FAMILY HIS
KNOWLEI
UK 1992/3

by Keith and Tracey Park

CONTENTS

Page

INTRODUCTION

Welcome to the second edition of our rapidly growing Directory. This directory will both provide you with information, and increase your enjoyment of family history. Family historians, are detectives, whose search for clues, can lead them to hard facts, but can often open up all sorts of unexpected situations, and wider interests.

In this book we have tried to do more than just produce a super Directory, that is both many times bigger and better organised than anything attempted before. We have attempted to give those new to family history the basic information to take them in the right direction, and to those with experience, we hope to make think about other alternatives, sources, projects, studies, and ideas. We hope to demonstrate that family history is fun, exciting, and open to anyone.

If you compare this edition with the 91 edition you will find we now have less articles, but generally they are much larger. We have tried to split articles logically between the directory and the bi-monthly magazine 'Family Twigletts', so that articles appearing here are either those too large to go in a magazine, or beginners material essential to get you going in the right direction. Copies of the 91 directory are still available if you wanted it, details can be found in the advertising section (section H).

As with most books the best place to start is at the beginning, and Section A will tell you how to use the Directory elements fully, while the introduction to Section F (Articles and Projects), will give you an overview of the articles.

In constructing this Directory, we had a lot of help. Every County Record Office in the country except two, and I wouldn't be so unkind as to name them, helped us by displaying posters, and leaflets, which allowed a lot of the information to be collected. We thank the archivists in charge of each of these offices, for their help and for the many helpful, and constructive suggestions, the majority of which have been implemented.

Likewise many libraries and LDS Family History Centres also helped in the same way. A number of evening class lecturers distributed forms to their classes and a few Family History Societies, distributed forms to their members. Over 450 articles have appeared in newspapers and magazines, both looking at the 91 directory and giving information about our projects. This has led to many enquiries. We thank all of them for their help.

We thank all the hundreds of people who wrote to us to say how much the 91 edition had helped them, you made the whole project worth while for us, we really appreciated to hear from you all.

In addition to this Tracey and I have written to over 38,000 people. Many have replied, many submitting information.

First Published 1992
FAMILY HISTORY CLUB
Computer Club Ltd

Copies available from:
Family History Club
Computer Club Ltd
19 Penybryn, Mountain Ash
Mid Glamorgan CF45 3TJ
Tel/Fax:0443-475900
Credit Card Orders Accepted
Or any good bookshop

ISBN 1-873594-03-8 Library Edition (Hardback) £28.95 (P&P £2.85)
ISBN 1-873594-04-6 Paperback £18.95 (P&P £2.85)

Printed: Redwood Press Ltd, Pegasus Way, Bowerhill, Melksham, Wiltshire SN12 6TR

INTRODUCTION

We thank all the people you will find listed in Section D (Addresses) for submitting information and the authors of the Guest Articles in Section F1. Likewise we thank for a second time the staff or the Record Offices for providing the information for Section G (Useful Addresses). Our computer databases are constantly being updated, so if you find someone has moved, we can probably give you their new address. Likewise if you discover someone in the directory has moved, please let us know.

The production of this book has used the latest computer equipment, and involved over 90 special computer programs being produced in order to handle the various databases, handle the mail, generate the sections for this book, and do a vast amount of checking to reduce errors. It has been compiled and typeset on our computers, entirely by us, therefore all the errors are ours. We recognise that the only way not to have any errors, is not to do anything, but we have done everything we could think of to eliminate them. In order to process information it had to be keyed in, and nearly all the information you will find in sections C (Interests) and D (Addresses), as well as most of the rest has been entered by Tracey. While some of the source information was well written, a crystal ball was sometimes necessary.

The production of this book has been a team effort, involving both Tracey and I, in far more work than we originally thought it would, and whilst my name may appear on more articles, Tracey has put far more hours work in than I have. Tracey has run the Directory project, dealt with Record Offices, discussed and typeset the Guest Articles, collected together the information and done the data entry, and still found time to have a baby. I designed the sections, wrote all the computer programs, handled the incoming mail, prepared information for entry, helped with the large mailings, devised the articles and projects, and generally helped Tracey when I could. The sheer volume of information has been difficult to deal with and it has needed many months of very long days to get it all in, and resulted in us publishing several months later than we had originally hoped to.

While we have done everything possible to use the correct spelling in articles and good English, we don't want to know of any minor errors, but if you discover any errors in facts, such as the spelling of a name, the wrong address, or similar more important errors then please let us know. Please remember that some places have been, in different periods, in different counties, and the spelling of a place name could have also changed slightly. Although there is room for error here, we have as far as possible entered the information submitted rather than tried to edit it.

If you are one of our more experienced readers, and have already done some research, may I suggest you look this year at your information to check that it is complete in relation to when and where individuals died, and what they died of, and encourage anyone you help to also do this. I will apologise in advance to those of you who discover your Great Grandfather died aged 8 or 10 and that all your relations stretching back for hundreds of years now turns out to be someone else's family, but please don't throw it away before you have recorded what you have found in the British Genealogical Database, (see Section F2 Articles and Projects).

If you are new to family history, then welcome, you will find many others associated with the hobby are pleasant and helpful people. Remember at all times that it is a hobby, an interest, no matter how absorbing. It can be exciting, frustrating, and at times exhilarating. It is unusual in that people from around the world help each other without financial reward, whatever their nationality, race, religion, or situation in life. Please share your achievements with others, and make sure your work is properly recorded and available to help future generations following in the search. This book is the worlds largest Genealogical Directory, and lists so many people who will be only too pleased to help you.

If you have any comments, or ideas, then please feel free to write or call us on 0443-475900 or 478754, 9am to 9pm, Monday to Saturday.

Keith Park.
1st July 1992.

PS. Well that's that one out the way, and if I start now, perhaps I can get the super 94 edition, which should be out in the summer of 93 out on time.

Tracey

SECTION A
HOW TO USE THIS BOOK and HELPFUL HINTS

In this section we are going to look at how to get the most from this directory, and its special features. If you have used other directories, then you may feel it is obvious, but if you use this approach you will find less than a quarter of the possible entries worth exploring, and also miss a lot of the additional information provided.

An example of the coded information, is the different meanings in various sections, of names in capitals, as compared with normal type, or the additional name on some records in section D shown in brackets.

ARE YOU READY FOR THE QUICK TOUR - Ten step plan ?

We will have a quick tour and then go over it in detail. You will then appreciate the various other ways this information can be used.

Details about each section is also explained in detail at the beginning of the relevant section often with more background information.

LETS GET STARTED !!

Directory structure. - You will have seen from the contents that there are a large number of sections. Sections B, C and D are the main directory sections we are interested in now, together with Section E.

Step One - Identify the names and places you are interested in from your own knowledge or files.

Step Two - Use Section B - variants, to identify more possible names, entries could be under. Section B does not list the names in section C that has no known variants.

Step Three - Use the table of county codes on the last printed page in this book), and identify the codes for the counties that interest you. Remember that county names and borders have changed in the past, so also identify nearby county codes as well. Note also the area codes that may apply, such as West Country, Home Counties, South Wales, Wales etc.

Step Four - Look up the names in section C, under the names, you have identified in section B or the name you have, if not included in section B. Look under the county and area codes, and at the places. You will need a good map to see where each of these places are. Note the date ranges, information is known for, and currently being researched, and the Reference number. Repeat this for each name.

Step five - Using the reference numbers identify the individuals in Section D. You can also look at what else these people know and are researching, by using the names at the end of their address entry, and looking up these in section C. This list also tells you other variants found by that person. You may be able to identify variants from this list, that have not been notified to us as variants. Some appear obvious, but might not be, but we haven't guessed.

Step Six - If you found entries in section C with "ALL" in county code, and place columns, you may have come across a one name study, or one name society. You will also see some names start with an entry which defines that a person or group are involved in a study of a name. (In the 91 edition there were far fewer studies, but those contained gave more details of what they had in section E. We have not repeated this in this years directory).

Step Seven - From what you have found out plan the action you are going to take.

Identify,:-

Those you can help.
Those who may be able to help you.
One Name Societies or Studies.
People you can share the future research tasks with.
Any other's you should contact.

Step Eight - Write to each of these people. (Example letters later).

Step Nine - Look at section F Articles and Projects, and look particularly at the information you can submit to us towards the next edition of this directory, and how to submit your research to the British Genealogical Database. The article on the database also contains news on a useful method of keeping records, which you may find helpful. Extra information can be sent in at any time, so there is no advantage in waiting

Step Ten - Look at other sections, such as Place Studies, Useful Addresses, Reference etc to get other possible starting points. Read the articles and all section headings.

When you start getting replies to your letters, or have done other research, you will need to repeat the above, using the additional information obtained.

CODING EXPLAINED with examples

Section B (Variants)
This section is in order alphabetically. It contains all names with two or more known variants, so not all the names in section C, are listed here. There are two types of entries, those starting with a name in capitals for example "WEBB", and those in normal type for example "Webb".

The entries that start in normal type is for a name that is not itself listed in section C. The name is followed by one or more names in capitals that are listed in section C. They also appear as the second type of entry in this section.
Example:

```
Scuse SKEWES SKEWIS SKEWS
     SKUCE SKUES SKUSE
```

The entry that starts with a capitalised name, is in section C. The name is followed by one or more known variants. If they are in capitals then they are also an option to look up in section C, as entries exist for this variant. It also has its own variant list in this section, which may give you more variants. Names in normal

type are not in section C but may have other names that are linked to it in this section. If the record has more than three variants, the number of variants is shown.
Example:

```
SKUSE 10 Scues Scuse
      SKEWES SKEWIS SKEWS
      Skewys SKUCE SKUES
      Skuys
```

You will see from this that:-

* All names we know of with two or more variants are listed, but not names with only one known way of spelling.
* Names in capitals, have its own entry in this section and are contained in section C.
* Names in normal type, have no entries in section C and an entry under this name does not list all variants, but just those names that contain a full variant list.
* By looking up all names under all variants and repeating this process with other linked entries, a list of names worth exploring in section C can be made.
* Names not contained in this section, still need to be checked in section C.

It has been suggested that we could have asked for entries under each variant as other directories do, and by this eliminated this section. As others don't carry as much information, have as many entries, or in some cases lay out the information, they can do this. If we were to have taken this approach, a lot of people would not have listed all variants, and the size would have increased, and therefore the cost of the directory would have had to be much higher.

Section C contains 106,407 lines over 19,579 names, by using this section you can identify an additional 15,600 names, and in excess of 766,441 additional possibilities, by using known variants of the name others have come across. You will see this is equivalent to a directory with over 1,000,000 entries covering 35,179 names, many times the size of the Genealogical Research Directory, published in Australia, which contains entries covering 25 countries, rather than England, Scotland, Wales, and the two parts of Ireland as we do. If we buried these entries in section C, it would take longer to follow up, and take up a lot more space.

Section C (Interests)
This section is arranged alphabetically by name, with a block for each name. Within the block, entries are in alphabetical order by county or area code, and within this by place name. "ALL", and areas such as "NORTH" are positioned in front of "A", and unknowns shown with a "?" or "???" are positioned after "Z". Where there is not enough room on a line, two lines are used for the entry. Where a name study is being done in relation to the entry this is the first line.
Example:

```
SKUES
                ALL  ALL  39381 ALL Name Study
     1900 1990 1900 1990 39381 CHS North
     1700 1990 1700 1990 39381 CON ALL
     1850 1990 1850 1900 39381 KEN Dartford
     1887 1990 .... .... 39403 KEN Tonbridge
     1800 1990 1800 1990 39381 LND ALL
     1874 1882 .... .... 39403 MDX West
     1850 1990 1850 1990 39381 YKS West
```

The explanation of the county or area codes is the last printed page in this book. If you are familiar with the British Standard or the Chapman County Codes this set will be largely familiar to you. We have added a few of our own, to handle information supplied. There are a few entries we could not code without losing information, in these cases the entry is in text. You need to look carefully through these codes as there are often a number of codes which relate to the same area. For example SSX for Sussex, SXE for East Sussex, and SXW for West Sussex. You can also get old and new areas, currently Dyfed (DFD), is made up of a number of older counties, including Pembrokeshire (PEM). It is in Wales (WLS), and South Wales (SWL).

As the borders of some counties have changed you will find some places that were at one point in one county are at another time in another county. As county lines often follow rivers, some places may go over the county border.

We suggest you list all the codes that could apply, but also go through the place names, and use a good map or detailed road atlas to identify the places listed. You will find in the reference section we have done an analysis of counties and surrounding areas which may help you.

When more people worked on the land, a larger percentage of the population lived in the country, and you will not always find that the same parish or place is listed. They may have lived in one parish, and went to church, school, or shopping in the next and if that is located nearer, they may have entered this. There was movement of labour, not only from the country into the towns, but from one estate to another owned by the same person, and by changing employment. In most cases you will find as today, people move within fifteen miles of their last address. A good map or very detailed atlas is therefore essential.

The dates in the first two columns show the range of dates the person submitting the details has some knowledge of, while the date range in the next two columns shows the span they are currently researching. "ALL", means all dates, not necessarily that they know of every individual that ever lived there. In many cases we had to interpret the information provided to get it into this format, and sometimes this was not possible, so we identified the missing or unknown entry with a "?". Four dots .... have no special meaning, it appears where no information was provided and makes the columns easier to read.

Having identified the entries that interest you, make a note of the reference number. This number comprises a six digit number, made up of a five digit number and a check digit. The use of the check digit eliminates transposition errors, as well as most other types of transcription errors. In tests we found that the largest number of errors, in using other directories, come about by transposition errors for example writing 1234 as 1324, and this causes people to write to the wrong people, the result is often not to get a reply, from an inappropriate enquiry.

Section D (Names & Addresses)
This section is in alphabetical order, but is also in order by the reference number. There is an information block for each person submitting information.

This is made up of:-

* Name and address, with postcode. A name in brackets is the maiden name (name before marriage), when it was entered on the form.
* Telephone number, if the person completing the form chose the option to list it. It is usually best to write, and this especially applies when the person has opted not to have their number listed.
* Interest list. This is the list of names the person is researching. An entry in capitals indicates that you will find an entry under this name for this person in section C, while an entry in normal type indicates it is a variant they have come across, but entries are not listed separately. There may be entries in section C under this name, but not for this person. So that you can identify a name study we have not capitalised any of the variant names, unless of course they have their own entry for this person. Sometimes you can tell from the list of names that you are searching the same family, and you can always get a better understanding by seeing what others are looking for. Remember they may not have listed everything, I know I didn't.
* File number, this is a number starting with a "F" and in this directory is in the range F1 to F7454. It is the file number of the original data supplied to us, and is useful when updating information, or asking about changes of address. While the reference number, being connected with the alphabetic position will change from one directory to another, the persons file number will remain constant. Given the file number we have easy access to the source information, or corrections that we have been notified of.

Example:

```
34533 PARK Mrs Tracey June. (Skuse) 19 Penybryn,
      Mountain Ash, Mid Glamorgan, CF45 3TJ.
      Tel:0443-478754
      DILLMAN Scuse Skues SKULL SKUSE SQUIRES
      TYLER WALDRON WEBB  F1001
```

The name of the person may be slightly different to what you expect, for example some military officers, have requested for security reasons that they are listed as MR. We have not listed any initials after names, either honours, or membership of organisations. This was done to save space.

Section E (Special Studies)

This section contains both special studies and two indexes that you may find useful. One index lists all Maiden Names (these are shown in Section D in brackets) and their reference number. A second index lists One Name Studies, most of which you will find in Section C and again gives the reference number so you can identify the person in Section D. The advantage of this index list is that it is easier to spot similar names to your interest, which may not be linked up with the variant section. Use of the variant section is recommended as some variants are split widely alphabetically.

This section also contains two indexes of studies, the first of these is Place Studies, while the second is all other types of studies. You need to look through both of these lists as sometimes a particular study may be classified differently than you expect. The reference number is shown which will get you back to the individual in Section D. The number starting with an F is the file number of the individual and allows us to access and maintain the information.

We would like to hear of any special studies or interests you have.

Other Sections

You will see from the contents list, what the other sections contain. Generally they are articles, projects, news, or reference information. Section G contains the most complete list available of archives where you can see records that will help you. Telephone numbers and opening times are shown. Please read section F2, and help us to make both a larger and more complete directory next year, and to build other databases that will help you. There is never any cost to you in submitting information.

What to do if they have moved

Let us assume you have come across someone in this directory, or in fact anyone interested in family history who has moved, then what should you do ? .

If you do not know their new address - write to us, giving as much information as you can, but including the name of the individual, the last known address, and any previous addresses for that individual you know of. If they are in this directory, include the File number (beginning with a F), from the end of their entry. A stamped addressed envelope is appreciated, but if you forget we will of course still reply (eventually). If we do not know we will log your query, and if the address comes to our attention we will let you know. Please make it clear that you are requesting an address rather than providing update information.

If you know of their new address - write to us, giving the same information as above but also state the new address. This will help us to help others. Often when moving there is so much to do, that it is understandable for us to be overlooked, so please let us know.

If you come across someone who has died. Please let us know, quoting as much of the above information as possible.

Writing to People

First please remember at all times that this is a hobby, that means to most people it has a lower priority than many other things. Having said that we have all found when talking to people with different ancestors than ours, and detailing our research, we get about as much excitement as if we had produced last years holiday photographs. So anyone interested is more than welcome.

The approach I suggest, is one that is likely to get as high a response as possible. You want to know if there are possibilities, and produce momentum. We know that it is difficult to get people to "get around to it", we may even suffer ourselves from a lack of motivation on occasions.

The way we can increase the likelihood of a response is to make it as easy as possible. One way of doing this is to enclose a stamped addressed envelope for the reply. Make it a large enough envelope, not one of these very tiny ones. A good size is known as C5, and will hold A4 paper folded in half, the very smallest usable size is known as DL, these hold A4 paper folded in three. As folding in half is easier than folding in three, C5 has to be best.

We can further increase the speed of response if we enclose a reply card. This ideally will allow the correspondent, the opportunity to tick one of several options and post it immediately, even if the full reply is going to take time. At least you know it arrived, and is being dealt with. An example is at the end of this section.

You will recognise both of these features have been included in professional information packs sent to you, by leading companies or charities.

You need to either keep a copy of what you have sent or list the main points. Remember to note the date sent.

It is not a good idea to send a vast amount of information initially, if you think you have information of use to someone, it is better to give an overview if possible, and see if they are interested. Never send your only copy to anyone. Photocopies are available in many places now, including many libraries. The simplest and probably easiest overview you can do is an outline of the individuals on the branch or the family tree involved. Show names, dates and places only at this time.

If you are requesting information, then try to keep your enquiry as relevant and to the point as you can. If you make it to complicated, or don't ask specifically for the information you want, then in most cases you will only get back half of the information you were hoping for.

If you want to go to see someone, then still write first, giving them notice of your interest, and a chance to tell you if it is not convenient. If you just turn up, you will find many people are suspicious or even frightened. Having written, it still may be a good idea to telephone before visiting anyone.

If you do visit someone please don't expect to take all their records away. If you are a new found friend or relation, they will not like to say no, and they may avoid showing you more, especially photographs.

Some people find it difficult to write letters the two following examples are designed to be a guide. There is no correct or incorrect way, so do what you feel you would like to receive.

Some people have difficulty in knowing how to address a correspondent. Tradition used to be to use Sir, Madam, Mr Name, Mrs Name or the like, it is also common now to address people directly by their first name. Again there is no right and wrong, it is up to you, but I suggest you could be lead by the correspondent, if they list their first name in a directory, then you could use it, if they don't, then assume they prefer a more formal approach. If you wish to play it safe, then use the formal approach. When you have a reply from them, which you will normally find follows your example, you can sometimes get a better idea from their approach. Is it chatty, or formal. Tracey always signs her name Tracey Park, this confuses some people, who don't know how to address her, luckily most settle for Dear Tracey, but she does get quite a few addressed Dear Tracey Park, and a paragraph apologising for the method of address.

Examples:

REPLY CARD

Your letter received on ....(date)

The information you supplied is:-
relevant / not relevant to my knowledge known.
relevant / not relevant to my research.

I am able / not able to help further.

I expect to be able to reply in detail in ..... Days/weeks.
Additional notes.

FROM: ______________________________

Your Name
Your Address
tel number

date

Dear Mr Bloggs,

I have been studying the information provided in the directory, "Family History Knowledge - UK 1992/3".

I enclose a sheet showing the branch of my family tree that I feel we may have in common. I would be pleased to answer any questions on any part of this, and would be grateful for any additional information you may know, and if you can, the source of this information.

Please could you indicate what part you are currently researching, how you are going about this, areas already covered and any other relevant information that would allow us to cover different areas of the research. I will of course reply immediately if your plan includes areas I have already searched.

I enclose both a stamped addressed envelope, for your reply in detail, and a reply card, which I hope you will return immediately, so that I can plan my next action.

Yours sincerely,

You

CONTACTING PEOPLE IN OTHER COUNTRIES

You can obtain from post offices, IRC's (International Reply Coupons). They used to be worth the equivalent of standard surface mail, but I am told they are now worth the equivalent of standard Air Mail. If you enclose an IRC and an envelope it may speed up your response. If you receive IRC's you may find that financially it is a better idea to hold them and use them to send to other people, than exchange for cash.

Another alternative way of contacting people is by FAX. A fax machine connects to a telephone line and sends a page of information in a few seconds. You will find many high streets now have businesses offering fax facilities to the public as do most hotels. You may therefore find it a good idea to identify who can receive faxes for you and quote this in your correspondence.

SECTION B
NAME VARIANTS

Introduction to Section
How To Use This Section

Name Variants - Why They Occur

English Spelling - Brief History of Spelling

Listing of Known Variants.

How To Use This Section
The information contained in this section was obtained from information submitted. It is not a full list of all names contained within the interest section, but identifies where two or more variants of a name have been found. We have not treated different combinations of capital and little letters as separate variants, these are often the Mac MaC type of variations. As alphabetically they are in the same place this will not create you a problem. You will find some variants very similar, while others like Ambridge, Hambridge, Rambridge and Umbridge are widely separated alphabetically.

Items printed totally in capital letters identifies it as an entry in the main interests section (C). Where a name in lower case (small letters), starting with a capital are variants.

You will find this section contains two types of entries, those starting with a capitalised name (ie SMITH), which is followed by a list of known variants, and when there are 4 or more it also tells you how many there are. The capitalised words will all be found listed in both this section and in section C. Looking up these names in this section may identify yet more variants.

The other type of entry, starts with a lowercase name, starting with a capital (ie Smith). This entry is not followed by all known variants but lists just those contained in section C. You will find each of these in this section, and their full set of variants.

The section is arranged alphabetically. Lines inset by two characters are continuations of the line above. There are four columns per page.

You need to list all variants, and look up each of these in this section, and continue this process until all possible names have been identified. Remember only those shown in capitals are in the next section, although you will find names in the next section where no variants are known, and therefore not listed here.

Name Variants
Many people are sensitive about their surname, and not inclined initially to look at variants of it. With more knowledge of family history, and the general history of our ancestors, we get to understand why or how, the name could have devolved over time. In this article I want to look first specifically at name variants and then at the development of our peculiar English spelling in general.

To so many people the suggestion that their ancestors may have been illiterate, is taken as a personal insult. Of course it should not be, for we will see that few people could read and write, and those that could did not have a common standardised spelling as we do today.

Throughout history up to relatively recently, only a small minority of the population could write. Names were written down how they sounded, by Clerks or Clergymen. Often those with the ability to write came from a different social class, if not from a different area of the country. Add to this the very strong dialects that existed and you can see how many of the variants are possible.

It was not considered polite to show off and write your name, in front of relatives, who could not write. So even when some of our ancestors either could write or could have pointed out an error they quietly made their mark.

Many people were in service, and where a servant had the same surname as the household, usually the servant was known by a different name. This is therefore not only a variant but a change in name. Some employers did not want to bother to learn new names so a replacement had to answer to the surname of their predecessor. These and pet/nicknames are known as alias' and are not true variants.

Girls of the same social class, did not receive as good an education as their brothers. In 1727 Swift wrote, "It is very hard that not one Gentleman daughter in a thousand should be brought to read or understand her own native tongue, or be judge of the easiest books that are written in it."

In 1877 out of 1,972 failures in a Civil Service examination, 1,866 failed for poor spelling, although this was in the Victorian period where there was an unnecessary importance given to spelling. Amusing when you consider that Queen Victoria was a poor speller.

At a more practical level in our own family history research, we will find different lines showing signs of the ability to write at different points. One of my lines for example, includes the Webb's of Brinkworth in Wiltshire. Frederick Webb married Ellen Stanton in 1874, both were farm workers. Later they established a haulage business. Neither of them could read or write, although Frederick could add up numbers. Their sons, which included my grandfather George born in 1878 could read and write, and there are amusing stories of them buying items they were not supposed to have and getting them added to suppliers accounts knowing that their father could not read the invoice. A descendent of Frederick still runs a haulage business in Brinkworth, but now with a fleet of lorries rather than horses and carts. Ellen did not appreciate other people poking their nose into her business, and was inclined to create confusion by having different variations of the facts. I have not yet established positively that her maiden name was Stanton, or where she came from, although she said she was born in Marlow, Somerset in 1856, St Catherines House does not have a record of this birth.

Education for the public started in Scotland before it did in England, but you do not normally have to go far back before you reach ancestors who's priorities did not include education.

We receive many letters on name spellings, and it is a particular study I am interested in. One lady wrote from Scotland, and would not complete our form, as she felt we were insulting her ancestors by giving the impression that they could not write. Within two days we received another letter giving the opposite viewpoint, his ancestor had been involved in providing the water supply to Glasgow in the early part of the last century, and he mentioned a report that made interesting reading containing his ancestors name four times over three pages with three different spellings, two of which were on the same page. He has found his name spelt 125 ways although due to our use of capital and lowercase letters we only get 109.

Birth registration even today, involves you telling the Registrar the name you want to record the child under, they write it down, and the surname does not have to be the same as the parent. You can see where a birth occurs before a marriage, which was quite common in many areas, the mother may not know how to spell the name if she recorded it under the fathers name. Straight clerical errors will account for some other changes, and as people who could not write might well use documents they had, you can see one error could change a branch.

On marriage the wife's maiden name is sometimes included to form a hyphanised or double barrelled name and some surnames differentiate the generation by adding a son to the end or Mac, Mc or O' to the front. Likewise some older surnames have both Norman (French) and English equivalents.

At some points in history, such as at the time of war, some people did not wish to have a foreign sounding name and would modify it, or change it to make it sound more English. Likewise many immigrants have done the same.

British Spelling
The English language devolved from threads of the past, modified by local customs and dialects. It is a patchwork of Anglo-Saxon, old Norse, Norman French, Clerks Latin, with additions from Wessex, Kent, Mercia, and Northumbria to name a few. These being modified to suit the conventions of printers and others. England with its trading history, has always been the refuge for exiles, a new home for immigrants, and marriages with people with other languages, illustrated by a quick look at the Royal family.

It is thought that old English started in the 5th Century when Germanic invaders from the continent conquered or drove out the Celtic and Romano-British inhabitants of Britain. These immigrants came mainly from two tribes, the Angles and Saxons. It is thought that they brought the Germanic runic alphabet to Britain. Over the next two to three hundred years, with their conversion to Christianity, and missionary work, their language devolved away from the other Germanic languages, similar to the way American-English has devolved away from Westminster English today.

Through small kingdoms and politics, a number of dialects and spellings evolved, with by the end of the 8th Century, three dominant kingdoms and dialects: Northumbria, Mercia, and West Saxon (including Kent). In the 9th Century distant cousins of the Anglo-Saxons, the Norsemen who spoke a related language, invaded Britain and conquered most of Northumbia and Mercia, which then became known as Danelaw. Alfred, King of the West Saxons fought and won a battle in Wessex, (the Battle of Ethandum at Edington in Wiltshire). This stopped the Norsemen. The dividing line ran along the old Roman road between London and Chester known as Watling Street. This old division can still be seen today in the differences in place names, dialect and spelling on either side of the line.

In the 10th Century Alfreds' successors conquered the Danish areas, to form a unified England under the West Saxon Royal house. Writing from this period is rare, with the church writing in Latin. But from what there is, experts can distinguish four dialects: Northumbrian, Mercian, Kentish, and West Saxon, with four slightly different conventions of spelling, vocabulary and syntax in the four regions.

The West Saxon dialect and house style of spelling became the standard. There were at this time a number of word factories, performing translations and book copying. The scribes that undertook this work developed a universal standard of old English. This is the simple foundation on which the rickety structure of subsequent English spelling has been erected. The spelling was far more phonetic (spelt as it sounds), than it has ever been since, with each letter having a distinct sound and there being no silent letters. English was the only language in Europe that was widely used locally in official documents, and had a fully developed literary form and standard spelling.

Then came 1066, and all that, with the Norman Conquest. William and his noblemen spoke "langue d'oil" a language of northern France. This became the language of the court. Until the 14th Century, the English were a subject people divided from their rulers by both race and language. We can see the effect on the language with the Anglo-Saxon peasants, looking after the cows, calves, swine and sheep in the field, and developed such surnames as Shepherd and Hog-ward (Howard). When these creatures arrived at the table for the Normans to eat they became, beef, veal, pork, and mutton. The Normans did not suppress English, but had no use for it. With no national use, or official documents to set a standard, spellings soon started to vary. The Normans were far less literate than the Anglo-Saxons, and not great readers. They could generally not read or understand English, and the few books they had were in French or Latin.

Slowly the two races grew together and the two languages became one, helped by the actions of clerks, bailiffs, nurses, and foremen. The language devolved regionally again, because there was no standard set centrally. In 1350 the Black Death wiped out a third of the population, those that were left forgot the importance of inflection, and gender was dropped. Today about 40% (fourty percent) of the words in the English dictionary were derived from French. By this time we had developed the most irrational spelling in the world.

The Royal Court came to rest at Westminster, and again with centralised government the language started to become more common again. Had it settled in Oxford or the West Midlands, or just about anywhere else the language would be very different today. At about this time the spread of learning and growth of wealth, changed the demand for books. The University was founded and literacy spread amongst the new merchant classes. Cheaper paper replaced the expensive parchment, and brought books and reading and thereby standard spelling.

Elizabethan compositors (typesetters) often varied the spelling of words in order to justify a line of type, (to get a straight right side to the text). We do this today by adding more spaces between words. Their readers became used to seeing the same word spelt in various ways.

There would appear to have been a move to standardise spelling in the early 17th Century with the first issue of the King James Bible in 1611. The spelling used was that which best fitted line spacing, but by the issues of 1629 and 1638, most of the variant spellings had been removed. There were several philosophers of spelling or orthography, such as Sir Thomas Smith who published something on this in 1568, followed by John Hart in 1569, Richard Malcaster in 1582 and Alexander Gil in 1619.

Just prior to the English Civil War, a war of words in political pamphlets preceded the war with swords (1642-46). In the rush to get typeset, line justification lost importance. When printing work became scarce, printers turned to producing spelling books, with its obvious effect on their own spelling.

Johnsons dictionary first published in 1755, became the first to be universally accepted. Although it is said that at this time every Englishmans house had the Bible, Shakespeare and Johnsons dictionary, only a small percentage of the population was literate. Johnson followed the spelling used by the printers, and English writers of the period. Spelling has not changed very much since, yet hundreds of thousands of words have come into the language, as English has become a world language, developments and discoveries have occurred, and product names such as Hoover and Biro, have obtained wider meaning. At the same time thousands of words have dropped out of common use, many now forgotten. Other words have changed their meaning entirely. The following illustrates this:

nice woman	meant what we refer to as a fast woman.
nice man	meant touchy and irritable.
prestigious	meant tricky.

Johnson recognised several spellings for some words, but the Victorians settled on a single invariable one. A few variants did survive, and in many cases were attached to different meanings of the same word, for example inquire and enquire or grey and gray, and by this means some became different words such as metal and mettle, flour and flower.

American spelling branched off after Johnson, and a teacher and journalist Noah Webster produced a spelling book in 1783, which became a fundamental part of the standardised American spelling. By 1890 Websters Dictionary was in its 400th revision and sold more than 60 million copies. Websters dictionary today as it has since 1828, carries both English and American variations. In the same way as America is no longer controlled from Westminster, it no longer had to conform to London usage of the language.

There have been many attempts to make English spelling more sensible, these have varied from the move by the Royal Society to set up an academy, supported by Dryden, Eveln and Swift, and even the government gave its approval and backing in 1712 (nothing happened), to individual moves by Benjamin Franklin, Isaac Pitman, Tennyson, Darwin, Andrew Carnegie, and Bernard Shaw. None have achieved any major success with the exception of Webster who did have some effect on the American version. In the future it is likely that the English and American versions of the language will merge, as already a large percentage of my more specialist books are American, and Websters is the dictionary I use most often. While some politicians and other people influenced by the Victorian era may stress the importance of spelling, generally educational establishments are more interested in creativity than fixed usage. This book like more and more today, has not been set by a typesetter, there are no proofreaders, or editors to check on the English, punctuation or spelling, so a freer form will come through. Newspapers likewise are now using computer technology, which again will result in more variations arriving on the printed page. Even the automatic spell checkers we use cannot spot when a word is the wrong word or another variation, and the more we come to rely on our computers to correct our spelling, the more open we are to errors creeping in.

Finally, when you hear people complaining about pronunciation on television, or spelling or other word in text, remember that English is a living language, continually devolving, and what was the correct way yesterday need not be now or tomorrow.

Keith

CHECK LIST FOR INTERVIEWS

Date of interview.
Full name of person interviewed.
Address at the time of interview.
Occupation or profession at that time.
Any different occupation previously.
Why was the occupation changed, and when.
Date and place of birth.
Date and place of baptism/christening.
Names of godparents, their relationship ie friend, relation.
Religious denomination.
Names of schools attended, include names of any friends they can remember.
Date and place of marriage.
Full name of husband/wife.
Names of witnesses on their marriage.
Death date, cause and place.
Burial date and place.
Full names of any children, with the date and place of birth; date and place of baptism/christening; date, place and cause of death if applicable (ie died at birth) of each.
Fathers full name.
Fathers residence now, and his occupation.
Mothers full name and surname before marriage.
Date and place of parents' marriage.
Date and place of father's birth and christening.
Date, place and cause of father's death and burial.
Date and place of mother's birth and christening.
Date, place and cause of mothers death and burial.
Full names of mothers/fathers parents (grandparents).
Names and addresses of aunts/uncles.
Occupations for any of the others above.
Make notes of any family stories they tell you concerning relations, friends and stories of childhood etc.
Ask to see any documents, photographs, family bible etc.
See the Code List in the BGD article (Section F2) for other ideas.

A baer A'BEAR ATTE BERE BEAR BEARE BERE DE LA BERE
A bear A'BEAR ATTE BERE BEAR BEARE BERE DE LA BERE
A beare A'BEAR ATTE BERE BEAR BEARE BERE DE LA BERE
A beere A'BEAR ATTE BERE BEAR BEARE BERE DE LA BERE
A bere A'BEAR ATTE BERE BEAR BEARE BERE DE LA BERE
A beyre A'BEAR ATTE BERE BEAR BEARE BERE DE LA BERE
A'barre A'BEAR ATTE BERE BEAR BEARE BERE DE LA BERE
A'BEAR 42 A baer A bear A beare A beere A bere A beyre A'barre A'beare A'beere A'beyre Abair Abarre Abbeare Abbir Abear Abeard Abeare Abeer Abeere Abere Abeyre Abier Abore Abour Abuer Abure ATTE BERE BEAR BEARE Beire BERE Dalbeare De beare De bere De la bear De la beere DE LA BERE Delaber Delabere Dellabere Delliber
A'beare A'BEAR ATTE BERE BEAR BEARE BERE DE LA BERE
A'beere A'BEAR ATTE BERE BEAR BEARE BERE DE LA BERE
A'beyre A'BEAR ATTE BERE BEAR BEARE BERE DE LA BERE
A'COURT 8 Accott Acot ACOTT Acourt Aecot Aecott Aecourt
A'teuill ATTRILL
Aas AZE
Ab adam BADHAM
Ab adham BADHAM
Abair A'BEAR ATTE BERE BEAR BEARE BERE DE LA BERE
Abarre A'BEAR ATTE BERE BEAR BEARE BERE DE LA BERE
Abarrow BARROW
Abbeare A'BEAR ATTE BERE BEAR BEARE BERE DE LA BERE
ABBET 4 ABBOT ABBOTT Abbotts
Abbett ABBOTT
Abbingdon ABINGDON
Abbir A'BEAR ATTE BERE BEAR BEARE BERE DE LA BERE
ABBOT 6 ABBET ABBOTT Abbotts Abott Abut
ABBOTT 7 ABBET Abbett ABBOT Abbotts Abott Abut
Abbotts ABBET ABBOT ABBOTT
ABDALE Ebdale
Abear A'BEAR ATTE BERE BEAR BEARE BERE DE LA BERE
Abeard A'BEAR ATTE BERE BEAR BEARE BERE DE LA BERE
Abeare A'BEAR ATTE BERE BEAR BEARE BERE DE LA BERE
Abeer A'BEAR ATTE BERE BEAR BEARE BERE DE LA BERE
Abeere A'BEAR ATTE BERE BEAR BEARE BERE DE LA BERE
ABEL ABELL
ABELL ABEL
Aber ALBERRY AUBRAY AUBREY
ABERCROMBIE Abercromby
Abercromby ABERCROMBIE
Abere A'BEAR ATTE BERE BEAR BEARE BERE DE LA BERE
Abethell BETHEL BETHELL BITHEL BOTHELL
Abeyre A'BEAR ATTE BERE BEAR BEARE BERE DE LA BERE
Abier A'BEAR ATTE BERE BEAR BEARE BERE DE LA BERE
ABINGDON Abbingdon
Abitot D'ABITOT
Abore A'BEAR ATTE BERE BEAR BEARE BERE DE LA BERE
Abott ABBOT ABBOTT
Abour A'BEAR ATTE BERE BEAR BEARE BERE DE LA BERE
ABREY OBREY
Abri ALBERRY AUBRAY AUBREY
Abuer A'BEAR ATTE BERE BEAR BEARE BERE DE LA BERE
Abure A'BEAR ATTE BERE BEAR BEARE BERE DE LA BERE
Abut ABBOT ABBOTT
Acarnley ACKERNLEY ACORNLEY
ACASTER 5 Ackaster AKESTER AKISTER De acastre
Accott A'COURT ACOTT
Ace AZE
Acelin ADSETT ALLETT ARSLETT ASLETT AYLETT AZE
Acerley ACKERLEY
ACHANY 5 D'ANNETHE HANNA HANNAH HANNAY
ACHESON 5 Aitcheson AITCHISON Atcheson ATKINSON
Ackaster ACASTER AKESTER AKISTER
ACKERLEY 7 Acerley Ackersley Ackley Akeley Akerly Hackersley
ACKERMAN AKERMAN
ACKERNLEY Acarnley ACORNLEY
Ackersley ACKERLEY
Ackhurst AKEHURST
Ackley ACKERLEY
ACKROYD AKEROYD AKROYD
Ackurst AKEHURST
ACOMB ANSCOMB Ascomb
ACORNLEY Acarnley ACKERNLEY
Acot A'COURT ACOTT
ACOTT 10 A'COURT Accott Acot Acourt Aecot Aecott Aecourt EACOTT EYCOTT
Acourt A'COURT ACOTT
Adames ADAMS
ADAMS 4 Adames ADDAMS Adhams
ADDAMS ADAMS Adhams
Adden HADDON HADEN
ADDENBROOKE Anbrook
ADDERSON 4 ADDISON Addistone Aderson
Addes ADDIS ADDS
Addice ADDIS
Addies ADDIS
Addinsall ADDINSELL
ADDINSELL 5 Addinsall Addlesea Adinsall Adlesay
Addinson ADINSON
ADDIS 19 Addes Addice Addies Addiss ADDY Addyes Addys Ades ADEY Adice Adie Adis Adiss ADY ADYE Adyes Adys EDDY
ADDISON 6 ADDERSON Addisonne Addistone Aderson Adison
Addisonne ADDISON
Addiss ADDIS
Addistone ADDERSON ADDISON
Addlesea ADDINSELL
ADDS 5 Addes Ade Ades Adze
ADDY 7 ADDIS ADEY Adie ADY ADYE EDDY
Addyes ADDIS
Addys ADDIS
Ade ADDS
Aden HADEN HAYDEN HEYDON
Adenburgh ATTENBOROUGH
ADER ATHER
Aderson ADDERSON ADDISON
Ades ADDIS ADDS
ADEY 8 ADDIS ADDY Adie ADY ADYE EADY EDDY
Adgor ADGORE
ADGORE Adgor
Adhams ADAMS ADDAMS
Adice ADDIS
Adie ADDIS ADDY ADEY ADY ADYE EDDY
Adinsall ADDINSELL
ADINSON Addinson
Adis ADDIS
Adison ADDISON
Adiss ADDIS
ADKIN 5 ADKINS ATKIN Attkin Attkins
ADKINS 4 ADKIN ATKIN ATKINS
Adlesay ADDINSELL
Adman ADNAMS
Admans ADNAMS
ADNAM 7 ADNAMS Adnum Adnums Hadnam Hadnams Hadnum
ADNAMS 10 Adman Admans ADNAM Adnum Adnums Hadnam Hadnams Hadnum Hadnums
Adnum ADNAM ADNAMS
Adnums ADNAM ADNAMS
Adraen ADRIAN
Adrain ADRIAN
ADRIAN 7 Adraen Adrain Adrien Adryan Edrain Odrien
Adrien ADRIAN
Adryan ADRIAN
ADSETT 89 Acelin Aislet ALLETT Alote Anslett Arselet Arselott Arslet ARSLETT Arsolot Arthlote Arthlottes Artolatt As Ascelin Ascelot Ase Aseelina Aselett Aseplet Ashleat Ashlet Ashlett Ashlott Aslaf Aslat Aslate Aslatt Aslet Aslete ASLETT Asletts Asliate Aslit Aslitt Asllatt Asllett Aslot Aslote Aslott Aslotte Aslut Aslute Aslutt Asplaiet Asplet Asse Asselet Asselett Asselot Asselote Asset Assett Asslade Asslat Asslet Asslett Asslot Asslott Asstlat Ast Astbatt Astelat Astelet Astelot Astlat Astlatt Astlet Astlett Astlott Astolina Asttlet Atelett Atte lote Attlet Auselett Auslet Auslett Awnsellet AYLETT Ayslett AZE Azlack Azlitt Azo Azor De aisse Le asplott
ADSHEAD Adshed Atset
Adshed ADSHEAD
Adthy ATTEY ATTY
ADY 7 ADDIS ADDY ADEY Adie ADYE EDDY
ADYE 7 ADDIS ADDY ADEY Adie ADY EDDY
Adyes ADDIS
Adys ADDIS
Adze ADDS
Aecot A'COURT ACOTT
Aecott A'COURT ACOTT
Aecourt A'COURT ACOTT
Aella ELLA ELLEY
Aelle ELLA ELLEY
Aeste AUST
Agate HIGHGATE
Aggutters AGUTTER
Agtley ASHLEY ASTLE ASTLEY
AGUTTER 4 Aggutters Gutter Gutters
Aichinhead AITKENHEAD
AIKEN 29 Aikin AITKEN Aken Akins ATKIN Atkine Auchain Eakings Eakins Eakons Ekens EKINS Ekynes Ekyns Hackence Hackins Hakince Hakines Hakings Hakins HAWKINS Oaking OAKINS Okens OKINS Okyn Okyns Ouckins
Aikenhead AITKENHEAD
Aikenheid AITKENHEAD
Aikin AIKEN EKINS HAWKINS OAKINS OKINS
Ailard ALLWOOD ALYWARD AYLWARD HAILWOOD HALEWOOD HALWOOD HAYWOOD
Ailes AYLES EALES EELES EYLES HILES ILES ISLES
Ailesberry ALSBURY AYLESBURY
Ailesbery ALSBURY AYLESBURY
Ailesbry ALSBURY AYLESBURY
Ailesbury ALSBURY AYLESBURY
Ailing AYLING
Ailmer AYLMER
Ails AYLES EALES
Ailsberry ALSBURY AYLESBURY
Ailsbery ALSBURY AYLESBURY
Ailsbry ALSBURY AYLESBURY
Ailsbury ALSBURY

If the name you are interested in is not here, try Section C.

AYLESBURY
Ailward ALLWOOD ALYWARD AYLWARD HAILWOOD HALEWOOD HALWOOD HAYWOOD
AIME 5 Ame AMEY Amie AMY
Aimer AYLMER
Aimsbury AINSBURY AMESBURY
AINGER 4 ANGEL ANGELL ANGER
Ainland AINLEY
AINLEY 4 Ainland Aneley Anley
AINSBURY 5 Aimsbury AMESBURY Amsburie Amsbury
Ainsley AINSLIE
AINSLIE 8 Ainsley Ainsly Angely Annesly Aynesley Ennislie Enslie
Ainsly AINSLIE
Airmin ARMIN
Airmine ARMIN
Airming ARMIN
Airminge ARMIN
AIRTON AYRTON
AISH 6 AISHE ASH ASHE Aysh Ayshe
AISHE 9 AISH Aisshe ASH ASHE Asshe Aysshe De esse Esse
Aishley ASHLEY
AISLABIE AISLABY Aisleby
AISLABY AISLABIE
Aisleby AISLABIE
Aislet ADSETT ALLETT ARSLETT ASLETT AYLETT AZE
Aisshe AISHE ASHE
Aitcheson ACHESON AITCHISON
AITCHISON ACHESON Aitcheson
AITKEN 5 AIKEN AITKIN ATKIN Atkine
AITKENHEAD 7 Aichinhead Aikenhead Aikenheid Akenhead Akinhead Akinheid
AITKIN AITKEN
AKEHURST 4 Ackhurst Ackurst Akurst
Akeley ACKERLEY
Aken AIKEN EKINS HAWKINS OAKINS OKINS
Akenhead AITKENHEAD
Akerly ACKERLEY
AKERMAN ACKERMAN
AKEROYD ACKROYD AKROYD
AKESTER 5 ACASTER Ackaster AKISTER De acastre
Akinhead AITKENHEAD
Akinheid AITKENHEAD
Akins AIKEN EKINS HAWKINS OAKINS OKINS
AKISTER 5 ACASTER Ackaster AKESTER De acastre
AKROYD ACKROYD AKEROYD
Akurst AKEHURST
ALAIS 5 Alay Aley Alliace Allies
Alay ALAIS
Alberie ALBERRY AUBRAY AUBREY
ALBERRY 23 Aber Abri Alberie Albery Auberie Aubery AUBRAY Aubraye AUBREY Aubreye Aubrie Awberie Awbery Awberye Awbrey Awbreye Horberry Horbery Horbury Opberry Opbury Orbery
Alberton ALDERTON
Albery ALBERRY ALLBERRY AUBRAY AUBREY
Albeson ALBISTON
Albinson ALBISTON
Albinston ALBISTON
Albison ALBISTON
ALBISTON 5 Albeson Albinson Albinston Albison
Albray ALLBERRY
Albury ALLBERRY ALSBURY AYLESBURY
Alcard ALLCARD
ALCE Als
ALCOCK 6 ANCOCK AUCOCK Aucott Aukett Awcock
ALCROFT ALDCROFT Allcroft
ALDCROFT ALCROFT Allcroft
ALDEN 7 ALLDEN Aulden ELDEN ELDIN Eldon Hallden
ALDERDICE Alderdyce Allderdice
Alderdyce ALDERDICE
Alders ALDHOUSE ALDIS ALDOUS ALDUS AUDAS AWDAS ORDERS
ALDERSLEY Oldersley
ALDERSON 5 Aldersonne ANDERSON Auderson Aulderson
Aldersonne ALDERSON ANDERSON
Alderten ALDERTON
ALDERTON 6 Alberton Alderten Aldirton Allderton Halderton
ALDHAM OLDHAM
Aldhous ALDHOUSE ALDIS ALDOUS ALDUS AUDAS AWDAS ORDERS
ALDHOUSE 20 Alders Aldhous Aldhowse ALDIS Aldiss ALDOUS ALDUS Alduse Alldis Alldiss AUDAS Audiss AUDUS Auldis AWDAS Awdis Awdus Oldis ORDERS
Aldhowse ALDHOUSE ALDIS ALDOUS ALDUS AUDAS AWDAS ORDERS
Aldirton ALDERTON
ALDIS 20 Alders Aldhous ALDHOUSE Aldhowse Aldiss ALDOUS ALDUS Alduse Alldis Alldiss AUDAS Audiss AUDUS Auldis AWDAS Awdis Awdus Oldis ORDERS
Aldiss ALDHOUSE ALDIS ALDOUS ALDUS AUDAS AUDUS
ALDOUS 20 Alders Aldhous ALDHOUSE Aldhowse ALDIS Aldiss ALDUS Alduse Alldis Alldiss AUDAS Audiss AUDUS Auldis AWDAS Awdis Awdus Oldis ORDERS
ALDRICH ALDRIDGE OLDRIDGE
Aldrid ALDRIDGE OLDRIDGE OLDROYD
ALDRIDGE 10 ALDRICH Aldrid ALLDRIDGE ELDRIDGE Oldrid OLDRIDGE Oldroid OLDROYD Oldroyde
ALDUS 20 Alders Aldhous ALDHOUSE Aldhowse ALDIS Aldiss ALDOUS Alduse Alldis Alldiss AUDAS Audiss AUDUS Auldis AWDAS Awdis Awdus Oldis ORDERS
Alduse ALDHOUSE ALDIS ALDOUS ALDUS AUDAS AWDAS ORDERS
ALDWORTH 4 Alldworth Allworth Alworth
Alefleet ALFLATT ELFLETT
ALEFOUNDER ALFOUNDER
Alemar AYLMER
Alemer AYLMER
Alen ALLEN
Alengame ALLINGHAM
Alengham ALLINGHAM
Aleright ALLRIGHT ALLWRIGHT
Alesberry ALSBURY AYLESBURY
Alesbery ALSBURY AYLESBURY
Alesbry ALSBURY AYLESBURY
Alesbury ALSBURY AYLESBURY
ALEXANDER Macalexander Mcalexander
Aley ALAIS ELEY ELY HAILEY HALEY HEALEY
ALFF 11 ALP ALPE ALPHE ALPS AULPH HULF OLFE ULF ULFE ULPH
ALFLATT 5 Alefleet Elfleet ELFLETT Elflitt
ALFORD Allford HALFORD
ALFOUNDER ALEFOUNDER
Algarth HALLGARTH
Algate HALLGARTH
Algath HALLGARTH
Alick ALLICK
Alingame ALLINGHAM
Alingham ALLINGHAM
Alis ALLIS ALLISON ALLISS
Alison ALLIS ALLISON ALLISS
Alix ALLICK
Alken ALKIN ALLKINS
Alkens ALKIN ALLKINS
ALKER HOULKER
ALKIN 20 Alken Alkens Alkins Alkyn Alkyne Alkynes Alkyns Allckin Allcoin Allekin Allken Allkin ALLKINS Allkyn Allkyne Allkynes Aulkin Aulkyns Awlkyns
Alkins ALKIN ALLKINS
Alkyn ALKIN ALLKINS
Alkyne ALKIN ALLKINS
Alkynes ALKIN ALLKINS
Alkyns ALKIN ALLKINS
ALLABY Allobie
ALLAKER Elleker Ellerker
ALLAN ALLEN
ALLATT 4 ALLETT Allitt ALLOTT
ALLBERRY 4 Albery Albray Albury
Allblaster ARBLASTER
Allbut ALLPORT
Allcar ALLCARD
ALLCARD 4 Alcard Allcar Allcart
Allcart ALLCARD
Allckin ALKIN ALLKINS
Allcoin ALKIN ALLKINS
Allcroft ALCROFT ALDCROFT HOLDCROFT
ALLDEN 4 ALDEN Aulden Hallden
Allderdice ALDERDICE
Allderton ALDERTON
Alldis ALDHOUSE ALDIS ALDOUS ALDUS AUDAS AUDUS
Alldiss ALDHOUSE ALDIS ALDOUS ALDUS AUDAS AWDAS ORDERS
ALLDRIDGE ALDRIDGE OLDRIDGE
Alldworth ALDWORTH
Allekin ALKIN ALLKINS
ALLEN 5 Alen ALLAN ALLIN ALYN
ALLETT 92 Acelin ADSETT Aislet ALLATT Allitt ALLOTT Alote Anslett Arselet Arselott Arslet ARSLETT Arsolot Arthlote Arthlottes Artolatt As Ascelin Ascelot Ase Aseelina Aselett Aseplet Ashleat Ashlet Ashlett Ashlott Aslaf Aslat Aslate Aslatt Aslet Aslete ASLETT Asletts Asliate Aslit Aslitt Asllatt Asllett Aslot Aslote Aslott Aslotte Aslut Aslute Aslutt Asplaiet Asplet Asse Asselet Asselett Asselot Asselote Asset Assett Asslade Asslat Asslet Asslett Asslot Asslott Asstlat Ast Astbatt Astelat Astelet Astelot Astlat Astlatt Astlet Astlett Astlott Astolina Asttlet Atelett Atte lote Attlet Auselett Auslet Auslett Awnsellet AYLETT Ayslett AZE Azlack Azlitt Azo Azor De aisse Le asplott
Alleybone HALLYBONE
Allford ALFORD HALFORD
Alliace ALAIS
Allibone HALLYBONE
ALLICK 4 Alick Alix Allix
Allies ALAIS
ALLIN ALLEN
ALLINGHAM 6 Alengame Alengham Alingame Alingham HALLINGHAM
ALLINSON ALLISON
ALLIS 5 Alis Alison ALLISON ALLISS
ALLISON 6 Alis Alison ALLINSON ALLIS ALLISS
ALLISS 5 Alis Alison ALLIS ALLISON
Allist ELLIS
Alliste ELLIS
ALLIT AYLETT Haylet
Allitt ALLATT ALLETT ALLOTT
Allix ALLICK
Allken ALKIN ALLKINS
Allkin ALKIN ALLKINS
ALLKINS 20 Alken Alkens ALKIN Alkins Alkyn Alkyne Alkynes Alkyns Allckin Allcoin Allekin Allken Allkin Allkyn Allkyne Allkynes Aulkin Aulkyns Awlkyns
Allkyn ALKIN ALLKINS
Allkyne ALKIN ALLKINS
Allkynes ALKIN ALLKINS
ALLMAN ALMOND
ALLMARK Hallmark
Allobie ALLABY
ALLOTT 6 ALLATT ALLETT Allitt ELLIOT ELLOTT
ALLPORT 6 Allbut Alport Auport Aupott Awport
ALLRIGHT 7 Aleright

If the name you are interested in is not here, try Section C.

ALLWRIGHT Alright Alrite ALWRIGHT Alwrite
Allsberry ALSBURY AYLESBURY
Allsbery ALSBURY AYLESBURY
Allsbry ALSBURY AYLESBURY
Allsbury ALSBURY AYLESBURY
ALLSOP 5 ALLSOPP ALSOP Alsope Alsopp
ALLSOPP 4 ALLSOP ALSOP Alsope
ALLSWORTH 4 HALLSWORTH Hawlsworth Howlesworth
Allthorpe ALTHORPE
Allward ALLWOOD ALYWARD AYLWARD HAILWOOD HALEWOOD HALWOOD HAYWOOD
ALLWOOD 13 Ailard Ailward Allward Alward Alwart Alwood ALYWARD AYLWARD HAILWOOD HALEWOOD HALWOOD HAYWOOD
Allworth ALDWORTH
ALLWRIGHT 7 Aleright ALLRIGHT Alright Alrite ALWRIGHT Alwrite
Allybone HALLYBONE
Allys ELLIS
ALMON ALMOND
ALMOND ALLMAN ALMON
Alote ADSETT ALLETT ARSLETT ASLETT AYLETT AZE
Alott AYLETT ILOTT
ALP 11 ALFF ALPE ALPHE ALPS AULPH HULF OLFE ULF ULFE ULPH
ALPE 11 ALFF ALP ALPHE ALPS AULPH HULF OLFE ULF ULFE ULPH
ALPHE 11 ALFF ALP ALPE ALPS AULPH HULF OLFE ULF ULFE ULPH
Alport ALLPORT
ALPS 11 ALFF ALP ALPE ALPHE AULPH HULF OLFE ULF ULFE ULPH
Alright ALLRIGHT ALLWRIGHT ALWRIGHT
Alrite ALLRIGHT ALLWRIGHT ALWRIGHT
Als ALCE
Alsberry ALSBURY AYLESBURY
Alsbry ALSBURY AYLESBURY
ALSBURY 28 Ailesberry Ailesbery Ailesbry Ailesbury Ailsberry Ailsbery Ailsbry Ailsbury Albury Alesberry Alesbery Alesbry Alesbury Allsberry Allsbery Allsbry Allsbury Alsberry Alsbry Aylesberry Aylesbery Aylesbry AYLESBURY Aylsberry Aylsbery Aylsbury Elsbury
Alsebrook HALBROOK
ALSOP 5 ALLSOP ALLSOPP Alsope Alsopp
Alsope ALLSOP ALLSOPP ALSOP
Alsopp ALLSOP ALSOP
ALSTON 7 Alstone ASTON AUSTEN AUSTIN Hewsdon Ostin
Alstone ALSTON AUSTIN
ALTHORPE Allthorpe
ALVEY ELVEY ELVY
Alward ALLWOOD ALYWARD AYLWARD HAILWOOD HALEWOOD HALWOOD HAYWOOD
Alwart ALLWOOD ALYWARD AYLWARD HAILWOOD HALEWOOD HALWOOD HAYWOOD
Alwood ALLWOOD ALYWARD AYLWARD HAILWOOD HALEWOOD HALWOOD HAYWOOD
Alworth ALDWORTH
ALWRIGHT 6 ALLRIGHT ALLWRIGHT Alright Alrite Alwrite
Alwrite ALLRIGHT ALLWRIGHT ALWRIGHT
ALYN ALLEN
Alys ELLIS
ALYWARD 13 Ailard Ailward Allward ALLWOOD Alward Alwart Alwood AYLWARD HAILWOOD HALEWOOD HALWOOD HAYWOOD
AMANET 26 Amanethe Amanett Amanez Amaret Amenet Amenete Ammanet Ammenet Ammonet Ammonett Ammonette Ammonnet Amonest Amonet Amonette Amonnet Amonnett Amonret Amonuett Amouet Amounet Hammanett Hammonet Hamonett Uminett
Amanethe AMANET
Amanett AMANET
Amanez AMANET
Amaret AMANET
Ambage AMBRIDGE HAMBRIDGE RAMBRIDGE
Ambery AMBREY
Ambidge AMBRIDGE HAMBRIDGE RAMBRIDGE
Ambige AMBRIDGE HAMBRIDGE RAMBRIDGE
Ambrage AMBRIDGE HAMBRIDGE RAMBRIDGE
AMBREY 5 Ambery Ambrey-evans Ambury Evans-ambrey
Ambrey-evans AMBREY
AMBRIDGE 9 Ambage Ambidge Ambige Ambrage Bambridge HAMBRIDGE RAMBRIDGE Umbrage
Ambury AMBREY
Ame AIME AMEY AMY
Amenet AMANET
Amenete AMANET
AMER 4 AMOR Amore AMOUR
Amery AMORY EMERY IMRIE
AMESBURY 5 Aimsbury AINSBURY Amsburie Amsbury
Amesden AMSDEN
AMEY 6 AIME Ame Amie AMY AMYE
Amfleete AMPHLETT
Amflet AMPHLETT
Amflit AMPHLETT
Amie AIME AMEY AMY AMYE
AMIES 7 AMIS Amise Amiss Amisse AMYS Amyss
AMIS 7 AMIES Amise Amiss Amisse AMYS Amyss
Amisden AMSDEN
Amise AMIES AMIS AMYS
Amiss AMIES AMIS AMYS
Amisse AMIES AMIS AMYS
Ammanet AMANET
Ammenet AMANET
Ammonet AMANET
Ammonett AMANET
Ammonette AMANET
Ammonnet AMANET
Amonest AMANET
Amonet AMANET
Amonette AMANET
Amonnet AMANET
Amonnett AMANET
Amonret AMANET
Amonuett AMANET
AMOR 4 AMER Amore AMOUR
Amore AMER AMOR AMOUR
AMORY 4 Amery EMERY IMRIE
Amouet AMANET
Amounet AMANET
AMOUR 4 AMER AMOR Amore
Ampfleet AMPHLETT
Amphlet AMPHLETT
AMPHLETT 10 Amfleete Amflet Amflit Ampfleet Amphlet Anfleet Anfleete Anflet Anflete
Amsburie AINSBURY AMESBURY
Amsbury AINSBURY AMESBURY
AMSDEN 8 Amesden Amisden Amsdon Amysden Amysdon Armsden De ambrosdon
Amsdon AMSDEN
AMSEL 6 Amzell ANCELL ANSELL Anzell Hansil
AMY 6 AIME Ame AMEY Amie AMYE
AMYE 4 AMEY Amie AMY
AMYS 7 AMIES AMIS Amise Amiss Amisse Amyss
Amysden AMSDEN
Amysdon AMSDEN
Amyss AMIES AMIS AMYS
Amzell AMSEL ANCELL ANSELL
Anam ANNUM
Anams ANNUM
Anbrook ADDENBROOKE
ANCELL 7 AMSEL Amzell ANSELL Anzell Hansel Hansil
ANCOCK 6 ALCOCK AUCOCK Aucott Aukett Awcock
Anders ANDERSON ANDREW ANDREWS
Andersen ANDERSON
ANDERSON 16 ALDERSON Aldersonne Anders Andersen Anderwes ANDREW Andrewe Andrewes ANDREWS Andro Androess Androwes Andrus Auderson Aulderson
Anderwes ANDERSON ANDREW ANDREWS
ANDICOT Endicote
ANDREW 11 Anders ANDERSON Anderwes Andrewe Andrewes ANDREWS Andro Androess Androwes Andrus
Andrewe ANDERSON ANDREW ANDREWS
Andrewes ANDERSON ANDREW ANDREWS
ANDREWS 12 Anders ANDERSON Anderwes ANDREW Andrewe Andrewes Andro Androess Androwes Androws Andrus
Andro ANDERSON ANDREW ANDREWS
Androess ANDERSON ANDREW ANDREWS
Androwes ANDERSON ANDREW ANDREWS
Androws ANDREWS
Andrus ANDERSON ANDREW ANDREWS
Aneley AINLEY
Anfleet AMPHLETT
Anfleete AMPHLETT
Anflet AMPHLETT
Anflete AMPHLETT
ANGEL 4 AINGER ANGELL ANGER
ANGELL 4 AINGER ANGEL ANGER
Angely AINSLIE
ANGER 4 AINGER ANGEL ANGELL
Angoffe ANGOVE
ANGOVE 8 Angoffe Angowgh Angrosse Angrove Engoffe Engove Engrosse
Angowgh ANGOVE
Angrosse ANGOVE
Angrove ANGOVE
ANGUISH ANGUS
ANGUS ANGUISH
Anley AINLEY
ANNABALAH Hannibal Hannible
ANNALL Annel
Annanis ANNUM
Annel ANNALL
Annesly AINSLIE
ANNUM 7 Anam Anams Annanis Annums Anum Anums
Annums ANNUM
Anschamen HENCHMAN HENSMAN HINKSMAN HINXMAN HITCHMAN
ANSCOMB ACOMB Ascomb
ANSELL 8 AMSEL Amzell ANCELL Ansiel Ansill Anzell Hansil
Ansiel ANSELL
Ansill ANSELL
Anslett ADSETT ALLETT ARSLETT ASLETT AYLETT AZE
Anstee ANSTEY
ANSTEY 4 Anstee Anstie ANSTY
Anstice ANSTIS
Anstie ANSTEY ANSTY
ANSTIS Anstice Anstiss
Anstiss ANSTIS
ANSTY ANSTEY Anstie
Antcliff ANTLIFF
Antcliffe ANTLIFF
Antel ANTELL
ANTELL 4 Antel Antil Antle
Anthorn HAWTHORN HAWTHORNE HORTON HOUGHTON ORTON
Antil ANTELL
Antle ANTELL
ANTLIFF 4 Antcliff Antcliffe Antliffe
Antliffe ANTLIFF
Anum ANNUM
Anums ANNUM
Anzell AMSEL ANCELL ANSELL
Ap adam BADHAM
Ap adham BADHAM
Ap eignion BENYON
Ap howell HOWELL POWELL
Ap ithel BETHEL BETHELL BITHEL BOTHELL
Ape APPS
Apelton APPLETON
Apgenti ARGENT
Aple APLEY APPLE
Apleton APPLETON
APLEY 9 Aple Aply Aplye Aplyn Appeley APPLE Appley Applye

If the name you are interested in is not here, try Section C.

APLIN APPLON
Aplton APPLETON
Aply APLEY APPLE
Aplye APLEY APPLE
Aplyn APLEY APPLE
APPELBEE 4 APPLEBEE APPLEBIE APPLEBY
Appeley APLEY APPLE
Appeling APPLIN
Appelton APPLETON
Apperby APPLEBEE APPLEBY
Appes APPS
APPLE 9 Aple APLEY Aply Aplye Aplyn Appeley Appley Applye
APPLEBEE 6 APPELBEE Apperby APPLEBIE APPLEBY Appulbee
APPLEBIE 4 APPELBEE APPLEBEE APPLEBY
APPLEBY 6 APPELBEE Apperby APPLEBEE APPLEBIE Appulbee
APPLETON 7 Apelton Apleton Aplton Appelton Applton Appulton
Appley APLEY APPLE
APPLIN Appeling
APPLON APLIN
Applton APPLETON
Applye APLEY APPLE
Appos APPS
APPS 5 Ape Appes Appos Apt
Appulbee APPLEBEE APPLEBY
Appulton APPLETON
Apt APPS
ARBER 4 Arbor ARBOUR HARBER
ARBLASTER Allblaster Hallblaster
Arbor ARBER ARBOUR HARBER
ARBOUR ARBER Arbor
Arbridge HARBRIDGE
ARCH Arche De arches
ARCHARD 7 Archart ORCHARD Orchart Orcheard Orchet Orchett
Archart ARCHARD ORCHARD
Archbald ARCHBOLD ARCHIBALD
ARCHBOLD 10 Archbald Archbould ARCHIBALD Archibalde Archibauld Archibaulde Archibold Archibould Archiboulde
Archbould ARCHBOLD ARCHIBALD
Arche ARCH
ARCHER ORCHARD
ARCHIBALD 10 Archbald ARCHBOLD Archbould Archibalde Archibauld Archibaulde Archibold Archibould Archiboulde
Archibalde ARCHBOLD ARCHIBALD
Archibauld ARCHBOLD ARCHIBALD
Archibaulde ARCHBOLD ARCHIBALD
Archibold ARCHBOLD ARCHIBALD
Archibould ARCHBOLD ARCHIBALD
Archiboulde ARCHBOLD ARCHIBALD
Arcle ARKLE
ARDEN ARDERN HARDEN
ARDERN ARDEN HARDEN
Ardy GARRAD GARRARD GARRAT GARRATT GARRETT GARROD GERARD GERRARD GERRETT JARRARD JARRATT JARRET JARRETT JARROLD JARVIS JERRARD JERRETT YARD
Argant ARGENT
ARGENT Apgenti Argant
ARIS AYRES
Arkenstall ARKINSTALL
Arkingstall ARKINSTALL
Arkingston ARKINSTALL
ARKINSTALL 8 Arkenstall Arkingstall Arkingston Arkinston Arkinstone Harkinstall Harkinstone
Arkinston ARKINSTALL
Arkinstone ARKINSTALL
ARKLE Arcle
ARKWRIGHT 9 Arthright Arthwright Atrick Atricks Atrix Attrick Attricks Harkwright
ARLET Arlett
Arlett ARLET
Arlosh LOSH
ARM 5 Arme ARMES ARMS Harm
ARMAN 11 Armar ARMER ARMOUR HAMER HARMAN Harmar Harmen HARMER Harmon Harmour
Armantage ARMITAGE
Armar ARMAN ARMER ARMOUR HAMER HARMAN HARMER
ARMATAGE ARMITAGE
Arme ARM ARMES ARMS
Armen ARMON FORMAN NORMAN ORMAN
ARMER 11 ARMAN Armar ARMOUR HAMER HARMAN Harmar Harmen HARMER Harmon Harmour
ARMES 5 ARM Arme ARMS Harm
ARMIN 17 Airmin Airmine Airming Airminge Armine Arming Arminge Armyn Armyne Armyng Armynge Ayrmin Ayrmine Ayrming Ayrminge Ermyn
Armine ARMIN
Arming ARMIN
Arminge ARMIN
ARMITAGE Armantage ARMATAGE
ARMON 6 Armen FORMAN NORMAN ORMAN Ormen
ARMOUR 11 ARMAN Armar ARMER HAMER HARMAN Harmar Harmen HARMER Harmon Harmour
ARMS 5 ARM Arme ARMES Harm
Armsden AMSDEN
Armsworth HARMSWORTH
Armyn ARMIN
Armyne ARMIN
Armyng ARMIN
Armynge ARMIN
Arnald ARNALL ARNOLD
ARNALL 5 Arnald ARNOLD Arnolde Ernald
Arnason ARNISON
Arneson ARNISON
ARNISON 4 Arnason Arneson Arnisson
Arnisson ARNISON
ARNOLD 6 Arnald ARNALL Arnolde Ernald Yarnold
Arnolde ARNALL ARNOLD
ARNOT ARNOTT
ARNOTT ARNOT
ARREQUER 9 ARRIKER ARWAKER Arwicker EARWACKER EARWAKER EARWICKER EOFORWACER ERRICKER
ARRIKER 9 ARREQUER ARWAKER Arwicker EARWACKER EARWAKER EARWICKER EOFORWACER ERRICKER
Arselet ADSETT ALLETT ARSLETT ASLETT AYLETT AZE
Arselott ADSETT ALLETT ARSLETT ASLETT AYLETT AZE
Arslet ADSETT ALLETT ARSLETT ASLETT AYLETT AZE
ARSLETT 89 Acelin ADSETT Aislet ALLETT Alote Anslett Arselet Arselott Arslet Arsolot Arthlote Arthlottes Artolatt As Ascelin Ascelot Ase Aseelina Aselett Aseplet Ashleat Ashlet Ashlett Ashlott Aslaf Aslat Aslate Aslatt Aslet Aslete ASLETT Asletts Asliate Aslit Aslitt Asllatt Asllett Aslot Aslote Aslott Aslotte Aslut Aslute Aslutt Asplaiet Asplet Asse Asselet Asselett Asselot Asselote Asset Assett Asslade Asslat Asslet Asslett Asslot Asslott Asstlat Ast Astbatt Astelat Astelet Astelot Astlat Astlatt Astlet Astlett Astlott Astolina Asttlet Atelett Atte lote Attlet Auselett Auslet Auslett Awnsellet AYLETT Ayslett AZE Azlack Azlitt Azo Azor De aisse Le asplott
Arsolot ADSETT ALLETT ARSLETT ASLETT AYLETT AZE
Artar ARTER ARTHUR
ARTER 6 Artar ARTHUR Arthurs AUTHERS Authurs
Arthlote ADSETT ALLETT ARSLETT ASLETT AYLETT AZE
Arthlottes ADSETT ALLETT ARSLETT ASLETT AYLETT AZE
Arthright ARKWRIGHT
ARTHUR 6 Artar ARTER Arthurs AUTHERS Authurs
Arthurs ARTER ARTHUR AUTHERS
Arthwright ARKWRIGHT
ARTLEY HARTLEY
Artolatt ADSETT ALLETT ARSLETT ASLETT AYLETT AZE
ARWAKER 9 ARREQUER ARRIKER Arwicker EARWACKER EARWAKER EARWICKER EOFORWACER ERRICKER
Arwicker ARREQUER ARRIKER ARWAKER EARWACKER EARWAKER EARWICKER EOFORWACER ERRICKER
As ADSETT ALLETT ARSLETT ASLETT AYLETT AZE
Asborn OSBAND OSBORN OSBORNE OSBOURN OSBOURNE
Ascelin ADSETT ALLETT ARSLETT ASLETT AYLETT AZE
Ascelot ADSETT ALLETT ARSLETT ASLETT AYLETT AZE
Ascham ASKAM ASKHAM
Aschfeilde ASHFIELD
Ascomb ACOMB ANSCOMB
Ascue ASKEW AYSCOUGH
Ase ADSETT ALLETT ARSLETT ASLETT AYLETT AZE
Aseelina ADSETT ALLETT ARSLETT ASLETT AYLETT AZE
Aselett ADSETT ALLETT ARSLETT ASLETT AYLETT AZE
Aseplet ADSETT ALLETT ARSLETT ASLETT AYLETT AZE
ASH 8 AISH AISHE ASHE Ask Aske Aysh Ayshe
ASHDOWN ASHDOWNE
ASHDOWNE ASHDOWN
ASHE 11 AISH AISHE Aisshe ASH Asshe Aysh Ayshe Aysshe De esse Esse
Ashelby ESHELBY EXELBY
ASHFIELD Aschfeilde
Ashin ASHLING
Ashleat ADSETT ALLETT ARSLETT ASLETT AYLETT AZE
Ashlet ADSETT ALLETT ARSLETT ASLETT AYLETT AZE
Ashlett ADSETT ALLETT ARSLETT ASLETT AYLETT AZE
ASHLEY 9 Agtley Aishley Ashly Assheley Astely Asterley ASTLE ASTLEY
ASHLING Ashin
Ashlott ADSETT ALLETT ARSLETT ASLETT AYLETT AZE
Ashly ASHLEY
Ashmale ASHMOLE
Ashmall ASHMOLE
Ashmele ASHMOLE
Ashmell ASHMOLE
Ashmenall ASHMOLE
ASHMOLE 7 Ashmale Ashmall Ashmele Ashmell Ashmenall Ashmoll
Ashmoll ASHMOLE
ASHWELL Ashwill
Ashwill ASHWELL
Ashwode ASHWOOD
ASHWOOD Ashwode
Ask ASH
ASKAM 4 Ascham Askem ASKHAM
Aske ASH
Askell HASKELL HASWELL HUSSELL HUZZELL OSWALD RUSSELL URSELL UZZELL
Askem ASKAM ASKHAM
ASKEW Ascue AYSCOUGH
ASKHAM 4 Ascham ASKAM Askem
Aslaf ADSETT ALLETT ARSLETT ASLETT AYLETT AZE
Aslat ADSETT ALLETT ARSLETT ASLETT AYLETT AZE
Aslate ADSETT ALLETT ARSLETT ASLETT AYLETT AZE
Aslatt ADSETT ALLETT ARSLETT ASLETT AYLETT AZE
Aslet ADSETT ALLETT

If the name you are interested in is not here, try Section C.

ARSLETT ASLETT AYLETT AZE HASLETT
Aslete ADSETT ALLETT ARSLETT ASLETT AYLETT AZE
ASLETT 122 Acelin ADSETT Aislet ALLETT Alote Anslett Arselet Arselott Arslet ARSLETT Arsolot Arthlote Arthlottes Artolatt As Ascelin Ascelot Ase Aseelina Aselett Aseplet Ashleat Ashlet Ashlett Ashlott Aslaf Aslat Aslate Aslatt Aslet Aslete Asletts Asliate Aslit Aslitt Asllatt Asllett Aslot Aslote Aslott Aslotte Aslut Aslute Aslutt Asplaiet Asplet Asse Asselet Asselett Asselot Asselote Asset Assett Asslade Asslat Asslet Asslett Asslot Asslott Asstlat Ast Astbatt Astelat Astelet Astelot Astlat Astlatt Astlet Astlett Astlott Astolina Asttlet Atelett Atte lote Attlet Auselett Auslet Auslett Awnsellet AYLETT Ayslett AZE Azlack Azlitt Azo Azor De aisse Haislett Harselett Harset Harslat Harslet Harslett Haselett Haselette Haslat Hasle Haslet HASLETT Haslit Haslitt Haslot Haslott Haslotte Haslut Haslutt Hassett Hasslat Hasslett Hastlet Hayslett Hazlett Hazlitt Heaslett Heazlett Hesellette Heslet Hoselett Hosleed Huslett Le asplott
Asletts ADSETT ALLETT ARSLETT ASLETT AYLETT AZE
Asley ASTLE ASTLEY
Asliate ADSETT ALLETT ARSLETT ASLETT AYLETT AZE
ASLIN Astlin ASTLING
Aslit ADSETT ALLETT ARSLETT ASLETT AYLETT AZE
Aslitt ADSETT ALLETT ARSLETT ASLETT AYLETT AZE
Asllatt ADSETT ALLETT ARSLETT ASLETT AYLETT AZE
Asllett ADSETT ALLETT ARSLETT ASLETT AYLETT AZE
Aslot ADSETT ALLETT ARSLETT ASLETT AYLETT AZE
Aslote ADSETT ALLETT ARSLETT ASLETT AYLETT AZE
Aslott ADSETT ALLETT ARSLETT ASLETT AYLETT AZE
Aslotte ADSETT ALLETT ARSLETT ASLETT AYLETT AZE
Aslut ADSETT ALLETT ARSLETT ASLETT AYLETT AZE
Aslute ADSETT ALLETT ARSLETT ASLETT AYLETT AZE
Aslutt ADSETT ALLETT ARSLETT ASLETT AYLETT AZE
Asnep ASNIP
ASNIP Asnep Asnipp
Asnipp ASNIP
ASPDEN ASPIN
ASPIN ASPDEN
ASPINALL Aspinwall
Aspinwall ASPINALL
ASPITAL Aspitall
Aspitall ASPITAL
Asplaiet ADSETT ALLETT ARSLETT ASLETT AYLETT AZE
ASPLAN ASPLIN
Asplet ADSETT ALLETT ARSLETT ASLETT AYLETT AZE
ASPLIN ASPLAN
Asse ADSETT ALLETT ARSLETT ASLETT AYLETT AZE
Asselet ADSETT ALLETT ARSLETT ASLETT AYLETT AZE
Asselett ADSETT ALLETT ARSLETT ASLETT AYLETT AZE
Asselot ADSETT ALLETT ARSLETT ASLETT AYLETT AZE
Asselote ADSETT ALLETT ARSLETT ASLETT AYLETT AZE
Assenden OSENTON
Assendon OSENTON
Asset ADSETT ALLETT ARSLETT ASLETT AYLETT AZE
Assett ADSETT ALLETT ARSLETT ASLETT AYLETT AZE
Asshe AISHE ASHE
Assheley ASHLEY
Asslade ADSETT ALLETT ARSLETT ASLETT AYLETT AZE
Asslat ADSETT ALLETT ARSLETT ASLETT AYLETT AZE
Asslet ADSETT ALLETT ARSLETT ASLETT AYLETT AZE
Asslett ADSETT ALLETT ARSLETT ASLETT AYLETT AZE
Asslot ADSETT ALLETT ARSLETT ASLETT AYLETT AZE
Asslott ADSETT ALLETT ARSLETT ASLETT AYLETT AZE
Asst AUST
Asstlat ADSETT ALLETT ARSLETT ASLETT AYLETT AZE
Ast ADSETT ALLETT ARSLETT ASLETT AUST AYLETT AZE
Astbatt ADSETT ALLETT ARSLETT ASLETT AYLETT AZE
Aste AUST
Astelat ADSETT ALLETT ARSLETT ASLETT AYLETT AZE
Astelet ADSETT ALLETT ARSLETT ASLETT AYLETT AZE
Asteley ASTLE ASTLEY
ASTELL Asthill Astill
Astelot ADSETT ALLETT ARSLETT ASLETT AYLETT AZE
Astely ASHLEY ASTLE ASTLEY
Asterley ASHLEY ASTLE ASTLEY
Astes AUST
Asthill ASTELL
Asthy HASTE
Astill ASTELL
Astin AUSTEN AUSTIN
Astlat ADSETT ALLETT ARSLETT ASLETT AYLETT AZE
Astlatt ADSETT ALLETT ARSLETT ASLETT AYLETT AZE
ASTLE 8 Agtley ASHLEY Asley Asteley Astely Asterley ASTLEY
Astlet ADSETT ALLETT ARSLETT ASLETT AYLETT AZE
Astlett ADSETT ALLETT ARSLETT ASLETT AYLETT AZE
ASTLEY 8 Agtley ASHLEY Asley Asteley Astely Asterley ASTLE
Astlin ASLIN ASTLING
ASTLING ASLIN Astlin
Astlott ADSETT ALLETT ARSLETT ASLETT AYLETT AZE
Astolina ADSETT ALLETT ARSLETT ASLETT AYLETT AZE
ASTON ALSTON AUSTEN
Astrage ASTRIDGE
Astride ASTRIDGE
ASTRIDGE Astrage Astride
Astte AUST
Asttlet ADSETT ALLETT ARSLETT ASLETT AYLETT AZE
Astwick AUSTWICK
Aswell HASKELL HASWELL HUSSELL HUZZELL OSWALD RUSSELL URSELL UZZELL
Atcheson ACHESON
Atelett ADSETT ALLETT ARSLETT ASLETT AYLETT AZE
Atey ATTEY ATTY
Athe ATTEY ATTY
Athee ATTEY ATTY
ATHER ADER
Atherol ATHROLL
Atherold ATHROLL
Atheroll ATHROLL
ATHERSICH ATHERSUCH ATHERSYCH
ATHERSUCH ATHERSICH ATHERSYCH
ATHERSYCH ATHERSICH ATHERSUCH
ATHERTON Hatherton
Athew ATTEY ATTY
Athey ATTEY ATTY
Athie ATTEY ATTY
Athrol ATHROLL
Athrole ATHROLL
ATHROLL 9 Atherol Atherold Atheroll Athrol Athrole Athrowl Earthroll Earthrowl
Athrowl ATHROLL
Aththe ATTEY ATTY
Aththew ATTEY ATTY
Aththy ATTEY ATTY
Athy ATTEY ATTY
Athye ATTEY ATTY
ATKIN 6 ADKIN ADKINS AIKEN AITKEN Atkine
Atkine AIKEN AITKEN ATKIN
ATKINS ADKINS HATKINS
ATKINSON ACHESON
Atral ATTRILL
Atree ATTREE TREE
Atrick ARKWRIGHT
Atricks ARKWRIGHT
Atril ATTRILL
Atrill ATTRILL
Atrix ARKWRIGHT
Atset ADSHEAD
Att ree ATTREE TREE
Attay ATTEY ATTY
ATTE BERE 42 A baer A bear A beare A beere A bere A beyre A'barre A'BEAR A'beare A'beere A'beyre Abair Abarre Abbeare Abbir Abear Abeard Abeare Abeer Abeere Abere Abeyre Abier Abore Abour Abuer Abure BEAR BEARE Beire BERE Dalbeare De beare De bere De la bear De la beere DE LA BERE Delaber Delabere Dellabere Delliber
Atte lote ADSETT ALLETT ARSLETT ASLETT AYLETT AZE
Atte ree ATTREE TREE
Atte ATTEY ATTY
Attee ATTEY ATTY
Attenboro ATTENBOROUGH
ATTENBOROUGH 5 Adenburgh Attenboro Attenborrow Attenburgh
Attenborrow ATTENBOROUGH
Attenburgh ATTENBOROUGH
Atterill ATTRILL
Atterwell ATTEWELL ATTWELL ATWILL OTTEWELL
ATTEWELL 9 Atterwell Attewill ATTWELL Atwell Atwells ATWILL OTTEWELL Ottwell
Attewill ATTEWELL ATTWELL ATWILL OTTEWELL
ATTEY 28 Adthy Atey Athe Athee Athew Athey Athie Aththe Aththew Aththy Athy Athye Attay Atte Attee Attha Atthe Atthers Atthew Atthey Atthie Atthy Atti ATTY Attye Authey Hathey
ATTFIELD HADFIELD Matfield
Attha ATTEY ATTY
Atthe ATTEY ATTY
Atthers ATTEY ATTY
Atthew ATTEY ATTY
Atthey ATTEY ATTY
Atthie ATTEY ATTY
Atthy ATTEY ATTY
Atti ATTEY ATTY
Attkin ADKIN
Attkins ADKIN
Attlet ADSETT ALLETT ARSLETT ASLETT AYLETT AZE
Attre ATTREE TREE
ATTREE 6 Atree Att ree Atte ree Attre TREE
Attrick ARKWRIGHT
Attricks ARKWRIGHT
ATTRILL 6 A'teuill Atral Atril Atrill Atterill
ATTWELL 9 Atterwell ATTEWELL Attewill

If the name you are interested in is not here, try Section C.

Atwell Atwells ATWILL OTTEWELL Ottwell
Attwoll ATTWOOLL
ATTWOOD ATWOOD
Attwool ATTWOOLL
ATTWOOLL 5 Attwoll Attwool Atwool Atwooll
ATTY 28 Adthy Atey Athe Athee Athew Athey Athie Aththe Aththew Aththy Athy Athye Attay Atte Attee ATTEY Attha Atthe Atthers Atthew Atthey Atthie Atthy Atti Attye Authey Hathey
Attye ATTEY ATTY
Attyoe ATYED
Atwell ATTEWELL ATTWELL ATWILL OTTEWELL
Atwells ATTEWELL ATTWELL ATWILL OTTEWELL
ATWILL 9 Atterwell ATTEWELL Attewill ATTWELL Atwell Atwells OTTEWELL Ottwell
ATWOOD ATTWOOD
Atwool ATTWOOLL
Atwooll ATTWOOLL
ATYED Attyoe Atyeo
Atyeo ATYED
Auberie ALBERRY AUBRAY AUBREY
Aubery ALBERRY AUBRAY AUBREY
AUBRAY 23 Aber Abri Alberie ALBERRY Albery Auberie Aubery Aubraye AUBREY Aubreye Aubrie Awberie Awbery Awberye Awbrey Awbreye Horberry Horbery Horbury Opberry Opbury Orbery
Aubraye ALBERRY AUBRAY AUBREY
AUBREY 23 Aber Abri Alberie ALBERRY Albery Auberie Aubery AUBRAY Aubraye Aubreye Aubrie Awberie Awbery Awberye Awbrey Awbreye Horberry Horbery Horbury Opberry Opbury Orbery
Aubreye ALBERRY AUBRAY AUBREY
Aubrie ALBERRY AUBRAY AUBREY
Auchain AIKEN EKINS HAWKINS OAKINS OKINS
Auckley OAKLEY
AUCOCK 6 ALCOCK ANCOCK Aucott Aukett Awcock
Aucott ALCOCK ANCOCK AUCOCK
AUDAS 20 Alders Aldhous ALDHOUSE Aldhowse ALDIS Aldiss ALDOUS ALDUS Alduse Alldis Alldiss Audiss AUDUS Auldis AWDAS Awdis Awdus Oldis ORDERS
Auders AUDUS ORDERS
Auderson ALDERSON ANDERSON
Audis AUDUS ORDERS
Audiss ALDHOUSE ALDIS ALDOUS ALDUS AUDAS AUDUS
Audridge AUTRIDGE
AUDUS 14 ALDHOUSE ALDIS Aldiss ALDOUS ALDUS Alldis AUDAS Auders Audis Audiss Auldis Oldis ORDERS
Aughton HAUGHTON HORTON ORTON
Augustin AUSTIN
Augustine AUSTIN
Aukett ALCOCK ANCOCK AUCOCK
Aulden ALDEN ALLDEN
Aulderson ALDERSON ANDERSON
Auldis ALDHOUSE ALDIS ALDOUS ALDUS AUDAS AUDUS
Aulkin ALKIN ALLKINS
Aulkyns ALKIN ALLKINS
AULPH 11 ALFF ALP ALPE ALPHE ALPS HULF OLFE ULF ULFE ULPH
Auport ALLPORT
Aupott ALLPORT
Auselett ADSETT ALLETT ARSLETT ASLETT AYLETT AZE
Auslet ADSETT ALLETT ARSLETT ASLETT AYLETT AZE
Auslett ADSETT ALLETT ARSLETT ASLETT AYLETT AZE
AUST 9 Aeste Asst Ast Aste Astes Astte Auste Awst
Auste AUST
AUSTEN 6 ALSTON Astin ASTON AUSTIN Austyn
AUSTIN 10 ALSTON Alstone Astin Augustin Augustine AUSTEN Austyn Hewsdon Ostin
AUSTWICK Astwick
Austyn AUSTEN AUSTIN
AUTEY 7 Autie AUTY AWTEY Awty Hawty Oute
Autheridg AUTRIDGE
Autheridge AUTRIDGE
AUTHERS 5 ARTER ARTHUR Arthurs Authurs
Authey ATTEY ATTY
Authurs ARTER ARTHUR AUTHERS
Autie AUTEY AWTEY
AUTRIDGE 12 Audridge Autheridg Autheridge Awdridg Awdridge Awtridg Awtridge Odrigd Odrigde Ottridg Ottridge
AUTY 4 AUTEY Awty Oute
Avan AVANN
AVANN Avan Avenn
Avason AVESTON
Avenn AVANN
AVES AVIS
AVESTON Avason Avoison
AVIS 5 AVES HAVERS Havies Havors
Avoison AVESTON
Awain OWEN
Awberie ALBERRY AUBRAY AUBREY
Awbery ALBERRY AUBRAY AUBREY
Awberye ALBERRY AUBRAY AUBREY
Awbrey ALBERRY AUBRAY AUBREY
Awbreye ALBERRY AUBRAY AUBREY
Awcock ALCOCK ANCOCK AUCOCK
AWDAS 15 Alders Aldhous ALDHOUSE Aldhowse ALDIS ALDOUS ALDUS Alduse Alldiss AUDAS Awdis Awdus Oldis ORDERS
Awdis ALDHOUSE ALDIS ALDOUS ALDUS AUDAS AWDAS ORDERS
Awdridg AUTRIDGE
Awdridge AUTRIDGE
Awdus ALDHOUSE ALDIS ALDOUS ALDUS AUDAS AWDAS ORDERS
Awlkyns ALKIN ALLKINS
Awnsellet ADSETT ALLETT ARSLETT ASLETT AYLETT AZE
Awport ALLPORT
Awst AUST
AWTEY AUTEY Autie
Awtridg AUTRIDGE
Awtridge AUTRIDGE
Awty AUTEY AUTY
Axall HACKWELL HAXELL
Axcel EXCEL EXCELL
Axcell EXCEL EXCELL HACKWELL HAXELL
Axel EXCEL EXCELL
Axell EXCEL EXCELL HACKWELL HAXELL
AXTENCE 4 Exten Extence Extens
AXUP Haxup
Ayels AYLES EALES
AYERS 6 AYRES EYERS EYRE EYRES Heires
AYLES 12 Ailes Ails Ayels EALES EELES EYLES HILES Hyles ILES IVES Yeeles
Aylesberry ALSBURY AYLESBURY
Aylesbery ALSBURY AYLESBURY
Aylesbry ALSBURY AYLESBURY
AYLESBURY 28 Ailesberry Ailesbery Ailesbry Ailesbury Ailsberry Ailsbery Ailsbry Ailsbury Albury Alesberry Alesbery Alesbry Alesbury Allsberry Allsbery Allsbry Allsbury Alsberry Alsbry ALSBURY Aylesberry Aylesbery Aylesbry Aylsberry Aylsbery Aylsbury Elsbury
AYLETT 98 Acelin ADSETT Aislet ALLETT ALLIT Alote Alott Anslett Arselet Arselott Arslet ARSLETT Arsolot Arthlote Arthlottes Artolatt As Ascelin Ascelot Ase Aseelina Aselett Aseplet Ashleat Ashlet Ashlett Ashlott Aslaf Aslat Aslate Aslatt Aslet Aslete ASLETT Asletts Asliate Aslit Aslitt Asllatt Asllett Aslot Aslote Aslott Aslotte Aslut Aslute Aslutt Asplaiet Asplet Asse Asselet Asselett Asselot Asselote Asset Assett Asslade Asslat Asslet Assiett Asslot Asslott Asstlat Ast Astbatt Astelat Astelet Astelot Astlat Astlatt Astlet Astlett Astlott Astolina Asttlet Atelett Atte lote Attlet Auselett Auslet Auslett Awnsellet Aylott Ayslett AZE
Azlack Azlitt Azo Azor De aisse Eylett Haylet Ilet ILETT Ilette ILOTT Le asplott
AYLING Ailing
Aylmar AYLMER
AYLMER 8 Ailmer Aimer Alemar Alemer Aylmar Elmar Elmer
Aylott AYLETT ILOTT
Aylsberry ALSBURY AYLESBURY
Aylsbery ALSBURY AYLESBURY
Aylsbury ALSBURY AYLESBURY
AYLWARD 13 Ailard Ailward Allward ALLWOOD Alward Alwart Alwood ALYWARD HAILWOOD HALEWOOD HALWOOD HAYWOOD
AYLWIN Aylwyn
Aylwyn AYLWIN
Aynesley AINSLIE
AYRE 6 AYRES Eayre EYRE Hair HARE
AYRES 11 ARIS AYERS AYRE Eayre EYERS EYRE EYRES Hair HARE Heires
Ayrmin ARMIN
Ayrmine ARMIN
Ayrming ARMIN
Ayrminge ARMIN
AYRTON AIRTON
AYSCOUGH Ascue ASKEW
Aysh AISH ASH ASHE
Ayshe AISH ASH ASHE
Ayslett ADSETT ALLETT ARSLETT ASLETT AYLETT AZE
Aysshe AISHE ASHE
AZE 92 Aas Ace Acelin ADSETT Aislet ALLETT Alote Anslett Arselet Arselott Arslet ARSLETT Arsolot Arthlote Arthlottes Artolatt As Ascelin Ascelot Ase Aseelina Aselett Aseplet Ashleat Ashlet Ashlett Ashlott Aslaf Aslat Aslate Aslatt Aslet Aslete ASLETT Asletts Asliate Aslit Aslitt Asllatt Asllett Aslot Aslote Aslott Aslotte Aslut Aslute Aslutt Asplaiet Asplet Asse Asselet Asselett Asselot Asselote Asset Assett Asslade Asslat Asslet Asslett Asslot Asslott Asstlat Ast Astbatt Astelat Astelet Astelot Astlat Astlatt Astlet Astlett Astlott Astolina Asttlet Atelett Atte lote Attlet Auselett Auslet Auslett Awnsellet AYLETT Ayslett Azlack Azlitt Azo Azor Azzo De aisse Le asplott
Azelwood HAZELWOOD HAZLEWOOD
Azlack ADSETT ALLETT ARSLETT ASLETT AYLETT AZE
Azlewood HAZELWOOD HAZLEWOOD
Azlitt ADSETT ALLETT ARSLETT ASLETT AYLETT AZE
Azo ADSETT ALLETT ARSLETT

If the name you are interested in is not here, try Section C.

ASLETT AYLETT AZE
Azor ADSETT ALLETT ARSLETT ASLETT AYLETT AZE
Azzo AZE
Baalaam BALAM BALLAM BELAM BELLAM
Babar BABER BEAVER
BABBINGTON 4 BABINGTON BEBBINGTON Bebington
BABER 6 Babar Babor Babre Babur BEAVER
BABINGTON 4 BABBINGTON BEBBINGTON Bebington
Babor BABER BEAVER
Babre BABER
Babur BABER
BACCHUS 4 BACKHOUSE Backhus BACKUS
Baccus BACKHOUSE BACKUS BEAKHOUSE
BACH BACHE
BACHE BACH
BACHELOR 6 BATCHELDER Batcheldor BATCHELER Batchellor BATCHELOR
Bachin BALCHIN
BACKAULLER Backoller
BACKHOUSE 17 BACCHUS Baccus Backhurst Backhus Backhust BACKUS Bakehouse Barckus Bauckas Baugust Bawgurst BEAKHOUSE Beakhurst Beaks Beakus Beckus
Backhurst BACKHOUSE BACKUS BEAKHOUSE
Backhus BACCHUS BACKHOUSE BACKUS
Backhust BACKHOUSE BACKUS BEAKHOUSE
Backingam BECKINGHAM
Backinggam BECKINGHAM
Backinggame BECKINGHAM
Backoller BACKAULLER
BACKUS 17 BACCHUS Baccus BACKHOUSE Backhurst Backhus Backhust Bakehouse Barckus Bauckas Baugust Bawgurst BEAKHOUSE Beakhurst Beaks Beakus Beckus
BACON 5 Beaken Beakon Becan Becon
Badam BADHAM
Baddam BADHAM
Baddames BADHAM
Baddarley BAGGALEY BAGLEY BAGULEY
Baddgeer BADGER
Badgary BADGERY
Badgeary BADGERY
BADGER 5 Baddgeer Badier Badjer Bagger
Badgerry BADGERY
BADGERY 10 Badgary Badgeary Badgerry Badgeworthy Bagery Bagworthy Bajurey Bargery Budgery
Badgeworthy BADGERY
BADHAM 9 Ab adam Ab adham Ap adam Ap adham Badam Baddam Baddames Badhams
Badhams BADHAM
Badier BADGER
Badjer BADGER
BADMAN Bedman BODMAN
Badtemp BATEUP
Baetson BATSON
Baettson BATSON
Baffin BAUGHEN BOFFIN
Bagalew BAGGALEY BAGGLEY BAGLEY
Bagalow BAGGALEY BAGGLEY BAGLEY
Bagan BAGGALEY BAGGIN BUGGINS
Bageley BAGGALEY BAGLEY BAGULEY
Bagelie BAGGALEY BAGLEY BAGULEY
Bagenal BAGNALL BAGNELL
Bagery BADGERY
Baggalew BAGGALEY BAGGLEY BAGLEY
BAGGALEY 32 Baddarley Bagalew Bagalow Bagan Bageley Bagelie Baggalew Baggalin Baggalow Baggan Bagge Baggeley Baggen Baggerley Baggiley BAGGIN BAGGLEY Bagguley Bagilye Bagin Baglay BAGLEY Baglie Bagly Bagney Bagueley Baguely BAGULEY Biggin Bigin BUGGINS
Baggalin BAGGALEY BAGGIN BUGGINS
Baggalow BAGGALEY BAGGLEY BAGLEY BAGULEY
Baggan BAGGALEY BAGGIN BUGGINS
Baggazzi BREGAZZIE
Bagge BAGGALEY BAGGIN BUGGINS
Baggeley BAGGALEY BAGLEY BAGULEY
Baggen BAGGALEY BAGGIN BUGGINS
Bagger BADGER
Baggerley BAGGALEY BAGLEY BAGULEY
Baggetripe BRODRIBB
BAGGETT 4 Baggot Baggott BAGOT
Baggiley BAGGALEY BAGLEY BAGULEY
BAGGIN 11 Bagan BAGGALEY Baggalin Baggan Bagge Baggen Bagin Biggin Bigin BUGGINS
BAGGLEY 7 Bagalew Bagalow Baggalew BAGGALEY Baggalow BAGLEY
Baggot BAGGETT BAGOT
Baggott BAGGETT BAGOT
Bagguley BAGGALEY BAGLEY BAGULEY
Bagilye BAGGALEY BAGLEY BAGULEY
Bagin BAGGALEY BAGGIN BUGGINS
Baglay BAGGALEY BAGLEY BAGULEY
BAGLEY 24 Baddarley Bagalew Bagalow Bageley Bagelie Baggalew BAGGALEY Baggalow Baggeley Baggerley Baggiley BAGGLEY Bagguley Bagilye Baglay Baglie Bagly Bagney Bagueley Baguely BAGULEY BAYLEY BEGLEY
Baglie BAGGALEY BAGLEY BAGULEY
Bagly BAGGALEY BAGLEY BAGULEY
BAGNALL Bagenal BAGNELL
BAGNELL Bagenal BAGNALL
Bagney BAGGALEY BAGLEY BAGULEY
BAGOT 4 BAGGETT Baggot Baggott
BAGSHAW Bagshawe
Bagshawe BAGSHAW
Bagueley BAGGALEY BAGLEY BAGULEY
Baguely BAGGALEY BAGLEY BAGULEY
BAGULEY 18 Baddarley Bageley Bagelie BAGGALEY Baggalow Baggeley Baggerley Baggiley Bagguley Bagilye Baglay BAGLEY Baglie Bagly Bagney Bagueley Baguely
Bagworthy BADGERY
Baigbie BEGBIE
BAIGENT Baijeant Baijent
Baignard BANIARD BANYARD
Baijeant BAIGENT
Baijent BAIGENT
Baikbie BEGBIE
Bail BALE BEALE
BAILDON Bayldon
Baile BAILEY
BAILEY 15 Baile BAILLIE Bailly BAILY BALEY Bayle BAYLEY Baylie BAYLIS BAYLISS BAYLY BEALEY BEELEY Beley
BAILLIE 4 BAILEY Bailly BAILY
Bailly BAILEY BAILLIE BAILY
BAILY 8 BAILEY BAILLIE Bailly Baylie BAYLIS BAYLISS BAYLY
BAIN 9 BAINE BAINES BAINS Ban Bane Baun BAWN Bayne
Bainard BANIARD BANYARD
BAINBRIDGE 17 Bainbrig Bainebrigge Bambrig Bambrigge Banbrig Baynbrig Baynbrigge Baynebrigge Beanbrig Bembrig Bembrigge Benbridge Benbrig Benbrigge Beynbrig Brainbridge
Bainbrig BAINBRIDGE
BAINE BAIN Bayne
Baineard BANIARD BANYARD
Bainebrigge BAINBRIDGE
BAINES 7 BAIN BAINS Bane BANES Banns BAYNES
BAINS 5 BAIN BAINES Banns BAYNES
BAINTON BAYNTON BAYTON
BAIRD Beaird BEARD
BAISBROWN 4 Besbrowne Bisborwn Bysbrown
Baisy BAIZEY
BAIZEY Baisy Bayesy
Bajurey BADGERY
BAKE BAKES
Bakehouse BACKHOUSE BACKUS BEAKHOUSE
BAKES BAKE
Baketerpe BRODRIBB
Balaam BALAM BALLAM BELAM BELLAM
BALAM 18 Baalaam Balaam Balan Balem Balen Balham BALLAM Baylam Baylham BELAM Belan Belane Belem Belen Belham BELLAM Bellham
Balan BALAM BALLAM BELAM BELLAM
Balch BAULCH BOLCH
Balchen BALCHIN
Balchild BALCHIN
BALCHIN 15 Bachin Balchen Balchild Balchine Balchylde Baldchild Ballchin Ballchine Balshin Baulchen Baulchin Belshim Bolchen Bolchin
Balchine BALCHIN
Balchylde BALCHIN
BALCOMB 15 BALCOMBE Balcoumb Balcourt Balkam BALKHAM Ballcomb Ballcombe Baucomb Baucombe Baukham Baulcomb Bawcom Bawcomb Bawcombe
BALCOMBE 15 BALCOMB Balcoumb Balcourt Balkam BALKHAM Ballcomb Ballcombe Baucomb Baucombe Baukham Baulcomb Bawcom Bawcomb Bawcombe
Balcoumb BALCOMB BALCOMBE BALKHAM
Balcourt BALCOMB BALCOMBE BALKHAM
Baldchild BALCHIN
Balden BALDING BOLDEN BOULDEN BOULDING BOWLING
Baldery BALDRY
BALDING 15 Balden Baulden BOLDEN Boldin Bolding Bolling Bollyng Bolynge BOULDEN Bouldin BOULDING Bowlden Bowldinge BOWLING
Baldrey BALDRY
BALDRY 4 Baldery Baldrey Bauldry
BALDWIN BALDWYN
BALDWYN BALDWIN
BALE Bail BEALE
Balem BALAM BALLAM BELAM BELLAM
Balen BALAM BALLAM BELAM BELLAM
BALES BALLS BEALES
BALEY 4 BAILEY BEALEY BEELEY
Balham BALAM BALLAM BELAM BELLAM
Balhevd BALLARD
Balinger BALLINGER
Balkam BALCOMB BALCOMBE BALKHAM
BALKHAM 15 BALCOMB BALCOMBE Balcoumb Balcourt Balkam Ballcomb Ballcombe Baucomb Baucombe Baukham Baulcomb Bawcom Bawcomb Bawcombe
BALL Balle BALLS
Ballad BALLARD
BALLAM 18 Baalaam Balaam BALAM Balan Balem Balen Balham Baylam Baylham BELAM Belan Belane Belem Belen Belham BELLAM Bellham
Ballanger BALLINGER
BALLANTINE BALLANTYNE
BALLANTYNE 4 BALLANTINE Ballenden Bellenden
BALLARD 4 Balhevd Ballad Ballarde
Ballarde BALLARD
Ballchin BALCHIN
Ballchine BALCHIN
Ballcomb BALCOMB BALCOMBE BALKHAM
Ballcombe BALCOMB BALCOMBE BALKHAM

If the name you are interested in is not here, try Section C.

Balle BALL BALLS
Ballenden BALLANTYNE
BALLINGER 4 Balinger Ballanger Bollinger
BALLS 5 BALES BALL Balle BEALES
Ballson BOLLSOM
BALM BALME BAUM
BALME BALM
BALMENT BAMENT
BALMFORD BALMFORTH BAMFORD
BALMFORTH 6 BALMFORD Balmforthe BAMFORD BAMFORTH Bamforthe
Balmforthe BALMFORTH BAMFORTH
Balshin BALCHIN
Balsom BOLLSOM
Balson BOLLSOM
Balthrop BARLTROP BARTROP
Baltrop BARLTROP BARTROP
Baltrope BARLTROP BARTROP
BAMBER Baumber
Bambridge AMBRIDGE HAMBRIDGE RAMBRIDGE
Bambrig BAINBRIDGE
Bambrigge BAINBRIDGE
BAMENT BALMENT
BAMFORD BALMFORD BALMFORTH
BAMFORTH 4 BALMFORTH Balmforthe Bamforthe
Bamforthe BALMFORTH BAMFORTH
Bamis BEAMISH
Ban BAIN BAWN
Banbrig BAINBRIDGE
Banckes BANKS
Bancks BANKS
Bane BAIN BAINES BAWN BAYNES
BANES BAINES
BANFIELD BARNFIELD BENFIELD
BANG 5 Bange Banges Bango BANGS
Bangam BINGHAM
BANGAY Bangey Bangy
Bange BANG BANGS
Banges BANG BANGS
Bangey BANGAY
Bangiard BANIARD BANYARD
Bango BANG BANGS
BANGS 5 BANG Bange Banges Bango
Bangy BANGAY
BANHAM Beenham BENHAM
BANIARD 10 Baignard Bainard Baineard Bangiard Banniard BANYARD Benyeard Bunyard Bunyeard
Bank BANKS
Bankes BANKS
BANKS 5 Banckes Bancks Bank Bankes
Banniard BANIARD BANYARD
Banns BAINES BAINS BAYNES
BANSBACH 4 Bansback Banspach Banspack
Bansback BANSBACH
Bansgrove BRANSGROVE
Banspach BANSBACH
Banspack BANSBACH
Bantack BANTICK
BANTICK Bantack
BANTON Bouant
BANYARD 10 Baignard Bainard Baineard Bangiard BANIARD Banniard Benyeard Bunyard Bunyeard
Baragwanath BARAGWANNAH
BARAGWANNAH Baragwanath
Baray BERRY
Barbar BARBER BARBOUR
Barbarr BARBER BARBOUR
BARBER 5 Barbar Barbarr Barbor BARBOUR
Barbor BARBER BARBOUR
BARBOUR 5 Barbar Barbarr BARBER Barbor
Barcker BARKER
Barckus BACKHOUSE BACKUS BEAKHOUSE
BARCLAY Barcley BARKLEY
Barcley BARCLAY BARKLEY
Bardesley BARDLEY BARDSLEY
BARDLEY 8 Bardesley Bardsea Bardsey BARDSLEY Barseley Barsley Barsly
Bardsea BARDLEY BARDSLEY
Bardsey BARDLEY BARDSLEY
BARDSLEY 8 Bardesley BARDLEY Bardsea Bardsey Barseley Barsley Barsly
Bare BEAR BEARE BERE
BAREFOOT 4 Bareford BARFOOT BARFORD
Bareford BAREFOOT
Barelegge BARLEY
BARFOOT BAREFOOT BARFORD
BARFORD BAREFOOT BARFOOT
Bargery BADGERY
BARGH Barghe
Barghe BARGH
BARKER Barcker
BARKLEY BARCLAY Barcley
BARKSHIRE 4 BERKSHIRE Birkshire Burkshire
Barland BORELAND BORLAND BURLAND
Barlee BARLEY
Barleigh BARLEY
BARLEY 6 Barelegge Barlee Barleigh Barlie Barly
Barlie BARLEY
Barlin BARLING
BARLING 5 Barlin Barlinge Barlyng Barmyng
Barlinge BARLING
BARLOW Barlowe
Barlowe BARLOW
BARLTROP 8 Balthrop Baltrop Baltrope Barthrop Barthropp Bartrip BARTROP
Barly BARLEY
Barlyng BARLING
Barmyng BARLING
BARNARD 5 BARNET BARNETT BENNETT BERNARD
Barnehurst BARNHURST
BARNELL Barnhill
BARNES 4 BARNS BURNES BURNS
BARNET 5 BARNARD BARNETT BENNETT BERNARD
BARNETT 5 BARNARD BARNET BENNETT BERNARD
BARNFIELD BANFIELD BENFIELD
Barnhill BARNELL
BARNHURST Barnehurst
BARNS 4 BARNES BURNES BURNS
Barnsberry BARNSBURY BARNSBY
BARNSBURY Barnsberry BARNSBY
BARNSBY Barnsberry BARNSBURY
Baro BARROW
Baroman BARROWMAN
BARON BARRON Beron
BARRADELL Barrowdale Boradale
BARRAT 5 BARRATT BARRET BARRETT Barrott
BARRATT 6 BARRAT BARRET BARRETT Barrot BERRETT
Barrel BORRELL BURRELL BURRILL
BARRET 5 BARRAT BARRATT BARRETT Barrott
BARRETT 9 BARRAT BARRATT BARRET Barrit BARRITT Barrot Barrott BERRETT
Barrit BARRETT BARRITT
BARRITT BARRETT Barrit
Barro BARROW
BARRON BARON
Barrot BARRATT BARRETT
Barrotcluff BARROWCLIFFE
Barrott BARRAT BARRET BARRETT
Barrough BARROW
BARROW 8 Abarrow Baro Barro Barrough Barrows BURROUGHS BURROWS
BARROWCLIFFE Barrotcluff
Barrowdale BARRADELL
BARROWMAN 4 Baroman Boroman Borrowman
Barrows BARROW
BARRY BERRY
Barseley BARDLEY BARDSLEY
Barsley BARDLEY BARDSLEY
Barsly BARDLEY BARDSLEY
Bartan BARTON BARTRAM BERTRAM BETON BOURTON BRETON BURTON BYRON
Bartane BARTON BARTRAM BERTRAM BETON BOURTON BRETON BURTON BYRON
Bartel BARTLE
BARTELL 11 BARTLE BARTWELL Boatell Botel BOTTELL Boughtell Boutell BOWTELL Bowttell Buddell
Barthrop BARLTROP BARTROP
Barthropp BARLTROP BARTROP
BARTLE 4 Bartel BARTELL BARTWELL
BARTLET BARTLETT
BARTLETT BARTLET
BARTON 42 Bartan Bartane Bartone Bartoun Bartrahame BARTRAM Bartrem Bauerton Bertane Berton Bertoun Bertown Bertowne BERTRAM Betan BETON Biron Biroun Birun Bortane Bouerton BOURTON Braton BRETON Bretun Burntoun Buron BURTON Burun BYRON De barton De berton De beton De birton De bret De briton De burton De burun Le bret Le bretun Le burone
Bartone BARTON BARTRAM BERTRAM BETON BOURTON BRETON BURTON BYRON
Bartoun BARTON BARTRAM BERTRAM BETON BOURTON BRETON BURTON BYRON
Bartrahame BARTON BARTRAM BERTRAM BETON BOURTON BRETON BURTON BYRON
BARTRAM 42 Bartan Bartane BARTON Bartone Bartoun Bartrahame Bartrem Bauerton Bertane Berton Bertoun Bertown Bertowne BERTRAM Betan BETON Biron Biroun Birun Bortane Bouerton BOURTON Braton BRETON Bretun Burntoun Buron BURTON Burun BYRON De barton De berton De beton De birton De bret De briton De burton De burun Le bret Le bretun Le burone
Bartrem BARTON BARTRAM BERTRAM BETON BOURTON BRETON BURTON BYRON
Bartrip BARLTROP BARTROP
BARTROP 8 Balthrop Baltrop Baltrope BARLTROP Barthrop Barthropp Bartrip
BARTWELL BARTELL BARTLE
Bascavill BASKERFIELD BASKERVILLE
Bascomb BASCOMBE
BASCOMBE Bascomb Bascum
Bascum BASCOMBE
Baseleigh BAZELEY BAZELY BAZLEY BEAZLEY
Baseley BAZELEY BAZELY BAZLEY BEAZLEY
Basely BAZELEY BAZELY BAZLEY BEAZLEY
Baser BEAZER BESSER
BASEY Bassey
Basfor BESFORD
Basil BASSIL
Basill BASSIL
Baskavil BASKERFIELD BASKERVILLE
Baskavill BASKERFIELD BASKERVILLE
Baskaville BASKERFIELD BASKERVILLE
Baskcavill BASKERFIELD BASKERVILLE
Baskerfeelde BASKERFIELD BASKERVILLE
BASKERFIELD 16 Bascavill Baskavil Baskavill Baskaville Baskcavill Baskerfeelde Baskervil Baskervile BASKERVILLE Baskevile Baskevill Baskeville Baskvyle Beskerville Bnascaville
Baskervil BASKERFIELD BASKERVILLE
Baskervile BASKERFIELD BASKERVILLE
BASKERVILLE 16 Bascavill Baskavil Baskavill Baskaville Baskcavill Baskerfeelde BASKERFIELD Baskervil Baskervile Baskevile Baskevill Baskeville Baskvyle Beskerville Bnascaville
Baskevile BASKERFIELD BASKERVILLE
Baskevill BASKERFIELD BASKERVILLE
Baskeville BASKERFIELD BASKERVILLE
Baskvyle BASKERFIELD BASKERVILLE
BASLINGTON 4 Basslington Bazlington Bazlinton
Bason BATE BATES BEATSON
BASSE 6 Boos Boose Bos BOSS Bosse
BASSET BASSETT
BASSETT BASSET
Bassey BASEY
BASSIL 4 Basil Basill

If the name you are interested in is not here, try Section C.

Bassill
Bassill BASSIL
Basslington BASLINGTON
BATCHELDER 6 BACHELOR Batcheldor BATCHELER Batchellor BATCHELOR
Batcheldor BACHELOR BATCHELDER BATCHELER BATCHELOR
BATCHELER 6 BACHELOR BATCHELDER Batcheldor Batchellor BATCHELOR
Batchellor BACHELOR BATCHELDER BATCHELER BATCHELOR
BATCHELOR 7 BACHELOR BATCHELDER Batcheldor BATCHELER Batchellor BATCHELOUR
BATCHELOUR BATCHELOR
BATE 6 Bason BATES Beats BEATSON BETTS
BATES 7 Bason BATE Beats BEATSON Bets BETTS
BATESON 11 BATSON Battenson Battison Battisson BETTINSON Bettison BUTSON Pattenson PATTINSON PATTISON
BATEUP 4 Badtemp Batup Beatup
BATEY 7 BATTY BATY Batye Bayty BEATTIE Beaty
BATH BATHE
Bathal BETHEL BETHELL BITHEL BOTHELL
BATHE BATH
Bathel BETHEL BETHELL BITHEL BOTHELL
BATHER Bathoe
Bathoe BATHER
BATHY Bethy Bothy
BATLEY Battlay
Batrie BUTTERISS BUTTERY BUTTRESS BUTTREY BUTTRY
BATSON 6 Baetson Baettson BATESON Battson BUTSON
Batte BATTEY BATTY BATTYE
BATTEN 5 Battin Batting Batton Battyn
Battenson BATESON BETTINSON PATTINSON PATTISON
BATTEY 5 Batte Battie BATTY BATTYE
Battie BATTEY BATTY BATTYE
Battin BATTEN
Batting BATTEN
Battison BATESON BETTINSON PATTINSON PATTISON
Battisson BATESON BETTINSON PATTINSON PATTISON
Battlay BATLEY
Batton BATTEN
Battson BATSON
BATTY 9 BATEY Batte BATTEY Battie BATTYE BATY BEATTIE Beaty
BATTYE 5 Batte BATTEY Battie BATTY
Battyn BATTEN
Batup BATEUP
BATY 7 BATEY BATTY Batye Bayty BEATTIE Beaty
Batye BATEY BATY
Baubin BOBIN
Bauch BAUGH BOUCH BOUGH
Bauche BAUGH BOUCH BOUGH
Bauckas BACKHOUSE BACKUS BEAKHOUSE
Baucke BAUGH BOUCH BOUGH
Baucomb BALCOMB BALCOMBE BALKHAM
Baucombe BALCOMB BALCOMBE BALKHAM
Baucot BAWCUTT
Baudrip BRODRIBB
Bauerton BARTON BARTRAM BERTRAM BETON BOURTON BRETON BURTON BYRON
Bauffin BAUGHEN BOFFIN
BAUGH 14 Bauch Bauche Baucke Baughe BOFF BOUCH Bouche Boucke BOUGH Boughe Bowch Bowche Bowgh
Baugham BAUGHEN BOFFIN
Baughan BAUGHEN BOFFIN
Baughe BAUGH BOUCH BOUGH
BAUGHEN 6 Baffin Bauffin Baugham Baughan BOFFIN
Baugust BACKHOUSE BACKUS BEAKHOUSE
Baukham BALCOMB BALCOMBE BALKHAM
BAULCH 4 Balch BOLCH Bolche
Baulchen BALCHIN
Baulchin BALCHIN
Baulcomb BALCOMB BALCOMBE BALKHAM
Baulden BALDING BOLDEN BOULDEN BOULDING BOWLING
Bauldry BALDRY
BAUM BALM
Baumber BAMBER
Baun BAIN BAWN
BAVERSTOCK STOCK
Bavins BEVAN BEVIN BEVINS BIFFIN
Bawcock BOOCOCK BUCKOKE BULCOCK BULCOCKE BULLOCK
Bawcom BALCOMB BALCOMBE BALKHAM
Bawcomb BALCOMB BALCOMBE BALKHAM
Bawcombe BALCOMB BALCOMBE BALKHAM
Bawcut BAWCUTT
BAWCUTT Baucot Bawcut
BAWDEN Boaden BOWDEN
Bawgurst BACKHOUSE BACKUS BEAKHOUSE
BAWN 5 BAIN Ban Bane Baun
BAWTREE Bawtrey Bawtry
Bawtrey BAWTREE
Bawtry BAWTREE
BAX BOX
Baycroft BEACROFT BEECROFT
Bayesy BAIZEY
Baylam BALAM BALLAM BELAM BELLAM
Bayldon BAILDON
Bayle BAILEY
Baylet BOYLETT
Baylett BOYLETT
BAYLEY 4 BAGLEY BAILEY BEGLEY
Baylham BALAM BALLAM BELAM BELLAM
Baylie BAILEY BAILY BAYLIS BAYLISS BAYLY
BAYLIS 6 BAILEY BAILY Baylie BAYLISS BAYLY
BAYLISS 6 BAILEY BAILY Baylie BAYLIS BAYLY
BAYLY 6 BAILEY BAILY Baylie BAYLIS BAYLISS
BAYMAN 5 BEAMAN BEAMOND BEAMONT BEAUMONT
Baymont BEAUMONT
Baynbrig BAINBRIDGE
Baynbrigge BAINBRIDGE
Bayne BAIN BAINE
Baynebrigge BAINBRIDGE
BAYNES 5 BAINES BAINS Bane Banns
BAYNTON BAINTON BAYTON
BAYTON BAINTON BAYNTON
Bayty BATEY BATY
BAZELEY 8 Baseleigh Baseley Basely BAZELY BAZLEY BEAZLEY Bezley
BAZELY 8 Baseleigh Baseley Basely BAZELEY BAZLEY BEAZLEY Bezley
Bazer BEAZER BESSER
BAZLEY 8 Baseleigh Baseley Basely BAZELEY BAZELY BEAZLEY Bezley
Bazlington BASLINGTON
Bazlinton BASLINGTON
Bazoni BAZZONE
BAZZONE Bazoni Bazzoni
Bazzoni BAZZONE
BEACHAM 12 Beachamp Beachen Beachim Beaching Beaucham BEAUCHAMP Bechan BEECHAM Beechen Beechim BEECHING
Beachamp BEACHAM BEAUCHAMP BEECHAM
BEACHELL BEACHILL Bearchill
Beachen BEACHAM BEECHING
Beacher BEECHER
BEACHILL BEACHELL Bearchill
Beachim BEACHAM BEAUCHAMP BEECHAM
Beaching BEACHAM BEECHING
BEACROFT 4 Baycroft Becroft BEECROFT
BEADLE Biddell BIDDLE
Beadmead BIDMEAD
Beadnall BEDNELL
Beagbie BEGBIE
Beagby BEGBIE
Beaird BAIRD BEARD
Beaken BACON
Beakerfield WAKEFIELD
BEAKHOUSE 15 Baccus BACKHOUSE Backhurst Backhust BACKUS Bakehouse Barckus Bauckas Baugust Bawgurst Beakhurst Beaks Beakus Beckus
Beakhurst BACKHOUSE BACKUS BEAKHOUSE
Beakon BACON
Beaks BACKHOUSE BACKUS BEAKHOUSE
Beakus BACKHOUSE BACKUS BEAKHOUSE
BEAL 9 BEALE Beall Beel Beeles VEAL VEALE VEALL Vele
BEALE 5 Bail BALE BEAL Beall
BEALES BALES BALLS
BEALEY 4 BAILEY BALEY BEELEY
Bealin BOYLIN BYOLIN
Beall BEAL BEALE
BEAMAN 10 BAYMAN Beamand Beament BEAMOND BEAMONT BEAUMONT Beeman Behmen BEMAN
Beamand BEAMAN BEAUMONT
Beament BEAMAN BEAUMONT
BEAMISH 9 Bamis BEAMS Beaumes Belmeis Bemayes Bemis Bemysh Bewmays
Beamon BEAUMONT
BEAMOND 5 BAYMAN BEAMAN BEAMONT BEAUMONT
BEAMONT 5 BAYMAN BEAMAN BEAMOND BEAUMONT
BEAMS BEAMISH
BEAN Beane Been
Beanbrig BAINBRIDGE
Beane BEAN
BEAR 46 A baer A bear A beare A beere A bere A beyre A'barre A'BEAR A'beare A'beere A'beyre Abair Abarre Abbeare Abbir Abear Abeard Abeare Abeer Abeere Abere Abeyre Abier Abore Abour Abuer Abure ATTE BERE Bare BEARE BEER BEERE Beire BERE Bier Dalbeare De beare De bere De la bear De la beere DE LA BERE Delaber Delabere Dellabere Delliber
Bearchill BEACHELL BEACHILL
BEARD BAIRD Beaird
Bearda BEARDER
Beardah BEARDER
Beardall BEARDER
Beardar BEARDER
Beardaw BEARDER
Bearden BEARDER
BEARDER 15 Bearda Beardah Beardall Beardar Beardaw Bearden Beardin Beardo Beardoe Beardon Beardow Berdall Berdoe Berdow
Beardin BEARDER
Beardo BEARDER
Beardoe BEARDER
Beardon BEARDER
Beardow BEARDER
Beardsal BEARDSALL BIRDSALL
BEARDSALL 14 Beardsal Beardsel Beardsell Birdsal BIRDSALL Birdsel Birdsell Boardsall Boardsell Burdsal Burdsall Burdsel Burdsell
Beardsel BEARDSALL BIRDSALL
Beardsell BEARDSALL BIRDSALL
BEARE 46 A baer A bear A beare A beere A bere A beyre A'barre A'BEAR A'beare A'beere A'beyre Abair Abarre Abbeare Abbir Abear Abeard Abeare Abeer Abeere Abere Abeyre Abier Abore Abour Abuer Abure ATTE BERE Bare BEAR BEER BEERE Beire BERE Bier Dalbeare De beare De bere De la bear De la beere DE LA BERE Delaber Delabere Dellabere Delliber
Bearhop BEARHOPE BEARUP
BEARHOPE 5 Bearhop Bearop BEARUP Beerup
Bearop BEARHOPE BEARUP
BEARUP 5 Bearhop BEARHOPE Bearop Beerup
BEASANT BESSANT
Beaseley BEASLEY BEAZLEY BEESLEY BESLEY
Beasle BEASLEY BEAZLEY

If the name you are interested in is not here, try Section C.

BEESLEY BESLEY
BEASLEY 34 Beaseley Beasle Beasly Beazeley BEAZLEY Beazly Beeasly Beeseley Beesely Beeslay Beesle Beeslee BEESLEY Beesly Beezeley Beezely Beezley Beezly Beisley Beisly Beseley BESLEY Besly Bessley Beuisley Beysley Bezeley Biesley Biesly Biezley Bisley Bisly Byesley
Beasly BEASLEY BEAZLEY BEESLEY BESLEY
Beathel BETHEL BETHELL BITHEL BOTHELL
Beathell BETHEL BETHELL BITHEL BOTHELL
Beathelle BETHEL BETHELL BITHEL BOTHELL
Beathil BETHEL BETHELL BITHEL BOTHELL
Beathill BETHEL BETHELL BITHEL BOTHELL
BEATON 8 BEATSON BEESON Beeston BEETSON BETHUNE BETSON BETTON
Beatrice BETTERIDGE BETTRIDGE
Beats BATE BATES BETTS
BEATSON 9 Bason BATE BATES BEATON BEESON Beeston BEETSON BETSON
BEATTIE 6 BATEY BATTY BATY BEATTY Beaty
BEATTY BEATTIE
Beatup BATEUP
Beaty BATEY BATTY BATY BEATTIE
Beaucham BEACHAM BEAUCHAMP BEECHAM
BEAUCHAMP 8 BEACHAM Beachamp Beachim Beaucham BEECHAM Beechim De beauchamp
Beaucock BOOCOCK BUCKOKE BULCOCK BULCOCKE BULLOCK
Beaumes BEAMISH
BEAUMONT 16 BAYMAN Baymont BEAMAN Beamand Beament Beamon BEAMOND BEAMONT Beeman Behmen BEMAN Bemond Bemont De beaumont DE NEWBURGH
BEAVAN 8 BEAVEN BEVAN BEVEN BEVIN Bivyen HOCKETT VIVIAN
Beavans BEVAN BEVIN BEVINS BIFFIN
BEAVEN 4 BEAVAN BEVAN BEVIN
BEAVER 4 Babar BABER Babor
Beavins BEVAN BEVIN BEVINS BIFFIN
BEAVIS 4 Beves BEVIS Bevys
Beazeley BEASLEY BEAZLEY BEESLEY BESLEY
BEAZER 32 Baser Bazer BEDER Bedger BEDR BEDSAR BEDSER BEDSIR BEDSOR BEDSTER Beeser BELSER Beser Besor BESSER Betcher BETR BETSAR BETSER BETSHER BETSO BETSOR BETSTER BETTSER BETTSOR BETZAR BETZER Bezer Bezoar Bodser Butzer
BEAZLEY 41 Baseleigh Baseley Basely BAZELEY BAZELY BAZLEY Beaseley Beasle BEASLEY Beasly Beazeley Beazly Beeasly Beeseley Beesely Beeslay Beesle Beeslee BEESLEY Beesly Beezeley Beezely Beezley Beezly Beisley Beisly Beseley BESLEY Besly Bessley Beuisley Beysley Bezeley Bezley Biesley Biesly Biezley Bisley Bisly Byesley
Beazly BEASLEY BEAZLEY
BEBBINGTON 4 BABBINGTON BABINGTON Bebington
Bebe BEEBY
Bebington BABBINGTON BABINGTON BEBBINGTON
Beby BEEBY
Bec BECK
Becan BACON
Bechan BEACHAM BEECHING
Becher BEECHER
BECK 5 Bec Becke Beek Bek
Becke BECK
BECKERLEG BECKERLEGGE
BECKERLEGGE BECKERLEG
BECKET BECKETT
BECKETT 5 BECKET Becquet Bequet BEQUETTE
BECKINGHAM 6 Backingam Backinggam Backinggame Berkingham Bickingham
Beckus BACKHOUSE BACKUS BEAKHOUSE
Becon BACON
Becquet BECKETT BEQUETTE
Becroft BEACROFT BEECROFT
Bedall BEEDALL
Beddingfeld BEDDINGFIELD BEDINGFIELD
BEDDINGFIELD 8 Beddingfeld Bedinfield Bedingfeld BEDINGFIELD Beningfield Bennifield Benningfield
Beddoe BEDDOES BEDDOW BEDDOWS
BEDDOES 4 Beddoe BEDDOW BEDDOWS
BEDDOW 4 Beddoe BEDDOES BEDDOWS
BEDDOWS 6 Beddoe BEDDOES BEDDOW BEDHOUSE Bedhows
BEDELL 6 Bedil Beedale Beedel Beedele BEEDLE
BEDER 27 BEAZER Bedger BEDR BEDSAR BEDSER BEDSIR BEDSOR BEDSTER BELSER BESSER Betcher BETR BETSAR BETSER BETSHER BETSO BETSOR BETSTER BETTSER BETTSOR BETZAR BETZER Bezer Bezoar Bodser Butzer
BEDFORD Bedforth
Bedforth BEDFORD
Bedger BEAZER BEDER BEDR BEDSAR BEDSER BEDSIR BEDSOR BEDSTER BELSER BESSER BETR BETSAR BETSER BETSHER BETSO BETSOR BETSTER BETTSER BETTSOR BETZAR BETZER
BEDHOUSE BEDDOWS Bedhows
Bedhows BEDDOWS BEDHOUSE
Bedil BEDELL BEEDLE
Bedinfield BEDDINGFIELD BEDINGFIELD
Bedingfeld BEDDINGFIELD BEDINGFIELD
BEDINGFIELD 8 Beddingfeld BEDDINGFIELD Bedinfield Bedingfeld Beningfield Bennifield Benningfield
Bedman BADMAN
BEDNELL Beadnall
BEDR 27 BEAZER BEDER Bedger BEDSAR BEDSER BEDSIR BEDSOR BEDSTER BELSER BESSER Betcher BETR BETSAR BETSER BETSHER BETSO BETSOR BETSTER BETTSER BETTSOR BETZAR BETZER Bezer Bezoar Bodser Butzer
BEDSAR 27 BEAZER BEDER Bedger BEDR BEDSER BEDSIR BEDSOR BEDSTER BELSER BESSER Betcher BETR BETSAR BETSER BETSHER BETSO BETSOR BETSTER BETTSER BETTSOR BETZAR BETZER Bezer Bezoar Bodser Butzer
BEDSER 27 BEAZER BEDER Bedger BEDR BEDSAR BEDSIR BEDSOR BEDSTER BELSER BESSER Betcher BETR BETSAR BETSER BETSHER BETSO BETSOR BETSTER BETTSER BETTSOR BETZAR BETZER Bezer Bezoar Bodser Butzer
BEDSIR 27 BEAZER BEDER Bedger BEDR BEDSAR BEDSER BEDSOR BEDSTER BELSER BESSER Betcher BETR BETSAR BETSER BETSHER BETSO BETSOR BETSTER BETTSER BETTSOR BETZAR BETZER Bezer Bezoar Bodser Butzer
BEDSOR 27 BEAZER BEDER Bedger BEDR BEDSAR BEDSER BEDSIR BEDSTER BELSER BESSER Betcher BETR BETSAR BETSER BETSHER BETSO BETSOR BETSTER BETTSER BETTSOR BETZAR BETZER Bezer Bezoar Bodser Butzer
BEDSTER 27 BEAZER BEDER Bedger BEDR BEDSAR BEDSER BEDSIR BEDSOR BELSER BESSER Betcher BETR BETSAR BETSER BETSHER BETSO BETSOR BETSTER BETTSER BETTSOR BETZAR BETZER Bezer Bezoar Bodser Butzer
BEDWARD Bedwood
Bedwood BEDWARD
Beeasly BEASLEY BEAZLEY BEESLEY BESLEY
Beebe BEEBY
Beebee BIBBINS
Beebey BEEBY
BEEBY 5 Bebe Beby Beebe Beebey
BEECHAM 7 BEACHAM Beachamp Beachim Beaucham BEAUCHAMP Beechim
Beechen BEACHAM BEECHING
BEECHENO Bircheno
BEECHER 4 Beacher Becher Bychar
Beechim BEACHAM BEAUCHAMP BEECHAM
BEECHING 6 BEACHAM Beachen Beaching Bechan Beechen
BEECROFT 4 Baycroft BEACROFT Becroft
Beedale BEDELL BEEDLE
BEEDALL Bedall Bidle
Beedel BEDELL BEEDLE
Beedele BEDELL BEEDLE
BEEDLE 7 BEDELL Bedil Beedale Beedel Beedele BIDDLE
Beeford BYFORD
Beeforth BYFORD
Beek BECK
Beel BEAL
Beeles BEAL
BEELEY 4 BAILEY BALEY BEALEY
Beeman BEAMAN BEAUMONT
Been BEAN
Beenham BANHAM BENHAM
BEER 5 BEAR BEARE BEERE Bier
BEERE 4 BEAR BEARE BEER
Beerup BEARHOPE BEARUP
Beeseley BEASLEY BEAZLEY BEESLEY BESLEY
Beesely BEASLEY BEAZLEY BEESLEY BESLEY
Beeser BEAZER BESSER
Beeslay BEASLEY BEAZLEY BEESLEY BESLEY
Beesle BEASLEY BEAZLEY BEESLEY BESLEY
Beeslee BEASLEY BEAZLEY BEESLEY BESLEY
BEESLEY 33 Beaseley Beasle BEASLEY Beasly Beazeley BEAZLEY Beeasly Beeseley Beesely Beeslay Beesle Beeslee Beesly Beezeley Beezely Beezley Beezly Beisley Beisly Beseley BESLEY Besly Bessley Beuisley Beysley Bezeley Biesley Biesly Biezley Bisley Bisly Byesley
Beesly BEASLEY BEAZLEY BEESLEY BESLEY
BEESON 6 BEATON BEATSON Beeston BEETSON BETSON
Beeston BEATON BEATSON BEESON BEETSON BETSON
BEETHAM BETHAM
Beethell BETHEL BETHELL BITHEL BOTHELL
Beetleson BEETLESTONE
Beetleston BEETLESTONE
BEETLESTONE 6 Beetleson Beetleston Bittleson Bittlestone
BEETSON 6 BEATON BEATSON BEESON Beeston BETSON
Beezeley BEASLEY BEAZLEY BEESLEY BESLEY
Beezely BEASLEY BEAZLEY BEESLEY BESLEY
Beezley BEASLEY BEAZLEY BEESLEY BESLEY
Beezly BEASLEY BEAZLEY BEESLEY BESLEY
Beford BYFORD
Begazzi BREGAZZIE
Begbee BEGBIE
Begbey BEGBIE
BEGBIE 11 Baigbie Baikbie Beagbie Beagby Begbee Begbey Begbio Begby Bigbie Bigby
Begbio BEGBIE
Begby BEGBIE
BEGLEY BAGLEY BAYLEY
Behmen BEAMAN BEAUMONT BEMAN
Beire A'BEAR ATTE BERE BEAR BEARE BERE DE LA BERE

If the name you are interested in is not here, try Section C.

Beisley BEASLEY BEAZLEY BEESLEY BESLEY
Beisly BEASLEY BEAZLEY BEESLEY BESLEY
Bek BECK
Belainy BELANEY
BELAM 18 Baalaam Balaam BALAM Balan Balem Balen Balham BALLAM Baylam Baylham Belan Belane Belem Belen Belham BELLAM Bellham
Belan BALAM BALLAM BELAM BELLAM
Belane BALAM BALLAM BELAM BELLAM
BELANEY Belainy Belanie
Belanie BELANEY
BELCHAMBER 4 BELCHAMBERS BELLCHAMBER BELLCHAMBERS
BELCHAMBERS 4 BELCHAMBER BELLCHAMBER BELLCHAMBERS
BELCHER BELLSHEAR
Beldam BELDHAM
BELDHAM Beldam
Belem BALAM BALLAM BELAM BELLAM
Belen BALAM BALLAM BELAM BELLAM
BELERBY 18 BELLABE BELLABEE BELLABEY BELLABIE BELLABY BELLARBE Bellarbey BELLARBIE BELLARBY BELLARBYE BELLEBY BELLERBIE BELLERBY BELLERBYE BELLIBIE BELLOBIE BELLOBYE
Belet BILLETT
Belett BILLETT
Beleus BELLAS BELLIS
Beley BAILEY
Belfrage BERRIDGE
Belham BALAM BALLAM BELAM BELLAM
Belinus BELLINGER BILLIN BILLING BILLINGE BILLINGS
Belitha BELITHER
BELITHER 7 Belitha Blitha Bolitha Bolither BOLITHO Bolithoe
BELLABE 18 BELERBY BELLABEE BELLABEY BELLABIE BELLABY BELLARBE Bellarbey BELLARBIE BELLARBY BELLARBYE BELLEBY BELLERBIE BELLERBY BELLERBYE BELLIBIE BELLOBIE BELLOBYE
BELLABEE 18 BELERBY BELLABE BELLABEY BELLABIE BELLABY BELLARBE Bellarbey BELLARBIE BELLARBY BELLARBYE BELLEBY BELLERBIE BELLERBY BELLERBYE BELLIBIE BELLOBIE BELLOBYE
BELLABEY 18 BELERBY BELLABE BELLABEE BELLABIE BELLABY BELLARBE Bellarbey BELLARBIE BELLARBY BELLARBYE BELLEBY BELLERBIE BELLERBY BELLERBYE BELLIBIE BELLOBIE BELLOBYE
BELLABIE 18 BELERBY BELLABE BELLABEE BELLABEY BELLABY BELLARBE Bellarbey BELLARBIE BELLARBY BELLARBYE BELLEBY BELLERBIE BELLERBY BELLERBYE BELLIBIE BELLOBIE BELLOBYE
BELLABY 18 BELERBY BELLABE BELLABEE BELLABEY BELLABIE BELLARBE Bellarbey BELLARBIE BELLARBY BELLARBYE BELLEBY BELLERBIE BELLERBY BELLERBYE BELLIBIE BELLOBIE BELLOBYE
Bellaies BELLAS BELLIS
BELLAM 18 Baalaam Balaam BALAM Balan Balem Balen Balham BALLAM Baylam Baylham BELAM Belan Belane Belem Belen Belham Bellham
BELLARBE 18 BELERBY BELLABE BELLABEE BELLABEY BELLABIE BELLABY Bellarbey BELLARBIE BELLARBY BELLARBYE BELLEBY BELLERBIE BELLERBY BELLERBYE BELLIBIE BELLOBIE BELLOBYE
Bellarbey BELERBY BELLABE BELLABEE BELLABEY BELLABIE BELLABY BELLARBE BELLARBIE BELLARBY BELLARBYE BELLEBY BELLERBIE BELLERBY BELLERBYE BELLIBIE BELLOBIE BELLOBYE
BELLARBIE 18 BELERBY BELLABE BELLABEE BELLABEY BELLABIE BELLABY BELLARBE Bellarbey BELLARBY BELLARBYE BELLEBY BELLERBIE BELLERBY BELLERBYE BELLIBIE BELLOBIE BELLOBYE
BELLARBY 18 BELERBY BELLABE BELLABEE BELLABEY BELLABIE BELLABY BELLARBE Bellarbey BELLARBIE BELLARBYE BELLEBY BELLERBIE BELLERBY BELLERBYE BELLIBIE BELLOBIE BELLOBYE
BELLARBYE 18 BELERBY BELLABE BELLABEE BELLABEY BELLABIE BELLABY BELLARBE Bellarbey BELLARBIE BELLARBY BELLEBY BELLERBIE BELLERBY BELLERBYE BELLIBIE BELLOBIE BELLOBYE
BELLAS 6 Beleus Bellaies Bellasse BELLIS Belows
Bellasse BELLAS BELLIS
BELLCHAMBER 4 BELCHAMBER BELCHAMBERS BELLCHAMBERS
BELLCHAMBERS 4 BELCHAMBER BELCHAMBERS BELLCHAMBER
BELLEBY 18 BELERBY BELLABE BELLABEE BELLABEY BELLABIE BELLABY BELLARBE Bellarbey BELLARBIE BELLARBY BELLARBYE BELLERBIE BELLERBY BELLERBYE BELLIBIE BELLOBIE BELLOBYE
Bellenden BALLANTYNE
BELLERBIE 18 BELERBY BELLABE BELLABEE BELLABEY BELLABIE BELLABY BELLARBE Bellarbey BELLARBIE BELLARBY BELLARBYE BELLEBY BELLERBY BELLERBYE BELLIBIE BELLOBIE BELLOBYE
BELLERBY 18 BELERBY BELLABE BELLABEE BELLABEY BELLABIE BELLABY BELLARBE Bellarbey BELLARBIE BELLARBY BELLARBYE BELLEBY BELLERBIE BELLERBYE BELLIBIE BELLOBIE BELLOBYE
BELLERBYE 18 BELERBY BELLABE BELLABEE BELLABEY BELLABIE BELLABY BELLARBE Bellarbey BELLARBIE BELLARBY BELLARBYE BELLEBY BELLERBIE BELLERBY BELLIBIE BELLOBIE BELLOBYE
Bellett BILLETT
BELLEW PELLEW
Bellham BALAM BALLAM BELAM BELLAM
BELLIBIE 18 BELERBY BELLABE BELLABEE BELLABEY BELLABIE BELLABY BELLARBE Bellarbey BELLARBIE BELLARBY BELLARBYE BELLEBY BELLERBIE BELLERBY BELLERBYE BELLOBIE BELLOBYE
Bellin BELLINGER BILLIN BILLING BILLINGE BILLINGS BOYLIN BYOLIN
Belling BELLINGER BILLIN BILLING BILLINGE BILLINGS
Bellinge BELLINGER BILLIN BILLING BILLINGE BILLINGS
BELLINGER 22 Belinus Bellin Belling Bellinge Bellings Bellins Billa BILLIN BILLING BILLINGE Billinger BILLINGS Billyng Billynge Billynges Bylling Byllinge Byllinges Byllyng Byllynge Byllynges
Bellings BELLINGER BILLIN BILLING BILLINGE BILLINGS
Bellins BELLINGER BILLIN BILLING BILLINGE BILLINGS
BELLIS 6 Beleus Bellaies BELLAS Bellasse Belows
Bellman BELMAN
BELLOBIE 18 BELERBY BELLABE BELLABEE BELLABEY BELLABIE BELLABY BELLARBE Bellarbey BELLARBIE BELLARBY BELLARBYE BELLEBY BELLERBIE BELLERBY BELLERBYE BELLIBIE BELLOBYE
BELLOBYE 18 BELERBY BELLABE BELLABEE BELLABEY BELLABIE BELLABY BELLARBE Bellarbey BELLARBIE BELLARBY BELLARBYE BELLEBY BELLERBIE BELLERBY BELLERBYE BELLIBIE BELLOBIE
BELLSHEAR BELCHER
BELLWOOD Belwood
BELMAN Bellman
Belmeis BEAMISH
Belows BELLAS BELLIS
BELSER 27 BEAZER BEDER Bedger BEDR BEDSAR BEDSER BEDSIR BEDSOR BEDSTER BESSER Betcher BETR BETSAR BETSER BETSHER BETSO BETSOR BETSTER BETTSER BETTSOR BETZAR BETZER Bezer Bezoar Bodser Butzer
Belshim BALCHIN
BELSTEN 4 Belstone Bilstone Bulstone
Belstone BELSTEN
Belwood BELLWOOD
BEMAN 4 BEAMAN BEAUMONT Behmen
Bemayes BEAMISH
Bembrig BAINBRIDGE
Bembrigge BAINBRIDGE
Bemis BEAMISH
Bemond BEAUMONT
Bemont BEAUMONT
Bemysh BEAMISH
Benats BENNET BENNETT
BENBOW Bendbow
Benbridge BAINBRIDGE
Benbrig BAINBRIDGE
Benbrigge BAINBRIDGE
Benches BINKS
Bendbow BENBOW
Benet BENNET BENNETT BENNETTS
Benetot BENTOTE
Benets BENNETS BENNETT BENNETTS
Benett BENNET BENNETT
Benewith BENNEWITH
Beneworth BENNIWITH
BENFIELD BANFIELD BARNFIELD
BENHAM 4 BANHAM Beenham BONHAM
Benian BENIANS BENNION BENYON
BENIANS 9 Benian Benion Benions Benyan Benyans Benyen BENYON Benyons
Beningfield BEDDINGFIELD BEDINGFIELD
Benion BENIANS BENNION BENYON
Benions BENIANS BENYON
Benit BENNET BENNETT
Benitt BENNET BENNETT
BENNAS Bennis
Bennat BENNET BENNETT BENNETTS
Bennats BENNETS BENNETTS
Bennatt BENNET BENNETT BENNETTS
Bennatts BENNET BENNETS BENNETT BENNETTS
BENNET 16 Benats Benet Benett Benit Benitt Bennat Bennatt Bennatts BENNETT BENNETTS Bennit Bennitt Bonnet BUNNET BUNNETT
BENNETS 6 Benets Bennats Bennatts BENNETT BENNETTS
BENNETT 22 BARNARD BARNET BARNETT Benats Benet Benets Benett Benit Benitt Bennat Bennatt Bennatts BENNET BENNETS

If the name you are interested in is not here, try Section C.

BENNETTS Bennit Bennitt BERNARD Bonnet BUNNET BUNNETT
BENNETTS 10 Benet Benets Bennat Bennats Bennatt Bennatts BENNET BENNETS BENNETT
BENNEWITH Benewith Benneworth
Benneworth BENNEWITH
Bennifield BEDDINGFIELD BEDINGFIELD
Bennimore FENNIMORE FILMER FINMORE FINNEMORE PHILLIMORE VENNIMORE
Benningfield BEDDINGFIELD BEDINGFIELD
BENNION 5 Benian Benion Benyen BENYON
Bennis BENNAS
Bennit BENNET BENNETT
Bennitt BENNET BENNETT
BENNIWITH Beneworth Benworth
BENSKIN Benskyn
Benskyn BENSKIN
BENTALL Benthall
Bentcliff BILLCLIFF
Benteley BENTLEY BENTLY
Benthall BENTALL
BENTLEY 4 Benteley BENTLY Bentlye
BENTLY 4 Benteley BENTLEY Bentlye
Bentlye BENTLEY BENTLY
Bentole BENTOTE
Bentot BENTOTE
BENTOTE 4 Benetot Bentole Bentot
Benworth BENNIWITH
Benyan BENIANS BENYON
Benyans BENIANS BENYON
Benyeard BANIARD BANYARD
Benyen BENIANS BENNION BENYON
BENYON 11 Ap eignion Benian BENIANS Benion Benions BENNION Benyan Benyans Benyen Benyons
Benyons BENIANS BENYON
Bequet BECKETT BEQUETTE
BEQUETTE 4 BECKETT Becquet Bequet
Berant BESANT BESSANT
Berbridge BURBIDGE BURBRIDGE
Berdall BEARDER
Berdoe BEARDER
Berdow BEARDER
BERE 48 A baer A bear A beare A beere A bere A beyre A'barre A'BEAR A'beare A'beere A'beyre Abair Abarre Abbeare Abbir Abear Abeard Abeare Abeer Abeere Abere Abeyre Abier Abore Abour Abuer Abure ATTE BERE Bare BEAR BEARE Beire Bire Bur BURGH BURR Burre Dalbeare De beare De bere De la bear De la beere DE LA BERE Delaber Delabere Dellabere Delliber
BERESFORD 4 BERISFORD Berresford BERRISFORD
Bergam BURGHAM BURGUM
Bergham BURGHAM BURGUM
Bergidge BURBIDGE BURBRIDGE
BERGIN BURGIN
Bergis BURGES BURGESS BURGIS
Bergum BURGHAM BURGUM
Beriall BORRELL BURRELL BURRILL
Beridge BERRIDGE
Berie BERRY
Berig BERRIDGE
Berige BERRIDGE
BERISFORD 4 BERESFORD Berresford BERRISFORD
Berkenshaw BIRKENSHAW BIRKINSHAW BURKINSHAW
Berkingham BECKINGHAM
Berkinhead BIRKENHEAD
Berkinshaw BIRKENSHAW BIRKINSHAW BURKINSHAW
BERKSHIRE 4 BARKSHIRE Birkshire Burkshire
Berkumshaw BIRKENSHAW BIRKINSHAW BURKINSHAW
Bermingham BIRMINGHAM
BERNARD 5 BARNARD BARNET BARNETT BENNETT
Beron BARON
Berresford BERESFORD BERISFORD BERRISFORD
BERRETT BARRATT BARRETT
Berrey BERRY BURY
BERRIDGE 5 Belfrage Beridge Berig Berige
Berrie BERRY
Berrill BORRELL BURRELL BURRILL
BERRISFORD 4 BERESFORD BERISFORD Berresford
BERRY 13 Baray BARRY Berie Berrey Berrie Berrye Bery Burey Burie Burrey BURRY BURY
Berrye BERRY
Bert BIRT BURT BURTE BUST BUTT
Bertane BARTON BARTRAM BERTRAM BETON BOURTON BRETON BURTON BYRON
Berton BARTON BARTRAM BERTRAM BETON BOURTON BRETON BURTON BYRON
Bertoun BARTON BARTRAM BERTRAM BETON BOURTON BRETON BURTON BYRON
Bertown BARTON BARTRAM BERTRAM BETON BOURTON BRETON BURTON BYRON
Bertowne BARTON BARTRAM BERTRAM BETON BOURTON BRETON BURTON BYRON
BERTRAM 42 Bartan Bartane BARTON Bartone Bartoun Bartrahame BARTRAM Bartrem Bauerton Bertane Berton Bertoun Bertown Bertowne Betan BETON Biron Biroun Birun Bortane Bouerton BOURTON Braton BRETON Bretun Burntoun Buron BURTON Burun BYRON De barton De berton De beton De birton De bret De briton De burton De burun Le bret Le bretun Le burone
Bertwell BERTWISTLE
Bertwisle BERTWISTLE BIRTWHISTLE BIRTWISLE
BERTWISTLE 13 Bertwell Bertwisle Betwisell Birkwistle Birthwistle Birtwell BIRTWHISTLE BIRTWISLE Birtwistle Birtwizle Botweazle Burtwistle
Bervil BURVILL BURVILLE
Bervill BURVILL BURVILLE
Berville BURVILL BURVILLE
Berwill BURVILL BURVILLE
Berwille BURVILL BURVILLE
Bery BERRY
BESANT 5 Berant Besent BESSANT Bezzant
Besbrowne BAISBROWN
Beseley BEASLEY BEAZLEY BEESLEY BESLEY
Besent BESANT
Beser BEAZER BESSER
Besfor BESFORD
BESFORD 4 Basfor Besfor Bestford
Besgrove BISGROVE
Besgrow BISGROVE
Beskerville BASKERFIELD BASKERVILLE
BESLEY 33 Beaseley Beasle BEASLEY Beasly Beazeley BEAZLEY Beeasly Beeseley Beesely Beeslay Beesle Beeslee BEESLEY Beesly Beezeley Beezely Beezley Beezly Beisley Beisly Beseley Besly Bessley Beuisley Beysley Bezeley Biesley Biesly Biezley Bisley Bisly Byesley
Besly BEASLEY BEAZLEY BEESLEY BESLEY
Besor BEAZER BESSER
BESS BEST
BESSANT 5 BEASANT Berant BESANT Bezzant
BESSER 32 Baser Bazer BEAZER BEDER Bedger BEDR BEDSAR BEDSER BEDSIR BEDSOR BEDSTER Beeser BELSER Beser Besor Betcher BETR BETSAR BETSER BETSHER BETSO BETSOR BETSTER BETTSER BETTSOR BETZAR BETZER Bezer Bezoar Bodser Butzer
Besset BISSET
Bessley BEASLEY BEAZLEY BEESLEY BESLEY
Bessot BISSET
BEST BESS
Bestford BESFORD
Beswatherick BESWETHERICK
Beswathick BESWETHERICK
BESWETHERICK 7 Beswatherick Beswathick Bosvathic Bosvathick Boswatherick Boswathick
BESWORTH BOSWORTH
Betan BARTON BARTRAM BERTRAM BETON BOURTON BRETON BURTON BYRON
Betcher BEAZER BEDER BEDR BEDSAR BEDSER BEDSIR BEDSOR BEDSTER BELSER BESSER BETR BETSAR BETSER BETSHER BETSO BETSOR BETSTER BETTSER BETTSOR BETZAR BETZER
Beteridge BETTERIDGE BETTRIDGE
Bethall BETHEL BETHELL BITHEL BOTHELL
BETHAM BEETHAM
Betheall BETHEL BETHELL BITHEL BOTHELL
BETHEL 30 Abethell Ap ithel Bathal Bathel Beathel Beathell Beathelle Beathil Beathill Beethell Bethall Betheall Betheldo Bethele BETHELL Bethelle Bethill Bethll Bethold Bethole Betholl Bettell Beythell BITHEL BOTHELL Bythall Bythel Bythell Ithell
Betheldo BETHEL BETHELL BITHEL BOTHELL
Bethele BETHEL BETHELL BITHEL BOTHELL
BETHELL 29 Abethell Ap ithel Bathal Bathel Beathel Beathell Beathelle Beathil Beathill Beethell Bethall Betheall BETHEL Betheldo Bethele Bethelle Bethill Bethold Bethole Betholl Bettell Beythell BITHEL BOTHELL Bythall Bythel Bythell Ithell
Bethelle BETHEL BETHELL BITHEL BOTHELL
Bethill BETHEL BETHELL BITHEL BOTHELL
Bethll BETHEL BITHEL
Bethold BETHEL BETHELL BITHEL BOTHELL
Bethole BETHEL BETHELL BITHEL BOTHELL
Betholl BETHEL BETHELL BITHEL BOTHELL
BETHUNE BEATON BETTON
Bethy BATHY
Betleston BEETLESTONE
BETON 42 Bartan Bartane BARTON Bartone Bartoun Bartrahame BARTRAM Bartrem Bauerton Bertane Berton Bertoun Bertown Bertowne BERTRAM Betan Biron Biroun Birun Bortane Bouerton BOURTON Braton BRETON Bretun Burntoun Buron BURTON Burun BYRON De barton De berton De beton De birton De bret De briton De burton De burun Le bret Le bretun Le burone
BETR 27 BEAZER BEDER Bedger BEDR BEDSAR BEDSER BEDSIR BEDSOR BEDSTER BELSER BESSER Betcher BETSAR BETSER BETSHER BETSO BETSOR BETSTER BETTSER BETTSOR BETZAR BETZER Bezer Bezoar Bodser Butzer
Betridge BETTERIDGE BETTRIDGE
Bets BATES BETTS
BETSAR 27 BEAZER BEDER Bedger BEDR BEDSAR BEDSER BEDSIR BEDSOR BEDSTER BELSER BESSER Betcher BETR BETSER BETSHER BETSO BETSOR BETSTER BETTSER BETTSOR BETZAR BETZER Bezer Bezoar Bodser Butzer
BETSER 27 BEAZER BEDER Bedger BEDR BEDSAR BEDSER BEDSIR BEDSOR BEDSTER BELSER BESSER Betcher BETR BETSAR BETSHER BETSO BETSOR BETSTER BETTSER BETTSOR BETZAR BETZER Bezer

If the name you are interested in is not here, try Section C.

Bezoar Bodser Butzer
BETSHER 27 BEAZER BEDER Bedger BEDR BEDSAR BEDSER BEDSIR BEDSOR BEDSTER BELSER BESSER Betcher BETR BETSAR BETSER BETSO BETSOR BETSTER BETTSER BETTSOR BETZAR BETZER Bezer Bezoar Bodser Butzer
BETSO 27 BEAZER BEDER Bedger BEDR BEDSAR BEDSER BEDSIR BEDSOR BEDSTER BELSER BESSER Betcher BETR BETSAR BETSER BETSHER BETSOR BETSTER BETTSER BETTSOR BETZAR BETZER Bezer Bezoar Bodser Butzer
BETSON 6 BEATON BEATSON BEESON Beeston BEETSON
BETSOR 27 BEAZER BEDER Bedger BEDR BEDSAR BEDSER BEDSIR BEDSOR BEDSTER BELSER BESSER Betcher BETR BETSAR BETSER BETSHER BETSO BETSTER BETTSER BETTSOR BETZAR BETZER Bezer Bezoar Bodser Butzer
BETSTER 27 BEAZER BEDER Bedger BEDR BEDSAR BEDSER BEDSIR BEDSOR BEDSTER BELSER BESSER Betcher BETR BETSAR BETSER BETSHER BETSO BETSOR BETTSER BETTSOR BETZAR BETZER Bezer Bezoar Bodser Butzer
BETSWORTH Bettsworth
Bettell BETHEL BETHELL BITHEL BOTHELL
Bettenson BETTINSON
Betteredge BETTERIDGE BETTRIDGE
BETTERIDGE 8 Beatrice Beteridge Betridge Betteredge BETTRIDGE Bitteredge Pethridge
BETTINSON 10 BATESON Battenson Battison Battisson Bettenson Bettison Pattenson PATTINSON PATTISON
Bettison BATESON BETTINSON PATTINSON PATTISON
BETTON BEATON BETHUNE
BETTRIDGE 8 Beatrice Beteridge Betridge Betteredge BETTERIDGE Bitteredge Pethridge
BETTS 5 BATE BATES Beats Bets
BETTSER 27 BEAZER BEDER Bedger BEDR BEDSAR BEDSER BEDSIR BEDSOR BEDSTER BELSER BESSER Betcher BETR BETSAR BETSER BETSHER BETSO BETSOR BETSTER BETTSOR BETZAR BETZER Bezer Bezoar Bodser Butzer
BETTSOR 27 BEAZER BEDER Bedger BEDR BEDSAR BEDSER BEDSIR BEDSOR BEDSTER BELSER BESSER Betcher BETR BETSAR BETSER BETSHER BETSO BETSOR BETSTER BETTSER BETZAR BETZER Bezer Bezoar Bodser Butzer
Bettsworth BETSWORTH
Betwisell BERTWISTLE BIRTWISLE
BETZAR 27 BEAZER BEDER Bedger BEDR BEDSAR BEDSER BEDSIR BEDSOR BEDSTER BELSER BESSER Betcher BETR BETSAR BETSER BETSHER BETSO BETSOR BETSTER BETTSER BETTSOR BETZER Bezer Bezoar Bodser Butzer
BETZER 27 BEAZER BEDER Bedger BEDR BEDSAR BEDSER BEDSIR BEDSOR BEDSTER BELSER BESSER Betcher BETR BETSAR BETSER BETSHER BETSO BETSOR BETSTER BETTSER BETTSOR BETZAR Bezer Bezoar Bodser Butzer
Beuglas BOOKLESS BUGLASS
Beuisley BEASLEY BEAZLEY BEESLEY BESLEY
BEVAN 14 Bavins BEAVAN Beavans BEAVEN Beavins Bevance Bevans BEVEN Bevens BEVIN Bevince BEVINS BIFFIN
Bevance BEVAN BEVIN BEVINS BIFFIN
Bevans BEVAN BEVIN BEVINS BIFFIN
Bevele BEVILL
Bevelle BEVILL
BEVEN 4 BEAVAN BEVAN BEVIN
Bevens BEVAN BEVIN BEVINS BIFFIN
Beverlee BEVERLEY
BEVERLEY Beverlee Beverly
Beverly BEVERLEY
Beves BEAVIS BEVIS
Bevile BEVILL
BEVILL 5 Bevele Bevelle Bevile Beville
Beville BEVILL
BEVIN 14 Bavins BEAVAN Beavans BEAVEN Beavins BEVAN Bevance Bevans BEVEN Bevens Bevince BEVINS BIFFIN
Bevince BEVAN BEVIN BEVINS BIFFIN
BEVINS 11 Bavins Beavans Beavins BEVAN Bevance Bevans Bevens BEVIN Bevince BIFFIN
BEVIS 4 BEAVIS Beves Bevys
Bevys BEAVIS BEVIS
BEWICK Bewicke
Bewicke BEWICK
Bewmays BEAMISH
Bewshea BEWSHER
Bewshear BEWSHER
BEWSHER Bewshea Bewshear
Beynbrig BAINBRIDGE
BEYNON Bynon
Beysley BEASLEY BEAZLEY BEESLEY BESLEY
Beythell BETHEL BETHELL BITHEL BOTHELL
Bezeley BEASLEY BEAZLEY BEESLEY BESLEY
Bezer BEAZER BEDER BEDR BEDSAR BEDSER BEDSIR BEDSOR BEDSTER BELSER BESSER BETR BETSAR BETSER BETSHER BETSO BETSOR BETSTER BETTSER BETTSOR BETZAR BETZER
Bezley BAZELEY BAZELY BAZLEY BEAZLEY
Bezoar BEAZER BEDER BEDR BEDSAR BEDSER BEDSIR BEDSOR BEDSTER BELSER BESSER BETR BETSAR BETSER BETSHER BETSO BETSOR BETSTER BETTSER BETTSOR BETZAR BETZER
Bezzant BESANT BESSANT
Bibbel BIBLE
Bibbey BIBBY
BIBBINS Beebee
Bibble BIBLE
BIBBY Bibbey
Bibel BIBLE
BIBLE 4 Bibbel Bibble Bibel
Bick BIX
Bickerdyke BIGGADIKE
BICKERTON Bigerton Biggerton
Bickes BIX
Bickingham BECKINGHAM
Bicks BIX
Bickston PEXTON PICKSTONE PICTON
Biday BYTHEWAY
Biddel BIDDLE BIDEL BIDEWELL BIDWELL
Biddell BEADLE BIDDLE
BIDDER Bydder
BIDDLE 13 BEADLE BEEDLE Biddel Biddell BIDEL Bidell BIDEWELL Bidle BIDWELL Bidwill Bydall Bydewell
BIDEL 10 Biddel BIDDLE Bidell BIDEWELL Bidle BIDWELL Bidwill Bydall Bydewell
Bidell BIDDLE BIDEL BIDEWELL BIDWELL
BIDEWELL 10 Biddel BIDDLE BIDEL Bidell Bidle BIDWELL Bidwill Bydall Bydewell
BIDGOOD 14 Biggott BIGWOOD Bregewood Bridewood Bridgewood Bridgewoodde Bridgood BRIDGWOOD Bridgwoode Bridwood Brigoods Brigwood Broodgwood
Bidle BEEDALL BIDDLE BIDEL BIDEWELL BIDWELL
Bidmade BIDMEAD
BIDMEAD 5 Beadmead Bidmade Bidmeade Bidmeed
Bidmeade BIDMEAD
Bidmeed BIDMEAD
BIDWELL 10 Biddel BIDDLE BIDEL Bidell BIDEWELL Bidle Bidwill Bydall Bydewell
Bidwill BIDDLE BIDEL BIDEWELL BIDWELL
Bier BEAR BEARE BEER
Biesley BEASLEY BEAZLEY BEESLEY BESLEY
Biesly BEASLEY BEAZLEY BEESLEY BESLEY
Biezley BEASLEY BEAZLEY BEESLEY BESLEY
BIFFIN 11 Bavins Beavans Beavins BEVAN Bevance Bevans Bevens BEVIN Bevince BEVINS
Biford BYFORD BYFORT
Bigadag BIGGADIKE
Bigadyke BIGGADIKE
Bigbie BEGBIE
Bigby BEGBIE
Bigerton BICKERTON
BIGGADIKE 10 Bickerdyke Bigadag Bigadyke Biggerdag Biggerdike Dickerday Dickerdyke Digadag Diggerdyke
Biggazzi BREGAZZIE
Biggerdag BIGGADIKE
Biggerdike BIGGADIKE
Biggerton BICKERTON
Biggin BAGGALEY BAGGIN BUGGINS
Biggott BIDGOOD BIGWOOD BRIDGWOOD
BIGHAM 9 Bingam Bingeham BINGHAM Binghame Bingum Binham Byngham Bynghame
Bigin BAGGALEY BAGGIN BUGGINS
Bignal BIGNEL BIGNELL
Bignall BIGNEL BIGNELL
BIGNEL 4 Bignal Bignall BIGNELL
BIGNELL 5 Bignal Bignall BIGNEL Bignoll
Bignoll BIGNELL
BIGWOOD 14 BIDGOOD Biggott Bregewood Bridewood Bridgewood Bridgewoodde Bridgood BRIDGWOOD Bridgwoode Bridwood Brigoods Brigwood Broodgwood
Bilbeart GILBARD GILBERT
Bilbie BILBY
Bilborough BILBROUGH
BILBROUGH 6 Bilborough Bilbruck Bilbruff BILLBROUGH Billbruff
Bilbruck BILBROUGH
Bilbruff BILBROUGH
BILBY Bilbie
BILKEY Bilky
Bilky BILKEY
Billa BELLINGER BILLIN BILLING BILLINGE BILLINGS
BILLBROUGH BILBROUGH Billbruff
Billbruff BILBROUGH BILLBROUGH
BILLCLIFF 4 Bentcliff Biltcliff Bintcliff
BILLETT 5 Belet Belett Bellett Billot
BILLIN 22 Belinus Bellin Belling Bellinge BELLINGER Bellings Bellins Billa BILLING BILLINGE Billinger BILLINGS Billyng Billynge Billynges Bylling Byllinge Byllinges Byllyng Byllynge Byllynges
BILLING 22 Belinus Bellin Belling Bellinge BELLINGER Bellings Bellins Billa BILLIN BILLINGE Billinger BILLINGS Billyng Billynge Billynges Bylling Byllinge Byllinges Byllyng Byllynge Byllynges
BILLINGE 22 Belinus Bellin Belling Bellinge BELLINGER Bellings Bellins Billa BILLIN BILLING Billinger BILLINGS Billyng Billynge Billynges Bylling Byllinge Byllinges Byllyng Byllynge Byllynges
Billinger BELLINGER BILLIN BILLING BILLINGE BILLINGS

If the name you are interested in is not here, try Section C.

BILLINGS 22 Belinus
Bellin Belling Bellinge
BELLINGER Bellings
Bellins Billa BILLIN
BILLING BILLINGE
Billinger Billyng
Billynge Billynges
Bylling Byllinge
Byllinges Byllyng
Byllynge Byllynges
Billot BILLETT
Billyng BELLINGER BILLIN
BILLING BILLINGE
BILLINGS
Billynge BELLINGER BILLIN
BILLING BILLINGE
BILLINGS
Billynges BELLINGER
BILLIN BILLING BILLINGE
BILLINGS
Bilstone BELSTEN
Biltcliff BILLCLIFF
BINDLEY BINGLEY BINLEY
BING 5 Binge BYNG Bynge
Ping
Bingam BIGHAM BINGHAM
Binge BING BYNG
Bingeham BIGHAM BINGHAM
BINGHAM 10 Bangam BIGHAM
Bingam Bingeham
Binghame Bingum Binham
Byngham Bynghame
Binghame BIGHAM BINGHAM
BINGLEY BINDLEY BINLEY
Bingum BIGHAM BINGHAM
Binham BIGHAM BINGHAM
BINKS Benches
BINLEY BINDLEY BINGLEY
Bintcliff BILLCLIFF
Biram BYRAM BYRON
Birbage BURBIDGE
BURBRIDGE
BIRBECK 4 Birchbeck
BIRKBECK Burkbeck
Birbidge BURBIDGE
BURBRIDGE
Birbridge BURBIDGE
BURBRIDGE
BIRCH BURCH Byrch
Birchbeck BIRBECK
BIRKBECK
Birchenall BIRCHENOUGH
Birchenhough BIRCHENOUGH
Bircheno BEECHENO
BIRCHENOUGH 6 Birchenall
Birchenhough Birchinall
Birchinhough
Byrchenhaughe
BIRCHER BURCHER
Birchinall BIRCHENOUGH
Birchinhead BIRKENHEAD
Birchinhough BIRCHENOUGH
BIRD 5 BIRT Burd BURT
Byrd
Birdsal BEARDSALL
BIRDSALL
BIRDSALL 15 Beardsal
BEARDSALL Beardsel
Beardsell Birdsal
Birdsel Birdsell
Birdsill Boardsall
Boardsell Burdsal
Burdsall Burdsel
Burdsell
Birdsel BEARDSALL
BIRDSALL
Birdsell BEARDSALL
BIRDSALL
Birdsill BIRDSALL
Bire BERE BURGH BURR
Birges BURGES BURGESS
BURGIS
Birk BURKE
BIRKBECK 4 BIRBECK
Birchbeck Burkbeck
BIRKENHEAD 4 Berkinhead
Birchinhead Birkinhead
BIRKENSHAW 7 Berkenshaw
Berkinshaw Berkumshaw
BIRKINSHAW Burkenshaw
BURKINSHAW
Birkinhead BIRKENHEAD
BIRKINSHAW 7 Berkenshaw
Berkinshaw Berkumshaw
BIRKENSHAW Burkenshaw
BURKINSHAW
Birkmyer BIRKMYRE
BIRKMYRE Birkmyer
Birkshire BARKSHIRE
BERKSHIRE
Birkwistle BERTWISTLE
BIRTWHISTLE BIRTWISLE
BIRMINGHAM Bermingham
Birnes BURNES BURNS
Birns BURNES BURNS
Biron BARTON BARTRAM
BERTRAM BETON BOURTON
BRETON BURTON BYRON
Biroun BARTON BARTRAM
BERTRAM BETON BOURTON
BRETON BURTON BYRON
BIRT 15 Bert BIRD Birte
Birtt Bortt Bourt
Burrtt BURT BURTE Burtt
BUST BUTT Byrt Byrtt
BIRTCHNELL BURCHNALL
Birte BIRT BURT BURTE
BUST BUTT
Birthwistle BERTWISTLE
BIRTWHISTLE BIRTWISLE
Birtt BIRT BURT BURTE
BUST BUTT
Birtwell BERTWISTLE
BIRTWHISTLE BIRTWISLE
BIRTWHISTLE 10 Bertwisle
BERTWISTLE Birkwistle
Birthwistle Birtwell
BIRTWISLE Birtwistle
Birtwizle Burtwistle
BIRTWISLE 12 Bertwisle
BERTWISTLE Betwisell
Birkwistle Birthwistle
Birtwell BIRTWHISTLE
Birtwistle Birtwizle
Botweazle Burtwistle
Birtwistle BERTWISTLE
BIRTWHISTLE BIRTWISLE
Birtwizle BERTWISTLE
BIRTWHISTLE BIRTWISLE
Birun BARTON BARTRAM
BERTRAM BETON BOURTON
BRETON BURTON BYRON
Bisacker BISSACRE
Bisbie BISBY
Bisborwn BAISBROWN
BISBY 5 Bisbie Biszby
Bizbie Bizby
Biscomb BUSCOMBE
Biscumb BUSCOMBE
Biset BISSET
BISGROVE 8 Besgrove
Besgrow Bosgrove
HISGROVE Isgro ISGROVE
Isgroves
BISH 6 Bishe Bisshe BYSH
Byshe Bysshe
Bishe BISH BYSH
BISHOP Bishopp Bisshop
Bishopp BISHOP
Bisit BISSET
Bisley BEASLEY BEAZLEY
BEESLEY BESLEY
Bisly BEASLEY BEAZLEY
BEESLEY BESLEY
Bisot BISSET
BISS BISSE
BISSACRE Bisacker
Bissat BISSET
BISSE BISS
BISSET 16 Besset Bessot
Biset Bisit Bisot
Bissat Bissit Bissot
Bizat Bizet Bizett
Bizit Bizot Bizzet
Bysset
Bisshe BISH BYSH
Bisshop BISHOP
Bissit BISSET
Bissot BISSET
Biszby BISBY
BITHEL 30 Abethell Ap
ithel Bathal Bathel
Beathel Beathell
Beathelle Beathil
Beathill Beethell
Bethall Betheall BETHEL
Betheldo Bethele
BETHELL Bethelle
Bethill Bethll Bethold
Bethole Betholl Bettell
Beythell BOTHELL
Bythall Bythel Bythell
Ithell
Bitheway BYTHEWAY
Bitteredge BETTERIDGE
BETTRIDGE
Bittleson BEETLESTONE
Bittlestone BEETLESTONE
Biurst BYHURST
Bivyen BEAVAN HOCKETT
VIVIAN
BIX 8 Bick Bickes Bicks
Bixe Bixx Byx Byxe
Bixe BIX
Bixx BIX
Bizat BISSET
Bizbie BISBY
Bizby BISBY
Bizet BISSET
Bizett BISSET
Bizit BISSET
Bizot BISSET
Bizzet BISSET
BLABER Blabir Blabour
Blabir BLABER
Blabour BLABER
BLACK 5 Blacke BLAKE Blek
Leblake
BLACKAH BLACKER BLAKEY
BLACKALL BLACKHALL
Blackden BLAGDON
Blacke BLACK
Blackeley BLACKLEY
BLAKELEY BLAKELY
BLACKER BLACKAH BLAKEY
BLACKET BLACKETT
BLACKETT BLACKET
BLACKGROVE BLAGRAVE
BLAGROVE
BLACKHALL BLACKALL
Blackie BLAIKIE
Blacklay BLAKELEY BLAKELY
BLAKEY
BLACKLEY 9 Blackeley
BLAKELEY BLAKELY
Blakley Bleackley
BLEAKLEY Bleekley
Blekley
BLACKLOCK 4 Blaiklock
BLAYLOCK Blellock
Blacknee BLACKNEY
BLAKENEY
BLACKNEY Blacknee
BLAKENEY
BLACKWELL BLAKEWELL
BLADEN 8 Bladin BLADON
Blaiden Blaidon Blayden
BLAYDON Bleadon
Bladin BLADEN BLADON
BLAYDON
BLADON 8 BLADEN Bladin
Blaiden Blaidon Blayden
BLAYDON Bleadon
Blagden BLAGDON
BLAGDON Blackden Blagden
BLAGRAVE BLACKGROVE
BLAGROVE
BLAGROVE BLACKGROVE
BLAGRAVE
Blaickie BLAIKIE
Blaiden BLADEN BLADON
BLAYDON
Blaidon BLADEN BLADON
BLAYDON
BLAIKIE Blackie Blaickie
Blaiklock BLACKLOCK
BLAYLOCK
Blakalay BLAKELEY BLAKELY
BLAKEY
BLAKE 4 BLACK Blek
Leblake
Blakelah BLAKELEY BLAKELY
BLAKEY
Blakelay BLAKELEY BLAKELY
BLAKEY
BLAKELEY 12 Blackeley
Blacklay BLACKLEY
Blakalay Blakelah
Blakelay BLAKELY BLAKEY
Blaklah Blaklay Blakley
BLAKELY 16 Blackeley
Blacklay BLACKLEY
Blakalay Blakelah
Blakelay BLAKELEY
BLAKEY Blaklah Blaklay
Blakley Bleackley
BLEAKLEY Bleekley
Blekley
BLAKENEY Blacknee
BLACKNEY
Blakesley BLAXLEY
BLAKEWELL BLACKWELL
BLAKEY 11 BLACKAH BLACKER
Blacklay Blakalay
Blakelah Blakelay
BLAKELEY BLAKELY
Blaklah Blaklay
Blaklah BLAKELEY BLAKELY
BLAKEY
Blaklay BLAKELEY BLAKELY
BLAKEY
Blakley BLACKLEY BLAKELEY
BLAKELY
Blan BLANN
BLANCHARD Blanched
BLANSHARD
Blanched BLANCHARD
BLANSHARD
BLANCHET BLANCHETT
BLANCHETT BLANCHET
BLANDFORD BLANFORD
BLANFORD BLANDFORD
BLANN Blan Blans
Blans BLANN
BLANSHARD BLANCHARD
Blanched
Blatnauer PLATNAUER
Blatner PLATNAUER
BLAXLEY Blakesley
Blay BLEAY
Blayden BLADEN BLADON
BLAYDON
BLAYDON 8 BLADEN Bladin
BLADON Blaiden Blaidon
Blayden Bleadon
BLAYLOCK 4 BLACKLOCK
Blaiklock Blellock
Bleackley BLACKLEY
BLAKELY BLEAKLEY
Bleadon BLADEN BLADON
BLAYDON
Bleak BLEEK
BLEAKLEY 6 BLACKLEY
BLAKELY Bleackley
Bleekley Blekley
BLEAY Blay Bley

If the name you are interested in is not here, try Section C.

BLEEK 4 Bleak Blleck Blsack
Bleekley BLACKLEY BLAKELY BLEAKLEY
Blek BLACK BLAKE
Blekley BLACKLEY BLAKELY BLEAKLEY
Blellock BLACKLOCK BLAYLOCK
Blencko BLENCOWE BLINCOW
Blenckoe BLENCOWE BLINCOW
Blenckow BLENCOWE BLINCOW
Blenco BLENCOWE BLINCOW
Blencoe BLENCOWE BLINCOW
Blencow BLENCOWE BLINCOW
BLENCOWE 23 Blencko Blenckoe Blenckow Blenco Blencoe Blencow Blenko Blenkoe Blenkow Blincko Blinckoe Blinckow Blinco Blincoe BLINCOW Blincowe Blinko Blyncho Blynchoo Blyncko Blynckoe Blynckow
BLENKIN Blenking
Blenking BLENKIN
Blenko BLENCOWE BLINCOW
Blenkoe BLENCOWE BLINCOW
Blenkow BLENCOWE BLINCOW
Blessard BLEZARD
Bley BLEAY
BLEZARD Blessard
Blie BLISS
Blincko BLENCOWE BLINCOW
Blinckoe BLENCOWE BLINCOW
Blinckow BLENCOWE BLINCOW
Blinco BLENCOWE BLINCOW
Blincoe BLENCOWE BLINCOW
BLINCOW 23 Blencko Blenckoe Blenckow Blenco Blencoe Blencow BLENCOWE Blenko Blenkoe Blenkow Blincko Blinckoe Blinckow Blinco Blincoe Blincowe Blinko Blyncho Blynchoo Blyncko Blynckoe Blynckow
Blincowe BLENCOWE BLINCOW
Blinko BLENCOWE BLINCOW
Blis BLISS
Blise BLISS
BLISS 8 Blie Blis Blise Blisse Blys Blyse Blyss
Blisse BLISS
Blitha BELITHER BOLITHO
Blleck BLEEK
Bloar BLORE BLOWER
BLOCK 4 Blog BLOGG Bloog
Blockey BLOCKLEY
BLOCKLEY 5 Blockey Blockly Blookley Brockley
Blockly BLOCKLEY
Bloer BLORE BLOWER
Blog BLOCK BLOGG
BLOGG 4 BLOCK Blog Bloog
Bloice BLOIS BLOSS BLOYS
BLOIS 10 Bloice Bloise BLOSS Blosse Bloy Bloyce Bloye BLOYS Bloyse
Bloise BLOIS BLOSS BLOYS
BLOMFIELD BLOOMFIELD
Blon BLUNN
BLOOD Blud Bludd
Bloog BLOCK BLOGG
Blookley BLOCKLEY
BLOOMFIELD 9 BLOMFIELD BLUMFIELD Bramfield BROMFIELD BROOMFIELD Brounfield Brownfield BRUMFIELD
BLOOR 4 Bloore BLORE BLOWER
Bloore BLOOR BLORE BLOWER
BLORE 6 Bloar Bloer BLOOR Bloore BLOWER
BLOSS 10 Bloice BLOIS Bloise Blosse Bloy Bloyce Bloye BLOYS Bloyse
Blosse BLOIS BLOSS BLOYS
BLOWER 6 Bloar Bloer BLOOR Bloore BLORE
Bloy BLOIS BLOSS BLOYS
Bloyce BLOIS BLOSS BLOYS
Bloye BLOIS BLOSS BLOYS
BLOYS 10 Bloice BLOIS Bloise BLOSS Blosse Bloy Bloyce Bloye Bloyse
Bloyse BLOIS BLOSS BLOYS
Blsack BLEEK
Blud BLOOD
Bludd BLOOD
Bluecock SLUCOCK
Blumell BLUMER
BLUMER Blumell Blummel
BLUMFIELD BLOOMFIELD
Blummel BLUMER
BLUMSOM Blumson Blumsum
Blumson BLUMSOM
Blumsum BLUMSOM
BLUNDEN Blundon
Blundon BLUNDEN
Blundred BUNDRED
Blune BLUNN
BLUNN 4 Blon Blune Blunne
Blunne BLUNN
Blyncho BLENCOWE BLINCOW
Blynchoo BLENCOWE BLINCOW
Blyncko BLENCOWE BLINCOW
Blynckoe BLENCOWE BLINCOW
Blynckow BLENCOWE BLINCOW
Blys BLISS
Blyse BLISS
Blyss BLISS
Bnascaville BASKERFIELD BASKERVILLE
Boaden BAWDEN BOWDEN
BOAG 5 BOAK Boake Boeg Boog
BOAK 5 BOAG Boake Boeg Boog
Boake BOAG BOAK
Boaler BOLER BOWLER
Boar BOOR BOORN BORE BOURN BOURNE
BOARD Bord
Boarder BORDER
Boardsall BEARDSALL BIRDSALL
Boardsell BEARDSALL BIRDSALL
Boarland BORELAND BORLAND BURLAND
Boas BOASE BOWES
BOASE 5 Boas Boaz Bose BOWES
BOAST Bost
Boatell BARTELL BOTTELL BOWTELL
Boaz BOASE BOWES
Bobain BOBIN
BOBBET Bobit
BOBIN 7 Baubin Bobain Bobine Bobing Boubine Bowbin
Bobine BOBIN
Bobing BOBIN
Bobit BOBBET
Bocock BOOCOCK BUCKOKE BULCOCK BULCOCKE BULLOCK
Bococke BOOCOCK BUCKOKE BULCOCK BULCOCKE BULLOCK
Bocoke BOOCOCK BUCKOKE BULCOCK BULCOCKE BULLOCK
BODDAN 4 Bodden BODEN BOWDEN
Bodden BODDAN BODEN BOWDEN
Boddeworth BUDWORTH
Boddeworthe BUDWORTH
Boddewurth BUDWORTH
Boddimead BODIMEADE
Boddimeade BODIMEADE
Boddimede BODIMEADE
BODDY BODY
Boddymead BODIMEADE
Boddymeade BODIMEADE
Boddymede BODIMEADE
BODEN 4 BODDAN Bodden BOWDEN
Bodener BODINNAR
Bodeworth BUDWORTH
Bodeworthe BUDWORTH
Bodewurth BUDWORTH
BODFISH Botfish
Bodimaid BODIMEADE
Bodimead BODIMEADE
BODIMEADE 17 Boddimead Boddimeade Boddimede Boddymead Boddymeade Boddymede Bodimaid Bodimead Bodimeaid Bodimede Bodiment Bodyman Bodymand Bodymead Bodymeade Bodymede
Bodimeaid BODIMEADE
Bodimede BODIMEADE
Bodiment BODIMEADE
Bodinar BODINNAR
Bodiner BODINNAR
BODINNAR 4 Bodener Bodinar Bodiner
BODMAN BADMAN Bodmin
Bodmin BODMAN
Bodser BEAZER BEDER BEDR BEDSAR BEDSER BEDSIR BEDSOR BEDSTER BELSER BESSER BETR BETSAR BETSER BETSHER BETSO BETSOR BETSTER BETTSER BETTSOR BETZAR BETZER
BODY BODDY
Bodyman BODIMEADE
Bodymand BODIMEADE
Bodymead BODIMEADE
Bodymeade BODIMEADE
Bodymede BODIMEADE
Boeg BOAG BOAK
Boelare BOWDLER
BOFF 4 BAUGH Boof BOUGH
BOFFIN 6 Baffin Bauffin Baugham Baughan BAUGHEN
Bog BOGG
BOGG 5 Bog Bogge Boggs Bogs
Bogge BOGG
BOGGIS Bogis
Boggs BOGG
Bogis BOGGIS
Bogs BOGG
Bohan BOHEN BOHUN
BOHEN Bohan BOHUN
BOHUN Bohan BOHEN
BOIES 6 BOISE BOYCE BOYES BOYS BOYSE
BOILES BOYLES
Boilet BOYLETT
Boilett BOYLETT
Boils BOYLE BOYLES
BOISE 6 BOIES BOYCE BOYES BOYS BOYSE
Boist BUIST
Boland BORELAND BORLAND BURLAND
Bolbrook HALBROOK
BOLCH 4 Balch BAULCH Bolche
Bolche BAULCH BOLCH
Bolchen BALCHIN
Bolchin BALCHIN
BOLD BOULD
BOLDEN 15 Balden BALDING Baulden Boldin Bolding Bolling Bollyng Bolynge BOULDEN Bouldin BOULDING Bowlden Bowldinge BOWLING
Boldin BALDING BOLDEN BOULDEN BOULDING BOWLING
Bolding BALDING BOLDEN BOULDEN BOULDING BOWLING
BOLER 4 Boaler Bouler BOWLER
Boleyn BOLLEN BULLEN BULLIN
Bolitha BELITHER BOLITHO
Bolither BELITHER
BOLITHO 5 BELITHER Blitha Bolitha Bolithoe
Bolithoe BELITHER BOLITHO
BOLLEN 4 Boleyn BULLEN BULLIN
Bolling BALDING BOLDEN BOULDEN BOULDING BOWLING
Bollinger BALLINGER
BOLLSOM 4 Ballson Balsom Balson
Bollyng BALDING BOLDEN BOULDEN BOULDING BOWLING
BOLTON BOULTON
Bolynge BALDING BOLDEN BOULDEN BOULDING BOWLING
Bondred BUNDRED
BONE 6 BOON BOONE BOWEN BOWN Bowun
Boneface BONIFACE
BONEHAM Boomham
BONEHILL 8 Bonel BONELL Bonhil Bonhill Bonill Bonnel Bonnell
Bonel BONEHILL BONELL
BONELL 8 BONEHILL Bonel Bonhil Bonhill Bonill Bonnel Bonnell
Boner BONNER
BONES 5 BORNE BOURN BOURNE BOWNESS
Boneyface BONIFACE
BONHAM BENHAM
Bonhil BONEHILL BONELL
Bonhill BONEHILL BONELL
BONIFACE 7 Boneface Boneyface Bonneyface Bonniface Bonnyface Bonyface
Bonill BONEHILL BONELL
Bonite BONITHAN
BONITHAN Bonite Bonity
Bonity BONITHAN
Bonnel BONEHILL BONELL
Bonnell BONEHILL BONELL
BONNER Boner
Bonnet BENNET BENNETT BUNNET BUNNETT
BONNEY 5 BONNY Buney BUNNEY Bunny
Bonneyface BONIFACE
Bonniface BONIFACE
BONNY BONNEY
Bonnyface BONIFACE
BONSER BONSOR
BONSOR BONSER

If the name you are interested in is not here, try Section C.

Bontavern BONTHRON
Bontawern BONTHRON
Bontemps BONTEMS
BONTEMS Bontemps
Bonthorn BONTHRON
Bonthorne BONTHRON
Bonthoux BONTOUX
BONTHRON 7 Bontavern Bontawern Bonthorn Bonthorne Bonthrone Bunthorn
Bonthrone BONTHRON
BONTOUX Bonthoux Bontus
Bontus BONTOUX
Bonyface BONIFACE
BOOCOCK 25 Bawcock Beaucock Bocock Bococke Bocoke Boococks Bookcok Bookecocke Boolcock Boulcock Bowcoc Bowcock Bowcocke Bowcoocke Bowkoke BUCKOKE BULCOCK BULCOCKE Bulcok Bulcoke Bulkok Bulkoke Bullcock BULLOCK
Boococks BOOCOCK BUCKOKE BULCOCK BULCOCKE BULLOCK
BOODLE BUDDLE
Boof BOFF
Boog BOAG BOAK
Bookcok BOOCOCK BUCKOKE BULCOCK BULCOCKE BULLOCK
Bookecocke BOOCOCK BUCKOKE BULCOCK BULCOCKE BULLOCK
BOOKER BROOKER
Booking BROOKING
BOOKLESS 7 Beuglas Buckles BUGLASS Bugless Buickless Buigloss
Boolcock BOOCOCK BUCKOKE BULCOCK BULCOCKE BULLOCK
Boomham BONEHAM
BOON 4 BONE BOONE BOWEN
BOONE 4 BONE BOON BOWEN
BOOR 8 Boar BOORN Boorne BORE Born BOURN BOURNE
BOORMAN BOREMAN BOWMAN
BOORN 8 Boar BOOR Boorne BORE Born BOURN BOURNE
Boorne BOOR BOORN BORE BOURN BOURNE
Boos BASSE BOSS
Boose BASSE BOSS
BOOT 4 BOOTE Bootes Boots
BOOTE 4 BOOT Bootes Boots
Bootes BOOT BOOTE
BOOTH Boothe
BOOTHBY BOUTHBY
Boothe BOOTH
BOOTHROYD BUTHROYD
Boots BOOT BOOTE
Boplet POPLETT
Boradale BARRADELL
Bord BOARD
Borden BURDEN
BORDER Boarder
Bordland BORELAND BORLAND BURLAND
BORE 8 Boar BOOR BOORN Boorne Born BOURN BOURNE
BORELAND 8 Barland Boarland Boland Bordland BORLAND Bourland BURLAND
BOREMAN 6 BOORMAN BORMAN Bourman BOWERMAN BOWMAN
Boresbroke FOSBROKE FOSBROOK
BORLAND 8 Barland Boarland Boland Bordland BORELAND Bourland BURLAND
BORMAN 4 BOREMAN Bourman BOWERMAN
Born BOOR BOORN BORE BOURN BOURNE
BORNE 4 BONES BOURN BOURNE
BORODALE BORROWDALE
Boroman BARROWMAN
Borowes BURROWS
BORRELL 10 Barrel Beriall Berrill Borrill Burhill Burrall BURRELL BURRILL Buryll
Borrill BORRELL BURRELL BURRILL
BORROUGHS BURROUGHS BURROWS
BORROWDALE BORODALE
Borrowe BURROWS
Borrowes BURROWS
Borrowman BARROWMAN
Bortane BARTON BARTRAM BERTRAM BETON BOURTON BRETON BURTON BYRON
Bortt BIRT BURT BURTE BUST BUTT
Bos BASSE BOSS
Boscumb BUSCOMBE
Bose BOASE BOWES
Bosgrove BISGROVE
BOSS 6 BASSE Boos Boose Bos Bosse
Bosse BASSE BOSS
Bosstake BOSTOCK
Bossworth BOSWORTH
Bost BOAST
BOSTOCK 8 Bosstake Bostocke Bostok Bostoke De bostock De bostok De boxtoc
Bostocke BOSTOCK
Bostok BOSTOCK
Bostoke BOSTOCK
Bosvathic BESWETHERICK
Bosvathick BESWETHERICK
Boswatherick BESWETHERICK
Boswathick BESWETHERICK
BOSWORTH BESWORTH Bossworth
Botel BARTELL BOTTELL BOWTELL
BOTELER 6 Botelier Botteler BUTLER Buttlar Buttler
Botelier BOTELER BUTLER
Botfish BODFISH
BOTHAMLEY BOTTOMLEY
BOTHELL 29 Abethell Ap ithel Bathal Bathel Beathel Beathell Beathelle Beathil Beathill Beethell Bethall Betheall BETHEL Betheldo Bethele BETHELL Bethelle Bethill Bethold Bethole Betholl Bettell Beythell BITHEL Bythall Bythel Bythell Ithell
Bothy BATHY
Botoler BUTLER
Botollien BUTLER
Botrey BUTTERISS BUTTERY BUTTRESS BUTTREY BUTTRY
Botry BUTTERISS BUTTERY BUTTRESS BUTTREY BUTTRY
Botteler BOTELER BUTLER
BOTTELL 9 BARTELL Boatell Botel Boughtell Boutell BOWTELL Bowttell Buddell
Botterel BUTTERISS BUTTERY BUTTRESS BUTTREY BUTTRY
BOTTOMLEY BOTHAMLEY
Bottreaux BUTTERISS BUTTERY BUTTRESS BUTTREY
Bottrel BUTTERISS BUTTERY BUTTRESS BUTTREY BUTTRY
Bottris BUTTERISS BUTTERY BUTTRESS BUTTREY BUTTRY
Botweazle BERTWISTLE BIRTWISLE
Bouant BANTON
Boubine BOBIN
BOUCH 13 Bauch Bauche Baucke BAUGH Baughe Bouche Boucke BOUGH Boughe Bowch Bowche Bowgh
Bouche BAUGH BOUCH BOUGH
BOUCHER 6 BOUCHIER Bouchoer Boutcher Boutchoer BUTCHER
BOUCHIER BOUCHER
Bouchoer BOUCHER BUTCHER
Boucke BAUGH BOUCH BOUGH
Boud BOWD
Boude BOWD
Boudelers BOWDLER
Boudlers BOWDLER
Bouerton BARTON BARTRAM BERTRAM BETON BOURTON BRETON BURTON BYRON
BOUGH 14 Bauch Bauche Baucke BAUGH Baughe BOFF BOUCH Bouche Boucke Boughe Bowch Bowche Bowgh
Boughe BAUGH BOUCH BOUGH
Boughtell BARTELL BOTTELL BOWTELL
BOULBY Bowlby
Boulcock BOOCOCK BUCKOKE BULCOCK BULCOCKE BULLOCK
BOULD BOLD
BOULDEN 15 Balden BALDING Baulden BOLDEN Boldin Bolding Bolling Bollyng Bolynge Bouldin BOULDING Bowlden Bowldinge BOWLING
Bouldin BALDING BOLDEN BOULDEN BOULDING BOWLING
BOULDING 15 Balden BALDING Baulden BOLDEN Boldin Bolding Bolling Bollyng Bolynge BOULDEN Bouldin Bowlden Bowldinge BOWLING
Bouldy BOULTBY
Bouler BOLER BOWLER
Boultbee BOULTBY
Boultbey BOULTBY
Boultbie BOULTBY
BOULTBY 6 Bouldy Boultbee Boultbey Boultbie Boultley
Boultley BOULTBY
BOULTON BOLTON
Boun BOWN BROWN
Bounce BUNCE
BOUND 4 Boundry BOUNDY Bownd
Boundry BOUND BOUNDY
BOUNDY 4 BOUND Boundry Bownd
BOUNSALL Bounsell
Bounsell BOUNSALL
BOURCHIER Bourgchier BURCHER
Boure BOWER BOWERS
Bourgchier BOURCHIER BURCHER
Bouring BOWER BOWERING BOWERS BOWRING
BOURKE BURKE
Bourland BORELAND BORLAND BURLAND
Bourman BOREMAN BORMAN BOWERMAN
BOURN 10 Boar BONES BOOR BOORN Boorne BORE Born BORNE BOURNE
BOURNE 10 Boar BONES BOOR BOORN Boorne BORE Born BORNE BOURN
Bourt BIRT BURT BURTE BUST BUTT
BOURTON 42 Bartan Bartane BARTON Bartone Bartoun Bartrahame BARTRAM Bartrem Bauerton Bertane Berton Bertoun Bertown Bertowne BERTRAM Betan BETON Biron Biroun Birun Bortane Bouerton Braton BRETON Bretun Burntoun Buron BURTON Burun BYRON De barton De berton De beton De birton De bret De briton De burton De burun Le bret Le bretun Le burone
Bousefield BOUSFIELD
BOUSFIELD Bousefield
BOUTAL 10 Boutall Boutel Boutell BOUTLE BOWTAL Bowtall Bowtel BOWTELL BOWTLE
Boutall BOUTAL BOUTLE BOWTAL BOWTELL BOWTLE
Boutcher BOUCHER BUTCHER
Boutchoer BOUCHER BUTCHER
Boutel BOUTAL BOUTLE BOWTAL BOWTELL BOWTLE
Boutell BARTELL BOTTELL BOUTAL BOUTLE BOWTAL BOWTELL BOWTLE
BOUTHBY BOOTHBY
BOUTLE 10 BOUTAL Boutall Boutel Boutell BOWTAL Bowtall Bowtel BOWTELL BOWTLE
BOW BOWE
Bowbin BOBIN
Bowch BAUGH BOUCH BOUGH
Bowche BAUGH BOUCH BOUGH
Bowcoc BOOCOCK BUCKOKE BULCOCK BULCOCKE BULLOCK
Bowcock BOOCOCK BUCKOKE BULCOCK BULCOCKE BULLOCK
Bowcocke BOOCOCK BUCKOKE BULCOCK BULCOCKE BULLOCK
Bowcoocke BOOCOCK BUCKOKE BULCOCK BULCOCKE BULLOCK
BOWD 4 Boud Boude Bowde
Bowde BOWD
BOWDEN 14 BAWDEN Boaden BODDAN Bodden BODEN Voaden VODDEN Voddon VODEN Vodin Vouden VOUSDEN Vowden
Bowdle BOWDLER
BOWDLER 11 Boelare Boudelers Boudlers Bowdle De boeles De bollers De boulers De budlers De bullers De buthley

If the name you are interested in is not here, try Section C.

BOWE BOW
BOWEN 6 BONE BOON BOONE BOWN Bowun
BOWER 12 Boure Bouring Bowere BOWERING BOWERS BOWERY Bowre BOWRING Bowry BOWYER BOYER
Bowere BOWER BOWERS
BOWERING 5 Bouring BOWER BOWERS BOWRING
BOWERMAN 4 BOREMAN BORMAN Bourman
BOWERS 9 Boure Bouring BOWER Bowere BOWERING Bowre BOWRING Bowry
BOWERY BOWER
BOWES 5 Boas BOASE Boaz Bose
Bowgh BAUGH BOUCH BOUGH
Bowkoke BOOCOCK BUCKOKE BULCOCK BULCOCKE BULLOCK
BOWL Bowld BOWLE
Bowlby BOULBY
Bowld BOWL BOWLE
Bowlden BALDING BOLDEN BOULDEN BOULDING BOWLING
Bowldinge BALDING BOLDEN BOULDEN BOULDING BOWLING
BOWLE BOWL Bowld
BOWLER 4 Boaler BOLER Bouler
BOWLING 15 Balden BALDING Baulden BOLDEN Boldin Bolding Bolling Bollyng Bolynge BOULDEN Bouldin BOULDING Bowlden Bowldinge
BOWMAN BOORMAN BOREMAN
BOWN 5 BONE Boun BOWEN BROWN
BOWNASS BOWNESS
Bownd BOUND BOUNDY
BOWNESS BONES BOWNASS
Bowre BOWER BOWERS
BOWRING 5 Bouring BOWER BOWERING BOWERS
Bowry BOWER BOWERS
BOWSER Bowzer
BOWTAL 10 BOUTAL Boutall Boutel Boutell BOUTLE Bowtall Bowtel BOWTELL BOWTLE
Bowtall BOUTAL BOUTLE BOWTAL BOWTELL BOWTLE
Bowtel BOUTAL BOUTLE BOWTAL BOWTELL BOWTLE
BOWTELL 17 BARTELL Boatell Botel BOTTELL Boughtell BOUTAL Boutall Boutel Boutell BOUTLE BOWTAL Bowtall Bowtel BOWTLE Bowttell Buddell
BOWTLE 10 BOUTAL Boutall Boutel Boutell BOUTLE BOWTAL Bowtall Bowtel BOWTELL
Bowttell BARTELL BOTTELL BOWTELL
Bowun BONE BOWEN
BOWYER BOWER BOYER
Bowzer BOWSER
BOX BAX
BOY BOYS
BOYARD BYARD
BOYCE 7 BOIES BOISE BOYES BOYS BOYSE LANDER-BOYCE
Boyels BOYLE BOYLES
BOYER BOWER BOWYER
BOYES 6 BOIES BOISE BOYCE BOYS BOYSE
BOYLE 6 Boils Boyels BOYLES Boyls O'boyle
BOYLES 6 BOILES Boils Boyels BOYLE Boyls
Boylet BOYLETT
BOYLETT 10 Baylet Baylett Boilet Boilett Boylet Bylate Bylet Bylett Bylot
BOYLIN 7 Bealin Bellin Boyling BYOLIN Byollin Byolling
Boyling BOYLIN BYOLIN
Boyls BOYLE BOYLES
BOYS 9 BOIES BOISE BOY BOYCE BOYES BOYSE De boys De boyse
BOYSE 8 BOIES BOISE BOYCE BOYES BOYS De boys De boyse
Braban BRABON BRAYBAN
Brabant BRABIN
Braben BRABIN
Brabham BRABON BRAYBAN
BRABIN 4 Brabant Braben Brabing
Brabing BRABIN
BRABON 5 Braban Brabham BRAYBAN Braybon
Brabrook BRAYBROOK
Brabrooke BRAYBROOK
BRACHER BRAKER BREAKER
BRACKENRIDGE Brackenrig
Brackenrig BRACKENRIDGE
Bracknal BRACKNELL
Bracknall BRACKNELL
BRACKNELL Bracknal Bracknall
Brackpole BRACKPOOL
BRACKPOOL Brackpole Brappole
BRACKSTONE 12 Braxston Braxstone BRAXTON Braxtone Breckston Breckstone Brexston Brexton Brickston Brickstone BRIXTON
Bradach BRADDOCK BRADICK BRIDACK BRIDDICK
Braddick BRADDOCK BRADICK BRIDACK BRIDDICK
BRADDOCK 17 Bradach Braddick Braddocke BRADICK Braidack Bredack Breddack BRIDACK Briddack Briddeck BRIDDICK Briddock Brideck Bridick Bridock Broddock
Braddocke BRADDOCK BRADICK BRIDACK BRIDDICK
BRADICK 17 Bradach Braddick BRADDOCK Braddocke Braidack Bredack Breddack BRIDACK Briddack Briddeck BRIDDICK Briddock Brideck Bridick Bridock Broddock
BRADLEY BROADLEY
BRADSTOCK 4 BRADSTOCKE Bredestock Broadstock
BRADSTOCKE 4 BRADSTOCK Bredestock Broadstock
Brae BRAY
Braen BRAIN BRAYNE
Bragarri BREGAZZIE
Bragazzie BREGAZZIE
Braggazzi BREGAZZIE
Braidack BRADDOCK BRADICK BRIDACK BRIDDICK
Braikway BROCKWAY
Brailesford BRAILSFORD BRELLISFORD BRELSFORD BRILLISFORD
BRAILSFORD 7 Brailesford Brailsforth Braylesford BRELLISFORD BRELSFORD BRILLISFORD
Brailsforth BRAILSFORD BRELLISFORD BRELSFORD BRILLISFORD
BRAIN 6 Braen Braine Brane Braune BRAYNE
Brainbridge BAINBRIDGE
Braine BRAIN BRAYNE
Braithwait BRAITHWAITE
BRAITHWAITE Braithwait
Braizier BRASIER BRAZIER
Brakan BRECKON
BRAKER BRACHER BREAKER
Brakway BROCKWAY
Bramah BRAMALD BRAMALL BRAMHALL BRAMMER
BRAMALD 7 Bramah BRAMALL Bramar Brameld BRAMHALL BRAMMER
BRAMALL 63 Bramah BRAMALD Bramar Brambel Brambell BRAMBLE Bramel Brameld Bramell BRAMHALL BRAMHILL Bramma Brammal Brammall Brammell BRAMMER BRAMWELL Bremall Bremble Bremboll Bremel Bremhall Bremhill Bremil Bremmel Bremmell Bremwell Brimbel BRIMBLE Brimel Brimhall Brimhill BRIMMELL Brimwell Bromble Bromehill Bromel BROMELL Bromelle Bromhall Bromhill Bromil Bromill Brommel Brommell Brommelle Bromwell Bromyl Bromyll Broomall Broomell Broomhall Broomhill Broomill Broomville Broomyll Brumble Brumel Brumell Brumhall Brumhill Brummell
Bramar BRAMALD BRAMALL BRAMHALL BRAMMER
Brambel BRAMALL BRAMBLE BRAMHILL BRAMWELL BRIMBLE BRIMMELL BROMELL
Brambell BRAMALL BRAMBLE BRAMHILL BRAMWELL BRIMBLE BRIMMELL BROMELL
BRAMBLE 61 BRAMALL Brambel Brambell BRAMBLES Bramel Bramell BRAMHILL Brammal Brammall Brammell BRAMWELL Bremall Bremble Bremboll Bremel Bremhall Bremhill Bremil Bremmel Bremmell Bremwell Brimbel BRIMBLE Brimel Brimhall Brimhill BRIMMELL Brimwell Bromble Brombles Bromehill Bromel BROMELL Bromelle Bromhall Bromhill Bromil Bromill BROMLEY Brommel Brommell Brommelle Bromwell Bromyl Bromyll Broomall Broomell Broomhall Broomhill Broomill Broomville Broomyll Brumble BRUMBLEY Brumel Brumell Brumhall Brumhill Brumley Brummell
BRAMBLES 4 BRAMBLE Bromble Brombles
Bramby BRAMLEY
Bramel BRAMALL BRAMBLE BRAMHILL BRAMWELL BRIMBLE BRIMMELL BROMELL
Brameld BRAMALD BRAMALL BRAMHALL BRAMMER
Bramell BRAMALL BRAMBLE BRAMHILL BRAMWELL BRIMBLE BRIMMELL BROMELL
Bramfete BRAMFITT
Bramfield BLOOMFIELD BROMFIELD BROOMFIELD BRUMFIELD
Bramfit BRAMFITT
BRAMFITT 8 Bramfete Bramfit Bramfoot Brumfet Brumfit Brumfitt Brumphit
Bramfoot BRAMFITT
BRAMHALL 7 Bramah BRAMALD BRAMALL Bramar Brameld BRAMMER
BRAMHILL 56 BRAMALL Brambel Brambell BRAMBLE Bramel Bramell Brammal Brammall Brammell BRAMWELL Bremall Bremble Bremboll Bremel Bremhall Bremhill Bremil Bremmel Bremmell Bremwell Brimbel BRIMBLE Brimel Brimhall Brimhill BRIMMELL Brimwell Bromble Bromehill Bromel BROMELL Bromelle Bromhall Bromhill Bromil Bromill Brommel Brommell Brommelle Bromwell Bromyl Bromyll Broomall Broomell Broomhall Broomhill Broomill Broomville Broomyll Brumble Brumel Brumell Brumhall Brumhill Brummell
Bramich BROMWICH
BRAMLEY Bramby
Bramma BRAMALL
Brammal BRAMALL BRAMBLE BRAMHILL BRAMWELL BRIMBLE BRIMMELL BROMELL
Brammall BRAMALL BRAMBLE BRAMHILL BRAMWELL BRIMBLE BRIMMELL BROMELL
Brammell BRAMALL BRAMBLE BRAMHILL BRAMWELL BRIMBLE BRIMMELL BROMELL
BRAMMER 7 Bramah BRAMALD BRAMALL Bramar Brameld BRAMHALL
BRAMPTON De brampton
Bramsgrove BRANSGROVE
BRAMWELL 56 BRAMALL Brambel Brambell BRAMBLE Bramel Bramell BRAMHILL Brammal Brammall Brammell Bremall Bremble Bremboll Bremel

If the name you are interested in is not here, try Section C.

Bremhall Bremhill
Bremil Bremmel Bremmell
Bremwell Brimbel
BRIMBLE Brimel Brimhall
Brimhill BRIMMELL
Brimwell Bromble
Bromehill Bromel
BROMELL Bromelle
Bromhall Bromhill
Bromil Bromill Brommel
Brommell Brommelle
Bromwell Bromyl Bromyll
Broomall Broomell
Broomhall Broomhill
Broomill Broomville
Broomyll Brumble Brumel
Brumell Brumhall
Brumhill Brummell
BRAN BRAND Brann
BRANCH Branche
Branche BRANCH
BRAND BRAN Brann
Brandish BRUNDISH
BRANDSON BRANSON
Brane BRAIN BRAYNE
Brann BRAN BRAND
BRANNEN BRENNAN
BRANSGROVE Bansgrove Bramsgrove
BRANSON BRANDSON
BRANSTON BRAUNSTON
Brappole BRACKPOOL
Bras BRASS
Brasel BRASELL BRAZELL
BRASELL 12 Brasel Brashell Brasil Brassel Brassell Brassil Brazel BRAZELL Brazil Brazill Brazzille
Brashell BRASELL BRAZELL
Brasher BRASIER BRAZIER
BRASIER 5 Braizier Brasher Brayser BRAZIER
Brasil BRASELL BRAZELL
Brason BRISON
BRASS Bras Brasse
Brasse BRASS
Brassel BRASELL BRAZELL
Brassell BRASELL BRAZELL
Brassil BRASELL BRAZELL
Brat BRATT BRETT
BRATBY BRETBY
Braton BARTON BARTRAM BERTRAM BETON BOURTON BRETON BURTON BYRON
BRATT Brat BRETT
Braune BRAIN
BRAUNSTON BRANSTON
Braven BRAVIN
BRAVIN Braven Braving
Braving BRAVIN
Braxston BRACKSTONE BRAXTON BRIXTON
Braxstone BRACKSTONE BRAXTON BRIXTON
BRAXTON 12 BRACKSTONE Braxston Braxstone Braxtone Breckston Breckstone Brexston Brexton Brickston Brickstone BRIXTON
Braxtone BRACKSTONE BRAXTON BRIXTON
BRAY 4 Brae BREA Brey
BRAYBAN 5 Braban Brabham BRABON Braybon
Braybon BRABON BRAYBAN
BRAYBROOK 4 Brabrook Brabrooke Braybrooke
Braybrooke BRAYBROOK
Braylesford BRAILSFORD BRELLISFORD BRELSFORD BRILLISFORD
BRAYNE 5 Braen BRAIN Braine Brane
Brayser BRASIER BRAZIER
Brayson BRISON
Brazel BRASELL BRAZELL
BRAZELL 12 Brasel BRASELL Brashell Brasil Brassel Brassell Brassil Brazel Brazil Brazill Brazzille
BRAZIER 5 Braizier Brasher BRASIER Brayser
Brazil BRASELL BRAZELL
Brazill BRASELL BRAZELL
Brazzille BRASELL BRAZELL
BREA BRAY
BREADY Breddy
BREAKER BRACHER BRAKER
BREALEY 10 Brealy BREAREY BREARLEY Brearly Brereley Brerely Brerley BRIERLEY Bryerly
Brealy BREALEY BREARLEY BRIERLEY
BREAREY BREALEY BREARLEY
BREARLEY 11 BREALEY Brealy BREAREY Brearly Brereley Brerely Brerley Briarley BRIERLEY Bryerly
Brearly BREALEY BREARLEY BRIERLEY
Brebner BREMNER
Brecan BRECKON
Breckaw BRECKON
BRECKON 5 Brakan Brecan Breckaw Broccon
Breckston BRACKSTONE BRAXTON BRIXTON
Breckstone BRACKSTONE BRAXTON BRIXTON
Breda BRIDER
Bredack BRADDOCK BRADICK BRIDACK BRIDDICK
Breddack BRADDOCK BRADICK BRIDACK BRIDDICK
Breddy BREADY
Bredestock BRADSTOCK BRADSTOCKE
BREES BREESE BREEZE
BREESE BREES BREEZE
Breewood BREWARD
BREEZE BREES BREESE
Bregazzi BREGAZZIE
BREGAZZIE 9 Baggazzi Begazzi Biggazzi Bragarri Bragazzie Braggazzi Bregazzi Breggazi
Bregewood BIDGOOD BIGWOOD BRIDGWOOD
Breggazi BREGAZZIE
BRELLISFORD 7 Brailesford BRAILSFORD Brailsforth Braylesford BRELSFORD BRILLISFORD
BRELSFORD 7 Brailesford BRAILSFORD Brailsforth Braylesford BRELLISFORD BRILLISFORD
Bremall BRAMALL BRAMBLE BRAMHILL BRAMWELL BRIMBLE BRIMMELL BROMELL
Bremble BRAMALL BRAMBLE BRAMHILL BRAMWELL BRIMBLE BRIMMELL BROMELL
Bremboll BRAMALL BRAMBLE BRAMHILL BRAMWELL BRIMBLE BRIMMELL BROMELL
Bremel BRAMALL BRAMBLE BRAMHILL BRAMWELL BRIMBLE BRIMMELL BROMELL
Bremhall BRAMALL BRAMBLE BRAMHILL BRAMWELL BRIMBLE BRIMMELL BROMELL
Bremhill BRAMALL BRAMBLE BRAMHILL BRAMWELL BRIMBLE BRIMMELL BROMELL
Bremil BRAMALL BRAMBLE BRAMHILL BRAMWELL BRIMBLE BRIMMELL BROMELL
Bremmel BRAMALL BRAMBLE BRAMHILL BRAMWELL BRIMBLE BRIMMELL BROMELL
Bremmell BRAMALL BRAMBLE BRAMHILL BRAMWELL BRIMBLE BRIMMELL BROMELL
BREMNER 4 Brebner Brimner Brymer
Bremwell BRAMALL BRAMBLE BRAMHILL BRAMWELL BRIMBLE BRIMMELL BROMELL
BRENCHLEY BRENCHLY
BRENCHLY BRENCHLEY
BRENNAN BRANNEN
Brereley BREALEY BREARLEY BRIERLEY
Brerely BREALEY BREARLEY BRIERLEY
Brerley BREALEY BREARLEY BRIERLEY
Breslain BRUSLAUN
Breslawn BRUSLAUN
BRETBY BRATBY
BRETON 46 Bartan Bartane BARTON Bartone Bartoun Bartrahame BARTRAM Bartrem Bauerton´ Bertane Berton Bertoun Bertown Bertowne BERTRAM Betan BETON Biron Biroun Birun Bortane Bouerton BOURTON Braton Bretun BRITAIN BRITTAN BRITTEN BRITTON Burntoun Buron BURTON Burun BYRON De barton De berton De beton De birton De bret De briton De burton De burun Le bret Le bretun Le burone
BRETT 4 Brat BRATT Britt
Bretun BARTON BARTRAM BERTRAM BETON BOURTON BRETON BURTON BYRON
BREWARD Breewood Brewood
Brewes DE BRAOSE
BREWIN 7 Briten BRITTAN BRITTEN BRITTIN BRITTON BRUIN
Brewood BREWARD
Brexston BRACKSTONE BRAXTON BRIXTON
Brexton BRACKSTONE BRAXTON BRIXTON
Brey BRAY
BRIAN BRYAN Bryon
BRIAND BRIARD Briart
BRIANT 4 BRIND BRINE BRYANT
BRIARD BRIAND Briart
Briarley BREARLEY BRIERLEY
Briart BRIAND BRIARD
BRICE 16 Broase Brois Broise BRUCE Bruice Bruis Bruisone Bruisson Brus Bruse Brussee Brussoun Brussoune Brys BRYSON
BRICKEL BRICKELL Brickle
BRICKELL BRICKEL Brickle
Bricket BRICKETT
BRICKETT 6 Bricket Briket Brikett Brycket Bryckett
Brickle BRICKEL BRICKELL
Brickston BRACKSTONE BRAXTON BRIXTON
Brickstone BRACKSTONE BRAXTON BRIXTON
Brida BRIDER
BRIDACK 17 Bradach Braddick BRADDOCK Braddocke BRADICK Braidack Bredack Breddack Briddack Briddeck BRIDDICK Briddock Brideck Bridick Bridock Broddock
Briddack BRADDOCK BRADICK BRIDACK BRIDDICK
Briddeck BRADDOCK BRADICK BRIDACK BRIDDICK
Bridden BRIDDON BRYDEN
BRIDDICK 17 Bradach Braddick BRADDOCK Braddocke BRADICK Braidack Bredack Breddack BRIDACK Briddack Briddeck Briddock Brideck Bridick Bridock Broddock
Briddock BRADDOCK BRADICK BRIDACK BRIDDICK
BRIDDON 6 Bridden BRIDEN Bridon BRYDEN BRYDON
Brideck BRADDOCK BRADICK BRIDACK BRIDDICK
BRIDEN 5 BRIDDON Bridon BRYDEN BRYDON
BRIDER 4 Breda Brida Bryder
Bridewood BIDGOOD BIGWOOD BRIDGWOOD
BRIDGEMAN 4 BRIDGMAN Burgeman Burgman
BRIDGES 4 Briges BRIGGS Brigis
BRIDGETT Bridgewood
BRIDGEWATER Bridgwater
Bridgewood BIDGOOD BIGWOOD BRIDGETT BRIDGWOOD
Bridgewoodde BIDGOOD BIGWOOD BRIDGWOOD
BRIDGMAN 4 BRIDGEMAN Burgeman Burgman
Bridgood BIDGOOD BIGWOOD BRIDGWOOD
Bridgwater BRIDGEWATER
BRIDGWOOD 14 BIDGOOD Biggott BIGWOOD Bregewood Bridewood Bridgewood Bridgewoodde Bridgood Bridgwoode Bridwood Brigoods Brigwood Broodgwood
Bridgwoode BIDGOOD BIGWOOD BRIDGWOOD
Bridick BRADDOCK BRADICK BRIDACK BRIDDICK
Bridock BRADDOCK BRADICK BRIDACK BRIDDICK
Bridon BRIDDON BRIDEN BRYDEN BRYDON
Bridwood BIDGOOD BIGWOOD BRIDGWOOD
BRIERLEY 10 BREALEY

If the name you are interested in is not here, try Section C.

Brealy BREARLEY Brearly Brereley Brerely Brerley Briarley Bryerly
Brierly BYERLEY
Briges BRIDGES
BRIGGS BRIDGES
BRIGHT Brite
BRIGHTLY BRIGHTWELL
BRIGHTMAN 4 Britman Bryghtman Wrightwril
BRIGHTWELL BRIGHTLY
BRIGHTY Brity
Brigis BRIDGES
Brigoods BIDGOOD BIGWOOD BRIDGWOOD
Brigwood BIDGOOD BIGWOOD BRIDGWOOD
Briket BRICKETT
Brikett BRICKETT
BRILLISFORD 7 Brailesford BRAILSFORD Brailsforth Braylesford BRELLISFORD BRELSFORD
Brimacombe BRINICOMBE
Brimbel BRAMALL BRAMBLE BRAMHILL BRAMWELL BRIMBLE BRIMMELL BROMELL
BRIMBLE 56 BRAMALL Brambel Brambell BRAMBLE Bramel Bramell BRAMHILL Brammal Brammall Brammell BRAMWELL Bremall Bremble Bremboll Bremel Bremhall Bremhill Bremil Bremmel Bremmell Bremwell Brimbel Brimel Brimhall Brimhill BRIMMELL Brimwell Bromble Bromehill Bromel BROMELL Bromelle Bromhall Bromhill Bromil Bromill Brommel Brommell Brommelle Bromwell Bromyl Bromyll Broomall Broomell Broomhall Broomhill Broomill Broomville Broomyll Brumble Brumel Brumell Brumhall Brumhill Brummell
Brimel BRAMALL BRAMBLE BRAMHILL BRAMWELL BRIMBLE BRIMMELL BROMELL
Brimhall BRAMALL BRAMBLE BRAMHILL BRAMWELL BRIMBLE BRIMMELL BROMELL
Brimhill BRAMALL BRAMBLE BRAMHILL BRAMWELL BRIMBLE BRIMMELL BROMELL
Brimicombe BRINICOMBE
BRIMMEL BRIMMELL
BRIMMELL 57 BRAMALL Brambel Brambell BRAMBLE Bramel Bramell BRAMHILL Brammal Brammall Brammell BRAMWELL Bremall Bremble Bremboll Bremel Bremhall Bremhill Bremil Bremmel Bremmell Bremwell Brimbel BRIMBLE Brimel Brimhall Brimhill BRIMMEL Brimwell Bromble Bromehill Bromel BROMELL Bromelle Bromhall Bromhill Bromil Bromill Brommel Brommell Brommelle Bromwell Bromyl Bromyll Broomall Broomell Broomhall Broomhill Broomill Broomville Broomyll Brumble Brumel Brumell Brumhall Brumhill Brummell
Brimmicombe BRINICOMBE
Brimner BREMNER
BRIMSON Brinson
Brimwell BRAMALL BRAMBLE BRAMHILL BRAMWELL BRIMBLE BRIMMELL BROMELL
BRIND 7 BRIANT Brindad Brinded BRINDLEY BRINDY BRINE
Brindad BRIND BRINDLEY BRINDY
Brinded BRIND BRINDLEY BRINDY
BRINDELL BRINDLE
BRINDLE BRINDELL
BRINDLEY 5 BRIND Brindad Brinded BRINDY
BRINDY 5 BRIND Brindad Brinded BRINDLEY
BRINE BRIANT BRIND
Brinecombe BRINICOMBE
Bringloe BRINGLOW
BRINGLOW Bringloe Brinklo
BRINICOMBE 6 Brimacombe Brimicombe Brimmicombe Brinecombe Brinnacombe
BRINING Bryning
Brinklo BRINGLOW
Brinnacombe BRINICOMBE
Brinson BRIMSON
Briouze DE BRAOSE
BRISBY BRUSBY
BRISON 5 Brason Brayson Brisson BRYSON
Brisson BRISON
Bristo BRISTOL BRISTOW
Bristoe BRISTOW
BRISTOL Bristo BRISTOW
BRISTOW 5 Bristo Bristoe BRISTOL Bristowe
Bristowe BRISTOW
BRITAIN 9 BRETON Britan BRITON BRITTAIN BRITTAN BRITTEN BRITTIN BRITTON
Britan BRITAIN BRITON BRITTAIN BRITTEN BRITTIN BRITTON
Brite BRIGHT
Briten BREWIN BRITTAN BRITTEN BRITTIN BRITTON BRUIN
Britman BRIGHTMAN
Britnall BRITNELL
BRITNELL 4 Britnall Brutenell Brutennell
BRITON 7 BRITAIN Britan BRITTAIN BRITTEN BRITTIN BRITTON
Britt BRETT
BRITTAIN 7 BRITAIN Britan BRITON BRITTEN BRITTIN BRITTON
BRITTAN 9 BRETON BREWIN BRITAIN Briten BRITTEN BRITTIN BRITTON BRUIN
BRITTEN 12 BRETON BREWIN BRITAIN Britan Briten BRITON BRITTAIN BRITTAN BRITTIN BRITTON BRUIN
BRITTIN 11 BREWIN BRITAIN Britan Briten BRITON BRITTAIN BRITTAN BRITTEN BRITTON BRUIN
BRITTON 12 BRETON BREWIN BRITAIN Britan Briten BRITON BRITTAIN BRITTAN BRITTEN BRITTIN BRUIN
Brity BRIGHTY
BRIXTON 12 BRACKSTONE Braxston Braxstone BRAXTON Braxtone Breckston Breckstone Brexston Brexton Brickston Brickstone
Broach BROATCH
Broadbribb BRODRIBB
Broaderib BRODRIBB
Broaderibb BRODRIBB
Broadie BRODIE
BROADLEY BRADLEY
Broadrib BRODRIBB
Broadribb BRODRIBB
Broadrick BRODERICK
Broadrip BRODRIBB
Broadripp BRODRIBB
Broadstock BRADSTOCK BRADSTOCKE
Broase BRICE BRUCE BRYSON
BROATCH Broach
Broccon BRECKON
BROCKBANK BROCKLEBANK
Brockelhurst BROCKHURST BROCKLEHURST
BROCKELSBY BROCKLESBY
Brockhall BROCKLESS
BROCKHURST 4 Brockelhurst BROCKLEHURST Brockleyhurst
Brockle BROCKLESS
BROCKLEBANK BROCKBANK
BROCKLEHURST 4 Brockelhurst BROCKHURST Brockleyhurst
Brockles BROCKLESS
BROCKLESBY BROCKELSBY
BROCKLESS 9 Brockhall Brockle Brockles Brockleys Brocklis Brockliss Brocles Brocolo
Brockley BLOCKLEY
Brockleyhurst BROCKHURST BROCKLEHURST
Brockleys BROCKLESS
Brocklis BROCKLESS
Brockliss BROCKLESS
BROCKWAY 5 Braikway Brakway Brokeway Brokway
Brocles BROCKLESS
Brocolo BROCKLESS
Broddock BRADDOCK BRADICK BRIDACK BRIDDICK
Broderib BRODRIBB
Broderibb BRODRIBB
Broderibbe BRODRIBB
BRODERICK Broadrick Brodrick
Broderip BRODRIBB
Broderipp BRODRIBB
Broderybb BRODRIBB
BRODIE 4 Broadie Brydie Brydy
Brodrib BRODRIBB
BRODRIBB 22 Baggetripe Baketerpe Baudrip Broadbribb Broaderib Broaderibb Broadrib Broadribb Broadrip Broadripp Broderib Broderibb Broderibbe Broderip Broderipp Broderybb Brodrib Brodrip Brodripp Brodrybbe Broerib
Brodrick BRODERICK
Brodrip BRODRIBB
Brodripp BRODRIBB
Brodrybbe BRODRIBB
Broerib BRODRIBB
Broham BROUGHAM BROWHAM
Brois BRICE BRUCE BRYSON
Broise BRICE BRUCE BRYSON
BROKENSHA Brokenshaw Brokenshire
.Brokenshaw BROKENSHA
Brokenshire BROKENSHA
Brokeway BROCKWAY
Brokway BROCKWAY
Broman BROMHAM
Bromble BRAMALL BRAMBLE BRAMBLES BRAMHILL BRAMWELL BRIMBLE BRIMMELL BROMELL
Brombles BRAMBLE BRAMBLES
Bromehead BROOMHEAD
Bromehill BRAMALL BRAMBLE BRAMHILL BRAMWELL BRIMBLE BRIMMELL BROMELL
Bromel BRAMALL BRAMBLE BRAMHILL BRAMWELL BRIMBLE BRIMMELL BROMELL
BROMELL 56 BRAMALL Brambel Brambell BRAMBLE Bramel Bramell BRAMHILL Brammal Brammall Brammell BRAMWELL Bremall Bremble Bremboll Bremel Bremhall Bremhill Bremil Bremmel Bremmell Bremwell Brimbel BRIMBLE Brimel Brimhall Brimhill BRIMMELL Brimwell Bromble Bromehill Bromel Bromelle Bromhall Bromhill Bromil Bromill Brommel Brommell Brommelle Bromwell Bromyl Bromyll Broomall Broomell Broomhall Broomhill Broomill Broomville Broomyll Brumble Brumel Brumell Brumhall Brumhill Brummell
Bromelle BRAMALL BRAMBLE BRAMHILL BRAMWELL BRIMBLE BRIMMELL BROMELL
BROMFIELD 7 BLOOMFIELD Bramfield BROOMFIELD Brounfield Brownfield BRUMFIELD
Bromhall BRAMALL BRAMBLE BRAMHILL BRAMWELL BRIMBLE BRIMMELL BROMELL
BROMHAM 5 Broman Brooman Bruman Brumman
Bromhead BROOMHEAD
Bromhill BRAMALL BRAMBLE BRAMHILL BRAMWELL BRIMBLE BRIMMELL BROMELL
Bromidge BROMWICH
Bromil BRAMALL BRAMBLE BRAMHILL BRAMWELL BRIMBLE BRIMMELL BROMELL
Bromill BRAMALL BRAMBLE BRAMHILL BRAMWELL BRIMBLE BRIMMELL BROMELL
BROMLEY 4 BRAMBLE BRUMBLEY Brumley
Brommel BRAMALL BRAMBLE BRAMHILL BRAMWELL BRIMBLE BRIMMELL BROMELL

If the name you are interested in is not here, try Section C.

Brommell BRAMALL BRAMBLE BRAMHILL BRAMWELL BRIMBLE BRIMMELL BROMELL
Brommelle BRAMALL BRAMBLE BRAMHILL BRAMWELL BRIMBLE BRIMMELL BROMELL
Bromwell BRAMALL BRAMBLE BRAMHILL BRAMWELL BRIMBLE BRIMMELL BROMELL
BROMWICH 5 Bramich Bromidge Brumidge Brummage
Bromyl BRAMALL BRAMBLE BRAMHILL BRAMWELL BRIMBLE BRIMMELL BROMELL
Bromyll BRAMALL BRAMBLE BRAMHILL BRAMWELL BRIMBLE BRIMMELL BROMELL
Broodgwood BIDGOOD BIGWOOD BRIDGWOOD
BROOK 4 BROOKE BROOKES BROOKS
BROOKBANK Brookbanks
Brookbanks BROOKBANK
BROOKE 4 BROOK BROOKES BROOKS
BROOKER BOOKER
BROOKES 4 BROOK BROOKE BROOKS
Brookin BROOKING
BROOKING 4 Booking Brookin Brookings
Brookings BROOKING
Brookman BRUCKMANN
BROOKS 4 BROOK BROOKE BROOKES
BROOM Broome
Broomall BRAMALL BRAMBLE BRAMHILL BRAMWELL BRIMBLE BRIMMELL BROMELL
Brooman BROMHAM
Broome BROOM
Broomell BRAMALL BRAMBLE BRAMHILL BRAMWELL BRIMBLE BRIMMELL BROMELL
BROOMFIELD 7 BLOOMFIELD Bramfield BROMFIELD Brounfield Brownfield BRUMFIELD
Broomhall BRAMALL BRAMBLE BRAMHILL BRAMWELL BRIMBLE BRIMMELL BROMELL
BROOMHEAD Bromehead Bromhead
Broomhill BRAMALL BRAMBLE BRAMHILL BRAMWELL BRIMBLE BRIMMELL BROMELL
Broomill BRAMALL BRAMBLE BRAMHILL BRAMWELL BRIMBLE BRIMMELL BROMELL
Broomville BRAMALL BRAMBLE BRAMHILL BRAMWELL BRIMBLE BRIMMELL BROMELL
Broomyll BRAMALL BRAMBLE BRAMHILL BRAMWELL BRIMBLE BRIMMELL BROMELL
Broscom BROSCOMBE
Broscomb BROSCOMBE
BROSCOMBE 5 Broscom Broscomb Broskam Broskham
Broskam BROSCOMBE
Broskham BROSCOMBE
Brosnahan BROSNAN
Brosnahen BROSNAN
BROSNAN Brosnahan Brosnahen
Broton BROTTON
BROTTON Broton
BROUGHALL Brughall
BROUGHAM 5 Broham Browgham BROWHAM Browholme
Broun BROWN BROWNE
Broune BROWN BROWNE
Brounfield BLOOMFIELD BROMFIELD BROOMFIELD BRUMFIELD
BROWELL 5 Browl BRUEL BRUELL BRUYLL
Browgham BROUGHAM BROWHAM
BROWHAM 5 Broham BROUGHAM Browgham Browholme
Browholme BROUGHAM BROWHAM
Browl BROWELL BRUEL BRUELL BRUYLL
BROWN 6 Boun BOWN Broun Broune BROWNE
Brownbridge BROWNRIGG
BROWNE 4 Broun Broune BROWN
Brownell BROWNHILL
Brownfield BLOOMFIELD BROMFIELD BROOMFIELD BRUMFIELD
BROWNHILL Brownell
Brownienge BROWNING
BROWNING Brownienge
BROWNJOHN BROWNON
BROWNLEE Brownley BROWNLOW
Brownley BROWNLEE BROWNLOW
BROWNLOW BROWNLEE Brownley
BROWNON BROWNJOHN
BROWNRIGG Brownbridge
Brownsea BROWNSEY
BROWNSEY Brownsea
BRUCE 16 BRICE Broase Brois Broise Bruice Bruis Bruisone Bruisson Brus Bruse Brussee Brussoun Brussoune Brys BRYSON
BRUCKMANN Brookman Brueckman
Brueckman BRUCKMANN
BRUEL 5 BROWELL Browl BRUELL BRUYLL
BRUELL 5 BROWELL Browl BRUEL BRUYLL
BRUFF Brugh
Brugh BRUFF
Brughall BROUGHALL
Bruice BRICE BRUCE BRYSON
BRUIN 7 BREWIN Briten BRITTAN BRITTEN BRITTIN BRITTON
Bruis BRICE BRUCE BRYSON
Bruisone BRICE BRUCE BRYSON
Bruisson BRICE BRUCE BRYSON
Bruman BROMHAM
Brumble BRAMALL BRAMBLE BRAMHILL BRAMWELL BRIMBLE BRIMMELL BROMELL
BRUMBLEY 4 BRAMBLE BROMLEY Brumley
Brumel BRAMALL BRAMBLE BRAMHILL BRAMWELL BRIMBLE BRIMMELL BROMELL
Brumell BRAMALL BRAMBLE BRAMHILL BRAMWELL BRIMBLE BRIMMELL BROMELL
Brumfet BRAMFITT
BRUMFIELD 7 BLOOMFIELD Bramfield BROMFIELD BROOMFIELD Brounfield Brownfield
Brumfit BRAMFITT
Brumfitt BRAMFITT
Brumhall BRAMALL BRAMBLE BRAMHILL BRAMWELL BRIMBLE BRIMMELL BROMELL
Brumhill BRAMALL BRAMBLE BRAMHILL BRAMWELL BRIMBLE BRIMMELL BROMELL
Brumidge BROMWICH
Brumley BRAMBLE BROMLEY BRUMBLEY
Brummage BROMWICH
Brumman BROMHAM
Brummell BRAMALL BRAMBLE BRAMHILL BRAMWELL BRIMBLE BRIMMELL BROMELL
Brumphit BRAMFITT
BRUNDISH Brandish Brundishe
Brundishe BRUNDISH
Brundred BUNDRED
Brunskell BRUNSKILL
Brunskil BRUNSKILL
BRUNSKILL Brunskell Brunskil
Brus BRICE BRUCE BRYSON
BRUSBY BRISBY
Bruse BRICE BRUCE BRYSON DE BRAOSE
BRUSH Brushe Brusshe
Brushe BRUSH
BRUSLAUN Breslain Breslawn
Brussee BRICE BRUCE BRYSON
Brusshe BRUSH
Brussoun BRICE BRUCE BRYSON
Brussoune BRICE BRUCE BRYSON
Brutenell BRITNELL
Brutennell BRITNELL
BRUYLL 5 BROWELL Browl BRUEL BRUELL
BRYAN 5 BRIAN Bryans BRYANT Bryon
Bryans BRYAN
BRYANT BRIANT BRYAN
Brycket BRICKETT
Bryckett BRICKETT
BRYDEN 6 Bridden BRIDDON BRIDEN Bridon BRYDON
Bryder BRIDER
Brydie BRODIE
BRYDON 5 BRIDDON BRIDEN Bridon BRYDEN
Brydy BRODIE
Bryerly BREALEY BREARLEY BRIERLEY
Bryghtman BRIGHTMAN
Brymer BREMNER
Bryning BRINING
Bryon BRIAN BRYAN
Brys BRICE BRUCE BRYSON
BRYSON 17 BRICE BRISON Broase Brois Broise BRUCE Bruice Bruis Bruisone Bruisson Brus Bruse Brussee Brussoun Brussoune Brys
Bucby BUCKBY BUCKLEY
Buckbee BUCKBY BUCKLEY
BUCKBY 10 Bucby Buckbee Buckbye BUCKLEY Buckly Bugbee Bugby Buglee Bukby
Buckbye BUCKBY BUCKLEY
Buckel BUCKLE
Buckell BUCKLE
Buckemaister BUCKMASTER
BUCKENHAM BUCKINGHAM
BUCKERIDGE Buckridge
BUCKINGHAM BUCKENHAM
BUCKLAND 4 BUCKLE BUCKLEY Buckly
BUCKLE 6 Buckel Buckell BUCKLAND BUCKLEY Buckly
Buckles BOOKLESS BUGLASS
BUCKLEY 14 Bucby Buckbee BUCKBY Buckbye BUCKLAND BUCKLE Buckly Bugbee Bugby Buglee Bukby BULKELEY BULKLEY
Buckly BUCKBY BUCKLAND BUCKLE BUCKLEY
Buckmaister BUCKMASTER
BUCKMASTER 6 Buckemaister Buckmaister Buckmayster Buckminster Buckmuster
Buckmayster BUCKMASTER
Buckminster BUCKMASTER
Buckmuster BUCKMASTER
BUCKOKE 25 Bawcock Beaucock Bocock Bococke Bocoke BOOCOCK Boococks Bookcok Bookecocke Boolcock Boulcock Bowcoc Bowcock Bowcocke Bowcoocke Bowkoke BULCOCK BULCOCKE Bulcok Bulcoke Bulkok Bulkoke Bullcock BULLOCK
Buckridge BUCKERIDGE
Buckstone BUXTON
BUCKTON Bucton BUXTON
Bucton BUCKTON BUXTON
Buddell BARTELL BOTTELL BOWTELL
BUDDEN Butten BUTTON
Buddeworth BUDWORTH
Buddeworthe BUDWORTH
Buddewurth BUDWORTH
BUDDLE BOODLE
Budeworth BUDWORTH
Budeworthe BUDWORTH
Budewurth BUDWORTH
Budgery BADGERY
BUDWORTH 15 Boddeworth Boddeworthe Boddewurth Bodeworth Bodeworthe Bodewurth Buddeworth Buddeworthe Buddewurth Budeworth Budeworthe Budewurth Budworthe Budwurth
Budworthe BUDWORTH
Budwurth BUDWORTH
BUGBEARD Bugberd
Bugbee BUCKBY BUCKLEY
Bugberd BUGBEARD
Bugby BUCKBY BUCKLEY
BUGGINS 11 Bagan BAGGALEY Baggalin Baggan Bagge Baggen BAGGIN Bagin Biggin Bigin
BUGLASS 7 Beuglas BOOKLESS Buckles Bugless Buickless Buigloss
Buglee BUCKBY BUCKLEY
Bugless BOOKLESS BUGLASS
Buickless BOOKLESS BUGLASS
Buigloss BOOKLESS BUGLASS
BUIST 4 Boist Busst Buste
Bukby BUCKBY BUCKLEY

If the name you are interested in is not here, try Section C.

BULCOCK 25 Bawcock Beaucock Bocock Bococke Bocoke BOOCOCK Boococks Bookcok Bookecocke Boolcock Boulcock Bowcoc Bowcock Bowcocke Bowcoocke Bowkoke BUCKOKE BULCOCKE Bulcok Bulcoke Bulkok Bulkoke Bullcock BULLOCK
BULCOCKE 25 Bawcock Beaucock Bocock Bococke Bocoke BOOCOCK Boococks Bookcok Bookecocke Boolcock Boulcock Bowcoc Bowcock Bowcocke Bowcoocke Bowkoke BUCKOKE BULCOCK Bulcok Bulcoke Bulkok Bulkoke Bullcock BULLOCK
Bulcok BOOCOCK BUCKOKE BULCOCK BULCOCKE BULLOCK
Bulcoke BOOCOCK BUCKOKE BULCOCK BULCOCKE BULLOCK
BULKELEY BUCKLEY BULKLEY
BULKLEY BUCKLEY BULKELEY
Bulkok BOOCOCK BUCKOKE BULCOCK BULCOCKE BULLOCK
Bulkoke BOOCOCK BUCKOKE BULCOCK BULCOCKE BULLOCK
BULLAMORE Bullimore
Bullcock BOOCOCK BUCKOKE BULCOCK BULCOCKE BULLOCK
BULLEN 4 Boleyn BOLLEN BULLIN
Bullimore BULLAMORE
BULLIN 4 Boleyn BOLLEN BULLEN
BULLOCK 26 Bawcock Beaucock Bocock Bococke Bocoke BOOCOCK Boococks Bookcok Bookecocke Boolcock Boulcock Bowcoc Bowcock Bowcocke Bowcoocke Bowkoke BUCKOKE BULCOCK BULCOCKE Bulcok Bulcoke Bulkok Bulkoke Bullcock BULLOCKE
BULLOCKE BULLOCK
Bulstone BELSTEN
BUMBY Burmby
BUNCE Bounce Bunch
Bunch BUNCE
Buncombe BUNKHAM BUNKUM
BUNDAY BUNDY
Bundick BUNDOCK
BUNDOCK Bundick Bundwick
BUNDRED 4 Blundred Bondred Brundred
Bundt BUNT
Bundwick BUNDOCK
BUNDY BUNDAY
Buney BONNEY BUNNEY
BUNGAY BUNGEY Bungy
BUNGEY BUNGAY Bungy
Bungy BUNGAY BUNGEY
Bunion BUNYAN
Bunkam BUNKHAM BUNKUM
BUNKHAM 4 Buncombe Bunkam BUNKUM
BUNKUM 4 Buncombe Bunkam BUNKHAM
BUNNET 5 BENNET BENNETT Bonnet BUNNETT
BUNNETT 5 BENNET BENNETT Bonnet BUNNET
BUNNEY 4 BONNEY Buney Bunny
Bunnion BUNYAN
Bunny BONNEY BUNNEY
Bunnyon BUNYAN
Bunson BUNSTON
BUNSTON Bunson Bunstone
Bunstone BUNSTON
BUNT Bundt Bunte
Bunte BUNT
BUNTEN 7 Buntin Buntine BUNTING Buntinge BUNTON Buntynge
Bunthorn BONTHRON
Buntin BUNTEN BUNTING BUNTON
Buntine BUNTEN BUNTING BUNTON
BUNTING 7 BUNTEN Buntin Buntine Buntinge BUNTON Buntynge
Buntinge BUNTEN BUNTING BUNTON
BUNTON 7 BUNTEN Buntin Buntine BUNTING Buntinge Buntynge
Buntynge BUNTEN BUNTING BUNTON
BUNYAN 5 Bunion Bunnion Bunnyon Bunyon
Bunyard BANIARD BANYARD
Bunyeard BANIARD BANYARD
Bunyon BUNYAN
Bur BERE BURGH BURR
Burbage BURBIDGE BURBRIDGE
Burberry BURBERY
BURBERY Burberry
BURBIDGE 10 Berbridge Bergidge Birbage Birbidge Birbridge Burbage BURBRIDGE BURKETT BURKITT
BURBRIDGE 10 Berbridge Bergidge Birbage Birbidge Birbridge Burbage BURBIDGE BURKETT BURKITT
BURCH BIRCH Byrch
BURCHER 4 BIRCHER BOURCHIER Bourgchier
BURCHNALL BIRTCHNELL
Burd BIRD
Burdakin BURDEKIN
BURDEKIN 5 Burdakin Burdikin Burdykin Burkikin
BURDEN Borden BURDON
Burdet BURDICK
BURDICK Burdet Burdit
Burdikin BURDEKIN
Burdit BURDICK
BURDON BURDEN
Burdsal BEARDSALL BIRDSALL
Burdsall BEARDSALL BIRDSALL
Burdsel BEARDSALL BIRDSALL
Burdsell BEARDSALL BIRDSALL
Burdykin BURDEKIN
Burey BERRY BURY
Burgam BURGHAM BURGUM
BURGAR 5 BURGER Burghar Burgher Burghes
Burgeman BRIDGEMAN BRIDGMAN
BURGER 5 BURGAR Burghar Burgher Burghes
BURGES 8 Bergis Birges BURGESS BURGESSE BURGIS Burgiss Burigges
BURGESS 8 Bergis Birges BURGES BURGIS Burgiss Burigges Burrgiss
BURGESSE BURGES Burgiss
BURGH 6 BERE Bire Bur BURR Burre
BURGHAM 6 Bergam Bergham Bergum Burgam BURGUM
Burghar BURGAR BURGER
Burgher BURGAR BURGER
Burghes BURGAR BURGER
BURGIN BERGIN
BURGIS 7 Bergis Birges BURGES BURGESS Burgiss Burigges
Burgiss BURGES BURGESS BURGESSE BURGIS
Burgman BRIDGEMAN BRIDGMAN
Burgoin BURGOYNE
BURGOYNE Burgoin
BURGUM 6 Bergam Bergham Bergum Burgam BURGHAM
Burhill BORRELL BURRELL BURRILL
Burie BERRY
Burigges BURGES BURGESS BURGIS
BURK BURKE
Burkbeck BIRBECK BIRKBECK
BURKE 4 Birk BOURKE BURK
Burkenshaw BIRKENSHAW BIRKINSHAW BURKINSHAW
BURKETT 4 BURBIDGE BURBRIDGE BURKITT
Burkikin BURDEKIN
BURKINSHAW 8 Berkenshaw Berkinshaw Berkumshaw BIRKENSHAW BIRKINSHAW Burkenshaw BURTENSHAW
BURKITT 4 BURBIDGE BURBRIDGE BURKETT
Burkshire BARKSHIRE BERKSHIRE
BURLAND 8 Barland Boarland Boland Bordland BORELAND BORLAND Bourland
Burmby BUMBY
BURN BURNE BURNS
BURNE BURN
BURNELL BURNHOLE Burnoll
BURNES 9 BARNES BARNS Birnes Birns Burness BURNS Byrnes Byrns
Burness BURNES BURNS
BURNET BURNETT
BURNETT BURNET HICKLING-BURNETT
BURNHOLE BURNELL Burnoll
Burnoll BURNELL BURNHOLE
BURNS 11 BARNES BARNS Birnes Birns BURN BURNES Burness BYRNE Byrnes Byrns
Burntoun BARTON BARTRAM BERTRAM BETON BOURTON BRETON BURTON BYRON
Buron BARTON BARTRAM BERTRAM BETON BOURTON BRETON BURTON BYRON
BURR 6 BERE Bire Bur BURGH Burre
BURRAGE BURRIDGE
Burrall BORRELL BURRELL BURRILL
Burre BERE BURGH BURR
BURRELL 10 Barrel Beriall Berrill BORRELL Borrill Burhill Burrall BURRILL Buryll
Burrey BERRY
Burrgiss BURGESS
BURRIDGE BURRAGE
BURRILL 10 Barrel Beriall Berrill BORRELL Borrill Burhill Burrall BURRELL Buryll
BURROUGHS 4 BARROW BORROUGHS BURROWS
Burrowe BURROWS
Burrowes BURROWS
BURROWS 9 BARROW Borowes BORROUGHS Borrowe Borrowes BURROUGHS Burrowe Burrowes
Burrtt BIRT BURT BURTE BUST BUTT
BURRY BERRY
Burson BURSTON
BURSTON 4 Burson Burstone Busson
Burstone BURSTON
BURT 15 Bert BIRD BIRT Birte Birtt Bortt Bourt Burrtt BURTE Burtt BUST BUTT Byrt Byrtt
BURTE 14 Bert BIRT Birte Birtt Bortt Bourt Burrtt BURT Burtt BUST BUTT Byrt Byrtt
BURTENSHAW BURKINSHAW
BURTON 42 Bartan Bartane BARTON Bartone Bartoun Bartrahame BARTRAM Bartrem Bauerton Bertane Berton Bertoun Bertown Bertowne BERTRAM Betan BETON Biron Biroun Birun Bortane Bouerton BOURTON Braton BRETON Bretun Burntoun Buron Burun BYRON De barton De berton De beton De birton De bret De briton De burton De burun Le bret Le bretun Le burone
Burtt BIRT BURT BURTE BUST BUTT
Burtwistle BERTWISTLE BIRTWHISTLE BIRTWISLE
Burun BARTON BARTRAM BERTRAM BETON BOURTON BRETON BURTON BYRON
BURVILL 9 Bervil Bervill Berville Berwill Berwille BURVILLE Burwill Burwille
BURVILLE 9 Bervil Bervill Berville Berwill Berwille BURVILL Burwill Burwille
Burwill BURVILL BURVILLE
Burwille BURVILL BURVILLE
BURY 4 Berrey BERRY Burey
Buryll BORRELL BURRELL BURRILL
BUSCOMBE 5 Biscomb Biscumb Boscumb Buscumb
Buscumb BUSCOMBE
Bushal BUSHELL
Bushall BUSHELL
Bushay BUSHBY
Bushbee BUSHBY
Bushbie BUSHBY
BUSHBY 5 Bushay Bushbee Bushbie Bushbye
Bushbye BUSHBY
Bushel BUSHELL
BUSHELL 4 Bushal Bushall Bushel
BUSKIN BUSTIN
Busson BURSTON
Busst BUIST
BUST 14 Bert BIRT Birte Birtt Bortt Bourt Burrtt BURT BURTE Burtt BUTT Byrt Byrtt
Buste BUIST

If the name you are interested in is not here, try Section C.

BUSTIN BUSKIN
BUSWELL Buzell
BUTCHER 6 BOUCHER Bouchoer Boutcher Boutchoer BUTCHERS
BUTCHERS BUTCHER
Buteland BUTLAND
Buteraus BUTTERISS BUTTERY BUTTRESS BUTTREY
BUTHROYD BOOTHROYD
BUTLAND Buteland Buttland
Butlen BUTLIN
BUTLER 8 BOTELER Botelier Botoler Botollien Botteler Buttlar Buttler
BUTLIN 6 Butlen Butling Buttlen Buttlin Buttling
Butling BUTLIN
BUTSON BATESON BATSON
BUTT 14 Bert BIRT Birte Birtt Bortt Bourt Burtt BURT BURTE Burtt BUST Byrt Byrtt
Buttarass BUTTERISS BUTTERY BUTTRESS BUTTREY
Buttaress BUTTERISS BUTTERY BUTTRESS BUTTREY
Butten BUDDEN BUTTON
BUTTENSHAW Buttinshaw BUTTONSHAW
BUTTER BUTTERS
Butterick BUTTERISS BUTTERY BUTTRESS BUTTREY BUTTRY
Butteries BUTTERISS BUTTERY BUTTRESS BUTTREY BUTTRY
Butteris BUTTERISS BUTTERY BUTTRESS BUTTREY BUTTRY
BUTTERISS 25 Batrie Botrey Botry Botterel Bottreaux Bottrel Bottris Buteraus Buttarass Buttaress Butterick Butteries Butteris BUTTERY Buttree Buttres BUTTRESS BUTTREY Buttrie Buttries Buttriess Buttriss BUTTRY Buttrye
BUTTERS BUTTER
BUTTERY 25 Batrie Botrey Botry Botterel Bottreaux Bottrel Bottris Buteraus Buttarass Buttaress Butterick Butteries Butteris BUTTERISS Buttree Buttres BUTTRESS BUTTREY Buttrie Buttries Buttriess Buttriss BUTTRY Buttrye
Buttinshaw BUTTENSHAW BUTTONSHAW
Buttland BUTLAND
Buttlar BOTELER BUTLER
Buttlen BUTLIN
Buttler BOTELER BUTLER
Buttlin BUTLIN
Buttling BUTLIN
BUTTON BUDDEN Butten
BUTTONSHAW BUTTENSHAW Buttinshaw
Buttree BUTTERISS BUTTERY BUTTRESS BUTTREY BUTTRY
Buttres BUTTERISS BUTTERY BUTTRESS BUTTREY BUTTRY
BUTTRESS 25 Batrie Botrey Botry Botterel Bottreaux Bottrel Bottris Buteraus Buttarass Buttaress Butterick Butteries Butteris BUTTERISS BUTTERY Buttree Buttres BUTTREY Buttrie Buttries Buttriess Buttriss BUTTRY Buttrye
BUTTREY 25 Batrie Botrey Botry Botterel Bottreaux Bottrel Bottris Buteraus Buttarass Buttaress Butterick Butteries Butteris BUTTERISS BUTTERY Buttree Buttres BUTTRESS Buttrie Buttries Buttriess Buttriss BUTTRY Buttrye
Buttrie BUTTERISS BUTTERY BUTTRESS BUTTREY BUTTRY
Buttries BUTTERISS BUTTERY BUTTRESS BUTTREY
Buttriess BUTTERISS BUTTERY BUTTRESS BUTTREY
Buttriss BUTTERISS BUTTERY BUTTRESS BUTTREY BUTTRY
BUTTRY 19 Batrie Botrey Botry Botterel Bottrel Bottris Butterick Butteries Butteris BUTTERISS BUTTERY Buttree Buttres BUTTRESS BUTTREY Buttrie Buttriss Buttrye
Buttrye BUTTERISS BUTTERY BUTTRESS BUTTREY BUTTRY
Butzer BEAZER BEDER BEDR BEDSAR BEDSER BEDSIR BEDSOR BEDSTER BELSER BESSER BETR BETSAR BETSER BETSHER BETSO BETSOR BETSTER BETTSER BETTSOR BETZAR BETZER
BUXTON 4 Buckstone BUCKTON Bucton
Buzell BUSWELL
BYARD BOYARD
Bychar BEECHER
Bydall BIDDLE BIDEL BIDEWELL BIDWELL
Byday BYTHEWAY
Bydder BIDDER
Bydewell BIDDLE BIDEL BIDEWELL BIDWELL
BYERLEY Brierly
Byesley BEASLEY BEAZLEY BEESLEY BESLEY
BYFORD 6 Beeford Beeforth Beford Biford BYFORT
BYFORT Biford BYFORD
BYHURST Biurst
Bylate BOYLETT
Bylet BOYLETT
Bylett BOYLETT
Bylling BELLINGER BILLIN BILLING BILLINGE BILLINGS
Byllinge BELLINGER BILLIN BILLING BILLINGE BILLINGS
Byllinges BELLINGER BILLIN BILLING BILLINGE BILLINGS
Byllyng BELLINGER BILLIN BILLING BILLINGE BILLINGS
Byllynge BELLINGER BILLIN BILLING BILLINGE BILLINGS
Byllynges BELLINGER BILLIN BILLING BILLINGE BILLINGS
Bylot BOYLETT
BYNG 5 BING Binge Bynge Ping
Bynge BING BYNG
Byngham BIGHAM BINGHAM
Bynghame BIGHAM BINGHAM
Bynon BEYNON
BYOLIN 7 Bealin Bellin BOYLIN Boyling Byollin Byolling
Byollin BOYLIN BYOLIN
Byolling BOYLIN BYOLIN
BYRAM 4 Biram BYROM BYRON
Byrch BIRCH BURCH
Byrchenhaughe BIRCHENOUGH
Byrd BIRD
BYRNE 4 BURNS Byrnes Byrns
Byrnes BURNES BURNS BYRNE
Byrns BURNES BURNS BYRNE
BYROM BYRAM
BYRON 44 Bartan Bartane BARTON Bartone Bartoun Bartrahame BARTRAM Bartrem Bauerton Bertane Berton Bertoun Bertown Bertowne BERTRAM Betan BETON Biram Biron Biroun Birun Bortane Bouerton BOURTON Braton BRETON Bretun Burntoun Buron BURTON Burun BYRAM De barton De berton De beton De birton De bret De briton De burton De burun Le bret Le bretun Le burone
Byrt BIRT BURT BURTE BUST BUTT
Byrtt BIRT BURT BURTE BUST BUTT
Bysbrown BAISBROWN
BYSH 6 BISH Bishe Bisshe Byshe Bysshe
Byshe BISH BYSH
Bysset BISSET
Bysshe BISH BYSH
Bythall BETHEL BETHELL BITHEL BOTHELL
Bythel BETHEL BETHELL BITHEL BOTHELL
Bythell BETHEL BETHELL BITHEL BOTHELL
BYTHEWAY 4 Biday Bitheway Byday
Byx BIX
Byxe BIX
Cabble CABLE
CABLE Cabble
Cabourne CAFFYN CAPEN CAPON COBBIN COBBING COFFIN KIPPING
Cachpole CATCHPOLE
Cackbread CAKEBREAD
CADDEL 4 Caddell Caddle CAUDLE
Caddell CADDEL CAUDLE
Caddey CADDIE CADDY CADY
CADDIE 5 Caddey CADDY Cadie CADY
Caddle CADDEL CAUDLE
CADDOCK Caddocke
Caddocke CADDOCK
CADDY 5 Caddey CADDIE Cadie CADY
Cadel CAUDLE
CADELL CADLE
Cadge CAGE KEDGE
Cadie CADDIE CADDY CADY
CADLE CADELL
CADMAN Cartman
CADY 5 Caddey CADDIE CADDY Cadie
CAESAR 5 CAESER Ceasar Ceaser CESAR
CAESER 4 CAESAR Ceasar Ceaser
CAFFERY Caffrey
Caffrey CAFFERY
CAFFYN 86 Cabourne Capan CAPEN Capin CAPON Caponere Caponn Caporn Capoun Capping Cappinger Capyn Caupen Caupin Caupion Cawpen Chapyn Choping Choppen Choppin Chopping Choppinge Chopponn Choppyn Choppynge Chopyn Cobben COBBIN COBBING Cobin Cobyn Cobynge Coffen Coffeyn COFFIN Coffing Coffinge Coffyn Cofin Cofyn Coopene Cooping Coopinge Cooppin Cooppyn Cooppyng Coopyne Copenger Cophaen Cophen Cophin Cophynn Copiner Copinger Copingers Coppener Coppengar Coppenger Coppiner Coppinger Coppingers Coppner Coppynger Copynger Copyunore Cupen Cupenes Cupin Cuppeynge Cuppin Cuppyn Cuppyng Keoppen KIPPING Koppang Koppeians Koppeinge Koppen Koppin Kopping Koppyn Kopyn Kuping Kypping Kyppyng
CAGE 6 Cadge Kadge KEDGE Keg Ketch
CAHILL O'cahill O'FOGARTY
CAIN CANE KEANE
CAINAN Canaan CANNON
CAINES 8 CAINS Canes Caynes Kaines Kains Kaynes Keynes
CAINS 8 CAINES Canes Caynes Kaines Kains Kaynes Keynes
CAIRNS Kairns
Caish CASH
Caisned CHANEY CHAWNER CHENEY CHESNEY CHEYNE CHEYNEY
Caisnei CHANEY CHAWNER CHENEY CHESNEY CHEYNE CHEYNEY
Caisneto CHANEY CHAWNER CHENEY CHESNEY CHEYNE CHEYNEY
CAKE Kaake Kake
CAKEBREAD Cackbread
Calcleugh CALDCLEUGH
CALCOT 12 CALCOTT CALCUTT Callcot Callcott CALLCUT Callcutt CAULCOT Caulcott Cawcott Cawket Cawkett
CALCOTT 12 CALCOT CALCUTT Callcot Callcott CALLCUT Callcutt CAULCOT Caulcott Cawcott Cawket Cawkett
CALCUTT 10 CALCOT CALCOTT Callcott CALLCUT

If the name you are interested in is not here, try Section C.

Callcutt Caulcott
Cawcott Cawket Cawkett
CALDCLEUGH 6 Calcleugh
Caldeleugh Caldelough
Cartclough Coldcleugh
Caldeleugh CALDCLEUGH
Caldelough CALDCLEUGH
CALDER Caulder
Caldren COLDRON
Caldron COLDRON
CALDWELL 4 Calldwell
Caudwell CAULDWELL
Calhom CALLUM
CALKIN 4 CAULKIN CAWKEN
Cawkins
CALL Caul
CALLADINE 25 Callerdine
CANADINE CANARDINE
Canderdine CANDERDYNE
CANNADINE CANNADYNE
CARDEN CARDIN CARDING
CARDON Carodine
CARRADINE Carradyne
Carrodine CARWARDEN
Carwardin CARWARDINE
CARWARDYNE DE
KAREWARDYN KAWRDIN
Keanodine KENDERDINE
KENWARDEN
Callam CALLUM
CALLAWAY CALLOWAY
Callcot CALCOT CALCOTT
CAULCOT
Callcott CALCOT CALCOTT
CALCUTT CALLCUT CAULCOT
CALLCUT 10 CALCOT CALCOTT
CALCUTT Callcott
Callcutt Caulcott
Cawcott Cawket Cawkett
Callcutt CALCOT CALCOTT
CALCUTT CALLCUT
Calldwell CALDWELL
CAULDWELL
CALLENDER COTTENDEN
Callerdine CALLADINE
CANADINE CANARDINE
CANDERDYNE CANNADINE
CANNADYNE CARDEN CARDIN
CARDING CARDON
CARRADINE CARWARDEN
CARWARDINE CARWARDYNE
DE KAREWARDYN KAWRDIN
KENDERDINE KENWARDEN
CALLONS COLLINS
CALLOWAY CALLAWAY
CALLUM 6 Calhom Callam
Calum Collum CULM
Calton CARLTON
Calum CALLUM
CALVER 4 CLOVER COLVER
CULVER
CALVERLEY 4 Calverly
CARVELEY Caverly
Calverly CALVERLEY
CARVELEY
CAM CAME CAMM
Camack CAMMACK
Cambrey KEMBREY
Cambry KEMBREY
Camby CANBY
CAME CAM CAMM
CAMFIELD 5 Campfield
CANFIELD ROBBINS ROBINS
CAMM CAM CAME
CAMMACK Camack Cummock
CAMP 8 Campe CHAMP Cimp
KEMP Kempe Kimp Kimpe
Campain CAMPION
Campantin CHIAMPANTE
Campe CAMP KEMP
Campfield CAMFIELD
CANFIELD ROBBINS ROBINS
Camphilon CAMPLEJOHN
Campilyon CAMPLEJOHN
Campilyone CAMPLEJOHN
CAMPION Campain CHAMPION
Camplechon CAMPLEJOHN
Camplechone CAMPLEJOHN
Camplegean CAMPLEJOHN
Camplegin CAMPLEJOHN
Camplegon CAMPLEJOHN
Campleiane CAMPLEJOHN
Campleijohn CAMPLEJOHN
Camplejean CAMPLEJOHN
CAMPLEJOHN 27 Camphilon
Campilyon Campilyone
Camplechon Camplechone
Camplegean Camplegin
Camplegon Campleiane
Campleijohn Camplejean
Camplejoyne Camplesham
Campleshon Campleshone
Campleson Camplethon
Campleton Campleyon
Campligon Camplijohn
Camplisham Camplishon
Capleion Champloshon
Compleshon
Camplejoyne CAMPLEJOHN
Camplesham CAMPLEJOHN
Campleshon CAMPLEJOHN
Campleshone CAMPLEJOHN
Campleson CAMPLEJOHN
Camplethon CAMPLEJOHN
Campleton CAMPLEJOHN
Campleyon CAMPLEJOHN
Campligon CAMPLEJOHN
Camplijohn CAMPLEJOHN
Camplisham CAMPLEJOHN
Camplishon CAMPLEJOHN
Camville DE CAMVILLE
Canaan CAINAN CANNON
CANADINE 25 CALLADINE
Callerdine CANARDINE
Canderdine CANDERDYNE
CANNADINE CANNADYNE
CARDEN CARDIN CARDING
CARDON Carodine
CARRADINE Carradyne
Carrodine CARWARDEN
Carwardin CARWARDINE
CARWARDYNE DE
KAREWARDYN KAWRDIN
Keanodine KENDERDINE
KENWARDEN
CANARDINE 25 CALLADINE
Callerdine CANADINE
Canderdine CANDERDYNE
CANNADINE CANNADYNE
CARDEN CARDIN CARDING
CARDON Carodine
CARRADINE Carradyne
Carrodine CARWARDEN
Carwardin CARWARDINE
CARWARDYNE DE
KAREWARDYN KAWRDIN
Keanodine KENDERDINE
KENWARDEN
Canbe CANBY
CANBY Camby Canbe
Candalant CANDELENT
Candalent CANDELENT
Candalett CANDELENT
CANDELENT 6 Candalant
Candalent Candalett
Candelow Candlent
Candelow CANDELENT
Canderdine CALLADINE
CANADINE CANARDINE
CANDERDYNE CANNADINE
CANNADYNE CARDEN CARDIN
CARDING CARDON
CARRADINE CARWARDEN
CARWARDINE CARWARDYNE
DE KAREWARDYN KAWRDIN
KENDERDINE KENWARDEN
CANDERDYNE 25 CALLADINE
Callerdine CANADINE
CANARDINE Canderdine
CANNADINE CANNADYNE
CARDEN CARDIN CARDING
CARDON Carodine
CARRADINE Carradyne
Carrodine CARWARDEN
Carwardin CARWARDINE
CARWARDYNE DE
KAREWARDYN KAWRDIN
Keanodine KENDERDINE
KENWARDEN
Candle CAUDLE
Candlent CANDELENT
Candlewick CONDUCT
CONDUIT
Canduck CONDUCT CONDUIT
CANE CAIN
Canes CAINES CAINS
CANFIELD CAMFIELD
Campfield
CANNADINE 25 CALLADINE
Callerdine CANADINE
CANARDINE Canderdine
CANDERDYNE CANNADYNE
CARDEN CARDIN CARDING
CARDON Carodine
CARRADINE Carradyne
Carrodine CARWARDEN
Carwardin CARWARDINE
CARWARDYNE DE
KAREWARDYN KAWRDIN
Keanodine KENDERDINE
KENWARDEN
CANNADYNE 25 CALLADINE
Callerdine CANADINE
CANARDINE Canderdine
CANDERDYNE CANNADINE
CARDEN CARDIN CARDING
CARDON Carodine
CARRADINE Carradyne
Carrodine CARWARDEN
Carwardin CARWARDINE
CARWARDYNE DE
KAREWARDYN KAWRDIN
Keanodine KENDERDINE
KENWARDEN
CANNING CANNINGS CANNON
CANNINGS CANNING CANNON
CANNON 5 CAINAN Canaan
CANNING CANNINGS
Cansdale CANSELL
Cansdell CANSELL
CANSELL Cansdale Cansdell
CANSICK Chusick Kansick
CANT 52 Cante CANTER
Canterall Canterel
CANTERELL Canterelle
Canterhill Canterhulle
Cantlen Cantrall
Cantrel CANTRELL
Cantrelle Cantril
CANTRILL Cantrille
Cantrul Cantrule Cantt
Cantwall Cantwell CANTY
Caunton Chanterall
Chanterel Chanterell
Chanterelle Chantrel
CHANTRELL Chantrelle
Chantril Chantrill
Cointerel Cointerell
Coynterel Cuinterel
Cuinterell Cuonterel
Kant Kanterall
Kanterell Kanterill
Kantrall Kantrell
Kantrill Quantrell
QUANTRILL Quarntrill
Queinterell QUINTRELL
Quyntrel
Cante CANT CANTY
CANTELLO 7 Cantelo
Canteloe Cantelow
Cantelowe Cantle
Kantelo
Cantelo CANTELLO
Canteloe CANTELLO
Cantelow CANTELLO
Cantelowe CANTELLO
CANTER 48 CANT Canterall
Canterel CANTERELL
Canterelle Canterhill
Canterhulle Cantlen
Cantrall Cantrel
CANTRELL Cantrelle
Cantril CANTRILL
Cantrille Cantrul
Cantrule Cantwall
Cantwell Caunton
Chanterall Chanterel
Chanterell Chanterelle
Chantrel CHANTRELL
Chantrelle Chantril
Chantrill Cointerel
Cointerell Coynterel
Cuinterel Cuinterell
Cuonterel Kanterall
Kanterell Kanterill
Kantrall Kantrell
Kantrill Quantrell
QUANTRILL Quarntrill
Queinterell QUINTRELL
Quyntrel
Canterall CANT CANTER
CANTERELL CANTRELL
CANTRILL CHANTRELL
QUANTRILL QUINTRELL
Canterel CANT CANTER
CANTERELL CANTRELL
CANTRILL CHANTRELL
QUANTRILL QUINTRELL
CANTERELL 48 CANT CANTER
Canterall Canterel
Canterelle Canterhill
Canterhulle Cantlen
Cantrall Cantrel
CANTRELL Cantrelle
Cantril CANTRILL
Cantrille Cantrul
Cantrule Cantwall
Cantwell Caunton
Chanterall Chanterel
Chanterell Chanterelle
Chantrel CHANTRELL
Chantrelle Chantril
Chantrill Cointerel
Cointerell Coynterel
Cuinterel Cuinterell
Cuonterel Kanterall
Kanterell Kanterill
Kantrall Kantrell
Kantrill Quantrell
QUANTRILL Quarntrill
Queinterell QUINTRELL
Quyntrel
Canterelle CANT CANTER
CANTERELL CANTRELL
CANTRILL CHANTRELL
QUANTRILL QUINTRELL
Canterhill CANT CANTER
CANTERELL CANTRELL
CANTRILL CHANTRELL
QUANTRILL QUINTRELL
Canterhulle CANT CANTER
CANTERELL CANTRELL
CANTRILL CHANTRELL
QUANTRILL QUINTRELL
Cantill CANTRILL
Cantle CANTELLO
Cantlen CANT CANTER
CANTERELL CANTRELL
CANTRILL CHANTRELL
QUANTRILL QUINTRELL
Cantrall CANT CANTER
CANTERELL CANTRELL
CANTRILL CHANTRELL
QUANTRILL QUINTRELL
Cantrel CANT CANTER
CANTERELL CANTRELL

If the name you are interested in is not here, try Section C.

CANTRILL CHANTRELL QUANTRILL QUINTRELL
CANTRELL 48 CANT CANTER Canterall Canterel CANTERELL Canterelle Canterhill Canterhulle Cantlen Cantrall Cantrel Cantrelle Cantril CANTRILL Cantrille Cantrul Cantrule Cantwall Cantwell Caunton Chanterall Chanterel Chanterell Chanterelle Chantrel CHANTRELL Chantrelle Chantril Chantrill Cointerel Cointerell Coynterel Cuinterel Cuinterell Cuonterel Kanterall Kanterell Kanterill Kantrall Kantrell Kantrill Quantrell QUANTRILL Quarntrill Queinterell QUINTRELL Quyntrel
Cantrelle CANT CANTER CANTERELL CANTRELL CANTRILL CHANTRELL QUANTRILL QUINTRELL
Cantril CANT CANTER CANTERELL CANTRELL CANTRILL CHANTRELL QUANTRILL QUINTRELL
CANTRILL 49 CANT CANTER Canterall Canterel CANTERELL Canterelle Canterhill Canterhulle Cantill Cantlen Cantrall Cantrel CANTRELL Cantrelle Cantril Cantrille Cantrul Cantrule Cantwall Cantwell Caunton Chanterall Chanterel Chanterell Chanterelle Chantrel CHANTRELL Chantrelle Chantril Chantrill Cointerel Cointerell Coynterel Cuinterel Cuinterell Cuonterel Kanterall Kanterell Kanterill Kantrall Kantrell Kantrill Quantrell QUANTRILL Quarntrill Queinterell QUINTRELL Quyntrel
Cantrille CANT CANTER CANTERELL CANTRELL CANTRILL CHANTRELL QUANTRILL QUINTRELL
Cantrul CANT CANTER CANTERELL CANTRELL CANTRILL CHANTRELL QUANTRILL QUINTRELL
Cantrule CANT CANTER CANTERELL CANTRELL CANTRILL CHANTRELL QUANTRILL QUINTRELL
Cantt CANT CANTY
Cantwall CANT CANTER CANTERELL CANTRELL CANTRILL CHANTRELL QUANTRILL QUINTRELL
Cantwell CANT CANTER CANTERELL CANTRELL CANTRILL CHANTRELL QUANTRILL QUINTRELL
CANTY 5 CANT Cante Cantt Kant
Canville DE CAMVILLE
Capan CAFFYN CAPEN CAPON COBBIN COBBING COFFIN KIPPING
CAPEL Cappel Cappell
CAPELIN Caplin
CAPEN 87 Cabourne CAFFYN Capan Capin CAPON Caponere Caponn Caporn Capoun Cappen Capping Cappinger Capyn Caupen Caupin Caupion Cawpen Chapyn Choping Choppen Choppin Chopping Choppinge Chopponn Choppyn Choppynge Chopyn Cobben COBBIN COBBING Cobin Cobyn Cobynge Coffen Coffeyn COFFIN Coffing Coffinge Coffyn Cofin Cofyn Coopene Cooping Coopinge Cooppin Cooppyn Cooppyng Coopyne Copenger Cophaen Cophen Cophin Cophynn Copiner Copinger Copingers Coppener Coppengar Coppenger Coppiner Coppinger Coppingers Coppner Coppynger Copynger Copyunore Cupen Cupenes Cupin Cuppeynge Cuppin Cuppyn Cuppyng Keoppen KIPPING Koppang Koppeians Koppeinge Koppen Koppin Kopping Koppyn Kopyn Kuping Kypping Kyppyng
Capet CAPPITT
Capett CAPPITT
CAPIE 7 CAPPIE Cappy Kapie Keppey KEPPIE Keppy
Capin CAFFYN CAPEN CAPON COBBIN COBBING COFFIN KIPPING
Capis CAPPS
Capit CAPPITT
Capitt CAPPITT
Capleion CAMPLEJOHN
Caplin CAPELIN
CAPON 90 Cabourne CAFFYN Capan CAPEN Capin Caponere Caponn Caporn Capoun Cappen Capping Cappinger Capyn Caupen Caupin Caupion Cawpen Chapyn CHOPEN Choping Choppen Choppin Chopping Choppinge Chopponn Choppyn Choppynge Chopyn Cobben COBBIN COBBING COBHAM Cobin Cobyn Cobynge Coffen Coffeyn COFFIN Coffing Coffinge Coffyn Cofin Cofyn Coopene Cooping Coopinge Cooppin Cooppyn Cooppyng Coopyne Copenger Cophaen COPHAM Cophen Cophin Cophynn Copiner Copinger Copingers Coppener Coppengar Coppenger Coppiner Coppinger Coppingers Coppner Coppynger Copynger Copyunore Cupen Cupenes Cupin Cuppeynge Cuppin Cuppyn Cuppyng Keoppen KIPPING Koppang Koppeians Koppeinge Koppen Koppin Kopping Koppyn Kopyn Kuping Kypping Kyppyng
Caponere CAFFYN CAPEN CAPON COBBIN COBBING COFFIN KIPPING
Caponn CAFFYN CAPEN CAPON COBBIN COBBING COFFIN KIPPING
Caporn CAFFYN CAPEN CAPON COBBIN COBBING COFFIN KIPPING
Capoun CAFFYN CAPEN CAPON COBBIN COBBING COFFIN KIPPING
Cappel CAPEL
Cappell CAPEL
Cappen CAPEN CAPON
Cappes CAPPS
Cappet CAPPITT
Cappett CAPPITT
CAPPIE 7 CAPIE Cappy Kapie Keppey KEPPIE Keppy
Capping CAFFYN CAPEN CAPON COBBIN COBBING COFFIN KIPPING
Cappinger CAFFYN CAPEN CAPON COBBIN COBBING COFFIN KIPPING
Cappis CAPPS
Cappit CAPPITT
CAPPITT 8 Capet Capett Capit Capitt Cappet Cappett Cappit
Cappock COBBETT COPPOCK CORBET CORBETT
Cappocke COBBETT COPPOCK CORBET CORBETT
CAPPS 5 Capis Cappes Cappis Caps
Cappuch COBBETT COPPOCK CORBET CORBETT
Cappuck COBBETT COPPOCK CORBET CORBETT
Cappy CAPIE CAPPIE KEPPIE
Caps CAPPS
Capyn CAFFYN CAPEN CAPON COBBIN COBBING COFFIN KIPPING
Caraher CARRAHER
Caras CARIS CARUS
CARCAS 5 Carcass Carcasse Carcus Carkasse
Carcass CARCAS
Carcasse CARCAS
Carcus CARCAS
CARD 5 Carde CART Curt Kart
Carde CARD
Cardell CURDELL
CARDEN 26 CALLADINE Callerdine CANADINE CANARDINE Canderdine CANDERDYNE CANNADINE CANNADYNE CARDIN CARDING CARDON Carodine CARRADINE Carradyne Carrodine CARWARDEN Carwardin CARWARDINE CARWARDYNE Cawarden DE KAREWARDYN KAWRDIN Keanodine KENDERDINE KENWARDEN
CARDEW Cardue
CARDIN 25 CALLADINE Callerdine CANADINE CANARDINE Canderdine CANDERDYNE CANNADINE CANNADYNE CARDEN CARDING CARDON Carodine CARRADINE Carradyne Carrodine CARWARDEN Carwardin CARWARDINE CARWARDYNE DE KAREWARDYN KAWRDIN Keanodine KENDERDINE KENWARDEN
CARDING 25 CALLADINE Callerdine CANADINE CANARDINE Canderdine CANDERDYNE CANNADINE CANNADYNE CARDEN CARDIN CARDON Carodine CARRADINE Carradyne Carrodine CARWARDEN Carwardin CARWARDINE CARWARDYNE DE KAREWARDYN KAWRDIN Keanodine KENDERDINE KENWARDEN
CARDON 25 CALLADINE Callerdine CANADINE CANARDINE Canderdine CANDERDYNE CANNADINE CANNADYNE CARDEN CARDIN CARDING Carodine CARRADINE Carradyne Carrodine CARWARDEN Carwardin CARWARDINE CARWARDYNE DE KAREWARDYN KAWRDIN Keanodine KENDERDINE KENWARDEN
Cardue CARDEW
Cardwell CORDWELL
CAREFOOT 13 CARFOOT CRAFFORD CRAFORD CRAWFORD CRAYFORD CROFFORD CROFOOT Crofut CROWFOOT CROWFORD Crowfrothe KERFOOT
CARELESS 8 Carelesse Carles CARLESS Carlis Carlos Carriss Cayes
Carelesse CARELESS CARLESS
CAREW 9 Carewe Caro Caroe Carrew Carro CARROW Caru Carue
Carewe CAREW CARROW
CAREY CARY Kari
CARFOOT 13 CAREFOOT CRAFFORD CRAFORD CRAWFORD CRAYFORD CROFFORD CROFOOT Crofut CROWFOOT CROWFORD Crowfrothe KERFOOT
Cargenven CURGENVEN
CARIS 4 Caras Carous CARUS
Carkasse CARCAS
Carles CARELESS CARLESS
CARLESS 8 CARELESS Carelesse Carles Carlis Carlos Carriss Cayes
Carleton CARLTON CHARLETON HILLHOUSE MCKERRELL
CARLICK 13 Kallock Keilock Keleg KILLICK Killik Killok Killoke Killuck Killucke Kyelyche Kyllyk Kyllyke
CARLILE CARLISLE CARLYLE
CARLIN CAROLAN Caroline
CARLION Carlyan CARLYON
Carlis CARELESS CARLESS
CARLISLE CARLILE CARLYLE
Carlos CARELESS CARLESS
CARLTON 7 Calton Carleton Carton Cauton CAWTON COULTON
Carlyan CARLION CARLYON
CARLYLE CARLILE CARLISLE
CARLYON CARLION Carlyan
CARNEGIE Carnegy
Carnegy CARNEGIE
CARNOCHAN CARNON
CARNON CARNOCHAN

If the name you are interested in is not here, try Section C.

Caro CAREW CARROW
Carodine CALLADINE CANADINE CANARDINE CANDERDYNE CANNADINE CANNADYNE CARDEN CARDIN CARDING CARDON CARRADINE CARWARDEN CARWARDINE CARWARDYNE DE KAREWARDYN KAWRDIN KENDERDINE KENWARDEN
Caroe CAREW CARROW
Carol CARROL CARROLL CHARLETON HILLHOUSE MCKERRELL
CAROLAN CARLIN Caroline
Caroline CARLIN CAROLAN
Carous CARIS CARUS
Carpender CARPENTER CARPINTER
CARPENTER Carpender CARPINTER
CARPINTER Carpender CARPENTER
CARR KERR
CARRADINE 25 CALLADINE Callerdine CANADINE CANARDINE Canderdine CANDERDYNE CANNADINE CANNADYNE CARDEN CARDIN CARDING CARDON Carodine Carradyne Carrodine CARWARDEN Carwardin CARWARDINE CARWARDYNE DE KAREWARDYN KAWRDIN Keanodine KENDERDINE KENWARDEN
Carradyne CALLADINE CANADINE CANARDINE CANDERDYNE CANNADINE CANNADYNE CARDEN CARDIN CARDING CARDON CARRADINE CARWARDEN CARWARDINE CARWARDYNE DE KAREWARDYN KAWRDIN KENDERDINE KENWARDEN
CARRAHER Caraher
Carrew CAREW CARROW
Carriar CARRIER CARRYER
CARRIER 4 Carriar CARRYER Caryer
Carriss CARELESS CARLESS
Carro CAREW CARROW
Carrodine CALLADINE CANADINE CANARDINE CANDERDYNE CANNADINE CANNADYNE CARDEN CARDIN CARDING CARDON CARRADINE CARWARDEN CARWARDINE CARWARDYNE DE KAREWARDYN KAWRDIN KENDERDINE KENWARDEN
CARROL Carol CARROLL
CARROLL Carol CARROL
CARROW 9 CAREW Carewe Caro Caroe Carrew Carro Caru Carue
CARRYER 4 Carriar CARRIER Caryer
Carsell CARZELL
CARSEY Cassey
Carsford CASSFORD
Carslack CARSLAKE KERSLAKE
CARSLAKE 5 Carslack Cerslake KERSLAKE Keslake
Carsom CORBOM CORSON
CART 4 CARD Curt Kart
Cartclough CALDCLEUGH
Cartlech CARTLICH
CARTLEDGE CARTLIDGE
Cartlege CARTLICH
CARTLICH Cartlech Cartlege
CARTLIDGE CARTLEDGE
Cartman CADMAN
CARTMEL CARTMELL
CARTMELL CARTMEL
Carton CARLTON CAWTON COULTON
Caru CAREW CARROW
Carue CAREW CARROW
CARUS 4 Caras CARIS Carous
CARVAL Cerveil
CARVASSO Corvouso
Carvath CARVETH
Carveighe CARVETH
CARVELEY 4 CALVERLEY Calverly Caverly
Carverth CARVETH
Carverthe CARVETH
CARVETH 7 Carvath Carveighe Carverth Carverthe Carvolth Cerveth
CARVEY 4 Carvy Cavey Cavy
Carvolth CARVETH
Carvy CARVEY
CARWARDEN 25 CALLADINE Callerdine CANADINE CANARDINE Canderdine CANDERDYNE CANNADINE CANNADYNE CARDEN CARDIN CARDING CARDON Carodine CARRADINE Carradyne Carrodine Carwardin CARWARDINE CARWARDYNE DE KAREWARDYN KAWRDIN Keanodine KENDERDINE KENWARDEN
Carwardin CALLADINE CANADINE CANARDINE CANDERDYNE CANNADINE CANNADYNE CARDEN CARDIN CARDING CARDON CARRADINE CARWARDEN CARWARDINE CARWARDYNE DE KAREWARDYN KAWRDIN KENDERDINE KENWARDEN
CARWARDINE 26 CALLADINE Callerdine CANADINE CANARDINE Canderdine CANDERDYNE CANNADINE CANNADYNE CARDEN CARDIN CARDING CARDON Carodine CARRADINE Carradyne Carrodine CARWARDEN Carwardin CARWARDYNE Cawarden DE KAREWARDYN KAWRDIN Keanodine KENDERDINE KENWARDEN
CARWARDYNE 25 CALLADINE Callerdine CANADINE CANARDINE Canderdine CANDERDYNE CANNADINE CANNADYNE CARDEN CARDIN CARDING CARDON Carodine CARRADINE Carradyne Carrodine CARWARDEN Carwardin CARWARDINE DE KAREWARDYN KAWRDIN Keanodine KENDERDINE KENWARDEN
Carwood CAWOOD
CARY CAREY Kari
Caryer CARRIER CARRYER
Carysfort CASSFORD
CARZELL Carsell
Casball CASBAN CASBOLT CASBON
CASBAN 17 Casball Casbard Casbell Casben Casbill CASBOLT Casbolte CASBON Casborn Casborne Casboult Casbourn Casbourne Casbull Casburn Casburne
Casbard CASBAN CASBOLT CASBON
Casbell CASBAN CASBOLT CASBON
Casben CASBAN CASBOLT CASBON
Casbill CASBAN CASBOLT CASBON
Casbold CASBOLT
CASBOLT 19 Casball CASBAN Casbard Casbell Casben Casbill Casbold Casbolte CASBON Casborn Casborne Casbould Casboult Casbourn Casbourne Casbull Casburn Casburne
Casbolte CASBAN CASBOLT CASBON
CASBON 17 Casball CASBAN Casbard Casbell Casben Casbill CASBOLT Casbolte Casborn Casborne Casboult Casbourn Casbourne Casbull Casburn Casburne
Casborn CASBAN CASBOLT CASBON
Casborne CASBAN CASBOLT CASBON
Casbould CASBOLT
Casboult CASBAN CASBOLT CASBON
Casbourn CASBAN CASBOLT CASBON
Casbourne CASBAN CASBOLT CASBON
Casbull CASBAN CASBOLT CASBON
Casburn CASBAN CASBOLT CASBON
Casburne CASBAN CASBOLT CASBON
CASE CASS Casse
Caseford CASSFORD
Casfeild CASSFORD
Casfield CASSFORD
Casford CASSFORD
CASH Caish
Cashe CASS
Cashford CASSFORD
Casling CASTLING
Casneto CHANEY CHAWNER CHENEY CHESNEY CHEYNE CHEYNEY
Cason CASSON
CASS 4 CASE Cashe Casse
Casse CASE CASS
CASSELS Cassils
Cassey CARSEY COSSEY
CASSFORD 11 Carsford Carysfort Caseford Casfeild Casfield Casford Cashford Cosfort Kaysford Keysford
Cassils CASSELS
CASSON Cason
Castel CASTLE
CASTELL 4 Castelle CASTLE Castles
Castelle CASTELL CASTLE
Casterson KESTERTON
Casterton KESTERTON
CASTLE 5 Castel CASTELL Castelle Castles
Castles CASTELL CASTLE
CASTLING Casling
CATANACH Cattanach
CATCHPOLE Cachpole
Catcut CATCUTT
Catcute CATCUTT
CATCUTT 4 Catcut Catcute Kitkat
Catheral CATHERALL CATTERALL
CATHERALL 8 Catheral Cathral Catral Catrow Catteral CATTERALL Cattral
Cathral CATHERALL CATTERALL
CATLOW Chatlow
Catral CATHERALL CATTERALL
Catrow CATHERALL CATTERALL
Cattanach CATANACH
Catteral CATHERALL CATTERALL
CATTERALL 8 Catheral CATHERALL Cathral Catral Catrow Catteral Cattral
Catterment QUARTERMAIN QUARTERMAN
Cattral CATHERALL CATTERALL
Caudell CAUDLE
CAUDLE 10 CADDEL Caddell Caddle Cadel Candle Caudell Caudwell Caule Cawdle
Caudwell CALDWELL CAUDLE CAULDWELL
Cauker COAKER COCKER COKER
Caul CALL
CAULCOT 6 CALCOT CALCOTT Callcot Callcott Caulcott
Caulcott CALCOT CALCOTT CALCUTT CALLCUT CAULCOT
Caulder CALDER
Cauldren COLDRON
Cauldron COLDRON
CAULDWELL 4 CALDWELL Calldwell Caudwell
Caule CAUDLE
CAULFIELD Cawfield CORFIELD
Caulker COAKER COCKER COKER
CAULKIN 4 CALKIN CAWKEN Cawkins
Caundrel LAUNDREL
Caunton CANT CANTER CANTERELL CANTRELL CANTRILL CHANTRELL QUANTRILL QUINTRELL
Caupen CAFFYN CAPEN CAPON COBBIN COBBING COFFIN KIPPING
Caupin CAFFYN CAPEN CAPON COBBIN COBBING COFFIN KIPPING
Caupion CAFFYN CAPEN CAPON COBBIN COBBING COFFIN KIPPING
Cause CAWSE
Causebrook CODGBROOK
CAUSER Cawser Corser
Caut CAWTE
Caute CAWTE
Cauton CARLTON CAWTON COULTON
Cauws CAWSE
Caux CAWSE
CAVANAGH KAVANAGH
CAVE Ceave Kave
CAVELL CAVIL Cavill
Caverly CALVERLEY CARVELEY
Cavey CARVEY
CAVIL CAVELL Cavill
Cavill CAVELL CAVIL SAVIL SAVILE SAVILLE

If the name you are interested in is not here, try Section C.

Cavy CARVEY
Cawarden CARDEN CARWARDINE
Cawcott CALCOT CALCOTT CALCUTT CALLCUT
Cawdery CORDERY
Cawdle CAUDLE
Cawfield CAULFIELD CORFIELD
CAWKEN 4 CALKIN CAULKIN Cawkins
Cawket CALCOT CALCOTT CALCUTT CALLCUT
Cawkett CALCOT CALCOTT CALCUTT CALLCUT
Cawkins CALKIN CAULKIN CAWKEN
CAWLEY 83 Cawly Coahley Coale Coalee Coaley Coaleys Coalie Coalle Coalley Coally Coaly Coawly Coeley Coely Cohley Cohleye Coiley COLE Colee Colei Coleley Colely COLEY Coleye Coleyis Coli Colie Coliye Coll Collay Colle Collee Colles COLLEY Colleye Colli COLLIE Colliy COLLY Collye Coly Colye Cooaly COOLE Coolee COOLEY Cooleye Coolie Coolley Coolly Coollye Cooly Coolye Coorley CORLEY Coulah Coulay Couley Coulley Couly Couolley Coweley Cowely Cowlay Cowlaye Cowlee Cowleige COWLEY Cowleye Cowli Cowlie Cowllay Cowllea Cowllie Cowly Cowlye Coyleie Coyley Coyly Culey CULLEY De culegh
Cawly CAWLEY COLE COLEY COLLEY COLLIE COLLY COOLE COOLEY CORLEY COWLEY CULLEY
CAWOOD Carwood
Cawpen CAFFYN CAPEN CAPON COBBIN COBBING COFFIN KIPPING
Caws CAWSE
CAWSE 6 Cause Cauws Caux Caws Cawsse
Cawser CAUSER
Cawsse CAWSE
Cawt CAWTE
CAWTE 4 Caut Caute Cawt
CAWTHORN CAWTHORNE
CAWTHORNE CAWTHORN
CAWTON 5 CARLTON Carton Cauton COULTON
Caxton CLAXTON
Cayes CARELESS CARLESS
Caynes CAINES CAINS
Ceasar CAESAR CAESER CESAR
Ceaser CAESAR CAESER
Ceave CAVE
Ceep KEAP KEEP
Ceiling CELLING
CELLING Ceiling Selin
Cepe KEAP KEEP
Cerslake CARSLAKE
Cerveil CARVAL
Cerveth CARVETH
CESAR CAESAR Ceasar
CESSFORD Sissford
Cesterson KESTERTON
Cesterton KESTERTON
Cestreton KESTERTON
Cethin GETHIN
CHADDERTON Chaderton
Chaddock CHADWICK
Chaderton CHADDERTON
Chadford SHETFER
CHADWICK 4 Chaddock Chadwicke Chadwyck
Chadwicke CHADWICK
Chadwyck CHADWICK
CHAFFIN Chafyn
Chafyn CHAFFIN
Chainey CHANEY CHAWNER CHENEY CHESNEY CHEYNE CHEYNEY
Chainy CHANEY CHAWNER CHENEY CHESNEY CHEYNE CHEYNEY
CHALK 5 Chalke Chaulk Chok Choke
Chalke CHALK
Chalkeley CHALKLEY
CHALKLEY Chalkeley Chalkly
Chalkly CHALKLEY
Challanor CHALLENOR
CHALLENOR Challanor Challoner
Challoner CHALLENOR
CHAMBERLAIN 4 CHAMBERLAYNE Chamberlen CHAMBERLIN
CHAMBERLAYNE 4 CHAMBERLAIN Chamberlen CHAMBERLIN
Chamberlen CHAMBERLAIN CHAMBERLAYNE
CHAMBERLIN CHAMBERLAIN CHAMBERLAYNE
CHAMNESS Champness
CHAMP CAMP
Champante CHIAMPANTE
CHAMPION CAMPION
Champloshon CAMPLEJOHN
Champness CHAMNESS
Chana CHANEY CHAWNER CHENEY CHESNEY CHEYNE CHEYNEY
Chandeler CHANDLER
CHANDLER 5 Chandeler Chanler CHANTLER Chaundler
Chanee CHANEY CHAWNER CHENEY CHESNEY CHEYNE CHEYNEY
Chanel CHANNEL
Chaner CHANEY CHAWNER CHENEY CHESNEY CHEYNE CHEYNEY
CHANEY 52 Caisned Caisnei Caisneto Casneto Chainey Chainy Chana Chanee Chaner Channer Chany Chaune Chauner Chauney Chauneys Chaunies Chauny CHAWNER Chawney Chawny Chayney Chaynye Cheaney Cheany Cheene Cheenei Cheeney Cheeny Cheine Cheiney Cheiny Chenduit Chenduyt Chene Chenea Cheneiy CHENEY Chenie Chenney Chenny Chensy Cheny Chesnei Chesneto CHESNEY Chesneye CHEYNE CHEYNEY China Chiney Chinney
Chanler CHANDLER
CHANNEL 4 Chanel Cheynel Cheynell
Channer CHANEY CHAWNER CHENEY CHESNEY CHEYNE CHEYNEY
CHANT Chaunt
Chanterall CANT CANTER CANTERELL CANTRELL CANTRILL CHANTRELL QUANTRILL QUINTRELL
Chanterel CANT CANTER CANTERELL CANTRELL CANTRILL CHANTRELL QUANTRILL QUINTRELL
Chanterell CANT CANTER CANTERELL CANTRELL CANTRILL CHANTRELL QUANTRILL QUINTRELL
Chanterelle CANT CANTER CANTERELL CANTRELL CANTRILL CHANTRELL QUANTRILL QUINTRELL
CHANTLER CHANDLER
Chantrall CHANTRELL
Chantrel CANT CANTER CANTERELL CANTRELL CANTRILL CHANTRELL QUANTRILL QUINTRELL
CHANTRELL 49 CANT CANTER Canterall Canterel CANTERELL Canterelle Canterhill Canterhulle Cantlen Cantrall Cantrel CANTRELL Cantrelle Cantril CANTRILL Cantrille Cantrul Cantrule Cantwall Cantwell Caunton Chanterall Chanterel Chanterell Chanterelle Chantrall Chantrel Chantrelle Chantril Chantrill Cointerel Cointerell Coynterel Cuinterel Cuinterell Cuonterel Kanterall Kanterell Kanterill Kantrall Kantrell Kantrill Quantrell QUANTRILL Quarntrill Queinterell QUINTRELL Quyntrel
Chantrelle CANT CANTER CANTERELL CANTRELL CANTRILL CHANTRELL QUANTRILL QUINTRELL
Chantril CANT CANTER CANTERELL CANTRELL CANTRILL CHANTRELL QUANTRILL QUINTRELL
Chantrill CANT CANTER CANTERELL CANTRELL CANTRILL CHANTRELL QUANTRILL QUINTRELL
Chany CHANEY CHAWNER CHENEY CHESNEY CHEYNE CHEYNEY
Chapel CHAPELL CHAPPEL CHAPPELL CHAPPELLS CHAPPLE
CHAPELHOW Chaplow
CHAPELL 8 Chapel Chapels CHAPPEL CHAPPELL CHAPPELLE CHAPPELLS CHAPPLE
Chapels CHAPELL CHAPPEL CHAPPELL CHAPPELLS
Chaple CHAPPEL CHAPPLE
Chaplow CHAPELHOW
CHAPMAN JEPMAN
CHAPPEL 8 Chapel CHAPELL Chapels Chaple CHAPPELL CHAPPELLS CHAPPLE
CHAPPELL 8 Chapel CHAPELL Chapels CHAPPEL CHAPPELLE CHAPPELLS CHAPPLE
CHAPPELLE 4 CHAPELL CHAPPELL CHAPPLE
CHAPPELLS 6 Chapel CHAPELL Chapels CHAPPEL CHAPPELL
CHAPPLE 7 Chapel CHAPELL Chaple CHAPPEL CHAPPELL CHAPPELLE
Chapper CHIPPERFIELD
Chapyn CAFFYN CAPEN CAPON COBBIN COBBING COFFIN KIPPING
CHARLETON 10 Carleton Carol CHARLTON HILLHOUSE Kerrill Mackerel Mccarol MCKERRELL Mckerrill
CHARLTON CHARLETON
Charot CHARRETT
Charratt CHARRETT
Charretier CHARTIER
CHARRETT 4 Charot Charratt Charrot
Charrot CHARRETT
Charteris CHARTERS
CHARTERS Charteris
CHARTIER Charretier
CHASTER CHESTER
Chatfeild CHATFIELD
CHATFIELD Chatfeild Chetfield
Chatlow CATLOW
CHATTEN Chatton
Chatton CHATTEN
CHATWELL 6 CHATWIN Chatwynd Chetwall Chetwyn CHETWYND
CHATWIN 6 CHATWELL Chatwynd Chetwall Chetwyn CHETWYND
Chatwynd CHATWELL CHATWIN CHETWYND
Chaulk CHALK
Chaundler CHANDLER
Chaune CHANEY CHAWNER CHENEY CHESNEY CHEYNE CHEYNEY
Chauner CHANEY CHAWNER CHENEY CHESNEY CHEYNE CHEYNEY
Chauney CHANEY CHAWNER CHENEY CHESNEY CHEYNE CHEYNEY
Chauneys CHANEY CHAWNER CHENEY CHESNEY CHEYNE CHEYNEY
Chaunies CHANEY CHAWNER CHENEY CHESNEY CHEYNE CHEYNEY
Chaunt CHANT
Chauny CHANEY CHAWNER CHENEY CHESNEY CHEYNE CHEYNEY
CHAWNER 52 Caisned Caisnei Caisneto Casneto Chainey Chainy Chana Chanee Chaner CHANEY Channer Chany Chaune Chauner Chauney Chauneys Chaunies Chauny Chawney Chawny Chayney Chaynye Cheaney Cheany Cheene Cheenei Cheeney Cheeny Cheine Cheiney Cheiny Chenduit Chenduyt Chene Chenea Cheneiy CHENEY Chenie Chenney Chenny Chensy Cheny Chesnei Chesneto CHESNEY Chesneye CHEYNE CHEYNEY China Chiney Chinney
Chawney CHANEY CHAWNER CHENEY CHESNEY CHEYNE CHEYNEY
Chawny CHANEY CHAWNER CHENEY CHESNEY CHEYNE CHEYNEY

If the name you are interested in is not here, try Section C.

Chayney CHANEY CHAWNER CHENEY CHESNEY CHEYNE CHEYNEY
Chaynye CHANEY CHAWNER CHENEY CHESNEY CHEYNE CHEYNEY
Cheak CHEEKE CHEKE
Cheake CHEEKE CHEKE
Cheaney CHANEY CHAWNER CHENEY CHESNEY CHEYNE CHEYNEY
Cheany CHANEY CHAWNER CHENEY CHESNEY CHEYNE CHEYNEY
Chebbott CHIBBETT CUBITT
Checket CHECKETTS
Checkets CHECKETTS
CHECKETTS 4 Checket Checkets Chicket
Cheek CHEEKE CHEKE
CHEEKE 5 Cheak Cheake Cheek CHEKE
Cheene CHANEY CHAWNER CHENEY CHESNEY CHEYNE CHEYNEY
Cheenei CHANEY CHAWNER CHENEY CHESNEY CHEYNE CHEYNEY
Cheeney CHANEY CHAWNER CHENEY CHESNEY CHEYNE CHEYNEY
Cheeny CHANEY CHAWNER CHENEY CHESNEY CHEYNE CHEYNEY
CHEEPER Chipper
Cheesat JESSETT
CHEESEMAN 5 CHEESMAN Cheseman Chezsman Chiesman
CHEESMAN 5 CHEESEMAN Cheseman Chezsman Chiesman
Cheetam CHITTAM
Chefens CHEFFINS
CHEFFINS 5 Chefens Chefins Chevins Chivins
Chefins CHEFFINS
Chegwgen CHEGWYN KEIGWIN
Chegwidden CHEGWIN CHEGWYN KEIGWIN
CHEGWIN Chegwidden
CHEGWYN 13 Chegwgen Chegwidden Chegwyne Chegwynne Chigwin Chigwydden Chuckweedon Chygin Chygwen Chygwin KEIGWIN Sugweeden
Chegwyne CHEGWYN KEIGWIN
Chegwynne CHEGWYN KEIGWIN
Cheine CHANEY CHAWNER CHENEY CHESNEY CHEYNE CHEYNEY
Cheiney CHANEY CHAWNER CHENEY CHESNEY CHEYNE CHEYNEY
Cheiny CHANEY CHAWNER CHENEY CHESNEY CHEYNE CHEYNEY
CHEKE 5 Cheak Cheake Cheek CHEEKE
CHELEW Chillew
Chenduit CHANEY CHAWNER CHENEY CHESNEY CHEYNE CHEYNEY
Chenduyt CHANEY CHAWNER CHENEY CHESNEY CHEYNE CHEYNEY
Chene CHANEY CHAWNER CHENEY CHESNEY CHEYNE CHEYNEY
Chenea CHANEY CHAWNER CHENEY CHESNEY CHEYNE CHEYNEY
Cheneiy CHANEY CHAWNER CHENEY CHESNEY CHEYNE CHEYNEY
CHENEY 52 Caisned Caisnei Caisneto Casneto Chainey Chainy Chana Chanee Chaner CHANEY Channer Chany Chaune Chauner Chauney Chauneys Chaunies Chauny CHAWNER Chawney Chawny Chayney Chaynye Cheaney Cheany Cheene Cheenei Cheeney Cheeny Cheine Cheiney Cheiny Chenduit Chenduyt Chene Chenea Cheneiy Chenie Chenney Chenny Chensy Cheny Chesnei Chesneto CHESNEY Chesneye CHEYNE CHEYNEY China Chiney Chinney
Chenie CHANEY CHAWNER CHENEY CHESNEY CHEYNE CHEYNEY
Chenney CHANEY CHAWNER CHENEY CHESNEY CHEYNE CHEYNEY
Chenny CHANEY CHAWNER CHENEY CHESNEY CHEYNE CHEYNEY
Chenower CHYNOWETH
Chenoweth CHYNOWETH
Chenowethe CHYNOWETH
Chenowight CHYNOWETH
Chenowith CHYNOWETH
Chenoworth CHYNOWETH
Chenowth CHYNOWETH
Chenowyth CHYNOWETH
Chenswath CHYNOWETH
Chensweth CHYNOWETH
Chensy CHANEY CHAWNER CHENEY CHESNEY CHEYNE CHEYNEY
Chenwith CHYNOWETH
Cheny CHANEY CHAWNER CHENEY CHESNEY CHEYNE CHEYNEY
Chescae CHESCOE
Chescal CHESCOE
CHESCOE 12 Chescae Chescal Chescoll Chescow Chesko Chesso Chessoe Chexo Chisco Chisso Tescoe
Chescoll CHESCOE
Chescow CHESCOE
Cheseman CHEESEMAN CHEESMAN
Chesham CHESSUM
CHESHIRE Chesshire
Chesko CHESCOE
Cheslade CHISLETT
Cheslate CHISLETT
Chesnei CHANEY CHAWNER CHENEY CHESNEY CHEYNE CHEYNEY
Chesneto CHANEY CHAWNER CHENEY CHESNEY CHEYNE CHEYNEY
CHESNEY 52 Caisned Caisnei Caisneto Casneto Chainey Chainy Chana Chanee Chaner CHANEY Channer Chany Chaune Chauner Chauney Chauneys Chaunies Chauny CHAWNER Chawney Chawny Chayney Chaynye Cheaney Cheany Cheene Cheenei Cheeney Cheeny Cheine Cheiney Cheiny Chenduit Chenduyt Chene Chenea Cheneiy CHENEY Chenie Chenney Chenny Chensy Cheny Chesnei Chesneto Chesneye CHEYNE CHEYNEY China Chiney Chinney
Chesneye CHANEY CHAWNER CHENEY CHESNEY CHEYNE CHEYNEY
Chesshire CHESHIRE
Chesso CHESCOE
Chessoe CHESCOE
CHESSUM Chesham
CHESTER CHASTER
Chesterson KESTERTON
Chesterton KESTERTON
Chetemore KIDNER KYNE
Chetfield CHATFIELD
Chetten CHETWIN CHETWYND
CHETTLE Chitell CHITTLE
Chetwall CHATWELL CHATWIN CHETWYND
CHETWIN 6 Chetten Chetwind Chetwym Chetwyn CHETWYND
Chetwind CHETWIN CHETWYND
Chetwym CHETWIN CHETWYND
Chetwyn CHATWELL CHATWIN CHETWIN CHETWYND
CHETWYND 10 CHATWELL CHATWIN Chatwynd Chetten Chetwall CHETWIN Chetwind Chetwym Chetwyn
Chety CHITTY
Chetye CHITTY
Chevalier CHEVALLIER
CHEVALLIER Chevalier
Cheverton CHIVERTON
Chevins CHEFFINS
CHEW 5 TEW TOE Too Tue
Chexo CHESCOE
CHEYNE 52 Caisned Caisnei Caisneto Casneto Chainey Chainy Chana Chanee Chaner CHANEY Channer Chany Chaune Chauner Chauney Chauneys Chaunies Chauny CHAWNER Chawney Chawny Chayney Chaynye Cheaney Cheany Cheene Cheenei Cheeney Cheeny Cheine Cheiney Cheiny Chenduit Chenduyt Chene Chenea Cheneiy CHENEY Chenie Chenney Chenny Chensy Cheny Chesnei Chesneto CHESNEY Chesneye CHEYNEY China Chiney Chinney
Cheynel CHANNEL
Cheynell CHANNEL
CHEYNEY 52 Caisned Caisnei Caisneto Casneto Chainey Chainy Chana Chanee Chaner CHANEY Channer Chany Chaune Chauner Chauney Chauneys Chaunies Chauny CHAWNER Chawney Chawny Chayney Chaynye Cheaney Cheany Cheene Cheenei Cheeney Cheeny Cheine Cheiney Cheiny Chenduit Chenduyt Chene Chenea Cheneiy CHENEY Chenie Chenney Chenny Chensy Cheny Chesnei Chesneto CHESNEY Chesneye CHEYNE China Chiney Chinney
Cheynoweth CHYNOWETH
Chezsman CHEESEMAN CHEESMAN
CHIAMPANTE Campantin Champante
CHIBBETT 8 Chebbott Chibott Clibbott Cubett CUBITT Kybbet Kybet
Chibott CHIBBETT CUBITT
Chickall CHICKLE
Chicket CHECKETTS
CHICKLE Chickall
Chiddel CHISTELL
Chiddle CHISTELL
Chidtell CHISTELL
Chiesman CHEESEMAN CHEESMAN
Chiferton CHIVERTON
Chigwin CHEGWYN KEIGWIN
Chigwydden CHEGWYN KEIGWIN
CHILD 4 Childe CHILDS Chiles
Childe CHILD
CHILDERLEY Childrey
Childes CHILDS
Childrey CHILDERLEY
CHILDS 4 CHILD Childes Chiles
Chiles CHILD CHILDS
Chillew CHELEW
CHIMLEY Chimney
Chimney CHIMLEY
China CHANEY CHAWNER CHENEY CHESNEY CHEYNE CHEYNEY
CHINCHEN Chinchin
Chinchin CHINCHEN
Chiney CHANEY CHAWNER CHENEY CHESNEY CHEYNE CHEYNEY
Chinney CHANEY CHAWNER CHENEY CHESNEY CHEYNE CHEYNEY
CHIPPENDALE Chippindale
Chipper CHEEPER
Chipperfeald CHIPPERFIELD
Chipperfelde CHIPPERFIELD
CHIPPERFIELD 6 Chapper Chipperfeald Chipperfelde Chipperfold Chipperville
Chipperfold CHIPPERFIELD
Chipperville CHIPPERFIELD
Chippindale CHIPPENDALE
Chisco CHESCOE
Chislet CHISLETT
CHISLETT 8 Cheslade Cheslate Chislet Chisslet Chisslett Chizlet Chizlett
Chisslet CHISLETT
Chisslett CHISLETT
Chisso CHESCOE
CHISTELL 4 Chiddel Chiddle Chidtell
Chitell CHETTLE CHITTLE
CHITTAM Cheetam
Chittie CHITTY
CHITTLE CHETTLE Chitell
CHITTLEBOROUGH Chittleburrow
Chittleburrow CHITTLEBOROUGH
CHITTY 4 Chety Chetye Chittie
CHIVERTON 5 Cheverton Chiferton Churton Chyfertun
Chivins CHEFFINS
Chizlet CHISLETT
Chizlett CHISLETT
Chnweth CHYNOWETH
CHOATE Choit
CHOICE Choiyce CHOYCE
Choit CHOATE
Choiyce CHOICE

If the name you are interested in is not here, try Section C.

Chok CHALK
Choke CHALK
CHOPEN 4 CAPON COBHAM COPHAM
Choping CAFFYN CAPEN CAPON COBBIN COBBING COFFIN KIPPING
Choppen CAFFYN CAPEN CAPON COBBIN COBBING COFFIN KIPPING
Choppin CAFFYN CAPEN CAPON COBBIN COBBING COFFIN KIPPING
Chopping CAFFYN CAPEN CAPON COBBIN COBBING COFFIN KIPPING
Choppinge CAFFYN CAPEN CAPON COBBIN COBBING COFFIN KIPPING
Chopponn CAFFYN CAPEN CAPON COBBIN COBBING COFFIN KIPPING
Choppyn CAFFYN CAPEN CAPON COBBIN COBBING COFFIN KIPPING
Choppynge CAFFYN CAPEN CAPON COBBIN COBBING COFFIN KIPPING
Chopyn CAFFYN CAPEN CAPON COBBIN COBBING COFFIN KIPPING
Choul CHOULES CHOULS
Chould CHOULES CHOULS
Chouler CHOULES CHOULS
CHOULES 7 Choul Chould Chouler CHOULS Chowler Chowles
CHOULS 7 Choul Chould Chouler CHOULES Chowler Chowles
Choun SHUNN
Chowin CHOWINGS
Chowing CHOWINGS
CHOWINGS 4 Chowin Chowing Chowins
Chowins CHOWINGS
Chowler CHOULES CHOULS
Chowles CHOULES CHOULS
CHOYCE CHOICE
Chreche CRITCH
Chretche CRITCH
Chriche CRITCH
Chriginton CRUDGINGTON
Chrimes CRIMES
CHRISFIELD CRISFIELD
CHRISMAS CHRISTMAS
Christal CRISTALL
Christall CRISTALL
CHRISTIE Chrystie
CHRISTMAS CHRISMAS Cristmas
CHRISTOFFER CHRISTOPHER Christophers
CHRISTOPHER CHRISTOFFER Christophers
Christophers CHRISTOFFER CHRISTOPHER
Chritch CRITCH
Chryche CRITCH
Chrymes CRIMES
CHRYSTAL Chrystell Crystal
Chrystell CHRYSTAL
Chrystie CHRISTIE
Chuckweedon CHEGWYN KEIGWIN
Chun SHUNN
Churton CHIVERTON
Chusick CANSICK
Chyfertun CHIVERTON
Chygin CHEGWYN KEIGWIN
Chygwen CHEGWYN KEIGWIN
Chygwin CHEGWYN KEIGWIN
Chynouth CHYNOWETH
CHYNOWETH 17 Chenower Chenoweth Chenowethe Chenowight Chenowith Chenoworth Chenowth Chenowyth Chenswath Chensweth Chenwith Cheynoweth Chnweth Chynouth Chynowith Genower
Chynowith CHYNOWETH
Cimp CAMP KEMP
Ciplin KIPLIN KIPLING
Cirsop KERSHOPE KIRSOPP
CIVELL Civil De ceville
Civil CIVELL
Civill SAVILLE
Clabbone CLAYBORNE
Clabborn CLAYBORNE
Clabborne CLAYBORNE
Clabbourn CLAYBORNE
Clabbourne CLAYBORNE
Clabbun CLAYBORNE
Clabburn CLAYBORNE
Clace CLACEY
CLACEY 4 Clace Clacy Clasey
Clackson CLAXTON
Clacy CLACEY
Claden CLAYDEN CLAYDON CLAYTON
Cladingbold CLARINGBOLD CLARINGBOULD
Cladon CLAYDEN CLAYDON CLAYTON
Claiborn CLAYBORNE
Claiborne CLAYBORNE
Claiden CLAYDEN CLAYDON CLAYTON
Claidon CLAYDEN CLAYDON CLAYTON
Claik CLAKE CLEAK CLICK
Clair HOUDE
Claiton CLAYDEN CLAYDON CLAYTON CLEETON
CLAKE 18 Claik CLEAK Cleake Cleek Cleeke Cleik Cleike Clek Cleke CLICK Clike Clique Klaik Klake Kleek Kleike Kleke
Clap CLAPP
Clape CLAPP
CLAPP 5 Clap Clape Clappe Cloup
Clappe CLAPP
CLAPSHAW 7 Clapshew Clapshin Clapsho CLAPSHOE Clapshoo Clapshow
Clapshew CLAPSHAW CLAPSHOE
Clapshin CLAPSHAW CLAPSHOE
Clapsho CLAPSHAW CLAPSHOE
CLAPSHOE 7 CLAPSHAW Clapshew Clapshin Clapsho Clapshoo Clapshow
Clapshoo CLAPSHAW CLAPSHOE
Clapshow CLAPSHAW CLAPSHOE
CLARICOATES Clattercoats
CLARINGBOLD Cladingbold CLARINGBOULD
CLARINGBOULD Cladingbold CLARINGBOLD
CLARK 6 CLARKE Cleark Clerc CLERK Clerke
CLARKE 6 CLARK Cleark Clerc CLERK Clerke
CLARKESTONE CLARKSON CLARSON
CLARKSON 4 CLARKESTONE Clarkstone CLARSON
Clarkstone CLARKSON
CLARSON CLARKESTONE CLARKSON
Clasey CLACEY
Claspar CLASPER
CLASPER Claspar
Claton CLAYDEN CLAYDON CLAYTON CLEETON
Clattercoats CLARICOATES
Clatton CLAYTON CLEETON
CLATWORTHY CLOTWORTHY
CLAUGHTON Clauton Clawton
Clauton CLAUGHTON
Clawton CLAUGHTON
Claxon CLAXTON
Claxson CLAXTON
CLAXTON 7 Caxton Clackson Claxon Claxson Claxtone Claxtonn
Claxtone CLAXTON
Claxtonn CLAXTON
CLAY Claye
Claybon CLAYBORNE CLAYBURN
Clayborn CLAYBORNE CLAYBURN
CLAYBORNE 24 Clabbone Clabborn Clabborne Clabbourn Clabbourne Clabbun Clabburn Claiborn Claiborne Claybon Clayborn Claybourn Claybourne CLAYBURN Claybyn Cleborne Cleyburn Cleyburne Cliberon Cliborne Clibrone Cliburne Cliggon
Claybourn CLAYBORNE CLAYBURN
Claybourne CLAYBORNE CLAYBURN
CLAYBURN 7 Claybon Clayborn CLAYBORNE Claybourn Claybourne Claybyn
Claybyn CLAYBORNE CLAYBURN
CLAYDEN 12 Claden Cladon Claiden Claidon Claiton Claton CLAYDON CLAYTON CLEDEN Cledon Cleydon
CLAYDON 12 Claden Cladon Claiden Claidon Claiton Claton CLAYDEN CLAYTON CLEDEN Cledon Cleydon
Claye CLAY
CLAYTON 17 Claden Cladon Claiden Claidon Claiton Claton Clatton CLAYDEN CLAYDON Cleaton CLEETON Cleiton Cleton Cleydon Cleyton Cleytone
CLEAK 18 Claik CLAKE Cleake Cleek Cleeke Cleik Cleike Clek Cleke CLICK Clike Clique Klaik Klake Kleek Kleike Kleke
Cleake CLAKE CLEAK CLICK
CLEAL Cleall
Cleall CLEAL
Cleark CLARK CLARKE
Cleaton CLAYTON CLEETON
CLEAVE Cleeve
CLEAVER Clever Cllever
CLEAVES Cleeves
Cleborne CLAYBORNE
CLEDEN 4 CLAYDEN CLAYDON Cledon
Cledon CLAYDEN CLAYDON CLEDEN
Cleek CLAKE CLEAK CLICK
Cleeke CLAKE CLEAK CLICK
CLEETON 10 Claiton Claton Clatton CLAYTON Cleaton Cleiton Cleton Cleyton Cleytone
Cleeve CLEAVE
Cleeves CLEAVES
Cleik CLAKE CLEAK CLICK
Cleike CLAKE CLEAK CLICK
Cleiton CLAYTON CLEETON
Clek CLAKE CLEAK CLICK
Cleke CLAKE CLEAK CLICK
Clemason CLEMENTSON CLEMSON
CLEMENS CLEMENT CLEMENTS
CLEMENT 4 CLEMENS CLEMENTS Clemmet
CLEMENTS 4 CLEMENS CLEMENT CLEMETS
CLEMENTSON 4 Clemason Clemison CLEMSON
Clemet CLEMETT
CLEMETS CLEMENTS
CLEMETT Clemet
Clemison CLEMENTSON CLEMSON
Clemmet CLEMENT
Clemmings SLAYMAN SLEMANS SLEMMINGS SLEMONDS
CLEMMOW 5 CLEMO Clemow Climo CLYMO
CLEMO 5 CLEMMOW Clemow Climo CLYMO
Clemow CLEMMOW CLEMO
CLEMSON 4 Clemason CLEMENTSON Clemison
Cleperton CLIPPERTON
Clerc CLARK CLARKE
CLERK 5 CLARK CLARKE Clerke LE CLERK
Clerke CLARK CLARKE CLERK
Cleton CLAYTON CLEETON
Cleugh CLEUTH CLOUGH
Cleulow CLEWLOW CLULOW
CLEUTH Cleugh CLOUGH
Clever CLEAVER
CLEVERLEY CLEVERLY
CLEVERLY CLEVERLEY
Cleward CLUARD
CLEWER Cluer
CLEWES CLEWS CLOWES
CLEWLOW Cleulow CLULOW
CLEWS CLEWES CLOWES
Cleyburn CLAYBORNE
Cleyburne CLAYBORNE
Cleydon CLAYDEN CLAYDON CLAYTON
Cleyton CLAYTON CLEETON
Cleytone CLAYTON CLEETON
CLIBBORN CLYBORN
Clibbott CHIBBETT CUBITT
Cliberon CLAYBORNE
Cliborne CLAYBORNE
Clibrone CLAYBORNE
Cliburne CLAYBORNE
CLICK 18 Claik CLAKE CLEAK Cleake Cleek Cleeke Cleik Cleike Clek Cleke Clike Clique Klaik Klake Kleek Kleike Kleke
CLIFF CLIFFE CLIFT
CLIFFE 6 CLIFF CLIFT CLIVE CLIVES Clyve
Cliffeton CLIFTON
Clifften CLIFTON
CLIFT CLIFF CLIFFE
CLIFTON 4 Cliffeton Clifften Clyfton
Cligand CLINGAN
Cliggon CLAYBORNE
Clike CLAKE CLEAK CLICK
Climo CLEMMOW CLEMO CLYMO
CLIMPSON 4 Climson

If the name you are interested in is not here, try Section C.

Clympson Clymson
Climson CLIMPSON
CLINCH Clynch
CLINGAN 22 Cligand Clingand Clingane Clingen Clingham Clingin Clinging Clingon Clingzean Clinzeand Klingan Klingen Klingham Macclengen Macclingan Macclingand Macclingen Mcclengen Mcclingan Mcclingand Mcclingen
Clingand CLINGAN
Clingane CLINGAN
Clingen CLINGAN
Clingham CLINGAN
Clingin CLINGAN
Clinging CLINGAN
Clingon CLINGAN
Clingzean CLINGAN
CLINTON Clynton
Clinzeand CLINGAN
Cliperton CLIPPERTON
CLIPPERTON 8 Cleperton Cliperton Clippington Clippiton Clipton Clyperton Clyppington
Clippington CLIPPERTON
Clippiton CLIPPERTON
CLIPSON Clipston Clipstone
Clipston CLIPSON
Clipstone CLIPSON
Clipton CLIPPERTON
Clique CLAKE CLEAK CLICK
CLIVE 4 CLIFFE CLIVES Clyve
CLIVES 4 CLIFFE CLIVE Clyve
Cllever CLEAVER
CLOAK CLOAKE CLOKE
CLOAKE CLOAK CLOKE
CLOKE CLOAK CLOAKE
CLOTWORTHY CLATWORTHY
CLOUGH Cleugh CLEUTH
Cloughs CLOWES
CLOUNIE Cloutie
Cloup CLAPP
Clous CLOWES
Clout CLOUTT
Cloute CLOUTT
Cloutie CLOUNIE
CLOUTT 4 Clout Cloute Clowte
CLOVER 4 CALVER COLVER CULVER
Cloward CLUARD
CLOWES 6 CLEWES CLEWS Cloughs Clous Clows
Clows CLOWES
Clowte CLOUTT
CLUARD 5 Cleward Cloward Cluart Clueard
Cluart CLUARD
CLUB Clubb
Clubb CLUB
Clueard CLUARD
Cluer CLEWER
CLULOW Cleulow CLEWLOW
CLYBORN CLIBBORN
Clyfton CLIFTON
CLYMO 4 CLEMMOW CLEMO Climo
Clympson CLIMPSON
Clymson CLIMPSON
Clynch CLINCH
Clynton CLINTON
Clyperton CLIPPERTON
Clyppington CLIPPERTON
Clyve CLIFFE CLIVE CLIVES
Co COE
Coachwith COATSWITH COATSWORTH
COAD COADE Code
COADE COAD Code
Coahley CAWLEY COLE COLEY COLLEY COLLIE COLLY COOLE COOLEY CORLEY COWLEY CULLEY
Coakaloff COCKCROFT COCKROFT COLCLOUGH
COAKER 6 Cauker Caulker COCKER COKER Cooker
Coakleough COCKCROFT COCKROFT COLCLOUGH
Coal COLE
Coale CAWLEY COLE COLES COLEY COLLEY COLLIE COLLY COOLE COOLEY CORLEY COWLEY CULLEY
Coalee CAWLEY COLE COLEY COLLEY COLLIE COLLY COOLE COOLEY CORLEY COWLEY CULLEY
COALES Colles
Coaley CAWLEY COLE COLEY COLLEY COLLIE COLLY COOLE COOLEY CORLEY COWLEY CULLEY
Coaleys CAWLEY COLE COLEY COLLEY COLLIE COLLY COOLE COOLEY CORLEY COWLEY CULLEY
Coalie CAWLEY COLE COLEY COLLEY COLLIE COLLY COOLE COOLEY CORLEY COWLEY CULLEY
Coalle CAWLEY COLE COLEY COLLEY COLLIE COLLY COOLE COOLEY CORLEY COWLEY CULLEY
Coalley CAWLEY COLE COLEY COLLEY COLLIE COLLY COOLE COOLEY CORLEY COWLEY CULLEY
Coally CAWLEY COLE COLEY COLLEY COLLIE COLLY COOLE COOLEY CORLEY COWLEY CULLEY
COALMAN COLEMAN
Coals COLES
Coaly CAWLEY COLE COLEY COLLEY COLLIE COLLY COOLE COOLEY CORLEY COWLEY CULLEY
Coaney CONEY
COAP 4 Coape COPE COPP
Coape COAP COPE COPP
Coar COARE
COARE Coar
Coashman COUCHMAN
COATES COATS COTES
Coatesworth COATSWITH COATSWORTH
COATH 5 Coeth Coth Cothe Couth
COATS 4 COATES COTES GOATS
COATSWITH 9 Coachwith Coatesworth COATSWORTH Coatsworthe Coteswith Cotesworth Cotsworth Cotsworthe
COATSWORTH 9 Coachwith Coatesworth COATSWITH Coatsworthe Coteswith Cotesworth Cotsworth Cotsworthe
Coatsworthe COATSWITH COATSWORTH
Coawly CAWLEY COLE COLEY COLLEY COLLIE COLLY COOLE COOLEY CORLEY COWLEY CULLEY
Cob COBB COBBE
COBB 4 Cob COBBE Coobe
Cobbatt COBBETT
COBBE 4 Cob COBB Coobe
Cobbeldick COBBLEDICK COBELDICK CUPPLEDITCH
Cobbeldicke COBBLEDICK COBELDICK CUPPLEDITCH
Cobben CAFFYN CAPEN CAPON COBBIN COBBING COFFIN KIPPING
Cobbet COBBETT COPPOCK CORBET CORBETT
COBBETT 61 Cappock Cappocke Cappuch Cappuck Cobbatt Cobbet Cobbick Cobbit Cobbitt Cobbut Cobbutt Cobert Cobet Cobit Cobitt Coboke Cobot Cobut Cooppock Copack Coperoak Cophack Cophacke Copheick Cophocke Cophook Copock Copocke Copot Coppach Coppache Coppack Coppacke Coppaick Coppak Coppatk Coppeck Coppecke Coppert Coppick Coppicke Coppict Coppoch Coppochs COPPOCK Coppocke Coppocks Coppoe Coppok Coppoke Coppook Coppott Coppowe Coppuck Coppucks Copuch CORBET CORBETT Corbit Cowpoke
Cobbick COBBETT COPPOCK CORBET CORBETT
COBBIN 95 Cabourne CAFFYN Capan CAPEN Capin CAPON Caponere Caponn Caporn Capoun Capping Cappinger Capyn Caupen Caupin Caupion Cawpen Chapyn Choping Choppen Choppin Chopping Choppinge Chopponn Choppyn Choppynge Chopyn Cobben Cobbine Cobbines COBBING Cobbings Cobbins Cobin Cobine Cobines Cobing Cobings Cobins Cobyn Cobynge Coffen Coffeyn COFFIN Coffing Coffinge Coffyn Cofin Cofyn Coopene Cooping Cooping‌e Cooppin Cooppyn Cooppyng Coopyne Copenger Cophaen Cophen Cophin Cophynn Copiner Copinger Copingers Coppener Coppengar Coppenger Coppiner Coppinger Coppingers Coppner Coppynger Copynger Copyunore Cupen Cupenes Cupin Cuppeynge Cuppin Cuppyn Cuppyng Keoppen KIPPING Koppang Koppeians Koppeinge Koppen Koppin Kopping Koppyn Kopyn Kuping Kypping Kyppyng
Cobbine COBBIN COBBING
Cobbines COBBIN COBBING
COBBING 95 Cabourne CAFFYN Capan CAPEN Capin CAPON Caponere Caponn Caporn Capoun Capping Cappinger Capyn Caupen Caupin Caupion Cawpen Chapyn Choping Choppen Choppin Chopping Choppinge Chopponn Choppyn Choppynge Chopyn Cobben COBBIN Cobbine Cobbines Cobbings Cobbins Cobin Cobine Cobines Cobing Cobings Cobins Cobyn Cobynge Coffen Coffeyn COFFIN Coffing Coffinge Coffyn Cofin Cofyn Coopene Cooping Coopinge Cooppin Cooppyn Cooppyng Coopyne Copenger Cophaen Cophen Cophin Cophynn Copiner Copinger Copingers Coppener Coppengar Coppenger Coppiner Coppinger Coppingers Coppner Coppynger Copynger Copyunore Cupen Cupenes Cupin Cuppeynge Cuppin Cuppyn Cuppyng Keoppen KIPPING Koppang Koppeians Koppeinge Koppen Koppin Kopping Koppyn Kopyn Kuping Kypping Kyppyng
Cobbings COBBIN COBBING
Cobbins COBBIN COBBING
Cobbit COBBETT COPPOCK CORBET CORBETT
Cobbitt COBBETT COPPOCK CORBET CORBETT
COBBLEDICK 11 Cobbeldick Cobbeldicke Cobeldeke COBELDICK Cobeldycke Cobledick Copledike Copledyke CUPPLEDITCH De cobeldyk
Cobbut COBBETT COPPOCK CORBET CORBETT
Cobbutt COBBETT
Cobeldeke COBBLEDICK COBELDICK CUPPLEDITCH
COBELDICK 11 Cobbeldick Cobbeldicke COBBLEDICK Cobeldeke Cobeldycke Cobledick Copledike Copledyke CUPPLEDITCH De cobeldyk
Cobeldycke COBBLEDICK COBELDICK CUPPLEDITCH
Cobert COBBETT
Cobet COBBETT
COBHAM 4 CAPON CHOPEN COPHAM
Cobin CAFFYN CAPEN CAPON COBBIN COBBING COFFIN KIPPING
Cobine COBBIN COBBING
Cobines COBBIN COBBING
Cobing COBBIN COBBING
Cobings COBBIN COBBING
Cobins COBBIN COBBING
Cobit COBBETT
Cobitt COBBETT
Cobledick COBBLEDICK COBELDICK CUPPLEDITCH
COBLEY COOLEY
Coboke COBBETT COPPOCK CORBET CORBETT
Cobot COBBETT COPPOCK CORBET CORBETT
Cobstake COPESTAKE
COBURN 5 COCKBURN Cockburne Cokburn Cokburne
Cobut COBBETT COPPOCK CORBET CORBETT
Cobyn CAFFYN CAPEN CAPON COBBIN COBBING COFFIN

If the name you are interested in is not here, try Section C.

KIPPING
Cobynge CAFFYN CAPEN CAPON COBBIN COBBING COFFIN KIPPING
Cocadee COCKADAY
Cocayn COCKAYNE COCKING
COCHRAM COCKRAM
Cochsha COCKSHAW
COCK 4 COCKS COX COXE
COCKADAY 10 Cocadee Cockade Cockady Cockeday Cockerdee Cocqidez Coquide Coquidee Kokedes
Cockade COCKADAY
Cockady COCKADAY
Cockain COCKAYNE COCKING COCKINGS COCKINS
Cockaine COCKAYNE COCKING COCKINGS COCKINS
Cockaines COCKAYNE COCKING COCKINGS COCKINS
Cockains COCKAYNE COCKING COCKINGS COCKINS
Cockan COCKAYNE COCKING COCKINGS COCKINS
Cockayn COCKAYNE COCKING COCKINGS COCKINS
COCKAYNE 26 Cocayn Cockain Cockaine Cockaines Cockains Cockan Cockayn Cockaynes Cockeyn Cockin COCKING COCKINGS COCKINS Cokain Cokaine Cokaines Cokains Cokan Cokayn Cokayne Cokaynes Cokin Cokings Cokins Cokyn
Cockaynes COCKAYNE COCKING COCKINGS COCKINS
COCKBURN 7 COBURN Cockburne Cockeburn Cockeburne Cokburn Cokburne
Cockburne COBURN COCKBURN
COCKCROFT 12 Coakaloff Coakleough Cockliffe Cocklough COCKROFT Coclof COLCLOUGH Coleclough Coltclough Coughlough Cowloff
COCKE COCKS COX
Cockeburn COCKBURN
Cockeburne COCKBURN
Cockeday COCKADAY
COCKER 6 Cauker Caulker COAKER COKER Cooker
COCKERAM Cockerham
Cockerdee COCKADAY
Cockerham COCKERAM COCKRAM
COCKERILL COCKRILL
COCKERTON 5 Cockeson Cokerton Coketon Cokton
Cockeson COCKERTON
Cockeyn COCKAYNE COCKING
Cockin COCKAYNE COCKING
COCKING 26 Cocayn Cockain Cockaine Cockaines Cockains Cockan Cockayn COCKAYNE Cockaynes Cockeyn Cockin COCKINGS COCKINS Cokain Cokaine Cokaines Cokains Cokan Cokayn Cokayne Cokaynes Cokin Cokings Cokins Cokyn
COCKINGS 23 Cockain Cockaine Cockaines Cockains Cockan Cockayn COCKAYNE Cockaynes COCKING COCKINS Cokain Cokaine Cokaines Cokains Cokan Cokayn Cokayne Cokaynes Cokin Cokings Cokins Cokyn
COCKINS 23 Cockain Cockaine Cockaines Cockains Cockan Cockayn COCKAYNE Cockaynes COCKING COCKINGS Cokain Cokaine Cokaines Cokains Cokan Cokayn Cokayne Cokaynes Cokin Cokings Cokins Cokyn
Cockliffe COCKCROFT COCKROFT COLCLOUGH
Cocklough COCKCROFT COCKROFT COLCLOUGH
COCKRAM 5 COCHRAM Cockerham COCKRAN Cockrem
COCKRAN COCKRAM
Cockrell COCKRILL
Cockrem COCKRAM
COCKRILL COCKERILL Cockrell
COCKROFT 12 Coakaloff Coakleough COCKCROFT Cockliffe Cocklough Coclof COLCLOUGH Coleclough Coltclough Coughlough Cowloff
COCKS 5 COCK COCKE COX COXE
Cocksham COCKSHAW
Cockshatt COCKSHAW
COCKSHAW 6 Cochsha Cocksham Cockshatt Cockshay Cockshutt
Cockshay COCKSHAW
Cockshutt COCKSHAW
Cocksworth COXWORTH
Coclof COCKCROFT COCKROFT COLCLOUGH
Cocqidez COCKADAY
Cod CODD
CODD Cod
CODDINGTON COLLINGTON
Code COAD COADE
CODGBROOK 10 Causebrook Codgbrooke Codgebrook Codgebrooke Cosbrook Cosbrooke Cotesbrock Cotesbrook Cotsbrook
Codgbrooke CODGBROOK
Codgebrook CODGBROOK
Codgebrooke CODGBROOK
Codry COWDREY COWDRY
COE Co Cooe
Coeley CAWLEY COLE COLEY COLLEY COLLIE COLLY COOLE COOLEY CORLEY COWLEY CULLEY
Coely CAWLEY COLE COLEY COLLEY COLLIE COLLY COOLE COOLEY CORLEY COWLEY CULLEY
Coeth COATH
COFELL Coffell
Coffell COFELL
Coffen CAFFYN CAPEN CAPON COBBIN COBBING COFFIN KIPPING
Coffeyn CAFFYN CAPEN CAPON COBBIN COBBING COFFIN KIPPING
COFFIN 86 Cabourne CAFFYN Capan CAPEN Capin CAPON Caponere Caponn Caporn Capoun Capping Cappinger Capyn Caupen Caupin Caupion Cawpen Chapyn Choping Choppen Choppin Chopping Choppinge Chopponn Choppyn Choppynge Chopyn Cobben COBBIN COBBING Cobin Cobyn Cobynge Coffen Coffeyn Coffing Coffinge Coffyn Cofin Cofyn Coopene Cooping Coopinge Cooppin Cooppyn Cooppyng Coopyne Copenger Cophaen Cophen Cophin Cophynn Copiner Copinger Copingers Coppener Coppengar Coppenger Coppiner Coppinger Coppingers Coppner Coppynger Copynger Copyunore Cupen Cupenes Cupin Cuppeynge Cuppin Cuppyn Cuppyng Keoppen KIPPING Koppang Koppeians Koppeinge Koppen Koppin Kopping Koppyn Kopyn Kuping Kypping Kyppyng
Coffing CAFFYN CAPEN CAPON COBBIN COBBING COFFIN KIPPING
Coffinge CAFFYN CAPEN CAPON COBBIN COBBING COFFIN KIPPING
Coffyn CAFFYN CAPEN CAPON COBBIN COBBING COFFIN KIPPING
Cofin CAFFYN CAPEN CAPON COBBIN COBBING COFFIN KIPPING
Cofsins COSSENS COUSINS
Cofyn CAFFYN CAPEN CAPON COBBIN COBBING COFFIN KIPPING
Cogell COWELL COWGILL
Coger COGGER
COGGER 4 Coger Couger Cougger
Coggrave COLGRAVE CONGRAVE CONGREVE CONGRIEVE
Coghell COWELL COWGILL
COGHILL Cogle
Cogle COGHILL
Cognard CONYERS
Cohley CAWLEY COLE COLEY COLLEY COLLIE COLLY COOLE COOLEY CORLEY COWLEY CULLEY
Cohleye CAWLEY COLE COLEY COLLEY COLLIE COLLY COOLE COOLEY CORLEY COWLEY CULLEY
Coiles COYLE
Coiley CAWLEY COLE COLEY COLLEY COLLIE COLLY COOLE COOLEY CORLEY COWLEY CULLEY
Coils COYLE
Cointerel CANT CANTER CANTERELL CANTRELL CANTRILL CHANTRELL QUANTRILL QUINTRELL
Cointerell CANT CANTER CANTERELL CANTRELL CANTRILL CHANTRELL QUANTRILL QUINTRELL
Coistain MACQUISTEN MCQUISTON
Cokain COCKAYNE COCKING COCKINGS COCKINS
Cokaine COCKAYNE COCKING COCKINGS COCKINS
Cokaines COCKAYNE COCKING COCKINGS COCKINS
Cokains COCKAYNE COCKING COCKINGS COCKINS
Cokan COCKAYNE COCKING COCKINGS COCKINS
Cokayn COCKAYNE COCKING COCKINGS COCKINS
Cokayne COCKAYNE COCKING COCKINGS COCKINS
Cokaynes COCKAYNE COCKING COCKINGS COCKINS
Cokburn COBURN COCKBURN
Cokburne COBURN COCKBURN
COKE COOK COOKE
COKER 6 Cauker Caulker COAKER COCKER Cooker
Cokerton COCKERTON
Coketon COCKERTON
Cokin COCKAYNE COCKING COCKINGS COCKINS
Cokings COCKAYNE COCKING COCKINGS COCKINS
Cokins COCKAYNE COCKING COCKINGS COCKINS
Cokton COCKERTON
Cokyn COCKAYNE COCKING COCKINGS COCKINS
COLAM 5 Collam Coulam Coulhame Cowlam
COLBRAN 7 Colbrand Colbrun Colebran Colebrand Colebrun Collbran
Colbrand COLBRAN
Colbrun COLBRAN
COLCLOUGH 13 Coakaloff Coakleough COCKCROFT Cockliffe Cocklough COCKROFT Coclof Coleclough Coltclough Coughlough Cowclough Cowloff
Coldcleugh CALDCLEUGH
COLDRAKE Coldrick Couldrake
Coldren COLDRON
Coldrick COLDRAKE
COLDRON 8 Caldren Caldron Cauldren Cauldron Coldren Couldren Couldron
COLE 90 CAWLEY Cawly Coahley Coal Coale Coalee Coaley Coaleys Coalie Coalle Coalley Coally Coaly Coawly Coeley Coely Cohley Cohleye Coiley Colee Colei Coleley Colely COLES COLEY Coleye Coleyis Coli Colie Coliye Coll Collay Colle Collee Colles COLLEY Colleye Colli COLLIE Colliy COLLY Collye Coly Colye Cooaly COOL COOLE Coolee COOLEY Cooleye Coolie Cooll Coolley Coolly Coollye Cooly Coolye CORLEY Coulah Coulay Coule Couley Coulle Coulley Couly Couolley Coweley Cowely Cowlay Cowlaye Cowlee Cowleige COWLEY Cowleye Cowli Cowlie Cowllay Cowllea Cowllie Cowly Cowlye Coyleie Coyley Coyly Cul Culey CULL CULLEY De culegh
Colebran COLBRAN
Colebrand COLBRAN
Colebrun COLBRAN
Coleclough COCKCROFT COCKROFT COLCLOUGH
Colee CAWLEY COLE COLEY

If the name you are interested in is not here, try Section C.

COLLEY COLLIE COLLY
COOLE COOLEY CORLEY
COWLEY CULLEY
COLEGATE Colgate Colget
Colei CAWLEY COLE COLEY
COLLEY COLLIE COLLY
COOLE COOLEY CORLEY
COWLEY CULLEY
Coleley CAWLEY COLE COLEY
COLLEY COLLIE COLLY
COOLE COOLEY CORLEY
COWLEY CULLEY
Colely CAWLEY COLE COLEY
COLLEY COLLIE COLLY
COOLE COOLEY CORLEY
COWLEY CULLEY
COLEMAN COALMAN COLMAN
COLENSO Colensoe
Colensoe COLENSO
COLES 9 Coale Coals COLE
Coule COULES Coulle
COWLES Cowls
COLESELL 5 Coleshil
Colsel Coucell COULSELL
Coleshil COLESELL
COULSELL
Colet COLLET COLLETT
COLLICK
Colett COLLET COLLETT
Colewelle COLWELL
COLEY 82 CAWLEY Cawly
Coahley Coale Coalee
Coaley Coaleys Coalie
Coalle Coalley Coally
Coaly Coawly Coeley
Coely Cohley Cohleye
Coiley COLE Colee Colei
Coleley Colely Coleye
Coleyis Coli Colie
Coliye Coll Collay
Colle Collee Colles
COLLEY Colleye Colli
COLLIE Colliy COLLY
Collye Coly Colye
Cooaly COOLE Coolee
COOLEY Cooleye Coolie
Coolley Coolly Coollye
Cooly Coolye CORLEY
Coulah Coulay Couley
Coulley Couly Couolley
Coweley Cowely Cowlay
Cowlaye Cowlee Cowleige
COWLEY Cowleye Cowli
Cowlie Cowllay Cowllea
Cowllie Cowly Cowlye
Coyleie Coyley Coyly
Culey CULLEY De culegh
Coleye CAWLEY COLE COLEY
COLLEY COLLIE COLLY
COOLE COOLEY CORLEY
COWLEY CULLEY
Coleyis CAWLEY COLE COLEY
COLLEY COLLIE COLLY
COOLE COOLEY CORLEY
COWLEY CULLEY
COLFER Colfor
Colfor COLFER
Colgate COLEGATE
Colget COLEGATE
COLGRAVE 13 Coggrave
Colgreve CONGRAVE
Congraves Congreave
Congreaves Congreives
CONGREVE Congreves
CONGRIEVE Conigrave
Conygrave
Colgreve COLGRAVE
CONGRAVE CONGREVE
CONGRIEVE
Coli CAWLEY COLE COLEY
COLLEY COLLIE COLLY
COOLE COOLEY CORLEY
COWLEY CULLEY
Colie CAWLEY COLE COLEY
COLLEY COLLIE COLLY
COOLE COOLEY CORLEY
COWLEY CULLEY
Colier COLLIER COLLYER
COLYER
Colingwood COLLINGWOOD
Colins COLLIN COLLING
COLLINGE COLLINGS
COLLINS
Colinwood COLLINGWOOD
Coliye CAWLEY COLE COLEY
COLLEY COLLIE COLLY
COOLE COOLEY CORLEY
COWLEY CULLEY
Coll CAWLEY COLE COLEY
COLLEY COLLIE COLLY
COOLE COOLEY CORLEY
COWLEY CULLEY
Collam COLAM CULLUM
COLLAR COLLARD COLLER
COLLARD COLLAR
Collay CAWLEY COLE COLEY
COLLEY COLLIE COLLY
COOLE COOLEY CORLEY
COWLEY CULLEY
Collbran COLBRAN
Colle CAWLEY COLE COLEY
COLLEY COLLIE COLLY
COOLE COOLEY CORLEY
COWLEY CULLEY
Collect COLLET COLLETT
COLLICK
COLLEDGE 4 Coolidge
Coolledge Coollidge
Collee CAWLEY COLE COLEY
COLLEY COLLIE COLLY
COOLE COOLEY CORLEY
COWLEY CULLEY
COLLEN 5 COLLIN COLLINGS
COLLINS Colyn
COLLER COLLAR
Colles CAWLEY COALES COLE
COLEY COLLEY COLLIE
COLLIS COLLY COOLE
COOLEY CORLEY COWLEY
CULLEY
COLLET 5 Colet Colett
Collect COLLETT
COLLETT 6 Colet Colett
Collect COLLET COLLICK
COLLEY 82 CAWLEY Cawly
Coahley Coale Coalee
Coaley Coaleys Coalie
Coalle Coalley Coally
Coaly Coawly Coeley
Coely Cohley Cohleye
Coiley COLE Colee Colei
Coleley Colely COLEY
Coleye Coleyis Coli
Colie Coliye Coll
Collay Colle Collee
Colles Colleye Colli
COLLIE Colliy COLLY
Collye Coly Colye
Cooaly COOLE Coolee
COOLEY Cooleye Coolie
Coolley Coolly Coollye
Cooly Coolye CORLEY
Coulah Coulay Couley
Coulley Couly Couolley
Coweley Cowely Cowlay
Cowlaye Cowlee Cowleige
COWLEY Cowleye Cowli
Cowlie Cowllay Cowllea
Cowllie Cowly Cowlye
Coyleie Coyley Coyly
Culey CULLEY De culegh
Colleye CAWLEY COLE COLEY
COLLEY COLLIE COLLY
COOLE COOLEY CORLEY
COWLEY CULLEY
Colli CAWLEY COLE COLEY
COLLEY COLLIE COLLY
COOLE COOLEY CORLEY
COWLEY CULLEY
COLLICK 4 Colet Collect
COLLETT
COLLIE 82 CAWLEY Cawly
Coahley Coale Coalee
Coaley Coaleys Coalie
Coalle Coalley Coally
Coaly Coawly Coeley
Coely Cohley Cohleye
Coiley COLE Colee Colei
Coleley Colely COLEY
Coleye Coleyis Coli
Colie Coliye Coll
Collay Colle Collee
Colles COLLEY Colleye
Colli Colliy COLLY
Collye Coly Colye
Cooaly COOLE Coolee
COOLEY Cooleye Coolie
Coolley Coolly Coollye
Cooly Coolye CORLEY
Coulah Coulay Couley
Coulley Couly Couolley
Coweley Cowely Cowlay
Cowlaye Cowlee Cowleige
COWLEY Cowleye Cowli
Cowlie Cowllay Cowllea
Cowllie Cowly Cowlye
Coyleie Coyley Coyly
Culey CULLEY De culegh
COLLIER 4 Colier COLLYER
COLYER
COLLIN 9 Colins COLLEN
COLLING COLLINGE
COLLINGS COLLINS COLLIS
Colyn
COLLING 6 Colins COLLIN
COLLINGE COLLINGS
COLLINS
COLLINGE 6 Colins COLLIN
COLLING COLLINGS
COLLINS
COLLINGS 9 Colins COLLEN
COLLIN COLLING COLLINGE
COLLINS COLLIS Colyn
COLLINGTON CODDINGTON
COLLINGWOOD 4 Colingwood
Colinwood Collinwood
COLLINS 11 CALLONS Colins
COLLEN COLLIN COLLING
COLLINGE COLLINGS
COLLIS Colons Colyn
Collinwood COLLINGWOOD
COLLIS 6 Colles COLLIN
COLLINGS COLLINS
Colliss
Colliss COLLIS
Colliy CAWLEY COLE COLEY
COLLEY COLLIE COLLY
COOLE COOLEY CORLEY
COWLEY CULLEY
Collom CULLUM
Collomb CULLUM
Collombe CULLUM
Collum CALLUM
Collumbine COLUMBINE
COLLY 82 CAWLEY Cawly
Coahley Coale Coalee
Coaley Coaleys Coalie
Coalle Coalley Coally
Coaly Coawly Coeley
Coely Cohley Cohleye
Coiley COLE Colee Colei
Coleley Colely COLEY
Coleye Coleyis Coli
Colie Coliye Coll
Collay Colle Collee
Colles COLLEY Colleye
Colli COLLIE Colliy
Collye Coly Colye
Cooaly COOLE Coolee
COOLEY Cooleye Coolie
Coolley Coolly Coollye
Cooly Coolye CORLEY
Coulah Coulay Couley
Coulley Couly Couolley
Coweley Cowely Cowlay
Cowlaye Cowlee Cowleige
COWLEY Cowleye Cowli
Cowlie Cowllay Cowllea
Cowllie Cowly Cowlye
Coyleie Coyley Coyly
Culey CULLEY De culegh
Collye CAWLEY COLE COLEY
COLLEY COLLIE COLLY
COOLE COOLEY CORLEY
COWLEY CULLEY
COLLYER 4 Colier COLLIER
COLYER
COLMAN COLEMAN
Colomb CULLUM
Colons COLLINS
Colsel COLESELL COULSELL
Colson CORSON COULSON
COXON
Colt COULT
Coltas COULTOUS
Coltclough COCKCROFT
COCKROFT COLCLOUGH
Colthart COULTHARD
COULTHART
COLTHUP 4 Coltrip Coltrup
Coultrope
Colthurst COULTHURST
Coltrip COLTHUP
Coltrup COLTHUP
COLUMBELL GAMBLE
COLUMBINE Collumbine
Cullumbine
Colven COLVIN COLWELL
COLVER 4 CALVER CLOVER
CULVER
COLVERSON 4 Colverstone
Coverson Culverson
Colverstone COLVERSON
Colville COLVIN COLWELL
COLVIN 4 Colven Colville
COLWELL
Colwall COLWELL
COLWELL 6 Colewelle
Colven Colville COLVIN
Colwall
Coly CAWLEY COLE COLEY
COLLEY COLLIE COLLY
COOLE COOLEY CORLEY
COWLEY CULLEY
Colye CAWLEY COLE COLEY
COLLEY COLLIE COLLY
COOLE COOLEY CORLEY
COWLEY CULLEY
COLYER 4 Colier COLLIER
COLLYER
Colyn COLLEN COLLIN
COLLINGS COLLINS
COMAN 5 Comin Comyn
Cooman Cowman
COMBER 5 COMER COOMBER
Cumber CUMBOR
Comberlege CUMBLIDGE
Comberlidge CUMBLIDGE
COMBES COOMBES COOMBS
Comblidge CUMBLIDGE
COMBS COOMBES COOMBS
Comeada COWMEADOW
Comeaddowe COWMEADOW
Comeado COWMEADOW
Comeadow COWMEADOW
Comeadowe COWMEADOW
Comeda COWMEADOW
Comedo COWMEADOW
COMER COMBER COOMBER
COMERY Comrie
Comford CORNFOOT CORNFORD
COMFORT CORNFOOT CORNFORD
Comin COMAN
Commeda COWMEADOW
Commedo COWMEADOW
Commens COMMONS CUMMINGS

If the name you are interested in is not here, try Section C.

CUMMINS
Commins COMMONS CUMMINGS CUMMINS
Commody COWMEADOW
COMMONS 6 Commens Commins CUMMINGS CUMMINS Cummons
COMPER Cumber Cumper
Compleshon CAMPLEJOHN
Comrie COMERY
Comyn COMAN
COMYNS CUMMINS
Conachar CONCHA CONCHAR CONCHIE MCCONCHIE MCCONCHY MCCONOCHIE
Conch CONCHA CONCHAR CONCHIE MCCONCHIE MCCONCHY MCCONOCHIE
CONCHA 53 Conachar Conch Conchair CONCHAR Conchay Conchea Conchear Conched Concher Conchey Conchiar CONCHIE Conchier Conchor Conchy Concie Conckey Concky Conenochie Congie Coniqhar Conkey Conkie Conky Connachie Connalin Connochie Conqhar Conqhuar Conquer Conquher Conquie Conqut Couchie Counchie Maccanch Maccanchie Macconchie Maconochie Mccanchie Mcconch MCCONCHIE MCCONCHY Mcconcie Mccongie Mcconkie Mcconnachie Mcconnichie Mcconnochie MCCONOCHIE Mcconochy Mcconockie
Conchair CONCHA CONCHAR CONCHIE MCCONCHIE MCCONCHY MCCONOCHIE
CONCHAR 53 Conachar Conch CONCHA Conchair Conchay Conchea Conchear Conched Concher Conchey Conchiar CONCHIE Conchier Conchor Conchy Concie Conckey Concky Conenochie Congie Coniqhar Conkey Conkie Conky Connachie Connalin Connochie Conqhar Conqhuar Conquer Conquher Conquie Conqut Couchie Counchie Maccanch Maccanchie Macconchie Maconochie Mccanchie Mcconch MCCONCHIE MCCONCHY Mcconcie Mccongie Mcconkie Mcconnachie Mcconnichie Mcconnochie MCCONOCHIE Mcconochy Mcconockie
Conchay CONCHA CONCHAR CONCHIE MCCONCHIE MCCONCHY MCCONOCHIE
Conchea CONCHA CONCHAR CONCHIE MCCONCHIE MCCONCHY MCCONOCHIE
Conchear CONCHA CONCHAR CONCHIE MCCONCHIE MCCONCHY MCCONOCHIE
Conchect CONDUCT CONDUIT
Conched CONCHA CONCHAR CONCHIE MCCONCHIE MCCONCHY MCCONOCHIE
Concher CONCHA CONCHAR CONCHIE MCCONCHIE MCCONCHY MCCONOCHIE
Conchey CONCHA CONCHAR CONCHIE MCCONCHIE MCCONCHY MCCONOCHIE
Conchiar CONCHA CONCHAR CONCHIE MCCONCHIE MCCONCHY MCCONOCHIE
CONCHIE 53 Conachar Conch CONCHA Conchair CONCHAR Conchay Conchea Conchear Conched Concher Conchey Conchiar Conchier Conchor Conchy Concie Conckey Concky Conenochie Congie Coniqhar Conkey Conkie Conky Connachie Connalin Connochie Conqhar Conqhuar Conquer Conquher Conquie Conqut Couchie Counchie Maccanch Maccanchie Macconchie Maconochie Mccanchie Mcconch MCCONCHIE MCCONCHY Mcconcie Mccongie Mcconkie Mcconnachie Mcconnichie Mcconnochie MCCONOCHIE Mcconochy Mcconockie
Conchier CONCHA CONCHAR CONCHIE MCCONCHIE MCCONCHY MCCONOCHIE
Conchor CONCHA CONCHAR CONCHIE MCCONCHIE MCCONCHY MCCONOCHIE
Conchy CONCHA CONCHAR CONCHIE MCCONCHIE MCCONCHY MCCONOCHIE
Concie CONCHA CONCHAR CONCHIE MCCONCHIE MCCONCHY MCCONOCHIE
Conckey CONCHA CONCHAR CONCHIE MCCONCHIE MCCONCHY MCCONOCHIE
Concky CONCHA CONCHAR CONCHIE MCCONCHIE MCCONCHY MCCONOCHIE
Condie CONDUCT CONDUIT
Conduc CONDUCT CONDUIT
Conduck CONDUCT CONDUIT
CONDUCT 15 Candlewick Canduck Conchect Condie Conduc Conduck Condue Conduet Conduett CONDUIT Conduitt Condy Conditt Cundwick
Condue CONDUCT CONDUIT
Conduet CONDUCT CONDUIT
Conduett CONDUCT CONDUIT
CONDUIT 15 Candlewick Canduck Conchect Condie Conduc Conduck CONDUCT Condue Conduet Conduett Conduitt Condy Cunditt Cundwick
Conduitt CONDUCT CONDUIT
Condy CONDUCT CONDUIT
Conenochie CONCHA CONCHAR CONCHIE MCCONCHIE MCCONCHY MCCONOCHIE
Conet CONNETT
CONEY 6 Coaney CONWAY COWEN COWINS COWNEY
Coneybear CONEYBEARE CONIBEAR
CONEYBEARE 24 Coneybear Coneybeer CONIBEAR Conibeare Conibeer Connibear Connibeare Connibeer Conybear Conybeare Conybeer Cuneybear Cuneybeare Cuneybeer Cunibear Cunibeare Cunibeer Cunnibear Cunnibeare Cunnibeer Cunybear Cunybeare Cunybeer
Coneybeer CONEYBEARE CONIBEAR
Conford CORNFOOT CORNFORD
Congie CONCHA CONCHAR CONCHIE MCCONCHIE MCCONCHY MCCONOCHIE
CONGRAVE 13 Coggrave COLGRAVE Colgreve Congraves Congreave Congreaves Congreives CONGREVE Congreves CONGRIEVE Conigrave Conygrave
Congraves COLGRAVE CONGRAVE CONGREVE CONGRIEVE
Congreave COLGRAVE CONGRAVE CONGREVE CONGRIEVE
Congreaves COLGRAVE CONGRAVE CONGREVE CONGRIEVE
Congreives COLGRAVE CONGRAVE CONGREVE CONGRIEVE
CONGREVE 13 Coggrave COLGRAVE Colgreve CONGRAVE Congraves Congreave Congreaves Congreives Congreves CONGRIEVE Conigrave Conygrave
Congreves COLGRAVE CONGRAVE CONGREVE CONGRIEVE
CONGRIEVE 13 Coggrave COLGRAVE Colgreve CONGRAVE Congraves Congreave Congreaves Congreives CONGREVE Congreves Conigrave Conygrave
CONIBEAR 24 Coneybear CONEYBEARE Coneybeer Conibeare Conibeer Connibear Connibeare Connibeer Conybear Conybeare Conybeer Cuneybear Cuneybeare Cuneybeer Cunibear Cunibeare Cunibeer Cunnibear Cunnibeare Cunnibeer Cunybear Cunybeare Cunybeer
Conibeare CONEYBEARE CONIBEAR
Conibeer CONEYBEARE CONIBEAR
Conigrave COLGRAVE CONGRAVE CONGREVE CONGRIEVE
Coningston CONISTON
Coniqhar CONCHA CONCHAR CONCHIE MCCONCHIE MCCONCHY MCCONOCHIE
CONISTON 6 Coningston Conningston Cuniston Cunningston Cunniston
Conkey CONCHA CONCHAR CONCHIE MCCONCHIE MCCONCHY MCCONOCHIE
Conkie CONCHA CONCHAR CONCHIE MCCONCHIE MCCONCHY MCCONOCHIE
Conky CONCHA CONCHAR CONCHIE MCCONCHIE MCCONCHY MCCONOCHIE
CONLEY 4 CONNELLY Connerlly Connerly
Conliffe CUNLIFFE
Connachie CONCHA CONCHAR CONCHIE MCCONCHIE MCCONCHY MCCONOCHIE
Connah CUNNAH
Connalin CONCHA CONCHAR CONCHIE MCCONCHIE MCCONCHY MCCONOCHIE
CONNELLY 5 CONLEY Connerlly Connerly CONNOLLY
CONNER 6 CONNOR Conor O'CONNER O'CONNOR O'conor
Connerlly CONLEY CONNELLY
Connerly CONLEY CONNELLY
Connet CONNETT
CONNETT Conet Connet
Connibear CONEYBEARE CONIBEAR
Connibeare CONEYBEARE CONIBEAR
Connibeer CONEYBEARE CONIBEAR
Conningston CONISTON
Connochie CONCHA CONCHAR CONCHIE MCCONCHIE MCCONCHY MCCONOCHIE
CONNOLLY CONNELLY
CONNOR 6 CONNER Conor O'CONNER O'CONNOR O'conor
Conor CONNER CONNOR O'CONNER O'CONNOR
Conqhar CONCHA CONCHAR CONCHIE MCCONCHIE MCCONCHY MCCONOCHIE
Conqhuar CONCHA CONCHAR CONCHIE MCCONCHIE MCCONCHY MCCONOCHIE
Conquer CONCHA CONCHAR CONCHIE MCCONCHIE MCCONCHY MCCONOCHIE
Conquher CONCHA CONCHAR CONCHIE MCCONCHIE MCCONCHY MCCONOCHIE
Conquie CONCHA CONCHAR CONCHIE MCCONCHIE MCCONCHY MCCONOCHIE
Conqut CONCHA CONCHAR CONCHIE MCCONCHIE MCCONCHY MCCONOCHIE
CONRATH Conratt Courath
Conratt CONRATH
Constabile CONSTABLE
CONSTABLE Constabile Cunstable
CONWAY CONEY
Conybear CONEYBEARE CONIBEAR
Conybeare CONEYBEARE CONIBEAR
Conybeer CONEYBEARE CONIBEAR
CONYERS Cognard
Conygrave COLGRAVE CONGRAVE CONGREVE CONGRIEVE
Cooaly CAWLEY COLE COLEY COLLEY COLLIE COLLY COOLE COOLEY CORLEY COWLEY CULLEY
Coobe COBB COBBE
Cooe COE
COOK COKE COOKE
COOKE COKE COOK
Cooker COAKER COCKER COKER
Cookes COOKS
COOKS Cookes
COOKSON COXON
COOL 6 COLE COOLE Cooll Cul CULL
COOLE 86 CAWLEY Cawly Coahley Coale Coalee

If the name you are interested in is not here, try Section C.

Coaley Coaleys Coalie Coalle Coalley Coally Coaly Coawly Coeley Coely Cohley Cohleye Coiley COLE Colee Colei Coleley Colely COLEY Coleye Coleyis Coli Colie Coliye Coll Collay Colle Collee Colles COLLEY Colleye Colli COLLIE Colliy COLLY Collye Coly Colye Cooaly COOL Coolee COOLEY Cooleye Coolie Cooll Coolley Coolly Coollye Cooly Coolye CORLEY Coulah Coulay Couley Coulley Couly Couolley Coweley Cowely Cowlay Cowlaye Cowlee Cowleige COWLEY Cowleye Cowli Cowlie Cowllay Cowllea Cowllie Cowly Cowlye Coyleie Coyley Coyly Cul Culey CULL CULLEY De culegh

Coolee CAWLEY COLE COLEY COLLEY COLLIE COLLY COOLE COOLEY CORLEY COWLEY CULLEY

COOLEY 83 CAWLEY Cawly Coahley Coale Coalee Coaley Coaleys Coalie Coalle Coalley Coally Coaly Coawly COBLEY Coeley Coely Cohley Cohleye Coiley COLE Colee Colei Coleley Colely COLEY Coleye Coleyis Coli Colie Coliye Coll Collay Colle Collee Colles COLLEY Colleye Colli COLLIE Colliy COLLY Collye Coly Colye Cooaly COOLE Coolee Cooleye Coolie Coolley Coolly Coollye Cooly Coolye CORLEY Coulah Coulay Couley Coulley Couly Couolley Coweley Cowely Cowlay Cowlaye Cowlee Cowleige COWLEY Cowleye Cowli Cowlie Cowllay Cowllea Cowllie Cowly Cowlye Coyleie Coyley Coyly Culey CULLEY De culegh

Cooleye CAWLEY COLE COLEY COLLEY COLLIE COLLY COOLE COOLEY CORLEY COWLEY CULLEY

Coolidge COLLEDGE

Coolie CAWLEY COLE COLEY COLLEY COLLIE COLLY COOLE COOLEY CORLEY COWLEY CULLEY

Coolin COULING COWLING

COOLING Cullin CULLING

Cooll COLE COOL COOLE CULL

Coolledge COLLEDGE

Coolley CAWLEY COLE COLEY COLLEY COLLIE COLLY COOLE COOLEY CORLEY COWLEY CULLEY

Coollidge COLLEDGE

Coolly CAWLEY COLE COLEY COLLEY COLLIE COLLY COOLE COOLEY CORLEY COWLEY CULLEY

Coollye CAWLEY COLE COLEY COLLEY COLLIE COLLY COOLE COOLEY CORLEY COWLEY CULLEY

Cooly CAWLEY COLE COLEY COLLEY COLLIE COLLY COOLE COOLEY CORLEY COWLEY CULLEY

Coolye CAWLEY COLE COLEY COLLEY COLLIE COLLY COOLE COOLEY CORLEY COWLEY CULLEY

Cooman COMAN

COOMBER COMBER COMER

COOMBES 5 COMBES COMBS COOMBS Coomes

COOMBS 5 COMBES COMBS COOMBES Coomes

Coomes COOMBES COOMBS

COON 6 Coone COUN Coune Cune Kewn

Coone COON COUN

Coop COOPE COPE COUPE

Coopay COOPEY

COOPE 7 Coop COPE Coup COUPE Cowp Cowpe

Coopee COOPEY

Coopene CAFFYN CAPEN CAPON COBBIN COBBING COFFIN KIPPING

COOPER COUPER COWPER

COOPES 6 COOPS COUPES COUPS COWPES COWPS

COOPEY 4 Coopay Coopee Coupey

Cooping CAFFYN CAPEN CAPON COBBIN COBBING COFFIN KIPPING

Coopinge CAFFYN CAPEN CAPON COBBIN COBBING COFFIN KIPPING

Coopland COPELAND COUPLAND

Cooppin CAFFYN CAPEN CAPON COBBIN COBBING COFFIN KIPPING

Cooppock COBBETT COPPOCK CORBET CORBETT

Cooppyn CAFFYN CAPEN CAPON COBBIN COBBING COFFIN KIPPING

Cooppyng CAFFYN CAPEN CAPON COBBIN COBBING COFFIN KIPPING

COOPS 6 COOPES COUPES COUPS COWPES COWPS

Coopyne CAFFYN CAPEN CAPON COBBIN COBBING COFFIN KIPPING

Coorley CAWLEY CORLEY

Coose COOZE

COOT COOTE

Cootar COOTER COUTER

COOTE COOT

COOTER 6 Cootar Cootter Coutar COUTER Coutter

Cootter COOTER COUTER

COOZE 4 Coose Couse Kouse

Cop'yn COPPEN COPPIN COPPING COPPINS

Copack COBBETT COPPOCK CORBET CORBETT

Copan COPPEN COPPIN COPPING COPPINS

COPE 10 COAP Coape Coop COOPE COPP Coup COUPE Cowp Cowpe

Copeians COPPEN COPPIN COPPING COPPINS

Copein COPPEN COPPIN COPPING COPPINS

Copeing COPPEN COPPIN COPPING COPPINS

COPELAND 5 Coopland COUPLAND Cowpland Kaupaland

Copen COPPEN COPPIN COPPING COPPINS

Copenal COPPEN COPPIN COPPING COPPINS

Copenger CAFFYN CAPEN CAPON COBBIN COBBING COFFIN KIPPING

Copens COPPEN COPPIN COPPING COPPINS

Coperoak COBBETT COPPOCK CORBET CORBETT

COPESTAKE 7 Cobstake Copstake Coupestack Coupstak Coupstake Cowpstake

Cophack COBBETT COPPOCK CORBET CORBETT

Cophacke COBBETT COPPOCK CORBET CORBETT

Cophaen CAFFYN CAPEN CAPON COBBIN COBBING COFFIN KIPPING

COPHAM 4 CAPON CHOPEN COBHAM

Copheick COBBETT COPPOCK CORBET CORBETT

Cophen CAFFYN CAPEN CAPON COBBIN COBBING COFFIN KIPPING

Cophin CAFFYN CAPEN CAPON COBBIN COBBING COFFIN KIPPING

Cophocke COBBETT COPPOCK CORBET CORBETT

Cophook COBBETT COPPOCK CORBET CORBETT

Cophynn CAFFYN CAPEN CAPON COBBIN COBBING COFFIN KIPPING

Copians COPPEN COPPIN COPPING COPPINS

Copiens COPPEN COPPIN COPPING COPPINS

Copin COPPEN COPPIN COPPING COPPINS

Copine COPPEN COPPIN COPPING COPPINS

Copiner CAFFYN CAPEN CAPON COBBIN COBBING COFFIN KIPPING

Coping COPPEN COPPIN COPPING COPPINS

Copinge COPPEN COPPIN COPPING COPPINS

Copinger CAFFYN CAPEN CAPON COBBIN COBBING COFFIN KIPPING

Copingers CAFFYN CAPEN CAPON COBBIN COBBING COFFIN KIPPING

Copings COPPEN COPPIN COPPING COPPINS

Copini COPPEN COPPIN COPPING COPPINS

Copinne COPPEN COPPIN COPPING COPPINS

Copins COPPEN COPPIN COPPING COPPINS

Copion COPPEN COPPIN COPPING COPPINS

Copledike COBBLEDICK COBELDICK CUPPLEDITCH

Copledyke COBBLEDICK COBELDICK CUPPLEDITCH

Copock COBBETT COPPOCK CORBET CORBETT

Copocke COBBETT COPPOCK CORBET CORBETT

Copon COPPEN COPPIN COPPING COPPINS

Copons COPPEN COPPIN COPPING COPPINS

Copot COBBETT COPPOCK CORBET CORBETT

COPP 4 COAP Coape COPE

Coppach COBBETT COPPOCK CORBET CORBETT

Coppache COBBETT COPPOCK CORBET CORBETT

Coppack COBBETT COPPOCK CORBET CORBETT

Coppacke COBBETT COPPOCK CORBET CORBETT

Coppaick COBBETT COPPOCK CORBET CORBETT

Coppain COPPEN COPPIN COPPING COPPINS

Coppak COBBETT COPPOCK CORBET CORBETT

Coppan COPPEN COPPIN COPPING COPPINS

Coppatk COBBETT COPPOCK CORBET CORBETT

Coppeck COBBETT COPPOCK CORBET CORBETT

Coppecke COBBETT COPPOCK CORBET CORBETT

Coppege COPPEN COPPIN COPPING COPPINS

Coppeinge COPPEN COPPIN COPPING COPPINS

Coppejans COPPEN COPPIN COPPING COPPINS

COPPEN 72 Cop'yn Copan Copeians Copein Copeing Copen Copenal Copens Copians Copiens Copin Copine Coping Copinge Copings Copini Copinne Copins Copion Copon Copons Coppain Coppan Coppege Coppeinge Coppejans Coppenianssn Coppens Coppent Coppenzans Coppeynge Coppian Coppidge Coppien Coppims COPPIN Coppine Coppines COPPING Copping' Coppinge Coppinges Coppingg Coppings Coppinn COPPINS Coppon Coppoyn Coppum Coppyn Coppynat Coppyne Coppyng Coppynge Coppyngg Coppynggs Coppynn Coppyns Copyance Copyans Copyinge Copyn Copyne Copyng Copynge Copyns Copynson Copynyns De coppinis De coppum De copun

Coppener CAFFYN CAPEN CAPON COBBIN COBBING COFFIN KIPPING

Coppengar CAFFYN CAPEN CAPON COBBIN COBBING COFFIN KIPPING

Coppenger CAFFYN CAPEN CAPON COBBIN COBBING COFFIN KIPPING

Coppenianssn COPPEN COPPIN COPPING COPPINS

Coppens COPPEN COPPIN COPPING COPPINS

Coppent COPPEN COPPIN COPPING COPPINS

Coppenzans COPPEN COPPIN COPPING COPPINS

Coppert COBBETT COPPOCK CORBET CORBETT

Copperthwaite COPPERWHEAT

COPPERWHEAT 4 Copperthwaite Copperwhite Copperwick

Copperwhite COPPERWHEAT

Copperwick COPPERWHEAT

Coppeynge COPPEN COPPIN

If the name you are interested in is not here, try Section C.

COPPING COPPINS
Coppian COPPEN COPPIN COPPING COPPINS
Coppick COBBETT COPPOCK CORBET CORBETT
Coppicke COBBETT COPPOCK CORBET CORBETT
Coppict COBBETT COPPOCK CORBET CORBETT
Coppidge COPPEN COPPIN COPPING COPPINS
Coppien COPPEN COPPIN COPPING COPPINS
Coppims COPPEN COPPIN COPPING COPPINS
COPPIN 72 Cop'yn Copan Copeians Copein Copeing Copen Copenal Copens Copians Copiens Copin Copine Coping Copinge Copings Copini Copinne Copins Copion Copon Copons Coppain Coppan Coppege Coppeinge Coppejans COPPEN Coppenianssn Coppens Coppent Coppenzans Coppeynge Coppian Coppidge Coppien Coppims Coppine Coppines COPPING Copping' Coppinge Coppinges Coppingg Coppings Coppinn COPPINS Coppon Coppoyn Coppum Coppyn Coppynat Coppyne Coppyng Coppynge Coppyngg Coppynggs Coppynn Coppyns Copyance Copyans Copyinge Copyn Copyne Copyng Copynge Copyns Copynson Copynyns De coppinis De coppum De copun
Coppine COPPEN COPPIN COPPING COPPINS
Coppiner CAFFYN CAPEN CAPON COBBIN COBBING COFFIN KIPPING
Coppines COPPEN COPPIN COPPING COPPINS
Copping' COPPEN COPPIN COPPING COPPINS
COPPING 72 Cop'yn Copan Copeians Copein Copeing Copen Copenal Copens Copians Copiens Copin Copine Coping Copinge Copings Copini Copinne Copins Copion Copon Copons Coppain Coppan Coppege Coppeinge Coppejans COPPEN Coppenianssn Coppens Coppent Coppenzans Coppeynge Coppian Coppidge Coppien Coppims COPPIN Coppine Coppines Copping' Coppinge Coppinges Coppingg Coppings Coppinn COPPINS Coppon Coppoyn Coppum Coppyn Coppynat Coppyne Coppyng Coppynge Coppyngg Coppynggs Coppynn Coppyns Copyance Copyans Copyinge Copyn Copyne Copyng Copynge Copyns Copynson Copynyns De coppinis De coppum De copun
Coppinge COPPEN COPPIN COPPING COPPINS
Coppinger CAFFYN CAPEN CAPON COBBIN COBBING COFFIN KIPPING
Coppingers CAFFYN CAPEN CAPON COBBIN COBBING COFFIN KIPPING
Coppinges COPPEN COPPIN COPPING COPPINS
Coppingg COPPEN COPPIN COPPING COPPINS
Coppings COPPEN COPPIN COPPING COPPINS
Coppinn COPPEN COPPIN COPPING COPPINS
COPPINS 72 Cop'yn Copan Copeians Copein Copeing Copen Copenal Copens Copians Copiens Copin Copine Coping Copinge Copings Copini Copinne Copins Copion Copon Copons Coppain Coppan Coppege Coppeinge Coppejans COPPEN Coppenianssn Coppens Coppent Coppenzans Coppeynge Coppian Coppidge Coppien Coppims COPPIN Coppine Coppines COPPING Copping' Coppinge Coppinges Coppingg Coppings Coppinn Coppon Coppoyn Coppum Coppyn Coppynat Coppyne Coppyng Coppynge Coppyngg Coppynggs Coppynn Coppyns Copyance Copyans Copyinge Copyn Copyne Copyng Copynge Copyns Copynson Copynyns De coppinis De coppum De copun
Coppner CAFFYN CAPEN CAPON COBBIN COBBING COFFIN KIPPING
Coppoch COBBETT COPPOCK CORBET CORBETT
Coppochs COBBETT COPPOCK CORBET CORBETT
COPPOCK 55 Cappock Cappocke Cappuch Cappuck Cobbet COBBETT Cobbick Cobbit Cobbitt Cobbut Coboke Cobot Cobut Cooppock Copack Coperoak Cophack Cophacke Copheick Cophocke Cophook Copock Copocke Copot Coppach Coppache Coppack Coppacke Coppaick Coppak Coppatk Coppeck Coppecke Coppert Coppick Coppicke Coppict Coppoch Coppochs Coppocke Coppocks Coppoe Coppok Coppoke Coppook Coppott Coppowe Coppuck Coppucks Copuch CORBET CORBETT Corbit Cowpoke
Coppocke COBBETT COPPOCK CORBET CORBETT
Coppocks COBBETT COPPOCK CORBET CORBETT
Coppoe COBBETT COPPOCK CORBET CORBETT
Coppok COBBETT COPPOCK CORBET CORBETT
Coppoke COBBETT COPPOCK CORBET CORBETT
Coppon COPPEN COPPIN COPPING COPPINS
Coppook COBBETT COPPOCK CORBET CORBETT
Coppott COBBETT COPPOCK CORBET CORBETT
Coppowe COBBETT COPPOCK CORBET CORBETT
Coppoyn COPPEN COPPIN COPPING COPPINS
Coppuck COBBETT COPPOCK CORBET CORBETT
Coppucks COBBETT COPPOCK CORBET CORBETT
Coppum COPPEN COPPIN COPPING COPPINS
Coppyn COPPEN COPPIN COPPING COPPINS
Coppynat COPPEN COPPIN COPPING COPPINS
Coppyne COPPEN COPPIN COPPING COPPINS
Coppyng COPPEN COPPIN COPPING COPPINS
Coppynge COPPEN COPPIN COPPING COPPINS
Coppynger CAFFYN CAPEN CAPON COBBIN COBBING COFFIN KIPPING
Coppyngg COPPEN COPPIN COPPING COPPINS
Coppynggs COPPEN COPPIN COPPING COPPINS
Coppynn COPPEN COPPIN COPPING COPPINS
Coppyns COPPEN COPPIN COPPING COPPINS
Copsay COPSEY
COPSEY 4 Copsay Copsie Copsy
Copsie COPSEY
Copstake COPESTAKE
Copsy COPSEY
Copuch COBBETT COPPOCK CORBET CORBETT
Copyance COPPEN COPPIN COPPING COPPINS
Copyans COPPEN COPPIN COPPING COPPINS
Copyinge COPPEN COPPIN COPPING COPPINS
Copyn COPPEN COPPIN COPPING COPPINS
Copyne COPPEN COPPIN COPPING COPPINS
Copyng COPPEN COPPIN COPPING COPPINS
Copynge COPPEN COPPIN COPPING COPPINS
Copynger CAFFYN CAPEN CAPON COBBIN COBBING COFFIN KIPPING
Copyns COPPEN COPPIN COPPING COPPINS
Copynson COPPEN COPPIN COPPING COPPINS
Copynyns COPPEN COPPIN COPPING COPPINS
Copyunore CAFFYN CAPEN CAPON COBBIN COBBING COFFIN KIPPING
Coquide COCKADAY
Coquidee COCKADAY
Corbeet CORBER CORBET CORBETT CORBITT
Corben CORBIN CORBYN
CORBER 8 Corbeet CORBET CORBETT Corbit CORBITT Corbut CURBER
CORBET 59 Cappock Cappocke Cappuch Cappuck Cobbet COBBETT Cobbick Cobbit Cobbitt Cobbut Coboke Cobot Cobut Cooppock Copack Coperoak Cophack Cophacke Copheick Cophocke Cophook Copock Copocke Copot Coppach Coppache Coppack Coppacke Coppaick Coppak Coppatk Coppeck Coppecke Coppert Coppick Coppicke Coppict Coppoch Coppochs COPPOCK Coppocke Coppocks Coppoe Coppok Coppoke Coppook Coppott Coppowe Coppuck Coppucks Copuch Corbeet CORBER CORBETT Corbit CORBITT Corbut Cowpoke
CORBETT 59 Cappock Cappocke Cappuch Cappuck Cobbet COBBETT Cobbick Cobbit Cobbitt Cobbut Coboke Cobot Cobut Cooppock Copack Coperoak Cophack Cophacke Copheick Cophocke Cophook Copock Copocke Copot Coppach Coppache Coppack Coppacke Coppaick Coppak Coppatk Coppeck Coppecke Coppert Coppick Coppicke Coppict Coppoch Coppochs COPPOCK Coppocke Coppocks Coppoe Coppok Coppoke Coppook Coppott Coppowe Coppuck Coppucks Copuch Corbeet CORBER CORBET Corbit CORBITT Corbut Cowpoke
Corbey CORBY
Corbie CORBY
CORBIN Corben CORBYN
Corbit COBBETT COPPOCK CORBER CORBET CORBETT CORBITT
CORBITT 7 Corbeet CORBER CORBET CORBETT Corbit Corbut
CORBOM 5 Carsom Corsam Corsamme CORSON
Corbut CORBER CORBET CORBETT CORBITT
CORBY 5 Corbey Corbie Cosby Korby
CORBYN Corben CORBIN
CORCORAN Covernan
Corderie CORDERY
CORDERY Cawdery Corderie
Cordner CORNER
CORDWELL Cardwell
CORFIELD CAULFIELD Cawfield
CORK CORKE
CORKE CORK
CORLEY 83 CAWLEY Cawly Coahley Coale Coalee Coaley Coaleys Coalie Coalle Coalley Coally Coaly Coawly Coeley Coely Cohley Cohleye Coiley COLE Colee Colei Coleley Colely COLEY Coleye Coleyis Coli Colie Coliye Coll Collay Colle Collee Colles COLLEY Colleye Colli COLLIE Colliy COLLY Collye Coly Colye Cooaly COOLE Coolee

If the name you are interested in is not here, try Section C.

COOLEY Cooleye Coolie Coolley Coolly Coollye Cooly Coolye Coorley Coulah Coulay Couley Coulley Couly Couolley Coweley Cowely Cowlay Cowlaye Cowlee Cowleige COWLEY Cowleye Cowli Cowlie Cowllay Cowllea Cowllie Cowly Cowlye Coyleie Coyley Coyly Culey CULLEY De culegh
Corna CORNAH CORNALL CORNER
CORNAH 8 Corna CORNALL CORNER Gorna Gornah Gornall Gorner
Cornal CORNALL CORNELL
CORNALL 11 Corna CORNAH Cornal Cornel CORNELL CORNER Gorna Gornah Gornall Gorner
Cornel CORNALL CORNELL
CORNELL 4 Cornal CORNALL Cornel
CORNER 9 Cordner Corna CORNAH CORNALL Gorna Gornah Gornall Gorner
Cornewall CORNWALL CORNWELL
Cornewell CORNWALL CORNWELL
CORNFOOT 6 Comford COMFORT Conford CORNFORD Cornfort
CORNFORD 6 Comford COMFORT Conford CORNFOOT Cornfort
Cornfort CORNFOOT CORNFORD
CORNISH 7 Cornishe Cornisshe Cornys Cornysh Cornyshe Cornysshe
Cornishe CORNISH
Cornisshe CORNISH
CORNWALL 4 Cornewall Cornewell CORNWELL
CORNWELL 4 Cornewall Cornewell CORNWALL
Cornys CORNISH
Cornysh CORNISH
Cornyshe CORNISH
Cornysshe CORNISH
Coromeadow COWMEADOW
CORRIE 6 Currer CURRIE Currier Curror CURRY
CORRY 4 Currey CURRIE CURRY
Corsam CORBOM CORSON
Corsamme CORBOM CORSON
Corser CAUSER
CORSON 6 Carsom Colson CORBOM Corsam Corsamme
CORT COURT
Corvouso CARVASSO
Corzer CROSIER CROZIER
Cosbrook CODGBROOK
Cosbrooke CODGBROOK
Cosby CORBY
COSENS 4 COSSENS COUSENS COUSINS
Cosfort CASSFORD
Cosgrave COSGROVE
COSGROVE Cosgrave
Cosham COSSAM COSSUM
Coshar COSIER CROZIER
Coshier COSIER CROZIER
Coshum COSSAM COSSUM
COSIER 5 Coshar Coshier Cozier CROZIER
Cosner CUZNER
Coson COULSON COXON
COSSAM 5 Cosham Coshum Cossom COSSUM
COSSENS 9 Cofsins COSENS Cossons COUSENS COUSINS COUZENS Cufsons Cussons
COSSEY 5 Cassey Cossi Cossie Cossy
Cossi COSSEY
Cossie COSSEY
Cossom COSSAM COSSUM
Cossons COSSENS COUSENS COUZENS
COSSUM 5 Cosham Coshum COSSAM Cossom
Cossy COSSEY
Costa COSTER
COSTER Costa
Coteford CUDDIFORD CUTTIFORD
COTES COATES COATS
Cotesbrock CODGBROOK
Cotesbrook CODGBROOK
Coteswith COATSWITH COATSWORTH
Cotesworth COATSWITH COATSWORTH
Cotgrave COTGREAVE
COTGREAVE 4 Cotgrave Cotgreve Cottgrave
Cotgreve COTGREAVE
Coth COATH
Cothe COATH
Cotrel COTTEREL COTTERELL COTTRELL
Cotrell COTTEREL COTTERELL COTTRELL
Cotsbrook CODGBROOK
Cotsworth COATSWITH COATSWORTH
Cotsworthe COATSWITH COATSWORTH
COTTELL COTTLE
Cotten CUTTEN CUTTING
COTTENDEN 11 CALLENDER Cottendesa Cottendon Cottenson Cottenton Cotterden Cotterdon Cottingden Cottonden Cottynden
Cottendesa COTTENDEN
Cottendon COTTENDEN
Cottenson COTTENDEN
Cottenton COTTENDEN
Cotterden COTTENDEN
Cotterdon COTTENDEN
COTTEREL 6 Cotrel Cotrell COTTERELL Cottrel COTTRELL
COTTERELL 6 Cotrel Cotrell COTTEREL Cottrel COTTRELL
Cottgrave COTGREAVE
Cottingden COTTENDEN
COTTLE COTTELL
Cottonden COTTENDEN
Cottrel COTTEREL COTTERELL COTTRELL
COTTRELL 6 Cotrel Cotrell COTTEREL COTTERELL Cottrel
Cottynden COTTENDEN
Coucell COLESELL COULSELL
Couchie CONCHA CONCHAR CONCHIE MCCONCHIE MCCONCHY MCCONOCHIE
COUCHMAN 5 Coashman Coushman Cowchman Cushman
Couffley CUFFLEY CUFLEY
Coufley CUFFLEY CUFLEY
Couger COGGER
Cougger COGGER
Coughlough COCKCROFT COCKROFT COLCLOUGH
Coulah CAWLEY COLE COLEY COLLEY COLLIE COLLY COOLE COOLEY CORLEY COWLEY CULLEY
Coulam COLAM
Coulay CAWLEY COLE COLEY COLLEY COLLIE COLLY COOLE COOLEY CORLEY COWLEY CULLEY
Couldrake COLDRAKE
Couldren COLDRON
Couldron COLDRON
Coule COLE COLES
COULES 4 COLES COWLES Cowls
Couley CAWLEY COLE COLEY COLLEY COLLIE COLLY COOLE COOLEY CORLEY COWLEY CULLEY
Coulhame COLAM
Coulin COULING COWLING
COULING 4 Coolin Coulin COWLING
Coulle COLE COLES
Coulley CAWLEY COLE COLEY COLLEY COLLIE COLLY COOLE COOLEY CORLEY COWLEY CULLEY
COULSELL 5 COLESELL Coleshil Colsel Coucell
COULSON 4 Colson Coson COXON
COULT Colt
Coultas COULTOUS
COULTHARD Colthart COULTHART
COULTHART Colthart COULTHARD
Coulthirst COULTHURST
COULTHURST Colthurst Coulthirst
COULTON 5 CARLTON Carton Cauton CAWTON
COULTOUS 4 Coltas Coultas Cultas
COULTRIP Coultrup
Coultrope COLTHUP
Coultrup COULTRIP
Couly CAWLEY COLE COLEY COLLEY COLLIE COLLY COOLE COOLEY CORLEY COWLEY CULLEY
COUN 6 COON Coone Coune Cune Kewn
Counchie CONCHA CONCHAR CONCHIE MCCONCHIE MCCONCHY MCCONOCHIE
COUNDLEY Cownley
Coune COON COUN
Couolley CAWLEY COLE COLEY COLLEY COLLIE COLLY COOLE COOLEY CORLEY COWLEY CULLEY
Coup COOPE COPE COUPE
COUPE 7 Coop COOPE COPE Coup Cowp Cowpe
COUPER COOPER COWPER
COUPES 6 COOPES COOPS COUPS COWPES COWPS
Coupestack COPESTAKE
Coupey COOPEY
COUPLAND 6 Coopland COPELAND Cowpland Cpoeland Kaupaland
COUPS 6 COOPES COOPS COUPES COWPES COWPS
Coupstak COPESTAKE
Coupstake COPESTAKE
Courath CONRATH
COURCHE Courchja
Courchja COURCHE
Courson CURSON
COURT CORT
Courtenage COURTNEIDGE
Courtenay COURTNEY
COURTIS CURTIS
Courtnage COURTNEIDGE
Courtnay COURTNEY
Courtnedge COURTNEIDGE
Courtnege COURTNEIDGE
COURTNEIDGE 6 Courtenage Courtnage Courtnedge Courtnege Courtnidge
COURTNEY Courtenay Courtnay
Courtnidge COURTNEIDGE
Couse COOZE
Cousener CUZNER
COUSENS 7 COSENS COSSENS Cossons COUSINS COUZENS Cuzens
Coushman COUCHMAN
COUSINS 10 Cofsins COSENS COSSENS COUSENS Cousons COUZENS Cufsons Cussons Cuzens
Cousons COUSINS
Coutar COOTER COUTER
COUTER 6 Cootar COOTER Cootter Coutar Coutter
Couth COATH
Coutter COOTER COUTER
Couzener CUZNER
COUZENS 6 COSSENS Cossons COUSENS COUSINS Cuzens
COVELL Covil
COVENEY 5 Covenny Coveny Covney Koveney
Covenny COVENEY
Coveny COVENEY
Covernan CORCORAN
Coverson COLVERSON
Covil COVELL
Covney COVENEY
Cow COWIE
COWAN COWEN MCCOWAN
Cowchman COUCHMAN
Cowclough COLCLOUGH
Cowdery COWDREY COWDRY
Cowdray COWDREY COWDRY
COWDREY 5 Codry Cowdery Cowdray COWDRY
COWDRY 5 Codry Cowdery Cowdray COWDREY
Cowe COWIE
Coweddow COWMEADOW
Coweley CAWLEY COLE COLEY COLLEY COLLIE COLLY COOLE COOLEY CORLEY COWLEY CULLEY
COWELL 4 Cogell Coghell COWGILL
Cowely CAWLEY COLE COLEY COLLEY COLLIE COLLY COOLE COOLEY CORLEY COWLEY CULLEY
COWEN 5 CONEY COWAN COWINS COWNEY
COWGILL 4 Cogell Coghell COWELL
COWHILL Cowull
COWIE Cow Cowe
COWINS 4 CONEY COWEN COWNEY
Cowlam COLAM
Cowlay CAWLEY COLE COLEY COLLEY COLLIE COLLY COOLE COOLEY CORLEY COWLEY CULLEY
Cowlaye CAWLEY COLE COLEY COLLEY COLLIE COLLY COOLE COOLEY CORLEY COWLEY CULLEY
Cowlee CAWLEY COLE COLEY COLLEY COLLIE COLLY COOLE COOLEY CORLEY COWLEY CULLEY
Cowleige CAWLEY COLE COLEY COLLEY COLLIE

If the name you are interested in is not here, try Section C.

COLLY COOLE COOLEY CORLEY COWLEY CULLEY
COWLES 4 COLES COULES Cowls
COWLEY 82 CAWLEY Cawly Coahley Coale Coalee Coaley Coaleys Coalie Coalle Coalley Coally Coaly Coawly Coeley Coely Cohley Cohleye Coiley COLE Colee Colei Coleley Colely COLEY Coleye Coleyis Coli Colie Coliye Coll Collay Colle Collee Colles COLLEY Colleye Colli COLLIE Colliy COLLY Collye Coly Colye Cooaly COOLE Coolee COOLEY Cooleye Coolie Coolley Coolly Coollye Cooly Coolye CORLEY Coulah Coulay Couley Coulley Couly Couolley Coweley Cowely Cowlay Cowlaye Cowlee Cowleige Cowleye Cowli Cowlie Cowllay Cowllea Cowllie Cowly Cowlye Coyleie Coyley Coyly Culey CULLEY De culegh
Cowleye CAWLEY COLE COLEY COLLEY COLLIE COLLY COOLE COOLEY CORLEY COWLEY CULLEY
Cowli CAWLEY COLE COLEY COLLEY COLLIE COLLY COOLE COOLEY CORLEY COWLEY CULLEY
Cowlie CAWLEY COLE COLEY COLLEY COLLIE COLLY COOLE COOLEY CORLEY COWLEY CULLEY
COWLING 4 Coolin Coulin COULING
Cowllay CAWLEY COLE COLEY COLLEY COLLIE COLLY COOLE COOLEY CORLEY COWLEY CULLEY
Cowllea CAWLEY COLE COLEY COLLEY COLLIE COLLY COOLE COOLEY CORLEY COWLEY CULLEY
Cowllie CAWLEY COLE COLEY COLLEY COLLIE COLLY COOLE COOLEY CORLEY COWLEY CULLEY
Cowloff COCKCROFT COCKROFT COLCLOUGH
Cowls COLES COULES COWLES
Cowly CAWLEY COLE COLEY COLLEY COLLIE COLLY COOLE COOLEY CORLEY COWLEY CULLEY
Cowlye CAWLEY COLE COLEY COLLEY COLLIE COLLY COOLE COOLEY CORLEY COWLEY CULLEY
Cowmadow COWMEADOW
Cowman COMAN
Cowmaydo COWMEADOW
Cowmaydy COWMEADOW
Cowmeaddowe COWMEADOW
COWMEADOW 24 Comeada Comeaddowe Comeado Comeadow Comeadowe Comeda Comedo Commeda Commedo Commody Coromeadow Coweddow Cowmadow Cowmaydo Cowmaydy Cowmeaddowe Cowmeadowe Cowmeadoy Cowmeda Cowmeddow Cowmeddowe Cowmedo Cowmedow
Cowmeadowe COWMEADOW
Cowmeadoy COWMEADOW
Cowmeda COWMEADOW
Cowmeddow COWMEADOW
Cowmeddowe COWMEADOW
Cowmedo COWMEADOW
Cowmedow COWMEADOW
COWNEY 4 CONEY COWEN COWINS
Cownley COUNDLEY
Cowp COOPE COPE COUPE
Cowpe COOPE COPE COUPE
COWPER COOPER COUPER
COWPES 6 COOPES COOPS COUPES COUPS COWPS
Cowpland COPELAND COUPLAND
Cowpoke COBBETT COPPOCK CORBET CORBETT
COWPS 6 COOPES COOPS COUPES COUPS COWPES
Cowpstake COPESTAKE
Cowull COWHILL
COX 5 COCK COCKE COCKS COXE
COXE 4 COCK COCKS COX
COXON 5 Colson COOKSON Coson COULSON
COXWORTH Cocksworth
COYLE Coiles Coils
Coyleie CAWLEY COLE COLEY COLLEY COLLIE COLLY COOLE COOLEY CORLEY COWLEY CULLEY
Coyley CAWLEY COLE COLEY COLLEY COLLIE COLLY COOLE COOLEY CORLEY COWLEY CULLEY
Coyly CAWLEY COLE COLEY COLLEY COLLIE COLLY COOLE COOLEY CORLEY COWLEY CULLEY
Coynterel CANT CANTER CANTERELL CANTRELL CANTRILL CHANTRELL QUANTRILL QUINTRELL
Cozier COSIER CROZIER
Cpoeland COUPLAND
CRAB 4 CRABB CRABBE Craib
CRABB 4 CRAB CRABBE Craib
CRABBE 4 CRAB CRABB Craib
Cracklin CRACKNELL
Crackling CRACKNELL
Cracknel CRACKNELL
CRACKNELL 4 Cracklin Crackling Cracknel
Crackstone CROSTON CROXON CROXSON CROXTON CRUXTON
Crae CREE
Crafar CRAFER
CRAFER 4 Crafar Craffer Crapher
Craffer CRAFER
CRAFFORD 13 CAREFOOT CARFOOT CRAFORD CRAWFORD CRAYFORD CROFFORD CROFOOT Crofut CROWFOOT CROWFORD Crowfrothe KERFOOT
CRAFORD 13 CAREFOOT CARFOOT CRAFFORD CRAWFORD CRAYFORD CROFFORD CROFOOT Crofut CROWFOOT CROWFORD Crowfrothe KERFOOT
CRAFTS CROFTS
Craghead CRAIGHEAD
Cragheid CRAIGHEAD
Craib CRAB CRABB CRABBE
CRAIG CRAIK
CRAIGHEAD 4 Craghead Cragheid Craigheid
Craigheid CRAIGHEAD
CRAIK CRAIG
CRAIN CRAINE
CRAINE CRAIN
CRAM 4 Cramb CRAME Cramm
Cramb CRAM CRAME
CRAME 4 CRAM Cramb Cramm
Cramm CRAM CRAME
CRAMMOND CRAMOND
CRAMOND CRAMMOND
Crankshaw CRANSHAW CRONKSHAW CRONSHAW
CRANSHAW 4 Crankshaw CRONKSHAW CRONSHAW
Crapher CRAFER
Crasswell CROSSWELL
Craston CROSTON CROXON CROXSON CROXTON CRUXTON
Crastone CROSTON CROXON CROXSON CROXTON CRUXTON
Craswell CROSSWELL
Crathwell CRAUGHWELL
CRAUGHWELL Crathwell Crothwell
CRAWFORD 13 CAREFOOT CARFOOT CRAFFORD CRAFORD CRAYFORD CROFFORD CROFOOT Crofut CROWFOOT CROWFORD Crowfrothe KERFOOT
Crawlie CROWLY
Craxton CROSTON CROXON CROXSON CROXTON CRUXTON
CRAYFORD 13 CAREFOOT CARFOOT CRAFFORD CRAFORD CRAWFORD CROFFORD CROFOOT Crofut CROWFOOT CROWFORD Crowfrothe KERFOOT
CREAK 7 Creake CREEK Creeke Creyke CRICK Criyk
Creake CREAK CREEK CRICK
CREASEY CREASY Cresst
CREASY CREASEY Cresst
Crede CREED
Credgington CRUDGINGTON
CREE Crae
CREED Crede
CREEK 7 CREAK Creake Creeke Creyke CRICK Criyk
Creeke CREAK CREEK CRICK
Creepel CRIPWELL
Creeple CRIPWELL
Creichton CREIGHTON
CREIGHTON 6 Creichton CRICHTON CRIGHTON Criton Cryton
Crepell CRIPWELL
Creple CRIPWELL
Creppill CRIPWELL
Crepple CRIPWELL
Cresst CREASEY CREASY
CREW 6 CREWE CREWS Crewys CRUSE Cruyes
CREWE CREW
CREWES 5 CREWS CRUSE CRUWYS Cruze
CREWS 8 CREW CREWES Crewys CRUSE CRUWYS Cruyes Cruze
Crewys CREW CREWS CRUSE
Creyke CREAK CREEK CRICK
Crich CRITCH
Criche CRITCH
Crichlow CRITCHLEY
CRICHTON 6 Creichton CREIGHTON CRIGHTON Criton Cryton
CRICK 7 CREAK Creake CREEK Creeke Creyke Criyk
CRIDDLE Cridle
Cridle CRIDDLE
Crier CRYER
CRIGHTON 6 Creichton CREIGHTON CRICHTON Criton Cryton
CRIMES 5 Chrimes Chrymes Crims Crymins
Crims CRIMES
Cripil CRIPWELL
Criple CRIPWELL
Crippel CRIPWELL
Cripple CRIPWELL
CRIPPS CRIPS
CRIPS CRIPPS
Cripwel CRIPWELL
Cripwele CRIPWELL
CRIPWELL 13 Creepel Creeple Crepell Creple Creppill Crepple Cripil Criple Crippel Cripple Cripwel Cripwele
CRISFIELD CHRISFIELD
Crisopp KERSHOPE KIRSOPP
CRISP Crispe
Crispe CRISP
Cristal CRISTALL
CRISTALL 4 Christal Christall Cristal
Cristmas CHRISTMAS
CRITCH 11 Chreche Chretche Chriche Chritch Chryche Crich Criche Crych Cryche Crytche
CRITCHLEY 5 Crichlow CROUCHLEY Cruchlow CRUTCHLEY
Criton CREIGHTON CRICHTON CRIGHTON
Crittenden CRUTTENDEN
Criyk CREAK CREEK CRICK
CROASDALE Croasdell Croysdale#
Croasdell CROASDALE
Crocer CROSIER CROZIER
Crockat CROCKETT
Crockert CROCKETT
Crocket CROCKETT
CROCKETT 7 Crockat Crockert Crocket Crockhett Crockit Crockitt
Crockham CROCOMBE CROWCOMBE DE CRAUCUMBE
Crockhett CROCKETT
Crockit CROCKETT
Crockitt CROCKETT
Crocomb CROCOMBE CROWCOMBE DE CRAUCUMBE
CROCOMBE 10 Crockham Crocomb Crocome Crocumb CROWCOMBE De craucombe DE CRAUCUMBE De crawecumbe De crewecombe
Crocome CROCOMBE CROWCOMBE DE CRAUCUMBE
Crocumb CROCOMBE CROWCOMBE DE CRAUCUMBE
CROFFORD 13 CAREFOOT CARFOOT CRAFFORD CRAFORD CRAWFORD CRAYFORD CROFOOT Crofut CROWFOOT CROWFORD Crowfrothe KERFOOT
CROFOOT 13 CAREFOOT CARFOOT CRAFFORD CRAFORD CRAWFORD CRAYFORD CROFFORD Crofut CROWFOOT CROWFORD Crowfrothe KERFOOT
Crofs CROSS
Crofswell CROSSWELL

If the name you are interested in is not here, try Section C.

CROFT Crofte CROFTS
Crofte CROFT
CROFTS CRAFTS CROFT
Crofut CAREFOOT CARFOOT CRAFFORD CRAFORD CRAWFORD CRAYFORD CROFFORD CROFOOT CROWFOOT CROWFORD KERFOOT
Crokestone CROXTON CRUXTON
Crokson CROSTON CROXON CROXSON CROXTON CRUXTON
Croley CROWLY
CROMACK Crummack
CROMPTON CRUMPTON
CRON CRONE
Crondace CROUDACE
CRONE CRON
CRONKSHAW 4 Crankshaw CRANSHAW CRONSHAW
CRONSHAW 4 Crankshaw CRANSHAW CRONKSHAW
CROOM CROOME
CROOME CROOM
CROSBIE CROSBY
CROSBY CROSBIE
Crose CROSS
Croser CROSIER CROZIER
CROSIER 7 Corzer Crocer Croser Crossier Crosyer CROZIER
CROSLAND 4 CROSLEY CROSSLAND CROSSLEY
CROSLEY 5 CROSLAND Crosly CROSSLAND CROSSLEY
Crosly CROSLEY CROSSLEY
CROSS 4 Crofs Crose Crosse
Crossar CROSSER
Crosse CROSS
CROSSER 4 Crossar Crozar Crozer
Crossier CROSIER CROZIER
CROSSLAND 4 CROSLAND CROSLEY CROSSLEY
CROSSLEY 5 CROSLAND CROSLEY Crosly CROSSLAND
CROSSWELL 5 Crasswell Craswell Crofswell Croswell
CROSTON 22 Crackstone Craston Crastone Craxton Crokson Croxom CROXON CROXSON Croxstone CROXTON Cruckston Cruckton Cruston Cruxden Cruxen Cruxon Cruxsonne Cruxston Cruxstonne CRUXTON Cruzston
Croswell CROSSWELL
Crosyer CROSIER CROZIER
Crothwell CRAUGHWELL
CROUCHLEY CRITCHLEY CRUTCHLEY
CROUDACE Crondace Cruddass
Croutcher CRUTCHER
Crouter CRUTCHER
CROWCOMBE 10 Crockham Crocomb CROCOMBE Crocome Crocumb De craucombe DE CRAUCUMBE De crawecumbe De crewecombe
CROWDER CROWTHER
CROWFOOT 13 CAREFOOT CARFOOT CRAFFORD CRAFORD CRAWFORD CRAYFORD CROFFORD CROFOOT Crofut CROWFORD Crowfrothe KERFOOT
CROWFORD 13 CAREFOOT CARFOOT CRAFFORD CRAFORD CRAWFORD CRAYFORD CROFFORD CROFOOT Crofut CROWFOOT Crowfrothe KERFOOT
Crowfrothe CAREFOOT CARFOOT CRAFFORD CRAFORD CRAWFORD CRAYFORD CROFFORD CROFOOT CROWFOOT CROWFORD KERFOOT
CROWL Crowle
Crowle CROWL
CROWLY Crawlie Croley
CROWTHER CROWDER
Croxom CROSTON CROXON CROXSON CROXTON CRUXTON
CROXON 22 Crackstone Craston Crastone Craxton Crokson CROSTON Croxom CROXSON Croxstone CROXTON Cruckston Cruckton Cruston Cruxden Cruxen Cruxon Cruxsonne Cruxston Cruxstonne CRUXTON Cruzston
Croxsen CROXSON CROXTON
CROXSON 23 Crackstone Craston Crastone Craxton Crokson CROSTON Croxom CROXON Croxsen Croxstone CROXTON Cruckston Cruckton Cruston Cruxden Cruxen Cruxon Cruxsonne Cruxston Cruxstonne CRUXTON Cruzston
Croxstone CROSTON CROXON CROXSON CROXTON CRUXTON
CROXTON 24 Crackstone Craston Crastone Craxton Crokestone Crokson CROSTON Croxom CROXON Croxsen CROXSON Croxstone Cruckston Cruckton Cruston Cruxden Cruxen Cruxon Cruxsonne Cruxston Cruxstonne CRUXTON Cruzston
CROYDEN CROYDON
CROYDON CROYDEN
Croysdale# CROASDALE
Crozar CROSSER
Crozer CROSSER
CROZIER 11 Corzer Coshar Coshier COSIER Cozier Crocer Croser CROSIER Crossier Crosyer
Crucher CRUTCHER
Cruchlow CRITCHLEY
Cruckston CROSTON CROXON CROXSON CROXTON CRUXTON
Cruckton CROSTON CROXON CROXSON CROXTON CRUXTON
Crudas CRUDDAS
CRUDDAS Crudas
Cruddass CROUDACE
Crudgeton CRUDGINGTON
CRUDGINGTON 6 Chriginton Credgington Crudgeton Crudington Cruginton
Crudington CRUDGINGTON
Cruginton CRUDGINGTON
Crummack CROMACK
CRUMPTON CROMPTON
CRUSE 8 CREW CREWES CREWS Crewys CRUWYS Cruyes Cruze
Cruston CROSTON CROXON CROXSON CROXTON CRUXTON
CRUTCHER 4 Croutcher Crouter Crucher
CRUTCHLEY CRITCHLEY CROUCHLEY
CRUTTENDEN Crittenden
CRUWYS 5 CREWES CREWS CRUSE Cruze
Cruxden CROSTON CROXON CROXSON CROXTON CRUXTON
Cruxen CROSTON CROXON CROXSON CROXTON CRUXTON
Cruxon CROSTON CROXON CROXSON CROXTON CRUXTON
Cruxsonne CROSTON CROXON CROXSON CROXTON CRUXTON
Cruxston CROSTON CROXON CROXSON CROXTON CRUXTON
Cruxstonne CROSTON CROXON CROXSON CROXTON CRUXTON
CRUXTON 23 Crackstone Craston Crastone Craxton Crokestone Crokson CROSTON Croxom CROXON CROXSON Croxstone CROXTON Cruckston Cruckton Cruston Cruxden Cruxen Cruxon Cruxsonne Cruxston Cruxstonne Cruzston
Cruyes CREW CREWS CRUSE
Cruze CREWES CREWS CRUSE CRUWYS
Cruzston CROSTON CROXON CROXSON CROXTON CRUXTON
Crych CRITCH
Cryche CRITCH
CRYER Crier
Crymins CRIMES
Crysoppe KIRSOP KIRSOPP
Crystal CHRYSTAL
Crytche CRITCH
Cryton CREIGHTON CRICHTON CRIGHTON
Cubbadge CUBBAGE
CUBBAGE Cubbadge
Cubett CHIBBETT CUBITT
CUBITT 8 Chebbott CHIBBETT Chibott Clibbott Cubett Kybbet Kybet
Cudaford CUDDIFORD CUTTIFORD
Cuddeford CUDDIFORD CUTTIFORD
Cudden CUDDON
CUDDIFORD 7 Coteford Cudaford Cuddeford Cuteford Cutresfourd CUTTIFORD
CUDDON Cudden
Cuell CULE KEWELL
CUFF 4 CUFFE Cuffey Culf
CUFFE 13 CUFF Cuffey Culf Dob DUFF DUFFY KILDUFF Mcduff Mcduffey Mcilduff O'diff O'duffy
Cuffey CUFF CUFFE
CUFFIN 4 KIFFIN KYFFIN KYFFYN
CUFFLEY 8 Couffley Coufley Cuffly Cufflye CUFLEY Cufly Cuflye
Cuffly CUFFLEY CUFLEY
Cufflye CUFFLEY CUFLEY
CUFLEY 8 Couffley Coufley CUFFLEY Cuffly Cufflye Cufly Cuflye
Cufly CUFFLEY CUFLEY
Cuflye CUFFLEY CUFLEY
Cufsons COSSENS COUSINS
Cuill CULE KEWELL
Cuinterel CANT CANTER CANTERELL CANTRELL CANTRILL CHANTRELL QUANTRILL QUINTRELL
Cuinterell CANT CANTER CANTERELL CANTRELL CANTRILL CHANTRELL QUANTRILL QUINTRELL
Cuirc QUIRK QUIRKE
Cul COLE COOL COOLE CULL
CULE 10 Cuell Cuill Keuell Kevel Kevell Kewel KEWELL Kewylle Kul
Culey CAWLEY COLE COLEY COLLEY COLLIE COLLY COOLE COOLEY CORLEY COWLEY CULLEY
Culf CUFF CUFFE
CULL 6 COLE COOL COOLE Cooll Cul
Cullan CULLEN CURRAN
CULLEN 10 Cullan Cullin Cullindge CULLING Cullinge Cullyne CURRAN Curren Currin
CULLEY 83 CAWLEY Cawly Coahley Coale Coalee Coaley Coaleys Coalie Coalle Coalley Coally Coaly Coawly Coeley Coely Cohley Cohleye Coiley COLE Colee Colei Coleley Colely COLEY Coleye Coleyis Coli Colie Coliye Coll Collay Colle Collee Colles COLLEY Colleye Colli COLLIE Colliy COLLY Collye Coly Colye Cooaly COOLE Coolee COOLEY Cooleye Coolie Coolley Coolly Coollye Cooly Coolye CORLEY Coulah Coulay Couley Coulley Couly Couolley Coweley Cowely Cowlay Cowlaye Cowlee Cowleige COWLEY Cowleye Cowli Cowlie Cowllay Cowllea Cowllie Cowly Cowlye Coyleie Coyley Coyly Culey CULLY De culegh
Cullin COOLING CULLEN CULLING CURRAN
Cullindge CULLEN
CULLING 4 COOLING CULLEN Cullin
Cullinge CULLEN
Cullombe CULLUM
CULLUM 8 Collam Collom Collomb Collombe Colomb Cullombe Cullumbe
Cullumbe CULLUM
Cullumbine COLUMBINE
CULLY CULLEY
Cullyne CULLEN
CULM CALLUM
CULSHAW Kilshaw
Cultas COULTOUS
CULVER 4 CALVER CLOVER COLVER
Culverson COLVERSON
CUM Cumbe
Cumbe CUM
Cumber COMBER COMPER CUMBOR
Cumberlege CUMBLIDGE
Cumberlidge CUMBLIDGE
CUMBLIDGE 7 Comberlege Comberlidge Comblidge Cumberlege Cumberlidge Cumlege
CUMBOR COMBER Cumber
CUMING CUMMING CUMMINGS
Cumlege CUMBLIDGE
CUMMIN CUMMING

If the name you are interested in is not here, try Section C.

CUMMING 4 CUMING CUMMIN CUMMINGS
CUMMINGS 8 Commens Commins COMMONS CUMING CUMMING CUMMINS Cummons
CUMMINS 7 Commens Commins COMMONS COMYNS CUMMINGS Cummons
Cummock CAMMACK
Cummons COMMONS CUMMINGS CUMMINS
Cumper COMPER
Cunclife CUNLIFFE
Cuncliff CUNLIFFE
Cuncliffe CUNLIFFE
Cunclyfe CUNLIFFE
Cunclyffe CUNLIFFE
Cundeclif CUNLIFFE
Cundeclyve CUNLIFFE
Cunditt CONDUCT CONDUIT
Cundliff CUNLIFFE
Cundliffe CUNLIFFE
Cundwick CONDUCT CONDUIT
Cune COON COUN
Cuneybear CONEYBEARE CONIBEAR
Cuneybeare CONEYBEARE CONIBEAR
Cuneybeer CONEYBEARE CONIBEAR
Cunibear CONEYBEARE CONIBEAR
Cunibeare CONEYBEARE CONIBEAR
Cunibeer CONEYBEARE CONIBEAR
Cuniston CONISTON
Cunliff CUNLIFFE
CUNLIFFE 13 Conliffe Cunclife Cuncliff Cuncliffe Cunclyfe Cunclyffe Cundeclif Cundeclyve Cundliff Cundliffe Cunliff Cunteclyve
CUNNAH Connah
Cunnibear CONEYBEARE CONIBEAR
Cunnibeare CONEYBEARE CONIBEAR
Cunnibeer CONEYBEARE CONIBEAR
Cunningston CONISTON
Cunniston CONISTON
Cunstable CONSTABLE
Cunteclyve CUNLIFFE
Cunybear CONEYBEARE CONIBEAR
Cunybeare CONEYBEARE CONIBEAR
Cunybeer CONEYBEARE CONIBEAR
Cuonterel CANT CANTER CANTERELL CANTRELL CANTRILL CHANTRELL QUANTRILL QUINTRELL
Cupen CAFFYN CAPEN CAPON COBBIN COBBING COFFIN KIPPING
Cupenes CAFFYN CAPEN CAPON COBBIN COBBING COFFIN KIPPING
Cupin CAFFYN CAPEN CAPON COBBIN COBBING COFFIN KIPPING
Cuppeynge CAFFYN CAPEN CAPON COBBIN COBBING COFFIN KIPPING
Cuppin CAFFYN CAPEN CAPON COBBIN COBBING COFFIN KIPPING
CUPPLEDITCH 11 Cobbeldick Cobbeldicke COBBLEDICK Cobeldeke COBELDICK Cobeldycke Cobledick Copledike Copledyke De cobeldyk
Cuppyn CAFFYN CAPEN CAPON COBBIN COBBING COFFIN KIPPING
Cuppyng CAFFYN CAPEN CAPON COBBIN COBBING COFFIN KIPPING
Curam CURME
CURBER CORBER
CURDELL Cardell
Curem CURME
CURGENVEN Cargenven Curvengen
CURL 8 CURLE Kearl Kearle KEIRL Keirle KERLE KERLEY
CURLE 8 CURL Kearl Kearle KEIRL Keirle KERLE KERLEY
Curm CURME
CURME 8 Curam Curem Curm Curmi Curn Curom Currum
Curmi CURME
Curn CURME
Curnoe CURNOW
CURNOW Curnoe
Curom CURME
CURRALL Currel CURRELL
CURRAN 6 Cullan CULLEN Cullin Curren Currin
Curray CURRIE CURRY
Currel CURRALL CURRELL
CURRELL CURRALL Currel
Curren CULLEN CURRAN
Currer CORRIE CURRIE CURRY
Currey CORRY CURRIE CURRY
CURRIE 9 CORRIE CORRY Curray Currer Currey Currier Curror CURRY
Currier CORRIE CURRIE CURRY
Currin CULLEN CURRAN
Curror CORRIE CURRIE CURRY
Currum CURME
CURRY 9 CORRIE CORRY Curray Currer Currey CURRIE Currier Curror
CURSON Courson Curzon
Curt CARD CART
CURTIS COURTIS
Curvengen CURGENVEN
Curzon CURSON
Cusener CUZNER
Cushman COUCHMAN
Cusner CUZNER
Cussner CUZNER
Cussons COSSENS COUSINS
Cut CUTT CUTTS
Cuteford CUDDIFORD CUTTIFORD
CUTLER Cuttler
Cutresfourd CUDDIFORD CUTTIFORD
CUTT 4 Cut Cutte CUTTS
Cutte CUTT CUTTS
CUTTEN 6 Cotten Cuttin CUTTING Cutton Kutten
CUTTIFORD 7 Coteford Cudaford Cuddeford CUDDIFORD Cuteford Cutresfourd
Cuttin CUTTEN CUTTING
CUTTING 6 Cotten CUTTEN Cuttin Cutton Kutten
Cuttler CUTLER
Cutton CUTTEN CUTTING
CUTTS 4 Cut CUTT Cutte
Cuzens COUSENS COUSINS COUZENS
CUZNER 7 Cosner Cousener Couzener Cusener Cusner Cussner
Cyrmon SERMON SIRMAN SURMAN
D' escures DE SCURES
D'ABITOT Abitot
D'albamarle DAMEREL
D'alenston DALLISON
D'amirel DAMEREL
D'amll DAMEREL
D'ANNETHE 5 ACHANY HANNA HANNAH HANNAY
D'ARCY 5 Darcey Darcie Darcy Darsey
D'aubney DAUBNEY
D'aumarle DAMEREL
D'isigny DISNEY
D'isney DISNEY
D'raoul DORRELL DORRILL
Da hora HORA
DA VALL 4 Davell De vall Divall
Dabby DARBY DERBY
Dabhoirean DAVOREN
Dabie DAVEY DAVIE DAVY
Daby DAVEY DAVIE DAVY
Dackwell DAGWELL
DACRE 8 Dacres Daiker Daikers Daker Dakers Dayker Daykers
Dacres DACRE
DADD 5 Dades Darde DARDS Deards
Daddecot DELICATE
DADE Deed
Dades DADD DARDS
DADGE DODGE
DADLEY 4 Dadleye Dadlie Dadlye
Dadleye DADLEY
Dadlie DADLEY
Dadlye DADLEY
Dael DALE DEAL
Daeth DEATH
Daferon DAFFERN DAFFON DAFFORNE
Daffarn DAFFERN DAFFON DAFFORNE
Daffarne DAFFERN DAFFON DAFFORNE
DAFFERN 9 Daferon Daffarn Daffarne Dafferne DAFFON Dafforn DAFFORNE Daffron
Dafferne DAFFERN DAFFON DAFFORNE
DAFFON 9 Daferon Daffarn Daffarne DAFFERN Dafferne Dafforn DAFFORNE Daffron
Dafforn DAFFERN DAFFON DAFFORNE
DAFFORNE 9 Daferon Daffarn Daffarne DAFFERN Dafferne DAFFON Dafforn Daffron
Daffron DAFFERN DAFFON DAFFORNE
Dagmell DAGWELL
DAGNEN DEGNEN
Dagweell DAGWELL
Dagwel DAGWELL
DAGWELL 8 Dackwell Dagmell Dagweell Dagwel Dagwol Dakwell Gagwell
Dagwol DAGWELL
Daiker DACRE
Daikers DACRE
Dail DALE DEAL
Daill DALE
DAINTON 5 DAYTON Deaton DEIGHTON DENTON
Dair DARE DEAR DEER
Dairel DORRELL DORRILL
Dairey DARLEY
Dairy DARLEY
DAITON DAYTON
Dakaine DAKEYNE DAKIN DAYKIN
Dakayne DAKEYNE DAKIN DAYKIN
Daker DACRE
Dakers DACRE
Dakeyn DAKEYNE DAKIN DAYKIN
DAKEYNE 9 Dakaine Dakayne Dakeyn Dakeyns DAKIN Dakyn DAYKIN Dukeyne
Dakeyns DAKEYNE DAKIN DAYKIN
DAKIN 9 Dakaine Dakayne Dakeyn DAKEYNE Dakeyns Dakyn DAYKIN Dukeyne
Dakins DAKYNS
Dakwell DAGWELL
Dakyn DAKEYNE DAKIN DAYKIN
DAKYNS Dakins
Dalamer DALLIMORE DELAMERE
Dalamore DALLIMORE DELAMERE
Dalason DALLISON
Dalbeare A'BEAR ATTE BERE BEAR BEARE BERE DE LA BERE
DALBY 4 DAULBY Dobey DOLBY
DALE 5 Dael Dail Daill DEAL
Dalemore DALLIMORE DELAMERE
DALGLIESH DALGLISH Dolgleish
DALGLISH DALGLIESH Dolgleish
Dalimere DALLIMORE DELAMERE
Dalimore DALLIMORE DELAMERE
Dalison DALLISON
Dallamore DALLIMORE DELAMERE
Dallaston DALLISON
Dallemore DALLIMORE DELAMERE
Dallemory DALLIMORE DELAMERE
DALLEY 4 DALLY Dolley DOLLY
DALLIMORE 10 Dalamer Dalamore Dalemore Dalimere Dalimore Dallamore Dallemore Dallemory DELAMERE
Dallinson DALLISON
DALLISON 7 D'alenston Dalason Dalison Dallaston Dallinson Dallisson
Dallisson DALLISON
DALLY 4 DALLEY Dolley DOLLY
DALRYMPLE Derumple
Dalve DELVE DELVES
Damarel DAMEREL
Damarell DAMEREL
Dambrell DAMEREL
DAMEN DAMMON
DAMER Dammer
DAMEREL 16 D'albamarle D'amirel D'amll D'aumarle Damarel Damarell Dambrell Damerell Dameril Damerill Damiral Dammarel Dammarell Damrel Damrell

If the name you are interested in is not here, try Section C.

Damerell DAMEREL
Dameril DAMEREL
Damerill DAMEREL
Damiral DAMEREL
Dammarel DAMEREL
Dammarell DAMEREL
Dammer DAMER
DAMMON DAMEN
Damrel DAMEREL
Damrell DAMEREL
Danat DENNETT
DANE 7 DAWN Dawne DEAN DEANE DEANS DENE
Danel DANIEL DANIELL DANIELLS DANIELS
Danels DANIEL DANIELL DANIELLS DANIELS
Danet DENNETT
Danett DENNETT
DANFORD 21 Danforde Darneford Darneforde Darnford Darnforde Denford Denforde Derneford Derneforde Dernford Dernforde Donford Donforde Dorneford Dorneforde Dornford Dornforde DUNFORD Dunsford DURNFORD
Danforde DANFORD DUNFORD DURNFORD
DANIEL 10 Danel Danels DANIELL DANIELLS DANIELS Dannel Dannels Danyell Danyells
DANIELL 10 Danel Danels DANIEL DANIELLS DANIELS Dannel Dannels Danyell Danyells
DANIELLS 10 Danel Danels DANIEL DANIELL DANIELS Dannel Dannels Danyell Danyells
DANIELS 10 Danel Danels DANIEL DANIELL DANIELLS Dannel Dannels Danyell Danyells
Dannel DANIEL DANIELL DANIELLS DANIELS
Dannels DANIEL DANIELL DANIELLS DANIELS
Dannet DENNETT
DANSON DAWSON
Danyell DANIEL DANIELL DANIELLS DANIELS
Danyells DANIEL DANIELL DANIELLS DANIELS
Dar DARE DEAR DEER
Darbey DARBY DERBY
Darbie DARBY DERBY
Darbishire DARBYSHIRE DERBYSHIRE
DARBY 7 Dabby Darbey Darbie Derbey Derbie DERBY
DARBYSHIRE 4 Darbishire Derbishire DERBYSHIRE
Darcey D'ARCY
Darcie D'ARCY
Darcy D'ARCY
Darde DADD DARDS
DARDS 5 DADD Dades Darde Deards
DARE 5 Dair Dar DEAR DEER
Darell DORRELL DORRILL
Darkin DARKING
DARKING Darkin
Darlet DARLETT
DARLETT 4 Darlet Darlot Darlott
DARLEY Dairey Dairy
Darlot DARLETT
Darlott DARLETT
Darneford DANFORD DUNFORD DURNFORD
Darneforde DANFORD DUNFORD DURNFORD
Darnel DARNELL
DARNELL Darnel
Darnford DANFORD DUNFORD DURNFORD
Darnforde DANFORD DUNFORD DURNFORD
Darra DARRAGH DARRAH
DARRAGH Darra DARRAH
DARRAH Darra DARRAGH
Darral DORRELL DORRILL
Darrant DURRANT
Darrell DORRELL DORRILL
Darsey D'ARCY
Dartnail DARTNELL
Dartnal DARTNELL
Dartnale DARTNELL
Dartnall DARTNELL
Dartnel DARTNELL
DARTNELL 14 Dartnail Dartnal Dartnale Dartnall Dartnel Durtnal Durtnall Durtnel Durtnell Dutnail Dutnal Dutnale Dutnall
DARVALL Darvoll Dorvold
Darvoll DARVALL
DASHWOOD Daswood
Daswood DASHWOOD
Daubener DAUBNEY
Daubeney DAUBNEY
Daubeny DAUBNEY
Daubner DAUBNEY DOBNER
DAUBNEY 6 D'aubney Daubener Daubeney Daubeny Daubner
Daughty DOUGHTY
DAULBY DALBY DOLBY
Davall DEVALL
Davaries DE VRIES
Davell DA VALL
Davenish DENNISH DEVENISH DEVONISH
Davenishe DENNISH DEVENISH DEVONISH
DAVENPORT DEVENPORT DEVONPORT
Davenyshe DENNISH DEVENISH DEVONISH
Davenysshe DENNISH DEVENISH DEVONISH
Daveren DAVOREN
Daverin DAVOREN
Daverrennes DAVOREN
DAVEY 5 Dabie Daby DAVIE DAVY
Davice DAVIES DAVIS
DAVID DAVIES
DAVIDSON 5 Davieson DAVISON Davisson Davyson
DAVIE 6 Dabie Daby DAVEY DAVIES DAVY
DAVIES 6 Davice DAVID DAVIE DAVIS DAVY
Davieson DAVIDSON DAVISON
Davil DE VIELL DEAVILLE DUVALL
Daville DE VILLE DEAVILLE DEVELL DEVOLL
DAVIS 4 Davice DAVIES DAVISON
DAVISON 6 DAVIDSON Davieson DAVIS Davisson Davyson
Davisson DAVIDSON DAVISON
Davitt DEVITT
Davol DEVOLL DIVAL
Davole DEVOLL DIVAL
Davoll DEVOLL DIVAL
Davolle DEVOLL DIVAL
DAVOREN 9 Dabhoirean Daveren Daverin Daverrennes Davren Dubhdabhoireann O'davoren O'duvdavoren
Davren DAVOREN
DAVY 6 Dabie Daby DAVEY DAVIE DAVIES
Davyson DAVIDSON DAVISON
Dawdy DOUGHTY
DAWES DAWS
DAWN DANE Dawne
Dawne DANE DAWN
DAWS DAWES
DAWSON DANSON
DAY O'day
Dayker DACRE
Daykers DACRE
DAYKIN 9 Dakaine Dakayne Dakeyn DAKEYNE Dakeyns DAKIN Dakyn Dukeyne
DAYMAN 9 Dayment DAYMOND Dement DIAMOND DIMENT DIMOND DYMENT DYMOND
Dayment DAYMAN DAYMOND DIAMOND DIMENT DIMOND DYMENT DYMOND
DAYMOND 9 DAYMAN Dayment Dement DIAMOND DIMENT DIMOND DYMENT DYMOND
Daynish DENNISH DEVENISH DEVONISH
Dayrell DORRELL DORRILL
DAYTON 7 DAINTON DAITON DEACON Deaton DEIGHTON DENTON
De acastre ACASTER AKESTER AKISTER
De aisse ADSETT ALLETT ARSLETT ASLETT AYLETT AZE
De ambrosdon AMSDEN
De arches ARCH
De barton BARTON BARTRAM BERTRAM BETON BOURTON BRETON BURTON BYRON
De beare A'BEAR ATTE BERE BEAR BEARE BERE DE LA BERE
De beauchamp BEAUCHAMP
De beaumont BEAUMONT DE NEWBURGH DE WARWICK
De bere A'BEAR ATTE BERE BEAR BEARE BERE DE LA BERE
De berton BARTON BARTRAM BERTRAM BETON BOURTON BRETON BURTON BYRON
De beton BARTON BARTRAM BERTRAM BETON BOURTON BRETON BURTON BYRON
De birton BARTON BARTRAM BERTRAM BETON BOURTON BRETON BURTON BYRON
De boeles BOWDLER
De bollers BOWDLER
De bostock BOSTOCK
De bostok BOSTOCK
De boulers BOWDLER
DE BOUVERIE De bouveries
De bouveries DE BOUVERIE
De boxtoc BOSTOCK
De boys BOYS BOYSE
De boyse BOYS BOYSE
De brampton BRAMPTON
DE BRAOSE 6 Brewes Briouze Bruse De breuse De brewes
De bret BARTON BARTRAM BERTRAM BETON BOURTON BRETON BURTON BYRON
De breuse DE BRAOSE
De brewes DE BRAOSE
De briton BARTON BARTRAM BERTRAM BETON BOURTON BRETON BURTON BYRON
De budlers BOWDLER
De bullers BOWDLER
De burton BARTON BARTRAM BERTRAM BETON BOURTON BRETON BURTON BYRON
De burun BARTON BARTRAM BERTRAM BETON BOURTON BRETON BURTON BYRON
De buthley BOWDLER
DE CAMVILLE Camville Canville
De ceville CIVELL
de Cnol KNOWLES
De cobeldyk COBBLEDICK COBELDICK CUPPLEDITCH
De coppinis COPPEN COPPIN COPPING COPPINS
De coppum COPPEN COPPIN COPPING COPPINS
De copun COPPEN COPPIN COPPING COPPINS
De craucombe CROCOMBE CROWCOMBE DE CRAUCUMBE
DE CRAUCUMBE 10 Crockham Crocomb CROCOMBE Crocome Crocumb CROWCOMBE De craucombe De crawecumbe De crewecombe
De crawecumbe CROCOMBE CROWCOMBE DE CRAUCUMBE
De crewecombe CROCOMBE CROWCOMBE DE CRAUCUMBE
De culegh CAWLEY COLE COLEY COLLEY COLLIE COLLY COOLE COOLEY CORLEY COWLEY CULLEY
De esette DE ESSETE
De esse AISHE ASHE
De esset DE ESSETE
DE ESSETE 6 De esette De esset De essette De esshetes De excetes
De essette DE ESSETE
De esshetes DE ESSETE
De excetes DE ESSETE
De ferrers FERRERS
De ferrieres FERRERS
De fowell FOWELL
DE GAI De gay Gai
De gamaches GAMAGE
De gamage GAMAGE
De gamages GAMAGE
De gay DE GAI
De gorsuch GORSUCH
DE GOURNAY Gournay
De gryndenham GREENHAM
De hanslope HANSLOPE
De harcourt HARCOURT
De harley HARLEY
De heckele HICKLEY
De hekelinge DE HICKELING HICKLIN HICKLING ICKELING
De hekelingge DE HICKELING HICKLIN HICKLING ICKELING
De hekelyng DE HICKELING HICKLIN HICKLING ICKELING
De hekelyngg DE HICKELING HICKLIN HICKLING ICKELING
De helles HILLS
De heskayte HESKETH
De heskayth HESKETH
DE HEVER Hever
De hichelle HICKLEY
De hickel HICKLES ICKEL ICKELING
DE HICKELING 75 De

If the name you are interested in is not here, try Section C.

hekelinge De hekelingge De hekelyng De hekelyngg De hickelinge De hickelyng De hickelynges De hickland De hickling De hicklinge De hicklingge De hicling De higeling De hikeling De hikelinga De hikelinge De hikelinges De hikelingge De hikelyng De hikelynge De hikligg De hiklyng De hitling De hykeling De hykelinge De hykelingge De hykelinggs De hykelingh De hykelyng De hykelynge De hykelyngge De hykkelingh De ikeling De ikelinges De ykeling Eccling Echelinog Etcling Hiceling Hichelyng Hickelynge HICKLIN HICKLING Hicklinge Hicklings Hicklingse Hicklinse Hicling Hiclyng Hikeling Hikelyng Hikelyngg Hikkling Hiklynge Hixling Hyckelyng Hycklinge Hycklyng Hykeling Hykelyng Hykling Hyklyng Hyklynge Iceling ICKELING Ickling Icling Iclingas Ikeling Ikelinge Ikling Ycling Ykeling Ykling
De hickelinge DE HICKELING HICKLIN HICKLING ICKELING
De hickelle HICKLEY
De hickelyng DE HICKELING HICKLIN HICKLING ICKELING
De hickelynges DE HICKELING HICKLIN HICKLING ICKELING
De hickland DE HICKELING HICKLAND HICKLIN HICKLING ICKELING
De hickling DE HICKELING HICKLIN HICKLING ICKELING
De hicklinge DE HICKELING HICKLIN HICKLING ICKELING
De hicklingge DE HICKELING HICKLIN HICKLING ICKELING
De hicling DE HICKELING HICKLIN HICKLING ICKELING
De higeling DE HICKELING HICKLIN HICKLING ICKELING
De hikeland HICKLAND
De hikeling DE HICKELING HICKLIN HICKLING ICKELING
De hikelinga DE HICKELING HICKLIN HICKLING ICKELING
De hikelinge DE HICKELING HICKLIN HICKLING ICKELING
De hikelinges DE HICKELING HICKLIN HICKLING ICKELING
De hikelingge DE HICKELING HICKLIN HICKLING ICKELING
De hikelyng DE HICKELING HICKLIN HICKLING ICKELING
De hikelynge DE HICKELING HICKLIN HICKLING ICKELING
De hikligg DE HICKELING HICKLIN HICKLING ICKELING
De hiklyng DE HICKELING HICKLIN HICKLING ICKELING
De hitling DE HICKELING HICKLIN HICKLING ICKELING
De hora HORA
De hykeling DE HICKELING HICKLIN HICKLING ICKELING
De hykelinge DE HICKELING HICKLIN HICKLING ICKELING
De hykelingge DE HICKELING HICKLIN HICKLING ICKELING
De hykelinggs DE HICKELING HICKLIN HICKLING ICKELING
De hykelingh DE HICKELING HICKLIN HICKLING ICKELING
De hykelyng DE HICKELING HICKLIN HICKLING ICKELING
De hykelynge DE HICKELING HICKLIN HICKLING ICKELING
De hykelyngge DE HICKELING HICKLIN HICKLING ICKELING
De hykkelingh DE HICKELING HICKLIN HICKLING ICKELING
De ikeling DE HICKELING HICKLIN HICKLING ICKELING
De ikelinges DE HICKELING HICKLIN HICKLING ICKELING
DE KAREWARDYN 25 CALLADINE Callerdine CANADINE CANARDINE Canderdine CANDERDYNE CANNADINE CANNADYNE CARDEN CARDIN CARDING CARDON Carodine CARRADINE Carradyne Carrodine CARWARDEN Carwardin CARWARDINE CARWARDYNE KAWRDIN Keanodine KENDERDINE KENWARDEN
de Knol KNOWLES
de Knoll KNOWLES
de Knolle KNOWLES
De kynardsley KINNERSLEY KYNARDSLEY KYNNERSLEY
De kynnardsley KINNERSLEY KYNARDSLEY KYNNERSLEY
De kynnardsleye KINNERSLEY KYNARDSLEY KYNNERSLEY
De l'est EAST ESTE
De la bear A'BEAR ATTE BERE BEAR BEARE BERE DE LA BERE
De la beere A'BEAR ATTE BERE BEAR BEARE BERE DE LA BERE
DE LA BERE 42 A baer A bear A beare A beere A bere A beyre A'barre A'BEAR A'beare A'beere A'beyre Abair Abarre Abbeare Abbir Abear Abeard Abeare Abeer Abeere Abere Abeyre Abier Abore Abour Abuer Abure ATTE BERE BEAR BEARE Beire BERE Dalbeare De beare De bere De la bear De la beere Delaber Delabere Dellabere Delliber
DE LA HAYE DELAHAY Delahaye
De la mare DELAMERE
De la pole POLE POWELL
DE LA RISEBREGGE 7 RISBRIDGER RUSBRIDGER RYSBRUG Rysbrugg RYSEBRIGGER RYSHBRYGGE
De lawze LAW LAWES LAWS
DE LE CLUSE Le cluse
De lobbe LOBB
De lors LAW LAWES LAWS
de Luly LULY
De luttele LUTLEY
De lutteley LUTLEY
De lutteleye LUTLEY
DE MANDEVILLE MANDEVILLE
De masny MANNY
De medewe MEADOWS PIERREPONT
De meriet MERRETT MERRITT
De mineriis MINERS MYNORS
De miners MINERS MYNORS
De monbrun MOMBRUN
DE MORTAGNE 20 De mountanys plaine De muntein Demunteny Monntegne Montaigne Mountagne Mountaigne Mountaine Mountane Mountany Mountayne Mountenay Mounteney Mounteneye Mountenney Mounteny Mountnay MOUNTNEY Mowntayne
De mortemer MORTIMER
De mountanys plaine DE MORTAGNE MOUNTNEY
De muntein DE MORTAGNE MOUNTNEY
De mynors MINERS MYNORS
De neubourg DE NEWBURGH DE WARWICK
De neufmarche NEWMARCH
DE NEWBURGH 5 BEAUMONT De beaumont De neubourg DE WARWICK
De newmarch NEWMARCH
De odingsells ODINGSELLS
De ondeslowe ONSLOW
De pembridge PEMBRIDGE
De pemprugge PEMBRIDGE
De picquigny PINCKNEY PINKNEY
De pinkeni PINCKNEY PINKNEY
De puleston PULESTON
De pyuelisdon PULESTON
De pyvelisdon PULESTON
De pywelisdon PULESTON
De remevill REMEVILLE
De remeville REMEVILLE
De rie PROUSE PROWSE
DE SCURES D' escures
De st valery ST VALORY
De st valori ST VALORY
De st valory ST VALORY
De stavele HOWELL STAVOLD STAWELL STOWELL STOYLE
De stawele HOWELL STAVOLD STAWELL STOWELL STOYLE
De stawell HOWELL STAVOLD STAWELL STOWELL STOYLE
De stawelle HOWELL STAVOLD STAWELL STOWELL STOYLE
De stawille HOWELL STAVOLD STAWELL STOWELL STOYLE
De stawylle HOWELL STAVOLD STAWELL STOWELL STOYLE
De stoill HOWELL STAVOLD STAWELL STOWELL STOYLE
De stouill HOWELL STAVOLD STAWELL STOWELL STOYLE
De stoule HOWELL STAVOLD STAWELL STOWELL STOYLE
De stoville HOWELL STAVOLD STAWELL STOWELL STOYLE
De stowill HOWELL STAVOLD STAWELL STOWELL STOYLE
De stowille HOWELL STAVOLD STAWELL STOWELL STOYLE
De ticheners TICKNER
De tichenoure TICKNER
DE TOENI 5 De toni DE TONY Todnie Tony
De toni DE TOENI DE TONY
DE TONY DE TOENI De toni
De turberville TURBERVILL TURBERVILLE TURVILLE
De tykenore TICKNER
De vall DA VALL
De varenne DE WARENNE WARREN
De vesci VESEY VESSEY
De vial DE VIELL DEAVILLE DUVALL
DE VIELL 9 Davil De vial DEAVILLE Devile Deville Divel Divell DUVALL
De vignes DESVIGNES DEVINE
DE VILLE 10 Daville Deavell DEAVILLE DEVELL Devile Devill Deville DEVOLL Deyville
DE VRIES Davaries
DE WARENNE 5 De varenne De warren Warenne WARREN
De warren DE WARENNE WARREN
DE WARWICK 4 De beaumont De neubourg DE NEWBURGH
De welles WELLS
De welleton WILLERTON WOOLERTON
De wharton WALTON WARTON WHARTON WORTON
De wilghton WILLERTON WOOLERTON
De willeghton WILLERTON WOOLERTON
De wilughton WILLERTON WOOLERTON
De wylgton WILLERTON WOOLERTON
De wynder WINDER
De wythnesham MEADOWS PIERREPONT
De ykeling DE HICKELING HICKLIN HICKLING ICKELING
DEACON 18 DAYTON Decon DEIGHTON Dekon Diccon DICKENS DICKER Dicking DICKON DICKSON Diggen Dikkon Dikon DIXON Dyckon Dykon Dyxon
DEADMAN Dedman
DEAKEN DEAKIN
DEAKIN DEAKEN
DEAL 4 Dael Dail DALE
DEAN 5 DANE DEANE DEANS

If the name you are interested in is not here, try Section C.

DENE
DEANE 5 DANE DEAN DEANS DENE
DEANS 5 DANE DEAN DEANE DENE
DEAR 5 Dair Dar DARE DEER
Deards DADD DARDS
Dearl DEARLE
DEARLE 4 Dearl Derl Derle
Dearling DERLING DURLING
DEATH 5 Daeth Deathe Deeth Deith
Deathe DEATH
Deaton DAINTON DAYTON DEIGHTON DENTON
Deavalle DEVALL
Deavell DE VILLE DEAVILLE DEVELL DEVOLL
Deaven DEVON
DEAVILLE 16 Davil Daville De vial DE VIELL DE VILLE Deavell DEVELL Devile Devill Deville DEVOLL Deyville Divel Divell DUVALL
Deavon DEVON
DEBELL 7 Dibbell DIBBLE Dibbley Dibel Dible DIBLEY
Debnish DENNISH DEVENISH DEVONISH
Debrick DEDRICK
Decon DEACON DICKENS DICKER DICKON DICKSON DIXON
Deconson DICKINSON
Deddicott DELICATE
Dederich DEDRICK
Dederick DEDRICK
Dedicoat DELICATE
Dedicott DELICATE
Dedlick DEDRICK
Dedman DEADMAN
DEDRICK 7 Debrick Dederich Dederick Dedlick Dedvick Deidrick
Dedvick DEDRICK
Deed DADE
DEER 5 Dair Dar DARE DEAR
Deeth DEATH
Deforge DESFORGES
Deforges DESFORGES
DEGNEN DAGNEN
Deidrick DEDRICK
DEIGHTON 10 DAINTON DAYTON DEACON Deaton DENTON Dighton Diton Ditton Dyton
Deignen DIGNIN
Deith DEATH
DEJEANNE JAYNE
Dekon DEACON DICKENS DICKER DICKON DICKSON DIXON
Dela mare DELAMERE
Delaber A'BEAR ATTE BERE BEAR BEARE BERE DE LA BERE
Delabere A'BEAR ATTE BERE BEAR BEARE BERE DE LA BERE
DELAHAY DE LA HAYE Delahaye
Delahaye DE LA HAYE DELAHAY
DELAHOY DELANOY
Delamare DELAMERE
DELAMERE 15 Dalamer Dalamore Dalemore Dalimere Dalimore Dallamore Dallemore Dallemory DALLIMORE De la mare Dela mare Delamare Delimare Dellamare
DELANEY LANY
DELANOY DELAHOY
Delay DULLEA
Delicata DELICATE
DELICATE 24 Daddecot Deddicott Dedicoat Dedicott Delicata Delicati Delicoat Delicut Deligate Dellicate Dellicott Derricott Derriscott Didicoat Dilleket Dillicate Dillicoat Doddicott Gelicot Gelicut Jelicot Jellicott Jellicult
Delicati DELICATE
Delicoat DELICATE
Delicut DELICATE
Delieu DULIEU
Deligate DELICATE
Delimare DELAMERE
DELL Delph DELVE
Dellabere A'BEAR ATTE BERE BEAR BEARE BERE DE LA BERE
Dellamare DELAMERE
DELLAR DELLER
DELLER DELLAR
Delliber A'BEAR ATTE BERE BEAR BEARE BERE DE LA BERE
Dellicate DELICATE
Dellicott DELICATE
Dellow DULLOW
Delnot DILNOT DILNUTT
Delph DELL DELVE
Delues DELVE DELVES
Delvas DELVE DELVES
DELVE 7 Dalve DELL Delph Delues Delvas DELVES
DELVES 5 Dalve Delues Delvas DELVE
Delworth DILLWORTH DILWORTH
Dement DAYMAN DAYMOND DIAMOND DIMENT DIMOND DYMENT DYMOND
Demont DIMENT DIMOND DYMOND
Demunteny DE MORTAGNE MOUNTNEY
Dendal DENDLE
Dendall DENDLE
Dendell DENDLE
DENDLE 4 Dendal Dendall Dendell
DENE 5 DANE DEAN DEANE DEANS
Denesey DENZEY
Denford DANFORD DUNFORD DURNFORD
Denforde DANFORD DUNFORD DURNFORD
DENGATE 4 Dingate DUNGATE Dungett
DENHAM 4 DENHOLM DENMAN DUNHAM
DENHOLM DENHAM
Denier DENYER
Dening DENNING DINNING
Deninge DENNING DINNING
Deninson DENISON DENNISON
DENISON 4 Deninson DENNISON DENNISTON
DENKLEY 8 Doncklin Donkley Donklin DUNCKLEY Dunckling DUNKLEY Dunkling
DENLEY Denly
Denly DENLEY
DENMAN DENHAM DUNHAM
DENNETT 5 Danat Danet Danett Dannet
DENNEY DENNY
DENNING 5 Dening Deninge Dennings DINNING
Dennings DENNING
DENNISH 10 Davenish Davenishe Davenyshe Davenysshe Daynish Debnish DEVENISH DEVONISH Dovnish
DENNISON 5 Deninson DENISON DENNISTON Dineson
DENNISTON DENISON DENNISON
DENNY DENNEY
Densey DENZEY
Densi DENZEY
Densy DENZEY
DENTON 6 DAINTON DAYTON Deaton DEIGHTON RHODES DENTON
Denwoodie DINWOODIE
Denyare DENYER
DENYER Denier Denyare
Denze DENZEY
DENZEY 12 Denesey Densey Densi Densy Denze Denzi Denzy Dinze Dinzey Dinzi Dinzy
Denzi DENZEY
Denzy DENZEY
Derbey DARBY DERBY
Derbie DARBY DERBY
Derbishire DARBYSHIRE DERBYSHIRE
Derbridge DURBRIDGE
DERBY 7 Dabby Darbey Darbie DARBY Derbey Derbie
DERBYSHIRE 4 Darbishire DARBYSHIRE Derbishire
Dereham DERHAM
DERHAM 4 Dereham Dyrram Dyrrham
Derl DEARLE
Derle DEARLE
DERLING Dearling DURLING
Derneford DANFORD DUNFORD DURNFORD
Derneforde DANFORD DUNFORD DURNFORD
Dernford DANFORD DUNFORD DURNFORD
Dernforde DANFORD DUNFORD DURNFORD
Derricott DELICATE
Derriscott DELICATE
Derumple DALRYMPLE
DESFORGES 6 Deforge Deforges Difirjis Fergis Forges-de
Desney DISNEY
Desrochers HOUDE
Desruisseaux HOUDE
DESVIGNES 5 De vignes Devigne DEVINE Divine
Detanon DETNON
Detmar DETTMER
DETNON Detanon
DETTMER 4 Detmar Dittmar Dittmer
DEVALL Davall Deavalle
DEVELL 7 Daville DE VILLE Deavell DEAVILLE DEVOLL Deyville
Deven DEVON
DEVENISH 10 Davenish Davenishe Davenyshe Davenysshe Daynish Debnish DENNISH DEVONISH Dovnish
DEVENPORT DAVENPORT DEVONPORT
Deveraux DEVEREUX
Devereau DEVEREUX
DEVEREUX Deveraux Devereau
DEVERSON DEVESON Devison
DEVESON DEVERSON Devison
Devigne DESVIGNES DEVINE
Devile DE VIELL DE VILLE DEAVILLE DUVALL
Devill DE VILLE DEAVILLE
Deville DE VIELL DE VILLE DEAVILLE DUVALL
DEVINE 5 De vignes DESVIGNES Devigne Divine
Devison DEVERSON DEVESON
DEVITT 5 Davitt Dewitt Macdavitt Macdevitt
Devol DEVOLL DIVAL
Devole DEVOLL DIVAL
DEVOLL 30 Daville Davol Davole Davoll Davolle DE VILLE Deavell DEAVILLE DEVELL Devol Devole Devolle Deyville DIVAL Divale Divall Divalle Divol Divole Divoll Divolle Dyval Dyvale Dyvall Dyvalle Dyvol Dyvole Dyvoll Dyvolle
Devolle DEVOLL DIVAL
DEVON 4 Deaven Deavon Deven
DEVONISH 10 Davenish Davenishe Davenyshe Davenysshe Daynish Debnish DENNISH DEVENISH Dovnish
DEVONPORT DAVENPORT DEVENPORT
DEWDER Duder
DEWEL DEWELL
DEWELL DEWEL
DEWEY DEWY
Dewherst DEWHIRST DEWHURST
DEWHIRST 4 Dewherst DEWHURST Duhirst
DEWHURST 4 Dewherst DEWHIRST Duhirst
Dewitt DEVITT
DEWY DEWEY
DEY Die DYE
Deyville DE VILLE DEAVILLE DEVELL DEVOLL
DIAMOND 11 DAYMAN Dayment DAYMOND Dement Dimand DIMENT Dimmond DIMOND DYMENT DYMOND
Dibbell DEBELL DIBBLE DIBLEY
Dibben DIBDEN
DIBBLE 10 DEBELL Dibbell Dibblee Dibbley Dibel Dible DIBLEY Dibly Dybble
Dibblee DIBBLE DIBLEY
Dibbley DEBELL DIBBLE DIBLEY
DIBDEN 5 Dibben Dibdon Diffden Dirdin
Dibdon DIBDEN
Dibel DEBELL DIBBLE DIBLEY
Dible DEBELL DIBBLE DIBLEY
DIBLEY 9 DEBELL Dibbell DIBBLE Dibblee Dibbley Dibel Dible Dibly
Dibly DIBBLE DIBLEY
Diccon DEACON DICKENS DICKER DICKON DICKSON

If the name you are interested in is not here, try Section C.

DIXON
Dicconson DICKINSON
Dicisson DICKINSON
DICKENS 16 DEACON Decon Dekon Diccon DICKER Dicking DICKON DICKSON Diggen Dikkon Dikon DIXON Dyckon Dykon Dyxon
DICKENSON DICKINSON Dickison
DICKER 17 DEACON Decon Dekon Diccon DICKENS Dicking DICKON DICKSON Diggen Dikkon Dikon DIXON Docker Dyckon Dykon Dyxon
Dickerday BIGGADIKE
Dickerdyke BIGGADIKE
DICKERSON DICKINSON
DICKES DICKS DIX
Dicking DEACON DICKENS DICKER DICKON DICKSON DIXON
DICKINSON 9 Deconson Dicconson Dicisson DICKENSON DICKERSON Dickison Dikison Dixson
Dickison DICKENSON DICKINSON
DICKON 16 DEACON Decon Dekon Diccon DICKENS DICKER Dicking DICKSON Diggen Dikkon Dikon DIXON Dyckon Dykon Dyxon
DICKS DICKES DIX
DICKSON 17 DEACON Decon Dekon Diccon DICKENS DICKER Dicking DICKON Diggen Dikkon Dikon DIXON Dixson Dyckon Dykon Dyxon
Didicoat DELICATE
DIDLICK Didlock Didluck
Didlock DIDLICK
Didluck DIDLICK
Die DEY DYE
DIER DYER
Diffden DIBDEN
Difirjis DESFORGES
Digadag BIGGADIKE
Diggen DEACON DICKENS DICKER DICKON DICKSON DIXON
Diggerdyke BIGGADIKE
Diggery DIGGORY
DIGGORY Diggery
Dighton DEIGHTON
DIGNIN Deignen
DIKE DYKE
Dikison DICKINSON
Dikkon DEACON DICKENS DICKER DICKON DICKSON DIXON
Dikon DEACON DICKENS DICKER DICKON DICKSON DIXON
Dilleket DELICATE
Dillicate DELICATE
Dillicoat DELICATE
Dillnot DILNOT
Dillnott DILNOT
Dillnutt DILNOT DILNUTT
Dillsworth DILLWORTH DILWORTH
DILLWORTH 12 Delworth Dillsworth Dilsworth Dilsworthy Dilwart Dilwarth Dilwert Dilwerth Dilwort DILWORTH Dylworth
DILNOT 10 Delnot Dillnot Dillnott Dillnutt Dilnott DILNUTT Dylnet Dylnot Dylnott
Dilnott DILNOT DILNUTT
DILNUTT 8 Delnot Dillnutt DILNOT Dilnott Dylnet Dylnot Dylnott
Dilsworth DILLWORTH DILWORTH
Dilsworthy DILLWORTH DILWORTH
Dilwart DILLWORTH DILWORTH
Dilwarth DILLWORTH DILWORTH
Dilwert DILLWORTH DILWORTH
Dilwerth DILLWORTH DILWORTH
Dilwort DILLWORTH DILWORTH
DILWORTH 12 Delworth Dillsworth DILLWORTH Dilsworth Dilsworthy Dilwart Dilwarth Dilwert Dilwerth Dilwort Dylworth
Dimand DIAMOND DIMOND
DIMENT 10 DAYMAN Dayment DAYMOND Dement Demont DIAMOND DIMOND DYMENT DYMOND
Dimers DIMES
DIMES 5 Dimers Dimmes Dismes Dymes
Dimmes DIMES
DIMMOCK 4 DYMOCK Dymok DYMOKE
Dimmond DIAMOND DIMOND
DIMOND 12 DAYMAN Dayment DAYMOND Dement Demont DIAMOND Dimand DIMENT Dimmond DYMENT DYMOND
DINE DINES
DINES DINE
Dineson DENNISON
Dingate DENGATE DUNGATE
Dingel DINGLE DINGLEY
Dingell DINGLEY
DINGLE Dingel DINGLEY
DINGLEY 8 Dingel Dingell DINGLE Dingly Dinglye Dyngell Dyngle
Dingly DINGLEY
Dinglye DINGLEY
DINNING 4 Dening Deninge DENNING
Dinwiddie DINWOODIE
Dinwiddy DINWOODIE
Dinwood DINWOODIE
Dinwoodey DINWOODIE
DINWOODIE 11 Denwoodie Dinwiddie Dinwiddy Dinwood Dinwoodey Dinwoody Dunwiddie Dunwood Dunwoodie Dunwoody
Dinwoody DINWOODIE
Dinze DENZEY
Dinzey DENZEY
Dinzi DENZEY
Dinzy DENZEY
Dionysia DYSON
Dirdin DIBDEN
Disdal DISDELL
Disdale DISDELL
Disdall DISDELL
Disdel DISDELL
DISDELL 6 Disdal Disdale Disdall Disdel Disedale
Disedale DISDELL
Dismes DIMES
DISNEY 4 D'isigny D'isney Desney
Dison DYSON
DISS Disse Dysse
Disse DISS
Disun DYSON
Diton DEIGHTON
Dittmar DETTMER
Dittmer DETTMER
Ditton DEIGHTON
DIVAL 24 Davol Davole Davoll Davolle Devol Devole DEVOLL Devolle Divale Divall Divalle Divol Divole Divoll Divolle Dyval Dyvale Dyvall Dyvalle Dyvol Dyvole Dyvoll Dyvolle
Divale DEVOLL DIVAL
Divall DA VALL DEVOLL DIVAL
Divalle DEVOLL DIVAL
Divel DE VIELL DEAVILLE DUVALL
Divell DE VIELL DEAVILLE DUVALL
DIVERS Diverse
Diverse DIVERS
Divine DESVIGNES DEVINE
Divol DEVOLL DIVAL
Divole DEVOLL DIVAL
Divoll DEVOLL DIVAL
Divolle DEVOLL DIVAL
DIX DICKES DICKS
DIXON 17 DEACON Decon Dekon Diccon DICKENS DICKER Dicking DICKON DICKSON Diggen Dikkon Dikon Dixson Dyckon Dykon Dyxon
Dixson DICKINSON DICKSON DIXON
Doan DOANE DONE DONNE DUNN
DOANE 4 Doan DONE DONNE
Doary DORE DOREE DOREY
Dob CUFFE DUFF DUFFY KILDUFF
DOBBIE DOBIE
Dobble DOUBLE DUBLE
Dobell DOUBLE DUBLE
Dobey DALBY DOLBY
DOBIE DOBBIE
DOBNER Daubner
DOBSON 4 Dobston Dopson Dotson
Dobston DOBSON
DOCHERTY DOUGHERTY
Docker DICKER
DOCKERELL 4 Dockerill Dockrell Dockrill
Dockerill DOCKERELL
Dockrell DOCKERELL
Dockrill DOCKERELL
DOD DODD
DODD DOD
Doddicott DELICATE
Doddingsheles ODINGSELLS
DODDS Dods
DODGE 4 DADGE DOIDGE Doodge
DODGSON DODSON Dodsonne
Dods DODDS
DODSON DODGSON Dodsonne
Dodsonne DODGSON DODSON
DOE DOO Dooe
Dogerel DOGGRELL
Doggrel DOGGRELL
DOGGRELL 5 Dogerel Doggrel Dogrel Dogrell
Dogrel DOGGRELL
Dogrell DOGGRELL
DOIDGE DODGE Doodge
DOLAN 4 DOLIN Doolen Doolin
DOLBEAR Dolbeare
Dolbeare DOLBEAR
DOLBY 4 DALBY DAULBY Dobey
DOLEMAN 6 DOLMAN DOMAN Doulman DOWLMAN Dowman
Dolfin DOLPHIN
Dolgleish DALGLIESH DALGLISH
DOLIN 10 DOLAN Doling DOLLEN Dollin DOLLING Dollings Dollins Doolen Doolin
Doling DOLIN DOLLEN DOLLING
DOLLEN 7 DOLIN Doling Dollin DOLLING Dollings Dollins
Dolley DALLEY DALLY DOLLY
Dollin DOLIN DOLLEN DOLLING
DOLLING 7 DOLIN Doling DOLLEN Dollin Dollings Dollins
Dollings DOLIN DOLLEN DOLLING
Dollins DOLIN DOLLEN DOLLING
DOLLY 4 DALLEY DALLY Dolley
DOLMAN 6 DOLEMAN DOMAN Doulman DOWLMAN Dowman
DOLPHIN Dolfin
DOMAN 5 DOLEMAN DOLMAN Donan Dornan
DOMINI Dominii DOMINY
Dominii DOMINI DOMINY
DOMINY DOMINI Dominii
Don DONE DONNE DUN DUNNE
Donaghue DONOGHUE DONOHUE
Donahue DONOGHUE DONOHUE
Donan DOMAN
Doncalf DUNCALF
Doncklin DENKLEY DUNCKLEY DUNKLEY
DONE 9 Doan DOANE Don Donn DONNE DUN DUNN DUNNE
Donford DANFORD DUNFORD DURNFORD
Donforde DANFORD DUNFORD DURNFORD
DONISTHORPE Durandesthorpe
Donkley DENKLEY DUNCKLEY DUNKLEY
Donklin DENKLEY DUNCKLEY DUNKLEY
Donmawe DUNMO DUNMOW
Donmo DUNMO DUNMOW
Donmoe DUNMO DUNMOW
Donmow DUNMO DUNMOW
Donmowe DUNMO DUNMOW
Donn DONE DONNE DUN DUNNE
DONNE 8 Doan DOANE Don DONE Donn DUN DUNNE
Donning DUNHILL DUNNELL
DONOGHUE 5 Donaghue Donahue Donohoe DONOHUE
Donohoe DONOGHUE DONOHUE
DONOHUE 5 Donaghue Donahue DONOGHUE Donohoe
Donthon DUNTHORN DUNTHORNE DUNTON
DOO DOE Dooe
Doodge DODGE DOIDGE
Doodles DUDDLES
Dooe DOE DOO
Dooglas DOUGLAS
Dooglesh DOUGLAS
Dooglesse DOUGLAS
Doolen DOLAN DOLIN
Doolin DOLAN DOLIN
Dooray DORE DOREE DOREY
Doorbridge DURBRIDGE

If the name you are interested in is not here, try Section C.

Doorey DORE DOREE DOREY
Dopson DOBSON
DORE 10 Doary Dooray
Doorey DOREE DOREY
Dorrey Dorry Dory Doury
DOREE 10 Doary Dooray
Doorey DORE DOREY
Dorrey Dorry Dory Doury
Dorel DORRELL DORRILL
DOREY 10 Doary Dooray
Doorey DORE DOREE
Dorrey Dorry Dory Doury
Dorill DORRELL DORRILL
Dornan DOMAN
Dorneford DANFORD DUNFORD DURNFORD
Dorneforde DANFORD DUNFORD DURNFORD
Dornford DANFORD DUNFORD DURNFORD
Dornforde DANFORD DUNFORD DURNFORD
Dorrall DORRELL DORRILL
Dorrel DORRELL DORRILL
DORRELL 14 D'raoul Dairel Darell Darral Darrell Dayrell Dorel Dorill Dorrall Dorrel Dorril DORRILL Durrell
Dorrey DORE DOREE DOREY
Dorril DORRELL DORRILL
DORRILL 14 D'raoul Dairel Darell Darral Darrell Dayrell Dorel Dorill Dorrall Dorrel DORRELL Dorril Durrell
Dorry DORE DOREE DOREY
Dorsett DOSSET
Dorvold DARVALL
DORWARD Dorwood Durward
Dorwood DORWARD
Dory DORE DOREE DOREY
Dosser DOSSOR
DOSSET Dorsett
DOSSOR Dosser
DOTCHEN Dotchin
Dotchin DOTCHEN
Doten DOUGHTY
Dotson DOBSON
Doty DOUGHTY
DOUBLE 4 Dobble Dobell DUBLE
DOUBT 5 Doupt Dout Doute Dowt
DOUCE 6 DOUSE Dowce Dowes Dows DOWSE
Doudgen DOWDEN DOWDING
Doudin DOWDEN DOWDING
Dougat DUCKETT DUGGETT
DOUGHERTY DOCHERTY
DOUGHTY 8 Daughty Dawdy Doten Doty Doutty Dowty Duty
DOUGLAS 9 Dooglas Dooglesh Dooglesse Douglesh Douglis Dougliss Dowglles Duglas
Douglesh DOUGLAS
Douglis DOUGLAS
Dougliss DOUGLAS
Dougsmore DUGMORE
Doulman DOLEMAN DOLMAN DOWLMAN
Doupt DOUBT
Doury DORE DOREE DOREY
DOUSE 6 DOUCE Dowce Dowes Dows DOWSE
Dout DOUBT
Doute DOUBT
Doutty DOUGHTY
Doveton DUFTON
Dovnish DENNISH DEVENISH DEVONISH
DOW DOWE
Dowce DOUCE DOUSE DOWSE
DOWD O'dowd
Dowdall DOWDELL
DOWDELL Dowdall Dowdwll
DOWDEN 5 Doudgen Doudin Dowdin DOWDING
Dowdin DOWDEN DOWDING
DOWDING 5 Doudgen Doudin DOWDEN Dowdin
Dowdwll DOWDELL
DOWE DOW
Dowel DOWELL
DOWELL Dowel
Dowes DOUCE DOUSE DOWSE
Dowglles DOUGLAS
DOWLAN Dowland DOWLING
Dowland DOWLAN DOWLING
Dowlen DOWLING
Dowlin DOWLING
DOWLING 5 DOWLAN Dowland Dowlen Dowlin
DOWLMAN 5 DOLEMAN DOLMAN Doulman Dowman
Dowman DOLEMAN DOLMAN DOWLMAN
DOWNES DOWNS
DOWNEY DOWNIE
DOWNIE DOWNEY
DOWNS DOWNES
Dows DOUCE DOUSE DOWSE
DOWSE 6 DOUCE DOUSE Dowce Dowes Dows
Dowt DOUBT
Dowty DOUGHTY
Doyley DULLEY
Doylye DULLEY
Dracas DRACASS DRAKES
DRACASS 6 Dracas Dracus Drakas Drakehouse DRAKES
Dracopp DRACUP
Dracot DRAYCOTT
Dracote DRAYCOTT
Dracott DRAYCOTT
DRACUP Dracopp
Dracus DRACASS DRAKES
DRAITEN DRAYDEN DRAYTON
Drakas DRACASS DRAKES
Drakehouse DRACASS DRAKES
DRAKES 6 Dracas DRACASS Dracus Drakas Drakehouse
Draycot DRAYCOTT
Draycote DRAYCOTT
DRAYCOTT 6 Dracot Dracote Dracott Draycot Draycote
DRAYDEN DRAITEN DRAYTON
Drayhurst DRYHURST
DRAYTON DRAITEN DRAYDEN
Drelaud DRILLOT
Drellet DRILLOT
Drellett DRILLOT
DREW DREWE
DREWE DREW
DREWERY DREWRY DRURY
Drewes DREWS DRUCE
DREWETT 6 Drewit Drewith DREWITT Druet DRUETT
Drewit DREWETT DREWITT
Drewith DREWETT DREWITT
DREWITT 5 DREWETT Drewit Drewith Druet
DREWRY DREWERY DRURY
DREWS 5 Drewes Drewse DRUCE Druse
Drewse DREWS DRUCE
Drihurst DRYHURST
Drihurste DRYHURST
Drilliot DRILLOT
Drilliott DRILLOT
DRILLOT 6 Drelaud Drellet Drellett Drilliot Drilliott
DRISCOL DRISCOLL
DRISCOLL DRISCOL
Drisdale DRISDALL
DRISDALL Drisdale
Dritt TRITT
DRITTLER Trischler
DRUCE 5 Drewes DREWS Drewse Druse
Druet DREWETT DREWITT
DRUETT DREWETT
Drummey DRUMMY
DRUMMY Drummey
DRURY 4 DREWERY DREWRY Dury
Druse DREWS DRUCE
Drwyherst DRYHURST
Dryas DRYHURST
Dryasse DRYHURST
Dryerre DRYHURST
Dryers DRYHURST
Dryerst DRYHURST
Dryess DRYHURST
Dryherst DRYHURST
Dryhirst DRYHURST
Dryhirste DRYHURST
Dryhorst DRYHURST
Dryhouse DRYHURST
DRYHURST 17 Drayhurst Drihurst Drihurste Drwyherst Dryas Dryasse Dryerre Dryers Dryerst Dryess Dryherst Dryhirst Dryhirste Dryhorst Dryhouse Dryhurste
Dryhurste DRYHURST
Dubhdabhoireann DAVOREN
DUBLE 4 Dobble Dobell DOUBLE
Duccoths DUCKETT
DUCK Ducke
Duckat DUCKETT
Ducke DUCK
DUCKENFIELD Duckinfield
Ducket DUCKETT DUGGETT
DUCKETT 10 Dougat Duccoths Duckat Ducket DUCKIT Duckitt Duget Dugget DUGGETT
Duckinfield DUCKENFIELD
DUCKIT DUCKETT
Duckitt DUCKETT
DUDDLES Doodles Dudles
Duder DEWDER
Dudgen DUDGEON
DUDGEON Dudgen Dudgon
Dudgon DUDGEON
Dudles DUDDLES
DUFF 10 CUFFE Dob DUFFY KILDUFF Mcduff Mcduffey Mcilduff O'diff O'duffy
Duffen DUFFIN
DUFFIN Duffen
Duffton DUFTON
DUFFY 10 CUFFE Dob DUFF KILDUFF Mcduff Mcduffey Mcilduff O'diff O'duffy
Duftan DUFTON
DUFTON 4 Doveton Duffton Duftan
Dugand DUGARD
DUGARD Dugand
DUGDALE DUGDELL
DUGDELL DUGDALE
Duget DUCKETT DUGGETT
Dugget DUCKETT DUGGETT
DUGGETT 6 Dougat Ducket DUCKETT Duget Dugget
Duglas DOUGLAS
DUGMORE Dougsmore
Duhirst DEWHIRST DEWHURST
Dujarden DUJARDIN
DUJARDIN Dujarden
DUKES JUKES Juks
Dukeyne DAKEYNE DAKIN DAYKIN
Duley DULLEY
DULIEU Delieu Duliu
Duliu DULIEU
DULLEA Delay
Dullee DULLEY
Duller DULLOW
DULLEY 7 Doyley Doylye Duley Dullee Dyllie Dylly
DULLOW Dellow Duller
DUMBLETON DUMPLETON
DUMPLETON DUMBLETON
DUN 7 Don DONE Donn DONNE DUNN DUNNE
Dunc DUNK
DUNCALF 10 Doncalf Duncalfe Duncaph Duncaulf Dunceph Duncoff Duncroft Duncuff Duncuft
Duncalfe DUNCALF
DUNCAN Duncen
Duncaph DUNCALF
Duncaulf DUNCALF
Duncen DUNCAN
Dunceph DUNCALF
DUNCKLEY 8 DENKLEY Doncklin Donkley Donklin Dunckling DUNKLEY Dunkling
Dunckling DENKLEY DUNCKLEY DUNKLEY
Duncoff DUNCALF
Duncroft DUNCALF
Duncuff DUNCALF
Duncuft DUNCALF
Dunell DUNHILL DUNNELL DUNNILL DUNNING
DUNFORD 21 DANFORD Danforde Darneford Darneforde Darnford Darnforde Denford Denforde Derneford Derneforde Dernford Dernforde Donford Donforde Dorneford Dorneforde Dornford Dornforde Dunsford DURNFORD
DUNGATE 4 DENGATE Dingate Dungett
Dungett DENGATE DUNGATE
DUNHAM 4 DENHAM DENMAN Dunholm
DUNHILL 8 Donning Dunell Dunil Dunnel DUNNELL DUNNILL DUNNING
Dunholm DUNHAM
Dunil DUNHILL DUNNELL
DUNK 4 Dunc Dunke Durk
Dunke DUNK
DUNKERLEY DUNKLEY
DUNKLEY 9 DENKLEY Doncklin Donkley Donklin DUNCKLEY Dunckling DUNKERLEY Dunkling
Dunkling DENKLEY DUNCKLEY DUNKLEY
Dunmawe DUNMO DUNMORE DUNMOW
DUNMO 10 Donmawe Donmo Donmoe Donmow Donmowe Dunmawe Dunmoe DUNMOW Dunmowe
Dunmoe DUNMO DUNMOW
Dunmoore DUNMORE
DUNMORE 8 Dunmawe Dunmoore Dunmorr Dunnamore Dunnomore Dunsemore Dunsmore

If the name you are interested in is not here, try Section C.

Dunmorr DUNMORE
DUNMOW 10 Donmawe Donmo Donmoe Donmow Donmowe Dunmawe DUNMO Dunmoe Dunmowe
Dunmowe DUNMO DUNMOW
DUNN 5 Doan DONE DUN DUNNE
Dunnamore DUNMORE
DUNNE 7 Don DONE Donn DONNE DUN DUNN
Dunnel DUNHILL DUNNELL
DUNNELL 6 Donning Dunell DUNHILL Dunil Dunnel
Dunnicliff DUNNICLIFFE
DUNNICLIFFE Dunnicliff
DUNNILL 4 Dunell DUNHILL DUNNING
DUNNING 4 Dunell DUNHILL DUNNILL
Dunnomore DUNMORE
DUNSBEE DUNSBY
DUNSBY DUNSBEE
Dunsemore DUNMORE
Dunsford DANFORD DUNFORD DURNFORD
Dunsmore DUNMORE
DUNSTALL TUNSTALL
Dunthon DUNTHORN DUNTHORNE DUNTON
DUNTHORN 5 Donthon Dunthon DUNTHORNE DUNTON
DUNTHORNE 5 Donthon Dunthon DUNTHORN DUNTON
DUNTON 5 Donthon Dunthon DUNTHORN DUNTHORNE
Dunwiddie DINWOODIE
Dunwood DINWOODIE
Dunwoodie DINWOODIE
Dunwoody DINWOODIE
Dupe JUPE JUPP
Durandesthorpe DONISTHORPE
DURANT 4 Durent DURRANT Durrent
Durbidg DURBRIDGE
Durbidge DURBRIDGE
DURBRIDGE 5 Derbridge Doorbridge Durbidg Durbidge
DURCAN DURKIN
DURDALE Durdel Durdell
Durdel DURDALE
Durdell DURDALE
Durent DURANT DURRANT
Durk DUNK
DURKIN DURCAN
DURLING Dearling DERLING
DURNFORD 21 DANFORD Danforde Darneford Darneforde Darnford Darnforde Denford Denforde Derneford Derneforde Dernford Dernforde Donford Donforde Dorneford Dorneforde Dornford Dornforde DUNFORD Dunsford
Durocher HOUDE
Durrance DURRANS
Durrand DURRANT
Durrande DURRANT
DURRANS Durrance
DURRANT 7 Darrant DURANT Durent Durrand Durrande Durrent
Durrell DORRELL DORRILL
Durrent DURANT DURRANT
Durtnal DARTNELL
Durtnall DARTNELL
Durtnel DARTNELL
Durtnell DARTNELL
Durward DORWARD
Dury DRURY
Dussec DUSSEE
DUSSEE Dussec
Dutnail DARTNELL
Dutnal DARTNELL
Dutnale DARTNELL
Dutnall DARTNELL
Duty DOUGHTY
DUVALL 9 Davil De vial DEVIELL DEAVILLE Devile Deville Divel Divell
Dybble DIBBLE
Dyckon DEACON DICKENS DICKER DICKON DICKSON DIXON
DYE DEY Die
DYER DIER
DYKE DIKE
Dykon DEACON DICKENS DICKER DICKON DICKSON DIXON
Dyllie DULLEY
Dylly DULLEY
Dylnet DILNOT DILNUTT
Dylnot DILNOT DILNUTT
Dylnott DILNOT DILNUTT
Dylworth DILLWORTH DILWORTH
DYMENT 9 DAYMAN Dayment DAYMOND Dement DIAMOND DIMENT DIMOND DYMOND
Dymes DIMES
DYMOCK 4 DIMMOCK Dymok DYMOKE
Dymok DIMMOCK DYMOCK DYMOKE
DYMOKE 4 DIMMOCK DYMOCK Dymok
DYMOND 10 DAYMAN Dayment DAYMOND Dement Demont DIAMOND DIMENT DIMOND DYMENT
Dyngell DINGLEY
Dyngle DINGLEY
Dyotson DYSON
Dyrram DERHAM
Dyrrham DERHAM
DYSON 6 Dionysia Dison Disun Dyotson Dysone
Dysone DYSON
Dysse DISS
Dyton DEIGHTON
Dyval DEVOLL DIVAL
Dyvale DEVOLL DIVAL
Dyvall DEVOLL DIVAL
Dyvalle DEVOLL DIVAL
Dyvol DEVOLL DIVAL
Dyvole DEVOLL DIVAL
Dyvoll DEVOLL DIVAL
Dyvolle DEVOLL DIVAL
Dyxon DEACON DICKENS DICKER DICKON DICKSON DIXON
Eachewes EACHUS
Eachowes EACHUS
EACHUS 5 Eachewes Eachowes Etchewes Hatchous
EACOTT ACOTT EYCOTT
Eadall EDDOLLS EDDOLS
EADE 4 EADES EDE HEAD
EADEN EDEN
EADES 9 EADE Eads EDE Eedes Eeds HEAD Heeds YATES
Eads EADES
EADY ADEY
Eagan EGAN HAGAN HAGEN HEGAN HOGAN KEEGAN
Eagel EAGLE EAGLES
Eagele EAGLE EAGLES
Eagelle EAGLE EAGLES
Eagen EGAN KEEGAN
EAGERS Egars Eggars
Eagin EGAN HAGAN HAGEN HEGAN HOGAN KEEGAN
EAGLE 8 Eagel Eagele Eagelle EAGLES Egel Egle Egles
EAGLES 8 Eagel Eagele Eagelle EAGLE Egel Egle Egles
Eakings AIKEN EKINS HAWKINS OAKINS OKINS
Eakins AIKEN EKINS HAWKINS OAKINS OKINS
Eakons AIKEN EKINS HAWKINS OAKINS OKINS
Ealam ELAM ELLAM
EALES 16 Ailes Ails Ayels AYLES Eals EELES Eells EELS EYLES HALES HAYLES HILES Hyles ILES Yeeles
EALEY 33 Ealy Eele Eeley EELY Eieley Eile Eiley Eilley Elay Elea Elee ELEY Eleye Eli Elie ELLEY Ellie Elly ELY Elye Eyeley Eyely Eyle EYLEY Eyly Eylye HEELEY Heely Hele Heley Hely Iley
Eals EALES EELES EELS EYLES
Ealslie EELES ILLSLEY ILSLEY
Ealson ELSON
Ealy EALEY EELY ELEY ELLEY ELY EYLEY HEELEY
EAMES 6 Eams Eemes EMES HEAMES IMMS
Eams EAMES EMES HEAMES IMMS
EARDLEY Yearsley Yurdley
Eardy GARRAD GARRARD GARRAT GARRATT GARRETT GARROD GERARD GERRARD GERRETT JARRARD JARRATT JARRET JARRETT JARROLD JARVIS JERRARD JERRETT YARD
EARL EARLE
EARLAND Erland
EARLE EARL
EARLEY 4 EARLY Yearley Yearly
EARLY 4 EARLEY Yearley Yearly
EARP Erp
Earthroll ATHROLL
Earthrowl ATHROLL
EARWACKER 9 ARREQUER ARRIKER ARWAKER Arwicker EARWAKER EARWICKER EOFORWACER ERRICKER
EARWAKER 9 ARREQUER ARRIKER ARWAKER Arwicker EARWACKER EARWICKER EOFORWACER ERRICKER
EARWICKER 9 ARREQUER ARRIKER ARWAKER Arwicker EARWACKER EARWAKER EOFORWACER ERRICKER
EASEY 5 EASY HEASEY Heasie HEASY
Easlye EELES ILLSLEY ILSLEY
Easom ISOM
EAST 4 De l'est Est ESTE
Eastale EASTAUGH
EASTAUGH 18 Eastale Eastaw EASTER Easthaugh Eastho Easto Eastoe Eastoll Eastough Eastow Eastowe Eastugh Eatole Estaugh Estaughe Esto Estow
Eastaw EASTAUGH
EASTER EASTAUGH
EASTERLING Easterlinge
Easterlinge EASTERLING
EASTGATE Esgate ISGATE
Easthaugh EASTAUGH
Eastho EASTAUGH
EASTLAKE Estlake
Easto EASTAUGH
Eastoe EASTAUGH
Eastoll EASTAUGH
EASTON Eyston
Eastough EASTAUGH
Eastow EASTAUGH
Eastowe EASTAUGH
Eastugh EASTAUGH
EASY 5 EASEY HEASEY Heasie HEASY
Eatall EATWELL
Eatole EASTAUGH
EATON HEATON
EATWELL 4 Eatall Etwall Yetwale
EAVES Eves
Eayre AYRE AYRES EYRE HARE
Eb HEBB HIBBS
Ebb HEBB HIBBS
Ebbatt EBBOTT EBBUTT HIBBITT IBBOT
Ebbe HEBB HIBBS
Ebbert EBBOTT EBBUTT HIBBITT IBBOT
Ebbes HEBB HIBBS
Ebbet EBBOTT EBBUTT HIBBITT IBBOT
Ebbett EBBOTT
Ebbetts EBBOTT EBBUTT HIBBITT IBBOT
Ebbit EBBOTT EBBUTT HIBBITT IBBOT
Ebbitt EBBOTT EBBUTT HIBBITT IBBOT
Ebbot EBBOTT EBBUTT HIBBITT IBBOT
EBBOTT 28 Ebbatt Ebbert Ebbet Ebbett Ebbetts Ebbit Ebbitt Ebbot Ebbut EBBUTT Ebert Ebet Ebot Ebott Ebottes Ebytt Hibbit HIBBITT Hibbot Ibbet Ibbett Ibbitt IBBOT Ibbott Ibet Ibot Ibott
Ebbs HEBBES
Ebbut EBBOTT EBBUTT HIBBITT IBBOT
EBBUTT 26 Ebbatt Ebbert Ebbet Ebbetts Ebbit Ebbitt Ebbot EBBOTT Ebbut Ebert Ebet Ebott Ebottes Ebytt Hibbit HIBBITT Hibbot Ibbet Ibbett Ibbitt IBBOT Ibbott Ibet Ibot Ibott
Ebdale ABDALE
Ebert EBBOTT EBBUTT HIBBITT IBBOT
Ebet EBBOTT EBBUTT HIBBITT IBBOT
Ebot EBBOTT
Ebott EBBOTT EBBUTT HIBBITT IBBOT
Ebottes EBBOTT EBBUTT HIBBITT IBBOT
Ebus HEBB HIBBS
Ebytt EBBOTT EBBUTT HIBBITT IBBOT
ECCLES 5 Ekels Heckels HECKLES HICKLES
Eccleser ECCLESHALL

If the name you are interested in is not here, try Section C.

ECCLESHALL Eccleser Eckleshall
Eccling DE HICKELING HICKLIN HICKLING ICKELING
Echel HICKLES ICKEL ICKELING
Echelinog DE HICKELING HICKLIN HICKLING ICKELING
Eckersall ECKERSLEY
ECKERSLEY Eckersall
Eckleshall ECCLESHALL
Eckton ECTON
ECTON Eckton
Edbroke EDBROOK EDBROOKE
EDBROOK Edbroke EDBROOKE
EDBROOKE Edbroke EDBROOK
Eddells EDDOLLS EDDOLS
Eddels EDDOLLS EDDOLS
Edden EDEN EDENS
Eddens EDEN EDENS
Eddislaw EDGELAW
Eddisly EDGELAW
Eddlestone EDELSTON
Eddol EDDOLLS EDDOLS
EDDOLLS 14 Eadall Eddells Eddels Eddol EDDOLS Edels Edolls Edols Iddol Iddolls Iddols Idol Idols
EDDOLS 14 Eadall Eddells Eddels Eddol EDDOLLS Edels Edolls Edols Iddol Iddolls Iddols Idol Idols
Eddons EDEN EDENS
EDDY 8 ADDIS ADDY ADEY Adie ADY ADYE Edy
EDE 4 EADE EADES HEAD
Edels EDDOLLS EDDOLS
EDELSTON 4 Eddlestone Edleston Edlestone
EDEN 7 EADEN Edden Eddens Eddons EDENS Edon
EDENS 6 Edden Eddens Eddons EDEN Edon
Edgcock HEDGECOCK HISCOCK
Edgcocke HEDGECOCK HISCOCK
Edgcom EDGCOMBE EDGECOMBE
Edgcomb EDGCOMBE EDGECOMBE
EDGCOMBE 18 Edgcom Edgcomb Edgcum Edgcumb Edgcumbe Edgecomb EDGECOMBE Edgecome Edgecumb Edgecumbe Egcom Egcumbe Eggecom Eggecombe Eggecumbe Hedgecombe Hitchcombe
Edgcum EDGCOMBE EDGECOMBE
Edgcumb EDGCOMBE EDGECOMBE
Edgcumbe EDGCOMBE EDGECOMBE
Edgecock HEDGECOCK HISCOCK
Edgecocke HEDGECOCK HISCOCK
Edgecomb EDGCOMBE EDGECOMBE
EDGECOMBE 19 Edgcom Edgcomb EDGCOMBE Edgcum Edgcumb Edgcumbe Edgecomb Edgecome Edgecumb Edgecumbe Egcom Egcumbe Eggecom Eggecombe Eggecumbe Hedgecomb Hedgecombe Hitchcombe
Edgecome EDGCOMBE EDGECOMBE
Edgecumb EDGCOMBE EDGECOMBE
Edgecumbe EDGCOMBE EDGECOMBE
EDGELAR Edglar
EDGELAW 6 Eddislaw Eddisly Edglaw Edslaw Enslie
EDGELEY 6 Edgely Edgey EDGLEY Edgly Elgay
Edgely EDGELEY EDGLEY
EDGERTON 5 Egenton EGERTON Eggerton Eginton
Edges HEDGES HODGES
Edgey EDGELEY EDGLEY
EDGINGTON EDGINTON
EDGINTON EDGINGTON
Edglar EDGELAR
Edglaw EDGELAW
EDGLEY 6 EDGELEY Edgely Edgey Edgly Elgay
Edgly EDGELEY EDGLEY
Edleston EDELSTON
Edlestone EDELSTON
EDMISTON Edmonston
EDMOND 4 EDMONDS EDMUND EDMUNDS
EDMONDS 4 EDMOND EDMUND EDMUNDS
Edmons EDMUNDS
Edmonston EDMISTON
EDMUND 4 EDMOND EDMONDS EDMUNDS
EDMUNDS 5 EDMOND EDMONDS Edmons EDMUND
EDNAY EDNEY
EDNEY EDNAY
Edolls EDDOLLS EDDOLS
Edols EDDOLLS EDDOLS
Edon EDEN EDENS
Edrain ADRIAN
Edrup REDRUP
Edsar EDSER
Edsau EDSER
Edsaw EDSER
Edsawe EDSER
Edscer EDSER
EDSER 9 Edsar Edsau Edsaw Edsawe Edscer Edsir Edsor Edzcer
Edsir EDSER
Edslaw EDGELAW
Edsor EDSER
EDWARDS Edwoods
Edwoods EDWARDS
Edy EDDY
Edzcer EDSER
Eedes EADES
Eeds EADES YATES
Eelborn WHEELBAND WILBORN
Eele EALEY EELY ELEY ELLEY ELY EYLEY HEELEY
EELES 37 Ailes AYLES EALES Eals Ealslie Easlye Eells EELS Eesley Eesly Elesely Elesley Eleslye EYLES Hildesley Hildisley Hildsley HILES Hyles Iilsley Ildesley Ildslee Ildsley ILES Illesley ILLSLEY Illsly Ilseleye Ilselie Ilsey Ilslelye ILSLEY Ilsleye Ilslie Ilsly Yeeles
Eeley EALEY EELY ELEY ELLEY ELY EYLEY HEELEY
Eells EALES EELES EELS
EELS 6 EALES Eals EELES Eells EYLES
EELY 33 EALEY Ealy Eele Eeley Eieley Eile Eiley Eilley Elay Elea Elee ELEY Eleye Eli Elie
ELLEY Ellie Elly ELY Elye Eyeley Eyely Eyle EYLEY Eyly Eylye HEELEY Heely Hele Heley Hely Iley
Eemes EAMES EMES HEAMES IMMS
Eesley EELES ILLSLEY ILSLEY
Eesly EELES ILLSLEY ILSLEY
Effam ESSAM
Efsam ESSAM
EGAN 11 Eagan Eagen Eagin Egin Eighan KEEGAN Macaodhagain Macaogain Mcegan Mckeegan
Egars EAGERS
Egcom EDGCOMBE EDGECOMBE
Egcumbe EDGCOMBE EDGECOMBE
Egel EAGLE EAGLES
Egelton EGGLETON
Egenton EDGERTON EGERTON
EGERTON 5 EDGERTON Egenton Eggerton Eginton
Eggars EAGERS
Eggecom EDGCOMBE EDGECOMBE
Eggecombe EDGCOMBE EDGECOMBE
Eggecumbe EDGCOMBE EDGECOMBE
Eggelton EGGLETON
Eggerton EDGERTON EGERTON
Egges HEDGES HODGES
EGGLETON Egelton Eggelton
Egin EGAN KEEGAN
Eginton EDGERTON EGERTON
Egle EAGLE EAGLES
Egles EAGLE EAGLES
Eibbot HEBBERD HERBERT HIBBERT HUBBERT HUBERT
Eibert HEBBERD HERBERT HIBBERT HUBBERT HUBERT
Eieley EALEY EELY ELEY ELLEY ELY EYLEY HEELEY
Eighan EGAN KEEGAN
Eile EALEY EELY ELEY ELLEY ELY EYLEY HEELEY
Eiley EALEY EELY ELEY ELLEY ELY EYLEY HEELEY
Eilley EALEY EELY ELEY ELLEY ELY EYLEY HEELEY
Eirmonger IREMONGER IRONMONGER
Eirmunger IREMONGER IRONMONGER
Eit EITE EYTE
EITE 8 Eit Elte Eyde Eyt EYTE Eytt Eytte
Ekels ECCLES HECKLES HICKLES
Ekens AIKEN EKINS HAWKINS OAKINS OKINS
Ekings EKINS
EKINS 27 AIKEN Aikin Aken Akins Auchain Eakings Eakins Eakons Ekens Ekings Ekynes Ekyns Hackence Hackins Hakince Hakines Hakings Hakins HAWKINS Oaking OAKINS Okens OKINS Okyn Okyns Ouckins
Ekynes AIKEN EKINS HAWKINS OAKINS OKINS
Ekyns AIKEN EKINS HAWKINS OAKINS OKINS
ELAM 5 Ealam ELLAM Ellom Ellum
Elay EALEY EELY ELEY ELLEY ELY EYLEY HEELEY
Elbet ELLET ELLIOTT
ELBURN Elburne
Elburne ELBURN
ELCOAT 10 Ellcoat Hailcoat Hailcot Helcoat Hellcoat Hilcoat Hilcot Hilcote Hillcot
ELDEN 4 ALDEN ELDIN Eldon
ELDIN 4 ALDEN ELDEN Eldon
Eldon ALDEN ELDEN ELDIN
ELDRIDGE ALDRIDGE
Elea EALEY EELY ELEY ELLEY ELY EYLEY HEELEY
Elee EALEY EELY ELEY ELLEY ELY EYLEY HEELEY
ELEMES ELMES
Elesely EELES ILLSLEY ILSLEY
Elesley EELES ILLSLEY ILSLEY
Eleslye EELES ILLSLEY ILSLEY
Elesmore ELLSMORE
Elethorn ELLITHORN
ELEY 38 Aley EALEY Ealy Eele Eeley EELY Eieley Eile Eiley Eilley Elay Elea Elee Eleye Eli Elie ELLEY Ellie Elly ELY Elye Eyeley Eyely Eyle EYLEY Eyly Eylye HAILEY HALEY Haly HEALEY HEELEY Heely Hele Heley Hely Iley
Eleye EALEY EELY ELEY ELLEY ELY EYLEY HEELEY
Elfe YELF
ELFICK ELPHICK Elphicke
Elfleet ALFLATT ELFLETT
ELFLETT 5 Alefleet ALFLATT Elfleet Elflitt
Elflitt ALFLATT ELFLETT
Elgay EDGELEY EDGLEY
Eli EALEY EELY ELEY ELLEY ELY EYLEY HEELEY
Eliag ELIAZ
Eliaj ELIAZ
Eliay ELIAZ
ELIAZ 4 Eliag Eliaj Eliay
Elie EALEY EELY ELEY ELLEY ELY EYLEY HEELEY
Elingworth ELLINGWORTH ILLINGWORTH
ELIOT 11 ELIOTT Elliat Elliatt ELLIOT ELLIOTT Elliotte ELLOT Ellyot Helliot Helliott
ELIOTT 10 ELIOT Elliat Elliatt ELLIOT ELLIOTT ELLOT Ellyot Helliot Helliott
Elise ELLIS
Elithorn ELLITHORN
ELLA 11 Aella Aelle Ellah Ellar Ellay Elle Eller ELLEY Ellire Ellor
Ellah ELLA ELLEY
ELLAM 5 Ealam ELAM Ellom Ellum
Ellar ELLA ELLEY
Ellarby ELLERBY
Ellard HELLARD
Ellay ELLA ELLEY
Ellcoat ELCOAT
Elle ELLA ELLEY
Elleker ALLAKER
Eller ELLA ELLEY
Ellerbie ELLERBY
ELLERBY Ellarby Ellerbie
Ellerker ALLAKER
Ellesmore ELLSMORE
ELLET 4 Elbet ELLIOTT Illet

If the name you are interested in is not here, try Section C.

Ellethorn ELLITHORN
ELLEY 43 Aella Aelle
EALEY Ealy Eele Eeley
EELY Eieley Eile Eiley
Eilley Elay Elea Elee
ELEY Eleye Eli Elie
ELLA Ellah Ellar Ellay
Elle Eller Ellie Ellire
Ellor Elly ELY Elye
Eyeley Eyely Eyle EYLEY
Eyly Eylye HEELEY Heely
Hele Heley Hely Iley
Ellias ELLIOT ELLIS
Elliat ELIOT ELIOTT
ELLIOT ELLIOTT ELLOT
Elliatt ELIOT ELIOTT
ELLIOT ELLIOTT ELLOT
Ellice ELLIS
Ellie EALEY EELY ELEY
ELLEY ELY EYLEY HEELEY
Elliess ELLIS
ELLINGWORTH 6 Elingworth
Ellinworth Ilingworth
ILLINGWORTH Illinworth
Ellinworth ELLINGWORTH
ILLINGWORTH
ELLIOT 15 ALLOTT ELIOT
ELIOTT Ellias Elliat
Elliatt ELLIOTT
Elliotte ELLIS ELLOT
ELLOTT Ellyot Helliot
Helliott
ELLIOTT 16 Elbet ELIOT
ELIOTT ELLET Elliat
Elliatt ELLIOT Elliotte
ELLOT ELLOTT Ellyot
Elyett Helliot Helliott
Illet
Elliotte ELIOT ELLIOT
ELLIOTT
Ellire ELLA ELLEY
ELLIS 14 Allist Alliste
Allys Alys Elise Ellias
Ellice Elliess ELLIOT
Ellise Elliss Ellys
Hellis
Ellise ELLIS
Elliss ELLIS
ELLITHORN 6 Elethorn
Elithorn Ellethorn
Ellithorne Elythorn
Ellithorne ELLITHORN
Ellom ELAM ELLAM
Ellor ELLA ELLEY
ELLOT 11 ELIOT ELIOTT
Elliat Elliatt ELLIOT
ELLIOTT ELLOTT Ellyot
Helliot Helliott
ELLOTT 5 ALLOTT ELLIOT
ELLIOTT ELLOT
Ellsley ELSEY ELSLEY
ELLSMORE 4 Elesmore
Ellesmore Elsemore
Ellson ELSON
Ellston ELSON ELSTON
Ellstone ELSON ELSTON
Ellum ELAM ELLAM
ELLWELL ELWELL
Elly EALEY EELY ELEY
ELLEY ELY EYLEY HEELEY
Ellyot ELIOT ELIOTT
ELLIOT ELLIOTT ELLOT
Ellys ELLIS
Elmar AYLMER
Elmer AYLMER
ELMES ELEMES
ELPHICK ELFICK Elphicke
Elphicke ELFICK ELPHICK
Elphinston ELPHINSTONE
ELPHINSTONE Elphinston
ELSAM ELSOM
Elsams ELSOMS
Elsbury ALSBURY AYLESBURY
ELSEGOOD Elseygood
Elsigood
Elsemore ELLSMORE
ELSEY Ellsley ELSLEY
Elseygood ELSEGOOD
Elsigood ELSEGOOD
ELSLEY Ellsley ELSEY
ELSOM ELSAM
ELSOMS Elsams
ELSON 8 Ealson Ellson
Ellston Ellstone Elsone
ELSTON Elstone
Elsone ELSON ELSTON
ELSTON 6 Ellston Ellstone
ELSON Elsone Elstone
Elstone ELSON ELSTON
Elte EITE EYTE
Eltheridge ETHERIDGE
ELVE ELVEY ELVY
ELVEY 4 ALVEY ELVE ELVY
ELVIN Elwin
Elving ELWIG
ELVY 4 ALVEY ELVE ELVEY
ELWELL ELLWELL
ELWIG Elving Elwigg
Elwigg ELWIG
Elwin ELVIN
Elworlthie ELWORTHY
Elworthe ELWORTHY
ELWORTHY Elworlthie
Elworthe
ELY 38 Aley EALEY Ealy
Eele Eeley EELY Eieley
Eile Eiley Eilley Elay
Elea Elee ELEY Eleye
Eli Elie ELLEY Ellie
Elly Elye Eyeley Eyely
Eyle EYLEY Eyly Eylye
HAILEY HALEY Haly
HEALEY HEELEY Heely
Hele Heley Hely Iley
Elye EALEY EELY ELEY
ELLEY ELY EYLEY HEELEY
Elyett ELLIOTT
Elythorn ELLITHORN
Em EMM
Emans EMENS EMMANS EMMENS
HEMMING HEMMINGS
Emberry EMBERY EMBURY
EMBERY 8 Emberry EMBRIE
EMBRY Emburie EMBURY
EMERY IMBRIE
EMBRIE 5 EMBERY EMBRY
EMERY IMBRIE
EMBRY 6 EMBERY EMBRIE
EMBURY EMERY IMBRIE
Emburie EMBERY EMBURY
EMBURY 5 Emberry EMBERY
EMBRY Emburie
EMENS 14 Emans Eming
Emings EMMANS EMMENS
Emming Emmings Hemans
Hemens Heming Hemings
HEMMING HEMMINGS
Emerie EMERY
EMERSON EMMERSON
EMERY 15 Amery AMORY
EMBERY EMBRIE EMBRY
Emerie Emmery EMORY
Emrey Emry IMBRIE Imbry
IMRIE Imry
EMES 6 EAMES Eams Eemes
HEAMES IMMS
Emet EMMETT
Emets EMMETS
Emetts EMMETS
Eming EMENS EMMANS EMMENS
HEMMING HEMMINGS
Emings EMENS EMMANS
EMMENS HEMMING HEMMINGS
Emington HEMINGTON
Emit EMMETT
EMM 4 Em Emme EMMS
EMMANS 14 Emans EMENS
Eming Emings EMMENS
Emming Emmings Hemans
Hemens Heming Hemings
HEMMING HEMMINGS
Emme EMM
EMMENS 14 Emans EMENS
Eming Emings EMMANS
Emming Emmings Hemans
Hemens Heming Hemings
HEMMING HEMMINGS
EMMERSON EMERSON
Emmery EMERY EMORY IMRIE
Emmet EMMETT EMMOTT
EMMETS Emets Emetts
EMMETT 8 Emet Emit Emmet
Emmit Emmot EMMOTT Enit
Emming EMENS EMMANS
EMMENS HEMMING HEMMINGS
Emmings EMENS EMMANS
EMMENS HEMMING HEMMINGS
Emmington HEMINGTON
Emmit EMMETT
Emmot EMMETT EMMOTT
EMMOTT 4 Emmet EMMETT
Emmot
EMMS EMM
EMORY 4 EMERY Emmery Emry
Empey IMPEY
Empy IMPEY
Emrey EMERY
Emry EMERY EMORY
Emuss HEMUS
Endicote ANDICOT
Enefer ENEVER ENIFFER
ENNEVER
ENEVER 4 Enefer ENIFFER
ENNEVER
Enever-harvey
HARVEY-ENEVER
Enew ENNEW
Engel INGALL INGLE INGLES
Enger ENGERT
Engeram INGRAM
Engers ENGERT
ENGERT 4 Enger Engers
Engerth
Engerth ENGERT
ENGLAND Ingland
Englethorpe INGLETHORPE
Engoffe ANGOVE
Engove ANGOVE
Engrosse ANGOVE
ENIFFER 4 Enefer ENEVER
ENNEVER
Enit EMMETT
ENNEVER 4 Enefer ENEVER
ENIFFER
ENNEW Enew
ENNIS INNES
Ennislie AINSLIE
Ensign SINE
Enslie AINSLIE EDGELAW
Enston ENSTONE
ENSTONE 5 Enston Henston
Henstone INSTONE
ENTWISLE ENTWISTLE
ENTWISTLE ENTWISLE
EOFORWACER 9 ARREQUER
ARRIKER ARWAKER
Arwicker EARWACKER
EARWAKER EARWICKER
ERRICKER
Eplet EPLETT
EPLETT 5 Eplet Epplet
Epplett Eptlett
Epplet EPLETT
Epplett EPLETT
Eptlett EPLETT
ERBACH Erback
Erback ERBACH
Eritage HERITAGE
Erland EARLAND
Ermyn ARMIN
Ernald ARNALL ARNOLD
Erp EARP
ERREY Erry URRY
ERRICKER 9 ARREQUER
ARRIKER ARWAKER
Arwicker EARWACKER
EARWAKER EARWICKER
EOFORWACER
ERRINGTON Eryngton
Erry ERREY URRY
Ervine ERWIN IRVIN IRVINE
IRVING IRWIN
ERWIN 6 Ervine IRVIN
IRVINE IRVING IRWIN
Eryngton ERRINGTON
ESCRICK 8 ESCRICKE
Eskrett ESKRICK
Eskricke Eskrit Eskritt
Estrick
ESCRICKE 8 ESCRICK
Eskrett ESKRICK
Eskricke Eskrit Eskritt
Estrick
Esewyre ESSERY
Esgate EASTGATE ISGATE
Eshelbey ESHELBY EXELBY
Eshelbie ESHELBY EXELBY
ESHELBY 12 Ashelby
Eshelbey Eshelbie
Eshellby Eshlebie
Essebie Esselbie
Esselby EXELBY Exilbie
Exilby
Eshellby ESHELBY EXELBY
Eshlebie ESHELBY EXELBY
Eskrett ESCRICK ESCRICKE
ESKRICK
ESKRICK 8 ESCRICK
ESCRICKE Eskrett
Eskricke Eskrit Eskritt
Estrick
Eskricke ESCRICK ESCRICKE
ESKRICK
Eskrit ESCRICK ESCRICKE
ESKRICK
Eskritt ESCRICK ESCRICKE
ESKRICK
ESSAM Effam Efsam
Essary ESSERY
Esse AISHE ASHE
Essebie ESHELBY EXELBY
Esselbie ESHELBY EXELBY
Esselby ESHELBY EXELBY
Essell HASKELL HASWELL
HUSSELL HUZZELL OSWALD
RUSSELL URSELL UZZELL
ESSERY 7 Esewyre Essary
Essewyre Essiry Essory
Essury
Essewyre ESSERY
Essiry ESSERY
Essory ESSERY
Essury ESSERY
Est EAST ESTE
Estaugh EASTAUGH
Estaughe EASTAUGH
ESTE 4 De l'est EAST Est
Estlake EASTLAKE
Esto EASTAUGH
Estow EASTAUGH
Estrick ESCRICK ESCRICKE
ESKRICK
Etchewes EACHUS
Etcling DE HICKELING
HICKLIN HICKLING
ICKELING
ETHEREDGE 5 ETHERIDGE
Ethrige Etrich Etridge
Etheridg ETHERIDGE
ETHERIDGE 10 Eltheridge
ETHEREDGE Etheridg
Etherig Ethridge
Ethrige Etrich Etridge
Itheridge
Etherig ETHERIDGE
ETHERINGTON 6 EVERINGTON

If the name you are interested in is not here, try Section C.

Everinton EVERTON
Evrington HETHERINGTON
Ethridge ETHERIDGE
Ethrige ETHEREDGE ETHERIDGE
Etrich ETHEREDGE ETHERIDGE
Etridge ETHEREDGE ETHERIDGE
Etwall EATWELL
Euart EWART
Eudey EUDY
EUDY Eudey
Euington EVERINGTON EVINGTON
Eule EWELL HOOLE YOLE YOUELL YULE
Euren UREN
EUSTACE 7 EUSTICE Eustis Hewstice STACE STACEY Ustis
EUSTICE 7 EUSTACE Eustis Hewstice STACE STACEY Ustis
Eustis EUSTACE EUSTICE STACE STACEY
EVA 5 EVEA Ever Hyviu Yva
EVAN EVANS
EVANS EVAN EVINS
Evans-ambrey AMBREY
EVEA 5 EVA Ever Hyviu Yva
Eveington EVERINGTON EVINGTON
Evelegh EVELEIGH EVELY
EVELEIGH 5 Evelegh Eveley EVELY Everleigh
Eveley EVELEIGH EVELY
EVELY 4 Evelegh EVELEIGH Eveley
EVENDEN Everenden EVERNDEN
Eventon EVERINGTON EVINGTON
Ever EVA EVEA
EVERARD 5 EVERETT EVERITT Overard Overitt
Everenden EVENDEN EVERNDEN
EVERET 5 EVERETT Everit EVERITT Evert
EVERETT 9 EVERARD EVERET Everit EVERITT Everrit Evert Overard Overitt
EVERINGTON 11 ETHERINGTON Euington Eveington Eventon Everinton EVERTON EVINGTON Evinton Evrington Eyngton
Everinton ETHERINGTON EVERINGTON EVERTON
Everit EVERET EVERETT EVERITT
EVERITT 9 EVERARD EVERET EVERETT Everit Everrit Evert Overard Overitt
Everleigh EVELEIGH
EVERNDEN EVENDEN Everenden
Everrit EVERETT EVERITT
Evert EVERET EVERETT EVERITT
EVERTON 5 ETHERINGTON EVERINGTON Everinton Evrington
Eves EAVES
EVINGTON 8 Euington Eveington Eventon EVERINGTON Evinton Evrington Eyngton
EVINS EVANS
Evinton EVERINGTON EVINGTON
Evrington ETHERINGTON EVERINGTON EVERTON EVINGTON
EWART Euart
Ewel EWELL HOOLE YOLE YOUELL YULE
Eweles EWELL HOOLE YOLE YOUELL YULE
EWELL 90 Eule Ewel Eweles Ewels HOOLE Juel Jule Uhl Uhles Uiles Uoel Yeaull Yeel Yeell Yehl Yeil Yeill Yell Yeoale Yeouls Yeowell Yeuell Yeuille Yeul Yeules Yeull Yeulle Yewell Yewl Yoall Yoele Yoell Yol YOLE Yoll Yooil Yool Yooll Yoolo Yooly Youan Youel YOUELL Youels Youhill Youil Youile Youill Youille Youl Youle Youles Youlie Youll Youlla Youlle Youlley Youllie Youlo Youlow Youly Yowel Yowil Yowle Yual Yuall Yuel Yuell Yuelle Yuelo Yuial Yuie Yuiell Yuil Yuile Yuille Yuillie Yuills Yuir Yul YULE Yull Yulle Yullie Yullow Yuls Yuyll Ywill Zoule
Ewels EWELL HOOLE YOLE YOUELL YULE
EWEN EWENS EWIN
EWENS EWEN
EWIN EWEN
EWINGS 13 EWINS Hevens Hewen HEWENS Hewigns Hewing HEWINGS Hewons Howins Huings Huins YOUINGS
EWINS 13 EWINGS Hevens Hewen HEWENS Hewigns Hewing HEWINGS Hewons Howins Huings Huins YOUINGS
Exal EXALL EXCEL EXCELL
EXALL 4 Exal EXCEL EXCELL
EXCEL 10 Axcel Axcell Axel Axell Exal EXALL EXCELL Exel Exell
EXCELL 10 Axcel Axcell Axel Axell Exal EXALL EXCEL Exel Exell
Exel EXCEL EXCELL
EXELBY 12 Ashelby Eshelbey Eshelbie ESHELBY Eshellby Eshlebie Essebie Esselbie Esselby Exilbie Exilby
Exell EXCEL EXCELL
EXFORD Hecksford Hexford
Exilbie ESHELBY EXELBY
Exilby ESHELBY EXELBY
Exten AXTENCE
Extence AXTENCE
Extens AXTENCE
EYCOTT ACOTT EACOTT
Eyde EITE EYTE
Eyeley EALEY EELY ELEY ELLEY ELY EYLEY HEELEY
Eyely EALEY EELY ELEY ELLEY ELY EYLEY HEELEY
EYERS 4 AYERS AYRES EYRES
Eyle EALEY EELY ELEY ELLEY ELY EYLEY HEELEY
EYLES 13 Ailes AYLES EALES Eals EELES EELS HILES Hyles ILES ISLES IVES Yeeles
Eylett AYLETT ILETT ILOTT
EYLEY 33 EALEY Ealy Eele Eeley EELY Eieley Eile Eiley Eilley Elay Elea Elee ELEY Eleye Eli Elie ELLEY Ellie Elly ELY Elye Eyeley Eyely Eyle Eyly Eylye HEELEY Heely Hele Heley Hely Iley
Eyly EALEY EELY ELEY ELLEY ELY EYLEY HEELEY
Eylye EALEY EELY ELEY ELLEY ELY EYLEY HEELEY
Eyngton EVERINGTON EVINGTON
EYRE 8 AYERS AYRE AYRES Eayre EYRES Hair HARE
EYRES 5 AYERS AYRES EYERS EYRE
Eyrmonger IREMONGER IRONMONGER
Eyrmunger IREMONGER IRONMONGER
Eysteinn MACQUISTEN MCQUISTON
Eyston EASTON
Eyt EITE EYTE
EYTE 8 Eit EITE Elte Eyde Eyt Eytt Eytte
Eytt EITE EYTE
Eytte EITE EYTE
Ezzy HIZZY
Faber FABIAN FEBEN
FABIAN 8 Faber Fabyan Feban FEBEN Febin Pheban Pheben
Fabyan FABIAN
Faddes FIDDES
FAGAN Fagen Fagin
Fagen FAGAN
FAGG Fagge
Fagge FAGG
Fagin FAGAN
Faharty FAHERTY
FAHERTY 6 Faharty Fauarty Fauerty Feharty Feherty
FAIRALL 7 FAIRHALL VERRALL Verrell Verrells VERRILL Verrills
FAIRCHILD 15 Fairchilde Fairchilds Farchild Fayerchild Fayerchilde Fayrechchilde Fearchilde Ferchell Ferchild Ferchilde Varchild Verchell Verchild Verchilde
Fairchilde FAIRCHILD
Fairchilds FAIRCHILD
FAIRFAX Feerfox Foirefax
Fairfoul FAITHFUL FAITHFULL
Fairfoull FAITHFUL FAITHFULL
Fairfull FAITHFUL FAITHFULL
FAIRHALL 7 FAIRALL VERRALL Verrell Verrells VERRILL Verrills
Fairlamb FARLAM
FAIRLESS Frailes
Fairly FARLEIGH FARLEY FERLY
Fairnill FARNELL FARNOL
FAITHFUL 10 Fairfoul Fairfoull Fairfull FAITHFULL Fayrfowel Faythefull Faythfule Faythfull Ffaithfull
FAITHFULL 10 Fairfoul Fairfoull Fairfull FAITHFUL Fayrfowel Faythefull Faythfule Faythfull Ffaithfull
Fake FEAKES
Fakes FEAKES
Fala FALLA
Falbrick FULBROOK FULLBRICK PHILBRICK
Falbrook FULBROOK FULLBRICK PHILBRICK
FALCONER FAULKNER Fawkener
FALKNER FAULKNER
FALLA 7 Fala Fallah FALLAS Fallaw Fallow FELLOWS
Fallah FALLA FALLAS FELLOWS
FALLAS 4 FALLA Fallah FELLOWS
Fallaw FALLA
Fallbrick FULBROOK FULLBRICK PHILBRICK
Fallow FALLA FELLOW
FALLOWS FELLOWS Ffallowes
Faltham FELTHAM FELTON
Fancho PHANCO
Fanco PHANCO
Fanker PHANCO
Fanko PHANCO
Fanston FANSTONE VANSTONE
FANSTONE 5 Fanston Fanstonne Vanston VANSTONE
Fanstonne FANSTONE VANSTONE
Fantam FANTHAM FANTOM
FANTHAM 5 Fantam Fanthom FANTOM Fentham
Fanthom FANTHAM FANTOM
FANTOM 5 Fantam FANTHAM Fanthom Fentham
FAR 5 FARR Farre Ffar Ffarre
Farage FERRIDGE
Faranden FARRINGTON
Farchild FAIRCHILD
Fardel FARDELL
FARDELL Fardel Fardle
Farden FARTHING
Fardle FARDELL
FARENDEN Farnden Farrenden
Farendon FARRINGTON
Farindon FARRINGTON
FARLAM Fairlamb
Farle FARLEIGH FARLEY FERLY
FARLEIGH 7 Fairly Farle FARLEY Farlie Farly FERLY
FARLEY 9 Fairly Farle FARLEIGH Farlie Farly Farrally Fearley FERLY
Farlie FARLEIGH FARLEY FERLY
Farly FARLEIGH FARLEY FERLY
FARMARY FARMERY
FARMER 4 Farmor Fermer FERMOR
Farmerie FARMERY
FARMERY FARMARY Farmerie
Farmor FARMER FERMOR
FARNAGH 6 FARNARTH FARNATH FARNETH FARNORTH FARNOTH
Farnal FARNELL FARNOL
Farnall FARNELL FARNOL
Farnan FARNON
FARNARTH 6 FARNAGH FARNATH FARNETH FARNORTH FARNOTH
FARNATH 6 FARNAGH FARNARTH FARNETH

If the name you are interested in is not here, try Section C.

FARNORTH FARNOTH
Farnden FARENDEN FARRINGTON
Farnehill FARNELL FARNOL FURNELL
FARNELL 11 Fairnill Farnal Farnall Farnehill Farnhill Farnill FARNOL Farnoll Fernell FURNELL
FARNETH 6 FARNAGH FARNARTH FARNATH FARNORTH FARNOTH
Farnhill FARNELL FARNOL FURNELL
Farnill FARNELL FARNOL
Farnin FARNON
FARNOL 11 Fairnill Farnal Farnall Farnehill FARNELL Farnhill Farnill Farnoll Fernell FURNELL
Farnoll FARNELL FARNOL
FARNON Farnan Farnin
FARNORTH 6 FARNAGH FARNARTH FARNATH FARNETH FARNOTH
FARNOTH 6 FARNAGH FARNARTH FARNATH FARNETH FARNORTH
FARR 5 FAR Farre Ffar Ffarre
Farra FARRAR FARRER FERRAR
Farrage FERRIDGE
Farrah FARRAR FARRER FERRAR
Farrally FARLEY
FARRANCE 4 FARRANTS Farrents Pharrance
FARRANT 5 FARRAT FARRENT TARRANT TARRAT
FARRANTS 4 FARRANCE Farrents Pharrance
FARRAR 6 Farra Farrah FARRER FERRAR Ferrer
FARRAT 4 FARRANT TARRANT TARRAT
Farre FAR FARR
Farrenden FARENDEN FARRINGTON
FARRENT FARRANT
Farrents FARRANCE FARRANTS
FARRER 6 Farra Farrah FARRAR FERRAR Ferrer
Farrett FERRETT
Farrige FERRIDGE
Farringdon FARRINGTON
FARRINGTON 7 Faranden Farendon Farindon Farnden Farrenden Farringdon
FARRO FARROW
FARROW 4 FARRO PHAROAH PHARROW
Farthers FATHERS
FARTHING 4 Farden Farthinge Farthings
Farthinge FARTHING
Farthings FARTHING
Fashion FAZAN
Fately FAUTLEY
FATHERS Farthers
Fatherston FEATHERSTONE FETHERSTON HORNSEY NESFIELD
Fatherstone FEATHERSTONE FETHERSTON HORNSEY NESFIELD
Fatterstone FEATHERSTONE FETHERSTON HORNSEY NESFIELD
Fauarty FAHERTY
Faucit FAWCETT
Faudington FAWDINGTON
Fauerty FAHERTY
Faughteley FAUTLEY
Faulkes FAULKS FAWKES
Faulkingham FOLKINGHAM
FAULKNER 4 FALCONER FALKNER Fawkener
FAULKS Faulkes FAWKES
Faulty FAUTLEY
Fausbrook FOSBROKE FOSBROOK
Fausbrooke FOSBROKE FOSBROOK
Fausch FOCH
Faustbrook FOSBROKE FOSBROOK
Faustbrooke FOSBROKE FOSBROOK
Fauteley FAUTLEY
FAUTLEY 9 Fately Faughteley Faulty Fauteley Fautleys Fautly Fawtely Fortley
Fautleys FAUTLEY
Fautly FAUTLEY
Fauvaque FOVARGUE
Fauvargue FOVARGUE
FAUX FAWLK
Favel FLAVELL
FAVELL FLAVELL
Faviour FEAVIOUR FEVYER
Favour FEAVIOUR FEVYER
FAWCETT Faucit Fawcitt
Fawcitt FAWCETT
FAWDINGTON Faudington
Fawkener FALCONER FAULKNER
FAWKES Faulkes FAULKS
FAWLK FAUX
Fawtely FAUTLEY
Fayerchild FAIRCHILD
Fayerchilde FAIRCHILD
Fayrechchilde FAIRCHILD
Fayrfowel FAITHFUL FAITHFULL
Faythefull FAITHFUL FAITHFULL
Faythfule FAITHFUL FAITHFULL
Faythfull FAITHFUL FAITHFULL
FAZAN 4 Fashion Frassan Frazan
Feak FEAKES
Feake FEAKES
FEAKES 12 Fake Fakes Feak Feake Feaks Feek Ffoks FOAKES Fokes Foks Folkes
Feaks FEAKES
Fearchilde FAIRCHILD
Fearley FARLEY
FEARN 4 FEARNS FERN Ferns
Fearncombe VEARNCOMBE
FEARNS 4 FEARN FERN Ferns
FEAST FEIST Fiest
Featherston FEATHERSTONE FETHERSTON HORNSEY NESFIELD
FEATHERSTONE 17 Fatherston Fatherstone Fatterstone Featherston FETHERSTON Fetherstone Hornee Hornesey Hornsay Hornsaye Hornsea HORNSEY Hornsie Hornsy NESFIELD Tetherston
Feaveriere FEAVIOUR FEVYER
Feaveryear FEAVIOUR FEVYER
Feavier FEAVIOUR FEVYER
FEAVIOUR 11 Faviour Favour Feaveriere Feaveryear Feavier Feavour Feavyer Feavyour Fevier FEVYER
Feavour FEAVIOUR FEVYER
Feavyer FEAVIOUR FEVYER
Feavyour FEAVIOUR FEVYER
Feban FABIAN FEBEN
FEBEN 5 Faber FABIAN Feban Febin
Febin FABIAN FEBEN
Feddis FIDDES
Feedes FIDDES
Feek FEAKES
Feerfox FAIRFAX
Feese FICE FISE FITZ VICE
Feharty FAHERTY
Feherty FAHERTY
Feilder FIELDER
FEIST FEAST Fiest
Fel FELL
Felingham FELLINGHAM FELMINGHAM
Felipot PHILLPOTTS PHILPOT PHILPOTT PHILPOTTS
Feliskirke PHILLISKIRK
Felixkirke PHILLISKIRK
FELL 4 Fel FELLS Ffel
Fellender FELLINDER VALENDER
FELLINDER 6 Fellender Valendar VALENDER Velender Vellender
FELLINGHAM Felingham FELMINGHAM
Felloe FELLOW
FELLOW Fallow Felloe
FELLOWES FELLOWS
FELLOWS 7 FALLA Fallah FALLAS FALLOWS FELLOWES Ffallowes
FELLS FELL
FELMINGHAM Felingham FELLINGHAM
Felpot PHILLPOTTS PHILPOT PHILPOTT PHILPOTTS
Felps PHELPS
Feltam FELTHAM FELTON
FELTHAM 5 Faltham Feltam FELTON Veltam
Felthorpe FOLTHORPE
FELTON 5 Faltham Feltam FELTHAM Veltam
Felypot PHILLPOTTS PHILPOT PHILPOTT PHILPOTTS
Felyxkyrk PHILLISKIRK
Fen FENN FENNE
Fenamor FENNIMORE FILMER FINMORE FINNEMORE PHILLIMORE VENNIMORE
Fenemer FENNIMORE FILMER FINMORE FINNEMORE PHILLIMORE VENNIMORE
Fenemore FENNIMORE FILMER FINMORE FINNEMORE PHILLIMORE VENNIMORE
Fenimore FENNIMORE FILMER FINMORE FINNEMORE PHILLIMORE VENNIMORE
Fenmer FENNIMORE FILMER FINMORE FINNEMORE PHILLIMORE VENNIMORE
Fenmere FENNIMORE FILMER FINMORE FINNEMORE PHILLIMORE VENNIMORE
FENN Fen FENNE
FENNA 4 FENNAH PHENNA PHENNAH
FENNAH 4 FENNA PHENNA PHENNAH
Fennall FENNEL FUNNELL
Fennamore FENNIMORE FILMER FINMORE FINNEMORE PHILLIMORE VENNIMORE
FENNE Fen FENN
FENNEL 6 Fennall Fennil FUNNELL Vennal Vinell
Fennemore FENNIMORE FILMER FINMORE FINNEMORE PHILLIMORE VENNIMORE
Fennesey FINNESEY
Fenneymore FENNIMORE FILMER FINMORE FINNEMORE PHILLIMORE VENNIMORE
Fennick FENWICK
Fennil FENNEL FUNNELL
FENNIMORE 58 Bennimore Fenamor Fenemer Fenemore Fenimore Fenmer Fenmere Fennamore Fennemore Fenneymore Fennymore Fiddimore Fillmore FILMER Filmore Finamer Finamoore Finamore Finemer Finemere Finemor Finemore Finimor Finmer Finmere FINMORE Finnamoor Finnamoore Finnamore FINNEMORE Finneymoore Finneymore Finnymoor Finnymore Finymore Fynmer Fynnamore Fynnemore Fynneymoore Fynneymore Fynnimore Fynnymore Philimore PHILLIMORE Philmore Phinamor Phinamore Phinnamore Phinnemore Phinnmore Phynemore Phynnamore Phynnemore Phynneymore Phynnimore Phynnymore VENNIMORE
FENNING Fenwich FINNING
Fennymore FENNIMORE FILMER FINMORE FINNEMORE PHILLIMORE VENNIMORE
Fenteman FENTIMAN VENTERMAN
Fenterman FENTIMAN VENTERMAN
Fentham FANTHAM FANTOM
FENTIMAN 7 Fenteman Fenterman Fentoman Fentyman VENTERMAN Ventyman
Fentoman FENTIMAN VENTERMAN
Fentyman FENTIMAN VENTERMAN
Fenwich FENNING FINNING
FENWICK Fennick
Ferchell FAIRCHILD
Ferchild FAIRCHILD
Ferchilde FAIRCHILD
Ferdinand FERDINANDO
FERDINANDO Ferdinand Fernando
Feret FERRETT
Fergis DESFORGES
FERGUSON FERGUSSON
FERGUSSON FERGUSON
Ferige FERRIDGE
Ferit FERRETT
FERLY 7 Fairly Farle FARLEIGH FARLEY Farlie Farly
Fermer FARMER
FERMOR FARMER Farmor
FERN 4 FEARN FEARNS Ferns
Fernando FERDINANDO

If the name you are interested in is not here, try Section C.

Ferncombe VEARNCOMBE
FERNEE 5 Ferney Ferny Furney Furny
Fernell FARNELL FARNOL FURNELL
Ferney FERNEE
Ferns FEARN FEARNS FERN
Ferny FERNEE
Ferral FIRRELL VERRAL
FERRAR 6 Farra Farrah FARRAR FARRER Ferrer
Ferrer FARRAR FARRER FERRAR
FERRERS De ferrers De ferrieres
FERRETT 5 Farrett Feret Ferit Firit
Ferrian FURRIAN
FERRIDGE 6 Farage Farrage Farrige Ferige Ferrige
Ferrige FERRIDGE
Ferrul FIRRELL VERRAL
Fetford THETFORD TITFORD
FETHERSTON 17 Fatherston Fatherstone Fatterstone Featherston FEATHERSTONE Fetherstone Hornee Hornesey Hornsay Hornsaye Hornsea HORNSEY Hornsie Hornsy NESFIELD Tetherston
Fetherstone FEATHERSTONE FETHERSTON HORNSEY NESFIELD
Fettice FIDDES
Fettis FIDDES
Fettous FIDDES
Feuell FEWEL FUELL
Fevier FEAVIOUR FEVYER
Fevyear FEVYER
FEVYER 12 Faviour Favour Feaveriere Feaveryear Feavier FEAVIOUR Feavour Feavyer Feavyour Fevier Fevyear
FEWEL 5 Feuell Fewell Fuel FUELL
Fewell FEWEL FUELL
FEWKES 4 Fowks FUKES Furkes
Ffaithfull FAITHFUL FAITHFULL
Ffallowes FALLOWS FELLOWS
Ffar FAR FARR
Ffarre FAR FARR
Ffel FELL
FFIDOE Fidoe
Ffillopott PHILLPOTTS PHILPOT PHILPOTT PHILPOTTS
Ffillpot PHILLPOTTS PHILPOT PHILPOTT PHILPOTTS
Ffilpot PHILLPOTTS PHILPOT PHILPOTT PHILPOTTS
Ffilpott PHILLPOTTS PHILPOT PHILPOTT PHILPOTTS
Ffoks FEAKES FOAKES
Fforian FORRYAN
FFOULKES 4 Ffoulks FOULKES Foulks
Ffoulks FFOULKES FOULKES
Ffowell FOWELL
Ffranceys FRANCIS
Ffray FRY FRYE
Ffrude FROOD FROUD FROUDE
Ffulk FULKE
Ffulke FULKE
FIANDER Fyander Phyander
FICE 10 Feese Fis FISE Fits FITZ Fitze Fyz VICE Vise
Fichaw FITCHEW FITZHUGH
Ficher FISHER
Fichew FITCHEW FITZHUGH
FICKLIN FICKLING
FICKLING FICKLIN
FIDDES 11 Faddes Feddis Feedes Fettice Fettis Fettous Fiddies Fiddis Fieldes Fittis
Fiddies FIDDES
Fiddimore FENNIMORE FILMER FINMORE FINNEMORE PHILLIMORE VENNIMORE
Fiddis FIDDES
Fidgeon FITZJOHN
Fidoe FFIDOE
FIELD 4 Fieldes FIELDS Fyelde
FIELDER Feilder
Fieldes FIDDES FIELD FIELDS
FIELDS FIELD Fieldes
FIELDSON Fieldston Fieldstone
Fieldston FIELDSON
Fieldstone FIELDSON
FIENNES FINES
Fiest FEAST FEIST
FIFE FYFE
Fifed FIFET
FIFET 8 Fifed Fiffed Fiffet Fiffird Fiffoot Fifird Fifoot
Fiffed FIFET
Fiffet FIFET
Fiffird FIFET
Fiffoot FIFET
Fifird FIFET
Fifoot FIFET
FILBRICK PHILBRICK
Filday VILDAY
FILDES 4 FILES Fyldes FYLES
Filepot PHILLPOTTS PHILPOT PHILPOTT PHILPOTTS
FILES 4 FILDES Fyldes FYLES
FILEWOOD Fillwood Fylewood
Filiskirk PHILLISKIRK
Filiskyrke PHILLISKIRK
FILLARY Philery
Fillepotte PHILLPOTTS PHILPOT PHILPOTT PHILPOTTS
Filliskirke PHILLISKIRK
Fillmore FENNIMORE FILMER FINMORE FINNEMORE PHILLIMORE VENNIMORE
Fillpot PHILLPOTTS PHILPOT PHILPOTT PHILPOTTS
Fillpott PHILLPOTTS PHILPOT PHILPOTT PHILPOTTS
Fillpotte PHILLPOTTS PHILPOT PHILPOTT PHILPOTTS
Fillwood FILEWOOD
FILMER 58 Bennimore Fenamor Fenemer Fenemore Fenimore Fenmer Fenmere Fennamore Fennemore Fenneymore FENNIMORE Fennymore Fiddimore Fillmore Filmore Finamer Finamoore Finamore Finemer Finemere Finemor Finemore Finimor Finmer Finmere FINMORE Finnamoor Finnamoore Finnamore FINNEMORE Finneymoore Finneymore Finnymoor Finnymore Finymore Fynmer Fynnamore Fynnemore Fynneymoore Fynneymore Fynnimore Fynnymore Philimore PHILLIMORE Philmore Phinamor Phinamore Phinnamore Phinnemore Phinnmore Phynemore Phynnamore Phynnemore Phynneymore Phynnimore Phynnymore VENNIMORE
Filmore FENNIMORE FILMER FINMORE FINNEMORE PHILLIMORE VENNIMORE
Filp PHELPS PHILIPS PHILLIPS PHILP
Filpot PHILPOT PHILPOTT
Filpott PHILLPOTTS PHILPOT PHILPOTT PHILPOTTS
Filson PHILSON
Finamer FENNIMORE FILMER FINMORE FINNEMORE PHILLIMORE VENNIMORE
Finamoore FENNIMORE FILMER FINMORE FINNEMORE PHILLIMORE VENNIMORE
Finamore FENNIMORE FILMER FINMORE FINNEMORE PHILLIMORE VENNIMORE
FINCH 4 Finche Fink Fynche
Finche FINCH
Findal FINDON
Findall FINDON
Findalls FINDON
Findan FINDON
Finday FINDLAY FINLAY FINLEY
Findel FINDON
Findell FINDON
Finden FINDON
Findern FINDON
Finderne FINDON
FINDLAY 4 Finday FINLAY FINLEY
Findle FINDON
FINDON 12 Findal Findall Findalls Findan Findel Findell Finden Findern Finderne Findle Fyndorne
FINEGAN 4 Finigan FINNEGAN FINNIGAN
Finemer FENNIMORE FILMER FINMORE FINNEMORE PHILLIMORE VENNIMORE
Finemere FENNIMORE FILMER FINMORE FINNEMORE PHILLIMORE VENNIMORE
Finemor FENNIMORE FILMER FINMORE FINNEMORE PHILLIMORE VENNIMORE
Finemore FENNIMORE FILMER FINMORE FINNEMORE PHILLIMORE VENNIMORE
FINES FIENNES
Finigan FINEGAN FINNIGAN
Finimor FENNIMORE FILMER FINMORE FINNEMORE PHILLIMORE VENNIMORE
Fink FINCH
FINLAY 4 Finday FINDLAY FINLEY
FINLEY 4 Finday FINDLAY FINLAY
Finmer FENNIMORE FILMER FINMORE FINNEMORE PHILLIMORE VENNIMORE
Finmere FENNIMORE FILMER FINMORE FINNEMORE PHILLIMORE VENNIMORE
FINMORE 59 Bennimore Fenamor Fenemer Fenemore Fenimore Fenmer Fenmere Fennamore Fennemore Fenneymore FENNIMORE Fennymore Fiddimore Fillmore FILMER Filmore Finamer Finamoore Finamore Finemer Finemere Finemor Finemore Finimor Finmer Finmere Finnamoor Finnamoore Finnamore FINNEMORE Finneymoore Finneymore Finnymoor Finnymore Finymore Fynmer Fynmore Fynnamore Fynnemore Fynneymoore Fynneymore Fynnimore Fynnymore Philimore PHILLIMORE Philmore Phinamor Phinamore Phinnamore Phinnemore Phinnmore Phynemore Phynnamore Phynnemore Phynneymore Phynnimore Phynnymore VENNIMORE
Finnamoor FENNIMORE FILMER FINMORE FINNEMORE PHILLIMORE VENNIMORE
Finnamoore FENNIMORE FILMER FINMORE FINNEMORE PHILLIMORE VENNIMORE
Finnamore FENNIMORE FILMER FINMORE FINNEMORE PHILLIMORE VENNIMORE
FINNEGAN FINEGAN
FINNEMORE 58 Bennimore Fenamor Fenemer Fenemore Fenimore Fenmer Fenmere Fennamore Fennemore Fenneymore FENNIMORE Fennymore Fiddimore Fillmore FILMER Filmore Finamer Finamoore Finamore Finemer Finemere Finemor Finemore Finimor Finmer Finmere FINMORE Finnamoor Finnamoore Finnamore Finneymoore Finneymore Finnymoor Finnymore Finymore Fynmer Fynnamore Fynnemore Fynneymoore Fynneymore Fynnimore Fynnymore Philimore PHILLIMORE Philmore Phinamor Phinamore Phinnamore Phinnemore Phinnmore Phynemore Phynnamore Phynnemore Phynneymore Phynnimore Phynnymore VENNIMORE
FINNESEY 4 Fennesey Finnessy Finnissy
Finnessy FINNESEY
Finneymoore FENNIMORE FILMER FINMORE FINNEMORE PHILLIMORE VENNIMORE
Finneymore FENNIMORE FILMER FINMORE

If the name you are interested in is not here, try Section C.

FINNEMORE PHILLIMORE VENNIMORE
FINNIGAN FINEGAN Finigan
FINNING FENNING Fenwich
Finnissy FINNESEY
Finnymoor FENNIMORE FILMER FINMORE FINNEMORE PHILLIMORE VENNIMORE
Finnymore FENNIMORE FILMER FINMORE FINNEMORE PHILLIMORE VENNIMORE
Finymore FENNIMORE FILMER FINMORE FINNEMORE PHILLIMORE VENNIMORE
Firit FERRETT
FIRRELL 5 Ferral Ferrul Furrel VERRAL
Firrs FURSE FURZE
Firs FURSE FURZE
FIRTH Firthe FYRTH
Firthe FIRTH FYRTH
Fis FICE FISE FITZ VICE
Fischer FISHER
FISE 10 Feese FICE Fis Fits FITZ Fitze Fyz VICE Vise
FISH FISK FISKE
Fishaw FITCHEW FITZHUGH
Fishbone FISHBOURNE
FISHBOURNE Fishbone Fishburne
Fishburne FISHBOURNE
FISHENDEN Fishington FISSENDEN
FISHER Ficher Fischer
Fishew FITCHEW FITZHUGH
Fishington FISHENDEN FISSENDEN
FISHLOCK Vishlake
Fishugh FITCHEW FITZHUGH
FISK 7 FISH FISKE Fisks Fysck Fysk Fyske
FISKE 7 FISH FISK Fisks Fysck Fysk Fyske
Fisks FISK FISKE
FISON FYSON
FISSENDEN FISHENDEN Fishington
FITCHET FITCHETT
FITCHETT FITCHET
FITCHEW 7 Fichaw Fichew Fishaw Fishew Fishugh FITZHUGH
FITNESS 7 Fitnesse Fitnis Fittness Fytnes Fytnesse Fyttness
Fitnesse FITNESS
Fitnis FITNESS
Fits FICE FISE FITZ VICE
Fittis FIDDES
Fittness FITNESS
FITZ 10 Feese FICE Fis FISE Fits Fitze Fyz VICE Vise
Fitze FICE FISE FITZ VICE
FITZELL 4 Fizzel Fizzell Phizell
FITZHUGH 7 Fichaw Fichew Fishaw Fishew Fishugh FITCHEW
FITZJOHN Fidgeon Fugion
Fiveash VIVASH
Fizzel FITZELL
Fizzell FITZELL
FLANDERS FLINDERS
Flavel FLAVELL
FLAVELL 4 Favel FAVELL Flavel
Flecher FLETCHER
FLEEMING FLEMING
FLEET 4 Fleete FOOT FOOTE
Fleete FLEET FOOT FOOTE
FLEMING FLEEMING FLEMMING
FLEMMING FLEMING
FLETCHER Flecher Flicher
Flicher FLETCHER
FLINDERS FLANDERS
FLINN FLYNN
FLINT 4 Flinte Flynt Flynte
Flinte FLINT
FLINTHAM Flinton Flintum
Flinton FLINTHAM
Flintum FLINTHAM
FLOOK Flooke Fluke
Flooke FLOOK
FLORRY FLORY Flurry
FLORY FLORRY Flurry
Flowdie FLOWERDAY FLOWERDEW
Flowdy FLOWERDAY FLOWERDEW
FLOWER FLOWERS
FLOWERDAY 4 Flowdie Flowdy FLOWERDEW
FLOWERDEW 4 Flowdie Flowdy FLOWERDAY
FLOWERS FLOWER
FLOYD 5 LLOYD LLOYDE LOYD LOYDE
Fluke FLOOK
Flurry FLORRY FLORY
FLYN FLYNN
FLYNN FLINN FLYN
Flynt FLINT
Flynte FLINT
FOAKES 6 FEAKES Ffoks Fokes Foks Folkes
FOCH 9 Fausch FOCHE Fooch FOSH Fouache Fouch Fouche Foucher
FOCHE 8 FOCH Fooch FOSH Fouache Fouch Fouche Foucher
Foddeslie FROGLEY
Foghill FOWELL
Foil FOYLE
Foirefax FAIRFAX
Fokes FEAKES FOAKES
Foks FEAKES FOAKES
Folger FOULDS FOULGER FOULKES
Folkes FEAKES FOAKES FULKE
FOLKINGHAM Faulkingham
Follan FOLLAND FOLLON
FOLLAND 6 Follan Follard Follen Follin FOLLON
Follard FOLLAND FOLLON
Follen FOLLAND FOLLON
Follin FOLLAND FOLLON
FOLLON 6 Follan FOLLAND Follard Follen Follin
Folsetter FOLSTER
FOLSTER Folsetter
FOLTHORPE Felthorpe
Fooch FOCH FOCHE FOSH
Fookes FOOKS FOWKES
FOOKS Fookes FOWKES
FOORD 4 Foorde FORD FORDE
Foorde FOORD FORD FORDE
Foosbrooke FOSBROKE FOSBROOK
FOOT 6 FLEET Fleete FOOTE Foott Footte
FOOTE 6 FLEET Fleete FOOT Foott Footte
FOOTITT FOOTTIT Futtit
Foott FOOT FOOTE
Footte FOOT FOOTE
FOOTTIT FOOTITT Futtit
Forcebrok FOSBROKE FOSBROOK
Forcebroke FOSBROKE FOSBROOK
Forcebrook FOSBROKE FOSBROOK
Forcebrooke FOSBROKE FOSBROOK
FORD 4 FOORD Foorde FORDE
Fordam FORDHAM
Fordame FORDHAM
Fordar FORDER
Fordard FORDER
Fordat FORDER
FORDE 4 FOORD Foorde FORD
Forden FORDER
FORDER 7 Fordar Fordard Fordat Forden Forderd Fordet
Forderd FORDER
Fordet FORDER
FORDHAM 4 Fordam Fordame Fordom
Fordom FORDHAM
FOREMAN 8 Foremann FORMAN Formann Formen Fourman Fourmen Voorman
Foremann FOREMAN FORMAN
Foresbrok FOSBROKE FOSBROOK
Foresbrook FOSBROKE FOSBROOK
Foresbrooke FOSBROKE FOSBROOK
FORESTER FORRESTER
Forges-de DESFORGES
Forian FORRYAN
Fories FORREST
Forist FORREST
Forister FORREST
FORMAN 13 Armen ARMON FOREMAN Foremann Formann Formen Fourman Fourmen NORMAN ORMAN Ormen Voorman
Formann FOREMAN FORMAN
Formen FOREMAN FORMAN
FORREST 5 Fories Forist Forister Forret
FORRESTER FORESTER
Forret FORREST
Forrian FORRYAN
FORRYAN 5 Fforian Forian Forrian Foryan
Forsbroock FOSBROKE FOSBROOK
Forsbrook FOSBROKE FOSBROOK
Forsebrook FOSBROKE FOSBROOK
Forsebrooke FOSBROKE FOSBROOK
Forshall FORSHAW
FORSHAW Forshall
Forstbrook FOSBROKE FOSBROOK
Forstbrooke FOSBROKE FOSBROOK
Forstebrook FOSBROKE FOSBROOK
Forstebrooke FOSBROKE FOSBROOK
FORSTER FOSTER
FORSYTH FORSYTHE
FORSYTHE FORSYTH
Forte FORTEE
FORTEE Forte Fortey
FORTESCUE Fortesque
Fortesque FORTESCUE
Fortey FORTEE
FORTH Furth
Fortley FAUTLEY
Foryan FORRYAN
Fosbrock FOSBROKE FOSBROOK
FOSBROKE 34 Boresbroke Fausbrook Fausbrooke Faustbrook Faustbrooke Foosbrooke Forcebrok Forcebroke Forcebrook Forcebrooke Foresbrok Foresbrook Foresbrooke Forsbroock Forsbrook Forsebrook Forsebrooke Forstbrook Forstbrooke Forstebrook Forstebrooke Fosbrock FOSBROOK Fosbrooke Fossbrook Fossbrooke Fostbrook Fostbrooke Frossbrook Frostbrook Fursbrook Fushbrook Fussbrook
FOSBROOK 35 Boresbroke Fausbrook Fausbrooke Faustbrook Faustbrooke Foosbrooke Forcebrok Forcebroke Forcebrook Forcebrooke Foresbrok Foresbrook Foresbrooke Forsbroock Forsbrook Forsebrook Forsebrooke Forstbrook Forstbrooke Forstebrook Forstebrooke Fosbrock FOSBROKE Fosbrooke Fossbrook Fossbrooke Fostbrook Fostbrooke Frossbrook Frostbrook Fursbrook Fushbrook Fussbrook Hosbrook
Fosbrooke FOSBROKE FOSBROOK
FOSH 8 FOCH FOCHE Fooch Fouache Fouch Fouche Foucher
Fossbrook FOSBROKE FOSBROOK
Fossbrooke FOSBROKE FOSBROOK
Fostbrook FOSBROKE FOSBROOK
Fostbrooke FOSBROKE FOSBROOK
FOSTER FORSTER
FOTHERINGHAM Fotheringhame
Fotheringhame FOTHERINGHAM
Fouache FOCH FOCHE FOSH
Fouargur FOVARGUE
Fouch FOCH FOCHE FOSH
Fouche FOCH FOCHE FOSH
Foucher FOCH FOCHE FOSH
Fouhel FOWELL
Fouhell FOWELL
FOULDS 5 Folger FOULGER FOULKES Fulger
Foule FOWLE FOWLES
Foules FOWLE FOWLES
FOULGER 5 Folger FOULDS FOULKES Fulger
FOULIS FOWLIS
FOULKES 8 FFOULKES Ffoulks Folger FOULDS FOULGER Foulks Fulger
Foulks FFOULKES FOULKES
Foulton FULTON
Fourman FOREMAN FORMAN
Fourmen FOREMAN FORMAN
FOVARGUE 5 Fauvaque Fauvargue Fouargur Fovarque
Fovarque FOVARGUE
Fowel FOWELL
FOWELL 11 De fowell Ffowell Foghill Fouhel Fouhell Fowel Fowhell Fowhill Voghill Vowel
Fowhell FOWELL
Fowhill FOWELL
FOWKES Fookes FOOKS
Fowks FEWKES FUKES

If the name you are interested in is not here, try Section C.

FOWLE 4 Foule Foules FOWLES
FOWLES 4 Foule Foules FOWLE
FOWLIS FOULIS
FOX Foxe Foxes
Foxe FOX
Foxes FOX
FOXLEE FOXLEY
FOXLEY FOXLEE
FOY 7 JOY LEE Tay TEA TEE TOY
FOYLE Foil
Fozard FOZZARD
FOZZARD Fozard
Fragall FRIGALL
Fragell FRIGALL
Fragle FRIGALL
FRAHER 6 Frahir Frehr FRYOR Phraher Raher
Frahir FRAHER FRYOR
Frailes FAIRLESS
Fraiser FRASER FRAZER
Fraiter FRATER
FRANCES FRANCIS
Francies FRANCIS
FRANCIS 7 Ffranceys FRANCES Francies Francys Fraunceys Frauncys
Francland FRANKLAND
Francys FRANCIS
Frankeland FRANKLAND
FRANKLAND 5 Francland Frankeland FRANKLIN Frankling
FRANKLIN FRANKLAND Frankling
Frankling FRANKLAND FRANKLIN
Frapell FRAPWELL
Frappell FRAPWELL
Frapple FRAPWELL
FRAPWELL 6 Frapell Frappell Frapple Rappel Wrapple
FRASER 9 Fraiser Frasor FRAZER Freser Frissel Frissell Frizzel Frizzell
Frasor FRASER FRAZER
Frassan FAZAN
FRATER Fraiter
Fraunceys FRANCIS
Frauncys FRANCIS
Frazan FAZAN
FRAZER 9 Fraiser FRASER Frasor Freser Frissel Frissell Frizzel Frizzell
Freagell FRIGALL
Freagle FRIGALL
FREARSON 5 Freason Freerson Freeson Freeston
Freason FREARSON
Freedland FREELAND
Freedlander FREELAND
FREELAND 5 Freedland Freedlander Friedland Friedlander
FREEMAN Freman Fryman
Freerson FREARSON
Freeson FREARSON
Freeston FREARSON FREESTONE
FREESTONE 7 Freeston Freestonne Freston Freyston Frieston Friestone
Freestonne FREESTONE
Fregal FRIGALL
Fregwill FRIGALL
Frehr FRAHER FRYOR
Freman FREEMAN
Freser FRASER FRAZER
FRESHNEY 5 Freskney Frishney Friskeney FRISKNEY
Freskney FRESHNEY FRISKNEY
Freston FREESTONE
FRETTS Fritz
Frewen FRUEN
Freyston FREESTONE
Friant FRYATT
FRIAR 5 FRIER FRYAR FRYER FRYOR
Friate FRYATT
Friatt FRYATT
Frie FRY FRYE
Friedland FREELAND
Friedlander FREELAND
Frient FRYATT
FRIER 4 FRIAR FRYAR FRYER
Frieston FREESTONE
Friestone FREESTONE
Friett FRYATT
FRIGALL 10 Fragall Fragell Fragle Freagell Freagle Fregal Fregwill Friggell Friggle
Friggell FRIGALL
Friggle FRIGALL
Friitt FRYATT
Friott FRYATT
FRISBY FRIZBY
Frishney FRESHNEY FRISKNEY
Friskeney FRESHNEY FRISKNEY
FRISKNEY 5 FRESHNEY Freskney Frishney Friskeney
Frissel FRASER FRAZER
Frissell FRASER FRAZER
Fritz FRETTS
FRIZBY FRISBY
Frizzel FRASER FRAZER
Frizzell FRASER FRAZER
FROGLEY 4 Foddeslie Froglie Frogly
Froglie FROGLEY
Frogly FROGLEY
FROOD 7 Ffrude Froode FROUD FROUDE Fround Frude
Froode FROOD FROUD FROUDE
Froslick FROSTICK
Frossbrook FOSBROKE FOSBROOK
Frostbrook FOSBROKE FOSBROOK
FROSTICK Froslick
FROUD 8 Ffrude FROOD Froode FROUDE Fround Frowde Frude
FROUDE 8 Ffrude FROOD Froode FROUD Fround Frowde Frude
Fround FROOD FROUD FROUDE
Frowde FROUD FROUDE
Frude FROOD FROUD FROUDE
FRUEN Frewen
FRY 4 Ffray Frie FRYE
FRYAR 4 FRIAR FRIER FRYER
FRYATT 8 Friant Friate Friatt Frient Friett Friitt Friott
FRYE 4 Ffray Frie FRY
FRYER 4 FRIAR FRIER FRYAR
Fryman FREEMAN
FRYOR 7 FRAHER Frahir Frehr FRIAR Phraher Raher
Fuel FEWEL FUELL
FUELL 5 Feuell FEWEL Fewell Fuel
Fugion FITZJOHN
FUKES 4 FEWKES Fowks Furkes
Fulbrick FULBROOK FULLBRICK PHILBRICK
FULBROOK 10 Falbrick Falbrook Fallbrick Fulbrick Fulbrooke FULLBRICK Fullbrook PHILBRICK Philbrook
Fulbrooke FULBROOK
FULCHER Fulger Fulshire
Fulger FOULDS FOULGER FOULKES FULCHER
Fulk FULKE
FULKE 5 Ffulk Ffulke Folkes Fulk
Fullar FULLER
FULLARD Fullwood FULWOOD
FULLBRICK 8 Falbrick Falbrook Fallbrick Fulbrick FULBROOK PHILBRICK Philbrook
Fullbrook FULBROOK
FULLELOVE Fulleylove Fullilove
FULLER Fullar
Fulleylove FULLELOVE
Fullilove FULLELOVE
Fullwood FULLARD FULWOOD
Fulshire FULCHER
FULTHORP Fulthorpe
Fulthorpe FULTHORP
FULTON Foulton
FULWOOD FULLARD Fullwood
Funcko PHANCO
Funell FUNNELL
Funnel FUNNELL
FUNNELL 9 Fennall FENNEL Fennil Funell Funnel Funnelle Vennal Vinell
Funnelle FUNNELL
Furkes FEWKES FUKES
FURNAS 4 Furnass FURNESS FURNIS
Furnass FURNAS FURNESS
FURNELL 6 Farnehill FARNELL Farnhill FARNOL Fernell
FURNESS 4 FURNAS Furnass FURNIS
Furney FERNEE
FURNIS FURNAS FURNESS
Furny FERNEE
Furrel FIRRELL VERRAL
FURRIAN Ferrian
Furrs FURSE FURZE
Furs FURSE FURZE
Fursbrook FOSBROKE FOSBROOK
FURSE 7 Firrs Firs Furrs Furs Fursse FURZE
FURSEDON 4 Fursedonn Furssedon Furssedonn
Fursedonn FURSEDON
Fursse FURSE FURZE
Furssedon FURSEDON
Furssedonn FURSEDON
Furth FORTH
FURZE 7 Firrs Firs Furrs Furs FURSE Fursse
Fushbrook FOSBROKE FOSBROOK
Fussbrook FOSBROKE FOSBROOK
Futtit FOOTITT FOOTTIT
Fyander FIANDER
Fychan VAUGHAN VOGAN VOGHAN
Fyelde FIELD
FYFE FIFE
Fyldes FILDES FILES FYLES
FYLES 4 FILDES FILES Fyldes
Fylewood FILEWOOD
Fylleskyrke PHILLISKIRK
Fylopot PHILLPOTTS PHILPOT PHILPOTT PHILPOTTS
Fylpot PHILLPOTTS PHILPOT PHILPOTT PHILPOTTS
Fylpott PHILLPOTTS PHILPOT PHILPOTT PHILPOTTS
Fynche FINCH
Fyndorne FINDON
Fynmer FENNIMORE FILMER FINMORE FINNEMORE PHILLIMORE VENNIMORE
Fynmore FINMORE
Fynnamore FENNIMORE FILMER FINMORE FINNEMORE PHILLIMORE VENNIMORE
Fynnemore FENNIMORE FILMER FINMORE FINNEMORE PHILLIMORE VENNIMORE
Fynneymoore FENNIMORE FILMER FINMORE FINNEMORE PHILLIMORE VENNIMORE
Fynneymore FENNIMORE FILMER FINMORE FINNEMORE PHILLIMORE VENNIMORE
Fynnimore FENNIMORE FILMER FINMORE FINNEMORE PHILLIMORE VENNIMORE
Fynnymore FENNIMORE FILMER FINMORE FINNEMORE PHILLIMORE VENNIMORE
FYRTH FIRTH Firthe
Fysck FISK FISKE
Fysk FISK FISKE
Fyske FISK FISKE
FYSON FISON
Fytnes FITNESS
Fytnesse FITNESS
Fyttness FITNESS
Fyz FICE FISE FITZ VICE
GABBETT Garbed
GABBITAS Gabitas Gabittas
Gabitas GABBITAS
Gabittas GABBITAS
Gadie GAUDIE
Gady GAUDIE
GAGER 4 Gaiger Gaugeor Gauger
Gagie GEGGIE
Gagwell DAGWELL
Gai DE GAI
Gaiger GAGER
Gailham GILHAM GILLAM
Gailward GALWARD
GAINER Gaynor
GAIR GEAR
Gaiter GATER
Galder GAULDER GAULER
GALL GAULD
Galland GALLON GOILLON GOLDING GOLLAND GOWLAND
GALLON 14 Galland Gaulon Gaylinge Gealing Gilland GOILLON GOLDING GOLLAND Gollin GOWLAND Gowling Gulling Gullon
Galsthorp GELSTHORPE
Galsthorpe GELSTHORPE
GALT GAULT
Galtie GOULTY
Galty GOULTY
Galvan GALVIN
GALVIN Galvan Golvun
GALWARD Gailward
Gamaches GAMAGE

If the name you are interested in is not here, try Section C.

GAMAGE 7 De gamaches De gamage De gamages Gamaches Gamages GAMMIDGE
Gamages GAMAGE
GAMBEL GAMBLE Gambol
GAMBLE 4 COLUMBELL GAMBEL Gambol
Gambol GAMBEL GAMBLE
GAMESON GAMSON
GAMMAN GAMMON
GAMMIDGE GAMAGE
GAMMON GAMMAN
GAMSON GAMESON
Gan GANE GAWEN GOWN GOYNE JANE JAYNE
Gandal GENDALL GENDLE
Gandall GENDALL GENDLE
Gandar GANDER
Gandee GANDY
Gandell GENDALL GENDLE
GANDER Gandar
Gandey GANDY
Gandie GANDY
Gandle GENDALL GENDLE
GANDY 4 Gandee Gandey Gandie
GANE 13 Gan GAWEN Geon Geune Gilb Gonne GOWN GOYNE Guine Jaine JANE JAYNE
GANN Ganne
Ganne GANN
Garad GARRAD GARRARD GARRAT GARRATT GARRETT GARROD GERARD GERRARD GERRETT JARRARD JARRATT JARRET JARRETT JARROLD JARVIS JERRARD JERRETT YARD
Garard GARRAD GARRARD GARRAT GARRATT GARRETT GARROD GERARD GERRARD GERRETT JARRARD JARRATT JARRET JARRETT JARROLD JARVIS JERRARD JERRETT YARD
Garat GARRATT GARRETT
Garbart GARBUTT
Garbed GABBETT
Garbertt GARBUTT
GARBETT GARBUTT
Garbut GARBUTT
GARBUTT 5 Garbart Garbertt GARBETT Garbut
GARD 4 Gird GOURD GURD
Gardeiner GARDENER GARDINER GARDNER
GARDENER 4 Gardeiner GARDINER GARDNER
GARDINER 5 Gardeiner GARDENER GARDNER GARNER
GARDNER 5 Gardeiner GARDENER GARDINER GARNER
GARFIT Garfoot
Garfoot GARFIT
Garlet JARLETT
Garlett JARLETT
Garlot JARLETT
GARNER GARDINER GARDNER
GARNIER Guernier
GARRAD 82 Ardy Eardy Garad Garard GARRARD GARRAT GARRATT Garred Garretson GARRETT Garretts Garrettson Garrison Garrit Garritt GARROD GARROTT Garrould Gerad Geraddus Gerald Geralds GERARD Gerarde Gerardes Gerards Geratt Geraud Geret Gerold Gerrad GERRARD Gerratt Gerred GERRETT Gervaise Gervas Gervase Gervis Gorret Heardy Jarad Jarald Jarat Jared Jareld Jarelds Jaret Jarets Jarett Jaretts Jarrad JARRARD Jarrat JARRATT Jarred JARRET Jarrets JARRETT Jarretts Jarritt Jarrod JARROLD Jarrott Jarvie JARVIS Jeffette Jeofett Jeorrett Jereatt JERRARD Jerratt Jerreatt Jerred JERRETT Jerrold YARD Yarrat Yarratt Yarrott Yerratt
GARRARD 84 Ardy Eardy Garad Garard GARRAD GARRAT GARRATT Garred Garretson GARRETT Garretts Garrettson Garrison Garrit Garritt GARROD GARROTT Garrould Gerad Geraddus Gerald Geralds GERARD Gerarde Gerardes Gerards Geratt Geraud Geret Gerold Gerrad GERRARD Gerratt Gerred GERRETT Gervaise Gervas Gervase Gervis GODDARD Gorrard Gorret Heardy Jarad Jarald Jarat Jared Jareld Jarelds Jaret Jarets Jarett Jaretts Jarrad JARRARD Jarrat JARRATT Jarred JARRET Jarrets JARRETT Jarretts Jarritt Jarrod JARROLD Jarrott Jarvie JARVIS Jeffette Jeofett Jeorrett Jereatt JERRARD Jerratt Jerreatt Jerred JERRETT Jerrold YARD Yarrat Yarratt Yarrott Yerratt
GARRAT 82 Ardy Eardy Garad Garard GARRAD GARRARD GARRATT Garred GARRET Garretson GARRETT Garretts Garrettson Garrison Garrit Garritt GARROD Garrould Gerad Geraddus Gerald Geralds GERARD Gerarde Gerardes Gerards Geratt Geraud Geret Gerold Gerrad GERRARD Gerratt Gerred GERRETT Gervaise Gervas Gervase Gervis Gorret Heardy Jarad Jarald Jarat Jared Jareld Jarelds Jaret Jarets Jarett Jaretts Jarrad JARRARD Jarrat JARRATT Jarred JARRET Jarrets JARRETT Jarretts Jarritt Jarrod JARROLD Jarrott Jarvie JARVIS Jeffette Jeofett Jeorrett Jereatt JERRARD Jerratt Jerreatt Jerred JERRETT Jerrold YARD Yarrat Yarratt Yarrott Yerratt
GARRATT 83 Ardy Eardy Garad Garard Garat GARRAD GARRARD GARRAT Garred GARRET Garretson GARRETT Garretts Garrettson Garrison Garrit Garritt GARROD Garrould Gerad Geraddus Gerald Geralds GERARD Gerarde Gerardes Gerards Geratt Geraud Geret Gerold Gerrad GERRARD Gerratt Gerred GERRETT Gervaise Gervas Gervase Gervis Gorret Heardy Jarad Jarald Jarat Jared Jareld Jarelds Jaret Jarets Jarett Jaretts Jarrad JARRARD Jarrat JARRATT Jarred JARRET Jarrets JARRETT Jarretts Jarritt Jarrod JARROLD Jarrott Jarvie JARVIS Jeffette Jeofett Jeorrett Jereatt JERRARD Jerratt Jerreatt Jerred JERRETT Jerrold YARD Yarrat Yarratt Yarrott Yerratt
Garred GARRAD GARRARD GARRAT GARRATT GARRETT GARROD GERARD GERRARD GERRETT JARRARD JARRATT JARRET JARRETT JARROLD JARVIS JERRARD JERRETT YARD
GARRET 4 GARRAT GARRATT GARRETT
Garretson GARRAD GARRARD GARRAT GARRATT GARRETT GARROD GERARD GERRARD GERRETT JARRARD JARRATT JARRET JARRETT JARROLD JARVIS JERRARD JERRETT YARD
GARRETT 85 Ardy Eardy Garad Garard Garat GARRAD GARRARD GARRAT GARRATT Garred GARRET Garretson Garretts Garrettson Garrison Garrit Garritt GARROD GARROTT Garrould Gerad Geraddus Gerald Geralds GERARD Gerarde Gerardes Gerards Geratt Geraud Geret Gerold Gerrad GERRARD Gerratt Gerred GERRETT Gervaise Gervas Gervase Gervis Gorret Heardy Jarad Jaraitt Jarald Jarat Jared Jareld Jarelds Jaret Jarets Jarett Jaretts Jarrad JARRARD Jarrat JARRATT Jarred JARRET Jarrets JARRETT Jarretts Jarritt Jarrod JARROLD Jarrott Jarvie JARVIS Jeffette Jeofett Jeorrett Jereatt JERRARD Jerratt Jerreatt Jerred JERRETT Jerrold YARD Yarrat Yarratt Yarrott Yerratt
Garretts GARRAD GARRARD GARRAT GARRATT GARRETT GARROD GERARD GERRARD GERRETT JARRARD JARRATT JARRET JARRETT JARROLD JARVIS JERRARD JERRETT YARD
Garrettson GARRAD GARRARD GARRAT GARRATT GARRETT GARROD GERARD GERRARD GERRETT JARRARD JARRATT JARRET JARRETT JARROLD JARVIS JERRARD JERRETT YARD
Garrison GARRAD GARRARD GARRAT GARRATT GARRETT GARROD GERARD GERRARD GERRETT JARRARD JARRATT JARRET JARRETT JARROLD JARVIS JERRARD JERRETT YARD
Garrit GARRAD GARRARD GARRAT GARRATT GARRETT GARROD GERARD GERRARD GERRETT JARRARD JARRATT JARRET JARRETT JARROLD JARVIS JERRARD JERRETT YARD
Garritt GARRAD GARRARD GARRAT GARRATT GARRETT GARROD GERARD GERRARD GERRETT JARRARD JARRATT JARRET JARRETT JARROLD JARVIS JERRARD JERRETT YARD
GARROD 82 Ardy Eardy Garad Garard GARRAD GARRARD GARRAT GARRATT Garred Garretson GARRETT Garretts Garrettson Garrison Garrit Garritt GARROTT Garrould Gerad Geraddus Gerald Geralds GERARD Gerarde Gerardes Gerards Geratt Geraud Geret Gerold Gerrad GERRARD Gerratt Gerred GERRETT Gervaise Gervas Gervase Gervis Gorret Heardy Jarad Jarald Jarat Jared Jareld Jarelds Jaret Jarets Jarett Jaretts Jarrad JARRARD Jarrat JARRATT Jarred JARRET Jarrets JARRETT Jarretts Jarritt Jarrod JARROLD Jarrott Jarvie JARVIS Jeffette Jeofett Jeorrett Jereatt JERRARD Jerratt Jerreatt Jerred JERRETT Jerrold YARD Yarrat Yarratt Yarrott Yerratt
GARROTT 6 GARRAD GARRARD GARRETT GARROD GERRARD
Garrould GARRAD GARRARD GARRAT GARRATT GARRETT GARROD GERARD GERRARD GERRETT JARRARD JARRATT JARRET JARRETT JARROLD JARVIS JERRARD JERRETT YARD
Garsh GORSUCH
GARSIDE Garsyde GARTSIDE
Garstwich GORSUCH
Garstwick GORSUCH
Garsyde GARSIDE GARTSIDE
GARTHWAITE Girthwaite
Gartley GARTLY
GARTLY Gartley
GARTSIDE GARSIDE Garsyde
Garvan GARVIN
Garvasius JARVICE JARVIS JERVIS
Garven GARVIN
GARVIN 4 Garvan Garven Garvon
Garvis JARVIS JERVIS
Garvon GARVIN
Gasard GAZZARD
GASCOIGNE 6 GASCOINE GASCOYNE Gasken GASKIN GASKING
GASCOINE 6 GASCOIGNE GASCOYNE Gasken GASKIN GASKING
GASCOYNE 6 GASCOIGNE

If the name you are interested in is not here, try Section C.

GASCOINE Gasken GASKIN GASKING
Gasken GASCOIGNE GASCOINE GASCOYNE GASKIN GASKING
GASKIN 9 GASCOIGNE GASCOINE GASCOYNE Gasken Gaskine Gaskines GASKING Gaskins
Gaskine GASKIN
Gaskines GASKIN
GASKING 6 GASCOIGNE GASCOINE GASCOYNE Gasken GASKIN
Gaskins GASKIN
Gassard GAZZARD
Gasserd GAZZARD
GASSON GASTON
Gast GUEST
GASTON GASSON
GATER 4 Gaiter Gayter Gaytor
GATES YEATS
GATHERCOAL GATHERCOLE STANDLEY
GATHERCOLE GATHERCOAL STANDLEY
Gattey GATTY
GATTY Gattey
GAUDEN 4 GORDEN Gordin GORDON
GAUDIE Gadie Gady
Gaugeor GAGER
Gauger GAGER
GAUGHT 7 GAULT Gaut GAWGHT GAWT Goult Gout
GAULD GALL
GAULDER Galder GAULER
GAULER 4 Galder GAULDER GOLDING
Gaulon GALLON GOILLON GOLDING GOLLAND GOWLAND
Gaulson GOLDSTON GOLDSTONE
GAULT 8 GALT GAUGHT Gaut GAWGHT GAWT Goult Gout
Gaurstage GORSUCH
Gausby GOSBY
Gaut GAUGHT GAULT GAWGHT GAWT
GAWEN 13 Gan GANE Geon Geune Gilb Gonne GOWN GOYNE Guine Jaine JANE JAYNE
GAWGHT 7 GAUGHT GAULT Gaut GAWT Goult Gout
Gawman GORMAN GOWMAN
GAWT 7 GAUGHT GAULT Gaut GAWGHT Goult Gout
Gawthorp GOLDTHORP GOLDTHORPE
Gawthorpe GOLDTHORP GOLDTHORPE
Gawthrope GOLDTHORP GOLDTHORPE
Gawthropp GOLDTHORP GOLDTHORPE
GAY GAYE
GAYDEN 4 GAYDON Geaden GEDEN
GAYDON 4 GAYDEN Geaden GEDEN
GAYE GAY
Gaylinge GALLON GOILLON GOLDING GOLLAND GOWLAND
Gaynor GAINER
Gayter GATER
Gaytor GATER
Gazard GAZZARD
GAZZARD 12 Gasard Gassard Gasserd Gazard Gissard Gizard Gizzard Gossard Gozard Gozzard Guyzard
Geaden GAYDEN GAYDON GEDEN
Geadon GEDEN
Geal GEALE JEAL
GEALE 5 Geal JEAL Jeale Jeall
Gealing GALLON GOILLON GOLDING GOLLAND GOWLAND
GEAR 6 GAIR GEER GEIR Gere Ghere
GEARLE Girle
GEBBETT Gibett Jebett
Geckes JACKS JAKES JEX
Gecks JACKS JAKES JEX
Gedding GEDEN GIDDENS GIDDINGS GIDDINS
Geddy GEDYE GYDE
GEDEN 19 GAYDEN GAYDON Geaden Geadon Gedding Gedin Gedon Geeden Geedon Geyden Geydon GIDDENS GIDDINGS GIDDINS Gydding Gyddyng Gydin Gydon
GEDGE GEDYE GIDDY
Gedie GEDYE GYDE
Gedin GEDEN GIDDENS GIDDINGS GIDDINS
Gedon GEDEN GIDDENS GIDDINGS GIDDINS
Gedy GEDYE GYDE
GEDYE 12 Geddy GEDGE Gedie Gedy Geedie Geedy Geedye Geydye GIDDY GYDE Gydy
GEE JEE
Geeden GEDEN
Geedie GEDYE GYDE
Geedon GEDEN
Geedy GEDYE GYDE
Geedye GEDYE GYDE
GEER 4 GEAR Gere Ghere
GEESIN 7 GEESING Geeson Gesynge Geysinge Gissing Gysynge
GEESING 7 GEESIN Geeson Gesynge Geysinge Gissing Gysynge
Geeson GEESIN GEESING
Gefferie JEFFERY JEFFREY
Geffery JEFFERIES JEFFERY JEFFERYS JEFFREY JEFFREYS JEFFRIES
Gefferys JEFFERIES JEFFERY JEFFERYS JEFFREY JEFFREYS JEFFRIES
Geffry JEFFERIES JEFFERY JEFFERYS JEFFREY JEFFREYS JEFFRIES
Geffryes JEFFERIES JEFFERY JEFFERYS JEFFREY JEFFREYS JEFFRIES
GEGGIE Gagie
GEIR GEAR
Gelbert GILBARD GILBERT
GELDER GILDER Guelder
Gelding GILDEN GILDING GILDON
GELEIT 5 Gelert Gelleit Gileit GILLETT
Gelert GELEIT GILLETT
Gelicho JELLICOE
Gelico JELLICOE
Gelicot DELICATE
Gelicut DELICATE
Gellat GILLOTT JELLETT
Gellatt GILLOTT JELLETT
Gelleit GELEIT GILLETT
Gelles GELLY JELLIS
Gellesthorp GELSTHORPE
Gellesthorpe GELSTHORPE
Gelliart GILLIATT
Gellico JELLICOE
Gelliman JELLIMAN
Gellis GELLY JELLIS
Gellot GILLOTT JELLETT
Gellott GILLOTT JELLETT
GELLY 10 Gelles Gellis Jealys Jeles Jelleys JELLIS Jelly Jellys Jolys
Gelsthorp GELSTHORPE
GELSTHORPE 10 Galsthorp Galsthorpe Gellesthorp Gellesthorpe Gelsthorp Gillsthorp Gillsthorpe Gilsthorp Gilsthorpe
GELSTON GILSTON
Gen GINN
GENDALL 8 Gandal Gandall Gandell Gandle Gendell GENDLE Gengell
Gendell GENDALL GENDLE
GENDLE 8 Gandal Gandall Gandell Gandle GENDALL Gendell Gengell
Gengell GENDALL GENDLE
Genning JENKINS JENNINGS JENNINS
Gennings JENKINS JENNINGS JENNINS
Gennins JENKINS JENNINGS JENNINS
Genower CHYNOWETH
GENT 4 GHENT Jent Jhent
Geofery JEFFERIES JEFFERY JEFFERYS JEFFREY JEFFREYS JEFFRIES
Geoffry JEFFERIES JEFFERY JEFFERYS JEFFREY JEFFREYS JEFFRIES
Geon GANE GAWEN GOWN GOYNE JANE JAYNE
Georsich GORSUCH
Gerad GARRAD GARRARD GARRAT GARRATT GARRETT GARROD GERARD GERRARD GERRETT JARRARD JARRATT JARRET JARRETT JARROLD JARVIS JERRARD JERRETT YARD
Geraddus GARRAD GARRARD GARRAT GARRATT GARRETT GARROD GERARD GERRARD GERRETT JARRARD JARRATT JARRET JARRETT JARROLD JARVIS JERRARD JERRETT YARD
Gerald GARRAD GARRARD GARRAT GARRATT GARRETT GARROD GERARD GERRARD GERRETT JARRARD JARRATT JARRET JARRETT JARROLD JARVIS JERRARD JERRETT YARD
Geralds GARRAD GARRARD GARRAT GARRATT GARRETT GARROD GERARD GERRARD GERRETT JARRARD JARRATT JARRET JARRETT JARROLD JARVIS JERRARD JERRETT YARD
GERARD 81 Ardy Eardy Garad Garard GARRAD GARRARD GARRAT GARRATT Garred Garretson GARRETT Garretts Garrettson Garrison Garrit Garritt GARROD Garrould Gerad Geraddus Gerald Geralds Gerarde Gerardes Gerards Geratt Geraud Geret Gerold Gerrad GERRARD Gerratt Gerred GERRETT Gervaise Gervas Gervase Gervis Gorret Heardy Jarad Jarald Jarat Jared Jareld Jarelds Jaret Jarets Jarett Jaretts Jarrad JARRARD Jarrat JARRATT Jarred JARRET Jarrets JARRETT Jarretts Jarritt Jarrod JARROLD Jarrott Jarvie JARVIS Jeffette Jeofett Jeorrett Jereatt JERRARD Jerratt Jerreatt Jerred JERRETT Jerrold YARD Yarrat Yarratt Yarrott Yerratt
Gerarde GARRAD GARRARD GARRAT GARRATT GARRETT GARROD GERARD GERRARD GERRETT JARRARD JARRATT JARRET JARRETT JARROLD JARVIS JERRARD JERRETT YARD
Gerardes GARRAD GARRARD GARRAT GARRATT GARRETT GARROD GERARD GERRARD GERRETT JARRARD JARRATT JARRET JARRETT JARROLD JARVIS JERRARD JERRETT YARD
Gerards GARRAD GARRARD GARRAT GARRATT GARRETT GARROD GERARD GERRARD GERRETT JARRARD JARRATT JARRET JARRETT JARROLD JARVIS JERRARD JERRETT YARD
Geratt GARRAD GARRARD GARRAT GARRATT GARRETT GARROD GERARD GERRARD GERRETT JARRARD JARRATT JARRET JARRETT JARROLD JARVIS JERRARD JERRETT YARD
Geraud GARRAD GARRARD GARRAT GARRATT GARRETT GARROD GERARD GERRARD GERRETT JARRARD JARRATT JARRET JARRETT JARROLD JARVIS JERRARD JERRETT YARD
Gere GEAR GEER
Geret GARRAD GARRARD GARRAT GARRATT GARRETT GARROD GERARD GERRARD GERRETT JARRARD JARRATT JARRET JARRETT JARROLD JARVIS JERRARD JERRETT YARD
GERMAIN GERMAINE GERMAN
GERMAINE GERMAIN
GERMAN 5 GERMAIN JARMAN JERMAN Jermyn
Germany JERMY
Gerold GARRAD GARRARD GARRAT GARRATT GARRETT GARROD GERARD GERRARD GERRETT JARRARD JARRATT JARRET JARRETT JARROLD JARVIS JERRARD JERRETT YARD
Gerrad GARRAD GARRARD GARRAT GARRATT GARRETT GARROD GERARD GERRARD GERRETT JARRARD JARRATT JARRET JARRETT JARROLD JARVIS JERRARD JERRETT YARD
Gerram JERAM JERRAM
GERRARD 82 Ardy Eardy Garad Garard GARRAD GARRARD GARRAT GARRATT Garred Garretson GARRETT Garretts Garrettson Garrison Garrit Garritt GARROD GARROTT Garrould Gerad

If the name you are interested in is not here, try Section C.

Geraddus Gerald Geralds GERARD Gerarde Gerardes Gerards Geratt Geraud Geret Gerold Gerrad Gerratt Gerred GERRETT Gervaise Gervas Gervase Gervis Gorret Heardy Jarad Jarald Jarat Jared Jareld Jarelds Jaret Jarets Jarett Jaretts Jarrad JARRARD Jarrat JARRATT Jarred JARRET Jarrets JARRETT Jarretts Jarritt Jarrod JARROLD Jarrott Jarvie JARVIS Jeffette Jeofett Jeorrett Jereatt JERRARD Jerratt Jerreatt Jerred JERRETT Jerrold YARD Yarrat Yarratt Yarrott Yerratt
Gerratt GARRAD GARRARD GARRAT GARRATT GARRETT GARROD GERARD GERRARD GERRETT JARRARD JARRATT JARRET JARRETT JARROLD JARVIS JERRARD JERRETT YARD
Gerred GARRAD GARRARD GARRAT GARRATT GARRETT GARROD GERARD GERRARD GERRETT JARRARD JARRATT JARRET JARRETT JARROLD JARVIS JERRARD JERRETT YARD
GERRETT 81 Ardy Eardy Garad Garard GARRAD GARRARD GARRAT GARRATT Garred Garretson GARRETT Garretts Garrettson Garrison Garrit Garritt GARROD Garrould Gerad Geraddus Gerald Geralds GERARD Gerarde Gerardes Gerards Geratt Geraud Geret Gerold Gerrad GERRARD Gerratt Gerred Gervaise Gervas Gervase Gervis Gorret Heardy Jarad Jarald Jarat Jared Jareld Jarelds Jaret Jarets Jarett Jaretts Jarrad JARRARD Jarrat JARRATT Jarred JARRET Jarrets JARRETT Jarretts Jarritt Jarrod JARROLD Jarrott Jarvie JARVIS Jeffette Jeofett Jeorrett Jereatt JERRARD Jerratt Jerreatt Jerred JERRETT Jerrold YARD Yarrat Yarratt Yarrott Yerratt
Gerrison MARGERISON
Gersey GORSUCH
Gervais JARVICE JARVIS JERVIS
Gervaise GARRAD GARRARD GARRAT GARRATT GARRETT GARROD GERARD GERRARD GERRETT JARRARD JARRATT JARRET JARRETT JARROLD JARVICE JARVIS JERRARD JERRETT JERVIS YARD
Gervas GARRAD GARRARD GARRAT GARRATT GARRETT GARROD GERARD GERRARD GERRETT JARRARD JARRATT JARRET JARRETT JARROLD JARVIS JERRARD JERRETT YARD
Gervase GARRAD GARRARD GARRAT GARRATT GARRETT GARROD GERARD GERRARD GERRETT JARRARD JARRATT JARRET JARRETT JARROLD JARVICE JARVIS JERRARD JERRETT JERVIS YARD
Gervasius JARVICE JARVIS JERVIS
Gervayse JARVICE JARVIS JERVIS
GERVES JARVIS JERVIS
Gerveys JARVICE JARVIS JERVIS
Gervis GARRAD GARRARD GARRAT GARRATT GARRETT GARROD GERARD GERRARD GERRETT JARRARD JARRATT JARRET JARRETT JARROLD JARVICE JARVIS JERRARD JERRETT JERVIS YARD
Gesset JESSETT
Gessett JESSETT
Gessut JESSETT
GEST GUEST
Gesynge GEESIN GEESING
GETHIN 4 Cethin Gethine Gethyn
Gethine GETHIN
Gethyn GETHIN
Getlife GOODLIFFE GOODYER
Gettlif GOODLIFFE GOODYER
Gettliffe GOODLIFFE GOODYER
Geune GANE GAWEN GOWN GOYNE JANE JAYNE
Gevans GIVENS JEAVONS
Gex JACKS JAKES JEX
Geyden GEDEN
Geydon GEDEN
Geydye GEDYE GYDE
Geysinge GEESIN GEESING
Gheen GINN
GHENT 4 GENT Jent Jhent
Ghere GEAR GEER
Ghieyes GYNES JEENS JOYNES
Ghines GYNES JEENS JOYNES
Ghisnes GYNES JEENS JOYNES
Ghiyes GYNES JEENS JOYNES
Ghorst GORSE GORST
Ghuines GYNES JEENS JOYNES
Gibbson GIBSON
Gibett GEBBETT
GIBSON Gibbson
GIDDENS 11 Gedding GEDEN Gedin Gedon GIDDINGS GIDDINS Gydding Gyddyng Gydin Gydon
Giddey GIDDY GYDE
GIDDINGS 14 Gedding GEDEN Gedin Gedon GIDDENS GIDDINS Gittings GITTINS Gydding Gyddings Gyddyng Gydin Gydon
GIDDINS 11 Gedding GEDEN Gedin Gedon GIDDENS GIDDINGS Gydding Gyddyng Gydin Gydon
GIDDY 9 GEDGE GEDYE Giddey Giddye Gidi Gyddy GYDE Gydy
Giddye GIDDY GYDE
Gidi GIDDY GYDE
Gifkins JIFFKINS JIFKINS
Giggall RIGHALL
GIGGINS 11 Giggons Jeggeons Jeggins Jeggon Jegins Jegion Jegon JIGGINS Jiggons Jyggyns
Giggons GIGGINS JIGGINS
Gilanders GILLANDERS
Gilb GANE GAWEN GOWN GOYNE JANE JAYNE
GILBARD 9 Bilbeart Gelbert Gilbart Gilberd GILBERT Gilburd Gilburt Gillbard
Gilbart GILBARD GILBERT
Gilberay GILLBERRY
Gilberd GILBARD GILBERT
GILBERT 10 Bilbeart Gelbert GILBARD Gilbart Gilberd Gilburd Gilburt Gillbard JILBERT
Gilburd GILBARD GILBERT
Gilburt GILBARD GILBERT
GILDEN 10 Gelding GILDING GILDON Guilden Guilding Guildon Gylden Gylding Gyldynge
GILDER GELDER Guelder
Gildersleaves GILDERSLEEVES
GILDERSLEEVES Gildersleaves
GILDING 10 Gelding GILDEN GILDON Guilden Guilding Guildon Gylden Gylding Gyldynge
GILDON 10 Gelding GILDEN GILDING Guilden Guilding Guildon Gylden Gylding Gyldynge
Gileit GELEIT GILLETT
GILES Goyles Jiles
GILFOYLE Kilfoyle
Gilgan GILLIGAN
Gilgin GILLIGAN
GILHAM 8 Gailham Gilhem Gilhom GILLAM Gillham Gilliam GILLOM
Gilhem GILHAM GILLAM GILLOM
Gilhom GILHAM GILLAM GILLOM
GILLAM 8 Gailham GILHAM Gilhem Gilhom Gillham Gilliam GILLOM
Gilland GALLON GOILLON GOLDING GOLLAND GOWLAND
GILLANDER Gillinder
GILLANDERS Gilanders
Gillat GILLOTT JELLETT
Gillbard GILBARD GILBERT
GILLBERRY Gilberay Gillbury
Gillbury GILLBERRY
Gillens GILLINGS
Gillet GILLETT
GILLETT 6 GELEIT Gelert Gelleit Gileit Gillet
Gillette GILLOTT JILLOTT
Gillham GILHAM GILLAM
Gilliam GILHAM GILLAM
Gilliart GILLIATT
GILLIATT Gelliart Gilliart
GILLIGAN Gilgan Gilgin
Gillinder GILLANDER
Gilling JENKINS JENNINGS JENNINS
GILLINGS Gillens Jellings
Gillins GIVENS JEAVONS
Gilliot GILLOTT JILLOTT
GILLOM 5 GILHAM Gilhem Gilhom GILLAM
Gillot GILLOTT JELLETT JILLOTT
GILLOTT 20 Gellat Gellatt Gellot Gellott Gillat Gillette Gilliot Gillot Gyllot Gyllott Jellat Jellatt Jellet JELLETT Jellot Jellott Jillat Jillatt JILLOTT
GILLSON GILSON
Gillsthorp GELSTHORPE
Gillsthorpe GELSTHORPE
Gilmer GILMORE GILMOUR
GILMORE 4 Gilmer GILMOUR Gilmur
GILMOUR 4 Gilmer GILMORE Gilmur
Gilmur GILMORE GILMOUR
GILPIN Kilpin
GILSON GILLSON
Gilsthorp GELSTHORPE
Gilsthorpe GELSTHORPE
GILSTON GELSTON
Gilstrap GILTRAP
Gilthorp GILTRAP
Gilthrop GILTRAP
GILTRAP 4 Gilstrap Gilthorp Gilthrop
GIMBLETT GIMLETT
GIMLETT GIMBLETT
Gin GINN
Gines GYNES JEENS JOINES JOYNES
GINGELL 4 Gingle GYNGELL Gyngle
Gingle GINGELL
Ginks JENKES JENKS JINKS
GINMAN JANMAN
GINN 7 Gen Gheen Gin Ginne Gyn Gynne
Ginne GINN
Ginner JENNER
Ginning JENKINS JENNINGS JENNINS
Ginnings JENKINS JENNINGS JENNINS
Ginnins JENKINS JENNINGS JENNINS
GINSBERG Ginsburg
Ginsburg GINSBERG
Gird GARD GOURD GURD
Girle GEARLE
GIRLING GURLING
Girthwaite GARTHWAITE
GIRVAN Girven Girvin
Girven GIRVAN
Girvin GIRVAN
Gisbey GOSBY
Gisby GOSBY
Giset JESSETT
Gissard GAZZARD
Gissat JESSETT
Gissatt JESSETT
Gisset JESSETT
Gissett JESSETT
Gissing GEESIN GEESING
Gittings GIDDINGS GITTINS
GITTINS GIDDINGS Gittings
GIVENS 10 Gevans Gillins Javins Jeavins JEAVONS Jevins Jevons Jillins Jyvins
Giver GUIVER GUYVER
Gizard GAZZARD
Gizzard GAZZARD
Glaconbury GLASTONBURY
Gladdish GLADWISH
Gladish GLADWISH
GLADWISH 5 Gladdish Gladish Gladwishe Gledewysh
Gladwishe GLADWISH
Glaize GLASS
GLANISTER 5 Glenester GLENISTER GLENNERSTER Glinister
GLANVILLE 5 Granfield GRANVILLE Grenvill GRENVILLE
Glasan GLASSON
GLASCOCK 5 Glascoe Glascow GLASGOW Glasscock
Glascoe GLASCOCK GLASGOW

If the name you are interested in is not here, try Section C.

Glascow GLASCOCK GLASGOW
Glasen GLASSON
GLASGOW 4 GLASCOCK Glascoe Glascow
GLASIER 4 Glaysier Glayzier GLAZIER
Glason GLASSON
Glaspole GLASPOOL
GLASPOOL Glaspole
GLASS Glaize
Glassan GLASSON
Glasscock GLASCOCK
Glassen GLASSON
Glassenbury GLASTONBURY
GLASSON 10 Glasan Glasen Glason Glassan Glassen Glazan Glazen Glazon Glazzon
Glasspole GLASSPOOL GLASSPOOLE
GLASSPOOL Glasspole GLASSPOOLE
GLASSPOOLE Glasspole GLASSPOOL
GLASTONBURY Glaconbury Glassenbury
Glaysier GLASIER GLAZIER
Glayzier GLASIER GLAZIER
Glazan GLASSON
Glazen GLASSON
GLAZIER 4 GLASIER Glaysier Glayzier
Glazon GLASSON
Glazzon GLASSON
GLEADHILL GLEADLE GLEDHILL
GLEADLE GLEADHILL GLEDHILL
Glean GLENN GLINN
Gledewysh GLADWISH
GLEDHILL GLEADHILL GLEADLE
Glenester GLANISTER GLENISTER GLENNERSTER
GLENISTER 5 GLANISTER Glenester GLENNERSTER Glinister
GLENN 5 Glean GLINN Glyn Glynn
GLENNERSTER 5 GLANISTER Glenester GLENISTER Glinister
Glibberry GLIBBERY
GLIBBERY 5 Glibberry Glibbury Glibree Glibrey
Glibbury GLIBBERY
Glibree GLIBBERY
Glibrey GLIBBERY
GLIDDON Glidon Glyddon
Glidon GLIDDON
Glinister GLANISTER GLENISTER GLENNERSTER
GLINN 5 Glean GLENN Glyn Glynn
Gloyen GLOYN
GLOYN Gloyen
Glyddon GLIDDON
Glyn GLENN GLINN
Glynn GLENN GLINN
Gnawdaby NORDABY
Gnordaby NORDABY
GOAD 7 GOOD Goodge Googe Goud GOUDGE GOUGE
Goard GOURD
Goaring GORING GORRINGE
GOATS COATS
Gobel GOBLE
GOBLE Gobel
Godbear GODBER
Godbeare GODBER
Godbeer GODBER
Godbeere GODBER
GODBER 5 Godbear Godbeare Godbeer Godbeere
GODDARD GARRARD Gorrard
GODDEN GODDING Goddon
GODDERIDGE 13 Godderige Goderidge Goderige Godridge Godrige GOODRIDGE Goodrige GOTHERIDGE Gotherige Gothridge Gothrige GUTTERIDGE
Godderige GODDERIDGE GOODRIDGE GOTHERIDGE GUTTERIDGE
GODDING GODDEN
Goddlife GOODLIFFE GOODYER
Goddliffe GOODLIFFE GOODYER
Goddon GODDEN
Godeleif GOODLIFFE GOODYER
Godeleive GOODLIFFE GOODYER
Godeleve GOODLIFFE GOODYER
Goderidge GODDERIDGE GOODRIDGE GOTHERIDGE GUTTERIDGE
Goderige GODDERIDGE GOODRIDGE GOTHERIDGE GUTTERIDGE
Goderthe GOODWORTH
Godileif GOODLIFFE GOODYER
Godileive GOODLIFFE GOODYER
Godin GODWIN GODWINE GOODWIN GOODWYN
Godleif GOODLIFFE GOODYER
Godleive GOODLIFFE GOODYER
Godlif GOODLIFFE GOODYER
Godlife GOODLIFFE GOODYER
Godliffe GOODLIFFE GOODYER
Godlyf GOODLIFFE GOODYER
Godridge GODDERIDGE GOODRIDGE GOTHERIDGE GUTTERIDGE
Godrige GODDERIDGE GOODRIDGE GOTHERIDGE GUTTERIDGE
Godring GOLDRING
Godsal GODSALL
Godsale GODSALL
GODSALL 4 Godsal Godsale Godsell
Godsden GOSDEN GOSLING GOSSELIN
Godsell GODSALL
GODWIN 7 Godin GODWINE Godwyne GOODWIN GOODWYN Goodwyne
GODWINE 6 Godin GODWIN Godwyne GOODWIN GOODWYN
Godworth GOODWORTH
Godwyne GODWIN GODWINE GOODWIN GOODWYN
Goeman GORMAN GOWMAN
GOFF GOFFE GOUGH
GOFFE GOFF GOUGH
Gogan GOGGIN
Goggan GOGGIN
GOGGIN 4 Gogan Goggan Gogin
Gogin GOGGIN
GOILLON 14 Galland GALLON Gaulon Gaylinge Gealing Gilland GOLDING GOLLAND Gollin GOWLAND Gowling Gulling Gullon
Goimar GOYMER
Goimer GOYMER
Goimor GOYMER
Goimour GOYMER
Goimur GOYMER
Golbey GOLBY GOLDBY
GOLBY 4 Golbey Goldbey GOLDBY
GOLD GOULD
Goldbey GOLBY GOLDBY
GOLDBY 4 Golbey GOLBY Goldbey
GOLDEN GOLDING GOULDING
GOLDER Goldier GOULDER
Goldering GOLDRING
Goldier GOLDER GOULDER
GOLDING 17 Galland GALLON GAULER Gaulon Gaylinge Gealing Gilland GOILLON GOLDEN GOLLAND Gollin GOULDING GOWLAND Gowling Gulling Gullon
GOLDRING 16 Godring Goldering Goldringe Golering Goleringe Golring Gooldringe Gooldryng Goulderinge Gouldring Gouldringe Gowdringe Gowdringes Gowldring Gowring
Goldringe GOLDRING
GOLDSMITH Gouldsmith
GOLDSTON 5 Gaulson GOLDSTONE Golson Goulson
GOLDSTONE 5 Gaulson GOLDSTON Golson Goulson
GOLDTHORP 14 Gawthorp Gawthorpe Gawthrope Gawthropp GOLDTHORPE Goldthrop Goldthrope Golthorp Golthorpe Gouldthorp Gouldthorpe Gowthorp Gowthorpe
GOLDTHORPE 14 Gawthorp Gawthorpe Gawthrope Gawthropp GOLDTHORP Goldthrop Goldthrope Golthorp Golthorpe Gouldthorp Gouldthorpe Gowthorp Gowthorpe
Goldthrop GOLDTHORP GOLDTHORPE
Goldthrope GOLDTHORP GOLDTHORPE
Golering GOLDRING
Goleringe GOLDRING
GOLLAND 14 Galland GALLON Gaulon Gaylinge Gealing Gilland GOILLON GOLDING Gollin GOWLAND Gowling Gulling Gullon
Gollin GALLON GOILLON GOLDING GOLLAND GOWLAND
Golring GOLDRING
Golsney GOSNAY GOSNEY
Golsny GOSNAY GOSNEY
Golson GOLDSTON GOLDSTONE
Golthorp GOLDTHORP GOLDTHORPE
Golthorpe GOLDTHORP GOLDTHORPE
Golty GOULTY
Golvun GALVIN
GOM GOMME GUMM
Goman GORMAN GOWMAN
Gomeldon GUMBLETON
GOMM GOOM
GOMME GOM GUMM
Gommo GUMMOW
Gonne GANE GAWEN GOWN GOYNE JANE JAYNE
Gonstone GUNSON GUNSTON GUNSTONE
GOOCH GOUCH
GOOD 9 GOAD GOODE Goodee Goodge Googe Goud GOUDGE GOUGE
GOODAIR 13 Goodaire GOODARE Goodayre Goodear GOODEARE GOODER Goodere Goodheir GOODIER GOODYEAR Goodyeare Gudeare
Goodaire GOODAIR GOODARE GOODEARE GOODER GOODIER GOODYEAR GOODYER
GOODALE GOODALL Gooddall
GOODALL GOODALE Gooddall
GOODARE 13 GOODAIR Goodaire Goodayre Goodear GOODEARE GOODER Goodere Goodheir GOODIER GOODYEAR Goodyeare Gudeare
Goodayre GOODAIR GOODARE GOODEARE GOODER GOODIER GOODYEAR GOODYER
Goodbaudy GOODBODY
Goodberry GOODBODY
Goodboddie GOODBODY
GOODBODY 4 Goodbaudy Goodberry Goodboddie
Gooddall GOODALE GOODALL
GOODE 4 GOOD Goodee Goud
Goodear GOODAIR GOODARE GOODEARE GOODER GOODIER GOODYEAR
GOODEARE 14 GOODAIR Goodaire GOODARE Goodayre Goodear GOODER Goodere Goodheir GOODIER GOODYEAR Goodyeare GOODYER Gudeare
Goodee GOOD GOODE
GOODER 13 GOODAIR Goodaire GOODARE Goodayre Goodear GOODEARE Goodere Goodheir GOODIER GOODYEAR Goodyeare Gudeare
Goodere GOODAIR GOODARE GOODEARE GOODER GOODIER GOODYEAR
GOODES GOODS
GOODEY GOODY
Goodge GOAD GOOD GOUDGE GOUGE
Goodgeon GUDGEON
Goodgion GUDGEON
Goodheir GOODAIR GOODARE GOODEARE GOODER GOODIER GOODYEAR
GOODIER 14 GOODAIR Goodaire GOODARE Goodayre Goodear GOODEARE GOODER Goodere Goodheir GOODYEAR Goodyeare GOODYER Gudeare
GOODING GOODWIN
Goodinson GOODISON
GOODISON Goodinson
Goodleuf GOODLIFFE GOODYER
Goodlif GOODLIFFE GOODYER
GOODLIFFE 21 Getlife Gettlif Gettliffe Goddlife Goddliffe Godeleif Godeleive Godeleve Godileif Godileive Godleif Godleive Godlif Godlife Godliffe Godlyf Goodleuf Goodlif Goodlyf GOODYER
Goodlyf GOODLIFFE GOODYER
GOODRIDGE 13 GODDERIDGE Godderige Goderidge

If the name you are interested in is not here, try Section C.

Goderige Godridge
Godrige Goodrige
GOTHERIDGE Gotherige
Gothridge Gothrige
GUTTERIDGE
Goodrige GODDERIDGE
GOODRIDGE GOTHERIDGE
GUTTERIDGE
GOODS GOODES
Goodwel GOODWELL GOODWILL
GOODWELL 4 Goodwel
GOODWILL Goodwille
Goodwerth GOODWORTH
Goodwerthe GOODWORTH
GOODWILL 4 Goodwel
GOODWELL Goodwille
Goodwille GOODWELL
GOODWILL
GOODWIN 8 Godin GODWIN
GODWINE Godwyne GOODING
GOODWYN Goodwyne
Goodwith GOODWORTH
GOODWORTH 8 Goderthe
Godworth Goodwerth
Goodwerthe Goodwith
Goodworthy Gudworth
Goodworthy GOODWORTH
GOODWYN 6 Godin GODWIN
GODWINE Godwyne GOODWIN
Goodwyne GODWIN GOODWIN
GOODY GOODEY
GOODYEAR 13 GOODAIR
Goodaire GOODARE
Goodayre Goodear
GOODEARE GOODER Goodere
Goodheir GOODIER
Goodyeare Gudeare
Goodyeare GOODAIR GOODARE
GOODEARE GOODER GOODIER
GOODYEAR
GOODYER 25 Getlife
Gettlif Gettliffe
Goddlife Goddliffe
Godeleif Godeleive
Godeleve Godileif
Godileive Godleif
Godleive Godlif Godlife
Godliffe Godlyf
Goodaire Goodayre
GOODEARE GOODIER
Goodleuf Goodlif
GOODLIFFE Goodlyf
Googe GOAD GOOD GOUDGE
GOUGE
Gooldringe GOLDRING
Gooldryng GOLDRING
GOOM GOMM
GOOSE GORST
Goram GOREHAM
GORDEN 4 GAUDEN Gordin
GORDON
GORDGE Gorg Gorge
Gordin GAUDEN GORDEN
GORDON
GORDON 5 GAUDEN GORDEN
Gordin JORDAN
GOREHAM 4 Goram Gorham
Gorum
Goreing GORING GORRINGE
Goreman GORMAN GOWMAN
Gorg GORDGE
Gorge GORDGE
Gorham GOREHAM
Gorie GORRIE
GORING 6 Goaring Goreing
Goringe Gorring
GORRINGE
Goringe GORING GORRINGE
GORMAN 7 Gawman Goeman
Goman Goreman Gormon
GOWMAN
Gormon GORMAN GOWMAN
Gorna CORNAH CORNALL
CORNER
Gornah CORNAH CORNALL
CORNER
Gornall CORNAH CORNALL
CORNER
Gorner CORNAH CORNALL
CORNER
Gornish GORSUCH
Gorrard GARRARD GODDARD
Gorret GARRAD GARRARD
GARRAT GARRATT GARRETT
GARROD GERARD GERRARD
GERRETT JARRARD JARRATT
JARRET JARRETT JARROLD
JARVIS JERRARD JERRETT
YARD
GORRIE Gorie
Gorring GORING GORRINGE
GORRINGE 6 Goaring
Goreing GORING Goringe
Gorring
Gorsach GORSUCH
GORSE Ghorst GORST
Gorsedg GORSUCH
Gorsedge GORSUCH
Gorseeche GORSUCH
Gorsehidge GORSUCH
Gorsey GORSUCH
Gorsh GORSUCH
Gorshe GORSUCH
Gorshich GORSUCH
Gorshuch GORSUCH
Gorsich GORSUCH
Gorsiche GORSUCH
Gorsidg GORSUCH
Gorsiegh GORSUCH
Gorsige GORSUCH
Gorsitch GORSUCH
Gorsitche GORSUCH
Gorssage GORSUCH
Gorssuck GORSUCH
GORST 4 Ghorst GOOSE
GORSE
Gorstadge GORSUCH
Gorstage GORSUCH
Gorstige GORSUCH
Gorston GORSUCH
Gorstridge GORSUCH
Gorstwick GORSUCH
GORSUCH 50 De gorsuch
Garsh Garstwich
Garstwick Gaurstage
Georsich Gersey Gornish
Gorsach Gorsedg
Gorsedge Gorseeche
Gorsehidge Gorsey Gorsh
Gorshe Gorshich
Gorshuch Gorsich
Gorsiche Gorsidg
Gorsiegh Gorsige
Gorsitch Gorsitche
Gorssage Gorssuck
Gorstadge Gorstage
Gorstige Gorston
Gorstridge Gorstwick
Gorsuche Gorsuchill
Gorsuck Gorsutch
Gorsuth Gorsyche
Gortage Gortain Gortan
Gortelow Gorten Gorter
Gorth Gorthar Gorthy
Gossage
Gorsuche GORSUCH
Gorsuchill GORSUCH
Gorsuck GORSUCH
Gorsutch GORSUCH
Gorsuth GORSUCH
Gorsyche GORSUCH
Gortage GORSUCH
Gortain GORSUCH
Gortan GORSUCH
Gortelow GORSUCH
Gorten GORSUCH
Gorter GORSUCH
Gorth GORSUCH
Gorthar GORSUCH
Gorthy GORSUCH
Gorum GOREHAM
Gosbee GOSBY
Gosbey GOSBY
Gosbie GOSBY
GOSBY 8 Gausby Gisbey
Gisby Gosbee Gosbey
Gosbie Gousby
GOSDEN 11 Godsden Gosding
Gosdon Goslin Gosline
GOSLING Gosolon
GOSSELIN Gossline
Gozling
Gosding GOSDEN GOSLING
GOSSELIN
Gosdon GOSDEN GOSLING
GOSSELIN
GOSLETT Gostlett
Goslin GOSDEN GOSLING
GOSSELIN
Gosline GOSDEN GOSLING
GOSSELIN
GOSLING 13 Godsden GOSDEN
Gosding Gosdon Goslin
Gosline Goslon Gosolon
GOSSELIN Gossline
GOSTLING Gozling
Goslon GOSLING GOSTLING
Gosnai GOSNAY GOSNEY
GOSNALD GOSNOLD
GOSNAY 10 Golsney Golsny
Gosnai Gosne GOSNEY
Gosny Gossney Goznay
Gozney
Gosne GOSNAY GOSNEY
GOSNEY 10 Golsney Golsny
Gosnai GOSNAY Gosne
Gosny Gossney Goznay
Gozney
GOSNOLD GOSNALD
Gosny GOSNAY GOSNEY
Gosolon GOSDEN GOSLING
GOSSELIN
Gossage GORSUCH
Gossard GAZZARD
GOSSELIN 11 Godsden
GOSDEN Gosding Gosdon
Goslin Gosline GOSLING
Gosolon Gossline
Gozling
Gossline GOSDEN GOSLING
GOSSELIN
Gossney GOSNAY GOSNEY
Gostlett GOSLETT
GOSTLING GOSLING Goslon
GOTHERIDGE 13 GODDERIDGE
Godderige Goderidge
Goderige Godridge
Godrige GOODRIDGE
Goodrige Gotherige
Gothridge Gothrige
GUTTERIDGE
Gotherige GODDERIDGE
GOODRIDGE GOTHERIDGE
GUTTERIDGE
Gothridge GODDERIDGE
GOODRIDGE GOTHERIDGE
GUTTERIDGE
Gothrige GODDERIDGE
GOODRIDGE GOTHERIDGE
GUTTERIDGE
Gotsheim GOTYHEIN
GOTYHEIN Gotsheim
GOUCH GOOCH
Goud GOAD GOOD GOODE
GOUDGE GOUGE
GOUDGE 7 GOAD GOOD Goodge
Googe Goud GOUGE
GOUGE 7 GOAD GOOD Goodge
Googe Goud GOUDGE
GOUGH GOFF GOFFE
Gouinlock GOWANLOCK
GOWENLOCK
GOULD GOLD Guild
GOULDER GOLDER Goldier
Goulderinge GOLDRING
GOULDING GOLDEN GOLDING
Gouldring GOLDRING
Gouldringe GOLDRING
Gouldsmith GOLDSMITH
Gouldthorp GOLDTHORP
GOLDTHORPE
Gouldthorpe GOLDTHORP
GOLDTHORPE
Goulet GOWLETT
Goulson GOLDSTON
GOLDSTONE
Goult GAUGHT GAULT GAWGHT
GAWT
Goultie GOULTY
GOULTY 5 Galtie Galty
Golty Goultie
GOURD 5 GARD Gird Goard
GURD
GOURLAY GURLEY
Gournay DE GOURNAY
Gourney GURNEY
Gousby GOSBY
Gout GAUGHT GAULT GAWGHT
GAWT
Govanelokis GOWANLOCK
GOWENLOCK
Govanlock GOWANLOCK
GOWENLOCK
Govanlok GOWANLOCK
GOWENLOCK
Govenlock GOWANLOCK
GOWENLOCK
GOWAN GOWARD GOWEN
Gowanloch GOWANLOCK
GOWENLOCK
GOWANLOCK 8 Gouinlock
Govanelokis Govanlock
Govanlok Govenlock
Gowanloch GOWENLOCK
GOWARD GOWAN GOWEN
Gowdringe GOLDRING
Gowdringes GOLDRING
GOWEN GOWAN GOWARD
GOWENLOCK 8 Gouinlock
Govanelokis Govanlock
Govanlok Govenlock
Gowanloch GOWANLOCK
GOWLAND 14 Galland GALLON
Gaulon Gaylinge Gealing
Gilland GOILLON GOLDING
GOLLAND Gollin Gowling
Gulling Gullon
Gowldring GOLDRING
Gowlet GOWLETT
GOWLETT 5 Goulet Gowlet
Gowlette Gullet
Gowlette GOWLETT
Gowling GALLON GOILLON
GOLDING GOLLAND GOWLAND
GOWMAN 7 Gawman Goeman
Goman Goreman GORMAN
Gormon
GOWN 13 Gan GANE GAWEN
Geon Geune Gilb Gonne
GOYNE Guine Jaine JANE
JAYNE
Gowring GOLDRING
Gowthorp GOLDTHORP
GOLDTHORPE
Gowthorpe GOLDTHORP
GOLDTHORPE
Goyan GOYNE
GOYDER Gwydyr
Goyen GOYNE
Goyles GILES
Goymar GOYMER
GOYMER 10 Goimar Goimer
Goimor Goimour Goimur
Goymar Goymor Goymour
Goymur
Goymor GOYMER

If the name you are interested in is not here, try Section C.

Goymour GOYMER
Goymur GOYMER
GOYNE 15 Gan GANE GAWEN Geon Geune Gilb Gonne GOWN Goyan Goyen Guine Jaine JANE JAYNE
Gozard GAZZARD
Gozling GOSDEN GOSLING GOSSELIN
Goznay GOSNAY GOSNEY
Gozney GOSNAY GOSNEY
Gozzard GAZZARD
GRACE Grase Grease
Gradage GRADDAGE GRADIDGE
GRADDAGE 4 Gradage GRADIDGE Gradige
GRADDON GRATTON
GRADIDGE 4 Gradage GRADDAGE Gradige
Gradige GRADDAGE GRADIDGE
GRADY Gready
Graeme GRAHAM
Graeor GREER GRIER GRIEVE GRIEVES
Grafam GRAFHAM
Graffham GRAFHAM
GRAFHAM Grafam Graffham
GRAGSON GREGSON GRIGSON
GRAHAM 6 Graeme Grahame Grahme Grayham Grayme
Grahame GRAHAM
Grahme GRAHAM
GRAINGER GRANGER
Graistie GRESTY
Graisty GRESTY
Graless GRAYLIS
Gralis GRAYLIS
Graliss GRAYLIS
Grammond GRIMMOND
Granam GRANNUM
Granfield GLANVILLE GRANVILLE GRENVILLE
GRANGER GRAINGER
Granham GRANNUM
GRANLEESE 4 Granlese Granleze Granlise
Granlese GRANLEESE
Granleze GRANLEESE
Granlise GRANLEESE
GRANNUM 4 Granam Granham Granom
Granom GRANNUM
Granvill GRANVILLE GRENVILLE
GRANVILLE 6 GLANVILLE Granfield Granvill Grenvill GRENVILLE
GRASBY GREASBY
Grase GRACE
Grasty GRESTY
GRATTON GRADDON
GRAVE GRAVES GREAVES
Gravel GRAVIL
GRAVES 5 GRAVE GREAVES Greeves GRIEVES
GRAVIL 4 Gravel Gravill Graville
Gravill GRAVIL
Graville GRAVIL
GRAY GREY
Grayham GRAHAM
Grayless GRAYLIS
GRAYLIS 9 Graless Gralis Graliss Grayless Grealis Greles Grelis Greslas
Grayme GRAHAM
Grayr GREER GRIER GRIEVE GRIEVES
Gready GRADY
Greair GREER GRIER GRIEVE GRIEVES
Grealis GRAYLIS
Greaney GRINNEY
Greaor GREER GRIER GRIEVE GRIEVES
Greare GREER GRIER GRIEVE GRIEVES
Greares GREER GRIER GRIEVE GRIEVES
Grears GREER GRIER GRIEVE GRIEVES
Greary GREER GRIER GRIEVE GRIEVES
GREASBY GRASBY
Grease GRACE
GREATBACH GREATBATCH
GREATBATCH GREATBACH
GREAVES 6 GRAVE GRAVES Greeves GREVES GRIEVES
Greear GREER GRIER GRIEVE GRIEVES
Greeare GREER GRIER GRIEVE GRIEVES
Greeares GREER GRIER GRIEVE GRIEVES
Greears GREER GRIER GRIEVE GRIEVES
Greehar GREER GRIER GRIEVE GRIEVES
Greels GRILLS GRYLL GRYLLS
GREEN GREENE
GREENE GREEN
Greeneinge GREENING
GREENGRASS Greengrasse Grengres
Greengrasse GREENGRASS
GREENHAM 7 De gryndenham Greneham Grenham Grinham Gryndeham Gryndenham
Greenhoff GREENHOW
Greenhough GREENHOW
GREENHOW 4 Greenhoff Greenhough Greenhowe
Greenhowe GREENHOW
GREENING 13 Greeneinge Greeninge Greenings Greenyng Greninge Grenynge Grinen Grining Grininges Grinnen Grinnin Grinning
Greeninge GREENING
Greenings GREENING
Greenstead GREENSTED GRIMSTEAD GRINSTED
GREENSTED 5 Greenstead GRIMSTEAD Grinstead GRINSTED
Greeny GRINNEY
Greenyng GREENING
Greeor GREER GRIER GRIEVE GRIEVES
GREER 50 Graeor Grayr Greair Greaor Greare Greares Grears Greary Greear Greeare Greeares Greears Greehar Greeor Greere Greeres Greers Greery Greeve Greeves Greier Greir Greire Greires Greirs Greiw Greiwar Greor Grere Greres Griar Griars Griear Grieer GRIER Griere Grieres Grierr Griers Griev GRIEVE GRIEVES Grievs Grior Grire Grirre Griv Gryer Gryor
Greere GREER GRIER GRIEVE GRIEVES
Greeres GREER GRIER GRIEVE GRIEVES
Greers GREER GRIER GRIEVE GRIEVES
Greery GREER GRIER GRIEVE GRIEVES
Greesty GRESTY
GREET Greete
Greete GREET
Greeve GREER GRIER GRIEVE GRIEVES
Greeves GRAVES GREAVES GREER GRIER GRIEVE GRIEVES
GREG GREGG
GREGG GREG
Gregor GRIGOR MACGREGOR MCGREGOR
Gregorey GREGORY
Gregorie GREGORY
GREGORY 4 Gregorey Gregorie GREGREY
GREGREY GREGORY
Gregsby GRIBESBY
GREGSON GRAGSON GRIGSON
Greier GREER GRIER GRIEVE GRIEVES
GREIFF Grieff
GREIG 7 Grig GRIGG GRIGGE GRIGGOR GRIGGS GRIGS
Greir GREER GRIER GRIEVE GRIEVES
Greire GREER GRIER GRIEVE GRIEVES
Greires GREER GRIER GRIEVE GRIEVES
Greirs GREER GRIER GRIEVE GRIEVES
Greive GRIEVE
Greiw GREER GRIER GRIEVE GRIEVES
Greiwar GREER GRIER GRIEVE GRIEVES
Greles GRAYLIS
Grelis GRAYLIS GRELLIS
GRELLIS Grelis
Grells GRILLS GRYLL GRYLLS
Greneham GREENHAM
Greney GRINNEY
Grengres GREENGRASS
Grenham GREENHAM
Grening GRINNEY
Greninge GREENING
Grenney GRINNEY
Grennie GRINNEY
Grenny GRINNEY
Grenvill GLANVILLE GRANVILLE GRENVILLE
GRENVILLE 6 GLANVILLE Granfield Granvill GRANVILLE Grenvill
Grenynge GREENING
Greor GREER GRIER GRIEVE GRIEVES
Grere GREER GRIER GRIEVE GRIEVES
Greres GREER GRIER GRIEVE GRIEVES
Greslas GRAYLIS
Grestie GRESTY
GRESTY 8 Graistie Graisty Grasty Greesty Grestie Greysty Griesty
GREVES GREAVES
Grewby GRUBY
GREWCOCK GROCOCK GROOCOCK
GREY GRAY
Greysty GRESTY
Griar GREER GRIER GRIEVE GRIEVES
Griars GREER GRIER GRIEVE GRIEVES
Gribban GRIBBIN
Gribben GRIBBIN
Gribbens GRIBBIN
GRIBBIN 11 Gribban Gribben Gribbens Gribbing Gribbings Gribbins Gribbon Gribbons Gribin Gribyn
Gribbing GRIBBIN
Gribbings GRIBBIN
Gribbins GRIBBIN
Gribbon GRIBBIN
Gribbons GRIBBIN
GRIBESBY Gregsby
Gribin GRIBBIN
Gribyn GRIBBIN
Gridiley GRIDLEY
GRIDLEY Gridiley
Griear GREER GRIER GRIEVE GRIEVES
Grieer GREER GRIER GRIEVE GRIEVES
Grieff GREIFF
GRIER 50 Graeor Grayr Greair Greaor Greare Greares Grears Greary Greear Greeare Greeares Greears Greehar Greeor GREER Greere Greeres Greers Greery Greeve Greeves Greier Greir Greire Greires Greirs Greiw Greiwar Greor Grere Greres Griar Griars Griear Grieer Griere Grieres Grierr Griers Griev GRIEVE GRIEVES Grievs Grior Grire Grirre Griv Gryer Gryor
Griere GREER GRIER GRIEVE GRIEVES
Grieres GREER GRIER GRIEVE GRIEVES
Grierr GREER GRIER GRIEVE GRIEVES
Griers GREER GRIER GRIEVE GRIEVES
Griesty GRESTY
Griev GREER GRIER GRIEVE GRIEVES
GRIEVE 51 Graeor Grayr Greair Greaor Greare Greares Grears Greary Greear Greeare Greeares Greears Greehar Greeor GREER Greere Greeres Greers Greery Greeve Greeves Greier Greir Greire Greires Greirs Greive Greiw Greiwar Greor Grere Greres Griar Griars Griear Grieer GRIER Griere Grieres Grierr Griers Griev GRIEVES Grievs Grior Grire Grirre Griv Gryer Gryor
GRIEVES 52 Graeor GRAVES Grayr Greair Greaor Greare Greares Grears Greary GREAVES Greear Greeare Greeares Greears Greehar Greeor GREER Greere Greeres Greers Greery Greeve Greeves Greier Greir Greire Greires Greirs Greiw Greiwar Greor Grere Greres Griar Griars Griear Grieer GRIER Griere Grieres Grierr Griers Griev GRIEVE Grievs Grior Grire Grirre Griv Gryer Gryor
Grievs GREER GRIER GRIEVE GRIEVES
GRIFFITH GRIFFITHS
GRIFFITHS 6 GRIFFITH

If the name you are interested in is not here, try Section C.

Griffits Griffitts Griffs Griffus
Griffits GRIFFITHS
Griffitts GRIFFITHS
Griffs GRIFFITHS
Griffus GRIFFITHS
Grig GREIG GRIGG GRIGGE GRIGGOR GRIGGS GRIGS
GRIGG 7 GREIG Grig GRIGGE GRIGGOR GRIGGS GRIGS
GRIGGE 7 GREIG Grig GRIGG GRIGGOR GRIGGS GRIGS
GRIGGOR 7 GREIG Grig GRIGG GRIGGE GRIGGS GRIGS
GRIGGS 7 GREIG Grig GRIGG GRIGGE GRIGGOR GRIGS
GRIGOR 15 Gregor M'gregor M'grigor MACGREGOR Macgrigor Mackgregor Mackgrigor Mcgreagor Mcgreger MCGREGOR Mcgreogar Mcgrigor Mckgregor Mckgrigor
GRIGS 7 GREIG Grig GRIGG GRIGGE GRIGGOR GRIGGS
GRIGSON GRAGSON GREGSON
Grill GRILLS GRYLL GRYLLS
Grilles GRILLS GRYLL GRYLLS
GRILLS 11 Greels Grells Grill Grilles Grils GRYLL Grylles GRYLLS Gryls Gryrlls
Grils GRILLS GRYLL GRYLLS
GRIMBALDESTON Grimbaldestone
Grimbaldestone GRIMBALDESTON
GRIMES 5 Grimme GRYME Grymes Grymme
Grimesdale GRIMSDELL
Grimmand GRIMMOND
Grimme GRIMES GRYME
GRIMMOND 5 Grammond Grimmand Grimond Grummond
Grimond GRIMMOND
Grimsdal GRIMSDELL
Grimsdall GRIMSDELL
Grimsdel GRIMSDELL
GRIMSDELL 5 Grimesdale Grimsdal Grimsdall Grimsdel
GRIMSTEAD 6 Greenstead GREENSTED Grimsteed Grinstead GRINSTED
Grimsteed GRIMSTEAD
Grimston GRIMSTONE
GRIMSTONE Grimston
GRINDY GRUNDY
Grinen GREENING
Griney GRINNEY
Grinham GREENHAM
Grinime GRINNEY
Grining GREENING GRINNEY
Grininges GREENING
Grinnen GREENING
GRINNEY 12 Greaney Greeny Greney Grening Grenney Grennie Grenny Griney Grinime Grining Grinning
Grinnin GREENING
Grinning GREENING GRINNEY
Grinstead GREENSTED GRIMSTEAD GRINSTED
GRINSTED 5 Greenstead GREENSTED GRIMSTEAD Grinstead
Grior GREER GRIER GRIEVE GRIEVES
Grire GREER GRIER GRIEVE GRIEVES
Grirre GREER GRIER GRIEVE GRIEVES
Griv GREER GRIER GRIEVE GRIEVES
Groaes GROSE GROSS GROSSE
Groas GROSE GROSS GROSSE
Groass GROSE GROSS GROSSE
Groasse GROSE GROSS GROSSE
Grobety GROBITY
GROBITY Grobety
Groce GROSE GROSS GROSSE
Grocier GROSIER
GROCOCK GREWCOCK GROOCOCK
Gronnow GRONOW
Grono GRONOW
GRONOW 4 Gronnow Grono Gruno
Groobey GRUBY
Grooby GRUBY
GROOCOCK GREWCOCK GROCOCK
Groos GROSE GROSS GROSSE
Groose GROSE GROSS GROSSE
Gros GROSE GROSS GROSSE
GROSE 13 Groaes Groas Groass Groasse Groce Groos Groose Gros GROSS GROSSE Grouse Growse
GROSIER Grocier
GROSS 13 Groaes Groas Groass Groasse Groce Groos Groose Gros GROSE GROSSE Grouse Growse
GROSSE 13 Groaes Groas Groass Groasse Groce Groos Groose Gros GROSE GROSS Grouse Growse
Grosshurst GROVEHURST
GROSVENOR Grovenor Grovesnor
Grouse GROSE GROSS GROSSE
GROVE GROVES
GROVEHURST Grosshurst
Grovenor GROSVENOR
GROVES GROVE
Grovesnor GROSVENOR
Growse GROSE GROSS GROSSE
GRUBY 4 Grewby Groobey Grooby
Grudgefeild GRUDGEFIELD
Grudgefeld GRUDGEFIELD
GRUDGEFIELD 5 Grudgefeild Grudgefeld Grudgfield Grutchfield
Grudgfield GRUDGEFIELD
Gruit GRUT
Gruitt GRUT
Grummond GRIMMOND
GRUNDY GRINDY
Gruno GRONOW
GRUT 5 Gruit Gruitt Grute Grutt
Grutchfield GRUDGEFIELD
Grute GRUT
Grutt GRUT
Gryer GREER GRIER GRIEVE GRIEVES
GRYLL 11 Greels Grells Grill Grilles GRILLS Grils Grylles GRYLLS Gryls Gryrlls
Grylles GRILLS GRYLL GRYLLS
GRYLLS 11 Greels Grells Grill Grilles GRILLS Grils GRYLL Grylles Gryls Gryrlls
Gryls GRILLS GRYLL GRYLLS
GRYME 4 GRIMES Grimme Grymme
Grymes GRIMES
Grymme GRIMES GRYME
Gryndeham GREENHAM
Gryndenham GREENHAM
Gryor GREER GRIER GRIEVE GRIEVES
Gryrlls GRILLS GRYLL GRYLLS
Gudeare GOODAIR GOODARE GOODEARE GOODER GOODIER GOODYEAR
GUDGEON Goodgeon Goodgion
Gudworth GOODWORTH
Guelder GELDER GILDER
Guernier GARNIER
GUESS GUEST
GUEST 4 Gast GEST GUESS
Guild GOULD
Guilden GILDEN GILDING GILDON
Guilding GILDEN GILDING GILDON
Guildon GILDEN GILDING GILDON
GUILFOYLE Kilfoyle
Guine GANE GAWEN GOWN GOYNE JANE JAYNE
Guines GYNES JEENS JOYNES
GUIVER 4 Giver GUYVER Gyva
Gullet GOWLETT
GULLEY GULLY
GULLICK GULLOCK
Gulling GALLON GOILLON GOLDING GOLLAND GOWLAND
GULLOCK GULLICK
Gullon GALLON GOILLON GOLDING GOLLAND GOWLAND
GULLY GULLEY
GUM GUMM
Gumbelton GUMBLETON
GUMBLETON Gomeldon Gumbelton
GUMBLEY GUMLEY Gumly
GUMLEY GUMBLEY Gumly
Gumly GUMBLEY GUMLEY
GUMM 4 GOM GOMME GUM
GUMMOW Gommo
GUNSON 4 Gonstone GUNSTON GUNSTONE
Gunsten GUNSTON GUNSTONE
GUNSTON 5 Gonstone GUNSON Gunsten GUNSTONE
GUNSTONE 5 Gonstone GUNSON Gunsten GUNSTON
Gunthorp GUNTHORPE GUNTRIP
GUNTHORPE 5 Gunthorp Gunthrip Gunthrup GUNTRIP
Gunthrip GUNTHORPE GUNTRIP
Gunthrup GUNTHORPE GUNTRIP
GUNTRIP 5 Gunthorp GUNTHORPE Gunthrip Gunthrup
Gup JUP JUPE JUPP JUPPE
Gupp JUP JUPE JUPP JUPPE
Guppe JUP JUPE JUPP JUPPE
Gupps JUP JUPE JUPP JUPPE
GURD 4 GARD Gird GOURD
GURLEY GOURLAY
GURLING GIRLING
GURNEY 5 Gourney Gurnie Gurny Gurnye
Gurnie GURNEY
Gurny GURNEY
Gurnye GURNEY
GUTHERSON Gutterson
Gutter AGUTTER
GUTTERIDGE 13 GODDERIDGE Godderige Goderidge Goderige Godridge Godrige GOODRIDGE Goodrige GOTHERIDGE Gotherige Gothridge Gothrige
Gutters AGUTTER
Gutterson GUTHERSON
GUY Guye
Guye GUY
GUYVER 4 Giver GUIVER Gyva
Guyzard GAZZARD
GWINNETT 5 GWINNUTT Gwynedd Gwynett Gwynutt
GWINNUTT 5 GWINNETT Gwynedd Gwynett Gwynutt
Gwydyr GOYDER
Gwynedd GWINNETT GWINNUTT
Gwynett GWINNETT GWINNUTT
GWYNN GWYNNE
GWYNNE GWYNN
Gwynutt GWINNETT GWINNUTT
Gydding GEDEN GIDDENS GIDDINGS GIDDINS
Gyddings GIDDINGS
Gyddy GIDDY GYDE
Gyddyng GEDEN GIDDENS GIDDINGS GIDDINS
GYDE 15 Geddy Gedie Gedy GEDYE Geedie Geedy Geedye Geydye Giddey GIDDY Giddye Gidi Gyddy Gydy
Gydin GEDEN GIDDENS GIDDINGS GIDDINS
Gydon GEDEN GIDDENS GIDDINGS GIDDINS
Gydy GEDYE GIDDY GYDE
Gylden GILDEN GILDING GILDON
Gylding GILDEN GILDING GILDON
Gyldynge GILDEN GILDING GILDON
Gyllot GILLOTT JELLETT
Gyllott GILLOTT JELLETT
Gyn GINN
GYNES 12 Ghieyes Ghines Ghisnes Ghiyes Ghuines Gines Guines JEENS Jines JOYNES Jynes
GYNGELL GINGELL Gyngle
Gyngle GINGELL GYNGELL
Gynne GINN
Gyssett JESSETT
Gysynge GEESIN GEESING
Gyva GUIVER GUYVER
HABBERLEY 4 Habberly Haberley Haberly
Habberly HABBERLEY
Haber HAVER
Haberley HABBERLEY
Haberly HABBERLEY
HABERMEHL Haeffermehl Haffermehl
Haccleia HICKLEY
Hached HATCHARD HATCHETT
Hackelbridge HUCKLEBRIDGE
Hackence AIKEN EKINS HAWKINS OAKINS OKINS
Hackersley ACKERLEY
Hackerson HACKESON
HACKESON Hackerson Hacksun
HACKETT 7 Hurckett Hurcot Hurcott Hurcotte Hurcut HURKETT
HACKFORD Hackforth
Hackforth HACKFORD
Hackins AIKEN EKINS HAWKINS OAKINS OKINS
Hacksall HACKWELL HAXELL
HACKSHALL Hackshell Hacsell
Hackshell HACKSHALL
Hacksoll HACKWELL HAXELL
Hacksun HACKESON
HACKWELL 12 Axall Axcell Axell Hacksall Hacksoll

If the name you are interested in is not here, try Section C.

Haxall HAXELL Haxill
Haxoll Haxswel Haxwell
HACON 4 HAKEN Haking
Hakon
Hacraste HAYCRAFT
HAYCROFT MACROFT
MAYCRAFT MAYCROFT
MEDCROFT MOORCROFT
Hacsell HACKSHALL
Haddan HADDON HADEN
Haddcock HADDOCK
HADDEN 4 HADDON HADEN
Hadon
HADDERELL HADDRELL
HATHERELL
Haddick HADDOCK
HADDOCK 5 Haddcock
Haddick Hadduck Hadduk
HADDON 8 Adden Haddan
HADDEN HADEN Hadon
HAWDON HOLDEN
HADDRELL 5 HADDERELL
Haddrill Hadrill
HATHERELL
Haddrill HADDRELL
Hadduck HADDOCK
Hadduk HADDOCK
Hade HEAD
HADEN 10 Adden Aden
Haddan HADDEN HADDON
Hadon HAYDEN HAYDON
HEYDON
Hadenham HADINGHAM
Hadfeld HADFIELD HATFIELD
HADFIELD 5 ATTFIELD
Hadfeld HATFIELD
Matfield
Hadham HADINGHAM
HADINGHAM Hadenham Hadham
HADLAND HEADLAND
HADLER Hadlor
Hadlor HADLER
HADLOW Hadlowe
Hadlowe HADLOW
Hadnam ADNAM ADNAMS
Hadnams ADNAM ADNAMS
Hadnum ADNAM ADNAMS
Hadnums ADNAMS
Hadon HADDEN HADDON HADEN
Hadrill HADDRELL
Hadwen HADWIN
HADWIN Hadwen
Haeffermehl HABERMEHL
Haffer HAVER
Haffermehl HABERMEHL
HAFFNER 4 HAFNER Heffner
Hefner
HAFNER 4 HAFFNER Heffner
Hefner
HAGAN 15 Eagan Eagin
HAGEN Haggan Hagin
Haygan Heagan Heagin
Heagon HEGAN Heigan
Higan HOGAN O'hagan
Hagardston HAGGERSTON
Hagarston HAGGERSTON
HAGEN 15 Eagan Eagin
HAGAN Haggan Hagin
Haygan Heagan Heagin
Heagon HEGAN Heigan
Higan HOGAN O'hagan
Hagerston HAGGERSTON
Haggan HAGAN HAGEN HEGAN
HOGAN
Haggarston HAGGERSTON
HAGGERSTON 8 Hagardston
Hagarston Hagerston
Haggarston Hagreston
Hardageston
Hardargeston
Hagin HAGAN HAGEN HEGAN
HOGAN
Hagreston HAGGERSTON
HAGUE HAIG HAIGH

Haiden HAYDEN HAYDON
HAIG HAGUE
HAIGH HAGUE
Haigwood HOGWOOD
Hail HAILE HAILS HALE
HALES HAYLES
Hailcoat ELCOAT
Hailcot ELCOAT
HAILE Hail HALE
HAILEE 4 HAILEY Haily
HALEY
HAILEY 9 Aley ELEY ELY
HAILEE Haily HALEY Haly
HEALEY
Haills HAILS HALE HALES
HAYLES
HAILS 7 Hail Haills HALE
HALES Hayle HAYLES
HAILWOOD 13 Ailard
Ailward Allward ALLWOOD
Alward Alwart Alwood
ALYWARD AYLWARD
HALEWOOD HALWOOD
HAYWOOD
Haily HAILEE HAILEY HALEY
Hain HAINES HAYNES
HAINES 6 Hain Hains
HAYNES Heynes Heyns
HAINING 6 Hainning Haning
HANNING Hanyng Hayning
Hainning HAINING HANNING
Hains HAINES HAYNES
Hair AYRE AYRES EYRE HARE
Hairbrun HARBOURNE
HARBRON
Haire HARE
Hairsign HAIRSINE
HAIRSINE 7 Hairsign
Haresine Harsen Harsin
Harsine Hersan
Hais HAYES HAYS
Haise HAYES HAYS HAYSE
HEYS
HAISELL 5 Halsell Harsell
HASSELL HAZEL
Haislett ASLETT HASLETT
Haisom HAYSOM
Haison HAZON
Haither HATHER HEATHER
HAKEN 4 HACON Haking
Hakon
Hakince AIKEN EKINS
HAWKINS OAKINS OKINS
Hakines AIKEN EKINS
HAWKINS OAKINS OKINS
Haking HACON HAKEN
Hakings AIKEN EKINS
HAWKINS OAKINS OKINS
Hakins AIKEN EKINS
HAWKINS OAKINS OKINS
Hakon HACON HAKEN
Halas HALLAS
HALAY HALEY
HALBARD Halbert Holbard
Halbert HALBARD
HALBROOK 12 Alsebrook
Bolbrook Halbrooks
Haulbrook Haulbrooks
Holbrock HOLBROOK
Holdbrook Holdbrooks
Houlbrook Houlbrooks
Halbrooks HALBROOK
HALDEN HALDIN Hallden
Haldern HAWTHORN HORDEN
HORDERN
Halderton ALDERTON
HALDIN HALDEN Hallden
HALDSWORTHE HOLDSWORTH
HALE 10 Hail HAILE Haills
HAILS HALES Hayle
HAYLES HEAL Heale
HALES 8 EALES Hail Haills
HAILS HALE Hayle HAYLES
Halesse HALSE

HALEWOOD 13 Ailard
Ailward Allward ALLWOOD
Alward Alwart Alwood
ALYWARD AYLWARD
HAILWOOD HALWOOD
HAYWOOD
HALEY 10 Aley ELEY ELY
HAILEE HAILEY Haily
HALAY Haly HEALEY
HALFARD 5 Halfred
HALFYARD Halfyeard
HELLARD
HALFORD ALFORD Allford
Halfred HALFARD HALFYARD
HELLARD
HALFYARD 6 HALFARD
Halfred Halfyards
Halfyeard HELLARD
Halfyards HALFYARD
Halfyeard HALFARD
HALFYARD HELLARD
Halgarth HALLGARTH
Halgath HALLGARTH
Haliday HALLIDAY
HALIFAX HALLIFAX
Haliwell HALLIWELL
HELLIWELL
Hallabone HALLYBONE
Halladay HALLIDAY
HOLLIDAY
HALLAM SAXELBY Saxilby
HALLAS Halas Hallass
Hallass HALLAS
Hallblaster ARBLASTER
Hallden ALDEN ALLDEN
HALDEN HALDIN
Halleck HAYLOCK
Halleren HALLORAN
Halleron HALLORAN
HALLEY 13 HANLEY HAWLEY
HOOLEY Hooly Howley
Hullay HULLEY HULLY
ULLEY Ully UTLEY
Whooley
Halleybone HALLYBONE
HALLGARTH 6 Algarth
Algate Algath Halgarth
Halgath
Hallibon HOLLIBONE
Hallibone HALLYBONE
HALLIDAY 6 Haliday
Halladay HOLIDAY
HOLLIDAY Holyday
HALLIFAX HALIFAX
Hallin HALLING HALLINS
HOLLIN HOLLINGS HOLLINS
HALLING 15 Hallin
Hallinge Hallinges
Hallings HALLINS
Hauling Haulinge Hawlin
Hawling Hawlings HOLLIN
Holling HOLLINGS
HOLLINS
Hallinge HALLING
Hallinges HALLING
HALLINGHAM ALLINGHAM
Hallings HALLING HALLINS
HOLLIN HOLLINGS HOLLINS
HALLINS 8 Hallin HALLING
Hallings HOLLIN Holling
HOLLINGS HOLLINS
HALLIWELL 7 Haliwell
Hallowell Heliwell
HELLAWELL HELLIWELL
Hellowell
HALLKINS Holkins
Hallmark ALLMARK
HALLORAN 5 Halleren
Halleron Halloron
Holloran
Halloron HALLORAN
HALLOWAY 6 Hallowell
HOLLAWAY HOLLOWAY
HOLLOWELL Holoway

Hallowell HALLIWELL
HALLOWAY HELLAWELL
HELLIWELL HOLLAWAY
HOLLOWAY HOLLOWELL
HALLOWES HALLOWS Hollows
HALLOWS HALLOWES Hollows
Hallson HALSON
HALLSWORTH 4 ALLSWORTH
Hawlsworth Howlesworth
HALLYBONE 7 Alleybone
Allibone Allybone
Hallabone Halleybone
Hallibone
Hals HALSE
Halsand HALSON
HALSE Halesse Hals
Halsell HAISELL HASSELL
HAZEL
HALSON 4 Hallson Halsand
Halsone
Halsone HALSON
HALSTEAD Hasted Haystead
HALWOOD 13 Ailard Ailward
Allward ALLWOOD Alward
Alwart Alwood ALYWARD
AYLWARD HAILWOOD
HALEWOOD HAYWOOD
Haly ELEY ELY HAILEY
HALEY HEALEY
Haman HAYMAN
Hamblett HAMLET
HAMBLEY 4 HAMBLY HAMLEY
Hamly
HAMBLIN Hamblyn
HAMBLY 4 HAMBLEY HAMLEY
Hamly
Hamblyn HAMBLIN
HAMBRIDGE 9 Ambage
Ambidge Ambige Ambrage
AMBRIDGE Bambridge
RAMBRIDGE Umbrage
Hambroke HAMBROOK
HAMBROOK Hambroke
Hembrook
HAMER 11 ARMAN Armar
ARMER ARMOUR HARMAN
Harmar Harmen HARMER
Harmon Harmour
Hamersley HAMMERSLEY
HAMILTON Hamiltone
Hamiltown
Hamiltone HAMILTON
Hamiltown HAMILTON
HAMLET Hamblett
HAMLEY 4 HAMBLEY HAMBLY
Hamly
HAMLIN HAMLYN
Hamly HAMBLEY HAMBLY
HAMLEY
HAMLYN HAMLIN
Hammanett AMANET
HAMMERSLEY Hamersley
Hammersly
Hammersly HAMMERSLEY
HAMMOND 4 HAMMONDS HAMON
Hamptonne
HAMMONDS HAMMOND
Hammonet AMANET
HAMON 9 HAMMOND Hamptonne
Hoeman Holeman HOLLMAN
HOLMAN HOMAN Homanes
Hamonett AMANET
Hamptonne HAMMOND HAMON
Hanam HANHAM HANNAM
HANBY HANDLEY
Hance HAUNCH
HANCEFORD 5 Hancford
HANDSFORD HANSFARD
HANSFORD
Hancford HANCEFORD
HANDSFORD HANSFARD
HANSFORD
Hanch HAUNCH
Hanchant HANCHET HANCHETT

If the name you are interested in is not here, try Section C.

HATCHETT
Hanchatt HANCHET HANCHETT HATCHETT
Hanchent HANCHET HANCHETT HATCHETT
HANCHET 10 Hanchant Hanchatt Hanchent HANCHETT Hanchiott Hantchett Hatchet HATCHETT Henshot
HANCHETT 10 Hanchant Hanchatt Hanchent HANCHET Hanchiott Hantchett Hatchet HATCHETT Henshot
Hanchiott HANCHET HANCHETT HATCHETT
Hanchman HENCHMAN HENSMAN HINKSMAN HINXMAN HITCHMAN
HANCOCK HANDCOCK
HAND Hande HANDS
HANDCOCK HANCOCK
Hande HAND
Handes HANDS
HANDFORD Hanford
HANDLEY HANBY HANLEY
HANDS 6 HAND Handes Hannes Hanns Hans
Handscombe HANSCOMBE
HANDSEL HANSELL
Handsen HANSON HARRISON
HANDSFORD 5 HANCEFORD Hancford HANSFARD HANSFORD
Hanford HANDFORD
HANHAM Hanam HANNAM
Haning HAINING HANNING
HANKINSON Hankison Henkinson
Hankison HANKINSON
HANLEY 14 HALLEY HANDLEY HAWLEY HOOLEY Hooly Howley Hullay HULLEY HULLY ULLEY Ully UTLEY Whooley
HANNA 6 ACHANY D'ANNETHE HANNAH HANNAY HANNEY
HANNAH 6 ACHANY D'ANNETHE HANNA HANNAY HANNEY
HANNAM Hanam HANHAM
HANNAY 6 ACHANY D'ANNETHE HANNA HANNAH HANNEY
HANNENT Hannet
Hannes HANDS
Hannet HANNENT
HANNEY 4 HANNA HANNAH HANNAY
Hannibal ANNABALAH
Hannible ANNABALAH
HANNING 6 HAINING Hainning Haning Hanyng Hayning
Hanns HANDS
Hannton HAUNTON
Hans HANDS
Hansard HANSORD
Hansborough HENSBERGH
Hansbrow HENSBERGH
HANSCOMBE Handscombe
Hansel ANCELL
HANSELL HANDSEL
Hansemane HENCHMAN HENSMAN HINKSMAN HINXMAN HITCHMAN
Hansen HANSON HARRISON
HANSFARD 5 HANCEFORD Hancford HANDSFORD HANSFORD
HANSFORD 5 HANCEFORD Hancford HANDSFORD HANSFARD
Hanshmen HENCHMAN HENSMAN HINKSMAN HINXMAN HITCHMAN
Hansil AMSEL ANCELL ANSELL
HANSLOPE De hanslope
HANSON 5 Handsen Hansen Hantson HARRISON
HANSORD Hansard
Hantchett HANCHET HANCHETT HATCHETT
HANTON Hearnton
Hantson HANSON HARRISON
Hanyng HAINING HANNING
Haore HOAR HORE
HARAL 14 Harald Harall Harel Harell HAROLD Harolde Harould Harral Harrall Harrel HARRELL Harrill HARROLD
Harald HARAL HAROLD HARRELL HARROLD
Harall HARAL HAROLD HARRELL
Harbadge HARBRIDGE
Harbage HARBRIDGE
HARBER ARBER Arbor
Harberon HARBOURNE HARBRON
Harberson HARBERTSON HERBISON
HARBERT HERBERT
HARBERTSON 8 Harberson Harbison Harbutson Herberson Herbertson HERBISON Herbutson
Harbidge HARBRIDGE
Harbige HARBRIDGE
Harbison HARBERTSON HERBISON
Harbourn HARBOURNE HARBRON
HARBOURNE 7 Hairbrun Harberon Harbourn HARBRON Harbrun Harburn
Harbridg HARBRIDGE
HARBRIDGE 7 Arbridge Harbadge Harbage Harbidge Harbige Harbridg
HARBRON 7 Hairbrun Harberon Harbourn HARBOURNE Harbrun Harburn
Harbrun HARBOURNE HARBRON
Harburn HARBOURNE HARBRON
Harbutson HARBERTSON HERBISON
Harca HARKER
HARCOURT De harcourt
Harcur HARKER
Hardageston HAGGERSTON
Hardargeston HAGGERSTON
Hardcastell HARDCASTLE
HARDCASTLE Hardcastell Herdecastell
HARDEMAN 5 Hardeyman HARDIMAN HARDYMAN Wardeman
HARDEN 6 ARDEN ARDERN HARDING HARNDEN Hernden
HARDESTY Hardistie HARDISTY
Hardeyman HARDEMAN HARDIMAN HARDYMAN
HARDIE HARDY
HARDIMAN 6 HARDEMAN Hardeyman HARDMAN HARDYMAN Wardeman
Hardin HARTIN HAUGHTON HORTON HUTTON MARTIN
HARDING HARDEN
Hardistie HARDESTY HARDISTY
HARDISTY HARDESTY Hardistie
HARDMAN HARDIMAN
Hardwich HARDWIDGE
HARDWICK 4 Hardwicke Hardwyck Hordwyck
Hardwicke HARDWICK
HARDWIDGE Hardwich Hardwitch
Hardwitch HARDWIDGE
Hardwyck HARDWICK
HARDY HARDIE
HARDYMAN 5 HARDEMAN Hardeyman HARDIMAN Wardeman
HARE 8 AYRE AYRES Eayre EYRE Hair Haire HARES
Harel HARAL HAROLD HARRELL
Harell HARAL HAROLD HARRELL
HARES 11 HARE Haress HARIS Harise Hariss HARRIES HARRIS Harrise Harrisse Hawis
Haresine HAIRSINE
Haress HARES HARIS HARRIES HARRIS
HARGRAVE 6 HARGRAVES Hargreave HARGREAVES HARGROVE Hargroves
HARGRAVES 6 HARGRAVE Hargreave HARGREAVES HARGROVE Hargroves
Hargreave HARGRAVE HARGRAVES HARGREAVES HARGROVE
HARGREAVES 6 HARGRAVE HARGRAVES Hargreave HARGROVE Hargroves
HARGROVE 6 HARGRAVE HARGRAVES Hargreave HARGREAVES Hargroves
Hargroves HARGRAVE HARGRAVES HARGREAVES HARGROVE
HARINGTON 4 HARRINGTON Herington HERRINGTON
HARIS 10 HARES Haress Harise Hariss HARRIES HARRIS Harrise Harrisse Hawis
Harise HARES HARIS HARRIES HARRIS
Hariss HARES HARIS HARRIES HARRIS
HARKER 5 Harca Harcur Harkie Hearker
Harkie HARKER
Harkinstall ARKINSTALL
Harkinstone ARKINSTALL
Harkwright ARKWRIGHT
HARLEY 4 De harley Malherbe Malherve
Harm ARM ARMES ARMS
HARMAN 12 ARMAN Armar ARMER ARMOUR HAMER Harmand Harmar Harmen HARMER Harmon Harmour
Harmand HARMAN
Harmar ARMAN ARMER ARMOUR HAMER HARMAN HARMER
Harmen ARMAN ARMER ARMOUR HAMER HARMAN HARMER
HARMER 11 ARMAN Armar ARMER ARMOUR HAMER HARMAN Harmar Harmen Harmon Harmour
Harmon ARMAN ARMER ARMOUR HAMER HARMAN HARMER
Harmour ARMAN ARMER ARMOUR HAMER HARMAN HARMER
Harmswood HARMSWORTH
HARMSWORTH Armsworth Harmswood
Harn HEARN HEARNE HERN
HARNDEN HARDEN Hernden
Harneiss HARNESS
Harnes HARNESS
HARNESS 4 Harneiss Harnes Harniss
Harniss HARNESS
HAROLD 14 HARAL Harald Harall Harel Harell Harolde Harould Harral Harrall Harrel HARRELL Harrill HARROLD
Harolde HARAL HAROLD HARRELL HARROLD
Harould HARAL HAROLD HARRELL HARROLD
Harpam HARPHAM HARPUM
HARPER HARPUR
HARPHAM Harpam HARPUM
HARPUM Harpam HARPHAM
HARPUR HARPER
HARRAD HARWOOD
Harral HARAL HAROLD HARRELL
Harrall HARAL HAROLD HARRELL HARROLD
HARRAS HARRIS
Harrel HARAL HAROLD HARRELL HARROLD
HARRELL 14 HARAL Harald Harall Harel Harell HAROLD Harolde Harould Harral Harrall Harrel Harrill HARROLD
Harrhy HARRY
Harriatt HARRIOTT HERRIOTT
HARRIES 10 HARES Haress HARIS Harise Hariss HARRIS Harrise Harrisse Hawis
Harrill HARAL HAROLD HARRELL HARROLD
HARRINGTON 4 HARINGTON Herington HERRINGTON
HARRIOTT 4 Harriatt Hayyot HERRIOTT
HARRIS 12 HARES Haress HARIS Harise Hariss HARRAS HARRIES Harrise HARRISS Harrisse Hawis
Harrise HARES HARIS HARRIES HARRIS
HARRISON 6 Handsen Hansen HANSON Hantson Herrison
HARRISS HARRIS
Harrisse HARES HARIS HARRIES HARRIS
HARROD Herrod
HARROLD 10 HARAL Harald HAROLD Harolde Harould Harrall Harrel HARRELL Harrill
HARRY Harrhy
HARRYMAN Herriman
Harselett ASLETT HASLETT
Harsell HAISELL HASSELL HAZEL HORSELL
Harsen HAIRSINE
Harset ASLETT HASLETT
Harsin HAIRSINE
Harsine HAIRSINE
Harslat ASLETT HASLETT
Harslet ASLETT HASLETT
Harslett ASLETT HASLETT
HARTAS 5 Hartass Harters Hartis Hartiss
Hartass HARTAS
Harten HARTIN HAUGHTON HORTON HUTTON MARTIN
Harters HARTAS
HARTERY Hartrey
HARTIN 9 Hardin Harten Harting Harton HAUGHTON

If the name you are interested in is not here, try Section C.

HORTON HUTTON MARTIN
Harting HARTIN
Hartis HARTAS
Hartiss HARTAS
Hartknoll HARTNELL HARTNOLL
HARTLE HARTLEY
HARTLEY 4 ARTLEY HARTLE Heartley
HARTNELL 4 Hartknoll HARTNOLL Hurtnoll
HARTNOLL 4 Hartknoll HARTNELL Hurtnoll
Harton HARTIN HAUGHTON HORTON HUTTON MARTIN
Hartrey HARTERY
HARTSHORN Hartshorne
Hartshorne HARTSHORN
HARVEY-ENEVER Enever-harvey
HARWOOD 4 HARRAD Herod Heyward
Hascol HASKELL
Hascoll HASKELL
HASE HAYES
Hasel HASELL HASSELL HAZEL
Haseler HASLER
Haselett ASLETT HASLETT
Haselette ASLETT HASLETT
Haselgrove HASSELGRAVE
HASELL 4 Hasel HASSELL HAZEL
Haselwood HAZELWOOD HAZLEWOOD
HASKELL 34 Askell Aswell Essell Hascol Hascoll HASKOLL Hassel HASWELL Hawsell Haysel Hessell Hoswell Husle HUSSELL HUZZELL Israel Issel Osell OSWALD Ozell RUSSELL URSELL Urswell Ushil Ussell Ussol Ussould Uswell Uzald Uzle Uzzeel Uzzele UZZELL
HASKING 6 Haskings HASKINS HOSKING Hoskings HOSKINS
Haskings HASKING HASKINS
HASKINS 6 HASKING Haskings HOSKING Hoskings HOSKINS
HASKOLL HASKELL
Haslar HASLER
Haslat ASLETT HASLETT
Hasle ASLETT HASLER HASLETT
HASLER 5 Haseler Haslar Hasle Hastler
Haslet ASLETT HASLETT
HASLETT 35 Aslet ASLETT Haislett Harselett Harset Harslat Harslet Harslett Haselett Haselette Haslat Hasle Haslet Haslit Haslitt Haslot Haslott Haslotte Haslut Haslutt Hassett Hasslat Hasslett Hastlet Hayslett Hazlett Hazlitt Heaslett Heazlett Hesellette Heslet Hoselett Hosleed Huslett
Haslewood HAZELWOOD HAZLEWOOD
Haslipp HESLOP
Haslit ASLETT HASLETT
Haslitt ASLETT HASLETT
Haslot ASLETT HASLETT
Haslott ASLETT HASLETT
Haslotte ASLETT HASLETT
Haslut ASLETT HASLETT
Haslutt ASLETT HASLETT
Hasom HAYSOM
Hassel HASKELL HASWELL HUSSELL HUZZELL OSWALD RUSSELL URSELL UZZELL
HASSELGRAVE Haselgrove Hazlegrave
HASSELL 8 HAISELL Halsell Harsell Hasel HASELL HAZEL Hazzael
Hassett ASLETT HASLETT
Hasslat ASLETT HASLETT
Hasslett ASLETT HASLETT
Hasson HAZON
HASTE Asthy
Hasted HALSTEAD
Hastler HASLER
Hastlet ASLETT HASLETT
HASWELL 31 Askell Aswell Essell HASKELL Hassel Hawsell Haysel Hessell Hoswell Husle HUSSELL HUZZELL Israel Issel Osell OSWALD Ozell RUSSELL URSELL Urswell Ushil Ussell Ussol Ussould Uswell Uzald Uzle Uzzeel Uzzele UZZELL
Hat HATT
HATCHARD 6 Hached Hatchat Hatcherd Hatchet HATCHETT
Hatchat HATCHARD HATCHETT
Hatchel HATCHELL
HATCHELL Hatchel Hatchill
Hatcherd HATCHARD HATCHETT
Hatchet HANCHET HANCHETT HATCHARD HATCHETT
HATCHETT 14 Hached Hanchant Hanchatt Hanchent HANCHET HANCHETT Hanchiott Hantchett HATCHARD Hatchat Hatcherd Hatchet Henshot
Hatchill HATCHELL
Hatchous EACHUS
Hatchwell HATSWELL
HATFIELD Hadfeld HADFIELD
Hatharal HATHERELL
HATHAWAY HATHWAY Havaway
HATHER 4 Haither HEATHER Hother
HATHERELL 4 HADDERELL HADDRELL Hatharal
Hathersall HOTHERSALL
Hatherton ATHERTON
Hathey ATTEY ATTY
Hathorn HAWTHORN HAWTHORNE HORTON HOUGHTON ORTON
Hathorne HAWTHORN HAWTHORNE HORTON HOUGHTON ORTON
Hathornthwaite HAYTHORNTHWAITE
HATHWAY HATHAWAY Havaway
HATKINS ATKINS
HATSWELL Hatchwell Hatswill
Hatswill HATSWELL
HATT Hat Hatte
HATTAM Hattem
Hatte HATT
Hattem HATTAM
HAUGHTON 11 Aughton Hardin Harten HARTIN Harton HORTON HOUGHTON HUTTON MARTIN ORTON
Haulbrook HALBROOK
Haulbrooks HALBROOK
Hauling HALLING
Haulinge HALLING
HAUNCH Hance Hanch
Haunchman HENCHMAN HENSMAN HINKSMAN HINXMAN HITCHMAN
Haunsmen HENCHMAN HENSMAN HINKSMAN HINXMAN HITCHMAN
HAUNTON Hannton Hawnton
Haute HAWTE
Hauthni HAWTHORN HAWTHORNE HORTON HOUGHTON ORTON
Hauthorn HAWTHORN
HAUXWELL Hawkswell
Havaway HATHAWAY HATHWAY
HAVER 5 Haber Haffer Havre Havver
HAVERS 4 AVIS Havies Havors
Havies AVIS HAVERS
Havors AVIS HAVERS
Havre HAVER
Havver HAVER
HAW 11 HOARE HORE HOWE WARR WEARE Whore Woar Woare WOOR Woore
HAWARD 6 HAYWARD HAYWOOD Heyward HEYWOOD HOWARD
Hawat HEWETT HEWITT HOWAT HOWITT
HAWDON HADDON HOLDEN
Hawis HARES HARIS HARRIES HARRIS
Hawk HAWKE
Hawkard HAWKYARD
HAWKE Hawk
HAWKEN 5 HAWKIN HAWKINS HOCKEN HOCKIN
HAWKER 4 HAWKES HAWKINS HAWKS
HAWKES 4 HAWKER HAWKINS HAWKS
HAWKESFORD HAWKSFORD
Hawkhead HAWKYARD
HAWKIN 6 HAWKEN HAWKINS HOCKEN HOCKIN Hockins
Hawkince HAWKING HAWKINGS HAWKINS
HAWKING 4 Hawkince HAWKINGS HAWKINS
HAWKINGS 4 Hawkince HAWKING HAWKINS
HAWKINS 39 AIKEN Aikin Aken Akins Auchain Eakings Eakins Eakons Ekens EKINS Ekynes Ekyns Hackence Hackins Hakince Hakines Hakings Hakins HAWKEN HAWKER HAWKES HAWKIN Hawkince HAWKING HAWKINGS HAWKS HOCKEN HOCKIN Hockins HOPKINS HOWKINS Oaking OAKINS Okens OKINS Okyn Okyns Ouckins
HAWKS 4 HAWKER HAWKES HAWKINS
HAWKSFORD HAWKESFORD
HAWKSHAW OAKSHOTT Ockshaw
Hawkswell HAUXWELL
HAWKYARD Hawkard Hawkhead
HAWLEY 13 HALLEY HANLEY HOOLEY Hooly Howley Hullay HULLEY HULLY ULLEY Ully UTLEY Whooley
Hawlin HALLING
Hawling HALLING
Hawlings HALLING
Hawlsworth ALLSWORTH HALLSWORTH
Hawnton HAUNTON
Haword HOWARD
HAWORTH HOWARTH Howorth
Hawsell HASKELL HASWELL HUSSELL HUZZELL OSWALD RUSSELL URSELL UZZELL
HAWTE Haute
Hawthen HAWTHORN HAWTHORNE HORTON HOUGHTON ORTON
HAWTHORN 20 Anthorn Haldern Hathorn Hathorne Hauthni Hauthorn Hawthen HAWTHORNE Hawthornthwaite Hawtyn Haythorne HORDEN HORDERN Horethorn Horthorn HORTON Hothorne HOUGHTON ORTON
HAWTHORNE 16 Anthorn Hathorn Hathorne Hauthni Hawthen HAWTHORN Hawthornthwaite Hawtyn Haythorne Horethorn Horthorn HORTON Hothorne HOUGHTON ORTON
Hawthornthwaite HAWTHORN HAWTHORNE HAYTHORNTHWAITE HORTON HOUGHTON ORTON
Hawty AUTEY
Hawtyn HAWTHORN HAWTHORNE HORTON HOUGHTON ORTON
Hawyn OWEN
Haxall HACKWELL HAXELL
HAXELL 12 Axall Axcell Axell Hacksall Hacksoll HACKWELL Haxall Haxill Haxoll Haxswel Haxwell
Haxill HACKWELL HAXELL
Haxoll HACKWELL HAXELL
Haxswel HACKWELL HAXELL
Haxt HEXT
Haxup AXUP
Haxwell HACKWELL HAXELL
HAY 4 HAYE HAYES KAY
HAYCRAFT 15 Hacraste HAYCROFT Macraft Macraste MACROFT Makecraft Marcroft MAYCRAFT Maycraught MAYCROFT Mecraft Mecroft MEDCROFT MOORCROFT
HAYCROFT 15 Hacraste HAYCRAFT Macraft Macraste MACROFT Makecraft Marcroft MAYCRAFT Maycraught MAYCROFT Mecraft Mecroft MEDCROFT MOORCROFT
HAYDEN 6 Aden HADEN Haiden HAYDON HEYDON
HAYDON 5 HADEN Haiden HAYDEN HEYDON
HAYE HAY HAYES
HAYES 11 Hais Haise HASE HAY HAYE HAYS HAYSE Heays HEYES HEYS
Haygan HAGAN HAGEN HEGAN HOGAN
Hayhoe HEYHOE
Hayhow HEYHOE
HAYHURST 5 Herst Heyhurst HIRST HURST
Hayle HAILS HALE HALES HAYLES
HAYLES 8 EALES Hail Haills HAILS HALE HALES Hayle
Haylet ALLIT AYLETT

If the name you are interested in is not here, try Section C.

HAYLOCK Halleck
HAYMAN Haman HAYMEN
HAYMEN HAYMAN
HAYNES 6 Hain HAINES Hains Heynes Heyns
Hayning HAINING HANNING
HAYS 7 Hais Haise HAYES HAYSE Heays HEYS
Haysand HAZON
HAYSE 5 Haise HAYES HAYS HEYS
Haysel HASKELL HASWELL HUSSELL HUZZELL OSWALD RUSSELL URSELL UZZELL
Haysham HAYSOM
Hayslett ASLETT HASLETT
Haysman HEASMAN
HAYSOM 6 Haisom Hasom Haysham Haysome Hayson
Haysome HAYSOM
Hayson HAYSOM
Haystead HALSTEAD
Haythorne HAWTHORN HAWTHORNE HORTON HOUGHTON ORTON
HAYTHORNTHWAITE Hathornthwaite Hawthornthwaite
HAYWARD 6 HAWARD HAYWOOD Heyward HEYWOOD HOWARD
Hayway HEIGHWAY
HAYWOOD 28 Ailard Ailward Allward ALLWOOD Alward Alwart Alwood ALYWARD AYLWARD HAILWOOD HALEWOOD HALWOOD HAWARD HAYWARD Heignwood Henywood Heyward HEYWOOD Highner HIGHWOOD Hiner Hinor Hinord HYNARD HYNER Hynerd Hynor
Hayyot HARRIOTT HERRIOTT
Hayzen HAZON
HAZEL 7 HAISELL Halsell Harsell Hasel HASELL HASSELL
HAZELWOOD 8 Azelwood Azlewood Haselwood Haslewood HAZLEWOOD Hazzelwood Hazzlewood
Hazen HAZON
Hazeon HAZON
Hazlegrave HASSELGRAVE
Hazlett ASLETT HASLETT
HAZLEWOOD 8 Azelwood Azlewood Haselwood Haslewood HAZELWOOD Hazzelwood Hazzlewood
Hazlitt ASLETT HASLETT
Hazmalalch HEZMALHALCH
Hazmalhalch HEZMALHALCH
Hazmonalsh HEZMALHALCH
HAZON 9 Haison Hasson Haysand Hayzen Hazen Hazeon Hegesende Heisende
Hazzael HASSELL
Hazzelwood HAZELWOOD HAZLEWOOD
Hazzlewood HAZELWOOD HAZLEWOOD
HEAD 5 EADE EADES EDE Hade
HEADLAND HADLAND
Heagan HAGAN HAGEN HEGAN HOGAN
Heagin HAGAN HAGEN HEGAN HOGAN
Heagon HAGAN HAGEN HEGAN HOGAN
HEAL HALE Heale
Heale HALE HEAL
HEALEY 8 Aley ELEY ELY HAILEY HALEY Haly HEALY
HEALY HEALEY
HEAMES 6 EAMES Eams Eemes EMES IMMS
HEARD HERD
HEARDER Herder Hurder
Heardy GARRAD GARRARD GARRAT GARRATT GARRETT GARROD GERARD GERRARD GERRETT JARRARD JARRATT JARRET JARRETT JARROLD JARVIS JERRARD JERRETT YARD
Hearker HARKER
HEARN 30 Harn HEARNE Heiron HERN Herne HERON Hierne HIERON Highorne Hiorne HIORNS Hiren Hirens Hirin HIRON Hirone HIRONS HORN HORNE HURN Hyearnes Hyerne Hyorn Hyron Hyrone Hyrons Hyryn Iron IRONS
HEARNE 28 Harn HEARN Heiron HERN Herne HERON Hierne HIERON Highorne Hiorne HIORNS Hiren Hirens Hirin HIRON Hirone HIRONS HURN Hyearnes Hyerne Hyorn Hyron Hyrone Hyrons Hyryn Iron IRONS
Hearnton HANTON
HEARST 5 Herse Herst HIRST HURST
Heartley HARTLEY
Heaseman HEASMAN
HEASEY 5 EASEY EASY Heasie HEASY
Heasie EASEY EASY HEASEY HEASY
Heaslett ASLETT HASLETT
HEASMAN 9 Haysman Heaseman Heesman Heisman Heseman Hesman Hezman Hysman
HEASY 5 EASEY EASY HEASEY Heasie
HEATH Heoth HETH
HEATHER 7 Haither HATHER Heether Heither HETHER Hother
HEATON EATON
Heaxt HEXT
Heays HAYES HAYS
Heazlett ASLETT HASLETT
HEBB 14 Eb Ebb Ebbe Ebbes Ebus Hib Hibb Hibbes HIBBS Hybys Ibbes Ibbs Ibs
Hebbat HEBBERD HERBERT HIBBERT HUBBERT HUBERT
HEBBERD 15 Eibbot Eibert Hebbat Hebert Hepert HERBERT Hibbart HIBBERT Hibort Hobort Hubberd HUBBERT HUBERT Hybbart
HEBBES 4 Ebbs Hebbs Ibbs
Hebblethwait HEBBLETHWAITE
HEBBLETHWAITE 5 Hebblethwait HEBBLEWHITE Heblet Heblett
HEBBLEWHITE HEBBLETHWAITE
Hebbs HEBBES
Hebbton HEBDEN
Hebdain HEBDEN
Hebdan HEBDEN
HEBDEN 4 Hebbton Hebdain Hebdan
Hebert HEBBERD HERBERT HIBBERT HUBBARD HUBBERT HUBERT
Heblet HEBBLETHWAITE
Heblett HEBBLETHWAITE
HEBRON HEPBURN
HECK HICK HICKS
Heckeley HICKLEY
Heckels ECCLES HECKLES HICKLES
Hecklay HICKLEY
HECKLES 5 ECCLES Ekels Heckels HICKLES
Heckley HICKLEY
Heckly HICKLEY
HECKS HEX
Hecksford EXFORD
Heclay HICKLEY
Hedage HERRIDGE
Hedgcock HEDGECOCK HISCOCK HISCOCKS HISCOX HITCHCOCK
Hedgcocke HEDGECOCK HISCOCK
HEDGECOCK 12 Edgcock Edgcocke Edgecock Edgecocke Hedgcock Hedgcocke HISCOCK Hiscocke HISCOCKS HISCOX HITCHCOCK
Hedgecomb EDGECOMBE
Hedgecombe EDGCOMBE EDGECOMBE
HEDGES 5 Edges Egges Hegges HODGES
Heeds EADES YATES
Heekley HICKLEY
HEELEY 33 EALEY Ealy Eele Eeley EELY Eieley Eile Eiley Eilley Elay Elea Elee ELEY Eleye Eli Elie ELLEY Ellie Elly ELY Elye Eyeley Eyely Eyle EYLEY Eyly Eylye Heely Hele Heley Hely Iley
Heely EALEY EELY ELEY ELLEY ELY EYLEY HEELEY
Heesman HEASMAN
Heether HEATHER HETHER
HEFFER HEFFORD
Heffner HAFFNER HAFNER
HEFFORD HEFFER
Hefner HAFFNER HAFNER
HEGAN 15 Eagan Eagin HAGAN HAGEN Haggan Hagin Haygan Heagan Heagin Heagon Heigan Higan HOGAN O'hagan
Hegesende HAZON
Hegges HEDGES HODGES
Heghland HIGHLAND HYLAND HYLANDS
Heginbotham HIGGINBOTHAM HIGGINBOTTOM
Hegman HICKMAN HIGMAN
Heiat HIATT HYATT HYETT
Heicklay HICKLEY
Heigan HAGAN HAGEN HEGAN HOGAN
Heigham HIGHAM HYEM
Heigho HEYHOE
HEIGHWAY 4 Hayway Heywaye Highway
Heignwood HAYWOOD HYNARD HYNER
Heilland HIGHLAND HYLAND HYLANDS
Heinsby HENSBY
Heires AYERS AYRES
Heiron HEARN HEARNE HERON HIERON HIORNS HIRON HIRONS IRONS
Heisende HAZON
Heisman HEASMAN
Heither HEATHER HETHER
Hekle HICKLEY
Helcoat ELCOAT
Hele EALEY EELY ELEY ELLEY ELY EYLEY HEELEY
Heley EALEY EELY ELEY ELLEY ELY EYLEY HEELEY
Heliwell HALLIWELL HELLIWELL
HELLARD 6 Ellard HALFARD Halfred HALFYARD Halfyeard
HELLAWELL 5 HALLIWELL Hallowell HELLIWELL Hellowell
Hellcoat ELCOAT
Hellen HELLIN
Helles HILLS
HELLIER 6 HELLYER Helyar HILLIER HILLYER HOLLIER
HELLIN Hellen
Helliot ELIOT ELIOTT ELLIOT ELLIOTT ELLOT
Helliott ELIOT ELIOTT ELLIOT ELLIOTT ELLOT
Hellis ELLIS
HELLIWELL 7 Haliwell HALLIWELL Hallowell Heliwell HELLAWELL Hellowell
Hellowell HALLIWELL HELLAWELL HELLIWELL
HELLYER 5 HELLIER HILLIER HILLYER HILYEAR
HELM HELME
HELME HELM
HELMOTH 19 MEALEMOUTH MEALMOUTH Meldmouthis MELEMOUTH MELLMOUTHE Melmath MELMETH Melmore MELMOTH Melmoth-brooks Melmott MELMOUTH Melmouthes Melwoth Milmoth Milmouthes Molmoth WELMOTH
Hely EALEY EELY ELEY ELLEY ELY EYLEY HEELEY
Helyar HELLIER HILLIER HOLLIER
Hemans EMENS EMMANS EMMENS HEMMING HEMMINGS
HEMBER Hemborough
HEMBERY Hembry Hembury
Hemborough HEMBER
Hembrook HAMBROOK
Hembrough HEMBROW
HEMBROW Hembrough
Hembry HEMBERY
Hembury HEMBERY
Hemens EMENS EMMANS EMMENS HEMMING HEMMINGS
Hementon HEMINGTON
Heming EMENS EMMANS EMMENS HEMMING HEMMINGS
Hemings EMENS EMMANS EMMENS HEMMING HEMMINGS
HEMINGTON 6 Emington Emmington Hementon Heminton Hemmington
HEMINGWAY HEMMINGWAY
Heminton HEMINGTON
HEMMING 14 Emans EMENS Eming Emings EMMANS EMMENS Emming Emmings Hemans Hemens Heming Hemings HEMMINGS
HEMMINGS 14 Emans EMENS Eming Emings EMMANS EMMENS Emming Emmings Hemans Hemens Heming Hemings HEMMING
Hemmington HEMINGTON
HEMMINGWAY HEMINGWAY
HEMUS Emuss
HENBEST 7 Henrest Henvest

If the name you are interested in is not here, try Section C.

Hinbest Hinrest Hinves HINVEST
Henceman HENCHMAN HENSMAN HINKSMAN HINXMAN HITCHMAN
Hencheman HENCHMAN HENSMAN HINKSMAN HINXMAN HITCHMAN
HENCHMAN 47 Anschamen Hanchman Hansemane Hanshmen Haunchman Haunsmen Henceman Hencheman Henchmen Hengestman Hengestmannus Hengstman Hengysman Henseman Hensheman Henshman HENSMAN Henxceman Henxeman Henxman Henxmen Henxstman Heynceman Heynsman Hinchman Hinckesman Hincksman Hincxman Hinesman Hingman Hingston Hinkman HINKSMAN Hinksmann Hinkson Hinshman Hinskman Hinsman Hinxeman Hinxksman HINXMAN Hinxon HITCHMAN Hnksman Hyckesman Hyncksman
Henchmen HENCHMAN HENSMAN HINKSMAN HINXMAN HITCHMAN
HENDEBOURCK 8 Hendebourk Hendlebourck HEUDEBOURCK Heudebourk Heudebourq Hourdebourg Hudiberk
Hendebourk HENDEBOURCK HEUDEBOURCK
Hendlebourck HENDEBOURCK HEUDEBOURCK
Hendley HENLEY HENLY
Hendlie HENLEY HENLY
Hendly HENLEY HENLY
Henfree HENFREY
HENFREY Henfree
Hengestman HENCHMAN HENSMAN HINKSMAN HINXMAN HITCHMAN
Hengestmannus HENCHMAN HENSMAN HINKSMAN HINXMAN HITCHMAN
Hengstman HENCHMAN HENSMAN HINKSMAN HINXMAN HITCHMAN
Hengysman HENCHMAN HENSMAN HINKSMAN HINXMAN HITCHMAN
Henkinson HANKINSON
HENLEY 6 Hendley Hendlie Hendly Henlie HENLY
Henlie HENLEY HENLY
HENLY 6 Hendley Hendlie Hendly HENLEY Henlie
Henrest HENBEST HINVEST
Hensberg HENSBERGH
HENSBERGH 7 Hansborough Hansbrow Hensberg Hensborough Hensbrow Hinsbergh
Hensborough HENSBERGH
Hensbrow HENSBERGH
HENSBY Heinsby
Henseman HENCHMAN HENSMAN HINKSMAN HINXMAN HITCHMAN
Hensheman HENCHMAN HENSMAN HINKSMAN HINXMAN HITCHMAN
Henshman HENCHMAN HENSMAN HINKSMAN HINXMAN HITCHMAN
Henshot HANCHET HANCHETT HATCHETT
HENSMAN 47 Anschamen Hanchman Hansemane Hanshmen Haunchman Haunsmen Henceman Hencheman HENCHMAN Henchmen Hengestman Hengestmannus Hengstman Hengysman Henseman Hensheman Henshman Henxceman Henxeman Henxman Henxmen Henxstman Heynceman Heynsman Hinchman Hinckesman Hincksman Hincxman Hinesman Hingman Hingston Hinkman HINKSMAN Hinksmann Hinkson Hinshman Hinskman Hinsman Hinxeman Hinxksman HINXMAN Hinxon HITCHMAN Hnksman Hyckesman Hyncksman
Henston ENSTONE
Henstone ENSTONE
HENTON HINTON
Henvest HENBEST HINVEST
Henxceman HENCHMAN HENSMAN HINKSMAN HINXMAN HITCHMAN
Henxeman HENCHMAN HENSMAN HINKSMAN HINXMAN HITCHMAN
Henxman HENCHMAN HENSMAN HINKSMAN HINXMAN HITCHMAN
Henxmen HENCHMAN HENSMAN HINKSMAN HINXMAN HITCHMAN
Henxstman HENCHMAN HENSMAN HINKSMAN HINXMAN HITCHMAN
Henywood HAYWOOD HYNARD HYNER
Heoth HEATH
Hepbern HEPBURN
HEPBURN HEBRON Hepbern
Hepert HEBBERD HERBERT HIBBERT HUBBERT HUBERT
Hephale HEPPELL HEPPLE
Heple HEPPELL HEPPLE
Heppel HEPPELL HEPPLE
Heppele HEPPELL HEPPLE
HEPPELL 6 Hephale Heple Heppel Heppele HEPPLE
HEPPENSTALL 4 Heppinstall HEPTINSTALL HEPTONSTALL
Heppinstall HEPPENSTALL HEPTINSTALL HEPTONSTALL
HEPPLE 6 Hephale Heple Heppel Heppele HEPPELL
HEPTINSTALL 4 HEPPENSTALL Heppinstall HEPTONSTALL
HEPTONSTALL 4 HEPPENSTALL Heppinstall HEPTINSTALL
Herage HERRIDGE
Herberson HARBERTSON HERBISON
HERBERT 16 Eibbot Eibert HARBERT Hebbat HEBBERD Hebert Hepert Hibbart HIBBERT Hibort Hobort Hubberd HUBBERT HUBERT Hybbart
Herbertson HARBERTSON HERBISON
HERBISON 8 Harberson HARBERTSON Harbison Harbutson Herberson Herbertson Herbutson
Herbutson HARBERTSON HERBISON
HERD HEARD
Herdecastell HARDCASTLE
Herder HEARDER
HERDMAN Hirdman
Heredge HERRIDGE
Hereford HURFORD
Herington HARINGTON HARRINGTON HERRINGTON
HERITAGE 4 Eritage Herytayge Herytidge
Herle HURLE
HERMAN 5 Hermann HERMON Hirman HURMAN
Hermann HERMAN HURMAN
HERMON 4 HERMAN Hirman HURMAN
HERN 9 Harn HEARN HEARNE Herne HERON HORN HORNE HURN
Hernden HARDEN HARNDEN
Herne HEARN HEARNE HERN HERON HIERON HIORNS HIRON HIRONS HURN IRONS
Herod HARWOOD
HERON 28 HEARN HEARNE Heiron HERN Herne HERRON Hierne HIERON Highorne Hiorne HIORNS Hiren Hirens Hirin HIRON Hirone HIRONS HURN Hyearnes Hyerne Hyorn Hyron Hyrone Hyrons Hyryn Iron IRONS
HERRIDGE 4 Hedage Herage Heredge
Herriman HARRYMAN
HERRINGTON 4 HARINGTON HARRINGTON Herington
HERRIOTT 4 Harriatt HARRIOTT Hayyot
Herrison HARRISON
Herrod HARROD
HERRON HERON
Hersan HAIRSINE
HERSANT HERSENT
Herse HEARST HIRST HURST
HERSEBERGER 4 HIRCHBERG HIRSCHBERG HIRSHBERG
HERSENT HERSANT
Herst HAYHURST HEARST HIRST HURST
Herytayge HERITAGE
Herytidge HERITAGE
Hesellette ASLETT HASLETT
Heseman HEASMAN
Heshmonhalsh HEZMALHALCH
Heskaith HESKETH
Heskayte HESKETH
Heskayth HESKETH
HESKETH 6 De heskayte De heskayth Heskaith Heskayte Heskayth
Heslet ASLETT HASLETT
HESLOP Haslipp HYSLOP
Hesmalhalch HEZMALHALCH
Hesmalhalsh HEZMALHALCH
Hesman HEASMAN
Hesmanlanch HEZMALHALCH
Hesmaulansh HEZMALHALCH
Hesmelhals HEZMALHALCH
Hesmelhelch HEZMALHALCH
Hesmolash HEZMALHALCH
Hesmonhalsh HEZMALHALCH
Hessell HASKELL HASWELL HUSSELL HUZZELL OSWALD RUSSELL URSELL UZZELL
Hessenhanch HEZMALHALCH
Hessitt HEWITT
HETH HEATH
HETHER 4 HEATHER Heether Heither
HETHERINGTON ETHERINGTON
Hethersall HOTHERSALL
HEUDEBOURCK 8 HENDEBOURCK Hendebourk Hendlebourck Heudebourk Heudebourq Hourdebourg Hudiberk
Heudebourk HENDEBOURCK HEUDEBOURCK
Heudebourq HENDEBOURCK HEUDEBOURCK
Heusser HUZZARD
Hevens EWINGS EWINS HEWENS HEWINGS YOUINGS
Hever DE HEVER
Hewartson HEWITSON
Hewelet HEWITT HEWLETT
Hewen EWINGS EWINS HEWENS HEWINGS YOUINGS
HEWENS 13 EWINGS EWINS Hevens Hewen Hewigns Hewing HEWINGS Hewons Howins Huings Huins YOUINGS
Hewertson HEWETSON HEWITSON
HEWES HUGHES
Hewet HEWETT HEWITT HOWAT HOWITT
HEWETSON 9 Hewertson HEWITSON Hewittson HEWSON Hugheson Hughetson HUGHSON HUITSON
HEWETT 13 Hawat Hewet Hewiss Hewit HEWITT HOWAT Howatt HOWITT Huet Huett Huitt Huot
Hewigns EWINGS EWINS HEWENS HEWINGS YOUINGS
Hewing EWINGS EWINS HEWENS HEWINGS YOUINGS
HEWINGS 13 EWINGS EWINS Hevens Hewen HEWENS Hewigns Hewing Hewons Howins Huings Huins YOUINGS
HEWINS Huins
HEWISH 7 Hewishe Hiwis Huise HUISH Huishe Huyshe
Hewishe HEWISH HUISH
Hewison HEWITSON HEWSON HUGHSON HUSON
Hewiss HEWETT HEWITT HOWAT HOWITT
Hewit HEWETT HEWITT HOWAT HOWITT
HEWITSON 14 Hewartson Hewertson HEWETSON Hewison Hewittson HEWSON Hueson Hugheson Hughetson HUGHSON Huison HUITSON HUSON
HEWITT 17 Hawat Hessitt Hewelet Hewet HEWETT Hewiss Hewit HEWLETT HOWAT Howatt HOWITT Huet Huett Huit Huitt Huot
Hewittson HEWETSON HEWITSON HEWSON HUGHSON HUITSON
HEWLET 4 HEWLETT Hulet Hulett
HEWLETT 6 Hewelet HEWITT HEWLET Hulet Hulett
Hewons EWINGS EWINS HEWENS HEWINGS YOUINGS
Hews HUGHES
Hewsdon ALSTON AUSTIN
HEWSON 12 HEWETSON Hewison HEWITSON Hewittson Hueson Hugheson Hughetson HUGHSON Huison HUITSON HUSON

If the name you are interested in is not here, try Section C.

Hewstice EUSTACE EUSTICE STACE STACEY
HEX HECKS
Hexford EXFORD HUXFORD
HEXT 6 Haxt Heaxt Hexte Hix Hixt
Hexte HEXT
HEYDON 5 Aden HADEN HAYDEN HAYDON
HEYES HAYES
HEYHOE 4 Hayhoe Hayhow Heigho
Heyhurst HAYHURST HIRST HURST
Heynceman HENCHMAN HENSMAN HINKSMAN HINXMAN HITCHMAN
Heynes HAINES HAYNES
Heyns HAINES HAYNES
Heynsman HENCHMAN HENSMAN HINKSMAN HINXMAN HITCHMAN
HEYS 5 Haise HAYES HAYS HAYSE
HEYSETT Heyssett
Heyssett HEYSETT
Heyward HARWOOD HAWARD HAYWARD HAYWOOD HEYWOOD HOWARD
Heywaye HEIGHWAY
HEYWOOD 6 HAWARD HAYWARD HAYWOOD Heyward HIGHWOOD
HEZMALHALCH 17 Hazmalalch Hazmalhalch Hazmonalsh Heshmonhalsh Hesmalhalch Hesmalhalsh Hesmanlanch Hesmaulansh Hesmelhals Hesmelhelch Hesmolash Hesmonhalsh Hessenhanch Hezmolalch Hezmonalsh Hezmonhalch
Hezman HEASMAN
Hezmolalch HEZMALHALCH
Hezmonalsh HEZMALHALCH
Hezmonhalch HEZMALHALCH
Hiat HIATT HYATT HYETT
HIATT 9 Heiat Hiat Hiet Hiett Highet HYATT HYETT Hyot
Hib HEBB HIBBS
Hibard HIBBARD HIBBERD HIBBERT IBBOT
Hibb HEBB HIBBS
HIBBARD 11 Hibard Hibbart HIBBERD HIBBERT Hibbird Hiberd Hybard Hyberd Ibbert IBBOT
Hibbart HEBBERD HERBERT HIBBARD HIBBERD HIBBERT HUBBERT HUBERT IBBOT
HIBBERD 11 Hibard HIBBARD Hibbart HIBBERT Hibbird Hiberd Hybard Hyberd Ibbert IBBOT
HIBBERT 24 Eibbot Eibert Hebbat HEBBERD Hebert Hepert HERBERT Hibard HIBBARD Hibbart HIBBERD Hibbird Hiberd Hibort Hobort Hubberd HUBBERT HUBERT Hybard Hybbart Hyberd Ibbert IBBOT
Hibbes HEBB HIBBS
HIBBET HIBBETT
HIBBETT HIBBET
Hibbird HIBBARD HIBBERD HIBBERT
Hibbit EBBOTT EBBUTT HIBBITT IBBIT IBBOT
HIBBITT 26 Ebbatt Ebbert Ebbet Ebbetts Ebbit Ebbitt Ebbot EBBOTT Ebbut EBBUTT Ebert Ebet Ebott Ebottes Ebytt Hibbit Hibbot Ibbet Ibbett Ibbitt IBBOT Ibbott Ibet Ibot Ibott
Hibblet HIBLET
Hibblett HIBLET
Hibbot EBBOTT EBBUTT HIBBITT IBBOT
HIBBS 14 Eb Ebb Ebbe Ebbes Ebus HEBB Hib Hibb Hibbes Hybys Ibbes Ibbs Ibs
Hiberd HIBBARD HIBBERD HIBBERT IBBOT
Hibgame HIPKIN
Hibgin HIPKIN
HIBLET 4 Hibblet Hibblett Hiblett
Hiblett HIBLET
Hibort HEBBERD HERBERT HIBBERT HUBBERT HUBERT
Hiccle HICKLES ICKEL ICKELING
Hiccleton HICKLETON
Hicel HICKLES ICKEL ICKELING
Hiceling DE HICKELING HICKLIN HICKLING ICKELING
HICHCOCKE HITCHCOCK HITCHCOX
Hichelyn HICKLIN HICKLING
Hichelyng DE HICKELING HICKLIN HICKLING ICKELING
Hichen HITCHEN HITCHIN HITCHON
HICHENS Hitchens
HICK 4 HECK HICKES HICKS
Hickelle HICKLEY
Hickelynge DE HICKELING HICKLIN HICKLING ICKELING
HICKEN HICKIN HICKLIN
Hickens HICKMANS
HICKERSON Hickinson
HICKES HICK HICKS
HICKIN 4 HICKEN HICKLIN HOCKING
Hickingham HICKLINGAM
Hickinson HICKERSON
HICKISSON HICKSON
Hicklain HICKLIN HICKLING
HICKLAND De hickland De hikeland
Hicklen HICKLIN HICKLING
HICKLENTON 7 Hicklington Hicklinton Hicklonton Icelingtun Icelintone Yclinton
HICKLES 18 De hickel ECCLES Echel Ekels Heckels HECKLES Hiccle Hicel Hikal Hikel Icel Ichel ICKEL ICKELING Ickle Icles Ikel
HICKLETON 7 Hiccleton Hicklton Hikalton Hikelton Icheltone Ickleton
HICKLEY 18 De heckele De hichelle De hickelle Haccleia Heckeley Hecklay Heckley Heckly Heclay Heekley Heicklay Hekle Hickelle Hickly Hicklye Hikeley Hikley
HICKLIN 89 De hekelinge De hekelingge De hekelyng De hekelyngg DE HICKELING De hickelinge De hickelyng De hickelynges De hickland De hickling De hicklinge De hicklingge De hicling De higeling De hikeling De hikelinga De hikelinge De hikelinges De hikelingge De hikelyng De hikelynge De hikligg De hiklyng De hitling De hykeling De hykelinge De hykelingge De hykelinggs De hykelingh De hykelyng De hykelynge De hykelyngge De hykkelingh De ikeling De ikelinges De ykeling Eccling Echelinog Etcling Hiceling Hichelyn Hichelyng Hickelynge HICKEN HICKIN Hicklain Hicklen HICKLING Hicklinge Hicklings Hicklingse Hicklinse Hicklyn Hiclen Hiclin Hicling Hiclyng Hikeling Hikelyng Hikelyngg Hikkling Hiklynge Hixling Hyckelyng Hyckling Hycklyng Hykeling Hykelyn Hykelyng Hykling Hyklyng Hyklynge Icelin Iceling Ichelin ICKELING Ickling Iclans Icling Iclingas Ikeline Ikeling Ikelinge Ikling Yclin Ycling Ykeling Ykling
HICKLING 87 De hekelinge De hekelingge De hekelyng De hekelyngg DE HICKELING De hickelinge De hickelyng De hickelynges De hickland De hickling De hicklinge De hicklingge De hicling De higeling De hikeling De hikelinga De hikelinge De hikelinges De hikelingge De hikelyng De hikelynge De hikligg De hiklyng De hitling De hykeling De hykelinge De hykelingge De hykelinggs De hykelingh De hykelyng De hykelynge De hykelyngge De hykkelingh De ikeling De ikelinges De ykeling Eccling Echelinog Etcling Hiceling Hichelyn Hichelyng Hickelynge Hicklain Hicklen HICKLIN Hicklinge Hicklings Hicklingse Hicklinse Hicklyn Hiclen Hiclin Hicling Hiclyng Hikeling Hikelyng Hikelyngg Hikkling Hiklynge Hixling Hyckelyng Hycklinge Hycklyng Hykeling Hykelyn Hykelyng Hykling Hyklyng Hyklynge Icelin Iceling Ichelin ICKELING Ickling Iclans Icling Iclingas Ikeline Ikeling Ikelinge Ikling Yclin Ycling Ykeling Ykling
HICKLING-BURNETT BURNETT
HICKLINGAM 8 Hickingham Hicklingem Hiclingham Icelingham Icklingham Ikelingham Yclinham
Hicklinge DE HICKELING HICKLIN HICKLING ICKELING
Hicklingem HICKLINGAM
Hicklings DE HICKELING HICKLIN HICKLING ICKELING
Hicklingse DE HICKELING HICKLIN HICKLING ICKELING
Hicklington HICKLENTON
Hicklinse DE HICKELING HICKLIN HICKLING ICKELING
Hicklinton HICKLENTON
Hicklonton HICKLENTON
Hicklton HICKLETON
Hickly HICKLEY
Hicklye HICKLEY
Hicklyn HICKLIN HICKLING
HICKMAN 11 Hegman HICKMAR Hickmett Hickmore Higeman Higgman HIGMAN Higmann Hygman Hykman
Hickmanes HICKMANS
HICKMANS 5 Hickens Hickmanes Hickmas Hickmons
HICKMAR 4 HICKMAN Hickmett Hickmore
Hickmas HICKMANS
Hickmett HICKMAN HICKMAR
Hickmons HICKMANS
Hickmore HICKMAN HICKMAR
HICKS 6 HECK HICK HICKES HIGGS Hix
HICKSON 4 HICKISSON Hixon HIXSON
Hiclen HICKLIN HICKLING
Hiclin HICKLIN HICKLING
Hicling DE HICKELING HICKLIN HICKLING ICKELING
Hiclingham HICKLINGAM
Hiclyng DE HICKELING HICKLIN HICKLING ICKELING
HIDE HYDE
HIDER HYDER
Hielan HIGHLAND HYLAND HYLANDS
Hielaunde HIGHLAND HYLAND HYLANDS
Hierne HEARN HEARNE HERON HIERON HIORNS HIRON HIRONS IRONS
HIERON 25 HEARN HEARNE Heiron Herne HERON Hierne Highorne Hiorne HIORNS Hiren Hirens Hirin HIRON Hirone HIRONS Hyearnes Hyerne Hyorn Hyron Hyrone Hyrons Hyryn Iron IRONS
Hiet HIATT HYATT HYETT
Hiett HIATT HYATT HYETT
Higan HAGAN HAGEN HEGAN HOGAN
Higate HIGHGATE
Higdon HIGHTON HIGTON
Higeman HICKMAN HIGMAN
HIGGIN HIGGINS
HIGGINBOTHAM Heginbotham HIGGINBOTTOM
HIGGINBOTTOM Heginbotham HIGGINBOTHAM
HIGGINS HIGGIN
Higgman HICKMAN HIGMAN

If the name you are interested in is not here, try Section C.

HIGGS HICKS
HIGHAM 4 Heigham Hyam HYEM
Highet HIATT HYATT HYETT
HIGHGATE 5 Agate Higate Hyat Hygate
HIGHLAND 11 Heghland Heilland Hielan Hielaunde Highlande Highlands Hiland Hilands HYLAND HYLANDS
Highlande HIGHLAND HYLAND HYLANDS
Highlands HIGHLAND HYLAND HYLANDS
HIGHLEY HILEY Iley
Highner HAYWOOD HYNARD HYNER
Highorne HEARN HEARNE HERON HIERON HIORNS HIRON HIRONS IRONS
HIGHTON Higdon HIGTON
Highway HEIGHWAY
HIGHWOOD HAYWOOD HEYWOOD
HIGMAN 8 Hegman HICKMAN Higeman Higgman Higmann Hygman Hykman
Higmann HICKMAN HIGMAN
HIGTON Higdon HIGHTON
Hikal HICKLES ICKEL ICKELING
Hikalton HICKLETON
Hikel HICKLES ICKEL ICKELING
Hikeley HICKLEY
Hikeling DE HICKELING HICKLIN HICKLING ICKELING
Hikelton HICKLETON
Hikelyng DE HICKELING HICKLIN HICKLING ICKELING
Hikelyngg DE HICKELING HICKLIN HICKLING ICKELING
Hikkling DE HICKELING HICKLIN HICKLING ICKELING
Hikley HICKLEY
Hiklynge DE HICKELING HICKLIN HICKLING ICKELING
Hiland HIGHLAND HYLAND HYLANDS
Hilands HIGHLAND HYLAND HYLANDS
Hilard HILLIARD HILLIER
Hilborn HILBORNE
HILBORNE 7 Hilborn Hilbourn Hilbourne Hilburn Hillbourn Hillbourne
Hilbourn HILBORNE
Hilbourne HILBORNE
Hilburn HILBORNE
Hilcoat ELCOAT
Hilcot ELCOAT
Hilcote ELCOAT
Hildesley EELES ILLSLEY ILSLEY
Hildisley EELES ILLSLEY ILSLEY
Hildsley EELES ILLSLEY ILSLEY
HILES 10 Ailes AYLES EALES EELES EYLES Hyles ILES ISLES Yeeles
HILEY HIGHLEY Iley
Hilierd HILLIARD HILLIER
Hillbourn HILBORNE
Hillbourne HILBORNE
Hillcot ELCOAT
Hilles HILLS
HILLHOUSE 9 Carleton Carol CHARLETON Kerrill Mackerel Mccarol MCKERRELL Mckerrill
Hilliar HILLIARD HILLIER
HILLIARD 7 Hilard Hilierd Hilliar HILLIER Hillierd Hilliyard
HILLIEAR HILLIER HILLYER
HILLIER 13 HELLIER HELLYER Helyar Hilard Hilierd Hilliar HILLIARD HILLIEAR Hillierd HILLYER HILYEAR HOLLIER
Hillierd HILLIARD HILLIER
Hillindrake HOLLINRAKE
Hilliyard HILLIARD
HILLS 4 De helles Helles Hilles
Hillsden HILSDEN
Hillsdon HILSDEN
HILLYER 5 HELLIER HELLYER HILLIEAR HILLIER
HILSDEN 4 Hillsden Hillsdon Hilsdon
Hilsdon HILSDEN
HILYEAR HELLYER HILLIER
Hinard HYNARD HYNER
Hinbest HENBEST HINVEST
HINCE 5 HINES Hints INCE INNES
HINCHCLIFF 6 HINCHCLIFFE HINCHLIFF HINCHLIFFE Hinschliffe Inchliffe
HINCHCLIFFE 6 HINCHCLIFF HINCHLIFF HINCHLIFFE Hinschliffe Inchliffe
Hinchley HINCHLIFF INCHLEY
HINCHLIFF 9 HINCHCLIFF HINCHCLIFFE Hinchley HINCHLIFFE Hinschliffe INCHLEY Inchliff Inchliffe
HINCHLIFFE 6 HINCHCLIFF HINCHCLIFFE HINCHLIFF Hinschliffe Inchliffe
Hinchman HENCHMAN HENSMAN HINKSMAN HINXMAN HITCHMAN
Hinckesman HENCHMAN HENSMAN HINKSMAN HINXMAN HITCHMAN
Hincks HINKS
Hincksman HENCHMAN HENSMAN HINKSMAN HINXMAN HITCHMAN
Hincxman HENCHMAN HENSMAN HINKSMAN HINXMAN HITCHMAN
HIND 8 HINDE HINDS HINE Hynd Hynde Hyndes Hyne
HINDE 6 HIND HINE Hynd Hynde Hyne
HINDES HINES
HINDS 5 HIND HINES Hynd Hyndes
HINE 6 HIND HINDE Hynd Hynde Hyne
Hiner HAYWOOD HYNARD HYNER
HINES 7 HINCE HINDES HINDS Hints INCE INNES
Hinesman HENCHMAN HENSMAN HINKSMAN HINXMAN HITCHMAN
Hinge INGE
Hingman HENCHMAN HENSMAN HINKSMAN HINXMAN HITCHMAN
Hingston HENCHMAN HENSMAN HINKSMAN HINXMAN HITCHMAN
Hinkes HINKS
Hinkman HENCHMAN HENSMAN HINKSMAN HINXMAN HITCHMAN
HINKS Hincks Hinkes
HINKSMAN 47 Anschamen Hanchman Hansemane Hanshmen Haunchman Haunsmen Henceman Hencheman HENCHMAN Henchmen Hengestman Hengestmannus Hengstman Hengysman Henseman Hensheman Henshman HENSMAN Henxceman Henxeman Henxman Henxmen Henxstman Heynceman Heynsman Hinchman Hinckesman Hincksman Hincxman Hinesman Hingman Hingston Hinkman Hinksmann Hinkson Hinshman Hinskman Hinsman Hinxeman Hinxksman HINXMAN Hinxon HITCHMAN Hnksman Hyckesman Hyncksman
Hinksmann HENCHMAN HENSMAN HINKSMAN HINXMAN HITCHMAN
Hinkson HENCHMAN HENSMAN HINKSMAN HINXMAN HITCHMAN
Hinor HAYWOOD HYNARD HYNER
Hinord HAYWOOD HYNARD HYNER
Hinrest HENBEST HINVEST
Hinsbergh HENSBERGH
Hinschliffe HINCHCLIFF HINCHCLIFFE HINCHLIFF HINCHLIFFE
Hinshman HENCHMAN HENSMAN HINKSMAN HINXMAN HITCHMAN
Hinskman HENCHMAN HENSMAN HINKSMAN HINXMAN HITCHMAN
HINSLEY 5 Illsey Incley INSLEY Insly
Hinsman HENCHMAN HENSMAN HINKSMAN HINXMAN HITCHMAN
HINTON HENTON
Hints HINCE HINES INCE INNES
Hinves HENBEST HINVEST
HINVEST 7 HENBEST Henrest Henvest Hinbest Hinrest Hinves
Hinxeman HENCHMAN HENSMAN HINKSMAN HINXMAN HITCHMAN
Hinxksman HENCHMAN HENSMAN HINKSMAN HINXMAN HITCHMAN
HINXMAN 47 Anschamen Hanchman Hansemane Hanshmen Haunchman Haunsmen Henceman Hencheman HENCHMAN Henchmen Hengestman Hengestmannus Hengstman Hengysman Henseman Hensheman Henshman HENSMAN Henxceman Henxeman Henxman Henxmen Henxstman Heynceman Heynsman Hinchman Hinckesman Hincksman Hincxman Hinesman Hingman Hingston Hinkman HINKSMAN Hinksmann Hinkson Hinshman Hinskman Hinsman Hinxeman Hinxksman Hinxon HITCHMAN Hnksman Hyckesman Hyncksman
Hinxon HENCHMAN HENSMAN HINKSMAN HINXMAN HITCHMAN
Hiorne HEARN HEARNE HERON HIERON HIORNS HIRON HIRONS IRONS
HIORNS 27 HEARN HEARNE Heiron Herne HERON Hierne HIERON Highorne Hiorne Hiren Hirens Hirin HIRON Hirone HIRONS Hyearnes Hyerne Hyorn Hyron Hyrone Hyrons Hyryn Iorne Iorns Iron IRONS
Hipgam HIPKIN
Hipgham HIPKIN
HIPKIN 8 Hibgame Hibgin Hipgam Hipgham Hipkins Hypgame Hypgham
Hipkins HIPKIN
HIPSEY 4 Hipsy Ipsey Ipsy
Hipsy HIPSEY
HIRCHBERG 4 HERSEBERGER HIRSCHBERG HIRSHBERG
Hirdley HORDLEY HURDLEY
Hirdman HERDMAN
Hiren HEARN HEARNE HERON HIERON HIORNS HIRON HIRONS IRONS
Hirens HEARN HEARNE HERON HIERON HIORNS HIRON HIRONS IRONS
Hirin HEARN HEARNE HERON HIERON HIORNS HIRON HIRONS IRONS
Hirman HERMAN HERMON HURMAN
HIRON 27 HEARN HEARNE Heiron Herne HERON Hierne HIERON Highorne Hiorne HIORNS Hiren Hirens Hirin Hirone HIRONS HURN Hurne Hyearnes Hyerne Hyorn Hyron Hyrone Hyrons Hyryn Iron IRONS
Hirone HEARN HEARNE HERON HIERON HIORNS HIRON HIRONS IRONS
HIRONS 25 HEARN HEARNE Heiron Herne HERON Hierne HIERON Highorne Hiorne HIORNS Hiren Hirens Hirin HIRON Hirone Hyearnes Hyerne Hyorn Hyron Hyrone Hyrons Hyryn Iron IRONS
HIRSCHBERG 4 HERSEBERGER HIRCHBERG HIRSHBERG
HIRSHBERG 4 HERSEBERGER HIRCHBERG HIRSCHBERG
Hirsopp HORSUP
HIRST 7 HAYHURST HEARST Herse Herst Heyhurst HURST
HISCOCK 12 Edgcock Edgcocke Edgecock Edgecocke Hedgcock Hedgcocke HEDGECOCK Hiscocke HISCOCKS HISCOX HITCHCOCK
Hiscocke HEDGECOCK HISCOCK
HISCOCKS 6 Hedgcock HEDGECOCK HISCOCK HISCOX HITCHCOCK
HISCOX 6 Hedgcock HEDGECOCK HISCOCK

If the name you are interested in is not here, try Section C.

HISCOCKS HITCHCOCK
Hisgrave HISGROVE
HISGROVE 8 BISGROVE Hisgrave Hissgrove Hosegrave Isgro ISGROVE Isgroves
HISLOP HYSLOP
Hissgrove HISGROVE
Hissy HIZZY
HITCHCOCK 9 Hedgcock HEDGECOCK HICHCOCKE HISCOCK HISCOCKS HISCOX HITCHCOX Hitchicock
Hitchcombe EDGCOMBE EDGECOMBE
HITCHCOX HICHCOCKE HITCHCOCK
HITCHEN 4 Hichen HITCHIN HITCHON
Hitchens HICHENS
Hitchicock HITCHCOCK
HITCHIN 4 Hichen HITCHEN HITCHON
HITCHMAN 47 Anschamen Hanchman Hansemane Hanshmen Haunchman Haunsmen Henceman Hencheman HENCHMAN Henchmen Hengestman Hengestmannus Hengstman Hengysman Henseman Hensheman Henshman HENSMAN Henxceman Henxeman Henxman Henxmen Henxstman Heynceman Heynsman Hinchman Hinckesman Hincksman Hincxman Hinesman Hingman Hingston Hinkman HINKSMAN Hinksmann Hinkson Hinshman Hinskman Hinsman Hinxeman Hinxksman HINXMAN Hinxon Hnksman Hyckesman Hyncksman
HITCHON 4 Hichen HITCHEN HITCHIN
Hivel IFOULD IVIL
Hiwis HEWISH HUISH
Hix HEXT HICKS
Hixam HUXAM HUXHAM
Hixling DE HICKELING HICKLIN HICKLING ICKELING
Hixon HICKSON HIXSON
HIXSON HICKSON Hixon
Hixt HEXT
HIZZY 4 Ezzy Hissy Issy
Hnksman HENCHMAN HENSMAN HINKSMAN HINXMAN HITCHMAN
HOAR 8 Haore HOARE Hor HORE Whoore Whor Whore
Hoardley HORDLEY HURDLEY
HOARE 12 HAW HOAR Hooar HORE WARR WEARE Whore Woar Woare WOOR Woore
HOATH 5 HORTH Horthe Hoth Hothe
Hobbes HOBBS
Hobblae HOBLEY
Hobbley HOBLEY
HOBBS 5 Hobbes Hobes Hobs Hoobes
Hobes HOBBS
Hoblae HOBLEY
Hoble HOBLEY
HOBLEY 10 Hobblae Hobbley Hoblae Hoble Hobly Hublae Hubley Oble Obley
HOBLIN HOBLYN
Hobly HOBLEY
HOBLYN HOBLIN
Hobort HEBBERD HERBERT HIBBERT HUBBERT HUBERT
Hobs HOBBS
HOBSON HOPSON
Hockelburge HUCKLEBRIDGE
HOCKEN 5 HAWKEN HAWKIN HAWKINS HOCKIN
Hocket HOCKETT
HOCKETT 5 BEAVAN Bivyen Hocket VIVIAN
HOCKIN 6 HAWKEN HAWKIN HAWKINS HOCKEN Hockins
HOCKING 5 HICKIN HOSKIN HOSKINS Hoskyns
Hockins HAWKIN HAWKINS HOCKIN
HOCKLESS Hockliss Ockless
Hockliss HOCKLESS
Hocknall HOCKNELL
HOCKNELL 5 Hocknall HOCKNEY Ocknall Ocknell
HOCKNEY HOCKNELL
Hoddesden HODSDEN HODSDON
Hoddesdon HODSDEN HODSDON
Hoddie HODDY HODY HUDDY
Hoddles HUDDLESTON HUDDLESTONE
HODDY 4 Hoddie HODY HUDDY
Hode HOOD HUDD
HODENET HODNET HODNETT
Hodesdon HODSDON HODSON
Hodeson HODSDON HODSON
Hodg HODGE
HODGE 4 Hodg Hodgers HODGES
Hodgekins HODGEKISS
Hodgekinson HODGKINSON
HODGEKISS Hodgekins Hodgskiss
Hodgen HODGSON HODSON HUDSON
Hodgens HODGSHON HODGSON HODSON
Hodgeon HODGSHON HODGSON HODSON
Hodgers HODGE HODGES
HODGES 10 Edges Egges HEDGES Hegges HODGE Hodgers HODGETTS Hogges Hoghes
Hodgeson HODSDON HODSON
HODGET 4 Hodgets Hodgett HODGETTS
Hodgets HODGET HODGETTS
Hodgett HODGET HODGETTS
HODGETTS 5 HODGES HODGET Hodgets Hodgett
Hodgin HODGSHON HODGSON HODSON HUDSON
Hodgins HODGSHON HODGSON HODSON
HODGKIN HODGKINS Hodgskin
HODGKINS HODGKIN Hodgskin
HODGKINSON 7 Hodgekinson Hodgkison Hodgkisson Hodgskinson HODKINSON Hodskinson
Hodgkison HODGKINSON
Hodgkisson HODGKINSON
HODGSHON 7 Hodgens Hodgeon Hodgin Hodgins HODGSON HODSON
Hodgskin HODGKIN HODGKINS
Hodgskinson HODGKINSON
Hodgskiss HODGEKISS
HODGSON 10 Hodgen Hodgens Hodgeon Hodgin Hodgins HODGSHON Hodgsone HODSON Hogson
Hodgsone HODGSON HODSON
HODKINSON HODGKINSON Hodskinson
HODNET HODENET HODNETT
HODNETT HODENET HODNET
HODSDEN 4 Hoddesden Hoddesdon HODSDON
HODSDON 8 Hoddesden Hoddesdon Hodesdon Hodeson Hodgeson HODSDEN HODSON
Hodshon HODSON HUDSON
Hodskinson HODGKINSON HODKINSON
HODSON 16 Hodesdon Hodeson Hodgen Hodgens Hodgeon Hodgeson Hodgin Hodgins HODGSHON HODGSON Hodgsone HODSDON Hodshon Hogson HUDSON
HODY 4 Hoddie HODDY HUDDY
Hoeman HAMON HOLLMAN HOLMAN HOMAN
HOFF HOGG
HOGAN 15 Eagan Eagin HAGAN HAGEN Haggan Hagin Haygan Heagan Heagin Heagon HEGAN Heigan Higan O'hagan
HOGARTH HUGGART
HOGBEN Hogbin
Hogbin HOGBEN
HOGG HOFF
Hogges HODGES
Hoghes HODGES
Hogson HODGSON HODSON HUDSON HUTSON
HOGWOOD Haigwood
Hoiskins HOSKINS
Holas HOLLIS
Holbard HALBARD
Holbrock HALBROOK
HOLBROOK HALBROOK
HOLCRAFT HOLCROFT OCRAFT
HOLCROFT HOLCRAFT OCRAFT
Holcut HURKETT
Holcutt HURKETT
Holdbrook HALBROOK
Holdbrooks HALBROOK
HOLDCROFT 4 Allcroft Howlcrofte Oldcroft
HOLDEN 8 HADDON HAWDON HOLDING Holttum HOLTUM Houlden HOULTON
HOLDER HOULDER
Holderfield HOLYFIELD
HOLDICH Holditch Houlditch
HOLDING HOLDEN
HOLDIP 4 Holdup Holduppe Holdyp
Holditch HOLDICH
HOLDSWORTH HALDSWORTHE HOULDSWORTH
Holdup HOLDIP
Holduppe HOLDIP
Holdyp HOLDIP
Holeman HAMON HOLLMAN HOLMAN HOMAN
Holich HOLLICK
HOLIDAY 4 HALLIDAY HOLLIDAY Holyday
Holifield HOLYFIELD
Holihead HOLYHEAD
Holiock HOLYOAKE
Holiocke HOLYOAKE
Holkins HALLKINS
HOLLAND 4 HOLLANDS Hollon HULLAND
Hollandby HOLLINGSBEE
HOLLANDS HOLLAND
HOLLAWAY 5 HALLOWAY Hallowell HOLLOWAY HOLLOWELL
Hollehead HOLYHEAD
Hollenby HOLLINGSBEE
Hollendby HOLLINGSBEE
HOLLEY Holly
Holleyhead HOLYHEAD
HOLLIBONE Hallibon Holybone
HOLLICK 5 Holich Hollix Olick Ollick
HOLLIDAY 5 Halladay HALLIDAY HOLIDAY Holyday
HOLLIER 7 HELLIER Helyar HILLIER Hoyler Olier OLLIER
HOLLIES HOLLIS
Hollifield HOLYFIELD
HOLLIN 8 Hallin HALLING Hallings HALLINS Holling HOLLINGS HOLLINS
Holling HALLING HALLINS HOLLIN HOLLINGS HOLLINS
Hollingberry HOLLINGSBEE
Hollingrake HOLLINRAKE
HOLLINGS 8 Hallin HALLING Hallings HALLINS HOLLIN Holling HOLLINS
HOLLINGSBEE 5 Hollandby Hollenby Hollendby Hollingberry
HOLLINGSWORTH 5 HOLLINGWORTH Hollingworthe Hollyngeworth Hollyngworth
HOLLINGWORTH 5 HOLLINGSWORTH Hollingworthe Hollyngeworth Hollyngworth
Hollingworthe HOLLINGSWORTH HOLLINGWORTH
HOLLINRAKE Hillindrake Hollingrake
HOLLINS 8 Hallin HALLING Hallings HALLINS HOLLIN Holling HOLLINGS
Hollioake HOLLYOAK
HOLLIS Holas HOLLIES
HOLLISTER 4 Holsor Olester Olser
Hollix HOLLICK
HOLLMAN 14 HAMON Hoeman Holeman Hollyman HOLMAN HOLMWOOD Holyman HOMAN Homanes Homard HOMEWOOD Olman OMAN
Hollon HOLLAND
Holloran HALLORAN
HOLLOWAY 7 HALLOWAY Hallowell HOLLAWAY HOLLOWELL Holoway HOLWAY
HOLLOWELL 5 HALLOWAY Hallowell HOLLAWAY HOLLOWAY
Hollows HALLOWES HALLOWS
Holly HOLLEY
Hollyfield HOLYFIELD
Hollyhead HOLYHEAD
Hollyman HOLLMAN HOLMAN HOLMWOOD HOMEWOOD OMAN
Hollyngeworth HOLLINGSWORTH HOLLINGWORTH
Hollyngworth HOLLINGSWORTH HOLLINGWORTH
HOLLYOAK Hollioake
Holm HOLME HOLMES HUME
HOLMAN 14 HAMON Hoeman Holeman HOLLMAN Hollyman HOLMWOOD Holyman HOMAN Homanes Homard HOMEWOOD Olman

If the name you are interested in is not here, try Section C.

OMAN
HOLME 5 Holm HOLMES HULME HUME
HOLMES 6 Holm HOLME HOMES HULME HUME
Holmewood HOLMWOOD HOMEWOOD
HOLMWOOD 11 HOLLMAN Hollyman HOLMAN Holmewood Holyman Homard HOMEWOOD Homwood Olman OMAN
Holoway HALLOWAY HOLLOWAY HOLWAY
Holsor HOLLISTER
HOLT HOUGHT HOULT
HOLTOM HOLTON
HOLTON HOLTOM
Holttum HOLDEN HOLTUM HOULTON
HOLTUM 4 HOLDEN Holttum HOULTON
HOLWAY HOLLOWAY Holoway
Holybone HOLLIBONE
Holyday HALLIDAY HOLIDAY HOLLIDAY
HOLYFIELD 5 Holderfield Holifield Hollifield Hollyfield
HOLYHEAD 5 Holihead Hollehead Holleyhead Hollyhead
Holyman HOLLMAN HOLMAN HOLMWOOD HOMEWOOD OMAN
HOLYOAKE 4 Holiock Holiocke Holyoke
Holyoke HOLYOAKE
HOMAN 7 HAMON Hoeman Holeman HOLLMAN HOLMAN Homanes
Homanes HAMON HOLLMAN HOLMAN HOMAN
Homard HOLLMAN HOLMAN HOLMWOOD HOMEWOOD OMAN
Homerode OMEROD ORMEROD ORMROD
HOMES HOLMES
HOMEWOOD 11 HOLLMAN Hollyman HOLMAN Holmewood HOLMWOOD Holyman Homard Homwood Olman OMAN
Homwood HOLMWOOD HOMEWOOD
HONEY HONY
HONEYSETT 4 Honiset Honysett Hunniset
HONEYWOOD Honywood Hunniwood
Honiset HONEYSETT
HONNER 4 Honnour Honor HONOUR
HONNOR Honor HONOUR
Honnour HONNER HONOUR HORNER
Honor HONNER HONNOR HONOUR HORNER
HONOUR 11 HONNER HONNOR Honnour Honor Honoure Honrel Hornal Hornell HORNER Hornur
Honoure HONOUR HORNER
Honrel HONOUR HORNER
HONY HONEY
Honysett HONEYSETT
Honywood HONEYWOOD
Hooar HOARE HORE
Hoobes HOBBS
HOOD Hode HUDD
Hoodswell HUDGELL HUDSWELL
Hoogan WOGAN
HOOK HOOKE
HOOKE HOOK
HOOLE 90 Eule Ewel Eweles EWELL Ewels Juel Jule Uhl Uhles Uiles Uoel Yeaull Yeel Yeell Yehl Yeil Yeill Yell Yeoale Yeouls Yeowell Yeuell Yeuille Yeul Yeules Yeull Yeulle Yewell Yewl Yoall Yoele Yoell Yol YOLE Yoll Yooil Yool Yooll Yoolo Yooly Youan Youel YOUELL Youels Youhill Youil Youile Youill Youille Youl Youle Youles Youlie Youll Youlla Youlle Youlley Youllie Youlo Youlow Youly Yowel Yowil Yowle Yual Yuall Yuel Yuell Yuelle Yuelo Yuial Yuie Yuiell Yuil Yuile Yuille Yuillie Yuills Yuir Yul YULE Yull Yulle Yullie Yullow Yuls Yuyll Ywill Zoule
HOOLEY 13 HALLEY HANLEY HAWLEY Hooly Howley Hullay HULLEY HULLY ULLEY Ully UTLEY Whooley
Hooly HALLEY HANLEY HAWLEY HOOLEY HULLEY HULLY ULLEY UTLEY
HOOPER HOOPPER
HOOPPER HOOPER
HOPES Hoppes HOPPS
HOPKINS HAWKINS
Hoppes HOPES HOPPS
HOPPS HOPES Hoppes
HOPSON HOBSON
Hor HOAR HORE
HORA Da hora De hora
HORAM 4 HURAM ORAM Whoram
HORAN 5 Horen HORN HORNE Horon
Horberry ALBERRY AUBRAY AUBREY
Horbery ALBERRY AUBRAY AUBREY
Horbury ALBERRY AUBRAY AUBREY
HORDEN 4 Haldern HAWTHORN HORDERN
HORDERN 4 Haldern HAWTHORN HORDEN
HORDLEY 5 Hirdley Hoardley HURDLEY Hurlye
Hordwyck HARDWICK
HORE 16 Haore HAW HOAR HOARE Hooar Hor WARR WEARE Whoore Whor Whore Woar Woare WOOR Woore
Horen HORAN
Horethorn HAWTHORN HAWTHORNE HORTON HOUGHTON ORTON
HORN 5 HEARN HERN HORAN HORNE
Hornal HONOUR HORNER
HORNBY HORNSBY
HORNE 5 HEARN HERN HORAN HORN
Hornee FEATHERSTONE FETHERSTON HORNSEY NESFIELD
Hornell HONOUR HORNER
HORNER 9 Honnour Honor HONOUR Honoure Honrel Hornal Hornell Hornur
Hornesey FEATHERSTONE FETHERSTON HORNSEY NESFIELD
Hornsay FEATHERSTONE FETHERSTON HORNSEY NESFIELD
Hornsaye FEATHERSTONE FETHERSTON HORNSEY NESFIELD
HORNSBY HORNBY
Hornsea FEATHERSTONE FETHERSTON HORNSEY NESFIELD
HORNSEY 17 Fatherston Fatherstone Fatterstone Featherston FEATHERSTONE FETHERSTON Fetherstone Hornee Hornesey Hornsay Hornsaye Hornsea Hornsie Hornsy NESFIELD Tetherston
Hornsie FEATHERSTONE FETHERSTON HORNSEY NESFIELD
Hornsy FEATHERSTONE FETHERSTON HORNSEY NESFIELD
Hornur HONOUR HORNER
Horon HORAN
Horrall HORRELL HORROLL
HORRELL 4 Horrall Horrill HORROLL
Horrill HORRELL HORROLL
HORROCKS Horrox
HORROLL 4 Horrall HORRELL Horrill
Horrox HORROCKS
Horsall HORSELL
HORSAM 6 HORSHAM Hosam Hossam Hursam Hursham
HORSECRAFT HORSECROFT Hoscroth
HORSECROFT HORSECRAFT Hoscroth
HORSEFIELD HORSFIELD
HORSELL Harsell Horsall
HORSEMAN HORSMAN
HORSEWELL 4 HORSEWILL HORSWELL HORSWILL
HORSEWILL 4 HORSEWELL HORSWELL HORSWILL
HORSFALL 4 Horsfell HORSFIELD Hurstfield
Horsfell HORSFALL HORSFIELD
HORSFIELD 4 HORSEFIELD HORSFALL Horsfell
HORSHAM 6 HORSAM Hosam Hossam Hursam Hursham
Horshill HOSSILL
HORSMAN HORSEMAN
Horsop HORSUP
HORSTMAN Horstmann
Horstmann HORSTMAN
Horstus HURSTHOUSE
HORSUP 4 Hirsopp Horsop Horsupp
Horsupp HORSUP
HORSWELL 4 HORSEWELL HORSEWILL HORSWILL
HORSWILL 4 HORSEWELL HORSEWILL HORSWELL
HORTH 5 HOATH Horthe Hoth Hothe
Horthe HOATH HORTH
Horthorn HAWTHORN HAWTHORNE HORTON HOUGHTON ORTON
HORTON 27 Anthorn Aughton Hardin Harten HARTIN Harton Hathorn Hathorne HAUGHTON Hauthni Hawthen HAWTHORN HAWTHORNE Hawthornthwaite Hawtyn Haythorne Horethorn Horthorn Hothorne HOUGHTON Howton Hufton Hurton HUTTON MARTIN ORTON
Hosam HORSAM HORSHAM
Hosbon OSBAND OSBORN OSBORNE OSBOURN OSBOURNE
Hosborn OSBORN OSBORNE
Hosbrook FOSBROOK
Hoscroth HORSECRAFT HORSECROFT
Hosegood HOSGOOD
Hosegrave HISGROVE
Hoselett ASLETT HASLETT
HOSGOOD Hosegood
HOSKEN HOSKIN HOSKING
HOSKIN 6 HOCKING HOSKEN HOSKING HOSKINS Hoskyns
HOSKING 7 HASKING HASKINS HOSKEN HOSKIN Hoskings HOSKINS
Hoskings HASKING HASKINS HOSKING HOSKINS
HOSKINS 9 HASKING HASKINS HOCKING Hoiskins HOSKIN HOSKING Hoskings Hoskyns
Hoskyns HOCKING HOSKIN HOSKINS
Hosleed ASLETT HASLETT
Hossam HORSAM HORSHAM
HOSSILL Horshill
Hoswell HASKELL HASWELL HUSSELL HUZZELL OSWALD RUSSELL URSELL UZZELL
Hotchkis HOTCHKISS
HOTCHKISS Hotchkis
Hoter HUDSON HUTSON
Hoth HOATH HORTH
Hothe HOATH HORTH
Hother HATHER HEATHER
HOTHERSALL 4 Hathersall Hethersall Huthersall
Hothorne HAWTHORN HAWTHORNE HORTON HOUGHTON ORTON
HOUCHELL 6 Houchen Houtchell Howchell Howtchell Ouchell
Houchen HOUCHELL
HOUDE 12 Clair Desrochers Desruisseaux Durocher Houl Hould Houle Houlle Leclair Leclerc Oule
HOUGHT HOLT HOULT
HOUGHTON 20 Anthorn Hathorn Hathorne HAUGHTON Hauthni Hawthen HAWTHORN HAWTHORNE Hawthornthwaite Hawtyn Haythorne Horethorn Horthorn HORTON Hothorne HOUTON Howton Hufton ORTON
Houl HOUDE
Houlbrook HALBROOK
Houlbrooks HALBROOK
Hould HOUDE
Houlden HOLDEN
HOULDER HOLDER
Houlditch HOLDICH
HOULDSWORTH HOLDSWORTH
Houle HOUDE
HOULKER ALKER
Houlle HOUDE
HOULT HOLT HOUGHT
HOULTON 4 HOLDEN Holttum HOLTUM
Hourdebourg HENDEBOURCK HEUDEBOURCK
HOUSE HOWSE HULSE
HOUSEHAM HOUSHAM Howsam
HOUSHAM 5 HOUSEHAM Howsam Howsham Howsom

If the name you are interested in is not here, try Section C.

Houtchell HOUCHELL
HOUTON HOUGHTON
Hoveden OVENDEN
HOW HOWE
HOWARD 5 HAWARD Haword HAYWARD Heyward
HOWARTH HAWORTH Howorth
HOWAT 13 Hawat Hewet HEWETT Hewiss Hewit HEWITT Howatt HOWITT Huet Huett Huitt Huot
Howatt HEWETT HEWITT HOWAT HOWITT
Howchell HOUCHELL
HOWE HAW HOW
Howel HOWELL HOWL
Howele HOWELL HOWL
HOWELL 130 Ap howell De stavele De stawele De stawell De stawelle De stawille De stawylle De stoill De stouill De stoule De stoville De stowill De stowille Howel Howele Howelle HOWELLS HOWL Howlle Mcstoile Mcstole POWELL Showell Shoyell Stafeld Staile Stauwill STAVOLD Stavwill Stawel STAWELL Stawle Stawyll Stayell Stayle Steole Steul Stewell Stewill Steywel Stoal Stoale Stoall Stoel Stoell Stoelle Stoewell Stoffell Stohel Stohell Stohill Stohl Stoiel Stoiell Stoil Stoile Stoiles Stoils Stol Stole Stoles Stoll Stolle Stolles Stols Stool Stoole Stooles Stools Stoolus Stouall Stouel Stouell Stouil Stoul Stouwell Stoval Stovald Stovall Stovel Stoveld Stovell Stovill Stovold Stovoll Stowal Stowall Stowals Stoweel Stoweils Stowel Stoweld Stowele Stoweley STOWELL Stowells Stowels Stowhil Stowhill Stowil Stowilles Stowl Stowldwell Stowle Stowles Stowold Stowole Stowoll Stowvel Stowwell Stowyll Stoyel Stoyell Stoyels Stoyl STOYLE Stoyles Stoyll Stoylls Stoyls Stoyoll Stuell Stul Stule Stules Stull Stweall Stwell Styell
Howelle HOWELL HOWL
HOWELLS HOWELL
Howieson HOWISON
Howins EWINGS EWINS HEWENS HEWINGS YOUINGS
HOWISON Howieson
HOWITT 13 Hawat Hewet HEWETT Hewiss Hewit HEWITT HOWAT Howatt Huet Huett Huitt Huot
HOWKINS HAWKINS
HOWL 6 Howel Howele HOWELL Howelle Howlle
Howlcrofte HOLDCROFT
Howlesworth ALLSWORTH HALLSWORTH
Howlet HOWLETT
HOWLETT 4 Howlet Hullet Hullot
Howley HALLEY HANLEY HAWLEY HOOLEY HULLEY HULLY ULLEY UTLEY
Howlle HOWELL HOWL
Howorth HAWORTH HOWARTH
Howsam HOUSEHAM HOUSHAM
HOWSE HOUSE HULSE
Howsham HOUSHAM
Howsom HOUSHAM
Howtchell HOUCHELL
Howton HORTON HOUGHTON
HOY Hoye
Hoye HOY
Hoyler HOLLIER
Hubard HUBBALL HUBBARD
HUBBALL 4 Hubard Hubberd Huberte
HUBBARD 5 Hebert Hubard Hubbart HUBERT
Hubbart HUBBARD HUBERT
Hubberd HEBBERD HERBERT HIBBERT HUBBALL HUBBERT HUBERT
HUBBERT 15 Eibbot Eibert Hebbat HEBBERD Hebert Hepert HERBERT Hibbart HIBBERT Hibort Hobort Hubberd HUBERT Hybbart
HUBERT 17 Eibbot Eibert Hebbat HEBBERD Hebert Hepert HERBERT Hibbart HIBBERT Hibort Hobort HUBBARD Hubbart Hubberd HUBBERT Hybbart
Huberte HUBBALL
Hublae HOBLEY
Hubley HOBLEY
Hucclebridge HUCKLEBRIDGE
Huckberry HUCKLEBRIDGE
Huckelbridg HUCKLEBRIDGE
Huckelbridge HUCKLEBRIDGE
Huckelbrige HUCKLEBRIDGE
Huckelbrigge HUCKLEBRIDGE
Huckelburdge HUCKLEBRIDGE
Huckelburge HUCKLEBRIDGE
Huckellbridge HUCKLEBRIDGE
Huckellburge HUCKLEBRIDGE
Huckelsby HUCKLESBY
Huckeridge HUCKLEBRIDGE
Huckilbridge HUCKLEBRIDGE
Huckleberry HUCKLEBRIDGE
Hucklebourg HUCKLEBRIDGE
Hucklebridg HUCKLEBRIDGE
HUCKLEBRIDGE 29 Hackelbridge Hockelburge Hucclebridge Huckberry Huckelbridg Huckelbridge Huckelbrige Huckelbrigge Huckelburdge Huckelburge Huckellbridge Huckellburge Huckeridge Huckilbridge Huckleberry Hucklebourg Hucklebridg Huckleburdge Huckleburg Huckleburge Huckleburgh Huckleburie Hucklebury Huckleburye Huckridge Huckylbrygg Huclebridge Knucklebridge
Huckleburdge HUCKLEBRIDGE
Huckleburg HUCKLEBRIDGE
Huckleburge HUCKLEBRIDGE
Huckleburgh HUCKLEBRIDGE
Huckleburie HUCKLEBRIDGE
Hucklebury HUCKLEBRIDGE
Huckleburye HUCKLEBRIDGE
Hucklesbey HUCKLESBY
HUCKLESBY Huckelsby Hucklesbey
Huckridge HUCKLEBRIDGE
Hucksford HUXFORD
HUCKSTEP Huckstepp
Huckstepp HUCKSTEP
Huckylbrygg HUCKLEBRIDGE
Huclebridge HUCKLEBRIDGE
Hucutt SLUCUTT
HUDD Hode HOOD
Huddeswell HUDGELL HUDSWELL
Huddleson HUDDLESTON HUDDLESTONE
HUDDLESTON 6 Hoddles Huddleson HUDDLESTONE HUDLESTON Hurlstone
HUDDLESTONE 5 Hoddles Huddleson HUDDLESTON HUDLESTON
HUDDY 4 Hoddie HODDY HODY
HUDGELL 8 Hoodswell Huddeswell Hudgle Hudgwell Hudsell HUDSWELL Udgell
Hudgle HUDGELL HUDSWELL
Hudgwell HUDGELL HUDSWELL
Hudiberk HENDEBOURCK HEUDEBOURCK
HUDLESTON HUDDLESTON HUDDLESTONE
Hudsell HUDGELL HUDSWELL
HUDSON 8 Hodgen Hodgin Hodshon HODSON Hogson Hoter HUTSON
HUDSWELL 8 Hoodswell Huddeswell HUDGELL Hudgle Hudgwell Hudsell Udgell
HUEGDON Hugdon
Hueson HEWITSON HEWSON HUGHSON HUSON
Huet HEWETT HEWITT HOWAT HOWITT
Huett HEWETT HEWITT HOWAT HOWITT
HUFFERDINE UPPERDINE
Hufton HORTON HOUGHTON
Hugdon HUEGDON
HUGGART HOGARTH
Huggens HUGGIN HUGGINS
HUGGIN 5 Huggens HUGGINS Huggons Hugins
HUGGINS 5 Huggens HUGGIN Huggons Hugins
Huggons HUGGIN HUGGINS
HUGHES 6 HEWES Hews Hughs Huse Huses
Hugheson HEWETSON HEWITSON HEWSON HUGHSON HUITSON
Hughetson HEWETSON HEWITSON HEWSON HUGHSON HUITSON
Hughs HUGHES
HUGHSON 12 HEWETSON Hewison HEWITSON Hewittson HEWSON Hueson Hugheson Hughetson Huison HUITSON HUSON
Hugins HUGGIN HUGGINS
Huings EWINGS EWINS HEWENS HEWINGS YOUINGS
Huins EWINGS EWINS HEWENS HEWINGS HEWINS YOUINGS
Huisdean MACQUISTEN MCQUISTON
Huisdeinn MACQUISTEN MCQUISTON
Huise HEWISH HUISH
HUISH 7 HEWISH Hewishe Hiwis Huise Huishe Huyshe
Huishe HEWISH HUISH
Huison HEWITSON HEWSON HUGHSON HUSON
Huit HEWITT
HUITSON 8 HEWETSON HEWITSON Hewittson HEWSON Hugheson Hughetson HUGHSON
Huitt HEWETT HEWITT HOWAT HOWITT
HULBARD HULBERT
HULBERT HULBARD
Hulcut HURKETT
Hulcutt HURKETT
Hulet HEWLET HEWLETT
Hulett HEWLET HEWLETT
HULF 11 ALFF ALP ALPE ALPHE ALPS AULPH OLFE ULF ULFE ULPH
HULLAND HOLLAND
Hullay HALLEY HANLEY HAWLEY HOOLEY HULLEY HULLY ULLEY UTLEY
Hullet HOWLETT
HULLEY 13 HALLEY HANLEY HAWLEY HOOLEY Hooly Howley Hullay HULLY ULLEY Ully UTLEY Whooley
Hullice MULLIS
Hullious MULLIS
Hullis MULLIS
Hulliss MULLIS
Hullot HOWLETT
HULLY 13 HALLEY HANLEY HAWLEY HOOLEY Hooly Howley Hullay HULLEY ULLEY Ully UTLEY Whooley
HULME HOLME HOLMES
HULSE HOUSE HOWSE
HUMBERSTON HUMBERSTONE
HUMBERSTONE HUMBERSTON
HUME 4 Holm HOLME HOLMES
Humfreys HUMPHRIES
Humfries HUMPHRIES
Humphery HUMPHRIES HUMPHRY
Humpherys HUMPHREYS HUMPHRIES
Humphreas HUMPHREYS HUMPHRIES HUMPHRIS
HUMPHREY HUMPHRY
HUMPHREYS 7 Humpherys Humphreas HUMPHRIES HUMPHRIS HUMPHRISS Humphrys
HUMPHRIES 11 Humfreys Humfries Humphery Humpherys Humphreas HUMPHREYS HUMPHRIS HUMPHRISS HUMPHRY Humphrys
HUMPHRIS 6 Humphreas HUMPHREYS HUMPHRIES HUMPHRISS Humphrys
HUMPHRISS 5 HUMPHREYS HUMPHRIES HUMPHRIS Humphrys
HUMPHRY 4 Humphery HUMPHREY HUMPHRIES
Humphrys HUMPHREYS HUMPHRIES HUMPHRIS HUMPHRISS
HUNCKYNGE 4 HUNKIN HUNKING HUNKINS
HUNKIN 4 HUNCKYNGE HUNKING HUNKINS
HUNKING 4 HUNCKYNGE HUNKIN HUNKINS
HUNKINS 4 HUNCKYNGE HUNKIN HUNKING
Hunniset HONEYSETT
Hunniwood HONEYWOOD
HUNT Hunte HUNTER

If the name you are interested in is not here, try Section C.

Hunte HUNT HUNTER
HUNTER 5 HUNT Hunte Hunto Huntow
Huntinford HUNTINGFORD
HUNTINGDON HUNTINGTON
HUNTINGFORD Huntinford
HUNTINGTON HUNTINGDON
Hunto HUNTER
Huntow HUNTER
Huot HEWETT HEWITT HOWAT HOWITT
HURAM 4 HORAM ORAM Whoram
Hurben HURLEY
Hurckett HACKETT HURKETT
Hurcot HACKETT HURKETT
Hurcott HACKETT HURKETT
Hurcotte HACKETT HURKETT
Hurcut HACKETT HURKETT
Hurcutt HURKETT
HURDEN HURDING HURDON
Hurder HEARDER
HURDING HURDEN HURDON
HURDLEY 5 Hirdley Hoardley HORDLEY Hurlye
HURDON HURDEN HURDING
HURFORD Hereford
Hurket HURKETT
HURKETT 14 HACKETT Holcut Holcutt Hulcut Hulcutt Hurckett Hurcot Hurcott Hurcotte Hurcut Hurcutt Hurket Hurkitt
Hurkitt HURKETT
Hurl HURLE
HURLE 5 Herle Hurl Hurll HURRELL
Hurlen HURLEY
HURLEY Hurben Hurlen
Hurll HURLE
Hurlstone HUDDLESTON
Hurlye HORDLEY HURDLEY
HURMAN 5 HERMAN Hermann HERMON Hirman
HURN 9 HEARN HEARNE HERN Herne HERON HIRON Hurne Hyrons
Hurne HIRON HURN
HURRELL HURLE
HURREN Hurrian
Hurrian HURREN
Hursam HORSAM HORSHAM
Hursell HUSSELL
Hursham HORSAM HORSHAM
HURST 7 HAYHURST HEARST Herse Herst Heyhurst HIRST
Hurstfield HORSFALL
HURSTHOUSE Horstus Hursthowse
Hursthowse HURSTHOUSE
Hurtnoll HARTNELL HARTNOLL
Hurton HORTON
Huse HUGHES
Huses HUGHES
Husle HASKELL HASWELL HUSSELL HUZZELL OSWALD RUSSELL URSELL UZZELL
Huslett ASLETT HASLETT
HUSON 7 Hewison HEWITSON HEWSON Hueson HUGHSON Huison
Hussard HUZZARD
Hussel HUSSELL
Husselbe HUSSELBEE
HUSSELBEE 6 Husselbe Husselbury Husselby Husslebee Hustlebee
Husselbury HUSSELBEE
Husselby HUSSELBEE
HUSSELL 34 Askell Aswell Essell HASKELL Hassel HASWELL Hawsell Haysel Hessell Hoswell Hursell Husle Hussel Hustle HUZZELL Israel Issel Osell OSWALD Ozell RUSSELL URSELL Urswell Ushil Ussell Ussol Ussould Uswell Uzald Uzle Uzzeel Uzzele UZZELL
Husslebee HUSSELBEE
Hustle HUSSELL
Hustlebee HUSSELBEE
HUSTWAYTE 4 Hustwick Hustwit Hustwitt
Hustwick HUSTWAYTE
Hustwit HUSTWAYTE
Hustwitt HUSTWAYTE
Hutchens HUTCHINGS HUTCHINS
Hutchenson HUTCHESON HUTCHINSON HUTCHISON
HUTCHESON Hutchenson HUTCHISON
HUTCHIN 4 HUTCHING HUTCHINGS HUTCHINS
HUTCHING 4 HUTCHIN HUTCHINGS HUTCHINS
HUTCHINGS 5 Hutchens HUTCHIN HUTCHING HUTCHINS
HUTCHINS 5 Hutchens HUTCHIN HUTCHING HUTCHINGS
HUTCHINSON Hutchenson
HUTCHISON Hutchenson HUTCHESON
Huthersall HOTHERSALL
HUTHNANCE Huthnans Huthnes
Huthnans HUTHNANCE
Huthnes HUTHNANCE
HUTSON 4 Hogson Hoter HUDSON
HUTTON 8 Hardin Harten HARTIN Harton HAUGHTON HORTON MARTIN
HUXAM Hixam HUXHAM
HUXFORD Hexford Hucksford
HUXHAM Hixam HUXAM
Huyshe HEWISH HUISH
Huzerd HUZZARD
HUZZARD 5 Heusser Hussard Huzerd Uzzett
HUZZELL 31 Askell Aswell Essell HASKELL Hassel HASWELL Hawsell Haysel Hessell Hoswell Husle HUSSELL Israel Issel Osell OSWALD Ozell RUSSELL URSELL Urswell Ushil Ussell Ussol Ussould Uswell Uzald Uzle Uzzeel Uzzele UZZELL
Hyam HIGHAM HYEM
Hyat HIGHGATE
HYATT 9 Heiat Hiat HIATT Hiet Hiett Highet HYETT Hyot
Hybard HIBBARD HIBBERD HIBBERT IBBOT
Hybbart HEBBERD HERBERT HIBBERT HUBBERT HUBERT
Hyberd HIBBARD HIBBERD HIBBERT IBBOT
Hybys HEBB HIBBS
Hyckelyng DE HICKELING HICKLIN HICKLING ICKELING
Hyckesman HENCHMAN HENSMAN HINKSMAN HINXMAN HITCHMAN
Hycklinge DE HICKELING HICKLIN HICKLING ICKELING
Hycklyng DE HICKELING HICKLIN HICKLING ICKELING
HYDE HIDE
HYDER HIDER
Hyearnes HEARN HEARNE HERON HIERON HIORNS HIRON HIRONS IRONS
HYEM 4 Heigham HIGHAM Hyam
Hyerne HEARN HEARNE HERON HIERON HIORNS HIRON HIRONS IRONS
HYETT 9 Heiat Hiat HIATT Hiet Hiett Highet HYATT Hyot
Hygate HIGHGATE
Hygman HICKMAN HIGMAN
Hykeling DE HICKELING HICKLIN HICKLING ICKELING
Hykelyn HICKLIN HICKLING
Hykelyng DE HICKELING HICKLIN HICKLING ICKELING
Hykling DE HICKELING HICKLIN HICKLING ICKELING
Hyklyng DE HICKELING HICKLIN HICKLING ICKELING
Hyklynge DE HICKELING HICKLIN HICKLING ICKELING
Hykman HICKMAN HIGMAN
HYLAND 11 Heghland Heilland Hielan Hielaunde HIGHLAND Highlande Highlands Hiland Hilands HYLANDS
HYLANDS 11 Heghland Heilland Hielan Hielaunde HIGHLAND Highlande Highlands Hiland Hilands HYLAND
Hyles AYLES EALES EELES EYLES HILES ILES
HYNARD 12 HAYWOOD Heignwood Henywood Highner Hinard Hiner Hinor Hinord HYNER Hynerd Hynor
Hyncksman HENCHMAN HENSMAN HINKSMAN HINXMAN HITCHMAN
Hynd HIND HINDE HINDS HINE
Hynde HIND HINDE HINE
Hyndes HIND HINDS
Hyne HIND HINDE HINE
HYNER 12 HAYWOOD Heignwood Henywood Highner Hinard Hiner Hinor Hinord HYNARD Hynerd Hynor
Hynerd HAYWOOD HYNARD HYNER
Hynor HAYWOOD HYNARD HYNER
Hyorn HEARN HEARNE HERON HIERON HIORNS HIRON HIRONS IRONS
Hyot HIATT HYATT HYETT
Hypgame HIPKIN
Hypgham HIPKIN
Hyron HEARN HEARNE HERON HIERON HIORNS HIRON HIRONS IRONS
Hyrone HEARN HEARNE HERON HIERON HIORNS HIRON HIRONS IRONS
Hyrons HEARN HEARNE HERON HIERON HIORNS HIRON HIRONS HURN IRONS
Hyryn HEARN HEARNE HERON HIERON HIORNS HIRON HIRONS IRONS
HYSLOP HESLOP HISLOP
Hysman HEASMAN
Hyviu EVA EVEA
I'ANSON JANSON
Ibbert HIBBARD HIBBERD HIBBERT IBBOT
Ibbes HEBB HIBBS
Ibbet EBBOTT EBBUTT HIBBITT IBBOT
Ibbett EBBOTT EBBUTT HIBBITT IBBOT
IBBIT Hibbit
Ibbitt EBBOTT EBBUTT HIBBITT IBBOT
IBBOT 35 Ebbatt Ebbert Ebbet Ebbetts Ebbit Ebbitt Ebbot EBBOTT Ebbut EBBUTT Ebert Ebet Ebott Ebottes Ebytt Hibard HIBBARD Hibbart HIBBERD HIBBERT Hibbit HIBBITT Hibbot Hiberd Hybard Hyberd Ibbert Ibbet Ibbett Ibbitt Ibbott Ibet Ibot Ibott
Ibbott EBBOTT EBBUTT HIBBITT IBBOT
Ibbs HEBB HEBBES HIBBS
Ibet EBBOTT EBBUTT HIBBITT IBBOT
Ibot EBBOTT EBBUTT HIBBITT IBBOT
Ibott EBBOTT EBBUTT HIBBITT IBBOT
Ibs HEBB HIBBS
Icel HICKLES ICKEL ICKELING
Icelin HICKLIN HICKLING
Iceling DE HICKELING HICKLIN HICKLING ICKELING
Icelingham HICKLINGAM
Icelingtun HICKLENTON
Icelintone HICKLENTON
Ichel HICKLES ICKEL ICKELING
Ichelin HICKLIN HICKLING
Icheltone HICKLETON
ICKEL 14 De hickel Echel Hiccle Hicel HICKLES Hikal Hikel Icel Ichel ICKELING Ickle Icles Ikel
ICKELING 88 De hekelinge De hekelingge De hekelyng De hekelyngg De hickel DE HICKELING De hickelinge De hickelyng De hickelynges De hickland De hickling De hicklinge De hicklingge De hicling De higeling De hikeling De hikelinga De hikelinge De hikelinges De hikelingge De hikelyng De hikelynge De hikligg De hiklyng De hitling De hykeling De hykelinge De hykelingge De hykelinggs De hykelingh De hykelyng De hykelynge De hykelyngge De hykkelingh De ikeling De ikelinges De ykeling Eccling Echel Echelinog Etcling Hiccle Hicel Hiceling Hichelyng Hickelynge HICKLES

If the name you are interested in is not here, try Section C.

HICKLIN HICKLING Hicklinge Hicklings Hicklingse Hicklinse Hicling Hiclyng Hikal Hikel Hikeling Hikelyng Hikelyngg Hikkling Hiklynge Hixling Hyckelyng Hycklinge Hycklyng Hykeling Hykelyng Hykling Hyklyng Hyklynge Icel Iceling Ichel ICKEL Ickle Ickling Icles Icling Iclingas Ikel Ikeling Ikelinge Ikling Ycling Ykeling Ykling
Ickle HICKLES ICKEL ICKELING
Ickleton HICKLETON
Ickling DE HICKELING HICKLIN HICKLING ICKELING
Icklingham HICKLINGAM
Iclans HICKLIN HICKLING
Icles HICKLES ICKEL ICKELING
Icling DE HICKELING HICKLIN HICKLING ICKELING
Iclingas DE HICKELING HICKLIN HICKLING ICKELING
Iddens IDIENS
Iddol EDDOLLS EDDOLS
Iddolls EDDOLLS EDDOLS
Iddols EDDOLLS EDDOLS
IDIENS Iddens
Idol EDDOLLS EDDOLS
Idols EDDOLLS EDDOLS
Iermonger IREMONGER IRONMONGER
Iermunger IREMONGER IRONMONGER
Iernmonger IREMONGER IRONMONGER
Iernmunber IREMONGER IRONMONGER
Iesset JESSETT
Iffold IFOULD IVIL
Ifold IFOULD IVIL
Ifolde IFOULD IVIL
IFOULD 16 Hivel Iffold Ifold Ifolde Ival Ivall Ivel Ivell IVIL Ivol Ivold Ivolde Ivoll Ivould Ivoulde
Iilsley EELES ILLSLEY ILSLEY
Ikel HICKLES ICKEL ICKELING
Ikeline HICKLIN HICKLING
Ikeling DE HICKELING HICKLIN HICKLING ICKELING
Ikelinge DE HICKELING HICKLIN HICKLING ICKELING
Ikelingham HICKLINGAM
Ikling DE HICKELING HICKLIN HICKLING ICKELING
Ildesley EELES ILLSLEY ILSLEY
Ildslee EELES ILLSLEY ILSLEY
Ildsley EELES ILLSLEY ILSLEY
ILES 10 Ailes AYLES EALES EELES EYLES HILES Hyles ISLES Yeeles
Ilet AYLETT ILOTT
ILETT 5 AYLETT Eylett Ilette ILOTT
Ilette AYLETT ILETT ILOTT
Iley EALEY EELY ELEY ELLEY ELY EYLEY HEELEY HIGHLEY HILEY
Ilingworth ELLINGWORTH ILLINGWORTH
Illesley EELES ILLSLEY ILSLEY
Illet ELLET ELLIOTT
ILLINGWORTH 6 Elingworth ELLINGWORTH Ellinworth Ilingworth Illinworth
Illinworth ELLINGWORTH ILLINGWORTH
Illsey HINSLEY INSLEY
ILLSLEY 26 Ealslie Easlye EELES Eesley Eesly Elesely Elesley Eleslye Hildesley Hildisley Hildsley Iilsley Ildesley Ildslee Ildsley Illesley Illsly Ilseleye Ilselie Ilsey Ilslelye ILSLEY Ilsleye Ilslie Ilsly
Illsly EELES ILLSLEY ILSLEY
ILOTT 8 Alott AYLETT Aylott Eylett Ilet ILETT Ilette
Ilseleye EELES ILLSLEY ILSLEY
Ilselie EELES ILLSLEY ILSLEY
Ilsey EELES ILLSLEY ILSLEY
Ilslelye EELES ILLSLEY ILSLEY
ILSLEY 26 Ealslie Easlye EELES Eesley Eesly Elesely Elesley Eleslye Hildesley Hildisley Hildsley Iilsley Ildesley Ildslee Ildsley Illesley ILLSLEY Illsly Ilseleye Ilselie Ilsey Ilslelye Ilsleye Ilslie Ilsly
Ilsleye EELES ILLSLEY ILSLEY
Ilslie EELES ILLSLEY ILSLEY
Ilsly EELES ILLSLEY ILSLEY
IMBRIE 5 EMBERY EMBRIE EMBRY EMERY
Imbry EMERY IMRIE
IMMS 6 EAMES Eams Eemes EMES HEAMES
IMPEY 4 Empey Empy Impy
Impy IMPEY
IMRIE 7 Amery AMORY EMERY Emmery Imbry Imry
Imry EMERY IMRIE
INCE 5 HINCE HINES Hints INNES
INCHLEY 4 Hinchley HINCHLIFF Inchliff
Inchliff HINCHLIFF INCHLEY
Inchliffe HINCHCLIFF HINCHCLIFFE HINCHLIFF HINCHLIFFE
Incley HINSLEY INSLEY
ING 4 Inggs INGS Inngs
Ingal INGALL
Ingale INGALL
INGALL 9 Engel Ingal Ingale Ingel Ingell INGLE INGLES Ynkel
Ingam PINCOMBE PINKHAM
Ingamthorp INGLETHORPE
Ingarthorp INGLETHORPE
INGE Hinge
Ingel INGALL INGLE INGLES
Ingell INGALL INGLE INGLES
Inggs ING INGS
Ingland ENGLAND
INGLE 7 Engel INGALL Ingel Ingell INGLES Ynkel
INGLES 8 Engel INGALL Ingel Ingell INGLE INGLIS Ynkel
INGLETHORPE 6 Englethorpe Ingamthorp Ingarthorp Inglethrapp Inglethropp
Inglethrapp INGLETHORPE
Inglethropp INGLETHORPE
INGLIS INGLES
Ingo INGOE
INGOE Ingo
Ingraham INGRAM PINCOMBE PINKHAM
INGRAM Engeram Ingraham
Ingrarum PINCOMBE PINKHAM
INGS 4 ING Inggs Inngs
INNES 6 ENNIS HINCE HINES Hints INCE
Inngs ING INGS
INSLEY 5 HINSLEY Illsey Incley Insly
Insly HINSLEY INSLEY
INSTONE ENSTONE
Iorne HIORNS IRONS
Iorns HIORNS IRONS
Ipsey HIPSEY
Ipsy HIPSEY
IRELAND Irlond
IREMONGER 16 Eirmonger Eirmunger Eyrmonger Eyrmunger Iermonger Iermunger Iernmonger Iernmunber Iremunger IRONMONGER Ironmunger Yermonger Yermunger Yernmonger Yernmunger
Iremunger IREMONGER IRONMONGER
Irlond IRELAND
Iron HEARN HEARNE HERON HIERON HIORNS HIRON HIRONS IRONS
IRONMONGER 16 Eirmonger Eirmunger Eyrmonger Eyrmunger Iermonger Iermunger Iernmonger Iernmunber IREMONGER Iremunger Ironmunger Yermonger Yermunger Yernmonger Yernmunger
Ironmunger IREMONGER IRONMONGER
IRONS 27 HEARN HEARNE Heiron Herne HERON Hierne HIERON Highorne Hiorne HIORNS Hiren Hirens Hirin HIRON Hirone HIRONS Hyearnes Hyerne Hyorn Hyron Hyrone Hyrons Hyryn Iorne Iorns Iron
IRVIN 6 Ervine ERWIN IRVINE IRVING IRWIN
IRVINE 6 Ervine ERWIN IRVIN IRVING IRWIN
IRVING 6 Ervine ERWIN IRVIN IRVINE IRWIN
IRWIN 6 Ervine ERWIN IRVIN IRVINE IRVING
ISAAC 5 ISAACS Isaak Isaake Isack
ISAACS ISAAC Isack
Isaak ISAAC
Isaake ISAAC
Isack ISAAC ISAACS
ISARD 4 ISSARD IZARD IZZARD
Isbester ISBISTER
ISBISTER Isbester
Ischer USHER
ISGATE EASTGATE Esgate
Isgro BISGROVE HISGROVE ISGROVE
ISGROVE 5 BISGROVE HISGROVE Isgro Isgroves
Isgroves BISGROVE HISGROVE ISGROVE
ISLES 5 Ailes EYLES HILES ILES
ISMADE Ismead
Ismead ISMADE
ISOM Easom
Israel HASKELL HASWELL HUSSELL HUZZELL OSWALD RUSSELL URSELL UZZELL
ISSARD 4 ISARD IZARD IZZARD
Issel HASKELL HASWELL HUSSELL HUZZELL OSWALD RUSSELL URSELL UZZELL
Issy HIZZY
Ithell BETHEL BETHELL BITHEL BOTHELL
Itheridge ETHERIDGE
Ival IFOULD IVIL
Ivall IFOULD IVIL
Ivel IFOULD IVIL
Ivell IFOULD IVIL
Ivereigh IVORY
IVERSON IVESON
Ivery IVORY
IVES AYLES EYLES
IVESON IVERSON
IVIL 17 Hivel Iffold Ifold Ifolde IFOULD Ival Ivall Ivel Ivell Ivill Ivol Ivold Ivolde Ivoll Ivould Ivoulde
Ivill IVIL
Ivol IFOULD IVIL
Ivold IFOULD IVIL
Ivolde IFOULD IVIL
Ivoll IFOULD IVIL
IVORY 4 Ivereigh Ivery Ivry
Ivould IFOULD IVIL
Ivoulde IFOULD IVIL
Ivry IVORY
IZARD 4 ISARD ISSARD IZZARD
IZZARD 4 ISARD ISSARD IZARD
Jacett JESSETT
JACK JACKS
JACKLIN 5 Jackling Jaglen Jaglin Jaklin
Jackling JACKLIN
JACKMAN JAKEMAN Jakman
JACKS 13 Geckes Gecks Gex JACK JAKES Jeackes Jeakes Jeaks Jeckes Jecks JEX Jexe
JACOB JACOBS
JACOBS JACOB
Jacock JEACOCK
Jacocke JEACOCK
JACOM Jacomb
Jacomb JACOM
Jacott JEACOCK
Jacox JEACOCK
JACQUES JAKES JAQUES
JAFFRAY Jeffray JEFFREY
Jaglen JACKLIN
Jaglin JACKLIN
Jaine GANE GAWEN GOWN GOYNE JANE JAYNE
JAKEMAN JACKMAN Jakman
JAKES 15 Geckes Gecks Gex JACKS JACQUES JAQUES Jeackes Jeakes Jeaks JEAQUES Jeckes Jecks

If the name you are interested in is not here, try Section C.

JEX Jexe
Jaklin JACKLIN
Jakman JACKMAN JAKEMAN
JAMESON 10 Jammeson
Jemeson Jemison
Jemmerson JEMMESON
Jemmieson Jemmison
Jimmeson Jimmison
Jammeson JAMESON JEMMESON
Jancey JAUNCEY
Jandrell JANDRILL
JAUNDRELL
JANDRILL 4 Jandrell
JAUNDRELL Jaundrill
JANE 16 Gan GANE GAWEN
Geon Geune Gilb Gonne
GOWN GOYNE Guine Jaine
JAYNE Jeaine Jeine
Jeyne
JANMAN GINMAN
JANNEY Janny Jenney
Janniper JUNIPER
Janny JANNEY
JANSEN JANSON
JANSON I'ANSON JANSEN
JAQUES 4 JACQUES JAKES
JEAQUES
Jarad GARRAD GARRARD
GARRAT GARRATT GARRETT
GARROD GERARD GERRARD
GERRETT JARRARD JARRATT
JARRET JARRETT JARROLD
JARVIS JERRARD JERRETT
YARD
Jaraitt GARRETT JARRETT
Jarald GARRAD GARRARD
GARRAT GARRATT GARRETT
GARROD GERARD GERRARD
GERRETT JARRARD JARRATT
JARRET JARRETT JARROLD
JARVIS JERRARD JERRETT
YARD
Jarat GARRAD GARRARD
GARRAT GARRATT GARRETT
GARROD GERARD GERRARD
GERRETT JARRARD JARRATT
JARRET JARRETT JARROLD
JARVIS JERRARD JERRETT
YARD
Jared GARRAD GARRARD
GARRAT GARRATT GARRETT
GARROD GERARD GERRARD
GERRETT JARRARD JARRATT
JARRET JARRETT JARROLD
JARVIS JERRARD JERRETT
YARD
Jareld GARRAD GARRARD
GARRAT GARRATT GARRETT
GARROD GERARD GERRARD
GERRETT JARRARD JARRATT
JARRET JARRETT JARROLD
JARVIS JERRARD JERRETT
YARD
Jarelds GARRAD GARRARD
GARRAT GARRATT GARRETT
GARROD GERARD GERRARD
GERRETT JARRARD JARRATT
JARRET JARRETT JARROLD
JARVIS JERRARD JERRETT
YARD
Jaret GARRAD GARRARD
GARRAT GARRATT GARRETT
GARROD GERARD GERRARD
GERRETT JARRARD JARRATT
JARRET JARRETT JARROLD
JARVIS JERRARD JERRETT
YARD
Jarets GARRAD GARRARD
GARRAT GARRATT GARRETT
GARROD GERARD GERRARD
GERRETT JARRARD JARRATT
JARRET JARRETT JARROLD
JARVIS JERRARD JERRETT
YARD
Jarett GARRAD GARRARD
GARRAT GARRATT GARRETT
GARROD GERARD GERRARD
GERRETT JARRARD JARRATT
JARRET JARRETT JARROLD
JARVIS JERRARD JERRETT
YARD
Jaretts GARRAD GARRARD
GARRAT GARRATT GARRETT
GARROD GERARD GERRARD
GERRETT JARRARD JARRATT
JARRET JARRETT JARROLD
JARVIS JERRARD JERRETT
YARD
Jarlet JARLETT
JARLETT 6 Garlet Garlett
Garlot Jarlet Jarlot
Jarlot JARLETT
JARMAIN JARMAN Jarmin
JARMAN 6 GERMAN JARMAIN
Jarmin JERMAN Jermyn
Jarmin JARMAIN JARMAN
Jarmy JERMY
Jarrad GARRAD GARRARD
GARRAT GARRATT GARRETT
GARROD GERARD GERRARD
GERRETT JARRARD JARRATT
JARRET JARRETT JARROLD
JARVIS JERRARD JERRETT
YARD
JARRARD 81 Ardy Eardy
Garad Garard GARRAD
GARRARD GARRAT GARRATT
Garred Garretson
GARRETT Garretts
Garrettson Garrison
Garrit Garritt GARROD
Garrould Gerad Geraddus
Gerald Geralds GERARD
Gerarde Gerardes
Gerards Geratt Geraud
Geret Gerold Gerrad
GERRARD Gerratt Gerred
GERRETT Gervaise Gervas
Gervase Gervis Gorret
Heardy Jarad Jarald
Jarat Jared Jareld
Jarelds Jaret Jarets
Jarett Jaretts Jarrad
Jarrat JARRATT Jarred
JARRET Jarrets JARRETT
Jarretts Jarritt Jarrod
JARROLD Jarrott Jarvie
JARVIS Jeffette Jeofett
Jeorrett Jereatt
JERRARD Jerratt
Jerreatt Jerred JERRETT
Jerrold YARD Yarrat
Yarratt Yarrott Yerratt
Jarrat GARRAD GARRARD
GARRAT GARRATT GARRETT
GARROD GERARD GERRARD
GERRETT JARRARD JARRATT
JARRET JARRETT JARROLD
JARVIS JERRARD JERRETT
YARD
JARRATT 81 Ardy Eardy
Garad Garard GARRAD
GARRARD GARRAT GARRATT
Garred Garretson
GARRETT Garretts
Garrettson Garrison
Garrit Garritt GARROD
Garrould Gerad Geraddus
Gerald Geralds GERARD
Gerarde Gerardes
Gerards Geratt Geraud
Geret Gerold Gerrad
GERRARD Gerratt Gerred
GERRETT Gervaise Gervas
Gervase Gervis Gorret
Heardy Jarad Jarald
Jarat Jared Jareld
Jarelds Jaret Jarets
Jarett Jaretts Jarrad
JARRARD Jarrat Jarred
JARRET Jarrets JARRETT
Jarretts Jarritt Jarrod
JARROLD Jarrott Jarvie
JARVIS Jeffette Jeofett
Jeorrett Jereatt
JERRARD Jerratt
Jerreatt Jerred JERRETT
Jerrold YARD Yarrat
Yarratt Yarrott Yerratt
Jarred GARRAD GARRARD
GARRAT GARRATT GARRETT
GARROD GERARD GERRARD
GERRETT JARRARD JARRATT
JARRET JARRETT JARROLD
JARVIS JERRARD JERRETT
YARD
JARRET 81 Ardy Eardy
Garad Garard GARRAD
GARRARD GARRAT GARRATT
Garred Garretson
GARRETT Garretts
Garrettson Garrison
Garrit Garritt GARROD
Garrould Gerad Geraddus
Gerald Geralds GERARD
Gerarde Gerardes
Gerards Geratt Geraud
Geret Gerold Gerrad
GERRARD Gerratt Gerred
GERRETT Gervaise Gervas
Gervase Gervis Gorret
Heardy Jarad Jarald
Jarat Jared Jareld
Jarelds Jaret Jarets
Jarett Jaretts Jarrad
JARRARD Jarrat JARRATT
Jarred Jarrets JARRETT
Jarretts Jarritt Jarrod
JARROLD Jarrott Jarvie
JARVIS Jeffette Jeofett
Jeorrett Jereatt
JERRARD Jerratt
Jerreatt Jerred JERRETT
Jerrold YARD Yarrat
Yarratt Yarrott Yerratt
Jarrets GARRAD GARRARD
GARRAT GARRATT GARRETT
GARROD GERARD GERRARD
GERRETT JARRARD JARRATT
JARRET JARRETT JARROLD
JARVIS JERRARD JERRETT
YARD
JARRETT 82 Ardy Eardy
Garad Garard GARRAD
GARRARD GARRAT GARRATT
Garred Garretson
GARRETT Garretts
Garrettson Garrison
Garrit Garritt GARROD
Garrould Gerad Geraddus
Gerald Geralds GERARD
Gerarde Gerardes
Gerards Geratt Geraud
Geret Gerold Gerrad
GERRARD Gerratt Gerred
GERRETT Gervaise Gervas
Gervase Gervis Gorret
Heardy Jarad Jaraitt
Jarald Jarat Jared
Jareld Jarelds Jaret
Jarets Jarett Jaretts
Jarrad JARRARD Jarrat
JARRATT Jarred JARRET
Jarrets Jarretts
Jarritt Jarrod JARROLD
Jarrott Jarvie JARVIS
Jeffette Jeofett
Jeorrett Jereatt
JERRARD Jerratt
Jerreatt Jerred JERRETT
Jerrold YARD Yarrat
Yarratt Yarrott Yerratt
Jarretts GARRAD GARRARD
GARRAT GARRATT GARRETT
GARROD GERARD GERRARD
GERRETT JARRARD JARRATT
JARRET JARRETT JARROLD
JARVIS JERRARD JERRETT
YARD
Jarritt GARRAD GARRARD
GARRAT GARRATT GARRETT
GARROD GERARD GERRARD
GERRETT JARRARD JARRATT
JARRET JARRETT JARROLD
JARVIS JERRARD JERRETT
YARD
Jarrod GARRAD GARRARD
GARRAT GARRATT GARRETT
GARROD GERARD GERRARD
GERRETT JARRARD JARRATT
JARRET JARRETT JARROLD
JARVIS JERRARD JERRETT
YARD
JARROLD 81 Ardy Eardy
Garad Garard GARRAD
GARRARD GARRAT GARRATT
Garred Garretson
GARRETT Garretts
Garrettson Garrison
Garrit Garritt GARROD
Garrould Gerad Geraddus
Gerald Geralds GERARD
Gerarde Gerardes
Gerards Geratt Geraud
Geret Gerold Gerrad
GERRARD Gerratt Gerred
GERRETT Gervaise Gervas
Gervase Gervis Gorret
Heardy Jarad Jarald
Jarat Jared Jareld
Jarelds Jaret Jarets
Jarett Jaretts Jarrad
JARRARD Jarrat JARRATT
Jarred JARRET Jarrets
JARRETT Jarretts
Jarritt Jarrod Jarrott
Jarvie JARVIS Jeffette
Jeofett Jeorrett
Jereatt JERRARD Jerratt
Jerreatt Jerred JERRETT
Jerrold YARD Yarrat
Yarratt Yarrott Yerratt
Jarrott GARRAD GARRARD
GARRAT GARRATT GARRETT
GARROD GERARD GERRARD
GERRETT JARRARD JARRATT
JARRET JARRETT JARROLD
JARVIS JERRARD JERRETT
YARD
Jarvas JARVICE JARVIS
JERVIS
Jarves JARVICE JARVIS
JERVIS
JARVICE 20 Garvasius
Gervais Gervaise
Gervase Gervasius
Gervayse Gerveys Gervis
Jarvas Jarves Jarvies
JARVIS Jarviss Jerfeys
Jervaulx JERVIS Jervois
Jervoise Yarvie
Jarvie GARRAD GARRARD
GARRAT GARRATT GARRETT
GARROD GERARD GERRARD
GERRETT JARRARD JARRATT
JARRET JARRETT JARROLD
JARVIS JERRARD JERRETT
YARD
Jarvies JARVICE JARVIS
JERVIS
JARVIS 99 Ardy Eardy
Garad Garard GARRAD
GARRARD GARRAT GARRATT
Garred Garretson
GARRETT Garretts
Garrettson Garrison

If the name you are interested in is not here, try Section C.

Garrit Garritt GARROD
Garrould Garvasius
Garvis Gerad Geraddus
Gerald Geralds GERARD
Gerarde Gerardes
Gerards Geratt Geraud
Geret Gerold Gerrad
GERRARD Gerratt Gerred
GERRETT Gervais
Gervaise Gervas Gervase
Gervasius Gervayse
GERVES Gerveys Gervis
Gorret Heardy Jarad
Jarald Jarat Jared
Jareld Jarelds Jaret
Jarets Jarett Jaretts
Jarrad JARRARD Jarrat
JARRATT Jarred JARRET
Jarrets JARRETT
Jarretts Jarritt Jarrod
JARROLD Jarrott Jarvas
Jarves JARVICE Jarvie
Jarvies Jarviss
Jeffette Jeofett
Jeorrett Jereatt
Jerfeys JERRARD Jerratt
Jerreatt Jerred JERRETT
Jerrold Jervaulx JERVIS
Jervois Jervoise YARD
Yarrat Yarratt Yarrott
Yarvie Yerratt
Jarviss JARVICE JARVIS JERVIS
JARY JEARY
Jasett JESSETT
Jassat JESSETT
Jasset JESSETT
Jassett JESSETT
Jauncee JAUNCEY
JAUNCEY 5 Jancey Jauncee Jauncy Jaunsey
Jauncy JAUNCEY
JAUNDRELL 4 Jandrell JANDRILL Jaundrill
Jaundrill JANDRILL JAUNDRELL
Jaunsey JAUNCEY
Javins GIVENS JEAVONS
Jaycock JEACOCK
Jaycott JEACOCK
Jaycox JEACOCK
JAYNE 17 DEJEANNE Gan GANE GAWEN Geon Geune Gilb Gonne GOWN GOYNE Guine Jaine JANE Jeaine Jeine Jeyne
Jcock JEACOCK
Jeackes JACKS JAKES JEX
JEACOCK 17 Jacock Jacocke Jacott Jacox Jaycock Jaycott Jaycox Jcock Jeacocke Jeacocks Jeacott Jeacox Jecock Jecox Jeycock Jeycocks
Jeacocke JEACOCK
Jeacocks JEACOCK
Jeacott JEACOCK
Jeacox JEACOCK
Jeaine JANE JAYNE
Jeakes JACKS JAKES JEX
Jeaks JACKS JAKES JEX
JEAL 5 Geal GEALE Jeale Jeall
Jeale GEALE JEAL
Jeall GEALE JEAL
Jealous JELLIS JELLOWS
Jealys GELLY JELLIS
JEAQUES JAKES JAQUES
JEARY JARY
Jeaves JEEVES
Jeavins GIVENS JEAVONS
Jeavon JEAVONS JEVON
JEAVONS 12 Gevans Gillins GIVENS Javins Jeavins Jeavon Jevins JEVON Jevons Jillins Jyvins
Jebett GEBBETT
Jeckes JACKS JAKES JEX
Jecks JACKS JAKES JEX
Jecock JEACOCK
Jecox JEACOCK
JEE GEE
JEENS 12 Ghieyes Ghines Ghisnes Ghiyes Ghuines Gines Guines GYNES Jines JOYNES Jynes
Jeeve JEEVES
JEEVES 5 Jeaves Jeeve Jeve Jeves
JEFCOATE 8 Jefcut JEFFCOAT Jeffcoatt JEFFCOTT Jephcoat Jephcote JEPHCOTT
Jefcut JEFCOATE JEFFCOAT JEFFCOTT JEPHCOTT
Jeffary JEFFERIES JEFFERY JEFFERYS JEFFREY JEFFREYS JEFFRIES
Jeffarys JEFFERIES JEFFERY JEFFERYS JEFFREY JEFFREYS JEFFRIES
JEFFCOAT 8 JEFCOATE Jefcut Jeffcoatt JEFFCOTT Jephcoat Jephcote JEPHCOTT
Jeffcoatt JEFCOATE JEFFCOAT JEFFCOTT JEPHCOTT
JEFFCOTT 8 JEFCOATE Jefcut JEFFCOAT Jeffcoatt Jephcoat Jephcote JEPHCOTT
Jefferey JEFFERY JEFFREY
Jeffereys JEFFREYS JEFFRIES
Jefferie JEFFERIES JEFFERY JEFFERYS JEFFREY JEFFREYS JEFFRIES
JEFFERIES 26 Geffery Gefferys Geffry Geffryes Geofery Geoffry Jeffary Jeffarys Jefferie Jefferress JEFFERY Jefferye JEFFERYS Jeffre Jeffres Jeffress JEFFREY JEFFREYS JEFFRIES Jeffris Jeffry Jeffrys Jefrys Jeoffries Jeoffrys
Jefferress JEFFERIES JEFFERY JEFFERYS JEFFREY JEFFREYS JEFFRIES
JEFFERY 31 Gefferie Geffery Gefferys Geffry Geffryes Geofery Geoffry Jeffary Jeffarys Jefferey Jefferie JEFFERIES Jefferress Jefferye JEFFERYS Jeffre Jeffres Jeffress JEFFREY JEFFREYS Jeffrie JEFFRIES Jeffris Jeffry Jeffrys Jefrie Jefrys Jeoffries Jeoffrys Jeofrey
Jefferye JEFFERIES JEFFERY JEFFERYS JEFFREY JEFFREYS JEFFRIES
JEFFERYS 26 Geffery Gefferys Geffry Geffryes Geofery Geoffry Jeffary Jeffarys Jefferie JEFFERIES Jefferress JEFFERY Jefferye Jeffre Jeffres Jeffress JEFFREY JEFFREYS JEFFRIES Jeffris Jeffry Jeffrys Jefrys Jeoffries Jeoffrys
Jeffette GARRAD GARRARD GARRAT GARRATT GARRETT GARROD GERARD GERRARD GERRETT JARRARD JARRATT JARRET JARRETT JARROLD JARVIS JERRARD JERRETT YARD
Jeffray JAFFRAY JEFFREY
Jeffre JEFFERIES JEFFERY JEFFERYS JEFFREY JEFFREYS JEFFRIES
Jeffres JEFFERIES JEFFERY JEFFERYS JEFFREY JEFFREYS JEFFRIES
Jeffress JEFFERIES JEFFERY JEFFERYS JEFFREY JEFFREYS JEFFRIES
JEFFREY 33 Gefferie Geffery Gefferys Geffry Geffryes Geofery Geoffry JAFFRAY Jeffary Jeffarys Jefferey Jefferie JEFFERIES Jefferress JEFFERY Jefferye JEFFERYS Jeffray Jeffre Jeffres Jeffress JEFFREYS Jeffrie JEFFRIES Jeffris Jeffry Jeffrys Jefrie Jefrys Jeoffries Jeoffrys Jeofrey
JEFFREYES JEFFRIES Jeffrys
JEFFREYS 27 Geffery Gefferys Geffry Geffryes Geofery Geoffry Jeffary Jeffarys Jeffereys Jefferie JEFFERIES Jefferress JEFFERY Jefferye JEFFERYS Jeffre Jeffres Jeffress JEFFREY JEFFRIES Jeffris Jeffry Jeffrys Jefrys Jeoffries Jeoffrys
Jeffrie JEFFERY JEFFREY
JEFFRIES 28 Geffery Gefferys Geffry Geffryes Geofery Geoffry Jeffary Jeffarys Jeffereys Jefferie JEFFERIES Jefferress JEFFERY Jefferye JEFFERYS Jeffre Jeffres Jeffress JEFFREY JEFFREYES JEFFREYS Jeffris Jeffry Jeffrys Jefrys Jeoffries Jeoffrys
Jeffris JEFFERIES JEFFERY JEFFERYS JEFFREY JEFFREYS JEFFRIES
Jeffry JEFFERIES JEFFERY JEFFERYS JEFFREY JEFFREYS JEFFRIES
Jeffrys JEFFERIES JEFFERY JEFFERYS JEFFREY JEFFREYES JEFFREYS JEFFRIES
Jefkins JIFFKINS JIFKINS
Jefrie JEFFERY JEFFREY
Jefrys JEFFERIES JEFFERY JEFFERYS JEFFREY JEFFREYS JEFFRIES
Jeggeons GIGGINS JIGGINS
Jeggins GIGGINS JIGGINS
Jeggon GIGGINS JIGGINS
Jegins GIGGINS JIGGINS
Jegion GIGGINS JIGGINS
Jegon GIGGINS JIGGINS
Jeine JANE JAYNE
Jeles GELLY JELLIS
Jelico JELLICOE
Jelicot DELICATE
Jellat GILLOTT JELLETT
Jellatt GILLOTT JELLETT
Jellet GILLOTT JELLETT
JELLETT 17 Gellat Gellatt Gellot Gellott Gillat Gillot GILLOTT Gyllot Gyllott Jellat Jellatt Jellet Jellot Jellott Jillat Jillatt
Jelleys GELLY JELLIS
Jellice JELLIS JELLOWS
JELLICOE 5 Gelicho Gelico Gellico Jelico
Jellicott DELICATE
Jellicult DELICATE
JELLIMAN 4 Gelliman Jellyman Juliman
Jellings GILLINGS JENKINS JENNINGS JENNINS
JELLIS 13 Gelles Gellis GELLY Jealous Jealys Jeles Jelleys Jellice JELLOWS Jelly Jellys Jolys
Jellot GILLOTT JELLETT
Jellott GILLOTT JELLETT
JELLOWS 4 Jealous Jellice JELLIS
Jelly GELLY JELLIS
Jellyman JELLIMAN
Jellys GELLY JELLIS
Jemeson JAMESON JEMMESON
Jemison JAMESON JEMMESON
Jemmerson JAMESON JEMMESON
JEMMESON 10 JAMESON Jammeson Jemeson Jemison Jemmerson Jemmieson Jemmison Jimmeson Jimmison
Jemmieson JAMESON JEMMESON
Jemmison JAMESON JEMMESON
Jenckes JENKES JENKS JINKS
Jeneper JUNIPER
Jeneson JENNISON
Jenever JUNIPER
Jenifer JUNIPER
Jeniffer JUNIPER
Jenings JENKINS JENNINGS JENNINS
Jenivere JUNIPER
Jenken JENKIN JENKYN
JENKES 6 Ginks Jenckes JENKS Jenkys JINKS
JENKIN 5 Jenken Jenking JENKINS JENKYN
Jenking JENKIN JENKYN
JENKINS 21 Genning Gennings Gennins Gilling Ginning Ginnings Ginnins Jellings Jenings JENKIN JENKINSON Jenning JENNINGS JENNINS Jilling Jining JINKENS Jinkins Jinnings Jinnins
JENKINSON 4 JENKINS JINKENS Jinkins
JENKS 6 Ginks Jenckes JENKES Jenkys JINKS
JENKYN 4 Jenken JENKIN

If the name you are interested in is not here, try Section C.

Jenking
Jenkys JENKES JENKS
JENNER Ginner
Jennerson JENNISON
Jennever JUNIPER
Jenney JANNEY
Jenning JENKINS JENNINGS JENNINS
JENNINGS 17 Genning Gennings Gennins Gilling Ginning Ginnings Ginnins Jellings Jenings JENKINS Jenning JENNINS Jilling Jining Jinnings Jinnins
JENNINS 17 Genning Gennings Gennins Gilling Ginning Ginnings Ginnins Jellings Jenings JENKINS Jenning JENNINGS Jilling Jining Jinnings Jinnins
Jenniper JUNIPER
Jennipher JUNIPER
JENNISON Jeneson Jennerson
Jent GENT GHENT
Jeofett GARRAD GARRARD GARRAT GARRATT GARRETT GARROD GERARD GERRARD GERRETT JARRARD JARRATT JARRET JARRETT JARROLD JARVIS JERRARD JERRETT YARD
Jeoffries JEFFERIES JEFFERY JEFFERYS JEFFREY JEFFREYS JEFFRIES
Jeoffrys JEFFERIES JEFFERY JEFFERYS JEFFREY JEFFREYS JEFFRIES
Jeofrey JEFFERY JEFFREY
Jeorrett GARRAD GARRARD GARRAT GARRATT GARRETT GARROD GERARD GERRARD GERRETT JARRARD JARRATT JARRET JARRETT JARROLD JARVIS JERRARD JERRETT YARD
Jephcoat JEFCOATE JEFFCOAT JEFFCOTT JEPHCOTT
Jephcote JEFCOATE JEFFCOAT JEFFCOTT JEPHCOTT
JEPHCOTT 8 JEFCOATE Jefcut JEFFCOAT Jeffcoatt JEFFCOTT Jephcoat Jephcote
JEPMAN CHAPMAN
JERAM 4 Gerram Jerom JERRAM
Jereatt GARRAD GARRARD GARRAT GARRATT GARRETT GARROD GERARD GERRARD GERRETT JARRARD JARRATT JARRET JARRETT JARROLD JARVIS JERRARD JERRETT YARD
Jerfeys JARVICE JARVIS JERVIS
JERMAN 4 GERMAN JARMAN Jermyn
Jermany JERMY
JERMY 4 Germany Jarmy Jermany
Jermyn GERMAN JARMAN JERMAN
Jerom JERAM JEROME JERRAM
JEROME 4 Jerom Jorham Jorum
JERRAM 4 Gerram JERAM Jerom
JERRARD 81 Ardy Eardy Garad Garard GARRAD GARRARD GARRAT GARRATT Garred Garretson GARRETT Garretts Garrettson Garrison Garrit Garritt GARROD Garrould Gerad Geraddus Gerald Geralds GERARD Gerarde Gerardes Gerards Geratt Geraud Geret Gerold Gerrad GERRARD Gerratt Gerred GERRETT Gervaise Gervas Gervase Gervis Gorret Heardy Jarad Jarald Jarat Jared Jareld Jarelds Jaret Jarets Jarett Jaretts Jarrad JARRARD Jarrat JARRATT Jarred JARRET Jarrets JARRETT Jarretts Jarritt Jarrod JARROLD Jarrott Jarvie JARVIS Jeffette Jeofett Jeorrett Jereatt Jerratt Jerreatt Jerred JERRETT Jerrold YARD Yarrat Yarratt Yarrott Yerratt
Jerratt GARRAD GARRARD GARRAT GARRATT GARRETT GARROD GERARD GERRARD GERRETT JARRARD JARRATT JARRET JARRETT JARROLD JARVIS JERRARD JERRETT YARD
Jerreatt GARRAD GARRARD GARRAT GARRATT GARRETT GARROD GERARD GERRARD GERRETT JARRARD JARRATT JARRET JARRETT JARROLD JARVIS JERRARD JERRETT YARD
Jerred GARRAD GARRARD GARRAT GARRATT GARRETT GARROD GERARD GERRARD GERRETT JARRARD JARRATT JARRET JARRETT JARROLD JARVIS JERRARD JERRETT YARD
JERRETT 81 Ardy Eardy Garad Garard GARRAD GARRARD GARRAT GARRATT Garred Garretson GARRETT Garretts Garrettson Garrison Garrit Garritt GARROD Garrould Gerad Geraddus Gerald Geralds GERARD Gerarde Gerardes Gerards Geratt Geraud Geret Gerold Gerrad GERRARD Gerratt Gerred GERRETT Gervaise Gervas Gervase Gervis Gorret Heardy Jarad Jarald Jarat Jared Jareld Jarelds Jaret Jarets Jarett Jaretts Jarrad JARRARD Jarrat JARRATT Jarred JARRET Jarrets JARRETT Jarretts Jarritt Jarrod JARROLD Jarrott Jarvie JARVIS Jeffette Jeofett Jeorrett Jereatt JERRARD Jerratt Jerreatt Jerred Jerrold YARD Yarrat Yarratt Yarrott Yerratt
Jerrold GARRAD GARRARD GARRAT GARRATT GARRETT GARROD GERARD GERRARD GERRETT JARRARD JARRATT JARRET JARRETT JARROLD JARVIS JERRARD JERRETT YARD
Jervaulx JARVICE JARVIS JERVIS
JERVIS 22 Garvasius Garvis Gervais Gervaise Gervase Gervasius Gervayse GERVES Gerveys Gervis Jarvas Jarves JARVICE Jarvies JARVIS Jarviss Jerfeys Jervaulx Jervois Jervoise Yarvie
Jervois JARVICE JARVIS JERVIS
Jervoise JARVICE JARVIS JERVIS
Jessat JESSETT
Jesseit JESSETT
Jesset JESSETT
Jessete JESSETT
Jesseth JESSETT
JESSETT 34 Cheesat Gesset Gessett Gessut Giset Gissat Gissatt Gisset Gissett Gyssett Iesset Jacett Jasett Jassat Jasset Jassett Jessat Jesseit Jesset Jessete Jesseth Jessette Jessit Jessitt Jessott Jessut Jessutt Jeuset Jizat Jizet Juset Jusset Jyssett
Jessette JESSETT
Jessit JESSETT
Jessitt JESSETT
Jessott JESSETT
Jessut JESSETT
Jessutt JESSETT
Jeuit JEWITT
Jeuset JESSETT
Jeve JEEVES
Jeves JEEVES
Jevins GIVENS JEAVONS
JEVON 4 Jeavon JEAVONS Jevons
Jevons GIVENS JEAVONS JEVON
JEWEL 6 JEWELL JOULE Juel Juele Juell
JEWELL 5 JEWEL JOULE Juel Juele
Jewet JEWITT
Jewett JEWITT
Jewit JEWITT
JEWITT 8 Jeuit Jewet Jewett Jewit Jueit Juet Juit
JEWKES JUKES
JEX 12 Geckes Gecks Gex JACKS JAKES Jeackes Jeakes Jeaks Jeckes Jecks Jexe
Jexe JACKS JAKES JEX
Jeycock JEACOCK
Jeycocks JEACOCK
Jeyne JANE JAYNE
Jhent GENT GHENT
Jhonson JOHNSON JOHNSTON
JIFFKINS 4 Gifkins Jefkins JIFKINS
JIFKINS 4 Gifkins Jefkins JIFFKINS
JIGGINS 11 GIGGINS Giggons Jeggeons Jeggins Jeggon Jegins Jegion Jegon Jiggons Jyggyns
Jiggons GIGGINS JIGGINS
JILBERT GILBERT
Jiles GILES
Jillat GILLOTT JELLETT
Jillatt GILLOTT JELLETT
Jilling JENKINS JENNINGS JENNINS
Jillins GIVENS JEAVONS
JILLOTT 5 Gillette Gilliot Gillot GILLOTT
Jimmeson JAMESON JEMMESON
Jimmison JAMESON JEMMESON
Jines GYNES JEENS JOYNES
Jining JENKINS JENNINGS JENNINS
JINKENS 4 JENKINS JENKINSON Jinkins
Jinkins JENKINS JENKINSON JINKENS
JINKS 5 Ginks Jenckes JENKES JENKS
Jinnifer JUNIPER
Jinnings JENKINS JENNINGS JENNINS
Jinnins JENKINS JENNINGS JENNINS
Jizat JESSETT
Jizet JESSETT
JOANES Johnes JONES
Jobb JOBBINS
Jobbens JOBBINS
JOBBINS Jobb Jobbens
Joblin JOPLING
JOHN JOHNS JONES
Johnes JOANES JONES
JOHNS JOHN
JOHNSON 5 Jhonson JOHNSTON JOHNSTONE Jonson
JOHNSTON 4 Jhonson JOHNSON JOHNSTONE
JOHNSTONE JOHNSON JOHNSTON
JOICE 5 Joicey JOY JOYCE JOYS
Joicey JOICE
JOINER JOYNER
JOINES Gines JOYNES
Joins JOINT JOYNES
JOINSON JOYNSON
JOINT 5 Joins JOYNES Joyns Joynt
Joleffe JOLIFFE
Jolife JOLIFFE
JOLIFFE Joleffe Jolife
Jolys GELLY JELLIS
JONES 4 JOANES JOHN Johnes
Jonson JOHNSON
Joplin JOPLING
JOPLING 4 Joblin Joplin Joplyn
Joplyn JOPLING
Jordain JORDAN JORDEN JORDON
JORDAN 10 GORDON Jordain JORDEN JORDON Jordun Jurdain Jurden Jurdon Jurdun
JORDEN 9 Jordain JORDAN JORDON Jordun Jurdain Jurden Jurdon Jurdun
JORDON 9 Jordain JORDAN JORDEN Jordun Jurdain Jurden Jurdon Jurdun
Jordun JORDAN JORDEN JORDON
Jorham JEROME
Jorum JEROME
Josclen JOSLIN JOSLING
Joslen JOSLIN JOSLING
JOSLIN 5 Josclen Joslen JOSLING Joslyn
JOSLING 5 Josclen Joslen JOSLIN Joslyn

If the name you are interested in is not here, try Section C.

Joslyn JOSLIN JOSLING
JOULE 5 JEWEL JEWELL Juel Juele
JOULES Jowles
Jowles JOULES
JOY 10 FOY JOICE JOYCE JOYS LEE Tay TEA TEE TOY
JOYCE 4 JOICE JOY JOYS
JOYNER JOINER
JOYNES 17 Ghieyes Ghines Ghisnes Ghiyes Ghuines Gines Guines GYNES JEENS Jines JOINEŞ Joins JOINT Joyns Joynt Jynes
Joyns JOINT JOYNES
JOYNSON JOINSON
Joynt JOINT JOYNES
JOYS 4 JOICE JOY JOYCE
Jueit JEWITT
Juel EWELL HOOLE JEWEL JEWELL JOULE YOLE YOUELL YULE
Juele JEWEL JEWELL JOULE
Juell JEWEL
Juet JEWITT
Juit JEWITT
JUKES 4 DUKES JEWKES Juks
Juks DUKES JUKES
Jule EWELL HOOLE YOLE YOUELL YULE
Juliman JELLIMAN
Jumper JUNIPER
Junevar JUNIPER
Junifer JUNIPER
JUNIPER 17 Janniper Jeneper Jenever Jenifer Jeniffer Jenivere Jennever Jenniper Jennipher Jinnifer Jumper Junevar Junifer Junipher Juniver Junyver
Junipher JUNIPER
Juniver JUNIPER
Junyver JUNIPER
JUP 11 Gup Gupp Guppe Gupps JUPE Jupes JUPP JUPPE Juppes Jups
JUPE 12 Dupe Gup Gupp Guppe Gupps JUP Jupes JUPP JUPPE Juppes Jups
Jupes JUP JUPE JUPP JUPPE
JUPP 12 Dupe Gup Gupp Guppe Gupps JUP JUPE Jupes JUPPE Juppes Jups
JUPPE 11 Gup Gupp Guppe Gupps JUP JUPE Jupes JUPP Juppes Jups
Juppes JUP JUPE JUPP JUPPE
Jups JUP JUPE JUPP JUPPE
Jurdain JORDAN JORDEN JORDON
Jurden JORDAN JORDEN JORDON
Jurdon JORDAN JORDEN JORDON
Jurdun JORDAN JORDEN JORDON
Juset JESSETT
Jusset JESSETT
Jutten JUTTON
JUTTON Jutten
Jyggyns GIGGINS JIGGINS
Jynes GYNES JEENS JOYNES
Jyssett JESSETT
Jyvins GIVENS JEAVONS
Kaake CAKE
Kadge CAGE KEDGE
Kadwell KIDWELL
Kaines CAINES CAINS
Kains CAINES CAINS
Kairns CAIRNS
Kake CAKE
Kallock CARLICK KILLICK
Kalman KELMAN
KANE KEEN
Kansick CANSICK
Kant CANT CANTY
Kantelo CANTELLO
Kanterall CANT CANTER CANTERELL CANTRELL CANTRILL CHANTRELL QUANTRILL QUINTRELL
Kanterell CANT CANTER CANTERELL CANTRELL CANTRILL CHANTRELL QUANTRILL QUINTRELL
Kanterill CANT CANTER CANTERELL CANTRELL CANTRILL CHANTRELL QUANTRILL QUINTRELL
Kantrall CANT CANTER CANTERELL CANTRELL CANTRILL CHANTRELL QUANTRILL QUINTRELL
Kantrell CANT CANTER CANTERELL CANTRELL CANTRILL CHANTRELL QUANTRILL QUINTRELL
Kantrill CANT CANTER CANTERELL CANTRELL CANTRILL CHANTRELL QUANTRILL QUINTRELL
Kapie CAPIE CAPPIE KEPPIE
Kari CAREY CARY
KARSLAKE KERSLAKE
Kart CARD CART
Kaupaland COPELAND COUPLAND
KAVANAGH CAVANAGH
Kave CAVE
KAWRDIN 25 CALLADINE Callerdine CANADINE CANARDINE Canderdine CANDERDYNE CANNADINE CANNADYNE CARDEN CARDIN CARDING CARDON Carodine CARRADINE Carradyne Carrodine CARWARDEN Carwardin CARWARDINE CARWARDYNE DE KAREWARDYN Keanodine KENDERDINE KENWARDEN
KAY 5 HAY KAYE KEAY KEY
KAYE KAY KEAY
Kaynes CAINES CAINS
Kaysford CASSFORD
KEAN 5 KEANE KEEN KEENE KEENS
KEANE 6 CAIN KEAN KEEN KEENE KEENS
Keanodine CALLADINE CANADINE CANARDINE CANDERDYNE CANNADINE CANNADYNE CARDEN CARDIN CARDING CARDON CARRADINE CARWARDEN CARWARDINE CARWARDYNE DE KAREWARDYN KAWRDIN KENDERDINE KENWARDEN
KEAP 16 Ceep Cepe Keape Kebbe Kebe KEEP Keepe Keeppe Kep Kepe Kibbe Kibe Kipe Kippe Kyppe
Keape KEAP KEEP
Kearl CURL CURLE KEIRL
Kearle CURL CURLE KEIRL
KEARSEY KERSEY
KEARSLEY 6 Kearsly Kerseley KERSLEY Kersly Kiersley
Kearsly KEARSLEY KERSLEY
KEARTON 7 Keinton KERTON Kincton KINGTON Kinton KIRTON
Keavan KEVAN
KEAY KAY KAYE
Kebbe KEAP KEEP
Kebe KEAP KEEP
Keddall KIDDALL KIDDELL KIDDLE
KEDDIE 6 Keddy KID KIDD Kiddie Kiddy
Keddle KETTLE KIDDALL KIDDELL KIDDLE
Keddy KEDDIE KID KIDD
KEDGE 6 Cadge CAGE Kadge Keg Ketch
Kedwell KIDWELL
Keears KEERS KER
KEEGAN 11 Eagan Eagen Eagin EGAN Egin Eighan Macaodhagain Macaogain Mcegan Mckeegan
KEELEY KEELY
KEELY KEELEY
KEEMISH KEMISH
KEEN 6 KANE KEAN KEANE KEENE KEENS
KEENE 5 KEAN KEANE KEEN KEENS
Keenor KENNER KINNEAR
KEENS 5 KEAN KEANE KEEN KEENE
KEEP 16 Ceep Cepe KEAP Keape Kebbe Kebe Keepe Keeppe Kep Kepe Kibbe Kibe Kipe Kippe Kyppe
Keepe KEAP KEEP
Keeppe KEAP KEEP
KEERS 5 Keears Keirs KER Kiers
KEET 5 Kit KITT KITTS Kyte
Keevil KEEVILL
KEEVILL 5 Keevil Keeville Kevil Kevill
Keeville KEEVILL
Keg CAGE KEDGE
Keggan KEGGIN
KEGGIN Keggan Kiggin
KEHOE KEOGH KEOUGH
KEIGWIN 13 Chegwgen Chegwidden CHEGWYN Chegwyne Chegwynne Chigwin Chigwydden Chuckweedon Chygin Chygwen Chygwin Sugweeden
Keilock CARLICK KILLICK
KEILTY Kielty
Keinton KEARTON KERTON KINGTON KIRTON
KEIRL 6 CURL CURLE Kearl Kearle Keirle
Keirle CURL CURLE KEIRL KERLE
Keirs KEERS KER
Keleg CARLICK KILLICK
Kellacher KELLAGHER
KELLAGHER Kellacher
KELLAN KELLAND Kellane
KELLAND 4 KELLAN Kellane KELLOND
Kellane KELLAN KELLAND
KELLAWAY 4 KELLEWAY KELLOWAY KELWAY
KELLET KELLETT
KELLETT KELLET
KELLEWAY 4 KELLAWAY KELLOWAY KELWAY
KELLEY KELLIE
Kellick KELLOCK KILLICK
KELLIE KELLEY
KELLINGLEY 4 Kellinley Killingley Killinley
Kellinley KELLINGLEY
Kellman KELMAN
KELLOCK Kellick KILLICK
KELLOND KELLAND
KELLOWAY 4 KELLAWAY KELLEWAY KELWAY
KELMAN 4 Kalman Kellman Kelmon
Kelmon KELMAN
KELWAY 4 KELLAWAY KELLEWAY KELLOWAY
KEMBREY Cambrey Cambry
KEMISH KEEMISH
KEMP 7 CAMP Campe Cimp Kempe Kimp Kimpe
Kempe CAMP KEMP
Kempsell KEMPSHALL
KEMPSEY Kemsey
KEMPSHALL Kempsell
KEMPSON Kimpson
KEMPSTER Kimpster
Kemsey KEMPSEY
Kena KENNER KINNEAR
KENCH KINCH
KENCHINGTON Kenchinton Kinchington
Kenchinton KENCHINGTON
KENDAL 4 KENDALL Kendell Kendle
KENDALL 4 KENDAL Kendell Kendle
Kendell KENDAL KENDALL
KENDERDINE 25 CALLADINE Callerdine CANADINE CANARDINE Canderdine CANDERDYNE CANNADINE CANNADYNE CARDEN CARDIN CARDING CARDON Carodine CARRADINE Carradyne Carrodine CARWARDEN Carwardin CARWARDINE CARWARDYNE DE KAREWARDYN KAWRDIN Keanodine KENWARDEN
Kendle KENDAL KENDALL
KENE Kens
Keneally KENELY
Kenealy KENELY
Kenelly KENELY
KENELY 5 Keneally Kenealy Kenelly Kennely
Kenley KINLEY
Kennar KENNER KINNEAR
Kennely KENELY
KENNER 13 Keenor Kena Kennar Kennor Kenor Kiner KINNEAR Kinner Kinnuer Kinver Kyner Kynner
Kennet KENNETT
KENNETT Kennet
Kennor KENNER KINNEAR
Kenor KENNER KINNEAR
Kens KENE
KENSEY KINSEY
KENWARDEN 25 CALLADINE Callerdine CANADINE CANARDINE Canderdine CANDERDYNE CANNADINE CANNADYNE CARDEN CARDIN CARDING CARDON Carodine CARRADINE Carradyne Carrodine CARWARDEN Carwardin CARWARDINE CARWARDYNE DE KAREWARDYN KAWRDIN Keanodine KENDERDINE
KEOGH KEHOE KEOUGH
Keoppen CAFFYN CAPEN CAPON COBBIN COBBING COFFIN KIPPING
KEOUGH KEHOE KEOGH
Kep KEAP KEEP
Kepe KEAP KEEP
Keppey CAPIE CAPPIE KEPPIE
KEPPIE 7 CAPIE CAPPIE

If the name you are interested in is not here, try Section C.

Cappy Kapie Keppey Keppy
Keppy CAPIE CAPPIE KEPPIE
KER 6 Keears KEERS Keirs KERR Kiers
Kerby KIRBY KIRKBY
KERCHIN 4 Kerching Kirchin Kirching
Kerching KERCHIN
KERFOOT 13 CAREFOOT CARFOOT CRAFFORD CRAFORD CRAWFORD CRAYFORD CROFFORD CROFOOT Crofut CROWFOOT CROWFORD Crowfrothe
Keridge KERRIDGE
Kerkeby KIRBY KIRKBY
Kerkland KIRKLAND
KERLE 9 CURL CURLE Keirle KERLEY Kerrel Kierle Kirle Kyrle
KERLEY 4 CURL CURLE KERLE
KERR CARR KER
Kerrel KERLE
Kerrey KERRY
KERRIDGE Keridge
Kerrie KERRY
Kerrill CHARLETON HILLHOUSE MCKERRELL
KERRY Kerrey Kerrie
Kerseley KEARSLEY KERSLEY
KERSEY KEARSEY
KERSHOPE 4 Cirsop Crisopp KIRSOPP
KERSLAKE 5 Carslack CARSLAKE KARSLAKE Keslake
KERSLEY 6 KEARSLEY Kearsly Kerseley Kersly Kiersley
Kersly KEARSLEY KERSLEY
Kersop KIRSOP KIRSOPP
Kersoppe KIRSOP KIRSOPP
KERTON 7 KEARTON Keinton Kincton KINGTON Kinton KIRTON
KERWINY Kirwin
Keslake CARSLAKE KERSLAKE
KESSELL Kissell
Kesterson KESTERTON
KESTERTON 9 Casterson Casterton Cesterson Cesterton Cestreton Chesterson Chesterton Kesterson
Ketch CAGE KEDGE
Ketchen KETCHIN KITCHEN KITCHIN
KETCHIN 5 Ketchen Ketchyn KITCHEN KITCHIN
Ketchyn KETCHIN KITCHEN KITCHIN
Ketenor KIDNER KYNE
Ketland KIRKLAND
Ketner KIDNER KYNE
Ketridge KETTERIDGE
KETT KITT
KETTEL KETTLE
KETTERIDGE 4 Ketridge Kettridge Kitteredge
KETTLE 9 Keddle KETTEL KIDDLE Kiddle-white Kidel Kidell Kihol Kittle
Kettridge KETTERIDGE
Keuell CULE KEWELL
KEVAN 8 Keavan Kevand Keven Keveren KEVERN KEVERNE KEVERYN
Kevand KEVAN
Kevel CULE KEWELL
Kevell CULE KEWELL
Keven KEVAN
Keveren KEVAN KEVERN KEVERNE KEVERYN
KEVERN 5 KEVAN Keveren KEVERNE KEVERYN
KEVERNE 5 KEVAN Keveren KEVERN KEVERYN
KEVERYN 5 KEVAN Keveren KEVERN KEVERNE
Kevil KEEVILL
Kevill KEEVILL
Kewel CULE KEWELL
KEWELL 10 Cuell Cuill CULE Keuell Kevel Kevell Kewel Kewylle Kul
Kewn COON COUN
Kewylle CULE KEWELL
KEY KAY
Keynes CAINES CAINS
Keysford CASSFORD
Kibbe KEAP KEEP
Kibe KEAP KEEP
KID 6 KEDDIE Keddy KIDD Kiddie Kiddy
Kidal KIDDALL KIDDELL KIDDLE
KIDD 6 KEDDIE Keddy KID Kiddie Kiddy
KIDDALL 12 Keddall Keddle Kidal KIDDELL Kiddill KIDDLE Kidel Kidil Kydal Kydel Kydil
KIDDELL 12 Keddall Keddle Kidal KIDDALL Kiddill KIDDLE Kidel Kidil Kydal Kydel Kydil
Kiddie KEDDIE KID KIDD
Kiddill KIDDALL KIDDELL KIDDLE
KIDDLE 17 Keddall Keddle KETTLE Kidal KIDDALL KIDDELL Kiddill Kiddle-white Kidel Kidell Kidil Kihol Kittle Kydal Kydel Kydil
Kiddle-white KETTLE KIDDLE
Kiddy KEDDIE KID KIDD
Kidel KETTLE KIDDALL KIDDELL KIDDLE
Kidell KETTLE KIDDLE
Kidil KIDDALL KIDDELL KIDDLE
KIDNER 12 Chetemore Ketenor Ketner Kitner Kitnor Kittnor Kydenor KYNE Kytemore Kytner Kyttner
KIDWELL Kadwell Kedwell
Kiellar KIELLOR
Kieller KIELLOR
KIELLOR Kiellar Kieller
Kielty KEILTY
Kierle KERLE
Kiers KEERS KER
Kiersley KEARSLEY KERSLEY
KIFF Kiffet
Kiffet KIFF
KIFFIN 4 CUFFIN KYFFIN KYFFYN
KIFFT KIFT
KIFT KIFFT
Kiggin KEGGIN
Kihol KETTLE KIDDLE
Kikke KIKKIE
KIKKIE Kikke
Kilberry KILBURY
Kilbery KILBURY
KILBURY 4 Kilberry Kilbery Killberry
KILDUFF 11 CUFFE Dob DUFF DUFFY Killduff Mcduff Mcduffey Mcilduff O'diff O'duffy
Kilfoyle GILFOYLE GUILFOYLE
Killan KILLON
Killberry KILBURY
Killduff KILDUFF
KILLER 4 Killhard Killhare Kyllar
Killhard KILLER
Killhare KILLER
KILLICK 15 CARLICK Kallock Keilock Keleg Kellick KELLOCK Killik Killok Killoke Killuck Killucke Kyelyche Kyllyk Kyllyke
Killik CARLICK KILLICK
Killingley KELLINGLEY
Killinley KELLINGLEY
Killok CARLICK KILLICK
Killoke CARLICK KILLICK
KILLON Killan
Killuck CARLICK KILLICK
Killucke CARLICK KILLICK
Kilmaster KILMINSTER KILMISTER
KILMINSTER Kilmaster KILMISTER
KILMISTER Kilmaster KILMINSTER
Kilpin GILPIN
Kilshaw CULSHAW
KIMBER KIMMER Kymer
Kime KING
KIMMER KIMBER Kymer
KIMMINGS KIMMINS KIMMONS
KIMMINS KIMMINGS KIMMONS
KIMMONS KIMMINGS KIMMINS
Kimp CAMP KEMP
Kimpe CAMP KEMP
Kimpson KEMPSON
Kimpster KEMPSTER
Kinardsley KINNERSLEY KYNARDSLEY KYNNERSLEY
KINCH KENCH
Kinchington KENCHINGTON
Kincton KEARTON KERTON KINGTON KIRTON
Kiner KENNER KINNEAR
KING 6 Kime KINGE KINGS Kyng Kynge
KINGDOM 9 Kingdome Kingdomme KINGDON Kingdone Kingdonne Kyngdon Kyngedon Kyngedone
Kingdome KINGDOM KINGDON
Kingdomme KINGDOM KINGDON
KINGDON 9 KINGDOM Kingdome Kingdomme Kingdone Kingdonne Kyngdon Kyngedon Kyngedone
Kingdone KINGDOM KINGDON
Kingdonne KINGDOM KINGDON
KINGE 5 KING KINGS Kyng Kynge
Kingeet KINGETT
Kinget KINGETT
KINGETT 7 Kingeet Kinget Kingette Kinggett Kingzett Kynget
Kingette KINGETT
Kinggett KINGETT
KINGS KING KINGE
KINGSWELL 7 Kingswill KINGWELL Kingwill Kingwyll Kyngwill Kyngwyll
Kingswill KINGSWELL KINGWELL
KINGTON 7 KEARTON Keinton KERTON Kincton Kinton KIRTON
KINGWELL 7 KINGSWELL Kingswill Kingwill Kingwyll Kyngwill Kyngwyll
Kingwill KINGSWELL KINGWELL
Kingwyll KINGSWELL KINGWELL
Kingzett KINGETT
KINLEY Kenley
KINNEAR 13 Keenor Kena Kennar KENNER Kennor Kenor Kiner Kinner Kinnuer Kinver Kyner Kynner
Kinner KENNER KINNEAR
KINNERSLEY 9 De kynardsley De kynnardsley De kynnardsleye Kinardsley KYNARDSLEY Kynnardsley Kynnardsleye KYNNERSLEY
Kinnuer KENNER KINNEAR
KINSEY KENSEY
Kinton KEARTON KERTON KINGTON KIRTON
Kinver KENNER KINNEAR
Kipe KEAP KEEP
KIPLIN 6 Ciplin KIPLING Kiplinge Kypling Kyplinge
KIPLING 6 Ciplin KIPLIN Kiplinge Kypling Kyplinge
Kiplinge KIPLIN KIPLING
Kippe KEAP KEEP
KIPPING 86 Cabourne CAFFYN Capan CAPEN Capin CAPON Caponere Caponn Caporn Capoun Capping Cappinger Capyn Caupen Caupin Caupion Cawpen Chapyn Choping Choppen Choppin Chopping Choppinge Chopponn Choppyn Choppynge Chopyn Cobben COBBIN COBBING Cobin Cobyn Cobynge Coffen Coffeyn COFFIN Coffing Coffinge Coffyn Cofin Cofyn Coopene Cooping Coopinge Cooppin Cooppyn Cooppyng Coopyne Copenger Cophaen Cophen Cophin Cophynn Copiner Copinger Copingers Coppener Coppengar Coppenger Coppiner Coppinger Coppingers Coppner Coppynger Copynger Copyunore Cupen Cupenes Cupin Cuppeynge Cuppin Cuppyn Cuppyng Keoppen Koppang Koppeians Koppeinge Koppen Koppin Kopping Koppyn Kopyn Kuping Kypping Kyppyng
KIRBY 5 Kerby Kerkeby Kirkbey KIRKBY
Kirchin KERCHIN
Kirching KERCHIN
KIRK KIRKE
Kirkbey KIRBY KIRKBY
KIRKBRIDE KIRKBRIGHT
KIRKBRIGHT KIRKBRIDE
KIRKBY 5 Kerby Kerkeby KIRBY Kirkbey
KIRKE KIRK
KIRKLAND 6 Kerkland Ketland Kyrkeland Kyrkland Kyrklande
Kirkley KIRTLEY

If the name you are interested in is not here, try Section C.

Kirle KERLE
KIRSOP 6 Crysoppe Kersop Kersoppe KIRSOPP Kirsoppe
KIRSOPP 9 Cirsop Crisopp Crysoppe KERSHOPE Kersop Kersoppe KIRSOP Kirsoppe
Kirsoppe KIRSOP KIRSOPP
KIRTLEY Kirkley
KIRTON 7 KEARTON Keinton KERTON Kincton KINGTON Kinton
Kirwin KERWINY
Kissell KESSELL
Kit KEET KITT KITTS
KITCHEN 6 Ketchen KETCHIN Ketchyn KITCHIN KITCHING
KITCHIN 6 Ketchen KETCHIN Ketchyn KITCHEN KITCHING
KITCHING KITCHEN KITCHIN
KITE Kyte
Kitkat CATCUTT
Kitner KIDNER KYNE
Kitnor KIDNER KYNE
KITT 6 KEET KETT Kit KITTS Kyte
Kitteredge KETTERIDGE
Kittle KETTLE KIDDLE
Kittnor KIDNER KYNE
KITTO KITTOW
KITTOW KITTO
KITTS 5 KEET Kit KITT Kyte
Klaik CLAKE CLEAK CLICK
Klake CLAKE CLEAK CLICK
Kleek CLAKE CLEAK CLICK
Kleike CLAKE CLEAK CLICK
Kleke CLAKE CLEAK CLICK
Klingan CLINGAN
Klingen CLINGAN
Klingham CLINGAN
Knap KNAPP
KNAPP Knap NAPP
Kneeland NEELAND NEWLAND
Kneeves NEAVES NEEVES NEVES
Knef KNIFE NEAVE NEEVE
Kneland NEELAND NEWLAND
Kneves NEAVES NEEVES NEVES
Knieve KNIFE NEAVE NEEVE
KNIFE 16 Knef Knieve Kniffe Knyf Knyfe Knyff Knyffe NEAVE NEEVE Nif Nife Niff Niffe Nyfe Nyffe
Knifeton KNIFTON KNIGHTON KNIVETON
Kniffe KNIFE
KNIFTON 4 Knifeton KNIGHTON KNIVETON
KNIGHTLEY Knightly
Knightly KNIGHTLEY
KNIGHTON 4 Knifeton KNIFTON KNIVETON
Knisfield NESFIELD
KNIVET Kniyvet
KNIVETON 4 Knifeton KNIFTON KNIGHTON
Kniyvet KNIVET
Knol KNOWLES NOWELL
Knole KNOWLES
Knoles KNOWLES
Knoll KNOWLES NOWELL
Knolle KNOWLES
Knolles KNOWLES
Knollis KNOWLES
Knollys KNOWLES
Knolson KNOWLSON NOLSON
KNOTT Not NOTT
Knoulson KNOWLSON NOLSON
Knowden KNOWLDEN
KNOWLDEN 5 Knowden Knowleden Nolden Noulden
Knowleden KNOWLDEN
KNOWLES 19 de Cnol de Knol de Knoll de Knolle Knol Knole Knoles Knoll Knolle Knolles Knollis Knollys Noll Nolls Nowel NOWELL Nowles Nowls
Knowleson KNOWLSON NOLSON
KNOWLSON 8 Knolson Knoulson Knowleson Nollson NOLSON Nolsonne Nowlson
KNUCKEY Nuckey
Knucklebridge HUCKLEBRIDGE
Knuttesforde NUTSFORD
Knyf KNIFE
Knyfe KNIFE
Knyff KNIFE
Knyffe KNIFE
Kokedes COCKADAY
Koppang CAFFYN CAPEN CAPON COBBIN COBBING COFFIN KIPPING
Koppeians CAFFYN CAPEN CAPON COBBIN COBBING COFFIN KIPPING
Koppeinge CAFFYN CAPEN CAPON COBBIN COBBING COFFIN KIPPING
Koppen CAFFYN CAPEN CAPON COBBIN COBBING COFFIN KIPPING
Koppin CAFFYN CAPEN CAPON COBBIN COBBING COFFIN KIPPING
Kopping CAFFYN CAPEN CAPON COBBIN COBBING COFFIN KIPPING
Koppyn CAFFYN CAPEN CAPON COBBIN COBBING COFFIN KIPPING
Kopyn CAFFYN CAPEN CAPON COBBIN COBBING COFFIN KIPPING
Korby CORBY
Kouse COOZE
Koveney COVENEY
Kul CULE KEWELL
Kuping CAFFYN CAPEN CAPON COBBIN COBBING COFFIN KIPPING
Kutten CUTTEN CUTTING
Kybbet CHIBBETT CUBITT
Kybet CHIBBETT CUBITT
Kydal KIDDALL KIDDELL KIDDLE
Kydel KIDDALL KIDDELL KIDDLE
Kydenor KIDNER KYNE
Kydil KIDDALL KIDDELL KIDDLE
Kyelyche CARLICK KILLICK
KYFFIN 4 CUFFIN KIFFIN KYFFYN
KYFFYN 4 CUFFIN KIFFIN KYFFIN
Kyllar KILLER
Kyllyk CARLICK KILLICK
Kyllyke CARLICK KILLICK
Kymer KIMBER KIMMER
KYNARDSLEY 9 De kynardsley De kynnardsley De kynnardsleye Kinardsley KINNERSLEY Kynnardsley Kynnardsleye KYNNERSLEY
KYNE 13 Chetemore Ketenor Ketner KIDNER Kitner Kitnor Kittnor Kydenor Kynne Kytemore Kytner Kyttner
Kyner KENNER KINNEAR
Kyng KING KINGE
Kyngdon KINGDOM KINGDON
Kynge KING KINGE
Kyngedon KINGDOM KINGDON
Kyngedone KINGDOM KINGDON
Kynget KINGETT
Kyngwill KINGSWELL KINGWELL
Kyngwyll KINGSWELL KINGWELL
Kynnardsley KINNERSLEY KYNARDSLEY KYNNERSLEY
Kynnardsleye KINNERSLEY KYNARDSLEY KYNNERSLEY
Kynne KYNE
Kynner KENNER KINNEAR
KYNNERSLEY 9 De kynardsley De kynnardsley De kynnardsleye Kinardsley KINNERSLEY KYNARDSLEY Kynnardsley Kynnardsleye
Kypling KIPLIN KIPLING
Kyplinge KIPLIN KIPLING
Kyppe KEAP KEEP
Kypping CAFFYN CAPEN CAPON COBBIN COBBING COFFIN KIPPING
Kyppyng CAFFYN CAPEN CAPON COBBIN COBBING COFFIN KIPPING
Kyrkeland KIRKLAND
Kyrkland KIRKLAND
Kyrklande KIRKLAND
Kyrle KERLE
Kyte KEET KITE KITT KITTS
Kytemore KIDNER KYNE
Kytner KIDNER KYNE
Kyttner KIDNER KYNE
La marechal LE MARECHAL
LABAT Labatt
Labatt LABAT
LABBETT 4 LOBBETT Lobet Lobett
Labourn LAYBOURNE
LABRAM LABRUM
LABRUM LABRAM
Laburn LAYBOURNE
Lacelet LASLETT
LACEY 12 LACKEY Lackie LACY LAKEY Lakie Laky Lasey Lasy LEAKEY Leakie Leaky
Lachem LATCHAM
Lacie LACY
LACK Lacke
Lacke LACK
LACKEY 10 LACEY Lackie LACY LAKEY Lakie Laky LEAKEY Leakie Leaky
Lackie LACEY LACKEY LACY LAKEY LEAKEY
LACY 12 LACEY Lacie LACKEY Lackie LAKEY Lakie Laky Lasy LEAKEY Leakie Leaky
Lad LADD
Ladbroke LADBROOK LADBROOKE
LADBROOK Ladbroke LADBROOKE
LADBROOKE Ladbroke LADBROOK
LADD 4 Lad Ladde Lads
Ladde LADD
Lads LADD
Lafflin LAFLIN
LAFLIN 5 Lafflin Lafling Laughlin Laughling
Lafling LAFLIN
Lagnden LANDEN LANDON
LAIDLAW Laidley Laidlow
Laidley LAIDLAW
Laidlow LAIDLAW
Laight LATES
LAIGHTON 10 Laton LAYTON LEATON LEIGHTON Lighten LIGHTON Lyghton Lyton Lyttone
LAILEY LALEY LAYLEY
Laimbear LAIMBEER
LAIMBEER 4 Laimbear Limebear Limebeer
Lainson LAINSTON
LAINSTON 4 Lainson Lenson Leynstone
LAIT 4 Leait LIGHT LIGHTNING
Laitham LATHAM
LAKEY 10 LACEY LACKEY Lackie LACY Lakie Laky LEAKEY Leakie Leaky
Lakie LACEY LACKEY LACY LAKEY LEAKEY
Laky LACEY LACKEY LACY LAKEY LEAKEY
Lale LEALL LISLE
LALEY LAILEY LAYLEY
LAMACQ Lamaroq Larmacq
Lamaroq LAMACQ
Lambard LAMBERT LAMPARD LOMBARD LUMBARD LUMBER
Lambart LAMBERT LAMPARD
LAMBERT 16 Lambard Lambart Lamburd LAMBURN LAMPARD Lamperd LAMPERT LOMBARD Lombart Lombert LUMBARD Lumbart LUMBER Lumbert Lumbort
Lambley LAMBLY LAMLEY
LAMBLY Lambley LAMLEY
LAMBOURN LAMBOURNE
LAMBOURNE LAMBOURN
Lamburd LAMBERT LAMBURN
LAMBURN LAMBERT Lamburd
LAMDEN Lamdin
Lamdin LAMDEN
LAMLEY Lambley LAMBLY
Lammesse LUMMIS
LAMPARD 5 Lambard Lambart LAMBERT Lamperd
Lampayne LAMPEN
LAMPEN 6 Lampayne Lampin Lampine Lamppyn Lampyn
Lamperd LAMBERT LAMPARD
LAMPERT LAMBERT
Lampin LAMPEN
Lampine LAMPEN
Lamppyn LAMPEN
Lampyn LAMPEN
LANCASHIRE LANKESTER
Lanckum LANCUM
Lancomb LANCUM
Lancome LANCUM
Lancon LANCUM
LANCUM 5 Lanckum Lancomb Lancome Lancon
Landbridge LANGRIDGE LANGRISH
LANDEN 5 Lagnden LANDON Lanedon Llanden
LANDER LAUNDER LAVENDER
LANDER-BOYCE BOYCE
Landeriowe LANDERYOU
Landery LANDRY
LANDERYOU Landeriowe Lenderyou
LANDIMORE LANDYMORE
LANDON 6 Lagnden LANDEN Lanedon LANGDON Llanden
Landram LANDRUM
Landray LANDREY LANDRY
Landrem LANDRUM

If the name you are interested in is not here, try Section C.

LANDREY 7 Landray LANDRY Landy Laundrey Lawndrey Lawndrie
Landridge LANGRIDGE LANGRISH
Landrim LANDRUM
LANDRUM 4 Landram Landrem Landrim
LANDRY 10 Landery Landray LANDREY Landy Laundery Laundrey Laundry Lawndrey Lawndrie
Landsdale LANSDALE LANSDELL
Landsdell LANSDALE LANSDELL
Landsell LANSDALE LANSDELL
Landy LANDREY LANDRY
LANDYMORE LANDIMORE
Lanedon LANDEN LANDON
Langabear LANGSBEAR
Langabeare LANGSBEAR
Langabere LANGSBEAR
Langaman LANGMAN LONGMAN
Langbridge LANGRIDGE LANGRISH
Langcake LONGCAKE
Langdail LANGDALE
LANGDALE 5 Langdail Langdayle Langdell Langdill
Langdayle LANGDALE
Langdell LANGDALE
Langdill LANGDALE
LANGDON LANDON
Langeford LANGFORD LONGFORD
Langeforde LANGFORD LONGFORD
Langfit LANGFORD LONGFORD
LANGFORD 12 Langeford Langeforde Langfit Langforde Lankford Longeford Longeforde Longfford Longfforde LONGFORD Longforde
Langforde LANGFORD LONGFORD
Langland LONGLAND
Langlande LONGLAND
LANGLEY Langly
Langly LANGLEY
LANGMAID 10 Langmate LANGMEAD Langmede Longmaid Longmaide Longmate Longmead Longmeade Longmede
LANGMAN 4 Langaman Longeman LONGMAN
Langmate LANGMAID LANGMEAD
LANGMEAD 10 LANGMAID Langmate Langmede Longmaid Longmaide Longmate Longmead Longmeade Longmede
Langmede LANGMAID LANGMEAD
Langmoor LONGMORE LONGMUIR
Langmore LONGMORE LONGMUIR
Langmuir LONGMORE LONGMUIR
Langmuire LONGMORE LONGMUIR
Langredge LANGRIDGE LANGRISH
LANGRIDGE 6 Landbridge Landridge Langbridge Langredge LANGRISH
LANGRISH 6 Landbridge Landridge Langbridge Langredge LANGRIDGE
LANGSBEAR 6 Langabear Langabeare Langabere Langsbeare Langsbere
Langsbeare LANGSBEAR
Langsbere LANGSBEAR
LANGTHORN LANGTHORNE
LANGTHORNE LANGTHORN LONGTHORNE
LANGTON 4 LANKTON LONGLEY Longton
Langworthie LANGWORTHY
LANGWORTHY Langworthie
Lanion LANYON
LANKESTER LANCASHIRE
Lankford LANGFORD
LANKTON LANGTON
LANSDALE 6 Landsdale Landsdell Landsell Lansdall LANSDELL
Lansdall LANSDALE LANSDELL
LANSDELL 6 Landsdale Landsdell Landsell LANSDALE Lansdall
Lantley LUNTLEY
Lantly LUNTLEY
Lanwarn LLANWARNE
Lanwarne LLANWARNE
Lanwerne LLANWARNE
Lanworn LLANWARNE
LANY DELANEY
LANYON Lanion
LAPIDGE Lapish
Lapish LAPIDGE
LAPLEY 4 Leplay Lepley LIPLEY
LAPPIN LAPPING
LAPPING LAPPIN
Larad LARARD
Larance LAURENCE LAWRENCE
LARARD 6 Larad Larrad Larrard Larred Larrod
Larcomb LARCOMBE LARKAM LARKHAM
LARCOMBE 4 Larcomb LARKAM LARKHAM
LARK LARKE
LARKAM 4 Larcomb LARCOMBE LARKHAM
LARKE LARK
Larken LARKIN
Larkeworthy LARKWORTHY
LARKHAM 4 Larcomb LARCOMBE LARKAM
LARKIN Larken LARKINS
LARKINS LARKIN Larkinson
Larkinson LARKINS
LARKWORTHY Larkeworthy
Larmacq LAMACQ
Larrad LARARD
LARRANCE LAURENCE
Larrard LARARD
Larrat LARRATT LARRETT
LARRATT 4 Larrat LARRETT Larritt
Larred LARARD
LARRETT 4 Larrat LARRATT Larritt
Larritt LARRATT LARRETT
Larrod LARARD
Larse LAW LAWES LAWS
LARTER Lawter
Lasad SADE
LASENBY LAZENBY
Lasey LACEY
Lashbrok LASHBROOK
LASHBROOK 4 Lashbrok Lashbrooke Lashbrooks
Lashbrooke LASHBROOK
Lashbrooks LASHBROOK
LASKEY Lasky
Lasky LASKEY
Laslet LASLETT
LASLETT 7 Lacelet Laslet Laslye Lasslet Lauslet Luslet
Laslye LASLETT
Lasslet LASLETT
Lasy LACEY LACY
LATCHAM Lachem Latchem
Latchem LATCHAM
LATES Laight
LATHAM 7 Laitham Lathem Laytham Laythum Leetham Letham
Lathem LATHAM
Lathlane LATHLEAN
LATHLEAN Lathlane Lethlean
Laton LAIGHTON LAYTON LEATON LEIGHTON LIGHTON
Laud LORD LOYD
Lauday LAWDAY LOVEDAY
LAUDER LAWTHER LOWTHER
LAUGHER LAWER Lawgher
Laughlin LAFLIN
Laughling LAFLIN
LAUGHTON LAWTON
LAUNDER 4 LANDER Launders LAVENDER
Launders LAUNDER
Laundery LANDRY
LAUNDREL Caundrel
Laundrey LANDREY LANDRY
Laundry LANDRY
LAURANCE 5 LAURENCE LAWRANCE LAWRENCE Lorrens
LAURENCE 7 Larance LARRANCE LAURANCE LAWRANCE LAWRENCE Lorrens
Laurenson LAWRENSON
LAURIE LAWRIE
Lauslet LASLETT
LAVENDER LANDER LAUNDER
LAVER Lavor
Lavers LAVES
LAVES Lavers
Lavor LAVER
LAW 8 De lawze De lors Larse LAWES LAWS Lawse Mclaws
LAWDAY Lauday LOVEDAY
LAWER LAUGHER Lawgher
LAWES 8 De lawze De lors Larse LAW LAWS Lawse Mclaws
Lawgher LAUGHER LAWER
LAWMAN 6 Lohrman Lohrmann LORMAN Lormann LOWMAN
Lawndrey LANDREY LANDRY
Lawndrie LANDREY LANDRY
LAWRANCE 5 LAURANCE LAURENCE LAWRENCE Lorrens
LAWRENCE 6 Larance LAURANCE LAURENCE LAWRANCE Lorrens
LAWRENSON Laurenson
LAWREY LAWRY LOWRY
LAWRIE LAURIE
LAWRY LAWREY LOWRY
LAWS 8 De lawze De lors Larse LAW LAWES Lawse Mclaws
Lawse LAW LAWES LAWS
LAWSON 5 LAWTON LEIGHTON LOTON LOWSON
Lawter LARTER
LAWTHER LAUDER LOWTHER
LAWTON 6 LAUGHTON LAWSON LEIGHTON Longton LOTON
LAY 4 LEA LEE LEIGH
Laybourn LAYBOURNE
LAYBOURNE 8 Labourn Laburn Laybourn Layburn Leybourne Leyburn Leyburne
Layburn LAYBOURNE
Laybutt LEBUTT
Layden LEYDEN
LAYLAND LEYLAND
LAYLEY LAILEY LALEY
Laytham LATHAM
Laythum LATHAM
LAYTON 10 LAIGHTON Laton LEATON LEIGHTON Lighten LIGHTON Lyghton Lyton Lyttone
LAZENBY LASENBY
Le asplott ADSETT ALLETT ARSLETT ASLETT AYLETT AZE
Le bret BARTON BARTRAM BERTRAM BETON BOURTON BRETON BURTON BYRON
Le bretun BARTON BARTRAM BERTRAM BETON BOURTON BRETON BURTON BYRON
Le burone BARTON BARTRAM BERTRAM BETON BOURTON BRETON BURTON BYRON
LE CLERK CLERK
Le cluse DE LE CLUSE
Le felicekyrk PHILLISKIRK
LE MARECHAL 5 La marechal Le mareschal Le marishall Le marshall
Le mareschal LE MARECHAL
Le marishall LE MARECHAL
Le marshall LE MARECHAL
Le meneter MINTA MINTER
LE MESSURIER 6 Le mesurier Lemessurier Lemesurier Messurier Mesurier
Le mesurier LE MESSURIER
Le moigne MOIGNE MONCK MONK MONKS
LE RICHE LERICHE
Le sade SADE
Le scelleur LE SEELLEUR
LE SEELLEUR 4 Le scelleur Le selleur Le sulleur
Le selleur LE SEELLEUR
Le sulleur LE SEELLEUR
Le thundre THUNDER
LEA 11 LAY Leace Leas Lease LEE LEES LEESE LEGH LEIGH LEY
Leabeater LEADBEATER LEADBETTER
Leabourn LEIBORNE
Leabourne LEIBORNE
Leabter LEADBEATER LEADBETTER
Leace LEA LEE LEES LEESE
LEACH 4 LEECH Leich LEITCH
LEACK LEAK LEAKE
Leacky LEAKEY LECKIE
LEADBEATER 4 Leabeater Leabter LEADBETTER
LEADBETTER 4 Leabeater Leabter LEADBEATER
Leading LEEDEN
Leadon LEEDEN
Leadston LEADSTONE LEDSTON LESSON LIDSTONE LYDSTON
LEADSTONE 13 Leadston Ledestone LEDSTON Ledstone LESSON LIDSTONE Lisson Liston Lydeston LYDSTON Lydstone Lysson
Leait LAIT LIGHT LIGHTNING
LEAK LEACK LEAKE
LEAKE LEACK LEAK

If the name you are interested in is not here, try Section C.

LEAKEY 13 LACEY LACKEY Lackie LACY LAKEY Lakie Laky Leacky Leakie Leaky LECKIE Lickey
Leakie LACEY LACKEY LACY LAKEY LEAKEY LECKIE
Leaky LACEY LACKEY LACY LAKEY LEAKEY
Leal LEALL LISLE
LEALL 4 Lale Leal LISLE
Leamon LEMON
Leaper LEEPER
LEAR Leer Lyer
Leas LEA LEE LEES LEESE
Lease LEA LEE LEES LEESE
Leason LEESON LESSON
Leath LEITH
LEATHAN Lethan
LEATON 10 LAIGHTON Laton LAYTON LEIGHTON Lighten LIGHTON Lyghton Lyton Lyttone
LEAVER LEVER
Leavitt LEVETT LEVIT LEVITT
Leavitte LEVETT LEVIT LEVITT
Lebatt LEBUTT
Leblake BLACK BLAKE
Leborne LEIBORNE
Lebourn LEIBORNE
LEBUTT 4 Laybutt Lebatt Leybutt
Leckfold LICKFOLD
Leckford LICKFOLD
LECKIE 4 Leacky LEAKEY Leakie
Leclair HOUDE
Leclerc HOUDE
Leder LEEPER
Ledestone LEADSTONE LEDSTON LESSON LIDSTONE LYDSTON
LEDGARD 4 LEDGER Lidger Lydger
Ledgate LEGAT LEGATE LEGGATT LEGGETT LEGGOTT LIDGATE LIGGETT
LEDGER 4 LEDGARD Lidger Lydger
LEDSTON 13 Leadston LEADSTONE Ledestone Ledstone LESSON LIDSTONE Lisson Liston Lydeston LYDSTON Lydstone Lysson
Ledstone LEADSTONE LEDSTON LESSON LIDSTONE LYDSTON
LEE 17 FOY JOY LAY LEA Leace Leas Lease LEES LEESE LEGH LEIGH LEY Tay TEA TEE TOY
LEECH 4 LEACH Leich LEITCH
Leedam LEEDHAM
LEEDEN Leading Leadon
LEEDHAM Leedam
LEEKEY Leeky
Leeky LEEKEY
LEEPER Leaper Leder
Leer LEAR
LEES 7 LEA Leace Leas Lease LEE LEESE
LEESE 7 LEA Leace Leas Lease LEE LEES
LEESON Leason LESSON
Leetham LATHAM
Leevars LEIVERS LEVERS
LEFEAVER LEFEVRE
LEFEVRE LEFEAVER
Leffen LIFFEN
LEFFIN 9 Leffing LIFFEN Liffin Lifton Loffen Lyffin Lyffing Lyfton
Leffing LEFFIN LIFFEN
LEGASSICK Legassicke
Legassicke LEGASSICK
LEGAT 17 Ledgate LEGATE Legatt Leget Leggat Leggate LEGGATT LEGGETT Leggit Leggitt LEGGOT LEGGOTT Legot LEGOTT LIDGATE LIGGETT
LEGATE 10 Ledgate LEGAT Leget Leggate LEGGATT LEGGETT LEGGOTT LIDGATE LIGGETT
Legatt LEGAT LEGGATT LEGGOT LEGGOTT LEGOTT
Leget LEGAT LEGATE LEGGATT LEGGETT LEGGOTT LIDGATE LIGGETT
LEGEYT 6 Legeytt LEGGETT Legyett Legytt Leygett
Legeytt LEGEYT LEGGETT
Leggat LEGAT LEGGATT LEGGOT LEGGOTT LEGOTT
Leggate LEGAT LEGATE LEGGATT LEGGETT LEGGOTT LIDGATE LIGGETT
LEGGATT 17 Ledgate LEGAT LEGATE Legatt Leget Leggat Leggate LEGGETT Leggit Leggitt LEGGOT LEGGOTT Legot LEGOTT LIDGATE LIGGETT
LEGGETT 15 Ledgate LEGAT LEGATE Leget LEGEYT Legeytt Leggate LEGGATT LEGGOTT Legyett Legytt Leygett LIDGATE LIGGETT
Leggit LEGAT LEGGATT LEGGOT LEGGOTT LEGOTT
Leggitt LEGAT LEGGATT LEGGOT LEGGOTT LEGOTT
LEGGOT 10 LEGAT Legatt Leggat LEGGATT Leggit Leggitt LEGGOTT Legot LEGOTT
LEGGOTT 17 Ledgate LEGAT LEGATE Legatt Leget Leggat Leggate LEGGATT LEGGETT Leggit Leggitt LEGGOT Legot LEGOTT LIDGATE LIGGETT
LEGH 5 LEA LEE LEIGH LEY
Legot LEGAT LEGGATT LEGGOT LEGGOTT LEGOTT
LEGOTT 10 LEGAT Legatt Leggat LEGGATT Leggit Leggitt LEGGOT LEGGOTT Legot
Legyett LEGEYT LEGGETT
Legytt LEGEYT LEGGETT
LEIBORNE 8 Leabourn Leabourne Leborne Lebourn Leyborne Libourn Lybourn
Leich LEACH LEECH
LEIGH 7 LAY LEA LEE LEGH LEY Lygh
LEIGHTON 13 LAIGHTON Laton LAWSON LAWTON LAYTON LEATON Lighten LIGHTON LOTON Lyghton Lyton Lyttone
LEITCH LEACH LEECH
LEITH Leath Lythe
LEIVERS Leevars LEVERS
LEM 5 LEMM Lemme Lems Lemson
LEMAN Lemman LEMON
Lemas LOMAS LOMAX
Lemess LOMAS LOMAX
Lemessurier LE MESSURIER
Lemesurier LE MESSURIER
LEMM 5 LEM Lemme Lems Lemson
Lemman LEMAN LEMON
Lemme LEM LEMM
LEMON 4 Leamon LEMAN Lemman
Lems LEM LEMM
Lemson LEM LEMM
LENAN LINNANE
Lenane LENNANE LENNON
Lenderyou LANDERYOU
Lendfild LINDFIELD
Leningham LINNINGTON
Lenington LINNINGTON
Lennan LENNANE LENNON
LENNANE 4 Lenane Lennan LENNON
Lenningham LINNINGTON
Lennington LINNINGTON
LENNON 4 Lenane Lennan LENNANE
Lenson LAINSTON
Leplay LAPLEY LIPLEY
Lepley LAPLEY LIPLEY
LERICHE LE RICHE
Lerwell LERWILL
LERWILL Lerwell Lurwell
LESSON 15 Leadston LEADSTONE Leason Ledestone LEDSTON Ledstone LEESON LIDSTONE Lisson Liston Lydeston LYDSTON Lydstone Lysson
Lesster LESTER
LESTER Lesster
Letham LATHAM
Lethan LEATHAN
Lethlean LATHLEAN
Letteleye LUTLEY
LEVER LEAVER
LEVERS Leevars LEIVERS
Leverston LIVINGSTON LIVINGSTONE
Leverton LIVINGSTON LIVINGSTONE
Levet LEVETT LEVIT LEVITT
LEVETT 7 Leavitt Leavitte Levet LEVIT LEVITT Levvett
Levingston LIVINGSTON LIVINGSTONE
Levington LIVINGSTON LIVINGSTONE
LEVIT 6 Leavitt Leavitte Levet LEVETT LEVITT
LEVITT 7 Leavitt Leavitte Levet LEVETT LEVIT Levvett
Levvett LEVETT LEVITT
Lewar LEWER LUER
LEWER 4 Lewar Lewir LUER
LEWERS 16 Loures Lures Maclure Mcclewr Mcclour Mccloure Mcclower Mccluer Mccluir Mccluire MCCLURE Mciloure Mcilure Mclewer MCLURE
LEWES LEWIS
LEWIN Lewing
Lewing LEWIN
Lewingden LEWINGTON
Lewingdon LEWINGTON
LEWINGTON Lewingden Lewingdon
Lewir LEWER LUER
LEWIS LEWES
Lewtas LEWTUS
LEWTUS Lewtas
LEY 5 LEA LEE LEGH LEIGH
Leyborne LEIBORNE
Leybourne LAYBOURNE
Leyburn LAYBOURNE
Leyburne LAYBOURNE
Leybutt LEBUTT
LEYDEN Layden
Leygett LEGEYT LEGGETT
LEYLAND LAYLAND
Leynstone LAINSTON
Liant LYANT LYON LYONS
Lias LYUS
Libourn LEIBORNE
Libsy LIVESEY LUCY
Licfold LICKFOLD
Lickas LICKIS LICKISS
Lickass LICKIS LICKISS
Lickefolde LICKFOLD
Lickes LICKIS LICKISS
Lickess LICKIS LICKISS
Lickey LEAKEY
Lickfauld LICKFOLD
LICKFOLD 9 Leckfold Leckford Licfold Lickefolde Lickfauld Lickford Lyckfold Lykfauld
Lickford LICKFOLD
LICKIS 9 Lickas Lickass Lickes Lickess LICKISS Liclkas Likis Likiss
LICKISS 9 Lickas Lickass Lickes Lickess LICKIS Liclkas Likis Likiss
LICKLEY Likely Likly
Liclkas LICKIS LICKISS
LICRECE LIQUORISH
Liddel LIDDLE
LIDDELL LIDDLE Lyddel
LIDDIARD Lidiard LYDIARD
LIDDLE 4 Liddel LIDDELL Lyddel
Lideath LYDDIETH
LIDGATE 10 Ledgate LEGAT LEGATE Leget Leggate LEGGATT LEGGETT LEGGOTT LIGGETT
Lidger LEDGARD LEDGER
LIDGETT 8 Lidiart Ludgett Lydiart Lydiat Lydiate Lydiatt Lydyate
Lidiard LIDDIARD LYDIARD
Lidiart LIDGETT
LIDSTONE 13 Leadston LEADSTONE Ledestone LEDSTON Ledstone LESSON Lisson Liston Lydeston LYDSTON Lydstone Lysson
LIDWELL Lidwill
Lidwill LIDWELL
Lies LISE LYES
Lietwin LIGHTWING
LIFFEN 10 Leffen LEFFIN Leffing Liffin Lifton Loffen Lyffin Lyffing Lyfton
Liffin LEFFIN LIFFEN
Liford LYFORD
Lifton LEFFIN LIFFEN
LIGGAT Liggatt
Liggatt LIGGAT
LIGGETT 10 Ledgate LEGAT LEGATE Leget Leggate LEGGATT LEGGETT LEGGOTT LIDGATE
LIGHT 4 LAIT Leait LIGHTNING
LIGHTBOUND LIGHTBOWN
LIGHTBOWN LIGHTBOUND
Lighten LAIGHTON LAYTON LEATON LEIGHTON LIGHTON
Lighting LIGHTNING LIGHTWING
LIGHTNING 8 LAIT Leait LIGHT Lighting LIGHTWING Lightwyn Lightyn
LIGHTON 10 LAIGHTON Laton LAYTON LEATON LEIGHTON

If the name you are interested in is not here, try Section C.

Lighten Lyghton Lyton Lyttone
Lightwin LIGHTWING
Lightwine LIGHTWING
LIGHTWING 9 Lietwin Lighting LIGHTNING Lightwin Lightwine Lightwyn Lightyn Lytewing
Lightwyn LIGHTNING LIGHTWING
Lightyn LIGHTNING LIGHTWING
Likely LICKLEY
Likis LICKIS LICKISS
Likiss LICKIS LICKISS
Likly LICKLEY
LILE LILL Lille
Liley LILLEY LILLIE LILLY LILY
Liliman LILLIMAN
LILL LILE Lille
Lille LILE LILL
LILLEY 6 Liley LILLIE LILLY LILY Lyllye
Lilleyman LILLIMAN
LILLIE 6 Liley LILLEY LILLY LILY Lyllye
Lillieman LILLIMAN
LILLIMAN 10 Liliman Lilleyman Lillieman Lillyman Lilyman Lyliman Lylleyman Lylliman Lyllyman
LILLINGTON Lyllington
LILLY 6 Liley LILLEY LILLIE LILY Lyllye
Lillyman LILLIMAN
LILY 6 Liley LILLEY LILLIE LILLY Lyllye
Lilyman LILLIMAN
Limbard LIMBOARD LIMBORD
Limbart LIMBORD
Limbert LIMBORD
LIMBOARD Limbard LIMBORD
LIMBORD 6 Limbard Limbart Limbert LIMBOARD Limbort
Limbort LIMBORD
Limebear LAIMBEER
Limebeer LAIMBEER
LIMER Limmer
LIMESI LYMESEY LYMESY
Limmer LIMER
Linall LYNALL
Linam LINEHAM LYNAM
LINBERRY 4 Linbery Linbry Linbury
Linbery LINBERRY
Linbry LINBERRY
Linbury LINBERRY
LINCH LYNCH
Lind LINES LYND LYNDS LYNES LYNN
Lindar LINDER
Lindars LINDER
Linde LINES LYND LYNDS LYNES LYNN
LINDER 4 Lindar Lindars Lindor
LINDFIELD 15 Lendfild Linfeeld Linfeild Linfeile Linfield Linfields Linnild Linveild Linvile Linvill Linville Lyndfeild Lynfeild Lynfelde
LINDGREEN LINDGREN
LINDGREN LINDGREEN
LINDO 4 Lindoe Lindow Lyndo
Lindoe LINDO
LINDOP Lindup
Lindor LINDER
Lindow LINDO
Linds LINES LYND LYNDS LYNES LYNN
LINDSAY 4 LINDSEY LINSEY Linzer
LINDSEY 4 LINDSAY LINSEY Linzer
Lindup LINDOP
LINE 4 LINES LYNE LYNES
Lineall LYNALL
LINEHAM 4 Linam LYNAM Lyneham
Linehill LYNALL
Linele LINGLEY LINLEY
Linell LYNALL
LINES 12 Lind Linde Linds LINE LYND Lynde LYNDS LYNE LYNES LYNN Lyns
Linfeeld LINDFIELD
Linfeild LINDFIELD
Linfeile LINDFIELD
Linfield LINDFIELD
Linfields LINDFIELD
Lingey LINGLEY LINLEY
LINGLEY 6 Linele Lingey Lingly Lingy LINLEY
Lingly LINGLEY LINLEY
Lingy LINGLEY LINLEY
Linington LINNINGTON
LINLEY 6 Linele Lingey LINGLEY Lingly Lingy
LINNANE LENAN
Linnild LINDFIELD
LINNINGTON 6 Leningham Lenington Lenningham Lennington Linington
LINSEY LINDSAY LINDSEY
Linveild LINDFIELD
Linvile LINDFIELD
Linvill LINDFIELD
Linville LINDFIELD
Linzer LINDSAY LINDSEY
Lipet LIPPETT
LIPLEY 4 LAPLEY Leplay Lepley
LIPPETT Lipet
LIPTROT Liptrott
Liptrott LIPTROT
LIQUORISH LICRECE
LISE 6 Lies Lize LYES Lys Lyse
LISLE 4 Lale Leal LEALL
LISSAMAN Lyssaman
Lisson LEADSTONE LEDSTON LESSON LIDSTONE LYDSTON
LISTER LYSTER
Liston LEADSTONE LEDSTON LESSON LIDSTONE LYDSTON
Liteljohns LITTLEJOHN LITTLEJOHNS
Litldik LITTLEDYKE
Littdike LITTLEDYKE
Litteldyke LITTLEDYKE
Littledick LITTLEDYKE
Littledike LITTLEDYKE
Littledyck LITTLEDYKE
LITTLEDYKE 9 Litldik Littdike Litteldyke Littledick Littledike Littledyck Lytledikes Lytledycke
LITTLEJOHN 7 Liteljohns LITTLEJOHNS Littlejon Littlejons Lytteljohns Lytteljons
LITTLEJOHNS 7 Liteljohns LITTLEJOHN Littlejon Littlejons Lytteljohns Lytteljons
Littlejon LITTLEJOHN LITTLEJOHNS
Littlejons LITTLEJOHN LITTLEJOHNS
LITTLEWOOD Lyttlewood
Livans LIVINGS
Livard LYFORD
Livens LIVINGS
Liverd LYFORD
LIVESEY 4 Libsy Livsay LUCY
LIVINGS Livans Livens
LIVINGSTON 6 Leverston Leverton Levingston Levington LIVINGSTONE
LIVINGSTONE 6 Leverston Leverton Levingston Levington LIVINGSTON
Livord LYFORD
Livsay LIVESEY LUCY
Lize LISE LYES
Llanden LANDEN LANDON
Llanwarn LLANWARNE
LLANWARNE 6 Lanwarn Lanwarne Lanwerne Lanworn Llanwarn
Llewelin LLEWELLYN LLEWELYN
Llewellin LLEWELLYN LLEWELYN
LLEWELLYN 5 Llewelin Llewellin LLEWELYN LLEWHELLIN
LLEWELYN 5 Llewelin Llewellin LLEWELLYN LLEWHELLIN
LLEWHELLIN LLEWELLYN LLEWELYN
LLOYD 5 FLOYD LLOYDE LOYD LOYDE
LLOYDE 5 FLOYD LLOYD LOYD LOYDE
LOADER LODER
LOASBY Loseby Lowesby
Loaten LOATON LOTON
LOATON 4 Loaten Loten LOTON
Lob LOBB
LOBB 5 De lobbe Lob Lobbe Lobe
Lobbe LOBB
LOBBETT 4 LABBETT Lobet Lobett
Lobe LOBB
Lobet LABBETT LOBBETT
Lobett LABBETT LOBBETT
Lochawe LOCHORE
Lochery LOCHRIE LOUGHARY
Lochoar LOCHORE
LOCHORE Lochawe Lochoar
LOCHRIE 4 Lochery LOUGHARY Loughery
LOCK LOCKE
LOCKE LOCK
Locket LUCKET LUCKETT
LOCKEY LOCKIE
LOCKIE LOCKEY
LOCOCK LOWCOCK
LODER LOADER
Loemle LUMLEY
Loffen LEFFIN LIFFEN
LOFTHOUSE LOFTUS
LOFTUS LOFTHOUSE
Lohrman LAWMAN LORMAN
Lohrmann LAWMAN LORMAN
Loid LORD LOYD
Loines LOYNS
Loins LOYNS
Lollum LULHAM
Lomacks LOMAS LOMAX
Lomalghs LOMAS LOMAX
Lomalls LOMAS LOMAX
Lomals LOMAS LOMAX
LOMAS 26 Lemas Lemess Lomacks Lomalghs Lomalls Lomals Lomase Lomass Lomasse Lomath LOMAX Lomaxe Lomes Lomhas Lomis Lommas Lomos Lomous Lomus Loomas Loumas Lowmas Lumas Lumhales Lumhalghs
Lomase LOMAS LOMAX
Lomass LOMAS LOMAX
Lomasse LOMAS LOMAX
Lomath LOMAS LOMAX
LOMAX 26 Lemas Lemess Lomacks Lomalghs Lomalls Lomals LOMAS Lomase Lomass Lomasse Lomath Lomaxe Lomes Lomhas Lomis Lommas Lomos Lomous Lomus Loomas Loumas Lowmas Lumas Lumhales Lumhalghs
Lomaxe LOMAS LOMAX
LOMBARD 10 Lambard LAMBERT Lombart Lombert LUMBARD Lumbart LUMBER Lumbert Lumbort
Lombart LAMBERT LOMBARD LUMBARD LUMBER
Lombert LAMBERT LOMBARD LUMBARD LUMBER
Lomes LOMAS LOMAX
Lomhas LOMAS LOMAX
Lomis LOMAS LOMAX
Lommas LOMAS LOMAX
Lomos LOMAS LOMAX
Lomous LOMAS LOMAX
Lomus LOMAS LOMAX
Londnys LUMMIS
LONDON LONNON
Lonen LONNEN LONNON
LONGCAKE Langcake
Longeford LANGFORD LONGFORD
Longeforde LANGFORD LONGFORD
Longelande LONGLAND
Longeman LANGMAN LONGMAN
Longfford LANGFORD LONGFORD
Longfforde LANGFORD LONGFORD
LONGFORD 11 Langeford Langeforde Langfit LANGFORD Langforde Longeford Longeforde Longfford Longfforde Longforde
Longforde LANGFORD LONGFORD
LONGLAND 5 Langland Langlande Longelande Longlond
LONGLEY LANGTON Longton
Longlond LONGLAND
Longmaid LANGMAID LANGMEAD
Longmaide LANGMAID LANGMEAD
LONGMAN 4 Langaman LANGMAN Longeman
Longmate LANGMAID LANGMEAD
Longmead LANGMAID LANGMEAD
Longmeade LANGMAID LANGMEAD
Longmede LANGMAID LANGMEAD
Longmoor LONGMORE LONGMUIR
LONGMORE 8 Langmoor Langmore Langmuir Langmuire Longmoor LONGMUIR Longmuire
LONGMUIR 8 Langmoor Langmore Langmuir

If the name you are interested in is not here, try Section C.

Langmuire Longmoor LONGMORE Longmuire
Longmuire LONGMORE LONGMUIR
LONGSTAFF LONGSTAFFE
LONGSTAFFE LONGSTAFF
LONGTHORNE LANGTHORNE
Longton LANGTON LAWTON LONGLEY
LONNEN Lonen LONNON
Lonney LUMMIS
LONNON 4 LONDON Lonen LONNEN
Lonys LUMMIS
Loomas LOMAS LOMAX
LOOTES Loots
Loots LOOTES
LORAINE Lorraine
LORD 4 Laud Loid LOYD
LORIMER Lorrimer Lottimer
LORMAN 5 LAWMAN Lohrman Lohrmann Lormann
Lormann LAWMAN LORMAN
Lorraine LORAINE
Lorrens LAURANCE LAURENCE LAWRANCE LAWRENCE
Lorrimer LORIMER
Loseby LOASBY
LOSH Arlosh
Loten LOATON LOTON
LOTHIAN LOWTHIAN
LOTON 7 LAWSON LAWTON LEIGHTON Loaten LOATON Loten
Lottimer LORIMER
Louenes LUMMIS
Louenesse LUMMIS
LOUGHARY 4 Lochery LOCHRIE Loughery
Loughery LOCHRIE LOUGHARY
Loumas LOMAS LOMAX
Louneis LUMMIS
Loures LEWERS MCCLURE MCLURE
LOUTH 4 Louthe LOWTH Lowthe
Louthe LOUTH LOWTH
Louvell LOVELL
LOVAT 4 LOVATT LOVET LOVETT
LOVATT 4 LOVAT LOVET LOVETT
LOVE LOVES LOVETT
LOVEDAY Lauday LAWDAY
Lovekyn LUCKIN LUCKING
Lovel LOVELL
Lovelee LOVELY
Loveley LOVELY
LOVELL Louvell Lovel
LOVELY 4 Lovelee Loveley Lovlee
Lovenes LUMMIS
Loveness LUMMIS
Loveredg LOVERIDGE
Loveredge LOVERIDGE
LOVERIDGE 9 Loveredg Loveredge Loveridges Loverodg Loverodge Lovradge Lovridge Lovridges
Loveridges LOVERIDGE
Loverodg LOVERIDGE
Loverodge LOVERIDGE
LOVES LOVE LOVETT
LOVET 4 LOVAT LOVATT LOVETT
LOVETT 6 LOVAT LOVATT LOVE LOVES LOVET
Loveys LOVIS
LOVIS Loveys
Lovlee LOVELY
Lovradge LOVERIDGE
Lovridge LOVERIDGE
Lovridges LOVERIDGE

LOW LOWE
LOWCOCK LOCOCK
Lowder LOWTHER
LOWE LOW
LOWERY LOWREY
Lowesby LOASBY
Lowins LOYNS
LOWMAN LAWMAN
Lowmas LOMAS LOMAX
Lownes LUMMIS
LOWREY LOWERY
LOWRY LAWREY LAWRY
LOWSON LAWSON
LOWTH 4 LOUTH Louthe Lowthe
Lowthe LOUTH LOWTH
LOWTHER 4 LAUDER LAWTHER Lowder
LOWTHIAN LOTHIAN
LOYD 8 FLOYD Laud LLOYD LLOYDE Loid LORD LOYDE
LOYDE 5 FLOYD LLOYD LLOYDE LOYD
Loyn LOYNS
LOYNS 5 Loines Loins Lowins Loyn
LUCAS 4 Lucasse Lukas LUQUAS
Lucasse LUCAS
Lucken LUKENS
LUCKET Locket LUCKETT
LUCKETT Locket LUCKET
LUCKIN 5 Lovekyn LUCKING Luckyn Lukin
LUCKING 5 Lovekyn LUCKIN Luckyn Lukin
Luckyn LUCKIN LUCKING
LUCY 4 Libsy LIVESEY Livsay
Ludgett LIDGETT
LUDKIN 4 Lurkin Lurkins LUTKIN
LUER 4 Lewar LEWER Lewir
Lukas LUCAS
LUKENS Lucken
Lukin LUCKIN LUCKING
Lulha LULHAM
LULHAM 8 Lollum Lulha Lulhame Lulla Lullam Lullham Lullum
Lulhame LULHAM
Luliere LULY
Lulla LULHAM
Lullam LULHAM
Lullham LULHAM
Lulliere LULY
Lullum LULHAM
Lully LULY
LULY 5 de Luly Luliere Lulliere Lully
Lumas LOMAS LOMAX
LUMBARD 10 Lambard LAMBERT LOMBARD Lombart Lombert Lumbart LUMBER Lumbert Lumbort
Lumbart LAMBERT LOMBARD LUMBARD LUMBER
LUMBER 10 Lambard LAMBERT LOMBARD Lombart Lombert LUMBARD Lumbart Lumbert Lumbort
Lumbert LAMBERT LOMBARD LUMBARD LUMBER
Lumbort LAMBERT LOMBARD LUMBARD LUMBER
Lumhales LOMAS LOMAX
Lumhalghs LOMAS LOMAX
LUMKIN Lumpkin
LUMLEY Loemle Lymley
LUMMIS 16 Lammesse Londnys Lonney Lonys Louenes Louenesse Louneis Lovenes Loveness Lownes Lumnes Lumnis Lumys Lundnes Lunnis

Lumnes LUMMIS
Lumnis LUMMIS
Lumpkin LUMKIN
Lumys LUMMIS
LUN LUND LUNN
LUND LUN LUNN
Lundnes LUMMIS
LUNN LUN LUND
Lunnis LUMMIS
LUNTLEY 4 Lantley Lantly Luntly
Luntly LUNTLEY
LUQUAS LUCAS
Lures LEWERS MCCLURE MCLURE
Lurkin LUDKIN LUTKIN
Lurkins LUDKIN LUTKIN
Lurwell LERWILL
LUSH Lushe
Lushe LUSH
Luslet LASLETT
Lutas LUTUS
Lutely LUTLEY
LUTKIN 4 LUDKIN Lurkin Lurkins
Lutlay LUTLEY
LUTLEY 21 De luttele De lutteley De lutteleye Letteleye Lutely Lutlay Lutleye Lutlie Lutly Luttelay Luttele Luttelegh Lutteley Lutteleye Luttey Luttley Luttly Lyteleye Lytley Lytteleghe
Lutleye LUTLEY
Lutlie LUTLEY
Lutly LUTLEY
Luttelay LUTLEY
Luttele LUTLEY
Luttelegh LUTLEY
Lutteley LUTLEY
Lutteleye LUTLEY
Luttey LUTLEY
Luttley LUTLEY
Luttly LUTLEY
LUTUS Lutas
Luxal LUXALL
LUXALL 4 Luxal Luxel Luxell
Luxel LUXALL
Luxell LUXALL
Lyal LYALL LYELL
LYALL 5 Lyal Lyel LYELL LYLE
LYANT 5 Liant LYON LYONS Lyont
Lyas LYUS
Lybourn LEIBORNE
Lyckfold LICKFOLD
Lyddel LIDDELL LIDDLE
Lyddiatt LYDDIETH
LYDDIETH 9 Lideath Lyddiatt Lydeat Lydiat Lydiate Lydiath Lydiatt Lydieth
Lydeat LYDDIETH
Lydeston LEADSTONE LEDSTON LESSON LIDSTONE LYDSTON
Lydger LEDGARD LEDGER
LYDIARD LIDDIARD Lidiard
Lydiart LIDGETT
Lydiat LIDGETT LYDDIETH
Lydiate LIDGETT LYDDIETH
Lydiath LYDDIETH
Lydiatt LIDGETT LYDDIETH
Lydieth LYDDIETH
LYDSTON 13 Leadston LEADSTONE Ledestone LEDSTON Ledstone LESSON LIDSTONE Lisson Liston

Lydeston Lydstone Lysson
Lydstone LEADSTONE LEDSTON LESSON LIDSTONE LYDSTON
Lydyate LIDGETT
Lyel LYALL LYELL
LYELL 5 Lyal LYALL Lyel LYLE
Lyer LEAR
LYES 6 Lies LISE Lize Lys Lyse
Lyffin LEFFIN LIFFEN
Lyffing LEFFIN LIFFEN
LYFORD 7 Liford Livard Liverd Livord Lyvard Lyward
Lyfton LEFFIN LIFFEN
Lygh LEIGH
Lyghton LAIGHTON LAYTON LEATON LEIGHTON LIGHTON
Lykfauld LICKFOLD
LYLE LYALL LYELL
Lyliman LILLIMAN
Lylleyman LILLIMAN
Lylliman LILLIMAN
Lyllington LILLINGTON
Lyllye LILLEY LILLIE LILLY LILY
Lyllyman LILLIMAN
LYMESEY LIMESI LYMESY
LYMESY LIMESI LYMESEY
Lymley LUMLEY
LYNALL 8 Linall Lineall Linehill Linell Lynehill Lynell Lynold
LYNAM 4 Linam LINEHAM Lyneham
LYNAS Lynass
Lynass LYNAS
LYNCH LINCH
LYND 10 Lind Linde Linds LINES Lynde LYNDS LYNES LYNN Lyns
Lynde LINES LYND LYNDS LYNES LYNN
Lyndfeild LINDFIELD
Lyndo LINDO
LYNDS 10 Lind Linde Linds LINES LYND Lynde LYNES LYNN Lyns
LYNE 4 LINE LINES LYNES
Lyneham LINEHAM LYNAM
Lynehill LYNALL
Lynell LYNALL
LYNES 12 Lind Linde Linds LINE LINES LYND Lynde LYNDS LYNE LYNN Lyns
Lynfeild LINDFIELD
Lynfelde LINDFIELD
LYNN 10 Lind Linde Linds LINES LYND Lynde LYNDS LYNES Lyns
Lynold LYNALL
Lyns LINES LYND LYNDS LYNES LYNN
LYON 5 Liant LYANT LYONS Lyont
LYONS 5 Liant LYANT LYON Lyont
Lyont LYANT LYON LYONS
Lys LISE LYES
Lyse LISE LYES
Lyssaman LISSAMAN
Lysson LEADSTONE LEDSTON LESSON LIDSTONE LYDSTON
LYSTER LISTER
Lyteleye LUTLEY
Lytewing LIGHTWING
Lythe LEITH
Lytledikes LITTLEDYKE
Lytledycke LITTLEDYKE
Lytley LUTLEY
Lyton LAIGHTON LAYTON

If the name you are interested in is not here, try Section C.

LEATON LEIGHTON LIGHTON
Lytteleghe LUTLEY
Lytteljohns LITTLEJOHN LITTLEJOHNS
Lytteljons LITTLEJOHN LITTLEJOHNS
Lyttlewood LITTLEWOOD
Lyttone LAIGHTON LAYTON LEATON LEIGHTON LIGHTON
LYUS Lias Lyas
Lyvard LYFORD
Lyward LYFORD
M'caughan MCCAUGHAN
M'cristain MACQUISTEN MCQUISTON
M'cristan MACQUISTEN MCQUISTON
M'cuistan MACQUISTEN MCQUISTON
M'cuisten MACQUISTEN MCQUISTON
M'cuistin MACQUISTEN MCQUISTON
M'cuiston MACQUISTEN MCQUISTON
M'garran MCGHRAN
M'gilhauche MILHENCH
M'gilhauk MILHENCH
M'gregor GRIGOR MACGREGOR MCGREGOR
M'grigor GRIGOR MACGREGOR MCGREGOR
M'huchison MACQUISTEN MCQUISTON
M'huison MACQUISTEN MCQUISTON
M'hustan MACQUISTEN MCQUISTON
M'KENZIE MACKENZIE MCKENZIE
M'lean MACLEAN MCLEAN
M'qhuiston MACQUISTEN MCQUISTON
M'queaston MACQUISTEN MCQUISTON
M'queestan MACQUISTEN MCQUISTON
M'queeston MACQUISTEN MCQUISTON
M'queiftoun MACQUISTEN MCQUISTON
M'queisoun MACQUISTEN MCQUISTON
M'queistene MACQUISTEN MCQUISTON
M'queistine MACQUISTEN MCQUISTON
M'quesistein MACQUISTEN MCQUISTON
M'questan MACQUISTEN MCQUISTON
M'questen MACQUISTEN MCQUISTON
M'questin MACQUISTEN MCQUISTON
M'questine MACQUISTEN MCQUISTON
M'question MACQUISTEN MCQUISTON
M'queston MACQUISTEN MCQUISTON
M'quiestan MACQUISTEN MCQUISTON
M'quistan MACQUISTEN MCQUISTON
M'quistein MACQUISTEN MCQUISTON
M'quisten MACQUISTEN MCQUISTON
M'quistin MACQUISTEN MCQUISTON
M'quistine MACQUISTEN MCQUISTON
M'quistion MACQUISTEN MCQUISTON
M'quiston MACQUISTEN MCQUISTON
M'uistine MACQUISTEN MCQUISTON
M'utchon MACQUISTEN MCQUISTON
Maab MABE
Mabane MABIN MAVIN MAVINS
Mabb MABE
MABE 5 Maab Mabb Maib Mayab
MABELL MABLE Mables
MABEN 4 MABIN Mabine Mabon
MABIN 33 Mabane MABEN Mabine Mabon Mabyn Mauin Mauings Mauven Mauvin Mauving Mavein Maveing Maven Mavene MAVIN Mavine Maving Mavinge Mavings MAVINS Mavius Mawevyn Mawven Mawvin Maying Mayvan Mayvens Meavin Meavine Meven Mevens Mevins
Mabine MABEN MABIN
MABLE MABELL Mables
Mables MABELL MABLE
Mabon MABEN MABIN
Mabry MAYBERRY MAYBURY
Mabury MAYBERRY MAYBURY
Mabyn MABIN MAVIN MAVINS
Macalexander ALEXANDER
Macalpin MCALPINE
Macalpine MCALPINE
Macaodhagain EGAN KEEGAN
Macaogain EGAN KEEGAN
Macaughan MCCAUGHAN
Macauley MCAULEY
MACBRYDE Mcbryde
Maccanch CONCHA CONCHAR CONCHIE MCCONCHIE MCCONCHY MCCONOCHIE
Maccanchie CONCHA CONCHAR CONCHIE MCCONCHIE MCCONCHY MCCONOCHIE
Macclengen CLINGAN
Macclingan CLINGAN
Macclingand CLINGAN
Macclingen CLINGAN
Maccoistain MACQUISTEN MCQUISTON
Macconchie CONCHA CONCHAR CONCHIE MCCONCHIE MCCONCHY MCCONOCHIE
Maccreadie MCCREADIE MCCREADY MCCREDIE
Maccready MCCREADY
Maccuiston MACQUISTEN MCQUISTON
Macdavitt DEVITT
Macdevitt DEVITT
Macdewell MACDUELL
MACDONALD Macdonnell MCDONALD
Macdonnell MACDONALD
MACDUELL 4 Macdewell Mcdowel Mcduell
MACE 18 MACEY Mascry Masery Masgrave Masgreave Masgreve Masgrove Maskerie Maskery Maskerye MASKREY MASSEY MOSS Mosse MUSGRAVE MUSGROVE Mussegreffe
MACER 4 MARCER MASSER MERCER
Macewan MCEWAN MCEWEN MCKEOWN
MACEY 19 MACE Mascry Masery Masey Masgrave Masgreave Masgreve Masgrove Maskerie Maskery Maskerye MASKREY MASSEY MOSS Mosse MUSGRAVE MUSGROVE Mussegreffe
Macgilhauch MILHENCH
Macgillhench MILHENCH
MACGREGOR 15 Gregor GRIGOR M'gregor M'grigor Macgrigor Mackgregor Mackgrigor Mcgreagor Mcgreger MCGREGOR Mcgreogar Mcgrigor Mckgregor Mckgrigor
Macgrigor GRIGOR MACGREGOR MCGREGOR
MACHAM MATCHAM
Macharg MEHARG
Machomas THOMPSON THOMSON THOMSONE
Machuison MACQUISTEN MCQUISTON
Macilhench MILHENCH
MACINTOSH MACKINTOSH MCINTOSH
Macjore MCGEORGE MCJORE
MACKALL 4 Mackoll Macole Macoll
MACKAY MACKIE MCKAY
Mackeinder MACKENDER
MACKENDER Mackeinder
MACKENZIE M'KENZIE MCKENZIE
Mackerel CHARLETON HILLHOUSE MCKERRELL
MACKERELL 4 Mackerill Mackrell MACKRILL
Mackerill MACKERELL MACKRILL
MACKERNES Maquernes
Mackgregor GRIGOR MACGREGOR MCGREGOR
Mackgrigor GRIGOR MACGREGOR MCGREGOR
MACKIE 6 MACKAY Mccie MCKAY Mckey MCKIE
MACKINDER Makinder
MACKINTOSH MACINTOSH MCINTOSH
MACKMAN 35 Mackmen MACKMIN Mackminn Macmain Macmaine Macmane Macmean Macmin MAKEMAN Makmin Makmun MCMAIN Mcmean Mcmeans Mcmeen Mcmein Mcmen Mcmenn Mcmim Mcmin Mcmina Mcmine Mcmines MCMINN Mcminne Mcminnies Mcminnis Mcmuin Mcmunn Mcmuns Mcmyn Mcmyne Mcmynn Muckmen
Mackmen MACKMAN MACKMIN MCMAIN MCMINN
MACKMIN 35 MACKMAN Mackmen Mackminn Macmain Macmaine Macmane Macmean Macmin MAKEMAN Makmin Makmun MCMAIN Mcmean Mcmeans Mcmeen Mcmein Mcmen Mcmenn Mcmim Mcmin Mcmina Mcmine Mcmines MCMINN Mcminne Mcminnies Mcminnis Mcmuin Mcmunn Mcmuns Mcmyn Mcmyne Mcmynn Muckmen
Mackminn MACKMAN MACKMIN MCMAIN MCMINN
Macknamay MCNAMEE
Mackoll MACKALL
Mackrell MACKERELL MACKRILL
MACKRILL 4 MACKERELL Mackerill Mackrell
Macksted MAXTED
Mackuisten MACQUISTEN MCQUISTON
MACLEAN M'lean MCLEAN
MACLEOD MCLEOD
Maclure LEWERS MCCLURE MCLURE
Macmahon MCMAHON
Macmain MACKMAN MACKMIN MCMAIN MCMINN
Macmaine MACKMAN MACKMIN MCMAIN MCMINN
Macmane MACKMAN MACKMIN MCMAIN MCMINN
Macmean MACKMAN MACKMIN MCMAIN MCMINN
Macmin MACKMAN MACKMIN MCMAIN MCMINN
MACMYN Mcmyn
Macnee MAGNAY
Macole MACKALL
Macoll MACKALL
Maconochie CONCHA CONCHAR CONCHIE MCCONCHIE MCCONCHY MCCONOCHIE
Macqueechan MACQUISTEN MCQUISTON
Macqueifstoun MACQUISTEN MCQUISTON
Macquesten MACQUISTEN MCQUISTON
Macquestian MACQUISTEN MCQUISTON
Macquestion MACQUISTEN MCQUISTON
Macquiftion MACQUISTEN MCQUISTON
Macquistan MACQUISTEN MCQUISTON
Macquistani MACQUISTEN MCQUISTON
Macquistation MACQUISTEN MCQUISTON
MACQUISTEN 109 Coistain Eysteinn Huisdean Huisdeinn M'cristain M'cristan M'cuistan M'cuisten M'cuistin M'cuiston M'huchison M'huison M'hustan M'qhuiston M'queaston M'queestan M'queeston M'queiftoun M'queisoun M'queistene M'queistine M'quesistein M'questan M'questen M'questin M'questine M'question M'queston M'quiestan M'quistan M'quistein M'quisten M'quistin M'quistine M'quistion M'quiston M'uistine M'utchon Maccoistain Maccuiston Machuison Mackuisten Macqueechan Macqueifstoun Macquesten Macquestian Macquestion Macquiftion Macquistan Macquistani Macquistation Macquister Macquistin Macquistini Macquistion Macquiston Macuistian Macuiston Macwhistan Macwhiston Macwisdon Maquiston Mccrustian Mccuestian Mccuestion Mccuistain Mccuisten Mccuister Mccuistians Mccuistin Mccuistion

If the name you are interested in is not here, try Section C.

Mccuiston Mccusten
Mccustin Mccuston
Mchoustone Mchuistonn
Mchutcheon Mckqueistein
Mckquestein Mcquest
Mcquesten Mcquiften
Mcquifton Mcquinston
Mcquistan Mcquisten
Mcquistian Mcquistin
Mcquistion MCQUISTON
Mcquseten Mcqustin
Mcqustion Mcquston
Mcuisten Mcuisthon
Mcuistian Mcuistine
Mcuistion Mcuiston
Mcwhiston Meccustin
Mkhuthin Mkhutkhon
Mkquefton Mkquiton
Monfcuiftion
Macquister MACQUISTEN MCQUISTON
Macquistin MACQUISTEN MCQUISTON
Macquistini MACQUISTEN MCQUISTON
Macquistion MACQUISTEN MCQUISTON
Macquiston MACQUISTEN MCQUISTON
MACRAE MCRAE
Macraft HAYCRAFT HAYCROFT MACRO MACROFT MACROW MAYCRAFT MAYCROFT MEDCROFT MOORCROFT
Macraste HAYCRAFT HAYCROFT MACROFT MAYCRAFT MAYCROFT MEDCROFT MOORCROFT
Macready MCCREADIE MCCREADY MCCREDIE
MACRO 5 Macraft MACROW MAYCRAFT MAYCROFT
MACROFT 15 Hacraste HAYCRAFT HAYCROFT Macraft Macraste Makecraft Marcroft MAYCRAFT Maycraught MAYCROFT Mecraft Mecroft MEDCROFT MOORCROFT
MACROW 5 Macraft MACRO MAYCRAFT MAYCROFT
Macstead MAXTED
Macthomas THOMPSON THOMSON THOMSONE
Macuistian MACQUISTEN MCQUISTON
Macuiston MACQUISTEN MCQUISTON
Macwhistan MACQUISTEN MCQUISTON
Macwhiston MACQUISTEN MCQUISTON
Macwisdon MACQUISTEN MCQUISTON
Madaver MADDEVER
Madcalf MEDCRAFT MEDCROFT METCALF METCALFE
Madcalfe MEDCRAFT MEDCROFT METCALF METCALFE
Madchoff MEDCALF METCALFE
Maddaver MADDEVER
Maddeford MADDEVER
MADDEVER 14 Madaver Maddaver Maddeford Maddifor Maddiford Maddiver Madefield Madefor Madeford Madever Madifor Madiford Madiver
Maddifor MADDEVER
Maddiford MADDEVER
MADDISON MADISON
Maddiver MADDEVER
MADDOCKS MADDOX
MADDOX MADDOCKS
Made MEAD MEADE
Madefield MADDEVER
Madefor MADDEVER
Madeford MADDEVER
Madeleigh MADELEY
MADELEY 6 Madeleigh Madely Madlee Madley Maidley
Madely MADELEY
Madestone MAINSTONE MANSTONE
Madever MADDEVER
Madifor MADDEVER
Madiford MADDEVER
Madin MAIDEN MEADEN
MADISON MADDISON
Madiver MADDEVER
MADLE 6 Mailes MALE MALES Masle Mayles
Madlee MADELEY
Madley MADELEY
Mae MAUL MAULE MAW MAY MAYE
Magges MAGGS MEGGS MOGG
Magget MARGETTS MARGRAVE MARGRETT
Maggot MARGETTS MARGRAVE MARGRETT
Maggott MARGETTS MARGRAVE MARGRETT
MAGGS 6 Magges Mags Meg MEGGS MOGG
Magilhauche MILHENCH
MAGINNIS Mcinnis
Magit MARGETTS MARGRAVE MARGRETT
Magitt MARGETTS MARGRAVE MARGRETT
MAGLOCHLAINN MCLAUGHLIN
MAGNAY Macnee
Magot MARGETTS MARGRAVE MARGRETT
Magowan MCGOWAN
Mags MAGGS MEGGS MOGG
MAGSON 4 MEGGINSON MEGGISON MEGSON
Mahan MAHON MAHONE
Maharg MEHARG
MAHER 5 MARRS MAYER MEAGHER MYERS
MAHON 4 Mahan MAHONE Mohane
MAHONE 4 Mahan MAHON Mohane
MAHONEY 4 MAHONY O'mahoney O'mahony
MAHONY 4 MAHONEY O'mahoney O'mahony
Maib MABE
Maid MEAD MEADE
MAIDEN 4 Madin Mayden MEADEN
Maidley MADELEY
Maidstone MAINSTONE MANSTONE
Maie MAY MAYE
Maihoo MAYHEW MAYO
Mailes MADLE MALE MALES
MAIN 7 Maine MAINS MANE MAYNE MAYOR MEAR
Mainard MAYNARD
Maine MAIN MANNY MAYNE MAYNEY
Mainestone MAINSTONE MANSTONE
Mainewaring MAINWARING MANNERING
MAINS MAIN
MAINSBRIDGE MANSBRIDGE
Mainston MAINSTONE MANSTONE
MAINSTONE 12 Madestone Maidstone Mainestone Mainston Manestone Manston MANSTONE Mayneston Maynestone Maynston Maynstone
MAINT Mainte
Mainte MAINT
MAINWARING 5 Mainewaring MANNERING Manwaring Maynwaring
MAIR 7 MARE MAYER MAYERS MEAR MEYER MEYERS
MAIRIS 9 Mareis Mares Mareys Maries MARIS Marrays Marreys Marys
Mais MAYES MAYS
Maisters MASTERS
Makclouch MILHENCH
Makecraft HAYCRAFT HAYCROFT MACROFT MAYCRAFT MAYCROFT MEDCROFT MOORCROFT
MAKEMAN MACKMAN MACKMIN
Makerly MCCURLEY
Makgilhauch MILHENCH
Makgillhauch MILHENCH
Makinder MACKINDER
Making MAKINS
Makings MAKINS
MAKINS 7 Making Makings Meaking Meakings Meeking Meekings
Makkilauche MILHENCH
Makkillauche MILHENCH
Makmin MACKMAN MACKMIN MCMAIN MCMINN
Makmun MACKMAN MACKMIN MCMAIN MCMINN
Makoff MEDCALF METCALFE
Makylhauche MILHENCH
MALANDIE Malindine
MALCOM Malcome
Malcome MALCOM
MALE 7 MADLE Mailes MALES Masle Mayles MEAL
Malefant MALIPHANT
Malender MALLINDER MULLENDER MULLINDER
MALES 6 MADLE Mailes MALE Masle Mayles
Malherbe HARLEY
Malherve HARLEY
Malia MELIA O'MALLEY
MALIN Mallin
Malinder MALLINDER MULLENDER MULLINDER
Malindine MALANDIE
MALIPHANT 4 Malefant Malliphant Malophant
Malison MALLINSON
Malisone MALLINSON
Malisonn MALLINSON
MALKIN Maulkin
Mall MAUL MAULE MAW
MALLAT Mallet
Mallenson MALLESON MALLINSON
MALLERY Mallory Malory
MALLESON 4 Mallenson MALLINSON Mallison
Mallesonne MALLINSON
Mallet MALLAT MALLETT
MALLETT Mallet
Malley MELIA O'MALLEY
Mallin MALIN
MALLINDER 5 Malender Malinder MULLENDER MULLINDER
Mallingson MALLINSON
MALLINSON 10 Malison Malisone Malisonn Mallenson MALLESON Mallesonne Mallingson Mallison Mallyson
Malliphant MALIPHANT
Mallison MALLESON MALLINSON
Mallory MALLERY
Mallpress MALPRESS
Mallyson MALLINSON
Malnoury MANOURY
MALONEY MOLONEY
Malophant MALIPHANT
Malory MALLERY
MALPRESS Mallpress Maltpress
MALROY Melroy Milroy
MALTBY Maultby
Maltpress MALPRESS
Mambery MEMBREY MEMORY MOWBRAY
Mambrun MOMBRUN
MAN MANN Mans
Mancel MANSEL MANSELL
Mancell MANSEL MANSELL
Manday MONDAY MONDEY MUNDAY MUNDIE MUNDY
Mandefield MANDEVILLE MANTERFIELD
MANDER MAUNDER
Manderell MAUNDRELL
Manderfield MANDEVILLE MANTERFIELD
Manderville MANDEVILLE MANTERFIELD
MANDEVILLE 8 DE MANDEVILLE Mandefield Manderfield Manderville MANTERFIELD MANVELL Manville
Mandey MONDAY MONDEY MUNDAY MUNDIE MUNDY
Mandie MONDAY MONDEY MUNDAY MUNDIE MUNDY
Mandral MAUNDRELL
Mandrell MAUNDRELL
Mandril MAUNDRELL
Mandy MONDAY MONDEY MUNDAY MUNDIE MUNDY
MANE 5 MAIN MAYNE MAYOR MEAR
Manestone MAINSTONE MANSTONE
MANHIRE MENEAR Minear
MANION MANNION
MANN 4 MAN MANNS Mans
Mannakay MANNAKEE
MANNAKEE Mannakay Mannekee
Mannekee MANNAKEE
MANNERING 5 Mainewaring MAINWARING Manwaring Maynwaring
MANNING MANNION
MANNION MANION MANNING
Mannon MENNIM
MANNS MANN
MANNY 7 De masny Maine Mayenne MAYNE MAYNEY Meduana
MANOURY Malnoury
Mans MAN MANN
MANSBRIDGE MAINSBRIDGE
MANSEL 8 Mancel Mancell MANSELL Manxell Mauncell Maunsel Maunsell
MANSELL 8 Mancel Mancell MANSEL Manxell Mauncell Maunsel Maunsell
Mansey MENZIES
Manston MAINSTONE MANSTONE
MANSTONE 12 Madestone Maidstone Mainestone Mainston MAINSTONE Manestone Manston

If the name you are interested in is not here, try Section C.

Mayneston Maynestone
Maynston Maynstone
Mantel MANTELL MANTLE
MANTELL Mantel MANTLE
MANTERFIELD 5 Mandefield Manderfield Manderville MANDEVILLE
MANTLE Mantel MANTELL
MANVELL MANDEVILLE Manville
Manville MANDEVILLE MANVELL
Manwaring MAINWARING MANNERING
Manxell MANSEL MANSELL
Maote MAYOTT
Maoul MAUL MAULE MAW
MAP 4 MAPP Mapps Maps
Mapel MAPLE
Mapil MAPLE
MAPLE 6 Mapel Mapil Mappel Mappil Mapple
MAPP 4 MAP Mapps Maps
Mappel MAPLE
Mappil MAPLE
Mapple MAPLE
Mapps MAP MAPP
Maps MAP MAPP
Maquernes MACKERNES
Maquiston MACQUISTEN MCQUISTON
Mar-gerrison MARGERISON
MARA 4 Meara O'MARA O'meara
Marag MARRIAGE
Marage MARRIAGE
Maragh MARRIAGE
Marayge MARRIAGE
MARCER 4 MACER MASSER MERCER
MARCH Mars MARSH
MARCHANT 5 Marchante Marchent MERCHANT Merchante
Marchante MARCHANT MERCHANT
Marchden MARSDEN
Marchdene MARSDEN
Marchent MARCHANT MERCHANT
MARCHMENT 4 Marchmont Marshment Marshmont
Marchmont MARCHMENT
Marcklew MARKLEW
Marclsden MARSDEN
Marclu MARKLEW
Marcroft HAYCRAFT HAYCROFT MACROFT MAYCRAFT MAYCROFT MEDCROFT MOORCROFT
Mardin MARTEN MARTIN MARTYN
MARDLIN 4 MARLIN Maudley Mawdling
Mardon MERDON
MARE 10 MAIR MAYER MAYERS MAYOR MEAR MEARE MERE MEYER MEYERS
Maregge MARRIAGE
Mareis MAIRIS MARIS
Marely MARLEY
Marenchi MARENGO
Marenco MARENGO
MARENGO Marenchi Marenco
Mares MAIRIS MARIS MAYERS
MARET Marett
Marett MARET
Mareys MAIRIS MARIS
Marfel MARFELL
MARFELL Marfel Marfill
Marfill MARFELL
Margaret MARGETTS MARGRAVE MARGRETT
Margarete MARGETTS MARGRAVE MARGRETT
Margarets MARGETTS MARGRAVE MARGRETT
Margarett MARGETTS MARGRAVE MARGRETT
Margarette MARGETTS MARGRAVE MARGRETT
Margarettes MARGETTS MARGRAVE MARGRETT
Margaretts MARGETTS MARGRAVE MARGRETT
Margarott MARGETTS MARGRAVE MARGRETT
Margarts MARGETTS MARGRAVE MARGRETT
Margate MARGETTS MARGRAVE MARGRETT
Margates MARGETTS MARGRAVE MARGRETT
Margats MARGETTS MARGRAVE MARGRETT
Margattes MARGETTS MARGRAVE MARGRETT
Margatts MARGETTS MARGRAVE MARGRETT
Margeret MARGETTS MARGRAVE MARGRETT
Margerets MARGETTS MARGRAVE MARGRETT
Margeretts MARGETTS MARGRAVE MARGRETT
Margerinson MARGERISON
MARGERISON 8 Gerrison Mar-gerrison Margerinson Margesson Marginson Margison Marjoryson
Margerit MARGETTS MARGRAVE MARGRETT
Margerts MARGETTS MARGRAVE MARGRETT
Margesson MARGERISON
Marget MARGETTS MARGRAVE MARGRETT
Margets MARGETTS MARGRAVE MARGRETT
Margett MARGETTS MARGRAVE MARGRETT
Margetto MARGETTS MARGRAVE MARGRETT
MARGETTS 50 Magget Maggot Maggott Magit Magitt Magot Margaret Margarete Margarets Margarett Margarette Margarettes Margaretts Margarott Margarts Margate Margates Margats Margattes Margatts Margeret Margerets Margeretts Margerit Margerts Marget Margets Margett Margetto Margitt Margitts Margrat Margrata Margrate Margratt Margratte MARGRAVE Margreate Margreath Margret Margrete Margrets MARGRETT Margrette Margretts Margrit Margrits Margritt Marguerit
Marginson MARGERISON
Margison MARGERISON
Margitt MARGETTS MARGRAVE MARGRETT
Margitts MARGETTS MARGRAVE MARGRETT
Margrat MARGETTS MARGRAVE MARGRETT
Margrata MARGETTS MARGRAVE MARGRETT
Margrate MARGETTS MARGRAVE MARGRETT
Margratt MARGETTS MARGRAVE MARGRETT
Margratte MARGETTS MARGRAVE MARGRETT
MARGRAVE 50 Magget Maggot Maggott Magit Magitt Magot Margaret Margarete Margarets Margarett Margarette Margarettes Margaretts Margarott Margarts Margate Margates Margats Margattes Margatts Margeret Margerets Margeretts Margerit Margerts Marget Margets Margett Margetto MARGETTS Margitt Margitts Margrat Margrata Margrate Margratt Margratte Margreate Margreath Margret Margrete Margrets MARGRETT Margrette Margretts Margrit Margrits Margritt Marguerit
Margreate MARGETTS MARGRAVE MARGRETT
Margreath MARGETTS MARGRAVE MARGRETT
Margret MARGETTS MARGRAVE MARGRETT
Margrete MARGETTS MARGRAVE MARGRETT
Margrets MARGETTS MARGRAVE MARGRETT
MARGRETT 50 Magget Maggot Maggott Magit Magitt Magot Margaret Margarete Margarets Margarett Margarette Margarettes Margaretts Margarott Margarts Margate Margates Margats Margattes Margatts Margeret Margerets Margeretts Margerit Margerts Marget Margets Margett Margetto MARGETTS Margitt Margitts Margrat Margrata Margrate Margratt Margratte MARGRAVE Margreate Margreath Margret Margrete Margrets Margrette Margretts Margrit Margrits Margritt Marguerit
Margrette MARGETTS MARGRAVE MARGRETT
Margretts MARGETTS MARGRAVE MARGRETT
Margrit MARGETTS MARGRAVE MARGRETT
Margrits MARGETTS MARGRAVE MARGRETT
Margritt MARGETTS MARGRAVE MARGRETT
Marguerit MARGETTS MARGRAVE MARGRETT
Mariadge MARRIAGE
Mariag MARRIAGE
Mariage MARRIAGE
Mariche MARRIAGE
Maridge MARRIAGE
Maries MAIRIS MARIS
Marige MARRIAGE
Marigg MARRIAGE
Marilion MOURILYAN
Marillon MOURILYAN
Mariot MARRIOTT MARROTT MARWOOD MERRIT
MARIOTT MARRIOTT
MARIS 9 MAIRIS Mareis Mares Mareys Maries Marrays Marreys Marys
Marjoryson MARGERISON
MARK 4 MARKE MARKES MARKS
Markam MARKHAM
Markclew MARKLEW
MARKE MARK
Markelew MARKLEW
MARKES MARK MARKS
MARKHAM Markam
MARKLEW 8 Marcklew Marclu Markclew Markelew Marklewe Marklow Marklue
Marklewe MARKLEW
MARKLEY Muckley
Marklow MARKLEW
Marklue MARKLEW
MARKS MARK MARKES
MARKWICK Markwicke Marquique
Markwicke MARKWICK
Marlan MARLAND MARLIN
MARLAND 4 Marlan Marlande MARLIN
Marlande MARLAND MARLIN
MARLBOROUGH Marlbrough
Marlbrough MARLBOROUGH
Marleigh MARLEY
MARLEY 7 Marely Marleigh Marly Merely MORLEY Murlye
MARLIN 7 MARDLIN Marlan MARLAND Marlande Maudley Mawdling
Marly MARLEY
MARNER Marriner
Marod MARRIOTT MARROTT MARWOOD
Marquique MARKWICK
MARR 5 MOIR MOORE MORE MUIR
Marrage MARRIAGE
Marraige MARRIAGE
Marrays MAIRIS MARIS
Marredge MARRIAGE
Marrege MARRIAGE
Marrett MERRETT MERRITT
Marreys MAIRIS MARIS
Marriadg MARRIAGE
Marriag MARRIAGE
MARRIAGE 30 Marag Marage Maragh Marayge Maregge Mariadge Mariag Mariage Mariche Maridge Marige Marigg Marrage Marraige Marredge Marrege Marriadg Marriag Marriages Marrich Marriche Marridg Marridge Marrige Marriges Marryadge Marryage Maryadge Maryge
Marriages MARRIAGE
Marrich MARRIAGE
Marriche MARRIAGE
Marridg MARRIAGE
Marridge MARRIAGE
Marrige MARRIAGE
Marriges MARRIAGE
Marriner MARNER
MARRIOTT 11 Mariot MARIOTT Marod Marrit Marrod Marrot MARROTT MARWOOD Meriot MERRIT
Marrit MARRIOTT MERRIT
Marrod MARRIOTT MARROTT

If the name you are interested in is not here, try Section C.

MARWOOD
Marrot MARRIOTT MARROTT MARWOOD
MARROTT 7 Mariot Marod MARRIOTT Marrod Marrot MARWOOD
MARRS 4 MAHER MAYER MYERS
Marrten MARTEN MARTIN MARTYN
Marryadge MARRIAGE
Marryage MARRIAGE
Mars MARCH MARSH
Marschel MARSHAL MARSHALL
Marsdean MARSDEN
Marsdeane MARSDEN
MARSDEN 22 Marchden Marchdene Marclsden Marsdean Marsdeane Marsdene Marsdens MARSDIN Marsdon Marshdean Marshden Marskin MARSON MARSTON Marzden Mercden Merclden Merclesden Merlsden Mersceden Mersden
Marsdene MARSDEN
Marsdens MARSDEN MARSDIN MARSTON
MARSDIN 7 MARSDEN Marsdens Marsdon Marskin MARSTON Mersden
Marsdon MARSDEN MARSDIN MARSON MARSTON
MARSH 5 MARCH Mars MERSH Mesh
MARSHAL 5 Marschel MARSHALL Martial Mershal
MARSHALL 4 Marschel MARSHAL Martial
Marshdean MARSDEN
Marshden MARSDEN
Marshment MARCHMENT
Marshmont MARCHMENT
Marskin MARSDEN MARSDIN MARSTON
Marsom MARSON
MARSON 10 MARSDEN Marsdon Marsom MARSTON MASON MASSOM Masson MUSSON MUSTON
Marsten MARSTON MASTON
Marsters MASTER MASTERS
Marstin MARSTON MASTON
MARSTON 12 MARSDEN Marsdens MARSDIN Marsdon Marskin MARSON Marsten Marstin Masten MASTON Mersden
Martaine MARTEN MARTIN MARTYN
Marteham MARTEN MARTIN MARTYN
Martell MURTELL
MARTEN 17 Mardin Marrten Martaine Marteham Martens MARTIN Martine Marton MARTYN Moreten Moretin MORETON Morten MORTIN MORTON Myttyne
Martens MARTEN MARTIN
Martial MARSHAL MARSHALL
MARTIN 24 Hardin Harten HARTIN Harton HAUGHTON HORTON HUTTON Mardin Marrten Martaine Marteham MARTEN Martens Martine Marton MARTYN Moreten Moretin MORETON Morten MORTIN MORTON Myttyne
Martine MARTEN MARTIN MARTYN
Marton MARTEN MARTIN MORETON MORTIN MORTON
MARTYN 9 Mardin Marrten Martaine Marteham MARTEN MARTIN Martine Myttyne
MARWOOD 7 Mariot Marod MARRIOTT Marrod Marrot MARROTT
Maryadge MARRIAGE
MARYCHURCH Merrychurch
Maryge MARRIAGE
Marys MAIRIS MARIS
Marzden MARSDEN
Mascry MACE MACEY MASKREY MASSEY MOSS MUSGRAVE MUSGROVE
Masery MACE MACEY MASKREY MASSEY MOSS MUSGRAVE MUSGROVE
Masey MACEY
Masgrave MACE MACEY MASKREY MASSEY MOSS MUSGRAVE MUSGROVE
Masgreave MACE MACEY MASKREY MASSEY MOSS MUSGRAVE MUSGROVE
Masgreve MACE MACEY MASKREY MASSEY MOSS MUSGRAVE MUSGROVE
Masgrove MACE MACEY MASKREY MASSEY MOSS MUSGRAVE MUSGROVE
Maskerie MACE MACEY MASKREY MASSEY MOSS MUSGRAVE MUSGROVE
Maskery MACE MACEY MASKREY MASSEY MOSS MUSGRAVE MUSGROVE
Maskerye MACE MACEY MASKREY MASSEY MOSS MUSGRAVE MUSGROVE
MASKREY 18 MACE MACEY Mascry Masery Masgrave Masgreave Masgreve Masgrove Maskerie Maskery Maskerye MASSEY MOSS Mosse MUSGRAVE MUSGROVE Mussegreffe
Masle MADLE MALE MALES
MASON 7 MARSON MASSOM Masson MAYSON MUSSON MUSTON
Masprat MUSPRATT
Maspratt MUSPRATT
Massay MASSEY MASSY
MASSER 4 MACER MARCER MERCER
MASSEY 21 MACE MACEY Mascry Masery Masgrave Masgreave Masgreve Masgrove Maskerie Maskery Maskerye MASKREY Massay MASSY Massye MOSS Mosse MUSGRAVE MUSGROVE Mussegreffe
Massinger MESSENGER
MASSOM 5 MARSON MASON MUSSON MUSTON
Masson MARSON MASON
MASSY 4 Massay MASSEY Massye
Massye MASSEY MASSY
Masten MARSTON MASTON
MASTER Marsters MASTERS
MASTERS 6 Maisters Marsters MASTER Mesters Musters
MASTON 5 Marsten Marstin MARSTON Masten
MAT 4 Mats Matt MATTS
Matcalf MEDCALF METCALFE
MATCHAM MACHAM
Maten MATON MATTIN
Matfield ATTFIELD HADFIELD
MATHER MATHERS
MATHERS 7 MATHER MATHEW MATHEWS Mathus MATTHEW MATTHEWS
MATHESON MATHIESON
MATHEW 6 MATHERS MATHEWS Mathus MATTHEW MATTHEWS
MATHEWS 6 MATHERS MATHEW Mathus MATTHEW MATTHEWS
MATHIESON MATHESON
Mathus MATHERS MATHEW MATHEWS MATTHEW MATTHEWS
MATON 7 Maten Matten MATTIN Matton Matyn Matyne
Mats MAT MATTS
Matt MAT MATTS
Matten MATON MATTHEW MATTIN
MATTENLEY MATTENLY MATTINGLEY
MATTENLY MATTENLEY MATTINGLEY
MATTHEW 8 MATHERS MATHEW MATHEWS Mathus Matten MATTHEWS WATTHEW
MATTHEWS 6 MATHERS MATHEW MATHEWS Mathus MATTHEW
MATTHEWSON MATTINSON Mattison
MATTIN 7 Maten MATON Matten Matton Matyn Matyne
MATTINGLEY MATTENLEY MATTENLY
MATTINGLY Mattlingley
MATTINSON MATTHEWSON Mattison
Mattison MATTHEWSON MATTINSON
Mattlingley MATTINGLY
Matton MATON MATTIN
MATTS 4 MAT Mats Matt
Matyn MATON MATTIN
Matyne MATON MATTIN
MAUDIT 4 Mauditt Mauduit Mayduith
Mauditt MAUDIT
Maudley MARDLIN MARLIN
Maudrell MAUNDRELL
Mauduit MAUDIT
Mauin MABIN MAVIN MAVINS
Mauings MABIN MAVIN MAVINS
MAUL 6 Mae Mall Maoul MAULE MAW
MAULE 6 Mae Mall Maoul MAUL MAW
Maulkin MALKIN
Maultby MALTBY
Mauncell MANSEL MANSELL
MAUNDER MANDER
Maunderell MAUNDRELL
MAUNDRELL 15 Manderell Mandral Mandrell Mandril Maudrell Maunderell Maundrill Monderel Monderell Mondrell Mounderell Moundrell Munderell Mundrell
Maundrill MAUNDRELL
Maunsel MANSEL MANSELL
Maunsell MANSEL MANSELL
MAURICE 5 MORRICE MORRIS MORRISH MORRISS
Mauven MABIN MAVIN MAVINS
Mauvin MABIN MAVIN MAVINS
Mauving MABIN MAVIN MAVINS
Mavein MABIN MAVIN MAVINS
Maveing MABIN MAVIN MAVINS
Maven MABIN MAVIN MAVINS
Mavene MABIN MAVIN MAVINS
MAVIN 30 Mabane MABIN Mabyn Mauin Mauings Mauven Mauvin Mauving Mavein Maveing Maven Mavene Mavine Maving Mavinge Mavings MAVINS Mavius Mawevyn Mawven Mawvin Maying Mayvan Mayvens Meavin Meavine Meven Mevens Mevins
Mavine MABIN MAVIN MAVINS
Maving MABIN MAVIN MAVINS
Mavinge MABIN MAVIN MAVINS
Mavings MABIN MAVIN MAVINS
MAVINS 30 Mabane MABIN Mabyn Mauin Mauings Mauven Mauvin Mauving Mavein Maveing Maven Mavene MAVIN Mavine Maving Mavinge Mavings Mavius Mawevyn Mawven Mawvin Maying Mayvan Mayvens Meavin Meavine Meven Mevens Mevins
Mavius MABIN MAVIN MAVINS
MAW 6 Mae Mall Maoul MAUL MAULE
Mawdling MARDLIN MARLIN
MAWER MOORE MOWER
Mawevyn MABIN MAVIN MAVINS
Mawven MABIN MAVIN MAVINS
Mawvin MABIN MAVIN MAVINS
Maxstead MAXTED
Maxtead MAXTED
MAXTED 6 Macksted Macstead Maxstead Maxtead Mexstead
MAY 6 Mae Maie MAYE MAYES MAYS
Mayab MABE
MAYBANK Maybanke Maybanks
Maybanke MAYBANK
Maybanks MAYBANK
MAYBERRY 4 Mabry Mabury MAYBURY
MAYBORN Maybourn Maybourne
Maybourn MAYBORN
Maybourne MAYBORN
MAYBURY 4 Mabry Mabury MAYBERRY
MAYCOCK 4 Meacock Mecock Mecuk
MAYCRAFT 17 Hacraste HAYCRAFT HAYCROFT Macraft Macraste MACRO MACROFT MACROW Makecraft Marcroft Maycraught MAYCROFT Mecraft Mecroft MEDCROFT MOORCROFT
Maycraught HAYCRAFT HAYCROFT MACROFT MAYCRAFT MAYCROFT MEDCROFT MOORCROFT
MAYCROFT 17 Hacraste HAYCRAFT HAYCROFT Macraft Macraste MACRO MACROFT MACROW Makecraft Marcroft MAYCRAFT Maycraught Mecraft Mecroft MEDCROFT MOORCROFT
Mayde MEAD MEADE
Mayden MAIDEN MEADEN
Mayduith MAUDIT

If the name you are interested in is not here, try Section C.

MAYE 4 Mae Maie MAY
Mayenne MANNY MAYNE MAYNEY
MAYER 13 MAHER MAIR MARE MARRS MAYERS MAYOR MEAR MEARE MERE MEYER MEYERS MYERS
MAYERS 10 MAIR MARE Mares MAYER MEAR MEARE MERE MEYER MEYERS
MAYES 5 Mais MAY MAYS Maze
MAYHEW Maihoo MAYO
Maying MABIN MAVIN MAVINS
Mayles MADLE MALE MALES
MAYNARD 5 Mainard Maynards Mynard Mynards
Maynards MAYNARD
MAYNE 10 MAIN Maine MANE MANNY Mayenne MAYNEY MAYOR MEAR Meduana
Mayneston MAINSTONE MANSTONE
Maynestone MAINSTONE MANSTONE
MAYNEY 6 Maine MANNY Mayenne MAYNE Meduana
Maynston MAINSTONE MANSTONE
Maynstone MAINSTONE MANSTONE
Maynwaring MAINWARING MANNERING
MAYO 4 Maihoo MAYHEW MAYOH
MAYOH MAYO
MAYOR 8 MAIN MANE MARE MAYER MAYNE MEAR MEYER
Mayot MAYOTT
Mayots MAYOTT
MAYOTT 4 Maote Mayot Mayots
MAYS 4 Mais MAY MAYES
MAYSON MASON
Mayvan MABIN MAVIN MAVINS
Mayvens MABIN MAVIN MAVINS
Maze MAYES
Mc crackan MC CRACKEN
MC CRACKEN Mc crackan
Mcalexander ALEXANDER
MCALISTER MCALLISTER
MCALLISTER MCALISTER
Mcalpin MCALPINE
MCALPINE 8 Macalpin Macalpine Mcalpin Mccalpin Mccolpin Mccoppin Mccorpin
MCAULEY Macauley
Mcbryde MACBRYDE
MCCALL 4 Mccaul Mccaull MCCOLL
MCCALLAM 4 Mccullam Mcellam Mcellum
Mccalpin MCALPINE
Mccanchie CONCHA CONCHAR CONCHIE MCCONCHIE MCCONCHY MCCONOCHIE
Mccarol CHARLETON HILLHOUSE MCKERRELL
Mccau MCGAUGH
MCCAUGHAN 4 M'caughan Macaughan Mckeighan
Mccaul MCCALL MCCOLL
Mccaull MCCALL MCCOLL
Mccaw MCGAUGH
Mccie MACKIE MCKAY MCKIE
Mcclengen CLINGAN
Mcclewr LEWERS MCCLURE MCLURE
Mcclingan CLINGAN
Mcclingand CLINGAN
Mcclingen CLINGAN
MCCLOUD MCLEOD
Mcclour LEWERS MCCLURE MCLURE
Mccloure LEWERS MCCLURE MCLURE
Mcclower LEWERS MCCLURE MCLURE
Mccluer LEWERS MCCLURE MCLURE
Mccluir LEWERS MCCLURE MCLURE
Mccluire LEWERS MCCLURE MCLURE
MCCLURE 16 LEWERS Loures Lures Maclure Mcclewr Mcclour Mccloure Mcclower Mccluer Mccluir Mccluire Mciloure Mcilure Mclewer MCLURE
MCCLUSKEY 5 Mccluskie Mcclusky Mcluskie Mclusky
Mccluskie MCCLUSKEY
Mcclusky MCCLUSKEY
MCCOLL 4 MCCALL Mccaul Mccaull
Mccolpin MCALPINE
Mcconch CONCHA CONCHAR CONCHIE MCCONCHIE MCCONCHY MCCONOCHIE
MCCONCHIE 53 Conachar Conch CONCHA Conchair CONCHAR Conchay Conchea Conchear Conched Concher Conchey Conchiar CONCHIE Conchier Conchor Conchy Concie Conckey Concky Conenochie Congie Coniqhar Conkey Conkie Conky Connachie Connalin Connochie Conqhar Conqhuar Conquer Conquher Conquie Conqut Couchie Counchie Maccanch Maccanchie Macconchie Maconochie Mccanchie Mcconch MCCONCHY Mcconcie Mccongie Mcconkie Mcconnachie Mcconnichie Mcconnochie MCCONOCHIE Mcconochy Mcconockie
MCCONCHY 53 Conachar Conch CONCHA Conchair CONCHAR Conchay Conchea Conchear Conched Concher Conchey Conchiar CONCHIE Conchier Conchor Conchy Concie Conckey Concky Conenochie Congie Coniqhar Conkey Conkie Conky Connachie Connalin Connochie Conqhar Conqhuar Conquer Conquher Conquie Conqut Couchie Counchie Maccanch Maccanchie Macconchie Maconochie Mccanchie Mcconch MCCONCHIE Mcconcie Mccongie Mcconkie Mcconnachie Mcconnichie Mcconnochie MCCONOCHIE Mcconochy Mcconockie
Mcconcie CONCHA CONCHAR CONCHIE MCCONCHIE MCCONCHY MCCONOCHIE
Mccongie CONCHA CONCHAR CONCHIE MCCONCHIE MCCONCHY MCCONOCHIE
Mcconkie CONCHA CONCHAR CONCHIE MCCONCHIE MCCONCHY MCCONOCHIE
Mcconnachie CONCHA CONCHAR CONCHIE MCCONCHIE MCCONCHY MCCONOCHIE
Mcconnichie CONCHA CONCHAR CONCHIE MCCONCHIE MCCONCHY MCCONOCHIE
Mcconnochie CONCHA CONCHAR CONCHIE MCCONCHIE MCCONCHY MCCONOCHIE
MCCONOCHIE 53 Conachar Conch CONCHA Conchair CONCHAR Conchay Conchea Conchear Conched Concher Conchey Conchiar CONCHIE Conchier Conchor Conchy Concie Conckey Concky Conenochie Congie Coniqhar Conkey Conkie Conky Connachie Connalin Connochie Conqhar Conqhuar Conquer Conquher Conquie Conqut Couchie Counchie Maccanch Maccanchie Macconchie Maconochie Mccanchie Mcconch MCCONCHIE MCCONCHY Mcconcie Mccongie Mcconkie Mcconnachie Mcconnichie Mcconnochie Mcconochy Mcconockie
Mcconochy CONCHA CONCHAR CONCHIE MCCONCHIE MCCONCHY MCCONOCHIE
Mcconockie CONCHA CONCHAR CONCHIE MCCONCHIE MCCONCHY MCCONOCHIE
Mccoppin MCALPINE
Mccorley MCCURLEY
Mccorpin MCALPINE
MCCOWAN COWAN
MCCRACKEN MCCRACKIN
MCCRACKIN MCCRACKEN
Mccraddie MCCREADIE MCCREADY MCCREDIE
Mccradie MCCREADIE MCCREADY MCCREDIE
MCCREADIE 12 Maccreadie Macready Mccraddie Mccradie MCCREADY Mccreddie Mccreddy MCCREDIE Mccredy Mcgraddy Mcgrady
MCCREADY 14 Maccreadie Maccready Macready Mccraddie Mccradie MCCREADIE Mccreddie Mccreddy MCCREDIE Mccredy Mcgraddy Mcgrady Mcready
Mccreddie MCCREADIE MCCREADY MCCREDIE
Mccreddy MCCREADIE MCCREADY MCCREDIE
MCCREDIE 12 Maccreadie Macready Mccraddie Mccradie MCCREADIE MCCREADY Mccreddie Mccreddy Mccredy Mcgraddy Mcgrady
Mccredy MCCREADIE MCCREADY MCCREDIE
Mccrustian MACQUISTEN MCQUISTON
Mccuestian MACQUISTEN MCQUISTON
Mccuestion MACQUISTEN MCQUISTON
Mccuistain MACQUISTEN MCQUISTON
Mccuisten MACQUISTEN MCQUISTON
Mccuister MACQUISTEN MCQUISTON
Mccuistians MACQUISTEN MCQUISTON
Mccuistin MACQUISTEN MCQUISTON
Mccuistion MACQUISTEN MCQUISTON
Mccuiston MACQUISTEN MCQUISTON
Mccullam MCCALLAM
MCCUNE 4 MCEWAN MCEWEN MCKUNE
MCCURLEY Makerly Mccorley
Mccusten MACQUISTEN MCQUISTON
Mccustin MACQUISTEN MCQUISTON
Mccuston MACQUISTEN MCQUISTON
MCDONAL MCDONALD
MCDONALD 4 MACDONALD MCDONAL MCDONNELL
MCDONNELL MCDONALD
MCDOUGAL 4 MCDOWALL MCDOWELL Mcdugal
MCDOWALL 4 MCDOUGAL MCDOWELL Mcdugal
Mcdowel MACDUELL
MCDOWELL 4 MCDOUGAL MCDOWALL Mcdugal
Mcduell MACDUELL
Mcduff CUFFE DUFF DUFFY KILDUFF
Mcduffey CUFFE DUFF DUFFY KILDUFF
Mcdugal MCDOUGAL MCDOWALL MCDOWELL
Mceachern MCKECHNIE
Mcegan EGAN KEEGAN
Mcellam MCCALLAM
Mcellum MCCALLAM
MCEWAN 6 Macewan MCCUNE MCEWEN MCKEOWN MCKUNE
MCEWEN 6 Macewan MCCUNE MCEWAN MCKEOWN MCKUNE
MCFARLAN MCFARLANE
MCFARLANE MCFARLAN
MCGAUGH 5 Mccau Mccaw MCGEOUGH MCGOUGH
MCGEE MCGHEE Mcgie
Mcgenet MCJANNETT
MCGEO Mcgeogh
Mcgeogh MCGEO
MCGEORGE 4 Macjore MCJORE Mcjorys
MCGEOUGH MCGAUGH MCGOUGH
MCGHEE 4 MCGEE MCGHIE Mcgie
MCGHIE MCGHEE
MCGHRAN M'garran Mghren
Mcgie MCGEE MCGHEE
Mcgilhauch MILHENCH
Mcgoffock MCGUFFIE MCGUFFOG
Mcgoffog MCGUFFIE MCGUFFOG
MCGOUGH MCGAUGH MCGEOUGH
MCGOWAN Magowan Mcgurran
Mcgraddy MCCREADIE MCCREADY MCCREDIE
Mcgrady MCCREADIE MCCREADY MCCREDIE
Mcgreagor GRIGOR MACGREGOR MCGREGOR
MCGREAVY Mcgreevy
Mcgreevy MCGREAVY
Mcgreger GRIGOR MACGREGOR

If the name you are interested in is not here, try Section C.

MCGREGOR
MCGREGOR 15 Gregor GRIGOR M'gregor M'grigor MACGREGOR Macgrigor Mackgregor Mackgrigor Mcgreagor Mcgreger Mcgreogar Mcgrigor Mckgregor Mckgrigor
Mcgreogar GRIGOR MACGREGOR MCGREGOR
Mcgrigor GRIGOR MACGREGOR MCGREGOR
Mcgrouther MCGRUTHER
MCGRUTHER Mcgrouther
MCGUFFIE 4 Mcgoffock Mcgoffog MCGUFFOG
MCGUFFOG 4 Mcgoffock Mcgoffog MCGUFFIE
Mcgurran MCGOWAN
MCHALE MICHAEL
Mchoustone MACQUISTEN MCQUISTON
Mchuistonn MACQUISTEN MCQUISTON
Mchutcheon MACQUISTEN MCQUISTON
Mciihaush MILHENCH
Mcilduff CUFFE DUFF DUFFY KILDUFF
Mciloure LEWERS MCCLURE MCLURE
Mcilure LEWERS MCCLURE MCLURE
Mcinnis MAGINNIS
MCINTOSH MACINTOSH MACKINTOSH
Mciwham MEIKLEHAM
MCJANNETT 4 Mcgenet Mcjenet Mcjennett
Mcjenet MCJANNETT
Mcjennett MCJANNETT
MCJORE 4 Macjore MCGEORGE Mcjorys
Mcjorys MCGEORGE MCJORE
MCKAY 6 MACKAY MACKIE Mccie Mckey MCKIE
MCKECHNIE Mceachern
Mckeegan EGAN KEEGAN
Mckeighan MCCAUGHAN
MCKENZIE 4 M'KENZIE MACKENZIE Mckinzie
MCKEOWN 4 Macewan MCEWAN MCEWEN
MCKERRELL 9 Carleton Carol CHARLETON HILLHOUSE Kerrill Mackerel Mccarol Mckerrill
Mckerrill CHARLETON HILLHOUSE MCKERRELL
Mckey MACKIE MCKAY MCKIE
Mckgregor GRIGOR MACGREGOR MCGREGOR
Mckgrigor GRIGOR MACGREGOR MCGREGOR
MCKIE 5 MACKIE Mccie MCKAY Mckey
Mckilhauche MILHENCH
Mckinzie MCKENZIE
Mckqueistein MACQUISTEN MCQUISTON
Mckquestein MACQUISTEN MCQUISTON
MCKUNE 4 MCCUNE MCEWAN MCEWEN
Mclaghlin MCLAUGHLAN
MCLAREN 4 Mclauran Mclauren MCLAURIN
MCLAUGHLAN 4 Mclaghlin Mclauglan Mclauglin
MCLAUGHLIN MAGLOCHLAINN
Mclauglan MCLAUGHLAN
Mclauglin MCLAUGHLAN
Mclauran MCLAREN MCLAURIN
Mclauren MCLAREN MCLAURIN
MCLAURIN 4 MCLAREN Mclauran Mclauren
Mclaws LAW LAWES LAWS
MCLEAN M'lean MACLEAN
MCLEOD MACLEOD MCCLOUD
Mclewer LEWERS MCCLURE MCLURE
Mclquham MEIKLEHAM
MCLURE 16 LEWERS Loures Lures Maclure Mcclewr Mcclour Mccloure Mcclower Mccluer Mccluir Mccluire MCCLURE Mciloure Mcilure Mclewer
Mcluskie MCCLUSKEY
Mclusky MCCLUSKEY
MCMAHON Macmahon
MCMAIN 34 MACKMAN Mackmen MACKMIN Mackminn Macmain Macmaine Macmane Macmean Macmin Makmin Makmun Mcmean Mcmeans Mcmeen Mcmein Mcmen Mcmenn Mcmim Mcmin Mcmina Mcmine Mcmines MCMINN Mcminne Mcminnies Mcminnis Mcmuin Mcmunn Mcmuns Mcmyn Mcmyne Mcmynn Muckmen
Mcmean MACKMAN MACKMIN MCMAIN MCMINN
Mcmeans MACKMAN MACKMIN MCMAIN MCMINN
Mcmeen MACKMAN MACKMIN MCMAIN MCMINN
Mcmein MACKMAN MACKMIN MCMAIN MCMINN
Mcmen MACKMAN MACKMIN MCMAIN MCMINN
Mcmenn MACKMAN MACKMIN MCMAIN MCMINN
Mcmim MACKMAN MACKMIN MCMAIN MCMINN
Mcmin MACKMAN MACKMIN MCMAIN MCMINN
Mcmina MACKMAN MACKMIN MCMAIN MCMINN
Mcmine MACKMAN MACKMIN MCMAIN MCMINN
Mcmines MACKMAN MACKMIN MCMAIN MCMINN
MCMINN 34 MACKMAN Mackmen MACKMIN Mackminn Macmain Macmaine Macmane Macmean Macmin Makmin Makmun MCMAIN Mcmean Mcmeans Mcmeen Mcmein Mcmen Mcmenn Mcmim Mcmin Mcmina Mcmine Mcmines Mcminne Mcminnies Mcminnis Mcmuin Mcmunn Mcmuns Mcmyn Mcmyne Mcmynn Muckmen
Mcminne MACKMAN MACKMIN MCMAIN MCMINN
Mcminnies MACKMAN MACKMIN MCMAIN MCMINN
Mcminnis MACKMAN MACKMIN MCMAIN MCMINN
Mcmuin MACKMAN MACKMIN MCMAIN MCMINN
MCMULLEN MCMULLIN
MCMULLIN MCMULLEN
Mcmunn MACKMAN MACKMIN MCMAIN MCMINN
Mcmuns MACKMAN MACKMIN MCMAIN MCMINN
Mcmyn MACKMAN MACKMIN MACMYN MCMAIN MCMINN
Mcmyne MACKMAN MACKMIN MCMAIN MCMINN
Mcmynn MACKMAN MACKMIN MCMAIN MCMINN
Mcnairn NAIRN NAIRNE
Mcnairna NAIRN NAIRNE
Mcnairne NAIRN NAIRNE
Mcname MCNAMEE
MCNAMEE Macknamay Mcname
MCNEIL 4 MCNEILL NEIL NEILL
MCNEILL 4 MCNEIL NEIL NEILL
MCPHEE MCPHIE
MCPHIE MCPHEE
Mcquest MACQUISTEN MCQUISTON
Mcqueston MACQUISTEN MCQUISTON
Mcquiften MACQUISTEN MCQUISTON
Mcquifton MACQUISTEN MCQUISTON
Mcquinston MACQUISTEN MCQUISTON
Mcquistan MACQUISTEN MCQUISTON
Mcquisten MACQUISTEN MCQUISTON
Mcquistian MACQUISTEN MCQUISTON
Mcquistin MACQUISTEN MCQUISTON
Mcquistion MACQUISTEN MCQUISTON
MCQUISTON 109 Coistain Eysteinn Huisdean Huisdeinn M'cristain M'cristan M'cuistan M'cuisten M'cuistin M'cuiston M'huchison M'huison M'hustan M'qhuiston M'queaston M'queestan M'queeston M'queiftoun M'queisoun M'queistene M'queistine M'quesistein M'questan M'questen M'questin M'questine M'question M'queston M'quiestan M'quistan M'quistein M'quisten M'quistin M'quistine M'quistion M'quiston M'uistine M'utchon Maccoistain Maccuiston Machuison Mackuisten Macqueechan Macqueifstoun Macquesten Macquestian Macquestion Macquiftion Macquistan Macquistani Macquistation MACQUISTEN Macquister Macquistin Macquistini Macquistion Macquiston Macuistian Macuiston Macwhistan Macwhiston Macwisdon Maquiston Mccrustian Mccuestian Mccuestion Mccuistain Mccuisten Mccuister Mccuistians Mccuistin Mccuistion Mccuiston Mccusten Mccustin Mccuston Mchoustone Mchuistonn Mchutcheon Mckqueistein Mckquestein Mcquest Mcqueston Mcquiften Mcquifton Mcquinston Mcquistan Mcquisten Mcquistian Mcquistin Mcquistion Mcquseten Mcqustin Mcqustion Mcquston Mcuisten Mcuisthon Mcuistian Mcuistine Mcuistion Mcuiston Mcwhiston Meccustin Mkhuthin Mkhutkhon Mkquefton Mkquiton Monfcuiftion
Mcquseten MACQUISTEN MCQUISTON
Mcqustin MACQUISTEN MCQUISTON
Mcqustion MACQUISTEN MCQUISTON
Mcquston MACQUISTEN MCQUISTON
MCRAE MACRAE
Mcready MCCREADY
Mcstoile HOWELL STAVOLD STAWELL STOWELL STOYLE
Mcstole HOWELL STAVOLD STAWELL STOWELL STOYLE
Mcthomas THOMPSON THOMSON THOMSONE
Mcuisten MACQUISTEN MCQUISTON
Mcuisthon MACQUISTEN MCQUISTON
Mcuistian MACQUISTEN MCQUISTON
Mcuistine MACQUISTEN MCQUISTON
Mcuistion MACQUISTEN MCQUISTON
Mcuiston MACQUISTEN MCQUISTON
MCVAY MCVEIGH Mcvey
MCVEIGH MCVAY Mcvey
Mcvey MCVAY MCVEIGH
Mcwha MEWHA
Mcwhiston MACQUISTEN MCQUISTON
Meacock MAYCOCK
MEAD 11 Made Maid Mayde MEADE MEADS Meaith Meath Meatt Meed Mesid
MEADE 10 Made Maid Mayde MEAD Meaith Meath Meatt Meed Mesid
MEADEN 7 Madin MAIDEN Mayden Meadon Meaton Medam
Meades MEADS MEEDS
Meadon MEADEN
Meadowe MEADOWS PIERREPONT
MEADOWS 9 De medewe De wythnesham Meadowe Medew Medewe Medowe Midhouse PIERREPONT
MEADS 5 MEAD Meades Medes MEEDS
MEAGHER MAHER
Meaith MEAD MEADE
MEAKIN 7 Meaking Meakings MEAKINS MEEHAN Mekins O'meehan
Meaking MAKINS MEAKIN MEAKINS
Meakings MAKINS MEAKIN MEAKINS
MEAKINS 6 MEAKIN Meaking Meakings Meekins Mekins
MEAL 5 MALE Meale Meel Meele
Meale MEAL
MEALEMOUTH 19 HELMOTH MEALMOUTH Meldmouthis MELEMOUTH MELLMOUTHE Melmath MELMETH Melmore MELMOTH Melmoth-brooks Melmott MELMOUTH Melmouthes Melwoth Milmoth Milmouthes Molmoth WELMOTH
Mealey MELIA MELLEY

If the name you are interested in is not here, try Section C.

O'MALLEY
MEALMOUTH 19 HELMOTH MEALEMOUTH Meldmouthis MELEMOUTH MELLMOUTHE Melmath MELMETH Melmore MELMOTH Melmoth-brooks Melmott MELMOUTH Melmouthes Melwoth Milmoth Milmouthes Molmoth WELMOTH
Mean MIEN
MEAR 11 MAIN MAIR MANE MARE MAYER MAYERS MAYNE MAYOR MEYER MEYERS
Meara MARA O'MARA
MEARE 5 MARE MAYER MAYERS MERE
Meares MEARS MEERS MERES
MEARS 4 Meares MEERS MERES
Measley MESLEY
MEASURES Measurier
Measurier MEASURES
MEATCHAM Metcham MITCHAM
Meath MEAD MEADE
Meatheringham METHERINGHAM
Meaton MEADEN
Meatt MEAD MEADE
Meavin MABIN MAVIN MAVINS
Meavine MABIN MAVIN MAVINS
Meccustin MACQUISTEN MCQUISTON
Mechan MEEHAN
Meckleburgh MECKLENBURGH MICKLEBOROUGH MICKLEBURGH
MECKLENBURGH 7 Meckleburgh Mickelburgh Mickleboro MICKLEBOROUGH MICKLEBURGH Muckleburgh
Mecock MAYCOCK
Mecraft HAYCRAFT HAYCROFT MACROFT MAYCRAFT MAYCROFT MEDCROFT MOORCROFT
Mecroft HAYCRAFT HAYCROFT MACROFT MAYCRAFT MAYCROFT MEDCROFT MOORCROFT
Mecuk MAYCOCK
Medam MEADEN
MEDCALF 11 Madchoff Makoff Matcalf Medcalfe Medtcalf Medtcalfe METCALF METCALFE Metcalph Metcelf
Medcalfe MEDCALF METCALF METCALFE
MEDCRAFT 7 Madcalf Madcalfe MEDCROFT METCALF METCALFE Mitcraft
MEDCROFT 21 Hacraste HAYCRAFT HAYCROFT Macraft Macraste MACROFT Madcalf Madcalfe Makecraft Marcroft MAYCRAFT Maycraught MAYCROFT Mecraft Mecroft MEDCRAFT METCALF METCALFE Mitcraft MOORCROFT
Medes MEADS MEEDS
Medew MEADOWS PIERREPONT
Medewe MEADOWS PIERREPONT
MEDGETT 4 Megett Midgett Midgitt
Medgley MESLEY MIDGLEY
Medilton MIDDLETON
Medleton MIDDLETON
Medne MEDNIS
MEDNIS Medne
Medowe MEADOWS PIERREPONT
Medtcalf MEDCALF METCALF METCALFE
Medtcalfe MEDCALF METCALF METCALFE
Meduana MANNY MAYNE MAYNEY
Medulton MIDDLETON
MEE Meigh
Meechan MEEHAN
Meed MEAD MEADE
MEEDS 4 Meades MEADS Medes
MEEHAN 6 MEAKIN Mechan Meechan Michan O'meehan
Meeking MAKINS
Meekings MAKINS
Meekins MEAKINS
Meel MEAL
Meele MEAL
MEERS 4 Meares MEARS MERES
Meesham NEESHAM
MEETEN 6 Meetens Meeting Meetten MITTON MUTTON
Meetens MEETEN MITTON MUTTON
Meeting MEETEN MITTON MUTTON
Meetten MEETEN MITTON MUTTON
Meg MAGGS MEGGS MOGG
Megett MEDGETT
MEGGINSON 4 MAGSON MEGGISON MEGSON
MEGGISON 4 MAGSON MEGGINSON MEGSON
MEGGS 6 Magges MAGGS Mags Meg MOGG
MEGSON 4 MAGSON MEGGINSON MEGGISON
MEHARG Macharg Maharg
Meigh MEE
MEIKLEHAM Mciwham Mclquham
Mein MIEN
Mekins MEAKIN MEAKINS
MELBOURNE 4 MILBORNE MILBOURN MILBOURNE
Meldmouthis HELMOTH MEALEMOUTH MEALMOUTH MELEMOUTH MELLMOUTHE MELMETH MELMOTH MELMOUTH WELMOTH
Meldread MILDRED
MELEMOUTH 19 HELMOTH MEALEMOUTH MEALMOUTH Meldmouthis MELLMOUTHE Melmath MELMETH Melmore MELMOTH Melmoth-brooks Melmott MELMOUTH Melmouthes Melwoth Milmoth Milmouthes Molmoth WELMOTH
Melhish MELHUISH MELLISH
MELHUISH 4 Melhish MELLISH Melluish
MELIA 5 Malia Malley Mealey O'MALLEY
Melksham MELSOM MILSOM
MELLEY 4 Mealey Melly Meloy
Mellidge MILLEDGE
MELLISH 4 Melhish MELHUISH Melluish
MELLMOUTHE 19 HELMOTH MEALEMOUTH MEALMOUTH Meldmouthis MELEMOUTH Melmath MELMETH Melmore MELMOTH Melmoth-brooks Melmott MELMOUTH Melmouthes Melwoth Milmoth Milmouthes Molmoth WELMOTH
Mellrid MILDRED
MELLSOP Melsop Melsopp
Melluish MELHUISH MELLISH
Melly MELLEY
Melmath HELMOTH MEALEMOUTH MEALMOUTH MELEMOUTH MELLMOUTHE MELMETH MELMOTH MELMOUTH WELMOTH
MELMETH 19 HELMOTH MEALEMOUTH MEALMOUTH Meldmouthis MELEMOUTH MELLMOUTHE Melmath Melmore MELMOTH Melmoth-brooks Melmott MELMOUTH Melmouthes Melwoth Milmoth Milmouthes Molmoth WELMOTH
Melmore HELMOTH MEALEMOUTH MEALMOUTH MELEMOUTH MELLMOUTHE MELMETH MELMOTH MELMOUTH WELMOTH
MELMOTH 19 HELMOTH MEALEMOUTH MEALMOUTH Meldmouthis MELEMOUTH MELLMOUTHE Melmath MELMETH Melmore Melmoth-brooks Melmott MELMOUTH Melmouthes Melwoth Milmoth Milmouthes Molmoth WELMOTH
Melmoth-brooks HELMOTH MEALEMOUTH MEALMOUTH MELEMOUTH MELLMOUTHE MELMETH MELMOTH MELMOUTH WELMOTH
Melmott HELMOTH MEALEMOUTH MEALMOUTH MELEMOUTH MELLMOUTHE MELMETH MELMOTH MELMOUTH WELMOTH
MELMOUTH 19 HELMOTH MEALEMOUTH MEALMOUTH Meldmouthis MELEMOUTH MELLMOUTHE Melmath MELMETH Melmore MELMOTH Melmoth-brooks Melmott Melmouthes Melwoth Milmoth Milmouthes Molmoth WELMOTH
Melmouthes HELMOTH MEALEMOUTH MEALMOUTH MELEMOUTH MELLMOUTHE MELMETH MELMOTH MELMOUTH WELMOTH
Meloy MELLEY
Melroy MALROY
MELSOM 8 Melksham MELSOME Melson Melsum Milksham MILSOM Milsum
MELSOME MELSOM Melson
Melson MELSOM MELSOME
Melsop MELLSOP
Melsopp MELLSOP
Melsum MELSOM MILSOM
MELVILLE MELVIN
MELVIN MELVILLE
MELWAYE Millway
Melwoth HELMOTH MEALEMOUTH MEALMOUTH MELEMOUTH MELLMOUTHE MELMETH MELMOTH MELMOUTH WELMOTH
Melwyche MILLEDGE
Membery MEMBREY MEMORY MOWBRAY
MEMBREY 9 Mambery Membery Membry Memmery Memorry MEMORY Mowbery MOWBRAY
Membrun MOMBRUN
Membry MEMBREY MEMORY MOWBRAY
Memmery MEMBREY MEMORY MOWBRAY
Memorry MEMBREY MEMORY MOWBRAY
MEMORY 9 Mambery Membery MEMBREY Membry Memmery Memorry Mowbery MOWBRAY
Menadew MENADUE
Menadu MENADUE
MENADUE 5 Menadew Menadu Menardea Minidue
Menardea MENADUE
Menday MONDAY MONDEY MUNDAY MUNDIE MUNDY
Mendey MONDAY MONDEY MUNDAY MUNDIE MUNDY
Mendie MONDAY MONDEY MUNDAY MUNDIE MUNDY
Mendy MONDAY MONDEY MUNDAY MUNDIE MUNDY
MENEAR MANHIRE Minear
Meness MENZIES
Mengeis MENZIES
Menges MENZIES
Mengies MENZIES
Mengus MENZIES
Mengzies MENZIES
Meniss MENZIES
Mennar MENNIM
Mennell MEYNELL
Mennill MEYNELL MONNELL
MENNIM 4 Mannon Mennar Menon
Menon MENNIM
Mensies MENZIES
Menyeis MENZIES
Menzeis MENZIES
Menzie MENZIES
MENZIES 16 Mansey Meness Mengeis Menges Mengies Mengus Mengzies Meniss Mensies Menyeis Menzeis Menzie Minges Moinzies Mowncey
Mercden MARSDEN
MERCER 4 MACER MARCER MASSER
MERCHANT 5 MARCHANT Marchante Marchent Merchante
Merchante MARCHANT MERCHANT
MercIden MARSDEN
Merclesden MARSDEN
MERCOTE MURCOTT
Merdex MORDUE
MERDON Mardon
Merdox MORDUE
Merdu MORDUE
Merdy MORDUE
Merdyson MORDUE
MERE 5 MARE MAYER MAYERS MEARE
Merel MERRILL
Merelelew MERRELEW
Merelewe MERRELEW
Merell MERRILL
Merely MARLEY
MERES 4 Meares MEARS MEERS
Merick MERRICK MEYRICK
Merie MERRY MYRRY
Meriell MERRILL
Meriet MERRETT MERRITT
Merike MERRICK MEYRICK
Merill MERRILL
Meriman MERRIMAN MERRYMAN
Meriot MARRIOTT MERRIT
Merit MERRETT MERRITT
Meriton MERRINGTON
Merlsden MARSDEN

If the name you are interested in is not here, try Section C.

Merner MERNOR
MERNOR Merner
Merot MERRETT MERRITT
MERRALL Merrell MERRILL
Merrat MERRETT MERRITT
Merrel MERRILL
MERRELEW 4 Merelelew Merelewe Merrelewe
Merrelewe MERRELEW
Merrell MERRALL MERRILL MURRELL MURRELLS
Merrells MURRELL MURRELLS
MERRETT 10 De meriet Marrett Meriet Merit Merot Merrat Merriott MERRITT Meryt
MERRICK 10 Merick Merike Merricke Merryck Meryck MEYRICK Meyricke Myrech Myrick
Merricke MERRICK MEYRICK
Merrieman MERRIMAN MERRYMAN
Merril MERRILL
MERRILEES Moraly Morraleez
MERRILL 10 Merel Merell Meriell Merill MERRALL Merrel Merrell Merril Meryl
MERRIMAN 5 Meriman Merrieman MERRYMAN Mirryman
MERRINGTON Meriton
Merriott MERRETT MERRITT
MERRIT 5 Mariot MARRIOTT Marrit Meriot
MERRITT 10 De meriet Marrett Meriet Merit Merot Merrat MERRETT Merriott Meryt
MERRY 6 Merie Mirrey Mirrie Mirry MYRRY
Merrychurch MARYCHURCH
Merryck MERRICK MEYRICK
MERRYMAN 5 Meriman Merrieman MERRIMAN Mirryman
Mersceden MARSDEN
Mersden MARSDEN MARSDIN MARSTON
MERSH MARSH Mesh
Mershal MARSHAL
Mertell MURTELL
Merton MORETON MORTON MURTON
Meryck MERRICK MEYRICK
Meryl MERRILL
Meryt MERRETT MERRITT
Mesceter MESSETER
Meseter MESSETER
Mesh MARSH MERSH
Mesid MEAD MEADE
Mesiter MESSETER
MESLEY 4 Measley Medgley Messley
MESSENGER Massinger Messinger
MESSER Messom
MESSETER 5 Mesceter Meseter Mesiter Messiter
Messinger MESSENGER
Messiter MESSETER
Messley MESLEY
Messom MESSER
Messurier LE MESSURIER
Mesters MASTERS
Mesurier LE MESSURIER
METCALF 11 Madcalf Madcalfe MEDCALF Medcalfe MEDCRAFT MEDCROFT Medtcalf Medtcalfe METCALFE Mitcraft
METCALFE 16 Madcalf Madcalfe Madchoff Makoff Matcalf MEDCALF Medcalfe MEDCRAFT MEDCROFT Medtcalf Medtcalfe METCALF Metcalph Metcelf Mitcraft
Metcalph MEDCALF METCALFE
Metcelf MEDCALF METCALFE
Metcham MEATCHAM MITCHAM
Metherall METHERELL
METHERELL Metherall Mythrell
METHERINGHAM Meatheringham
Metsom METSON
METSON 4 Metsom Midsom Mitsom
Meulles MULES
Meurilyon MOURILYAN
Meven MABIN MAVIN MAVINS
Mevens MABIN MAVIN MAVINS
Mevins MABIN MAVIN MAVINS
MEWHA Mcwha
Mewles MULES
Mewrillon MOURILYAN
MEWTON Mouton Muton
Mexstead MAXTED
MEYER 8 MAIR MARE MAYER MAYERS MAYOR MEAR MEYERS
MEYERS 7 MAIR MARE MAYER MAYERS MEAR MEYER
MEYNELL 5 Mennell Mennill Minnell MONNELL
MEYRICK 10 Merick Merike MERRICK Merricke Merryck Meryck Meyricke Myrech Myrick
Meyricke MERRICK MEYRICK
Mghren MCGHRAN
Mial MIALL MYHILL
MIALL 4 Mial Myal MYHILL
MICHAEL MCHALE
Michan MEEHAN
MICHEL MITCHEL MITCHELL
MICHELL MITCHELL
MICHELSON 8 Michinson Mitcheison MITCHELSON Mitchenson Mitcheson MITCHINSON Mitchison
Michinson MICHELSON MITCHELSON MITCHINSON
Mickelburgh MECKLENBURGH MICKLEBOROUGH MICKLEBURGH
Mickelwricht MICKLEWRIGHT
Mickelwright MICKLEWRIGHT
Mickleboro MECKLENBURGH MICKLEBOROUGH MICKLEBURGH
MICKLEBOROUGH 7 Meckleburgh MECKLENBURGH Mickelburgh Mickleboro MICKLEBURGH Muckleburgh
MICKLEBURGH 7 Meckleburgh MECKLENBURGH Mickelburgh Mickleboro MICKLEBOROUGH Muckleburgh
MICKLEWRIGHT 4 Mickelwricht Mickelwright Micklwright
Micklwright MICKLEWRIGHT
Micol NICHOL
MIDDLETON 6 Medilton Medleton Medulton Midleton Myddleton
MIDGELEY MIDGLEY
Midgett MEDGETT
Midgitt MEDGETT
MIDGLEY Medgley MIDGELEY
Midhouse MEADOWS
Midleton MIDDLETON
Midsom METSON
MIDWINTER Mywynter
Miels MILES
MIEN Mean Mein
Miffling MIFLIN
MIFLIN Miffling Miphlin
Milage MILLEDGE
Milam MILEHAM MYLAM
MILBANK Millbank
MILBORNE 4 MELBOURNE MILBOURN MILBOURNE
MILBOURN 4 MELBOURNE MILBORNE MILBOURNE
MILBOURNE 4 MELBOURNE MILBORNE MILBOURN
Milden MILDON
MILDON 4 Milden Mylden Myldon
Mildread MILDRED
MILDRED 10 Meldread Mellrid Mildread Mildredge Mildrett Milldred Milred Milridge Mylrede
Mildredge MILDRED
Mildrett MILDRED
MILEHAM 4 Milam Millham MYLAM
Miler MILLER
MILES Miels
MILHENCH 17 M'gilhauche M'gilhauk Macgilhauch Macgillhench Macilhench Magilhauche Makclouch Makgilhauch Makgillhauch Makkilauche Makkillauche Makylhauche Mcgilhauch Mciihaush Mckilhauche Millhench
Milichamp MILLICHAMP MILLICHIP
Milichip MILLICHAMP MILLICHIP
Milinton MILLINGTON
Milksham MELSOM MILSOM
MILL 6 MILLES MILLS Miln MILNE Mylles
MILLAR MILLER MILNER
MILLARD MILLER MILLWARD
Millbank MILBANK
Milldred MILDRED
MILLEDGE 6 Mellidge Melwyche Milage Millidge Molledge
MILLER 9 Miler MILLAR MILLARD MILLNER Milnar MILNER Milnor Mylner
MILLES 4 MILL MILLS Mylles
Millham MILEHAM MYLAM
Millhench MILHENCH
MILLICHAMP 7 Milichamp Milichip Millichap MILLICHIP Millichop Millichope
Millichap MILLICHAMP
MILLICHIP 4 Milichamp Milichip MILLICHAMP
Millichop MILLICHAMP
Millichope MILLICHAMP
Millidge MILLEDGE
Milligeton MILLINGTON
MILLINER MILLNER MILNER
MILLINGTON 6 Milinton Milligeton Millinton Mulyncon Myllington
Millinton MILLINGTON
MILLNER 7 MILLER MILLINER Milnar MILNER Milnor Mylner
Millns MILNES
MILLS 5 MILL MILLES MILNES Mylles
Millstone MILSON
MILLWARD 5 MILLARD Millwood MILWARD Milwood
Millway MELWAYE
Millwood MILLWARD MILWARD
Milmoth HELMOTH MEALEMOUTH MEALMOUTH MELEMOUTH MELLMOUTHE MELMETH MELMOTH MELMOUTH WELMOTH
Milmouthes HELMOTH MEALEMOUTH MEALMOUTH MELEMOUTH MELLMOUTHE MELMETH MELMOTH MELMOUTH WELMOTH
Miln MILL MILNE
Milnar MILLER MILLNER MILNER
MILNE MILL Miln
MILNER 8 MILLAR MILLER MILLINER MILLNER Milnar Milnor Mylner
MILNES 4 Millns MILLS Milns
Milnor MILLER MILLNER MILNER
Milns MILNES
Milred MILDRED
Milridge MILDRED
Milroy MALROY
MILSOM 7 Melksham MELSOM Melsum Milksham MILSON Milsum
MILSON Millstone MILSOM
Milsum MELSOM MILSOM
MILWARD 4 MILLWARD Millwood Milwood
Milwood MILLWARD MILWARD
Mimack MIMMACK
Mimbrun MOMBRUN
Mimes MIMMS
MIMMACK Mimack Mimmock
Mimmes MIMMS
Mimmock MIMMACK
MIMMS 4 Mimes Mimmes Mims
Mims MIMMS
Minday MONDAY MONDEY MUNDAY MUNDIE MUNDY
Mindey MONDAY MONDEY MUNDAY MUNDIE MUNDY
Mindie MONDAY MONDEY MUNDAY MUNDIE MUNDY
Mindy MONDAY MONDEY MUNDAY MUNDIE MUNDY
Minear MANHIRE MENEAR
Minell MINNEY
MINERS 6 De mineriis De miners De mynors MINORS MYNORS
Miney MINNEY
Minges MENZIES
Minidue MENADUE
Minin MINNEY
Minnal MINNEY
Minnell MEYNELL MINNEY MONNELL
MINNEY 9 Minell Miney Minin Minnal Minnell Minnie Minny Miny
Minnie MINNEY
Minny MINNEY
MINORS MINERS
Minshall MINSHULL
MINSHULL Minshall Mynshule
MINTA 6 Le meneter MINTER Mintor Myntor Myntur
Mintar MINTER

If the name you are interested in is not here, try Section C.

MINTER 9 Le meneter MINTA Mintar Mintor Myntar Mynter Myntor Myntur
MINTERN Minterne MINTON
Minterne MINTERN MINTON
Mintie MINTY
MINTON MINTERN Minterne
Mintor MINTA MINTER
MINTY Mintie
Miny MINNEY
Miphlin MIFLIN
Mirrey MERRY
Mirrie MERRY MYRRY
Mirry MERRY MYRRY
Mirryman MERRIMAN MERRYMAN
Mirtell MURTELL
Mison MISSON MYSON
Misprat MUSPRATT
Mispratt MUSPRATT
MISSON 4 Mison MYSON Mysson
MITCHAM MEATCHAM Metcham
Mitcheison MICHELSON MITCHELSON MITCHINSON
MITCHEL MICHEL MITCHELL
MITCHELL 4 MICHEL MICHELL MITCHEL
Mitchellson MITCHELSON
MITCHELSON 9 MICHELSON Michinson Mitcheison Mitchellson Mitchenson Mitcheson MITCHINSON Mitchison
Mitchenson MICHELSON MITCHELSON MITCHINSON
Mitcheson MICHELSON MITCHELSON MITCHINSON
MITCHINSON 8 MICHELSON Michinson Mitcheison MITCHELSON Mitchenson Mitcheson Mitchison
Mitchison MICHELSON MITCHELSON MITCHINSON
Mitcraft MEDCRAFT MEDCROFT METCALF METCALFE
MITHAM 4 Mithem Mittham Mytham
Mithem MITHAM
Mitre MITTER
Mitsom METSON
MITTER Mitre
Mittham MITHAM
MITTON 7 MEETEN Meetens Meeting Meetten MUTTON MYTTON
Mkhuthin MACQUISTEN MCQUISTON
Mkhutkhon MACQUISTEN MCQUISTON
Mkquefton MACQUISTEN MCQUISTON
Mkquiton MACQUISTEN MCQUISTON
MOAR MOIR MORE
MOAT Moate Mote
Moate MOAT
MOBBERLEY 5 Mobberly MOBERLEY Moberly Mobley
Mobberly MOBBERLEY MOBERLEY
MOBERLEY 5 MOBBERLEY Mobberly Moberly Mobley
Moberly MOBBERLEY MOBERLEY
Mobley MOBBERLEY MOBERLEY
MOCK Mocke Mok
Mockcy MOXEY MOXLEY MOXSY
Mocke MOCK
Mockey MOXEY MOXLEY MOXSY
MOCKRIDGE MOGRIDGE Muckridge
Mocksay MOXEY MOXLEY MOXSY
Modell MUDDLE MUDLE
Modicliff MOLDICLIFF
Modicliffe MOLDICLIFF
Moels MULES
MOFFAT 6 MOFFATT Moffet Moffett Moffit MOFFITT
MOFFATT 6 MOFFAT Moffet Moffett Moffit MOFFITT
Moffet MOFFAT MOFFATT MOFFITT MORFETT MURFITT
Moffett MOFFAT MOFFATT MOFFITT MORFETT MURFITT
Moffit MOFFAT MOFFATT MOFFITT
MOFFITT 6 MOFFAT MOFFATT Moffet Moffett Moffit
MOGG 7 Magges MAGGS Mags Meg MEGGS MUGG
MOGRIDGE MOCKRIDGE Muckridge
Mohane MAHON MAHONE
Mohon MOHUN
MOHUN Mohon
MOIGNE 9 Le moigne MONCK MONK Monke MONKS Moyne Munck Munk
Moinzies MENZIES
MOIR 6 MARR MOAR MOORE MORE MUIR
Moise MORSE MOSS MOYES MOYSE
MOISEY 7 Moissy MOYSEY Moysie Moysse Moysy Moyzey
Moissy MOISEY MOYSEY
Mok MOCK
MOLD 8 Molde MOLE MOUL MOULD Moulde MOULE MOULES
Molde MOLD MOLE MOUL MOULD MOULE
MOLDICLIFF 12 Modicliff Modicliffe Moldicliffe Moodycliff Moodycliffe Mouldercliff Mouldercliffe Mouldeycliff Mouldeycliffe Mouldicliff Mouldicliffe
Moldicliffe MOLDICLIFF
MOLE 8 MOLD Molde MOUL MOULD Moulde MOULE MOULES
Molett MOLLET MOLLETT
Moleyns MOLINEUX MOLYNEUX
Molinaux MOLINEUX MOLYNEUX
Molineus MOLINEUX MOLYNEUX
MOLINEUX 17 Moleyns Molinaux Molineus Molinex Molino Mollenas Mollineaux Molyneaux MOLYNEUX Molynox Moulineaux Mulinex Mullenax Mullenneix Mulliner Mullinox
Molinex MOLINEUX MOLYNEUX
Molino MOLINEUX MOLYNEUX
Molis MULES
Molledge MILLEDGE
Mollenas MOLINEUX MOLYNEUX
MOLLET Molett MOLLETT
MOLLETT Molett MOLLET
Mollineaux MOLINEUX MOLYNEUX
Molmoth HELMOTH MEALEMOUTH MEALMOUTH MELEMOUTH MELLMOUTHE MELMETH MELMOTH MELMOUTH WELMOTH
MOLONEY MALONEY
Molyneaux MOLINEUX MOLYNEUX
MOLYNEUX 17 Moleyns Molinaux Molineus MOLINEUX Molinex Molino Mollenas Mollineaux Molyneaux Molynox Moulineaux Mulinex Mullenax Mullenneix Mulliner Mullinox
Molynox MOLINEUX MOLYNEUX
Mombrom MOMBRUN
Mombrum MOMBRUN
MOMBRUN 10 De monbrun Mambrun Membrun Mimbrun Mombrom Mombrum Monbrun Mornborn Mumbrun
Monbrun MOMBRUN
MONCK 9 Le moigne MOIGNE MONK Monke MONKS Moyne Munck Munk
MONCREIFF 4 Moncreiffe Moncrieff Moncrieffe
Moncreiffe MONCREIFF
Moncrieff MONCREIFF
Moncrieffe MONCREIFF
MONDAY 20 Manday Mandey Mandie Mandy Menday Mendey Mendie Mendy Minday Mindey Mindie Mindy MONDEY Mondie Mondy MUNDAY Mundey MUNDIE MUNDY
Monderel MAUNDRELL
Monderell MAUNDRELL
MONDEY 20 Manday Mandey Mandie Mandy Menday Mendey Mendie Mendy Minday Mindey Mindie Mindy MONDAY Mondie Mondy MUNDAY Mundey MUNDIE MUNDY
Mondie MONDAY MONDEY MUNDAY MUNDIE MUNDY
Mondrell MAUNDRELL
Monds MUNNS
Mondy MONDAY MONDEY MUNDAY MUNDIE MUNDY
MONEY 4 Monie Monies Monney
Monfcuiftion MACQUISTEN MCQUISTON
Mongsby MONKSBY
Monie MONEY
Monies MONEY
MONK 9 Le moigne MOIGNE MONCK Monke MONKS Moyne Munck Munk
Monke MOIGNE MONCK MONK MONKS
MONKS 9 Le moigne MOIGNE MONCK MONK Monke Moyne Munck Munk
MONKSBY Mongsby
MONNELL 4 Mennill MEYNELL Minnell
Monney MONEY
Monntegne DE MORTAGNE MOUNTNEY
MONTAGU MONTAGUE
MONTAGUE MONTAGU
Montaigne DE MORTAGNE MOUNTNEY
Montford MOUNTFORD
MONTGOMERY Mountgomery
MOODIE MOODY
MOODY MOODIE
Moodycliff MOLDICLIFF
Moodycliffe MOLDICLIFF
MOON MOONE
MOONE MOON
MOOR 6 MOCRE MOORES MOORS MORE MORES
Mooras MOORHOUSE
MOORCOCK Morecock
MOORCROFT 15 Hacraste HAYCRAFT HAYCROFT Macraft Macraste MACROFT Makecraft Marcroft MAYCRAFT Maycraught MAYCROFT Mecraft Mecroft MEDCROFT
MOORE 11 MARR MAWER MOIR MOOR MOORES MOORS MORE MORES MOWER MUIR
Moorehouse MOORHOUSE
Moorehowse MOORHOUSE
Mooreman MOORMAN MOREMAN
MOORES 6 MOOR MOORE MOORS MORE MORES
MOORHOUSE 5 Mooras Moorehouse Moorehowse MOREHOUSE
MOORLEN Morland Morlin
MOORMAN 4 Mooreman MOREMAN Morman
MOORS 6 MOOR MOORE MOORES MORE MORES
Moorton MORETON MORTON MURTON
MORALEE 13 Moraley Moralie Morallie Morally Moraly Morelee Morrale Morraley Morralle Morrerley Morrilee Morrowlee
Moraley MORALEE
Moralie MORALEE
Morallie MORALEE
Morally MORALEE
Moraly MERRILEES MORALEE
MORCOM Morcombe Morcome
Morcombe MORCOM
Morcome MORCOM
Mordall MORDUE
Morday MORDUE
Morddew MORDUE
Morddle MORDUE
Mordeu MORDUE
Mordew MORDUE
Mordex MORDUE
Mordey MORDUE
Mordle MORDUE
Mordne MORDUE
Mordow MORDUE
Mordu MORDUE
MORDUE 19 Merdex Merdox Merdu Merdy Merdyson Mordall Morday Morddew Morddle Mordeu Mordew Mordex Mordey Mordle Mordne Mordow Mordu Mordy
Mordy MORDUE
MORE 10 MARR MOAR MOIR MOOR MOORE MOORES MOORS MORES MUIR
Morecock MOORCOCK
MOREHOUSE MOORHOUSE
MORELAND 4 Morelands Morland MORLANDS
Morelands MORELAND MORLANDS
Morelee MORALEE
Morell MORRELL MORRILL
MOREMAN 4 Mooreman MOORMAN Morman
MORES 6 MOOR MOORE MOORES MOORS MORE
Moresby MORRISBY
Moreten MARTEN MARTIN MORETON MORTON
Moretin MARTEN MARTIN MORETON MORTIN MORTON
MORETON 15 MARTEN MARTIN Marton Merton Moorton

If the name you are interested in is not here, try Section C.

Moreten Moretin Morten MORTIN MORTON Mourton Murten Murtin MURTON
Morfat MORFETT MURFITT
MORFEE 5 Morfey MORPHEW Morphey MORPHY
Morfet MORFETT MURFITT
MORFETT 6 Moffet Moffett Morfat Morfet MURFITT
Morfey MORFEE MORPHEW MORPHY
MORGAN MORGANS
MORGANS MORGAN
Morillon MOURILYAN
Morish MORRICE MORRISH
MORISON MORRISON
Morland MOORLEN MORELAND MORLANDS
MORLANDS 4 MORELAND Morelands Morland
MORLEY MARLEY
Morlin MOORLEN
Morman MOORMAN MOREMAN
Mornborn MOMBRUN
MORPHEW 5 MORFEE Morfey Morphey MORPHY
Morphey MORFEE MORPHEW MORPHY
MORPHY 5 MORFEE Morfey MORPHEW Morphey
Morrale MORALEE
Morraleez MERRILEES
Morraley MORALEE
Morralle MORALEE
MORRAM Morvam
MORRAN 4 MORREN Morrin O'morren
Morrel MORRELL MORRILL
MORRELL 4 Morell Morrel MORRILL
MORREN 4 MORRAN Morrin O'morren
Morrerley MORALEE
MORRICE 8 MAURICE Morish Morrifs MORRIS MORRISH MORRISS Morryce
Morrifs MORRICE MORRIS MORRISS
Morrilee MORALEE
MORRILL 4 Morell Morrel MORRELL
Morrin MORRAN MORREN
MORRIS 7 MAURICE MORRICE Morrifs MORRISH MORRISS Morryce
MORRISBY Moresby Mosby
MORRISH 6 MAURICE Morish MORRICE MORRIS MORRISS
MORRISON 4 MORISON MORRISSON Mylevoirrey
MORRISS 6 MAURICE MORRICE Morrifs MORRIS MORRISH
MORRISSON MORRISON
MORRIT MORRITT
MORRITT MORRIT
Morrowlee MORALEE
Morryce MORRICE MORRIS
MORSE Moise MOSS
MORT MORTER
Mortbois MORTIBOY MORTIBOYS
Morteboyce MORTIBOY MORTIBOYS
Mortemer MORTIMER
Morten MARTEN MARTIN MORETON MORTON MURTON
MORTER MORT
MORTIBOY 5 Mortbois Morteboyce Mortiboyes MORTIBOYS
Mortiboyes MORTIBOY MORTIBOYS
MORTIBOYS 5 Mortbois Morteboyce MORTIBOY Mortiboyes
MORTIMER 4 De mortemer Mortemer MORTIMORE
MORTIMORE MORTIMER
MORTIN 7 MARTEN MARTIN Marton Moretin MORETON MORTON
MORTON 15 MARTEN MARTIN Marton Merton Moorton Moreten Moretin MORETON Morten MORTIN Mourton Murten Murtin MURTON
Morvam MORRAM
Mosbrate MUSPRATT
Mosby MORRISBY
Mosedale MOUSDALE
Mospert MUSPRATT
Mosprat MUSPRATT
Mospratt MUSPRATT
MOSS 20 MACE MACEY Mascry Masery Masgrave Masgreave Masgreve Masgrove Maskerie Maskery Maskerye MASKREY MASSEY Moise MORSE Mosse MUSGRAVE MUSGROVE Mussegreffe
Mosse MACE MACEY MASKREY MASSEY MOSS MUSGRAVE MUSGROVE
Mossprat MUSPRATT
Mote MOAT
MOTH Mothe
Mothe MOTH
MOUAT 4 Mouatt MOWAT MOWATT
Mouatt MOUAT MOWAT
MOUBRAY MOWBERRY MOWBRAY
Moudsdlae MOUSDALE
MOUL 7 MOLD Molde MOLE MOULD Moulde MOULE
MOULD 9 MOLD Molde MOLE MOUL Moulde MOULDS MOULE MOULES
Moulde MOLD MOLE MOUL MOULD MOULE
Mouldercliff MOLDICLIFF
Moulderclliffe MOLDICLIFF
MOULDEY Mouldie Mouldy
Mouldeycliff MOLDICLIFF
Mouldeycliffe MOLDICLIFF
Mouldicliff MOLDICLIFF
Mouldicliffe MOLDICLIFF
Mouldie MOULDEY
MOULDS MOULD
Mouldy MOULDEY
MOULE 7 MOLD Molde MOLE MOUL MOULD Moulde
MOULES 4 MOLD MOLE MOULD
Moulesdale MOUSDALE
Moulineaux MOLINEUX MOLYNEUX
Moulsdale MOUSDALE
Moulsdel MOUSDALE
Moulsdell MOUSDALE
MOUNCEY Mouncy
Mouncy MOUNCEY
Mounderell MAUNDRELL
Moundrell MAUNDRELL
Mountagne DE MORTAGNE MOUNTNEY
Mountaigne DE MORTAGNE MOUNTNEY
Mountaine DE MORTAGNE MOUNTNEY
Mountane DE MORTAGNE MOUNTNEY
Mountany DE MORTAGNE MOUNTNEY
Mountayne DE MORTAGNE MOUNTNEY
Mountenay DE MORTAGNE MOUNTNEY
Mounteney DE MORTAGNE MOUNTNEY
Mounteneye DE MORTAGNE MOUNTNEY
Mountenney DE MORTAGNE MOUNTNEY
Mounteny DE MORTAGNE MOUNTNEY
MOUNTFORD 4 Montford Mountfort MUNFORD
Mountfort MOUNTFORD
Mountgomery MONTGOMERY
Mountnay DE MORTAGNE MOUNTNEY
MOUNTNEY 20 DE MORTAGNE De mountanys plaine De muntein Demunteny Monntegne Montaigne Mountagne Mountaigne Mountaine Mountane Mountany Mountayne Mountenay Mounteney Mounteneye Mountenney Mounteny Mountnay Mowntayne
Mourilon MOURILYAN
MOURILYAN 8 Marilion Marillon Meurilyon Mewrillon Morillon Mourilon Murillon
Mourton MORETON MORTON MURTON
MOUSDALE 7 Mosedale Moudsdlae Moulesdale Moulsdale Moulsdel Moulsdell
Mousprat MUSPRATT
Mouton MEWTON
Movels MOWELS MOWLES
MOWAT 4 MOUAT Mouatt MOWATT
MOWATT MOUAT MOWAT
MOWBERRY MOUBRAY MOWBRAY
Mowbery MEMBREY MEMORY MOWBRAY
MOWBRAY 11 Mambery Membery MEMBREY Membry Memmery Memorry MEMORY MOUBRAY MOWBERRY Mowbery
MOWELS Movels MOWLES
MOWER MAWER MOORE
MOWLES Movels MOWELS
Mowncey MENZIES
Mowntayne DE MORTAGNE MOUNTNEY
Moxan MOXHAM MOXON
Moxay MOXEY MOXLEY MOXSY
Moxcay MOXEY MOXLEY MOXSY
Moxcey MOXEY MOXLEY MOXSY
Moxe MOXEY MOXLEY MOXSY
Moxem MOXHAM
MOXEY 29 Mockcy Mockey Mocksay Moxay Moxcay Moxcey Moxe Moxhae Moxhay Moxhaye Moxhey Moxie MOXLEY Moxsay Moxsaye Moxsey Moxseye Moxsie MOXSY Moxsye Moxxey Moxy Moxye Moxzay Moxzie Moxzye Mucksay Muoxhey
Moxhae MOXEY MOXLEY MOXSY
MOXHAM 4 Moxan Moxem MOXON
Moxhay MOXEY MOXLEY MOXSY
Moxhaye MOXEY MOXLEY MOXSY
Moxhey MOXEY MOXLEY MOXSY
Moxie MOXEY MOXLEY MOXSY
MOXLEY 29 Mockcy Mockey Mocksay Moxay Moxcay Moxcey Moxe MOXEY Moxhae Moxhay Moxhaye Moxhey Moxie Moxsay Moxsaye Moxsey Moxseye Moxsie MOXSY Moxsye Moxxey Moxy Moxye Moxzay Moxzie Moxzye Mucksay Muoxhey
MOXON Moxan MOXHAM
Moxsay MOXEY MOXLEY MOXSY
Moxsaye MOXEY MOXLEY MOXSY
Moxsey MOXEY MOXLEY MOXSY
Moxseye MOXEY MOXLEY MOXSY
Moxsie MOXEY MOXLEY MOXSY
MOXSY 29 Mockcy Mockey Mocksay Moxay Moxcay Moxcey Moxe MOXEY Moxhae Moxhay Moxhaye Moxhey Moxie MOXLEY Moxsay Moxsaye Moxsey Moxseye Moxsie Moxsye Moxxey Moxy Moxye Moxzay Moxzie Moxzye Mucksay Muoxhey
Moxsye MOXEY MOXLEY MOXSY
Moxxey MOXEY MOXLEY MOXSY
Moxy MOXEY MOXLEY MOXSY
Moxye MOXEY MOXLEY MOXSY
Moxzay MOXEY MOXLEY MOXSY
Moxzie MOXEY MOXLEY MOXSY
Moxzye MOXEY MOXLEY MOXSY
MOYCE MOYES MOYSE
MOYERS MYERS
MOYES 5 Moise MOYCE MOYSE Moyses
Moyne MOIGNE MONCK MONK MONKS
MOYSE 5 Moise MOYCE MOYES Moyses
Moyses MOYES MOYSE
MOYSEY 7 MOISEY Moissy Moysie Moysse Moysy Moyzey
Moysie MOISEY MOYSEY
Moysse MOISEY MOYSEY
Moysy MOISEY MOYSEY
Moyzey MOISEY MOYSEY
MQUAD Mquaid
Mquaid MQUAD
Muckleburgh MECKLENBURGH MICKLEBOROUGH MICKLEBURGH
Muckley MARKLEY
Muckmen MACKMAN MACKMIN MCMAIN MCMINN
Muckridge MOCKRIDGE MOGRIDGE
Mucksay MOXEY MOXLEY MOXSY
MUDDIE MUDIE
MUDDLE Modell MUDLE
Mudg MUDGE
MUDGE Mudg
MUDIE MUDDIE
MUDLE Modell MUDDLE
MUGG MOGG
Muggeson MUGGINSON
MUGGINSON 4 Muggeson Muggleston Mugliston
Muggleston MUGGINSON
MUGGLEWORTH Mugleworth
Mugleworth MUGGLEWORTH
Mugliston MUGGINSON
MUIR 5 MARR MOIR MOORE MORE
Mule MULES
MULES 14 Meulles Mewles Moels Molis Mule Mulles MULLICE Mullies MULLIS MULLISS Mullize Mullys Mulys
Mulin MULLIN MULLINS
Mulinex MOLINEUX MOLYNEUX
Mulins MULLIN MULLINS
MULLAN MULLEN

If the name you are interested in is not here, try Section C.

MULLEN MULLAN MULLIN
Mullenax MOLINEUX MOLYNEUX
MULLENDER 6 Malender Malinder MALLINDER MULLINDER Mulliner
Mullenneix MOLINEUX MOLYNEUX
Mulles MULES MULLICE MULLIS MULLISS
MULLEY Mully
MULLICE 9 MULES Mulles Mullies MULLIS MULLISS Mullize Mullys Mulys
Mullies MULES MULLICE MULLIS MULLISS
MULLIN 5 Mulin Mulins MULLEN MULLINS
MULLINDER 6 Malender Malinder MALLINDER MULLENDER Mulliner
Mulliner MOLINEUX MOLYNEUX MULLENDER MULLINDER
Mullinox MOLINEUX MOLYNEUX
MULLINS 4 Mulin Mulins MULLIN
MULLIS 13 Hullice Hullious Hullis Hulliss MULES Mulles MULLICE Mullies MULLISS Mullize Mullys Mulys
MULLISS 9 MULES Mulles MULLICE Mullies MULLIS Mullize Mullys Mulys
Mullize MULES MULLICE MULLIS MULLISS
Mully MULLEY
Mullys MULES MULLICE MULLIS MULLISS
Mulyncon MILLINGTON
Mulys MULES MULLICE MULLIS MULLISS
Mumbrun MOMBRUN
MUNCEY MUNSEY
Munck MOIGNE MONCK MONK MONKS
MUNDAY 20 Manday Mandey Mandie Mandy Menday Mendey Mendie Mendy Minday Mindey Mindie Mindy MONDAY MONDEY Mondie Mondy Mundey MUNDIE MUNDY
Munderell MAUNDRELL
Mundey MONDAY MONDEY MUNDAY MUNDIE MUNDY
MUNDIE 20 Manday Mandey Mandie Mandy Menday Mendey Mendie Mendy Minday Mindey Mindie Mindy MONDAY MONDEY Mondie Mondy MUNDAY Mundey MUNDY
Mundrell MAUNDRELL
MUNDY 20 Manday Mandey Mandie Mandy Menday Mendey Mendie Mendy Minday Mindey Mindie Mindy MONDAY MONDEY Mondie Mondy MUNDAY Mundey MUNDIE
MUNFORD MOUNTFORD
Munk MOIGNE MONCK MONK MONKS
MUNNS Monds
MUNSEY MUNCEY
Muoxhey MOXEY MOXLEY MOXSY
MURCOTT MERCOTE
MURDEN MURDIN
MURDIN MURDEN MURDING
MURDING MURDIN
MURDOCH MURDOCK
MURDOCK MURDOCH
Murfee MURPHY
MURFITT 6 Moffet Moffett Morfat Morfet MORFETT
Murillon MOURILYAN
Murlye MARLEY
MURPHY Murfee
MURRAY Murrey Murry
MURRELL 6 Merrell Merrells MURRELLS Murrill Murrills
MURRELLS 6 Merrell Merrells MURRELL Murrill Murrills
Murrey MURRAY
Murrill MURRELL MURRELLS
Murrills MURRELL MURRELLS
Murry MURRAY
Mursprat MUSPRATT
MURTELL 5 Martell Mertell Mirtell Myrtle
Murten MORETON MORTON MURTON
Murtin MORETON MORTON MURTON
MURTON 9 Merton Moorton MORETON Morten MORTON Mourton Murten Murtin
Musbert MUSPRATT
Muserate MUSPRATT
MUSGRAVE 18 MACE MACEY Mascry Masery Masgrave Masgreave Masgreve Masgrove Maskerie Maskery Maskerye MASKREY MASSEY MOSS Mosse MUSGROVE Mussegreffe
MUSGROVE 18 MACE MACEY Mascry Masery Masgrave Masgreave Masgreve Masgrove Maskerie Maskery Maskerye MASKREY MASSEY MOSS Mosse MUSGRAVE Mussegreffe
Mushprat MUSPRATT
Mushrat MUSPRATT
Mushratt MUSPRATT
MUSK 4 Muske Must Muste
Muske MUSK
Muspard MUSPRATT
Muspart MUSPRATT
Muspered MUSPRATT
Musperet MUSPRATT
Muspert MUSPRATT
Muspirt MUSPRATT
Musprate MUSPRATT
MUSPRATT 42 Masprat Maspratt Misprat Mispratt Mosbrate Mospert Mosprat Mospratt Mossprat Mousprat Mursprat Musbert Muserate Mushprat Mushrat Mushratt Muspard Muspart Muspered Musperet Muspert Muspirt Musprate Muspret Musprett Muspritt Musprot Musprote Musprotte Musprout Muspurt Muspurte Mussprat Musspratt Mustprat Mustpratt Mustrap Mustrop Mustrope Mustsprat Mustsprit
Muspret MUSPRATT
Musprett MUSPRATT
Muspritt MUSPRATT
Musprot MUSPRATT
Musprote MUSPRATT
Musprotte MUSPRATT
Musprout MUSPRATT
Muspurt MUSPRATT
Muspurte MUSPRATT
Mussegreffe MACE MACEY MASKREY MASSEY MOSS MUSGRAVE MUSGROVE
MUSSON 5 MARSON MASON MASSOM MUSTON
Mussprat MUSPRATT
Musspratt MUSPRATT
Must MUSK
Muste MUSK
Musters MASTERS
Musto MUSTOE
MUSTOE Musto
MUSTON 5 MARSON MASON MASSOM MUSSON
Mustprat MUSPRATT
Mustpratt MUSPRATT
Mustrap MUSPRATT
Mustrop MUSPRATT
Mustrope MUSPRATT
Mustsprat MUSPRATT
Mustsprit MUSPRATT
Muton MEWTON
MUTTON 6 MEETEN Meetens Meeting Meetten MITTON
Myal MIALL MYHILL
MYAS Myass MYERS
Myass MYAS MYERS
Myddleton MIDDLETON
Myer MYERS
MYERS 8 MAHER MARRS MAYER MOYERS MYAS Myass Myer
MYHILL 4 Mial MIALL Myal
MYLAM 4 Milam MILEHAM Millham
Mylden MILDON
Myldon MILDON
Mylevoirrey MORRISON
Mylles MILL MILLES MILLS
Myllington MILLINGTON
Mylner MILLER MILLNER MILNER
Mylrede MILDRED
Mynard MAYNARD
Mynards MAYNARD
MYNORS 5 De mineriis De miners De mynors MINERS
Mynshule MINSHULL
Myntar MINTER
Mynter MINTER
Myntor MINTA MINTER
Myntur MINTA MINTER
Myrech MERRICK MEYRICK
Myrick MERRICK MEYRICK
MYRRY 5 Merie MERRY Mirrie Mirry
Myrtle MURTELL
MYSON 4 Mison MISSON Mysson
Mysson MISSON MYSON
Mytham MITHAM
Mythrell METHERELL
MYTTON MITTON
Myttyne MARTEN MARTIN MARTYN
Mywynter MIDWINTER
NADEN 7 NADIN NADON NAIDEN NAYDEN NEDEN Neyden
NADIN 7 NADEN NADON NAIDEN NAYDEN NEDEN Neyden
NADON 7 NADEN NADIN NAIDEN NAYDEN NEDEN Neyden
Naern NAIRN NAIRNE
Naerne NAIRN NAIRNE
NAIDEN 7 NADEN NADIN NADON NAYDEN NEDEN Neyden
NAIL NEAL NEALE
NAILER 4 NAILOR NAYLER NAYLOR
NAILOR 4 NAILER NAYLER NAYLOR
NAIRN 13 Mcnairn Mcnairna Mcnairne Naern Naerne NAIRNE Nairon Narn Narne Narryn Neaum Neorne
NAIRNE 13 Mcnairn Mcnairna Mcnairne Naern Naerne NAIRN Nairon Narn Narne Narryn Neaum Neorne
Nairon NAIRN NAIRNE
NAISH 7 Naishe NASH Nashe Naysh Neace Nese
Naishe NAISH NASH
NALL 4 Naul Naule Nawle
Nankeval NANKIVELL
NANKIVELL 5 Nankeval Nanscuval Nanskievel Nanskivell
Nanscuval NANKIVELL
Nanskievel NANKIVELL
Nanskivell NANKIVELL
Naphthen NAPTHINE
Napkin NAPTHINE
NAPP KNAPP
Napten NAPTHINE
Napthen NAPTHINE
NAPTHINE 6 Naphthen Napkin Napten Napthen Napthing
Napthing NAPTHINE
Naramore NARRAMORE
Narey NARY NEARY
Narn NAIRN NAIRNE
Narne NAIRN NAIRNE
NARRAMORE Naramore
Narryn NAIRN NAIRNE
NARY Narey NEARY
Nasfield NESFIELD
NASH 7 NAISH Naishe Nashe Naysh Neace Nese
Nashe NAISH NASH
Nashfylde NESFIELD
NASON 4 Nasson Nassone Nassonne
Nasson NASON
Nassone NASON
Nassonne NASON
Nastfeild NESFIELD
Nastfield NESFIELD
Natcott NETCOTT
NATION Nations
Nations NATION
Natrup NAWTHORP NORTHROP
Naul NALL
Naule NALL
Nauthorp NAWTHORP NORTHROP
Nauthrop NAWTHORP NORTHROP
Navis NEVELL NEVES NEVILL NEVILLE
Nawdaby NORDABY
Nawle NALL
NAWTHORP 11 Natrup Nauthorp Nauthrop Northorp NORTHROP Northrope Northroppe Nortop Nortrap Notrup
NAYDEN 7 NADEN NADIN NADON NAIDEN NEDEN Neyden
NAYLER 4 NAILER NAILOR NAYLOR
NAYLOR 4 NAILER NAILOR NAYLER
Naysh NAISH NASH
Neace NAISH NASH
Neach NEECH

If the name you are interested in is not here, try Section C.

NEACOMB Neacombe
Neacombe NEACOMB
Neades NEADS NEEDS
NEADS Neades NEEDS
NEAL NAIL NEALE
Nealand NEELAND NEWLAND
NEALE 5 NAIL NEAL NEIL NEILL
Neames NIMS
NEARY Narey NARY
Nease NIAS
Neasham NEESHAM
NEAT NEATE
NEATE NEAT
Neathercot NETHERCOTT
Neathercotte NETHERCOTT
Neaum NAIRN NAIRNE
NEAVE 5 Knef Knieve KNIFE NEEVE
NEAVES 5 Kneeves Kneves NEEVES NEVES
Neavil NEVELL NEVES NEVILL NEVILLE
Neavill NEVELL NEVES NEVILL NEVILLE
Neaville NEVELL NEVES NEVILL NEVILLE
Nech NEECH
Neche NEECH
NEDEN 7 NADEN NADIN NADON NAIDEN NAYDEN Neyden
Nedham NEEDHAM
NEECH 8 Neach Nech Neche Neeche Nich Niche Nyche
Neeche NEECH
NEEDHAM Nedham
Needlay NEEDLER NEEDLEY
NEEDLER Needlay NEEDLEY
NEEDLEY Needlay NEEDLER
NEEDS Neades NEADS
NEELAND 8 Kneeland Kneland Nealand Neelands Neland NEWLAND Neyland
Neelands NEELAND NEWLAND
Neene NINNIS
Neenes NINNIS
NEESHAM 4 Meesham Neasham Nesham
NEEVE 5 Knef Knieve KNIFE NEAVE
NEEVES 5 Kneeves Kneves NEAVES NEVES
NEIL 5 MCNEIL MCNEILL NEALE NEILL
NEILL 5 MCNEIL MCNEILL NEALE NEIL
NEILSON NELSON
Neithercot NETHERCOTT
Neithercote NETHERCOTT
Neithercott NETHERCOTT
Neithercut NETHERCOTT
Neithercutt NETHERCOTT
Neland NEELAND NEWLAND
Nellis NELLIST
NELLIST Nellis
NELSON NEILSON
Nennis NINNIS
Neorne NAIRN NAIRNE
NESBIT 4 NESBITT NISBET NISBETT
NESBITT 4 NESBIT NISBET NISBETT
Nese NAISH NASH
Nesfeald NESFIELD
Nesfeeld NESFIELD
Nesfeld NESFIELD
Nesfelde NESFIELD
Nesfelld NESFIELD
NESFIELD 30 Fatherston Fatherstone Fatterstone Featherston FEATHERSTONE FETHERSTON Fetherstone Hornee Hornesey Hornsay Hornsaye Hornsea HORNSEY Hornsie Hornsy Knisfield Nasfield Nashfylde Nastfeild Nastfield Nesfeald Nesfeeld Nesfeld Nesfelde Nesfelld Nessfield Nestfield Nisfield Tetherston
Nesham NEESHAM
Nessfield NESFIELD
Nestfield NESFIELD
NETCOTT 4 Natcott Notcott Notcutt
Nethercoat NETHERCOTT
Nethercoate NETHERCOTT
Nethercoats NETHERCOTT
Nethercot NETHERCOTT
Nethercote NETHERCOTT
NETHERCOTT 15 Neathercot Neathercotte Neithercot Neithercote Neithercott Neithercut Neithercutt Nethercoat Nethercoate Nethercoats Nethercot Nethercote Nethercut Nethercutt
Nethercut NETHERCOTT
Nethercutt NETHERCOTT
NETTELL Nettle
Nettle NETTELL
NETTLEINGHAM NETTLINGHAM
NETTLINGHAM NETTLEINGHAM
Neufmarche NEWMARCH
Neufmenell NEWMARCH
Neuham NEWHAM
Neut NUTE
Nevel NEVELL NEVES NEVILL NEVILLE
NEVELL 13 Navis Neavil Neavill Neaville Nevel Nevelle NEVES Nevil NEVILL NEVILLE Nevis Nowis
Nevelle NEVELL NEVES NEVILL NEVILLE
NEVES 17 Kneeves Kneves Navis NEAVES Neavil Neavill Neaville NEEVES Nevel NEVELL Nevelle Nevil NEVILL NEVILLE Nevis Nowis
Nevil NEVELL NEVES NEVILL NEVILLE
Nevile NEVILLE
NEVILL 13 Navis Neavil Neavill Neaville Nevel NEVELL Nevelle NEVES Nevil NEVILLE Nevis Nowis
NEVILLE 14 Navis Neavil Neavill Neaville Nevel NEVELL Nevelle NEVES Nevil Nevile NEVILL Nevis Nowis
Neville-ussher USHER USSHER
Nevis NEVELL NEVES NEVILL NEVILLE
Newam NEWHAM
Newans NEWEN NEWENS NEWIN
NEWBERRY 6 NEWBERY Newbory NEWBURY Nuberry Nubory
NEWBERY 6 NEWBERRY Newbory NEWBURY Nuberry Nubory
Newbory NEWBERRY NEWBERY NEWBURY
NEWBURY 6 NEWBERRY NEWBERY Newbory Nuberry Nubory
NEWBY NUBY
NEWCOMB NEWCOMBE
NEWCOMBE NEWCOMB
NEWEN 5 Newans NEWENS NEWIN Newins
NEWENS 5 Newans NEWEN NEWIN Newins
NEWHAM 4 Neuham Newam Newum
NEWIN 5 Newans NEWEN NEWENS Newins
Newins NEWEN NEWENS NEWIN
NEWLAND 8 Kneeland Kneland Nealand NEELAND Neelands Neland Neyland
NEWMARCH 7 De neufmarche De newmarch Neufmarche Neufmenell Newmarsh Nova meinell
Newmarsh NEWMARCH
Newt NUTE
Newte NUTE
Newum NEWHAM
Neyden NADEN NADIN NADON NAIDEN NAYDEN NEDEN
Neyland NEELAND NEWLAND
NIAS Nease Nyers
Nich NEECH
Niche NEECH
NICHOL 7 Micol Nichole NICHOLL NICHOLLS NICOLL Nicolls
NICHOLAS 5 NICHOLLS NICHOLS Nickels Nickols
Nicholds NICHOLLS NICHOLS NICKOLDS
Nichole NICHOL
NICHOLL 5 NICHOL NICHOLLS NICOLL Nicolls
NICHOLLS 14 NICHOL NICHOLAS Nicholds NICHOLL NICHOLS Nickalls Nickels NICKLES NICKOLDS Nickoless Nickols NICOLL Nicolls
NICHOLS 11 NICHOLAS Nicholds NICHOLLS Nickalls Nickells Nickels NICKLES NICKOLDS Nickoless Nickols
NICHOLSON Nickleson NICOLSON
Nickalls NICHOLLS NICHOLS
Nickells NICHOLS
Nickels NICHOLAS NICHOLLS NICHOLS
Nickland NICKLEN
NICKLEN Nickland
NICKLES NICHOLLS NICHOLS
Nickleson NICHOLSON
NICKOLDS 6 Nicholds NICHOLLS NICHOLS Nickoless Nickols
Nickoless NICHOLLS NICHOLS NICKOLDS
Nickols NICHOLAS NICHOLLS NICHOLS NICKOLDS
NICKS NIX
NICKSON 8 Nigson Nixen NIXON Nixson Nixsone Noxon Nycson
NICOLL 5 NICHOL NICHOLL NICHOLLS Nicolls
Nicolls NICHOL NICHOLL NICHOLLS NICOLL
NICOLSON NICHOLSON
Nif KNIFE
Nife KNIFE
Niff KNIFE
Niffe KNIFE
Nigson NICKSON NIXON
Nimes NIMS
Nimms NIMS
NIMS 4 Neames Nimes Nimms
NINEHAM Ninham Ninnim
Ninham NINEHAM
NINNES NINNIS
Ninnim NINEHAM
NINNIS 5 Neene Neenes Nennis NINNES
NISBET 4 NESBIT NESBITT NISBETT
NISBETT 4 NESBIT NESBITT NISBET
Nisfield NESFIELD
NIX NICKS
Nixen NICKSON NIXON
NIXON 7 NICKSON Nigson Nixen Nixson Nixsone Noxon
Nixson NICKSON NIXON
Nixsone NICKSON NIXON
Noades NODES
Noak NOAKE NOAKES NOCK NOKES
NOAKE 11 Noak NOAKES Noaux NOCK Nocke Nok Noke NOKES Noks Nookes
NOAKES 11 Noak NOAKE Noaux NOCK Nocke Nok Noke NOKES Noks Nookes
Noaux NOAKE NOAKES NOCK NOKES
NOBLE NOBLES
NOBLES NOBLE
Nocetter NOSSETTER NOSSITER
NOCK 11 Noak NOAKE NOAKES Noaux Nocke Nok Noke NOKES Noks Nookes
Nocke NOAKE NOAKES NOCK NOKES
Nocyter NOSSETTER NOSSITER
NODES Noades
Noice NOYCE
Noise NOYCE NOYES NOYSE
Nok NOAKE NOAKES NOCK NOKES
Noke NOAKE NOAKES NOCK NOKES
NOKES 11 Noak NOAKE NOAKES Noaux NOCK Nocke Nok Noke Noks Nookes
Noks NOAKE NOAKES NOCK NOKES
Nolden KNOWLDEN
Noll KNOWLES NOWELL
NOLLER Nolly
Nolls KNOWLES
Nollson KNOWLSON NOLSON
Nolly NOLLER
NOLSON 8 Knolson Knoulson Knowleson KNOWLSON Nollson Nolsonne Nowlson
Nolsonne KNOWLSON NOLSON
Nonne NUNN NUNNS
Nookes NOAKE NOAKES NOCK NOKES
Norbery NORBURY
Norburie NORBURY
NORBURY Norbery Norburie
NORCOTE 4 NORCOTT NORKETT NORTHCOTE
NORCOTT 4 NORCOTE NORKETT NORTHCOTE
NORDABY 4 Gnawdaby Gnordaby Nawdaby
Norie NORRIE
Norington NORRINGTON
NORKETT 4 NORCOTE NORCOTT NORTHCOTE
NORMAN 6 Armen ARMON FORMAN ORMAN Ormen
NORRIE Norie
NORRINGTON Norington

If the name you are interested in is not here, try Section C.

NORRIS NORRISH
NORRISH NORRIS
Norsworthy NOSWORTHY
NORTH Northe
NORTHCOTE 4 NORCOTE NORCOTT NORKETT
Northe NORTH
NORTHERN Novderen
Northmoor NORTHMORE
Northmoore NORTHMORE
NORTHMORE Northmoor Northmoore
Northorp NAWTHORP NORTHROP
NORTHROP 11 Natrup Nauthorp Nauthrop NAWTHORP Northorp Northrope Northroppe Nortop Nortrap Notrup
Northrope NAWTHORP NORTHROP
Northroppe NAWTHORP NORTHROP
Nortop NAWTHORP NORTHROP
Nortrap NAWTHORP NORTHROP
NOSSETTER 4 Nocetter Nocyter NOSSITER
NOSSITER 4 Nocetter Nocyter NOSSETTER
NOSWORTHY Norsworthy
Not KNOTT NOTT
Notcott NETCOTT
Notcutt NETCOTT
NOTLEY Nottley
Notrup NAWTHORP NORTHROP
NOTT KNOTT Not
Nottley NOTLEY
Noulden KNOWLDEN
Nova meinell NEWMARCH
Novderen NORTHERN
NOVELL NOWELL
Nowel KNOWLES NOWELL
NOWELL 7 Knol Knoll KNOWLES Noll NOVELL Nowel
Nowis NEVELL NEVES NEVILL NEVILLE
Nowles KNOWLES
Nowls KNOWLES
Nowlson KNOWLSON NOLSON
Noxon NICKSON NIXON
NOY Noye
NOYCE 6 Noice Noise NOYES Noys NOYSE
Noye NOY
NOYES 5 Noise NOYCE Noys NOYSE
Noys NOYCE NOYES NOYSE
NOYSE 5 Noise NOYCE NOYES Noys
Nuberry NEWBERRY NEWBERY NEWBURY
Nubory NEWBERRY NEWBERY NEWBURY
NUBY NEWBY
Nuckey KNUCKEY
Nun NUNN NUNNS
NUNALY Nunnaly
NUNN 5 Nonne Nun NUNNS Nunny
Nunnaly NUNALY
NUNNS 5 Nonne Nun NUNN Nunny
Nunny NUNN NUNNS
NUTE 4 Neut Newt Newte
Nuthal NUTHALL
NUTHALL Nuthal
NUTSFORD Knuttesforde
Nyche NEECH
Nycson NICKSON
Nyers NIAS
Nyfe KNIFE
Nyffe KNIFE
O'boyle BOYLE
O'cahill CAHILL O'FOGARTY
O'CONNER 6 CONNER CONNOR Conor O'CONNOR O'conor
O'CONNOR 6 CONNER CONNOR Conor O'CONNER O'conor
O'conor CONNER CONNOR O'CONNER O'CONNOR
O'cuirc QUIRK QUIRKE
O'davoren DAVOREN
O'day DAY
O'diff CUFFE DUFF DUFFY KILDUFF
O'donaghue O'DONAHUE O'DONOGHUE
O'DONAHUE 5 O'donaghue O'DONOGHUE O'donohoe O'donohue
O'DONOGHUE 5 O'donaghue O'DONAHUE O'donohoe O'donohue
O'donohoe O'DONAHUE O'DONOGHUE
O'donohue O'DONAHUE O'DONOGHUE
O'dowd DOWD O'DOWDE
O'DOWDE O'dowd
O'duffy CUFFE DUFF DUFFY KILDUFF
O'duvdavoren DAVOREN
O'FOGARTY CAHILL O'cahill
O'hagan HAGAN HAGEN HEGAN HOGAN
O'keefe O'KEEFFE
O'KEEFFE O'keefe
O'livey OLIVEY
O'mahoney MAHONEY MAHONY
O'mahony MAHONEY MAHONY
O'MALLEY 5 Malia Malley Mealey MELIA
O'MARA 4 MARA Meara O'meara
O'meara MARA O'MARA
O'meehan MEAKIN MEEHAN
O'morren MORRAN MORREN
O'NEIL O'NEILL O'niel
O'NEILL O'NEIL O'niel
O'niel O'NEIL O'NEILL
O'OLLARD OLLARD
O'quirk QUIRK QUIRKE
O'RAW 5 O'rawe O'row RAW Rawe
O'rawe O'RAW RAW
O'row O'RAW RAW
O'SULLIVAN SULLIVAN
O'TOOL 4 O'TOOLE Tool TOOLE
O'TOOLE 4 O'TOOL Tool TOOLE
Oackley OAKLEY OCKLEY
Oackly OAKLEY OCKLEY
OAKELEY 4 OAKLEY Okeley Okely
Oakely OAKLEY OCKLEY
OAKES Oaks
OAKESHOTT Okeshot Oxeate
OAKEY OCKEY
Oaking AIKEN EKINS HAWKINS OAKINS OKINS
OAKINS 26 AIKEN Aikin Aken Akins Auchain Eakings Eakins Eakons Ekens EKINS Ekynes Ekyns Hackence Hackins Hakince Hakines Hakings Hakins HAWKINS Oaking Okens OKINS Okyn Okyns Ouckins
OAKLEY 29 Auckley Oackley Oackly OAKELEY Oakely Oaklie Oakly Occle Ochely Ockeley Ockle OCKLEY Ockly Ocle Oclee Ocley Ocleye Ocly Okelee Okeley Okelie Okely Okle Okly Rithoak Rithock Wreakoke Writhoak
Oaklie OAKLEY OCKLEY
Oakly OAKLEY OCKLEY
Oaks OAKES
OAKSHOTT HAWKSHAW Ockshaw
OASTLER Ostler
OATES OATS Otes
OATS OATES Otes
OBERY 4 OBREY Woberry Wooberry
Oble HOBLEY
Obley HOBLEY
OBREY 5 ABREY OBERY Woberry Wooberry
Occle OAKLEY OCKLEY
Ochely OAKLEY OCKLEY
Ockeley OAKLEY OCKLEY
OCKEY OAKEY
Ockle OAKLEY OCKLEY
Ockless HOCKLESS
OCKLEY 27 Oackley Oackly Oakely OAKLEY Oaklie Oakly Occle Ochely Ockeley Ockle Ockly Ocle Oclee Ocley Ocleye Ocly Okelee Okeley Okelie Okely Okle Okly Rithoak Rithock Wreakoke Writhoak
Ockly OAKLEY OCKLEY
Ocknall HOCKNELL
Ocknell HOCKNELL
Ockshaw HAWKSHAW OAKSHOTT
Ocle OAKLEY OCKLEY
Oclee OAKLEY OCKLEY
Ocley OAKLEY OCKLEY
Ocleye OAKLEY OCKLEY
Ocly OAKLEY OCKLEY
OCRAFT HOLCRAFT HOLCROFT
Odam ODHAMS
Oddie ODDY
ODDY Oddie
Odham ODHAMS
ODHAMS 4 Odam Odham Oldhams
ODINGSELLS De odingsells Doddingsheles -
Odrien ADRIAN
Odrigd AUTRIDGE
Odrigde AUTRIDGE
Oerton ORTON OVERTON
Offa OFFER
OFFELOW 8 OFFILER Offler OFFLEY Offlow Offly Ofley Ofly
OFFER Offa
OFFILER 5 OFFELOW Offler OFFLEY Offlow
Offler OFFELOW OFFILER OFFLEY
OFFLEY 8 OFFELOW OFFILER Offler Offlow Offly Ofley Ofly
Offlow OFFELOW OFFILER OFFLEY
Offly OFFELOW OFFLEY
Offspring OFSPRING
Ofley OFFELOW OFFLEY
Ofly OFFELOW OFFLEY
OFSPRING Offspring
Ogan WOGAN
Okelee OAKLEY OCKLEY
Okeley OAKELEY OAKLEY OCKLEY
Okelie OAKLEY OCKLEY
Okely OAKELEY OAKLEY OCKLEY
Okens AIKEN EKINS HAWKINS OAKINS OKINS
Okeshot OAKESHOTT
OKINES OKINS
OKINS 27 AIKEN Aikin Aken Akins Auchain Eakings Eakins Eakons Ekens EKINS Ekynes Ekyns Hackence Hackins Hakince Hakines Hakings Hakins HAWKINS Oaking OAKINS Okens OKINES Okyn Okyns Ouckins
Okle OAKLEY OCKLEY
Okly OAKLEY OCKLEY
Okyn AIKEN EKINS HAWKINS OAKINS OKINS
Okyns AIKEN EKINS HAWKINS OAKINS OKINS
OLD OULD
Oldcroft HOLDCROFT
OLDEN OLDING
Oldersley ALDERSLEY
OLDFIELD Ouldfield
OLDHAM ALDHAM Owdem
Oldhams ODHAMS
OLDING OLDEN
Oldis ALDHOUSE ALDIS ALDOUS ALDUS AUDAS AUDUS AWDAS ORDERS
Oldrid ALDRIDGE OLDRIDGE OLDROYD
OLDRIDGE 9 ALDRICH Aldrid ALDRIDGE ALLDRIDGE Oldrid Oldroid OLDROYD Oldroyde
Oldroid ALDRIDGE OLDRIDGE OLDROYD
OLDROYD 7 Aldrid ALDRIDGE Oldrid OLDRIDGE Oldroid Oldroyde
Oldroyde ALDRIDGE OLDRIDGE OLDROYD
Olerenshaw OLORENSHAW
Olester HOLLISTER
OLFE 11 ALFF ALP ALPE ALPHE ALPS AULPH HULF ULF ULFE ULPH
Olick HOLLICK
Olier HOLLIER OLLIER
Olivah OLIVEY
Olivee OLIVEY
OLIVER 6 OLLAY Olliver OLVER Olyiker Olyver
OLIVEY 7 O'livey Olivah Olivee Olivie Olivy Olyvye
Olivie OLIVEY
Olivy OLIVEY
OLLARD O'OLLARD
OLLAY OLIVER
Ollick HOLLICK
OLLIER HOLLIER Olier
Olliver OLIVER
Olman HOLLMAN HOLMAN HOLMWOOD HOMEWOOD OMAN
OLORENSHAW Olerenshaw
Olsborn OSBORN OSBORNE OSBOURN OSBOURNE
Olser HOLLISTER
OLVER OLIVER
Olyiker OLIVER
Olyver OLIVER
Olyvye OLIVEY
OMAN 9 HOLLMAN Hollyman HOLMAN HOLMWOOD Holyman Homard HOMEWOOD Olman
OMEROD 8 Homerode Omerode Omroyde ORMEROD Ormeroyd ORMROD Ormroyd
Omerode OMEROD ORMEROD ORMROD
Ominett AMANET
Omroyde OMEROD ORMEROD ORMROD
Ondeslowe ONSLOW
Oniens ONION ONIONS
ONION 8 Oniens ONIONS Onyen Onyon Union UNWIN

If the name you are interested in is not here, try Section C.

Unwyn
ONIONS 4 Oniens ONION Onyon
ONSLOW De ondeslowe Ondeslowe
Onwhynne UNWIN
ONWIN UNWIN
Onyen ONION UNWIN
Onyon ONION ONIONS
Opberry ALBERRY AUBRAY AUBREY
Opbury ALBERRY AUBRAY AUBREY
Opey OPIE
OPIE 5 Opey Oppie Oppy Opy
Opperman OPPERMANN
OPPERMANN Opperman
Oppie OPIE
Oppy OPIE
Opy OPIE
ORAM 6 HORAM HURAM ORRAM Orum Whoram
Orbal ORBELL
Orbel ORBELL
ORBELL 4 Orbal Orbel Orble
Orbery ALBERRY AUBRAY AUBREY
Orble ORBELL
ORCHARD 8 ARCHARD Archart ARCHER Orchart Orcheard Orchet Orchett
Orchart ARCHARD ORCHARD
Orcheard ARCHARD ORCHARD
Orchet ARCHARD ORCHARD
Orchett ARCHARD ORCHARD
ORDERS 18 Alders Aldhous ALDHOUSE Aldhowse ALDIS ALDOUS ALDUS Alduse Alldiss AUDAS Auders Audis AUDUS AWDAS Awdis Awdus Oldis
Orgil ORGILL
ORGILL Orgil
ORIEL 4 Oriell ORRIEL Orriell
Oriell ORIEL ORRIEL
ORMAN 9 Armen ARMON FORMAN NORMAN Ormand Ormen ORMOND Ormonde
Ormand ORMAN ORMOND
Ormen ARMON FORMAN NORMAN ORMAN
ORMEROD 8 Homerode OMEROD Omerode Omroyde Ormeroyd ORMROD Ormroyd
Ormeroyd OMEROD ORMEROD ORMROD
ORMOND 4 ORMAN Ormand Ormonde
Ormonde ORMAN ORMOND
ORMROD 8 Homerode OMEROD Omerode Omroyde ORMEROD Ormeroyd Ormroyd
Ormroyd OMEROD ORMEROD ORMROD
ORRAM ORAM
ORRELL ORRIEL
ORRIEL 5 ORIEL Oriell ORRELL Orriell
Orriell ORIEL ORRIEL
Orsborn OSBORN OSBORNE OSBOURN OSBOURNE
ORTON 21 Anthorn Aughton Hathorn Hathorne HAUGHTON Hauthni Hawthen HAWTHORN HAWTHORNE Hawthornthwaite Hawtyn Haythorne Horethorn Horthorn HORTON Hothorne HOUGHTON Oerton OVERTON Owerton
Orum ORAM
OSBALDESTON 11 Osbaldiston Osbalston Osbason Osbenson Osberson Osbiston Osbornson Osbosen Osboston Osbostone
Osbaldiston OSBALDESTON
Osbalston OSBALDESTON
Osban OSBAND OSBORN OSBORNE OSBOURN OSBOURNE
OSBAND 19 Asborn Hosbon Osban Osbon Osbond OSBORN OSBORNE OSBOURN OSBOURNE Osburn Osburne Ozborn Ozbourn Ozbourne Ozburn Ozburne Wasborn Washbourne
Osbason OSBALDESTON
Osbenson OSBALDESTON
Osberson OSBALDESTON
Osbiston OSBALDESTON
Osbon OSBAND OSBORN OSBORNE OSBOURNE
Osbond OSBAND OSBORN OSBORNE OSBOURN OSBOURNE
OSBORN 23 Asborn Hosbon Hosborn Olsborn Orsborn Osban OSBAND Osbon Osbond OSBORNE OSBOURN OSBOURNE Osburn Osburne Ozborn Ozborne Ozbourn Ozbourne Ozburn Ozburne Wasborn Washbourne
OSBORNE 23 Asborn Hosbon Hosborn Olsborn Orsborn Osban OSBAND Osbon Osbond OSBORN OSBOURN OSBOURNE Osburn Osburne Ozborn Ozborne Ozbourn Ozbourne Ozburn Ozburne Wasborn Washbourne
Osbornson OSBALDESTON
Osbosen OSBALDESTON
Osboston OSBALDESTON
Osbostone OSBALDESTON
OSBOURN 22 Asborn Hosbon Olsborn Orsborn Osban OSBAND Osbon Osbond OSBORN OSBORNE OSBOURNE Osburn Osburne Ozborn Ozborne Ozbourn Ozbourne Ozburn Ozburne Wasborn Washbourne
OSBOURNE 22 Asborn Hosbon Olsborn Orsborn Osban OSBAND Osbon Osbond OSBORN OSBORNE OSBOURN Osburn Osburne Ozborn Ozborne Ozbourn Ozbourne Ozburn Ozburne Wasborn Washbourne
Osburn OSBAND OSBORN OSBORNE OSBOURN OSBOURNE
Osburne OSBAND OSBORN OSBORNE OSBOURN OSBOURNE
Oseland OSLAND
Osell HASKELL HASWELL HUSSELL HUZZELL OSWALD RUSSELL URSELL UZZELL
OSEMAN OSMAN
Osenten OSENTON
OSENTON 4 Assenden Assendon Osenten
OSLAND Oseland Oslin
Oslin OSLAND
OSMAN OSEMAN
Ossie OUSEY
Ostin ALSTON AUSTIN
Ostler OASTLER
OSWALD 31 Askell Aswell Essell HASKELL Hassel HASWELL Hawsell Haysel Hessell Hoswell Husle HUSSELL HUZZELL Israel Issel Osell Ozell RUSSELL URSELL Urswell Ushil Ussell Ussol Ussould Uswell Uzald Uzle Uzzeel Uzzele UZZELL
Oter OTTER
Otes OATES OATS
OTTER Oter
OTTEWELL 12 Atterwell ATTEWELL Attewill ATTWELL Atwell Atwells ATWILL OTTIWELL Ottowell Ottwell Otwel
OTTIWELL 4 OTTEWELL Ottowell Otwel
Ottowell OTTEWELL OTTIWELL
Ottridg AUTRIDGE
Ottridge AUTRIDGE
Ottwell ATTEWELL ATTWELL ATWILL OTTEWELL
Otwel OTTEWELL OTTIWELL
Ouchell HOUCHELL
Ouckins AIKEN EKINS HAWKINS OAKINS OKINS
Ouerington OVERINGTON
OULD OLD Oulds
Ouldfield OLDFIELD
Oulds OULD
Oule HOUDE
Ous OWST
OUSEY 6 Ossie Owsie Owzy Ozey Ussey
Oust OWST
Oute AUTEY AUTY
OUTRAM OWTRAM
OVAL Ovel Ovell
Ovel OVAL
Ovell OVAL
OVENDEN Hoveden
Overard EVERARD EVERETT EVERITT
OVEREND OVERIN
OVERIN OVEREND
OVERINGTON Ouerington OVINGTON
Overitt EVERARD EVERETT EVERITT
OVERTON 4 Oerton ORTON Owerton
OVINGTON OVERINGTON
Owain OWEN
Owdem OLDHAM
OWEN 9 Awain Hawyn Owain OWENS Woewen Woewin Wowen Wowin
OWENS OWEN
Owerton ORTON OVERTON
Owest OWST
Oweste OWST
Owgan WOGAN
Owsie OUSEY
OWST 5 Ous Oust Owest Oweste
OWTRAM OUTRAM
Owzy OUSEY
Oxeate OAKESHOTT
OXENHAM 5 Oxinham Oxman OXNAM Oxsonham
Oxer OXLEY
Oxinham OXENHAM OXNAM
OXLEY Oxer Oxxe
Oxman OXENHAM OXNAM
OXNAM 5 OXENHAM Oxinham Oxman Oxsonham
Oxsonham OXENHAM OXNAM
Oxxe OXLEY
Ozborn OSBAND OSBORN OSBORNE OSBOURN OSBOURNE
Ozborne OSBORN OSBORNE OSBOURN OSBOURNE
Ozbourn OSBAND OSBORN OSBORNE OSBOURN OSBOURNE
Ozbourne OSBAND OSBORN OSBORNE OSBOURN OSBOURNE
Ozburn OSBAND OSBORN OSBORNE OSBOURN OSBOURNE
Ozburne OSBAND OSBORN OSBORNE OSBOURN OSBOURNE
Ozell HASKELL HASWELL HUSSELL HUZZELL OSWALD RUSSELL URSELL UZZELL
Ozey OUSEY
Paccard PACKARD
Paccarde PACKARD
PACE 11 PAICE Paise Pase PASS Payce PAYE Pays Payse Peise PYE
PACK 6 Packe Pake PARK Pax PECK
PACKARD 4 Paccard Paccarde Pakkarde
Packe PACK PARK PECK
PACKER PARKER
PACKHAM PECKHAM
PACKNELL Pocknell
Packson PAXSON PAXTON
PADBURY 6 Podbury Portberrie PORTBURY Potberry Potbury
Paddel PADDLE
Paddington PARTINGTON PATTENDEN
PADDLE 4 Paddel Padle Padwell
Paden PEDEN
PADGET 4 PADGETT PAGET PAGETT
PADGETT 4 PADGET PAGET PAGETT
Padle PADDLE
Padwell PADDLE
Pae PAY PAYE
Pafford PALSER PAVORD PAZZERD PURSER
Pagdan PAGDEN
PAGDEN Pagdan
PAGET 4 PADGET PADGETT PAGETT
PAGETT 4 PADGET PADGETT PAGET
PAICE 7 PACE Paise Payce Pays Payse Peise
Pailing PALIN PALING
PAILLING Paleing PALIN
PAIN 7 PAINE Pane PAYN PAYNE PINE PYNE
PAINE 5 PAIN Pane PAYN PAYNE
Paise PACE PAICE
Pait PATE PEAT PETT
Pake PACK PARK PECK
Pakkarde PACKARD
Palaie PALEY
Palay PALEY
Paleing PAILLING PALIN
Palet PALLETT PAULET POLLET POLLETT POLLITT
Palett PALLETT PAULET POLLET POLLETT POLLITT
PALEY 4 Palaie Palay Payley
PALFREY Parfrey
Palian PALIN PALING
PALIN 6 Pailing PAILLING Paleing Palian PALING

If the name you are interested in is not here, try Section C.

PALING 6 Pailing Palian PALIN Palling Payling
PALK PAUK
PALKE POLKEY
Pallet PALLETT PAULET PERRETT POLLET POLLETT POLLITT PORRETT PORRIT PORRITT
PALLETT 31 Palet Palett Pallet PAULET Paulett Paulit Paullet Paulot Pawlet Pawlete Pawlett Polet Polett Poliet Polit Pollert POLLET POLLETT Polliet Polliot Pollit POLLITT Pollitte Pollot Poolit Poulett Poulette Powlet Powlett Powlit
Palling PALING
PALSER 17 Pafford Parser Pasard Paser Pasher Passard Passer Passerd Passwer Payser Payzer Pazer Pazzard PAZZERD Posheart PURSER
Pammenter PARMENTER PARMENTIER
Panckhurst PANKHURST
Pancoast PANKHURST
Pancurst PANKHURST
Pancus PANKHURST
Pane PAIN PAINE PAYNE
Pangeram PINCOMBE PINKHAM
Pangerham PINCOMBE PINKHAM
Pankherst PANKHURST
PANKHURST 7 Panckhurst Pancoast Pancurst Pancus Pankherst Penkhurst
PANNIFER Pennifer
Pantin PONTIN PONTING
Parchall PURCHALL PURCHELL
Pardington PARTINGTON PATTENDEN
PARDOE PARDOW
PARDOW PARDOE
Parfet PARFETT PARFITT
PARFETT 4 Parfet Parfit PARFITT
Parfit PARFETT PARFITT
PARFITT 4 Parfet PARFETT Parfit
Parfrey PALFREY PUREFOY
Parinton PARRINGTON
PARISH PARRISH
PARK 9 PACK Packe Pake PARKE PARKES PARKS Pax PECK
PARKE 4 PARK PARKES PARKS
PARKER PACKER
PARKES 4 PARK PARKE PARKS
Parkeshouse PARSUS PERSEHOUSE
PARKIN 5 Parkyn Pearkins PERKIN PERKINS
PARKINS 10 Parkyns PERKINS Perkyns Pirkins Pirkyns Purkins Purkyns Pyrkins Pyrkyns
PARKS 4 PARK PARKE PARKES
Parkyn PARKIN
Parkyns PARKINS PERKINS
PARMENTER 4 Pammenter PARMENTIER Parminter
PARMENTIER 4 Pammenter PARMENTER Parminter
Parminter PARMENTER PARMENTIER
Parnacoat PARNACOTT PENICAD PENICOD PENICUD PENIKET PENIKETT PENNEKETT PENNICARD PENNICEARD PENNICODD PENNICORD PENNICOTT PENNICUD PENNIKETT PENNYCAD PENNYCOTT PENNYCUD PENNYEND
Parnacote PARNACOTT PENICAD PENICOD PENICUD PENIKET PENIKETT PENNEKETT PENNICARD PENNICEARD PENNICODD PENNICORD PENNICOTT PENNICUD PENNIKETT PENNYCAD PENNYCOTT PENNYCUD PENNYEND
PARNACOTT 119 Parnacoat Parnacote Parnecoat Parnecote Parnecott Parnecut Parnecutt Parnicoat Parnicote Parnicott Parnicutt Parnycoat Parnycote Parnycott Parnycutt Peenicott Penacot Penecad Peneceard Penecett Penecod Penecot Penecud Penekat Peneket Penekett Peneycud Peneycudd Peneycutt PENICAD Penicade Penicard Penicat Penicate Peniceard Peniced Penicet Penicoat Penicoate PENICOD Penicode Penicoot Penicord Penicorde Penicot Penicote Penicott PENICUD Penicudd Penicut Penicutt Peniend Penikat Penikate Peniked PENIKET PENIKETT Penikid Pennacott Pennaket Pennecett Penneket PENNEKETT Penneycidd Penneycod Penneycud Pennicad Pennicade PENNICARD Pennicarde Pennicate PENNICEARD Pennicoad Pennicoate Pennicod PENNICODD Pennicode Pennicood Pennicoot PENNICORD Pennicorde Pennicot Pennicote PENNICOTT Pennicotte PENNICUD Pennicudd Pennicutt Penniend Pennikat Pennikate Penniket PENNIKETT Pennikide PENNYCAD Pennycade Pennycard Pennycate Pennyceard Pennycid Pennycoad Pennycod Pennycodd Pennycode Pennycoed Pennycord Pennycorde Pennycot Pennycote PENNYCOTT PENNYCUD PENNYEND Pennykate Pennyrott Penocod Penycad Penycard Penycat
Parnall PARNELL
Parnecoat PARNACOTT PENICAD PENICOD PENICUD PENIKET PENIKETT PENNEKETT PENNICARD PENNICEARD PENNICODD PENNICORD PENNICOTT PENNICUD PENNIKETT PENNYCAD PENNYCOTT PENNYCUD PENNYEND
Parnecote PARNACOTT PENICAD PENICOD PENICUD PENIKET PENIKETT PENNEKETT PENNICARD PENNICEARD PENNICODD PENNICORD PENNICOTT PENNICUD PENNIKETT PENNYCAD PENNYCOTT PENNYCUD PENNYEND
Parnecott PARNACOTT PENICAD PENICOD PENICUD PENIKET PENIKETT PENNEKETT PENNICARD PENNICEARD PENNICODD PENNICORD PENNICOTT PENNICUD PENNIKETT PENNYCAD PENNYCOTT PENNYCUD PENNYEND
Parnecut PARNACOTT PENICAD PENICOD PENICUD PENIKET PENIKETT PENNEKETT PENNICARD PENNICEARD PENNICODD PENNICORD PENNICOTT PENNICUD PENNIKETT PENNYCAD PENNYCOTT PENNYCUD PENNYEND
Parnecutt PARNACOTT PENICAD PENICOD PENICUD PENIKET PENIKETT PENNEKETT PENNICARD PENNICEARD PENNICODD PENNICORD PENNICOTT PENNICUD PENNIKETT PENNYCAD PENNYCOTT PENNYCUD PENNYEND
Parnel PARNELL
PARNELL Parnall Parnel
Parnicoat PARNACOTT PENICAD PENICOD PENICUD PENIKET PENIKETT PENNEKETT PENNICARD PENNICEARD PENNICODD PENNICORD PENNICOTT PENNICUD PENNIKETT PENNYCAD PENNYCOTT PENNYCUD PENNYEND
Parnicote PARNACOTT PENICAD PENICOD PENICUD PENIKET PENIKETT PENNEKETT PENNICARD PENNICEARD PENNICODD PENNICORD PENNICOTT PENNICUD PENNIKETT PENNYCAD PENNYCOTT PENNYCUD PENNYEND
Parnicott PARNACOTT PENICAD PENICOD PENICUD PENIKET PENIKETT PENNEKETT PENNICARD PENNICEARD PENNICODD PENNICORD PENNICOTT PENNICUD PENNIKETT PENNYCAD PENNYCOTT PENNYCUD PENNYEND
Parnicutt PARNACOTT PENICAD PENICOD PENICUD PENIKET PENIKETT PENNEKETT PENNICARD PENNICEARD PENNICODD PENNICORD PENNICOTT PENNICUD PENNIKETT PENNYCAD PENNYCOTT PENNYCUD PENNYEND
Parnton PARRINGTON
Parnycoat PARNACOTT PENICAD PENICOD PENICUD PENIKET PENIKETT PENNEKETT PENNICARD PENNICEARD PENNICODD PENNICORD PENNICOTT PENNICUD PENNIKETT PENNYCAD PENNYCOTT PENNYCUD PENNYEND
Parnycote PARNACOTT PENICAD PENICOD PENICUD PENIKET PENIKETT PENNEKETT PENNICARD PENNICEARD PENNICODD PENNICORD PENNICOTT PENNICUD PENNIKETT PENNYCAD PENNYCOTT PENNYCUD PENNYEND
Parnycott PARNACOTT PENICAD PENICOD PENICUD PENIKET PENIKETT PENNEKETT PENNICARD PENNICEARD PENNICODD PENNICORD PENNICOTT PENNICUD PENNIKETT PENNYCAD PENNYCOTT PENNYCUD PENNYEND
Parnycutt PARNACOTT PENICAD PENICOD PENICUD PENIKET PENIKETT PENNEKETT PENNICARD PENNICEARD PENNICODD PENNICORD PENNICOTT PENNICUD PENNIKETT PENNYCAD PENNYCOTT PENNYCUD PENNYEND
Parrett PARROTT
Parrie PARRY PERRY
PARRINGTON Parinton Parnton
PARRISH PARISH
Parrot PARROTT
PARROTT Parrett Parrot
Parrow PERROW
PARRY 4 Parrie Pary PERRY
Parser PALSER PAZZERD PURSER
Parshall PURCHALL PURCHELL
Parshouse PARSUS PERSEHOUSE
Parsley PARSLOE PARSLOW
PARSLOE Parsley PARSLOW
PARSLOW Parsley PARSLOE
Parsnage PARSONAGE
PARSONAGE 4 Parsnage Pasnage Personage
PARSUS 5 Parkeshouse Parshouse PERSEHOUSE Pursehouse
PARTINGTON 12 Paddington Pardington Patdenden PATTENDEN Pattender Pattentine Pattenton Pattington Peddenden Peddington Petterden
Pary PARRY PERRY
Pasard PALSER PAZZERD PURSER
PASCO 4 PASCOE Pashco Paskow
PASCOE 4 PASCO Pashco Paskow
Pase PACE PASS PAYE PYE
Paser PALSER PAZZERD PURSER
Pashco PASCO PASCOE
Pasher PALSER PAZZERD PURSER
PASK Paske
Paske PASK
PASKENS Paskins
Paskins PASKENS
Paskow PASCO PASCOE
Pasnage PARSONAGE
PASS 5 PACE Pase PAYE PYE
Passard PALSER PAZZERD PURSER
Passer PALSER PAZZERD PURSER
Passerd PALSER PAZZERD PURSER
Passwer PALSER PAZZERD

If the name you are interested in is not here, try Section C.

PURSER
Patchen PATCHING
Patchin PATCHING
PATCHING Patchen Patchin
Patdenden PARTINGTON PATTENDEN
PATE 4 Pait PEAT PETT
PATERSON 4 PATTERSON PATTISON PETERSON
PATEY PEATY
PATTEN PATTERN
PATTENDEN 12 Paddington Pardington PARTINGTON Patdenden Pattender Pattentine Pattenton Pattington Peddenden Peddington Petterden
Pattender PARTINGTON PATTENDEN
Pattenson BATESON BETTINSON PATTINSON PATTISON
Pattentine PARTINGTON PATTENDEN
Pattenton PARTINGTON PATTENDEN
PATTERN PATTEN
PATTERSON 4 PATERSON PATTISON PETERSON
Patteson PATTINSON PATTISON
Pattesone PATTINSON PATTISON
Pattington PARTINGTON PATTENDEN
PATTINSON 11 BATESON Battenson Battison Battisson BETTINSON Bettison Pattenson Patteson Pattesone PATTISON
PATTISON 14 BATESON Battenson Battison Battisson BETTINSON Bettison PATERSON Pattenson PATTERSON Patteson Pattesone PATTINSON PETERSON
PAUK PALK
PAUL PAULL
PAULET 31 Palet Palett Pallet PALLETT Paulett Paulit Paullet Paulot Pawlet Pawlete Pawlett Polet Polett Poliet Polit Pollert POLLET POLLETT Polliet Polliot Pollit POLLITT Pollitte Pollot Poolit Poulett Poulette Powlet Powlett Powlit
Paulett PALLETT PAULET POLLET POLLETT POLLITT
PAULEY PAWLEY
Paulienge PAULIN PAULING
PAULIN 7 Paulienge PAULING Paulling Pawlin Pawling Pualing
PAULING 8 Paulienge PAULIN Paulling Pauwling Pawlin Pawling Pualing
Paulit PALLETT PAULET POLLET POLLETT POLLITT
PAULL PAUL
Paullet PALLETT PAULET POLLET POLLETT POLLITT
Paulling PAULIN PAULING
Paulot PALLETT PAULET POLLET POLLETT POLLITT
PAULSON PEARSON
Pauton PAWTON
Pauwling PAULING
Pavard PAVORD
Paverd PAVORD
PAVORD 4 Pafford Pavard Paverd
Pawlet PALLETT PAULET POLLET POLLETT POLLITT
Pawlete PALLETT PAULET POLLET POLLETT POLLITT
Pawlett PALLETT PAULET POLLET POLLETT POLLITT
PAWLEY PAULEY
Pawlin PAULIN PAULING
Pawling PAULIN PAULING
PAWTON Pauton Porton
Pax PACK PARK PECK
Paxen PAXSON PAXTON POGSON POXON POXSON POXTON
Paxon PAXSON PAXTON POGSON POXON POXSON POXTON
PAXSON 15 Packson Paxen Paxon PAXTON Pockson Pockton Pocson Pocton POGSON Poxan Poxen POXON POXSON POXTON
PAXTON 15 Packson Paxen Paxon PAXSON Pockson Pockton Pocson Pocton POGSON Poxan Poxen POXON POXSON POXTON
PAY Pae PAYE
PAYBODY 5 PEABODY PEBERDY PEBODY Pepperday
Payce PACE PAICE
PAYE 7 PACE Pae Pase PASS PAY PYE
Payley PALEY
Payling PALING
PAYN 4 PAIN PAINE PAYNE
PAYNE 7 PAIN PAINE Pane PAYN PEIN PINE
Pays PACE PAICE
Payse PACE PAICE
Payser PALSER PAZZERD PIZER POIZER POYSER PURSER PYZER
Payzer PALSER PAZZERD PURSER
Pazer PALSER PAZZERD PURSER
Pazzard PALSER PAZZERD PURSER
Pazzer PIZER POIZER POYSER PYZER
PAZZERD 17 Pafford PALSER Parser Pasard Paser Pasher Passard Passer Passerd Passwer Payser Payzer Pazer Pazzard Posheart PURSER
PEABODY 5 PAYBODY PEBERDY PEBODY Pepperday
Peacar PEAKER
PEACH 13 Peache PEACHEY Peachie PEACHY Peachye Pech Peche Pechie Peets Perts PETTS POTTS
Peache PEACH PEACHEY PEACHY
PEACHEY 9 PEACH Peache Peachie PEACHY Peachye Pech Peche Pechie
Peachie PEACH PEACHEY PEACHY
PEACHY 9 PEACH Peache PEACHEY Peachie Peachye Pech Peche Pechie
Peachye PEACH PEACHEY PEACHY
Peadon PEDEN
Peagan PEDEN
Peagram PINCOMBE PINKHAM
Peagrem PINCOMBE PINKHAM
Peagrim PINCOMBE PINKHAM
Peagrum PINCOMBE PINKHAM
Peagrym PINCOMBE PINKHAM
PEAK PEAKE
PEAKE PEAK
PEAKER 5 Peacar Peeker Pekar Peker
PEAL 8 Peale PEEL Peil PEILE Pele Piel Piele
Peale PEAL PEEL PEILE
Peapell PEPAL
Peaple PEPAL
PEARCE 7 PEARS PEARSE PEERCYE PEERS PEIRCE PIERCE
Pearcey PEARCY PIERCY
PEARCY 5 Pearcey Pearsey PERCY PIERCY
Pearkes PERKES PERKS
Pearkins PARKIN PERKIN PERKINS
Pearks PERKES PERKS
Pearless PEERLESS
PEARMAIN PEARMAN
PEARMAN 4 PEARMAIN PERMAIN Perman
PEARN Pearne Pern
Pearne PEARN
Pearpoint PEIRPOINT PIERPOINT
PEARS PEARCE
PEARSE 5 PEARCE PEERS PEIRCE PIERCE
Pearsey PEARCY PIERCY
PEARSON 5 PAULSON Pearsons PEIRSON PIERSON
Pearsons PEARSON
PEAT 5 Pait PATE PEET PETT
PEATER 6 Peiter PETER PETRE PETTER Petterd
PEATFIELD Petfield Pitfield
PEATY PATEY
PEBERDY 5 PAYBODY PEABODY PEBODY Pepperday
PEBODY 5 PAYBODY PEABODY PEBERDY Pepperday
Pech PEACH PEACHEY PEACHY
Peche PEACH PEACHEY PEACHY
Pechie PEACH PEACHEY PEACHY
PECK 6 PACK Packe Pake PARK Pax
Peckam PECKHAM
PECKET PECKITT PRICKETT
PECKHAM PACKHAM Peckam
PECKITT PECKET PRICKETT
Peckman PITMAN PITTMAN
PECKSTON PEXTON
Peckton PEXTON PICKSTONE PICTON
Pedan PEDEN
Peddenden PARTINGTON PATTENDEN
Peddington PARTINGTON PATTENDEN
Peddle PIDDLE
PEDEN 8 Paden Peadon Peagan Pedan Pedin Pedion Pedon
PEDERICK PETHERICK
Pedin PEDEN
Pedion PEDEN
Pedon PEDEN
Peeker PEAKER
PEEL 9 PEAL Peale Peele Peil PEILE Pele Piel Piele
Peele PEEL
Peenicott PARNACOTT PENICAD PENICOD PENICUD PENIKET PENIKETT PENNEKETT PENNICARD PENNICEARD PENNICODD PENNICORD PENNICOTT PENNICUD PENNIKETT PENNYCAD PENNYCOTT PENNYCUD PENNYEND
PEERCYE PEARCE
Peerles PEERLESS
PEERLESS Pearless Peerles
PEERS 5 PEARCE PEARSE PEIRCE PIERCE
PEET PEAT
Peets PEACH PETTS POTTS
Pegget PICKET PIGGOT PIGOT
PEGLAR PEGLER
PEGLER PEGLAR
Pegram PINCOMBE PINKHAM
Pegrem PINCOMBE PINKHAM
Pegrim PINCOMBE PINKHAM
Pegrum PINCOMBE PINKHAM
Pegrym PINCOMBE PINKHAM
Peil PEAL PEEL PEILE
PEILE 8 PEAL Peale PEEL Peil Pele Piel Piele
PEIN PAYNE PINE
PEIRCE 5 PEARCE PEARSE PEERS PIERCE
PEIRPOINT 4 Pearpoint Pheopoint PIERPOINT
PEIRSON PEARSON PIERSON
Peise PACE PAICE
Peiter PEATER PETER PETRE PETTER
Pekar PEAKER
Peker PEAKER
Pele PEAL PEEL PEILE
Pelgram PINCOMBE PINKHAM
Pelgrem PINCOMBE PINKHAM
Pelgrin PINCOMBE PINKHAM
Pelgrum PINCOMBE PINKHAM
Pelgrym PINCOMBE PINKHAM
PELLANT Pellen Pellent
Pellen PELLANT PELLIN PELLING
Pellent PELLANT
PELLEW BELLEW
PELLIN Pellen PELLING
PELLING Pellen PELLIN
PEMBLE 4 PIMBLE Pimblett Pymble
PEMBRIDGE 8 De pembridge De pemprugge Pembruge Pembrugge Penbrug Penbrugg Penebrugge
Pembruge PEMBRIDGE
Pembrugge PEMBRIDGE
Pemgram PINCOMBE PINKHAM
Pemgrem PINCOMBE PINKHAM
Pemgrin PINCOMBE PINKHAM
Pemgrum PINCOMBE PINKHAM
Pemgrym PINCOMBE PINKHAM
Pen PENN
Penacot PARNACOTT PENICAD PENICOD PENICUD PENIKET PENIKETT PENNEKETT PENNICARD PENNICEARD PENNICODD PENNICORD PENNICOTT PENNICUD PENNIKETT PENNYCAD PENNYCOTT PENNYCUD PENNYEND
Penbrug PEMBRIDGE
Penbrugg PEMBRIDGE
Penderel PENDRILL
Pendrell PENDRILL
PENDRILL Penderel Pendrell
Penebrugge PEMBRIDGE
Penecad PARNACOTT PENICAD PENICOD PENICUD PENIKET PENIKETT PENNEKETT PENNICARD PENNICEARD PENNICODD PENNICORD

If the name you are interested in is not here, try Section C.

PENNICOTT PENNICUD
PENNIKETT PENNYCAD
PENNYCOTT PENNYCUD
PENNYEND
Peneceard PARNACOTT
PENICAD PENICOD PENICUD
PENIKET PENIKETT
PENNEKETT PENNICARD
PENNICEARD PENNICODD
PENNICORD PENNICOTT
PENNICUD PENNIKETT
PENNYCAD PENNYCOTT
PENNYCUD PENNYEND
Penecett PARNACOTT
PENICAD PENICOD PENICUD
PENIKET PENIKETT
PENNEKETT PENNICARD
PENNICEARD PENNICODD
PENNICORD PENNICOTT
PENNICUD PENNIKETT
PENNYCAD PENNYCOTT
PENNYCUD PENNYEND
Penecod PARNACOTT PENICAD
PENICOD PENICUD PENIKET
PENIKETT PENNEKETT
PENNICARD PENNICEARD
PENNICODD PENNICORD
PENNICOTT PENNICUD
PENNIKETT PENNYCAD
PENNYCOTT PENNYCUD
PENNYEND
Penecot PARNACOTT PENICAD
PENICOD PENICUD PENIKET
PENIKETT PENNEKETT
PENNICARD PENNICEARD
PENNICODD PENNICORD
PENNICOTT PENNICUD
PENNIKETT PENNYCAD
PENNYCOTT PENNYCUD
PENNYEND
Penecud PARNACOTT PENICAD
PENICOD PENICUD PENIKET
PENIKETT PENNEKETT
PENNICARD PENNICEARD
PENNICODD PENNICORD
PENNICOTT PENNICUD
PENNIKETT PENNYCAD
PENNYCOTT PENNYCUD
PENNYEND
Penekat PARNACOTT PENICAD
PENICOD PENICUD PENIKET
PENIKETT PENNEKETT
PENNICARD PENNICEARD
PENNICODD PENNICORD
PENNICOTT PENNICUD
PENNIKETT PENNYCAD
PENNYCOTT PENNYCUD
PENNYEND
Peneket PARNACOTT PENICAD
PENICOD PENICUD PENIKET
PENIKETT PENNEKETT
PENNICARD PENNICEARD
PENNICODD PENNICORD
PENNICOTT PENNICUD
PENNIKETT PENNYCAD
PENNYCOTT PENNYCUD
PENNYEND
Penekett PARNACOTT
PENICAD PENICOD PENICUD
PENIKET PENIKETT
PENNEKETT PENNICARD
PENNICEARD PENNICODD
PENNICORD PENNICOTT
PENNICUD PENNIKETT
PENNYCAD PENNYCOTT
PENNYCUD PENNYEND
Peneni PINCKNEY PINKNEY
Peneycud PARNACOTT
PENICAD PENICOD PENICUD
PENIKET PENIKETT
PENNEKETT PENNICARD
PENNICEARD PENNICODD
PENNICORD PENNICOTT
PENNICUD PENNIKETT
PENNYCAD PENNYCOTT
PENNYCUD PENNYEND
Peneycudd PARNACOTT
PENICAD PENICOD PENICUD
PENIKET PENIKETT
PENNEKETT PENNICARD
PENNICEARD PENNICODD
PENNICORD PENNICOTT
PENNICUD PENNIKETT
PENNYCAD PENNYCOTT
PENNYCUD PENNYEND
Peneycutt PARNACOTT
PENICAD PENICOD PENICUD
PENIKET PENIKETT
PENNEKETT PENNICARD
PENNICEARD PENNICODD
PENNICORD PENNICOTT
PENNICUD PENNIKETT
PENNYCAD PENNYCOTT
PENNYCUD PENNYEND
PENGELLY PENGILLY
Pengeram PINCOMBE PINKHAM
Pengerham PINCOMBE
PINKHAM
PENGILLY PENGELLY
Pengram PINCOMBE PINKHAM
Pengrem PINCOMBE PINKHAM
Pengrim PINCOMBE PINKHAM
Pengrum PINCOMBE PINKHAM
Pengrym PINCOMBE PINKHAM
Penharood PENHORWOOD
Penharwood PENHORWOOD
Penhorad PENHORWOOD
Penhorn PINHORN
Penhorne PINHORN
PENHORWOOD 4 Penharood
Penharwood Penhorad
PENICAD 119 Parnacoat
Parnacote PARNACOTT
Parnecoat Parnecote
Parnecott Parnecut
Parnecutt Parnicoat
Parnicote Parnicott
Parnicutt Parnycoat
Parnycote Parnycott
Parnycutt Peenicott
Penacot Penecad
Peneceard Penecett
Penecod Penecot Penecud
Penekat Peneket
Penekett Peneycud
Peneycudd Peneycutt
Penicade Penicard
Penicat Penicate
Peniceard Peniced
Penicet Penicoat
Penicoate PENICOD
Penicode Penicoot
Penicord Penicorde
Penicot Penicote
Penicott PENICUD
Penicudd Penicut
Penicutt Peniend
Penikat Penikate
Peniked PENIKET
PENIKETT Penikid
Pennacott Pennaket
Pennecett Penneket
PENNEKETT Penneycidd
Penneycod Penneycud
Pennicad Pennicade
PENNICARD Pennicarde
Pennicate PENNICEARD
Pennicoad Pennicoate
Pennicod PENNICODD
Pennicode Pennicood
Pennicoot PENNICORD
Pennicorde Pennicot
Pennicote PENNICOTT
Pennicotte PENNICUD
Pennicudd Pennicutt
Penniend Pennikat
Pennikate Penniket
PENNIKETT Pennikide
PENNYCAD Pennycade
Pennycard Pennycate
Pennyceard Pennycid
Pennycoad Pennycod
Pennycodd Pennycode
Pennycoed Pennycord
Pennycorde Pennycot
Pennycote PENNYCOTT
PENNYCUD PENNYEND
Pennykate Pennyrott
Penocod Penycad
Penycard Penycat
Penicade PARNACOTT
PENICAD PENICOD PENICUD
PENIKET PENIKETT
PENNEKETT PENNICARD
PENNICEARD PENNICODD
PENNICORD PENNICOTT
PENNICUD PENNIKETT
PENNYCAD PENNYCOTT
PENNYCUD PENNYEND
Penicard PARNACOTT
PENICAD PENICOD PENICUD
PENIKET PENIKETT
PENNEKETT PENNICARD
PENNICEARD PENNICODD
PENNICORD PENNICOTT
PENNICUD PENNIKETT
PENNYCAD PENNYCOTT
PENNYCUD PENNYEND
Penicat PARNACOTT PENICAD
PENICOD PENICUD PENIKET
PENIKETT PENNEKETT
PENNICARD PENNICEARD
PENNICODD PENNICORD
PENNICOTT PENNICUD
PENNIKETT PENNYCAD
PENNYCOTT PENNYCUD
PENNYEND
Penicate PARNACOTT
PENICAD PENICOD PENICUD
PENIKET PENIKETT
PENNEKETT PENNICARD
PENNICEARD PENNICODD
PENNICORD PENNICOTT
PENNICUD PENNIKETT
PENNYCAD PENNYCOTT
PENNYCUD PENNYEND
Peniceard PARNACOTT
PENICAD PENICOD PENICUD
PENIKET PENIKETT
PENNEKETT PENNICARD
PENNICEARD PENNICODD
PENNICORD PENNICOTT
PENNICUD PENNIKETT
PENNYCAD PENNYCOTT
PENNYCUD PENNYEND
Peniced PARNACOTT PENICAD
PENICOD PENICUD PENIKET
PENIKETT PENNEKETT
PENNICARD PENNICEARD
PENNICODD PENNICORD
PENNICOTT PENNICUD
PENNIKETT PENNYCAD
PENNYCOTT PENNYCUD
PENNYEND
Penicet PARNACOTT PENICAD
PENICOD PENICUD PENIKET
PENIKETT PENNEKETT
PENNICARD PENNICEARD
PENNICODD PENNICORD
PENNICOTT PENNICUD
PENNIKETT PENNYCAD
PENNYCOTT PENNYCUD
PENNYEND
Penicoat PARNACOTT
PENICAD PENICOD PENICUD
PENIKET PENIKETT
PENNEKETT PENNICARD
PENNICEARD PENNICODD
PENNICORD PENNICOTT
PENNICUD PENNIKETT
PENNYCAD PENNYCOTT
PENNYCUD PENNYEND
Penicoate PARNACOTT
PENICAD PENICOD PENICUD
PENIKET PENIKETT
PENNEKETT PENNICARD
PENNICEARD PENNICODD
PENNICORD PENNICOTT
PENNICUD PENNIKETT
PENNYCAD PENNYCOTT
PENNYCUD PENNYEND
PENICOD 119 Parnacoat
Parnacote PARNACOTT
Parnecoat Parnecote
Parnecott Parnecut
Parnecutt Parnicoat
Parnicote Parnicott
Parnicutt Parnycoat
Parnycote Parnycott
Parnycutt Peenicott
Penacot Penecad
Peneceard Penecett
Penecod Penecot Penecud
Penekat Peneket
Penekett Peneycud
Peneycudd Peneycutt
PENICAD Penicade
Penicard Penicat
Penicate Peniceard
Peniced Penicet
Penicoat Penicoate
Penicode Penicoot
Penicord Penicorde
Penicot Penicote
Penicott PENICUD
Penicudd Penicut
Penicutt Peniend
Penikat Penikate
Peniked PENIKET
PENIKETT Penikid
Pennacott Pennaket
Pennecett Penneket
PENNEKETT Penneycidd
Penneycod Penneycud
Pennicad Pennicade
PENNICARD Pennicarde
Pennicate PENNICEARD
Pennicoad Pennicoate
Pennicod PENNICODD
Pennicode Pennicood
Pennicoot PENNICORD
Pennicorde Pennicot
Pennicote PENNICOTT
Pennicotte PENNICUD
Pennicudd Pennicutt
Penniend Pennikat
Pennikate Penniket
PENNIKETT Pennikide
PENNYCAD Pennycade
Pennycard Pennycate
Pennyceard Pennycid
Pennycoad Pennycod
Pennycodd Pennycode
Pennycoed Pennycord
Pennycorde Pennycot
Pennycote PENNYCOTT
PENNYCUD PENNYEND
Pennykate Pennyrott
Penocod Penycad
Penycard Penycat
Penicode PARNACOTT
PENICAD PENICOD PENICUD
PENIKET PENIKETT
PENNEKETT PENNICARD
PENNICEARD PENNICODD
PENNICORD PENNICOTT
PENNICUD PENNIKETT
PENNYCAD PENNYCOTT
PENNYCUD PENNYEND
Penicoot PARNACOTT
PENICAD PENICOD PENICUD
PENIKET PENIKETT
PENNEKETT PENNICARD
PENNICEARD PENNICODD
PENNICORD PENNICOTT
PENNICUD PENNIKETT

If the name you are interested in is not here, try Section C.

PENNYCAD PENNYCOTT
PENNYCUD PENNYEND
Penicord PARNACOTT
PENICAD PENICOD PENICUD
PENIKET PENIKETT
PENNEKETT PENNICARD
PENNICEARD PENNICODD
PENNICORD PENNICOTT
PENNICUD PENNIKETT
PENNYCAD PENNYCOTT
PENNYCUD PENNYEND
Penicorde PARNACOTT
PENICAD PENICOD PENICUD
PENIKET PENIKETT
PENNEKETT PENNICARD
PENNICEARD PENNICODD
PENNICORD PENNICOTT
PENNICUD PENNIKETT
PENNYCAD PENNYCOTT
PENNYCUD PENNYEND
Penicot PARNACOTT PENICAD
PENICOD PENICUD PENIKET
PENIKETT PENNEKETT
PENNICARD PENNICEARD
PENNICODD PENNICORD
PENNICOTT PENNICUD
PENNIKETT PENNYCAD
PENNYCOTT PENNYCUD
PENNYEND
Penicote PARNACOTT
PENICAD PENICOD PENICUD
PENIKET PENIKETT
PENNEKETT PENNICARD
PENNICEARD PENNICODD
PENNICORD PENNICOTT
PENNICUD PENNIKETT
PENNYCAD PENNYCOTT
PENNYCUD PENNYEND
Penicott PARNACOTT
PENICAD PENICOD PENICUD
PENIKET PENIKETT
PENNEKETT PENNICARD
PENNICEARD PENNICODD
PENNICORD PENNICOTT
PENNICUD PENNIKETT
PENNYCAD PENNYCOTT
PENNYCUD PENNYEND
PENICUD 119 Parnacoat
Parnacote PARNACOTT
Parnecoat Parnecote
Parnecott Parnecut
Parnecutt Parnicoat
Parnicote Parnicott
Parnicutt Parnycoat
Parnycote Parnycott
Parnycutt Peenicott
Penacot Penecad
Peneceard Penecett
Penecod Penecot Penecud
Penekat Peneket
Penekett Peneycud
Peneycudd Peneycutt
PENICAD Penicade
Penicard Penicat
Penicate Peniceard
Peniced Penicet
Penicoat Penicoate
PENICOD Penicode
Penicoot Penicord
Penicorde Penicot
Penicote Penicott
Penicudd Penicut
Penicutt Peniend
Penikat Penikate
Peniked PENIKET
PENIKETT Penikid
Pennacott Pennaket
Pennecett Penneket
PENNEKETT Penneycidd
Penneycod Penneycud
Pennicad Pennicade
PENNICARD Pennicarde
Pennicate PENNICEARD
Pennicoad Pennicoate
Pennicod PENNICODD
Pennicode Pennicood
Pennicoot PENNICORD
Pennicorde Pennicot
Pennicote PENNICOTT
Pennicotte PENNICUD
Pennicudd Pennicutt
Penniend Pennikat
Pennikate Penniket
PENNIKETT Pennikide
PENNYCAD Pennycade
Pennycard Pennycate
Pennyceard Pennycid
Pennycoad Pennycod
Pennycodd Pennycode
Pennycoed Pennycord
Pennycorde Pennycot
Pennycote PENNYCOTT
PENNYCUD PENNYEND
Pennykate Pennyrott
Penocod Penycad
Penycard Penycat
Penicudd PARNACOTT
PENICAD PENICOD PENICUD
PENIKET PENIKETT
PENNEKETT PENNICARD
PENNICEARD PENNICODD
PENNICORD PENNICOTT
PENNICUD PENNIKETT
PENNYCAD PENNYCOTT
PENNYCUD PENNYEND
Penicut PARNACOTT PENICAD
PENICOD PENICUD PENIKET
PENIKETT PENNEKETT
PENNICARD PENNICEARD
PENNICODD PENNICORD
PENNICOTT PENNICUD
PENNIKETT PENNYCAD
PENNYCOTT PENNYCUD
PENNYEND
Penicutt PARNACOTT
PENICAD PENICOD PENICUD
PENIKET PENIKETT
PENNEKETT PENNICARD
PENNICEARD PENNICODD
PENNICORD PENNICOTT
PENNICUD PENNIKETT
PENNYCAD PENNYCOTT
PENNYCUD PENNYEND
Penie PENNY WIMPENNY
Peniend PARNACOTT PENICAD
PENICOD PENICUD PENIKET
PENIKETT PENNEKETT
PENNICARD PENNICEARD
PENNICODD PENNICORD
PENNICOTT PENNICUD
PENNIKETT PENNYCAD
PENNYCOTT PENNYCUD
PENNYEND
Penikat PARNACOTT PENICAD
PENICOD PENICUD PENIKET
PENIKETT PENNEKETT
PENNICARD PENNICEARD
PENNICODD PENNICORD
PENNICOTT PENNICUD
PENNIKETT PENNYCAD
PENNYCOTT PENNYCUD
PENNYEND
Penikate PARNACOTT
PENICAD PENICOD PENICUD
PENIKET PENIKETT
PENNEKETT PENNICARD
PENNICEARD PENNICODD
PENNICORD PENNICOTT
PENNICUD PENNIKETT
PENNYCAD PENNYCOTT
PENNYCUD PENNYEND
Peniked PARNACOTT PENICAD
PENICOD PENICUD PENIKET
PENIKETT PENNEKETT
PENNICARD PENNICEARD
PENNICODD PENNICORD
PENNICOTT PENNICUD
PENNIKETT PENNYCAD
PENNYCOTT PENNYCUD
PENNYEND
PENIKET 119 Parnacoat
Parnacote PARNACOTT
Parnecoat Parnecote
Parnecott Parnecut
Parnecutt Parnicoat
Parnicote Parnicott
Parnicutt Parnycoat
Parnycote Parnycott
Parnycutt Peenicott
Penacot Penecad
Peneceard Penecett
Penecod Penecot Penecud
Penekat Peneket
Penekett Peneycud
Peneycudd Peneycutt
PENICAD Penicade
Penicard Penicat
Penicate Peniceard
Peniced Penicet
Penicoat Penicoate
PENICOD Penicode
Penicoot Penicord
Penicorde Penicot
Penicote Penicott
PENICUD Penicudd
Penicut Penicutt
Peniend Penikat
Penikate Peniked
PENIKETT Penikid
Pennacott Pennaket
Pennecett Penneket
PENNEKETT Penneycidd
Penneycod Penneycud
Pennicad Pennicade
PENNICARD Pennicarde
Pennicate PENNICEARD
Pennicoad Pennicoate
Pennicod PENNICODD
Pennicode Pennicood
Pennicoot PENNICORD
Pennicorde Pennicot
Pennicote PENNICOTT
Pennicotte PENNICUD
Pennicudd Pennicutt
Penniend Pennikat
Pennikate Penniket
PENNIKETT Pennikide
PENNYCAD Pennycade
Pennycard Pennycate
Pennyceard Pennycid
Pennycoad Pennycod
Pennycodd Pennycode
Pennycoed Pennycord
Pennycorde Pennycot
Pennycote PENNYCOTT
PENNYCUD PENNYEND
Pennykate Pennyrott
Penocod Penycad
Penycard Penycat
PENIKETT 119 Parnacoat
Parnacote PARNACOTT
Parnecoat Parnecote
Parnecott Parnecut
Parnecutt Parnicoat
Parnicote Parnicott
Parnicutt Parnycoat
Parnycote Parnycott
Parnycutt Peenicott
Penacot Penecad
Peneceard Penecett
Penecod Penecot Penecud
Penekat Peneket
Penekett Peneycud
Peneycudd Peneycutt
PENICAD Penicade
Penicard Penicat
Penicate Peniceard
Peniced Penicet
Penicoat Penicoate
PENICOD Penicode
Penicoot Penicord
Penicorde Penicot
Penicote Penicott
PENICUD Penicudd
Penicut Penicutt
Peniend Penikat
Penikate Peniked
PENIKET Penikid
Pennacott Pennaket
Pennecett Penneket
PENNEKETT Penneycidd
Penneycod Penneycud
Pennicad Pennicade
PENNICARD Pennicarde
Pennicate PENNICEARD
Pennicoad Pennicoate
Pennicod PENNICODD
Pennicode Pennicood
Pennicoot PENNICORD
Pennicorde Pennicot
Pennicote PENNICOTT
Pennicotte PENNICUD
Pennicudd Pennicutt
Penniend Pennikat
Pennikate Penniket
PENNIKETT Pennikide
PENNYCAD Pennycade
Pennycard Pennycate
Pennyceard Pennycid
Pennycoad Pennycod
Pennycodd Pennycode
Pennycoed Pennycord
Pennycorde Pennycot
Pennycote PENNYCOTT
PENNYCUD PENNYEND
Pennykate Pennyrott
Penocod Penycad
Penycard Penycat
Penikid PARNACOTT PENICAD
PENICOD PENICUD PENIKET
PENIKETT PENNEKETT
PENNICARD PENNICEARD
PENNICODD PENNICORD
PENNICOTT PENNICUD
PENNIKETT PENNYCAD
PENNYCOTT PENNYCUD
PENNYEND
Penil PENNILL PENNY PINEL
PINNEL PINNELL
Peniman PENNIMAN PENNYMAN
PENNYMON PENYMAN
Penion PINION
Penkhurst PANKHURST
PENN Pen Penne
Pennacott PARNACOTT
PENICAD PENICOD PENICUD
PENIKET PENIKETT
PENNEKETT PENNICARD
PENNICEARD PENNICODD
PENNICORD PENNICOTT
PENNICUD PENNIKETT
PENNYCAD PENNYCOTT
PENNYCUD PENNYEND
Pennaket PARNACOTT
PENICAD PENICOD PENICUD
PENIKET PENIKETT
PENNEKETT PENNICARD
PENNICEARD PENNICODD
PENNICORD PENNICOTT
PENNICUD PENNIKETT
PENNYCAD PENNYCOTT
PENNYCUD PENNYEND
Penne PENN
Pennecett PARNACOTT
PENICAD PENICOD PENICUD
PENIKET PENIKETT
PENNEKETT PENNICARD
PENNICEARD PENNICODD
PENNICORD PENNICOTT
PENNICUD PENNIKETT
PENNYCAD PENNYCOTT
PENNYCUD PENNYEND
Penneket PARNACOTT
PENICAD PENICOD PENICUD
PENIKET PENIKETT
PENNEKETT PENNICARD

If the name you are interested in is not here, try Section C.

PENNICEARD PENNICODD
PENNICORD PENNICOTT
PENNICUD PENNIKETT
PENNYCAD PENNYCOTT
PENNYCUD PENNYEND
PENNEKETT 119 Parnacoat
Parnacote PARNACOTT
Parnecoat Parnecote
Parnecott Parnecut
Parnecutt Parnicoat
Parnicote Parnicott
Parnicutt Parnycoat
Parnycote Parnycott
Parnycutt Peenicott
Penacot Penecad
Peneceard Penecett
Penecod Penecot Penecud
Penekat Peneket
Penekett Peneycud
Peneycudd Peneycutt
PENICAD Penicade
Penicard Penicat
Penicate Peniceard
Peniced Penicet
Penicoat Penicoate
PENICOD Penicode
Penicoot Penicord
Penicorde Penicot
Penicote Penicott
PENICUD Penicudd
Penicut Penicutt
Peniend Penikat
Penikate Peniked
PENIKET PENIKETT
Penikid Pennacott
Pennaket Pennecett
Penneket Penneycidd
Penneycod Penneycud
Pennicad Pennicade
PENNICARD Pennicarde
Pennicate PENNICEARD
Pennicoad Pennicoate
Pennicod PENNICODD
Pennicode Pennicood
Pennicoot PENNICORD
Pennicorde Pennicot
Pennicote PENNICOTT
Pennicotte PENNICUD
Pennicudd Pennicutt
Penniend Pennikat
Pennikate Penniket
PENNIKETT Pennikide
PENNYCAD Pennycade
Pennycard Pennycate
Pennyceard Pennycid
Pennycoad Pennycod
Pennycodd Pennycode
Pennycoed Pennycord
Pennycorde Pennycot
Pennycote PENNYCOTT
PENNYCUD PENNYEND
Pennykate Pennyrott
Penocod Penycad
Penycard Penycat
PENNEY 6 Pennie Penning
PENNY PENY PINNING
Penneycidd PARNACOTT
PENICAD PENICOD PENICUD
PENIKET PENIKETT
PENNEKETT PENNICARD
PENNICEARD PENNICODD
PENNICORD PENNICOTT
PENNICUD PENNIKETT
PENNYCAD PENNYCOTT
PENNYCUD PENNYEND
Penneycod PARNACOTT
PENICAD PENICOD PENICUD
PENIKET PENIKETT
PENNEKETT PENNICARD
PENNICEARD PENNICODD
PENNICORD PENNICOTT
PENNICUD PENNIKETT
PENNYCAD PENNYCOTT
PENNYCUD PENNYEND

Penneycud PARNACOTT
PENICAD PENICOD PENICUD
PENIKET PENIKETT
PENNEKETT PENNICARD
PENNICEARD PENNICODD
PENNICORD PENNICOTT
PENNICUD PENNIKETT
PENNYCAD PENNYCOTT
PENNYCUD PENNYEND
Penneyman PENNIMAN
PENNYMAN PENNYMON
PENYMAN
Pennicad PARNACOTT
PENICAD PENICOD PENICUD
PENIKET PENIKETT
PENNEKETT PENNICARD
PENNICEARD PENNICODD
PENNICORD PENNICOTT
PENNICUD PENNIKETT
PENNYCAD PENNYCOTT
PENNYCUD PENNYEND
Pennicade PARNACOTT
PENICAD PENICOD PENICUD
PENIKET PENIKETT
PENNEKETT PENNICARD
PENNICEARD PENNICODD
PENNICORD PENNICOTT
PENNICUD PENNIKETT
PENNYCAD PENNYCOTT
PENNYCUD PENNYEND
PENNICARD 119 Parnacoat
Parnacote PARNACOTT
Parnecoat Parnecote
Parnecott Parnecut
Parnecutt Parnicoat
Parnicote Parnicott
Parnicutt Parnycoat
Parnycote Parnycott
Parnycutt Peenicott
Penacot Penecad
Peneceard Penecett
Penecod Penecot Penecud
Penekat Peneket
Penekett Peneycud
Peneycudd Peneycutt
PENICAD Penicade
Penicard Penicat
Penicate Peniceard
Peniced Penicet
Penicoat Penicoate
PENICOD Penicode
Penicoot Penicord
Penicorde Penicot
Penicote Penicott
PENICUD Penicudd
Penicut Penicutt
Peniend Penikat
Penikate Peniked
PENIKET PENIKETT
Penikid Pennacott
Pennaket Pennecett
Penneket PENNEKETT
Penneycidd Penneycod
Penneycud Pennicad
Pennicade Pennicarde
Pennicate PENNICEARD
Pennicoad Pennicoate
Pennicod PENNICODD
Pennicode Pennicood
Pennicoot PENNICORD
Pennicorde Pennicot
Pennicote PENNICOTT
Pennicotte PENNICUD
Pennicudd Pennicutt
Penniend Pennikat
Pennikate Penniket
PENNIKETT Pennikide
PENNYCAD Pennycade
Pennycard Pennycate
Pennyceard Pennycid
Pennycoad Pennycod
Pennycodd Pennycode
Pennycoed Pennycord
Pennycorde Pennycot

Pennycote PENNYCOTT
PENNYCUD PENNYEND
Pennykate Pennyrott
Penocod Penycad
Penycard Penycat
Pennicarde PARNACOTT
PENICAD PENICOD PENICUD
PENIKET PENIKETT
PENNEKETT PENNICARD
PENNICEARD PENNICODD
PENNICORD PENNICOTT
PENNICUD PENNIKETT
PENNYCAD PENNYCOTT
PENNYCUD PENNYEND
Pennicate PARNACOTT
PENICAD PENICOD PENICUD
PENIKET PENIKETT
PENNEKETT PENNICARD
PENNICEARD PENNICODD
PENNICORD PENNICOTT
PENNICUD PENNIKETT
PENNYCAD PENNYCOTT
PENNYCUD PENNYEND
PENNICEARD 119 Parnacoat
Parnacote PARNACOTT
Parnecoat Parnecote
Parnecott Parnecut
Parnecutt Parnicoat
Parnicote Parnicott
Parnicutt Parnycoat
Parnycote Parnycott
Parnycutt Peenicott
Penacot Penecad
Peneceard Penecett
Penecod Penecot Penecud
Penekat Peneket
Penekett Peneycud
Peneycudd Peneycutt
PENICAD Penicade
Penicard Penicat
Penicate Peniceard
Peniced Penicet
Penicoat Penicoate
PENICOD Penicode
Penicoot Penicord
Penicorde Penicot
Penicote Penicott
PENICUD Penicudd
Penicut Penicutt
Peniend Penikat
Penikate Peniked
PENIKET PENIKETT
Penikid Pennacott
Pennaket Pennecett
Penneket PENNEKETT
Penneycidd Penneycod
Penneycud Pennicad
Pennicade PENNICARD
Pennicarde Pennicate
Pennicoad Pennicoate
Pennicod PENNICODD
Pennicode Pennicood
Pennicoot PENNICORD
Pennicorde Pennicot
Pennicote PENNICOTT
Pennicotte PENNICUD
Pennicudd Pennicutt
Penniend Pennikat
Pennikate Penniket
PENNIKETT Pennikide
PENNYCAD Pennycade
Pennycard Pennycate
Pennyceard Pennycid
Pennycoad Pennycod
Pennycodd Pennycode
Pennycoed Pennycord
Pennycorde Pennycot
Pennycote PENNYCOTT
PENNYCUD PENNYEND
Pennykate Pennyrott
Penocod Penycad
Penycard Penycat
Pennicoad PARNACOTT
PENICAD PENICOD PENICUD

PENIKET PENIKETT
PENNEKETT PENNICARD
PENNICEARD PENNICODD
PENNICORD PENNICOTT
PENNICUD PENNIKETT
PENNYCAD PENNYCOTT
PENNYCUD PENNYEND
Pennicoate PARNACOTT
PENICAD PENICOD PENICUD
PENIKET PENIKETT
PENNEKETT PENNICARD
PENNICEARD PENNICODD
PENNICORD PENNICOTT
PENNICUD PENNIKETT
PENNYCAD PENNYCOTT
PENNYCUD PENNYEND
Pennicod PARNACOTT
PENICAD PENICOD PENICUD
PENIKET PENIKETT
PENNEKETT PENNICARD
PENNICEARD PENNICODD
PENNICORD PENNICOTT
PENNICUD PENNIKETT
PENNYCAD PENNYCOTT
PENNYCUD PENNYEND
PENNICODD 119 Parnacoat
Parnacote PARNACOTT
Parnecoat Parnecote
Parnecott Parnecut
Parnecutt Parnicoat
Parnicote Parnicott
Parnicutt Parnycoat
Parnycote Parnycott
Parnycutt Peenicott
Penacot Penecad
Peneceard Penecett
Penecod Penecot Penecud
Penekat Peneket
Penekett Peneycud
Peneycudd Peneycutt
PENICAD Penicade
Penicard Penicat
Penicate Peniceard
Peniced Penicet
Penicoat Penicoate
PENICOD Penicode
Penicoot Penicord
Penicorde Penicot
Penicote Penicott
PENICUD Penicudd
Penicut Penicutt
Peniend Penikat
Penikate Peniked
PENIKET PENIKETT
Penikid Pennacott
Pennaket Pennecett
Penneket PENNEKETT
Penneycidd Penneycod
Penneycud Pennicad
Pennicade PENNICARD
Pennicarde Pennicate
PENNICEARD Pennicoad
Pennicoate Pennicod
Pennicode Pennicood
Pennicoot PENNICORD
Pennicorde Pennicot
Pennicote PENNICOTT
Pennicotte PENNICUD
Pennicudd Pennicutt
Penniend Pennikat
Pennikate Penniket
PENNIKETT Pennikide
PENNYCAD Pennycade
Pennycard Pennycate
Pennyceard Pennycid
Pennycoad Pennycod
Pennycodd Pennycode
Pennycoed Pennycord
Pennycorde Pennycot
Pennycote PENNYCOTT
PENNYCUD PENNYEND
Pennykate Pennyrott
Penocod Penycad
Penycard Penycat

If the name you are interested in is not here, try Section C.

Pennicode PARNACOTT
PENICAD PENICOD PENICUD
PENIKET PENIKETT
PENNEKETT PENNICARD
PENNICEARD PENNICODD
PENNICORD PENNICOTT
PENNICUD PENNIKETT
PENNYCAD PENNYCOTT
PENNYCUD PENNYEND
Pennicood PARNACOTT
PENICAD PENICOD PENICUD
PENIKET PENIKETT
PENNEKETT PENNICARD
PENNICEARD PENNICODD
PENNICORD PENNICOTT
PENNICUD PENNIKETT
PENNYCAD PENNYCOTT
PENNYCUD PENNYEND
Pennicoot PARNACOTT
PENICAD PENICOD PENICUD
PENIKET PENIKETT
PENNEKETT PENNICARD
PENNICEARD PENNICODD
PENNICORD PENNICOTT
PENNICUD PENNIKETT
PENNYCAD PENNYCOTT
PENNYCUD PENNYEND
PENNICORD 119 Parnacoat
Parnacote PARNACOTT
Parnecoat Parnecote
Parnecott Parnecut
Parnecutt Parnicoat
Parnicote Parnicott
Parnicutt Parnycoat
Parnycote Parnycott
Parnycutt Peenicott
Penacot Penecad
Peneceard Penecett
Penecod Penecot Penecud
Penekat Peneket
Penekett Peneycud
Peneycudd Peneycutt
PENICAD Penicade
Penicard Penicat
Penicate Peniceard
Peniced Penicet
Penicoat Penicoate
PENICOD Penicode
Penicoot Penicord
Penicorde Penicot
Penicote Penicott
PENICUD Penicudd
Penicut Penicutt
Peniend Penikat
Penikate Peniked
PENIKET PENIKETT
Penikid Pennacott
Pennaket Pennecett
Penneket PENNEKETT
Penneycidd Penneycod
Penneycud Pennicad
Pennicade PENNICARD
Pennicarde Pennicate
PENNICEARD Pennicoad
Pennicoate Pennicod
PENNICODD Pennicode
Pennicood Pennicoot
Pennicorde Pennicot
Pennicote PENNICOTT
Pennicotte PENNICUD
Pennicudd Pennicutt
Penniend Pennikat
Pennikate Penniket
PENNIKETT Pennikide
PENNYCAD Pennycade
Pennycard Pennycate
Pennyceard Pennycid
Pennycoad Pennycod
Pennycodd Pennycode
Pennycoed Pennycord
Pennycorde Pennycot
Pennycote PENNYCOTT
PENNYCUD PENNYEND
Pennykate Pennyrott
Penocod Penycad
Penycard Penycat
Pennicorde PARNACOTT
PENICAD PENICOD PENICUD
PENIKET PENIKETT
PENNEKETT PENNICARD
PENNICEARD PENNICODD
PENNICORD PENNICOTT
PENNICUD PENNIKETT
PENNYCAD PENNYCOTT
PENNYCUD PENNYEND
Pennicot PARNACOTT
PENICAD PENICOD PENICUD
PENIKET PENIKETT
PENNEKETT PENNICARD
PENNICEARD PENNICODD
PENNICORD PENNICOTT
PENNICUD PENNIKETT
PENNYCAD PENNYCOTT
PENNYCUD PENNYEND
Pennicote PARNACOTT
PENICAD PENICOD PENICUD
PENIKET PENIKETT
PENNEKETT PENNICARD
PENNICEARD PENNICODD
PENNICORD PENNICOTT
PENNICUD PENNIKETT
PENNYCAD PENNYCOTT
PENNYCUD PENNYEND
PENNICOTT 119 Parnacoat
Parnacote PARNACOTT
Parnecoat Parnecote
Parnecott Parnecut
Parnecutt Parnicoat
Parnicote Parnicott
Parnicutt Parnycoat
Parnycote Parnycott
Parnycutt Peenicott
Penacot Penecad
Peneceard Penecett
Penecod Penecot Penecud
Penekat Peneket
Penekett Peneycud
Peneycudd Peneycutt
PENICAD Penicade
Penicard Penicat
Penicate Peniceard
Peniced Penicet
Penicoat Penicoate
PENICOD Penicode
Penicoot Penicord
Penicorde Penicot
Penicote Penicott
PENICUD Penicudd
Penicut Penicutt
Peniend Penikat
Penikate Peniked
PENIKET PENIKETT
Penikid Pennacott
Pennaket Pennecett
Penneket PENNEKETT
Penneycidd Penneycod
Penneycud Pennicad
Pennicade PENNICARD
Pennicarde Pennicate
PENNICEARD Pennicoad
Pennicoate Pennicod
PENNICODD Pennicode
Pennicood Pennicoot
PENNICORD Pennicorde
Pennicot Pennicote
Pennicotte PENNICUD
Pennicudd Pennicutt
Penniend Pennikat
Pennikate Penniket
PENNIKETT Pennikide
PENNYCAD Pennycade
Pennycard Pennycate
Pennyceard Pennycid
Pennycoad Pennycod
Pennycodd Pennycode
Pennycoed Pennycord
Pennycorde Pennycot
Pennycote PENNYCOTT
PENNYCUD PENNYEND
Pennykate Pennyrott
Penocod Penycad
Penycard Penycat
Pennicotte PARNACOTT
PENICAD PENICOD PENICUD
PENIKET PENIKETT
PENNEKETT PENNICARD
PENNICEARD PENNICODD
PENNICORD PENNICOTT
PENNICUD PENNIKETT
PENNYCAD PENNYCOTT
PENNYCUD PENNYEND
PENNICUD 119 Parnacoat
Parnacote PARNACOTT
Parnecoat Parnecote
Parnecott Parnecut
Parnecutt Parnicoat
Parnicote Parnicott
Parnicutt Parnycoat
Parnycote Parnycott
Parnycutt Peenicott
Penacot Penecad
Peneceard Penecett
Penecod Penecot Penecud
Penekat Peneket
Penekett Peneycud
Peneycudd Peneycutt
PENICAD Penicade
Penicard Penicat
Penicate Peniceard
Peniced Penicet
Penicoat Penicoate
PENICOD Penicode
Penicoot Penicord
Penicorde Penicot
Penicote Penicott
PENICUD Penicudd
Penicut Penicutt
Peniend Penikat
Penikate Peniked
PENIKET PENIKETT
Penikid Pennacott
Pennaket Pennecett
Penneket PENNEKETT
Penneycidd Penneycod
Penneycud Pennicad
Pennicade PENNICARD
Pennicarde Pennicate
PENNICEARD Pennicoad
Pennicoate Pennicod
PENNICODD Pennicode
Pennicood Pennicoot
PENNICORD Pennicorde
Pennicot Pennicote
PENNICOTT Pennicotte
Pennicudd Pennicutt
Penniend Pennikat
Pennikate Penniket
PENNIKETT Pennikide
PENNYCAD Pennycade
Pennycard Pennycate
Pennyceard Pennycid
Pennycoad Pennycod
Pennycodd Pennycode
Pennycoed Pennycord
Pennycorde Pennycot
Pennycote PENNYCOTT
PENNYCUD PENNYEND
Pennykate Pennyrott
Penocod Penycad
Penycard Penycat
Pennicudd PARNACOTT
PENICAD PENICOD PENICUD
PENIKET PENIKETT
PENNEKETT PENNICARD
PENNICEARD PENNICODD
PENNICORD PENNICOTT
PENNICUD PENNIKETT
PENNYCAD PENNYCOTT
PENNYCUD PENNYEND
Pennicutt PARNACOTT
PENICAD PENICOD PENICUD
PENIKET PENIKETT
PENNEKETT PENNICARD
PENNICEARD PENNICODD
PENNICORD PENNICOTT
PENNICUD PENNIKETT
PENNYCAD PENNYCOTT
PENNYCUD PENNYEND
Pennie PENNEY PENNY
Penniend PARNACOTT
PENICAD PENICOD PENICUD
PENIKET PENIKETT
PENNEKETT PENNICARD
PENNICEARD PENNICODD
PENNICORD PENNICOTT
PENNICUD PENNIKETT
PENNYCAD PENNYCOTT
PENNYCUD PENNYEND
Pennifer PANNIFER
Pennikat PARNACOTT
PENICAD PENICOD PENICUD
PENIKET PENIKETT
PENNEKETT PENNICARD
PENNICEARD PENNICODD
PENNICORD PENNICOTT
PENNICUD PENNIKETT
PENNYCAD PENNYCOTT
PENNYCUD PENNYEND
Pennikate PARNACOTT
PENICAD PENICOD PENICUD
PENIKET PENIKETT
PENNEKETT PENNICARD
PENNICEARD PENNICODD
PENNICORD PENNICOTT
PENNICUD PENNIKETT
PENNYCAD PENNYCOTT
PENNYCUD PENNYEND
Penniket PARNACOTT
PENICAD PENICOD PENICUD
PENIKET PENIKETT
PENNEKETT PENNICARD
PENNICEARD PENNICODD
PENNICORD PENNICOTT
PENNICUD PENNIKETT
PENNYCAD PENNYCOTT
PENNYCUD PENNYEND
PENNIKETT 119 Parnacoat
Parnacote PARNACOTT
Parnecoat Parnecote
Parnecott Parnecut
Parnecutt Parnicoat
Parnicote Parnicott
Parnicutt Parnycoat
Parnycote Parnycott
Parnycutt Peenicott
Penacot Penecad
Peneceard Penecett
Penecod Penecot Penecud
Penekat Peneket
Penekett Peneycud
Peneycudd Peneycutt
PENICAD Penicade
Penicard Penicat
Penicate Peniceard
Peniced Penicet
Penicoat Penicoate
PENICOD Penicode
Penicoot Penicord
Penicorde Penicot
Penicote Penicott
PENICUD Penicudd
Penicut Penicutt
Peniend Penikat
Penikate Peniked
PENIKET PENIKETT
Penikid Pennacott
Pennaket Pennecett
Penneket PENNEKETT
Penneycidd Penneycod
Penneycud Pennicad
Pennicade PENNICARD
Pennicarde Pennicate
PENNICEARD Pennicoad
Pennicoate Pennicod
PENNICODD Pennicode
Pennicood Pennicoot

If the name you are interested in is not here, try Section C.

PENNICORD Pennicorde
Pennicot Pennicote
PENNICOTT Pennicotte
PENNICUD Pennicudd
Pennicutt Penniend
Pennikat Pennikate
Penniket Pennikide
PENNYCAD Pennycade
Pennycard Pennycate
Pennyceard Pennycid
Pennycoad Pennycod
Pennycodd Pennycode
Pennycoed Pennycord
Pennycorde Pennycot
Pennycote PENNYCOTT
PENNYCUD PENNYEND
Pennykate Pennyrott
Penocod Penycad
Penycard Penycat
Pennikide PARNACOTT
PENICAD PENICOD PENICUD
PENIKET PENIKETT
PENNEKETT PENNICARD
PENNICEARD PENNICODD
PENNICORD PENNICOTT
PENNICUD PENNIKETT
PENNYCAD PENNYCOTT
PENNYCUD PENNYEND
Pennil PENNILL PENNY
PINEL PINNEL PINNELL
PENNILL 9 Penil Pennil
PENNY PINEL Pinell
PINNEL PINNELL Pynnell
PENNIMAN 7 Peniman
Penneyman PENNYMAN
PENNYMON PENYMAN
Ponnyman
Penning PENNEY PINNING
PENNY 17 Penie Penil
PENNEY Pennie Pennil
PENNILL PENY PINEL
Pinell PINNEL PINNELL
Pynnell Whimpenie
Wimpennie WIMPENNY
Winpenny
PENNYCAD 119 Parnacoat
Parnacote PARNACOTT
Parnecoat Parnecote
Parnecott Parnecut
Parnecutt Parnicoat
Parnicote Parnicott
Parnicutt Parnycoat
Parnycote Parnycott
Parnycutt Peenicott
Penacot Penecad
Peneceard Penecett
Penecod Penecot Penecud
Penekat Peneket
Penekett Peneycud
Peneycudd Peneycutt
PENICAD Penicade
Penicard Penicat
Penicate Peniceard
Peniced Penicet
Penicoat Penicoate
PENICOD Penicode
Penicoot Penicord
Penicorde Penicot
Penicote Penicott
PENICUD Penicudd
Penicut Penicutt
Peniend Penikat
Penikate Peniked
PENIKET PENIKETT
Penikid Pennacott
Pennaket Pennecett
Penneket PENNEKETT
Penneycidd Penneycod
Penneycud Pennicad
Pennicade PENNICARD
Pennicarde Pennicate
PENNICEARD Pennicoad
Pennicoate Pennicod
PENNICODD Pennicode
Pennicood Pennicoot
PENNICORD Pennicorde
Pennicot Pennicote
PENNICOTT Pennicotte
PENNICUD Pennicudd
Pennicutt Penniend
Pennikat Pennikate
Penniket PENNIKETT
Pennikide Pennycade
Pennycard Pennycate
Pennyceard Pennycid
Pennycoad Pennycod
Pennycodd Pennycode
Pennycoed Pennycord
Pennycorde Pennycot
Pennycote PENNYCOTT
PENNYCUD PENNYEND
Pennykate Pennyrott
Penocod Penycad
Penycard Penycat
Pennycade PARNACOTT
PENICAD PENICOD PENICUD
PENIKET PENIKETT
PENNEKETT PENNICARD
PENNICEARD PENNICODD
PENNICORD PENNICOTT
PENNICUD PENNIKETT
PENNYCAD PENNYCOTT
PENNYCUD PENNYEND
Pennycard PARNACOTT
PENICAD PENICOD PENICUD
PENIKET PENIKETT
PENNEKETT PENNICARD
PENNICEARD PENNICODD
PENNICORD PENNICOTT
PENNICUD PENNIKETT
PENNYCAD PENNYCOTT
PENNYCUD PENNYEND
Pennycate PARNACOTT
PENICAD PENICOD PENICUD
PENIKET PENIKETT
PENNEKETT PENNICARD
PENNICEARD PENNICODD
PENNICORD PENNICOTT
PENNICUD PENNIKETT
PENNYCAD PENNYCOTT
PENNYCUD PENNYEND
Pennyceard PARNACOTT
PENICAD PENICOD PENICUD
PENIKET PENIKETT
PENNEKETT PENNICARD
PENNICEARD PENNICODD
PENNICORD PENNICOTT
PENNICUD PENNIKETT
PENNYCAD PENNYCOTT
PENNYCUD PENNYEND
Pennycid PARNACOTT
PENICAD PENICOD PENICUD
PENIKET PENIKETT
PENNEKETT PENNICARD
PENNICEARD PENNICODD
PENNICORD PENNICOTT
PENNICUD PENNIKETT
PENNYCAD PENNYCOTT
PENNYCUD PENNYEND
Pennycoad PARNACOTT
PENICAD PENICOD PENICUD
PENIKET PENIKETT
PENNEKETT PENNICARD
PENNICEARD PENNICODD
PENNICORD PENNICOTT
PENNICUD PENNIKETT
PENNYCAD PENNYCOTT
PENNYCUD PENNYEND
Pennycod PARNACOTT
PENICAD PENICOD PENICUD
PENIKET PENIKETT
PENNEKETT PENNICARD
PENNICEARD PENNICODD
PENNICORD PENNICOTT
PENNICUD PENNIKETT
PENNYCAD PENNYCOTT
PENNYCUD PENNYEND
Pennycodd PARNACOTT
PENICAD PENICOD PENICUD
PENIKET PENIKETT
PENNEKETT PENNICARD
PENNICEARD PENNICODD
PENNICORD PENNICOTT
PENNICUD PENNIKETT
PENNYCAD PENNYCOTT
PENNYCUD PENNYEND
Pennycode PARNACOTT
PENICAD PENICOD PENICUD
PENIKET PENIKETT
PENNEKETT PENNICARD
PENNICEARD PENNICODD
PENNICORD PENNICOTT
PENNICUD PENNIKETT
PENNYCAD PENNYCOTT
PENNYCUD PENNYEND
Pennycoed PARNACOTT
PENICAD PENICOD PENICUD
PENIKET PENIKETT
PENNEKETT PENNICARD
PENNICEARD PENNICODD
PENNICORD PENNICOTT
PENNICUD PENNIKETT
PENNYCAD PENNYCOTT
PENNYCUD PENNYEND
Pennycord PARNACOTT
PENICAD PENICOD PENICUD
PENIKET PENIKETT
PENNEKETT PENNICARD
PENNICEARD PENNICODD
PENNICORD PENNICOTT
PENNICUD PENNIKETT
PENNYCAD PENNYCOTT
PENNYCUD PENNYEND
Pennycorde PARNACOTT
PENICAD PENICOD PENICUD
PENIKET PENIKETT
PENNEKETT PENNICARD
PENNICEARD PENNICODD
PENNICORD PENNICOTT
PENNICUD PENNIKETT
PENNYCAD PENNYCOTT
PENNYCUD PENNYEND
Pennycot PARNACOTT
PENICAD PENICOD PENICUD
PENIKET PENIKETT
PENNEKETT PENNICARD
PENNICEARD PENNICODD
PENNICORD PENNICOTT
PENNICUD PENNIKETT
PENNYCAD PENNYCOTT
PENNYCUD PENNYEND
Pennycote PARNACOTT
PENICAD PENICOD PENICUD
PENIKET PENIKETT
PENNEKETT PENNICARD
PENNICEARD PENNICODD
PENNICORD PENNICOTT
PENNICUD PENNIKETT
PENNYCAD PENNYCOTT
PENNYCUD PENNYEND
PENNYCOTT 119 Parnacoat
Parnacote PARNACOTT
Parnecoat Parnecote
Parnecott Parnecut
Parnecutt Parnicoat
Parnicote Parnicott
Parnicutt Parnycoat
Parnycote Parnycott
Parnycutt Peenicott
Penacot Penecad
Peneceard Penecett
Penecod Penecot Penecud
Penekat Peneket
Penekett Peneycud
Peneycudd Peneycutt
PENICAD Penicade
Penicard Penicat
Penicate Peniceard
Peniced Penicet
Penicoat Penicoate
PENICOD Penicode
Penicoot Penicord
Penicorde Penicot
Penicote Penicott
PENICUD Penicudd
Penicut Penicutt
Peniend Penikat
Penikate Peniked
PENIKET PENIKETT
Penikid Pennacott
Pennaket Pennecett
Penneket PENNEKETT
Penneycidd Penneycod
Penneycud Pennicad
Pennicade PENNICARD
Pennicarde Pennicate
PENNICEARD Pennicoad
Pennicoate Pennicod
PENNICODD Pennicode
Pennicood Pennicoot
PENNICORD Pennicorde
Pennicot Pennicote
PENNICOTT Pennicotte
PENNICUD Pennicudd
Pennicutt Penniend
Pennikat Pennikate
Penniket PENNIKETT
Pennikide PENNYCAD
Pennycade Pennycard
Pennycate Pennyceard
Pennycid Pennycoad
Pennycod Pennycodd
Pennycode Pennycoed
Pennycord Pennycorde
Pennycot Pennycote
PENNYCUD PENNYEND
Pennykate Pennyrott
Penocod Penycad
Penycard Penycat
PENNYCUD 119 Parnacoat
Parnacote PARNACOTT
Parnecoat Parnecote
Parnecott Parnecut
Parnecutt Parnicoat
Parnicote Parnicott
Parnicutt Parnycoat
Parnycote Parnycott
Parnycutt Peenicott
Penacot Penecad
Peneceard Penecett
Penecod Penecot Penecud
Penekat Peneket
Penekett Peneycud
Peneycudd Peneycutt
PENICAD Penicade
Penicard Penicat
Penicate Peniceard
Peniced Penicet
Penicoat Penicoate
PENICOD Penicode
Penicoot Penicord
Penicorde Penicot
Penicote Penicott
PENICUD Penicudd
Penicut Penicutt
Peniend Penikat
Penikate Peniked
PENIKET PENIKETT
Penikid Pennacott
Pennaket Pennecett
Penneket PENNEKETT
Penneycidd Penneycod
Penneycud Pennicad
Pennicade PENNICARD
Pennicarde Pennicate
PENNICEARD Pennicoad
Pennicoate Pennicod
PENNICODD Pennicode
Pennicood Pennicoot
PENNICORD Pennicorde
Pennicot Pennicote
PENNICOTT Pennicotte
PENNICUD Pennicudd
Pennicutt Penniend
Pennikat Pennikate
Penniket PENNIKETT

If the name you are interested in is not here, try Section C.

Pennikide PENNYCAD
Pennycade Pennycard
Pennycate Pennyceard
Pennycid Pennycoad
Pennycod Pennycodd
Pennycode Pennycoed
Pennycord Pennycorde
Pennycot Pennycote
PENNYCOTT PENNYEND
Pennykate Pennyrott
Penocod Penycad
Penycard Penycat
PENNYEND 119 Parnacoat
Parnacote PARNACOTT
Parnecoat Parnecote
Parnecott Parnecut
Parnecutt Parnicoat
Parnicote Parnicott
Parnicutt Parnycoat
Parnycote Parnycott
Parnycutt Peenicott
Penacot Penecad
Peneceard Penecett
Penecod Penecot Penecud
Penekat Peneket
Penekett Peneycud
Peneycudd Peneycutt
PENICAD Penicade
Penicard Penicat
Penicate Peniceard
Peniced Penicet
Penicoat Penicoate
PENICOD Penicode
Penicoot Penicord
Penicorde Penicot
Penicote Penicott
PENICUD Penicudd
Penicut Penicutt
Peniend Penikat
Penikate Peniked
PENIKET PENIKETT
Penikid Pennacott
Pennaket Pennecett
Penneket PENNEKETT
Penneycidd Penneycod
Penneycud Pennicad
Pennicade PENNICARD
Pennicarde Pennicate
PENNICEARD Pennicoad
Pennicoate Pennicod
PENNICODD Pennicode
Pennicood Pennicoot
PENNICORD Pennicorde
Pennicot Pennicote
PENNICOTT Pennicotte
PENNICUD Pennicudd
Pennicutt Penniend
Pennikat Pennikate
Penniket PENNIKETT
Pennikide PENNYCAD
Pennycade Pennycard
Pennycate Pennyceard
Pennycid Pennycoad
Pennycod Pennycodd
Pennycode Pennycoed
Pennycord Pennycorde
Pennycot Pennycote
PENNYCOTT PENNYCUD
Pennykate Pennyrott
Penocod Penycad
Penycard Penycat
Pennykate PARNACOTT
PENICAD PENICOD PENICUD
PENIKET PENIKETT
PENNEKETT PENNICARD
PENNICEARD PENNICODD
PENNICORD PENNICOTT
PENNICUD PENNIKETT
PENNYCAD PENNYCOTT
PENNYCUD PENNYEND
PENNYMAN 7 Peniman
Penneyman PENNIMAN
PENNYMON PENYMAN
Ponnyman
PENNYMON 7 Peniman
Penneyman PENNIMAN
PENNYMAN PENYMAN
Ponnyman
Pennyrott PARNACOTT
PENICAD PENICOD PENICUD
PENIKET PENIKETT
PENNEKETT PENNICARD
PENNICEARD PENNICODD
PENNICORD PENNICOTT
PENNICUD PENNIKETT
PENNYCAD PENNYCOTT
PENNYCUD PENNYEND
Penocod PARNACOTT PENICAD
PENICOD PENICUD PENIKET
PENIKETT PENNEKETT
PENNICARD PENNICEARD
PENNICODD PENNICORD
PENNICOTT PENNICUD
PENNIKETT PENNYCAD
PENNYCOTT PENNYCUD
PENNYEND
Penrhys PENRICE
PENRICE Penrhys Penrise
Penrise PENRICE
Pensar PENZER
Pensor PENZER
PENSTON Penstone
Penstone PENSTON
Pentelo PENTELOW PENTLOE
PENTLOW
Penteloe PENTELOW PENTLOE
PENTLOW
PENTELOW 7 Pentelo
Penteloe Pentler Pentlo
PENTLOE PENTLOW
Pentler PENTELOW PENTLOE
PENTLOW
Pentlo PENTELOW PENTLOE
PENTLOW
PENTLOE 7 Pentelo
Penteloe PENTELOW
Pentler Pentlo PENTLOW
PENTLOW 7 Pentelo
Penteloe PENTELOW
Pentler Pentlo PENTLOE
PENVELL 4 Penvil Penvill
Penville
Penvil PENVELL
Penvill PENVELL
Penville PENVELL
Penwell PINWILL
Penwill PINWILL
PENY PENNEY PENNY
Penycad PARNACOTT PENICAD
PENICOD PENICUD PENIKET
PENIKETT PENNEKETT
PENNICARD PENNICEARD
PENNICODD PENNICORD
PENNICOTT PENNICUD
PENNIKETT PENNYCAD
PENNYCOTT PENNYCUD
PENNYEND
Penycard PARNACOTT
PENICAD PENICOD PENICUD
PENIKET PENIKETT
PENNEKETT PENNICARD
PENNICEARD PENNICODD
PENNICORD PENNICOTT
PENNICUD PENNIKETT
PENNYCAD PENNYCOTT
PENNYCUD PENNYEND
Penycat PARNACOTT PENICAD
PENICOD PENICUD PENIKET
PENIKETT PENNEKETT
PENNICARD PENNICEARD
PENNICODD PENNICORD
PENNICOTT PENNICUD
PENNIKETT PENNYCAD
PENNYCOTT PENNYCUD
PENNYEND
PENYMAN 7 Peniman
Penneyman PENNIMAN
PENNYMAN PENNYMON
Ponnyman
PENZER Pensar Pensor
People PEPAL
PEPAL 4 Peapell Peaple
People
Pepeat PEPPIAT PEPPIATT
Pepiat PEPPIAT PEPPIATT
Pepiatt PEPPIAT PEPPIATT
Pepitt PEPPIAT PEPPIATT
Pepperday PAYBODY PEABODY
PEBERDY PEBODY
Peppett PEPPIAT PEPPIATT
PEPPIAT 10 Pepeat Pepiat
Pepiatt Pepitt Peppett
PEPPIATT Peppit
Peppytte Pepyat
PEPPIATT 10 Pepeat Pepiat
Pepiatt Pepitt Peppett
PEPPIAT Peppit Peppytte
Pepyat
Peppit PEPPIAT PEPPIATT
Peppytte PEPPIAT PEPPIATT
Pepyat PEPPIAT PEPPIATT
Perceval PERCIVAL
PERCIVAL Perceval
Percivall
Percivall PERCIVAL
PERCY PEARCY PIERCY
Perdu PURDUE
PEREGRINE Pergrin
Peren PERING PERREN
PERRIN PERRING
Pergrin PEREGRINE
Perham PERIAM PERRIAM
PERIAM 4 Perham PERRIAM
Peryam
Perie PIRIE
Periman PERRYMAN
Perin PERING PERREN
PERRIN PERRING
PERING 10 Peren Perin
PERREN PERRIN PERRING
Perringe Perryn
Perrynge Peryn
PERKES 10 Pearkes Pearks
PERKS Pierkes Pierks
Pirkes Pirks Purkes
Purks
PERKIN 4 PARKIN Pearkins
PERKINS
PERKINS 13 PARKIN PARKINS
Parkyns Pearkins PERKIN
Perkyns Pirkins Pirkyns
Purkins Purkyns Pyrkins
Pyrkyns
Perkis PURKIS
PERKS 10 Pearkes Pearks
PERKES Pierkes Pierks
Pirkes Pirks Purkes
Purks
Perkyns PARKINS PERKINS
PERMAIN PEARMAN Perman
Perman PEARMAN PERMAIN
Pern PEARN
Perow PERROW
Perowe PERROW
PERREN 10 Peren Perin
PERING PERRIN PERRING
Perringe Perryn
Perrynge Peryn
Perres PERRIS
PERRETT 9 Pallet POLLET
POLLETT POLLITT Porret
PORRETT PORRIT PORRITT
PERRIAM 4 Perham PERIAM
Peryam
Perrie PERRY
Perriman PERRYMAN
PERRIN 10 Peren Perin
PERING PERREN PERRING
Perringe Perryn
Perrynge Peryn
PERRING 10 Peren Perin
PERING PERREN PERRIN
Perringe Perryn
Perrynge Peryn
Perringe PERING PERREN
PERRIN PERRING
PERRIS Perres
PERROW 4 Parrow Perow
Perowe
PERRY 6 Parrie PARRY Pary
Perrie Pery
Perryer PERYER
PERRYMAN Periman Perriman
Perryn PERING PERREN
PERRIN PERRING
Perrynge PERING PERREN
PERRIN PERRING
PERSEHOUSE 5 Parkeshouse
Parshouse PARSUS
Pursehouse
Pershall PURCHALL
PURCHELL
Personage PARSONAGE
Persuire PURSER
Perts PEACH PETTS POTTS
Perver PURVER
Perveur PURVER
Pery PERRY
Peryam PERIAM PERRIAM
PERYER Perryer
Peryn PERING PERREN
PERRIN PERRING
PETER 7 PEATER Peiter
PETERS PETRE PETTER
Petterd
PETERS PETER
PETERSON 4 PATERSON
PATTERSON PATTISON
Petfield PEATFIELD
PETHERICK PEDERICK
Pethridge BETTERIDGE
BETTRIDGE
Petifer PETTIFER
Petipher PETTIFER
Petit PETITT PETTET
PETTIT PETTITT PETTY
PETYT
Petite PETTIT
PETITT 5 Petit PETTET
PETTIT PETTITT
Petle PETLEY
PETLEY 5 Petle Pettely
Pitle Pittley
PETRE 6 PEATER Peiter
PETER PETTER Petterd
PETT 4 Pait PATE PEAT
Pettely PETLEY
PETTER 6 PEATER Peiter
PETER PETRE Petterd
Petterd PEATER PETER
PETRE PETTER
Petterden PARTINGTON
PATTENDEN
PETTET 5 Petit PETITT
PETTIT PETTITT
Pettie PETTY PETYT
PETTIFER 4 Petifer
Petipher Pettipher
Pettingale PETTINGILL
Pettingall PETTINGILL
Pettingel PETTINGILL
PETTINGILL 5 Pettingale
Pettingall Pettingel
Portingall
Pettipher PETTIFER
PETTIT 8 Petit Petite
PETITT PETTET Pettite
PETTITT PETTY
Pettite PETTIT
PETTITT 5 Petit PETITT
PETTET PETTIT
PETTS 5 PEACH Peets Perts
POTTS
PETTY 6 Petit Pettie
PETTIT Pettyt PETYT
Pettyt PETTY PETYT

If the name you are interested in is not here, try Section C.

PETYT 5 Petit Pettie
  PETTY Pettyt
PEWSEY Pisey PUSEY
PEXTON 15 Bickston
  PECKSTON Peckton
  Pickstan Pickston
  PICKSTONE Pickstones
  PICTON Pigston Pixston
  Pixstone Pixton Pixtone
  Theckston
PEYMAN Pyeman
Pfankuch PHANCO
PHANCO 7 Fancho Fanco
  Fanker Fanko Funcko
  Pfankuch
PHAROAH FARROW
Pharrance FARRANCE
  FARRANTS
PHARROW FARROW
Phathain PHETHEAN
  PHYTHIAN
Phathian PHETHEAN
  PHYTHIAN
Pheban FABIAN
Pheben FABIAN
Phelip PHELPS PHILIPS
  PHILLIPS PHILP
Phelipot PHILLPOTTS
  PHILPOT PHILPOTT
  PHILPOTTS
Phelipote PHILLPOTTS
  PHILPOT PHILPOTT
  PHILPOTTS
Phelipott PHILLPOTTS
  PHILPOT PHILPOTT
  PHILPOTTS
Pheliskyrk PHILLISKIRK
Phelp PHELPS PHILIPS
  PHILLIPS PHILP
Phelpot PHILLPOTTS
  PHILPOT PHILPOTT
  PHILPOTTS
Phelpotte PHILLPOTTS
  PHILPOT PHILPOTT
  PHILPOTTS
Phelpottes PHILLPOTTS
  PHILPOT PHILPOTT
  PHILPOTTS
PHELPS 9 Felps Filp
  Phelip Phelp PHILIPS
  PHILLIPS PHILP Philps
PHENNA 4 FENNA FENNAH
  PHENNAH
PHENNAH 4 FENNA FENNAH
  PHENNA
Pheopoint PEIRPOINT
  PIERPOINT
PHETHEAN 6 Phathain
  Phathian Phethian
  Phthyan PHYTHIAN
Phethian PHETHEAN
  PHYTHIAN
Phicocks PHILCOX
PHILBRICK 9 Falbrick
  Falbrook Fallbrick
  FILBRICK Fulbrick
  FULBROOK FULLBRICK
  Philbrook
Philbrook FULBROOK
  FULLBRICK PHILBRICK
Philcock PHILPOT PHILPOTT
Philcocks PHILCOX
Philcott PHILPOT PHILPOTT
PHILCOX 4 Phicocks
  Philcocks Phillcox
Philepot PHILLPOTTS
  PHILPOT PHILPOTT
  PHILPOTTS
Philery FILLARY
Philickerke PHILLISKIRK
Philimore FENNIMORE
  FILMER FINMORE
  FINNEMORE PHILLIMORE
  VENNIMORE

PHILIP 4 PHILIPS PHILLIP
  PHILLIPS
Philipot PHILLPOTTS
  PHILPOT PHILPOTT
  PHILPOTTS
Philipott PHILLPOTTS
  PHILPOT PHILPOTT
  PHILPOTTS
Philippot PHILLPOTTS
  PHILPOT PHILPOTT
  PHILPOTTS
Philippotte PHILLPOTTS
  PHILPOT PHILPOTT
  PHILPOTTS
Philipps PHILIPS
  PHILLIPPS PHILLIPS
PHILIPS 12 Filp Phelip
  Phelp PHELPS PHILIP
  Philipps PHILLIP
  PHILLIPPS PHILLIPS
  PHILP Philps
Phillcox PHILCOX
PHILLIMORE 58 Bennimore
  Fenamor Fenemer
  Fenemore Fenimore
  Fenmer Fenmere
  Fennamore Fennemore
  Fenneymore FENNIMORE
  Fennymore Fiddimore
  Fillmore FILMER Filmore
  Finamer Finamoore
  Finamore Finemer
  Finemere Finemor
  Finemore Finimor Finmer
  Finmere FINMORE
  Finnamoor Finnamoore
  Finnamore FINNEMORE
  Finneymoore Finneymore
  Finnymoor Finnymore
  Finymore Fynmer
  Fynnamore Fynnemore
  Fynneymoore Fynneymore
  Fynnimore Fynnymore
  Philimore Philmore
  Phinamor Phinamore
  Phinnamore Phinnemore
  Phinnmore Phynemore
  Phynnamore Phynnemore
  Phynneymore Phynnimore
  Phynnymore VENNIMORE
PHILLIP 4 PHILIP PHILIPS
  PHILLIPS
Phillipott PHILLPOTTS
  PHILPOT PHILPOTT
  PHILPOTTS
PHILLIPPS 4 Philipps
  PHILIPS PHILLIPS
PHILLIPS 12 Filp Phelip
  Phelp PHELPS PHILIP
  Philipps PHILIPS
  PHILLIP PHILLIPPS PHILP
  Philps
PHILLISKIRK 13 Feliskirke
  Felixkirke Felyxkyrk
  Filiskirk Filiskyrke
  Filliskirke Fylleskyrke
  Le felicekyrk
  Pheliskyrk Philickerke
  Philliskirke Phyllykyrk
Philliskirke PHILLISKIRK
Phillpot PHILLPOTTS
  PHILPOT PHILPOTT
  PHILPOTTS
Phillpott PHILLPOTTS
  PHILPOT PHILPOTT
PHILLPOTTS 45 Felipot
  Felpot Felypot
  Ffillopott Ffillpot
  Ffilpot Ffilpott
  Filepot Fillepotte
  Fillpot Fillpott
  Fillpotte Filpott
  Fylopot Fylpot Fylpott
  Phelipot Phelipote
  Phelipott Phelpot
  Phelpotte Phelpottes
  Philepot Philipot
  Philipott Philippot
  Philippotte Phillipott
  Phillpot Phillpott
  Philpootte PHILPOT
  Philpote PHILPOTT
  Philpotte PHILPOTTS
  Philputt Philypot
  Philypott Phylpot
  Phylpott Phylpotte
  Phylypot Phylypotte
Philmore FENNIMORE FILMER
  FINMORE FINNEMORE
  PHILLIMORE VENNIMORE
PHILP 8 Filp Phelip Phelp
  PHELPS PHILIPS PHILLIPS
  Philps
Philpootte PHILLPOTTS
  PHILPOT PHILPOTT
  PHILPOTTS
PHILPOT 49 Felipot Felpot
  Felypot Ffillopott
  Ffillpot Ffilpot
  Ffilpott Filepot
  Fillepotte Fillpot
  Fillpott Fillpotte
  Filpot Filpott Fylopot
  Fylpot Fylpott Phelipot
  Phelipote Phelipott
  Phelpot Phelpotte
  Phelpottes Philcock
  Philcott Philepot
  Philipot Philipott
  Philippot Philippotte
  Phillipott Phillpot
  Phillpott PHILLPOTTS
  Philpootte Philpote
  PHILPOTT Philpotte
  PHILPOTTS Philputt
  Philypot Philypott
  Phylpot Phylpote
  Phylpott Phylpotte
  Phylypot Phylypotte
Philpote PHILLPOTTS
  PHILPOT PHILPOTT
  PHILPOTTS
PHILPOTT 49 Felipot
  Felpot Felypot
  Ffillopott Ffillpot
  Ffilpot Ffilpott
  Filepot Fillepotte
  Fillpot Fillpott
  Fillpotte Filpot
  Filpott Fylopot Fylpot
  Fylpott Phelipot
  Phelipote Phelipott
  Phelpot Phelpotte
  Phelpottes Philcock
  Philcott Philepot
  Philipot Philipott
  Philippot Philippotte
  Phillipott Phillpot
  Phillpott PHILLPOTTS
  Philpootte PHILPOT
  Philpote Philpotte
  PHILPOTTS Philputt
  Philypot Philypott
  Phylpot Phylpote
  Phylpott Phylpotte
  Phylypot Phylypotte
Philpotte PHILLPOTTS
  PHILPOT PHILPOTT
  PHILPOTTS
PHILPOTTS 44 Felipot
  Felpot Felypot
  Ffillopott Ffillpot
  Ffilpot Ffilpott
  Filepot Fillepotte
  Fillpot Fillpott
  Fillpotte Filpott
  Fylopot Fylpot Fylpott
  Phelipot Phelipote
  Phelipott Phelpot
  Phelpotte Phelpottes
  Philepot Philipot
  Philipott Philippot
  Philippotte Phillipott
  Phillpot PHILLPOTTS
  Philpootte PHILPOT
  Philpote PHILPOTT
  Philpotte Philputt
  Philypot Philypott
  Phylpot Phylpott
  Phylpotte Phylypot
  Phylypotte
Philps PHELPS PHILIPS
  PHILLIPS PHILP
Philputt PHILLPOTTS
  PHILPOT PHILPOTT
  PHILPOTTS
PHILSON Filson
Philypot PHILLPOTTS
  PHILPOT PHILPOTT
  PHILPOTTS
Philypott PHILLPOTTS
  PHILPOT PHILPOTT
  PHILPOTTS
Phinamor FENNIMORE FILMER
  FINMORE FINNEMORE
  PHILLIMORE VENNIMORE
Phinamore FENNIMORE
  FILMER FINMORE
  FINNEMORE PHILLIMORE
  VENNIMORE
Phinnamore FENNIMORE
  FILMER FINMORE
  FINNEMORE PHILLIMORE
  VENNIMORE
Phinnemore FENNIMORE
  FILMER FINMORE
  FINNEMORE PHILLIMORE
  VENNIMORE
Phinnmore FENNIMORE
  FILMER FINMORE
  FINNEMORE PHILLIMORE
  VENNIMORE
PHIPPS PHIPS
PHIPS PHIPPS
Phizell FITZELL
Phraher FRAHER FRYOR
Phthyan PHETHEAN PHYTHIAN
Phyander FIANDER
Phyllykyrk PHILLISKIRK
Phylpot PHILLPOTTS
  PHILPOT PHILPOTT
  PHILPOTTS
Phylpote PHILPOT PHILPOTT
Phylpott PHILLPOTTS
  PHILPOT PHILPOTT
  PHILPOTTS
Phylpotte PHILLPOTTS
  PHILPOT PHILPOTT
  PHILPOTTS
Phylypot PHILLPOTTS
  PHILPOT PHILPOTT
  PHILPOTTS
Phylypotte PHILLPOTTS
  PHILPOT PHILPOTT
  PHILPOTTS
Phynemore FENNIMORE
  FILMER FINMORE
  FINNEMORE PHILLIMORE
  VENNIMORE
Phynnamore FENNIMORE
  FILMER FINMORE
  FINNEMORE PHILLIMORE
  VENNIMORE
Phynnemore FENNIMORE
  FILMER FINMORE
  FINNEMORE PHILLIMORE
  VENNIMORE
Phynneymore FENNIMORE
  FILMER FINMORE
  FINNEMORE PHILLIMORE
  VENNIMORE
Phynnimore FENNIMORE

If the name you are interested in is not here, try Section C.

FILMER FINMORE FINNEMORE PHILLIMORE VENNIMORE
Phynnymore FENNIMORE FILMER FINMORE FINNEMORE PHILLIMORE VENNIMORE
PHYTHIAN 6 Phathain Phathian PHETHEAN Phethian Phthyan
Piat PYATT PYETT
PICK PIKE
PICKET 4 Pegget PIGGOT PIGOT
PICKETT 4 PIKET PIKETT Pykett
PICKLES 4 Picles Pigheles PIGHILLS
Pickman PITMAN PITTMAN
Pickstan PEXTON PICKSTONE PICTON
Pickston PEXTON PICKSTONE PICTON
PICKSTONE 14 Bickston Peckton PEXTON Pickstan Pickston Pickstones PICTON Pigston Pixston Pixstone Pixton Pixtone Theckston
Pickstones PEXTON PICKSTONE PICTON
Pickthorn PICKTON PICTON
PICKTON Pickthorn PICTON
Picles PICKLES PIGHILLS
PICTON 16 Bickston Peckton PEXTON Pickstan Pickston PICKSTONE Pickstones Pickthorn PICKTON Pigston Pixston Pixstone Pixton Pixtone Theckston
Piddell PIDDLE
PIDDLE 5 Peddle Piddell Pydele Pydell
Pidgin PIGGIN PIGGINS
Piel PEAL PEEL PEILE
Piele PEAL PEEL PEILE
PIERCE 7 PEARCE PEARSE PEERS PEIRCE PIERSE PRICE
PIERCY 5 Pearcey PEARCY Pearsey PERCY
Pierkes PERKES PERKS
Pierks PERKES PERKS
PIERPOINT 4 Pearpoint PEIRPOINT Pheopoint
PIERREPONT 8 De medewe De wythnesham Meadowe MEADOWS Medew Medewe Medowe
PIERSE PIERCE
PIERSON PEARSON PEIRSON
PIFF PITT PITTS
Pigeon PIGGIN
Piggen PIGGIN PIGGINS
PIGGIN 8 Pidgin Pigeon Piggen Pigging Piggings PIGGINS Pigin
Pigging PIGGIN PIGGINS
Piggings PIGGIN PIGGINS
PIGGINS 6 Pidgin Piggen PIGGIN Pigging Piggings
PIGGOT 4 Pegget PICKET PIGOT
Pigheles PICKLES PIGHILLS
PIGHILLS 4 PICKLES Picles Pigheles
Pigin PIGGIN
PIGOT 4 Pegget PICKET PIGGOT
Pigram PINCOMBE PINKHAM
Pigrem PINCOMBE PINKHAM
Pigrim PINCOMBE PINKHAM
Pigrum PINCOMBE PINKHAM
Pigrym PINCOMBE PINKHAM
Pigston PEXTON PICKSTONE PICTON
PIKE PICK PYKE
PIKET 4 PICKETT PIKETT Pykett
PIKETT 4 PICKETT PIKET Pykett
PILBEAM 6 Pilbeame Pilbean Pilbin Pillbeam Pilvin
Pilbeame PILBEAM
Pilbean PILBEAM
Pilbin PILBEAM
Pilgram PINCOMBE PINKHAM
Pilgrem PINCOMBE PINKHAM
Pilgrin PINCOMBE PINKHAM
Pilgrum PINCOMBE PINKHAM
Pilgrym PINCOMBE PINKHAM
PILKINGTON Pilkinton
Pilkinton PILKINGTON
PILLAER PILLER
Pillbeam PILBEAM
PILLER PILLAER
Pilston PULESTON
Pilvin PILBEAM
PIM 4 PIMM PYM Pymm
PIMBLE 4 PEMBLE Pimblett Pymble
Pimblett PEMBLE PIMBLE
Pimgram PINCOMBE PINKHAM
Pimgrem PINCOMBE PINKHAM
Pimgrin PINCOMBE PINKHAM
Pimgrum PINCOMBE PINKHAM
Pimgrym PINCOMBE PINKHAM
PIMM 4 PIM PYM Pymm
Pinchene PINCKNEY PINKNEY
Pinchengi PINCKNEY PINKNEY
Pincheni PINCKNEY PINKNEY
Pinck PINK
Pinckam PINCOMBE PINKHAM
Pincke PINK
Pinckham PINCOMBE PINKHAM
PINCKNEY 17 De picquigny De pinkeni Peneni Pinchene Pinchengi Pincheni Pinkeigni Pinkeney Pinkeni Pinkeny PINKNEY Pyncknaye Pyncknye Pynhenye Pynkenheye Pynkney
Pinckomb PINCOMBE PINKHAM
Pinckombe PINCOMBE PINKHAM
Pincomb PINCOMBE PINKHAM
PINCOMBE 86 Ingam Ingraham Ingrarum Pangeram Pangerham Peagram Peagrem Peagrim Peagrum Peagrym Pegram Pegrem Pegrim Pegrum Pegrym Pelgram Pelgrem Pelgrin Pelgrum Pelgrym Pemgram Pemgrem Pemgrin Pemgrum Pemgrym Pengeram Pengerham Pengram Pengrem Pengrim Pengrum Pengrym Pigram Pigrem Pigrim Pigrum Pigrym Pilgram Pilgrem Pilgrin Pilgrum Pilgrym Pimgram Pimgrem Pimgrin Pimgrum Pimgrym Pinckam Pinckham Pinckomb Pinckombe Pincomb Pingeram Pingerham Pingram Pingrem Pingrim Pingrum Pingrym Pinkam PINKHAM Pinkomb Pinkombe Pringham Pygrem Pygrim Pygrum Pygrym Pylgram Pylgrem Pylgrin Pylgrum Pylgrym Pymgram Pymgrem Pymgrin Pymgrum Pymgrym Pyngeram Pyngerham Pyngram Pyngrem Pyngrim Pyngrum Pyram
Pincot PINCOTT
PINCOTT Pincot
PINE 5 PAIN PAYNE PEIN PYNE
PINEL 9 Penil Pennil PENNILL PENNY Pinell PINNEL PINNELL Pynnell
Pinell PENNILL PENNY PINEL PINNEL PINNELL
Ping BING BYNG
Pingeram PINCOMBE PINKHAM
Pingerham PINCOMBE PINKHAM
Pingram PINCOMBE PINKHAM
Pingrem PINCOMBE PINKHAM
Pingrim PINCOMBE PINKHAM
Pingrum PINCOMBE PINKHAM
Pingrym PINCOMBE PINKHAM
PINHORN 5 Penhorn Penhorne Pinhorne Pynhorn
Pinhorne PINHORN
Pinhoul PINWILL
Pinin PINNING
Pining PINNING
Pininge PINNING
Pinins PINNING
PINION 4 Penion Pinnion Pinnions
PINK 4 Pinck Pincke Pinke
Pinkam PINCOMBE PINKHAM
Pinke PINK
Pinkeigni PINCKNEY PINKNEY
Pinkeney PINCKNEY PINKNEY
Pinkeni PINCKNEY PINKNEY
Pinkeny PINCKNEY PINKNEY
PINKHAM 86 Ingam Ingraham Ingrarum Pangeram Pangerham Peagram Peagrem Peagrim Peagrum Peagrym Pegram Pegrem Pegrim Pegrum Pegrym Pelgram Pelgrem Pelgrin Pelgrum Pelgrym Pemgram Pemgrem Pemgrin Pemgrum Pemgrym Pengeram Pengerham Pengram Pengrem Pengrim Pengrum Pengrym Pigram Pigrem Pigrim Pigrum Pigrym Pilgram Pilgrem Pilgrin Pilgrum Pilgrym Pimgram Pimgrem Pimgrin Pimgrum Pimgrym Pinckam Pinckham Pinckomb Pinckombe Pincomb PINCOMBE Pingeram Pingerham Pingram Pingrem Pingrim Pingrum Pingrym Pinkam Pinkomb Pinkombe Pringham Pygrem Pygrim Pygrum Pygrym Pylgram Pylgrem Pylgrin Pylgrum Pylgrym Pymgram Pymgrem Pymgrin Pymgrum Pymgrym Pyngeram Pyngerham Pyngram Pyngrem Pyngrim Pyngrum Pyram
PINKNEY 17 De picquigny De pinkeni Peneni Pinchene Pinchengi Pincheni PINCKNEY Pinkeigni Pinkeney Pinkeni Pinkeny Pyncknaye Pyncknye Pynhenye Pynkenheye Pynkney
Pinkomb PINCOMBE PINKHAM
Pinkombe PINCOMBE PINKHAM
PINNEL 9 Penil Pennil PENNILL PENNY PINEL Pinell PINNELL Pynnell
PINNELL 9 Penil Pennil PENNILL PENNY PINEL Pinell PINNEL Pynnell
Pinni PINNING
Pinnin PINNING
PINNING 16 PENNEY Penning Pinin Pining Pininge Pinins Pinni Pinnin Pinninge Pinnings Pins Pynin Pynnin Pynning Pynninge
Pinninge PINNING
Pinnings PINNING
Pinnion PINION
Pinnions PINION
Pinoil PINWILL
Pins PINNING
Pinwell PINWILL
PINWILL 6 Penwell Penwill Pinhoul Pinoil Pinwell
Piotvain PUTWAIN
PIPER 4 Pipers Pipper PYER
Pipers PIPER PYER
Pipper PIPER PYER
PIRIE Perie Pirrie
Pirkes PERKES PERKS
Pirkins PARKINS PERKINS
Pirks PERKES PERKS
Pirkyns PARKINS PERKINS
Pirrie PIRIE
Pisey PEWSEY PUSEY
PITE Pyte
Pitfield PEATFIELD
PITHAM PITTAM Pittum
PITHER Pithers
Pithers PITHER
Pitle PETLEY
PITMAN 5 Peckman Pickman Pitmon PITTMAN
Pitmon PITMAN PITTMAN
Pits PITTS
PITT PIFF PITTS
PITTAM PITHAM Pittum
Pittes PITTS
Pittis PITTS
Pittley PETLEY
PITTMAN 5 Peckman Pickman PITMAN Pitmon
PITTOCK Pttock-buss
PITTS 7 PIFF Pits PITT Pittes Pittis Pyttes
Pittum PITHAM PITTAM
Pixston PEXTON PICKSTONE PICTON
Pixstone PEXTON PICKSTONE PICTON
Pixton PEXTON PICKSTONE PICTON
Pixtone PEXTON PICKSTONE PICTON
PIZER 14 Payser Pazzer Poiser POIZER POYSER Poysor Poyzer Pysor PYZER Spizer Spoiser Spoizer Spyzer
Pladal PLEYDELL
Pladall PLEYDELL
Pladel PLEYDELL
Pladell PLEYDELL
Pladle PLEYDELL
Pladwel PLEYDELL
Pladwell PLEYDELL
Plaidal PLEYDELL
Plaidall PLEYDELL
Plaidel PLEYDELL
Plaidell PLEYDELL
Plaidwel PLEYDELL

If the name you are interested in is not here, try Section C.

Plaidwell PLEYDELL
Plaistead PLAISTED
PLAISTED 5 Plaistead Plastead Playstead Playsted
Plastead PLAISTED
Platel PLEYDELL
Platfoot PLAYFORD
Platmaner PLATNAUER
Platnancer PLATNAUER
PLATNAUER 6 Blatnauer Blatner Platmaner Platnancer Platner
Platner PLATNAUER
Platwall PLEYDELL
Playdal PLEYDELL
Playdall PLEYDELL
Playdel PLEYDELL
Playdell PLEYDELL
Playdwel PLEYDELL
Playdwell PLEYDELL
PLAYFAIR PLAYFERE
PLAYFERE PLAYFAIR
PLAYFOOT Splayfoot
PLAYFORD Platfoot Splayfoot
Playstead PLAISTED
Playsted PLAISTED
Pleadal PLEYDELL
Pleadall PLEYDELL
Pleadel PLEYDELL
Pleadell PLEYDELL
Pleadles PLEYDELL
Pleadwel PLEYDELL
Pleadwell PLEYDELL
PLEASANCE PLEASANT
PLEASANT PLEASANCE
Pledal PLEYDELL
Pledall PLEYDELL
Pleddle PLEYDELL
Pledel PLEYDELL
Pledell PLEYDELL
Pledle PLEYDELL
Pledwel PLEYDELL
Pledwell PLEYDELL
Pleidal PLEYDELL
Pleidall PLEYDELL
Pleidel PLEYDELL
Pleidell PLEYDELL
Pleidwel PLEYDELL
Pleidwell PLEYDELL
PLEYDELL 46 Pladal Pladall Pladel Pladell Pladle Pladwel Pladwell Plaidal Plaidall Plaidel Plaidell Plaidwel Plaidwell Platel Platwall Playdal Playdall Playdel Playdell Playdwel Playdwell Pleadal Pleadall Pleadel Pleadell Pleadles Pleadwel Pleadwell Pledal Pledall Pleddle Pledel Pledell Pledle Pledwel Pledwell Pleidal Pleidall Pleidel Pleidell Pleidwel Pleidwell Ploydel Ploydell Plydel
PLIMMER PLUMMER Plymer
Plokenet PLUCKNET
Ploydel PLEYDELL
Ploydell PLEYDELL
Pluckenet PLUCKNET
PLUCKNET 7 Plokenet Pluckenet Plukenet Plukent Plunkenet Plunknet
Plukenet PLUCKNET
Plukent PLUCKNET
PLUM PLUMB
PLUMB PLUM
PLUMBLEY Plumbly
Plumbly PLUMBLEY PLUMLEY
PLUMLEY Plumbly Plumly
Plumly PLUMLEY
PLUMMER PLIMMER Plymer
Plunkenet PLUCKNET
Plunknet PLUCKNET
Plydel PLEYDELL
Plymer PLIMMER PLUMMER
Pocknell PACKNELL
Pockson PAXSON PAXTON POGSON POXON POXSON POXTON
Pockton PAXSON PAXTON POGSON POXON POXSON POXTON
Pocson PAXSON PAXTON POGSON POXON POXSON POXTON
Pocton PAXSON PAXTON POGSON POXON POXSON POXTON
Podbury PADBURY PORTBURY
Podevin PUTWAIN
POGSON 14 Paxen Paxon PAXSON PAXTON Pockson Pockton Pocson Pocton Poxan Poxen POXON POXSON POXTON
POINFON 4 POINTER POINTUR PUINTUR
POINTER 5 POINFON POINTUR Poynder PUINTUR
Pointin POINTING
POINTING 4 Pointin Pointinge Poynting
Pointinge POINTING
POINTON POYNTON
POINTUR 4 POINFON POINTER PUINTUR
Poiser PIZER POIZER POYSER PYZER
Poitvine PUTWAIN
POIZER 14 Payser Pazzer PIZER Poiser POYSER Poysor Poyzer Pysor PYZER Spizer Spoiser Spoizer Spyzer
Poke POOK
Polan POLAND
POLAND 4 Polan Polland Powland
POLDEN Polten POULDEN
POLE 7 De la pole POOL POOLE Poolley POWEL POWELL
Polentine POLLENDINE POLLINGTON POLLINTINE
Polet PALLETT PAULET POLLET POLLETT POLLITT
Polett PALLETT PAULET POLLET POLLETT POLLITT
Poleykett POLLICOTT POLLIKETT
Polglaise POLGLASE
POLGLASE 4 Polglaise Polglass Polglaze
Polglass POLGLASE
Polglaze POLGLASE
Polick POLLOCK
Poliet PALLETT PAULET POLLET POLLETT POLLITT
Polintine POLLENDINE POLLINGTON POLLINTINE
Polinton POLLENDINE POLLINGTON POLLINTINE
Polit PALLETT PAULET POLLET POLLETT POLLITT
Politt POLLITT
POLKEY PALKE
POLKINGHORN POLKINGHORNE
POLKINGHORNE POLKINGHORN
POLL POWELL POWLES
Pollak POLLOCK
Polland POLAND
POLLARD POLLETT
Pollecutt POLLICOTT POLLIKETT
POLLENDINE 9 Polentine Polintine Polinton Pollentine Pollindyne POLLINGTON POLLINTINE Polyngton
Pollentine POLLENDINE POLLINGTON POLLINTINE
Pollert PALLETT PAULET POLLET POLLETT POLLITT
POLLET 36 Palet Palett Pallet PALLETT PAULET Paulett Paulit Paullet Paulot Pawlet Pawlete Pawlett PERRETT Polet Polett Poliet Polit Pollert POLLETT Polliet Polliot Pollit POLLITT Pollitte Pollot Poolit Porret PORRETT PORRIT PORRITT Poulett Poulette Powlet Powlett Powlit
POLLETT 37 Palet Palett Pallet PALLETT PAULET Paulett Paulit Paullet Paulot Pawlet Pawlete Pawlett PERRETT Polet Polett Poliet Polit POLLARD Pollert POLLET Polliet Polliot Pollit POLLITT Pollitte Pollot Poolit Porret PORRETT PORRIT PORRITT Poulett Poulette Powlet Powlett Powlit
Polleycutt POLLICOTT POLLIKETT
Pollick POLLOCK
Pollicke POLLOCK
POLLICOTT 6 Poleykett Pollecutt Polleycutt Pollicutt POLLIKETT
Pollicutt POLLICOTT POLLIKETT
Polliet PALLETT PAULET POLLET POLLETT POLLITT
POLLIKETT 6 Poleykett Pollecutt Polleycutt POLLICOTT Pollicutt
Pollindyne POLLENDINE POLLINGTON POLLINTINE
POLLINGTON 9 Polentine Polintine Polinton POLLENDINE Pollentine Pollindyne POLLINTINE Polyngton
POLLINTINE 9 Polentine Polintine Polinton POLLENDINE Pollentine Pollindyne POLLINGTON Polyngton
Polliot PALLETT PAULET POLLET POLLETT POLLITT
Pollique POLLOCK
Pollit PALLETT PAULET POLLET POLLETT POLLITT
POLLITT 37 Palet Palett Pallet PALLETT PAULET Paulett Paulit Paullet Paulot Pawlet Pawlete Pawlett PERRETT Polet Polett Poliet Polit Politt Pollert POLLET POLLETT Polliet Polliot Pollit Pollitte Pollot Poolit Porret PORRETT PORRIT PORRITT Poulett Poulette Powlet Powlett Powlit
Pollitte PALLETT PAULET POLLET POLLETT POLLITT
Polloc POLLOCK
POLLOCK 8 Polick Pollak Pollick Pollicke Pollique Polloc Pollok
Pollok POLLOCK
Pollot PALLETT PAULET POLLET POLLETT POLLITT
POLSON Poulson
Polten POLDEN POULDEN
Polton POULTON
Polvertoft PULVERTAFT PULVERTOFT
Polvertofte PULVERTAFT PULVERTOFT
Polyngton POLLENDINE POLLINGTON POLLINTINE
POMEROY 6 Pomery POMROY Pomry Pumeroy Pumrey
Pomery POMEROY POMROY
POMROY 6 POMEROY Pomery Pomry Pumeroy Pumrey
Pomry POMEROY POMROY
Ponder SPONDER
Poney POWNEY
Ponnyman PENNIMAN PENNYMAN PENNYMON PENYMAN
Ponten PONTIN
PONTIN 6 Pantin Ponten PONTING PONTON Pontyn
PONTING 5 Pantin PONTIN PONTON Pontyn
PONTON PONTIN PONTING
Pontyn PONTIN PONTING
Poock POOK
Pooer POWER
POOK 4 Poke Poock Pooke
Pooke POOK
POOL 5 POLE POOLE POWELL Pull
POOLE 6 POLE POOL POOLEY POWELL Pull
POOLER 5 Pouler PULAR PULLAR PULLER
POOLEY 5 POOLE Pooly POWLEY Powly
Poolit PALLETT PAULET POLLET POLLETT POLLITT
Poolley POLE POWELL
Poolton POULTON
Pooly POOLEY POWLEY
Popeley POPELY
POPELY Popeley Popley
Popkess POPKISS
POPKISS Popkess
Poplet POPLETT
POPLETT 8 Boplet Poplet Popplett Puplet Puplett Pupplett Toplett
Popley POPELY
Popplett POPLETT
PORCH PORTCH
Porchel PURCHALL PURCHELL
Pordvine PUTWAIN
Porit PORRIT PORRITT
Poritt PORRIT PORRITT
Porret PERRETT POLLET POLLETT POLLITT PORRETT PORRIT PORRITT
PORRETT 9 Pallet PERRETT POLLET POLLETT POLLITT Porret PORRIT PORRITT
PORRIT 11 Pallet PERRETT POLLET POLLETT POLLITT Porit Poritt Porret PORRETT PORRITT
PORRITT 11 Pallet PERRETT POLLET POLLETT POLLITT Porit Poritt Porret PORRETT PORRIT
Portberrie PADBURY PORTBURY
Portbery PORTBURY

If the name you are interested in is not here, try Section C.

Portbeurye PORTBURY
PORTBURY 10 PADBURY
Podbury Portberrie
Portbery Portbeurye
Potberie Potberry
Potbeury Potbury
PORTCH PORCH
PORTEOUS Portice
Portice PORTEOUS
Portingall PETTINGILL
Porton PAWTON
Portwine PUTWAIN
Posheart PALSER PAZZERD
PURSER
Postan POSTON
Posten POSTON
Postern POSTON
Posterne POSTON
POSTON 5 Postan Posten
Postern Posterne
Potberie PORTBURY
Potberry PADBURY PORTBURY
Potbeury PORTBURY
Potbury PADBURY PORTBURY
Pothecary POTTICARY
Potisain PUTWAIN
POTT POTTS
POTTER Potterf Pottier
Potterf POTTER
POTTERTON POTTINGTON
POTTOTON
Potticarie POTTICARY
POTTICARY Pothecary
Potticarie
Pottier POTTER
POTTINGTON POTTERTON
POTTOTON
POTTOTON POTTERTON
POTTINGTON
POTTS 6 PEACH Peets Perts
PETTS POTT
Potvine PUTWAIN
Poudich POWDITCH
Poudrel POWDERILL
POWDRILL
POULDEN POLDEN Polten
Pouler POOLER
Poulett PALLETT PAULET
POLLET POLLETT POLLITT
Poulette PALLETT PAULET
POLLET POLLETT POLLITT
Poulson POLSON
POULTER Powlter POWTER
POULTON 4 Polton Poolton
Pulton
Pounal POWNALL
Pounall POWNALL
POUND POUNDS
POUNDS POUND
Pouny POWNEY
Poutney POWNEY
Poutrell POWDERILL
Powderell POWDRILL
POWDERILL 9 Poudrel
Poutrell Powdril
Powtrell Pultrel Putel
Putrel Putrell
Powdich POWDITCH
POWDITCH Poudich Powdich
POWDRICH Powdridge
Powdridge POWDRICH
Powdril POWDERILL
POWDRILL Poudrel
Powderell
POWEL POLE POWELL
POWELL 12 Ap howell De la
pole HOWELL POLE POLL
POOL POOLE Poolley
POWEL POWLES POWNALL
POWER Pooer
Powland POLAND
POWLES POLL POWELL
Powlet PALLETT PAULET
POLLET POLLETT POLLITT

Powlett PALLETT PAULET
POLLET POLLETT POLLITT
POWLEY 4 POOLEY Pooly
Powly
Powlit PALLETT PAULET
POLLET POLLETT POLLITT
Powlter POULTER POWTER
Powly POOLEY POWLEY
Pownal POWNALL
POWNALL 5 Pounal Pounall
POWELL Pownal
POWNEY 5 Poney Pouny
Poutney Powny
Powny POWNEY
POWTER POULTER Powlter
Powtrell POWDERILL
Poxan PAXSON PAXTON
POGSON POXON POXSON
POXTON
Poxen PAXSON PAXTON
POGSON POXON POXSON
POXTON
POXON 14 Paxen Paxon
PAXSON PAXTON Pockson
Pockton Pocson Pocton
POGSON Poxan Poxen
POXSON POXTON
POXSON 14 Paxen Paxon
PAXSON PAXTON Pockson
Pockton Pocson Pocton
POGSON Poxan Poxen
POXON POXTON
POXTON 14 Paxen Paxon
PAXSON PAXTON Pockson
Pockton Pocson Pocton
POGSON Poxan Poxen
POXON POXSON
Poynder POINTER
Poynting POINTING
POYNTON POINTON
POYSER 14 Payser Pazzer
PIZER Poiser POIZER
Poysor Poyzer Pysor
PYZER Spizer Spoiser
Spoizer Spyzer
Poysor PIZER POIZER
POYSER PYZER
Poyzer PIZER POIZER
POYSER PYZER
PRACEY PRACY
PRACY PRACEY
PRAGNELL 5 Prangell
Prangle Prangnall
PRANGNELL
Prangell PRAGNELL
PRANGNELL
Prangle PRAGNELL
PRANGNELL
Prangnall PRAGNELL
PRANGNELL
PRANGNELL 5 PRAGNELL
Prangell Prangle
Prangnall
Pratellis PROUSE PROWSE
PRATER Preater Preator
Preace PREECE PREES
PRIEST REECE REES
Preas PREECE PREES PRIEST
REECE REES
Preast PREECE PREES
PRIEST REECE REES
Preater PRATER
Preator PRATER
Preaux PROUSE PROWSE
Precias PRECIOUS
Precions PRECIOUS
PRECIOUS 21 Precias
Precions Precise
Prescious Preshas
Presheas Preshous
Preshouse Preshus
Presise Presses
Pressius Presson
Pressus Pretcious

Preticouss Pretious
Pretiouss Pretius
Pretyus
Precise PRECIOUS
PREECE 9 Preace Preas
Preast PREES Preest
PRIEST REECE REES
PREEN Preene Prene
Preene PREEN
PREES 9 Preace Preas
Preast PREECE Preest
PRIEST REECE REES
Preest PREECE PREES
PRIEST REECE REES
Preist PRIEST
Preistland PRESLAND
Prene PREEN
Presburrie PRESBURY
PRESBURY 6 Presburrie
Presby Prestbury
Prisbrey Prisbry
Presby PRESBURY
Prescious PRECIOUS
PRESCOT Prescott
Prescott PRESCOT
PRESTHOPE RANDOLPH
Preshas PRECIOUS
Presheas PRECIOUS
Preshous PRECIOUS
Preshouse PRECIOUS
Preshus PRECIOUS
Presise PRECIOUS
PRESLAND 5 Preistland
Pressland Prestland
Prisland
Presses PRECIOUS
Pressic PRESSICK PRISSICK
PRESSICK 6 Pressic
Preswick Prissic
PRISSICK Prisswick
Pressius PRECIOUS
Pressland PRESLAND
Presson PRECIOUS
Pressus PRECIOUS
Prest PRIEST
Prestbury PRESBURY
PRESTHOPE Prescott
RANDOLPH
Prestland PRESLAND
Preswick PRESSICK
PRISSICK
Pretcious PRECIOUS
Prethero PROTHERO
PROTHEROE
Pretheroe PROTHERO
PROTHEROE
Prethro PROTHERO
PROTHEROE
Prethroe PROTHERO
PROTHEROE
Preticouss PRECIOUS
Pretious PRECIOUS
Pretiouss PRECIOUS
Pretius PRECIOUS
PRETLOVE 4 Pretluv
Prettlove Prettluv
Pretluv PRETLOVE
Prettlove PRETLOVE
Prettluv PRETLOVE
PRETTY Prety PRITTY
Prety PRETTY PRITTY
Pretyus PRECIOUS
Preux PROUSE PROWSE
Prevost PROVIS PROVOST
Prewen PRUEN
PREWETT 4 Pruet Pruett
Pruitt
Prewin PRUEN
Prewine PRUEN
Prewne PRUEN
PRIAL PRYAL PRYALL
PRICE PIERCE PRYCE
PRICHARD 4 Prichit
PRITCHARD Pritchet

Prichit PRICHARD
PRITCHARD
PRICKETT PECKET PECKITT
Prickter PRICTER
PRICTER Prickter Prictor
Prictor PRICTER
PRIER 5 PRIOR Prower
Pryer PRYOR
PRIEST 11 Preace Preas
Preast PREECE PREES
Preest Preist Prest
REECE REES
PRIESTLEY Priestnall
Priestnall PRIESTLEY
Pringham PINCOMBE PINKHAM
PRINGLE Pringles
Pringleton
Pringles PRINGLE
Pringleton PRINGLE
PRIOR 5 PRIER Prower
Pryer PRYOR
Prisbrey PRESBURY
Prisbry PRESBURY
Prisland PRESLAND
Prissic PRESSICK PRISSICK
PRISSICK 6 Pressic
PRESSICK Preswick
Prissic Prisswick
Prisswick PRESSICK
PRISSICK
PRITCHARD 4 PRICHARD
Prichit Pritchet
Pritchet PRICHARD
PRITCHARD
Prithro PROTHERO
PROTHEROE
Prithroe PROTHERO
PROTHEROE
PRITTY PRETTY Prety
Probait PROBERT
Probard PROBERT PROBETTS
Probards PROBERT PROBETTS
Probart PROBERT PROBETTS
Probarts PROBERT PROBETTS
Probat PROBERT PROBETTS
Probate PROBERT PROBETTS
Probates PROBERT PROBETTS
Probats PROBERT PROBETTS
Probatt PROBERT PROBETTS
Probatts PROBERT PROBETTS
PROBERT 21 Probait
Probard Probards
Probart Probarts Probat
Probate Probates
Probats Probatt
Probatts Proberts
Probet Probets Probett
PROBETTS Probit Probits
Probitt Probitts
Proberts PROBERT PROBETTS
Probet PROBERT PROBETTS
Probets PROBERT PROBETTS
Probett PROBERT PROBETTS
PROBETTS 20 Probard
Probards Probart
Probarts Probat Probate
Probates Probats
Probatt Probatts
PROBERT Proberts Probet
Probets Probett Probit
Probits Probitt
Probitts
Probit PROBERT PROBETTS
Probits PROBERT PROBETTS
Probitt PROBERT PROBETTS
Probitts PROBERT PROBETTS
Probus PROUSE PROWSE
Prockter PROCTER PROCTOR
Procktor PROCTER PROCTOR
PROCTER 4 Prockter
Procktor PROCTOR
PROCTOR 4 Prockter
Procktor PROCTER
Proeuen PRUEN

If the name you are interested in is not here, try Section C.

PROFFIT Profit Prophet
Profit PROFFIT
Prom PROOM
PROOM 6 Prom Proome Prum Prume Prumme
Proome PROOM
Prophet PROFFIT
PROTHERO 15 Prethero Pretheroe Prethro Prethroe Prithro Prithroe PROTHEROE Protherough Prothro Prothroe Prydderch Prytherch Prythro Prythroe
PROTHEROE 15 Prethero Pretheroe Prethro Prethroe Prithro Prithroe PROTHERO Protherough Prothro Prothroe Prydderch Prytherch Prythro Prythroe
Protherough PROTHERO PROTHEROE
Prothro PROTHERO PROTHEROE
Prothroe PROTHERO PROTHEROE
Prouen PRUEN
Prouin PRUEN
PROUSE 10 De rie Pratellis Preaux Preux Probus Prouz Prouze Provs PROWSE
PROUT Sprout
Prouz PROUSE PROWSE
Prouze PROUSE PROWSE
Provest PROVIS PROVOST
PROVICE PROVIS
PROVIS 5 Prevost Provest PROVICE PROVOST
PROVOST 4 Prevost Provest PROVIS
Provs PROUSE PROWSE
Prowen PRUEN
Prower PRIER PRIOR PRYOR
Prowne PRUEN
PROWSE 10 De rie Pratellis Preaux Preux Probus PROUSE Prouz Prouze Provs
Prowyne PRUEN
Pruan PRUEN
PRUDAMES Prudham Prudome
Prudham PRUDAMES
Prudome PRUDAMES
PRUEN 24 Prewen Prewin Prewine Prewne Proeuen Prouen Prouin Prowen Prowne Prowyne Pruan Pruene Pruenen Pruine Prun Prune Prunne Prunnen Pruyn Pruyne Pruynen Pruynes Pryne
Pruene PRUEN
Pruenen PRUEN
Pruet PREWETT
Pruett PREWETT
Pruine PRUEN
Pruitt PREWETT
Prum PROOM
Prume PROOM
Prumme PROOM
Prun PRUEN
Prune PRUEN
Prunne PRUEN
Prunnen PRUEN
Pruyn PRUEN
Pruyne PRUEN
Pruynen PRUEN
Pruynes PRUEN
PRYAL PRIAL PRYALL
PRYALL PRIAL PRYAL
PRYCE PRICE
Prydderch PROTHERO PROTHEROE
Pryer PRIER PRIOR PRYOR
Pryne PRUEN
PRYOR 5 PRIER PRIOR Prower Pryer
Prytherch PROTHERO PROTHEROE
Prythro PROTHERO PROTHEROE
Prythroe PROTHERO PROTHEROE
Pttock-buss PITTOCK
Pualing PAULIN PAULING
PUDDEPHATT PUDDIFOOT
PUDDIFOOT PUDDEPHATT
Puddington PURRINTON
Pudener PUDNER
Pudeney PUDNEY
Pudnar PUDNER
PUDNER 8 Pudener Pudnar Pudnor Putnar Putner Putnor Puttener
PUDNEY Pudeney Putney
Pudnor PUDNER
Pue PUGH
PUGH Pue
PUINTUR 4 POINFON POINTER POINTUR
PULAR 4 POOLER PULLAR PULLER
PULEE TULEE
PULESTON 12 De puleston De pyuelisdon De pyvelisdon De pywelisdon Pilston Pulieston Puliston Pulleston Pyuelisdon Pyvelisdon Pywelisdon
Pulieston PULESTON
Puliston PULESTON
Pull POOL POOLE
PULLAN Pullein Pulleyn
PULLAR 4 POOLER PULAR PULLER
Pullein PULLAN
PULLER 4 POOLER PULAR PULLAR
Pulleston PULESTON
Pulleyn PULLAN
Pulton POULTON
Pultrel POWDERILL
PULVERTAFT 5 Polvertoft Polvertofte PULVERTOFT Pulvertofte
PULVERTOFT 5 Polvertoft Polvertofte PULVERTAFT Pulvertofte
Pulvertofte PULVERTAFT PULVERTOFT
Pumeroy POMEROY POMROY
Pumrey POMEROY POMROY
Puplet POPLETT
Puplett POPLETT
Pupplett POPLETT
Purcas PURCHASE PURKESS PURKIS PURKISS
Purcass PURCHASE PURKESS PURKIS PURKISS
Purceur PURVER
Purchal PURCHALL PURCHELL
PURCHALL 12 Parchall Parshall Pershall Porchel Purchal Purchel PURCHELL Purchil Purchill Purshale Purshall
Purchas PURCHASE PURKESS PURKIS PURKISS
PURCHASE 15 Purcas Purcass Purchas Purchass Purches Purckis Purckuse Purkas Purkass Purkes PURKESS Purkies PURKIS PURKISS
Purchass PURCHASE PURKESS PURKIS PURKISS
Purchel PURCHALL PURCHELL
PURCHELL 12 Parchall Parshall Pershall Porchel Purchal PURCHALL Purchel Purchil Purchill Purshale Purshall
Purches PURCHASE PURKESS PURKIS PURKISS
Purchil PURCHALL PURCHELL
Purchill PURCHALL PURCHELL
Purckis PURCHASE PURKESS PURKIS PURKISS
Purckuse PURCHASE PURKESS PURKIS PURKISS
Purdie PURDY
PURDUE Perdu
PURDY Purdie
PUREFOY Parfrey Purfrey
Purfrey PUREFOY
Purington PURRINTON
Purkas PURCHASE PURKESS PURKIS PURKISS
Purkass PURCHASE PURKESS PURKIS PURKISS
Purkes PERKES PERKS PURCHASE PURKESS PURKIS PURKISS
PURKESS 15 Purcas Purcass Purchas PURCHASE Purchass Purches Purckis Purckuse Purkas Purkass Purkes Purkies PURKIS PURKISS
Purkies PURCHASE PURKESS PURKIS PURKISS
Purkins PARKINS PERKINS
PURKIS 16 Perkis Purcas Purcass Purchas PURCHASE Purchass Purches Purckis Purckuse Purkas Purkass Purkes PURKESS Purkies PURKISS
PURKISS 15 Purcas Purcass Purchas PURCHASE Purchass Purches Purckis Purckuse Purkas Purkass Purkes PURKESS Purkies PURKIS
Purks PERKES PERKS
Purkyns PARKINS PERKINS
Purrington PURRINTON
PURRINTON 4 Puddington Purington Purrington
Pursehouse PARSUS PERSEHOUSE
PURSER 19 Pafford PALSER Parser Pasard Paser Pasher Passard Passer Passerd Passwer Payser Payzer Pazer Pazzard PAZZERD Persuire Posheart Pursuir
Purshale PURCHALL PURCHELL
Purshall PURCHALL PURCHELL
Pursuir PURSER
PURVER 11 Perver Perveur Purceur Purveure Purvey Purveyor Purvier Purviour Purvor Purvur
Purveure PURVER
Purvey PURVER
Purveyor PURVER
Purvier PURVER
Purviour PURVER
Purvor PURVER
Purvur PURVER
PUSEY PEWSEY Pisey
Putel POWDERILL
Putman PUTNAM
PUTNAM 4 Putman PUTTENHAM Puttnam
Putnar PUDNER
Putner PUDNER
Putney PUDNEY
Putnor PUDNER
Putrel POWDERILL
Putrell POWDERILL
Puttener PUDNER
PUTTENHAM PUTNAM Puttnam
Puttnam PUTNAM PUTTENHAM
PUTWAIN 8 Piotvain Podevin Poitvine Pordvine Portwine Potisain Potvine
PYATT Piat PYETT
Pydele PIDDLE
Pydell PIDDLE
PYE 5 PACE Pase PASS PAYE
Pyeman PEYMAN
PYER 4 PIPER Pipers Pipper
PYETT Piat PYATT
Pygrem PINCOMBE PINKHAM
Pygrim PINCOMBE PINKHAM
Pygrum PINCOMBE PINKHAM
Pygrym PINCOMBE PINKHAM
PYKE PIKE
Pykett PICKETT PIKET PIKETT
Pylgram PINCOMBE PINKHAM
Pylgrem PINCOMBE PINKHAM
Pylgrin PINCOMBE PINKHAM
Pylgrum PINCOMBE PINKHAM
Pylgrym PINCOMBE PINKHAM
PYM 4 PIM PIMM Pymm
Pymble PEMBLE PIMBLE
Pymgram PINCOMBE PINKHAM
Pymgrem PINCOMBE PINKHAM
Pymgrin PINCOMBE PINKHAM
Pymgrum PINCOMBE PINKHAM
Pymgrym PINCOMBE PINKHAM
Pymm PIM PIMM PYM
Pyncknaye PINCKNEY PINKNEY
Pyncknye PINCKNEY PINKNEY
PYNE PAIN PINE
Pyngeram PINCOMBE PINKHAM
Pyngerham PINCOMBE PINKHAM
Pyngram PINCOMBE PINKHAM
Pyngrem PINCOMBE PINKHAM
Pyngrim PINCOMBE PINKHAM
Pyngrum PINCOMBE PINKHAM
Pynhenye PINCKNEY PINKNEY
Pynhorn PINHORN
Pynin PINNING
Pynkenheye PINCKNEY PINKNEY
Pynkney PINCKNEY PINKNEY
Pynnell PENNILL PENNY PINEL PINNEL PINNELL
Pynnin PINNING
Pynning PINNING
Pynninge PINNING
Pyram PINCOMBE PINKHAM
Pyrkins PARKINS PERKINS
Pyrkyns PARKINS PERKINS
Pysor PIZER POIZER POYSER PYZER
Pyte PITE
Pyttes PITTS
Pyuelisdon PULESTON
Pyvelisdon PULESTON
Pywelisdon PULESTON
PYZER 14 Payser Pazzer PIZER Poiser POIZER POYSER Poysor Poyzer Pysor Spizer Spoiser Spoizer Spyzer

If the name you are interested in is not here, try Section C.

QUAIN Quan QUINN
Quan QUAIN QUINN
Quantrell CANT CANTER CANTERELL CANTRELL CANTRILL CHANTRELL QUANTRILL QUINTRELL
QUANTRILL 48 CANT CANTER Canterall Canterel CANTERELL Canterelle Canterhill Canterhulle Cantlen Cantrall Cantrel CANTRELL Cantrelle Cantril CANTRILL Cantrille Cantrul Cantrule Cantwall Cantwell Caunton Chanterall Chanterel Chanterell Chanterelle Chantrel CHANTRELL Chantrelle Chantril Chantrill Cointerel Cointerell Coynterel Cuinterel Cuinterell Cuonterel Kanterall Kanterell Kanterill Kantrall Kantrell Kantrill Quantrell Quarntrill Queinterell QUINTRELL Quyntrel
Quarntrill CANT CANTER CANTERELL CANTRELL CANTRILL CHANTRELL QUANTRILL QUINTRELL
Quarrey QUARRY
Quarrie QUARRY
QUARRY Quarrey Quarrie
Quarterly QUARTLY
QUARTERMAIN 6 Catterment Quartermaine QUARTERMAN Quartermane Quatremaine
Quartermaine QUARTERMAIN QUARTERMAN
QUARTERMAN 6 Catterment QUARTERMAIN Quartermaine Quartermane Quatremaine
Quartermane QUARTERMAIN QUARTERMAN
Quartley QUARTLY
QUARTLY Quarterly Quartley
Quatremaine QUARTERMAIN QUARTERMAN
Queinterell CANT CANTER CANTERELL CANTRELL CANTRILL CHANTRELL QUANTRILL QUINTRELL
Queney QUINEY QUINNEY
Quhyt WHITE WHYTE
QUIDDINGTON Quittenden
Quie QUY
QUIGG TWIGG
QUINCE 7 QUINCEY Quincie Quincy Quinse Quinsey Quinsy
QUINCEY 7 QUINCE Quincie Quincy Quinse Quinsey Quinsy
Quincie QUINCE QUINCEY
Quincy QUINCE QUINCEY
QUINEY 5 Queney QUINNEY Quiny Quyney
QUINN QUAIN Quan
QUINNEY 5 Queney QUINEY Quiny Quyney
Quinse QUINCE QUINCEY
Quinsey QUINCE QUINCEY
Quinsy QUINCE QUINCEY
Quinterle QUINTRELL
Quintral QUINTRELL
QUINTRELL 50 CANT CANTER Canterall Canterel CANTERELL Canterelle Canterhill Canterhulle Cantlen Cantrall Cantrel CANTRELL Cantrelle Cantril CANTRILL Cantrille Cantrul Cantrule Cantwall Cantwell Caunton Chanterall Chanterel Chanterell Chanterelle Chantrel CHANTRELL Chantrelle Chantril Chantrill Cointerel Cointerell Coynterel Cuinterel Cuinterell Cuonterel Kanterall Kanterell Kanterill Kantrall Kantrell Kantrill Quantrell QUANTRILL Quarntrill Queinterell Quinterle Quintral Quyntrel
Quiny QUINEY QUINNEY
QUIRK 5 Cuirc O'cuirc O'quirk QUIRKE
QUIRKE 5 Cuirc O'cuirc O'quirk QUIRK
Quitesyd WHITESIDE
Quittenden QUIDDINGTON
Quoy QUY
Quoye QUY
QUY 5 Quie Quoy Quoye Quye
Quye QUY
Quyney QUINEY QUINNEY
Quyntrel CANT CANTER CANTERELL CANTRELL CANTRILL CHANTRELL QUANTRILL QUINTRELL
Qwittwham WHITHAM WHITTAM WITHAM WITTAM
Qwythedws WHITESIDE
Rabey RABY
RABY Rabey
RACE Raice Rase
RACKSTRAW Rakestraw
RADBURN 5 Redbourn REDBURN Rodbourn Rodbur
Radciff RADCLIFF RADCLIFFE RATCLIFF RATCLIFFE RATLIEFF
Radcleff RADCLIFF RADCLIFFE RATCLIFF RATCLIFFE RATLIEFF
Radcleife RADCLIFF RADCLIFFE RATCLIFF RATCLIFFE RATLIEFF
RADCLIFF 28 Radciff Radcleff Radcleife RADCLIFFE Radclyff Radclyffe Raddlyff Ratckif Ratclif RATCLIFF RATCLIFFE Ratclifft Ratclift Ratclyffe Ratleff Ratley RATLIEFF Ratlif Ratlife Ratliff Ratliffe Ratly Ratlyff Rattcliffe Rattlif Rattliff Retcliffe
RADCLIFFE 28 Radciff Radcleff Radcleife RADCLIFF Radclyff Radclyffe Raddlyff Ratckif Ratclif RATCLIFF RATCLIFFE Ratclifft Ratclift Ratclyffe Ratleff Ratley RATLIEFF Ratlif Ratlife Ratliff Ratliffe Ratly Ratlyff Rattcliffe Rattlif Rattliff Retcliffe
Radclyff RADCLIFF RADCLIFFE RATCLIFF RATCLIFFE RATLIEFF
Radclyffe RADCLIFF RADCLIFFE RATCLIFF RATCLIFFE RATLIEFF
Raddlyff RADCLIFF RADCLIFFE RATCLIFF RATCLIFFE RATLIEFF
RADNAGE 5 RADNEDGE Radnege RADNIDGE Ranedge
RADNEDGE 5 RADNAGE Radnege RADNIDGE Ranedge
Radnege RADNAGE RADNEDGE RADNIDGE
RADNIDGE 5 RADNAGE RADNEDGE Radnege Ranedge
Radway RODWAY
RAE 4 RAY REA WRAY
Raeny RENNIE
Rafeil RAFFELL RAFFILL RAFFLE
Raffaell RAFFELL RAFFILL RAFFLE
Raffel RAFFELL RAFFILL RAFFLE
RAFFELL 21 Rafeil Raffaell Raffel Raffil RAFFILL Raffille RAFFLE Rafflle Rafield Rafil Rafill Rapgael Raphall Raphel Raphele Raphell Raphiel Raphil Rasil Rassel
Raffil RAFFELL RAFFILL RAFFLE
RAFFILL 21 Rafeil Raffaell Raffel RAFFELL Raffil Raffille RAFFLE Rafflle Rafield Rafil Rafill Rapgael Raphall Raphel Raphele Raphell Raphiel Raphil Rasil Rassel
Raffille RAFFELL RAFFILL RAFFLE
RAFFLE 21 Rafeil Raffaell Raffel RAFFELL Raffil RAFFILL Raffille Rafflle Rafield Rafil Rafill Rapgael Raphall Raphel Raphele Raphell Raphiel Raphil Rasil Rassel
Rafflle RAFFELL RAFFILL RAFFLE
Raffmel RATHMELL
Rafield RAFFELL RAFFILL RAFFLE
Rafil RAFFELL RAFFILL RAFFLE
Rafill RAFFELL RAFFILL RAFFLE
Rafmel RATHMELL
RAFTER RAFTON
RAFTON RAFTER
RAGG WRAGG
Raher FRAHER FRYOR
Raice RACE
RAILTON 7 Ralton RAYTON Relton RULTON Wrayton Wreaton
Raily RAWLEIGH RAWLEY ROWLEY
Raiment RAYMENT
RAINBIRD 4 Rainburd Raynbeard Raynbird
Rainburd RAINBIRD
RAINE 4 RAINES RAYNE Raynes
RAINER 4 Rainor RAYNER RAYNOR
RAINES 6 RAINE Rainsraynes RAYNE Raynes Rayns
Rainesdale RAMSDALE RAVENSDALE
RAINEY Ranye
RAINFORD RAINFORTH
RAINFORTH RAINFORD
Rainie RENNIE
Rainne RENNIE
Rainnie RENNIE
Rainny RENNIE
Rainor RAINER RAYNER RAYNOR
Rainsdale RAMSDALE RAVENSDALE
Rainsraynes RAINES
Rainy RENNIE
Raisey RAZEY
Rakestraw RACKSTRAW
Raley RAWLEIGH RAWLEY ROWLEY
RALF 10 RALPH REALF Realff RELF RELFE RELPH ROLF ROLFE ROLPH
Rall RAWLE RAWLL
RALPH 9 RALF REALF RELF RELFE RELPH ROLF ROLFE ROLPH
Ralston ROWLSTONE
Ralton RAILTON RULTON
RAM 4 Rame Ramm Ramme
RAMBRIDGE 9 Ambage Ambidge Ambige Ambrage AMBRIDGE Bambridge HAMBRIDGE Umbrage
Rame RAM REAMES
Rames REAMES
Ramm RAM
Ramme RAM
RAMSAY RAMSEY
RAMSDALE 10 Rainesdale Rainsdale Ranesdale Ranesdall Ransdale Ransdall Ravenesdale RAVENSDALE Revenedale
Ramsel RAMSELL
RAMSELL 6 Ramsel Romsel Romsell Rumsel Rumsell
RAMSEY RAMSAY
Ramskar RAMSKER
RAMSKER Ramskar
Ranbie RANBY
RANBY Ranbie Randbie
RANCE Raunce
RANDAL 5 RANDALL Randel RANDELL RANDLE
RANDALL 11 RANDAL Randel RANDELL RANDLE RANDLES Randole Randoll Ranulf Rendele RUNDLE
Randbie RANBY
Randel RANDAL RANDALL RANDELL RANDLE
RANDELL 9 RANDAL RANDALL Randel RANDLE RANDLES Randole Randoll Ranulf
RANDLE 10 RANDAL RANDALL Randel RANDELL RANDLES Randole Randoll Ranulf RENDLE
RANDLES 7 RANDALL RANDELL RANDLE Randole Randoll Ranulf
Randole RANDALL RANDELL RANDLE RANDLES
Randoll RANDALL RANDELL RANDLE RANDLES
RANDOLPH Prescott PRESTHOPE
Ranedge RADNAGE RADNEDGE RADNIDGE
Ranesdale RAMSDALE RAVENSDALE

If the name you are interested in is not here, try Section C.

Ranesdall RAMSDALE RAVENSDALE
Raney RENNIE
RANKIN RANKINE
RANKINE RANKIN
Rannolds REYNOLDS
Ranny RENNIE
Ransdale RAMSDALE RAVENSDALE
Ransdall RAMSDALE RAVENSDALE
Ranulf RANDALL RANDELL RANDLE RANDLES
Rany RENNIE
Ranye RAINEY
Rapgael RAFFELL RAFFILL RAFFLE
Raphall RAFFELL RAFFILL RAFFLE
Raphel RAFFELL RAFFILL RAFFLE
Raphele RAFFELL RAFFILL RAFFLE
Raphell RAFFELL RAFFILL RAFFLE
Raphiel RAFFELL RAFFILL RAFFLE
Raphil RAFFELL RAFFILL RAFFLE
Rappel FRAPWELL
Rapsey RAPSON
Rapsin RAPSON
RAPSON 5 Rapsey Rapsin Rapsyn Wrapson
Rapsyn RAPSON
RASBERRY Rasbury RESBURY
Rasbury RASBERRY RESBURY
Raschelegh RASHLEIGH
Raschelye RASHLEIGH
Rase RACE
Rasely RASHLEIGH
Rasey RAZEY
RASHLEIGH 8 Raschelegh Raschelye Rasely Rasle Rasselegh Rasshelegh Rayshelegh
Rasil RAFFELL RAFFILL RAFFLE
Rasiman ROSAMOND
Rasle RASHLEIGH
Rassel RAFFELL RAFFILL RAFFLE
Rasselegh RASHLEIGH
Rasshelegh RASHLEIGH
Rasy RAZEY
Ratckif RADCLIFF RADCLIFFE RATCLIFF RATCLIFFE RATLIEFF
Ratclif RADCLIFF RADCLIFFE RATCLIFF RATCLIFFE RATLIEFF
RATCLIFF 28 Radciff Radcleff Radcleife RADCLIFF RADCLIFFE Radclyff Radclyffe Raddlyff Ratckif Ratclif RATCLIFFE Ratclifft Ratclift Ratclyffe Ratleff Ratley RATLIEFF Ratlif Ratlife Ratliff Ratliffe Ratly Ratlyff Rattcliffe Rattlif Rattliff Retcliffe
RATCLIFFE 28 Radciff Radcleff Radcleife RADCLIFF RADCLIFFE Radclyff Radclyffe Raddlyff Ratckif Ratclif RATCLIFF Ratclifft Ratclift Ratclyffe Ratleff Ratley RATLIEFF Ratlif Ratlife Ratliff Ratliffe Ratly Ratlyff Rattcliffe Rattlif Rattliff Retcliffe
Ratclifft RADCLIFF RADCLIFFE RATCLIFF RATCLIFFE RATLIEFF
Ratclift RADCLIFF RADCLIFFE RATCLIFF RATCLIFFE RATLIEFF
Ratclyffe RADCLIFF RADCLIFFE RATCLIFF RATCLIFFE RATLIEFF
RATHBONE RATHBUN Rathburn
RATHBUN RATHBONE Rathburn
Rathburn RATHBONE RATHBUN
RATHEL 13 Rathell RATHIL Rathill RATHWELL Rothell Rothill ROTHWELL Wrathel Wrathwell Wrothall Wrothel Wrothwell
Rathell RATHEL RATHIL
RATHIL 5 RATHEL Rathell Rathill Wrathel
Rathill RATHEL RATHIL RATHWELL ROTHWELL
Rathmall RATHMELL
RATHMELL 5 Raffmel Rafmel Rathmall Rathnell
Rathnell RATHMELL
RATHWELL 10 RATHEL Rathill Rothell Rothill ROTHWELL Wrathwell Wrothall Wrothel Wrothwell
Ratleff RADCLIFF RADCLIFFE RATCLIFF RATCLIFFE RATLIEFF
Ratley RADCLIFF RADCLIFFE RATCLIFF RATCLIFFE RATLIEFF
RATLIEFF 28 Radciff Radcleff Radcleife RADCLIFF RADCLIFFE Radclyff Radclyffe Raddlyff Ratckif Ratclif RATCLIFF RATCLIFFE Ratclifft Ratclift Ratclyffe Ratleff Ratley Ratlif Ratlife Ratliff Ratliffe Ratly Ratlyff Rattcliffe Rattlif Rattliff Retcliffe
Ratlif RADCLIFF RADCLIFFE RATCLIFF RATCLIFFE RATLIEFF
Ratlife RADCLIFF RADCLIFFE RATCLIFF RATCLIFFE RATLIEFF
Ratliff RADCLIFF RADCLIFFE RATCLIFF RATCLIFFE RATLIEFF
Ratliffe RADCLIFF RADCLIFFE RATCLIFF RATCLIFFE RATLIEFF
Ratly RADCLIFF RADCLIFFE RATCLIFF RATCLIFFE RATLIEFF
Ratlyff RADCLIFF RADCLIFFE RATCLIFF RATCLIFFE RATLIEFF
Rattcliffe RADCLIFF RADCLIFFE RATCLIFF RATCLIFFE RATLIEFF
RATTERY RATTRAY
Rattlif RADCLIFF RADCLIFFE RATCLIFF RATCLIFFE RATLIEFF
Rattliff RADCLIFF RADCLIFFE RATCLIFF RATCLIFFE RATLIEFF
RATTRAY RATTERY
Raudinge RAWDON RHODEN RODEN ROWDEN ROYDEN
Raunce RANCE
Rauson RAWSON
Rausone RAWSON
Ravel REVEL REVELL REVILL
Ravenesdale RAMSDALE RAVENSDALE
RAVENSDALE 10 Rainesdale Rainsdale RAMSDALE Ranesdale Ranesdall Ransdale Ransdall Ravenesdale Revenedale
RAW 7 O'RAW O'rawe O'row Rawe ROE ROWE
Rawden RAWDING RAWDON
Rawdin RAWDING RAWDON
RAWDING 4 Rawden Rawdin RAWDON
RAWDON 58 Raudinge Rawden Rawdin RAWDING Raydon Reuden Rhoaden Rhodan Rhoddan Rhodden RHODEN Rhodin Rhoding Rhodon Roadding Roaden Roading Roadinge Roadon Rodan Rodden Roddin Rodding Roddon RODEN Rodend Rodene Rodhenn Rodin Rodine Roding Rodinge Rodinn Rodon Rodone Rodyn Roeden Roedon Rohden Roiden Rooden Roodin Rooding Roodinge Roodon Roodyng Roudan Rouden Rowadon Rowdan ROWDEN Rowdin Rowding Rowdinge Rowdon ROYDEN Woden
Rawe O'RAW RAW ROE ROWE
Rawel RAWLE RAWLL
RAWES 5 Raws Rawse Rowes Rows
Rawl RAWLE RAWLL
RAWLE 8 Rall Rawel Rawl RAWLL Rorel Rorell Rorle
RAWLEIGH 6 Raily Raley RAWLEY Rawly ROWLEY
Rawlen RAWLINGS RAWLINS
Rawlens RAWLINGS RAWLINS
RAWLETT Rollett
RAWLEY 6 Raily Raley RAWLEIGH Rawly ROWLEY
Rawlin RAWLINGS RAWLINS
RAWLINGS 6 Rawlen Rawlens Rawlin RAWLINS Rollings
RAWLINS 6 Rawlen Rawlens Rawlin RAWLINGS Rollings
RAWLINSON 6 Rolison ROLLASON ROLLINSON Rollison Rowlinson
RAWLL 8 Rall Rawel Rawl RAWLE Rorel Rorell Rorle
Rawly RAWLEIGH RAWLEY ROWLEY
Raws RAWES
Rawse RAWES
RAWSON 5 Rauson Rausone Rawsone Rawsonne
Rawsone RAWSON
Rawsonne RAWSON
RAY 5 RAE Raye REA WRAY
Raydon RAWDON RHODEN RODEN ROWDEN ROYDEN
Raye RAY WRAY
Rayle ROYAL ROYALL ROYLE
Raymant RAYMENT
RAYMENT 6 Raiment Raymant Raymint Raymont Reyment
Raymint RAYMENT
Raymont RAYMENT
Raynbeard RAINBIRD
Raynbird RAINBIRD
RAYNE 4 RAINE RAINES Raynes
RAYNER 4 RAINER Rainor RAYNOR
Raynes RAINE RAINES RAYNE
RAYNOR 4 RAINER Rainor RAYNER
Rayns RAINES
Rayshelegh RASHLEIGH
RAYTON 4 RAILTON Wrayton Wreaton
Razee RAZEY
RAZEY 6 Raisey Rasey Rasy Razee Razy
Razy RAZEY
Re'foy REFOY
Re-foy REFOY
REA 4 RAE RAY WRAY
READ 8 READE Rede REED REEDE REID Rheed Ried
READE READ REED
READER REEDER Reider
READING Redding
REAKES REEKS
REAL ROYAL RYAL
REALF 11 RALF RALPH RELF RELFE RELPH RICOLFIS RICWULF RIULF ROLF ROLFE
Realff RALF RELF RELFE RELPH ROLPH
Realme REAM RHEAM
REAM 5 Realme Reame RHEAM Rheame
Reame REAM RHEAM
REAMES 15 Rame Rames Reem Reeme Reemes Reems Reme Remes Rhame Rhames Rheem Rheeme Rheemes Rheems
REAR 6 Reare Reares Reeher Reer Reir
Reare REAR
Reares REAR
REAVELY Revely
Recard RICKARD
Recassel REUCASSEL
Reccard RICKARD
Recceard RICKARD
Receard RICKARD
Recerd RICKARD
Rechard RICKARD
Recheard RICKARD
Recherd RICKARD
Reckard RICKARD
Reckeard RICKARD
Recks REEKS RICKS
Record RICKARD
Redbourn RADBURN REDBURN
REDBURN 5 RADBURN Redbourn Rodbourn Rodbur
Redding READING RIDDING
Reddit REDDY REDHEAD
Redditt REDHEAD REDITT
REDDY Reddit REDHEAD
Rede READ REED REEDE REID
Redge RIDGE
REDHEAD 6 Reddit Redditt REDDY Redit REDITT
Redit REDHEAD REDITT
REDITT 4 Redditt REDHEAD Redit
Redknap REDKNAPP
REDKNAPP Redknap Rednap
Rednap REDKNAPP
Redout RIDEOUT RIDOUT
REDRUP 4 Edrup Rethrop Rudroppe
REECE 13 Preace Preas Preast PREECE PREES Preest PRIEST REES Reese Rheese Rhys RICE

If the name you are interested in is not here, try Section C.

REED 8 READ READE Rede REEDE REID Rheed Ried
REEDE 4 READ Rede REED
REEDER READER Reider
Reeher REAR
REEKS 4 REAKES Recks RICKS
Reem REAMES
Reeme REAMES
Reemes REAMES
Reems REAMES
Reer REAR
REES 13 Preace Preas Preast PREECE PREES Preest PRIEST REECE Reese Rheese Rhys RICE
Reese REECE REES RICE
REESON Rightson
REEVE REEVES REVE
REEVES REEVE
REFOY Re'foy Re-foy
Reg RIDGE
REID 5 READ Rede REED Ried
Reider READER REEDER
Reinolds REYNOLDS
Reir REAR
RELF 13 RALF RALPH REALF Realff RELFE RELPH RICOLFIS RICWULF RIULF ROLF ROLFE ROLPH
RELFE 10 RALF RALPH REALF Realff RELF RELPH ROLF ROLFE ROLPH
RELPH 13 RALF RALPH REALF Realff RELF RELFE RICOLFIS RICWULF RIULF ROLF ROLFE ROLPH
Relton RAILTON RULTON
Reme REAMES
Remes REAMES
Remevill REMEVILLE
REMEVILLE 4 De remevill De remeville Remevill
Ren WREN
Renakers RUNACRES
RENARD 4 Rennard Rennerd Reynard
Renault RENNOLDS REYNOLDS
RENCHER Rensher
Rendel RENDELL RENDLE
Rendele RANDALL
RENDELL Rendel RENDLE
RENDLE 5 RANDLE Rendel RENDELL Renuall
Rennard RENARD
Rennaulds RENNOLDS REYNOLDS
Renne WREN
RENNEL 4 Rennell RINNEL Rinnell
Rennell RENNEL RINNEL
Rennels REYNOLDS
Rennerd RENARD
RENNIE 14 Raeny Rainie Rainne Rainnie Rainny Rainy Raney Ranny Rany Renny Reny Rinn Rynn
RENNOLDS 5 Renault Rennaulds Renold REYNOLDS
Rennoles REYNOLDS
Rennols REYNOLDS
Renny RENNIE
Renold RENNOLDS REYNOLDS
Renoldeg REYNOLDS
Renshen RENCHER
RENTON Rentone
Rentone RENTON
Rentoul RINTOUL
Rentroul RINTOUL
Renuall RENDLE
Reny RENNIE
RESBURY RASBERRY Rasbury
Restarick RESTORICK
RESTORICK Restarick Restrick
Restrick RESTORICK
Retallic RETALLICK
RETALLICK Retallic Rettalack
Retcliffe RADCLIFF RADCLIFFE RATCLIFF RATCLIFFE RATLIEFF
Rethrop REDRUP
Rettalack RETALLICK
Reubotham ROWBOTTOM
REUCASSEL 4 Recassel Rowcassel Rucassel
Reuden RAWDON RHODEN RODEN ROWDEN ROYDEN
REVE REEVE
REVEL 5 Ravel REVELL REVILL Ryell
REVELL 5 Ravel REVEL REVILL Ryell
Revely REAVELY
Revenedale RAMSDALE RAVENSDALE
REVILL 5 Ravel REVEL REVELL Ryell
Revit REVITT RIVET RIVETT
REVITT 4 Revit RIVET RIVETT
Rew ROW ROWE
Rewbotham ROWBOTTOM
Rewbury RUBERY
Reyment RAYMENT
Reynard RENARD
REYNOLDS 11 Rannolds Reinolds Renault Rennaulds Rennels RENNOLDS Rennoles Rennols Renold Renoldeg
Rezle RISDALE
Rhame REAMES
Rhames REAMES
RHEAM 5 Realme REAM Reame Rheame
Rheame REAM RHEAM
Rheed READ REED
Rheem REAMES
Rheeme REAMES
Rheemes REAMES
Rheems REAMES
Rheese REECE REES
Rhoaden RAWDON RHODEN RODEN ROWDEN ROYDEN
RHOADES 8 Rhode RHODES Roades ROADS Rodes Roode Roodes
Rhodan RAWDON RHODEN RODEN ROWDEN ROYDEN
Rhoddan RAWDON RHODEN RODEN ROWDEN ROYDEN
Rhodden RAWDON RHODEN RODEN ROWDEN ROYDEN
Rhode RHOADES RHODES
RHODEN 55 Raudinge RAWDON Raydon Reuden Rhoaden Rhodan Rhoddan Rhodden Rhodin Rhoding Rhodon Roadding Roaden Roading Roadinge Roadon Rodan Rodden Roddin Rodding Roddon RODEN Rodend Rodene Rodhenn Rodin Rodine Roding Rodinge Rodinn Rodon Rodone Rodyn Roeden Roedon Rohden Roiden Rooden Roodin Rooding Roodinge Roodon Roodyng Roudan Rouden Rowadon Rowdan ROWDEN Rowdin Rowding Rowdinge Rowdon ROYDEN Woden
RHODES DENTON DENTON
RHODES 8 RHOADES Rhode Roades ROADS Rodes Roode Roodes
Rhodin RAWDON RHODEN RODEN ROWDEN ROYDEN
Rhoding RAWDON RHODEN RODEN ROWDEN ROYDEN
Rhodon RAWDON RHODEN RODEN ROWDEN ROYDEN
Rhodus ROADHOUSE
Rhyad RHYED
RHYED Rhyad
Rhys REECE REES
Ribbens RIBBINS
RIBBINS Ribbens
Ricard RICKARD
Riccard RICKARD
Riccord RICKARD RICKCORD
Riccords RICKCORD
RICE 4 REECE REES Reese
RICHARDS 4 RICHES Ridges Ritchies
RICHARDSON 4 Richenson Richerson Richinson
RICHE Richie
Richenson RICHARDSON
Richerson RICHARDSON
RICHES 4 RICHARDS Ridges Ritchies
Richie RICHE
Richinson RICHARDSON
RICKABY RICKERBY
RICKARD 20 Recard Reccard Recceard Receard Recerd Rechard Recheard Recherd Reckard Reckeard Record Ricard Riccard Riccord Rickarde RICKARDS Rickeard Rickerd Ricord
Rickarde RICKARD
RICKARDS RICKARD Rickeard
RICKCORD 9 Riccord Riccords Rickcords Rickoard Rickord Rickords Ricord Ricords
Rickcords RICKCORD
Rickeard RICKARD RICKARDS
RICKERBY RICKABY
Rickerd RICKARD
RICKET RICKETS RICKETTS
RICKETS RICKET RICKETTS
RICKETTS RICKET RICKETS
Rickoard RICKCORD
Rickord RICKCORD
Rickords RICKCORD
RICKS Recks REEKS
RICKSON RIXON RIXSON
RICOLFIS 6 REALF RELF RELPH RICWULF RIULF
Ricord RICKARD RICKCORD
Ricords RICKCORD
RICWULF 6 REALF RELF RELPH RICOLFIS RIULF
Ridal RIDDEL RIDDELL RIDDLE RIDLEY RUDDELL
Riddal RIDDEL RIDDELL RIDDLE RIDLEY RUDDELL
Riddall RIDDEL RIDDELL RIDDLE RIDLEY RUDDELL
RIDDEL 13 Ridal Riddal Riddall RIDDELL RIDDLE RIDLEY Ridlon Ruddal Ruddel RUDDELL Rydall Ryedale
RIDDELL 13 Ridal Riddal Riddall RIDDEL RIDDLE RIDLEY Ridlon Ruddal Ruddel RUDDELL Rydall Ryedale
RIDDICK 4 RUDDICK Ruddoch RUDDOCK
RIDDING Redding
RIDDLE 13 Ridal Riddal Riddall RIDDEL RIDDELL RIDLEY Ridlon Ruddal Ruddel RUDDELL Rydall Ryedale
RIDEOUT 8 Redout Ridet RIDETT Ridhett RIDOUT Ridoutt Ridoux
RIDER RYDER
Ridet RIDEOUT RIDETT RIDOUT
RIDETT 5 RIDEOUT Ridet Ridhett RIDOUT
RIDGE 4 Redge Reg Rydge
Ridges RICHARDS RICHES
Ridhett RIDEOUT RIDETT RIDOUT
RIDING 5 RIDINGS Ryden RYDING Rydings
RIDINGS 4 RIDING RYDING Rydings
RIDLEY 13 Ridal Riddal Riddall RIDDEL RIDDELL RIDDLE Ridlon Ruddal Ruddel RUDDELL Rydall Ryedale
Ridlon RIDDEL RIDDELL RIDDLE RIDLEY RUDDELL
RIDOUT 8 Redout RIDEOUT Ridet RIDETT Ridhett Ridoutt Ridoux
Ridoutt RIDEOUT RIDOUT
Ridoux RIDEOUT RIDOUT
Ridsdall RIDSDILL
Ridsdell RIDSDILL
RIDSDILL 5 Ridsdall Ridsdell Risdall Risdell
Ried READ REED REID
Rigal RIGHALL
RIGHALL 4 Giggall Rigal Ryeauld
Right WRIGHT
Rightson REESON
Rigley WRIGLEY
RILEY RYLEY
Rimel RIMER RIMMER RYMER
RIMELL 4 Rymell Rymill Rymyll
RIMER 5 Rimel RIMMER Rymel RYMER
RIMMER 6 Rimel RIMER Rymel RYMER Rymmer
RING RINGE Wring
RINGE RING Wring
RINGSTEAD Ringsted
Ringsted RINGSTEAD
Rinn RENNIE
RINNEL 4 RENNEL Rennell Rinnell
Rinnell RENNEL RINNEL
RINTOUL Rentoul Rentroul
Ripen RIPPIN RIPPON
Ripin RIPPIN RIPPON
Riping RIPPIN RIPPON
RIPLEY Rippley
Ripon RIPPIN RIPPON
Rippen RIPPIN RIPPON
RIPPIN 8 Ripen Ripin Riping Ripon Rippen Ripping RIPPON
Ripping RIPPIN RIPPON
Rippley RIPLEY
RIPPON 8 Ripen Ripin Riping Ripon Rippen RIPPIN Ripping
RISBRIDGER 7 DE LA RISEBREGGE RUSBRIDGER RYSBRUG Rysbrugg RYSEBRIGGER RYSHBRYGGE
Risdal RISDALE
RISDALE 7 Rezle Risdal Wrassell Wresle Wressell Wrossell
Risdall RIDSDILL

If the name you are interested in is not here, try Section C.

Risdell RIDSDILL
RISELEY 8 Risely RISLEY Risly Rizley Ryseley Rysley Wrisley
Risely RISELEY
RISHFORTH 5 Rishworth RUSHFIRTH RUSHFORTH RUSHWORTH
Rishin RUSHENT
Rishworth RISHFORTH RUSHFIRTH RUSHFORTH RUSHWORTH
RISLEY 4 RISELEY Rizley Wrisley
Risly RISELEY
Ritchies RICHARDS RICHES
Rite WRIGHT
Rithoak OAKLEY OCKLEY
Rithock OAKLEY OCKLEY
RIULF 6 REALF RELF RELPH RICOLFIS RICWULF
RIVER 4 RIVERS Ryver Ryvers
RIVERS 4 RIVER Ryver Ryvers
RIVET 4 Revit REVITT RIVETT
RIVETT 4 Revit REVITT RIVET
RIXON RICKSON RIXSON
RIXSON RICKSON RIXON
Rizley RISELEY RISLEY
ROACH 4 Roache ROCH ROCHE
Roache ROACH
Roadding RAWDON RHODEN RODEN ROWDEN ROYDEN
Roaden RAWDON RHODEN RODEN ROWDEN ROYDEN
Roades RHOADES RHODES
ROADHOUSE Rhodus
Roading RAWDON RHODEN RODEN ROWDEN ROYDEN
Roadinge RAWDON RHODEN RODEN ROWDEN ROYDEN
Roadon RAWDON RHODEN RODEN ROWDEN ROYDEN
ROADS RHOADES RHODES
Roadway RODWAY
Roantree ROWNTREE
Robarts ROBERTS
Robbarts ROBERTS
Robben ROBBENS ROBBINS ROBIN ROBINS
ROBBENS 8 Robben Robbin ROBBINS Roben Robens ROBIN ROBINS
Robberts ROBERTS
Robbin ROBBENS ROBBINS ROBIN ROBINS
ROBBINS 11 CAMFIELD Campfield Robben ROBBENS Robbin Roben Robens ROBIN ROBINS ROBINSON
Roben ROBBENS ROBBINS ROBIN ROBINS
Robens ROBBENS ROBBINS ROBIN ROBINS
ROBERT ROBERTS
ROBERTS 5 Robarts Robbarts Robberts ROBERT
ROBERTSON ROBINSON ROBSON
Robery RUBERY
ROBEY ROBY
ROBIN 8 Robben ROBBENS Robbin ROBBINS Roben Robens ROBINS
ROBINET 6 ROBINETT Robinette Robnet Robnett Robnette
ROBINETT 6 ROBINET Robinette Robnet Robnett Robnette
Robinette ROBINET ROBINETT
ROBINS 11 CAMFIELD Campfield Robben ROBBENS Robbin ROBBINS Roben Robens ROBIN ROBINSON
ROBINSON 5 ROBBINS ROBERTSON ROBINS ROBSON
Robnet ROBINET ROBINETT
Robnett ROBINET ROBINETT
Robnette ROBINET ROBINETT
ROBSON 4 ROBERTSON ROBINSON Robsun
Robsun ROBSON
ROBY ROBEY
Roccker ROCKER
ROCH ROACH ROCHE
ROCHE ROACH ROCH
ROCHESTER 4 ROSENSTRAUGH Rotchester RUDCHESTER
ROCK Rocks
ROCKER Roccker Rockerby
Rockerby ROCKER
Rocks ROCK
Rocliffe ROUTLEY ROWTCLIFF
Rod RODD
Rodan RAWDON RHODEN RODEN ROWDEN ROYDEN
Rodbourn RADBURN REDBURN
Rodbur RADBURN REDBURN
RODD Rod
Rodden RAWDON RHODEN RODEN ROWDEN ROYDEN
Roddin RAWDON RHODEN RODEN ROWDEN ROYDEN
Rodding RAWDON RHODEN RODEN ROWDEN ROYDEN
Roddon RAWDON RHODEN RODEN ROWDEN ROYDEN
RODEN 57 Raudinge RAWDON Raydon Reuden Rhoaden Rhodan Rhoddan Rhodden RHODEN Rhodin Rhoding Rhodon Roadding Roaden Roading Roadinge Roadon Rodan Rodden Roddin Rodding Roddon Rodend Rodene Rodhenn Rodin Rodine Roding Rodinge Rodinn Rodon Rodone Rodyn Roeden Roedon Rohden Roiden Rooden Roodin Rooding Roodinge Roodon Roodyng Roudan Rouden Rowadon Rowdan ROWDEN Rowdin Rowding Rowdinge Rowdon ROYDEN Roydon Ryden Woden
Rodend RAWDON RHODEN RODEN ROWDEN ROYDEN
Rodene RAWDON RHODEN RODEN ROWDEN ROYDEN
Rodes RHOADES RHODES
RODGER RODGERS ROGERS
RODGERS RODGER ROGERS
Rodhenn RAWDON RHODEN RODEN ROWDEN ROYDEN
Rodin RAWDON RHODEN RODEN ROWDEN ROYDEN
Rodine RAWDON RHODEN RODEN ROWDEN ROYDEN
Roding RAWDON RHODEN RODEN ROWDEN ROYDEN
Rodinge RAWDON RHODEN RODEN ROWDEN ROYDEN
Rodinn RAWDON RHODEN RODEN ROWDEN ROYDEN
Rodon RAWDON RHODEN RODEN ROWDEN ROYDEN
Rodone RAWDON RHODEN RODEN ROWDEN ROYDEN
RODWAY Radway Roadway
Rodyn RAWDON RHODEN RODEN ROWDEN ROYDEN
ROE 5 RAW Rawe ROW ROWE
Roeden RAWDON RHODEN RODEN ROWDEN ROYDEN
Roedon RAWDON RHODEN RODEN ROWDEN ROYDEN
ROFFE ROLFE
ROGERS 4 RODGER RODGERS ROGGERS
ROGGERS ROGERS
Rohden RAWDON RHODEN RODEN ROWDEN ROYDEN
Roial ROYAL ROYALL ROYLE RYAL
Roiden RAWDON RHODEN RODEN ROWDEN ROYDEN
Roiston ROYSTON
ROLES ROLLS Rowls
Roleston ROLSTONE ROWLSTONE
Rolestone ROLSTONE ROWLSTONE
ROLF 9 RALF RALPH REALF RELF RELFE RELPH ROLFE ROLPH
ROLFE 10 RALF RALPH REALF RELF RELFE RELPH ROFFE ROLF ROLPH
Rolison RAWLINSON ROLLINSON
ROLLASON RAWLINSON Rollison
Rollett RAWLETT
Rollings RAWLINGS RAWLINS
ROLLINSON 4 RAWLINSON Rolison Rowlinson
Rollison RAWLINSON ROLLASON
ROLLS ROLES Rowls
Rollston ROWLSTONE
ROLPH 9 RALF RALPH Realff RELF RELFE RELPH ROLF ROLFE
ROLSTONE 6 Roleston Rolestone Rowlestone Rowlston ROWLSTONE
Rolt ROUGHT
ROMAIN ROMAINE
ROMAINE ROMAIN
Romsel RAMSELL
Romsell RAMSELL
Rontrey ROWNTREE
Rooby RUBY
Roode RHOADES RHODES
Rooden RAWDON RHODEN RODEN ROWDEN ROYDEN
Roodes RHOADES RHODES
Roodin RAWDON RHODEN RODEN ROWDEN ROYDEN
Rooding RAWDON RHODEN RODEN ROWDEN ROYDEN
Roodinge RAWDON RHODEN RODEN ROWDEN ROYDEN
Roodon RAWDON RHODEN RODEN ROWDEN ROYDEN
Roodyng RAWDON RHODEN RODEN ROWDEN ROYDEN
ROOK ROOKE
ROOKE ROOK
ROOTHAM 5 Rotham Roton Wrootham Wrotham
Rorel RAWLE RAWLL
Rorell RAWLE RAWLL
Rorle RAWLE RAWLL
Rosaman ROSAMOND
ROSAMOND 8 Rasiman Rosaman Rosamund Rosemunde Rosiman Rosoman Rosomand
Rosamund ROSAMOND
Roscho ROSCOE ROSCOW
Roschow ROSCOE ROSCOW
Rosco ROSCOE ROSCOW
ROSCOE 9 Roscho Roschow Rosco ROSCOW Roscowe Roskow Rosow Rosscho
ROSCOW 9 Roscho Roschow Rosco ROSCOE Roscowe Roskow Rosow Rosscho
Roscowe ROSCOE ROSCOW
ROSE 4 ROZE ROZEE Ruse
Rosemunde ROSAMOND
ROSENSTRAUGH ROCHESTER
ROSEVEAR ROSEVEARE Rosevere
ROSEVEARE ROSEVEAR Rosevere
Rosevere ROSEVEAR ROSEVEARE
Rosey ROSIE
ROSIE 4 Rosey Rosy Rozie
Rosiman ROSAMOND
Roskow ROSCOE ROSCOW
Rosoman ROSAMOND
Rosomand ROSAMOND
Rosow ROSCOE ROSCOW
ROSSALL ROSSELL
Rosscho ROSCOE ROSCOW
ROSSELL ROSSALL
Rosy ROSIE
Rotchester ROCHESTER RUDCHESTER
Rotham ROOTHAM
Rothell RATHEL RATHWELL ROTHWELL
Rothero ROTHEROE
ROTHEROE Rothero Rotherough
Rotherough ROTHEROE
Rothill RATHEL RATHWELL ROTHWELL
ROTHWELL 10 RATHEL Rathill RATHWELL Rothell Rothill Wrathwell Wrothall Wrothel Wrothwell
Roton ROOTHAM
Rouby RUBY
Rouckston RUXTON
Rouckstone RUXTON
Roudan RAWDON RHODEN RODEN ROWDEN ROYDEN
Rouden RAWDON RHODEN RODEN ROWDEN ROYDEN
ROUGHT 4 Rolt Roult Rowlt
Roukston RUXTON
Roukstone RUXTON
Roult ROUGHT
Rouncefield ROUNSEFELL
ROUNDTREE Rountree
ROUNSEFELL 5 Rouncefield Rounsevell Rounsfull Rounsifield
Rounsevell ROUNSEFELL
Rounsfull ROUNSEFELL
Rounsifield ROUNSEFELL
Rountree ROUNDTREE ROWNTREE
ROUS ROUSE
ROUSE 4 ROUS Rousi ROWSE
Rousi ROUSE ROWSE
Roussel ROUSSELL RUSELL RUSSEL RUSSELL
ROUSSELL 6 Roussel RUSELL RUSSEL RUSSELL Russells
Roust RUST
Routcliff ROUTLEY ROWTCLIFF
Routleff ROUTLEY ROWTCLIFF
Routleft ROWTCLIFF
ROUTLEY 11 Rocliffe Routcliff Routleff Routliff Routly Rowcliff Rowcliffe ROWTCLIFF Rowtcliffe Rowtly

If the name you are interested in is not here, try Section C.

Routliff ROUTLEY ROWTCLIFF
Routly ROUTLEY
ROW 4 Rew ROE ROWE
Rowadon RAWDON RHODEN RODEN ROWDEN ROYDEN
Rowarth ROWORTH
Rowberry RUBERY
Rowbery RUBERY
Rowbory RUBERY
ROWBOTTOM Reubotham Rewbotham
Rowbree RUBERY
Rowbrey RUBERY
Rowbury RUBERY
Rowcassel REUCASSEL
Rowcliff ROUTLEY ROWTCLIFF
Rowcliffe ROUTLEY ROWTCLIFF
Rowdan RAWDON RHODEN RODEN ROWDEN ROYDEN
ROWDEN 57 Raudinge RAWDON Raydon Reuden Rhoaden Rhodan Rhoddan Rhodden RHODEN Rhodin Rhoding Rhodon Roadding Roaden Roading Roadinge Roadon Rodan Rodden Roddin Rodding Roddon RODEN Rodend Rodene Rodhenn Rodin Rodine Roding Rodinge Rodinn Rodon Rodone Rodyn Roeden Roedon Rohden Roiden Rooden Roodin Rooding Roodinge Roodon Roodyng Roudan Rouden Rowadon Rowdan Rowdin Rowding Rowdinge Rowdon ROYDEN Roydon Ryden Woden
Rowdin RAWDON RHODEN RODEN ROWDEN ROYDEN
Rowding RAWDON RHODEN RODEN ROWDEN ROYDEN
Rowdinge RAWDON RHODEN RODEN ROWDEN ROYDEN
Rowdon RAWDON RHODEN RODEN ROWDEN ROYDEN
ROWE 6 RAW Rawe Rew ROE ROW
Rowel ROWELL
ROWELL 5 Rowel Rowil ROWLE ROWLEY
Rowentree ROWNTREE
Rowes RAWES
Rowil ROWELL
ROWLAND ROWLANDS
ROWLANDS ROWLAND
Rowlate ROWLATT ROWLETT
ROWLATT Rowlate ROWLETT
ROWLE ROWELL ROWLEY
Rowlestone ROLSTONE ROWLSTONE
ROWLETT Rowlate ROWLATT
ROWLEY 8 Raily Raley RAWLEIGH RAWLEY Rawly ROWELL ROWLE
Rowlinson RAWLINSON ROLLINSON
Rowls ROLES ROLLS
Rowlston ROLSTONE ROWLSTONE
ROWLSTONE 8 Ralston Roleston Rolestone Rollston ROLSTONE Rowlestone Rowlston
Rowlt ROUGHT
ROWNTREE 5 Roantree Rontrey Rountree Rowentree
ROWORTH Rowarth
Rows RAWES
ROWSE ROUSE Rousi

ROWTCLIFF 11 Rocliffe Routcliff Routleff Routleft ROUTLEY Routliff Rowcliff Rowcliffe Rowtcliffe Rowtly
Rowtcliffe ROUTLEY ROWTCLIFF
Rowtly ROUTLEY ROWTCLIFF
ROYAL 13 Rayle REAL Roial Royale ROYALL Royals ROYEL ROYLE RYAL Ryals Ryell Ryle
Royale ROYAL ROYALL ROYLE
ROYALL 12 Rayle Roial ROYAL Royale Royals ROYEL ROYLE RYAL Ryals Ryell Ryle
Royals ROYAL ROYALL ROYLE RYAL
ROYDEN 57 Raudinge RAWDON Raydon Reuden Rhoaden Rhodan Rhoddan Rhodden RHODEN Rhodin Rhoding Rhodon Roadding Roaden Roading Roadinge Roadon Rodan Rodden Roddin Rodding Roddon RODEN Rodend Rodene Rodhenn Rodin Rodine Roding Rodinge Rodinn Rodon Rodone Rodyn Roeden Roedon Rohden Roiden Rooden Roodin Rooding Roodinge Roodon Roodyng Roudan Rouden Rowadon Rowdan ROWDEN Rowdin Rowding Rowdinge Rowdon Roydon Ryden Woden
Roydon RODEN ROWDEN ROYDEN
ROYEL 4 ROYAL ROYALL ROYLE
ROYLANCE ROYLE
ROYLE 13 Rayle Roial ROYAL Royale ROYALL Royals ROYEL ROYLANCE RYAL Ryals Ryell Ryle
ROYSTON Roiston
ROZE ROSE
ROZEE ROSE Ruse
Rozie ROSIE
Rubbery RUBERY
Rubbra RUBERY
Rubby RUBY
Ruberry RUBERY
RUBERY 14 Rewbury Robery Rowberry Rowbery Rowbory Rowbree Rowbrey Rowbury Rubbery Rubbra Ruberry Rubra Rubrey
Rubey RUBY
Rubie RUBY
Rubra RUBERY
Rubrey RUBERY
RUBY 6 Rooby Rouby Rubby Rubey Rubie
Rucassel REUCASSEL
Rud RUDD
RUDCHESTER ROCHESTER Rotchester
RUDD Rud Rudde
Ruddal RIDDEL RIDDELL RIDDLE RIDLEY RUDDELL
Rudde RUDD
Ruddel RIDDEL RIDDELL RIDDLE RIDLEY RUDDELL
RUDDELL 13 Ridal Riddal Riddall RIDDEL RIDDELL RIDDLE RIDLEY Ridlon Ruddal Ruddel Rydall Ryedale
RUDDICK 4 RIDDICK Ruddoch RUDDOCK

RUDDLE Rudell
Ruddoch RIDDICK RUDDICK RUDDOCK
RUDDOCK 4 RIDDICK RUDDICK Ruddoch
Rudell RUDDLE
Rudroppe REDRUP
Ruegg RUGG
RUFFELL RUFFIED RUFFLE
RUFFIED RUFFELL
RUFFLE RUFFELL
Rug RUGG
RUGG Ruegg Rug
Ruggman RUGMAN
RUGMAN 4 Ruggman Rugmand Rvgman
Rugmand RUGMAN
Rukston RUXTON
RULTON 4 RAILTON Ralton Relton
RUMENS 5 Rumings Rummens Rummings Rummins
Rumings RUMENS
Rumlea RUMLEY
RUMLEY Rumlea
Rummens RUMENS
RUMMERY 4 RUMMEY Rummy RUMNEY
RUMMEY 4 RUMMERY Rummy RUMNEY
Rummings RUMENS
Rummins RUMENS
Rummy RUMMERY RUMMEY RUMNEY
RUMNEY 4 RUMMERY RUMMEY Rummy
Rumsel RAMSELL
Rumsell RAMSELL
Runacles RUNACRES RUNAGALL
Runacre RUNACRES RUNAGALL
RUNACRES 17 Renakers Runacles Runacre Runacus RUNAGALL Runagle Runeckles Runicles Runnacre Runnacres Runnacus Runnagall Runnalces Runnegar Runnicles Runnigar
Runacus RUNACRES RUNAGALL
RUNAGALL 16 Runacles Runacre RUNACRES Runacus Runagle Runeckles Runicles Runnacre Runnacres Runnacus Runnagall Runnalces Runnegar Runnicles Runnigar
Runagle RUNACRES RUNAGALL
Rundeel RUNDELL
Rundeil RUNDELL
RUNDELL 5 Rundeel Rundeil Rundiel RUNDLE
Rundiel RUNDELL
RUNDLE RANDALL RUNDELL
Runeckles RUNACRES RUNAGALL
Runicles RUNACRES RUNAGALL
Runnacre RUNACRES RUNAGALL
Runnacres RUNACRES RUNAGALL
Runnacus RUNACRES RUNAGALL
Runnagall RUNACRES RUNAGALL
Runnalces RUNACRES RUNAGALL
Runnegar RUNACRES RUNAGALL
Runnicles RUNACRES RUNAGALL

Runnigar RUNACRES RUNAGALL
RUSBRIDGER 7 DE LA RISEBREGGE RISBRIDGER RYSBRUG Rysbrugg RYSEBRIGGER RYSHBRYGGE
Ruse ROSE ROZEE
RUSELL 6 Roussel ROUSSELL RUSSEL RUSSELL Russells
RUSHBROOK Rushbrooke
Rushbrooke RUSHBROOK
Rushen RUSHENT
RUSHENT 4 Rishin Rushen Rushin
RUSHFIRTH 5 RISHFORTH Rishworth RUSHFORTH RUSHWORTH
RUSHFORTH 5 RISHFORTH Rishworth RUSHFIRTH RUSHWORTH
Rushin RUSHENT
RUSHWORTH 5 RISHFORTH Rishworth RUSHFIRTH RUSHFORTH
Rusland RUSSLAND
Ruslin RUSLING
RUSLING Ruslin Rustling
RUSS Russe
Russe RUSS
RUSSEL 6 Roussel ROUSSELL RUSELL RUSSELL Russells
RUSSELL 36 Askell Aswell Essell HASKELL Hassel HASWELL Hawsell Haysel Hessell Hoswell Husle HUSSELL HUZZELL Israel Issel Osell OSWALD Ozell Roussel ROUSSELL RUSELL RUSSEL Russells URSELL Urswell Ushil Ussell Ussol Ussould Uswell Uzald Uzle Uzzeel Uzzele UZZELL
Russells ROUSSELL RUSELL RUSSEL RUSSELL
RUSSLAND Rusland
RUST Roust
Rustling RUSLING
RUTHEN 8 Rutheson Ruthsen Ruthson Ruthvan RUTHVEN Ruthvin Ruttum
Rutheson RUTHEN RUTHVEN
Ruthsen RUTHEN RUTHVEN
Ruthson RUTHEN RUTHVEN
Ruthvan RUTHEN RUTHVEN
RUTHVEN 8 RUTHEN Rutheson Ruthsen Ruthson Ruthvan Ruthvin Ruttum
Ruthvin RUTHEN RUTHVEN
Ruttum RUTHEN RUTHVEN
RUXTON 6 Rouckston Rouckstone Roukston Roukstone Rukston
Rvgman RUGMAN
RYAL 9 REAL Roial ROYAL ROYALL Royals ROYLE Ryals Ryell
Ryals ROYAL ROYALL ROYLE RYAL
Rydall RIDDEL RIDDELL RIDDLE RIDLEY RUDDELL
Ryden RIDING RODEN ROWDEN ROYDEN RYDING
RYDER RIDER
Rydge RIDGE
RYDING 5 RIDING RIDINGS Ryden Rydings
Rydings RIDING RIDINGS RYDING
Ryeauld RIGHALL
Ryedale RIDDEL RIDDELL RIDDLE RIDLEY RUDDELL
Ryell REVEL REVELL REVILL ROYAL ROYALL ROYLE RYAL

If the name you are interested in is not here, try Section C.

Ryle ROYAL ROYALL ROYLE
RYLEY RILEY
Rymel RIMER RIMMER RYMER
Rymell RIMELL
RYMER 6 Rimel RIMER RIMMER Rymel Rymmer
Rymill RIMELL
Rymmer RIMMER RYMER
Rymyll RIMELL
Rynn RENNIE
RYSBRUG 7 DE LA RISEBREGGE RISBRIDGER RUSBRIDGER Rysbrugg RYSEBRIGGER RYSHBRYGGE
Rysbrugg DE LA RISEBREGGE RISBRIDGER RUSBRIDGER RYSBRUG RYSEBRIGGER RYSHBRYGGE
RYSEBRIGGER 7 DE LA RISEBREGGE RISBRIDGER RUSBRIDGER RYSBRUG Rysbrugg RYSHBRYGGE
Ryseley RISELEY
RYSHBRYGGE 7 DE LA RISEBREGGE RISBRIDGER RUSBRIDGER RYSBRUG Rysbrugg RYSEBRIGGER
Rysley RISELEY
Ryver RIVER RIVERS
Ryvers RIVER RIVERS
SABAN Seaban
SABELL SABLE
Saber SAUBERE
SABIN SABINE Sabyn
SABINE SABIN Sabyn
SABLE SABELL
Sabyn SABIN SABINE
Sacar SAKER SECKER
SACH SAICH
Sacket SACKETT
SACKETT 4 Sacket Sackette Saket
Sackette SACKETT
SACKFIELD SACKVILLE
SACKVILLE SACKFIELD Saqueville
SADE Lasad Le sade
Sadgrave SADGROVE
Sadgrouge SADGROVE
SADGROVE 13 Sadgrave Sadgrouge Sadgrowe Salgrove Satgrove Sedgrave Sedgreves Sedgrove Sedgrow Sidgrave Sudgrave Sudgrove
Sadgrowe SADGROVE
Saerson SARSON SEARSON
SAGAR 8 SAGER Saghar Sagher Seagar SEAGER SEGAR Seiger
SAGER 8 SAGAR Saghar Sagher Seagar SEAGER SEGAR Seiger
Saghar SAGAR SAGER SEAGER SEGAR
Sagher SAGAR SAGER SEAGER SEGAR
SAICH SACH
Sainsberry SAINSBURY SAINTSBURY SAINTSBURYE SAYNSBURY SEINESBERIA SEYNISBURY
SAINSBURY 9 Sainsberry SAINTSBURY SAINTSBURYE SAYNSBURY SEINESBERIA SEYNISBURY Seynsbury Sinisbury
SAINT 4 SAINTY SANT SAUNT
SAINTSBURY 9 Sainsberry SAINSBURY SAINTSBURYE SAYNSBURY SEINESBERIA SEYNISBURY Seynsbury Sinisbury
SAINTSBURYE 9 Sainsberry SAINSBURY SAINTSBURY SAYNSBURY SEINESBERIA SEYNISBURY Seynsbury Sinisbury
SAINTY 4 SAINT SANT SAUNT
Sais SAYCE
Saissal SAYSELL
SAKER 4 Sacar SECKER Seeker
Saket SACKETT
SALAMAN 32 Slammon Slamon SLAYMAN SLEAMAN SLEMAN SLEMANS Slemen Slemens Slemmen Slemmens Slemming SLEMMINGS SLEMMON SLEMMONDS SLEMMONS SLEMON SLEMONS Sleuthman SLIMAN SLIMANS Slimin Sliming Slimings Slimmand SLIMMANDS SLIMMING SLIMMINGS Slimond Slymand Slymin Slymins
SALAMON 5 SALOMON Salomons SOLOMON Solomons
SALE 7 SALES SAYELL SAYLE SAYLES SEAL SEARLE
SALES 5 SALE SAYLE SAYLES SEARLE
SALESBURY SALISBURY Salusbury
Salgrove SADGROVE
SALISBURY SALESBURY Salusbury
SALLABANK Sallabanks
Sallabanks SALLABANK
SALMON 6 SALOMON Saman Sammond Sammons Samon
SALOMON 6 SALAMON SALMON Salomons SOLOMON Solomons
Salomons SALAMON SALOMON SOLOMON
Salsters SALTER
SALTER 4 Salsters Salters Saltters
Salters SALTER
SALTMARSH Saltmarshe Saltmash
Saltmarshe SALTMARSH
Saltmash SALTMARSH
Saltters SALTER
Salusbury SALESBURY SALISBURY
Sam SAMMES SAMS
Saman SALMON
Sambidge SAMBRIDGE
SAMBRIDGE Sambidge
Same SAMMES SAMS
Sames SAMMES SAMS
SAMFER SANDFORD SANFORD
SAMMES 6 Sam Same Sames Samms SAMS
Sammond SALMON
Sammons SALMON
Samms SAMMES SAMS
Samon SALMON
Sampear SAMPHIRE
Sampeere SAMPHIRE
Samper SAMPHIRE
Sampher SAMPHIRE
Samphey SAMPHIRE
Samphier SAMPHIRE
SAMPHIRE 12 Sampear Sampeere Samper Sampher Samphey Samphier Samphur Sampier Sampieri Sampiers Sampire
Samphur SAMPHIRE
Sampier SAMPHIRE
Sampieri SAMPHIRE
Sampiers SAMPHIRE
Sampire SAMPHIRE
SAMPSON 4 Samsen SAMSON SANSOM
SAMS 6 Sam Same Sames SAMMES Samms
Samsen SAMPSON SAMSON
SAMSON 4 SAMPSON Samsen SANSOM
SAMUEL SAMUELS
SAMUELS SAMUEL
Sanda SANDOE
Sandah SANDOE
SANDELANDS SANDILANDS
SANDER SAUNDERS
SANDERS Saunder SAUNDERS
SANDERSON SANDISON SAUNDERSON
SANDFORD SAMFER SANFORD
SANDILANDS SANDELANDS
SANDISON SANDERSON
Sando SANDOE
SANDOE 6 Sanda Sandah Sando Sandow Sandowe
Sandow SANDOE
Sandowe SANDOE
SANDS SANDYS Sans
SANDYS SANDS Sans
SANFORD SAMFER SANDFORD
SANHAM 7 Sanhum Sannam Sannum Sanom Seniohm Sinom
Sanhum SANHAM
Sannam SANHAM
Sannum SANHAM
Sanom SANHAM
Sans SANDS SANDYS
SANSOM 5 SAMPSON SAMSON SANSOME SANSUM
SANSOME SANSOM SANSUM
SANSUM SANSOM SANSOME
SANT 4 SAINT SAINTY SAUNT
SANTER SAUNTER
Saqueville SACKVILLE
Sara SARAH SEARY
SARAH Sara
SARGARTSON 5 Sargeantson SARGISSON Seargantson Sergisson
SARGEANT 9 Sargeaunt SARGENT SARJEANT Sarjeaunt Sarjent Seargent SERGEANT SERJEANT
Sargeantson SARGARTSON SARGISSON
Sargeaunt SARGEANT SARGENT SARJEANT
SARGENT 10 SARGEANT Sargeaunt SARJEANT Sarjeaunt Sarjent Seargent SERGEANT Sergent SERJEANT
SARGISSON 5 SARGARTSON Sargeantson Seargantson Sergisson
SARJEANT 10 SARGEANT Sargeaunt SARGENT Sarjeaunt Sarjent SERGEANT Sergent Serjant SERJEANT
Sarjeaunt SARGEANT SARGENT SARJEANT
Sarjent SARGEANT SARGENT SARJEANT SERGEANT SERJEANT
Sarle SEARLE
SARSON Saerson SEARSON
SARVIS SERVICE Servis
Sary SEARY
Sasel SAYSELL
SATES Seyts
Satgrove SADGROVE
SAUBERE 4 Saber Sober Sobere
Saueri SAVERY SAVORY
Sauery SAVERY SAVORY
Sauland SUNDERLAND SUTHERLAND
Saunder SANDERS
SAUNDERS SANDER SANDERS
SAUNDERSON SANDERSON
SAUNT 4 SAINT SAINTY SANT
SAUNTER SANTER
SAVAGE SAVIDGE SAVIGE
Saval SAVIL SAVILE SAVILLE
Savare SAVERY SAVORY
Savari SAVERY SAVORY
Savarie SAVERY SAVORY
Savary SAVERY SAVORY
Saveall SAVIL SAVILE SAVILLE
Savell SAVIL SAVILE SAVILLE
Saverey SAVERY SAVORY
Saveri SAVERY SAVORY
Saverie SAVERY SAVORY
SAVERY 20 Saueri Sauery Savare Savari Savarie Savary Saverey Saveri Saverie Saverye Savoery Savori Savorie SAVORY Savourey Savouri Savourie Savoury Severy
Saverye SAVERY SAVORY
SAVIDGE SAVAGE SAVIGE
SAVIGE SAVAGE SAVIDGE
SAVIL 12 Cavill Saval Saveall Savell SAVILE SAVILLE Savle Seavell Sevil SEVILL Seville
SAVILE 9 Cavill Saval Saveall Savell SAVIL SAVILLE Savle Seavell
SAVILLE 13 Cavill Civill Saval Saveall Savell SAVIL SAVILE Savle Seavell Sevil SEVILL Seville
Savle SAVIL SAVILE SAVILLE
Savoery SAVERY SAVORY
Savori SAVERY SAVORY
Savorie SAVERY SAVORY
SAVORY 20 Saueri Sauery Savare Savari Savarie Savary Saverey Saveri Saverie SAVERY Saverye Savoery Savori Savorie Savourey Savouri Savourie Savoury Severy
Savourey SAVERY SAVORY
Savouri SAVERY SAVORY
Savourie SAVERY SAVORY
Savoury SAVERY SAVORY
Sawden SOWDEN
Sawuer SAWYER
SAWYER Sawuer Soughyer
SAXBY Saxilby
SAXELBY HALLAM Saxilby
Saxilby HALLAM SAXBY SAXELBY
SAXTON 4 Sextan Sextin SEXTON
SAYCE Sais Sayse
Saycele SAYSELL
Saycell SAYSELL
Saycil SAYSELL
SAYELL SALE SAYLE
SAYER SAYERS Sayr
SAYERS SAYER
SAYLE 5 SALE SALES SAYELL SAYLES
SAYLES 4 SALE SALES SAYLE
SAYNSBURY 9 Sainsberry SAINSBURY SAINTSBURY SAINTSBURYE SEINESBERIA

If the name you are interested in is not here, try Section C.

SEYNISBURY Seynsbury Sinisbury
Sayr SAYER
Saysal SAYSELL
Sayse SAYCE
SAYSELL 12 Saissal Sasel Saycele Saycell Saycil Saysal Saysill Saysol Seysel Siscel Sysel
Saysill SAYSELL
Saysol SAYSELL
SAYWELL SEWELL
SCADDAN 5 SCADDEN SCADDING Scaddon SCADENG
SCADDEN 5 SCADDAN SCADDING Scaddon SCADENG
SCADDING 5 SCADDAN SCADDEN Scaddon SCADENG
Scaddon SCADDAN SCADDEN SCADDING SCADENG
SCADENG 5 SCADDAN SCADDEN SCADDING Scaddon
Scair SCARR
SCALES SKALES
Scaltock SCOLTOCK
SCAMEL SCAMELL SCAMMELL
SCAMELL SCAMEL SCAMMELL
SCAMMELL SCAMEL SCAMELL
SCAPENS Scapings
Scapings SCAPENS
SCAPLAN 4 Scapland Scapslan Scapsland
Scapland SCAPLAN
Scapslan SCAPLAN
Scapsland SCAPLAN
Scar SCARR SKAR
Scarf SCARFE SCARFF
SCARFE 4 Scarf SCARFF Scarffe
SCARFF 4 Scarf SCARFE Scarffe
Scarffe SCARFE SCARFF
SCARLETT Scorlett
SCARMAN Searman
SCARNELL SCARNING
SCARNING SCARNELL
SCARR 5 Scair Scar SKAR Skarr
Scarratt SKERRATT SKERRETT SKERRITT
SCARROW 4 SKERO SKERROW SKIRROW
Scawtock SCOLTOCK
Schackespaer SHAKESPEARE
Schackespaere SHAKESPEARE
Schackespaerr SHAKESPEARE
Schackespear SHAKESPEARE
Schackespeare SHAKESPEARE
Schackespearr SHAKESPEARE
Schackespeer SHAKESPEARE
Schackespeere SHAKESPEARE
Schackespeir SHAKESPEARE
Schackespeire SHAKESPEARE
Schackespeirr SHAKESPEARE
Schackespeirre SHAKESPEARE
Schackesper SHAKESPEARE
Schackesperr SHAKESPEARE
Schackesperre SHAKESPEARE
Schackespier SHAKESPEARE
Schackespiere SHAKESPEARE
Schackespierr SHAKESPEARE
Schackespir SHAKESPEARE
Schackespirr SHAKESPEARE
Schackespyrr SHAKESPEARE
Schacklock SHACKLOCK
Schaexspaer SHAKESPEARE
Schaexspaere SHAKESPEARE
Schaexspaerr SHAKESPEARE
Schaexspear SHAKESPEARE
Schaexspeare SHAKESPEARE
Schaexspearr SHAKESPEARE
Schaexspeer SHAKESPEARE
Schaexspeere SHAKESPEARE
Schaexspeir SHAKESPEARE
Schaexspeire SHAKESPEARE
Schaexspeirr SHAKESPEARE
Schaexspeirre SHAKESPEARE
Schaexsper SHAKESPEARE
Schaexspere SHAKESPEARE
Schaexsperr SHAKESPEARE
Schaexspier SHAKESPEARE
Schaexspiere SHAKESPEARE
Schaexspierr SHAKESPEARE
Schaexspierre SHAKESPEARE
Schaexspir SHAKESPEARE
Schaexspirr SHAKESPEARE
Schaexspyr SHAKESPEARE
Schaexspyrr SHAKESPEARE
Schaften SHAFTEN SHAFTO SHAFTOE
Schaftin SHAFTEN SHAFTO SHAFTOE
Schafting SHAFTEN SHAFTO SHAFTOE
Schafto SHAFTEN SHAFTO SHAFTOE
Schafton SHAFTEN SHAFTO SHAFTOE
Schaickspaer SHAKESPEARE
Schaickspaere SHAKESPEARE
Schaickspaerr SHAKESPEARE
Schaickspear SHAKESPEARE
Schaickspeare SHAKESPEARE
Schaickspearr SHAKESPEARE
Schaickspeer SHAKESPEARE
Schaickspeere SHAKESPEARE
Schaickspeire SHAKESPEARE
Schaickspeirr SHAKESPEARE
Schaickspeirre SHAKESPEARE
Schaicksper SHAKESPEARE
Schaickspere SHAKESPEARE
Schaicksperr SHAKESPEARE
Schaicksperre SHAKESPEARE
Schaickspier SHAKESPEARE
Schaickspiere SHAKESPEARE
Schaickspierr SHAKESPEARE
Schaickspierre SHAKESPEARE
Schaickspir SHAKESPEARE
Schaickspirr SHAKESPEARE
Schaickspyr SHAKESPEARE
Schaickspyrr SHAKESPEARE
Schaiksspaer SHAKESPEARE
Schaiksspaere SHAKESPEARE
Schaiksspaerr SHAKESPEARE
Schaiksspear SHAKESPEARE
Schaiksspeare SHAKESPEARE
Schaiksspearr SHAKESPEARE
Schaiksspeer SHAKESPEARE
Schaiksspeere SHAKESPEARE
Schaiksspeir SHAKESPEARE
Schaiksspeire SHAKESPEARE
Schaiksspeirr SHAKESPEARE
Schaiksspeirre SHAKESPEARE
Schaikssper SHAKESPEARE
Schaiksspere SHAKESPEARE
Schaiksspert SHAKESPEARE
Schaikssperre SHAKESPEARE
Schaiksspier SHAKESPEARE
Schaiksspiere SHAKESPEARE
Schaiksspierr SHAKESPEARE
Schaiksspierre SHAKESPEARE
Schaiksspir SHAKESPEARE
Schaiksspirr SHAKESPEARE
Schaiksspyr SHAKESPEARE
Schaquespaer SHAKESPEARE
Schaquespaere SHAKESPEARE
Schaquespaerr SHAKESPEARE
Schaquespear SHAKESPEARE
Schaquespeare SHAKESPEARE
Schaquespearr SHAKESPEARE
Schaquespeer SHAKESPEARE
Schaquespeere SHAKESPEARE
Schaquespeir SHAKESPEARE
Schaquespeirr SHAKESPEARE
Schaquespeirre SHAKESPEARE
Schaquesper SHAKESPEARE
Schaquespere SHAKESPEARE
Schaquesperr SHAKESPEARE
Schaquesperre SHAKESPEARE
Schaquespier SHAKESPEARE
Schaquespiere SHAKESPEARE
Schaquespierr SHAKESPEARE
Schaquespierre SHAKESPEARE
Schaquespir SHAKESPEARE
Schaquespirr SHAKESPEARE
Schaquespyr SHAKESPEARE
Schaquespyrr SHAKESPEARE
Schayxpyr SHAKESPEARE
Schayxspaer SHAKESPEARE
Schayxspaere SHAKESPEARE
Schayxspaerr SHAKESPEARE
Schayxspear SHAKESPEARE
Schayxspeare SHAKESPEARE
Schayxspearr SHAKESPEARE
Schayxspeer SHAKESPEARE
Schayxspeere SHAKESPEARE
Schayxspeir SHAKESPEARE
Schayxspeire SHAKESPEARE
Schayxspeirr SHAKESPEARE
Schayxspeirre SHAKESPEARE
Schayxsper SHAKESPEARE
Schayxspere SHAKESPEARE
Schayxsperr SHAKESPEARE
Schayxsperre SHAKESPEARE
Schayxspier SHAKESPEARE
Schayxspiere SHAKESPEARE
Schayxspierr SHAKESPEARE
Schayxspierre SHAKESPEARE
Schayxspir SHAKESPEARE
Schayxspirr SHAKESPEARE
Schayxspyrr SHAKESPEARE
Scheackespaer SHAKESPEARE
Scheackespaere SHAKESPEARE
Scheackespaerr SHAKESPEARE
Scheackespear SHAKESPEARE
Scheackespeare SHAKESPEARE
Scheackespearr SHAKESPEARE
Scheackespeer SHAKESPEARE
Scheackespeere SHAKESPEARE
Scheackespeir SHAKESPEARE
Scheackespeire SHAKESPEARE
Scheackespeirr SHAKESPEARE
Scheackespeirre SHAKESPEARE
Scheackesper SHAKESPEARE
Scheackespere SHAKESPEARE
Scheackesperr SHAKESPEARE
Scheackesperre SHAKESPEARE
Scheackespier SHAKESPEARE
Scheackespiere SHAKESPEARE
Scheackespierr SHAKESPEARE
Scheackespierre SHAKESPEARE
Scheackespir SHAKESPEARE
Scheackespirr SHAKESPEARE
Scheackespyr SHAKESPEARE
Scheackespyrr SHAKESPEARE
Scheikspaer SHAKESPEARE
Scheikspaere SHAKESPEARE
Scheikspaerr SHAKESPEARE
Scheikspear SHAKESPEARE
Scheikspeare SHAKESPEARE
Scheikspearr SHAKESPEARE
Scheikspeer SHAKESPEARE
Scheikspeir SHAKESPEARE
Scheikspeire SHAKESPEARE
Scheikspeirr SHAKESPEARE
Scheikspeirre SHAKESPEARE
Scheiksper SHAKESPEARE
Scheikspere SHAKESPEARE
Scheiksperr SHAKESPEARE
Scheiksperre SHAKESPEARE
Scheikspier SHAKESPEARE
Scheikspiere SHAKESPEARE
Scheikspierr SHAKESPEARE
Scheikspierre SHAKESPEARE
Scheikspir SHAKESPEARE
Scheikspirr SHAKESPEARE
Scheikspyr SHAKESPEARE
Scheikspyrr SHAKESPEARE
Scheixspeirr SHAKESPEARE
Scheppyn SHIPPEN
Scheykespaer SHAKESPEARE
Scheykespaere SHAKESPEARE
Scheykespaerr SHAKESPEARE
Scheykespear SHAKESPEARE
Scheykespeare SHAKESPEARE
Scheykespearr SHAKESPEARE
Scheykespeer SHAKESPEARE
Scheykespeere SHAKESPEARE
Scheykespeir SHAKESPEARE
Scheykespeire SHAKESPEARE
Scheykespeirr SHAKESPEARE
Scheykespeirre SHAKESPEARE
Scheykesper SHAKESPEARE
Scheykespere SHAKESPEARE
Scheykesperr SHAKESPEARE
Scheykesperre SHAKESPEARE
Scheykespier SHAKESPEARE
Scheykespiere SHAKESPEARE
Scheykespierr SHAKESPEARE
Scheykespierre SHAKESPEARE
Scheykespir SHAKESPEARE
Scheykespirr SHAKESPEARE
Scheykespyrr SHAKESPEARE
Scheyquespaer SHAKESPEARE
Scheyquespaere SHAKESPEARE
Scheyquespaerr SHAKESPEARE
Scheyquespear SHAKESPEARE
Scheyquespeare SHAKESPEARE
Scheyquespearr SHAKESPEARE
Scheyquespeer SHAKESPEARE
Scheyquespeere SHAKESPEARE
Scheyquespeir SHAKESPEARE
Scheyquespeire SHAKESPEARE
Scheyquespeirr SHAKESPEARE
Scheyquespeirre SHAKESPEARE
Scheyquesper SHAKESPEARE
Scheyquespere SHAKESPEARE
Scheyquesperr SHAKESPEARE
Scheyquesperre SHAKESPEARE
Scheyquespier SHAKESPEARE
Scheyquespiere SHAKESPEARE
Scheyquespierr SHAKESPEARE
Scheyquespierre SHAKESPEARE
Scheyquespir SHAKESPEARE
Scheyquespirr SHAKESPEARE
Scheyquespyrr SHAKESPEARE
Schieldt SCHILDT
SCHILDT Schieldt
Schlobohm SLOBOM
Schlobohn SLOBOM
SCHOFIELD 5 SCHOLEFIELD

If the name you are interested in is not here, try Section C.

Scholfield Scolefield Scorefield
SCHOLEFIELD 4 SCHOFIELD Scholfield Scorefield
SCHOLEY SCOLEY
Scholfield SCHOFIELD SCHOLEFIELD
Schoor SHORE
Schoore SHORE
Schor SHORE
SCHULZE Schutze
Schutze SCHULZE
Sciner SKINNER
Sclaitter SCLATER SLATER
SCLATER 4 Sclaitter Sklaitter SLATER
Scoates SKOTS
Scolefield SCHOFIELD
Scoles SKOYLES
SCOLEY SCHOLEY
SCOLTOCK Scaltock Scawtock
SCOONES SCOONS
SCOONS SCOONES
Scope SCOPES
SCOPES 4 Scope Skoopes Skopes
Scorefield SCHOFIELD SCHOLEFIELD
Scorlett SCARLETT
Scorr SCURR
Scorre SCURR
SCORRILL 6 SCURRILL SKORRELL SQUIRRELL SQUORRELL SQURIEL
Scorrs SCURR
Scorse SCOURSE
SCOT SCOTT
SCOTT SCOT
SCOULAR SCOULLER
Scoulcroft SCOWCROFT
SCOULLER SCOULAR
Scource SCOURSE
SCOURFIELD Scurfield
SCOURSE Scorse Scource
SCOWCROFT Scoulcroft
SCRACE SCRASE
SCRASE SCRACE
SCREACH Screech
SCREATON 6 Screeton Screton SCRUTON Skreetan Skreeton
Screech SCREACH
Screeton SCREATON SCRUTON
Screton SCREATON SCRUTON
Screyvener SCRIVENER
Scribner SCRIVENER
Scribnor SCRIVENER
SCRIVEN SCRIVENS
SCRIVENER 5 Screyvener Scribner Scribnor Scrivenor
Scrivenor SCRIVENER
SCRIVENS SCRIVEN
Scruce SCRUSE
SCRUSE Scruce
SCRUTON 6 SCREATON Screeton Screton Skreetan Skreeton
SCUDAMORE 7 Skidgemore Skidgmore SKIDMORE Skidsmore Skitmore Skudemore
Scues SKEWES SKEWIS SKEWS SKUCE SKUES SKUSE
Scull SKULL
Scur SCURR
Scure SCURR
Scurfield SCOURFIELD
Scurlock SHERLOCK SHURLOCK
SCURR 10 Scorr Scorre Scorrs Scur Scure Scurre Scurres Skur Skurr
Scurre SCURR
Scurres SCURR
SCURRILL 6 SCORRILL SKORRELL SQUIRRELL SQUORRELL SQURIEL
Scuse SKEWES SKEWIS SKEWS SKUCE SKUES SKUSE
SEA SEE
Seaban SABAN
SEABORNE 7 Seabourne Seaburne Sebron Sebronde Seybon Shebrond
Seabourne SEABORNE
Seaburne SEABORNE
Seacombe SECCOMBE
Seagall SEAGULL
Seagar SAGAR SAGER SEAGER SEGAR
SEAGER 11 SAGAR SAGER Saghar Sagher Seagar SEGAR Seger Seiger Zeager Zeger
SEAGERS Segers
Seagle SEAGULL
SEAGO Seagoe
Seagoe SEAGO
Seagul SEAGULL
SEAGULL 5 Seagall Seagle Seagul Segull
SEAL SALE
Sealwood SELLWOOD SELWOOD
SEALY SILLEY
SEAMAR 6 Seamer Seamour Semer Seymer SEYMOUR
Seamer SEAMAR SEYMOUR
Seamor SEANOR SEYMOUR
Seamour SEAMAR SEYMOUR
SEANOR Seamor
SEAR 6 SEARS Seear Seears Sier Siers
Search SURCH
SEARCY Sercy
SEARE Seayre Seer
Seargantson SARGARTSON SARGISSON
Seargent SARGEANT SARGENT SERGEANT
SEARL 4 SEARLE Serl Serle
SEARLE 8 SALE SALES Sarle SEARL SEARLES Serl Serle
SEARLES SEARLE
Searman SCARMAN
SEARS 8 SEAR Seear Seears Seeres SEERS Sier Siers
SEARSON Saerson SARSON
Searston SEARSTONE SEASTON
SEARSTONE 4 Searston SEASTON Shearston
SEARY 5 Sara Sary Seery Sery
SEASTON 5 Searston SEARSTONE SESTON Shearston
SEATH SETH
Seavell SAVIL SAVILE SAVILLE
Seaverne SEVERNE
Seayre SEARE
Sebron SEABORNE
Sebronde SEABORNE
Seccomb SECCOMBE
SECCOMBE 4 Seacombe Seccomb Secombe
SECKER 4 Sacar SAKER Seeker
Secombe SECCOMBE
Seddan SEDDON
Sedden SEDDON
SEDDON Seddan Sedden
Sedgbear SEDGBEER
SEDGBEER 7 Sedgbear Sedgberry Sedgbury Sedgebear Sedgeberry Sedgebury
Sedgberry SEDGBEER
Sedgbury SEDGBEER
Sedgebear SEDGBEER
Sedgeberry SEDGBEER
Sedgebury SEDGBEER
SEDGEFIELD Sedgfeild Sedyfeild
SEDGELEY Sedgely
Sedgely SEDGELEY
SEDGEWICK 5 SEDGWICK Sidgewick Sidgwick Sigiswick
Sedgfeild SEDGEFIELD
Sedgrave SADGROVE
Sedgreves SADGROVE
Sedgrove SADGROVE
Sedgrow SADGROVE
SEDGWICK SEDGEWICK SHEDWICK
Sedyfeild SEDGEFIELD
SEE SEA
Seear SEAR SEARS
Seears SEAR SEARS SEERS
Seeker SAKER SECKER
Seem SIMS SYMES
Seer SEARE
Seeres SEARS SEERS
SEERS 4 SEARS Seears Seeres
Seery SEARY
SEFTON SEPHTON
SEGAR 9 SAGAR SAGER Saghar Sagher Seagar SEAGER Seger Seiger
Seger SEAGER SEGAR
Segers SEAGERS
SEGRAVE 4 SIGRAVE SIGROVE SYGROVE
Segull SEAGULL
Seiger SAGAR SAGER SEAGER SEGAR
SEINESBERIA 9 Sainsberry SAINSBURY SAINTSBURY SAINTSBURYE SAYNSBURY SEYNISBURY Seynsbury Sinisbury
Selance SELLEN SELLENS SILENCE SILLENCE
Selar SELLAR SELLER
Selbie SELBY
SELBY Selbie
Selcock SILCOCK SILCOX
Selcocks SILCOCK SILCOX
Selence SELLEN SELLENS SILENCE SILLENCE
Seler SELLAR SELLER
SELF SELFE SELTH
SELFE SELF SELTH
Selin CELLING
SELLAR 6 Selar Seler SELLARS SELLER SELLERS
SELLARS 4 SELLAR SELLER SELLERS
SELLEN 16 Selance Selence Sellence SELLENS Sellon SILENCE SILLENCE Sillince Sillins Sillons Sollons Sullence Sullens Sullince Sullins
Sellence SELLEN SELLENS SILENCE SILLENCE
SELLENS 15 Selance Selence SELLEN Sellence SILENCE SILLENCE Sillince Sillins Sillons Sollons Sullence Sullens Sullince Sullins
SELLER 6 Selar Seler SELLAR SELLARS SELLERS
SELLERS 4 SELLAR SELLARS SELLER
SELLEY 6 Selly Sulley SULLY Zelley Zelly
SELLINGS 7 Selvin Selwin Selwyer SELWYN Selwynne Sulivan
Sellon SELLEN
SELLWOOD 6 Sealwood SELWOOD Sillwood Tillwood ZILLWOOD
Selly SELLEY SULLY
SELMAM Silmam
SELMAN Selmon
Selmon SELMAN
SELTH SELF SELFE
Selvin SELLINGS SELWYN
Selwin SELLINGS SELWYN
SELWOOD Sealwood SELLWOOD
Selwyer SELLINGS SELWYN
SELWYN 7 SELLINGS Selvin Selwin Selwyer Selwynne Sulivan
Selwynne SELLINGS SELWYN
Semens SEMMONS SIMMONDS SIMMONS SYMONDS
Semer SEAMAR SEYMOUR
SEMMONS 5 Semens SIMMONDS SIMMONS SYMONDS
Sems SIMS SYMES
Sencicle SENSICLE
Seneschal SENSICLE
Senet SINNOTT
Seniohm SANHAM
Sennett SINNOTT
Sennitt SINNOTT
Sensical SENSICLE
Sensicall SENSICLE
SENSICLE 5 Sencicle Seneschal Sensical Sensicall
SEPHTON SEFTON
Sercy SEARCY
SERGEANT 9 SARGEANT SARGENT SARJEANT Sarjent Seargent Sergent Serjant SERJEANT
Sergent SARGENT SARJEANT SERGEANT SERJEANT
Sergisson SARGARTSON SARGISSON
Serich SERREDGE
Serjant SARJEANT SERGEANT
SERJEANT 7 SARGEANT SARGENT SARJEANT Sarjent SERGEANT Sergent
Serl SEARL SEARLE
Serle SEARL SEARLE
Serman SERMON SIRMAN SURMAN
SERMON 6 Cyrmon Serman SIRMAN Sirmon SURMAN
SERREDGE Serich
SERVICE SARVIS Servis
Servis SARVIS SERVICE
Sery SEARY
SESTON SEASTON
Setchall SETCHELL
SETCHELL Setchall
SETH SEATH
Seven SEVERN
Sevens SEVERN
SEVERN 5 Seven Sevens Severns Sivorn
SEVERNE Seaverne
Severns SEVERN
Severy SAVERY SAVORY
Sevil SAVIL SAVILLE SEVILL
SEVILL 5 SAVIL SAVILLE Sevil Seville

If the name you are interested in is not here, try Section C.

Seville SAVIL SAVILLE SEVILL
SEWELL SAYWELL SHEWELL
Sextan SAXTON SEXTON
Sextin SAXTON SEXTON
SEXTON 4 SAXTON Sextan Sextin
Seybon SEABORNE
Seymer SEAMAR SEYMOUR
SEYMOUR 7 SEAMAR Seamer Seamor Seamour Semer Seymer
SEYNISBURY 9 Sainsberry SAINSBURY SAINTSBURY SAINTSBURYE SAYNSBURY SEINESBERIA Seynsbury Sinisbury
Seynsbury SAINSBURY SAINTSBURY SAINTSBURYE SAYNSBURY SEINESBERIA SEYNISBURY
Seysel SAYSELL
Seyts SATES
SHACKELL SHACKLE
SHACKLE SHACKELL
SHACKLOCK 9 Schacklock Shacklocke Shadlock Shalselock Shatlock Shocklach Shokelach Sholiche
Shacklocke SHACKLOCK
SHADDICK Shaddock
Shaddock SHADDICK
Shade SHEAVES
Shadlock SHACKLOCK
SHAFTEN 11 Schaften Schaftin Schafting Schafto Schafton Shaftin Shafting SHAFTO SHAFTOE Shafton
Shaftin SHAFTEN SHAFTO SHAFTOE
Shafting SHAFTEN SHAFTO SHAFTOE
SHAFTO 11 Schaften Schaftin Schafting Schafto Schafton SHAFTEN Shaftin Shafting SHAFTOE Shafton
SHAFTOE 11 Schaften Schaftin Schafting Schafto Schafton SHAFTEN Shaftin Shafting SHAFTO Shafton
Shafton SHAFTEN SHAFTO SHAFTOE
SHAKESPEARE 459
Schackespaer
Schackespaere
Schackespaerr
Schackespear
Schackespeare
Schackespearr
Schackespeer
Schackespeere
Schackespeir
Schackespeire
Schackespeirr
Schackespeirre
Schackesper
Schackesperr
Schackesperre
Schackespier
Schackespiere
Schackespierr
Schackespir
Schackespirr
Schackespyrr
Schaexspaer
Schaexspaere
Schaexspaerr
Schaexspear
Schaexspeare
Schaexspearr
Schaexspeer
Schaexspeere
Schaexspeir
Schaexspeire
Schaexspeirr
Schaexspeirre
Schaexsper Schaexspere
Schaexsperr Schaexspier
Schaexspiere
Schaexspierr
Schaexspierre
Schaexspir Schaexspirr
Schaexspyr Schaexspyrr
Schaickspaer
Schaickspaere
Schaickspaerr
Schaickspear
Schaickspeare
Schaickspearr
Schaickspeer
Schaickspeere
Schaickspeire
Schaickspeirr
Schaickspeirre
Schaicksper
Schaickspere
Schaicksperr
Schaicksperre
Schaickspier
Schaickspiere
Schaickspierr
Schaickspierre
Schaickspir
Schaickspirr
Schaickspyr
Schaickspyrr
Schaiksspaer
Schaiksspaere
Schaiksspaerr
Schaiksspear
Schaiksspeare
Schaiksspearr
Schaiksspeer
Schaiksspeere
Schaiksspeir
Schaiksspeire
Schaiksspeirr
Schaiksspeirre
Schaikssper
Schaiksspere
Schaiksspeerr
Schaikssperre
Schaiksspier
Schaiksspiere
Schaiksspierr
Schaiksspierre
Schaiksspir
Schaiksspirr
Schaiksspyr
Schaquespaer
Schaquespaere
Schaquespaerr
Schaquespear
Schaquespeare
Schaquespearr
Schaquespeer
Schaquespeere
Schaquespeir
Schaquespeirr
Schaquespeirre
Schaquesper
Schaquespere
Schaquesperr
Schaquesperre
Schaquespier
Schaquespiere
Schaquespierr
Schaquespierre
Schaquespir
Schaquespirr
Schaquespyr
Schaquespyrr Schayxpyr
Schayxspaer
Schayxspaere
Schayxspaerr
Schayxspear
Schayxspeare
Schayxspearr
Schayxspeer
Schayxspeere
Schayxspeir
Schayxspeire
Schayxspeirr
Schayxspeirre
Schayxsper Schayxspere
Schayxsperr
Schayxsperre
Schayxspier
Schayxspiere
Schayxspierr
Schayxspierre
Schayxspir Schayxspirr
Schayxspyrr
Scheackespaer
Scheackespaere
Scheackespaerr
Scheackespear
Scheackespeare
Scheackespearr
Scheackespeer
Scheackespeere
Scheackespeir
Scheackespeire
Scheackespeirr
Scheackespeirre
Scheackesper
Scheackespere
Scheackesperr
Scheackesperre
Scheackespier
Scheackespiere
Scheackespierr
Scheackespierre
Scheackespir
Scheackespirr
Scheackespyr
Scheackespyrr
Scheikspaer
Scheikspaere
Scheikspaerr
Scheikspear
Scheikspeare
Scheikspearr
Scheikspeer Scheikspeir
Scheikspeire
Scheikspeirr
Scheikspeirre
Scheiksper Scheikspere
Scheiksperr
Scheiksperre
Scheikspier
Scheikspiere
Scheikspierr
Scheikspierre
Scheikspir Scheikspirr
Scheikspyr Scheikspyrr
Scheixspeirr
Scheykespaer
Scheykespaere
Scheykespaerr
Scheykespear
Scheykespeare
Scheykespearr
Scheykespeer
Scheykespeere
Scheykespeir
Scheykespeire
Scheykespeirr
Scheykespeirre
Scheykesper
Scheykespere
Scheykesperr
Scheykesperre
Scheykespier
Scheykespiere
Scheykespierr
Scheykespierre
Scheykespir
Scheykespirr
Scheykespyrr
Scheyquespaer
Scheyquespaere
Scheyquespaerr
Scheyquespear
Scheyquespeare
Scheyquespearr
Scheyquespeer
Scheyquespeere
Scheyquespeir
Scheyquespeire
Scheyquespeirr
Scheyquespeirre
Scheyquesper
Scheyquespere
Scheyquesperr
Scheyquesperre
Scheyquespier
Scheyquespiere
Scheyquespierr
Scheyquespierre
Scheyquespir
Scheyquespirr
Scheyquespyrr
Shakesperr Shaykspaer
Shaykspaere Shaykspaerr
Shaykspear Shaykspearr
Shaykspeer Shaykspeere
Shaykspeir Shaykspeire
Shaykspeirr
Shaykspeirre Shaykspeer
Shaykspere Shayksperr
Shayksperre Shaykspier
Shaykspiere Shaykspierr
Shaykspierre Shaykspir
Shaykspirr Shaykspyr
Shaykspyrr Shayxpaer
Shayxpaere Shayxpaerr
Shayxpear Shayxpeare
Shayxpearr Shayxpeer
Shayxpeere Shayxpeire
Shayxpeirr Shayxpeirre
Shayxper Shayxpere
Shayxperr Shayxperre
Shayxpiere Shayxpierr
Shayxpierre Shayxpir
Shayxpirr Shayxpyr
Shayxpyrr Sheackespaer
Sheackespaere
Sheackespaerr
Sheackespeare
Sheackespearr
Sheackespeer
Sheackespeere
Sheackespeir
Sheackespeire
Sheackespeirr
Sheackespeirre
Sheackesper
Sheackespere
Sheackesperr
Sheackesperre
Sheackespier
Sheackespiere
Sheackespiero
Sheackespierr
Sheackespierre
Sheackespir
Sheackespirr
Sheackespyr
Sheackespyrr
Sheacksspeare
Sheacksspearr
Sheacksspeere
Sheacksspeire
Sheacsspier Sheaksspaer
Sheaksspaere
Sheaksspaerr
Sheaksspear Sheaksspeer
Sheaksspeir
Sheaksspeirre
Sheakssper Sheaksspere

If the name you are interested in is not here, try Section C.

Sheaksspperr
Sheaksspperre
Sheaksspiere
Sheaksspierr
Sheaksspierre
Sheaksspir Sheaksspirr
Sheaksspyr Sheaksspyrr
Sheaquespaer
Sheaquespaere
Sheaquespaerr
Sheaquespear
Sheaquespeare
Sheaquespearr
Sheaquespeer
Sheaquespeere
Sheaquespeir
Sheaquespeire
Sheaquespeirr
Sheaquesper
Sheaquespere
Sheaquesperr
Sheaquesperre
Sheaquespier
Sheaquespiere
Sheaquespierr
Sheaquespierre
Sheaquespir
Sheaquespirr
Sheaquespyr Sheckespaer
Sheckespaere
Sheckespaerr
Sheckespear
Sheckespeare
Sheckespearr
Sheckespeer Sheckespeir
Sheckespeire
Sheckespeirr
Sheckespeirre
Sheckesper Sheckespere
Sheckesperr
Sheckesperre
Sheckespier
Sheckespierr
Sheckespierre
Sheckespir Sheckespirr
Sheckespyrr Sheixspaer
Sheixspaere Sheixspaerr
Sheixspear Sheixspeare
Sheixspearr Sheixspeer
Sheixspeere Sheixspeir
Sheixspeire
Sheixspeirre Sheixsper
Sheixspere Sheixsperr
Sheixsperre Sheixspier
Sheixspiere Sheixspierr
Sheixspierre Sheixspir
Sheixspyr Sheixspyrr
Shekespaer Shekespaere
Shekespaerr Shekespear
Shekespeare Shekespearr
Shekespeer Shekespeere
Shekespeir Shekespeire
Shekespeirr
Shekespeirre Shekesper
Shekespere Shekesperr
Shekesperre Shekespier
Shekespiere Shekespierr
Shekespierre Shekespir
Shekespirr Shexpaerr
Shexspaer Shexspaere
Shexspear Shexspeare
Shexspearr Shexspeer
Shexspeere Shexspeir
Shexspeire Shexspeirr
Shexspeirre Shexsper
Shexspere Shexsperr
Shexsperre Shexspier
Shexspiere Shexspierr
Shexspierre Shexspir
Shexspirr Shexspyr
Shexspyrr Sheykspaer
Sheykspaere Sheykspaerr
Sheykspeare Sheykspearr
Sheykspeer Sheykspeere
Sheykspeir Sheykspeire
Sheykspeirr
Sheykspeirre Sheyksper
Sheykspere Sheyksperr
Sheyksperre Sheykspier
Sheykspiere Sheykspierr
Sheykspierre Sheykspir
Sheykspirr Sheykspyr
Sheykspyrr
Shakesperr SHAKESPEARE
Shalcroft SHALLCROSS SHAWCROFT
Shalcross SHALLCROSS SHAWCROSS
Shalcrosse SHALLCROSS SHAWCROSS
SHALDERS Shaulders
Shallcroft SHALLCROSS SHAWCROFT
SHALLCROSS 10 Shalcroft Shalcross Shalcrosse Shallcroft Shallcrosse SHAWCROFT SHAWCROSS Shawcrosse Shorecroft
Shallcrosse SHALLCROSS SHAWCROSS
Shalselock SHACKLOCK
SHAMBROOK Shambrooke Sharnbrook
Shambrooke SHAMBROOK
Shankiland SHANKLAND
SHANKLAND Shankiland Skanlin
Shanksmith SHOUKSMITH
Shapcot SHAPCOTT
Shapcote SHAPCOTT
SHAPCOTT 4 Shapcot Shapcote Shepcote
SHAPLAND Shappland
Shapleigh SHAPLEY
SHAPLEY 4 Shapleigh Shaplie Shaplye
Shaplie SHAPLEY
Shaplye SHAPLEY
Shappland SHAPLAND
Shares SHEAVES
Shargold SHERGOLD
Sharlock SHERLOCK SHURLOCK
Sharlocke SHERLOCK SHURLOCK
Sharly SHIRLEY
SHARMAN 4 SHEARMAN SHERMAN Starman
Sharnbrook SHAMBROOK
SHARP SHARPE
SHARPE SHARP
Sharpenton SHARPINGTON
Sharpentyne SHARPINGTON
Sharperton SHARPINGTON
Sharpertone SHARPINGTON
Sharpertonn SHARPINGTON
Sharpertonne SHARPINGTON
SHARPINGTON 9 Sharpenton Sharpentyne Sharperton Sharpertone Sharpertonn Sharpertonne Sharpinton Sheppington
Sharpinton SHARPINGTON
SHARPLES Sharpless Sharplesse
Sharpless SHARPLES
Sharplesse SHARPLES
SHARPLIN SHARPLING
SHARPLING SHARPLIN
Sharrard SHERRARD
Sharred SHERRARD SHERRATT
Sharrier SHAYER
SHARROCK SHORROCK
Sharrog SHEARWOOD SHERWOOD
Sharyer SHAYER
Shatlock SHACKLOCK
Shaulders SHALDERS
Shaves SHEAVES
SHAW SHAWE
SHAWCROFT 6 Shalcroft Shallcroft SHALLCROSS Shawcrosse Shorecroft
SHAWCROSS 6 Shalcross Shalcrosse SHALLCROSS Shallcrosse Shawcrosse
Shawcrosse SHALLCROSS SHAWCROFT SHAWCROSS
SHAWE SHAW
Shaxon SHAXTON
SHAXTON Shaxon
SHAYER Sharrier Sharyer
Shaykspaer SHAKESPEARE
Shaykspaere SHAKESPEARE
Shaykspaerr SHAKESPEARE
Shaykspear SHAKESPEARE
Shaykspearr SHAKESPEARE
Shaykspeer SHAKESPEARE
Shaykspeere SHAKESPEARE
Shaykspeir SHAKESPEARE
Shaykspeire SHAKESPEARE
Shaykspeirr SHAKESPEARE
Shaykspeirre SHAKESPEARE
Shayksper SHAKESPEARE
Shaykspere SHAKESPEARE
Shaykspèrr SHAKESPEARE
Shayksperre SHAKESPEARE
Shaykspier SHAKESPEARE
Shaykspiere SHAKESPEARE
Shaykspierr SHAKESPEARE
Shaykspierre SHAKESPEARE
Shaykspir SHAKESPEARE
Shaykspirr SHAKESPEARE
Shaykspyr SHAKESPEARE
Shaykspyrr SHAKESPEARE
Shayxpaer SHAKESPEARE
Shayxpaere SHAKESPEARE
Shayxpaerr SHAKESPEARE
Shayxpear SHAKESPEARE
Shayxpeare SHAKESPEARE
Shayxpearr SHAKESPEARE
Shayxpeer SHAKESPEARE
Shayxpeere SHAKESPEARE
Shayxpeire SHAKESPEARE
Shayxpeirr SHAKESPEARE
Shayxpeirre SHAKESPEARE
Shayxper SHAKESPEARE
Shayxpere SHAKESPEARE
Shayxperr SHAKESPEARE
Shayxperre SHAKESPEARE
Shayxpiere SHAKESPEARE
Shayxpierr SHAKESPEARE
Shayxpierre SHAKESPEARE
Shayxpir SHAKESPEARE
Shayxpirr SHAKESPEARE
Shayxpyr SHAKESPEARE
Shayxpyrr SHAKESPEARE
Sheackespaer SHAKESPEARE
Sheackespaere SHAKESPEARE
Sheackespaerr SHAKESPEARE
Sheackespeare SHAKESPEARE
Sheackespearr SHAKESPEARE
Sheackespeer SHAKESPEARE
Sheackespeere SHAKESPEARE
Sheackespeir SHAKESPEARE
Sheackespeire SHAKESPEARE
Sheackespeirr SHAKESPEARE
Sheackespeirre SHAKESPEARE
Sheackesper SHAKESPEARE
Sheackespere SHAKESPEARE
Sheackesperr SHAKESPEARE
Sheackesperre SHAKESPEARE
Sheackespier SHAKESPEARE
Sheackespiere SHAKESPEARE
Sheackespiero SHAKESPEARE
Sheackespierr SHAKESPEARE
Sheackespierre SHAKESPEARE
Sheackespir SHAKESPEARE
Sheackespirr SHAKESPEARE
Sheackespyr SHAKESPEARE
Sheackespyrr SHAKESPEARE
Sheacksspeare SHAKESPEARE
Sheacksspearr SHAKESPEARE
Sheacksspeere SHAKESPEARE
Sheacksspeire SHAKESPEARE
Sheacsspier SHAKESPEARE
SHEAF Sheaff
Sheaff SHEAF
Sheaksspaer SHAKESPEARE
Sheaksspaere SHAKESPEARE
Sheaksspaerr SHAKESPEARE
Sheaksspear SHAKESPEARE
Sheaksspeer SHAKESPEARE
Sheaksspeir SHAKESPEARE
Sheaksspeirre SHAKESPEARE
Sheakssper SHAKESPEARE
Sheaksspere SHAKESPEARE
Sheaksspèrr SHAKESPEARE
Sheaksspèrre SHAKESPEARE
Sheaksspiere SHAKESPEARE
Sheaksspierr SHAKESPEARE
Sheaksspierre SHAKESPEARE
Sheaksspir SHAKESPEARE
Sheaksspirr SHAKESPEARE
Sheaksspyr SHAKESPEARE
Sheaksspyrr SHAKESPEARE
Sheappheard SHEPHERD SHEPPARD
Sheaquespaer SHAKESPEARE
Sheaquespaere SHAKESPEARE
Sheaquespaerr SHAKESPEARE
Sheaquespear SHAKESPEARE
Sheaquespeare SHAKESPEARE
Sheaquespearr SHAKESPEARE
Sheaquespeer SHAKESPEARE
Sheaquespeere SHAKESPEARE
Sheaquespeir SHAKESPEARE
Sheaquespeire SHAKESPEARE
Sheaquespeirr SHAKESPEARE
Sheaquesper SHAKESPEARE
Sheaquespere SHAKESPEARE
Sheaquesperr SHAKESPEARE
Sheaquesperre SHAKESPEARE
Sheaquespier SHAKESPEARE
Sheaquespiere SHAKESPEARE
Sheaquespierr SHAKESPEARE
Sheaquespierre SHAKESPEARE
Sheaquespir SHAKESPEARE
Sheaquespirr SHAKESPEARE
Sheaquespyr SHAKESPEARE
SHEAR 19 Sheare Sheares SHEARS SHEER Sheere Sheeres SHEERS Sheir Sheire Sheires Sheirs Shere Sheres Shier Shiere Shiers SHIRE Shires
SHEARDOWN 5 Sheerdown Sheredonne Sheredown Sheredowne
Sheare SHEAR SHEARS SHEER SHEERS SHIRE
Sheares SHEAR SHEARS SHEER SHEERS SHIRE
Sheargold SHERGOLD
Shearlock SHERLOCK SHURLOCK
SHEARMAN SHARMAN
SHEARS 19 SHEAR Sheare Sheares SHEER Sheere Sheeres SHEERS Sheir Sheire Sheires Sheirs Shere Sheres Shier Shiere Shiers SHIRE Shires
Shearston SEARSTONE SEASTON
SHEARWOOD Sharrog SHERWOOD
SHEAVES 4 Shade Shares Shaves
Shebrond SEABORNE
Sheckespaer SHAKESPEARE

If the name you are interested in is not here, try Section C.

Sheckespaere SHAKESPEARE
Sheckespaerr SHAKESPEARE
Sheckespear SHAKESPEARE
Sheckespeare SHAKESPEARE
Sheckespearr SHAKESPEARE
Sheckespeer SHAKESPEARE
Sheckespeir SHAKESPEARE
Sheckespeire SHAKESPEARE
Sheckespeirr SHAKESPEARE
Sheckespeirre SHAKESPEARE
Sheckesper SHAKESPEARE
Sheckespere SHAKESPEARE
Sheckesperr SHAKESPEARE
Sheckesperre SHAKESPEARE
Sheckespier SHAKESPEARE
Sheckespierr SHAKESPEARE
Sheckespierre SHAKESPEARE
Sheckespir SHAKESPEARE
Sheckespirr SHAKESPEARE
Sheckespyrr SHAKESPEARE
SHEDDEN Sheddon Sheeden
Sheddon SHEDDEN
SHEDWICK SEDGWICK
Sheeden SHEDDEN
SHEEN SHIN
Sheepheard SHEPARD SHEPHERD SHEPPERD
Sheepherd SHEPARD SHEPHERD SHEPPERD
SHEER 19 SHEAR Sheare Sheares SHEARS Sheere Sheeres SHEERS Sheir Sheire Sheires Sheirs Shere Sheres Shier Shiere Shiers SHIRE Shires
Sheerdown SHEARDOWN
Sheere SHEAR SHEARS SHEER SHEERS SHIRE
Sheeres SHEAR SHEARS SHEER SHEERS SHIRE
SHEERS 19 SHEAR Sheare Sheares SHEARS SHEER Sheere Sheeres Sheir Sheire Sheires Sheirs Shere Sheres Shier Shiere Shiers SHIRE Shires
Sheetford SHETFER
Sheil SHIELDS SHIELL
Sheild SHIELD SHILL
Sheill SHIELDS SHIELL
Sheils SHIELDS SHIELS
Sheir SHEAR SHEARS SHEER SHEERS SHIRE
Sheire SHEAR SHEARS SHEER SHEERS SHIRE
Sheires SHEAR SHEARS SHEER SHEERS SHIRE
Sheirs SHEAR SHEARS SHEER SHEERS SHIRE
Sheixspaer SHAKESPEARE
Sheixspaere SHAKESPEARE
Sheixspaerr SHAKESPEARE
Sheixspear SHAKESPEARE
Sheixspeare SHAKESPEARE
Sheixspearr SHAKESPEARE
Sheixspeer SHAKESPEARE
Sheixspeere SHAKESPEARE
Sheixspeir SHAKESPEARE
Sheixspeire SHAKESPEARE
Sheixspeirre SHAKESPEARE
Sheixsper SHAKESPEARE
Sheixspere SHAKESPEARE
Sheixsperr SHAKESPEARE
Sheixsperre SHAKESPEARE
Sheixspier SHAKESPEARE
Sheixspiere SHAKESPEARE
Sheixspierr SHAKESPEARE
Sheixspierre SHAKESPEARE
Sheixspir SHAKESPEARE
Sheixspyr SHAKESPEARE
Sheixspyrr SHAKESPEARE
Shekespaer SHAKESPEARE
Shekespaere SHAKESPEARE
Shekespaerr SHAKESPEARE
Shekespear SHAKESPEARE
Shekespeare SHAKESPEARE
Shekespearr SHAKESPEARE
Shekespeer SHAKESPEARE
Shekespeere SHAKESPEARE
Shekespeir SHAKESPEARE
Shekespeire SHAKESPEARE
Shekespeirr SHAKESPEARE
Shekespeirre SHAKESPEARE
Shekesper SHAKESPEARE
Shekespere SHAKESPEARE
Shekesperr SHAKESPEARE
Shekesperre SHAKESPEARE
Shekespier SHAKESPEARE
Shekespiere SHAKESPEARE
Shekespierr SHAKESPEARE
Shekespierre SHAKESPEARE
Shekespir SHAKESPEARE
Shekespirr SHAKESPEARE
SHELDON 4 SHELTON SHILDON SHILTON
SHELTON 4 SHELDON SHILDON SHILTON
SHENTON Shinton
SHEPARD 10 Sheepheard Sheepherd SHEPERD Shepheard SHEPHERD SHEPPARD SHEPPERD Shepphard Sheppherd
Shepcote SHAPCOTT
SHEPERD SHEPARD SHEPHERD
SHEPHARD SHEPPARD
Shepheard SHEPARD SHEPHERD SHEPPARD SHEPPERD
SHEPHERD 11 Sheappheard Sheepheard Sheepherd SHEPARD SHEPERD Shepheard SHEPPARD SHEPPERD Shepphard Sheppherd
SHEPHERDLEY Shipherdley
SHEPPARD 9 Sheappheard SHEPARD SHEPHARD Shepheard SHEPHERD SHEPPERD Shepphard Sheppherd
SHEPPERD 7 Sheepheard Sheepherd SHEPARD Shepheard SHEPHERD SHEPPARD
Shepphard SHEPARD SHEPHERD SHEPPARD
Sheppherd SHEPARD SHEPHERD SHEPPARD
Sheppington SHARPINGTON
Sherard SHERRARD SHERRATT
SHERBORN 7 SHERBORNE Sherbourne Shirborne Shurbon Shurbone Shurbun
SHERBORNE 8 SHERBORN Sherbourne Sherburn Shirborne Shurbon Shurbone Shurbun
Sherbourne SHERBORN SHERBORNE
Sherburn SHERBORNE
Shere SHEAR SHEARS SHEER SHEERS SHIRE
Sheredonne SHEARDOWN
Sheredown SHEARDOWN
Sheredowne SHEARDOWN
Sheres SHEAR SHEARS SHEER SHEERS SHIRE
Shergall SHERGOLD
SHERGOLD 6 Shargold Sheargold Shergall Shergoll Shirgold
Shergoll SHERGOLD
Sherifs SHIRREFFS
Sherley SHIRLEY
Sherloc SHERLOCK SHURLOCK
SHERLOCK 8 Scurlock Sharlock Sharlocke Shearlock Sherloc Shirlock SHURLOCK
SHERMAN SHARMAN Starman
Sherrad SHERRARD SHERRATT
SHERRARD 10 Sharrard Sharred Sherard Sherrad SHERRATT Sherreard Sherred Sherret Sherrott
SHERRATT 9 Sharred Sherard Sherrad SHERRARD Sherreard Sherred Sherret Sherrott
Sherreard SHERRARD SHERRATT
Sherred SHERRARD SHERRATT
Sherret SHERRARD SHERRATT
SHERRIES SHERRIS SHERRY
SHERRIF Sherriff
Sherriff SHERRIF
Sherrifs SHIRREFFS
SHERRIS SHERRIES SHERRY
Sherrott SHERRARD SHERRATT
SHERRY SHERRIES SHERRIS
SHERWEN SHERWIN
SHERWIN SHERWEN
SHERWOOD 5 Sharrog SHEARWOOD SHEWARD Shuard
Shetfar SHETFER
Shetfard SHETFER
SHETFER 12 Chadford Sheetford Shetfar Shetfard Shetfor Shethford Shitford Shittford Shudford Shutford Shutforth
Shetfor SHETFER
Shethford SHETFER
Shettle SHUTTLE
SHEWARD SHERWOOD Shuard
Shewbridge SHOEBRIDGE SHOOBRIDGE
Shewel SHEWELL
SHEWELL SEWELL Shewel
Shewker SHUKER
Shewry SHUREY
Shexpaerr SHAKESPEARE
Shexspaer SHAKESPEARE
Shexspaere SHAKESPEARE
Shexspear SHAKESPEARE
Shexspeare SHAKESPEARE
Shexspearr SHAKESPEARE
Shexspeer SHAKESPEARE
Shexspeere SHAKESPEARE
Shexspeir SHAKESPEARE
Shexspeire SHAKESPEARE
Shexspeirr SHAKESPEARE
Shexspeirre SHAKESPEARE
Shexsper SHAKESPEARE
Shexspere SHAKESPEARE
Shexsperr SHAKESPEARE
Shexsperre SHAKESPEARE
Shexspier SHAKESPEARE
Shexspiere SHAKESPEARE
Shexspierr SHAKESPEARE
Shexspierre SHAKESPEARE
Shexspir SHAKESPEARE
Shexspirr SHAKESPEARE
Shexspyr SHAKESPEARE
Shexspyrr SHAKESPEARE
Sheykspaer SHAKESPEARE
Sheykspaere SHAKESPEARE
Sheykspaerr SHAKESPEARE
Sheykspeare SHAKESPEARE
Sheykspearr SHAKESPEARE
Sheykspeer SHAKESPEARE
Sheykspeere SHAKESPEARE
Sheykspeir SHAKESPEARE
Sheykspeire SHAKESPEARE
Sheykspeirr SHAKESPEARE
Sheykspeirre SHAKESPEARE
Sheyksper SHAKESPEARE
Sheykspere SHAKESPEARE
Sheyksperr SHAKESPEARE
Sheyksperre SHAKESPEARE
Sheykspier SHAKESPEARE
Sheykspiere SHAKESPEARE
Sheykspierr SHAKESPEARE
Sheykspierre SHAKESPEARE
Sheykspir SHAKESPEARE
Sheykspirr SHAKESPEARE
Sheykspyr SHAKESPEARE
Sheykspyrr SHAKESPEARE
Shiel SHIELDS SHIELL
SHIELD 4 Sheild SHIELDS SHILL
SHIELDS 8 Sheil Sheill Sheils Shiel SHIELD SHIELL SHIELS
SHIELL 6 Sheil Sheill Shiel SHIELDS SHILL
SHIELS Sheils SHIELDS
Shier SHEAR SHEARS SHEER SHEERS SHIRE
Shiere SHEAR SHEARS SHEER SHEERS SHIRE
Shiers SHEAR SHEARS SHEER SHEERS SHIRE
Shifeley SHIFLEY
Shifferley SHIFLEY
SHIFLEY Shifeley Shifferley
SHILDON 4 SHELDON SHELTON SHILTON
SHILL 4 Sheild SHIELD SHIELL
SHILLABEER Shillibeer
Shillibeer SHILLABEER
SHILLING Shillinge Shillings
Shillinge SHILLING
Shillings SHILLING
SHILTON 4 SHELDON SHELTON SHILDON
Shimpton SHRIMPTON
SHIN SHEEN
Shingelton SHINGLETON SINGLETON
SHINGLETON 4 Shingelton Singelton SINGLETON
Shinton SHENTON
SHIP SHIPP
Shipherdley SHEPHERDLEY
SHIPP SHIP
SHIPPEN 5 Scheppyn Shippin Shippon SHIPTON
Shippin SHIPPEN
Shippon SHIPPEN
SHIPTON SHIPPEN
Shirborne SHERBORN SHERBORNE
SHIRE 19 SHEAR Sheare Sheares SHEARS SHEER Sheere Sheeres SHEERS Sheir Sheire Sheires Sheirs Shere Sheres Shier Shiere Shiers Shires
Shires SHEAR SHEARS SHEER SHEERS SHIRE
Shirgold SHERGOLD
SHIRLEY 5 Sharly Sherley Shirly Shurley
Shirlock SHERLOCK SHURLOCK
Shirly SHIRLEY
SHIRREFFS Sherifs Sherrifs
SHIRT SHURT
Shitford SHETFER
Shittford SHETFER
Shoal SHOLL

If the name you are interested in is not here, try Section C.

Shoale SHOLL
Shoar SHORE
SHOARD 4 Shoord Shord Shorde
Shoare SHORE
Shobridge SHOEBRIDGE SHOOBRIDGE
Shocklach SHACKLOCK
SHOEBRIDGE 7 Shewbridge Shobridge SHOOBRIDGE Shoubridge Shrowbridge Shubridge
Shokelach SHACKLOCK
Shole SHOLL
Sholiche SHACKLOCK
SHOLL 5 Shoal Shoale Shole Showle
Shonksmith SHOUKSMITH
SHOOBRIDGE 7 Shewbridge Shobridge SHOEBRIDGE Shoubridge Shrowbridge Shubridge
Shooker SHUKER
Shooksmith SHOUKSMITH
Shoord SHOARD
Shoot SHUTE SHUTT
Shor SHORE
Shord SHOARD
Shorde SHOARD
SHORE 7 Schoor Schoore Schor Shoar Shoare Shor
Shorecroft SHALLCROSS SHAWCROFT
SHORROCK SHARROCK
Shortal SHORTALL
SHORTALL 7 Shortal Shortel Shortell Shorthill Shortill Shortle
Shortel SHORTALL
Shortell SHORTALL
Shorthill SHORTALL
Shortill SHORTALL
Shortle SHORTALL
Shoubridge SHOEBRIDGE SHOOBRIDGE
Shoucksmith SHOUKSMITH
SHOUKSMITH 6 Shanksmith Shonksmith Shooksmith Shoucksmith Shucksmith
Showell HOWELL STAVOLD STAWELL STOWELL STOYLE
Showle SHOLL
Shoyell HOWELL STAVOLD STAWELL STOWELL STOYLE
SHREEVE 6 Shreeves Shreve Shreves Shrieve Shrieves
Shreeves SHREEVE
Shreve SHREEVE
Shreves SHREEVE
SHREWSBURY 4 Shrosbury Shroseberie Shrowsbury
Shrieve SHREEVE
Shrieves SHREEVE
SHRIMPTON Shimpton Srimpton
Shrosbury SHREWSBURY
Shroseberie SHREWSBURY
Shroudley STROUDLEY
Shrowbridge SHOEBRIDGE SHOOBRIDGE
Shrowsbury SHREWSBURY
SHRUBB Shurb
Shuard SHERWOOD SHEWARD
Shubridge SHOEBRIDGE SHOOBRIDGE
Shucker SHUKER
Shucksmith SHOUKSMITH
Shudford SHETFER
SHUFFLEBOTHAM 4 Shufflebothom Shufflebottam SHUFFLEBOTTOM
Shufflebothom SHUFFLEBOTHAM SHUFFLEBOTTOM
Shufflebottam SHUFFLEBOTHAM SHUFFLEBOTTOM
SHUFFLEBOTTOM 4 SHUFFLEBOTHAM Shufflebothom Shufflebottam
Shugar SHUKER
SHUKER 10 Shewker Shooker Shucker Shugar Shulker Sucker Sugar Suger Suker
Shulker SHUKER
Shun SHUNN
SHUNN 4 Choun Chun Shun
Shurb SHRUBB
Shurbon SHERBORN SHERBORNE
Shurbone SHERBORN SHERBORNE
Shurbun SHERBORN SHERBORNE
SHUREY 4 Shewry Shurrey Shury
Shurley SHIRLEY
SHURLOCK 8 Scurlock Sharlock Sharlocke Shearlock Sherloc SHERLOCK Shirlock
Shurrey SHUREY
SHURT SHIRT
Shury SHUREY
SHUTE Shoot SHUTT
Shutford SHETFER
Shutforth SHETFER
SHUTT Shoot SHUTE
Shuttel SHUTTLE
Shuttell SHUTTLE
SHUTTLE 4 Shettle Shuttel Shuttell
SIDAL 4 SIDDAL SIDDALL SIDLE
SIDDAL 4 SIDAL SIDDALL SIDLE
SIDDALL 5 SIDAL SIDDAL SIDLE SIDWELL
Sidgewick SEDGEWICK
Sidgrave SADGROVE
Sidgwick SEDGEWICK
SIDLE 4 SIDAL SIDDAL SIDDALL
SIDNEY 4 Sidny SYDNEY Sydny
Sidny SIDNEY SYDNEY
SIDWELL SIDDALL
Sier SEAR SEARS SYRE
Siers SEAR SEARS
SIEVEWRIGHT Suvaret
Sigiswick SEDGEWICK
Sign SINE
SIGRAVE 4 SEGRAVE SIGROVE SYGROVE
SIGROVE 4 SEGRAVE SIGRAVE SYGROVE
Sikes SYKES
SILCOCK 7 Selcock Selcocks SILCOCKS SILCOX Sillcock Sillcocks
SILCOCKS SILCOCK SILCOX
SILCOX 7 Selcock Selcocks SILCOCK SILCOCKS Sillcock Sillcocks
SILENCE 15 Selance Selence SELLEN Sellence SELLENS SILLENCE Sillince Sillins Sillons Sollons Sullence Sullens Sullince Sullins
SILK Silke Silks
Silke SILK
Silks SILK
Silkston SILKSTONE
SILKSTONE Silkston
SILLARS SILLERS
Sillcock SILCOCK SILCOX
Sillcocks SILCOCK SILCOX
SILLENCE 15 Selance Selence SELLEN Sellence SELLENS SILENCE Sillince Sillins Sillons Sollons Sullence Sullens Sullince Sullins
SILLERS SILLARS
SILLEY SEALY
Sillince SELLEN SELLENS SILENCE SILLENCE
Sillins SELLEN SELLENS SILENCE SILLENCE
Sillons SELLEN SELLENS SILENCE SILLENCE
Sillwood SELLWOOD ZILLWOOD
Silmam SELMAM
SILVERTHORN SILVERTHORNE
SILVERTHORNE SILVERTHORN
SILVESTER Silwester SYLVESTER
Silwester SILVESTER SYLVESTER
Sim SIME SIMES
Simcens SIMKIN SIMKINS SIMPKIN SIMPKINS
SIME 6 Sim SIMES Simm Sym Symm
SIMES 6 Sim SIME Simm Sym Symm
SIMKIN 6 Simcens SIMKINS SIMPKIN SIMPKINS Sympkins
SIMKINS 6 Simcens SIMKIN SIMPKIN SIMPKINS Sympkins
Simm SIME SIMES
SIMMONDS 9 Semens SEMMONS SIMMONS SIMONDS SIMONS Symmonds SYMONDS SYMONS
SIMMONS 7 Semens SEMMONS SIMMONDS SIMONS SYMONDS SYMONS
SIMMS SIMS
SIMON 4 SIMONDS SIMONS SYMON
SIMONDS 8 SIMMONDS SIMON SIMONS Symmonds SYMON SYMONDS SYMONS
SIMONS 7 SIMMONDS SIMMONS SIMON SIMONDS SYMON SYMONS
SIMPKIN 6 Simcens SIMKIN SIMKINS SIMPKINS Sympkins
SIMPKINS 6 Simcens SIMKIN SIMKINS SIMPKIN Sympkins
SIMPSON 4 SIMSON SYMPSON Symson
SIMS 7 Seem Sems SIMMS SYMES Symmes Symms
SIMSON 4 SIMPSON SYMPSON Symson
SINE Ensign Sign
SINFIELD 7 Singfeild Singfield Sinkfeild Sinkfield SWINCKFIELD Synfield
SING 8 Singe Singes SINGS Sinns Sins Syng Synge
Singe SING SINGS
Singelton SHINGLETON SINGLETON
Singes SING SINGS
Singfeild SINFIELD SWINCKFIELD
Singfield SINFIELD SWINCKFIELD
SINGLETON 4 Shingelton SHINGLETON Singelton
SINGS 8 SING Singe Singes Sinns Sins Syng Synge
Sinisbury SAINSBURY SAINTSBURY SAINTSBURYE SAYNSBURY SEINESBERIA SEYNISBURY
Sinkfeild SINFIELD SWINCKFIELD
Sinkfield SINFIELD SWINCKFIELD
Sinnatt SINNOTT
Sinnett SINNOTT
SINNOTT 9 Senet Sennett Sennitt Sinnatt Sinnett Sionoid Synot Synott
Sinns SING SINGS
Sinom SANHAM
Sins SING SINGS
Sionoid SINNOTT
SIRMAN 6 Cyrmon Serman SERMON Sirmon SURMAN
Sirmon SERMON SIRMAN SURMAN
Sirret SYRETT
Siscel SAYSELL
Siser SIZER SYER
Sissford CESSFORD
SIVETER Siviter
Siviter SIVETER
Sivorn SEVERN
Sizar SIZER
SIZER 8 Siser Sizar Sizor SYER Syser Syzar Syzer
Sizor SIZER
SKALES SCALES
Skanlin SHANKLAND
SKAR 4 Scar SCARR Skarr
Skarr SCARR SKAR
Skarratt SKERRATT SKERRETT SKERRITT
Skayles SKOYLES
Skeeles SKEELS
SKEELS Skeeles
Skeg SKEGG SKEGGS SKIGGS
SKEGG 9 Skeg Skegge SKEGGS Skegs Skig Skigg SKIGGS Skigs
Skegge SKEGG SKEGGS SKIGGS
SKEGGS 9 Skeg SKEGG Skegge Skegs Skig Skigg SKIGGS Skigs
Skegs SKEGG SKEGGS SKIGGS
Skelden SKELDING SKELDON
SKELDING Skelden SKELDON
SKELDON Skelden SKELDING
Skelleton SKELTON SKILTON
SKELTON Skelleton SKILTON
SKERM 4 Skirm SKYRM SKYRME
SKERO 4 SCARROW SKERROW SKIRROW
SKERRATT 5 Scarratt Skarratt SKERRETT SKERRITT
SKERRETT 5 Scarratt Skarratt SKERRATT SKERRITT
SKERRITT 5 Scarratt Skarratt SKERRATT SKERRETT
SKERROW 4 SCARROW SKERO SKIRROW
Sketch SKITCH
SKEWES 10 Scues Scuse SKEWIS SKEWS Skewys SKUCE SKUES SKUSE Skuys
SKEWIS 10 Scues Scuse SKEWES SKEWS Skewys

If the name you are interested in is not here, try Section C.

SKUCE SKUES SKUSE Skuys
SKEWS 10 Scues Scuse
SKEWES SKEWIS Skewys
SKUCE SKUES SKUSE Skuys
Skewys SKEWES SKEWIS
SKEWS SKUCE SKUES SKUSE
Skich SKITCH
Skidgemore SCUDAMORE
SKIDMORE
Skidgmore SCUDAMORE
SKIDMORE
SKIDMORE 7 SCUDAMORE
Skidgemore Skidgmore
Skidsmore Skitmore
Skudemore
Skidsmore SCUDAMORE
SKIDMORE
Skig SKEGG SKEGGS SKIGGS
Skigg SKEGG SKEGGS SKIGGS
SKIGGS 9 Skeg SKEGG
Skegge SKEGGS Skegs
Skig Skigg Skigs
Skigs SKEGG SKEGGS SKIGGS
SKILTON Skelleton SKELTON
Skiner SKINNER
SKINNER 4 Sciner Skiner
Skynner
Skirm SKERM SKYRM SKYRME
SKIRROW 4 SCARROW SKERO
SKERROW
SKITCH Sketch Skich
Skitmore SCUDAMORE
SKIDMORE
Skitterall SKITTRALL
SKITTRALL Skitterall
Skittrell
Skittrell SKITTRALL
Sklaitter SCLATER SLATER
Skoils SKOYLES
Skoopes SCOPES
Skopes SCOPES
SKORRELL 6 SCORRILL
SCURRILL SQUIRRELL
SQUORRELL SQURIEL
Skotes SKOTS
SKOTS Scoates Skotes
SKOYLES 4 Scoles Skayles
Skoils
Skreetan SCREATON SCRUTON
Skreeton SCREATON SCRUTON
SKUCE 10 Scues Scuse
SKEWES SKEWIS SKEWS
Skewys SKUES SKUSE
Skuys
Skudemore SCUDAMORE
SKIDMORE
SKUES 10 Scues Scuse
SKEWES SKEWIS SKEWS
Skewys SKUCE SKUSE
Skuys
SKULL Scull
Skur SCURR
Skurr SCURR
SKUSE 10 Scues Scuse
SKEWES SKEWIS SKEWS
Skewys SKUCE SKUES
Skuys
Skuys SKEWES SKEWIS SKEWS
SKUCE SKUES SKUSE
Skynner SKINNER
SKYRM 4 SKERM Skirm
SKYRME
SKYRME 4 SKERM Skirm
SKYRM
SLACK Slacke
Slacke SLACK
Sladdin SLADEN
SLADEN Sladdin Sladin
Sladin SLADEN
Slammon SALAMAN SLAYMAN
SLEAMAN SLEMAN SLEMANS
SLEMMINGS SLEMMON
SLEMMONDS SLEMMONS
SLEMON SLEMONS SLIMAN
SLIMANS SLIMMANDS
SLIMMING SLIMMINGS
Slamon SALAMAN SLAYMAN
SLEAMAN SLEMAN SLEMANS
SLEMMINGS SLEMMON
SLEMMONDS SLEMMONS
SLEMON SLEMONS SLIMAN
SLIMANS SLIMMANDS
SLIMMING SLIMMINGS
Slason SLAWSON
SLATER 6 Sclaitter
SCLATER Sklaitter
SLATTER SLAUGHTER
Slatery SLATTERY
SLATTER SLATER SLAUGHTER
SLATTERY Slatery
SLAUGHTER SLATER SLATTER
SLAWSON 5 Slason Slawston
Sloson Slowson
Slawston SLAWSON
SLAYMAN 36 Clemmings
SALAMAN Slammon Slamon
SLEAMAN SLEMAN Slemands
SLEMANS Slemen Slemens
Slemmen Slemmens
Slemming SLEMMINGS
SLEMMON SLEMMONDS
SLEMMONS SLEMON
SLEMONDS SLEMONS
Sleuthman Sleymans
SLIMAN SLIMANS Slimin
Sliming Slimings
Slimmand SLIMMANDS
SLIMMING SLIMMINGS
Slimond Slymand Slymin
Slymins
SLEAMAN 32 SALAMAN
Slammon Slamon SLAYMAN
SLEMAN SLEMANS Slemen
Slemens Slemmen
Slemmens Slemming
SLEMMINGS SLEMMON
SLEMMONDS SLEMMONS
SLEMON SLEMONS
Sleuthman SLIMAN
SLIMANS Slimin Sliming
Slimings Slimmand
SLIMMANDS SLIMMING
SLIMMINGS Slimond
Slymand Slymin Slymins
SLEEP Sleepe
Sleepe SLEEP
SLEIGHTHOLME Slightholm
Slitom
SLEMAN 32 SALAMAN Slammon
Slamon SLAYMAN SLEAMAN
SLEMANS Slemen Slemens
Slemmen Slemmens
Slemming SLEMMINGS
SLEMMON SLEMMONDS
SLEMMONS SLEMON SLEMONS
Sleuthman SLIMAN
SLIMANS Slimin Sliming
Slimings Slimmand
SLIMMANDS SLIMMING
SLIMMINGS Slimond
Slymand Slymin Slymins
Slemands SLAYMAN SLEMANS
SLEMMINGS SLEMONDS
SLEMANS 36 Clemmings
SALAMAN Slammon Slamon
SLAYMAN SLEAMAN SLEMAN
Slemands Slemen Slemens
Slemmen Slemmens
Slemming SLEMMINGS
SLEMMON SLEMMONDS
SLEMMONS SLEMON
SLEMONDS SLEMONS
Sleuthman Sleymans
SLIMAN SLIMANS Slimin
Sliming Slimings
Slimmand SLIMMANDS
SLIMMING SLIMMINGS
Slimond Slymand Slymin
Slymins
Slemen SALAMAN SLAYMAN
SLEAMAN SLEMAN SLEMANS
SLEMMINGS SLEMMON
SLEMMONDS SLEMMONS
SLEMON SLEMONS SLIMAN
SLIMANS SLIMMANDS
SLIMMING SLIMMINGS
Slemens SALAMAN SLAYMAN
SLEAMAN SLEMAN SLEMANS
SLEMMINGS SLEMMON
SLEMMONDS SLEMMONS
SLEMON SLEMONS SLIMAN
SLIMANS SLIMMANDS
SLIMMING SLIMMINGS
Slemmen SALAMAN SLAYMAN
SLEAMAN SLEMAN SLEMANS
SLEMMINGS SLEMMON
SLEMMONDS SLEMMONS
SLEMON SLEMONS SLIMAN
SLIMANS SLIMMANDS
SLIMMING SLIMMINGS
Slemmens SALAMAN SLAYMAN
SLEAMAN SLEMAN SLEMANS
SLEMMINGS SLEMMON
SLEMMONDS SLEMMONS
SLEMON SLEMONS SLIMAN
SLIMANS SLIMMANDS
SLIMMING SLIMMINGS
Slemming SALAMAN SLAYMAN
SLEAMAN SLEMAN SLEMANS
SLEMMINGS SLEMMON
SLEMMONDS SLEMMONS
SLEMON SLEMONS SLIMAN
SLIMANS SLIMMANDS
SLIMMING SLIMMINGS
SLEMMINGS 36 Clemmings
SALAMAN Slammon Slamon
SLAYMAN SLEAMAN SLEMAN
Slemands SLEMANS Slemen
Slemens Slemmen
Slemmens Slemming
SLEMMON SLEMMONDS
SLEMMONS SLEMON
SLEMONDS SLEMONS
Sleuthman Sleymans
SLIMAN SLIMANS Slimin
Sliming Slimings
Slimmand SLIMMANDS
SLIMMING SLIMMINGS
Slimond Slymand Slymin
Slymins
SLEMMON 32 SALAMAN
Slammon Slamon SLAYMAN
SLEAMAN SLEMAN SLEMANS
Slemen Slemens Slemmen
Slemmens Slemming
SLEMMINGS SLEMMONDS
SLEMMONS SLEMON SLEMONS
Sleuthman SLIMAN
SLIMANS Slimin Sliming
Slimings Slimmand
SLIMMANDS SLIMMING
SLIMMINGS Slimond
Slymand Slymin Slymins
SLEMMONDS 32 SALAMAN
Slammon Slamon SLAYMAN
SLEAMAN SLEMAN SLEMANS
Slemen Slemens Slemmen
Slemmens Slemming
SLEMMINGS SLEMMON
SLEMMONS SLEMON SLEMONS
Sleuthman SLIMAN
SLIMANS Slimin Sliming
Slimings Slimmand
SLIMMANDS SLIMMING
SLIMMINGS Slimond
Slymand Slymin Slymins
SLEMMONS 32 SALAMAN
Slammon Slamon SLAYMAN
SLEAMAN SLEMAN SLEMANS
Slemen Slemens Slemmen
Slemmens Slemming
SLEMMINGS SLEMMON
SLEMMONDS SLEMON
SLEMONS Sleuthman
SLIMAN SLIMANS Slimin
Sliming Slimings
Slimmand SLIMMANDS
SLIMMING SLIMMINGS
Slimond Slymand Slymin
Slymins
SLEMON 32 SALAMAN Slammon
Slamon SLAYMAN SLEAMAN
SLEMAN SLEMANS Slemen
Slemens Slemmen
Slemmens Slemming
SLEMMINGS SLEMMON
SLEMMONDS SLEMMONS
SLEMONS Sleuthman
SLIMAN SLIMANS Slimin
Sliming Slimings
Slimmand SLIMMANDS
SLIMMING SLIMMINGS
Slimond Slymand Slymin
Slymins
SLEMONDS 7 Clemmings
SLAYMAN Slemands
SLEMANS SLEMMINGS
Sleymans
SLEMONS 32 SALAMAN
Slammon Slamon SLAYMAN
SLEAMAN SLEMAN SLEMANS
Slemen Slemens Slemmen
Slemmens Slemming
SLEMMINGS SLEMMON
SLEMMONDS SLEMMONS
SLEMON Sleuthman SLIMAN
SLIMANS Slimin Sliming
Slimings Slimmand
SLIMMANDS SLIMMING
SLIMMINGS Slimond
Slymand Slymin Slymins
Sleuthman SALAMAN SLAYMAN
SLEAMAN SLEMAN SLEMANS
SLEMMINGS SLEMMON
SLEMMONDS SLEMMONS
SLEMON SLEMONS SLIMAN
SLIMANS SLIMMANDS
SLIMMING SLIMMINGS
Slewcock SLUCOCK
Slewcott SLUCOCK SLUCUTT
Sleymans SLAYMAN SLEMANS
SLEMMINGS SLEMONDS
Slie SLY SLYE
Slightholm SLEIGHTHOLME
SLIGO Slingo
SLIMAN 32 SALAMAN Slammon
Slamon SLAYMAN SLEAMAN
SLEMAN SLEMANS Slemen
Slemens Slemmen
Slemmens Slemming
SLEMMINGS SLEMMON
SLEMMONDS SLEMMONS
SLEMON SLEMONS
Sleuthman SLIMANS
Slimin Sliming Slimings
Slimmand SLIMMANDS
SLIMMING SLIMMINGS
Slimond Slymand Slymin
Slymins
SLIMANS 32 SALAMAN
Slammon Slamon SLAYMAN
SLEAMAN SLEMAN SLEMANS
Slemen Slemens Slemmen
Slemmens Slemming
SLEMMINGS SLEMMON
SLEMMONDS SLEMMONS
SLEMON SLEMONS
Sleuthman SLIMAN Slimin
Sliming Slimings
Slimmand SLIMMANDS
SLIMMING SLIMMINGS
Slimond Slymand Slymin
Slymins
Slimin SALAMAN SLAYMAN
SLEAMAN SLEMAN SLEMANS
SLEMMINGS SLEMMON

If the name you are interested in is not here, try Section C.

SLEMMONDS SLEMMONS
SLEMON SLEMONS SLIMAN
SLIMANS SLIMMANDS
SLIMMING SLIMMINGS
Sliming SALAMAN SLAYMAN
SLEAMAN SLEMAN SLEMANS
SLEMMINGS SLEMMON
SLEMMONDS SLEMMONS
SLEMON SLEMONS SLIMAN
SLIMANS SLIMMANDS
SLIMMING SLIMMINGS
Slimings SALAMAN SLAYMAN
SLEAMAN SLEMAN SLEMANS
SLEMMINGS SLEMMON
SLEMMONDS SLEMMONS
SLEMON SLEMONS SLIMAN
SLIMANS SLIMMANDS
SLIMMING SLIMMINGS
Slimmand SALAMAN SLAYMAN
SLEAMAN SLEMAN SLEMANS
SLEMMINGS SLEMMON
SLEMMONDS SLEMMONS
SLEMON SLEMONS SLIMAN
SLIMANS SLIMMANDS
SLIMMING SLIMMINGS
SLIMMANDS 32 SALAMAN
Slammon Slamon SLAYMAN
SLEAMAN SLEMAN SLEMANS
Slemen Slemens Slemmen
Slemmens Slemming
SLEMMINGS SLEMMON
SLEMMONDS SLEMMONS
SLEMON SLEMONS
Sleuthman SLIMAN
SLIMANS Slimin Sliming
Slimings Slimmand
SLIMMING SLIMMINGS
Slimond Slymand Slymin
Slymins
SLIMMING 32 SALAMAN
Slammon Slamon SLAYMAN
SLEAMAN SLEMAN SLEMANS
Slemen Slemens Slemmen
Slemmens Slemming
SLEMMINGS SLEMMON
SLEMMONDS SLEMMONS
SLEMON SLEMONS
Sleuthman SLIMAN
SLIMANS Slimin Sliming
Slimings Slimmand
SLIMMANDS SLIMMINGS
Slimond Slymand Slymin
Slymins
SLIMMINGS 32 SALAMAN
Slammon Slamon SLAYMAN
SLEAMAN SLEMAN SLEMANS
Slemen Slemens Slemmen
Slemmens Slemming
SLEMMINGS SLEMMON
SLEMMONDS SLEMMONS
SLEMON SLEMONS
Sleuthman SLIMAN
SLIMANS Slimin Sliming
Slimings Slimmand
SLIMMANDS SLIMMING
Slimond Slymand Slymin
Slymins
Slimond SALAMAN SLAYMAN
SLEAMAN SLEMAN SLEMANS
SLEMMINGS SLEMMON
SLEMMONDS SLEMMONS
SLEMON SLEMONS SLIMAN
SLIMANS SLIMMANDS
SLIMMING SLIMMINGS
Slingo SLIGO
Slitom SLEIGHTHOLME
Sloacomb SLOCOMBE
STOCKHAM
Sloacombe SLOCOMBE
STOCKHAM
Sloban SLOBOM
Slobin SLOBOM
SLOBOM 8 Schlobohm
Schlobohn Sloban Slobin
Sloburn Slowbohm
Slowburn
Sloburn SLOBOM
Slockem SLOCOMBE STOCKHAM
Slockham SLOCOMBE
STOCKHAM
Slocock SLUCOCK
Slocomb SLOCOMBE STOCKHAM
SLOCOMBE 15 Sloacomb
Sloacombe Slockem
Slockham Slocomb
Slocome Slocum Slocumb
Slocumbe Slokeham
Slowcomb Slowcombe
STOCKHAM Stocombe
Slocome SLOCOMBE STOCKHAM
Slocum SLOCOMBE STOCKHAM
Slocumb SLOCOMBE STOCKHAM
Slocumbe SLOCOMBE
STOCKHAM
Slocutt SLUCUTT
Slokeham SLOCOMBE
STOCKHAM
SLOMAN Slowman
Sloocock SLUCOCK
Sloson SLAWSON
Slowbohm SLOBOM
Slowburn SLOBOM
Slowcock SLUCOCK
Slowcoke SLUCOCK
Slowcomb SLOCOMBE
STOCKHAM
Slowcombe SLOCOMBE
STOCKHAM
Slowman SLOMAN
Slowson SLAWSON
Slucett SLUCUTT
SLUCOCK 8 Bluecock
Slewcock Slewcott
Slocock Sloocock
Slowcock Slowcoke
Slucott SLUCUTT
SLUCUTT 8 Hucutt Slewcott
Slocutt Slucett Slucott
Sluggate Sluggut
Sluggate SLUCUTT
Sluggut SLUCUTT
SLY Slie SLYE
SLYE Slie SLY
Slymand SALAMAN SLAYMAN
SLEAMAN SLEMAN SLEMANS
SLEMMINGS SLEMMON
SLEMMONDS SLEMMONS
SLEMON SLEMONS SLIMAN
SLIMANS SLIMMANDS
SLIMMING SLIMMINGS
Slymin SALAMAN SLAYMAN
SLEAMAN SLEMAN SLEMANS
SLEMMINGS SLEMMON
SLEMMONDS SLEMMONS
SLEMON SLEMONS SLIMAN
SLIMANS SLIMMANDS
SLIMMING SLIMMINGS
Slymins SALAMAN SLAYMAN
SLEAMAN SLEMAN SLEMANS
SLEMMINGS SLEMMON
SLEMMONDS SLEMMONS
SLEMON SLEMONS SLIMAN
SLIMANS SLIMMANDS
SLIMMING SLIMMINGS
SMAIL Smaill Smeill
SMAILES SMALES SMILES
Smaill SMAIL
Smaleman SMALLMAN
SMALES SMAILES
Smaley SMALLEY
Smalie SMALLEY
SMALLEY 7 Smaley Smalie
Smallie Smally Smaly
Smalye
SMALLFIELD Smallvel
Smallie SMALLEY
SMALLMAN Smaleman Smalman
Smallshare SMALLSHAW
SMALLSHIRE
SMALLSHAW 15 Smallshare
Smallsher SMALLSHIRE
Smalschaghe Smalschawhe
Smalsha Smalshagh
Smalshaw Smalshawe
Smalshew Smalshey
Smalshire Smalshowe
Smawshaw
Smallsher SMALLSHAW
SMALLSHIRE
SMALLSHIRE 6 Smallshare
SMALLSHAW Smallsher
Smalshaw Smalshire
Smallvel SMALLFIELD
Smally SMALLEY
Smalman SMALLMAN
Smalschaghe SMALLSHAW
Smalschawhe SMALLSHAW
Smalsha SMALLSHAW
Smalshagh SMALLSHAW
Smalshaw SMALLSHAW
SMALLSHIRE
Smalshawe SMALLSHAW
Smalshew SMALLSHAW
Smalshey SMALLSHAW
Smalshire SMALLSHAW
SMALLSHIRE
Smalshowe SMALLSHAW
Smaly SMALLEY
Smalye SMALLEY
Smardon SMERDON
Smawshaw SMALLSHAW
Smeill SMAIL
SMELLIE Smillie Smylie
Smerden SMERDON
SMERDON Smardon Smerden
Smethy SMITHY
SMIDDITT Smithet
SMILES SMAILES
SMILEY 7 SMILIE Smilley
Smillie Smyley Smylie
Smyly
SMILIE 7 SMILEY Smilley
Smillie Smyley Smylie
Smyly
Smilley SMILEY SMILIE
Smillie SMELLIE SMILEY
SMILIE
SMIRK Smirke
Smirke SMIRK
SMITH 5 SMYTH
Thurleigh-smith
Thurley-smith
Tyrley-smith
Smithet SMIDDITT
SMITHY 4 Smethy Smythees
Smythies
Smyley SMILEY SMILIE
Smylie SMELLIE SMILEY
SMILIE
Smyly SMILEY SMILIE
SMYTH SMITH Smythe
Smythe SMYTH
Smythees SMITHY
Smythies SMITHY
SNADAN Snedan
Snaw SNOW
Snazel SNEAZWELL
Snazwell SNEAZWELL
SNEAZWELL Snazel Snazwell
Snedan SNADAN
Sneesbie SNEESBY
SNEESBY 4 Sneesbie
Snesbie Snezby
SNELGAR 6 Snelger
Snelgrau Snelgrave
SNELGROVE SNELLGROVE
Snelger SNELGAR SNELGROVE
SNELLGROVE
Snelgrau SNELGAR
SNELGROVE SNELLGROVE
Snelgrave SNELGAR
SNELGROVE SNELLGROVE
SNELGROVE 6 SNELGAR
Snelger Snelgrau
Snelgrave SNELLGROVE
SNELL SNELLING
SNELLGROVE 6 SNELGAR
Snelger Snelgrau
Snelgrave SNELGROVE
SNELLING SNELL
Snesbie SNEESBY
Snezby SNEESBY
Snoad SNODE
Snocks SNOOK SNOOKS
SNODE Snoad
SNOOK 6 Snocks SNOOKS
Snouke Snoukes Snouks
SNOOKS 6 Snocks SNOOK
Snouke Snoukes Snouks
Snouke SNOOK SNOOKS
Snoukes SNOOK SNOOKS
Snouks SNOOK SNOOKS
SNOW Snaw Snowe
SNOWDEN SNOWDON SOWDEN
SNOWDON SNOWDEN
Snowe SNOW
SOAMES SOMES
SOANE 4 Soanes SOANS SONE
Soanes SOANE SOANS SONE
SOANS 4 SOANE Soanes SONE
Soaper SOPER
Soapper SOPER
SOAR 5 Soare Soer SORE
SWORD
Soare SOAR SORE SWORD
Sobee SOBEY SOBIE
Sober SAUBERE
Sobere SAUBERE
SOBEY 5 Sobee SOBIE Soby
Sobye
SOBIE 5 Sobee SOBEY Soby
Sobye
Soby SOBEY SOBIE
Sobye SOBEY SOBIE
Sockburn STOCKBURN
SOCKET SOCKETT
SOCKETT SOCKET
Soer SOAR SORE
Soileux SOILLEUX
SOILLEUX Soileux
SOLES Soules
Solesby SOULSBY
Sollons SELLEN SELLENS
SILENCE SILLENCE
SOLOMON 5 SALAMON SALOMON
Salomons Solomons
Solomons SALAMON SALOMON
SOLOMON
Solsby SOULSBY
Solsbye SOULSBY
SOMERVILLE SOMMERVILLE
SOMES SOAMES
SOMIRELL SUMMERHILL
Summerlille
SOMMERAYNS Sommerijns
Sommerijns SOMMERAYNS
SOMMERS 4 SOMNER SUMMERS
SUMNER
SOMMERVILLE SOMERVILLE
SOMNER SOMMERS SUMNER
SONE 4 SOANE Soanes SOANS
SONLEY 4 Sonly Sunlay
SUNLEY
Sonly SONLEY SUNLEY
SOPER 4 Soaper Soapper
Sopper
Sopper SOPER
SORE 5 SOAR Soare Soer
SWORD
Sotham SOUTHAM SOUTHIN
SOUTHORN SOUTHWELL
SUTHERS SUTTON
Sothams SOUTHAM SOUTHIN
SOUTHORN SOUTHWELL
SUTHERS SUTTON
Sotheran SOUTHAM SOUTHIN

If the name you are interested in is not here, try Section C.

SOUTHORN SOUTHWELL SUTHERS SUTTON
Sothern SOUTHAM SOUTHIN SOUTHORN SOUTHWELL SUTHERS SUTTON
Sotherne SOUTHAM SOUTHIN SOUTHORN SOUTHWELL SUTHERS SUTTON
Sothoran SOUTHAM SOUTHIN SOUTHORN SOUTHWELL SUTHERS SUTTON
Souden SOUTHAM SOUTHIN SOUTHORN SOUTHWELL SUTHERS SUTTON
Soughthe SOUTHEE SOUTHEY
Soughyer SAWYER
SOULARD Soullard
Soulbie SOULSBY
Soules SOLES
Soulesby SOULSBY
Soullard SOULARD
SOULSBY 9 Solesby Solsby Solsbye Soulbie Soulesby Soulsbye Sowleby Sowlesby
Soulsbye SOULSBY
SOUTAR 6 SOUTER Souttar SOUTTER SOWTER SUTER
SOUTER 6 SOUTAR Souttar SOUTTER SOWTER SUTER
SOUTHAM 37 Sotham Sothams Sotheran Sothern Sotherne Sothoran Souden Southan Southarn Southart Southen Southham SOUTHIN Southon SOUTHORN Southorne Southoun Southran Southren Southron Southurn SOUTHWELL Souton Soutten Sowtan Sowtharn Sowthern Sowton Sowtun Sutham Suthern Sutherns SUTHERS Suthon Suthorn SUTTON
Southan SOUTHAM SOUTHIN SOUTHORN SOUTHWELL SUTHERS SUTTON
SOUTHARD 9 Southers Sudders Suthast SUTHERS Sutherst Suthert Suthworth Suttherd
Southarn SOUTHAM SOUTHIN SOUTHORN SOUTHWELL SUTHERS SUTTON
Southart SOUTHAM SOUTHIN SOUTHORN SOUTHWELL SUTHERS SUTTON
Southay SOUTHEE SOUTHEY
Southcote SOUTHCOTT
SOUTHCOTT Southcote
Southe SOUTHEE SOUTHEY
SOUTHEE 9 Soughthe Southay Southe SOUTHEY Southie Southy Sowthe Sowthy
Southen SOUTHAM SOUTHIN SOUTHORN SOUTHWELL SUTHERS SUTTON
SOUTHERN Sutheran
Southers SOUTHARD SUTHERS
SOUTHEY 11 Soughthe Southay Southe SOUTHEE Southie SOUTHIN Southy Sowethee Sowthe Sowthy
Southham SOUTHAM SOUTHIN SOUTHORN SOUTHWELL SUTHERS SUTTON
Southie SOUTHEE SOUTHEY
SOUTHIN 39 Sotham Sothams Sotheran Sothern Sotherne Sothoran Souden SOUTHAM Southan Southarn Southart Southen SOUTHEY Southham Southon SOUTHORN Southorne Southoun Southran Southren Southron Southurn SOUTHWELL Souton Soutten Sowethee Sowtan Sowtharn Sowthern Sowton Sowtun Sutham Suthern Sutherns SUTHERS Suthon Suthorn SUTTON
Southon SOUTHAM SOUTHIN SOUTHORN SOUTHWELL SUTHERS SUTTON
SOUTHORN 37 Sotham Sothams Sotheran Sothern Sotherne Sothoran Souden SOUTHAM Southan Southarn Southart Southen Southham SOUTHIN Southon Southorne Southoun Southran Southren Southron Southurn SOUTHWELL Souton Soutten Sowtan Sowtharn Sowthern Sowton Sowtun Sutham Suthern Sutherns SUTHERS Suthon Suthorn SUTTON
Southorne SOUTHAM SOUTHIN SOUTHORN SOUTHWELL SUTHERS SUTTON
Southoun SOUTHAM SOUTHIN SOUTHORN SOUTHWELL SUTHERS SUTTON
Southran SOUTHAM SOUTHIN SOUTHORN SOUTHWELL SUTHERS SUTTON
Southren SOUTHAM SOUTHIN SOUTHORN SOUTHWELL SUTHERS SUTTON
Southron SOUTHAM SOUTHIN SOUTHORN SOUTHWELL SUTHERS SUTTON
Southurn SOUTHAM SOUTHIN SOUTHORN SOUTHWELL SUTHERS SUTTON
SOUTHWARD Suddart
SOUTHWELL 37 Sotham Sothams Sotheran Sothern Sotherne Sothoran Souden SOUTHAM Southan Southarn Southart Southen Southham SOUTHIN Southon SOUTHORN Southorne Southoun Southran Southren Southron Southurn Souton Soutten Sowtan Sowtharn Sowthern Sowton Sowtun Sutham Suthern Sutherns SUTHERS Suthon Suthorn SUTTON
Southy SOUTHEE SOUTHEY
Souton SOUTHAM SOUTHIN SOUTHORN SOUTHWELL SUTHERS SUTTON
Souttar SOUTAR SOUTER SOUTTER SOWTER SUTER
Soutten SOUTHAM SOUTHIN SOUTHORN SOUTHWELL SUTHERS SUTTON
SOUTTER 6 SOUTAR SOUTER Souttar SOWTER SUTER
SOWDEN Sawden SNOWDEN
Sowethee SOUTHEY SOUTHIN
Sowleby SOULSBY
Sowlesby SOULSBY
Sowtan SOUTHAM SOUTHIN SOUTHORN SOUTHWELL SUTHERS SUTTON
SOWTER 6 SOUTAR SOUTER Souttar SOUTTER SUTER
Sowtharn SOUTHAM SOUTHIN SOUTHORN SOUTHWELL SUTHERS SUTTON
Sowthe SOUTHEE SOUTHEY
Sowthern SOUTHAM SOUTHIN SOUTHORN SOUTHWELL SUTHERS SUTTON
Sowthy SOUTHEE SOUTHEY
Sowton SOUTHAM SOUTHIN SOUTHORN SOUTHWELL SUTHERS SUTTON
Sowtun SOUTHAM SOUTHIN SOUTHORN SOUTHWELL SUTHERS SUTTON
SPACKMAN 5 Spakeman Spakman SPEAKMAN Speckman
Spake SPEAK SPEAKE
Spakeman SPACKMAN SPEAKMAN
Spakman SPACKMAN
Spaldon SPALTON SPAWTON
SPALTON 6 Spaldon Spaulton Spawlton SPAWTON Spolton
Spander SPONDER
SPANTON Spenton
Spare SPEAR
Sparehawke SPARHAWKE
SPARHAWKE Sparehawke Sparrowhawk
SPARKES SPARKS
SPARKS SPARKES
Sparrowhawk SPARHAWKE
Spate SPEAK SPEAKE
Spaul SPAWL
Spaulton SPALTON SPAWTON
Spaunder SPONDER
Spawder SPONDER
SPAWL Spaul Sporle
Spawlton SPALTON SPAWTON
Spawnder SPONDER
SPAWTON 6 Spaldon SPALTON Spaulton Spawlton Spolton
SPEAK 10 Spake Spate SPEAKE Speakes Speaks Specke Speecke Speke Spoake
SPEAKE 10 Spake Spate SPEAK Speakes Speaks Specke Speecke Speke Spoake
Speakes SPEAK SPEAKE
SPEAKMAN SPACKMAN Spakeman
Speaks SPEAK SPEAKE
SPEAR 10 Spare Speare Spears SPEER Speers Speir SPEIRS SPIER SPIERS
Speare SPEAR SPEER
SPEARING 5 SPIRING Spuring Spyring Spyryng
Spears SPEAR SPEER SPEIRS SPIER SPIERS
Specke SPEAK SPEAKE
Speckman SPACKMAN
SPEECHLEY SPEECHLY
SPEECHLY SPEECHLEY
Speecke SPEAK SPEAKE
SPEER 9 SPEAR Speare Spears Speers Speir SPEIRS SPIER SPIERS
Speers SPEAR SPEER SPEIRS SPIER SPIERS
SPEIGHT Speyght
Speir SPEAR SPEER SPEIRS SPIER SPIERS SPIRES
SPEIRS 14 SPEAR Spears SPEER Speers Speir SPIER SPIERS Spire SPIRES Spyer Spyers Spyre Spyres
Speke SPEAK SPEAKE
SPENCE 4 SPENCER SPENSE SPENSER
SPENCER 4 SPENCE SPENSE SPENSER
Spendalow SPENDELOW
SPENDELOW Spendalow Spendillo
Spendillo SPENDELOW
SPENSE 4 SPENCE SPENCER SPENSER
SPENSER 4 SPENCE SPENCER SPENSE
Spenton SPANTON
SPERLING SPURLING
Spettiswood SPOTTISWOODE
Speyght SPEIGHT
Spibey SPIBY SPIVEY SPIVY
SPIBY 4 Spibey SPIVEY SPIVY
SPIER 14 SPEAR Spears SPEER Speers Speir SPEIRS SPIERS Spire SPIRES Spyer Spyers Spyre Spyres
SPIERS 14 SPEAR Spears SPEER Speers Speir SPEIRS SPIER Spire SPIRES Spyer Spyers Spyre Spyres
SPILLSBERY Spilsbery SPILSBURY
Spilsbery SPILLSBERY SPILSBURY
SPILSBURY SPILLSBERY Spilsbery
Spinck SPINK SPINKS
Spinckes SPINKS
Spincks SPINK SPINKS
SPINK 4 Spinck Spincks SPINKS
Spinkes SPINKS
SPINKS 6 Spinck Spinckes Spincks SPINK Spinkes
Spire SPEIRS SPIER SPIERS SPIRES
SPIRES 10 Speir SPEIRS SPIER SPIERS Spire Spyer Spyers Spyre Spyres
SPIRING 5 SPEARING Spuring Spyring Spyryng
Spitell SPITTAL SPITTLE SPITTLES
SPITTAL 10 Spitell Spittall SPITTLE SPITTLES Spitull Spytell Spyttle Spytull Spytyll
Spittall SPITTAL SPITTLE SPITTLES
SPITTLE 10 Spitell SPITTAL Spittall SPITTLES Spitull Spytell Spyttle Spytull Spytyll
SPITTLES 10 Spitell SPITTAL Spittall SPITTLE Spitull Spytell Spyttle Spytull Spytyll
Spitull SPITTAL SPITTLE SPITTLES
SPIVEY 4 Spibey SPIBY SPIVY
SPIVY 4 Spibey SPIBY SPIVEY
Spizer PIZER POIZER POYSER PYZER
Splayfoot PLAYFOOT

If the name you are interested in is not here, try Section C.

PLAYFORD
Spoad SPOARD SPODE
Spoade SPOARD SPODE
Spoake SPEAK SPEAKE
SPOARD 8 Spoad Spoade Spoarde SPODE Spood Spoode Spoward
Spoarde SPOARD SPODE
SPODE 8 Spoad Spoade SPOARD Spoarde Spood Spoode Spoward
Spoiser PIZER POIZER POYSER PYZER
Spoizer PIZER POIZER POYSER PYZER
Spok SPOKES
Spoke SPOKES
SPOKES 5 Spok Spoke Spookes Spooks
Spolton SPALTON SPAWTON
Spon SPONG
SPONDER 6 Ponder Spander Spaunder Spawder Spawnder
SPONG 5 Spon Sponge Spoung Spounge
Sponge SPONG
Spood SPOARD SPODE
Spoode SPOARD SPODE
Spookes SPOKES
Spooks SPOKES
SPOOR SPOORS Spours
SPOORS SPOOR Spours
Spor SPUR SPURR
Sporle SPAWL
SPOTTISWOODE Spettiswood
Spoung SPONG
Spounge SPONG
Spours SPOOR SPOORS
Spoward SPOARD SPODE
Spranklin SPRANKLING
SPRANKLING Spranklin
SPRAY Sprey SPRY
Sprey SPRAY SPRY
Spriddell SPRIDDLE
SPRIDDLE Spriddell
Sprig SPRIGGS
Sprigg SPRIGGS
Sprigge SPRIGGS
SPRIGGS 6 Sprig Sprigg Sprigge Sprigs Sprydge
Sprigs SPRIGGS
SPRINGALL 5 Springat SPRINGATE Springet SPRINGETT
Springat SPRINGALL SPRINGATE SPRINGETT
SPRINGATE 5 SPRINGALL Springat Springet SPRINGETT
Springbat SPRINGFORD
Springbatt SPRINGFORD
Springbett SPRINGFORD
Springet SPRINGALL SPRINGATE SPRINGETT
SPRINGETT 5 SPRINGALL Springat SPRINGATE Springet
SPRINGFORD 4 Springbat Springbatt Springbett
SPROD Sprood
Sprood SPROD
SPROT SPROTT
SPROTT SPROT
Sprout PROUT
SPRY SPRAY Sprey
Sprydge SPRIGGS
SPUR 4 Spor SPURR Spurre
SPURDEN Spurgon
Spurgon SPURDEN
Spuring SPEARING SPIRING
SPURLING SPERLING
SPURR 4 Spor SPUR Spurre
Spurre SPUR SPURR
Spyer SPEIRS SPIER SPIERS SPIRES
Spyers SPEIRS SPIER SPIERS SPIRES
Spyre SPEIRS SPIER SPIERS SPIRES
Spyres SPEIRS SPIER SPIERS SPIRES
Spyring SPEARING SPIRING
Spyryng SPEARING SPIRING
Spytell SPITTAL SPITTLE SPITTLES
Spyttle SPITTAL SPITTLE SPITTLES
Spytull SPITTAL SPITTLE SPITTLES
Spytyll SPITTAL SPITTLE SPITTLES
Spyzer PIZER POIZER POYSER PYZER
SQUANCE SQUINCE Squints
Squar SQUARE SQUIRE
SQUARE 4 Squar Squarr SQUIRE
Squarr SQUARE SQUIRE
SQUIER SQUIRE SQUIRES
SQUINCE SQUANCE Squints
Squints SQUANCE SQUINCE
SQUIRE 6 Squar SQUARE Squarr SQUIER SQUIRES
SQUIRES SQUIER SQUIRE
SQUIRRELL 6 SCORRILL SCURRILL SKORRELL SQUORRELL SQURIEL
SQUORRELL 6 SCORRILL SCURRILL SKORRELL SQUIRRELL SQURIEL
SQURIEL 6 SCORRILL SCURRILL SKORRELL SQUIRRELL SQUORRELL
Srimpton SHRIMPTON
ST CLAIR ST CLARE ST CLERE
ST CLARE ST CLAIR ST CLERE
ST CLERE ST CLAIR ST CLARE
St valeri ST VALORY
St valery ST VALORY
ST VALORY 6 De st valery De st valori De st valory St valeri St valery
Stabeler STABLER
Stabelor STABLER
Stabil STIBBLES STIBLIS STUBBLES
Stableford STAPLEFORD
STABLER 7 Stabeler Stabelor Stabley Stablor Stabulor Steabler
Stabley STABLER
Stablis STIBBLES STIBLIS STUBBLES
Stablor STABLER
Stabulor STABLER
Stabyl STIBBLES STIBLIS STUBBLES
STACE 7 EUSTACE EUSTICE Eustis Hewstice STACEY Ustis
STACEY 12 EUSTACE EUSTICE Eustis Hewstice STACE Staci Stacie STACY Stasey Stasy Ustis
Staci STACEY STACY
Stacie STACEY STACY
Stackwell STOCKWELL
STACY 6 STACEY Staci Stacie Stasey Stasy
Staddan STADDON
Stadden STADDON
STADDON Staddan Stadden
STADHAM 9 Statames Statems STATHAM STATHAMS Statmas Statms Stattam Stattum
Stafeld HOWELL STAVOLD STAWELL STOWELL STOYLE
STAFFORD 8 Stafforde Staford Staforde Stefford Stifford Stofford STRATFORD
Stafforde STAFFORD STRATFORD
Staford STAFFORD STRATFORD
Staforde STAFFORD STRATFORD
Staile HOWELL STAVOLD STAWELL STOWELL STOYLE
Stailey STALEY STARLEY STOYLE
STAINER 5 STANIER Stayner Steiner STENNER
STAINFORTH STANNIFORTH
Stainsgair STANGER
STAINTON Stenton
STAIRS 4 STARES STEARS Steres
STALEY 20 Stailey Stalley Stally Staly STARLEY Staueelley Stauley STAVELEY Stavely Stayle Stayleigh Stayley Stayly Stealy Steley Stelly Sterley STOYLE Tally
Stalley STALEY
Stally STALEY STAVELEY
Staly STALEY STARLEY STOYLE
STAMFORD 4 Stamforth STANDFORD STANFORD
Stamforth STAMFORD
Stammer STAMMERS
STAMMERS Stammer Stammus
Stammus STAMMERS
Stanage STANIDGE
STANAWAY STANWAY
STANBRIDGE Stansbridge
STANBURY STANSBURY
STANCOMB Stancombe
Stancombe STANCOMB
Standaven STANDEVEN
Standavens STANDEVEN
STANDEAVEN 5 STANDEVEN Standhaven Standheaven Standiven
Standeen STANDEVEN
Standeeven STANDEVEN
STANDEN STANDING
Standeon STANDEVEN
Standering STANDRING
Standevan STANDEVEN
Standevans STANDEVEN
STANDEVEN 25 Standaven Standavens STANDEAVEN Standeen Standeeven Standeon Standevan Standevans Standevens Standever Standevins Standhaven Standhavens Standheaven Standheavens Standheven Standivan Standiven Standiver Standoven Standven Standwen Standwin Stannonen
Standevens STANDEVEN
Standever STANDEVEN
Standevins STANDEVEN
STANDFORD 6 STAMFORD STANDFORTH STANFORD STANFORTH Staniford
STANDFORTH STANDFORD STANFORTH
Standhaven STANDEAVEN STANDEVEN
Standhavens STANDEVEN
Standheaven STANDEAVEN STANDEVEN
Standheavens STANDEVEN
Standheven STANDEVEN
STANDING STANDEN
Standivan STANDEVEN
Standiven STANDEAVEN STANDEVEN
Standiver STANDEVEN
STANDLEY 5 GATHERCOAL GATHERCOLE STANLEY Stanly
Standmore STANMORE
Standoven STANDEVEN
Standrin STANDRING
STANDRING Standering Standrin
Standven STANDEVEN
Standwen STANDEVEN
Standwin STANDEVEN
STANFIELD STANSFIELD
STANFORD 4 STAMFORD STANDFORD Staniford
STANFORTH STANDFORD STANDFORTH
STANGER 4 Stainsgair Stenger Stensgarth
STANIDGE Stanage
STANIER 5 STAINER Stayner Steiner STENNER
Staniford STANDFORD STANFORD
STANLEY STANDLEY Stanly
Stanly STANDLEY STANLEY
Stanmer STANMORE
STANMORE 4 Standmore Stanmer Stansmore
STANNIFORTH STAINFORTH
STANNING Stonige
Stannonen STANDEVEN
Stansbridge STANBRIDGE
STANSBURY STANBURY
STANSFIELD STANFIELD
Stansmore STANMORE
STANTON STAUNTON
STANWAY STANAWAY
Stapilton STAPLETON STAPYLTON
STAPLE STAPOL
STAPLEFORD Stableford
STAPLETON Stapilton STAPYLTON
STAPOL STAPLE
STAPYLTON Stapilton STAPLETON
STARES 4 STAIRS STEARS Steres
Staresmore STARMORE STARSMORE
STARKEY Starkie Starky
Starkie STARKEY
Starky STARKEY
STARLEY 12 Stailey STALEY Staly Staueelley Stauley Stayle Stayleigh Stelly Sterley STOYLE Tally
Starman SHARMAN SHERMAN
STARMORE 5 Staresmore Starsmeare Starsmor STARSMORE
Starsmeare STARMORE STARSMORE
Starsmor STARMORE STARSMORE
STARSMORE 5 Staresmore STARMORE Starsmeare Starsmor
START 5 Starte Stert Stirret STURT
Starte START STURT
Stasey STACEY STACY

If the name you are interested in is not here, try Section C.

Stasy STACEY STACY
Statames STADHAM STATHAM STATHAMS
Statems STADHAM STATHAM STATHAMS
Staters STATHERS STATTERS
STATHAM 9 STADHAM Statames Statems STATHAMS Statmas Statms Stattam Stattum
STATHAMS 9 STADHAM Statames Statems STATHAM Statmas Statms Stattam Stattum
STATHERS Staters STATTERS
Statmas STADHAM STATHAM STATHAMS
Statms STADHAM STATHAM STATHAMS
Stattam STADHAM STATHAM STATHAMS
STATTERS Staters STATHERS
Stattum STADHAM STATHAM STATHAMS
Stauelley STALEY STARLEY STOYLE
Stauley STALEY STARLEY STOYLE
STAUNTON STANTON
Stauwill HOWELL STAVOLD STAWELL STOWELL STOYLE
STAVELEY 5 STALEY Stally Stavely Stayley
Stavely STALEY STAVELEY
STAVOLD 122 De stavele De stawele De stawell De stawelle De stawille De stawylle De stoill De stouill De stoule De stoville De stowill De stowille HOWELL Mcstoile Mcstole Showell Shoyell Stafeld Staile Stauwill Stavwill Stawel STAWELL Stawle Stawyll Stayell Stayle Steole Steul Stewell Stewill Steywel Stoal Stoale Stoall Stoel Stoell Stoelle Stoewell Stoffell Stohel Stohell Stohill Stohl Stoiel Stoiell Stoil Stoile Stoiles Stoils Stol Stole Stoles Stoll Stolle Stolles Stols Stool Stoole Stooles Stools Stoolus Stouall Stouel Stouell Stouil Stoul Stouwell Stoval Stovald Stovall Stovel Stoveld Stovell Stovill Stovold Stovoll Stowal Stowall Stowals Stoweel Stoweils Stowel Stoweld Stowele Stoweley STOWELL Stowells Stowels Stowhil Stowhill Stowil Stowilles Stowl Stowldwell Stowle Stowles Stowold Stowole Stowoll Stowvel Stowwell Stowyll Stoyel Stoyell Stoyels Stoyl STOYLE Stoyles Stoyll Stoylls Stoyls Stoyoll Stuell Stul Stule Stules Stull Stweall Stwell Styell
Stavwill HOWELL STAVOLD STAWELL STOWELL STOYLE
Stawel HOWELL STAVOLD STAWELL STOWELL STOYLE
STAWELL 122 De stavele De stawele De stawell De stawelle De stawille De stawylle De stoill De stouill De stoule De stoville De stowill De stowille HOWELL Mcstoile Mcstole Showell Shoyell Stafeld Staile Stauwill STAVOLD Stavwill Stawel Stawle Stawyll Stayell Stayle Steole Steul Stewell Stewill Steywel Stoal Stoale Stoall Stoel Stoell Stoelle Stoewell Stoffell Stohel Stohell Stohill Stohl Stoiel Stoiell Stoil Stoile Stoiles Stoils Stol Stole Stoles Stoll Stolle Stolles Stols Stool Stoole Stooles Stools Stoolus Stouall Stouel Stouell Stouil Stoul Stouwell Stoval Stovald Stovall Stovel Stoveld Stovell Stovill Stovold Stovoll Stowal Stowall Stowals Stoweel Stoweils Stowel Stoweld Stowele Stoweley STOWELL Stowells Stowels Stowhil Stowhill Stowil Stowilles Stowl Stowldwell Stowle Stowles Stowold Stowole Stowoll Stowvel Stowwell Stowyll Stoyel Stoyell Stoyels Stoyl STOYLE Stoyles Stoyll Stoylls Stoyls Stoyoll Stuell Stul Stule Stules Stull Stweall Stwell Styell
Stawle HOWELL STAVOLD STAWELL STOWELL STOYLE
Stawyll HOWELL STAVOLD STAWELL STOWELL STOYLE
Stayell HOWELL STAVOLD STAWELL STOWELL STOYLE
Stayle HOWELL STALEY STARLEY STAVOLD STAWELL STOWELL STOYLE
Stayleigh STALEY STARLEY STOYLE
Stayley STALEY STAVELEY
Stayly STALEY
Stayner STAINER STANIER STENNER
STAYT Steyt
Steabler STABLER
STEAD 6 Steade Sted Stede STEED Steede
Steade STEAD STEED
STEADMAN 8 STEDMAN STEEDMAN Steidman Stidman Stiedman Stoodman Studman
Stealy STALEY
Stean STEANE
STEANE Stean
STEARN STERN
STEARS 4 STAIRS STARES Steres
Steart STEWARD STEWART STUART STURT
Stebben STEBBENS STEBBING STEBBINGS STEBBINS
STEBBENS 6 Stebben Stebbin STEBBING STEBBINGS STEBBINS
Stebbin STEBBENS STEBBING STEBBINGS STEBBINS
STEBBING 10 Stebben STEBBENS Stebbin STEBBINGS STEBBINS Stebling Stubben STUBBINGS STUBBINS
STEBBINGS 9 Stebben STEBBENS Stebbin STEBBING STEBBINS Stubben STUBBINGS STUBBINS
STEBBINS 6 Stebben STEBBENS Stebbin STEBBING STEBBINGS
Stebling STEBBING
Steckland STICKLAND STICKLER
Stecklen STICKLAND STICKLER
Stecklian STICKLAND STICKLER
Steclin STICKLAND STICKLER
Stecquelin STICKLAND STICKLER
Sted STEAD STEED
Stede STEAD STEED
STEDMAN 8 STEADMAN STEEDMAN Steidman Stidman Stiedman Stoodman Studman
Steeble STIBBLES STIBLIS STUBBLES
STEED 7 STEAD Steade Sted Stede Steede STEEDS
Steede STEAD STEED
STEEDMAN 8 STEADMAN STEDMAN Steidman Stidman Stiedman Stoodman Studman
STEEDS STEED
STEEL 7 STEELE STEIL STEILL Stele Stiel Stile
STEELE 5 STEEL Stele Stiel Stile
Steelman STILLMAN
STEER 4 Steere Steeres STEERS
Steere STEER STEERS
Steeres STEER STEERS
STEERS 4 STEER Steere Steeres
STEEVENS 5 Stephans STEPHENS STEVENS Stevins
Steevins STEPHENS STEVENS
Steff STIFF
Steffe STIFF
Stefford STAFFORD STRATFORD
Steggall STEGGALS
Steggalls STEGGALS STEGGLES
STEGGALS 7 Steggall Steggalls Steggells Steggels Stiggles Stiggold
Steggells STEGGALS STEGGLES
Steggels STEGGALS
STEGGLES 6 Steggalls Steggells Stigals Stygals Stygles
Steidman STEADMAN STEDMAN STEEDMAN
STEIL STEEL STEILL
STEILL STEEL STEIL
Steiner STAINER STANIER STENNER
Stekland STICKLAND STICKLER
Steklen STICKLAND STICKLER
Stele STEEL STEELE
Steley STALEY
Stelly STALEY STARLEY STOYLE
Stenger STANGER
STENNER 5 STAINER STANIER Stayner Steiner
Stensgarth STANGER
STENSON STINSON
Stenton STAINTON
Steole HOWELL STAVOLD STAWELL STOWELL STOYLE
Steph STIFF
Stephans STEEVENS STEPHENS STEVENS
Stephe STIFF
STEPHEN STEPHENS Steven
STEPHENS 7 STEEVENS Steevins Stephans STEPHEN STEVENS Stevins
STEPHENSON STEVENSON
Stequelain STICKLAND STICKLER
Stequelin STICKLAND STICKLER
Stere STERREY STERRY
Steres STAIRS STARES STEARS
Sterley STALEY STARLEY STOYLE
STERN STEARN
STERREY 6 Stere STERRY Stirri Stirrie Stirry
STERRY 6 Stere STERREY Stirri Stirrie Stirry
Stert START STEWARD STEWART STUART STURT
Stettle STUTTLE
Steuard STEWARD STEWART STUART STURT
Steuarde STEWARD STEWART STUART STURT
Steuart STEWARD STEWART STUART STURT
Steuarte STEWARD STEWART STUART STURT
Steul HOWELL STAVOLD STAWELL STOWELL STOYLE
Stevarde STEWARD STEWART STUART STURT
Stevarte STEWARD STEWART STUART STURT
Steven STEPHEN
STEVENS 6 STEEVENS Steevins Stephans STEPHENS Stevins
STEVENSON STEPHENSON
Stevins STEEVENS STEPHENS STEVENS
STEWARD 24 Steart Stert Steuard Steuarde Steuart Steuarte Stevarde Stevarte STEWART Stirt Stiuard Stiubhard Stiubhart Stiward Stuard Stuarde STUART Stuerd STURT Stuward Stwyarde Styward Stywarde
STEWART 24 Steart Stert Steuard Steuarde Steuart Steuarte Stevarde Stevarte STEWARD Stirt Stiuard Stiubhard Stiubhart Stiward Stuard Stuarde STUART Stuerd STURT Stuward Stwyarde Styward Stywarde
Stewart-cole STUART-COLE
Stewell HOWELL STAVOLD STAWELL STOWELL STOYLE
Stewill HOWELL STAVOLD

If the name you are interested in is not here, try Section C.

STAWELL STOWELL STOYLE
Stewkley STUTLEY
Steyt STAYT
Steywel HOWELL STAVOLD STAWELL STOWELL STOYLE
Stibbillis STIBBLES STIBLIS STUBBLES
STIBBLES 15 Stabil Stablis Stabyl Steeble Stibbillis Stibils Stibles STIBLIS Stibls Stibulis Stibull STUBBLES Stubil Stubyl
Stibils STIBBLES STIBLIS STUBBLES
Stibles STIBBLES STIBLIS STUBBLES
STIBLIS 15 Stabil Stablis Stabyl Steeble Stibbillis STIBBLES Stibils Stibles Stibls Stibulis Stibull STUBBLES Stubil Stubyl
Stibls STIBBLES STIBLIS STUBBLES
Stibulis STIBBLES STIBLIS STUBBLES
Stibull STIBBLES STIBLIS STUBBLES
Stichberry STICHBURY
STICHBURY 6 Stichberry Stickbury Stitchberry Stitchbury Strichbury
Stichling STICKLAND STICKLER
Stickbury STICHBURY
Stickeland STICKLAND STICKLER
Stickeling STICKLAND STICKLER
Stickelonde STICKLAND STICKLER
Sticklaine STICKLAND STICKLER
Sticklan STICKLAND STICKLER
STICKLAND 35 Steckland Stecklen Stecklian Steclin Stecquelin Stekland Steklen Stequelain Stequelin Stichling Stickeland Stickeling Stickelonde Sticklaine Sticklan Sticklane Sticklang Sticklen Sticklend STICKLER Sticklin Stickling Sticklinge Sticklings Sticklonde Sticland Stictland Stikland STRICKLAND Stuckland Styckland Stycklinge Stycland Stykklande
Sticklane STICKLAND STICKLER
Sticklang STICKLAND STICKLER
Sticklen STICKLAND STICKLER
Sticklend STICKLAND STICKLER
STICKLER 34 Steckland Stecklen Stecklian Steclin Stecquelin Stekland Steklen Stequelain Stequelin Stichling Stickeland Stickeling Stickelonde Sticklaine Sticklan STICKLAND Sticklane Sticklang Sticklen Sticklend Sticklin Stickling Sticklinge Sticklings Sticklonde Sticland Stictland Stikland Stuckland Styckland Stycklinge Stycland Stykklande
Sticklin STICKLAND STICKLER
Stickling STICKLAND STICKLER
Sticklinge STICKLAND STICKLER
Sticklings STICKLAND STICKLER
Sticklonde STICKLAND STICKLER
Sticland STICKLAND STICKLER
Stictland STICKLAND STICKLER
Stidman STEADMAN STEDMAN STEEDMAN
Stiedman STEADMAN STEDMAN STEEDMAN
Stief STIFF
Stiel STEEL STEELE
Stife STIFF
STIFF 8 Steff Steffe Steph Stephe Stief Stife Stiffe
Stiffe STIFF
Stifford STAFFORD STRATFORD
Stigals STEGGLES
Stiggles STEGGALS
Stiggold STEGGALS
Stikland STICKLAND STICKLER
Stile STEEL STEELE
STILES STYLES
STILLMAN Steelman
STIMPSON STIMSON
STIMSON STIMPSON
Stingermore STINJEMOR
Stingjemor STINJEMOR
Stinjamore STINJEMOR
STINJEMOR 4 Stingermore Stingjemor Stinjamore
STINSON STENSON
Stirret START STURT
Stirri STERREY STERRY
Stirrie STERREY STERRY
Stirry STERREY STERRY
Stirt STEWARD STEWART STUART STURT
STIRZAKER STORZAKER Sturzaker
Stitchberry STICHBURY
Stitchbury STICHBURY
Stiuard STEWARD STEWART STUART STURT
Stiubhard STEWARD STEWART STUART STURT
Stiubhart STEWARD STEWART STUART STURT
Stiward STEWARD STEWART STUART STURT
Stoal HOWELL STAVOLD STAWELL STOWELL STOYLE
Stoale HOWELL STAVOLD STAWELL STOWELL STOYLE
Stoall HOWELL STAVOLD STAWELL STOWELL STOYLE
Stoat STOTE
Stoate STOTE
Stoatt STOTE
STOBBIE STOBIE
STOBIE STOBBIE STOBO
STOBO STOBIE
STOCK BAVERSTOCK
Stockborn STOCKBURN
Stockborne STOCKBURN
Stockbourn STOCKBURN
Stockbourne STOCKBURN
STOCKBURN 6 Sockburn Stockborn Stockborne Stockbourn Stockbourne
Stocken STOCKTON
STOCKHAM 15 Sloacomb Sloacombe Slockem Slockham Slocomb SLOCOMBE Slocome Slocum Slocumb Slocumbe Slokeham Slowcomb Slowcombe Stocombe
STOCKTON Stocken Stocton
STOCKWELL 4 Stackwell Stockwill Stokewell
Stockwill STOCKWELL
Stocombe SLOCOMBE STOCKHAM
Stocton STOCKTON
Stoel HOWELL STAVOLD STAWELL STOWELL STOYLE
Stoell HOWELL STAVOLD STAWELL STOWELL STOYLE
Stoelle HOWELL STAVOLD STAWELL STOWELL STOYLE
Stoewell HOWELL STAVOLD STAWELL STOWELL STOYLE
Stoffell HOWELL STAVOLD STAWELL STOWELL STOYLE
Stofford STAFFORD STRATFORD
Stohel HOWELL STAVOLD STAWELL STOWELL STOYLE
Stohell HOWELL STAVOLD STAWELL STOWELL STOYLE
Stohill HOWELL STAVOLD STAWELL STOWELL STOYLE
Stohl HOWELL STAVOLD STAWELL STOWELL STOYLE
Stoiel HOWELL STAVOLD STAWELL STOWELL STOYLE
Stoiell HOWELL STAVOLD STAWELL STOWELL STOYLE
Stoil HOWELL STAVOLD STAWELL STOWELL STOYLE
Stoile HOWELL STAVOLD STAWELL STOWELL STOYLE
Stoiles HOWELL STAVOLD STAWELL STOWELL STOYLE
Stoils HOWELL STAVOLD STAWELL STOWELL STOYLE
Stokald STOKER STOKOE
STOKE STOKES
Stokel STOKER STOKOE
Stokeld STOKER STOKOE
Stokell STOKER STOKOE
STOKER 6 Stokald Stokel Stokeld Stokell STOKOE
STOKES STOKE
Stokewell STOCKWELL
STOKOE 6 Stokald Stokel Stokeld Stokell STOKER
Stol HOWELL STAVOLD STAWELL STOWELL STOYLE
Stole HOWELL STAVOLD STAWELL STOWELL STOYLE
Stoles HOWELL STAVOLD STAWELL STOWELL STOYLE
Stoll HOWELL STAVOLD STAWELL STOWELL STOYLE
Stolle HOWELL STAVOLD STAWELL STOWELL STOYLE
Stolles HOWELL STAVOLD STAWELL STOWELL STOYLE
Stols HOWELL STAVOLD STAWELL STOWELL STOYLE
Stonige STANNING
Stoodman STEADMAN STEDMAN STEEDMAN
Stool HOWELL STAVOLD STAWELL STOWELL STOYLE
Stoole HOWELL STAVOLD STAWELL STOWELL STOYLE
Stooles HOWELL STAVOLD STAWELL STOWELL STOYLE
Stools HOWELL STAVOLD STAWELL STOWELL STOYLE
Stoolus HOWELL STAVOLD STAWELL STOWELL STOYLE
Storah STORER
STORAR STORER
STORER Storah STORAR
STORES STORRES
STOREY STORY
STORIE STORY
STORRES STORES
STORY STOREY STORIE
STORZAKER STIRZAKER
STOTE 4 Stoat Stoate Stoatt
Stouall HOWELL STAVOLD STAWELL STOWELL STOYLE
Stouel HOWELL STAVOLD STAWELL STOWELL STOYLE
Stouell HOWELL STAVOLD STAWELL STOWELL STOYLE
Stouil HOWELL STAVOLD STAWELL STOWELL STOYLE
Stoul HOWELL STAVOLD STAWELL STOWELL STOYLE
Stouwell HOWELL STAVOLD STAWELL STOWELL STOYLE
Stoval HOWELL STAVOLD STAWELL STOWELL STOYLE
Stovald HOWELL STAVOLD STAWELL STOWELL STOYLE
Stovall HOWELL STAVOLD STAWELL STOWELL STOYLE
Stovel HOWELL STAVOLD STAWELL STOWELL STOYLE
Stoveld HOWELL STAVOLD STAWELL STOWELL STOYLE
Stovell HOWELL STAVOLD STAWELL STOWELL STOYLE
Stovill HOWELL STAVOLD STAWELL STOWELL STOYLE
Stovold HOWELL STAVOLD STAWELL STOWELL STOYLE
Stovoll HOWELL STAVOLD STAWELL STOWELL STOYLE
Stowal HOWELL STAVOLD STAWELL STOWELL STOYLE
Stowall HOWELL STAVOLD STAWELL STOWELL STOYLE
Stowals HOWELL STAVOLD STAWELL STOWELL STOYLE
Stoweel HOWELL STAVOLD STAWELL STOWELL STOYLE
Stoweils HOWELL STAVOLD STAWELL STOWELL STOYLE
Stowel HOWELL STAVOLD STAWELL STOWELL STOYLE
Stoweld HOWELL STAVOLD STAWELL STOWELL STOYLE
Stowele HOWELL STAVOLD STAWELL STOWELL STOYLE
Stoweley HOWELL STAVOLD STAWELL STOWELL STOYLE
STOWELL 122 De stavele De stawele De stawell De stawelle De stawille De stawylle De stoill De stouill De stoule De stoville De stowill De stowille HOWELL Mcstoile Mcstole Showell Shoyell Stafeld Staile Stauwill STAVOLD Stavwill Stawel STAWELL Stawle Stawyll Stayell Stayle Steole Steul Stewell Stewill Steywel Stoal Stoale Stoall Stoel Stoell Stoelle Stoewell Stoffell Stohel Stohell Stohill Stohl Stoiel Stoiell Stoil Stoile Stoiles Stoils Stol Stole Stoles Stoll Stolle

If the name you are interested in is not here, try Section C.

Stolles Stols Stool
Stoole Stooles Stools
Stoolus Stouall Stouel
Stouell Stouil Stoul
Stouwell Stoval Stovald
Stovall Stovel Stoveld
Stovell Stovill Stovold
Stovoll Stowal Stowall
Stowals Stoweel
Stoweils Stowel Stoweld
Stowele Stoweley
Stowells Stowels
Stowhil Stowhill Stowil
Stowilles Stowl
Stowldwell Stowle
Stowles Stowold Stowole
Stowoll Stowvel
Stowwell Stowyll Stoyel
Stoyell Stoyels Stoyl
STOYLE Stoyles Stoyll
Stoylls Stoyls Stoyoll
Stuell Stul Stule
Stules Stull Stweall
Stwell Styell
Stowells HOWELL STAVOLD STAWELL STOWELL STOYLE
Stowels HOWELL STAVOLD STAWELL STOWELL STOYLE
Stowhil HOWELL STAVOLD STAWELL STOWELL STOYLE
Stowhill HOWELL STAVOLD STAWELL STOWELL STOYLE
Stowil HOWELL STAVOLD STAWELL STOWELL STOYLE
Stowilles HOWELL STAVOLD STAWELL STOWELL STOYLE
Stowl HOWELL STAVOLD STAWELL STOWELL STOYLE
Stowldwell HOWELL STAVOLD STAWELL STOWELL STOYLE
Stowle HOWELL STAVOLD STAWELL STOWELL STOYLE
Stowles HOWELL STAVOLD STAWELL STOWELL STOYLE
Stowold HOWELL STAVOLD STAWELL STOWELL STOYLE
Stowole HOWELL STAVOLD STAWELL STOWELL STOYLE
Stowoll HOWELL STAVOLD STAWELL STOWELL STOYLE
Stowvel HOWELL STAVOLD STAWELL STOWELL STOYLE
Stowwell HOWELL STAVOLD STAWELL STOWELL STOYLE
Stowyll HOWELL STAVOLD STAWELL STOWELL STOYLE
Stoyel HOWELL STAVOLD STAWELL STOWELL STOYLE
Stoyell HOWELL STAVOLD STAWELL STOWELL STOYLE
Stoyels HOWELL STAVOLD STAWELL STOWELL STOYLE
Stoyl HOWELL STAVOLD STAWELL STOWELL STOYLE
STOYLE 132 De stavele De stawele De stawell De stawelle De stawille De stawylle De stoill De stouill De stoule De stoville De stowill De stowille HOWELL Mcstoile Mcstole Showell Shoyell Stafeld Staile Stailey STALEY Staly STARLEY Stauelley Stauley Stauwill STAVOLD Stavwill Stawel STAWELL Stawle Stawyll Stayell Stayle Stayleigh Stelly Steole Sterley Steul Stewell Stewill Steywel Stoal Stoale Stoall Stoel Stoell Stoelle Stoewell Stoffell Stohel Stohell Stohill Stohl Stoiel Stoiell Stoil Stoile Stoiles Stoils Stol Stole Stoles Stoll Stolle Stolles Stols Stool Stoole Stooles Stools Stoolus Stouall Stouel Stouell Stouil Stoul Stouwell Stoval Stovald Stovall Stovel Stoveld Stovell Stovill Stovold Stovoll Stowal Stowall Stowals Stoweel Stoweils Stowel Stoweld Stowele Stoweley STOWELL Stowells Stowels Stowhil Stowhill Stowil Stowilles Stowl Stowldwell Stowle Stowles Stowold Stowole Stowoll Stowvel Stowwell Stowyll Stoyel Stoyell Stoyels Stoyl Stoyles Stoyll Stoylls Stoyls Stoyoll Stuell Stul Stule Stules Stull Stweall Stwell Styell Tally
Stoyles HOWELL STAVOLD STAWELL STOWELL STOYLE
Stoyll HOWELL STAVOLD STAWELL STOWELL STOYLE
Stoylls HOWELL STAVOLD STAWELL STOWELL STOYLE
Stoyls HOWELL STAVOLD STAWELL STOWELL STOYLE
Stoyoll HOWELL STAVOLD STAWELL STOWELL STOYLE
STRACHAN 5 Strahan STRAIN Strauchan Strawn
Strafair STRAUGHAIR
Straffair STRAUGHAIR
Strafhair STRAUGHAIR
Strahan STRACHAN
STRAIN STRACHAN
Strainge STRANGE
Straith STRATH
Stranach STRANACK
STRANACK 5 Stranach Strannach Strannack Strannock
STRANGE Strainge
Strangeway STRANGEWAYS
Strangewayes STRANGEWAYS
STRANGEWAYS 5 Strangeway Strangewayes Strangway Strangways
Strangway STRANGEWAYS
Strangways STRANGEWAYS
Strannach STRANACK
Strannack STRANACK
Strannock STRANACK
STRATFIELD STRATFORD Stratfull
STRATFORD 10 STAFFORD Stafforde Staford Staforde Stefford Stifford Stofford STRATFIELD Stratfull
Stratfull STRATFIELD STRATFORD
STRATH Straith Stroath
Strauchan STRACHAN
STRAUGHAIR 7 Strafair Straffair Strafhair Straugheir Straughier Strawhair
STRAUGHAN Strofen
Straugheir STRAUGHAIR
Straughier STRAUGHAIR
Strawhair STRAUGHAIR
Strawn STRACHAN
Streadar STREDDER
Streader STREDDER
STREATER 4 STREETER Streter Strether
STREATFEILD 4 STREATFIELD STREETFIELD Streitfield
STREATFIELD 4 STREATFEILD STREETFIELD Streitfield
STREDDER 4 Streadar Streader Streder
Streder STREDDER
STREETER 4 STREATER Streter Strether
STREETFIELD 4 STREATFEILD STREATFIELD Streitfield
Streitfield STREATFEILD STREATFIELD STREETFIELD
Streter STREATER STREETER
Strether STREATER STREETER
Strichbury STICHBURY
STRICKLAND STICKLAND
Striddick STRUDWICK
Stridduck STRUDWICK
Stroad STROUD
Stroath STRATH
STROBRIDGE 5 Strobryg Strobrygge Strowbridge Strubridge
Strobryg STROBRIDGE
Strobrygge STROBRIDGE
Strode STROOD STROUD
Stroehle STROHLE
Stroele STROHLE
Strofair STROPHAIR
Strofare STROPHAIR
Strofen STRAUGHAN
Stroffair STROPHAIR
Stroghare STROUGHAIR
Strohl STROHLE
STROHLE 5 Stroehle Stroele Strohl Strole
Strole STROHLE
STRONG Stronge
Stronge STRONG
STROOD Strode STROUD
STROPHAIR 5 Strofair Strofare Stroffair Stropheir
Stropheir STROPHAIR
STROUD 6 Stroad Strode STROOD Stroude Strowd
Stroude STROUD
STROUDLEY Shroudley
STROUGHAIR 4 Stroghare Stroughare Strowhair
Stroughare STROUGHAIR
Strowbridge STROBRIDGE
Strowd STROUD
Strowhair STROUGHAIR
Strubridge STROBRIDGE
STRUDWICK Striddick Stridduck
Stuard STEWARD STEWART STUART STURT
Stuarde STEWARD STEWART STUART STURT
STUART 24 Steart Stert Steuard Steuarde Steuart Steuarte Stevarde Stevarte STEWARD STEWART Stirt Stiuard Stiubhard Stiubhart Stiward Stuard Stuarde Stuerd STURT Stuward Stwyarde Styward Stywarde
STUART-COLE Stewart-cole
Stubben STEBBING STEBBINGS STUBBINGS STUBBINS
STUBBINGS 5 STEBBING STEBBINGS Stubben STUBBINS
STUBBINS 5 STEBBING STEBBINGS Stubben STUBBINGS
STUBBLES 15 Stabil Stablis Stabyl Steeble Stibbillis STIBBLES Stibils Stibles STIBLIS Stibls Stibulis Stibull Stubil Stubyl
Stubil STIBBLES STIBLIS STUBBLES
Stubyl STIBBLES STIBLIS STUBBLES
Stuckland STICKLAND STICKLER
Studman STEADMAN STEDMAN STEEDMAN
Stuell HOWELL STAVOLD STAWELL STOWELL STOYLE
Stuerd STEWARD STEWART STUART STURT
Stul HOWELL STAVOLD STAWELL STOWELL STOYLE
Stule HOWELL STAVOLD STAWELL STOWELL STOYLE
Stules HOWELL STAVOLD STAWELL STOWELL STOYLE
Stull HOWELL STAVOLD STAWELL STOWELL STOYLE
STUMP STUMPE
STUMPE STUMP
Sturde STURDY
Sturdie STURDY
STURDY 4 Sturde Sturdie Sturdye
Sturdye STURDY
STURT 27 START Starte Steart Stert Steuard Steuarde Steuart Steuarte Stevarde Stevarte STEWARD STEWART Stirret Stirt Stiuard Stiubhard Stiubhart Stiward Stuard Stuarde STUART Stuerd Stuward Stwyarde Styward Stywarde
Sturzaker STIRZAKER
Stutely STUTLEY
STUTLEY Stewkley Stutely
Stuttell STUTTLE
STUTTLE Stettle Stuttell
Stuward STEWARD STEWART STUART STURT
Stweall HOWELL STAVOLD STAWELL STOWELL STOYLE
Stwell HOWELL STAVOLD STAWELL STOWELL STOYLE
Stwyarde STEWARD STEWART STUART STURT
Styckland STICKLAND STICKLER
Stycklinge STICKLAND STICKLER
Stycland STICKLAND STICKLER
Styell HOWELL STAVOLD STAWELL STOWELL STOYLE
Stygals STEGGLES
Stygles STEGGLES
Stykklande STICKLAND STICKLER
STYLES STILES
Styward STEWARD STEWART STUART STURT
Stywarde STEWARD STEWART STUART STURT
Sucker SHUKER
Sudard SUDDARDS
Suddard SUDDARDS
SUDDARDS 12 Sudard Suddard Suddart Sudderd Sudderds Suddert Sudderth Suddorth

If the name you are interested in is not here, try Section C.

Sudert Sudord Suthard
Suddart SOUTHWARD SUDDARDS
Sudderd SUDDARDS
Sudderds SUDDARDS
Sudders SOUTHARD SUTHERS
Suddert SUDDARDS
Sudderth SUDDARDS
Suddorth SUDDARDS
Sudert SUDDARDS
Sudgrave SADGROVE
Sudgrove SADGROVE
Sudord SUDDARDS
Sugar SHUKER
Suger SHUKER
Sugweeden CHEGWYN KEIGWIN
Suker SHUKER
Sulivan SELLINGS SELWYN
Sullence SELLEN SELLENS SILENCE SILLENCE
Sullens SELLEN SELLENS SILENCE SILLENCE
Sulley SELLEY SULLY
Sullince SELLEN SELLENS SILENCE SILLENCE
Sullins SELLEN SELLENS SILENCE SILLENCE
SULLIVAN O'SULLIVAN
SULLY 8 SELLEY Selly Sulley Zelley Zelly Zolie Zullie
SULMAN Sunman
Sumerhill SUMMERHILL SUMMERILL
Sumeril SUMMERHILL SUMMERILL
Sumerill SUMMERHILL SUMMERILL
SUMMERELL SUMMERHILL Summerille
SUMMERHILL 10 SOMIRELL Sumerhill Sumeril Sumerill SUMMERELL Summeril SUMMERILL Summerille Summerlille
Summeril SUMMERHILL SUMMERILL
SUMMERILL 6 Sumerhill Sumeril Sumerill SUMMERHILL Summeril
Summerille SUMMERELL SUMMERHILL
Summerlille SOMIRELL SUMMERHILL
SUMMERS SOMMERS
SUMNER SOMMERS SOMNER
SUNDERLAND 8 Sauland Surrland Sutheland SUTHERLAND Suthland Suylerland Suyrland
Sunlay SONLEY SUNLEY
SUNLEY 4 SONLEY Sonly Sunlay
Sunman SULMAN
SURCH Search
SURMAN 6 Cyrmon Serman SERMON SIRMAN Sirmon
Surrland SUNDERLAND SUTHERLAND
SUTCLIFFE Sutliff
SUTER 6 SOUTAR SOUTER Souttar SOUTTER SOWTER
Sutham SOUTHAM SOUTHIN SOUTHORN SOUTHWELL SUTHERS SUTTON
Suthard SUDDARDS
Suthast SOUTHARD SUTHERS
Sutheland SUNDERLAND SUTHERLAND
Sutheran SOUTHERN
SUTHERLAND 8 Sauland SUNDERLAND Surrland Sutheland Suthland Suylerland Suyrland
Suthern SOUTHAM SOUTHIN SOUTHORN SOUTHWELL SUTHERS SUTTON
Sutherns SOUTHAM SOUTHIN SOUTHORN SOUTHWELL SUTHERS SUTTON
SUTHERS 45 Sotham Sothams Sotheran Sothern Sotherne Sothoran Souden SOUTHAM Southan SOUTHARD Southarn Southart Southen Southers Southham SOUTHIN Southon SOUTHORN Southorne Southoun Southran Southren Southron Southurn SOUTHWELL Souton Soutten Sowtan Sowtharn Sowthern Sowton Sowtun Sudders Sutham Suthast Suthern Sutherns Sutherst Suthert Suthon Suthorn Suthworth Suttherd SUTTON
Sutherst SOUTHARD SUTHERS
Suthert SOUTHARD SUTHERS
Suthland SUNDERLAND SUTHERLAND
Suthon SOUTHAM SOUTHIN SOUTHORN SOUTHWELL SUTHERS SUTTON
Suthorn SOUTHAM SOUTHIN SOUTHORN SOUTHWELL SUTHERS SUTTON
Suthworth SOUTHARD SUTHERS
Sutliff SUTCLIFFE
Suttaby SUTTERBY
Sutterbee SUTTERBY
Sutterbie SUTTERBY
SUTTERBY 4 Suttaby Sutterbee Sutterbie
Suttherd SOUTHARD SUTHERS
SUTTON 37 Sotham Sothams Sotheran Sothern Sotherne Sothoran Souden SOUTHAM Southan Southarn Southart Southen Southham SOUTHIN Southon SOUTHORN Southorne Southoun Southran Southren Southron Southurn SOUTHWELL Souton Soutten Sowtan Sowtharn Sowthern Sowton Sowtun Sutham Suthern Sutherns SUTHERS Suthon Suthorn
Suvaret SIEVEWRIGHT
Suylerland SUNDERLAND SUTHERLAND
Suyrland SUNDERLAND SUTHERLAND
SWADLING Swatling
SWAFFIELD 4 Swafield Swathfield Swayfield
Swafield SWAFFIELD
Swailes SWALES
Swails SWALES
SWAIN 5 SWAINE Swane Swanne SWAYNE
SWAINE 6 SWAIN Swane Swanne SWAYNE SWEAINE
SWAINSON 4 SWAINSTON SWANSON SWANSTON
SWAINSTON 4 SWAINSON SWANSON SWANSTON
SWAISLAND Swaseland
SWALES Swailes Swails
SWAN SWANN
Swane SWAIN SWAINE SWAYNE
Swanel SWANNELL
Swanil SWANNELL
SWANN SWAN
Swanne SWAIN SWAINE SWAYNE
SWANNELL 4 Swanel Swanil Swannil
Swannil SWANNELL
SWANSON 4 SWAINSON SWAINSTON SWANSTON
SWANSTON 4 SWAINSON SWAINSTON SWANSON
SWARBROOK Swarbrooke Swarbrooks
Swarbrooke SWARBROOK
Swarbrooks SWARBROOK
Swaseland SWAISLAND
Swathfield SWAFFIELD
Swatling SWADLING
Swayesland SWAYSLAND
Swayfield SWAFFIELD
SWAYNE 6 SWAIN SWAINE Swane Swanne SWEAINE
Swayseland SWAYSLAND
SWAYSLAND Swayesland Swayseland
SWEAINE SWAINE SWAYNE
Sweating SWEETING
Sweatman SWEETMAN
Sweatnam SWEETMAN
Sweeney SWENY
Sweeny SWENY
Sweetange SWEETING
Sweeteing SWEETING
SWEETING 7 Sweating Sweetange Sweeteing Sweeton Swetinge Swetten
SWEETMAN 4 Sweatman Sweatnam Sweetnam
Sweetnam SWEETMAN
Sweeton SWEETING
Swenarton SWINNERTON
Swenerton SWINNERTON
Sweney SWENY
SWENY 7 Sweeney Sweeny Sweney Swiney Swiny Swiyny
Swetinge SWEETING
Swetten SWEETING
Swinarton SWINNERTON
SWINCKFIELD 7 SINFIELD Singfeild Singfield Sinkfeild Sinkfield Synfield
SWINDELLS Swindles Swyndells
Swindles SWINDELLS
SWINERD 4 SWINNARD SWINYARD Swynnyard
Swinerton SWINNERTON
Swiney SWENY
SWINFIELD Swingfield Swynfield
Swingfield SWINFIELD
SWINNARD 4 SWINERD SWINYARD Swynnyard
SWINNERTON 8 Swenarton Swenerton Swinarton Swinerton Swinnington Swynerton Swynnerton
Swinnington SWINNERTON
Swiny SWENY
SWINYARD 4 SWINERD SWINNARD Swynnyard
SWIRE Swyre
Swiyny SWENY
SWORD 5 SOAR Soare SORE SWORDS
SWORDS SWORD
Swyndells SWINDELLS
Swynerton SWINNERTON
Swynfield SWINFIELD
Swynnerton SWINNERTON
Swynnyard SWINERD SWINNARD SWINYARD
Swyre SWIRE
SYDNEY 4 SIDNEY Sidny Sydny
Sydny SIDNEY SYDNEY
SYER 4 Siser SIZER Syser
SYGROVE 4 SEGRAVE SIGRAVE SIGROVE
SYKES Sikes
SYLVESTER SILVESTER Silwester
Sym SIME SIMES
SYMES 6 Seem Sems SIMS Symmes Symms
Symm SIME SIMES
Symmes SIMS SYMES
Symmonds SIMMONDS SIMONDS SYMONDS
Symms SIMS SYMES
SYMON 4 SIMON SIMONDS SIMONS
SYMONDS 8 Semens SEMMONS SIMMONDS SIMMONS SIMONDS Symmonds SYMONS
SYMONS 6 SIMMONDS SIMMONS SIMONDS SIMONS SYMONDS
Sympkins SIMKIN SIMKINS SIMPKIN SIMPKINS
SYMPSON 4 SIMPSON SIMSON Symson
Symson SIMPSON SIMSON SYMPSON
Synfield SINFIELD SWINCKFIELD
Syng SING SINGS
Synge SING SINGS
Synot SINNOTT
Synott SINNOTT
SYRE Sier
SYRETT Sirret
Sysel SAYSELL
Syser SIZER SYER
Syzar SIZER
Syzer SIZER
Tabat TABBAT TALBOT
TABBAT 9 Tabat Tabbatt Tabbit Tabet TALBOT Tawbutt Tbet Tibbot
Tabbatt TABBAT TALBOT
Tabbit TABBAT TALBOT
Tabet TABBAT TALBOT
Tachell TATCHELL TEAGLE TEAGUE
Tackel TEAGLE TEAGUE
Tackle TEAGLE TEAGUE
Tadway TUDWAY
Taff TATE TEFT
Tagle TEAGLE TEAGUE
Tague TEAGLE TEAGUE
Tailer TAILOR TAYLER TAYLOR TYLER
Tailles TALLIS TALLISS
Taillis TALLIS TALLISS
TAILOR 7 Tailer Taler Talor TAYLER TAYLOR TYLER
TAINTON Taynton
TAIT TATE
Talantire TALLANTIRE
Talantyre TALLANTIRE
Talbert TALBOT
Talbirt TALBOT
TALBOT 15 Tabat TABBAT Tabbatt Tabbit Tabet Talbert Talbirt TALBOTT Talbut Taleboth Talfirth Tawbutt Tbet Tibbot
TALBOTT TALBOT Talbut
Talbut TALBOT TALBOTT
Tale TALL TOLL
Taleboth TALBOT
Talentire TALLANTIRE

If the name you are interested in is not here, try Section C.

Talentyre TALLANTIRE
Taler TAILOR TAYLER TAYLOR
Talfirth TALBOT
Talintire TALLANTIRE
Talintyre TALLANTIRE
TALL 5 Tale Talle TOLL Tolle
TALLANTIRE 12 Talantire Talantyre Talentire Talentyre Talintire Talintyre Tallantyre Tallentire Tallentyre Tallintire Tallintyre
Tallantyre TALLANTIRE
Talle TALL TOLL
Tallentire TALLANTIRE
Tallentyre TALLANTIRE
Tallintire TALLANTIRE
Tallintyre TALLANTIRE
TALLIS 7 Tailles Taillis TALLISS Tayles Taylis Tolas
TALLISS 7 Tailles Taillis TALLIS Tayles Taylis Tolas
Tally STALEY STARLEY STOYLE
Talmadge TALMAGE
TALMAGE Talmadge
Talmin TOULMIN
Talor TAILOR TAYLER TAYLOR
Taltersale TATTERSHALL
Tam TAME
Tamblenson TAMBLINSON
Tambleson TAMBLINSON
TAMBLIN 6 Tambling TAMLIN Thomlin TOMLIN TOMLYN
Tambling TAMBLIN TAMLIN TOMLIN TOMLYN
Tamblingson TAMBLINSON
TAMBLINSON 4 Tamblenson Tambleson Tamblingson
TAME Tam Taym
TAMES Tamms TAMS
TAMLIN 6 TAMBLIN Tambling Thomlin TOMLIN TOMLYN
Tamms TAMES TAMS
Tampen TAMPIN
TAMPIN 4 Tampen Tampion Tempan
Tampion TAMPIN
TAMS TAMES Tamms
Tanar TANNER
Taner TANNER
Tannat TANNATT
TANNATT Tannat
TANNER 5 Tanar Taner Tannors Tanor
Tannors TANNER
Tanor TANNER
TANSER Tansur
Tansur TANSER
Tap TAPP
TAPLIN 4 Tapling TUPLIN TUPLING
Tapling TAPLIN TUPLIN TUPLING
TAPP 4 Tap Tappe Taype
Tappe TAPP
Tarbart TARBERT
Tarbat TARBERT
TARBERT 4 Tarbart Tarbat Tarbet
Tarbet TARBERT
Tarle TARREL TEARLE TERRELL TIRRELL TURRALL TYRRELL
Tarlin TARLING
TARLING 5 Tarlin Teirling Thurling Torlon
Tarrall TARREL TEARLE TERRELL TIRRELL TURRALL TYRRELL
TARRANT 4 FARRANT FARRAT TARRAT
TARRAT 4 FARRANT FARRAT TARRANT
TARREL 76 Tarle Tarrall Tarrell Tarrill Taurel TEARLE Terall Terel Terell Terill Terle Terold Terrald Terrall Terrel TERRELL Terril Terrill Terroll Terryl Teryl Tirall Tirel Tirell Tirolde Tirral Tirrall Tirrel TIRRELL Tirril Tirrill Tirrold Tirrolde Tirroll Torell Torill Torrell Tourell Tourle Tourlle Turel Turell Turil Turill Turl Turle Turral TURRALL Turrel Turrell Turril Turrill Turrle Turrold Turroll Tyrald Tyrall Tyrel Tyrell Tyrie Tyril Tyrill Tyrol Tyrold Tyroll Tyrral Tyrrall Tyrrel TYRRELL Tyrril Tyrrill Tyrrol Tyrrold Tyrrolde Tyrroll
Tarrell TARREL TEARLE TERRELL TIRRELL TURRALL TYRRELL
Tarrill TARREL TEARLE TERRELL TIRRELL TURRALL TYRRELL
Tarvall TURVILL TURVILLE
Tatarsole TATTERSHALL
Tatashall TATTERSHALL
Tatchel TATCHELL
TATCHELL Tachell Tatchel
TATE 6 Taff TAIT Tatt Teatt TEFT
Tatersall TATTERSHALL
Tatershal TATTERSHALL
Tatersole TATTERSHALL
Tateshale TATTERSHALL
Tateshalle TATTERSHALL
Tather TATLER TATLOW TATTER TETHER TITHER
TATLER 7 Tather Tatley TATLOW TATTER Tattle Tattler
Tatley TATLER TATLOW TATTER
TATLOW 7 Tather TATLER Tatley TATTER Tattle Tattler
Tatt TATE TEFT
TATTER 7 Tather TATLER Tatley TATLOW Tattle Tattler
TATTERSHALL 18 Taltersale Tatarsole Tatashall Tatersall Tatershal Tatersole Tateshale Tateshalle Tattsal Tattsil Titsel Titterel Tittersal Tittersale Tittersall Tittersell Totterel
Tattle TATLER TATLOW TATTER
Tattler TATLER TATLOW TATTER
Tattsal TATTERSHALL
Tattsil TATTERSHALL
Taurel TARREL TEARLE TERRELL TIRRELL TURRALL TYRRELL
Tavendale TEVENDALE TIVENDALE
Tavener TAVERNER
TAVERNER Tavener
Tavidale TEVENDALE TIVENDALE
Taviotdale TEVENDALE TIVENDALE
Tawbutt TABBAT TALBOT
Tawcock TOCOCK TWOCOCK
TAWS Tawse
Tawse TAWS
Tay FOY JOY LEE TEA TEE TOY
TAYLER 7 Tailer TAILOR Taler Talor TAYLOR TYLER
Tayles TALLIS TALLISS
Taylis TALLIS TALLISS
TAYLOR 8 Tailer TAILOR Taler Talor TAYLER TOWLER TYLER
Taym TAME
Taynton TAINTON
Taype TAPP
Tbet TABBAT TALBOT
TEA 7 FOY JOY LEE Tay TEE TOY
Teaby TEBAY
Tead TEDD TIDD
Teag TEAGLE TEAGUE
Teage TEAGLE TEAGUE
TEAGLE 15 Tachell Tackel Tackle Tagle Tague Teag Teage Teagse TEAGUE Teakle Teaqu Teege Tegel Tegle
TEAGOE Tego
Teagse TEAGLE TEAGUE
TEAGUE 16 Tachell Tackel Tackle Tagle Tague Teag Teage TEAGLE Teagse Teakle Teaqu Teege Tegel Tegle Tigue
Teakle TEAGLE TEAGUE
TEAL TEALE TEALL
TEALE TEAL
TEALL TEAL
Teaqu TEAGLE TEAGUE
TEARLE 76 Tarle Tarrall TARREL Tarrell Tarrill Taurel Terall Terel Terell Terill Terle Terold Terrald Terrall Terrel TERRELL Terril Terrill Terroll Terryl Teryl Tirall Tirel Tirell Tirolde Tirral Tirrall Tirrel TIRRELL Tirril Tirrill Tirrold Tirrolde Tirroll Torell Torill Torrell Tourell Tourle Tourlle Turel Turell Turil Turill Turl Turle Turral TURRALL Turrel Turrell Turril Turrill Turrle Turrold Turroll Tyrald Tyrall Tyrel Tyrell Tyrie Tyril Tyrill Tyrol Tyrold Tyroll Tyrral Tyrrall Tyrrel TYRRELL Tyrril Tyrrill Tyrrol Tyrrold Tyrrolde Tyrroll
Teather TETHER TITHER
Teatt TATE TEFT
Tebaud TEBBIT TEBBUT THEOBALD TIBBIT
TEBAY Teaby
Tebbel TEBBLE
Tebbet TEBBETT TEBBIT TEBBUT TEBBUTT THEOBALD TIBBIT
TEBBETT Tebbet TEBBUTT
TEBBIT 15 Tebaud Tebbet Tebbot TEBBUT Tebet Tebit Tebot THEOBALD Thibaud Thibault Tibaud Tibbet Tibbets TIBBIT
TEBBLE Tebbel
Tebbot TEBBIT TEBBUT THEOBALD TIBBIT
TEBBUT 15 Tebaud Tebbet TEBBIT Tebbot Tebet Tebit Tebot THEOBALD Thibaud Thibault Tibaud Tibbet Tibbets TIBBIT
TEBBUTT Tebbet TEBBETT
Tebet TEBBIT TEBBUT THEOBALD TIBBIT
Tebit TEBBIT TEBBUT THEOBALD TIBBIT
Tebot TEBBIT TEBBUT THEOBALD TIBBIT
Techener TICKNER
Techiner TICKNER
Techinor TICKNER
Technear TICKNER
Teckner TICKNER
Tecner TICKNER
Ted TEDD TIDD
TEDD 9 Tead Ted Tedde Tedds Tede Teds TIDD Tudd
Tedde TEDD TIDD
Tedds TEDD TIDD
Tede TEDD TIDD
Tedford THETFORD TITFORD
Teds TEDD TIDD
Tedway TUDWAY
TEE 7 FOY JOY LEE Tay TEA TOY
TEECE Tees Teese
Teege TEAGLE TEAGUE
Tees TEECE
Teese TEECE
TEFT 5 Taff TATE Tatt Teatt
Tegel TEAGLE TEAGUE
Tegle TEAGLE TEAGUE
Tego TEAGOE
Teirling TARLING
Teisser TESSIER
Teitgen TEITYEN
TEITYEN Teitgen Tietgen
Teknor TICKNER
TELFER TELFORD
TELFORD TELFER
Tempan TAMPIN
TENANT TENNANT
TENNANT TENANT
Terall TARREL TEARLE TERRELL TIRRELL TURRALL TYRRELL
Terel TARREL TEARLE TERRELL TIRRELL TURRALL TYRRELL
Terell TARREL TEARLE TERRELL TIRRELL TURRALL TYRRELL
Terevall TURVILL TURVILLE
Terill TARREL TEARLE TERRELL TIRRELL TURRALL TYRRELL
Terle TARREL TEARLE TERRELL TIRRELL TURRALL TYRRELL
Terold TARREL TEARLE TERRELL TIRRELL TURRALL TYRRELL
Terrald TARREL TEARLE TERRELL TIRRELL TURRALL TYRRELL
Terrall TARREL TEARLE TERRELL TIRRELL TURRALL TYRRELL
Terrel TARREL TEARLE TERRELL TIRRELL TURRALL TYRRELL
TERRELL 76 Tarle Tarrall

If the name you are interested in is not here, try Section C.

TARREL Tarrell Tarrill
Taurel TEARLE Terall
Terel Terell Terill
Terle Terold Terrald
Terrall Terrel Terril
Terrill Terroll Terryl
Teryl Tirall Tirel
Tirell Tirolde Tirral
Tirrall Tirrel TIRRELL
Tirril Tirrill Tirrold
Tirrolde Tirroll Torell
Torill Torrell Tourell
Tourle Tourlle Turel
Turell Turil Turill
Turl Turle Turral
TURRALL Turrel Turrell
Turril Turrill Turrle
Turrold Turroll Tyrald
Tyrall Tyrel Tyrell
Tyrie Tyril Tyrill
Tyrol Tyrold Tyroll
Tyrral Tyrrall Tyrrel
TYRRELL Tyrril Tyrrill
Tyrrol Tyrrold Tyrrolde
Tyrroll
Terril TARREL TEARLE
TERRELL TIRRELL TURRALL
TYRRELL
Terrill TARREL TEARLE
TERRELL TIRRELL TURRALL
TYRRELL
Terroll TARREL TEARLE
TERRELL TIRRELL TURRALL
TYRRELL
Terryl TARREL TEARLE
TERRELL TIRRELL TURRALL
TYRRELL
Tervil TURVILL TURVILLE
Teryl TARREL TEARLE
TERRELL TIRRELL TURRALL
TYRRELL
Tescoe CHESCOE
TESSIER Teisser
Tetchener TICKNER
Tetchner TICKNER
Tetford THETFORD TITFORD
Tetforde THETFORD TITFORD
Tethe TETHER TITHER
TETHER 6 Tather Teather
Tethe Tetther TITHER
Tetheridge TITHERADGE
Tetherston FEATHERSTONE
FETHERSTON HORNSEY
NESFIELD
TETLOW Tettlow Tettlowe
TETSER 4 TIDSER TITSALL
TITTENSOR
Tettford THETFORD TITFORD
Tetther TETHER TITHER
Tettlow TETLOW
Tettlowe TETLOW
Teturton TITTERTON
TEVENDALE 11 Tavendale
Tavidale Taviotdale
Tevidale Tevindale
Teviotdale TIVENDALE
Tividale Tivindale
Tiviotdale
Tevidale TEVENDALE
TIVENDALE
Tevindale TEVENDALE
TIVENDALE
Teviotdale TEVENDALE
TIVENDALE
TEVLEN Tevlin
Tevlin TEVLEN
TEW 5 CHEW TOE Too Tue
TEWLEY 4 TOOLEY TULEY
Tuly
TEWSON Tulson Tuson
Thadford THETFORD TITFORD
Thaik THAKE
THAIN Thaine
Thaine THAIN

THAKE Thaik Theak
Thalford THETFORD TITFORD
Thamson THOMPSON THOMSON
THOMSONE
Thamsone THOMPSON THOMSON
THOMSONE
THARP 4 Tharpe THORP
THORPE
Tharpe THARP THORP THORPE
Thatfoord THETFORD
TITFORD
Thatford THETFORD TITFORD
Thatfur THETFORD TITFORD
Thaxton THEXTON
Theak THAKE
Theaxton THEXTON
Thecher TREACHER TRICKER
Theckford THETFORD
TITFORD
Theckston PEXTON
PICKSTONE PICTON
THEXTON
Thedford THETFORD TITFORD
Thedforde THETFORD
TITFORD
Thefford THETFORD TITFORD
Theford THETFORD TITFORD
Thelfar THETFORD TITFORD
Thelford THETFORD TITFORD
THEOBALD 15 Tebaud Tebbet
TEBBIT Tebbot TEBBUT
Tebet Tebit Tebot
Thibaud Thibault Tibaud
Tibbet Tibbets TIBBIT
Theoford THETFORD TITFORD
Thetfer THETFORD TITFORD
Thetfird THETFORD TITFORD
Thetfor THETFORD TITFORD
THETFORD 34 Fetford
Tedford Tetford
Tetforde Tettford
Thadford Thalford
Thatfoord Thatford
Thatfur Theckford
Thedford Thedforde
Thefford Theford
Thelfar Thelford
Theoford Thetfer
Thetfird Thetfor
Thetforde Thetforth
Thetfur Thettfford
Thettforthe Thiford
Thitford Thotford
Thutfer Titfoord
TITFORD Tytford
Thetforde THETFORD
TITFORD
Thetforth THETFORD
TITFORD
Thetfur THETFORD TITFORD
Thettfford THETFORD
TITFORD
Thettforthe THETFORD
TITFORD
Theuld THOULD
THEWLIS Thoulouse
THEXTON 4 Thaxton
Theaxton Theckston
Thibaud TEBBIT TEBBUT
THEOBALD TIBBIT
Thibault TEBBIT TEBBUT
THEOBALD TIBBIT
THICKET Thickett
Thickett THICKET
Thiford THETFORD TITFORD
Thirkell THIRKILL
THRELKELD
Thirkettle THURKETTLE
THIRKILL Thirkell
THRELKELD
THIRP Thirpe
Thirpe THIRP
THISTLETHWAITE
Thistlewhate

Thistlewhate
THISTLETHWAITE
Thitford THETFORD TITFORD
Thold THOULD
Thole THOULD
THOM 4 Thoms TOM TOMS
THOMAS 10 Thomasina
Thombes Thoms THOMSON
TOMAS Tombes TOMBS
Tomes TOMS
Thomasina THOMAS THOMSON
THOMASON THOMPSON
THOMASSON 7 Thomisson
THOMPSON THOMSON
Tomasson Tomisson
TOMSON
Thombes THOMAS TOMBS
Thomisson THOMASSON
THOMPSON THOMSON TOMSON
Thomlin TAMBLIN TAMLIN
TOMLIN TOMLYN
Thomlinson TOMLINSON
Thompset THOMPSETT
TOMPSETT TOMSETT
THOMPSETT 10 Thompset
Thomsat Thomsett
Tompset TOMPSETT Tomsat
Tomsatt Tomset TOMSETT
THOMPSON 16 Machomas
Macthomas Mcthomas
Thamson Thamsone
THOMASON THOMASSON
Thomisson THOMSON
THOMSONE Tomasson
Tomeson Tomisson
TOMPSON TOMSON
Thoms THOM THOMAS TOM
TOMBS TOMS
Thomsat THOMPSETT
TOMPSETT TOMSETT
Thomsett THOMPSETT
TOMPSETT TOMSETT
THOMSON 17 Machomas
Macthomas Mcthomas
Thamson Thamsone THOMAS
Thomasina THOMASSON
Thomisson THOMPSON
THOMSONE Tomasson
Tomeson Tomisson
TOMPSON TOMSON
THOMSONE 8 Machomas
Macthomas Mcthomas
Thamson Thamsone
THOMPSON THOMSON
Thonder THUNDER
Thondir THUNDER
Thondyer THUNDER
Thondyr THUNDER
Thondyrr THUNDER
THORN 4 THORNE Thornne
Thurn
THORNE 4 THORN Thornne
Thurn
THORNELL 6 Thornelough
THORNHILL Thornhull
Thornill Thorningly
Thornelough THORNELL
THORNHILL
THORNELY Thorniley
THORNLEY
THORNHILL 6 THORNELL
Thornelough Thornhull
Thornill Thorningly
Thornhull THORNELL
THORNHILL
Thorniley THORNELY
THORNLEY
Thornill THORNELL
THORNHILL
Thorningly THORNELL
THORNHILL
THORNLEY THORNELY
Thorniley
Thornne THORN THORNE

THORP 5 THARP Tharpe
THORPE Thorrp
THORPE 5 THARP Tharpe
THORP Thorrp
Thorrp THORP THORPE
Thory THURLEY
Thotford THETFORD TITFORD
THOULD 6 Theuld Thold
Thole Thowell Thowld
Thoulouse THEWLIS
Thounder THUNDER
Thowell THOULD
Thowld THOULD
Thownson TOWNSON
Thoytes THOYTS
THOYTS Thoytes
THREADER 4 Thredder
Treader Tredder
THREADGOLD 4 TREADGOLD
Tredgold Tredgould
Thredder THREADER
THRELKELD Thirkell
THIRKILL
Thrumboy TRIMBY
Thrymbie TRIMBY
Thubboron THUBRON
Thubbron THUBRON
THUBRON Thubboron
Thubbron
THULBORN Thurborn
Thurlborn
THUNDER 14 Le thundre
Thonder Thondir
Thondyer Thondyr
Thondyrr Thounder
Thundere Thundir
Thundre Thundyr Tunder
Tundur
Thundere THUNDER
Thundir THUNDER
Thundre THUNDER
Thundyr THUNDER
Thurborn THULBORN
Thure THURLEY
THURKETTLE Thirkettle
Thurkle THURTLE
Thurlborn THULBORN
Thurleigh-smith SMITH
THURLEY Thory Thure
Thurley-smith SMITH
Thurling TARLING
Thurn THORN THORNE
THURNALL Thurnel
Thurnel THURNALL
THURSTAIN THURSTON
THURSTON THURSTAIN
THURTLE Thurkle
Thutfer THETFORD TITFORD
Thwait THWAITES TWAITE
TWAITES TWAITS TWITE
THWAITES 9 Thwait Thwaits
Twait TWAITE TWAITES
TWAITS TWITE WAITES
Thwaits THWAITES TWAITE
TWAITES TWAITS TWITE
Tibaud TEBBIT TEBBUT
THEOBALD TIBBIT
Tibbet TEBBIT TEBBUT
THEOBALD TIBBIT
Tibbets TEBBIT TEBBUT
THEOBALD TIBBIT
TIBBIT 15 Tebaud Tebbet
TEBBIT Tebbot TEBBUT
Tebet Tebit Tebot
THEOBALD Thibaud
Thibault Tibaud Tibbet
Tibbets
Tibbot TABBAT TALBOT
Tibott TYBBOT
TICEHURST TYHURST
Tichenar TICKNER
Tichener TICKNER
Tichenner TICKNER
Tichiner TICKNER

If the name you are interested in is not here, try Section C.

Tichinor TICKNER
Tichinour TICKNER
Tichmour TICKNER
Tichnar TICKNER
Tichner TICKNER
Tichnore TICKNER
Tickat TIQUET
Tickerner TICKNER
Tickernor TICKNER
Ticket TIQUET
Tickett TIQUET
Tickiner TICKNER
Tickinor TICKNER
Ticknar TICKNER
TICKNER 94 De ticheners De tichenoure De tykenore Techener Techiner Techinor Technear Teckner Tecner Teknor Tetchener Tetchner Tichenar Tichener Tichenner Tichiner Tichinor Tichinour Tichmour Tichnar Tichner Tichnore Tickerner Tickernor Tickiner Tickinor Ticknar Tickno Ticknor Ticknore Ticknour Ticne Ticner Ticnor Tikner Tinchiner Titcharton Titchener Titchenor Titchiner Titchner Titchoner Tochener Tockne Tockner Touchener Trikner Tuchener Tuchenor Tuchiner Tuchinor Tuckne Tuckner Tupne Tutchener Tutchiner Twichener Twychener Twychenor Tycenare Tychenar Tychener Tychenor Tychenour Tychiner Tychinor Tychyner Tyckener Tyckner Tycknor Tycknore Tycknour Tycne Tycner Tyeknor Tygnor Tykenar Tykener Tykenor Tykenore Tykenour Tyknar Tyknare Tykner Tyknere Tyknor Tyknore Tyknour Tylkenor Tynchiner Tynchyner Tynckor Tytchenor
Tickno TICKNER
Ticknor TICKNER
Ticknore TICKNER
Ticknour TICKNER
Ticne TICKNER
Ticner TICKNER
Ticnor TICKNER
Ticquet TIQUET
TIDD 9 Tead Ted TEDD Tedde Tedds Tede Teds Tudd
Tidderton TITTERTON
Tideman TIDYMAN
Tideswell TIDSALL TISDALL
Tidiman TIDYMAN
Tidridge TITHERADGE
TIDSALL 5 Tideswell Tidsell Tidza TISDALL
Tidsell TIDSALL TISDALL
TIDSER 4 TETSER TITSALL TITTENSOR
Tidway TUDWAY
TIDYMAN 6 Tideman Tidiman Tydeman Tydiman Tydman
Tidza TIDSALL TISDALL
Tietgen TEITYEN
TIFFEN TIFFIN
TIFFIN TIFFEN
Tigal TIGGALL TIGWELL
Tigalle TIGGALL TIGWELL
TIGGALL 6 Tigal Tigalle TIGWELL Tygal Tyghall
TIGHE TYE
Tigue TEAGUE
TIGWELL 6 Tigal Tigalle TIGGALL Tygal Tyghall
Tikner TICKNER
TILBIE TILBY Tilbye
TILBY TILBIE Tilbye
Tilbye TILBIE TILBY
TILDESLEY 5 Tildsley Tildsly TINSLEY TYLDESLEY
Tildsley TILDESLEY TINSLEY
Tildsly TILDESLEY TINSLEY
TILER TYLER
Tiley TILY
Tillar TILLER
Tillemuth TILLMUTH TILMOUSE TILMOUTH
TILLER 5 Tillar Tillier Tilyer Tylyer
TILLEY 4 TILLIE TILLY Tylley
TILLIE 4 TILLEY TILLY Tylley
Tillier TILLER
TILLMUTH 5 Tillemuth TILMOUSE TILMOUTH Tyllemuth
TILLOT Tillott
Tillott TILLOT
Tillstone TILSTON
Tillwood SELLWOOD ZILLWOOD
TILLY 4 TILLEY TILLIE Tylley
TILMOUSE 5 Tillemuth TILLMUTH TILMOUTH Tyllemuth
TILMOUTH 5 Tillemuth TILLMUTH TILMOUSE Tyllemuth
TILSTON Tillstone Tylston
TILY Tiley
Tilyer TILLER
Timber TIMBERS
TIMBERLAKE Timberlick Timlic
Timberlick TIMBERLAKE
TIMBERS Timber
Timbs TIMMS TIMS
Times TIMMS TIMS
Timlic TIMBERLAKE
TIMMS 4 Timbs Times TIMS
TIMS 4 Timbs Times TIMMS
Tinchiner TICKNER
TINDAL 5 TINDALE TINDALL Tyndale TYNDALL
TINDALE 7 TINDAL TINDALL TINDELL TINDLE Tyndale TYNDALL
TINDALL 8 TINDAL TINDALE Tindel TINDELL TINDLE Tyndale TYNDALL
Tindel TINDALL TINDLE
TINDELL 5 TINDALE TINDALL TINDLE Tyndale
TINDLE 6 TINDALE TINDALL Tindel TINDELL Tyndale
Tindley TINGLEY TINLEY
TINDSLEY Tindsly Tynsly
Tindsly TINDSLEY
TINGLEY Tindley TINLEY
TINLEY Tindley TINGLEY
Tinmoth TINMOUTH
TINMOUTH 4 Tinmoth Tynemouth Tynmouth
Tinne TUNNEY
TINSLEY 5 TILDESLEY Tildsley Tildsly TYLDESLEY
Tiping TIPPING
TIPLADY Typlady Typladye
Tipp TRIP TRIPP
TIPPING 6 Tiping Tippinge Typinge Typping Typpinge
Tippinge TIPPING
TIQUET 5 Tickat Ticket Tickett Ticquet
Tirall TARREL TEARLE TERRELL TIRRELL TURRALL TYRRELL
Tirel TARREL TEARLE TERRELL TIRRELL TURRALL TYRRELL
Tirell TARREL TEARLE TERRELL TIRRELL TURRALL TYRRELL
Tirolde TARREL TEARLE TERRELL TIRRELL TURRALL TYRRELL
Tirral TARREL TEARLE TERRELL TIRRELL TURRALL TYRRELL
Tirrall TARREL TEARLE TERRELL TIRRELL TURRALL TYRRELL
Tirrel TARREL TEARLE TERRELL TIRRELL TURRALL TYRRELL
TIRRELL 76 Tarle Tarrall TARREL Tarrell Tarrill Taurel TEARLE Terall Terel Terell Terill Terle Terold Terrald Terrall Terrel TERRELL Terril Terrill Terroll Terryl Teryl Tirall Tirel Tirell Tirolde Tirral Tirrall Tirrel Tirril Tirrill Tirrold Tirrolde Tirroll Torell Torill Torrell Tourell Tourle Tourlle Turel Turell Turil Turill Turl Turle Turral TURRALL Turrel Turrell Turril Turrill Turrle Turrold Turroll Tyrald Tyrall Tyrel Tyrell Tyrie Tyril Tyrill Tyrol Tyrold Tyroll Tyrral Tyrrall Tyrrel TYRRELL Tyrril Tyrrill Tyrrol Tyrrold Tyrrolde Tyrroll
Tirril TARREL TEARLE TERRELL TIRRELL TURRALL TYRRELL
Tirrill TARREL TEARLE TERRELL TIRRELL TURRALL TYRRELL
Tirrol TYRRELL
Tirrold TARREL TEARLE TERRELL TIRRELL TURRALL TYRRELL
Tirrolde TARREL TEARLE TERRELL TIRRELL TURRALL TYRRELL
Tirroll TARREL TEARLE TERRELL TIRRELL TURRALL TYRRELL
TISDALL 5 Tideswell TIDSALL Tidsell Tidza
Tison TYSON
Tissard TIZARD TIZZARD
Titcharton TICKNER
Titchener TICKNER
Titchenor TICKNER
Titchiner TICKNER
Titchner TICKNER
Titchoner TICKNER
Titfoord THETFORD TITFORD
TITFORD 34 Fetford Tedford Tetford Tetforde Tettford Thadford Thalford Thatfoord Thatford Thatfur Theckford Thedford Thedforde Thefford Theford Thelfar Thelford Theoford Thetfer Thetfird Thetfor THETFORD Thetforde Thetforth Thetfur Thettfford Thettforthe Thiford Thitford Thotford Thutfer Titfoord Tytford
TITHER 7 Tather Teather Tethe TETHER Tetther Tyther
TITHERADGE 5 Tetheridge Tidridge Titheridge Tytheridge
Titheridge TITHERADGE
TITSALL 4 TETSER TIDSER TITTENSOR
Titsel TATTERSHALL
TITTENSOR 4 TETSER TIDSER TITSALL
Titterel TATTERSHALL
Tittersal TATTERSHALL
Tittersale TATTERSHALL
Tittersall TATTERSHALL
Tittersell TATTERSHALL
TITTERTON 4 Teturton Tidderton Tydrington
TIVENDALE 11 Tavendale Tavidale Taviotdale TEVENDALE Tevidale Tevindale Teviotdale Tividale Tivindale Tiviotdale
Tividale TEVENDALE TIVENDALE
Tivindale TEVENDALE TIVENDALE
Tiviotdale TEVENDALE TIVENDALE
TIZARD 4 Tissard TIZZARD Tyzard
TIZZARD 4 Tissard TIZARD Tyzard
Toakely TOAKLEY
TOAKLEY 4 Toakely Toaklove Tockeley
Toaklove TOAKLEY
Tochener TICKNER
Tockeley TOAKLEY
Tocker TUCKER
Tockne TICKNER
Tockner TICKNER
TOCOCK 6 Tawcock Toecock Toocock Towcock TWOCOCK
TOD TODD TOOD
TODD TOD TOOD
Todnie DE TOENI
Todway TUDWAY
TOE 5 CHEW TEW Too Tue
Toecock TOCOCK TWOCOCK
Toel TOLE TOLL
Toesland TOSELAND
TOFIELD Topfield
TOIN 4 TOINE TOYN TOYNE
TOINE 4 TOIN TOYN TOYNE
Toker TUCKER
Tolas TALLIS TALLISS
TOLE 7 Toel TOLL Tolle Towl TOWLE TULL
Tolefree TOLFREE
Toler TOLLER
TOLFREE 5 Tolefree Tolfrey Tollfrey Tolvery
Tolfrey TOLFREE

If the name you are interested in is not here, try Section C.

TOLL 7 Tale TALL Talle Toel TOLE Tolle
Tolle TALL TOLE TOLL
TOLLER Toler
Tollfrey TOLFREE
Tolmin TOULMIN
Tolmine TOULMIN
Tolming TOULMIN
TOLSON TOULSON
Tolvery TOLFREE
TOM 4 THOM Thoms TOMS
Tomalin TOMLIN
TOMAS 4 THOMAS Tomes TOMS
Tomasson THOMASSON THOMPSON THOMSON TOMLINSON TOMSON
Tombes THOMAS TOMBS
Tomblin TOMLIN
TOMBS 7 THOMAS Thombes Thoms Tombes Tomes TOOMBS
Tomes THOMAS TOMAS TOMBS TOMS TOOMBS
Tomeson THOMPSON THOMSON TOMPSON TOMSON
Tominson TOMLINSON
Tomisson THOMASSON THOMPSON THOMSON TOMSON
TOMKINS TOMPKINS
TOMLIN 8 TAMBLIN Tambling TAMLIN Thomlin Tomalin Tomblin TOMLYN
TOMLINSON 4 Thomlinson Tomasson Tominson
TOMLYN 6 TAMBLIN Tambling TAMLIN Thomlin TOMLIN
TOMPKINS TOMKINS
Tompset THOMPSETT TOMPSETT TOMSETT
TOMPSETT 10 Thompset THOMPSETT Thomsat Thomsett Tompset Tomsat Tomsatt Tomset TOMSETT
TOMPSON 5 THOMPSON THOMSON Tomeson TOMSON
TOMS 7 THOM THOMAS Thoms TOM TOMAS Tomes
Tomsat THOMPSETT TOMPSETT TOMSETT
Tomsatt THOMPSETT TOMPSETT TOMSETT
Tomset THOMPSETT TOMPSETT TOMSETT
TOMSETT 10 Thompset THOMPSETT Thomsat Thomsett Tompset TOMPSETT Tomsat Tomsatt Tomset
TOMSON 9 THOMASSON Thomisson THOMPSON THOMSON Tomasson Tomeson Tomisson TOMPSON
TONDRA Tonra
TONG TONGE TONGUE
TONGE TONG TONGUE
TONGUE TONG TONGE
TONKE TONKS
Tonkein TONKIN TONKYN
Tonken TONKIN TONKYN
TONKENS Tonkins
TONKIN 5 Tonkein Tonken Tonking TONKYN
Tonking TONKIN
Tonkins TONKENS
Tonkiss TONKS
TONKS TONKE Tonkiss
TONKYN 4 Tonkein Tonken TONKIN
Tonra TONDRA
Tonshet TOUCHET
Tonstal TUNSTALL TUNSTILL
Tony DE TOENI
Too CHEW TEW TOE
Toocock TOCOCK TWOCOCK
TOOD TOD TODD
TOOK Tooke TUCK
Tooke TOOK
Tool O'TOOL O'TOOLE TOOLE
TOOLE 4 O'TOOL O'TOOLE Tool
TOOLEY 4 TEWLEY TULEY Tuly
TOOMBS TOMBS Tomes
TOON 4 TOONE Toones Toons
TOONE 4 TOON Toones Toons
Toones TOON TOONE
Toons TOON TOONE
Tootal TOOTELL TOOTHILL TOOTILL
Tootel TOOTELL TOOTHILL TOOTILL
TOOTELL 6 Tootal Tootel TOOTHILL TOOTILL Tootle
TOOTHILL 6 Tootal Tootel TOOTELL TOOTILL Tootle
TOOTILL 6 Tootal Tootel TOOTELL TOOTHILL Tootle
Tootle TOOTELL TOOTHILL TOOTILL
TOOVEY Toovye Tovy
Toovye TOOVEY
Tooze TWOSE
Toozer TOZER
Topfield TOFIELD
Toplett POPLETT
TOPP TOPPE
TOPPE TOPP
Torell TARREL TEARLE TERRELL TIRRELL TURRALL TYRRELL
Torill TARREL TEARLE TERRELL TIRRELL TURRALL TYRRELL
Torlon TARLING
Torrell TARREL TEARLE TERRELL TIRRELL TURRALL TYRRELL
TORRIE Tory
Torvill TURVILL TURVILLE
Tory TORRIE
TOSELAND Toesland Tosland
Tosere TOZER
Tosland TOSELAND
Totley TOTTY
Totlie TOTTY
Totly TOTTY
TOTNAM TOTTENHAM
TOTTENHAM 4 TOTNAM Tottingham Tottnam
Totterdale TOTTERDELL
TOTTERDELL Totterdale
Totterel TATTERSHALL
Tottey TOTTY
Tottie TOTTY
Tottingham TOTTENHAM
Tottnam TOTTENHAM
TOTTY 6 Totley Totlie Totly Tottey Tottie
Touchener TICKNER
TOUCHET 8 Tonshet Touchette Toutchet Tuchett Tuchette Tushet Tutchet
Touchette TOUCHET
Toudell TWADDLE TWEDALE TWEDDLE
Toulman TOULMIN
TOULMIN 14 Talmin Tolmin Tolmine Tolming Toulman Toulmine Toulming Towline Towlinge Towlmin Towlmine Towlming Towlminge
Toulmine TOULMIN
Toulming TOULMIN
TOULSON TOLSON
Tounsend TOWNSEND TOWNSHEND TOWNSIN
Tourell TARREL TEARLE TERRELL TIRRELL TURRALL TYRRELL
Tourle TARREL TEARLE TERRELL TIRRELL TURRALL TYRRELL
Tourlle TARREL TEARLE TERRELL TIRRELL TURRALL TYRRELL
Tourt TWORT
Toutchet TOUCHET
TOVEY 4 Tovi Tovie Tovy
Tovi TOVEY
Tovie TOVEY
Tovy TOOVEY TOVEY
Towan TOWN TOWNE
Towcock TOCOCK TWOCOCK
Towen TOWN TOWNE
Towenson TOWNSON
Towick TREWICK
Towl TOLE TOWLE TULL
TOWLE 4 TOLE Towl TULL
TOWLER TAYLOR
Towline TOULMIN
Towlinge TOULMIN
Towlmin TOULMIN
Towlmine TOULMIN
Towlming TOULMIN
Towlminge TOULMIN
TOWN 6 Towan Towen TOWNE Townes Towns
TOWNDROW Townerowe TOWNROW
TOWNE 6 Towan Towen TOWN Townes Towns
TOWNEND TOWNSEND TOWNSHEND
Townerowe TOWNDROW TOWNROW
Townes TOWN TOWNE
Townesend TOWNSEND TOWNSHEND TOWNSIN
TOWNROW TOWNDROW Townerowe
Towns TOWN TOWNE
TOWNSEND 6 Tounsend TOWNEND Townesend TOWNSHEND TOWNSIN
TOWNSHEND 6 Tounsend TOWNEND Townesend TOWNSEND TOWNSIN
TOWNSIN 5 Tounsend Townesend TOWNSEND TOWNSHEND
TOWNSON Thownson Towenson
TOY 9 FOY JOY LEE Tay TEA TEE TOYE TYE
TOYE TOY
TOYN 4 TOIN TOINE TOYNE
TOYNE 4 TOIN TOINE TOYN
TOZER Toozer Tosere
TRACE TRACEY TRACY
TRACEY TRACE TRACY
Tracher TREACHER TRICKER
TRACY TRACE TRACEY
Traganza TREGENZA
Tragenza TREGENZA
Traharne TREHARNE
Trahearn TRAHERNE TREHERNE
Trahern TRAHERNE TREHERNE
TRAHERNE 7 Trahearn Trahern Trehearn Trehearne Trehern TREHERNE
TRAIL TRAILL
TRAILL TRAIL
Train TREIN
Trait TRITT
Traker TREACHER TRICKER
Tramer TRANMER
Trammer TRANMER
TRANMER Tramer Trammer
TRAPNELL 4 Tratnell Tropinel Trumpmell
Tratcher TREACHER TRICKER
Trate TRITT
TRATHAN TRATHEN TRATTAN
TRATHEN 4 TRATHAN TRATTAN Tratten
Tratnell TRAPNELL
Tratt TROTT
TRATTAN 4 TRATHAN TRATHEN Tratten
Tratten TRATHEN TRATTAN
Traughton TROUGHTON
Travas TRAVERS TRAVES TRAVIS TREVIS
Travena TREVENA
Travenor TREVENA
TRAVERS 12 Travas Traverse TRAVES TRAVIS Traviss Trevass Trevers Treverse Treves TREVIS Trives
Traverse TRAVERS TRAVES TRAVIS TREVIS
TRAVES 8 Travas TRAVERS Traverse TRAVIS Traviss Trevass TREVIS
TRAVIS 12 Travas TRAVERS Traverse TRAVES Traviss Trevass Trevers Treverse Treves TREVIS Trives
Traviss TRAVERS TRAVES TRAVIS TREVIS
TRAWLEY Trolley Trolly
TREACHER 10 Thecher Tracher Traker Tràtcher Treker TRICKER Troacher Trocker Trouchor
TREADAWAY 4 Treadway Tredaway Tredway
Treader THREADER
TREADGOLD 4 THREADGOLD Tredgold Tredgould
Treadle TREADWELL TREDWELL
Treadway TREADAWAY
TREADWELL 7 Treadle Treddell Treddle TREDWELL Treedle Truddle
TREBILCOCK Trebilcook
Trebilcook TREBILCOCK
Tredacke TREDINNICK
Tredanic TREDINNICK
Tredaway TREADAWAY
Treddell TREADWELL TREDWELL
Tredder THREADER
Treddinnick TREDINNICK
Treddle TREADWELL TREDWELL
Tredenack TREDINNICK
Tredeneck TREDINNICK
Tredenicke TREDINNICK
Tredeser TRESEDER TRESIDDER
TREDGET 4 TREDGETT Treget Trudget
TREDGETT 4 TREDGET Treget Trudget
Tredgold THREADGOLD TREADGOLD
Tredgould THREADGOLD TREADGOLD
Tredick TREDINNICK
Tredinick TREDINNICK
TREDINNICK 11 Tredacke Tredanic Treddinnick Tredenack Tredeneck Tredenicke Tredick Tredinick Tredyck Tredynnacke
Tredway TREADAWAY

If the name you are interested in is not here, try Section C.

TREDWELL 7 Treadle TREADWELL Treddell Treddle Treedle Truddle
Tredyck TREDINNICK
Tredynnacke TREDINNICK
TREE 6 Atree Att ree Atte ree Attre ATTREE
Treedle TREADWELL TREDWELL
Treeman TRUEMAN TRUMAN
TREFOR TREVOR
Treganza TREGENZA
Tregensa TREGENZA
Tregensagh TREGENZA
Tregensith TREGENZA
Tregenso TREGENZA
Tregensoe TREGENZA
Tregensow TREGENZA
Tregensyth TREGENZA
TREGENZA 14 Traganza Tragenza Treganza Tregensa Tregensagh Tregensith Tregenso Tregensoe Tregensow Tregensyth Tregenzo Treginsa Treginza
Tregenzo TREGENZA
Treget TREDGET TREDGETT
Treginsa TREGENZA
Treginza TREGENZA
Treglawn TREGLOAN TREGLOWN
TREGLOAN 9 Treglawn Treglohan Treglone Treglorn Treglorne Treglowan Treglowhan TREGLOWN
Treglohan TREGLOAN TREGLOWN
Treglone TREGLOAN TREGLOWN
Treglorn TREGLOAN TREGLOWN
Treglorne TREGLOAN TREGLOWN
Treglowan TREGLOAN TREGLOWN
Treglowhan TREGLOAN TREGLOWN
TREGLOWN 9 Treglawn TREGLOAN Treglohan Treglone Treglorn Treglorne Treglowan Treglowhan
TREGONING TREGONNING Tregony
TREGONNING TREGONING Tregony
Tregony TREGONING TREGONNING
Treharn TREHARNE
TREHARNE Traharne Treharn
Trehearn TRAHERNE TREHERNE
Trehearne TRAHERNE TREHERNE
Trehern TRAHERNE TREHERNE
TREHERNE 7 Trahearn Trahern TRAHERNE Trehearn Trehearne Trehern
TREIN Train Trien
Treker TREACHER TRICKER
TRELEVEN Treliving
Trelisick TRELISSICK
TRELISSICK 4 Trelisick Trelizick Trelysick
Treliving TRELEVEN
Trelizick TRELISSICK
Trelvalscois TREVALSCUS
Trelysick TRELISSICK
TREMAIN TREMAINE TREMAYNE
TREMAINE TREMAIN TREMAYNE
TREMAYNE TREMAIN TREMAINE
Trembe TRIMBY
TREMBLETT TREMLETT
TREMLETT TREMBLETT
TRENBERTH Trenbirth
Trenbirth TRENBERTH
Treouran TREWREN
TREPAS 7 TREPASSE TREPES TREPESS TREPPASS TREPPESS TREPUS
TREPASSE 7 TREPAS TREPES TREPESS TREPPASS TREPPESS TREPUS
TREPES 7 TREPAS TREPASSE TREPESS TREPPASS TREPPESS TREPUS
TREPESS 7 TREPAS TREPASSE TREPES TREPPASS TREPPESS TREPUS
TREPPASS 7 TREPAS TREPASSE TREPES TREPESS TREPPESS TREPUS
TREPPESS 7 TREPAS TREPASSE TREPES TREPESS TREPPASS TREPUS
TREPUS 7 TREPAS TREPASSE TREPES TREPESS TREPPASS TREPPESS
Tresedder TRESEDER TRESIDDER
TRESEDER 10 Tredeser Tresedder TRESIDDER Tresider Tresodern Tresseder Trezedar Trezeder Trezodar
TRESIDDER 10 Tredeser Tresedder TRESEDER Tresider Tresodern Tresseder Trezedar Trezeder Trezodar
Tresider TRESEDER TRESIDDER
Tresise TRESIZE TREZISE
TRESIZE 4 Tresise TREZISE TUSISE
Tresodern TRESEDER TRESIDDER
Tresseder TRESEDER TRESIDDER
Trethack TRETHAKE
TRETHAKE Trethack
Trethevy TRETHEWEY
Tretheway TRETHEWEY
TRETHEWEY 5 Trethevy Tretheway Trethewy Trethue
Trethewy TRETHEWEY
Trethue TRETHEWEY
TREVALSCUS Trelvalscois Trevascus
Trevascus TREVALSCUS
Trevass TRAVERS TRAVES TRAVIS TREVIS
TREVENA 6 Travena Travenor Trevenor Trevin Trivin
Trevenor TREVENA
Trevers TRAVERS TRAVIS TREVIS
Treverse TRAVERS TRAVIS TREVIS
Treves TRAVERS TRAVIS TREVIS
Trevick TREWICK
Trevilian TREVYLLIAN
Trevillian TREVYLLIAN
Trevin TREVENA
TREVIS 12 Travas TRAVERS Traverse TRAVES TRAVIS Traviss Trevass Trevers Treverse Treves Trives
TREVOR TREFOR
TREVYLLIAN Trevilian Trevillian
TREW TRUE
Trewalla TREWOLLA
TREWICK 5 Towick Trevick Truick Tyrwhitt
Trewman TRUEMAN TRUMAN
TREWOLLA Trewalla Trewoola
Trewoola TREWOLLA
Trewran TREWREN
TREWREN 5 Treouran Trewran Truran Truren
Trezedar TRESEDER TRESIDDER
Trezeder TRESEDER TRESIDDER
TREZISE Tresise TRESIZE
Trezodar TRESEDER TRESIDDER
Tribb TRIBE
TRIBE Tribb Trybe
TRICE 4 Trise Tryce Tryse
TRICKER 10 Thecher Tracher Traker Tratcher TREACHER Treker Troacher Trocker Trouchor
TRICKS Trix
Trien TREIN
Trig TRIGG TRIGGS
TRIGG 4 Trig Trigge TRIGGS
Trigge TRIGG TRIGGS
TRIGGS 4 Trig TRIGG Trigge
Trikner TICKNER
Trimbie TRIMBY
TRIMBY 6 Thrumboy Thrymbie Trembe Trimbie Trymbie
Trindal TRINDER
TRINDER Trindal
TRIP 4 Tipp Tripe TRIPP
Tripe TRIP TRIPP
TRIPP 4 Tipp TRIP Tripe
Trischler DRITTLER
Trise TRICE
TRITT 5 Dritt Trait Trate Tritten
Tritten TRITT
Trives TRAVERS TRAVIS TREVIS
Trivin TREVENA
Trix TRICKS
Troacher TREACHER TRICKER
Troath TROTH
Trobarge TROBRIDGE TROWBRIDGE
TROBE TROLLOPE
Troberege TROBRIDGE TROWBRIDGE
TROBRIDGE 8 Trobarge Troberege Troubridge TROWBRIDGE Trowerbridge Trubreg Trubridge
Trocker TREACHER TRICKER
Trolley TRAWLEY
TROLLOPE TROBE
Trolly TRAWLEY
Tropinel TRAPNELL
TROTH Troath Trough
TROTT Tratt
Troubridge TROBRIDGE TROWBRIDGE
Trouchor TREACHER TRICKER
Trough TROTH
TROUGHTON 4 Traughton Trouton Trowton
Trouton TROUGHTON
TROWBRIDGE 8 Trobarge Troberege TROBRIDGE Troubridge Trowerbridge Trubreg Trubridge
Trowerbridge TROBRIDGE TROWBRIDGE
Trowton TROUGHTON
Trublevill TURBERVILL TURBERVILLE TURVILLE
Trubleville TURBERVILL TURBERVILLE TURVILLE
TRUBODY TRUEBODY
Trubreg TROBRIDGE TROWBRIDGE
Trubridge TROBRIDGE TROWBRIDGE
TRUCKEL 4 TRUCKELL TRUCKELLS TRUCKELS
TRUCKELL 4 TRUCKEL TRUCKELLS TRUCKELS
TRUCKELLS 4 TRUCKEL TRUCKELL TRUCKELS
TRUCKELS 4 TRUCKEL TRUCKELL TRUCKELLS
Truddle TREADWELL TREDWELL
TRUDGEON Trudgian
Trudget TREDGET TREDGETT
Trudgian TRUDGEON
TRUE TREW
TRUEBODY TRUBODY
TRUEMAN 5 Treeman Trewman TRUMAN Trwman
Truick TREWICK
TRUMAN 5 Treeman Trewman TRUEMAN Trwman
TRUMPLET Trumplett
Trumplett TRUMPLET
Trumpmell TRAPNELL
Truran TREWREN
Truren TREWREN
Trwman TRUEMAN TRUMAN
Trybe TRIBE
Tryce TRICE
Trymbie TRIMBY
Tryse TRICE
Tuchener TICKNER
Tuchenor TICKNER
Tuchett TOUCHET
Tuchette TOUCHET
Tuchiner TICKNER
Tuchinor TICKNER
TUCK TOOK
TUCKER Tocker Toker
Tuckne TICKNER
Tuckner TICKNER
Tudd TEDD TIDD
Tudwaie TUDWAY
TUDWAY 8 Tadway Tedway Tidway Todway Tudwaie Tudwaye Tudwey
Tudwaye TUDWAY
Tudwey TUDWAY
Tue CHEW TEW TOE
Tuedell TWADDLE TWEDALE TWEDDLE
Tuffen TUFFIN
TUFFIN Tuffen
TUFTON 10 Tupen Tupenn TUPPEN Tuppenn Tuppin Tuppyn Tuppyne Tuppyng Tupton
TULEE PULEE
TULEY 4 TEWLEY TOOLEY Tuly
TULL 4 TOLE Towl TOWLE
Tulson TEWSON
Tuly TEWLEY TOOLEY TULEY
Tunder THUNDER
Tundur THUNDER
TUNE Tunes
Tunes TUNE
TUNNA 5 TUNNAH TUNNEY Tunnie Tunno
TUNNAH 5 TUNNA TUNNEY Tunnie Tunno
TUNNEY 6 Tinne TUNNA TUNNAH Tunnie Tunno
Tunnie TUNNA TUNNAH TUNNEY
Tunno TUNNA TUNNAH TUNNEY

If the name you are interested in is not here, try Section C.

Tunstale TUNSTALL TUNSTILL
TUNSTALL 5 DUNSTALL Tonstal Tunstale TUNSTILL
TUNSTILL 4 Tonstal Tunstale TUNSTALL
Tupen TUFTON TUPPEN
Tupenn TUFTON TUPPEN
TUPLIN 4 TAPLIN Tapling TUPLING
TUPLING 4 TAPLIN Tapling TUPLIN
Tupne TICKNER
TUPPEN 10 TUFTON Tupen Tupenn Tuppenn Tuppin Tuppyn Tuppyne Tuppyng Tupton
Tuppenn TUFTON TUPPEN
Tuppin TUFTON TUPPEN
Tuppyn TUFTON TUPPEN
Tuppyne TUFTON TUPPEN
Tuppyng TUFTON TUPPEN
Tupton TUFTON TUPPEN
Turbervile TURBERVILL TURBERVILLE TURVILLE
TURBERVILL 8 De turberville Trublevill Trubleville Turbervile TURBERVILLE Turbill TURVILLE
TURBERVILLE 8 De turberville Trublevill Trubleville Turbervile TURBERVILL Turbill TURVILLE
Turbill TURBERVILL TURBERVILLE TURVILLE
Turel TARREL TEARLE TERRELL TIRRELL TURRALL TYRRELL
Turell TARREL TEARLE TERRELL TIRRELL TURRALL TYRRELL
Turil TARREL TEARLE TERRELL TIRRELL TURRALL TYRRELL
Turill TARREL TEARLE TERRELL TIRRELL TURRALL TYRRELL
Turl TARREL TEARLE TERRELL TIRRELL TURRALL TYRRELL
Turle TARREL TEARLE TERRELL TIRRELL TURRALL TYRRELL
TURP Turps
Turps TURP
Turral TARREL TEARLE TERRELL TIRRELL TURRALL TYRRELL
TURRALL 76 Tarle Tarrall TARREL Tarrell Tarrill Taurel TEARLE Terall Terel Terell Terill Terle Terold Terrald Terrall Terrel TERRELL Terril Terrill Terroll Terryl Teryl Tirall Tirel Tirell Tirolde Tirral Tirrall Tirrel TIRRELL Tirril Tirrill Tirrold Tirrolde Tirroll Torell Torill Torrell Tourell Tourle Tourlle Turel Turell Turil Turill Turl Turle Turral Turrel Turrell Turril Turrill Turrle Turrold Turroll Tyrald Tyrall Tyrel Tyrell Tyrie Tyril Tyrill Tyrol Tyrold Tyroll Tyrral Tyrrall Tyrrel TYRRELL Tyrril Tyrrill Tyrrol Tyrrold Tyrrolde Tyrroll
Turrel TARREL TEARLE TERRELL TIRRELL TURRALL TYRRELL
Turrell TARREL TEARLE TERRELL TIRRELL TURRALL TYRRELL
Turril TARREL TEARLE TERRELL TIRRELL TURRALL TYRRELL
Turrill TARREL TEARLE TERRELL TIRRELL TURRALL TYRRELL
Turrle TARREL TEARLE TERRELL TIRRELL TURRALL TYRRELL
Turrold TARREL TEARLE TERRELL TIRRELL TURRALL TYRRELL
Turroll TARREL TEARLE TERRELL TIRRELL TURRALL TYRRELL
Turte TWORT
Turuell TURVILL TURVILLE
Turuill TURVILL TURVILLE
Turval TURVILL TURVILLE
Turveile TURVILL TURVILLE
Turvell TURVILL TURVILLE
TURVILL 12 Tarvall Terevall Tervil Torvill Turuell Turuill Turval Turveile Turvell TURVILLE Turvyle
TURVILLE 19 De turberville Tarvall Terevall Tervil Torvill Trublevill Trubleville Turbervile TURBERVILL TURBERVILLE Turbill Turuell Turuill Turval Turveile Turvell TURVILL Turvyle
Turvyle TURVILL TURVILLE
Tushet TOUCHET
TUSISE TRESIZE
Tuson TEWSON
Tutchener TICKNER
Tutchet TOUCHET
Tutchiner TICKNER
Tutching TWITCHIN
TUTT 4 Tutte TUTTY Tuttye
Tutte TUTT TUTTY
TUTTY 4 TUTT Tutte Tuttye
Tuttye TUTT TUTTY
TUXFORD TUXWORTH
TUXWORTH TUXFORD
Twaddel TWADDLE TWEDALE TWEDDLE
TWADDLE 8 Toudell Tuedell Twaddel TWEDALE Tweddell TWEDDLE Twodell
Twaemlow TWAMLOW
Twait THWAITES TWAITE TWAITES TWAITS TWITE
TWAITE 8 Thwait THWAITES Thwaits Twait TWAITES TWAITS TWITE
TWAITES 8 Thwait THWAITES Thwaits Twait TWAITE TWAITS TWITE
TWAITS 8 Thwait THWAITES Thwaits Twait TWAITE TWAITES TWITE
TWAMLOW Twaemlow
Tweady TWEEDY
TWEDALE 11 Toudell Tuedell Twaddel TWADDLE Tweddale Tweddell TWEDDLE TWEEDALE Twodell Twydale
Tweddale TWEDALE TWEDDLE TWEEDALE
Tweddell TWADDLE TWEDALE TWEDDLE
TWEDDLE 11 Toudell Tuedell Twaddel TWADDLE TWEDALE Tweddale Tweddell TWEEDALE Twodell Twydale
Tweddy TWIDDY
Twedey TWEEDY
Twedge TWIGGE
Twedy TWEEDY
TWEEDALE 5 TWEDALE Tweddale TWEDDLE Twydale
TWEEDY 5 Tweady Twedey Twedy TWIDDY
TWELFTREE 8 Twelftrees Twelftrick Twelftricks TWELVETREE Twelvetrees Twelvetrick Twelvetricks
Twelftrees TWELFTREE TWELVETREE
Twelftrick TWELFTREE TWELVETREE
Twelftricks TWELFTREE TWELVETREE
Twell TWELLS TWELVES
TWELLS Twell TWELVES
TWELVES Twell TWELLS
TWELVETREE 8 TWELFTREE Twelftrees Twelftrick Twelftricks Twelvetrees Twelvetrick Twelvetricks
Twelvetrees TWELFTREE TWELVETREE
Twelvetrick TWELFTREE TWELVETREE
Twelvetricks TWELFTREE TWELVETREE
Twichener TICKNER
Twidal TWIDLE
Twidale TWIDLE
TWIDDY Tweddy TWEEDY
Twidel TWIDLE
Twidell TWIDLE
TWIDLE 7 Twidal Twidale Twidel Twidell Twydale Twydle
TWIGG QUIGG
TWIGGE Twedge
Twining TWYNING
Twiny TWYNING
Twis TWIST
Twiss TWIST
TWIST Twis Twiss
Twitchen TWITCHIN
TWITCHIN Tutching Twitchen
TWITE 8 Thwait THWAITES Thwaits Twait TWAITE TWAITES TWAITS
TWOCOCK 6 Tawcock TOCOCK Toecock Toocock Towcock
Twodell TWADDLE TWEDALE TWEDDLE
TWORT Tourt Turte
TWOSE Tooze
Twychener TICKNER
Twychenor TICKNER
Twydale TWEDALE TWEDDLE TWEEDALE TWIDLE
Twydle TWIDLE
TWYNING 4 Twining Twiny Twyny
Twyny TWYNING
TYACK 4 Tyacke Tyacks TYERS
Tyacke TYACK TYERS
Tyacks TYACK TYERS
TYBBOT Tibott
Tycenare TICKNER
Tychenar TICKNER
Tychener TICKNER
Tychenor TICKNER
Tychenour TICKNER
Tychiner TICKNER
Tychinor TICKNER
Tychyner TICKNER
Tyckener TICKNER
Tyckner TICKNER
Tycknor TICKNER
Tycknore TICKNER
Tycknour TICKNER
Tycne TICKNER
Tycner TICKNER
Tydeman TIDYMAN
Tydiman TIDYMAN
Tydman TIDYMAN
Tydrington TITTERTON
TYE TIGHE TOY
Tyeknor TICKNER
TYERMAN Tyreman
TYERS 4 TYACK Tyacke Tyacks
Tygal TIGGALL TIGWELL
Tyghall TIGGALL TIGWELL
Tygnor TICKNER
TYHURST TICEHURST
Tykenar TICKNER
Tykener TICKNER
Tykenor TICKNER
Tykenore TICKNER
Tykenour TICKNER
Tyknar TICKNER
Tyknare TICKNER
Tykner TICKNER
Tyknere TICKNER
Tyknor TICKNER
Tyknore TICKNER
Tyknour TICKNER
TYLDESLEY TILDESLEY TINSLEY
TYLER 7 Tailer TAILOR TAYLER TAYLOR TILER Tylor
Tylkenor TICKNER
Tyllemuth TILLMUTH TILMOUSE TILMOUTH
Tylley TILLEY TILLIE TILLY
Tylor TYLER
Tylston TILSTON
Tylyer TILLER
Tynchiner TICKNER
Tynchyner TICKNER
Tynckor TICKNER
Tyndale TINDAL TINDALE TINDALL TINDELL TINDLE TYNDALL
TYNDALL 5 TINDAL TINDALE TINDALL Tyndale
Tynemouth TINMOUTH
Tynmouth TINMOUTH
Tynsly TINDSLEY
Typinge TIPPING
Typlady TIPLADY
Typladye TIPLADY
Typping TIPPING
Typpinge TIPPING
Tyrald TARREL TEARLE TERRELL TIRRELL TURRALL TYRRELL
Tyrall TARREL TEARLE TERRELL TIRRELL TURRALL TYRRELL
Tyrel TARREL TEARLE TERRELL TIRRELL TURRALL TYRRELL
Tyrell TARREL TEARLE TERRELL TIRRELL TURRALL TYRRELL
Tyreman TYERMAN
Tyrie TARREL TEARLE TERRELL TIRRELL TURRALL TYRRELL

If the name you are interested in is not here, try Section C.

Tyril TARREL TEARLE TERRELL TIRRELL TURRALL TYRRELL
Tyrill TARREL TEARLE TERRELL TIRRELL TURRALL TYRRELL
Tyrley-smith SMITH
Tyrol TARREL TEARLE TERRELL TIRRELL TURRALL TYRRELL
Tyrold TARREL TEARLE TERRELL TIRRELL TURRALL TYRRELL
Tyroll TARREL TEARLE TERRELL TIRRELL TURRALL TYRRELL
Tyrral TARREL TEARLE TERRELL TIRRELL TURRALL TYRRELL
Tyrrall TARREL TEARLE TERRELL TIRRELL TURRALL TYRRELL
Tyrrel TARREL TEARLE TERRELL TIRRELL TURRALL TYRRELL
TYRRELL 77 Tarle Tarrall TARREL Tarrell Tarrill Taurel TEARLE Terall Terel Terell Terill Terle Terold Terrald Terrall Terrel TERRELL Terril Terrill Terroll Terryl Teryl Tirall Tirel Tirell Tirolde Tirral Tirrall Tirrel TIRRELL Tirril Tirrill Tirrol Tirrold Tirrolde Tirroll Torell Torill Torrell Tourell Tourle Tourlle Turel Turell Turil Turill Turl Turle Turral TURRALL Turrel Turrell Turril Turrill Turrle Turrold Turroll Tyrald Tyrall Tyrel Tyrell Tyrie Tyril Tyrill Tyrol Tyrold Tyroll Tyrral Tyrrall Tyrrel Tyrril Tyrrill Tyrrol Tyrrold Tyrrolde Tyrroll
Tyrril TARREL TEARLE TERRELL TIRRELL TURRALL TYRRELL
Tyrrill TARREL TEARLE TERRELL TIRRELL TURRALL TYRRELL
Tyrrol TARREL TEARLE TERRELL TIRRELL TURRALL TYRRELL
Tyrrold TARREL TEARLE TERRELL TIRRELL TURRALL TYRRELL
Tyrrolde TARREL TEARLE TERRELL TIRRELL TURRALL TYRRELL
Tyrroll TARREL TEARLE TERRELL TIRRELL TURRALL TYRRELL
Tyrwhitt TREWICK
TYSON Tison
Tytchenor TICKNER
Tytford THETFORD TITFORD
Tyther TITHER
Tytheridge TITHERADGE
Tyzard TIZARD TIZZARD
U'ren UREN
Udel UDELL
UDELL 5 Udel Yewdale Youdall Youdle
Udgell HUDGELL HUDSWELL
Uhl EWELL HOOLE YOLE YOUELL YULE
Uhles EWELL HOOLE YOLE YOUELL YULE
Uiles EWELL HOOLE YOLE YOUELL YULE
ULF 11 ALFF ALP ALPE ALPHE ALPS AULPH HULF OLFE ULFE ULPH
ULFE 11 ALFF ALP ALPE ALPHE ALPS AULPH HULF OLFE ULF ULPH
ULLATHORNE Ullithorne
ULLEY 13 HALLEY HANLEY HAWLEY HOOLEY Hooly Howley Hullay HULLEY HULLY Ully UTLEY Whooley
Ullithorne ULLATHORNE
Ully HALLEY HANLEY HAWLEY HOOLEY HULLEY HULLY ULLEY UTLEY
Ullyat ULYAT ULYATT
Ullyett ULYAT ULYATT
ULPH 11 ALFF ALP ALPE ALPHE ALPS AULPH HULF OLFE ULF ULFE
ULYAT 6 Ullyat Ullyett Ulyate ULYATT Ulyet
Ulyate ULYAT ULYATT
ULYATT 6 Ullyat Ullyett ULYAT Ulyate Ulyet
Ulyet ULYAT ULYATT
Umbrage AMBRIDGE HAMBRIDGE RAMBRIDGE
Union ONION UNWIN
UNWIN 9 ONION Onwhynne ONWIN Onyen Union Unwine Unwins Unwyn
Unwine UNWIN
Unwins UNWIN
Unwyn ONION UNWIN
Uoel EWELL HOOLE YOLE YOUELL YULE
UPCHER Upsher
UPPERDINE HUFFERDINE
Upsher UPCHER
UREN 7 Euren U'ren Urin Urine Yorren Youren
Urin UREN
Urine UREN
URRY ERREY Erry
URSELL 31 Askell Aswell Essell HASKELL Hassel HASWELL Hawsell Haysel Hessell Hoswell Husle HUSSELL HUZZELL Israel Issel Osell OSWALD Ozell RUSSELL Urswell Ushil Ussell Ussol Ussould Uswell Uzald Uzle Uzzeel Uzzele UZZELL
Urswell HASKELL HASWELL HUSSELL HUZZELL OSWALD RUSSELL URSELL UZZELL
Urswick URWICK
Urswyk URWICK
URWICK Urswick Urswyk
USHER 4 Ischer Neville-ussher USSHER
Ushil HASKELL HASWELL HUSSELL HUZZELL OSWALD RUSSELL URSELL UZZELL
Ussell HASKELL HASWELL HUSSELL HUZZELL OSWALD RUSSELL URSELL UZZELL
Ussey OUSEY
USSHER Neville-ussher USHER
Ussol HASKELL HASWELL HUSSELL HUZZELL OSWALD RUSSELL URSELL UZZELL
Ussould HASKELL HASWELL HUSSELL HUZZELL OSWALD RUSSELL URSELL UZZELL
Usteison VSTEISON
Ustis EUSTACE EUSTICE STACE STACEY
Uswell HASKELL HASWELL HUSSELL HUZZELL OSWALD RUSSELL URSELL UZZELL
Uteridge UTTERIDGE
Utler UTLEY UTTLEY
UTLEY 16 HALLEY HANLEY HAWLEY HOOLEY Hooly Howley Hullay HULLEY HULLY ULLEY Ully Utler Uttler UTTLEY Whooley
Utridge UTTERIDGE
Utterage UTTERIDGE
UTTERIDGE 7 Uteridge Utridge Utterage Uttrage Uttrege Uttridge
Uttler UTLEY UTTLEY
UTTLEY 4 Utler UTLEY Uttler
Uttrage UTTERIDGE
Uttrege UTTERIDGE
Uttridge UTTERIDGE
Uzald HASKELL HASWELL HUSSELL HUZZELL OSWALD RUSSELL URSELL UZZELL
Uzle HASKELL HASWELL HUSSELL HUZZELL OSWALD RUSSELL URSELL UZZELL
Uzzeel HASKELL HASWELL HUSSELL HUZZELL OSWALD RUSSELL URSELL UZZELL
Uzzele HASKELL HASWELL HUSSELL HUZZELL OSWALD RUSSELL URSELL UZZELL
UZZELL 31 Askell Aswell Essell HASKELL Hassel HASWELL Hawsell Haysel Hessell Hoswell Husle HUSSELL HUZZELL Israel Issel Osell OSWALD Ozell RUSSELL URSELL Urswell Ushil Ussell Ussol Ussould Uswell Uzald Uzle Uzzeel Uzzele
Uzzett HUZZARD
Vage VAGUE
Vagg VAGUE
Vaghan VAUGHAN VOGAN VOGHAN
VAGUE 4 Vage Vagg Veague
Vahan VAUGHAN VOGAN VOGHAN
Vaisey VASEY VESEY
Valance VALENCE VALLANCE VALLENCE
VALE 7 VEAL VEALE VEALL VEEL Veile Vele
VALENCE 5 Valance VALLANCE VALLENCE Vallens
Valendar FELLINDER VALENDER
VALENDER 6 Fellender FELLINDER Valendar Velender Vellender
Valeran WALDRON WALROND
VALLANCE 5 Valance VALENCE VALLENCE Vallens
VALLAR 4 VALLER Vollar VOLLER
VALLENCE 5 Valance VALENCE VALLANCE Vallens
Vallens VALENCE VALLANCE VALLENCE
VALLER 4 VALLAR Vollar VOLLER
Valpi VALPY
VALPY Valpi
Van der avert VANDERAVORT
Van der avoird VANDERAVORT
Van der avoirt VANDERAVORT
Van der avoort VANDERAVORT
Van der avort VANDERAVORT
Van vaulconburgh VAN VAULKENBURGH
VAN VAULKENBURGH Van vaulconburgh
Vander avort VANDERAVORT
VANDERAVORT 7 Van der avert Van der avoird Van der avoirt Van der avoort Van der avort Vander avort
Vanston FANSTONE VANSTONE
VANSTONE 5 Fanston FANSTONE Fanstonne Vanston
Vapent VIPAN VIPOND VIPONT
Vapont VIPAN VIPOND VIPONT
Vappers VIPAN VIPOND VIPONT
Vappon VIPAN VIPOND VIPONT
Vara VEAR
Varchild FAIRCHILD
Varco VARCOE VERCOE
VARCOE 4 Varco Verco VERCOE
Vard VEAR
VARE VEAR Veire
Varer VEAR
VARNHAM 5 Varnon Verham Vernham VERNON
Varnol VERNALL
Varnon VARNHAM VERNON
Varow VEAR
Varrant VERRANT
Varrd VEAR
Varrde VEAR
Varrent VERRANT
Varrow VEAR
VASEY Vaisey VESEY
Vasey-Simons VAZIE-SIMONS
Vasie-Simons VAZIE-SIMONS
Vauden VODDEN VODEN
VAUGHAN 12 Fychan Vaghan Vahan VOGAN VOGHAN Vogin Vougan Voughan Voughen Voughn Voughon
Vaus VAUSE WASE WASS WASSE
VAUSE 7 Vaus Was WASE WASS WASSE Waus
Vauss VOSS
Vautier VOTIER
Vawden VODDEN VODEN
Vazey-Simons VAZIE-SIMONS
VAZIE-SIMONS 4 Vasey-Simons Vasie-Simons Vazey-Simons
Vazy VEASY
Veaco VEECOCK
Veacock VEECOCK
Veague VAGUE
VEAL 9 BEAL VALE VEALE VEALL VEEL Veil Veile Vele
VEALE 8 BEAL VALE VEAL VEALL VEEL Veile Vele
VEALL 8 BEAL VALE VEAL VEALE VEEL Veile Vele
Veapond VIPAN VIPOND VIPONT
VEAR 17 Vara Vard VARE Varer Varow Varrd Varrde Varrow Veara Vearah Veard Vearer

If the name you are interested in is not here, try Section C.

Veire Verah Vere Verer
Veara VEAR
Vearah VEAR
Veard VEAR
Vearer VEAR
Vearine VEARING
VEARING Vearine
VEARNCOMBE 4 Fearncombe Ferncombe Verncombe
VEASY Vazy
VEECOCK Veaco Veacock
VEEL 7 VALE VEAL VEALE VEALL Veile Vele
Veepon VIPAN VIPOND VIPONT
Veepond VIPAN VIPOND VIPONT
Veepont VIPAN VIPOND VIPONT
Veil VEAL
Veile VALE VEAL VEALE VEALL VEEL
Veipon VIPAN VIPOND VIPONT
Veire VARE VEAR
Vele BEAL VALE VEAL VEALE VEALL VEEL
Velender FELLINDER VALENDER
Vellender FELLINDER VALENDER
Veltam FELTHAM FELTON
Venes VENESS VENICE VENUS
VENESS 4 Venes VENICE VENUS
VENICE 4 Venes VENESS VENUS
VENING VENNING
Vennal FENNEL FUNNELL
VENNIMORE 58 Bennimore Fenamor Fenemer Fenemore Fenimore Fenmer Fenmere Fennamore Fennemore Fenneymore FENNIMORE Fennymore Fiddimore Fillmore FILMER Filmore Finamer Finamoore Finamore Finemer Finemere Finemor Finemore Finimor Finmer Finmere FINMORE Finnamoor Finnamoore Finnamore FINNEMORE Finneymoore Finneymore Finnymoor Finnymore Finymore Fynmer Fynnamore Fynnemore Fynneymoore Fynneymore Fynnimore Fynnymore Philimore PHILLIMORE Philmore Phinamor Phinamore Phinnamore Phinnemore Phinnmore Phynemore Phynnamore Phynnemore Phynneymore Phynnimore Phynnymore
VENNING VENING
VENTERMAN 7 Fenteman Fenterman FENTIMAN Fentoman Fentyman Ventyman
Ventyman FENTIMAN VENTERMAN
VENUS 4 Venes VENESS VENICE
Vepans VIPAN VIPOND VIPONT
Vepend VIPAN VIPOND VIPONT
Veping VIPAN VIPOND VIPONT
Vepoint VIPAN VIPOND VIPONT
Vepon VIPOND VIPONT
Vepond VIPAN VIPOND VIPONT
Veponn VIPAN VIPOND VIPONT
Vepound VIPAN VIPOND VIPONT
Vepoynte VIPAN VIPOND VIPONT
Veppine VIPAN VIPOND VIPONT
Veppon VIPOND VIPONT
Verah VEAR
Verchell FAIRCHILD
Verchild FAIRCHILD
Verchilde FAIRCHILD
Verco VARCOE VERCOE
VERCOE 4 Varco VARCOE Verco
Vere VEAR WEIR
Verer VEAR
Verham VARNHAM VERNON
VERINDER Verrender VERRINDER
VERIOD Veriot
Veriot VERIOD
Verley WHORLEY
Verli WHORLEY
Verly WHORLEY
Vernal VERNALL
VERNALL 9 Varnol Vernal Vernalls Vernals Vernel Vernell Vernoll Vernols
Vernalls VERNALL
Vernals VERNALL
Verncombe VEARNCOMBE
Vernel VERNALL
Vernell VERNALL
Vernham VARNHAM VERNON
Vernoll VERNALL
Vernols VERNALL
VERNON 5 VARNHAM Varnon Verham Vernham
Verpende VIPAN VIPOND VIPONT
Verpent VIPAN VIPOND VIPONT
Verpond VIPAN VIPOND VIPONT
VERRAL 5 Ferral Ferrul FIRRELL Furrel
VERRALL 7 FAIRALL FAIRHALL Verrell Verrells VERRILL Verrills
VERRAN Verron
VERRANT 4 Varrant Varrent Verrent
Verrell FAIRALL FAIRHALL VERRALL VERRILL
Verrells FAIRALL FAIRHALL VERRALL VERRILL
Verrender VERINDER VERRINDER
Verrent VERRANT
VERRILL 7 FAIRALL FAIRHALL VERRALL Verrell Verrells Verrills
Verrills FAIRALL FAIRHALL VERRALL VERRILL
VERRINDER VERINDER Verrender
Verron VERRAN
VESEY 7 De vesci Vaisey VASEY VESSEY Vessie Vessy
VESSEY De vesci VESEY
Vessie VESEY
Vessy VESEY
Veterepond VIPAN VIPOND VIPONT
Veterepont VIPAN VIPOND VIPONT
VEY Vie VYE
Vial VIALLS VIALS
Viall VIALLS VIALS
VIALLS 4 Vial Viall VIALS
VIALS 4 Vial Viall VIALLS
Vian VYAN
VIAR Viard
Viard VIAR
VICARS 13 Vicas VICCARS VICKARS VICKERS Vickhouse Vickous Vicr Vicres Vicrs Vicus VIGERS Vuckis
VICARY VICKERY
Vicas VICARS VICCARS VICKARS VICKERS VIGERS
VICCARS 13 VICARS Vicas VICKARS VICKERS Vickhouse Vickous Vicr Vicres Vicrs Vicus VIGERS Vuckis
VICE 12 Feese FICE Fis FISE Fits FITZ Fitze Fyz Vise VYSE Vyze
VICKARS 13 VICARS Vicas VICCARS VICKERS Vickhouse Vickous Vicr Vicres Vicrs Vicus VIGERS Vuckis
VICKARY VICKERY
VICKERAGE Vickress Vickris
VICKERS 13 VICARS Vicas VICCARS VICKARS Vickhouse Vickous Vicr Vicres Vicrs Vicus VIGERS Vuckis
VICKERY VICARY VICKARY
Vickhouse VICARS VICCARS VICKARS VICKERS VIGERS
Vickous VICARS VICCARS VICKARS VICKERS VIGERS
Vickress VICKERAGE
Vickris VICKERAGE
Vicr VICARS VICCARS VICKARS VICKERS VIGERS
Vicres VICARS VICCARS VICKARS VICKERS VIGERS
Vicrs VICARS VICCARS VICKARS VICKERS VIGERS
Vicus VICARS VICCARS VICKARS VICKERS VIGERS
Vie VEY VYE
VIGERS 15 VICARS Vicas VICCARS VICKARS VICKERS Vickhouse Vickous Vicr Vicres Vicrs Vicus VIGUS Vuckis Wvigus
Vigors VIGUS
Vigours VIGUS
Vigues VIGURS
VIGURS Vigues
VIGUS 6 VIGERS Vigors Vigours Vikers Wvigus
Vikers VIGUS
VILDAY Filday Vildey
Vildey VILDAY
Vilsone WILLSON WILSON
Vinceant VINCENT
VINCENT Vinceant
Vinell FENNEL FUNNELL
Vineyard WINYARD
VINTER Vynter
Vipam VIPAN VIPOND VIPONT
VIPAN 74 Vapent Vapont Vappers Vappon Veapond Veepon Veepond Veepont Veipon Vepans Vepend Veping Vepoint Vepond Veponn Vepound Vepoynte Veppine Verpende Verpent Verpond Veterepond Veterepont Vipam Vipant Vipart Vipe Vipeham Vipehan Vipen Vipend Vipent Viper Viphan Viphill Viphirs Viphors Viphours Vipin Vipind Viping Vipoint Vipon VIPOND Viponde VIPONT Viport Vipos Vipound Vipounde Vipount Vipounte Vipout Vippars Vippen Vippin Vippon Vippur Vipun Vipus Vitropent Vitropond Vuipent Vupend Vypant Vypend Vyping Vypointe Vypond Vyponde Vypont Vyponte Vypounde
Vipant VIPAN VIPOND VIPONT
Vipart VIPAN VIPOND VIPONT
Vipe VIPAN VIPOND VIPONT
Vipeham VIPAN VIPOND VIPONT
Vipehan VIPAN VIPOND VIPONT
Vipen VIPAN VIPOND VIPONT
Vipend VIPAN VIPOND VIPONT
Vipent VIPAN VIPOND VIPONT
Viper VIPAN VIPOND VIPONT
Viphan VIPAN VIPOND VIPONT
Viphill VIPAN VIPOND VIPONT
Viphirs VIPAN VIPOND VIPONT
Viphors VIPAN VIPOND VIPONT
Viphours VIPAN VIPOND VIPONT
Vipin VIPAN VIPOND VIPONT
Vipind VIPAN VIPOND VIPONT
Viping VIPAN VIPOND VIPONT
Vipoint VIPAN VIPOND VIPONT
Vipon VIPAN VIPOND VIPONT
VIPOND 77 Vapent Vapont Vappers Vappon Veapond Veepon Veepond Veepont Veipon Vepans Vepend Veping Vepoint Vepon Vepond Veponn Vepound Vepoynte Veppine Veppon Verpende Verpent Verpond Veterepond Veterepont Vipam VIPAN Vipant Vipart Vipe Vipeham Vipehan Vipen Vipend Vipent Viper Viphan Viphill Viphirs Viphors Viphours Vipin Vipind Viping Vipoint Vipon Viponde VIPONT Viport Vipos Vipound Vipounde Vipount Vipounte Vipout Vippan Vippars Vippen Vippin Vippon Vippur Vipun Vipus Vitropent Vitropond Vuipent Vupend Vypant Vypend Vyping Vypointe Vypond Vyponde Vypont Vyponte Vypounde
Viponde VIPAN VIPOND VIPONT
VIPONT 77 Vapent Vapont Vappers Vappon Veapond Veepon Veepond Veepont Veipon Vepans Vepend

If the name you are interested in is not here, try Section C.

Veping Vepoint Vepon Vepond Veponn Vepound Vepoynte Veppine Veppon Verpende Verpent Verpond Veterepond Veterepont Vipam VIPAN Vipant Vipart Vipe Vipeham Vipehan Vipen Vipend Vipent Viper Viphan Viphill Viphirs Viphors Viphours Vipin Vipind Viping Vipoint Vipon VIPOND Viponde Viport Vipos Vipound Vipounde Vipount Vipounte Vipout Vippan Vippars Vippen Vippin Vippon Vippur Vipun Vipus Vitropent Vitropond Vuipent Vupend Vypant Vypend Vyping Vypointe Vypond Vyponde Vypont Vyponte Vypounde
Viport VIPAN VIPOND VIPONT
Vipos VIPAN VIPOND VIPONT
Vipound VIPAN VIPOND VIPONT
Vipounde VIPAN VIPOND VIPONT
Vipount VIPAN VIPOND VIPONT
Vipounte VIPAN VIPOND VIPONT
Vipout VIPAN VIPOND VIPONT
Vippan VIPOND VIPONT
Vippars VIPAN VIPOND VIPONT
Vippen VIPAN VIPOND VIPONT
Vippin VIPAN VIPOND VIPONT
Vippon VIPAN VIPOND VIPONT
Vippur VIPAN VIPOND VIPONT
Vipun VIPAN VIPOND VIPONT
Vipus VIPAN VIPOND VIPONT
Virly WHORLEY
Vise FICE FISE FITZ VICE VYSE
Vishlake FISHLOCK
Vitropent VIPAN VIPOND VIPONT
Vitropond VIPAN VIPOND VIPONT
VIVASH 5 Fiveash Viveash Vivish Vivosh
Viveash VIVASH
VIVIAN 6 BEAVAN Bivyen HOCKETT VIVYAN Vyvyan
Vivish VIVASH
Vivosh VIVASH
VIVYAN VIVIAN Vyvyan
Voaden BOWDEN VODDEN VODEN VOUSDEN
VOAK 4 VOAKE Vouk Vouke
VOAKE 4 VOAK Vouk Vouke
Voakes VOKES
Voaks VOKES
VODDEN 11 BOWDEN Vauden Vawden Voaden Voddon VODEN Vodin Vouden VOUSDEN Vowden
Voddon BOWDEN VODDEN VODEN VOUSDEN
VODEN 11 BOWDEN Vauden Vawden Voaden VODDEN Voddon Vodin Vouden VOUSDEN Vowden
Vodin BOWDEN VODDEN VODEN VOUSDEN
VOGAN 12 Fychan Vaghan Vahan VAUGHAN VOGHAN Vogin Vougan Voughan Voughen Voughn Voughon
VOGHAN 12 Fychan Vaghan Vahan VAUGHAN VOGAN Vogin Vougan Voughan Voughen Voughn Voughon
Voghill FOWELL
Vogin VAUGHAN VOGAN VOGHAN
Voiter VOTIER
VOKES Voakes Voaks
Vollar VALLAR VALLER VOLLER
VOLLER 4 VALLAR VALLER Vollar
Voorman FOREMAN FORMAN
Vos VOSS
VOSS 4 Vauss Vos Vox
Votia VOTIER
VOTIER 5 Vautier Voiter Votia Votyer
Votyer VOTIER
Vouden BOWDEN VODDEN VODEN VOUSDEN
Vougan VAUGHAN VOGAN VOGHAN
Voughan VAUGHAN VOGAN VOGHAN
Voughen VAUGHAN VOGAN VOGHAN
Voughn VAUGHAN VOGAN VOGHAN
Voughon VAUGHAN VOGAN VOGHAN
Vouk VOAK VOAKE
Vouke VOAK VOAKE
VOUSDEN 9 BOWDEN Voaden VODDEN Voddon VODEN Vodin Vouden Vowden
Vowden BOWDEN VODDEN VODEN VOUSDEN
Vowel FOWELL
Vox VOSS
VSTEISON Usteison
Vuckis VICARS VICCARS VICKARS VICKERS VIGERS
Vuipent VIPAN VIPOND VIPONT
Vupend VIPAN VIPOND VIPONT
VYAN Vian
VYE VEY Vie
Vylie WYLIE WYLLIE
Vynter VINTER
Vypant VIPAN VIPOND VIPONT
Vypend VIPAN VIPOND VIPONT
Vyping VIPAN VIPOND VIPONT
Vypointe VIPAN VIPOND VIPONT
Vypond VIPAN VIPOND VIPONT
Vyponde VIPAN VIPOND VIPONT
Vypont VIPAN VIPOND VIPONT
Vyponte VIPAN VIPOND VIPONT
Vypounde VIPAN VIPOND VIPONT
VYSE 4 VICE Vise Vyze
Vyvyan VIVIAN VIVYAN
Vyze VICE VYSE
Waddam WADHAM WADHAMS WADMAN
Waddams WADHAM WADHAMS WADMAN
Waddan WADHAM WADHAMS WADMAN
WADDELOW 7 Waddilow Waddilowe Wadelow Wadiloe WADLOW Wadlowe
Wadden WADHAM WADHAMS WADMAN
Waddilow WADDELOW WADLOW
Waddilowe WADDELOW WADLOW
Waddingham WADDINGTON
WADDINGTON Waddingham
Waddon WADHAM WADHAMS WADMAN
WADE WARD Warde
Wadelow WADDELOW WADLOW
WADHAM 9 Waddam Waddams Waddan Wadden Waddon WADHAMS Wadim WADMAN
WADHAMS 9 Waddam Waddams Waddan Wadden Waddon WADHAM Wadim WADMAN
Wadiloe WADDELOW WADLOW
Wadim WADHAM WADHAMS WADMAN
WADLOW 7 WADDELOW Waddilow Waddilowe Wadelow Wadiloe Wadlowe
Wadlowe WADDELOW WADLOW
WADMAN 9 Waddam Waddams Waddan Wadden Waddon WADHAM WADHAMS Wadim
Waeich WAEICK
WAEICK Waeich
Waggestaff WAGSTAFF WAGSTAFFE
Waggon WAGHORN
Waggstaf WAGSTAFF WAGSTAFFE
Waggstafe WAGSTAFF WAGSTAFFE
Waggstaff WAGSTAFF WAGSTAFFE
Waggstaffe WAGSTAFF WAGSTAFFE
WAGHORN 4 Waggon Waghorne Wagon
Waghorne WAGHORN
Wagon WAGHORN
Wagstaf WAGSTAFF WAGSTAFFE
Wagstafe WAGSTAFF WAGSTAFFE
WAGSTAFF 9 Waggestaff Waggstaf Waggstafe Waggstaff Waggstaffe Wagstaf Wagstafe WAGSTAFFE
WAGSTAFFE 9 Waggestaff Waggstaf Waggstafe Waggstaff Waggstaffe Wagstaf Wagstafe WAGSTAFF
Waight WAIT WAITE WAITES WAYTE WAYTH WEIGHT WHAITES
Waights WAIT WAITE WAITES WAYTE WAYTH WEIGHT WHAITES
Wailes WALES
WAIN 10 WAINE Wainer Wane Wayne Wayner Wean Weane Wein Wene
Waindman WAINEMAN WAINMAN
WAINE 10 WAIN Wainer Wane Wayne Wayner Wean Weane Wein Wene
WAINEMAN 5 Waindman WAINMAN Wayneman Waynman
Wainer WAIN WAINE
WAINMAN 6 Waindman WAINEMAN WAYMAN Wayneman Waynman
Waistell WASTELL
WAIT 22 Waight Waights WAITE WAITES Waithe Waits Wate Wates Wayt WAYTE Waytes WAYTH Waythe Wayths WEIGHT Weighte Weights Whaite WHAITES Whaits Whayte
WAITE 22 Waight Waights WAIT WAITES Waithe Waits Wate Wates Wayt WAYTE Waytes WAYTH Waythe Wayths WEIGHT Weighte Weights Whaite WHAITES Whaits Whayte
WAITES 23 THWAITES Waight Waights WAIT WAITE Waithe Waits Wate Wates Wayt WAYTE Waytes WAYTH Waythe Wayths WEIGHT Weighte Weights Whaite WHAITES Whaits Whayte
Waithe WAIT WAITE WAITES WAYTE WAYTH WEIGHT WHAITES
Waits WAIT WAITE WAITES WAYTE WAYTH WEIGHT WHAITES
WAKEFIELD 5 Beakerfield WAKEFORD Weakfield Woakfield
WAKEFORD WAKEFIELD WEAKFORD
WAKEHAM Weakham
WAKELAM Wakelem Whakelam
Wakelem WAKELAM
Wakelen WAKELIN WAKELING
WAKELEY 5 WAKELIN WAKELY WAKERLEY Wakerly
WAKELIN 8 Wakelen WAKELEY WAKELING WAKELY WAKERLEY Wakerly WEAKLIM
WAKELING Wakelen WAKELIN
WAKELY 5 WAKELEY WAKELIN WAKERLEY Wakerly
Wakelyn WALKLIN
WAKERLEY 10 WAKELEY WAKELIN WAKELY Wakerly WAKLEY WALKERLEY WALKEY WALKLEY WEAKLEY
Wakerly WAKELEY WAKELIN WAKELY WAKERLEY
Waklet WALKLATE
WAKLEY 6 WAKERLEY WALKERLEY WALKEY WALKLEY WEAKLEY
Walborn WALBRAN WALBURN
Walborne WALBRAN WALBURN
Walbourn WALBRAN WALBURN
Walbourne WALBRAN WALBURN
WALBRAN 8 Walborn Walborne Walbourn Walbourne WALBURN Walburne Welburn
WALBURN 8 Walborn Walborne Walbourn Walbourne WALBRAN Walburne Welburn
Walburne WALBRAN WALBURN
WALCH 6 WALSH Walshe WELCH WELSH Welshe
WALDEGRAVE 7 Waldgrave Walgraur Walgrave Walgrove Walsgrave Walsgrove
WALDEN 6 Waldin WALDING WALDREN WALDRON Wallden
Waldgrave WALDEGRAVE
Waldin WALDEN WALDING WALDRON
WALDING 5 WALDEN Waldin WALDREN Wallden
WALDREN 4 WALDEN WALDING Wallden
WALDRON 15 Valeran WALDEN Waldin Waldrond Waleran Walerand Waleraund

If the name you are interested in is not here, try Section C.

Wallrond Walran Walrand Walrauen Walraund Walron WALROND
Waldrond WALDRON WALROND
WALE WHALE WHEALE
Waleran WALDRON WALROND
Walerand WALDRON WALROND
Waleraund WALDRON WALROND
Walerton WILLERTON WOOLERTON
WALES 9 Wailes WALLS Wals Weals Whailes WHALES Whalls Whals
Waley WALLEY WHALEY WHALLEY
Walgraur WALDEGRAVE
Walgrave WALDEGRAVE
Walgrove WALDEGRAVE
Walin WALLIN
Walkelate WALKLATE
WALKERLEY 6 WAKERLEY WAKLEY WALKEY WALKLEY WEAKLEY
WALKEY 6 WAKERLEY WAKLEY WALKERLEY WALKLEY WEAKLEY
Walklat WALKLATE
WALKLATE 8 Waklet Walkelate Walklat Walklet Walklett Walklot Wauklet
Walklet WALKLATE
Walklett WALKLATE
WALKLEY 6 WAKERLEY WAKLEY WALKERLEY WALKEY WEAKLEY
WALKLIN Wakelyn
Walklot WALKLATE
Walkman WORKMAN
WALL 5 WALLE WALLER Whall Whalle
WALLACE WALLIS
WALLAGE WORLEDGE
Wallden WALDEN WALDING WALDREN
WALLE 4 WALL WALLER Whalle
Wallen WALLIN
WALLER 4 WALL WALLE Whalle
Wallerton WILLERTON WOOLERTON
Walles WALLIS
WALLEY 5 Waley WHALEY WHALLEY Whawley
WALLIN Walin Wallen
WALLIS 5 WALLACE Walles Wallish WALLS
Wallish WALLIS WALLS
Wallrond WALDRON WALROND
WALLS 9 WALES WALLIS Wallish Wals Weals WHALES Whalls Whals
WALMSLEY 4 Wamsley Warmsley WORMSLEY
WALPOLE 4 Walpoole Warpole Worpel
Walpoole WALPOLE
Walran WALDRON WALROND
Walrand WALDRON WALROND
Walrauen WALDRON WALROND
Walraund WALDRON WALROND
Walron WALDRON WALROND
WALROND 13 Valeran WALDRON Waldrond Waleran Walerand Waleraund Wallrond Walran Walrand Walrauen Walraund Walron
Wals WALES WALLS WHALES
Walsgrave WALDEGRAVE
Walsgrove WALDEGRAVE
WALSH 6 WALCH Walshe WELCH WELSH Welshe
WALSHAW Welshaw
Walshe WALCH WALSH WELCH WELSH
Walten WALTON
WALTER 6 WALTERS Waltiar WARLTIER WARLTIRE Wartyre
WALTERS 4 WALTER WATERS WATTERS
Waltiar WALTER WARLTIER WARLTIRE
WALTON 8 De wharton Walten WARTON Werfton WHARTON Whartonne WORTON
Wamsley WALMSLEY WORMSLEY
Wancklen WANKLIN WANKLING
Wand WAUD
Wane WAIN WAINE
WANKLIN 4 Wancklen WANKLING Wanklyn
WANKLING 4 Wancklen WANKLIN Wanklyn
Wanklyn WANKLIN WANKLING
Wannister WINNISTER
Wansborough WANSBROUGH
WANSBROUGH Wansborough
Warberton WARBLETON WARBURTON
Warbey WARBOYS WORBEY WORBY
WARBLETON Warberton WARBURTON
Warbois WARBOYS
Warboise WARBOYS
WARBOYS 7 Warbey Warbois Warboise Warby WORBEY WORBY
WARBURTON Warberton WARBLETON
Warby WARBOYS WORBEY WORBY
WARD WADE Warde
WARDALE WARDLE
Warde WADE WARD
Wardele WARDELL
WARDELL 5 Wardele WARDIELL Wardill WARDLE
Wardeman HARDEMAN HARDIMAN HARDYMAN
WARDIELL WARDELL WARDLE
Wardill WARDELL WARDLE
WARDLE 5 WARDALE WARDELL WARDIELL Wardill
WARDLEY 5 WOODLEY WORDLEY WORDLY WORTLEY
WARDNER WARNER
WARE 5 WEAR WEARE WERE WHEARE
WAREHAM 4 WARHAM Wearham Werham
Wareing WARING
Waren WARN WARNE WEARNE
Warenne DE WARENNE WARREN
WARHAM WAREHAM Werham
Warie WARRY WHARRY
WARING 4 Wareing WARREN Wearing
Warkman WORKMAN
Warlan WARLAND
WARLAND 4 Warlan Warlon Warlond
Warle WHORLEY
Warley WHORLEY
Warlon WARLAND
Warlond WARLAND
WARLOW Whollo WHORLOW
WARLTIER 5 WALTER Waltiar WARLTIRE Wartyre
WARLTIRE 5 WALTER Waltiar WARLTIER Wartyre
Warmsley WALMSLEY WORMSLEY
WARN 7 Waren WARNE Wearn WEARNE WORN Worne
WARNE 9 Waren WARN WARNER WARREN Wearn WEARNE WORN Worne
WARNER 4 WARDNER WARNE WARREN
WARNHAM 7 WERNHAM Wirdnam WIRNHAM WORNHAM WYRDENHAM WYRNHAM
Warpman WORKMAN
Warpole WALPOLE
WARR 10 HAW HOARE HORE WEARE Whore Woar Woare WOOR Woore
WARRAD 7 WARWOOD WHARRAD Wharrod WHORWOOD WORRAD WORROD
WARRE 6 WARREY WARRIE WARRY WARRYE WHARRY
Warrell WORRELL
WARREN 9 De varenne DE WARENNE De warren Warenne WARING WARNE WARNER Warring
Warrenton WARRINGTON WORTHINGTON
WARREY 6 WARRE WARRIE WARRY WARRYE WHARRY
WARRICK WARWICK
WARRIE 6 WARRE WARREY WARRY WARRYE WHARRY
Warring WARREN
WARRINGTON 6 Warrenton Worlich Worlington Worrington WORTHINGTON
Warrity WHERTY
WARRY 9 Warie WARRE WARREY WARRIE WARRYE Wary WHARRY Worie
WARRYE 6 WARRE WARREY WARRIE WARRY WHARRY
WARTON 7 De wharton WALTON Werfton WHARTON Whartonne WORTON
Wartyre WALTER WARLTIER WARLTIRE
WARWICK WARRICK
WARWOOD 8 WARRAD WHARRAD Wharrod WHORWOOD WORRAD WORROD WORWOOD
Wary WARRY WHARRY
Was VAUSE WASE WASS WASSE
Wasborn OSBAND OSBORN OSBORNE OSBOURN OSBOURNE
Wasdal WESTALL WORSDELL
Wasdall WESTALL WORSDELL
WASE 7 Vaus VAUSE Was WASS WASSE Waus
Wasgate WASKETT
Washbourne OSBAND OSBORN OSBORNE OSBOURN OSBOURNE
Wasket WASKETT
WASKETT 5 Wasgate Wasket Wosket Woskett
Wasmecoat WESTMACOT WESTMACOTE WESTMACOTT WESTMANCOAT WESTMANCOTT WESTNACOTT
WASS 7 Vaus VAUSE Was WASE WASSE Waus
WASSALL WASSELL
WASSE 7 Vaus VAUSE Was WASE WASS Waus
WASSELL WASSALL
WASTELL Waistell
Wat WATT
WATCHAM Watsham
Wate WAIT WAITE WAITES WAYTE WAYTH WEIGHT WHAITES
Water WATERS WATTERS WATTIS WATTS
WATERAGE Wateridge
Wateridge WATERAGE
Waterlo WATERLOW
WATERLOW Waterlo
WATERS 13 WALTERS Water Wates Wats WATTERS Wattes Wattie WATTIS WATTS Wattus Worters Worts
Wates WAIT WAITE WAITES WATERS WATTERS WATTIS WATTS WAYTE WAYTH WEIGHT WHAITES
Watheridge WITHERIDGE
WATHEW 5 Wathews Wathey WATTHEW WATTHEWS
Wathews WATHEW WATTHEW WATTHEWS
Wathey WATHEW WATTHEW WATTHEWS
WATKIN WATKINS
WATKINS WATKIN
Watley WOTTLEY
WATMER 8 Watmoor Watmor WATMORE WATMOUGH WATTMORE Whatmoore WHATMORE
Watmoor WATMER WATMORE WATTMORE WHATMORE
Watmor WATMER WATMORE WATTMORE WHATMORE
WATMORE 8 WATMER Watmoor Watmor WATMOUGH WATTMORE Whatmoore WHATMORE
WATMOUGH 5 WATMER WATMORE WATTMORE WHATMORE
Wats WATERS WATTERS WATTIS WATTS
Watsham WATCHAM
WATT Wat
WATTERS 13 WALTERS Water WATERS Wates Wats Wattes Wattie WATTIS WATTS Wattus Worters Worts
Wattes WATERS WATTERS WATTIS WATTS
WATTHEW 6 MATTHEW WATHEW Wathews Wathey WATTHEWS
WATTHEWS 5 WATHEW Wathews Wathey WATTHEW
Wattie WATERS WATTERS WATTIS WATTS
WATTIS 12 Water WATERS Wates Wats WATTERS Wattes Wattie WATTS Wattus Worters Worts
WATTMORE 8 WATMER Watmoor Watmor WATMORE WATMOUGH Whatmoore WHATMORE
WATTON WHATTON
WATTS 12 Water WATERS Wates Wats WATTERS Wattes Wattie WATTIS Wattus Worters Worts
Wattus WATERS WATTERS WATTIS WATTS
WAUD 7 Wand Waude Waudebie Waudie Waund Woad
Waude WAUD
Waudebie WAUD
Waudie WAUD
Wauklet WALKLATE
Waund WAUD
Waus VAUSE WASE WASS WASSE
Wavin WEAVING
Wawley WHORLEY
WAY WHALE
WAYMAN WAINMAN
Wayne WAIN WAINE
Wayneman WAINEMAN WAINMAN

If the name you are interested in is not here, try Section C.

Wayner WAIN WAINE
Waynman WAINEMAN WAINMAN
Wayt WAIT WAITE WAITES WAYTE WAYTH WEIGHT WHAITES
WAYTE 22 Waight Waights WAIT WAITE WAITES Waithe Waits Wate Wates Wayt Waytes WAYTH Waythe Wayths WEIGHT Weighte Weights Whaite WHAITES Whaits Whayte
Waytes WAIT WAITE WAITES WAYTE WAYTH WEIGHT WHAITES
WAYTH 22 Waight Waights WAIT WAITE WAITES Waithe Waits Wate Wates Wayt WAYTE Waytes Waythe Wayths WEIGHT Weighte Weights Whaite WHAITES Whaits Whayte
Waythe WAIT WAITE WAITES WAYTE WAYTH WEIGHT WHAITES
Wayths WAIT WAITE WAITES WAYTE WAYTH WEIGHT WHAITES
Weakfield WAKEFIELD
WEAKFORD WAKEFORD
Weakham WAKEHAM
WEAKLEY 6 WAKERLEY WAKLEY WALKERLEY WALKEY WALKLEY
WEAKLIM WAKELIN
Weakly WEEKLEY WICKLIN
Weal WEALE WHEAL WHEALE
WEALAND Wealands
Wealands WEALAND
Wealby WELBY WELSBY WILBY
WEALE 5 Weal WHEAL WHEALE Wheel
Weals WALES WALLS WHALES
Wean WAIN WAINE
Weane WAIN WAINE
WEAR 5 WARE WEARE WERE WHEARE
WEARE 14 HAW HOARE HORE WARE WARR WEAR WERE WHEARE Whore Woar Woare WOOR Woore
Wearham WAREHAM
Wearing WARING
Wearn WARN WARNE WEARNE
WEARNE 5 Waren WARN WARNE Wearn
WEARY 7 Werrey Werrie WERRY Wheary Wheery WHERRY
Weastherell WETHERAL
Weatherald WETHERALD
WEATHERALL Witherall
Weatheredge WITHERIDGE
Weathereg WITHERIDGE
WEATHERHEAD 4 Wetherhead Wetherherd Whetherherd
Weatheridge WITHERIDGE
Weatherige WITHERIDGE
Weathers WITHERS
Weatherspoon WITHERSPOON WOTHERSPOON
Weaven WEAVING
Weavin WEAVING
WEAVING 4 Wavin Weaven Weavin
Webbel WEBBERLEY WEBLEY WHIBLEY
Webbeley WEBBERLEY WEBLEY WHIBLEY
WEBBERLEY 11 Webbel Webbeley Webbly WEBLEY Webly Weebyly Weobley WHIBLEY Wibelai Wibley
Webbly WEBBERLEY WEBLEY WHIBLEY
WEBDAY Wibday
Webkin WIEBKIN
WEBLEY 11 Webbel Webbeley WEBBERLEY Webbly Webly Weebyly Weobley WHIBLEY Wibelai Wibley
Webly WEBBERLEY WEBLEY WHIBLEY
WEBSTER Websture
Websture WEBSTER
WEDDALL WEDDELL
WEDDELL WEDDALL
Wedderspon WITHERSPOON WOTHERSPOON
Weddon WHEADON WHEATON WHITTON
WEDLAKE WIDLAKE
Weebyly WEBBERLEY WEBLEY WHIBLEY
Weekerson WILKINSON
WEEKES WEEKS
WEEKLEY 4 Weakly Wickland WICKLIN
WEEKS WEEKES
Weeldig WILDIG WILDIN WILDING
Weelebee WELBY WELSBY WILBY
Weeler WHEELER WHELLER
WEETMAN 6 Weightman Wetman Wheatman WHITEMAN WIGHTMAN
WEIGHT 22 Waight Waights WAIT WAITE WAITES Waithe Waits Wate Wates Wayt WAYTE Waytes WAYTH Waythe Wayths Weighte Weights Whaite WHAITES Whaits Whayte
Weighte WAIT WAITE WAITES WAYTE WAYTH WEIGHT WHAITES
Weightman WEETMAN WHITEMAN WIGHTMAN
WEIGHTON Wighton
Weights WAIT WAITE WAITES WAYTE WAYTH WEIGHT WHAITES
Wein WAIN WAINE
WEIR Vere Wier
Welband WHEELBAND WILBORN
Welbe WELBY WELSBY WILBY
Welbeaby WELBY WELSBY WILBY
Welbee WELBY WELSBY WILBY
Welbey WELBY WELSBY WILBY
Welbie WELBY WELSBY WILBY
Welborn WHEELBAND WILBORN WILBOURNE
Welborne WILBOURNE
Welbourn WHEELBAND WILBORN
WELBROCK Welbrook
Welbrook WELBROCK
Welburn WALBRAN WALBURN WILBOURNE
WELBY 23 Wealby Weelebee Welbe Welbeaby Welbee Welbey Welbie Welbye Wellbe Wellbee Wellbey Wellbie Wellby Wellbye Wellebye Welliaby WELSBY Whelby Wheleby WILBY Willby Willebey
Welbye WELBY WELSBY WILBY
WELCH 6 WALCH WALSH Walshe WELSH Welshe
WELCHMAN Welshman
Welden WELDON WELDONE
WELDON 5 Welden WELDONE Wellden Welldon
WELDONE 5 Welden WELDON Wellden Welldon
Welerton WILLERTON WOOLERTON
Weles WELLS
WELFARE Welfer
Welfer WELFARE
WELFORD 5 Welfords Welfors Wellford WILFORD
Welfords WELFORD WILFORD
Welfors WELFORD WILFORD
Welladvised WILLAVISE
WELLARD Wellerd Willard
Wellavise WILLAVISE
Wellbe WELBY WELSBY WILBY
Wellbee WELBY WELSBY WILBY
Wellbey WELBY WELSBY WILBY
Wellbie WELBY WELSBY WILBY
Wellby WELBY WELSBY WILBY
Wellbye WELBY WELSBY WILBY
Wellden WELDON WELDONE
Welldig WILDIG WILDIN WILDING
Welldon WELDON WELDONE
Wellebye WELBY WELSBY WILBY
Wellerd WELLARD
Wellerton WILLERTON WOOLERTON
Welles WELLS
Wellford WELFORD WILFORD
Welliaby WELBY WELSBY WILBY
WELLMAN Welman
WELLS 6 De welles Weles Welles Wels WILLS
Welman WELLMAN
WELMOTH 19 HELMOTH MEALEMOUTH MEALMOUTH Meldmouthis MELEMOUTH MELLMOUTHE Melmath MELMETH Melmore MELMOTH Melmoth-brooks Melmott MELMOUTH Melmouthes Melwoth Milmoth Milmouthes Molmoth
Wels WELLS
WELSBY 23 Wealby Weelebee Welbe Welbeaby Welbee Welbey Welbie WELBY Welbye Wellbe Wellbee Wellbey Wellbie Wellby Wellbye Wellebye Welliaby Whelby Wheleby WILBY Willby Willebey
WELSH 6 WALCH WALSH Walshe WELCH Welshe
Welshaw WALSHAW
Welshe WALCH WALSH WELCH WELSH
Welshman WELCHMAN
WENDEN 4 Wending Wendon Windin
Wending WENDEN
Wendon WENDEN
Wene WAIN WAINE
WENHAM 4 Whenham Whonham Wonham
WENMOTH Wenmouth
Wenmouth WENMOTH
Wenns WENS
WENS Wenns
WENTWORTH Wintworth
Weobley WEBBERLEY WEBLEY WHIBLEY
Werden WORDEN
WERE 5 WARE WEAR WEARE WHEARE
Werfton WALTON WARTON WHARTON WORTON
Werham WAREHAM WARHAM
Werkman WORKMAN
WERNHAM 7 WARNHAM Wirdnam WIRNHAM WORNHAM WYRDENHAM WYRNHAM
Werrey WEARY WERRY WHERRY
Werrie WEARY WERRY WHERRY
WERRY 7 WEARY Werrey Werrie Wheary Wheery WHERRY
Wersley WORSLEY
Werth WORTH
Wesbrook WESTBROOK WESTBROOKE
Wesdal WESTALL WORSDELL
Wesdall WESTALL WORSDELL
WESLEY WESTLEY
Wesmacott WESTMACOT WESTMACOTE WESTMACOTT WESTMANCOAT WESTMANCOTT WESTNACOTT
Wesmicot WESTMACOT WESTMACOTE WESTMACOTT WESTMANCOAT WESTMANCOTT WESTNACOTT
Wesmoor WESTMORE
Wesmoore WESTMORE
Wesmor WESTMORE
Wesmore WESTMORE
Wessmor WESTMORE
Wesson WESTON
Westabee WESTOBY
Westabie WESTOBY
Westaby WESTOBY
Westabye WESTOBY
Westal WESTALL WORSDELL
WESTALL 21 Wasdal Wasdall Wesdal Wesdall Westal Wisdal Wisdall Wordsell Worsdale Worsdall Worsdel WORSDELL Worsdoll Worstall Worstoll Wosdale Wosdell Wostil Wostill Wostoll
Westauby WESTOBY
Westawaie WESTAWAY
WESTAWAY 7 Westawaie Westawaye Westerway Westeway Westoway Westway
Westawaye WESTAWAY
Westbe WESTOBY
Westbie WESTOBY
Westbroke WESTBROOK WESTBROOKE
WESTBROOK 4 Wesbrook Westbroke WESTBROOKE
WESTBROOKE 4 Wesbrook Westbroke WESTBROOK
Westby WESTOBY
Westebee WESTOBY
Westebey WESTOBY
Westebie WESTOBY
Westeby WESTOBY
Westebye WESTOBY
Westemecott WESTMACOT WESTMACOTE WESTMACOTT WESTMANCOAT WESTMANCOTT WESTNACOTT
Westemore WESTMORE
Westerbey WESTOBY
Westerbie WESTOBY
Westerby WESTOBY
Westerbye WESTOBY
Westerway WESTAWAY
Westetun WESTON
Westeway WESTAWAY
Westgarten WESTGARTH
WESTGARTH Westgarten
Westibie WESTOBY
Westiby WESTOBY
Westibye WESTOBY
Westington WESTON
WESTLEY WESLEY

If the name you are interested in is not here, try Section C.

Westmacet WESTMACOT WESTMACOTE WESTMACOTT WESTMANCOAT WESTMANCOTT WESTNACOTT
Westmackit WESTMACOT WESTMACOTE WESTMACOTT WESTMANCOAT WESTMANCOTT WESTNACOTT
Westmacoat WESTMACOT WESTMACOTE WESTMACOTT WESTMANCOAT WESTMANCOTT WESTNACOTT
WESTMACOT 28 Wasmecoat Wesmacott Wesmicot Westemecott Westmacet Westmackit Westmacoat WESTMACOTE WESTMACOTT Westmacotte Westmacutt Westmaggott Westmaket WESTMANCOAT Westmancote WESTMANCOTT Westmancourt Westmarrott Westmarutt Westmecet Westmecott Westmicott Westmoncoat Westmoncote Westmuchett Westmuckett WESTNACOTT
WESTMACOTE 28 Wasmecoat Wesmacott Wesmicot Westemecott Westmacet Westmackit Westmacoat WESTMACOT WESTMACOTT Westmacotte Westmacutt Westmaggott Westmaket WESTMANCOAT Westmancote WESTMANCOTT Westmancourt Westmarrott Westmarutt Westmecet Westmecott Westmicott Westmoncoat Westmoncote Westmuchett Westmuckett WESTNACOTT
WESTMACOTT 28 Wasmecoat Wesmacott Wesmicot Westemecott Westmacet Westmackit Westmacoat WESTMACOT WESTMACOTE Westmacotte Westmacutt Westmaggott Westmaket WESTMANCOAT Westmancote WESTMANCOTT Westmancourt Westmarrott Westmarutt Westmecet Westmecott Westmicott Westmoncoat Westmoncote Westmuchett Westmuckett WESTNACOTT
Westmacotte WESTMACOT WESTMACOTE WESTMACOTT WESTMANCOAT WESTMANCOTT WESTNACOTT
Westmacutt WESTMACOT WESTMACOTE WESTMACOTT WESTMANCOAT WESTMANCOTT WESTNACOTT
Westmaggott WESTMACOT WESTMACOTE WESTMACOTT WESTMANCOAT WESTMANCOTT WESTNACOTT
Westmaket WESTMACOT WESTMACOTE WESTMACOTT WESTMANCOAT WESTMANCOTT WESTNACOTT
WESTMANCOAT 28 Wasmecoat Wesmacott Wesmicot Westemecott Westmacet Westmackit Westmacoat WESTMACOT WESTMACOTE WESTMACOTT Westmacotte Westmacutt Westmaggott Westmaket Westmancote WESTMANCOTT Westmancourt Westmarrott Westmarutt Westmecet Westmecott Westmicott Westmoncoat Westmoncote Westmuchett Westmuckett WESTNACOTT
Westmancote WESTMACOT WESTMACOTE WESTMACOTT WESTMANCOAT WESTMANCOTT WESTNACOTT
WESTMANCOTT 28 Wasmecoat Wesmacott Wesmicot Westemecott Westmacet Westmackit Westmacoat WESTMACOT WESTMACOTE WESTMACOTT Westmacotte Westmacutt Westmaggott Westmaket WESTMANCOAT Westmancote Westmancourt Westmarrott Westmarutt Westmecet Westmecott Westmicott Westmoncoat Westmoncote Westmuchett Westmuckett WESTNACOTT
Westmancourt WESTMACOT WESTMACOTE WESTMACOTT WESTMANCOAT WESTMANCOTT WESTNACOTT
Westmare WESTMORE
Westmarrott WESTMACOT WESTMACOTE WESTMACOTT WESTMANCOAT WESTMANCOTT WESTNACOTT
Westmarutt WESTMACOT WESTMACOTE WESTMACOTT WESTMANCOAT WESTMANCOTT WESTNACOTT
Westmecet WESTMACOT WESTMACOTE WESTMACOTT WESTMANCOAT WESTMANCOTT WESTNACOTT
Westmecott WESTMACOT WESTMACOTE WESTMACOTT WESTMANCOAT WESTMANCOTT WESTNACOTT
Westmeer WESTMORE
Westmer WESTMORE
Westmicott WESTMACOT WESTMACOTE WESTMACOTT WESTMANCOAT WESTMANCOTT WESTNACOTT
Westmoncoat WESTMACOT WESTMACOTE WESTMACOTT WESTMANCOAT WESTMANCOTT WESTNACOTT
Westmoncote WESTMACOT WESTMACOTE WESTMACOTT WESTMANCOAT WESTMANCOTT WESTNACOTT
Westmond WESTMORE
Westmoor WESTMORE
Westmoore WESTMORE
Westmor WESTMORE
WESTMORE 14 Wesmoor Wesmoore Wesmor Wesmore Wessmor Westemore Westmare Westmeer Westmer Westmond Westmoor Westmoore Westmor
Westmuchett WESTMACOT WESTMACOTE WESTMACOTT WESTMANCOAT WESTMANCOTT WESTNACOTT
Westmuckett WESTMACOT WESTMACOTE WESTMACOTT WESTMANCOAT WESTMANCOTT WESTNACOTT
WESTNACOTT 28 Wasmecoat Wesmacott Wesmicot Westemecott Westmacet Westmackit Westmacoat WESTMACOT WESTMACOTE WESTMACOTT Westmacotte Westmacutt Westmaggott Westmaket WESTMANCOAT Westmancote WESTMANCOTT Westmancourt Westmarrott Westmarutt Westmecet Westmecott Westmicott Westmoncoat Westmoncote Westmuchett Westmuckett
Westobe WESTOBY
Westobie WESTOBY
WESTOBY 28 Westabee Westabie Westaby Westabye Westauby Westbe Westbie Westby Westebee Westebey Westebie Westeby Westebye Westerbey Westerbie Westerby Westerbye Westibie Westiby Westibye Westobe Westobie Westobye Westorby Westorebie Westybye Whesterby
Westobye WESTOBY
WESTON 8 Wesson Westetun Westington Westone Westun WHISTON WISTON
Westone WESTON
Westorby WESTOBY
Westorebie WESTOBY
Westoway WESTAWAY
Westun WESTON
Westway WESTAWAY
Westybye WESTOBY
Wether WITHERS
WETHERAL 4 Weastherell Wetherill Whetherill
WETHERALD Weatherald
Wetheredg WITHERIDGE
Wetheredge WITHERIDGE
Wetherhead WEATHERHEAD
Wetherherd WEATHERHEAD
Wetheridge WITHERIDGE
Wetherill WETHERAL
Wethers WITHERS
Wetherspoon WITHERSPOON WOTHERSPOON
Wetherudge WITHERIDGE
Wetheryde WITHERIDGE
Wetheryg WITHERIDGE
Wetman WEETMAN WHITEMAN WIGHTMAN
Weyle WYLIE WYLLIE
Whailes WALES
Whaite WAIT WAITE WAITES WAYTE WAYTH WEIGHT WHAITES
WHAITES 22 Waight Waights WAIT WAITE WAITES Waithe Waits Wate Wates Wayt WAYTE Waytes WAYTH Waythe Wayths WEIGHT Weighte Weights Whaite Whaits Whayte
Whaits WAIT WAITE WAITES WAYTE WAYTH WEIGHT WHAITES
Whakelam WAKELAM
WHALE 9 WALE WAY WHALES Whayle WHEAL WHEALE Wheall Whoal
Whalen WHELAN
WHALES 13 WALES WALLS Wals Weals WHALE Whalls Whals Whayle WHEAL WHEALE Wheall Whoal
WHALEY 5 Waley WALLEY WHALLEY Whawley
Whall WALL
Whalle WALL WALLE WALLER
WHALLEY 5 Waley WALLEY WHALEY Whawley
Whalls WALES WALLS WHALES
Whals WALES WALLS WHALES
Wharley WHORLEY
WHARRAD 7 WARRAD WARWOOD Wharrod WHORWOOD WORRAD WORROD
Wharrod WARRAD WARWOOD WHARRAD WHORWOOD WORRAD WORROD
WHARRY 9 Warie WARRE WARREY WARRIE WARRY WARRYE Wary Worie
WHARTON 7 De wharton WALTON WARTON Werfton Whartonne WORTON
Whartonne WALTON WARTON WHARTON WORTON
Wharty WHERTY
Whatley WOTTLEY
Whatmoore WATMER WATMORE WATTMORE WHATMORE
WHATMORE 8 WATMER Watmoor Watmor WATMORE WATMOUGH WATTMORE Whatmoore
WHATTON WATTON
Whawley WALLEY WHALEY WHALLEY WHORLEY
Whayle WHALE WHALES WHEAL WHEALE
Whayte WAIT WAITE WAITES WAYTE WAYTH WEIGHT WHAITES
WHEADON 5 Weddon WHEATON WHITTON Widdon
WHEAL 10 Weal WEALE WHALE WHALES Whayle WHEALE Wheall Wheel Whoal
WHEALE 11 WALE Weal WEALE WHALE WHALES Whayle WHEAL Wheall Wheel Whoal
Whealer WHEELER WHELLER
Wheall WHALE WHALES WHEAL WHEALE
WHEARE 5 WARE WEAR WEARE WERE
Whearly WHORLEY
Wheary WEARY WERRY WHERRY
WHEATLEY 4 Wheatly Whetley WHETLY
Wheatly WHEATLEY WHETLY
Wheatman WEETMAN WHITEMAN WIGHTMAN
WHEATON 5 Weddon WHEADON WHITTON Widdon
Wheel WEALE WHEAL WHEALE
Wheelan WHELAN
Wheelar WHEELER WHELLER
WHEELBAND 6 Eelborn Welband Welborn Welbourn WILBORN
WHEELDON WHEELTON Whelton
WHEELER 10 Weeler Whealer Wheelar Wheeller Wheiler Wheler WHELLER Whiler Whylr
Wheeller WHEELER WHELLER
WHEELTON WHEELDON Whelton
Wheery WEARY WERRY WHERRY
Wheiler WHEELER WHELLER
WHELAN Whalen Wheelan
Whelby WELBY WELSBY WILBY
Wheleby WELBY WELSBY WILBY
Wheler WHEELER WHELLER
Whelerton WILLERTON WOOLERTON
WHELLER 8 Weeler Whealer Wheelar WHEELER Wheeller Wheiler Wheler
Whelton WHEELDON WHEELTON
Whenham WENHAM
Wherden WORDEN
Wherley WHORLEY
Wherly WHORLEY

If the name you are interested in is not here, try Section C.

WHERRY 7 WEARY Werrey Werrie WERRY Wheary Wheery
WHERTY Warrity Wharty
Whesterby WESTOBY
Whetherherd WEATHERHEAD
Whetherige WITHERIDGE
Whetherill WETHERAL
Whetley WHEATLEY WHETLY
WHETLY 4 WHEATLEY Wheatly Whetley
WHIBLEY 11 Webbel Webbeley WEBBERLEY Webbly WEBLEY Webly Weebyly Weobley Wibelai Wibley
Whicker WHITCHER
Whiddington WHITTINGTON
Whidley WHITBY
WHIFFEN 8 WHIFFIN Whiffing Whiffyn Whyfyn Wifen Wiffen Wiffin
WHIFFIN 7 WHIFFEN Whiffing Whiffyn Whyfyn Wiffen Wiffin
Whiffing WHIFFEN WHIFFIN
Whiffyn WHIFFEN WHIFFIN
Whigam WHIGHAM
WHIGHAM Whigam
Whildig WILDIG WILDIN WILDING
Whiler WHEELER
Whilerton WILLERTON WOOLERTON
WHILLANCE Whillans WILLANS
Whillans WHILLANCE WILLANS
Whillerton WILLERTON WOOLERTON
Whilson WILLSON WILSON
Whimpenie PENNY WIMPENNY
Whinam WHINHAM
WHINCUP Winckup Wincop
Whinfrey WINFREY
WHINHAM 6 Whinam Whinholm Whinnem Whinnim Whinnom
Whinholm WHINHAM
Whinn WINN WYNN WYNNE
Whinnem WHINHAM
Whinnim WHINHAM
Whinnom WHINHAM
Whinyates WINGATE
Whirley WHORLEY
Whisken WHISKIN WISKEN WISKIN
WHISKIN 11 Whisken Whisking Whiskins Whiskyn WISKEN Wiskens WISKIN Wisking Wiskins Wyskin
Whisking WHISKIN WISKEN WISKIN
Whiskins WHISKIN WISKEN WISKIN
Whiskyn WHISKIN WISKEN WISKIN
Whisler WHISTLER
WHISTLER 4 Whisler Wisler Wistler
WHISTON WESTON WISTON
WHITAKER Whitechar WHITTAKER
Whitam WHITHAM WHITTAM WITHAM WITTAM WITTON
Whitamore WHITTAMORE WHITTEMORE
Whitbourn WHITBURN
Whitbourne WHITBURN
WHITBURN Whitbourn Whitbourne
WHITBY Whidley
WHITCHER 4 Whicker Whitear Whitier
Whitchomb WHITCOMB WHITCOMBE
WHITCOMB 4 Whitchomb WHITCOMBE Whittcomb
WHITCOMBE 7 Whitchomb WHITCOMB Whittcomb Witcom Witcomb WITCOMBE
WHITE 4 Quhyt Whyt WHYTE
Whitear WHITCHER
Whiteaway WHITEWAY
Whitechar WHITAKER WHITTAKER
WHITEFOORD WHITEFORD Whitfoord
WHITEFORD WHITEFOORD Whitfoord
WHITEING 4 WHITING WHITTING WITTING
WHITELEY WHITLEY
WHITELOCK 5 Whitelocke WHITLOCK Whitlocke Wittlock
Whitelocke WHITELOCK WHITLOCK
Whitely WHITLEY
WHITEMAN 6 WEETMAN Weightman Wetman Wheatman WIGHTMAN
Whitemore WHITMORE
WHITEROD 4 WHITROD Whitrood Witrod
WHITESIDE 11 Quitesyd Qwythedws Whitesides Whitsid Whitside Whitsyd Whittsyde Whyteside Whytsd Whytsyd
Whitesides WHITESIDE
WHITEWAY Whiteaway
Whitfoord WHITEFOORD WHITEFORD
WHITHAM 12 Qwittwham Whitam Whitquam WHITTAM Whittham Whitwam Whitwham WITHAM WITTAM Wittom WITTON
Whitier WHITCHER
Whitimore WHITTAMORE WHITTEMORE
WHITING 4 WHITEING WHITTING WITTING
WHITLEY 5 WHITELEY Whitely Whittley Wittley
WHITLOCK 5 WHITELOCK Whitelocke Whitlocke Wittlock
Whitlocke WHITELOCK WHITLOCK
WHITMORE Whitemore
WHITNEY 11 Whitteney Whittney Whittneye Whyteneye Witeneie Witenie WITNEY Wittney Wyteney Wytteneye
Whitquam WHITHAM WHITTAM WITHAM WITTAM
WHITROD 4 WHITEROD Whitrood Witrod
Whitrood WHITEROD WHITROD
Whitsid WHITESIDE
Whitside WHITESIDE
Whitsyd WHITESIDE
WHITTA 4 Whittaw Whitto WHITTON
WHITTAKER WHITAKER Whitechar
WHITTAM 11 Qwittwham Whitam WHITHAM Whitquam Whittham Whitwam Whitwham WITHAM WITTAM Wittom
WHITTAMORE 5 Whitamore Whitimore WHITTEMORE Whittimore
Whittaw WHITTA WHITTON
Whittcomb WHITCOMB WHITCOMBE
WHITTEMORE 5 Whitamore Whitimore WHITTAMORE Whittimore
Whittenberie WHITTENBURY
Whittenberrye WHITTENBURY
Whittenborough WHITTENBURY
Whittenburrough WHITTENBURY
WHITTENBURY 7 Whittenberie Whittenberrye Whittenborough Whittenburrough Witenbury Wittenburg
Whitteney WHITNEY
Whittham WHITHAM WHITTAM WITHAM WITTAM
Whittimore WHITTAMORE WHITTEMORE
WHITTING 4 WHITEING WHITING WITTING
WHITTINGTON Whiddington
Whittleton WITTLETON
Whittley WHITLEY
Whittney WHITNEY WITNEY
Whittneye WHITNEY WITNEY
Whitto WHITTA WHITTON
WHITTON 8 Weddon WHEADON WHEATON WHITTA Whittaw Whitto Widdon
Whittsyde WHITESIDE
Whitwam WHITHAM WHITTAM WITHAM WITTAM
Whitwham WHITHAM WHITTAM WITHAM WITTAM
Whoal WHALE WHALES WHEAL WHEALE
Wholley WOOLEY WOOLLEY
Whollo WARLOW WHORLOW
Whonham WENHAM
Whooley HALLEY HANLEY HAWLEY HOOLEY HULLEY HULLY ULLEY UTLEY
Whoore HOAR HORE
Whor HOAR HORE
Whoram HORAM HURAM ORAM
Whorden WORDEN
Whore HAW HOAR HOARE HORE WARR WEARE WOOR
Whorely WHORLEY
Whorlay WHORLEY
Whorle WHORLEY
WHORLEY 22 Verley Verli Verly Virly Warle Warley Wawley Wharley Whawley Whearly Wherley Wherly Whirley Whorely Whorlay Whorle Whorlie Whorlly Whorly Wirley Worlye
Whorlie WHORLEY
Whorlly WHORLEY
WHORLOW WARLOW Whollo
Whorly WHORLEY
Whorm WORMS
Whormes WORMS
WHORRALL WORALL WORRALL
WHORWOOD 7 WARRAD WARWOOD WHARRAD Wharrod WORRAD WORROD
Whyat WYATT
Whyatt WYATT
WHYBROW 7 Widbrow WYBORN Wybrew Wybroo WYBROW Wyburn
Whyfyn WHIFFEN WHIFFIN
Whylr WHEELER
Whyt WHITE WHYTE
WHYTE 4 Quhyt WHITE Whyt
Whyteneye WHITNEY
Whyteside WHITESIDE
Whytsd WHITESIDE
Whytsyd WHITESIDE
Wiat WYATT
Wiatt WYATT
Wiatte WYATT
Wibday WEBDAY
Wibelai WEBBERLEY WEBLEY WHIBLEY
Wibkin WIEBKIN
Wibley WEBBERLEY WEBLEY WHIBLEY
Wiborn WYBORN
Wichington WICKINGTON WIGGINTON
WICKENS 6 Wickince WICKINS Wiggens WIGGINS Wikins
Wickerson WILKINSON
WICKES WICKS WIX
Wickeson WILKINSON
Wickince WICKENS WICKINS
WICKINGTON 5 Wichington Wiggington WIGGINTON Wigington
WICKINS 4 WICKENS Wickince Wikins
Wickland WEEKLEY WICKLIN
WICKLIN 4 Weakly WEEKLEY Wickland
WICKS WICKES WIX
WICKSTEAD Wicksteed Wixsted
Wicksteed WICKSTEAD
Widbrow WHYBROW WYBORN WYBROW
WIDCOMBE Witcom
Widdig WILDIG WILDIN WILDING
Widdon WHEADON WHEATON WHITTON
WIDLAKE WEDLAKE
WIDMORE WIGMORE
WIEBKIN 4 Webkin Wibkin Wiebking
Wiebking WIEBKIN
Wier WEIR
Wifen WHIFFEN
Wiffen WHIFFEN WHIFFIN
Wiffin WHIFFEN WHIFFIN
Wiggens WICKENS WIGGINS
Wiggington WICKINGTON WIGGINTON
WIGGINS WICKENS Wiggens
WIGGINTON 5 Wichington WICKINGTON Wiggington Wigington
WIGHTMAN 6 WEETMAN Weightman Wetman Wheatman WHITEMAN
Wighton WEIGHTON
Wigington WICKINGTON WIGGINTON
WIGMORE WIDMORE
Wigsell WIGZELL
WIGZELL Wigsell
Wikins WICKENS WICKINS
WILBORN 6 Eelborn Welband Welborn Welbourn WHEELBAND
Wilbourn WILBOURNE
WILBOURNE 5 Welborn Welborne Welburn Wilbourn
WILBY 24 Wealby Weelebee Welbe Welbeaby Welbee Welbey Welbie WELBY Welbye Wellbe Wellbee Wellbey Wellbie Wellby Wellbye Wellebye Welliaby WELSBY Whelby Wheleby Willby Willebey WILLOUGHBY

If the name you are interested in is not here, try Section C.

Wilce WILKES WILKS
WILCOCK 6 WILCOCKS WILCOX Willcock WILLCOCKS WILLCOX
WILCOCKS 6 WILCOCK WILCOX Willcock WILLCOCKS WILLCOX
WILCOX 6 WILCOCK WILCOCKS Willcock WILLCOCKS WILLCOX
WILD 4 WILDE Wyld WYLDE
Wilddigg WILDIG WILDIN WILDING
WILDE 4 WILD Wyld WYLDE
Wildeck WILDIG WILDIN WILDING
Wildeg WILDIG WILDIN WILDING
Wildegg WILDIG WILDIN WILDING
Wildegge WILDIG WILDIN WILDING
Wilderidge WILDRIDGE
Wildes WILES WYLDE
WILDEY WILDY Willdey
WILDGOOSE Willgoose
Wildic WILDIG WILDIN WILDING
Wildick WILDIG WILDIN WILDING
Wildicke WILDIG WILDIN WILDING
Wildidd WILDIG WILDIN WILDING
WILDIG 52 Weeldig Welldig Whildig Widdig Wilddigg Wildeck Wildeg Wildegg Wildegge Wildic Wildick Wildicke Wildidd Wildigage Wildige Wildiges Wildigg Wildigge Wildiggs Wildigh Wildigs Wildike WILDIN WILDING Wildinge Wildis Wilduck Willdeck Willdeg Willdege Willdegg Willdegge Willdic Willdick Willdicke Willdidge Willdig Willdige Willdigg Willdigge Willdike Willdin Willding Willdinge Willdizz Willdog Willduck Willgig Wooldig Wyldig Wyldigg
Wildigage WILDIG WILDIN WILDING
Wildige WILDIG WILDIN WILDING
Wildiges WILDIG WILDIN WILDING
Wildigg WILDIG WILDIN WILDING
Wildigge WILDIG WILDIN WILDING
Wildiggs WILDIG WILDIN WILDING
Wildigh WILDIG WILDIN WILDING
Wildigs WILDIG WILDIN WILDING
Wildike WILDIG WILDIN WILDING
WILDIN 52 Weeldig Welldig Whildig Widdig Wilddigg Wildeck Wildeg Wildegg Wildegge Wildic Wildick Wildicke Wildidd WILDIG Wildigage Wildige Wildiges Wildigg Wildigge Wildiggs Wildigh Wildigs Wildike WILDING Wildinge Wildis Wilduck Willdeck Willdeg Willdege Willdegg Willdegge Willdic Willdick Willdicke Willdidge Willdig Willdige Willdigg Willdigge Willdike Willdin Willding Willdinge Willdizz Willdog Willduck Willgig Wooldig Wyldig Wyldigg
WILDING 52 Weeldig Welldig Whildig Widdig Wilddigg Wildeck Wildeg Wildegg Wildegge Wildic Wildick Wildicke Wildidd WILDIG Wildigage Wildige Wildiges Wildigg Wildigge Wildiggs Wildigh Wildigs Wildike WILDIN Wildinge Wildis Wilduck Willdeck Willdeg Willdege Willdegg Willdegge Willdic Willdick Willdicke Willdidge Willdig Willdige Willdigg Willdigge Willdike Willdin Willding Willdinge Willdizz Willdog Willduck Willgig Wooldig Wyldig Wyldigg
Wildinge WILDIG WILDIN WILDING
Wildis WILDIG WILDIN WILDING
Wildredge WILDRIDGE
WILDRIDGE Wilderidge Wildredge
Wilds WILES WYLDE
Wilduck WILDIG WILDIN WILDING
WILDY WILDEY Willdey
Wilerton WILLERTON WOOLERTON
WILES 9 Wildes Wilds Willes Wyld WYLDE Wyldes Wylds Wyles
Wilet WILLET WILLETT
WILEY 4 Wily Wylay WYLIE
WILFORD 5 WELFORD Welfords Welfors Wellford
Wilis WILLIS
Wiliss WILLIS
WILKES 6 Wilce WILKS Willetts Willkes Wilts
WILKINS Willkins
WILKINSON 4 Weekerson Wickerson Wickeson
WILKS 6 Wilce WILKES Willetts Willkes Wilts
Willabay WILLOUGHBY
WILLANS WHILLANCE Whillans
Willard WELLARD
Willarton WILLERTON WOOLERTON
Willatan WILLERTON WOOLERTON
Willaton WILLERTON WOOLERTON
WILLAVISE Welladvised Wellavise
Willbey WILLOUGHBY
Willbie WILLOUGHBY
Willbo WILLOUGHBY
Willby WELBY WELSBY WILBY
Willcock WILCOCK WILCOCKS WILCOX WILLCOCKS WILLCOX
WILLCOCKS 6 WILCOCK WILCOCKS WILCOX Willcock WILLCOX
WILLCOX 6 WILCOCK WILCOCKS WILCOX Willcock WILLCOCKS
Willdeck WILDIG WILDIN WILDING
Willdeg WILDIG WILDIN WILDING
Willdege WILDIG WILDIN WILDING
Willdegg WILDIG WILDIN WILDING
Willdegge WILDIG WILDIN WILDING
Willdey WILDEY WILDY
Willdic WILDIG WILDIN WILDING
Willdick WILDIG WILDIN WILDING
Willdicke WILDIG WILDIN WILDING
Willdidge WILDIG WILDIN WILDING
Willdig WILDIG WILDIN WILDING
Willdige WILDIG WILDIN WILDING
Willdigg WILDIG WILDIN WILDING
Willdigge WILDIG WILDIN WILDING
Willdike WILDIG WILDIN WILDING
Willdin WILDIG WILDIN WILDING
Willding WILDIG WILDIN WILDING
Willdinge WILDIG WILDIN WILDING
Willdizz WILDIG WILDIN WILDING
Willdog WILDIG WILDIN WILDING
Willduck WILDIG WILDIN WILDING
Willebey WELBY WELSBY WILBY
Willemore WILMER
Willemot WILLMOT WILLMOTT WILMOT
Willemote WILLMOT WILLMOTT WILMOT
WILLERTON 36 De welleton De wilghton De willeghton De wilughton De wylgton Walerton Wallerton Welerton Wellerton Whelerton Whilerton Whillerton Wilerton Willarton Willatan Willaton Willertone Willinton Willirton Williton Willoughton Wilughton Wolerton Woliton Wollarton Wollaton Wollerton Woolarton WOOLERTON Woollaton Woollerton Woolorton Wooloton Wylarton Wyllerton
Willertone WILLERTON WOOLERTON
Willes WILES WYLDE
Willesden WILSDON
WILLET 6 Wilet WILLETT Willoit Willot Wylett
WILLETS WILLIS
WILLETT 6 Wilet WILLET Willoit Willot Wylett
Willetts WILKES WILKS
Willgig WILDIG WILDIN WILDING
Willgoose WILDGOOSE
WILLIAM WILLIAMS
WILLIAMS WILLIAM
Willinton WILLERTON WOOLERTON
Willirton WILLERTON WOOLERTON
WILLIS 6 Wilis Wiliss WILLETS Williss WILLS
Williss WILLIS
Williton WILLERTON WOOLERTON
Willkes WILKES WILKS
Willkins WILKINS
Willmer WILMER
WILLMORE WILMER
WILLMOT 6 Willemot Willemote WILLMOTT WILMOT WILMOTT
WILLMOTT 6 Willemot Willemote WILLMOT WILMOT WILMOTT
WILLNER 6 Willnor Wilnal Wilnall Wilner Wilnor
Willnor WILLNER
Willoghby WILLOUGHBY
Willoit WILLET WILLETT
Willot WILLET WILLETT
WILLOUGHBY 8 WILBY Willabay Willbey Willbie Willbo Willoghby Willowby
Willoughton WILLERTON WOOLERTON
Willowby WILLOUGHBY
WILLS WELLS WILLIS
Willsden WILSDON
Willsdon WILSDON
Willsher WILTSHIRE
Willshire WILSHER WILSHIRE WILTSHIRE
WILLSON 6 Vilsone Whilson WILSON Wilsone Wulson
WILMER 5 Willemore Willmer WILLMORE Wilmore
Wilmore WILMER
WILMOT 6 Willemot Willemote WILLMOT WILLMOTT WILMOTT
WILMOTT 4 WILLMOT WILLMOTT WILMOT
WILMSHURST 6 Wimpset Wimpshurst Wimset Wimsherst Wimshurst
Wilnal WILLNER
Wilnall WILLNER
Wilner WILLNER
Wilnor WILLNER
Wilsden WILSDON
WILSDON 5 Willesden Willsden Willsdon Wilsden
Wilshear WILTSHIRE
Wilsheir WILTSHIRE
WILSHER 4 Willshire Wilshier WILTSHIRE
WILSHERE 4 WILSHIRE Wiltsheir WILTSHIRE
Wilshier WILSHER WILSHIRE WILTSHIRE
WILSHIRE 6 Willshire WILSHERE Wilshier Wiltsheir WILTSHIRE
WILSON 7 Vilsone Whilson WILLSON Wilsone Wilsonne Wulson
Wilsone WILLSON WILSON
Wilsonne WILSON
Wilts WILKES WILKS
Wiltsheir WILSHERE WILSHIRE WILTSHIRE
WILTSHIRE 10 Willsher

If the name you are interested in is not here, try Section C.

Willshire Wilshear Wilsheir WILSHER WILSHERE Wilshier WILSHIRE Wiltsheir
Wilughton WILLERTON WOOLERTON
Wily WILEY WYLIE WYLLIE
Wimpennie PENNY WIMPENNY
WIMPENNY 6 Penie PENNY Whimpenie Wimpennie Winpenny
Wimpset WILMSHURST
Wimpshurst WILMSHURST
Wimset WILMSHURST
Wimsherst WILMSHURST
Wimshurst WILMSHURST
Win WINN WYNN WYNNE
WINCHCOMB WINCHCOMBE
WINCHCOMBE WINCHCOMB
Winckup WHINCUP
Wincop WHINCUP
WINDEBANK Windibank Windybank
WINDER De wynder Wynder
Windgate WINGATE
Windgeat WINGATE
Windibank WINDEBANK
Windin WENDEN
WINDSOR WINSOR
Windwood WINWOOD
Windyates WINGATE
Windybank WINDEBANK
WINFREY Whinfrey
WINGAT WINGATE
WINGATE 9 Whinyates Windgate Windgeat Windyates WINGAT Wingeatt Wingett Wynniatt
Wingeatt WINGATE
Wingett WINGATE
WINGRAVE WINGROVE
WINGROVE WINGRAVE
Winister WINNISTER
WINN 5 Whinn Win WYNN WYNNE
WINNE WINNEY
Winnester WINNISTER
WINNEY WINNE Winny
WINNISTER 4 Wannister Winister Winnester
Winny WINNEY
Winpenny PENNY WIMPENNY
Winsar WINSOR WINZAR
WINSCOM 5 Winscomb Winscombe Winscome Winskum
Winscomb WINSCOM
Winscombe WINSCOM
Winscome WINSCOM
Winskum WINSCOM
WINSOR 4 WINDSOR Winsar WINZAR
WINTER WINTERS
WINTERS WINTER
Wintworth WENTWORTH
WINWOOD Windwood
WINYARD Vineyard
WINZAR Winsar WINSOR
Wiot WYATT
Wirdnam WARNHAM WERNHAM WIRNHAM WORNHAM WYRDENHAM WYRNHAM
Wirley WHORLEY
WIRNHAM 7 WARNHAM WERNHAM Wirdnam WORNHAM WYRDENHAM WYRNHAM
Wirth WORTH
Wisbey WISBY
WISBY Wisbey
Wisdal WESTALL WORSDELL
Wisdall WESTALL WORSDELL
WISE Wyse
Wisehart WISHART
WISHAM 4 Wissam Wyssam Wyssom
Wishard WISHART
WISHART 4 Wisehart Wishard Wisheart
Wisheart WISHART
WISKEN 11 Whisken WHISKIN Whisking Whiskins Whiskyn Wiskens WISKIN Wisking Wiskins Wyskin
Wiskens WHISKIN WISKEN WISKIN
WISKIN 11 Whisken WHISKIN Whisking Whiskins Whiskyn WISKEN Wiskens Wisking Wiskins Wyskin
Wisking WHISKIN WISKEN WISKIN
Wiskins WHISKIN WISKEN WISKIN
Wisler WHISTLER
Wissam WISHAM
Wistler WHISTLER
WISTON WESTON WHISTON
Witcom WHITCOMBE WIDCOMBE WITCOMBE
Witcomb WHITCOMBE WITCOMBE
WITCOMBE 4 WHITCOMBE Witcom Witcomb
Witenbury WHITTENBURY
Witeneie WHITNEY WITNEY
Witenie WHITNEY
WITHAM 12 Qwittwham Whitam WHITHAM Whitquam WHITTAM Whittham Whitwam Whitwham WITTAM Wittom WITTON
Wither WITHERS
Witherage WITHERIDGE
Witherall WEATHERALL
Witheredg WITHERIDGE
Witheredge WITHERIDGE
Witheridg WITHERIDGE
WITHERIDGE 22 Watheridge Weatheredge Weathereg Weatheridge Weatherige Wetheredg Wetheredge Wetheridge Wetherudge Wetheryde Wetheryg Whetherige Witherage Witheredg Witheredge Witheridg Wyderidge Wyetherayge Wytheridge Wytherug Wytherydg
WITHERS 6 Weathers Wether Wethers Wither Wythers
WITHERSPOON 6 Weatherspoon Wedderspon Wetherspoon Witherspoons WOTHERSPOON
Witherspoons WITHERSPOON WOTHERSPOON
WITNEY 5 WHITNEY Whittney Whittneye Witeneie
Witrod WHITEROD WHITROD
WITTAM 11 Qwittwham Whitam WHITHAM Whitquam WHITTAM Whittham Whitwam Whitwham WITHAM Wittom
Witte WITTY
Wittenburg WHITTENBURY
WITTING 4 WHITEING WHITING WHITTING
WITTLETON Whittleton
Wittley WHITLEY
Wittlock WHITELOCK WHITLOCK
Wittney WHITNEY
Wittom WHITHAM WHITTAM WITHAM WITTAM
WITTON 4 Whitam WHITHAM WITHAM
WITTY Witte
WIX WICKES WICKS
Wixsted WICKSTEAD
Woad WAUD
Woakfield WAKEFIELD
Woans WONES
Woar HAW HOARE HORE WARR WEARE WOOR
Woare HAW HOARE HORE WARR WEARE WOOR
Woberry OBERY OBREY
Woddle WOODALL
Woddwys WOOD WOODIS WOODWIS
Wodebine WOODBINE
Wodehouse WOODHOUSE
Woden RAWDON RHODEN RODEN ROWDEN ROYDEN
Wodier WOODGER
Wodin WOODDEN WOODDIN WOODEN
Wodman WOODMAN
Woewen OWEN
Woewin OWEN
Woff WOLFE WOOF
Woffe WOLFE WOOF
WOGAN 4 Hoogan Ogan Owgan
Wolen WOLLAND WOOLLAMS WOOLLAND
Wolens WOLLAND WOOLLAMS WOOLLAND
Wolerton WILLERTON WOOLERTON
Woley WOOLEY WOOLLEY
Wolf WOLFE WOOF
WOLFE 7 Woff Woffe Wolf WOOF Wooff WOOLFE
WOLFENDEN 7 Wolfendon Wolfinden WOOLFENDEN Woolfendon Woolfinden Woolindon
Wolfendon WOLFENDEN WOOLFENDEN
Wolfinden WOLFENDEN WOOLFENDEN
Wolford WOLFORTH WOOLFORD
Wolfork WOLFORTH WOOLFORD
Wolfort WOLFORTH WOOLFORD
WOLFORTH 8 Wolford Wolfork Wolfort WOOLFORD Woolforth Worfolk Worfolke
Wolfreys WOOLFRIES
Wolfries WOOLFRIES
Wolgar WOLGER WOOLGAR WORGER
WOLGER 6 Wolgar WOOLGAR Woolger Woollgar WORGER
Woliton WILLERTON WOOLERTON
Wollacot WOLLACOTT WOOLLACOTT
WOLLACOTT 5 Wollacot Woolacott Woollacot WOOLLACOTT
Wollam WOLLAND WOOLLAMS WOOLLAND
Wollams WOLLAND WOOLLAMS WOOLLAND
Wollan WOLLAND WOOLLAMS WOOLLAND
WOLLAND 37 Wolen Wolens Wollam Wollams Wollan Wollands Wollans Wollen Wollend Wollens Wollin Wollins Wolloms Wollon Wollons Woolam Woolams Woolan Woolans Woolen Woolham WOOLLAMS WOOLLAND Woollands Woollans Woollen Woollend Woollends Woollens Woollham Woollhams Woolliams Woollin Woollins Woollon Woollons
Wollands WOLLAND WOOLLAMS WOOLLAND
Wollans WOLLAND WOOLLAMS WOOLLAND
Wollard WOOLARD WOOLLARD WOOLWARD
Wollarton WILLERTON WOOLERTON
Wollaston WOOLASTON
Wollaton WILLERTON WOOLERTON
Wollen WOLLAND WOOLLAMS WOOLLAND
Wollend WOLLAND WOOLLAMS WOOLLAND
Wollens WOLLAND WOOLLAMS WOOLLAND
Woller WOOLLER
Wollerton WILLERTON WOOLERTON
Wolley WOOLEY WOOLLEY
Wollin WOLLAND WOOLLAMS WOOLLAND
Wollings WOOLLINGS
Wollins WOLLAND WOOLLAMS WOOLLAND
Wolloms WOLLAND WOOLLAMS WOOLLAND
Wollon WOLLAND WOOLLAMS WOOLLAND
Wollons WOLLAND WOOLLAMS WOOLLAND
Wolridge WOOLDRIDGE WOOLRICH
Wolrych WOOLDRIDGE WOOLRICH
Wolseley WOOZLEY
Wolstancroft WOLSTENCROFT
WOLSTENCROFT 5 Wolstancroft Woolstancroft Woolstencroft Worstencroft
Wolvert WOOLVETT
Womball WOMBWELL
Wombel WOMBWELL
Wombell WOMBWELL
Wombewell WOMBWELL
Wombill WOMBWELL
Womble WOMBWELL
Wombwel WOMBWELL
WOMBWELL 14 Womball Wombel Wombell Wombewell Wombill Womble Wombwel Womel Womell Womewell Woombell Woombill Woombwell
Womel WOMBWELL
Womell WOMBWELL
Womewell WOMBWELL
WONES Woans
Wonham WENHAM
Wooard WOOLLARD
Wooberry OBERY OBREY
WOOD 8 Woddwys Woodde Woode WOODIS WOODS WOODWIS Woodys
Woodal WOODALL WOODHALL
WOODALL 8 Woddle Woodal Wooddall Wooddle Woodell WOODHALL Woodle
Woodbin WOODBINE
WOODBINE 4 Wodebine Woodbin Woodbyne
Woodbyne WOODBINE
WOODCOCK WOODCOCKE Woodkok
WOODCOCKE WOODCOCK
Wooddall WOODALL
Woodde WOOD WOODS

If the name you are interested in is not here, try Section C.

WOODDEN 6 Wodin WOODDIN WOODEN Woodin WOODING
WOODDIN 5 Wodin WOODDEN WOODEN Woodin
WOODDISS 9 WOODIS WOODISE Woodiwis Woodiwise WOODIWISSE WOODWIS WOODWISE WOODWISS
Wooddle WOODALL WOODHALL
Woode WOOD WOODS
Woodell WOODALL WOODHALL
WOODEN 5 Wodin WOODDEN WOODDIN Woodin
WOODGER 5 Wodier Woodgier Woodier Woodyear
Woodgier WOODGER
WOODHALL 6 Woodal WOODALL Wooddle Woodell Woodle
WOODHOUSE 5 Wodehouse WOODHURST WOODISS Woodus
WOODHURST WOODHOUSE Woodus
Woodier WOODGER
Woodin WOODDEN WOODDIN WOODEN
WOODING WOODDEN
WOODIS 12 Woddwys WOOD WOODDISS WOODISE Woodiwis Woodiwise WOODIWISSE WOODWIS WOODWISE WOODWISS Woodys
WOODISE 9 WOODDISS WOODIS Woodiwis Woodiwise WOODIWISSE WOODWIS WOODWISE WOODWISS
WOODISS WOODHOUSE
Woodiwis WOODDISS WOODIS WOODISE WOODIWISS WOODIWISSE WOODWIS WOODWISE WOODWISS
Woodiwise WOODDISS WOODIS WOODISE WOODIWISSE WOODWIS WOODWISE WOODWISS
WOODIWISS Woodiwis
WOODIWISSE 9 WOODDISS WOODIS WOODISE Woodiwis Woodiwise WOODWIS WOODWISE WOODWISS
Woodkok WOODCOCK
Woodle WOODALL WOODHALL
WOODLEY 4 WARDLEY WORDLEY WORDLY
WOODLIFF WOODLIFFE
WOODLIFFE WOODLIFF
WOODMAN Wodman
Woodmancey WOODMANSEE WOODMANSEY
WOODMANSEE Woodmancey WOODMANSEY
WOODMANSEY Woodmancey WOODMANSEE
Woodrofe WOODROFF WOODROFFE WOODRUFF
WOODROFF 6 Woodrofe WOODROFFE Woodroofe WOODRUFF Woodrus
WOODROFFE 7 Woodrofe WOODROFF Woodroofe Woodrooffe WOODRUFF Woodrus
Woodroofe WOODROFF WOODROFFE WOODRUFF
Woodrooffe WOODROFFE WOODRUFF
WOODRUFF 7 Woodrofe WOODROFF WOODROFFE Woodroofe Woodrooffe Woodrus
Woodrus WOODROFF WOODROFFE WOODRUFF
WOODS 4 WOOD Woodde Woode
Woodus WOODHOUSE WOODHURST
WOODWALL Woodwell
WOODWARD WOOLWARD
Woodwell WOODWALL
WOODWIS 12 Woddwys WOOD WOODDISS WOODIS WOODISE Woodiwis Woodiwise WOODIWISSE WOODWISE WOODWISS Woodys
WOODWISE 9 WOODDISS WOODIS WOODISE Woodiwis Woodiwise WOODIWISSE WOODWIS WOODWISS
WOODWISS 9 WOODDISS WOODIS WOODISE Woodiwis Woodiwise WOODIWISSE WOODWIS WOODWISE
Woodyear WOODGER
Woodys WOOD WOODIS WOODWIS
WOOF 6 Woff Woffe Wolf WOLFE Wooff
Wooff WOLFE WOOF
Woolacott WOLLACOTT WOOLLACOTT
Woolam WOLLAND WOOLLAMS WOOLLAND
Woolams WOLLAND WOOLLAMS WOOLLAND
Woolan WOLLAND WOOLLAMS WOOLLAND
Woolans WOLLAND WOOLLAMS WOOLLAND
WOOLARD 4 Wollard WOOLLARD WOOLWARD
Woolarton WILLERTON WOOLERTON
WOOLASTON Wollaston
Wooldig WILDIG WILDIN WILDING
WOOLDRIDGE 7 Wolridge Wolrych WOOLRICH Woolriche Woolridge Woolrych
Woolen WOLLAND WOOLLAMS WOOLLAND
Wooler WOOLLER
WOOLERTON 37 De welleton De wilghton De willeghton De wilughton De wylgton Walerton Wallerton Welerton Wellerton Whelerton Whilerton Whillerton Wilerton Willarton Willatan Willaton WILLERTON Willertone Willinton Willirton Williton Willoughton Wilughton Wolerton Woliton Wollarton Wollaton Wollerton Woolarton Woollaton Woollerton Woolloton Woolorton Wooloton Wylarton Wyllerton
WOOLEY 5 Wholley Woley Wolley WOOLLEY
WOOLFE WOLFE
WOOLFENDEN 7 WOLFENDEN Wolfendon Wolfinden Woolfendon Woolfinden Woolindon
Woolfendon WOLFENDEN WOOLFENDEN
Woolfinden WOLFENDEN WOOLFENDEN
WOOLFORD 8 Wolford Wolfork Wolfort WOLFORTH Woolforth Worfolk Worfolke
Woolforth WOLFORTH WOOLFORD
Woolfreys WOOLFRIES
WOOLFRIES 4 Wolfreys Wolfries Woolfreys
WOOLGAR 6 Wolgar WOLGER Woolger Woollgar WORGER
Woolger WOLGER WOOLGAR WORGER
Woolham WOLLAND WOOLLAMS WOOLLAND
Woolindon WOLFENDEN WOOLFENDEN
Woolings WOOLLINGS
Woollacot WOLLACOTT WOOLLACOTT
WOOLLACOTT 5 Wollacot WOLLACOTT Woolacott Woollacot
WOOLLAMS 37 Wolen Wolens Wollam Wollams Wollan WOLLAND Wollands Wollans Wollen Wollend Wollens Wollin Wollins Wolloms Wollon Wollons Woolam Woolams Woolan Woolans Woolen Woolham WOOLLAND Woollands Woollans Woollen Woollend Woollends Woollens Woollham Woollhams Woolliams Woollin Woollins Woollon Woollons
WOOLLAND 37 Wolen Wolens Wollam Wollams Wollan WOLLAND Wollands Wollans Wollen Wollend Wollens Wollin Wollins Wolloms Wollon Wollons Woolam Woolams Woolan Woolans Woolen Woolham WOOLLAMS Woollands Woollans Woollen Woollend Woollends Woollens Woollham Woollhams Woolliams Woollin Woollins Woollon Woollons
Woollands WOLLAND WOOLLAMS WOOLLAND
Woollans WOLLAND WOOLLAMS WOOLLAND
WOOLLARD 5 Wollard Wooard WOOLARD WOOLWARD
Woollaton WILLERTON WOOLERTON
Woollen WOLLAND WOOLLAMS WOOLLAND
Woollend WOLLAND WOOLLAMS WOOLLAND
Woollends WOLLAND WOOLLAMS WOOLLAND
Woollens WOLLAND WOOLLAMS WOOLLAND
WOOLLER Woller Wooler
Woollerton WILLERTON WOOLERTON
WOOLLEY 5 Wholley Woley Wolley WOOLEY
Woollgar WOLGER WOOLGAR WORGER
Woollham WOLLAND WOOLLAMS WOOLLAND
Woollhams WOLLAND WOOLLAMS WOOLLAND
Woolliams WOLLAND WOOLLAMS WOOLLAND
Woollin WOLLAND WOOLLAMS WOOLLAND
WOOLLINGS Wollings Woolings
Woollins WOLLAND WOOLLAMS WOOLLAND
Woollman WOOLMAN
Woollon WOLLAND WOOLLAMS WOOLLAND
Woollons WOLLAND WOOLLAMS WOOLLAND
Woolloton WOOLERTON
WOOLMAN Woollman
WOOLNER Woolno WOOLNOUGH
Woolno WOOLNER WOOLNOUGH
WOOLNOUGH WOOLNER Woolno
Woolorton WILLERTON WOOLERTON
Wooloton WILLERTON WOOLERTON
WOOLRICH 7 Wolridge Wolrych WOOLDRIDGE Woolriche Woolridge Woolrych
Woolriche WOOLDRIDGE WOOLRICH
Woolridge WOOLDRIDGE WOOLRICH
Woolrych WOOLDRIDGE WOOLRICH
Woolstancroft WOLSTENCROFT
Woolstencroft WOLSTENCROFT
WOOLVEN WOOLVIN
WOOLVETT Wolvert Woolvitt
WOOLVIN WOOLVEN
Woolvitt WOOLVETT
WOOLWARD 5 Wollard WOODWARD WOOLARD WOOLLARD
Woombell WOMBWELL
Woombill WOMBWELL
Woombwell WOMBWELL
WOOR 10 HAW HOARE HORE WARR WEARE Whore Woar Woare Woore
Woore HAW HOARE HORE WARR WEARE WOOR
Woosencroft WOSONCROFT
Woosley WOOZLEY
Wooster WORSTER
WOOTEN WOOTON WOOTTON
WOOTON WOOTEN WOOTTON
WOOTTON WOOTEN WOOTON
WOOZLEY Wolseley Woosley
WORALL WHORRALL WORRALL
WORBEY 5 Warbey WARBOYS Warby WORBY
WORBY 5 Warbey WARBOYS Warby WORBEY
Worcester WORSTER
Worcestre WORSTER
WORDEN 4 Werden Wherden Whorden
WORDLEY 4 WARDLEY WOODLEY WORDLY
WORDLY 4 WARDLEY WOODLEY WORDLEY
Wordsell WESTALL WORSDELL
Worel WORRELL
Worell WORRELL
Worfolk WOLFORTH WOOLFORD
Worfolke WOLFORTH WOOLFORD
WORGER 6 Wolgar WOLGER WOOLGAR Woolger Woollgar
Worie WARRY WHARRY
Workeman WORKMAN
WORKMAN 7 Walkman Warkman Warpman Werkman Workeman Wourkman
WORLEDGE WALLAGE
Worlich WARRINGTON WORTHINGTON
Worlington WARRINGTON WORTHINGTON
Worlye WHORLEY
WORMALD 4 WORMALL Wormeald Wormeall
WORMALL 4 WORMALD

If the name you are interested in is not here, try Section C.

Wormeald Wormeall
Wormeald WORMALD WORMALL
Wormeall WORMALD WORMALL
WORMS Whorm Whormes
WORMSLEY 4 WALMSLEY Wamsley Warmsley
WORN 4 WARN WARNE Worne
Worne WARN WARNE WORN
WORNHAM 7 WARNHAM WERNHAM Wirdnam WIRNHAM WYRDENHAM WYRNHAM
Worpel WALPOLE
WORRAD 7 WARRAD WARWOOD WHARRAD Wharrod WHORWOOD WORROD
WORRALL WHORRALL WORALL
Worrel WORRELL
WORRELL 6 Warrell Worel Worell Worrel Worrill
Worrill WORRELL
Worrington WARRINGTON WORTHINGTON
WORROD 7 WARRAD WARWOOD WHARRAD Wharrod WHORWOOD WORRAD
Worsdale WESTALL WORSDELL
Worsdall WESTALL WORSDELL
Worsdel WESTALL WORSDELL
WORSDELL 21 Wasdal Wasdall Wesdal Wesdall Westal WESTALL Wisdal Wisdall Wordsell Worsdale Worsdall Worsdel Worsdoll Worstall Worstoll Wosdale Wosdell Wostil Wostill Wostoll
Worsdoll WESTALL WORSDELL
Worsetar WORSTER
Worseter WORSTER
WORSFOLD Worsfolde
Worsfolde WORSFOLD
WORSLEY Wersley
Worstall WESTALL WORSDELL
Worstencroft WOLSTENCROFT
WORSTER 11 Wooster Worcester Worcestre Worsetar Worseter Worsyter Wosetar Woseter Woster Wyssetour
Worstoll WESTALL WORSDELL
Worsyter WORSTER
Worters WATERS WATTERS WATTIS WATTS
WORTH Werth Wirth
Worthan WORTHEN
WORTHEN 5 Worthan Worthin Worthing Worthon
Worthin WORTHEN
Worthing WORTHEN
WORTHINGTON 6 Warrenton WARRINGTON Worlich Worlington Worrington
Worthon WORTHEN
WORTLEY WARDLEY
WORTON 7 De wharton WALTON WARTON Werfton WHARTON Whartonne
Worts WATERS WATTERS WATTIS WATTS
WORWOOD WARWOOD
Wosdale WESTALL WORSDELL
Wosdell WESTALL WORSDELL
Wosencroft WOSONCROFT
Wosetar WORSTER
Woseter WORSTER
Wosket WASKETT
Woskett WASKETT
WOSONCROFT Woosencroft Wosencroft
Woster WORSTER
Wostil WESTALL WORSDELL
Wostill WESTALL WORSDELL
Wostoll WESTALL WORSDELL
WOTHERSPOON 6 Weatherspoon Wedderspon Wetherspoon WITHERSPOON Witherspoons
WOTTLEY Watley Whatley
Wourkman WORKMAN
Wowen OWEN
Wowin OWEN
WRAGG RAGG
Wrapple FRAPWELL
Wrapson RAPSON
Wrassell RISDALE
Wrathel RATHEL RATHIL
Wrathwell RATHEL RATHWELL ROTHWELL
WRAY 5 RAE RAY Raye REA
WRAYFORD WREFORD WREYFORD
Wrayforde WREFORD
Wrayton RAILTON RAYTON
Wreakoke OAKLEY OCKLEY
Wreaton RAILTON RAYTON
WREFORD 4 WRAYFORD Wrayforde WREYFORD
WREN 4 Ren Renne Wrenne
Wrenne WREN
Wresle RISDALE
Wressell RISDALE
WREYFORD WRAYFORD WREFORD
WRIGHT Right Rite
Wrightwril BRIGHTMAN
WRIGLEY Rigley
Wring RING RINGE
Wrisley RISELEY RISLEY
Writhoak OAKLEY OCKLEY
Wrootham ROOTHAM
Wrossell RISDALE
Wrothall RATHEL RATHWELL ROTHWELL
Wrotham ROOTHAM
Wrothel RATHEL RATHWELL ROTHWELL
Wrothwell RATHEL RATHWELL ROTHWELL
Wulson WILLSON WILSON
Wvigus VIGERS VIGUS
Wyat WYATT
WYATT 8 Whyat Whyatt Wiat Wiatt Wiatte Wiot Wyat
WYBORN 9 WHYBROW Wiborn Widbrow Wyborne Wybrew Wybroo WYBROW Wyburn
Wyborne WYBORN
Wybrew WHYBROW WYBORN WYBROW
Wybroo WHYBROW WYBORN WYBROW
WYBROW 7 WHYBROW Widbrow WYBORN Wybrew Wybroo Wyburn
Wyburn WHYBROW WYBORN WYBROW
Wyderidge WITHERIDGE
Wyetherayge WITHERIDGE
Wylarton WILLERTON WOOLERTON
Wylay WILEY WYLIE
Wyld WILD WILDE WILES WYLDE
WYLDE 11 WILD WILDE Wildes Wilds WILES Willes Wyld Wyldes Wylds Wyles
Wyldes WILES WYLDE
Wyldig WILDIG WILDIN WILDING
Wyldigg WILDIG WILDIN WILDING
Wylds WILES WYLDE
Wyles WILES WYLDE
Wylett WILLET WILLETT
WYLIE 9 Vylie Weyle WILEY Wily Wylay WYLLIE Wylly Wylye
Wyllerton WILLERTON WOOLERTON
WYLLIE 7 Vylie Weyle Wily WYLIE Wylly Wylye
Wylly WYLIE WYLLIE
Wylye WYLIE WYLLIE
Wynder WINDER
WYNN 5 Whinn Win WINN WYNNE
WYNNE 5 Whinn Win WINN WYNN
Wynniatt WINGATE
WYRDENHAM 7 WARNHAM WERNHAM Wirdnam WIRNHAM WORNHAM WYRNHAM
WYRNHAM 7 WARNHAM WERNHAM Wirdnam WIRNHAM WORNHAM WYRDENHAM
Wyse WISE
Wyskin WHISKIN WISKEN WISKIN
Wyssam WISHAM
Wyssetour WORSTER
Wyssom WISHAM
Wyteney WHITNEY
Wytheridge WITHERIDGE
Wythers WITHERS
Wytherug WITHERIDGE
Wytherydg WITHERIDGE
Wytteneye WHITNEY
YALE Yales
Yales YALE
Yandal YANDLE YENDALL
Yandall YANDLE YENDALL
Yandell YANDLE YENDALL
YANDLE 7 Yandal Yandall Yandell YENDALL Yendell Yendle
Yap YAPP
YAPP Yap Yappe
Yappe YAPP
YARD 81 Ardy Eardy Garad Garard GARRAD GARRARD GARRAT GARRATT Garred Garretson GARRETT Garretts Garrettson Garrison Garrit Garritt GARROD Garrould Gerad Geraddus Gerald Geralds GERARD Gerarde Gerardes Gerards Geratt Geraud Geret Gerold Gerrad GERRARD Gerratt Gerred GERRETT Gervaise Gervas Gervase Gervis Gorret Heardy Jarad Jarald Jarat Jared Jareld Jarelds Jaret Jarets Jarett Jaretts Jarrad JARRARD Jarrat JARRATT Jarred JARRET Jarrets JARRETT Jarretts Jarritt Jarrod JARROLD Jarrott Jarvie JARVIS Jeffette Jeofett Jeorrett Jereatt JERRARD Jerratt Jerreatt Jerred JERRETT Jerrold Yarrat Yarratt Yarrott Yerratt
YARDLEY YEARDLEY
Yarnold ARNOLD
Yarrat GARRAD GARRARD GARRAT GARRATT GARRETT GARROD GERARD GERRARD GERRETT JARRARD JARRATT JARRET JARRETT JARROLD JARVIS JERRARD JERRETT YARD
Yarratt GARRAD GARRARD GARRAT GARRATT GARRETT GARROD GERARD GERRARD GERRETT JARRARD JARRATT JARRET JARRETT JARROLD JARVIS JERRARD JERRETT YARD
Yarrott GARRAD GARRARD GARRAT GARRATT GARRETT GARROD GERARD GERRARD GERRETT JARRARD JARRATT JARRET JARRETT JARROLD JARVIS JERRARD JERRETT YARD
Yarvie JARVICE JARVIS JERVIS
YATES 6 EADES Eeds Heeds YEATES YEATS
Yclin HICKLIN HICKLING
Ycling DE HICKELING HICKLIN HICKLING ICKELING
Yclinham HICKLINGAM
Yclinton HICKLENTON
Yealding YIELDING
Yealf YELF
Yeaman YEOMAN
Yeamon YEOMAN
YEARBY Yerby
YEARDLEY YARDLEY
Yearl YEARLE
YEARLE 4 Yearl Yerl Yerle
Yearley EARLEY EARLY
Yearly EARLEY EARLY
Yearsley EARDLEY
YEATES YATES
YEATS GATES YATES
Yeaull EWELL HOOLE YOLE YOUELL YULE
Yeauman YEOMAN
Yeel EWELL HOOLE YOLE YOUELL YULE
Yeeles AYLES EALES EELES EYLES HILES ILES
Yeell EWELL HOOLE YOLE YOUELL YULE
Yehl EWELL HOOLE YOLE YOUELL YULE
Yeil EWELL HOOLE YOLE YOUELL YULE
Yeill EWELL HOOLE YOLE YOUELL YULE
YELF 5 Elfe Yealf Yelfe Yellowes
Yelfe YELF
Yell EWELL HOOLE YOLE YOUELL YULE
Yellowes YELF
YENDALL 7 Yandal Yandall Yandell YANDLE Yendell Yendle
Yendell YANDLE YENDALL
Yendle YANDLE YENDALL
Yeoale EWELL HOOLE YOLE YOUELL YULE
YEOMAN 8 Yeaman Yeamon Yeauman Yeouman Yeoumans Yomans Youman
Yeouls EWELL HOOLE YOLE YOUELL YULE
Yeouman YEOMAN
Yeoumans YEOMAN
Yeowell EWELL HOOLE YOLE YOUELL YULE
Yerby YEARBY
Yerl YEARLE
Yerle YEARLE
Yermonger IREMONGER IRONMONGER
Yermunger IREMONGER IRONMONGER
Yernmonger IREMONGER IRONMONGER
Yernmunger IREMONGER IRONMONGER
Yerratt GARRAD GARRARD GARRAT GARRATT GARRETT GARROD GERARD GERRARD GERRETT JARRARD JARRATT

If the name you are interested in is not here, try Section C.

JARRET JARRETT JARROLD JARVIS JERRARD JERRETT YARD
Yetwale EATWELL
Yeuell EWELL HOOLE YOLE YOUELL YULE
Yeuille EWELL HOOLE YOLE YOUELL YULE
Yeul EWELL HOOLE YOLE YOUELL YULE
Yeules EWELL HOOLE YOLE YOUELL YULE
Yeull EWELL HOOLE YOLE YOUELL YULE
Yeulle EWELL HOOLE YOLE YOUELL YULE
Yewdale UDELL
Yewell EWELL HOOLE YOLE YOUELL YULE
Yewl EWELL HOOLE YOLE YOUELL YULE
YIELDING Yealding
Ykeling DE HICKELING HICKLIN HICKLING ICKELING
Ykling DE HICKELING HICKLIN HICKLING ICKELING
Ynkel INGALL INGLE INGLES
Yoall EWELL HOOLE YOLE YOUELL YULE
Yocksall YOXALL
Yoele EWELL HOOLE YOLE YOUELL YULE
Yoell EWELL HOOLE YOLE YOUELL YULE
Yol EWELL HOOLE YOLE YOUELL YULE
YOLE 90 Eule Ewel Eweles EWELL Ewels HOOLE Juel Jule Uhl Uhles Uiles Uoel Yeaull Yeel Yeell Yehl Yeil Yeill Yell Yeoale Yeouls Yeowell Yeuell Yeuille Yeul Yeules Yeull Yeulle Yewell Yewl Yoall Yoele Yoell Yol Yoll Yooil Yool Yooll Yoolo Yooly Youan Youel YOUELL Youels Youhill Youil Youile Youill Youille Youl Youle Youles Youlie Youll Youlla Youlle Youlley Youllie Youlo Youlow Youly Yowel Yowil Yowle Yual Yuall Yuel Yuell Yuelle Yuelo Yuial Yuie Yuiell Yuil Yuile Yuille Yuillie Yuills Yuir Yul YULE Yull Yulle Yullie Yullow Yuls Yuyll Ywill Zoule
Yoll EWELL HOOLE YOLE YOUELL YULE
Yoltan YOULTON
Yolten YOULTON
Yolton YOULTON
Yomans YEOMAN
Yong YONGE YOUNG
YONGE 4 Yong YOUNG Younge
Yongue YOUNG
Yooil EWELL HOOLE YOLE YOUELL YULE
Yool EWELL HOOLE YOLE YOOLE YOUELL YUILL YULE
YOOLE 10 Yool Yuil Yuile YUILL Yuille YULE Zuil Zuill Zuille
Yooll EWELL HOOLE YOLE YOUELL YULE
Yoolo EWELL HOOLE YOLE YOUELL YULE
Yooly EWELL HOOLE YOLE YOUELL YULE
YORK YORKE
YORKE YORK
Yorren UREN
Youan EWELL HOOLE YOLE YOUELL YULE
Youdall UDELL
Youdle UDELL
Youel EWELL HOOLE YOLE YOUELL YULE
YOUELL 90 Eule Ewel Eweles EWELL Ewels HOOLE Juel Jule Uhl Uhles Uiles Uoel Yeaull Yeel Yeell Yehl Yeil Yeill Yell Yeoale Yeouls Yeowell Yeuell Yeuille Yeul Yeules Yeull Yeulle Yewell Yewl Yoall Yoele Yoell Yol YOLE Yoll Yooil Yool Yooll Yoolo Yooly Youan Youel Youels Youhill Youil Youile Youill Youille Youl Youle Youles Youlie Youll Youlla Youlle Youlley Youllie Youlo Youlow Youly Yowel Yowil Yowle Yual Yuall Yuel Yuell Yuelle Yuelo Yuial Yuie Yuiell Yuil Yuile Yuille Yuillie Yuills Yuir Yul YULE Yull Yulle Yullie Yullow Yuls Yuyll Ywill Zoule
Youels EWELL HOOLE YOLE YOUELL YULE
Youhill EWELL HOOLE YOLE YOUELL YULE
Youil EWELL HOOLE YOLE YOUELL YULE
Youile EWELL HOOLE YOLE YOUELL YULE
Youill EWELL HOOLE YOLE YOUELL YULE
Youille EWELL HOOLE YOLE YOUELL YULE
YOUINGS 13 EWINGS EWINS Hevens Hewen HEWENS Hewigns Hewing HEWINGS Hewons Howins Huings Huins
Youl EWELL HOOLE YOLE YOUELL YULE
Youle EWELL HOOLE YOLE YOUELL YULE
Youles EWELL HOOLE YOLE YOUELL YULE
Youlie EWELL HOOLE YOLE YOUELL YULE
Youll EWELL HOOLE YOLE YOUELL YULE
Youlla EWELL HOOLE YOLE YOUELL YULE
Youlle EWELL HOOLE YOLE YOUELL YULE
Youlley EWELL HOOLE YOLE YOUELL YULE
Youllie EWELL HOOLE YOLE YOUELL YULE
Youlo EWELL HOOLE YOLE YOUELL YULE
Youlow EWELL HOOLE YOLE YOUELL YULE
Youltan YOULTON
Youlten YOULTON
Youltin YOULTON
YOULTON 7 Yoltan Yolten Yolton Youltan Youlten Youltin
Youly EWELL HOOLE YOLE YOUELL YULE
Youman YEOMAN
YOUNG 5 Yong YONGE Yongue Younge
Younge YONGE YOUNG
Youren UREN
Yowel EWELL HOOLE YOLE YOUELL YULE
Yowil EWELL HOOLE YOLE YOUELL YULE
Yowle EWELL HOOLE YOLE YOUELL YULE
YOXALL Yocksall
Yual EWELL HOOLE YOLE YOUELL YULE
Yuall EWELL HOOLE YOLE YOUELL YULE
Yuel EWELL HOOLE YOLE YOUELL YULE
Yuell EWELL HOOLE YOLE YOUELL YULE
Yuelle EWELL HOOLE YOLE YOUELL YULE
Yuelo EWELL HOOLE YOLE YOUELL YULE
Yuial EWELL HOOLE YOLE YOUELL YULE
Yuie EWELL HOOLE YOLE YOUELL YULE
Yuiell EWELL HOOLE YOLE YOUELL YULE
Yuil EWELL HOOLE YOLE YOOLE YOUELL YUILL YULE
Yuile EWELL HOOLE YOLE YOOLE YOUELL YUILL YULE
YUILL 10 Yool YOOLE Yuil Yuile Yuille YULE Zuil Zuill Zuille
Yuille EWELL HOOLE YOLE YOOLE YOUELL YUILL YULE
Yuillie EWELL HOOLE YOLE YOUELL YULE
Yuills EWELL HOOLE YOLE YOUELL YULE
Yuir EWELL HOOLE YOLE YOUELL YULE
Yul EWELL HOOLE YOLE YOUELL YULE
YULE 95 Eule Ewel Eweles EWELL Ewels HOOLE Juel Jule Uhl Uhles Uiles Uoel Yeaull Yeel Yeell Yehl Yeil Yeill Yell Yeoale Yeouls Yeowell Yeuell Yeuille Yeul Yeules Yeull Yeulle Yewell Yewl Yoall Yoele Yoell Yol YOLE Yoll Yooil Yool YOOLE Yooll Yoolo Yooly Youan Youel YOUELL Youels Youhill Youil Youile Youill Youille Youl Youle Youles Youlie Youll Youlla Youlle Youlley Youllie Youlo Youlow Youly Yowel Yowil Yowle Yual Yuall Yuel Yuell Yuelle Yuelo Yuial Yuie Yuiell Yuil Yuile YUILL Yuille Yuillie Yuills Yuir Yul Yull Yulle Yullie Yullow Yuls Yuyll Ywill Zoule Zuil Zuill Zuille
Yull EWELL HOOLE YOLE YOUELL YULE
Yulle EWELL HOOLE YOLE YOUELL YULE
Yullie EWELL HOOLE YOLE YOUELL YULE
Yullow EWELL HOOLE YOLE YOUELL YULE
Yuls EWELL HOOLE YOLE YOUELL YULE
Yurdley EARDLEY
Yuyll EWELL HOOLE YOLE YOUELL YULE
Yva EVA EVEA
Ywill EWELL HOOLE YOLE YOUELL YULE
Zeager SEAGER
Zeger SEAGER
Zelley SELLEY SULLY
Zelly SELLEY SULLY
ZILLWOOD 4 SELLWOOD Sillwood Tillwood
Zolie SULLY
Zoule EWELL HOOLE YOLE YOUELL YULE
Zuil YOOLE YUILL YULE
Zuill YOOLE YUILL YULE
Zuille YOOLE YUILL YULE
Zullie SULLY

HOW CURRENT IS YOUR DIRECTORY

It is said that 20% of addresses go out of date each year. This table works on the basis of 20% of the remaining. From this you can see that after 3 years nearly half the addresses are already out of date.

ELAPSED YEARS	% CORRECT	ELAPSED YEARS	% CORRECT
0	100	11	9
1	80	12	7
2	64	13	5
3	51	14	4
4	41	15	4
5	33	16	3
6	26	17	2
7	21	18	2
8	17	19	1
9	13	20	1
10	11		

If the name you are interested in is not here, try Section C.

SECTION C
INTERESTS SECTION

Brief Overview of Section
This section is arranged alphabetically by Surname, and within this;-

"ALL" comes first, followed by
counties or regions alphabetically by code,
followed by ??? for unknown.

Within each of these the entries are arranged alphabetically by place name, but with "ALL" and areas such as North, South coming first.

Where there is a study being carried out to contain everyone of that name, this will be the first entry under that name. It is particularly important therefore to use the Variant Section B to identify these studies, which are only listed under one variant of the name in most cases.

Column Descriptions
KNOWN FROM AND TO

This is the range of dates that the person who submitted this entry has known information for.

RESEARCHING FROM AND TO

This is the range of dates that the person who submitted this entry is currently researching, or would like to find out more about.

REFERENCE NUMBER

This is the reference number that allows you to identify the person who submitted the entry and their address. Their address is found in section D, which is in order by reference number, and also alphabetically.

The number is made up of a 5 digit number starting from 10000, with a check digit added to the end. The use of the check digit, greatly reduces the chance of transcription and other errors. This is the check digit method that has the highest error detection capabilities, and can be a number from 0 to 9 or an X representing 10. To avoid confusion we have not used codes which would end with an X, so there will appear to be some gaps in the number sequence.

Last years numbers were 5 digits long, the move for this year to a 6 digit number follows research that shows you make less errors when copying down groups of 3 numbers. Therefore look on a number 123456 as 123 456, for ease of use.

COUNTY CODE

This is a 3 digit code, used as an abbreviation for the county. A full list of the county codes is the very last printed page of this directory. The codes used are very similar to both the British Standard Set, and those known as the Chapman County Codes. In most cases they are obvious abbreviations, but sometimes to avoid confusion, they have been slightly modified. In general you will find the county codes are the same as in other sets, but we have added some area codes, such as one to cover the Home Counties. If you are familiar with the other sets then please look through the list to see any differences that are relevant to you. We would have preferred to have printed the county names in full, but this would have quite drastically increased the size and thereby the price of both the book and postage. As all other directories use county codes, we decided to follow. We will be reviewing this in the future so if you have strong feelings on this please let us know.

PLACE

This is the name of a place, or an area of the county.

Additional Points
Not everyones form was easy to enter into the format we are using. While we could translate mid 18th Century into a number, sometimes the information provided could not be translated, and on these occasions you will see a question mark (?). Where there is missing information such as a county, we have not guessed, but have put three question marks (???) and put it at the end of the list.

County boundaries have changed, and at some points in history, small islands of land in the middle of a county could be part of another county, or a county could be in two or more separated pieces.

Because of the above, and the fact that there can be places with the same name in more than one county, we have not edited the information provided but entered it as submitted.

As many places can be classified in many ways, under various county codes old and new, under area and others, you will need a good map and it will involve you in some detective work to find all the possibilities that may interest you. You may find the county chart in section I (Reference) is helpful, which highlights the old and equivalent new counties together with the surrounding counties.

Remember to fully use the variant section to make sure nothing is missed. Even if you are interested in only one spelling for some reason, you need to find the variants, and using this section finds the entries in section D. Following the name and address in section D, you will find the known variants of the name that the person has submitted. It is likely therefore that the name and period you are interested in could be classified under the other variants. While some people submitted entries under several variants some have just entered information under the oldest known form, and entered later variations as variants. If you do not check this you could miss some of the best discoveries open to you.

If you are interested in all the people from a place please see the Place and Special Studies in Section E.

OTHER USEFUL PAGES

Please remember to send in your information.
Why not do it now !!!

Known From	To	Researching From	To	Ref	Cty	Place
A'BEAR						
....	....	ALL	ALL	124974	ALL	Name Study
....	....	ALL	ALL	124974	ALL	ALL
....	....	1795	1810	124974	BKM	Aylesbury
1840	1850	1825	1850	124974	BKM	Eton
1470	1928	1066	1992	124974	BRK	Harehatch
1855	1860	1600	1900	124974	BRK	Hurst
1775	1780	1600	1900	124974	BRK	Reading
1325	1928	1066	1992	124974	BRK	Wargrave
1810	1815	1790	1825	124974	CON	Scilly Isles
1919	1979	....	....	124974	GLS	Aldsworth
1844	1889	1820	1890	124974	LND	Marylebone
1884	1979	1850	1979	124974	MDX	Fulham
1878	1937	1870	1940	124974	MDX	Hendon
1838	1930	1810	1930	124974	MDX	Isleworth
1783	1888	1600	1900	124974	OXF	Bix
1895	1899	1890	1900	124974	OXF	Dunsden
1851	1858	1830	1859	124974	OXF	Garsington
1859	1920	1859	1920	124974	OXF	Headington
1560	1578	1538	1919	124974	OXF	Henley
1783	1818	1600	1900	124974	OXF	Middle Assendon
1813	1883	1600	1900	124974	OXF	Rotherfield Greys
1900	1919	....	....	124974	OXF	Rotherfield Peppard
1807	1829	1066	1992	124974	OXF	Shiplake
1853	1900	1837	1900	124974	SRY	Lambeth
A'COURT						
....	....	ALL	ALL	142549	ALL	ALL
1850	1900	ALL	ALL	142549	DOR	Fifehead Magdelen
1850	1900	ALL	ALL	142549	WIL	Sutton Veny
AARONS						
1880	1920	1880	1900	114529	LND	East End
ABBA						
1860	....	....	....	164062	WES	Staveley
ABBERLEY						
....	....	1700	1900	179531	STS	Abbots Bromley
ABBET						
1745	....	ALL	1745	168602	CAM	Burwell
....	....	1650	1690	103713	SFK	Wickhambrook
ABBEY						
1720	1800	1600	1992	167592	LAN	Liverpool
?	1820	?	?	147400	LEI	Cottesmore
....	....	1700	1900	101958	NFK	ALL
?	1820	?	?	147400	RUT	North Luffenham
1750	?	1750	1992	167592	SCT	Glasgow
ABBOT						
1744	1745	1680	1780	105333	DEV	Buckland In The Moor
1744	1745	1680	1780	105333	DEV	Holne
1744	1745	1680	1780	105333	DEV	Ilsington
1744	1745	1680	1780	105333	DEV	Lydford
1744	1745	1680	1780	105333	DEV	Widecombe In The Moor
1712	1720	1700	1800	127116	HAM	North Baddesley
1640	1840	1500	1850	105333	LAN	Brownedge
1640	1840	1500	1850	105333	LAN	Chorley
1740	1763	ALL	ALL	135909	LAN	Mcuh Hoole
1640	1840	1500	1850	105333	LAN	Preston
1640	1840	1500	1850	105333	LAN	Samlesbury
1640	1840	1500	1850	105333	LAN	Walton Le Dale
1845	....	....	....	108375	MDX	Enfield
....	1823	1786	1840	133639	SOM	Coker
1786	....	1786	1850	133639	SOM	Lonnington
1800	....	....	....	117579	SOM	Witham Friary
1786	1820	1750	1786	145327	WYK	Wath
ABBOTT						
....	....	ALL	1800	158577	BDF	Sharnbrook
1851	1980	1700	1850	170178	BKM	High Wycombe
1680	1940	....	....	128996	CAM	Thorney
1778	1861	1700	1992	140090	DEV	North Molton
1915	1915	1850	1915	103640	ESS	Stratford
1813	1992	1700	1820	116416	HRT	Redbourn
1794	1850	....	1794	108839	HUN	Houghton
1794	1830	1750	1800	115681	HUN	St Neots
?	?	?	?	154687	KEN	Herne
1840	1890	ALL	ALL	159034	KEN	Snodland
1884	1992	?	1884	153613	LAN	ALL
1773	1846	1700	1773	160474	LAN	Blackburn
1771	1862	....	....	138851	LAN	Blackrod
1771	1862	....	....	138851	LAN	Horwich
1826	....	ALL	ALL	112275	LEI	North West
1714	1918	1500	1714	175072	LIN	Belchford
1820	1860	1750	1820	165018	LIN	Hogsthorpe
1812	1851	1700	1812	170178	LND	Westminster
1820	1838	ALL	1820	159077	NTH	Aldwinkle
ABBOTT contd.						
1839	1851	1780	1861	160903	NTH	Islip
1839	1851	1780	1861	160903	NTH	Twywell
....	....	ALL	1750	178411	NTT	Oxton
1600	1625	ALL	1600	131059	SFK	Hadleigh
1810	1850	1700	1820	133892	SFK	Ipswich
1618	1652	....	....	101028	SFK	Lidgate
1781	1992	1700	1781	174378	SFK	Otley
1880	1980	1800	1880	110647	SFK	Somersham
1799	1808	ALL	1799	169730	SRY	Kingston
1871	1935	?	1871	136611	WAR	Aston
1681	1992	1550	1681	142646	WES	Clifton
1884	1992	?	1884	153613	YKS	ALL
ABBS						
1900	1992	1900	1992	163600	MDX	North
1791	1859	....	....	135437	NFK	Billingford
1680	....	1650	1700	179035	NFK	Burston
1855	1855	....	....	135437	NFK	E Dereham
1863	1876	....	....	135437	NFK	Fulmodestone
1818	1861	....	....	135437	NFK	N Elmham
1881	1985	....	....	135437	NFK	Stibbard
1815	1815	....	....	135437	NFK	Swanton Morley
ABDALE						
1730	1850	1700	1850	125881	NFK	Fakenham
ABDY						
1870	....	....	....	151785	YKS	Handsworth
ABEL						
1836	1992	ALL	1836	100021	GMP	Dyce Old Machor
ALL	1900	....	....	132756	HEF	???
ALL	1900	....	....	132756	LAN	???
1870	1900	....	....	132756	LEI	Staunton Harold
1790	1810	....	....	102318	LIN	Threckingham
1880	1914	....	....	132756	NTH	Pottersbury
1700	1800	1600	1700	128317	NTH	Weedon
1773	1800	....	....	129747	SFK	Elmsett
1750	....	....	....	129747	SFK	Wattisfield
1820	1880	....	....	102318	SRY	East
1700	1980	1600	1700	159115	SRY	London
1860	1965	....	....	132756	STS	Penkhull
1860	1965	....	....	132756	STS	Stoke On Trent
1776	1878	1700	1800	135550	WOR	North
ABELL						
....	....	1700	1900	108766	DEV	Hatherleigh
1789	1798	1700	1798	148288	YKS	Rotherham
1789	1798	1700	1798	148288	YKS	Wakefield
ABERCROMBIE						
1790	1840	1760	1790	134139	BRK	Cookham
ABERNETHY						
1300	1350	1200	1300	154881	SCT	ALL
1750	1965	....	....	137820	SHI	Fetlar
1720	1965	....	....	137820	SHI	Mid Yell
1760	1965	....	....	137820	SHI	North Yell
1758	1965	....	....	137820	SHI	Northmavine
1720	1965	....	....	137820	SHI	South Yell
ABERY						
1718	1770	1650	1992	101419	BRK	ALL
1866	1884	1800	1900	116742	MDX	Notting Hill
ABET						
1754	1782	....	1754	177504	SFK	Clopton
ABINGDON						
1900	....	....	....	127086	ALL	ALL
ABLE						
....	....	ALL	1852	114030	NFK	Horstead
ABLETHORPE						
1715	1770	1715	1770	148156	BKM	Hanslope
ABLETT						
....	....	1827	1859	140244	CAM	Bourn
....	....	1803	....	140244	CAM	Gamlingay
ABLITT						
1838	1864	1750	1850	171441	LND	Westminster
ABON						
1851	1900	1750	1850	172472	NFK	Norwich
ABRAHALL						
1863	1992	1750	1863	149519	MON	Monmouth
ABRAHAM						
?	?	?	?	138622	ALL	ALL
1780	1797	....	1780	142166	BDF	Cranfield
1829	1905	1750	1829	118486	BDF	Eaton Bray
1655	1750	1600	1750	164674	DEV	Ashburton
1750	1830	1700	1830	144657	ESS	Chingford
1750	1830	1700	1830	144657	ESS	Loughton
1773	1874	1750	1874	158658	GLA	Llansamlet
1773	1874	1750	1874	158658	GLA	Swansea
1790	1925	1750	1790	157074	HAM	Tichfield

Surname	Known From	To	Researching From	To	Ref	Cty	Place
ABRAHAM contd.							
	1840	1960	....	....	100048	LND	Greenwich
	1847	1992	....	1847	100064	MEA	Hayes
	1800	1840	1700	1800	100048	SRY	Bermondsey
	1750	1851	ALL	1750	145203	YKS	Easington
ABRAHAMS							
	1758	1824	ALL	ALL	124982	SOM	North
ABRAM							
	?	1982	....	....	100072	LAN	Liverpool
	1881	1992	ALL	1881	100072	NTH	Northampton
	1911	?	1911	ALL	100072	SFK	Bury St Edmunds
	1655	....	1575	....	118591	WES	East Ward
ABRAMS							
	1725	1825	1600	1725	175781	WIL	Bromham
	1725	1825	1600	1725	175781	WIL	Devizes
ABREY							
	1873	1974	1790	1875	112135	SFK	Mildenhall
ABSALON							
	1750	1800	1700	1992	167592	SFK	Yarmouth
ABURROW							
	....	....	1560	1840	166448	HAM	???
	....	....	1840	1900	166448	SSX	???
ACASTER							
	1130	1202	1066	1250	178640	YKS	Acaster
	1800	1825	1750	1870	178675	YKS	Brotherton
	1870	1992	1800	1870	178675	YKS	Goole
	1250	1401	1200	1500	178640	YKS	York
ACHANY							
	....	....	1066	....	130745	ENG	South
ACHESON							
	1758	1839	ALL	ALL	111295	FER	Enniskillen
ACHILLES							
	1820	1900	?	?	102512	IRL	Dublin
ACKERLEY							
	1740	1790	1700	1900	103632	LAN	Salford
ACKERMAN							
	1824	1866	1820	1875	118354	BKM	Chalfont St Peter
	1726	1812	1500	1726	138614	DOR	Bridport
	....	....	1900	1992	109894	DOR	Weymouth
	1874	1917	1860	1920	135933	OXF	Charlbury
ACKERNLEY							
	1742	1992	....	1742	141968	YKS	Kildwick
ACKERS							
	1798	1841	ALL	ALL	107913	LAN	Scarisbrick
ACKLAM							
	1550	1700	1450	1550	109959	EYK	Reighton
ACKLAND							
	1777	1857	....	....	172030	DEV	Luppitt
	1800	1920	1800	1920	160814	DEV	Plymouth
	1664	1820	....	....	167053	HAM	Basing
ACKLING							
	1800	1860	1700	1900	153826	BRK	Abingdon
ACKRELL							
	1800	1992	1800	?	166235	YKS	East Riding
ACKRILL							
	1750	1850	....	....	124621	LIN	Stallingborough
ACKROYD							
	1880	1900	1800	1950	119180	DUR	North
	1780	1992	1700	1992	100099	WRY	Bradford
	1700	1800	....	....	100099	WRY	Thornton
	1920	1992	ALL	ALL	162027	WYK	Bradford
	1886	1960	....	1886	176702	WYK	Bradford
	1770	1860	1770	1860	153621	WYK	Clayton
	1828	1992	1700	1828	100110	WYK	Farsley
	1810	1851	1750	1810	178993	YKS	Bruntcliffe
	1855	1881	1881	1992	130990	YKS	Doncaster
	1790	1992	ALL	1992	100102	YKS	Heckmondwike
	1850	1930	....	....	127574	YKS	Whitby
ACLAND							
	1904	1992	1820	1904	150487	AVN	Bristol
	1890	1992	1700	1890	150487	DEV	???
ACOMB							
	1741	....	1600	1741	116637	YKS	Long Marston
	1790	1816	1600	1800	134368	YKS	Ripon
ACORNLEY							
	1500	....	ALL	ALL	169277	LAN	ALL
	1500	....	ALL	ALL	169277	WYK	ALL
ACOTT							
	1850	1900	....	....	113514	GLA	Cardiff
	....	....	1770	1850	113514	GLS	???
ACRES							
	....	....	ALL	ALL	100544	ALL	Name Study
	1742	1936	1600	1992	100129	KEN	East
	1890	1920	1800	1992	100129	KEN	Canterbury
ACRES contd.							
	1840	1936	1800	1992	100129	KEN	Maidstone
	1742	1880	1700	1742	100129	KEN	Pluckley
	1880	1930	1850	1880	100129	KEN	Ramsgate
	1808	1870	1750	1800	100129	KEN	Smarden
	1705	1775	1705	1775	174084	SRY	Wimbledon
	1815	1982	1700	1815	179043	YKS	North
ACRILL							
	1800	1850	1600	1800	145688	LIN	Grimsby
	1680	1725	....	....	145688	LIN	Keelby
	1650	1700	....	....	145688	LIN	Stallingborough
ACTON							
	1900	1960	ALL	ALL	100137	STS	Burton On Trent
ADAIR							
	1740	1815	1700	1992	133450	IRL	Dublin
	1740	1815	1700	1992	133450	LAN	Manchester
	1740	1815	1700	1992	133450	???	London
ADAM							
	1795	1950	ALL	ALL	147087	ABD	ALL
	1720	1900	....	1720	174246	ABD	Easter Beltie
	1720	1900	....	1720	174246	ABD	Kncardine O'neil
	1801	1908	....	1801	160652	ABD	Rathen
	1760	....	....	....	151351	ANS	Arbroath
	1773	1849	....	....	171654	AYR	Kilmarnock
	1807	1900	1700	1800	144037	FIF	Anstruther
	1750	1980	....	1760	174246	KCD	Bush
	1864	1934	1700	1864	100145	RFW	Glasgow
ADAMI							
	1790	1840	1770	1790	134139	LND	Westminster
ADAMS							
	1781	1781	ALL	....	115355	BDF	ALL
	1795	1881	1700	1950	159964	BKM	Thornborough
	1802	....	1700	1802	123307	BRK	Kintbury
	....	1855	1800	1880	128961	BRK	Newbury
	....	....	1600	1850	143219	BRK	Windsor
	1806	1872	1700	1806	125784	CAM	Whittels Ford
	1834	1992	ALL	1834	105465	CHS	Prestbury
	....	....	1700	1799	138126	CMN	???
	1600	1800	ALL	ALL	166537	CON	North
	1843	1869	1750	1843	168173	CON	Camborne
	1700	1750	1650	1700	132942	CON	Feock
	1900	1965	1800	1900	177717	CON	Launceston
	1780	1850	ALL	ALL	100161	CON	St Germans
	1814	....	....	....	155608	DBY	ALL
	1780	1940	1800	1992	133450	DEV	ALL
	1820	1840	1820	1840	110361	DEV	Chulmleigh
	1829	1900	1700	1829	109983	DEV	Devonport
	1871	1881	....	....	133922	DEV	Exeter
	1782	1992	ALL	1782	100285	DEV	Northlew
	1780	1835	1814	1835	110361	DEV	South Molton
	....	....	1750	1825	156795	DOR	East
	1725	1900	1650	1725	160458	DOR	Frampton
	1793	1992	1700	1793	150223	DOR	Winterbourne Zelston
	....	....	ALL	ALL	116823	DOW	Greyabbey
	1870	1992	1600	1870	176915	DUR	Stockton On Tees
	1870	1992	1600	1870	176915	DUR	Witton Park
	....	....	1600	1725	100226	EAG	ALL
	....	....	ALL	1840	104442	ESS	Great Warley
	....	....	ALL	1800	128627	ESS	North Weald
	1858	....	ALL	ALL	107255	ESS	Saffron Walden
	1725	1800	1600	1725	100226	ESS	Theydon Garnon
	1888	1909	....	....	143928	ESS	Witham
	1820	....	....	....	137936	FIF	Auchtermuchty
	....	....	1865	1910	100188	GLA	Cardiff
	....	1947	1887	1947	101427	GLA	Cardiff
	....	....	1700	1800	100188	GLA	Merthyr Tydfil
	....	....	1868	1881	100188	GLA	Penarth
	1850	1900	....	1850	159972	GLS	Bristol
	....	....	1700	1786	150150	GLS	Duntisborne Abbotts
	1811	1914	1700	1820	117773	GLS	West Dean
	1782	1871	ALL	ALL	150169	HAM	Alton
	1650	1812	1813	1992	166804	HAM	Andover
	1850	1940	1941	1989	136859	HAM	Portsmouth
	1857	1874	1700	1857	167819	HAM	Southampton
	1740	1763	ALL	1750	169730	HAM	Weston Patrick
	1820	1880	ALL	ALL	115002	HAM	Whitchurch
	1835	1980	1770	1835	168386	KCD	Stonehaven
	1842	1850	ALL	1850	109819	KEN	South West
	....	....	ALL	ALL	100153	KEN	Deptford
	1818	1880	ALL	1880	100269	KEN	Faversham
	....	....	ALL	ALL	100153	KEN	Luddesdown
	....	....	ALL	ALL	100153	KEN	Rochester
	1790	1820	1700	1820	133817	KEN	Rochford

Known From	To	Researching From	To	Ref	Cty	Place
ADAMS contd.						
1721	?	?	?	166642	KEN	???
1840	1880	1840	1890	103225	LAN	Liverpool
1820	1880	1880	1992	100196	LEI	Anstey
1870	1870	1850	1950	135925	LND	North East
....	....	1830	1860	123390	LND	Bow
1910	1950	1800	1910	137685	LND	Canning Town
1828	1859	1650	1828	139769	LND	Covent Garden
1855	1916	1855	1992	100226	LND	Muswell Hill
1800	1992	1750	1800	100277	LND	Shoreditch
1760	1820	1760	1820	100277	LND	Stepney
1835	1992	....	1835	129461	LND	???
1818	1861	....	....	101028	MDX	Hoxton
1818	1861	....	....	101028	MDX	London
1778	1801	1700	1777	131245	MDX	Shoreditch
1816	1825	ALL	ALL	149683	MDX	Southgate
1900	....	....	....	104337	MDX	???
1881	1885	1750	1880	100188	MON	Ebbw Vale
1850	1992	1840	1900	116661	NTH	ALL
1855	1992	1799	1855	166855	NTH	Brockhall
1700	1800	....	....	137111	NTH	Farthinghoe
1790	1890	1890	1992	133507	NTH	Pattishall
1777	1777	1700	1780	128449	NTT	Nottingham
1850	1900	1750	1850	174513	OXF	Broughton Poggs
1813	1921	ALL	1940	132217	PEM	Cilgerran
1840	1900	1780	1840	103845	PEM	Monkton
1840	1900	1780	1840	103845	PEM	Pembroke Dock
1847	....	....	....	129747	SFK	Combs
1833	....	....	....	129747	SFK	Great Bricett
1870	1920	....	....	129747	SFK	Ipswich
1850	1992	1850	1992	100161	SFK	Lowestoft
1803	1809	....	....	129747	SFK	Wattisfield
1600	1720	1600	1680	142018	SOM	East
1815	1992	1800	1981	143928	SOM	Ashill
1749	1992	1700	1749	123153	SOM	Bath
1900	....	1850	1930	142549	SOM	Batheaston
1844	1865	1700	1900	102326	SOM	Coleford Kilmersdon
1851	....	....	....	174750	SOM	Haselbury Plucknett
....	....	1750	1820	129356	SOM	Martock
1820	1846	1820	1846	133922	SOM	Montacute
1700	1750	1600	1725	144606	SOM	Odcombe
1850	1900	....	1850	159972	SOM	Weston
1839	1880	1750	1850	112526	SRY	Walworth
1806	1837	ALL	ALL	149683	SSX	Harting
....	....	1700	1800	118834	SSX	Prinsted
1650	1850	....	....	153397	SSX	West Grinsted
1800	1800	ALL	ALL	149683	SSX	Westfield
....	....	1830	1860	123390	STI	Baldernock
1625	1725	1550	1750	133450	STS	Cheswardine
1851	1900	1800	1851	156574	STS	Little Pits
1800	1800	1750	1850	134627	STS	Walsall
1649	1669	1600	1700	167002	SXE	Waldron
1780	1940	1800	1992	133450	WAR	ALL
1820	1880	1880	1992	100196	WAR	Birmginham
1820	1880	1880	1992	100196	WAR	Coventry
1700	1800	1550	1840	100420	WAR	Meriden
1850	1899	1700	1992	122742	WIL	Box
1850	1900	1750	1850	174513	WIL	Little Hinton
1830	1920	1650	1830	148113	YKS	Doncaster
1780	1850	1750	1850	166081	YKS	Heck
1830	1880	1800	1900	166081	YKS	Kippax
1852	1900	1600	1852	131261	YKS	Sheffield
?	1839	ALL	ALL	111295	???	???
ADAMSON						
1802	1926	ALL	ALL	112844	ABD	Slains
1785	1785	ALL	1785	154563	CUL	Alston
1815	1838	1800	1992	165603	DUR	Long Newton
1880	1930	1800	1930	123048	DUR	Sunderland
1890	1992	....	....	175099	DUR	???
1859	1992	1700	1859	179566	LAN	Preston
1930	1989	1800	1930	174939	YKS	Driffield
....	1671	1650	1700	138584	YKS	Rothwell
ADCOCK						
1834	1921	1700	1850	117013	NFK	Dereham
1750	1750	1600	1750	174130	RUT	Prestland
1823	1992	1700	1823	161446	STS	Penkridge
1600	1800	....	....	100420	WAR	Great Packington
1600	1800	....	....	100420	WAR	Little Packington
1600	1800	....	....	100420	WAR	Meriden
1700	1760	1760	1992	172782	YKS	Ainsty
ADDAMS						
1690	....	....	....	151351	DOR	Piddlehinton
1773	1870	1700	1780	145963	SRY	Rotherhithe
ADDENBROOKE						
1500	1700	ALL	1800	160873	WOR	Old Swinford
ADDERLEY						
1788	1835	1600	1847	125806	WAR	Birmingham
ADDERSON						
1767	1793	1650	1766	131245	WAR	Stretton On Dunsmore
ADDICOAT						
1736	1873	ALL	ALL	104191	CON	Penzance
ADDIMAN						
1728	1788	1700	1850	137561	YKS	Barwick In Elmet
ADDINGTON						
1835	....	....	....	154296	ALL	???
1750	1900	1700	1760	137243	NTH	Potterspury
ADDINSELL						
1641	1992	1500	1800	100307	NTT	North
ADDIS						
....	....	ALL	ALL	100323	ALL	Name Study
1909	1992	ALL	1909	174017	BRE	Brynmawr
1811	1992	....	1811	100315	LND	Stepney
1883	1992	ALL	1883	174017	MON	Llanhilleth
....	....	....	....	141054	STS	Black Country
....	....	....	....	141054	WOR	Black Country
ADDISON						
1835	1878	1800	1835	159980	CUL	Thursby
1660	1730	1660	1730	127655	HUN	Glatton
1793	....	....	....	111856	NFK	Wimbotsham
1650	1660	1600	1650	121339	NYK	Lythe
1583	1840	....	....	117404	STS	Eccleshall
1848	....	1600	1848	132802	STS	Wolverhampton
1755	1773	1700	1800	116505	WES	Morland
?	?	....	....	154113	WES	The Levens
1790	1835	ALL	1790	136913	YKS	Great Ouseburn
1820	1840	1700	1820	167843	YKS	Sandend
1840	1900	1840	1900	167843	YKS	Thornaby On Tees
1850	1992	1700	1850	172782	???	Wickersfield
ADDLESEE						
1695	1900	ALL	ALL	171379	LIN	ALL
ADDLESHAW						
1695	1760	ALL	ALL	171379	LIN	Stainton By Langworth
ADDLEY						
1963	1992	....	....	173932	WIL	Bradford On Avon
ADDS						
1698	1744	1670	1744	167002	SXE	Hailsham
1670	1727	1650	1750	167002	SXE	Ticehurst
1636	1680	1600	1700	167002	SXE	Withyham
ADDY						
....	....	1862	1911	103187	EYK	York
1694	1712	1675	1694	101796	YKS	Darfield
ADENBROOKE						
1684	1724	1680	1730	160873	HEF	Upper Sapey
1639	1671	1600	1700	160873	STS	Kingswinford
ADER						
1762	....	....	1762	171441	DUR	Wolviston
ADEY						
....	....	ALL	1914	173177	DBY	Winshull
1700	1880	1600	1920	119040	DOR	Poole
1820	1906	1846	1906	133175	GLS	Kingswood
1793	1900	1700	ALL	135127	HAM	Hordle
1800	1829	1800	1898	142530	HAM	Hordle
1751	1992	1660	1750	121673	STS	Burntwood
1820	1906	1846	1906	133175	WIL	Kingswood
ADGORE						
1649	1680	1600	1700	171441	KEN	Pluckley
ADIAR						
1808	1834	1800	1808	139483	WIG	Stoneykirk
ADIN						
1787	1834	1660	1786	100358	DBY	Derby
1852	1959	1834	1852	100358	LAN	Manchester
ADINSON						
1682	1730	ALL	ALL	141615	LAN	Warton
ADKIN						
1700	....	ALL	1700	131059	ESS	Bocking
1833	1896	1751	1911	102296	LIN	Binbook
1864	1880	1813	1938	102296	LIN	Ludborough
1825	1825	1750	1825	142085	NTT	Bingham
1696	1753	1600	1696	116637	SFK	Barrow
1800	1900	1700	1800	125660	SFK	Bungay
1800	1900	1700	1800	125660	SFK	Bury St Edmunds
1727	1727	1650	1726	131245	WAR	Long Itchington
ADKINS						
1785	1799	1500	1800	137170	BDF	Billington
1669	1801	1650	1801	125520	ESS	Stock Havard

Known From To Researching From To Ref Cty Place

ADKINS contd.
.... 1700 1799 142409 NFK ???
1820 1880 1820 1890 112925 NTH Wicken
1754 1830 1700 1850 118397 OXF Coggs
1832 1906 1700 1832 156914 STS Aldridge
1715 ALL .... 117048 STS Harborne
ADLAM
.... ALL ALL 100366 ALL Name Study
1600 1700 1600 1700 165999 GLS Westbury On Trym
1840 1883 1700 1900 133175 SOM Stanton Drew
1800 1860 1700 1900 162345 SOM Wookey
ADLARD
.... ALL ALL 105503 LIN ALL
1792 1865 .... 178330 LND Smithfield
1792 1865 .... 178330 LND Stockwell
ADLINBTON
1784 1840 1784 1860 113301 DBY Dronfield
ADNAM
1753 1851 ALL 1851 127094 BRK Newbury
1884 1890 1850 1884 119059 STS West Bromwich
ADNAMS
1753 1851 ALL 1851 127094 BRK Newbury
ADRIAN
.... ALL ALL 100374 ALL Name Study
ADSETT
.... 1800 1950 100382 ALL ALL
1733 1960 1550 1960 100382 SRY ALL
1733 1960 1550 1960 100382 SSX ALL
.... 1811 ALL 132349 SSX North Chapel
ADSHEAD
.... 1840 1750 1840 163686 CHS Cheadle
ADY
.... 1600 1650 154873 KEN Upchurch
ADYE
1450 1750 ALL 1992 133450 KEN Barham
.... 1350 1700 154873 KEN Barham
.... 1350 1700 154873 KEN Doddington
.... 1350 1700 154873 KEN Lynsted
.... 1350 1700 154873 KEN Nurstead
1825 1900 ALL ALL 162434 WIL Bradford On Avon
AERAY
.... 1600 1700 116173 CUL St Bees
AFFLECK
1800 .... 100633 DUR ???
1780 1800 ALL ALL 130508 FIF Pittenweem
1800 1850 ALL ALL 130508 FIF St Monanace
1744 1900 1700 1900 159964 KKD Kirkpatrick Durham
1887 1890 ALL ALL 100390 LAN Manchester
.... 1850 1950 159964 LAN Manchester
AGAR
.... ALL ALL 100404 ALL Name Study
1837 1922 .... 100404 ALL ALL
1820 1900 1800 1911 108278 ANT Belfast
1700 1800 1600 1700 113204 DOW Holywood
1800 1850 .... 117064 DUR Boldon
1794 1885 1600 1992 130125 DUR Durham
? ? ? ? 100692 MDX St George East
1754 1800 ALL 1754 143731 SFK Hartismere
1804 1992 .... 100404 YKS Langton
AGER
.... 1700 1992 122009 ESS East
1857 1959 1700 1857 138673 ESS Birdrook
1743 1821 1743 1821 114308 NTH ALL
1877 1992 1800 1877 100412 SFK Mendlesham
1820 1870 ALL ALL 150347 WAR Birmingham
AGLAND
1862 .... 1700 1862 117927 DEV Exeter
AGNEW
1853 1874 ALL ALL 149489 ARM Lurgan
1800 1870 1700 1800 100145 DFS Dumfries
1866 1881 ALL ALL 149489 HAM Portsmouth
1860 1880 1800 1930 136174 TYR Garvaghey
1850 1870 1800 1870 156280 TYR ???
AGUS
1750 1910 1600 1850 173223 EAG ???
AGUTTER
.... ALL ALL 100420 ALL Name Study
ALL ALL ALL ALL 100420 ALL ALL
AHERNE
1843 1992 1700 1843 133108 IRL Limerick
AHLERS
1867 1867 1810 1900 105333 MDX London
1868 1906 1800 1868 103640 MDX Poplar

Known From To Researching From To Ref Cty Place

AHSMAN
1850 1992 1700 1849 156876 SOM Coleford
AHSTON
1740 1958 1600 1750 172006 LAN Bury
1740 1958 1600 1750 172006 LAN Middleton
AICKEN
1846 1934 1750 1900 176621 ANT Randalstown
1846 1934 1750 1900 176621 ANT Toome Bridge
AIKEN
1844 1992 1700 1844 100447 ANT Ballydaie
1670 1671 1650 1671 108510 CLK Clackmannan
1844 1992 1700 1844 100447 MDX London
AILWORTH
1650 1750 1650 1750 165999 GLS Henbury
AIME
1780 1880 1750 1900 176206 LND Lambeth
AIMERS
.... 1700 1800 149187 ANS Panbride
AIMIS
1800 1877 1700 1800 125806 STS Kingswinford
AINGE
1841 1925 1700 1840 152552 LND ???
1790 1840 1750 1790 140309 WOR Inkberrow
AINGER
1813 1887 1700 1830 175218 NFK North West
AINLEY
1778 1817 1778 1841 132845 WYK Birstal
1800 1992 1650 1900 134678 WYK Golcar
1764 1850 ALL 1850 113611 WYK Hatfield
1800 1992 1650 1900 134678 WYK Huddersfield
1641 1750 1600 1780 170348 YKS Almondbury
AINSBURY
1800 1850 1700 1800 142913 GLS Mangotsfield
1750 1800 1800 1900 142913 WOR Dudley
AINSBY
1841 1900 1800 1900 146269 MDX Chelsea
AINSCOUGH
1775 1926 .... 116602 LAN West
AINSCOW
1800 .... 126497 LAN Leyland
AINSLIE
1732 1770 1730 1800 149063 BEW Duns
1800 1905 .... 100455 CMA Grizedale
1679 1880 .... 100455 ELN Haddington
1680 1800 1650 1850 149063 ELN Haddington
1617 1680 .... 100455 MLN Newbattle
1617 1700 ALL 1750 149063 MLN Newbattle
1841 1936 1936 1992 145335 NBL Howick
.... 1760 1830 145335 ROX ALL
1460 1655 .... 100455 ROX Fala
1570 1828 .... 100455 ROX Jedburgh
1250 1500 .... 100455 ROX Oxnam
1907 1910 1910 1992 141771 SOM Ditcheat
1765 1800 .... 100455 WES Kendal
AINSWORTH
.... 1740 .... 1740 100463 BDF Caddington
1800 .... 1800 .... 100463 BDF Cardington
1797 .... 1797 1817 100463 HRT Essendon
1748 1780 1748 1780 100463 HRT Kings Warden
1900 1992 1900 1992 109347 LAN Accrington
1620 1908 1770 1992 133450 LAN Manchester
1706 1900 1600 1800 109347 LAN Padiham
1770 1800 1770 1810 145602 LAN Salmesbury
1850 1920 1850 1920 100463 MDX Hammersmith
1850 1890 1850 .... 100463 MDX Newington
1860 1900 1600 1992 178268 STS Kingsley
1793 1820 ALL 1793 102350 YKS Brayton
AIR
1775 1992 ALL 1775 100536 ??? ???
AIRE
1898 .... 1850 .... 134589 YKS Castleford
AIREY
? ? .... 100471 CMA ???
1769 1820 1700 1769 111236 CUL Middleton
? ? .... 100471 LAN Blackburn
1784 1909 1750 1784 138347 SFK Earl Soham
AIRNS
.... ALL ALL 109924 ALL Name Study
AIRTON
.... 1748 .... 121940 WRY Gisburn
.... 1748 .... 121940 WRY Long Preston
AISBETT
1824 1840 1800 1992 146331 DUR Pittington

Known From	To	Researching From	To	Ref	Cty	Place
AISH						
....	....	ALL	ALL	101974	ALL	Name Study
1700	1900	ALL	ALL	101974	ALL	ALL
....	....	1800	1920	134694	DOR	Stalbridge
AISHE						
1700	1900	ALL	ALL	101974	ALL	ALL
AISLABIE						
1725	1793	1700	1793	118192	MDX	ALL
AISLABY						
....	....	ALL	ALL	141844	ALL	Name Study
AITCHISON						
1870	1874	1850	1890	172855	LKS	Cadder
1828	1835	1538	1835	118893	NBL	Horncliffe
1809	1881	1538	1881	118893	NBL	Wooler
....	....	1800	1900	146110	SCT	ALL
1750	1965	....	....	137820	SHI	Fetlar
1720	1965	....	....	137820	SHI	Mid Yell
1760	1965	....	....	137820	SHI	North Yell
1758	1965	....	....	137820	SHI	Northmavine
1720	1965	....	....	137820	SHI	South Yell
AITKEN						
....	....	1830	1992	167932	ANS	Montrose
1838	1857	1700	1838	166723	BEW	Belville
1809	....	1800	1900	164402	CUL	Dalston
1825	1992	1600	1864	100579	DOW	Donaghdee
1872	....	1700	1992	131423	DUR	Jarrow On Tyne
1820	1840	1780	1840	130915	FIF	St Andrews
1840	1917	1800	1992	102407	FIF	St Manance
1867	1872	1800	1900	129453	LAN	Warrington
....	....	1700	1850	179574	LKS	Lanark
....	....	1800	1850	176079	MDX	Shadwell
1774	1863	1650	1800	179000	STI	Bannockburn
AITKENHEAD						
1500	1992	1500	1992	146846	LTN	ALL
1500	1992	1500	1992	146846	STI	ALL
AITKIN						
1820	....	1800	1850	102016	MDX	Shadwell
AITON						
1775	....	....	....	120804	LKS	Stonehouse
AKED						
1937	....	....	....	176885	NTT	Sutton In Ashfield
1770	1803	1750	1803	155969	YKS	Halifax
1709	1730	1650	1750	155969	YKS	Otley
AKEHURST						
....	....	1750	1800	159115	SRY	Ewell
....	....	1750	1800	159115	SRY	Newington
1754	1992	ALL	1754	100536	SSX	Burwash
1880	1900	1880	1940	139688	SSX	Hellingly
AKER						
1845	1925	1700	1845	176052	STS	Birmingham
AKERMAN						
1786	1960	1786	1960	163317	DEV	Seaton
1725	1794	1700	1800	163317	DOR	Bridport
1843	1971	1840	1936	163317	SOM	West
AKEROYD						
1805	1812	1780	1840	170348	YKS	Warley In Halifax
AKERS						
....	....	1800	1880	107891	HRT	Cheshunt
1822	1992	1700	1822	101540	HRT	Hertford
1880	1935	1880	1950	107891	MDX	Tottenham
1926	1928	1890	1950	107891	STI	Stirling
1850	....	1750	....	116920	WAR	Birmingham
1869	1968	1800	1869	135461	WAR	Birmingham
AKESTER						
1750	1900	1500	1750	178640	YKS	Hull
AKISTER						
1762	1901	1600	1750	100552	CMA	Grange Over Sands
1762	1901	1600	1750	100552	CMA	Lindale
AKNOS						
1750	1844	1650	1750	159115	SRY	Epsom
AKROYD						
1350	1800	1350	1800	153621	WYK	Wadsworth
AKVOS						
1790	....	1750	1790	159115	SRY	Ewell
ALABASTER						
....	....	ALL	ALL	130087	ALL	Name Study
1592	1992	ALL	ALL	130087	ALL	ALL
ALAIS						
....	....	ALL	ALL	158437	ALL	Name Study
1800	1992	ALL	1800	158437	LND	???
ALAND						
1716	1865	1700	1900	143928	WIL	Chippenham
1650	1750	ALL	1650	175994	WIL	Chippenham

Known From	To	Researching From	To	Ref	Cty	Place
ALAVOINE						
1831	1884	1700	1830	160601	LND	???
ALBAN						
....	....	ALL	ALL	160857	ALL	Name Study
ALBANY						
?	?	?	?	100560	BDF	Bedford
?	?	?	?	100560	BDF	Marston Morteyn
?	?	?	?	100560	BDF	Wooton
1800	1992	ALL	1800	100560	HRT	Stansted Abbott
1800	1992	ALL	1800	100560	HRT	Ware
ALBERRY						
1837	1900	1750	1837	172472	LND	Shoreditch
ALBERT						
....	1834	1800	1860	142018	HAM	Southampton
ALBIN						
1873	1900	ALL	ALL	139459	IRL	Ulster
ALBISTON						
....	....	ALL	1820	101761	CHS	ALL
....	....	ALL	1820	101761	LAN	ALL
ALBON						
1730	1780	1680	1780	135941	SFK	Glemsford
ALBORN						
1560	1700	1560	1700	167924	BDF	Southill
ALBUTT						
1810	1992	1600	1810	100579	WAR	Birmingham
ALCE						
1840	1890	ALL	ALL	152226	SSX	ALL
ALCHORN						
1784	1813	....	....	139971	SSX	Eastbourne
ALCHORNE						
1600	1800	....	....	164038	SXE	Arlington
1600	1700	....	....	164038	SXW	Wilmington
ALCOCK						
....	....	1700	ALL	111724	ALL	ALL
1787	....	ALL	ALL	115371	ALL	ALL
1767	1940	....	....	128996	CAM	Thorney
1841	....	1841	ALL	115371	LAN	Aughton
1787	....	ALL	ALL	115371	LAN	Ince Blundell
1792	....	ALL	ALL	115371	LAN	Liverpool
1819	....	1819	ALL	115371	LAN	Lydiate
....	1720	ALL	1720	134511	NTT	Linby
1820	1850	1650	1992	167592	STS	Burslem
1800	1850	1650	1992	167592	STS	Potteries
1837	1860	....	....	163287	WAR	Birmingham
1747	....	....	....	117196	YKS	Danby Wiske
ALCROFT						
1891	ALL	ALL	ALL	130788	AYR	Ayr
1891	ALL	ALL	ALL	130788	AYR	Prestwick
1877	1881	ALL	ALL	130788	LAN	Birkenhead
1877	1881	ALL	ALL	130788	LAN	Liverpool
ALDAM						
1694	1840	1600	1700	162396	LIN	Belton
ALDCROFT						
1766	....	....	....	131210	LND	Covent Garden
ALDEN						
1866	1992	ALL	ALL	118613	GLS	Westbury
1750	1880	1600	1750	164860	SFK	Marlesford
1880	1914	1800	1914	166928	YKS	Bridlington
ALDEN-MONTAGUE						
1882	1920	ALL	ALL	100595	LND	???
ALDER						
1802	1802	1600	1802	152080	BRK	Moulsford
1810	1824	1700	1810	102881	DUR	Sunderland
1820	1835	1780	1835	171441	OXF	Oxford
ALDERDICE						
....	....	ALL	ALL	139734	ALL	Name Study
....	....	ALL	ALL	139726	ALL	Name Study
ALDERMAN						
1770	1950	ALL	ALL	100617	BKM	Beckhampton
1770	1992	ALL	ALL	100617	BKM	Swanbourne
1724	1940	....	....	128996	CAM	Thorney
1800	1992	1600	1800	100609	HAM	ALL
1650	1812	1600	1992	166804	HAM	ALL
1600	1900	ALL	ALL	100617	HAM	Andover
....	....	1740	1780	160806	NTH	ALL
1730	1800	ALL	ALL	100617	NTH	Barnack
1730	1800	ALL	ALL	100617	NTH	Duddington
1600	1800	ALL	ALL	100617	NTH	Gt Harrauden
1600	1800	ALL	ALL	100617	NTH	Hannington
1600	1800	ALL	ALL	100617	NTH	Holcot
1690	1920	ALL	ALL	100617	NTH	Nassington
1700	1850	ALL	ALL	100617	NTH	Peterborough
1616	1830	ALL	ALL	100617	NTH	Rothwell
1778	1807	1500	1778	125695	NTH	Rothwell

Known From	To	Researching From	To	Ref	Cty	Place
ALDERMAN contd.						
1590	1700	ALL	ALL	100617	NTT	Burton Latimer
1520	1700	ALL	ALL	100617	NTT	Kettering
1600	1900	ALL	ALL	100617	NTT	Northampton
1700	1992	ALL	ALL	100617	NTT	Titchmarsh
1818	1835	1750	1850	126470	WIL	Wroughton
ALDERSLEY						
....	....	ALL	ALL	108332	ALL	Name Study
ALDERSON						
....	....	ALL	ALL	100625	ALL	Name Study
....	....	ALL	ALL	100633	ALL	Name Study
....	....	1700	1850	177776	CLV	Newport
1850	1857	1800	1850	121339	DUR	Darlington
1700	1992	ALL	ALL	100633	ENG	North
1800	1832	1700	1820	117013	NFK	East Rudham
1770	1777	1600	1770	121339	NYK	Gunnerside
1743	1821	1600	1743	102571	WES	Brough
1800	1851	....	....	104302	YKS	Arkengarthdale
1820	1837	ALL	ALL	112267	YKS	Arkengarthdale
1837	1873	....	....	112267	YKS	Burley
1800	1900	1700	1900	161411	YKS	Holtby
1794	1811	ALL	ALL	119504	YKS	Romaldkirk
1873	1906	....	....	112267	YKS	Skipton
1790	1890	1750	1850	121509	YKS	Swaledale
ALDERTON						
1558	1992	ALL	ALL	100641	EAG	???
1765	1790	ALL	ALL	100641	NFK	Cringleford
1789	1832	1750	1850	136719	NFK	Hedenham
1787	1851	ALL	ALL	100641	NFK	Intwood
1820	1992	ALL	ALL	100641	NFK	Norwich
1770	1850	ALL	ALL	100641	NFK	Saxlingham
1755	1789	ALL	ALL	100641	NFK	Wreningham
1760	1931	ALL	ALL	100641	SFK	Bury St Edmunds
1797	1816	....	....	135070	SFK	Ipswich
1791	1943	ALL	ALL	100641	SFK	Preton
1800	1860	1700	1800	139106	SRY	Horsell
1620	1992	1700	1992	100668	SSX	East
ALDHAM						
1800	1992	1800	1992	133450	DEV	Plymouth
1700	1900	ALL	ALL	142565	NFK	Norwich
ALDHOUSE						
1400	....	....	....	100676	ALL	ALL
ALDINGTON						
1747	1830	....	....	151475	WOR	Elmley Castle
ALDIS						
1400	....	....	....	100676	ALL	ALL
1830	1880	1750	1830	146285	MDX	Holborn
ALDOM						
1700	1900	ALL	1730	133183	GLS	???
ALDOUS						
1400	....	....	....	100676	ALL	ALL
1788	1920	1586	1788	102512	NFK	Surlington
1700	1700	1650	1700	155276	SFK	Fressingfield
ALDRED						
1786	1839	1700	1786	178500	DBY	Ilkeston
1788	1872	1780	1881	170143	HAM	East Meon
1744	1992	1700	1830	110116	HAM	Headley
1788	1872	1780	1881	170143	HAM	Steep
1620	1710	1620	1710	127655	HUN	Godmanchester
1650	1750	1650	1750	152404	LAN	Hulton
1750	1760	1700	1992	167592	SFK	Lowestoft
1820	1850	1750	1820	176516	WYK	Rotherham
1770	1789	1700	1789	148288	YKS	Rotherham
1770	1789	1700	1789	148288	YKS	Wakefield
ALDREN						
1893	1992	1803	1983	100684	LAN	Lancaster
....	....	1888	1926	100684	NFK	Kings Lynn
ALDRICH						
1850	1920	1750	1850	112704	SFK	Southwold
1855	1900	1823	1855	176028	???	???
ALDRIDGE						
1800	1950	1700	1800	128376	AVN	Bristol
1785	1810	ALL	1850	118737	BRK	Brightwalton
1811	1851	ALL	1811	118737	BRK	Inkpen
1700	1750	1600	1750	174599	DOR	Motcombe
1878	1940	1878	1940	145319	GLA	Pontypridd
1850	1870	1750	1850	123870	HAM	Southampton
1874	1981	1800	1900	126918	LND	ALL
1874	1981	1800	1900	126918	LND	South
?	?	?	?	100692	MDX	London
1780	1800	1700	1800	148792	MDX	Shoreditch
1704	....	....	1720	160873	NBL	Chollerton
....	....	1700	1992	140627	NFK	Puham
1722	1992	ALL	1722	119652	NFK	Yarmouth

Known From	To	Researching From	To	Ref	Cty	Place
ALDRIDGE contd.						
1816	1850	1750	1850	171484	SFK	Ampton
1845	1878	1845	1878	143642	SFK	Cowlinge
1790	....	1700	1900	171484	SFK	Tunstall
....	....	1700	1992	140627	SFK	Walpole
....	....	....	....	160806	SRY	West Horsley
....	....	1850	1900	173355	WAR	Birmingham
1500	1600	....	....	100420	WAR	Meriden
1600	1750	1500	1700	174599	WIL	Bratton
1805	1867	....	....	115606	WIL	Shalbo
1720	1740	1700	1760	160873	WOR	Little Witley
1749	1770	1740	1780	160873	WOR	Shrawley
ALDUS						
1874	1874	1830	1890	150568	CLV	Hartlepool
1880	1920	1880	1920	150568	DUR	South Shields
ALDWIN						
1900	1960	1700	1900	158976	BKM	South
ALDWORTH						
1600	1992	1600	1992	146420	IRL	Cork
1600	1992	1600	1992	146420	IRL	Kerry
ALEFOUNDER						
....	....	ALL	ALL	100706	ALL	Name Study
1340	1992	ALL	ALL	100706	ALL	ALL
ALEXANDER						
1890	1985	1840	1890	160431	ABD	Ellon
1850	1992	1800	1850	174653	ANS	Dundee
1870	1950	1830	1870	160431	ANS	Fettercairn
1792	1830	....	....	154849	AYR	???
1793	1992	1700	....	110264	BAN	Gamrie
1884	1960	1750	1884	166723	CUL	Cockermouth
1787	1793	1787	1793	147125	DUR	Bishopwearmouth
1839	1860	....	....	171492	ESS	???
1792	....	1750	1850	117560	HAM	Andover
1800	1900	1700	1800	136840	HAM	Andover
1777	1843	1600	1777	150169	HAM	Bradley
1868	....	1800	1960	101907	KEN	Hollingbourne
1842	1876	1800	1876	171441	KEN	Lenham
1842	1876	1800	1876	171441	KEN	Nonnington
1860	1900	1859	1900	163317	LAN	Liverpool
1855	1973	1700	1855	138568	LDY	???
1715	1992	1690	1992	153273	LKS	Leadhills
....	....	1840	....	116866	LKS	???
1846	1846	1830	1992	137863	LND	Islington
1860	1892	1750	1900	103888	LND	???
1839	1860	....	....	171492	LND	???
1809	1918	1770	1881	124001	MDX	East London
1808	1900	1700	1807	131245	MDX	Whitechapel
1802	1859	1789	1879	163317	NIR	Belfast
....	....	....	1850	116866	NIR	???
1767	1839	1650	1767	150614	SCT	Port Glasgow
1820	1840	1800	1900	111325	SFK	Ashbocking
....	....	1760	1787	147125	SFK	Ipswich
....	....	1700	1900	140627	SFK	Trimley
1711	1754	1690	1770	170143	SRY	Horsell
1733	1733	1550	1720	102830	WAR	Tanworth
1800	1992	1600	1800	100730	WIG	Whithorn
1650	1830	1600	1750	153451	WIL	Great Sumerford
1650	1830	1600	1750	153451	WIL	Rodbourne
ALF						
ALL	ALL	ALL	ALL	171964	ALL	ALL
ALFF						
ALL	ALL	ALL	ALL	171964	ALL	ALL
ALFFEWE						
1400	1450	1300	1400	154881	LND	ALL
ALFLATT						
1700	1850	1700	1850	134759	NFK	ALL
ALFORD						
1815	1850	1815	1850	164399	DEV	Bratten Clovelly
....	....	1600	1992	137588	DEV	Dolton
1800	1840	1600	1840	154342	WIL	Heytesbury
1813	1895	1793	1895	132845	WIL	Mere
1850	1992	1650	1850	100765	WIL	Whiteparish
1821	1900	1700	1900	135968	WOR	Worcester
1790	....	1700	1790	171441	WOR	Worcester
ALFOUNDER						
1583	1638	1500	1750	159956	SFK	Great Barton
ALFREY						
1729	....	1600	1729	164879	SSX	Poynings
1740	1770	1700	1770	103446	SSX	Pyecombe
ALGAR						
1820	1830	1500	1980	164992	DEV	Ideford
1820	1830	1500	1980	164992	DEV	Topsham
1797	1830	1700	1800	152552	SFK	Blythburgh
1797	....	....	1797	101761	SFK	???

Known From	To	Researching From	To	Ref	Cty	Place
ALGAR contd.						
1870	1950	1500	1980	164992	SRY	Battersea
ALGER						
1732	1810	1600	1732	167355	ESS	Gt Bentley
ALIBASTER						
1800	1881	1700	1800	111945	SFK	Cookley
ALID						
1770	1800	1770	1836	100862	LND	Bethnal Green
ALINGTON						
1854	1914	....	....	153176	MAY	Castlebar
ALISTER						
1811	1919	1750	1919	121134	ANT	Lisburn
ALKER						
1783	1850	1750	1900	177636	LAN	Balckburn
1590	1687	ALL	ALL	141615	LAN	Ormskirk
ALKIN						
1659	1771	1600	1800	175633	STS	Uttoxeter
ALLABY						
....	....	ALL	ALL	100781	ALL	Name Study
ALLAKER						
....	....	ALL	ALL	134147	ALL	Name Study
ALLAMBRIDGE						
....	....	1650	1750	131962	DOR	Sherborne
ALLAN						
1792	1792	1700	1820	170178	ABD	Kinellar
1860	1900	....	....	154849	ABD	Marykirk
1850	1926	ALL	ALL	112844	ABD	Slains
1854	....	ALL	ALL	117889	ANS	Kirriemuir
1817	1834	1700	1817	122394	AYR	Graigie
?	?	?	?	100838	BAN	Rothiemay
1670	1710	ALL	1710	149063	BEW	Lauder
1851	1871	1851	1900	126705	CHS	Wirral
1860	1992	1700	1860	100846	CLK	Clackmanan
1750	1910	1750	1910	110523	CON	Manaccan
1824	1876	....	....	101001	ELN	ALL
....	....	ALL	1637	119326	ELN	Tranent
1920	1992	1855	1920	147311	FIF	Kincardine
1720	....	ALL	ALL	130508	FIF	St Monance
....	....	1700	1800	149187	FIF	St Monance
1800	1838	1700	1838	148288	FIF	Strathmiglo
1754	1944	1700	1754	119881	KCD	Maryculter
1867	1941	....	....	105473	KEN	Gravesend
1830	1992	1700	1830	164208	LAN	Kirkham
1850	1857	ALL	ALL	135909	LKS	Glasgow
1819	1850	1800	1819	101796	LKS	Glassford
1768	1992	ALL	ALL	146366	LND	ALL
1887	1902	ALL	ALL	135909	LND	Regents Park
1580	1992	....	....	100811	MLN	Gogol
1768	1992	ALL	ALL	146366	MOR	Bishopmill
1768	1992	ALL	ALL	146366	MOR	Speymouth
1876	1992	1700	1876	100803	NYK	Richmond
1775	1992	....	....	101990	OKI	Eday
1775	1992	....	....	101990	OKI	Sanday
1775	1992	....	....	101990	OKI	Stronsay
1670	1710	ALL	1710	149063	ROX	Melrose
1886	1961	1700	1886	165859	SCT	Kirkintulloch
1768	1922	1700	1992	108154	STI	Falkirk
....	....	ALL	ALL	152048	STI	Larbert
....	....	ALL	ALL	152048	STI	Linlithgow
1850	1880	1850	1880	147338	WRY	Bowling
1850	1850	1820	1850	147338	WRY	Frizinghall
1840	....	1800	....	134589	YKS	Long Marston
ALLARD						
1900	....	1850	1992	133450	DEV	Plymouth
1705	1759	1650	1700	167533	GLS	Bristol
1650	1732	1650	1750	155896	GLS	Sandhurst
1850	1920	1700	1850	102210	KEN	Wye
1900	1992	1600	1992	112003	LEI	Osgathorpe
1769	1916	1769	1916	117579	SOM	Frome
1800	1900	1800	1992	120499	SOM	Frome
ALLARDICE						
1780	1900	1700	1800	133787	AYR	Kilmarnock
ALLARDYCE						
1862	1903	1903	1992	146560	LKS	Coatbride
ALLARS						
1794	1910	1700	1800	100862	LND	East
1794	1910	1700	1800	100862	LND	Stepney
ALLATT						
1870	1992	ALL	1870	102407	SYK	West Bretton
ALLAWAY						
1724	1840	1600	1724	163163	WIL	Bradford On Avon
ALLBERRY						
....	....	ALL	ALL	100870	ALL	Name Study
1850	1950	1750	1850	146587	LND	Holborn

Known From	To	Researching From	To	Ref	Cty	Place
ALLBERRY contd.						
1818	1900	1700	1992	128163	SSX	West
ALLBONE						
1770	1800	1700	1770	111198	BDF	Biggleswade
ALLBRIGHT						
1770	1800	1730	1800	155691	BKM	North
ALLBROOK						
1835	1900	1600	1835	113263	MDX	London
ALLCARD						
....	....	ALL	ALL	155861	ALL	Name Study
ALLCHURCH						
?	?	?	?	142514	KEN	Greenwich
ALLCOCK						
1760	....	....	....	135771	CHS	Central
1860	1992	1860	1992	115479	DBY	Codnor
1750	1800	1650	1750	162396	LIN	North
1880	1968	1860	1900	118168	MDX	East London
1830	1930	1700	1900	118168	NFK	Great Yarmouth
1848	1881	1800	1848	175951	NTT	Silston
1650	1800	....	1800	133086	SFK	Barrow
ALLCORN						
1800	1800	1500	1800	174009	SSX	ALL
1890	1900	ALL	1890	108197	SSX	Chailey
1841	1878	1800	1878	140058	SXE	Battle
1841	1878	1800	1878	140058	SXE	Hastings
1841	1878	1800	1878	140058	SXE	Lewes
ALLDAY						
1850	1875	1750	1850	121010	WAR	Birmingham
ALLDEN						
1780	1950	1700	1800	142395	WOR	Stourbridge
ALLDRIDGE						
1720	....	1700	1800	113662	GLS	Bisley
ALLDRITT						
1810	1860	1820	1830	125938	WAR	Castle Bromwich
ALLE						
1635	1635	1590	1635	124974	BRK	Hampstead Marshall
ALLEINE						
1640	1680	1600	1800	151653	SOM	Bridgwater
ALLEN MAY						
1912	1912	1850	1992	173096	SCT	Lockerbie
ALLEN						
1829	1889	....	....	149675	ALL	ALL
1900	1992	1850	1900	155594	ANT	Ballymena
1882	1992	1790	1882	155594	ANT	Belfast
1850	1992	1750	1850	107697	ARM	Newton Sibbold
1880	....	1880	....	149284	AVN	Bristol
1800	1850	1700	1800	139203	AYR	Beith
1840	1860	1800	1900	141933	BDF	Harold
1840	1860	1800	1900	141933	BDF	Kempston
1732	1771	ALL	1771	108642	BDF	Souldrop
1696	1696	1600	1750	117005	BKM	Haversham
1740	1890	1740	1890	172960	BRK	South
1764	1811	1725	1820	176621	BRK	Abingdon
1538	1720	1538	1750	172960	BRK	Bucklebury
1800	1850	1780	1800	138894	BRK	Newbury
1831	1860	ALL	1900	100919	BRK	Pangbourne
1830	1900	1800	1900	172960	BRK	Reading
1783	....	1700	1850	170178	BRK	Shefford
1751	1838	....	....	115290	BRK	Waltham St Lawrence
1658	1675	....	1675	108839	CAM	Harlton
1653	1940	....	....	128996	CAM	Thorney
1800	....	1800	....	134813	CON	Liskeard
1813	1849	1700	1813	128368	CON	Madron
1700	....	1700	1850	116920	CON	Mevagissey
....	1868	1750	1868	177938	CON	Panzance
1770	1992	1727	1770	139416	CON	Perranzabloe
1831	....	1800	1831	114332	CON	Perranzabuloe
1775	....	1700	1800	175838	CON	St Agnes
....	....	1829	1863	116602	CON	Stoke Climsland
1896	1941	ALL	1896	115355	DBY	ALL
1800	1900	ALL	ALL	156604	DBY	Ashover
1800	1850	1700	1800	143243	DBY	Brimington
1764	1992	1700	1800	101044	DBY	Wirksworth
....	....	ALL	1860	140848	DEV	ALL
1810	1960	1500	1810	104140	DEV	Devenport
1810	1960	1500	1810	104140	DEV	Lapford
1685	1992	1600	1685	100900	DEV	Okehampton
1844	1890	ALL	ALL	126098	DOR	Loders
1769	1858	1760	1858	162825	DOR	Portland
1770	1850	1650	1750	136840	DOR	Wareham
1753	1874	1600	1992	130125	DOR	Winfrith N
....	....	1700	1850	179531	DUR	Chester Le Street
1940	1992	1850	1992	131679	ESS	Rayleigh
1900	1992	1600	1900	140953	GLA	St Mellons

Known From	To	Researching From	To	Ref	Cty	Place
ALLEN contd.						
1820	....	1700	1820	130389	GLA	Swansea
1816	....	....	....	124982	GLS	Berkeley
1870	?	1700	1992	167096	GLS	Berkley
1720	1725	1680	1750	142018	GLS	Bristol
....	....	ALL	1854	121827	GLS	Stroud
1823	1992	1750	1992	136719	HAM	Basingstoke
1823	1858	1750	1880	136719	HAM	Deane
1782	1793	....	....	156647	HAM	Godshill
1840	1870	1700	1850	126772	HAM	Havant
1781	1992	1700	1780	142700	HAM	Laverstoke
1824	1845	1750	1850	101036	HAM	Minstead
1836	1992	1780	1837	100986	HAM	Portsea
1840	1992	ALL	1992	101036	HAM	Southampton
1891	....	ALL	1891	133957	HAM	???
1881	1931	1857	1881	177555	HEF	???
1800	1850	ALL	ALL	114235	HRT	Luton
1890	1992	1800	1992	127353	HUN	Conington
1850	1900	1800	1900	142875	HUN	Conington
1846	....	1846	1920	127353	HUN	Sawtry
1672	1910	1910	1992	122793	IOW	ALL
1792	1818	1770	1820	126667	IOW	Godshill
1780	1850	1700	1800	136840	IOW	Godshill
1830	....	ALL	ALL	166839	IRL	Queens County
1810	1850	1800	1900	126179	KEN	Appledore
....	....	?	1855	100935	KEN	Ashurst
1860	1950	1850	1950	159034	KEN	Deptford
1819	1823	1750	1819	110051	KEN	Dover
1838	1862	....	1838	171646	KEN	Eastry
1862	1933	ALL	1862	100897	KEN	Greenwich
1748	1816	....	....	101028	KEN	Maidstone
1816	1860	....	....	101028	KEN	Smarden
1670	1992	1670	1992	137308	KEN	Sundridge
....	....	1837	1900	162000	KEN	Swale
....	....	1700	1790	119431	KEN	Swingfield
....	....	1826	1920	116912	KEN	Woolwich
1850	1944	1700	1850	131601	LAN	Lancaster
1866	1886	?	?	124451	LAN	Liverpool
1896	1941	ALL	1896	115355	LEI	ALL
1672	1708	ALL	ALL	141615	LEI	Kings Norton
1730	1780	1650	1730	160458	LEI	Osgathorpe
1810	1992	1700	1810	158917	LEI	Thorpe Satchville
1870	....	1870	....	162663	LIN	West
1765	1815	1815	1865	117072	LIN	Friskney
1855	1876	1800	....	109282	LND	Central
1940	1960	1900	1960	135925	LND	East
1850	1940	1840	1920	160504	LND	South East
1854	1861	ALL	1861	121827	LND	South
1900	1950	1900	1950	159034	LND	Greenwich
....	....	1806	1992	131601	LND	Stratford
....	....	1800	1992	138053	LND	Wandsworth
1888	1947	1800	1888	138053	LND	West Ham
....	....	1806	1992	131601	LND	West Hamshire
....	....	1800	1992	125857	MDX	Enfield
1880	1949	....	....	101028	MDX	Finchley
1880	1949	....	....	101028	MDX	Hackney
1866	....	....	1866	126519	MDX	Hackney
1880	1949	....	....	101028	MDX	Highbury
1880	1992	1800	1992	164607	MDX	Holborn
1798	....	1750	1869	149292	MDX	London
1890	....	....	....	153885	MDX	Stroud Green
1834	....	ALL	1834	112887	NFK	Denver
1787	1851	ALL	1787	169730	NFK	Docking
1770	1860	ALL	1770	108197	NFK	Hemsby
1750	1992	1600	1992	135860	NFK	Hemsby
1800	1950	1700	1800	160296	NFK	Neatishead
....	....	1806	1992	131601	NFK	Norwich
....	....	1806	1992	131601	NFK	Thorpe
1697	1697	ALL	1697	115126	NTH	Moulton
1719	1917	ALL	1719	175862	NTH	Syresham
1750	1900	ALL	ALL	114235	NTH	???
1829	1992	....	....	172529	OXF	Barton
1834	1870	1750	1834	134627	OXF	Deddington
1801	....	....	....	170623	OXF	Watlington
1749	1992	ALL	1992	101079	PEM	ALL
1793	....	1700	1793	138355	RUT	Brisbrook
1775	1915	1700	1820	112038	RUT	Carlby
1794	1845	1780	1861	123404	RUT	Whitwell
....	1800	ALL	1800	177695	SAL	Madeley
1624	1671	1550	1624	152110	SFK	Glemsford
1851	1992	ALL	1851	105465	SLI	Sligo
1841	1841	1800	1844	121568	SOM	Ash Priors
1856	1880	1800	1900	165824	SOM	Batheaston
....	....	1890	1992	131555	SOM	Stone
....	....	1700	1940	131555	SOM	Street
1660	1730	1660	1750	142018	SOM	Taunton
1820	1826	ALL	ALL	159034	SRY	Croydon
1862	1885	1800	1885	174343	SRY	Kingston
1858	1865	1850	1870	159034	SRY	Lambeth
1896	1969	1700	1896	108588	SRY	Malden
1859	....	1600	1865	175641	SRY	Rotherhithe
1815	1834	1835	1870	115819	STS	Burslem
1843	1870	1840	1885	165441	STS	Chell
1824	1900	1750	1820	173452	STS	Gornal
....	....	1860	1992	154105	STS	Wednesbury
....	....	1670	1904	100935	SXE	Withyham
1840	1900	1800	1920	136174	TYR	Garvaghey
1800	1838	1830	1850	102245	WAR	Arley
1849	1849	....	....	127426	WAR	Aston
1800	1992	1700	1800	152366	WAR	Atherstone
1760	1800	ALL	1760	102245	WAR	Bickenhill
1823	1823	....	....	127426	WAR	Birmingham
1835	1945	1700	1836	100110	WAR	Foleshill
1875	1875	....	....	127426	WAR	Lozells
1847	1858	1858	1992	102245	WAR	Over Whitacre
1775	1790	1750	1840	136719	WIL	Swallowfield
1805	1887	ALL	1805	115126	WOR	Bartons Norton
1850	1935	1850	1935	173185	WYK	Heckmondwike
1806	1853	1700	1806	128031	YKS	Sheffield
1650	1921	1600	1650	165417	YKS	???
....	....	1800	1992	125857	???	Birmingham
1837	1869	1800	1900	132489	???	Bristol
ALLENBY						
1760	1992	1700	1800	113786	LIN	Aylesby
1760	1992	1700	1800	113786	LIN	Brocklesby
1700	1900	ALL	ALL	110477	LIN	Fotherby
1700	1900	ALL	ALL	110477	LIN	Louth
ALLERTON						
1840	1900	1705	1840	139483	LAN	Bootle
ALLETT						
1538	1992	1538	1992	101087	LIN	ALL
1789	1980	1700	1992	101087	LIN	Central
1700	1789	1700	1992	101087	LIN	South
1880	1980	1700	1992	101087	LIN	Alford
1700	1789	1700	1992	101087	LIN	Boston
1850	1875	1700	1992	101087	LIN	Great Steeping
1789	1880	1700	1992	101087	LIN	Willoughby
ALLEY						
1800	1850	....	....	113514	WIL	Northlease
ALLEYN						
1770	1992	1727	1770	139416	CON	Rose
ALLICK						
1820	1870	1780	1820	161519	CAM	Whittlesey
ALLIN						
1610	1840	ALL	1610	158577	BRK	East Hendred
....	....	ALL	1650	158577	BRK	Harwell
1700	....	ALL	1700	158577	OXF	Iffley
1700	....	ALL	1700	158577	OXF	Littlemore
1700	....	ALL	1700	158577	OXF	Sandford
ALLINGHAM						
1725	1992	ALL	1992	132055	KEN	ALL
1700	1800	1700	1800	169781	SRY	Burstow
ALLINSON						
1750	1992	1750	1992	169250	DUR	Middleton In Teesdale
1806	1818	1750	1806	179086	YKS	Bradford
1850	....	1700	1850	104566	YKS	Easingwold
1850	1992	1700	1850	104566	YKS	York
ALLIS						
1850	1900	1800	1900	142875	LIN	???
....	....	1881	....	118850	WAR	Birmingham
ALLISON						
1691	1880	1600	1691	152196	CMA	Gosforth
1754	1818	ALL	1754	158445	DUR	Durham
1880	1992	1800	1910	145556	KEN	Sydenham
1779	1828	ALL	ALL	141615	LAN	Over Kellet
1800	1992	....	....	176125	LIN	Asterby
1800	1992	....	....	176125	LIN	Goulceby
1880	1992	1800	1910	145556	LND	South
1918	1992	ALL	ALL	112674	LND	Islington
1860	1860	1800	1920	145556	MLN	Edinburgh
1880	1992	1800	1910	145556	SRY	Battersea
1880	1992	1800	1910	145556	SRY	Richmond
....	....	ALL	1817	123412	WAR	Birmingham
1821	1848	ALL	ALL	119504	WES	Appleby
1821	1871	ALL	ALL	119504	WES	Brough
1761	1771	1700	1761	160474	WES	Grasmere

Known From	To	Researching From	To	Ref	Cty	Place
ALLISON contd.						
1870	1992	1800	1992	132810	YKS	Elland
....	....	1800	1900	101095	???	Sunderland
ALLISS						
1822	1992	1790	1822	114545	LIN	Fens
1822	1992	1790	1822	114545	LIN	Mid Ville
ALLISTON						
1812	1857	1700	1992	101141	LND	North
ALLISTONE						
....	....	ALL	ALL	101117	ALL	Name Study
ALLIT						
1776	1776	ALL	1776	129283	NFK	Felbrigg
ALLKINS						
1840	1880	1800	1900	175633	LIN	Horncastle
....	1930	1600	1992	175633	STS	ALL
ALLMAN						
1770	1801	1650	1770	150614	CHS	Davenham
1865	1865	1700	1900	112089	LAN	Manchester
1730	1794	1650	1730	125105	NFK	Great Yarmouth
1761	1866	1650	1760	131245	SFK	Great Yarmouth
1800	1992	1800	1950	163511	STS	Stoke
ALLMAND						
1800	1900	1800	1850	108693	FLN	Manmer
ALLMARK						
....	....	ALL	ALL	169072	ALL	Name Study
ALLOTT						
1851	....	1800	1851	103772	RUT	???
1745	1745	1700	1750	128449	YKS	Birstall
1789	1832	1600	1789	133132	YKS	Sheffield
ALLOWAY						
1630	1820	....	....	140554	OXF	Mapledurham
ALLPORT						
1700	1730	1690	1740	160873	SAL	Sheriffhales
1500	1880	ALL	1900	160873	STS	ALL
1800	1880	1770	1900	160873	WAR	Birmingham
1620	1730	1600	1780	160873	WAR	Sutton Coldfield
1500	1880	ALL	1900	160873	WOR	ALL
ALLRIGHT						
1764	1840	1600	1764	101125	KEN	Canterbury
1840	1920	1700	1840	101125	MDX	London
ALLSOP						
....	....	ALL	ALL	173967	ALL	Name Study
1850	1960	1700	1850	113735	DBY	Bakewell
....	1760	ALL	1760	134511	DBY	North Wingfield
ALL	ALL	ALL	ALL	155608	DBY	Ripley
....	....	1700	1900	153079	LIN	Whaplode
1882	1926	ALL	ALL	125288	NTT	Edwindstowe
....	1992	1800	1992	101184	NTT	Nottingham
....	....	1743	1800	115142	WAR	Austrey
1850	1900	1700	1850	113735	YKS	Sheffield
....	....	1787	1890	101184	YKS	York
ALLSOPP						
1754	1925	ALL	1754	147877	LEI	Fleckney
ALLSWORTH						
....	....	1800	1900	149462	MDX	London
ALLUM						
1800	1802	1600	1802	152080	BRK	Marcham
1830	1852	1800	1900	143693	LND	St Pancras
1863	....	1800	1900	143693	MDX	Hayes
1800	1890	....	....	135984	NFK	Yarmouth
....	....	1600	....	127833	SFK	North
1800	1890	....	....	135984	SFK	Horham
1813	1992	1300	1813	100196	SFK	Walsham Le Willows
ALLWOOD						
1797	1822	1700	1822	101133	LIN	Dunholm Ludford
1821	1906	1800	1821	169803	LND	Wandsworth
1850	....	1850	1992	133450	LND	???
1733	1811	1700	....	101133	NTT	Tuxforo
....	....	1800	1900	102318	SOM	Bath
....	....	1750	1820	105244	SOM	Taunton
....	....	1700	1821	169803	SOM	Taunton
1820	1939	1800	1992	105244	SRY	Wandsworth
ALLWRIGHT						
....	....	1600	1764	101125	ALL	ALL
....	....	1100	1992	101141	ALL	ALL
....	....	1700	1850	101141	LND	City
1851	1992	1851	1992	147230	LND	East End
1779	1787	1770	1802	101141	MDX	London
1812	1846	1846	1992	101141	MDX	Shoreditch
1790	1850	ALL	ALL	177989	OXF	Goring
1851	1992	1787	1992	147230	SOM	Bath
ALMER						
....	....	1800	1881	173371	DUR	Tramfield

Known From	To	Researching From	To	Ref	Cty	Place
ALMON						
1728	1728	1650	1728	167452	BKM	Beaconsfield
ALMOND						
1785	1885	1600	1785	167355	ESS	Gt Bentley
1851	1928	1700	1992	153672	HRT	Codicote
1851	1928	1700	1992	153672	HRT	Hitchin
....	....	1700	1840	160601	KEN	Kingsnorth
1718	1732	ALL	ALL	141615	LAN	Aughton
?	....	?	?	116610	LAN	Blackburn
?	1760	....	....	138851	LAN	Bolton
1780	1890	....	1780	101168	LAN	Sefton
1720	1803	....	1720	109622	LAN	Woodplumpton
1680	1825	1600	1825	170291	LIN	Kesteven
1862	1930	1840	1900	160601	LND	East
1851	1928	1700	1992	153672	MDX	Enfield
1870	1890	....	1870	125202	SRY	Surbiton
1900	1992	1900	1992	113743	SSX	Northiam
ALMONDROYD						
1792	1851	....	1792	146013	YKS	Bradford
ALP						
ALL	ALL	ALL	ALL	171964	ALL	ALL
1780	1820	1700	1780	124605	SFK	Wenhaston
ALPE						
ALL	ALL	ALL	ALL	171964	ALL	ALL
ALPHE						
ALL	ALL	ALL	ALL	171964	ALL	ALL
ALPHEIGH						
1400	1450	1300	1400	154881	LND	ALL
ALPS						
ALL	ALL	ALL	ALL	171964	ALL	ALL
ALRED						
1620	1710	1620	1710	127655	HUN	Godmanchester
ALSAGER						
1740	1860	1740	1860	100420	WAR	Great Packington
1740	1860	1740	1860	100420	WAR	Meriden
ALSBURY						
1900	1980	1800	1992	101176	DBY	ALL
....	....	1600	1992	101176	GLS	ALL
....	....	1800	1992	101176	NTT	ALL
....	....	1600	1992	101176	SOM	ALL
1900	1950	1600	1800	101176	WIL	ALL
ALSFORD						
1851	1881	1840	1920	119008	BKM	Amersham
1806	1860	1700	1860	119008	BKM	Dorney
ALSOP						
1680	1700	1600	1800	162620	DUR	Ryton
1684	1775	ALL	1684	141224	GLS	South
1760	1920	1740	1900	120995	GLS	Bristol
1699	1699	1600	1699	174130	LEI	Garthorpe
1699	1699	1600	1699	174130	LEI	Melton Mowbray
....	....	1935	1992	101184	LND	Harringay
....	1992	1800	1992	101184	NTT	Nottingham
1750	1750	1550	1730	102830	STS	Kingswinford
1720	ALL	....	....	142158	WIL	Malmesbury
1760	1880	1650	1880	102490	WIL	Stanton St Quinton
1810	1830	ALL	1850	113611	WYK	Stainforth
....	....	1787	1890	101184	YKS	York
ALSPATH						
1100	1400	....	....	100420	WAR	Meriden
ALSTON						
1718	1906	1732	1906	116424	ESS	North East
1844	1856	1800	1844	122483	IOM	Douglas
1790	1830	1700	1900	167177	PEE	???
1800	1900	1700	1800	125660	SRY	Lingfield
ALTESTON						
....	....	....	....	177318	???	???
ALTHOFF						
?	?	....	....	114642	MDX	London
ALTHORPE						
1839	1845	1700	1838	131245	NFK	Norwich
ALTON						
1653	1653	1550	1640	102830	DBY	Carsington
ALL	ALL	ALL	ALL	101192	IRL	Palatine Connections
ALTREE						
1850	1915	1850	1915	140724	WAR	Birmingham
1795	1850	1795	1850	140724	WOR	Inkberrow
ALTY						
1744	1861	ALL	1744	122858	LAN	Lydiate
ALVES						
1797	1992	ALL	1797	127523	ABD	Aberdeen
ALVEY						
....	....	ALL	ALL	101206	ALL	Name Study

Known From	To	Researching From	To	Ref	Cty	Place
ALVIS						
1837	1837	1790	1837	156981	GLS	???
1840	1880	1800	1840	165468	SOM	Bristol
ALWAY						
1750	1850	1700	1780	144657	SOM	Wellington
1745	1745	1670	1745	165530	WIL	Sherston
ALWRIGHT						
1660	1750	1600	1750	125032	BRK	Arborfield
1609	1709	1538	1710	125032	BRK	Hurst
ALYN						
1565	....	1500	1550	153591	SSX	West
ALYWARD						
....	1868	....	....	147869	KEN	???
AMALRIC						
1775	1850	1775	1850	146226	LAN	Manchester
AMANET						
....	....	ALL	ALL	101222	ALL	Name Study
1700	1992	ALL	ALL	101222	LND	East
1700	1992	ALL	ALL	101222	LND	North
AMAS						
....	1771	1700	1800	176621	KEN	Canterbury
AMATT						
1613	1640	ALL	1640	129283	ESS	Kelvedon
AMBLER						
1751	1860	1715	1750	162523	HRT	Shenley
1895	1992	1895	1992	114308	NTH	Kislingbury
1870	1895	1870	1895	114308	WIL	Devizes
1840	....	ALL	ALL	166839	WYK	Keighley
1800	....	1750	....	134589	YKS	Barwick In Elmet
1800	1900	1600	1992	122084	YKS	Halifax
1800	1840	1750	1850	130974	YKS	Hunslett
1307	1904	1307	1904	170038	YKS	Northowram
1852	1869	1852	1869	114308	YKS	Pudsey
1808	1838	1770	1800	130877	YKS	Swillington
1301	1900	1851	1870	114308	YKS	West Riding
1773	1781	1770	1800	130877	YKS	Whitkirk
AMBREY						
1689	1891	1600	1730	117773	GLS	English Bicknor
1689	1891	1600	1730	117773	HEF	Peterstow
1861	1891	1861	1891	138398	HEF	Ross
AMBRIDGE						
....	....	ALL	ALL	106925	ALL	Name Study
1650	1985	ALL	ALL	106925	ALL	ALL
1800	1992	ALL	ALL	101230	CHS	???
1800	1992	ALL	ALL	101230	LAN	???
AMBROSE						
1750	1810	1650	1800	136840	HAM	Fordingbridge
1874	1992	....	....	137952	HRT	???
1800	1850	1750	1800	130214	MDX	St Pancras
AMER						
?	?	?	?	133418	HRT	Bushey
1786	1800	1700	1840	142018	SOM	Rode
1715	1840	1680	1840	142018	WIL	Trowbridge
AMES						
1860	1920	1837	1860	120731	DOR	Blandford
1677	1717	1650	1717	107573	SOM	Frome
AMESBURY						
1720	1850	1650	1900	156515	GLS	Mangotsfield
1710	1850	1600	1710	101249	SOM	Kenn
1710	1850	1600	1710	101249	SOM	Wedmore
1850	1992	....	....	101249	???	Bristol
AMEY						
1540	1660	1537	1660	101346	DEV	Exeter
1839	1992	....	1839	161071	DOR	Fordington
1676	1900	1600	1850	101257	ESS	North West
....	....	1850	1890	158410	HAM	Christcurch
1700	1700	....	....	101346	HAM	Eling
AMHURST						
1697	1740	1600	1700	122920	KEN	Marden
AMIEL						
ALL	ALL	ALL	ALL	147575	ALL	ALL
AMIES						
1732	1992	....	....	140414	NFK	Norwich
1837	1935	1700	1837	117110	STS	Nordley
AMIS						
1850	1880	1850	1880	157171	LND	St Georges Hanover Sq
1650	1718	1600	1650	154881	MGY	Llandyssil
1770	1860	1770	1860	157171	NFK	Barton Turf
1885	1940	1885	1940	157171	SRY	Camberwell
AMMONY						
1770	1940	....	....	128996	CAM	Thorney
AMNER						
1880	1992	?	1880	159514	SFK	Hoxton

Known From	To	Researching From	To	Ref	Cty	Place
AMOR						
1910	....	....	....	122505	CHS	???
1799	....	....	....	122505	DEV	Sidbury
1820	....	....	....	122505	LND	ALL
....	....	1800	1899	104884	SOM	Bath
....	....	1700	1799	104884	WIL	Bradford On Avon
1696	1920	1660	1907	101265	WIL	Bromham
1770	1790	1650	1770	101265	WIL	Melksham
1790	1992	1600	1790	101273	WIL	Pewsey
AMORRY						
1694	1738	1650	1695	162396	LIN	Crowle
AMORY						
1665	1940	....	....	128996	CAM	Thorney
AMOS DEAN						
....	....	1700	1900	119210	ALL	ALL
AMOS						
1836	1968	ALL	1992	104299	GLS	Bristol
1615	1849	ALL	1844	137774	KEN	South East
1850	1880	....	....	121185	KEN	South
?	?	1500	1992	101303	LIN	ALL
1795	1992	1500	1795	101303	LIN	Grantham
1803	1947	1700	1850	117013	NFK	East Lexham
1750	1992	ALL	ALL	101281	NTH	ALL
1900	1992	1600	1900	149713	NTH	Raunds
1781	....	ALL	1800	104299	SAL	ALL
1800	1840	1840	1900	148199	SCT	Edinburgh
....	....	1830	1900	114170	WLS	South
?	?	1800	1992	101303	YKS	Leeds
AMOUR						
....	....	1800	1900	137685	LND	Fulham
AMPHLETT						
....	....	ALL	ALL	112151	ALL	Name Study
1754	1781	....	....	131229	WOR	Claines
1370	1980	1980	1992	101311	WOR	Ombersley
AMPLEFORD						
1841	1841	1700	1841	174130	NFK	Holt
1855	1925	1800	1855	174130	NFK	Shirehall Plain
AMSDEN						
....	....	ALL	ALL	101338	ALL	Name Study
1547	1992	ALL	ALL	101338	ALL	ALL
AMSEL						
1761	1821	....	1821	137405	CAM	Rampton
AMY						
....	....	ALL	ALL	101346	ALL	Name Study
1650	1992	1650	1992	101346	CON	North
1700	1900	1700	1992	146943	CON	St Teath
1650	1660	1605	1992	101346	DEV	Exeter
1802	1877	1750	1802	141356	JSY	St Helier
AMYE						
1490	1750	1450	1800	101257	CAM	South West
1540	1660	1537	1660	101346	DEV	Exeter
AMYS						
1699	1880	ALL	1699	100536	???	Norwich
ANALL						
....	....	1674	1992	170453	FIF	ALL
ANCELL						
1701	1790	....	....	137405	CAM	Willingham
1775	1793	ALL	1775	175080	SSX	Funtington
1775	1793	ALL	1775	175080	SSX	West Dean
ANCHOR						
1797	1871	?	1797	144800	CAM	Whitlesey
ANCHRET						
1728	1792	1650	1800	144460	SAL	Dawley
ANCKLEY						
1700	1800	1700	1800	167924	BDF	Upper Gravenhurst
ANCOCK						
1850	1850	1800	1850	147478	GLS	???
ANDERSON WILLIAMS						
1848	1992	1700	1848	137219	GLS	Barton St Mary
ANDERSON						
1793	1793	1785	1820	141046	ANS	Coupar-Angus
1820	1855	1800	1900	144177	ANS	Tannadice
1690	1760	....	....	126497	BAN	Cullen
1900	1969	1700	1900	152730	BEW	Coldstream
1818	....	....	....	117560	BKM	Burnham
1836	1856	?	1836	112356	BKM	Maids Morton
....	....	1650	1840	160911	CAM	Ely
1747	....	ALL	1747	168602	CAM	Littleport
1850	1900	....	....	133361	CAM	Peterborough
1780	1850	1700	1992	104671	CON	Falmouth
1810	1992	1810	1992	146129	DFS	Durisdeer Parish
....	....	1840	1900	175161	DFS	Palnackie
1795	1992	....	1795	175374	DFS	Sanquhar
....	....	....	1890	116866	DNB	???

Known From	To	Researching From	To	Ref	Cty	Place
ANDERSON contd.						
....	....	ALL	ALL	116823	DOW	ALL
1800	1840	ALL	ALL	101400	DUR	South Shields
1500	1530	ALL	1550	149063	ELN	Haddington
....	....	1793	1992	170453	FIF	ALL
1821	1887	ALL	ALL	101370	FIF	Dunfermline
1858	....	....	....	111457	FIF	Falkirk
1780	....	ALL	ALL	130508	FIF	Pittenweem
1881	1881	ALL	1881	131881	HAM	Portsmouth
1867	1966	....	....	136905	HEF	Weobley
1650	1850	....	....	138037	HRT	North East
1880	1992	....	....	133361	HRT	Hemel Hempstead
1841	1992	1650	1840	160911	HUN	St Ives
1829	1930	1800	1854	119105	IRL	Dublin
1843	....	1800	1850	146331	IRL	???
1778	1787	1700	1778	153605	KCD	Banchory Ternan
....	....	1700	1770	172871	KCD	Catterline
1778	1787	1700	1778	153605	KCD	Durris
....	....	1700	1770	172871	KCD	Kinneff
1880	1900	1800	1950	145556	KEN	Sydenham
1850	1900	1850	1900	122254	LAN	Liverpool
1850	1888	....	....	166189	LAN	Liverpool
1780	1890	1600	1780	133329	LIN	Alford
1770	1860	1800	1860	177350	LIN	Caistor
1550	1600	1550	1846	156647	LIN	Manby
1843	1903	1903	1992	146560	LKS	Coatbride
1797	1850	1700	1797	149004	LKS	Glasgow
1830	....	ALL	1830	112887	LKS	???
....	....	....	1890	116866	LKS	???
1880	1992	1700	1880	101419	LND	ALL
1880	1900	1800	1950	145556	LND	South
1910	1985	1800	1910	171034	LND	???
1780	1870	1780	1870	167924	MDX	Chelsea
1908	1960	....	....	120340	MDX	Enfield
1868	....	1750	1868	121010	MDX	Shoreditch
1860	1860	1800	1900	145556	MLN	Edinburgh
1789	1900	1750	1789	101427	MLN	Liberton
1776	1833	1776	1833	149403	NBL	Bywell
....	1720	ALL	1740	162507	NBL	Newcastle Upon Tyne
1840	1881	ALL	ALL	101400	NBL	North Shields
1866	1890	1830	1865	173118	NBL	Seaton Delaval
1829	1878	ALL	1829	166847	NBL	Tynemouth
1761	1787	1740	1787	147311	NYK	Scarborough
1806	1855	1600	1855	148482	OKI	Birsay
1789	1836	1600	1789	136905	OXF	South
1716	1992	1680	1715	101397	PER	Baledgarno
1810	1860	1740	1890	128244	PER	Blairgowrie
....	....	ALL	1762	119326	PER	Dull
1810	1860	1740	1890	128244	PER	Lethendy
1850	1888	....	1850	166189	RFW	Millinoaff
1920	1950	1750	1920	158976	RFW	Paisley
1640	1645	1550	1640	139084	ROX	Melrose
1789	1858	1700	1800	166723	ROX	Melrose
1851	1880	1800	1850	115541	SCT	Barrhead
1869	?	ALL	ALL	101370	SCT	Bothwell
1885	1992	ALL	ALL	101370	SCT	Evanton
1806	....	ALL	1806	102350	SCT	Fife
1830	1869	ALL	ALL	101370	SCT	Glasgow
1805	1805	1800	1830	126667	SCT	Montrose
1780	1860	1780	1860	122254	SCT	Perthshire
1872	?	ALL	ALL	101370	SCT	Strathavon
1750	1965	....	....	137820	SHI	Fetlar
1720	1965	....	....	137820	SHI	Mid Yell
1760	1965	....	....	137820	SHI	North Yell
1758	1965	....	....	137820	SHI	Northmavine
1720	1965	....	....	137820	SHI	South Yell
1841	ALL	....	....	117560	SRY	Egham
1860	1920	1800	1950	145556	SRY	Richmond
1860	1920	1800	1950	145556	SRY	Vauxhall
1780	1880	....	....	132756	STS	Bagnell
1780	1880	....	....	132756	STS	Longton
1780	1880	....	....	132756	STS	Trentham
1794	1840	ALL	ALL	101370	SUT	Clyne
1781	....	....	....	101370	SUT	???
1500	1900	1500	1900	170216	WIL	ALL
1797	1870	1790	1870	171549	YKS	Bingley
1870	1992	1700	1870	155497	YKS	Hull
1870	1890	1870	1992	171549	YKS	Keighley
1800	1862	1750	1800	129623	YKS	Staveley
1811	1830	1750	1830	110426	???	Dundee
1811	1830	1750	1830	110426	???	Forfarshire
1770	1850	ALL	1770	128481	???	Marykirk
ANDERTON						
1600	1850	1600	1850	175897	CHS	???

Known From	To	Researching From	To	Ref	Cty	Place
ANDERTON contd.						
1600	1850	1600	1850	175897	DBY	???
1670	1827	1650	1830	136328	LAN	Heath Charnock
1847	1903	1847	1903	136328	LAN	Manchester
1600	1850	1600	1850	175897	LAN	???
1750	1890	ALL	1900	113611	LIN	Barton On Humber
1710	1750	ALL	1750	113611	LIN	Wrawby
1829	1858	1700	1829	118168	MDX	Clerkenwell
1858	1925	1850	1992	118168	SRY	Croydon
1876	1960	1700	1876	125415	WAR	Birmingham
1932	1992	....	....	116041	YKS	Bradford
1758	1797	1700	1800	141097	YKS	Holme
1758	1797	1700	1800	141097	YKS	Spalding Moor
ANDICOT						
1854	1861	1700	1992	170518	SOM	Taunton
ANDO						
1500	1992	1500	1992	130672	SOM	Huntspill
1500	1992	1500	1992	130672	SOM	Weston Zoyland
ANDOE						
1500	1992	1500	1992	130672	SOM	Glastonbury
1500	1992	1500	1992	130672	SOM	Pitney
ANDOW						
....	....	ALL	ALL	103543	HAM	Southampton
1500	1992	1500	1992	130672	SOM	Weston Super Mare
ANDREW						
1745	....	....	1745	101761	CAI	Bower
1796	1859	....	....	138851	CHS	Hyde
1796	1859	....	....	138851	CHS	Romiley
1833	1891	1800	1900	137561	CON	Barren Downs
1840	1880	1800	1888	165824	CON	Redruth
1800	1899	1700	1800	162507	CON	Truro
1750	1992	1750	1992	106593	DEV	North West
1550	1800	1300	1850	105333	DEV	Buckland In The Moor
1550	1800	1300	1850	105333	DEV	Holne
1550	1800	1300	1850	105333	DEV	Ilsington
1550	1800	1300	1850	105333	DEV	Lydford
1550	1800	1300	1850	105333	DEV	Widecombe In The Moor
1770	1886	1750	1890	101435	HEF	Ross On Wye
1694	1757	1757	1780	101443	KCD	Fordoun
1820	1980	1790	1820	128724	KEN	Charing
1860	1943	1840	ALL	145386	LAN	Manchester
1800	1900	1800	1900	123765	LIN	East
1750	1900	1650	1750	162396	LIN	Snitterby
1830	1975	ALL	1830	172901	LND	ALL
....	....	1840	ALL	145386	MAY	Thurlough Park
1780	1900	1780	1992	101443	NRY	Skelton
1750	1790	1729	1812	107360	NTH	Long Buckby
1860	1950	ALL	1860	154555	NTH	???
1601	1790	1601	1790	101494	NYK	Hinderwell
1727	1772	1662	1840	101435	SAL	Whittington
1760	1860	1700	1860	110906	SSX	Eastdene
1750	?	1750	?	101435	WOR	ALL
1813	1858	1813	1925	101435	WOR	Bengeworth
1850	1992	1700	1850	101478	WOR	Bengeworth
1810	1900	1750	1810	165018	YKS	Swanland
ANDREWARTHA						
1817	1885	1700	1817	176575	CON	St Hilary
ANDREWARTHER						
1808	1868	1800	1900	137561	CON	Breage
1808	1868	1800	1900	137561	CON	Perranuthnoe
ANDREWS						
1740	?	ALL	ALL	101370	ANT	Portglenone
1874	1925	....	....	151238	BDF	Toddington
1765	....	1720	1765	102024	BRK	C Hurst
1749	1888	....	....	135437	CHS	Chester
1777	1783	....	....	135437	CHS	Nantwich
....	1756	ALL	1756	134511	DBY	Norton
1870	....	....	....	172030	DEV	Newton St Cyres
1874	1992	1800	1875	179167	DEV	Plymouth
1725	1900	1600	1900	162043	DEV	Shaugh Prior
1679	1851	1600	1851	170267	DEV	South West Dartmoor
1780	1800	....	....	100277	DOR	Upwey
1815	1992	1815	1992	148091	ESS	Environs
1800	1850	1700	1800	100048	ESS	Great Leighs
1815	1992	1815	1992	148091	ESS	Littlebury
1815	1992	1815	1992	148091	ESS	London
1815	1992	1815	1992	148091	ESS	Plaistow
1815	1992	1815	1992	148091	ESS	Saffron Walden
1780	1900	1750	1900	152528	ESS	Waltham Abbey
1882	1992	1864	1882	120278	EYK	Kingston Upon Hull
1854	1854	1800	1880	125032	GLS	Bristol
1810	1852	1750	1900	174521	GLS	Bristol

Known From	To	Researching From	To	Ref	Cty	Place
ANDREWS contd.						
1890	1920	1800	1900	119083	GLS	Gloucester
....	....	1690	1750	142018	GLS	Gloucester
1814	1814	1750	1814	133000	HAM	Alverstoke
1720	1870	ALL	ALL	131490	HAM	Binstead
?	?	1789	1843	117919	HAM	Fareham
1800	1992	ALL	1800	106224	HAM	Gosport
1780	1909	ALL	1780	153028	HAM	Plaitford
1840	1840	1800	1840	133000	HAM	Porstmouth
1883	....	1855	1883	121827	HAM	Southampton
1838	1931	1838	1931	163635	HAM	Southampton
1685	1720	ALL	ALL	131490	HAM	W Meon
1650	1850	....	....	138037	HRT	North East
1775	1775	ALL	1775	167959	HRT	Stanstead Abbots
1750	1992	1600	1890	108693	HRT	Therfield
1714	1992	1600	1700	164119	HRT	Ware
1844	1992	1700	1844	167541	IRL	Dublin
1703	1935	1700	1992	144355	KEN	South
1724	1813	1650	1723	161357	KEN	Ash
1751	....	....	1751	171441	KEN	Sittingbourne
1813	1900	1700	1800	112569	KEN	Westwell
1848	1848	....	....	135437	LAN	Liverpool
....	1842	ALL	1842	102350	LAN	Manchester
1735	1809	....	1735	101761	LIN	Welton Le Marsh
1780	1800	1800	1900	133507	LND	Clapham
1865	1890	1700	1865	119083	LND	Southark
1811	....	1811	1992	101494	LND	Wapping
1800	1900	1700	1800	133507	MDX	Poplar
1830	1900	1700	1830	124362	NFK	Diss
1788	....	ALL	1788	158445	NFK	Gt Witchingham
1877	1891	1875	1923	121827	NFK	Sprowston
1830	1900	1700	1830	124362	NFK	Tackolneston
1718	1718	1650	1750	167002	NTH	Holdenby
1830	1920	1830	1920	101494	NYK	Farlington
1800	1878	ALL	ALL	131490	SRY	Farnham
....	....	ALL	ALL	174033	SRY	Wimbledon
1885	1885	ALL	ALL	101486	STS	Stoke Upon Trent
1700	1774	ALL	ALL	113700	WIL	Bishops Canning
1809	1878	ALL	1878	168696	WIL	Brinkworth
1774	1810	ALL	ALL	113700	WIL	Bromham
1700	1730	1680	1750	142018	WIL	Cleverton
1718	1750	1700	1770	142018	WIL	Marlborough
1766	1766	....	....	115606	WIL	Overton
....	....	ALL	1820	151602	WIL	Ramsbury
1548	1557	1500	1600	145459	WIL	West Dean
....	....	1700	1856	120278	WIL	???
1687	1992	1600	1992	135704	WOR	Hampton
1811	1887	1800	1992	116653	WOR	Shrawley
1851	1889	1700	1900	121150	YKS	Barnsley
1750	1883	1700	1750	160024	YKS	Clayton
....	....	1700	1880	102148	YKS	Hull
1851	1889	1700	1900	121150	YKS	Smithies
1856	1864	....	....	120278	???	London
1800	1830	1800	1830	101494	???	Newcastle On Tyne
ANDROS						
1680	....	....	....	137693	CHI	Guernsey
ANEAR						
1779	1826	ALL	1826	168718	CON	South East
ANFEYLD						
1573	1629	....	1608	108839	CAM	Harlton
ANGEL						
....	....	ALL	ALL	101516	ALL	Name Study
1420	1992	ALL	ALL	101516	ALL	ALL
....	....	1700	1992	110248	ALL	ALL
1858	1992	1700	1858	179051	BDF	Kings Walden
1824	1897	1700	1900	137901	CHS	Stockport
1721	1760	ALL	1721	128082	CON	Laneust
1721	1760	ALL	1721	128082	CON	Scilly Isles
....	....	1800	1900	101508	DEV	Plymouth
....	....	1800	1900	101508	DEV	Plympton
1742	1850	1600	1700	161950	DOR	Portland
1680	1713	1600	1800	162620	DOR	???
1803	1803	1600	1803	112410	FLN	Halkyn
1780	1850	1750	1880	123536	HUN	Brington
1780	1850	1750	1880	123536	HUN	Great
1780	1850	1750	1880	123536	HUN	Molesworth
1795	1852	1795	1992	109819	NFK	Great Yarmouth
1846	1873	1750	1845	131245	NFK	Norwich
1587	1761	1421	1992	101516	SAL	Stottesdon
1786	1786	1700	1992	101516	SAL	Sutton Maddock
1841	1841	1800	1992	101516	STS	Dudley
1847	1847	1850	1992	101516	STS	Kingswinford
1776	1800	1700	1776	159158	WIL	Lacock

Known From	To	Researching From	To	Ref	Cty	Place
ANGELL						
1904	....	....	....	110736	AVN	Bristol
1785	1858	....	....	104817	HAM	Breamore
1837	1868	ALL	ALL	122106	IRL	Waterford
1810	1920	1780	1920	176982	KEN	Hoo
....	....	1800	1860	176435	MDX	Bow
1870	1992	1870	1992	101516	STS	Cannock
1805	1858	1805	1858	104817	WIL	Whiteparish
ANGER						
1900	1932	ALL	ALL	123323	HAM	Farnborough
1720	1930	ALL	ALL	123323	WIL	Watchfield
ANGIER						
1770	1800	1700	1800	124605	ESS	Gt Clacton
ANGOLD						
1830	1900	1500	1992	126799	LND	???
ANGOVE						
1720	1992	1400	1720	101524	CON	ALL
....	....	1700	1800	175838	CON	Redruth
ANGRAVE						
1798	1900	1600	1900	124834	NTT	East Leake
ANGUISH						
?	?	1830	1867	134406	IRL	ALL
1750	1800	1700	1800	100927	NFK	Aldeby
1750	1800	1700	1800	100927	SFK	Aldeby
1867	1867	ALL	ALL	134406	YKS	Scarborough
ANGUS						
1760	1940	ALL	1760	154563	DUR	Weardale
1820	1910	1820	1950	144290	INV	Inverness
1819	1821	....	....	112909	NBL	Newcastle
ANKERS						
1820	1870	ALL	ALL	137987	CHS	Dodleston
1750	1850	ALL	ALL	137987	CHS	Malpas
1750	1850	ALL	ALL	137987	CHS	Tilston
1870	1900	1870	1900	115932	LAN	Manchester
1870	1900	1870	1900	115932	LAN	Oldham
ANMEAR						
1841	1950	1700	1841	165182	CON	Gwennap
ANNABALAH						
1820	1840	ALL	1840	132217	NTT	Sutton In Ashfield
ANNABLE						
1810	....	1700	1900	131148	DBY	Duffield
ANNABLES						
1752	1940	....	....	128996	CAM	Thorney
ANNALL						
1740	1810	ALL	1900	113492	FIF	???
ANNALS						
1860	1860	ALL	1860	131849	SRY	Clapham
ANNAN						
1821	1851	1820	1861	110728	NBL	East
ANNETS						
1650	1812	1600	1992	166804	HAM	ALL
ANNETT						
....	....	ALL	ALL	121371	ALL	Name Study
1700	1830	1530	1980	101532	HAM	Portsmouth
1750	1914	1555	1750	126462	NBL	Widdrington
1830	1950	1530	1980	101532	SRY	East London
ANNETTE						
1900	1992	1530	1900	132551	HAM	Herriard
ANNETTS						
1758	1758	....	....	115606	HAM	Linkenholt
ANNING						
....	....	ALL	ALL	145270	ALL	Name Study
....	....	1791	1816	145270	DEV	Colyton
....	....	ALL	ALL	104159	LND	Hackney
ANNIS						
1753	....	ALL	1753	147362	LEI	East
1753	....	ALL	1753	147362	LEI	Sproxton
1800	1950	1800	1950	137464	WOR	Pershore
ANNISON						
1790	1860	....	1860	135275	MDX	Enfield
ANNUM						
1868	....	1863	1880	133639	SAL	Broseley
1843	1863	1810	1890	133639	WOR	Shrawley
ANSCOMB						
....	....	ALL	ALL	137243	ALL	Name Study
ANSCOMBE						
1835	1920	1700	1835	164178	HAM	???
....	....	1800	1890	153931	LND	Hackney
1835	1920	1700	1835	164178	SXW	???
ANSDELL						
1760	1780	1760	1780	135429	DEV	Exeter
1800	1840	1800	1840	135429	DEV	Topsham
1780	1840	1780	1840	135429	DEV	Woodbury
1816	1914	ALL	ALL	140821	HUM	Kingston Upon Hull

Known From	To	Researching From	To	Ref	Cty	Place
ANSDELL contd.						
1800	....	1700	1850	110914	LAN	Bold
1800	....	1700	1850	110914	LAN	Farnworth
....	....	ALL	ALL	140821	LAN	Liverpool
ANSELL						
....	1778	1740	1830	128961	HRT	Hatfield
1846	....	1790	1840	121479	LND	Woolwich
1788	1810	1700	1850	139386	SRY	Lambeth
1814	1814	1790	1830	105333	WIL	Downton
ANSLOW						
1780	1831	1700	1780	179116	STS	Penkridge
ANSON						
1678	....	....	....	138401	CUL	Penrith
1788	1870	1780	1890	166316	MDX	St Pancras
1820	....	1780	1850	102016	SRY	Newington
1575	1992	ALL	1992	133450	STS	Penkridge
1760	1860	....	....	141984	YKS	Hambleton
1762	1992	1600	1770	101575	YKS	Hull
1762	1992	1600	1770	101575	YKS	Knottingley
1762	1992	1600	1770	101575	YKS	Selby
ANSPACH						
1800	1900	1800	1900	107476	LND	Tottenham
ANSTEY						
1900	1992	1750	1900	146374	CON	St Gluvius
1812	1827	1812	1848	101583	DEV	Culmstock
1743	1763	....	....	101583	DEV	Tiverton
1848	1857	1857	1920	101583	DEV	Topsham
1794	1806	....	....	101583	DEV	West Anstey
1786	1852	?	1900	136611	GLS	Dirham
1786	1852	?	1900	136611	GLS	Hinton
ANSTIS						
....	....	ALL	ALL	101591	ALL	Name Study
ALL	ALL	ALL	ALL	101591	ALL	ALL
1600	1770	....	....	106240	CON	Duloe
1600	1700	....	....	106240	CON	Liskeard
1650	1770	....	....	106240	CON	St Neot
1640	1708	1500	1670	121932	DEV	Lifton
....	....	1829	1900	145394	DEV	Plymouth
1700	1764	....	....	106240	SRY	Mortlake
ANSTY						
1579	1773	ALL	1775	174289	DOR	ALL
1579	1725	....	1590	174270	DOR	???
ANTELL						
1822	1847	1600	1900	110329	DOR	North
....	....	1500	1830	166863	DOR	Holwell
1629	1861	1600	1861	101605	DOR	Stour Provost
ANTHONEY						
1896	1972	1896	1972	100722	DUB	Dublin
1838	1972	1700	1838	100722	NBL	North Sheilds
ANTHONY						
1830	....	....	1885	147672	CON	Hayle
1700	1900	1700	1900	160814	DEV	Wembury
1786	1803	1700	1800	112216	DOR	Milborne St Andrew
1790	1880	....	....	140317	MDX	Islington
1830	....	1800	1900	143758	NFK	Clay
1850	....	1800	1900	143758	NFK	Hunworth
1797	1812	1725	1841	116114	NFK	Welbourne
ANTLIFF						
1748	1992	1650	1748	169889	NTT	Caunton
ANTROBUS						
1900	1980	1800	1900	109487	CHS	Wilslow
APLETREFEUD						
1250	1300	1200	1250	154881	KEN	Cudham
APLEY						
1554	1612	....	....	174319	DEV	Barnstaple
APLIN						
....	....	1750	1800	162566	DEV	Offwell
....	....	1750	1850	162566	DOR	Lyme Regis
1640	1697	....	....	142522	MDX	St Jiles
1850	1870	1500	1850	148598	STS	???
APLON						
....	....	1500	1800	129577	DOR	???
APPELBEE						
1540	1992	....	....	168653	ALL	ALL
APPERLEY						
1820	....	....	....	101613	GLS	Cheltenham
1800	1992	1700	1800	148059	GNT	Chepstow
APPLE						
1838	....	....	....	172820	LND	St Martins In Field
APPLEBEE						
1540	1992	ALL	ALL	168653	ALL	ALL
APPLEBIE						
1540	1992	....	....	168653	ALL	ALL
APPLEBY						
....	....	ALL	ALL	168653	ALL	Name Study
1540	1992	ALL	ALL	168653	ALL	ALL
1753	1886	1650	1886	101621	BDF	Bedford
1612	1850	1550	1660	102830	DBY	ALL
1886	1992	....	....	101621	LAN	Greater Manchester
1818	1930	1600	1818	148954	LND	East
1830	1870	....	....	140317	MDX	Hackney
1730	....	ALL	1992	119695	SOM	West Pennard
1810	1830	1830	1860	148113	WAR	Aston
1810	1830	1830	1860	148113	WAR	Birmingham
1840	1900	1700	1820	139297	YKS	Birdforth
1780	1837	1750	1837	102563	YKS	Branton Green
1840	1900	1700	1820	139297	YKS	Felixkirk
1840	1900	1700	1820	139297	YKS	Gilling
1840	1900	1700	1820	139297	YKS	Ripon
1860	1890	1830	1860	148113	YKS	Sheffield
1801	1851	1800	1992	165603	YKS	Staindrop
1800	1960	1725	1800	105503	YKS	Swaledale
APPLEDORE						
1385	1992	1200	1992	148377	ALL	ALL
APPLEGATE						
1850	1992	1700	1850	119261	NFK	Kings Lynn
....	....	ALL	1610	149349	NFK	???
APPLETON						
1841	1851	....	....	131202	DUR	Hutton Henry
1863	1960	1860	1900	168629	DUR	Sayberge
....	....	ALL	ALL	157260	HAM	North
....	....	ALL	ALL	157260	HAM	Kingsclere
1810	1850	1700	1850	148792	HAM	Tadley
1810	1881	1500	1810	129577	IOW	???
1845	1992	?	1845	119296	KEN	Staple
1864	1992	1700	1864	117595	KEN	Whitstable
1725	1792	....	....	138851	LAN	Aspul
1798	1874	1700	1798	101648	LAN	Liverpool
1874	1874	1874	1900	101648	LAN	Salford
1717	1804	1550	1750	167533	MDX	Harmondsworth
1784	1841	1500	1841	168629	NYK	Cowton
1786	1992	1600	1786	134570	YKS	Thirks
APPLEYARD						
1845	1911	1750	1850	112526	DUB	Balbriggan
?	1716	1560	1800	170267	YKS	Batley
1776	1992	1776	?	166235	YKS	Halifax
1742	1816	1700	1851	170267	YKS	Holbeck
1795	1851	1750	1870	116386	YKS	Leeds
....	....	?	?	115592	YKS	Outwood
1880	1920	1600	1880	175382	YKS	Wakefield
1742	1816	1700	1851	170267	YKS	Wortley
APPLIN						
1830	1850	1800	1850	108243	GLS	Bristol
1850	....	1840	1860	148989	MDX	Bow
1888	1945	1850	1888	160768	SXW	Chichester
....	....	1860	1870	108243	YKS	Leeds
APPLON						
1810	1881	1500	1810	129577	IOW	???
APPS						
1857	1861	1820	1880	127361	CON	St Endellion
1780	1850	ALL	1780	150983	HAM	Portsea
1800	1830	1830	1884	131385	KEN	Tunbridge Wells
1820	1890	1820	1900	113743	SSX	Brede
1730	1780	1700	1730	156140	SSX	Chailey
?	?	1850	1920	109843	SSX	Fairlight
....	1700	....	....	174564	SSX	Ninfield
1880	1881	1850	1899	119199	SSX	Wadhurst
1793	1851	1813	1851	101656	SXE	Sedlecombe
APTED						
1780	1815	1750	1815	147974	SRY	Reigate
APTER						
1680	1747	1600	1992	117609	DEV	Brixham
APTHORP						
....	....	ALL	ALL	101664	ALL	Name Study
1680	1800	1660	1900	101664	CAM	ALL
1680	1800	1660	1900	101664	HUN	ALL
APTOR						
1600	1750	1400	1760	105333	DEV	Buckland In The Moor
1600	1750	1400	1760	105333	DEV	Holne
1600	1750	1400	1760	105333	DEV	Ilsington
1600	1750	1400	1760	105333	DEV	Lydford
1600	1750	1400	1760	105333	DEV	Widecombe In The Moor
ARABIN						
1685	1992	1600	1900	101672	IRL	???
?	?	ALL	1900	117919	MDX	London

Surname	Known From	Known To	Researching From	Researching To	Ref	Cty	Place
ARBER							
	1676	1827	....	....	152110	CAM	Burwell
	1804	1924	1800	1930	133043	NTH	Creaton
	1771	1824	1700	1900	133043	NTH	Islip
	1716	1992	1700	1992	133043	NTH	Twynell
	1744	1820	1700	1820	133043	NTH	Woodford
ARBLASTER							
	1800	1860	....	....	137111	STS	Norton Cames
ARBON							
	1797	1900	1700	1992	112402	SFK	Bury St Edmunds
ARBOUIN							
	....	....	1700	1800	176036	MDX	London
ARBOUR							
	1690	1992	....	1770	101834	NFK	South West
ARBUTHNOT							
	1814	1839	1700	1900	158666	ANS	Montrose
	1799	1810	1750	1799	101796	ARL	Kilcalmonell
ARCH							
	....	....	ALL	ALL	101680	ALL	Name Study
ARCHARD							
	1850	1950	1750	1850	122599	NFK	Yarmouth
	1712	1881	ALL	1712	157791	WIL	Calne
ARCHBELL							
	....	....	....	1830	116866	YKS	Tadcaster
ARCHBOLD							
	....	....	1750	1841	177059	NBL	Central
	1841	1900	....	....	177059	NBL	Newcastle Upon Tyne
	1830	1950	ALL	ALL	178470	NBL	Walker
ARCHDEACON							
	....	....	1837	1985	122971	ENG	ALL
	....	....	1837	1985	122971	WLS	ALL
ARCHER							
	1700	1730	1650	1700	172901	DBY	???
	1854	1923	....	....	148733	ESS	High Ongar
	1800	1992	1700	1992	156701	ESS	Woodford
	1788	1875	1800	1992	156698	ESS	Woodford
	1790	1790	1750	1790	149152	ESS	???
	1760	1795	1720	1820	105333	HAM	Isle Of Wight
	1650	1750	1720	1799	105694	HAM	Portsea
	1675	1725	1720	?	105694	HAM	Winchester
	1770	1822	1730	1770	162523	HRT	Shenley
	1830	1890	1700	1830	102210	IRL	???
	1825	1846	1798	1825	117269	KEN	Gravesend
	1820	1820	ALL	ALL	130575	LEI	Leicester
	....	....	1840	1890	164984	LIN	Boston
	1817	....	1700	1850	102881	MDX	Shoreditch
	1600	1930	ALL	ALL	140686	NFK	ALL
	1676	1800	....	....	165999	NTT	East
	1710	1720	1650	1720	169749	NTT	Hulm Pierre Point
	1803	1813	1780	1830	135763	SAL	Bridgnorth
	1870	1970	1870	1992	125687	SAL	Dawley
	1794	1881	1700	1794	154288	SFK	Flowton
	1835	1860	1835	1860	103764	WAR	Alcester
	1841	1872	1800	1915	171298	WAR	Atherstone
	1800	1855	1800	1855	103764	WAR	Beaudesert
	1840	1932	1700	1840	126349	WAR	Coventry
	1817	....	1700	1817	172022	WAR	Coventry
	1812	1960	....	....	115495	YKS	Armley
	1870	1960	1870	1907	115495	YKS	Cleckheaton
ARCHIBALD							
	1810	1992	1700	1810	123374	ABD	Tough
	1855	....	1800	1900	146536	AYR	Kilbirnie
	1800	1875	1786	1875	146536	LKS	Lanark
	1755	....	1755	1895	146536	LKS	Libberton
	....	....	ALL	1741	119326	MLN	Inveresk
	....	....	ALL	ALL	101702	SCT	ALL
ARCOLL							
	....	....	1750	1825	177229	DEV	ALL
ARDEN							
	....	....	1750	1880	163260	LIN	South
ARDERN							
	1850	1940	ALL	ALL	119253	CHS	High Lane
ARDERSLEY							
	1811	1992	ALL	1811	100803	NYK	Gargrave
ARENY							
	1761	1798	1600	1760	108413	SOM	Banwell
ARFMAN							
	1839	1856	1800	1910	166677	HAM	Southampton
ARGALL							
	1736	1814	1650	1736	127590	CON	Madron
ARGENT							
	....	....	ALL	ALL	118796	ALL	Name Study
	1788	1900	1600	1900	127108	ESS	Halstead
	1600	1800	1600	1800	114529	ESS	Tilbury Juxta Clare
ARGENT contd.							
	1700	1799	1700	1790	135941	SFK	Glemsford
	1600	1800	1600	1800	114529	SFK	Stoke By Clare
ARGENTI							
	1200	1950	ALL	ALL	162620	ALL	ALL
ARGYLE							
	....	....	1600	ALL	115142	ALL	ALL
ARIS							
	....	1788	....	....	130079	OXF	Bicester
ARKELL							
	....	1700	....	....	174564	OXF	???
ARKILL							
	1687	1732	1540	1730	156515	GLS	Sevenhampton
ARKINSTALL							
	1830	1900	1600	1830	165247	SAL	ALL
	1830	1900	1600	1830	165247	STS	ALL
ARKLE							
	....	....	ALL	ALL	101710	ALL	Name Study
	1830	1848	....	1548	176761	NBL	Acklington
	1830	1848	....	1548	176761	NBL	Amble
	1823	1848	ALL	1823	176761	NBL	Broomhill
ARKLESS							
	1820	1900	1750	1850	112704	DUR	Newcastle
ARKWRIGHT							
	....	....	ALL	ALL	101729	ALL	Name Study
ARLET							
	1770	1800	1700	1800	136840	HAM	Andover
ARM							
	....	....	ALL	ALL	120626	ALL	ALL
	1781	1992	ALL	ALL	127078	ALL	ALL
	1800	1992	ALL	....	120626	STS	Walsall
ARMAN							
	1797	1888	ALL	ALL	151580	LND	Limehouse
ARMATAGE							
	1871	1992	1700	1871	101745	NBL	Newcastle On Tyne
ARMER							
	1810	1836	1750	1840	179299	LND	Fulham
	1769	1829	....	....	118354	YKS	Dent
ARMES							
	1735	1769	....	1735	142166	BDF	Cranfield
	....	....	1700	1992	140627	NFK	Norwich
	1846	1908	1800	1851	135461	WAR	Birmingham
ARMFIELD							
	1640	1780	1640	1890	100420	STS	Penn
	1640	1780	1640	1890	100420	STS	Wolverhampton
	1770	1850	1640	1890	100420	WAR	Birmingham
ARMIGER							
	1840	....	1840	....	156892	NFK	E Barsham
ARMIN							
	....	....	ALL	ALL	101753	ALL	Name Study
	1164	1992	1164	1992	101753	ALL	ALL
	1164	1992	1164	1992	101753	LIN	???
	1164	1992	1164	1992	101753	YKS	???
ARMISON							
	1822	1825	....	....	135518	NTT	Mansfield
ARMITAGE							
	1780	1807	?	1790	103934	HRT	Willian
	1860	1890	1600	1860	175382	LAN	Dewsbury
	1871	1992	1700	1871	101745	NBL	Newcastle On Tyne
	1925	1992	1900	1925	171247	TIP	Cloughjordan
	1778	....	....	1778	101761	WRY	Honley
	1798	1992	....	1798	101761	WRY	Huddersfield
	1830	1870	1800	1850	103721	WRY	Leeds
	1751	1790	1700	1750	170348	YKS	Almondbury
	1730	1783	ALL	1730	169730	YKS	Cawthorne By Barnsley
	....	1747	1700	1747	160024	YKS	Clayton
	1814	1840	....	....	139483	YKS	Doncaster
	....	....	1700	1780	147613	YKS	High Hoyland
	1780	1855	....	1780	144800	YKS	Huddersfield
	1835	1860	1800	1992	146331	YKS	Huddersfield
	1800	1840	1750	1800	139483	YKS	Sheffield
ARMITT							
	....	....	ALL	ALL	143014	ALL	ALL
ARMON							
	1797	1888	ALL	ALL	151580	LND	Limehouse
ARMOUR							
	1750	1792	ALL	ALL	129933	ARL	Campbeltown
	1740	1760	1700	1740	157708	AYR	Dreghorn
	1750	1815	1700	1750	101796	AYR	Irvine
	1810	1992	1770	1810	141070	AYR	Kilmarnock
	1900	1910	1600	1907	101788	AYR	Kilwinning
	1841	1925	1791	1841	101788	DOW	Newtownards
	1810	1992	1600	1841	101788	LKS	Airdrie

Known From	To	Researching From	To	Ref	Cty	Place
ARMOUR contd.						
1925	1954	....	....	101788	MLN	Rosewell
ARMS						
....	....	....	....	158747	ALL	ALL
1788	1871	ALL	1788	158445	NFK	Gt Witchingham
ARMSTRONG						
1865	1960	1600	1865	127507	ANT	Ballycor
?	....	?	?	177679	AYR	ALL
1797	1881	1797	1992	141798	BRE	Brecon
....	....	1650	1780	101826	BRK	Reading
1686	1940	....	....	128996	CAM	Thorney
1838	1872	1838	1872	117803	CAV	Kingscourt
1900	....	?	?	176842	CHS	Birkenhead
1822	1992	ALL	1822	100528	CLA	Portumna
1789	1879	1700	1789	120278	CLV	Hartlepool
1785	1893	1751	1893	102482	CMA	Carlisle
1833	1880	1700	1833	142883	CUL	Carlisle
1768	1886	1768	1886	149403	CUL	Castle Carrock
1811	1845	1800	1900	130990	CUL	Sebergham
1770	1950	1700	1770	144231	DFS	Glencairn
1770	1950	1650	1770	128376	DUR	Chester Le Street
1874	1992	1700	1874	101842	DUR	Gateshead
1882	1944	1600	1882	169595	DUR	Gateshead
1842	1924	....	....	102881	DUR	Sunderland
1783	1992	ALL	1600	163945	ENG	West Country
1795	1992	1750	1992	138584	FER	Colmon Island
1820	....	....	....	174750	FER	Gortgarron
1783	1992	ALL	1600	163945	FER	???
1772	1992	1700	1800	101826	HAM	Basingstoke
1830	1830	1780	1830	133000	HAM	Portsmouth
....	....	?	1820	103934	HRT	Woolwich
1852	1887	ALL	1852	116092	IRL	???
....	1881	1500	1881	175072	LAN	St Helens
1800	1898	1820	1898	171654	LKS	Glasgow
1835	1910	1700	1835	179574	LOU	Dundalk
1783	1992	ALL	1600	163945	MAY	???
1755	1815	1730	1775	135410	NBL	Haltwhistle
1750	1992	....	....	142417	NBL	Haltwhistle
1750	1820	1700	1750	149152	NBL	Longhoughton
1874	1992	1700	1874	101842	NBL	Newcaslte Upon Tyne
....	....	1700	1815	102881	NBL	North Shields
....	....	1650	1750	135410	NBL	Thorngrafton
1793	1917	1793	1917	142662	NBL	Wooler
1800	1992	1600	1900	101834	NFK	Central
1800	1992	1600	1900	101834	NFK	West
1800	1900	....	....	150371	ROX	Newcastleton
1784	1826	ALL	ALL	144568	ROX	???
1783	1992	ALL	1600	163945	SLI	???
1873	1936	1848	1873	116653	STS	Wolverhampton
1814	....	1800	1900	139114	WEX	Newton Barry
ARMYAS						
1650	1718	1600	1650	154881	MGY	Llandyssil
ARMYTAGE						
1559	1559	1500	1560	176451	YKS	Kirkburton
ARNALL						
1722	1763	1650	1701	150894	CON	Tintagel
ARNATI						
1830	1860	1800	1992	148784	ALL	ALL
ARNDALE						
1860	1900	1860	1900	170119	SSX	Eastbourne
ARNDELL						
....	....	1700	1797	152269	MDX	ALL
ARNELL						
1800	1850	ALL	ALL	113700	LND	Clerkenwell
1875	1927	1800	1875	118168	MDX	Walthamstow
1852	1881	1852	1992	143944	NRY	ALL
ARNFIELD						
1790	1818	....	....	138851	CHS	Mellor
1790	1818	....	....	138851	DBY	Mellor
ARNISON						
....	....	ALL	ALL	101850	ALL	Name Study
ARNOLD						
1750	1800	1750	1800	101877	BDF	Farndish
....	....	....	....	101877	BDF	Gravenhurst
1086	....	1086	....	101877	BDF	Houghton Conquest
1740	1860	1740	1800	101877	BDF	Leighton Buzzard
1700	1900	1700	1800	101877	BDF	Luton
1750	1800	1750	1800	101877	BDF	Poddington
1560	1900	1560	1860	101877	BDF	Shillington
1762	....	1725	1800	102016	BRK	Appleton With Eaton
1690	1940	....	....	128996	CAM	Thorney
1700	1800	1600	1800	145602	DEV	Bideford
1643	1774	1643	1789	121681	DOR	Puddletown
1740	1750	1740	1750	154210	DOR	Tolpuddle
ARNOLD contd.						
....	....	1800	1900	146390	ESS	Fordham
1750	1866	ALL	1750	173304	ESS	Orsett
1840	....	....	....	145068	HAM	Southampton
1700	1900	1840	1880	101877	HRT	Hitchin
1780	1880	1780	1880	101877	HRT	London Colney
1790	1900	1790	1880	101877	HRT	North Mimms
1730	1900	1780	1850	101877	HRT	Offley
1560	1900	1560	1880	101877	HRT	Pirton
1750	1880	1750	1880	101877	HRT	Ridge
1780	1880	1780	1880	101877	HRT	Shenley
1790	1900	1790	1880	101877	HRT	South Mimms
1720	1900	1740	1860	101877	HRT	St Albans
1820	1920	1920	1992	109851	KEN	North
1890	1930	1870	1950	101907	KEN	Rochester
1820	1850	1700	1820	101907	KEN	Sheerness
1860	1870	1850	1900	101907	KEN	Snodland
1647	1717	ALL	ALL	141615	LEI	Billesdon
1767	1870	1600	1770	126772	LEI	Thurgarton
....	....	ALL	ALL	101885	LIN	Boston
1850	1900	1860	1880	101877	LND	Bloomsbury
1840	1880	1840	1860	101877	LND	City
1780	1900	1800	1880	101877	LND	Clerkenwell
1800	1920	1800	1870	101877	LND	Holborn
1860	1920	1860	1880	101877	LND	Islington
1780	1900	1800	1880	101877	LND	Shoreditch
1819	1880	1819	1873	101915	LND	Shoreditch
....	....	1700	1900	129275	LND	Southwark
1780	1870	1800	1880	101877	LND	St Lukes
1800	1900	1800	1880	101877	LND	St Pancras
1767	1992	ALL	1767	101869	LND	???
1795	1850	1750	1850	160849	MON	Trelleck
1815	....	....	1815	177504	SFK	Holbrook
1894	1895	1800	1893	131245	SRY	Camberwell
....	....	1858	1992	139343	SSX	Crowborough
1781	1992	1700	1781	130257	SSX	Donnington
1879	1901	1901	1992	139343	SSX	Eastbourne
1783	1826	1700	1900	144703	WAR	ALL
1866	1955	1800	1992	122203	WAR	Birmingham
1800	1900	1650	1800	107042	WAR	Flecknoe
1782	1800	1780	1800	150479	WAR	Radford Semele
1739	1793	ALL	1992	102245	WAR	Tysoe
1880	1910	1850	1900	111821	YKS	Armley
1823	1900	1800	1950	111821	YKS	North Bierley
....	....	1750	1900	163082	YKS	North Stainley
1880	1992	1880	1992	101915	YKS	Sheffield
1866	1955	1800	1992	122203	???	London
ARNOT						
1764	1780	1755	1780	108510	FIF	Aberdour
1761	1808	ALL	1890	108510	FIF	Auchtertool
1820	1992	1650	1820	173665	NYK	Bulmer
ARNOTT						
1820	1870	ALL	1890	108510	FIF	Beath
1871	1881	1860	1890	108510	FIF	Dunfermline
1150	1992	....	....	151130	FIF	Woodmylne
1750	1965	....	....	137820	SHI	Fetlar
1720	1965	....	....	137820	SHI	Mid Yell
1760	1965	....	....	137820	SHI	North Yell
1758	1965	....	....	137820	SHI	Northmavine
1720	1965	....	....	137820	SHI	South Yell
1963	1992	....	....	173932	WIL	Bradford On Avon
ARNOUX						
1850	1900	1840	1992	167592	STS	Stoke
ARRANDELL						
1818	1863	1750	1863	141097	YKS	Hull
ARREQUER						
1560	1590	ALL	1992	121797	ALL	ALL
ARRIKER						
1600	1699	ALL	1992	121797	ALL	ALL
ARROWSMITH						
....	....	1796	1992	121940	CHS	Stockport
1740	1763	ALL	1740	154563	DUR	Teesdale
1879	1992	1700	1879	105163	FLN	Antani
1770	1914	1700	1881	160636	LAN	Denton
1750	1800	....	....	126497	LAN	Leyland
1815	1816	1700	1815	104728	LAN	Liverpool
1800	1850	1700	1800	158232	LND	East
1810	1875	1750	1900	167983	STS	Stafford
....	....	1850	1910	159220	WLS	Mold
ARSCOTT						
1800	1860	1700	1800	101931	DEV	Buckfastleigh
1800	1840	....	....	102946	DEV	Buckfastleigh
....	....	1700	1800	174130	DEV	Dunsford
1530	1642	1530	1960	115436	DEV	Tawton

Known Researching
From To From To Ref Cty Place
ARSCOTT contd.
1852 1953 1700 1852 170542 DEV Totnes
ARSELING
1742 1940 .... 128996 CAM Thorney
ARSLETT
1841 1872 1750 1841 122068 HAM Yateley
1841 1872 1750 1841 122068 SRY Guildford
ARSSOLOM
1792 1881 1700 1880 156566 MON Croesyceiliog
ARTER
1850 1985 1700 1850 160318 HAM Portsmouth
1883 .... 1840 1900 131547 LND ALL
1770 1992 1700 1770 101958 NFK ALL
ARTHUR
1830 1850 ALL ALL 129933 AYR Dalmellington
1782 1810 ALL ALL 129933 AYR Kirkmichael
1745 1765 ALL ALL 129933 AYR Maybole
.... 1800 1830 117137 BRE Abergwesyn
.... 1650 1850 129550 CON Lostwithel
1725 1735 .... 102644 DEV Stoodleigh
.... 1800 ALL 149187 FIF Abdie
1780 .... 130915 FIF Auchtermuchty
.... 1800 ALL 149187 FIF Ceves
.... 1800 ALL 149187 FIF Kirkcaldy
1851 1992 ALL ALL 142034 GLA Rhondda
1785 1992 1600 1785 103098 HAM Fawley
1757 1760 .... 131229 HEF ALL
1861 .... ALL ALL 129933 LKS Glasgow
1771 1812 1700 1771 144037 NBL Hartburn
1770 1992 1700 1770 101958 NFK ALL
1841 1851 1700 1841 119075 NTH Burton Latimer
1700 1992 1650 1855 104914 SHI ALL
1750 1965 .... 137820 SHI Fetlar
1720 1965 .... 137820 SHI Mid Yell
1760 1965 .... 137820 SHI North Yell
1758 1965 .... 137820 SHI Northmavine
1720 1965 .... 137820 SHI South Yell
1716 ? ALL 1716 156388 WIL Bramshaw
ARTHURSON
1750 1965 .... 137820 SHI Fetlar
1720 1965 .... 137820 SHI Mid Yell
1760 1965 .... 137820 SHI North Yell
1758 1965 .... 137820 SHI Northmavine
1720 1965 .... 137820 SHI South Yell
ARTIS
1750 1778 1778 1891 125105 NFK Great Yarmouth
1650 1777 1538 1650 125105 SFK Kirkley
ARTLETT
1853 1937 ALL 1874 108642 KEN Dover
ARTLEY
1776 .... ALL 1776 104299 YKS Barnsley
ARUNDEL
1871 1896 1800 1871 109649 YKS Castleford
1850 1918 .... 145912 YKS Stanley
ARUNDELL
1750 1800 1600 1750 168351 CON Truro
1700 1700 1650 1750 133450 DEV Bampton
ARWAKER
1500 1700 ALL 1992 121797 ALL ALL
ASBURY
.... ALL ALL 173088 SAL Bridgnorth
ASBY
1860 1890 .... 104450 CAM Six Mile Bottom
1860 1890 .... 104450 SFK Newmarket
ASCOUGH
1850 1920 1920 1950 125253 DUR Barnard Castle
1850 1920 1920 1950 125253 DUR Darlington
.... 1840 1860 125253 LAN Rochdale
.... 1840 1860 125253 LAN Todmordem
1830 1870 1870 1930 125253 NYK Bedale
1650 1830 1830 1930 125253 NYK Hunton
1793 1842 ALL 1793 125253 YKS Hornby
1793 1842 ALL 1793 125253 YKS Patrick Brempton
ASH
.... ALL ALL 101974 ALL Name Study
1600 1900 ALL ALL 101974 ALL ALL
1850 1992 .... 100056 CHS Dukinfield
1720 1800 1600 1900 153354 CON North Hill
.... 1600 1992 137588 DEV Totnes
1590 1725 1550 1600 156795 DOR East
1850 1940 1720 1850 105716 GLS South East
1850 1992 .... 100056 LAN Ashton Under Lyne
1700 1840 .... 100056 LIN Fleet
1700 1840 .... 100056 LIN Holbeach

Known Researching
From To From To Ref Cty Place
ASH contd.
1700 1840 .... 100056 LIN Kirton In Holland
1797 1909 1820 1909 151211 LIN Surfleet
1860 .... 135771 LND East
1839 .... 132888 LND St Pancras
1600 1900 ALL ALL 101974 MDX London
1803 1992 1700 1803 152056 NTT Radford
1740 1800 1650 1740 121339 NYK Lastingham
.... 1800 1906 170879 SOM Bath
1750 1800 1700 1800 144657 SOM Milverton
.... 1750 1850 163082 SRY Kingston
.... ? .... 143499 STS Leek
.... 1700 .... 137456 WAR Stockton
ASHALL
1690 1850 .... 126497 LAN Leyland
1816 1866 1700 1866 178233 LAN St Helens
1770 1910 1770 1910 126500 LAN Wigan
1770 1800 1600 1770 113204 YKS Sheffield
ASHBRIDGE
.... ALL ALL 101982 ALL Name Study
ASHBROOK
1795 1880 .... 160482 CHS Tabley
ASHBURNER
1687 1862 1687 1900 118168 LAN Ulverston
ASHBURNHAM
1430 1480 1350 1430 154881 SSX Ashburnham
ASHBY
.... ALL ALL 110698 ALL Name Study
1760 1800 1700 1760 135496 GLS Warwick Border
1748 1980 1700 1992 142360 HRT Rickmansworth
1850 .... 101990 HUN Ellington
1850 .... 132500 LAN Preston
.... 1700 1806 102008 LEI ALL
1806 1866 1780 1806 102008 LEI Kibworth
1800 1850 ALL ALL 113700 LND Islington
1474 1791 1721 1791 142360 MDX Harefield
1879 1900 1800 1879 152684 NTH Bugbrooke
1600 1900 .... 153583 NTH Bugbrooke
.... 1800 1900 168653 SRY Southwark
1849 1930 .... 102008 YKS Leeds
ASHCROFT
1778 1785 1700 1778 102016 GLS Bristol
1730 1950 ALL ALL 154490 HUN Yelling
.... ALL ALL 115371 LAN ALL
1760 .... ALL ALL 115371 LAN Gillmoss
1877 .... ALL 1877 148172 LAN Manchester
1749 1863 1749 1863 178489 LAN Prescot
1782 1782 1700 1782 163783 LAN Preston
1785 1992 ALL ALL 108464 LAN Standish
1850 1860 1800 1850 102016 MDX Mile End Old Town
1800 1820 1790 1850 102016 MDX Shadwell
1785 .... 1785 1800 102016 MDX St Lukes
1800 1920 ALL ALL 157864 SCT ALL
1796 1849 1796 1849 105147 STS ALL
ASHDOWN
1930 1992 1850 1930 140546 KEN Burham
1846 1851 1800 1865 160776 KEN Southborough
1790 1820 1700 1850 156280 KEN Tonbridge
1848 .... 160776 KEN Tonbridge
1880 .... 160776 LND City
.... 1896 1907 160776 MDX Islington
1871 .... 160776 MDX St Marylebone
1834 1992 1800 1992 165603 SRY Limpsfield
1874 1875 .... 160776 SRY Peckham
1850 .... 1830 1900 127760 SSX Brighton
1806 1850 1800 1900 156280 SSX Brighton
1890 1899 1890 1899 113743 SSX Rye
ASHDOWNE
1600 1632 1550 1600 154881 KEN Chiddingstone
ASHE
.... ALL ALL 102032 ALL Name Study
1600 1900 ALL ALL 101974 ALL ALL
1600 1992 ALL 1992 102032 ALL ALL
1890 1900 ALL 1890 148385 DUB Dublin
1600 1900 ALL ALL 101974 MDX London
ASHER
1799 1878 1850 1900 161861 HAM Littleann
1728 1848 .... 165999 LEI Bottesford
1820 1900 1700 1825 166561 LEI Old Dalby
1728 1848 .... 165999 LIN Claypole
1858 1939 .... 133248 NTH Rothwell
1728 1848 .... 165999 NTT Newark
ASHFIELD
.... ALL ALL 102040 ALL Name Study

Known From	To	Researching From	To	Ref	Cty	Place
ASHFORD						
1870	1992	....	1870	102059	CHS	Northwich
1841	1900	1500	1841	148679	DEV	East
1690	1900	1500	1690	179396	HAM	Portsmouth
1841	1865	1800	1880	142018	HAM	Southampton
1720	1820	1700	1850	167126	SFK	Earl Soham
1780	1950	1650	1780	128376	SOM	S Brewham
1720	1807	1750	1810	166685	SOM	Somerton
1771	1867	ALL	1771	102067	SOM	Witham Friary
1693	1923	ALL	ALL	125873	WAR	Birmingham
1852	1852	....	1852	102059	WAR	Erdington
ASHFORTH						
1786	....	1750	1800	170348	YKS	Sheffield
ASHLEY						
1617	1699	1600	1617	152196	CMA	Bridekirk
1686	1742	ALL	1686	154563	DBY	North Wingfield
1551	1700	1500	1550	145459	HAM	East Dean
1850	....	....	....	112348	LAN	Liverpool
....	....	ALL	ALL	166812	LAN	Manchester
1861	1900	1850	1900	105953	LAN	Shevington
1740	1992	1680	1900	131075	LIN	North
1800	1992	....	....	176125	LIN	Asterby
1800	1992	....	....	176125	LIN	Goulceby
1770	1790	1750	1770	125318	MDX	London
1881	1992	1850	1880	139173	MGY	Berriew
1816	1816	....	....	135437	NFK	N Elmham
1846	1846	....	....	108901	NTT	Cuckney
1871	....	1871	1903	146773	NTT	Sherwood
1857	1981	1800	1900	102075	SAL	Bomere Heath
1780	1820	1780	1850	173665	SAL	Wem
1772	1992	1700	1920	105953	SOM	North
1900	1960	ALL	ALL	100137	STS	ALL
1867	1867	1850	1900	105953	STS	Wolstanton
1843	1855	1780	1843	149918	WIL	Marston
1892	1903	1871	1903	146773	YKS	Hull
ASHLING						
1774	1940	....	....	128996	CAM	Thorney
1738	1881	1650	1738	116440	CAM	Whittlesey
1888	....	1870	1920	165492	LND	Stepney
ASHMAN						
1718	1791	1600	1718	125784	CAM	Fulbourn
1800	1923	1820	1840	125784	CAM	Swaffham Prior
1796	1796	1796	1796	136808	SFK	Bury St Edmunds
1731	1759	1700	1800	176923	SOM	Kilmersdon
1815	1817	1600	1815	115525	SOM	Leigh On Mendip
ASHMOLE						
1800	1992	1600	1992	111147	DBY	ALL
ASHMORE						
1849	1890	ALL	1992	179205	DBY	Pilsley
1753	1992	1700	1753	126527	HUN	Alconbury
1853	1992	1750	1853	116513	WAR	Birmingham
ASHPOLE						
1695	1830	1600	1830	102938	BDF	Sharnbrook
ASHPOOL						
1900	1992	....	....	158607	NTH	Peterborough
ASHTON						
1560	1700	1560	1700	167924	BDF	Shillington
1690	1749	....	....	166189	BKM	Eton
1690	1749	....	....	166189	BKM	Langley
1790	1880	1750	1830	174912	CAE	Caernarfon
1851	1881	1851	1930	156833	CHS	Macclesfield
1770	....	1600	1992	168637	CON	Poughill
1811	1927	1811	....	118761	DBY	Matlock
1600	1670	1550	1697	102830	DBY	Winster
1769	1795	....	....	145297	DEV	Bradworthy
1736	1841	1600	1992	168637	DEV	Bradworthy
1762	1825	1600	1992	168637	DEV	Clovelly
1826	1835	1600	1992	168637	DEV	Woolsery
1690	1750	....	....	102091	EYK	Catwick
1820	1880	....	....	102091	EYK	Kirk Ella
1580	1690	....	....	102091	EYK	Leven
1755	1840	....	....	102091	EYK	Ottringham
1790	1820	....	....	102091	EYK	Sutton On Hull
1900	1992	1800	1900	113514	EYK	???
1750	1775	1725	1750	101796	LAN	Ashton Under Lyne
1665	1992	ALL	1665	102083	LAN	Blackburn
1668	1870	ALL	1668	102083	LAN	Middleton
1815	....	....	1820	101761	LAN	Moston
1880	1900	1860	1880	142492	LAN	Singleton
?	....	....	....	102105	LAN	???
1860	....	1800	1900	168785	LEI	Melton Mowbray
1900	1950	1800	1925	123293	LIN	ALL
1801	1855	ALL	1801	107964	LIN	Boston
1881	1992	ALL	1881	165751	LIN	Spilsby
ASHTON contd.						
1834	1900	1800	1834	172898	LND	Shoreditch
1837	1894	....	....	147621	MDX	Edmonton
1620	1992	....	1780	137634	NTT	Littleborough
1834	1992	1800	1992	165603	SRY	Limpsfield
1750	1960	1750	1992	150479	WAR	Birmingham
1779	1795	1750	1800	141097	YKS	North Newbald
1860	1880	1850	1930	173452	YKS	Rawmarsh
1840	1840	1700	1900	121762	YKS	Sheffield
ASHURST						
1810	1871	....	....	116602	LAN	West
1847	1860	1800	1847	100757	LAN	Ashton In The Willows
1770	....	....	....	126497	LAN	Leyland
ASHWELL						
1780	1820	1760	1780	133671	BDF	Bassingbourne
1804	1885	1804	1885	124915	BDF	Silsoe
1775	1838	ALL	1838	118990	ESS	Aveley
1800	....	1700	1800	105457	LEI	???
1840	1841	1841	1881	164232	SFK	Butley
ASHWOOD						
1780	1970	1600	1780	102113	LND	Marylebone
....	1500	ALL	1500	177695	SAL	Astley Abbots
1751	1813	?	1751	179515	SAL	Madeley
ASHWORTH						
....	....	ALL	ALL	102121	ALL	Name Study
1801	1940	....	....	128996	CAM	Thorney
1907	....	1870	1907	146773	LAN	Blackburn
1800	1870	1870	1992	162256	LAN	Edgworth
1789	1886	1785	1886	102121	LAN	Rochdale
1784	1878	1750	1784	117196	LAN	Rochdale
1806	1878	1750	1806	117218	LAN	Rochdale
1825	....	1800	1871	147281	LAN	Rossendale
1829	1871	1750	1900	105554	WES	Kendal
1911	1911	1877	1911	146773	YKS	Skipton
ASKAM						
1780	1992	1600	1780	133825	YKS	Knottingley
1860	1890	1800	1860	172510	YKS	Sheffield
ASKEN						
1833	1852	1813	1851	174602	LIN	Spilsby
ASKEW						
1797	1832	....	....	168602	BDF	Odell
1710	1742	ALL	1710	168602	BDF	Stevington
1710	1742	ALL	1710	168602	BDF	Wootton
1799	1861	1700	1799	104310	ESS	???
1800	1855	1600	1800	102571	LAN	Broughton In Furness
....	....	1600	1720	116173	LAN	Furness
1686	....	....	....	129747	LIN	Claypole
....	....	1700	1800	174947	NTH	Woodford
1822	1960	1700	1822	113425	SFK	Ipswich
....	....	ALL	ALL	150924	YKS	North
ASKEY						
....	....	ALL	ALL	134414	ALL	Name Study
ASKFORD						
1736	1736	1695	1736	174211	LIN	Washingborough
ASKHAM						
ALL	1770	....	....	170798	WRY	Thurlstone
1723	1771	1700	1723	177393	YKS	Ferry Fryston
1860	1890	1800	1860	172510	YKS	Sheffield
ASKIN						
1779	....	1700	1799	154601	WYK	Horbury
ASLETT						
....	....	ALL	ALL	102156	ALL	Name Study
ALL	ALL	ALL	ALL	102156	ALL	ALL
1900	1950	ALL	ALL	122866	HAM	Liss
ASLIN						
1713	1992	1700	1992	102164	NTT	Gedling
1582	1713	1500	1700	102164	NTT	Southwell
ASNIP						
1800	1883	1700	1900	135623	ALL	ALL
ASPDEN						
1720	1850	ALL	1750	102172	LAN	Darwen
1800	1880	1880	1992	162256	LAN	Tockholes
ASPELING						
....	....	ALL	ALL	102180	ALL	Name Study
ASPIN						
1810	1840	1770	1840	151912	YKS	Waddington
ASPINALL						
1920	1940	1920	1940	171441	BKM	Winslow
1800	1900	1750	1800	132268	LAN	Bolton
1864	1880	1800	1880	171441	LAN	Liverpool
1804	1830	1700	1800	129453	LAN	Wigan
1890	1910	1890	1910	171441	MON	Newport

Known From	To	Researching From	To	Ref	Cty	Place
ASPINALL contd.						
1815	1992	1800	1992	132810	YKS	Elland
ASPITAL						
1820	1870	1700	1820	112038	NTH	Castor
ASPLAN						
1797	1862	1700	1797	145823	CAM	Over
ASPLIN						
1810	1840	1700	1850	125423	HUN	St Ives
ASQUE						
1839	1900	1800	1850	149446	NFK	???
ASQUITH						
1838	1838	1500	1838	142069	LAN	Burnley
1800	1950	1600	1800	131261	LND	Holborn
1871	1992	ALL	1992	104299	YKS	Barnsley
1820	1840	1750	1992	167592	YKS	Castleford
1838	1838	1500	1838	142069	YKS	Colne
1752	1992	1700	1752	102199	YKS	Scholes Cleckheaton
1860	?	1750	1992	167592	YKS	Whitwood
1860	1871	ALL	1871	104299	YKS	Worsborough Common
1875	1915	1875	1992	165603	YKS	Yarm
ASSHETON						
1650	1778	ALL	ALL	102202	CHS	Ashley
1200	1800	ALL	ALL	102202	LAN	Ashton Under Lyne
1450	1800	ALL	ALL	102202	LAN	Middleton
ASSHETON-SMITH						
1778	1992	ALL	ALL	102202	CAE	Vaynol
1778	1992	ALL	ALL	102202	HAM	Tedworth
ASSINDER						
1800	1992	ALL	ALL	102210	ALL	ALL
ASTBURY						
1800	1830	1800	1992	167592	CHS	Manchester
1779	1799	ALL	ALL	124982	FLN	ALL
1845	....	1800	1845	105538	SAL	Ketley
1690	1720	1500	1992	167592	STS	Lane Delph
1730	1750	1500	1992	167592	STS	Shelton
1690	1730	1500	1992	167592	STS	Stoke
ASTELL						
1876	1985	1800	1876	100412	LND	Islington
1876	1985	1800	1876	100412	MDX	Islington
1774	1890	1774	1890	102237	MDX	Westminster
1737	1796	1722	1812	102237	NTH	Rockingham
ASTEN						
1757	1757	1700	1760	125032	BRK	Bucklebury
ASTINGTON						
1800	1850	1700	1800	142905	CHS	Cheadle
ASTLE						
1825	1840	1700	1900	141569	STS	Burton On Trent
ASTLEY						
1350	1400	1250	1350	154881	DEN	Ruthyn
1840	1900	1800	ALL	104590	LAN	Bury
....	....	1790	1840	104590	LAN	Golborne
1840	1900	1800	ALL	104590	LAN	Oldham
1670	1731	1550	1675	118958	LAN	???
1800	1992	ALL	1992	102245	STS	Gnosall
1850	1890	1700	1850	133701	???	Birmingham
ASTLING						
1860	....	1700	1850	120596	LIN	???
1860	....	1700	1850	120596	NTT	???
ASTON						
1856	1856	ALL	1856	126225	ARM	???
1560	1585	....	....	135437	CHS	Moston
1600	1992	ALL	1600	165395	CHS	Tarporey
1809	1809	....	....	135437	GLS	St Briavels
1788	1824	1725	1825	129356	MDX	Bishopsgate
1801	....	....	1801	133566	MDX	Stepney
1861	1940	1800	1861	105538	SAL	Madeley Wood
1820	1872	1820	1890	169323	STS	Darlaston
1795	1824	1600	1824	162035	WOR	Ripple
ASTRIDGE						
....	....	ALL	ALL	176850	ALL	Name Study
1870	1871	1800	1900	171247	DEV	Holbeton
1800	1860	1800	1900	102636	HAM	Cliddesden
1750	1850	1700	1850	102636	HAM	Overton
1868	1916	1800	1930	102636	HAM	Tunworth
1724	1853	1724	1853	107514	WIL	Savernake
1724	1853	1724	1853	107514	WIL	Shalbourne
ATCHINSON						
1764	1764	1600	1800	130125	NBL	Chatton
ATHER						
1762	....	....	1762	171441	DUR	Wolviston
ATHERALL						
1850	1900	1600	1850	123587	SSX	Withyham
ATHERDEN						
1736	1900	1600	1900	151599	KEN	Dover
ATHERFOLD						
1867	1984	1771	1867	105473	SSX	Hartfield
ATHERLEY						
....	....	1750	1800	115142	WAR	Mancetter
ATHERSICH						
1790	1992	1550	1992	102261	WAR	Birmingham
ATHERSUCH						
1750	1992	1500	1992	102261	AVN	Bristol
1750	1992	1500	1992	102261	GLS	Bristol
1750	1992	1500	1992	102261	SOM	Bristol
1540	1850	1500	1992	102261	STS	???
1620	1992	1550	1992	102261	WAR	Coventry
1540	1850	1500	1992	102261	WAR	???
1540	1850	1500	1992	102261	WOR	???
ATHERSYCH						
1620	1992	1550	1992	102261	WAR	Coventry
ATHERTON						
1800	1850	1800	1850	135941	CAM	Bartlow
1850	1910	1850	1910	135941	CAM	Horseheath
1850	1910	1850	1910	135941	CAM	Shudy Camps
1838	1838	1800	1850	126705	CHS	Chester
1750	1850	1600	1850	119172	CHS	Holywell
1800	1850	1800	1850	135941	ESS	Ashdon
1700	1799	1660	1800	135941	ESS	Radwinter
....	....	1800	1860	118575	FLN	Holywell
1851	1900	1840	1900	118575	GLA	West
1720	1750	1720	1750	138479	GLS	Horfield
1821	1852	1700	1852	178233	LAN	Blackrod
1889	1920	1850	1900	124796	LAN	Penketh
1860	1940	1760	1860	100358	LAN	Salford
....	....	1800	1880	124796	LAN	St Helens
....	....	1800	1880	124796	LAN	Warrington
1785	1869	1700	1785	102997	LAN	Wigan
1818	1992	1818	1992	110396	LAN	Wigan
1753	1790	1700	1753	168912	LAN	Wigan
1869	1889	ALL	1869	104167	SFK	Brandon Hall
1900	1992	1900	1992	135941	SFK	Great Thurlow
1824	....	1824	1869	104167	SFK	Mildenhall
ATHROLL						
1750	1992	1500	1750	102288	SFK	Woodbridge
ATKIN						
1882	1882	1840	1890	174289	DBY	Ashbourne
....	1750	ALL	1750	134511	DBY	Norton
1864	1864	1066	1864	108669	DUR	Sunderland
1833	1896	1751	1911	102296	LIN	Binbrook
1806	1992	1700	1806	102342	LIN	Isle Of Axholme
1864	1880	1813	1938	102296	LIN	Ludborough
1715	1780	1500	1715	175072	LIN	Metheringham
1770	1790	1700	1850	160636	LIN	Wellingore
1792	1828	?	1800	164976	NTT	Nottingham
ATKINS						
1750	1850	1700	1900	177180	BKM	Aston Abbots
1879	1992	1600	1879	122963	BKM	Newton Longville
1722	1722	....	....	115606	BRK	Bray
1770	1880	1600	1770	104469	BRK	Coleshill
1653	1940	....	....	128996	CAM	Thorney
1800	....	....	1992	151270	CAM	Whittlesey
1610	1820	1610	1820	127655	COR	Firville
1610	1820	1610	1820	127655	COR	Mallow
1890	1988	1750	1890	165271	GLS	ALL
1638	1820	....	....	117404	GLS	Chipping Campden
1745	1992	1700	1745	102342	HAM	Portsea
1750	1800	1700	1800	136840	HAM	Portsmouth
1820	1880	ALL	ALL	115002	HAM	Whitchurch
1820	....	1820	1822	151750	HRT	Aldbury
1850	1880	1830	1900	111325	KEN	Greenwich
1819	1850	1700	1819	138584	LAN	Manchester
1930	1980	1850	1930	107476	LEI	Leicester
1800	1900	ALL	ALL	131873	LND	Hackney
1800	1900	ALL	ALL	131873	LND	Islington
1800	1900	ALL	ALL	131873	LND	Westminster
1830	1992	1700	1850	102326	MDX	Hoxton
1779	....	1750	1800	163775	MDX	Stepney
....	....	1839	....	103217	MON	Mathern
1840	1860	1800	1850	158658	NFK	Postwick
1797	1876	1795	1880	171654	NTH	Grafton Regis
1930	1980	1850	1930	107476	NTH	Northampton
....	1837	1800	1850	128961	OXF	Chipping Norton
1820	1905	....	....	174556	SFK	Oakley
1820	1905	....	....	174556	SFK	Wetheringbett
1860	1930	1800	1860	112747	SOM	Litton
1750	1828	1700	1750	172871	SOM	Norton St Philip
1800	1850	1850	1992	102318	SRY	East
1869	1892	ALL	1890	127094	SRY	Camberwell

Known From	To	Researching From	To	Ref	Cty	Place
ATKINS contd.						
1780	1800	....	....	102318	SRY	Dorking
1761	1992	....	....	134619	STS	Milford
1882	1930	....	....	105147	STS	West Bromwich
1800	1910	1700	1851	151513	WAR	Baddesley Ensor
1680	1727	1650	1750	142018	WIL	ALL
....	....	1900	1992	122963	WMD	Birmingham
1890	1988	1750	1890	165271	WOR	Broadway
ATKINSON						
....	....	1800	1900	146978	CMA	Kendal
....	....	1800	1900	146978	CMA	Windermere
....	....	....	1810	114812	CON	???
1727	....	....	....	138401	CUL	Hesket In The Forest
1797	....	1700	1797	105457	CUL	???
1847	1949	1750	1900	102415	DUB	Dublin
1798	....	ALL	1798	158445	DUR	Bishopw'mth
1672	1679	ALL	ALL	130508	DUR	Boldon
1849	1992	....	....	113395	DUR	Chester Le Street
1860	1961	1850	1961	123250	DUR	Consett
1774	1800	1700	1774	121339	DUR	Hamsterley
....	....	?	....	155349	DUR	Shadforth
....	....	....	....	155349	DUR	Sherburn in Elmet
1867	....	1700	1850	161721	DUR	South Shields
1830	1960	1800	1960	110728	DUR	Sunderland
1780	....	....	....	131202	DUR	Tanfield
1843	1860	....	....	131202	DUR	Thornley
....	1795	1750	1795	128961	ESS	Stratford
1860	1881	1700	1860	140953	EYK	Eastrington
1843	1992	ALL	1843	162027	EYK	Hull
1660	1832	1660	1832	169552	LAN	Cartmel
1842	....	ALL	1842	102350	LAN	Dalton In Furness
1705	1785	1705	1787	169552	LAN	Hawkshead
1825	....	....	....	147486	LAN	Lancaster
1743	1858	1734	1858	169552	LAN	Lindale In Cartmel
1600	1700	1600	1700	169781	LAN	Low Wray
1699	1792	ALL	ALL	141615	LAN	Priest Hutton
1738	1824	1500	1738	175072	LIN	Belchford
1788	1992	1700	1788	102342	LIN	Broughton
1840	1920	....	....	163465	LIN	Gosberton
1880	1899	1850	1937	101923	LIN	Legbourne
1680	1720	....	....	165999	LIN	Lincoln
1850	1861	1800	1980	159018	LIN	Market Rasen
1800	1880	....	....	118206	LIN	North Thoresby
1760	1992	....	....	163465	LIN	Rippingale
1825	1872	1750	1875	136042	LND	East
....	....	1800	1850	135089	LND	North
1877	1951	1843	1877	107247	LND	Hoxton
1744	....	....	1744	160873	NBL	Chollerton
1799	1900	1700	1799	164267	NBL	Hexham
1800	1820	....	....	131202	NBL	Wallsend
1805	1806	1700	1805	104728	NBL	???
1825	1851	1800	1830	143944	NRY	Hawsker
1744	1936	1600	1744	162248	NRY	Sandhutton
1825	1851	1800	1830	143944	NRY	Whitby
1700	1770	....	....	127655	NTH	ALL
1750	1800	1700	1800	116823	NYK	Baldersby
1861	1992	....	....	102393	NYK	Danby
1811	1871	ALL	1811	169846	NYK	Hampstwaite
1580	1826	....	....	102393	NYK	Lastingham
1811	1871	ALL	1811	169846	NYK	Leeds
1861	1992	....	....	102393	NYK	Northallerton
1860	....	1860	....	109967	SRY	Camberwell
1839	1861	1839	1900	173940	WES	Appleby
1755	1858	1754	1858	169552	WES	Beetham
1657	1680	1657	1680	169552	WES	Burton In Kendal
1700	1756	1600	1700	152196	WES	Heversham
1772	1871	1769	1875	169552	WES	Heversham
1754	1774	1744	....	138401	WES	Kendal
....	....	1700	1800	147613	WES	Kendal
1662	1723	1662	1725	169552	WES	Kirkby Lonsdale
1840	1883	1837	1883	169552	WES	Milnthorpe
1741	1853	1735	1853	169552	WES	Underbarrow
1664	1849	1596	1664	102571	WES	Whinhowe Orton
1676	1865	1671	1865	169552	WES	Witherslack
1843	1992	ALL	1843	162027	WYK	Leeds
1796	1810	ALL	1796	152234	WYK	Methley
1848	....	ALL	ALL	155373	YKS	North
1838	1860	1850	1992	172782	YKS	Aberford
....	....	1650	1750	147613	YKS	Addingham
1796	1824	1750	1800	151912	YKS	Bolton By Bowland
1736	1804	1500	1736	125695	YKS	Bubwith
1812	1900	1700	1900	102377	YKS	Holme On Spalding Moor
ATKINSON contd.						
1840	1900	1800	1840	114812	YKS	Huddersfield
....	....	....	....	114812	YKS	Kippax
1792	1886	ALL	1792	158445	YKS	Kirk Ella
1704	1850	1600	1704	154172	YKS	Knottingley
1900	1992	....	....	102377	YKS	Leeds
1850	1900	1800	1850	165468	YKS	Leeds
1867	1992	1750	1867	111813	YKS	Levisham
?	....	?	....	155349	YKS	Masham
1756	....	....	....	151351	YKS	Otley
1867	1992	1750	1867	111813	YKS	Rosedale Abbey
1780	1880	1600	1780	108308	YKS	Rosedale
1772	1992	1600	1772	123951	YKS	Sand Hutton
1830	1900	1700	1830	177296	YKS	Settle
1890	1992	....	....	102369	YKS	Sheffield
1849	1992	....	....	113395	YKS	Sheffield
1866	1992	....	....	159018	YKS	Sheffield
1666	....	....	....	151351	YKS	Tadcaster
1748	....	1600	1748	116637	YKS	Whixley
1765	1992	ALL	1765	102350	YKS	Wragby
ATLEE						
1827	1855	1700	1860	166960	MDX	London
ATMORE						
....	....	1700	1992	140627	NFK	Seething
ATTCHISON						
1822	1900	1600	1900	176133	SCT	???
ATTE BERE						
1318	1341	1066	1470	124974	BRK	Wargrave
ATTENBOROUGH						
1849	1905	1700	1849	138509	DBY	Belper
1550	1900	1400	1992	148288	NTT	Clifton
....	1755	ALL	1755	134511	NTT	East Leake
1861	1910	....	....	144096	NTT	Nottingham
1550	1900	1400	1992	148288	NTT	Stapleford
ATTER						
1770	1992	1700	1770	101958	NFK	ALL
ATTEWELL						
1905	1992	1905	1992	111600	HAM	Lymington
ATTEY						
1720	1765	1700	1770	103632	DUR	Sedgefield
1840	1926	1840	1950	103632	DUR	Sunderland
1767	1788	....	....	103632	YKS	Whitby
ATTFIELD						
....	....	1600	1850	131989	SRY	Wonesh
ATTHILL						
1821	1831	1818	1847	168181	FER	Magheraculmony
1815	1815	1805	1820	168181	TYR	Fintona
ATTON						
1700	1745	1600	1700	174130	RUT	Braunston
ATTREE						
....	....	ALL	ALL	102423	ALL	Name Study
ATTRILL						
....	....	ALL	ALL	144118	ALL	Name Study
1783	1947	1750	1900	113212	IOW	Arreton
ATTRYDE						
1882	1928	....	....	116602	KEN	Medway
1857	1866	1863	1871	116602	MDX	Bethnal Green
1836	1871	....	....	116602	MDX	Chelsea
1799	1825	....	....	116602	SRY	Long Ditton
ATTWELL						
....	....	ALL	ALL	144959	ALL	Name Study
....	....	1700	1899	174963	BDF	Battlesden
....	....	1700	1899	174963	BDF	Toddington
1849	1948	1800	1960	141046	BRK	Wokingham
1200	1992	1500	1950	102431	LND	ALL
1500	1992	1500	1950	102431	MDX	ALL
ATTWOOD						
1900	1992	1500	1900	110310	BRK	ALL
1755	1988	1600	1755	162035	GLS	Teddington
1757	1951	1650	1757	100277	SSX	Wartling
1805	1826	1500	1805	104825	WOR	Shipston On Stour
ATTWOODS						
1770	1825	ALL	1770	167878	WIL	Burbage
ATTWOOLL						
....	....	ALL	ALL	102458	ALL	Name Study
....	....	ALL	ALL	102466	DOR	Portland
ATTY						
1910	1992	1800	1910	174645	YKS	Bedale
ATWILL						
1300	1900	1300	1900	160814	DEV	Walkhampton
ATWOOD						
1650	1850	1650	1850	176508	SRY	Sanderstead
ATYED						
....	....	ALL	ALL	102474	ALL	Name Study

Known From	To	Researching From	To	Ref	Cty	Place
AUBERT						
1890	1950	1820	1890	118982	LND	Highbury
1890	1950	1820	1890	118982	LND	Islington
AUBRAY						
1605	1806	1066	1605	175935	BRK	Chieveley
AUBREY						
1730	1992	1730	1850	111538	HEF	Aston Ingham
....	....	1600	1750	111538	HEF	???
1823	1855	1750	1823	133760	LAN	???
....	....	1250	1700	111538	WLS	South
1834	....	1800	1850	137308	WLS	Llannefydd
AUCHINLECK						
....	1500	ALL	1500	162507	SCT	Glenbervie
AUCHMUTY						
1850	1950	1800	1900	173746	FIF	Auchtermuchty
AUCHTERLONIE						
1888	1912	1880	1890	172855	STI	Falkirk
AUCHTERLONY						
....	1500	ALL	1600	162507	SCT	???
AUCKLAND						
1707	1779	1740	1800	158712	LIN	Ingham
AUCOCK						
....	....	ALL	ALL	101354	SSX	East
1789	1890	....	....	101354	SSX	Alfriston
1640	1900	....	....	101354	SSX	Eastbourne
AUDAER						
1685	1960	1685	1992	172227	ALL	ALL
AUDAS						
1760	1840	....	....	102946	YKS	Ecclesfield
1760	1790	....	....	102946	YKS	Thurscoe
AUDLEY						
1580	....	ALL	1580	179515	NFK	Old Breckenham
AUDSLEY						
1760	1770	ALL	1760	162256	MDX	Covent Garden
AUDUS						
1790	1940	....	....	102946	YKS	Sheffield
AUFRERE						
1720	1781	....	....	156647	LIN	Manby
AUGARDE						
1790	1992	1500	1780	114944	LND	???
AUGUST						
1812	1850	ALL	1836	133957	HAM	Ringwood
1754	1754	1700	1754	125105	NFK	Stalham
AULD						
1821	1992	ALL	1992	100102	AYR	Ayr
1888	1950	1700	1888	148423	AYR	Golyton
1750	1891	1750	1950	119725	LKS	Glasgow
AULEY						
1780	1780	1700	1740	124427	NFK	Snoring
AULIFF						
1850	....	1850	1950	101656	MAY	Ballina
AULPH						
ALL	ALL	ALL	ALL	171964	ALL	ALL
AULT						
1813	1880	1800	....	169250	DBY	Ticknall
AUNGER						
1821	1821	1700	1821	177520	CON	St Clether
AUST						
ALL	ALL	ALL	ALL	102539	ALL	ALL
1750	1800	1750	1800	135429	SOM	Bath
AUSTEN						
1752	1951	1750	1951	144355	KEN	South
1830	1850	1700	1830	112569	KEN	Aldington
1850	1992	1800	1850	179442	KEN	Hythe
....	1850	....	....	114642	KEN	Tenterden
1842	1915	1841	1920	108278	KEN	Westwell
1703	1778	....	....	165999	SSX	Angmering
AUSTERBERRY						
....	....	ALL	ALL	102547	ALL	Name Study
1700	1992	ALL	ALL	102547	ALL	ALL
AUSTICK						
1733	1860	ALL	1733	102350	YKS	Kellington
AUSTIN						
1590	1992	1590	1992	102628	ALL	ALL
1809	1841	1809	1841	139971	BDF	Podington
1841	....	1800	1880	156833	CHS	Hatherton
1841	....	1800	1880	156833	CHS	Hunterston
1767	1854	1767	1854	111228	CHS	Wybunbury
1751	1992	1720	1751	102598	DEV	Brixham
1810	1860	1860	1920	171239	DEV	East Bubleigh
1600	1700	1600	1700	106305	ENG	Titchfield
1780	1992	1780	1992	152129	GLA	Llanrhydian
1840	1890	1840	1890	152129	GLA	Swansea
1750	1778	....	....	131660	GLS	Naunton By Stowe
AUSTIN contd.						
1853	1875	....	....	127426	HUN	Eynesbury
1804	1841	1760	1804	169021	HUN	Ramsey
1748	1748	....	....	127426	KEN	Aylesford
1835	1861	1800	1871	102563	KEN	Canterbury
1800	1992	1500	1800	145157	KEN	Canterbury
1721	....	....	1721	171441	KEN	Frinstead
1800	1992	1500	1800	145157	KEN	Maidstone
1824	1880	1500	1880	169439	KEN	Snave
1777	1871	ALL	1777	143278	KEN	Sutton
?	?	?	?	166642	KEN	???
1881	....	1861	....	156833	LAN	Liverpool
1871	....	1861	....	156833	LAN	Salford
1890	1896	1870	1890	177393	LND	Hammersmith
1890	1910	1910	1992	171239	MDX	Hammersmith
1742	1855	....	....	127426	NTH	Earls Barton
1781	1818	1740	1781	149039	NTH	Northampton
1836	1836	....	....	127426	SFK	???
1810	1820	1750	1840	165824	SOM	Bath
1854	1888	1700	1854	169676	SOM	Brewham
1800	1870	1750	1800	138959	SRY	Chessington
1800	1870	1750	1800	138959	SRY	Ewell
1800	1870	1750	1800	138959	SRY	Long Ditlar
....	....	1865	1890	177393	SRY	Southwark
1800	1870	1750	1800	138959	SRY	Tolworth
1812	....	....	....	144088	STS	Eccleshall
1905	1920	....	....	127426	WAR	Birmingham
1882	1882	....	....	127426	WAR	Handsworth
1875	1875	....	....	127426	WAR	Lozells
1788	1989	1600	1788	102571	WES	Howgill
AUSTRIDGE						
1910	1916	1916	1950	102636	HAM	Portsmouth
1916	1928	1900	1950	102636	SRY	Aldershot
1940	1950	1940	1980	102636	SRY	Weybridge
AUSTWICK						
1716	1716	1650	1750	167002	CAM	Cambridge
1800	1940	1700	1992	110477	WRY	Knottingley
....	....	1700	1892	144452	YKS	Brotherton
AUTEY						
1800	1850	1800	1850	123595	YKS	Huddersfield
AUTHERS						
1883	....	....	....	102644	DEV	Burlescombe
1857	....	....	....	102644	DEV	Sampford Peverell
1785	1857	1725	1785	102644	DEV	Stoodleigh
1785	1857	1725	1785	102644	DEV	Stoodley
1908	....	....	....	102644	SOM	North Petherton
AUTHERTON						
1700	1799	1660	1880	135941	ESS	Radwinter
AUTIN						
1800	1900	1800	1900	102555	WAR	Leek Wooton
AUTRIDGE						
1615	1858	1550	1614	128082	CON	ALL
1771	1903	1679	1800	128082	DEV	ALL
1851	1952	....	....	128082	WLS	Cardiff
AUTY						
1857	....	1830	1880	163775	SRY	Bermondsey
AUVACHE						
1580	1992	....	....	108448	LND	East
AVANN						
....	....	ALL	ALL	161993	ALL	Name Study
1837	1840	ALL	ALL	161993	GLS	ALL
1837	1840	ALL	ALL	161993	KEN	ALL
1837	1840	ALL	ALL	161993	LAN	ALL
1837	1840	ALL	ALL	161993	MDX	ALL
1837	1840	ALL	ALL	161993	SSX	ALL
1837	1840	ALL	ALL	161993	STS	ALL
1842	1992	ALL	ALL	161993	WAR	Birmingham
AVARBRIETER						
1860	....	1700	....	130435	CHS	Astbury
AVARD						
1740	1760	ALL	1760	115282	KEN	East
1700	1900	1700	1900	162736	KEN	Borders
1795	1865	1700	1800	132640	SSX	Warbleton
AVELING						
1670	1940	....	....	128996	CAM	Thorney
AVEN						
1660	1850	....	....	128759	SOM	Berkley
AVENS						
....	....	ALL	ALL	102652	ALL	Name Study
AVENT						
1660	1750	1600	1750	167088	DEV	Modbury
AVERALL						
....	....	1600	1920	108812	STD	Motherwell

Known From	To	Researching From	To	Ref	Cty	Place
AVERILL						
1640	1700	ALL	1640	131059	KEN	Ash By Ridley
1779	1800	1750	1830	125288	STS	Ashley
AVERN						
1800	1900	1700	1992	102164	LND	St Mary In The Field
AVERY						
1800	1850	1800	1850	141682	CON	Falmouth
1700	1720	1675	1850	133450	CON	Liskeard
1700	1800	1700	1800	141682	CON	St Agnes
....	....	1871	1992	109193	CON	St Austell
....	1863	ALL	1863	114030	DEV	Bratton Cloveley
1850	1920	ALL	1992	163821	DEV	Exminster
1697	1980	1600	1700	102679	DEV	Wembury
1849	1851	ALL	1992	163821	DEV	West Buckland
1872	1939	1300	1992	152501	ESS	East Ham
1815	1850	1815	1850	107522	KEN	Tenterden
....	....	1835	1870	109193	KEN	Woolwich
1820	1917	ALL	ALL	157864	LND	Walworth
1650	1650	1600	1700	133450	SOM	West
1800	1860	1800	1860	173428	SSX	Wadhurst
....	....	1800	1992	150762	WIL	Mere
AVES						
1820	1825	1790	1820	155934	CAM	Cambridge
1753	....	1600	1753	116637	SFK	Barrow
AVESTON						
1774	1992	1500	1774	140279	PEM	Dale
1774	1992	1500	1774	140279	PEM	Pwllecrochan
AVIS						
....	....	ALL	ALL	158100	ALL	Name Study
1550	....	ALL	1550	131059	KEN	Cowden
....	1760	....	....	103144	KEN	???
1870	1932	....	....	135070	LND	Poplar
1800	1870	1760	1800	176311	SRY	Wandsworth
....	....	1700	1930	100935	SSX	East
....	1760	....	....	103144	SSX	East
1770	1820	1700	1770	135879	SSX	Rottingdean
AVISON						
....	....	1773	1992	121940	CHS	Cheadle
1766	1796	1766	1796	149403	WYK	Crofton
1793	1992	ALL	1850	114553	YKS	Huddersfield
AVLING						
1880	1930	1880	....	144983	SSX	Hastings
AWDAS						
1785	1950	....	....	102946	YKS	Sheffield
AWDREY						
1833	....	....	1992	103942	WIL	Chippenham
AWRE						
1669	1706	1600	1750	155896	GLS	Awre
AWSON						
1700	1840	1750	1840	159247	WAR	Coventry
AWTEY						
1695	1770	1550	1700	173452	YKS	High Melton
AXE						
1860	1920	1750	1860	172510	YKS	Sheffield
AXENALL						
....	....	ALL	ALL	130850	LND	ALL
AXFORD						
1569	1657	1200	1569	168637	CON	Botus Fleming
1924	1934	1924	1928	133922	DEV	Exeter
1820	1967	....	....	133922	DOR	Bournemouth
1820	1967	1866	1921	133922	HAM	Fair Oak
1600	ALL	....	....	153397	HAM	New Forest
1886	1889	....	....	173932	HAM	Twyford
1805	1840	1700	1900	177873	SOM	???
1816	1816	1770	1850	133922	WIL	Heytesbury
1847	1854	....	....	173932	WIL	Heytesbury
1837	....	....	....	173932	WIL	Lindfield Slaugham
....	....	ALL	1800	151602	WIL	Ramsbury
1750	1798	1777	1850	133922	WIL	Sutton Veny
1857	1866	....	....	173932	WIL	Sutton Veny
1802	1843	1777	1850	133922	WIL	Tytherington
1857	....	....	....	173932	WIL	Warminster
1794	....	....	....	173932	WIL	West Lavington
1819	....	....	....	173932	WIL	Westwood
1849	1872	1700	....	135259	WIL	Wilton
1917	....	....	....	133922	YKS	Wakefield
AXON						
1800	1860	....	1800	102059	LAN	Haughton
1770	1992	ALL	1992	104299	YKS	Barnsley
AXTELL						
....	....	ALL	1992	112941	HAM	Southampton
AXTEN						
1820	1850	1820	1850	128740	LND	Holborn

Known From	To	Researching From	To	Ref	Cty	Place
AXTENCE						
1800	1825	1700	1800	156795	DOR	North
AXUP						
1815	1861	1750	1900	116742	YKS	Rawcliffe
AXWORTHY						
1807	1844	1780	1850	176982	DEV	Plymouth
AYERS						
1750	1992	1600	1750	159115	DEV	Kentisbeare
1760	1910	1740	1910	122122	GLS	Ampney St Peter
1800	1870	1800	1870	128287	GLS	Chedworth
1700	1780	1740	1780	128287	GLS	Fairford
1750	1992	1600	1750	159115	GSY	St Peter Port
1750	1992	1600	1750	159115	GSY	St Sampson
1723	1800	1600	1723	166804	SFK	Kirkley
1682	1766	ALL	1682	168602	SFK	Lowestoft
1675	1680	1650	1700	105120	SSX	Brighton
AYLEN						
1772	1772	1770	1810	176672	ESS	ALL
AYLES						
1820	....	....	....	117579	DOR	Poole
1789	1992	1759	1789	146056	HAM	New Forest
1789	1992	1759	1789	146056	HAM	Ringwood
1850	....	....	....	117579	SRY	Southwark
AYLESBURY						
1877	1992	....	....	104760	SRY	Walworth
1750	1877	ALL	1750	104760	WIL	Corsley
AYLESWORTH						
1829	1850	1700	1829	165859	LND	St Martin The Field
AYLETT						
1871	1902	1902	1992	129100	MDX	Mary Le Bone
1837	1880	1837	....	145807	WAR	Birmingham
AYLING						
....	....	ALL	ALL	161608	ENG	South
1800	1850	1750	1800	152404	HAM	Headley
1815	1815	1750	1850	141151	KEN	ALL
1600	1850	1600	1850	152404	SSX	Houghton
....	....	1840	1874	168777	SSX	Warningcamp
1735	1790	1720	1820	105333	SSX	Woolavington
1820	1871	1820	1871	175196	SSX	Worthing
AYLMER						
1823	1824	1700	1823	144126	BDF	Biggleswade
1745	....	1720	1760	163775	MDX	Cripplegate
1854	1992	1824	1854	144126	MDX	London
AYLWARD						
....	....	1700	1900	129275	LND	Walworth
AYLWIN						
....	....	ALL	ALL	143995	ALL	Name Study
AYNSLEY						
....	1762	....	....	132756	MDX	London
1500	1800	....	....	132756	NBL	Chollerton
1500	1800	....	....	132756	NBL	Harelaws
1500	1800	....	....	132756	NBL	Hartburn
1500	1800	....	....	132756	NBL	Hexham
1500	1800	....	....	132756	NBL	Highlaws
1500	1800	....	....	132756	NBL	Little Harle
1500	1800	....	....	132756	NBL	Shaftoe
ALL	1550	....	....	132756	ROX	Falla
1750	1900	....	....	132756	STS	Longton
AYRE						
1825	....	1815	1850	123404	DBY	Cundor
1730	1815	1700	1850	123404	LEI	Coleorton
1898	....	1850	....	134589	YKS	Castleford
1820	1845	1800	1900	144908	YKS	Hull
1800	1830	1700	1850	158208	YKS	York
AYRES						
1750	1860	1700	1860	145750	BDF	Wootton
1834	1851	1700	1834	170321	BKM	Chilton
1828	1860	ALL	1828	115126	BKM	Gt Missenden
1835	1856	....	....	121754	BKM	Wendover
....	....	ALL	1835	121754	BKM	Wycombe
1808	1869	1780	1880	176982	DEV	Devonport
1863	....	ALL	1863	164623	DEV	East Stonehouse
1770	1992	ALL	ALL	146803	HAM	ALL
1795	1864	1750	1864	148156	HUN	Central
1795	1864	1750	1864	148156	HUN	North
1850	....	1800	1900	127353	HUN	Holme
1800	1840	ALL	1840	174815	LEI	Leicester
....	....	1875	1883	102709	LND	Chelsea
....	....	1846	1875	102709	LND	Pimlico
....	....	1883	1902	102709	LND	Shepherds Bush
1750	1850	1700	1850	126799	NFK	Lowestoft
1750	1900	1750	1880	130567	NTH	Kislingbury
....	1788	....	....	130079	OXF	Bicester
1800	1839	?	1900	127612	SRY	Battersea

Known From	To	Researching From	To	Ref	Cty	Place
AYRES contd.						
1806	?	?	1806	136611	WIL	Corsley
?	?	?	?	169064	YKS	Sheffield
AYRTON						
1740	1992	ALL	1740	100803	NYK	Long Preston
....	....	1688	1730	155039	YKS	Litton
AYSCOUGH						
1730	1800	1600	1800	129496	LIN	Colsterworth
1846	1863	1800	1846	164259	LIN	Manby
AYTO						
1750	1992	ALL	ALL	150169	LIN	ALL
AYTON						
....	....	ALL	ALL	102725	ALL	Name Study
ALL	ALL	ALL	ALL	102725	ALL	ALL
1750	1980	....	....	102741	DUR	Consett
1750	1980	....	....	102741	DUR	Wolsingham
1800	1900	....	....	125199	MDX	Bethnal Green
1815	1890	1785	1920	105759	NBL	Newcastle
1840	1920	1600	1850	118907	NFK	ALL
AZE						
1680	1980	1680	1980	102768	DEV	Barnstaple
1680	1980	1680	1980	102768	DEV	Plymouth
....	....	1080	1400	102768	HAM	???
....	....	1080	1200	102768	SSX	???
....	....	1080	1400	102768	WIL	???
AZEVEDO						
1770	1992	1660	1950	152064	LND	East End
BABB						
....	....	ALL	ALL	114677	ALL	Name Study
1600	1980	1400	1992	114677	ALL	ALL
1700	1730	1680	1780	142018	SOM	Taunton
BABBINGTON						
1816	1860	1750	1816	133787	???	Birmingham
BABER						
....	....	ALL	ALL	102776	ALL	Name Study
....	....	ALL	ALL	118249	ALL	Name Study
ALL	ALL	ALL	ALL	102776	ALL	ALL
....	....	ALL	ALL	102776	SOM	ALL
....	1746	1500	1746	175072	SOM	Nailsea
BABINGTON						
1748	1775	....	....	138851	CHS	North Central
....	....	1816	1952	157244	DEV	???
1775	1891	....	....	138851	LAN	Manchester
....	....	1816	1952	157244	OXF	Noxford
1800	1980	1700	1800	160709	SRY	Southwark
BABYSTOCK						
1797	1797	....	....	115606	WIL	Eat Knoyle
BACCHUS						
1770	1850	1700	1830	117005	BKM	Astwood
BACH						
1813	1850	1813	1992	105147	SAL	Stoke St Milborough
BACHE						
1790	1992	ALL	1800	116408	WAR	Birmingham
BACHELOR						
1876	1992	1876	1992	172952	KEN	Tonbridge
1806	1831	1700	1851	165972	SRY	Lambeth
BACHILER						
....	....	1550	1632	143138	KEN	Sandwich At Hamburg
....	....	1550	1632	143138	???	Fleisching
BACK						
1678	1989	ALL	1716	107719	DEV	Crediton
1678	1989	ALL	1846	107719	DEV	Tedburn St Mary
1740	1804	1740	1810	144355	KEN	South
1766	1897	1766	1897	173142	KEN	Ashford
1860	....	....	1860	164011	KEN	Folkestone
1897	1908	....	....	173142	KEN	Sittingbourne
....	....	1861	1920	102784	LND	Hackney
1840	1851	1851	1930	102784	LND	Stratford
1786	1886	1886	1920	102784	NBL	Berwick Upon Tweed
1641	1992	1500	1641	154288	NFK	Walsingham
1760	1770	1770	1780	102784	SCT	Kelso
1825	1850	1700	1900	107719	SOM	Bath
1825	1850	1700	1900	107719	SOM	Frome
BACKAULLER						
....	....	?	?	104310	DEV	Hawkchurch
....	....	?	?	104310	DOR	Stoke Abbott
BACKHOUSE						
1700	1800	1700	1800	169781	DUR	Darlington
1540	1647	ALL	ALL	141615	LAN	Borwick
1700	1800	....	....	146854	LAN	Lancaster
1600	1700	1600	1700	169781	LAN	Yealand Conyers
1863	1901	1863	1992	110132	MDX	Clerkenwell
1863	1901	1863	1992	110132	MDX	St Giles
1786	1851	1851	1900	116505	SFK	Orford
BACKHOUSE contd.						
....	....	1800	1881	110132	SRY	???
1778	1881	....	....	152234	WYK	Garforth
1743	1760	1700	1992	114901	YKS	Barmwick Elmet
1816	1840	1840	....	157139	YKS	Leeds
1780	1825	1700	1992	114901	YKS	Wakefield
BACKLER						
?	?	1750	1850	109843	LND	Cripplegate
?	?	1750	1850	109843	LND	Spitalfield
?	?	1700	1850	109843	LND	St Pancras
1850	1992	1700	1850	109843	WAR	Birmingham
BACKSHALL						
1757	1832	1700	1757	175951	SSX	Ardingly
BACKUS						
1613	1772	1538	1613	125105	OXF	Bix
BACON						
1742	1940	....	....	128996	CAM	Thorney
1814	1936	1780	1840	124788	DBY	Greatlongstone
1700	1750	1600	1700	151769	DBY	Ticknall
1712	1712	1700	1750	149152	DBY	Wirkworth
1805	1918	ALL	ALL	127175	ESS	East
1805	1918	ALL	ALL	127175	ESS	North
1833	1992	ALL	1820	151602	ESS	High Beach
1831	1850	1800	1870	105120	ESS	Thorrington
1830	1840	1810	1900	170992	IRL	Newton Limavady
1831	1919	?	1830	136611	LIN	Minting
1875	1895	ALL	1890	155853	MDX	Shoreditch
1771	1844	1750	1800	143308	NFK	Saxthorpe
....	1620	1500	1620	148288	NTT	Nottingham
....	....	....	....	177393	NTT	Nottingham
....	1620	1500	1620	148288	NTT	Stapleford
1726	1765	....	1726	101761	NTT	Wellow
1788	1840	1770	1880	105333	SSX	Birdham
1788	1840	1770	1880	105333	SSX	Oving
1611	1704	1600	1611	175781	WIL	Bromham
1822	1822	1750	1822	101060	WIL	Salisbury
1700	1740	1700	1760	142018	WIL	Salisbury
1750	1880	1700	1750	149152	YKS	Sheffield
BADBY						
....	....	ALL	ALL	102792	ALL	Name Study
BADCOCK						
1708	1992	1670	1708	132004	CAM	Burwell
1771	1858	ALL	1858	168718	CON	South East
1864	1881	1864	1992	172596	CON	Paul
1800	....	1600	1800	149608	DEV	Shebbear
1785	1860	1700	1860	102806	DEV	South Molton
1630	1714	....	....	165999	SSX	Angmering
....	1800	....	....	174564	SSX	???
BADDELEY						
1750	1790	1600	1992	167592	LAN	Liverpool
1750	1790	1600	1992	167592	STS	Shelton
1750	1790	1600	1992	167592	STS	Stoke On Trent
BADDLEY						
1810	1840	1750	1810	121053	STS	Darlaston
BADGER						
....	....	1850	ALL	159026	DBY	Buxton
....	....	ALL	ALL	159026	DBY	Dronfield
....	....	ALL	ALL	159026	DBY	Hathersage
....	....	1820	1850	117137	GLA	Merthyr
1812	1862	1750	1810	162396	OXF	Horton
1869	1869	ALL	1900	128171	STS	Wolverhampton
....	....	ALL	ALL	159026	YKS	Barnsley
1557	1837	ALL	ALL	159026	YKS	Doncaster
1542	1900	ALL	ALL	159026	YKS	Rotherham
1560	1900	ALL	ALL	159026	YKS	Sheffield
....	....	1840	ALL	159026	YKS	York
BADGERS						
....	....	ALL	ALL	159026	ALL	Name Study
BADGERY						
....	....	1600	1783	102814	CON	???
....	....	1600	1783	102814	DEV	???
....	....	1600	1783	102814	DOR	???
1803	1814	....	....	102814	LND	???
1783	....	....	....	102814	SOM	Yeovil
....	....	1600	1783	102814	SOM	???
1803	1814	....	....	102814	SRY	Bermondsey
1818	1992	....	....	102814	WOR	Worcester
BADGLIE						
1559	1704	1500	1610	102830	DBY	ALL
BADHAM						
....	....	ALL	ALL	102822	ALL	Name Study
....	....	ALL	ALL	102822	ALL	ALL
1874	1960	....	....	148202	GLA	Aberdare
1822	1823	....	1825	102822	HEF	???

Known From	To	Researching From	To	Ref	Cty	Place
BADHAM contd.						
1823	1920	....	....	102822	LND	North West
1824	1871	1700	1824	148202	PEM	Williamston
1822	1823	....	1825	102822	WOR	???
BADLAND						
1861	1907	1834	1860	153907	WOR	Bewdley
1829	1834	1700	1828	153907	WOR	Lindridge
BADLESMERE						
1200	1355	1100	1200	154881	KEN	Sittingbourne
BADMAN						
1801	1824	1700	1881	176923	SOM	Holcombe
1882	....	1700	1992	176923	SOM	Paulton
....	1686	1748	....	115290	SOM	Wedmore
BADNAGE						
....	1830	....	1950	130168	WAR	Birmingham
BADSEY						
1740	1992	ALL	ALL	170097	ALL	Ledbury
BAGEHOT						
1740	1900	1740	1900	151653	SOM	Langport
BAGG						
1854	....	....	....	119911	SOM	Dracott
BAGGALEY						
1730	1992	1730	1770	130877	NTT	Mansfield
BAGGALLAY						
1907	1992	1790	1907	102849	LND	Brixton
BAGGARIDGE						
1770	1796	....	1796	149055	GLS	Bristol
BAGGETT						
....	....	1700	1800	146927	GLS	???
....	1800	1700	1800	146927	LND	Westminster
BAGGIN						
....	....	1820	1860	113514	SYK	Sheffield
BAGGLEY						
1850	1850	1850	1850	109347	DBY	Ashford
BAGGS						
1530	1992	....	....	124699	HAM	Central
1422	1949	ALL	ALL	105015	HAM	Hannington
1807	1960	1780	1960	122122	???	Bristol
BAGIER						
1839	1900	ALL	1850	106283	ESS	Romford
1900	1916	ALL	ALL	106283	SCT	Edinburgh
BAGLEY						
1790	1821	1700	1790	179116	STS	Bilston
1847	1870	1870	1992	179116	WAR	Birmingham
BAGLIN						
1800	1850	1700	1800	128163	GLS	ALL
BAGNALL						
1830	1900	1800	1900	130567	CHS	Sandbach
....	....	1800	1899	158240	IRL	Dublin
1930	....	1900	1930	177768	NFK	Fransham
1851	....	1800	1880	156833	STS	Stafford
BAGNELL						
1827	1992	1700	1827	118532	YKS	Sheffield
BAGOT						
1693	1839	1650	....	120634	LAN	Pilling
1500	1600	....	....	100420	WAR	Meriden
1800	....	ALL	1900	174637	WOR	???
BAGSHAW						
1750	1820	1500	1750	107972	NTT	Nether Langwith
....	1670	1600	1700	152560	STS	Narrowdale
1798	1904	1750	1800	103039	YKS	Sheffield
1830	1992	....	1830	114812	YKS	Shefield
BAGULEY						
1550	1840	1550	1840	102830	DBY	ALL
1550	1840	1550	1840	102830	LAN	ALL
1200	1840	1200	1840	102830	NTT	ALL
BAGWELL						
....	....	ALL	1992	146986	ALL	ALL
....	....	ALL	ALL	172413	DEV	East
BAIGENT						
....	....	ALL	ALL	102857	ALL	Name Study
1500	1900	1500	1800	102865	BRK	ALL
1500	1900	1500	1800	102865	HAM	ALL
1758	....	1700	1758	157732	HAM	Alton
1500	1900	1500	1800	102865	SRY	ALL
1854	1883	1700	1854	167231	SRY	Addlestone
1500	1900	1500	1800	102865	SSX	ALL
1770	1992	1650	1770	102873	SSX	Midhurst
BAIKIE						
1771	1992	1600	1992	148482	OKI	Orkney
BAILDON						
1861	1906	1851	1879	160164	LAN	Manchester
1800	1850	1780	1865	160164	YKS	Huddersfield

Known From	To	Researching From	To	Ref	Cty	Place
BAILES						
1828	1852	1750	1830	132454	DUR	St Mary Le Bow
1810	1865	1700	1810	102881	DUR	Sunderland
1885	1914	....	....	102881	NBL	Newcastle Upon Tyne
1800	1900	1800	1900	102490	YKS	Staveley
BAILEY						
1750	1850	1600	1992	177180	BKM	Astin Abbots
1764	1791	1740	1764	119059	BKM	Brill
1750	1890	1600	1992	177180	BKM	Ivinghoe
1801	1992	1700	1900	102938	BKM	Olney
1700	1992	1600	1992	102970	BRK	Chieveley
1655	1940	....	....	128996	CAM	Thorney
1672	1729	1600	....	169498	CAM	Thorney
1820	1940	1820	1940	154466	CAM	Wicken
1740	1770	1590	1780	172006	CHS	Cheadle
1848	1888	1851	1888	169498	CHS	Chester
1841	1989	1700	1841	170569	CHS	Gatley
1840	1992	....	1840	102911	CON	Camborne
1836	....	1836	1900	133264	DBY	Mackworth
1800	1850	1700	1800	145017	DEV	ALL
1851	1934	1800	1851	128368	DEV	Newton Abbot
1800	1870	1800	1810	124028	DEV	Plymouth
1844	1880	1844	1992	145009	DEV	Sidbury
1900	1992	1800	1900	164240	DOR	Wimborne St Giles
....	....	1865	1885	137618	DUR	Chester Le Street
....	....	1750	1850	137618	DUR	Felling
1835	1992	1700	1835	159212	DUR	Gateshead
1893	1950	1800	1900	129593	DUR	Haswell
....	....	1800	1900	129593	DUR	Hurworth
1872	1929	ALL	1872	159204	ESS	Chelmsford
1872	1929	ALL	1872	159204	ESS	Writtle
1765	1793	ALL	1795	113611	EYK	Hull
1850	1900	1850	1900	139920	GLA	Treherbert
1635	1835	1635	1835	165999	GLS	ALL
1730	1800	1600	1800	154342	GLS	Bitton
1700	1900	1700	1900	131962	HAM	Inland
1760	1950	1700	1800	136840	HAM	Portsmouth
1790	1860	ALL	1900	173614	HAM	Portsmouth
1889	1970	ALL	ALL	103543	HAM	Southampton
1840	1950	1780	1840	161284	HEF	Burghill
1850	1950	1800	1992	177180	HRT	Lilley
1820	1880	1848	1992	102954	IRL	Burrishoole
1800	1825	ALL	1825	131059	KEN	Bonnington
1914	1992	1914	1992	102989	KEN	Dartford
....	1900	....	....	112429	LAN	Lancaster
1892	1962	....	1892	166189	LAN	Liverpool
1868	1992	ALL	ALL	127000	LAN	Manchester
1830	1850	....	....	126497	LAN	Pemberton
....	....	1750	1800	100129	LEI	Harston
1729	1878	1650	1729	175064	LIN	Billinghau
1798	1878	1750	1992	169498	LIN	Holbeach
ALL	ALL	ALL	ALL	163716	LND	ALL
1840	1940	1800	1840	104124	LND	Battersea
1829	1956	1700	1900	172316	LND	Bethnal Green
1869	1921	1750	1870	102903	LND	Bloomsbury
1840	1940	1800	1840	104124	LND	Hoborn
1869	1921	1750	1870	102903	LND	Islington
1860	1900	1700	1992	165255	LND	Lambeth
1850	1992	1700	1850	157449	LND	Penge
1840	1875	ALL	1992	159174	LND	Southwark
1829	1956	1700	1900	172316	LND	Whitechapel
1851	1880	ALL	1851	169730	MDX	Chiswick
1880	1881	1855	1905	110051	MDX	Old Ford
1884	1914	1854	....	102989	MDX	Pancras
1779	....	1775	1785	163775	MDX	Stepney
1860	1900	....	....	165255	MDX	Westminster
1881	....	....	....	137618	NBL	Newcastle
....	....	1850	1870	137618	NBL	Tynemouth
?	?	?	?	150975	NFK	Hingham
1725	1754	ALL	1725	115126	NTH	Finedon
....	1800	....	1800	177695	NTH	Irthlingborough
1829	1942	1820	1921	150053	NTH	Kettering
1860	1992	1700	1860	119261	NTH	Potterspury
1785	1890	....	....	102946	NTT	Nottingham
1800	1912	?	1880	129046	OXF	Benson
....	....	1858	....	140767	SAL	Dawley
1826	1940	1726	1826	177490	SFK	Burgate
1700	1750	1700	1750	144657	SOM	Banwell
1760	1825	1700	1800	145149	SOM	Chard
1790	1871	1750	1992	178020	SOM	Halse
1700	1850	1600	1700	108677	SOM	Nynehead
1790	1871	1750	1992	178020	SOM	Wiveliscombe
1820	1992	1820	1992	102954	SSX	Chichester
....	....	1700	1800	118834	SSX	Pagham

Known From	To	Researching From	To	Ref	Cty	Place
BAILEY contd.						
1780	1880	1700	1780	146285	SSX	Pagham
1820	1992	1820	1992	102954	SSX	Rumboldswyk
1750	1870	1700	1900	162736	SSX	Ticehurst
1828	1992	....	....	129291	STS	Biddulph
1860	1940	1700	1900	137731	STS	Biddulph
1785	1992	ALL	1785	146056	STS	Biddulph
....	....	1800	1870	137111	STS	Bilston
1800	1900	1558	1800	153427	STS	Blurton
1824	1847	ALL	1824	106909	STS	Highland
1830	1855	1800	1898	108510	STS	Kidsgrove
1800	1850	1500	1850	136794	STS	Leigh
1800	1900	1558	1800	153427	STS	Newcastle
1840	1910	1800	1898	108510	STS	Tunstall
1880	1940	ALL	....	120626	STS	Walsall
1812	1910	1750	1910	123285	SYK	Hoyland
1790	1802	1750	1900	122327	WAR	Nuneaton
1901	....	1700	1901	172111	WIL	Tinhead
1806	1890	....	1806	132837	WIL	Trowbridge
....	....	1885	1900	137618	WRY	Pool In Wharfdale
....	1797	1700	1797	110531	WYK	Kirkburton
1800	1860	1700	1900	130419	YKS	Barnoldswick
1750	1975	1750	1975	104612	YKS	Holmfirth
1750	1780	1700	1780	123595	YKS	Holmfirth
1820	1860	....	....	125199	YKS	Normanton
1850	1992	....	....	102946	YKS	Sheffield
1760	1851	ALL	1760	169730	YKS	Silkstone
BAILEY-CHURCHILL						
1875	1898	1875	1992	102938	LIN	Tattershall
BAILIE						
1600	1630	ALL	....	104515	LIN	Beckingham
BAILISS						
....	....	ALL	ALL	165646	LEI	???
BAILLIE						
1804	1831	1770	1820	102962	LKS	Hamilton
1750	1810	1650	1810	154881	ROC	Eddleston
1450	1500	1350	1450	154881	ROC	Lamington
....	1400	ALL	1510	162507	SCT	Lamington
BAILY						
1800	1860	1800	1860	167924	KEN	Chatham
1790	1920	....	....	168041	LND	City
1830	1900	1830	1900	167924	MDX	St Pancras
ALL	1686	....	....	170178	WIL	Bishops Cannings
1787	1839	....	....	115606	WIL	Ramsbury
BAIN						
1750	1900	....	....	126497	CAI	Halkirk
....	1889	ALL	1895	127000	CAI	Keiss
1760	1920	1760	1920	126500	CAI	Wick Halkirk
1860	1900	....	....	110159	GAL	Galway
1868	1992	1700	1868	102997	LAN	Ashton
1887	1907	1700	1887	153605	LAN	Liverpool
1807	1862	1600	1807	147346	MLN	Edinburgh
1790	1891	1700	1992	171875	ROC	Rogart
1769	1796	1500	1769	129577	SCT	Wick
1750	1965	....	....	137820	SHI	Fetlar
1720	1965	....	....	137820	SHI	Mid Yell
1760	1965	....	....	137820	SHI	North Yell
1758	1965	....	....	137820	SHI	Northmavine
1720	1965	....	....	137820	SHI	South Yell
BAINBRIDGE						
1906	1992	....	....	160148	CLV	Grangetown
1851	1882	....	....	160148	CLV	Middlesborough
1750	1980	1600	1750	167584	DUR	Aukland
1775	1992	1700	1775	103039	DUR	Bishop Auckland
1781	1851	1700	1781	160148	DUR	Hartlepool
1550	1700	1550	1700	117706	DUR	Middleton In Teesdale
1660	1740	1620	1700	108871	DUR	Weadale
1604	1992	1500	1604	159182	LAN	Carnforth
1849	1890	1829	1849	134309	LAN	Lancaster
1550	1750	1550	1700	117706	MDX	London
1780	1992	1700	1900	160725	NBL	Newcastle Upon Tyne
1580	1620	1550	1700	117706	YKS	Coverham
1700	1800	1700	1800	117706	YKS	Coxwold
1600	1670	1550	1700	117706	YKS	Killinghall
1570	1650	1550	1700	117706	YKS	Knaresborough
1640	1670	1550	1700	117706	YKS	Leeds
1670	1684	1600	1700	117706	YKS	Lindley
....	....	1750	1790	177393	YKS	Ottringham
1550	1600	1550	1700	117706	YKS	Pately Bridge
1600	1750	1550	1700	117706	YKS	Ripon
1550	1700	1550	1700	117706	YKS	Romaldkirk
BAINBRIGG						
1699	1699	ALL	1699	154563	NBL	Haltwistle
BAINE						
1831	1881	....	....	168203	PER	Findo Gask
1802	1804	....	....	168203	RFW	Paisley
BAINES						
1550	1992	....	....	103047	ALL	ALL
1815	1870	1815	1870	134031	CAM	Burwell
1735	1940	....	....	128996	CAM	Thorney
1711	1732	ALL	1711	163341	ESS	Clavering
1711	1732	ALL	1711	162108	ESS	Clavering
1813	1875	....	....	159131	LAN	Preston
1850	1880	1850	1880	134031	LND	Dulwich
1790	1840	1790	1840	154210	NYK	Bedale
1700	1899	1700	1850	135941	SFK	Haverhill
1901	1992	1700	1900	122114	WAR	Birmingham
....	....	1700	ALL	151629	WYK	Halifax
1761	1852	1700	1761	152196	YKS	Dent
1801	1829	1700	1800	176451	YKS	Ingleton
BAINS						
1820	1920	ALL	ALL	122297	DUR	South Shields
1710	1800	ALL	ALL	122297	FIF	Pittenweem
1880	1950	....	....	135968	LEI	Sewstern
1786	1880	1600	1900	135968	RUT	Market Overton
BAINTON						
1827	1871	1700	1827	174831	WIL	Trowbridge
BAIRD						
1770	1980	1700	1770	123374	ABD	Leochel-Cushnie
1800	....	ALL	ALL	130508	ABD	Peterhead
1807	1846	1725	1875	143251	ANT	Belfast
1800	1992	1650	1850	103055	ANT	Glenarm
1880	1992	1700	1890	136573	FIF	Kirkcaldy
1802	1992	1700	1806	103063	HAM	Portsmouth
1800	1894	1750	1894	179000	LKS	Airdrie
1859	1881	1859	1881	146528	MLN	Edinburgh
1790	1850	1790	1850	133795	SCT	ALL
1728	....	1700	1750	146536	STI	Muiravonside
BAIRNSON						
1750	1800	1700	1992	104671	SHI	Dunrossness
BAIRSTOWN						
1751	1801	1720	1800	146897	YKS	Halifax
BAISBROWN						
1731	1890	1568	1869	169552	LAN	Hawkshead
1670	1837	1670	1837	169552	LAN	Poulton Le Fylde
1749	1890	1633	1932	169552	LAN	Troutbeck
1651	1959	1651	1959	169552	WES	Staveley
1755	1812	1720	1812	169552	WES	Winster
BAISTER						
1811	1840	1750	1840	125466	DUR	Brancepeth
BAITSON						
1700	1992	1600	1700	102342	LIN	Corringham
BAIZEY						
1756	1758	ALL	1760	129283	ESS	Rochford
BAKE						
1872	1961	1872	1961	103071	DUR	Bishop Auckland
....	....	ALL	ALL	103071	YKS	ALL
1750	1780	1650	1750	103071	YKS	Appletreewick
1780	1872	1780	1872	103071	YKS	Grassington
1696	1807	ALL	1696	145203	YKS	Skipton
BAKER						
1839	1992	ALL	1839	160199	ALL	Coastal Ports
1809	1850	1700	1809	111198	BDF	Sandy
1793	1856	1760	1793	119059	BKM	Brill
1670	1695	....	....	145688	BRK	Bray
1710	1720	....	....	145688	BRK	Warfield
1860	1950	1800	1860	129445	CAM	Cambridge
1720	1992	1580	1720	175870	CAM	Pampisford
1673	1940	....	....	128996	CAM	Thorney
1741	1832	ALL	ALL	115126	CHI	ALL
1660	1775	1500	1690	121932	CON	Jacobstow
....	....	1750	1850	177725	CON	Launcells
1900	1939	1900	1992	121932	CON	North Petherwin
1660	1775	1500	1690	121932	CON	Tremaine
1702	1702	ALL	1702	154563	DBY	Bolsover
1800	1850	1750	1800	121592	DEV	Axminster
1735	1816	1700	1850	134376	DEV	Blackawton
....	....	1650	1685	176893	DEV	Bowhays
....	....	1650	1685	176893	DEV	Dunchidoeck
1800	1842	1600	1800	133132	DEV	Exeter
1840	1880	1840	1880	135429	DEV	Exmouth
1815	1833	1750	1850	121568	DEV	Knowstone
1860	1861	1800	1875	136042	DEV	Ottersy St Mary
1830	....	....	....	172030	DEV	Pilton
1806	1937	1317	1806	137537	DEV	Plymouth
1841	1861	1600	1890	170518	DEV	St Giles In The Heath

Known From	To	Researching From	To	Ref	Cty	Place
BAKER contd.						
1790	1890	1750	1830	138487	DEV	Widworthy
1770	1797	1650	1770	118958	DEV	???
1780	1800	1780	1800	154210	DOR	Coombe Keynes
1792	1810	1700	1793	127116	DOR	Iwerneminster
1690	1730	....	....	151351	DOR	Piddletrenthide
1860	1900	1700	1920	107115	DOR	Sherborne
1800	1850	1750	1800	121592	DOR	Thorncombe
1813	1906	1813	1912	154733	DOR	Winfrith
1642	....	1642	1992	127035	DOR	???
1830	1880	1700	1840	106267	ESS	Aythorp Roding
1750	1800	1725	1850	149152	ESS	Colcehster
1847	....	1780	....	116297	ESS	Finchingfield
1790	1900	1766	1790	122572	GLS	ALL
1834	1853	ALL	1906	168696	GLS	Bedminster
1700	1850	1700	1875	142158	GLS	Berkeley
1860	1900	1860	1992	152943	GLS	Bristol
1769	1812	....	....	148261	GLS	Cheltenham
1800	1830	1800	1860	157171	GLS	Cowley
1520	1704	1308	1788	142859	GLS	Kings Stanley
1800	1899	ALL	ALL	146633	HAM	ALL
1745	1851	1700	1900	103160	HAM	Fawley
1745	1863	1711	1745	145459	HAM	Fawley
1770	1992	1600	1770	103098	HAM	Hythe
1826	1992	1800	1900	103225	HAM	Kingsclere
1760	1780	....	....	153397	HAM	New Forest
1850	1950	....	....	106240	HAM	Portsmouth
....	1771	ALL	ALL	129933	HAM	Portsmouth
1755	1778	1548	1755	150169	HAM	Priors Dean
1860	1976	....	....	145394	HAM	Southampton
1750	1850	ALL	1800	115282	KEN	East
....	....	1746	1792	130060	KEN	Brookland
1861	1945	1768	1861	107247	KEN	Deal
1780	1920	1780	1920	120235	KEN	Deptford
....	....	1750	1808	121037	KEN	Dover
....	1833	1800	1833	164321	KEN	Dover
1750	1800	1700	1900	111589	KEN	Edenbridge
1760	1850	1650	1840	129976	KEN	Folkestone
1802	1832	....	1802	177504	KEN	Halling
1854	1858	1791	1900	139114	KEN	Leeds
1700	1900	....	....	152978	KEN	Maidstone
1820	1880	1820	1880	107522	KEN	Sittingbourne
1800	1900	1700	1800	166022	KEN	Sittingbourne
1811	1848	....	1848	103349	KEN	Staplehurst
1814	1891	1800	1891	157597	KEN	Tunbridge Wells
....	....	1746	1792	130060	KEN	Winchelsea
1758	1992	1600	1758	103195	KEN	Worth
1874	1903	1904	1950	178284	KEN	Worth
1840	1914	....	1840	101168	LAN	Liverpool
1850	1960	1890	1960	132683	LAN	Liverpool
1852	1877	1600	1852	150150	LAN	Liverpool
1830	1840	1800	1830	117196	LAN	Rochdale
....	1684	1600	1684	117234	LAN	Walton
1808	1862	....	....	108057	LEI	Leicester
1839	1877	1800	1900	137626	LEI	Newbold Verdon
1765	....	....	....	163155	LEI	Shepshed
1838	1894	1750	1838	149519	LIN	Gainsborough
1739	1808	....	....	108057	LIN	Stamford
1885	1929	1700	1885	109223	LND	ALL
1790	1900	1766	1790	122572	LND	ALL
1800	1899	ALL	ALL	146633	LND	ALL
1865	1992	ALL	1865	149071	LND	Clerkenwell
1865	1992	ALL	1865	149071	LND	Hackney
1830	1908	ALL	1869	101362	LND	Islington
1889	1889	1880	1890	158089	LND	Southwark
1884	1992	1800	1884	149365	MDX	Acton
1867	....	1750	1867	121010	MDX	Bethnal Green
1865	....	1800	1865	154202	MDX	Chelsea
....	1833	....	1833	164321	MDX	East London
1860	1870	1830	1900	176648	MDX	Edmondon
1865	....	1800	1865	154202	MDX	Fulham
1880	1890	....	....	105759	MDX	Islington
1800	1850	....	....	106240	MDX	London
1800	1840	1800	1992	137448	MDX	Poplar
1808	1833	....	....	121037	MDX	Shoreditch
1858	1924	1830	1924	157678	MDX	St Pancras
1835	1875	1835	1875	142158	MON	Marshfield
1734	1992	1700	1734	156035	NFK	Bale
1799	1960	1799	1960	116726	NFK	Cromer
....	....	1750	1810	143308	NFK	Hindolveston
1740	1947	1740	1947	175153	NFK	North Yorks
1880	1930	1930	1940	162485	NFK	Norwich
1850	1960	1890	1960	132683	NFK	Scratby
1870	1880	1800	1870	162485	NFK	Yarmouth

Known From	To	Researching From	To	Ref	Cty	Place
BAKER contd.						
1843	1928	....	....	121231	NTH	Barnwell
1793	....	....	1820	171441	OXF	Broadwell
1820	1835	1800	1835	171441	OXF	Oxford
1700	1850	1700	1850	136239	SAL	Bridgenorth
1850	1960	ALL	ALL	162469	SFK	North
1718	1750	ALL	ALL	121487	SFK	Elmswell
1722	1750	1650	1800	159956	SFK	Elmswell
1900	....	ALL	ALL	121487	SFK	Hadleigh
1816	1871	1871	1900	116505	SFK	Ipswich
1820	1880	....	....	157864	SFK	Rumburgh
1800	1861	1800	1900	170852	SFK	Stowmarket
....	....	1840	ALL	114022	SFK	???
1792	1992	1700	1920	105953	SOM	North
1760	1850	1700	1760	103675	SOM	Banwell
1759	1992	1700	1800	138487	SOM	Bridgwater
1850	1900	1850	1900	138479	SOM	Butcombe
1760	1849	1650	1790	100013	SOM	Dinder
1700	1800	1700	1800	165999	SOM	Dinder
1732	1819	1700	1841	176923	SOM	Holcombe
1752	....	1752	1992	139602	SOM	Ilton
1856	1870	1800	1860	166316	SOM	Lydeard St Lawrence
1680	1720	....	....	171654	SOM	Middle Chinnock
1860	1900	1700	1860	130389	SOM	Milbourne Port
....	....	1600	1992	123242	SOM	Minehead
1805	1980	ALL	ALL	153516	SOM	Nempnett Thrubwell
1810	1828	1750	1850	121568	SOM	North Petherton
1840	1862	1700	1840	153281	SOM	North Petherton
1750	1800	1700	1800	144657	SOM	Wellington
1780	1992	1600	1780	133825	SOM	West Hornington
1867	1903	1850	1900	129607	SRY	North East
1845	1900	1800	1900	145866	SRY	Bermondsey
1813	1890	1792	1976	148067	SRY	Bermondsey
1800	1900	ALL	ALL	141704	SRY	Croydon
1890	1900	1830	1900	176648	SRY	Mitcham
1800	1899	ALL	ALL	146633	SRY	Richmond
1866	....	....	....	124559	SRY	Southwark
1593	1869	....	....	165999	SSX	Angmering
1860	....	1860	....	135488	SSX	Brighton
....	....	ALL	ALL	168610	SSX	Brighton
....	....	ALL	1840	178403	SSX	Broadwater
1586	1992	1500	1586	153591	SSX	Easebourne
....	....	ALL	ALL	103241	SSX	East Grinstead
1586	1992	1500	1586	153591	SSX	Ewhurst
....	1800	....	....	174564	SSX	Guestling
1778	1830	1778	1929	127183	SSX	Horsted Keynes
1828	1828	ALL	1820	165263	SSX	Mayfield
1819	1819	1750	1819	174807	SSX	Mayfield
1586	1992	1500	1586	153591	SSX	Salehurst
....	....	ALL	ALL	103241	SSX	Turners Hill
....	1800	....	....	174564	SSX	Westfield
....	....	1700	1839	137626	STS	Burton Upon Trent
1803	1861	1590	1803	133752	STS	Cheslyn Hay
1850	1870	1700	1850	132284	STS	Essington
1645	1800	1600	1820	160873	STS	Kingswinford
1800	1832	1700	1800	126357	STS	Longton
1800	1842	1600	1800	133132	STS	Rugeley
1801	1823	1600	1850	170178	SXE	Glynde
1760	1850	1600	1780	170178	SXE	Rye
1724	1724	1680	1750	167002	SXE	Warbleton
1840	1890	1700	1890	161411	WAR	Birmingham
1830	1853	ALL	1830	174815	WAR	Birmingham
1750	1900	1700	1900	119938	WAR	Stratford
1734	1743	1700	1734	152196	WES	Grasmere
1775	1887	1725	1779	137057	WIL	Alfriston
?	....	?	?	143499	WIL	Bradford On Avon
1830	1860	1810	1840	165530	WIL	Chippenham
1763	1851	1600	1880	150576	WIL	Dinton
1780	1818	1780	1818	137057	WIL	Lewes
1820	1850	1775	1820	172901	WOR	Dudley
1800	1830	....	1830	102822	WOR	Halesowen
1805	1960	1700	1805	153346	WOR	Old Swinford
1725	1771	....	....	148261	WOR	Pershore
1813	1957	ALL	ALL	168610	WOR	Worcester
1826	1992	1600	1826	160172	YKS	East Rdg
1860	1881	....	....	139823	YKS	Heslerton
1750	1825	1500	1800	103888	YKS	Leeds
....	....	1600	1650	115142	???	Mancetter
1740	1947	1740	1947	175153	???	South Kilvington
1740	1947	1740	1947	175153	???	Winfarthing
BAKES						
....	....	ALL	ALL	103276	ALL	Name Study
1820	1856	1700	1820	144177	WRY	Calverley
1745	1795	1600	1992	102520	YKS	Eccleshill

Known From	To	Researching From	To	Ref	Cty	Place
BAKEWELL						
....	....	1800	1900	135496	NTT	Nottingham
BAKHEN						
ALL	ALL	....	....	153397	SSX	West Grinsted
BALAM						
1086	1992	ALL	ALL	105333	ALL	ALL
BALCHIN						
....	....	ALL	ALL	128856	ALL	Name Study
1500	1992	1500	1992	128856	ALL	ALL
1815	1860	1700	1815	122378	NTT	Nottingham
1559	1777	1500	1800	159581	SRY	Bramley
1794	1818	1740	1800	172871	SRY	Godalming
1823	1992	550	1992	103292	SRY	Wonersh
1900	1940	ALL	ALL	175536	SSX	Central
1774	1861	ALL	....	132349	SSX	Kirdford
1820	1992	1700	1820	103306	SSX	Wisburough Green
BALCKER						
1840	1850	1800	1855	160164	SOM	Combe St Nicholas
BALCKETT						
1794	1896	1600	1794	167355	YKS	Welbury
BALCOMB						
1776	1920	1700	1776	163082	SRY	Sutton
1801	1829	1801	1829	138312	SSX	Ticehurst
BALCOMBE						
1842	1899	1842	ALL	153214	KEN	Brambrook
1698	1698	....	....	139971	SSX	Herstmonceux
1842	1899	1842	ALL	153214	SSX	Ticehurst
BALD						
1841	1992	ALL	ALL	127000	ELN	Garvald
1841	1992	ALL	ALL	127000	ELN	Ormiston
BALDCOCK						
1800	1886	1700	1800	121525	SSX	Wadhurst
BALDERSON						
1733	1940	....	....	128996	CAM	Thorney
1733	1992	1700	1733	169730	CAM	Thorney
1881	1881	1800	1900	178446	LIN	Lincoln
BALDERSTONE						
1033	1992	1033	1992	108138	ALL	ALL
BALDIE						
?	?	?	?	167169	FIF	St Monans
BALDING						
1888	1978	1800	1888	164879	CAR	Bagnalstown
1788	1892	1700	1850	117013	NFK	Dersingham
BALDOCK						
1750	1820	1750	1820	135232	KEN	Canterbury
1587	1680	1500	1587	145971	KEN	Charing
1733	1771	....	....	171654	LIN	Brinkhill
1820	1910	1750	1820	145424	SRY	Brixton
BALDRY						
1600	1700	1500	1800	177180	BDF	Eaton Bray
1881	1906	1881	1992	131768	KEN	Gillingham
1841	1881	1841	1881	131768	NFK	Great Yarmouth
1789	1800	ALL	ALL	154830	SFK	Barking
....	....	1800	1841	131768	SFK	Denham
1815	1860	1750	1820	132640	SFK	Ipswich
BALDWIN						
....	....	1600	1699	155292	BKM	ALL
1773	1858	1600	1773	103330	BKM	Shabbington
1666	1739	1689	1739	165999	GLS	Brockworth
1750	1992	....	....	118672	GLS	Withington
1580	1580	....	....	115606	HAM	Froyle
1897	1992	....	....	103330	HAM	Liss
1770	1902	ALL	ALL	125873	KEN	Wrotham
1745	1760	1740	1800	155969	LAN	Burnley
1870	1992	1870	1900	172855	LAN	Church
1659	1700	1600	1700	109347	LAN	Grindleton
1880	1980	1880	1980	114936	LAN	Higher Walton
....	....	1700	1870	138614	LAN	Lytham
....	....	1770	1820	155969	LAN	Manchester
1659	1700	1600	1700	109347	LAN	Sawley
1868	1992	1800	1863	103322	LAN	Wigan
1817	1850	1800	1850	107026	MDX	Hayes
1793	1805	1700	1900	118168	NFK	Blackney
1831	1861	1800	1900	118168	NFK	Great Yarmouth
?	?	1773	1846	114308	NTH	Kislingbury
1827	1848	1790	1827	166707	RUT	Liddington Thorpe By Water
1809	1870	1780	1880	169323	SAL	Tong
1858	1897	....	....	103330	SSX	Blackdown
1850	1920	1800	1890	115614	SSX	Hastings
1840	1850	1830	1880	169323	STS	Darlaston
1861	1904	1850	1910	169323	STS	Wednesbury
1794	1992	1750	1900	157597	SXE	Wadhurst
1800	1891	1760	1800	128333	YKS	Giggleswick
BALDWIN contd.						
1765	1845	1760	1850	155969	YKS	Halifax
1853	1900	1841	1853	165026	YKS	Weardley
....	....	1800	....	146668	???	London
BALDWINSON						
....	....	ALL	ALL	113115	ALL	Name Study
BALDWYN						
1265	1992	ALL	1265	103357	GLS	???
1794	1822	1700	1850	138193	HEF	Upton Bishop
1265	1992	ALL	1265	103357	WOR	Ashton Under Hill
1850	....	....	....	105996	WOR	Ashton Upon Hill
BALDY						
1772	?	?	?	166642	SSX	???
BALE						
1850	1992	1700	1850	174041	DEV	Barnstaple
1802	1838	....	....	103373	DEV	Braughton
?	?	1800	1870	157023	DEV	Sidmouth
1850	1931	1800	1850	113352	ESS	Latchingdon
1550	1650	1650	1850	142913	LEI	Carlton Curlieu
1779	1911	1700	1779	178926	LEI	Hisbands Bosworth
1779	1911	1700	1779	178926	LEI	Willoughby Waterless
....	....	ALL	ALL	143340	LEI	???
1800	1959	1750	1900	154881	LND	ALL
1700	1800	1600	1800	154342	SOM	Porlock
1823	1857	ALL	1823	114987	SOM	Staple Fitzpaine
1837	1992	1800	1837	103365	SRY	Camberwell
BALES						
1853	1902	1700	1853	124907	HRT	Hemel Hempstead
1860	1880	1750	1860	146285	SSX	Framfield
1840	1940	1800	1840	167568	YKS	Castleton
BALEY						
....	....	1720	1780	145211	WRY	Stainburn
BALFOUR						
1805	1992	ALL	1805	115355	ANS	Montrose
1400	1992	....	....	100536	SCT	???
BALFOUR-OGILVY						
1400	1992	....	....	100536	SCT	???
BALHATCHET						
....	....	ALL	ALL	168637	ALL	ALL
1709	1799	1600	1992	168637	CON	Stratton
BALK						
1737	1877	1600	1737	120278	EYK	Skirlaugh
BALKHAM						
1763	1868	....	....	177601	SSX	Hastings
BALKWILL						
1550	1992	1700	....	103381	DEV	North
1550	1992	1700	....	103381	DEV	South
1813	1870	ALL	1830	107816	DEV	Hatherleigh
BALL						
....	....	ALL	ALL	144959	ALL	Name Study
....	....	1880	1960	159220	ALL	ALL
1820	....	....	....	152099	ABD	Aberdeen
1801	1863	ALL	1863	108642	BDF	Odell
....	1890	1850	1900	128961	BKM	High Wycombe
1861	1890	1600	1992	170518	BRK	Faringdon
1796	1800	1700	1800	137901	CHS	Stockport
1800	1900	1800	1900	171077	CON	St Breock
1677	1954	ALL	ALL	171301	CON	St Columb
1863	1970	1700	1863	103411	CON	St Mawgan
1851	1871	1700	1900	177873	CON	???
....	?	?	?	127442	DBY	???
....	1730	ALL	ALL	129933	DEV	Holne
1770	1980	ALL	1770	103438	DEV	Mary Tavy
1745	1790	1700	1800	171549	DEV	West Putford
1913	1992	1850	1992	159220	GLS	Dursley
....	....	1800	1840	148113	GLS	Olveston
1900	1910	1880	1910	159220	GLS	Tetbury
1913	1992	1700	1913	105163	GLS	Uley
1800	1850	1500	1850	175463	HAM	ALL
1825	1901	?	1825	113360	HAM	Longparish
1820	1850	1820	....	135895	HAM	Portsmouth
1880	1924	....	....	133922	HAM	Twyford
1900	1992	1800	1900	108618	LAN	Everton Brow
1779	1806	1750	1779	163783	LAN	Kirkham
1750	1770	1600	1992	167592	LAN	Liverpool
1779	1806	1750	1779	163783	LAN	Ormskirk
1700	1940	1550	1700	173169	LEI	North West
1776	1776	1600	1992	110787	LEI	Gilmorton
1832	1992	1700	1832	119261	LEI	Wigston
1852	1852	....	1900	171646	LND	South
....	....	ALL	ALL	118400	LND	Islington
1851	1924	....	....	133922	LND	Kensington
1700	1820	1700	1820	167924	MDX	Ealing

Known From	To	Researching From	To	Ref	Cty	Place
BALL contd.						
1801	1863	ALL	1863	108642	MDX	London
1760	?	1600	1992	167592	MDX	London
....	?	?	?	127442	NTT	Normanton
1751	....	1700	1800	143693	OXF	Crowell
1843	....	....	....	152099	ROX	Melrose
1812	....	ALL	1812	131725	SAL	Dawley Magna
1855	1855	1800	1855	121568	SOM	Ashwick
1803	?	ALL	ALL	153516	SOM	Congresbury
1818	1890	1818	1890	103403	SOM	Dunster
1803	?	ALL	ALL	153516	SOM	Hewish
1851	1924	1851	1870	133922	SOM	Kilmington
1500	1820	1500	1820	103403	SOM	Piminster
1700	1720	1650	1700	156140	SSX	Hastings
1770	1850	1750	1850	146803	SSX	Rogate
....	....	ALL	1875	173177	STS	Rugeley
1809	....	ALL	1809	131725	STS	Wolverhampton
1851	1992	1700	1851	174297	WAR	Birmingham
....	....	1780	1820	117137	WIL	Warminster
....	1630	ALL	ALL	127809	WIL	???
....	....	1700	1820	147613	YKS	Darton
....	....	1800	1840	147613	YKS	Hemsworth
....	....	1740	1780	147613	YKS	High Hoyland
....	....	ALL	ALL	103454	???	???
BALLAM						
1881	1925	....	1881	103470	MDX	St George
BALLANCE						
1831	....	ALL	ALL	103837	YKS	East
BALLANTINE						
1778	1850	1700	1860	171662	MLN	Edinburgh
1850	1870	1750	1900	100501	PER	Perth
1750	1770	1700	1800	138878	SCT	ALL
1820	1900	1820	1900	177814	SCT	Hamilton
1850	1870	1750	1992	100501	???	Dalkeith
1850	1870	1750	1992	100501	???	Haddington
BALLANTYNE						
1764	1880	1760	1942	171654	AYR	Kirkoswald
1865	1925	1925	1992	146560	LKS	Coatbride
1734	1992	1400	1992	148482	OKI	Evie
....	....	1500	1750	103497	ROX	ALL
1750	1880	ALL	1992	119105	ROX	Castleton
....	....	1500	1750	103497	SEL	ALL
BALLARD						
....	....	ALL	ALL	103500	ALL	Name Study
1900	1992	1800	1900	113514	EYK	Hull
1825	1851	1820	1855	106321	GLA	Llantwit Major
1855	1935	1840	1922	106321	GLA	Merthyr Tydfil
1760	1760	1710	1800	105333	HAM	Isle Of Wight
1780	1992	1780	1992	131156	HAM	Lyndhurst
....	....	1700	1850	110914	HAM	Portsea
1800	1992	1700	1992	165557	HAM	Portsmouth
....	....	1600	....	154377	HUN	ALL
1830	1880	1700	1900	129755	KEN	Dover
1907	1992	1800	1992	117293	KEN	Gravesend
1679	1880	1544	1679	103500	KEN	Tenterden
1850	1900	1800	1850	172898	LND	Chelsea
1881	1992	ALL	1881	141704	SRY	Croydon
1880	1992	....	....	103500	SSX	Hastings
1593	1761	1580	1761	127604	WAR	Ansty
1700	....	1600	1992	151475	WOR	Central
1700	1865	....	....	151475	WOR	Eckington
1700	1865	....	....	151475	WOR	Fladbury
1700	1865	....	....	151475	WOR	Netherton
BALLEINE						
1500	1992	....	....	119105	JSY	ALL
BALLETT						
1860	1920	1837	1860	120731	DOR	Poole
BALLINGALL						
1831	1831	1821	1880	126918	LND	South
1831	1831	1821	1880	126918	LND	City
BALLINGER						
1880	1961	ALL	1880	103489	GAL	Gort
1726	1800	1600	1725	108413	GLS	Chedworth
1885	1942	ALL	ALL	151408	LND	Willesden
1884	....	1860	1884	102989	MDX	Pancras
1813	1885	ALL	ALL	151408	WOR	Dormston
1813	1885	ALL	ALL	151408	WOR	Evesham
BALLS						
1839	....	1800	1850	103934	DBY	Bakewell
1770	1870	1680	1800	169137	ESS	Wormingford
....	....	1850	1900	118834	LND	???
1826	1869	1700	1826	153109	NFK	Norwich
....	....	?	1825	103934	NFK	???
1737	1810	ALL	1737	168602	SFK	Middleton
BALLS contd.						
1748	....	....	1748	133566	SFK	Redisham
1737	1810	ALL	1737	168602	SFK	Theberton
1846	....	1845	1860	103934	YKS	Hull
BALLUER						
1801	1820	1801	1992	105147	SAL	Myddle
BALM						
....	....	ALL	ALL	103519	ALL	Name Study
1745	1784	1600	1744	131245	LEI	Countesthorpe
BALME						
1790	1860	1790	1860	133450	YKS	Halifax
BALMENT						
1822	1992	1600	1822	103551	DEV	Barnstaple
BALMER						
1810	?	1700	1992	167592	FLN	Buckley
1800	1900	ALL	1800	126322	FLN	Mold
1807	1865	1500	1807	125695	HUN	???
1870	1900	1800	1992	126322	LAN	Manchester
1800	1992	1700	1992	177652	LEI	Waltham
1788	....	1700	1788	101443	NRY	Loftus
BALMFORD						
1808	1831	1804	1833	126276	WRY	Salithwaite
BALMFORTH						
1871	1920	1800	1871	109509	LAN	Ashton Under Lyne
1900	1960	1700	1900	158976	LND	Strand
1770	1800	1700	1770	121339	NYK	Whitby
1818	1992	ALL	1818	111384	WYK	Halifax
1871	1920	ALL	1890	109509	WYK	Holmfirth
1818	1992	ALL	1818	111384	WYK	Leeds
BALMONT						
1851	1940	1700	1851	165581	SOM	Bristol
BALORT						
1820	1820	1770	1820	155276	SFK	Walton
BALSDON						
1830	1874	....	....	138134	SOM	Bristol
1887	1926	1800	1887	174955	SSX	Aldrington
BALSHAW						
1870	1900	1800	1870	105198	LAN	Ormskirk
BALZEBY						
....	....	1750	1850	129127	NFK	Norwich
....	....	1698	1850	129127	SFK	Ipwsich
BAMBER						
1790	1992	1650	1992	103535	LAN	Brockholes
1790	1992	1650	1992	103535	LAN	Chipping
1850	1907	ALL	1850	147222	LAN	Liverpool
1790	1992	1650	1992	103535	LAN	Longridge
1790	1992	1650	1992	103535	LAN	Whittingham
1790	1992	1650	1992	103535	LAN	Wyresdale
1800	1820	1750	1850	100129	LIN	Helpingham
1565	1980	....	....	103527	LIN	???
BAMBROUGH						
1851	1992	ALL	ALL	103543	HAM	Southampton
1825	....	ALL	ALL	103543	NBL	Newcastle
BAMBURGH						
1450	1500	1350	1450	154881	KEN	Paddlesworth
BAMENT						
1822	1992	1600	1822	103551	DEV	Barnstaple
BAMFIELD						
1786	1874	1770	1880	177016	LIN	Grantham
1814	....	1800	1900	177016	LND	Camberwell
1814	....	1800	1900	177016	LND	St Giles
1841	1894	1840	1900	177016	MDX	London
BAMFORD						
1868	1900	1800	1900	129178	CWD	Wrexham
1719	1857	....	1774	101761	LAN	Middleton
1730	1871	ALL	ALL	120669	LAN	Pilkington
1730	1871	ALL	ALL	120669	LAN	Radcliffe
1800	1900	1800	1900	110523	LAN	Rochdale
1795	1883	....	1723	134902	NTH	Harrington
1750	1880	1750	1880	130567	NTH	Scaldwell
1690	1712	1600	1712	148288	NTT	Stapleford
BAMFORTH						
1800	1850	1600	1800	113654	WAR	Birmingham
1850	1992	1600	1992	120677	WYK	Lingards
1802	1992	1770	1992	147311	WYK	Slaithwaite
BAMLETT						
1700	1900	1625	1900	110884	DUR	???
BAMPKIN						
1750	1992	ALL	ALL	103578	ALL	ALL
BAN DER BEN						
....	....	1851	1992	126241	DUR	Gateshead
....	....	1851	1992	126241	LND	Marylebone
BANBERY						
....	....	1800	1899	179612	DEV	Sampford Courtenay

Known From	To	Researching From	To	Ref	Cty	Place
BANBROOK						
1716	1861	1500	1716	126918	ESS	ALL
....	1861	1500	1716	126918	LND	Clerkenwell
BANBURY						
1771	1865	....	....	115606	BRK	Bray
BANCE						
1700	1900	....	....	163511	BRK	Newbury
1800	1900	1800	1900	163511	HAM	Southampton
BANCROFT						
1780	1900	1700	1850	124788	DBY	Bradwell
1750	1920	1700	1900	145866	DBY	Sinfin
1861	1881	1800	1840	106968	LAN	Salford
....	....	ALL	1860	145548	LEI	Belton
....	1750	1500	1860	175072	LIN	ALL
....	....	1677	1810	177725	LIN	Skidbrook
1810	1870	....	....	177725	LIN	Theddlesthorpe
BAND						
1623	1960	1623	1960	103586	ALL	ALL
1866	....	1866	1936	103586	HAM	Gosport
BANES						
1550	1827	1550	1827	102830	STS	Kingswinford
BANFIELD						
1750	1800	1600	1800	124761	DEV	North West
1800	1900	1800	1900	124761	NFK	Gt Yarmouth
BANFORD						
....	....	ALL	ALL	100153	MON	???
BANG						
....	....	....	....	103608	ALL	ALL
BANGAY						
....	....	ALL	ALL	103594	ALL	Name Study
BANGER						
1746	1746	1733	1746	107573	WIL	Hindon
BANGHAM						
1750	1992	....	1750	117110	KEN	Canterbury
BANGS						
....	....	ALL	ALL	103608	ALL	Name Study
1500	1983	1500	1983	103608	ALL	ALL
1870	1950	1870	1950	135925	LND	Holloway
1800	1900	1750	1992	148784	MDX	St Pancras
1712	1853	1640	1860	135941	SFK	Lakenheath
BANHAM						
....	....	ALL	ALL	150207	ALL	Name Study
1817	1881	1750	1850	175722	NFK	???
1817	1881	1750	1850	175722	SFK	???
BANIARD						
1750	1800	1600	1750	102288	SFK	Bealings
BANISTER						
1760	1970	1760	1970	103616	ESS	Fryerning
BANKIN						
1750	1992	ALL	ALL	103578	ALL	ALL
BANKS						
....	....	ALL	ALL	157449	ALL	Name Study
1772	....	....	1772	146935	CHS	???
1850	1960	ALL	ALL	162469	CUL	North
1851	....	?	1860	164976	DBY	Stanton By Dale
1640	1680	1640	1700	117145	DBY	Tideswell
1920	1992	1700	1920	103640	ESS	Stratford
....	....	1700	1992	125857	GLS	ALL
1841	1861	1861	1920	142042	GLS	Stroud
1831	1879	1700	1831	173797	HAM	Lymington
1714	1850	1650	1750	141283	IOM	Douglas
1712	1992	1640	1840	117145	LAN	Bolton
1859	1992	1750	1850	125350	LAN	Haslingdon
1802	1854	....	....	103624	LAN	Manchester
1712	1992	1640	1840	117145	LAN	Manchester
1846	1897	1897	1992	117099	LAN	Manchester
1771	1847	1700	1847	141062	LAN	Pendleton
1550	1802	....	....	103624	LAN	Ulverstone
1825	1880	1700	1900	144037	LAN	Warrington
1805	1810	1700	1800	107344	LIN	Bourne
1818	....	1750	1850	141739	LKS	Glasgow
1869	1920	1868	1923	100951	LND	North
1850	1992	1700	1850	157449	LND	Battersea
1920	1992	1700	1920	103640	LND	Brixton
1850	1992	1700	1850	157449	LND	Marylebone
1890	1890	....	....	103632	MDX	Chiswick
1920	1992	1700	1920	103640	MDX	Islington
1857	1857	....	....	103632	MDX	Islington
1854	1989	....	....	103624	NBL	Tynemouth
1740	1893	1700	1893	103632	NTH	Northampton
1770	1822	ALL	1770	164364	NTT	Gringley On The Hill
1850	1910	....	....	177776	NYK	Bossall
1820	1850	....	....	177776	NYK	Husthwait
BANKS contd.						
1780	1820	1700	1780	177776	NYK	Pickhill
1840	1850	1841	1861	100951	SOM	Bath
1830	1955	1830	1981	100951	SOM	Bristol
?	1851	1750	1851	165220	SSX	Lewes
....	....	1800	1992	125857	STS	ALL
....	....	1800	1992	125857	WAR	ALL
1821	1846	1846	1992	117099	WAR	Birmingham
....	....	1700	1992	125857	WIL	ALL
1700	1800	1650	1750	142042	WIL	Berwick Bassett
1800	1860	1700	1800	142042	WIL	Bremhill
1600	1800	1600	1992	100951	WIL	Castle Coombe
1819	1819	1780	1820	142042	WIL	Yatton Keynell
1800	1965	1800	1930	123145	WMD	Birmingham
1871	1992	1855	1871	164364	YKS	Sheffield
BANN						
1760	1800	1700	1760	155500	CHS	Prestbury
BANNAN						
1857	1920	ALL	ALL	157864	SCT	ALL
BANNATYNE						
1827	1849	....	....	127140	LKS	Glasgow
1750	1800	....	....	127140	LKS	New Lanark
BANNELL						
1664	1992	ALL	1664	107239	NFK	Grimstow
BANNER						
1723	1850	1841	1900	130192	KEN	Stockbury
....	....	1790	1992	170402	WOR	Bromsgove
BANNERMAN						
1835	1835	1750	1900	112089	IRL	Belfast
BANNING						
ALL	ALL	ALL	ALL	125482	ALL	ALL
1827	1874	....	....	122955	LAN	Liverpool
....	....	1066	1827	122955	LAN	Ribble Valley
1839	1860	1750	1850	137421	OXF	Burford
1770	1900	1500	1770	174661	WIL	ALL
BANNISTER						
1730	1820	1650	1830	174599	IOW	Godshill
1791	1812	1500	1791	117234	LAN	Trawden
1830	1900	1800	1830	125350	LAN	Warton
1790	1960	1725	1790	105503	LIN	Willoughton
1880	1930	1850	1930	166154	LND	Tooting
1790	1830	1790	1850	174599	MDX	Marylebone
BANNOCK						
1832	1949	1700	1832	165867	LND	Rotherhythe
BANNOCKS						
1825	1992	1825	1992	156973	GLS	Gloucester
1825	1992	1825	1992	156973	LND	???
BANNON						
1820	1854	1800	1911	121746	TIP	Ballycahill
BANSBACH						
....	....	....	1850	131962	LND	Stepney
BANT						
1750	1840	1800	1840	159247	WAR	Coventry
BANTAN						
....	....	1800	1900	147613	LAN	Tatham
....	....	1800	1900	147613	YKS	Bentham
BANTCOCK						
1773	1867	1600	1773	154288	SFK	Combs
BANTICK						
1849	....	1800	1849	128724	SFK	Ixworth
BANTIN						
1837	1837	1750	1837	117633	LND	Bermondsey
BANTING						
1800	1992	1600	1800	103667	HAM	Andover
1800	1992	1600	1800	103667	HAM	Hambledon
1830	1992	ALL	ALL	110388	HAM	Newtown
BANTON						
1863	1900	1860	1900	140295	SOM	Bridgwater
BANWELL						
....	....	ALL	ALL	103675	ALL	Name Study
ALL	ALL	ALL	ALL	103675	ALL	ALL
1900	1992	1500	1800	143154	OXF	Adderbury
1800	1992	1500	1800	143154	OXF	Chastleton
1800	1992	1500	1800	143154	OXF	Little Tew
BANYARD						
1839	1992	....	....	103683	LND	Bow
1839	1992	....	....	103683	NFK	Great Yarmouth
....	....	1600	1880	129763	NFK	Uppwell
BANYER						
1871	1992	1750	1871	103691	NFK	Bacton
BARACLOUGH						
1900	1992	ALL	1900	102407	WYK	Bradford
1900	1992	ALL	1900	102407	WYK	Shipley
1822	1822	1800	1840	141097	YKS	Adwick Le Street

Known From	To	Researching From	To	Ref	Cty	Place
BARAGWANNAH						
1670	1691	1600	1670	102571	CON	Ludgvan
BARAN						
1890	1992	1890	1992	128619	LAN	Liverpool
BARBER						
1819	1922	1750	1850	103756	ANT	Glenwhirry
....	....	1800	1950	103713	CAM	Ashley
1899	1968	1850	1899	161861	CAM	Manae
1665	1940	....	....	128996	CAM	Thorney
1720	1755	1560	1800	103764	CHS	Adlington
1850	1900	ALL	1850	107719	DEV	Exeter
1800	1980	?	1850	127833	ESS	West
1796	1846	ALL	ALL	155373	ESS	Burnham On Crouch
1805	1830	1750	1805	121339	ESS	Romford
1720	1730	1650	1750	136840	HAM	Hamble
1822	....	ALL	ALL	151327	HEF	???
....	....	1750	1850	126144	HRT	???
1820	1880	1820	1880	126144	KEN	West
1750	1775	1700	1850	103764	LAN	Didsbury
1700	1992	....	....	157805	LAN	Prescott
1775	1920	1700	1920	103764	LAN	Withington
1835	1877	1700	1877	165476	LND	Bethnal Green
1684	1902	1600	1806	163562	LND	City
1824	1845	1800	1824	177490	LND	Whitechapel
....	....	ALL	1878	169943	MDX	Shoreditch
1813	1992	1750	1900	148660	NFK	East
1740	1792	1700	1837	118362	NFK	East Ruston
....	....	1720	1750	103713	NFK	Hevingham
1835	....	ALL	ALL	107425	NFK	Norwich
1805	1926	1700	1805	170542	NFK	Woodton
1698	1698	ALL	1698	115126	NTH	Kingsthorpe
1700	1742	1675	1700	147311	NYK	Seamer
ALL	ALL	ALL	ALL	174793	SCT	Edinburgh
....	....	1600	1850	127833	SFK	South
1886	1954	1800	1900	123811	SFK	Ipswich
1800	....	1807	1858	164232	SFK	Theberton
....	....	1750	1780	103713	SFK	Wickhambrook
1850	....	1850	1950	101656	SLI	Coola
1900	1930	1800	1900	149128	SRY	London
1750	1851	1600	1820	157716	YKS	Holmfirth
1586	1676	1550	1670	170348	YKS	Kirkburton
1850	1940	ALL	1900	142301	YKS	Leeds
BARBERO						
1920	1980	ALL	1920	179027	GLA	Penarth
BARBOUR						
1803	1900	1700	1803	143812	RFW	Lochwinnoch
BARCHARD						
....	....	ALL	ALL	100781	ALL	Name Study
BARCLAY						
1826	1992	1600	1826	146137	ABD	East
1842	1917	1700	1842	169676	ELN	Preston Pans
1841	....	ALL	ALL	147621	FLN	Mold
....	....	1900	1992	167177	HAM	Portsmouth
1815	1915	1700	1992	167177	MLN	Edinburgh
1833	1840	1813	1840	151106	MOR	Bellie
1840	1870	1750	1900	100501	PER	Kinkell
BARDEN						
....	....	?	?	110507	KEN	Lenham
1900	....	1600	1800	165476	SSX	Hastings
1773	1773	1700	1800	117331	SSX	Withyham
1690	1992	....	....	168521	YKS	Huddersfield
BARDGETT						
1544	1992	1544	1992	129038	ALL	ALL
BARDILL						
1825	1850	1750	1825	172901	DBY	???
BARDLEY						
....	....	1800	....	128627	CAM	Soham
BARDSLEY						
....	....	ALL	ALL	103780	ALL	Name Study
ALL	ALL	ALL	ALL	103780	ALL	ALL
1800	1992	....	1800	102059	LAN	Denton
1870	1880	1870	1900	115932	LAN	Oldham
1865	....	?	1870	164976	LAN	Oldham
BARDWELL						
1800	....	....	....	126543	SFK	Charsfield
1800	....	....	....	126543	SFK	Wickham Market
BAREFOOT						
1700	1800	1600	1800	177180	BKM	Hardwick
1734	1738	ALL	ALL	132004	CAM	Horningsea
1760	1992	....	....	132004	CAM	Swaffham Bulbeck
BAREHAM						
1840	1880	1800	1900	135283	ESS	Ridgewell
BARFF						
1585	1955	?	?	104329	YKS	???
BARFOOT						
1789	1819	1760	1820	119059	BKM	Brill
1800	....	ALL	ALL	138533	DBY	Ticknall
1802	1838	1750	1802	173770	HAM	South
1729	1980	1650	1750	169234	HAM	Botley
....	1760	ALL	1760	134511	LEI	Husband Bosworth
BARFOOTE						
1600	1700	....	....	100420	WAR	Meriden
BARFORD						
1812	....	1500	1812	145718	BDF	Eversholt
1820	1848	1500	1820	145718	BDF	Luton
1848	1874	1700	1874	145718	BRK	Cookham
1822	....	1700	1900	145718	BRK	Maidenhead
1830	1840	ALL	1840	158437	BRK	Maidenhead
1859	1859	1800	1900	145718	SRY	Egham
1876	1876	1800	1950	145718	WAR	Birmingham
1600	1700	....	....	100420	WAR	Meriden
BARGE						
1885	1933	1800	1933	149519	BKM	Quainton
BARGENT						
....	....	ALL	ALL	156442	HAM	Portsmouth
BARGER						
1750	1800	1700	1900	103578	PEM	Angle
BARGH						
....	....	1750	1800	148113	DBY	Dronfield
1446	1968	?	?	104329	YKS	???
BARHAM						
1778	1881	....	....	144282	KEN	Northfleet
1880	1950	1800	1980	135283	LND	Marylebone
1840	1860	1800	1900	135283	NFK	Norwich
1799	1964	1665	1799	122815	SFK	Middleton
1727	1964	1665	1727	122815	SFK	Sibton
BARJEW						
1600	1800	1600	1800	131962	WIL	South
BARK						
....	....	ALL	ALL	103802	SOM	Leamington
....	....	ALL	ALL	103799	WIL	Great Knutsford
1539	1884	?	?	104329	YKS	???
BARKBY						
1771	1992	1600	1771	170747	LEI	Whitwich
BARKER						
1865	....	1860	1900	142638	BRK	Sunningdale
1865	....	1860	1900	142638	BRK	Winkfield
1690	1810	1600	1690	176311	BRK	Wokingham
1748	1777	....	1800	137405	CAM	Harston South
1828	?	1750	1841	168033	CHS	Astbury
1800	1850	1700	1800	114472	CHS	Bollington
1840	1960	1800	1880	107476	CHS	Nantwich
1703	1757	....	....	138851	CHS	Wearverham
1800	1992	ALL	1800	158437	DBY	Bakewell
1790	1925	1700	1950	169889	DBY	Derby
1816	1992	1700	1816	117447	DBY	Glossop
1707	1887	1650	1707	103004	DBY	Winster
1707	1855	1700	1860	163635	DBY	Winster
1903	1992	1700	1903	172316	ENG	ALL
1800	1840	1750	1800	166316	ESS	Navestock
1814	1887	ALL	ALL	162108	ESS	Purleigh
1781	1879	ALL	ALL	162108	HRT	ALL
1753	1992	1600	1753	103853	HRT	Graveley
1871	1961	1780	1871	103853	HRT	Hitchin
1854	1992	ALL	ALL	115762	HRT	Wheathampstead
1940	1950	1850	1940	101907	KEN	Chatham
1830	1860	1830	1880	166383	KEN	Deptford
1780	1920	1780	1920	130400	KEN	Loose
1850	1930	1750	1850	137782	LAN	Wigan
....	1992	....	....	149675	LEI	Knighton
1790	1818	1700	1790	162396	LIN	Central
1930	1992	1700	1930	171913	LIN	Lincoln
1835	1992	....	....	103810	LND	East
1903	1992	1700	1900	172316	LND	Bethnal Green
1869	1992	1800	1900	149012	LND	Fulham
1832	1992	1800	....	169250	LND	Shoreditch
1832	1992	1800	....	169250	LND	Southwark
1810	1903	1700	1900	166960	MDX	London
1778	1844	1700	1778	100447	MDX	Stepney
1859	....	....	....	121835	NFK	Kings Lynn
1840	1880	1750	1830	159115	NFK	Norwich
1802	....	....	....	121835	NFK	Snettisham
1700	1820	ALL	1700	135143	NFK	Sutton
1836	....	....	....	121835	NFK	Swaffham
1918	1973	ALL	ALL	118885	NRY	Middlesborough
1700	1765	1700	1900	168327	NTH	Lowick
....	1992	....	....	149675	NTH	???
1852	....	1700	1852	110108	NTT	Hucknall

Known		Researching				
From	To	From	To	Ref	Cty	Place
BARKER contd.						
....	....	1800	1852	178411	NTT	Nottingham
1785	....	ALL	ALL	105481	NTT	Radford
1800	1900	1600	1800	137162	NTT	???
1763	1940	1650	1750	125458	NYK	Stokesley
1763	1940	1650	1750	125458	NYK	Thirsk
1719	1903	....	....	117404	SAL	Much Wenlock
1822	....	ALL	ALL	112275	SAL	Worford
1860	1900	1780	1860	129895	SFK	Kettleburgh
1820	1880	1750	1820	164860	SFK	Otley
1806	1848	1700	1805	119164	SFK	Tannington
1796	1833	1700	1893	163953	SFK	Tuddenham
....	....	1750	1850	174114	SFK	???
1860	1865	1800	1860	177393	SRY	Reigate
1830	1930	1800	1890	124648	SRY	Southwark
1840	1880	1750	1830	159115	SRY	Walworth
1619	1981	1500	1619	110639	STS	Fenton
1862	1992	1500	1862	136107	STS	Five Towns
1619	1981	1500	1619	110639	STS	Longton
1621	1746	1550	1730	102830	STS	Sedgely
1871	1960	....	....	137499	STS	Stafford
1841	1860	1700	1840	137499	STS	Tean
1700	1740	1675	1992	114901	YKS	Barwick Elmet
1761	1796	1650	1850	137561	YKS	Barwick In Elmet
1803	1883	1700	1803	160024	YKS	Clayton
1772	....	....	....	151351	YKS	Coverham
....	....	1700	1885	121452	YKS	Haddlesey
1849	1872	....	....	169013	YKS	Halifax
1800	1992	ALL	ALL	103837	YKS	Hull
1900	1920	1750	1900	103845	YKS	Scarborough
....	....	ALL	1810	171794	YKS	Sowerby
1853	1898	1600	1930	172863	YKS	York
BARKLE						
1700	1850	1600	1850	143766	CON	Gwinear
BARKLEY						
1851	....	....	....	100676	LND	East
1852	1921	1750	1852	154539	LND	City
1822	1907	1700	1822	170747	SAL	???
BARKS						
1800	1850	1700	1800	162396	LIN	South
1770	1785	1700	1770	120529	NTT	Collingham
BARKSHIRE						
1750	1900	1600	1900	160946	SSX	Petworth
BARKUS						
1766	1826	ALL	1766	113689	DUR	Whickham
BARLEY						
....	....	ALL	ALL	103861	ALL	Name Study
....	....	1850	1920	103713	BDF	Bedford
....	....	1820	1850	103713	BDF	Biggleswade
1830	1900	1700	1840	106267	SFK	Central
1796	1850	....	....	169528	YKS	Thorne
BARLING						
1800	1940	1800	1940	154466	KEN	Sheerness
1640	1770	....	....	154873	KEN	Sittingbourne
....	....	1200	1610	154873	KEN	Weald
BARLINGHAM						
1300	1350	1200	1300	154881	ALL	ALL
BARLOW						
1763	1821	1763	1821	103977	BRK	Aldworth
1763	1821	1763	1821	103977	BRK	Basildon
1821	1870	1821	1870	103977	BRK	Reading
1763	1821	1763	1821	103977	BRK	Streatley
1824	1992	....	1824	178365	BRK	Sutton Courtenay
....	....	1800	ALL	164615	CHS	Hyde
1768	1786	....	....	138851	CHS	Lower Peover
1814	1841	ALL	1814	171476	CHS	Northwich
1849	....	?	1850	164976	DBY	Derby
1813	....	1780	1870	119970	DUB	Raheny
ALL	....	....	....	151416	HAM	Southampton
1800	1950	1800	1950	141410	HUN	Peterborough
1667	1980	1600	1980	141410	HUN	Somersham
1811	1835	1700	1850	168815	LAN	ALL
1750	1850	1700	1750	132268	LAN	Bolton
1850	1871	1800	1871	165824	LAN	Bolton
1870	1910	1800	1870	106968	LAN	Bury
1800	1900	1700	1800	129534	LAN	Bury
1771	1861	1740	1890	129313	LAN	Droylsden
....	....	1800	1885	160393	LAN	Eccles
1735	1992	1600	1735	160962	LAN	Eccles
1750	1850	1700	1750	132268	LAN	Farnworth
1735	1760	1735	1760	140724	LAN	Gorton
1850	1910	1750	1850	132632	LAN	Heywood
1784	1813	1745	1841	174211	LAN	Little Heaton
1802	1824	?	1802	128910	LAN	Pilsworth
BARLOW contd.						
1735	1760	1735	1760	140724	LAN	Reddish
1764	1765	1700	1800	159964	LAN	Ringley
1885	1992	1800	1885	160393	LAN	Salford
1850	1910	1750	1850	132632	LAN	Shaw
1758	1899	1900	1992	162256	LAN	Tottington
1784	1813	1745	1841	174211	LAN	Unsworth
1735	1992	1600	1735	160962	LAN	Warrington
1666	1728	1550	1675	118958	LAN	???
1826	....	1800	1840	164976	LEI	Loughborough
1850	1940	1850	1940	138193	MDX	Harlington
ALL	....	....	....	151416	SSX	Brighton
1865	1960	1600	1950	156825	STS	Birmingham
1803	1836	....	....	102733	STS	Brewood
1868	1980	1600	1950	156825	STS	Tamworth
1789	1812	....	1789	163031	SYK	Wickersley
1865	1960	1600	1950	156825	WAR	Birmingham
1600	1700	....	....	146854	WES	Orton
1865	1960	1600	1950	156825	WOR	Birmingham
BARLTROP						
1650	1992	1500	1800	103888	ESS	???
BARMS						
1655	....	....	1655	160873	STS	South
BARNACLE						
....	....	ALL	ALL	165069	LEI	Leicester
BARNACOTT						
1750	1800	1750	1890	110523	CON	Manaccan
BARNARD						
1804	....	1800	1850	119970	BKM	Finmere
1814	....	1800	1850	119970	BKM	Water Stratford
1807	1807	1770	1850	125032	BRK	Aldermaston
....	....	....	1704	137405	CAM	Great Eversden
1654	1710	....	....	165999	ESS	Great Waltham
1900	1970	1900	1970	118842	ESS	Ilford
1864	1895	ALL	ALL	120057	ESS	Mile End
1800	....	1800	1850	119970	GLS	Childs Wickham
1632	1672	1557	1847	142859	GLS	Frampton On Severn
1730	1810	ALL	ALL	103896	HRT	Sawbridgeworth
1837	1992	1837	1992	126217	KEN	Sheerness
1833	1870	....	....	172812	KEN	Sheerness
1815	1817	1800	1850	118842	LND	North
1816	1830	1790	1816	118842	LND	City
1818	1955	1750	1900	118842	MDX	ALL
1870	....	1870	1900	118842	MDX	Camberwell
1812	1919	1650	1992	123552	MDX	London
1856	1856	1800	1870	160903	MDX	Marylebone
1818	1879	1780	1920	118842	MDX	Shoreditch
1861	....	ALL	1861	120057	MDX	St George
1844	....	1844	1880	118842	MDX	Stepney
1809	....	1800	1850	119970	MGY	Darowen
1812	1919	1650	1992	123552	NFK	Attleborough
1800	1900	ALL	ALL	126721	NTT	Radcliffe
1800	1900	1700	1850	116823	NYK	Fylingdales
1850	1992	1850	1920	111562	OXF	Oxford
ALL	ALL	ALL	ALL	114502	SOM	ALL
BARNARDIER						
1700	1850	1700	1850	155195	LND	Bethnal Green
BARNBY						
1900	1920	1850	1900	114251	ALL	ALL
BARNDEN						
....	1660	....	....	103144	SSX	East
BARNELL						
....	....	ALL	ALL	119814	ALL	Name Study
BARNERDSHIL						
1207	1330	1329	1480	104027	RUT	Barnsdale
BARNES						
1780	1840	1780	1860	119059	BDF	Leighton Buzzard
1806	1860	1780	1806	119059	BKM	Brill
1814	1871	1750	1850	176451	CHS	Stockport
1812	1834	1700	1812	152196	CMA	Harris Park
1811	1940	ALL	ALL	121398	CON	Paul
1850	1900	1800	1875	166901	CON	Phillack
1850	1960	ALL	ALL	162469	CUL	North
1818	1857	....	1857	103349	CUL	Bolton
1827	1836	1810	1844	169552	CUL	Brampton
1841	1881	1790	1882	169552	CUL	Farlam
1797	1992	1700	1797	130141	DBY	Eyam
1812	....	1812	1900	149578	DEV	Brixham
1859	1960	1600	1859	162671	DEV	East Allington
....	....	1883	....	174963	DEV	Plymouth
1801	1850	1700	1992	167460	DEV	Torquay
1859	1960	1600	1859	162671	DEV	West Allington
1810	1900	....	....	122106	DOR	Portland
1791	1992	1770	1992	103993	DOR	Shaftesbury

BARNES contd.

Known From	To	Researching From	To	Ref	Cty	Place
1745	1775	1720	1820	105333	DOR	Wimborne Minster
1800	1860	1750	1900	138517	DUB	Dublin
1820	1860	1820	1880	105376	DUR	Barnard Castle
1750	1840	ALL	1840	105376	DUR	City
1840	1860	1800	1840	103985	ESS	Tendring
1830	1980	1830	1930	119474	ESS	Wickham St Paul
1770	1860	1600	1800	158542	HAM	Brockenhurst
....	....	?	1778	103934	HAM	Crondall
1800	1820	1770	1860	124974	HAM	Kingsclere
1745	1800	1720	1820	105333	HAM	Ringwood
1786	1828	....	....	127779	HAM	Ringwood
1800	1900	1800	1992	158542	HAM	South Stoneham
1845	1992	1700	1845	103950	HAM	Southampton
1930	1992	ALL	ALL	103543	HAM	Southampton
1890	1930	1820	1890	103985	HAM	Southampton
1851	....	?	1860	103934	HRT	Thundridge
1730	1804	1500	1730	129577	IOW	???
1840	1870	1870	1992	160458	IRL	Navan
1835	1845	1835	1845	103934	KEN	Bromley
1777	1830	1700	1777	145971	KEN	Hothfield
1860	1900	....	....	151572	KEN	Sevenoaks
1790	1857	ALL	1832	155683	LAN	Accrington
1912	1992	1912	1992	138827	LAN	Ashton Under Lyme
1821	1848	1750	1820	151912	LAN	Blackburn
1857	1881	1856	1883	169552	LAN	Dalton In Furness
1816	1906	1750	1992	179078	LAN	Haslingden
1907	1992	ALL	1940	128171	LAN	Liverpool
1843	1855	1800	1860	114464	LAN	Manchester
1791	1791	....	....	159492	LAN	Manchester
1766	1787	1722	1770	109622	LAN	Preston
1808	1862	....	....	112429	LAN	Wesham
1880	1992	?	1880	153613	LAN	???
....	1780	....	....	174564	LEI	Redmile
1628	1728	....	....	165999	LEI	Stathern
1750	1992	....	1750	103926	LIN	Lincoln
1628	1728	....	....	165999	LIN	Sedgebrook
1750	1992	....	1750	103926	LIN	Skellingthorpe
1920	1970	1920	1970	114316	LND	Chiswick
1820	1992	1800	1860	103985	LND	Whitechapel
1824	1920	1824	1920	103977	MDX	Feltham
1770	1800	1770	1800	148288	MDX	London
....	....	ALL	ALL	172413	MDX	Staines
1824	1920	1824	1920	103977	MDX	Sunbury
1824	1920	1824	1920	103977	MDX	Teddington
1840	1870	1800	1900	139386	MDX	Westminster
1800	1820	1800	1820	126209	NBL	Ancroft
1873	....	....	....	121835	NFK	Heigham
1800	....	....	....	121835	NFK	Langham
1700	....	....	....	121835	NFK	Sculthorpe
....	....	1750	1900	104000	NFK	Wymondham
....	1850	....	....	174564	NTT	Egmanton
1800	1860	1600	1800	168211	OXF	Bloxham
1633	1750	1600	1755	107565	OXF	Cuddesdon
1597	1851	1545	1597	103918	OXF	Standlake
1806	1860	1780	1806	119059	OXF	Thame
1851	1871	1851	1871	111090	SCT	Roxborough
1750	1861	1700	1750	111945	SFK	Chediston
1860	1920	1860	1920	114316	SFK	Ipswich
1850	1900	....	....	151572	SOM	Bath
....	....	ALL	ALL	100153	SRY	ALL
1786	1835	?	1835	103934	SRY	Godalming
1750	1900	1700	1850	144657	SRY	Godstone
1750	1850	1700	1850	144657	SRY	Horne
1786	1835	?	1835	103934	SRY	Ripley
1786	1835	?	1835	103934	SRY	Sutton
1888	....	....	....	163112	SSX	Brighton
1831	1871	ALL	1815	165263	SSX	Chiddingly
1800	1992	1700	1800	170771	SSX	Dallington
....	....	1565	1850	173150	SXE	Brede
1910	1965	1724	1977	169552	WES	Ambleside
1791	1908	1731	1963	169552	WES	Appleby
1789	1926	1754	1946	169552	WES	Beetham
1817	1874	1813	1874	169552	WES	Brough Under Stainmore
1796	1965	1717	1971	169552	WES	Burneside
1624	1814	1559	1871	169552	WES	Crosby Garrett
1803	1812	1713	1812	169552	WES	Grasmere
1821	1921	1813	1923	169552	WES	Grayrigg
1798	1806	1776	1972	169552	WES	Great Musgrave
1881	1906	1842	1906	169552	WES	Holme
1876	1949	1732	1956	169552	WES	Hugill
1894	1935	1701	1935	169552	WES	Kentmere
1781	1946	1781	1973	169552	WES	Kirkby Lonsdale

BARNES contd.

Known From	To	Researching From	To	Ref	Cty	Place
1814	1861	1813	1861	169552	WES	Kirkby Stephen
1884	1910	1827	1981	169552	WES	Langdale
1854	1913	1813	1913	169552	WES	Milnthorpe
1948	1953	1777	1953	169552	WES	Natland
1686	1814	1654	1814	169552	WES	Orton
1813	1929	1813	1947	169552	WES	Selside
1874	1965	1871	1965	169552	WES	Skelsmergh
1854	1868	1813	1932	169552	WES	Troutbeck
1827	1949	1813	1972	169552	WES	Warcop
1848	1945	1613	1945	169552	WES	Windermere
1793	1803	1671	1942	169552	WES	Witherslack
....	....	1680	1760	133604	WIL	Aldbourne
1776	1808	ALL	1850	167029	WIL	Chilton Foliat
1725	....	ALL	ALL	116394	WIL	Eastcott
1790	1813	1700	1790	144711	WIL	Hannington
1790	1813	1700	1790	144711	WIL	Highworth
1822	1972	....	....	103969	WIL	Malmsbury
1700	....	ALL	ALL	116394	WIL	Mardon
....	....	1700	1830	133604	WIL	Seend
1853	1992	1799	1853	178241	YKS	Ellerburn
1837	1848	1693	1886	169552	YKS	Garsdale
1848	1924	1800	1924	169552	YKS	Sedbergh
1828	1992	1803	1950	178241	YKS	Thornton Dale
1858	1929	1858	....	164135	???	Syston

BARNET

Known From	To	Researching From	To	Ref	Cty	Place
....	....	1700	1800	149187	ANS	Monifieth
1777	1813	1700	1800	143693	BKM	Hughenden
1813	....	1700	1850	143693	BKM	Penn
1713	1940	....	....	128996	CAM	Thorney
....	1857	1500	1857	175072	CHS	Macclesfield
1759	....	1700	1780	162507	CON	Truro
1850	1860	1800	1850	146102	LAN	Prestwich
1773	1773	1700	1820	105333	SOM	Creech St Michael
1773	1773	1700	1820	105333	SOM	Stoke St Gregory
1773	1773	1700	1820	105333	SOM	Taunton
1773	1773	1700	1820	105333	SOM	Thornfalcon
1667	1705	1550	1666	102830	STS	Ellastone
1500	1800	....	....	100420	WAR	Meriden

BARNETT

Known From	To	Researching From	To	Ref	Cty	Place
1783	1869	1783	1869	149403	BKM	Penn
1785	1870	ALL	1950	118737	BRK	Appleton
1771	1919	....	....	115606	BRK	Bray
1660	1817	1500	1900	153354	CON	Gwennap
1870	1992	1800	1870	124117	GLA	Aberdare
1580	1750	1550	1681	102830	GLS	Withington
1870	1882	1800	1890	167983	HEF	Hereford
1787	....	....	1800	171441	KEN	Hoath
1822	....	....	1850	171441	KEN	Tonge
1780	1992	ALL	1780	102083	KEN	Tudeley
1867	....	1830	1880	146102	LAN	Salford
1820	1940	1780	1820	138258	LIN	Anwick
1827	1854	1700	1900	110191	MDX	London
1829	1900	1800	1900	140325	MDX	Tottenham
1838	....	1700	1850	126772	NTT	Nottingham
1810	1915	1600	1810	156914	RAD	Huntington
....	....	1800	1900	153281	SOM	Bridgewater
?	?	?	?	159913	SOM	Catcott
?	?	?	?	108758	SRY	Alfold
?	?	?	?	108758	SSX	???
....	....	1795	1850	115142	STS	Wolverhampton
1851	1869	ALL	1851	115355	WAR	ALL
1869	1869	ALL	ALL	115355	WAR	Coventry
1760	1814	1600	1760	116637	WES	Kirkby Stephen
1776	1800	1500	1776	115134	WIL	Bishopstone
....	....	1800	1992	140759	WIL	Christian Malford
....	....	1800	1992	140759	WIL	Trowbridge

BARNEY

Known From	To	Researching From	To	Ref	Cty	Place
1857	1932	1750	1857	158275	HAM	Alton
1742	1922	1742	....	116394	HAM	Beaulieu
1770	1922	....	....	116394	HAM	Fareham
1857	1932	1750	1857	158275	HAM	Sholing
1860	1881	1860	1881	118192	NFK	Norwich
?	?	1770	1770	114308	OXF	Bambury
1856	1856	....	....	139971	SCT	Dundee

BARNEYSDALE

Known From	To	Researching From	To	Ref	Cty	Place
1453	1517	1420	1530	104027	NFK	Bearwick
1453	1517	1420	1530	104027	NFK	West Rudham

BARNFIELD

Known From	To	Researching From	To	Ref	Cty	Place
1821	1916	1750	1821	178381	GLS	Cranham
1790	1810	1750	1810	162825	GLS	Horsley

BARNHURST

Known From	To	Researching From	To	Ref	Cty	Place
....	....	ALL	ALL	104019	ALL	Name Study

Known From	To	Researching From	To	Ref	Cty	Place
BARNS						
1801	1850	1700	1992	167460	DEV	Torquay
1700	1750	1600	1750	154342	GLS	Bitton
1807	1862	1807	1862	144878	HRT	St Stephens
1900	....	1850	1920	124796	LND	Islington
1784	1831	1757	1784	178241	YKS	Helmsley
1786	1799	1575	1837	178241	YKS	Sproxton
BARNSBURY						
1730	1800	1650	1800	136840	HAM	Southwick
BARNSBY						
ALL	ALL	ALL	ALL	106054	???	???
BARNSDALE						
1450	1600	1450	1600	104027	GLS	Alkington
1450	1600	1450	1600	104027	GLS	Berkeley
1450	1600	1450	1600	104027	GLS	Frampton On Severn
1450	1600	1450	1600	104027	GLS	Stone
1690	1854	1690	1854	104027	LIN	Donnington In Holland
1690	1854	1690	1854	104027	LIN	Wilsford Claypole
1850	1898	1850	1898	104027	LND	St George East
1850	1898	1850	1898	104027	LND	St Pauls
1600	1762	1600	1762	104027	NTT	Balderton
1600	1762	1600	1762	104027	NTT	Epperton
1870	1946	1870	1946	104027	SSX	Brighton
BARNSHAW						
1898	1992	1567	1652	177105	BKM	Burnham
1898	1992	1567	1652	177105	CHS	Audlem
1898	1992	1567	1652	177105	CHS	Congleton
....	1805	1750	1850	126659	CHS	Macclesfield
1898	1992	1567	1652	177105	CHS	Macclesfield
1898	1992	1567	1652	177105	CHS	Stockport
1870	1992	1700	1880	177105	???	Heburn
BARNSLEY						
1818	1842	1700	1881	160636	CHS	Poynton
1809	1928	1700	1820	118958	CHS	???
1760	....	....	1760	101761	NTT	Burton Joyce
1830	1850	1800	1900	177997	SOM	Bath
1820	1945	1800	1945	123145	WMD	Birmingham
1870	1900	1800	1900	177997	YKS	Bradford
1885	1902	1750	1885	118516	???	Birmingham
BARNUM						
1800	1969	ALL	ALL	161012	ALL	ALL
BARNWELL						
1800	1922	1750	1900	154881	WAR	Clifton
BARON						
1800	....	1800	....	134813	CON	Bodmin
1800	1925	?	?	131458	CON	Charlestown
1700	1992	1700	1900	123234	CON	Mevagissey
1731	1830	....	....	174319	CON	Mevagissey
1600	1900	1600	1900	131458	CON	St Austell
....	....	ALL	ALL	178152	HAM	Southampton
1747	1859	1700	1747	115460	HRT	Hitchin
1728	1748	1726	1780	104043	LAN	Brindle
1861	1902	1840	1900	104043	LAN	Darwen
1701	1744	1600	1700	104043	LAN	Great Harwood
1897	1907	1896	....	104043	LAN	Manchester
1881	1960	1700	1881	146021	LAN	Rochdale
1834	1850	1826	1870	104043	LAN	Salford
1732	1800	1650	1800	179078	LAN	Shuttleworth
1775	1820	1744	1800	104043	LAN	Wigan
1746	1929	1735	1896	107166	SSX	Worthing
1660	1760	1660	1760	107522	WRY	Todmorden
BARR						
1928	1992	1500	1928	104051	AYR	Irvine
....	....	1500	1780	138614	DFS	Holywood
1876	1957	1600	1876	150940	GLS	???
1870	....	....	....	106852	LKS	Carluke
1725	1790	....	....	171654	LKS	Carluke
....	....	1500	1800	166863	LKS	East Kilbride
....	....	1500	1800	166863	LKS	Hamilton
1801	1889	1700	1800	153656	LKS	Lesmahagow
1780	1820	1740	1800	128244	LKS	Shotts
1800	1900	ALL	ALL	128279	LND	Bethnal Green
1886	1900	1800	1886	149365	MDX	Acton
1840	1920	1800	1920	124605	MDX	East London
1820	?	1700	1992	167592	MDX	London
1750	1790	1700	1750	117765	RFW	Bridge Of Weir
1893	1947	1800	1893	146110	SCT	ALL
1876	1957	1600	1876	150940	WAR	???
1780	1840	1700	1992	167592	WOR	Worcester
1800	1992	1750	1950	115622	YKS	East Riding
1666	1812	1600	1666	179043	YKS	Hawnby
1892	....	....	....	161136	YKS	Hull
1571	1972	?	?	104329	YKS	???

Known From	To	Researching From	To	Ref	Cty	Place
BARRACK						
1728	1822	1500	1800	100013	ESS	Dunmow
BARRACLOUGH						
?	?	?	?	104078	WYK	Pemstowe
1750	1850	1700	1900	138517	YKS	Bradford
BARRACLUFF						
1851	1906	1830	1851	109878	LND	ALL
BARRADELL						
1804	1875	....	1804	161691	DBY	Breaston
BARRANCE						
ALL	ALL	ALL	ALL	104086	ALL	ALL
BARRAS						
1743	1992	ALL	1743	165204	YKS	West Ardsley
1847	1880	ALL	ALL	150401	???	Cockermouth
1858	....	ALL	ALL	150401	???	Little Barcock
BARRASS						
1780	1992	1700	1780	160571	DUR	West Rainton
1762	1930	ALL	1760	178543	NBL	Easdon
BARRAT						
1948	1992	....	....	104094	ESS	Chelmsford
1922	1948	....	....	104094	ESS	Leytonstone
1881	1896	....	....	104094	ESS	Plaistow
1803	1816	....	....	104094	MDX	Westminster
1839	1861	....	....	104094	SRY	Lambeth
BARRATT						
....	....	ALL	ALL	143839	ALL	Name Study
1796	1810	1700	1796	161225	BDF	Turvey
1748	1971	1590	1750	172006	CHS	Cheadle
....	....	ALL	ALL	126098	DOR	???
1871	1926	1800	1950	150576	HAM	Romsey
1865	1900	1900	1992	137626	LEI	Packington
1726	1881	1755	1888	124826	LIN	Winteringham
1844	1900	ALL	ALL	110442	MAY	ALL
....	....	1700	1865	137626	NTH	Towcester
1800	1850	....	....	138118	SAL	Market Drayton
1733	1891	....	1827	155055	STS	Gnosall
1775	....	1775	....	124842	STS	Newcastle
1871	1914	1829	1871	171298	STS	Stoke-On-Trent
1830	1840	1800	1840	137413	WAR	Coventry
....	....	1600	ALL	115142	WAR	???
1773	1851	ALL	1900	150576	WIL	Donhead St Andrew
1780	1930	....	....	143839	WIL	Trowbridge
BARRE						
1430	1490	1330	1430	154881	HRT	Knebworth
BARRELL						
1875	1939	1986	1992	176826	HEF	Long Town
1700	1830	1700	1830	151297	HEF	???
BARREN						
1732	1752	ALL	1732	154563	CUL	Alston
BARRET						
1789	1851	1700	1850	170569	CHS	Ringway
1809	1850	1800	1851	108251	DEV	Exeter
1700	1725	ALL	ALL	130508	HAM	Andover
1890	1920	1890	1920	115932	LAN	Manchester
1890	1920	1890	1920	115932	LAN	Oldham
1890	1920	1890	1920	115932	LAN	Salford
1749	1749	1500	1749	169439	OXF	Lower Heyford
1717	1761	ALL	1717	168602	SFK	Henstead
1717	1761	ALL	1717	168602	SFK	Lowestoft
BARRETT						
....	....	ALL	ALL	104116	ALL	Name Study
1812	?	1600	1812	108588	BDF	Luton
1835	1890	1800	1835	179604	BDF	Luton
1850	1945	1800	1850	104124	BKM	Wycombe
1670	1750	....	....	104132	BRK	Ashbury
1860	1920	ALL	ALL	116416	CHS	ALL
1650	1900	1500	1650	104140	CON	Duloe
1650	1900	1500	1650	104140	CON	St Germans
1650	1900	1500	1650	104140	CON	St Keyne
1801	1850	1700	1801	118958	CON	???
1900	1960	....	....	104140	DEV	Plymouth
....	....	1800	1900	167401	DEV	Plymouth
1800	1930	1775	1800	163635	DEV	Stoke Dameral
1800	1863	1800	1992	101532	DEV	Totnes
1801	1850	1700	1801	118958	DEV	???
....	....	1750	1810	161357	DOR	West
1840	1880	1700	1840	126322	DOR	Alton Pancras
1752	1818	....	....	161357	DOR	Beaminster
1795	1851	....	....	164631	ESS	Waltham Holy X
1880	1920	1880	1992	126322	FLN	Northrop
1732	1877	1650	1732	148938	GLS	Berkeley
1795	1992	ALL	1795	151777	GLS	Gloucester
1795	1992	ALL	1795	151777	GLS	Stroud
1815	1855	1815	1840	110159	IRL	Dublin

Known From	To	Researching From	To	Ref	Cty	Place
BARRETT contd.						
1800	1900	1800	1900	126144	KEN	Gravesend
1754	1790	....	1850	171441	KEN	Rodmersham
....	1839	....	1839	161888	KID	Castledermot
1860	1914	?	1860	171298	KID	Kildare
....	....	1800	1850	147613	LAN	Tatham
1855	1992	....	1855	115150	LKS	Glasgow
1800	1890	1800	1992	101532	LND	Bethnal Green
....	....	1800	1900	120456	LND	Greenwich
1840	1920	1840	1900	171417	LND	Holborn
1830	1900	....	....	164631	LND	Limehouse
1841	1900	1820	1940	160601	LND	???
....	1850	ALL	ALL	122866	MDX	East
1786	1841	1700	1818	167533	MDX	Bethnal Green
1897	1948	1897	....	113875	MDX	London
1813	....	....	....	161136	MON	Chepstow
1920	1945	1880	1920	130346	NBL	Newcastle Upon Tyne
1850	1992	ALL	1850	169692	NIR	Crogranamore
1746	1802	....	....	104817	NTH	Arthingworth
....	....	1721	1747	139831	NTH	Arthingworth
1746	1802	....	....	104817	NTH	Haselbech
1842	1860	ALL	ALL	162108	OXF	Burford
1890	1992	1500	1890	140279	PEM	Pembroke
1600	1700	....	1700	177695	SAL	Stockton
1720	1780	....	....	145688	SFK	Maer
1790	1860	1790	1880	121878	SOM	Barrington
1770	1810	1750	1810	166685	SOM	Somerton
....	....	1700	1840	160601	SOM	???
1860	1896	1860	1896	110159	STS	Lichfield
1800	1992	1800	1992	133833	STS	Winshill
1704	1992	....	....	104132	WIL	Aldbourne
1700	1850	1700	1850	145661	WIL	Aldbourne
1700	1780	1700	1780	156930	WIL	Aldbourne
1800	1840	1600	1840	154342	WIL	Heytesbury
1520	1670	....	....	104132	WIL	Stratton St Margaret
1860	1992	1700	1850	151955	WIL	Swindon
1845	....	....	....	171166	WRY	Burton Leonard
....	1920	....	....	171166	WRY	Leeds
....	1890	....	....	171166	WRY	Moor Allerton
1632	1880	....	....	151351	YKS	Harewood
1587	1660	....	....	151351	YKS	Kildwick In Craven
1839	....	....	....	161136	YKS	Sheffield
1726	1779	1700	1726	130206	YKS	Skipton
BARRIBALL						
1650	1700	1600	1800	153354	CON	North Hill
1705	1750	ALL	1705	129267	CON	North Petherwin
1750	1980	....	....	129267	CON	Werrington
1800	1900	1700	1800	151300	DEV	ALL
BARRICK						
1600	....	....	....	153397	ALL	ALL
....	....	1560	1700	106054	YKS	Halifax
BARRIE						
1837	1871	1800	1881	108227	FIF	Arngask
1900	....	1850	1992	168637	SCT	Larkhall
BARRINGER						
1844	1844	1780	1860	133000	HUN	Abbotsley
1901	1966	....	....	140406	LEI	Leicester
1840	1900	1800	1840	140406	LND	Westminster
1731	1801	1700	1800	100048	MDX	West Drayton
BARRINGTON						
1785	1900	1500	1785	114634	LEX	Cullenagh
....	....	ALL	ALL	104159	LND	Hackney
1814	1861	1700	1861	162035	MDX	Chelsea
1730	1830	1500	1850	105333	SOM	Crrech St Michael
1730	1830	1500	1850	105333	SOM	Stoke St Gregory
1730	1830	1500	1850	105333	SOM	Taunton
1730	1830	1500	1850	105333	SOM	Thornfalcon
BARRITT						
1810	1992	1760	1810	159573	YKS	Halifax
BARROM						
1690	1964	1665	1700	122815	SFK	Bedfield
BARRON NEE WELLER						
1890	1950	1890	1950	178799	KEN	Gillingham
BARRON						
1692	1725	ALL	1692	168602	CAM	Burwell
1724	1940	....	....	128996	CAM	Thorney
1731	1992	ALL	ALL	163112	CON	Mevagissey
1735	1904	1700	1850	161721	DUR	South Shields
1900	1980	1880	1980	178799	KEN	Gillingham
1806	1870	1700	1900	148008	LIN	ALL
1770	1992	....	1770	114812	LIN	Owston
1770	1992	....	1770	114812	LIN	Scotton
1808	1825	1700	1992	137855	MOR	Dyke
BARRON contd.						
1808	1825	1700	1992	137855	MOR	Kintesack
BARROW						
....	....	ALL	ALL	104175	ALL	Name Study
....	....	1700	1850	139432	DEV	Bratton
1450	1850	ALL	1992	133450	GLS	ALL
....	....	....	1705	130060	KEN	Hawkhurst
1755	1850	1600	1755	119822	LAN	Bolton
1798	1840	1750	1800	118354	LAN	Manchester
1700	1800	1600	1700	121118	LAN	St Michael On Wyre
1860	....	1800	1900	136042	LND	East
1841	1861	ALL	ALL	104167	MDX	Berkeley Square
1846	1850	1700	1900	166073	MDX	Shoreditch
1824	....	1750	1850	104167	MDX	St Georges
1857	1859	1840	1860	104167	SRY	Brixton
1861	....	1860	1870	104167	SRY	Kingston On Thames
1871	....	1870	ALL	104167	SRY	Mortlake
1881	1889	1889	ALL	104167	SRY	Wandsworth
1589	1979	?	?	104329	YKS	???
BARROWCLIFF						
1767	1795	1600	1770	126772	LEI	Rolleston
BARROWCLIFFE						
....	1731	1650	1731	148288	NTT	Stapleford
BARROWCLOUGH						
....	1730	?	1730	128910	DBY	West Hallam
BARROWMAN						
....	....	1770	1790	122904	LDY	Newton Limvady
1840	1913	1790	1840	122904	LKS	Airdrie
BARRY						
1800	1933	ALL	1933	100102	AYR	Givan
....	....	?	?	167592	CHS	???
1841	1992	1700	1841	109177	COR	???
1879	....	ALL	ALL	104191	IRL	Cork
1870	1930	1870	1870	145580	LAN	Liverpool
1706	1992	....	....	175374	LEI	Upton Sibson
1850	1992	1700	1992	115460	LIM	Kilfinney
1864	....	....	....	151270	LIM	Newcastle West
1845	....	1800	1845	116572	LIM	Newcastle
1839	1919	1919	1992	164127	STD	Muirburn
BARSBY						
1843	1880	1830	1900	102334	MDX	Aldgate
1843	1880	1830	1900	102334	MDX	Bethnal Green
1820	1825	1820	1825	102334	MDX	Paddington
BARSON						
1639	1641	....	....	151351	NTT	Bunny
1641	1687	....	....	151351	NTT	Clifton
1679	1725	....	....	151351	NTT	South Wilford
BARSTED						
1803	1871	1700	1803	101842	NFK	Hindolveston
BARTELL						
1710	1730	1600	1710	102571	CON	Constantine
BARTER						
?	?	?	?	117528	DEV	Ipplepen
?	?	?	?	117528	DEV	Kings Kerswell
ALL	ALL	....	....	153397	HAM	New Forest
1785	1903	1785	....	123609	SOM	Frome
BARTHOLMEW						
....	....	ALL	ALL	157260	WIL	Shalbourne
BARTHOLOMEW						
1875	1992	1875	1899	104213	DBY	Ecclesall Bierlow
1804	1826	ALL	ALL	170968	HAM	Fareham
1590	1590	1560	1590	124974	HAM	Kintbury
1798	1950	1700	1800	103896	HAM	Titchfield
1707	1765	1600	1707	170542	HAM	Titchfield
1823	1853	1800	1853	148121	KEN	Rochester
1838	1862	1838	1862	104213	STS	Handsworth
1675	1713	ALL	1713	156175	SXE	Ninfield
1875	1992	1875	1899	104213	SYK	Sheffield
1838	1862	1838	1862	104213	WAR	Birmingham
....	....	....	1785	109290	YKS	Sheffield
BARTLE						
....	....	1700	1820	136972	CON	Camborne
1700	1850	1600	1850	143766	CON	Gwinear
1782	1800	....	1782	146811	CON	St Erth
1818	1851	1800	1818	146811	GLA	Margam
1793	1992	ALL	1793	104221	NFK	Clenchwarton
1745	1846	....	....	136247	NFK	Oulton
....	....	1900	1992	136247	NFK	Reepham
1700	1940	1700	1940	105511	NTT	Laxton
1700	1940	1700	1940	105511	NTT	Worksop
....	1819	1750	1820	120529	YKS	Leeds
BARTLESON						
1750	1965	....	....	137820	SHI	Fetlar
1720	1965	....	....	137820	SHI	Mid Yell

Known From	Known To	Researching From	Researching To	Ref	Cty	Place
BARTLESON contd.						
1760	1965	....	....	137820	SHI	North Yell
1758	1965	....	....	137820	SHI	Northmavine
1720	1965	....	....	137820	SHI	South Yell
BARTLET						
1700	1830	1600	1840	105333	DEV	Buckland In The Moor
1700	1830	1600	1840	105333	DEV	Holne
1700	1830	1600	1840	105333	DEV	Ilsington
1700	1830	1600	1840	105333	DEV	Lydford
1818	1857	....	....	115274	DEV	Milton Combe
1700	1830	1600	1840	105333	DEV	Widecombe In The Moor
1658	1765	ALL	1658	172901	OXF	ALL
1795	....	....	1825	152803	SOM	Hardington
1895	1900	1871	1930	139130	WLS	Pontypridd
BARTLETT						
1724	1870	1700	1900	176044	BRK	Marcham
1612	1870	1612	1870	178705	BRK	Reading
....	....	1600	1800	104256	CON	Calstock
1792	1871	1700	1792	104256	CON	Menheniot
1759	1965	1690	1873	109053	CON	North Hill
1881	1938	....	....	104256	DEV	Buckfastleigh
1818	1820	1800	1818	141798	DEV	Plymouth
1850	....	ALL	1900	168696	DEV	Tavistock
1760	1820	1740	1830	120995	DEV	Teignmouth
1680	1730	1550	1680	147583	DOR	North
1700	1770	1600	1770	154342	DOR	Broadwindsor
1718	1806	ALL	1718	165735	DOR	Broadwindsor
1710	1780	....	....	137480	DOR	Chideock
1850	....	1700	....	127760	DOR	Lytchett Maltravers
1800	1840	1800	1950	160539	DOR	Sherborne
1740	1778	....	....	112887	DOR	???
....	....	1890	1920	117137	GLA	Bargoed
1880	1910	1800	1900	173428	GLA	???
1770	1850	1600	1850	154342	GLS	Bitton
1814	1900	1814	1900	165735	GLS	Hanham
....	....	1870	1900	117137	GLS	Ruardean
1761	....	....	....	102733	GLS	South Cerney
1826	....	ALL	1826	139459	GLS	Stonehouse
1800	1850	1700	1800	123978	HAM	Isle Of Wight
1830	1850	1800	1835	155691	HAM	Ringwood
1750	1850	1750	1850	141682	HAM	Silchester
1729	1992	1525	1729	104248	IOW	St Helens
1780	1813	1780	1853	102806	IOW	???
1740	1992	1700	1992	124699	KEN	East
1902	....	1890	1930	171441	KEN	Chatham
1750	1790	1650	1750	139106	LND	London
1898	1977	1770	1898	158267	MDX	London
1795	....	1750	1850	102016	MDX	St George Hanover Square
....	....	1750	1850	157201	NFK	Martham
1860	1900	ALL	1860	169692	OXF	Banbury
1546	1546	1500	1700	159956	SFK	Bury St Edmunds
ALL	ALL	ALL	ALL	114502	SOM	ALL
1850	1870	ALL	1850	141224	SOM	ALL
1600	1992	....	....	153397	SOM	ALL
1842	1860	1800	1842	144177	SOM	Blackford
1862	1952	ALL	1850	131695	SOM	Bristol
1730	1850	1550	1730	147583	SOM	East Chinnock
1800	1840	1800	1950	160539	SOM	Sutton Montis
1800	1900	1800	1900	134031	SRY	Kingston On Thames
1782	1969	....	....	108200	SRY	Kingston
1733	1763	....	....	108200	SRY	Leatherhead
1730	1790	1730	1790	132721	SSX	Amberley
1800	1992	1700	1992	165344	WAR	Aston
1792	1929	1700	1930	171441	WAR	Ilmington
1761	1851	....	....	102733	WIL	Latton
1806	1814	....	....	165735	???	Keynsham
BARTLEY						
1871	....	ALL	ALL	150924	ARM	Scarva
?	....	....	....	147184	IRL	???
1850	1890	1800	1850	144606	MDX	Pimlico
BARTON						
1740	1770	1650	1740	101834	CAM	Grantchester
....	....	1730	1810	103713	CAM	Isleham
1687	1940	....	....	128996	CAM	Thorney
1791	1820	1791	1820	147532	CHS	Great Budworth
1816	....	....	....	124982	GLS	Berkeley
1800	1992	ALL	1992	104299	GLS	Bristol
1827	1899	ALL	1827	129682	GLS	Cheltenham
1669	1752	1600	1722	145289	HAM	Isle Of Wight
1839	1860	1830	1860	171999	HRT	Hinxworth
1762	1775	....	1762	108839	HUN	Needingworth
BARTON contd.						
1750	1900	ALL	ALL	104272	IOW	ALL
1699	....	1650	1700	126667	IOW	Calbourne
1600	1992	ALL	ALL	129577	IOW	???
1837	1891	ALL	ALL	157856	KEN	Boughton
1750	1992	1600	1800	104302	KEN	Deal
1821	1870	....	....	164631	KEN	Deptford
1830	1860	1830	1880	166383	KEN	Deptford
1815	1840	1790	1840	154873	KEN	Dover
1832	1840	1700	1832	113425	KEN	Eastwell
1815	1840	1790	1840	154873	KEN	Folkestone
1837	1891	ALL	ALL	157856	KEN	Monchelsea
1765	1851	1700	1851	178233	LAN	Aughton
1880	1992	1750	1880	126985	LAN	Coastal
1850	1907	1800	1850	109878	LAN	Liverpool
1861	1871	....	1861	149918	LEI	Leicester
1846	1992	....	1846	104280	LIN	South
1784	1800	....	....	164631	MDX	St Marylebone
1777	1777	ALL	1780	113611	NYK	Whitby
1850	1960	ALL	ALL	162469	SFK	North
1704	1750	ALL	1704	142107	SFK	Stratford St Mary
1815	1960	1700	1815	165980	SSX	Warbleton
1800	1880	....	....	132756	STS	Cradley
1750	1900	1650	1850	172928	STS	Handsworth
1800	1880	....	....	132756	STS	Rowley
1750	1900	1650	1850	172928	STS	West Bromwich
1850	1900	ALL	ALL	115002	WOR	Upton On Severn
1850	1992	1750	1850	110442	WYK	Castleford
1200	1511	1200	1873	113484	YKS	Barton
1785	1856	ALL	1860	104299	YKS	Ecclesall Bierlow
BARTRAM						
1800	1861	....	1861	158305	DUR	Heworth
ALL	....	....	....	123641	LIN	Stamford
1857	1871	....	....	123641	MDX	Islington
1861	1882	....	....	132829	NBL	Longhoughton
1820	1840	1700	1820	153281	SOM	Bridgwater
BARTROP						
....	1880	1880	1950	133639	MDX	Islington
BARTRUM						
1819	1841	1819	1992	147230	NFK	Diss
BARTTRAM						
1760	1780	ALL	....	104515	LIN	Haydour
BARTWELL						
1792	1992	ALL	1992	160938	NFK	North
BARTY						
1833	1884	1700	1850	175307	LIN	Boston
1853	1932	1800	1950	175307	SRY	Croyden
BARTY-KING						
1900	1992	1900	1992	133450	KEN	???
1900	1992	1900	1992	133450	SSX	???
BARUGH						
1549	1986	1700	1753	104329	YKS	Dishforth
BARWELL						
1832	1845	1832	1992	115355	LEI	ALL
1800	1850	1750	1800	135879	LND	Marylebone
1805	....	1700	1851	176923	SOM	Apulton
1755	1800	1600	1750	108413	SOM	Hinton Blewett
....	....	1650	1800	115142	WAR	Kingsbury
BARWICK						
1751	1825	....	....	162825	DEV	Parracombe
1800	1899	....	....	121835	NFK	Gaywood
1800	1899	....	....	121835	NFK	Kings Lynn
1615	1800	ALL	....	100536	SFK	???
BARWIS						
1798	1900	....	....	130648	CON	West
1234	1992	....	....	130648	CUL	North
BASCOMBE						
1820	1850	ALL	ALL	115266	DOR	ALL
BASE						
?	?	1810	1992	104337	MDX	Mile End Old Town
BASEBE						
1860	1992	1500	1860	139033	LND	Camden Town
1860	1992	1500	1860	139033	SRY	Wallington
1860	1992	1500	1860	139033	SSX	Brighton
BASETON						
1727	....	ALL	....	104515	LIN	Heckington
BASEY						
1855	1917	1750	1855	116440	NFK	Norwich
BASFORD						
1801	1875	....	1801	133566	MDX	Stepney
1715	1850	1650	1715	147885	NTH	Towcester
BASHAM						
1747	1900	1700	1900	126586	SFK	???

Known From	To	Researching From	To	Ref	Cty	Place
BASHFORD						
1818	1932	1700	1818	152544	KEN	Chiddingstone
1890	1920	....	1890	102059	YKS	Barnsley
BASKCOMB						
1850	1992	1700	1850	113786	ESS	Barking
BASKER						
....	....	ALL	ALL	104345	ALL	Name Study
1790	1930	1550	1790	104345	LIN	ALL
BASKERFIELD						
1713	1737	1600	1800	166359	DEV	???
BASKERVILLE						
1800	1980	....	....	121061	CHS	Alderley
1793	1992	1500	1793	140279	DEV	North
1793	1992	1500	1793	140279	DEV	Ashwater
1811	1831	1700	1831	126357	TIP	Youghal
1830	1880	1830	1970	104353	WRY	Bradford
1900	....	ALL	ALL	114847	???	Bristol
BASKETT						
1800	1850	1800	1850	108693	???	London
BASKOTT						
1827	1900	1827	1900	146617	WAR	Marton
BASLEY						
....	....	1750	1810	104361	HAM	Dogmersfield
1800	1950	1800	1915	104361	MDX	Brentford
1800	1950	1800	1915	104361	MDX	Southall
BASLINGTON						
....	....	ALL	ALL	104388	ALL	Name Study
1612	1992	1612	1992	104388	LIN	ALL
BASNETT						
1831	1909	1700	1831	150614	CHS	Sutton
1858	1881	ALL	ALL	149489	STS	Leek
BASS						
1877	1992	ALL	1877	115355	BDF	ALL
1780	1860	ALL	1780	115282	KEN	East
1840	1850	1800	1870	124311	LAN	Liverpool
1877	1992	ALL	1877	115355	LEI	ALL
1870	1992	1750	1870	128732	NTH	Nothampton
1877	1992	ALL	1877	115355	NTT	ALL
1812	1866	1800	1836	136581	POW	Brecon
1780	1870	1750	1780	149993	WAR	Honiley
1825	1992	1650	1825	151092	WOR	Alvechurch
BASSAGE						
....	....	1750	1800	154873	KEN	Maidstone
BASSANO						
....	....	ALL	ALL	146641	ALL	Name Study
BASSE						
1753	1753	....	....	147869	LND	Stepney
BASSENDEN						
1800	1992	....	....	104426	KEN	Ash
1730	1770	....	....	104426	KEN	Wye
BASSET						
1170	1241	1100	1231	124974	BKM	High Wycombe
1900	1992	....	....	135666	GLA	Coed Y Mynach
BASSETT						
1887	1919	1887	1992	108979	BDF	Leighton Buzzard
1800	1855	....	....	130281	DEV	Holsworthy
1800	1844	1700	1810	100013	ESS	Pleshey
1500	....	....	....	100536	GLA	Beaupre
1821	....	1800	1830	171441	KEN	Canterbury
1800	....	....	1830	171441	KEN	Hythe
1836	1920	1800	1900	116173	LEI	Leicester
1690	1770	1670	1800	100420	LEI	Medbourne
1775	1850	1600	1775	160784	LEI	Ridlington
1823	1856	1800	1856	110175	LND	Lewisham
1823	1856	1800	1856	110175	LND	Rushey Green
....	....	....	1860	161667	LND	Walworth
1624	1703	....	....	142522	SRY	Dorking
1375	1992	....	....	168467	STS	Blore
1700	1992	1600	1700	141879	STS	Butterton
BASSETT-SMITH						
1800	1969	ALL	....	100536	???	London
BASSIL						
....	....	....	....	127272	HRT	Sawbridgeworth
1820	1857	1750	1820	174203	HRT	Sawbridgeworth
BASSINGHAM						
1767	1839	1700	1780	103896	LND	City
BASSINGTHWAIGHTE						
1763	1790	1790	....	156027	NFK	Happisburg
1763	1790	1760	....	156027	NFK	North Walsham
BASSINGTON						
1750	1992	1566	1750	104442	MDX	Edmonton
1750	1992	1566	1750	104442	MDX	Hoxton
1750	1992	1566	1750	104442	MDX	Islington
1750	1992	1566	1750	104442	MDX	Poplar

Known From	To	Researching From	To	Ref	Cty	Place
BASSINGTON contd.						
1550	1600	ALL	1550	104442	SRY	Camberwell
BASTABLE						
....	....	1600	1992	137588	DEV	Newton St Cyres
1800	1850	1700	1900	159093	DOR	Marhull
....	....	1800	1850	147079	SOM	ALL
BASTARD						
....	....	ALL	ALL	161209	ALL	Name Study
1820	?	ALL	ALL	129399	DEV	Great Torrington
....	....	1750	....	108677	DOR	Sherborne
....	....	ALL	1880	161209	LND	Central
1818	....	1818	....	156027	MDX	Cripplegate
1840	....	1840	....	156027	MDX	Lambeth
....	....	ALL	1880	161209	NFK	Norfolk
1759	1759	....	....	135437	NFK	Wood Norton
BASTICK						
1822	1854	....	1822	164321	MDX	East London
BASTIN						
1780	1880	1500	1780	104140	DEV	Devonport
1780	1880	1880	1992	104140	DEV	Ottery St Mary
BASTOCK						
?	?	1732	1775	114308	WAR	South
BASTON						
1890	1945	....	....	104450	HRT	High Barnet
1841	....	1800	1900	101508	SRY	Newington
BASTOW						
1877	....	....	....	132500	LAN	Oldham
BATCHELDER						
1780	1880	....	....	179396	NFK	Norwich
1780	1880	....	....	179396	NFK	Swannington
BATCHELER						
1770	1992	1600	1770	104469	BKM	Buckingham
BATCHELOR						
1720	1720	ALL	1720	112631	BKM	Amersham
1717	1740	1740	1797	104485	BKM	Beaconsfield
1740	1800	1715	1740	104485	BKM	Chesham
1770	1846	1700	1900	116742	BKM	Chesham
....	....	1700	1900	108766	DEV	???
1712	1950	1710	1950	109827	HAM	Southampton
1740	1860	....	....	145394	HAM	Southampton
1792	1930	1700	1930	153133	HRT	Great Gaddesden
1744	1765	1765	1774	104485	HRT	Harpenden
1807	1914	ALL	1850	112720	HRT	Tring
1713	1717	1680	1773	104485	HRT	Wigginton
1820	1950	1800	1980	153990	KEN	Bredhurst
1850	1924	1750	1850	153990	KEN	Gillingham
1862	1992	1862	1992	164313	KEN	Maidstone
1831	1879	ALL	1879	156175	KEN	Medway
1831	1879	ALL	1879	156175	KEN	Northfllet
1862	1938	....	....	148733	KEN	Street Hadlow
1782	1855	1750	1855	164313	KEN	Tonbridge
1876	1992	1876	1992	172952	KEN	Tonbridge
1816	1837	1837	1888	104485	MDX	Heston
1822	1877	....	....	104485	MDX	Isleworth
1800	1856	....	....	150762	MON	Blaenavon
1800	....	....	....	150762	MON	Ebbw Vale
1888	1931	1857	1888	104485	SRY	Camberwell
1819	1837	1837	1888	104485	SRY	Richmond
1731	1760	1700	1800	164313	SSX	Balcombe
1860	1900	1875	1900	113743	SSX	Brede
1778	1888	1700	1778	174807	SSX	Cuckfield
1854	1854	ALL	1992	125113	SSX	East Dean
1750	1850	1700	1900	162736	SSX	Hartfield
1814	1814	ALL	1992	102245	WAR	Armscote
1790	....	....	....	150762	WIL	Bradford On Avon
....	....	1881	1895	133221	WIL	Devizes
....	....	1700	1752	150150	WOR	Cleeve Prior
BATCHELOUR						
1834	1855	1800	1855	108391	MDX	London
BATCHER						
1792	1810	1700	1900	141569	WAR	Birmingham
BATCOCK						
1838	....	....	....	173932	SRY	Ashtead
BATE						
1719	1965	1551	1871	109053	CON	Linkinhorne
1756	1820	....	....	165999	CON	Stoke Climsland
....	....	1750	1810	118834	DOR	Devonport
....	....	1750	1810	118834	DOR	East Stonehouse
....	....	1850	1920	147826	KEN	???
....	....	1825	1992	121940	LAN	Winwick
....	....	1600	1631	150150	NTH	Naseby
1700	1800	....	1800	177695	STS	Essington
....	1800	....	1800	177695	STS	Gt Wyrley
1800	1880	1780	1880	137111	WAR	Birmingham

Known From	To	Researching From	To	Ref	Cty	Place
BATE contd.						
1829	1930	1750	1835	117722	WAR	Dudley
1800	1827	1700	1827	133876	WOR	Alvechurch
1800	1827	1700	1827	133876	WOR	Bromsgrove
BATELEY						
1771	1771	ALL	1771	129283	NFK	St Ibbard
BATEMAN						
1800	1900	ALL	1800	120332	BRK	Burford
1890	1900	1950	1950	126179	CHI	Guernsey
1850	1900	1700	1850	113735	DBY	Bakewell
1840	....	....	....	134007	DBY	Hartington
1836	1876	1700	1876	131199	DBY	Winster
1820	1860	ALL	1820	141224	GLS	South
1570	1770	ALL	ALL	128449	GLS	Bitton
1805	1960	ALL	1900	131334	GLS	Bitton
1860	1870	ALL	ALL	128449	GLS	Bristol St George
1770	1830	ALL	ALL	128449	GLS	Mangotsfield
1830	1860	ALL	ALL	128449	GLS	Stapleton
1470	1650	1470	1650	104507	KEN	ALL
1570	1992	1570	1992	104507	KEN	Folkestone
1850	1900	....	....	178330	LND	Brixton
1826	....	....	....	124508	LND	City
1840	....	....	....	134007	LND	London
1700	1850	....	....	114243	LND	???
....	....	1750	1850	178330	NFK	Norwich
1820	1900	....	....	120332	OXF	Bampton
....	....	1750	1840	100188	PEM	Harrisey
1820	....	1700	1820	128090	WAR	Birmingham
1740	1770	1700	1770	153249	WOR	Abeley Kings
1740	1770	1700	1770	153249	WOR	Kidderminster
....	?	....	....	141941	???	London
BATES						
1819	1940	1700	1819	116378	BDF	Eddlesborough
1851	1945	ALL	1851	106151	BDF	Luton
1850	1930	1800	1930	127353	BKM	Drayton Parslow
1825	1880	1770	1825	118354	BKM	Lillingston Lovell
1831	1900	....	1900	171441	BKM	West Wycombe
1650	1690	ALL	1700	118338	BRK	Cookham
1880	1920	1860	1880	103985	CAM	Chatteris
1853	....	1800	1850	140473	CAM	Ely
1890	1930	1800	1930	103985	CAM	Outwell
1669	1940	....	....	128996	CAM	Thorney
1890	1930	1800	1930	103985	CAM	Wisbech
1750	1800	....	....	118354	DBY	Duffield
1790	1870	1790	....	116394	DEV	Devonport
1815	1992	1700	1815	151467	KEN	East
1820	1840	1750	1820	132640	KEN	Lewisham
1830	1900	1700	1830	144681	KEN	Maidstone
1900	1960	ALL	ALL	100137	LEI	ALL
1665	1983	ALL	ALL	141615	LEI	Leicester
1798	1820	1700	1800	102008	LIN	Althorpe
1798	1902	....	....	114545	LIN	Boston
1750	1900	1750	1900	136484	LND	Bloomsbury
1813	1992	1500	1992	175498	LND	Lambeth
1850	ALL	1700	1850	130397	LND	London
1865	1870	1865	....	116394	LND	St Pancras
1750	1900	1750	1900	136484	LND	Whitechapel
1740	1800	1700	1800	176672	NFK	ALL
1736	1904	1736	1992	104531	NFK	Great Witchingham
1831	1948	1831	1992	104531	NFK	Weston Longville
1690	1838	1650	1840	127604	NTH	West
1825	1860	1800	1860	143774	NTH	Barnwell
....	....	1700	1992	124400	NTH	Boughton
1800	1830	1800	1830	143774	NTH	Cotterstock
1789	1806	ALL	ALL	124176	NTH	Litchborough
1869	1919	1849	1943	125717	NTH	Northampton
1875	1968	1800	1900	133531	NTH	Northampton
1776	1838	1650	1776	131377	NTH	Rothwell
1824	1900	....	....	125709	NTH	Rushden
1824	1900	....	....	125709	NTH	Sywell
1782	....	....	1782	133566	SRY	Clapham
1890	1904	1890	1930	171441	SRY	Farncombe
1890	1904	1890	1930	171441	SRY	Godalming
1828	1875	....	....	118354	STS	Anslow
1749	1797	1700	1760	170348	YKS	Almondbury
1846	1899	1827	1992	104299	YKS	Barnsley
1750	1950	1750	1950	110280	YKS	Birchencliffe
....	....	1800	1960	104523	YKS	Halifax
1706	1750	1700	1720	170348	YKS	Huddersfield
1750	1800	1750	1800	123595	YKS	Kirkheaton
1751	1820	....	....	170348	YKS	Kirkheaton
1781	1847	1600	1800	101575	YKS	Knottingley
1750	1950	1750	1950	110280	YKS	Lindley
1781	1847	1600	1800	101575	YKS	Pontefract

Known From	To	Researching From	To	Ref	Cty	Place
BATES contd.						
1827	....	ALL	1846	104299	YKS	Skelmanthorpe
1836	1890	....	....	102008	YKS	Wakefield
BATESON						
1700	1992	1600	1900	137405	CAM	South
....	....	....	1900	137405	HRT	North
1835	1933	1800	1950	179132	LAN	Bolton
....	....	1650	1700	147613	LAN	Melling#
BATEUP						
1860	1916	....	1860	165484	SSX	Wadhurst
BATEY						
1750	1800	1750	1800	133817	DUR	Jarrow
1815	1871	1600	1950	158399	NBL	Newcastle
1880	1992	1800	1900	167843	YKS	Thornaby On Tees
BATH						
....	....	ALL	ALL	104558	ALL	Name Study
1830	1885	1750	1830	101931	CON	Wendron
?	?	?	?	142018	GLS	Bristol
1855	1859	1840	1870	142018	GLS	Gloucester
1696	1955	1650	1800	151467	KEN	North West
1776	1784	ALL	ALL	129933	LND	Limehouse
1835	1845	1780	1860	123870	MDX	London
1800	1820	1700	1800	112410	STS	Burslem
1800	1900	1600	1800	132586	WIL	Broad Blunsdon
1793	1865	....	....	161861	WIL	Idmiston
?	?	?	?	142018	WIL	Salisbury
1896	1920	1066	1920	108669	WYK	Hemsworth
BATHE						
1815	1917	1700	1992	123552	BRK	Thatcham
1815	1917	1700	1992	123552	MDX	London
BATHEN						
1813	1814	1700	1911	121746	STS	Uttoxeter
BATHER						
1683	....	1600	1700	160873	STS	Walsall
BATHGATE						
1810	1839	....	1839	161888	WLN	Bathgate
BATHMAKER						
1814	1900	ALL	ALL	122211	SRY	Lambeth
BATHOLOMEW						
1799	....	ALL	1800	119687	SSX	Beckley
BATHURST						
1720	....	1650	1750	139386	KEN	Cranbrook
BATHY						
1703	1703	1100	1703	117749	CON	Mawgan In Meneage
BATLEY						
1598	1671	....	1598	101761	WRY	Horbury
1730	1992	....	....	157694	YKS	Holmfirth
1730	1992	....	....	157694	YKS	Huddersfield
1730	1992	....	....	157694	YKS	Whitkirk
BATMAN						
1600	1992	1600	1992	104566	YKS	Copmanthorpe
1600	1992	1600	1992	104566	YKS	York
BATSER						
1600	....	ALL	1992	106119	KEN	???
1572	1603	ALL	1992	106119	SRY	Guildford
BATSON						
....	....	1612	1992	127035	BKM	???
1653	1940	....	....	128996	CAM	Thorney
ALL	....	....	....	150975	NFK	Hingham
ALL	....	....	....	150975	NFK	Norwich
1790	1825	1750	1850	158658	NFK	Norwich
....	....	1612	1992	127035	OXF	???
1800	1992	1700	1992	177652	WAR	Aston
1704	1789	1680	1720	170348	WIL	Purton
BATT						
1794	1833	1600	1794	102571	CON	Gwennap
....	....	1650	1750	156795	HAM	West
1779	....	1700	1779	121010	HAM	Amport
1868	1958	....	....	104574	HAM	Porstmouth
1806	1868	1700	1868	104574	KEN	Isle Of Sheppy
1600	1750	1600	1750	142018	SOM	ALL
BATTALIA						
1800	1850	1800	1850	106631	MDX	Westminster
BATTAM						
1760	1900	1650	1760	141372	KEN	East
BATTCOCK						
ALL	ALL	ALL	ALL	172324	ENG	South
BATTEN						
....	....	ALL	ALL	104582	ALL	Name Study
1766	1813	1700	1766	167452	BKM	Radnage
1775	....	....	....	151750	BRK	Thatcham
1832	1992	1700	1832	161446	CON	Camborne
1680	1718	1600	1680	102571	CON	Perranzabuloe
1740	1794	1500	1740	132993	CON	Quethiock

Known From	To	Researching From	To	Ref	Cty	Place
BATTEN contd.						
1725	1780	1700	1725	173118	CON	Talland
1792	1930	1700	1792	139815	DEV	Bradford
1817	1881	1750	1850	120146	DEV	Highampton
BATTERSBY						
ALL	ALL	ALL	ALL	122629	GLS	Bristol
ALL	1925	ALL	ALL	122629	GLS	Fairford
1800	1890	1700	1800	110914	LAN	Wigan
1912	1981	....	....	140406	LEI	Leicester
1810	1911	1750	1810	140406	NTT	Nottingham
1742	1790	1650	1740	167533	YKS	Anston
BATTERSON						
1838	1865	1800	1890	116386	BDF	Henlow
....	....	ALL	ALL	149349	IRL	???
BATTEY						
....	....	1700	1800	147613	LAN	Tunstall
BATTINSON						
....	....	ALL	ALL	165190	ALL	Name Study
1600	1992	ALL	ALL	165190	ALL	ALL
BATTISFORD						
1200	1400	1200	1400	154881	ALL	ALL
BATTLE						
1800	1804	1700	1800	139084	ESS	Takeley
1812	1914	....	1812	132837	WIL	Trowbridge
BATTS						
1743	1743	ALL	1800	168696	OXF	Abingdon
1748	1748	ALL	1800	168696	OXF	Fyfield
1780	1900	1500	1900	125725	OXF	Stanton Harcourt
1700	1872	ALL	1872	168696	OXF	Stanton Harcourt
BATTY						
1860	....	1700	....	130435	CHS	Astbury
1584	1992	ALL	ALL	150797	LIN	South
1871	1871	1850	1920	105333	MDX	London
1871	1871	1850	1920	105333	MDX	Notting Hill
1799	1860	1700	1799	122378	NTT	Newark On Trent
1845	....	ALL	ALL	138533	NYK	Burton In Lonsdale
1858	1919	....	1858	163031	SOM	Yeovil
1839	1871	1820	1920	105333	SRY	Putney
1769	1855	1750	1850	106429	WRY	Campsall
1756	1761	1650	1750	129453	WRY	North Craven
ALL	1730	....	....	170798	WRY	Silkstone
....	....	1750	1800	147613	YKS	Darton
1806	1938	1796	1992	136808	YKS	Hedon
1854	1975	1500	1854	132233	YKS	Huddersfield
1548	1673	....	....	168513	YKS	Kirkburton
....	....	....	....	127272	YKS	Stocksbridge
BATTYE						
1740	1800	1740	1820	123595	YKS	Holmfirth
1890	1992	1600	1890	104612	YKS	Huddersfield
1890	1992	1600	1890	104612	YKS	Scholes
BATY						
....	....	ALL	ALL	155284	ALL	Name Study
1800	1920	1770	1992	126632	CMA	Rockcliffe
1700	1790	1700	1800	148474	CUL	Kirkandrews On Esk
BAUDRIER						
1889	....	....	....	153400	LND	Marylebone
BAUGH						
....	....	ALL	ALL	125989	ALL	Name Study
....	....	ALL	ALL	125989	ALL	ALL
1832	1920	1600	1832	104620	HEF	Almeley
1832	1920	1600	1832	104620	HEF	Bromyard
1832	1920	1600	1832	104620	HEF	Marden
1832	1920	1600	1832	104620	HEF	Moreton Jeffries
1800	1878	ALL	1800	146226	LAN	Manchester
1821	1870	ALL	1821	143278	WAR	Birmingham
BAUGHEN						
....	....	ALL	ALL	104639	ALL	Name Study
BAULCH						
1800	1820	1770	1810	168580	SOM	Muchelney
BAULDIE						
....	....	1780	....	149187	FIF	Abdie
BAULDING						
1812	1814	....	....	158712	LIN	Tealby
BAULDOCK						
....	1768	ALL	1768	152838	LIN	Marshchapel
BAUM						
....	....	1700	1900	135968	LEI	ALL
BAUMFORTH						
....	1640	1600	1700	138584	YKS	Kippax
....	1670	1600	1700	138584	YKS	Rothwell
BAVE						
1806	1806	1600	1806	144851	SSX	Battle
BAVENHILL						
1802	1890	1830	1916	165441	STS	Wednesbury

Known From	To	Researching From	To	Ref	Cty	Place
BAVERSTOCK						
1790	1806	ALL	1793	161292	DOR	Blandford
1860	1900	1700	1860	113247	HAM	Andover
1795	1943	?	1795	113360	HAM	Hurstbourne Priors
1821	1965	1763	1820	175846	HAM	Portsea
BAVRIDGE						
1840	1900	....	1900	109568	LND	Lambeth
BAWCUTT						
1749	1749	1745	1755	107360	NTH	Crick
1750	1790	1736	1812	107360	NTH	Welton
BAWDEN						
1630	1652	1560	1630	102571	CON	Gwennap
....	....	1600	1750	174319	CON	Lanlivery
1690	1710	1600	1690	102571	CON	Marazion
?	....	?	?	143499	CON	Porthleven
1770	....	1750	1800	178845	CON	Stithians
1850	1900	1800	1900	161349	CON	???
....	....	ALL	1900	173614	DEV	North
1840	1880	1840	1880	135429	DEV	Heasley Mill
1857	1900	ALL	1900	173614	DEV	South Moulton
1755	1848	1740	1850	160644	SOM	East Brent
1860	1992	1860	1992	160644	SOM	Weston Super Mare
BAWN						
1830	1950	1700	1830	143421	GLS	Oldland
1882	....	....	....	135488	LND	Camberwell
1850	....	1830	1850	148121	LND	Poplar
BAWTREE						
....	....	ALL	ALL	174963	ALL	ALL
BAX						
1742	1797	ALL	1992	125113	KEN	Minster
1860	....	....	....	172723	SOM	Barrow Gurney
1801	1824	1801	1824	138312	SRY	Dorking
BAXENDALE						
1700	1800	....	....	126497	LAN	Wigan
1760	1830	1760	1800	126500	LAN	Wigan
BAXTER						
1650	1992	1650	1992	104671	ABD	Footdee
1782	....	....	....	138401	CUL	Hesket In The Forest
1840	....	....	....	128945	DUR	New Cassop
1766	1810	1650	1766	158143	FIF	Newburgh
1760	....	1700	1760	166723	GLS	Stroud
1870	1917	ALL	1870	131881	HAM	Portsmouth
1851	1889	....	1900	137405	HRT	Hertford
....	....	....	1835	137405	HRT	North Mimms
....	....	....	1845	137405	HRT	Park Street
1839	1847	1700	1839	100447	HUN	Offord
1650	1992	1650	1992	104671	KCD	Nigg
1700	ALL	1700	ALL	125512	KEN	Bromley
1892	....	1700	1992	168637	LEI	Carlton
1726	1880	....	....	165999	LEI	Harlaxton
1813	1890	ALL	1813	131881	LIN	Boston
1809	1886	....	....	169226	LIN	Boston
1726	1880	....	....	165999	LIN	Hougham
1850	1920	1850	1900	143774	LND	East
1850	1920	1850	1900	143774	LND	North
1861	1861	1830	1900	104663	LND	Chelsea
1820	1920	1820	1920	155195	LND	Fulham
....	....	1700	1820	169226	LND	Greenwich
1895	1895	1895	1944	104663	LND	Kensington
1861	1992	1861	1992	104663	LND	???
....	....	....	1820	137405	MDX	Harrow
1760	1840	1660	1840	155195	NFK	Forncett
1790	1850	1750	1850	127604	NTH	ALL
....	....	....	1860	110817	NTH	Kings Cliffe
1673	....	....	....	148156	NTH	Old
1848	1934	1800	1850	153656	PEE	Drumelzier
....	....	1750	1850	174114	SFK	???
1897	1950	....	....	126187	SRY	Richmond
1726	1880	....	....	165999	STS	Stapenhill
....	....	1750	1900	115142	WAR	Polesworth
1844	1844	1800	1869	127361	WRY	Pontefract
1815	1835	1790	1835	147311	WYK	Almondbury
1775	1775	1775	1775	109347	YKS	Gisburn
1798	1951	1750	1798	133760	YKS	Linthwaite
1800	1882	1760	1800	133760	YKS	Slaithwaite
....	1903	....	1903	133906	YKS	???
1939	1992	....	....	126187	???	Bristol
1867	1992	1800	1891	105899	???	Haddington
1867	1992	1800	1891	105899	???	Tranent
BAY						
1726	1800	1500	1726	129577	IOW	???
BAYBUTT						
1800	1900	....	....	146854	LAN	Southport

Known From	To	Researching From	To	Ref	Cty	Place
BAYFIELD						
1787	1840	....	....	131660	NFK	Norwich
BAYFORD						
1836	1900	1700	1836	168963	ESS	Gt Burstead
1772	1992	1500	1772	132233	HRT	Furneux Pelham
BAYLES						
1800	1900	1600	1800	104701	DUR	Romaldkirk
1555	1950	1555	1950	104698	SFK	Wilby
BAYLEY						
....	....	ALL	1800	104728	ALL	???
1818	1822	1860	1900	104728	CHS	ALL
1865	1886	....	1900	118117	DBY	Derby
1850	1850	1800	1992	133450	DEV	Plymouth
1620	1660	1660	1700	155896	GLS	Awre
1750	....	1750	1870	119458	KEN	Smeeth
1841	1871	1872	1900	104728	LAN	Liverpool
1600	1900	1600	1992	133450	LAN	Manchester
1690	1780	1600	1690	173312	SAL	North
1737	1793	....	....	117404	SAL	Dawley Magna
1650	1800	1600	1800	142018	SOM	Rode
1800	1850	....	....	103721	STS	Darlaston
1768	1838	1700	1767	166464	STS	Gentleshaw
1850	1900	1800	1900	103721	WAR	Birmingham
1900	1950	....	1900	148342	WAR	Birmingham
....	....	1600	1750	115142	WAR	Mancetter
....	....	1750	1850	142549	WIL	Sutton Veny
BAYLIFFE						
....	....	1750	1850	147613	LAN	Melling
BAYLIS						
1750	1830	ALL	1750	141224	GLS	South
....	....	1800	1900	168386	GLS	Cheltenham
1812	1880	1700	1812	134368	HEF	Welland
1520	....	....	....	109991	OXF	Enstone
1800	1900	1700	1800	174513	OXF	Somerton
1800	1900	1700	1800	174513	OXF	Upper Heyford
1820	1920	1750	1820	173444	WAR	North
1799	1850	1750	1810	137413	WOR	Lower Mitton
BAYLISS						
1801	1801	1700	1900	178322	GLS	Leckhampton
1859	1920	ALL	1859	168742	LND	London
1830	1992	1600	1830	156914	RAD	Huntington
1790	1886	1700	1900	159107	STS	Brockmoor
1850	1992	1700	1850	161349	WAR	Birmingham
1830	1845	....	1850	152803	WOR	Worcester
BAYLY						
1610	1634	1600	1650	177938	DOR	Netherbury
BAYMAN						
1700	ALL	1725	1900	107379	HRT	Hitchin
BAYNES						
....	....	1800	....	128627	ESS	Thaxted
....	....	ALL	1700	151629	EYK	Wistow
1768	1794	ALL	ALL	130508	FIF	Kilconquhar
1830	1832	ALL	ALL	115126	HAM	Bishops Waltham
1829	1844	1500	1844	157538	LIN	East Butterwick
1829	1844	1500	1844	157538	LIN	West Butterwick
1860	1933	ALL	....	136018	LND	Hoxton
1860	1933	ALL	....	136018	MDX	Hoxton
BAYNHAM						
1860	1880	ALL	ALL	140740	HEF	Weobley
1860	1992	ALL	ALL	140740	MON	Newport
1830	1860	ALL	ALL	140740	RAD	Presteign
BAYNTON						
1625	1992	ALL	1625	104752	SOM	ALL
1861	1866	1700	1827	174831	WIL	Westbury
1764	1992	1600	1764	163856	WOR	Stone
BAYTHROP						
1820	1880	1700	1850	146110	LAN	Priest Hutton
BAYTON						
1760	1992	1700	1769	164267	SRY	Kingston
BAYTUP						
1820	1874	1700	1900	100536	GLS	Campden
BAZELEE						
1674	1706	1640	1670	167533	LND	Wapping
BAZELEY						
1600	1780	....	....	106240	CON	St Columb
1780	1880	....	....	106240	CON	St Ives
1800	1950	....	....	106240	DEV	ALL
BAZELY						
1721	1764	ALL	1721	154563	DEV	ALL
1790	1992	....	....	104760	KEN	Deptford
1743	1790	ALL	1743	104760	SRY	Southwark
BAZLEY						
1900	1992	....	....	104779	CHS	Runcorn
1777	1777	ALL	ALL	104779	DEV	Bradninch
BAZLEY contd.						
1782	1820	....	....	104779	DEV	Broad Clyst
1814	1870	....	....	104779	DEV	Pinhoe
1822	1875	....	....	171557	DOR	Lyme Regis
1792	1800	....	....	104779	DOR	Uplyme
1911	1926	....	....	104779	GLA	Barry Dock
1921	1951	....	....	104779	GLA	Cardiff
1938	1945	....	....	104779	GLA	Porthcawl
1890	1921	....	....	104779	GLS	Staverton
1878	1900	....	....	104779	HEF	Leominster
1870	1947	....	....	104779	HEF	Stoke Prior
1700	ALL	....	....	117684	LAN	ALL
1701	1992	....	....	104779	LAN	Manchester
1900	1992	....	....	104779	LIN	Gainsborough
1903	1980	....	....	104779	LIN	Scunthorpe
1822	1875	....	....	171557	LND	Highgate
1880	1930	....	....	104779	LND	???
1894	1912	....	....	104779	SAL	Ludlow
1820	1899	....	....	104779	SOM	Hennington
1912	1939	....	....	104779	WAR	Birmingham
1867	1878	....	....	104779	WIL	Hilperton
1939	1987	....	....	104779	WOR	Kidderminster
....	1870	....	....	171557	???	Birmingham
BAZZONE						
....	....	ALL	ALL	104787	ALL	Name Study
BEACH						
1772	1799	1500	1772	110310	KEN	Benenden
1900	1992	....	1900	171131	OXF	Evesham
BEACHAM						
1850	1900	1700	1850	118915	ESS	Fobbing
1890	1992	ALL	1890	104795	GLS	Adlestrop
1890	1992	ALL	1890	104795	GLS	Bledington
1890	1992	ALL	1890	104795	GLS	Braodwell
1890	1992	ALL	1890	104795	GLS	Daylesford
1890	1992	ALL	1890	104795	GLS	Evenlode
1890	1992	ALL	1890	104795	GLS	Icomb
1890	1992	ALL	1890	104795	GLS	Maugersbury
1890	1992	ALL	1890	104795	GLS	Oddington
1890	1992	ALL	1890	104795	GLS	Prestbury
1890	1992	ALL	1890	104795	GLS	Stow On The Wold
....	....	1800	1899	174963	LND	ALL
1860	1870	1860	1870	121460	LND	Westminster
1600	1992	ALL	1600	104795	OXF	Kingham
....	....	ALL	ALL	174963	SOM	Kilmersden
....	....	ALL	ALL	174963	SOM	Mells
BEACHELL						
1755	1795	ALL	1755	102350	YKS	Monk Fryston
BEACHILL						
1750	1840	1750	1850	141984	YKS	Monk Fryston
BEACON						
1872	1992	....	....	172529	LIN	Grantham
1878	?	1878	?	140422	LND	City
1874	?	1874	?	140422	SRY	Lambeth
BEACROFT						
1881	1992	1600	1881	151092	KEN	New Cross
BEADLE						
1781	....	1700	1781	144746	ESS	Heybridge
1817	1860	1750	1850	124311	KEN	Lewisham
1900	1900	ALL	ALL	127787	LND	Peckham
1830	1860	1700	....	104809	SRY	Bermondsey
1850	....	1850	....	117250	???	Lewisham
BEADSON						
1759	1759	1759	1800	126705	LAN	Rochdale
BEAGLEHOLE						
1820	1850	1700	1850	156442	DEV	Dartmouth
1840	1880	1840	1900	156442	LND	Stepney
BEAGLES						
1801	....	....	....	135488	CAM	Elm
1746	1940	....	....	128996	CAM	Thorney
1800	....	....	....	135488	CAM	Wisbech
BEAGLEY						
1805	1860	1750	1860	126586	HAM	Bentley
1650	1780	1600	1800	144657	HAM	Farringdon
1811	1992	1700	1811	139777	SRY	Hambledon
BEAK						
1760	1850	1700	1992	173096	SOM	Bridgwater
BEAKE						
1780	1790	1650	1780	177164	SOM	Middlezoy
BEAKHOUSE						
1793	1992	1700	1793	125105	OXF	Rotherfield Grays
BEAL						
....	....	1800	1900	119784	BKM	Wycombe
1550	1800	1600	1650	133450	CON	Central
1650	1750	1650	1992	133450	CON	Advent

Known From	To	Researching From	To	Ref	Cty	Place
BEAL contd.						
....	....	1550	1700	117803	ERY	ALL
1657	1881	....	....	117803	ERY	Skirpenbeck
1795	1875	ALL	ALL	169730	HAM	Mapledurwell
....	....	ALL	ALL	166812	KEN	Isle Of Thanet
1750	1881	....	....	177687	LIN	Strubby
....	....	1550	1700	117803	NRY	ALL
1750	1800	ALL	....	143944	NRY	Terrington
1825	1860	1500	1850	104825	OXF	Banbury
1865	1930	1700	1900	115894	YKS	North
1865	1930	1700	1900	115894	YKS	West
1865	1865	....	....	141097	YKS	North Newbald
BEALE						
....	....	1800	1900	119784	BKM	Wycombe
1890	1950	1700	1992	121215	DBY	Glossop
....	1780	1700	1780	121010	GLS	Newent
1600	1800	1600	1800	144657	HAM	Farringdon
1400	1600	1400	1600	144657	HAM	Priors Dean
1800	1902	1700	1800	174068	HRT	Cheshunt
1700	1725	....	....	145688	LIN	Great Coates
1870	....	ALL	ALL	116394	LND	???
....	1700	....	....	174564	OXF	???
1763	1864	1720	1920	105333	SSX	Birdham
BEALES						
1841	1920	....	....	122319	NFK	Norwich
BEALEY						
1802	1813	....	1802	125954	DEV	Merton
BEAMAN						
1850	1930	1800	1950	145556	KEN	Sydenham
1811	1855	1700	1855	115347	LAN	Liverpool
1850	1930	1800	1950	145556	LND	South
1850	1930	1800	1950	145556	SRY	South London
BEAMISH						
....	....	ALL	ALL	104833	ALL	Name Study
1594	1992	1108	1992	104833	ALL	ALL
1826	1946	....	....	151548	WAR	Coventry
BEAMOND						
1780	1805	....	....	128082	MGY	Churchstoke
BEAMONT						
1640	1684	ALL	ALL	141615	LEI	Leicester
1780	1820	1700	1780	155500	SAL	Wistanstow
BEAMS						
1750	1840	....	....	110124	SRY	Ewell
1800	1900	1700	1800	144681	SRY	Ewell
....	....	1600	1750	110124	SRY	???
BEAN						
1814	....	ALL	ALL	155632	CHI	Guernsey
1814	....	ALL	ALL	155632	CHI	Jersey
1750	1780	1740	1780	136980	HAM	Hayling Island
1750	1820	1700	1800	136840	HAM	Hayling
1710	1734	1675	1992	114901	HAM	Portsea
1734	1760	1734	1992	114901	HAM	South Hayling
1842	....	....	....	104841	HAM	Winchester
1773	1853	....	....	104841	KEN	Bethersden
1856	1870	....	....	104841	KEN	Bexley
1540	1606	1538	1707	104841	KEN	Chislet
1763	1837	....	....	104841	KEN	Deptford
1588	1841	1558	1849	104841	KEN	Dover
1464	1665	1572	1665	104841	KEN	Elham
1551	1849	....	....	104841	KEN	Folkestone
1876	1943	....	....	104841	KEN	Great Chart
1572	1719	1560	1600	104841	KEN	Hythe
1716	1797	1715	1808	104841	KEN	Rochester
1716	1797	1715	1808	104841	KEN	Strood
1815	1834	....	....	104841	KEN	Tenterden
1687	1855	1547	1837	104841	KEN	Tonbridge
1784	1796	1702	1796	104841	KEN	Tudeley Cum Capel
1747	1865	....	....	104841	LND	Deptford
1820	1930	1800	1930	103225	LND	Holborn
1680	1873	....	....	104841	LND	St Marylebone
1780	1800	1780	1800	136980	MDX	Picadilly
1865	....	....	....	104841	MON	Rockfield
1836	1867	....	....	104841	SRY	Croydon
1866	1869	....	....	104841	SRY	Wimbledon
1588	1684	....	....	104841	SSX	Alfriston
1795	1837	....	1880	104841	SSX	Bexhill
1792	1929	1777	1906	104841	SSX	Brighton
1814	1980	....	....	104841	SSX	Burwash
1757	1762	....	....	104841	SSX	Chiddingly
1642	1674	1568	1759	104841	SSX	Denton
1567	1885	1566	1889	104841	SSX	East Blatchington
1716	1752	....	....	104841	SSX	East Dean
1812	1862	1812	1862	104841	SSX	East Grinstead
1787	1855	1754	1901	104841	SSX	East Guldeford
BEAN contd.						
1681	1913	....	....	104841	SSX	Eastbourne
1651	1839	....	....	104841	SSX	Frant
1704	1735	1704	1737	104841	SSX	Friston
1690	1907	1558	1970	104841	SSX	Hastings
1861	1992	1846	1992	104841	SSX	Heathfield
....	1851	1815	1880	104841	SSX	Hooe
1835	....	....	....	104841	SSX	Hurstpierpoint
1723	1799	1723	1874	104841	SSX	Iden
1809	1909	1754	1948	104841	SSX	Isfield
1870	1930	1870	....	144983	SSX	Isfield
1661	1743	1661	1783	104841	SSX	Jevington
1804	1892	....	....	104841	SSX	Lewes
1706	1809	1593	1809	104841	SSX	Litlington
1817	1864	1813	1857	104841	SSX	Mayfield
1720	1858	1813	1837	104841	SSX	Pett
1569	1773	1569	1773	104841	SSX	Petworth
1743	....	....	....	104841	SSX	Piddinghoe
1653	1723	....	....	104841	SSX	Ringmer
1832	1861	1813	1847	104841	SSX	Rotherfield
1737	1846	1764	1772	104841	SSX	Rottingdean
1576	....	1596	....	104841	SSX	Rye
1559	1845	1559	1880	104841	SSX	Seaford
1587	1588	....	....	104841	SSX	Southease
....	1625	1604	1754	104841	SSX	Southeighton
1796	1917	1640	1973	104841	SSX	Uckfield
1799	1904	1793	1840	104841	SSX	Waldron
1882	1950	1882	1950	104841	SSX	Warbleton
1816	1851	....	....	104841	SSX	Westbourne
1609	1752	1690	1840	104841	SSX	Willingdon
1729	1835	....	....	104841	SSX	Wivelsfield
1760	1800	....	....	177393	YKS	Arksey
1700	1992	1650	1992	134589	YKS	Dalby
1826	1860	....	....	177393	YKS	Doncaster
1720	1760	1680	1720	177393	YKS	Fishlake
1660	1930	1660	1930	150118	YKS	Kirkby Wharfe
BEAR						
1780	1830	1730	1840	120995	DEV	Kenton
1725	1861	1700	1880	171549	DEV	West Putford
1770	1888	1770	1992	108251	KEN	Medway
1860	1920	ALL	ALL	111732	LND	East
1813	1992	1800	1920	130621	LND	Hackney
1813	1992	1800	1920	130621	LND	Marylebone
BEARD						
1720	1830	1700	1720	151866	CAM	Haslingfield
1752	1940	....	....	128996	CAM	Thorney
1680	1992	1680	1992	178357	CHS	ALL
1806	1835	1800	1850	124788	DBY	Glossop
1812	1851	ALL	1812	179086	DBY	Glossop
1800	1830	1750	1800	160458	DBY	Hayfield
....	....	1500	1779	138614	DEV	Exeter
1730	1830	1730	1840	120995	DEV	Kenton
1933	1936	1933	1992	104876	DOR	Bournemouth
1600	1900	1600	1900	104868	GLS	Painswick
1790	....	ALL	1822	152641	GLS	Stanley St Leonard
1680	1992	1680	1992	178357	LAN	ALL
1867	....	ALL	ALL	127205	LAN	Holcombe Brook
1890	1992	1500	1890	134600	LND	ALL
1933	1939	1939	1992	104876	SSX	Brighton
1710	1710	1680	1730	105120	SSX	Brighton
1723	1992	....	....	135844	SSX	East Grinstead
1800	1992	1750	1800	104884	STS	ALL
1926	1935	1935	1992	104876	???	Birmingham Ladywood
BEARDER						
1760	1780	1650	1760	175986	DBY	North
1804	1900	1780	1804	175986	YKS	Bradford
1804	1900	1780	1804	175986	YKS	Halifax
BEARDMORE						
....	1779	....	1779	128910	DBY	Duffield
1800	1850	1700	1800	151769	DBY	Ironville
1837	....	1700	1900	175307	STS	Cheadle
1759	1760	1700	1800	149098	STS	Newcastle
BEARDSALL						
1709	1709	....	....	159492	LAN	Oldham
BEARDSHALL						
1662	1876	1662	1880	169900	YKS	Silkstone
1778	1837	1778	1841	169900	YKS	Worsbrough
BEARDSLEY						
1600	1860	1600	1810	166952	DBY	Crich
1874	1940	1500	1992	117900	DBY	Ilkeston
1770	1980	1700	1770	162213	DBY	Ilkeston
1600	1860	1600	1810	166952	DBY	South Wingfield
1864	1938	....	1864	121002	DBY	???

Known From	To	Researching From	To	Ref	Cty	Place
BEARDSMORE						
1885	1992	....	....	104892	STS	Lichfield
1790	1910	1550	1891	104892	STS	Rugeley
BEARE						
1838	....	....	1838	152242	CON	Penzance
BEARHOPE						
1790	1870	1790	1900	142557	SCT	Galashiels
BEARMAN						
1825	1925	1700	1825	170887	ESS	Bocking
BEARNE						
....	....	1700	1799	174963	DEV	Kingsteignton
BEARSBY						
....	....	ALL	ALL	158704	ALL	Name Study
1796	1992	?	1796	158704	ALL	ALL
BEART						
....	....	ALL	ALL	100889	ALL	Name Study
BEARUP						
....	....	ALL	ALL	142557	DUR	ALL
....	....	ALL	ALL	142557	ENG	Borders
1770	1850	1700	1900	142557	NBL	Newcastle
....	....	ALL	ALL	142557	SCT	Borders
....	....	ALL	ALL	142557	YKS	ALL
....	....	ALL	ALL	142557	???	Newcastle
BEASANT						
....	....	1785	1843	130958	WIL	Bremhill
BEASLEY						
1790	1840	1700	1860	120472	BRK	Bray
1790	1840	1700	1860	120472	BRK	Cookham
1790	1840	1700	1860	120472	BRK	Maidenhead
1840	1892	1750	1920	120472	BRK	Reading
1800	1860	1860	1992	117110	KEN	Canterbury
1834	1992	....	1834	141968	KEN	Greenwich
1799	1806	1785	1812	120472	LND	Clerkenwell
1770	1800	1600	1770	117110	MDX	London
1900	1980	1750	1900	158976	SRY	Roehampton
BEASTON						
1717	1756	ALL	1717	154946	ERY	Eastringham
BEATER						
1780	1950	1600	1780	162876	DEV	Kingsteignton
BEATHAM						
1800	....	....	....	131822	CMA	Glassonby
1700	1820	1700	1850	143553	WES	Crosby Rav
BEATON						
1860	1992	1600	1860	146137	ABD	Ellon
1860	1992	1600	1860	146137	ABD	Monquhitter
1685	1775	1660	1800	150002	ANS	Forfar
1793	....	ALL	ALL	105481	NTT	Strelley
1750	1816	1650	1816	144606	SOM	South
1874	1900	ALL	ALL	177989	WOR	Oldbury
1874	1900	ALL	ALL	177989	WOR	West Bromwivh
BEATSON						
....	....	ALL	ALL	104906	ALL	Name Study
1800	1851	ALL	ALL	142204	LAN	Bury
1851	1871	1871	1900	142204	LAN	Manchester
BEATTIE						
1875	1902	1841	1891	124001	ABD	Insch
1898	1963	1800	1992	116009	ANT	Belfast
1800	1855	ALL	1855	100102	AYR	Saltcoats
1874	1992	ALL	1874	123749	CAV	Tarmore
1836	1992	ALL	ALL	140813	CMA	ALL
1825	1845	1825	1845	149403	CUL	Castle Carrock
1853	1883	1700	1853	138584	LAN	Liverpool
1873	1922	1836	1922	140813	SCT	???
1800	1850	1800	1850	149403	SCT	???
1700	1992	1700	1992	104914	SHI	ALL
BEATTY						
1800	1850	1600	1850	133590	TYR	Stewartstown
1839	....	1800	1860	169625	TYR	???
BEAUCHAMP						
....	....	ALL	ALL	174963	ALL	Bristol
1100	1450	....	....	100536	ALL	???
1860	1992	1500	1860	139033	LAN	Rossendale Valley
1860	1992	1500	1860	139033	LND	Kingston Upon Thames
1860	1992	1500	1860	139033	SRY	Kingston Upon Thames
1268	1449	1268	1317	124974	WAR	Warwick
1804	1992	1770	1900	104957	WMD	Coventry
1100	1268	1100	1268	124974	WOR	Elmley
BEAUFORT						
1372	1464	....	....	100536	ALL	???
BEAUFOY						
1400	1992	1400	1992	100420	NTH	ALL
1400	1992	1400	1992	100420	WAR	ALL
BEAUFOY contd.						
....	....	1700	1900	104965	???	Coventry
BEAUMAN						
1736	1755	....	1790	171441	KEN	Stansted
BEAUMONT						
1761	1843	1761	1930	115797	HEF	West
1789	....	....	1789	108839	HUN	Somersham
1066	1118	1066	1100	124974	LEI	Leicester
1340	1600	1200	1600	154881	LEI	Thringston
1869	1944	....	1869	123714	NFK	Horningthorpe
1775	1816	1650	1774	131245	SFK	Hadleigh
1790	1960	1700	1850	168734	WAR	Coventry
1838	1930	1760	1838	132039	WIL	Salisbury
1786	1862	....	1786	101761	WRY	Almondbury
1781	....	....	1781	101761	WRY	Cumberworth
1768	....	....	1768	101761	WRY	Thornhill
1880	1992	ALL	1900	162027	WYK	Huddersfield
1831	1921	1800	1921	147311	WYK	Leeds
1760	1800	1730	1800	123595	YKS	Almondbury
1762	1880	1700	1800	170348	YKS	Almondbury
1859	1992	....	....	131628	YKS	Bradford
1780	1850	?	1780	144800	YKS	Holmfirm
1867	1989	1700	1866	136859	YKS	Huddersfield
1818	1992	1800	1852	166960	YKS	Huddersfield
1666	1727	1640	1740	170348	YKS	Huddersfield
1859	1992	....	....	131628	YKS	Keighley
1578	1610	1560	1650	170348	YKS	Mirfield
BEAVAN						
1685	1915	1545	1992	107514	HAM	Chalton
1829	1866	1750	1829	176931	HEF	Leominster
1855	1870	....	1855	122378	KEN	Ightham
1925	1992	1800	1925	106186	MDX	Hammersmith
....	....	1650	1800	106461	WIL	ALL
1685	1915	1545	1992	107514	WIL	Salisbury
1829	1866	1750	1829	176931	WOR	Leominster
BEAVEN						
1600	1850	1600	1800	104981	WIL	???
1859	....	1700	1859	172448	WOR	Worcester
BEAVER						
1804	1855	ALL	1804	112313	LAN	Manchester
1920	....	....	....	135968	LEI	Leicester
BEAVERS						
1800	1900	1700	1900	124621	TYR	ALL
1800	1900	1700	1900	132446	TYR	ALL
BEAVES						
1720	1825	1700	1800	131911	HAM	Romsey
BEAVIS						
1760	1803	ALL	1760	154563	DOR	Broadwey
1833	1900	1600	1992	159956	ESS	Copford
1833	1900	1700	1992	159956	ESS	Pluden
BEAZER						
1864	1879	ALL	1992	143197	WIL	Trowbridge
BEAZLEY						
1792	1931	1760	1900	105325	CAM	Ely
1880	1992	1800	1992	176982	HAM	Southampton
....	....	ALL	ALL	175943	IOW	Ryde
1775	1838	1600	1775	151092	LND	???
1820	1915	ALL	ALL	175943	SSX	Brighton
BEAZOR						
1810	1880	1700	1810	122599	NFK	Yarmouth
BEBB						
1880	1919	1880	1919	125148	AVN	Bristol
1823	....	ALL	1823	125148	HEF	Baston
BEBBINGTON						
1790	1910	1600	1912	130621	CHS	South
1710	1992	1600	1710	174378	CHS	Barthomley
1700	1948	1700	1992	128171	CHS	Malpas
1790	1850	ALL	ALL	161292	CHS	Weaverham
....	....	1700	1992	128171	SAL	Whitchurch
BEBEE						
1671	1940	....	....	128996	CAM	Thorney
BECK						
1850	1900	1750	1850	167789	ANT	???
1767	1992	1650	1992	101419	BRK	ALL
1769	1951	ALL	ALL	105015	BRK	Hurley
1786	1786	1750	1800	125032	BRK	Sonning
1875	1880	1820	1920	102482	CMA	Carlisle
1850	1900	1750	1850	167789	DOW	???
1916	1942	1880	1915	102482	ESS	Dovercourt
1830	....	....	....	167037	GLS	Stroud
1834	....	1834	....	158011	LEI	Newbold Verdun
....	....	1700	1850	112208	LND	St Pancras
....	....	1840	1870	100218	MDX	Kensington
1720	1816	1700	1800	162272	MDX	Southgate

Surname	Known From	Known To	Researching From	Researching To	Ref	Cty	Place
BECK contd.							
	1900	1992	....	....	105058	MDX	Uxbridge
	1863	1880	1840	1860	173118	NBL	Corenside
	1754	1992	1600	1754	125105	NFK	Catfield
	1815	1815	ALL	1815	129283	NFK	Haddiscoe
	1851	1881	1700	1850	169994	NTT	Nottingham
	1767	1992	1650	1992	101419	OXF	ALL
	1760	1992	1700	1760	105031	SFK	Kettleburgh
	....	1818	ALL	ALL	129933	SOM	Bridgewater
	1830	1906	1700	1830	162035	SRY	Rotherhythe
	1870	1980	1800	1900	169404	SSX	Eastbourne
	....	....	1838	1909	105058	SSX	Haywards Heath
	1840	1900	1700	1840	170801	SSX	Lewes
	1876	1903	....	....	105058	SSX	Worthing
	1837	....	1600	1837	105023	STS	Elford
	1881	1962	1700	1881	105023	STS	Tamworth
	1861	....	1700	1861	105023	STS	Walsall
	1863	....	1700	1863	105023	WAR	Ashted
BECKENHAM							
	....	....	1700	1920	105074	BRK	Reading
	....	....	1820	1920	105074	LND	Lambeth
	1870	1970	1700	1870	105074	MDX	Brentford
	1870	1970	1700	1870	105074	MDX	St Pancras
	1870	1970	1700	1870	105074	SRY	Croydon
BECKENSALE							
	1776	....	....	....	142360	OXF	Bampton
BECKERLEG							
	....	....	ALL	ALL	105082	ALL	Name Study
	....	....	1600	1850	105082	CON	Ashton
	....	....	1600	1850	105082	CON	Breage
	....	....	1600	1850	105082	CON	Gwennap
	....	....	1600	1850	105082	CON	Madron
	....	....	1066	ALL	105090	CON	Mousehole
	....	....	1600	1850	105082	CON	Paul
	1726	1830	1700	1726	153605	CON	Paul
	....	....	1066	ALL	105090	DEV	Bickleton
	....	....	1066	ALL	105090	HUM	Bicker
	....	....	1066	ALL	105090	NYK	Bickerton
BECKERLEGGE							
	1838	1992	....	....	105090	CON	Marazion
	1250	....	1250	1617	105090	DEV	Bickleigh
BECKET							
	1765	1785	ALL	1800	118737	BRK	Appleton
	1821	1829	....	....	121827	SFK	Orford
	1821	1829	....	....	121827	SFK	Yoxford
BECKETT							
	1930	1980	1850	1930	158976	BKM	South
	1892	1965	1880	1965	127353	HAM	Sherrish Heath
	....	....	ALL	ALL	143340	LAN	???
	1825	1876	1825	....	113875	LIN	Coddington
	1825	1965	1700	1825	110620	LND	East End
	1795	....	....	....	164232	OXF	Shipton
	1831	1940	1831	1910	164232	SFK	Bury St Edmunds
	1800	1992	1500	1800	145157	SFK	Woodbridge
	1850	1890	1800	1900	173436	WAR	Stratford Upon Avon
	1841	1881	ALL	....	153214	WIL	Teffort Erias Ridge
BECKHAM							
	....	....	ALL	ALL	105112	ALL	Name Study
	ALL	ALL	ALL	ALL	105112	ALL	ALL
	1839	1900	1800	1850	149446	NFK	???
BECKINGHAM							
	1738	1830	1738	1830	107514	WIL	Great Bedwyn
	1775	1828	1700	1775	166782	WIL	Great Bedwyn
	1770	1841	1700	1850	105120	WIL	Marlborough
	1772	1855	1700	1900	105120	WIL	Overton
	1738	1830	1738	1830	107514	WIL	Savernake
	1828	1992	1700	1775	166782	WIL	Savernake
BECKINSALE							
	1663	ALL	ALL	ALL	162108	ALL	ALL
	1867	1992	ALL	ALL	162108	LND	ALL
	1663	1867	ALL	ALL	162108	OXF	ALL
BECKLEY							
	1698	1988	1698	1829	153257	BKM	Wendover
	1920	1992	1850	1992	151459	ESS	South
	1920	1992	1850	1992	151459	LND	???
BECKTON							
	1890	1930	1850	1992	151521	YKS	Leeds
	1890	1930	1850	1992	151521	YKS	Sheffield
BECKWITH							
	1800	1900	1700	1800	135054	YKS	Middleham
BEDDARD							
	1800	....	ALL	ALL	112461	WOR	ALL
BEDDING							
	1851	....	1700	1851	159271	LND	East
BEDDING contd.							
	1920	1992	1700	1920	130044	MDX	Bethnal Green
BEDDINGFIELD							
	1835	1900	1700	1835	139335	NFK	Norwich
BEDDINGTON							
	1819	1840	1790	1819	142360	WIL	Hullavington
BEDDOES							
	1867	....	1680	....	123471	SAL	Clunbury
BEDDOW							
	?	?	1848	1875	131733	CWD	Llangollen
	1800	1815	1750	1830	158658	GLA	Lougher
	1898	....	....	....	161136	GLA	Port Talbot
	1751	1790	1700	1800	162280	SAL	Broseley
BEDDOWES							
	1850	1869	1800	1870	165824	YKS	Barnsley
BEDDOWS							
	1800	1860	1700	1800	132268	LAN	Horwich
BEDELL							
	....	1830	1700	1830	104809	SRY	Bermondsey
BEDELLA							
	1748	1813	1700	1748	168173	CON	Merther
BEDENHAM							
	....	....	ALL	ALL	105147	ALL	Name Study
	1795	1992	1795	1992	105147	WOR	Besford
BEDER							
	1714	....	ALL	1992	106119	BRK	???
	1715	....	ALL	1992	106119	SRY	???
BEDESOR							
	1296	....	ALL	1992	106119	SSX	???
BEDESTER							
	1838	....	ALL	1992	106119	SRY	???
BEDFORD							
	1771	1800	1700	1771	170593	BKM	Twyford
	1841	1841	1750	1870	171662	BRK	Reading
	1810	1945	ALL	1810	114928	CON	???
	....	....	1650	1799	105171	DEV	Crediton
	....	....	1799	1992	105171	DEV	Exeter
	1799	1848	....	....	105171	DEV	Kenn-Kenford
	1895	1910	....	....	104272	KEN	Loose
	1827	1910	1750	1827	153974	KEN	Tunbridge
	1811	....	ALL	....	104515	LIN	Heckington
	1880	1950	ALL	ALL	135127	LND	St Mary Newington
	....	....	1700	1770	177393	NTT	Retford
	1750	1840	ALL	ALL	106313	OXF	Hook Norton
	1850	1992	1700	1850	105201	SRY	Southwark
	1706	1830	1700	1850	150304	WRY	East Ardsley
	1839	1855	....	....	150304	WRY	Gildersome
	1822	....	....	....	126276	WRY	Gowdall
	....	1847	....	....	126276	WRY	Thorne
	1746	1838	1700	1850	150304	WRY	West Ardsley
	1746	1838	1700	1850	150304	WRY	Woodkirk
	1873	1992	1700	1873	105163	WYK	Pontefract
	1858	1992	1700	1900	167606	WYK	Sowery Bridge
	1800	1980	1750	1850	105198	YKS	Ardsley East
	1790	1810	1750	1790	177393	YKS	Bawtry
	1826	1992	1650	1826	168513	YKS	Hampole
	1803	1836	1700	1803	166723	YKS	Leeds
	1839	1905	1700	1839	179043	YKS	Leeds
	....	....	1850	1880	159220	YKS	Pontefract
	....	....	1890	1992	105171	???	London
BEDHOUSE							
	1616	1759	1550	1658	102830	STS	Sedgely
BEDIENT							
	1684	1761	....	....	142522	MDX	Staines
BEDINGFIELD							
	....	....	1700	1710	161357	KEN	Margate
	1800	1992	1750	1900	105228	SFK	East
BEDLAKE							
	1703	1706	ALL	1720	168718	CON	South East
BEDLINGTON							
	1800	1920	ALL	ALL	122297	DUR	South Shields
BEDNALL							
	....	....	1675	1725	153478	DBY	???
	....	....	1675	1725	153478	LEI	???
	....	....	1675	1725	153478	SAL	???
	1725	1992	1675	1725	153478	STS	Walsall
	....	....	1675	1725	153478	WAR	???
BEDNELL							
	1810	....	....	....	118931	STS	???
	1851	1852	1851	....	118931	WAR	Coventry
BEDR							
	1715	....	ALL	1992	106119	SRY	???
BEDROCK							
	....	1888	....	1888	105236	CHS	Chester

Known From	To	Researching From	To	Ref	Cty	Place
BEDROCK contd.						
1900	1992	....	....	105236	CHS	Port Sunlight
1890	1900	....	....	105236	GYN	Trawsfynydd
BEDSAR						
1679	....	ALL	1992	106119	SRY	???
BEDSER						
....	....	ALL	ALL	105244	ALL	Name Study
1750	1992	1500	1992	105244	ALL	ALL
1702	1992	ALL	1992	106119	BRK	???
1900	1992	ALL	1992	106119	EAG	???
1723	1992	ALL	1992	106119	HAM	???
1900	1992	ALL	1992	106119	HRT	???
1729	1992	ALL	1992	106119	MDX	???
1695	1992	ALL	1992	106119	SRY	???
BEDSIR						
1812	....	ALL	1992	106119	SRY	???
BEDSON						
1500	1600	....	....	100420	WAR	Meriden
BEDSOR						
1716	....	ALL	1992	106119	HAM	???
BEDSTER						
1782	1784	ALL	1992	106119	BRK	???
1900	....	ALL	1992	106119	HRT	???
1859	1902	1700	1900	106119	KEN	Faversham
1900	....	ALL	1992	106119	LND	???
1729	....	ALL	1992	106119	SRY	???
BEDSUM						
1703	....	ALL	1992	106119	SRY	???
BEDWARD						
....	....	ALL	ALL	104493	ALL	Name Study
BEDWELL						
1710	1897	ALL	ALL	166804	ALL	ALL
1803	1992	1650	1803	101419	BRK	ALL
1803	1992	1650	1803	101419	BRK	Steventon
1775	1920	1700	1992	132799	BRK	Steventon
1803	1856	1857	1870	101419	OXF	Bampton
BEE						
1600	1700	1600	1700	169781	DUR	Durham
1764	1766	1720	1800	105333	HAM	Isle Of Wight
1660	1900	1600	1800	113654	LAN	Garstang
1850	1880	1750	1880	136565	LAN	Preston
1846	1931	1846	1931	151211	LIN	Louth
....	1715	1500	1715	175072	LIN	Metheringham
1689	1689	....	....	121835	LIN	Waddington
1538	1992	....	1538	105252	LIN	???
1805	1899	1700	1805	160024	NFK	Kings Lynn
BEEBY						
1798	1849	ALL	1798	146315	HUN	Farcet
1756	....	?	1770	164976	HUN	Houghton
1798	1849	ALL	1798	146315	HUN	Titmarsh
....	1900	ALL	1900	146315	LAN	Hartshead
1628	1900	1620	1628	129909	NTH	East
1700	1730	1730	1770	174947	NTH	Kettering
1700	1730	1730	1770	174947	NTH	Thrapston
1838	?	1700	1838	108588	NTH	Wellingborough
1700	1730	1730	1770	174947	NTH	Woodford-Tuxta
BEEBYE						
1650	1650	1600	1650	174130	LEI	Houghton On The Hill
BEECH						
1828	1880	1750	1830	135763	CHS	Sandbach
1779	1779	1700	1800	147575	KEN	Deal
1871	1881	....	....	135348	LAN	Oldham
ALL	....	....	1743	140716	NTH	Blisworth
1743	....	1600	1743	140716	NTH	Milton
....	....	....	1870	129313	STS	Biddulph
1825	1887	1725	1825	134473	STS	Longton
1850	1992	1850	1992	105279	WAR	Birmingham
1780	1850	....	....	105279	WOR	Hartlebury
BEECHAM						
1710	1880	ALL	....	104515	LIN	South
BEECHENO						
....	....	ALL	ALL	150878	ALL	Name Study
ALL	ALL	ALL	ALL	148997	ALL	ALL
1835	1992	ALL	1835	148997	???	London
BEECHER						
....	....	ALL	ALL	177148	ALL	Name Study
1900	....	1800	....	100536	???	???
BEECHEY						
1817	1840	ALL	1817	150967	BRK	Abingdon
1780	1880	1700	1900	166804	GLS	Lechlade
....	....	1770	1800	150967	KEN	Spensus
1860	1890	1800	1860	132187	LND	Brompton
1885	1920	....	....	150967	LND	Kensal Town
BEECHEY contd.						
1750	1850	1750	1992	133450	OXF	Burford
BEECHING						
....	....	ALL	ALL	105287	ALL	ALL
1700	1992	1600	1992	105287	KEN	ALL
1710	....	....	1750	171441	KEN	Bathersden
1757	1891	ALL	ALL	157856	KEN	Monchelsea
1750	1850	1700	1950	105287	SSX	East
BEECROFT						
....	....	1700	1850	152390	HUN	???
1822	1900	1600	1992	172863	YKS	Harrogate
1821	1871	ALL	1850	114553	YKS	Spofforth
BEEDALL						
1790	1972	1752	1972	103012	LIN	ALL
BEEDELL						
1860	1947	1800	1947	139327	LND	Lambeth
1860	1947	1800	1947	139327	SRY	Lambeth
BEEDIE						
1873	1903	....	....	172871	ANS	Montrose
....	....	1750	1800	172871	KCD	Arbuthnott
1818	1891	1800	1818	172871	KCD	Bervie
BEEDLE						
1675	....	1600	1700	124796	BKM	Water Stratford
1824	1847	1600	1823	156779	DEV	Exeter
1700	1800	1600	1992	114596	DEV	Tiverton
....	?	....	1872	105155	MDX	Westminster
1774	1992	....	1774	105295	NYK	Wykeham
1813	1918	....	....	117161	YKS	Fylingdales
BEEDOM						
1637	1710	?	1637	158569	HRT	ALL
BEEKEN						
1800	1870	1700	1800	132640	KEN	Tenterden
1826	1912	ALL	1826	159077	LIN	Crowland
BEEKIN						
1811	1900	....	....	164631	LIN	Spalding
BEELEY						
1851	1920	....	....	153796	CHS	Hyde
1780	1821	....	....	153796	CHS	Stockport
BEER						
1837	1909	1538	1837	144479	AVN	Bath
1880	1930	1880	1930	132721	CAM	Cambridge
....	....	1600	1900	179531	CON	Tywardreath
1750	1992	1500	1992	166758	DEV	South
?	?	?	?	156671	DEV	Beer
1806	1900	1806	1900	118540	DEV	Montleigh
1860	1880	1830	1920	142875	DEV	Newton Abbot
1756	1790	1650	1756	172898	DEV	Woodleigh
1900	1992	....	....	135666	GLA	Pentyrch
....	....	1800	1840	165824	GLS	Bristol
....	....	1600	1950	134546	IOW	Brading
1786	1828	1700	1786	117110	KEN	Deal
1619	1952	ALL	ALL	137774	KEN	Dover
1890	....	....	....	136565	LAN	Liverpool
1840	1983	1840	1983	165824	SOM	Bath
1851	....	....	....	174750	SOM	Haselbury Plucknett
BEERE						
1848	....	1700	1869	115967	SOM	Bath
BEERS						
1808	1808	1750	1830	159905	WAR	Bubbenhall
BEESLEY						
1860	1863	1600	1860	165697	BKM	Slough
....	....	1700	1850	117587	LAN	South West
1560	1992	1560	1861	160237	LAN	South
1860	1863	1600	1860	165697	SFK	Mildenhall
....	....	ALL	....	120839	WAR	???
BEESON						
1803	1992	ALL	1803	115126	BKM	Gt Missenden
....	....	ALL	1890	175323	DBY	Derby
1894	1992	1700	1894	105309	LND	East
BEETHAM						
1700	1784	....	....	136565	WES	Burton In Kendal
1880	1992	1600	1880	166103	YKS	Bishop Monkton
1800	1950	ALL	1950	144290	YKS	Doncaster
1700	1850	ALL	1850	144290	YKS	East Ardsley
1750	1850	ALL	1850	144290	YKS	Hooten Pagnell
BEETLESTONE						
1740	1760	1650	1760	160849	SAL	Worfield
BEETON						
1580	1900	1650	1900	105317	SFK	North West
1800	1992	1600	1800	166103	SFK	Cowlinge
BEETS						
1750	1850	1700	1900	156701	KEN	Dover
BEETSON						
1796	1925	1760	1950	126705	LAN	South

Known From	To	Researching From	To	Ref	Cty	Place
BEEVER						
1861	1992	....	....	115258	YKS	Clayton West
1780	1800	1750	1800	123595	YKS	Holmfirth
BEEVERS						
1796	1833	1770	1850	123285	SYK	Rawmarsh
BEEVIS						
1900	1992	....	1900	137642	KEN	Maidstone
BEEXLEY						
1792	1931	1760	1900	105325	CAM	Ely
BEGBIE						
1819	1992	1819	1900	175196	AVN	Bristol
1870	1901	ALL	ALL	176419	AYR	Kilmarnock
1880	1950	1881	....	170623	BRK	Windsor
1584	1992	1584	1800	175196	ELN	ALL
1857	1857	1857	1857	175196	LAN	Liverpool
1833	1870	1833	1870	170623	LND	Pancras
1779	1992	1750	1900	175196	MDX	Westminster
1805	....	....	....	170623	SCT	???
BEGGS						
1853	1992	1700	1853	105899	ANT	???
1882	1942	....	....	151548	NIR	Belfast
BEGLEY						
1840	1870	1820	1880	100218	WAR	Coventry
BEHAGG						
?	?	ALL	ALL	174432	HUN	Wistow
BEHAN						
1840	....	....	....	122335	WES	Kilbeggan
BEHENNA						
....	....	1800	1850	153745	CON	Kenwyn
....	....	ALL	1850	166499	CON	St Gluvias
....	....	ALL	1874	166499	???	London
BEILBY						
1780	1790	1700	1800	168297	YKS	???
BELAM						
....	....	ALL	ALL	105333	ALL	Name Study
1400	1992	ALL	ALL	105333	ALL	ALL
BELANEY						
....	....	ALL	ALL	148970	ALL	Name Study
BELBIN						
....	....	ALL	ALL	105341	ALL	Name Study
BELCHAMBER						
1803	1861	1790	....	102989	KEN	Deptford
1766	1803	1766	....	102989	KEN	St Mary Cary
BELCHAMBERS						
1770	1800	1700	1800	136840	KEN	Westerham
BELCHER						
....	....	ALL	ALL	105368	ALL	Name Study
1849	1925	1800	1850	125628	BRK	Beenham
1596	1855	1500	1600	125628	BRK	Denchworth
1841	1992	1700	1992	149659	BRK	Hagbourne
1889	1901	ALL	1889	119504	DUR	Brandon
1813	1992	ALL	1890	105376	LIN	Bourne
1875	1970	1850	1992	145572	LND	Hackney
1875	1970	1850	1992	145572	LND	Shoreditch
1855	1900	....	....	130281	LND	Somers Town
1850	1930	1700	1850	102903	NTH	Wellingborough
1770	1820	1700	1800	105767	WOR	South
....	....	ALL	1880	173045	YKS	Pontefract
BELDHAM						
1697	1705	1670	1720	131547	SRY	Okewood
BELERBY						
1581	....	....	....	105481	DUR	St Oswald
BELGROVE						
1824	1880	1700	1824	160601	OXF	Cassington
BELITHER						
1800	1860	1860	1900	133396	KEN	Plumstead
1800	1860	1860	1900	133396	LND	Plumstead
BELKNAPPE						
1450	1500	1350	1450	154881	KEN	Boughton Aluph
BELL						
....	....	ALL	ALL	105430	ALL	Name Study
1860	1900	1800	1900	167258	ABD	Fraserburgh
1815	1817	....	....	127140	ARL	Glenaray
1815	1817	....	....	127140	ARL	Sallachary
....	....	1840	....	150711	AVN	Bedminster
1870	1980	1700	1870	160989	BEW	Berwick
1700	1900	1500	1700	174661	CAM	Cambridge
1720	1780	1600	1720	101834	CAM	Dry Drayton
1800	1950	1830	1992	121320	CHS	Wallasey
1750	1800	....	....	148261	CUL	Alston
1732	1837	1700	1850	160873	CUL	Arthuret
....	....	1750	1850	148474	CUL	Hayton
1759	1782	1600	1800	130125	CUL	Sebergham
1843	1845	1840	1850	160873	CUL	Wigton
BELL contd.						
1799	1799	ALL	1799	154563	DBY	Whitwell
1864	1888	1830	1950	134376	DEV	Ivybridge
1864	1888	1830	1950	134376	DEV	Plymouth
....	....	....	1850	145939	DFS	Dumfries
1854	1992	1820	1854	105422	DUR	Barnard Castle
1856	1958	1800	1992	147982	DUR	Darlington
1814	1814	1538	1890	118893	DUR	Gateshead Fell
1878	....	1878	....	161721	DUR	South Shields
1853	1979	1800	1900	177970	DUR	Tantobie
1840	1850	1830	1880	118281	DUR	Weardale
1850	1960	1700	1850	158208	DUR	Weardale
1769	1769	ALL	1769	154563	DUR	Whickham
1800	....	1700	....	116920	DUR	???
?	?	?	?	150215	HAM	Romsey
?	?	....	....	160679	HAM	???
1800	1877	1800	1860	146358	HIL	Aberdeen
1790	1877	1700	1860	146358	KCD	Maryculter
1817	1992	ALL	1817	105406	KEN	East Farleigh
....	....	1790	1799	165476	KEN	Frinstead
1893	1992	....	....	105473	KEN	Gillingham
1817	1992	ALL	1817	105406	KEN	Maidstone
?	?	?	?	166642	KEN	Whitstable
1754	1845	1600	1900	132977	KKD	Gatehouse Of Fleet
1834	1851	1834	1851	147486	LAN	Arkholme
1851	1900	1851	1900	147486	LAN	Burnley
1825	....	1825	....	147486	LAN	Lancaster
1871	1982	ALL	ALL	160733	LAN	Liverpool
....	....	ALL	ALL	166812	LAN	Manchester
1790	1992	1700	1790	105392	LIN	Market Rasen
1859	1903	1859	....	162175	LKS	Old Monkland
1828	1848	1750	1828	149004	LND	Southwark
1840	1992	1700	1840	108618	LND	St Pancras
1800	....	....	....	126543	MDX	Brentford
1800	....	....	....	126543	MDX	Chelsea
1865	....	1865	1900	144703	MDX	Kentish Town
1690	1732	1690	1800	117706	MDX	London
....	1912	1875	1992	144703	MDX	Tottenham
....	....	ALL	1803	119326	MLN	Edinburgh
1790	1810	1780	1830	176982	MLN	Edinburgh
....	....	ALL	1803	119326	MLN	Inveresk
1820	1854	1750	1854	105422	MLN	Leith
1712	....	1689	....	148644	MLN	Leith
1789	1850	....	....	148261	NBL	Allendale
1851	1893	1700	1850	132764	NBL	Aydon
1848	....	1845	1850	160873	NBL	Belford
1800	1860	ALL	ALL	122386	NBL	Bellingham
1816	1992	ALL	1816	154520	NBL	Bolam
1821	1929	1700	1820	147346	NBL	Corbridge
1800	1860	ALL	ALL	122386	NBL	Halton Wark
1876	1992	1800	1900	105414	NBL	Newcastle On Tyne
1867	1881	1850	1900	160873	NBL	Newcastle On Tyne
1849	1866	ALL	1900	171751	NBL	Newcastle Upon Tyne
1862	1992	1700	1862	139084	NBL	Newcastle
1800	1899	1800	1899	169781	NBL	Newcastle
1851	....	1848	1890	160873	NBL	Tweedmouth
1825	1992	1750	1865	105422	NBL	Willington Quay
1837	1844	1800	1900	110132	NBL	???
1844	?	ALL	ALL	166243	NFK	Barnhambroom
1640	1900	1850	1900	155853	NFK	Burnhams
1730	1800	ALL	1800	155853	NFK	Calthorpe
1794	1874	....	....	135437	NFK	Gt Ryburgh
1821	?	ALL	ALL	166243	NFK	Haveringland
1769	1833	....	....	135437	NFK	Hindringham
1798	1917	1700	1850	117013	NFK	Little Barningham
1827	1879	....	....	135437	NFK	Lt Ryburgh
1846	1846	....	....	135437	NFK	Norwich
1830	1947	....	....	135437	NFK	Stibbard
1800	?	ALL	ALL	166243	NFK	Swannington
1764	1764	....	....	135437	NFK	Wells
....	....	1860	1930	147613	NIR	Belfast
....	....	1830	1880	147613	NIR	Newtownbreda
....	....	1750	1850	147613	NIR	Temple Patrick
1780	1855	1538	1865	118893	NRY	Fangdalebeck
1720	1765	1538	1890	118893	NRY	Great Broughton
1770	1820	1538	1890	118893	NRY	Great Busby
1720	1765	1538	1830	118893	NRY	Kirkby
1760	1780	1538	1890	118893	NRY	Kirklevington
1772	1814	1700	1772	162248	NRY	Sandhutton
1770	1820	1538	1890	118893	NRY	Stokesley
1800	1992	1750	1850	138967	NTH	Peterborough
1745	1900	1700	1745	105457	NTH	Wilbarston
1698	1698	1650	1740	167002	NYK	Topcliffe
1800	1860	1800	1860	147184	NYK	Wensleydale

Known From	To	Researching From	To	Ref	Cty	Place
BELL contd.						
1800	1884	....	....	141798	PER	Carse Of Gowrie
1835	1855	ALL	....	150835	PER	Greenloaning
1790	1869	1841	1891	146560	PER	Perth
1840	1900	1830	1880	170992	SCT	Port Glasgow
1850	1900	1700	1850	142670	SEL	Hawick
1827	1927	1780	1900	102075	SRY	Newington
1827	1927	1780	1900	102075	SRY	Southwark
1870	1900	ALL	1870	119105	TIP	Creighton's Grange
1840	1880	1800	1920	136174	TYR	Garvaghey
1852	1861	1852	1865	144703	WAR	Birmingham
1790	1870	ALL	1820	142301	WES	Grasmere
1783	1805	1700	1800	105449	WES	Kendal
1830	1830	1600	1992	144703	WES	Kendal
1828	1834	1828	1834	147486	WES	Kirby Lonsdale
1828	1828	1600	1992	144703	WES	Kirkby Stephen
1500	1900	1500	1900	170216	WIL	ALL
1841	1851	1841	1851	124001	WIL	Winterslow
1825	1830	1700	1850	118281	YKS	Arkengarthdale
1793	....	1750	1793	176885	YKS	Church Fenton
1860	1952	1700	1860	148113	YKS	Doncaster
1793	1827	1800	1992	172782	YKS	Eastrington
1805	1992	1805	1992	105449	YKS	Hull
1912	1960	1912	1992	121320	YKS	Leeds
1856	1958	1800	1992	147982	YKS	Leeds
1750	1800	1800	1992	172782	YKS	Portington Hall
1750	1850	1750	1850	123463	YKS	Richmond
1912	1960	1912	1992	121320	YKS	Ripon
1772	1992	1600	1772	123951	YKS	Sand Hutton
1847	1900	1800	1900	167843	YKS	Thornaby On Tees
1801	1992	1780	1992	144460	YKS	West Breton
1793	1828	1793	1828	147486	YKS	West Witton
1735	1775	1700	1992	114901	YKS	Wheldrake
BELLABE						
1571	?	ALL	ALL	105481	YKS	Elland
BELLABEE						
1742	?	ALL	ALL	105481	NTH	Stoke Albany
BELLABEY						
1825	1900	ALL	ALL	105481	NTT	Radford
1696	?	ALL	ALL	105481	STS	Uttoxeter
1712	1900	ALL	ALL	105481	YKS	Silkcone
BELLABIE						
1636	?	ALL	ALL	105481	YKS	Barwick In Elmet
BELLABY						
1642	1992	1642	1992	105481	DBY	Belper
1642	1992	1642	1992	105481	DBY	Derby
1642	1992	1642	1992	105481	NTT	Nottingham
BELLAM						
1780	1850	1700	1780	100129	HUN	Stilton
BELLAMORE						
1748	1770	1550	1770	174343	HAM	Hambledon
BELLAMY						
1800	1880	....	....	174556	AVN	Yatton
1840	1877	1700	1840	164267	BDF	Potten
1688	1940	....	....	128996	CAM	Thorney
1567	1956	1567	1956	107638	DEV	Plymouth
1703	1800	1600	1900	135968	LEI	Great Glen
1745	1992	1700	1745	105503	LIN	Croft
1744	....	....	1744	101761	LIN	Friskney
1789	1878	1500	1789	175072	LIN	Kettlethorpe
1860	1960	1800	1860	166421	LND	North
1830	1870	1800	1900	152528	LND	Bethnal Green
1770	1792	....	1770	161888	LND	???
1860	1980	ALL	ALL	105511	NTT	Beeston
1700	1860	1700	1860	105511	NTT	Laxton
1600	1992	ALL	ALL	105511	NTT	Nottingham
1732	1757	1732	1757	165999	SOM	Croscombe
1732	1757	1732	1757	165999	SOM	Dinder
?	?	ALL	1900	117919	WOR	Old Swinford
1820	1853	1820	1853	153257	WOR	Old Swinford
BELLARBE						
1707	?	ALL	ALL	105481	SSX	Rumboldswick
BELLARBIE						
1549	?	ALL	ALL	105481	DUR	Eaglecliffe
BELLARBY						
1588	?	ALL	ALL	105481	DUR	St Oswald
BELLARBYE						
1500	1600	ALL	ALL	105481	ENG	North
BELLARS						
1850	1992	ALL	....	155713	DUR	Stockton On Tees
1850	1992	ALL	....	155713	YKS	Stockton On Tees
BELLAS						
1600	1987	1500	1600	173711	CMA	Murton Cum Hilton
1066	1622	....	....	140678	DUR	???

Known From	To	Researching From	To	Ref	Cty	Place
BELLAS contd.						
1690	1800	1600	1800	135550	WES	North
1714	1992	1550	1714	142646	WES	Bolton
1622	1821	....	1821	140678	WES	Long Marton
1714	1992	1550	1714	142646	WES	Long Marton
1750	1800	1650	1850	143553	WES	Long Marton
1788	1839	....	1788	165484	YKS	Wakefield
BELLASIS						
1066	1622	....	....	140678	DUR	???
1622	1821	....	1821	140678	WES	Long Marton
BELLCHAMBER						
1766	1850	1600	1900	130125	KEN	Westerham
1750	....	1700	1900	113743	SSX	Warbleton
BELLCHAMBERS						
1825	....	1700	1825	154059	KEN	Deptford
BELLEBY						
1840	?	....	....	105481	NTT	Radford
BELLERBIE						
1583	?	ALL	ALL	105481	DUR	Long Newton
BELLERBY						
1811	1850	1750	1811	155810	DUR	Esh
1581	?	ALL	ALL	105481	DUR	St Oswald
1860	....	....	....	119768	YKS	Cowthorpe
....	1760	1700	1760	174858	YKS	Rillington
BELLERBYE						
1560	1600	ALL	ALL	105481	ENG	North
BELLEW						
1770	1800	1700	1800	116432	CON	Tremaine
BELLHOUSE						
....	....	1800	1860	113220	LIN	Ashby De La Launde
....	....	1860	1992	113220	LIN	Grantham
BELLIBIE						
1628	?	ALL	ALL	105481	SFK	Sudbury
BELLIE						
....	....	1600	1855	148482	OKI	Birsay
BELLINGER						
1792	1800	1770	1792	127116	HAM	Tidworth
1792	1800	1770	1792	127116	WIL	Tidworth
BELLINGHAM						
1836	1865	....	1836	178853	KEN	Maidstone
1680	1850	1680	1750	105546	LAN	Hawkshead
1650	1650	1650	1650	105546	LAN	Warton
1833	1900	ALL	ALL	141186	STS	Central
1833	1900	ALL	ALL	141186	STS	North
1400	1870	1600	1820	105546	WES	Kendal
BELLIS						
1740	1912	ALL	ALL	124982	FLN	ALL
?	....	ALL	1895	124842	FLN	Bagilt
1768	1881	....	....	147621	FLN	Northop
1875	ALL	ALL	1875	124842	STS	Hanley
1850	1890	....	....	156485	???	Birkenhead
BELLISSON						
1600	1800	....	....	100420	WAR	Meriden
BELLOBIE						
1594	?	....	....	105481	YKS	Monk Frystone
1603	?	....	....	105481	YKS	Whitkirk
BELLOBYE						
1611	?	ALL	ALL	105481	SFK	Sudbury
BELLOM						
1789	1940	....	....	128996	CAM	Thorney
BELLSHEAR						
1771	1798	1650	1770	131245	WAR	Stretton On Dunsmore
BELLWOOD						
1850	1985	1750	1992	130036	DUR	Eppleby
1827	1881	1800	1950	105554	LAN	Liverpool
1925	1957	1925	1957	105554	YKS	Barnsley
1661	1708	ALL	ALL	105554	YKS	Skipwith
1736	1836	ALL	ALL	105554	YKS	Thorganby
BELMAN						
1873	1965	1800	1900	105562	WAR	Birmingham
BELSER						
1610	1680	ALL	1992	106119	LND	Southwark
BELSEY						
1780	1800	1650	1780	128090	KEN	East
BELSON						
?	?	?	?	166642	SRY	Frimley
BELSTEN						
1851	1950	1851	1950	170267	AVN	Bristol
1768	1816	1744	1954	170267	SOM	Keynsham
BELTON						
1700	1800	1600	1700	174130	LEI	Goadby
1766	1802	ALL	1992	159174	LIN	Long Sutton
1787	1940	1700	1900	159042	LIN	Stamford

Known From	To	Researching From	To	Ref	Cty	Place
BELTON contd.						
1881	1992	1700	1880	169994	NTT	Nottingham
....	....	1845	1851	159042	RAD	Knighton
BELTZUNG						
....	....	ALL	ALL	105570	ALL	Name Study
BEMAN						
1689	1870	1600	1689	145459	HAM	Bursledon
BEMAND						
1846	1901	1750	1900	114456	SAL	ALL
BEMBRICK						
....	....	1800	1920	107816	LND	Westminster
BEMEY						
?	?	?	?	150215	SSX	Hastings
BEMI						
1820	ALL	ALL	1858	116734	MDX	Bishopsgate
1820	ALL	ALL	1858	116734	MDX	London
1820	ALL	ALL	1858	116734	MDX	St Botolph
BEMROSE						
1700	1950	ALL	....	144290	LIN	Caythorpe
BENBOW						
....	....	ALL	ALL	105589	ALL	Name Study
....	....	ALL	ALL	105589	ALL	ALL
1650	1700	1700	1800	105589	ESS	London
1798	....	....	....	144169	HEF	Hentland
1829	....	....	....	144169	HEF	Llanwarne
1793	....	....	....	144169	HEF	Peterston
1650	1700	1700	1800	105589	KEN	London
1650	1700	1700	1800	105589	MDX	London
1650	1700	1600	1800	105589	SAL	Shrewsbury
1800	1900	1558	1800	153427	STS	Barcaston
BENCE						
1761	1800	1760	1800	179337	GLS	Marshfield
1752	....	....	....	142859	GLS	Woodchester
1760	1900	1760	1900	163406	SOM	Bath
....	1792	ALL	1792	175080	SOM	Swainswick
1750	1946	....	....	114669	SOM	Twerton
BENDALL						
1800	....	ALL	1800	144053	BRK	???
1829	1932	....	....	131660	GLS	Cam
1800	....	ALL	1800	144053	HAM	???
BENDER						
1829	1900	1780	1900	140325	LND	Southwark
BENDING						
....	....	ALL	ALL	105597	ALL	Name Study
BENFIELD						
....	....	1650	1780	118834	DOR	Corfe Castle
1780	1851	....	....	118834	HAM	Portsmouth
1814	....	1700	1813	105600	LEI	Twycross
1780	1900	1500	1900	125725	OXF	Leafield
1875	1940	ALL	ALL	107336	SRY	Bermondsey
1853	1960	....	....	105600	STS	Dudley
1853	1960	....	....	105600	STS	Tipton Coseley
1853	1960	....	....	105600	STS	Wolverhampton
BENGE						
1860	....	....	....	142158	KEN	Plumstead
1866	1866	ALL	1866	131849	SSX	Brighton
BENHAM						
1830	1850	1830	1850	120472	BRK	Bray
1830	1850	1830	1850	120472	BRK	Maidenhead
1748	1870	1700	1900	136719	HAM	Basingstoke
1819	....	....	1920	175315	HAM	Binstead
1800	1980	1600	1810	170607	HAM	Porstmouth
1819	....	....	1920	175315	HAM	Winchester
1821	1851	1800	1860	119059	HAM	???
....	....	1850	1950	156523	SSX	Brighton
1500	1900	1500	1900	170216	WIL	ALL
BENIAMS						
1725	1897	ALL	1897	118990	SAL	ALL
BENIANS						
....	....	ALL	ALL	105619	ALL	Name Study
1782	1992	ALL	1800	105619	HMC	???
BENISON						
1821	....	....	....	117579	CAV	???
1847	1853	....	....	117579	STS	Bilston
1853	1886	1853	1886	117579	WOR	Balsall Heath
1880	1897	....	....	117579	WOR	Kings Heath
BENJAFIELD						
1700	1830	1700	1850	105627	DOR	Gillingham
1700	1830	1700	1850	105627	SOM	Cucklington
BENJAMIN						
1800	1900	1800	1900	177032	AVN	Bristol
1785	1950	1750	1949	152668	CMA	Askham In Furness
1796	1871	....	....	147621	FLN	Holywell
1845	1850	....	....	125202	LAN	Liverpool
BENJAMIN contd.						
1923	....	....	....	135968	LEI	Leicester
1800	1823	1800	1992	110205	MDX	London
ALL	1800	ALL	1800	152668	WLS	???
1880	1894	....	1880	125202	WRY	Bradford
BENN						
1720	1836	1600	1720	152196	CMA	Haile
1600	1700	1500	1700	167088	CMA	Whitehaven
1796	1992	1861	1992	125172	CUL	Cockermouth
ALL	ALL	ALL	ALL	105813	CUL	Corney
1796	1992	1861	1992	125172	CUL	Maryport
1796	1992	1861	1992	125172	CUL	St Bees
1750	1800	1700	1850	138878	CUL	St Bees
1783	1900	1750	1890	177636	CUL	St Bees
ALL	ALL	ALL	ALL	105813	CUL	Whitehaven
1750	1800	1700	1850	138878	CUL	Whitehaven
1850	1865	1800	1900	123536	DUR	Shildon
1783	1950	1700	1950	177636	LAN	Merseyside
1790	1825	1750	1850	123536	YKS	Bradford
1790	1825	1750	1850	123536	YKS	Clayton
1800	1810	1750	1830	116386	YKS	Leeds
1730	1770	1700	1800	157651	YKS	Sutton On Forest
BENNALLACK						
1897	1969	1800	1897	160156	CON	Truro
BENNAS						
1901	....	1700	1901	115967	NTH	Tynemouth
BENNELL						
....	....	ALL	ALL	136735	BKM	Andridge
BENNER						
1822	1989	ALL	1822	112313	NTT	Nottingham
1822	1989	ALL	1822	112313	RUT	Essendine
BENNET						
1710	1770	1500	1750	143693	CON	Cambrone
1700	1800	1700	1800	171077	CON	St Merryn
....	....	1764	1992	121940	DBY	Chinley
1850	1920	1850	1920	118540	DOW	Rathfriland
1780	....	1780	1900	106410	GLS	Berkeley
1780	1800	1700	1800	136840	HAM	Winchester
1640	1700	....	1720	171441	KEN	Meopham
1870	1870	....	....	115258	KEN	Ramsgate
1700	1796	....	1820	171441	KEN	Ridley
1760	1800	1700	1800	135941	MLN	Gilmerton
1780	1850	1770	1860	135941	MLN	Lauriston
1820	1860	1810	1860	135941	MLN	St Cuthberts
1800	1830	1700	1840	135941	MLN	Stockbridge
1720	1840	1600	1720	109142	PER	Muthil
1582	1670	ALL	ALL	162280	SAL	Bridgnorth
1532	1702	1500	1702	102830	STS	Sedgely
1785	1840	1752	1800	120146	WIL	Wootton Rivers
BENNETS						
1800	1850	1700	1800	159441	CON	ALL
BENNETT						
....	....	1700	1900	105678	ALL	ALL
1799	1877	1700	1799	134732	ARM	???
1817	1893	....	1817	108839	BDF	Clifton
1740	1915	ALL	ALL	112518	BRK	Appleton
1720	1770	1680	1730	156930	BRK	Avington
1760	1805	1700	1760	175307	BRK	Newbury
1900	1918	1900	1918	108839	BRK	Slough
1838	1923	ALL	1838	151777	BRK	Windsor
1781	1992	....	1992	157244	CAM	Ramsay
1757	1900	1700	1770	135496	CHS	North
....	....	1800	ALL	164615	CHS	Hyde
1844	1919	....	....	179523	CHS	Over
1750	1880	1700	1800	155500	CHS	Preston On The Hill
1802	1992	1700	1992	137901	CHS	Stockport
1844	1919	....	....	179523	CHS	Wharton
1809	1992	....	....	169412	CHS	???
1686	1721	....	....	106240	CON	Bodmin
1830	1850	1750	1850	142123	CON	Camborne
1810	....	1750	1810	142905	CON	Gwinear
1578	1800	....	....	106240	CON	Launceston
1750	1820	....	....	106240	CON	Lostwithiel
....	....	....	1800	114812	CON	St Agnes
1700	1776	....	....	106240	CON	St Neot
1764	1930	ALL	1760	177482	CON	Tywardreath
1870	1920	1800	1870	129437	CON	???
1740	1900	1650	1800	156442	COR	Bandon
1822	1870	....	1825	178853	DEV	Moreton Hampstead
1856	1861	....	1856	117234	DEV	Plymouth
1780	1820	1750	1850	135658	DEV	Plymouth
1749	1839	1700	1839	162825	DOR	Portland
1770	1850	1770	1800	174599	DOR	Shaftesbury
1700	1946	1700	1992	147125	DUR	Winlaton

Known From	To	Researching From	To	Ref	Cty	Place
BENNETT contd.						
1829	....	1865	1900	110868	ENG	???
....	....	1750	1850	105678	ESS	ALL
1735	1860	1650	1750	100048	ESS	Brentwood
1800	1992	1700	1800	105767	GLS	ALL
....	....	1750	1900	105678	GLS	ALL
1840	....	ALL	ALL	156558	GLS	Cheltenham
1830	1880	1700	1830	145904	GLS	Newnham On Severn
....	....	1700	1760	105651	GLS	Ripple
1830	1880	1700	1830	145904	GLS	Ruarden
1738	1835	1650	1738	166723	GLS	Stroud
1790	1860	1700	1790	105651	GLS	Twyning
1740	1770	1700	1800	155896	GLS	Westbury On Severn
1677	1879	1500	1676	172006	GLS	Westbury On Severn
....	....	1600	1850	127833	HAM	East
1600	1940	....	....	127833	HAM	Portsmouth
1860	1891	1860	1890	172634	HAM	Southampton
1850	1900	....	1900	129151	HEF	Kingsland
1840	1940	1700	1850	145904	HEF	Ross On Wye
1850	1900	....	1900	129151	HEF	Yarpole
1833	?	....	....	162108	HRT	???
1870	1878	1870	1878	108839	HUN	Ramsey
1848	1930	1600	1848	167819	IOW	Shalfleet
1756	1794	1500	1756	129577	IOW	???
1800	1850	1750	1850	126144	KEN	West
?	?	?	?	151505	LAN	Cartmel
1869	1886	1869	1911	146773	LAN	Hindley
1827	1892	....	1827	109622	LAN	Manchester
1910	1939	....	....	151505	LAN	Scaforth
1869	1886	1869	1933	146773	LAN	Wigan
1806	1910	ALL	ALL	113700	LND	Hoxton
1851	?	?	1851	136611	LND	Long Lane
1790	1992	1765	1992	105759	LND	Spitalfields
1841	1870	....	1841	108839	LND	St Pancras
1880	1989	ALL	....	136018	LND	Wandsworth
....	1700	....	....	174564	LND	???
1830	1906	....	....	127779	MDX	Clerkenwell
1855	1880	1800	1900	155357	MDX	London
1800	1850	1800	1900	106631	MDX	Westminster
1740	1815	1700	1800	131431	MGY	Trefegwlys
1844	....	....	....	153524	MON	Tredegar
1850	1960	1700	1850	134074	NFK	Feltwell
1805	1992	1750	1992	110906	NFK	West Lynn
1918	....	1918	....	108839	NFK	Yarmouth
1813	1832	1800	1871	167002	NTT	Clayworth
1798	1851	1700	1881	167002	NTT	East Stoke
1789	1796	1700	1871	167002	NTT	Halam
1795	1850	1700	1795	138584	NTT	Kingston On Soar
1818	1902	1750	1902	167002	NTT	Newark
1900	1950	1850	1900	165891	NTT	Retford
1776	1840	....	....	132756	OXF	ALL
1887	1992	1870	1887	177539	OXF	Cumnor
1700	1850	1750	1825	172634	OXF	Deddington
1776	1840	....	....	132756	OXF	Oxford
1846	1974	1846	1974	149403	OXF	Oxford
1813	1894	1700	1813	118605	SAL	South
1811	1814	1764	1839	160059	SAL	Astley Abbots
1841	1919	1839	1900	160059	SAL	Billingsley
1841	1864	ALL	ALL	136735	SAL	Minsterley
1836	1837	1780	1845	160059	SAL	Rindleford
1836	1837	1780	1845	160059	SAL	Worfield
1900	1992	1818	1900	129895	SFK	Debenham
1688	1820	1600	1800	107565	SOM	Corston
1780	1920	ALL	1780	138169	SOM	Huntspill
1820	1920	....	....	138169	SOM	Lympsham
1800	1992	1750	1850	108243	SOM	???
....	....	1750	1800	131431	SOM	???
1888	1920	1800	1887	131245	SRY	Bermondsey
1750	1960	1650	1750	105716	SSX	West
1700	1800	1700	1800	152404	SSX	W Chiltington
1840	1900	1840	1900	105724	STS	Burton On Trent
1821	1907	1600	1821	112410	STS	Hanley
1783	1809	1700	1783	156248	STS	Sedgley
1861	1927	1760	1861	134473	STS	Stoke On Trent
1831	1846	1700	1846	164879	STS	Wednesbury
1860	1900	ALL	ALL	117870	STS	West Bromwich
1780	1840	1700	1992	167592	STS	Woolstanton
1800	1850	1800	1850	103764	WAR	Alcester
....	....	1750	1850	154458	WAR	Birmingham
1820	....	....	....	116432	WAR	Newton
1750	1800	1750	1800	103764	WAR	Wixford
?	?	?	?	151505	WES	Crosthwaite
1800	1937	1800	1937	172634	WIL	Highworth
1701	1841	?	1850	103934	WIL	Tollard Royal
BENNETT contd.						
1800	1992	1700	1800	105767	WOR	South
1860	1992	....	....	105651	WOR	Bredon
1890	1936	1880	1905	160059	WOR	Kidderminster
1850	....	ALL	ALL	112461	WOR	Stourbridge
1814	1820	1785	1992	114901	YKS	Braham
1812	1814	1785	1992	114901	YKS	Harewood
1850	1880	1880	1950	138584	YKS	Keighley
1774	1992	1700	1774	166723	YKS	Leeds
1860	1880	....	....	153397	YKS	Sheffield
1911	1933	1869	1911	146773	YKS	Skipton
BENNETTO						
1600	1900	?	1900	131458	CON	St Austell
BENNETTS						
1841	1992	1700	1841	105635	CON	Gwennad
1660	1706	1600	1660	102571	CON	St Just In Penwith
BENNEWITH						
....	....	ALL	ALL	105783	ALL	Name Study
BENNICKE						
1777	....	....	1777	155667	???	Devonport
1777	....	....	1777	155667	???	Stoke Damerelin
BENNIE						
1800	1842	1780	1992	122416	LKS	Barony
BENNINGTON						
1880	1930	ALL	1992	156078	LIN	???
1835	....	1700	1865	105635	NFK	Walsham
1865	1992	1835	1865	105635	STS	Dudley
1762	1762	ALL	ALL	128449	WAR	Coventry
BENNION						
....	....	ALL	ALL	111384	CHS	Chester
1860	1900	1800	1900	126322	CHS	Chester
1780	1920	1700	1780	173312	CHS	Eccleston
1836	1843	....	1850	169412	CHS	Over
1850	1950	1850	1950	108693	CHS	Wem
1862	1863	....	....	142859	FLN	Mold
1877	1956	....	....	142859	LAN	Manchester
1869	....	....	....	142859	LAN	Warrington
1627	....	ALL	1627	143278	NTH	Brockhall
....	....	ALL	ALL	111384	NYK	Scarborough
1866	....	....	....	142859	SAL	Ironbridge
....	....	ALL	1860	126322	SAL	Welshpool
1843	1960	1800	1910	165441	STS	Stoke On Trent
1838	1992	1819	1838	111384	WYK	Leeds
1860	....	....	....	142859	YKS	Bramley
BENNISON						
1788	1850	1700	1788	165182	YKS	Whitby
1713	1734	1600	1715	101575	YKS	Wressle
BENNIWITH						
1739	1778	1600	1739	156779	SFK	Kersey
1739	1778	1600	1739	156779	SFK	Layham
BENNS						
1828	1871	1700	1828	100226	NFK	ALL
BENNY WILLIAMS						
1857	1872	ALL	1857	152013	DEV	Plymouth
BENNYMEN						
1817	1937	1628	1817	137537	DEV	Plymouth
BENSKIN						
1480	1800	1480	1992	142174	LEI	North
BENSLEY						
1780	1800	1700	1850	176672	NFK	Woodton
1900	1992	1800	1900	142417	NFK	???
BENSON						
1880	1930	1800	1992	116009	ANT	Belfast
1800	1992	1700	1800	164208	CMA	Kendal
1600	1700	1500	1700	167088	CMA	Whitehaven
....	....	1650	1750	116173	CUL	West
1700	1850	1700	1850	143553	CUL	Addingham
1704	1902	1650	1704	105805	DUB	Dublin
....	1764	1500	1764	175072	LIN	Belchford
1881	1940	....	....	144495	LND	Stoke Newington
?	?	?	?	132136	LND	???
1866	1992	?	1866	156337	MDX	Kensington
1699	1788	1650	1699	160474	WES	Grasmere
....	....	1700	1750	177393	YKS	Cawcod
1700	1770	....	....	140554	YKS	Cawood
1806	1850	1800	1850	101044	YKS	Harrogate
ALL	ALL	ALL	ALL	105813	YKS	Ripley
BENSTEAD						
1713	1800	1600	1700	125784	CAM	Bottisham
1799	1848	1799	1851	136808	CAM	Soham
1771	1893	1600	1770	125784	CAM	Swaffham Prior
1950	1992	1950	1992	133450	KEN	???
1820	1950	ALL	ALL	157864	NFK	Gt Yarmouth
1865	1921	1865	....	113875	NTT	ALL

Known From	To	Researching From	To	Ref	Cty	Place
BENSTEAD contd.						
1950	1992	1950	1992	133450	SSX	???
BENSTED						
1765	1818	1765	1818	149403	KEN	Eastling
1840	1920	1840	1940	136271	MDX	Willesden
BENT						
1826	1886	1800	1850	149772	LAN	Blackburn
1750	1992	1700	1750	155500	LAN	Rixton
1743	1743	1707	1750	107360	NTH	Badby
BENTALL						
1780	1992	1500	1780	112127	ESS	Halstead
....	1804	1760	1861	128961	ESS	Halstead
BENTERMAN						
1890	1973	1700	1890	153702	LND	Leyton
BENTHAM						
1835	1880	ALL	ALL	119253	CHS	Stockport
1825	1835	ALL	ALL	119253	LAN	Caton
1844	1992	1600	1844	172332	WYK	Bradford
1778	1840	....	....	118354	YKS	Dent
1731	1761	1700	1731	152196	YKS	Dent
BENTING						
....	....	ALL	ALL	107077	ALL	Name Study
BENTLEY						
....	....	1810	1830	103713	CAM	Cheveley
....	....	1750	1810	103713	CAM	Woodditton
1783	....	ALL	ALL	119253	CHS	Weaverham
1836	1992	1836	1992	147001	DEV	Devonport
1720	1820	....	....	165999	ESS	Aldham
1720	1820	....	....	165999	ESS	Copford
1813	1992	1813	1992	177962	ESS	Manuden
1805	1850	1750	1850	160903	HRT	Barkway
1730	1833	ALL	1840	137774	KEN	South East
1840	1860	....	1860	178861	KEN	Dartford
1733	?	?	?	166642	KEN	???
1858	1940	1800	1900	129623	LAN	Bolton
1700	....	1700	....	109347	LAN	Huncoat
1750	1790	1700	1992	167592	LAN	Liverpool
....	....	1750	1830	149632	LAN	Manchester
1820	1849	ALL	ALL	149632	LKS	Glasgow
1844	1855	ALL	ALL	121754	LND	???
1832	1992	1700	1832	158917	SAL	Sutton Maddock
1844	....	ALL	ALL	121754	SRY	Kennington
1696	1845	....	....	131210	SRY	Merton
1720	1820	1820	1992	148180	STS	North
1880	1900	1850	1900	134627	STS	Walsall
1858	1880	1850	1880	134627	STS	West Bromwich
1836	1836	1800	1850	134627	WAR	Morton Baggott
1772	1848	....	1772	176702	WYK	Queensbury
1771	....	....	1771	146013	YKS	Bradford
1735	1795	1650	1735	177393	YKS	Felkirk
....	....	1275	1950	105821	YKS	Halifax
1840	1992	ALL	1840	136875	YKS	Sandal
1743	1992	1500	1900	105821	YKS	Southowram
1840	1992	ALL	1840	136875	YKS	Wakefield
BENTLY						
1850	1992	1700	1870	148563	CHS	Wirral
BENTON						
....	....	1799	1832	137405	CAM	Swavesey
1550	1992	1550	1992	105848	ESS	ALL
....	....	1700	1850	129364	ESS	???
....	....	ALL	ALL	105864	HUN	Earith
1877	1992	?	1877	105856	KEN	???
1700	....	....	1700	150851	LIN	Boston
....	....	ALL	ALL	105864	LND	Camberwell
....	....	ALL	ALL	105864	LND	Peckham
1877	1992	?	1877	105856	MDX	???
1877	1992	?	1877	105856	SRY	???
1819	1992	....	....	134619	STS	Milford
1813	1992	1650	1813	151092	STS	Wolverhampton
BENTOTE						
1740	1743	1685	1785	105872	KEN	Canterbury
1763	1853	1685	1900	105872	LND	Bethnal Green
1861	1881	1845	1891	105872	SFK	Lavenham
1861	1861	1853	1868	105872	SFK	Sudbury
1870	1905	1860	1992	105872	SRY	Reigate
BENWELL						
....	1779	1750	1820	128961	HAM	Whitchurch
....	1779	1750	1820	128961	KEN	Dover
BENYON						
1450	1850	....	....	175439	SAL	Great Ash
1822	1851	1800	1851	165441	SAL	Whitchurch
....	....	1805	1842	111767	???	Berriew
BEQUETTE						
....	....	ALL	ALL	105104	ALL	Name Study

Known From	To	Researching From	To	Ref	Cty	Place
BERE						
1738	1929	1730	1920	176982	CON	Egloshayle
BERESFORD						
....	....	ALL	ALL	105880	ALL	Name Study
1812	1992	ALL	1812	111384	DBY	Belper
1830	1900	1830	1900	111791	DBY	Staveley
....	1878	ALL	1878	153958	DBY	Swanwick
1774	....	ALL	1800	139459	SAL	Donington
1837	....	1750	1900	109894	STS	Uttoxeter
1846	1992	ALL	....	111384	WYK	Howden
1846	1992	ALL	....	111384	WYK	Leeds
BERG						
1827	1881	1750	1840	155225	LND	City
BERGER						
....	....	1849	1877	115010	MDX	London
....	....	1849	1877	115010	WIL	Salisbury
BERGIN						
1850	1860	1840	1860	111589	IRL	Kilkenny
BERISFORD						
1600	1700	1600	1700	103764	STS	Alstonfield
BERJEW						
....	....	ALL	ALL	122041	ALL	Name Study
1600	1850	1600	1800	131962	DOR	North
BERKELEY						
1400	1480	1300	1400	154881	GLS	Beverstone
BERKIN						
1839	1894	1800	1894	147311	STS	Barlaston
BERKS						
1720	1780	1650	1720	173312	STS	Wolstanton
BERKSHIRE						
1878	1881	....	....	155756	SRY	Bermondsey
1872	1878	1800	1872	155756	SRY	Newington
1881	1897	....	....	155756	SRY	Rotherhithe
BERLE						
1800	1899	1800	1899	147575	LND	Bethnal Green
BERNARD						
1858	1992	1800	1858	111163	ENG	ALL
1712	1850	1712	1850	133450	LIN	???
BERNERS						
1750	1900	1500	1750	175269	SFK	Woolverstone
BERRETT						
1871	1891	1860	1899	163775	WIL	Pewsey
BERRIDGE						
1300	1992	ALL	ALL	105910	ALL	ALL
1866	1988	....	....	162655	CAM	Dry Drayton
1697	1940	....	....	128996	CAM	Thorney
1800	1830	1800	1841	164895	LEI	Thurmaston
1755	1992	1600	1755	105929	NTH	Cotterstock
1800	1840	ALL	1800	162655	NTH	Fineshade
1619	1850	1550	1619	176249	NTT	South West
1828	1876	1876	1900	169374	RUT	Great Casterton
1795	1814	1814	1828	169374	RUT	Greetham
BERRIFF						
1836	1980	1820	1836	120731	LND	Paddington
BERRIL						
1730	1816	1700	1816	166111	NTH	Bozeat
BERRIMAN						
?	?	?	?	136999	CON	Fulval
1800	1920	ALL	ALL	166537	CON	Whitstone
1665	1688	1600	1665	102571	CON	Zennor
1800	ALL	1500	1870	145378	LND	Nunhead
BERRINGTON						
1809	1850	1700	1900	135968	LEI	ALL
....	....	1850	1900	164801	MON	Abergavenny
1879	1903	1800	1879	133604	WIL	Chippenham
BERRISFORD						
1851	1864	1851	1864	173851	AVN	Bristol
BERRY						
1815	1865	1750	1880	123536	BDF	Eaton Socon
1815	1870	ALL	ALL	130664	BDF	Eaton Socon
1817	1970	1700	1817	117110	CHS	Hyde
1800	1890	1800	1900	105945	CON	Illogan
1828	1861	ALL	1828	114987	DEV	Coldridge
1774	1800	1700	1800	105945	DEV	Combe Martin
1755	1790	1755	1790	117323	DEV	Crediton
1826	....	1826	....	146900	DEV	Ipplepen
1815	1895	1700	1912	110949	DOR	Chideock
1681	1739	1600	1739	156515	GLS	Guiting Power
1800	1850	1800	1850	105953	HAM	Christchurch
1815	1870	ALL	ALL	130664	HUN	Eaton Socon
1890	....	....	....	160385	IOM	Douglas
1840	....	1800	1840	160385	IRL	Down
1900	1950	1800	1900	138649	IRL	Dublin
1808	1870	....	1808	101761	IRL	???

Known From	To	Researching From	To	Ref	Cty	Place
BERRY contd.						
1860	1900	1860	1900	142158	KEN	Plumstead
1764	1805	1700	1992	172243	KEN	Plumstead
1885	1920	1885	1920	105953	LAN	Barrow In Furness
1650	1800	1650	1800	152404	LAN	Hulton
1825	1992	....	1850	147818	LAN	Worsley
....	....	?	?	110507	LEI	Leicester
1729	....	....	1729	175374	LEI	Upton Sibson
1855	1886	1790	1855	175064	LIN	Billinghau
1876	1885	ALL	ALL	130664	LIN	Pinchbeck
1858	....	ALL	ALL	117889	LKS	Shotts
1860	....	....	....	130079	LND	Deptford
1860	1992	1700	1860	105988	LND	Wandsworth
1900	1910	1900	1910	105953	MON	Risca
1772	1844	1700	1900	178322	NTH	Appletree
1760	1876	1650	1780	106313	NTH	Chipping Warden
1730	1950	1550	1730	105937	SFK	Sudbury
1842	....	....	....	163392	SFK	Troston
....	....	1720	1800	172871	SOM	Norton St Philip
1850	1992	1850	1992	105953	SOM	Timsbury
1890	1914	....	....	164720	SOM	Weston Super Mare
1821	1853	1700	1821	162035	SRY	Rotherhythe
1828	1871	ALL	1810	165263	SSX	Rotherfield
1880	1992	1750	1880	177237	WAR	Emscote
1600	1700	....	....	100420	WAR	Meriden
1880	1992	1750	1880	177237	WAR	Warwick
....	....	ALL	1800	151602	WIL	Ramsbury
....	....	1870	1992	124117	WIL	Salisbury
1750	1850	1700	1750	165530	WIL	Sherston
1865	1992	....	....	122157	WIL	Swindon
1900	1950	1800	1900	138649	WMD	Birmingham
1809	1833	....	....	105996	WOR	Honington
1619	....	....	....	105996	WOR	Tredington
1814	....	....	1814	101761	WRY	Almondbury
1750	1900	1750	1900	177288	WYK	Halifax
1785	1870	1700	1920	173452	YKS	South
1785	1870	1700	1920	173452	YKS	West
1690	1992	ALL	1690	110027	YKS	Almondbury
1682	1840	1650	1710	170348	YKS	Almondbury
1881	....	....	....	104078	YKS	Horbury
1786	1816	1600	1992	102520	YKS	Idle
1690	1992	ALL	1690	110027	YKS	Ripponden
1690	1992	ALL	1690	110027	YKS	Scammonden
BERRYMAN						
1600	1750	....	....	139491	CON	Zennor
BERSEY						
1883	....	ALL	ALL	158879	CON	Plymouth
1883	....	ALL	ALL	158879	DEV	Falmouth
BERTIE						
1731	1900	1500	1900	170216	DOR	ALL
BERTRAM						
....	....	1800	ALL	149187	JSY	Grouville
1850	1908	1750	1850	170054	KEN	Chatham
....	....	....	....	132829	???	???
BERTRIM						
....	....	ALL	1760	132829	NBL	North
BERTWISTLE						
1250	1850	....	....	102172	LAN	ALL
BERWICK						
1750	1759	....	....	130605	DUR	???
1750	1759	....	....	130605	NBL	???
1825	1841	1750	1900	105244	SRY	Totting
BESANT						
1791	1840	1750	1785	133639	DOR	Melcombe Regis
1781	1840	1750	1785	133639	DOR	Weymouth
1781	1840	1750	1785	133639	DOR	Wyke Regis
BESFORD						
1790	1992	1550	1790	106038	NFK	Walcot
BESLEY						
1790	....	1790	1850	169625	OXF	Crowell
BESS						
1750	1800	1600	1750	147583	DOR	Rampisham
BESSANT						
....	....	ALL	ALL	177083	ALL	Name Study
1840	1900	1700	ALL	135127	HAM	Sopley
BESSER						
1890	1900	ALL	ALL	132276	SSX	Eastbourne
BESSTON						
1876	1953	1800	1900	144630	NFK	Sporle
BEST						
1856	1992	1700	1850	106399	AVN	Bristol
1750	1750	1700	1800	133450	CON	Roche
1775	1825	1700	1775	128325	CON	St Stephen In Brannel

Known From	To	Researching From	To	Ref	Cty	Place
BEST contd.						
1561	1570	1560	1571	106054	CUL	Carlisle
....	....	1700	1992	153540	DEV	Devonport
1837	1838	1700	1850	106399	DEV	Exeter St Sidwell
1800	1870	1700	ALL	131253	DEV	Great Torrington
1800	1851	1700	1881	119040	DOR	Poole
1800	1851	1700	1881	119040	DOR	Wareham
1700	1800	....	....	117064	DUR	Hamsterley
1744	....	ALL	1744	154946	ERY	Eastringham
1861	1900	....	1861	124710	KEN	Canterbury
1627	1646	....	1650	171441	KEN	Canterbury
1908	1936	1800	1908	152544	KEN	Chiddingstone
1584	1584	....	....	127426	KEN	Lenham
1820	1840	1750	1840	174599	MDX	Harlington
1800	1920	1800	1920	141577	MGY	ALL
1740	1992	....	....	123609	SOM	Norton Sub Hamdon
1850	1914	1800	1992	106046	SRY	Croydon
1690	1850	1500	1992	106046	SSX	Forest Row
1736	1884	....	....	117579	STS	Bilston
1718	1833	....	....	117579	STS	Wednesbury
1745	1800	1680	1745	143332	WIL	Bemerton
1621	1707	....	....	117579	WOR	Elmley Lovet
1760	....	1600	1760	145432	WOR	Feckinham
1573	1992	....	1573	106054	WOR	Hartlebury
1778	1801	1700	1778	164577	WOR	Worcester
....	....	....	1936	100579	WYK	Halifax
1731	1992	1650	1800	168513	YKS	Almondbury
1560	1992	1512	1570	106054	YKS	Romaldkirk
BESTER						
1820	1840	ALL	1840	154490	HUN	Godmanchester
....	1895	....	1895	160652	LIN	Grimsby
BESTWICK						
1815	1815	1766	1815	122572	DBY	ALL
1750	1900	1750	1900	173681	DBY	Hartington
1815	1815	1766	1815	122572	LEI	ALL
1815	1870	1790	1820	128333	STS	Leek
BESWETHERICK						
1900	1992	1600	1900	106070	CON	Falmouth
1800	1992	1650	1800	106070	CON	Lanlivery
BESWICK						
1843	1992	ALL	1843	160008	CHS	Manchester
1843	1992	ALL	1843	160008	CHS	Stockport
1760	1800	1750	1820	117145	LAN	Bolton
....	1825	ALL	ALL	176737	LAN	Manchester
1782	1854	ALL	ALL	151580	LND	Marylebone
1742	1900	1540	1742	176249	NTT	South West
....	....	1600	1992	160245	NTT	Sutton Bonington
BESWORTH						
1794	....	....	1794	108839	HUN	Houghton
BETCHAR						
1792	....	ALL	1992	106119	BRK	???
BETHAM						
1694	1789	1600	1694	102571	WES	Crosby Ravensworth
BETHEL						
....	....	ALL	ALL	106100	ALL	Name Study
1600	1992	1600	1992	106100	ALL	ALL
BETHELL						
1450	1992	1450	1992	106100	ALL	ALL
1604	1992	1604	1992	106100	GLS	Bitton
1604	1992	1604	1992	106100	GLS	Bristol
1604	1992	1604	1992	106100	GLS	Painswick
1723	1835	ALL	ALL	135208	GLS	Painswick
1604	1992	1604	1992	106100	GLS	Tormarton
1575	1776	1575	1776	106100	HAM	Winchester
1730	1881	1600	1992	139181	HEF	Allensmore
1730	1881	1600	1992	139181	HEF	Clehonger
1550	1814	1550	1814	106100	HEF	Maunsell Gamage
1800	1850	1750	1800	157708	HEF	Staunton On Wye
1840	1900	ALL	ALL	135208	KEN	Greenwich
1850	1920	1830	1992	139181	LAN	Earlestown
....	1868	ALL	1868	127000	LAN	Manchester
1840	1900	ALL	ALL	135208	LND	Greenwich
1814	1874	1814	1910	164232	SFK	Stowmarket
1561	1992	1561	1992	106100	SOM	North Petherton
1719	1992	1719	1992	106100	WIL	Bradford On Avon
1719	1992	1719	1992	106100	WIL	Chilton Foliot
1591	1992	1591	1992	106100	YKS	Rise
BETHUNE						
1755	1855	....	....	137936	FIF	Ceres
1830	1900	1830	1900	119725	LKS	Glasgow
1781	1830	1830	1850	119725	ROC	Rosskeen
BETHWIN						
1695	1747	1600	1992	122211	SRY	Lambeth

Known From	To	Researching From	To	Ref	Cty	Place
BETON						
1845	1898	1787	1845	107557	LND	St Pancras
BETR						
1864	1992	ALL	1992	106119	MDX	???
BETSAR						
1620	....	ALL	1992	106119	HAM	???
1625	....	ALL	1992	106119	SRY	???
1599	....	ALL	1992	106119	SSX	Eastbourne
BETSEN						
1851	1992	ALL	1992	106119	SRY	???
BETSER						
....	....	ALL	ALL	106119	ALL	Name Study
1620	1818	1600	1900	106119	HAM	ALL
1900	1992	ALL	1992	106119	HRT	???
1753	1992	ALL	1992	106119	KEN	???
1770	1992	ALL	1992	106119	MDX	???
1572	1885	1296	1992	106119	SRY	Chertsey
1572	1885	1296	1992	106119	SRY	Guildford
1572	1885	1296	1992	106119	SRY	Midhurst
1590	1600	1600	1960	106119	SSX	Eastborne
BETSHER						
1764	....	ALL	1992	106119	SRY	???
BETSHUR						
1748	....	ALL	1992	106119	SRY	???
BETSO						
1717	1992	ALL	1992	106119	SRY	???
BETSON						
....	....	1837	1900	162000	KEN	Medway
1500	1600	....	....	100420	WAR	Meriden
....	?	?	....	134457	YKS	Hull
BETSOR						
1635	....	ALL	1992	106119	HAM	???
1583	1722	ALL	1992	106119	SRY	???
BETSTER						
1803	....	ALL	1992	106119	SRY	???
BETSWORTH						
1850	1880	1750	1850	129712	MDX	London
1774	....	ALL	1992	106119	SRY	???
1697	1740	1670	1760	170143	SSX	Trotton
BETTELEY						
1800	1945	1750	1992	154881	LND	ALL
BETTELHEIM						
1870	1920	1850	1870	109878	LND	ALL
BETTERIDGE						
1700	....	....	1700	106127	BRK	ALL
1808	1992	ALL	1992	159174	DBY	Hartshorne
1838	1992	ALL	1992	159174	DBY	Woodville
1640	1992	1640	1992	122769	GLS	Upper Swell
1771	1905	ALL	1852	123013	GLS	???
1811	1817	1811	1840	106143	HAM	Chilworth
1862	1942	1600	1862	167355	LND	Bermondsey
1700	....	....	1700	106127	OXF	ALL
1640	1992	1640	1992	122769	OXF	Chipping Norton
1785	1802	1700	1785	167452	OXF	Emmington
1700	....	....	1700	106127	SOM	ALL
1705	1783	ALL	1992	159174	WAR	Nether Whitacre
1700	....	....	1700	106127	WIL	ALL
1811	1817	1811	1840	106143	WIL	Alderbury
BETTERRIDGE						
1858	1929	1858	1929	106143	GLS	Iron Acton
1858	1929	1858	1929	106143	WIL	Alderbury
BETTESS						
1740	1950	....	....	165999	CON	Lewannick
1740	1950	....	....	165999	CON	St Teath
1740	1950	....	....	165999	NTT	Newark
BETTINSON						
....	....	ALL	ALL	106135	ALL	Name Study
BETTLES						
1746	1746	ALL	....	115355	BDF	ALL
....	....	1780	1800	103713	BDF	Bletsoe
....	....	1790	1830	103713	BDF	Riseley
BETTON						
1812	1812	1790	1812	111414	SAL	Pontesbury
1790	1790	1750	1851	111414	SAL	Westbury
BETTRIDGE						
1540	1809	1500	1540	102830	GLS	Upper Swell
1557	1992	ALL	1557	169935	OXF	Kelmscott
1557	1840	1485	1557	169943	OXF	Kelmscott
1887	1929	1887	1929	106143	WIL	Alderbury
BETTS						
....	....	ALL	ALL	106151	ALL	Name Study
1851	1945	ALL	1851	106151	BDF	Luton
1806	1836	1750	1840	176621	BDF	Potton
....	1840	....	1840	161888	ESS	Halstead
BETTS contd.						
....	1820	....	1850	161888	ESS	Wethergate
1830	1992	....	....	169145	GNT	Newport
....	....	1840	1900	134694	HAM	Southampton
....	....	1800	1890	134694	IRL	Killucan
....	....	1838	1840	134694	IRL	Limerick
....	....	1800	1890	134694	IRL	Westmeath
1778	1804	ALL	ALL	169145	IRL	???
....	....	1800	1950	162000	KEN	Medway
....	....	1800	1950	162000	KEN	Swale
1873	1880	1880	1960	174831	LND	Battersea
1830	1850	1800	1850	123722	LND	Camberwell
1860	1983	ALL	1860	106151	LND	Charlton
....	....	1770	1820	162647	LND	City
1860	1870	1850	1992	176281	LND	St Pancras
1737	1992	ALL	1737	106178	NFK	Central
1737	1992	ALL	1737	106178	NFK	South
1800	1814	....	....	176885	NFK	Elsing
1770	1799	1700	1770	176885	NFK	North Tuddenham
1750	1870	1600	1992	114596	NFK	Shropham
1762	....	....	....	157554	NFK	Tibbenham
1701	1758	1650	1758	159905	OXF	Shenington
1811	1873	1873	1900	174831	SXW	Cuckfield
1888	1936	1880	1888	138495	WAR	Redditch
BETTSER						
1792	....	ALL	1992	106119	KEN	???
1664	....	ALL	1992	106119	SRY	???
BETTSOR						
1770	....	ALL	1992	106119	SSX	???
BETTY						
1794	1914	1700	1794	104310	CON	Bodmin
1803	1883	1700	1803	159093	CON	Ladock
1803	1883	1700	1803	159093	CON	Probus
1685	1750	1685	1750	133450	CON	Tregony
1719	1911	1500	1911	172294	SOM	ALL
BETZAR						
1648	....	ALL	1992	106119	SRY	???
1648	1700	ALL	1992	106119	SSX	???
BETZER						
1696	1708	ALL	1992	106119	SRY	???
BEVAN						
1879	1992	ALL	ALL	164550	COR	Bantry
1879	1992	ALL	ALL	164550	COR	Dunmanonsey
1813	1871	1770	1813	118079	DEV	Tavistock
1800	1890	1700	1800	105767	GLA	Gower
1800	1900	1750	1850	168750	GLA	Llangefelach
1841	1851	1841	1851	125717	GLA	Llanguick
1695	1992	ALL	1695	142034	GLA	Llangyfelach
....	....	1700	1900	100188	GLA	Moriston
1860	1910	1825	1910	142794	GLA	Mountain Ash
....	....	1800	1930	129232	GLA	Neath
1774	1818	?	1774	121665	GLS	Bristol
1796	1870	1600	1795	106208	HEF	Bodenham
1796	1870	1600	1795	106208	HEF	Ullingswick
....	....	1700	1900	131555	IRL	Cork
1800	1960	1700	1960	105287	LAN	Liverpool
1900	....	....	....	113018	LND	???
1821	1859	ALL	1992	102245	MDX	Westminster
1850	1930	1750	1850	105740	MON	Chepstow
....	....	ALL	1790	136514	SAL	Roddington
1850	1860	1800	1850	106194	SAL	Weston
1793	1904	....	....	116505	SFK	Ipswich
1854	1854	ALL	1900	168696	SOM	Yatton
1732	1834	1732	1834	167029	WIL	Aldbourne
1845	1920	1840	1880	106194	WMD	Dudley
1850	1879	1750	1850	138339	WOR	Whittington
1850	1879	1750	1850	138339	WOR	Worcester
BEVEN						
1795	1795	....	....	135437	SOM	Shepton Mallet
BEVERIDGE						
1851	1871	1700	1850	129305	ANS	Dundee
1750	....	ALL	ALL	130508	FIF	Abbotshall
1790	1850	1600	1850	130125	NBL	Beford
1822	1890	1800	1920	123536	NBL	Newcastle On Tyne
BEVERLEY						
....	....	ALL	ALL	104647	ALL	Name Study
1846	1912	1826	1846	142891	LIN	Rothwell
1826	1846	1800	1850	142891	YKS	Hull
BEVILL						
1760	1857	1600	1900	171522	SSX	Hastings
BEVIN						
1879	1992	ALL	ALL	164550	COR	Dunmanonsey
1750	1780	1700	1850	145661	WIL	Aldbourne

Surname	Known From	Known To	Researching From	Researching To	Ref	Cty	Place
BEVINGTON							
	1560	1650	1500	1760	173983	WAR	Honnington
	1830	1992	ALL	1830	160938	???	Ashchurch
BEVINS							
	1714	1800	1600	1714	131350	DEV	Arlington
	1820	1850	1820	1850	167029	HAM	Kingsclere
	....	....	1600	1800	179531	STS	West Bromley
BEVIS							
	....	....	ALL	ALL	106224	ALL	Name Study
	1434	1992	ALL	ALL	106224	ALL	ALL
	1737	1992	ALL	1737	106232	HAM	Fareham
	1880	1992	ALL	1800	106224	HAM	Fareham
	1880	1992	ALL	1800	106224	HAM	Gosport
	1737	1992	ALL	1737	106232	HAM	Gosport
	1785	1818	1740	1840	105333	HAM	Isle Of Wight
	1737	1992	ALL	1737	106232	HAM	Portsmouth
	1665	....	1640	1680	142018	LND	???
	1650	1685	1600	1690	142018	SOM	Chard
BEWEN							
	1830	1940	....	....	140317	ESS	East Donyland
BEWES							
	1800	1992	ALL	ALL	106240	ALL	ALL
	1600	1750	....	....	106240	CON	Launceston
	1700	1740	....	....	106240	CON	St Neot
	1730	1900	....	....	106240	DEV	Plymouth
BEWGLASS							
	1843	1938	?	?	106259	IRL	???
	?	1890	?	?	106259	LDY	Magherafelt
	1841	1857	?	?	106259	MOG	???
	1866	?	?	?	106259	SCT	Greenoch
	1820	1840	?	?	106259	TYR	ALL
BEWICK							
	....	....	ALL	ALL	130605	ALL	Name Study
	1843	1878	1700	1878	178233	CMA	Whitehaven
	1827	1885	1700	1827	176052	DUR	Hetton Le Hole
	1700	1992	1500	1700	106267	NBL	South
	1799	1801	ALL	ALL	119504	WES	Barrowdale Beck
BEWLEY							
	1886	1992	1840	1886	145084	CMA	Wythburn
BEWSEY							
	1851	1884	1800	1851	130184	LND	Southwark
	....	....	1700	1850	143685	SOM	Taunton
BEWSHER							
	....	....	ALL	ALL	160512	ALL	Name Study
BEXHILL							
	1645	1645	1600	1645	174807	SSX	Woodmancote
BEXTON							
	1795	1850	1700	1795	138584	NTT	Kingston On Soar
BEYNON							
	1869	1992	1800	1869	124427	CGN	Borth
	....	....	1800	1900	179027	CGN	Pembray
	1841	1918	1841	1918	159743	CMN	St Clears Mydrim
	1650	....	ALL	1992	105767	GLA	ALL
	1850	1900	1750	1850	179027	GLA	Nelson
BEZANCE							
	1800	1840	ALL	ALL	124605	SFK	Gorleston
BEZANTS							
	1750	1880	ALL	ALL	124605	NFK	Great Yarmouth
BIBB							
	....	....	ALL	1855	125393	STS	Birmingham
	....	....	ALL	1855	125393	WAR	Birmingham
	1810	1900	1700	1810	106283	WOR	Stourport
BIBBINS							
	1721	....	....	1750	160873	STS	Bilston
	1790	1992	1740	1790	161284	STS	Wolverhampton
BIBBY							
	1755	1875	1700	1755	152196	CMA	Manchester
	1829	1937	1700	1829	117927	CUL	Manchester
	1781	1900	1750	1850	177636	LAN	Balckburn
	?	1763	....	....	138851	LAN	Bolton
	1840	1870	1840	1880	117145	LAN	Heath Charnock
	1779	1840	ALL	ALL	135909	LAN	Kirkby Ireleth
	1693	1721	ALL	ALL	141615	LAN	Pilling
	1853	1887	1750	1850	129453	LAN	Warrington
	1905	1992	1700	1905	105007	LAN	???
BIBLE							
	....	....	ALL	ALL	122025	ALL	Name Study
	1850	ALL	1800	1850	171190	DEV	Barnstaple
BIBLEY							
	1848	1886	ALL	1992	125113	GLS	Coleford
BICE							
	....	....	?	?	112453	CON	Colan
BICKELL							
	1640	1992	1640	1992	168882	DEV	Milton Abbot
BICKERDIKE							
	1743	....	ALL	1743	119326	NRY	Brafferton
	1743	....	ALL	1743	119326	WRY	Gt Ouseburn
	1900	1992	1700	1900	107018	YKS	ALL
	1780	1850	1700	1800	165468	YKS	Kippax
	1840	1900	1700	1840	167762	YKS	Spofforth
BICKERS							
	1733	1828	ALL	ALL	141127	SFK	East
	1815	1890	1815	1900	111791	SFK	Southwold
BICKERSTAFF							
	1748	1891	ALL	1748	154563	LAN	ALL
	1790	1840	ALL	ALL	135909	LAN	Much Hoole
	1774	1878	1700	1900	135704	WOR	Bretforton
	1748	1891	ALL	1748	154563	YKS	ALL
BICKERSTAFFE							
	1836	1900	1700	1836	146021	LAN	St Helens
BICKERTON							
	1800	1850	1740	1860	142174	SAL	Dawley
	1815	1900	1700	1992	116742	YKS	Rawcliffe
BICKERTON-PRATT							
	....	....	1860	1992	100188	BRE	Cardiff
BICKFORD							
	1756	1870	1500	1800	132993	CON	Sheviock
	1800	1810	1810	1890	104140	DEV	Dartmouth
BICKHAM							
	1747	1768	1740	1780	142018	GLS	Bristol
	1781	1784	1770	1800	142018	LND	???
	1774	....	1770	1780	142018	SOM	Bath
BICKLE							
	....	....	1700	1900	171891	DEV	Broadwoodwidger
	1800	1822	1780	1800	145297	DEV	Tavistock
BICKLEY							
	1830	1870	1800	1900	165662	SAL	Wem
	1760	1800	1600	1760	158968	STS	Pelsall
BICKNELL							
	1841	1891	1700	1900	122181	HAM	Overton
	1790	1992	1790	1992	106305	LEI	Kirkby Malory
	1853	1853	1854	1950	118583	MDX	London
	1820	1860	1820	1860	155764	SRY	Haslemere
	1874	1893	ALL	ALL	128449	STS	Black Country
	1500	1992	1790	1992	106305	WAR	Nuneaton
BIDDER							
	1727	1850	....	....	160458	DEV	???
	1826	1890	1800	1992	152943	GLS	Bristol
	1727	1850	....	....	160458	LND	???
BIDDLE							
	1783	1822	1752	1858	106321	BRE	Clyro Glasbury
	....	....	....	1745	142409	ENG	Midlands
	1840	1922	1835	1922	106321	GLA	Merthyr Tydfil
	....	....	1715	1754	106321	HEF	ALL
	1799	1846	1700	1992	159956	LND	St James Garlick Hythe
	1928	1992	1925	1992	106321	SFK	Ipswich
	....	....	1696	1760	106321	STS	ALL
	....	....	1616	1795	106321	WAR	ALL
	1750	1900	ALL	ALL	106313	WAR	Harbury
BIDDLECOMBE							
	1830	1839	1840	1992	127787	DOR	Wimborne
	1600	1940	....	....	127833	HAM	Portsmouth
	1822	1850	1790	1860	156310	LND	???
BIDDLESCOMBE							
	1782	1898	1782	1898	126187	DOR	Bridport
BIDDLESTONE							
	1825	1888	1750	1825	178551	STS	Smethwick
	1825	1888	1750	1825	178551	STS	West Bromwich
BIDDULPH							
	....	....	ALL	ALL	106348	ALL	Name Study
	....	....	1066	1992	106348	ALL	ALL
	1800	1900	1780	1900	108510	SAL	Shifnal
	1789	1800	1760	1800	108510	SAL	Wrockwardine
BIDEL							
	....	....	1600	1800	106356	NFK	???
BIDEN							
	1800	1992	1700	1850	122513	HAM	Portsea
	1841	1860	ALL	1841	131881	HAM	Portsmouth
BIDEWELL							
	1750	1900	1600	1992	106356	NFK	???
BIDGOOD							
	1808	1808	1700	1808	116106	DEV	North East
BIDMEAD							
	1744	1880	....	....	118737	BRK	Beenham
	1750	1992	ALL	ALL	128449	WAR	Coventry
BIDWELL							
	....	....	ALL	ALL	106364	ALL	Name Study

Known From	To	Researching From	To	Ref	Cty	Place
BIDWELL contd.						
....	....	ALL	ALL	105864	HUN	Earith
BIELBY						
1808	1992	ALL	1808	178942	EYK	Thwing
1793	1822	ALL	1793	154946	YKS	Sledmere
1830	1877	....	....	139351	YKS	Weaverthorpe
....	....	ALL	1822	178942	YKS	Wintringham
BIFFEN						
1859	1920	ALL	ALL	158070	LND	Edmonton
BIFFIN						
1694	1834	ALL	1834	167029	WIL	Aldbourne
BIGGADIKE						
1700	1900	ALL	ALL	159530	LIN	ALL
BIGGAR						
1828	1912	....	....	128457	ANT	Belfast
1660	1740	1600	1660	117234	IRL	???
1660	1740	1600	1660	117234	SCT	???
BIGGERSTAFF						
1800	1900	1750	1900	177180	HRT	Bovingdon
BIGGINS						
1820	1830	1800	1860	169641	CUL	Westward
1782	....	1782	1820	154474	LAN	Lancaster
BIGGS						
1800	1900	1800	1900	110353	AVN	Bristol
1766	1871	1700	1871	145750	BDF	Marston
....	....	ALL	ALL	172324	ENG	London
1791	1854	ALL	1791	100528	HUN	St Ives
1848	....	....	....	116254	LND	Hammersmith
1672	1830	1600	1830	162280	SAL	ALL
1798	1863	1700	1863	174300	SOM	Bath
....	....	ALL	ALL	172324	SRY	???
1862	....	....	....	134430	SSX	St Leonards
1672	1830	1600	1830	162280	STS	ALL
BIGHAM						
1700	1850	1700	1850	154881	ALL	ALL
BIGLAND						
1700	1800	1500	1700	175269	LEI	Long Whatton
1750	1965	....	....	137820	SHI	Fetlar
1720	1965	....	....	137820	SHI	Mid Yell
1760	1965	....	....	137820	SHI	North Yell
1758	1965	....	....	137820	SHI	Northmavine
1720	1965	....	....	137820	SHI	South Yell
BIGLEN						
1720	1760	....	....	142158	GLS	Norton
BIGLIN						
1830	....	1700	1850	106380	YKS	Holderness
BIGNEL						
1787	1923	ALL	ALL	158070	SSX	Clayton
1787	1923	ALL	ALL	158070	SSX	Keymer
BIGNELL						
1800	1992	1800	1992	143014	ALL	ALL
1850	1992	....	....	127221	DEV	Appledore
1927	1969	1750	1898	106402	HAM	Hedge End
1927	1969	1750	1898	106402	HAM	West End
....	....	1700	1900	106402	LND	Kensington
1680	1760	....	....	132756	OXF	Bicester
BIGWOOD						
1705	1882	ALL	1705	158445	WIL	Westbury
BILBROUGH						
1700	1900	1700	1900	106429	WRY	Campsall
1850	1950	1850	1950	106429	WRY	Grenoside
1713	1736	1650	1765	101575	YKS	Wressle
1800	1930	1800	1930	150118	YKS	York
BILBY						
1673	1702	1600	1725	109290	NFK	Central
1810	1940	1720	1940	153303	NTT	Clifton
BILES						
1870	1871	1750	1895	171247	DEV	Holbeton
1810	....	....	....	119911	DOR	Powerstock
1895	1930	1895	1930	171247	HAM	Odiham
1881	....	....	....	112380	LND	Forest Gate
BILKE						
1712	1924	ALL	ALL	154563	DOR	Weymouth
BILKEY						
....	....	1800	1860	137111	CON	East Newlyn
....	....	1750	1800	174319	CON	St Erme
BILL						
1890	....	....	....	152420	LND	Shoreditch
1750	1850	1700	1992	177180	STS	Sedgley
BILLANY						
1950	1992	1950	1992	133450	DOR	???
1820	1910	1750	1910	115622	YKS	East Riding
BILLBROUGH						
1800	1825	1800	1900	161586	YKS	Pontefract

BIL

Known From	To	Researching From	To	Ref	Cty	Place
BILLCLIFF						
1756	1804	1700	1992	151521	YKS	Penistone
BILLEAU						
....	....	1700	1992	179531	ALL	ALL
BILLET						
....	....	1600	1730	148792	HAM	Whitchurch
BILLETT						
1700	1900	ALL	ALL	115266	DOR	ALL
BILLIN						
....	....	1750	1800	115142	LEI	Higham On The Hill
BILLING						
....	....	1200	1992	106445	ALL	ALL
980	1992	1120	1992	106453	ALL	ALL
1738	1738	1738	1738	145580	DBY	Edlaston
1800	1850	....	....	124621	LIN	Driby
1700	1830	1550	1850	162043	NTH	Whitfield
1750	1772	....	1772	171441	OXF	Stanton St John
1799	1815	ALL	1799	114987	SOM	Buckland St Mary
1826	1992	1826	1992	174483	STS	Smethwick
BILLINGE						
....	....	1200	1992	106445	ALL	ALL
BILLINGHAM						
1853	....	1830	1870	163775	MDX	Bethnal Green
1770	1850	....	....	153583	NTH	Bugbrooke
1750	1900	1700	1750	105457	NTH	Weedon
1820	1910	ALL	ALL	149535	SRY	Lambeth
1820	1870	ALL	ALL	149535	SRY	Newington
1870	1880	ALL	ALL	149535	SRY	Southwark
1829	1923	....	....	112232	STS	Cradley Heath
1786	1992	1600	1786	128139	STS	Cradley Heath
1786	1992	1600	1786	128139	WOR	Dudley
1816	1895	....	1816	129771	WOR	Old Swinford
1511	1575	ALL	1511	129992	WOR	Worcester
BILLINGHURST						
1818	1873	1818	1873	114308	SSX	Lewis
BILLINGS						
....	....	ALL	ALL	106453	ALL	Name Study
....	....	1200	1992	106445	ALL	ALL
....	....	1600	1800	149608	CON	St Agnes
1540	1713	1500	1625	102830	DBY	Carsington
1857	1896	ALL	ALL	115355	LEI	ALL
1900	1992	1600	1992	112003	LEI	Osgathorpe
....	1737	....	1737	151688	NTH	Etton
1772	1992	1650	1772	105902	NTH	Eye
1820	1838	....	....	171654	SRY	Newington
1825	1830	1700	1825	134058	STS	Harborne
1806	1992	1700	1920	102326	STS	Lichfield
1810	1841	1700	1841	134058	WAR	Birmingham
BILLINGSLEY						
1798	1856	....	1798	178365	BRK	Sutton Courtenay
BILLINGTON						
1809	....	....	....	130192	CHS	Wybunbury
1780	1895	1780	1870	145130	LAN	Upholland
1662	1662	1600	1662	163783	LAN	Woodplumpton
1821	1906	1700	1840	117005	OXF	Somerton
1840	1900	1840	1900	138118	STS	Madeley
1850	1992	1750	1850	156574	STS	Red Street
BILLMAN						
1788	1992	1700	1788	106488	NFK	Hockham
BILLOP						
1500	1600	1500	1600	169781	ERY	Beverley
BILLOPP						
1600	1700	1600	1700	169781	LND	???
BILLYARD						
....	....	ALL	ALL	125644	ALL	Name Study
BILNEY						
1835	1992	1500	1835	106496	CAM	ALL
1835	1992	1500	1835	106496	NFK	ALL
1835	1992	1500	1835	106496	SFK	ALL
1800	1992	1500	1800	106496	SFK	Stradbroke
BILSON						
....	....	ALL	....	133515	LEI	Somerby
BILTON						
?	?	?	?	118044	LIN	Farlesthorpe
1860	....	....	....	163465	NTT	Misterton
1792	1887	ALL	1792	178411	NTT	Nottingham
1852	1889	1800	1850	131806	SCT	Auckinleck
1835	1900	1700	1850	160350	SRY	Lingfield
BINDING						
1800	1950	1700	1800	106518	MDX	London
BINDLEY						
1850	1992	1570	1992	129410	ALL	ALL
BINE						
1761	1835	1500	1761	153591	KEN	High Halstow

Known From	To	Researching From	To	Ref	Cty	Place
BINE contd.						
1761	1835	1500	1761	153591	SSX	Peasmarsh
BINES						
1800	1850	....	....	131059	ESS	Canewdon
1775	1800	ALL	1775	131059	ESS	Danbury
1825	1925	....	....	131059	ESS	Hawkwell
1775	1850	ALL	1775	131059	ESS	Purleigh
BING						
1800	1850	ALL	ALL	106534	KEN	Canterbury
1845	1992	ALL	ALL	106534	KEN	Thanet
BINGHAM						
....	....	1780	1820	148113	CHS	Stalybridge
1750	1850	....	....	153397	HAM	New Forest
1738	1794	1650	1738	115460	HRT	Kensworth
1870	1992	1650	1992	173517	LIN	North
1789	1794	1785	1800	108901	LIN	Corringham
1750	1992	1600	1750	102342	LIN	Gainsborough
1876	1891	1876	1992	173517	LIN	Gainsborough
1793	1822	1700	1830	159042	LIN	Stamford
1823	1901	1700	1823	134732	LIN	Thorganby
1750	1992	1600	1900	106569	NTT	North
1700	1992	1650	1992	173517	NTT	North
1650	1875	1500	1650	106542	NTT	Claborough
1750	1820	1750	1900	106569	NTT	Clayworth
1700	1850	1500	1650	106542	NTT	North Wheaten
1810	1861	1800	1880	106569	NTT	North Wheatley
1875	1992	1875	1992	173517	WYK	Huddersfield
1875	1884	1875	1884	173517	WYK	Leeds
1906	1992	1906	1992	173517	WYK	Rotherham
1880	1985	1880	1985	173517	WYK	Sheffield
1841	1856	1841	1992	173517	WYK	Worsbrough
1850	1992	1800	1992	173517	YKS	ALL
1877	1944	1800	1877	149578	YKS	???
BINGLE						
....	....	ALL	ALL	163198	GLS	Minchinhampton
BINGLEY						
1400	1750	1400	1750	154881	ALL	ALL
1450	1900	1450	1900	106577	CHS	Chester
1450	1600	1450	1600	106577	FLN	Hawarden
....	....	1900	1930	143685	LIN	Grimsby
1150	1992	1150	1992	106577	YKS	South
1807	....	1760	1840	170348	YKS	Braithwell
BININGTON						
1770	1780	1770	1780	149403	YKS	Humbleton
BINKLEY						
1813	1851	?	1813	128910	NTT	Kirkby In Ashfield
BINKS						
1940	1950	ALL	1950	111678	DUR	Stockton
1750	1854	....	....	129747	ESS	Halstead
1820	1992	1700	1820	166804	MDX	Bethnal Green
1700	1803	1538	1820	118893	NRY	Romaldkirk
1700	1845	1538	1830	118893	NRY	???
1822	....	ALL	1822	171573	NYK	Bradford
1822	....	ALL	1822	171573	NYK	Oxley
1940	1950	ALL	1950	111678	NYK	Stockton
1822	....	ALL	1822	171573	NYK	Well
1874	1900	....	....	129747	SFK	Ipswich
1784	1850	1784	1992	165603	YKS	Fingall
1785	1992	....	....	171972	YKS	Malton
1785	1992	....	....	171972	YKS	Norton
1818	1888	1750	1818	117196	YKS	Richmond
1780	1885	1700	1780	117218	YKS	Richmond
1853	1860	....	1853	121002	???	London
BINLEY						
ALL	ALL	ALL	ALL	106585	ALL	ALL
BINNEY						
1838	1860	1700	1880	113107	ANS	Arbroath
1813	1935	1813	1992	103810	YKS	Rotherham
1813	1935	1813	1992	103810	YKS	Sheffield
1797	1844	1700	1797	128368	YKS	Sheffield
BINNING						
1775	1780	1650	1780	166928	YKS	Hunmanby
BINNINGTON						
1810	1866	1810	1866	149403	YKS	Hull
1833	1888	1800	1833	171565	YKS	Hull
BINNS						
1840	1900	1840	1900	110523	LAN	Rochdale
1802	1919	1775	1802	149047	LAN	Salford
1815	1850	1790	1815	155489	SRY	Kennington
ALL	1820	....	....	170798	WRY	Adwalton
ALL	1820	....	....	170798	WRY	Birstall
1820	....	....	....	170798	WRY	Leeds
1840	....	ALL	ALL	166839	WYK	Bradford
1788	....	ALL	ALL	166839	WYK	Haworth
BINNS contd.						
1851	1900	1700	1900	113778	YKS	Hunsworth
1663	1836	ALL	ALL	105015	YKS	Kildwick
....	....	1750	1800	149047	YKS	North Owran
1773	1992	1700	1773	160148	YKS	Plompton
BINSTEAD						
1801	1928	1700	1801	170542	HAM	Bishops Waltham
BINSTED						
1719	1748	1700	1750	170143	HAM	Buriton
1719	1748	1700	1750	170143	HAM	East Meon
BINT						
1770	1800	....	....	100420	WAR	Meriden
BINYON						
....	....	1700	1992	131903	LAN	Manchester
BIRBECK						
....	....	1800	1900	144401	SAL	Telford
BIRCH						
1816	1885	....	....	167444	BRK	Brightwell
1665	1940	....	....	128996	CAM	Thorney
1750	1908	1750	1908	130567	CHS	Stockport
1791	1992	1700	1791	170542	HAM	East Woodhay
1767	1831	1767	1831	151750	HRT	Wigginton
1771	1869	1700	1771	170542	KEN	Tilmanstone
1715	1777	1650	1777	141062	LAN	Pendleton
1800	1879	....	....	171824	LAN	St Helens
1670	1815	1600	1815	109630	LIN	Cockerington
1823	1845	....	....	168092	MDX	Shoreditch
1881	1886	1881	1992	156426	NBL	Woodhorn
1846	....	ALL	1846	147877	SRY	Benhilton
1835	1865	1700	1835	141402	SSX	St Leonards
1827	1841	1800	1886	156426	STS	North
1580	1650	1450	1580	154881	STS	Cavil
1840	1900	1750	1840	106607	STS	Leek
1665	1707	1600	1665	120049	STS	Wetton
1841	1881	1841	1881	156426	WAR	Aston
1800	1900	ALL	ALL	100897	WAR	???
1800	1992	1800	1850	106593	WOR	Bendley
1781	1803	....	....	102733	WOR	Tardebigge
1823	....	....	....	119911	YKS	Dichforth
1796	1890	1796	1890	138703	YKS	Sheffield
BIRCHALL						
1810	1854	1780	1810	118435	LAN	Liverpool
1828	1930	....	....	139483	LAN	Liverpool
1872	1897	1872	1900	165824	LAN	Skelmersdale
....	....	1840	1871	165824	LAN	St Helens
1841	1848	1700	1848	178233	LAN	St Helens
1600	1800	1600	1765	145130	LAN	Upholland
1803	....	1750	1828	139483	LAN	Whiston
1890	1940	1890	1970	100218	WAR	Coventry
1790	....	1750	1850	102016	WAR	Lighthorne
1890	1970	1840	1890	100218	WAR	Wolvey
BIRCHENOUGH						
....	....	ALL	ALL	106615	ALL	Name Study
BIRCHENSTY						
1350	1500	1300	1500	154881	SSX	Birchensty
BIRCHER						
1800	1950	....	....	155225	GLS	Barnwood
1690	1800	1600	1700	155225	GLS	Blaisdon
1800	1950	....	....	155225	GLS	Churchdown
1873	1906	1870	1920	117722	STS	Bilston
....	....	1800	1875	117722	WAR	Atherstone
BIRCHETT						
....	....	ALL	ALL	110841	ALL	ALL
BIRD						
1670	1760	ALL	1760	137286	BDF	Houghton Conquest
1836	1960	1600	1830	168211	BDF	Luton
1800	1846	1760	1851	153508	BKM	Medmenham
1737	1970	1600	1737	100447	BKM	Stokenchurch
....	....	1600	1830	127884	BRK	Cookham
1859	1922	1700	1900	140066	CHS	???
....	....	ALL	1770	119326	ELN	Aberlady
1746	1780	1650	1750	100013	ESS	Chignal St James
1760	1857	1600	1760	139084	ESS	Great Canfield
1966	1992	ALL	1966	147087	GLS	ALL
1720	1760	1680	1720	165530	GLS	Horsley
1850	1910	1700	1850	145904	HEF	Kings Pyon
1854	1881	ALL	1881	138819	LAN	Preston
1800	1900	....	....	126497	LAN	Wigan
1800	1900	1800	1900	126500	LAN	Wigan
1675	1778	ALL	ALL	141615	LEI	Gaulby
....	....	1700	1800	136743	LEI	Seagrave
1787	1936	1700	1800	131377	LIN	Ancaster
1720	1850	1620	1720	162396	LIN	Wrawby
1880	1930	1880	1930	166154	LND	Battersea

Known From	To	Researching From	To	Ref	Cty	Place
BIRD contd.						
1889	1901	1901	1992	122807	LND	Lisson Grove
1790	1850	....	....	104477	LND	Shoreditch
1830	1900	ALL	1830	169943	MDX	Bloomsbury
1827	1853	1700	1827	169935	MDX	Bloomsbury
1800	1850	1800	1850	106631	MDX	Clerkenwell
1881	1892	1861	1950	160903	MDX	Hackney
1800	1850	ALL	ALL	127884	MDX	Hammersmith
1820	1840	ALL	ALL	127884	MDX	Kensington
1881	1892	1861	1950	160903	MDX	Shoreditch
1773	1845	1700	1850	118281	MDX	St Pancras
1700	1880	ALL	ALL	107425	NFK	South
1760	1820	1700	1760	101958	NFK	Syderstone
1560	1850	....	....	129763	NTH	West
1525	1861	1300	1700	160903	NTH	Benefield
1800	1917	1649	1892	150053	NTH	Brigstock
1868	....	1800	1868	154202	NTH	Lutton
1737	1970	1600	1737	100447	OXF	Ibstone
1775	1850	....	....	132756	SAL	Buildwas
1724	1754	....	....	101028	SFK	Barrow
1830	1910	1750	1830	164860	SFK	Clopton
1723	1776	....	....	129747	SFK	Glemsford
1895	1925	1862	1895	106623	SRY	Guildford
1861	1881	1828	1861	106623	SRY	Woking
1797	1861	1780	1900	160873	STS	Brierley Hill
1580	1650	1450	1580	154881	STS	Cavil
1880	....	....	....	145009	STS	Handsworth
1797	1841	1780	1900	160873	STS	Kingswinford
1854	1873	1700	1854	164879	STS	Walsall
1833	1861	1800	1860	119059	WAR	Birmingham
1850	1903	1700	1905	117722	WAR	Dudley
....	....	1550	1650	115142	WAR	Mancetter
1841	1992	?	1841	174181	WAR	Rugby
1841	1992	?	1841	174181	WAR	Warwick
1630	1770	....	....	140309	WOR	Bretforton
1824	....	....	1824	160873	WOR	Halesowen
1815	1897	1815	1992	174475	WOR	Stourbridge
1813	1833	1813	1833	139807	YKS	ALL
1812	1992	....	....	175161	???	Church Eaton
BIRDBRIDGE						
1740	1818	1700	1900	118168	KEN	Bromley
BIRDE						
1691	1716	1500	1700	164909	ESS	Widford
BIRDSALL						
....	....	ALL	ALL	171166	ALL	Name Study
....	....	ALL	ALL	171166	ALL	ALL
1844	1923	1700	1844	141542	ALL	Manchester
1770	1881	1770	1881	171166	WRY	Kirk Fenton
1832	1900	1832	1900	171166	WRY	Leeds
1800	1881	1800	1881	171166	WRY	Towton
1868	1944	1868	1926	176885	YKS	Castleford
1793	....	1750	1826	176885	YKS	Church Fenton
1863	....	1850	1868	176885	YKS	Hazlewood
1859	1866	1847	1868	176885	YKS	Saxton In Elmet
1826	1847	1826	1847	176885	YKS	Stutton
BIRDSEYE						
....	1820	....	....	130079	OXF	Merton
BIRHIE						
....	....	1800	1900	129275	LND	West Ham
BIRKBECK						
....	....	ALL	ALL	106674	ALL	Name Study
1700	1900	1600	1900	106674	YKS	Grinton
1850	1900	....	....	106674	YKS	Settle
BIRKELMANS						
1882	....	1850	1900	119180	MDX	Islington
BIRKENHEAD						
1776	1926	1600	1776	120200	CHS	Northwich
1776	1926	1600	1776	120200	LAN	Warrington
BIRKENSHAW						
1777	1826	....	....	160458	LND	???
1777	1826	....	....	160458	NBL	???
BIRKETT						
1843	....	1555	1814	126462	CMA	Buttermere
1770	1992	1700	1770	106682	CUL	Muncaster
1850	1900	1750	1850	159212	CUL	Workington
1691	1992	1691	....	125172	LAN	Hawkshead
1740	1750	1700	1740	151769	LIN	Horbling
1720	1740	1650	1720	151769	LIN	Threckingham
1789	1853	1700	1820	163740	NTT	Newark
1691	1992	1691	....	125172	WES	Winster
1745	1830	1700	1745	136220	YKS	Melsonby
BIRKHEAD						
1649	1677	ALL	ALL	141615	LEI	Leicester
BIRKIN						
1790	1992	ALL	ALL	156000	DBY	ALL
1891	....	?	1900	164976	DBY	Borrowash
1812	1871	ALL	ALL	126721	NTT	Hucknall
BIRKINSHAW						
1770	1850	1650	1780	132659	WRY	Darfield
BIRKITT						
1833	1870	1800	1833	175951	YKS	Drax
BIRKMIRE						
1840	1880	1840	1880	106690	SAL	Bridgnorth
1870	1930	1870	1930	106690	WAR	Birmingham
BIRKMYRE						
1770	1870	1700	1900	106690	KKD	???
1800	1900	1750	1940	106690	LAN	Liverpool
1750	1900	1700	1900	106690	LKS	Glasgow
1800	1900	1700	1900	106690	RFW	North
1855	1873	....	....	139971	SCT	Port Glasgow
1770	1870	1700	1900	106690	WIG	???
BIRKS						
1825	....	....	....	121827	CHS	Holmes Chapel
1845	....	1845	....	159247	DBY	Chesterfield
1828	1920	?	1850	164976	DBY	Chesterfield
1800	1992	1700	1800	157740	DBY	Derby
1851	1858	1800	1900	121827	LND	Lambeth
1862	1992	1500	1862	136107	STS	Five Towns
1830	....	1830	....	159247	WAR	Coventry
BIRMINGHAM						
....	....	1790	1850	162825	DEV	Braod Clyst
1826	....	1790	....	162825	DEV	Ilfracombe
1906	1992	1800	1906	110752	IRL	???
1906	1992	1800	1906	110752	LND	???
BIRRANE						
1830	1850	1836	1852	111090	IRL	Killia
BIRRELL						
?	?	....	....	170453	FIF	ALL
BIRSTY						
1530	1750	1500	1750	154881	KEN	Hever
BIRT						
1750	1850	ALL	ALL	139564	DOR	Swanage
1700	1875	ALL	1992	133450	GLS	Coleford
1670	1890	1738	1789	106712	GLS	Painswick
ALL	ALL	ALL	ALL	103543	HAM	Christchurch
BIRTCHNELL						
1790	1900	ALL	1790	127949	BDF	Woburn
1952	1992	....	....	106720	BRK	Windsor
BIRTLES						
....	....	ALL	1820	178403	CAM	ALL
1790	1840	ALL	1790	145254	CHS	Knutsford
1840	1875	1875	1950	145254	LAN	Manchester
BIRTWHISTLE						
....	....	ALL	ALL	106739	ALL	Name Study
1200	1850	1850	1992	106739	ALL	ALL
BIRTWISLE						
1560	1992	1560	1881	166952	CHS	Northwich
BISBY						
1760	1930	1600	1760	173452	YKS	ALL
1880	1923	....	....	106747	YKS	Mexborough
BISGROVE						
1750	1992	ALL	1992	156272	ALL	ALL
1816	1816	....	....	135437	DEV	Churchstanton
BISH						
1758	1868	1700	1900	152285	SSX	???
BISHOP						
1850	1992	1850	1992	153818	BKM	Aston Clinton
1850	1992	1700	1900	140805	BKM	Chesham
1850	1992	1700	1900	140805	BKM	Cholesbury
1790	1885	1790	1900	153818	BKM	Cholesbury
1804	1859	1780	1880	176982	DEV	Devonport
1857	1880	....	....	102601	DEV	Ebford Woodbury
1840	1880	1840	1880	135429	DEV	Exmouth
1770	1850	1740	1900	171158	DEV	Farway
1850	1851	1750	1851	107662	DEV	Selsey
1817	1858	....	1858	102601	DEV	Topsham
1786	1857	....	1786	102601	DEV	Zeal Monachorum
1750	1992	1600	1992	106763	DOR	Central
1760	1787	1500	1760	138614	DOR	Bridport
1750	1850	1700	1810	174599	DOR	Burton Bradstock
1840	1863	1810	1880	133639	DOR	Melcombe Regis
1850	1851	1750	1851	107662	DOR	Portland
1840	1863	1810	1880	133639	DOR	Weymouth
1691	1766	ALL	1691	154563	DOR	Weymouth
1840	1863	1810	1880	133639	DOR	Wyke Regis
?	?	?	?	140104	DUR	Gateshead
1890	1992	1890	1992	106798	ESS	???

Known From	To	Researching From	To	Ref	Cty	Place
BISHOP contd.						
1880	1992	....	....	102601	GLA	Cardiff
1778	1860	1700	1900	178322	GLS	Leckhampton
1881	1992	ALL	ALL	173355	GLS	Minchinhampton
....	....	1843	1868	173355	GLS	Shipton Moyne
1670	1910	1560	1700	138150	GLS	Westerleigh
1730	1850	1600	1900	149128	HAM	Ampfield
1600	1940	1600	1992	127833	HAM	Portsmouth
1837	1837	ALL	ALL	172251	HAM	Portsmouth
1680	1740	1600	1750	136840	HAM	Winchester
1840	1945	1800	1900	149128	HAM	Winchester
....	....	1600	1850	127833	HAM	???
1797	1867	ALL	1867	118990	HEF	ALL
1800	1900	1750	1900	119938	HEF	Cradley
1650	1750	ALL	ALL	131873	HRT	Much Hormead
1700	1830	1700	1890	128740	KEN	East Peckham
1880	1900	1880	1900	147486	LAN	Burnley
1870	1992	1870	1992	106763	LAN	Preston
1799	....	ALL	....	104515	LIN	Osbournby
1820	1890	1820	1890	106798	LND	Marylebone
1820	1830	1825	1830	101877	LND	St Pancras
1845	1847	1800	1900	151181	MDX	Hackney
1800	1855	1800	1900	117870	MDX	London
?	?	?	?	140104	MDX	Poplar
1796	1872	1750	1830	129356	MDX	Shoreditch
1845	1845	ALL	....	109258	MDX	Yiewsley-Hillingdon
1780	1850	1720	1780	128333	MLN	Currie
1760	1860	1760	1860	101877	NFK	Beeston Regis
1750	1790	1700	1900	117463	NFK	Blakeney
1538	1860	1538	1860	101877	NFK	Burnham
1767	1884	ALL	1767	161330	NFK	Mileham
1790	1840	1750	1790	165948	SFK	Great Barton
1500	1820	1500	1820	125679	SOM	South East
....	....	1830	1900	114170	SOM	Bristol
1864	1891	1827	1891	106771	SOM	Henstridge
1850	1900	1800	1930	114677	SOM	Taunton
1848	1921	1848	1921	143286	SOM	Wellington
....	....	1500	1880	137472	SRY	Dorking
....	....	1500	1880	137472	SRY	Holmwood
1889	1893	....	1903	153982	SRY	Rotherhithe
1823	1841	1800	1900	118192	SSX	Brighton
1870	1890	1800	1870	120308	SSX	Old Shoreham
1772	1834	1500	1772	110310	SSX	Salehurst
1730	1871	1680	1730	114871	SSX	Ticehurst
1730	1871	1680	1730	114871	SSX	Westfield
....	1800	....	....	174564	SSX	Westfield
1600	1787	ALL	1751	156175	SXE	Ninfield
....	....	1600	1850	127833	SXW	???
1881	1881	1881	1900	178322	WAR	Aston
1850	1871	ALL	1850	112615	WOR	Cradley
1778	1856	ALL	1778	103004	YKS	Sheffield
BISHOPPS						
1798	?	?	?	166642	KEN	???
BISKET						
ALL	ALL	ALL	ALL	166758	ALL	ALL
BISS						
1710	1830	....	....	135437	SOM	Stogursey
BISSACRE						
1585	1686	1580	1992	122211	SRY	Lambeth
BISSE						
1780	1800	1700	1785	174599	WIL	Warminster
BISSELL						
....	1833	ALL	1900	127000	STS	Dudley
....	1833	ALL	1900	127000	WOR	???
BISSENDEN						
1821	1848	....	1821	177601	SSX	Hastings
BISSET						
1820	1840	1700	1880	159379	FIF	Newburgh
1796	1876	1796	1800	102121	SCT	Edinburgh
BISSETT						
1821	1821	ALL	ALL	130508	FIF	Cameron
1865	1871	1700	1865	109223	GMP	Newpitsligo
1804	1947	1775	1804	150312	WLN	Carriden
BISSMIRE						
....	....	ALL	ALL	170364	ALL	Name Study
BI3TOW						
1750	1830	1750	1830	173533	NTH	South
BITHEL						
1824	1874	ALL	ALL	125288	STS	Gnosall
1836	1870	ALL	ALL	125288	STS	Norton Canes
BITHELL						
1870	....	....	....	127086	HAM	ALL
BIX						
....	....	ALL	ALL	118222	ALL	Name Study

Known From	To	Researching From	To	Ref	Cty	Place
BIX contd.						
1564	1900	1560	1992	118222	ALL	ALL
BIZLEY						
....	1992	....	....	122157	WIL	Swindon
BLABER						
1700	1950	1600	1840	106828	SSX	ALL
1558	1710	....	....	165999	SSX	Angmering
BLABY						
1660	1720	1600	1660	149373	KEN	Bermondsey
1660	1720	1600	1660	149373	LND	City
1660	1720	1600	1660	149373	LND	Deptford
BLACK						
....	....	ALL	ALL	102180	ALL	Name Study
1800	1880	1700	1800	106887	ABD	Deskford
1869	1992	1800	1900	105414	ABD	Old Machar
1800	1880	1700	1800	106887	ABD	Rathven
1869	1992	1800	1900	105414	ABD	Tarves
1800	1850	ALL	ALL	103896	ANT	Ballycastle
1870	1992	1750	1870	118052	ANT	Ballycastle
1650	1850	1500	1650	113204	ANT	Belfast
1791	1881	1700	1791	106836	ARL	Mull
1793	1810	1700	1900	168246	AYR	New Cumnock
1841	1841	1800	1841	179116	AYR	Old Cummock
ALL	ALL	ALL	1930	158275	BRK	Newbury
1837	1870	1800	1880	147788	CUL	Carlisle
1830	1992	1700	1830	106879	DFS	Eskdalemuir
1792	1872	ALL	ALL	101370	DUR	Durham
ALL	ALL	1780	1880	110671	DUR	South Shields
1830	1992	1830	1900	159905	DUR	South Shields
1813	1836	ALL	ALL	101370	FIF	Burntisland
....	....	1700	ALL	149187	FIF	Carnbee
1844	1862	ALL	ALL	101370	FIF	Dunfermline
....	....	1700	ALL	149187	FIF	Kilrenny
1723	1750	ALL	1723	131881	FIF	Kirkaldy
1710	....	....	....	130915	FIF	Leuchars
1830	1830	1700	1900	112089	IRL	???
1825	1838	1780	1850	131547	KCD	Tulliallan
1791	....	....	1800	171441	KEN	Faversham
1800	1909	1700	1800	160474	LAN	Prescot
1920	1977	....	....	141674	LEI	No Mans Heath
1690	1860	ALL	1785	168718	LEI	Queniborough
1900	1950	1900	1950	138479	LIN	Sudbrooke
1858	1891	1800	1900	120146	LKS	Cambusnethen
1791	1881	1881	1992	106836	LKS	Glasgow
1890	....	....	....	106852	LKS	Walston
1830	1869	ALL	1869	101362	LND	Islington
1857	1975	1800	1860	103896	LND	Poplar
....	....	ALL	ALL	106860	MDX	Camden Town
....	....	ALL	1811	119326	MLN	Temple
1886	1992	1850	1886	130877	NBL	Bedlington
1790	1850	1760	1870	159905	NBL	Blyth
1770	1820	1770	1870	160121	NBL	Newcastle
1790	1992	1790	1992	146366	NBL	Rothbury
1830	1850	1830	1850	159905	NBL	Tynemouth
1696	1759	ALL	1759	162507	NFK	Norwich
1805	1860	....	....	132756	NTT	Blyth
1853	....	1840	1870	131547	OXF	Banbury
1806	1816	1800	1840	172162	RFW	Greenock
1790	1992	1790	1992	146366	ROX	Eckford
1900	1980	1800	1900	119784	SCT	Anderston
1850	1905	1800	1905	147095	SCT	Edingburgh
1852	1992	ALL	1852	106860	SFK	Ipswich
1886	1934	1880	1900	131547	SRY	Dorking
1790	1890	1700	1920	167207	STI	Falkirk
1800	1909	1700	1800	160474	WES	Grasemere
1870	1900	1900	ALL	171174	YKS	Scarborough
BLACKADDER						
1875	....	1700	1900	153354	ELN	Dirleton
BLACKADER						
1719	1719	ALL	1719	131881	FIF	Kirkaldy
BLACKAH						
1866	1940	....	....	167150	HAM	Portsmouth
1824	1851	1700	1824	167150	YKS	Pateley Bridge
BLACKALER						
....	....	1800	1992	153540	DEV	Devonport
BLACKALL						
1797	1825	1700	1825	111953	BKM	Turville Heath
1843	1992	1843	....	106895	BRK	Bradfield
1840	1920	....	....	177776	BRK	Reading
1843	1992	1843	....	106895	OXF	Bradfield
1800	1850	....	....	125997	???	London
BLACKALLER						
1699	1807	....	....	112887	LND	???

Known From	Known To	Researching From	Researching To	Ref	Cty	Place
BLACKBEARD						
1770	1800	1600	1900	112372	YKS	Nidderdale
BLACKBOURN						
1850	1880	1550	1850	147265	LIN	Mid
BLACKBOURNE						
1562	1592	1500	1560	176451	YKS	Kirkburton
BLACKBURN						
1895	1906	1837	1931	147257	BKM	Wingrave
1802	1950	....	1820	106917	CHS	Over
1700	1800	....	1700	106917	CHS	Wettenhall
1802	1950	....	1820	106917	CHS	Wharton
1832	1915	....	....	151912	LAN	Blackburn
1700	1849	1700	1860	145602	LAN	Chorley
1826	1847	1800	1850	133043	LDY	Carrowclare
....	....	1850	1900	123765	LIN	Grimsby
1793	1851	1793	1871	147257	LIN	Horbling
1873	....	....	....	147257	LIN	Kirton
1850	1880	1550	1850	147265	LIN	Mid
1769	1793	1769	1793	147257	LIN	Normanton
1868	1971	1868	1927	147257	MDX	Chiswick
1742	1742	1700	1760	159042	RUT	Whissendine
1793	1992	ALL	1793	106909	YKS	Burnsall
1825	1985	1750	1850	106925	YKS	Mirfield
1811	1832	1740	1832	151912	YKS	West Bradford
BLACKER						
1733	....	1600	1750	100013	SOM	Chilcompton
1695	1791	1695	1791	154733	SOM	Clutton
BLACKET						
1702	1720	ALL	1702	154563	DUR	Weardale
BLACKETT SHELDON						
1846	1979	1600	1846	167355	NBL	Newcastle
BLACKETT						
1840	1900	1840	1900	106933	LAN	Salford
1709	1992	1650	1700	129038	WES	North
1650	1900	1650	1900	106933	WES	Appleby
BLACKFORD						
1734	1734	1600	1733	131245	WAR	Leek Wootton
BLACKGROVE						
1450	1992	1450	1992	107069	ALL	ALL
BLACKHALL						
1696	1750	1750	1992	175412	DEV	Exeter
1865	1865	1865	1992	175412	KEN	Canterbury
1816	1870	1870	1992	175412	LND	Hackney
1600	1650	1650	1992	175412	OXF	Abingdon
BLACKHURST						
1900	1992	1800	1992	177881	CUL	Barrow In Furness
....	....	1750	1805	179523	LAN	Liverpool
1900	1992	1800	1992	177881	LKS	Glasgow
BLACKISTON						
1774	1992	....	....	127221	SSX	ALL
BLACKLEDGE						
1668	1683	ALL	ALL	141615	LAN	Winmarly
BLACKLEY						
....	....	1800	1900	118834	KEN	Canterbury
....	....	1800	1900	118834	KEN	Dover
BLACKLOCK						
1841	1871	1700	1840	106968	CUL	Bolton
1860	1920	1700	1860	106968	CUL	Castle Sowerby
1843	1915	1800	1992	106941	DBY	Derby
1800	1880	ALL	ALL	116823	DUR	Stockton
1865	1915	1800	1992	106941	SSX	Highbrook
BLACKLOCKS						
1638	?	?	?	166642	KEN	Postling
BLACKMAN						
1788	1992	ALL	1788	106984	BKM	Burnham
ALL	ALL	ALL	1930	158275	BRK	Inkpen
1735	1735	1700	1750	125032	BRK	Wokingham
1736	1760	1650	1736	178608	HRT	Reed
....	....	ALL	1788	106984	OXF	Henley
1870	....	1870	....	162663	SRY	Lambeth
....	1600	....	....	174564	SSX	Hooe
1831	1900	1700	1854	164402	WIL	Lyneham
BLACKMORE						
1808	1897	1750	1851	122882	DEV	Broadclyst
1759	1853	....	....	135437	DEV	Clayhidon
1700	1992	1650	1992	156701	DEV	Thelbridge
1720	1992	1650	1992	156698	DEV	Thelbridge
1830	1850	ALL	ALL	131253	DEV	Torre
?	?	ALL	ALL	100897	KEN	Greenwich
1860	1865	1800	1950	106976	LND	Lambeth
1828	1860	1750	1860	106976	SOM	Bath
1812	1885	ALL	1812	114987	SOM	Church Stanton
1838	1992	1700	1838	154415	SOM	Churchstanton
1830	1930	1700	1830	112992	SOM	Weston Super Mare
BLACKMORE contd.						
1850	1992	1600	1850	117838	???	Bristol
BLACKNEY						
1699	1730	1500	1700	104825	BRK	Reading
BLACKSHAL						
1813	1900	1700	1850	117005	SFK	Sudbury
BLACKSHAW						
1530	1992	....	1530	144363	CHS	Withington
BLACKSTONE						
1760	1836	....	....	106992	YKS	Beverley
BLACKWELL						
ALL	ALL	ALL	1930	158275	BRK	Newbury
1861	1900	ALL	ALL	112518	BRK	Shippon
1700	1860	1600	1700	176311	CAM	Burwell
1676	1829	1500	1992	102520	CON	Crowan
....	....	1600	1738	134104	DBY	ALL
1701	....	ALL	ALL	105481	DBY	Ilkeston
1760	1810	1700	1760	160458	DBY	Matlock
1738	1920	1600	1738	134104	DEN	Llanverres
1840	1900	1842	1878	178683	GLS	Horsley
1849	1851	1800	1850	123978	HAM	Southampton
1780	1825	ALL	1825	107026	LND	Marylebone
1825	1930	1800	1992	107026	MDX	Uxbridge
....	....	1780	1810	110450	NTH	ALL
1653	1851	1580	1652	166820	NTH	Harpole
1800	1860	1750	1900	138517	SOM	???
1810	1834	1780	1992	122416	TIP	Roscrea
1800	1992	1600	1800	107018	YKS	Kirbymoorside
BLACKWOOD						
1718	1739	ALL	ALL	174777	AYR	Kames
1718	1739	ALL	ALL	174777	AYR	Muirkeirk
1830	1930	1790	1830	107042	TYR	???
BLADEN						
1850	1992	1700	1850	139335	KEN	Rochester
BLADES						
1770	1992	ALL	1992	151319	LAN	ALL
1811	ALL	ALL	ALL	122629	LAN	Preston
1800	1992	....	....	176125	LIN	Asterby
1800	1992	....	....	176125	LIN	Goulceby
1770	1992	ALL	1992	151319	YKS	ALL
1750	1850	1700	1850	110612	YKS	North
1881	1930	1800	1881	102415	YKS	Sheffield
BLADON						
1790	1837	ALL	1992	107050	WAR	ALL
1790	1837	ALL	1992	107050	WAR	Solihull
1790	1837	ALL	1992	107050	WAR	Tamworth
1800	1940	ALL	1992	107050	WOR	Kings Norton
BLAGDON						
1800	1840	1600	1840	154342	DEV	Bere Alston
1800	1860	1600	1860	154342	GLS	Bristol
1784	1805	1700	1800	123137	SOM	Limington
1666	1758	1600	1992	122211	SRY	Lambeth
BLAGG						
....	....	1800	1900	103667	CHS	???
1900	1992	1793	1992	108901	DBY	Whitwell
....	....	1800	1900	103667	LAN	???
1769	1793	1769	1793	108901	NTT	East Markham
1793	1900	1793	1900	108901	NTT	Ordsall
....	....	1800	1900	103667	SAL	???
BLAGRAVE						
1450	1992	1450	1992	107069	ALL	ALL
BLAGROVE						
1450	1992	1450	1992	107069	ALL	ALL
BLAIKIE						
1690	1730	ALL	1730	149063	MLN	Stow
1720	1860	1720	1860	149063	ROX	Melrose
1816	1900	1700	1835	133787	SAL	Oswestry
BLAIN						
1784	1814	1784	1992	143987	NIR	Belfast
BLAINEY						
1834	1860	1700	1900	169536	SAL	ALL
BLAIR						
....	....	1700	1850	134546	ANS	Dundee
....	....	1700	1850	134546	ANS	Kingoldrum
1860	1911	1800	1911	108278	ANT	Ballymoney
1831	1837	1700	1900	175889	ARL	Islay
1831	1837	1700	1900	175889	ARL	Kilmun
1793	1861	1750	1840	124028	BUT	Rothesay
1812	....	....	....	136964	CON	St Agnes Truro
1799	1900	1700	1850	106380	DUR	???
1780	1820	....	....	140554	ELN	Stenton
1861	1884	....	....	168203	LKS	Hamilton
1766	1930	1600	1766	147346	MDX	London
1766	1822	1740	1822	147311	NYK	Scarborough

Known From	To	Researching From	To	Ref	Cty	Place
BLAIR contd.						
1786	1945	....	1850	170461	RFW	Renfrew
1785	1850	1785	1850	133795	SCT	Camelon
1800	1840	1750	1992	104671	SHI	ALL
1805	1884	....	....	168203	STI	Drymen
1845	1861	....	....	168203	STI	Kippen
1799	1900	1700	1850	106380	YKS	Guisborough
BLAKE						
....	....	ALL	ALL	107107	ALL	Name Study
1863	1944	1700	1992	178373	AVN	Bristol
1802	1879	1750	1802	107093	BKM	Ashendon
1867	1897	....	....	137790	CHS	Crewe
1800	1850	1700	1992	167592	CHS	Northwich
1690	1778	1500	1720	121932	CON	Jacobstow
1760	1870	1700	1900	169641	CON	Jacobstow
1690	1778	1500	1720	121932	CON	Week St Mary
....	....	ALL	1860	178403	DBY	ALL
1679	1807	1625	1851	149047	DEV	North Molton
....	....	1600	1950	136379	HAM	South
1830	1873	1830	1873	155381	HAM	Alverstoke
1500	1650	1400	1600	144657	HAM	Andover
1816	1992	1650	1816	179272	HAM	Andover
1500	1650	1400	1600	144657	HAM	Enham
1841	1847	1800	1841	133442	HAM	Hurstbourne Tarrant
1760	1820	1700	1820	148288	HAM	Portsea
1909	1992	ALL	ALL	178373	HAM	West Wellow
1853	1895	ALL	1853	166847	HRT	Cheshunt
1850	1992	1700	1850	157872	LND	Walworth
1850	1992	1700	1850	157872	LND	Woolwich
1880	1960	1880	1960	107115	MDX	Hammersmith
1870	1890	1850	1920	100242	MDX	Hillingdon
1833	1854	1750	1880	166898	MDX	St Pancras
1844	1988	1844	1992	107980	NFK	Rockland St Mary
1814	1983	1740	1850	155381	NFK	Yarmouth
....	....	1800	1870	100242	OXF	Nettlebed
1852	1862	1750	1852	158267	SFK	Bacton
1814	1983	1740	1850	155381	SFK	Gorleston
1830	1880	ALL	1830	110078	SFK	Ipswich
1828	1850	ALL	ALL	125466	SFK	Occold
1829	1975	1829	1875	133175	SOM	Banwell
1600	1750	1600	1750	151653	SOM	Bridgwater
....	....	1550	1750	130591	SOM	Halse
1650	1720	1600	1800	151653	SOM	Langport
1770	1880	1700	1840	144657	SOM	Milverton
1830	ALL	1700	1830	160741	SRY	Bermondsey
1820	?	1750	1992	167592	STS	Burslem
1790	1868	1790	....	116394	WIL	Chippenham
1800	1860	1700	1900	107115	WIL	Devizes
1732	....	....	....	170348	WIL	Long Newnton
....	....	1700	1750	170348	WIL	Purton
1600	1992	1600	1992	110361	WIL	Woodford
BLAKEBURN						
1770	1950	1650	1770	128376	DUR	Chester Le Street
BLAKELEY						
1805	1992	1700	1805	107123	CHS	Macclesfield
....	....	?	?	119997	LND	London
1737	1992	1600	1737	107123	STS	Burslem
1737	1992	1600	1737	107123	STS	Stoke
1743	1767	1700	1743	107123	WOR	Old Swinford
1684	1840	1600	1700	154601	WYK	Batley
1658	1949	....	....	109142	YKS	Batley
?	?	?	?	119997	YKS	Dewsbury
1626	1658	1550	1626	109142	YKS	Hartshead
BLAKELOCK						
1784	1784	1750	1800	141461	DUR	North West
BLAKELY						
1580	1932	1500	1850	154881	ALL	ALL
1580	1932	1500	1850	154881	DOW	ALL
1580	1932	1500	1850	154881	NBL	ALL
BLAKEMAN						
1867	1871	1800	1900	165824	DEV	Plymouth
1873	1881	1800	1900	165824	SOM	Bath
BLAKEMORE						
1840	1880	ALL	1880	121053	STS	Darlaston
1844	1906	1800	1844	149039	STS	West Bromwich
BLAKENEY						
1687	1736	1650	1736	125032	BRK	Reading
1730	1800	1750	1870	125032	BRK	Waltham St Lawrence
1761	1800	1750	1810	125032	BRK	Windsor
1774	1880	ALL	ALL	119105	GAL	Eyrefield
BLAKER						
1546	1992	1546	1992	107166	SSX	Worthing
BLAKEWAY						
1650	1900	1650	1900	120251	SAL	ALL

Known From	To	Researching From	To	Ref	Cty	Place
BLAKEWELL						
1732	1802	1550	1731	102830	LIN	Krikby Green
BLAKEY						
1827	1899	1800	1900	103632	DUR	Sunderland
1797	1848	1797	1848	143286	LAN	Accrington
1800	1992	1650	1800	143944	NRY	ALL
....	....	1776	1992	121940	WRY	Long Preston
BLAMEY						
1749	1992	1749	1992	149810	CON	Mevagissey
1846	1992	1846	1992	149810	CON	St Austell
1632	1992	1632	1992	107174	CON	Veryan
1640	1992	1500	1640	150142	CON	Veryan
1632	1992	1632	1992	149810	CON	Veryan
BLAMIRE						
1700	1800	....	....	146854	WES	Orton
BLAMIRES						
....	1930	....	1900	154784	YKS	Cleckheaton
BLANCART						
1656	1940	....	....	128996	CAM	Thorney
BLANCE						
1600	1900	1600	1800	104914	SHI	ALL
1750	1965	....	....	137820	SHI	Fetlar
1720	1965	....	....	137820	SHI	Mid Yell
1760	1965	....	....	137820	SHI	North Yell
1758	1965	....	....	137820	SHI	Northmavine
1720	1965	....	....	137820	SHI	South Yell
BLANCHARD						
1892	1940	....	....	128996	CAM	Thorney
1680	1735	....	....	151351	DOR	Alton Pancras
1647	1800	1500	1647	150169	HAM	East Tisted
1760	1820	1760	1900	150169	HAM	Newton Valence
1890	1903	1800	1992	178446	LIN	Friskney
1859	....	....	....	140023	LND	ALL
1864	....	....	....	150762	MON	Blaenavon
1864	....	....	....	150762	MON	Ebbw Vale
1720	1800	1600	1720	164879	SRY	ALL
1743	1851	1600	1743	164879	SRY	Chorleywood
....	....	1800	1860	179361	WIL	Bower Chalke
1700	....	ALL	ALL	116394	WIL	Semley
....	....	1796	1960	150762	WIL	Trowbridge
1791	....	1700	1800	115967	YKS	Whitby
BLANCHER						
1700	1800	....	....	100056	CAM	Thorney
1763	1869	1600	1770	101575	LIN	Billinghay
BLANCHET						
1750	1850	1750	1850	144657	HAM	Farringdon
BLANCHETT						
1810	1811	1750	1850	167002	BKM	Upton Cum Chalvey
BLANCHFIELD						
1796	1838	1700	1796	171476	KEN	Chillendon
BLANCHFLOWER						
1860	1900	1860	1900	140864	MDX	Edmonton
1860	1900	1860	1900	140864	MDX	Islington
1800	1850	1750	1800	140864	NFK	Swaffham
BLANCHFORD						
....	....	1600	1900	126055	DEV	ALL
BLAND						
1865	1915	1820	1870	107182	CHS	Altrincham
1831	1879	1879	1992	107204	DUR	Stockton
1720	1780	1700	1800	144657	ESS	Chingford
1841	1875	1800	1841	108103	KEN	Crayford
1800	1992	1800	1992	134880	KEN	Gravesend
1625	1625	....	....	127426	KEN	Harrietsham
1720	1751	ALL	ALL	141615	LAN	Borwick
1805	1880	1700	1900	144703	LEI	ALL
1809	....	ALL	1809	107964	LIN	Leake
1850	1930	1800	1850	146285	MDX	Islington
1814	1830	1700	1814	149632	MLN	Edinburgh
1850	1900	ALL	ALL	108960	NFK	ALL
1800	1820	1600	1820	101834	NFK	South West
1726	1881	1700	1992	175722	NFK	Stokesby
1860	1931	1750	1860	153974	NFK	???
1600	1900	1900	1992	129763	NTH	West
1808	1831	1700	1808	107204	NYK	Grinton
1808	1831	1700	1808	107204	NYK	Reeth
1714	1815	1600	1714	172871	SFK	Bury St Edmunds
....	1860	ALL	1802	166847	SFK	Bury
....	1860	ALL	1802	166847	SFK	Hessett
1679	1992	1540	1679	142646	WES	Little Strickland
1679	1992	1540	1679	142646	WES	Morland
1869	1992	1758	1869	107190	WES	Orton
1815	1820	1700	1850	107182	WYK	Esholt
1815	1820	1700	1850	107182	WYK	Otley
1801	1925	?	?	176702	WYK	Queensbury

```
 Known     Researching
 From  To  From  To    Ref    Cty   Place
BLAND  contd.
 1700 1920 ALL  ALL   163252 YKS North
 1806 1924 1750 1900 157384 YKS Silsden
BLANDFORD
 .... .... ALL  ALL   107212 ALL ALL
 1806 1982 1700 1806 107212 HAM Boldre
 1500 1900 1500 1900 170216 WIL ALL
BLANDIMORE
 .... .... ALL  1750 175331 DOR ALL
 .... .... ALL  1750 175331 SOM ALL
 .... .... ALL  1750 175331 WIL ALL
BLANDY
 1797 1853 1797 1853 173738 BRK Hungerford
BLANE
 1880 1920 1920 1940 145408 LND Sydenham
BLANEY
 1811 1900 1700 1825 145882 DOR Old Swanwick
BLANFORD
 1685 1752 1640 1780 105333 WIL Semley
 1685 1752 1640 1780 105333 WIL Tisbury
BLANKING
 1840 1992 1800 1992 114642 MDX Stepney
BLANKS
 1820 1992 1600 1820 152633 ESS East Hanningfield
BLANN
 .... .... ALL  ALL   125911 ALL Name Study
 .... .... ALL  ALL   125911 ALL ALL
 1714 1881 1714 1992 107220 SSX Beeding
 1714 1880 ALL  1714 125911 SSX Upper Beeding
BLANSHARD
 1711 1760 1500 1711 125695 YKS Bubwith
 1700 1800 1700 1800 130052 YKS East Riding
BLANTACII
 1855 1855 1800 1992 116122 SCT Blythswood
BLANTHEM
 1760 1780 1700 1770 173312 STS Stone
BLASDON
 1820 1850 ALL  ALL   107352 DEV Alverdiscott
BLASKET
 1798 ?    ?    ?     166642 SSX ???
BLASSON
 1704 1862 .... .... 134007 NTH Higham Ferrers
BLATCHFORD
 1800 1900 1700 1900 142875 CON Truro
 1858 1938 .... .... 159301 CON ???
 1870 1930 1800 1870 173770 DEV Plymouth
BLATCHLEY
 1819 1992 ALL  1819 107239 SOM Bath
BLATHWAYT
 ALL  ALL  .... .... 137332 ??? ???
BLAUNT
 1800 1810 1750 1850 100129 LEI Ullesthorpe
BLAXHILL
 1820 1900 1820 1950 140171 HRT Clothall
BLAXILL
 1682 1887 ALL  ALL   162108 ALL ALL
BLAXLAND
 .... .... 1600 1811 101125 KEN ALL
 1811 1900 1700 1811 101125 KEN Seasalter
BLAXLEY
 1648 1861 1640 1871 170143 NTH Lamport
 1648 1861 1640 1871 170143 NTH Walgrave
BLAYDON
 1939 1945 .... .... 107255 ARL Campbletown
 1881 1939 ALL  ALL   107255 ESS West
 1945 1950 .... .... 107255 LND Putney
 1752 1885 ALL  ALL   107255 SFK West
 1972 1992 .... .... 107255 SFK Ipswich
 1950 1992 ALL  ALL   107255 SRY West
 1974 1988 .... .... 107255 SSX Arundel
 1974 1988 .... .... 107255 SSX Worthing
BLAYLOCK
 1808 1851 ALL  1808 111988 CMA
                           Kirkandrews Upon Esk
 1819 1992 1600 1819 169595 CUL Brampton
 1835 1835 ALL  ALL   145335 CUL Carlisle
BLAZE
 1650 1700 1650 1992 133450 LAN Liverpool
 1679 1897 1600 1730 101575 LIN Tattershall
 1679 1897 1600 1730 101575 NTT Castle Bytham
 1679 1897 1600 1730 101575 NTT Newark
BLAZEDALE
 .... 1770 ALL  1770 134511 NTT Arnold
BLAZELY
 1791 .... .... 1992 136964 HRT Baldock
BLAZER
 .... .... 1700 1800 163260 NFK Middleton
BLEACH
 .... ?    .... .... 141941 HAM Portsmouth
BLEAKLEY
 .... .... ALL  ALL   129941 ALL Name Study
BLEARS
 1820 1851 .... .... 118729 LAN Eccles
BLEASE
 .... 1836 1700 1850 172405 LAN Liverpool
BLEAY
 1726 1890 1700 1750 111953 OXF Marston
BLECHYNDEN
 1562 1871 ALL  1800 137774 KEN South East
BLEE
 1774 1992 1700 1774 159859 CON Breage
 1700 1900 1700 1900 110523 CON St Hilary
 1808 1818 .... .... 173932 SRY
                         Kingston Upon Thames
 1836 1838 .... .... 173932 SRY Thames Ditton
BLEEK
 .... .... ALL  ALL   107263 ALL Name Study
 1870 1953 ALL  1870 175145 NTH Lois Weedon
BLEEKE
 1660 1699 1600 1750 155896 GLS Gloucester
BLENCARN
 1600 1750 1600 1750 167924 YKS Terrington
BLENCH
 1786 1842 1600 1786 144711 CAM Doddington
 1786 1842 1600 1786 144711 CAM March
BLENCOWE
 .... .... ALL  ALL   120936 ALL Name Study
 1790 1881 1891 1992 107271 ALL ALL
 ALL  ALL  ALL  ALL   120936 ALL ALL
 1720 1800 ALL  ALL   173436 NTH Helmdon
 1655 1770 1650 1780 103632 NTH Whilton
 1850 1992 1850 1920 111562 OXF Banbury
 1861 1992 1860 ALL   173436 STS Wolverhampton
 1830 1860 1830 1860 173436 WAR Warwick
BLENCOWES
 .... .... ALL  ALL   173436 ALL Name Study
BLENHEIM
 .... .... 1830 1992 151920 SRY Egham
BLENKARN
 1565 1992 ALL  ALL   143944 NRY Terrington
BLENKEY
 1834 1853 1550 1850 147265 YKS North
BLENKIN
 1778 1847 1750 1778 171565 YKS ALL
BLENNER HASSETT
 1852 .... .... 1852 129518 KER Tralee
BLETCHER
 .... .... ALL  ALL   166812 LAN Manchester
BLETSOE
 1791 1860 .... .... 147486 NTH Chelveston
BLEWART
 1660 1800 ALL  1900 115347 WES ALL
BLEWER
 1803 1878 1750 1900 120146 ESS West Thurrock
BLEWETT
 1760 1800 1700 1850 142875 CON Gwinear
 1720 1860 1700 1860 102369 CON Mousehole
 1871 1881 1871 1992 172596 CON Paul
BLEWITT
 1810 1992 1750 1880 166901 CON Crowan
 1800 .... .... .... 135402 ESS Romford
 1780 1850 1750 1800 123595 NTH Duston
BLEZARD
 .... .... 1650 1992 121940 WRY Bolton By Bowland
 .... .... 1650 1992 121940 WRY Slaidburn
BLICK
 1811 1811 1700 1850 170178 BKM Hughenden
 1700 1992 1700 1992 161276 BKM Wycombe
 1890 1992 1850 1992 161276 BRK Maidenhead
BLIGH
 .... .... ALL  ALL   107336 ALL Name Study
 .... .... ALL  ALL   107336 KEN ALL
 1797 1980 ALL  ALL   107336 KEN Sevenoaks
 1830 1940 ALL  ALL   107336 SRY Newington
BLIGHT
 1787 1864 1500 1800 132993 CON Ludgvan
 1840 1880 1750 1850 116432 CON Saltash
```

Known From	To	Researching From	To	Ref	Cty	Place
BLIGHT contd.						
1782	....	1700	1781	110345	CON	St Cleer
1700	1800	1700	1800	110434	CON	St Germans
ALL	ALL	ALL	ALL	107352	DEV	North
1836	1864	1800	1836	135879	DEV	Newton St Petrock
1834	1860	1800	1834	173118	DEV	Wolfardisworthy
1886	1992	1800	1886	147230	LND	East End
BLIN						
1867	....	....	....	153885	DEV	Crediton
BLINCOW						
1740	1960	1700	1900	107360	NTH	Long Buckby
BLINKHORN						
1863	1868	1800	1863	103322	LAN	Wigan
BLINMAN						
1880	1940	....	....	137693	GLS	Winterbourne
BLINSHAM						
....	....	?	?	104310	DEV	St Giles In The Wood
BLISS						
....	....	ALL	ALL	107387	ALL	Name Study
1760	1811	1740	1811	119059	GLS	Moreton In Marsh
1850	1900	1850	ALL	113603	MDX	Bethnal Green
1740	1850	1740	ALL	113603	MDX	Enfield
1720	1740	1720	ALL	113603	MDX	South Mimms
1777	1874	1770	1875	171654	NTH	Potterspury
1770	1800	....	....	100420	WAR	Meriden
1850	1960	1800	1992	171670	YKS	Sheffield
BLISSITT						
1910	1984	1850	1910	107395	NTT	Grantham
BLITHE						
1847	1930	ALL	ALL	168335	CON	Calstock
1851	1926	ALL	ALL	168335	DEV	Chillaton
1840	1926	1840	1926	168335	DEV	Marystone
1800	1930	ALL	ALL	168335	DEV	Milton Abbot
1800	1930	ALL	ALL	168335	DEV	Stowford
BLITHMAN						
1798	1798	....	....	141097	YKS	Adwick On Dearne
BLIZZARD						
1670	1730	....	....	142522	GLS	???
1815	1839	1790	....	156191	WIL	Malmesbury
BLOCH						
?	?	?	?	138622	ALL	ALL
BLOCK						
....	....	ALL	ALL	107409	ALL	Name Study
1714	1714	1650	1714	155276	SFK	Bucklesham
BLOCKLEY						
1890	1992	ALL	ALL	107417	ALL	ALL
1780	1850	1700	1900	107417	LEI	Claybrook
1650	1900	ALL	ALL	177997	LEI	Claybrook
1890	1895	1850	1920	107417	LEI	Leicester
1803	1808	1770	1850	107417	NTH	Kingsthorpe
1683	1724	1600	1800	162280	SAL	Bridgnorth
1830	1851	ALL	1851	115355	WAR	ALL
1650	1750	ALL	ALL	177997	WAR	Churchover
1824	1824	ALL	ALL	115355	WAR	Coventry
....	1775	1750	1790	132586	WAR	Nuneaton
1842	1862	....	1842	111767	???	Forden
BLOGG						
1760	1992	1610	1760	138029	LAN	Chorley
1760	1992	1610	1760	138029	NFK	Sheringham
BLOIS						
ALL	ALL	ALL	ALL	149845	ALL	ALL
ALL	ALL	ALL	ALL	107425	ALL	???
1761	1761	1730	1761	149845	SFK	ALL
BLOM						
1900	1930	1800	1900	159441	LND	ALL
BLOMBERG						
1860	1992	1500	1992	175498	ALL	ALL
BLOMFIELD						
....	....	ALL	ALL	167185	ALL	Name Study
....	....	....	....	107433	ALL	ALL
1780	1800	1750	1800	129003	SFK	Ipswich
1738	1813	1600	1900	159956	SFK	Ousden
BLOMILEY						
1869	1869	1800	1870	146315	LAN	Didsbury
BLOOD						
1823	1946	1700	1950	178616	LEI	Shepshed
1833	1992	1820	1833	161284	STS	Checkley
BLOODWORTH						
....	....	1700	1992	149225	ALL	ALL
1772	1901	ALL	1772	115355	CAM	ALL
1860	1900	1850	1870	112038	HUN	North
1772	1971	1772	1992	115355	HUN	Ufford
1772	1971	1772	1992	115355	LIN	Ufford
BLOODWORTH contd.						
1772	1901	ALL	1772	115355	NTH	ALL
....	....	1750	1870	112038	NTH	North
1772	1971	1772	1992	115355	NTH	Ufford
1772	1901	ALL	1772	115355	RUT	ALL
1772	1971	1772	1992	115355	RUT	Ufford
1741	....	1715	1741	115819	WIL	Ramsbury
....	....	1700	1992	149225	WIL	Trowbridge
BLOOM						
1700	1798	1650	1700	167533	NFK	Rockland St Mary
1738	1820	1600	1750	101575	NFK	Wells Next The Sea
1744	1746	1744	1746	156922	SYK	Barnby Dun
BLOOMER						
1790	1850	1700	1800	142395	WOR	Cradley
BLOOMFIELD						
1830	1851	ALL	1900	144347	NFK	ALL
1780	1860	1700	1860	173223	NFK	???
1830	1870	1790	1830	158380	SFK	Bury St Edmunds
1600	1920	1600	1920	114316	SFK	Ipswich
1832	1862	1800	1862	145106	SFK	Worlingham
BLOOR						
1800	1900	1800	1900	130567	CHS	Wheelock
1837	1837	ALL	1837	108642	HRT	Flamstead
1820	1992	1750	1820	134317	STS	North
1838	1992	1700	1838	127388	STS	Penkridge
1838	1992	1700	1838	127388	STS	Wolverhampton
BLORE						
1846	....	1846	1992	168572	DBY	Belper
1800	1850	1600	1850	132306	LAN	Liverpool
1750	1840	1750	1840	110434	LAN	Manchester
1846	....	1846	1992	168572	NTT	Rapley
1200	1300	....	....	168467	STS	Blore
....	....	ALL	ALL	149306	STS	Dove Valley
BLOSS						
1700	1750	....	....	157724	SFK	???
BLOUET						
1866	1980	1870	1950	107468	MDX	London
BLOUNT						
....	....	1760	1830	107484	DBY	Alfreton
1880	1992	ALL	1880	126489	DBY	Darley Abbey
1789	1992	....	....	107484	DBY	Shirland
....	....	1700	1800	107484	DBY	South Wingfield
1700	1760	1600	1740	107476	SAL	Claverley
1740	1820	1740	1820	107476	STS	Pattingham
1637	....	ALL	1992	161470	???	Normanton
BLOW						
1826	1880	1500	1900	157538	KEN	Blackheath
1783	1829	1700	1783	170593	LIN	Blanknew
1800	1850	....	....	177687	LIN	Bradley
1815	1960	1725	1815	105503	LIN	Clee
1850	1960	1700	1850	135801	YKS	Sheffield
BLOWER						
1792	1845	1700	1792	148938	GLS	Puriton
1831	1882	1800	1900	124788	LND	Shoreditch
1887	....	....	....	126187	STS	Wolverhampton
1730	1855	1700	1851	151513	WAR	Grendon
1900	1992	....	....	126187	???	Bristol
BLOWERS						
1750	1850	ALL	ALL	100161	SFK	North
1790	1860	1700	1790	164860	SFK	Hasketon
1730	1780	1700	1730	124605	SFK	Wenhaston
BLOWEY						
1820	....	....	....	153400	CON	Golant
BLOWFIELD						
....	....	1770	1825	118354	BKM	Lillingston Lovell
BLOWMAN						
1820	1910	1700	1850	120839	EYK	???
BLOWS						
1800	1850	1780	1870	123676	CAM	Bassingbourne
....	....	1700	1900	143359	ESS	Aveley
BLOXHAM						
1740	1764	ALL	1740	115126	OXF	Banbury
1803	1829	1760	1829	159905	OXF	Shenington
BLOYS						
1728	1766	1700	1800	128961	ESS	Colchester
BLUCK						
1715	....	....	....	131229	WOR	Naunton Beauchamp
BLUET						
1676	1690	....	....	101028	SFK	Lidgate
BLUETT						
1770	1852	1700	1800	121932	CON	Egloskerry
1770	1852	1700	1800	121932	CON	Tremaine
1719	1992	1670	1719	102083	SOM	Taunton

Known From	To	Researching From	To	Ref	Cty	Place
BLUMER						
1865	1920	1700	1992	113778	CLV	Hartlepool
BLUMFIELD						
1743	1776	1700	1743	103632	RUT	Greetham
1720	1750	1650	1770	151769	RUT	Greetham
BLUMSOM						
1806	1950	1800	1950	107891	LND	Bethnal Green
1803	1950	1800	1950	107891	LND	Shoreditch
BLUNDEL						
1799	1821	ALL	1799	126942	LAN	Kirkham
BLUNDELL						
1793	1812	1750	1793	147885	CHS	Birkenhead
1800	1992	1500	1980	107492	HAM	ALL
?	?	ALL	1800	117919	KEN	Chelsfield
1585	1992	1550	....	169250	KEN	Chelsfield
1858	1992	....	....	131504	LAN	Banks
1700	....	ALL	ALL	112461	LAN	Birkdale
....	....	ALL	ALL	147222	LAN	Liverpool
1585	1992	1550	....	169250	SRY	Horley
1585	1992	1550	....	169250	SRY	Lambeth
BLUNDEN						
1680	1870	ALL	ALL	107565	SSX	Pulborough
1700	1800	1600	1700	163015	SSX	Pulborough
BLUNDY						
1700	1992	1650	1992	107514	WIL	Brubage
1700	1992	1650	1992	107514	WIL	Shalbourne
BLUNN						
1800	1881	1530	1800	169986	WOR	Lickey Hills
1840	1881	1700	1840	150738	WOR	Rubery
BLUNT						
....	....	....	....	124206	ALL	ALL
1807	1992	1800	1992	106119	ENG	South East
1805	1880	....	....	140570	FLN	???
1819	....	ALL	1819	124206	GLS	???
1608	1834	....	....	142530	HAM	Christchurch
1798	1798	1798	1798	149403	OXF	Thame
1700	1760	1600	1740	107476	SAL	Claverley
1740	1820	1740	1820	107476	STS	Pattingham
1823	1830	....	1823	125954	WAR	Claines
1837	1945	1700	1837	177113	WLS	Brymbo
....	....	ALL	1820	178403	WMD	Birmingham
ALL	ALL	ALL	ALL	124206	WOR	Worcester
BLUNTACH						
1740	1740	1700	1992	116122	BAN	Alvah
1730	1736	1700	1992	116122	BAN	???
1838	1838	1830	1992	116122	DEV	Plymouth
1793	1793	1780	1992	116122	INV	???
1786	1853	1780	1992	116122	MOR	Dallas
1663	1795	1660	1992	116122	MOR	Dyke
1772	1851	1770	1992	116122	MOR	Forres
1941	1941	1780	1992	116122	MOR	Kellas
1756	1788	1750	1992	116122	MOR	Kinloss
1790	1821	1780	1992	116122	MOR	Rafford
1763	1763	1760	1992	116122	MOR	St Andrews Lhambryd
1851	1851	1800	1992	116122	NAI	Alves
1710	1733	1700	1992	116122	NAI	???
1793	1840	1780	1992	116122	SCT	Lanark Barony
1820	1820	1800	1992	116122	???	Elgin
1965	1967	1920	1992	116122	???	Wolverhampton
BLUNTISH						
1848	1860	1795	1870	116122	GAL	???
1870	1871	1795	1870	116122	KID	???
1840	1876	1785	1992	116122	LAN	Manchester
1780	1949	1780	1992	116122	MDX	N London
1817	1817	1812	1840	116122	SAL	Llanyblodwell
1780	1939	1780	1992	116122	SRY	S London
1780	1947	1780	1992	116122	???	London
BLYDE						
1880	1897	1800	1900	168947	LAN	Manchester
1800	1992	1700	1992	165344	WAR	Birmingham
?	?	?	?	168947	???	London
BLYKE						
1430	1500	1350	1500	154881	SAL	Astley
BLYTH						
1810	1930	ALL	1810	122823	ANS	Mains
1724	1807	1700	1800	169218	FIF	St Monance
1775	1916	ALL	1775	118222	NFK	Bessingham
1790	1792	1750	1789	131245	NFK	Norwich
1917	1992	1700	1917	157872	SFK	Bury St Edmunds
1800	1992	1700	1992	165344	WAR	Birmingham
1771	1773	1650	1770	131245	WIL	Salisbury
BLYTHE						
1750	1992	1700	1800	172642	DOW	Hillborough
?	?	?	?	158372	LND	ALL
BLYTHE contd.						
1814	1992	1700	1861	105899	ROX	Melrose
1800	1992	1700	1992	165344	WAR	Bordesley
BLYTON						
1790	1992	1790	1930	103225	ALL	ALL
1804	1992	1700	1805	161772	NTT	Masnfield
BOA						
1788	....	....	1788	175552	ROX	Jedburgh
BOAG						
....	....	ALL	ALL	127906	ALL	Name Study
1750	1800	ALL	1800	144533	DUR	ALL
1750	1800	ALL	1800	144533	NBL	ALL
1750	1800	ALL	1800	144533	YKS	ALL
BOAGEY						
1850	1992	ALL	1992	144533	ALL	ALL
BOAK						
....	1763	ALL	1763	175080	HAM	Widley
1863	1941	1700	1863	111198	NYK	Pickering
BOAM						
1800	1876	1700	1876	131199	DBY	Winster
BOARD						
1850	1992	?	....	161780	AVN	Bristol
1711	1924	1700	1930	163317	SOM	West
1706	1758	1650	1758	113069	SOM	Berrow
1706	1758	1650	1758	124990	SOM	Berrow
1738	1860	1700	1860	113069	SOM	Huntspill
1738	1860	1700	1860	124990	SOM	Huntspill
BOARDMAN						
1700	1760	1650	1700	150614	CHS	Over
1860	1980	1700	1860	113026	LAN	Billinge
1760	1780	1700	1992	167592	LAN	Liverpool
1769	1992	1650	1769	166138	LAN	Manchester
1842	1891	1750	1851	142204	LAN	Rumwoth
1780	1860	1600	1860	113026	LAN	West Derby
....	....	ALL	ALL	130524	MDX	Hackney
....	....	ALL	ALL	130524	MDX	Homerton
1850	1860	1835	1860	107522	WRY	Dewsbury
1830	1870	1750	1870	107182	WYK	Barnsley
1830	1870	1750	1870	107182	WYK	Hunslet
BOASE						
1600	1870	ALL	1860	137286	CON	West
1790	....	....	1790	152242	CON	West
1880	1950	1700	1880	107530	CON	Ludgvan
1609	1850	....	....	125628	CON	Newlyn
1769	1816	1730	1769	169021	CON	Penzance
1845	1992	1730	1845	169021	CON	St Buryan
1807	....	1700	1807	130141	CON	St Just In Penwith
BOAST						
1800	1900	1700	1800	145319	NFK	Bawbugh
BOATER						
....	....	ALL	ALL	107549	ENG	ALL
BOBBET						
1857	....	....	1757	177504	SFK	Hasketon
BOBBIN						
1810	1992	1700	1810	161772	NFK	Thorp
BOBBINS						
1861	1875	1875	1890	177393	LND	St George Hanover Square
1820	1851	1700	1820	177393	NFK	Kings Lynn
BOBBY						
....	....	ALL	ALL	126004	ALL	Name Study
1703	1882	1650	1750	105775	SFK	Mellis
1870	1870	1850	1870	105775	SFK	Otley
1798	1850	1850	1992	105775	SFK	Wortham
1703	1882	1650	1750	105775	SFK	Yaxley
BOBIN						
1702	1702	ALL	ALL	115126	CHI	ALL
1744	1992	1690	1745	107557	KEN	Deptford
1685	1785	....	1992	107557	MDX	Bromley By Bow
BOCK						
ALL	ALL	ALL	ALL	102296	ALL	ALL
1748	1830	....	....	102296	ESS	Witham
1800	1900	....	....	102296	LND	West Ham
1900	1992	....	....	102296	OXF	Headington
BOCKING						
1900	1992	1900	1992	107522	KEN	Gillingham
1855	1910	1800	1992	100862	SRY	Lambeth
1855	1910	1800	1992	100862	SRY	Southwark
1870	1900	1870	1900	107522	WRY	Sheffield
BODD						
1730	....	....	....	149284	DEV	???
BODDAN						
1851	....	1700	1851	122394	AYR	Graigie
1857	....	1700	1851	122394	AYR	Tarbolton

Surname	Known From	Known To	Researching From	Researching To	Ref	Cty	Place
BODDAN contd.							
	1853	....	1700	1851	122394	AYR	West Kilbride
	1880	1889	1700	1880	122394	DFS	Sanquhar
	1881	1884	1700	1851	122394	DNB	Kilmaronock
	1865	....	1700	1851	122394	KKD	Troqueer
BODDINGTON							
	1867	1992	1700	1867	121258	NTH	Rounds
	1794	1895	1750	1900	145300	OXF	Standlake
	1700	1800	....	....	100420	WAR	Meriden
BODDY							
	1800	1900	1700	1920	128805	BKM	ALL
	1840	1950	1700	1950	128813	BKM	Marlow
	1690	1781	ALL	1781	168718	CON	South East
	1881	....	1800	1900	171441	DUR	Hartlepool
	1848	1871	....	1900	171441	YKS	Middlesborough
BODEN							
	1780	1840	....	....	133361	BKM	Drayton Parslow
	1900	1992	ALL	ALL	112275	DBY	Matlock
	1806	1863	1700	1806	136816	DBY	Matlock
	1806	1863	1700	1806	136816	DBY	Tansley
	1750	1833	1600	1992	165697	DBY	???
	1836	1953	1700	1836	150614	LAN	Liverpool
	1809	1931	1809	1880	107581	SAL	Benthall
	1888	1941	ALL	ALL	107581	WAR	Birmingham
	1740	1890	ALL	ALL	128449	WAR	Birmingham
BODENHAM							
	....	....	1700	1850	144703	HEF	ALL
	1784	1810	1700	1850	144703	SAL	ALL
BODFISH							
	....	....	ALL	ALL	107603	ALL	Name Study
	....	....	1805	1828	118850	OXF	Tad Marton
BODGENER							
	1815	1846	1700	1850	115681	LND	???
BODGER							
	1770	1800	ALL	1800	151815	CAM	Bourn
	1770	1880	1790	1863	112291	CAM	March
	1800	1870	1830	1870	112291	HUN	Somersham
	1870	1900	1870	1900	112291	MDX	Clerkenwell
	1763	1839	ALL	ALL	135208	NTH	Eye
	1763	1839	ALL	ALL	135208	NTH	Gunsthorpe
	1763	1839	ALL	ALL	135208	NTH	Werrington
BODIMEADE							
	....	....	ALL	ALL	147958	ALL	Name Study
	1600	....	ALL	ALL	147958	ALL	ALL
BODINGTON							
	1603	1649	ALL	1603	168602	BDF	Turvey
BODINNAR							
	1700	1870	ALL	1870	137286	CON	West
BODKIN							
	1920	....	1800	1960	101907	KEN	Gillingham
BODLE							
	1850	1960	....	....	164038	SSX	Alfriston
	1579	1890	ALL	1800	163945	SSX	Brighton
	1579	1890	ALL	1800	163945	SSX	Hailsham
BODLEY							
	1727	1827	....	....	158747	DEV	Exeter
BODMAN							
	....	....	ALL	ALL	107611	ALL	Name Study
	1770	1992	1500	1800	107611	SOM	Farleigh Hungerford
	1795	1992	1700	1795	107611	SOM	Tellisford
	1850	1992	1700	1850	107611	WAR	Aston
	1740	1860	1690	1850	126276	WIL	Chippenham
	1800	1992	1500	1800	107611	WIL	Wingfield
BODMEAD							
	1800	1887	1700	1800	169730	KEN	Lewisham
BODNUM							
	1777	1851	1700	1777	148938	GLS	Arlingham
BODSOR							
	1668	1735	ALL	1992	106119	SRY	???
BODULGATE							
	1400	1470	1300	1470	154881	ALL	ALL
BODY							
	1828	1847	1750	1850	142999	BKM	Chenies
	1723	1992	?	1992	107638	CON	Launceston
	1704	1848	ALL	1704	165735	DEV	Crediton
	1723	1992	?	1992	107638	DEV	Launceston
	1800	1820	1750	1850	167126	SOM	Pitminster
	1848	1992	....	....	165735	???	Bristol
BODYCOMBE							
	....	....	1780	1830	117137	GLA	Llansamlet
	....	....	1830	1900	117137	GLA	Rhondda
BODYCOT							
	1852	1882	1766	1852	122572	LEI	ALL
	1852	1882	1766	1852	122572	LND	ALL
BODYLL							
	1800	....	1500	1700	164038	SXE	Hailsham
BOELS							
	1827	1864	1750	1827	128368	DEV	Ipplepen
BOES							
	1880	1912	1860	1880	174580	LND	Clerkenwell
BOESE							
	1886	1889	1880	1890	165174	WOR	Hartlebury
	1853	1886	1831	1889	165174	WOR	Kidderminster
BOFF							
	....	....	ALL	ALL	107646	ALL	Name Study
	1739	1859	ALL	ALL	107646	BDF	Woburn
	1811	1873	ALL	ALL	107646	CHS	Chester
	1789	?	1700	1789	166898	HRT	Rebourn
	1789	1992	ALL	ALL	107646	HRT	St Albans
	1793	1943	1793	1856	166898	HRT	St Albans
	1807	1992	ALL	ALL	107646	MDX	Islington
	....	....	ALL	ALL	107646	STS	Wolverhampton
	1846	1992	ALL	ALL	107646	WAR	Coventry
BOFFIN							
	1769	1800	....	....	124672	OXF	Bicester
	1830	1950	....	....	124672	OXF	Oxford
BOGG							
	....	....	ALL	ALL	115568	ALL	Name Study
BOGGIS							
	1807	1854	1750	1850	148725	NFK	Kenninghall
	1726	1800	1690	1760	173630	SFK	Ringsfield
BOHEN							
	1080	....	1066	1166	148121	WIL	Tockenham
BOHLING							
	1790	1992	ALL	ALL	122149	ALL	ALL
BOHUN							
	1276	1305	1270	1350	148121	ESS	Pleshey
	1370	....	1350	1400	148121	HEF	???
	1066	....	1066	1276	148121	NFK	Tateford
	1603	1798	1500	1800	148121	NFK	???
	1312	....	1312	1400	148121	NTH	Caldecot
	1824	....	1750	1824	148121	SFK	Beccles
BOIES							
	1066	1992	1066	1992	108626	ALL	ALL
BOILES							
	1846	1992	ALL	1882	108642	WAR	Whichford
BOILING							
	1875	1930	....	....	160768	SXW	Chichester
	1800	1888	1700	1800	160768	SXW	Felpham
BOISE							
	1066	1992	1066	1992	108626	ALL	ALL
BOISTON							
	1740	1960	1600	1740	155810	NBL	Elsdon
BOLAM							
	1737	1774	1650	1800	173983	NBL	Rochester
BOLCH							
	1630	1650	....	....	171654	SOM	West Chinnock
BOLD							
	1700	1800	1700	1800	100536	LAN	???
BOLDEN							
	1750	1992	ALL	ALL	107670	ESS	Tilty
BOLDERSTONE							
	1033	1992	1033	1992	108138	ALL	ALL
	1733	1898	ALL	1733	169730	CAM	Thorney
BOLDY							
	1846	1915	1846	1915	139661	YKS	Snaith
BOLE							
	1848	1869	1770	1915	176621	TYR	Oritor
BOLER							
	1715	1746	1680	1720	170348	YKS	Laughton En Le Morthern
BOLES							
	1580	1830	1580	1830	127655	COR	Ballinacorra
BOLEY							
	1800	1900	1700	1900	106631	SOM	Bleadon
BOLGER							
	....	....	1830	1900	159840	LAN	Manchester
BOLITHO							
	1600	1992	1600	1940	107689	CON	West
	1610	1800	1500	1700	107697	CON	Wendron
BOLLAND							
	1688	1907	1907	1992	151688	NTH	Maxey
	1730	1800	1730	1820	154210	NYK	Kirklevington
	1601	1703	....	....	151688	RUT	Empingham
	1561	1772	....	....	151688	RUT	Hambleton
	1840	1950	1780	1840	139483	YKS	Sheffield
BOLLARD							
	1778	1850	1700	1850	133876	WAR	Birmingham

Known From	To	Researching From	To	Ref	Cty	Place
BOLLARD contd.						
1778	1850	1700	1850	133876	WAR	Solihull
1778	1850	1700	1850	133876	WOR	Northfield
BOLLEN						
1880	1992	1600	1880	173207	DOR	Dorchester
1830	....	1500	1839	147672	SOM	Yeovil
BOLLONS						
1754	1850	1850	1992	151688	LIN	Deeping St James
1853	1868	1868	1992	151688	LIN	Langtoft
1880	1938	1938	1992	151688	LIN	Whaplode Fen
BOLLSOM						
1852	1852	1845	1855	130877	CON	Tutwell
BOLSOVER						
....	....	ALL	ALL	165964	ALL	Name Study
1611	1992	ALL	ALL	165964	DBY	North East
BOLT						
1840	1989	ALL	1940	107719	CON	Gunnislake
1837	1839	1837	1992	114596	DEV	Ash Regney
1772	1989	ALL	1796	107719	DEV	Broad Woodkelly
1849	1900	1901	1950	148903	DEV	Plymouth
1800	1989	ALL	1880	107719	DEV	Whitchurch
1680	....	....	1680	101761	LIN	Marsh Chapel
1797	1883	1700	1900	152285	LND	Bethnal Green
1714	1780	ALL	1759	154946	WES	Appleby
1759	1801	ALL	1759	154946	WES	Bongate
BOLTER						
1825	1872	....	....	115606	BKM	Burnham
BOLTON						
1697	1728	1600	1700	143693	BKM	Amersham
1704	....	1600	1750	143693	BKM	Beaconsfield
1850	1992	1650	1850	157872	BRK	Peasemore
1840	1900	1700	1840	167762	CLA	Ennis
1791	1992	ALL	1791	110000	CMA	Cockermouth
1880	1900	1700	1900	126802	ENG	Midlands
....	1860	....	1950	130168	ENG	Midlands
....	....	....	1834	121169	KEN	???
1810	1831	1783	1831	159492	LAN	Bolton
1799	....	1700	1850	110914	LAN	Coppull
....	....	....	1846	154024	LAN	Manchester
1831	1992	1831	1992	159492	LAN	Oldham
1800	1870	1700	1992	114596	LAN	Southport
1735	1845	1700	1900	175633	LIN	Horncastle
....	....	1700	1992	127299	LND	ALL
1850	1940	1800	1855	155691	LND	Newington
1826	1945	1700	1826	120367	NFK	South East
1795	1900	1500	1992	140872	NFK	???
1851	1861	ALL	1992	111384	NYK	Scarborough
1851	1861	ALL	1992	111384	NYK	Thornton
1850	1900	1700	1850	118915	OXF	Oxford
1858	1878	1800	1900	174661	SCT	Glasgow
ALL	1865	....	....	110000	SFK	Woodbridge
1795	1900	1500	1992	140872	SFK	???
1801	1801	1750	1800	179337	WIL	Langley Burrell
1758	1840	ALL	ALL	166839	WYK	Cullingworth
1758	1812	....	....	166839	WYK	Haworth
1874	1894	1894	1992	111384	WYK	Leeds
1788	....	....	....	166839	WYK	Morton
1818	1851	1818	1861	170267	YKS	Bramley
1819	1992	1790	1850	118354	YKS	Haworth
....	....	1700	1750	177393	YKS	Riccall
1684	1794	1660	1851	170267	YKS	West Tanfield
BOLTWOOD						
1786	1844	1700	1786	172553	ESS	Wickham Bishops
BONAKER						
1770	1800	....	....	100420	WAR	Meriden
BONAS						
1800	1992	ALL	ALL	166537	NFK	Castle Acre
BONCEY						
1600	1850	1600	1850	126446	SRY	Woking
BOND						
1850	1890	1830	1900	172960	BRK	Reading
1826	1992	1700	1826	140449	CON	Ludgvan
1680	1886	1580	1680	107751	CON	St Austell
?	?	?	?	111937	CON	Trenarren
1700	1800	1700	1800	100536	CON	???
1766	1865	1700	1870	107565	DEV	Axminster
1800	1865	1750	1880	139890	DEV	Bishops Nympton
1600	1743	1600	1770	107565	DEV	Chardstock
1744	1752	ALL	ALL	129933	DEV	Exeter
1750	1790	1700	1810	171158	DEV	Farway
1820	1881	....	1820	145939	DEV	Plymouth
....	....	1700	1992	122742	DOR	Weymouth
1822	1841	1600	1822	175781	DOR	Weymouth
....	....	ALL	ALL	121320	GLS	Cirencester

Known From	To	Researching From	To	Ref	Cty	Place
BOND contd.						
1843	1918	?	1849	113360	HAM	Andover
1850	1900	1850	1900	134767	KEN	Sevenoaks
1850	1900	1850	1900	134767	KEN	Tonbridge
1800	1834	ALL	ALL	124982	LAN	Lancaster
1886	1992	....	....	107751	LAN	Liverpool
1774	1857	1751	1891	159492	LAN	Manchester With Salford
1880	1992	1700	1880	138657	LAN	Manchester
1696	1907	1660	....	120634	LAN	Preston
1733	1733	1600	1733	174130	LEI	Goadby
1890	1980	1700	1890	171913	LIN	Lincoln
1830	1992	ALL	1830	107751	LND	Bow
....	....	1800	1900	129011	LND	Clerkenwell
1850	1992	1850	1892	153257	LND	Lambeth
1799	1875	1600	1875	129011	MDX	London
1654	1992	1600	1992	107735	NFK	Diss
1797	1850	1700	1800	152552	NFK	Little Walsingham
1810	1850	1810	1850	103764	OXF	Neithrop
1876	1911	1876	1911	113670	SOM	Ashill
1770	1825	1770	1850	160504	SOM	Bath
1811	1900	1650	1811	153281	SOM	Bridgwater
1776	1820	....	1820	152803	SOM	Glastonbury
1927	1927	1800	1927	121568	SOM	Thornfalcon
1840	1860	1840	1860	160504	SRY	Lambeth
1802	1992	1700	1802	102342	STS	Abbots Bromley
1735	1886	1700	1735	166464	STS	Blithfield
1817	1992	1700	1817	107743	TYR	Fawney
1780	1860	1790	1861	172960	WIL	Cheverall
1770	1800	1700	1770	152196	YKS	Garstang
1539	1914	1500	1914	129798	YKS	Tong
....	....	1600	1800	171794	YKS	Tong
BONDS						
1812	?	1812	1890	108006	CON	ALL
1820	?	1820	?	108006	JSY	St Helier
1840	1890	1840	1890	108006	KEN	Deptford
BONE						
1780	1890	1840	1900	177350	BKM	Chesham
1780	1839	1700	1810	121932	CON	Botus Fleming
1780	1839	1700	1810	121932	CON	Egloskerry
1870	....	1800	1992	129348	CON	Falmouth
1688	1700	1600	1750	130125	CUL	Dalston
1860	1960	1750	1860	118478	DUR	Tow Law
1820	1840	1700	1830	126772	HAM	Alton
1800	1992	1700	1800	107778	HAM	Basingstoke
1674	1835	1660	1835	170143	HAM	Buriton
1674	1835	1660	1835	170143	HAM	East Meon
1796	1955	1760	1955	107786	HAM	Hawkley
1796	1955	1760	1955	107786	HAM	Oakhanger
1850	1890	1850	1890	132721	HAM	Portsea
1804	1839	1750	1992	127299	HAM	Portsmouth
1785	1835	....	1785	100064	NFK	Cockley Cley
1769	....	1700	1769	176885	NFK	Costessey
1766	1766	ALL	1800	129283	NFK	Ditchingham
1770	1900	1700	1900	169641	NFK	Marham
1754	1895	ALL	1754	157511	SXW	Chichester
BONEHAM						
....	....	ALL	ALL	169196	ALL	Name Study
1800	1992	1700	1992	165344	WAR	Dunchurch
1740	1992	1740	1992	169196	WAR	Dunchurch
BONEHILL						
1822	1955	1700	1822	169854	WAR	Birmingham
BONELL						
1820	1900	1700	1900	132950	STS	Lichfield
1793	1936	1720	1792	166464	STS	Walsall
BONES						
1560	1900	1500	1560	132942	DUR	Aukland
1790	1970	1600	1840	178470	DUR	Aycliffe
1773	1889	?	1773	125059	DUR	Bishop Auckland
1763	1778	1717	1779	144037	DUR	Chester Le Street
....	....	....	....	109207	ESS	???
1740	1870	1700	1900	167126	LND	???
1837	1900	....	....	100536	SSX	???
BONFIELD						
1700	1807	ALL	1800	168718	BDF	North West
1825	1850	1700	1850	145882	DOR	Swanage
BONHAM						
1870	1992	....	....	161969	BKM	Fenny Stratford
1870	1992	....	....	161969	IOW	Cowes
BONICK						
1790	1820	1700	1800	171182	HRT	Broxbourne
BONIFACE						
....	....	ALL	ALL	107808	ALL	Name Study
1837	1940	....	....	128996	CAM	Thorney

Known From	To	Researching From	To	Ref	Cty	Place
BONIFACE contd.						
1650	1871	1600	1650	166723	SSX	Friston
BONIFANT						
1725	1832	1600	1850	132403	LIN	North
1725	1832	1600	1850	132403	NTT	North
BONITHAN						
1700	1800	1700	1800	171549	DEV	Buckfastleigh
BONNEAU						
1757	1815	1700	1820	152285	LND	Bethnal Green
BONNER						
1852	1900	1600	1852	127507	ANT	Racavan
....	....	1600	1900	124273	DEV	Silverton
1828	1855	1750	1828	154911	ENG	South
1803	1966	1750	1966	121134	LIN	West
....	....	1600	1900	124273	SOM	Wiveliscombe
1802	....	1750	....	152064	WIL	Chippenham
1856	1881	1700	1856	157767	WIL	Clack
1796	1836	1700	1796	157767	WIL	Devizes
....	....	ALL	1600	164631	WOR	ALL
BONNETT						
1550	1980	ALL	ALL	111406	LEI	Whitwick
BONNEY						
1850	1900	1700	1910	106356	MDX	London
1773	1992	1650	1773	169676	SFK	Sudbury
1900	1910	1850	1910	106356	SFK	???
BONNICK						
1750	....	ALL	1600	131059	KEN	Tonbridge
BONNIN						
1770	1851	ALL	1770	107824	ALL	ALL
BONNY						
1740	1830	1700	1850	101028	KEN	Cranbrook
1768	1992	1700	1800	105201	KEN	Hartlip
1805	1855	ALL	1805	106909	KEN	Rainham
BONSALL						
ALL	ALL	ALL	ALL	107832	ALL	ALL
....	....	1700	1850	176400	DBY	Alfreton
1600	1683	1683	1776	107832	DBY	Alstonfield
1830	1860	ALL	1890	176400	DBY	Heage
1641	1699	1620	1640	107832	DBY	Mouldbridge
1880	1900	ALL	ALL	101230	DBY	???
1880	1900	ALL	ALL	101230	LAN	???
1643	1698	1619	1643	107832	STS	Mary Wood
1550	1683	1680	1680	107832	STS	Sheen
BONSER						
....	....	ALL	ALL	122173	ALL	Name Study
1778	1900	1700	1900	135968	LEI	Whitwick
1841	1880	1700	1850	126950	NTT	Kinoulton
BONSOR						
1720	1770	ALL	ALL	107840	NTT	Retford
1900	1942	1700	1800	105023	STS	Tamworth
1800	1900	1700	1800	105023	WAR	Birmingham
BONTEMS						
1811	1896	ALL	1811	151424	LND	St Pancras
BONTHRON						
1500	1992	ALL	1992	107859	ALL	ALL
1800	1992	1500	1992	107859	FIF	ALL
BONTOUX						
....	....	ALL	ALL	107867	ALL	Name Study
BONVILE						
1300	1600	1300	1600	154881	ALL	ALL
BONWELL						
....	....	ALL	ALL	107875	ALL	ALL
1600	1992	1500	1600	107875	YKS	ALL
BONWICK						
1825	1900	1700	1825	135844	SSX	East Grinstead
BONY						
1670	....	....	....	112429	LAN	Lytham
BOOBYER						
1673	1918	1500	1918	172294	SOM	ALL
BOOCOCK						
1840	1900	....	....	107883	WRY	Kildwick
....	....	1820	1860	107883	WRY	Lothersdale
....	....	1820	1850	107883	WRY	Thornton In Graven
....	....	1820	1840	107883	YKS	Barnoldswick
BOODLE						
1780	1850	ALL	ALL	137987	FLN	Bangor On Dee
1720	1900	ALL	ALL	137987	SAL	North West
BOOK						
1764	1850	1600	1764	149888	GLS	Bristol
BOOKE						
1609	....	1550	1640	143138	DEV	Tiverton
BOOKER						
1818	1818	1800	1818	128368	DBY	Over Haddon
1830	1992	1700	1830	160571	DUR	Sunderland

Known From	To	Researching From	To	Ref	Cty	Place
BOOKER contd.						
1814	1992	1700	1814	102342	HAM	Portsea
1795	1811	1700	1811	134058	HAM	Portsea
1800	1892	1800	1992	115673	SRY	Upper Norwood
1780	1816	ALL	ALL	149004	SSX	Tortington
1880	1992	ALL	....	120626	STS	Walsall
1800	1920	1800	1992	115673	SXW	Arundel
1784	1992	1700	1784	128368	YKS	Sheffield
BOOKLAND						
ALL	1740	....	....	170178	WIL	Cherhill
BOOKLESS						
....	....	ALL	ALL	133396	ALL	ALL
1720	1850	1680	1900	133396	BEW	Cockburnspath
1720	1850	1680	1900	133396	BEW	Coldingham
1720	1850	1680	1900	133396	NBL	Berwick
BOOKMASTER						
1745	1770	....	1770	171441	SRY	Puttenham
BOOLE						
1730	1813	1600	1750	144606	SOM	South
BOOMER						
1838	1881	1045	1992	118893	DUR	Merrington
1738	1881	1045	1992	118893	DUR	St Oswalds
1732	1738	1045	1992	118893	NRY	Guisborough
BOON						
1800	1850	1600	1992	176494	CAM	ALL
1750	1830	1750	1830	151297	DEV	Modbury
1820	1855	1750	1900	158666	ENG	ALL
1860	1880	1800	1992	126322	MDX	London
1831	1900	1800	1992	107891	NFK	West
1792	1900	1700	1900	135968	NFK	Walpole
1850	1860	1800	1890	126322	SFK	Sutton
1700	1880	1600	1992	140872	SFK	???
BOONE						
1712	1992	ALL	1712	169919	DEV	Bishopsteighton
....	1830	....	....	174564	GLS	Cheltenham
1700	1843	....	....	149888	SOM	Cossington
1775	1780	1750	1800	124990	SOM	Otter Hampton
1775	1780	1750	1800	113069	SOM	Otterhampton
1772	1841	1600	1851	113069	SOM	Paulett
1772	1841	1600	1851	124990	SOM	Pawlett
1670	1790	1600	1900	149888	SOM	Pawlett
BOOR						
1883	1890	1700	1883	153362	LAN	Liverpool
BOORER						
1700	1800	1700	1800	169781	SRY	Burstow
BOORMAN						
....	....	1850	1859	173274	KEN	Snave
BOORN						
1773	1960	1650	1772	161853	HEF	Bishopstone
BOOSEY						
....	....	1800	1880	154261	ESS	Foulness Island
....	....	1800	1992	154261	ESS	Southend On Sea
BOOT						
1750	1922	1650	1750	138185	DBY	South Normanton
....	....	....	....	107433	DUR	???
1540	1900	1900	1992	129763	NTH	Byfield
1766	1793	ALL	ALL	130575	NTH	Byfield
1811	1819	1700	1832	142085	NTT	Stanton On The Wolds
1795	1820	1750	1820	142085	NTT	Willoughby
BOOTE						
1851	1920	1850	1950	165441	CHS	Nantwich
BOOTH						
....	....	ALL	ALL	107921	ALL	Name Study
1790	1825	ALL	ALL	140902	ABD	Ellon
1825	1855	ALL	ALL	140902	ABD	Foveran
....	1860	ALL	ALL	136948	CHS	Alderley
1794	1868	1794	1923	122440	CHS	Hyde
1800	1820	1819	....	160164	CHS	Macclesfield
1786	1924	....	1786	163228	CHS	Marple
1862	1886	?	1862	128910	DBY	Clay Cross
1849	1992	1829	1992	146625	DBY	Dronfield
1689	1780	1500	1700	107972	DBY	Eckington
1800	1950	1700	1800	120383	DBY	Eckington
1820	1900	ALL	1820	128414	DUR	Auckland
1741	1860	1700	1880	122610	GLS	Tewkesbury
1595	1770	1590	1650	165417	HAM	Cherewell
1814	?	1600	1992	172332	JSY	Grouville
1850	1992	1800	1900	137715	LAN	South
1770	1845	1770	1845	107522	LAN	Ashton Under Lyme
1880	1969	1700	1880	118915	LAN	Ashton Under Lyne
1820	1900	1820	1900	148911	LAN	Manchester
1837	1917	1820	1917	168920	LAN	Manchester
1862	1900	1850	1862	113050	LAN	Newton Heath

Known From	To	Researching From	To	Ref	Cty	Place
BOOTH contd.						
1750	1785	1700	1750	155500	LAN	Newton Le Willows
1700	1800	1600	1700	107905	LAN	Orford
1743	1817	1743	1817	179078	LAN	Redvales
1861	1906	1861	1906	160164	LAN	Salford
1700	1800	....	....	146854	LAN	Warton
1600	1624	ALL	ALL	141615	LEI	Billesdon
1796	1828	1750	1860	176621	LIN	Long Sutton
....	....	1800	1992	108502	LND	Stepney
1710	1890	1500	1710	107972	NTT	Mansfield Woodhouse
1800	1840	....	1850	102822	NTT	Nottingham
1820	....	1840	1880	135429	SOM	Bath
1780	1830	1600	1800	113654	STS	Stoke
1850	1910	ALL	1850	128171	STS	Wolverhampton
1729	....	1500	....	107972	SYK	Thorpe Salvin
1809	1992	1700	1809	176710	WAR	Coventry
1920	1940	....	1920	157406	WRY	Halifax
1815	1879	1790	1870	147311	WYK	Almondbury
1763	1766	1700	1800	160253	WYK	Almondbury
1629	1967	....	....	145327	WYK	Batley
1629	1967	....	....	145327	WYK	Birstal
1629	1967	....	....	145327	WYK	Drighlington
1795	1795	1700	1828	101486	WYK	Rishworth
1828	1836	ALL	ALL	101486	WYK	Scammonden
1820	1840	1800	1860	109525	YKS	Brompton By Sawton
1840	1870	1700	1850	118915	YKS	Holmfirth
1740	1820	....	....	145688	YKS	Hunslet
1870	1930	1800	1870	105392	YKS	Peniston
1827	1851	ALL	1850	152838	YKS	Rotherham
1650	1850	1600	1850	119717	YKS	Roxby
1796	1855	1750	1900	144622	YKS	Royston
1869	1992	1849	1992	146625	YKS	Stannington
1833	1853	ALL	1833	104299	YKS	Wakefield
BOOTHBY						
1897	1933	1800	1897	159735	GLA	Swansea
1690	1770	ALL	....	104515	LIN	ALL
1884	....	1880	1890	163775	MDX	Clerkenwell
1679	1848	1600	1679	159735	SAL	Pontesbury
1760	1992	1750	1992	104396	YKS	East Riding
BOOTHMAN						
....	....	1700	1791	160474	IRL	???
1791	1870	1700	1791	160474	LAN	Blackburn
1791	1870	1700	1791	160474	LAN	Colne
1791	1870	1700	1791	160474	LAN	Tottington
BOOTHROYD						
....	1910	....	....	132500	LAN	Oldham
1800	1900	1750	1840	109517	WRY	Holmfirth
1750	1950	1750	1850	123595	YKS	Almondbury
1800	1836	ALL	1870	158445	YKS	Halifax
1769	1905	1730	1769	133760	YKS	Netherthong
BOOTLE						
1915	1992	ALL	1915	127167	LND	Mile End
BOOTY						
1750	1821	1700	1950	107980	NFK	Horsford
1825	1950	1820	1950	107980	NFK	Norwich
BORDER						
1840	1880	1500	1840	104825	HRT	Northchurch
BORDON						
1857	1857	1700	1857	106887	ABD	New Deer
BORE						
1850	1895	1800	1850	128775	LND	East
BOREHAM						
1803	1844	1600	1992	159956	ESS	Moreton
....	?	?	....	114642	SFK	Rede
....	....	1760	1769	173274	SFK	Whatfield
1877	1992	ALL	ALL	115762	SFK	Whepstead
BORELAND						
ALL	ALL	ALL	ALL	108014	ALL	ALL
BOREMAN						
1704	1749	....	1704	177504	KEN	Strood
BORLAND						
1840	1960	1840	1900	128651	RFW	Kildarchan
1780	1800	1700	1800	128651	RFW	Paisley
BORLASE						
1539	1624	1500	1539	102571	CON	Sithney
1700	1750	1600	1700	107697	CON	St Michael Penkivel
BORLEY						
1820	1864	1700	1820	165182	SFK	Bury St Edmunds
BORMAN						
1920	1992	1700	1920	161772	DBY	???
BORMAY						
1819	....	....	1849	158305	LIN	Frampton
BORNE						
1813	1888	1750	1900	165972	DEV	Central

Known From	To	Researching From	To	Ref	Cty	Place
BORODALE						
1759	1801	ALL	1759	154946	WES	Appleby
1759	1801	ALL	1759	154946	WES	Bongate
BORRELL						
....	....	ALL	ALL	177598	ALL	Name Study
BORRIDGE						
1870	1992	ALL	1870	136875	YKS	Bradford
BORRINGTON						
1589	....	....	....	170380	DEV	Ideford
1851	1954	....	....	170380	LND	Islington
1760	1930	....	....	170380	SFK	Bury St Edmunds
BORROR						
....	....	ALL	ALL	139246	ALL	Name Study
BORROUGHS						
1700	1775	1700	1800	171549	CON	Lanteglos By Fowey
BORROWDALE						
1756	1806	ALL	1756	154946	WES	Kirkby Stephens
BORROWLONG						
1805	1824	1600	1805	102571	LAN	Manchester
BORROWS						
1750	1820	ALL	1800	173177	CAM	Levrington
BORSLEY						
....	....	1800	....	137456	WAR	Dunchurch
BORTHWICK						
1800	1960	....	....	126497	NBL	Berwick Upon Tweed
1820	1900	1800	1900	126500	NBL	Berwick Upon Tween
BORTON						
1840	1920	1800	1992	171417	LND	Holborn
....	....	1807	1838	143480	NTH	Aynho
BORWICK						
1837	1940	1837	1940	148091	CUL	Lowick Bridge
BOSANKO						
1798	1850	1798	1845	164402	CON	Carnmenellis
1798	1850	1798	1845	164402	CON	Wendron
1825	1920	1800	1900	164402	DUR	Haswell
BOSCAWEN						
1510	1538	1500	1510	102571	CON	Tregothian
BOSHARDE						
....	....	ALL	1837	122971	WOR	Claines
BOSHER						
1860	1930	1860	1930	135666	GLA	Abertridwr
1840	1992	....	....	135666	GLA	Merthyr Tydfil
1840	1992	....	....	135666	GLA	Mountain Ash
1860	1930	....	....	135666	GLA	New Tredegar
1960	1989	1960	1989	135666	GLA	Whitchurch
BOSLEY						
1834	1861	1750	1880	125903	LAN	Manchester
1878	....	....	....	125903	OXF	South Weston
BOSS						
....	1833	1750	1833	176389	NYK	South Otterington
1800	1860	1720	1930	108049	OXF	Banbury
1760	1812	....	....	108049	WAR	South
BOSSA						
1830	1870	1750	1830	128538	ALL	ALL
BOSSISTOW						
....	....	1800	....	140082	CON	Truro
BOSSON						
1758	1992	....	....	108057	CHS	ALL
BOSTOCK						
....	....	1600	1700	134104	CHS	ALL
....	....	1600	1800	130621	CHS	South
1080	1515	1066	1216	124974	CHS	Bostock
1801	1830	1775	1801	175951	CHS	Sandbach
1706	1935	1600	1700	134104	DEN	Holt
1706	1935	1600	1700	134104	DEN	Ridley
....	....	1680	1880	130621	NTT	Blidworth
....	....	1680	1880	130621	NTT	Greasley
1842	1955	1500	1842	176974	STS	Tean
1854	....	ALL	1854	176842	WLS	Wrexham
BOSTRIDGE						
1840	1930	....	....	104922	LND	ALL
1785	1840	1700	1785	104922	LND	Deptford
BOSWARD						
1700	1800	1700	1800	103764	WAR	Bidford On Avon
BOSWELL						
1780	1992	1740	1950	166952	CHS	Northwich
....	....	....	....	107433	DUR	???
1801	....	....	....	172545	KEN	Dover
....	....	ALL	....	172219	LND	???
1804	....	....	....	121835	NFK	Kings Lynn
1840	1880	1750	1992	172545	OXF	Garsington
1500	....	1500	....	100536	SCT	???
....	....	....	....	107433	WAR	???
1700	1725	1675	1992	114901	YKS	Selby

Known From	To	Researching From	To	Ref	Cty	Place
BOSWORTH						
1797	1860	1600	1797	165697	CAM	Chatteris
1812	1845	1790	1850	119008	DBY	Sawley
1871	1881	1866	1950	119008	ESS	West Ham
1797	1840	1750	1800	111236	LEI	Breedon On The Hill
1779	1791	1700	1850	119008	LEI	Castle Donnington
1910	1912	....	....	171883	LEI	Congerstone
1779	1791	1700	1850	119008	LEI	Hemington
1845	1866	1845	1870	119008	LIN	Lincoln
1798	1900	1600	1900	124834	NTT	East Leake
1865	1915	1700	1865	179647	WAR	Birmingham
1750	1820	1600	1992	114596	WAR	Coleshill
1600	1800	....	....	100420	WAR	Meriden
1855	1952	ALL	ALL	171883	WAR	Nuneaton
BOTELER						
1832	1900	1600	1832	110019	DBY	West
1832	1900	1600	1832	110019	LND	Shoreditch
BOTEREL						
1757	1767	1600	1900	102520	CON	Crowan
BOTHAMLEY						
....	....	1810	1850	174289	ALL	ALL
1843	1850	1750	1875	174270	DOR	ALL
1843	1920	1800	1843	174289	DOR	Hampreston
1830	1894	1750	1900	145750	LIN	Sutton Bridge
BOTHEL						
....	....	1806	1930	131032	YKS	Doncaster
BOTHELL						
....	....	1806	1930	131032	WES	???
1933	1948	1806	1930	131032	YKS	Thorn
BOTILER						
1100	1400	....	....	100420	WAR	ALL
BOTT						
1700	1730	1600	1700	151769	DBY	Ticknall
1810	1900	1800	1900	136484	LND	Spitalfields
....	....	....	1840	123412	STS	Birmingham
1758	1840	1700	1757	166464	STS	Shenstone
1800	1900	1800	1900	105147	STS	Tipton
1800	1900	1750	1992	177180	STS	Tipton
1850	1900	1700	1850	169676	WAR	Birmingham
BOTTELL						
....	....	ALL	ALL	108065	ALL	ALL
BOTTERILL						
....	....	ALL	ALL	108073	ALL	Name Study
1800	1860	1860	1900	133396	KEN	Plumstead
1800	1860	1860	1900	133396	LND	Plumstead
BOTTERS						
1700	1725	1675	1750	171549	CON	Lanteglos By Fowey
BOTTFIELD						
1800	1850	1800	1850	126209	SAL	South
BOTTING						
1772	1992	1600	1772	119512	SSX	Cuckfield
1840	1860	ALL	ALL	162108	SSX	Cuckfield
1750	1992	1650	1750	154016	SSX	Shipley
BOTTLE						
....	....	ALL	ALL	108081	ALL	Name Study
1450	1992	ALL	1992	108081	ALL	ALL
1786	1992	1600	1786	108065	KEN	Central
1786	1992	1600	1786	108065	KEN	East
BOTTOMLEY						
1740	1795	....	....	138851	CHS	Mottram
1743	1992	1650	1743	105902	NTH	Peterborough
1790	1960	1790	1960	153621	WYK	Halifax
....	....	1500	1900	168017	YKS	West
1800	1850	1750	1800	123595	YKS	Halifax
1777	1805	1700	1850	157716	YKS	Ripponden
BOTTOMS						
1750	1780	1700	1850	122602	BDF	Flitton With Silspe
1715	1740	1650	1800	122602	BDF	Uppergravenhurst
BOTTRELL						
1665	1863	ALL	1665	134783	CON	West Penwith
BOTTRILL						
1780	1800	....	....	147486	NTH	Northampton
BOTWRIGHT						
1740	1850	1700	1740	105031	SFK	Friston
1800	1821	1750	1800	155276	SFK	Friston
....	....	1750	1800	106356	SFK	???
BOUCH						
1711	1795	1600	1711	152196	CMA	Egremont
1871	....	1780	1851	128511	CUL	Carlisle
1851	....	....	....	128511	CUL	Wigton
1784	1802	ALL	1992	159174	LIN	Long Sutton
1851	....	ALL	1992	159174	LND	Camden Town
1835	1848	ALL	1992	159174	LND	Euston
1853	1858	ALL	1992	159174	LND	Kentish Town
BOUCH contd.						
1867	1875	ALL	1992	159174	LND	Pimlico
1827	....	ALL	1992	159174	LND	Southwark
1863	....	ALL	1992	159174	LND	St Pancras
BOUCHER						
1500	1700	1400	1500	120189	AVN	Bristol
....	1903	1890	1950	133639	SOM	Coker
1509	1750	1400	1509	120189	SOM	East Harptree
BOUCHET						
1768	1777	ALL	1800	154067	LND	Bermondsey
BOUCHIER						
1780	1992	1750	1992	108510	YKS	Leeds
BOUFFEY						
1758	....	ALL	1992	159174	STS	Wolverhampton
BOUGH						
1773	1900	1700	1900	122122	HEF	Cradley
1718	1811	1718	1811	157171	WOR	Cradley
1840	1880	1800	1900	157171	WOR	Leigh
1870	1975	1870	1975	157171	WOR	Malvern
....	....	1820	1843	133639	WOR	Shrawley
BOUGHTON						
1716	1900	1650	1716	128937	GLS	Elmore
BOUGHTWOOD						
1790	1850	1750	1870	171158	ESS	Writtle
BOULBY						
1813	1820	1700	1992	114901	YKS	Ackworth
1815	1820	1700	1992	114901	YKS	Hull
BOULCOTT						
1740	1800	....	1850	102822	HEF	Bosbury
BOULD						
1843	1968	1500	1843	176974	STS	Longton
1772	1854	....	....	114669	WYK	Leeds
BOULDEN						
1780	1900	1600	1900	108111	KEN	North East
1760	1900	1600	1800	113654	KEN	Maidston
1600	1850	1300	1992	108146	KEN	???
1745	1900	1650	1750	109703	YKS	Bradfield
BOULDERSTONE						
1033	1992	1033	1992	108138	ALL	ALL
1816	1918	....	....	116602	CHS	Stockport
BOULDING						
1450	1992	1300	1992	108146	KEN	???
1745	1900	1650	1750	109703	YKS	Bradfield
BOULDRAM						
1760	1810	....	....	145688	LIN	Winterton
BOULT						
1831	1874	1700	1830	153664	???	???
BOULTBY						
....	....	1806	ALL	175625	NTT	Basford
....	....	1806	ALL	175625	NTT	Gotham
BOULTER						
1830	1851	1800	1900	127612	SRY	Battersea
1840	1898	1750	1840	150614	SSX	Brighton
1887	1900	ALL	ALL	123706	STS	ALL
1887	1900	ALL	ALL	123706	STS	Cannock
1738	1911	1738	1911	139807	WIL	ALL
....	1822	1690	1850	126276	WIL	Chippenham
BOULTON						
1840	1900	1700	1900	126322	CHS	Chester
1840	1881	1840	1992	149098	DUR	Sunderland
1847	1867	1750	1847	146102	GLS	Cheltenham
....	....	1753	1850	101478	GLS	Cotswolds
1800	1850	1780	1850	142360	GLS	Kempsford
?	?	?	?	101214	HAM	Fratton
1867	1896	1800	1870	146102	LAN	Stretford
1826	1945	1700	1826	120367	NFK	South East
1830	1840	1770	1850	168580	NTH	Burton Latimer
1770	1790	1700	1770	121339	NYK	Osmotherley
1798	1851	1780	1850	166316	SOM	Wells
?	?	?	?	101214	SRY	Lambeth
1759	1880	1600	1800	149098	STS	Burslem
1820	1841	1750	1850	155152	STS	Penkridge
1600	1800	1600	1800	131040	WIL	Ashton Keynes
1790	1900	ALL	1900	153184	WIL	Ashton Keynes
1820	1890	1700	1800	146102	WIL	Cricklade
1681	1992	1681	1992	131156	WIL	Somerford Keynes
1750	1850	1850	1992	127477	WOR	Feckenham
1820	1845	1750	1850	108154	YKS	Halifax
....	....	....	....	123471	???	???
BOUND						
1817	1992	1700	1817	102342	HAM	Porstmouth
1800	1920	ALL	1930	146986	WIL	Coombe Bissett
1805	1887	ALL	1805	146986	WIL	Martin

Known From	To	Researching From	To	Ref	Cty	Place
BOUNDS						
1865	1952	ALL	1887	101281	NTH	Northampton
BOUNDY						
1776	....	ALL	ALL	110272	CON	Altarnun
1821	1860	1821	1992	114596	DEV	Ash Reigney
1752	1900	ALL	ALL	108162	SRY	ALL
BOUNSALL						
1741	1805	1600	1741	148040	CON	Launceston
BOURCHIER						
1250	1550	1200	1550	154881	ESS	Halstead
1250	1550	1200	1550	154881	ESS	Little Easton
1250	1550	1200	1550	154881	HRT	Ware
1250	1550	1200	1550	154881	KEN	Halstead
BOURKE						
1798	1992	....	....	139971	MAY	Ballycastle
1600	1900	ALL	ALL	127930	MAY	Killala
1850	1880	1800	1992	163848	TIP	Liscahill
BOURN						
1830	1870	ALL	ALL	171379	LIN	Boston
....	....	ALL	ALL	126098	SOM	Beckington
1800	1850	ALL	ALL	126098	SOM	Road
....	....	1700	1900	108766	SSX	Balcombe
1800	1850	ALL	ALL	126098	WIL	North Bradley
1800	1936	ALL	ALL	126098	WIL	Road
BOURNE						
1824	1884	ALL	ALL	116548	BRK	Sandhurst
1650	1707	1650	1750	176982	CON	Egloshayle
1760	1840	1600	1760	108197	ESS	Maldon
1779	1779	....	....	144355	KEN	South
1600	1860	1500	1900	102520	KEN	Hothfield
1817	1899	ALL	1817	119687	KEN	Lydd
1817	1899	ALL	1817	119687	KEN	New Romney
1806	....	....	....	108200	LND	Blackfriars
1840	1920	....	....	108200	LND	Camberwell
ALL	ALL	ALL	ALL	177601	MID	ALL
1850	1890	....	....	163465	NTT	Collingham
1700	ALL	....	....	163465	NTT	North Muskham
1750	1850	1700	1800	178454	SSX	North
1869	1992	....	....	119687	SSX	Rye
1791	1856	ALL	ALL	105015	SSX	Warnham
1720	1880	1650	1880	160849	STS	Norton In The Moors
1611	1750	1500	1600	110639	STS	Stoke On Trent
1809	....	ALL	1809	131725	STS	Wolverhampton
BOURNER						
1840	1905	1835	1905	107522	KEN	Tenterden
BOURREE						
....	....	ALL	ALL	108170	ALL	Name Study
BOURTON						
1811	1992	1800	1810	108227	SOM	Beckington
1800	1980	1780	1800	161322	SOM	Border
BOUSFIELD						
....	....	ALL	ALL	108235	ALL	Name Study
1830	1992	1700	1830	155810	LND	Soho
BOUSKILL						
....	....	1780	1900	147613	LAN	Tatham
BOUSTEAD						
1830	1860	1700	1880	146714	CUL	West
....	....	1700	1880	146714	T&W	Wallsend
BOUTAL						
....	....	ALL	ALL	108243	ALL	Name Study
1700	1992	1650	1930	108243	HRT	???
BOUTHBY						
1700	1748	ALL	1760	113611	LIN	Barrow On Humber
BOUTLE						
1800	....	....	....	112534	CAM	ALL
1800	1820	1800	....	112534	ESS	Stansted
1800	1820	1800	....	112534	HRT	Stansted
BOVEY						
1747	1797	1747	1837	168416	CON	Gorran
1782	1992	1782	1992	168416	CON	St Blazey
1747	1755	1747	1755	168416	CON	Stewe
1750	1800	1700	1800	149144	CON	Tregoney
BOVINDON						
....	....	ALL	ALL	158100	ALL	Name Study
BOVINGTON						
1827	1942	1790	1942	162450	SRY	Egham
BOVIS						
1600	1992	1600	1992	108251	ALL	ALL
1783	1992	1780	1992	108251	KEN	West
BOW						
1860	1870	1836	1880	117145	IRL	ALL
BOWATER						
1750	1825	1638	1835	145572	KEN	Ramsgate
1700	1810	1638	1835	145572	KEN	Woolwich
BOWATER contd.						
....	....	1700	1785	149977	STS	South
1785	1797	....	....	149977	STS	Kingswinford
....	....	1780	1900	147613	STS	Rowley Regis
1638	1810	1638	1835	145572	WAR	Coventry
1845	1900	1800	1900	142875	WOR	Dudley
BOWD						
1697	1697	1650	1720	167002	CAM	Cambridge
1689	1689	1650	1720	167002	CAM	Histon
BOWDEN						
1804	1992	1700	1804	161446	CAM	Soham
1740	1879	....	....	138851	CHS	Davenham
1740	1879	....	....	138851	CHS	Lostick Gralam
1820	1992	1650	1820	173665	CHS	Malpas
1829	....	1700	1828	110345	CHS	Marple
1800	....	1800	....	177466	CHS	Marple
1829	1889	1700	1828	110345	CHS	Stalybridge
1832	1832	1100	1832	117749	CON	Contantine
1840	1992	....	....	109444	CON	Phillack
1820	1913	1700	1850	156450	CON	Phillack
1820	1913	1700	1850	156450	CON	Uny-Lelant
1800	1992	1600	1800	108286	DEV	North
1800	1841	....	....	102946	DEV	Ashburton
1782	1836	1700	1809	162825	DEV	East Down
....	....	1600	1992	137588	DEV	North Tawton
1785	1820	1750	1820	170852	DEV	South Molton
1866	1870	1700	1866	117064	DEV	Torquay
1880	1930	1880	1930	117064	DUR	Brandon
1816	1935	ALL	1816	129658	KEN	Woolwich
....	....	1700	1850	130931	LAN	Salford
1850	....	1850	....	159247	LAN	Warrington
1840	1850	1800	1840	146587	MDX	Uxbridge
1785	1862	1600	1785	147346	NBL	Branton
1780	1900	....	....	137693	SOM	Backwell
1840	1880	1840	1880	135429	SOM	Heasley Mill
1808	1892	ALL	1808	167878	SOM	Shapwick
1900	1950	....	1900	148342	WAR	Birmingham
BOWDING						
1800	1820	1750	1900	151653	SOM	Langport
BOWDITCH						
1830	1880	....	1830	133434	DOR	Upway
ALL	ALL	ALL	ALL	114502	SOM	ALL
BOWDLER						
....	....	ALL	ALL	108294	ALL	Name Study
1096	1992	....	....	174378	MGY	Montgomery
1102	1992	1102	1900	108294	SAL	Chirbury
1856	1881	1800	1856	105538	SAL	Madeley Wood
?	....	....	?	166065	SAL	Shrewsbury
BOWE						
1760	1992	1550	1760	108308	YKS	North
BOWEN						
1800	1917	?	1800	158704	BRE	Ystrdgynlais
1817	1851	1817	1851	176958	CGN	Cardigan
1845	1950	ALL	1845	122572	CMN	ALL
1688	1775	....	....	176958	CMN	Cambrose
....	....	1700	1850	123110	CMN	Trelech
1800	1845	1700	1992	107204	CMN	???
1780	....	....	1780	146013	DBY	Longford
....	1850	1750	1850	146927	ENG	London
1845	1950	ALL	1845	122572	HAM	ALL
1843	....	1700	1843	145971	HAM	Portsea
1770	1961	1770	1881	118664	HEF	Burghill
1770	1850	1700	1850	172642	HEF	Burghill
1770	1850	1700	1850	172642	HEF	Hereford
1770	1961	1770	1881	118664	HEF	Wellington
1873	1992	1700	1873	144754	KEN	Halstead
1845	1950	ALL	1845	122572	LND	ALL
1880	....	....	....	171905	LND	Strand
1871	1927	....	....	171905	MDX	Saint Giles
1821	....	1821	....	171905	MDX	Westminster
1817	1851	1817	1851	176958	PEM	Llantood
1326	1600	1070	1600	176923	PEM	Loch Meilir
1843	1897	1750	1850	121886	PEM	Monkton
1688	1775	....	....	176958	PEM	Poyston
1866	1943	1830	1920	151041	WLS	Bersham
1787	1907	1700	1787	179647	WOR	Grimley
1787	1907	1700	1787	179647	WOR	Powick
BOWER						
....	....	1780	1850	108472	DEV	Ottery St Mary
1820	1829	1750	1850	150320	DEV	Ottery St Mary
1860	1992	1700	1860	108324	DEV	???
1760	1800	ALL	1800	115266	DOR	ALL
ALL	ALL	1500	1800	118559	DOR	ALL
....	1880	....	1880	103470	DOR	Corfe

Known From	To	Researching From	To	Ref	Cty	Place
BOWER contd.						
1700	1850	....	....	108677	DOR	Iwerne
1890	1975	....	....	114227	GLA	Cardiff
1590	1892	1664	1992	114227	GLS	Gloucester
1880	1992	....	1880	103470	LND	Walthamstow
1550	1713	1619	1713	108375	NTH	Aynho
1583	1634	1583	1634	108375	NTH	Gretton
1700	1730	1650	1700	121339	NYK	Pickering
1515	1777	1650	1777	108375	OXF	Souldern
1589	....	....	....	108375	OXF	Stoke Lyne
1703	....	....	1703	108375	OXF	Witney
1843	1992	ALL	1850	114553	YKS	Bradford
1860	1992	1700	1860	108324	YKS	???
1868	1992	ALL	1868	105465	???	Kirkcaldy
BOWERING						
....	....	1730	1860	108472	DEV	Axminster
1798	1847	....	....	114545	LIN	Lincoln
....	....	1750	1900	108472	SOM	Exmoor
BOWERMAN						
1900	1970	ALL	1900	166545	DEV	Wellington
1820	1850	....	....	132756	NTH	Brackley
ALL	ALL	ALL	ALL	108340	OXF	ALL
1790	1850	....	....	132756	OXF	Bicester
1570	1850	....	....	132756	OXF	Charlbury
1750	1810	ALL	1750	163341	OXF	Charlbury
1570	1850	....	....	132756	OXF	Finstock
1570	1850	....	....	132756	OXF	Ramsden
1570	1850	....	....	132756	OXF	Witney
BOWERS						
1821	1894	1821	1900	168564	CHS	North
1820	1829	1750	1850	150320	DEV	Ottery St Mary
1800	1802	1700	1900	159956	ESS	Tillingham
1780	1950	1750	1950	146803	HAM	ALL
1900	1992	1750	1900	158275	HAM	Sholing
1849	1890	....	....	108375	MDX	Bishopsgate
1708	1910	1708	1910	108375	MDX	City
1770	1845	1777	1779	108375	MDX	Enfield
1776	1776	....	....	108375	MDX	Low Leyton
1837	1844	1700	1844	102326	NFK	Wretton
1820	1823	1750	1850	141569	NTH	Slipton
1811	1875	....	1811	102059	SAL	South
?	1971	ALL	1971	100072	SFK	Bury St Edmunds
1780	1880	1750	1950	146803	SRY	ALL
1779	....	....	1779	108375	SRY	Streatham
1780	1820	1750	1900	146803	SSX	ALL
1798	1841	ALL	ALL	122106	STS	Madeley
1861	1992	1800	1861	158526	SXE	Brighton
BOWERY						
1750	1800	1600	1800	154342	GLS	Mangotsfield
BOWES						
1750	1880	1650	1750	179663	DUR	Heworth
1750	1880	1650	1750	179663	DUR	Stanhope
1715	1743	....	1750	171441	KEN	Bapchild
1715	1743	....	1750	171441	KEN	Milstead
1865	1992	1800	1880	135623	LAN	Liverpool
1839	1860	1700	1839	135151	WES	Brampton
BOWIE						
1929	1940	....	....	159964	LAN	Bolton
1800	1890	1700	1920	167177	MLN	Edinburgh
1800	1890	1700	1920	167177	MLN	Leith
1845	1929	1800	1900	159964	RFW	Glasgow
BOWKER						
1812	1843	1812	1843	143286	LAN	Accrington
1830	1850	1820	1850	123595	LAN	Clitheroe
1853	1992	1650	1853	108405	LAN	Manchester
1853	1992	1650	1853	108405	LAN	Salford
....	....	ALL	1939	172502	SCT	???
1855	1983	?	?	104329	YKS	???
BOWL						
1781	1850	1550	1780	108413	GLS	Central
BOWLAND						
1821	1940	....	....	128996	CAM	Thorney
1730	1800	1730	1820	154210	NYK	Kirklevington
BOWLE						
1848	?	ALL	ALL	153516	SOM	Kewstoke
BOWLER						
....	....	1780	1900	103713	BDF	Elstow
1761	1900	1600	1900	108421	BDF	Husborne Crawley
1850	1920	....	....	113735	DBY	Drigdehay
1781	1894	1600	1781	150150	LAN	Snarestone
1886	1886	1840	1886	114448	LND	Chelsea
1789	1791	ALL	1790	112887	MDX	Shoreditch
1850	1920	....	....	113735	STS	Alton
1743	1992	1743	1992	155993	STS	Alton

Known From	To	Researching From	To	Ref	Cty	Place
BOWLER contd.						
1850	1920	....	....	113735	STS	Cauldon
....	....	1850	1900	109134	WAR	Birmingham
BOWLES						
1857	1884	1500	1857	175072	CHS	Macclesfield
1580	1830	1580	1830	127655	COR	Ballinacorra
1818	1850	ALL	1818	175994	GLS	Siddington
1750	1850	1700	1850	102970	HAM	East Woodhay
1650	1962	ALL	1910	137774	KEN	Dover
1836	1836	1815	1840	128449	KEN	Ramsgate
1817	1817	1800	1836	128449	KEN	Sandwich
1830	1850	1800	1830	136522	MDX	Clerkenwell
1858	1992	1800	1858	126586	MDX	London
1850	1900	1700	1992	122114	WAR	Birmingham
BOWLEY						
1870	1900	1800	1870	116432	DEV	Plymouth
1840	1992	ALL	ALL	164887	HRT	Watford
....	....	1650	1950	124656	LEI	Shepshed
....	....	1600	1900	124656	LEI	???
1860	....	1860	....	109967	SRY	Camberwell
1800	1830	ALL	ALL	164887	SSX	South
1769	1944	....	....	115606	WIL	Buttermere
1800	1900	1800	1900	137464	WIL	Great Bedwyn
BOWLING						
1821	1940	....	....	128996	CAM	Thorney
1300	1750	1300	1992	108146	KEN	???
BOWMAN						
1850	1992	1750	1850	107697	ANT	Belfast
1746	1992	1600	1740	167312	CMA	Hodyoad Lamplugh
1803	1992	ALL	1803	104221	CMA	Whitehaven
1892	1944	1600	1892	179566	DBY	Bakewell
1831	1841	ALL	1880	101001	FIF	East
1831	1841	ALL	1880	101001	FIF	South
1700	1800	1700	1800	123722	GLS	Pucklechurch
1860	1992	1800	1860	108448	HAM	Pamber
1860	1992	1800	1860	108448	HAM	Tadley
1750	1850	1750	1850	141682	HAM	Tadley
1914	1914	....	....	148334	MDX	Chelsea
1866	1980	....	....	101001	MLN	Cockpen
1866	1980	....	....	101001	MLN	Lasswade
1730	1798	....	1730	101761	NTT	Ragnall
1870	1940	1500	1900	137502	SFK	Ipswich
1800	1870	1800	1870	134422	SOM	Bristol
BOWMER						
1700	1800	1700	1800	169781	DUR	Wickham
1800	1899	1800	1899	169781	NBL	Long Benton
1754	1900	1600	1992	130125	NBL	Woodhorn
BOWN						
....	....	ALL	ALL	143839	ALL	Name Study
....	....	....	1804	154024	DBY	Bolsover
1835	1950	1700	1850	153230	DBY	Hognaston
1799	1844	ALL	ALL	143839	ESS	Romford
....	....	ALL	1775	164631	GLS	ALL
1804	1841	....	....	164631	GLS	Stow On Wold
1815	1830	....	1840	157139	HAM	Isle Of Wight
1750	1800	1750	1800	135941	SFK	Clare
1700	1840	1700	1840	102490	SOM	Middlezoy
1760	1872	1813	1871	170623	SOM	West Cranmore
....	....	1800	....	137456	WAR	Dunchurch
BOWNAS						
1880	1992	ALL	1900	111678	CMA	Witherslack
BOWNASS						
1871	....	1871	1992	159468	LAN	North East
1700	1881	1700	1992	159468	WES	South East
BOWNESS						
1773	1889	?	1773	125059	DUR	Bishop Auckland
1874	1992	ALL	ALL	108464	LAN	Liverpool
....	....	1850	1992	131628	WES	Kendal
1700	1750	....	....	146854	WES	Orton
BOWNS						
1830	1880	?	1820	158569	GLS	Stroud
BOWRIN						
....	....	ALL	ALL	147222	STS	Handsworth
....	....	ALL	ALL	147222	STS	Willenhall
BOWRING						
1840	1874	1800	1874	124990	AVN	Bristol
1760	1830	1799	1830	118095	LIN	Horsington
1788	1853	1700	1788	121010	MDX	Islington
1841	1860	1841	1917	118095	NBL	Bothal
BOWSER						
1760	1850	1600	1760	167584	NYK	Barton
1749	1802	1600	1850	123250	YKS	Cranswick
1749	1802	1600	1850	123250	YKS	Hutton

Known From	To	Researching From	To	Ref	Cty	Place
BOWSHER						
....	....	1800	1900	171891	BRK	Reading
....	....	1750	ALL	175366	ESS	ALL
1760	1800	1760	1820	175366	LND	Bishopsgate
BOWSKILL						
1680	1750	1680	1815	130621	NTT	Blidworth
1680	1750	1680	1815	130621	NTT	Mansfield Woodhouse
BOWTAL						
....	....	1700	1850	108243	ESS	???
BOWTELL						
ALL	ALL	ALL	ALL	108480	CAM	ALL
ALL	ALL	ALL	ALL	108480	ESS	ALL
....	....	....	....	108480	LND	Tower Hamletts
....	....	....	....	108480	SCT	ALL
ALL	ALL	ALL	ALL	108480	SFK	ALL
....	....	....	....	108480	SFK	Thaxstead
BOWTLE						
1830	1992	1750	1830	166634	ESS	Wethersfield
BOWYER						
....	....	ALL	ALL	108499	ALL	Name Study
ALL	ALL	ALL	ALL	108499	ALL	ALL
1772	1794	ALL	1772	168602	BRK	Bray
1772	1794	ALL	1772	168602	BRK	Cookham
1750	1992	ALL	1750	108502	BRK	Winkfield
1787	1803	1803	1915	118079	LND	East
....	....	1800	1830	108510	SAL	Much Wenlock
1847	1992	1800	1830	108510	SAL	Shifnal
1945	....	....	....	173932	SRY	Epsom
1675	....	ALL	....	108499	WIL	South Wraxall
BOX						
....	....	1750	1825	142999	CON	Minster
1675	?	?	?	166642	KEN	Canterbury
1799	1900	ALL	ALL	171379	LIN	ALL
1873	....	1800	1873	176931	MON	Newport
1774	1992	1774	1992	127035	SRY	Lambeth
1863	1900	1500	1863	153494	WAR	Birmingham
1863	1900	1500	1863	153494	WAR	Warwick
BOXALL						
1841	....	1841	1992	149055	HAM	Bramshott
1830	1860	1800	1900	126535	KEN	Bromley
1857	1880	1850	1880	129607	SRY	Southwark
1780	1960	1700	1850	124311	SSX	West
1815	1850	1600	1850	113654	SSX	Brighton
1838	1867	1700	1838	138673	SSX	Horsham
BOXER						
1760	1900	1800	1900	151653	MIL	Royal Navy
BOXSHALL						
1870	1890	....	....	167525	MDX	Kensington
1820	1870	1800	1820	167525	SRY	Richmond
BOY						
1734	....	ALL	1734	104299	YKS	Carlton
BOYARD						
1806	1863	1700	1851	151513	WAR	Atherstone
BOYCE						
1066	1992	1066	1992	108626	ALL	ALL
....	....	1750	1850	127949	BKM	Newport Pagnell
1654	1940	....	....	128996	CAM	Thorney
....	....	ALL	1850	135607	DEV	Teignmouth
1874	1900	1800	1900	125431	LDY	Coleraine
1877	1992	1700	1877	170054	LND	Bow
1850	1950	....	....	135607	MDX	North London
1778	1857	1750	1857	147311	NYK	Scalby
1790	1851	1770	1900	156965	WIL	Marlborough
BOYCOTT						
1750	....	ALL	1750	179515	SAL	Uppington
BOYD						
....	....	ALL	ALL	108545	ALL	Name Study
1300	1600	1300	1600	154881	ALL	ALL
1870	1992	1750	1870	118052	ANT	Ballycastle
1824	....	1750	1824	108596	AYR	ALL
1730	1740	....	....	127140	AYR	Ayr
1790	1815	....	1820	146811	AYR	Beith
1792	1895	ALL	1800	101079	AYR	Newmilns
1835	....	....	....	132381	BUT	Rothesay
1808	1810	1700	1808	100846	CLK	???
1860	1992	....	....	143855	DEV	Plymouth
....	....	1700	1860	143855	DON	Killybegs
1840	1992	1650	1992	176621	DOW	Newtownards
1900	1920	ALL	ALL	120154	DUR	Sunderland
1858	....	ALL	1858	133957	HAM	Southampton
1833	....	1700	1833	177865	IRL	???
1864	1932	ALL	1864	108537	LAN	Liverpool
1890	1992	1890	1992	109436	LAN	Manchester
1846	1895	1750	....	109282	LND	Central

Known From	To	Researching From	To	Ref	Cty	Place
BOYD contd.						
1800	1901	1775	1850	150312	PER	Perth
....	1700	....	1700	177695	SAL	???
1858	....	ALL	1858	133957	SCT	ALL
1853	1992	....	....	108529	SCT	Glasgow
....	....	1700	1831	126357	SLI	???
1830	1855	1750	1900	126977	WIG	Portpatrick
1831	1951	1800	1831	175447	YKS	Bradford
1831	1951	1800	1831	175447	YKS	Lesterdyke
BOYDE						
?	?	....	....	154113	BKM	Langley
?	?	....	....	154113	BRK	Wokingham
BOYDEN						
1834	1992	1700	1834	151866	ESS	Colchester
1872	1902	1800	1950	113638	MDX	Tottenham
BOYDEN-ROBERTS						
1830	1873	1800	1830	164828	MDX	Bloomsbury
BOYELL						
1861	1928	1700	1928	104485	MDX	Marylebone
BOYER						
1820	1950	1700	1880	148652	CHS	Gt Budworth
1800	....	1800	1992	164054	CHS	Hollingworth
1800	....	1800	1992	164054	CHS	Tintwistle
1750	1992	ALL	ALL	150797	LIN	Corby Glen
1750	1992	ALL	ALL	150797	LIN	Thurlby By Bourn
1770	1806	1700	1841	160636	LIN	Woolsthorpe
1837	1850	1800	1850	126446	MDX	South West
1841	1992	1538	1841	131318	NTH	Walton
BOYERS						
1840	1860	1800	1850	137618	LAN	Wigan
1795	1918	1700	1795	143448	LIN	???
1820	1870	ALL	ALL	142611	YKS	Hatfield
BOYES						
....	....	ALL	ALL	108626	ALL	Name Study
1066	1992	1066	1992	108626	ALL	ALL
1850	1992	1700	1992	108618	DFS	Dunscore
1763	1885	....	....	131660	GLS	Eastleach Turville
1797	1860	ALL	1797	115126	HAM	Bishops Waltham
1620	1992	....	1620	148237	HAM	Hambledon
1780	1800	1700	1780	121339	NYK	Whitby
1686	1729	....	....	131660	SFK	Newmarket
1620	1992	....	1620	148237	SSX	New Fishbourne
....	....	1700	1885	166863	YKS	Leeds
1796	1900	1700	1795	132764	YKS	Wensleydale
1660	1733	1540	1700	174858	YKS	Wintingham
BOYLE						
1840	1980	1700	1840	140260	DON	Dungloe
1800	1870	1740	1830	146927	DON	Rathmelton
1830	1945	1800	1992	166081	LAN	Preston
....	....	1770	1790	122904	LDY	Newton Limvady
1860	....	....	....	132381	LKS	Glasgow
....	....	1750	1850	146358	STD	Glasgow
BOYLES						
1846	1992	ALL	1882	108642	BDF	Sharnbrook
1850	1900	1800	1900	104868	BKM	Brill
1814	1851	ALL	1814	164623	DEV	Barnstaple
1750	1860	1750	1860	107352	DEV	Braunton
1550	1750	1550	1750	107352	DEV	East Down
BOYLETT						
....	....	ALL	ALL	108650	ALL	Name Study
....	....	ALL	ALL	108650	ALL	ALL
1540	1881	1881	1992	108650	SRY	Ash
1540	1881	1881	1992	108650	SRY	Guildford
1540	1881	1881	1992	108650	SRY	Pirbright
1540	1881	1881	1992	108650	SRY	Woplesdon
BOYLIN						
1860	1880	1600	1860	122084	LND	Bethnal Green
BOYNE						
1832	1870	1830	1870	148911	CAR	Tullow
1907	1992	1907	1992	148911	HAM	Wealdstone
BOYS						
....	....	1500	1800	108677	ALL	ALL
1066	1992	1066	1992	108626	ALL	ALL
1680	1860	....	....	108677	DOR	Sherborne
1767	1797	....	....	103632	DUR	Sunderland
1818	1902	1066	1992	108669	DUR	Sunderland
1700	1950	1500	1800	108677	HAM	South East
1855	....	....	....	170526	HAM	Fareham
1841	1955	....	....	170526	HAM	Portsmouth
1200	1850	1800	1950	108677	KEN	East
1096	1735	1096	1696	150894	KEN	Goodnestone
1096	1735	1096	1696	150894	KEN	Kingston
1626	1626	....	....	127426	KEN	Ulcombe
1550	1700	1550	1700	108677	LND	ALL

Known From	To	Researching From	To	Ref	Cty	Place
BOYS contd.						
1600	1700	....	1600	108677	SOM	Bath
1902	1964	....	....	108669	WYK	Leeds
1797	1797	....	....	144568	YKS	???
BOYSE						
1066	1992	1066	1992	108626	ALL	ALL
BOYTON						
1842	1856	....	....	133221	BDF	Bedford
1752	1765	....	....	133221	ESS	Clavering
1654	1679	ALL	1680	129283	ESS	Kelvedon
1792	1835	1835	1842	133221	HRT	Bishops Stortford
BRABBINS						
1750	1800	1700	1900	142875	NFK	Thurlton
BRABFORD						
1830	1900	1830	1900	178675	YKS	Knottingley
1800	1830	1750	1830	178675	YKS	Pontefract
BRABIN						
1650	1900	1650	1900	109045	DEV	???
BRABON						
1800	1992	....	....	135860	SSX	Burwash
BRACE						
1890	1930	1800	1930	103985	CAM	March
1776	1940	....	....	128996	CAM	Thorney
1860	1890	1800	1860	103985	CAM	Upwell
1890	1930	1800	1930	103985	CAM	Wisbech
1776	....	1730	1800	131547	GLS	Long Newnton
....	....	....	....	127272	HRT	Sawbridgeworth
1822	....	....	1822	108839	HUN	Somersham
1845	1896	1800	1896	177113	WOR	St Andrews
BRACEBRIDGE						
1640	1765	ALL	ALL	141615	LEI	Leicester
BRACER						
1661	1940	....	....	128996	CAM	Thorney
BRACEWELL						
1774	....	....	1774	149624	LAN	Colne
....	....	....	....	108685	MDX	???
1916	1992	1916	1992	108685	WAR	Coventry
1916	1992	1916	1992	108685	WAR	Nuneaton
1794	1942	1700	1800	112224	YKS	Keighley
1825	1992	1825	1992	108685	YKS	Leeds
BRACEY						
1845	....	1800	1845	106062	BDF	Stanbridge
1600	1980	1500	1600	173169	GLS	South
1720	1992	1700	1992	108693	HRT	Graveley
1550	1650	1500	1550	173169	LND	London
1800	1992	1750	1992	107514	NFK	South East
1836	1892	1800	1910	141666	NFK	Broads
1800	1992	1700	1800	179035	NFK	Yarmouth
BRACHER						
1500	1900	1500	1900	170216	WIL	ALL
1770	....	1700	1770	121010	WIL	Sedgehill
1788	1845	1788	1845	137898	WIL	Sutton Mandeville
BRACK						
1812	....	....	....	146447	DUR	Sunderland
BRACKENBURY						
....	....	....	1745	130060	KEN	Lydd
....	911	800	1992	175072	LIN	ALL
1800	1992	....	....	176125	LIN	Asterby
1821	....	....	....	114545	LIN	Butterwick
1821	....	....	....	114545	LIN	Fens
1800	1992	....	....	176125	LIN	Goulceby
1800	1890	ALL	ALL	111155	LIN	Wrangle
BRACKENRIDGE						
1788	....	1700	1800	115967	AYR	Kirkoswald
BRACKER						
1784	1854	ALL	1804	108642	BDF	Odell
BRACKLEY						
1800	1864	ALL	1800	126721	BKM	North Crawley
BRACKNELL						
1822	1876	....	....	126926	MDX	Bethnal Green
....	....	1733	1822	126926	MDX	Shoreditch
....	....	1733	1822	126926	MDX	Stepney
BRACKPOOL						
....	....	ALL	ALL	108707	ALL	Name Study
BRACKSTONE						
1815	1870	1500	1992	109436	DEV	South Molton
1550	1850	1500	1992	109436	HAM	Longparish
1674	1696	1600	1674	115819	WIL	Ramsbury
BRADBEER						
1804	1817	1800	1812	117579	SOM	Corfe
1860	1900	1700	1860	130389	SOM	North Curry
1800	1900	1800	1900	106410	SOM	Pitminster
1758	1801	1750	1812	117579	SOM	Pitminster
BRADBERRY						
1829	....	ALL	1829	151424	YKS	Ripon
BRADBURN						
1830	....	1800	1900	146978	LAN	Farnworth
1798	1986	....	1798	123358	LAN	Liverpool
BRADBURY						
1878	1902	1700	1878	172049	CHS	Denton
1860	1882	1800	1860	142786	DBY	Brough
1790	1830	1750	1790	160458	DBY	Hayfield
1844	1925	1800	1900	124788	DBY	Little Longstone
1851	1992	1700	1992	153672	HRT	ALL
1882	1884	1884	1900	142786	LAN	Ashton Under Lyne
1878	1902	1700	1878	172049	LAN	Bredbury
....	....	ALL	ALL	167827	LAN	Manchester
1886	1992	1800	1886	108715	LAN	Oldham
?	?	....	....	132500	LAN	Oldham
1750	1840	1600	1750	113158	LAN	Saddleworth
1877	1992	....	....	132500	LAN	Shaw
....	1881	1500	1881	175072	LAN	St Helens
1860	1870	1830	1860	108731	LND	Islington
....	....	1700	1756	149977	STS	West
1900	1980	1900	1980	108723	STS	Boney Hay
....	....	1850	1950	108723	STS	Burntwood
1817	1992	1700	1900	108723	STS	Cannock Wood
....	....	1700	1900	108723	STS	Gentleshaw
1756	1840	....	....	149977	STS	Gnosall
1841	1890	....	....	149977	STS	Wolverhampton
1775	1775	ALL	1775	122017	WYK	Saddleworth
1750	1840	1600	1750	113158	YKS	Saddleworth
....	....	ALL	ALL	167827	YKS	Saddleworth
....	....	1900	1950	142786	YKS	Sheffield
BRADD						
1812	1900	1750	1812	129712	HRT	Bishop Stortford
BRADDEN						
1848	1848	1800	1860	127361	DEV	Putford
BRADDOCK						
1836	1900	1815	1850	122351	CHS	Macclesfield
BRADDON						
1809	1992	1700	1809	164917	CON	Polperro
BRADEN						
....	....	ALL	ALL	114308	SSX	Brighton
BRADER						
1790	1860	1700	1790	135879	LND	Westminster
BRADEY						
1803	....	1700	1803	139386	NTT	Gamston
BRADFIELD						
....	1960	1700	....	108758	BRK	Milton
1795	1816	1700	1795	107344	LIN	Spalding
1765	1992	1500	1992	141585	SRY	Wimbledon
BRADFORD						
1800	1830	....	....	113514	CAM	Newmarket
1866	1925	1866	1925	108782	DEV	Exeter
....	....	1800	1846	116165	DEV	Pinhoe
1717	1787	1650	1717	148938	GLS	Arlingham
1800	1840	1760	1800	176311	HEF	Ledbury
1800	1850	1700	1850	107611	HEF	Prestiegn
1743	1992	1700	1900	148725	HRT	Brent Pelham
1744	1900	ALL	....	104515	LIN	South
....	....	1500	1900	108766	SSX	ALL
1600	1900	1600	1900	108766	SSX	Eastbourne
1752	1770	1700	1820	160873	STS	Sedgley
1830	1970	....	....	113514	WYK	Leeds
BRADFURTH						
1632	1660	1600	1680	170348	YKS	Huddersfield
BRADGATE						
1631	1659	ALL	ALL	141615	LEI	Claybrooke
BRADICK						
1856	1856	1800	1880	127981	MDX	London
BRADLAUGHE						
....	....	ALL	ALL	136832	ALL	Name Study
1400	1600	....	....	136832	NFK	ALL
1275	1700	....	....	136832	SFK	ALL
BRADLEN						
1802	1919	ALL	1992	100196	YKS	Drighlington
BRADLEY						
....	....	1600	1900	108812	ARM	Charlemont
1700	1800	1700	1900	125679	BRK	Thatcham
1820	1992	....	....	177202	CAM	Murrow
1726	1812	1600	1726	177202	CAM	Whittlesey
1819	....	1700	1840	143243	DBY	Chesterfield
1871	1893	1850	1893	128449	DBY	Derby
1796	....	1790	1796	148121	DBY	North Wingfield
1796	....	1750	1800	148121	DBY	Wingerworth
1817	....	1600	1817	132802	DOR	Leigh

Known From	To	Researching From	To	Ref	Cty	Place
BRADLEY contd.						
1688	1768	1658	1688	139149	ERY	Southburn
1774	1812	1700	1900	109282	ESS	South East
1711	1747	1700	1747	107573	HAM	Alton
1780	1840	1700	1850	136840	HAM	Winchester
....	....	1700	1810	166863	IRL	Meath
1862	1992	ALL	1862	136875	IRL	???
1733	1841	1600	1733	170542	KEN	Ash
1863	1960	1840	1863	173673	KEN	Chatham
?	?	?	?	100692	LAN	Ardwick
1856	1871	....	....	169013	LAN	Manchester
1700	1992	ALL	1700	112771	LAN	Oldham
1730	1815	....	....	169528	LAN	Preston
1766	....	1700	1770	130214	LEI	Kegworth
1800	1992	1700	1800	162396	LIN	Central
1736	1811	....	1736	101761	LIN	Friskney
1750	1778	....	....	121835	LIN	Salmonby
1745	1799	1600	1750	101575	LIN	Wrawby By Brigg
1849	1851	1700	1992	166073	LND	Bethnall Green
....	....	1800	1900	146978	LOU	Carlingford
1815	1840	1700	1992	166073	MDX	St Dunstans
1815	1840	1700	1992	166073	MDX	Stepney
1790	1825	1700	1800	131377	NTH	Rothwell
1822	1871	1750	1881	160636	NTT	Newark
....	1793	....	....	128910	NTT	Southwell
1745	1745	ALL	1800	168696	OXF	Stanton Harcourt
....	....	1750	1992	167789	SOM	Bath
....	....	....	1770	147818	SRY	???
1863	1960	1840	1863	173673	STS	Rushall
1502	1730	1470	1730	102830	STS	Sedgely
1871	1930	1800	1930	133426	STS	Wednesbury
1900	1992	1700	1900	108812	TYR	Killyman
1846	1895	1840	1900	108804	WOR	Abbots Morton
1821	1844	1820	1850	108804	WOR	Salwarpe
1740	1844	1660	1740	170348	YKS	Almondbury
1862	1992	ALL	1862	136875	YKS	Bradford
1774	1840	....	....	170348	YKS	Braithwell
1800	1992	....	....	117625	YKS	Great Ayton
1776	1992	1776	?	166235	YKS	Halifax
1800	1820	1750	1850	123536	YKS	Hawnby
1797	1992	ALL	1826	154946	YKS	Huddersfield
1850	1900	1700	1850	108790	YKS	Keighley
1860	1870	1800	1900	148458	YKS	Langcliffe
....	....	....	1770	147818	YKS	Lower Wharfedale
....	....	1700	1800	147613	YKS	Marton In Craven
1849	1880	1881	1890	170348	YKS	Rawmarsh
1712	1746	1700	1760	170348	YKS	Throapham
1782	....	1782	1800	117625	YKS	Yarm
BRADMAN						
1804	1808	ALL	ALL	177989	HAM	Kingsclere
BRADRIDGE						
1820	1860	1550	1820	146587	DEV	Ugborough
BRADSHAW						
1700	ALL	1745	1905	107379	ALL	ALL
1822	1921	....	....	168602	BDF	Harrold
1822	1921	....	....	168602	BDF	Odell
1806	....	1750	1830	169625	CAM	Ely
1716	1992	1566	1992	108839	CAM	Sutton
1700	1800	....	....	100056	CAM	Thorney
1746	1940	....	....	128996	CAM	Thorney
1788	1881	1788	1992	113956	DBY	Darley
1883	....	1880	1889	169625	ESS	Chelmsford
1856	1895	ALL	1856	166847	HRT	Wormley
1790	1850	....	....	140317	HUN	Upwood
....	....	1700	1992	131903	LAN	Manchester
1775	1888	1650	1880	173622	LAN	Manchester
1800	1850	1750	1800	121509	LAN	Padiham
1737	1742	ALL	1737	146226	LAN	Prestwich
1845	1992	1700	1845	118923	LAN	St Helens
1748	1748	1650	1747	131245	LEI	Quorndon
1728	1747	1650	1747	131245	LEI	Woodhouse
1800	1900	1700	1850	126268	LND	Bethnal Green
1886	....	1750	1992	179183	MDX	Bromley
1850	1944	?	?	143464	MDX	Islington
1902	1992	ALL	1902	152013	MDX	Islington
1723	1749	1720	1750	107360	NTH	Crick
1795	1830	....	1830	174912	NTH	Roade
1805	1822	ALL	1805	168602	NTH	Wellingboro
....	....	ALL	ALL	160733	SAL	ALL
?	?	ALL	ALL	100897	SRY	???
1880	1992	ALL	1880	108847	STS	Armitage
1840	1900	1830	1900	138444	WAR	Rugby
BRADSTOCK						
1593	1634	....	1600	174270	DOR	???
BRADSTOCK contd.						
....	....	....	1593	174270	WOR	Worcester
BRADSTOCKE						
1630	1650	1560	1630	174289	DOR	Witchampton
....	....	ALL	1650	174289	WOR	ALL
BRADSTREET						
1602	....	1602	....	121487	SFK	Hessett
BRADWELL						
1714	1777	1650	1720	152110	CAM	Burwell
1715	1880	1700	1860	143774	DBY	Bradwell
BRADY						
1839	ALL	ALL	1880	116734	CAV	Belturbet
1839	ALL	ALL	1880	116734	CAV	Templeport
....	....	1780	1880	108863	CAV	???
1900	1992	1850	1992	108855	DUR	Durham
1796	1845	1796	1992	142735	ESS	Romford
1900	1915	1875	1992	117609	HAM	Alverstoke
1839	ALL	ALL	1880	116734	IRL	???
....	....	1800	1900	108855	MOG	???
BRADYLL						
1500	1540	....	....	126497	LAN	Wigan
BRAGG						
1805	....	1750	1840	160873	CUL	Ireby
1800	1950	1650	1800	141372	DEV	Sandford
1840	1920	1700	1840	152587	ESS	Brightlingsea
1888	1938	ALL	1888	152641	KEN	Woolwich
1855	1870	1855	1900	167002	MDX	Islington
1792	1992	1700	1792	115096	SOM	Yeovil
BRAHAM						
1902	1920	1850	1992	128473	LND	South East
BRAID						
1829	1831	....	....	127140	LKS	New Monkland
BRAIDFORD						
1845	1855	1845	1855	108871	BDF	Luton
....	....	1800	1845	108871	BEW	???
1870	1970	....	....	108871	DUR	North West
....	....	1700	1800	108871	NBL	North
1860	1880	....	....	108871	NBL	Newcastle Upon Tyne
1855	1860	1855	1860	108871	STS	South
BRAIDWOOD						
1850	1992	....	....	108898	LAN	Liverpool
1814	1992	ALL	1814	108898	LKS	Roberton
1814	1992	ALL	1814	108898	LKS	Wiston
BRAILEY						
1820	1950	1700	1850	160725	DEV	North
....	....	1800	1880	163791	LND	Marylebone
BRAILSFORD						
1797	1992	1851	1881	108901	SYK	Sheffield
BRAIM						
1800	1850	....	....	177474	YKS	Knottingley
BRAIN						
1687	1900	ALL	1900	131334	GLS	ALL
1840	1992	ALL	ALL	108928	GLS	Bitton
1740	1800	1600	1800	154342	GLS	Bitton
1840	1992	ALL	ALL	108928	GLS	Bristol
?	?	?	?	136395	GLS	Bristol
1860	1870	1858	1868	138398	HEF	Ross
1890	1915	1830	1890	104124	OXF	Banbury
?	?	?	?	136395	SOM	Bristol
1687	1900	ALL	1900	131334	WIL	ALL
1777	1840	1500	1777	108928	WIL	Ashton Keynes
1777	1840	1500	1777	108928	WIL	Leigh
BRAITHWAITE						
1896	1992	....	....	176362	OXF	Banbury
....	....	1750	1950	176362	WES	Kendal
1748	1846	1700	1850	123536	YKS	Bedale
ALL	1850	....	....	176362	YKS	Sedberg
BRAITHWATE						
1757	1871	1720	1871	162825	CUL	Melmerby
BRAKE						
1700	1847	1558	....	112968	DOR	Yetminster
1600	1900	1600	1900	152226	DOR	Yetminster
1820	1900	1600	1900	120677	SOM	St Georges
BRAKER						
1753	1808	1700	1753	174289	DOR	West Parley
1751	1791	1700	1751	174289	HAM	Christchurch
BRALIND						
....	....	ALL	ALL	147303	DEV	Paignton
....	....	ALL	ALL	147303	DEV	Torquay
BRAMALD						
1885	1895	....	....	110833	DBY	Matlock
1745	1885	....	....	110833	YKS	South
BRAMALL						
1720	1730	ALL	ALL	110833	DBY	Tideswell

Known From	Known To	Researching From	Researching To	Ref	Cty	Place
BRAMALL contd.						
1806	1820	ALL	....	120626	STS	Walsall
1713	1797	1720	1797	124826	WRY	Holmfirth
BRAMBLE						
1650	1992	1650	1992	136867	CON	Penzance
1891	1992	ALL	1891	175994	GLS	Coates
1797	1841	ALL	1797	175994	GLS	Siddington
1780	1804	ALL	1804	168718	LEI	Queniborough
1774	1830	1750	1830	179337	WIL	Chippenham
BRAMBLES						
1800	1880	1750	1900	131075	YKS	Muston
1840	1880	....	....	131075	YKS	Scarborough
BRAMFITT						
....	....	1800	1900	108936	DUR	Chester Le Street
....	....	1850	1900	108936	DUR	Houghton Le Spring
1850	1900	1800	1900	108936	DUR	Lumley
1900	1992	1850	1992	108936	DUR	Wheatley Hill
1900	1992	1850	1992	108936	DUR	Wingate
1790	1810	1750	1820	108936	DUR	???
1800	1900	ALL	1800	108936	YKS	Bradford
1800	1900	ALL	1800	108936	YKS	Leeds
1771	1885	1700	1775	176451	YKS	Otley
BRAMHALL						
1860	1956	1860	....	144827	DBY	Glossop
BRAMHAM						
1845	?	1820	1878	108944	NYK	Great Ayton
1850	1870	1850	1900	119938	YKS	Carlton
BRAMHILL						
1818	1958	1700	1992	134023	LIN	Eastoft
BRAMLEY						
1780	1900	1700	1780	145645	LEI	North
1791	1992	1750	1791	137944	LEI	Braunstone
....	....	1500	1992	161470	LEI	Wymeswold
1780	1845	1780	1845	153621	NYK	Nidderdale
1754	1776	ALL	1754	154563	YKS	Fewston
1702	1730	1670	1700	156302	YKS	Ripon
1720	1770	1680	1720	130877	YKS	Sutton Bonington
BRAMMAGE						
....	....	ALL	ALL	109231	ALL	Name Study
BRAMMAR						
1850	1950	1700	1850	122424	STS	Stoke Upon Trent
BRAMMEL						
1856	....	1700	....	132128	KEN	Graves Wilton
BRAMMER						
1792	1848	1750	1800	170348	DBY	Whitwell
1755	1854	....	....	132381	DUR	Heworth
1755	1932	....	....	132381	LKS	Glasgow
BRAMPTON						
1757	1900	1700	1757	176257	BDF	Leighton
1740	1790	1700	1740	121339	NYK	Wensley
1180	1350	1066	1240	124974	RAD	Stanage
1100	1350	1066	1240	124974	SAL	Brampton
1100	1130	1066	1240	124974	SAL	Kinlet
BRAMSKILL						
1785	1810	1720	1820	168912	LAN	Wigan
BRAMWELL						
1870	1880	1750	1870	125431	ANT	Belfast
1797	1816	1800	1816	113484	FIF	Inverkeithing
?	?	?	?	109975	LND	Kings Cross
1820	1861	1820	1861	113484	PER	Perth
1700	1767	1500	1800	167843	YKS	Kirby Ravensworth
1840	....	1800	1900	102164	YKS	Sheffield
BRAN						
1815	1850	1700	1815	164267	KEN	Wittersham
BRANCH						
1750	1770	1730	1750	140317	ESS	Fingerinhoe
1860	....	ALL	1860	154091	MDX	Hackney
1725	1824	1633	1730	117773	MDX	Whitechapel
1725	1824	1633	1730	117773	SRY	Peckham Rye
BRANCHETT						
1824	1992	....	1992	171441	KEN	Dunkirk
BRAND						
1730	1760	....	....	165999	ESS	Chapel
1683	1910	1556	1683	118079	ESS	Chrishall
1683	1910	1556	1683	118079	ESS	Elmdon
1730	1760	....	....	165999	ESS	Great Tey
1843	1904	1800	1843	102849	ESS	Maldon
1795	1816	1700	1800	117315	KCD	Glenbervie
1780	1870	1700	1780	114871	KEN	Beckley
1870	1880	....	....	114871	KEN	Speldhurst
1789	1789	ALL	1789	168742	NTT	Balderton
1742	1835	1700	1835	103160	SRY	Walton On Thames
BRANDON						
1300	1600	1300	1600	154881	ALL	ALL
BRANDON contd.						
1871	1992	1800	1871	167932	BDF	Leighton Buzzard
1858	1992	1850	1992	159018	BRK	Windsor
1850	1950	ALL	ALL	108960	LND	East
1821	1900	1821	1900	108952	LND	Shoreditch
BRANDRYTH						
....	....	ALL	1780	178403	DBY	Smalley
BRANDSON						
1680	1680	1600	1680	155276	SFK	Bucklesham
BRANFOOT						
1750	1992	ALL	ALL	108979	ALL	ALL
BRANNAN						
?	?	?	?	112437	LKS	Salsburgh
BRANNEN						
1841	1864	1700	1841	117595	KEN	Canterbury
BRANSBY						
1770	1830	1700	1770	147710	NFK	Norwich
1685	1746	1500	1750	148121	NFK	Shotesham
1685	1798	1600	1800	148121	NFK	???
BRANSCOMBE						
1825	1830	1700	1840	153826	DEV	???
BRANSGROVE						
1682	1792	ALL	1861	156582	MDX	Hanwell
BRANSON						
1740	1992	1600	1740	108995	HUN	Sawtry
BRANSTON						
1760	1840	1700	1900	126179	HAM	Harbridge
1815	1820	1700	1815	157767	LND	???
BRANT						
1750	1900	1750	1917	109002	BRK	Arborfield
1839	1880	1789	1900	109002	BRK	Binfield
1850	1872	1830	1872	151599	BRK	Bracknell
1839	1880	1789	1900	109002	BRK	Warfield
1750	1900	1750	1917	109002	BRK	Wokingham
1800	1850	1700	1800	172898	LND	Holborn
1834	1861	....	1860	171646	WOR	Norton Juxta Kempsey
1794	1956	ALL	1794	109029	WOR	Pershore
1794	1956	ALL	1794	109029	WOR	White Ladies Aston
BRASELL						
1731	1875	....	....	117803	BKM	Hogshaw
1852	1863	....	....	117803	SRY	Barnes
BRASH						
1818	1992	1750	1850	141739	LKS	Glasgow
1814	1960	1710	1814	134473	MDX	Lambeth
1814	1960	1710	1814	134473	SRY	Lambeth
BRASHEAR						
....	....	ALL	ALL	166014	ALL	Name Study
BRASIER						
?	?	?	?	169544	HAM	Winslade
1803	....	1700	1803	178608	KEN	Stone
1899	1950	1800	1899	169803	LND	Hackney
BRASS						
....	....	ALL	ALL	109037	ALL	Name Study
1855	1992	....	....	101990	OKI	Sandwick
1745	1910	1700	1745	129038	WES	North
BRASSAR						
1661	1940	....	....	128996	CAM	Thorney
BRASSEY						
1851	1992	1700	1850	158755	CHS	Bruerton
BRASSINGTON						
1824	1846	1750	1824	147850	LND	Mary Le Bone
1824	1846	1750	1824	147850	LND	St Pancras
1806	1842	1780	1806	156426	STS	North
1857	1877	1750	1860	169234	STS	Wrinehill
BRATBY						
1851	1992	....	....	121290	DBY	Derby
1711	1851	....	....	121290	DBY	Holland Ward
1771	1789	1650	1770	131245	DBY	Sandiacre
1789	1881	1800	1910	131245	LEI	ALL
1871	1871	1850	1900	131245	NTT	ALL
1900	1960	1900	1960	131245	WAR	ALL
BRATFIELD						
ALL	1716	....	....	170178	WIL	Bishops Cannings
....	....	1750	1810	109746	WOR	Tardebigge
BRATFORD						
....	1723	?	1723	128910	WAR	Bulkington
BRATLEY						
....	....	ALL	ALL	109916	ALL	Name Study
BRATT						
1550	1950	1550	1950	148857	CHS	ALL
1860	....	1800	1900	143758	WAR	Kimmerston
BRAUND						
1750	1992	1750	1850	106593	DEV	North West

Known From	To	Researching From	To	Ref	Cty	Place
BRAUNSTON						
1778	1778	ALL	ALL	171816	NTH	Duston
BRAVANT						
1803	1803	1770	1840	124974	HAM	Lambourne
BRAVIN						
1650	1992	1600	1992	109045	ALL	???
BRAWLEY						
?	?	?	?	159913	SOM	???
BRAWN						
1802	1992	1700	1905	109053	CON	Lezant
1667	1801	....	1850	155055	GLS	Sandhurst
1562	1900	1560	1900	148156	NTH	Grendon
BRAXTON						
1820	1840	ALL	1820	150983	HAM	Portsea
BRAY						
1794	1876	1800	1880	173762	BRK	Inkpen
1765	1843	1600	1765	149888	BRK	Radley
1841	1875	1790	1875	130877	CON	ALL
1800	1992	1700	1800	177520	CON	Altarnum
1740	1992	1600	1730	163562	CON	Bodmin
1791	1992	1700	1791	161446	CON	Budock
1791	1992	1700	1791	161446	CON	Falmouth
1630	1850	1630	1992	109088	CON	Gwennap
1812	....	1812	....	123099	CON	Mullion
1826	....	1826	....	123099	CON	Roseworthy
1600	1992	1500	1992	133450	CON	S Gennys
1800	1883	1700	1992	137448	CON	Sellan
1215	1630	1215	1630	109088	CON	St Cleer
....	....	1640	1992	173592	CON	St Gennys
1842	1878	1800	1992	102407	CON	???
1790	1992	1700	1790	141348	DEV	North
1820	1860	1820	1860	109088	DEV	Bere Alston
1780	1992	1600	1780	161543	DEV	Cullompton
1786	1820	1700	1820	121886	DEV	Plymouth
....	....	1800	....	161543	DOR	Bridport
1700	1700	1600	1800	162620	HEF	???
....	....	1600	1800	103888	IRL	???
1840	1992	1600	1840	109061	KEN	East
1840	1992	1600	1840	109061	KEN	Medway
1890	1918	1837	1918	144525	KEN	St Margarets
1815	1840	1800	1840	147974	LEI	Lutterworth
1832	1900	1600	1900	176133	LIN	Lincolnshire
1799	1807	1770	1830	102075	LND	West
....	....	1800	1900	117714	LND	West
1826	1992	1650	1826	154660	LND	Bethnal Green
1826	1847	1700	1850	154660	LND	Stepney
1816	1820	1700	1820	154660	LND	Westminster
1886	1925	....	....	139831	MDX	Fulham
1800	1870	1700	1800	128090	MDX	Harefield
1866	1900	....	....	139831	MDX	Notting Hill
1720	1750	1700	1750	147974	MDX	St Martin At Fields
1829	1946	1750	1915	163740	MDX	St Marylebone
1833	1833	1750	1833	156914	MGY	Churchstoke
1800	1899	ALL	ALL	146633	NTH	ALL
1573	1837	....	....	139831	NTH	Brixworth
1828	1864	....	....	139831	NTH	Northampton
....	....	ALL	ALL	115231	SFK	Bury St Edmonds
....	....	1828	1992	161543	SRY	Rotherhite
1728	1803	1675	1760	129356	SSX	Hellingly
1750	1800	1700	1850	123722	WIL	Bradford On Avon
1820	1930	1800	1950	143839	WIL	Bradford On Avon
1800	1899	ALL	ALL	146633	WIL	Gt Bedwyn
1830	1970	1700	1830	168726	WIL	Melksham
1840	1858	1800	1870	137561	WOR	Bewdley
1632	....	1600	1660	170348	YKS	Almondbury
1760	1840	1650	1860	122602	YKS	Hinley
BRAYBAN						
1820	?	ALL	1820	134805	SXE	???
BRAYBROOK						
1876	1902	ALL	ALL	143529	BDF	Ampthill
....	....	1600	1850	134546	BDF	Bletsoe
....	....	1600	1850	134546	BDF	Sharnbrook
....	....	1600	1850	134546	BDF	Souldrop
BRAYLEY						
1820	1950	1700	1850	160725	DEV	North
BRAYN						
1920	1992	1700	1992	121150	LEI	Lutterworth
BRAYNE						
1761	1800	1750	1992	122211	SRY	Lambeth
1830	1890	1700	1992	122203	WAR	Hockley Heath
1830	1890	1700	1992	122203	WAR	Stratford
1885	1930	1700	1992	122203	???	Birmingham
BRAYSHAW						
1822	1862	1700	1900	102660	WRY	Idle
BRAYSHAW contd.						
1822	1862	1700	1900	102660	WRY	Thackley
1777	1898	1600	1992	102520	YKS	Idle
BRAZELL						
1570	1992	1570	1992	109096	ALL	ALL
1800	1860	1700	1860	109525	CMN	Llannon
BRAZIER						
1703	1901	1586	1703	102512	BDF	Milton Bry
1723	1770	1723	....	115576	BRK	Cheveley
1773	1800	1700	1851	126381	ESS	North
1823	1871	1700	1823	160709	LND	Westminster
....	1700	....	....	174564	SSX	???
1820	1850	1700	1900	113492	WIL	South
....	....	1900	1992	122963	WMD	Birmingham
BREA						
1500	1540	1480	1500	102571	CON	Paul
BREACH						
1876	1881	1876	1992	172596	CON	Newlyn St Peters
1878	1902	1878	1992	172596	SFK	Lowestoft
1850	1880	1800	1850	136522	SSX	Pevensey
BREADNER						
1834	1850	1830	....	156019	LAN	Liverpool
1851	1937	....	....	156019	LAN	Manchester
BREADON						
1885	1992	1885	1920	124826	LAN	Manchester
1847	1992	1847	1911	124826	TYR	Fivemiletown
BREADY						
1740	1800	1600	1800	154342	GLS	Stapleton
BREAKER						
1794	1808	1500	1800	174270	DOR	West Parley
1747	1802	1500	1800	174270	HAM	Christchurch
BREAKS						
1851	....	1820	1900	179078	LAN	Lancaster
1737	....	1650	1800	179078	WES	Kirby Lonsdale
1830	1992	1830	1992	179078	YKS	Bolton By Bowland
BREAKSPEAR						
1700	1800	1800	1800	141682	GLS	Bledington
BREALEY						
....	....	ALL	ALL	175668	ALL	ALL
1680	1850	ALL	ALL	175668	DBY	ALL
1800	1920	ALL	ALL	175668	STS	ALL
BREAREY						
1599	1992	1500	1992	154784	YKS	ALL
BREARLEY						
1778	1848	1650	1778	134015	LAN	Rochdale
1760	1992	1485	1760	109118	WYK	Elland
1854	1992	1750	1860	135623	YKS	Elland
1815	1992	1700	1815	100757	YKS	Halifax
1780	1800	1760	1780	159573	YKS	Halifax
....	....	....	....	127272	YKS	Stocksbridge
1903	1975	....	....	149497	???	Birmingham
BREAY						
....	....	ALL	1850	166499	CON	St Gluvias
BRECHIN						
1860	1900	1700	1860	123986	DNB	Cumbernauld
1862	1892	1840	1900	151106	LKS	Old Monkland
....	....	1850	1900	145637	MLN	Edinburgh
BRECK						
1756	1855	1600	1855	148482	OKI	Birsay
BRECKELL						
1802	1992	1770	1802	123706	LAN	Liverpool
BRECKON						
....	....	ALL	ALL	101443	ALL	Name Study
1720	1973	ALL	ALL	101443	ALL	ALL
1814	1900	1700	1814	148806	NYK	Egton
1740	1830	1550	1740	150843	YKS	Danby In Cleveland
BREE						
1796	1938	....	....	151548	NTH	Long Buckby
1803	1817	....	1881	131229	SRY	Camberwell
1725	1734	....	1881	131229	STS	Hamstall Ridware
1621	1700	....	1881	131229	WAR	Hatton
BREED						
1750	1930	1600	1930	147710	HRT	ALL
BREEDEN						
1750	1890	1700	1750	172898	LND	Southwark
BREEDON						
1620	1950	1600	1900	124974	BRK	Pangbourne
1663	1708	1600	1725	124974	BRK	South Moreton
1808	1848	1750	1850	172251	NTT	Southwell
BREEN						
1780	1900	1780	1900	120995	SOM	Stoke Lane
BREENS						
....	1700	1650	1700	161357	ESS	Great Easton

Known From	To	Researching From	To	Ref	Cty	Place
BREES						
....	....	1823	1850	176893	MGY	Llangurig
....	....	1823	1850	176893	MGY	Llanidloes
1802	....	1750	1841	176877	MON	Llangurig
BREESE						
1790	1992	....	1832	138320	MON	Llanbrynmair
1785	1851	1600	1785	165298	WIL	ALL
BREEZE						
1857	1878	1800	1900	142360	BRK	Reading
1865	1897	1861	1897	176877	HEF	Kington
1821	?	ALL	ALL	109126	MDX	Bethanl Green
....	....	ALL	ALL	109126	NFK	ALL
1713	1753	....	1713	151688	NFK	East Ruston
1830	1847	1750	1847	118192	NFK	Sidestrand
1856	1992	1700	1856	154164	NFK	Terrington St Clements
1826	1854	1800	1881	176877	RAD	Llanddewi
BREGAZZIE						
1865	1900	....	....	140201	MDX	London
1831	1865	1800	1865	140201	NTT	Nottingham
BREHONY						
....	1960	....	....	151963	SLI	???
BRELLISFORD						
1750	1992	....	....	109134	ALL	ALL
BRELSFORD						
1788	1850	1788	1800	130567	CHS	Stockport
BREMNER						
1810	1820	1700	1810	109142	ABD	Auchterless
1700	1900	1750	1900	145467	ABD	Glenbuchat
1860	1920	1860	ALL	171530	ANS	Arbroath
1870	1900	1855	ALL	171530	ANS	Carnoustie
1750	1940	1750	1940	126500	BAN	Wick
1730	1950	....	....	126497	CAI	Wick
1796	1800	ALL	1900	171530	FIF	Crail
1804	1860	ALL	ALL	171530	FIF	Peat Inn
1830	1881	ALL	1900	171530	FIF	St Andrews
1850	1880	1800	1900	153877	GLS	Coleford
1850	1880	1800	1900	153877	GLS	Forest Of Dean
1747	1992	....	....	128643	OKI	Westray
BRENCHLEY						
1764	1992	1450	1764	109169	KEN	Charing
1600	1992	....	....	117854	KEN	Charing
1843	1992	1700	1843	162000	KEN	Medway
....	....	1800	1950	162000	KEN	Swale
1668	....	....	1700	171441	KEN	Wormshill
1900	1992	....	....	117854	YKS	Leeds
BRENCHLY						
1764	1992	1450	1764	109169	KEN	Charing
BRENDON						
1648	1714	1600	1800	134562	DEV	North
BRENNAN						
1852	1873	1780	1850	155098	AYR	Kilmarnock
1834	1863	1750	1880	100439	DOW	Hillsborough
1834	1992	1700	1834	109177	FER	Enniskillen
1900	1920	1800	1910	122475	IRL	ALL
1879	1992	1800	1900	122475	KEN	Woolwich
1750	1800	ALL	1992	170909	KIK	Castlecomer
1890	1900	1850	1890	135658	LAN	Lancaster
....	....	1800	1890	138614	LAN	Liverpool
....	....	1800	1940	139203	LAN	Manchester
BRENNAND						
....	....	ALL	1850	147109	LAN	Bowland
1839	1920	....	....	147109	LAN	Chipping
1690	1800	ALL	1880	123048	WRY	Slaidburn
....	....	ALL	1850	147109	YKS	Bowland
BRENT						
1700	1775	....	....	106240	DEV	Plymouth
1838	1883	1700	1838	165859	LND	???
1838	1883	1700	1838	165859	MDX	???
BRENTLEY						
1920	1992	ALL	ALL	101494	ALL	ALL
BRENTNALL						
....	1640	ALL	1640	134511	NTT	Krikby In Ashfield
BRENTON						
1775	1992	1700	1775	140473	CON	Fowey
1855	1929	1700	1855	173886	CON	St Columb Mincer
1803	1851	ALL	1837	101362	CON	St Columb
BRERETON						
?	?	?	?	169811	CHS	Birkenhead
?	?	?	?	169811	CHS	Holt
?	?	?	?	169811	CHS	Malpas
1830	1992	1100	1992	125520	CHS	Stanleybridge
1840	1900	1840	1900	134597	CHS	Stapeley
1770	1845	1700	1850	134597	CHS	Wybunbury

Known From	To	Researching From	To	Ref	Cty	Place
BRETBY						
1711	1851	....	....	121290	DBY	Holland Ward
BRETON						
....	....	1600	1706	150150	NTH	Naseby
BRETT						
1724	1940	....	....	128996	CAM	Thorney
1802	1821	1750	1820	102717	ESS	Berden
1809	1877	1600	1809	159239	ESS	Colchester
1600	1800	1600	1800	114529	ESS	Tilbury Juxta Clare
1782	1793	1782	1881	156647	HAM	Niton
1821	1870	1820	1900	102717	HRT	Little Hadham
1820	1920	1700	1992	122742	IOW	Shanklin
1820	1920	1700	1992	122742	IOW	Wentnor
1890	1992	....	1900	147818	LND	East
1821	1963	ALL	ALL	175005	MDX	London
1854	1992	....	....	122564	NFK	Gt Yarmouth
1726	1808	....	....	122564	NFK	Itteringham
1846	1854	....	....	122564	NFK	Norwich
1639	1701	1528	1639	122564	NFK	Salle
1730	1776	ALL	1776	129283	NFK	St Ibbard
1820	1895	1750	1820	164860	SFK	Clopton
1600	1800	1600	1800	114529	SFK	Stoke By Clare
1814	1992	1750	1960	166898	SLI	Dromore
BRETTEL						
1780	1800	1700	1992	167592	CHS	Northwich
1800	1830	1700	1992	167592	STS	Burslem
1800	1850	1800	1992	167592	STS	Potteries
1700	1850	ALL	1800	141305	WOR	ALL
BRETTELL						
1639	....	....	1640	160873	STS	Kingswinford
1639	....	....	1640	160873	WOR	Old Swinford
BRETTON						
....	....	1800	1900	102318	ESS	West
BREW						
1862	1910	ALL	ALL	112275	SAL	Central
BREWARD						
....	....	ALL	ALL	109185	ALL	Name Study
1850	1900	1800	1850	152471	LEI	Leicester
BREWER						
1798	1861	1700	1798	144177	CON	Padstow
1828	1867	1700	1828	173886	CON	St Columb Mincer
1860	1992	1700	1860	109193	CON	St Eval
1864	1938	1800	1864	128368	DEV	Teignmouth
1731	1900	1500	1900	170216	DOR	ALL
1808	....	1750	1850	109894	DOR	Bere Regis
1765	1780	1700	1800	105333	DOR	Cranborne
1700	1730	1500	1800	170933	DOR	Edmondsham
1823	1883	1800	1823	127116	DOR	Whichampton
1839	1919	1600	1839	178101	DOW	Waringstown
1916	....	1850	1916	113352	ESS	Chelmsford
....	....	....	....	109207	ESS	???
1731	1900	1500	1900	170216	HAM	ALL
1790	1992	1700	1992	170933	HAM	New Forest
1725	1848	1700	1880	105333	HAM	Ringwood
1850	1940	ALL	1920	108642	KEN	Dover
1814	1881	1600	1814	169595	LIN	Lissington
1823	1992	1770	1823	113719	LIN	Normanby By Spital
....	....	ALL	ALL	174033	MDX	Edmonton
1715	1778	....	....	114669	SFK	Rendham
....	....	1550	1750	130591	SOM	Brompton Ralph
....	....	1750	1800	130591	SOM	Lydeard St Lawrence
1868	1980	....	1868	106100	SOM	Wells
1792	1920	1700	1792	168173	SRY	Burstow
1792	1920	1700	1792	168173	SRY	Redhill
....	....	1650	1800	106461	WIL	ALL
1835	1850	ALL	ALL	154008	WIL	Avebury
?	?	?	?	168548	???	???
BREWERTON						
....	....	1800	1840	128732	ESS	N Aylesford
1864	1918	1700	1864	109223	LND	Hammersmith
1823	1992	1700	1823	161446	OXF	North Aston
BREWIN						
....	....	ALL	ALL	109231	ALL	Name Study
1880	1910	1750	1880	117153	CAM	Wisbeach
1732	1795	ALL	1732	147877	LEI	Ravenstone
1799	1822	....	....	163155	LEI	Stanton Under Bardon
BREWIS						
1800	1992	....	....	100633	DUR	???
1881	1900	1881	1900	124001	MDX	North London
1841	1880	1841	1881	124001	NBL	Newcastle
1800	1992	....	....	100633	???	Newcastle Upon Tyne
BREWSTER						
1800	....	1800	1834	109266	KEN	Maidstone

Known From	To	Researching From	To	Ref	Cty	Place
BREWSTER contd.						
1766	1923	ALL	1871	156310	LIN	Grantham
?	?	?	?	126306	LIN	Skegness
....	....	ALL	ALL	130850	LND	ALL
1840	1869	ALL	ALL	109266	LND	London
?	?	?	?	126306	NTT	Nottingham
1750	1800	1750	1800	162329	SFK	West
1768	1870	1700	1870	152110	SFK	Glemsford
1834	....	1834	1840	109266	SFK	Horningsheath
BREYMAYER						
....	....	ALL	ALL	141135	ALL	Name Study
1861	1958	1847	1861	141135	LAN	Manchester
BRIAN						
1763	1785	ALL	ALL	141615	NTH	Wilbarston
1770	1992	1600	1770	148059	SCT	ALL
1847	1992	ALL	1847	110000	WIC	Vale Of Avoca
BRIAND						
1750	1770	1700	1992	167592	MDX	London
1740	1750	1600	1992	167592	STS	Newcastle Under Lyme
BRIANT						
1660	1745	1500	1800	153354	CON	Cury
1811	1811	1700	1850	177881	KEN	Minster In Sheppey
1773	?	ALL	ALL	153516	SOM	Congresbury
1820	1900	1600	1900	120677	SOM	Pensford
....	1700	....	....	174564	SSX	???
1724	1992	1500	1992	109274	WIL	Shalbourne
BRIARD						
1692	1992	1550	1692	166480	GSY	ALL
1692	1992	1550	1692	166480	JSY	ALL
BRICE						
1650	1800	ALL	ALL	131873	DEV	Exeter
1812	1900	1837	1890	124001	HAM	Stockbridge
1892	1950	1900	1963	124001	KEN	Charlton
1820	1900	1700	1820	148342	LEI	Harston
1820	1960	1700	....	148342	LIN	Grantham
1883	1890	1880	1900	124001	SRY	South West
BRICK						
....	....	ALL	ALL	143340	IRL	Limerick
1813	....	1700	1800	136891	WLS	Montgomeryshire
BRICKEL						
1873	1936	1700	1873	138436	MDX	Shoreditch
1873	1936	1700	1873	138436	MDX	Whitechapel
BRICKELL						
1670	1750	1600	1750	174599	DOR	Motcombe
1870	1992	....	....	113018	DOR	Shaftesbury
1670	1880	1600	1800	174599	DOR	Shaftesbury
BRICKENDEN						
1776	....	....	1776	155667	KEN	Acrise
BRICKETT						
....	....	ALL	ALL	113468	ALL	Name Study
BRIDACK						
1700	1800	1600	1800	169617	NBL	Hexham
BRIDCUT						
1850	1930	1700	1880	146064	WOR	Birmingham
BRIDDICK						
1780	1940	1500	1800	169617	DUR	ALL
BRIDDON						
1830	?	ALL	ALL	107352	DBY	Crich
1800	?	ALL	ALL	107352	DBY	South Wingfield
BRIDE						
1806	1839	1770	1806	103365	KEN	Brompton
1839	1851	1851	1992	103365	KEN	Sheerness
BRIDEN						
1823	1943	1810	1823	120731	LND	Paddington
BRIDEOAKE						
1680	1910	1600	1700	155500	LAN	Leigh
1680	1910	1600	1700	155500	LAN	Manchester
BRIDER						
1810	1980	....	1810	156906	HAM	Portsmouth
1810	1980	....	1810	156906	HAM	Southampton
1828	1860	1750	1850	142999	LND	Lambeth
1800	1850	....	1850	156906	LND	???
?	?	?	?	156906	SRY	???
1860	1992	1860	....	156906	???	Newcastle On Tyne
BRIDGE						
1804	....	1750	1810	152110	CAM	Burwell
1673	1765	....	....	138401	CHS	Chester
1812	1872	....	....	173827	DBY	Newhall
1762	1847	....	....	138401	DEN	Eglwysbach
1650	1900	1500	1992	162620	DOR	Piddletrenthide
1820	1835	1780	1850	174912	ESS	Bradwell-On-Sea
1790	1992	1700	1790	151165	ESS	Rochford
1818	1851	1818	1851	116114	KEN	Ashford

BRI

Known From	To	Researching From	To	Ref	Cty	Place
BRIDGE contd.						
1841	1992	1750	....	110264	LAN	St Helens
?	?	?	?	135615	LAN	Turton
1780	1900	1780	1992	162620	LND	???
1840	1860	1800	1900	135283	NFK	Norwich
BRIDGEFORD						
1740	1800	ALL	ALL	137243	ABD	Kincardine O'neil
BRIDGEMAN						
....	....	1600	1750	128082	CON	East
1850	1900	1700	1850	156531	DEV	West
1886	....	ALL	ALL	177547	LND	St Giles
1886	1923	ALL	ALL	177547	MDX	St Giles
....	....	ALL	ALL	104884	WIL	ALL
?	?	?	?	167894	WIL	Little Somerford
BRIDGEN						
1790	1900	1770	1900	170097	STS	Whittington
BRIDGER						
1837	1851	ALL	ALL	166243	HAM	Bramshot
1837	1851	ALL	ALL	166243	HAM	Liphook
1861	1925	ALL	ALL	166243	SRY	Godstone
1797	1837	ALL	ALL	166243	SRY	Puttenham
....	....	ALL	ALL	172057	SSX	Ringmer
1841	1855	1770	1855	120561	SSX	Wisborough Green
BRIDGES						
1820	1928	1750	1820	141321	BRK	Abington
1800	....	....	1800	171441	BRK	Buckland
1820	1928	1750	1820	141321	BRK	Wooton
1780	1850	....	1780	110027	HAM	Droxford
1850	1850	1550	1850	102830	HUN	Peterborough
1880	1920	1880	....	109290	LKS	ALL
1625	1875	1550	1875	109290	NFK	Central
....	....	1800	....	109290	NFK	North West
1792	1992	1700	1800	117013	NFK	Flitcham
....	....	1700	1900	140627	NFK	Norwich
1850	1870	1800	1900	136867	NFK	Swaffham
1550	1700	....	....	164631	WAR	Alchester
....	....	ALL	1600	164631	WOR	South Littleton
1835	1875	1830	....	109290	YKS	South
....	....	1840	....	109290	YKS	Hull
BRIDGETT						
1750	1830	1600	1830	119172	STS	Dilhorne
BRIDGEWATER						
?	1792	....	....	134732	GLA	???
BRIDGFORD						
1769	....	ALL	1992	159174	DBY	Derby
1822	1882	1792	1882	147486	NTH	Chelveston
BRIDGLAND						
1880	1992	ALL	ALL	158798	KEN	West
1796	1887	1824	1887	103608	KEN	Kempsing
BRIDGMAN						
1720	1860	....	....	104132	WIL	Aldbourne
BRIDGWOOD						
1800	1900	1600	1800	109304	STS	North
BRIDLE						
1840	1992	....	....	101036	CHI	Guernsey
1800	1850	ALL	1850	101036	DOR	Lyme Regis
1795	1900	1700	1795	168351	LND	Westminster
....	....	1700	....	164038	WIL	ALL
1720	1850	....	1720	110027	WIL	Whiteparish
BRIENT						
1820	....	....	1820	155667	CON	Launceston
1820	....	....	1820	155667	CON	St Stephen
BRIERE						
1845	....	1700	1992	168637	LND	City
BRIERHURST						
1761	....	1700	1800	100129	LIN	Fulbeck
BRIERLEY						
1791	1952	....	....	116602	LAN	ALL
1775	1875	1775	ALL	104590	LAN	Bacup
....	....	1846	1860	162221	LAN	Bury
1820	1868	ALL	1820	162221	LAN	Heywood
1775	1875	1775	ALL	104590	LAN	Rochdale
1800	1992	1800	1992	110523	LAN	Rochdale
1820	1868	ALL	1820	162221	LAN	Rochdale
1775	1875	1775	ALL	104590	LAN	Whitworth
....	....	ALL	ALL	135968	LEI	ALL
1810	1810	1750	1810	176079	STS	Bilston
1747	1809	....	....	126276	WRY	Saddleworth
1500	1700	1500	1700	109347	YKS	Gisburn
1870	1992	1700	1900	109312	YKS	Huddersfield
1850	1870	....	....	109312	YKS	Saddleworth
1860	....	....	....	161136	YKS	Sheffield
BRIERS						
1800	1970	1750	1800	109703	YKS	Ecclesfield

Surname	Known From	Known To	Researching From	Researching To	Ref	Cty	Place
BRIGDEN							
	1847	1992	1650	1847	152544	KEN	Chiddingstone
	1750	1910	ALL	1750	109320	SSX	Cuckfield
BRIGG							
	1550	1950	....	....	108677	YKS	ALL
BRIGGES							
	1605	....	ALL	....	104515	LIN	Great Ponton
BRIGGS							
	1805	1813	1700	1750	143693	BKM	Hughenden
	1813	....	1700	1750	143693	BKM	Penn
	....	....	1650	1750	137405	CAM	Cottenham
	....	....	1650	1750	137405	CAM	Rampton.
	1723	1940	....	....	128996	CAM	Thorney
	....	....	1700	1800	116173	CUL	West
	1780	1890	1600	1800	113654	DBY	Denby
	1838	1992	ALL	1838	109339	DUR	Brandon
	1818	1881	ALL	1818	158445	DUR	Durham
	1699	1725	ALL	1699	154563	DUR	Teesdale
	1730	1910	1600	1730	102210	KEN	Great Chart
	1804	1882	1700	1940	110051	KEN	Northfleet
	1850	1992	1850	1992	109347	LAN	Accrington
	1750	1900	1750	1900	125237	LAN	Darwen
	1800	1880	1880	1992	162256	LAN	Darwen
	1700	....	1700	....	109347	LAN	Grindleton
	1830	1912	1750	1851	151912	LAN	Sabden
	1830	1915	ALL	ALL	171948	LAN	Scales
	1820	1918	1800	1820	137944	LEI	Desford
	1801	1866	1700	1800	143448	LIN	Grimsby
	1730	1840	1730	1860	117323	MDX	Acton
	1890	1992	1890	1992	147966	NFK	Norwich
	1681	1681	ALL	1681	115126	NTH	Brixworth
	1846	1865	1700	1880	115967	NTH	Tynemouth
	1830	1900	1800	1900	118540	NTT	Southwell
	1820	1880	1750	1820	159115	SRY	Newington
	1820	1880	1750	1820	159115	SRY	Walworth
	1856	1992	1856	1992	158011	STS	Burton On Trent
	1820	1840	1750	1820	160458	WRY	Heptonstall
	1720	1970	1720	1970	153621	WYK	Queensbury
	1769	1992	....	1769	176702	WYK	Queensbury
	1840	1900	1800	1900	155098	YKS	Batley
	1750	....	1700	1840	134589	YKS	Bilbrough
	1800	....	1800	....	109347	YKS	Gisburn
	1874	1989	1750	1874	174939	YKS	Harrogate
	1800	1900	1750	1900	116386	YKS	Leeds
	1770	1820	1750	1820	119717	YKS	No Frodingham
	1833	1992	1700	1832	105988	YKS	North Bierley
	1874	1893	ALL	1980	136891	YKS	South Bank
	....	....	?	?	115592	YKS	Wakefield
	....	....	ALL	1818	158445	YKS	???
BRIGHAM							
	....	....	1700	1900	179531	LND	ALL
	1720	1900	1700	1720	154873	NBL	Holy Island
BRIGHOUSE							
	1814	1850	1800	1850	145750	LAN	Aughton
BRIGHT							
	1800	1840	1800	1840	135429	DEV	Colaton Raleigh
	1760	1850	1600	1760	134090	DEV	Dolton
	1760	1830	1760	1830	107352	DEV	Langtree
	1760	1850	1600	1760	134090	DEV	Monachorum
	1830	1890	1830	1890	107352	DEV	Petrock
	1760	1850	1600	1760	134090	DEV	Zeal
	1783	1992	1700	....	106895	ESS	The Rodings
	1830	1992	1750	1830	154415	GLS	Westbury Upon Severn
	1700	1800	1600	1700	148792	HAM	North West
	....	....	1750	1850	120456	LND	???
	1850	1870	....	....	144371	LND	???
	1775	1811	1700	1775	169528	MDX	London
	1783	1879	1700	1780	130443	NTH	???
	1770	1830	1700	1770	177229	SAL	Bishops Castle
	1830	ALL	1830	1845	160164	SOM	Buckland St Mary
	1768	1856	1700	1860	113638	WIL	Ramsbury
	....	....	1785	1795	177229	YKS	Leeds
	....	....	1700	1820	132241	YKS	Saddleworth
BRIGHTLING							
	1900	1992	1763	1900	148075	ENG	Midlands
	1900	1992	1763	1900	148075	SRY	Garshalton
	1900	1992	1763	1900	148075	WLS	Abergavenny
BRIGHTLY							
	1806	1810	ALL	1806	168602	CAM	Littleport
BRIGHTMAN							
	1797	1992	1700	1797	146021	BDF	Little Barford
	1826	1935	....	....	172812	KEN	Sheerness
	1849	1890	1890	1992	109851	NBL	North Shields
BRIGHTMAN contd.							
	1796	1812	1750	1812	107360	NTH	Blisworth
	1723	1786	1694	1837	107360	NTH	Chapel Brampton
	1832	1870	1812	1880	107360	NTH	Long Buckby
	1666	1722	1660	1755	107360	NTH	Northampton
	1845	1874	1800	1900	125865	NTH	Northhampton
	1823	1829	1791	1860	107360	NTH	Wappenham
BRIGHTMAR							
	....	....	1874	1880	145270	LND	Marylebone
BRIGHTON							
	1830	1940	1830	1940	152668	LAN	Manchester
	1830	1940	1830	1940	152668	NFK	ALL
BRIGHTWELL							
	....	....	1800	1940	139777	MDX	London
	1844	....	1800	1900	110604	MDX	St Pancras
BRIGHTWEN							
	....	1730	1700	1731	128961	ESS	Coggeshall
BRIGHTY							
	1863	1881	1750	1862	131245	NFK	Norwich
BRIGNAL							
	1892	....	1892	....	161721	DUR	South Shields
BRIGNOLL							
	1601	1787	....	....	173916	YKS	???
BRIGSTOCK							
	1790	1992	1790	1850	116661	NTH	Weldon
BRILL							
	1800	1900	1800	1900	178047	BKM	Aylesbury
	1880	1890	1860	1900	142174	WRY	Leeds
BRILLISFORD							
	....	....	1700	1749	109134	SAL	???
BRIMBLE							
	1790	1980	ALL	ALL	153516	SOM	Chew Magna
	1808	1835	1700	1808	177075	SOM	Paulton
BRIMFIELD							
	1700	1900	1700	1900	114790	DEV	Ottery St Mary
BRIMMEL							
	1845	1867	1845	1867	157171	WOR	Claines
BRIMMELL							
	....	....	....	?	141216	GLS	Gloucester
BRIMMICOMB							
	1851	ALL	ALL	1851	116734	ALL	ALL
BRIMSON							
	....	....	ALL	ALL	109371	ALL	Name Study
	ALL	ALL	ALL	ALL	109371	ALL	ALL
	1851	1855	1820	1880	159964	DOR	Poole
	1881	1897	1860	1900	159964	HRT	Great Munden
BRIND							
	1855	1881	?	1855	111155	LND	Bow
	1798	1874	1794	1992	142735	WIL	Highworth
	1828	1881	?	1828	111155	WIL	Westbury
BRINDELL							
	1804	....	ALL	1800	115118	HRT	Great Amwell
BRINDLE							
	1784	1810	ALL	1784	126942	LAN	Chorley
	1810	1850	ALL	ALL	138886	LAN	Preston
	1800	1880	1880	1992	162256	LAN	Tockholes
BRINDLEY							
	1830	1850	ALL	1881	175757	DBY	Cheshire Boundary
	1855	1992	ALL	ALL	169315	DUR	East
	1822	1882	1700	1950	170054	SRY	Bermondsey
BRINDY							
	1812	1926	1600	1812	103853	NFK	Geldeston
BRINE							
	ALL	ALL	ALL	ALL	124206	ALL	ALL
	1714	1777	1679	1714	157511	DOR	Swanage
	1881	1980	1800	1900	124206	GLA	ALL
	1874	1915	1800	1900	124206	HAM	ALL
	1885	1940	1750	1885	125601	HAM	Bournemouth
	1881	1980	1800	1900	124206	SOM	ALL
BRINER							
	1841	1860	....	1841	131385	LND	Whitechapel
BRINGINSHAW							
	....	....	ALL	ALL	161934	ALL	Name Study
BRINGLOW							
	....	....	ALL	ALL	117757	ALL	Name Study
BRINICOMBE							
	1830	1900	ALL	ALL	141127	DEV	South
	1792	1992	1700	1792	128368	DEV	Ilsington
BRINING							
	ALL	....	1840	1880	135429	DEV	ALL
	1875	1992	1875	1992	109347	LAN	Accrington
	1700	....	1700	....	109347	LAN	Ellel
	1850	....	1850	....	109347	YKS	Bradford
	1825	....	1825	....	109347	YKS	Huddersfield

Known From	To	Researching From	To	Ref	Cty	Place
BRINING contd.						
1825	....	1825	....	109347	YKS	Sowerby
BRINKLOW						
1835	1992	1800	1835	176257	BDF	Eaton Bray
BRINKWELL						
1700	1800	1700	1800	152404	SSX	Wiston
BRINNING						
ALL	....	1840	1880	135429	DEV	ALL
1840	1900	1840	1920	135429	DEV	Exmouth
1840	1900	1840	1920	135429	DEV	Littleham
BRINSFORTH						
1700	1730	1650	1700	165662	YKS	Sheffield
BRINSLEY						
1790	....	ALL	ALL	174637	DOR	Beaminster
BRINT						
1840	1950	1750	1840	128538	ALL	ALL
BRIODY						
1910	1960	1800	1910	151793	DUB	Dunloughaire
BRION						
1793	1880	....	....	168890	BKM	High Wycombe
BRISBANE						
1866	1940	1800	1900	137758	LKS	Glasgow
1792	1793	ALL	1792	112887	MLN	Edinburgh
1793	....	....	....	112887	PER	Blairgowrie
1793	....	....	....	112887	PER	Perth
BRISBY						
1780	1830	1700	1780	102393	NYK	Hawnby
1780	1830	1700	1780	102393	NYK	Helmsley
BRISCALL						
1730	1843	1650	1730	150614	CHS	Middlewich
BRISCOE						
1800	1840	1700	1800	124133	CHS	Chester
1810	1880	1600	1880	126837	LAN	Liverpool
1839	....	....	....	144169	LAN	Liverpool
1864	1992	1800	1864	109398	SAL	Wellington
BRISLAND						
1850	1900	1839	1949	173215	GLS	ALL
....	....	1720	1992	173215	HEF	ALL
....	....	1720	1992	173215	IRL	ALL
BRISLEY						
1750	1900	....	....	154466	KEN	Borden
BRISON						
....	....	ALL	ALL	109401	ALL	Name Study
1784	1904	1700	1784	167533	GLS	Bristol
1776	1850	1700	1776	169242	HAM	Portsmouth
BRISSLEY						
1795	1840	1700	1840	134880	KEN	Elmsted
BRISTOL						
1806	1852	....	1806	101761	STS	Buslem
1806	1852	....	1806	101761	STS	Wolstanton
BRISTOR						
....	....	ALL	ALL	172413	BRK	Central
BRISTOW						
1740	1767	1650	1750	143693	BKM	Hughenden
1714	....	1690	1750	124796	BKM	Princes Risborough
1687	1767	1600	1687	167452	BKM	Princes Risborough
1861	1882	1841	1992	145009	CON	Liskeard
1756	....	....	....	164038	ESS	Wilmington
1775	1970	1600	1850	123293	GLS	Tetbury
1600	1870	....	....	103837	LIN	ALL
1805	....	ALL	....	104515	LIN	Ruskington
1880	1992	1800	1880	147230	LND	Southwark
1824	1956	....	1824	164321	MDX	East London
1813	1850	1700	1813	153346	SAL	Bridgnorth
1760	1992	1500	1760	131830	SRY	Burstow
1760	1992	1500	1760	131830	SSX	???
1861	1882	1841	1992	145009	SSX	???
1750	1900	....	....	110124	WIL	Chippenham
1775	1970	1600	1850	123293	WIL	Chippenham
1784	1810	1750	1784	165530	WIL	Chippenham
....	....	1800	1900	171794	YKS	Airmyn
....	....	1800	1900	171794	YKS	Eastrington
....	....	1800	1900	171794	YKS	Goole
1871	1992	ALL	ALL	103837	YKS	Hessle
BRITAIN						
1790	1992	1650	1790	139769	WAR	Birmingham
BRITCLIFFE						
....	....	1750	1810	151912	LAN	Accrington
1810	1851	....	....	151912	LAN	Sabden
BRITEE						
1882	1890	ALL	ALL	100595	ESS	???
1882	1890	ALL	ALL	100595	LND	???
BRITNELL						
1777	1865	1600	1900	143693	BKM	Bledlow

Known From	To	Researching From	To	Ref	Cty	Place
BRITNELL contd.						
1568	1894	1500	1900	143693	BKM	Princes Risborough
1799	....	1700	1900	143693	BKM	West Wycombe
1604	1707	1500	1900	143693	OXF	Chinnor
1727	1756	1500	1900	143693	OXF	Crowell
BRITON						
1828	1971	1700	1828	169226	LKS	Glasgow
BRITTAIN						
1827	1850	ALL	1827	122823	BDF	Colmworth
1800	1850	....	....	155950	CAM	Laverington
1736	1940	....	....	128996	CAM	Thorney
1750	1800	1700	1750	155950	NTH	Peterborough
1813	1962	1800	1962	133280	WAR	Birmingham
1900	1992	....	....	161349	WAR	Birmingham
1728	1787	1278	1787	133280	WAR	Knowle
1800	1900	1750	1800	126179	WIL	Calne
1806	1992	1700	1992	128600	YKS	Sheffield
....	....	1800	1900	161349	YKS	???
BRITTAN						
1876	....	1800	1876	156132	ESS	Dagenham
BRITTEN						
1807	1850	1750	1810	147397	NTH	Moulton
....	....	1750	1850	170879	SOM	Saltford
1825	1992	....	....	131288	SOM	Shepton Mallet
BRITTIN						
....	....	1850	1950	134546	NTH	Chelveston
BRITTON						
1703	1870	1500	1771	102830	DBY	Derby
1800	1825	1600	1825	154342	DEV	Exeter
1800	1880	ALL	1800	141224	GLS	South
1833	1856	ALL	1906	168696	GLS	Bedminster
1811	....	1700	1816	126357	LET	Manor Hamilton
1828	1851	1750	1828	129445	NFK	Great Bircham
1800	1870	....	....	177393	YKS	Brayton
1865	1892	1700	1992	102377	YKS	Cawood
1700	1750	1650	1700	177393	YKS	Kirkby Wharfe
1750	1800	....	....	177393	YKS	Ryther
BRIXTON						
1870	1992	1870	1992	109436	GLA	Cardiff
BROAD						
....	....	1790	1800	133183	AVN	Bristol
1740	1992	....	....	109444	CON	East
1746	1833	ALL	1833	168718	CON	South East
1750	1900	1700	1900	136239	CON	Duloe
1631	1800	....	....	174319	CON	Gorran
1780	1850	1750	1870	171549	CON	Pelynt
1839	ALL	1700	1839	148628	CON	St Ives
....	....	?	?	104310	DEV	Merton
1830	1992	1700	1830	168084	GLS	Twerton
1880	1900	....	....	149667	HAM	Mottisfont
1845	1890	1550	1900	106119	IRL	Cork
1810	1840	1810	1840	128740	KEN	East Malling
1818	1892	1700	1900	172073	KEN	St Marys Platt
1790	1960	1790	1900	109452	KEN	Staplehurst
1827	1978	1700	1978	159271	LND	East
1856	1960	1700	1910	165476	LND	Bethnal Green
1820	....	....	....	161527	MDX	Paddington
1820	1900	1790	1820	161527	SOM	Bath
....	....	1800	1900	170879	SOM	Saltford
BROADBANK						
1818	1871	1700	1818	122793	SSX	Bosham
BROADBENT						
1807	1877	1770	1877	160636	CHS	Dunkinfield
1838	1919	....	1836	147672	DBY	Hadfield
1865	1881	1800	1865	108715	LAN	Ashton Under Lyme
1788	1870	ALL	1788	154563	LIN	Gainsborough
1815	1870	1740	1815	167932	LIN	Sedgebrook
1850	1992	1750	1850	109479	WRY	Delph
1802	1822	1780	1822	147338	WRY	Ripponden
1850	1992	1750	1850	109479	WRY	Saddleworth
1900	1980	1800	1900	109487	WYK	Elland
1900	1980	1800	1900	109487	WYK	Jaggergreen
1632	1992	1590	1630	109495	YKS	Saddleworth
BROADBRIDGE						
1783	....	1750	1850	154962	KEN	Whitstable
1820	1870	ALL	ALL	162205	SSX	Brighton
1838	1900	ALL	ALL	163112	SSX	Brighton
BROADFOOT						
1796	1841	1700	1841	178233	CMA	Whitehaven
1900	1951	1800	1951	151181	FLN	Prestatyn
1857	....	1800	1992	151181	GLA	Swansea
1876	1876	1850	1950	151181	LAN	Liverpool
BROADHEAD						
1776	....	....	1776	101761	WRY	Almondbury

Known From	To	Researching From	To	Ref	Cty	Place
BROADHEAD contd.						
1780	1992	1500	1800	109517	WRY	Wooldale
1600	1699	1600	1699	154601	WYK	Horbury
1792	1850	1750	1900	144622	YKS	Carlton
1700	1840	1700	1840	156027	YKS	Kirkburton
1700	1799	1700	1799	169781	YKS	Monk Bretton
BROADHURST						
1820	1845	1790	1820	139149	CHS	Macclesfield
1800	....	1750	....	177466	CHS	Marple
1843	....	1800	1900	139114	CHS	Stockport
1800	1930	ALL	ALL	122866	HAM	Silchester
BROADIST						
1796	1839	....	....	167479	GLS	Windrush
1839	1860	....	....	167479	OXF	Brize Norton
BROADLEY						
1844	1852	1800	1860	147338	ERY	Hutton Cranswick
1723	1903	1693	1723	139149	ERY	Kirkburn
1795	1992	1700	1795	161179	LAN	Blackburn
1795	1992	1700	1795	161179	LAN	Clayton Le Moors
1850	1992	1750	1900	144622	YKS	York
BROADWAY						
1780	1780	1780	1780	147575	DOR	Motcombe
1839	1992	1700	1839	113166	OXF	Watlington
1851	1912	....	....	130958	SOM	Road
1820	1900	....	....	143030	SOM	Rode
1840	1860	....	....	143030	WIL	North Bradley
BROADWOOD						
1640	1660	1500	1800	162620	NBL	Allendale
1675	1700	....	....	106798	SCT	Borders
1800	1900	1700	1992	106798	SRY	???
BROADY						
....	....	ALL	ALL	132179	ALL	Name Study
1800	1900	ALL	ALL	132179	ALL	ALL
1800	1900	....	....	132179	CHS	Appleton
1871	1900	....	....	132179	CHS	Stockton Heath
BROATCH						
....	....	ALL	ALL	109541	ALL	Name Study
BROCK						
1783	1992	ALL	ALL	109568	ALL	ALL
1843	1992	1700	1843	130257	DEV	Abbotsham
1783	1830	ALL	ALL	109568	DEV	Exbourne
1768	1819	ALL	ALL	165972	DEV	Okehampton
....	....	....	1770	130060	KEN	Winchelsea
....	....	1810	1850	109568	LND	Bishopsgate
1770	1870	ALL	1900	156310	NFK	Great Dunham
1781	1838	1800	1880	107573	NFK	Market ???
1770	1851	....	....	110965	OKI	ALL
1750	1850	1700	1920	156086	SOM	Lympsham
BROCKBANK						
1830	1910	1800	1992	130036	CUL	West Ward
1800	....	1700	....	116920	LAN	Colton
1832	1992	1832	1992	108391	MDX	London
1723	1900	1500	1850	108618	WES	Crosthwaite
1723	1900	1500	1850	108618	WES	Underbarrow
?	?	?	?	108391	WES	Underbarrow
1780	1810	1750	1850	130869	YKS	Hull
1798	1832	1790	1832	108391	???	Newcastle Upon Tyne
BROCKELL						
1780	1840	1700	1992	114596	YKS	Bellerby
BROCKELSBY						
1833	1893	ALL	1992	179205	LIN	Boston
BROCKENSHIRE						
1670	1800	1550	1850	133450	CON	Central
1750	1800	1600	1750	165549	CON	Roche
BROCKET						
1600	1685	1500	1600	154881	HRT	ALL
BROCKHURST						
1546	1580	1500	1580	102830	WAR	Tanworth
BROCKLEBANK						
1871	1881	1861	1900	116173	AGY	Beaumaris
1870	1890	1850	1920	116173	CHS	Birkenhead
1820	1900	1700	1820	130230	CMA	Dalton In Furness
1718	1860	1600	1720	116173	CUL	West
1820	1900	1700	1820	130230	LAN	Dalton In Furness
1870	1890	1850	1920	116173	LAN	Liverpool
1719	1805	1600	1719	152196	LAN	Torver
1820	1880	....	....	133329	LIN	Waltham
1790	1820	1600	1790	133329	YKS	Anlaby
1780	1810	1750	1850	130869	YKS	Hull
BROCKLEHURST						
1837	1980	....	....	132136	CHS	Allostock
1820	1920	1800	1992	128384	CHS	Macclesfield
BROCKLESBY						
1790	1830	1750	1850	123145	LIN	Halton Holegate
BROCKLESS						
1580	1980	....	....	137146	BKM	???
1580	1980	....	....	137146	NTH	???
1580	1980	....	....	137146	OXF	???
....	....	1750	1850	137146	???	Liverpool
BROCKMAN						
1884	1992	1700	1884	109576	DEV	Plymouth
....	....	1760	1800	161357	KEN	East
1724	1813	1650	1723	161357	KEN	Ash
1676	1837	....	....	161357	KEN	Birchington
1635	1800	....	....	161357	KEN	Folkestone
....	....	ALL	ALL	118400	KEN	Margate
1775	1847	....	....	161357	KEN	Margate
1860	....	....	1860	118400	KEN	Southborough
1836	1857	....	....	161357	SRY	Southwark
BROCKWAY						
....	1765	1700	1765	128961	HAM	Isle Of Wight
....	1765	1700	1765	128961	HAM	Ringwood
....	....	1600	1899	115975	WIL	East
....	....	1755	1830	107247	WIL	East Knoyle
BROCKWELL						
1818	1992	1750	1850	110604	KEN	Chatham
1820	1900	1840	1900	123021	KEN	Chatham
1853	1875	1840	1853	118281	MDX	Paddington
1830	1880	1700	1900	118281	SFK	Cavendish
BRODERICK						
1800	....	1750	1800	123870	IRL	???
....	....	1750	1850	163082	LND	Stepney
BRODHURST-HILL						
....	....	1850	1992	129550	CHS	Chester
BRODIE						
1845	1895	1800	1845	178896	ANS	Dundee
....	....	1500	1786	138614	CAI	Canisbay
1853	1880	1750	1992	124044	CAI	Dunnett
1686	1794	1686	1794	131881	FIF	Kirkaldy
1775	1811	?	1820	103934	LND	???
BRODRIBB						
....	....	ALL	ALL	140708	ALL	ALL
....	....	ALL	ALL	170240	ALL	ALL
1725	1900	ALL	ALL	140708	GLS	ALL
1816	....	....	....	124982	GLS	Berkeley
1725	1900	ALL	ALL	140708	SOM	ALL
1767	1900	ALL	ALL	140708	WIL	ALL
BROGAN						
1835	1835	1700	1835	146358	IRL	Donegal
1881	1897	1881	1900	146358	RFW	Langbank
BROGDEN						
1740	1900	1700	1900	110612	LAN	Clitheroe
1740	1900	1700	1900	110612	LAN	Manch
1731	1755	1650	1790	133574	YKS	Kirkby Overblow
BROKEHOUSE						
1750	1800	1700	1750	128368	LEI	Mountsorrel
BROKENSHA						
....	....	1600	1820	109584	CON	Mexagessey
1840	1950	1800	1860	109584	CON	Penrith
BROMAGE						
1831	....	....	....	158895	MDX	London
BROME						
1400	1800	1400	1700	100420	WAR	ALL
BROMELL						
....	....	ALL	ALL	109592	ALL	Name Study
BROMERLEY						
1675	....	1675	....	109347	LAN	Padiham
1600	....	1600	....	109347	LAN	Tottington
BROMFIELD						
1861	1894	....	....	135437	DEV	Churchstanton
1816	1851	....	....	135437	DEV	Clayhidon
1841	1841	....	....	135437	DEV	Culmstock
1775	1820	....	....	135437	DEV	Hemyock
1700	1900	1700	1900	114790	DEV	Ottery St Mary
1830	1890	1800	1830	155691	HAM	Ringwood
1800	1850	....	....	172634	HAM	???
1860	1900	1865	1895	172634	LAN	Liverpool
1860	1900	1865	1895	172634	LAN	Manchester
BROMHAM						
....	....	1750	1850	142751	WIL	Calne
1791	1812	1750	1850	142751	WIL	Corsham
BROMILEY						
1840	1910	1800	1840	108154	LAN	Bolton
BROMLEY						
1762	1850	ALL	1762	108642	BDF	Riseley
1762	1850	ALL	1762	108642	BDF	Souldrop
1883	1905	1750	1883	109606	CHS	Hyde Gee Cross
....	....	ALL	1875	173177	DBY	Winshull

Known From	To	Researching From	To	Ref	Cty	Place
BROMLEY contd.						
1860	1957	1830	1925	154334	EYK	Hull
1821	1940	1700	1821	139785	KEN	Gravesend
1823	1830	ALL	ALL	138886	LAN	Chorley
1821	1940	1700	1821	139785	LND	Woolwich
1876	1890	1850	1950	178799	MDX	Clerkenwell
1860	1972	1860	1972	107980	MDX	Hackney
1876	1890	1850	1950	178799	MDX	Holborn
1741	....	....	....	131210	SRY	Carshalton
1837	1915	1800	1836	166464	STS	Darlaston
1530	1992	1530	1992	162817	WAR	Stratford
1530	1992	1530	1992	162817	WAR	Warwick
1800	1850	1800	1900	154334	WYK	Goole
1765	1843	1750	1900	154334	WYK	Selby
1802	?	ALL	1800	165883	???	Chorley
BROMMAGE						
1718	1751	1650	1800	159905	WAR	Brailes
BROMWICH						
1817	1841	1700	1817	119075	LEI	Market Harborough
1750	1992	1600	1750	169676	WAR	Edgebaston
BRONNE						
1870	1940	1840	1940	124745	SRY	Southwark
BRONSON						
1691	1776	ALL	1992	115126	BKM	Langley Marrish
BROOK						
1860	1970	1700	1860	156450	AVN	Bristol
....	....	1750	1817	109673	CHS	Prestbury
1840	1900	1800	1900	147958	DEV	Bridestowe
1820	1920	1800	1850	166316	ESS	Chelmsford
1870	1992	....	....	153397	HAM	Eastleigh
1793	1807	1770	1807	144878	HRT	Rickmansworth
1691	1713	1700	1750	153192	LAN	Bolton
1841	1890	....	....	109622	LAN	Manchester
1898	1950	1850	1992	113476	LAN	Nelson
1840	1992	....	....	153397	SOM	Taunton
1840	1992	....	....	153397	SOM	Yeovil
1600	1680	....	....	165999	SSX	Angmering
1871	1992	....	....	165352	SSX	Hailsham
1834	....	....	1834	101761	WRY	Birstall
1790	1840	1750	1850	150304	WRY	Dewsbury
1790	1840	1750	1850	150304	WRY	Thornhill
1841	1992	1779	1841	109630	WYK	Birstall
1835	1870	1835	1870	149403	WYK	Wakefield
1784	1799	1730	1800	108510	YKS	Batley
1697	1992	1600	1700	109703	YKS	Ecclesfield
1748	1794	1700	1748	133760	YKS	Holmfirth
1818	1858	1793	1794	109622	YKS	Huddersfield
1825	....	....	....	123951	YKS	Huddersfield
1870	1899	?	1870	144800	YKS	Huddersfield
1788	1844	1768	1788	168521	YKS	Huddersfield
1635	1720	....	....	145688	YKS	Keighley
1830	1848	1800	1830	128368	YKS	Leeds
1840	1992	....	....	124354	YKS	Mirfield
1866	1981	1750	1866	175587	YKS	Morley
1798	1946	1700	1820	163740	YKS	Pontefract
1780	1900	1700	1780	149152	YKS	Sheffield
1796	1900	1600	1796	154172	YKS	Wyke
....	....	....	....	107433	YKS	???
BROOKBANK						
....	....	ALL	ALL	109665	ALL	Name Study
BROOKE						
1850	1900	1750	1850	128538	ALL	ALL
1808	....	....	....	109673	CHS	Macclesfield
1700	1800	1700	1800	144657	DEV	Hemyock
1695	1807	ALL	ALL	125121	ESS	Malden
....	....	1700	1770	154873	KEN	Marden
....	....	1700	1770	154873	KEN	Tonbridge
....	....	1845	1870	131962	LAN	Liverpool
1860	1900	1850	1992	165603	LND	Croydon
1870	1900	....	....	131962	LND	Highgate
....	....	1700	1770	131962	SRY	Caterham
1800	1860	1800	1992	165603	SRY	Warlingham
1804	1900	....	1804	101761	WRY	Almondbury
1741	....	....	1741	101761	WRY	Horbury
1700	1792	....	1700	101761	WRY	Huddersfield
1665	....	....	1665	101761	WRY	Wakefield
1848	1936	1820	1847	115495	YKS	Cleckheaton
1697	1992	1600	1700	109703	YKS	Ecclesfield
1678	....	1700	1750	153192	YKS	Elland
1675	....	1700	1750	153192	YKS	Fixby
1590	1669	1550	1669	128449	YKS	Hartshead
1737	1768	1700	1780	170348	YKS	Huddersfield
1725	....	1680	1750	170348	YKS	Kirkheaton
....	....	....	....	107433	YKS	???

Known From	To	Researching From	To	Ref	Cty	Place
BROOKER						
1700	1800	1750	....	175234	BRK	Blewbury
1868	1878	1860	1878	131563	GLS	Newland
....	....	ALL	1870	178403	HAM	???
....	....	ALL	ALL	118400	KEN	Hadlow
1875	....	....	1875	118400	KEN	Southborough
1700	....	1700	....	100536	LND	???
....	....	1871	1896	161357	SRY	Camberwell
1850	1935	?	?	108189	SRY	Charlwood
1851	1871	ALL	1992	125113	SRY	Charlwood
1780	1850	1500	1850	175463	SRY	Horley
1861	1871	....	....	161357	SRY	Oxted
1799	1992	1700	1799	176257	SRY	Rotherhithe
....	....	1871	1896	161357	SRY	Southwark
1835	1839	1800	1835	161357	SSX	East Grinstead
1711	1835	ALL	ALL	156140	SSX	Framfield
1832	1846	1700	1832	132543	SSX	Horsham
1745	1773	1700	1800	131563	SSX	Kirdford
1700	1992	1600	1700	148237	SSX	Lavant Chichester
1800	1881	1800	1992	131563	SSX	Lurgashall
1776	1881	1776	1992	131563	SSX	Northchapel
1780	1850	1500	1850	175463	SSX	Worth
1675	1706	ALL	1700	156175	SXE	Ninfield
1914	1928	1832	1914	132543	WAR	Birmingham
1821	1976	ALL	1821	100072	???	Wrestlingworth
BROOKES						
1790	1870	....	....	132225	CHS	Tattenhall
1840	1880	1750	1880	136840	GLS	Bristol
1903	1903	1850	1903	103640	HAM	Southampton
1791	1845	ALL	1791	178926	LEI	Enderby
1810	1858	1700	1850	163562	LND	Marylebone
1847	1870	1700	1870	119849	MDX	London
1875	1910	1800	1875	160156	NTH	Lutterworth
1814	1814	....	....	130877	NTT	Sutton In Ashfield
1680	1807	1650	1992	122211	SRY	Lambeth
1730	1910	1558	1730	153427	STS	Endon
1795	1840	1700	1900	173452	STS	Gornal
1790	....	1700	1900	159468	STS	Tipton
1829	1880	1800	1900	128929	STS	Whampton
1850	1900	ALL	ALL	150347	WAR	Birmingham
....	....	ALL	1820	167029	WIL	Savernake
?	?	1799	1869	117919	WOR	Old Swinford
1697	1992	1600	1700	109703	YKS	Ecclesfield
BROOKING						
....	....	ALL	ALL	109711	ALL	Name Study
ALL	ALL	ALL	ALL	166758	ALL	ALL
1656	1870	....	....	165999	CON	Stoke Climsland
1700	1820	1500	1840	105333	DEV	Buckland In The Moor
1700	1820	1500	1840	105333	DEV	Holne
1700	1820	1500	1840	105333	DEV	Ilsington
1700	1820	1500	1840	105333	DEV	Lydford
1828	....	ALL	1847	121436	DEV	Stokenham
1700	1820	1500	1840	105333	DEV	Widecombe In The Moor
BROOKLAND						
1800	1840	1700	1992	132799	BRK	Sutton Courtney
BROOKS						
1771	1839	1700	1771	123307	BRK	Chieveley
1711	1808	1690	1711	115819	BRK	Longworth
1746	1919	ALL	ALL	175005	CAM	West
1812	1992	1700	1812	145696	CHS	Stalybridge
1856	1924	1700	1924	162280	CHS	Stockport
1809	1826	1780	1851	113719	DBY	Ashover
1843	1992	1843	1992	113719	DBY	Chesterfield
....	....	1800	1850	148113	DBY	???
1813	1860	1700	1900	119202	DEV	Plymouth
1844	1844	1826	1846	124915	ESS	Danbury
1856	?	1800	1992	137294	ESS	Rettendon
1880	1992	1800	1992	137294	ESS	Stanford Le Hope
1834	1992	1700	1854	166987	HAM	???
1780	1900	1780	1900	129151	HEF	Eye
1780	1900	1780	1900	129151	HEF	Yarpole
1730	1788	1700	1850	179256	HRT	Wigginton
1795	1992	....	....	152765	IRL	Dublin
1854	1877	ALL	1992	125113	KEN	Birchington
1874	1904	1300	1950	152501	KEN	Chatham
....	....	....	....	153117	KEN	Maidstone
1900	1948	....	....	136948	KEN	Sydenham
1778	1992	ALL	1778	110000	LAN	Ainsworth
1815	1850	1700	1815	109681	LAN	Ashton Under Lyme
1812	1992	1700	1812	145696	LAN	Ashton Under Lyne
1774	1850	1600	1774	119822	LAN	Bolton
....	1872	ALL	ALL	129933	LAN	Liverpool

Known From	To	Researching From	To	Ref	Cty	Place
BROOKS contd.						
1840	....	1816	1840	147281	LAN	Manchester
1785	1974	?	1859	164976	LAN	Oldham
....	....	....	....	178926	LEI	Countesthorpe
1791	1845	ALL	1791	178926	LEI	Enderby
....	....	....	....	178926	LEI	Hisbands Bosworth
....	....	....	....	178926	LEI	Kilby
1760	1900	....	....	103721	LIN	Epworth
1863	1866	1750	1880	177970	LKS	North
1800	....	....	....	153117	LND	East
1874	1904	1300	1950	152501	LND	Battersea
1868	1900	ALL	ALL	136948	LND	Lambeth
1824	1865	1800	1880	173436	LND	Marylebone
1792	1884	....	1792	164321	MDX	East London
1830	1857	1800	1857	108391	MDX	London
1874	....	1500	....	110310	MDX	London
1800	1867	1750	1800	121037	MDX	Shoreditch
1946	....	1940	1950	163775	MON	Swansea
1710	1850	1700	1800	105627	NFK	Larling
1895	1917	1850	1930	170143	NTH	Great Creaton
....	1760	ALL	1760	134511	NTT	Tibshelf
1777	1798	1700	1800	159905	OXF	Chadlington
1790	1854	1750	1820	124648	OXF	Witney
1825	1861	....	....	116505	SFK	Hadleigh
1848	1855	1855	1871	116505	SFK	Lawshall
1803	1839	1803	1839	116505	SFK	Washbrook
1784	1828	ALL	ALL	153516	SOM	Bridgwater
1784	1828	ALL	ALL	153516	SOM	Kenn
1795	1992	....	....	152765	SOM	Nailsea
1788	....	....	....	148768	SRY	Lambeth
....	....	1600	1830	113085	SSX	Shipley
1820	1940	1750	1820	132640	SSX	Shipley
1862	1888	1700	1861	136735	STS	Wolverhampton
1711	1711	1550	1710	102830	WAR	Bickenhill
1828	1850	1700	1827	136735	WAR	Birmingham
....	....	1750	1850	142751	WIL	Calne
1791	1812	1750	1850	142751	WIL	Corsham
?	?	1799	1869	117919	WOR	Old Swinford
BROOKSBANK						
1826	1860	....	1826	125954	YKS	Bradford
BROOKSBY						
1730	1809	1650	1860	147958	LND	???
BROOM						
1759	1786	1759	1786	165999	AVN	Bristol
1809	1921	....	1809	131385	DEV	Topsham
1780	1820	1750	1850	171158	DEV	Uffculme
1808	....	ALL	1850	125466	ESS	Colchester
1840	1880	1800	1880	120219	WOR	Kidderminster
BROOMFIELD						
1795	1825	1760	1795	168912	DEV	Burlescombe
1853	1861	1770	1870	122327	DUB	Dublin
1870	1900	1870	1920	133922	HAM	Bramshaw
1790	1880	ALL	1790	167665	HAM	New Forest
1850	1868	1850	1992	151106	LEX	Mountrath
1847	1907	....	ALL	168912	SOM	Cheddon Fitzpaine
1847	1907	....	ALL	168912	SOM	Monkton
1800	1860	1800	1992	152943	SOM	Taunton
....	....	1700	1800	172871	SRY	Godalming
1708	1992	ALL	ALL	109746	WOR	Bromsgrove
BROOMHEAD						
1821	1900	1600	1900	176133	DBY	Derbyshire
1807	1807	1770	1833	174289	DBY	Hartington
1833	1950	1790	1833	174289	DBY	Monyash
1779	1850	1725	1779	105503	LIN	Horncastle
1650	1670	1600	1650	177393	NTT	South Wheatley
1590	1700	1550	1700	160849	NTT	Wheatley
1840	1890	1700	1840	148113	YKS	Rotherham
1830	1950	1850	1980	135801	YKS	Sheffield
BROOMING						
ALL	ALL	ALL	ALL	109754	CON	ALL
ALL	ALL	ALL	ALL	109754	DEV	ALL
BROPHY						
1800	1900	1700	1950	118680	LEX	???
BROSCH						
1850	1992	1850	1992	119989	ALL	???
BROSCOMBE						
1731	1972	....	1731	109762	WYK	Liversedge
BROSNAN						
....	....	1800	1900	109770	IRL	Kerry
1843	1874	....	....	117803	KER	Killeentierna
....	....	1900	1950	109770	???	Bristol
BROSTER						
1770	1992	ALL	1770	110000	CHS	Bollington
ALL	1650	....	....	110000	CHS	Bosley

Known From	To	Researching From	To	Ref	Cty	Place
BROSTER contd.						
ALL	1650	....	....	110000	CHS	Macclesfield
1821	1821	ALL	1872	143634	STS	Tamworth
BROTCHIE						
....	1828	ALL	1900	127000	OKI	South Walls
BROTHERIDGE						
1800	1900	1700	1900	128163	GLS	ALL
BROTHERS						
1700	1800	1700	1800	167924	BDF	Upper Gravenhurst
1700	1740	1700	1740	167924	HRT	Pirton
BROTHERTON						
1870	1880	1840	1870	109878	LAN	Burnley
1870	1880	1840	1870	109878	LAN	Habergham Eaves
1790	1825	1700	1790	155500	LAN	Leigh
1650	1950	1590	1700	105821	LAN	Pendle
1850	1881	1790	1850	138363	YKS	Dales
1806	1820	1750	1900	158976	YKS	Hampsthwaite
1832	1992	1600	1992	172863	YKS	Harrogate
BROTHWELL						
1810	1830	ALL	1830	151254	LIN	Scredington
BROTTON						
1680	1700	1600	1680	121339	NYK	Brotton
BROUGH						
1911	1975	1700	1911	172448	CHS	Macclesfield
1801	1830	ALL	1900	145734	CMA	West
1794	....	1750	1800	148121	DBY	???
1801	1881	1790	1800	108227	FIF	Strathmiglo
....	....	1837	1910	109797	LAN	Ardwick
....	....	1837	1910	109797	LAN	Manchester
1760	1800	....	....	150304	NRY	Lastingham
1860	1940	1700	1900	137731	STS	Biddulph
1837	1967	1841	1881	150304	WRY	Gildersome
1825	1834	....	....	150304	WRY	Rothwell
1700	1830	1700	1830	167924	YKS	Crambe
1545	1975	?	?	104329	YKS	???
BROUGHALL						
1760	1860	1600	1760	139203	MON	???
1756	1756	1700	1756	179116	SAL	Whitchurch
BROUGHAM						
....	....	ALL	ALL	166421	ALL	Name Study
1820	1970	1600	1820	166421	ALL	ALL
1539	1992	1600	1992	179450	ALL	ALL
BROUGHTON						
1855	1920	1700	1860	148962	CHS	Chester
1750	1820	1750	1820	154377	DBY	Chesterfield
....	....	ALL	ALL	105864	HAM	Portsmouth
1806	1887	1800	1900	176982	KEN	Teynham
1794	1840	....	....	118354	LAN	Salford
1759	1790	1600	1850	144703	LEI	East
1675	1719	ALL	ALL	141615	LEI	Gaulby
1770	1992	1770	1992	144703	LEI	Leicester
1800	1992	....	....	176125	LIN	Asterby
1800	1992	....	....	176125	LIN	Goulceby
....	....	1750	1850	105864	LND	ALL
1790	1860	ALL	1800	155853	NFK	Walsingham
1800	1900	1800	1900	154377	NTH	Peterborough
1865	1912	1851	1912	165441	SAL	Ruyton Xi Towns
1800	1850	1700	1800	116572	YKS	Bawtry
1750	1800	1700	1750	143243	YKS	Leeds
1800	1850	1700	1800	116572	YKS	Loversall
BROWELL						
1530	1824	1248	1530	109800	DUR	ALL
1538	1824	1480	1538	109800	NBL	ALL
1296	1595	1199	1296	109800	NBL	Warkworth
BROWHAM						
....	....	ALL	ALL	179450	ALL	Name Study
BROWN						
1830	1992	1755	1840	131792	ABD	Crathie
....	....	1700	1860	100838	ABD	Kintore
1792	1860	1700	1880	113107	ANS	Arbroath
....	....	1700	....	149187	ANS	Panbride
1865	1900	1600	1865	127507	ANT	Ballycor
1900	1935	ALL	1884	173045	ANT	Kells
1871	1875	1830	1854	146757	AYR	Ayr
1871	1875	1830	1854	146757	AYR	Fenwick
1591	1992	1500	1600	153656	AYR	Stewaton
1810	1880	1700	1810	118419	BAN	Forglen
ALL	....	....	....	150975	BDF	Biggleswade
1797	1830	1700	1800	179574	BEW	Berwick On Tween
1800	1992	....	1800	110027	BEW	Coldingham
1849	1851	1829	1851	119059	BKM	Brill
1840	....	1700	1850	143693	BKM	Fingest
1810	1836	1700	1850	143693	BKM	Hambleden
1726	1761	1850	1900	143693	BKM	Stokenchurch

Known From	To	Researching From	To	Ref	Cty	Place
BROWN contd.						
1834	1859	1700	1850	143693	BKM	West Wycombe
1744	1744	1700	1744	124974	BRK	Speen
1690	1900	1650	1900	102970	BRK	Welford
1835	1870	1800	1900	142360	BRK	White Waltham
1804	1865	1750	1900	126381	CAM	Castle Camps
1874	....	....	1874	101761	CAM	Sawston
1654	1940	....	....	128996	CAM	Thorney
1830	1919	ALL	1830	126942	CAM	Tydd St Giles
....	....	1800	1840	113514	CAM	???
1842	1873	1550	1890	147265	CHS	East
1840	1860	1750	1900	143189	CHS	Runcorn
1805	1859	1700	1805	152196	CMA	Egremont
....	....	ALL	ALL	141534	CMA	Whitehaven
1780	1890	....	....	174319	CON	Grampound
1824	1850	1824	1850	109819	CON	Hayle
1709	....	1850	1900	178845	CON	Redruth
1660	1708	1600	1750	153354	CON	Saint Gluvias
1718	1775	....	....	174319	CON	St Erme
1850	1900	1750	1850	100978	CON	Stratton
1800	1970	1700	1970	146293	CON	Stratton
1900	1961	ALL	1900	177482	CON	Tywardreath
1770	1820	1700	1850	138878	CUL	Egremont
1700	1800	1650	1850	138878	CUL	Rockcliffe
1814	....	ALL	ALL	105481	DBY	Duffield
1769	1790	ALL	1769	175080	DEV	Beer
1730	1850	ALL	1730	135143	DEV	Bideford
1846	....	1830	1855	142034	DEV	Dawlish
1741	1992	1500	1741	164798	DEV	Lifton
....	....	1880	1992	179213	DEV	Plymouth
1769	1790	ALL	1769	175080	DEV	Seaton
1400	1450	1400	1450	135429	DEV	South Molton
1820	1858	1821	1992	110876	DOR	Eastown
1880	1940	1850	1992	152226	DOR	Poole
1793	1850	1725	1850	152579	DOR	Preston
1856	1992	1600	1856	178101	DOW	Waringstown
1830	1899	....	....	111260	DUR	Darlington
....	1837	1780	1837	103322	DUR	Great Stainton
1843	1927	1538	1927	118893	DUR	Ireshopeburn
1848	1848	1700	1890	153001	DUR	Monkwearmouth
....	....	ALL	ALL	141534	DUR	Murton
1882	1992	....	1882	151270	DUR	Stanhope
1850	1992	1800	1850	115312	DUR	Sunderland
1825	1861	1800	1861	171425	DUR	Tanfield
1762	1762	ALL	1762	154563	DUR	Teesdale
1893	1900	1893	1900	118893	DUR	Waterhouses
1790	1930	1700	1790	132942	DUR	Whickham
1773	1773	ALL	1773	129283	ESS	Firstead
1900	1950	1900	1960	135925	ESS	Ford End
1840	....	....	....	162833	ESS	Hankwell
1917	....	1900	1992	117609	ESS	???
1540	1750	1450	1540	109959	EYK	Beeford
1815	1815	ALL	1820	113611	EYK	Hull
1840	1846	1750	1850	171662	FIF	Cupar
1750	1800	....	....	130915	FIF	Kilconquhar
1820	....	ALL	ALL	130508	FIF	Pittenweem
1700	1800	1650	1900	152692	FLN	Llanasa
....	....	1818	1992	142034	GLA	Neath
1855	1992	1845	1855	142034	GLA	Rhigos
1858	1868	1820	1871	110876	GLA	St Brides Major
1895	1898	....	....	150762	GLA	Swansea
1730	1740	ALL	1730	141224	GLS	South
1850	1992	1800	1992	129240	GLS	Bristol
1800	1850	1600	1850	154342	GLS	Bristol
1800	1920	1650	1800	109886	GLS	Burford
1855	1866	....	....	167037	GLS	Cheltenham
1854	1905	1835	1905	159700	GLS	Coombe Hill
1890	ALL	....	....	167037	GLS	Forest Green
1812	1992	1750	1812	164917	GLS	Forest Of Dean
1860	1964	ALL	ALL	113662	GLS	Gloucester
1825	1970	1700	1970	121150	GLS	Horsley
1800	1850	1800	1850	108251	GLS	Iron Action
....	....	1796	....	174963	GLS	Stoud
1798	1830	1760	1815	159700	GLS	Stow On The Wold
1830	....	....	....	167037	GLS	Stroud
1850	1992	1700	1850	148059	GNT	Tintern
1795	....	1700	1900	141151	HAM	ALL
1892	1953	1800	1900	123811	HAM	Aldershot
1857	1857	ALL	1992	170909	HAM	Atherfield
1782	1782	1750	1800	107573	HAM	Bighton
1850	1900	1800	1900	135925	HAM	Bournemouth
1870	1992	1870	1900	109827	HAM	Brown Candover
1800	1950	1600	1900	120677	HAM	Crawley
1723	1992	1600	1723	166804	HAM	Odiham

Known From	To	Researching From	To	Ref	Cty	Place
BROWN contd.						
1847	1881	1800	1900	176982	HAM	Romsey
1861	1957	ALL	ALL	156884	HAM	Southampton
1750	....	ALL	1800	169730	HRT	Benington
1791	1940	1700	1992	153672	HRT	Hitchin
1770	1910	1700	1770	157074	HRT	Little Berkhamstead
1770	....	....	....	140317	HUN	Little Stukeley
1836	1849	....	1836	129305	IOM	Port St Mary
1699	1754	1650	1780	126667	IOW	Calbourne
?	?	?	?	173274	IRL	Antrim
1739	....	....	1739	117234	IRL	Down
?	?	ALL	1846	101281	IRL	Dublin
1818	1890	ALL	1818	167878	KEN	ALL
....	....	1600	1670	161357	KEN	Birchington
1820	1835	1700	1900	136034	KEN	Chatham
1720	....	....	....	171441	KEN	Cuxton
1769	1992	....	....	138231	KEN	Deal
1874	1899	1700	1874	178608	KEN	Deptford
1769	1992	....	....	138231	KEN	Dover
1200	1350	1150	1350	154881	KEN	Edenbridge
1900	1992	....	....	141267	KEN	Faversham
1860	1900	1800	1860	154873	KEN	Faversham
1809	1846	ALL	1850	129283	KEN	Greenwich
1646	1646	....	....	127426	KEN	Harrietsham
1860	1900	1800	1860	154873	KEN	Sittingbourne
1701	....	....	....	171441	KEN	Strood
1850	1992	1850	1992	109347	LAN	Accrington
1850	1950	1800	1992	143189	LAN	Aigburth
1800	....	1800	....	109347	LAN	Bury
1775	1881	1700	1881	160636	LAN	Denton
1600	1700	1600	1700	109347	LAN	Downham
1830	1875	1875	1950	102660	LAN	Failsworth
1750	1810	1500	1750	120049	LAN	Kirkham
1775	1867	ALL	1775	126942	LAN	Kirkham
1873	1976	1873	1873	145580	LAN	Liverpool
1769	1992	....	....	138231	LAN	Manchester
1720	1808	1600	1810	110787	LEI	Cosby
1871	1910	ALL	1817	161330	LEI	Eastwell
1865	1874	1865	1874	131563	LIN	Croft
....	....	1750	1830	172847	LIN	Grantham
1660	1830	ALL	....	104515	LIN	Heckington
1790	1830	ALL	1790	152021	LIN	Horncastle
1751	1801	1700	1900	149098	LIN	Louth
....	1764	....	....	128910	LIN	Ownby
1700	1865	1560	1875	131563	LIN	Pinchbeck
1808	1992	....	....	109835	LIN	Tattershall
1695	1740	....	....	145688	LIN	Thorpe St Peter
1784	1826	1700	1850	125865	LIN	Ulcrby By Barton
1790	1992	1700	1790	102342	LIN	Worlaby
1779	....	....	....	120804	LKS	Stonehouse
1852	1852	....	1900	171646	LND	South
1915	1920	1850	1915	165689	LND	West
1891	1944	1750	1891	142697	LND	Battersea
1769	1992	....	....	138231	LND	Camberwell
....	....	1880	ALL	108065	LND	East Ham
1818	....	ALL	1818	164623	LND	Greenwich
....	....	1700	1900	109894	LND	Shoreditch
1850	1940	1750	1850	156132	LND	Shoreditch
1873	1895	1825	1900	136042	LND	Stepney
1877	....	1875	1992	109894	LND	Stoke Newington
....	1847	ALL	ALL	129933	LND	Whitechapel
1917	....	1900	1992	117609	LND	???
1790	1832	1841	1891	146560	LTN	Dalmeny
1790	1832	1841	1891	146560	LTN	Leith
1790	1832	1841	1891	146560	LTN	Queensferry
1846	1846	ALL	....	109258	MDX	Cowley
1838	1838	....	1890	171646	MDX	East London
1780	1900	1700	1780	179663	MDX	East London
1940	....	1935	1945	163775	MDX	Hackney
1884	1930	1800	1884	171662	MDX	Hackney
1887	1961	1800	1887	102849	MDX	Kentishtown
1881	1885	1855	1905	110051	MDX	Old Ford
1850	1920	1850	1920	144657	MDX	Paddington
1800	1992	ALL	ALL	137847	MDX	Popular
1847	1937	1846	1992	167959	MDX	Tottenham
1830	1870	1700	1830	167649	MGY	Bettws Cedewain
1859	....	....	....	150762	MON	Blaenavon
1800	1992	ALL	ALL	137847	MON	Chepstow
....	....	ALL	ALL	121363	MON	Newport
1758	1758	1720	1780	159905	NBL	Blyth
1867	1890	1840	1865	173118	NBL	Elsdon
1841	1875	1800	1900	160563	NBL	Great Whittington
1764	....	....	1770	160873	NBL	Hartburn

Known From	To	Researching From	To	Ref	Cty	Place
BROWN contd.						
1840	1870	1700	1880	100439	NBL	Netherton By Bedlington
1845	1850	1800	1850	145602	NBL	Newcastle Upon Tyne
1824	1841	....	1850	146811	NBL	Tynemouth
1600	1650	1500	1800	162620	NBL	West Allendale
1718	1945	1718	1945	142662	NBL	Wooler
....	....	1700	1850	152390	NFK	Costessey
1760	1800	1700	1760	172898	NFK	Kings Lynn
1803	1820	1800	1830	109819	NFK	Norwich
....	....	1700	1992	140627	NFK	Norwich
1800	1940	1700	1992	109924	NFK	Shropham
1841	1860	1750	1900	126799	NFK	Upwell
1800	1860	1750	1900	126799	NFK	Wretton
1715	1730	....	....	110159	NRY	Kirkleatham
1730	1747	....	....	110159	NRY	Yarm
1800	1876	ALL	ALL	135208	NTH	Eye
1766	1789	....	....	171654	NTH	Grafton Regis
1800	1876	ALL	ALL	135208	NTH	Gunsthorpe
1846	1970	1850	1921	101281	NTH	Northampton
1800	1876	ALL	ALL	135208	NTH	Werrington
1808	1850	1780	1810	177393	NTT	Bingham
1720	1875	1600	1719	131245	NTT	Blidworth
1821	1843	1790	1821	147745	NTT	Egmanton
1830	1850	....	....	172847	NTT	Hickling
1830	1992	1700	1830	110108	NTT	Hucknall
1920	1992	1700	1920	110108	NTT	Nottingham
1840	1870	1700	1850	130133	NTT	Wymondham
1740	1764	1720	1764	147311	NYK	Scarborough
1900	1992	....	....	128643	OKI	Westray
1800	1920	1650	1800	109886	OXF	Burford
1700	1772	ALL	1772	168696	OXF	Enstone
1726	1761	1600	1750	143693	OXF	Stokenchurch
1800	1992	....	1800	110027	PEE	Peebles
1850	1992	1700	1992	135429	PEM	Milford Haven
1450	1850	1750	1850	135429	PEM	Monkton
1450	1850	1750	1850	135429	PEM	Pembroke
....	....	1750	ALL	149187	PER	Collace
1790	1810	1841	1891	146560	PER	Perth
1824	....	ALL	1824	112887	PER	???
1855	1992	....	1855	115150	RFW	Barrhead
1822	....	1800	1850	146536	RFW	Greenock
1842	1861	1800	1842	146358	RFW	Port Glasgow
1820	1839	1700	1820	139084	ROX	Ancrum
1840	1860	1700	1850	179191	ROX	Hawick
1800	1900	....	....	150371	ROX	Newcastleton
1780	1908	1800	1881	122238	SAL	Broseley
1801	1830	....	....	144568	SAL	Sheriff Hales
1798	1992	ALL	1798	110000	SCT	Airdrie
1830	1869	ALL	ALL	101370	SCT	Bothwell
1900	1914	....	....	158941	SCT	Edinburgh
....	....	ALL	1775	103284	SCT	Glasgow
....	....	1800	1900	179248	SCT	Hawick
1750	1810	ALL	ALL	107425	SCT	Kirkliston
ALL	1800	....	....	110000	SCT	New Monkland
1825	....	1800	....	109347	SCT	???
1613	1753	....	....	129747	SFK	Glemsford
1818	1848	1750	1850	152110	SFK	Glemsford
1680	1680	1600	1680	155276	SFK	Grundesburg
1830	1987	1750	1830	134015	SFK	Ipswich
1830	1987	1750	1830	134015	SFK	Marlesford
1707	1707	1650	1707	155276	SFK	Needham
1750	1965	....	....	137820	SHI	Fetlar
1720	1965	....	....	137820	SHI	Mid Yell
1760	1965	....	....	137820	SHI	North Yell
1758	1965	....	....	137820	SHI	Northmavine
1720	1965	....	....	137820	SHI	South Yell
1818	....	1750	1845	142034	SOM	Bath
1700	1790	....	1800	179213	SOM	Croscombe
....	....	1800	1992	179213	SOM	Shepton Mallet
1843	1867	ALL	1843	171468	SOM	Twerton
1796	?	ALL	ALL	153516	SOM	Wedmore
1817	1931	1400	....	135259	SOM	Yeovil
1840	1870	1700	1880	170607	SSX	Cavendish
1815	1868	ALL	....	132349	SSX	Maresfield
1793	1837	1750	1793	147745	STI	Campsie
1790	1800	1700	1800	103764	STS	Alstonfield
1900	1950	ALL	ALL	158941	STS	Burslem
1776	1800	1600	1776	110639	STS	Milwich
1800	1850	1600	1800	143014	STS	Stoke On Trent
1850	1992	1700	1850	117005	WAR	Coventry
1808	1992	1828	1992	118931	WAR	Coventry
1760	1940	1600	1992	128279	WES	South
1850	1900	1850	1950	119865	WES	Ambleside

Known From	To	Researching From	To	Ref	Cty	Place
BROWN contd.						
1763	1992	ALL	1763	175994	WIL	Calne
1763	1992	ALL	1763	175994	WIL	Chippenham
1780	1790	1780	1790	154210	WIL	Ford
1730	1920	1600	1730	177253	WIL	Idmiston
1700	1730	1600	1700	177253	WIL	Imber
1700	1861	1700	1861	108251	WIL	Oaksey
1700	1870	1700	1850	178047	WIL	Oaksey
1750	1900	1650	1750	177253	WIL	Porton
1845	1881	1800	1900	176982	WIL	Salisbury
1684	....	1650	1720	170348	WIL	Sutton Benger
1792	1881	1700	1900	120146	WIL	Woodborough
1859	....	....	....	150762	WOR	???
1750	1875	1600	1900	102660	WRY	Idle
1750	1875	1600	1900	102660	WRY	Thackley
1841	1841	1700	1841	100110	WYK	Bradford
1794	1900	ALL	1794	100587	WYK	Yeadon
....	....	1587	1736	174858	YKS	Barton Fleming
1826	1868	1826	1868	139661	YKS	Bothwell
1860	1890	....	....	177393	YKS	Brotherton
1725	1960	1650	1730	137278	YKS	Cowesby
1834	1854	ALL	1851	179086	YKS	Elmsall
1764	1779	1700	1800	176621	YKS	Farsley
1890	1920	....	....	177393	YKS	Featherstone
1932	1945	1700	1900	166766	YKS	Gargrave
1760	1839	1740	1760	133760	YKS	Holmfirth
1736	1830	....	....	174858	YKS	Hunmanby
1780	1800	....	....	117196	YKS	Mansfield
1810	1850	....	....	124168	YKS	Middleton Tyas
1760	1835	1725	1835	141097	YKS	North Newbald
1757	....	....	....	151351	YKS	Otley
1764	1900	1700	1764	150096	YKS	Rawmarsh
1764	1823	1740	1780	170348	YKS	Rawmarsh
1829	1881	1829	1881	173851	YKS	Scarborough
1750	....	1700	....	134589	YKS	Wigginton
1883	1948	....	1883	165484	YKS	Woolley
1840	1935	ALL	1935	100102	YKS	York
1830	1899	....	....	111260	YKS	York
....	....	1750	1860	113514	YKS	York
1800	1992	1750	1900	138371	YKS	York
1850	1950	1600	1950	135968	YKS	???
1829	....	....	....	120804	???	Isle Of Tiree
BROWNBILL						
1800	1992	ALL	1992	110140	ALL	ALL
1800	1992	ALL	1992	110140	LAN	Liverpool
....	....	1700	1850	117587	LAN	???
BROWNE						
1829	1992	1650	1829	101419	BRK	Wargrave
1790	1865	1840	1860	166685	CMA	Carlisle
1621	1621	1500	1620	131245	DBY	North Wingfield
1630	1809	....	....	146676	DEV	Branscombe
1630	1809	....	....	146676	DEV	Colyton
1750	1850	1700	1750	108677	DEV	Crediton
1930	1992	1600	1930	137588	DEV	Newton St Cyres
1780	1800	1780	1790	110159	DEV	Tiverton
1815	1840	1840	1890	166685	ESS	Leytonstone
1835	1835	ALL	1815	165263	HEF	ALL
1815	1850	1839	1850	110159	IRL	Dublin
....	....	1600	1690	154873	KEN	Ashford
....	....	1800	1840	154873	KEN	Canterbury
....	....	1584	1800	106054	KEN	Maidstone
....	....	1800	1830	154873	KEN	Rainham
?	?	?	?	166642	KEN	???
....	1890	1800	1890	142697	LND	Battersea
1800	1850	1700	1850	103055	NFK	Diss
1786	1992	1780	1992	110205	NFK	Norwich
1819	1992	1700	1819	118265	NFK	Norwich
1830	1890	1800	1900	158658	NFK	Norwich
1892	1892	....	....	173061	NFK	Norwich
1840	1900	1800	1900	129496	NTT	Nottingham
1870	....	1700	1870	118923	SAL	High Evcall
1830	1880	1830	1850	110159	SFK	Ipswich
1733	1755	1675	1775	129356	SOM	Chilthorne Domer
1860	1870	....	....	110159	STS	Alrewas
1860	1890	1860	1890	110159	STS	Lichfield
1815	1850	....	....	110159	WAR	Birmingham
BROWNER						
1850	1992	....	....	108898	LAN	Liverpool
BROWNHILL						
1800	1900	1700	1850	142395	DBY	Baslow
BROWNING						
1724	1940	....	....	128996	CAM	Thorney
1770	....	1770	1900	139114	CON	Laucestor
1859	1930	....	....	118494	CON	Pensilva

Known From	Known To	Researching From	Researching To	Ref	Cty	Place
BROWNING contd.						
ALL	....	1840	1880	135429	DEV	ALL
1791	1890	1700	1791	120146	DEV	Drewsteignton
....	....	1838	1859	118494	DEV	Sheepstor
1803	1894	1700	1803	121525	DEV	Sowton
....	....	1804	1841	118494	DEV	Walkhampton
....	....	1778	1803	118494	DEV	Widecombe In The Moor
....	....	....	1631	174270	DOR	ALL
....	....	1550	1625	174289	DOR	ALL
....	....	1700	1900	106402	HAM	Chalk Hill
1808	1881	1700	1950	158399	HAM	New Milton
....	....	1700	1900	106402	HAM	Southampton
1750	1780	1700	1780	136840	HAM	Sparsholt
1796	1842	ALL	ALL	150886	HUN	Great Staughton
1683	1712	....	1750	171441	KEN	Canterbury
1794	1946	1700	1946	113638	KEN	Hastingleigh
1800	1860	ALL	ALL	139564	KEN	Malling
....	....	1774	1823	161667	KEN	Sutton At Hone
1716	1922	1700	1906	110213	KEN	Whitstable
1717	?	?	?	166642	KEN	???
1814	1851	1700	1814	179116	OXF	Dukclington
BROWNINGS						
1807	1809	1700	1850	124907	SSX	Twineham
BROWNJOHN						
1700	1770	ALL	ALL	158798	SOM	Central
BROWNLEE						
1902	1992	ALL	ALL	150681	ANT	Cogry
BROWNLIE						
1857	1897	ALL	ALL	106860	LKS	Glasgow
1867	1901	1700	1992	155713	LKS	Hamilton
1867	1901	1700	1992	155713	LKS	Stonehouse
1820	1860	....	1860	116866	LKS	???
....	....	1800	1900	146110	SCT	ALL
BROWNLOW						
1806	1858	?	1860	164976	NTT	Burton Joyce
1560	1992	ALL	1560	135143	NTT	Mattesley
BROWNON						
?	?	?	?	121185	KEN	South
BROWNRIDGE						
?	?	?	?	110221	YKS	Barwick
BROWNRIGG						
1749	1898	1400	1749	140678	CUL	Matterdale
1749	1898	1400	1749	140678	CUL	Watermillock
BROWNSELL						
1700	1800	1700	1800	161705	NFK	North
....	....	1840	1900	138142	NFK	Swaffham
1904	1904	1800	1904	121568	SOM	Bickenhall
BROWNSEY						
....	....	1700	1992	110248	ALL	ALL
BROWNSTON						
1644	1881	ALL	ALL	165972	DEV	Morchard Bishop
BROWSTER						
....	....	1700	ALL	149187	FIF	Carnbee
....	....	1700	ALL	149187	FIF	Kilrenny
BROXHAM						
1830	1900	ALL	ALL	143294	LEI	Hinckley
BROXHOLME						
1818	1856	1800	1920	165034	LIN	Barton On Humber
1530	1600	1530	1600	169323	LIN	Yawthorpe
BROXTON						
....	....	ALL	ALL	151750	ALL	Name Study
ALL	ALL	ALL	ALL	151750	ALL	ALL
BRUAN						
1869	1933	1869	1992	166804	ALL	ALL
BRUCE						
....	....	ALL	1750	110256	ABD	Aberdeen
....	....	1700	1850	110256	ABD	Alford
....	....	1550	1750	110256	ABD	Kildrummy
....	....	1796	....	149187	ABD	Lonmay
1755	1871	1700	1920	114898	ANS	ALL
1829	1992	1700	1919	110264	BAN	King Edward
1806	....	....	1806	101761	CAI	Bower
1700	1750	....	....	126497	CAI	Canisbay
1765	1992	1700	1992	128481	CAI	Watten
1850	....	1750	1900	171700	CAM	Whittlesey
1820	1870	1820	?	114944	ESS	ALL
?	?	?	?	127701	ESS	Great Clacton
1750	1920	1750	1920	105317	ESS	St Osyth
1835	1876	1700	1835	150614	LAN	Liverpool
1800	1900	1800	1900	167843	LAN	Manchester
1775	1908	....	....	160458	LND	???
1775	1908	....	....	160458	NBL	???
1785	1893	ALL	1785	120022	NTH	Holcote
BRUCE contd.						
1810	....	....	....	157554	PER	Little Dunkeld
1790	1820	ALL	1820	152048	RFW	Eastwood
1692	1800	1500	1600	153591	SCT	Environ
1755	1880	1700	1920	114898	SCT	Forfar
1692	1800	1500	1600	153591	SCT	Spott
1800	1870	1739	1870	132381	SHI	Unst
1802	1808	1750	1850	165824	SOM	Bath
1820	1900	1820	1900	165824	SOM	Saltford
1750	1883	1700	1750	141798	STI	St Ninians
1740	1900	1740	1900	110280	YKS	Batley
1704	1760	1704	1760	110280	YKS	Halifax
1740	1900	1740	1900	110280	YKS	Heckmondwike
1700	1704	1700	1704	110280	YKS	Settle
BRUCKER						
1766	1828	....	....	116017	LND	East
1766	1828	....	....	116017	LND	City
BRUCKMANN						
1841	1992	1841	1992	141267	MDX	Mile End
1841	1992	1841	1992	141267	MDX	Wapping
BRUDENELL						
....	....	ALL	ALL	110299	HUN	???
1837	1900	....	....	110299	NTH	Irchester
1724	1851	....	....	139157	NTH	Warmington
BRUDENWELL						
1490	1992	ALL	1490	129992	NTH	Dean
BRUEL						
1275	1275	1066	1275	109800	LAN	ALL
1198	1199	1066	1198	109800	LND	London
1296	1587	1066	1296	109800	NBL	Felton
BRUELL						
1248	1248	1066	1248	109800	ERY	ALL
BRUERTON						
1840	1900	1740	1840	172928	STS	Darlaston
1840	1900	1740	1840	172928	STS	Wednesbury
BRUETON						
1803	1992	....	1803	125954	WAR	Birmingham
BRUFF						
1830	....	....	1914	147672	CAM	Cambridge
1890	1920	....	....	104450	LND	Tower Hamlets
BRUFORD						
1880	1992	....	....	169528	LAN	Liverpool
1791	1880	1700	1800	169528	SOM	Bridgewater
BRUIN						
1620	1750	1550	1650	155950	LEI	Wigston
BRUMBLEY						
1817	1851	1700	1817	177202	LIN	Dowsby
1851	1891	1750	1851	177202	LIN	Helpringham
1770	1817	1700	1851	177202	NTH	Helpston
BRUMBY						
1830	1992	?	1830	143952	LIN	Gainsborough
1850	1992	1750	1850	102342	LIN	Grasby
....	....	1700	1850	112208	LND	St Pancras
....	....	1800	1850	112208	MDX	Uxbridge
BRUMFIELD						
1750	1850	....	1750	118907	WOR	South East
BRUMMET						
1929	....	1925	1930	163775	ESS	West Ham
BRUMPTON						
1776	1776	1745	1800	174211	LIN	Branston
1851	1861	1800	1900	159018	LIN	Market Rasen
1866	1881	1800	1880	159018	YKS	Sheffield
BRUNDISH						
....	....	ALL	ALL	110302	ALL	Name Study
BRUNDRITT						
1790	1992	ALL	ALL	143537	ALL	ALL
BRUNGAR						
1810	1860	....	....	101028	KEN	Bethersden
BRUNSDEN						
1770	1885	1500	1770	141925	BRK	Bucklebury
BRUNSDON						
1844	1992	1500	....	110310	BRK	ALL
1840	1840	1500	1840	110310	WIL	ALL
BRUNSKILL						
1800	1900	1800	1992	133450	DEV	Dartmouth
1750	1800	1700	1800	143553	WES	Milburn
1718	1788	1600	1718	145327	WYK	Hampsthwaite
1799	....	ALL	ALL	119504	YKS	Muker
BRUNSWICK						
1798	1853	1854	1992	132764	DUR	South Shields
BRUNT						
1778	1814	?	1825	103934	DBY	Bakewell
....	....	1600	1870	166863	DOR	Holwell
....	....	1750	1851	111414	HEF	Leintwardine

Known From	To	Researching From	To	Ref	Cty	Place
BRUNT contd.						
1957	1957	1957	1957	162442	SCT	Glasgow
1800	1889	1600	1800	110329	SOM	Wedmore
1800	1850	1650	1800	151084	STS	North
....	....	1600	1800	179531	STS	Ellastone
1740	1885	1640	1740	172006	STS	Hollinsclough
....	....	1800	1850	166960	TYR	Magheralough
1820	....	1800	1841	169625	TYR	Magheralough
BRUNTON						
....	....	ALL	1783	119326	MLN	Newbattle
1795	....	....	1795	175552	ROX	Jedburgh
BRUNYEE						
1861	1992	1628	1992	134023	LIN	Crowle
1800	1840	1750	1840	104396	YKS	Hull
BRUSBY						
1780	1830	1700	1780	102393	NYK	Hawnby
1780	1830	1700	1780	102393	NYK	Helmsley
BRUSH						
1750	1823	1700	1750	165123	CON	Rame
1900	1992	1900	1992	176990	GLA	Loughor
1550	1880	1500	1800	167770	GLS	Tewkesbury
1726	1907	1600	1992	176990	POW	Bodenham
1767	1800	1600	1992	176990	POW	Bosbury
1726	1907	1600	1992	176990	POW	Clifford
1726	1907	1600	1992	176990	POW	Dorstone
1790	1880	1600	1992	176990	POW	Hardwick By Hay
1726	1907	1600	1992	176990	POW	Hay On Wye
1746	1852	1600	1992	176990	POW	Hereford
1836	1867	1700	1836	179647	WOR	Worcester
BRUSLAUN						
1798	1992	1798	1992	163848	WIC	Monaseed
BRUTON						
....	....	ALL	ALL	110337	ALL	Name Study
1883	1923	ALL	1883	147087	GLS	ALL
1850	1900	1700	....	111724	HRT	Watford
BRUTY						
1600	1800	1600	1800	114529	ESS	Tilbury Juxta Clare
1900	1980	ALL	ALL	132977	LND	ALL
1600	1800	1600	1800	114529	SFK	Stoke By Clare
BRUYLL						
1538	1586	1066	1538	109800	NBL	Hadston
BRYAN						
1850	1900	1600	1850	112097	DBY	Stapleford
1809	1900	1700	1809	134368	GLS	Gloucester
1881	1992	1700	1880	110345	LAN	Liverpool
1700	1830	1600	1700	152463	LEI	Walton On Wolds
....	....	1750	1800	102717	MDX	London
1893	....	ALL	ALL	105481	NTT	Belper
1850	1900	1600	1850	112097	NTT	Sandiacre
1653	1852	1600	1992	176877	SAL	Clun
1700	1920	1660	1720	173649	STS	Sheriffhales
1778	1809	1700	1800	134368	YKS	East
BRYANT						
....	....	ALL	ALL	100382	ALL	Name Study
....	....	ALL	ALL	160555	ALL	Name Study
1851	1992	1700	ALL	110353	AVN	Abson
1851	1992	1700	ALL	110353	AVN	Wick
1786	1870	1750	1786	133221	BDF	Bedford
1781	1785	1750	1780	133221	BDF	Potton
1863	1992	1863	1936	177792	CHS	Birkenhead
1863	1992	1863	1936	177792	CHS	Wallasey
1819	1846	1750	1850	143251	CON	Lanhydrock
1819	1846	1750	1850	143251	CON	Lanivet
1819	1846	1750	1850	143251	CON	Lanlivery
1819	1846	1750	1850	143251	CON	St Winnow
1887	1992	1800	1887	109193	CON	Wadebridge
1880	1920	1700	1920	112003	DBY	Newhall
1700	1992	1700	1992	110361	DEV	Plymouth
1625	1992	1625	1992	110361	DEV	Plymstock
1881	1960	1700	1850	106380	DUR	Stockton
1840	1894	1700	1992	122742	GLS	Littledean
1810	1850	1800	1850	106801	GLS	St George
1898	1992	ALL	ALL	150681	HAM	Portsea
1700	1960	1700	1960	100382	KEN	Rolvenden
1808	1889	....	....	135968	KEN	Rolvenden
1700	1960	1700	1960	100382	KEN	Tenterden
1885	1992	1800	1992	117293	MDX	Hammersmith
1900	1950	1850	1900	110353	MON	Tredegar
1770	1900	1700	1770	105392	SFK	North
1800	1835	1611	1865	160555	SOM	Ansford
1834	....	....	....	167037	SOM	Bath
1802	1893	1610	1889	160555	SOM	Castle Cary
1784	1852	1735	1855	160407	SOM	Frome
1852	....	1820	1860	177792	SOM	Kingsbury Episcopi

Known From	To	Researching From	To	Ref	Cty	Place
BRYANT contd.						
1670	1690	1650	1670	128724	SSX	ALL
1842	1881	ALL	....	153214	SSX	Framfeild
....	....	1550	1750	100382	SSX	Northiam
1699	1830	1650	1800	166154	SSX	Ringmer
1835	1931	....	1835	136778	WIL	Corsham
1781	1785	1735	1855	160407	WIL	Corsley
1810	1917	....	....	100536	WLS	???
1852	1880	ALL	1880	106380	WOR	Kidderminster
1886	1941	1700	1886	100110	WYK	Halifax
1840	1950	1800	1950	123862	???	Bristol
1839	1875	1700	1839	153206	???	???
BRYCE						
1804	1835	1700	1804	144967	CUL	Borwick
1851	1992	1835	1841	144967	LAN	Bolton
1826	1835	1700	1804	144967	LAN	Glasson Dock
1841	1992	1835	1841	144967	LAN	Preston
1850	....	ALL	ALL	135453	LKS	Liberton
1870	....	ALL	ALL	117889	LKS	Newbiggins
1880	1899	....	....	111260	LND	Bethnal Green
1800	1890	1850	1860	111260	LTN	Edinburgh
1839	1992	ALL	ALL	110388	SCT	Edinburgh
1839	1992	ALL	ALL	110388	SCT	Glasgow
BRYDELL						
1850	....	1700	....	164038	SSX	Chichester
1500	....	....	....	164038	WIL	???
BRYDEN						
1745	1992	1745	1992	110396	CUL	Milburn
1745	1992	1745	1992	110396	DFS	???
1850	1992	1850	1992	108278	LKS	Glasgow
BRYDON						
1794	1840	ALL	1794	128481	ANS	Montrose
1838	....	....	....	166723	BEW	Leitholm
1830	1900	1700	1850	144037	LKS	Glasgow
1780	....	ALL	ALL	128481	NBL	Newcastle
1834	1992	....	....	172529	SCT	Yarrow
BRYER						
1823	1851	....	....	133221	BDF	Bedford
1750	1800	1650	1750	118745	DBY	Mackworth
1800	1850	1700	1800	138010	HAM	Southampton
BRYNKENELL						
1100	1700	....	....	100420	WAR	Meriden
BRYSON						
1781	1992	....	....	149616	DFS	Dornock
1784	1792	1700	1792	167533	GLS	Bristol
1790	1923	1790	1923	133795	SCT	Cumbernauld
BUBB						
?	?	?	?	175145	GLS	Lower Swell
....	....	ALL	ALL	171816	WAR	Birmingham
1800	1850	ALL	ALL	171816	WOR	Powick
BUBBERS						
1884	1960	1700	1900	165476	LND	Bethnal Green
BUBBINGS						
....	....	1700	1900	140627	NFK	Salhouse
BUCHAN						
....	....	1850	1900	142298	ABD	Ellon
1856	1910	....	....	116165	ABD	Fraserburgh
1800	1960	1750	1850	140864	ABD	Fraserburgh
....	....	ALL	1800	119326	ELN	Cockenzie
1875	1890	....	1875	152927	FIF	???
1861	1910	....	....	168203	LKS	Hamilton
1806	1840	....	....	168203	PER	Crieff
1834	1881	....	....	168203	PER	Fowlis Wester
1897	1950	....	....	168203	PER	Huntingtower
1875	1890	....	1875	152927	PER	Perth
1861	1871	....	....	168203	STI	Drymen
BUCHANAN						
....	....	ALL	ALL	148466	ALL	Name Study
....	....	ALL	1890	173045	ANT	Ballyalbana
....	....	ALL	1890	173045	ANT	Ballynashee
....	1836	1500	1850	153591	ELN	Haddington
1900	1970	1800	1992	110418	FER	Enniskillen
1825	1862	1800	1900	139114	LKS	Balfrom
1849	1864	1800	1900	110426	LKS	Glasgow
1780	1780	1700	1780	149632	LKS	Glasgow
1820	1860	1800	1880	169641	LKS	Glasgow
1800	1925	?	1930	103934	SCT	Aberdeen
1780	1821	1700	1830	179000	SCT	Riccarton
1800	1925	?	1930	103934	SCT	Skye
BUCHANON						
1835	1840	1700	1878	173622	TYR	Drumskinny
BUCHER						
1590	1600	1550	1610	124796	BKM	Chesham
1610	....	1590	1650	124796	BKM	Great Hampden

Known From	To	Researching From	To	Ref	Cty	Place
BUCHMAN						
1825	1862	1862	1900	139114	LKS	Balfrom
BUCK						
1599	1680	ALL	1600	154563	DOR	Abbotsbury
1766	1797	ALL	ALL	154563	DOR	Wyke Regis
1779	1900	1750	1930	110434	ESS	Chelmsford
1770	1780	1730	1800	110434	ESS	Chignall St James
....	....	ALL	1790	155470	ESS	Newport
1900	1910	1880	1920	151947	GLA	Aberdare
1836	1920	1750	1920	110434	HAM	Isle Of Wight
1847	....	1840	1900	127353	HUN	Sawtry
1840	1880	1750	1960	157171	LAN	Colne
1600	1992	?	?	114944	LND	ALL
1671	1717	ALL	1840	104531	NFK	Great Witchingham
1812	1920	1812	1920	173061	NFK	Hempnall
....	....	ALL	ALL	104531	NFK	Weston Longville
....	....	1500	1785	166863	SOM	ALL
1806	1806	1750	1846	121568	SOM	Bath
1846	1846	1806	1846	121568	SOM	Dunkerton
1870	1992	1800	1870	110442	WYK	Pontefract
1895	....	ALL	ALL	112461	YKS	ALL
1760	1809	....	....	129216	YKS	Harthill
1801	1812	1750	1850	141097	YKS	North Newbald
BUCKBY						
....	....	ALL	ALL	110450	ALL	ALL
....	....	1720	1805	110450	LEI	Little Bowden
....	....	1810	1940	110450	NTH	Burton Latimer
....	....	1780	1860	110450	NTH	Cranford
....	....	1690	1780	110450	NTH	Desborough
....	....	1710	1810	110450	NTH	Great Oxenden
....	....	1800	1910	110450	NTH	Kettering
....	....	1720	1780	110450	NTH	Maidwell
1720	1800	1690	1720	134139	NTH	Maidwell
....	....	1820	1870	110450	NTH	Pytchley
....	....	1700	1820	110450	NTH	Rothwell
....	....	1760	1800	110450	NTH	Rushton
BUCKENHAM						
1720	1780	1600	1720	101834	NFK	South West
1548	1744	....	....	129747	SFK	Debenham
1615	1750	ALL	1615	131059	SFK	Hadleigh
BUCKERDIGE						
1500	1992	1500	1992	110469	ALL	ALL
BUCKERIDGE						
1841	1863	1700	1860	160601	BRK	Tilehurst
BUCKETT						
1786	1909	1750	1910	126667	IOW	Newchurch
1800	1920	1800	1920	176176	OXF	Henley On Thames
BUCKHAM						
1790	1890	1790	1890	168998	DUR	Lanchester
1790	1890	1790	1890	168998	DUR	Ovington
1700	1900	1800	1900	117064	ROX	Kelso
BUCKINGHAM						
1730	1880	1500	1900	110485	CON	North Hill
....	1740	....	1740	110485	DEV	Ashwater
1930	1960	1900	1960	110485	DEV	Exeter
1827	1880	1800	1830	150320	DEV	Paignton
1880	1930	1880	1930	110485	DEV	Shaldon
1855	....	....	1855	171441	LND	Kensington
1836	1859	ALL	ALL	124176	OXF	Handborough
1755	....	....	....	102733	OXF	Northleigh
1799	1992	1799	1992	178705	OXF	Northmoor
1700	1850	1700	1850	173681	OXF	Oxford
1746	1862	1653	1888	129194	OXF	Steeple Barton
1784	1784	1750	1784	155276	SFK	Bredfield
1700	....	?	?	136999	SSX	Brighton
BUCKLAND						
1848	1921	1848	1921	131970	DBY	Borrowash
1819	1819	1819	1819	131970	DBY	Normanton On Soar
1400	1450	1300	1400	154881	KEN	Shoreham
1805	1851	....	....	139971	SRY	Bookham
1765	1805	....	....	139971	SRY	Clandon
1721	1992	1650	1721	126454	SRY	Ripley
1620	1800	1620	1760	142018	WIL	Melksham
1846	1992	1800	1845	157619	WIL	Potterne
BUCKLE						
1750	1900	1750	1900	161276	BRK	Newbury
1750	1900	1750	1900	161276	BRK	Wallingford
....	....	1700	1800	147613	CAM	Chatteris
....	....	1700	....	141216	GLS	Mid
1811	1913	ALL	ALL	107255	LND	ALL
1798	1965	ALL	1798	169846	NYK	Hunsingore
1854	1892	1800	1900	123811	SFK	Mendlesham
1620	1992	1620	1850	110361	WIL	Nettleton
BUCKLER						
....	....	1700	1850	120715	CON	ALL
1710	1743	ALL	1743	168718	CON	South East
....	....	1700	1850	120715	CON	Morwenstowe
1896	1928	1800	1950	176184	LEI	???
1650	1800	1700	1750	142018	WIL	Warminster
BUCKLEY						
ALL	ALL	ALL	ALL	110558	ALL	ALL
1847	1878	1847	1878	117668	CHS	Anderton
1819	1819	1800	1839	117668	CHS	Over
1839	1847	1839	1847	117668	CHS	Pickmere
1861	1867	1800	1860	155934	COR	Cork
....	....	?	?	110507	DUR	Sunderland
1672	1740	1600	1672	110515	GLS	Atherstone On Stour
1871	1900	1850	1870	132438	GLS	Little Dean
1592	....	....	....	153397	HAM	Sway
....	....	....	....	161888	IRL	Cork
?	?	....	....	147184	IRL	???
1807	1992	1600	1807	119822	LAN	Bolton
1805	1841	1700	1900	178233	LAN	Bury
1719	....	1700	1850	179078	LAN	Bury
1809	....	....	....	115371	LAN	Liverpool
1900	1920	....	....	177709	LAN	Liverpool
1870	....	1700	1950	126160	LAN	Manchester
1700	1837	ALL	ALL	178292	LAN	Oldham
....	....	ALL	ALL	178292	LAN	Rochdale
1752	1843	ALL	ALL	178292	LAN	Royton
1704	1837	ALL	ALL	178292	LAN	Shaw
1847	1847	1750	1870	171662	LND	Chelsea
1853	1881	ALL	1881	171751	NBL	Gallowgate
1917	1939	ALL	1939	171751	NBL	Gosforth
1853	1881	ALL	1881	171751	NBL	Newcastle Upon Tyne
1844	1950	1740	1820	173649	STS	Bramshall
1676	1791	1600	1770	179116	STS	Mid
1538	1980	1538	1980	110558	WIL	ALL
1742	1880	....	....	110515	WOR	Alvechurgh
1802	1880	1750	1810	137413	WOR	Lower Mitton
1720	1740	1680	1800	126276	WRY	Saddleworth
1850	1873	1750	1850	110531	WYK	Hepworth
....	....	ALL	ALL	178292	WYK	Saddleworth
1803	1861	ALL	1803	179086	YKS	Doncaster
1859	1880	1700	1992	102377	YKS	Leeds
1721	1780	1650	1750	126411	YKS	Saddleworth
....	....	1700	1860	132241	YKS	Saddleworth
BUCKMAN						
1843	1970	ALL	1970	158070	SSX	Ditchling
1843	1970	ALL	1970	158070	SSX	Plumpton
BUCKMASTER						
....	....	1580	1812	110566	BDF	Barton In Clay
....	1757	1602	1812	110566	BDF	Battlesden
....	....	1560	1812	110566	BDF	Biggleswade
....	....	1580	1812	110566	BDF	Caddington
1669	1798	1539	1812	110566	BDF	Chalgrove
....	....	1538	1812	110566	BDF	Cockayne
1602	1763	1602	1763	110566	BDF	Eaton Bray
....	....	1538	1812	110566	BDF	Edworth
....	....	1538	1812	110566	BDF	Eyeworth
....	1685	1581	1812	110566	BDF	Flitton In Silsoe
1603	1733	1602	1812	110566	BDF	Harlington
....	....	1560	1812	110566	BDF	Holcote
1670	1676	1538	1678	110566	BDF	Houghton Regis
1589	1851	1559	1851	110566	BDF	Ivinghoe
1816	1851	1725	1851	110566	BDF	Ledburn
1580	1861	1580	1861	110566	BDF	Leighton Buzzard
....	....	1560	1812	110566	BDF	Lidlington
1700	1871	1575	1871	110566	BDF	Linslade
1816	1851	1725	1851	110566	BDF	Mentmore
1673	1686	1558	1812	110566	BDF	Millbrook
1729	1759	1559	1812	110566	BDF	Milton Bryan
....	1803	1602	1812	110566	BDF	Potsgrove
....	....	1560	1812	110566	BDF	Salford
1630	1851	1630	1851	110566	BDF	Slapton
1728	1776	1559	1812	110566	BDF	Stotford
....	....	1580	1812	110566	BDF	Streatley
....	....	1580	1812	110566	BDF	Sundon
....	....	1538	1812	110566	BDF	Sutton
1608	1746	1602	1740	110566	BDF	Totternhoe
....	....	1560	1812	110566	BDF	Westoning
1582	1744	1582	1744	110566	BDF	Whipsnade
1671	1678	1558	1812	110566	BDF	Woburn
....	....	1538	1812	110566	BDF	Wrestingsworth
....	....	1739	1763	110566	BKM	Aston Abbotts
1659	1677	1582	1812	110566	BKM	Cheddington
....	....	1576	1810	110566	BKM	Cholesbury

Known From	To	Researching From	To	Ref	Cty	Place
BUCKMASTER contd.						
....	....	1737	1769	110566	BKM	Cublington
....	....	1730	1760	110566	BKM	Dunston
1595	1799	1568	1812	110566	BKM	Edlesborough
....	....	1730	1760	110566	BKM	Grove
....	1874	1677	1737	110566	BKM	Pitstone
1623	1754	1623	1754	110566	BKM	Soulbury
1595	1631	1545	1715	110566	BKM	Stewkley
1589	1589	1565	1836	110566	BKM	Swanbourne
1704	1713	1680	1722	110566	BKM	Whaddon
1546	1804	1546	1804	110566	BKM	Wing
1751	1760	1675	1762	110566	BKM	Wingrave
1881	1907	1881	1907	110566	NTH	Bugbrook
BUCKNALL						
1763	1850	1700	1850	128163	ALL	ALL
....	1645	1600	1675	152560	NTT	Sutton In Ashfield
BUCKNELL						
1851	1992	1830	1850	106208	LND	Battersea
1851	1992	1830	1850	106208	LND	Stepney
1851	1992	1830	1850	106208	LND	Wandsworth
....	....	1750	1830	106208	SFK	Walsham Le Willows
BUCKOKE						
1600	1900	?	1600	158569	HRT	ALL
1693	1987	1700	1992	110574	HRT	Abbots Langley
1693	1987	1700	1992	110574	HRT	Kings Langley
BUCKSEY						
1849	1870	1800	1900	116297	KEN	Frindsbury
BUCKTHORPE						
1820	1850	ALL	ALL	113581	LND	???
1841	....	....	....	135402	MDX	Islington
BUCKTON						
1866	1879	1863	1887	157813	MER	Corwen
1763	1831	1763	1831	129747	YKS	Armley
1763	1831	1763	1831	129747	YKS	Wortley
BUCKWELL						
1712	1742	1700	1742	128724	SSX	ALL
BUCKWORTH						
1746	1940	....	....	128996	CAM	Thorney
BUDD						
1750	1850	1750	1850	159409	BRK	ALL
1860	1870	1870	1992	110582	DBY	Derby
1850	....	1700	1856	149608	DEV	Pyworthy
....	....	1700	1992	110582	GLS	Bristol
....	....	1700	1992	110582	GLS	Gloucester
1800	1850	1750	1825	145343	HAM	ALL
1849	1911	....	....	170526	HAM	Ulnsor In Eling
1852	1978	1700	1978	159271	LND	East
....	....	1600	1700	130591	SOM	Bradford On Tone
....	....	1300	1600	130591	SOM	Wellington
1700	1797	ALL	ALL	166243	SRY	Puttenham
1500	1550	....	....	142522	SRY	Wandsworth
1650	1881	1650	1890	170852	SSX	Felpham
1741	1765	1600	1741	164879	SSX	Upper Beeding
1750	1863	1860	1992	110582	STS	Elford
1750	1863	1860	1992	110582	STS	Lichfield
BUDDEN						
....	....	1650	1750	156795	DOR	East
1687	1992	1660	1992	172995	DOR	Canford Magna
1841	....	ALL	ALL	126098	DOR	Loders
....	1778	1700	1800	176621	DOR	Poole
1500	1900	1500	1900	170216	HAM	ALL
1500	1900	1500	1900	170216	WIL	ALL
BUDDING						
....	....	ALL	1876	145548	GLS	Stroud
....	....	ALL	1876	145548	MON	Risca
BUDDLE						
1817	1817	1760	1850	159905	DUR	South Shields
1743	1921	1600	1743	170542	KEN	Goodnestone
BUDDLES						
1851	1950	1826	1992	145041	DUR	South East
BUDDS						
1690	1690	....	....	159883	KEN	Canterbury
BUDGE						
....	....	1500	1992	110590	CON	ALL
....	....	1500	1992	110590	DEV	ALL
1812	1992	1700	1812	130257	DEV	Ermington
....	....	1500	1992	110590	DOR	ALL
1790	1852	....	1852	167037	INV	Kilmuir
1868	1890	....	....	118729	LAN	Liverpool
1868	1881	....	....	118729	LND	St Georges
1500	1992	1500	1992	110590	SOM	South
1500	1992	1500	1992	110590	SOM	West
1767	1992	1700	1800	110604	SOM	Chillington
BUDGEN						
1778	1778	ALL	1992	125113	SSX	Worth
BUDGETT						
....	....	1750	1900	174696	AVN	Bristol
1640	1850	1550	1850	110612	SOM	Frome
BUDWORTH						
....	....	ALL	ALL	110620	ALL	Name Study
1820	....	....	....	115371	LAN	Aughton
....	....	1600	1800	110620	LEI	Barwell
1800	1992	....	....	110620	LEI	Leicester
BUERDSALL						
1874	1877	1700	1877	141542	CHS	Chester
BUERDSELL						
1844	1923	1700	1844	141542	ALL	Manchester
BUES						
1645	....	1600	1680	114332	DEV	Sutcombe
BUFFERY						
....	....	....	....	165433	GLS	???
BUFFET						
1700	1899	1700	1830	135941	SFK	Hundon
BUFFREY						
....	....	....	....	165433	GLS	???
BUFFRY						
....	....	....	....	165433	GLS	???
BUFTON						
1845	....	....	....	167517	SOM	Bristol
BUGBEARD						
1746	1800	ALL	ALL	113743	MDX	ALL
BUGBIRD						
1746	1800	1700	1850	113743	MDX	Ruislip
BUGDEN						
1880	1992	....	....	121444	KEN	Tenterden
BUGG						
1796	1824	1700	1796	117471	DOR	Folke
1796	1824	1700	1796	117471	DOR	Stalbridge
1808	1836	ALL	1900	146390	ESS	Fordham
1672	1684	1630	1672	172871	SFK	Bury St Edmonds
1816	1867	....	....	172871	SFK	Drinkstone
1750	1992	1500	1750	110647	SFK	Offton
1704	1812	....	....	172871	SFK	Whelnetham
1850	1916	ALL	1850	100072	???	???
BUGGINS						
1800	1850	1600	1800	121118	OXF	Wootton
....	....	1900	1992	136743	WAR	Coventry
....	....	1800	1900	136743	WAR	Frankton
BUGLASS						
1619	1880	....	1992	129739	BEW	ALL
1830	1840	1800	1860	107476	LND	East
1840	1900	1800	1860	107476	SFK	Bury St Edmunds
BUGLER						
?	?	?	?	177938	DOR	Beaminster
BUGNIO						
....	....	1800	1874	102849	HUM	Hull
BUHLER						
....	....	1700	1900	135968	ALL	ALL
BUIK						
1802	1840	1802	1840	156019	ANS	Dundee
BUIST						
....	....	ALL	ALL	110655	ALL	Name Study
BULBECK						
1887	1992	ALL	1992	179205	LND	Paddington
1887	1992	ALL	1992	179205	LND	St Pancras
1812	1887	ALL	1992	179205	SXW	Bognor
1812	1887	ALL	1992	179205	SXW	Chichester
BULCH						
1847	1992	1700	1992	110663	YKS	North
BULCOCK						
....	....	1770	1825	107883	LAN	Colne
1600	....	1600	....	109347	LAN	Newchurch In Pendle
1600	1700	1600	1700	109347	LAN	Twiston
....	....	1820	1860	107883	WRY	Lothersdale
1800	1850	1600	1850	107883	WRY	Thornton In Craven
1800	1850	1780	1840	107883	YKS	Barnoldswick
1600	....	1600	....	109347	YKS	Gisburn
BULCOCKE						
1663	....	....	1663	149624	LAN	Colne
BULEY						
1779	1854	ALL	1779	175080	DEV	Topsham
1720	1810	1650	1720	173312	FLN	Halkin
BULGER						
....	....	1775	1820	159840	DUB	Dublin
....	....	1830	1900	159840	LAN	Manchester
1866	....	1800	1950	122688	LND	East
1866	....	1800	1950	122688	LND	Poplar

Known From	To	Researching From	To	Ref	Cty	Place
BULGER contd.						
1866	....	1800	1950	122688	LND	Shadwell
BULGIN						
1805	....	ALL	1805	112887	WIL	Bradford On Avon
BULHAND						
1740	1820	1740	1820	158712	LIN	Tealby
BULKELEY						
1540	1620	....	....	107085	BDF	Odell
1764	1854	ALL	ALL	147621	FLN	Halkyn
BULKLEY						
1650	1992	....	....	118672	FLN	Whitford
BULL						
1700	1799	....	....	114243	BDF	Bedford
....	....	1700	1800	134546	BDF	Souldap
1793	1900	ALL	ALL	115681	BDF	St Neots
....	....	1700	1800	134546	BDF	Thurleigh
1759	1811	1759	ALL	175854	BKM	Aston Clinton
1760	1980	....	....	114243	BKM	Newport Pagnell
1490	1992	1450	1992	136794	DBY	ALL
1750	1768	....	....	156647	HAM	Arreton
1780	1980	1600	1780	136859	HAM	Boldre
1699	1787	1600	1767	145289	HAM	Isle Of Wight
1720	1800	1720	1800	127655	HEF	Woofferton
1777	1800	?	1800	164976	HUN	Houghton
1793	1900	ALL	ALL	115681	HUN	St Neots
1845	1992	1700	1845	109177	IOW	Brading
1539	1931	ALL	1870	137774	KEN	South East
1840	1880	1840	1880	167924	KEN	Lewisham
1826	1862	1700	1826	165220	LEI	Leicester
1860	1900	1860	1930	117641	LND	Camberwell
1860	1884	....	1860	131385	LND	Islington
1795	1880	1795	1880	167924	MDX	Stepney
1840	1850	1800	1840	146587	MDX	Uxbridge
1700	1799	....	....	114243	NTH	Irthlingboro
1675	1933	?	1675	177806	OXF	Wardington
1729	1743	1700	1730	103632	RUT	Greetham
1700	1730	1600	1700	151769	RUT	Greetham
1720	1800	1720	1800	127655	SAL	Richards Castle
1702	1833	ALL	1702	129283	SFK	Blundeston
1900	1992	1900	1992	133450	SFK	???
1600	1810	ALL	ALL	112968	SOM	Crewkerne
?	?	ALL	1850	117919	SOM	Kilmersdon
1780	ALL	....	....	142158	SOM	Tintinhull
1580	1992	ALL	1580	106232	SSX	Albourne
1580	1992	ALL	1580	106232	SSX	Cowfold
1800	....	....	....	164038	SSX	???
1490	1992	1450	1992	136794	STS	ALL
1800	1935	....	....	122491	???	Bristol
BULLAMORE						
1790	1830	1700	1790	155950	CAM	Whittlesey
1748	1770	....	1748	151688	NFK	Mundesley
1830	1850	....	....	155950	NTH	Peterborough
BULLARD						
....	....	1700	1900	154377	HRT	ALL
1810	1992	1700	1992	153672	HRT	Hitchin
1700	1930	1700	1930	154377	HUN	ALL
BULLAS						
1802	1820	1700	1802	133167	WAR	Oldbury
1750	1839	1839	1877	110027	YKS	Doncaster
BULLED						
1785	1850	1700	1800	156698	DEV	Witheridge
BULLEN						
1869	1992	1800	1869	161861	CAM	Southery
1860	1880	1800	1880	168998	CHS	Stockport
1815	1845	1700	1800	156795	DOR	North
1840	1860	1700	1930	113646	KEN	Bomley
1779	1820	1750	1820	103632	LAN	Liverpool
1850	1930	1800	1950	176281	LAN	Liverpool
1820	1835	1800	1835	103632	LAN	Manchester
1700	1820	1700	1850	158712	LIN	Tealby
1880	1940	1891	1917	147257	LND	Bow
1869	1992	1800	1869	161861	NFK	Southery
1793	1855	1700	1790	178543	NFK	Swaffham
1784	1877	1700	1900	159581	SRY	Guildford
1892	1992	1850	1892	161861	YKS	Roystone
BULLENT						
1847	1870	1800	1900	178624	NFK	Gorlestone
BULLER						
1800	....	1750	1850	169625	CAM	Haddenham
1805	....	1800	1830	169625	LND	Hoxton
1738	1738	....	1738	136212	OXF	Somerton
1786	1786	....	....	135437	SOM	Kilton
BULLEY						
1791	1992	1700	1791	167541	DEV	Plymouth

Known From	To	Researching From	To	Ref	Cty	Place
BULLEY contd.						
1777	1945	1700	1777	150657	DEV	Torquay
BULLIN						
1840	1874	1840	1900	165654	GLA	Swansea
1780	1876	ALL	1812	165654	SRY	Esher
BULLINGER						
1748	1992	1700	1748	176257	MDX	Stepney
BULLINGHAM						
1800	....	ALL	ALL	125466	NFK	Brockdish
1880	1910	1800	1880	149705	SFK	Saxmundham
BULLIONS						
1756	1916	1700	1916	162442	SCT	ALL
BULLIVANT						
1850	1900	1800	1850	115134	LIN	ALL
1718	1750	1660	1718	177393	NTT	Askham
1740	1760	....	....	177393	NTT	Weston
BULLMORE						
1800	1900	1700	1800	129445	CON	Falmouth
1800	1900	1700	1800	129445	CON	Newlyn East
BULLOCH						
1869	1937	1937	1992	146560	LKS	Coatbride
BULLOCK						
1800	1820	1770	1800	125318	BDF	Woburn
1870	1992	1870	1900	107131	CHS	Macclesfield
1800	1825	ALL	ALL	112496	CON	Mid
1800	1850	1650	1800	115452	CON	Mid
1735	1740	1700	1750	133450	CON	Roche
1770	1850	1700	1800	121312	CON	St Enoder
1750	1900	1780	1900	123773	CON	St Enoder
1800	1850	1700	1800	165549	CON	St Stephen In Brannel
1818	....	ALL	ALL	156558	CON	St Stephen
1862	....	1862	....	123773	CON	Truro
1820	1848	1800	1992	117609	DEV	Devonport
1843	1966	1800	1850	173649	ESS	Gt Dunmow
1700	1750	1600	1750	174513	GLS	Blaisdon
1880	1986	1763	1880	177539	HAM	Heckfield
1762	1910	1910	1992	122793	IOW	ALL
1912	1912	ALL	ALL	109258	MDX	Hounslow
1710	1790	ALL	1720	142301	NBL	Warkworth
1809	1964	1700	1850	117013	NFK	Banningham
1765	1843	1700	1850	117013	NFK	Edgefield
1778	1805	ALL	1810	113611	NFK	Hockwold
....	....	1700	1900	110914	NFK	Holt
1821	1851	1775	1850	101923	NFK	Titchwell
1860	1879	1860	1880	114715	NTT	Sneinton
1820	1895	1820	1895	125318	SSX	Harting
....	....	1700	1900	110914	STS	Burton On Trent
1696	1992	1600	1696	123153	WIL	Nettleton
1600	1700	....	....	167924	YKS	Pocklington
1830	1900	1700	1830	177296	YKS	Settle
BULLOCKE						
1817	1820	1790	1846	126918	LND	South
1817	1820	1790	1846	126918	LND	Clerkenwell
BULMAN						
1830	1860	1700	1880	100439	CMA	Torpenhow
1783	1992	1740	1783	174173	CUL	Irthington
1803	1955	1700	1800	142883	CUL	Scaleby
1760	1950	1650	1760	128376	DUR	Chester Le Street
1816	1890	1816	1890	110396	DUR	Crook
1816	1890	1816	1890	110396	DUR	North Shields
BULMER						
1859	1992	1700	1859	123943	CHS	Hyde
1800	1850	1700	1850	126845	DUR	Darlington
1833	1881	1045	1992	118893	DUR	Merrington
1738	1881	1045	1992	118893	DUR	St Oswalds
1807	1858	1780	1862	144878	HRT	Aldenham
1848	1865	1800	1992	126977	LAN	Litherland
1732	1738	1045	1992	118893	NRY	Guisborough
....	....	1066	1155	124974	WRY	Appletreewick
1800	1862	1750	1800	174203	YKS	Oldmalton
1800	1838	1800	1992	165603	YKS	Skilton
1838	1895	1838	1992	165603	YKS	Yarm
BULPITT						
1800	1850	ALL	ALL	130508	HAM	Andover
1868	1871	1840	1871	119059	WAR	Birmingham
BULT						
1901	1923	1855	1901	166898	SSX	Hastings
BULTITUDE						
1760	1992	1600	1992	135860	NFK	Martham
BUMBY						
1780	1870	1700	1780	157074	ESS	Layer Breton
BUMSTEAD						
....	1700	....	....	174564	SSX	???

Known From	To	Researching From	To	Ref	Cty	Place
BUNBURY						
1839	1839	1600	1839	152080	IRL	Dublin
BUNCE						
1757	....	1650	1770	143693	BKM	Amersham
1840	1892	1700	1850	143693	BKM	Beaconsfield
1900	....	1850	1950	143693	BKM	Cores End
1792	1940	1600	1970	143693	BKM	High Wycombe
1758	1821	1650	1770	143693	BKM	Penn
1894	....	1800	1900	143693	BKM	Princes Risborough
1794	....	1700	1850	143693	BKM	Wooburn
....	....	1700	1850	169471	HRT	???
1692	....	....	1692	171441	KEN	Cheriton
1820	1880	1800	1870	155047	LND	Bethnal Green
1869	1946	1750	1869	153974	MDX	London
1760	1800	1700	1800	177989	OXF	Goring
1760	1800	1700	1800	177989	OXF	Whitchurh
1720	1950	ALL	ALL	117307	WIL	North East
BUNCHAM						
1860	1900	1860	1900	118540	GLS	Forest Of Dean
BUNDAY						
1795	1818	1795	ALL	170968	HAM	Fareham
1836	1900	1700	1836	158232	WIL	Downton
BUNDLE						
1839	....	....	....	173932	LND	Marylebone
1841	....	....	....	173932	LND	St Pancras
1835	....	....	....	173932	SRY	Ashtead
1742	1810	....	....	173932	SRY	Headley
1747	1786	....	....	173932	SRY	Walton On The Hill
BUNDOCK						
....	....	ALL	ALL	114073	ALL	Name Study
1812	1833	....	....	158178	ESS	Gt Braxted
1777	1812	1538	1777	158178	ESS	Layer Breton
1754	1770	1754	1770	114073	ESS	Woodham Walter
1800	1850	....	....	125199	HAM	Exton
1798	1823	1798	1823	114073	LND	Southwark
BUNDRED						
1759	1992	1700	1992	110728	ALL	ALL
BUNDY						
1801	1890	1750	1992	144908	BDF	Eaton Socon
1902	1911	1900	1992	144908	HUN	Little Paxton
1902	1992	1900	1992	144908	HUN	St Neots
1894	1901	1890	1910	144908	SSX	Ringmore
1840	1860	1820	1900	126640	WIL	Alderbury
1763	1836	1700	1850	118397	WIL	Downton
....	....	1800	1900	179361	WIL	Downton
BUNGAY						
....	....	ALL	ALL	110744	ALL	Name Study
1865	1871	1850	1900	171441	BRK	Stanford In The Vale
....	1992	1843	1900	115924	HAM	Southsea
....	1992	1843	1900	115924	MDX	Stanwell
1700	....	....	....	126543	SFK	Old Newton
BUNGEY						
1875	1907	....	....	153397	HAM	New Forest
BUNKER						
1820	1860	....	....	127779	MDX	Holborn
BUNKHAM						
1802	1992	1700	1802	110752	DEV	East Ogwell
BUNKUM						
1700	1800	1600	1700	126357	CON	Menheniot
BUNN						
1730	1760	ALL	1730	115266	DOR	ALL
1903	1903	....	....	148334	HRT	Northcurch
1835	1992	1600	1835	123420	LND	East
1784	1924	1700	1808	110922	NFK	ALL
1740	1875	1700	1740	114871	NFK	Blofield
1800	1992	1700	1800	141402	NFK	Filby
1808	1924	1750	ALL	110922	NFK	Great Yarmouth
1740	1875	1700	1740	114871	NFK	Moulton
1735	1810	1735	1810	116483	SSX	Bury
1600	1700	....	....	100420	WAR	Meriden
BUNNET						
1753	1778	....	....	'35437	NFK	Corpusty
1710	1797	1797	1813	156582	NFK	Corpusty
1710	1805	....	....	135437	NFK	Saxthorpe
1710	1797	1797	1813	156582	NFK	Saxthorpe
BUNNETT						
....	....	ALL	ALL	110760	ALL	Name Study
BUNNEY						
....	....	ALL	ALL	110779	ALL	Name Study
1904	1925	1885	1992	113719	GLA	Penrhiwceiber
1752	1850	1700	1752	127116	HAM	Hursley
1884	1885	1850	1884	113719	LAN	Skelmers Dale
BUNNING						
....	....	ALL	ALL	110787	ALL	Name Study
1575	1699	1550	1575	102830	LIN	Bourne
BUNSTON						
1719	1760	ALL	ALL	107565	SOM	Wayford
BUNT						
1750	1800	1700	1850	148784	CON	Fowey
1837	1992	1600	1873	110795	CON	Lostwithiel
1800	1900	1800	1900	171077	CON	St Breock
1813	1900	1800	1992	148784	HAM	Portsea
BUNTEN						
1800	1940	....	....	135453	RFW	Cathcart
BUNTING						
....	....	ALL	ALL	110809	ALL	Name Study
1820	1844	1700	1844	121932	DBY	Bonsall
1820	1844	1700	1844	121932	DBY	Crich
1641	1651	1600	1641	147745	DBY	Matlock
1750	1870	1700	1750	160458	DBY	Matlock
1820	1844	1700	1844	121932	DBY	Tansley
1820	1870	1750	1950	115215	LKS	Glasgow
1840	1899	1800	1900	169978	LND	City
1767	1767	....	....	135437	NFK	Fakenham
1800	1992	1600	1800	166103	SFK	Cowlinge
1700	....	....	....	114642	SFK	Exning
1604	1606	ALL	1628	156175	SXE	???
BUNTON						
1720	1900	1650	1720	124168	DUR	Witton Gilbert
1788	1905	1788	1905	108006	ESS	Hempstead
BUNYAN						
1851	1980	1837	1851	119059	BKM	Brill
....	....	....	1900	110817	HRT	Hertford
....	....	....	1900	110817	LND	Bethnal Green
....	....	....	1920	110817	LND	Hampstead
....	....	....	1920	110817	LND	Marylebone
1875	1992	1875	1992	110825	MDX	London
BURBERY						
1817	1903	1700	1817	176575	LEI	Seagrave
BURBIDGE						
1837	1980	ALL	ALL	172251	HAM	Portsmouth
....	....	ALL	1900	116181	LEI	Leicester
1773	1825	1706	1772	162825	NTH	Paston
1840	1881	1825	1881	162825	NTH	Peterborough
1764	1771	1594	1812	107360	NTH	Upton
1830	1880	1820	1880	159700	WIL	Amesbury
1800	1840	1800	1840	178705	WIL	Salisbury
BURBRIDGE						
....	....	....	1830	137405	HUN	St Ives
1854	1939	1855	1950	160067	MDX	Tottenham
1800	1861	1780	1871	160067	SRY	Kew
1800	1840	1800	1840	178705	WIL	Salisbury
BURCH						
1775	1850	1735	....	110833	ESS	North East
1850	ALL	1850	ALL	110833	LND	Bermondsey
1880	ALL	1850	ALL	110833	LND	Greenwich
1890	ALL	1850	ALL	110833	LND	West Ham
1780	1820	1750	1850	124605	NTH	Kings Sutton
....	....	ALL	1775	110833	SFK	South
1853	1992	ALL	ALL	133051	SFK	Stowupland
1630	1750	1630	1730	156930	WIL	Aldbourne
BURCHALL						
1850	1900	1700	1850	118915	OXF	ALL
BURCHELL						
1800	1850	1750	1850	152900	KEN	Deptford
1907	1941	1750	1908	129143	PEM	Lamphey
1907	1941	1750	1908	129143	PEM	Pembroke
....	....	?	?	143499	WIL	Hilmarton
1841	1853	1841	1853	118931	WIL	Lyneham
BURCHER						
1784	1850	1700	1784	118079	SSX	Arundel
BURCHETT						
....	....	ALL	ALL	110841	ALL	ALL
1850	1865	1850	1870	154873	KEN	Chatham
1800	1850	1800	1900	111147	NFK	ALL
1650	1700	1650	1730	110841	SSX	East Dean
1814	1860	1750	1814	154873	SSX	Rye
1732	1844	1700	1732	100277	SSX	Wartling
BURCHILL						
ALL	1800	ALL	1800	142425	GLS	South
BURCHNALL						
1500	1860	1600	1910	169323	LEI	Thurcaston
BURDEKIN						
....	....	ALL	ALL	161462	ALL	Name Study
1890	1930	1890	1930	177792	LAN	St Helens
1759	1896	1700	1900	109290	YKS	South

Known From	To	Researching From	To	Ref	Cty	Place
BURDEN						
?	?	1900	1992	167096	BRK	Windsor
1830	....	1700	1881	152722	DOR	Wareham
1830	1851	1700	....	152722	DOR	Worgret
1867	1882	....	....	155594	DOW	Hillsborough
....	....	1820	1860	155594	DOW	Rathfriland
1761	1794	ALL	1761	158445	DUR	Durham
1855	1992	1800	1855	179442	HAM	Boarhunt Mill
1810	....	1840	1992	110868	LEX	Ireland
1940	1950	1900	1960	167096	LND	Islington
?	1880	1700	1992	167096	OXF	St Clements
....	....	1800	1890	126136	SSX	Bosham
?	?	1890	1992	167096	WAR	Birmingham
1700	1992	1650	1700	133434	WIL	Semley
1704	....	1680	1740	170348	WIL	Wroughton
BURDES						
1858	1992	1700	1860	161772	ENG	???
BURDETT						
1735	1795	....	1735	116777	ESS	Eastwood
1700	1800	....	1800	177695	LEI	Bringhust
1765	1900	1700	1765	124583	LEI	Gumley
....	....	1600	1710	150150	LEI	Husbands Bosworth
1880	1911	1880	1933	109223	LND	ALL
1840	1940	1840	1942	100951	LND	North
1818	1841	1818	1950	100951	NFK	St Faiths
1710	1992	1600	1710	150150	NTH	ALL
1848	1880	1700	1880	109223	YKS	Knostrope
BURDFIELD						
1800	1900	1750	1900	155357	SXW	Itchenfield
BURDGE						
....	....	ALL	ALL	110876	ALL	Name Study
1826	1894	1826	1992	110876	SOM	Bridgewater
BURDICK						
....	....	ALL	ALL	150134	ALL	Name Study
BURDON						
1650	1851	1600	1900	110884	DUR	???
1756	1777	1700	1780	141046	PER	Crieff
BURFIELD						
1798	1855	1700	1800	103896	BRK	Hungerford
1730	1736	1700	1750	123137	KEN	West Peckham
BURFOOT						
1566	1846	1850	1950	110892	KEN	Cowden
1558	1836	1836	1950	110892	KEN	Haldow
....	....	1560	1900	110892	KEN	Headcorn
1632	1849	1849	1900	110892	KEN	Hever
1578	1840	1840	1900	110892	SRY	Horley
1747	1848	1848	1900	110892	SSX	Horsham
BURFORD						
1739	1739	1650	1800	148938	GLS	Berkeley
1815	1871	....	....	160482	GLS	Dowdeswell
....	....	1650	1750	110515	GLS	Preston On Stour
1760	1778	....	....	160482	GLS	Whittington
1815	1871	....	....	160482	GLS	Withington
1840	1890	1500	1890	137472	KEN	Chatham
1840	1890	1500	1890	137472	KEN	Gillingham
1840	1890	1500	1890	137472	KEN	North Aylesford
1840	1890	1500	1890	137472	KEN	Rochester
1840	1890	1500	1890	137472	KEN	Strood
1810	1900	1600	1810	170194	LND	ALL
1750	1800	1750	1800	126209	WOR	Dormston
1881	1927	....	....	121290	WOR	Dudley
BURGAR						
1740	1992	1492	1770	110965	OKI	ALL
1773	1835	ALL	1773	167878	OKI	Pap Westray
BURGE						
1820	1850	1770	1820	149462	CON	Breage
ALL	ALL	ALL	ALL	124206	DOR	ALL
BURGEN						
1637	1768	1637	1768	103977	HRT	Aldenham
BURGER						
1800	1992	1800	1992	125679	LND	ALL
BURGES						
1780	1807	1700	1850	140260	BRK	Thatcham
1773	1795	ALL	ALL	124982	SOM	ALL
1760	1820	1700	1800	136840	SOM	Brendon Hills
....	....	1600	1830	166863	SOM	Bristrol
BURGESS						
1739	....	1700	1800	162280	ABD	Cabrach
1802	1809	1802	1860	110922	BDF	Barton In The Clay
1707	1802	1602	1812	110922	BDF	Luton
1701	1940	....	....	128996	CAM	Thorney
....	....	1790	1850	110930	CHS	Acton
1873	1877	1873	1873	145580	CHS	Bromborough
1850	1883	....	....	110930	CHS	Burleydam

Known From	To	Researching From	To	Ref	Cty	Place
BURGESS contd.						
1800	1900	1740	1850	155047	CHS	Burleydam
....	....	1760	1800	110930	CHS	Cholmeston
1800	1850	1700	1980	124133	CHS	Northwich
1850	1901	1800	1850	141135	CHS	Wilmslow
1850	1992	1700	1850	110914	CHS	???
1800	1900	1800	1900	139718	CON	Camborne
1727	1861	ALL	ALL	165972	DEV	Witheridge
1760	1800	....	....	159883	DOR	Bere Regis
1860	1900	....	....	159883	DOR	Holt
1820	1870	....	....	159883	DOR	Tarrant Launceston
1740	1800	1600	1750	120839	EYK	???
1800	1850	1750	1850	173428	HAM	Buriton
1841	....	....	....	170526	HAM	Portsmouth
1802	1992	1750	1900	148725	HRT	Cheshunt
1825	1950	ALL	ALL	164887	HRT	Rickmansworth
1800	1893	1700	1900	116742	HRT	Stanstead
1880	1900	....	....	164631	KEN	Burham
1712	1850	....	....	164631	KEN	Cranbrook
1849	1900	....	....	164631	KEN	Goudhurst
1600	1712	....	....	164631	KEN	Tonbridge
1783	1900	ALL	1783	119687	KEN	Wittersham
1790	1980	1700	1850	159964	KKD	Kirkpatrick Durham
1897	1987	....	....	145580	LAN	Liverpool
1866	1992	1700	1866	116181	LEI	West
1844	1900	1750	1844	138010	LEI	Leicester
....	1759	1700	1800	163201	LEI	Leicester
1680	1980	ALL	ALL	111406	LEI	Whitwick
1700	1920	ALL	1700	168955	LIN	ALL
....	....	ALL	ALL	143014	LND	ALL
1850	1950	1850	1900	111791	LND	Greenwich
1883	1902	1700	1950	172316	LND	Shoreditch
1897	1983	1890	ALL	110922	LND	Tooting
1883	1902	1700	1950	172316	LND	Walworth
ALL	1825	ALL	1825	102334	MDX	Paddington
1825	1872	1820	ALL	110922	MDX	Wesminster
1816	....	....	....	135518	NTT	Radford
1855	1941	....	....	110930	SAL	Whitchurch
....	....	?	?	173851	SCT	???
....	....	1600	1830	166863	SOM	Bristrol
1832	1918	ALL	ALL	122386	SOM	Long Ashton
....	....	ALL	ALL	143014	SRY	ALL
1650	1750	ALL	1700	115282	SSX	East
1880	1992	1700	1925	110949	SSX	Brighton
1800	1850	1700	1800	139106	SSX	???
....	....	1800	....	137456	WAR	Dunchurch
1790	1840	....	1790	113891	WIL	Calne
1761	1797	ALL	1761	158445	WIL	Potterne
....	....	ALL	1740	151602	WIL	Wilcot
BURGESSE						
1683	1751	1650	1760	123404	NFK	North Elmham
1675	....	1600	1683	123404	NFK	Weasenham
BURGH						
1805	1810	1800	1830	118842	LND	Strand
1875	1978	1870	1980	118842	MDX	North
1867	1873	1840	1900	118842	MDX	Bethnal Green
1869	1932	1800	1869	118842	MDX	Chelsea
1931	1933	1930	1935	118842	MDX	Fulham
1863	1864	1860	1890	118842	MDX	Kensington
1866	....	1840	1880	118842	MDX	Paddington
1940	1978	1900	1940	118842	MDX	Ruislip
1832	1856	1830	1900	118842	MDX	St Pancras
1882	1937	1856	1882	118842	MDX	Tottenham
BURGHAM						
1789	1992	1650	1789	110957	GLS	Little Dean
BURGIN						
....	....	1600	1800	136743	LEI	Saltby
BURGIS						
....	....	ALL	ALL	143510	ALL	Name Study
BURGOYNE						
....	....	ALL	ALL	110973	ALL	Name Study
1789	1808	1789	1808	136808	CAM	Cambridge
BURGUM						
....	....	ALL	ALL	110981	ALL	Name Study
1580	1992	ALL	ALL	110981	ALL	ALL
BURK						
....	....	1650	1700	177393	YKS	Wiston
BURKE						
1803	....	1750	1835	148288	ARM	Keady
1830	1860	1800	1880	118435	CHS	Birkenhead
1850	1850	1100	1850	117749	GAL	???
1897	1971	1800	1897	103853	HAM	Ringwood
1860	1900	....	....	110159	IRL	West
1750	1800	ALL	1992	170909	KIK	Muckalee

Known From	To	Researching From	To	Ref	Cty	Place
BURKE contd.						
1890	1992	1700	1890	131903	LAN	Manchester
1900	1950	1920	1940	110159	LND	ALL
1841	1890	ALL	....	153214	MDX	Somers Town
1841	1890	ALL	....	153214	MDX	St Pancras
1850	1945	1840	1945	100218	WAR	Coventry
1815	1840	....	....	110159	WRY	Bradford
1857	1992	1830	1857	141879	YKS	Rotherham
....	....	1650	1700	177393	YKS	Wiston
BURKETT						
1733	1837	....	1851	137405	CAM	Willingham
BURKIN						
....	....	ALL	ALL	177857	ALL	Name Study
BURKINSHAW						
1870	1900	1700	1870	126772	YKS	Sheffield
BURKITT						
1760	1992	ALL	ALL	154806	LIN	Alford
BURLAND						
1760	1780	1750	1800	153451	HEF	Kent Church
1800	1880	1800	1880	153451	???	Bristol
BURLE						
1676	1690	1676	1690	178705	BRK	Reading
BURLETON						
1826	1988	1750	1826	165271	ALL	ALL
BURLEY						
1300	1450	1250	1450	154881	ALL	ALL
1700	1930	....	....	153745	CON	Tregony Gwennap
1865	....	1800	1900	139114	DEV	Plymouth
1816	....	....	....	124982	GLS	Berkeley
1694	1753	....	....	165999	LIN	Lincoln
1850	1992	....	....	126101	WAR	???
1850	1992	....	....	126101	???	Birmingham
BURLING						
....	....	1730	1820	103713	CAM	Waterbeach
BURLINGHAM						
....	....	....	....	125466	NFK	ALL
1710	1720	1650	1710	155276	SFK	Earl Stonham
1788	1850	ALL	ALL	125466	SFK	Wattisfield
BURLOW						
1680	1900	1680	1992	138193	GLS	Dymock
BURLTON						
1600	1960	....	....	166510	ENG	???
BURMAN						
1881	1890	1881	1890	101877	LND	Clerkenwell
1750	1992	1750	1992	111007	LND	Islington
1858	1862	1858	1862	101877	LND	St Lukes
1750	1910	....	....	168041	NFK	Great Yarmouth
1788	1858	1788	1858	101877	SFK	Bramford
1826	1865	1826	1865	101877	SFK	Ipswich
BURN						
1816	1846	1600	1816	115169	DUR	Darlington
1750	1880	1750	1880	117641	HAM	Test Valley
....	....	1700	1850	179191	PER	Blairingone
1797	....	....	....	103942	SRY	Newington
1802	1815	....	1992	103942	SRY	Walworth
1900	1948	1800	1992	113956	T&W	Dunston
1900	1948	1800	1992	113956	T&W	Gateshead
1750	1992	1650	1750	102342	WRY	Adlingfleet
1820	1880	....	....	131717	???	Clonsalee
BURNAND						
1765	1796	1700	1800	162248	NRY	Aldborough
BURNARD						
1790	1992	1650	1790	154415	CON	Altarnun
1750	....	1750	1900	106410	SOM	Long Sutton
BURNE						
1800	1840	1700	1900	162132	CMA	Penrith
1700	1762	1600	1992	103942	CUL	Alston
1793	1800	1750	1992	103942	CUL	Penrith
1790	1924	1800	1992	103942	NBL	Newbiggin
1756	1790	1700	1992	103942	NBL	Temple Sowerby
BURNELL						
1797	1840	1700	1797	168351	BKM	Quainton
1836	....	1750	1836	105457	LND	???
1548	1727	1727	1832	169889	NTT	Winkburn
1790	1850	1700	1850	136840	SOM	Brendon Hills
1800	1992	1600	1800	148059	SOM	Cannington
1895	1959	1840	1895	126470	SRY	Lambeth
1707	1707	....	....	103632	WAR	Edgbaston
BURNES						
1881	1890	1877	1886	111090	DUR	???
BURNET						
1586	1586	1500	1600	176389	NYK	Eryholme
BURNETT						
....	....	ALL	ALL	111015	ALL	Name Study

Known From	To	Researching From	To	Ref	Cty	Place
BURNETT contd.						
1750	1960	1750	1850	140864	ABD	Fraserburgh
1800	1820	1800	1820	121096	ABD	Howburn
1845	....	1845	1859	129305	ANS	Dundee
1856	1957	1800	1992	129739	CMA	Cockermouth
1800	1856	1800	1992	129739	CMA	Workington
1710	1789	ALL	1789	168718	CON	South East
1830	1870	1800	1900	126799	HAM	Abbotts Ann
1775	1800	1700	1775	121010	HAM	Andover
1828	1851	1828	1851	131970	HAM	Andover
1800	1830	1750	1850	126799	HAM	Portsea
1880	1992	1830	1880	103985	HAM	Portsmouth
1828	1851	1828	1874	131970	HAM	Southampton
....	....	1800	1850	123277	HEF	Bramyard
1837	1912	1837	1900	153990	LND	???
1794	1803	....	....	133299	MDX	London
1818	1918	1850	1992	129739	MSY	Liverpool
1884	1940	....	....	114715	NIR	Cook Town
1810	1860	ALL	1860	149063	ROX	Sprouston
1760	1900	1600	1760	149888	SOM	Cossington
1860	1992	1700	1860	117633	SRY	Croydon
1625	1670	1600	1720	160873	STS	Kingswinford
1841	1881	1800	1841	127116	WIL	Amesbury
1860	....	....	....	161136	YKS	Sheffield
BURNEY						
1762	1913	1700	1760	156221	HAM	Gosport
1794	1846	1750	1794	144223	IRL	Armagh
BURNHAM						
1830	1870	1830	1870	107980	DUR	South Shields
1861	1992	....	....	111023	LAN	Manchester
1775	1871	1871	1992	111023	LIN	Spalding
1810	1840	1700	1820	131377	NTH	Rothwell
BURNHOLE						
1830	1992	1700	1830	148059	SOM	Cannington
BURNINGHAM						
1530	1876	....	....	115606	HAM	Froyle
BURNISTON						
....	....	ALL	ALL	111058	ALL	Name Study
1830	1992	1700	1830	111058	DEV	Plymouth
1792	1992	ALL	ALL	111058	HAM	Basingstoke
....	....	1750	1820	111058	MDX	Barnet
....	....	ALL	ALL	111058	YKS	ALL
BURNS						
1725	1992	1700	1725	169897	ANS	Arbroath
1889	1992	....	....	132918	ANS	Dundee
....	1833	1750	1850	101893	CAM	Hrston
1831	1850	....	....	132918	FIF	Cupar
1750	1992	1700	1725	169897	FIF	Cupar
1800	1830	1800	1850	153354	IRL	Carvan
....	....	1800	1858	160474	IRL	Wicklow
1854	1881	ALL	ALL	106216	IRL	???
1870	1960	1700	1870	125415	IRL	???
1840	1860	1500	1992	175498	IRL	???
1850	1856	....	....	132918	JSY	St Hellier
1866	1886	....	....	111066	KEN	Rochester
1700	....	1600	....	116920	LAN	Colton
....	....	....	1851	145742	LAN	Manchester
1821	1952	....	....	171824	LAN	Rainford
1858	1909	1800	1858	160474	LAN	Ulverston
1826	1992	1850	1992	111074	LET	???
1840	1860	1500	1992	175498	LND	Blackfriars
1850	1960	1850	1960	117641	LND	Hampstead
?	....	....	?	111104	LND	???
1859	1864	....	....	132918	LTN	Leith
....	....	1800	1910	126217	MDX	Poplar
....	....	1700	1850	179191	PER	Blairingone
1824	1826	ALL	1825	112887	PER	???
1881	....	....	....	137936	RFW	Glasgow
1841	1870	1800	1841	146358	RFW	Paisley
1841	1870	1800	1841	146358	RFW	Port Glasgow
?	....	....	?	111104	SRY	Sutton
1832	1913	....	....	135453	STI	Falkirk
1847	1982	1777	1847	147060	YKS	Leeds
1826	1992	1850	1992	111074	???	Glasgow
BURR						
....	....	1800	....	137456	BDF	Cople
1790	1900	1700	1992	113743	BKM	ALL
1850	1874	1850	1992	111112	HEF	Barnet
1867	1909	1850	1992	111112	HEF	London Colney
1785	1808	1600	1800	111112	HEF	St Albans
1830	1880	1800	1900	113743	HRT	Tring
1705	1732	....	....	171654	LIN	Tetford
1850	1900	1800	1900	113743	MDX	Harrow
1811	1850	1800	1850	111112	MDX	London Enfield

Known From	To	Researching From	To	Ref	Cty	Place
BURR contd.						
1863	1992	1600	1862	110795	NIR	Londonderry
BURRAGE						
....	....	ALL	ALL	135062	DOR	Compton Abbas
1870	1992	1700	1870	148865	LND	???
BURREE						
....	....	ALL	ALL	111120	ALL	Name Study
1760	1775	ALL	1760	111120	DOR	ALL
1755	1780	ALL	1755	111120	SOM	ALL
1757	1782	ALL	1757	111120	WIL	ALL
BURRELL						
1820	....	....	....	146870	DBY	Chester Le Street
1636	1709	1500	1636	175072	LIN	Billinghay
1765	1852	1730	1765	157775	LND	Newington
....	....	1700	1800	128627	LND	???
....	....	1823	1880	176893	MGY	Llangurig
....	....	1823	1880	176893	MGY	Llanidloes
1600	1992	1600	1992	111147	NFK	ALL
....	....	1700	1850	140627	NFK	Norwich
1776	1992	....	....	139351	NFK	Smallburgh
1775	1945	ALL	1775	131091	SSX	ALL
BURREN						
1840	1890	1750	1840	132632	KEN	Staplehurst
1840	1890	1750	1840	132632	KEN	Tunbridge Wells
BURRIDGE						
1780	1850	....	....	165255	BDF	Eaton Bray
1772	1807	1500	1772	129577	IOW	???
?	?	?	?	129577	SOM	???
BURRILL						
1763	1869	1600	1770	101575	LIN	Billinghay
BURRIS						
....	....	....	....	165433	GLS	???
BURROUGH						
....	....	ALL	1600	138169	DEV	North Petherton
1700	1800	ALL	1700	138169	DEV	White Stuanton
BURROUGHS						
1830	1850	1750	1830	128775	BRK	Reading
1863	1992	1600	1862	178101	DUR	W Hartlepoll
1850	1886	1800	1850	169757	ESS	ALL
1700	1700	1700	1700	136808	HRT	Barkway
1769	....	....	1769	171441	OXF	Stanton St John
1750	1917	1750	1917	163813	SAL	Cockshutt
1810	1875	1750	1810	167533	SFK	Bury St Edmund
1820	1840	1750	1900	139386	SFK	Cotton
1840	....	....	1840	164011	WOR	Worcester
BURROW						
1550	1900	1550	1900	106593	CON	Morewentow
1780	1992	1780	1992	106593	DEV	Woolfardisworthy
1547	1610	ALL	ALL	141615	LAN	Whittington
1640	1700	1640	1710	142018	SOM	ALL
1857	1992	1800	1857	111163	SRY	Lambeth
1764	....	....	1860	171441	WOR	Ombersley
1764	1826	....	1860	171441	WOR	Worcester
1841	1888	1700	1841	167355	YKS	Fylingdale
BURROWS						
1700	1950	1600	1700	101400	BDF	South
1900	1940	1700	1900	151955	BKM	Aylesbury
1863	1910	....	....	177407	BRK	Reading
1840	1880	1800	1840	173312	CHS	Chester
1821	....	1821	....	147532	CUL	Heskett In The Forest
1830	1850	1830	1850	140295	GLS	Cheltenham
1900	1992	1800	1900	150061	GLS	Gloucester
1792	1853	1750	1880	125563	GLS	Westbury On Severn
1750	1860	1750	1860	167924	HRT	Holwell
1750	1850	1750	1850	167924	HRT	Ickleford
1850	1961	1750	1880	113476	LAN	Burnley
1795	1795	1745	1830	174211	LAN	Burnley
1700	1992	1700	1992	158038	LAN	Cronton
....	1823	1800	1900	146978	LAN	Farnworth
1700	1992	1700	1992	158038	LAN	Farnworth
....	....	1700	1800	147613	LAN	Melling
1764	1819	ALL	ALL	107913	LAN	St Helens
1700	1992	1700	1992	158038	LAN	Tarbock
1600	1820	1600	1820	100420	LEI	ALL
1721	1763	1550	1575	102830	LIN	Kirkby Green
1800	1900	ALL	ALL	131873	LND	Westminster
1831	1980	1800	1870	140325	MDX	Pinner
1860	1890	....	....	166189	MDX	Uxbridge
1800	1837	1800	1837	140295	MON	Penwaine
1700	1950	1550	1700	129763	NTH	West
1770	1795	1600	1820	100420	NTH	Claycoton
1700	1863	1600	1700	177407	NTH	Long Buckby
1850	1900	1800	1850	116823	NTT	ALL
BURROWS contd.						
1798	1900	1600	1900	124834	NTT	East Leake
1900	1992	....	....	162183	NTT	Nottingham
1820	1900	1750	1820	164860	SFK	Clopton
1800	1890	ALL	ALL	111155	SFK	Leiston
1809	1813	1750	1850	159956	SFK	Market Weston
?	1850	ALL	ALL	111155	SFK	Parliam
1837	1992	1750	1827	176257	SFK	Sweffling
1695	1800	1600	1992	122211	SRY	Lambeth
....	....	1800	1900	167916	STS	Simethwick
1730	1820	1600	1820	100420	WAR	Willey
1740	1760	1700	1740	160458	WES	Heversham
1900	1960	1700	1900	151955	WIL	Swindon
....	....	1700	1800	147613	YKS	Bentham
BURRUP						
1670	1783	1670	1783	165999	GLS	ALL
BURRY						
1807	1862	ALL	1800	117366	BRK	Abingdon
BURSBY						
1800	....	....	....	126993	ALL	ALL
BURSEY						
1700	1900	1500	1992	126799	HAM	Holdenhurst
1709	1842	1650	1709	174289	HAM	Holdenhurst
BURSLEM						
1730	1765	1650	1730	120049	STS	Horton
BURSTON						
1875	1992	1871	1992	121568	GLA	Cardiff
1772	1992	1700	1992	121568	SOM	Ash Priors
1939	1945	1900	1992	121568	SRY	Croydon
BURSTOW						
1858	1960	1750	1858	134473	KEN	Lewisham
1869	1917	1800	1869	174955	SSX	Broadwater
BURT						
1700	ALL	1795	1845	107379	BKM	W'ton Turville
1750	....	1600	1750	149608	CON	Jacobstow
1739	1992	1600	1739	127116	DOR	Witchampton
1700	ALL	1830	1900	107379	HRT	Tring
1800	1900	ALL	ALL	175285	IOW	ALL
1830	1860	1800	1830	125318	KEN	Harbledown
1858	ALL	ALL	1858	116734	MDX	London
1858	ALL	ALL	1858	116734	MDX	Shorditch
1750	1880	1650	1800	144606	SOM	South
1704	1794	1657	1794	170143	SRY	Brupham
1704	1794	1657	1794	170143	SRY	Worplesdon
1850	1900	1800	1900	129976	SSX	Hastings
1500	1900	1500	1900	170216	WIL	ALL
BURTE						
1614	1614	1550	1660	105333	DEV	Buckland In The Moor
1614	1614	1550	1660	105333	DEV	Holne
1614	1614	1550	1660	105333	DEV	Ilsington
1614	1614	1550	1660	105333	DEV	Lydford
1614	1614	1550	1660	105333	DEV	Widecombe In The Moor
BURTENSHAW						
?	?	?	?	121185	KEN	ALL
1760	1992	1500	1760	164879	SSX	ALL
1860	....	1860	....	135488	SSX	Brighton
1795	1812	1600	1795	147885	SSX	West Grinstead
BURTOFT						
1926	....	ALL	ALL	119180	DUR	North
BURTON						
1813	1864	1700	1813	144711	CAM	Doddington
1887	1930	1880	1950	179701	CHS	Hough
1867	....	ALL	1867	160008	CHS	Stockport
1813	1992	1750	1950	117609	CON	Bodmin
1813	1992	1750	1950	117609	CON	Constantine
1813	1992	1750	1950	117609	CON	Redruth
1830	1900	1757	1830	125636	DBY	Long Eaton
1830	1900	1757	1830	125636	DBY	Shardlow
1815	1840	1750	1815	111236	DBY	Winster
1761	1829	1827	ALL	154946	ERY	Pickering
1569	1708	....	....	165999	ESS	Earls Colne
1924	....	1920	1930	163775	ESS	West Ham
....	1790	....	....	174564	ESS	???
1819	1900	1790	1819	158739	GLA	Pendoylan
1840	1860	1800	1840	148113	HRT	Hoddesdon
1572	1848	1550	1572	102830	HUN	Orton Waterville
1800	1900	....	....	151785	HUN	Spaldwick
....	1780	ALL	1780	152889	HUN	St Neots
1774	1810	1700	1773	144711	HUN	Upwood
1733	1736	....	1750	171441	KEN	Bethersden
1819	1830	1700	1819	148113	KEN	Dartford
1802	....	1802	....	117250	KEN	Dungeness

Known From	To	Researching From	To	Ref	Cty	Place
BURTON contd.						
1800	1921	1750	1992	147982	KEN	Eltham
1800	1921	1750	1992	147982	KEN	Orpington
1832	1861	1750	1861	100390	LAN	???
1824	1850	1700	1900	135968	LEI	Woodhouse
1900	1960	1800	1920	112038	LIN	Bourne
1868	1891	1800	1992	117609	LND	Camberwell
....	....	1840	1880	148113	LND	Chelsea
1768	1851	1750	1851	124028	MDX	Chelsea
1840	....	ALL	1840	174637	MDX	London
1888	1902	ALL	1888	146714	NBL	ALL
1805	1881	1800	1900	123021	NFK	Aylsham
1850	?	1750	1850	171034	NFK	Great Yarmouth
1901	1982	....	....	176966	NTT	Hucknall
1800	1820	1800	1820	151599	NTT	Nottingham
1816	....	ALL	ALL	105481	NTT	Old Basford
1780	1850	1700	1800	137618	NTT	Sutton In Ashfield
1700	1750	1600	1700	172901	NTT	???
1800	1805	1700	1800	121339	NYK	Felixkirk
1766	1782	1740	1782	147311	NYK	Whitby
....	1856	....	....	128988	PER	Alyth
ALL	1856	....	....	128988	RFW	Paisley
....	....	ALL	ALL	111228	SAL	South
1880	1920	ALL	ALL	126659	SAL	Clee Hill
1811	1889	1800	1992	179701	SAL	Cold Hatton
....	1928	ALL	ALL	165484	SAL	High Ercall
1800	1850	1700	1850	135941	SFK	Great Wratting
1800	1850	1700	1850	135941	SFK	Little Thurlow
....	....	1800	1950	170879	SOM	Bath
1575	1770	....	....	160539	SOM	Sutton Montis
1820	1890	1750	1900	145556	SSX	Buxted
1790	1790	....	....	139971	SSX	Eastbourne
1820	1890	1750	1900	145556	SSX	Uckfield
1820	1890	1750	1900	145556	SSX	West Firle
....	....	ALL	1888	146714	STS	Cheadle
1814	1814	1750	1814	179116	STS	Ipstones
1867	1887	1850	1890	179701	STS	Onneley
....	....	1875	....	118850	WAR	Birmingham
1800	1900	1700	1800	171182	WIL	South
1800	1900	1700	1800	171182	WIL	West
1819	1838	ALL	1819	175080	WIL	Donhead St Andrew
1772	1850	1600	1900	150576	WIL	Tisbury
1750	1900	1700	1750	157708	WOR	Hagley
1696	....	....	....	131229	WOR	Worcester
1880	1960	....	....	137618	WRY	Castleford
1826	1889	....	1826	111171	WYK	Bradford
....	....	ALL	1839	111384	WYK	Brotherton
1600	1756	1600	1900	154601	WYK	Horbury
1830	1950	1600	1830	152730	YKS	Cottingham
1869	1992	1800	1992	111201	YKS	Sheffield
1848	....	1555	1848	126462	YKS	Sutton On The Forest
1850	1910	1700	1850	118478	YKS	Whitby
1802	1839	1727	1839	117250	???	Lewisham
....	1804	1727	1804	117250	???	Southend
BURVILL						
1815	1836	ALL	1815	119296	KEN	Sandwich
BURVILLE						
....	....	ALL	ALL	111244	ALL	Name Study
BURWASH						
1250	1350	1200	1350	154881	SSX	Burwash
BURWIN						
1776	1830	1776	1830	153621	WYK	Oxenhope
BURWOOD						
1750	1850	1700	1850	126799	NFK	Lowestoft
1700	1992	1500	1950	111252	NFK	Yarmouth
1700	1992	1500	1950	111252	SFK	Aldeburgh
1730	1750	1700	1750	129003	SFK	Hollesley
1700	1992	1500	1950	111252	SFK	Lowestoft
1700	1992	1500	1950	111252	SFK	Southwold
BURY						
1750	1900	1750	1900	125237	LAN	Darwen
1800	1880	1880	1992	162256	LAN	Darwen
BUSAIN						
....	1830	ALL	1850	118338	KEN	???
BUSBY						
1850	1860	1800	1850	109533	BKM	North Crawley
1880	1965	1880	1963	140295	GLA	Cardiff
1809	1865	1800	1889	103640	MDX	Bethnal Green
1809	1865	1800	1889	103640	MDX	Holborn
1850	1890	1890	1930	109533	MDX	St Pancras
1820	1850	1800	1820	109533	MDX	Strand
1742	1796	1550	1741	102830	NTH	Bythorn
1835	1845	ALL	ALL	176060	OXF	Deddington

Known From	To	Researching From	To	Ref	Cty	Place
BUSBY contd.						
1740	1875	1740	1890	140295	OXF	Minster Lovell
1723	1835	ALL	1723	176060	OXF	Minster Lovell
1800	1820	....	....	145394	OXF	North Leigh
1867	1883	1860	1884	140295	???	Bristol
BUSCOMBE						
1805	1970	1700	1805	111279	CON	ALL
1805	1970	1700	1805	111279	DEV	Braunton
BUSFEILD						
1650	1992	1500	1850	124079	YKS	ALL
BUSFIELD						
1848	1992	ALL	1898	111066	WRY	ALL
BUSH						
....	1860	....	....	135682	BRK	Childrey
1560	1585	....	....	135682	BRK	Great Faringdon
1600	....	....	....	135682	BRK	Langford
1600	1860	....	....	135682	BRK	Sparsholt
....	....	....	1800	173177	CAM	Elm
1650	1750	ALL	1650	115266	DOR	ALL
1850	1930	1700	1850	118915	ESS	Fobbing
1746	1914	1650	1746	145823	ESS	Halstead
1786	1887	ALL	1887	114030	ESS	Saffron Walden
1746	1914	1650	1746	145823	ESS	Stambourne
1470	1560	....	....	135682	GLS	Northleach
1720	1770	1650	1770	136840	HAM	Fordingbridge
....	....	1750	1850	124702	HRT	Bishops Stortford
1823	1974	ALL	1992	179205	LIN	Bolingbroke
1823	1974	ALL	1992	179205	LIN	Boston
1790	....	ALL	....	104515	LIN	Potterhanworth
1823	1974	ALL	1992	179205	LIN	Wyberton
1820	1992	ALL	1820	134805	NFK	Hardingham
1790	1992	ALL	1720	134805	NFK	Hingham
1790	1870	1790	1992	111287	NFK	Norwich
1759	1809	....	....	139211	NFK	Tottington
1750	1790	1750	1992	111287	NFK	Wymondham
1742	1775	1600	1741	131245	WAR	Frankton
BUSHBY						
....	....	ALL	ALL	111309	ALL	Name Study
ALL	ALL	ALL	ALL	111309	ALL	ALL
1831	1842	....	....	128511	CUL	Brampton
1900	1971	....	....	128511	CUL	Carlisle
1797	1802	1650	1797	128511	CUL	Penrith
1851	....	....	....	128511	DUR	Durham
1809	1992	1700	1809	110639	MDX	???
1802	1871	....	....	128511	NBL	Hexham
1809	1992	1700	1809	110639	SSX	???
1740	1800	1650	1800	138878	WES	ALL
BUSHELL						
1871	1871	1800	1914	166146	BKM	Hanslope
1781	1935	1700	1935	134880	ESS	Asheldam
1825	1992	....	1930	171441	KEN	Mid
1772	1935	ALL	ALL	119296	KEN	Walmer
1800	1992	1600	1800	142042	KEN	Wlmer
1914	1960	1914	1960	166146	NTH	Holcott
1797	....	1700	1797	125806	OXF	Banbury
1800	1880	1800	1900	123145	STS	Tipton
1600	1992	1600	1800	145513	WIL	Great Bedwyn
1700	1799	ALL	ALL	146633	WIL	Milton Lilbourne
1760	1780	ALL	1780	167029	WIL	Shalbourne
BUSHNELL						
1857	1867	1707	1992	139955	ALL	Bray
1800	1900	ALL	ALL	177989	OXF	Whitchurch
BUSHROD						
1850	1992	1700	1850	113530	DOR	East Burton
?	?	?	?	117528	DOR	Sherborne
1765	....	1700	1765	152579	DOR	Whitchurch
1765	....	1700	1765	152579	DOR	Winterborne
BUSKIN						
1700	1800	1600	1800	154342	SOM	Minehead
1790	1850	1600	1850	154342	SOM	Porlock
BUSLEY						
1743	1788	1700	1743	148938	GLS	Hardwicke
BUSS						
1800	1840	ALL	ALL	125318	ESS	Ardleigh
1707	1850	....	....	113093	SSX	Brightling
....	1700	....	....	174564	SSX	???
BUSSELL						
1800	1920	....	....	137693	SOM	Bath
1830	1860	1750	1830	171859	SOM	Taunton
BUSSEY						
1840	1880	ALL	ALL	107425	NFK	Norwich
1827	1893	1750	1900	155152	NTT	Nottingham
1733	....	ALL	1733	148172	YKS	Stillingfleet

Known From	To	Researching From	To	Ref	Cty	Place
BUST						
....	1774	ALL	ALL	129933	HAM	Odiham
BUSTIN						
1760	1818	1760	1818	154040	DEV	Braunton
1791	1791	1790	1793	154040	DEV	West Down
1850	1870	1800	1920	141445	WAR	ALL
BUSTON						
1818	1900	1800	1950	107980	NFK	Norwich
BUSWELL						
1870	1950	1870	1900	177571	BKM	Stony Stratford
1790	1931	1700	1790	119075	LEI	Market Harborough
1790	1820	ALL	1850	177571	LEI	Market Harborough
1820	1870	1820	1900	177571	NTH	Desborough
1750	1850	ALL	ALL	114235	NTH	???
....	....	1850	1875	107484	NTT	Welford
1650	1745	....	....	171654	WAR	Monks Kirby
BUTCHART						
1801	1948	ALL	1801	102350	SCT	St Andrews
BUTCHER						
....	....	1780	1870	103713	CAM	Isleham
1747	1778	ALL	1747	168602	CAM	Littleport
1754	1832	1750	1832	126667	DOR	West Lulworth
1780	1850	1700	1850	117617	ESS	Colchester
....	....	....	....	109207	ESS	???
1880	1960	....	....	113514	GLA	Barry
1810	1900	ALL	1900	131334	GLS	ALL
1810	1861	1700	1810	162035	GLS	Bristol
1800	1809	1500	1800	129577	IOW	???
1822	1992	1700	1820	112445	KEN	Aldington
1822	1992	1700	1820	112445	KEN	Ashurst
1755	1992	....	1755	146013	KEN	Seasalter
1837	1992	1700	1837	105163	KEN	Strood
1797	1797	....	....	127426	KEN	Ulcombe
1794	1794	1700	1850	141151	KEN	Whitstable
1763	1763	....	....	127426	KEN	???
1897	1900	1800	1897	128368	LND	Chelsea
1830	1850	1800	1850	109517	NFK	Upwell
1850	1910	1700	1850	167010	SFK	Bury St Edmunds
1860	1960	1800	1980	135283	SFK	Friston
1895	1961	....	....	105708	SFK	Lowestoft
1866	ALL	ALL	1902	116734	SOM	ALL
1800	....	....	1992	151270	SOM	Misterton
1875	1992	....	....	153397	SRY	ALL
?	?	ALL	1746	114308	SRY	Godalming
1739	1839	1700	1850	127183	SSX	East Grinstead
1810	1900	ALL	1900	131334	WIL	ALL
ALL	1778	....	....	170178	WIL	Cliffe Pypard
1752	1865	....	....	115606	WIL	Little Bedwyn
1770	1870	....	....	113514	WIL	North Bradley
BUTCHERS						
1802	1900	1700	1802	148938	GLS	Wraxall
1891	1891	1891	1930	113743	SSX	Rye
BUTEUX						
1820	1860	....	1820	169188	EAG	Saffron Waldon
BUTHROYD						
1751	1773	1720	1740	170348	YKS	Kirkheaton
BUTLAND						
....	....	ALL	ALL	174327	ALL	Name Study
1838	1851	1700	1838	138673	DEV	Plymouth
BUTLER						
....	....	ALL	ALL	111392	ALL	Name Study
1850	1992	1750	1850	118052	ANT	Ballycastle
1850	1910	1800	1992	116009	ANT	???
1724	1811	1600	1850	143693	BKM	Bledlow
1810	1855	1600	1850	143693	BKM	Burnham
....	....	?	1740	111376	BKM	Invinghoe
1761	1799	1500	1850	143693	BKM	Stokenchurch
1830	1911	1800	1830	172162	BRK	Beedon
1791	....	1700	1800	143693	BRK	Beenham
1850	1900	1840	1900	151599	BRK	Bracknell
1745	....	1700	1800	143693	BRK	Bradfield
1713	1730	....	1750	171441	BRK	Faringdon
1790	1974	1500	1790	141925	BRK	Frilsham
1773	....	1700	1800	143693	BRK	Tidmarsh
1868	....	1800	1900	143693	BRK	Tilehurst
1870	1992	....	....	138959	CAM	Hook
1790	1890	....	....	132225	CHS	Beeston
1845	....	1750	1860	175838	CON	Redruth
1850	1932	1700	1992	122114	DBY	Central
1575	1630	....	....	131857	DOR	Gillingham
1700	1800	ALL	ALL	131873	ESS	Manuden
1805	....	1700	1805	113352	ESS	Rivenhall
1870	1900	1860	1910	111325	ESS	Stewardstonebury
1656	1690	ALL	ALL	155896	GLS	Awre
BUTLER contd.						
1775	1992	ALL	1775	111333	HAM	North West
1808	1827	....	1808	161691	HAM	Appleshaw
1776	1776	1750	1800	125032	HAM	Newnham
1750	1775	1700	1760	127116	HAM	Romsey
1830	1880	....	....	164631	HEF	Ledbury
1700	ALL	1807	1881	107379	HRT	Berkhamsted
....	....	1740	1800	111376	HRT	Berkhamsted
1700	ALL	1807	1881	107379	HRT	Hemel Hempstead
1800	1870	1700	1800	138959	HUN	Overton
?	?	ALL	ALL	174432	HUN	Ramsey
1800	1870	1700	1800	138959	HUN	Waterville
1840	1860	ALL	1840	115282	KEN	East
....	....	1890	1910	106356	KEN	Broad Oak
1796	....	1750	1850	139386	KEN	Chatham
1830	1940	....	....	111392	KEN	Eltham
1830	1940	....	....	111392	KEN	Hither Green
1850	1920	1825	1992	133450	KEN	Sandwich
1679	1714	....	1720	171441	KEN	Wychling
1815	1980	1860	ALL	152064	KER	Killorglin
....	....	1890	1992	147613	LAN	Barrow In Furness
1895	1925	ALL	1849	146315	LAN	Chorlton
1820	1886	1820	....	109622	LAN	Kirkham
1895	1925	ALL	1949	146315	LAN	Manchester
1798	1920	1790	1950	142875	LIN	Saxilby
1700	1992	1800	1992	111422	LND	ALL
1820	1839	....	1820	142166	LND	Bethnal Green
1804	1827	1800	1830	115193	LND	Finsbury
1872	....	1840	1875	148156	LND	Fulham
1911	1970	1700	1911	111449	LND	Islington
1820	1900	ALL	ALL	110442	MAY	ALL
1850	1870	1750	1900	106356	MDX	Bethnal Green
1835	1859	1780	1860	129356	MDX	Bloomsbury
1880	1970	1700	1880	158976	MDX	Hillingdon
1800	1900	1750	1900	126446	MDX	Holborn
1860	1900	....	....	111368	MDX	Marylebone
1780	1800	1750	1850	129356	MDX	Shoreditch
....	1866	1700	1866	144754	MDX	South Hackney
1800	1870	1800	1900	111325	MDX	St Georges
1785	1890	1715	....	111392	MDX	St Pancras
1819	1840	1770	1820	102717	MDX	Strand
....	....	1800	1850	111376	MDX	Wapping
ALL	1772	....	....	105368	MDX	???
1797	1860	ALL	1797	154946	NRY	Hoveringham
?	?	1500	1795	101303	NTT	Hucknall
?	?	1500	1795	101303	NTT	Mansfield
?	?	1500	1795	101303	NTT	Nottingham
1720	1830	....	1830	137634	NTT	Rampton
1795	1992	1500	1795	101303	NTT	Skegby
1741	1815	1700	1820	124796	OXF	Bletchingdon
1863	1992	1800	1900	145513	OXF	Henley On Thames
1738	1857	1700	1760	124796	OXF	Holton
1796	....	1750	1800	124796	OXF	Kidlington
1737	1992	1700	1800	111392	OXF	Tetsworth
1660	1740	1600	1740	160849	SAL	Billingsley
1750	1880	1750	1880	130567	SAL	Newtown By Wem
1827	1895	1820	1900	115193	SOM	Bristol
1690	1900	1650	1900	120995	SOM	Frome
1824	....	....	1850	152803	SOM	Glastonbury
1792	1829	ALL	1792	175080	SOM	Swainswick
1870	1992	....	....	138959	SRY	Ewell
1812	....	....	....	101613	SSX	Battle
1867	....	1867	....	148156	SSX	Brighton
1855	1895	1800	1855	174807	SSX	Laughton
1721	1762	1690	1800	160873	STS	Bilston
1885	1909	....	....	164631	STS	Burton On Trent
1650	1750	1600	1950	177180	STS	Darlaston
1840	1900	....	....	132756	STS	Trentham
....	1660	....	....	111392	TIP	Moyally
1800	1841	....	....	164631	WAR	Birmingham
1100	1400	....	....	100420	WAR	Meriden
1861	1917	....	....	108200	WAR	Netherwhiteacre
1852	1858	1800	1992	116009	WAT	???
....	....	1800	1850	133604	WIL	Corsham
1756	1835	ALL	1900	165654	WIL	Melksham
1840	1992	1700	1840	152633	WIL	Ramsbury
1650	1800	ALL	1650	164631	WOR	Kidderminster
1680	1762	1650	1710	170348	YKS	Almondbury
1841	1851	1851	1881	154946	YKS	Appleton Le Moors
1869	1992	ALL	1869	136875	YKS	Bradford
1700	1725	1700	1725	141097	YKS	Braithwell
1700	1735	1650	1750	160873	YKS	Elvington
1881	1915	ALL	1881	154946	YKS	Huddersfield
1650	1680	1620	1700	170348	YKS	Huddersfield

Known From	To	Researching From	To	Ref	Cty	Place
BUTLER contd.						
1817	1868	1790	1817	175951	YKS	Pontefract
1820	1992	ALL	1992	157902	YKS	Skipton
BUTLIN						
....	....	ALL	ALL	100323	ALL	Name Study
1827	1992	1800	1992	108391	MDX	London
1650	1820	ALL	1650	164887	NTH	Whilton
BUTSER						
1743	....	ALL	1992	106119	ESS	???
BUTSON						
1805	1838	1750	1805	103896	BRK	Newbury
1750	1780	1650	1750	142999	CON	Padstow
1750	1780	1650	1750	142999	CON	St Merryn
1760	1992	1700	1992	161322	DEV	Border
1760	1992	1700	1992	161322	SOM	Border
BUTT						
1800	1850	1750	1900	135925	BKM	Stoke Poges
1724	1940	....	....	128996	CAM	Thorney
1851	1851	1851	1881	136808	CAM	Whittlesey
1867	1926	1800	....	122661	CHI	Jersey
1600	1700	1600	1700	142018	DOR	ALL
....	....	1700	1800	156795	DOR	North
1766	1992	1636	1766	116513	GLS	Deerhurst
1760	1850	1720	1860	122122	GLS	Frampton Cotterell
1850	1900	1850	1900	122122	GNT	Bleanavon
....	....	1800	....	145998	IOW	???
1873	1881	1873	1910	126705	LAN	Manchester
1600	1750	1600	1750	142018	SOM	ALL
1500	1900	1500	1900	170216	WIL	ALL
1821	1992	1750	1900	113212	WIL	Salisbury
1825	1826	1700	1825	138355	YKS	York
BUTTANSHAW						
....	....	ALL	ALL	172812	ALL	ALL
BUTTENSHAW						
....	....	ALL	ALL	172812	ALL	ALL
1811	1992	1600	1811	151092	SSX	Hastings
BUTTER						
1710	....	1650	1710	130214	ANS	Fowlis
1710	....	1650	1710	130214	ANS	Lundie
ALL	ALL	ALL	ALL	137731	SAL	Cheswardine
BUTTERFIELD						
....	....	1700	1850	118923	CMA	Whitehaven
1850	1900	1780	1850	114499	ESS	Barking
1776	1811	ALL	ALL	120650	YKS	South
1888	1888	ALL	1888	146315	YKS	Leeds
BUTTERISS						
ALL	ALL	ALL	ALL	111473	ALL	ALL
BUTTERS						
1875	1928	1800	1928	111279	CON	ALL
1830	1840	1800	1870	111279	DEV	ALL
1780	1800	ALL	ALL	130508	FIF	Autchtermuchty
1848	1870	1800	1848	111279	HAM	Lymington
1800	1992	....	....	176125	LIN	Asterby
1800	1992	....	....	176125	LIN	Goulceby
1750	1782	1782	1850	149519	LIN	Tattersall
1850	1935	1700	1850	174920	NFK	Necton
1860	1910	1837	1950	130036	NYK	Harrogate
1840	1900	1700	1840	167762	SFK	East
1825	1860	1750	1880	100439	STS	Wolverhampton
BUTTERWORTH						
....	....	ALL	ALL	100005	ALL	Name Study
....	....	ALL	ALL	111481	ALL	Name Study
ALL	ALL	ALL	ALL	111481	ALL	ALL
1850	1992	1850	1992	109347	LAN	Accrington
1843	1866	1700	1843	129046	LAN	Aston Under Lyne
1850	1980	1750	1850	111503	LAN	Blackburn
1845	1899	ALL	ALL	161713	LAN	Blackburn
1700	....	1700	....	109347	LAN	Clayton Le Moors
1830	1930	ALL	1830	162256	LAN	Edgworth
1782	1884	1650	1992	110205	LAN	Heywood
1875	1930	1837	1875	166464	LAN	Manchester
1793	1841	1750	1820	174211	LAN	Manchester
1793	1841	1750	1820	174211	LAN	Middleton
1834	1871	1700	1900	178233	LAN	Moston
1760	1900	1700	1760	111511	LAN	Oldham
1850	1992	....	....	132500	LAN	Oldham
1775	1800	1775	1800	109347	LAN	Pendleton
1813	1875	....	....	159131	LAN	Preston
1800	....	1800	....	109347	LAN	Read
1837	1862	....	1837	109622	LAN	Royton
1760	1900	1700	1760	111511	LAN	Royton
1800	1900	....	....	146854	LAN	Southport
1800	....	1800	....	109347	LAN	Whalley
1822	1822	1820	1822	108901	NTT	Averham
BUTTERWORTH contd.						
1750	1900	1650	1800	109517	WRY	Cartworth
1862	1862	1800	1880	171662	YKS	Eston
BUTTERY						
1880	1890	ALL	1930	125830	LIN	Central
1790	1830	ALL	1840	165212	NTT	Worksop
1749	1992	....	....	134619	STS	Milford
BUTTI						
1800	1900	1800	....	109452	LND	Holborn
BUTTINGTON						
1778	....	....	1780	171441	KEN	Littlebourne
BUTTIS						
1840	1900	1700	1840	167762	SFK	East
BUTTLE						
1750	1880	1700	1800	154601	EYK	Aughton
1750	1880	1700	1800	154601	EYK	Howden
1750	1880	1700	1800	154601	EYK	Selby
1844	....	1700	1844	144614	GLS	Charlton Abbots
1850	....	1750	1850	108596	YKS	Pickering
BUTTMAN						
1775	1840	ALL	1780	142301	MDX	Hornsey
BUTTON						
1730	1850	ALL	1730	163341	ESS	Clavering
1880	1992	1856	1880	177539	ESS	Rochford
1796	1841	ALL	1796	123641	LIN	Bishop Norton
1800	1830	ALL	ALL	103837	LIN	Stainton Le Vale
1805	1850	1700	1900	131199	LIN	Stainton Le Vale
1785	1895	....	....	102946	NTT	Nottingham
1700	1840	1800	1850	111422	SFK	ALL
1776	1776	1700	1776	155276	SFK	Leiston
1760	1860	1700	1860	147958	SOM	Coleford
....	....	1700	1799	174963	SOM	Kilmersden
1752	1897	1700	1752	159158	WIL	Lacock
BUTTONSHAW						
1786	1992	ALL	1992	172812	ALL	ALL
BUTTRESS						
....	....	ALL	ALL	111473	ALL	Name Study
1900	1992	1900	1992	134910	CAM	Fulbourn
BUTTREY						
....	....	ALL	ALL	111538	ALL	ALL
1520	1840	1480	1840	111538	NTH	Marston St Lawrence
1824	1981	1700	1825	128465	SAL	High Ercall
1735	1800	1735	1992	111538	WRY	Farnley
1720	1992	1720	1992	111538	WRY	Gildersome
BUTTRIDGE						
1640	1992	1640	1992	122769	OXF	Churchill
BUTTRY						
1780	1861	1750	1870	116386	YKS	Gildersome
BUTTS						
1730	1778	ALL	1730	122106	DOR	Portland
BUTZOR						
1691	....	ALL	1992	106119	HAM	???
BUXEY						
1830	....	1800	1900	116297	KEN	Hoo
BUXTON						
1170	1795	....	....	144304	DBY	Chelmorton
....	1809	?	1809	128910	DBY	Swanwick
1756	1831	1650	1756	163783	LAN	Garstang
1799	....	1600	1992	110787	LEI	Cosby
1790	1940	1600	1790	152463	LEI	Walton On The Wolds
1840	1860	1840	1860	130567	MDX	St Pancras
1795	1815	1538	1795	126942	SFK	Debenham
1756	1831	1650	1756	163783	WES	Heversham
1858	1860	1858	1860	129747	YKS	Burley
1763	1831	1763	1831	129747	YKS	Leeds
1833	1857	1700	1833	128031	YKS	Sheffield
BUYCE						
....	....	1800	1899	142409	NFK	???
BUYERS						
1810	1920	1810	1920	128740	DUR	South Shields
BUZZA						
....	1850	1750	1850	146927	CON	St Just
1865	1992	?	1865	129615	???	Liverpool
BUZZARD						
1700	1992	1740	1992	111562	ALL	ALL
1792	1992	1740	1851	111562	NTH	Northampton
BYARD						
....	....	ALL	ALL	136956	ALL	Name Study
ALL	ALL	ALL	ALL	136956	ALL	ALL
1580	1992	....	....	142158	GLS	Newent
BYATT						
1790	1840	ALL	1800	106739	ESS	ALL
1787	1835	1600	1787	165298	ESS	Thaxted
1660	1992	....	....	142158	GLS	Gloucester

Known From	To	Researching From	To	Ref	Cty	Place
BYE						
1789	1839	....	....	117374	BRK	Thatcham
1789	1839	....	....	117374	BRK	Wantage
1775	1992	1775	1992	111570	ESS	Manuden
1792	....	1700	1900	141151	HAM	ALL
1781	1781	1740	1850	124974	HAM	Kingsclere
1880	1992	1880	1992	111570	HRT	Bishops Stortford
BYERLEY						
1705	1742	....	....	129747	IOW	Gatcombe
1775	....	....	....	129747	IOW	Thorley
1697	....	....	....	129747	IOW	West Cowes
BYERS						
1680	1680	1500	1800	162620	CUL	???
1850	1900	1850	1940	127914	DUB	Dublin
1700	1700	1500	1800	162620	NBL	???
1860	1950	1860	1900	137618	WRY	Kippax
1825	1925	1800	1850	165468	YKS	Kippax
BYETT						
....	....	ALL	ALL	142158	ALL	Name Study
BYFORD						
1832	1892	....	....	168963	ESS	Rayleigh
1790	1992	1600	1790	118788	SFK	Glemsford
1600	1799	1640	1750	135941	SFK	Wickhambrook
1750	1900	1750	1900	111589	YKS	ALL
1800	1870	1750	1900	111589	YKS	Castleford
BYFORT						
?	....	....	....	168963	ESS	???
BYGLANDE						
....	....	1500	1700	175269	LAN	Cartmel
BYGRAVE						
1800	1840	1800	1870	111325	NFK	Norwich
BYHURST						
1850	1949	....	....	160106	KEN	Swanscombe
BYLES						
1700	1992	1700	1992	111597	MDX	Ickenham
BYNER						
1796	1850	1700	1850	149160	HRT	Hertingfordbury
BYNG						
1550	1640	1450	1640	154881	KEN	Wrotham
1741	1788	1741	1788	156892	NBL	Howden Pans
BYNORTH						
1800	1850	1700	1800	129003	HRT	Hertford
BYOLIN						
1841	1872	1815	1872	163813	SAL	Tetchill
BYRAM						
1800	1850	1700	1800	118745	MGY	Manafon
1837	1860	1700	1837	153346	STS	Kingswinford
BYRNE						
1864	1864	1848	....	120057	IRL	Dublin
....	1797	1600	1850	175641	IRL	Wicklow
1800	1830	....	....	126497	LET	???
1893	1992	1700	1893	148334	SRY	Lambeth
BYROM						
1830	1880	1750	1880	135771	LAN	South East
1811	....	....	1815	101761	WRY	Honley
BYRON						
1615	1780	....	....	100358	LAN	Manchester
....	1800	ALL	1800	134511	NTT	Nottingham
BYSH						
1716	1716	1650	1750	167002	SRY	Burstow
BYSHOP						
1755	1765	1730	1800	171158	DEV	Uffculme
BYSOUTH						
1699	1923	1600	1800	178608	HRT	Reed
....	1818	1800	1818	178608	MDX	Enfield
BYTHEWAY						
1820	1851	ALL	ALL	119504	HAM	Portsmouth
1750	1850	1700	1850	174297	SAL	South
1794	1795	ALL	ALL	119504	SAL	???
1670	1770	1550	1670	134104	WOR	Evesham
BYWORTH						
1801	1978	1700	1800	169854	BDF	Woburn
1859	1900	1600	1860	144045	YKS	York
CABLE						
1820	1830	1750	1820	144150	ANS	Dundee
1793	1805	1793	....	115940	ESS	Bocking
1844	1980	1844	1980	115940	ESS	Chadwellheath
1819	1861	1799	....	102989	ESS	Halstead
1860	1920	1800	1930	134589	NFK	Aylmerton
1773	1848	ALL	1800	165654	WIL	Durnford
CABON						
1674	1800	....	....	121835	LIN	Market Stainton
CABORN						
1773	1869	1730	1812	149845	LIN	ALL

Known From	To	Researching From	To	Ref	Cty	Place
CABOURN						
1750	1800	....	....	124621	LIN	Boston
CACKET						
1679	1741	....	1750	171441	KEN	Pluckley
CACKETT						
1780	1940	1780	1900	143502	ESS	ALL
1750	1780	1650	ALL	143502	KEN	ALL
CADD						
1741	1842	1700	1741	170593	BKM	Hillesden
CADDALL						
....	....	ALL	1712	119326	PER	Clunie
CADDEL						
1748	1863	1748	1863	176303	GLS	Great Rissington
1871	1992	1871	1992	176303	STS	Walsall
CADDICK						
1726	1830	1600	1992	167592	LAN	Liverpool
....	1836	....	1836	140767	STS	Sedgley
CADDIE						
1737	1775	1650	1737	117471	DOR	Holwell
CADDOCK						
1700	1750	1600	1992	167592	LAN	Liverpool
CADDY						
1785	1851	1780	1860	124001	CON	Phillack
1824	1864	....	....	127957	CON	Phillack
1784	1857	....	....	127957	CON	St Hilary
1780	1860	1700	1780	109983	CON	Wendron
1748	1992	ALL	1992	111600	DOR	ALL
1744	1933	ALL	1950	111600	DOR	Piddlehinton
1866	1992	1850	1992	111600	HAM	Cymington
1906	1992	1850	ALL	111600	HAM	Southampton
1890	1992	1880	1992	165441	STS	Rugeley
CADE						
....	....	1800	1900	141275	LIN	North Willingham
....	....	1800	1900	141275	LIN	Welton
1750	1770	1700	1750	120529	LIN	West Ashby
CADELL						
1726	1777	....	....	115290	WIL	Heddington
CADGINE						
....	....	1785	1856	118133	CLK	ALL
....	....	1622	1855	118133	FIF	ALL
1825	1825	1617	1684	118133	FIF	Dunfermline
1847	1847	....	....	118133	LKS	Lesmahagow
1866	1881	1861	1866	118133	SCT	Bridgeton
CADIC						
1830	1890	....	....	175390	GSY	St Peter Port
CADLE						
1866	1992	1800	1866	131806	GLS	Gloucester
CADMAN						
1846	1897	1799	1897	151432	FLN	Holywell
....	1700	....	1700	177695	NTH	Irthlingborough
1753	....	....	1753	101761	NTT	Epperstone
CADWALLADER						
1869	1926	1700	1869	155101	STS	Wolverhampton
CADY						
....	....	1850	1880	126519	CON	Marazion
CAESAR						
1826	1900	1750	1900	121177	HAM	Silchester
CAESER						
1915	1965	....	1915	137073	LIN	Pinchbeck
1905	1915	....	1905	137073	YKS	Rawmarsh
CAFFERY						
....	....	1600	1860	138614	IRL	???
....	....	1850	1911	138614	LAN	Lytham
CAFFIN						
1850	1900	1700	1850	120723	LND	Bermondsey
CAFFYN						
....	....	....	....	164542	SSX	ALL
CAGE						
1805	....	1780	1835	123404	NFK	Gaywood
CAHILL						
1820	1930	1885	1992	163848	DUB	Dublin City
1700	1850	1700	1992	163848	WIC	Rathleasty
CAIE						
1850	1992	1650	1992	104671	ABD	Footdee
1850	1992	1650	1992	104671	KCD	Nigg
CAIGER						
1730	1870	ALL	ALL	104191	MDX	London
?	?	?	?	154938	SSX	Sidlesham
CAILLET						
1657	1940	....	....	128996	CAM	Thorney
CAIN						
1800	1850	ALL	1992	170909	ARM	Milltown
1788	1806	....	....	156647	IOM	Kirk Micheal
1841	1863	1750	1890	137235	LEI	Leicester

Known From	To	Researching From	To	Ref	Cty	Place
CAIN contd.						
....	....	1871	1992	124117	LND	Ealing
....	....	1877	1992	124117	LND	Isleworth
1940	1992	1850	1940	124117	WIL	Warminster
CAINAN						
....	....	ALL	ALL	118222	ALL	Name Study
1750	1980	1700	1992	118222	ALL	ALL
CAINE						
1875	1989	ALL	1875	111619	IOM	Patrick
1834	1992	....	....	111619	IOM	Ramsey
1900	1992	....	....	164062	LAN	Darwen
CAINES						
1822	1992	1700	1822	115096	DOR	Hazelbury Brian
CAINK						
1792	1797	1750	1850	170100	MGY	???
1792	1797	1797	1850	170100	SAL	Oswestry
CAINS						
....	....	ALL	ALL	111627	ALL	Name Study
1927	1933	1910	1992	111627	CAM	Saffron Walden
1900	1900	1850	1992	111627	DEV	Plymouth
1864	1877	1850	1992	111627	DEV	Totnes
1750	1992	1600	1992	111627	GLS	South
1773	1873	....	1773	149888	GLS	Bristol
1801	1992	1600	1801	156183	GLS	Bristol
1848	1919	1800	1992	111627	MDX	London
1882	1928	1850	1992	111627	SOM	Shepton Mallet
1855	1910	1850	1992	111627	SOM	Street
CAIRN						
1716	1716	1511	1716	141291	IOM	Rushen
CAIRNE						
1716	1716	1511	1716	141291	IOM	Rushen
CAIRNS						
1760	1930	ALL	1760	115118	DUR	Chester Le Street
1895	1960	1600	1850	128899	DUR	Dunston
1895	1960	1600	1850	128899	DUR	Lowhand
1849	....	1849	....	161721	DUR	South Shields
1910	1920	ALL	1910	179515	IRL	Ulster
1754	1845	1750	1845	171654	LKS	Dalserf
1864	1950	1860	1950	135925	LND	Kingston
1830	1950	1800	1900	135925	LND	Stepney
1816	1818	1790	1820	159905	NBL	Alnwick
1850	1960	1600	1850	128899	NBL	Byker
CAISLEY						
....	....	ALL	ALL	169048	ALL	ALL
1886	1959	ALL	ALL	169048	EYK	Goole
....	....	ALL	ALL	169048	HUM	Hemmingbrough
CAISTER						
1693	1834	....	1860	171441	KEN	Lyminge
1693	1834	....	1860	171441	KEN	Newington
1693	1834	....	1860	171441	KEN	Stowting
1792	....	....	1860	171441	KEN	Waltham
CAITHNESS						
1770	1810	1700	1770	130214	ANS	Panbride
CAKE						
....	....	ALL	ALL	111635	ALL	Name Study
CAKEBREAD						
....	....	ALL	ALL	111643	ALL	Name Study
1860	1901	1600	1860	101222	ESS	Saffron Walden
CALADINE						
1920	1992	1800	1950	171689	DBY	Holmewood
CALBERRY						
1850	1870	1800	1850	121339	DUR	Sunderland
1850	1870	1800	1850	121339	NYK	Scorton
CALBERSON						
....	....	ALL	ALL	111651	ALL	Name Study
CALCOT						
1790	1890	1650	1790	151084	SAL	???
CALCOTT						
1800	1850	1700	1992	167592	CHS	Chester
1800	1850	1700	1992	167592	CHS	Malpas
CALCRAFT						
1835	1895	1800	1855	155691	KEN	Dover
....	....	1800	1835	155691	SFK	Ipswich
CALCROFT						
1700	1760	....	....	165999	LEI	Redmile
CALCUTT						
....	....	1800	1900	176508	LND	Islington
1815	1966	1881	1992	179116	OXF	Cogges
1782	1871	1700	1782	179116	OXF	Stanton Harcourt
1490	....	ALL	....	162302	OXF	???
1857	1881	1881	1992	179116	STS	West Bromwich
CALDCLEUGH						
....	....	ALL	ALL	165506	ALL	Name Study
....	....	1837	ALL	165506	ALL	ALL

Known From	To	Researching From	To	Ref	Cty	Place
CALDCLEUGH contd.						
1870	1989	1870	ALL	165506	DUR	Bishop Auckland
1700	1900	1600	1700	117218	DUR	City
1655	1860	1600	1655	117196	DUR	Durham
1704	1945	1704	ALL	165506	DUR	Durham
ALL	1610	....	....	165506	NBL	Allendale
1610	1630	....	....	165506	NBL	Corbridge
1630	1650	....	....	165506	NBL	Newcastle
CALDER						
1740	1920	....	....	152927	ABD	Coull
1840	1865	1750	1930	159379	ABD	Gartly
1740	1920	....	1740	152927	ABD	Lumphanan
1740	1920	....	?	152927	ABD	Tarland
1792	1830	1650	1850	112089	BEW	???
1784	1992	1700	1784	167703	CAI	Dunnet
1799	1801	....	....	127140	CAI	Wick
1795	1874	1700	1900	112089	CAI	???
1827	1939	....	....	127140	LKS	Glasgow
1800	....	....	....	127140	LKS	New Lanark
....	....	ALL	1805	119326	PER	Pitfurie
1824	....	....	....	127140	RFW	Greenock
1762	1796	1500	1762	129577	SCT	Nairn
1830	1870	1800	1850	120286	WOR	St Clement
CALDERBANK						
1820	1900	1700	1830	159166	LAN	South
1861	1992	1790	1861	103322	LAN	Chorley
1750	....	....	....	126497	LAN	Leyland
CALDERWOOD						
1840	1900	1840	1850	111678	CMA	Wigton
1840	1992	ALL	1850	111678	IRL	???
....	....	1700	1799	104884	WIG	ALL
CALDICOT						
1700	1854	....	1790	137405	CAM	South
CALDICOTT						
1880	1900	....	....	125938	STS	Walsall
CALDON						
1870	1900	1600	1900	111686	IRL	South
1840	1980	1800	1900	111686	LND	Central
CALDWELL						
1814	1820	1795	1820	128147	ANT	Clady
1780	1860	....	....	117684	CHS	Knutsford
1780	1860	....	....	117684	CHS	Leigh
1850	1910	....	....	117684	CHS	Mobberley
1760	1780	1650	1992	167592	CHS	Nantwich
1850	1900	1850	1992	127248	LAN	Ince In Makerfield
1820	1860	1750	1820	155500	LAN	Ince
1900	1900	1900	1900	145580	LAN	Liverpool
1770	1850	1500	1850	127248	LAN	Wigan
....	....	1765	1820	128147	SCT	Glasgow
1810	1860	1750	1992	167592	STS	Audley
1780	1830	1700	1992	167592	STS	Newcastle Under Lym
CALHOUN						
1723	?	ALL	ALL	101370	IRL	???
1800	1830	1690	1830	158313	TYR	???
CALKIN						
1800	1860	1700	1800	168734	SAL	Shrewsbury
CALL						
....	....	ALL	ALL	111716	ALL	Name Study
1680	1850	1600	1680	158402	DEV	???
CALLACK						
....	1825	ALL	1825	108197	ESS	Maldon
CALLADINE						
1582	1900	1390	1900	156809	DBY	Boulton
1825	1825	1825	1825	156809	IRL	Limerick
CALLAGHAN						
1700	1900	....	....	111724	COR	???
....	....	?	?	110507	DOW	Down Patrick
1890	1980	1800	1890	124036	GLA	Merthyr Tydfil
1700	1900	1700	....	111724	IRL	???
....	....	ALL	ALL	143340	IRL	???
1820	1860	1700	1900	138517	???	Cork
CALLAHAN						
1860	....	1700	1860	172588	MDX	London
CALLAN						
1894	1992	1700	1873	157112	LAN	Manchester
1872	1894	1800	1872	157112	LAN	Simsx Widnes
1857	1900	1790	1857	111740	SSX	Brighton
CALLANAN						
1828	1845	1800	1850	167711	GAL	Kiltormer
CALLANDER						
1848	1964	1750	1874	140678	DFS	Terregles
CALLARD						
1606	1742	1600	1800	171549	DEV	Buckfastleigh
1400	1860	1400	1992	114596	DEV	Burrington

Known From	To	Researching From	To	Ref	Cty	Place
CALLAWAY						
1859	1970	1700	1859	111279	CON	ALL
ALL	ALL	ALL	ALL	160261	HAM	ALL
1826	1873	1700	1826	164178	HAM	Fordingbridge
1921	1981	1870	1921	164127	WAR	Rugby
1790	1820	1790	1820	154210	WIL	Winterbourne Earls
CALLCUT						
1700	1900	1650	1920	111759	MDX	Bethnal Green
CALLEAR						
1790	1820	1600	1790	176052	SAL	Wellington
CALLEN						
1600	1992	1500	1992	150576	ALL	ALL
1600	1992	1500	1992	150576	HAM	ALL
1764	1861	1700	1870	179299	HAM	Bishopstoke
1880	1930	1700	ALL	159255	LND	Walhamstow
1800	1820	1800	1820	135429	SOM	Bath
CALLENDER						
....	1882	ALL	1882	122017	CAM	Cambridge
CALLER						
1780	1900	1700	1992	126012	KEN	Meopham
CALLICOTE						
1767	1777	1730	1767	157775	HAM	Honeybourne
CALLINGHAM						
....	....	ALL	ALL	112828	ALL	Name Study
....	....	1790	1815	143480	HAM	Aldershot
1843	1992	1600	1992	112828	SRY	ALL
....	....	1790	1803	143480	SRY	Farnham
1660	1684	1630	1992	114901	SRY	Godalming
CALLINSWOOD						
1850	1877	....	....	105147	STS	Wolverhampton
CALLIS						
1870	1970	1700	1870	105074	MDX	Acton
1850	1870	1700	1850	105074	MDX	Chiswick
CALLISTER						
1871	1930	1820	1871	111767	IOM	Marrow
1853	....	....	....	160385	IOM	Maughold
1713	1740	1706	1740	141291	IOM	Rushen
CALLONS						
1680	1720	ALL	1680	115266	DOR	ALL
CALLOW						
1816	1838	1790	1850	155918	BDF	Luton
1816	1866	1750	1816	127973	KEN	Canterbury
1839	1967	1839	1967	155918	LND	Bermondsey
1890	1992	1700	1890	103640	SFK	Beccles
1700	1812	ALL	1850	156140	STS	Tipton
CALLOWAY						
1860	1940	1840	1940	117641	LND	Bethnal
1774	1872	1774	1872	105147	STS	Tipton
1800	1815	1650	1720	156140	STS	Tipton
CALLUM						
1735	1775	1700	1775	146846	BAN	Keith
1771	1827	1600	1771	149888	BRK	Faringdon
....	....	1830	1906	146706	CAV	Manor Hamilton
1701	1799	1650	1750	176621	FIF	Aberdour
1854	1883	1837	1883	150827	MDX	London
1650	1900	1500	1992	146846	SCT	North
CALOW						
1842	1861	1700	1842	111775	LEI	Hinkley
1864	1891	1851	1864	111775	LEI	Loughborough
1858	1918	1800	1858	174203	MDX	Islington
CALPSON						
1829	1918	1829	1918	136158	KEN	Riverhead
CALROW						
1560	1790	1560	1790	111783	CHS	Prestbury
1790	1992	1790	1860	111783	LAN	Bury
1811	1992	1750	1850	111783	MDX	London
CALTENACH						
....	....	1800	1900	146110	SCT	ALL
CALTHORPE						
1847	1936	1800	1846	157619	NFK	Broome
CALTHROP						
1828	1846	1700	1900	116742	LIN	Boston
CALVELEY						
1780	1810	1700	1799	139858	ALL	ALL
CALVER						
1825	1850	1800	1992	106941	LND	Rotherhithe
1799	1867	1750	1992	106941	NFK	Gt Yarmouth
1830	1992	1830	1900	111791	NFK	Topcroft
1850	1880	1700	1850	155497	SFK	Stanton
1850	1930	1800	1992	106941	SSX	East Grinstead
CALVERLEY						
1780	1810	1700	1799	139858	ALL	ALL
CALVERT						
1880	1936	1700	1881	139203	DUR	Sunderland
CALVERT contd.						
1638	1938	1638	1992	143065	LAN	Great Harwood
1638	1936	1912	1992	143065	LAN	Oswaldtwisle
1856	1907	1700	1856	119075	LAN	Preston
....	....	....	....	116351	NBL	Newcastle
1800	1900	1650	1800	147729	NYK	Muker
1850	1920	1600	1850	113263	SRY	London
1834	....	....	1834	101761	WRY	Birstall
1825	1830	1700	1850	118281	YKS	Arkengarthdale
1799	1860	1750	1820	135550	YKS	Dales
1724	1740	1650	1724	177393	YKS	Hemingbrough
1860	1992	1860	1992	104612	YKS	Huddersfield
1809	1878	1700	1809	123005	YKS	Huddersfield
1860	1992	1860	1992	104612	YKS	Kirkheaton
1800	1850	1750	1800	111511	YKS	Leeds
....	....	....	....	116351	YKS	Muker
1813	1848	1750	1848	135011	YKS	Pately Bridge
1829	1902	ALL	1829	151424	YKS	Ripon
....	....	....	....	116351	YKS	Swaledale
1775	1808	1700	1900	116742	YKS	Swaledale
1809	1878	1700	1809	123005	YKS	Wakefield
1600	1992	1500	1790	167843	YKS	Wensleydale
CALVOCURESSI						
1500	1950	ALL	ALL	162620	ALL	ALL
CAM						
1550	1640	1450	1650	154881	LND	ALL
CAMB						
1950	1992	1802	1950	111805	LAN	Lower Bentham
1950	1992	1802	1950	111805	YKS	Lower Bentham
CAMBAGE						
1800	1950	1800	1950	110612	YKS	North
CAMBER						
1590	1590	1560	1590	124974	HAM	Kingsclere
CAMBERS						
1713	1992	....	....	111813	BDF	Cardington
1713	1992	....	....	111813	BDF	Cople
....	....	1800	....	137456	BDF	Cople
CAMBOURN						
1820	1850	1700	1992	118753	WIL	Marlborough
CAMBRAY						
1300	1400	1300	1992	113840	SAL	ALL
CAMBRIDGE						
1838	....	1750	1850	138185	MDX	???
CAMDEN						
1850	1930	1850	1910	132683	CHS	Altrincham
CAME						
1550	1640	1450	1650	154881	LND	ALL
CAMERON						
1856	1900	....	....	154849	ABD	Marykirk
....	....	1700	1900	175889	ARL	Dunoon
1799	1874	1750	1850	111848	ARL	Kilmalie
1776	1809	1750	1860	111848	ARL	Ranachan
....	....	1700	1900	175889	ARL	Tiree
1800	1940	1700	1800	146587	BAN	Ruthven
1817	....	....	....	127140	INV	Achentore
1871	....	1800	1881	165824	INV	Boleskine
1785	1817	....	....	127140	INV	Kilmallie
1900	1992	1700	1900	178659	INV	Tain
1849	1851	....	....	127140	LKS	Glasgow
1789	1797	1700	1992	159956	LKS	Glasgow
1750	1785	....	1800	176540	PER	Kenmore
1700	1799	1600	1799	132802	PER	Lochtay
1815	1835	1740	1850	143251	ROC	Black Isle
1815	1835	1740	1850	143251	ROC	Culgo
1815	1835	1740	1850	143251	ROC	Easter Culbo
1780	1800	1750	1800	111821	ROC	Logie Wester
1815	1835	1740	1850	143251	ROC	Resolis
1800	1992	1750	1800	111821	ROC	Urray
....	....	1789	....	135380	SCT	St Andrews
1832	1900	....	....	148016	SCT	???
....	1839	....	....	161888	SCT	???
1851	1871	....	....	135380	???	Bristol
CAMFIELD						
1894	1943	....	....	103373	MON	Newport
CAMICE						
1836	1840	1810	1992	111864	SAL	Madeley Wood
CAMIES						
1855	1884	1855	1884	111864	HAM	Winchester
1827	1840	1810	1992	111864	SAL	Lawley Bank
CAMISH						
1640	1796	1520	....	111864	HAM	Hinton Ampner
CAMISHE						
1562	1630	1520	1784	111864	HAM	Medstead

Known From	To	Researching From	To	Ref	Cty	Place
CAMM						
....	1849	....	1849	146919	LAN	Austwick
1804	1992	1750	1800	116076	LEI	Tilton
1801	1846	....	....	167517	LIN	Grantham
1822	1885	1750	1822	174289	MDX	London
1804	1992	1750	1800	116076	NTT	Nottingham
1800	....	1700	....	134589	YKS	Little Ribston
CAMMACK						
1800	1870	1750	1900	147958	LIN	Upton Cum Kexby
CAMMEL						
1764	....	ALL	ALL	127078	HAM	Portsmouth
CAMMIES						
1700	1784	1520	1784	111864	HAM	Hinton Ampner
1700	1784	1520	1789	111864	HAM	Medstead
1827	1840	1810	1992	111864	SAL	Dawley Magna
1827	1840	1810	1992	111864	SAL	Wellington
1907	1913	1907	1913	111864	SRY	Worcester Park
1904	1992	1810	1992	111864	STS	Bilston
1904	1992	1810	1992	111864	STS	Darlaston
1904	1992	1810	1992	111864	STS	West Bromwich
1814	1992	1784	1992	111864	WAR	Birmingham
1840	1992	1810	1992	111864	WMD	Wolverhampton
CAMMIS						
1779	1779	1750	1800	136719	BRK	Inkpen
1779	1779	1750	1800	136719	HAM	Bentworth
1562	1646	1520	1784	111864	HAM	Bramdean
CAMMISH						
....	....	ALL	ALL	111872	ALL	Name Study
1640	....	....	....	111864	HAM	Medstead
CAMMISHE						
1562	1646	1520	1784	111864	HAM	Medstead
CAMMISSE						
1562	1634	1520	1784	111864	HAM	Medstead
CAMP						
1803	1827	1600	1900	159956	ESS	Moreton
1739	1753	....	....	101028	HRT	Sawbridgenorth
?	?	?	?	111457	SCT	Dalgety
1750	1810	1650	1750	165018	WYK	Ferrisby
CAMPBELL						
1700	1821	....	....	100536	ALL	???
1835	1890	1800	1835	126357	ABD	Inverurie
1849	1871	1849	1992	131423	ABD	Towie
1900	1930	ALL	1884	173045	ANT	Ahoghill
1750	1800	1600	1900	144290	ARL	Bragleen
1850	1854	....	....	127140	ARL	Drimfearn
1863	1992	1600	1863	175889	ARL	Dunoon
1850	1854	....	....	127140	ARL	Glenary
1800	1850	....	....	127140	ARL	Inverinan
1800	1850	....	....	127140	ARL	Kilchrenan
1730	1770	1730	1770	106305	ARL	Kilmartin
1840	1850	....	....	127140	ARL	Kilmore
1840	1850	....	....	127140	ARL	Lochavichside
1800	1850	....	....	127140	ARL	Lochaweside
1800	1850	ALL	1992	170909	ARM	???
1810	1850	1700	1800	145017	AYR	Ardrossan
1740	1750	1730	1740	101796	AYR	Irvine
1820	1840	ALL	1820	146757	AYR	New Cumnock
1820	1840	ALL	1820	146757	AYR	Old Cumnock
1780	1800	....	....	126497	CAI	Halkirk
1840	1857	1840	1857	117455	CLK	Clackmannan
1759	1782	....	....	116602	DBY	Derby
1837	1992	1802	1837	111899	DNB	Dumbarton
1700	1825	1600	1825	154881	DOR	Poole
1783	1854	1700	1783	121525	GAL	Galway
1870	1900	1870	1900	121177	HAM	Winchester
1819	1826	1700	1849	131423	INV	Kiltarlity
1874	1964	1750	1874	140678	KKD	Colvend
1874	1964	1750	1874	140678	KKD	Dalbeattie
1865	1900	1600	1865	144932	LAN	Liverpool
1828	1888	1700	1828	145971	LAN	Manchester
1828	1888	1700	1828	145971	LAN	Salford
1785	1844	1700	1800	134732	LDY	Kilrea
1826	1920	1700	1992	108278	LDY	Limavady
1876	1992	1876	1992	112305	LKS	Airdrie
1850	1930	....	....	124532	LKS	Glasgow
....	....	1811	1885	132381	LKS	Glasgow
1800	1837	1750	1837	123536	LND	Holborn St Andrew
1806	....	ALL	1992	159174	LND	Shoreditch
1830	1837	1837	1992	146560	LTN	Queensferry
1830	1870	1830	1870	136360	MDX	Highgate
1748	1830	1700	1750	149152	NBL	Earsdon
1837	1853	1830	1860	123536	NBL	Newcastle On Tyne
1825	1825	ALL	1825	161330	NTT	Awsworth
1800	1850	1700	1850	117455	PER	Killen

Known From	To	Researching From	To	Ref	Cty	Place
CAMPBELL contd.						
1766	....	....	....	127140	PER	Killin
1766	....	....	....	127140	PER	Lochtayside
1750	1900	1700	1800	120286	PER	Logierait
1838	....	ALL	ALL	172057	PER	???
1805	1861	1780	1861	124028	RFW	Greenock
1880	1992	ALL	1880	142263	ROC	Dingwall
1850	1900	1700	1850	144150	ROC	Dingwall
....	....	?	?	134201	SCT	Glasgow
....	....	1600	1840	123390	STI	Baldernock
1804	1891	....	....	117803	SUT	Creich
1850	1920	ALL	1850	142069	???	Glasgow
....	....	1700	1850	126357	???	Loch Carron
CAMPER						
....	....	ALL	ALL	111902	ALL	Name Study
CAMPION						
....	....	ALL	ALL	111910	ALL	Name Study
1760	1880	ALL	....	104515	LIN	South
1850	....	....	1850	162086	LND	Islington
1700	1850	....	....	114642	SFK	West
1877	1900	1600	1877	131261	YKS	Sheffield
CAMPKIN						
?	?	ALL	ALL	111929	ALL	ALL
1774	1811	1700	1800	136042	HRT	Kimpton
1775	1775	ALL	1775	167959	HRT	Stanstead Abbots
1779	1992	1700	1779	111929	KEN	???
CAMPLEJOHN						
....	....	ALL	ALL	161616	ALL	Name Study
CAMPLING						
1636	1800	1636	1800	167126	NFK	Norwich
CAMPS						
1897	1992	ALL	ALL	142492	LAN	Preston
CAN						
1772	1804	1750	1830	105120	WIL	Milton Lilbourne
CANADINE						
1733	1745	1700	1900	156809	GLS	Gloucester
1733	1745	1700	1900	156809	GLS	Twekesbury
CANARDINE						
1638	1638	1638	1638	156809	ESS	Hadleigh
CANBY						
....	....	1800	1992	173053	DUR	Coundon
1800	....	1700	....	134589	YKS	Easingwold
....	....	1800	1992	173053	???	Hurst
....	....	1800	1992	173053	???	Sedbergh
CANDELENT						
1745	1992	ALL	ALL	145807	STS	Birmingham
CANDERDYNE						
?	1552	1550	1875	156809	STS	Marston
CANDIE						
1800	1992	1700	....	158364	ANS	Aberlemno
CANDISH						
1820	1826	ALL	ALL	159034	SRY	Croydon
CANDLER						
1834	....	1834	....	117560	LND	Westminster
....	....	....	....	107085	NTH	Northampton
CANDO						
1800	1992	1700	1992	158364	ANS	Aberlemno
CANDOW						
1800	1992	1700	1992	158364	ANS	Aberlemno
CANDY						
1800	1992	1700	1992	158364	ANS	Aberlemno
1850	1890	1800	1850	166316	SOM	Bath
CANE						
1837	....	1837	1992	149055	HAM	Grayshott
1800	1860	ALL	....	145556	SSX	Ripe
1729	1776	1680	1790	176621	SSX	Westham
CANESFORD						
1208	?	1208	1992	179086	ALL	ALL
CANFANY						
....	....	ALL	ALL	110086	ALL	Name Study
CANFIELD						
....	....	ALL	ALL	145599	ALL	Name Study
1826	1846	1750	1826	144711	GLS	Kempsford
1860	1890	....	....	144711	HAM	Kingsclere
CANHAM						
1751	1940	....	....	128996	CAM	Thorney
1860	....	....	1860	164011	HRT	Hatfield
?	....	?	....	104337	MDX	Mile End Old Town
1779	....	....	....	132853	NFK	Wicklewood
1750	1820	1750	1992	162884	SFK	Bucklesham
CANN						
?	?	?	?	111937	DEV	South Tawton
1800	1870	1700	1870	166650	DEV	South Tawton
1806	1934	1700	1806	107654	DEV	Throwleigh

Known From	To	Researching From	To	Ref	Cty	Place
CANN contd.						
1839	1927	1700	1839	169730	MDX	Bloomsbury
1839	1890	1700	1839	118168	MDX	London
CANNADINE						
....	....	ALL	ALL	156809	ALL	Name Study
1725	1729	1700	1900	156809	CHS	Wilmslow
1705	1837	1630	1988	156809	SAL	Broseley
1705	1837	1630	1988	156809	SAL	Meole Brace
1797	1980	1700	1985	156809	WAR	Warwick
1797	1980	1700	1985	156809	WOR	Aston
1797	1980	1700	1985	156809	WOR	Belbroughton
1797	1980	1700	1985	156809	WOR	Birmingham
1797	1980	1700	1985	156809	WOR	Chaddesley Corbett
1797	1980	1700	1985	156809	WOR	Coventry
1797	1980	1700	1985	156809	WOR	Cradley
1797	1980	1700	1985	156809	WOR	Dudley
1797	1980	1700	1985	156809	WOR	Feckenham
1797	1980	1700	1985	156809	WOR	Halesowen
1797	1980	1700	1985	156809	WOR	Kidderminster
1797	1980	1700	1985	156809	WOR	Northampton
1797	1980	1700	1985	156809	WOR	Oldswinford
1797	1980	1700	1985	156809	WOR	Wolverhampton
CANNADYNE						
1539	1850	1539	1900	156809	LEI	Shepshed
1590	1850	1539	1900	156809	LND	ALL
CANNAN						
1762	1797	1600	1797	152080	BRK	Sutton Courtenay
CANNELL						
....	....	ALL	ALL	109924	ALL	Name Study
1872	1898	ALL	ALL	174505	DUR	Gateshead
1794	1864	....	....	156647	IOM	???
1860	1870	1700	1992	109924	KEN	ALL
1898	1900	1800	1992	108421	LND	Shoreditch
1850	1860	1700	1992	109924	MDX	ALL
1700	1800	1500	1992	109924	NFK	ALL
1858	1861	1800	1881	109924	SFK	Bury St Edmunds
CANNEY						
1600	1630	1600	1630	106305	ENG	???
CANNIFORD						
1750	1992	ALL	1750	115177	DEV	Broad Hembury
CANNING						
1810	1855	1700	1900	178322	GLS	Bristol
....	ALL	ALL	....	100153	KIK	Kilkenny City
1827	1856	1800	1870	149292	KKD	Castle Douglas
1846	1869	1800	1900	149292	LAN	Liverpool
1850	1951	1700	1850	168653	LND	Chelsea
1798	1874	....	....	165514	WAR	Warwick
1819	1857	1750	1865	110922	WIL	ALL
1790	1820	1780	1820	154210	WIL	Great Wishford
CANNINGS						
1770	1992	1580	1770	175870	SOM	Batheaston
1820	1850	1820	1850	154210	WIL	Winterbourne Earls
CANNOCK						
1767	1851	1700	1767	148938	GLS	Westbury On Severn
CANNON						
1773	1818	1770	1818	164704	BRK	Reading
1709	1779	1650	1750	135550	CUL	East
1840	1992	1700	1840	111961	DEV	Plymouth
1690	1800	1690	1820	125903	HRT	Anstey
1700	1800	1650	1850	125903	HRT	Barley
1743	1900	1838	1900	125903	HRT	Gt Hormead
1815	1992	1690	1880	125903	HRT	Walkern
1781	?	ALL	1781	162108	HRT	???
1838	....	ALL	ALL	163988	KKD	???
1809	1827	1700	1809	106054	LND	ALL
1830	1945	ALL	ALL	113700	MAY	Castlebar
1830	1945	ALL	ALL	113700	MAY	Westport
....	....	1800	1900	166960	MDX	London
1831	1992	....	....	172529	OXF	Dunstew
1891	1992	....	1891	125202	SRY	???
CANNONS						
1820	1848	1700	1820	111953	BRK	East Ilsley
CANON						
1672	1672	....	....	115606	BRK	Cookham
CANSELL						
....	....	ALL	ALL	107328	ALL	Name Study
CANSICK						
....	....	ALL	ALL	151149	ALL	Name Study
CANT						
1760	1900	ALL	ALL	111988	ANS	ALL
....	1918	....	1918	175137	NBL	ALL
1760	1900	ALL	ALL	111988	TAY	ALL
CANTELLO						
ALL	ALL	ALL	ALL	111996	ALL	ALL
CANTELLS						
1700	1935	1700	1935	152536	JSY	???
CANTELUPE						
1300	1600	1300	1600	154881	ALL	ALL
CANTER						
1863	1873	1863	1900	176893	DUB	South
1650	1820	1600	1820	176893	GLS	Minchinhampton
1832	1900	1820	1900	176893	YKS	Barnsley
CANTERBURY						
1696	1841	....	....	104310	DOR	Stoke Abbott
CANTERELL						
1700	1850	1650	1992	177180	HRT	Gt Gaddesden
CANTLON						
1880	1930	1700	1880	124931	IRL	Tralee
CANTON						
....	....	ALL	ALL	160857	ALL	Name Study
CANTRELL						
1802	1896	1700	1800	138185	DBY	ALL
1500	ALL	1500	ALL	125512	DBY	Kings Newton
1500	ALL	1500	ALL	125512	DBY	Melbourne
1897	1976	1700	1897	100110	DEV	Cockington
1800	ALL	1800	ALL	125512	LEI	Asby De La Zouche
1610	1620	1600	1650	103764	STS	Alstonfield
1750	1950	1700	1950	114529	YKS	Sheffield
1590	1930	1590	1930	114529	YKS	Swaledale
CANTRILL						
....	....	ALL	ALL	112003	ALL	Name Study
1177	1992	1177	1992	112003	ALL	ALL
1800	1900	1650	1800	170194	DBY	Derby
1898	1992	....	....	100986	STS	Leak
1800	1900	....	....	167843	YKS	Grinton
CANTY						
1830	1992	1802	1871	124826	LIN	Barton Upon Humber
CAPEL						
1889	1920	1800	1889	110639	IRL	???
1850	1890	ALL	ALL	171816	NTH	ALL
1889	1920	1800	1889	110639	SCT	???
CAPELIN						
1803	1849	1750	1810	172871	SRY	Godalming
1803	1849	1750	1810	172871	SRY	Ripley
1778	1829	1650	1829	112178	SRY	Ripley-Send
CAPELL						
1825	1992	1700	1825	174076	LEI	Smeeton-Westerby
1850	1890	ALL	ALL	171816	NTH	ALL
CAPEN						
1811	1839	1811	1839	131970	DOR	Poole
CAPES						
1860	1864	....	....	101877	BKM	Bletchley
1846	1900	1846	1900	101877	CAM	Cambridge
1750	1800	1750	1800	123765	LIN	East
1870	1920	1880	1890	101877	LND	Bermondsey
1900	1913	....	....	101877	LND	Chelsea
1864	1900	1864	1900	101877	LND	Pimlico
1720	1800	1720	1800	101877	NFK	Billingford
1837	1846	1837	1846	101877	NFK	Old Buckenham
1800	1810	1800	1810	101877	NFK	Tibenham
1810	1846	1810	1846	101877	NFK	Winfarthing
1770	1860	1800	1840	101877	SFK	Drayton
1800	1900	1860	1880	101877	SFK	Plomersgate
1770	1860	1800	1840	101877	SFK	Tittleshall
1860	1880	1860	1880	101877	SFK	Tunstall
CAPEWELL						
1860	1992	ALL	1860	108847	STS	Kingsley
1890	1890	1870	1900	134627	STS	Walsall
1840	1860	1750	1840	137421	STS	Walsall
CAPIE						
1790	1890	....	....	139300	FIF	ALL
1790	1890	....	....	139300	LKS	ALL
CAPLE						
....	....	1770	1800	103713	BDF	Bletsoe
1790	1880	1790	1880	140295	SOM	Uphill
CAPLEHORN						
1776	1814	1700	1850	107417	HAM	Michelmersh
CAPLEHORNE						
1800	1900	ALL	ALL	107417	ALL	ALL
CAPNER						
1745	1850	1700	1900	149993	WAR	Solihull
CAPON						
....	....	ALL	ALL	112011	ALL	Name Study
....	....	1500	1760	138614	DOR	Bridport
1730	1992	1650	1730	155276	SFK	Bredfield
1750	1840	1700	1900	115746	SOM	Taunton
CAPP						
1541	1670	1540	1992	103144	BKM	Great Horwood

Known From	To	Researching From	To	Ref	Cty	Place
CAPP contd.						
1693	1724	1540	1992	103144	BKM	Soulbury
1810	1860	1540	1992	103144	BKM	Stewkley
1724	1810	1540	1992	103144	BKM	Wing
1860	1900	1860	1992	103144	HRT	Waltham Cross
1700	1800	1650	1700	151769	LIN	Fulbeck
1900	1960	1900	1960	103144	MDX	Enfield
1700	1899	1600	1840	135941	SFK	Lakenheath
1700	1899	1600	1840	135941	SFK	Wangford
CAPPER						
1840	1880	....	....	137790	CHS	Acton
1840	1880	....	....	137790	CHS	Nantwich
....	....	1800	....	146188	CHS	Nantwich
1750	....	....	....	148768	MDX	Clerkenwell
1750	....	....	....	148768	MDX	Strand
....	1798	1700	1820	100048	SRY	Bermondsey
1820	1992	....	....	144088	STS	Biddulph
CAPPIE						
1850	1900	....	....	139300	ELN	ALL
1850	1900	....	....	139300	FIF	ALL
CAPPITT						
....	....	ALL	ALL	112038	ALL	ALL
1565	1640	....	....	112038	LIN	Creatford
1800	1992	....	....	112038	LIN	Thurlby
CAPPS						
....	....	ALL	ALL	127515	ALL	Name Study
1782	1804	1750	1782	145424	MDX	London
1896	1900	....	1896	171743	YKS	???
CAPSTICK						
1900	1910	1840	1900	109878	LAN	Burnley
1900	1910	1840	1900	109878	LAN	Habergham Eaves
1808	1870	1750	1900	118443	YKS	Hawes
CAPTAIN						
....	....	1600	1855	148482	OKI	Birsay
CARADIN						
1722	1869	1700	1900	156809	YKS	Leeds
1722	1869	1700	1900	156809	???	Clapham
CARBERRY						
....	....	ALL	ALL	136638	GLS	Gloucester
....	....	ALL	ALL	136638	IRL	ALL
....	....	ALL	ALL	166812	OFF	Killelary
....	....	ALL	ALL	166812	OFF	Lynally
....	....	ALL	ALL	166812	OFF	Tullamore
CARBIS						
1804	1804	1700	1900	100536	CON	Falmouth
1834	1940	1750	1840	177938	CON	Penzance
CARBUTT						
....	....	ALL	ALL	104531	LIN	ALL
1849	1933	1700	1849	139025	YKS	York
CARCAS						
....	....	ALL	ALL	112054	ALL	Name Study
1810	1992	ALL	1810	112054	ALL	ALL
CARD						
1871	1992	....	....	108030	GNT	Newport
1850	1992	ALL	1850	100803	KEN	Bidborough
1852	1852	?	1852	113360	LND	Bermondsey
1860	1992	1860	1992	146846	MDX	London
1841	1851	1800	1841	108030	SOM	Rodney Stoke
1820	1900	1600	1820	123587	SSX	Rotherfield
1687	1752	1600	1687	165980	SSX	Warbleton
CARDALL						
1650	1992	1650	1992	114790	SAL	Market Drayton
CARDEN						
1650	1950	1400	1992	112062	ALL	ALL
1839	1839	....	....	140414	KEN	Penhurst
CARDER						
1800	1880	1700	1800	115541	ESS	Wethersfield
CARDEW						
1801	1812	1750	1860	110922	CON	ALL
1847	1960	1700	1847	111279	CON	East
1700	....	ALL	1800	168696	CON	East
1847	1960	1700	1847	111279	DEV	Plymouth
1812	....	1812	1880	110922	MDX	Westminster
CARDIGAN						
....	....	1800	1850	167088	COR	???
CARDIN						
1614	1823	1550	1677	102830	DBY	ALL
CARDING						
1841	1861	1841	1861	159492	LAN	Chorlton With Manchester
CARDO						
1803	1889	....	....	140384	WMD	Birmingham
1803	1889	....	....	140384	WMD	Dudley
1803	1889	....	....	140384	WMD	Oldswinford
CARDO contd.						
1803	1889	....	....	140384	WMD	Yardley
CARDON						
1697	1858	1600	1900	156809	SAL	Ashford Carbonell
1697	1858	1600	1900	156809	SAL	Bishops Castle
1697	1858	1600	1900	156809	SAL	Bridgenorth
1697	1858	1600	1900	156809	SAL	Condover
1697	1858	1600	1900	156809	SAL	Dawley Magna
1697	1858	1600	1900	156809	SAL	Easthope
1697	1858	1600	1900	156809	SAL	Ellesmere
1697	1858	1600	1900	156809	SAL	Little Wenlock
1697	1858	1600	1900	156809	SAL	Ludlow
1697	1858	1600	1900	156809	SAL	Lydbury North
1697	1858	1600	1900	156809	SAL	Madeley
1697	1858	1600	1900	156809	SAL	Priors Lee
1697	1858	1600	1900	156809	SAL	Shawbury
1697	1858	1600	1900	156809	SAL	Shrewsbury
1697	1858	1600	1900	156809	SAL	Whitchurch
CARDOZA						
....	....	ALL	ALL	112070	ALL	Name Study
CARDY						
1840	1890	1820	1840	103985	ESS	Clacton
1850	1875	1840	1900	168947	LND	Woolwich
CARE						
1862	1992	1700	1930	112089	ENG	ALL
1710	1710	....	....	121355	LND	Stepney
1862	1992	1700	1930	112089	SCT	ALL
CAREFOOT						
ALL	1800	1700	1800	116785	ALL	ALL
CARELESS						
1850	1980	1600	1850	112097	BDF	Bedford
1850	1980	1600	1850	112097	HUN	Huntingdon
CAREW						
....	....	ALL	ALL	159190	ALL	Name Study
1086	1992	....	....	159190	ALL	ALL
CAREY						
1700	1800	....	....	137693	CHI	Guernsey
1824	1881	1806	1890	116424	DEV	East Stonehouse
ALL	ALL	ALL	ALL	175927	KEN	ALL
1848	1869	ALL	1848	108537	LAN	Liverpool
1700	1992	1600	1700	100536	LND	???
1806	1824	1806	1824	116424	SOM	Baltonsborough
1750	1800	1700	1850	103055	SRY	Brixton
1750	1800	1700	1850	103055	SRY	Lambeth
1775	1992	ALL	1775	112100	SSX	East
ALL	ALL	ALL	ALL	175927	SSX	East
ALL	ALL	ALL	ALL	175927	SSX	West
....	1700	....	....	174564	SSX	Hooe
....	1700	....	....	174564	SSX	Pevensey
....	....	1800	....	146668	???	London
CARFOOT						
ALL	1800	1700	1800	116785	ALL	ALL
CARFRAE						
....	....	1750	1850	159964	MLN	ALL
CARGILL						
1800	1820	1700	1800	100978	ANS	Craig
CARHART						
1723	1725	1700	1775	133450	CON	Roche
CARIOLI						
1783	1853	1816	1900	149756	NYK	Whitby
CARIS						
1384	1992	1384	1925	119741	DUR	???
1384	1992	1384	1925	119741	NBL	???
CARKEEK						
....	....	1800	1839	118494	CON	Gwennap
1839	1930	....	....	118494	CON	Pensilva
CARKWOOD						
....	....	1820	1992	112305	LKS	???
CARL						
1842	1847	1800	1867	102563	LND	Shoreditch
CARLAW						
1849	1992	1700	1850	112127	DUR	Gateshead
1849	1992	1700	1850	112127	DUR	Newcastle
1800	1882	1750	1830	179000	STI	Falkirk
CARLESS						
1747	1890	1740	1890	103632	NTH	Maidford
CARLICK						
1850	1950	1600	1850	154059	ESS	Terling
CARLIER						
1829	1875	1800	1829	119628	MLN	Edinburgh
1829	1875	1800	1829	119628	YKS	Sheffield
CARLILE						
1850	1920	1700	1880	160954	MSY	Liverpool
1800	1934	1700	1800	148865	WYK	Pudsey

Known From	To	Researching From	To	Ref	Cty	Place
CARLIN						
1700	ALL	....	....	117684	CUL	ALL
1780	ALL	....	....	117684	LAN	ALL
1800	1850	1750	1900	107611	WAR	Aston
CARLING						
1730	1750	1700	1730	121339	NYK	K Reavensworth
1830	1980	1760	1830	151068	YKS	Pateley Bridge
CARLION						
....	....	1750	1850	105082	CON	Breage
....	....	1750	1850	105082	CON	Gwennapp
CARLISLE						
1800	1934	1700	1800	148865	WYK	Pudsey
1792	1851	1792	1851	160237	YKS	Sheffield
CARLOW						
1780	1850	1700	1992	126012	KEN	Meopham
CARLSTROM						
1830	1911	1830	1911	136530	MDX	London
CARLTON						
1400	1470	1300	1470	154881	ALL	ALL
1840	1850	1750	1900	143502	CAM	Cambridge
1760	1900	1600	1760	121339	DUR	Dalrington
1759	1809	1759	1809	149403	DUR	Lamesley
....	....	ALL	1801	106178	NFK	Central
....	....	ALL	1801	106178	NFK	West
1801	1992	ALL	1801	106178	NFK	Norwich
1800	1900	1800	1900	121339	WYK	Leeds
1865	1919	1500	1919	169439	YKS	Middlestown
CARLYLE						
1800	1934	1700	1800	148865	WYK	Pudsey
CARLYON						
1576	1670	....	....	174319	CON	St Austell
CARMAN						
1869	1935	1760	1869	139777	LND	Holborn
CARMICHAEL						
....	....	ALL	ALL	108383	ALL	Name Study
1850	....	....	....	132381	LKS	Glasgow
1790	1900	....	....	133388	NBL	Newcastle Upon Tyne
....	....	1650	1800	133388	SCT	ALL
CARNABY						
ALL	1550	....	....	132756	NBL	???
CARNALL						
....	....	1725	1825	120855	DBY	North
....	....	1725	1825	120855	YKS	South
CARNE						
1470	1540	1470	1540	137340	CON	East Newlyn
1767	1867	1600	1767	173886	CON	St Columb Mincer
1561	1750	....	....	176958	GLA	Nash
CARNEEY						
1678	....	....	....	151351	ANS	Arbroath
CARNEGIE						
1800	?	ALL	ALL	101370	FIF	Dunfermline
CARNELL						
1800	1800	ALL	ALL	147389	DEV	South
1800	1839	1750	1839	174629	DEV	Talaton
1845	1992	1700	1845	161772	KEN	Shoreham
CARNELLEY						
1751	1849	....	....	156922	SYK	???
CARNES						
1726	1726	1700	1775	144606	DUR	Heworth
CARNEY						
1866	1927	1860	1927	134422	FER	Brookeborough
CARNOCHAN						
1812	1834	1700	1812	117234	SCT	Ayr
1805	1885	....	....	106852	WIG	Wigtown
CARNON						
1847	1897	1807	1900	110914	HAM	Portsea
1817	1850	1600	1850	110914	SCT	Kirkcudbright
CARNSEW						
1550	1900	1400	1900	143766	CON	ALL
CAROLAN						
1812	1992	1787	1992	163244	CAV	???
CARPENTER						
....	....	ALL	ALL	108219	ALL	Name Study
1850	1992	1750	1850	112194	AVN	Bristol
1800	1940	1800	1940	112186	AVN	Bristol
1796	1796	1760	1800	108510	BRK	Reading
1738	....	1650	1750	143693	CON	Illogan
1806	1880	1800	1900	121312	CON	Padstow
1850	1992	1650	1850	148059	DEV	Exeter
1813	1950	ALL	ALL	122866	HAM	East
1811	1875	....	....	156647	HAM	Boldre
1650	1740	1650	1750	144657	HAM	Farringdon
1796	1895	1700	1796	126772	HAM	Ropley
1850	1992	1700	1870	112216	HEF	Ross On Wye
CARPENTER contd.						
1788	1992	1750	1992	153133	HRT	Great Gaddesden
1850	1960	....	....	161969	IOW	Cowes
1850	1960	....	....	161969	IOW	Newport
1675	1685	1550	1725	133450	IRL	Ardstagh
1822	1914	1700	1822	152544	KEN	Chiddingstone
1750	1890	1700	1800	112224	KEN	Dover
1776	1870	1700	1776	126454	KIK	Thomastown
1850	1992	1600	1900	132306	LAN	Liverpool
1790	1814	....	....	121355	LND	Stepney
1870	1890	1850	1890	112216	MON	Central
1590	1850	1570	1850	166804	OXF	Bampton
1841	1890	1700	1992	170518	OXF	Banbury
1880	1992	1700	1880	112208	SFK	Mildenhall
1640	1780	1640	1780	142018	SOM	Bath
1755	1815	1730	1815	107573	SOM	Frome
1800	1830	1700	1800	103888	SOM	???
1761	1803	....	....	173932	SRY	Abinger
1800	1805	1770	1800	176257	SRY	Croydon
1747	1992	1650	1794	112178	SRY	Ripley-Send
1811	1849	....	....	173932	SRY	Wotton
1810	1830	1830	1900	155322	SSX	Chalvington
1800	1860	ALL	ALL	154008	WIL	Calne
....	1850	....	1850	161888	WIL	Deverill
1755	1815	1730	1815	107573	WIL	Somerset Border
1707	1743	1670	1710	170348	WIL	Swindon
1500	1992	1660	1992	112186	WOR	Bromsgrove
CARPINTER						
1873	1935	1800	1873	127590	GLS	Bristol
CARR						
1800	1900	1700	1900	146943	BKM	Central
1804	1851	ALL	1804	145335	CUL	Caldbeck
....	....	....	1776	109290	DBY	North
1819	1870	ALL	1870	177695	DUR	Beamish
1744	1772	1600	1744	116637	DUR	Bishop Middleham
1815	1830	1700	1850	144037	DUR	Gateshead
1780	1800	1600	1900	162620	DUR	Gateshead
1775	1800	1600	1775	116637	DUR	Long Newton
1837	1930	1700	1837	153001	DUR	Stockton
1851	1861	1800	1871	171425	DUR	Sunderland
1846	1876	....	1846	166510	ENG	Central
1860	1870	1800	1860	128090	IRL	Dublin
1840	1992	....	....	101621	LAN	Ashton Under Lyne
1800	1900	ALL	ALL	140708	LAN	Colne
1776	1840	....	....	101621	LAN	Garstang
1749	1786	ALL	ALL	135909	LAN	Much Hoole
....	....	ALL	ALL	140708	LAN	Preston
1600	1699	1600	1699	169781	LAN	Yealand Redmayne
1800	1860	1860	1900	132438	LEI	Gaddesby
1852	1992	....	....	175803	LND	Kentish Town
1849	1851	1800	1850	130656	LND	???
1830	....	....	....	126497	NBL	Berwick Upon Tweed
1728	1769	ALL	1728	132829	NBL	Embleton
1760	1992	....	....	132829	NBL	Longbenton
1851	1861	1800	1871	171425	NBL	Newcastle
1800	1920	1800	1992	162620	NBL	North Shields
1690	1790	1650	1690	160458	NBL	Ovingham
1770	....	....	....	146447	NBL	Rothbury
1720	1800	1600	1800	101834	NFK	Hingham
1839	1860	1800	1839	155217	NFK	Norwich
1777	1794	1539	1850	107360	NTH	Kingsthorpe
1845	....	1800	1900	115967	NTH	Tynemouth
1800	1815	1750	1800	121339	NYK	Richmond
1760	1992	ALL	1760	135143	OXF	Oxford
1814	1835	1814	1835	149403	OXF	Oxford
1850	1992	1700	1850	148423	PER	Balinluig
....	....	1850	1900	175102	SFK	Felixstowe
....	....	1850	1900	175102	SFK	Walton
1805	1992	1805	1992	112232	STS	???
1805	1992	1805	1992	112232	WAR	???
1750	1840	1700	1750	168076	WIL	Edington
?	?	?	?	174297	WOR	Beoley
1805	1992	1805	1992	112232	WOR	???
1705	1799	1682	1799	153273	WRY	Ingleton
1703	1747	1600	1992	102520	YKS	Fewston
1837	1992	ALL	ALL	112240	YKS	Leeds
1760	1860	1700	1760	173452	YKS	Rawmarsh
1785	1851	1750	1785	171565	YKS	Rise
1785	1851	1750	1785	171565	YKS	Riston
1800	1850	1775	1992	114901	YKS	Selby
1775	1800	1750	1992	114901	YKS	Stillingfleet
1785	1851	1750	1785	171565	YKS	Swine
....	1750	ALL	1750	148172	YKS	York

Known From	To	Researching From	To	Ref	Cty	Place
CARRADINE						
1552	1850	1550	1850	156809	HEF	Ashperton
1552	1850	1550	1850	156809	HEF	Bishops Frome
1552	1850	1550	1850	156809	HEF	Bosbury
1552	1850	1550	1850	156809	HEF	Castle Frome
1552	1850	1550	1850	156809	HEF	Hereford
1552	1850	1550	1850	156809	HEF	Ledbury
1552	1850	1550	1850	156809	HEF	Much Marcle
1552	1850	1550	1850	156809	HEF	Munsley
1552	1850	1550	1850	156809	HEF	Pencombe
1552	1850	1550	1850	156809	HEF	Tarrington
1552	1850	1550	1850	156809	HEF	Yarkhill
1624	1868	1589	1900	156809	LND	Aldgate
1624	1868	1589	1900	156809	LND	Bishopsgate
1624	1868	1589	1900	156809	LND	Cripplegate
1624	1868	1589	1900	156809	LND	Finsbury
1624	1868	1589	1900	156809	LND	Holborn
1624	1868	1589	1900	156809	LND	Shoreditch
1624	1868	1589	1900	156809	LND	Stepney
1624	1868	1589	1900	156809	LND	Westminster
1624	1868	1589	1900	156809	LND	Whitechapel
1615	1868	1500	1900	156809	WOR	Alfrick
1615	1868	1500	1900	156809	WOR	Bushley
1615	1868	1500	1900	156809	WOR	Chaddesley Corbett
1615	1868	1500	1900	156809	WOR	Claines
1615	1868	1500	1900	156809	WOR	Cradley
1615	1868	1500	1900	156809	WOR	Dudley
1615	1868	1500	1900	156809	WOR	Hallow
1615	1868	1500	1900	156809	WOR	Hanbury
1615	1868	1500	1900	156809	WOR	Hanley Castle
1615	1868	1500	1900	156809	WOR	Hartlebury
1615	1868	1500	1900	156809	WOR	Kidderminster
1615	1868	1500	1900	156809	WOR	Leigh
1615	1868	1500	1900	156809	WOR	Lulsley
1615	1868	1500	1900	156809	WOR	Nelland
1615	1868	1500	1900	156809	WOR	Old Swinford
1615	1868	1500	1900	156809	WOR	Powick
1615	1868	1500	1900	156809	WOR	Ripple
1615	1868	1500	1900	156809	WOR	Suckley
1615	1868	1500	1900	156809	WOR	Worcester
CARRAHER						
1790	1900	1750	1900	136840	IRL	Coast
CARRAT						
1774	1861	1861	?	128910	LIN	Brattleby
1717	1774	?	1717	128910	LIN	Hackthorne
CARRE						
1802	1836	ALL	ALL	115126	CHI	ALL
CARRICK						
1809	1965	....	....	135453	LKS	Glasgow
CARRIER						
1838	1870	....	....	112259	BKM	Wolverton
1600	1700	1600	1800	133450	DBY	Wirkworth
1716	1740	1680	1750	142018	GLS	Bristol
1698	1838	ALL	ALL	112259	KEN	North West
....	....	1830	1880	137685	NFK	Gt Yarmouth
1840	1875	....	....	112259	OXF	Oxford
1700	1716	1680	1720	142018	WIL	Fisherton Anger
1875	1992	....	....	112259	WIL	Swindon
CARRINGTON						
1700	1900	1500	1980	114197	ALL	ALL
1711	1940	....	....	128996	CAM	Thorney
1733	1750	1680	1733	147885	CHS	Wirral
1900	1992	ALL	ALL	112275	DBY	Ripley
1744	1800	1744	....	116394	DEV	Exeter
1794	1825	1744	....	116394	DEV	Topsham
1696	1753	1600	1750	176621	ESS	Bradfield
1684	1744	1684	....	116394	LND	Holborn
1841	....	1841	....	116394	SRY	Newington
CARROL						
....	....	1800	1840	135658	IRL	???
1840	1850	1800	1840	135658	LAN	Liverpool
CARROLL						
1880	1992	....	....	124354	IRL	Dublin
1897	1992	1800	1900	140147	IRL	???
1864	1864	1800	1875	171662	KIK	Kilkenny
1897	1992	1800	1900	140147	LND	Battersea
1870	1895	1800	1900	121762	YKS	South
1919	....	1900	1930	163775	YKS	Barnsley
CARRON						
ALL	1842	....	....	172693	IRL	???
CARROW						
1700	1800	1700	1800	167924	PEM	Tenby
CARROWDYNE						
1624	1649	1589	1900	156809	LND	Bishopsgate
CARROWDYNE contd.						
1624	1649	1589	1900	156809	LND	Cripplegate
1624	1649	1589	1900	156809	LND	Westminster
CARRUTHERS						
1820	....	1820	....	168882	AYR	Muirkirk
....	....	1800	1900	168386	DFS	Dalton
1855	1890	1700	1855	169501	DFS	Lochmaben
1755	1828	1600	1755	140678	WES	Newbiggen
1755	1828	1600	1755	140678	WES	T. Sowerby
CARRYER						
1716	1808	....	1850	171441	KEN	Milstead
CARSBY						
....	....	ALL	ALL	130524	MDX	London
CARSEY						
1808	1851	ALL	1808	160008	WYK	Scarborough
CARSLAKE						
....	....	ALL	ALL	174904	ALL	Name Study
1550	1992	1500	1700	135429	ALL	ALL
1824	....	....	....	131822	CON	ALL
1840	1992	1600	1840	117285	DEV	???
CARSLEY						
1700	1800	1700	1800	120529	WLS	Ellesmere
CARSON						
....	....	ALL	ALL	115231	IRL	???
ALL	1876	....	....	179701	IRL	???
1854	1992	ALL	1854	112313	KKD	Anworth
1876	1950	1876	1950	179701	LAN	Liverpool
1905	1992	1905	1992	112305	LKS	Chapelhall
1790	1820	1750	1850	111821	RFW	Greenock
1884	1905	1840	1905	112305	TYR	???
1800	1830	1690	1840	158313	TYR	???
CART						
1685	1900	1600	1950	146846	KEN	Canterbury
CARTER						
1600	1700	1600	1700	167924	BDF	Campton
1810	1810	1750	1850	147958	BDF	Flitton
1810	1840	1800	1840	102970	BDF	Westoning
1851	....	1700	1850	170178	BKM	Penn
1585	1800	ALL	1585	168211	BKM	Swanbourne
1838	1876	....	1838	101761	BKM	Upton Cum Chalbey
1792	1871	1780	1871	113069	BRK	Abingdon
1850	1950	1700	1850	149632	BRK	Binfield
1690	1916	1600	1900	115681	BRK	Buckland
1797	1988	1600	1797	162035	CAM	Cambridge
....	1832	1500	1751	125695	CAM	Little Abington
1823	1860	1700	1823	153079	CAM	March
1850	1908	ALL	1850	129658	CAM	St Neots
1833	1992	1833	....	112380	CHS	Bowdon
1860	1992	1800	1900	165662	CHS	Nantwich
1851	1992	1851	1871	112380	CHS	Pennys Lane
1845	1992	1845	1992	147249	CHS	Warrington
1734	1758	1600	1734	102571	CON	Breage
1700	1850	1700	1800	107530	CON	Breage
1800	1900	1800	1992	133450	CON	Breage
1837	1992	1700	1837	130257	CON	Camborne
1700	1735	1650	1700	145297	CON	Kenwyn
1800	1900	1800	1992	133450	CON	Mardon
1775	1800	1725	1775	172901	DBY	Ilkeston
1847	1953	1700	1847	177938	DEV	St Thomas
1896	1992	1700	1896	158275	DOR	Ferndown
1896	1992	1700	1896	158275	DOR	Hampreston
1771	1830	1700	1850	119040	DOR	Hamworthy
1730	1850	....	....	151351	DOR	Okeford Fitzpaine
1771	1830	1700	1850	119040	DOR	Poole
1695	1746	....	....	151351	DOR	Shillingstone
1806	1980	1790	1890	135895	DOR	Weymouth
1825	1880	....	....	151351	DOR	Winterborne Monkton
....	....	1600	1992	108812	DOW	Rathriland
1860	1992	1700	1860	128325	DUR	Darlington
1786	1921	ALL	1806	108642	ESS	Debden
1802	1819	....	....	105619	ESS	Thorpe Le Soken
....	....	1870	1890	117137	GLA	Deri
....	....	1840	1870	117137	GLA	Merthyr
1870	1960	1600	1890	176664	GLS	Bitton
1760	1835	1760	1835	178705	GLS	Coln St Aldwyn
1795	1795	1750	1825	178004	GLS	Horton
1725	1747	1600	1725	108413	GLS	Painswick
1870	1960	1600	1890	176664	GLS	Wick
1881	1992	1881	1992	172952	HAM	Bitterne
1600	1730	1500	1700	144657	HAM	Farringdon
....	?	....	....	141941	HAM	Portsmouth
1786	1921	ALL	1806	108642	HRT	Bishops Stortford
1857	1916	....	1857	175579	HRT	Harpenden
1825	1870	1825	1870	107522	KEN	Edenbridge

Known From	To	Researching From	To	Ref	Cty	Place
CARTER contd.						
1854	1970	1789	1895	143480	KEN	Greenwich
1810	1835	1700	1820	117110	KEN	Sandwich
1720	1757	1599	1720	141291	LAN	Lancaster
1729	1734	ALL	ALL	141615	LAN	Lancaster
....	1861	....	1861	146919	LAN	Lancaster
....	....	1799	1855	155039	LAN	Liverpool
1876	....	....	....	144169	LAN	Manchester
1854	....	1854	....	160164	LAN	Salford
1772	1932	1700	....	112348	LEI	Goadby Marwood
1900	1920	1800	1950	117870	LEI	Netherseal
1790	1835	1750	1790	120529	LIN	Goltho
1740	....	....	....	156647	LIN	Manby
1851	1992	1851	1992	147230	LND	East End
1860	1950	1800	1860	159212	LND	Holbonr
1863	1992	1700	1992	112402	LND	Islington
1803	1803	....	....	121355	LND	Whitechapel
1893	1917	1800	1992	166197	MDX	Hampstead
1840	1885	1819	1885	105619	MDX	Harrow
1840	1885	1819	1885	105619	MDX	Marylebone
1855	1992	1700	1855	109967	MDX	St Georges
1885	....	....	1600	136557	MDX	???
1812	1895	1812	1895	119695	MON	Overmonnow
1825	1850	....	....	135070	NFK	East Dereham
1861	1950	1700	1861	179051	NFK	Wareham
1865	1992	....	....	128643	OKI	Westray
1792	1871	1780	1871	124990	OXF	Abingdon
1550	1600	1500	1900	166804	OXF	Bampton
1742	1743	1600	1743	115681	OXF	Langford
1880	1970	1750	1900	175978	OXF	Marsh Baldon
1848	1880	1800	1880	177938	OXF	St Thomas
1800	1992	1500	1800	151483	SAL	Iron Bridge
1610	....	....	1950	120391	SAL	???
1787	....	1787	1992	147230	SFK	Ipswich
1770	1800	1700	1800	105619	SFK	Nayland
1753	1811	1700	1841	176923	SOM	Apulton
1884	....	....	1884	163031	SOM	Exmoor
....	....	1800	1840	117137	SOM	Paulton
1765	1863	1700	1768	177075	SOM	Paulton
1850	1870	1830	1870	109371	SOM	Yeovil
1786	1921	ALL	1806	108642	SRY	Morden
1813	1930	1813	1930	169323	STS	Darlaston
1760	1830	1700	1800	136840	WIL	Avon Valley
1812	1840	1700	1840	109363	WIL	Calne
....	....	1750	1840	101478	WOR	Broadway
1828	1900	1750	1828	137278	YKS	Bedale
1838	1992	1700	1868	109649	YKS	Halifax
1834	1992	1700	1834	109649	YKS	Huddersfield
1818	1833	1818	1833	160164	YKS	Pontefract
ALL	ALL	ALL	ALL	105813	YKS	Sowerby
?	?	ALL	ALL	174432	YKS	Wombleton
1900	1992	1800	1900	111813	???	Hartlepool
CARTERET						
1750	....	....	....	137693	CHI	Guernsey
CARTHEW						
1819	1821	....	....	147672	CON	Redruth
1700	1992	1600	1700	156566	DEV	South
1840	1940	1820	1992	105333	KEN	Woolwich
1840	1940	1820	1992	105333	MDX	London
CARTLEDGE						
1795	1847	1600	1795	152463	LEI	Long Whatton
....	....	1820	1840	177725	LIN	Holton Beckering
1860	1881	ALL	1860	144029	YKS	Ecclesfield
1860	1881	ALL	1860	144029	YKS	Ripon
1860	1881	ALL	1860	144029	YKS	Sheffield
CARTLICH						
1639	1750	1500	1639	110639	STS	Stoke On Trent
CARTLIDGE						
1849	1881	ALL	1849	106909	STS	Burslem
1830	1861	1700	1830	112410	STS	Penkhull
CARTMEL						
1853	1897	1821	1897	161861	CMA	Keswick
1837	1880	1837	1880	173568	LAN	Burscough
CARTMELL						
1950	....	....	....	112429	LAN	Liverpool
1796	1918	....	....	112429	LAN	Lytham Moss Side
1719	1804	....	....	112429	LAN	Marton
1670	1804	....	....	112429	LAN	North Meols
1896	?	....	....	112429	LAN	Wesham
CARTWRIGHT						
1842	1851	1840	1851	129283	CAM	Cambridge
1788	1840	1700	1800	135496	CHS	North
1847	1848	1750	1847	155845	CHS	Northwich
1844	1851	1844	1851	129283	HAM	Portsmouth
CARTWRIGHT contd.						
....	....	1850	1992	108502	HUN	Abbotsley
1854	1870	1851	1870	129283	KEN	Gravesend
1784	1900	1700	1900	135968	LEI	Blaby
1780	1800	1700	1850	155950	LEI	Leicester
1820	1840	....	....	167517	LIN	Grantham
1700	1800	....	....	100056	LIN	Salmonby
1700	1800	....	....	100056	LIN	Spilsby
1795	1868	ALL	1820	129283	MDX	Shorditch
1821	1830	....	1821	122378	NTT	Newark On Trent
1730	1794	1650	1730	150614	SAL	Ellesmere
1860	....	1800	1900	168785	SAL	Ellesmere
1860	1992	....	....	128716	SAL	Wellington
1844	1919	ALL	1992	159174	STS	Burton On Trent
1825	....	ALL	1992	159174	STS	Rugeley
1833	....	ALL	1992	159174	STS	Salt
1810	1875	1750	1900	113697	STS	Stafford
1669	1770	1640	1800	160873	STS	Womborne
1788	?	1700	1788	171476	WAR	Mancetter
1863	1906	1800	1863	149977	WOR	Dudley
....	....	1800	1851	111414	WOR	Oldbury
1814	....	....	....	152455	WOR	???
1700	....	1600	....	134589	YKS	Rufforth
1863	1863	1800	1863	128368	YKS	Sheffield
1800	1866	1700	1900	177369	YKS	York
CARTY						
?	?	?	?	112437	LKS	Shotts
1920	1992	1700	1920	165573	LKS	???
?	?	?	?	112437	LTN	Faldhouse
CARUS						
1500	....	1400	1600	129011	CUL	Kendal
1850	1900	1900	1992	162256	LAN	Darwen
CARUTH						
1836	1863	1863	1992	146560	LKS	Coatbride
CARVAL						
1780	....	....	....	129747	IRL	???
CARVASSO						
1620	1750	....	....	139491	CON	St Just
CARVELEY						
1842	1871	ALL	ALL	111384	WYK	Hunslet
1842	1871	ALL	ALL	111384	WYK	Leeds
1842	1871	ALL	ALL	111384	WYK	Rothwell
CARVER						
1800	1825	1800	1825	178705	GLA	Cardiff
1800	....	ALL	ALL	116394	HAM	Titchfield
1799	1992	1600	1799	112445	HAM	Upham
1799	1992	1600	1799	112445	IOW	Shorewell
1780	1809	1700	1809	118168	LAN	Colton
1805	1900	1750	1810	156957	NTT	Gotham
....	....	ALL	ALL	100153	SFK	Bedfield
....	....	ALL	ALL	100153	SFK	Framlingham
1820	1860	1850	1855	110159	SFK	Ipswich
CARVETH						
....	....	ALL	ALL	140732	ALL	Name Study
....	....	?	?	112453	CON	St Allen
CARVEY						
1780	1920	1750	1950	166804	BRK	Shrivenham
1760	1770	1700	1800	166804	WIL	Aldbourne
CARVOSSO						
1645	1747	....	....	143596	CON	Mousehole
CARWARDEN						
1450	1650	1450	1650	112062	ALL	ALL
CARWARDINE						
1626	1626	1626	1626	156809	ESS	Asheldham
1800	1889	1574	1900	156809	ESS	Earls Colne
1750	1850	1700	1750	118745	GLS	Gloucester
1574	1770	1552	1850	156809	HEF	ALL
1770	1850	1600	1900	130125	HEF	Bosbury
1574	1770	1552	1850	156809	HEF	Preston
1552	1850	1550	1850	156809	HEF	Stoke Edith
....	....	1500	1650	112062	HEF	Thinghill
1574	1770	1552	1850	156809	HEF	Withington
1574	1770	1552	1850	156809	HEF	Wynne
1601	1866	1589	1900	156809	LND	Bethnal Green
1601	1866	1589	1900	156809	LND	Cripplegate
1601	1866	1589	1900	156809	LND	Finsbury
1601	1866	1589	1900	156809	LND	Hanover Square
1601	1866	1589	1900	156809	LND	Holborn
1601	1866	1589	1900	156809	LND	Shoreditch
1601	1866	1589	1900	156809	LND	St Pancras
1601	1866	1589	1900	156809	LND	Stepney
1601	1866	1589	1900	156809	LND	Westminster
1612	1855	1600	1900	156809	SAL	Bettus
1612	1855	1600	1900	156809	SAL	Bridgenorth

Known From	To	Researching From	To	Ref	Cty	Place
CARWARDINE	contd.					
1612	1855	1600	1900	156809	SAL	Burford
1612	1855	1600	1900	156809	SAL	Chirbury
1612	1855	1600	1900	156809	SAL	Clun
1612	1855	1600	1900	156809	SAL	Condover
1612	1855	1600	1900	156809	SAL	Ludford
1612	1855	1600	1900	156809	SAL	Ludlow
1612	1855	1600	1900	156809	SAL	Neen Sollars
1612	1855	1600	1900	156809	SAL	Pontesbury
1612	1855	1600	1900	156809	SAL	Stanton Lacy
1612	1855	1600	1900	156809	SAL	Stoke St Milborough
1612	1855	1600	1900	156809	SAL	Wellington
1612	1855	1600	1900	156809	SAL	Wistanston
CARWARDYNE						
1394	1588	1066	1588	156809	STS	Malpas
1394	1588	1066	1588	156809	STS	Mavesyn Ridware
CARWELL						
....	....	1500	1825	166863	KEN	ALL
CARY						
....	....	1800	1870	107727	LND	London
1853	1930	ALL	1853	119695	MON	Overmonnow
1820	1920	ALL	1800	138169	SOM	Lympsham
CARYESFORD						
ALL	ALL	ALL	ALL	112461	ALL	ALL
CARYL						
....	....	1500	1600	175269	???	London
CARYSFORTH						
1863	1992	ALL	ALL	112461	ALL	ALL
CARZELL						
1770	....	....	....	127140	AYR	???
CASBAN						
1541	1869	1541	1869	120308	CAM	Melborne
1541	1869	1541	1869	120308	CAM	Meldreth
1870	1992	1870	1930	120308	SRY	Croydon
CASBOLT						
....	....	ALL	ALL	112488	ALL	Name Study
1520	1989	1500	1992	112488	ALL	ALL
1750	1850	ALL	ALL	112496	CAM	South
1750	1850	ALL	ALL	112496	ESS	North West
1750	1850	ALL	ALL	112496	SFK	South West
CASBON						
1920	1992	1850	1920	151955	ALL	ALL
1920	1992	1850	1920	151955	WMD	???
CASE						
1764	1908	ALL	1992	133930	CAM	Cambridge
1773	1776	1700	1800	116173	CUL	West
1745	1865	1600	1800	115681	DOR	Bridport
1730	1800	1700	1800	174599	DOR	Shaftesbury
1870	1922	1870	1922	133930	LND	West Ham
CASELDEN						
1840	1865	....	....	144371	KEN	Hunton
CASELEY						
1700	1750	1680	1780	142018	SOM	Taunton
CASEY						
1840	1840	ALL	1840	119636	CLA	Kilrush
1840	1900	1800	1850	133787	LKS	Motherwell
1841	1910	ALL	ALL	112518	MDX	Marylebone
1736	1970	1600	1750	112526	OXF	Clifton Hampdon
1844	....	1700	1844	111953	OXF	Marston
CASH						
1800	1880	....	....	179701	CHS	Upton
1828	1880	1800	1880	166677	HAM	Sherfield English
1800	1850	1750	1900	174599	HAM	Sherfield English
1700	1850	....	....	100056	LIN	Holbeach
1700	1850	....	....	100056	LIN	Sutterton
CASHELL						
1850	1970	ALL	ALL	112526	IRL	ALL
CASHMORE						
1882	1882	1859	1882	157678	LAN	Liverpool
1590	1690	1500	1900	177180	STS	West Bromwich
1800	1850	1750	1900	107611	WAR	Aston
1828	1856	1856	1992	174262	WAR	Birmingham
1700	1992	1700	1992	114790	WAR	Hatton
CASIER						
....	....	1600	1700	156531	CON	ALL
CASLAKE						
....	....	ALL	ALL	125040	ALL	Name Study
CASLEY						
1850	1870	ALL	ALL	162205	DEV	Buckfastleigh
CASPER						
1842	1992	1842	1992	112534	NYK	Hull
1842	1992	1842	1992	112534	NYK	Scarborough
1842	1992	1842	1992	112534	NYK	York

Known From	To	Researching From	To	Ref	Cty	Place
CASS						
1660	1752	....	1660	101761	WRY	Wakefield
CASSADY						
1818	1836	1700	1818	149632	MDX	Stepney
CASSELDINE						
....	....	1600	1700	150150	RUT	Caldecott
CASSELL						
1850	....	1700	1850	145378	LND	Rotherhithe
CASSELS						
1850	1992	ALL	1850	149829	LKS	ALL
1797	1839	1790	1840	171654	LKS	Carluke
CASSERLEY						
1850	1900	1800	1992	177180	STS	Smethwick
CASSFORD						
1577	1715	1577	1750	129194	HAM	Lymington
1571	1992	1571	1900	129194	IOW	ALL
1700	1800	1700	1750	135089	IOW	???
1669	1909	1669	1909	129194	KEN	ALL
1610	1985	1610	1900	129194	LND	ALL
CASSIDY						
....	....	ALL	ALL	152048	ANT	???
1872	1876	1850	1890	126705	COR	???
1902	1992	1890	1992	126705	LAN	Manchester
CASSON						
1727	1742	1703	1727	141291	CUL	Ulpha
1740	1896	ALL	1900	113611	EYK	Hull
1878	1992	1700	1878	178225	LAN	Everton
1662	1814	....	....	120634	LAN	Holton On Lune
1878	1992	1700	1878	178225	LAN	Liverpool
1820	1840	1820	1840	113611	LIN	Lincoln
1870	1890	1800	1869	131245	NFK	East Dereham
1891	1892	1800	1890	131245	SRY	Dulwich
CASTE						
1785	1895	....	....	102946	LEI	Knighton
1785	1895	....	....	102946	NTT	Nottingham
CASTELL						
1871	1908	ALL	ALL	160776	ALL	ALL
?	?	?	?	142514	ABD	Aberdeen
?	?	?	?	142514	ABD	Rhynie
?	?	?	?	142514	ABD	Tarves
1750	1800	....	....	165999	ESS	ALL
1800	1850	1750	1900	106631	MDX	London
1750	1800	....	....	165999	NFK	ALL
CASTELLO						
1800	1992	1800	1992	112550	WAR	Birmingham
CASTILL						
1750	....	....	....	160385	IOM	Bride
CASTILLION						
....	....	1500	1750	153397	BRK	ALL
....	....	1500	1750	153397	MDX	London
....	....	1500	1750	153397	SRY	Godalming
....	....	1500	1750	153397	SRY	Guildford
CASTLE						
1660	1960	1600	1960	126500	ABD	Fyvie
1700	1900	1700	1900	149233	ABD	Fyvie
1660	1900	....	....	126497	ABD	Lyvie
1766	1793	1500	1850	157538	BRK	ALL
1685	1890	1540	1900	155616	BRK	???
1800	1850	1800	1850	124761	KEN	North East
1804	1980	1700	1804	110019	KEN	Canterbury
....	1770	ALL	1800	152889	KEN	Dover
1790	1830	1700	1830	108111	KEN	Wingham
1850	1950	....	....	126497	MLN	Edinburgh
1775	1800	1700	1800	172901	NTT	Bilborough
1780	1890	1750	1780	135518	NTT	Radford
1810	1832	1750	1850	105120	OXF	Banbury
1908	1914	....	....	151416	SCT	Aberdeen
1871	1900	....	....	117560	SRY	Clapham
?	?	?	?	163279	WMD	Wolverhampton
1756	1992	....	1804	101761	WRY	Kirkheaton
1780	1800	1730	1820	123595	YKS	Holmfirth
1750	1800	1700	1900	138517	YKS	Holmfirth
1841	1900	1600	1840	124176	YKS	Hull
CASTLEDINE						
1678	1746	1600	1800	141569	NTH	Fotheringhay
1808	....	1800	....	162744	NTT	Bingham
CASTLEDOWN						
1894	....	ALL	ALL	105481	NTT	Radford
CASTLEHOWE						
1790	1910	1700	1790	155810	CUL	Penrith
CASTLETON						
1740	1815	1700	1850	149152	YKS	Sheffield
CASTLING						
....	....	ALL	ALL	137871	ALL	Name Study

Known From	To	Researching From	To	Ref	Cty	Place
CASTREE						
1869	1939	1700	1869	127566	STS	Lichfield
1869	1939	1700	1869	127566	STS	Tettenhall
CASWELL						
1811	....	1700	1811	126357	CLA	Doonass
1698	1749	1700	1800	144037	NBL	Hartburn
?	1790	?	1790	158569	SAL	Shrewsbury
1808	1849	1750	1808	164259	WOR	Kidderminster
CATANACH						
1816	1841	1750	1816	118427	ABD	Glenmuick
CATCHESIDE						
1595	1808	1580	1812	178470	DUR	Chester Le Street
1595	1808	1580	1812	178470	DUR	Durham
1595	1808	1580	1812	178470	DUR	Lamesley
1820	1905	....	....	112577	NBL	Newcastle
1710	1820	1650	1850	112577	NBL	Stamfordham
1710	....	1650	1750	112577	NBL	Wylam
CATCHPOLE						
?	1830	....	1930	160164	LAN	Manchester
1864	1871	1864	1871	160164	LAN	Salford
1800	1820	1800	1820	160164	NFK	Yarmouth
1852	1852	1852	1852	173851	SFK	Bury St Edmonds
1700	1700	1650	1700	155276	SFK	Fressingfield
1790	1865	1700	1790	164860	SFK	Hasketon
1800	1992	1600	1800	164461	SFK	Kessingland
1845	1848	1845	1848	160164	SFK	Lowestoft
1755	1992	1700	1755	105031	SFK	Tunstall
1850	1853	1853	1853	160164	SRY	Newington
CATCUM						
....	1920	....	....	159999	MDX	Brentford
CATCUTT						
1780	1800	ALL	1780	115266	DOR	ALL
CATER						
....	....	1800	1850	116238	DEV	Knighton
1800	....	....	....	135488	ESS	Colchester
1765	1881	1700	1940	110051	GLS	Stapleton
1840	1860	1750	1840	137421	HUN	Huntingdon
....	....	1800	1850	116238	KEN	Dover
1700	1992	1700	1992	177687	LIN	Louth
1870	1900	1830	1900	116238	MDX	Marylebone
1858	1904	1856	1960	110051	SCT	ALL
CATES						
1810	1890	1750	1900	131792	LND	Westminster
CATHARDINE						
1772	....	1772	....	112364	ESS	Great Leighs
CATHCART						
1885	1965	1700	1885	157996	LAN	St Helens
CATHERALL						
1750	1800	1600	1992	167592	CHS	Chester
1700	1860	1500	1992	167592	FLN	Buckley
1675	1861	1861	1875	112585	FLN	Ewloe
1892	1992	....	....	112585	LAN	Bolton
1861	1992	....	....	134430	LND	Watford
1881	....	1861	1892	112585	STS	Thursfield
1875	1879	1879	1892	112585	STS	Wedgewood
CATHERY						
1796	1815	1775	1992	114901	HAM	Warblington
CATHRALL						
1825	1992	1825	1900	157376	FLN	Hope
CATLEY						
1766	....	ALL	1766	119326	ERY	Bilton In Ainsty
CATLIN						
1800	1900	1800	1900	134767	HRT	Hemel Hempstead
1844	1900	1844	1900	134767	KEN	Sevenoaks
1800	1900	1800	1900	134767	MDX	Islington
1670	1702	1750	1900	123285	SYK	Worsbrough
CATLING						
1760	1820	ALL	1750	152889	BDF	Tilbrook
1712	1940	....	....	128996	CAM	Thorney
1770	1803	1524	1835	118893	NFK	Kenninghall
CATLOW						
1871	1973	1861	1973	108952	LAN	Burnley
1795	1820	1500	1820	169439	LAN	Church
1815	1917	1700	1881	160636	LAN	Denton
CATON						
1824	1923	ALL	1923	114030	ESS	Wimbish
....	....	1850	1970	111503	LAN	Blackburn
....	....	1700	1900	111503	LAN	Lancaster
....	....	1800	1850	137111	LAN	Lancaster
1840	1850	1800	1850	137111	WOR	Worcester
CATT						
1150	1439	1150	1439	107980	NFK	Hevingham
1909	....	1875	1910	113743	SSX	Brede
1800	1851	ALL	1800	131849	SSX	Willingdon
CATTELL						
1820	1850	....	....	112593	NFK	Norwich
1800	1820	1750	1820	112593	SFK	Gorleston
CATTERALL						
....	....	ALL	1992	112607	LAN	Catterall
....	....	ALL	1992	112607	LAN	Colne
....	....	ALL	1992	112607	LAN	Croston
....	....	ALL	1992	112607	LAN	Euxton
1820	1880	1750	1820	128384	LAN	Manchester
....	....	ALL	1992	112607	NYK	Giggleswick
....	....	ALL	1992	112607	NYK	Rathmeli
....	....	ALL	1992	112607	NYK	Wigglesworth
CATTERHOLD						
....	....	1700	1750	140716	SFK	Baddingham
CATTERSON						
1820	....	1820	1853	169625	LIN	Great Grimsby
1600	....	1600	1800	169625	YKS	Hull
CATTLE						
1769	1992	1700	1769	141348	DOR	East
CATTLEY						
1747	1890	1700	1861	160903	HRT	Anstey
1747	1890	1700	1861	160903	HRT	Barkway
CATTO						
1750	1850	1750	1800	140864	ABD	Foveran
CATTON						
1904	....	1850	1950	112615	LAN	Stockport
1814	1900	ALL	1814	140813	NFK	Field Dalling
1860	1900	1800	1860	123811	SFK	Barningham
1845	1871	1700	1992	159468	STS	Tipton
1851	....	1700	1800	112615	YKS	Huddersfield
1830	....	1700	1800	112615	YKS	Mirfield
CAUDERY						
1940	1992	ALL	ALL	112631	ALL	ALL
1800	....	ALL	ALL	112631	BKM	ALL
CAUDLE						
....	....	ALL	ALL	112658	ALL	ALL
1720	1850	ALL	1850	115908	GLS	North
....	....	1720	1726	112658	GLS	Temple Guiting
CAULCOT						
1790	1890	1650	1790	151084	STS	???
CAULDOCK						
1850	1850	1800	1850	146587	LND	Finsbury
CAULDWELL						
1815	1909	1600	1815	143146	DBY	Alderwasley
1802	1880	ALL	1802	168742	NTT	Egmanton
CAULEY						
1861	1992	1750	1861	112666	CON	South East
1861	1992	1750	1861	112666	DEV	South West
CAULFIELD						
1820	1825	1800	1850	123536	ANT	ALL
1900	1980	1800	1900	105198	ANT	Kells
1825	1871	1800	1880	123536	NBL	Alnwick
CAULKIN						
1800	1860	1700	1800	168734	SAL	Chetwynd
1790	1900	1700	1992	168734	SAL	Newport
CAULKINS						
1600	1649	ALL	ALL	122211	WLS	Borders
CAULTON						
1818	....	ALL	ALL	155608	DBY	Denby
1880	1900	ALL	ALL	155608	DBY	Ripley
CAUNCE						
1790	1953	....	....	116602	LAN	West
....	....	1700	1992	131601	LAN	Accrington
....	....	1700	1992	131601	LAN	Croston
....	....	1700	1992	131601	LAN	Merebrow
CAUNT						
1840	1930	1835	1940	160164	LAN	Manchester
1802	1830	ALL	....	104515	LIN	Old Somerby
1785	1840	1785	1840	160164	NTT	Balderton
1851	1893	1851	1893	160164	NTT	Bury
1830	....	1830	....	160164	NTT	Collingham
1814	....	1814	....	160164	NTT	East Bridgford
1800	1992	ALL	1800	123854	NTT	Hucknall
1851	1854	1851	1854	160164	NTT	Salford
1785	1840	1785	1840	160164	NTT	Southscarle
1841	1851	1841	1851	160164	NTT	Stockport
1770	....	1770	1850	135429	SOM	Bath
CAUNTER						
1550	1880	1300	1900	105333	DEV	Buckland In The Moor
1550	1880	1300	1900	105333	DEV	Holne
1550	1880	1300	1900	105333	DEV	Ilsington
1550	1880	1300	1900	105333	DEV	Lydford

Known From	To	Researching From	To	Ref	Cty	Place
CAUNTER contd.						
1550	1880	1300	1900	105333	DEV	Widecombe In The Moor
CAUSER						
1760	1851	ALL	ALL	101486	SAL	South East
1960	1960	ALL	ALL	100137	STS	ALL
1862	1871	ALL	ALL	136735	WAR	Aston
1827	1849	ALL	ALL	136735	WAR	Birmingham
1849	1861	ALL	ALL	136735	WOR	Yadley
CAUSTON						
1815	1925	1815	1992	133450	LND	Southwark
CAUTLEY						
1811	1940	....	....	128996	CAM	Thorney
CAVANAGH						
1890	1960	1800	1890	175595	TYR	Belfast
CAVE						
....	....	ALL	ALL	112690	ALL	Name Study
....	....	ALL	ALL	112682	ALL	Name Study
1066	1992	1066	1992	112682	ALL	ALL
1066	ALL	1066	ALL	112690	ALL	ALL
ALL	ALL	ALL	ALL	159530	ALL	ALL
1803	1834	....	1803	108839	CAM	Sutton
1833	1900	....	....	129801	CAM	Sutton
1722	1940	....	....	128996	CAM	Thorney
1600	1992	ALL	ALL	112674	GLS	ALL
1762	1819	1700	1762	114928	HAM	Isle Of Wight
1858	1938	1800	1858	175447	LAN	Royton
1678	1851	ALL	ALL	126381	LEI	Leicester
1632	1632	1580	1660	156396	LEI	Swinford
....	....	1700	1992	139343	LND	Islington
1780	1840	1720	1850	173029	NTT	Carlton
1770	1840	1700	1770	172847	NTT	Gedling
1790	1840	ALL	ALL	143839	WIL	Trowbridge
CAVEEN						
....	....	ALL	ALL	153982	ALL	Name Study
1844	1870	....	1870	153982	LAN	Liverpool
CAVELL						
1737	....	ALL	1750	104299	SOM	Old Cleeve
1667	1992	1500	1700	112704	SOM	Old Cleeve
CAVENDISH						
....	....	ALL	1680	178403	DBY	Doveridge
....	....	ALL	1630	178403	STS	Tutbury
CAVENEY						
....	1876	1800	1876	103322	YKS	Tadcaster
CAVERS						
1820	1850	ALL	1850	149063	MLN	Stow
1833	1894	1700	1833	166723	ROX	Ashkirk
1800	1850	1800	1850	149063	ROX	Cavers
1780	1800	ALL	1800	149063	SEL	Ettrick
1760	1820	ALL	1825	149063	SEL	Roberton
CAVETT						
....	....	ALL	ALL	112712	ALL	ALL
1860	1900	....	....	112712	SCT	Thornhill
CAVIL						
....	....	1750	1900	162388	SOM	Ubley
CAVLEY						
1900	1992	ALL	ALL	135321	SLI	Mullaghmore
CAVNETT						
....	....	ALL	ALL	136549	ALL	Name Study
CAW						
1770	1793	1700	1770	124427	FIF	Tulliallan
1636	1969	....	....	149616	PER	Crieff
CAWARDIN						
1390	1390	1390	1390	156809	DBY	Hartington
CAWKEN						
1800	1900	1700	1800	168734	SAL	Shrewsbury
CAWLEY						
1850	1950	1770	1850	130192	CHS	Bunbury
1813	1843	1788	1843	169099	CHS	Chester
1854	1992	1700	1850	116416	MDX	Camden
1826	1911	1826	1911	132543	SFK	Bardwell
CAWOOD						
....	....	1850	1890	103713	NRY	Scarborough
1739	1771	1730	1780	170143	SSX	Trotton
....	....	1810	1850	103713	WRY	Barwick In Elmet
....	....	1810	1850	103713	WRY	Leeds
....	....	1770	1810	103713	WRY	Whitkirk
1823	1846	1760	1900	144460	YKS	Halifax
CAWSE						
1770	1840	1800	1900	168580	CON	Looe
1670	1750	1650	1760	168580	CON	St Neot
1833	1900	1700	1830	114162	DEV	Holbeton
1780	1830	1700	1830	114162	DEV	Newton Ferrers

Known From	To	Researching From	To	Ref	Cty	Place
CAWSTON						
1500	1600	1400	1600	154881	KEN	Orpington
1814	....	....	....	136999	SFK	Bury St Edmunds
CAWTE						
....	....	ALL	ALL	112720	ALL	Name Study
....	....	ALL	ALL	112720	ENG	ALL
1546	1992	1200	1700	112720	HAM	ALL
1800	1900	1700	1800	101826	HAM	Longstock
1800	1900	1700	1800	101826	HAM	Stockbridge
CAWTHORN						
?	?	?	?	160679	ALL	ALL
1837	....	1700	1850	160679	CAM	???
1837	....	1700	1850	160679	LIN	???
1731	1992	1600	1750	101575	YKS	Goole
1731	1992	1600	1750	101575	YKS	Hull
1731	1992	1600	1750	101575	YKS	Knottingley
1837	....	1700	1850	160679	YKS	???
CAWTHORNE						
....	....	ALL	ALL	160679	ALL	Name Study
?	?	?	?	160679	ALL	ALL
1910	1992	1700	1910	112739	LND	Bethnal Green
1890	....	....	....	154695	WRY	Ossett
CAWTHRA						
1810	1870	1750	1810	117633	WYK	Bradford
CAWTON						
1842	1849	1842	1860	147125	DUR	Bishop Auckland
CAYFORD						
1760	1800	1640	1760	149373	SOM	Saltford
CAYGILL						
1820	1890	1760	1820	137278	YKS	Snape
CAZNELL						
1820	1870	....	....	128759	NFK	West Dereham
CEALY						
1800	1800	1700	1800	132640	SSX	Warbleton
CECIL						
1825	1963	....	....	130958	MDX	Bethnal Green
CELLING						
....	....	1780	1820	109533	ALL	ALL
1820	1860	....	....	109533	DEV	Plymouth
CERNAN						
1854	ALL	ALL	1854	116734	CAV	Belturbet
1854	ALL	ALL	1854	116734	CAV	Templeport
1854	ALL	ALL	1854	116734	IRL	???
CESAR						
....	....	ALL	ALL	112755	ALL	Name Study
CESSFORD						
....	....	ALL	ALL	130877	ALL	Name Study
1760	1881	1760	1881	130877	NBL	ALL
CHAD						
ALL	1763	....	....	105368	SOM	Shepton
CHADBOURNE						
....	....	ALL	ALL	163368	DBY	???
1873	....	ALL	ALL	125202	LAN	Manchester
....	....	ALL	ALL	163368	NTT	???
1850	1850	....	....	125202	WOR	Stourbridge
CHADBURN						
....	....	1650	1900	131555	LEI	Ashby De La Zouch
CHADD						
?	1940	....	....	104450	LND	Camden Town
CHADDERDON						
....	....	ALL	ALL	112763	ALL	Name Study
CHADDERTON						
1800	1992	1700	1800	163570	ALL	ALL
1700	1992	ALL	1700	112771	LAN	Oldham
1775	1900	....	1900	147818	LAN	Oldham
CHADWICK						
....	....	ALL	ALL	112798	ALL	Name Study
....	....	ALL	ALL	112801	ALL	Name Study
....	....	1800	1850	168815	CHS	ALL
1820	1992	1700	1820	129208	CHS	Macclesfield
1790	1840	1790	1840	140724	CHS	Stockport
....	1725	1700	1725	152560	DBY	Ashlehay
....	....	1800	1850	168815	LAN	ALL
1857	1926	ALL	ALL	104531	LAN	Bolton
?	?	?	?	176842	LAN	Earlestown
1830	1850	1830	1850	140724	LAN	Heaton Norris
1850	1992	1800	1850	139475	LAN	Liverpool
1850	1900	1800	1900	166960	LAN	Liverpool
1845	1860	1845	1860	140724	LAN	Manchester
1839	1908	1839	1916	129216	LAN	Marsden
1851	....	1816	1841	136565	LAN	Preston
1859	....	?	1860	164976	LAN	Prestwick
1740	1790	1740	1790	140724	LAN	Reddish
1785	1910	....	....	116602	LAN	Rochdale

Known From	To	Researching From	To	Ref	Cty	Place
CHADWICK contd.						
1868	1912	1750	1900	126977	LAN	???
....	....	ALL	ALL	130818	LND	Camberwell
1827	1936	1827	1936	140724	WAR	Warwick
1868	1912	1750	1900	126977	YKS	???
CHAFFE						
1600	1992	1600	1900	166545	DEV	Buckfastleigh
CHAFFER						
1800	1890	1780	1920	170038	LAN	Worsthorne
CHAFFERS						
1750	1780	1650	1992	167592	LAN	Liverpool
CHAFFEY						
1800	1850	1700	1800	118915	SOM	ALL
CHAFFIN						
....	....	ALL	ALL	120642	ALL	Name Study
1550	1950	1550	1700	108677	DOR	Sherborne
1550	1950	1550	1700	108677	SOM	ALL
CHALCROFT						
1842	1842	1825	1842	107573	ESS	Woodford
1865	1871	1865	1871	138398	GLS	Stanton
1835	1861	1835	1861	138398	HEF	Dixon
1860	1860	1840	1860	126640	LND	Kennington
1861	1881	1861	1881	138398	MON	Abertillery
CHALDER						
1790	1970	1600	1840	178470	DUR	East
1790	1970	1600	1840	178470	YKS	Arkengarthdale
CHALFONT						
....	....	1330	1420	154873	BKM	Chalfont
CHALK						
1779	1992	1700	1779	167800	DEV	Hartland
1779	1992	1700	1779	167800	DEV	Parkham
1657	1883	....	....	101028	ESS	High Easter
1850	1860	1820	1860	155691	LND	Newington
1816	....	....	....	112836	LND	Paddington
1846	?	1700	1800	112836	LND	St Pancras
1850	1851	1700	1800	112836	MDX	Chelsea
1870	....	....	....	153397	SSX	Portslade
1869	1875	....	....	112836	WAR	Aston
1860	1869	....	....	112836	WAR	Leamington
1700	1730	1650	1800	174599	WIL	Downton
CHALKER						
1700	1869	....	....	151351	DOR	Netherbury
1728	1830	....	....	151351	DOR	Powerstock
1846	....	1840	....	156027	MDX	Hammersmith
1815	....	1810	....	156027	SFK	Bungay
CHALKLEY						
1720	1746	ALL	ALL	141623	ESS	???
1788	1928	1788	1813	103853	HRT	Ashwell
....	....	1600	1788	103853	HRT	Essendon
1740	1820	1740	1820	171999	HRT	Ippollitts
1740	1820	1740	1820	171999	HRT	Kings Walden
1829	1992	1750	1829	176257	MDX	Tottenham
CHALLAND						
1800	1840	1700	....	152722	NTT	E Bridgford
CHALLANDS						
1785	1992	ALL	1785	107239	LEI	Bottesford
CHALLENGER						
1680	1863	1600	1900	149047	SOM	Balgdon
....	....	1700	1900	133329	YKS	Doncaster
1900	1992	....	1900	135674	YKS	???
CHALLENOR						
1818	1843	1750	1818	134627	SAL	Oswestry
1843	1880	1830	1900	134627	STS	Willenhall
CHALLESS						
1808	1882	1700	1808	138673	EAG	???
CHALLICE						
1870	1910	ALL	1904	114030	DEV	Torquay
CHALLINGSWORTH						
1870	1950	1850	1900	131431	GNT	Newport
CHALLIS						
....	....	....	1730	137405	CAM	South
....	1811	1765	....	123609	ESS	Faulkbourne
1888	1972	1600	1888	147893	MDX	Hampton
?	....	....	?	169358	SFK	Bury St Edmunds
CHALMERS						
1840	1930	1800	1930	167258	ABD	Fraserburgh
1770	1900	1750	1900	149233	ABD	Fyvie
1850	1860	1750	1900	135925	ABD	Kintore
1768	1992	1725	1768	112844	ABD	Strichen
1770	1900	1750	1900	149233	ABD	Strichen
....	....	1800	1900	105198	ABD	???
1820	1860	....	....	159883	ANS	Dundee
1814	....	1800	1855	146536	AYR	Ardrafan
1860	1940	1700	1860	155136	AYR	???

Known From	To	Researching From	To	Ref	Cty	Place
CHALMERS contd.						
1822	1901	1750	1820	153656	LKS	Carnwath
1828	1897	1790	1850	179000	LKS	Chapelhall
....	....	ALL	1802	119326	MLN	Newbattle
1807	1992	1700	1838	166987	OKI	Stronsay
1801	....	....	....	106852	PER	Kilmadock
1828	1912	1750	1828	140678	PER	Kinclaven
1801	....	....	....	106852	PER	Logie
1830	1910	1800	1900	160563	TAY	Dundee
1830	1910	1800	1900	160563	TAY	Lochee
CHALONER						
1900	1906	1850	1906	141135	LAN	Manchester
1851	1881	1800	1900	119008	LIN	Lincoln
CHALONS						
1735	1735	1700	1735	128368	LIN	Coleby
CHALTON						
1802	1803	?	1803	158569	LND	Marylebone
1767	....	1767	....	141194	SRY	Caterham
CHAM						
1700	....	1600	....	134589	YKS	Knaresborough
CHAMBERLAIN						
....	....	1700	1800	123137	BDF	Stotfold
1781	1872	1700	1781	123307	BRK	Chieveley
1865	1940	1794	1865	107247	DEV	Bampton
1853	1992	1700	1800	172820	HRT	Great Amwell
1750	1785	....	....	142360	HRT	Rickmansworth
1130	1500	1130	1500	104736	LEI	ALL
1823	....	....	1823	171441	LND	Bethnal Green
1840	1970	....	....	119334	LND	Chelsea
1859	1992	ALL	ALL	115762	LND	Islington
1870	1950	1800	1870	108103	NFK	???
1736	1850	1700	1736	135747	NTH	Burton Latimer
1848	1892	1800	1992	134988	NTT	Bradmore
1848	1892	1800	1992	134988	NTT	Bunny
1490	1600	1490	1600	104736	OXF	Shirborne
1750	1800	1650	1750	166804	SFK	Lowestoft
1900	1940	1800	1945	115746	SOM	Central
1772	1841	ALL	1850	165654	SOM	Shepton Mallet
1800	1850	ALL	ALL	171816	WAR	Birmingham
1739	1822	1700	1739	101796	WAR	Monks Kirby
1810	1880	1700	1810	162884	WIL	Charlton
1736	1896	1660	1750	163562	WOR	Worcester
1780	1850	1600	1992	167592	WOR	Worcester
1800	1950	1700	1950	138045	???	Birmingham
1900	1992	1700	1900	112860	???	London
CHAMBERLAINE						
1857	1915	1828	1915	104604	LND	Battersea
CHAMBERLAYNE						
1800	1992	1800	1992	104736	HAM	Southampton
1730	1830	1730	1830	104736	KEN	Greenwich
1730	1830	1730	1830	104736	KEN	Rolvenden
1630	1700	1630	1700	104736	OXF	Wickham
1600	1800	1600	1800	104736	???	London
CHAMBERLIN						
1680	1830	....	....	116017	DEV	North
1830	1900	....	....	116017	LND	Haggerston
1816	....	1800	1850	142638	LND	St Giles
1810	....	1780	1820	128724	MDX	London
CHAMBERS						
1690	1690	ALL	1690	115126	BKM	Datchet
1728	1924	....	1728	108839	CAM	Coveney
1800	1870	1700	1800	129208	CHS	Macclesfield
1850	1900	....	....	143243	DBY	Staveley
1700	1710	1680	1710	165530	GLS	Berkeley
1800	1850	ALL	1800	145939	HAM	Bedhampton
1750	1800	1750	1800	167924	HRT	Icleford
1809	1953	1805	1953	138312	KEN	Central
1753	1860	....	1860	171441	KEN	Faversham
....	....	1700	1900	162000	KEN	Swale
....	1800	....	1800	177695	LEI	Leicester
1794	1800	1750	1850	110191	MDX	London
1900	....	....	....	148504	MOR	Redditch
....	....	1700	1800	116173	NTT	North
1800	1850	1700	1800	143243	NTT	Eastwood
1745	....	ALL	ALL	105481	NTT	Nuthall
1840	1992	1600	1840	167010	SFK	Wilby
1773	1979	1750	1992	112879	WAR	Birmingham
1800	....	....	....	148504	WAR	Studley
1700	1750	1700	1780	149691	WAR	Studley
1630	1664	1600	1630	152196	WES	Heversham
1800	1818	1700	1800	137901	YKS	Handsworth
1814	1900	1700	1837	176370	YKS	Leeds
CHAMBLEY						
1789	1854	1675	1875	157716	ALL	ALL

Known From	To	Researching From	To	Ref	Cty	Place
CHAMBLEY contd.						
1833	1851	1750	1870	157716	WES	Appleby
1819	1851	1700	1920	157716	YKS	West Riding
CHAMNESS						
1800	1900	ALL	1850	149691	ESS	ALL
CHAMNEY						
....	1700	ALL	1700	162507	YKS	Colton
CHAMP						
....	....	ALL	ALL	161454	ALL	Name Study
1823	1859	1600	1823	152080	BRK	Sutton Courtenay
1811	1865	1725	1811	105503	DEV	Seaton
1773	1832	1700	1773	177555	DOR	Lulworth
1850	1953	1830	1953	132608	LND	???
1894	1946	1890	1992	104663	SFK	Southwold
1773	1775	ALL	1774	112887	SRY	Weybridge
CHAMPION						
1790	1992	....	....	138134	CON	Camborne
1804	1833	1780	1900	157341	CON	Crowan
1847	....	1847	....	173266	CON	Penzance
....	....	1750	1850	147710	ESS	Chelsford
1784	1843	1500	1784	110310	HAM	Odiham
1780	1992	1780	1992	178705	HAM	Odiham
1801	1825	1750	1848	149640	HAM	Titchfield
1825	1879	1725	1903	149640	HAM	Winchester
1863	1890	1863	1890	131997	KEN	Central
1797	....	....	1800	171441	KEN	Bredgar
1743	....	....	1800	171441	KEN	Newnham
1775	....	....	1800	171441	KEN	Tonge
1836	1870	1700	1836	139696	KEN	Woolwich
1692	1703	....	1740	171441	KEN	Wormshill
1830	1864	1825	1895	149640	MDX	Hammersmith
1800	1850	1800	1850	128724	MDX	London
1864	1882	1860	1895	149640	MDX	London
1823	....	1800	1850	116572	NTT	Burton Joyce
1790	1880	1770	1880	142018	SOM	Bath
1600	1850	1600	1850	142018	SOM	Shepton Mallet
....	1540	ALL	1546	112178	SRY	Godalming
CHANCE						
1800	1940	1813	1940	130222	BDF	Eversholt
....	....	1670	1832	143480	BDF	Marston Moretaine
1800	1810	1800	1810	130222	BDF	Toddington
1840	1885	ALL	1885	118990	BRK	Wlatham St Laurence
1855	1992	....	....	143480	HAM	Fareham
1800	1900	1800	1900	173681	WOR	Lye
CHANCELLOR						
1720	1900	1500	1900	155543	SOM	Bridgewater
1720	1900	1500	1900	155543	SOM	Street
CHANDLER						
....	....	ALL	ALL	112917	ALL	Name Study
ALL	ALL	ALL	ALL	112917	ALL	ALL
1750	1850	1700	1900	177180	BKM	Aston Abbots
1700	1800	1500	1800	177180	BKM	Mentmore
1754	1850	1700	1850	132608	BRK	Lambourn
1905	1905	1905	1905	147575	BRK	Maidenhead
....	....	1600	1992	146099	BRK	Sonning
1750	1800	1730	1820	123145	BRK	Stratfield Mortimer
1840	?	1840	?	128112	ESS	Purfleet
1843	1867	1843	1867	147575	GLS	Bishops Cleene
1800	1800	1800	1800	145580	GLS	Bristol
1817	1851	1700	1817	169730	HAM	Basing
1770	1856	1700	1770	114871	KEN	Chartham
1808	1863	1808	1900	110051	KEN	Northfleet
1812	1860	1700	1869	147575	KEN	Thanet
1747	?	?	?	166642	KEN	???
1830	1922	....	....	145580	LAN	Liverpool
1800	1900	ALL	ALL	112933	LEI	Alk Village
1800	1900	ALL	ALL	112933	LEI	Gilmorton
1800	1900	ALL	ALL	112933	LEI	Marborough
1840	1967	....	....	140023	LND	ALL
1850	1872	1830	1872	151599	LND	East
1800	1900	1800	1930	147575	MDX	Fulham
1800	1900	1800	1900	177180	MDX	Kilburn
1720	1992	1600	1850	101834	NFK	South West
1722	1920	....	1722	100064	NFK	Northwold
1840	1890	....	....	144371	OXF	Oxford
1580	1768	1580	1770	159581	SRY	Bramley
1859	1870	....	....	112909	SRY	Morsley Down
1819	1821	....	....	112909	SRY	Southwark
....	....	1806	1885	119431	SSX	Burwash
1754	1800	1700	1754	170747	SSX	Mayfield
1800	1824	1750	1800	133671	WIL	Churchdown
1732	1850	1700	1850	132608	WIL	Ramsbury
1778	....	1778	....	147575	WIL	???
CHANEY						
1860	1992	ALL	1992	153311	DEV	???
1834	1867	1830	1870	161942	KEN	Dover
....	....	ALL	ALL	153311	KEN	???
1750	1920	1600	1920	160946	NFK	ALL
CHANN						
1700	....	1600	....	134589	YKS	Knaresborough
CHANNALL						
1828	1861	1700	1828	138673	SSX	Rudgwick
CHANNEL						
1649	1696	1600	1649	145459	HAM	Bursledon
1799	1867	?	1799	136611	LIN	Atterby
CHANNELL						
1851	1861	1861	1900	149357	DEV	Axminster
CHANNING						
1897	1917	1915	1917	139343	KEN	Chatham
1857	1865	1800	1992	139343	LND	Islington
CHANNON						
1796	1798	1770	1798	133000	DEV	Axminster
1750	1800	1750	1800	135429	DEV	Aylesbeare
....	....	1898	1953	134694	DEV	Exeter
1720	....	1600	1720	168637	DEV	Exter
....	....	1840	1900	134694	DEV	Gittisham
....	....	1800	1870	134694	DEV	Salcombe Regis
CHANT						
1840	1890	1840	1930	166685	AVN	Bristol
1803	1870	1750	1803	102598	DEV	Brixham
1800	1840	1795	1840	166685	SOM	Queen Camel
1746	1800	1740	1800	166685	SOM	Somerton
1845	1992	1750	1845	112941	SOM	South Petherton
1700	1900	ALL	1700	112968	SOM	Stoke Sub Hamdon
1700	1900	ALL	1700	112968	SOM	West Chinnock
CHANTER						
?	?	?	?	151556	YKS	Bradford
CHANTLER						
1600	1700	1550	1600	156140	SSX	Barcombe
CHANTRELL						
1840	1880	1800	1840	161519	LAN	Liverpool
CHANTREY						
1880	....	1600	1800	112976	LAN	Wigan
CHANTS						
1866	?	....	....	129100	MDX	Whitechapel
CHAPELHOW						
1751	1803	ALL	ALL	145335	CUL	Kirkoswald
CHAPELL						
1739	1980	1600	1740	159646	CON	Cawsand
1739	1763	1600	1739	159646	CON	Padstow
1739	1909	1700	1739	165123	CON	Padstow
1765	1992	1600	1765	133493	CON	Rame
1690	1720	1720	1765	133493	CON	St Columb Major
1900	1992	ALL	ALL	148520	KEN	Sittingbourne
CHAPLIN						
....	1783	1700	1786	128961	ESS	Halstead
1692	1792	1600	1692	138584	LEI	Kegworth
1809	1870	1809	1870	167924	LEI	Leicester
1920	1992	....	....	113018	LND	Hackney
1800	1870	1800	1870	145750	NFK	Kings Lynn
1661	1708	ALL	ALL	121487	SFK	Hessett
1886	1905	1800	1885	123811	SFK	Ipswich
1780	1980	1600	1780	112992	SOM	Weston Super Mare
1780	1980	1600	1780	112992	SOM	Wick St Lawrence
1865	1900	1800	1865	126535	SRY	East Hampstead
1700	1850	1700	1850	167924	WAR	Bedworth
1600	1700	....	....	100420	WAR	Meriden
CHAPLYN						
ALL	ALL	ALL	ALL	111066	KEN	Rochester
CHAPMAN						
1859	1887	1850	1890	113107	BAN	Newton Of Panbride
1820	1860	1790	1860	113107	BAN	Port Gordon
1810	1900	1750	1900	147958	BDF	Flitton
1613	1789	....	....	172731	BDF	Luton
....	....	1600	1800	104469	BKM	Buckingham
1791	1860	1700	1791	105562	BKM	Stoke Goldington
?	?	?	?	159069	BKM	Wendover
1824	....	1790	1824	176885	BKM	Wendover
1863	1946	ALL	ALL	144762	BRK	Hungerford
....	....	1760	1840	103713	CAM	Ashley
1773	ALL	ALL	1800	116734	CAM	Balsham
1736	1940	....	....	128996	CAM	Thorney
1805	1980	1700	1805	132640	CAM	Wisbeach
1792	1867	1650	1800	165549	CON	Laniuet
1900	....	ALL	ALL	159026	CUL	Carlisle
1877	....	ALL	ALL	159026	CUL	Kirby Stephen
....	....	1764	1870	115142	DBY	South

Known From	To	Researching From	To	Ref	Cty	Place
CHAPMAN contd.						
1892	1992	1860	1992	146625	DBY	Huddersfield
1824	1992	1700	1824	173770	DEV	South
1845	....	....	....	170623	DEV	Hennock
1804	....	....	....	177687	DEV	Plymouth
1750	1830	1700	1850	105422	DUR	Cockfield
1816	1885	ALL	1816	128414	DUR	Trimdon
1698	1698	ALL	1698	154563	DUR	Weardale
1800	1900	ALL	ALL	132977	ESS	Coggeshall
1936	1947	1900	1992	129984	ESS	Forest Gate
1681	1749	....	....	165999	ESS	Great Baddow
1826	....	....	....	170623	ESS	Great Dunmow
1806	1863	1800	1863	134880	ESS	Southminster
1850	1900	1850	1900	126799	ESS	West Ham
1700	....	ALL	ALL	130508	FIF	St Monance
?	?	ALL	ALL	156671	GLA	Porthcawl
1767	....	1700	1767	166723	GLS	Randwick
....	....	1800	1850	149306	HAM	Porstmouth
1800	1992	1700	1800	167649	HRT	ALL
1560	1800	1560	1800	167924	HRT	Bennington
1798	1880	....	....	172731	HRT	Wheathamstead
1797	1841	1700	1800	116378	HUN	Diddington
1750	1830	ALL	ALL	114235	HUN	???
1811	1900	1811	ALL	165522	IOM	Douglas
1778	1799	ALL	ALL	165522	IRL	Dublin
1874	1891	1850	1992	155896	KEN	Bexley Heath
....	....	1831	?	130079	KEN	Bexley
1863	....	1840	1870	171441	KEN	Eythorn
1826	1890	1820	1890	144878	KEN	Faversham
1850	1871	1850	1900	176982	KEN	Greenwich
1753	1849	....	....	144282	KEN	Northfleet
1753	1849	....	....	144282	KEN	Sutton At Hone
1900	1925	1900	1992	165522	LAN	Liverpool
1785	1853	1700	1785	113050	LAN	Worsley
....	....	1850	1900	133531	LEI	Leicester
1790	1992	1700	1850	169560	LIN	North
1720	1730	....	....	103721	LIN	Althorpe
1785	....	....	1785	101761	LIN	Croft
1804	1992	1804	1992	177687	LIN	Fotherby
1790	1850	ALL	1790	152021	LIN	Horncastle
....	1733	....	....	128910	LIN	Laughton
1700	1921	1550	1850	139866	LIN	Louth
1650	1750	1550	1800	139866	LIN	Skegness
....	1871	1700	1900	126292	LND	East End
1837	1992	ALL	ALL	115762	LND	Marylebone
1803	1803	....	....	121355	LND	St George In The East
1800	1841	1700	1800	168033	MDX	Chiswick
1800	1841	1700	1800	168033	MDX	Turnham Green
....	....	1650	1800	117587	NFK	Cnetral
1750	1900	1700	1900	126799	NFK	Great Bircham
1840	1960	1750	1840	171034	NFK	Thurgarton
1675	1992	ALL	ALL	143944	NTH	East Haddon
1734	1794	1734	1802	104817	NTH	Kettering
1757	1794	1650	1760	131377	NTH	Rothwell
1750	1830	ALL	ALL	114235	NTH	???
1790	1830	1830	1880	148113	NTT	Lowdham
1881	1891	1881	1891	113085	OXF	Benson
1850	1881	1850	1881	113085	OXF	Brightwell Baldwin
1750	1800	1750	1800	108693	RUT	Liddington
1750	1800	1750	1800	108693	RUT	Seaton
1790	1880	1700	1900	172073	SFK	Middleton
1784	....	1780	1800	169625	SFK	Norton
1810	1880	1700	1810	164860	SFK	Stradbroke
1811	1881	1700	1992	176923	SOM	Apulton
1803	1822	1700	1881	176923	SOM	Farrington Gurney
1750	1992	1500	ALL	113093	SOM	Frome
?	?	1700	1850	123668	SOM	Harptree
1838	....	1600	1838	164879	SRY	Bermondsey
1815	1840	1815	1841	113085	SRY	Bletchingley
1750	1880	....	....	113042	SSX	Brighton
1867	1992	1837	1867	114995	SSX	Eastbourne
1766	1779	ALL	....	132349	SSX	Framfield
....	....	?	1760	113042	SSX	New Shoreham
1754	1782	1700	1754	100277	SSX	Wartling
1806	1830	1750	1850	129356	SSX	Wartling
1850	1900	1700	1900	117870	STS	Litchfield
1900	1945	1880	1900	113050	STS	Smethwick
1840	1910	1800	1940	136174	TYR	Augmnacloy
1850	1900	1700	1900	117870	WAR	Birmingham
1800	1920	ALL	ALL	143839	WIL	Bradford On Avon
1863	1946	ALL	ALL	144762	WIL	Hungerford
....	1828	ALL	1828	167878	WIL	West Lavington
1798	1992	1700	1798	102342	WRY	Whitgift

Known From	To	Researching From	To	Ref	Cty	Place
CHAPMAN contd.						
1861	1982	1800	1861	136301	YKS	Barnsley
1694	1694	1650	1700	141097	YKS	Braithwell
1821	1851	ALL	1821	145203	YKS	Cargrave
1841	1902	1700	1841	167355	YKS	Fylingdale
1740	1800	1700	1800	119717	YKS	Hemingbrough
1770	1830	....	1830	113034	YKS	Scarborough
....	....	....	1850	114812	YKS	Shefield
1909	1985	1909	1992	165603	YKS	Stockton
CHAPPEL						
1624	1850	1562	1624	177903	CON	Blisland
1624	1850	1562	1624	177903	CON	Truro
1865	1917	1917	1945	169374	DUR	Sunderland
1760	1900	1730	1900	118540	SOM	North
1758	1758	....	....	135437	SOM	Stogumber
CHAPPELL						
1845	1992	1700	1845	128325	CON	Penzance
....	....	1790	1890	159646	CON	Plymouth
....	....	1790	1890	159646	DEV	Plymouth
1797	1866	1780	1900	103896	ESS	Witham
1890	1925	ALL	ALL	164887	HRT	Watford
1837	1880	1862	1880	172235	KEN	Milton
1837	1880	1862	1880	172235	KEN	Sittingbourne
1827	1871	ALL	ALL	153516	SOM	Ashwick
CHAPPELLE						
....	....	1790	1890	159646	CON	Plymouth
....	....	1790	1890	159646	DEV	Plymouth
CHAPPELLS						
....	....	ALL	1800	111988	CHS	Macclesfield
1790	1992	ALL	1790	111988	STS	Leek
CHAPPERLIN						
1650	1750	1650	1750	142018	WIL	ALL
CHAPPLE						
1797	1829	ALL	ALL	104191	CON	Penzance
....	....	1790	1890	159646	CON	Plymouth
1879	....	....	1879	163031	DEV	North
1839	1860	1700	1880	116394	DEV	Chittlehampton
1800	1810	ALL	1800	145564	DEV	Chittlehampton
1524	1720	ALL	1720	142506	DEV	Exeter
....	....	1790	1890	159646	DEV	Plymouth
1772	1821	1700	1830	142506	DEV	St Sidwell
1800	1850	1700	1850	116823	DEV	Totnes
1700	1800	ALL	ALL	131873	ESS	Manuden
1700	1750	ALL	ALL	131873	HRT	Much Hormead
1900	1947	....	....	121444	MDX	London
....	....	....	1879	163031	SOM	???
CHAPPUIS						
1707	....	1109	1707	168505	LND	Chelsea
CHAPRONIERE						
....	....	ALL	ALL	134740	ALL	Name Study
CHARD						
1782	1782	....	....	135437	DEV	Clayhidon
1757	1762	....	....	135437	DEV	Hemyock
1900	1950	1800	1900	119040	GLA	Pontycymmer
1806	1806	....	....	135437	GLS	Bristol
1820	....	....	....	101613	MDX	Marylebone
ALL	ALL	ALL	ALL	114502	SOM	ALL
1700	1992	ALL	ALL	173363	SOM	South
1700	1992	ALL	ALL	173363	SOM	West
1803	1803	....	....	135437	SOM	Bedminster
1781	1782	....	....	135437	SOM	Chew Stoke
1900	1970	1800	1900	119040	SOM	Clutton
1806	1806	1700	1850	105333	SOM	Creech St Michael
1715	1992	ALL	ALL	173363	SOM	Pitney
1806	1806	1700	1850	105333	SOM	Stoke St Gregory
1806	1806	1700	1850	105333	SOM	Taunton
1806	1806	1700	1850	105333	SOM	Thornfalcon
CHARGE						
1870	....	1800	....	162752	HRT	???
CHARIE						
1880	1992	1550	1880	167932	ENG	ALL
CHARITY						
1762	1940	....	....	128996	CAM	Thorney
1794	1879	1794	1879	113131	CAM	Wimblington
1821	1974	1821	1850	113131	CHS	Haslington
1815	1920	1815	1852	113131	HUN	Huntingdon
1600	1920	1600	1850	113131	LEI	Croxton Kerrial
1600	1920	1600	1850	113131	LEI	Roxton
1773	1850	1773	1850	113131	LIN	Barholm
1619	1737	1619	1737	113131	NTH	Maxey
1735	1992	1735	1912	113131	NTH	Northborough
1618	1980	1618	1850	113131	RUT	Seaton
1798	1980	1798	1950	113131	SFK	Boyton

Known From	To	Researching From	To	Ref	Cty	Place
CHARKER						
1880	1992	1840	1992	135429	MDX	Islington
CHARLES						
1860	1920	ALL	ALL	156604	ABD	New Aberbour
....	....	1800	1900	134546	BDF	Yielden
1841	1992	1750	1841	149918	CHS	Barrow
....	....	1800	1860	158259	DEN	Brymbo
1765	1790	ALL	ALL	129933	DEV	Exeter
1708	1870	1600	1780	177555	DOR	South
1830	1950	1830	1950	152935	GLS	Bristol
1707	1784	1707	1784	165999	GLS	Henbury
1740	1740	1740	1740	136808	HRT	Barkway
1850	1880	....	....	147486	HRT	Barnet
1864	1900	1800	1900	113174	LDY	Desertmartin
1864	1900	1800	1900	113174	LDY	Draperstown
....	....	1888	1900	113174	LND	Hackney
1874	1931	1860	1935	129879	LND	Shoreditch
1852	1992	1700	1852	113166	MDX	St Andrew Holborn
....	....	ALL	1786	119326	MLN	Newbattle
1830	1890	1700	1819	113158	SRY	Camberwell
1857	1900	1790	1857	111740	SSX	Brighton
1860	1880	1840	1860	148113	STS	Sedgeley
....	....	1800	1900	113174	TYR	Cookstown
....	....	1860	1940	113174	WAR	Bromsgrove
1800	1840	1700	1800	148113	WAR	Dudley
1880	1890	1890	1920	148113	YKS	Sheffield
CHARLESON						
1750	1965	....	....	137820	SHI	Fetlar
1720	1965	....	....	137820	SHI	Mid Yell
1760	1965	....	....	137820	SHI	North Yell
1758	1965	....	....	137820	SHI	Northmavine
1720	1965	....	....	137820	SHI	South Yell
CHARLESVORTH						
1800	....	....	....	141208	MDX	Twickenham
CHARLESWORTH						
1904	1963	1800	1900	110345	CHS	North
1727	1857	1700	1860	108510	CHS	Coppenhall
1727	1860	ALL	ALL	108510	CHS	Minshull Vernon
....	....	1800	1900	110345	DBY	Charlesworth
1798	1852	ALL	1798	168742	LEI	Buckminster
1925	1933	1892	1927	109509	LIN	Redbourne
1830	1830	1790	1880	158658	NFK	Norwich
1875	1920	1800	1900	178454	NTT	Nottingham
1782	1801	ALL	ALL	105481	NTT	Old Basford
1820	1860	ALL	ALL	108510	STS	Audley
....	....	ALL	ALL	111384	SYK	Silkstone
....	....	ALL	ALL	111384	SYK	Thurgoland
1541	1784	1723	1784	124826	WRY	Holmfirth
ALL	1780	....	....	170798	WRY	Penistone
ALL	1780	....	....	170798	WRY	Thurlstone
....	....	ALL	ALL	111384	WYK	Carlton
....	....	ALL	ALL	111384	WYK	Cawthorn
1892	1932	ALL	1892	109509	WYK	Cleckheaton
1820	1861	ALL	ALL	111384	WYK	Lofthouse
1820	1861	ALL	ALL	111384	WYK	Rothwell
1760	....	1720	1800	170348	YKS	Almondbury
1818	1881	ALL	1900	104299	YKS	Barnsley
1720	1800	1700	1800	123595	YKS	Holmfirth
1800	1830	1750	1850	146803	YKS	Leeds
1800	1900	1850	1900	105546	YKS	Wooldale
CHARLETON						
....	....	ALL	ALL	113190	ALL	Name Study
ALL	ALL	ALL	ALL	113182	ALL	ALL
....	....	ALL	ALL	113190	ALL	ALL
CHARLETT						
1820	....	....	....	101613	SRY	Lambeth
CHARLEY						
1700	1992	1500	1700	113204	ANT	Dunmurry
....	....	1650	1900	136166	DEV	Kentisbury
....	....	1852	1900	136166	GLA	Llandaff
CHARLTON						
1834	1851	....	....	116637	CUL	Brampton
1776	1863	....	1776	124524	DUR	Gainford
1930	1984	1830	1984	126241	DUR	Gateshead
1846	1881	1881	1992	113220	DUR	Pelton
1786	1786	1750	1790	103632	DUR	Sedgefield
....	....	1865	1890	126241	DUR	South Shields
1910	1930	1850	1950	179671	DUR	South Shields
1777	1846	ALL	1777	113220	DUR	Whickham
1850	1900	1800	1850	165018	EYK	Beverley
1850	1860	1830	1900	113212	GNT	Blaina
1600	1800	1600	1800	152404	LAN	Eccles
1904	1937	1800	1904	127116	LND	St Mary Le Bone
1790	....	1600	1790	116637	NBL	Corbridge
CHARLTON contd.						
1871	1881	1881	1992	113220	NBL	Gosforth
1810	1900	1600	1810	130885	NBL	Hartburn
1796	1821	1760	1796	130877	NBL	Hexham
....	....	1830	1881	126241	NBL	Wallsend
1780	1850	1600	1780	172901	NTT	Bilborough
1780	1850	1600	1780	172901	NTT	Strelley
1700	1830	1700	1900	113212	SOM	Brewham
1700	1830	1700	1900	113212	SOM	Nunney
1809	1830	1800	1900	165034	YKS	Gt Ayton
CHARLWOOD						
1804	1900	ALL	ALL	115010	SSX	Horsham
CHARMAN						
1800	1900	1500	1900	113239	KEN	ALL
1800	1900	1500	1900	113239	LND	ALL
1500	1900	1500	1900	113239	SRY	ALL
1800	1900	....	....	151572	SRY	Cranley
1808	1967	1700	1808	118710	SRY	Unstid Mill
1500	1900	1500	1900	113239	SSX	ALL
CHARNEY						
1835	1992	1750	1835	111813	YKS	Greenfield
CHARNLEY						
1830	1860	1830	1860	137804	LAN	Bolton
1800	1992	ALL	1800	112771	LAN	Dalton
1802	1958	1700	1800	169854	LAN	Furness
1800	1820	....	....	137804	LAN	Garstang
1800	1820	1780	1830	137804	LAN	Kirkham
....	....	1650	1800	147613	LAN	Melling
1860	1900	1850	1900	137804	LAN	Rochdale
1644	1800	1600	1850	179078	LAN	Tatham
CHARNOCK						
....	....	1700	1992	111503	LAN	Chorley
....	....	1700	1992	111503	LAN	Leyland
1750	1806	....	....	175439	LAN	Leyland
1750	1806	....	....	175439	LAN	Wigan
CHARRETT						
1780	1950	ALL	1992	113247	HAM	Andover
1780	1950	ALL	1992	113247	HAM	Portsmouth
1780	1950	ALL	1992	113247	HAM	Southampton
1800	1840	1800	1850	113247	LAN	Liverpool
1820	....	1800	1992	113247	PEM	Pembroke
1800	....	1800	1992	113247	WYK	Mezborough
CHARSLEY						
1906	1992	1850	1992	130036	CHS	Birkenhead
CHARTER						
1800	1936	ALL	ALL	151815	CAM	Arrington
1780	1800	1600	1780	164577	NBL	North Shields
CHARTERS						
1799	1851	1700	1900	139203	DFS	Wamphray
1850	1992	1700	1850	113786	YKS	Hull
CHARTIER						
1756	1800	1700	1756	108448	LND	East
CHASE						
1400	1600	1400	1600	144657	HAM	Liss
CHASEN						
1818	1846	1800	1846	134422	LAN	Liverpool
1818	1846	1800	1846	134422	LAN	West Derby
CHASLEY						
1735	....	....	....	101613	MDX	Paddington
CHASSELS						
....	....	....	1860	116866	LKS	???
CHASTER						
1798	1851	1600	1798	156779	NFK	Plumstead
CHASTNEY						
1770	1855	1620	1770	138029	NFK	Seringham
CHATAWAY						
....	....	....	1860	116866	WAR	???
CHATER						
1850	1880	....	....	151998	BKM	Little Kimble
1900	1950	....	....	151998	DEV	Tiverton
1852	1935	....	....	178926	LEI	Leicester
1788	1852	1700	1788	178926	NTH	Long Buckby
1850	1877	1850	1877	139408	WAR	Aston
1750	1760	....	....	125423	WOR	Hanbury
CHATFIELD						
....	....	ALL	ALL	113255	ALL	Name Study
1811	1835	1780	1811	175951	SSX	Ditchling
?	?	1880	1920	109843	SSX	Fairlight
1750	1992	1600	1750	109843	SSX	Greatham
1750	1992	1600	1750	109843	SSX	Pulborough
1800	1851	1780	1860	105333	SSX	Yapton
CHATTEN						
1850	1992	1750	1992	102032	EAG	???
....	....	1770	....	145688	SFK	Weybread

Known From	To	Researching From	To	Ref	Cty	Place
CHATTER						
1750	1760	1700	1780	125423	WOR	Hanbury
CHATTERS						
1680	1890	1680	1890	114316	ESS	Belchamps
1840	1945	1840	1945	114316	SFK	Cavendish
CHATTERTON						
1768	1768	....	1768	108510	DBY	New Mills
1580	1881	1500	1992	152277	LIN	ALL
1850	1920	1800	1992	133450	LND	???
1740	1890	....	....	152277	MDX	London
1850	1992	1600	1850	113263	YKS	???
CHATTING						
1900	1930	1800	1940	173746	LND	ALL
CHATWELL						
1680	1750	1600	1800	160849	SAL	Acton Burnell
CHATWIN						
1816	1906	1750	1816	164224	???	Scarborough
CHAVASSIE						
1750	1850	....	....	137111	STS	Coseley
CHAWNER						
1853	1945	1800	1853	118710	KEN	Deal
CHAWORTH						
1000	1450	1000	1450	154881	ALL	ALL
CHEAL						
1830	1992	1700	1830	160571	DUR	Hartlepool
1792	....	ALL	ALL	156558	SSX	East Grinstead
1780	1825	1750	1825	100277	SSX	Salehurst
CHEALE						
1600	1800	....	....	164038	SXE	Henfield
CHEATER						
1800	1850	ALL	ALL	151998	WIL	Boyton
CHEATLE						
1800	1819	1800	1819	160164	LEI	Ashby De La Zouch
CHEATTER						
1865	1865	....	....	108901	NTT	Ordsall
CHECKER						
....	....	1750	1850	132586	WIL	Highworth
CHECKETTS						
1700	1881	....	....	130680	WAR	Aston Cantlow
CHECKLEY						
1620	1850	1550	1620	129763	NTH	South
1889	1992	1500	1889	153494	WAR	ALL
CHEEKE						
1740	1750	1700	1800	123536	DOR	Wareham
CHEEPER						
1810	1870	1700	1992	113751	ALL	ALL
CHEESEMAN						
1753	1804	1725	1961	132845	KEN	Marden
1796	1850	1796	1911	109002	SRY	Chobham
1796	1850	1796	1911	109002	SRY	Windlesham
1680	1850	1600	1850	132950	SSX	Portslade
....	1800	....	....	174564	SSX	Salehurst
CHEESMAN						
1740	1800	1700	1800	146633	KEN	Horsmonden
1720	1966	1600	1800	112224	KEN	Mereworth
1783	1829	1700	1850	131547	SRY	Capel
1880	....	1800	1850	131547	SRY	Dorking
1794	1992	1500	1950	172995	SRY	Egham
1829	....	1800	1850	131547	SRY	Ockley
....	1800	....	....	174564	SSX	Salehurst
CHEETHAM						
1799	....	....	....	129747	CHS	Bramhall
1837	1859	....	....	129747	CHS	Stockport
1800	1900	....	....	121061	LAN	Aldham
1781	1841	1841	1860	101648	LAN	Ashton Under Lyne
1800	1841	ALL	ALL	107913	LAN	Downholland
1860	1860	1860	1900	101648	LAN	Salford
1742	1857	....	....	132500	LAN	Shaw
....	....	1800	1899	124796	LAN	???
1778	1843	1730	1843	100307	NTT	North
1830	1900	1700	1830	172901	NTT	Nottingham
CHEFFINS						
1813	1870	1750	1900	148725	HRT	Furneux Pelham
1756	1881	ALL	ALL	117072	LIN	Hundelby
CHEGWIDEN						
....	....	1650	1750	174319	CON	St Allen
CHEGWIN						
1650	1741	1100	1741	117749	CON	Constantine
CHEGWYN						
....	....	ALL	ALL	112399	ALL	Name Study
1524	1970	....	....	112399	ALL	ALL
1524	1970	1283	1600	112399	CON	ALL
CHEKE						
....	....	ALL	ALL	113271	ALL	Name Study

Known From	To	Researching From	To	Ref	Cty	Place
CHEKEMBRA						
1630	1649	1600	1630	102571	CON	Zennor
CHELEW						
1585	1745	1550	1585	102571	CON	Ludgvan
CHELL						
....	....	ALL	ALL	166812	LAN	Manchester
1790	1920	1790	1920	149853	STS	Dilhorne
CHELLEW						
1600	1900	1700	1890	107530	CON	Ludgvan
CHELTON						
1836	1850	1800	1836	175951	SAL	???
CHENEY						
1747	1805	ALL	1747	154563	DOR	Puncknowle
1715	1992	1450	1992	113298	NTH	East
1750	1768	1600	1750	150150	NTH	Naseby
CHENNELL						
1883	1920	1880	1992	105333	LND	Eltham
1890	1992	ALL	ALL	176222	LND	Southwark
1869	1903	1830	1900	113301	SRY	Capel
CHENNELLS						
1800	1992	1700	1850	114081	HRT	Great Gaddesdon
1850	1950	1800	1992	177180	HRT	Gt Gaddesden
CHEQUER						
....	....	1750	1850	132586	WIL	Highworth
CHERRETT						
1750	1940	1700	1940	152226	DOR	Kinson
CHERRY						
1758	1992	1700	1913	113336	AVN	Bristol
1600	1700	1600	1700	167924	BDF	Meppersall
1700	1800	1700	1800	167924	BDF	Shillington
....	....	1800	1850	167401	KEN	Romney
1765	....	1700	1800	179078	LAN	Warton
1860	1890	1850	1900	167401	MDX	Stoke Newington
1730	1860	1600	1730	113328	NTH	Kilsby
1600	1800	1550	1600	173169	OXF	Banbury
1799	1820	1791	1799	163686	OXF	Stratten Audley
1850	1950	ALL	ALL	113328	WAR	Birmingham
1840	1850	ALL	ALL	113328	WAR	Coventry
1700	1900	1700	1900	106674	YKS	Grinton
CHESCOE						
1799	1992	1700	1992	113344	BRK	Reading
CHESHIRE						
1840	....	ALL	1847	121436	BDF	Eaton Bray
1850	1870	1840	1880	137111	GLS	Cheltenham
1800	1830	ALL	ALL	139181	HEF	Abbey Dore
1825	1845	1780	1850	174912	MDX	London
....	....	1800	1900	154458	WAR	Birmingham
1815	1861	1700	1815	111775	WAR	Nuneaton
CHESLETT						
1857	1992	....	....	107158	KEN	New Cross
CHESNEY						
1856	1881	1700	1856	154164	NFK	Terrington St Clements
CHESSON						
1865	1902	1700	1865	167355	KEN	Maidstone
CHESSUM						
....	....	ALL	ALL	130729	ALL	Name Study
CHESTER						
....	....	1700	1850	152390	HUN	Hamerton
1830	1855	1700	1829	110345	LAN	Liverpool
1800	1810	1700	1800	121339	LIN	Alford
1907	....	1850	1950	113352	LND	West Norwood
1769	1826	1650	1768	131245	MDX	Shoreditch
1800	1900	1780	1837	165948	NTH	Marston St Lawrence
1566	1825	1600	1675	150150	NTH	Naseby
1853	....	?	1860	164976	NTT	Nottingham
1746	1770	1720	1770	147311	NYK	Wykeham
1775	1855	....	1855	155055	SAL	Grinshill
1850	....	ALL	ALL	112275	SAL	Madely
CHESTERS						
1872	1939	1700	1872	113573	CHS	Copenhall
1848	....	....	....	105988	CWD	Harwarden
CHESWORTH						
1840	1940	1800	1840	117765	LAN	Liverpool
CHETTER						
1870	1930	1850	1900	161292	CHS	Warrington
1820	1920	1750	1850	143502	SAL	ALL
1810	1830	ALL	ALL	161292	SAL	Ludlow
1860	1930	1860	1930	133426	SAL	Shifnal
1820	1850	ALL	ALL	161292	SAL	Shifnal
CHETTLE						
1780	1868	1600	1780	126772	LEI	Leicester
CHETWIN						
1850	1900	1800	1850	107611	STS	Rugely

Known From	Known To	Researching From	Researching To	Ref	Cty	Place
CHETWYND						
1750	1960	1750	1960	151513	WAR	Grendon
1600	1765	1700	1800	151513	WAR	Kingsbury
1100	1400	....	....	100420	WAR	Meriden
CHEVALLIER						
900	1992	900	1850	176362	CHI	Jersey
CHEVELEY						
1808	1851	....	1808	108839	HRT	Ware
CHEVILL						
1800	1840	1700	1800	107743	CAM	Littleport
CHEW						
1750	1800	1600	1800	154342	GLS	Bisley
1800	1992	1600	1992	154342	GLS	Bristol
1813	1834	ALL	1900	146315	NTH	Northborough
1750	1900	ALL	ALL	114235	NTH	???
CHEWTER						
1680	1800	1536	1700	130516	SRY	Windlesham
1832	1873	1800	1832	119512	SSX	Crowborough
CHEYNE						
1660	....	....	....	126497	ABD	Fyvie
1902	1929	1800	1893	131938	GLA	Mountain Ash
1750	1965	....	....	137820	SHI	Fetlar
1720	1965	....	....	137820	SHI	Mid Yell
1760	1965	....	....	137820	SHI	North Yell
1758	1965	....	....	137820	SHI	Northmavine
1720	1965	....	....	137820	SHI	South Yell
CHEYNEY						
1150	1230	1100	1230	154881	ALL	ALL
CHIAMPANTE						
1603	1660	1550	1660	145459	HAM	Hursley
CHIBBETT						
1500	1992	1500	1992	139556	DEV	North
1500	1850	1500	1850	139556	SOM	Carhampton Hundred
CHICK						
1862	1886	1800	1862	149004	DEV	Chardstock
....	....	....	....	158747	DOR	ALL
1841	1881	....	....	116475	IOW	Godsill
....	....	1906	1956	102709	LND	Chiswick
1820	1842	1700	1820	153281	SOM	Aller
1800	1851	1600	1992	170518	SOM	Alowenshay
1820	1842	1700	1820	153281	SOM	Middlezoy
1820	1842	1700	1820	153281	SOM	Moorlinch
1820	1842	1700	1820	153281	SOM	North Curry
1820	1842	1700	1820	153281	SOM	North Newton
1820	1842	1700	1820	153281	SOM	North Petherton
1820	1842	1700	1820	153281	SOM	Othery
1820	1842	1700	1820	153281	SOM	Stoke St Gregory
1820	1842	1700	1820	153281	SOM	Thurloxton
1878	1974	1870	1970	116238	SRY	Rotherhithe
CHICKIE						
1600	1675	....	....	172987	IOW	Newport Parish
CHICKLE						
1780	1869	1700	1900	116742	SFK	Hartest
CHIDGLEY						
1600	1880	1600	1880	146064	SOM	Watchet
CHIDWICK						
1830	1900	1700	1830	103195	KEN	Walmer
CHIFNEY						
....	....	ALL	ALL	122262	ALL	ALL
CHILCOT						
1665	1844	....	....	127221	CON	Tintagel
CHILCOTT						
1876	1992	....	1876	163031	DEV	Plymouth
1910	1920	1910	1992	121568	HAM	Basingstoke
1855	1880	1840	1900	151106	MDX	???
1870	1870	1830	1920	121568	SOM	West
CHILD						
1802	1891	1500	1810	164909	BRK	Oakley Green
1802	1891	1500	1810	164909	BRK	Windsor
1790	1841	ALL	1800	149446	GLS	Bristol
1612	1730	....	....	165999	GLS	Henbury
1750	1880	1700	1900	177180	HRT	Bushey
1810	1860	1750	1810	127973	LIN	Crowland
1853	1992	?	1853	113360	LND	South
1680	1740	1680	1740	159557	MDX	Fulham
1860	....	1860	1900	149446	MDX	Mile End
....	1740	ALL	1740	134511	NTT	Oxton
1698	1725	1650	1740	131547	SSX	Rudgwick
1674	....	1600	1700	131547	SSX	Wisborough Green
1810	1820	1600	1992	167592	STS	Newcastle Under Lyme
1730	1820	1600	1992	167592	STS	Tunstall
1700	1890	1700	1890	159557	WIL	Castle Combe
1530	1800	1530	1800	159557	WIL	Heddington
CHILD contd.						
1627	1706	....	1627	101761	WRY	Emley
CHILDERLEY						
1751	1860	1700	1751	109533	CAM	Etisley
1870	1980	1870	1980	171999	HUN	St Neots
CHILDEROY						
1754	....	1650	1754	121010	HAM	Amport
CHILDERSTONE						
1456	1915	....	1456	133566	SFK	Mildenhall
CHILDS						
1790	1900	1700	1790	111198	BDF	Blunham
1802	1891	1500	1810	164909	BRK	Oakley Green
1843	1971	....	....	167444	BRK	Reading
1847	1851	1830	1870	160601	BRK	Wallingford
1802	1891	1500	1810	164909	BRK	Windsor
1762	....	1575	1762	108839	CAM	Sutton
1780	1936	1756	1792	136816	DBY	Chesterfield
1780	1936	1756	1792	136816	DBY	Hasland
1765	1820	ALL	1800	115266	DOR	ALL
1890	....	ALL	....	121487	ESS	Colchester
1850	1992	1700	1880	118532	ESS	???
1833	1992	1760	1880	145149	HAM	Kilmiston
1830	1919	1700	1919	178233	HAM	Petersfield
....	....	1800	1850	160601	OXF	Woodcott
....	....	1700	1930	119520	PEM	Lawrenny
1625	1675	1600	1992	114901	SRY	Thursley
1919	....	1900	1930	163775	YKS	Barnsley
CHILLERY						
1861	1871	1871	1920	109533	HUN	Ramsey
CHILLORY						
1813	1813	1790	1813	133000	HUN	Abbotsley
CHILMAN						
1764	....	....	....	173932	SRY	Epsom
1753	1854	....	....	173932	SRY	Great Bookham
1755	....	....	....	173932	SRY	Leatherhead
1756	1757	....	....	173932	SRY	Merstham
1772	1772	....	1772	136212	SRY	Stoke D'abernon
1741	....	....	....	173932	SRY	Sutton
1762	....	....	....	173932	SRY	Walton On The Hill
CHILTON						
....	....	ALL	ALL	113379	ALL	Name Study
1712	1777	ALL	ALL	122386	DUR	Blaydon
1712	1777	ALL	ALL	122386	DUR	Ryton
1700	1850	1680	1992	173096	GLS	Coaley
1777	1880	ALL	ALL	122386	NBL	Newburn
1820	1900	1600	1820	169862	SAL	Lilleshall
1796	....	ALL	1796	131725	SAL	Shifnal
CHILVERS						
1750	1992	1750	1900	164437	NFK	ALL
1750	1850	1700	1850	126799	NFK	Docking
1794	1861	ALL	1794	168602	SFK	Bungay
1600	1940	1600	1940	114316	SFK	Cransford
1834	1933	1800	1834	124095	SFK	Gorleston
1794	1861	ALL	1794	168602	SFK	Mettingham
CHIMLEY						
....	....	ALL	ALL	113387	ALL	ALL
1800	1980	1600	1900	113387	LIN	ALL
CHINCHEN						
1735	1735	ALL	1735	115266	DOR	ALL
....	....	1605	1970	123439	DOR	Purbeck
CHINERY						
1862	1962	ALL	1862	167959	ESS	Thundersley
CHINN						
1845	....	1700	1845	102210	WAR	Birmingham
....	....	1750	1850	112879	WAR	Coventry
1822	1992	1700	1822	123951	WAR	Coventry
CHINNAH						
1764	1780	ALL	1764	173304	OXF	Henley On Thames
CHINNER						
1799	1992	1700	1799	161446	OXF	Middleton Cheney
CHINNEREY						
1700	....	1600	1700	169862	SFK	Mildenhall
CHINNERY						
1928	1929	1928	1929	128740	SRY	Croydon
CHINNOCK						
1823	....	1823	1870	133639	SOM	Coker
1781	1816	1760	1900	166898	SOM	East Pennard
1714	1804	1700	1804	107573	SOM	Frome
1851	1861	1851	1900	166898	WIL	Dinton
CHIPCHASE						
....	....	1500	1899	115975	DUR	Stockton On Tees
....	....	1750	1890	110671	NBL	North Shields
CHIPPENDALE						
....	....	ALL	ALL	151734	ALL	Name Study

Known From	To	Researching From	To	Ref	Cty	Place
CHIPPERFIELD						
ALL	ALL	ALL	ALL	113395	ALL	ALL
1876	1992	1850	1876	113395	DUR	Chester Le Street
1732	1812	ALL	1732	162108	ESS	???
1876	1900	1800	1876	113395	NFK	Great Yarmouth
CHIRSTIE						
1750	1800	1700	1750	157708	AYR	Kilwinning
CHISHOLM						
....	....	1740	1770	159905	DUR	Tanfield
1807	1824	1750	1850	149292	INV	Kilmorack
1890	1905	....	....	155381	KEN	Sydenham
1840	1863	ALL	ALL	110388	MLN	Edinburgh
1796	1798	1790	1850	159905	NBL	North Shields
....	....	....	1834	130060	SCT	???
CHISLETT						
....	....	ALL	ALL	113409	ALL	Name Study
CHISNALL						
....	....	1790	1861	139831	ESS	Dovercourt
1765	1795	....	....	139831	SFK	Stoke By Nayland
CHISTELL						
....	....	1700	1800	156795	HAM	West
CHISWELL						
ALL	ALL	....	....	113417	ALL	ALL
CHITTAM						
1716	1716	1600	1750	126918	ESS	Widford
1695	1721	1550	1694	102830	LIN	Kirkby Green
CHITTENDEN						
....	....	1760	1850	143480	HAM	Portsea
....	....	ALL	ALL	121754	KEN	Yalding
CHITTLE						
1700	1930	....	....	158275	BRK	Chievely
1755	1820	ALL	1830	167029	HAM	Burghclere
1790	1820	ALL	1830	167029	HAM	Kingsclere
CHITTLEBOROUGH						
1806	1840	1806	1840	164232	SFK	Sudbourne
CHITTUCK						
1760	1800	1700	1760	139688	SFK	Aldham
CHITTY						
1800	1831	ALL	ALL	107352	EYK	Harpham
1790	1850	ALL	ALL	107352	EYK	Nafferton
1831	....	1600	1855	168637	HAM	Warblington
1842	....	....	....	173932	SRY	Ashtead
1540	1763	1500	1765	159581	SRY	Cranleigh
1660	1685	1630	1992	114901	SRY	Godalming
1540	1763	1500	1765	159581	SRY	Godalming
1867	1901	1700	1992	168637	SRY	Great Bookham
1820	....	....	....	173932	SSX	Chiddingfold
CHIVERS						
1773	1880	1700	1773	148962	HAM	Penton Mewsey
1840	1900	1600	1900	112828	LND	ALL
1789	1811	1700	1789	144711	SOM	High Littleton
1808	1872	....	....	103373	WIL	Avebury
1700	1799	ALL	ALL	146633	WIL	Burbage
1815	1895	1700	1895	174300	WIL	Melksham
CHIVERTON						
1895	1960	....	....	102601	GLA	Cardiff
1771	1771	ALL	1771	131881	HAM	Brixton
1870	1895	....	....	102601	IOW	Cowes
1713	1875	1230	1713	102601	IOW	Freshwater
1700	1839	1500	1700	129577	IOW	???
1812	....	1812	1860	133639	SOM	Coker
CHOAT						
1898	....	....	....	175919	LND	Bow
CHOATE						
1650	1720	1650	1720	133817	SFK	Buxhall
CHOICE						
....	....	ALL	ALL	163333	ALL	Name Study
....	....	ALL	ALL	163325	ALL	Name Study
CHOLMELEY						
1600	....	....	....	167037	LIN	Kirkby
1600	....	....	....	167037	MDX	London
CHOPEN						
1790	1800	1750	1830	115746	SOM	Taunton
CHORLEY						
1840	1880	1800	1900	122343	DUR	Seaham
1765	1871	ALL	ALL	113433	LAN	Prescot
1791	....	....	....	117196	LAN	Warrington
CHORLTON						
1839	....	1750	1839	178381	LAN	Pendleton
CHOULES						
1816	1992	....	....	167444	HAM	Gt Bedwyn
CHOULS						
1850	1936	1700	1850	113441	ESS	Billericay
1880	1908	1700	1850	113441	SRY	Great Bookham
CHOULS contd.						
1770	1822	ALL	1770	167878	WIL	Great Bedwyn
CHOWINGS						
....	....	ALL	ALL	113468	ALL	Name Study
CHOWN						
1790	1830	1750	1860	105333	DEV	Exeter
1733	1867	1867	1992	125105	DEV	Exminster
1818	1850	1750	1880	100439	DEV	Ottery St Mary
1569	1733	1538	1992	125105	DEV	Ottery St Mary
1790	1841	1750	1860	105333	MDX	London
1730	1800	1600	1730	171182	WIL	South
1730	1800	1600	1730	171182	WIL	West
CHOWNE						
....	....	ALL	ALL	171638	ALL	ALL
CHOYCE						
1850	1926	1800	1850	174866	CUL	Whitehaven
CHRISFIELD						
1400	1900	....	....	116998	KEN	Lenham
CHRISHOLM						
1773	1992	1700	1773	150363	BEW	Channelkirk
CHRISMAS						
1880	1900	1850	1900	111325	MDX	Barnet
1716	1724	1650	1750	131547	SSX	Kirdford
1580	1716	1500	1750	131547	SSX	North Chapel
1755	1764	1700	1800	131547	SSX	Petworth
1841	1851	1841	1992	140058	SXE	Battle
1841	1851	1841	1992	140058	SXE	Hastings
1878	1967	1878	1992	140058	SXE	Lewes
CHRISTELOW						
1866	1943	1800	1900	141461	DUR	ALL
CHRISTER						
1807	1908	1800	1900	151106	KEN	Tonbridge
CHRISTIAN						
1758	1815	1730	1800	141283	IOM	Douglas
1712	1760	1600	1712	135151	IOM	Maughold
1847	1871	1790	1847	108103	KEN	Crayford
1789	1878	ALL	1878	164623	LAN	Liverpool
1749	1814	1700	1900	135968	LEI	Melton
1790	1820	1700	1790	151769	LIN	Barkstone
1790	1820	1700	1790	151769	LIN	Long Bennington
1850	1890	1850	1900	143065	LIN	Louth
CHRISTIE						
1810	1841	1700	1810	163201	ABD	Huntly
1840	1992	1700	1920	113492	FIF	???
1740	1992	1750	1992	133450	HRT	Hoddesdon
1765	1858	ALL	ALL	135909	KKD	New Galloway
ALL	ALL	ALL	ALL	163716	LND	ALL
?	....	1800	1850	148121	MDX	Tottenham
1815	....	1600	1815	132802	PER	Killin
1800	....	1800	1900	139114	PER	Locherlour
1866	1992	?	1866	124540	SCT	Glasgow
1750	1965	....	....	137820	SHI	Fetlar
1720	1965	....	....	137820	SHI	Mid Yell
1760	1965	....	....	137820	SHI	North Yell
1758	1965	....	....	137820	SHI	Northmavine
1720	1965	....	....	137820	SHI	South Yell
1825	1869	1820	1870	107573	SRY	Lambeth
1740	....	....	....	141798	STI	St Ninians
1828	....	1800	1828	153699	STI	Stirling
CHRISTIENSEN						
1860	1890	ALL	1860	176060	DUR	South Shields
CHRISTIRE						
1900	1992	1900	1992	147575	LND	???
CHRISTMAS						
....	....	ALL	ALL	113506	ALL	Name Study
1655	1900	1600	1650	133671	CAM	Bassingbourne
1828	....	ALL	1850	106739	ESS	Aldham
1720	1880	1600	1800	110116	HAM	East Worldham
1870	1930	ALL	ALL	113581	LND	ALL
1790	1811	1750	1830	131547	SRY	Capel
CHRISTOE						
1840	1992	1650	1840	177245	CON	Truro
CHRISTOFFER						
1808	1900	ALL	1808	179663	MDX	East London
CHRISTOPHER						
1685	1812	1600	1685	102571	CON	Zennor
1800	1880	1760	1900	125970	DOR	Sherborne
1844	1921	1800	1891	141461	DOR	Sherborne
1780	1850	1700	1900	148652	DOR	Weymouth
1700	1775	ALL	1700	131059	KEN	Ash By Ridley
1730	1900	1730	1900	114146	KEN	Medway
1562	1760	1560	1760	114146	KEN	Seal
1829	1992	1800	1840	118354	LAN	Wigan

Known From	To	Researching From	To	Ref	Cty	Place
CHRISTOPHERSON						
1600	....	1600	1900	116920	LAN	Colton
CHRISTY						
1642	1939	....	....	168777	SCT	Watergate
1642	1939	....	....	168777	SSX	Watergate
CHROM						
1830	1840	1800	1830	157775	SCT	Lochmaben
CHROMN						
1830	1840	1800	1830	157775	SCT	Lochmaben
CHRYSTAL						
1840	1860	1800	1860	103632	DUR	Sunderland
CHUBB						
1779	1992	1700	1779	167436	CON	Northill
1850	1992	1750	1850	154415	DEV	Tamerton Folliot
1851	1900	1790	1851	175846	DOR	Beaminster
ALL	ALL	ALL	ALL	114502	SOM	ALL
1776	1992	1700	1820	116289	WIL	Langford
CHUDLEIGH						
....	....	1600	1992	137588	DEV	Newton Abbot
CHUGG						
1700	1880	1800	1870	132721	DEV	North
CHUMBLEY						
1890	1929	1800	1992	138088	SRY	Croydon
CHUME						
1860	1860	1800	1860	148431	SAL	Shrewsbury
CHURCH						
....	....	ALL	ALL	113522	ALL	Name Study
1778	1829	....	....	115606	BRK	Cookham
1754	....	....	1780	171441	BRK	East Hendred
1822	1992	ALL	1795	133930	BRK	Wantage
1795	1992	ALL	1795	133930	BRK	Woolstone
1804	....	?	1804	155667	CON	Liskeard
1830	1900	1600	1830	151025	ESS	Netteswell
1920	1992	....	1930	113514	GLA	Barry
....	....	1880	1930	113514	GLA	Cardiff
....	....	1700	1880	144452	GLS	Cinderford
1806	....	....	1850	152803	HRT	Welwyn
1670	?	?	?	166642	KEN	Canterbury
1847	1938	1800	1900	166960	KEN	Maidstone
1882	1992	1700	1882	102148	LND	East End
1864	1923	ALL	ALL	118168	MDX	East London
1770	1799	1700	1800	117013	NFK	Erpingham
1715	1736	1700	1736	166707	NTH	Maidwell
1822	1829	1700	1822	113425	SFK	Ipswich
1775	1870	1870	1950	172073	SFK	Kenton
1818	1870	1870	1950	172073	SFK	Middleton
1775	1826	....	1775	122815	SFK	Worlingham
....	....	....	1900	113514	SOM	???
....	....	1850	1880	164801	WIL	Devizes
1881	1988	....	....	144452	YKS	Castleford
CHURCHER						
1674	1903	1674	1903	174343	HAM	Hambledon
1800	1992	1800	1900	161586	HAM	Langstone
1865	1992	1750	1900	136042	HAM	Portsmouth
1604	1670	1550	1670	174343	HAM	Wickham
1871	1975	1850	1992	100242	LND	South
....	....	1798	1817	114308	LND	Shoreditch
1850	1850	1750	1900	136042	SRY	Rotherhithe
1786	1987	1700	1786	100277	SSX	Worthing
CHURCHHOUSE						
1869	1953	1700	1880	142212	SOM	Henton
CHURCHILD						
1777	1778	1750	1800	123536	HAM	Portsea
CHURCHILL						
1678	1715	ALL	1715	122106	DEV	Beer
1678	1715	ALL	1715	122106	DEV	Seaton
1665	1700	ALL	1665	115266	DOR	ALL
1853	....	1700	1992	110418	DOR	Bourton
1556	1641	ALL	1641	122106	DOR	Bradford Peverill
1790	1865	1600	1790	158984	DOR	Cerne Abbas
1798	1798	1650	1800	120081	DOR	Corscombe
1836	1992	....	1836	161071	DOR	Fordington
1798	....	....	....	151351	DOR	Maiden Newton
1725	1781	ALL	1725	154563	DOR	Portesham
1847	....	....	....	151351	DOR	St Peters Dorchester
1887	1992	1840	1887	113530	GLA	Cardiff
1900	1992	1850	1992	161071	LND	???
1830	....	....	....	174750	OXF	Woodstock
1715	1744	ALL	1715	122106	SOM	Crewkerne
....	....	1819	....	174963	SOM	Farnborough
1800	1850	ALL	ALL	124176	WAR	Erdington
CHURCHMAN						
1660	1760	1600	1700	101834	CAM	Dry Drayton

Known From	To	Researching From	To	Ref	Cty	Place
CHURCHWARD						
....	....	ALL	ALL	113549	ALL	Name Study
CHURCHYARD						
1880	1909	....	....	127582	LND	Balham
1850	1992	ALL	ALL	146218	MDX	ALL
1824	1860	1800	1824	117196	SFK	Ipswich
CHUTER						
1854	1911	....	....	135070	ESS	East Ham
1854	1911	....	....	135070	ESS	West Ham
1845	1850	....	....	135070	KEN	Maidstone
1911	1992	....	....	135070	MDX	Poplar
1795	1861	1770	1871	170143	SRY	Stoke Next Guildford
CHYNE						
1660	1840	1600	1840	126500	ABD	Fyvie
CHYNOWETH						
1770	1850	1600	1770	143812	CON	St Agnes
CINDEREY						
....	....	1879	....	149497	???	Forest Of Dean
CITTIL						
1836	....	....	....	150282	STI	Falkirk
CIVELL						
1665	ALL	....	....	167037	NFK	Mulbarton
CLABON						
1800	1992	1750	1800	115312	NFK	???
CLACEY						
1700	1832	1650	1750	125032	BRK	Arborfield
1754	1830	1700	1900	125032	BRK	Barkham
1730	1900	1700	1950	125032	BRK	Finchampstead
CLACK						
1789	1900	1700	1789	152552	BKM	Missenden
1740	1860	1740	1860	116831	HUN	Warboys
....	....	1900	1960	173355	KEN	Ramsgate
1847	1870	1800	1847	128724	MDX	London
....	....	1700	1800	152552	MDX	???
CLADERWOOD						
1836	1897	ALL	1992	102245	NBL	Newcastle Upon Tyne
CLAFTON						
?	....	?	?	119997	YKS	Horbury
CLAKE						
1650	1950	1550	1900	113883	DEV	ALL
CLAMP						
1862	1863	1852	1864	156582	KEN	Plumstead
1807	1833	ALL	1833	156582	KEN	Sevenoaks
1812	1875	ALL	1812	116157	LND	Lambeth
1834	1980	?	1834	113557	SRY	Carshalton
1836	1881	1833	1881	156582	SRY	Carshalton
CLANCEY						
1820	1820	1700	1820	157031	IRL	???
CLANFIELD						
1800	1840	1800	1992	135429	OXF	Cuddesdon
1717	....	1717	1793	108375	OXF	Witney
CLAPCOTT						
1830	1910	ALL	ALL	162205	DOR	Haselbury Bryan
CLAPHAM						
....	....	....	....	113565	CAM	Cambridge
1777	1940	....	....	128996	CAM	Thorney
1845	1968	1845	1920	120103	CMA	Natland
1860	1920	1860	....	120103	LAN	North
1845	1968	1845	1920	120103	LAN	Clapham
....	....	....	....	113565	LAN	Manchester
1770	1783	1700	1841	160636	LIN	Hackthorne
1683	....	1066	1683	113565	YKS	Batley
1683	....	1066	1683	113565	YKS	Binstall
1720	1750	1600	1750	175382	YKS	Giggleswick
....	1992	....	....	113565	???	London
CLAPP						
....	....	ALL	ALL	135429	ALL	Name Study
ALL	ALL	ALL	ALL	135429	ALL	ALL
1740	1992	1600	1992	114596	DEV	Cruwys Morchard
CLAPPERTON						
1840	1992	ALL	1840	131849	SRY	Clapham
CLAPSHAW						
1827	1862	1810	1900	124974	LND	Shoreditch
1789	1827	1750	1850	124974	SRY	Farnham
CLAPSHOE						
1688	1688	1680	1690	124974	BRK	Hampstead Marshall
1706	1735	1702	1750	124974	BRK	Warfield
....	....	ALL	ALL	124974	HAM	North East
1661	1735	1640	1740	124974	HAM	Basingstoke
....	....	1700	1825	124974	HAM	Bentley
....	....	1700	1825	124974	HAM	Bentworth
....	....	1700	1825	124974	HAM	Binstead
....	....	1600	1800	124974	HAM	Dummer

Known From	To	Researching From	To	Ref	Cty	Place
CLAPSHOE contd.						
1701	1790	1692	1800	124974	HAM	Froyle
1640	1715	1600	1750	124974	HAM	Mapledurwell
1630	1649	1620	1670	124974	HAM	Micheldever
1510	1740	1530	1750	124974	HAM	North Waltham
1676	1749	1630	1770	124974	HAM	Odiham
1665	1665	1620	1680	124974	HAM	Sherborne St John
1652	1694	1600	1700	124974	HAM	Steventon
1670	1670	1630	1670	124974	HAM	Sydmonton
CLAPSON						
1795	1830	1700	1800	132640	SSX	Warbleton
1801	1861	ALL	1851	156175	SXE	Hellingly
CLARE						
1791	1858	1750	1800	149047	CHS	Warrington
1816	1839	1800	1845	163775	IRL	Dublin
1891	1940	ALL	ALL	113581	LND	Clerkenwell
1700	1765	ALL	ALL	113581	WAR	ALL
1840	1890	ALL	ALL	113581	WAR	Birmingham
CLAREBROUGH						
1571	1850	1500	1571	138584	YKS	Rothwell
CLARGO						
1745	1880	1600	1745	101419	BRK	ALL
1745	1880	1600	1745	101419	BRK	Bucklebury
CLARICOATES						
....	....	ALL	ALL	131520	ALL	Name Study
CLARIDGE						
1764	1791	ALL	1764	115126	BKM	Aylesbury
1760	1800	1760	1800	118540	GLS	Bristol
1840	1950	1800	1920	113883	LEI	ALL
1847	1910	1847	ALL	113603	MDX	Bethnal Green
1823	1992	1700	1823	161446	OXF	Bicester
1810	1830	1810	1830	113603	SOM	Bath
1830	1847	1830	ALL	113603	SOM	Bristol
CLARINGBOLD						
1700	1935	1700	1935	115517	KEN	East
1800	1820	1770	1800	134139	KEN	Littlebourn
CLARINGBOULD						
....	....	1500	1950	164992	ALL	ALL
CLARK						
1860	1930	....	1900	174246	ABD	ALL
1758	1830	....	....	146870	ABD	Crathie
....	....	1700	ALL	149187	ANS	Panbride
1790	1945	1790	1860	133884	ARL	Balachulish
....	....	1600	1800	175889	ARL	Dunoon
1829	?	1700	1881	102997	AYR	Stewarton
1780	1920	1700	1780	123374	BAN	Marnoch
1720	1860	1700	1860	126500	BAN	Wick Latheron
1819	1992	1700	1819	105902	BDF	Luton
1738	1992	1600	1738	167541	BKM	Great Marlow
1750	1790	1700	1780	117005	BKM	Newport Pagnell
1700	1890	1600	1900	177180	BKM	The Lee
1830	1850	1700	1850	170178	BKM	Wycombe
1860	1920	....	1880	120529	BRK	Reading
1829	1850	1700	1829	111953	BRK	Uffington
1700	1860	....	....	126497	CAI	Latheron
1760	1860	1700	1800	140864	CAM	Bassingbourn
1845	1916	1700	1845	133930	CAM	Cambridge
....	....	1720	1750	103713	CAM	Waterbeach
1850	1910	ALL	1910	175757	CHS	Dukinfield
1800	1992	....	....	175099	CMA	???
1740	1900	1700	1900	121126	CON	Kenwyn
1797	1866	1700	1797	127590	CON	Perranzabuloe
1845	1992	1845	1992	113719	DBY	Chesterfield
1540	1880	1800	1860	132721	DEV	North
1850	....	ALL	1900	168696	DEV	Tavistock
1904	1914	....	....	133922	DOR	Bournemouth
1841	1871	1750	1841	168033	DOR	Dorchester
1845	1851	1800	1900	149160	ESS	Downham
1800	1870	....	....	140317	ESS	East Donyland
1791	1951	1600	1791	167355	ESS	Gt Bentley
1850	1881	1850	1950	149160	ESS	Ramsden Bellhouse
1762	1792	1700	1762	172553	ESS	Rivenhall
1680	1691	1650	1800	169218	FIF	St Monance
1700	1799	1700	1799	169781	GLS	Bristol
1816	1987	....	....	178683	GLS	Oxenhall
1760	1992	1760	1992	110361	GLS	Stinchcombe
1940	1992	1940	1992	133922	HAM	Ashurst
1875	1914	1860	1960	133922	HAM	Fair Oak
?	?	?	?	153931	HAM	Lymington
1820	1840	1750	1850	136840	HAM	Portsmouth
1800	1890	1750	1800	140864	HRT	Barkway
1800	1981	ALL	ALL	132977	HRT	Bushey Heath
1809	1992	1750	1809	115460	HRT	Hexton
1750	1850	1750	1850	167924	HRT	Ickleford

Known From	To	Researching From	To	Ref	Cty	Place
CLARK contd.						
1650	1750	ALL	ALL	131873	HRT	Little Hadham
1800	1890	1750	1800	140864	HRT	Royston
1800	1900	1800	1900	126144	KEN	West
1870	1953	1700	1870	100846	KEN	Dover
....	....	1800	....	140333	KEN	Frith
1881	1945	....	....	105473	KEN	Gravesend
1814	1843	ALL	1850	129283	KEN	Greenwich
1880	1940	1800	1992	145556	KEN	Penge
1860	1900	1700	1860	174572	KEN	Sheerness
1750	1992	1600	1750	113654	LAN	Kirkham
1860	1992	1850	1992	126705	LAN	Manchester
1900	....	....	....	156868	LAN	Oldham
1720	1899	....	....	165999	LEI	Leicester
1750	1992	ALL	1750	134511	LEI	Wigston
1762	1782	....	1762	101761	LIN	Bilsby
1790	1980	1750	1900	123145	LIN	Friskney
1859	1890	ALL	1859	116157	LND	Bethnal Green
1851	1900	....	....	167517	LND	City
1837	1925	....	....	133922	LND	Herne Hill
1839	1839	1800	1839	149578	LND	Holborn
1880	1940	1840	1940	147958	LND	Islington
....	....	1750	1900	129275	LND	Soho
....	....	1750	1880	113697	LND	Southwark
1870	1920	1758	1992	146870	LND	Stepney
....	....	1750	1900	129275	LND	Westminster
1780	1992	1700	1780	177490	LND	Whitechapel
1847	1848	1848	1874	160776	MDX	Dalston
1850	1900	1800	1950	102016	MDX	Poplar
1799	1835	1750	1800	177024	MDX	St Marylebone
1851	1942	1700	1850	117013	MDX	St Pancras
1831	1854	1700	1992	118168	MDX	St Pancras
1746	1768	1700	1770	144797	MDX	Stepney
....	....	1848	1874	160776	MDX	Stoke Newington
1830	....	1800	1850	102016	MDX	???
....	....	1600	1900	134155	MLN	Tranent
....	....	1800	1992	126462	NBL	Felton
1775	1830	1600	1850	130125	NBL	Longbenton
1876	1876	1800	1900	105414	NBL	Newcastle On Tyne
1750	1980	....	....	132837	NBL	???
1760	1772	1600	1759	131245	NFK	Norwich
1810	1860	....	....	142522	NIR	???
1800	1940	1870	1940	173533	NTH	ALL
1694	1741	ALL	1694	154555	NTH	Daventry
1739	1739	....	....	127426	NTH	Earls Barton
1800	1992	1700	1800	105902	NTH	Eye
1778	1819	1750	1820	178411	NTT	Calverton
1821	1823	1800	1845	113719	NTT	Mansfield
1764	1780	1650	1780	139386	NTT	Marnham
1787	1787	1600	1786	131245	NTT	Nottingham
1804	1807	....	....	139386	NTT	Ordsall
1860	1930	1850	1920	106569	NTT	Tuxford
1783	1812	....	....	151351	NTT	Upton
1700	1992	1100	1700	100803	NYK	Long Preston
1830	1860	1800	1830	120529	OXF	Caversham
1806	1816	1800	1850	172162	RFW	Greenock
1852	1898	1832	1852	118435	RFW	Paisley
1800	1850	1700	1900	167207	ROX	???
1719	1719	1600	1992	110787	RUT	Oakham
1719	1719	1600	1992	110787	RUT	Stamford Barton
....	1800	....	1800	177695	SAL	Dawley
1850	1870	1800	1992	165573	SCT	West Calder
1700	1723	1670	1700	128724	SFK	Little Saxham
1800	1850	1700	1800	149705	SFK	Wetheringsett
1750	1965	....	....	137820	SHI	Fetlar
1720	1965	....	....	137820	SHI	Mid Yell
1760	1965	....	....	137820	SHI	North Yell
1758	1965	....	....	137820	SHI	Northmavine
1720	1965	....	....	137820	SHI	South Yell
1800	1900	1850	1900	154903	SOM	Godney
1810	1850	1700	1850	179477	SOM	Shipham
....	....	1842	1847	160776	SRY	Brixton
1700	1830	ALL	1730	138169	SRY	Carshalton
1720	1752	....	....	139971	SSX	Laughton
1780	1800	1700	1900	171522	SSX	Seaford
....	1851	1700	1851	170178	SSX	Winchelsea
1750	1900	1650	1750	151084	STS	North
1720	1750	....	....	145688	STS	Burslem
1800	1850	....	....	145688	STS	Hanley
1798	1854	....	....	102733	WAR	Kinwarten
1850	1930	ALL	ALL	123048	WAR	Leamington Spa
1800	1881	ALL	1881	175757	WAR	Pailton
1790	1850	1700	1850	119938	WAR	Stratford
....	....	1700	1800	147613	WES	Kendal

Known From	To	Researching From	To	Ref	Cty	Place
CLARK contd.						
1790	....	....	....	115576	WIL	Bromham
1830	1845	ALL	1845	168696	WIL	Dauntsey
1825	1900	1780	1841	113727	WIL	Kennet-Avon Canal
ALL	1805	....	....	170178	WIL	Lyneham
1803	1992	1803	1992	110361	WIL	Nettleton
1735	1992	ALL	ALL	113662	WIL	Sherston Parva
1822	1910	1822	1910	178683	WOR	Pendock
1700	1992	1100	1700	100803	WYK	Long Preston
1800	1910	1800	1900	130621	YKS	Alverthorpe
1800	1850	1700	1900	130419	YKS	Clapham
1803	1910	....	....	117161	YKS	Fylingdales
1727	1797	1600	1750	174858	YKS	Helmsley
1800	1910	1800	1900	130621	YKS	Leeds
1830	....	1800	1880	152129	YKS	Leeds
1666	1693	1600	1670	176451	YKS	Long Preston
1800	1899	1800	1899	133833	YKS	Morley
1800	1900	1800	1900	140236	YKS	Morley
1800	1850	ALL	ALL	131873	YKS	Sculcoates
....	....	1750	1820	147613	YKS	Sheffield
1850	1902	ALL	1850	154563	YKS	Sheffield
1800	1841	....	....	102946	YKS	Thirsk
1850	1992	1600	1850	108308	YKS	Thirsk
1863	1992	ALL	1863	149071	???	Blackmore
1850	1920	1850	1992	179477	???	Bristol
1863	1992	ALL	1863	149071	???	Chelmsford
1863	1992	ALL	1863	149071	???	Ingatestone
CLARKE						
....	....	....	....	143316	ALD	???
....	....	1700	1960	172111	ANT	Ahoghill
1881	1992	1700	1992	113778	ARM	Market Hill
1840	1860	1840	1860	130222	BDF	Benefield
1536	1719	1500	1750	124796	BKM	Adstock
1832	....	1730	1850	124796	BKM	Akeley
1750	1845	1700	1900	173878	BKM	Bow Brickhill
1746	1809	1730	1825	124796	BKM	Lillingstone Dayrell
1803	....	1775	1805	124796	BKM	Maids Moreton
1719	1799	1700	1800	124796	BKM	Steeple Claydon
1826	1909	1800	1992	115673	BRK	Reading
1860	1920	....	1880	120529	BRK	Reading
1760	1790	1760	1800	124605	CAM	Brinkley
1900	1925	1925	1992	117099	CHS	Birkenhead
1873	1873	1873	1873	145580	CHS	Bromborough
1859	1992	1700	1859	123943	CHS	Hyde
1900	1992	1800	1900	113867	CHS	Middlewich
1851	1871	1800	1881	149330	CHS	Middlewich
1880	1992	1880	1992	113778	CLV	Middlesbrough
1800	1992	....	....	175099	CMA	???
1750	1850	1700	1850	136840	CON	Maker
1880	1992	1850	1880	154741	DBY	Codnor
1869	1992	1700	1869	113808	DBY	Ilkeston
1675	....	1600	1980	112348	DBY	Stanton By Bridge
1788	1860	1788	1992	114596	DEV	Ash Regney
1800	1992	1800	1900	131288	DEV	Braunton
1877	....	1850	1890	177350	DEV	High Wick
1880	1980	1800	1880	173770	DEV	Plymouth
1814	1855	ALL	1814	121525	DEV	Sidmouth
1890	1992	1700	1890	113794	DOW	Belfast
1850	1992	1750	1992	157651	DUR	South Sheilds
1762	1792	1700	1762	172553	ESS	Rivenhall
....	....	1800	1900	102644	GLS	Amberley
1752	1777	1700	1752	148938	GLS	Arlingham
....	....	?	....	141216	GLS	Hasfield
....	....	?	....	141216	GLS	Tirley
1803	1803	1750	1803	147575	GLS	Wickwar
1760	1861	1600	1880	110183	HAM	Alton
1739	1776	ALL	1739	169730	HAM	Herriard
1890	1930	1700	1900	113859	HAM	Portsmouth
1825	1896	1750	1850	172251	HAM	Portsmouth
1750	ALL	1812	1881	107379	HRT	Hemel Hempstead
1830	....	1800	1830	148156	HUN	East
....	....	....	....	157058	HUN	Hilton
1700	1840	1500	1700	129577	IOW	???
1839	1884	....	....	150282	IRL	Wixford
....	?	....	....	141941	IRL	???
1742	1773	1700	1742	128724	KEN	Postling
1900	1992	1800	1900	113867	LAN	Liverpool
1900	1925	1925	1992	117099	LAN	Liverpool
1889	1956	1870	1920	124826	LAN	Manchester
1900	....	....	....	156868	LAN	Oldham
1731	1749	ALL	ALL	141615	LEI	Chadwell
1860	1992	1860	1992	144703	LEI	Leicester
1800	1992	....	....	176125	LIN	Asterby

Known From	To	Researching From	To	Ref	Cty	Place
CLARKE contd.						
1800	1992	....	....	176125	LIN	Goulceby
1793	1800	....	....	121835	LIN	Lincoln
1715	1793	....	....	121835	LIN	Waddington
1850	1870	1800	1900	142050	LIN	???
....	....	1800	1900	174114	LND	Haggerston
1830	1930	1800	1900	113859	LND	Peckham
....	....	1800	1900	129275	LND	Southwark
1780	1790	1775	1800	124796	LND	St Giles In The Fields
....	....	1800	1900	129275	LND	Woolwich
1861	1890	1800	1861	175595	MAY	???
1865	1900	1800	1900	113859	MDX	Fulham
1740	1745	1700	1760	105120	MDX	Harmondsworth
1840	1940	1800	....	147958	MDX	London
1844	1844	1800	1850	125032	MDX	Westminster
1850	1900	1700	1900	160954	MSY	Liverpool
1843	1887	....	....	139874	NBL	North Shields
1889	1992	1852	1889	113786	NFK	Belton
1800	1850	1800	1850	158658	NFK	Great Yarmouth
1801	....	....	....	121827	NFK	Lyng
1830	1870	1800	1900	111821	NFK	Norwich
....	....	1800	1900	129275	NFK	Norwich
1872	1967	1872	1992	139041	NTH	Blisworth
1692	1714	1600	1800	159956	NTH	Buton Latimer
1804	1879	ALL	1804	115126	NTH	Collintree
1694	1741	ALL	1694	154555	NTH	Daventry
1853	1992	1700	1853	121258	NTH	Harpole
1916	?	ALL	ALL	100072	NTH	Naseby
1873	1940	1873	1900	147281	NTH	Northampton
1811	....	1811	....	148156	NTH	Sutton
1818	1854	1700	1854	150150	NTH	Thornhaugh
1876	1938	ALL	1876	100072	NTH	Welton
1764	1764	ALL	ALL	171816	NTH	Welton
1600	1640	....	....	103632	NTH	Whilton
....	....	1790	1850	115142	NTT	South
1778	1819	1750	1820	178411	NTT	Calverton
1798	1900	1600	1900	124834	NTT	East Leake
1865	1875	1800	1865	177393	NTT	Eastwood
1860	1988	1860	1988	106569	NTT	Retford
1749	1992	?	1749	128910	NTT	Watnall
1830	1860	1800	1830	120529	OXF	Caversham
1700	1800	1700	1992	139203	PER	Errol
1800	....	....	....	126993	ROX	Jedburgh
1870	....	1870	....	162663	RUT	Oakham
1860	1963	1746	1860	129895	SFK	Brandeston
....	....	1850	1859	173274	SFK	Hadleigh
1818	1992	1800	1900	166960	SFK	???
1792	1940	ALL	ALL	153516	SOM	Banwell
1750	1850	1750	1850	142018	SOM	Bath
1792	1940	ALL	ALL	153516	SOM	Kewstoke
1673	1728	....	1673	149888	SOM	Pawlett
1803	1900	1750	1900	118540	SOM	Stockland Bristol
1810	1925	1834	1914	133922	SRY	Brixton
1811	1968	1780	1968	124028	SRY	Camberwell
1750	....	1700	1850	153397	SRY	Cobham
1892	1926	1750	1892	143316	SRY	Eastbourne
1868	1931	1868	1900	133922	SRY	Kennington
1810	1931	1876	1914	133922	SRY	Lambeth
1830	1910	1750	1992	106941	SSX	Highbrook
1850	....	ALL	ALL	172057	SSX	???
1816	1900	1800	1920	160873	STS	Brierly Hill
1662	1816	1600	1820	160873	STS	Sedgley
1860	1992	1800	1950	136174	TYR	Redargen
....	1708	?	1708	128910	WAR	Bedworth
1801	1861	1700	1992	144703	WAR	Bedworth
1750	1850	1700	1850	154210	WAR	Bedworth
1760	1850	1730	1850	100420	WAR	Birmingham
1600	1700	....	....	100420	WAR	Meriden
1730	1760	1730	1850	100420	WOR	Belbroughton
1758	1820	1700	1760	149993	WOR	Bewdley
....	....	?	....	141216	WOR	Eldersfield
1830	1870	1800	1850	120286	WOR	St Clement
1777	1832	ALL	1850	113611	WYK	Kirhouse Green
1777	1832	ALL	1850	113611	WYK	Kirk Bramwith
1832	1900	ALL	1900	113611	WYK	Thorne
1700	1830	....	....	156922	YKS	Rawmarsh
CLARKESTONE						
1780	1900	1600	1780	152463	NTT	Sutton Bonnington
CLARKSON						
1750	1850	1700	1800	129003	KEN	Hornchurch
....	....	1700	1900	168815	LAN	ALL
1855	1871	1700	1855	119075	LAN	Blackburn
1634	1702	ALL	ALL	141615	LAN	Garstang

Known From	To	Researching From	To	Ref	Cty	Place
CLARKSON contd.						
1700	1800	1700	1800	123722	LAN	Preston
1758	....	....	1758	101761	LIN	Croft
1800	1840	ALL	....	104515	LIN	Grantham
....	....	....	....	108898	LKS	Roberton
1850	1950	ALL	1992	108898	LKS	Wiston
1815	1876	1555	1815	126462	NYK	Whitby
....	....	1800	1900	109894	STS	Uttoxeter
....	....	ALL	ALL	103837	YKS	ALL
1700	1800	1700	1800	167924	YKS	Bugthorpe
1840	1871	....	1992	108367	YKS	Dewsbury
1684	1744	1660	1684	101796	YKS	Doncaster
1692	1760	1650	1692	177393	YKS	Hemingbrough
1820	1840	ALL	1820	108367	YKS	High Hoyland
1770	1817	ALL	ALL	103837	YKS	Hull
1825	1850	1750	1825	150096	YKS	Kippax
1600	1800	1600	1800	167924	YKS	Kirby Underdale
1857	....	ALL	1857	151424	YKS	Leeds
1784	1807	....	....	151351	YKS	Masham
1827	1863	1700	1900	115401	YKS	Mirfield
1787	1870	....	....	177393	YKS	Selby
1900	1967	1800	1900	167843	YKS	Stokesley
1880	1992	1700	1880	167916	???	???
CLARRICOATES						
1854	1985	1854	....	113875	DBY	Derby
1648	1992	1651	1992	113875	LIN	ALL
1851	1983	1851	....	113875	LND	ALL
1800	1992	1800	....	113875	NTT	Newark
1862	1992	1862	....	113875	YKS	York
CLARRIDGE						
1840	1950	1800	1920	113883	LEI	ALL
CLARSON						
1789	1960	1600	1789	152463	LEI	Longwhatton
CLARVIS						
1807	1870	1700	1900	148008	LIN	ALL
CLARY						
1836	....	1800	1836	128724	SFK	Denham
CLASBY						
1760	1920	1550	1760	113891	HAM	ALL
1830	1849	1750	1849	118192	SSX	Brighton
CLASPER						
....	....	1300	1900	113980	ALL	ALL
1780	1850	1700	1960	101907	DUR	Sunderland
1797	1871	1600	1871	171425	DUR	Sunderland
1797	1871	1600	1871	171425	NBL	Newcastle
CLATER						
1780	1900	1780	1900	137634	NTT	East Retford
1760	1780	....	1780	137634	NTT	Whatton
CLATWORTHY						
1830	1850	....	....	113905	CON	Falmouth
1750	1800	....	....	113905	CON	Saltash
1700	1750	....	....	113905	CON	St Dominick
1800	1830	....	....	113905	DEV	Plymouth
....	....	....	1700	113905	DEV	South Molton
1850	1870	....	....	113905	LAN	Liverpool
1870	1925	....	....	113905	LND	South East
1850	1870	....	....	113905	LND	Shoreditch
1925	1970	....	....	113905	SRY	Weybridge
CLAUGHAN						
1800	1900	1750	1900	110884	DUR	North
CLAUGHTON						
....	....	ALL	ALL	113921	ALL	Name Study
1700	1900	....	....	131474	YKS	Leeds
CLAXTON						
....	....	ALL	ALL	113948	ALL	Name Study
1749	1992	ALL	ALL	141127	NFK	South
1826	1900	ALL	1826	141704	NFK	Wearsted
1749	1992	ALL	ALL	141127	SFK	North
CLAY						
1214	1650	1200	1650	113956	DBY	ALL
....	....	1550	1700	115142	DBY	South
1638	1922	1600	1992	113956	DBY	Darley
1634	1654	1500	1633	131245	DBY	Eckington
....	1719	....	....	154024	DBY	North Wingfield
1627	1752	1600	1992	113956	DBY	Youlgreave
1780	1850	1700	1780	157074	ESS	Canewdon
1756	1813	1750	1813	171654	ESS	Canewdon
1900	1992	1700	1850	113964	LEI	Belgrave
1850	1920	1850	1920	116483	LIN	Kirton End
1761	1977	1761	1977	151211	LIN	Quadring
1761	1977	1761	1977	151211	LIN	Surfleet
....	1780	ALL	1780	134511	NTT	East Leake
1752	1770	1650	1751	131245	NTT	Woodborough
1811	1834	1811	1834	113670	SOM	Freshford
CLAY contd.						
1800	1992	1700	1992	120677	WYK	Slaithwaite
1810	1992	ALL	1810	100803	WYK	Sowerby
1810	1920	1650	1810	170194	YKS	Halifax
1739	1820	1700	1841	170267	YKS	Soothill
1820	1881	1800	1881	170267	YKS	Wortley
CLAYALL						
1818	1842	ALL	1818	161500	SOM	Crewkerne
CLAYBORNE						
1552	1621	ALL	ALL	156906	NFK	Kings Lynn
1066	1699	ALL	ALL	156906	WES	Cliburn
....	....	ALL	ALL	156906	YKS	???
CLAYBURN						
....	....	ALL	ALL	113980	ALL	Name Study
....	....	1300	1900	113980	ALL	ALL
CLAYDEN						
1718	1850	ALL	1718	163341	ESS	Clavering
1726	1825	ALL	1726	162108	ESS	Clavering
1826	1992	1700	1826	152552	ESS	Stebbing
1653	1700	....	....	172987	IOW	???
CLAYDON						
1850	1980	1750	1850	119164	ESS	Bocking
....	1851	1750	1851	101893	ESS	Chelmsford
1800	1950	1700	1800	133582	ESS	Earlscolne
1775	1848	1700	1775	114871	ESS	Hempstead
1750	1992	1700	1750	113352	ESS	Rivenhall
1810	1850	1775	1810	114871	ESS	Steeple Bumpstead
1870	1915	....	....	114871	LND	Willesden
1750	1890	....	....	169129	NFK	Kings Lynn
1750	1890	....	....	169129	NFK	Swaffham
CLAYSON						
1761	1834	ALL	1761	115126	NTH	Weston Flavel
CLAYTON						
1811	1992	1811	1992	142182	ALL	ALL
1850	1900	1850	1900	114006	BKM	Great Marlow
1714	1850	1800	1850	114006	BKM	Hambleden
1770	1930	....	....	116602	BRK	ALL
1800	1850	1800	1850	114006	BRK	Reading
1800	....	1780	1800	135771	CHS	North East
1900	1940	1800	1900	157058	CHS	Hyde
1740	1765	....	....	138851	CHS	Romiley
1860	1880	1700	1860	143103	CHS	Stockport
1768	1874	1800	1860	108510	DBY	Glossop
1694	1874	1800	1860	108510	DBY	New Mills
1650	1850	....	....	138037	HRT	North East
1913	1987	....	....	111619	IOM	Peel
1700	1800	1600	1800	154903	KEN	Deal
1803	1903	....	....	121061	LAN	Aldham
1880	1890	....	....	143103	LAN	Ashton Under Lyne
1890	1902	....	....	143103	LAN	Bolton
1852	....	1852	1909	129747	LAN	Liverpool
1840	1900	1800	1900	167843	LAN	Manchester
1809	1882	....	1809	170461	LAN	Tockholes
1477	1992	1600	1750	124176	LEI	Melton Mowbray
1907	1920	....	....	148989	MDX	North East
1797	....	?	1800	164976	NTT	West Bridgeford
1800	1900	1800	1850	114006	OXF	Checkendon
1600	1960	1800	1900	114006	OXF	Henley
1800	1900	1800	1850	114006	OXF	Ipsden
1748	1866	1748	1866	114006	OXF	Pyrton
....	1793	....	....	146811	SAL	Wellington
1850	1960	ALL	ALL	162469	SFK	North
1836	1867	1750	1880	113638	SRY	Bermondsey
1830	1880	ALL	1830	102016	SRY	Newington
1830	1880	ALL	1830	102016	SRY	Walworth
1750	1992	1750	1950	123463	SSX	Selsey
1692	1821	1600	1900	115991	SXW	Selsey
....	1860	....	1950	130168	WAR	Birmingham
1850	....	1800	1900	143758	WAR	Solihull
1836	1902	1700	1850	145882	WYK	Tickhill
....	....	1800	1900	171794	YKS	Bradford
....	....	1800	1900	171794	YKS	Cleckheaton
1750	1778	1700	1760	170348	YKS	Illingworth
1860	1910	1910	ALL	171174	YKS	Leeds
CLEAK						
....	....	ALL	ALL	114014	ALL	ALL
1650	1950	1550	1900	113883	DEV	ALL
....	....	1880	1970	153265	KEN	Medway
....	....	1785	1980	153265	LND	???
CLEAL						
....	....	1800	ALL	136476	DOR	Weymouth
....	....	1500	ALL	114022	DOR	???
1830	1880	1830	1880	152250	SOM	Chard
1818	1842	ALL	1818	161500	SOM	Crewkerne

Known From	To	Researching From	To	Ref	Cty	Place
CLEAL contd.						
....	....	1500	ALL	114022	SOM	???
CLEAN						
1600	1992	1600	1992	143014	ALL	ALL
CLEAR						
....	1805	....	1805	120529	BRK	Cookham
CLEARS						
1679	1800	1600	1700	159956	SFK	Market Weston
CLEARY						
....	....	ALL	ALL	166812	LAN	Manchester
....	....	ALL	ALL	166812	OFF	Tullamore
CLEASBY						
1835	1992	ALL	1835	165301	DUR	South
1533	1580	1500	1600	176389	NYK	Great Ayton
1800	1876	ALL	ALL	119504	WES	Brough
1780	1780	1750	1780	131342	WES	Great Musgrave
1780	....	ALL	ALL	119504	YKS	Askrigg
1780	1800	ALL	ALL	119504	YKS	Ravenseat
1680	....	ALL	ALL	119504	YKS	Stonesdale
CLEAVE						
1300	1980	1100	1980	114197	ALL	ALL
1800	1880	ALL	ALL	149535	BRK	Windsor
1723	1932	1723	1932	114030	CON	Egloshayle
1592	1700	ALL	1592	114030	CON	St Kew
1870	1992	1800	1870	109193	CON	St Wenn
1550	1850	1300	1850	105333	DEV	Buckland In The Moor
1861	1936	....	....	154121	DEV	Chudleigh
1863	1863	1800	1875	136042	DEV	Exeter
1550	1850	1300	1850	105333	DEV	Holne
1550	1850	1300	1850	105333	DEV	Ilsington
1550	1850	1300	1850	105333	DEV	Lydford
1550	1850	1300	1850	105333	DEV	Widecombe In The Moor
1860	1900	ALL	ALL	149535	SRY	Wandsworth
CLEAVER						
1811	1841	....	....	137049	BRK	Wargrave
1841	1980	....	....	137049	MDX	North East London
1800	1900	....	1800	177695	NTH	Northampton
1827	1847	1827	1860	114715	NTT	Carlton
1726	1811	1500	1726	137049	OXF	Baldon
1726	1811	1500	1726	137049	OXF	Dist
1746	1773	1600	1746	169935	OXF	Duns Tew
....	1800	....	1800	177695	WAR	Braunston
CLEAVES						
....	....	1700	1950	116335	AVN	Bristol
1800	1805	1770	1820	126144	KEN	Gillingham
CLEDEN						
1736	1992	ALL	ALL	160288	BRK	Reading
1736	1992	ALL	ALL	160288	HAM	Andover
CLEET						
1800	1900	ALL	ALL	122297	DUR	South Shields
CLEETON						
1740	1992	1500	1750	114049	SAL	ALL
CLEGG						
....	....	ALL	ALL	108294	ALL	Name Study
1785	1930	1700	1992	179078	LAN	Bacup
1786	1817	....	....	120901	LAN	Burnley
1841	1992	....	....	128716	LAN	Liverpool
1850	1880	....	....	128856	LAN	Manchester
1840	1901	1810	1901	147281	LAN	Manchester
1842	1958	1800	1850	103896	LAN	Rochdale
1806	....	....	....	132500	LAN	Shaw
1790	1860	1600	1790	117633	WYK	Dewsbury
1780	1992	ALL	1780	100803	WYK	Erringden
1850	1860	1700	1850	145688	YKS	Dewsbury
1819	1850	1700	1900	177873	YKS	Halifax
1814	1819	1780	1830	116114	YKS	Heptonstall
1766	1832	ALL	1766	102350	YKS	Ledston
CLEGGS						
1850	1860	1700	1992	167592	YKS	Castleford
CLEGHORN						
1840	1900	1800	1992	127124	ALL	ALL
1756	1768	1700	1800	114057	DUR	Swalwell
1530	1900	1530	1992	127124	ENG	ALL
....	....	1830	1880	114057	LND	Bermondsey
1857	1928	1928	1992	114057	NBL	North Shields
1790	1992	....	1790	110027	PEE	Peebles
1480	1900	1480	1900	127124	SCT	ALL
CLELAND						
1734	1992	....	....	148644	LAN	Mouse Hill
CLELLAND						
1830	1900	....	....	176540	AYR	Dalry
1740	1770	1700	1740	122904	WLN	Bo'ness

Known From	To	Researching From	To	Ref	Cty	Place
CLEMAS						
1819	1992	1600	1992	114065	CON	???
1780	1992	1780	1992	114065	DEV	???
1809	1992	1809	1992	114065	DOR	???
1780	1985	1780	1985	114065	SRY	???
CLEMENS						
?	?	?	?	166642	KEN	???
CLEMENT						
1092	1183	1066	1600	176923	BRE	Talyllyn
1183	1400	1066	1600	176923	CGN	Tregaron
1697	1950	1600	1992	176923	GLA	Pontlliw
1850	1900	1700	1850	171174	NYK	East Rounton
1850	1900	1700	1850	171174	NYK	West Rounton
1811	1860	1780	1811	173118	PEM	Nevern
1773	1875	ALL	1773	154946	YKS	Barford
1850	1904	1904	ALL	154946	YKS	Startforth
CLEMENTS						
1720	....	ALL	1720	131059	ESS	Bocking
1900	1992	1600	1900	127469	GLS	Bristol
1660	1721	1600	1740	155896	GLS	Painswick
1832	....	....	....	138061	HAM	Portsea
1770	1803	....	....	165999	LEI	Long Clawson
1805	1805	1700	1804	131245	LIN	Frieston
1700	1770	....	....	165999	LIN	Harlaxton
1770	1830	1700	1770	108448	LND	East
1860	1900	1800	1900	114081	LND	Mary Le Bone
1870	1903	1850	1992	145009	MDX	Bethnal Green
1575	1625	1500	1600	109290	NFK	Central
1850	1992	1700	1850	150886	NFK	North East
....	....	1700	1838	117846	NFK	Ashill
1867	....	1800	1900	114480	NFK	Norwich
1840	1870	1687	1992	139351	SFK	Debenham
1817	1817	1700	1890	153001	SFK	Ipswich
1900	1992	1600	1900	127469	SOM	Bristol
1864	....	1864	1955	141194	SRY	Bermondsey
CLEMENTSON						
1853	1992	1700	1807	172820	CUL	Penrith
1800	1820	ALL	ALL	130508	DUR	Swalwell
1770	1830	1750	1830	173428	NBL	Allendale
CLEMETS						
....	....	1800	1899	174963	MDX	Islington
CLEMETT						
....	....	ALL	ALL	114103	ALL	Name Study
CLEMMEY						
1846	1992	1780	1846	176257	ALL	ALL
CLEMMOW						
1900	1963	1800	1900	134856	CON	Grampound
....	....	1700	1838	134856	CON	St Enoder
CLEMO						
1817	....	1700	1900	162388	CON	St Austell
CLEMPSON						
1606	....	....	1606	160873	STS	Willenhall
CLEMSON						
1760	1860	1600	1760	139203	MON	Alberbury
1740	1800	....	1800	176540	SAL	Alberbury
1802	1887	1750	1802	157775	SRY	Newington
....	1825	....	1825	150495	STS	Martley
CLENCH						
1790	1820	1700	1820	163473	DOR	Bere Regis
CLENDINNEN						
1786	1941	ALL	ALL	131415	BEW	Earlston
CLEOBURY						
1830	1890	1800	1830	156302	STS	Walsall
CLERK						
1700	1860	....	....	126497	CAI	Latheron
1786	1806	1780	1810	146536	PEE	Broughton
CLEUTH						
1800	1850	1600	1850	133590	NBL	Newcastle Upon Tyne
CLEVELAND						
1770	1830	1700	1830	139688	SFK	Ipswich
1775	....	ALL	1775	148172	YKS	Stillingfleet
CLEVERDON						
1807	1951	1700	1807	139815	DEV	Parkham
CLEVERLEY						
1660	1782	1683	1782	104817	HAM	Soberton
CLEVERLY						
1810	1850	1780	1960	115797	BRK	Great Shefford
1732	1822	ALL	ALL	117307	HAM	Romsey
1754	1836	....	....	115290	WIL	Heddington
1850	....	ALL	1850	106984	WIL	Overton
CLEWER						
....	....	1790	1856	160385	ENG	???
1918	1918	ALL	1918	122572	HAM	ALL
1856	1992	1856	1992	160385	IOM	Douglas

Known From	To	Researching From	To	Ref	Cty	Place
CLEWER contd.						
?	?	?	?	174297	WOR	ALL
1841	1881	1841	1881	108901	WOR	Dodderhill
1812	1830	1808	1841	108901	WOR	Hanbury
1821	1841	1815	1851	108901	WOR	Himbleton
1880	1880	1841	1881	108901	WOR	Tibberton
CLEWES						
1800	1850	1700	1992	167592	STS	Burslem
1800	1850	1700	1992	167592	STS	Cobridge
1853	1883	1700	1853	138509	STS	Wolverhampton
CLEWLOW						
1873	1895	ALL	ALL	125288	STS	Stafford
....	1700	....	....	174564	STS	Stafford
CLEWS						
....	....	ALL	ALL	108588	ALL	ALL
1810	1840	1810	1840	173681	DBY	Leecote Farm
1800	....	....	....	130486	STS	Stafford
....	....	?	?	177334	WOR	???
CLIBBON						
1800	1992	1700	1992	108618	HRT	Ware
CLIBBORN						
....	....	1700	1800	163244	DUB	???
....	....	1700	1800	163244	OFF	???
CLICK						
1795	1950	1700	1795	113883	GLS	ALL
CLIFF						
....	1750	ALL	1750	134511	NTT	ALL
1820	1840	1780	1850	163791	SAL	Whitchurch
1790	1992	ALL	1790	102245	WAR	Coleshill
1834	....	....	....	175587	YKS	Gildersome
1674	1877	1620	1740	109622	YKS	Huddersfield
1785	1909	1750	1910	116386	YKS	Leeds
1719	....	....	....	151351	YKS	Otley
1770	1793	1740	1800	160873	YKS	York
CLIFFE						
1300	1980	1200	1980	114197	ALL	ALL
1829	1980	1825	1992	134406	LAN	Manchester
1829	1980	1825	1992	134406	LAN	Salford
?	1892	1500	1992	101303	SAL	ALL
1890	1892	1500	1890	101303	SAL	Wreakin
1798	1809	1750	1840	134406	YKS	Huddersfield
CLIFFORD						
....	....	ALL	ALL	114138	ALL	Name Study
1850	1992	1700	1850	144762	CAM	Wood Ditton
1700	....	....	....	142158	GLS	Norton
....	....	ALL	1782	164631	GLS	Stow On Wold
1600	1700	1600	1750	118338	HAM	Fordingbridge
1600	1700	1600	1750	118338	HAM	Ringwood
1850	1874	1800	1874	141097	HEF	Morse Ruardean
1851	1851	1700	1851	144762	KEN	Chatham
....	....	1700	1730	161357	KEN	Margate
1849	1875	1700	1849	144762	SFK	Newmarket
1670	1750	1670	1770	142018	WIL	Marlborough
1874	1901	1874	1901	141097	YKS	Rotherham
1300	1480	....	....	175439	???	???
CLIFT						
1830	1899	1800	1900	106119	CON	???
1797	1853	1700	1800	100013	ESS	Great Waltham
....	....	1790	1850	137685	NFK	Gt Yarmouth
1800	1900	ALL	ALL	166537	WOR	Dudley
CLIFTON						
1770	1820	1700	1770	167711	BDF	Oakley
1820	1919	1820	1919	170631	DEV	Coryton
1867	1895	1867	1895	170631	DEV	Lewtrenchard
1821	1913	1821	1919	170631	DEV	Stowford
1845	1852	1800	1992	137448	GLS	???
1750	1840	ALL	ALL	146633	KEN	ALL
1659	1847	1538	1659	125105	NFK	Great Yarmouth
1800	1850	1600	1850	168211	OXF	Bloxham
....	1935	....	....	118451	WES	Windermere
1830	....	....	1830	118451	WES	Witherslack
1850	....	....	1850	164011	WOR	Worcester
CLIMPSON						
....	....	ALL	....	134244	HAM	Portsmouth
1640	1684	....	....	127426	KEN	Harrietsham
1670	1960	1589	1960	144525	KEN	Maidstone
CLINCH						
1550	1919	1550	1919	114146	GLS	Cirencester
1550	1830	1550	1830	114146	GLS	Fairford
1830	ALL	1500	1830	145378	KEN	Bolton Manor
1730	1992	....	1850	171441	KEN	Bredgar
1730	1992	....	1850	171441	KEN	Stockbury
1790	1850	1790	1830	114146	MDX	London
1770	1900	1770	1830	114146	OXF	Witney

Known From	To	Researching From	To	Ref	Cty	Place
CLINCH contd.						
1750	1992	....	....	175439	OXF	Witney
CLING						
1760	1992	ALL	1760	131393	DEV	Bideford
1760	1992	ALL	1760	131393	DEV	Hartland
CLINGAN						
....	....	ALL	ALL	114154	ALL	ALL
1772	1992	1600	1772	114154	KKD	Kirkpatrick Durham
CLINGO						
1860	1870	1700	....	135259	LND	???
CLINKERBERRY						
1730	1992	1580	1730	175870	BRK	Bisham
CLINNGH						
1890	1980	1700	1890	171913	LIN	Lincoln
CLINTON						
1845	1923	....	....	114162	CON	Truro
1923	1935	....	....	114162	DEV	Exeter
1822	1992	1800	....	156191	DUR	Chester Le Street
1850	....	1850	1868	104043	IRL	???
1822	1992	1800	....	156191	LND	???
1822	1992	1800	....	156191	NBL	Newcastle
1831	....	....	....	163031	SLI	???
1861	1992	....	1992	163031	SYK	???
CLIPPERTON						
1900	1970	1600	1900	114170	ALL	ALL
....	....	1700	1750	114170	GAL	ALL
1850	1970	1750	1850	114170	LND	ALL
1800	1970	1600	1800	114170	NFK	ALL
CLIPSON						
1805	1927	1700	1805	141569	NTH	Slipton
CLISBY						
?	?	1750	ALL	117919	MDX	London
CLISSOLD						
1750	1850	1700	1900	128163	GLS	Central
1800	1850	1750	1800	101524	GLS	Stroud
1890	....	....	....	167037	GLS	Stroud
CLIST						
1750	1840	1700	1840	144657	DEV	Hemyock
1805	....	....	....	149284	DEV	???
CLITHEROE						
1704	1801	ALL	1704	169943	LAN	Leyland
1676	1824	1600	1676	169935	LAN	Leyland
CLIVE						
1300	1985	800	1985	114197	ALL	ALL
1750	1800	1600	1992	167592	STS	Tunstall
CLIVELY						
1809	1992	1600	1809	114189	MDX	London
CLIVES						
....	....	ALL	ALL	114197	ALL	Name Study
CLOAK						
1800	....	1650	....	116920	CON	Mevagissey
1800	1900	1800	1900	134031	CON	Perranarworthal
CLOAKE						
....	....	....	....	135488	KEN	Ashford
1780	1855	1700	1780	152587	KEN	Tenterden
CLOCKIE						
1819	....	....	....	106852	WIG	Sorbie
CLOGG						
1800	1815	1780	1820	168580	CON	Crumplehorn
1815	1845	1810	1860	168580	CON	Morval
CLOKE						
1800	....	1650	....	116920	CON	Mevagissey
1582	1980	1582	1980	137529	CON	Pillaton
CLOKIE						
1870	1890	1750	1992	167592	YKS	Castleford
CLONEY						
1750	1992	ALL	1750	134996	WEX	???
CLOPTON						
1300	1400	1300	1400	154881	ALL	ALL
CLOSE						
1827	1871	1871	1992	122653	CMA	Ulverston
....	....	1750	1850	151084	LND	East
1890	1943	1870	ALL	145386	SRY	Lambeth
1800	1850	1800	....	118591	WES	East Ward
1750	1850	1650	....	118591	WRY	Gunnerside
....	1745	1700	1780	174858	YKS	Brompton
1814	1850	....	....	174858	YKS	Helmsley
1780	1790	1785	1815	174858	YKS	Over Silton
1781	1815	1700	1800	122653	YKS	Swaledale
CLOSSON						
1762	1913	1600	1760	156221	HAM	Southampton
CLOTHIER						
....	....	ALL	ALL	114200	ALL	Name Study
....	....	1750	1950	109770	ENG	ALL

Known From	To	Researching From	To	Ref	Cty	Place
CLOTHIER contd.						
1859	1992	1538	1859	131318	SOM	Bristol
1740	....	....	....	142158	SOM	Cadbury
CLOTWORTHY						
1850	1900	1750	1850	167789	ANT	???
1700	1750	....	....	113905	CON	St Dominick
....	....	....	1700	113905	DEV	South Molton
1500	1600	1150	1500	174319	DEV	???
1850	1900	1750	1850	167789	DOW	???
CLOUD						
1844	1930	....	....	169102	MDX	???
....	....	ALL	1820	169102	SAL	Shrewsbury
CLOUDSLEY						
1740	....	....	....	126993	ALL	ALL
CLOUGH						
1840	1930	1800	1950	133450	DEV	Tavistock
1900	1992	1800	1900	116823	DUR	Eshwinning
1900	1992	ALL	1850	136077	LAN	East
1800	1950	....	....	126497	LAN	Leyland
1790	1860	1700	1790	165530	LAN	Rochdale
1820	1980	1800	1900	126500	LAN	Wigan
1845	1992	1840	1900	149845	LIN	ALL
1775	....	....	1775	101761	LIN	Willoughby
1770	1992	1700	1992	126632	NBL	Cramlington
1875	1960	1750	1875	130885	NBL	Cramlington
....	....	1700	1900	108677	YKS	ALL
1870	1992	1870	1992	125687	YKS	Bradford
1845	1992	1840	1900	149845	YKS	Dewsbury
1870	1992	1870	1992	125687	YKS	Huddersfield
CLOUNIE						
1805	1806	1750	1850	159964	KKD	Kelton
CLOUTT						
1563	1873	1563	1900	170143	KEN	Brenchley
1563	1873	1563	1900	170143	KEN	Marden
CLOUTTE						
1876	1889	1876	1889	170143	DEV	Plympton
1899	1905	1895	1907	170143	KEN	Margate
1899	1905	1895	1907	170143	KEN	Westgate
1910	1920	1900	1944	170143	MDX	Ealing
1867	1878	1867	1881	170143	MDX	Turnham Green
1862	1870	1843	1871	170143	WIL	Corsham
CLOVER						
1806	1827	1750	1850	162396	NTT	Collingham
1780	1820	1700	1780	102288	SFK	Barking
CLOWES						
1750	1850	1600	1992	167592	CHS	Chester
1650	1680	1600	1750	117706	CHS	Gawsworth
1650	1660	1600	1992	167592	CHS	Lawton
1900	?	1800	1992	167592	CHS	Macclesfield
1650	1670	1500	1992	167592	CHS	Old Rode
1560	1870	1560	1900	154598	LEI	South
1680	....	1500	1992	167592	MDX	London
1899	1956	1956	1992	179116	STS	Dudley
1780	1958	ALL	ALL	179116	STS	Ipstones
1780	1820	1600	1992	167592	STS	Longport
1833	1956	1800	1833	110213	STS	Stoke On Trent
1810	?	1600	1992	167592	STS	Woolstanton
1870	1992	1860	1920	154598	YKS	Sheffield
CLOWTING						
1816	1945	....	....	135070	MDX	Stepney
1788	1816	....	....	135070	SFK	Eyke
CLUARD						
ALL	ALL	ALL	ALL	114219	ALL	ALL
CLUB						
....	....	ALL	ALL	101109	ALL	Name Study
CLUBBE						
1810	1992	1750	1810	138282	CHS	Farndon
CLUBLEY						
1880	1920	1800	1900	116823	NYK	Patley Bridge
CLUCAS						
1731	1733	1729	1733	141291	IOM	Arbory
....	....	1780	1820	131962	IOM	Marown
1723	1749	1511	1749	141291	IOM	Rushen
1740	1830	ALL	1850	115347	LAN	Liverpool
CLUGSTON						
1800	1830	1690	1830	158313	MOG	Carrickmacross
CLULOE						
....	....	1700	1900	179531	STS	Leek
CLULOW						
....	....	ALL	ALL	104159	LND	Hackney
....	....	ALL	ALL	128929	STS	ALL
....	....	1558	1810	153427	STS	Leek
CLUNE						
1849	1918	1800	1849	173339	CLA	Kilnona

Known From	To	Researching From	To	Ref	Cty	Place
CLUNES						
1750	1790	1650	1750	144150	INV	Inverness
CLUNESS						
1750	1965	....	....	137820	SHI	Fetlar
1720	1965	....	....	137820	SHI	Mid Yell
1760	1965	....	....	137820	SHI	North Yell
1758	1965	....	....	137820	SHI	Northmavine
1720	1965	....	....	137820	SHI	South Yell
CLUTTERBUCK						
1857	1857	....	....	163287	GLS	Cheltenham
1790	1992	1790	1810	114227	GLS	Gloucester
1790	....	....	....	114227	GLS	Newent
CLUTTON						
1810	1880	1600	1810	134104	DEN	Is Y Coed
....	....	1840	1860	137723	SFK	Horham
1750	1800	1700	1800	115614	SFK	Mettingham
CLYBORN						
....	....	1800	1900	147079	OFF	ALL
CLYDE						
1870	1920	1800	1900	111821	LKS	Govan
CLYMO						
1819	1847	....	....	130176	CON	Camborne
1837	1885	1885	1992	162973	CON	Liskeard
CLYNICK						
1863	1920	1700	1992	112003	STS	Burton Upon Trent
CLYST						
1808	1808	1808	1808	143286	DEV	Burlescombe
COACHIFOR						
1806	1810	1806	1826	153303	LIN	Tetford
COAD						
1818	1828	1700	1828	137901	CON	Northill
....	....	1800	1900	122076	CON	St Cleer
1746	1830	1746	1830	156019	CON	St Keverne
....	....	1750	1880	143359	CON	Truro
1869	1873	1860	1901	108391	MDX	London
COADE						
1700	1853	1853	1992	139203	CON	???
COAKER						
1200	1992	ALL	ALL	105333	ALL	ALL
COAKLEY						
1850	1910	ALL	ALL	106283	LAN	Salford
COALES						
....	....	ALL	ALL	114235	ALL	ALL
1850	1980	....	....	114243	BKM	Newport Pagnell
1850	1900	ALL	ALL	114235	NFK	Wisbech
1540	1850	....	....	114243	NTH	ALL
1650	1900	1500	1700	114235	NTH	Aldwinckle
1860	1900	ALL	ALL	143677	SRY	Bermondsey
COALMAN						
1770	1840	1600	1840	154342	GLS	Mangotsfield
COAP						
1789	1800	ALL	ALL	128821	DBY	Denby
COARE						
....	....	ALL	ALL	114251	ALL	Name Study
1800	1992	1700	1900	114251	ALL	ALL
COATES						
1812	1992	ALL	1851	100536	ALL	???
1661	1940	....	....	128996	CAM	Thorney
1672	1672	1550	1672	102830	DBY	Matlock
1846	1846	1800	1850	159042	DOW	Killyleagh
1850	1920	1800	1900	159220	DUR	Hartlepool
1600	1700	1600	1700	169781	DUR	Langley Ford
1600	1700	1600	1700	169781	DUR	Lynesack
1774	1774	1550	1774	102830	GLS	Aston Blank
....	....	ALL	ALL	166812	LAN	Manchester
1850	1875	1800	1900	171921	LAN	Manchester
1873	1873	1846	1900	159042	LAN	Salford
1860	....	1860	....	135488	LAN	St Helens
1885	1992	?	1885	153613	LAN	???
1870	1992	....	....	171921	LIN	Grimsby
....	....	1750	1850	116262	LKS	Glasgow
1820	1900	1800	1992	136867	LND	ALL
1708	....	ALL	1708	119326	NRY	Coxwold
....	....	1838	1900	117803	NRY	Yarm
1700	1810	1700	1810	127655	NTH	Byfield
1700	1850	1600	1992	177725	NYK	Kirkby Mooreside
....	....	1800	1932	159042	RFW	Paisley
?	....	?	?	177679	SCT	Borders
1740	1850	1650	1740	118745	SSX	Alciston
1860	1992	1700	1860	100803	WYK	Halifax
1834	1847	1700	1834	103268	YKS	Bempton
1680	....	....	....	145688	YKS	Keighley
1897	?	1700	1800	159336	YKS	Mere Whitwood
1700	1830	1650	1830	119717	YKS	No Frodingham

Known From	To	Researching From	To	Ref	Cty	Place
COATES contd.						
1772	1838	1700	1900	116742	YKS	Swaledale
1775	1992	1700	1800	122513	YKS	Thirlby
1775	1799	1710	1780	135763	YKS	York
1790	1800	1600	1992	102520	YKS	???
1885	1992	?	1885	153613	YKS	???
COATH						
....	....	ALL	ALL	114278	ALL	Name Study
1798	1820	1500	1800	132993	CON	East
1808	1851	1800	1851	170267	DEV	Plymouth
1755	1783	1748	1831	170267	DEV	Plymstock
COATS						
1790	1850	1700	1790	132268	WAR	Butlers Marston
COATSWITH						
1840	1860	1800	1850	137278	NBL	Benton
COATSWORTH						
1724	1773	1600	1750	101575	LIN	Wrawby By Brigg
1700	1992	1550	1700	171395	YKS	Rothwell
COBB						
1620	1750	....	....	114294	BRK	North Moreton
1842	1940	....	....	128996	CAM	Thorney
1750	1800	1750	1800	154210	DOR	Coombe Keynes
1800	1900	1700	1800	114286	DOR	Wareham
1800	1900	1700	1800	114286	DOR	Wimbourne
1750	1901	1750	1950	134880	KEN	Greenwich
....	....	1820	1850	164364	LIN	East Kirkby
1800	1870	1800	1914	118818	LIN	Heckington
1600	1700	....	....	169129	NFK	Tilney
1560	1992	1250	1560	114294	OXF	Dorchester On Thames
1720	1850	....	....	114294	OXF	Navington
1752	1763	1700	1800	146269	SRY	Richmond
1850	1880	....	....	164364	YKS	Howden
1850	1880	....	....	164364	YKS	Melton
1864	1900	1830	1864	142360	YKS	York
COBBE						
1650	1750	ALL	ALL	137987	CHS	Wybunbury
COBBEAL						
1768	1788	1750	1799	163775	MDX	Shoreditch
COBBETT						
....	....	ALL	ALL	114308	ALL	Name Study
1332	1992	1332	1992	114308	ALL	ALL
....	....	1800	1847	143707	SRY	Egham
....	....	1800	1900	121592	SRY	Woking
COBBIN						
1550	1960	1550	1960	114316	SFK	ALL
COBBING						
....	....	ALL	ALL	114324	ALL	Name Study
COBBLEDICK						
1820	1860	1750	1900	122688	CON	St Teath
1530	1992	1530	1992	114332	CON	???
1530	1992	1530	1992	114332	DEV	???
COBEAN						
1800	1830	1690	1830	158313	TYR	???
COBELDICK						
....	....	ALL	ALL	114332	ALL	Name Study
COBHAM						
1200	1270	1170	1270	154881	KEN	Hever
....	....	1600	1900	124273	LND	Bermondsey
....	....	1600	1900	124273	LND	Southwark
1830	1840	1800	1850	115746	SOM	Taunton
COBIE						
1893	....	....	1600	136557	DEV	???
1863	....	....	1600	136557	MDX	???
COBLEY						
1800	1825	1800	1825	178705	SOM	Pensford
COBURN						
....	....	1700	1830	174300	SOM	Bath
COCHRAM						
1860	1919	....	1890	166510	ENG	London
COCHRANE						
1852	1992	1852	1992	106291	CWD	Abergele
1800	1856	1800	1856	146536	DOW	Inch
1900	1992	1880	1900	140198	HRT	Hatfield
1900	1992	1880	1900	140198	HRT	Hyde
1900	1992	1880	1900	140198	HRT	Lemsford
1900	1992	1880	1900	140198	HRT	Welwyn Garden City
1889	1889	1600	1889	147885	SCT	Glasgow
....	....	1750	1880	140198	SCT	Wishaw
COCK						
1796	1822	....	....	109002	BRK	Winkfield
1750	1900	1750	1900	160814	CON	Roche
1762	1762	1725	1825	133450	CON	S Gennys
....	....	1700	1800	174319	CON	St Allen
COCK contd.						
....	....	1700	1800	174319	CON	St Erme
1838	1855	1700	1992	124044	CON	St Wenn
1770	1860	1600	1870	162043	CON	Truro
1745	....	....	....	166723	CON	Warbstow
1800	1900	1700	1800	133019	CON	???
1790	1992	1700	1992	167800	DEV	Northam
1821	1841	1800	1851	116505	ESS	Colcester
1775	1800	ALL	1775	131059	ESS	Purleigh
1800	1992	1700	1800	116440	ESS	Sible Hedingham
1700	1800	ALL	1700	115282	KEN	East
....	1720	ALL	1720	152889	KEN	Folkestone
1798	1905	1800	1860	116831	KEN	Woolwich
1769	....	....	1800	171441	KEN	Worth
1790	1820	1790	1820	157171	LAN	Colne
1766	1992	1700	1775	102342	LIN	Flixborough
1756	1756	....	....	108901	LIN	Flixborough
1720	1730	1650	1720	151769	LIN	Threckingham
1847	1925	....	....	116505	LND	City
1740	1770	1730	1782	135828	NFK	Pulham St Mary
1782	1910	1782	1889	135828	SFK	Mettingham
1780	....	1750	....	119695	SOM	East Pannard
1788	?	ALL	ALL	153516	SOM	Wedmore
1822	1917	1841	1933	109002	SRY	Bagshot
COCKADAY						
1607	1992	1775	1920	114359	NFK	Norwich
1850	1960	1700	1850	163732	NFK	Norwich
COCKAYNE						
....	....	1770	1850	130346	DBY	Wirksworth
1774	1851	?	1780	164976	NTT	Nottingham
COCKBAIN						
1820	1864	1790	1820	117196	CHS	Congleton
1560	1830	1500	1900	149292	CUL	Keswick
1560	1830	1500	1900	149292	CUL	Threlkeld
1830	1888	1500	1900	149292	LAN	Liverpool
COCKBURN						
....	....	ALL	ALL	114375	ALL	Name Study
1791	1992	1690	1790	114367	BEW	Eccles
1791	1992	1690	1790	114367	BEW	Fogo
1791	1992	1690	1790	114367	BEW	Langton
1781	1992	1600	1992	130125	CUL	ALL
....	....	1700	1830	162620	DUR	Chester Le Street
1730	1850	1600	1730	142328	ELN	Haddington
1530	1580	ALL	1600	149063	ELN	Haddington
1730	1850	1600	1730	142328	ELN	Ormston
1850	1920	....	....	121185	KEN	ALL
1800	1899	ALL	ALL	146633	LND	ALL
1820	1992	1700	1992	162620	NBL	North Shields
1889	1889	1600	1889	147885	SCT	Glasgow
1664	1850	ALL	1664	102350	SCT	???
....	....	1700	1800	162620	SEL	Tushielaw
1800	1899	ALL	ALL	146633	SRY	ALL
COCKCROFT						
1809	1864	1750	1809	169056	YKS	Halifax
1840	1851	1700	1840	175900	YKS	Halifax
COCKE						
....	1900	1800	1900	117501	ESS	Steeple Bumpstead
1762	1851	1715	1800	170143	SRY	Chobham
1762	1851	1715	1800	170143	SRY	Pirbirhgt
COCKER						
1870	1920	ALL	ALL	129119	LAN	Bury
1906	....	1800	1906	103322	LAN	Heath Charnock
1800	1880	1880	1992	162256	LAN	Tockholes
COCKERAM						
1800	1900	1800	1900	161705	DBY	Derby
1665	1703	1640	1703	153273	LAN	Tatham
COCKERELL						
1880	1984	ALL	1880	172901	LND	ALL
COCKERILL						
1790	1830	1790	1830	141232	DUR	Sunderland
1700	1850	....	....	156922	NTH	Collingtree
1740	1850	....	....	156922	NTH	Gayton
1839	1856	1800	1839	104124	NTH	Hellidon
1800	1900	1700	1800	114383	NTH	Wolverhampton
1790	1992	1700	1992	114383	STS	Wolverhampton
1700	1750	1700	1800	114383	WAR	Napton
1820	1930	1750	1820	123102	WAR	Priors Marsden
COCKEROM						
1790	1851	1700	1790	111198	NYK	Lythe
COCKERTON						
1599	1860	1327	1599	162655	CAM	West
1760	1900	1700	1900	167088	LND	???
COCKFIELD						
....	....	1800	1900	129593	DUR	ALL

Known From	To	Researching From	To	Ref	Cty	Place
COCKFIELD contd.						
1893	....	1800	1900	129593	DUR	Hurworth
1800	1850	1800	1850	143553	WES	Milburn
COCKING						
1670	1980	ALL	1670	134783	CON	St Ives
1784	1834	1719	1784	154024	DBY	Staveley
1834	1976	....	....	154024	LAN	Manchester
1908	1992	1830	1908	113719	LIN	Lincoln
1750	1950	1750	1950	114529	YKS	Sheffield
COCKINGS						
....	....	ALL	ALL	114391	ALL	Name Study
1154	1992	ALL	ALL	114391	ALL	ALL
COCKINS						
1550	1800	1450	1550	174513	OXF	Upper Heyford
COCKRAM						
1728	1928	1680	1943	121568	DEV	North East
1742	1817	1700	1820	114405	DEV	Cheriton Fitzpaine
1813	1860	1700	1813	148814	DEV	Chulmleigh
1750	1870	1700	1900	114405	DEV	Stockleigh Pomeroy
1870	1902	1800	1870	174068	LND	Lambeth
1850	1920	1850	1920	114405	LND	Marylebone
1902	1913	1871	1992	121568	SOM	Brompton Regis
COCKRAN						
1806	1853	....	1806	161691	MDX	Shoreditch
COCKRILL						
1800	1830	1700	1800	167983	LAN	Rossendale
1803	1827	....	1803	177504	SFK	East Bergholt
1748	1823	1700	1730	158089	SFK	Hawstead
1748	1823	1700	1730	158089	SFK	Pakenham
COCKROFT						
1820	1822	1800	1890	136034	STS	???
1780	1860	1770	1860	153621	WYK	Queensbury
COCKS						
1860	1880	....	....	121185	KEN	South
1880	1968	1880	1970	117501	KEN	Woolwich
COCKSEDGE						
1780	....	1700	1800	149845	SFK	ALL
COCKSHAW						
1700	1790	1600	1700	132659	ERY	York
COCKSHOOT						
1793	1882	1793	1882	124613	LAN	Leigh
1882	1992	1793	1992	124613	LAN	Reddish
COCKSHOTT						
1830	1900	1830	1922	110183	YKS	Keighley
COCKSHUT						
1622	....	....	....	151351	YKS	Kildwick In Craven
CODD						
....	....	ALL	ALL	114421	ALL	Name Study
1687	....	....	....	114413	WLS	South
CODDELL						
1805	....	1805	....	145726	DOR	Weymouth
CODDINGTON						
1887	1920	ALL	ALL	117366	KEN	Greenwich
1734	1890	1734	1890	123404	LEI	Wymeswold
CODGBROOK						
....	....	ALL	ALL	100927	ALL	Name Study
1684	1992	1350	1992	100927	NTH	Rushden
CODLIN						
1852	1992	1790	1852	114448	MDX	Hackney
CODLING						
1859	1873	1859	1880	123404	LEI	Wymeswold
1788	1992	1700	1788	102342	LIN	Bottesford
1818	1880	1700	1818	102148	LIN	Leadham
1837	1900	1500	1837	141089	NFK	ALL
1795	1833	1700	1860	123404	NFK	Hempton
1830	1883	1820	1883	123404	NFK	Kings Lynn
1756	1817	1700	1800	129593	YKS	Staithes
CODNER						
1830	1830	1700	....	131253	DEV	Ipplepen
CODRINGTON						
1837	....	ALL	1837	169374	GLS	Iron Acton
1791	1803	1803	1837	169374	GLS	Westerleigh
CODY						
1899	1992	....	1899	139033	CAM	Cambridge
1899	1992	....	1899	139033	IRL	ALL
COE						
1500	1900	1830	1992	118907	CAM	Cambridge
1825	1992	1815	1830	114472	CHS	Bollington
1769	1992	1700	1777	114464	DEV	Plymouth
?	?	?	?	117528	ESS	Great Halstead
1804	1820	1750	1810	114472	LAN	Manchester
1894	....	1894	1992	101141	LND	North
1700	1860	1650	1900	110183	NFK	Field Dalling
1818	1850	ALL	1818	164623	NTT	Weston
COFELL						
....	....	ALL	ALL	114480	ENG	ALL
COFFEE						
1827	1845	1700	1827	117927	LND	Stepney
COFFEEY						
1700	....	....	1650	136557	COR	???
COFFEL						
....	....	1800	1850	129933	IRL	???
....	1840	ALL	ALL	129933	LKS	Glasgow
COFFEY						
1850	1992	1800	1850	114499	IRL	ALL
COFFIN						
1786	1850	ALL	ALL	158585	HAM	Bishops Waltham
1800	1900	1800	1900	178705	HAM	Bishops Waltham
1700	....	....	....	153397	HAM	Boldre
COGAN						
ALL	ALL	ALL	ALL	114502	GLA	Cardiff
....	....	1830	1850	121479	LAN	Liverpool
1811	1811	....	....	121355	LND	Shoreditch
COGDON						
1837	1881	1837	1881	175188	DUR	Sunderland
COGGAN						
1760	1992	1700	1760	102342	LIN	Isle Of Axholme
ALL	ALL	ALL	ALL	114502	SOM	ALL
COGGER						
....	....	1700	1930	165247	KEN	ALL
1661	1683	1500	1700	170178	KEN	Sandhurst
1727	1864	....	1727	177504	KEN	Shorn
....	....	1800	1930	165247	LND	Central
....	....	1800	1930	165247	LND	South
....	....	1800	1930	165247	SRY	ALL
COGGESHALL						
1681	1961	1600	1849	124435	SFK	Dallinghoo
COGGINS						
?	?	?	?	136395	GLS	Bristol
1793	1992	1700	1793	105902	NTH	Irthlingboro
1840	1970	ALL	ALL	164887	OXF	Weston On The Green
?	?	?	?	136395	SOM	Bristol
COGGRELLE						
1592	....	....	....	153397	HAM	Milford
COGHAN						
1860	1930	1800	1930	113743	NBL	Newcastle
COGHILL						
....	....	ALL	ALL	114510	ALL	Name Study
1850	1860	1700	1992	167592	DBY	Derby
1800	1870	1700	1992	167592	LAN	Liverpool
COGMAN						
....	....	1700	1950	140627	NFK	Norwich
COHEN						
1850	1992	1750	1992	114596	LAN	Manchester
1700	1980	1851	1881	114529	LND	???
COHN						
1850	1992	1700	1900	160725	ALL	ALL
COKE						
1650	1705	1600	1750	171549	DEV	Buckfastleigh
COKER						
....	....	ALL	ALL	105333	ALL	Name Study
1200	1992	ALL	ALL	105333	ALL	ALL
1850	1870	ALL	1850	168343	BKM	Pitstone
1672	1992	1672	1992	152994	DEV	Bigbury
1825	1906	1800	1900	102717	ESS	South
1850	1870	ALL	1850	168343	HRT	???
COKKES						
1100	1400	....	....	100420	WAR	Meriden
COLAM						
....	....	ALL	ALL	114537	ALL	Name Study
COLBAK						
1743	1743	ALL	1800	168696	OXF	Abingdon
COLBECK						
1763	1992	1680	1763	114545	LIN	Lincoln
COLBERT						
1823	....	1780	1825	148199	NYK	East Cottingwith
COLBOUNRE						
....	1850	1820	1870	118338	BRK	Twyford
....	....	1750	1840	118338	WAR	Leamington Spa
COLBOURN						
1820	1916	1800	1920	135925	BRK	Kintbury
1659	1940	....	....	128996	CAM	Thorney
COLBRAN						
1837	1960	1500	1700	107948	SXE	Hurstmonceux
1750	1837	1650	1750	107948	SXE	Ninfield
COLBRIDGE						
1804	1830	1650	1804	139769	LIN	Luddington
1825	1825	ALL	1830	113611	WYK	Thorne

Known From	To	Researching From	To	Ref	Cty	Place
COLBRIDGE contd.						
1802	....	....	....	161136	YKS	Thorne
COLBY						
1845	1850	1800	1845	175951	NTH	Northampton
1734	1830	....	....	127779	SFK	Henley
1800	1992	ALL	1800	114650	SFK	Lowestoft
COLCHIN						
1734	1788	1700	1850	145661	ENG	ALL
COLCLOUGH						
1848	1881	1500	1848	176974	STS	Longton
COLCOCK						
....	1831	1770	1900	128961	LND	Finsbury Park
COLDICOTT						
1812	1851	1750	1870	169323	GLS	Cow Honeybourne
1883	1934	1883	1934	169323	NTH	Wellingborough
1866	1881	1850	1890	169323	SRY	Newington
1880	1890	1800	1900	149993	WAR	Shustoke
COLDRAKE						
1861	....	1845	1880	171441	KEN	Dover
1847	....	1820	1860	171441	LND	Highgate
1841	....	1820	1860	171441	LND	St Pancras
1814	1858	....	....	171441	SFK	Lowestoft
1814	....	....	1840	171441	WIL	Westbury
COLDRON						
1820	1840	....	....	120782	LIN	Hykeham
1840	1992	....	....	120782	LIN	Lincoln
COLDWELL						
1790	1992	ALL	1850	114553	YKS	Holmfirth
1861	1911	1750	1920	119008	YKS	Kirkburton
1790	1992	ALL	1850	114553	YKS	Penistone
1700	1799	1700	1799	169781	YKS	Royston
1861	1911	1750	1920	119008	YKS	Upper Thong
COLE						
1815	1883	1883	1992	153168	BDF	Dunton
1774	1853	....	....	116602	BRK	Bradfield
1816	1861	1750	1900	114626	BRK	Brimpton Common
1909	....	ALL	1950	170674	CAM	Cambridge
1861	....	....	....	114626	CMA	Barrow In Furness
1066	1992	....	....	114944	CON	Polapit Tamar
1100	1992	1100	1992	114596	DEV	Ashreigney
1859	1900	1859	1890	164399	DEV	Bickington
1724	1992	....	....	165735	DEV	Bishops Nympton
1688	1992	1500	1688	114588	DEV	Dawlish
1066	1992	....	....	114944	DEV	Hillsleigh
1800	1874	1700	1992	117609	DEV	Kingskerswell
1687	1900	1687	1900	163406	DEV	South Molton
1802	1910	1700	1802	147389	DEV	Tavistock
1850	1850	1800	1992	133450	DEV	???
1771	1850	ALL	1900	111600	DOR	Piddlehinton
1720	1860	1800	1860	177032	DOR	Stourpaine
....	....	1600	1800	108677	DOR	Wimborne
1677	1677	ALL	1677	154563	DUR	Auckland St Helen
1851	....	ALL	ALL	155608	DUR	Hewarth
1789	1992	ALL	1789	106909	ESS	Colchester
1750	1850	1500	1750	109959	ESS	Dovercourt
1800	1992	1750	1800	165336	ESS	Little Clacton
1825	1835	1800	1850	105120	ESS	Thorrington
1840	1880	1800	1900	152528	ESS	Waltham Abbey
1848	1880	1830	1891	113719	GLS	Bristol
1853	1888	1750	1880	163740	GLS	Bristol
1815	1900	1800	1900	169250	GLS	Painswick
1620	....	1620	1700	142158	GLS	Stone
....	....	1600	1860	158968	GLS	Tuffley
1740	1800	1700	1750	138150	GLS	Westerleigh
1734	1800	1700	1800	121010	HAM	Chilbolton
1733	1759	1700	1733	127116	HAM	Fawley
1771	....	1750	1800	114642	HAM	Isle Of Wight
1735	1801	1735	1801	106747	HAM	Longstock
1780	1900	1750	1900	124605	HEF	Hereford
1709	1715	....	....	101028	HRT	Thundridge
1796	1992	....	....	139165	KEN	Canterbury
1871	1954	1790	1960	124001	KEN	Chatham
1854	1865	....	....	114626	LAN	Coniston
1850	1854	....	....	114626	LAN	Croston
1792	1848	1550	1791	102830	LIN	Digby
1934	....	1800	1970	170674	LND	Islington
1880	1900	1850	1900	155691	LND	Lambeth
1870	1992	1600	1870	100730	LND	London
1900	1950	1800	1900	118214	LND	Paddington
1806	1992	....	....	172529	LND	???
1880	1900	1860	1890	114642	MDX	Bow
1889	....	ALL	1889	167711	MDX	Chiswick
1780	1861	1780	1992	156698	MDX	Holloway
1850	....	....	....	103624	NBL	Tynemouth
COLE contd.						
1781	1992	1816	1992	145238	NFK	North
1728	1794	1728	1794	142980	NTH	Long Buckby
1896	1896	....	....	108901	NTT	Ordsall
1728	1750	1700	1750	147311	NYK	Hinderwell
1700	1800	1600	1700	174513	OXF	Adderbury
....	....	1840	1890	142751	PEM	Pembroke
1865	1886	1770	1870	142751	PEM	Presceli
1800	1850	1700	1900	100129	RUT	Luffenham
1820	....	1800	1900	114626	RUT	Oakham
1800	1880	ALL	ALL	132276	SFK	Capel
1600	1800	ALL	ALL	132276	SFK	Chattisham
1870	1950	1880	1950	132276	SFK	East Bergholt
1772	1881	ALL	ALL	140155	SOM	Backwell
1788	?	ALL	ALL	153516	SOM	Bridgwater
1814	1992	1600	1814	114634	SOM	Bristol
1800	1940	1650	1800	175811	SOM	Wellow
1881	1914	ALL	ALL	140155	SOM	Weston Super Mare
1814	1870	1780	1870	114642	SRY	Alfold
1789	1810	1600	1830	116580	SRY	Richmond
....	....	ALL	1940	152544	SRY	Tatsfield
1860	1880	1880	1910	140880	SSX	East
1696	1809	....	....	165999	SSX	West
....	....	1500	1825	103624	SSX	Brighton
1900	1940	ALL	ALL	170801	SSX	Brighton
1844	1900	ALL	ALL	170801	SSX	Lewes
1700	1850	1841	1900	165263	SSX	Rotherfield
1700	1850	1841	1900	165263	SSX	Withyham
1800	1930	1700	1930	107611	WAR	Aston
1795	1847	1795	1847	142980	WAR	Birmingham
1800	1900	1700	1850	132950	WIL	Calne
1670	1784	1600	1670	165530	WIL	Chippenham
1790	1820	1790	1820	154210	WIL	Winterbourne Monkton
1704	1820	1670	1720	170348	WIL	Wroughton
1803	1940	1803	1940	142980	WYK	Bradford
1872	1981	1700	1872	174939	YKS	Driffield
COLEBROOK						
1850	1900	....	....	104272	KEN	East Farleigh
1850	1900	....	....	104272	KEN	Loose
COLEBROOKE						
1660	1750	1600	1800	149993	HAM	Twyford
COLEBY						
1869	1992	....	....	114669	SFK	Lakenheath
1800	1992	ALL	1800	114650	SFK	Lowestoft
COLEGATE						
....	....	ALL	ALL	128767	ALL	Name Study
COLEMAN						
....	....	ALL	ALL	134961	ALL	Name Study
1700	1800	ALL	1900	113492	BDF	North
1811	1875	1800	1890	127353	BKM	Great Brickhill
1650	1750	1600	1800	177180	BKM	Soulbury
1845	1940	1845	1992	165395	BRK	Reading
1900	1992	1900	1992	164704	BRK	Thatcham
1300	1992	1700	1992	130478	CON	Bodmin
1850	1992	ALL	1850	156078	CON	???
1740	1900	1740	1900	164704	DEV	Ugborough
1841	1888	1750	1841	107662	DOR	Ilsington
1750	1900	1750	1850	111007	ESS	Barking
1750	1900	1750	1850	111007	ESS	Loughton
1780	1860	1770	1800	158380	ESS	Mashbury
1760	1765	ALL	ALL	141623	ESS	Waltham Abbey
1850	1992	1800	1992	129240	GLS	Bristol
1845	1940	1845	1992	165395	GLS	Bristol
1850	1960	1700	1850	114685	GLS	Newland
....	....	1800	....	145998	IOW	???
....	1840	....	....	126276	IRL	???
1692	1992	1692	1992	133450	KEN	Ash
1830	1992	....	....	159883	KEN	Ash
1720	1830	....	....	159883	KEN	Godmersham
1741	1870	1650	1741	145823	KEN	Romney Marsh
1700	1850	....	....	114723	KEN	Whitstable
....	....	ALL	1800	162833	LEI	Glooston
1785	1823	1785	1840	114715	LEI	Kimcote-Walton
1720	1840	1720	1840	114715	LEI	Lutterworth
1860	1880	1800	1900	112704	LND	Hammersmith
1730	1800	1700	1730	172898	LND	Whitechapel
....	....	ALL	1900	178403	LND	???
1857	....	1700	....	123552	MDX	London
1850	1960	1700	1850	114685	MON	Trelleck
1813	1900	1700	1900	114480	NFK	Blofield
1778	1841	1700	1900	114480	NFK	Hardley
1813	1992	1700	1900	114480	NFK	???
1708	1717	1650	1717	150150	NTH	Great Easton

Known From	To	Researching From	To	Ref	Cty	Place
COLEMAN contd.						
1800	1870	1600	1800	101389	NTH	Rothwell
1860	1890	1860	1890	114715	NTT	Central
1845	1850	1845	1850	114715	NTT	Carlton
1890	1940	1820	1940	114715	NTT	Sneinton
1695	1882	1650	1700	172871	SFK	Cockfield
1695	1882	1650	1700	172871	SFK	Rougham
1695	1882	1650	1700	172871	SFK	Rushbrooke
1824	1900	ALL	1824	157899	SOM	Bath
ALL	1930	ALL	ALL	161292	SOM	Bedminster
1845	1940	1845	1992	165395	SOM	Bristol
1824	1900	ALL	1824	157899	SOM	Walcot
1868	1890	1820	1868	140880	SSX	East
1780	1811	1700	1850	145556	SSX	Eastbourne
1744	....	1650	1744	166723	SSX	Hailsham
1812	1842	1700	1812	166723	SSX	Wartling
1759	1841	1700	1800	176621	SSX	Westfield
1840	1850	1840	1850	126276	STS	Rugeley
1766	1850	1650	1850	174300	WIL	Berwick Bassett
1829	1873	1800	1855	142360	WIL	Braod Blunsdon
1750	1840	1650	1750	168076	WIL	Edington
1851	1992	1750	1850	114693	YKS	Forcett
COLENSO						
1800	1850	1600	1992	176494	CON	ALL
1850	1992	1650	1992	104671	CON	Penzance
1850	1860	1850	1900	136867	CON	Penzance
COLES						
?	?	1700	1850	123668	BDF	Luton
1719	....	1650	1720	124796	BKM	Steeple Claydon
1805	1829	....	....	115290	BKM	Wendover
1736	1940	....	....	128996	CAM	Thorney
1888	1992	1500	1888	141089	CHI	Guernsey
1888	1992	1500	1888	141089	CHI	Jersey
....	....	1700	1850	175242	DEV	Gittisham
....	....	1700	1850	175242	DEV	Honiton
ALL	ALL	ALL	ALL	150169	HAM	Empshott
1783	1992	1700	1783	114731	HAM	Milford
....	1850	ALL	1850	152889	HUN	Gt Catworth
1840	....	....	1840	164011	KEN	Dover
1810	1837	1700	1810	130257	LEI	Leicester
1797	1832	1797	1832	151211	LIN	Little Oakley
1750	1900	1740	1900	130494	MDX	ALL
1823	1850	1800	1823	107093	MDX	Knightsbridge
1797	1832	1797	1832	151211	NTH	Barnwel
1800	1900	....	1800	177695	NTH	Northampton
....	1800	....	1800	177695	NTH	Wilby
1773	....	1700	1800	124796	OXF	Chalgrove
1778	1806	1750	1825	124796	OXF	Lewknor
1773	1852	1600	1773	149888	OXF	Milton
1900	1940	1800	1945	115746	SOM	Central
1800	1850	1700	1800	149306	SOM	Central
1829	....	1800	....	152722	SOM	Butleigh
1555	1937	1538	1600	150940	SOM	Evercreech
1850	1850	1800	1900	121568	SOM	Kilmersdon
1822	1850	1800	1822	101524	SOM	North Petherton
1855	1910	ALL	ALL	164887	SOM	Shepton Mallet
1820	1860	1770	1900	130494	WAR	Birmingham
COLESBY						
1800	1900	1700	1800	154458	WAR	Birmingham
COLESELL						
1743	1860	1720	1861	153508	BKM	Langley Marish
COLESHILL						
....	....	ALL	1890	178403	BKM	???
COLEY						
1267	1920	1066	1920	114758	ALL	ALL
1740	1881	1740	1951	173851	BKM	Great Bradwell
1850	1941	1850	1941	132675	LIN	Crowland
....	....	1850	1859	173274	MDX	London
....	....	ALL	1870	125393	STS	Birmingham
....	....	ALL	1870	125393	WAR	Birmingham
COLFER						
....	....	ALL	ALL	114766	ALL	Name Study
1878	1992	ALL	ALL	114766	AVN	Central
1880	1960	ALL	ALL	114766	WAT	East
1850	1960	ALL	ALL	114766	WEX	South
COLFOX						
1751	1810	1200	1850	135763	SAL	Preston Gubbalds
COLGAN						
1892	....	....	....	145742	IRL	Dublin
COLGRAVE						
ALL	....	....	....	123641	NTT	Worksop
COLIN						
1850	1992	1700	1850	146110	WAR	ALL

Known From	To	Researching From	To	Ref	Cty	Place
COLINSON						
1720	1770	....	....	103721	LIN	Althorpe
COLK						
1725	1850	1700	1992	114774	NFK	Bacton
1850	1992	1850	1992	114774	YKS	Sheffield
COLLAR						
1814	1928	ALL	ALL	175862	WIL	ALL
COLLARD						
1806	1860	1750	1840	160350	DEV	Bampton
1810	1888	1780	1810	147745	KEN	Stodmarsh
1870	1950	1850	1950	106429	LND	???
1734	1963	1500	1754	115134	SOM	Taunton
1784	1870	1600	1788	114634	SOM	Wickwar
1770	1910	1740	1910	106801	SOM	Wiveliscombe
1783	....	....	....	170623	SOM	Wiveliscombe
1500	1916	1500	1992	178020	SOM	Wiveliscombe
1775	1842	1600	1775	147729	WIL	Trowbridge
COLLEDGE						
1780	1840	1269	1780	115576	DBY	Wirksworth
1810	1864	1750	1900	148725	HRT	Bayford
....	....	1850	1880	114782	SSX	???
COLLEIS						
1781	....	....	....	147486	WIL	Bromham
COLLEN						
1888	1992	ALL	ALL	115762	LND	Lambeth
1888	1992	ALL	ALL	115762	SRY	Lambeth
COLLER						
1848	1848	1800	1850	136042	LND	East
COLLET						
1790	....	1750	1790	120030	CON	???
COLLETT						
1883	1945	1700	1880	170615	CON	Mid
1800	1850	....	....	153745	CON	Philleigh
1700	1900	1700	1900	128708	CON	Roseland
1780	1992	1700	1850	106186	CON	St Austell
....	....	1700	1899	174963	GLS	Leonard Stanley
1729	1795	1600	1729	118877	GLS	Lower Slaughter
....	....	1700	1899	174963	GLS	Woodchester
....	....	1700	1899	115975	LND	London
1840	....	1800	1900	139114	LND	???
1857	1931	ALL	ALL	155454	MDX	Chelsea
1857	1931	ALL	ALL	155454	MDX	Fulham
....	....	1860	....	174963	MON	Newport
1860	1881	1860	1910	123862	NTT	Eastwood
1839	1900	ALL	ALL	124176	OXF	Combe
1800	1860	1750	1880	123862	SFK	Yoxwood
....	....	1870	ALL	174963	SOM	Bath
1760	1870	1760	1870	114790	WAR	Stretton In Dunsmore
1666	1673	....	....	151351	YKS	Barwick In Elmet
1689	1800	....	....	151351	YKS	Harewood
COLLEY						
1750	1992	1750	1992	133450	DEV	Plymouth
1900	1931	1800	1931	138045	HEF	Webley
....	1757	1600	1750	153591	KEN	High Halstow
1767	1810	1810	ALL	146226	LAN	Prestolee
1761	1788	ALL	1761	154563	LIN	Knaith
1674	1818	ALL	1674	146226	NTT	Harworth
1831	1835	ALL	1835	165735	SOM	Bath
1829	1831	ALL	1829	165735	SOM	Castle Cary
1800	1992	....	....	115258	WIL	Wootton Rivers
1882	1920	ALL	ALL	169315	YKS	North
....	....	1700	1900	169315	YKS	Hemsley
1835	1992	....	....	165735	???	Bristol
1790	1992	ALL	1790	114804	???	Wolverhampton
COLLIAR						
1682	1682	1682	1682	107573	WAR	Nether Whitacre
COLLICK						
1800	1900	1700	1800	107530	CON	Breage
1860	1940	1860	1940	104027	LND	Tottenham
COLLICOTT						
1800	1980	1700	1800	114820	CON	Mabe
1800	1980	1700	1800	114820	CON	Roche
1800	1980	1700	1800	114820	CON	St Wenn
COLLIE						
1790	1890	1500	1750	106267	KCD	East
COLLIER						
....	....	ALL	ALL	114839	ALL	Name Study
1803	1803	1700	1803	112216	DOR	Puddletown
1835	1845	1700	1870	112216	DOR	Swanage
1851	1992	1800	1872	123080	GLS	Bristol
....	1850	1750	1850	146927	KEN	London
1844	1844	1844	1891	159492	LAN	Oldham
1890	1920	1800	1900	173029	LEI	Leicester

Known From	To	Researching From	To	Ref	Cty	Place
COLLIER contd.						
1802	1894	....	1802	142166	LND	Bethnal Green
1850	1900	1700	1850	102903	LND	Bloomsbury
1850	1900	1700	1850	102903	LND	Islington
1700	1750	1650	1750	151742	NRY	North York Moors
1700	1900	....	....	108677	OXF	Witney
1851	1992	1800	1872	123080	SOM	Bristol
1780	....	1780	1930	119458	SRY	Southwark
1800	1992	1700	1992	165344	WAR	Dunchurch
1803	....	1600	1803	164879	WIL	ALL
1740	1860	1700	1750	170348	WIL	Lydiard Millicent
1620	1760	1550	1800	174599	WIL	Sutton Veny
1800	1900	1800	1900	142549	WIL	Warminster
1793	....	1770	1790	145297	WIL	Westbury
1630	1730	1630	1730	164941	WRY	Leeds
COLLIN						
1880	1992	1800	1880	109193	BEW	Eyemouth
1803	1855	ALL	ALL	151815	CAM	Arrington
1731	1752	1600	1775	110787	RUT	Langham
1731	1752	1600	1775	110787	RUT	Uppingham
COLLINE						
1900	1992	1600	1900	114944	ESS	Billericay
COLLING						
1680	1700	ALL	1700	168718	CON	South East
1891	1891	1800	1891	121568	SOM	Stocklinch Ottersay
COLLINGE						
1840	1850	1700	1840	170178	LAN	Ardwick
1751	1796	1600	1751	119822	LAN	Bolton
1751	1796	1600	1751	119822	LAN	Oldham
COLLINGRIDGE						
1765	1850	....	1765	136212	OXF	Somerton
COLLINGS						
1800	1992	ALL	1800	147389	CON	Calstock
?	?	1700	1960	123668	DEV	Plymouth
1860	1960	1700	1860	157996	GLA	Cardiff
1860	1960	1700	1860	157996	GLA	Cowbridge
....	....	1700	1860	157996	GLS	Thornbury
....	....	1750	1850	118834	KEN	Canterbury
....	....	1750	1850	118834	KEN	Dover
1500	1795	1795	1820	114855	SFK	Debenham
1875	1960	1875	1960	114855	SFK	Frostenden
1820	1875	1820	1875	114855	SFK	Kelsale
1830	1840	ALL	1850	107026	SOM	Freshford
1800	....	....	....	167037	SSX	Hastings
COLLINGTON						
1809	1840	ALL	1809	122823	SRY	Croyden
COLLINGWOOD						
1787	1982	1700	1950	177091	DOR	Poole
1840	1882	....	....	102741	DUR	Stanhope
1840	1882	....	....	102741	DUR	Tow Law
1688	1737	1660	1740	161624	ESS	Lambourne
1713	1716	1713	1716	161624	ESS	Romford
1718	1730	1718	1730	161624	KEN	Brentwood
1738	1791	1700	1738	137383	KEN	East Greenwich
1786	1831	1786	1860	161624	KEN	Greenwich
1760	....	1760	1790	161624	KEN	Rochester
1850	1930	1850	1930	161624	LAN	Liverpool
1792	1881	1700	1792	176885	LIN	Grantham
1897	1983	....	....	176885	LND	Kensington
1600	1650	1500	1900	166804	OXF	ALL
1792	1940	1792	1940	161624	OXF	Oxford
COLLINRIDGE						
1780	1985	....	....	140791	BKM	Haddenham
COLLINS						
1830	1890	1870	1950	114871	AVN	Bristol
....	....	1700	1899	174963	BDF	Battlesden
1860	1900	1800	1900	130427	BDF	Cardington
1833	1845	1750	1992	114901	BKM	Flackwell Heath
1778	1801	1600	1778	167541	BKM	Great Marlow
1800	1980	1700	1900	143693	BKM	High Wycombe
1798	1845	1750	1992	114901	BKM	Little Harlow
1816	1930	1700	1900	143693	BKM	West Wycombe
....	....	ALL	1820	167029	BRK	Speen
1750	1750	1700	1750	124974	BRK	Wokingham
1870	1992	1867	1992	123099	CON	Camborne
1894	1906	1800	1992	117609	CON	Constantine
....	....	1838	1867	123099	CON	Gwennap
1820	1840	1700	1950	114898	COR	ALL
1650	1725	1600	1750	171549	DEV	Buckfastleigh
1800	1900	1825	1900	172642	DEV	Witheridge
1774	1781	1500	1800	174270	DOR	West Parley
1863	....	1800	1900	139114	DOW	Drummiller
1800	1880	1750	1900	119865	ESS	???
1855	1891	1840	1900	114898	GLA	ALL
COLLINS contd.						
1850	1860	1850	1900	114898	GLA	Cardiff
1900	1920	1800	1900	179027	GLA	Penarth
1850	1860	1850	1900	114898	GLA	Swansea
1816	....	....	....	124982	GLS	Berkeley
1815	1830	ALL	ALL	113662	GLS	Hasfield
1750	1850	1650	1750	174513	GLS	Leigh
....	....	1600	1700	148792	HAM	North West
1773	1873	1714	1881	153508	HAM	Alton
1576	1812	1500	1842	174270	HAM	Christchurch
1822	1858	1858	1900	124559	HAM	Crondall
1870	1992	1750	1870	118516	HAM	Hampshire
1812	1812	1750	1812	174289	HAM	Holdenhurst
1812	1842	1500	1842	174270	HAM	Holdenhurst
1851	1926	1851	1926	151408	HAM	Portsmouth
1790	1851	....	....	104477	HAM	Titchfield
1800	1917	1700	1800	103896	HAM	Titchfield
....	....	1600	1900	131962	HAM	Winchester
1838	1838	1838	1838	136808	HRT	Barkway
1859	1861	1859	1992	114901	HRT	Watford
1760	1830	1700	1820	114871	IRL	Cork
1820	1850	1820	1992	133450	IRL	Cork
1673	1845	1500	1673	139084	KEN	Shipbourne
1860	1992	1860	1992	114936	LAN	Blackburn
1840	1992	1600	1840	148954	LND	East
1863	1863	1840	1863	114448	LND	Battersea
1872	1992	ALL	1992	150630	LND	Camberwell
1827	1914	....	....	171557	LND	Highgate
1900	1992	....	1900	159514	LND	Hoxton
1860	....	....	....	170623	LND	Marylebone
1820	1830	1820	1830	114871	LND	Moorfields
1801	....	....	1810	171441	LND	Saffron Hill
1835	1841	1835	1992	106666	LND	Shoreditch
1867	1870	....	....	121460	LND	St Pancras
....	....	1700	1992	122742	LND	???
1730	1800	1730	1800	167924	MDX	Ealing
1767	ALL	ALL	1770	116734	MDX	London
1839	....	1700	....	123552	MDX	London
1794	1842	1650	1794	139769	MDX	London
....	....	1800	1868	130184	MDX	Marylebone
1767	ALL	ALL	1770	116734	MDX	Shorditch
1767	ALL	ALL	1770	116734	MDX	St Leonards
....	....	1800	....	137456	NTH	Cottesbrooke
....	....	ALL	ALL	114308	NTH	Kislingbury
1780	1831	1750	1905	148288	NTT	Costock Bunny
1762	....	ALL	ALL	105481	NTT	Hucknall
1795	....	1700	1850	143693	OXF	Chalgrove
1795	....	1700	1850	143693	OXF	Chargrove
1635	1720	....	....	142522	OXF	???
1731	1752	1600	1775	110787	RUT	Langham
1731	1752	1600	1775	110787	RUT	Uppingham
1720	1980	1700	1900	123145	SAL	Bishops Gate
1910	1992	1989	1992	114979	SAL	Shrewsbury
....	1700	....	1700	177695	SAL	???
1300	1910	1300	1910	111422	SFK	ALL
1728	1750	1680	1728	155276	SFK	Bucklesham
1600	1750	1600	1750	142018	SOM	Chard
1670	1730	1660	1740	142018	SOM	Taunton
1750	1825	1700	1830	147575	SOM	Yeovil
1925	1992	1700	1930	158836	SRY	ALL
1832	1845	1800	1832	138347	SRY	Beddington
1826	1837	....	....	117560	SRY	Bermondsey
1790	1820	1750	1800	143502	SRY	Farnham
1727	1992	1650	1727	114928	SRY	Richmond
1865	1920	1750	1865	166634	SRY	Southwark
1840	1945	1800	1950	144908	SSX	Brighton
1690	1960	1200	1690	162671	SSX	Burwash
1695	1773	....	....	139971	SSX	Eastbourne
1695	1773	....	....	139971	SSX	Friston
....	....	ALL	1850	165263	SSX	Heathfield
....	....	ALL	1870	165263	SSX	Mayfield
....	....	1876	ALL	165263	SSX	Rotherfield
1881	1890	ALL	1881	165263	SSX	Wadhurst
1780	1831	1600	1810	145432	STS	Enville St Mary
1689	....	....	1690	160873	STS	Sedgley
1790	1869	....	....	155055	STS	Wolverhampton
1827	1992	1800	1827	147850	SXE	Bexhill
1827	1992	1800	1827	147850	SXE	Hastings
1700	1861	1700	1851	151513	WAR	Baddesley Ensor
1770	1820	1700	1841	151513	WAR	Kingsbury
1773	1793	1750	1775	137057	WIL	Alfriston
....	1840	ALL	1840	167878	WIL	Preshute
1890	1900	1800	1890	131350	WLS	Swansea
1742	1796	1710	1800	123404	WOR	Inkberrow

Known From	To	Researching From	To	Ref	Cty	Place
COLLINS contd.						
....	....	1800	1880	129232	WOR	Kidderminster
1820	1890	1800	1900	143502	WOR	Powick
1850	1880	1800	?	143502	WOR	Worcester
....	....	1700	1740	177393	YKS	Birkin
1761	....	1730	1815	167932	YKS	Cayton
1827	1914	....	....	171557	YKS	???
COLLINSON						
1903	1992	1877	1903	114995	KEN	Chatham
1881	....	....	....	129216	NTT	Mansfield
1850	1870	1700	1992	167592	STS	Burslem
1830	1992	....	....	117161	YKS	Fylingdales
....	....	1789	1830	117161	YKS	Goathland
1790	1876	1750	1790	128368	YKS	Leeds
1790	1876	1750	1790	128368	YKS	Sheffield
1790	1876	1750	1790	128368	YKS	Thornhill
COLLIS ELLIOT						
....	....	ALL	ALL	161470	LIN	Stamford
....	....	ALL	ALL	161470	NTH	Daventry
COLLIS						
1783	1809	1700	1900	122394	CAM	Fordham
1700	1992	ALL	ALL	115002	HAM	Winchester
....	....	1780	1820	168777	HAM	???
1820	1869	1815	1869	167002	LIN	Boston
1809	1816	1700	1900	122394	LIN	Grimsby
1810	1817	1800	1850	167002	LIN	Spilsby
1844	1864	1800	1891	118192	MDX	Shoreditch
....	....	ALL	ALL	161470	NTH	Daventry
1697	1817	1550	1850	167002	NTH	West Haddon
1808	....	ALL	1992	159174	SSX	Arundel
1799	....	ALL	1992	159174	SSX	Lyminster
COLLS						
....	....	ALL	ALL	166812	NFK	Horstead
....	....	ALL	ALL	166812	NFK	Norwich
COLLY						
1804	1804	1600	1800	172332	LIN	Epworth
COLLYER						
1858	1992	ALL	1858	115010	ENG	South
1850	1920	?	?	143464	MDX	Islington
1801	1879	1800	1881	170143	SRY	Kingfield
1801	1879	1800	1881	170143	SRY	Woking
COLMAN						
1785	1830	1760	1860	105333	DOR	Corfe Mullen
....	1856	1700	1856	154164	NFK	North West
1795	1881	....	1800	125202	NFK	West Newton
1780	1860	1700	1860	158054	NFK	???
COLOGNE						
1900	1912	1915	1960	112569	KEN	Mersham
COLQUHOUN						
1873	1900	....	....	127140	RFW	Greenock
COLSTON						
1789	1819	1760	1819	119059	BKM	Brill
1850	1893	1850	1878	131938	GLA	Aberdare
1850	1893	1850	1878	131938	GLA	Mountain Ash
1800	1850	1700	1800	133493	SOM	Shepton Mallet
COLTART						
1800	1880	1800	?	136522	DFS	Annan
COLTHUP						
1760	1992	1500	1760	115037	KEN	East
COLTMAN						
1860	....	1700	....	130435	LEI	Wogston
1770	1900	1650	1770	141372	LND	Greenwich
COLTON						
....	1800	....	....	174564	LEI	Egmanton
1788	1833	1735	1847	156817	LEI	Loughborough
1801	1864	ALL	1801	168742	NTT	Egmanton
COLUMBELL						
1572	1588	1500	1571	102830	DBY	Darley
COLUMBINE						
1791	1899	ALL	1899	104299	YKS	Barnsley
COLVARD						
1826	....	1750	1992	174408	ESS	???
1780	....	....	....	163910	YKS	Darton
COLVER						
1770	1850	1500	1970	115045	LEI	Earl Shilton
1900	1960	1900	1965	115045	NTT	Nottingham
1700	1980	ALL	1700	115045	YKS	Sheffield
COLVERD						
1826	....	1750	1992	174408	ESS	???
1829	1937	ALL	ALL	165972	MDX	East
COLVERSON						
1818	1992	1750	1992	115797	HAM	East Meon
COLVIN						
1850	1950	....	....	140864	ABD	Fraserburgh
COLVIN contd.						
1850	1950	....	....	140864	ABD	Peterhead
1720	1950	1600	1720	128376	DUR	Wolsingham
1780	1820	1800	1850	140864	KCD	Stonehaven
?	?	....	....	114642	KEN	Maidstone
1792	1820	1750	1850	114642	KEN	Tenterden
1875	1882	....	1875	129771	SSX	Chiddingly
COLWELL						
....	....	ALL	ALL	115053	ALL	Name Study
....	....	1100	1992	115053	ALL	ALL
1764	1944	1700	1992	115053	BKM	ALL
....	....	1500	1992	115053	CON	ALL
....	....	1500	1992	115053	DEV	ALL
1300	1509	1300	1992	115053	ESS	ALL
1606	1992	1450	1992	115053	GLS	ALL
1789	....	1769	1789	173851	GLS	Longney
1739	1992	1500	1992	115053	HAM	ALL
....	....	1600	1992	115053	HEF	Aston
....	....	1600	1992	115053	HEF	Ingham
....	....	1478	1600	115053	KEN	Faversham
1801	1823	1750	1801	155845	SRY	Walworth
1756	1992	1500	1992	115053	SSX	ALL
1778	1850	1500	1800	170178	SXE	East Dean
COLWILL						
1790	1850	1790	1850	118540	CON	Kilkham
1790	1850	1790	1850	118540	DEV	Bradworthy
COLYER						
1694	1857	1694	1857	103977	BRK	Reading
1822	1992	1765	1882	126926	MDX	Stepney
....	....	1795	1855	126926	MDX	Whitechapel
1630	1730	1630	1730	164941	WRY	Leeds
COMAN						
....	?	?	?	127442	DBY	???
....	?	?	?	127442	NTT	???
COMBELLACK						
1750	1900	1700	1850	119865	CON	Sevorgan
1750	1900	1700	1850	119865	CON	Tregunstis
1750	1900	1700	1850	119865	CON	Wendron
COMBEN						
1700	1890	1700	1890	164674	DOR	Portland
COMBER						
1820	1960	ALL	ALL	158593	KEN	ALL
1861	1904	1800	1861	174807	SSX	Brighton
1612	1780	1600	1780	147885	SSX	Lindfield
1813	1813	1813	1813	136808	SXE	Withyam
COMBES						
....	....	1800	1890	126136	SSX	Bosham
COMBRIDGE						
1500	1650	1450	1650	154881	KEN	Penshurst
COMBS						
1796	1871	1700	1881	124788	LAN	Oldham
ALL	ALL	ALL	ALL	161551	MDX	London
1751	1893	1500	1914	174009	SSX	East
COMER						
1725	1970	....	....	144088	CHS	Basford
1795	1847	1750	1850	105732	CHS	Wrenbury
1769	1821	ALL	1769	175080	DEV	Topsham
1800	1948	1800	1948	138045	MON	Ebbw Vale
1753	1992	1600	1753	115096	NFK	Cawston
1798	1821	1700	1850	121568	SOM	West
1800	1890	1800	1900	138045	???	Nantglow
COMERFORD						
1891	1894	1890	1950	132454	DUR	Chester Le Street
1866	1878	1700	1866	132454	KIK	???
COMERY						
1744	1890	1700	1744	178543	NTT	Bulwell
COMFORT						
1820	1840	1800	1850	176494	LND	ALL
COMLEY						
1815	1881	1851	1881	151335	HEF	Kings Caple
1866	1948	ALL	ALL	152919	OXF	Clanfield
COMMOFORD						
1869	1992	ALL	1869	136875	YKS	Bradford
COMMONS						
1750	1780	1750	1780	142018	GLS	Bristol
1730	1750	1720	1800	142018	SOM	Bridgwater
....	1728	1700	1750	142018	SOM	Donyatt
COMPER						
1798	1992	ALL	1800	115118	SSX	Northchapel
COMPLIN						
1850	1870	1700	1850	111732	HAM	Yately
COMPTON						
1771	....	ALL	1771	123013	GLS	???
1791	1850	1700	1791	121010	HAM	Amport

Known From	To	Researching From	To	Ref	Cty	Place
COMPTON contd.						
1725	1992	1600	1750	173878	HAM	Amport
....	....	....	1883	158763	HEF	Orcop
1730	?	1650	1992	167592	LAN	Charnock
1730	?	1650	1992	167592	LAN	Chorley
1824	1860	1820	1870	112925	NTH	Deasnhanger
1724	1724	....	....	135437	SSX	Chichester
1743	1766	....	....	135437	SSX	Sidlesham
1500	1900	1500	1900	170216	WIL	ALL
....	....	....	....	100013	???	???
COMYNS						
....	....	1808	1818	130656	ANT	Belfast
CON						
1777	1777	1550	1800	147265	ABD	???
1777	1777	1550	1800	147265	BAN	???
CONCHA						
1903	1971	1900	1992	131423	MLN	Edinburgh
CONCHAR						
1818	1840	1700	1992	131423	DFS	Kirkmahoe
1772	1800	1700	1992	131423	KCD	Crossmichael
CONCHIE						
1828	1842	1700	1992	131423	DFS	Dunscore
1855	1900	1700	1992	131423	DFS	Kirkmahoe
1820	1866	ALL	....	149004	NIR	???
CONDLIFFE						
....	....	ALL	ALL	137669	ALL	Name Study
CONDON						
1877	1896	1500	1877	110310	LAN	Liverpool
1820	1840	1700	1820	172022	LEI	Sileby
CONDUCT						
1775	1992	ALL	1775	115126	HAM	Bishops Waltham
1776	1843	1700	1900	162280	HAM	Bishops Waltham
CONDUIT						
1859	1900	1800	1992	176869	HAM	Winchester
CONEY						
1700	ALL	1807	1881	107379	BKM	Stoke Poges
1700	ALL	1807	1881	107379	HRT	ALL
1800	1992	1400	1790	115134	LIN	ALL
1760	....	1750	1775	124796	OXF	Oxford
1737	1786	1700	1800	124796	OXF	Tackley
....	....	1840	ALL	118060	WIL	Salisbury
CONEYBEARE						
1810	1830	....	....	118729	DEV	Devonport
....	....	1850	1992	178799	DEV	Holbeton
1763	1992	1600	1763	150487	DEV	Morchard Bishop
CONGDON						
1745	1800	1700	1850	171549	CON	Duloe
CONGRAVE						
1703	1900	ALL	1750	169730	CAM	Elm
1553	....	1589	1992	115142	WAR	Polesworth
CONGREVE						
....	....	ALL	ALL	132330	ALL	Name Study
ALL	ALL	ALL	ALL	132330	ALL	ALL
1703	1940	....	....	128996	CAM	Thorney
1777	1790	1760	1777	132330	DBY	Wirksworth
1833	1836	ALL	1833	169730	HUN	Woodstone
1794	1816	1794	1816	132330	KEN	Chatham
1794	?	1782	1794	132330	LND	Central
1761	1992	ALL	1761	132330	YKS	Sheffield
CONGRIEVE						
1703	1853	ALL	1703	169730	CAM	Thorney-Wisbech
CONIBEAR						
1806	1856	1500	1806	153095	DEV	North
CONISTON						
1700	1870	1870	1992	168726	YKS	East
CONLAN						
?	....	?	?	116610	LND	Bethnal Green
?	....	?	?	116610	LND	Whitechaple
CONLEY						
1854	1856	1854	1856	168289	FIF	Dunfermline
1851	1915	1800	1870	179299	LND	St Georges In The East
1867	....	1850	1890	163775	MDX	Stepney
CONN						
1777	1777	1550	1800	147265	ABD	???
1777	1777	1550	1800	147265	BAN	???
CONNATTY						
1850	1860	....	....	156043	MDX	Clerkenwell
1826	1860	....	....	156043	MDX	Cripplegate
1800	1826	1700	1800	156043	MDX	Shoreditch
CONNELL						
1849	1935	1750	1849	110426	COR	???
1820	1860	1820	1860	125997	STD	Kilmarnock
CONNELLY						
1870	....	1800	1870	126985	COR	???
1860	1900	1820	1900	113107	GLA	Dowlais
1843	1843	1750	1843	179647	IRL	Amagh
1870	....	1800	1870	126985	KER	???
CONNELY						
1820	1854	1820	1854	168289	LKS	Glasgow
CONNER						
1843	1843	1750	1843	179647	IRL	Sligo
1855	1992	....	1855	115150	LKS	Glasgow
1726	1772	1700	1726	170593	RFW	Greenock
CONNERTON						
1821	1903	ALL	1821	159077	CUL	Carlisle
CONNETT						
1870	1992	1700	1870	142042	DEV	Buckerell
1680	1756	1600	1756	179299	DEV	Dunsford
CONNINGTON						
1865	1938	....	....	173142	WAR	Birmingham
CONNOLD						
1900	1960	1800	1900	167010	SFK	Stradbroke
CONNOLLY						
....	1900	1800	1900	172138	CAR	Old Derrig
1850	1992	1800	1900	107700	LAN	Liverpool
1891	1920	1800	1992	126233	LAN	Liverpool
1881	1891	1800	1992	126233	LAN	Manchester
1850	1992	1800	1850	107700	LARNE	Temple
CONNOLY						
....	....	ALL	ALL	166812	OFF	Geashill
....	....	ALL	ALL	166812	OFF	Tullamore
CONNOR						
1830	1830	1750	1860	171662	COR	Cork
....	....	1800	1900	159336	IRL	???
1820	1923	....	....	141356	JSY	St Helier
1814	....	....	....	131210	KEN	Woolwich
1842	1875	1800	1842	100277	LND	Shoreditch
1850	1992	1700	1850	118532	TIP	Clogheen
CONOLLY						
1870	1928	1840	1870	125288	STS	Great Barr
1870	1928	1840	1870	125288	STS	Queslett
CONQUEST						
....	....	ALL	ALL	133841	ALL	Name Study
1856	....	1700	1856	152269	BDF	ALL
1818	....	ALL	1840	170674	BKM	Gt Linford
CONRATH						
....	....	1800	1992	131962	LND	St Pancras
CONROY						
1860	1880	1850	1880	132470	GLA	ALL
1860	1880	1850	1880	132470	MON	ALL
CONSIT						
1851	1900	1700	1850	172782	YKS	East Riding
CONSITT						
1800	1900	1900	1992	172782	YKS	Waghen
CONSTABLE						
1750	1900	1700	1900	134627	CAM	Coveney
....	....	1770	1830	103713	CAM	Grantchester
1750	1850	1700	1850	134627	CAM	Witchford
....	....	....	1792	142409	ENG	Midlands
1765	1850	1700	1950	114898	FIF	ALL
1729	1871	1650	1900	114898	FIF	North
1770	1850	1770	1950	171522	KEN	Boxley
1863	1992	ALL	ALL	115177	LND	Holborn
1790	1810	1700	1900	114898	MDX	London
1863	1992	ALL	ALL	115177	MDX	Paddington
1850	1900	1700	1992	114898	MLN	ALL
1850	1925	1800	1992	114898	MLN	Edinburgh
....	....	1550	1650	130591	SOM	Lydeard St Lawrence
1778	1819	ALL	1992	125113	SSX	Worth
1600	1900	1500	1900	171522	SSX	???
1758	1992	ALL	ALL	124281	YKS	Beverley
1580	1900	1814	1900	158712	YKS	Bridlington
1629	1859	1600	1859	147311	YKS	Wolds
CONSTANT						
1842	1877	ALL	1842	108553	SSX	Selsey
CONSTANTINE						
1750	1900	....	....	157805	LAN	Blackburn
1826	1992	1700	1826	115185	LAN	Manchester
....	....	1800	1840	165190	LND	Bethnal Green
1790	1850	1840	1850	110159	WRY	Bradford
1500	1850	....	....	157805	YKS	Burnsall
1783	....	1760	1800	165190	YKS	Giggleswick
1783	....	1760	1800	165190	YKS	Long Preston
CONTENCIN						
1728	1920	ALL	ALL	157848	ALL	ALL

Known From	To	Researching From	To	Ref	Cty	Place
CONWAY						
1882	1970	....	....	115207	CHS	Birkenhead
1897	1980	....	1897	160652	DEV	Plymouth
1776	1981	1750	1939	154709	DOR	ALL
1572	1621	1572	1621	151858	DOR	Powerstock
1830	1900	1730	1950	118680	IRL	Kings County
....	....	1700	1840	143006	IRL	???
1840	1940	1840	1900	143006	LAN	Manchester
1640	....	....	....	156647	LIN	???
1894	1964	1700	1894	148423	NTT	Hucknall
....	....	1830	1900	115207	WAR	Birmingham
CONYARD						
1800	1895	1550	1800	150843	NFK	Martham
CONYERS						
1700	1870	1090	1880	139807	ALL	ALL
1070	1800	1070	1800	150916	DUR	North
1809	....	ALL	ALL	138533	NFK	Martham
....	1676	?	1676	162507	???	???
CONZON						
1800	1860	....	....	145939	DEV	Corn Wood
COOBIN						
1813	1841	....	....	110167	LAN	Preston
COOCH						
1763	1800	....	1763	125954	DEV	Standford
COOK						
....	....	1800	....	137456	BDF	Cople
1760	....	1700	1760	100129	BDF	Sutton
1787	1940	1700	1787	105562	BKM	Ravenstone
1920	1992	1500	1920	110310	BRK	Basingstoke
1571	1889	ALL	ALL	151815	CAM	Longstowe
1844	1844	1840	1850	126705	CHS	Holmes Chapel
1800	1832	1700	1808	100846	CLK	???
1820	1840	....	....	115274	CON	Calstock
1790	1803	....	....	115274	CON	Quethiock
1803	1820	....	....	115274	CON	St Ive
1841	1848	....	....	115274	CON	Torpoint
1834	1875	ALL	1875	175757	DBY	Cheshire Boundary
....	....	....	....	174793	DBY	???
1751	1780	1700	1780	133000	DEV	Axminster
1818	1960	....	....	115274	DEV	Buckland Monachorum
1740	1810	1700	1760	171158	DEV	Halberton
1815	1992	1700	1815	133914	DEV	Molland Cross
1800	1860	1800	1870	136239	DEV	Stoke Damerel
....	....	....	1890	116866	DNB	???
1800	1850	1750	1880	134376	DOR	Charmouth
1757	1786	1700	1757	127116	DOR	Durweston
1750	1860	1600	1750	164844	DUR	North
1842	1842	1066	1842	108669	DUR	Sunderland
....	....	ALL	ALL	115231	DUR	Sunderland
1794	1885	1750	1900	110728	DUR	Whickham
1773	1992	1600	1773	117676	ESS	Central
1820	1860	1700	1860	152587	ESS	Brightlingsea
1800	1830	1790	1830	173428	ESS	Chelmsford
1765	....	....	....	117196	ESS	Great Dunmow
1868	1880	1800	1992	116297	ESS	Harlow
1768	1787	1720	1768	172871	ESS	Stanway
1829	1942	....	....	157554	FIF	Dunfermline
1880	1904	1800	1880	126519	GLA	Swansea
1733	1871	....	....	135437	GLS	Bristol
1788	....	....	....	176958	GLS	Bristol
1861	1869	1869	1900	118982	GLS	Painswick
1801	1801	1750	1801	179647	GLS	Weston
1823	1867	ALL	1823	115223	HAM	Dogmers Field
1880	1950	1800	1900	136840	HAM	Portsmouth
1700	1900	....	....	152978	HEF	Bromyard
1779	1863	1775	1900	102717	HRT	Braughing
1845	1876	1700	1845	138509	HRT	Flamstead
1770	1779	1700	1780	102717	HRT	Layston
1780	1861	....	....	117560	HUN	Leigton
1850	1900	1850	1900	136484	KEN	Aylesford
1800	1940	1530	1992	145769	KEN	Canterbury
1840	....	1300	1992	152501	KEN	Chatham
1823	....	....	1830	171441	KEN	Folkestone
1810	1840	1810	1840	128740	KEN	Snodland
....	....	1870	1915	124265	LAN	Caton
1800	....	1700	1850	135348	LAN	Kirkham
1891	1920	1800	1992	126233	LAN	Liverpool
1822	1845	1790	1845	108510	LAN	Luzley
1880	1890	1800	1992	126233	LAN	Manchester
?	1816	....	....	138851	LAN	Manchester
1819	1960	1600	1819	152463	LEI	Long Whatton
1702	1841	....	1702	101761	LIN	Gayton
1702	1841	....	1702	101761	LIN	Manby
1702	1735	1500	1702	175072	LIN	Potterhanworth
COOK contd.						
1724	1804	1550	1779	102830	LIN	Ruskington
1790	1820	1790	1900	153303	LIN	South Kelsey
1730	1870	ALL	ALL	115215	LKS	Cambuslang
1800	1920	ALL	ALL	115215	LKS	Glasgow
....	....	....	1890	116866	LKS	???
1866	1900	1800	1900	123765	LND	ALL
1874	1992	1300	1900	152501	LND	Battersea
1872	....	1840	1875	148156	LND	Fulham
1867	1967	....	....	151122	LND	Kensington
1890	ALL	....	....	117560	LND	Mile End
1750	1900	1750	1900	122521	LND	Southwark
1750	1800	1750	1800	167924	LND	St Giles Cripplegate
1817	1907	1788	1830	151122	LND	St Marylebone
?	?	ALL	ALL	100897	LND	???
1755	....	ALL	1750	115118	LND	???
1870	1992	....	....	115258	LND	???
1811	....	....	1811	177504	MDX	London
1870	1992	....	....	115258	MDX	???
1880	1992	ALL	1880	115282	NFK	Diss
1870	1992	....	....	115258	NFK	Great Yarmouth
1835	1843	1700	1834	131245	NFK	Norwich
1900	1900	1900	1900	170143	NTH	Great Creaton
1812	1906	1700	1812	127590	NTH	Hexham
1800	1900	....	1800	177695	NTH	Northampton
1700	1850	....	....	177725	NYK	Kirkby Mooreside
1789	1880	ALL	ALL	154830	SFK	Barking
1577	1708	....	....	129747	SFK	Glemsford
1910	1992	1910	1992	135941	SFK	Great Thurlow
1780	1780	1700	1780	155276	SFK	Kirton
1820	1882	1700	1820	164860	SFK	Letheringham
1910	1992	1910	1992	135941	SFK	Little Thurlow
1775	1960	1600	1775	115304	SFK	Lowestoft
1655	....	1600	1660	135941	SFK	Sudbury
1677	1915	1677	1915	135941	SFK	Wickhambrook
1841	1841	....	....	135437	SOM	Bedminster
1798	1867	ALL	ALL	153516	SOM	Berrow
1798	1867	ALL	ALL	153516	SOM	Bleadon
1789	1871	1600	1789	115525	SOM	Chew Stoke
1807	1852	?	1807	119296	SOM	Clutton
1787	1914	....	....	115290	SOM	Wedmore
1748	1992	1700	1748	161446	SOM	Wrington
1845	1850	1750	1850	100048	SOM	???
1832	1842	....	....	173932	SRY	Ashtead
1826	1883	1800	1900	131792	SRY	Ewell
1837	....	ALL	1837	147877	SRY	Farnham
....	....	1720	1860	166634	SRY	Kingston
1815	1823	....	....	173932	SRY	Wotton
....	....	1800	1850	172871	SSX	Hove
1850	1890	1800	1899	113743	SSX	Rye
....	....	1800	1850	172871	SSX	Steyning
1796	1941	1700	1820	179000	STI	Kilsyth
1800	1830	1690	1830	158313	TYR	Strabane
1770	1800	....	....	100420	WAR	Meriden
....	....	1700	1800	176125	WIL	Latton
1808	1853	....	....	115606	WIL	Martin
1737	1892	....	....	176125	WIL	Mildenhall
1826	1840	1700	1840	109363	WIL	Urchfont
1873	1926	1800	1873	127590	WLS	Glamorgan
1711	....	....	1720	160873	WOR	Dudley
1819	1819	1700	1900	178322	WOR	Halesowen
....	....	ALL	1800	133361	YKS	Hull
1600	1700	1600	1700	167924	YKS	Thornton
1850	1900	1850	1992	120499	???	London
....	....	ALL	1850	144932	???	???
COOKE						
1900	1905	....	....	125997	AVN	Bristol
1655	1940	....	....	128996	CAM	Thorney
1794	1892	....	....	108057	CHS	ALL
1726	1858	1600	1726	152196	CMA	Coulderton
1794	1794	ALL	ALL	113360	CON	Perranzabuloe
1835	1880	1800	1926	117536	DUR	South Shields
1731	1992	1700	1731	160148	DUR	Whickham
1855	1970	1800	1851	111163	DUR	???
1674	1700	1670	1700	161624	ESS	Romford
1754	1767	1665	....	131210	ESS	Waltham Abbey
1700	1800	1700	1800	144657	ESS	Waltham Holy Cross
1851	1933	1800	1851	155225	GLS	Gloucester
1817	1837	1600	1837	145289	HAM	Isle Of Wight
1715	1765	1675	1800	149993	HAM	Micheldever
1859	1915	1859	1920	164542	HAM	Porstmouth
1700	1840	1600	1900	139068	HEF	Wormbridge
....	....	1850	1900	175102	HUN	Brampton

Known From	To	Researching From	To	Ref	Cty	Place
COOKE contd.						
1775	1797	1500	1775	129577	IOW	???
1799	1945	1700	1881	160636	LAN	Denton
1850	1992	1800	1850	113964	LEI	Melton Mowbray
1900	1992	1700	1900	171913	LIN	Branston
1800	1992	1700	1800	102342	LIN	Hibaldstow
1850	1992	1800	1850	113964	LIN	Melton Mowbray
1810	1992	1750	1810	115312	LIN	???
1820	1992	1500	1992	175498	LND	St Georges In East
1750	1992	1700	1900	115339	NFK	Garboldisham
....	1636	1550	1636	148288	NTT	Costock Bunny
1866	....	1760	1939	149845	SFK	Bury St Edmunds
1700	1750	....	....	157724	SFK	Groton
1801	1992	ALL	ALL	115762	SFK	Whepstead
....	....	ALL	ALL	118400	SRY	Felsham
....	....	ALL	ALL	118400	SRY	Leatherhead
1870	1870	ALL	1844	165263	SRY	Leatherhead
?	?	ALL	ALL	100897	SRY	Walworth
1867	....	1867	....	148156	SSX	Brighton
1742	1926	1600	1800	164542	SSX	Brighton
1700	1992	1600	1700	124184	STS	Colton
1700	1992	1600	1700	124184	STS	Colwich
1830	1860	....	....	145688	STS	Longton
1700	1992	1600	1700	124184	STS	Moreton
1573	1776	1550	1660	102830	STS	Sedgely
1770	1800	....	....	100420	WAR	Meriden
1580	1680	1500	1680	154881	WEX	Tomduff
1900	1992	1750	1900	155780	WIL	Wroughton
....	....	1850	1890	169722	YKS	West
1896	1992	1700	1896	138436	YKS	Sheffield
COOKNELL						
....	....	1600	1800	147613	NTT	ALL
....	....	1750	1800	147613	OXF	Spelsbury
COOKS						
1730	1860	1730	1860	127655	WAR	Norton Lindsey
1730	1860	1730	1860	127655	WAR	Snitterfield
COOKSEY						
....	....	ALL	ALL	115363	ALL	Name Study
1550	1992	1550	1992	115363	ALL	ALL
1881	1900	....	....	144096	STS	Hedneford
....	....	1600	1700	147613	STS	Rowley Regis
?	?	?	?	144096	WOR	Dudley
COOKSLEY						
1850	1860	....	....	106798	DEV	Torquay
COOKSON						
....	....	ALL	ALL	115398	ALL	Name Study
1760	....	ALL	ALL	115371	ALL	ALL
1814	1875	1790	1860	168947	CHS	Warrington
1814	1875	1790	1860	168947	CHS	Winsford
1790	1814	1785	1825	168947	ENG	North
1760	1992	ALL	1760	115371	LAN	ALL
1760	....	ALL	1992	115371	LAN	Fylde
1816	....	ALL	ALL	115371	LAN	Little Crosby
1858	....	1858	1992	115371	LAN	Liverpool
1719	1758	....	....	112429	LAN	Lytham
1808	1845	ALL	1845	113611	LIN	Louth
1770	1800	....	....	100420	WAR	Meriden
1837	1992	1750	1860	135623	???	West Kirby
COOL						
....	....	ALL	ALL	109789	ALL	Name Study
....	....	ALL	1992	131083	AVN	Bristol
1830	1930	1750	1900	177784	AVN	Bristol
1700	1850	1650	1900	152528	GLS	Bitton
1700	1850	1650	1900	152528	GLS	Siston
....	....	1820	ALL	118060	WIL	Fonthill
COOLE						
1792	1824	....	....	102733	GLS	South Cerney
COOLEY						
1760	1860	1700	1760	166804	BRK	North
1834	1860	1860	1992	146560	LKS	Coatbride
....	....	1700	1825	110620	LND	Finsbury
1800	1880	ALL	ALL	156604	LND	Paddington
1827	1992	1700	1827	115401	LND	???
COOLING						
1803	1840	1750	1851	160636	LIN	Lincoln
1800	1992	1700	1850	120596	LIN	???
1800	1992	1700	1850	120596	NTT	???
1864	....	....	....	165387	OXF	Burford
1815	....	1700	....	123552	OXF	???
....	1911	ALL	1911	123188	WAR	Stratford Upon Avon
1911	?	1911	ALL	123188	WLS	Swansea
COOMBE						
1878	....	ALL	1878	164755	CMA	Millom
1676	1690	....	1676	149888	CON	Lezant
COOMBE contd.						
1810	1870	....	1810	125954	DEV	Exeter
1770	1800	1700	1770	159115	DEV	Kentisbeare
1797	1840	1700	1800	126772	DEV	Torquay
1817	1920	....	....	144495	LND	Holborn
COOMBER						
1820	1960	ALL	ALL	158593	KEN	ALL
1734	1788	1700	1850	145661	KEN	Chatham
1734	1788	1700	1850	145661	KEN	Maidstone
1760	1890	....	1760	122378	KEN	Plaxtol
1820	1920	1600	1820	123587	KEN	Tonbridge
1891	1992	1800	1959	116378	NTH	Northampton
1800	1890	1700	1950	171522	SSX	Eastbourne
COOMBES						
1809	1870	1809	1960	115436	CHI	???
1800	1992	....	....	122467	DEV	Chudleigh
1900	1920	1800	1900	162760	DEV	Exmouth
1809	1870	1809	1960	115436	DEV	Kentisbeare
1797	....	1700	1797	170321	DEV	Stoke In Teighnhead
....	....	ALL	ALL	147303	DEV	Torquay
....	....	1500	1765	166863	DOR	Holwell
1788	1848	1700	1788	117471	DOR	Iwerne Minster
1821	1900	1700	1821	103195	IOW	Shalfleet
1830	1855	1750	1840	100048	MDX	Chelsea
1818	1843	1780	1820	101427	SOM	Central
1840	1900	1840	1992	117870	WAR	Birmingham
1845	1950	1558	1700	153427	WOR	???
1840	1950	1840	1950	123862	???	Bristol
COOMBS						
1800	1940	ALL	ALL	115444	AVN	Bristol
1820	1900	1700	1830	142670	DOR	Buckhorn Weston
1756	1800	1600	1800	110329	DOR	Holwell
1630	1800	1600	1700	174599	DOR	Shaftesbury
1806	1838	1800	1838	145602	HAM	Christchurh
1800	1900	1700	1900	149691	HAM	Fordingbridge
1850	1900	ALL	1992	128260	HAM	Soton
....	....	1800	1840	153842	HAM	???
1613	1900	1560	1613	179353	KEN	East
1850	1992	1700	1850	157449	LND	Marylebone
1611	1800	ALL	ALL	115444	SOM	North Petherton
1740	1820	1600	1740	108413	SOM	Portbury
ALL	....	....	....	156221	SOM	Thornton
....	....	1700	1825	174270	WIL	Ebbesbourne Wake
....	....	1775	1835	174289	WIL	Ebbesbourne Wake
1838	1880	1838	1900	145602	WIL	Salisbury
COOMER						
1725	1970	....	....	144088	CHS	Basford
1750	1914	1700	1750	104728	CHS	???
?	?	1703	1728	163813	CHS	???
1750	1914	1700	1750	104728	LAN	???
1728	1992	1702	1728	163813	STS	Madeley
COON						
1650	1992	1600	1960	115452	CON	Mid
1550	1800	1600	1800	115452	DEV	South
COONEY						
1850	1992	1700	1992	115460	LIM	Kilfinney
1863	1941	1863	1992	165727	LND	East
1860	1900	1887	1992	112232	TIP	Roscrea
COOPE						
1720	1770	1700	1720	165530	LAN	South East
COOPER						
1590	1992	1590	1992	102628	ALL	ALL
1820	1920	1700	1820	123374	ABD	Kincardine O'neil
1771	1950	1600	1992	167673	ABD	Old Pitsligo
1877	1939	1897	1936	110035	ARL	Oban
....	....	1690	1980	135046	AVN	Bristol
1830	1850	1830	1850	140724	BDF	Luton
....	....	1600	1750	147613	BDF	Shillington
1777	....	?	1780	103934	BDF	Southill
1594	1635	....	1635	103349	BKM	Olney
1832	1860	ALL	1835	108642	BKM	Podbury
1767	1782	1700	1767	119075	BKM	Weston Underwood
1725	1756	1650	1800	176621	BRK	Hurst
1719	1871	....	1770	137405	CAM	South
1800	1846	ALL	ALL	151815	CAM	Bourn
1820	1992	ALL	ALL	172103	CAM	Ely
1719	1871	....	1770	137405	CAM	Foxton
1750	1962	1600	1750	150614	CHS	Preston On The Hill
1830	1992	....	....	118729	CHS	Wallasey
....	....	1875	1955	145084	CMA	Maryport
1810	1860	1700	1810	148059	CMA	Ulverstone
1800	1871	1700	1800	145629	DBY	Shottle
....	1729	....	....	154024	DBY	Whittington
1915	1970	....	....	162183	DBY	???

Known From	To	Researching From	To	Ref	Cty	Place
COOPER contd.						
1840	1992	....	....	115479	DEV	Axemouth
1827	1830	1770	1830	132470	DEV	Burrington
1810	1830	....	....	118729	DEV	Devonport
....	....	....	....	124206	DUR	Seaham Harbour
1876	1897	ALL	ALL	120154	DUR	Sunderland
1700	1992	1700	....	123609	ESS	Braintree
1890	1920	ALL	ALL	121487	ESS	Colchester
1816	1980	1800	1880	115797	ESS	Paglesham
1880	1950	....	....	168041	ESS	West Ham
....	....	1690	1980	135046	GLS	Cheltenham
1777	1818	1750	1992	116653	GLS	Frampton On Severn
1770	1800	1600	1770	118877	GLS	Lower Slaughter
1750	1830	....	....	137693	GLS	Wootten Under Edge
1840	1900	1840	1900	126640	HAM	North
1793	1992	ALL	1800	169730	HAM	Basing
1872	1937	....	....	138630	HAM	Bournemouth
1749	1992	1600	1749	115525	HAM	Brighstone
1720	1813	1700	1820	159581	HAM	Crondall
1750	1800	1600	1900	166804	HAM	East Woodham
1747	1992	1600	1747	103098	HAM	Fawley
1550	1620	1500	1620	144657	HAM	Micheldever
1903	1931	1700	1903	103640	HAM	Southampton
1590	1660	1590	1660	102628	HAM	Tytherley
1788	1800	1700	1788	157147	HAM	Upton Grey
1710	1735	1675	1992	114901	HAM	Warblington
1830	1915	1750	1850	175978	HRT	Ashwell
1660	1992	1660	1992	102628	IRL	ALL
1860	1992	1800	1880	113646	KEN	Gravesend
1810	....	1780	1810	128724	KEN	Gravesend
1816	1860	1780	1830	166154	KEN	Maidstone
1870	1880	1800	1940	101907	KEN	Strood
....	....	1750	1850	178284	KEN	Wingham
....	....	1806	1896	170437	LAN	Blackrod
1890	1910	ALL	ALL	138886	LAN	Preston
1800	1900	1600	1800	144932	LAN	Preston
1850	1992	1700	1930	158216	LAN	Salford
1808	1844	1700	1808	152196	LAN	Ulverston
1840	1992	....	....	115479	LEI	Grantham
1643	1693	ALL	ALL	141615	LEI	Hinckley
1773	....	....	....	120804	LEI	Ullesthorpe
1892	1971	ALL	ALL	135224	LIN	Cleethorpes
1892	1971	ALL	ALL	135224	LIN	Grimsby
1840	1992	....	....	115479	LIN	Lincoln
1850	1930	....	....	127833	LND	South East
....	....	1800	1910	137618	LND	Bermondsey
....	....	1870	....	151610	LND	Chertsey
1872	1937	....	....	138630	LND	Croydon
1878	....	1850	....	167290	LND	Holborn
1900	1900	1850	1950	135925	LND	Holloway
1832	1860	ALL	1835	108642	LND	Pimlico
1875	....	1750	1900	109894	LND	Shoreditch
1860	1992	1800	1860	114448	LND	Westminster
1871	1939	1864	1900	170348	LND	Woolwich
1840	1992	....	....	129291	LND	???
....	....	ALL	ALL	161608	LND	???
1792	1825	1841	1891	146560	LTN	Dalmeny
1792	1825	1841	1891	146560	LTN	Leith
1792	1825	1841	1891	146560	LTN	Queensferry
1860	1992	1860	1992	163600	MDX	East
1860	1992	1860	1992	163600	MDX	North
....	....	ALL	ALL	130524	MDX	Hackney
....	....	ALL	ALL	130524	MDX	Haggerstone
1877	1988	1850	1877	159522	MDX	Harefield
1850	1880	1750	1850	146285	MDX	Holborn
1850	1964	1800	1850	111163	MDX	New Brentford
1870	....	1750	1870	179183	MDX	Shadwell
1842	....	1842	1864	170348	MIL	ARMY
1862	1900	1850	1920	118540	MON	Llantarnam
1748	1882	1700	1750	149152	NBL	Blyth
1803	1803	1700	1820	117013	NFK	Edgefield
....	1809	1750	1850	128961	NFK	Holt
....	1788	1750	1850	128961	NFK	North Walsham
1810	1840	1700	1810	177490	NFK	Wymondham
1850	1900	1700	1992	112097	NYK	Helmsley
1773	1807	1600	1841	115630	SAL	Lilleshall
1741	1868	1700	1741	174289	SAL	Lilleshall
....	....	1868	1918	174289	SAL	Newport
1600	1700	1560	1800	155462	SAL	Norton In Hales
....	....	1800	....	137456	SAL	Shifnal
1838	1908	1807	1908	115630	SAL	Wrockwardine Wood
1801	1992	ALL	1801	157511	SCT	Loanhead
1800	1830	1600	1850	127833	SFK	East
1820	1980	1750	1820	132187	SFK	South
1800	1900	1700	1860	115614	SFK	Benhall
1860	....	1800	1900	126144	SFK	Bradwell
....	....	ALL	ALL	172103	SFK	Brandon
1750	1850	1750	1850	133817	SFK	Buxhall
1850	1992	1800	1992	115614	SFK	Leiston
1800	1880	1700	1800	164860	SFK	Pettistree
1745	1880	1650	1900	126586	SFK	Stansfield
1769	1806	1700	1769	155276	SFK	Trimley
1811	1864	1750	1811	155276	SFK	Ufford
1822	1872	ALL	1822	161500	SOM	Crewkerne
1819	1844	1600	1819	164879	SRY	Albury
1653	1992	1590	1992	102628	SRY	Byfleet
....	....	1700	1800	163082	SRY	Godstone
1840	1870	1700	1880	170607	SSX	Cavendish
1780	1890	1700	1780	115541	SSX	East Grinstead
1789	1930	1700	1992	124389	SSX	Graffham
1693	1811	1570	1820	116580	SSX	Kirdford
1750	1810	....	....	118729	SSX	Storrington
1852	1892	1800	1920	146358	STD	Glasgow
1813	1813	1800	1830	108510	STS	Audley
1818	1820	1790	1820	108510	STS	Biddulph
1796	1830	1760	1850	160873	STS	Bilston
1780	1851	1700	1780	125288	STS	Fradley
1814	....	ALL	1814	174815	STS	Handsworth
1806	1900	1600	1806	112410	STS	Hanford
1771	1812	1750	1850	155462	STS	High Offley
1746	1841	ALL	1992	122106	STS	Madeley
1691	1751	1600	1800	155462	STS	Mucklestone
1800	1880	1600	1800	158968	STS	Pelsall
1820	1900	1700	1820	141658	STS	Rugeley
1612	1709	....	....	117404	STS	Shareshill
1815	1830	1780	1845	170348	STS	Stone
1770	1810	1700	1850	179116	STS	Trentham
1750	1820	1700	1750	170488	STS	Walsall
1831	1861	1800	1890	101486	STS	Wolverhampton
....	....	1835	1992	124389	SXW	East Dean
1885	1952	....	1885	115509	WAR	Birmingham
1850	1875	1850	1875	140724	WAR	Birmingham
1803	1979	1750	1850	112879	WAR	Coventry
1860	1920	1860	1920	116483	WAR	Leamington Spa
1784	1900	1700	1900	135968	WAR	Poleworth
1805	1808	1500	1808	169439	WAR	Shipston On Stour
....	....	1750	1820	116173	WAR	Southam
....	....	1600	1750	134104	WAR	Stratford Upon Avon
....	....	1750	1841	151513	WAR	Wilncote
1880	1920	1820	1920	133922	WIL	Devizes
1590	1660	1590	1660	102628	WIL	Downton
1741	1807	1700	1850	118397	WIL	Downton
....	....	1690	1980	135046	WIL	Hankerton
1766	....	....	....	115576	WIL	Heddington
1683	1812	....	1840	121169	WIL	Longbridge Deverill
1831	1850	....	1850	152803	WIL	Old Basing
1750	1930	1600	1750	134104	WOR	Evesham
1906	1992	ALL	1906	111066	WRY	ALL
1850	1900	1700	1900	163902	YKS	South
1850	1880	1850	1880	135429	YKS	Brighouse
1700	1800	....	....	167924	YKS	Crambe
1850	1880	1850	1880	135429	YKS	Gate Hemsley
1810	1900	1750	1900	142875	YKS	Grazebrook
1820	1950	1800	1870	123595	YKS	Greetland
1823	....	1800	....	134589	YKS	Kirby Grindalythe
1735	1800	1700	1800	176621	YKS	Rastrick
1800	1900	....	....	100633	YKS	Ripon
1670	1992	1670	1992	116742	YKS	Swaledale
1830	1992	1800	1850	171670	YKS	Wentworth
1825	1850	1700	1825	108308	YKS	Westerdale
COOPES						
ALL	ALL	ALL	ALL	115657	ALL	ALL
COOPEY						
1814	1879	1814	ALL	133930	GLS	Churcham
....	....	1700	1800	115649	GLS	Gloucester
1850	1960	1830	1850	115649	MDX	London
....	....	1800	1840	115649	WIL	Trowbridge
COOPS						
....	....	ALL	ALL	115657	ALL	Name Study
ALL	ALL	ALL	ALL	115657	ALL	ALL
COOT						
....	....	1600	1680	154873	KEN	Barden
....	....	1600	1680	154873	KEN	Canterbury
1703	1732	....	....	135437	SSX	Binstead
1755	1755	....	....	135437	SSX	Eastergate
COOTE						
1739	1865	1600	1739	117676	ESS	Central

Known From	Known To	Researching From	Researching To	Ref	Cty	Place
COOTE contd.						
....	....	1700	1900	129275	ESS	Thaxted
....	....	ALL	ALL	172413	ESS	Witham
....	....	1800	1900	129275	LND	Bermondsey
....	....	1860	1900	129275	LND	Camberwell
1849	1960	1700	1849	164178	LND	Halstead
....	....	1700	1880	129275	LND	Southwark
COOTER						
....	....	ALL	ALL	115665	ALL	Name Study
ALL	ALL	ALL	ALL	115665	ALL	ALL
COOZE						
1800	1992	1660	1992	115673	LND	ALL
COPE						
1843	1931	1700	1843	146021	BDF	Tempsford
1720	1930	1600	1720	115703	GLS	Berkeley
1720	1930	1600	1720	115703	GLS	Pucklechurch
1720	1930	1600	1720	115703	GLS	Westerleigh
1850	1870	ALL	ALL	130508	HAM	Andover
1788	1992	1700	1992	115681	LND	ALL
1815	1910	1780	1815	165107	LND	Paddington
1840	1930	1700	1900	108618	LND	St Apncras
1818	1842	ALL	1818	154288	LND	Stepney
....	....	1800	1910	118834	LND	???
1798	1806	1753	1809	153257	OXF	Thame
1862	1932	1700	1992	122114	WAR	Birmingham
1862	1932	1700	1992	122114	WAR	West Bromwich
1800	1900	ALL	1992	174157	WIC	Baltinglass
COPELAND						
1860	1930	1700	1860	115738	DOW	Warrenpoint
1700	....	1650	....	116920	DUR	???
1800	1850	1800	1900	117781	EYK	Hull
1816	1992	1700	1816	110752	LND	???
1840	1992	1650	1850	115711	SFK	Bury St Edmunds
COPEMAN						
1895	1905	1850	1970	138215	CAM	Pondersbridge
1795	1881	....	....	138215	NFK	North
1737	1837	ALL	1737	168602	SFK	Beccles
COPESTAKE						
1855	1855	....	....	145580	CHS	Birkenhead
1880	1992	ALL	1880	126489	DBY	Derby
1754	1836	1754	1754	145580	DBY	Snelston
1855	1867	....	....	145580	DBY	Tissington
1869	1988	....	....	145580	LAN	Liverpool
1820	1850	ALL	ALL	113581	LND	???
....	....	1754	1754	145580	STS	???
....	1293	1474	....	145580	YKS	???
COPHAM						
1790	1983	1700	1992	115746	ALL	ALL
COPITHORNE						
1849	1992	1600	1849	158461	IRL	???
COPITTS						
1749	1760	....	....	131202	DUR	Stanphope
COPLAND						
1850	1992	ALL	1850	109851	ESS	???
1850	1992	ALL	1850	109851	KEN	???
1750	1965	....	....	137820	SHI	Fetlar
1720	1965	....	....	137820	SHI	Mid Yell
1760	1965	....	....	137820	SHI	North Yell
1758	1965	....	....	137820	SHI	Northmavine
1720	1965	....	....	137820	SHI	South Yell
COPLEY						
....	....	1850	1992	168815	CHS	ALL
....	....	1850	1992	168815	DBY	ALL
1690	1760	....	....	103721	ERY	Adlingfleet
....	....	1700	1850	110914	HAM	???
1600	....	1800	1992	164054	WRY	Wortley
1684	1694	1600	1700	154601	WYK	Batley
1802	1876	1750	1802	138584	YKS	Bradford
1870	1950	1750	1950	115622	YKS	West Riding
COPNER						
1748	1800	1700	1992	116653	GLS	Harescombe
1772	1821	ALL	1796	123013	GLS	???
COPP						
1800	1900	1850	1900	154903	DEV	Exeter
1800	1900	1840	1900	172634	DEV	Tiverton
COPPARD						
....	....	ALL	ALL	115754	ALL	Name Study
1848	1851	1800	1848	177393	LND	Islington
....	....	1800	1848	177393	LND	Shoreditch
....	....	1800	1840	177393	SAL	Ludlow
1750	1850	1700	1900	103993	SSX	Eastbourne
1770	1790	ALL	ALL	147567	SSX	Henfield
1752	1781	....	....	139971	SSX	West Firle
1730	1830	ALL	ALL	147567	SSX	Woodmancote
COPPARD contd.						
1901	1992	ALL	1900	100536	SSX	???
COPPEN						
1746	1992	ALL	ALL	115762	ESS	Hatfield Peverell
COPPENDALE						
1555	....	1555	....	158305	YKS	Barnby
....	1555	....	1555	158305	YKS	Beverley
1666	....	....	1666	158305	YKS	Wookirk
COPPERWHEAT						
1800	1900	1700	1900	177180	BDF	Mursley
COPPIN						
1730	1820	1700	1900	179191	CON	Cardinham
1720	1750	....	1780	171441	KEN	Mid
1770	1840	ALL	1770	122823	KEN	West Wickham
COPPINDALE						
....	....	1700	1740	177393	YKS	Beeston
COPPING						
....	....	1100	1900	115770	ALL	ALL
1774	....	....	1780	171441	KEN	Borden
1749	....	....	1780	171441	KEN	Milton
1800	1870	....	....	101028	KEN	Smarden
1786	1806	1780	1810	175153	NFK	Winfarthing
1675	1730	....	1675	101761	SFK	Pakenham
1730	1940	1700	1800	101664	SFK	Wortham
COPPINS						
1850	1920	1700	1850	102210	KEN	Ashford
COPPLESTONE						
1860	1930	1800	1870	168947	LAN	Liverpool
COPPOCK						
1830	....	1800	....	115789	OXF	Bicester
1545	1770	....	....	115789	OXF	Cuddesdon
1685	1832	....	....	115789	OXF	Great Haseley
1690	1850	1600	1900	115789	OXF	Great Milton
1849	1927	1800	1927	115789	OXF	Headington Quarry
1750	1900	1750	1900	115789	OXF	Headington
1700	1800	1700	1850	115789	OXF	Henley On Thames
1840	1870	1840	1870	115789	OXF	Launton
....	....	1700	1900	115789	OXF	Oxford
....	....	1750	1850	115789	OXF	Tetsworth
COPPS						
1850	1900	1850	1900	108693	HRT	Weston
COPSEY						
....	....	ALL	ALL	115800	ALL	Name Study
1820	1920	1800	1850	166316	ESS	Chelmsford
1713	1992	1670	1992	115797	ESS	Gosfield
1813	....	1750	1813	113352	ESS	Writtle
1715	1787	....	....	101028	SFK	Little Saxham
COPSON						
....	....	1600	1850	137014	STS	ALL
....	....	1600	1850	137014	WAR	ALL
1819	....	....	....	125202	WAR	Nuneaton
COPUS						
1736	1736	1700	1750	170143	SRY	Stoke Next Guildford
CORBER						
....	....	ALL	ALL	178772	ALL	ALL
1680	1800	1600	1800	167088	DEV	Cornwood
1600	1985	1700	1985	178772	DEV	Plymouth
CORBET						
....	....	ALL	ALL	151572	ALL	Name Study
1040	1992	1040	1992	151572	ALL	ALL
1830	1958	1700	1860	154881	DOW	Ballyward
1040	1300	1040	1300	154881	SAL	Caus
1852	1944	....	....	176354	SAL	Hopton Waters
1040	1100	....	....	156647	WAR	Alcester
CORBETT						
1838	1946	1700	1992	156493	BDF	Bedford
1801	1825	1750	1850	159964	BKM	Adstock
1750	1830	1650	1750	151769	DBY	Derby
1800	1821	ALL	1821	152641	DBY	Long Whatton
....	1840	ALL	1870	152641	DBY	Sawley
1830	1890	....	1800	164631	DBY	Sawley
1832	1946	1832	1905	159700	GLS	Coombe Hill
1830	1932	1780	1817	164232	HAM	Bishops Sutton
1795	1809	1780	1809	164232	HAM	Old Alresford
1795	1826	1750	1826	159700	HEF	Cradley
....	....	ALL	1800	164631	LEI	ALL
....	1861	ALL	1870	152641	LEI	Castle Donnington
....	....	ALL	1800	164631	LEI	Long Whatton
1700	ALL	....	....	163465	LIN	Rippingale
1870	1987	1987	1992	146560	LKS	Coatbride
1787	1829	1740	1787	115819	MLN	Edinburgh
1835	1890	1811	1890	109819	MOG	Drumreenagh
1765	1907	1790	1907	134686	ROC	Black Isle

Known Researching
From To From To Ref Cty Place
CORBETT contd.
1789 1907 1700 .... 134686 ROS Avoch
1887 1961 1700 1887 128465 SAL Ironbridge
1902 1957 1780 1992 164232 SFK Bury St Edmunds
1947 1992 1780 1992 164232 SFK Ispwich
1870 1894 1894 1992 152641 STS Burton On Trent
1862 1925 .... 164631 STS Burton On Trent
1870 1992 1750 1900 178136 STS Longton
1813 1992 1845 1914 140767 STS Sedgley
ALL ALL .... 1720 106054 WAR Nuneaton
1813 1992 1845 1914 140767 WOR Dudley
.... 1847 ALL 174963 ??? Birmingham
CORBIN
.... ALL ALL 115827 ALL Name Study
1741 1821 1675 1741 174289 DOR West Parley
.... 1750 1800 119199 HAM ALL
.... 1750 1800 119199 WIL ALL
CORBISHLEY
1780 1992 ALL ALL 106658 CHS Macclesfield
1750 1880 1790 1880 115835 LAN Lancaster
1880 1992 1880 1992 115835 LAN Preston
1750 1880 1790 1880 115835 LAN Thurnham
1780 1992 ALL ALL 106658 STS Cheadle
CORBITT
1825 1828 1800 1992 114057 DUR Gateshead
CORBLE
1750 1782 .... 1750 101761 SFK Pakenham
1788 1992 ALL 1788 115843 SFK South Lopham
CORBOM
1750 1868 1700 1900 146129 DFS Dumfries
1750 1868 1700 1900 146129 DFS Morton Parish
CORBRIDGE
1650 1800 1600 1992 148288 YKS Hemsworth
1790 1850 1600 1992 148288 YKS Wakefield
CORBY
.... ALL ALL 115851 ALL Name Study
1707 1780 1690 1800 119059 BKM Waddesdon
1350 1450 1300 1450 154881 KEN Boughton Malherbe
1770 1900 ALL 1770 157899 LEI Sharnford
1820 1840 1750 1825 112038 LIN Toft
1820 1920 1785 1881 124001 MDX East London
1840 1860 1700 1839 131245 MDX Hackney
1760 1850 1760 1850 159905 NBL Blyth
1729 1992 1500 1729 125695 NTH Boughton
CORBYN
1650 1800 .... 177474 DEV Ilsington
1850 1992 ALL ALL 120456 LND Greenwich
CORCORAN
.... 1975 1965 1975 115886 BKM Denham
.... ALL 1900 137774 IRL South
1833 1935 1800 1992 115886 LND Central
1833 1935 1800 1992 115886 LND North
.... 1846 .... 140767 MAY ???
1901 1924 1800 1965 115886 MDX ALL
1846 .... 1851 .... 140767 YKS Leeds
CORDELL
1880 1940 1860 .... 116297 ESS Harlow
1856 .... 156329 LND Islington
CORDEN
1740 1765 .... 145688 LIN Grainsby
1780 1850 .... 145688 LIN Grimsby
1765 1780 .... 145688 LIN North Thoresby
CORDER
1712 1779 1763 1851 128961 ESS Fiering
CORDERY
1827 1992 1653 1827 124559 BRK Swallowfield
1790 1800 1700 1820 174386 HAM Heckfield
1870 1900 1700 1900 140171 HRT Barnet
1840 1850 1800 1840 146587 MDX Uxbridge
CORDINER
1800 1850 1700 1800 148342 ABD Peterhead
1780 1992 1700 1992 130869 MOR Peterhead
CORDING
1910 1970 1700 1960 115894 MDX London
CORDINGLEY
.... 1800 1899 171794 YKS Tong
CORDOCK
1750 1859 ALL ALL 135224 ??? ???
CORDRAN
1761 1791 1700 1761 127116 NFK Norwich
CORDUKES
.... 1800 1837 132381 LKS Glasgow
CORDWELL
.... 1840 1930 115908 ALL ALL

Known Researching
From To From To Ref Cty Place
CORDWELL contd.
.... 1840 1930 115908 ENG South West
1800 1900 1800 ALL 115908 GLS North
1900 .... 148989 LND ???
CORDWENT
1802 1855 ALL 1802 114987 SOM Trull
CORFIELD
.... ALL ALL 115916 ALL Name Study
1730 1800 1700 1800 167088 SOM Winscombe
1654 1671 1550 1670 102830 STS Darlaston
1671 .... 1680 160873 STS Darlaston
CORJEAGE
1785 1802 1700 1785 135151 IOM Michael
CORK
1720 1920 1650 1750 135496 GLS Warick Border
1908 1992 ALL ALL 153281 KEN Borstal
1746 1992 1700 1800 105201 KEN Rodmersham
1798 1850 ALL .... 120839 SRY ???
CORKE
.... 1992 1066 1894 115924 HAM Southsea
1760 1992 1750 1992 143650 KEN Sevenoaks
1798 1850 ALL .... 120839 SRY ???
CORKER
1800 1840 ALL .... 115355 LEI ALL
CORKIN
1700 1800 1800 1930 148849 DUR South Shields
CORKISH
1730 1825 ALL 1730 160385 IOM Bride
CORLETT
1800 1900 1700 1800 113204 IOM Ballaugh
.... ALL 1850 147109 IOM Ballaugh
1865 1947 .... 160385 IOM Douglas
.... 1800 1900 147109 IOM Santon
1788 1806 1788 1992 156647 IOM ???
1855 1992 1820 1855 147109 LAN Liverpool
CORLEY
1806 1826 1700 1826 132543 SFK ALL
CORMACK
1826 1948 .... 135739 CAI Canisbay
.... 1500 1813 138614 CAI Canisbay
1770 1800 .... 126497 CAI Killinster
CORMIE
.... 1700 ALL 149187 MOR Duffies
.... 1700 ALL 149187 MOR Urquhart
CORNAH
1780 1992 1780 1992 115932 LAN Fylde
CORNALL
1780 1992 1780 1992 115932 LAN Fylde
CORNBROUGH
1727 1777 1600 1750 124257 YKS Crambe
1727 1777 1600 1750 124257 YKS Whitwell
CORNELIUS
1876 1992 1876 1992 149810 CON Roche
1840 1900 1840 1900 149810 CON Wadebridge
.... ALL 1950 145548 CON ???
.... ? ? 132195 SOM Wellington
CORNELL
1818 .... 1750 1818 176885 ESS Little Dunmow
1730 1880 .... 1730 100064 NBL Newmarket
1700 1770 1550 1850 139866 SFK Gazeley
1726 1860 1700 1900 136980 SFK Haverhill
CORNER
.... 1800 ALL 164615 CHS Hyde
1772 1772 1772 1772 143286 DEV Burlescombe
1782 1799 .... 116602 DUR Chester Le Street
1832 1853 1830 1855 103632 DUR Sunderland
1799 1918 1700 1799 142883 HEF Eignbrook
1800 1848 1750 1820 151912 LAN Chipping Stonyhurst
1600 1900 1600 1900 135968 LEI Great Dalby
1630 1680 1600 1630 121339 NYK Lythe
1700 .... 1600 .... 134589 YKS Haxby
1688 1900 .... 173916 YKS Ruswarp
CORNES
1810 1907 1700 1840 135763 CHS Over
1810 1907 1700 1840 135763 CHS Wearver
1810 1907 1700 1840 135763 CHS Wistaston
1900 1992 1800 1900 108618 LAN Liverpool
CORNEY
1862 1931 ALL 1862 108642 CUL Northaw
.... 1819 1900 151203 IOW Sandown
.... 1770 1800 103713 WRY Barwick In Elmet
CORNFOOT
1808 1841 1700 1860 122394 FIF Pittenweem

Known From	To	Researching From	To	Ref	Cty	Place
CORNFORD						
....	....	ALL	ALL	139653	ALL	Name Study
1770	1992	1700	1950	105287	KEN	ALL
1844	1939	1800	1844	174807	SRY	Godstone
1706	1890	ALL	1900	151017	SRY	Warlingham
1794	1794	1600	1794	113743	SSX	ALL
1860	1992	....	....	115940	SSX	Brighton
1812	1880	1812	1880	115940	SSX	West Firle
1793	1864	1700	1795	165980	SSX	???
CORNFORTH						
1900	1992	1883	1900	115967	DUR	Hartlepool
1825	1883	1700	1825	115967	YKS	Whitby
CORNISH						
....	....	ALL	ALL	115991	ALL	Name Study
1400	1992	1400	1992	115991	ALL	ALL
1829	....	1700	1900	131148	CON	Gwennap
1715	1992	1500	1992	115991	DEV	South
1800	1900	1750	1992	133450	DEV	Dartmouth
1800	1850	1750	1850	146374	DEV	Modbury
1827	1828	1827	1828	145106	ESS	Althorne
1826	1827	1825	1830	145106	ESS	Burnham On Crouch
....	....	1800	1992	115975	MDX	Stepney
1500	1900	....	....	115983	NFK	ALL
1829	?	1827	1855	145106	NFK	Harleston
1749	1835	....	....	127426	NTH	Earls Barton
1830	1831	1665	1941	132497	OXF	Oxford
....	....	1750	1992	127299	PEM	Patur
1500	1900	....	....	115983	SFK	ALL
1855	1881	1855	1881	145106	SFK	Worlingworth
1792	1992	1750	1792	176257	SRY	Rotherhithe
CORNMELL						
1730	1762	1500	1730	104825	BRK	Shottesbrook
1730	1730	1700	1750	125032	BRK	Shottesbrook
CORNOCK						
1800	1850	ALL	ALL	154008	ALL	ALL
CORNS						
1813	1861	1750	1815	155500	STS	Madeley
CORNTHWAITE						
1693	1820	1600	1693	138401	WES	Heversham
1664	1699	1600	1664	152196	WES	Heversham
1693	1820	1600	1693	138401	WES	Old Hutton
CORNWALL						
1845	1869	1845	1869	100668	SSX	East
....	....	1600	1750	108812	TYR	Dungannon
ALL	1100	....	....	132756	???	???
CORNWELL						
1850	1880	ALL	1850	108847	CAM	Ely
1890	1923	1700	1890	144150	CAM	Fulbourn
....	....	ALL	1728	119326	ELN	Tranent
1833	1856	ALL	1833	166847	SRY	Newington
1821	1957	1750	1821	174807	SSX	Framfield
1787	1807	....	1787	117234	SSX	Frant
1838	1934	1838	1934	100668	SSX	Mayfield
CORP						
1780	1820	1750	1820	124605	NFK	Great Yarmouth
CORPES						
....	....	1786	1840	114308	SSX	Empshot
CORPS						
1856	1856	ALL	1856	131881	HAM	Portsmouth
CORREN						
1817	1845	ALL	ALL	151580	LND	Bloomsbury
CORRI						
1830	1870	1820	1830	134139	IRL	Dublin
1800	1820	1770	1800	134139	SCT	Edinburgh
CORRIE						
1792	1886	ALL	ALL	104191	MDX	London
CORRIGAN						
....	1847	ALL	1847	153710	LAN	Whiston
1800	1900	....	....	126497	LET	???
....	....	ALL	ALL	166812	NBL	Newcastle
CORRON						
1820	1820	1700	1820	157031	IRL	???
CORRY						
1898	1992	1800	1992	116009	ANT	Belfast
1810	1850	1600	1810	148954	LND	Lambeth
1790	1900	1760	1850	100617	SOM	Charlton Adam
CORSELLIS						
1570	1900	1570	1960	131822	ALL	ALL
CORSON						
....	....	ALL	ALL	115029	ALL	Name Study
1804	1887	1600	1804	132977	KKD	Gatehouse Of Fleet
CORSTORPHINE						
ALL	....	....	....	151416	SCT	ALL

Known From	To	Researching From	To	Ref	Cty	Place
CORT						
1704	....	....	1704	177504	KEN	Strood
CORWEN						
1725	1766	ALL	ALL	141615	LAN	Pilling
CORY						
1583	1992	1773	1900	106593	CON	Morwenstow
1500	1850	1500	1850	131911	CON	Stratton
1300	1992	1600	1900	106593	DEV	North West
CORYNDON						
1800	1874	1800	1874	175196	MDX	Westminster
COSENS						
1800	1840	1700	1900	136034	GLS	Wotton Under Edge
COSFORD						
1800	1880	1880	1992	134708	HUN	Kimbolton
1780	1800	1800	1992	134708	NTH	Ringstead
COSGROVE						
1818	1992	1700	1992	116025	DOW	Henryville
COSH						
1808	1916	1700	1808	126292	DOR	ALL
COSHILL						
1792	1864	1700	1864	107573	OXF	Crowell
COSIER						
1760	1790	1700	1790	148288	MDX	London
1900	1947	1875	1899	118850	WAR	Birmingham
COSS						
1881	1992	1820	1992	116041	IRL	Borris In Ossory
COSSAM						
1800	....	ALL	1800	115282	SSX	East
COSSAR						
1803	1898	ALL	ALL	109266	LKS	Dolphinton
COSSENS						
1806	1807	....	1820	171441	LND	City
COSSEY						
1851	1881	1840	1940	110051	KEN	ALL
1780	1881	1700	1940	110051	NFK	ALL
1800	1881	1700	1900	110051	SFK	North
COSSHAM						
1740	1900	1500	1900	149934	GLS	Thornbury
COSSINS						
1860	....	....	....	164003	LND	Holborn
1818	1960	1700	1818	134074	SOM	Crewkerne
1818	1973	....	1818	106100	SOM	Hinton St George
....	....	ALL	ALL	106100	WLS	South
1789	1992	1750	1790	116076	YKS	Hawnby
1789	1992	1750	1790	116076	YKS	York
COSSLETT						
1790	?	ALL	ALL	126071	GLA	Cardiff
1786	1890	ALL	ALL	126071	GLA	Castleton
1865	1900	ALL	ALL	126071	GLA	Leckwith
1750	1786	ALL	ALL	126071	MON	Machen
COSSUM						
1863	1992	1630	1900	116084	SSX	Hastings
COSTAIN						
1731	1738	1511	1738	141291	IOM	Arbory
COSTELLO						
1864	1894	1860	1900	130370	CHS	Macclesfield
1894	1992	1894	1992	130370	LAN	Manchester
1885	1890	1860	1885	110043	LND	???
1890	1929	1880	1940	113743	NBL	Newcastle
COSTER						
....	....	1780	1850	143480	HAM	Fareham
1750	1839	1500	1750	153095	KEN	Central
1804	1930	1750	1950	147958	LND	???
COSTIDELL						
....	....	1800	1900	125660	KEN	Westerham
COSTIN						
1650	1750	1600	1800	177180	BKM	Northall
1835	1860	1500	1835	104825	HRT	Berkhamstead
1858	....	1750	1858	134473	KEN	Lewisham
COSWAY						
1650	1980	1650	1980	139807	ALL	ALL
COTCHIEFER						
1800	1992	....	....	176125	LIN	Asterby
1800	1992	....	....	176125	LIN	Goulceby
COTES						
1800	1931	ALL	1800	167878	DBY	Belper
1800	1810	1750	1800	165530	GLS	Hawkesbury
COTGREAVE						
....	....	1066	1272	124974	CHS	Hargrave
COTGROVE						
....	....	ALL	ALL	134333	ALL	Name Study
COTHER						
1780	1992	ALL	1992	172812	ALL	ALL
1740	1806	1700	1837	159158	GLS	Pitchcombe

Known From	To	Researching From	To	Ref	Cty	Place
COTMAN						
1780	1880	1880	1992	117072	LIN	Friskney
COTON						
1870	1992	ALL	1870	163368	STS	Clifton Campville
1839	1946	1750	1900	136530	WAR	Birmingham
COTSELL						
....	....	1811	1873	116092	ALL	ALL
....	....	1797	....	116092	HAM	Farnham
COTTAM						
1780	1881	1740	1780	174211	LAN	Clitheroe
1780	1881	1740	1780	174211	LAN	Downham
1830	1850	1750	1830	121509	LAN	Woodplumpton
1795	1878	1850	1878	149845	LIN	ALL
1726	....	ALL	....	104515	LIN	Stapleford
1780	1881	1740	1780	174211	YKS	Bolton By Bowland
1811	1992	1500	1870	151483	YKS	Firbeck
1700	1800	....	....	124621	YKS	Hull
1864	1957	1800	1864	128368	YKS	Sheffield
1839	1992	1500	1870	151483	YKS	Sheffield
COTTEE						
....	....	ALL	ALL	111317	ALL	Name Study
COTTELL						
1755	1824	1740	1850	105333	HAM	Isle Of Wight
COTTENDEN						
1810	1992	1643	1810	132322	KEN	North
1600	1643	1643	1810	132322	KEN	South
1810	1870	1650	1810	120774	KEN	West
1180	....	1180	1992	132322	SXE	Cottenden
COTTER						
1866	1992	1700	1866	101419	GLA	Merthyr Tydfil
....	....	1750	1900	174696	IRL	Cork
COTTERALL						
1853	1875	1841	1890	125717	LEI	St Margarets
1830	1850	ALL	1850	105376	LIN	Lenton
COTTEREL						
....	....	1800	1900	125660	HAM	Winchester
1549	1708	1500	1549	102830	WAR	Tanworth
COTTERELL						
1896	1940	1896	1940	126705	CHS	Wirral
1900	1992	1837	1992	179302	HRT	St Albans
1810	1813	1800	1860	176281	NTH	Northampton
....	....	1700	1850	101273	WIL	Beechingstoke
COTTERILL						
1797	1797	1750	1841	142921	CHS	Wincle
1840	1845	ALL	1840	105376	NTH	ALL
1828	1859	1800	1850	142921	STS	Lane End
?	?	?	?	100692	STS	Smethwick
COTTEY						
1887	1992	....	1887	171743	SOM	Nitaunton
COTTIER						
1803	1992	1700	1992	160385	IOM	ALL
COTTINGHAM						
....	....	1790	1870	171638	LAN	Manchester
1550	1850	....	....	152277	LIN	ALL
1886	1901	1850	1885	113719	LIN	Lincoln
1783	1867	1750	1881	160636	LIN	West Barkwith
COTTLE						
....	....	1700	1750	142026	DEV	Clovelly
1880	1930	1880	1930	124605	MDX	Hackney
1786	1786	1700	1800	121568	SOM	North East
1840	1880	1750	1880	124605	SOM	Bath
1700	1810	ALL	ALL	112968	SOM	Crewkerne
1788	1803	1788	1815	124915	SOM	Wellow
COTTOM						
1746	1835	1700	1746	152196	LAN	Bolton Le Sands
COTTON						
....	....	ALL	ALL	116130	ALL	Name Study
ALL	1848	ALL	1844	107638	ALL	ALL
1671	1679	....	....	138401	CHS	Chester
1671	1679	....	....	138401	CHS	Weston Under Lizard
1789	1881	ALL	1821	123013	GLS	Cumbleton
1860	1880	1840	1900	133922	HAM	Fawley
1840	1960	1840	1840	151165	HAM	Porstmouth
1830	1910	ALL	1992	150630	HAM	Portsmouth
1870	1987	ALL	1987	111600	HAM	Southampton
1870	1900	1830	1870	102024	LAN	Manchester
1765	1765	ALL	1765	173290	LAN	Winwick
1820	1887	....	....	122319	NFK	Norwich
1730	1940	1700	1800	101664	SFK	Wortham
1380	1736	....	....	168777	SSX	Warblington
1780	1804	1700	1780	179116	STS	Penkridge
1820	1880	ALL	1920	173436	WOR	Bretforton
1861	1871	1800	1905	109746	WOR	Bromsgrove
1801	1823	1770	1823	147311	WYK	Huddersfield
COTTON-BLUNTISH						
1922	1947	1870	1992	116122	LND	Brixton
1922	1929	1870	1992	116122	LND	Clapham
1947	1947	1870	1992	116122	LND	Penge
COTTRELL						
1800	1915	1790	1900	103128	DBY	Brampton
1800	1840	1600	1840	102490	DEV	Payhembury
1870	1992	1830	1870	139157	ESS	Romford
....	....	1830	1851	139157	HAM	East
1837	1992	1837	1992	179302	HRT	Bushey
1830	1850	1800	1900	135925	LND	Kensington
1840	1960	1800	1960	102490	SOM	Congresbury
COTTY						
1500	1600	1500	1600	154881	KEN	Edenbridge
COUBROUGH						
1750	1860	1700	1900	137758	STI	Campsie
COUCH						
1800	1815	ALL	1900	168696	CON	East
1600	....	1550	1600	135771	CON	North
1750	1850	1700	1800	148377	CON	North Hill
1800	1857	....	....	145394	CON	St Breoch
1630	1900	1600	1880	127361	CON	St Endellion
?	?	?	?	117528	DEV	North
1630	1900	1600	1630	168777	DEV	Aveton Gifford
1777	....	....	....	170623	DEV	Teigngrace
1880	1950	1700	1880	171913	???	???
COUCHE						
1887	1950	ALL	1887	122572	CON	ALL
1887	1950	ALL	1887	122572	DEV	ALL
COUCHER						
1830	1992	ALL	1830	151602	LND	ALL
COUCHMAN						
1800	1810	ALL	1810	152889	KEN	Hawkhurst
1700	1992	1600	1700	143170	KEN	Lynsted
1700	1992	1600	1700	143170	KEN	Tunstall
....	....	1850	1950	137685	LND	Sydenham
1850	1880	ALL	ALL	131172	SXE	Rye
COUGHLAN						
....	....	ALL	1875	116157	IRL	Cork
1820	1820	1750	1850	136840	IRL	Dungarven
1875	1992	ALL	1875	116157	LND	Central
COUGHLIN						
....	....	ALL	1875	116157	IRL	Cork
1875	1992	ALL	1875	116157	LND	Central
COUL						
1828	1860	1800	1860	113107	BAN	Port Gordon
COULES						
1750	1850	1600	1850	154342	GLS	Mangotsfield
1770	....	....	1770	163295	SSX	West
COULING						
1803	1900	1750	1900	125563	GLS	Kempsford
COULL						
1670	1992	ALL	ALL	137758	ANS	ALL
1820	1850	1700	1820	100978	ANS	Craig
1810	1860	1780	1860	146803	ANS	Craig
1826	1919	....	....	116165	BAN	Portgordon
COULMAN						
1780	1881	....	....	159751	DEV	Braod Hempston
COULSELL						
1860	1920	1920	1992	153729	MDX	Tower Hamlets
1814	1860	ALL	1814	153729	SRY	Southwark
COULSON						
1800	1950	1750	1850	109517	CAM	Guyhirn
1770	1840	1700	1850	134627	CAM	Milton
1770	1840	1700	1850	134627	CAM	Witchford
1850	....	....	1850	114812	DBY	Chesterfield
1770	....	ALL	ALL	130508	DUR	Sunderland
1768	1874	1500	1768	175072	LIN	Glentham
1851	1881	1800	1900	178446	LIN	Lincoln
1893	1900	1880	1992	123250	LIN	Skirbeck
1827	1827	1820	1827	107573	MDX	Westminster
1789	1881	1700	1820	130877	NBL	Tynedale
1807	1899	1500	1807	103624	NBL	Tynemouth
1830	1847	1830	ALL	113603	SOM	Bristol
1914	1992	1900	1992	123250	YKS	Hull
1820	1850	1780	1820	149462	YKS	Knaresborough
COULSTING						
1832	....	1800	1900	167045	???	Bristol
COULSTON						
1830	1847	1830	ALL	113603	SOM	Bristol
COULT						
1890	1992	1860	1930	122297	DUR	South Shields
1786	....	....	1786	101761	YKS	Warmsworth

Known From	To	Researching From	To	Ref	Cty	Place
COULTASS						
?	?	?	?	133728	EYK	West Of Hull
COULTER						
....	....	1700	1900	179531	ALL	ALL
1848	1890	1800	1848	149004	ANT	Aghalee
1800	1865	1750	1800	177024	AYR	Ballantrae
....	....	1800	1992	135127	LND	???
1800	....	ALL	ALL	172057	MOG	???
....	....	1800	1900	145343	NIR	ALL
COULTHARD						
1795	1880	....	....	116173	CUL	West
1735	1735	1720	1735	159905	CUL	Arthuret
1655	1707	1620	1750	159905	CUL	Brackenhill
1763	1880	1760	1900	159905	CUL	Cumwhinton
1693	1735	1670	1750	159905	CUL	Hallburn
1835	1860	1750	1835	159212	CUL	Whitehaven
....	....	1700	1800	116173	DFS	ALL
1810	1950	....	....	108871	DUR	North West
1835	1992	1835	1900	159905	DUR	South Shields
1650	1810	1650	1750	108871	DUR	Weardale
1782	1850	1770	1850	131911	HAM	Alton
?	?	?	?	130354	NBL	Baxwell
?	?	?	?	130354	NBL	Throckley
COULTHART						
1840	1900	1750	1840	161365	LAN	Blackburn
COULTHURST						
1760	1992	1760	1992	101494	LAN	ALL
COULTON						
1900	1960	ALL	ALL	100137	LEI	ALL
1788	1833	1735	1847	156817	LEI	Loughborough
COULTOUS						
1890	1916	ALL	1960	121622	YKS	ALL
1890	1916	ALL	1960	121622	YKS	Thorne
COULTRIP						
1800	1850	1800	1850	124761	KEN	Sheppey
COUN						
....	....	1820	ALL	136476	ESS	High Ongar
COUNDLEY						
1743	1758	1710	1780	160873	WOR	Rock
COUNTER						
1835	1900	1700	1850	107719	DEV	South Zeal
COUPAR						
....	....	1500	1770	138614	CAI	Olrig
COUPE						
?	?	ALL	1900	116203	LAN	Amounderness
1819	1992	1700	1819	116181	NTT	Blidworth
COUPER						
1866	1992	1700	1866	108316	LKS	Rutherglen
COUPES						
ALL	ALL	ALL	ALL	115657	ALL	ALL
COUPLAND						
1290	1960	1560	1992	163589	CMA	Furness
1787	1865	1700	1787	178926	LEI	Broughton Astley
1787	1865	1700	1787	178926	LEI	Markfield
1100	1630	1630	1800	144649	LIN	Eppleby
1800	1992	1630	1800	144649	LIN	Sibsey
1100	1630	1630	1800	144649	YKS	Eppleby
COUPS						
ALL	ALL	ALL	ALL	115657	ALL	ALL
COURCHE						
1723	....	1700	1750	163775	MDX	Stepney
COURT						
....	....	1800	1850	116238	DEV	Knighton
1796	1825	1796	1850	169161	DEV	Totnes
....	....	ALL	ALL	101354	GLS	North
1742	1775	1600	1742	115169	GLS	Bourton On The Hill
1856	....	....	....	144169	HEF	Llandwarne
....	....	1800	1850	116238	KEN	Dover
1850	1908	1800	1992	169161	LAN	Liverpool
1690	....	ALL	1690	179515	LND	London
1850	1900	1800	1900	116238	MDX	Marylebone
1824	1940	ALL	ALL	153516	SOM	Banwell
1828	1958	....	....	116211	SOM	Bristol
1800	1980	1700	1800	158925	SOM	Dunster
1785	1810	....	....	143596	SOM	Exford
....	1769	....	....	116211	SOM	Luccombe
1702	1769	....	....	116211	SOM	Luecombe
1799	1854	....	....	116211	SOM	Minehead
1680	....	....	....	116211	SOM	Porlock
1739	1828	....	....	116211	SOM	Wootton Courtney
1825	....	1825	1880	149284	SOM	???
....	....	ALL	ALL	101354	WAR	West
....	....	ALL	ALL	101354	WOR	East
?	?	?	?	174297	WOR	Beoley

Known From	To	Researching From	To	Ref	Cty	Place
COURTBIE						
1605	....	ALL	ALL	105481	DBY	Ilkeston
COURTER						
....	....	ALL	ALL	147915	DEV	Moretonshampstead
COURTHOPE						
1190	1974	?	1992	163945	KEN	???
1190	1974	?	1992	163945	LND	???
COURTIES						
1700	....	ALL	ALL	116394	DEV	North
COURTIS						
1700	1910	1700	1910	110523	CON	St Hilary
COURTNEIDGE						
1760	1992	1500	1760	128872	SRY	Ashstead
COURTNELL						
1800	1870	1700	1800	135844	SRY	Mitcham
COURTNEY						
....	....	1780	1850	118575	DEV	North
1738	1992	1650	1738	130966	DOR	Sydling St Nicholas
1819	1863	....	....	117579	KEN	Greenwich
1785	....	....	....	117579	KER	???
1780	1800	1780	1800	168920	KER	???
....	....	ALL	ALL	102083	LND	Holborn
1858	1876	....	....	117579	MDX	Islington
1819	1866	1800	1900	168920	???	London
COUSANS						
1820	1950	1820	1950	144290	LIN	Lincoln
COUSENS						
1798	1803	1700	1825	168149	GLS	Bristol
1757	1785	1700	1800	178004	HAM	Portsmouth
1806	1806	1750	1850	178004	HAM	South Hayling
1828	1865	1810	1870	168149	MDX	London
....	....	?	1800	168149	WLS	???
COUSINS						
1888	1888	1800	1900	102962	BRK	Bracknell
1870	1940	1860	1900	102962	BRK	Winkfield
1870	1950	1750	1870	153893	CAM	Guyhirn
1825	1880	1700	1825	172588	CHS	North
1763	1880	1750	1900	126187	DOR	Poorstock
1824	1851	1800	1900	102962	HAM	Fareham
1800	1917	1800	1900	117617	LIN	Hibaldstow
1835	1900	1700	1835	129445	NFK	Outwell
1850	1960	ALL	ALL	162469	SFK	North
1871	1871	1840	1870	102962	SFK	Mildenhall
COUSSENS						
1782	1782	ALL	1782	154563	SSX	Hastings
COUTER						
1761	1770	....	....	127795	SSX	Berwick
COUTNAGE						
1800	1900	1700	1900	121762	SSX	West
COUTS						
1800	1840	1700	1800	100978	ABD	Peterhead
COUTT						
1790	1840	....	....	176540	PER	Methven
COUTTIE						
1871	1907	ALL	1871	172502	SCT	???
COUTTS						
....	....	ALL	ALL	116262	ALL	Name Study
....	....	ALL	ALL	116262	ALL	ALL
1800	1868	1750	1850	137057	ABD	Auchendoir
1787	1992	ALL	1785	147087	ABD	Huntly
1811	1975	....	1811	175552	ABD	Kintore
1787	1992	ALL	1785	147087	ABD	Rhynies Essie
....	....	1850	1900	142298	ABD	???
1775	1900	1600	1992	108510	FIF	Dunfermline
1675	1960	ALL	1992	108510	FIF	Kincardine On Forth
1790	1862	1700	1720	146358	KCD	Maryculter
1842	1950	....	....	132381	LKS	Glasgow
....	....	1790	1845	132381	MLN	Edinburgh
1775	1917	1695	1775	141313	SCT	ALL
1750	1965	....	....	137820	SHI	Fetlar
1720	1965	....	....	137820	SHI	Mid Yell
1760	1965	....	....	137820	SHI	North Yell
1758	1965	....	....	137820	SHI	Northmavine
1720	1965	....	....	137820	SHI	South Yell
COUZENS						
1769	1860	1669	1769	132748	HAM	Cathrington
1820	1850	1820	1992	114901	HAM	Emsworth
1795	1850	1795	1992	114901	HAM	Havant
1775	1795	1750	1992	114901	HAM	Portsea
1850	1875	1850	1992	114901	SSX	West Dean
COUZNER						
1755	1765	1740	1780	145297	WIL	Westbury
COVE						
1844	1992	1700	1844	178500	STS	West Bromwich

Known From	To	Researching From	To	Ref	Cty	Place
COVELL						
1702	1821	....	1830	137405	CAM	Rampton
COVENEY						
1806	1810	1700	1850	110051	KEN	East
COVENTRY						
1880	1960	....	....	151572	ALL	ALL
1850	1992	1700	1850	112208	BRK	Buckland
1800	1900	....	....	132225	CHS	Wallasey
1800	1992	....	....	170313	HAM	Kingsclere
1871	1906	....	....	120057	LND	North
COVERDALE						
1800	1943	1700	1800	148806	NYK	Helmsley
COVERLEY						
1700	1820	1600	1850	144606	MDX	ALL
1760	1817	1700	1760	150738	WAR	Nuneaton
COVEY						
?	?	?	?	108758	SRY	???
?	?	?	?	108758	SSX	???
COVILL						
1698	....	....	1700	160873	YKS	Sutton On Derwent
COWAN						
1820	1840	1750	1820	139378	AYR	Coylton
1820	1840	1750	1820	139378	AYR	Stair
1881	1992	ALL	1881	106860	AYR	???
1790	1850	1800	1900	119725	ROX	Hownam
1819	1885	....	....	139874	SCT	Glasgow
1819	1885	....	....	139874	SCT	Troon
1700	1743	1700	1750	146536	STI	Falkirk
1731	1773	1700	1780	146536	STI	Muiravonside
1820	1822	1700	1840	136891	YKS	Sculcoats
COWAP						
1920	....	....	....	159492	CHI	Jersey
1920	....	....	....	159492	LAN	Oldham
COWARD						
1750	1992	1600	1750	128554	CMA	Lake District
1700	1730	1600	1900	162620	DOR	Sherborne
1840	1845	1800	1840	103640	HAM	Fareham
1702	1992	1600	1702	116289	HAM	Southampton
1687	1900	1600	1700	116173	LAN	Furness
1850	1880	ALL	ALL	138886	LAN	Preston
1731	1733	ALL	ALL	141615	LAN	Stalmine
1773	1932	1700	1932	154709	LND	ALL
1800	1870	1600	1900	162620	LND	Kensington
....	....	1760	1810	159115	LND	St Marylebone
1761	....	ALL	1992	119695	SOM	West Pennard
....	....	1760	1810	159115	SRY	Lambeth
....	....	?	?	110507	WIL	Bath
....	....	?	?	110507	WIL	Bradford On Avon
1770	1787	1746	1787	165492	WIL	Maiden Bradley
1800	....	1750	....	134589	YKS	Acomb York
1731	1890	1600	1731	178209	YKS	Beal
1818	1914	ALL	1980	136891	YKS	Bridlington
1700	1992	....	....	134619	YKS	Kellington
1783	1834	1750	1783	175951	YKS	Knottingly
1731	1798	ALL	1731	102350	YKS	Pontefract
COWCHER						
1880	1939	....	....	151718	LND	West Ham
COWDALL						
1500	1740	1500	1800	100420	LEI	ALL
1730	1800	1500	1800	100420	NTH	Naseby
COWDEN						
....	....	1700	1850	147613	DFS	ALL
COWDEREY						
1881	....	....	1881	108839	NTH	Nothampton
1805	1846	....	1805	108839	OXF	Abingdon
COWDREY						
1846	1880	1700	....	116297	KEN	Deptford
1846	1880	1700	....	116297	SRY	Lingfield
1838	1880	1700	1838	116297	SRY	St Saviours
1846	1880	1700	....	116297	SRY	???
COWDRY						
1771	1872	....	....	115290	WIL	All Cannings
1872	1940	....	....	115290	WIL	Wroughton
COWELL						
1841	1863	1863	ALL	158690	DOR	Sherborne
1851	1970	1774	1992	132705	ESS	Tolleshunt Major
1809	1902	ALL	ALL	158690	HRT	Ware
1694	1878	ALL	ALL	158690	NFK	Kings Lynn
1774	1900	ALL	ALL	158690	SRY	Southwark
1800	1899	1800	1899	169781	WLS	???
COWEN						
....	1897	1871	1873	151041	CHS	Wallasey
1773	1926	1700	1773	152196	CMA	Whitehaven
1810	1820	1700	1820	146730	CUL	Workington
COWEN contd.						
....	....	1864	1866	151041	CWD	???
....	....	1872	1938	151041	LAN	Beaforth
1700	1730	1600	1750	160873	NBL	Morpeth
COWERN						
1840	1897	1700	1840	115185	STS	Leek
COWEY						
1822	1905	1700	1822	159093	ESS	Great Oakley
COWFIELD						
....	....	ALL	1864	119326	MLN	Edinburgh
COWGILL						
1690	1765	1660	1690	122904	LAN	Colne
1700	1992	1700	1992	147788	YKS	Leeds
COWHAM						
1789	....	....	....	151211	CAM	Whittlesea
COWHILL						
1831	....	1700	1831	165182	LAN	Lower Wearsdalt
COWIE						
1868	1992	ALL	1868	154482	ABD	Peterhead
1850	1900	1600	....	161268	BAN	Ordiquhill Marnoch
....	....	1700	1850	152390	LND	Ilford
....	....	1860	1900	129275	LND	West Ham
....	....	1700	1850	152390	NFK	???
....	....	1750	1900	129275	SCT	Peterhead
COWIN						
1841	1992	1815	1841	116475	IOM	Lonan
COWING						
1820	1843	1700	1850	144037	NBL	Corbridge
COWINS						
1730	1820	1700	1850	160873	NBL	Bothal
COWLAND						
....	....	1700	ALL	111724	ALL	ALL
COWLES						
1831	1851	1800	1831	132853	NFK	Attleborough
1800	1850	ALL	ALL	100161	SFK	North
1769	....	....	....	132853	SFK	???
1838	1890	1750	1838	169242	SOM	Tweton
COWLEY						
....	....	1800	....	116335	AVN	Bristol
....	....	1700	1992	134546	BDF	Elstow
....	....	1700	1992	134546	BDF	Yielden
1815	1915	1750	1840	155691	BKM	North
1760	1860	1700	1760	166804	BRK	North
1799	1940	....	....	128996	CAM	Thorney
1846	1847	1846	1900	110051	GLS	Bristol
....	....	1700	1850	147613	IOM	Peel
1830	1900	1700	1900	142875	IRL	Dublin
....	....	1750	1800	108677	KEN	Upchurch
....	....	1800	1900	117714	LND	West
1813	1877	1700	1992	101419	NTH	Ringstead
1790	1850	....	....	102946	WAR	Ansty
1840	1890	....	....	102946	YKS	Sheffield
COWLING						
1808	1992	1700	1808	140449	CON	Gwennap
1781	1790	1604	1781	137537	CON	St Mellion
1729	1763	1650	1729	150894	CON	Tintagel
1780	1840	....	....	129267	CON	Treneglos
1570	1800	ALL	ALL	120529	GLS	Kempsford
1835	1963	1807	1835	116378	HUN	Buckden
1802	1847	1750	1820	135550	LIN	North
1828	1829	1800	1828	116378	LND	East
1720	1750	1600	1720	121339	NYK	Blades
1625	1700	....	....	100099	WRY	Northowram
1730	1760	1550	1730	150843	YKS	Easingwold
1830	1992	1800	1900	116386	YKS	Leeds
1830	1939	1600	1900	112372	YKS	Nidderdale
1800	1861	1750	1850	116386	YKS	Pateley Bridge
1868	1875	1700	1868	138673	YKS	Pateley Bridge
COWLISHAW						
....	1716	ALL	1716	134511	DBY	Tibshelf
1804	1821	1800	1840	108901	NTT	Cuckney
1816	1871	1800	1816	128368	YKS	Sheffield
COWMEADOW						
1540	1992	ALL	ALL	154768	ALL	ALL
1819	1821	ALL	ALL	154768	CHS	Southport
1809	1879	ALL	ALL	154768	GLA	Cardiff
1826	1874	ALL	ALL	154768	HAM	Alvertoke
....	....	ALL	ALL	154768	HEF	ALL
1819	1821	ALL	ALL	154768	LAN	Liverpool
1819	1821	ALL	ALL	154768	LAN	???
1600	1700	ALL	ALL	154768	LND	Greenwich
1675	....	ALL	ALL	154768	LND	Jewry
1700	1800	ALL	ALL	154768	LND	Kensington
....	....	ALL	ALL	154768	WLS	South

Known From	To	Researching From	To	Ref	Cty	Place
COWNE						
1538	1730	ALL	ALL	131164	DEV	Ugborough
COWNEY						
1730	1820	1700	1850	160873	NBL	Bothal
COWPER						
1696	1909	ALL	1696	116025	ABD	Clatt
1740	1800	1700	1800	169560	ANS	Kettins
1840	1992	1700	1840	157457	CUL	Penrith
1798	....	ALL	1798	154946	ERY	Howden
ALL	1750	....	....	170798	NRY	Cundall
1786	1855	1700	1992	116653	WOR	Shrawley
COWPERTHWAITE						
1600	1800	1750	1800	143553	WES	Kentmere
1750	1800	1700	1850	143553	WES	Long Marton
COWPES						
ALL	ALL	ALL	ALL	115657	ALL	ALL
COWPS						
ALL	ALL	ALL	ALL	115657	ALL	ALL
COWSLADE						
....	....	1650	1700	176621	BRK	Newbury
COWTON						
1637	1756	1500	1670	174858	YKS	Hunmanby
COX						
....	....	ALL	ALL	116491	ALL	Name Study
1700	1815	1650	1750	122351	BDF	Cardington
1823	1851	1800	1850	104183	BDF	Luton
1811	1973	1600	1811	108588	BDF	Luton
1800	1850	1800	1850	167924	BDF	Shillington
1753	1924	1700	1900	117005	BKM	Shenley
1734	1734	1721	1796	107360	BKM	Stewkley
1781	1870	....	....	124672	BRK	Faringdon
....	....	1700	1992	132799	BRK	Hanney
1724	1724	1700	1725	108510	BRK	Hurst
1860	1900	1700	1992	132799	BRK	Steventon
1870	1875	....	1875	102822	BRK	Winkfield
1796	1822	....	....	109002	BRK	Winkfield
1730	ALL	1700	1740	134627	CAM	Coveney
1819	1850	....	1819	136212	CAM	Whittlesey
1815	1815	....	1840	102822	CHS	Nantwich
1829	1872	1750	1872	141062	CHS	Sutton
....	1893	1850	1900	116467	CON	Mousehole
1821	....	....	....	170623	CON	St Austell
1766	1920	1650	1766	163163	DBY	Bolsover
1776	1992	1600	1776	116432	DEV	North
1796	1851	1776	1851	163317	DEV	Seaton
1840	1992	ALL	1840	116459	DOR	Bridport
1851	1858	1851	1861	174416	DOR	Cerne Abbas
1746	1892	1558	....	112968	DOR	Rampisham
....	....	1700	1900	139254	DOR	Shillingstone
1785	1810	1700	1810	107565	DOR	Whitechurch Canonicorum
1850	1860	ALL	1850	147567	DOR	Whitechurch
1813	1912	1813	1912	154733	DOR	Winfrith
1837	1850	1770	1837	117471	GLS	Avening
1806	1830	....	....	135437	GLS	Bristol
1850	1900	1850	1900	154342	GLS	Bristol
1796	1860	ALL	ALL	113662	GLS	Newington Bagpath
1853	1928	1800	1853	128937	GLS	Quedgley
1788	....	1700	1780	178845	GLS	Slimbridge
1780	1870	1801	1873	126276	HAM	Portsea
1830	1858	1830	1858	147486	HAM	Portsea
1826	1863	1700	1826	120707	HRT	ALL
1785	1805	1700	1992	124044	HRT	Rickmansworth
1801	1828	1750	1801	147575	HRT	St Mimms
1823	1851	1840	1850	104183	HRT	Tring
....	....	1800	1923	108243	HRT	Ware
1841	1871	....	....	119334	HUN	Godmanchester
1795	1831	1750	1900	174521	IRL	Cork
1870	1930	....	....	102822	KEN	Bromley
1890	1972	ALL	ALL	153281	KEN	Canterbury
1890	1972	ALL	ALL	153281	KEN	Deal
1770	1885	1750	1800	149373	KEN	Deptford
1850	1960	1825	1897	131997	KEN	East Farleigh
1750	1880	1750	1880	103993	KEN	Frittenden
1850	1950	1700	1850	132942	KEN	Northfleet
1700	1775	ALL	1700	131059	KEN	Shorne
1861	1933	....	....	121967	LEI	Melton Mowbray
1890	1930	1800	1900	179671	LEI	Turlangton
1797	1992	....	1797	101761	LIN	Gainsborough
1870	....	ALL	ALL	169897	LKS	Blantyre
1860	1992	ALL	1992	116408	LND	ALL
1857	1992	1700	1857	171980	LND	Hackney
1895	1958	1870	1895	117358	LND	Islington
1859	....	....	....	124559	LND	Lambeth
COX contd.						
1836	1837	....	....	153885	LND	Newington
1822	1845	1780	1822	177393	LND	Shoreditch
1880	1923	1840	1880	143707	LND	Stratford
....	....	....	1918	171743	LND	???
1800	1810	1810	1900	162876	MDX	Central
1790	1830	....	1890	113034	MDX	Brentford
1834	1870	1834	1874	168289	MDX	Harrow
1805	1841	1700	1992	124044	MDX	Hillingdon
1818	1818	1818	1818	137898	MDX	London Wall
1867	1992	....	1866	129461	MDX	Marylebone
1848	1992	1700	1848	113166	MDX	St Leonard
1904	1930	1930	1930	166189	MDX	Uxbridge
1816	1825	1800	1830	163775	MDX	Westminster
1822	1842	1820	1822	159522	NFK	Norwich
1806	1835	1750	1835	148156	NTH	Central
1806	1835	1750	1835	148156	NTH	South
1800	1880	ALL	1800	156922	NTH	Dingley
1865	1992	1700	1865	105902	NTH	Raunds
1798	....	1798	....	148156	NTH	Upper Heyford
1600	1992	1600	1900	161276	OXF	Blackthorn
1740	1850	1740	1850	140295	OXF	Minster Lovell
1719	1852	....	....	102733	OXF	Northleigh
....	....	1800	1900	142131	OXF	Shiplake
1800	1830	....	....	103764	SAL	Broseley
1815	1874	1815	1874	130370	SAL	Loppington
1860	1880	1850	1900	109525	SFK	Cavenham
1819	1956	1750	1820	135763	SOM	Bath
1814	1866	....	....	135437	SOM	Bedminster
1600	1850	1600	1900	154342	SOM	Bedminster
1791	....	1600	1791	115525	SOM	Cheddar
1776	1784	....	....	135437	SOM	Chew Stoke
1823	....	1811	1850	133639	SOM	Coker
1698	....	ALL	ALL	122106	SOM	Cricket Malherbie
1750	1794	1650	1750	174130	SOM	Dundry
1819	1956	1750	1820	135763	SOM	Twerton
1841	1842	....	....	170623	SOM	Williton
1783	....	....	....	170623	SOM	Wiveliscombe
1800	1992	1700	1800	161446	SOM	Yeovil
1822	1917	1841	1933	109002	SRY	Bagshot
1900	1900	1900	1992	168149	SRY	Balham
....	....	1800	1992	116467	SRY	Ewell
1870	1957	....	....	144282	SRY	Merstham
1736	1864	....	....	144282	SSX	Barcombe
1800	1900	....	....	162590	SSX	Brighton
1805	1870	1805	1870	116483	SSX	Buxted
1800	1900	....	....	162590	SSX	Hove
1847	1992	1700	1847	128465	SSX	Loughton
1817	1881	1700	1900	125865	STS	Kingswinford
1830	....	1800	1850	102016	WAR	Arrow
....	1729	?	1729	128910	WAR	Bedworth
1900	1992	....	....	116408	WAR	Birmingham
1791	1851	....	....	165514	WAR	Hampton On The Hill
1100	1400	....	....	100420	WAR	Meriden
1790	1900	1650	1790	170194	WAR	Nuneaton
1769	1992	1700	1769	116513	WAR	Ratley
1711	1992	1711	....	116394	WIL	Central
....	....	ALL	1828	175080	WIL	Fifield
1815	1830	1500	1815	104825	WIL	Great Cheverell
1780	1840	1570	1870	155616	WIL	Keevil
1800	1810	1750	1850	165824	WIL	Steeple Ashton
1890	1910	1840	1890	164852	WIL	Swindon
1920	1940	1940	1960	164852	WIL	Warminster
1800	1920	1750	1850	130516	WOR	Claines
1830	1925	1800	1830	120286	WOR	St Clement
1781	1835	?	1781	121665	WOR	Stourport
1849	1849	1750	1849	156914	???	West Bromwich
....	....	ALL	1820	178403	???	???
COXALL						
....	....	ALL	ALL	116521	ALL	ALL
1600	1900	1600	1900	116521	CAM	ALL
1737	1926	1700	1926	116521	CAM	Haslingfield
COXE						
1800	1992	ALL	1800	100536	???	???
COXHEAD						
1804	1855	1700	1900	136034	BRK	East Carston
1744	1795	1700	1750	103896	BRK	Hungerford
1841	1913	1820	1900	142360	BRK	Kintbury
....	....	1600	1992	127833	BRK	Newbury
1850	1870	1830	1890	120529	BRK	Reading
COXON						
1800	1820	1820	1992	148180	DBY	???
1766	1898	ALL	ALL	116548	DUR	North
1700	1950	1600	1700	128376	DUR	Chester Le Street

Known From	To	Researching From	To	Ref	Cty	Place
COXON contd.						
1700	1750	ALL	ALL	130508	DUR	Gateshead
1840	1850	1840	1850	113611	EYK	Hull
1808	1845	ALL	1860	113611	LIN	Louth
1800	1820	1820	1992	148180	STS	???
COXWORTH						
1800	1881	1800	1881	104396	YKS	East Riding
COYLE						
1875	1972	1800	1875	128937	DUR	ALL
COYNE						
....	....	1600	1850	146099	IRL	Mayo
1889	1992	1850	....	116556	LAN	Blackburn
....	....	1800	1850	176362	LAN	Liverpool
....	....	1800	1890	166456	NBL	Newcastle
....	....	1800	1840	176362	WEM	Kilbeggan
COYSTEN						
1850	1900	1700	1950	175056	ESS	ALL
COYSTON						
1850	1900	1700	1950	175056	ESS	ALL
1850	1900	1700	1950	175056	LND	London
COZENS						
....	....	ALL	ALL	116564	ALL	Name Study
CRAB						
....	....	ALL	ALL	116599	ALL	ALL
CRABB						
1850	1992	?	1850	163864	ANS	Kirriemuir
1749	1822	....	1749	177504	CAM	Littleport
1700	1881	1700	1881	141178	CON	South East
1897	1992	....	1897	171743	DEV	Upottery
1820	1900	1790	1820	175846	DOR	Beaminster
1820	1855	1700	1820	116572	DOR	Bridport
....	....	1800	1870	138991	ESS	South West
1868	1880	1800	1992	116297	ESS	Harlow
1674	1732	ALL	ALL	169730	ESS	Sheering
1780	1854	1700	1810	147958	LND	???
1800	1900	1800	1900	106410	SOM	Beer Crocombe
1758	1861	1758	1861	117579	SOM	Beer Crocombe
1840	1870	1840	1900	106410	SOM	Wellington
1851	1869	....	....	117579	SOM	Wellington
CRABBE						
....	....	ALL	ALL	116599	ALL	Name Study
CRABTREE						
1788	1818	....	....	178330	CHS	Gawsworth
1765	1860	1799	1841	102121	LAN	Rochdale
1788	1907	....	....	116602	LAN	Rochdale
1900	1950	1900	1950	118540	NTT	Retford
....	....	ALL	ALL	125202	WRY	Bradford
1790	1830	1750	1800	160458	WRY	Heptonstall
....	....	1818	1830	178330	WYK	Anston
1841	1873	1800	1880	133574	YKS	Horsforth
1795	1853	1760	1800	170348	YKS	Pellon In Halifax
1740	1835	1650	1740	110027	YKS	Scammonden
CRACKNELL						
1817	1992	1700	1817	145823	ESS	Ridgewell
1900	1940	1700	1960	101907	KEN	Strood
1900	1980	1700	1920	103314	LND	East
?	?	?	?	116610	LND	Camberwell
1820	1992	1800	1992	122769	MDX	London
1820	1992	1800	1992	122769	SRY	Bow
1820	1992	1800	1992	122769	SRY	Stepney
CRADDICK						
1795	1822	1750	1992	147982	KEN	Sheerness
CRADDOCK						
1637	1868	1600	1868	127604	NTH	ALL
....	....	ALL	ALL	123196	NTH	Northampton
1788	1821	1760	1821	147311	NYK	Hinderwell
....	....	1700	1781	149977	STS	ALL
1723	1840	1700	1722	166464	STS	Cannock Wood
1816	1859	....	....	149977	STS	Salt
1781	1813	....	....	149977	STS	Sandon
1850	1900	1850	1900	107476	STS	Wolverhampton
1870	1992	....	....	126101	WOR	Bromsgrove
1871	....	....	....	102733	WOR	Redditch
1770	1840	1500	1700	167843	YKS	Preston Under Scar
CRADOCK						
1776	1868	1700	....	100536	CON	Bodmin
1760	1804	1700	1790	121932	CON	Treneglos
1769	1778	1700	1850	159956	NTH	Wellingborough
CRAFER						
....	....	ALL	ALL	116629	ALL	Name Study
1802	1889	1790	1889	132608	LND	???
CRAFFORD						
ALL	1800	1450	1700	116785	ALL	ALL
1824	1900	1700	1824	159093	LND	Hammersmith

Known From	To	Researching From	To	Ref	Cty	Place
CRAFORD						
ALL	1800	1450	1700	116785	ALL	ALL
CRAFTS						
1807	1874	1700	1900	178616	NTT	Lambley
1807	1874	1700	1900	178616	NTT	Nottingham
1700	1811	....	....	142085	NTT	Plumtre
CRAGG						
1600	1850	1550	1850	114383	CMA	Millom
1800	1980	1600	1800	112097	LEI	Quorndon
1670	1691	1600	1670	152196	WES	Burton In Kendal
CRAGGS						
1845	1950	1700	1845	104701	DUR	ALL
1720	1840	1600	1720	116637	DUR	Boldon
....	....	1700	1800	159980	DUR	Lamesley
....	....	1600	1720	116637	DUR	Sedgefield
1840	1992	....	....	116637	DUR	Sunderland
1720	....	1600	1720	116637	DUR	Wolsingham
1837	1920	....	....	159980	ENG	ALL
1800	1830	....	....	102946	LIN	Brent Broughton
1760	1800	....	....	102946	NTT	Balderton
1825	1992	1700	1825	128325	NYK	Gilling
1837	1920	....	....	159980	WLS	ALL
CRAGO						
....	....	1800	1899	116645	CON	Dobwalls
CRAIG						
1875	1900	1600	1875	127507	ANT	Glynn
....	....	1700	1960	172111	ANT	Port Glenone
1790	1992	....	....	144088	AYR	ALL
....	....	1700	1800	169501	AYR	Dalry
1820	1992	1700	1820	168246	AYR	New Cumnock
1840	1900	....	....	169501	AYR	New Cumnock
....	....	ALL	ALL	129933	AYR	Stewarton
1796	1895	....	....	135739	CAI	Bower
1755	1900	1700	1755	173134	CAI	Wick
1808	1861	1808	1861	173711	CMA	Murton Cum Hilton
1700	1800	1600	1700	113204	DOW	Carricknab
1846	1880	ALL	1900	177695	DUR	Croxdale
....	....	1780	1987	126241	DUR	South Shields
1765	1910	....	....	122343	DUR	Sunderland
1830	1830	1770	1830	146803	GAL	Stranraer
1772	....	....	....	127140	LKS	Glasgow
1740	1780	1700	1740	122904	LKS	Gorbals
1761	....	1720	1761	115819	MLN	Edinburgh
1980	1987	1780	1987	126241	NBL	ALL
1772	....	....	....	127140	NIR	Belfast
1772	....	....	....	127140	RFW	Greenock
1850	1962	1850	1850	166189	RFW	Paisley
1840	1860	1840	1992	165603	WIC	Keiss
1778	1788	1740	1840	177970	???	Glasgow
CRAIGHEAD						
1738	1782	1606	1992	116688	ANS	Mains
1635	1673	1606	1992	116688	ANS	Monifieth
1738	1782	1606	1992	116688	ANS	Strathmartine
1782	1797	1606	1992	116688	ANS	Tealing
1799	1870	1606	1992	116688	FIF	Newburgh
1674	1700	1606	1992	116688	PER	Inchture
1870	1986	1606	1992	116688	SEL	Galashiels
CRAIGIE						
....	....	1650	1992	127299	ABD	Aberdeen
1634	?	ALL	ALL	101370	FIF	Balchristie
1840	1900	1800	1840	120286	PER	Coupar Angus
CRAIGS						
....	....	1780	1987	126241	DUR	South Shields
1980	1987	1780	1987	126241	NBL	ALL
1860	1900	ALL	1860	134260	NBL	Blyth
CRAIK						
....	....	1700	1850	134546	ANS	Glenisla
....	....	1700	1850	134546	ANS	Oathlaw
CRAIN						
....	....	1700	1850	147613	IOM	Peel
CRAINE						
1750	1795	1700	1750	174130	LEI	Tugby
CRAM						
....	....	ALL	ALL	116718	ALL	Name Study
1780	1820	1700	1900	130915	ELN	Dirleton
CRAME						
....	1936	....	....	147869	BRK	Hungerford
....	1936	....	....	147869	WIL	???
CRAMMOND						
1790	1880	1550	1920	179655	SCT	Forfar
CRAMOND						
....	....	ALL	ALL	179655	ALL	Name Study
1823	1992	1700	1823	172014	BDS	Coldstream

Known From	To	Researching From	To	Ref	Cty	Place
CRAMP						
1670	1850	1580	1992	173096	KEN	St Lawrence
1620	1850	1580	1992	173096	KEN	St Peters
1905	1908	1900	1982	120987	LEI	Leicester
1780	1870	1600	1780	152463	LEI	Seagrave
1600	1900	1600	1900	122521	SSX	Crowhurst
CRAMPE						
1550	1650	1500	1992	173096	KEN	Birchington
CRAMPTON						
1550	1850	1550	1850	134759	KEN	Cranbrook
1835	1930	ALL	ALL	113859	KEN	Tonbridge Wells
1880	1900	1800	1880	147478	SSX	Hastings
1600	1970	1400	1600	114634	WIC	Dublin
1870	1992	1700	1850	115584	YKS	Outlane
CRANCH						
1796	....	ALL	1796	137545	DEV	Exeter
CRANE						
1726	1940	....	....	128996	CAM	Thorney
1860	1900	1700	1992	167592	CHS	Chester
1900	1992	1700	1900	132772	DBY	???
1851	1992	1450	1850	127787	DOR	ALL
....	....	1700	1900	132772	GAL	???
....	....	?	....	128589	HRT	Baldock
1822	....	1700	1822	179183	HRT	Grat Amwell
1808	1872	1700	1808	160709	KEN	Maidstone
1800	1820	1700	1992	167592	LAN	Liverpool
1870	1907	1908	1992	127787	LEI	Leicester
1755	1814	1650	1760	131377	LIN	Corringham
1880	1910	1850	1992	176281	MDX	Ealing
1885	1960	1885	1960	116726	NFK	Cromer
1740	1860	1600	1860	100927	NFK	Great Yarmouth
1835	1867	1750	1850	131377	NFK	Hevingham
1814	1890	1650	1890	116726	NFK	North Walsham
....	1915	ALL	ALL	118885	NRY	Middlesborough
1830	1890	1750	1830	179140	SFK	Chelmondiston
1785	1940	1750	1785	159158	SFK	Kelsale
1897	ALL	ALL	1850	116734	WAR	Birmingham
1849	1872	1872	1900	145513	WIL	Oxenwood
CRANFIELD						
....	....	ALL	ALL	116742	ALL	Name Study
ALL	ALL	ALL	ALL	116742	ALL	ALL
1820	....	....	....	103608	ESS	Wickford
1840	....	1800	....	134686	LAN	Manchester
CRANFORD						
1720	1850	1700	1750	124699	HAM	East
CRANMER						
....	....	1800	....	156833	STS	???
CRANN						
1914	1960	ALL	1960	146315	YKS	Leeds
CRANNA						
1780	1870	....	....	130915	ABD	Tarves
CRANSHAW						
1834	1894	1500	1992	117900	LAN	Bamber Bridge
CRANSON						
1795	1800	....	....	145688	KEN	Woolwich
CRANSTON						
ALL	1831	....	....	105368	CAV	Virginia
1850	1932	1850	1950	146536	LKS	Shotts
1840	1900	1700	1840	143812	LND	ALL
1700	1900	1700	....	111724	MLN	???
1825	1992	ALL	1825	157198	NBL	Kirknewton
1825	1992	ALL	1825	157198	SCT	???
CRANSTOUN						
1801	1880	1700	1800	168386	LKS	Crawford
CRANTON						
1780	1820	1700	1780	112569	KEN	Whareborn
CRAPNELL						
1861	1870	1800	1900	123811	SFK	Copton
CRAPP						
1840	....	1800	1900	139114	DEV	Plymouth
1813	1992	1500	1992	175498	LND	Lambeth
CRASE						
1860	1960	1860	....	116750	ENG	Rudruthford
CRASKE						
....	....	ALL	ALL	139769	ALL	Name Study
1750	1840	1600	1800	118907	LND	East End
1770	1800	ALL	1770	108197	NFK	Cromer
1783	1855	1650	1783	139769	NFK	Lyng
....	....	1700	1800	140627	NFK	Norwich
1825	1850	1750	1825	132640	SRY	Lambeth
CRATE						
1775	1882	1841	1881	116769	HAM	Stoke Charity
1882	1992	1882	1992	116769	NBL	ALL
CRATHERN						
1872	1940	1700	1872	137049	MDX	North East London
CRAUGHWELL						
....	1860	....	....	126276	IRL	Galway
1862	1876	1861	1881	126276	STS	Hammerwich
CRAVEN						
1707	....	1650	1750	179078	LAN	Tatham
1860	1992	?	?	176702	WYK	Bingley
1849	1910	1823	1849	146706	YKS	Allerston
1800	1960	1800	1900	167851	YKS	Bridlington
....	....	1700	1756	146706	YKS	Ebberston
1699	1850	1699	1850	177814	YKS	Ebberston
1690	1750	1650	1992	114901	YKS	Harewood
1805	1915	ALL	1805	106909	YKS	Heaton
1733	1817	ALL	1733	102350	YKS	Kellington
1733	1992	....	....	134619	YKS	Kellington
1766	1780	1730	1790	149152	YKS	Leeds
1800	1960	1800	1900	167851	YKS	Scarborough
1832	1905	1832	1900	149152	YKS	Sheffield
1750	....	1700	1750	160024	YKS	Thornton
CRAW						
1800	1897	1700	1960	118680	LEX	ALL
CRAWFORD						
....	....	ALL	ALL	175692	ALL	Name Study
ALL	ALL	ALL	1800	116785	ALL	ALL
1832	1851	ALL	1832	149632	AYR	Ardrossan
....	1780	ALL	ALL	129933	AYR	Kirkmichael
1780	1850	1600	1800	167983	AYR	Largs
....	....	1800	1900	175889	BUT	Rothesay
1800	....	1800	1900	116793	CHS	Nantwich
1848	1992	1600	1848	100579	DOW	Ballyhay
1636	1636	ALL	ALL	130508	DUR	Gateshead
1813	1860	ALL	1813	122386	DUR	Ryton
1813	1860	ALL	1813	122386	DUR	Winlaton
ALL	1800	ALL	ALL	116785	ENG	ALL
1750	1800	1600	1750	142670	FIF	Dunfermline
....	....	1700	1850	175889	INV	Isle Of Barra
....	....	1750	1850	153486	KEN	Woolwich
1800	1992	....	....	176125	LIN	Asterby
1767	1880	1600	1760	116815	LIN	Coningsby
1767	1880	1600	1760	116815	LIN	Frithville
1800	1992	....	....	176125	LIN	Goulceby
1915	1960	1800	1915	134074	LND	Fulham
1837	1858	1800	1858	126586	MDX	Whitechapel
1698	1750	1600	1750	130125	NBL	Bamburgh
1790	1820	ALL	1820	152048	RFW	Eastwood
1852	1873	1800	1992	124044	SRY	Weybridge
1780	1870	....	....	142670	SSX	Brighton
1750	....	....	....	141798	STI	St Ninians
1840	1880	ALL	ALL	150347	WAR	Birmingham
1740	1790	1700	1740	122904	WLN	Torpichen
ALL	1800	ALL	ALL	116785	WLS	ALL
1847	1871	ALL	1871	151645	WOR	Bromsgrove
1800	1900	1700	1800	124257	YKS	Hawnby
1800	1900	1700	1800	124257	YKS	Huby
CRAWLEY						
1830	1992	1800	1920	118869	BDF	Bedford
1850	1980	1850	1992	171417	DEV	Plymouth
1800	1830	1620	1830	118869	HRT	Hitchen
1838	1917	ALL	ALL	104183	HRT	Tring
1860	1960	1700	1860	134074	IRL	Cork
1850	ALL	....	....	117560	MDX	Shoreditch
1805	1851	1700	1804	131245	MDX	Spitalfields
CRAWSHAW						
1816	1893	ALL	1816	160008	WYK	Mirfield
1796	1818	ALL	1818	104299	YKS	Barnsley
1860	1870	1800	1860	110078	YKS	Dewsbury
CRAXFORD						
1811	1992	1700	1811	105902	NTH	Middleton
CRAY						
1800	1850	1750	1800	115649	SRY	Lambeth
1800	1850	1750	1800	115649	WIL	Trowbridge
CRAYFORD						
ALL	1800	1450	1700	116785	ALL	ALL
CRAYSTON						
1600	1992	1600	1992	152196	WES	Heversham
CRAZE						
1865	1992	ALL	1865	134783	CON	Phillack
CREAK						
1745	1774	....	....	129747	NFK	North Wotton
CREAMER						
1818	1884	1700	1850	175218	NFK	North West
CREASER						
1778	1810	....	....	167479	YKS	Dunnington

Known From	To	Researching From	To	Ref	Cty	Place
CREASER contd.						
1830	1992	1700	1830	132241	YKS	Huddersfield
1830	1992	1700	1830	132241	YKS	Meltham
1810	1904	....	....	167479	YKS	Strensall
CREASEY						
1785	1825	....	....	114871	KEN	Catsfield
1750	1785	1700	1750	114871	KEN	Ninfield
1825	1870	....	....	114871	KEN	Speldhurst
1750	1992	ALL	1750	158437	LIN	Billinghay
....	1710	1500	1710	175072	LIN	Billinghay
1800	1900	....	....	111368	MDX	Marylebone
1786	1820	ALL	1786	143731	SFK	Hartismere
CREASY						
1854	1992	....	1900	137642	DEV	Ilsington
1854	1992	....	1900	137642	LND	Islington
CREATON						
1813	1821	1813	1821	136980	SRY	Southwark
CREBER						
1835	1880	....	....	169722	DEV	Sheepstor
....	....	1750	1835	169722	DEV	Walkhampton
CRECHLO						
....	....	ALL	1750	103284	LND	???
CREE						
....	....	ALL	ALL	165964	ALL	Name Study
1721	1992	1600	1900	165964	AYR	???
1783	1826	1700	1900	165964	CLA	Ennis
1850	....	....	....	151785	DBY	Beighton
1643	1992	1600	1900	165964	DBY	???
1775	1992	1775	1992	133450	DEV	Plymouth
....	....	ALL	ALL	116823	DOW	Carrowdore
1840	1992	1600	1900	165964	DOW	???
1760	1910	1700	1900	165964	DUR	Aukland
1847	1992	1847	1992	116823	DUR	Wolniston
1694	1992	1600	1900	165964	FIF	???
1775	1850	1700	1775	179574	LKS	Biggar
1694	1992	1600	1900	165964	LKS	Glasgow
1775	1850	1700	1775	179574	LKS	Lanark
1571	1992	1500	1900	165964	PER	???
1700	1900	1800	1992	133450	SCT	Perth
CREED						
1781	1860	1775	1875	145300	BKM	Waddesden
1840	1900	....	....	157724	BRK	Reading
1840	1980	1840	1880	116831	COR	Kildorrery
1850	1950	1850	1950	145300	HRT	Watford
1777	1800	1700	1777	142328	KEN	ALL
1840	1925	1840	1925	142891	KEN	Plumstead
1880	1918	1880	ALL	110922	LND	Lambeth
1850	1900	1837	1900	118540	MDX	Islington
1838	1918	1838	ALL	110922	MDX	Westminster
1792	1851	ALL	ALL	105015	NFK	Lynn
1733	1800	1700	1800	145300	OXF	Bicester
1756	1885	1650	1885	110922	OXF	Oxford
1800	1966	1700	1800	171182	SOM	ALL
1795	1795	....	....	127426	WAR	Edgbaston
CREEK						
1800	1992	1400	1800	116858	CAM	Isle Of Ely
1775	1881	1740	1910	118079	ESS	Chrishall
1775	1881	1740	1910	118079	ESS	Heydon
1753	....	ALL	1730	130079	OXF	Bicester
CREEMER						
....	....	1750	1825	177229	DEV	Exbourne
CREEN						
....	....	1700	1900	179531	ALL	ALL
CREER						
1804	1832	....	1804	111767	IOM	Union Mills
CREESY						
1825	....	1700	1825	157147	SRY	Newington
CREETON						
1800	1835	1600	1800	176133	HUM	Sutton In Holderness
CREIGHTON						
1825	1868	1868	1900	140880	BRK	Hungerford
1825	1868	1868	1900	140880	BRK	Inken
1680	1750	....	....	152277	DUR	Chester Le Street
1875	1940	ALL	ALL	120154	DUR	Sunderland
1770	1850	....	....	152277	LIN	Louth
1810	1850	....	....	152277	MDX	London
....	....	1750	1825	140880	SCT	ALL
1735	1840	....	....	152277	WES	Bampton
1872	1950	ALL	1872	146315	YKS	Kexborough
1872	1950	ALL	1872	146315	YKS	S Elmsall
CREIGHTON-BROWNE						
1800	....	1770	1820	160822	???	???
CRELLIN						
1839	....	1820	1839	111767	IOM	Kirk German
CREMAR						
1780	1850	1600	1780	158046	???	London
CREMER						
1818	1992	1500	1818	141089	NFK	ALL
1835	1860	1835	1900	129607	SRY	Bermondsey
CREPIN						
....	....	ALL	ALL	129755	ALL	Name Study
1870	1992	ALL	ALL	129755	KEN	Dover
1840	1860	ALL	ALL	129755	KEN	Gravesend
CRERAR						
1830	1904	1750	1904	140678	PER	Weem
CRESPEL						
....	....	ALL	ALL	154067	ALL	Name Study
1745	1875	ALL	ALL	154067	LND	Westminster
1650	1700	ALL	ALL	154067	NFK	Norwich
CRESSE CLARA						
....	1937	1937	....	166197	???	???
CRESSELL						
1771	1771	1700	1771	128449	WAR	Coventry
CRESSEY						
....	1820	1750	1840	120529	YKS	Doncaster
1700	1830	1600	1830	119717	YKS	Hemingbrough
CRESSWELL						
1832	1870	ALL	ALL	100919	BKM	Hambleden
....	....	ALL	ALL	100919	BKM	Marlow
1803	....	ALL	ALL	155608	DBY	Alfreton
1790	1939	1700	1790	178500	DBY	Selston
1814	....	1800	1830	116572	DEV	Plymouth
1830	....	1750	1850	102016	ESS	Copford
1690	1710	....	1730	116866	HEF	???
1767	1824	1700	1767	122580	LND	East
1800	....	1770	1840	169625	NTT	Nottingham
1650	1750	....	....	140554	OXF	Mapledurham
1900	1940	ALL	1940	115045	STS	West Bromwich
....	....	1700	1800	147613	STS	Wolverhampton
1728	1869	1700	1870	116866	WOR	???
CRESWELL						
1860	....	....	....	116874	MDX	Hoxten
....	....	ALL	ALL	116874	NTT	???
CRESWICK						
1890	1930	1890	1930	119474	YKS	Liverton Mines
CRESWICKE						
....	....	ALL	1700	103284	SOM	Bristol
CRETON						
1872	1935	ALL	1872	146315	YKS	Kexborough
1872	1935	ALL	1872	146315	YKS	S Elmsall
CREW						
1700	1850	1850	1992	110124	BDF	Luton
1790	1850	1850	1992	166804	BRK	Faringdon
1870	1992	1800	1900	101265	DOR	Beaminster
1784	1823	?	1900	136611	GLS	Dirham
1660	1800	1500	1660	148113	GLS	Hawkesbury
1784	1823	?	1900	136611	GLS	Hinton
1676	1738	1500	1676	129577	IOW	???
1856	....	1700	....	132128	LND	Poplar
1848	1848	1800	1850	178004	WIL	Sopworth
CREWE						
....	....	ALL	ALL	116882	CHS	ALL
1602	1900	1602	1763	160237	CHS	Bunbury
1602	1900	1602	1763	160237	CHS	Sandbach
1808	1843	....	....	116602	LAN	Liverpool
1795	1848	1795	1821	160237	STS	Pottries
CREWES						
....	....	1700	1880	135046	CON	Roseland
CREWS						
....	....	ALL	ALL	116890	ALL	Name Study
1790	1830	1790	1830	148377	CON	Saltash
1742	1860	1650	1742	166723	CON	Stoke Climsland
1810	1812	1750	1860	121568	SOM	West
CREYE						
1200	1300	1200	1300	154881	KEN	Paulin Creye
CRIBB						
1776	1992	ALL	ALL	115126	DOR	Blandford
CRICHTON						
1818	1850	1750	1820	117943	ANS	Dundee
1879	1881	1875	1992	116904	CUL	Carlisle
1820	....	1750	1992	116904	DFS	???
....	....	1836	1863	116912	DUB	Kilmainham
1863	1865	1862	1867	116904	DUR	Sunderland
....	....	1780	....	149187	FIF	Abdie
1863	1992	1820	1863	116912	KEN	Woolwich
....	1400	ALL	1513	162507	SCT	Cranston Riddel

Known From To Researching From To Ref Cty Place

CRICHTON contd.
1851 1875 1841 1900 116904 WAR Coventry
CRICK
1900 1960 .... 110124 BDF Luton
1780 1780 1750 1800 166677 CAM Kirtling
1874 1992 1750 1874 121703 CAM Peteroborugh
.... 1700 1900 110124 HRT Kings Walden
.... 1800 1900 110124 HRT Lilley
.... 1800 1900 110124 HRT Offley
1844 1860 1800 1875 136042 LND Poplar
1780 1840 1700 1850 126268 LND Westminster
1820 1890 ALL ALL 162205 NTH Geddington
1753 .... ALL 1730 130079 OXF Bicester
1840 1992 1700 1840 116939 RAD Knighton
1870 1931 1850 1940 136042 SSX Cuckfield
.... 1700 1840 116939 ??? Westhorpe
CRICKETT
1700 1700 .... 159883 KEN Sandwich
CRICKMAY
1802 .... 1841 .... 116947 WIL Hindon
1889 .... 1889 1992 116947 ??? London
CRICKMORE
1856 1992 1700 1856 118265 SFK Lowestoft
CRIDDLE
1800 1992 ALL ALL 155454 SOM Williton
1800 1992 ALL ALL 155454 WLS Cardiff
CRIDLAND
1774 1877 .... 175439 LND Spitalfields
1811 1880 1700 1811 171980 SOM Bridgwater
1774 1877 .... 175439 ??? Bristol
CRIGHTON
1854 1992 1800 1900 116963 LAN Manchester
CRILLY
1800 1875 .... 138150 STD East Kilbride
CRIMBLE
1678 1708 1650 1700 177555 DOR South
CRIMES
1750 1980 1550 1900 149837 CHS ALL
1800 1900 ALL 1800 126322 CHS Chester
CRIMP
1650 ALL .... 103381 CON Kingsbridge
CRINGLE
1750 1900 .... 1750 136212 NFK Wells
CRINKLEY
1833 1980 .... 166855 NBL South
CRINNION
1800 1992 1800 1992 125679 DUR ALL
CRIPPEN
.... ALL ALL 116971 ALL Name Study
1837 1992 1066 1992 116971 ALL ALL
CRIPPS
1865 1918 1830 1865 142360 BRK Chaddleworth
1761 1840 .... 153176 BRK Sunningwell
1900 1948 1880 1992 121568 GLS Birdlip
1850 1923 1788 1923 141550 GLS Cirencester
1853 1876 1800 1900 170526 HAM Portsmouth
.... 1800 1900 170283 KEN Tonbridge
1857 .... 1850 1900 170283 LND St Benit
1850 1923 1788 1923 141550 LND ???
1802 1850 ALL 1802 108642 MDX Soho
1743 1769 .... 148261 SOM Kingstone
1810 1840 .... 127779 SRY Egham
CRIPS
1780 .... 142158 WIL Aldbourne
CRIPWELL
1580 1870 1400 1580 172847 NTT Barton In Fabis
1580 1870 1400 1580 172847 NTT Bunny
1580 1870 1400 1580 172847 NTT Ruddington
CRISFIELD
1400 1900 .... 116998 KEN Lenham
CRISFORD
1795 1900 1700 1900 177288 SSX Kent Border
CRISP
1851 1860 1700 1851 172049 BDF Ampthill
1864 .... ALL 1870 170674 CAM Willingham
1813 1839 1600 1813 116637 DUR Bishopwearmouth
1813 1839 1600 1813 116637 DUR Sunderland
1800 .... 145920 HAM ???
1796 1800 1750 1850 110191 MDX London
1770 1802 1700 1820 117013 NFK Erpingham
1726 1968 1600 1750 117013 NFK Snettisham
.... 1700 .... 1700 177695 NTH Long Buckby
1680 1820 ALL ALL 128449 NTT Nottingham
1739 .... 129747 SFK Parham

CRISP contd.
1838 .... 1800 1838 176885 SRY Lambeth
1851 1860 1700 1851 172049 STS Lichfield
1762 1969 1700 1762 143707 WIL Bradford On Avon
1822 1846 1700 1822 151300 WOR Worcester
CRISPIN
.... 1900 1992 109894 DOR Weymouth
CRISTALL
1820 1850 1750 1820 144150 ANS Dundee
CRITCH
1750 1980 .... 117021 ALL ALL
1770 1960 1560 1770 117021 KEN ALL
1770 1850 1960 .... 117021 LAN Manchester
1765 1960 1565 1765 117021 LND ALL
CRITCHELL
1700 1880 1600 1900 104361 DOR Abbotsbury
CRITCHETT
1810 .... 1800 1850 102016 LND St Benet
1800 .... 1750 1850 102016 SRY Bermondsey
CRITCHLEY
1778 1822 .... 138851 LAN Bolton
1840 1900 1800 1870 178489 LAN Rainhill
CRITCHLOW
1884 1890 1770 1777 107832 STS Sheen
CRITTAL
.... 1900 1940 166979 KEN Tonbridge
CROAD
1847 1914 1847 1914 127817 DOR Weymouth
1886 1965 1847 1900 127817 HAM Portsmouth
CROASDALE
.... ALL ALL 173126 ALL Name Study
CROCKER
1800 1840 .... 174556 CGN Lampeter
1854 1920 1820 1854 158267 CON Ladock
1795 1800 1750 1840 168580 CON Ladock
.... 1750 1850 117714 CON St Mawes
1779 1812 1700 1850 115681 DOR Bridport
1820 .... 1800 1880 135429 SOM Bath
1817 .... ALL 1840 174815 SOM Bristol
1813 ? ? 1813 136611 SOM Thorn St Margaret
CROCKETT
1906 1992 ALL 1906 144053 ALL ALL
.... ALL ALL 152226 ALL ALL
1800 1853 1750 1800 100277 BKM Bhesham
1834 1992 ALL 1850 115177 LND St Pancras
1820 1880 1800 1880 102717 MDX Chelsea
1846 1870 1700 1890 112216 MON Central
1880 1905 1880 1920 102717 SRY Camberwell
1715 1992 ALL 1715 117048 STS Smethwick
CROCKETT-SCOTT
1851 1910 1826 1851 112720 LEI Leicester
CROCKFORD
.... 1700 ALL 111724 ALL ALL
CROCKWELL
1750 1850 .... 177474 DEV Coffinswell
CROCOMBE
.... ALL ALL 117056 ALL Name Study
1569 ALL 1560 ALL 117056 ALL ALL
1850 1992 1850 1992 126322 CHS Chester
1800 1850 1700 1800 131350 DEV Lynton
.... 1800 1992 126322 MON Cwmbran
CROFFORD
ALL 1800 1700 1800 116785 ALL ALL
CROFOOT
ALL 1800 1500 1800 116785 ALL ALL
CROFT
1750 .... 123641 DBY Chesterfield
.... 1000 1100 124974 HEF Croft
.... 1700 1992 125091 KEN Benenden
.... 1700 1992 125091 KEN Tenterden
1785 1960 1700 1900 164097 LAN Bickerstaffe
1785 1960 1700 1900 164097 LAN Liverpool
1826 1923 1780 1950 118443 LAN Preesall
1800 1975 1780 1980 168920 LAN Tockholes
1579 1636 ALL ALL 141615 LAN Warton
1750 1800 ALL ALL 152021 LIN Ashby Puerorum
1805 1805 ALL 1810 113611 NYK Whitby
1712 1931 1700 1851 129194 SFK East
1775 1775 .... 139971 SSX East Hoathly
1732 1960 1600 1737 124257 YKS Acaster
1732 1960 1600 1737 124257 YKS Naburn
CROFTON
1600 1940 1600 1940 117064 DUR Central

Known From	To	Researching From	To	Ref	Cty	Place
CROFTS						
1783	....	....	....	142360	CAM	Ely
1823	1860	1700	1890	153079	CAM	March
1764	1787	1740	1764	147885	CHS	West Kirby
1763	?	?	?	166642	KEN	Boxley
1792	1913	ALL	1792	114553	NTT	Retford
1790	1900	1750	1900	112879	WAR	Burton Hastings
....	....	1800	1880	133604	WIL	Chippenham
CROKER						
1790	1855	1790	1855	114073	HAM	South Stoneham
1770	....	ALL	ALL	116394	IRL	Dublin
1700	1900	1700	1900	127582	WAT	Waterford
CROMACK						
1745	1900	....	....	141984	YKS	South Milford
1900	1920	....	....	141984	YKS	Whitwood
CROME						
1840	1992	1800	1992	117080	LND	???
1750	1992	....	1992	117080	NFK	ALL
1784	....	....	....	115576	NFK	Swaffham
1840	1910	1800	1992	100862	SRY	Lambeth
1840	1910	1800	1992	100862	SRY	Southwark
CROMER						
1350	1450	1350	1450	154881	CAM	Willingham
CROMP						
1785	1785	....	....	144355	KEN	South
CROMPE						
1466	1587	1400	1600	173096	KEN	Bredger
CROMPORN-BUSH						
?	?	?	?	124702	HRT	Bishops Stortford
CROMPTON						
1840	1920	....	....	102369	LAN	Bolton
1765	....	....	1765	111767	LAN	Bolton
1820	1992	1600	1820	119822	LAN	Bolton
1870	1880	1800	1870	146110	LAN	Bolton
1845	1992	1700	1845	117099	LAN	Manchester
1655	1705	1655	1705	159492	LAN	Oldham
1779	1916	?	1800	164976	LAN	Oldham
1796	1888	1700	1800	126411	LAN	Prestwich
1785	1992	....	....	144088	STS	Biddulph
1870	1880	1700	1870	133701	WOR	Lower Mitton
1810	1814	1810	1814	141097	YKS	Beeford
1770	1808	1700	1810	141097	YKS	Bridlington
1815	1825	1815	1825	141097	YKS	Nafferton
1837	1900	1750	1875	141097	YKS	North Newbald
1780	1850	1700	1780	124362	YKS	Ripponden
CROMWELL						
1087	1940	900	1087	105074	ALL	ALL
CRON						
1785	1865	1700	1785	126772	DFS	Durisdeer
1786	1903	1750	1786	144231	DFS	Durrisdeer
CRONE						
?	?	?	?	158372	LND	ALL
CRONEY						
1814	....	1710	1814	134473	SRY	Lambeth
CRONIN						
....	....	1800	1887	130141	COR	Boherbue
....	....	1800	1887	130141	COR	Kanturk
1770	1795	1700	1770	114871	IRL	Cork
CRONKSHAW						
1802	1802	1500	1802	169439	LAN	Haslingden
CRONSHAW						
1781	1841	1700	1880	178233	LAN	Blackrod
CROOK						
ALL	1900	1840	1880	135429	DEV	Broadclyst
1900	1992	1840	1880	135429	DEV	Exminster
1800	1850	1700	1830	117129	DEV	Tiverton
....	....	1820	1840	117137	GLS	Absom
1800	1840	1700	1900	136034	GLS	Bisley
1884	1926	1700	1884	147761	GLS	Forest Of Dean
1800	1850	1750	1850	106631	GLS	Stroud
1830	1850	1820	1870	117129	GNT	Abergavenny
1813	1992	1800	1930	117145	LAN	Bolton
1820	1920	1700	1820	132632	LAN	Fylde
1813	1992	1800	1930	117145	LAN	Tockholes
1813	1988	1600	1813	159522	LAN	Walton Le Dale
....	1875	1890	1950	106518	MDX	London
1700	....	....	....	148768	MDX	Marylebone
1850	1920	....	....	117137	MON	Abertillery
....	....	1840	1870	117137	MON	Risca
1750	1992	1770	1992	124699	NFK	Central
1731	1848	1500	1731	132853	NFK	Attleborough
1770	1850	1650	1850	107611	SOM	Farleigh Hungerford
....	....	1780	1820	117137	WIL	Melksham
1787	1875	....	....	115606	WIL	Ogbourne St Andrew
CROOK contd.						
1850	1900	1700	1850	100765	WIL	Shiteparish
1759	1802	1740	1810	142018	WIL	Whiteparish
CROOKE						
....	....	1800	1860	176036	KEN	Bromley
1500	1800	1500	1900	170216	WIL	ALL
CROOKES						
1796	1968	1700	1800	176516	WYK	Rotherham
1796	1968	1700	1800	176516	WYK	Sheffield
CROOKS						
1780	1800	1700	1850	130915	ELN	Dirleton
1810	1871	1750	1809	172006	LAN	St Helens
1780	1815	....	....	129747	LIN	Stow In Lindsey
1796	1798	1790	1850	159905	NBL	North Shields
CROOKSHANK						
....	....	1860	1992	171638	ALL	ALL
CROOM						
1850	1992	1750	1850	117153	DOR	ALL
1680	1723	....	....	165999	GLS	Cromhall
CROOME						
1700	1750	ALL	1700	141224	GLS	South
1726	1787	1650	1726	148938	GLS	Cromhall
1750	1900	....	....	108677	GLS	North Cerney
1680	....	....	....	107085	SCT	Edinburgh
CROOT						
1800	1850	1780	1850	103225	CAM	Camlingay
CROOTE						
1792	1939	1500	1792	125695	CAM	Gamlingay
CROPLEY						
1750	1810	1600	1810	170291	LIN	Folkingham
1689	....	ALL	....	104515	LIN	Welboure
CROPPER						
1850	1865	1850	1865	136980	CHS	Stockport
CROSBIE						
1880	1930	1860	1900	123145	LOG	Longford
1740	1850	....	....	168777	SSX	Fishbourne
CROSBY						
1750	1992	1600	1992	130125	CUL	Bolton
1833	1891	1800	1841	171425	DUR	Sunderland
1770	1992	1700	1770	105392	LIN	Thurlby
1793	1851	1720	1850	176621	SFK	Ixworth Thorpe
1776	1800	1700	1800	126586	SFK	???
1806	1806	1750	1830	136042	SOM	Bath
1700	1870	1400	1700	140678	WES	Long Marton
1840	1870	....	....	102946	YKS	Farlington
1780	1840	....	....	102946	YKS	Felixkirk
1740	1992	1700	1740	117161	YKS	Fylingdales
1800	1840	....	....	102946	YKS	Kilburn
1780	1800	....	....	102946	YKS	Kilvington
CROSFIELD						
1599	1725	ALL	ALL	141615	LAN	Morecambe
CROSIER						
1822	1860	1811	1860	109819	MOG	Drumswords
CROSLAND						
1730	1850	1700	1850	123595	YKS	Holmfirth
1868	1910	1918	ALL	154946	YKS	Huddersfield
....	....	1750	1830	133760	YKS	Lindley
CROSLEY						
1700	1770	1660	1700	122904	LAN	Burnley
1796	1850	1700	1900	102520	YKS	Thornton
CROSS						
1700	1850	ALL	1850	117188	ANS	Coupar Angus
1830	1830	1790	1830	159905	ARM	???
....	....	1690	1880	135046	AVN	Bristol
1820	1992	1700	1820	117242	CAM	Ely
1780	1992	1700	1800	117218	CHS	Northwich
1780	1992	1700	1780	117196	CHS	Northwich
1880	1910	1600	1880	118648	CMA	Whitehaven
1815	1854	....	1815	160652	CON	Calstock
1630	1674	1600	1630	102571	CON	Lanlivery
1600	1900	1600	1900	160814	CON	Mevagissey
1747	....	....	....	172030	DEV	Halberton
1844	1992	1750	1844	154415	DEV	Plymouth
....	....	1750	1850	164798	DEV	Tiverton
1811	1891	....	....	139513	DOR	East
1811	1891	....	....	139513	DOR	West
1754	1992	....	....	139513	DOR	Buckhorn Weston
1778	1804	....	....	139513	DOR	Kington Magna
1806	....	1806	....	139513	DOR	Marnhill
1811	1891	....	....	139513	DOR	Provost
1811	1891	....	....	139513	DOR	Stours
1710	1800	1600	1710	158984	DOR	Wyke Regis
1870	1900	1870	1900	159905	DUR	South Shields
1840	1960	1700	1840	152587	ESS	Brightlingsea

Known From	To	Researching From	To	Ref	Cty	Place
CROSS contd.						
1855	?	1800	1854	167568	ESS	Stamford Le Hope
1877	....	1800	1900	160407	GLS	Bristol
1800	1890	1750	1900	108359	HUN	Easton
1780	1800	1700	1800	113204	IOM	Ballaugh
1800	1900	1700	1992	122742	IOW	Newport
1793	1855	1770	1793	117269	KEN	Brenchley
1790	1992	1700	1790	161179	LAN	Blackburn
1790	1992	1700	1790	161179	LAN	Chipping
1786	1878	1700	1786	163783	LAN	Woodplumpton
1791	1992	1700	1790	117226	LEI	Breedon On Hill
1850	1900	1700	1850	173452	LEI	Breedon On The Hill
1800	1921	....	....	162833	LEI	Leicester
1791	1992	1700	1790	117226	LEI	Loughborough
1600	1992	....	....	100633	LIN	???
1839	1866	1800	1900	139114	MDX	London
1870	1900	1800	1900	137618	MDX	Marylebone
1854	1855	....	1854	117234	MDX	Westminster
1860	1992	1850	1992	116807	MON	Newport
1770	1890	1600	1830	101834	NFK	South West
1866	1894	1840	1894	151599	NFK	Bawdswell
1920	1930	1850	1950	135925	NFK	Thornham
ALL	ALL	ALL	ALL	106054	NFK	Walpole St Peter
1804	1832	1800	1992	110205	NTT	Nottingham
1600	1992	....	....	100633	NTT	???
....	....	ALL	1770	114308	OXF	Bambury
1700	1818	ALL	1992	168696	OXF	Enstone
1700	1850	ALL	1850	117188	PER	Cargill
1756	1992	1700	1756	158143	PER	Redgorton
1800	....	1700	1950	141151	SFK	ALL
1806	1840	ALL	1806	139513	SOM	Abbascombe
1742	1826	....	....	139513	SOM	Bayford
1793	1821	1600	1992	115525	SOM	Blagdon
1877	....	1800	1900	160407	SOM	Bristol
1658	1901	....	....	139513	SOM	Cucklington
1811	....	1810	1811	139513	SOM	Frome
1690	1972	1735	1780	160407	SOM	Frome
1570	1826	....	....	139513	SOM	Horsington
1650	1860	1650	1992	112941	SOM	Lydeard St Lawrence
1776	1781	1735	1776	160407	SOM	Marston Bigot
1742	1826	....	....	139513	SOM	Stoke Trister
1806	1840	ALL	1806	139513	SOM	Stowell
....	....	1690	1880	135046	SOM	Taunton
1780	1830	1750	1800	144657	SOM	West Buckland
1730	1857	1700	1737	150320	SOM	West Buckland
1741	1992	....	....	139513	SOM	Wincanton
1800	1840	1700	1900	138517	SOM	???
1935	1980	....	....	135925	SRY	Farnham
....	....	1900	1930	137618	STI	Kirkintilloch
....	....	ALL	1850	142298	TYR	???
1803	1846	?	1803	158569	WAR	Monks Kirby
1862	1976	....	....	139513	WIL	Bonham
1787	1923	1735	1787	160407	WIL	Corsley
1757	1886	....	1757	165484	WIL	East Knoyle
1790	1790	1750	1820	174599	WIL	Kilmington
1848	1850	1800	1992	146331	WIL	???
1786	1814	1750	1820	148121	YKS	Hull
CROSSER						
....	....	ALL	ALL	116068	ALL	Name Study
CROSSFIELD						
1700	1775	1600	1992	114901	YKS	Harewood
1650	1700	1600	1992	114901	YKS	Weardley
CROSSKILL						
....	....	ALL	ALL	148393	ALL	Name Study
CROSSLAND						
1858	1930	1930	1992	117277	CHS	Newton
1814	1868	1868	1992	117277	DBY	Chapel En Le Frith
....	....	ALL	ALL	115231	DBY	???
1793	1814	1700	1793	117277	LAN	Manchester
....	....	1700	1800	134848	LAN	Manchester
1880	1950	....	....	126276	WRY	Barnsley
1900	1988	....	....	126276	WRY	Mexborough
1817	....	1880	ALL	166138	YKS	Holbeck
1850	1900	1600	1850	115134	YKS	Sheffield
CROSSLEY						
1764	1828	1730	1880	123404	DBY	Lullington
1825	1930	1700	1992	116742	LAN	Burnley
1817	1817	1775	1817	174211	LAN	Burnley
....	....	1700	1900	118923	LAN	Manchester
1873	....	....	....	132500	LAN	Oldham
1873	....	....	....	132500	LAN	Rochdale
1873	....	....	....	132500	LAN	Shaw
1866	1899	1839	1899	118354	SRY	Mitcham
1700	1730	1700	1730	107522	WRY	Todmorden
CROSSLEY contd.						
1811	1992	ALL	1811	100803	WYK	Erringden
1800	1900	1700	1800	173452	YKS	South
....	....	1850	1890	169722	YKS	West
1800	1900	1700	1800	173452	YKS	West
1820	1850	1750	1850	116742	YKS	Halifax
....	....	ALL	1800	167665	YKS	Leeds
1764	1855	1764	1855	177547	YKS	Peniston
1800	1900	....	....	167665	YKS	Rothwell
1820	1830	1800	1850	123536	YKS	Thornton
CROSSMAN						
1700	1821	1700	1821	145602	DEV	Bideford
1800	1848	1650	1800	141372	DEV	Sandford
1500	1774	....	....	165999	GLS	Almondsbury
1500	1774	....	....	165999	GLS	Henbury
1880	1907	1840	1880	172170	MDX	London
1687	1869	1600	1900	149888	SOM	Cossingdon
CROSSWELL						
1760	1992	1600	1760	117285	HAM	Basingstoke
1790	1980	1700	1800	107611	NFK	Great Yarmouth
CROSTON						
1841	1891	1800	1891	142204	LAN	Westhoughton
CROTON						
1800	1860	1750	1900	138517	LAN	Aston Under Lyne
CROTOSHINSKY						
1903	1954	1850	1900	145424	ALL	ALL
CROTTY						
1864	1900	1864	1900	111457	LKS	???
CROUCH						
....	....	1750	1796	168777	HAM	Nether Wallop
1641	1680	1600	1800	141151	HRT	Buntingford
?	1992	1741	1992	172235	KEN	Headcorn
?	1992	1741	1992	172235	KEN	Marden
1890	1924	1800	1950	115886	LND	Central
1885	1911	1800	1970	115886	LND	South
1840	1860	1800	1900	152528	LND	Camberwell
1837	1872	1800	1837	149578	LND	Tottenham
1867	1992	1867	1992	117293	MDX	Brentford
1850	....	1850	1881	142638	MDX	Cricklewood
1797	1797	ALL	1797	117293	MDX	Hanwell
1800	1866	1700	1866	117293	MDX	Isleworth
1852	1950	ALL	ALL	100161	MDX	London
1832	1992	1750	1832	131806	MDX	Tottenham
1870	1950	1870	1992	100161	SFK	Lowestoft
1797	1881	1770	1900	115886	WIL	Collingbourne Kingston
1821	....	1800	1850	142638	WIL	Horningsham
CROUCHER						
1899	1900	1690	1900	100765	HAM	Southampton
1855	1855	ALL	1880	117307	KEN	Charing
1762	1873	1762	1873	138312	SRY	Dorking
1713	1832	1650	1713	119512	SSX	Felpham
CROUCHLEY						
1771	1820	1700	1800	117315	CHS	Daresbury
1820	1960	1700	1900	112372	HAM	Portsmouth
CROUCHMAN						
1880	1900	ALL	ALL	117323	ESS	Harlow
1926	1926	1700	1926	153206	HRT	???
1800	1900	ALL	ALL	117323	LND	ALL
1890	1920	ALL	ALL	117323	MDX	Enfield
CROUDACE						
1849	1885	1700	1869	129305	DUR	Evenwood
CROUTCH						
1820	1850	1600	1820	123587	SSX	Rotherfield
CROW						
1740	1992	1740	1890	106305	DUB	???
1790	1820	....	....	128759	HAM	Portsmouth
....	....	ALL	ALL	166812	HAM	Portsmouth
1820	1870	1700	1820	135348	LAN	Oldham
1670	1790	1600	1670	177024	LIN	Spridlington
1760	1760	ALL	ALL	162620	NBL	Newcastle
1800	1852	1795	1850	109819	NFK	Great Yarmouth
1700	1899	1640	1840	135941	SFK	Lakenheath
1500	1700	1500	1700	100420	WAR	Coventry
1500	1700	1500	1700	100420	WAR	Meriden
CROWCHER						
1680	1680	1650	1710	105333	SSX	Singleton
1800	1820	1780	1820	105333	SSX	West Stoke
CROWCOMBE						
1839	1892	1749	1892	107573	SOM	Bridgwater
1840	1900	1750	1840	145351	SOM	Langford Budville
CROWDER						
....	....	1890	....	136913	DUR	Sunderland
1830	1880	1830	1960	117536	LND	Peckham

Known From	To	Researching From	To	Ref	Cty	Place
CROWDER contd.						
1800 ?		ALL	ALL	172251	NTT	???
....	....	1865	....	136913	YKS	Hunslet
CROWE						
1830	1890	1800	1992	139203	FER	???
1920	1992	1900	1992	133450	KEN	???
....	....	ALL	1820	164631	LND	Mile End
1800	1900	ALL	ALL	131873	LND	Soho
1800	1850	ALL	ALL	131873	SOM	Bristol
1881	1940	1700	1881	146609	YKS	Ilkley
CROWELL						
1823	....	ALL	ALL	110272	CON	St Clether
CROWFOOT						
ALL	1800	1500	1800	116785	ALL	ALL
1873	1873	1800	1900	114685	LND	Marylebone
CROWFORD						
....	....	ALL	ALL	116785	ALL	Name Study
ALL	1800	1600	1800	116785	ALL	ALL
CROWFORTHE						
ALL	1800	1450	1600	116785	ALL	ALL
CROWGIE						
1670	1687	1600	1670	102571	CON	Gwennap
CROWHURST						
1734	....	....	1750	171441	KEN	Wormshill
....	....	?	1730	100935	SSX	ALL
1822	1844	1800	1822	128724	SSX	ALL
1820	1820	1700	1850	128163	SSX	East
1851	1992	....	....	165352	SSX	Hailsham
1872	1900	1600	1900	135968	SSX	Hartfield
1730	1900	....	....	100935	SSX	Withyam
1773	1992	1700	1800	117331	SSX	Withyham
CROWL						
1830	1900	1700	1830	165549	CON	St Stephens In Brannel
CROWLEY						
1883	1992	1800	1912	105899	DFS	Dumfries
....	1920	....	....	159999	IRL	Dublin
ALL	1826	....	....	105368	KER	???
1825	1860	1860	1992	137448	KER	???
1855	1992	ALL	ALL	117366	LAN	Liverpool
1873	1992	1700	1873	141143	LAN	Liverpool
1840	1980	1820	1840	145009	STS	West Bromwich
1796	1820	1700	1796	133167	WAR	Oldbury
CROWLSEY						
....	....	1770	1890	103713	BDF	Wilstead
CROWLY						
1578	1656	ALL	1578	168602	BDF	Campton
CROWMEADOW						
....	....	ALL	ALL	154768	ALL	Name Study
CROWMER						
1370	1613	1300	1600	154881	KEN	Sittingbourne
CROWSON						
....	....	ALL	ALL	104531	LIN	ALL
CROWTHER						
....	....	1800	1820	177725	EYK	Hull
1841	1992	1841	1899	145505	GLS	Blcokley
1863	1900	1800	1863	118354	LAN	Manchester
1800	1992	1700	1800	132268	LAN	Newton Heath
1730	1750	1650	1820	123145	SAL	Stoke St Milborough
1900	1928	1870	1959	152773	STS	Smethwick
1720	1910	1720	1910	107522	WRY	Todmorden
1832	1854	ALL	ALL	101486	WYK	Elland
1750	1810	1700	1760	170348	YKS	Almondbury
1841	1860	ALL	1841	173290	YKS	Halifax
1860	....	ALL	ALL	175587	YKS	Morley
CROXALL						
....	....	....	1800	117714	CON	St Just In Roseland
....	....	1750	1850	117714	CON	St Mawes
CROXFORD						
1800	1900	1700	1800	176257	ESS	ALL
1848	1878	1750	1848	150614	MDX	Hackney
CROXON						
1730	1935	1730	1920	156353	CAM	Haddenham
CROXSON						
1821	1821	1800	1850	100242	BRK	Reading
CROXTON						
1610	1900	1610	1830	127655	HUN	Great Catworth
1790	1850	....	1790	174025	OXF	Blackthorn
1665	1715	....	....	108871	WES	Warcop
CROYDEN						
1830	1844	1830	1900	122335	SFK	Woodbridge
CROYDON						
1840	1850	1800	1880	137111	GLS	Bristol

Known From	To	Researching From	To	Ref	Cty	Place
CROZIER						
....	....	1800	1880	138991	ESS	Chelmsford
1662	1803	1600	1662	174858	YKS	Hunmanby
CRUDDAS						
1750	1770	1700	1750	121339	DUR	Hamsterley
1775	1851	1700	1775	160148	DUR	Hamsterly
CRUDDINGTON						
....	....	ALL	ALL	134635	ALL	Name Study
CRUDGE						
....	....	ALL	ALL	149888	ALL	Name Study
ALL	ALL	ALL	ALL	103160	ALL	ALL
ALL	ALL	ALL	ALL	149888	ALL	ALL
1600	1750	1500	1750	132993	CON	West
1800 ?		ALL	1800	117382	DEV	Bampton
1713	1900	1600	1992	149888	DEV	Oakford
CRUDGINGTON						
1540	1992	1540	1992	134635	LND	???
1420	1992	1420	1992	134635	SAL	ALL
1786	....	1600	1800	145432	STS	???
1540	1992	1540	1992	134635	WOR	ALL
CRUICKSHANK						
1862	1920	1800	1900	126586	ABD	Cruden
1770	....	....	....	126497	ABD	Fyvie
1873	1873	1700	1873	106887	ABD	Grange
1820	1866	1820	1866	109819	ABD	Old Machar
1862	1920	1800	1900	126586	ABD	Peterhead
1806	1992	1700	1806	102997	GMP	Marnoch
1806	1992	1700	1806	102997	GMP	Rothiemay
CRUIKSHANK						
....	....	1810	1900	148210	ABD	Achterless
1811	1878	....	1878	175552	ABD	Daviot
CRUISE						
1841	1960	1841	1960	150827	IRL	???
1841	1960	1841	1960	150827	LAN	Liverpool
CRUMACK						
1815	1892	1700	1815	171611	YKS	Rotherham
CRUMBLE						
1810	1810	1500	1810	110310	LAN	Chaigley
CRUMLEY						
ALL	1900	1840	1920	136786	ALL	ALL
CRUMP						
1690	1992	ALL	1750	128171	CHS	Malpas
1769	....	1600	1769	125121	ESS	Barking
ALL	ALL	ALL	ALL	117390	HEF	ALL
1730	1780	ALL	ALL	139181	HEF	Clehonger
1630	1680	1500	1650	156515	HEF	Orleton
1782	1985	1760	1900	102806	HUN	Buckden
1859	1880	1790	1859	117471	LND	Bethnal Green
1850	1900	1800	1900	107611	WAR	Aston
CRUMPTON						
1740	1992	1740	1992	117412	GLS	Bristol
1815	1833	1767	1815	163686	WAR	Birmingham
1870	1880	1700	1870	133701	WOR	Lower Mitton
CRUMWELL						
1881	1950	1850	1950	178799	DOW	Kilhorne Annalong
CRUSCOMBE						
1540	1720	ALL	1540	158739	DEV	Braunton
CRUSE						
1772	1860	1700	1772	179663	CON	Stoke Climsland
1842	1950	1700	1900	140066	LAN	Liverpool
1859	1992	1800	1860	166316	MDX	Teddington
CRUTCHER						
1840	1920	1700	1900	119040	DOR	Cranborne
....	....	1700	1840	119040	HAM	New Forest
CRUTCHLEY						
1841	1910	1800	1841	175447	LAN	Oldham
1791	1906	1720	....	149039	NTH	Northampton
1630	1930	....	....	129054	SAL	???
....	....	1650	1730	149977	STS	Central
1771	1817	....	....	149977	STS	Ingestre
1816	1860	1700	1960	137499	STS	Rudeley
1730	1770	....	....	149977	STS	Stowe By Chartley
1794	1919	1700	1919	156973	STS	Wolverhampton
1630	1930	....	....	129054	STS	???
CRUTCHLOW						
1680	1800	1800	1840	148954	WAR	Bedworth
CRUTTENDEN						
....	....	ALL	ALL	117420	ALL	Name Study
1700	1850	1700	1850	176672	SSX	ALL
1787	1787	1500	1787	174009	SSX	Hastings
CRUWYS						
1800	1870	1700	1820	166375	DEV	North
1839	1859	1750	1860	121568	DEV	Knowstone

Known From	To	Researching From	To	Ref	Cty	Place
CRUXTON						
....	....	ALL	ALL	117439	ALL	Name Study
....	....	1880	1920	117439	CWD	Wrexham
1800	1900	1700	1800	117439	SAL	Wellington
....	....	1750	1900	158941	SAL	Wellington
....	....	1850	1970	117439	STS	South
1900	1992	ALL	ALL	158941	STS	Burslem
1880	1900	1900	1970	117439	STS	Stoke On Trent
....	....	1850	1970	117439	WAR	North
....	....	1850	1970	117439	WMD	Birmingham
CRWAFORD						
....	....	1790	1845	132381	MLN	Edinburgh
CRYER						
1830	1934	1703	1830	163686	LAN	Wardle
1850	....	....	....	172723	SOM	Barrow Gurney
1750	1825	1700	1750	176516	WYK	Rotherham
1855	1992	1650	1855	117447	WYK	Sheffield
CUBBAGE						
1800	1880	1550	1800	114928	OXF	Nettlebed
CUBBIN						
....	....	1600	1950	137014	IOM	???
....	....	1800	1850	134848	LAN	Liverpool
....	....	1800	1950	137014	WAR	Birmingham
CUBBON						
1731	1740	1511	1740	141291	IOM	Arbory
1871	1900	ALL	ALL	165522	IOM	Onchan
CUBBY						
1853	1903	ALL	1853	159077	CUL	Carlisle
CUBIS						
1780	1820	1730	1780	133671	CAM	Bassingbourne
CUBITT						
1861	1992	1700	1861	117463	DUR	ALL
1785	1850	....	....	160458	LND	???
1861	1992	1700	1861	117463	NBL	ALL
1500	1750	1500	1750	168343	NFK	ALL
1726	1992	1600	1726	117463	NFK	Blakeney
1786	1992	1600	1786	117463	NFK	Salthouse
1785	1850	....	....	160458	NFK	???
CUBLEY						
1760	1900	1650	1760	170194	DBY	Derby
CUCKNEY						
1720	1992	1600	1992	179388	SSX	Sompting
1720	1992	1600	1992	179388	SSX	Steyning
CUCKOW						
1785	1989	1700	1851	122467	KEN	Dartford
CUDBIRD						
1820	1936	ALL	1820	159204	NFK	Hingham
1820	1936	ALL	1820	159204	NFK	Norwich
CUDD						
1700	1800	....	....	100420	WAR	Meriden
CUDDIE						
1795	1839	1700	1795	158143	FIF	Dunfermline
CUDDIFORD						
1750	1900	1700	1750	143170	DEV	Cheriton Fitzpaine
CUDDON						
1805	1992	....	1805	112143	SFK	Hadleigh
CUDLIP						
1798	1824	1700	1798	133523	DEV	Devonport
?	?	?	?	164348	DEV	Plymouth
CUDLIPP						
1600	1800	1600	1800	168882	DEV	Tavistock
CUDWORTH						
....	....	1770	1830	103713	CAM	Isleham
CUFF						
1775	1992	1580	1775	117471	DOR	Folke
1775	1992	1580	1775	117471	DOR	Holwell
....	1850	1750	1850	146927	KEN	???
....	....	1851	1881	156833	LAN	Liverpool
1850	1850	1850	1900	106666	LND	Shoreditch
....	1850	1750	1850	146927	???	London
CUFFE						
....	....	ALL	ALL	117498	ALL	Name Study
1572	1626	....	....	165999	GLS	Gloucester
1572	1626	....	....	165999	GLS	Westbury On Trym
CUFFIN						
1789	1843	1789	1845	140422	DEN	Llanfairtalherarn
CUFFLEY						
all	ALL	ALL	ALL	117501	ALL	ALL
CUFFLIN						
1839	1900	....	....	163155	LEI	Belton
1664	1853	....	....	163155	LEI	Ratby & Groby
CUFLEY						
....	....	ALL	ALL	117501	ALL	Name Study
all	ALL	ALL	ALL	117501	ALL	ALL
CUGAN						
1861	1884	1500	1861	141089	NFK	ALL
CULBERT						
1800	1850	1800	1850	106305	DOW	???
CULE						
1737	1992	1737	1992	155160	GLA	St Nicholas
CULL						
1810	1870	1700	1810	156795	DOR	East
1830	1850	1800	1860	169323	GLS	Cow Honeybourne
1820	1830	1800	1845	169323	GLS	Toddington
1863	1920	1800	1863	145459	HAM	Fawley
1800	1880	1800	1880	126438	HAM	Lymington
CULLEDGE						
1900	1920	1800	1900	173029	LEI	Leicester
CULLEN						
1600	1992	?	?	114944	CON	St Revesue
1893	1950	1800	1890	159336	IRL	Dunnganon
1400	1850	ALL	1850	117544	KEN	ALL
1600	1992	ALL	ALL	125083	KEN	South East
1830	1856	1700	1992	159468	KEN	Ashford
1770	?	?	?	166642	KEN	Mersham
....	....	ALL	1900	144347	KID	ALL
?	?	?	?	173800	LND	South
1825	1900	1825	1900	118540	NTT	ALL
?	?	?	?	117528	NTT	Radford
1850	1900	ALL	1850	144347	OFF	ALL
1832	1851	1832	1992	144347	OFF	???
1600	1992	?	....	114944	SOM	Weston Toyland
CULLEY						
1700	1900	1700	1900	135968	NTT	Bingham
1801	1851	1770	1820	115886	WIL	Pewsey
CULLIFORD						
1757	1757	1757	1757	107573	SOM	Bridgwater
1773	1807	ALL	ALL	153516	SOM	Congresbury
1724	1992	1724	1992	106410	SOM	High Ham
1871	1894	....	....	117579	SOM	High Ham
1724	1992	1724	1992	106410	SOM	Long Sutton
1724	1820	1724	1820	117579	SOM	Long Sutton
1724	1992	1724	1992	106410	SOM	Somerton
1820	....	....	....	117579	SOM	Somerton
CULLIMORE						
....	....	1866	1992	172685	AYR	ALL
1761	1992	ALL	ALL	172685	BRK	ALL
....	....	ALL	ALL	172685	GLS	ALL
1800	1800	1700	1850	147575	GLS	Tytherington
....	....	1700	1800	171182	HAM	Rowner
1800	1930	ALL	ALL	147575	SWL	???
1878	1992	ALL	1900	147109	WAT	???
1878	1992	ALL	1900	147109	WEX	???
....	....	1300	1992	172685	WIL	ALL
1900	1992	ALL	ALL	172685	YKS	ALL
CULLINANE						
....	....	1800	1992	119156	IRL	???
CULLING						
....	....	ALL	ALL	117587	ALL	Name Study
....	....	1500	1900	117587	ALL	ALL
1400	1850	ALL	1850	117544	KEN	ALL
CULLINGHAM						
1700	1750	1650	1800	117595	SFK	Lowestoft
1800	1992	1700	1800	117595	SRY	Croydon
CULLIS						
1750	1900	1600	1850	117609	CON	Bodmin
1815	....	1766	1815	122572	DBY	ALL
1815	....	1766	1815	122572	GLS	ALL
1781	1861	1700	1781	115819	GLS	Slimbridge
1750	1900	1600	1850	117609	LND	Holborn
1750	1900	1600	1850	117609	MDX	???
1815	....	1766	1815	122572	NTT	ALL
1818	1886	1750	1992	117609	WAR	Leamington
CULLISS						
?	?	?	?	160326	SAL	Central
CULLUM						
1946	1992	ALL	ALL	117935	CMA	Ulverston
1623	1670	....	....	174319	CON	Tywardreath
1800	1950	ALL	ALL	122866	HAM	East
1916	1992	ALL	ALL	111333	HAM	???
....	....	....	....	122866	LND	???
1780	1880	1500	1780	134708	SFK	Rougham
CULLY						
1800	1850	1700	1800	145408	WIL	Marlborough
CULM						
1825	1875	1750	1875	100390	CHS	Chester
....	....	ALL	ALL	100390	LAN	Manchester
1860	1900	1800	1860	178209	LAN	Manchester

Known From	To	Researching From	To	Ref	Cty	Place
CULPAN						
1815	1992	1700	1815	100757	YKS	Halifax
CULSHAW						
1784	1890	....	....	116602	LAN	West
1800	1880	1750	1850	177636	LAN	Balckburn
1747	1846	....	1747	109622	LAN	Ormskirk
1840	....	1800	1900	139114	LAN	Ormskirk
1832	1950	....	....	109622	LAN	Preston
1806	1992	1800	1992	120901	LAN	Rufford
CULVER						
1688	1700	....	....	142522	ENG	???
....	....	1798	1850	116912	KEN	Woolwich
CULVERHOUSE						
ALL	ALL	ALL	ALL	151750	ALL	ALL
1640	1820	1500	1900	169536	BKM	Wing
1820	1992	1820	1992	169536	MDX	St Pancras
CULVERWELL						
1813	1850	1770	1860	174912	GLA	St Fagens
1893	1965	1965	1992	104728	GLS	Bristol
1742	1841	ALL	1742	114987	SOM	Church Stanton
CULY						
1724	1940	....	....	128996	CAM	Thornley
CULYER						
1600	1992	1300	1900	117617	NFK	Norwich
1600	1992	1300	1900	117617	NFK	Wymondham
CUM						
....	....	1700	1800	147613	YKS	Giggleswick
CUMBERLAND						
1889	1918	1700	1992	168181	NTT	Bradmore
....	....	1700	1992	168181	NTT	Bunny
1732	1950	ALL	1732	178411	NTT	Willoughby On The Wolds
....	....	1650	1720	147613	YKS	Bentham
CUMBERS						
1750	1800	1700	1800	144657	ESS	Chingford
CUMBERTON						
1836	1880	ALL	1900	117889	RFW	Port Glasgow
CUMBERWORTH						
1836	1920	1836	1851	151211	LIN	East Marsh
1836	1920	1836	1851	151211	LIN	Wold
CUMBLIDGE						
....	....	ALL	ALL	150886	ALL	ALL
1800	1992	ALL	ALL	150886	HUN	Wistow
CUMBOR						
1848	1879	1828	1848	117625	DUR	Heighington
1814	1828	1770	1814	117625	YKS	Brignall
1854	1992	....	....	117625	YKS	Doncaster
1852	1992	....	....	117625	YKS	Great Ayton
CUMING						
1842	1992	....	1842	137642	DEV	Dartmoor
1800	1830	1700	1800	126772	DEV	North Bovey
CUMINGS						
1681	1681	....	....	135437	SOM	Stogursey
CUMMIN						
1829	1856	1800	1829	144177	DOW	Mourne
1777	1860	1700	1800	163740	YKS	Kirkby Fleetham
CUMMING						
1787	1992	1700	1787	144010	ABD	Fintray
....	....	1815	1870	148210	BAN	Fordyce
1800	....	1750	1850	173134	CAI	Dunbeath
1660	1680	1500	1730	105333	DEV	Buckland In The Moor
1660	1680	1500	1730	105333	DEV	Holne
1660	1680	1500	1730	105333	DEV	Ilsington
1660	1680	1500	1730	105333	DEV	Lydford
1820	1860	1700	1840	177717	DEV	Torquay
1660	1680	1500	1730	105333	DEV	Widecombe In The Moor
1800	1900	1600	1800	121118	INV	Spey Valley
1874	....	....	1874	118400	LND	East
1800	1850	1750	1850	141739	SCT	???
....	1807	....	....	153176	YKS	Topcliffe
CUMMINGS						
1886	1886	1800	1900	117633	DUR	Darlington
1800	1840	1750	1850	116823	NYK	Fylingdales
1850	1880	1800	1900	117870	WAR	Birmingham
1905	1992	1885	1920	117633	WYK	Bradford
1814	1884	1790	....	132381	???	Aberdeen
CUMMINS						
1700	1870	1670	1850	124974	BRK	Kingsclere
1826	1854	1750	1826	150614	DEV	Shaldon
1750	1800	1700	1750	177024	GLS	Newent
1750	1800	1700	1900	166804	HAM	Hurstbourne
1750	1800	1700	1900	166804	HAM	Tarrant
CUMMINS contd.						
1770	1929	1700	1950	159964	WIL	Stockton
CUMNER						
1850	1992	1850	1992	117641	LND	Rotherhithe
1660	1890	1660	1890	117641	WIL	East
CUMYN						
1200	1340	1200	1350	154881	ALL	ALL
CUNCLINGTON						
....	....	1800	1850	159905	NBL	Earsdon
CUNDALL						
1750	....	1700	....	134589	YKS	Newton On Ouse
1830	1890	....	1900	147818	YKS	Nun Monkton
CUNDY						
1851	....	1800	1851	102849	ESS	Southend
1920	1992	ALL	ALL	156175	GLA	Swansea
CUNINGHAME						
....	....	1700	1800	142670	AYR	Kilmarnock
CUNLIFFE						
....	....	1890	1915	151041	LAN	Bootle
1870	1885	1849	1888	117668	LAN	Haydock
1846	1876	1700	1846	109649	LAN	Rishton
1885	1975	1885	1975	117668	LAN	Rishton
....	....	1890	1915	151041	LAN	Seaforth
1849	1849	1800	1870	117668	LAN	Winstanley
1849	1916	1849	1992	165603	YKS	Stockton
1849	1916	1849	1992	165603	YKS	Yarm
CUNNAH						
1700	1790	1600	1700	134104	DEN	Wrexham
CUNNINGHAM						
....	....	ALL	ALL	117692	AYR	Beith
1843	1910	1840	1920	146536	AYR	Beith
1870	1906	ALL	ALL	117692	BDF	Luton
1849	1870	....	....	161675	CLK	Tillicoutry
1820	1992	1650	1820	128554	CMA	Keswick
1820	1992	1650	1820	128554	CMA	Ulverston
1850	1950	1600	1850	154059	ESS	Colchester
1800	1850	1600	1800	154059	ESS	Holland On Sea
1760	....	ALL	ALL	130508	FIF	St Monance
....	1800	....	1800	108197	IRL	Cork
1890	1970	1890	1970	126144	KEN	Gravesend
1728	1992	1500	1728	139084	KEN	Shipbourne
1728	1992	1500	1728	139084	KEN	Tonbridge
1851	1928	1840	1992	115673	LAN	Liverpool
1880	1920	....	....	117684	LAN	Liverpool
ALL	1880	....	....	117684	MAY	Ballinar
....	....	ALL	1864	119326	MLN	Edinburgh
1860	....	1800	1900	126144	SFK	Bradwell
CUNNINGTON-CROSS						
1850	1910	1850	1910	117323	MDX	Old Brentford
CUPER						
1700	1800	....	1780	108375	ESS	Billercay
CUPHIS						
1780	1810	1700	1900	110051	KEN	Northfleet
CUPIT						
1704	1733	1600	1703	131245	DBY	Shirland
CUPITT						
1770	1840	1600	1770	104469	SRY	Wandsworth
CUPPLEDITCH						
1707	1992	1680	1992	114332	LIN	???
CUPPLEDYKE						
1570	1640	ALL	1700	158283	ERY	ALL
CURANT						
1765	1930	1700	1765	117714	CON	Falmouth
CURBER						
....	....	ALL	ALL	178772	ALL	ALL
1600	1958	1700	1958	178772	DEV	Plymouth
CURD						
1757	1900	1650	1757	120774	KEN	Dartford
1722	1885	1722	1885	173142	KEN	Deptford
....	....	1690	1820	109533	KEN	Sussex Borders
1888	1992	1800	1888	110094	KEN	Watering Bury
1888	1992	1800	1888	110094	KEN	Yalding
1835	1992	1700	1835	118788	SSX	Rye
....	....	1690	1739	109533	SXE	ALL
1739	1992	....	....	109533	SXE	Rye
1789	....	1600	1850	170178	SXE	Rye
CURDELL						
....	....	1500	1738	138614	CON	Perranuthnoe
CURE						
1832	....	....	....	120804	WAR	Withy Brook
CURELL						
1800	1860	1700	1900	138517	HEF	???
CURETON						
1825	1875	1700	1875	117722	SAL	Upton Magna

Known From	To	Researching From	To	Ref	Cty	Place
CURETON contd.						
1875	1992	1875	1910	117722	STS	Bilston
CURGENVEN						
1745	1950	1600	1745	111279	CON	ALL
CURL						
1790	1900	....	....	177725	SOM	Long Sutton
CURLE						
1800	1992	....	....	153397	HAM	New Forest
1876	1992	1700	1876	117730	LND	East
1876	1992	1700	1876	117730	LND	City
1861	....	....	....	135402	SRY	Camberwell
CURLING						
1600	1851	1817	1851	176958	HAM	???
1600	1851	1817	1851	176958	KEN	Chilton
1796	1815	1600	1851	176958	LND	???
1600	1851	1817	1851	176958	SOM	Bristol
CURLINGTON						
....	....	....	1600	109290	NFK	South West
CURME						
....	....	ALL	ALL	164100	ALL	Name Study
1500	ALL	ALL	ALL	164100	ALL	ALL
CURNOCKE						
1720	1790	1680	1720	165530	GLS	Ozleworth
CURNOW						
1819	1849	1800	1819	128368	CON	Gulval
1680	1900	....	....	153745	CON	Gwennap
1673	1712	1500	1800	153354	CON	Gwennap
1670	1875	1600	1920	108510	CON	Ludgvan
1580	1800	1580	1800	150126	CON	Mawgan In Meneage
1770	1875	1600	1920	108510	CON	St Ives
1650	1850	1650	1750	168750	CON	St Ives
1700	1992	1100	1700	117749	CON	St Martin In Meneage
1640	1900	1640	1960	112712	CON	Towedcack
1643	1738	1600	1643	102571	CON	Towednack
1670	1875	1600	1920	108510	CON	Towednack
1590	1718	....	....	139491	CON	Towednack
1819	1849	1800	1819	128368	CON	Zennor
CURPHEY						
1748	1840	1715	1812	141283	IOM	Braddan
CURR						
1747	1807	ALL	1807	118737	BRK	West Woodhay
1767	....	....	....	161136	DUR	Lanchester
1800	....	....	....	161136	YKS	Sheffield
CURRALL						
1833	1870	1786	1833	163686	WAR	Barford
CURRAN						
1860	1992	ALL	1860	117765	LAN	Liverpool
1838	1920	1838	....	162175	ROS	Kilmacknort
CURRELL						
1780	1980	1800	1830	117773	HRT	Hertford
1810	1955	....	....	148350	NFK	Norwich
CURRIE						
1817	1901	1750	1850	122882	ARL	Skipness
1743	1960	1700	1750	153656	AYR	Fenwick
1822	1987	1750	1840	111848	AYR	New Cumnock
....	1770	....	1770	136085	BAN	Fordyce
1833	1854	1800	1870	169161	CHS	Macclesfield
1670	1780	1670	1780	151297	DFS	Annan
1730	1912	ALL	ALL	145092	DFS	Hoddam
1845	1900	1800	1845	126470	DUR	South Shields
1848	1927	....	....	132381	LKS	Glasgow
1815	1860	1750	1850	133787	LKS	Larkhall
1800	1850	1700	1800	139092	MDX	Westminster
....	....	1800	1900	143685	MLN	Edinburgh
....	....	1750	1900	174319	MLN	???
1800	1899	ALL	ALL	145092	NTT	Nottingham
1831	1992	....	....	127434	ROX	Darnick
1831	1992	....	....	127434	ROX	Melrose
1650	1992	1650	1992	166758	SCT	???
1770	1790	ALL	1800	149063	SEL	Ettrick
1737	1831	1695	1737	127434	SEL	Ettrickbridgend
CURROUGHS						
?	?	?	?	176842	LAN	Earlestown
CURRY						
1903	1913	....	....	117803	DUB	Dublin
1800	1860	ALL	1860	128414	DUR	Rainton
1767	1767	....	....	103632	DUR	Sunderland
1729	1729	ALL	1729	154563	DUR	Weardale
1820	1957	1820	1850	117781	EYK	Hull
1800	1890	1800	1890	151297	GLA	Neath
1855	1929	....	....	131660	GLS	Bristol
1864	1903	1857	1863	117803	LEX	Abbeyleix
....	....	ALL	1886	116351	NBL	Annitsford

Known From	To	Researching From	To	Ref	Cty	Place
CURRY contd.						
....	....	ALL	1886	116351	NBL	Bedlington
1796	1850	1700	1850	117781	NBL	Tyne And Wear
1842	1851	1800	1900	126470	NFK	Foulden
1832	1838	....	....	117803	NRY	East Witton
1838	1839	....	....	117803	NRY	Middleham
1826	1992	1547	....	175803	SOM	North Curry
1811	1902	1811	1902	154709	SRY	Lambeth
1822	1840	....	1840	161888	TYR	Omagh
1860	1867	....	....	117803	WIL	Gt Bedwyn
1855	1861	1855	1879	117803	WRY	Bradford
1852	1855	....	....	117803	WRY	Cleckheaton
1841	1852	....	....	117803	WRY	Dewsbury
1752	1881	....	....	117803	WRY	Knaresborough
1821	1881	....	....	117803	WRY	Pateley Bridge
1839	1841	....	....	117803	WRY	Pool
....	....	1500	1752	117803	YKS	ALL
1841	1962	?	1841	136611	???	Bristol
CURSON						
1838	1992	1700	1838	117846	NFK	Ashill
CURTICE						
1850	1900	....	....	129267	CON	St Stephens By Launceston
CURTIN						
....	....	ALL	ALL	100153	COR	Cork City
CURTIS						
1727	1761	1500	1727	125695	BDF	Gamlingay
....	....	ALL	ALL	154970	BRK	Beedon
1804	1840	1800	1850	172162	BRK	Beedon
1788	1840	1730	1788	102024	BRK	Caversham
1700	1800	1700	....	175234	BRK	East Ilsley
1750	1860	1650	1750	101834	CAM	Dry Drayton
1750	1780	1700	1810	124605	CAM	Stetchworth
1806	1884	....	....	138339	CON	Flushing Mylor
1806	1992	1700	1806	140449	CON	Gwennap
1700	1910	1700	1992	110523	CON	Manaccan
....	....	1770	1806	138339	CON	St Sampson
....	....	ALL	ALL	100153	COR	Cork City
1784	1865	1700	1784	175064	DOR	Buckland Newton
1855	1915	....	....	165514	DOR	Marnhull
....	....	?	?	110507	DUR	Sunderland
1840	1992	1700	1840	109576	ESS	West Ham
1852	....	....	....	135402	EYK	Anlaby
1800	1860	1700	1800	135658	GLS	Bristol
....	1823	1500	1823	175072	GLS	Bristol
1850	1992	1600	1850	117838	GLS	Frampton Cotterell
1653	1788	1550	1652	102830	GLS	Turkdean
....	....	1700	1820	166863	IRL	Cavan
1800	1850	ALL	ALL	131873	IRL	Cork
1825	1992	ALL	1825	133930	LND	ALL
1800	1900	ALL	ALL	131873	LND	Westminster
....	....	1832	ALL	178403	LND	???
1850	....	1750	1900	106356	MDX	Bethnal Green
1847	1860	1800	1847	172871	MDX	Marylebone
....	....	1800	1899	142409	NFK	???
1750	1850	....	....	153583	NTH	Bugbrooke
1805	1890	1805	1890	147486	NTH	Chelueston
....	....	1750	1850	110450	NTH	Denford
1881	1992	1881	1992	147486	NTH	Northampton
1851	1900	1851	1992	147486	NTH	Stanwick
1781	....	1781	....	147486	NTH	Titchmarsh
1840	1992	1600	1800	109576	SFK	Tuddenham
1770	1992	1700	1770	105031	SFK	Woodbridge
1800	1850	ALL	ALL	131873	SOM	Bristol
....	....	....	1814	130079	SOM	Crewkerne
1840	1840	ALL	1992	125113	SOM	Wells
....	....	1832	ALL	178403	SRY	???
1870	1900	ALL	ALL	115126	STS	Rugeley
1900	1992	1800	1899	156876	WIL	Crockerton
1701	1701	....	1701	121169	WIL	Longbridge Deverill
1820	ALL	....	....	142158	WIL	Malmesbury
1672	....	....	....	142859	WIL	Minety
1700	1800	1700	1820	108456	WIL	Warminster
1815	1872	1750	1872	141062	WIL	Warminster
1812	1870	1750	1812	176451	YKS	Wakefield
1826	1871	....	....	135380	???	Bristol
CURTLER						
....	....	?	?	178349	ALL	ALL
....	....	?	?	178349	LND	ALL
....	....	?	?	178349	LND	Camberwell
....	....	?	?	178349	LND	St Pancras
....	....	?	?	178349	WOR	North Claines
....	....	?	?	178349	WOR	Salwarpe
....	....	?	?	178349	???	Birmingham

Known From	To	Researching From	To	Ref	Cty	Place
CURWEN						
1817	1879	....	....	118729	LAN	Cockerham
1802	1992	1750	1800	164216	LAN	Myerscough
CURWOOD						
....	....	1700	1850	145688	LND	St Botolph
CUSENS						
1816	1861	1780	1816	101427	HAM	Portsmouth
CUSHION						
1823	1992	1750	1830	117862	SRY	London
CUSHWAY						
1765	1992	1765	1992	117641	LND	East End
1767	ALL	ALL	1790	116734	MDX	Bethnal Green
1784	1851	1700	1860	144797	MDX	Bethnal Green
1767	ALL	ALL	1790	116734	MDX	Bishopsgate
1767	ALL	ALL	1790	116734	MDX	London
1767	ALL	ALL	1790	116734	MDX	St Matthews
CUSICK						
1850	1900	1800	1900	138371	YKS	Sheffield
CUSS						
1890	1900	1890	1900	153052	WIL	Ashton Keynes
CUSTARD						
1687	1851	1586	1687	102512	DUR	Newbottle
CUSWORTH						
1781	1853	1750	1850	123285	SYK	Elsecar
1835	1992	1700	1835	165212	WYK	Rotherham
1835	1992	1700	1835	165212	WYK	Sheffield
1700	1966	1650	1800	129623	YKS	???
CUTBUSH						
....	....	ALL	1800	152978	KEN	Maidstone
CUTCLIFFE						
1786	1992	1700	1992	122548	DEV	North
CUTHBERT						
1832	....	1800	1850	170348	ABD	Aberdeen
1800	1860	....	....	159883	ANS	Dundee
1750	1850	1700	1900	156280	LIN	Barnetby
1876	1992	1876	1992	112305	LKS	Coatbridge
1700	1899	1750	1880	135941	SFK	Hundon
1789	1820	1600	1789	156779	SFK	Kersey
1800	1884	1700	1992	102377	YKS	Hinderwell Runswick
....	....	1820	....	119768	YKS	Wakefield
CUTHBERTSON						
1809	1851	1800	1832	174602	NBL	Ancroft
1809	1851	1800	1832	174602	NBL	Belford
1829	....	....	....	132381	RFW	Paisley
CUTHILL						
1895	....	....	....	137936	ABD	Peterhead
1800	....	....	....	137936	ANS	Inverkeillour
1881	1900	....	....	137936	RFW	Glasgow
CUTLACK						
....	....	ALL	ALL	146641	ALL	Name Study
CUTLER						
1750	1850	1700	1992	177180	BKM	Edlesborough
1600	1700	1500	1900	177180	BKM	Eton
1721	1822	1712	1800	107360	BKM	Stewkley
1720	1740	1743	1796	107360	BKM	Wing
1725	1992	ALL	1725	117897	BKM	Wing
1850	1900	1850	1900	107476	DBY	Chesterfield
1700	1825	1600	1700	156795	DOR	East
1802	1830	1750	1830	120197	DOR	???
1766	1790	1740	1992	114901	HAM	South Hayling
1872	1951	1800	1872	175595	IRL	Longford
1907	1941	ALL	ALL	129178	LAN	Liverpool
1850	1900	1700	1850	156795	LND	North
1840	1900	1800	1840	133221	LND	Bermondsey
1900	1900	1960	1992	168149	MDX	Hounslow
1830	1970	1800	1850	120197	SSX	Brighton
1830	1900	1830	1900	107476	STS	South
1850	1900	1850	1900	107476	STS	Oldbury
1830	1900	1800	1900	107476	WOR	Dudley
....	....	1780	1900	161594	YKS	Doncaster
1790	1820	ALL	1820	158003	YKS	Hull
....	....	1840	1900	161594	YKS	Leeds
....	....	1780	1900	161594	YKS	Thorne
CUTMER						
1764	1764	1700	1800	159964	HRT	Great Munden
CUTMORE						
1815	1909	1700	1909	117617	MDX	London
1765	1821	....	1800	137405	SFK	Bury St Edmunds
CUTT						
1883	....	....	....	173932	SRY	Epsom
CUTTEN						
....	....	ALL	ALL	117919	ALL	Name Study
ALL	ALL	ALL	ALL	117919	ALL	ALL
CUTTER						
1867	1957	1700	1867	112143	NFK	Diss
....	1781	1600	1781	132209	NFK	Shropham
CUTTIFORD						
1650	1750	1600	1650	143170	DEV	Ide
1880	1992	1800	1880	113964	LEI	Leicester
CUTTING						
1850	1875	....	....	151351	DBY	Brampton
1799	....	....	....	151351	DBY	Derby
1711	1800	1600	1850	176621	ESS	Thorpe
1802	1850	....	....	151351	NTT	Basford
1849	1867	1700	1867	112143	SFK	Palgrave
CUTTS						
1650	1850	....	....	138037	HRT	North East
1797	....	....	1820	171441	HRT	Datchworth
CUZNER						
....	....	ALL	ALL	123293	ALL	Name Study
1750	1992	ALL	ALL	123293	ALL	ALL
CYPHER						
1800	1850	1700	1800	176753	GLS	Tetbury
CYSTER						
1844	1890	ALL	ALL	112631	BKM	Aylesbury
1880	1992	ALL	1880	142263	BKM	Chalfont St Peter
1809	1992	ALL	1992	112631	BKM	Farnham Royal
D'ABITOT						
1066	1110	1066	1110	124974	WOR	Worcester
D'AGUILAR						
1870	1920	1700	1992	171638	ALL	ALL
D'ANNETHE						
....	....	1066	....	130745	ENG	South
D'ARCY						
1831	1894	ALL	1900	113611	EYK	Hull
1700	1847	....	....	164410	IRL	Ballyhaunis
1890	1992	1847	1890	164410	LAN	Liverpool
?	1913	....	....	150185	ROS	Castlreach
D'IFFANGAR						
....	....	ALL	ALL	137731	LND	ALL
D'ORR						
1857	1911	1700	....	135259	LND	???
....	....	1400	....	135259	NFK	Diss
D'OYLY						
1310	1992	1066	1992	176672	NFK	ALL
1310	1992	1066	1992	176672	SFK	ALL
D'UZES						
1066	1206	1066	1206	154881	ALL	ALL
DA VALL						
1885	1960	1812	1885	134872	SSX	Brighton
DABBS						
1761	....	....	....	166723	LND	Cripplegate
1822	1992	1700	1820	117927	MDX	St Mary
1743	1992	1700	1743	161284	SAL	Wellington
DABLE						
1880	1900	1860	1895	103128	DBY	Staveley
DABORNE						
1548	1664	1550	1650	106119	SRY	Guildford
DACBY						
1804	1821	1700	1992	116653	GLS	Hempsted
DACK						
1800	1941	ALL	ALL	117935	NFK	ALL
....	....	1700	1850	117587	NFK	???
DACRE						
....	....	ALL	ALL	157074	ALL	Name Study
....	....	ALL	ALL	157074	ALL	ALL
1804	1827	1700	1850	122653	CMA	ALL
1790	1992	1700	1790	157074	WYK	Whitkirk
1300	1500	....	....	100536	???	???
DADD						
1800	1850	1650	1800	141372	DEV	Totnes
1880	....	ALL	ALL	153281	KEN	Rochester
1902	1982	ALL	ALL	153281	YKS	Sheffield
DADDOW						
....	....	1600	1700	174319	CON	Gorran
DADDY						
1759	1875	1700	1760	162396	LIN	Snitterby
DADE						
1850	1870	1750	1900	106356	NFK	Saxlingham
1840	1919	1840	1992	104663	SFK	East
1749	1782	....	....	123129	SFK	Hawkedon
....	....	1700	1749	123129	SFK	Risby
DADGE						
1776	1825	1700	1850	126667	GLS	Gloucester
DADLEY						
....	....	ALL	ALL	115487	ALL	Name Study

Known From	To	Researching From	To	Ref	Cty	Place
DADSWELL						
1800	1900	1900	....	116297	SSX	Rotherfield
DAFFERN						
....	1760	1700	1760	103268	LIN	???
DAFFON						
....	....	ALL	ALL	176060	STS	ALL
1878	1992	ALL	1878	176060	STS	West Bromwich
DAFFORNE						
1750	1800	1700	1760	117943	BRK	Maidenhead
1679	1800	1600	1679	117943	KEN	Chatham
1800	1900	1500	1680	117943	LND	ALL
DAFT						
ALL	ALL	ALL	ALL	167347	ALL	ALL
DAGLEISH						
1841	1908	1700	1900	149756	???	Hartlepool
DAGLISH						
1820	1851	1851	1866	117951	DUR	Gateshead
1792	1808	1808	1820	117951	DUR	Ryton
1596	1839	1760	1790	117951	DUR	Whickham
1767	1767	ALL	1767	154563	DUR	Whickham
1780	1850	....	....	160458	LAN	???
1921	1953	1881	1921	117951	NBL	Ashington
1866	1881	1881	1893	117951	NBL	Blyth
1780	1850	....	....	160458	NBL	???
DAGNEN						
1816	1816	1700	1816	146358	IRL	ALL
DAGWELL						
1700	1705	1700	1725	117994	HAM	Bishops Waltham
....	1962	....	1962	117994	HAM	Bordon
1835	1870	1800	1890	117994	HAM	Easton
....	....	1775	1871	143480	HAM	Fareham
1675	1681	ALL	1675	117994	HAM	Kilmeston
....	....	1775	1871	143480	HAM	Lymington
1734	1781	1700	1800	117994	HAM	Ovington
1833	1861	1801	1873	126276	HAM	Portsea
....	....	1775	1871	143480	HAM	Portsea
1926	....	1920	....	117994	HAM	Selborne
1853	1935	1850	1935	117994	PEM	Haverfordwest
DAGWORTHY						
....	....	ALL	ALL	163481	ALL	Name Study
1840	1992	ALL	ALL	163481	DEV	Central
1840	1992	ALL	ALL	163481	DEV	East
1700	1745	ALL	ALL	163481	DOR	South
1800	1820	ALL	ALL	163481	HAM	Portsea
1840	1900	ALL	ALL	163481	LND	Kensington
DAILLEY						
1827	1860	1800	1840	100862	DEV	Plymouth
1827	1860	1800	1840	100862	SRY	Lambeth
DAIN						
1770	1787	1600	1770	102571	LAN	Manchester
DAINES						
1815	1960	1700	1815	124362	LND	East
....	....	1700	1992	140627	NFK	Langley
DAINTON						
1720	1992	1720	....	118672	GLS	Dursley
1745	....	1745	1800	145505	GLS	Dursley
....	....	....	....	118001	SOM	Trowbridge
....	....	....	....	118001	WIL	Bradford
....	....	....	....	118001	WIL	Winsley
DAINTRY						
1812	1820	1792	1820	165441	CHS	Macclesfield
DAINTY						
1772	1992	ALL	1640	118028	GLS	???
....	....	1820	1910	118028	LEI	???
1800	1860	1700	1800	157708	SAL	Wellington
1820	1900	1800	1820	157708	WOR	Dudley
DAISLEY						
1889	....	1916	....	135488	CAM	Cambridge
DAITON						
1804	1851	ALL	ALL	179116	MDX	Marylebone
DAKEYNE						
1600	1712	1600	1750	118036	DBY	Bonsall
1725	1900	1700	1900	118036	DBY	Darley Dale
1800	1982	1800	1982	118036	???	Manchester
DAKIN						
....	....	....	....	142085	LEI	Hemington
1811	1811	1750	1810	131245	LEI	Loughborough
1865	....	1800	1865	147362	STS	Tutbury
ALL	1730	....	....	170798	WRY	Penistone
DAKYNS						
1767	1927	....	....	100536	???	Holy Isle
1767	1927	....	....	100536	???	Lindisfarne
DALBY						
....	....	1800	....	113352	ESS	Great Waltham
DALBY contd.						
....	1645	1600	1675	152560	LEI	Castle Donington
1862	1896	1962	1982	120987	LEI	Leicester
....	....	1600	1992	115975	LND	London
1800	1820	1700	1800	112593	SFK	Yoxford
1850	1900	1700	1900	156280	YKS	Dewsbury
1850	1900	1700	1900	156280	YKS	Leeds
1760	1910	1700	1760	130877	YKS	Spofforth
1760	1910	1700	1760	130877	YKS	Wetherby
DALE						
....	....	1650	1900	179531	CHS	Astbury
1832	1859	1750	1832	155845	CHS	Congleton
1781	....	....	....	136964	CON	St Agnes Truro
1600	1750	1500	1800	138878	CUL	St Bees
1833	1850	1700	1900	159956	ESS	Copford
1805	1876	ALL	1876	113611	EYK	Hull
1870	1884	1846	1900	163317	HAM	Aldershot
1852	....	....	1890	171441	KEN	???
1873	1992	ALL	1873	115878	LEI	Somerby
1746	1960	....	....	157694	NBL	Newcastle
1746	1960	....	....	157694	NBL	North Shields
1700	1750	1700	1780	154210	NYK	Kirklevington
1780	1840	1700	1780	134627	OXF	Milcombe
1682	1834	1834	1900	169374	RUT	Great Casterton
....	....	....	1859	130060	SCT	???
1849	....	1800	1849	140880	SSX	Falmer
1796	1944	1600	1796	103853	SSX	Horsham
1883	1906	ALL	ALL	156256	STS	North
1800	1830	1750	1830	177210	STS	Biddulph
1763	1850	1750	1850	165441	STS	Bucknall
1770	1800	....	....	100420	WAR	Meriden
1764	1803	ALL	ALL	146145	YKS	Danby
1600	1746	....	....	157694	YKS	Fylingdales
1803	1893	ALL	ALL	146145	YKS	Lastingham
1600	1700	....	....	167924	YKS	Terrington
DALES						
1805	1876	ALL	1873	113611	EYK	Hull
1750	1850	1650	1750	121339	LIN	Alford
?	?	?	?	118044	LIN	Grimoldby
1722	1800	....	....	100536	LND	???
....	....	1800	1899	171794	YKS	Goole
....	....	1800	1899	171794	YKS	Kilpin
1910	1946	1910	1992	108979	YKS	Thirsk
DALEY						
1800	1992	1700	1800	167584	LIM	Limerick
DALGLEISH						
1838	1860	ALL	ALL	145386	LAN	Manchester
1803	....	1803	ALL	145386	LND	???
1800	1980	1650	1980	171662	MLN	ALL
1789	1840	1700	1800	174319	MLN	???
1841	1908	1700	1900	149756	???	Berwick On Tweed
DALGLESH						
1800	....	1770	ALL	166138	LAN	Manchester
DALGLIESH						
1820	?	ALL	ALL	129399	SCT	Galashiels
DALGLISH						
1750	1850	1650	1750	107905	LKS	Glasgow
DALLAT						
1850	1992	1600	1850	118052	ANT	Dunloy
DALLEN						
1260	1820	1750	1900	126586	MDX	London
DALLEY						
....	....	1600	ALL	118060	DOR	Beaminster
....	1660	ALL	1630	118060	SOM	Wells
1770	1800	1600	1770	147583	SRY	Walton On Thames
1770	1850	ALL	1770	118060	WIL	Chilmark
DALLIBER						
1600	1675	....	....	142522	DOR	Stoke Abbott
DALLIMORE						
....	....	ALL	ALL	118192	GLS	ALL
1862	1907	1862	1907	118192	GLS	Cheltenham
1849	1859	....	....	118192	GLS	Tortworth
1825	1825	ALL	ALL	118192	HAM	ALL
1639	1950	ALL	ALL	118192	IOW	ALL
1725	1992	ALL	ALL	118192	SOM	ALL
DALLIN						
1800	1870	1700	1800	119164	DEV	Barnstaple
DALLING						
1760	1980	ALL	ALL	129119	DFS	Moffat
DALLISON						
....	....	ALL	ALL	118087	ALL	Name Study
1738	1992	1650	1738	118087	DBY	Derby
....	....	1650	1730	118087	LEI	???
1540	1900	....	....	118087	LIN	Laughton

Known From	To	Researching From	To	Ref	Cty	Place
DALLISON contd.						
....	....	1650	1730	118087	NTT	???
DALLMAN						
1841	1992	1600	1840	132403	LND	???
1841	1992	1600	1840	132403	MDX	???
DALLOW						
1850	1930	1800	1950	131431	HEF	Little Dewchurch
DALLY						
1890	1960	1890	1960	131938	GLA	Mountain Ash
1792	1792	1792	1792	161950	IOW	ALL
1847	1910	1800	1846	108227	SOM	Shepton Beauchamp
DALMON						
1891	....	....	....	145521	SSX	Wiston
DALRYMPLE						
....	....	ALL	ALL	118109	ALL	Name Study
ALL	ALL	ALL	ALL	118109	ALL	ALL
1808	1992	1600	1807	132977	KKD	Gatehouse Of Fleet
1779	1992	1813	1992	118095	NBL	Newcastle On Tyne
1772	1930	....	....	175439	WLN	Polmont
DALTON						
....	....	ALL	ALL	118125	ALL	Name Study
1590	1992	1500	1992	164658	ALL	ALL
1650	1992	1400	1650	164658	CAM	ALL
1764	1766	1720	1800	159905	CUL	Cumwhinton
1830	1860	1700	1830	174661	DUR	ALL
....	....	....	....	172324	IRL	ALL
1850	1877	1850	1877	134767	KEN	Crayford
1898	1992	....	....	104760	KEN	Greenwich
1898	1992	....	....	104760	KEN	Lewisham
1672	....	....	1700	171441	KEN	Meopham
....	....	ALL	ALL	147222	LAN	Liverpool
1882	1992	ALL	1882	118117	LAN	Manchester
1880	1992	1800	1880	139475	LAN	Manchester
1640	1992	1640	1992	159492	LAN	Oldham
1800	1992	1500	1800	164658	LAN	Oldham
1744	1850	ALL	1744	104760	MDX	Camden Town
1744	1850	ALL	1744	104760	MDX	Hampstead
1744	1850	ALL	1744	104760	MDX	Isleworth
1830	1830	1800	1830	134627	NTH	Appletree
1830	1830	1800	1830	134627	NTH	Aston-Le-Walls
1850	1898	....	....	104760	SRY	Walworth
1850	1877	1850	1877	134767	YKS	Barwick In Elmet
1860	1900	1800	1900	165662	YKS	Sheffield
DALY						
1722	1722	....	....	115606	BRK	Bray
....	....	1800	1880	164798	COR	???
....	....	1800	1880	164798	LIM	???
1886	1992	1860	1886	118133	SCT	Bridgeton
DALZIEL						
1750	1800	1750	1800	123463	DFS	Dumfires
DAMANT						
1860	1890	1700	1860	178136	SFK	Woodbridge
DAMBY						
1797	1797	1750	1800	150002	WOR	Ribbesford
DAMEN						
....	....	....	....	119911	DOR	St Martin
1838	....	....	....	119911	DOR	Winterborne
DAMER						
....	....	ALL	1750	175331	DOR	ALL
....	....	ALL	1750	175331	SOM	ALL
....	....	ALL	1750	175331	WIL	ALL
DAMEREL						
....	....	ALL	ALL	154148	ALL	Name Study
....	....	ALL	ALL	154148	ALL	ALL
1835	1840	1800	1850	120243	KEN	Lee
DAMMANN						
1873	1882	....	....	139874	NBL	North Sheilds
DAMMERELL						
1756	1790	1650	1756	172898	DEV	Woodleigh
DAMMON						
1720	1795	1650	1850	110205	DOR	Abbotsbury
DAMMS						
1850	1942	1700	1850	176516	WYK	Sheffield
DAMP						
1820	1852	1700	1820	164178	IOW	Ryde
ALL	ALL	ALL	ALL	165158	SOM	Chard
DAMPIER						
....	....	1720	1800	165158	SOM	Axmouth
1700	1980	1500	1700	118141	SOM	Queen Camel
1744	1800	1700	1743	165158	SOM	Wambrook
DAMPIERRE						
1600	1970	1400	1600	118141	CHS	Bramall
DAMPNEY						
1742	1914	1500	1742	110329	DOR	North
DAMPNEY contd.						
....	....	1500	1860	166863	DOR	Holwell
DAMSELL						
1000	1850	ALL	....	139009	GLS	???
1600	1850	1850	1992	139009	LND	???
1850	1992	....	....	139009	???	Liverpool
DAMYON						
1822	1992	ALL	ALL	118168	MDX	London
DAN						
1787	1820	....	1787	129771	SSX	Charlington
DANBY						
ALL	ALL	ALL	ALL	103160	ALL	ALL
1780	1820	1760	1850	176281	MDX	St Pancras
DANCE						
1804	1962	1780	1992	116653	GLS	Ashelworth
....	....	?	?	118176	HEF	Callow
....	....	ALL	ALL	104159	LND	Hackney
1680	1822	1500	1800	155152	NTT	Nottingham
1643	1900	ALL	1643	135062	STS	Old Swinford
1860	1874	1700	1874	109010	WIL	Froxfield
1780	1880	1780	1880	109010	WIL	Preshute
1711	1852	1700	1852	132608	WIL	Ramsbury
DANCER						
1643	1900	ALL	1643	135062	STS	Old Swinford
DANDO						
1900	1950	1850	1950	146277	GLA	Cardiff
....	....	1500	1980	164992	GLS	Bristol
....	....	ALL	ALL	146277	SOM	North
....	....	1600	1900	146277	SOM	High Littleton
1789	1850	1600	1790	108413	SOM	Hinton Blewett
....	....	1770	1880	146277	SOM	Paulton
1800	1900	1635	1950	146277	SOM	Timsbury
DANDRIDGE						
1828	1868	1828	1868	149403	OXF	Stadhampton
DANDY						
1738	1783	ALL	ALL	135909	LAN	Croston
1738	1783	ALL	ALL	135909	LAN	Much Hoole
1810	1840	1700	1850	126586	LAN	North Meols
DANE						
1840	1930	1700	1840	134899	KEN	East
1840	1930	1700	1840	134899	KEN	Faversham
1674	....	....	1700	171441	KEN	Wychling
1830	....	ALL	1830	179515	MIL	Surgeon General
DANELLE						
1600	1699	....	....	137960	MDX	London
DANES						
1745	1835	1700	1745	134317	NTH	Kingsthorpe
DANFORD						
1883	ALL	ALL	1861	116734	LIM	???
1883	ALL	ALL	1861	116734	TIP	???
DANFORTH						
1512	1802	....	....	104302	SFK	Framlingham
DANGERFIELD						
....	....	ALL	ALL	170151	ALL	Name Study
1800	....	ALL	1822	152641	GLS	Eastington
1790	1970	1700	1930	125423	STS	Tipton
1800	1903	1800	1900	108693	WIL	Marlborough
DANIEL						
....	....	1066	1992	118206	ALL	ALL
1663	1793	ALL	1793	151254	CHS	Wilmslow
1680	1697	1600	1680	102571	CON	St Agnes
1826	1992	ALL	1826	118184	CON	St Austell
1800	1992	....	....	109444	CON	St Cleer
1814	1862	1770	1814	130141	CON	St Just In Penwith
1750	1850	1750	1850	135666	DEN	Henllan
1806	1852	ALL	1806	114987	DEV	Torquay
1773	1838	1773	1838	158658	GLA	Llansamlet
1798	....	1798	....	148156	HUN	Hemingford Abbots
1540	1600	1500	1600	154881	KEN	Farningham
1848	1848	ALL	1848	108537	LAN	Liverpool
1793	1900	1793	1992	151254	LAN	Salford
1793	1900	1793	1992	151254	LAN	Tyldesley
1750	1800	....	....	126497	LAN	Wigan
....	1852	1700	1852	159271	LND	East
1844	1964	1800	1850	149012	LND	East End
1900	1912	....	....	118192	MDX	Chiswick
1783	1825	1720	1825	118192	MDX	Stepney
1845	....	1800	1881	110132	MDX	???
1767	1806	1700	1820	117013	NFK	Dersingham
1750	1850	1700	1850	139068	NTH	Northampton
1774	1774	1700	1900	178322	OXF	Wardington
1800	....	ALL	ALL	126098	SOM	Hemington
1807	1851	1807	1900	118192	SRY	Lambeth
1819	1893	1819	1900	118192	SRY	Southwark

Known From	To	Researching From	To	Ref	Cty	Place
DANIEL contd.						
1680	1850	1500	1992	167592	STS	Burslem
1720	1800	1500	1992	167592	STS	Cobridge
1750	1800	1600	1992	167592	STS	Longton
1780	1840	1600	1992	167592	STS	Stoke
1857	1992	1750	1857	163090	STS	Stone
1890	....	....	....	154695	WRY	Ossett
....	....	1066	1500	118206	YKS	ALL
1660	1720	1640	1720	118206	YKS	Cayton
1590	1800	1400	1660	118206	YKS	Collingham
1700	1730	....	....	118206	YKS	Hull
1730	1992	....	....	118206	YKS	Scarborough
1707	1801	1600	1707	116637	YKS	Whixley
DANIELL						
....	....	1800	1881	110132	SRY	???
1625	1943	1550	1625	118214	WIL	Imber
DANIELLS						
1839	1880	?	1839	112356	LND	London
DANIELS						
1840	1840	1840	1850	113050	CHS	Altincham
1835	....	ALL	1835	144053	CHS	Heaton Mersey
1837	1900	1700	1837	168653	ESS	ALL
1804	1895	....	....	144282	GLS	N'ton Bagpath
1820	1920	1820	1920	106631	GLS	Stroud
1700	1900	1700	1900	133833	GLS	Stroud
1804	1895	....	....	144282	GLS	Tresham
1781	1822	1700	1900	131296	HAM	ALL
1800	1890	1736	1992	103144	HRT	Hemel Hempstead
1740	?	?	?	166642	KEN	Paddlesworth
1825	1829	....	....	139831	NFK	Hethersett
....	....	1803	1824	139831	NFK	Ketteringham
1903	1992	1800	1903	127787	NFK	Norwich
....	....	1830	1871	139831	NFK	Norwich
....	....	1700	1900	131296	SRY	ALL
1895	1980	....	....	144282	SRY	Merstham
....	1891	1891	1992	166197	WAR	Birmingham
1855	1900	1600	1900	145165	WIL	Imber
1816	1899	1500	1815	130184	WIL	Upton Scudamore
DANIELSON						
1750	1965	....	....	137820	SHI	Fetlar
1720	1965	....	....	137820	SHI	Mid Yell
1760	1965	....	....	137820	SHI	North Yell
1758	1965	....	....	137820	SHI	Northmavine
1720	1965	....	....	137820	SHI	South Yell
DANILY						
?	?	1750	1900	114456	MGY	ALL
1809	1840	1750	1900	114456	SAL	ALL
DANKS						
....	....	ALL	ALL	118257	ALL	Name Study
1752	1773	ALL	ALL	135127	WOR	Dudley St Thomas
1841	1872	....	....	102733	WOR	Redditch
DANN						
1780	1800	1700	1780	133493	CON	Looe
1804	1825	ALL	ALL	141615	LEI	Wigston
1800	....	ALL	1800	104442	MDX	Poplar
1851	1886	1800	1850	125628	NFK	Briston
1844	1992	1700	1844	118265	NFK	Great Witchingham
1841	1960	1700	1841	167061	SSX	Herstmonceux
DANNAN						
1885	1920	1850	1992	171670	???	Plymouth
DANSON						
1817	1858	1700	1992	113476	LAN	Kirkham
DANTON						
1840	1842	1700	1850	105775	KEN	St Lawrence
DANZEY						
1422	1992	1422	1992	123099	LEI	Somerby
1848	1988	1750	1850	165271	MDX	London
DARBY						
1861	1992	1650	1860	160911	CAM	Sutton
1732	1800	....	....	161357	DOR	West
1696	1730	....	....	151351	DOR	Beaminster
1725	1730	....	....	151351	DOR	Powerstock
....	....	1700	1780	161357	DOR	South Perrott
1772	1815	1750	1840	118273	KEN	Birchington
1835	1901	1832	1916	118273	KEN	Rochester
1887	1890	1890	1992	120022	LEI	Loughborough
1859	1960	1859	1960	118273	MDX	Stepney
....	....	1700	1780	161357	SOM	East
1837	1888	1700	1992	124966	SOM	Yeovil
....	....	1700	1799	138592	STS	South
1799	1835	....	....	138592	STS	Bilston
....	....	1789	....	151610	STS	Rowley Regis
1847	1887	....	....	138592	STS	Wolverhampton
1780	1780	....	....	127426	WAR	Birmingham
DARBY contd.						
1690	1742	1680	1750	142018	WIL	Ashton Keyens
1830	1980	1800	1950	123145	WMD	Birmingham
1836	1846	....	....	138592	WOR	Dudley
DARBYSHIRE						
1850	1870	ALL	1992	136077	LAN	East
1800	1880	1700	1800	118281	LAN	Chorley
1800	1880	1700	1800	118281	LAN	Rivington
1792	1880	1750	1850	101044	YKS	Arkendale
DARDS						
1664	1688	1650	1700	161624	ESS	Lambourne
DARE						
1801	1900	1650	1800	118303	ESS	Steeple Bumpstead
1730	1850	1700	1992	173096	KEN	Ramsgate
1650	1800	1600	1992	173096	KEN	Sandwich
1780	1900	1700	1992	118303	SFK	ALL
1750	1800	1700	1900	118303	SFK	Bury St Edmunds
1780	1870	1750	1870	168912	SOM	Monkton
DAREY						
1827	1870	1800	1850	100242	BKM	Heston
DARGUE						
1800	1807	1750	1800	176451	CMA	Kirby Lonsdale
1871	1940	1863	1992	158399	NBL	Newcastle
DARGUES						
....	....	ALL	ALL	158399	ALL	ALL
DARIDGE						
1800	1900	1700	1992	101532	DOR	Weymouth
DARK						
1740	1800	ALL	1750	115266	DOR	ALL
1890	....	....	1879	121908	WOR	Overbury
DARKE						
1839	1918	1839	....	121436	DEV	Exeter
DARKER						
....	....	....	....	151270	NTH	Marholm
1799	1799	....	....	130877	NTT	Arnold
DARKING						
1660	1960	1500	1660	137049	SFK	Haverhill
DARKYNHOLL						
1380	1450	1300	1450	154881	ALL	ALL
DARLETT						
1700	ALL	1742	1796	107379	BKM	ALL
1700	ALL	1742	1796	107379	HRT	ALL
DARLEY						
1580	1820	1300	1600	132993	CON	North Hill
1580	1820	1300	1600	132993	NFK	???
1763	1843	....	....	174858	YKS	Helmsley
1733	1763	1600	1733	174858	YKS	Rillington
1830	....	ALL	1850	134503	YKS	Withernwick
1580	1820	1300	1600	132993	YKS	???
DARLING						
1892	1992	1815	1892	174017	LND	Chelsea
1740	1840	1800	1860	122424	NBL	Bamborough
1710	1767	ALL	1767	149063	ROX	Melrose
1850	1870	1800	1900	122424	STS	Stoke Upon Trent
DARLINGTON						
1760	1797	1650	1760	150614	CHS	Davenham
1855	....	1750	1855	108596	LAN	ALL
....	....	1798	1851	155039	LAN	Liverpool
1838	1992	1700	1838	161446	MDX	London
1830	....	ALL	1830	112887	MLN	Edinburgh
1850	1880	1850	1880	100420	WAR	Meriden
DARLOW						
....	....	1700	1800	163260	LIN	Spalding
DARN						
1862	1930	ALL	ALL	113700	GLS	Gloucester
DARNBROUGH						
1772	1992	1700	1992	161640	YKS	Bradford
1925	1935	1875	1925	109479	YKS	Methley
DARNELL						
1800	1992	ALL	1900	113492	BDF	North
1815	1940	....	....	128996	CAM	Thornley
1840	1871	1700	1890	141445	LIN	Whaplode
1759	1826	1730	1830	127604	NTH	Rushden
1890	1967	1881	1967	141445	NTT	Nottingham
DARNLEY						
....	....	ALL	ALL	136115	CHS	Birkenhead
....	....	ALL	ALL	136115	CHS	Chester
....	....	ALL	ALL	136115	STS	Norton Caines
....	....	ALL	ALL	136115	WAR	Birmingham
DARRAGH						
1850	1992	1750	1850	118052	ANT	Ballycastle
1850	1900	1700	1900	138517	???	Belfat
DARRAH						
1800	1925	1800	1925	119091	LAN	Fylde

Known From	To	Researching From	To	Ref	Cty	Place
DARRAH contd.						
1800	1925	1800	1925	119091	LAN	Manchester
1795	1875	1750	1900	119091	LND	East
1870	1900	1870	1900	119091	LND	Rotherhithe
1880	1915	1880	1920	119091	LND	Southwark
DARROCH						
1790	1860	1750	1992	167983	AYR	Irvine
DART						
1775	1825	1600	1900	158399	DOR	Dorchester
DARTNELL						
....	....	ALL	ALL	113468	ALL	Name Study
DARTON						
1750	1992	1600	1992	147710	HRT	ALL
1785	1872	1700	1785	167649	HRT	Ardley
DARTS						
1819	1930	ALL	1819	100072	???	Wrestlingworth
DARVALL						
....	....	ALL	ALL	118338	ALL	Name Study
1500	....	ALL	ALL	118338	BKM	???
1640	....	ALL	ALL	118338	BRK	???
1600	....	ALL	ALL	118338	LND	???
DARVEL						
1727	....	1650	1750	143693	BKM	Hughenden
DARVELL						
....	....	....	1850	156698	LND	???
DARVELL-STEVENS						
1800	1900	1750	1900	156701	ALL	ALL
DARWEN						
1650	1700	1600	1650	120049	LAN	Leyland
DARWENT						
1936	1950	1700	1936	156221	NFK	ALL
DARWIN						
1873	1873	....	....	108901	NTT	Retford
DARWOOD						
1885	....	1885	....	135488	CAM	West Walton
1885	....	1885	....	135488	NFK	West Walton
DASHWOOD						
....	....	ALL	ALL	113468	ALL	Name Study
1710	1860	....	....	137480	DOR	Almer
DATSON						
1700	1840	1700	1890	118346	CON	Deay
DAUBER						
1890	1900	....	....	175099	YKS	Pickering
DAUBNEY						
1841	1900	1841	1900	153303	LIN	Belchford
1743	1743	1700	1743	174211	LIN	Canwick
1734	1773	ALL	ALL	110477	LIN	Thornton By Horncastle
1743	1743	1700	1743	174211	LIN	Waddington
DAUGHTON						
....	....	1730	1800	117137	WIL	Mildenhall
DAULBY						
1838	1861	1700	1838	106968	LAN	Liverpool
DAULMAN						
....	....	1600	1756	137014	STS	Polesworth
....	....	1600	1756	137014	STS	Tamworth
DAUNCEY						
1807	1832	....	....	117579	SOM	Butleigh
DAUNT						
....	....	ALL	ALL	166022	ALL	ALL
1780	1820	1600	1800	166022	IRL	Cork
DAVE						
1810	1850	ALL	1810	145564	DEV	Swimbridge
DAVENPORT						
1826	1992	1600	1826	118656	BRE	Newbridge On Wye
....	....	ALL	ALL	130850	CHS	ALL
1766	1835	ALL	ALL	119253	CHS	Ashton On Mersey
1500	1621	....	....	135437	CHS	Boughton
1600	1970	1400	1600	118141	CHS	Bramall
1632	1632	....	....	135437	CHS	Chester
1780	1800	1600	1992	167592	CHS	Manchester
1823	1861	1800	1850	140090	CHS	Nantwich
1780	1800	1600	1992	167592	CHS	Stalybridge
1750	1800	1600	1992	167592	CHS	Stockport
1800	1850	1600	1992	167592	CHS	Withington
1400	1500	....	....	135437	CHS	Woodford
1858	1900	ALL	1858	147222	IRL	Cork
1820	1841	ALL	1891	146390	LAN	Astley
1858	1900	ALL	1858	147222	LAN	Liverpool
1800	1992	ALL	1800	112771	LAN	Manchester
....	....	ALL	ALL	130850	LAN	Manchester
....	....	ALL	ALL	130850	LAN	Salford
1780	1900	....	....	126497	LAN	Wigan
1720	1769	1650	1719	131245	LEI	Quorndon

Known From	To	Researching From	To	Ref	Cty	Place
DAVENPORT contd.						
1853	1855	1800	1853	174289	SAL	Lilleshall
1826	1992	1600	1826	118656	SAL	Ludlow
1750	?	1600	1992	167592	STS	Burslem
1780	1850	1700	1992	167592	STS	Cobridge
1780	1850	1700	1992	167592	STS	Longport
1780	1850	1700	1992	167592	STS	Longton
1900	1992	1750	1900	108723	WAR	Nuneaton
DAVEY						
1715	1828	....	....	121754	BKM	Wendover
1715	1829	....	....	143596	CON	Gulval
1850	1992	1600	1850	123242	CON	Kea
1500	1992	1500	1992	160423	CON	Linkinhorne
....	1911	1800	1911	177938	CON	Millbrook
1715	1829	....	....	143596	CON	Paul
1850	1992	1600	1850	123242	CON	Perranarworthal
1841	....	1800	1850	165824	CON	Redruth
1715	1829	....	....	143596	CON	Sancreed
1752	1980	1980	1992	140139	CON	Sheviock
1715	1829	....	....	143596	CON	St Buryan
1936	1940	1800	1936	158623	CUL	Barrow In Furness
1736	1992	1736	1900	106593	DEV	North West
1779	1865	....	....	165735	DEV	Bishops Nympton
1750	1850	ALL	ALL	131873	DEV	Exeter
1907	1992	....	....	118389	DEV	Torquay
1858	1907	ALL	1858	118389	DEV	Torrington
....	....	ALL	1858	118389	DEV	???
1872	1992	1800	1875	118354	ESS	Kirby Le Soken
ALL	1781	....	....	105368	ESS	???
1850	1992	1700	1850	148059	GNT	Chepstow
1795	1830	ALL	1830	131067	HAM	Portsea
1800	1900	ALL	ALL	131873	LND	Hackney
1850	ALL	1850	1950	107379	MDX	Southall
1808	1841	1700	1880	150118	NFK	Great Yarmouth
1823	1843	1750	1823	118397	SFK	Hoxne Hundred
1865	1900	....	....	165735	SOM	Bristol
....	....	ALL	1858	118389	SOM	???
1822	1861	1780	1822	131326	YKS	Hull
1871	1898	1600	1992	172863	YKS	Otley
DAVID						
1770	1992	1700	1770	118583	CMN	Laugharne
1802	1830	1780	1830	158658	CMN	Pembrey
1850	....	ALL	ALL	175587	GAL	Hafod
1824	....	ALL	ALL	175587	GAL	Llandeilo-Talybont
1840	1950	1840	1850	140295	GLA	Cardiff
1800	1850	1700	1850	156442	GLA	Cardiff
1800	1900	1700	1800	166022	GLA	Llanharan
....	....	1800	1840	117137	GLA	Llansannor
1737	1821	....	....	176559	GLA	St Bridges Minor
....	....	1800	1840	117137	GLA	St Hilary
1830	1873	1800	1873	140295	GLA	Welsh St Donats
1894	....	....	1894	118400	LND	East
....	....	ALL	ALL	118400	LND	Finchley
1770	1900	1700	1900	118540	PEM	Cilymaenllwyd
DAVIDGE						
1772	1937	ALL	ALL	175862	DOR	Blandford Forum
1850	1875	1850	1900	111007	LND	East
DAVIDSON						
1832	1992	ALL	ALL	166596	ABD	Cruden
1660	....	....	....	126497	ABD	Darnabo
1739	1992	1696	1739	116025	ABD	Kennethmont
1857	1857	1700	1857	106887	ABD	Rathen
1720	1744	1550	1750	147265	ABD	???
1810	1900	1700	1810	118419	BAN	Rathven
1770	1870	1700	1870	126500	BAN	Wick
1720	1744	1550	1750	147265	BAN	???
1784	1992	....	....	132381	CAI	Watten
1760	1870	....	....	126497	CAI	Wick
....	....	1700	1900	102881	CUL	Brampton
1805	1992	ALL	1800	112771	CUL	Stapleton
....	....	1850	1910	142417	DUR	South Shields
1812	1865	1790	1815	128333	FIF	Inverkeithing
1780	....	ALL	ALL	130508	FIF	St Monance
1840	1900	ALL	1850	162507	HAM	Gosport
1780	1800	1650	1780	100978	KCD	Bervie
1840	1850	ALL	ALL	117145	LAN	Bolton
1835	1974	1800	1974	152668	LAN	Manchester
1705	1762	1700	1800	163562	LKS	Yetholme
1860	1910	ALL	....	136018	LND	Hoxton
1895	1961	1800	1895	103853	LND	Kings Cross
1851	....	1840	1880	130877	NBL	Ancroft
1841	1856	1700	1841	103268	NBL	Newcast On Tyne
1865	1950	....	....	102881	NBL	Newcastle Upon Tyne
1829	1840	ALL	ALL	117145	NBL	Newcastle

Known From	To	Researching From	To	Ref	Cty	Place
DAVIDSON contd.						
1700	1850	1800	1850	117064	ROX	Kelso
1840	1880	....	....	117064	ROX	Newcastleton
1800	1900	....	....	150371	ROX	Newcastleton
....	....	1800	1880	140805	SCT	Aberdeen
1835	1974	1800	1974	152668	SCT	???
....	....	ALL	1840	162507	SCT	???
1900	1920	1850	1900	117153	SEL	Galashiels
1750	1965	....	....	137820	SHI	Fetlar
1720	1965	....	....	137820	SHI	Mid Yell
1760	1965	....	....	137820	SHI	North Yell
1758	1965	....	....	137820	SHI	Northmavine
1720	1965	....	....	137820	SHI	South Yell
1841	1841	....	....	135437	SRY	Beddington
1839	1839	....	....	135437	SRY	Bermondsey
1851	1901	....	....	135437	SRY	Kingston On Thames
1876	1876	....	....	135437	SRY	Lambeth
1816	1816	....	....	135437	SRY	Wandsworth
1876	1992	ALL	1876	116408	WAR	Birmingham
1830	1861	....	....	131628	YKS	Bingley
1830	1861	....	....	131628	YKS	Keighley
1830	1861	....	....	131628	YKS	Steeton
DAVIE						
1700	1992	1500	1850	124079	DEV	ALL
1612	....	1600	1620	114332	DEV	Moreton Hampstead
1790	1800	1800	1900	162876	DOR	Lyme Regis
1700	1740	1660	1760	142174	LEI	Scraptoft
1800	1830	ALL	....	104515	LIN	Lenton
....	....	ALL	1900	151602	LND	Battersea
....	....	ALL	1900	151602	SCT	Edinburgh
1807	....	....	....	141798	STI	Bannockburn
DAVIES						
1806	1830	1780	1806	127116	AGY	Llanfaelog
1860	1930	1715	1950	129143	BRE	Beulah
1820	1920	1750	1850	112704	BRE	Llanelly
1860	1930	1715	1950	129143	BRE	Llanfan
1801	1879	1801	1880	177008	BRE	Merthur Cynog
1840	1860	1800	1840	139793	BRE	Tal-Y-Llyn
1797	1900	1900	1992	158704	BRE	Ystradgynlais
1688	1927	1688	1927	104027	CAE	Glanwydden
1688	1927	1688	1927	104027	CAE	Llandudno
1640	1820	1640	1790	115614	CAE	Nefyn
1830	1920	1800	1830	115614	CAE	Trevor
1800	1830	1800	1830	135666	CGN	Cardigan
1780	1850	....	....	176958	CGN	Cardigan
1860	1960	ALL	1840	179612	CGN	Llanbadarnfawr
1776	1844	ALL	1844	154032	CGN	Llangranog
1745	....	1600	....	118591	CGN	Llanwenog
1802	....	1780	1860	169625	CGN	New Quay
1877	1958	1700	1877	141542	CHS	Chester
....	....	1840	1875	174289	CHS	Liverpool
1771	1827	....	1771	124524	CHS	Northwich
1920	1936	1903	1950	118524	CHS	Wallasey
1840	1864	....	....	118729	CHS	Wallasey
1830	1900	1780	1830	129119	CHS	Wrenbury
1695	....	ALL	ALL	131415	CMN	North
1800	1992	....	1800	138320	CMN	Abergwily
1800	1900	1700	1800	123102	CMN	Carmarthen
1851	1851	1800	1851	123110	CMN	Cilrmedyn
1852	1871	....	....	142034	CMN	Cwmaman
1800	1850	1750	1880	118575	CMN	Ffairfach Llandeilo
1806	....	ALL	1806	142034	CMN	Llanddeusant
1840	1900	1750	1850	168750	CMN	Llandebie
1720	....	1600	1800	176923	CMN	Llandebie
1865	1871	1800	1871	142794	CMN	Llandeilo
1797	1815	1750	1851	176923	CMN	Llandeilo
1841	1900	ALL	ALL	114987	CMN	Llandevaelog
1841	1881	1750	1841	123129	CMN	Llangennech
1820	1821	1750	1850	129135	CMN	Meidrim
1851	1851	1800	1851	123110	CMN	Trelech
1818	....	1700	1800	136891	CMN	???
1700	....	1600	....	116920	CON	Mevagissey
1750	1780	1650	1750	142999	CON	Padstow
1700	....	1600	....	116920	CON	Roseland Peninsular
1750	1780	1650	1750	142999	CON	St Merryn
1840	....	....	....	160385	DBY	???
....	....	1800	1860	142093	DEN	Abergele
1754	1872	?	1754	171298	DEN	Colwyn
1728	1992	....	....	138401	DEN	Llangermyw
1770	1992	1770	....	118672	DEN	Llangynhafal
1750	1820	1750	1820	135666	DEN	Llannefydd
1750	1800	1750	1800	135666	DEN	Llansannan
1728	1992	....	....	138401	DEN	Llansannan
1864	1949	1800	1900	177210	DEN	Nantglyn

Known From	To	Researching From	To	Ref	Cty	Place
DAVIES contd.						
1830	1871	....	1830	157791	DEN	Rhosimaedri
1830	1871	....	1830	157791	DEN	Ruabon
1806	1837	1700	1806	100110	DFD	Fishguard
1700	1720	....	....	151351	DOR	Piddletrenthide
....	....	1840	1870	167401	ESS	Chelmsford
....	....	1800	1992	162620	ESS	Southminster
1770	1850	1750	1900	152528	ESS	Waltham Abbey
1800	1992	1700	1800	118702	FLN	Bodfari
1762	1960	1700	1800	138304	FLN	Holywell
1760	1846	ALL	ALL	147621	FLN	Holywell
1850	1992	1700	1850	110957	GLA	Abertillery
1840	1900	1800	1900	131431	GLA	Caerphilly
1850	1992	....	....	129232	GLA	Crynant
1860	1870	1840	1870	158658	GLA	Dowlais
1840	1870	1870	1950	178845	GLA	Dowlais
1858	1858	1800	1880	178004	GLA	Dyffryn Clydach
1890	1950	1890	1950	142794	GLA	Garnant
1830	....	....	....	142158	GLA	Llandarne
1824	....	ALL	1824	174777	GLA	Llansamlet
1881	1881	ALL	ALL	107255	GLA	Merthyr Tydfil
1886	1886	....	....	127426	GLA	Merthyr Tydfil
1817	1992	....	1854	138320	GLA	Merthyr Tydfil
1830	1900	1750	1830	139793	GLA	Neath Abbey
1845	1858	ALL	1845	174777	GLA	Penclawdd
1844	....	1844	1992	168572	GLA	Penmark
?	?	?	?	104205	GLA	Penrhiwceiber
1855	....	ALL	1992	159174	GLA	Pentyrch
?	....	....	....	118508	GLA	Penygraig
1863	1924	1863	1876	125717	GLA	Pontadawe
1860	1950	1860	1950	118575	GLA	Pontardawe
1828	1936	1820	1936	159743	GLA	Pontlottyn
1890	?	1890	1992	174262	GLA	Pontypridd
1920	1950	1800	1920	141402	GLA	Port Talbot
1870	1950	1750	1870	123102	GLA	Swansea
1859	1950	....	....	169013	GLA	Swansea
1806	....	ALL	1992	159174	GLA	Tregochas
1884	1992	1800	1884	118710	GLA	Treharris
1860	1950	1860	1950	118575	GLA	Ystalyfera
1860	1880	....	....	127426	GLA	???
....	....	ALL	ALL	146471	GLS	Iron Acton
1800	ALL	1800	1844	151475	GLS	???
1724	1992	ALL	1724	171611	GYN	Nefyn
1899	1899	....	....	107255	HAM	Southsea
1772	1772	1500	1772	110310	HAM	Southwick
1810	1840	1780	1840	159700	HEF	Hay
1864	....	ALL	ALL	138533	HEF	Hereford
1853	1877	1700	1853	141542	HEF	Leintwardine
1780	1800	1600	1780	104469	HEF	Leominster
1800	....	....	....	144169	HEF	Netherton
1800	....	....	....	144169	HEF	Pencoyd
1720	1740	1650	1800	133450	IRL	Donnyebrook
1839	1884	....	....	150282	IRL	Wixford
1888	1940	1800	1940	141461	LAN	Ashton Under Lyne
1854	1883	ALL	1854	176842	LAN	Earlestown
1846	1898	....	1992	124524	LAN	Hulme
1864	1875	....	....	118729	LAN	Liverpool
1890	1903	1875	1903	118524	LAN	Liverpool
1881	....	....	....	138401	LAN	Liverpool
1831	....	1680	1831	177865	LAN	Liverpool
1830	1840	....	....	118729	LAN	Manchester
....	1846	ALL	1846	127000	LAN	Manchester
....	1838	1800	1838	138584	LAN	Manchester
1856	1856	1800	1856	175447	LAN	Manchester
1850	....	....	....	132500	LAN	Oldham
1834	1900	1700	1834	146021	LAN	Pendleton
1880	....	1880	....	135488	LND	Camberwell
1818	1886	1786	1930	103160	LND	Hackney
1842	1922	1700	1842	154288	LND	Holborn
....	....	1800	1900	162620	LND	Shoreditch
1880	1945	1860	1945	100218	MDX	Kensington
1840	1930	1700	1840	109398	MDX	Marylebone
1870	1880	....	....	167401	MDX	Pancras
1788	....	1780	1790	163775	MDX	Shoreditch
1834	1900	1750	1850	163244	MDX	Southwark
1862	1910	1700	1862	111775	MGY	Carno
1778	1850	1600	1778	156914	MGY	Llanfyllin
....	....	1800	1851	111414	MGY	Llanllwchaiarn
1880	1900	1850	1890	131431	MGY	Newtown
1820	1840	1700	1820	174343	MGY	Welshpool
....	1800	....	1800	177695	MGY	Welshpool
1829	1865	1770	1829	119628	MLN	Edinburgh
1837	1900	1800	1900	118540	MON	Cwmbran
....	....	1837	1940	123315	MON	Cymsyfiog

Known From	To	Researching From	To	Ref	Cty	Place
DAVIES contd.						
1840	1904	1850	1904	159743	MON	Pontllanfraith
?	?	?	?	159743	MON	Risca
1828	1840	1820	1850	159743	MON	Tredegar
1850	ALL	....	....	142158	MON	Trevethin
1900	1992	....	1900	118451	NTH	Northampton
....	1881	....	1881	140767	NTT	Sutton In Ashfield
1870	1875	1870	1890	100218	OXF	North Leigh
1791	1885	1800	1900	156744	PEM	Fishguard
1799	1928	1799	1881	104213	PEM	Haverfordwest
1895	1946	1700	1895	142212	PEM	Haverfordwest
1811	1839	1780	1811	173118	PEM	Letterston
1842	1864	1842	1864	104213	PEM	Llanboidy
1791	1885	1800	1900	156744	PEM	Llanychaer
1842	1864	1842	1864	104213	PEM	Narberth
1799	1928	1799	1881	104213	PEM	Pembroke Dock
....	....	1800	1860	142093	PEM	Spittal
1801	1992	1500	1801	140279	PEM	Steyton
1799	1928	1799	1881	104213	PEM	Tenby
1841	....	ALL	ALL	131415	PEM	Treffgarne
1830	1830	1800	1840	158658	POW	Brecon
1800	1870	1700	1800	101524	POW	Llandinam
1720	1841	1600	1881	176877	RAD	Beguildy
1881	1965	ALL	ALL	112275	SAL	Bridgnorth
1845	1870	1780	1845	118486	SAL	Claverley
....	....	1853	....	140767	SAL	Dawley
1900	1950	1800	1900	108359	SAL	Hook A Gate
1708	1770	ALL	1708	179515	SAL	Hopesay
1742	1845	1600	1881	176877	SAL	Llanfair Waterdine
1870	1890	1870	1885	100218	SAL	Ludlow
1800	1889	1800	1889	177695	SAL	Madeley
1862	1992	1700	1862	118605	SAL	Minsterley
1870	1930	1820	1870	109878	SAL	Oswestry
1822	1849	1780	1822	154024	SAL	Shrewsbury
1870	1880	....	....	124516	SAL	Yokleton
....	....	1840	1870	124516	SAL	???
1812	....	1750	1810	178845	SOM	Backwell
....	....	1750	1900	162388	SOM	West Super Mare
1850	1900	ALL	ALL	162620	SRY	Epsom
1780	1866	1700	1780	132853	SRY	Lambeth
1840	1900	1700	1992	162620	SRY	Wandsworth
....	....	1820	1870	167401	SSX	Eastbourne
1800	1900	1800	1800	177695	STS	Cannock
1861	1992	1792	....	144088	STS	Knutton
1800	....	....	....	130486	STS	Stafford
1740	1850	ALL	ALL	117870	WAR	Birmingham
1800	ALL	1800	1844	151475	WAR	Birmingham
1880	1945	1880	1945	100218	WAR	Coventry
1888	....	....	....	126926	WLS	Mold
1850	1992	1700	1850	118532	WLS	Swansea
1852	1878	1827	1852	118435	WLS	???
1843	1900	ALL	ALL	135127	WOR	Dudley St Thomas
....	....	1500	1992	119792	WOR	Dudley
1831	1863	1775	1830	149977	WOR	Dudley
1836	1930	1700	1836	109398	WOR	Little Comberton
1836	1930	1700	1836	109398	WOR	Pershore
1850	1930	1750	1850	179086	YKS	Bradford
DAVILL						
1850	1960	ALL	ALL	162469	YKS	North
DAVIS						
....	....	....	....	173037	ANT	Hillsborough
1740	1800	1740	1800	167924	BDF	Shillington
1796	1863	1700	1796	179116	BRK	Denchworth
1770	1800	1700	1850	140260	BRK	Wokingham
....	....	1800	....	128627	CAM	???
1880	1950	1880	1992	122238	CHS	Port Sunlight
1666	1842	?	1666	128910	DBY	Heanor
1812	1992	1812	....	118761	DBY	Matlock
1800	1870	1650	1800	120774	DEV	South East
1700	1900	1500	1700	179396	DEV	Ottery St Mary
1750	1850	....	....	108677	DOR	Cerne Abbas
1800	1900	1800	1900	112712	DOR	Puddletown
1858	1992	1850	1992	112216	DOR	Studland
1747	1843	1700	1900	112216	DOR	Winterborne Whitchurch
....	....	....	....	173037	DOW	Lisburn
1700	1800	1700	1800	169781	DUR	Whickham
1815	1851	ALL	1860	118737	ESS	Colchester
1750	1850	ALL	1850	106380	ESS	Cold Norton
1750	1850	ALL	1850	106380	ESS	Purliegh
1750	1850	ALL	1850	106380	ESS	Stow Maries
1900	....	....	....	126926	ESS	West Ham
1782	1861	1700	1782	101486	EYK	Hull
1880	1890	....	....	134376	GLA	Bristol

Known From	To	Researching From	To	Ref	Cty	Place
DAVIS contd.						
1800	1992	1700	1800	118745	GLS	Badgeworth
1765	1845	1700	1850	105333	GLS	Bisley
1800	1992	1700	1800	118745	GLS	Boddington
....	....	1800	1899	104884	GLS	Bristol
1881	1920	1881	ALL	110922	GLS	Bristol
1860	1942	1860	1942	165395	GLS	Bristol
1700	1750	....	....	176958	GLS	Bristol
1871	1871	1871	1871	143286	GLS	Cheltenham
....	....	ALL	ALL	151998	GLS	Coleford
1797	1900	1700	1850	118753	GLS	Durlsey
1800	1851	1750	1851	125865	GLS	Gloucester
1833	1861	1700	1833	173797	GLS	Gloucester
1765	1845	1700	1850	105333	GLS	Horsley
....	....	1700	1780	148113	GLS	King Stanley
1590	1750	1553	1791	142859	GLS	Leonard Stanley
1827	1866	1700	1900	172073	GLS	Moreton In Marsh
1772	1790	1750	1800	136980	GLS	Parish St George
1740	1780	1600	1780	154342	GLS	Siston
1800	1992	1700	1800	118745	GLS	Staverton
1800	1992	ALL	ALL	103152	GLS	Stroud
1785	1795	1760	1815	105333	GLS	Tetbury
1819	1841	1750	1819	148938	GLS	Westbury On Severn
1732	1897	1600	1732	172006	GLS	Westbury On Severn
1700	1830	1700	1830	151297	GNT	Tintern
1907	....	....	....	153397	HAM	Brockenhurst
1767	1855	1700	1767	133949	HAM	Christchurch
1792	1837	1792	....	115576	HAM	Clanukke
1750	1792	....	....	153397	HAM	New Forest
....	....	1700	1850	110078	HAM	Romsey
1500	1800	1300	1500	123390	HEF	Dymock
1850	1860	1800	1850	140309	HEF	Shobdon
....	1863	....	....	101370	IRL	???
1844	1914	1800	1940	139203	KEN	Beckenham
1808	1992	1700	1808	118788	KEN	Hawkhurst
1825	1850	1780	1825	108413	KEN	Lynsted
1890	1980	....	....	110078	LAN	Lees
....	....	1800	....	118826	LAN	Manchester
1890	1980	....	....	110078	LAN	Oldham
1890	1980	....	....	110078	LAN	Rochdale
1780	1800	1700	1780	155950	LEI	Leicester
1838	1850	1750	1900	134376	LIN	Stamford
....	....	1860	1900	166022	LKS	Motherwell
1872	1992	1872	ALL	110922	LND	ALL
1860	1968	1800	1860	174068	LND	ALL
1800	1900	ALL	ALL	131873	LND	East
1788	....	1788	1992	165727	LND	Aldgate
1851	1880	1750	1851	172472	LND	Holborn
1825	1850	1780	1825	108413	LND	Lambeth
1920	1934	1920	....	118516	LND	London
1903	1968	1700	1923	166073	LND	Paddington
1800	....	....	....	153117	LND	Stepney
1900	1914	....	....	130281	LND	Waterloo
....	....	1800	....	118826	LND	???
....	....	1869	1910	118834	LND	???
....	....	ALL	ALL	151998	MDX	Bloomsbury
1800	1900	1750	1900	116742	MDX	Heston
1790	1836	ALL	1800	142301	MDX	London
1850	1920	1850	1920	144541	MDX	London
....	1817	1800	1817	133639	MDX	Marylebone
1809	1974	....	1809	133566	MDX	Paddington
1840	1880	ALL	1840	102016	MDX	St Pancras
1842	1881	ALL	1881	164186	NTH	Rothesthorpe
1844	1912	1600	1844	143146	NTT	Annesley
1785	1895	....	....	102946	NTT	Nottingham
1800	1900	1803	1900	122238	SAL	Broseley
1750	1803	1750	1803	122238	SAL	Mid
1854	1930	ALL	ALL	101370	SCT	Maxwelltown
1700	1750	1700	1770	142018	SOM	Bath
1860	1942	1860	1942	165395	SOM	Bath
1830	1950	1700	1830	145017	SOM	Bishops Lydyard
1750	1950	1700	1900	136840	SOM	Brendon Hills
1846	1950	1700	1846	132039	SOM	Bristol
1770	1870	1770	1870	156744	SOM	Castle Cary
1808	1839	ALL	1808	161500	SOM	Crewkerne
1770	1870	1770	1870	156744	SOM	Long Ashton
1770	1850	1700	1992	178020	SOM	Nettlecombe
ALL	....	....	....	156221	SOM	Stogursey
1800	1992	1600	1800	135313	SOM	Stowey
1770	1870	1770	1870	156744	SOM	West Lavington
1777	1867	ALL	ALL	153516	SOM	Worle
1887	1930	....	....	172073	SRY	Battersea
1865	1887	1850	1900	118737	SRY	Lambeth
1843	1864	....	....	121835	SRY	Malden

Known From	To	Researching From	To	Ref	Cty	Place
DAVIS contd.						
1828	1840	1800	1840	146803	SRY	Seale
1832	1860	1800	1900	133922	SSX	Bosham
1750	1850	1700	1900	138517	SSX	Ewhurst
1826	1840	1800	1826	176257	SSX	Lewes
1904	1904	....	....	144096	STS	Hednesford
1800	1860	1700	1800	166022	STS	Sedgeley
1840	1851	1851	1900	172073	WAR	Alveston
1886	....	ALL	1900	139459	WAR	Birmingham
1839	1921	1800	1850	117773	WAR	Kidderminster
1698	1728	1550	1697	131245	WAR	Rowington
1886	....	ALL	1900	139459	WAR	Saltley
1886	....	ALL	1900	139459	WAR	Small Heath
1825	1992	....	....	157805	WAR	St Martin
1704	?	ALL	1700	171573	WES	Sowlby
....	....	1650	1800	106461	WIL	ALL
1783	1868	1750	1783	145513	WIL	Collingbourne
1783	1868	1750	1783	145513	WIL	Ducis
1860	....	1800	1860	176931	WIL	Lea
1716	....	1716	1992	101656	WIL	Salisbury
1764	1835	1700	1765	176125	WIL	Savernake
1835	1977	....	....	176125	WIL	Wootton Rivers
1839	1900	1839	1900	111457	WLS	Cardiff
1880	?	ALL	1900	165646	WLS	Welshpool
1750	1880	1700	1850	126438	WOR	Alvechurch
1790	1825	....	....	157805	WOR	Alvechurch
1778	1788	1700	1800	159107	WOR	Bellbroughton
1797	1846	....	....	151351	WOR	Bengeworth
1851	1871	1850	1900	134376	WOR	Birmingham
1700	1850	1700	1850	103993	WOR	Broadway
1829	1873	1750	1992	166197	WOR	Eldersfield
1671	1881	1650	ALL	110922	WOR	Inkberrow
1860	1870	....	....	110078	YKS	Dewsbury
1875	1900	1860	1900	166022	YKS	Rotherham
DAVIS-ISAAC						
1782	1801	1740	1801	101486	ENG	ALL
DAVISON						
....	....	ALL	ALL	118907	ALL	Name Study
1852	1920	1600	1852	127507	ANT	Racavan
1820	1852	1820	1852	154563	DUR	ALL
1770	1950	1600	1770	167584	DUR	Aukland
....	....	....	....	144215	DUR	Chester Moor
1811	1825	1538	1992	118893	DUR	Heworth
1840	1875	1538	1992	118893	DUR	Houghton Le Spring
1770	1880	....	....	102741	DUR	Hunwick
1842	1855	1538	1992	118893	DUR	Ryhope
1771	1771	1538	1992	118893	DUR	Ryton
1837	1891	1538	1992	118893	DUR	Seaham Harbourn
1870	1950	1700	1870	165182	DUR	Shildom
1770	1880	....	....	102741	DUR	St Helens Auckland
....	....	ALL	1886	116351	DUR	Sunderland
1772	1818	1538	1992	118893	DUR	Tanfield
1773	1793	ALL	1773	154563	DUR	Teesdale
1805	1811	1538	1992	118893	DUR	Whickham
1794	1900	ALL	ALL	122386	DUR	Whickham
1800	1900	....	....	100633	DUR	???
1789	1824	....	1824	165484	FIF	Kirkcaldy
1830	1992	1600	1830	118907	LND	ALL
1878	1992	1800	1878	122068	LND	North West
1767	1850	....	....	121355	LND	Bethnal Green
1767	1850	....	....	121355	LND	Limehouse
1767	1850	....	....	121355	LND	Shoreditch
1857	1936	ALL	....	109258	MDX	Enfield Wash
1850	1880	1850	1880	118869	MDX	London
1810	1875	1770	1810	147745	NBL	Alnwick
1886	1988	ALL	1886	116351	NBL	Annitsford
1799	1992	ALL	1799	154520	NBL	Bedlington
1886	1988	ALL	1886	116351	NBL	Blythe
1825	1840	1538	1992	118893	NBL	Churton
1886	1988	ALL	1886	116351	NBL	Cowpen
1721	1744	1700	1750	123536	NBL	Embleton
1840	1878	ALL	1992	102245	NBL	Newcastle Upon Tyne
1837	1992	....	....	169110	NBL	North Shields
1810	1820	1810	1820	154563	NBL	Ovingham
1812	1837	1700	1812	169110	NBL	Shotley Fields
1823	1824	1700	1845	152609	NBL	Wooperton
1800	....	....	....	169129	NFK	East
1830	1850	1830	1850	130222	NTH	Aldwinkle St Peters
1735	1980	1600	1735	107042	NYK	Scarborough
1780	1810	ALL	1780	154563	SSX	Hastings
1829	1920	1700	1829	167886	YKS	North Allerton
1750	1800	....	....	167843	YKS	Redmire Cum Bolton
1716	1757	1600	1760	101575	YKS	Rothwell
1818	1992	1700	1818	123951	YKS	Sand Hutton
DAVISON contd.						
1857	1992	1700	1857	123943	YKS	Sheffield
1800	1900	1750	1850	153990	???	Chester Le Street
DAVOREN						
....	....	ALL	ALL	174637	ALL	Name Study
ALL	1992	ALL	ALL	174637	ALL	ALL
DAVY						
1861	1880	1800	1861	155217	DEV	Coryton
1729	1850	1850	1900	145963	DEV	Crediton
1750	1992	1500	1750	118915	DEV	Heavitree
1750	1992	1500	1750	118915	DEV	Totnes
1827	1827	1550	1830	147265	DUR	???
1819	....	ALL	1819	104299	GLS	Bristol
1760	1950	1650	1760	128376	NBL	Horton
1790	1857	1857	1891	125105	NFK	Great Yarmouth
1767	1860	....	....	127779	SFK	Burgh
....	....	1850	1900	145963	SOM	Bristol
1840	1992	....	1840	133825	YKS	Bradford
....	....	....	....	160180	YKS	Embsay
1591	....	....	....	160180	YKS	Kildwick
DAVYS						
1570	1992	1500	1992	145750	ALL	ALL
DAW						
1796	1992	....	1796	160652	CON	Callington
1800	1900	1600	1800	179396	DEV	Ottery St Mary
1817	1980	1650	1748	141372	DEV	Sandford
1790	1992	....	1800	179213	DEV	Totnes
1720	....	ALL	ALL	110272	DOR	Cheddington
1796	1941	1700	1796	161225	GLS	Thornbury
1744	1963	1700	1850	117013	NFK	Dersingham
1751	1845	1700	1751	100277	SSX	Wartling
DAWBER						
1783	1951	1700	1783	178500	NTT	Newark
DAWE						
1894	1963	1750	1894	153974	BKM	High Wycombe
....	....	1883	1884	158763	CON	Callington
1841	1861	1700	1838	130656	CON	Tresmeer
1800	1850	1750	1800	159441	DEV	ALL
1630	1850	1600	1900	177091	DEV	South
1807	....	1800	1838	130656	DEV	Bratton Clovelly
1847	1926	1850	1926	121584	DEV	Stoke Damerel
1850	1870	1800	1850	143898	DEV	Tavistock
1870	1878	1850	1870	130656	GLA	Llwynyppia
1875	1930	1860	1875	143898	LND	Southwark
1867	1940	1750	1867	153974	MDX	London
DAWES						
1700	1900	1600	1900	154342	GLS	Stapleton
1827	1938	1938	1980	115819	LAN	Salford
1800	1900	1700	1850	107948	MDX	Brentford
1722	1816	1797	1829	156582	NFK	Norwich
....	....	1800	1860	176494	NTT	ALL
1870	1992	1700	1870	118923	SAL	High Evcall
1755	1881	1650	1755	119512	SSX	Cuckfield
DAWKINS						
1734	1992	....	....	100900	BKM	Great Horwood
1813	1856	1700	1813	120707	HAM	ALL
1885	1910	....	....	164232	SRY	Lambeth
DAWLEY						
1750	1870	1750	1870	167924	STS	ALL
DAWN						
1705	1750	1500	1705	138614	CON	Perranuthnoe
DAWS						
1740	1796	....	....	159492	ALL	ALL
1773	....	1770	1820	142018	GLS	Wickwar
1835	1992	1834	1992	159492	LAN	Oldham
1886	1965	1700	1886	173479	NFK	Norwich
DAWSON						
1854	1992	ALL	1700	124303	BDF	Clapham
1838	1899	ALL	1838	149950	BDF	Clapham
1877	1878	ALL	ALL	115355	BDF	Dean
1835	1836	1800	1880	123536	BDF	Eaton Socon
1800	1900	1830	1880	108847	CAM	Ely
1650	1800	1800	1900	110930	CHS	Burleydam
1810	1850	1750	1810	168912	CHS	Macclesfield
1780	1800	....	....	164631	CMA	Ely
1850	....	1700	1920	126160	CUL	Eskdale
1850	....	1700	1920	126160	CUL	Gosforth
1750	1800	1700	1750	102172	CUL	Matterdale
1713	1800	1600	1713	158739	CUL	St Bees
1850	....	1700	1920	126160	CUL	Wastdale
?	?	?	?	151556	CUL	???
1881	....	1851	1881	156833	DBY	Glossop
1881	....	1851	1881	156833	DBY	Hadfield
....	....	1790	1831	156833	DBY	Ludworth

Known From	To	Researching From	To	Ref	Cty	Place
DAWSON contd.						
1846	1846	1800	1846	137413	DEV	Crediton
1780	1895	1538	1895	118893	DUR	St Johns
....	....	....	....	116637	DUR	Sunderland
1796	1867	ALL	1796	154563	DUR	Weardale
1767	1992	1700	1767	118982	ESS	Stratford
1767	1992	1700	1767	118982	ESS	Tedring
....	1780	ALL	1780	152889	HUN	Hail Weston
1859	1911	1800	1859	114545	HUN	Sawtry
1880	1992	ALL	1880	119652	IRL	Belfast
1907	1992	....	....	164631	KEN	Dartford
1775	1820	....	....	161357	KEN	Margate
1758	1851	....	....	118729	LAN	Eccles
1830	1845	1800	1830	101796	LAN	Farnworth
1800	1840	....	....	102172	LAN	Halton
1790	1920	ALL	1992	151254	LAN	Leigh
....	....	1750	1900	100390	LAN	Littleborough
1771	1777	1735	1777	174211	LAN	Prestwich
1812	1851	ALL	1812	133159	LAN	Seathwaite
1790	1920	ALL	1992	151254	LAN	Tyldesley
1577	1806	ALL	ALL	141615	LAN	Warton
1771	1777	1735	1777	174211	LAN	Whitefield
1698	1992	1560	1700	118958	LAN	???
....	....	1700	ALL	115142	LEI	South
1729	1737	ALL	ALL	141615	LEI	Leicester
1800	1992	....	....	176125	LIN	Asterby
1860	1885	1800	1850	112038	LIN	Bourne
1790	1850	....	....	102946	LIN	Brant Broughton
1790	1850	....	....	102946	LIN	Fulbeck
1800	1992	....	....	176125	LIN	Goulceby
1812	1900	....	....	164631	LIN	Spalding
1840	....	1840	....	162663	LIN	Stainby
1790	1850	....	....	102946	LIN	Welton Le Marsh
1808	1953	1300	1850	152501	LND	Pimlico
1808	1953	1300	1850	152501	LND	Westminster
1847	1851	1847	1861	146528	MDX	Paddington
1700	1830	....	....	148261	NBL	Allendales
1822	1847	1800	1850	152609	NBL	Burradon
1822	1847	1800	1850	152609	NBL	Colt Park
1740	1881	1700	1900	167487	NFK	Bracon Ash
1740	1760	1700	1740	141402	NFK	Hedenham
1863	1863	1750	1862	131245	NFK	Norwich
1837	....	1837	....	151041	NIR	Belfast
1857	1900	1857	1900	117803	NRY	Scruton
1833	1844	....	....	117803	NRY	Thornton Watlass
1879	1900	1879	1900	117803	NRY	Yarm
1779	1781	1754	1804	107360	NTH	Duston
1747	1763	1740	1770	107360	NTH	Kingsthorpe
1844	1845	1841	1851	146528	NTH	Rushden
1788	1813	1858	1880	107360	NTH	Scaldwell
1837	....	1837	....	151041	SCT	Anderston
1800	1900	1800	1992	177180	STS	Coseley In Sedgley
1800	1850	1800	1992	177180	WAR	Aston
1727	1732	1705	....	138401	WES	Heversham
1869	1869	1800	1880	127361	WRY	Bradford
1698	1920	1698	1920	117803	WRY	Marton Cum Grafton
1867	1879	....	....	117803	WRY	Minskip
1781	1877	....	1781	101761	WRY	Mirfield
....	....	1750	1850	100390	WYK	Keighley
1820	1940	1760	1920	103616	WYK	Tickhill
1850	1890	1700	1890	163902	YKS	South
1779	1860	1680	1760	170348	YKS	Almondbury
1840	1880	1500	1840	104140	YKS	Brighouse
1813	1881	1783	1881	118974	YKS	Churwell
1881	1949	1800	1950	109460	YKS	Golcar
1848	1992	1650	1848	168513	YKS	Huddersfield
1726	....	1680	1750	170348	YKS	Huddersfield
1784	1858	1784	1858	149403	YKS	Hull
1840	1880	1880	1992	104140	YKS	Kirkburton
1756	1791	1600	1750	101575	YKS	Leeds
1790	....	1600	1790	116637	YKS	Robin Hoods Bay
1800	1850	1700	1850	166928	YKS	Seamer
1840	1890	....	....	102946	YKS	Sheffield
1750	....	1700	....	134589	YKS	Swillington
DAY						
1742	1823	ALL	1742	126721	BDF	Shefford
1780	1824	ALL	ALL	168211	BDF	Woburn
1780	1824	ALL	ALL	168211	BKM	Fenny Stratford
1782	1816	....	1850	171441	BRK	Kingston Lisle
....	....	1750	1810	103713	CAM	Cheveley
1820	1992	1700	1820	117242	CAM	Ely
1691	1940	....	....	128996	CAM	Thornley
1830	....	1750	1900	109894	DOR	Bere Regis
1802	1843	1700	1802	113425	ESS	East Donyland

Known From	To	Researching From	To	Ref	Cty	Place
DAY contd.						
1755	1835	1650	1750	100013	ESS	High Easter
1763	1774	1730	1850	128961	ESS	Stansted
1838	1841	ALL	ALL	149683	GLS	Kemerton
1740	1850	1700	1740	124362	GLS	Lechlade
1770	1896	1700	1770	159565	GLS	Longborough
1851	1992	1700	1992	119040	GLS	Lower Slaughter
1759	1815	1700	1759	134627	GLS	Sutton Under Brailles
1859	1910	....	....	102601	IOW	Cowes
1750	1860	....	....	102601	IOW	Shalfleet
1749	1799	....	....	127957	IOW	Shalfleet
1700	1816	1500	1700	129577	IOW	???
1874	1992	1700	1879	139335	KEN	Peckham
1827	1900	ALL	ALL	141704	LND	Bermondsey
1900	1992	1700	1900	133647	LND	East End
1827	1900	ALL	ALL	141704	LND	Horsleydown
1874	1992	1700	1879	139335	LND	Peckham
1827	1900	ALL	ALL	141704	LND	Southwark
1827	1900	ALL	ALL	141704	LND	St Olave
1800	1830	1700	1850	126268	LND	Stepney
1924	....	....	....	173932	LND	Stoke Newington
1800	....	1700	1800	128090	LND	Whitechapel
1780	1833	1750	1830	107093	MDX	Westminster
1690	1690	1600	1675	176672	NFK	ALL
1840	1845	1845	1850	113646	NTH	Deventry
1992	1992	ALL	1743	119067	NTH	Peterborough
1865	1870	1700	1870	113778	NYK	Allerton Mauleverer
....	....	ALL	1800	103284	OXF	Clifton
1719	....	....	....	102733	OXF	Northleigh
1860	1900	1800	1900	111325	SFK	Washbrook
1820	1850	1800	1820	101524	SOM	Lyng
1959	....	....	....	173932	SRY	Horley
1800	1840	1750	1840	107093	SRY	Lambeth
1870	1938	ALL	....	153214	SRY	Wandsworth
1850	1872	....	1850	129771	SSX	Hailsham
1876	1932	1780	1876	175846	SSX	Hastings
1798	....	ALL	1800	115118	SSX	Northchapel
1850	1970	1750	1900	107611	WAR	Aston
1796	ALL	....	....	117048	WAR	Birmingham
1750	1780	1600	1850	130125	WAR	Hatton
1800	1840	ALL	1800	145564	WIL	Chippenway
1780	1881	1700	1992	159468	WIL	Corsham
....	....	ALL	1825	151602	WIL	Hindon
1750	1825	ALL	1850	167029	WIL	Ramsbury
1879	1969	ALL	ALL	149683	WOR	South
....	....	ALL	ALL	143502	WOR	Worcester
1796	1840	....	....	151351	YKS	Bedale
1755	1800	1700	1787	119032	YKS	Boston Spa
1775	1781	....	....	151351	YKS	Ripon
1600	1630	1500	1992	114901	YKS	Thirkleby
1860	1900	1800	1900	164518	YKS	Wakefield
....	1900	....	1900	119024	???	Birmingham
1828	1900	....	....	100536	???	Horstead
DAYCOCK						
....	....	?	?	147869	ALL	ALL
DAYE						
1580	1670	1400	1992	102520	YKS	Rylstone
DAYER						
1900	1966	1966	....	109967	BKM	Chesham
DAYKIN						
1794	1803	1766	1794	122572	DBY	ALL
1794	1803	1766	1794	122572	NTT	ALL
1830	1873	ALL	ALL	143677	NTT	Greasley
DAYMAN						
....	....	ALL	ALL	119083	ALL	Name Study
DAYMOND						
....	....	ALL	1992	119083	ALL	ALL
1735	1850	ALL	1992	119083	DEV	East
DAYSH						
?	?	ALL	1850	117919	HAM	Wickham
DAYTON						
1753	1992	ALL	1992	168718	NTH	East
DE ACTON						
ALL	1400	....	....	132756	NBL	???
DE BAR						
1740	1820	1300	1820	154881	ALL	ALL
DE BEAUREGARD						
1785	1785	ALL	ALL	154067	SRY	Croydon
1830	1872	1825	1890	154067	STS	ALL
DE BEAUREGARDE						
1785	1856	ALL	1900	154067	LND	ALL
DE BIDDLESTON						
ALL	1240	....	....	132756	NBL	???

Known From	To	Researching From	To	Ref	Cty	Place
DE BOARD						
1800	1950	1700	1800	146110	ENG	ALL
DE BOHUN						
1066	1400	1066	1400	154881	ALL	ALL
DE BOUVERIE						
....	....	1560	1650	154873	KEN	Canterbury
....	....	1560	1650	154873	KEN	Sandwich
....	....	1560	1650	154873	LND	???
DE BRAOSE						
....	....	1066	1230	124974	GNT	Abergavenny
1066	1300	1066	1300	154881	RAD	Radnor
DE BREANSKI						
1850	1900	ALL	ALL	129178	LND	Greenwich
DE BRYN						
....	....	1200	1300	154873	LAN	???
DE CAEN						
1650	1992	ALL	1950	119105	JSY	ALL
DE CAMVILLE						
....	....	1066	1150	124974	DEV	ALL
1140	1180	1100	1200	124974	OXF	Stanton Harcourt
DE CARLE						
1752	1791	....	....	116602	NFK	Norwich
1840	1864	1800	1861	155381	SFK	Bury St Edmunds
DE CARTERET						
1608	1845	ALL	1608	115126	CHI	ALL
1700	1980	1700	1980	119113	GSY	ALL
....	....	ALL	ALL	155632	JSY	Channel Islands
1000	1565	1000	1900	119113	JSY	St Ouens
1566	1940	1566	1980	119113	SRK	ALL
DE CHAIR						
1654	....	....	....	131822	ESS	???
1654	....	....	....	131822	LND	???
DE CLAVERING						
1250	1330	1200	1330	154881	NRY	Coverham
DE CLAXTON						
ALL	1550	....	....	132756	NBL	Dilston
ALL	1550	....	....	132756	NBL	Horden
DE CLIFFORD THORNTON						
1811	1876	?	1811	109975	LND	Islington
DE CRAUCUMBE						
1140	1253	1066	1590	117056	ALL	ALL
DE CREON						
ALL	1200	....	....	132756	NBL	???
DE CROSS GONZALES						
1880	1920	1800	1890	147494	LND	London
DE DULIN						
1880	1992	....	....	119121	ALL	ALL
DE DUNLOP						
1260	1992	....	1492	144363	SCT	Irvine
DE EMELDON						
ALL	1400	....	....	132756	NBL	Newcastle
DE ESSETE						
....	....	ALL	ALL	124974	ALL	ALL
1066	1275	1066	1480	124974	SSX	Exceat
DE FELTON						
ALL	1380	....	....	132756	NBL	Edlingham
DE FRESNE						
1830	1860	1800	1880	170143	JSY	St Helier
1830	1860	1800	1880	170143	JSY	St Martin
DE GAI						
....	....	1140	1210	124974	BKM	ALL
DE GOURNAY						
....	....	1066	1120	124974	NFK	Great Yarmouth
DE GRESLEY						
1060	1166	....	....	157120	STS	ALL
DE GRUCHY						
1300	1992	....	....	115126	CHI	ALL
1901	....	....	....	113484	CHI	Jersey
1870	1992	1700	1870	119156	CHI	Jersey
....	1930	....	....	113484	DOR	Weymouth
DE HADINDEN						
1200	1400	1200	1400	154881	KEN	Sundridge
DE HARTLYNGTON						
1240	1520	....	....	134953	YKS	Hartlington
DE HERLINETUN						
1100	1520	....	....	134953	YKS	Hartlington
DE HEVER						
1030	1087	1000	1100	124974	KEN	Hever
DE HEVRE						
1150	1220	1100	1250	154881	KEN	Hever
DE HICKELING						
1150	1477	ALL	ALL	133299	ALL	ALL
1237	....	....	....	133299	BKM	Oving
1317	....	....	....	133299	DBY	Derby
DE HICKELING contd.						
1364	1372	....	....	133299	DBY	Matlock
1348	....	....	....	133299	DBY	Repton
1325	....	....	....	133299	KEN	Faversham
1327	1330	....	....	133299	LEI	Frisby On The Wreake
1327	....	....	....	133299	LEI	Harby
1325	....	....	....	133299	MDX	Woolwich
1301	1326	....	....	133299	NFK	Basingham
1328	1348	....	....	133299	NFK	Burnham
1216	....	....	....	133299	NFK	Dilham
1344	1376	....	....	133299	NFK	Great Yarmouth
1150	1408	....	....	133299	NFK	Hickeling
1307	1347	....	....	133299	NFK	Mautby
1313	1328	....	....	133299	NFK	Norton
1294	1477	....	....	133299	NFK	Norwich
1328	....	....	....	133299	NFK	Weybridge Priory
1272	1306	....	....	133299	NFK	Wissingset
1204	1206	....	....	133299	NTH	Pattishall
1170	1234	....	....	133299	NTT	Hickeling
1273	....	....	....	133299	NTT	Newstead In Sherwood
1351	....	....	....	133299	NTT	Newthorpe
1276	....	....	....	133299	NTT	Nottingham
1335	....	....	....	133299	NTT	Oxton
1318	1345	....	....	133299	SFK	Beauchamps
1336	1350	....	....	133299	SFK	Brome
1318	1345	....	....	133299	SFK	Heigham Hill
1336	1350	....	....	133299	SFK	Occold
1316	1380	....	....	133299	SFK	Rishangles
1300	1345	....	....	133299	SFK	Shelfanger
1336	1350	....	....	133299	SFK	Stuston
1297	1307	....	....	133299	SSX	Chinting Seaford
1328	1341	....	....	133299	STS	Cresswell
1327	1342	....	....	133299	STS	Draycott In The Clay
1324	....	....	....	133299	WOR	Langebergh
1318	....	....	....	133299	YKS	Patrington
1275	....	....	....	133299	YKS	York
DE KAREWARDYN						
1292	1430	1292	1430	156809	HEF	???
DE L'AUNE						
....	....	1700	1750	150967	LND	Spitalfields
DE LA BERE						
....	....	ALL	ALL	124974	ALL	ALL
1318	1341	1066	1992	124974	BRK	Wargrave
1292	1450	1250	1500	124974	GLA	Weobley
1600	1820	....	....	124974	GLS	Bishops Cleeve
1600	1820	....	....	124974	GLS	Southam
1500	1640	....	....	124974	GLS	Tibberton
1333	1428	1300	1428	124974	HAM	Binstead
1376	1514	1376	1514	124974	HAM	Clehonger
1066	1514	1066	1514	124974	HAM	Hereford
1340	1520	1300	1520	124974	HAM	Kinnersley
1316	1325	1066	1992	124974	OXF	ALL
1297	1297	1250	1350	124974	SSX	Thornham
DE LA CHAMBRE						
....	....	1500	....	164038	SSX	Hailsham
DE LA HAYE						
1870	1992	1700	1870	166480	JSY	ALL
DE LA PIERRE						
1660	1738	1660	1738	154873	KEN	Canterbury
DE LA QUEULLE						
1500	1560	1450	1560	154881	ALL	ALL
DE LA RISEBREGGE						
1276	1332	1200	1700	131547	SRY	Reigate
DE LACY EVANS						
....	....	ALL	ALL	138673	ALL	ALL
DE LE CLUSE						
1640	1992	1640	1992	141380	ALL	ALL
DE LEYBURNE						
1220	1350	1200	1350	154881	ALL	ALL
DE LONGFORD						
1170	1610	....	....	157120	DBY	ALL
1170	1610	....	....	157120	STS	ALL
DE LOUVAINE						
1200	1397	1200	1400	154881	ESS	Little Easton
DE MANDEVILLE						
1150	1200	1100	1200	154881	ESS	ALL
....	....	1066	1155	124974	ESS	Pleshey
DE MASKELL						
1940	1992	1850	1940	112399	MDX	London
DE MERLE						
1800	1900	1800	1900	151653	SOM	Congresbury

Surname	Known From	Known To	Researching From	Researching To	Ref	Cty	Place
DE MOLTON							
	ALL	1240	....	....	132756	NBL	???
DE MONTFORT							
	950	1350	900	1350	154881	ALL	ALL
DE MORTAGNE							
	....	....	942	1443	145580	ENG	ALL
	....	....	1177	....	145580	ESS	???
	....	....	1161	1350	145580	SFK	Old Newton
DE NEWBURGH							
	1066	1242	1066	1242	124974	WAR	Warwick
DE NOYERS							
	....	....	1700	1750	150967	LND	Spitalfields
DE PRADINES							
	1790	1992	ALL	....	136018	LND	Woolwich
DE PUTRON							
	....	....	1540	1950	125296	GSY	???
DE QUERTON							
	....	1300	....	....	135399	WES	Appleby Assises
DE QUINCY							
	1150	1300	1100	1300	154881	NTH	Bushby
DE RIDELSFORD							
	1150	1250	1150	1250	154881	WIC	Bray
DE ROS							
	....	....	1066	1350	154873	KEN	???
DE ROUFFIGNAC							
	1685	1992	1685	1992	108081	ALL	ALL
DE SANDFORD							
	1150	1300	1150	1300	154881	ALL	ALL
DE SAY							
	1100	1400	1100	1400	154881	ALL	ALL
DE SCURES							
	1100	1499	1100	1499	163805	HAM	ALL
DE SEGRAVE							
	1100	1350	1100	1350	154881	LEI	Seagrave
DE SMITH							
	1885	1905	ALL	ALL	125318	LND	Hackney
DE SMYTHETON							
	ALL	1350	....	....	132756	NBL	???
DE STAFFORD							
	1041	1166	....	....	157120	STS	ALL
DE STIRRUP							
	1840	....	ALL	1840	160660	ALL	ALL
DE STUTEVILLE							
	1150	1250	1100	1250	154881	ALL	ALL
DE TOENI							
	1102	1309	....	....	157120	ALL	ALL
	1041	1088	....	....	157120	STS	ALL
DE TONY							
	1066	1350	1066	1350	154881	HRT	Flamstead
DE TRIE							
	1100	1205	1100	1205	154881	ALL	ALL
DE VALLERIES							
	1150	1250	1150	1250	154881	ESS	ALL
DE VEAR							
	1810	1880	1750	1810	143332	LND	Westminster
DE VIELL							
	1830	1992	1700	1830	119164	DEV	ALL
DE VILLE							
	....	....	ALL	ALL	119172	ALL	Name Study
	1855	....	ALL	ALL	119180	DBY	West
	1877	1883	ALL	ALL	119180	STS	Burton On Trent
	1600	1830	1600	1830	119172	STS	Marchington
	1883	1992	ALL	ALL	119180	YKS	Leeds
DE VILLERS							
	1076	1245	....	....	172537	LAN	Crosby
	1245	1400	....	....	172537	LEI	Brooksby
	1115	1347	....	....	172537	SSX	Tryford
DE VRIES							
	1825	1838	1780	1815	157481	BRK	Various
	1795	1809	1725	1820	157481	LND	St Georges Hanover Square
	1837	1920	1835	1920	157481	MDX	Chiswick
DE WAER							
	1066	1170	1066	1170	154881	NFK	ALL
DE WARENNE							
	1066	1374	1066	1138	124974	NFK	Castle Acre
	1066	1374	1066	1138	124974	SSX	Lewels
	1066	1374	1066	1138	124974	WRY	Conisborough
DE WARWICK							
	1184	1242	1066	1242	124974	WAR	Warwick
DE WAUTHAM							
	1100	1200	1100	1200	154881	ALL	ALL
DE WESTON							
	1200	1350	1200	1350	154881	LIN	Boston
DE-REDING							
	1854	1920	....	....	173282	HAM	Portsmouth
DEACKES							
	1812	....	....	....	148768	KEN	Strood
DEACON							
	1806	1878	1600	1806	149888	CON	Antony
	1700	1800	1700	1890	126403	CON	Duloe
	1747	1790	1700	1809	171549	CON	Duloe
	1800	1840	1800	1840	126403	CON	Millbrook
	1753	1992	1600	1753	116432	CON	St Stephens Saltash
	1753	1992	1600	1753	116432	CON	Stoke Climsland
	1856	1856	1700	1850	168734	DEV	Plymouth
	1770	1992	1740	1800	119199	HAM	Fordingbridge
	1790	1862	1750	1880	105333	HAM	Isle Of Wight
	1820	1821	1780	1830	105333	HAM	Portsmouth
	....	....	1600	1780	119199	IOW	ALL
	1810	1860	1700	1860	135275	MDX	Enfield
	1818	1851	1600	1992	115525	SOM	Shepton Mallett
	1820	1900	ALL	ALL	158798	WIL	West
	1750	1800	1600	1780	119199	WIL	Ramsbury
	1798	....	....	....	119911	YKS	Askrigg
DEADMAN							
	1770	1800	1770	1800	174343	HAM	East Worldham
	1730	1770	1730	1770	174343	HAM	Portchester
	1711	1730	1550	1730	174343	HAM	Portsea
	1832	1887	1800	1900	151246	SSX	Hailsham
	1880	1992	1880	1992	151246	SSX	Hastings
	1802	1835	1750	1850	151246	SSX	Wartling
	1890	1965	....	1890	137073	SXW	North Berstead
DEAKEN							
	1725	1738	ALL	ALL	141615	LEI	North
DEAKIN							
	1824	1992	....	....	102083	LAN	Bolton
	1898	1992	....	....	163155	LEI	Coalville
	1730	1865	1600	1730	120839	SAL	North
	1670	1992	ALL	1670	102083	SAL	Preston Brockhurst
	?	....	....	....	102105	SAL	???
	....	....	....	1898	163155	WAR	Birmingham
	1810	1900	1500	1810	169986	WOR	Stoke Prior
DEAKINS							
	1891	1992	ALL	1891	133957	HAM	Portsmouth
DEAL							
	1840	1880	1700	1840	152587	KEN	Dover
DEAMER							
	1850	1900	ALL	ALL	168211	BDF	Luton
	1880	1970	1700	1880	158976	MDX	Hillingdon
DEAN							
	1806	1871	1806	1856	125229	BKM	Gt Missenden
	1599	1887	1599	1887	125229	BKM	Hughenden
	....	....	1700	1850	101273	BKM	Hughendon
	1586	1892	1586	1892	125229	BKM	Lt Missenden
	1740	1805	1700	1850	125032	BRK	Easthampstead
	1992	1992	....	....	119210	BRK	Wokingham
	1771	1796	1700	1796	141062	CHS	Goostrey
	1744	1980	1700	1980	168920	CHS	Liscard
	1800	1870	....	....	132225	CHS	Wallasey
	1727	1918	1727	1918	121681	DOR	Bridport
	1770	1820	1770	1820	154210	DOR	Christchurch
	?	?	?	?	175390	DOR	Sherborne
	1720	1794	1500	1794	174270	DOR	West Parley
	1812	1875	ALL	1812	160008	EYK	Goole
	1800	1860	1700	1800	135658	GLS	Bristol
	1702	1794	1500	1794	174270	HAM	Christchurch
	1751	1751	1700	1770	174289	HAM	Christchurch
	....	....	....	1794	174270	HAM	Holdenhurst
	1880	1926	1880	1992	119210	KEN	Beckenham
	1861	....	1800	1992	140058	KEN	Capel
	1871	1874	1874	1992	140058	KEN	Chiddingstone Heath
	1740	....	....	1800	171441	KEN	Lynstead
	1861	....	1800	1992	140058	KEN	Sittingbourne
	1861	....	1800	1992	140058	KEN	Tonbridge
	1767	1870	1750	1870	119385	LAN	Accrington
	1852	1992	ALL	1992	143197	LAN	Barton
	1790	1920	1700	1790	161365	LAN	Barton
	1738	1936	1700	1870	131709	LAN	Didsbury
	1792	1950	ALL	1800	131695	LAN	Manchester
	1859	1992	1800	1859	175447	LAN	Manchester
	1870	1930	1870	1930	119385	LAN	Preston
	1796	1820	ALL	ALL	138886	LAN	Preston
	1750	1829	....	....	118354	LAN	Wigan
	1876	1879	....	....	119210	LIN	Melton Mowbray
	1810	1870	1780	1810	133221	LND	Bermondsey
	....	....	1800	1900	145688	LND	Islington
	1823	1845	....	....	168092	MDX	Finsbury St Lukes

Known From	To	Researching From	To	Ref	Cty	Place
DEAN contd.						
1880	1886	....	....	119210	MDX	Hackney
1820	1823	....	....	135437	MDX	Hackney
1912	1992	....	....	119210	MDX	Hendon
1767	1897	1750	1897	107573	MDX	Heston
....	....	1600	1900	176508	MDX	Pancras
1866	....	1845	1866	176885	MDX	St Pancras
1845	....	1838	1866	176885	MDX	Strand
1800	1850	1700	1860	135941	SFK	Great Thurlow
1800	1850	1700	1860	135941	SFK	Little Thurlow
1823	1840	1700	1830	112216	SFK	Southwold
1839	1839	....	....	135437	SRY	Bermondsey
1838	....	1800	1838	176885	SRY	Lambeth
1790	1824	1799	1826	152129	SRY	Richmond
1844	1854	1854	1876	119210	SSX	Brighton
1810	1892	1800	1840	108510	STS	Audley
1860	1860	1830	1892	108510	STS	Burslem
1770	1870	1700	1870	134627	STS	Rushall
1792	1828	?	1792	121665	STS	Wolverhampton
1885	1950	1850	1950	127353	WIL	Seend
1861	....	ALL	1861	170674	WOR	Worcester
?	?	?	?	122645	YKS	Addingham
1703	1777	1500	1703	125695	YKS	Everingham
?	?	?	?	122645	YKS	Ilkley
?	?	?	?	122645	YKS	Nesfield
1840	1940	....	....	145912	YKS	South Leeds
DEANE						
....	....	ALL	1736	103284	BKM	Hambleden
1776	1850	1750	1850	102970	BRK	Speen
1829	1992	1700	1829	160962	CHS	Wirral
1886	1937	ALL	ALL	149489	GLS	Cheltenham
....	1831	1790	1850	128961	KEN	Dover
1829	1992	1700	1829	160962	LAN	North
1829	1992	1700	1829	160962	LAN	Liverpool
1750	1750	1700	1750	147575	LND	Hackney
1829	1992	1700	1829	160962	YKS	???
DEANEY						
1880	1987	1800	1992	162183	DBY	ALL
1880	1987	1800	1992	162183	DBY	Ilkston
DEANS						
1838	1862	1800	1900	144231	AYR	Neilston
1839	....	ALL	ALL	172057	BEW	Axton
1900	....	ALL	....	119237	ENG	South
1828	1850	1800	1828	101796	RFW	Pollockshaws
1634	1992	1546	1880	141798	ROX	Hawick
1803	....	ALL	....	119237	T&W	South Sheilds
DEAR						
1850	1960	1850	1900	108693	BDF	Arlesey
....	....	ALL	ALL	174963	BDF	Arlesey
....	....	ALL	ALL	174963	BDF	Shillington
1775	1800	1740	1812	123536	HAM	Portsea
1650	1800	1600	1992	173096	KEN	Sandwich
1730	1850	1700	1992	173096	KEN	St Lawrence
1790	1860	....	....	165999	LEI	Leicester
1550	1800	....	....	165999	LIN	ALL
1550	1800	....	....	165999	LIN	Glentham
1550	1800	....	....	165999	LIN	Lincoln
....	....	1800	1850	145688	LND	St Pancras
1829	1854	1600	1829	132802	PER	Kenmore
....	....	1780	1850	118834	SSX	West Wittering
1830	1884	....	....	152722	WIL	Salisbury
....	....	ALL	ALL	151696	???	???
DEARDEN						
1861	1881	1840	1900	126705	LAN	South
1830	1943	ALL	1830	121525	LAN	Burnley
1850	1875	ALL	ALL	119253	LAN	Hulme
1875	1935	ALL	ALL	119253	LAN	Monton
1873	1992	1801	1992	111805	LAN	Rossendale
1812	....	1750	1825	137782	WYK	Stainland
DEARLE						
....	....	ALL	ALL	164380	ALL	Name Study
1658	1960	ALL	ALL	164380	ALL	ALL
DEARLOVE						
....	....	ALL	ALL	103136	ALL	ALL
1920	1992	....	....	153397	MDX	London
1920	1992	....	....	153397	SRY	ALL
DEARMAN						
1774	1807	1730	1807	144460	CAM	Weston
1816	....	....	1850	171441	HRT	Offley
1450	1920	....	....	139866	YKS	Sheffield
?	?	?	?	169781	YKS	Thorne
DEARMER						
1825	?	1700	1825	108588	HRT	Harpenden
DEARN						
1896	1992	1800	1900	127523	WAR	Birmingham
DEARNLEY						
1807	1992	1700	1800	160253	WYK	Fulstone
1840	1970	ALL	1840	143022	YKS	Huddersfield
DEARSLEY						
1830	....	1750	1850	102016	NFK	Carbrooke
DEASE						
....	....	....	1830	163201	MAY	Cloonmore
DEATH						
1785	....	....	....	103608	ESS	Boxted
1777	1900	1750	1900	119091	LND	Hackney
1837	1900	1800	1900	119091	LND	Paddington
1777	1900	1750	1900	119091	LND	Shoreditch
1837	1900	1800	1900	119091	LND	St Pancras
1707	1820	1700	1900	119091	LND	Whitechapel
1895	1960	1875	1930	119091	MDX	Edmonton
1720	1850	ALL	ALL	154008	SFK	ALL
1700	1800	1700	1800	162329	SFK	West
1646	1875	1600	1840	119091	SFK	Edwardstone
1770	1850	1770	1850	105848	SFK	Hitcham
1581	1800	1580	1840	119091	SFK	Lt Waldingfield
1619	1807	1600	1840	119091	SFK	Milden
1650	1800	1500	1800	144657	SFK	Stoke Next Nayland
1815	1870	1750	1815	172871	SFK	Whelnetham
1830	1840	1800	1840	119091	SRY	Kew
DEAVILLE						
1854	1976	1835	1854	110213	STS	Stoke On Trent
DEBBRIDGE						
1770	1780	1770	1780	127655	LND	Grosvenor Square
DEBELL						
1600	1800	....	....	103381	CON	Looe
DEBENER						
1655	1940	....	....	128996	CAM	Thornley
DEBENHAM						
1776	1992	1650	1776	136727	SFK	Chevington Whepstead
DEBNEY						
....	....	ALL	ALL	119288	ALL	Name Study
DEBOO						
1643	1940	....	....	128996	CAM	Thornley
DECAY						
1652	1940	....	....	128996	CAM	Thornley
DEDE						
1731	1737	1700	1750	144797	MDX	Spitalfields
1730	1856	1650	1730	179663	MDX	Spitalfields
DEDRICK						
1800	1950	1800	1850	120405	KEN	Maidstone
1800	1930	1750	1850	120405	MDX	Poplar
1650	1930	1750	1850	120405	MDX	Stepney
DEE						
1650	1700	1550	1650	145688	BRK	Warfield
1650	1700	1550	1650	145688	BRK	Winkfield
....	....	1850	1992	146307	DEV	Teignmouth
1894	1992	1800	1890	109398	ESS	Islington
1894	1992	1800	1890	109398	ESS	Walthamstow
1797	....	ALL	ALL	107336	KEN	Eynsford
DEEBLE						
1748	1847	1650	1748	167533	LND	Old Fish Street
DEEKS						
1800	....	....	....	131822	SFK	G-Berguolt
DEELEY						
1891	1893	?	1891	119296	BRK	Reading
DEELYE						
?	?	ALL	1800	117919	WOR	Old Swinford
DEEMING						
1818	1818	1810	1840	134627	STS	Arley
1818	1818	1810	1840	134627	STS	Hareley
1840	1920	1820	1840	134627	STS	Willenhall
DEER						
....	....	1700	1736	172871	SFK	Bury St Edmunds
1752	1992	1710	1866	107573	SOM	The Quantocks
DEERE						
1610	1760	ALL	1610	158739	GLA	Llanblethian
1690	1795	1795	1850	158739	GLA	St Georges
DEFTY						
1720	1780	ALL	ALL	130508	DUR	Chester Le Street
1680	1720	ALL	ALL	130508	DUR	Gateshead
1780	1890	ALL	ALL	130508	DUR	Sunderland
DEGGE						
1627	1899	1899	1992	165158	STS	Uttoxeter
DEGNEN						
1869	1869	1837	1869	146358	RFW	Langbank

Known From	To	Researching From	To	Ref	Cty	Place
DEHANY						
1895	1992	....	....	119318	CHS	Wallasey
1870	1910	1850	1940	119318	LAN	Liverpool
1830	1992	....	....	119318	WAR	ALL
DEIELIES						
1752	1761	....	....	127426	KEN	???
DEIGHTON						
1717	1747	ALL	ALL	130508	DUR	Stanhope
1860	1870	....	....	119334	HUN	Godmanchester
1810	1860	1770	1810	119334	HUN	Huntingdon
1870	1970	....	....	119334	LND	Kensington
1880	1900	1800	1880	130044	MDX	London
1738	....	ALL	1738	119326	NYK	Maundby
....	....	1800	1900	100234	YKS	Coxwold
1600	1900	ALL	ALL	102202	YKS	Kirk Deighton
1874	?	ALL	1878	171573	YKS	North Milford
DEINSHBACK						
1838	1839	1770	1880	131792	LND	Southwark
DEITON						
....	?	?	....	134457	NTH	Wellingborough
DEJEANNE						
1618	1714	ALL	ALL	111295	???	Bristol
DELACOURT						
1540	1873	1500	1900	101427	DOR	South
DELAHAY						
1718	1750	ALL	ALL	154032	BRE	Llanigon
DELAHOY						
1643	1940	....	....	128996	CAM	Thornley
DELAMERE						
1922	1922	ALL	ALL	143634	LND	Islington
1940	1992	1940	ALL	143634	WYK	Wakefield
DELANEY						
1830	1930	1800	1992	168327	IRL	Thurles
DELANOY						
1751	1802	ALL	1751	169730	CAM	Thorney-Wisbech
1644	1940	....	....	128996	CAM	Thornley
DELAVAL						
1075	1550	....	....	132756	NBL	ALL
1075	1550	....	....	132756	NBL	Horton
1075	1550	....	....	132756	NBL	Seaton Delaval
DELAWARE						
1200	1380	1200	1400	154881	KEN	Brasted
DELEHAYE						
1643	1940	....	....	128996	CAM	Thornley
DELEMONT						
1810	....	1810	1860	133639	SOM	Coker
DELESPIER						
1644	1940	....	....	128996	CAM	Thornley
DELETO						
1870	1870	1800	1890	152285	HAM	Portsmouth
DELICATE						
....	....	ALL	ALL	170755	ALL	Name Study
ALL	ALL	ALL	ALL	170755	ALL	ALL
DELL						
1817	1992	1700	1817	105902	BDF	Luton
1800	1865	1700	1850	143693	BKM	Bledlow
1894	....	1800	1900	143693	BKM	Princes Risborough
1830	1853	1750	1900	143693	BKM	Saunderton
1830	....	1750	1850	143693	BKM	Speen
1614	1676	1750	1830	118575	DEV	Barnstaple
1890	1927	....	....	167509	LND	Ealing
1830	....	....	....	167509	LND	Shepherds Bush
1927	1961	....	....	167509	MDX	Ickenham
....	....	....	....	173932	SRY	Kingston Upon Thames
1590	1650	1550	1992	114901	SRY	Thursley
1862	....	....	....	167509	WLS	Tonypandy
DELLA ROCCA						
1810	1910	1830	1890	128732	LND	Lambeth
DELLAMAYNE						
....	....	1500	1600	174319	CON	St Austell
DELLAR						
....	....	1801	1860	138142	CAM	Oakington
1820	1845	1750	1820	133671	CAM	Whaddon
1800	1923	1750	1850	119342	ESS	Nazeing
1886	1937	1800	1886	119342	ESS	Waltham Abbey
1792	1846	1700	1792	115460	HRT	Lilley
1792	1846	1700	1792	115460	HRT	Offley
DELLCHAR						
1832	1832	1750	1850	112089	???	???
DELLER						
....	....	ALL	ALL	119350	ALL	Name Study
1792	1846	1700	1792	115460	HRT	Lilley
1792	1846	1700	1792	115460	HRT	Offley
DELLER contd.						
....	....	ALL	1800	155470	HRT	???
....	....	1800	1851	132519	MDX	Enfield
1853	1910	1825	1851	132519	MDX	Islington
1830	1850	1780	1830	145424	MDX	Tottenham
1855	1858	....	....	132519	MDX	Uxbridge
DELMAGE						
1807	1841	1790	1841	144223	LIM	Adare
DELVE						
1550	1880	1750	1870	132721	DEV	North
1807	1970	1700	1807	119369	DEV	Bow
1761	1868	1700	1770	162825	DEV	East Down
1755	1827	1660	1860	165972	DEV	Morchard Bishop
1832	1841	1820	1845	118575	DEV	Swimbridge
DELVES						
1844	1960	1700	1844	134074	NFK	Great Yarmouth
1736	1881	1837	1881	171727	SAL	Hodnet
DEMAINE						
1640	1949	1600	1992	119377	YKS	Barden
DEMAN						
....	....	ALL	1900	178403	SSX	Billingshurst
DEMATT						
1759	1769	1750	1800	133787	MDX	London
DEMELLWEEK						
1799	1992	....	1799	160652	DEV	Plymouth
DEMPSEY						
1855	1892	1800	1900	110426	MDX	???
DEMPSTER						
1795	1802	1760	1845	142751	ABD	Culsalmond
1780	....	1750	1780	108596	AYR	ALL
1700	1992	....	....	123374	KCD	St Cyrus
1750	1965	....	....	137820	SHI	Fetlar
1720	1965	....	....	137820	SHI	Mid Yell
1760	1965	....	....	137820	SHI	North Yell
1758	1965	....	....	137820	SHI	Northmavine
1720	1965	....	....	137820	SHI	South Yell
DENBEIGH						
1843	....	ALL	ALL	127078	DOR	Shaftesbury
DENBY						
....	....	1700	1900	160253	WYK	Snaith
DENCH						
1812	1836	1812	1836	156027	HAM	Andover
1780	1800	1800	....	156027	HAM	Vernhams Dean
1820	1947	1822	1900	110175	LND	Deptford
1802	1992	1802	1900	163406	SOM	Bath
1758	1800	1758	1800	163406	WIL	Ogborne St George
DENDLE						
....	....	ALL	ALL	119393	ALL	Name Study
DENDY						
1790	1948	1700	1790	164879	SSX	North
1600	1690	1600	1700	159581	SSX	Horsham
DENE						
1868	1992	1700	1868	145033	DEV	Horwood
DENGATE						
1812	1992	1600	1812	151092	KEN	Newenden
1730	1859	1730	1860	138312	SSX	Ticehurst
DENHAM						
1660	1800	1600	1750	121207	BDF	Haynes
1750	1800	1750	1800	121207	BDF	Luton
1896	1946	1890	1919	176958	DUR	South Shields
1742	1808	1600	1800	155152	LIN	Stamford
1800	1920	1800	1920	131857	LND	Barnet
1800	1920	1800	1920	131857	LND	Edmonton
1817	?	1700	1817	176141	MDX	Paddington
1896	1946	1890	1919	176958	YKS	Normanton
1900	1992	1700	1900	119733	YKS	Rastrick
1896	1946	1890	1919	176958	YKS	Wakefield
1896	....	1870	1920	176958	???	Jarrow
DENHOLM						
1820	1850	1750	1850	141739	LKS	Glasgow
1770	1866	1700	1800	174319	MLN	???
1802	1902	1800	1900	167487	SCT	Edinburgh
1790	1870	1700	1900	147095	SCT	Edingburgh
DENIELS						
1890	1940	1890	1992	103144	MDX	Enfield
DENISON						
....	....	1500	1870	168017	YKS	North
DENKLEY						
1725	1880	1600	1750	127833	BKM	Dunton
1725	1880	1600	1750	127833	BKM	Winslow
1760	1940	1600	1800	127833	CAM	Ely
1800	1940	1600	1800	127833	HUN	St Ives
1900	1980	....	....	127833	KEN	Dover
1900	1980	....	....	127833	KEN	Folkestone

```
 Known      Researching
 From  To  From  To    Ref    Cty   Place
DENKLEY  contd.
 1865 1970 .... .... 127833 LAN Ormskirk
 1836 1900 1600 1900 127833 LND East End
 1750 1980 .... .... 127833 MDX Enfield
 1880 1940 .... .... 127833 SRY Croydon
DENLEY
 .... .... ALL  ALL  103993 ALL Name Study
 1680 1992 1100 1992 103993 ALL ALL
 1677 1755 1550 1700 156515 GLS Kempsford
DENMAN
 1600 1700 1600 1700 121207 BDF Barton In Clay
 ?    ?    ?    ?    140716 BRK ALL
 1800 1920 1700 1900 112976 DOR Portland
 1726 .... 1500 1726 140716 LIN ALL
 1800 .... 1600 1800 140716 LND ALL
 1800 1900 1600 1900 112976 LND Clerkenwell
 1891 1992 ?    1891 156337 LND Fulham
 1828 1933 1800 1900 108391 MDX London
 1781 .... ALL  ALL  127078 SOM South Petherton
 1816 1880 .... 1992 125113 SRY Charlwood
 1802 1890 1750 1850 101427 SSX North
 1700 1820 1500 1992 125113 SSX Worth
 1834 .... 1800 1850 108391 YKS Finningley
 1801 1861 .... .... 151548 ??? Bristol
DENN
 1560 1620 1500 1700 132942 DUR Aycliffe
DENNE
 1850 1920 1800 1850 121185 KEN ALL
 1575 1630 .... .... 142522 KEN Ripple
 1765 .... .... 1820 171441 KEN Thanet
DENNET
 1828 1846 1700 1846 178233 LAN Wigan
DENNETT
 1800 1843 ALL  ALL  173290 LAN Cuerdley
 1670 1700 .... .... 177318 LAN Farnworth
 1720 1781 1700 1780 119407 LAN Hale Bank
 1822 1963 ALL  ALL  173290 LAN Warrington
 1781 1947 ALL  ALL  119407 LAN Widnes
 1811 1881 1770 1811 162892 SOM Stogumber
 1824 1969 1780 1824 174807 SSX Brighton
DENNEY
 1834 1934 ALL  1834 103489 KEN Chatham
 1834 1934 ALL  1834 103489 KEN Gravesend
 1799 1827 1750 1850 126705 LAN Manchester
DENNING
 .... .... ALL  ALL  119415 ALL Name Study
 1870 1992 1820 1870 119423 MON South
DENNINGTON
 1800 1860 1700 1800 163732 NFK Ravingham
DENNIS
 .... .... ALL  ALL  119466 ALL Name Study
 1874 1942 1881 .... 170623 BRK Windsor
 1785 1888 1600 1785 117730 CAM Littleport
 1804 1992 1700 1804 161446 CAM Soham
 1762 1813 1624 1762 108839 CAM Sutton
 1766 1854 1700 1861 160636 CHS Little Barrow
 1843 .... ALL  ALL  110272 CON Altarnun
 1832 1908 1800 1900 137561 CON Paul
 1645 1670 1600 1650 121932 CON St Neot
 1815 1896 1750 1815 136816 DBY Measham
 1790 1850 1790 1850 132721 DEV North
 1750 1830 1700 1830 138487 DEV Braton Fleming
 .... .... 1850 1900 109894 DOR Weymouth
 1785 1785 1700 1880 156493 NTT Nottingham
 1731 .... ALL  ALL  105481 NTT Nuthall
 1851 1871 1851 1871 170623 OXF Britwell Salome
 1781 1881 1841 1881 170623 OXF Watlington
 1830 1900 1800 1880 138487 SOM Wookey
 1750 1830 1700 1800 144657 SRY Lingfield
 .... .... ALL  ALL  145343 WIL ALL
 1822 1863 1740 1850 135763 YKS Sheriffhutton
DENNISH
 1500 1992 1500 1992 119644 ESS ALL
 1500 1992 1500 1992 119644 SFK ALL
DENNISON
 1725 1940 .... .... 128996 CAM Thornley
 .... .... 1750 1834 142751 COR Cork
 1834 1881 1825 1881 142751 LAN Manchester
 1780 1800 1750 1800 109525 NYK Fylingdales
 1679 1700 1600 1679 102571 WES Eskew Beck
 .... .... .... .... 119474 WES Kendal
 .... .... 1841 1871 131628 WES Kendal
 1874 1940 1850 1874 131628 WES Kirkby Lonsdale
 .... 1782 1700 1782 110531 WYK Hemsworthy
```

```
 Known      Researching
 From  To  From  To    Ref    Cty   Place
DENNISON  contd.
 1871 1992 1836 1871 131628 YKS Bradford
 1760 1780 1750 1760 130877 YKS Leeds
DENNISTON
 .... .... ALL  ALL  119482 ALL Name Study
DENNY
 .... .... ALL  ALL  119490 ALL Name Study
 1800 1838 1800 1838 103608 ESS Dedham
 1756 1860 1756 1900 107980 NFK Raveningham
 1777 1779 ALL  1780 156175 SFK Haughley
 1828 1880 .... .... 140988 SFK Lound
 1850 1880 .... .... 140988 SRY Wimbledon
DENSHAM
 .... .... 1800 1900 122203 SOM ???
 .... .... 1800 1900 122203 SRY Cranmore
DENSON
 1828 1843 1828 1850 126705 LAN Liverpool
DENT
 1880 1940 1880 1960 157937 CMA Barrow In Furness
 1851 1894 .... .... 135739 DUR North
 1849 1851 ALL  ALL  119504 DUR Crook
 1701 1863 1600 1850 102881 DUR Romaldkirk
 1849 1851 ALL  ALL  119504 DUR Willington
 1809 1809 ALL  1809 129283 ESS Hatfield Peveril
 1850 1871 1850 1900 161586 HAM Havant
 1880 1940 1880 1960 157937 LAN Barrow In Furness
 1600 1860 1500 1860 157937 LAN Warton
 1600 1900 1600 1900 135968 LEI Hallaton
 1852 1881 1750 1852 153109 LIN Grantham
 1803 1803 ?    1803 158569 LND Marylebone
 1650 1983 1600 1700 143944 NTH ALL
 ?    ?    1540 1650 142646 WES Morland
 1832 1853 1750 1831 131245 WOR Worcester
 1732 .... 1600 1732 116637 YKS Romaldkirk
 1794 1992 ALL  1794 119504 YKS Romaldkirk
DENTITH
 1810 1992 1750 1810 120170 CHS Christleton
DENTON
 1800 1992 .... .... 103047 ALL ALL
 1800 1900 1800 1900 118869 BDF North
 1798 1847 1700 1900 105562 BKM Emberton
 1896 .... 1850 1900 122661 BRK Culham
 1700 .... 1700 1900 116920 DUR Hartlepool
 1850 1850 1700 1860 133892 HAM ALL
 .... .... 1600 1950 134546 IOW Brighston
 .... .... 1600 1950 134546 IOW Newport
 .... .... 1600 1950 134546 IOW Shorewell
 1860 ?    ALL  1860 127388 LAN Manchester
 1825 1850 ALL  ALL  100390 LAN Milnrow
 1850 1881 1750 1900 133574 YKS Bramley
 1559 1579 1500 1560 176451 YKS Kirkburton
 1820 1992 1650 1820 102148 YKS Leeds
 1820 1992 1650 1820 102148 YKS Rothwell
DENYER
 .... .... 1800 1940 116467 SRY Ewell
 1625 1800 1600 1992 114901 SRY Thursley
 .... .... 1900 1992 116467 SSX Hastings
 1854 .... 1700 1900 143448 SSX North Chapel
DENZEY
 1500 1599 ALL  1800 119520 BKM Lillington Dayrell
 1500 1700 ALL  1650 119520 BRK Waltham St Lawrence
 1400 1700 ALL  1900 119520 NTH Chacombe
 1485 1992 ALL  1900 119520 OXF Banbury
 1327 1800 ALL  1800 119520 WAR Tamworth
DEPEAR
 1776 1900 .... .... 164631 LIN Spalding
DEPLEDGE
 .... .... .... .... 160180 YKS ???
DERBY
 1841 1992 1841 1992 119539 IRL Monaghan
DERBYSHIRE
 1810 .... 1700 1800 131148 DBY Duffield
 1900 1992 1850 1900 174335 DBY Garston
 1830 1890 1700 1850 153230 DBY Kniveton
 1900 1992 1850 1900 174335 DBY Liverpool
 1841 1861 1768 .... 118761 DBY Matlock
 1811 .... 1800 1900 131148 DBY West Hallam
 1820 1881 1820 1881 136565 LAN Lower Darwen
 1780 1800 1700 1780 173312 LAN Preston
 1820 1890 .... .... 114545 NTT Nottingham
DERGES
 1838 1859 1750 1992 124044 DEV Holm
DERHAM
 .... .... ALL  ALL  169684 ALL Name Study
```

Known From	To	Researching From	To	Ref	Cty	Place
DERHAM contd.						
1066	1840	1700	1840	174130	GLS	Rington
1066	1840	1700	1840	174130	SOM	Rington
DERING						
1160	1992	....	....	150983	KEN	ALL
DERLING						
1640	1790	1600	1800	105333	SSX	Singleton
1740	1740	1710	1790	105333	SSX	West Stoke
DERRETT						
1816	1816	1750	1816	148938	GLS	Kingswood
DERRICK						
1862	1924	1750	....	123560	AVN	Weston Super Mare
....	....	ALL	1850	141224	GLS	Bristol
1818	1944	....	....	115495	NTT	Barton In Fabis
1815	1992	1700	1825	166561	NTT	Wysall
....	....	ALL	1850	141224	SOM	Bristol
DERRY						
....	1920	1874	1920	151041	IOM	???
....	1920	1874	1920	151041	LAN	Bootle
....	1920	1874	1920	151041	LAN	Seaforth
1840	1860	1600	1840	118877	NBL	Berwick On Tween
1864	1877	1864	1877	143286	WAR	Ston
DERUSETT						
....	....	ALL	ALL	119547	ALL	Name Study
DESBOROUGH						
1700	1750	1700	1750	116831	CAM	Eltisley
?	1940	....	....	128996	CAM	Thornley
DESBOUGH						
1813	1900	1813	1900	119563	WAR	Birmingham
DESCON						
1800	1900	1844	1900	162140	CAM	Alconbury Weston
DESCOUS						
1654	1940	....	....	128996	CAM	Thornley
DESFORGES						
1682	....	1682	1890	119571	ENG	ALL
1682	....	....	....	119571	LIN	ALL
1682	1850	ALL	ALL	171379	LIN	ALL
DESLANDES						
1810	1989	ALL	ALL	113700	LND	Bethnal Green
DESOER						
1830	1918	....	....	138118	LAN	Manchester
DESORT						
1566	1992	1560	1660	125520	KEN	Canterbury
DESPERQUES-COUTANCHE						
....	....	ALL	ALL	155632	CHI	Guernsey
....	....	ALL	ALL	155632	CHI	Jersey
DESVIGNES						
1640	1800	1600	ALL	111155	LND	East
DETHICK						
1540	1600	1450	1700	121614	DBY	ALL
DETNON						
1824	1874	1820	1880	163775	MDX	Bethnal Green
DETTMER						
1828	1833	1790	1840	155683	MDX	St Pancras
DEUCHARS						
....	....	1843	ALL	149187	ANS	Dundee
DEVALL						
....	....	ALL	ALL	119598	ALL	Name Study
DEVAN						
1800	1830	1750	1850	131431	MDX	London
DEVANNEY						
....	....	ALL	1859	176656	IRL	???
1859	1920	1859	1920	176656	LIN	Grimsby
1850	1980	....	....	118370	???	Coventry
DEVELL						
1500	1600	....	....	100420	WAR	Meriden
DEVENISH						
....	....	1250	1992	119644	ALL	ALL
....	....	1500	1992	119644	ESS	ALL
1765	1790	1600	1790	145289	HAM	Isle Of Wight
....	....	1500	1992	119644	MDX	ALL
DEVENPORT						
1790	1820	1700	1800	154245	BRK	Windsor
1830	1930	1830	1930	126500	LAN	Wigan
....	....	1800	....	137456	WAR	Edgbaston
DEVENSHER						
....	....	1650	1760	174319	CON	Mevagissy
DEVERAL						
1679	....	....	....	151351	NTT	South Wilford
DEVERELL						
1605	1727	ALL	1600	168211	BKM	Swanbourne
1794	1818	1700	1794	166723	GLS	Rodborough
DEVEREUX						
1066	1100	1066	1150	154881	ALL	ALL
DEVEREUX contd.						
....	....	1800	....	137456	BDF	Campton
....	....	1750	1850	146927	GLS	???
....	....	1700	1860	106682	IRL	???
1861	1929	....	....	106682	LAN	Accrington
1799	1807	1770	1830	102075	SRY	Rotherhithe
1066	1125	1066	1140	124974	WIL	Salisbury
DEVERSON						
1803	1880	1803	1880	125970	SRY	Southwark
DEVESON						
1838	1992	1650	1838	151092	KEN	???
DEVINE						
1784	1992	1750	1875	133043	MEA	Boyerstown
1784	1992	1750	1875	133043	MEA	Navan
DEVIS						
....	....	1700	1800	154458	WAR	???
DEVITT						
....	....	ALL	ALL	119601	ALL	Name Study
DEVLIN						
1850	1992	1750	1850	118052	ANT	Ballycastle
1830	1850	1750	1870	148288	ARM	Keady
1850	1937	....	....	136824	CUL	Keswick
1834	1834	ALL	1855	119636	DOW	Ballynahinch
1831	1906	1825	1885	119628	RFW	Greenock
1800	1992	1800	1950	119865	TYR	Arboe
DEVOLL						
1500	1840	1500	1700	120960	DOR	ALL
DEVON						
....	....	ALL	ALL	153125	ALL	Name Study
DEVONALD						
1800	1900	1750	1900	118540	CMN	Meline
1760	1928	1800	1881	104213	PEM	Narberth
DEVONISH						
....	....	ALL	ALL	119644	ALL	Name Study
....	....	1250	1992	119644	ALL	ALL
1500	1992	1500	1992	119644	ESS	ALL
1500	1992	1500	1992	119644	MDX	London
DEVONPORT						
ALL	1780	....	....	170798	NTT	Sutton Bonnington
DEVONSHIRE						
....	....	ALL	ALL	158100	ALL	Name Study
1848	1929	....	....	114545	BDF	Stanford
....	....	1800	1860	113514	WYK	Leeds
DEW						
1800	1992	1700	1800	155977	NFK	Baconsthorpe
1600	1750	1600	1750	167924	NFK	Tavenham
....	....	ALL	1749	114308	SRY	Godalming
....	....	1790	1816	130184	WIL	Dilton
1850	1900	ALL	ALL	164593	WIL	South Wraxall
1890	1920	1800	1920	172421	WIL	Westbury
DEWAR						
1780	1850	1700	1900	124427	PER	Strathard
1823	1900	1823	1900	138827	PER	Weem
1834	1992	....	....	128716	SCT	Edinburgh
1875	....	1800	1875	144711	STS	Tixall
DEWDER						
....	....	ALL	ALL	155233	ALL	Name Study
DEWEL						
1857	1992	1300	1992	152501	ESS	East Ham
DEWELL						
1570	1992	ALL	1570	119652	KEN	East
1845	1992	1300	1992	152501	KEN	???
1730	1730	1650	1730	155276	SFK	Bredfield
DEWES						
1772	....	....	....	151351	NTT	Nottingham
1800	1873	1600	1800	106054	OXF	Chipping Norton
1801	....	....	....	117579	OXF	Chipping Norton
....	....	....	....	107433	WAR	???
DEWEY						
....	....	1860	1900	134694	DOR	Poole
....	....	1860	1900	134694	DOR	Wimborne
....	....	1860	1940	134694	HAM	Sutton Scotney
....	....	1860	1940	134694	HAM	Wonston
....	....	1700	1800	107344	LIN	Bourne
1770	1814	1770	1850	123404	LIN	Bourne
1763	1795	1730	1800	123404	LIN	Grantham
....	....	1600	1800	119660	SSX	West
1800	1992	1600	1800	119660	WIL	Donhead St Andrew
1845	1980	1700	1845	137707	WIL	Great Bedwin
1845	1980	1700	1845	137707	WIL	Shrewton
1859	1986	1727	1859	107247	WIL	Tilshead
DEWGATE						
1805	1823	ALL	1823	156175	SXE	Crowhurst

Known From	To	Researching From	To	Ref	Cty	Place
DEWHIRST						
1730	1840	1700	1730	122904	LAN	Padham
DEWHURST						
1750	1750	1700	1750	163783	LAN	Goosnargh
1718	1724	1500	1718	110310	LAN	Stonehurst
1750	1950	1650	1750	121509	LAN	Whalley
1786	....	1786	....	160164	YKS	Sowerby
DEWICK						
1680	1992	ALL	ALL	117005	ALL	ALL
1850	1992	....	....	115479	NTT	Laxton
....	....	1700	1800	131652	WMD	???
DEWIRD						
1842	....	....	....	100668	SSX	East
DEWSON						
1820	1862	1820	1890	137235	LAN	Liverpool
1860	1880	ALL	ALL	124605	MDX	Marylebone
1773	1817	1700	1850	137235	STS	Wolverhampton
DEWY						
1672	1750	ALL	....	104515	LIN	Sedgebrook
DEXTER						
1700	1850	1600	1700	151769	DBY	Ticknall
1790	1830	1700	1790	151769	LEI	Diseworth
1790	1830	1700	1790	151769	LEI	Thornton
1855	1870	1800	1855	121010	NFK	Kings Lynn
1600	1675	....	....	148261	NTH	Bristol
1813	1834	1700	1813	131377	NTH	Rothwell
1872	1935	1700	1872	138673	YKS	Leeds
DEY						
1873	1942	1700	1873	106887	ABD	Grange
1796	1826	1700	1796	160024	YKS	Heck
DEYELL						
1750	1965	....	....	137820	SHI	Fetlar
1720	1965	....	....	137820	SHI	Mid Yell
1760	1965	....	....	137820	SHI	North Yell
1758	1965	....	....	137820	SHI	Northmavine
1720	1965	....	....	137820	SHI	South Yell
DIACK						
1794	1866	ALL	1794	106909	ABD	Kincardine O'neil
DIAMOND						
1900	1930	1800	1930	138371	YKS	York
DIBB						
1840	1860	1750	1992	167592	YKS	Allerton
1840	1860	1750	1992	167592	YKS	Castleford
1840	1860	1750	1992	167592	YKS	Whitwood
DIBBLE						
....	....	1790	1830	127388	LIN	Epworth
1682	1795	1680	1795	171654	SOM	Chiselborough
1801	1801	....	....	135437	SOM	Ilton
1828	1847	ALL	ALL	175005	SRY	Dorking
1744	1876	....	....	135437	SSX	Sidlesham
DIBBS						
1793	....	1770	1793	133639	MDX	Marylebone
DIBDEN						
....	....	ALL	ALL	166774	ALL	Name Study
1820	1992	....	....	153397	MDX	New Forest
1719	1783	1600	1719	145459	WIL	Bramshaw
DIBLEY						
....	....	ALL	ALL	101559	ALL	Name Study
1640	1992	1640	1992	146099	ALL	ALL
1800	1850	1700	1800	134848	HAM	Candover
....	....	1700	1820	101559	HAM	Gosport
1760	....	ALL	1760	119687	KEN	Lamberhurst
1694	1722	ALL	1760	119687	KEN	Lower Halling
1805	1927	1700	1900	101559	LND	South
1760	1936	....	....	119687	SSX	Frant
1840	1936	....	....	119687	SSX	Rye
DICE						
....	....	1700	1992	122742	LND	???
DICK						
1792	1926	1700	1792	112844	ABD	Crimond
1797	1992	1700	1797	144010	AYR	Ayr
1820	1850	1700	1820	139378	AYR	Barr
1815	1820	....	....	127140	AYR	Dundonald
1770	1803	....	....	127140	AYR	Irvine
1823	1840	....	....	127140	AYR	Kilmarnock
1820	1850	1700	1820	139378	AYR	Kirkoswald
1820	1850	1700	1820	139378	AYR	Pailly
1808	1867	1800	1868	163317	BAN	Aberchirder
1807	1950	....	....	127140	LKS	Glasgow
1933	1935	1870	1933	117358	LND	Islington
1798	1851	1750	1798	101427	MLN	Edinburgh
....	....	1700	ALL	149187	MOR	Duffies
1828	....	1700	1885	131423	MOR	Duffus
1853	1896	1853	1896	142840	NBL	Newcastle

DIC

Known From	To	Researching From	To	Ref	Cty	Place
DICK contd.						
1835	1875	....	....	118354	YKS	Hull
DICKEN						
1900	1960	ALL	ALL	100137	DBY	ALL
1900	1960	ALL	ALL	100137	STS	ALL
1825	1851	1700	1900	141569	STS	Burton On Trent
DICKENS						
1815	1850	ALL	1815	168602	LIN	Tallington
1700	1800	....	1800	177695	OXF	Banbury
DICKENSON						
1844	....	1800	1845	106062	BKM	Edelsborough
....	....	1829	....	174963	LND	ALL
1759	1890	....	....	119709	OXF	Abingdon
1759	1890	....	....	119709	OXF	Oxford
1830	1870	1870	1992	108367	YKS	Flockton
DICKER						
1767	....	1650	1800	143693	BRK	Aldermarston
1812	1992	1700	1812	130257	DEV	Yealmpton
1823	....	1750	1800	103292	SSX	Horsham
1635	1663	1500	1663	153591	SSX	Salehurst
DICKERSON						
1700	1992	1600	1992	148377	HUN	Huntingdon
1817	1881	1750	1900	126381	NFK	Wells
DICKES						
1742	1770	ALL	ALL	113662	GLS	Cherington
DICKETTS						
1826	1841	1800	1851	165824	WIL	East Knoyle
DICKIE						
....	....	1760	1820	172871	ANS	Montrose
1930	1992	1800	1930	119733	YKS	Huddersfield
DICKINS						
1819	....	1750	1819	103772	SAL	???
DICKINSON						
1750	1904	1700	1980	168947	CHS	Warrington
1750	1904	1700	1980	168947	CHS	Winsford
1756	1897	1700	1756	152196	CMA	Gosforth
1674	1992	....	1674	144363	CUL	Sample
1834	1843	1834	1843	121304	DBY	Glossop
1800	1900	1780	1900	127353	KEN	Saltwood
1811	....	1800	1860	169625	LAN	Altcar
1800	1882	1700	1882	178233	LAN	Anderton
1799	1810	1764	1830	169552	LAN	Cartmel Fell
1742	1793	1724	1794	169552	LAN	Cartmel
1814	1833	1725	1840	169552	LAN	Finsthwaite
1795	1837	1750	1850	177792	LAN	Liverpool
1800	1950	1700	1800	142905	LAN	Manchester
1869	1970	ALL	ALL	138886	LAN	Preston
1653	1806	ALL	ALL	141615	LAN	Stalmine
1775	1800	1700	1775	151769	LIN	Horbling
1739	1864	1740	1864	171654	LIN	Hundleby
....	....	1798	1855	101818	LIN	Wainfleet
1789	1789	1700	1789	174130	LND	Blackheath
1764	1900	?	1900	103934	LND	Edmonton
1700	1989	1500	1989	152536	LND	Various
1500	1992	1500	1930	119741	NBL	South West
1895	1961	....	....	101818	NFK	Blakeney
1857	1937	....	....	101818	NFK	Wells Next Sea
1718	1790	....	....	151351	NTT	South Wilford
1780	....	....	....	164232	SFK	Sudbourne
1789	1789	1700	1789	174130	SOM	Rington
1819	1868	1732	1974	169552	WES	Hugill
1761	1897	1761	1897	121304	WES	Lyth
1807	1864	1807	1864	169552	WES	Selside
1728	1812	1728	1812	169552	WES	Staveley
1769	1871	1720	1871	169552	WES	Winster
1694	1926	1694	1926	121304	WES	Witherslack
1770	1855	1600	1770	124257	YKS	Colton
....	....	1820	....	119768	YKS	Hull
1830	1850	1800	1900	129496	YKS	Morley
1770	1855	1600	1770	124257	YKS	Saxton
1786	....	1750	1800	170348	YKS	Sheffield
1770	1855	1600	1770	124257	YKS	Towton
DICKISSON						
1682	....	....	1682	101761	NTT	Radcliffe On Trent
DICKLEY						
1852	1877	1650	1900	176621	ANT	Ballymacilroy
DICKMAN						
1720	1786	ALL	1720	167878	WIL	Great Bedwyn
DICKON						
1757	1848	ALL	ALL	175773	ERY	ALL
1669	1745	....	1780	175773	LIN	ALL
DICKONSON						
1870	1870	1700	1870	112097	YKS	Wakefield

Known From	To	Researching From	To	Ref	Cty	Place
DICKS						
1700	1800	1600	1800	144657	GLS	Hanham Abbots
1890	1940	1885	1940	170933	HAM	Goodworth Clatferd
1919	1992	1900	1992	170933	HAM	Southampton
1798	....	....	....	148768	KEN	Strood
1780	1850	1700	1800	144657	SOM	Bristol
1731	1880	1700	1900	170933	WIL	Idmiston
1731	1880	1700	1900	170933	WIL	Porton
1800	1850	1700	1800	174513	WOR	Kemerton
DICKSON						
?	1940	ALL	1940	126195	BAN	Banff
1800	1840	ALL	1840	149063	BEW	Coldstream
1821	1992	1800	1846	140473	DEV	Stonehouse
1470	1525	ALL	1550	149063	ELN	Haddington
1770	1790	1700	1800	130915	FIF	Leuchars
1720	1799	1650	1850	169218	FIF	St Monance
1850	1920	1837	1920	164569	GLS	Forest Of Dean
ALL	1808	....	....	105368	IRL	Belfast
1862	1940	....	....	134430	KEN	Maidstone
1840	....	1800	1840	144010	KID	Kildare
1722	1865	....	....	165999	LEI	Hinckley
1722	1865	....	....	165999	LEI	Leicester
1722	1865	....	....	165999	LEI	Lutterworth
1669	1745	....	1780	175773	LIN	ALL
1869	1876	1700	1870	115967	MLN	Edinburgh
....	....	ALL	1864	119326	MLN	Edinburgh
1805	1930	1800	ALL	148652	MLN	Edinburgh
1790	1850	1700	1790	161292	NFK	Briston
1809	1992	ALL	1809	130605	PEE	Drumelzier
1800	1840	ALL	1840	149063	ROX	Kelso
1800	....	....	....	133590	SCT	???
1910	1992	....	....	146862	STI	Stenhousemuir
1610	....	....	....	145688	YKS	Keighley
DIDCOAT						
1600	1693	1550	1692	102830	GLS	Notgrove
DIDCOCK						
1850	1975	1600	1850	119784	BRK	Aston Upthorpe
DIDHAM						
1850	1900	ALL	ALL	139890	DEV	East
DIDLICK						
1603	1992	1500	1603	119792	SAL	ALL
DIDSBURY						
1840	1850	1800	1840	114472	CHS	Tarvin
DIER						
1726	1844	1700	1726	121584	CON	Lanlivery
DIFFEY						
1803	1842	1750	1850	102970	DOR	Stinsford
DIFFIELD						
1820	1830	1820	1830	128112	LND	Southwark
DIGBY						
1743	1992	ALL	1743	119067	CAM	Wisbech
1743	1992	ALL	1743	119067	LEI	Burton Lazars
1785	1992	1700	1785	176079	LND	Westminster
1500	1900	1500	1900	100420	WAR	Coleshill
1500	1800	1500	1900	100420	WAR	Meriden
DIGBY-GREEN						
?	....	?	....	104337	MDX	Mile End Old Town
DIGGLE						
1834	1847	1847	1992	103365	DEV	Stoke Damerel
1799	1869	1700	....	134686	LAN	Bolton
1861	1881	1800	1992	121215	LAN	Denton
1809	1834	1770	1809	103365	MDX	Westminster
DIGGORY						
....	....	ALL	ALL	119830	ALL	Name Study
1854	1881	1820	1900	139173	MGY	Forgen
DIGHT						
....	1840	1800	1840	128090	DOR	Christchurch
1780	1920	....	....	159972	SOM	Milverton
....	....	ALL	ALL	128090	SOM	???
DIGNALL						
1879	1912	1800	1900	100307	ALL	ALL
DIGNEY						
....	....	ALL	ALL	119849	ALL	ALL
DIGNIN						
1840	1845	ALL	1992	170909	ROS	Elphin
DIGSWELL						
1880	1920	1920	1992	140198	HRT	Welwyn
DIGWEED						
....	....	ALL	ALL	139947	ALL	Name Study
DIKE						
....	....	1600	1650	151602	WIL	Bishops Cannings
1860	1900	1580	1860	132373	WIL	Bradford On Avon
1710	1730	1690	1740	145297	WIL	Horningsham

Known From	To	Researching From	To	Ref	Cty	Place
DILKE						
1700	1820	1650	1900	127051	LND	Westminster
1820	1900	1800	1900	127051	SOM	Bristol
1650	1730	1650	1730	127051	STS	Lichfield
DILKS						
1872	1873	1860	1880	164992	HAM	Winchester
1871	1891	1850	1980	164992	KEN	Elham
DILLEY						
?	?	....	....	154113	BKM	Stoke Poges
DILLINGHAM						
1612	1627	1550	1650	156396	LEI	Cotesbach
1810	1810	ALL	1810	107557	LND	St Pancras
1597	1725	1550	1703	102830	NTH	Nassington
DILLMAN						
?	?	1700	1900	153222	DOR	Kinson
DILLON						
1830	1880	1700	1800	123870	IRL	???
1830	1880	1800	1880	123870	LND	Ilford
....	1870	1700	1870	178608	MDX	Limehouse
1810	1838	1800	1850	176982	MLN	Edinburgh
DILLOW						
1880	1980	1750	1880	122556	HAM	ALL
DILLWORTH						
1753	1804	ALL	ALL	179310	LAN	Slaidburn
DILNOT						
....	....	ALL	ALL	123137	ALL	Name Study
....	....	ALL	ALL	123137	ALL	ALL
1500	1992	ALL	ALL	123137	KEN	ALL
1812	1936	1700	1812	145823	KEN	Thanet
DILNUTT						
1850	1992	ALL	ALL	123137	LND	ALL
DILWORTH						
1500	1992	ALL	ALL	119857	ALL	ALL
1500	1992	ALL	ALL	119857	MDX	London
1850	1992	1700	1890	160954	MSY	Liverpool
1750	1800	1650	1900	130419	YKS	Slaidburn
1771	1992	1700	1992	179078	YKS	Slaidburn
DIMBERLINE						
1851	1931	1851	1931	122270	SYK	Doncaster
DIMBLEBY						
1748	1944	1600	1748	169595	LIN	Glentham
1678	1688	1600	1750	141569	NTH	Wilbarston
DIMELOW						
1880	1885	1885	1992	117099	LAN	Manchester
DIMENT						
1834	1992	1700	1834	130257	DEV	Abbotsham
1834	1992	1700	1834	130257	DEV	Beaford
1792	1846	1700	1792	173843	DOR	Allington
1727	1837	1725	1840	151858	DOR	Corscombe
1800	1830	1700	1900	142050	SOM	South
DIMES						
1682	1992	ALL	ALL	115681	HAM	North East
1750	1992	ALL	ALL	115681	LND	ALL
1540	1992	ALL	ALL	115681	SRY	West
DIMITRESCO						
1900	1950	1870	1900	171034	LND	???
DIMMACK						
1850	1920	1800	1890	164607	MDX	Clerkenwell
DIMMOCK						
1840	1900	1800	1900	118540	BDF	Luton
1721	1730	1721	1796	107360	BKM	Stewkley
1780	1900	1750	1900	165441	STS	Shelton Under Harley
DIMOND						
....	....	ALL	ALL	171158	DEV	ALL
1880	....	1870	1880	135429	DEV	Exeter
1800	1992	1700	1800	167649	DEV	Monkton
1800	1992	1700	1800	167649	DEV	Upottery
1710	1860	1500	1710	132802	DOR	Leigh
1890	1992	1700	1890	166480	JSY	ALL
1780	1820	1700	1820	139688	SOM	Winsham
DINAN						
1850	1971	1800	1992	158186	LND	West
DINE						
1788	1809	1770	1820	161322	KEN	East
DINES						
1772	1977	ALL	1977	118990	ESS	ALL
1845	1937	1750	1845	145823	ESS	Gt Totham
1700	1725	ALL	ALL	130508	HAM	Andover
1788	1809	1770	1820	161322	KEN	East
1800	1992	....	....	169129	NFK	Kings Lynn
DINGLE						
1740	1992	ALL	ALL	104183	CON	Central
1778	1992	1600	1778	119873	CON	Duloe

Known From	To	Researching From	To	Ref	Cty	Place
DINGLE contd.						
1750	1900	1700	1900	136239	CON	Duloe
1818	1828	1700	1828	137901	CON	Northill
1778	1992	1600	1778	119873	CON	Pelynt
1800	1881	1700	1800	116432	CON	Stoke Climsland
1851	1861	1800	1861	137901	DEV	Mamhead
1827	1890	1827	1900	173339	DEV	???
1889	1901	1901	1992	122807	LND	Euston Road
1791	1845	1700	1791	127116	NFK	Norwich
DINGLEY						
1600	1650	1600	1650	171549	HAM	Arreton
1850	1992	....	....	144088	STS	Rowley Regis
1860	1992	ALL	1949	168718	WAR	Birmingham
DINGMAN						
1763	1765	1700	1763	117277	LAN	Manchester
DINGWALL						
1775	1850	1700	1775	119881	ABD	Logie Coldstone
1864	1958	1958	1992	146560	LKS	Coatbride
1850	1900	1700	1850	144150	ROC	Dingwall
DINNAGE						
1817	1871	ALL	ALL	149489	SSX	Horsham
DINNEN						
1686	1686	1650	1800	162620	DOR	Sherborne
DINNER						
1884	1900	1800	1884	126403	CON	Duloe
1887	1906	1906	1940	109533	MDX	Finchley
....	....	1830	1887	109533	MDX	Islington
DINNING						
1650	1940	1650	1940	110884	NBL	South
1824	1880	ALL	1880	138819	T&W	Swallwell
DINSDALE						
1700	1992	1600	1700	102342	LIN	Searby Cum Owmby
1831	1917	ALL	ALL	153753	STS	Walsall
....	....	ALL	ALL	119938	YKS	ALL
1794	....	....	....	119911	YKS	Askrigg
1840	1860	1600	1890	119903	YKS	Bradford
1794	....	....	....	119911	YKS	Crakehall
1840	1860	1600	1890	119903	YKS	Hawes
1860	1890	1860	1890	119938	YKS	Scarborough
1670	1850	1600	1670	121509	YKS	Wensleydale
1700	1900	ALL	ALL	119938	YKS	York
DINSMORE						
....	....	ALL	1880	173045	ANT	Kells
DINWOODIE						
....	....	ALL	ALL	119946	ALL	Name Study
DIPLOCK						
1850	1900	1850	1900	134767	KEN	Sevenoaks
1850	1900	1850	1900	134767	KEN	Tonbridge
1850	ALL	1500	1850	145378	SSX	Buxted
1783	1828	1750	1880	100242	SSX	Chailey
1800	ALL	1500	1800	145378	SSX	Framfield
1830	ALL	1500	1830	145378	SSX	Little Horstead
DIPPLE						
1779	....	1770	1790	163775	MDX	Stepney
DIROM						
1720	1800	1650	1750	142670	BAN	Muiresk
DISBROW						
1671	1707	1500	1670	100013	CAM	Soham
DISDELL						
1800	1890	ALL	ALL	107417	ALL	ALL
1890	1900	1850	1950	107417	LEI	Leciester
1846	1881	1800	1900	107417	LIN	Long Sutton
DISHMAN						
1800	1850	1600	1800	145688	LIN	North Coates
DISLEY						
1819	1884	ALL	1819	122858	LAN	Haskayne
1919	1992	....	....	141534	LND	Holloway
DISMORE						
1800	1890	1800	1890	163511	LAN	Liverpool
1700	1850	1700	1850	163511	LND	City
1800	1940	1800	1940	163511	MDX	Cranford
DISNEY						
1650	1850	1650	1850	119970	ALL	ALL
1800	1830	ALL	ALL	119962	CAR	Whole
1700	1850	ALL	1700	138169	ESS	Colchester
1790	1840	ALL	ALL	119962	KIK	North
1800	....	ALL	ALL	119962	LEX	Archerstown
1780	....	1700	1780	177296	LIN	Ropsley
1700	1850	1690	1700	109703	NFK	Norton Subcourse
....	1841	1800	1841	115495	NTT	Keyworth
....	....	1600	1700	138169	SFK	Acton
....	....	ALL	1600	138169	SFK	Ixworth
DISS						
....	....	ALL	ALL	119989	ALL	Name Study
DISS contd.						
1563	1900	1200	1900	119989	CAM	ALL
1520	1900	1200	1900	119989	ESS	ALL
1288	1900	1200	1900	119989	NFK	ALL
1420	1900	1200	1900	119989	SFK	ALL
DISTON						
1789	....	....	....	135488	DEV	Plymouth
1809	....	1924	....	135488	LND	Bermondsey
DITCHAM						
....	....	ALL	ALL	169080	SFK	Ipswich
DITE						
1790	1992	....	1790	159972	SOM	Milverton
DITMAS						
1770	1992	ALL	1770	131067	YKS	???
DITMASS						
1770	1992	ALL	1770	131067	YKS	???
DITSON						
1860	1992	1750	1860	176486	NBL	Blyth
DITZEL						
....	....	ALL	ALL	167517	ALL	Name Study
1840	ALL	ALL	ALL	167517	ALL	ALL
DIVAL						
1750	1920	1700	1850	166154	SSX	ALL
DIVE						
1800	1899	1800	1899	147575	???	???
DIVER						
1812	1917	....	....	146560	DON	Kilbarron
....	....	ALL	ALL	100153	DON	???
1857	1986	1986	1992	146560	LKS	Coatbride
....	....	1815	1851	116912	NBL	Newcastle On Tyne
1750	1950	1800	1950	162329	SFK	???
DIVERS						
1594	1830	1500	1594	138584	YKS	Rothwell
DIVES						
1800	1900	1600	1800	125660	BDF	Bromham
1800	1900	1600	1800	125660	SRY	Lingfield
DIVIANI						
1830	1850	1500	1992	164992	MDX	Clerkenwell
1858	1992	ALL	ALL	127981	MDX	London
DIX						
1760	1992	1650	1760	149713	BDF	Westoning
1880	1920	ALL	ALL	112518	MDX	Marylebone
1815	1830	1700	1830	162078	SAL	Wellington
1880	1992	1800	1950	129976	WAR	Birmingham
DIXEY						
1850	1900	1700	1850	118915	YKS	Hull
DIXON						
1750	1920	....	....	175439	BKM	Marlow
1845	1880	1845	1900	120049	CHS	Birkenhead
1845	1900	1845	1992	120049	CHS	Chester
1700	1850	1650	1850	167088	CMA	Whitehaven
1858	1902	ALL	ALL	164887	COR	Cork
1850	1960	ALL	ALL	162469	CUL	North
1783	1826	1700	1782	132764	CUL	Ainstable
1730	1760	1700	1800	138878	CUL	Gosforth
1820	1848	1700	1820	124427	DFS	Kirkton
1849	1875	1845	1875	130990	DUR	Houghton Le Spring
1848	1848	....	....	103632	DUR	Ludworth
1849	1870	1538	1992	118893	DUR	Seaham Harbour
1700	1820	1600	1700	167584	DUR	Staindrop
1780	1840	....	....	103632	DUR	Sunderland
1900	1912	1538	1992	118893	DUR	Waskerley
1800	1992	1800	1992	108243	ESS	Chelmsford
1800	1992	1700	1800	103098	HAM	Fawley
....	....	ALL	ALL	103543	HAM	Southampton
....	....	ALL	ALL	120057	KEN	ALL
1850	1992	1500	1992	120014	KEN	East
1930	1961	1871	1893	161667	KEN	Dartford
1714	1940	1700	1992	142735	KEN	Deal
1900	....	1880	1950	126144	KEN	Gravesend
1857	1992	....	....	112380	KEN	Maistone
1755	1850	ALL	ALL	120057	KEN	Molash
1835	1942	ALL	ALL	113662	KEN	Willesborough
1791	1901	1680	1901	153273	LAN	Dalton In Furness
1825	1860	1825	1860	120049	LAN	Eccles
1740	1825	1700	1825	120049	LAN	Kirkham
1872	....	....	....	132500	LAN	Kirkham
1800	1900	....	....	146854	LAN	Liverpool
1839	1910	ALL	1910	157902	LAN	Liverpool
1803	1849	1600	1803	102571	LAN	Manchester
1813	1930	1800	1850	124826	LAN	Manchester
1841	1920	1830	1900	124826	LAN	Newton Heath
1846	....	....	....	171824	LAN	Newton Le Willow
1800	1900	1700	1800	178209	LAN	Oldham

Known From	To	Researching From	To	Ref	Cty	Place
DIXON contd.						
1784	1858	1784	1858	143286	LAN	Peel
1860	1992	1700	1992	114596	LAN	Penketh
1709	1760	1600	1709	120049	LAN	Preston
1825	1860	1825	1860	120049	LAN	Salford
....	....	1820	1992	147613	LAN	Tatham
1825	1870	1825	1870	120049	LAN	Warrington
1722	1865	....	....	165999	LEI	Hinckley
1722	1865	....	....	165999	LEI	Leicester
1722	1865	....	....	165999	LEI	Lutterworth
1825	1960	1650	1825	120081	LIN	East
1802	....	ALL	ALL	103837	LIN	Alford
1866	1919	1919	1992	130990	LIN	Gainsborough
1795	1992	ALL	1851	156310	LND	Central
1840	1992	ALL	....	120057	LND	North
1814	1881	....	....	167517	LND	St Georges
1816	1850	....	1850	102822	LND	St Pancras
1875	1925	1800	1875	115460	LND	Stepney
1859	1884	ALL	1859	122386	NBL	North
1733	1770	1700	1800	123536	NBL	Allendale
1812	1826	1800	1850	130990	NBL	Allendale
1785	1785	1538	1992	118893	NBL	Branxton
1770	1900	1750	1800	127965	NBL	Hexhamshire
1810	1897	ALL	1992	102245	NBL	Newcastle Upon Tyne
1830	1850	1800	1850	103764	NBL	Newcastle
1803	1943	1538	1992	118893	NBL	Spittal
1790	1850	1700	1790	161292	NFK	Briston
1843	1849	1538	1992	118893	NRY	Marske
1741	1764	....	....	117803	NRY	Sessay
1838	1843	1538	1992	118893	NRY	Whitby
1774	1820	ALL	ALL	135208	NTH	Eye
1774	1820	ALL	ALL	135208	NTH	Gunsthorpe
1774	1820	ALL	ALL	135208	NTH	Werrington
1842	1900	....	....	132756	NTT	Barnby Moor
1842	1900	....	....	132756	NTT	Bothamstall
1870	1930	....	....	132756	NTT	Retford
1850	1900	1800	1900	116823	NYK	Baldersby
1890	1945	....	....	132756	OXF	Bicester
1750	1920	....	....	175439	OXF	Henley
1870	1878	1800	1870	145351	SRY	Lambeth
1880	1992	1880	1992	120049	STS	Biddulph
1850	1900	1850	1900	103764	STS	Smethwick
1900	1992	1900	1992	120049	STS	Stoke On Trent
1828	1960	1800	1960	151513	WAR	Grendon
1780	1800	1700	1828	151513	WAR	Kingsbury
?	?	?	?	151505	WES	Kendal
1689	1850	1540	1860	155616	WIL	East
....	....	1700	1820	153184	WIL	North
1825	1840	1750	1825	133671	WIL	Avebury
1809	?	....	....	153184	WIL	Brinkworth
1822	1992	ALL	1822	120022	WOR	Upton On Severn
1700	1801	1700	1815	124826	WRY	Holmfirth
1713	1797	1650	1713	117803	WRY	Marton Cum Grafton
1882	....	....	....	100579	WYK	Leeds
....	....	1800	1992	166936	YKS	Batley-Morley
....	....	1733	1892	155039	YKS	Bishopdale
1807	1910	ALL	1807	102350	YKS	Brotherton
1800	1900	1600	1900	132306	YKS	Dent
....	....	1800	1992	166936	YKS	Gildersome
....	....	1700	1899	174963	YKS	Hoarwooddale
1825	1845	1700	1825	108790	YKS	Keighley
1800	1917	1700	1920	134589	YKS	Langton
....	....	1700	1850	152390	YKS	Leeds
1837	....	1800	1850	103462	YKS	Northowram
1864	1870	....	....	132756	YKS	Sheffield
1742	1846	1560	1742	133132	YKS	Sheffield
1788	1865	1700	1871	124788	YKS	Thornhill
DIZON						
....	....	1640	1720	103713	SFK	Wickhambrook
DOANE						
1889	1934	ALL	1889	160008	STS	Newcastle Under Lyme
DOBBIE						
1700	1950	....	....	108677	AYR	ALL
1700	1950	....	....	108677	ESS	Saling
....	....	ALL	1750	108677	SCT	ALL
....	....	ALL	ALL	152048	STI	Falkirk
DOBBING						
1840	1992	1740	1840	160075	DUR	Sunderland
DOBBINS						
ALL	ALL	ALL	ALL	124206	ALL	ALL
1754	ALL	ALL	1836	116734	DUB	Dublin
1754	ALL	ALL	1836	116734	LEX	Shabally
1754	ALL	ALL	1836	116734	WEM	???
DOBBS						
1770	1800	1750	1770	133442	LIN	Belchford
DOBBY						
1870	ALL	ALL	ALL	135240	YKS	Lower Dales
DOBEDOE						
1815	1870	1750	1815	123978	KEN	Chatham
DOBIE						
....	....	ALL	1870	129119	LAN	Liverpool
1800	1900	....	....	150371	MLN	Edinburgh
DOBLE						
1760	1900	1740	1950	171158	DEV	Broadhembury
1805	1884	1750	1804	175846	DEV	Kingsbury
1650	1800	....	....	169528	SOM	Church Stanton
1780	1884	1700	1780	175846	SOM	Wedmore
DOBNER						
1810	1880	1780	1810	147583	BRK	Windsor
1780	1830	1700	1780	147583	MDX	Staines
DOBNEY						
1655	1940	....	....	128996	CAM	Thornley
DOBSON						
....	....	ALL	ALL	120111	ALL	Name Study
....	....	ALL	ALL	120138	ALL	Name Study
1820	1870	1820	1870	150479	AGY	Holyhead
1737	1748	1600	1737	111198	BDF	Willington
1750	1820	1700	1820	150479	BRK	Ramsbury
1840	1900	1800	1920	105945	CHS	Chester
1800	1900	1700	1900	126802	DUR	ALL
1575	1702	1542	1642	141291	LAN	Aldingham
1800	1880	1600	1800	102172	LAN	Billington
1800	1880	1700	1800	102172	LAN	Blackburn
1851	1926	ALL	ALL	125202	LAN	Liverpool
1873	1926	ALL	ALL	125202	LAN	Manchester
1890	1980	1750	1890	139521	LIN	Louth
ALL	1930	....	....	106747	LIN	North Somercoates
1840	1863	....	....	102733	MDX	London
?	....	?	....	104337	MDX	Mile End Old Town
1798	1992	1650	1800	130885	NBL	Hexham
1815	....	....	....	125202	NBL	Newcastle
1800	1900	1800	1900	116823	NYK	Sandhutton
1860	1860	ALL	1992	156078	SCT	ALL
1759	1992	ALL	1880	120103	WES	Brough
1759	1992	ALL	1880	120103	WES	Kendal
1825	1853	1800	1825	133671	WIL	Avebury
1775	1820	1700	1775	133671	WIL	Ogbourne Standrew
....	....	ALL	1825	151602	WIL	Ramsbury
ALL	1754	....	....	170178	WIL	Ramsbury
1926	1992	ALL	ALL	125202	WRY	Halifax
1800	1940	1700	1992	110477	WRY	Knottingley
1857	1860	1700	1857	176141	WYK	Scholes
1810	1825	1775	1825	141097	YKS	Doncaster
1890	1980	1750	1890	139521	YKS	Hull
1756	1905	1700	1992	151521	YKS	Rotherham
1775	1799	....	....	166030	YKS	Rothwell
1884	1992	1700	1900	171689	YKS	Wortley
DOCHERTY						
1785	1878	....	....	146560	DON	South
1845	1912	1800	1890	120146	LKS	Glasgow
1810	....	....	....	132381	PEE	Manor
DOCKERELL						
1880	1890	1800	1950	128805	ESS	Barking
DOCKING						
1811	1871	1700	1811	145033	CON	Egloshayle
DOCKREE						
....	....	ALL	ALL	112542	ALL	Name Study
ALL	ALL	ALL	ALL	112542	ALL	ALL
1770	1985	....	1850	112542	HRT	St Albans
1820	1985	....	1850	112542	LND	Clerkenwall
DOCTOR						
1900	1965	ALL	ALL	120154	SCT	Glasgow
DOD						
1780	1815	1700	1780	114472	CHS	Barrow
....	....	1450	1600	111538	CHS	Shocklack
1630	1700	1630	1700	111538	HRT	Bennington
1774	1774	1745	1812	107360	NTH	Blisworth
1600	1700	1600	1700	111538	NTH	???
1834	1857	1750	1834	178381	SAL	Marchamley
DODD						
....	....	1800	1830	117137	BRE	Llangattoch
1774	1918	1700	1774	160474	CHS	Bickerton
1810	1830	1700	1900	138363	CHS	Chester
....	....	ALL	ALL	178691	CUL	Farlam
1774	1918	1700	1774	160474	CWD	Chirk
1750	1850	1600	1750	134104	DEN	Gresford
1838	1861	1800	1861	106968	DEV	Topsham

Known From	To	Researching From	To	Ref	Cty	Place
DODD contd.						
1780	1800	1780	1800	124605	ESS	Black Notley
1800	1980	1800	1980	178705	GNT	Blackwood
1800	1929	1750	1800	160318	LAN	Liverpool
1897	1928	....	....	138827	LAN	Ormskirk
....	....	1800	1870	107727	LND	London
1600	1800	....	....	153583	NTH	Bugbrooke
1750	1765	1730	1770	107360	NTH	Tiffield
1806	1854	ALL	1806	135143	OXF	Oxford
....	....	ALL	ALL	143502	SAL	Central
1680	1850	....	1850	155055	SAL	Hadnall
1819	1819	1780	1830	124915	SSX	Brighton
1820	?	....	....	160067	SSX	Brighton
....	....	ALL	ALL	114308	WAR	South
1759	1800	1700	1759	152196	WES	Kendal
1800	1900	1800	1900	126640	WLS	South
1824	1992	1750	1824	120170	WOR	Rock
DODDINGTON						
1500	1600	1500	1600	154881	ALL	ALL
DODDRELL						
....	....	1700	1992	120189	ALL	ALL
1635	1937	1785	1840	176958	GLS	Bristol
1635	1937	1785	1840	176958	SCT	Glasgow
1640	1900	1500	1640	120189	SOM	Shepton Mallet
1635	1937	1785	1840	176958	SOM	Shepton Mallet
1824	1900	1500	1824	120189	WIL	Mere
DODDS						
1753	1850	....	....	160458	ALL	ALL
1865	1930	1750	1870	100501	BRK	High Wycombe
1889	1905	ALL	1889	119504	DUR	Brandon
1883	1912	1800	1992	128937	DUR	Burnhope Holmside
1825	1871	1780	1880	123536	DUR	Washington
1871	1960	1700	1871	151440	NBL	ALL
....	....	1890	1992	175137	NBL	ALL
1800	1850	....	....	151440	NBL	Anwick
....	....	1798	1890	151440	NBL	Berwick Upon Tweed
1810	1835	ALL	1835	149063	NBL	Carham
1850	1980	1800	1980	123536	NBL	Newcastle On Tyne
1720	1800	1650	1720	170488	NBL	Shoreswood
1860	1992	1700	1860	117153	ROX	Crailing
1835	1860	1800	1860	149063	ROX	Kelso
1860	ALL	1860	ALL	149063	ROX	Melrose
1773	1828	....	1773	175552	ROX	Melrose
1903	1934	ALL	1934	138819	T&W	Newcastle Upon Tyne
....	....	1770	....	174963	YKS	Scalby
DODGE						
1720	1810	1700	1750	121932	CON	Jacobstow
1718	1840	1718	1840	133639	SOM	Coker
1732	1846	ALL	1732	161500	SOM	Crewkerne
DODGESHUN						
1780	1920	1700	1992	129496	YKS	Morley
DODGSHON						
1765	....	....	....	117196	CMA	Hawkshead
DODGSON						
1672	1731	ALL	ALL	130508	DUR	Sunderland
1784	1992	1700	1784	178993	YKS	Leeds
1807	1830	1600	1820	175382	YKS	Settle
1800	1880	1750	1850	157651	YKS	Thirsk
1850	1900	1750	1900	157651	YKS	York
DODMAN						
1781	1940	....	....	128996	CAM	Thornley
1820	1822	1700	1850	135496	NFK	Weybourne
DODSON						
....	....	1600	1850	131962	ESS	Epping
1717	1816	1717	1816	103977	HRT	Aldenham
1650	1661	1650	1661	102628	SRY	Kingston On Thames
1777	1945	1700	1850	120197	SSX	Brighton
1200	1900	1800	1900	163511	SSX	Brighton
1765	1789	1700	1800	129356	SSX	Hellingly
1777	1945	1700	1850	120197	SSX	Lewes
1700	1800	1700	1800	163511	SSX	Lewes
DODSWORTH						
1706	1730	1600	1706	116637	DUR	Chester Le Street
1850	1900	1750	1850	134651	LIN	Langriville
DODWELL						
1700	1850	1700	1850	100420	WAR	Great Packington
1700	1850	1700	1850	100420	WAR	Meriden
DOE						
....	1750	ALL	ALL	122866	CAM	ALL
1780	1801	1750	1850	171158	ESS	Terling
DOEL						
....	1863	....	1863	161888	WIL	???
DOFFIN						
1790	1800	1700	1850	126268	LND	Stepney

Known From	To	Researching From	To	Ref	Cty	Place
DOGGETT						
1749	1940	....	....	128996	CAM	Thornley
DOGGRELL						
....	....	1700	1815	156795	DOR	North
DOGOOD						
....	1599	....	1599	109622	LIN	Gunness
DOHERTY						
....	....	ALL	ALL	120421	ALL	Name Study
1840	1900	1700	1840	140260	DON	Dungloe
1841	1865	....	....	150282	IRL	Dublin
1840	1958	1600	1840	103195	KIK	Kilkenny
1895	....	....	....	146455	LAN	Toxteth Park
1866	1881	1845	1866	146773	YKS	Hull
DOHORTY						
1800	1992	....	....	139971	MAY	Ballycastle
DOIDGE						
1841	1870	....	....	161675	CON	Gwennap
1800	....	1800	1850	142638	DEV	Lamerton
1841	1912	ALL	1866	118184	DEV	???
DOIG						
1850	1860	1800	1900	179604	OXF	Oxford
DOKE						
1847	1847	1847	1992	116653	STS	Tamworth
DOLAN						
1867	1992	1700	1867	120200	LAN	Warrington
1880	1920	....	....	138150	PER	Perth
1850	1880	....	....	138150	STI	Stirling
DOLBEAR						
1807	1840	1750	1810	176796	MDX	Marylebone
....	....	1750	1800	176796	MDX	St Pancras
DOLBY						
1870	1953	....	....	121967	HUN	Ramsey
1805	1890	1700	1805	107344	NTH	Oundle
DOLEMAN						
1750	1782	1700	1750	128317	DBY	Breadsall
DOLIN						
1850	1880	1800	1850	116432	CON	Torpoint
DOLLAR						
1858	1960	ALL	ALL	120219	STI	Falkirk
....	....	....	....	120219	STI	Grangemouth
DOLLEN						
1800	1850	1500	1900	135542	SOM	West
DOLLERY						
1796	1900	1700	1860	130451	BRK	???
....	....	1640	1715	125032	HAM	Bramley
....	....	1800	1874	101001	HAM	Portsmouth
DOLLIMORE						
1812	1836	1800	1850	171999	HRT	St Pauls Walden
DOLLING						
....	....	ALL	ALL	101559	ALL	Name Study
1797	1820	1700	1800	101559	HAM	Beaulieu
1784	1820	1700	1800	101559	HAM	Bramshaw
1829	1980	1700	1900	101559	LND	???
DOLLY						
1834	....	1750	1910	131210	SRY	Merton
DOLMAN						
1842	1885	1800	1885	144223	DBY	Repton
1895	1992	1500	1895	139033	LAN	Manchester
1895	1992	1500	1895	139033	LAN	Swinton
1820	1850	ALL	ALL	157864	NFK	Rougham
1895	1992	1500	1895	139033	STS	ALL
1750	1870	1700	1850	132950	WIL	Bremhill
DOLPHIN						
1780	1830	1700	1780	121339	NYK	Marrick
1802	1992	ALL	1802	100587	WAR	Birmingham
....	....	....	....	135704	WAR	Birmingham
1892	1934	....	1892	134724	???	???
DOLTON						
1859	1890	1800	1859	161810	HRT	Barnet
1835	1853	ALL	ALL	130508	LND	Holborn
DOMAN						
1857	1859	1700	1860	126772	LEI	Whitwick
DOMINEY						
1910	1992	1850	1950	141461	DOR	Poole
DOMING						
1757	1765	1700	1757	127116	DOR	Tarrant Hinton
DOMINI						
1650	1740	1500	1800	132055	KEN	Dover
DOMINY						
1852	1852	ALL	ALL	149683	SOM	Burnham On Sea
1853	1853	ALL	ALL	149683	SRY	Battersea
DOMLEO						
1860	1900	1800	1880	121886	DBY	Derby
1800	1850	1700	1850	121886	NTT	Sutton Bonnington

Known From	To	Researching From	To	Ref	Cty	Place
DOMMETT						
1774	1804	1650	1774	120227	DEV	Seaton Beer
1804	1940	....	....	120227	DEV	Stoke Damerel
DOMONEY						
1879	1911	1815	1878	167568	LND	Chobham
DONACHIE						
1862	1976	1800	1862	150673	ANT	Central
DONALD						
....	....	1770	1850	148210	ABD	Old Machar
1880	1992	ALL	1880	142263	AYR	Beith
1815	1900	1750	1900	120235	AYR	Dundonald
1819	....	....	....	106852	AYR	Stair
....	....	1800	1899	104884	BAN	Fordyce
1830	1850	1700	1850	126802	CUL	ALL
1772	1772	1600	1800	130125	DFS	Langholm
....	1801	....	....	146811	RFW	Mearns
DONALDSON						
1790	1900	1700	1790	118419	BAN	Rathven
1750	1900	1700	1900	126802	CUL	ALL
1797	1797	1780	1810	120243	FIF	Aberdour
1750	1770	1650	1750	100978	KCD	Kinneff
1902	1950	1851	1902	108405	LAN	Salford
1791	1859	1700	1791	152196	LAN	Ulverston
1902	1950	1851	1902	108405	LKS	Glasgow
1902	1950	1851	1902	108405	LKS	Hutcheson Town
....	....	1750	1860	100390	LKS	West Kilbride
1852	1890	1850	1992	145602	LND	Camden Town
1852	1890	1850	1992	145602	LND	St Pancras
1835	1881	1750	1890	152285	LND	Stepney
1850	1900	1850	1900	123463	RFW	New Kilpatrick
1800	1899	1800	1899	169781	SCT	Comrie
1790	....	....	....	167037	SCT	Edinburgh
1750	1965	....	....	137820	SHI	Fetlar
1720	1965	....	....	137820	SHI	Mid Yell
1760	1965	....	....	137820	SHI	North Yell
1758	1965	....	....	137820	SHI	Northmavine
1720	1965	....	....	137820	SHI	South Yell
1800	1899	1800	1899	169781	SRY	Roehampton
1835	1930	....	....	120243	STI	Polmont
1800	1823	1750	1835	120243	WLN	Carriden
1820	1870	1770	1820	122904	WLN	Torpichen
DONAVAN						
1855	1960	1700	1855	146021	LAN	Manchester
1855	1960	1700	1855	146021	LAN	Salford
1863	1863	1863	1992	165727	LND	East
DONAWAY						
1838	....	1750	1850	138185	IRL	???
DONE						
1700	1850	1700	1850	120251	CHS	Bunbury
1200	1680	1200	1680	120251	CHS	Delamere
1850	1900	1700	1850	161349	CHS	Eaton
1850	1930	1850	1930	120251	CHS	Malpas
1860	1970	1800	1860	137278	LAN	Manchester
1850	1992	....	....	101249	LND	Chelsea
1850	1992	....	....	101249	LND	Fulham
1850	1992	....	....	101249	LND	Wandsworth
DONEY						
1850	1980	1700	1850	114820	CON	South East
1850	1980	1700	1850	114820	CON	Lerryn
1850	1980	1700	1850	114820	CON	St Veeo
DONGWORTH						
1800	1890	1800	1890	161276	LIN	ALL
DONISTHORPE						
1470	1875	ALL	ALL	141615	LEI	North
DONKERSLEY						
1894	....	ALL	ALL	138533	WYK	Keighley
1840	1950	ALL	1840	143022	YKS	Huddersfield
DONKIN						
1765	1787	ALL	1765	154563	DUR	Durham
1807	1891	....	....	120278	EYK	Driffiled
1891	1992	....	....	120278	EYK	Kingston Upon Hull
1830	1870	ALL	ALL	162620	NBL	Long Horseley
1850	1870	ALL	ALL	162620	NBL	North Shields
1820	1850	1700	1900	162620	NBL	Rothbury
....	....	1700	1899	125148	T&W	Sunderland
DONNE						
1720	1992	1600	1720	120294	MDX	London
DONNELLY						
1870	1992	1750	1870	118052	ANT	Armoy
1850	1992	1750	1850	118052	ANT	Ballycastle
1850	1992	1780	1850	120308	GLA	Cardiff
1862	....	....	....	103608	IRL	Kilkenney
1818	1910	1818	1841	162809	LAN	Bolton
1850	1900	1700	1850	173037	MOG	Castle Brayney

Known From	To	Researching From	To	Ref	Cty	Place
DONNELLY contd.						
....	....	1750	1850	116262	ROS	Moore
1830	1863	1700	1863	116300	TIP	???
1861	1937	1861	1937	163554	TYR	Fintona
DONNISON						
1861	....	1861	....	158305	DUR	Heworth
1900	1992	1800	1900	140546	LIN	Boston
1860	....	....	1860	158305	NBL	Newcastle
1864	1870	1864	....	158305	YKS	Hunslet
1878	1992	1878	....	158305	YKS	Mexborough
1875	1878	1875	....	158305	YKS	Rotherham
DONNITHORNE						
1797	....	1600	1850	167223	CON	St Agnes
....	....	1600	1900	167223	HEF	???
DONOGHUE						
....	....	ALL	ALL	151971	ALL	Name Study
1881	1920	1880	1992	113778	CLV	Middlesbrough
1861	1992	1700	1992	113778	GLA	Merthyr Tydfil
DONOHUE						
1780	1800	ALL	1805	165654	WAT	ALL
DONOVAN						
1860	....	ALL	....	153214	COR	???
....	....	1850	....	140333	IRL	Skibbereen
1838	....	1750	1850	138185	IRL	???
1850	1910	1700	1910	152536	IRL	???
1847	1992	ALL	1850	115177	LND	East
....	....	1900	....	140333	LND	South East
1850	1910	1700	1910	152536	SRY	Caterham
DOO						
....	....	ALL	ALL	120324	ALL	Name Study
1580	1992	1500	1580	120324	CAM	ALL
1580	1992	1500	1580	120324	ESS	ALL
1580	1992	1500	1580	120324	KEN	ALL
1580	1992	1500	1580	120324	LND	ALL
1580	1992	1500	1580	120324	MDX	ALL
1580	1992	1500	1580	120324	NFK	ALL
1580	1992	1500	1580	120324	SFK	ALL
1580	1992	1500	1580	120324	SRY	ALL
DOOLEY						
....	....	1820	1903	155039	CHS	Chester
1790	1840	1700	1800	151769	DBY	Ashover
1790	1840	1700	1800	151769	DBY	Ockbrook
....	....	1830	1903	155039	LAN	Liverpool
....	....	....	....	120332	WAT	Portlaw
DOOLITTLE						
1700	1800	1650	1850	150002	WOR	Kidderminster
DOORBAR						
1785	1992	....	....	144088	STS	Biddulph
DOORE						
1815	1992	1700	1815	125024	BKM	Stoke
DORAN						
1866	....	....	....	145742	IRL	Dublin
1863	1890	....	....	134686	LAN	Manchester
1807	1861	1800	1861	165972	MDX	East
DORCAS						
1725	1747	ALL	1747	152838	LIN	Marshchapel
DORE						
1600	1750	1500	1900	170216	BRK	ALL
1833	1923	ALL	ALL	118192	IOW	ALL
1850	1900	ALL	ALL	127884	LND	North West
1700	1992	1550	1992	114596	OXF	Charlbury
DOREE						
1834	1834	1700	ALL	172316	LND	Bethnal Green
DOREY						
....	....	ALL	ALL	100234	ALL	Name Study
....	....	1500	1992	100234	ALL	ALL
1757	....	1700	1800	126667	DOR	East Stoke
....	....	1700	1840	100234	DOR	Lytchett
?	?	?	?	100234	DOR	Wimbourne
1794	....	ALL	1794	122572	GLS	ALL
1850	1992	1700	1885	100234	HAM	Southampton
DORKS						
1850	1900	ALL	1850	156078	HUN	???
DORLING						
....	....	ALL	ALL	132861	ALL	Name Study
DORMAN						
....	....	1750	1780	157406	KEN	Ashford
1860	1915	....	....	168165	LEI	Leicester
1847	1847	1800	1847	144177	LND	???
1768	1885	1886	1920	169374	RUT	Pickworth
1780	1992	....	1780	157406	RUT	Uppingham
DORMER						
1900	1992	1736	1900	120375	PER	Dunblane
1900	1992	....	....	120375	STI	Stirling

Known Researching
From To From To Ref Cty Place

DORMOR
1800 1958 1500 1800 141925 MDX Hampton
DORNEY
1712 1822 ALL ALL 124982 GLS South
DORR
1775 1810 .... 1775 100064 NFK Hilborough
DORRELL
.... ALL ALL 120391 ALL Name Study
ALL ALL ALL ALL 120391 ALL ALL
1775 1875 1700 1840 163740 WOR Rock
1769 1882 1740 1882 146897 WOR Wolverhampton
DORRILL
1699 1715 1650 1750 167002 GLS Willersey
1741 1747 1730 1780 167002 WAR Atherstone On Stour
1753 1765 1750 1800 167002 WAR Old Dtratford
DORRINGTON
1760 1900 1700 1800 150916 GLS St Briavels
1839 1992 1750 1840 101540 HRT Hoddesdon
DORROFIELD
1794 1843 1700 1850 172294 HRT ALL
DORWARD
1700 1900 1700 1850 120405 ANS Arbirlot
1734 1900 1700 1900 120405 ANS Arbroath
1850 1992 1800 1850 174653 ANS Kinnettles
1734 1900 1700 1900 120405 ANS St Vigeans
DOSSET
1780 1847 ALL 1992 112631 BKM Amersham
DOSSOR
1770 1920 ALL ALL 107824 ALL ALL
DOSWELL
.... 1900 .... 1900 119024 SOM Frome
DOTCHEN
.... 1772 ALL 1772 164623 DUR Gateshead
DOUASTON
1786 1817 1786 1817 163813 SAL Oswestry
DOUBELL
.... 1800 1900 125660 SRY Lingfield
DOUBLE
1590 1760 ALL 1590 131059 SFK Ipswich
1725 1884 .... 131822 SFK Molton St Mary
.... 1800 1899 173274 SFK Raydon
DOUBT
.... ALL ALL 120413 ALL Name Study
DOUCE
1798 1925 .... 101028 MDX Holborn
1798 1925 .... 101028 MDX London
DOUCH
1750 1791 1700 1750 139084 KEN Shipbourne
DOUGAL
1752 .... 1700 1800 169218 FIF St Monance
DOUGH
1725 1750 1700 1725 177024 ESS North East
DOUGHERTY
1816 1821 1700 1816 146358 IRL ALL
1851 1992 1816 1850 146358 STD Greenock
1851 1992 1816 1850 146358 STD Paisley
DOUGHLY
1757 1800 1600 1850 130125 WAR Studley
DOUGHTY
.... ALL ALL 120448 ALL Name Study
1844 1844 1844 1844 175196 AVN Bristol
1855 1870 .... 118729 CHS Wallasey
.... 1865 1951 149497 CON Redruth
.... 1850 .... 129593 DBY Buxton
1730 1950 ALL ALL 120456 KEN Thanet
1584 1899 1713 1872 124826 LIN Barton Upon Humber
ALL ALL ALL ALL 120456 LND ALL
1830 1992 1790 1992 120456 LND Greenwich
1855 1868 .... 1855 163031 NYK Whitby
1811 1864 .... 118729 SAL Broseley
1850 1939 1800 1850 156035 WOR Worcester
.... 1800 .... 129593 YKS Whitby
1850 .... 131024 ??? Kidderminster
DOUGLAS
.... 115967 AYR Kirkoswald
1818 1857 .... 1857 103349 CUL Bolton
1799 .... ALL 1850 158445 DUR Monkw'mth
1669 1720 ALL 1720 122386 DUR Ryton
1820 1860 ALL ALL 130508 DUR Sunderland
1791 1828 1700 1900 159956 FIF Cupar
1753 1819 1780 1792 177199 KEN Rochester
1873 1901 1873 1901 103608 LND Mary Le Bone
ALL 1450 .... 132756 NBL Borders
.... 1850 .... 1850 136085 NBL Redesdale

Known Researching
From To From To Ref Cty Place

DOUGLAS contd.
1800 1992 1700 1900 116823 NYK Whitby
ALL 1450 .... 132756 ROX Borders
1700 1775 ALL 1700 115118 ROX Cavers
1770 1835 .... 141798 ROX Hawick
1800 1900 .... 150371 ROX Newcastleton
1753 1819 1753 1819 177199 SSX Brighton
1763 1766 1600 1763 123390 STI Baldernock
.... 1850 1920 148210 TYR Stewartstown
1775 .... 1775 120464 WIG Kirkmaiden
1775 .... 1775 120464 WIG Stoneykirk
1803 1880 1750 1992 126977 WIG Stranraer
1800 1820 1820 1860 177199 WLS Aberystwyth
.... 1830 116866 YKS ???
DOUGLASS
1858 1900 1800 1900 126217 KEN Sheerness
1828 1828 1828 1860 167711 MDX Bow
.... 1830 1840 130877 NBL Longhoughton
1850 1870 1800 1900 144622 YKS York
DOULL
1840 1860 1800 1980 135631 CAI Wick
1780 1840 1750 1980 135631 WES Middleton Fell
DOURNELLE
1658 1940 .... 128996 CAM Thornley
DOUSE
1825 1881 1600 1825 139084 NBL ALL
1600 1725 1500 1750 109274 WIL Great Bedwyn
DOUST
.... ALL ALL 120480 ALL Name Study
.... ALL ALL 120057 ALL ALL
1874 1896 ALL ALL 120057 KEN Christchurch
DOVE
ALL ALL ALL ALL 146080 KEN ALL
1702 1749 .... 127426 KEN Boughton Monchelsea
1724 1724 .... 127426 KEN Canty St Mary Bred
1695 1695 .... 127426 KEN East Malling
1773 1934 1700 1950 134880 KEN Elmsted
1765 1765 1700 1800 134880 KEN Rochester
1850 1970 1820 1850 115207 LAN Merseyside
1632 .... 165999 LIN Lincoln
1721 1721 .... 144568 LIN ???
1817 1992 1700 1817 141143 LND ALL
1826 1850 1750 1850 101664 LND Clapton
1840 1850 1840 1850 134880 LND Victoria
1826 1960 1750 1850 101664 MDX ALL
.... 1750 1880 169471 MDX ???
1760 1790 1538 1820 118893 NFK ???
.... 1700 1847 109223 NTH Towcester
1847 .... 1800 1847 109223 SOM Easton
1770 1900 1600 1800 120499 SOM Wincanton
.... 1800 1900 115207 YKS Whitby
DOVE-SMITH
.... 150924 YKS North
DOVER
.... 1750 1900 104000 NFK Wymondham
DOVERNER
1800 1992 1600 1800 135054 YKS Bradford
1800 1992 1600 1800 135054 YKS Leeds
DOVEY
1775 1840 1700 1775 127116 HAM Abbotts Ann
1690 1732 1600 1700 156515 SAL Stanton Lacy
1825 1845 .... 138118 WOR Worcester
DOW
.... 1702 1650 1720 128961 ESS Coggeshall
1776 1945 1600 1776 159239 ESS Colchester
1703 1765 1720 1756 120502 ESS Great Wigborough
1827 1970 1700 1827 120510 ESS Kelvedon Hatch
1756 1762 1720 1756 120502 ESS Layer Marney
1850 1890 1800 1920 167177 FIF Dunfermlin
1850 1890 1800 1920 167177 FIF Inverkeithing
1819 1825 1800 1819 101796 LKS Glassford
1829 1900 1780 1850 131482 MLN Edinburgh
1871 1920 1871 1920 142840 NFK Aslacton
1873 1920 .... 142840 NFK Forncett St Peter
1780 1850 1650 1800 160296 NFK Hemsby
1800 1822 .... 168203 PER Methven
1801 1888 .... 168203 PER Moneydie
1831 1900 1700 1800 100536 SSX ???
1831 1900 1700 1800 100536 ??? Croydon
DOWD
1875 1885 .... 153842 HRT Barnet
.... ALL 1860 153842 IRL Carlow
.... ALL 1860 153842 IRL Kildare
1861 1870 1845 1860 153842 LND Hackney

Known From	To	Researching From	To	Ref	Cty	Place
DOWD contd.						
1861	1870	1845	1860	153842	LND	Islington
....	1820	ALL	ALL	120529	YKS	Doncaster
DOWDELL						
1673	1759	1670	1759	151858	DOR	Corfe Castle
DOWDEN						
1750	1880	1700	1750	141402	HAM	Isle Of Wight
1863	....	1863	1992	149055	LND	Regents Park
1820	1846	....	....	153397	MDX	New Forest
1806	1840	1750	1806	172871	WIL	Westbury
DOWDESWELL						
1066	1992	1810	1992	120545	GLS	Havescombe
1840	1856	ALL	ALL	174505	MDX	Islington
DOWDING						
....	....	....	1850	120553	DOR	???
....	....	....	1850	120553	GLS	???
1800	1870	1800	1992	175498	LND	Limhouse
1850	1910	....	....	120553	LND	???
....	....	....	1850	120553	SOM	???
1790	1800	1700	1800	123870	WIL	Hilperton
1800	1992	....	....	150762	WIL	Mere
....	....	....	1850	120553	WIL	???
1906	1985	....	1906	136778	???	Bristol
DOWE						
1871	1920	1871	1920	142840	NFK	Aslacton
DOWELL						
1856	....	1800	1856	133639	DOR	Melcombe Regis
1856	....	1800	1856	133639	DOR	Wyke Regis
1735	....	....	....	106852	WIG	???
DOWINING						
1841	1880	1830	1850	170852	DBY	Tibshelf
DOWLAN						
1775	....	1775	1850	139483	IRL	???
DOWLER						
1880	....	....	....	163392	LND	Poplar
1830	1850	1750	1850	142395	WAR	Nuneaton
1750	1870	ALL	1750	103438	WMD	Birmingham
1840	....	....	....	163392	???	Birmingham
DOWLING						
1837	1894	1814	....	132381	LKS	Glasgow
1883	1992	1600	1883	123420	LND	South East
1841	1854	1700	1992	170518	SOM	Chard
1600	1720	1600	1720	142018	SOM	Norton St Philip
1854	1936	1700	1992	170518	SOM	Taunton
1834	1850	1790	1834	139483	WIG	Penninghame
1670	1708	1660	1720	142018	WIL	Marlborough
....	....	1750	1800	168777	WIL	Winterslow
DOWLMAN						
1720	1800	1600	1720	177024	LIN	North East
DOWN						
1809	1864	1800	1811	101427	DEV	Devonport
1841	1864	1841	1947	101427	DEV	Kings Teignton
1748	1837	1700	1851	134880	DEV	Northlew
1818	1930	1818	1900	109053	DEV	Princetown
1774	1865	1700	1774	150320	DEV	Winkleigh
1732	1909	1700	1909	154709	DOR	ALL
....	....	1700	1880	179477	GLS	ALL
1755	1831	1755	1831	146056	HAM	Holdenhurst
1852	1954	1841	1954	134880	KEN	Hythe
1671	1719	....	....	127426	KEN	Lenham
1880	1900	1880	1940	139688	SSX	Frant
1755	1831	1755	1831	146056	WIL	Holdenhurst
....	....	1850	1950	179477	???	Bristol
DOWNBOROUGH						
1750	1834	1750	1850	175153	YKS	Halifax
1750	1834	1750	1850	175153	YKS	Northowram
DOWNE						
1670	1670	....	....	127426	KEN	Harrietsham
1850	1900	1700	1850	118915	YKS	Barton Upon Humber
DOWNEHAM						
1600	1700	ALL	ALL	131873	HRT	Much Hormead
DOWNER						
1689	1900	1500	1992	145289	HAM	Isle Of Wight
1792	1900	1740	1900	105333	WIL	Downton
1792	1900	1740	1900	105333	WIL	Salisbury
DOWNES						
1920	1992	1700	1920	106038	ESS	Colchester
1864	1870	....	1864	120588	LAN	South West
1870	1992	1871	1881	120588	LAN	Southport
1880	1940	1880	1992	120561	LND	South
1859	1992	1700	1859	172944	LND	Bethnal Green
1780	1870	....	....	140864	MDX	Edmonton
1780	1870	....	....	140864	MDX	Enfield
....	1846	....	....	140767	ROS	???
DOWNES contd.						
1850	1880	1800	1900	129607	SRY	North East
1780	1900	1700	1992	120561	SRY	Croydon
1780	1900	1700	1992	120561	SRY	Guildford
1766	1800	1730	1830	117773	SRY	Walworth
1910	1989	ALL	1910	175323	SSX	Uckfield
1812	1845	1750	1812	126454	WAR	Birmingham
1846	....	1853	....	140767	YKS	Leeds
DOWNEY						
1677	1747	1650	1800	165972	DEV	Witheridge
1831	1904	1700	1832	156051	DUB	City
1817	1817	ALL	ALL	120650	IRL	Kilkenny
1852	1900	ALL	ALL	120650	LIN	Crowle
1922	1922	1800	1992	140147	LND	Battersea
1918	1984	1800	1918	151793	NIR	Belfast
DOWNIE						
1870	1992	....	....	108898	LAN	Liverpool
1859	1881	1859	1881	146528	MLN	Currie
DOWNING						
1800	1890	1840	1890	103403	CON	Stratton
1800	1890	1700	1900	103403	DEV	North
1807	1919	1780	1880	176982	DEV	Plymouth
....	....	....	....	156922	HEF	Hereford
1750	1850	1650	1750	163732	NFK	Roydon
1782	1836	ALL	1808	101281	NTH	Towcester
....	....	1700	1992	147613	STS	Rowley Regis
....	....	1850	1900	106429	WRY	Ecclesfield
1851	1851	ALL	1851	102334	???	London
DOWNS						
1779	1857	....	1880	171441	KEN	Boughton Under Blean
1838	1992	1800	1992	100129	LIN	Stamford
1800	1863	1800	1863	141097	LIN	Sturton
1806	1831	ALL	1806	102350	NTT	Sturton
1730	1770	....	1770	137634	NTT	Worksop
....	1846	....	....	140767	ROS	???
1737	1868	1700	1900	100129	RUT	Tinwell
1762	1842	1762	1842	102563	YKS	Darley
1846	....	1853	....	140767	YKS	Leeds
1733	....	1700	1762	102563	YKS	Pateley Bridge
DOWNTON						
1802	1882	1700	1802	149578	DEV	Ugborough
1791	....	1791	1820	133639	DOR	Leigh
1770	1825	1600	1900	158399	DOR	Leigh
1813	....	1791	1813	133639	DOR	Yetminster
1840	1860	1800	1900	142050	LIN	???
....	....	1800	1850	147826	LND	Islington
1800	1880	1700	1900	142050	SOM	South
DOWRICK						
1794	1826	1700	1794	168173	CON	Probus
1794	1826	1700	1794	168173	CON	Tregony
DOWSE						
....	....	ALL	ALL	175129	ALL	Name Study
ALL	ALL	ALL	ALL	175129	ALL	ALL
1733	1881	1700	1900	101923	LIN	Saltfleet
1733	1881	1700	1900	101923	LIN	Trusthorpe
DOWSETT						
1767	....	1650	1767	100013	ESS	Pleshey
1830	1852	1700	1830	125105	ESS	Rochford
1884	1893	1800	1900	127302	LND	Westminster
1780	1801	1750	1850	134481	SRY	Bletchingley
DOWSING						
....	....	1857	1900	157643	ESS	Manningtree
1740	1850	1650	1850	139688	SFK	Bredfield
1822	1838	1800	1850	146269	SFK	Lowestoft
DOWSLING						
1780	1800	1780	1800	119938	YKS	Scarborough
DOWSON						
1580	1760	....	....	102741	DUR	Hamsterley
1698	1738	1670	1750	123536	DUR	Hamsterley
1719	1719	ALL	1719	154563	DUR	Weardale
1850	1992	1700	1850	158208	DUR	Weardale
1800	1900	1700	1800	170801	MDX	London
1900	1910	1880	1992	165603	SRY	Carshalton
1792	1840	1730	1792	177393	YKS	Bawtry
1840	1870	1870	1930	170801	YKS	Grosmont
DOXEY						
1700	1740	1600	1700	120049	STS	Horton
....	....	1700	1800	155497	???	???
DOY						
1789	1890	1700	1850	175218	NFK	North West
DOYLE						
1793	....	....	....	131210	KEN	Sheerness
1860	1980	1700	1860	146021	LAN	Manchester

Known From	To	Researching From	To	Ref	Cty	Place
DOYLE contd.						
1860	1980	1700	1860	146021	LAN	Salford
1810	....	....	....	131210	LND	Christchurch
1800	1850	1700	1900	171522	SSX	Hastings
....	1850	1600	1850	175641	WEX	???
DRABBLE						
1776	1808	ALL	1776	102350	YKS	Throapham
DRACASS						
....	....	ALL	1808	145335	YKS	Hull
1841	1871	1871	1992	145335	YKS	Sheffield
DRACUP						
1798	1992	1600	1800	174580	YKS	Great Horton
....	....	1600	1800	174580	YKS	Idle
DRAGE						
1820	1889	1800	1890	120561	HRT	Stapleford
1780	1900	ALL	ALL	114235	HUN	Molesworth
1750	1992	1600	1750	166111	NTH	Bozeat
DRAIN						
....	....	1850	1960	137685	ESS	Southend
....	....	1850	1910	137685	SRY	Godalming
1908	1912	1850	1950	137685	STS	Tunstall
DRAITEN						
....	....	1700	1800	135089	IOW	???
DRAKE						
1835	1884	1800	1835	128724	BRK	Henley
1860	1900	ALL	ALL	120650	DBY	Chesterfield
1713	1851	1691	1822	170267	DEV	Cheriton
1802	1851	1750	1836	170267	DEV	Crediton
1818	1822	1800	1992	117609	DEV	Devonport
1790	1992	ALL	1790	137545	DEV	Exeter
1815	1830	1700	1815	116106	DEV	Hemyock
1700	1869	....	....	101249	HAM	Romsey
1807	1851	....	....	130079	KEN	Deal
1540	1599	1540	1599	143162	KEN	Medway
....	....	1760	1850	147613	LAN	Tunstall
1836	1880	1800	1880	103616	LEI	Nether Broughton
1812	1814	ALL	ALL	120650	LEI	Thurmaston
1816	1827	ALL	ALL	120650	LIN	Sleaford
1850	1901	1850	1935	129879	LND	East
1895	1940	....	....	101249	LND	Battersea
1830	1880	1800	1922	176281	LND	City
1880	1920	....	....	121460	LND	Lambeth
1811	1811	1700	1811	120367	NFK	Norwich
1863	1910	1863	1910	114626	NFK	Watlington
1835	1860	ALL	ALL	120650	NTT	Mansfield
1827	1835	ALL	ALL	120650	NTT	Newark
1820	1929	1820	1929	114626	RUT	Oakham
1721	1807	ALL	ALL	121487	SFK	Elmswell
1700	1740	1640	1740	135941	SFK	Lakenheath
1820	1940	1820	1880	176281	SRY	Croydon
1820	1850	1750	1820	132640	SRY	Lambeth
1825	1850	1750	1825	140309	WAR	Wellesbourne
1830	1930	1830	1930	143588	WYK	Bradford
1850	1900	1700	1850	110345	YKS	Ackworth
1808	1906	1750	1820	136301	YKS	Dewsbury
1781	1812	1760	1835	146897	YKS	Halifax
1699	1899	1650	1900	175153	YKS	Halifax
1778	1824	1600	1790	101575	YKS	Holbeck
1778	1824	1600	1790	101575	YKS	Leeds
1699	1899	1650	1900	175153	YKS	Northowram
1808	1906	1750	1820	136301	YKS	Thornhill
1790	1860	1600	1790	154172	YKS	Wyke
DRAKEFIELD						
1771	1870	1700	1890	137235	LEI	Hemington
1771	1870	1700	1890	137235	LEI	Lockington
1679	1791	1600	1800	137235	STS	Tutbury
DRAKEFORD						
1870	1900	1700	1870	121258	WAR	Coventry
DRAKES						
1780	1850	1850	1900	145408	LIN	Lindsey
DRANE						
1792	1792	ALL	1800	129283	NFK	Thwaite St Mary
1785	1937	1600	1785	179647	SFK	Hopton
DRANSFIELD						
1650	1992	1400	1992	114596	LAN	Dewsbury
1750	1992	1600	1992	120677	WYK	Almondbury
DRAPER						
....	....	ALL	ALL	120693	ALL	Name Study
1816	1824	1800	1850	144908	BDF	Bolnhurst
1892	1992	1880	1992	144908	BDF	Great Barford
1805	1892	1780	1920	144908	BDF	Wilden
1860	1910	1860	1992	149055	CAM	???
1822	1852	1700	1822	120707	ENG	Hertford
1801	1860	1700	1992	153672	HRT	ALL
DRAPER contd.						
1740	1800	1650	1740	120685	HRT	Ardeley
1740	1800	1650	1740	120685	HRT	Cottered
1740	1800	1650	1740	120685	HRT	Stevenage
1836	1992	1755	1836	129712	KEN	West
....	....	1750	1840	169056	LAN	Bolton
1849	1855	1844	1865	148121	LND	City
1840	1900	1800	1840	146587	LND	Edmonton
1823	....	1800	1855	148121	LND	Islington
....	....	1750	1850	137685	NFK	Gt Yarmouth
1820	1910	1820	1910	173533	NTH	South
1776	1798	1700	1850	144908	NTH	Grendon
1750	1850	ALL	1750	176516	NTT	Sutton Cum Lound
1900	1920	1750	1900	158976	SRY	Ash
1750	1992	1650	1750	102873	SRY	Bagshot
1743	1955	ALL	ALL	109002	SRY	Bagshot
1750	1992	1650	1750	102873	SRY	Windlesham
1743	1955	ALL	ALL	109002	SRY	Windlesham
1800	1992	1700	1992	165344	WAR	Rugby
1770	1770	1770	1770	147575	WIL	Alton Barnes
1753	1770	1700	1753	147575	WIL	Market Lavington
1750	1992	1500	1750	170194	WIL	Urchfont
1836	1872	ALL	1836	102350	YKS	Ferrybridge
1836	1872	ALL	1836	102350	YKS	Rawmarsh
DRAPPER						
1880	1960	1800	1880	126675	KEN	Gillingham
DRAVER						
....	....	ALL	1800	110965	OKI	North Isles
DRAWBRIDGE						
1790	1992	1700	1800	142395	KEN	Cranbrook
1600	1660	....	....	119431	SXE	Warblton
DRAY						
1870	1992	1790	1870	177539	SSX	Chiddingly
1866	1992	1700	1900	125385	WOR	Rochford
DRAYCOTT						
1895	1992	1700	1900	171689	DBY	Dronfield
1822	1992	1750	1822	137944	LEI	Anstey
DRAYDEN						
....	....	1700	1800	135089	IOW	???
DRAYDON						
1815	1985	ALL	ALL	171980	ALL	ALL
DRAYTON						
....	....	1700	1800	135089	IOW	???
....	....	ALL	ALL	115142	LEI	???
....	....	1530	1700	151513	WAR	Mancetter
....	....	ALL	ALL	115142	WAR	???
DREA						
....	....	1800	1940	142549	ALL	ALL
1890	1910	1880	1920	163775	ESS	Grays
....	....	ALL	ALL	142549	IRL	Kilkenny
DREDGE						
1813	1856	1813	1856	108391	MDX	London
1784	1792	1700	1850	118192	MDX	Stepney
1780	1850	1700	1850	174300	SOM	Frome
DRESSER						
1710	1850	1600	1850	176338	EYK	Holderness
1850	1992	1850	1992	176338	EYK	Hull
DRESSLER						
1890	1900	1800	1992	167592	LAN	Birkenhead
1880	1920	1800	1992	167592	STS	Stoke
DREW						
1800	1850	ALL	1850	137286	CON	West
1800	1992	1750	1992	125563	CON	Breage
1667	1820	ALL	1667	148385	CON	Landrake
1790	1840	1600	?	127833	CON	Penzance
1800	1992	1750	1992	125563	CON	Phillack
1667	1820	ALL	1667	148385	CON	Saltash
1699	1850	ALL	1699	148385	CON	St Germans
....	....	1600	1780	146730	CUL	Passim
1799	1881	ALL	ALL	165972	DEV	Morchard Bishop
1779	1854	ALL	1779	175080	DEV	Tavistock
1811	....	ALL	1811	104299	GLS	Birstol
1572	1732	....	....	165999	GLS	Hartpury
1820	1992	....	1820	159972	HAM	Ambersham
....	....	1830	....	121827	IRL	???
?	?	?	?	121185	KEN	South
1850	1880	....	....	174955	KEN	Ashford
1822	1886	ALL	1886	157902	LIM	Limerick
1858	1992	ALL	ALL	108464	LND	Islington
1851	....	ALL	1851	121827	LND	Lambeth
....	....	1500	1850	164992	MDX	ALL
1790	1810	1700	1850	126799	NFK	Great Bircham
....	....	1600	1805	101125	SOM	ALL
1770	1782	1760	1800	142018	SOM	Bath

Known From	To	Researching From	To	Ref	Cty	Place
DREW contd.						
1805	1950	1600	1805	101125	SOM	Taunton
1910	1912	1870	1992	121568	SOM	Templecombe
1820	ALL	....	....	117560	SRY	Egham
1670	....	1675	....	130621	WIL	Bishops Cannings
1737	1793	1700	1737	115819	WIL	Sopworth
DREWE						
1863	1866	1830	1862	120731	KEN	Canterbury
DREWEATT						
1900	1992	1900	1992	121738	BRK	Reading
DREWERY						
1796	1992	1700	1796	120758	LIN	Little Grimsby
1800	1850	1700	1800	171921	LIN	Louth
DREWETT						
1850	1875	1800	1900	160563	BRK	Reading
1870	1900	1830	1900	121738	HAM	Kingsclere
1713	....	....	1730	171441	HAM	Monk Sherborne
....	....	1858	ALL	132349	WIL	Patney
DREWITT						
1850	1900	ALL	ALL	173657	BRK	Faringdon
1831	1852	1700	1831	111953	OXF	Marston
DREWMILK						
1828	1850	....	....	174955	MDX	Marylebone
....	....	1750	1813	174955	NFK	Brockdish
1813	1820	....	....	174955	SFK	Brandon
DREWRY						
1762	1792	1700	1762	172553	ESS	Bradwell
DREWS						
1780	1820	1700	1820	139688	SOM	Lopen
DRIFFIELD						
1800	1862	1700	1800	134732	LIN	Bishop Norton
1842	1900	1600	1842	123307	SFK	East Bergholt
DRILLOT						
1671	1948	ALL	ALL	115126	CHI	Sark
DRING						
1818	1886	1750	1818	160911	HUN	Warboys
1820	1900	1820	1900	120782	LIN	Baston
1800	1820	....	....	120782	LIN	Haconby
1789	1810	....	....	120782	LIN	Kirkby Underwood
1900	1992	1900	1992	120782	LIN	Lincoln
....	....	1700	1789	120782	LIN	Mid
DRINKWATER						
1833	1870	....	....	166189	BKM	Langley
1810	1811	1790	1810	117196	CHS	Northwich
1880	1970	1700	1880	149624	CHS	Tattunhall
....	....	1700	....	141216	GLS	Mid
....	....	?	....	141216	GLS	Sandhurst
1781	1851	1700	1851	120790	GLS	Tewksbury
1834	1852	1680	1834	138029	LAN	Chorley
1750	1780	1600	1992	167592	LAN	Liverpool
1800	1840	1750	1800	142905	LAN	Manchester
ALL	1850	....	....	114642	MDX	London
1851	1992	1800	1992	120790	NTT	Chilwell
DRISCOL						
....	....	1800	1881	110132	COR	???
DRISCOLL						
1907	....	....	....	150762	GLA	Cardiff
1840	....	....	....	110833	IRL	???
1898	1981	1750	1898	168025	KEN	Chislehurst
1881	....	....	....	110833	LND	East
DRISDALL						
1815	1846	1800	1850	163775	IRL	Dublin
1848	1868	1840	1870	163775	SRY	Bermondsey
1847	....	1845	1850	163775	WAR	Birmingham
DRITTLER						
....	....	ALL	1881	120588	ALL	ALL
1887	1992	1865	1887	120588	LAN	Southport
DRIVER						
1750	1950	1800	1950	162329	CAM	???
1759	1821	1726	1759	103918	KEN	Lynsted
1780	1800	1700	1800	126837	LAN	Lancaster
1827	1992	....	1827	174076	LEI	Medbourne
1820	1900	1800	1900	153877	LEI	Syston
1715	1818	1715	1818	104817	NTH	Kettering
1716	1819	1716	1819	139831	NTH	Kettering
1790	1880	1700	1800	136840	SFK	Finningham
1834	1860	1750	1834	155845	SRY	Newington
1797	1861	1750	1797	155845	SRY	Southwark
DRODGE						
1783	1850	....	....	153397	HAM	New Forest
DRONSFIELD						
1851	1851	1800	1851	108715	LAN	Oldham
DROUGHT						
1700	1820	....	....	155683	DUB	ALL

Known From	To	Researching From	To	Ref	Cty	Place
DROUGHT contd.						
1850	1992	1750	1850	167789	DUB	Dublin
DROVER						
1880	1992	....	....	173827	WAR	Edgbaston
DROWET						
1550	1604	1500	1604	154881	KEN	ALL
DROWN						
....	....	1800	1900	139432	DEV	Tavistock
DRUCE						
1789	1815	1700	1789	176885	BRK	Clewer
1800	1840	1700	1800	121509	ESS	???
1850	....	....	....	114642	MDX	London
1850	1932	1800	1850	112925	NTH	Potterspury
1850	1932	1800	1850	112925	NTH	Yardley Gobion
DRUERY						
1830	1915	1700	1900	142875	LIN	???
DRUETT						
1800	1840	1750	1800	135879	LND	Aldersgate
DRULY						
1800	1850	ALL	ALL	130508	HAM	Andover
DRUMMOND						
1841	1841	....	....	168203	CAI	Wick
1857	1992	1700	1857	100110	DUR	Sunderland
1802	1806	....	....	168203	ELN	Haddington
1790	1830	1740	1790	128244	FIF	Saline
1790	1830	1740	1790	128244	FIF	Torryburn
....	....	ALL	ALL	120618	IRL	???
1840	1900	1800	1900	117781	NYK	Scarborough
1300	1400	1300	1400	154881	PER	Stobhall
1850	1860	ALL	ALL	120618	SRY	London
DRUMMY						
1840	1890	....	....	111368	MDX	Marylebone
DRURY						
1762	1792	1700	1762	172553	ESS	Bradwell
1595	1850	1460	1662	120820	GLS	Weston Sub Edge
1790	1822	1700	1790	113425	KEN	Benenden
1840	....	....	....	117579	KEN	Charlton
1795	1992	1795	....	120812	KEN	Medway
1900	1925	1900	1992	165522	LAN	Liverpool
1897	1930	1895	1930	151599	LEI	Loughborough
1950	1992	1850	1950	177199	LIN	Brigg
1801	1900	1780	1900	151599	LIN	Eagle
1801	1900	1780	1900	151599	LIN	Hykeham
1700	1992	1600	1700	102342	LIN	Springthorpe
1842	1954	ALL	1813	106283	LIN	Trent Valley Villages
1950	1992	1850	1950	177199	LIN	Willoughton
1780	1840	1780	1800	168920	LND	Holborn
1749	1760	1700	1760	168920	LND	Shoreditch
1749	1834	....	....	117579	LND	???
1730	1840	1700	1900	120812	NFK	Great Yarmouth
1753	1758	1700	1800	159905	OXF	Chadlington
1460	1595	1460	1662	120820	SAL	Shrewsbury
1066	1460	....	....	120820	SFK	Bury St Edmunds
1066	1700	....	....	168777	SFK	Thurston
....	....	1845	ALL	174963	SOM	???
1706	1860	1650	1706	120774	SSX	East
1800	1850	1700	1900	171522	SSX	Seaford
1558	1740	1460	1662	120820	WOR	Bretforton
1851	1888	1811	1888	146773	YKS	Hull
DRUST						
ALL	ALL	ALL	ALL	104272	ALL	ALL
1600	1900	ALL	ALL	104272	LIN	ALL
DRY						
1800	1940	ALL	....	120839	EYK	Driffield
....	....	1500	1800	166863	HAM	Basingstoke
1690	1750	1600	1750	122920	LND	ALL
DRYDEN						
1820	....	....	....	150657	CON	Gwennap
1755	1811	ALL	1755	154563	CUL	Alston
1820	1992	1800	1850	122297	DUR	Gateshead
1835	1886	1886	1992	143049	NBL	Belford
1796	1834	1700	1796	165182	YKS	Stakesley
DRYHURST						
....	....	ALL	ALL	120847	ALL	Name Study
1285	1992	1354	1992	120847	DEN	Denbigh
1900	1992	1900	1992	120847	ESS	Chelmsford
1790	1992	1790	1992	120847	LAN	Liverpool
1830	1992	1830	1992	120847	LAN	Manchester
1825	1992	1825	1992	120847	WMD	Birmingham
DRYLAND						
1788	1837	1750	1837	144355	KEN	South
1863	1992	ALL	ALL	118370	KEN	Aldington
1710	1800	1650	1710	173312	KEN	Tonbridge

Known From	To	Researching From	To	Ref	Cty	Place
DRYNAN						
1762	1875	1760	1875	171654	WIG	Port Patrick
1888	1901	1800	1888	174807	WIG	Sandhead
DRYSDALE						
1909	....	1909	....	127647	SCT	???
1821	1914	1750	1821	147745	STI	Campsie
DU HEAUME						
1824	1881	....	....	141356	JSY	St Oven
DU PAY						
1780	1800	1750	1992	104671	CON	ALL
DUBB						
1880	1992	1650	1880	120863	DEV	Bideford
DUBERY						
....	....	1650	1992	140120	LND	Islington
DUBLE						
1764	?	?	?	166642	KEN	Cranbrook
DUBOIS						
1643	1940	....	....	128996	CAM	Thornley
DUCAT						
1800	1850	ALL	1900	117188	ANS	Kettins
DUCE						
1780	1850	1600	1780	173207	SAL	South
1830	....	....	1992	120391	SAL	???
1700	1760	1700	1760	133817	SFK	Long Melford
DUCK						
1770	1992	....	....	144304	ARM	???
1770	1992	....	....	144304	COR	???
1786	1851	1831	1919	167533	GLS	Bristol
1856	?	1700	1856	120871	HAM	Alverstoke
....	....	ALL	ALL	154571	NRY	ALL
1620	1660	1600	1620	121339	NYK	Lythe
1846	?	1700	1846	120871	PEM	Pembroke
1868	....	1600	1868	137812	WIL	Chippenham
1820	....	1600	1868	137812	WIL	Trowbridge
1810	1830	1750	1880	144622	YKS	Thrybergh
DUCKENFIELD						
1830	1900	1750	1830	172510	YKS	Aughton
1830	1900	1750	1830	172510	YKS	Sheffield
DUCKETT						
....	....	ALL	ALL	120898	ALL	Name Study
ALL	ALL	ALL	ALL	120898	ALL	ALL
1792	1866	1600	1866	164704	BRK	Sulhampstead
1886	1940	1700	1850	111554	GLS	Shurdington
1776	1778	1770	1780	125032	HAM	Mapledurwell
1778	1782	1770	1790	125032	HAM	Newnham
1819	1827	1810	1830	125032	HAM	Rotherwick
1818	1876	1810	1880	125032	HAM	Sherborne St John
1775	1845	1750	1900	125032	HAM	Sherfield On Loddon
1700	1820	1670	1800	125032	HAM	Tunworth
1775	1856	1725	1775	170100	LAN	Garstang
1852	1900	1841	1900	171166	LAN	Liverpool
1605	1800	1550	1605	170100	SAL	Neen Savage
ALL	ALL	1800	1850	111554	SOM	Mark
1730	1810	1680	1730	103675	SOM	Wedmore
1734	1780	....	....	115290	SOM	Wedmore
1785	1820	1780	1820	171166	WRY	Clapham
DUCKHAM						
1810	1842	ALL	ALL	175005	DEV	Loxbere
1850	....	....	....	145742	WAR	Coventry
DUCKINS						
1691	1767	....	1758	137405	CAM	Rampton
DUCKIT						
....	....	1730	1992	121940	WRY	Giggleswick
DUCKWORTH						
1840	1880	ALL	1840	146757	CHS	Warrington
1779	1985	1650	1779	167886	FLN	Ewloe
1828	....	....	....	136565	LAN	Billington
1753	1992	1690	1992	120901	LAN	Burnley
1830	1992	1700	1830	117447	LAN	Haslingden
1775	....	1775	....	109347	LAN	Lower Darwen
1825	....	1825	....	109347	LAN	Oswaldtwistle
1764	....	?	1764	103934	LND	???
1802	1896	ALL	1896	157902	YKS	South
1802	1896	ALL	1896	157902	YKS	West
1849	1902	1827	1849	134309	YKS	Saddleworth
DUCY						
1600	1755	1600	1770	142018	SOM	ALL
DUDBRIDGE						
....	....	ALL	ALL	120928	GLS	Amberley
....	....	1500	1599	120928	GLS	Bisley
ALL	ALL	1500	1599	120928	GLS	Minchinghampton
ALL	1500	ALL	1599	120928	GLS	Stroud
DUDDEN						
1724	1992	1700	1724	161446	SOM	Cameley
DUDDLES						
1650	1900	ALL	ALL	159530	LIN	ALL
DUDDLESTON						
1760	1780	1700	1770	173312	SAL	Prees
DUDDRIDGE						
1893	1944	ALL	ALL	106216	SOM	Bridgwater
DUDGEON						
....	....	ALL	ALL	108820	ALL	Name Study
DUDLEY						
....	....	1600	1835	137014	CAM	ALL
1700	1900	1700	1900	156086	CHS	Davenham
1745	1930	ALL	1745	120944	CON	West
....	....	1600	1835	137014	HUN	ALL
1840	....	....	....	117560	MDX	London
1830	....	1750	1900	102016	MDX	St Lukes
....	....	1600	1835	137014	NTH	ALL
1800	1830	....	....	117560	WAR	Birmingham
1812	1812	1750	1820	128449	WAR	Birmingham
1839	1945	1500	1850	164909	WOR	Oldbury
....	....	1800	1910	110108	WOR	Worcester
1805	1851	1700	1805	168033	YKS	York
DUDLEY-WARD						
1800	1900	1700	1800	135054	LAN	Liverpool
DUDMAN						
....	....	1810	....	106623	SRY	Woking
DUE						
....	....	ALL	ALL	114308	SRY	Godalming
DUEL						
....	....	1800	1900	133604	WIL	Littleton Panell
DUELL						
....	....	1800	1900	129593	YKS	Barrowby
....	....	1750	1900	129593	YKS	Borrowby
DUERDEN						
1700	1810	1700	1850	151912	LAN	Pendleton
1700	1810	1700	1850	151912	LAN	Whalley
DUESE						
1790	1800	1700	1790	172901	NTT	Mansfield
DUFALL						
....	....	ALL	ALL	120960	ALL	Name Study
1840	1992	1840	1880	120960	DOR	ALL
DUFF						
....	....	ALL	ALL	113077	ALL	Name Study
1776	1857	1750	1860	146536	AYR	Kilbirnie
1770	....	1770	1850	146536	AYR	Largs
1810	1923	1700	1810	158143	FIF	Newburgh
1785	1810	....	....	168203	FIF	Scoonie
1789	1872	1789	1992	143472	PER	Ballinluig
1767	1950	....	....	168203	PER	Methven
1795	1810	1700	1795	158143	PER	Perth
1789	1872	1789	1992	143472	PER	Pitlochry
1799	1915	....	....	168203	PER	Redgorton
1900	1950	....	....	168203	PER	Tibbermore
1825	1851	1851	1900	161586	SSX	Midhurst
1850	1860	1830	1870	138444	WAR	Dudley
DUFFAUT						
1880	1992	1880	1992	165786	NBL	Blyth
1880	1992	1880	1992	165786	NBL	Tynemouth
DUFFELLS						
1803	1808	1750	1820	131547	SRY	Betchworth
1802	....	1750	1820	131547	SRY	Capel
DUFFETT						
1950	1992	1800	1950	150010	DOR	Weymouth
1798	1800	1700	1797	166820	MDX	London
DUFFIELD						
1821	1900	ALL	1821	121525	ESS	Mile End Old Town
1810	1992	1700	1810	148334	MDX	Chelsea
1790	1840	1790	1840	161705	NFK	North
1760	1851	....	....	122319	NFK	Norwich
1787	1821	ALL	1787	161330	NTT	Nottingham
1836	1890	1600	1836	123420	SFK	Newmarket
1840	1862	1650	1840	145432	WOR	Bromsgrove
1865	1901	1885	1992	145432	WOR	Kidderminster
1871	1881	....	....	121290	???	Derby
DUFFILL						
1786	1992	....	1786	120979	WOR	Bromsgrove
1840	1901	1600	1830	145432	WOR	Woodcote Green
DUFFIN						
1870	1992	1870	1920	173614	DEV	North
1800	1850	ALL	1900	173614	HAM	South
1836	1836	ALL	1860	173614	HAM	Titchfield
1758	1761	1700	1758	157147	HAM	Upton Grey
1789	1830	1760	1841	164895	LEI	Thurmaston
1750	1850	1700	1950	100439	LIN	Boston
1750	1850	1700	1950	100439	LIN	Wainfleet St Mary

Known From	To	Researching From	To	Ref	Cty	Place
DUFFIN contd.						
1790	1870	1750	1870	146803	SRY	Windlesham
1750	1850	1750	1950	177180	STS	Tipton
1792	1798	1600	1992	120987	WAR	Aston Cantlow
1910	1951	1600	1992	120987	WAR	Bilton
1862	1940	1800	1900	120987	WAR	Claverdon
1771	1811	1600	1900	120987	WAR	Great Alne
1700	1800	1500	1800	177180	WAR	Snitterfield
1865	1945	1600	1992	120987	WAR	Southam
1850	1950	1850	1992	177180	WAR	Stretton On Dunsmore
DUFFY						
1840	1840	ALL	1840	108367	IRL	???
1856	....	ALL	ALL	172057	OFF	Killourney
1840	1850	1850	1900	108367	YKS	Barnsley
1840	1850	1850	1900	108367	YKS	Wakefield
DUFTON						
ALL	ALL	ALL	ALL	170267	ALL	ALL
DUFTY						
1837	1992	ALL	ALL	101362	DEV	Central
1843	1843	....	....	108901	NTT	Epperstone
DUGARD						
1760	1800	ALL	ALL	128449	WOR	ALL
1796	1992	ALL	ALL	128449	WOR	Birmingham
1760	1780	ALL	ALL	128449	WOR	Feckenham
1779	1807	ALL	ALL	128449	WOR	Hagley
1780	1800	ALL	ALL	128449	WOR	Hartlebury
1780	1800	ALL	ALL	128449	WOR	Kidderminster
1799	1799	ALL	ALL	128449	WOR	Worcester
DUGDALE						
1620	1620	1580	1650	174289	DOR	ALL
1585	1598	1558	1585	174270	DOR	Tarrant Hinton
1826	1900	1600	1826	177644	DOR	???
1850	1853	1700	1890	174270	LAN	ALL
....	....	1740	1830	151912	LAN	Blacko Colne
1830	1881	....	....	151912	LAN	Clitheroe
1830	1900	1700	1830	121509	LAN	Colne
1812	1830	ALL	ALL	138886	LAN	Kirkham
1839	1980	ALL	1839	122858	LAN	Manchester
1830	1900	1700	1830	121509	LAN	Marsden
1737	1870	1737	1870	160237	LAN	Tatham
1720	1730	1600	1730	175382	YKS	Barnoldwick
DUGDELL						
1811	1906	1700	1811	111945	SFK	Brampton
DUGGAN						
1800	1900	1700	1900	103578	PEM	Angle
1700	1992	1600	1700	121010	RAD	Old Radnor
1857	1992	....	1857	121002	RAD	???
1810	1880	1750	1810	121509	TIP	Casmel
DUGGETT						
1681	1702	1660	1681	101796	SFK	Ipswich
DUGGIN						
1855	1857	1838	1855	167959	KEN	Chatham
DUGGINS						
1850	1992	1538	1850	154792	WOR	ALL
DUGMORE						
....	....	ALL	ALL	141763	ALL	Name Study
DUGUID						
1740	....	....	....	126497	ABD	Fyvie
1832	1860	1780	1860	126586	ABD	Fyvie
1740	1780	1740	1780	126500	ABD	Fyvie
DUJARDIN						
....	....	ALL	ALL	121029	ALL	Name Study
DUKE						
1730	1821	1700	1830	176672	ALL	ALL
1840	1880	1700	1850	107719	CHI	Jersey
....	....	ALL	1860	140848	DEV	ALL
....	....	1600	1950	134546	HAM	Portsea
....	....	1600	1950	134546	HAM	Portsmouth
....	....	1600	1950	134546	IOW	Bewbridge
....	....	1600	1950	134546	IOW	Brading
1706	?	?	?	166642	KEN	Throwley
1850	1900	ALL	ALL	170801	SSX	Brighton
1664	1708	1600	1750	167002	SXE	Iden
1731	1780	1700	1800	167002	SXE	Mayfield
1659	1706	1600	1750	167002	SXE	Playden
1750	1930	ALL	1750	115282	TAY	ALL
DUKER						
1809	....	1750	1850	154962	HRT	South East
DUKES						
1780	1834	....	....	153397	HAM	New Forest
DULANTY						
....	1846	....	....	140767	IRL	???
1858	....	1858	....	140767	YKS	???
DULIEU						
1695	1975	ALL	1776	121355	LND	Bethnal Green
1690	1992	1690	1992	117641	LND	East End
1695	1975	ALL	1776	121355	LND	Hackney Wick
1695	1975	ALL	1776	121355	LND	Stepney
DULIN						
1800	1985	ALL	1800	119121	ALL	ALL
1800	1985	ALL	1800	119121	LND	ALL
DULING						
....	....	....	....	108340	LND	???
DULLEA						
1777	1808	ALL	1808	129283	IRL	Cork
1808	1861	1808	1880	129283	MDX	St George In The East
DULLEY						
1697	1992	1550	1992	121037	ALL	ALL
DULLOW						
1812	1842	1800	1900	176982	KEN	Hoo
DULY						
1900	1960	1700	1950	165476	KEN	Rochester
1900	1992	1900	1992	124613	SSX	Hastings
DUMARESQ						
1873	1922	ALL	ALL	121045	HAM	Alvestoke
1792	?	ALL	ALL	121045	SAL	Bushel Hall
DUMBELTON						
....	....	1800	1860	169471	HRT	South
....	....	1750	1800	169471	OXF	North
DUMBER						
....	....	1500	1885	121088	HAM	ALL
DUMBILL						
1800	1950	1700	1800	129534	LAN	Warrington
DUMBLE						
1780	1868	ALL	1868	168718	CON	South East
DUMBLETON						
1763	1881	1760	1950	153818	OXF	North Newington
1830	1900	1830	1900	121053	STS	Darlaston
1800	1830	1700	1800	121053	WAR	Stratford Upon Avon
DUMBRELL						
....	....	ALL	1851	175323	SSX	East Grinstead
DUMONT						
1780	....	1780	1800	169625	???	Lambeth Palace
DUMPER						
....	....	ALL	ALL	121088	ALL	Name Study
1885	1950	1500	1885	121088	HAM	ALL
DUMPLETON						
1846	....	ALL	ALL	121436	HRT	Tring
DUN						
1791	1796	1600	1791	123390	STI	Baldernock
DUNBABIN						
....	....	1800	1992	166936	CHS	Runcorn
DUNBAR						
....	....	ALL	ALL	112984	ALL	Name Study
1840	1840	ALL	ALL	173657	CON	St Austell
1843	1920	....	....	146811	LKS	Glasgow
1799	1836	....	1799	146811	MOR	Forres
1830	1850	1850	1880	148113	WAR	Birmingham
....	....	1880	1920	148113	YKS	Sheffield
DUNBARTON						
1862	1862	ALL	1862	108642	BKM	Amersham
DUNBAVAN						
1720	1770	1600	1992	167592	LAN	Liverpool
DUNBIBBIN						
1720	1770	1600	1992	167592	LAN	Liverpool
DUNCALF						
....	....	ALL	ALL	114561	ALL	Name Study
....	....	ALL	ALL	114561	ALL	ALL
DUNCAN						
1835	1835	1700	1835	106887	ABD	Boyndie
1791	1992	1600	1791	146137	ABD	Buchan
1796	1871	1700	1796	118427	ABD	Cortachy
1780	1850	....	....	126497	ABD	Forgue
1820	1850	1700	1820	100978	ABD	Old Deer
1806	1842	1700	1830	103462	ABD	Peterhead
....	....	1870	1910	111708	ABD	Peterhead
1800	....	ALL	ALL	130508	ABD	Peterhead
1650	1800	1600	1800	154881	ANS	Forfar
1850	1992	1750	1850	118052	ANT	Ballycastle
1794	1824	1770	1830	121126	ANT	Belfast
1900	1920	....	....	177709	CHS	Wallasy
1800	1840	1740	1800	128244	DNB	Kirktilloch
1862	1862	1800	1900	142921	DUR	South Shields
1795	1992	1700	1795	170453	FIF	ALL
....	....	1750	1850	145637	FIF	Collessie
....	....	1860	....	149187	FIF	Newport

Known From	To	Researching From	To	Ref	Cty	Place
DUNCAN contd.						
1750	....	ALL	ALL	130508	FIF	St Monance
1750	1992	1600	1750	121118	FIF	St Monans
1860	....	....	1860	164011	HAM	Portsmouth
1740	1800	1740	1800	121096	KCD	Banchory Devenick
1790	1830	1790	1830	121096	KCD	Strachan
1815	1992	....	....	121142	LAN	Liverpool
1797	....	....	1797	148830	LTN	Carriden
....	....	ALL	1769	119326	MLN	Newbattle
1860	1992	1800	1992	164518	MOR	ALL
1800	1820	1700	1900	103403	MOR	Boharm
1871	1878	....	....	121142	PER	Bellyclone
1860	1992	....	....	121142	PER	Clunie
1871	1878	....	....	121142	PER	Fowlis Wester
1854	1878	....	....	121142	PER	Moneydie
1765	1874	1841	1891	146560	PER	Perth
1800	1900	....	....	150371	SCT	Glasgow
1944	1992	ALL	1944	165263	SCT	???
1860	....	....	1860	148830	TYR	???
DUNCANSON						
1749	1879	ALL	ALL	108510	CLK	ALL
1749	1879	ALL	ALL	108510	FIF	ALL
1749	1879	ALL	ALL	108510	FIF	Kincardine On Forth
1595	1899	ALL	ALL	108510	SCT	ALL
DUNCKLEY						
1689	1911	ALL	1689	174157	DUB	Dublin
1689	1911	ALL	1689	174157	WIC	Baltinglass
DUNCOMBE						
?	1896	?	?	127841	DUR	ALL
?	1896	1800	?	127841	YKS	ALL
DUNDAS						
1850	1992	1800	1850	174653	ANS	Dundee
1850	1992	1800	1850	174653	ANS	Kirriemuir
DUNDERDALE						
1740	1992	1600	1800	113654	LAN	St Michaels
1780	1820	1600	1992	167592	YKS	Castleford
1760	1780	1600	1992	167592	YKS	Leeds
DUNDON						
1804	1805	1780	1832	151181	MDX	London
DUNFORD						
1810	....	....	....	145688	CAM	Cambridge
?	?	1800	1850	121185	KEN	ALL
1750	1900	1650	1900	121177	WIL	Great Cheverelle
1650	1840	....	1840	121169	WIL	Longbridge Deverill
1600	1779	....	....	168513	YKS	Middlestown
DUNGATE						
....	....	1250	1992	121193	KEN	ALL
....	....	1500	1992	121193	SRY	ALL
1850	1980	1250	1850	121193	SSX	ALL
DUNHAM						
1660	1850	1660	1850	121207	BDF	Haynes
1850	1900	1850	1900	121207	BDF	Luton
1700	1800	1700	1800	167924	BDF	Shillington
1770	1770	1700	1770	134627	CAM	Witchford
1754	1870	1700	1900	121207	HUN	Kimbolton
1879	1992	1879	1930	121207	LAN	Oldham
1804	1889	1800	1889	139645	LIN	Skidbrook With Saltfleet
1790	1830	ALL	1790	108197	NFK	Somerton
1800	1850	1700	1800	160296	NFK	Somerton
1589	1700	ALL	1700	101079	NTT	Scrooby
1930	1970	1930	1970	121207	SRY	Ewell
1875	1920	1875	1920	121207	YKS	Bradford
1875	1920	1875	1920	121207	YKS	Wakefield
DUNHILL						
1837	1980	1800	1940	117781	EYK	Hull
DUNK						
1769	....	....	1800	171441	KEN	Bethersden
1823	1826	1700	1850	105775	KEN	Chislet
1832	1871	ALL	1940	156175	KEN	Meopham
1772	1852	....	1772	177601	SSX	Catsfield
1772	1852	....	1772	177601	SSX	Hastings
DUNKERLEY						
1821	1861	1700	1992	121215	CHS	Stockport
1862	1907	....	1862	179221	LAN	Aston Under Lyne
1861	1992	1700	1992	121215	LAN	Denton
1700	1966	1850	1966	121223	LAN	Manchester
1800	1850	1700	1800	178209	LAN	Oldham
1930	1960	1700	1992	121215	LAN	Poulton
1800	1850	1700	1800	178209	LAN	Sholver
DUNKERTON						
1795	1902	ALL	1992	119695	SOM	West Pennard
DUNKIN						
....	....	1700	1800	174696	ESS	Woodham Mortimer
DUNKINSON						
1849	....	....	....	153397	HAM	Brockenhurst
DUNKLEY						
1750	1850	ALL	1850	137286	BDF	Houghton Conquest
1840	1992	1700	1840	108618	HRT	Hadley
1736	1850	?	1850	103934	HUN	Ellington
1736	1850	?	1850	103934	HUN	Kimbolton
1736	1850	?	1850	103934	HUN	St Neots
1850	1950	ALL	1800	142301	MDX	London
1743	1743	1720	1750	107360	NTH	Badby
1890	1992	1700	1890	141275	NTH	East Haddon
1806	1822	ALL	1806	115126	NTH	Flore
1867	1900	1700	1867	121258	NTH	Great Creaton
1744	1816	1729	1837	107360	NTH	Long Buckby
1738	1738	1730	1740	103632	NTH	Maidford
1920	1940	1870	1920	104124	WAR	Leamington
DUNKOIN						
1830	1992	1800	1992	152528	LND	???
DUNLOP						
1820	1887	ALL	1820	146757	AYR	Ayr
1700	1724	....	....	171654	AYR	Dunlop
1832	1992	....	....	144088	AYR	Stewarton
1740	1760	1700	1760	130915	ELN	Dirleton
1824	1940	1750	1825	126535	HAM	Portsmouth
1824	....	ALL	1824	169919	RFW	Courock
DUNMALL						
1889	1971	1750	1889	168025	KEN	Chislehurst
DUNMAN						
....	....	ALL	ALL	177857	ALL	Name Study
DUNMILL						
1804	1826	ALL	1804	146986	KEN	Maidstone
DUNMO						
1803	1992	1800	1900	166960	KEN	Bromley
DUNMORE						
....	....	ALL	ALL	121266	ALL	Name Study
all	ALL	ALL	ALL	121266	ALL	ALL
....	....	1850	1900	134546	BDF	Dean
1738	1759	1700	1760	171654	ESS	Mundon
1810	1860	1700	1810	172847	LEI	Buckminster
1810	1860	1700	1810	172847	LEI	Walton On The Wolds
1930	....	1930	....	162663	LIN	Gunby
1728	1955	1700	1955	170143	NTH	Broughton
1728	1955	1700	1955	170143	NTH	Burton Latimer
1728	1955	1700	1955	170143	NTH	Walgrave
1840	1880	....	....	172847	NTT	Nottingham
1763	1787	ALL	1992	102245	WAR	Stivichall
DUNMOW						
....	....	ALL	ALL	100250	ALL	Name Study
1837	1980	ALL	ALL	100250	ALL	ALL
DUNN						
1790	1890	1750	1850	111821	AGY	Dunoon
1831	1831	1831	1831	145580	ANS	Dundee
1760	1830	1700	1850	154881	ANT	ALL
1900	1905	ALL	1992	163821	AVN	Bedminster
ALL	1900	ALL	1992	163821	AVN	Bristol
1840	1851	1800	1860	116114	BRK	Windsor
1809	1815	1800	1830	126705	CHS	Crappenhall
1738	1858	....	....	138851	CHS	Davenham
1750	1789	1650	1750	150614	CHS	Leftwich
1770	1860	1700	1900	146803	CLK	Alloa
1800	....	?	?	136999	CON	Gwinear
1730	1750	1700	1992	133450	CON	Helston
1729	1837	1650	1730	121312	CON	Illogan
1729	1837	1650	1730	121312	CON	Redruth
1837	1960	1837	1920	121312	CON	Truro
1820	1870	1800	1870	124605	DBY	Derby
1772	1992	....	....	144053	DEV	ALL
1842	1871	1800	1842	176869	DEV	Burliscombe
1810	1992	1500	1800	121282	DEV	Putford
1810	1992	1500	1800	121282	DEV	West Woolfardisworth
1840	1992	1790	1840	101788	DOW	Greyabbey
1845	1876	1845	1876	130990	DUR	Durham
1844	....	1840	....	156191	DUR	Framwellgate Moor
....	....	1960	1992	111341	ESS	Dagenham
1815	1823	1800	1825	113611	EYK	Hull
1858	1992	1600	1858	172332	EYK	Hull
1789	1820	ALL	1795	113611	EYK	Skirlaugh
1827	1871	ALL	1871	104299	GLS	Bristol
1884	1992	1700	1884	172944	HAM	Portsmouth
1700	1900	1660	1900	121274	KEN	East
1803	1882	1795	1900	121274	KEN	Canterbury
1790	1800	1750	1830	105120	KEN	Chatham
1850	1897	1845	1950	118737	KEN	Chatham

Known From	To	Researching From	To	Ref	Cty	Place
DUNN contd.						
....	1862	1750	1862	121010	KEN	Chatham
1760	1881	1760	1900	121274	KEN	Deal
1790	1992	ALL	1992	132055	KEN	Dover
1789	1847	1700	1789	161225	KEN	Folkestone
1732	1790	1732	1800	121274	KEN	Northbourne
1790	1820	1700	1850	159964	KKD	Kirkpatrick Durham
1869	1875	1860	1885	126705	LAN	Manchester
1904	1950	1850	1904	145254	LAN	Manchester
1750	1800	1600	1800	152404	LAN	Manchester
1833	1833	1830	1850	126705	LAN	Preston
1863	1900	1860	1930	121274	LAN	Warington
1809	1815	1800	1830	126705	LAN	Warrington
1800	1840	1700	1800	116106	LIN	Brant Broughton
1808	....	1750	1820	100390	LKS	West Kilbride
....	1914	ALL	ALL	130818	LND	Peckham Rye
1840	1870	1840	1950	116114	MDX	Hammersmith
1881	1950	1870	1992	116114	MDX	Old Brentford
1800	1830	1800	1830	138894	MDX	Stepney
1832	1963	1813	1929	153176	NBL	Tynemouth
1730	1870	....	....	155853	NFK	North
....	....	1700	1850	140627	NFK	Trowse
1800	1880	1800	1880	155764	NTH	???
1800	1880	1800	1880	155764	OXF	???
1700	1970	1700	1992	121320	PER	Auchterarder
1844	....	....	....	102733	SAL	???
1844	1951	1820	1844	118133	SCT	Glasgow
1800	1980	1700	1800	126322	SFK	Alderton
1772	1992	....	....	144053	SOM	ALL
1850	1945	ALL	1992	163821	SOM	Taunton
....	1843	....	1843	140767	WOR	Dudley
1777	1790	1750	1820	123404	WOR	Inkberrow
?	?	ALL	1850	117919	WOR	Old Swinford
1790	1860	1750	1790	155810	YKS	Bedale
1730	1800	1700	1800	105449	YKS	Beeford
....	....	1600	1740	174858	YKS	Hunmanby
1800	1865	1800	1900	105449	YKS	North Frodingham
1850	1850	1840	1860	126705	YKS	Rotherham
1850	1948	1800	1850	128368	YKS	Sheffield
1702	1730	1600	1730	105449	YKS	Skipsea
1740	1798	....	....	174858	YKS	Thwing
1680	1700	1650	1992	114901	YKS	Wheldrake
1900	1992	1800	1900	101788	???	Glasgow
1833	1992	1750	1833	101893	???	Maryborough
DUNNACHIE						
1860	1900	1700	1960	124931	LKS	Glasgow
DUNNE						
1860	1960	1840	1860	121339	DUR	Darlington
1870	1910	1800	1900	147079	IRL	Dublin
....	....	1700	1860	121339	IRL	???
1850	1897	1845	1950	118737	KEN	Chatham
1856	....	ALL	ALL	172057	OFF	Killourney
DUNNELL						
1740	1814	ALL	ALL	104531	NFK	Weston Longville
DUNNET						
1821	1992	....	1821	115355	CAI	Canisbay
DUNNETT						
....	1798	ALL	1860	127000	CAI	Canisbay
1800	1992	1600	1800	164461	SFK	North East
....	....	1700	1900	140627	SFK	Cookley
1788	1867	ALL	1867	156175	SFK	Shotley
DUNNICLIFFE						
....	....	ALL	ALL	121347	ALL	Name Study
DUNNILL						
1785	1860	1785	1860	140767	YKS	Leeds
1785	1860	1785	1860	140767	YKS	York
DUNNING						
1830	1920	1600	1830	155497	DEV	Throwleigh
1800	1950	1700	1800	155497	DEV	Wonson
1790	1790	1750	1830	105333	HAM	Isle Of Wight
1860	1895	1850	1860	153842	LND	Kensington
1768	....	ALL	1768	119326	NRY	Brafferton
....	....	1800	1850	108510	SAL	Dawley
1804	1841	1700	1804	153842	WIL	Chapmanslade
1768	....	....	....	158895	WIL	Corsham
1828	1828	....	1828	113034	YKS	Farndale
1800	1900	1800	1992	139203	YKS	York
DUNNINGHAM						
1871	1897	1750	1992	137863	ABD	Aberdeen
DUNNINGTON						
1800	1850	....	....	144029	YKS	Sheffield
DUNSBEE						
1795	....	1800	1850	102016	MDX	???
DUNSBY						
....	....	....	....	141720	DOR	???
....	....	....	....	141720	HAM	???
DUNSCOMBE						
1800	1900	ALL	ALL	121363	DEV	East
DUNSDON						
1846	....	1840	1850	163775	SRY	Newington
DUNSTALL						
....	....	ALL	ALL	121371	ALL	Name Study
DUNSTAN						
1790	1825	ALL	ALL	140902	ABD	Ellon
1840	1900	....	....	130230	CMA	Ulverstone
1820	1948	1700	1900	168068	CON	Lelant
1850	1860	1810	1900	173835	CON	Mylor Bridge
1826	1960	1700	1826	130230	CON	Perran Ar Worthal
....	....	1800	1992	122076	CON	Redruth
1826	1960	1700	1826	130230	CON	Redruth
1820	1948	1700	1900	168068	CON	St Ives
1826	1960	1700	1826	130230	CON	Stithians
....	....	1800	1992	122076	CON	Truro
DUNSTER						
ALL	1724	....	....	105368	SOM	Ilminster
1868	1954	1830	1900	143677	SRY	Bermondsey
DUNSTONE						
1791	1844	1700	1791	148938	GLS	Evercreech
DUNT						
1776	1820	ALL	....	172812	BRK	ALL
DUNTHORN						
1762	1840	....	1762	100064	SFK	Lidgate
DUNTHORNE						
....	....	1700	1992	140627	NFK	Norwich
DUNTHORPE						
1852	1952	1700	1851	131245	NFK	Norwich
DUNTON						
1707	1814	1650	1850	109290	NFK	Central
DUNVILLE						
1840	1900	ALL	ALL	121428	CHS	ALL
DUPERRON						
1810	1849	ALL	1810	179345	LND	Marylebone
DUPRE						
1705	1774	1650	1705	101222	LND	East
DUPUIS						
1780	1900	1750	1900	176281	LND	Westminster
DUR						
1850	1886	1886	1992	117625	DUR	Darlington
DURAN						
1725	1992	....	1725	174076	OXF	Steeple Aston
DURANT						
1820	1860	1750	1860	174912	DEV	North Tauton
....	....	1500	1870	137472	KEN	Chatham
....	....	1500	1870	137472	KEN	Gillingham
....	....	1500	1870	137472	KEN	Rochester
DURBAN						
1798	1817	....	....	101028	MDX	London
1798	1817	....	....	101028	MDX	Stepney
DURBRIDGE						
....	....	ALL	ALL	174637	ALL	Name Study
1600	1800	ALL	ALL	174637	ALL	ALL
DURCAN						
....	1874	....	....	146811	WYK	Halifax
DURDALE						
1700	1750	1600	1700	156795	DOR	East
DURE						
....	....	1800	....	140082	DEV	Stokenham
DUREL						
1620	1620	ALL	ALL	115126	CHI	ALL
DURELL						
....	....	1860	1895	115061	ESS	Leytonstone
....	....	1820	1890	115061	LND	Poplar
....	....	1820	1890	115061	LND	Stepney
....	....	1800	1880	115061	SRY	Camberwell
....	....	1800	1880	115061	SRY	Peckham
DURHAM						
....	....	ALL	ALL	121479	ALL	Name Study
1580	1850	1750	1850	121479	LAN	Fylde
1800	1900	1780	1820	121479	LAN	Liverpool
1680	1705	ALL	....	104515	LIN	Sedgebrook
1800	1992	1800	1992	121460	LND	Westminster
1800	1850	1807	1843	121444	MDX	London
....	....	1750	1850	121479	NIR	Antrim
1799	1892	1700	1799	150150	SYK	Wakefield
1870	1930	1700	1950	121452	YKS	Castleford
1800	....	1700	....	134589	YKS	Hemingbrough
1870	1930	1700	1950	121452	YKS	Selby

Known From	To	Researching From	To	Ref	Cty	Place
DURKEE						
....	....	ALL	ALL	129674	ALL	Name Study
DURKIN						
1762	1793	ALL	ALL	128449	WOR	Coventry
DURLING						
1831	1892	....	....	133248	PEM	Pembroke Dock
DURMAN						
....	....	1800	1910	160342	DOR	Weymouth
1800	1850	1700	1800	171182	HAM	Ringwood
1830	1870	....	....	171182	SSX	Midhurst
DURNFORD						
?	?	?	?	121185	DOR	South
1767	1789	1700	1800	163562	SOM	Castle Cary
....	....	1700	1774	130184	WIL	Upton Scudamore
DURNO						
1850	1900	....	....	148342	ABD	Huntly
DUROSE						
1891	1992	?	1900	164976	DBY	Borrowash
1850	1992	1700	1850	109894	STS	Uttoxeter
DURRAN						
1762	1847	1762	1847	149403	OXF	Steeple Aston
1725	1992	....	1725	174076	OXF	Steeple Aston
DURRANS						
1782	....	....	1782	101761	WRY	Kirkheaton
1866	1992	1500	1866	132233	YKS	Huddersfield
1715	1753	1660	1720	170348	YKS	Mirfield
DURRANT						
1765	1800	1500	1765	137170	BKM	Great Brickhill
1720	1760	1700	1760	103764	BKM	Marsh Gibbon
1800	1891	1700	1900	122181	BKM	Wendover
1740	1780	ALL	1740	115266	DOR	ALL
1667	....	....	....	153397	HAM	Boldre
1900	1930	1700	1900	147893	HAM	Gosport
1730	1780	1550	1730	150843	NFK	Caister On Sea
1730	1992	1730	1992	128384	NFK	Gt Yarmouth
1730	1992	1730	1992	128384	NFK	Norwich
....	....	....	1850	160601	NFK	Norwich
1850	1960	ALL	ALL	162469	SFK	North
1725	1754	1725	1754	121487	SFK	Elmswell
1777	1992	1777	1992	121487	SFK	Hadleigh
1781	1781	....	....	127426	SFK	Hadleigh
1575	1725	ALL	1600	121487	SFK	Hessett
1575	1725	ALL	1725	121487	SFK	Hitcham
1850	1900	1700	1850	130389	SOM	Milbourne Port
1840	1900	1700	1900	113859	SRY	Walworth
1800	1860	ALL	1800	131849	SSX	East
1920	1992	....	....	122130	SSX	Buxted
1741	1794	....	1741	129771	SSX	Chiddingly
1870	1880	....	....	122130	SSX	East Hoathly
1916	1920	....	....	122130	SSX	Framfield
1780	1930	....	....	122130	SSX	Waldron
1800	1860	ALL	1800	131849	SSX	Waldron
DURSLEY						
1832	1875	ALL	1900	104299	GLS	Bristol
1811	....	ALL	1850	104299	SOM	Nailsea
1898	1941	1800	1992	167045	???	Bristol
DURSTON						
1800	1960	1700	1800	103675	SOM	ALL
1730	1930	1700	1730	101427	SOM	Central
1690	....	1705	1850	159913	SOM	Catcott
DUSART						
1850	1900	1850	1900	132683	CHS	Altrincham
DUSSEE						
1760	1911	1760	1992	141267	MDX	Spitalfields
DUSTAN						
1790	1825	ALL	ALL	140902	ABD	Ellon
1700	1881	....	....	159751	DEV	Inwardleigh
DUSTIN						
1820	1850	1700	1820	158046	HAM	Portsea
DUTCH						
1788	1945	ALL	ALL	173673	ALL	ALL
1841	1920	1800	1992	121495	DOR	Sixpenny Handly
1750	1900	1700	1900	121495	WIL	Salisbury
DUTFIELD						
....	....	1751	1800	138339	WOR	Pershore
DUTHIE						
ALL	ALL	ALL	ALL	126896	ABD	Buchan
DUTTON						
1719	1834	1650	1719	150614	CHS	Hatton
1700	1845	....	....	160385	DBY	???
1845	1951	....	....	160385	LAN	Manchester
1815	1992	ALL	1815	136875	LND	Islington
1780	1861	....	....	160385	NTT	Gotham
....	....	1700	1900	122424	STS	North

Known From	To	Researching From	To	Ref	Cty	Place
DUTTON contd.						
1760	1860	1600	1900	133590	STS	Sedgley
1760	1860	1600	1900	133590	STS	Tipton
....	1700	....	....	174564	STS	???
1798	1798	1700	1800	124974	WAR	Barford
1815	1992	ALL	1815	136875	WOR	Dudley
1700	1880	1500	1700	169986	WOR	Kings Norton
....	1867	1750	1992	166197	WOR	Netherton
1700	1880	1500	1700	169986	WOR	Northfield
....	....	1800	1900	129046	WYK	Huddersfield
1726	1747	1700	1992	114901	YKS	Huddersfield
DUVAL						
1600	1900	....	....	116998	LND	Spitafield
DUVALL						
1797	1862	ALL	1797	161500	MDX	Fulham
1797	1862	ALL	1797	161500	MDX	Westminster
DUVIVIER						
1740	1760	1700	1992	167592	LND	Chelsea
1740	1760	1700	1992	167592	MDX	London
1780	1800	1700	1992	167592	STS	Newcastle Under Lyme
1780	1800	1700	1992	167592	STS	Stone
1760	?	1700	1992	167592	WOR	Worcester
DUXBURY						
....	....	ALL	ALL	121517	ALL	Name Study
1800	1992	1700	1800	121509	LAN	Accrington
1800	1992	1700	1800	121509	LAN	Colne
1700	1850	ALL	1750	102172	LAN	Darwen
1750	1900	1750	1900	125237	LAN	Darwen
1800	1880	1880	1992	162256	LAN	Darwen
1740	1992	1700	1740	121509	LAN	Simonstone
1600	....	1600	....	109347	YKS	Gisburn
DWYER						
1854	1992	1800	1854	113166	COR	???
DYALL						
....	....	ALL	ALL	155284	ALL	Name Study
1840	1900	1800	1900	142875	IRL	Cavan
DYBALL						
1842	1970	ALL	1842	160733	LEI	Asby De La Zouch
1687	1780	ALL	1800	156310	NFK	Central
1801	1849	1800	1850	123404	NFK	Buxton
DYCHE						
1886	1931	1700	1886	109223	STS	Burton On Trent
DYE						
1840	1900	1800	1840	176257	CAM	Oakington
1854	....	1700	1854	117927	LND	Blackfriars
....	....	ALL	ALL	127175	NFK	Central
1800	1992	ALL	ALL	127175	NFK	West
1817	1900	1700	1900	141127	SFK	Belton
DYER						
1630	1660	1600	1750	121533	BKM	Chesham
1700	1760	....	....	167797	BKM	Marsworth
1880	....	....	....	163392	BRK	Reading
1800	1900	1800	1920	162760	CON	Cambourn
1867	1889	1800	1900	121541	CON	North Hill
1813	1838	1700	1813	163953	DEV	Beer & Seaton
1800	....	1840	1880	135429	DEV	Exmouth
1726	1844	1844	1846	121584	DEV	Plympton
1737	1750	1680	1737	117471	DOR	North West
....	....	1700	1992	122009	ESS	East
1870	1930	1700	1900	140171	ESS	Braintree
1789	1814	1700	1900	178322	GLS	Ashton Under Hill
1770	1860	1600	1860	154342	GLS	Bristol
1725	1725	1695	1770	179337	GLS	Westerleigh
1900	1992	....	....	137200	GLS	Yate
1700	1920	1650	1920	121533	HAM	Alton
1750	1820	1700	1820	167088	HAM	Kingsclere
1782	1796	ALL	1782	131881	HAM	Portsmouth
1700	1760	....	....	167797	HRT	Tring
....	....	1600	1950	134546	IOW	Brading
1700	1900	1600	1700	121592	IOW	Carisbrooke
....	....	1600	1950	134546	IOW	Carisbrooke
1673	1715	1600	1673	162701	IOW	Niton
1865	1890	1890	1992	162701	IOW	Ryde
1667	1787	....	....	164631	KEN	Goudhurst
1884	1900	1861	1863	156639	LND	ALL
1800	1900	....	....	116998	LND	Bermondsey
1800	1860	....	....	132225	LND	East End
1890	1920	1890	1992	121533	LND	Maida Vale
1890	1920	1890	1992	121533	LND	Putney
1790	1992	1680	1992	121568	SOM	Thurloxton
1900	1920	1700	1910	135887	SRY	Thornton Heath
1820	1900	ALL	1900	151017	SSX	Brighton
1700	1900	....	....	116998	WIL	Boyton

Known From	To	Researching From	To	Ref	Cty	Place
DYER contd.						
1818	1870	1800	1870	158658	WIL	Holt
1790	1820	1750	1820	158658	WIL	Westbury
1826	....	1700	1826	150223	WIL	Wilton
1737	1770	ALL	1737	158445	WIL	???
....	....	ALL	ALL	121576	YKS	Hessle
....	....	ALL	ALL	121576	YKS	Selby
DYKE						
1891	1891	....	....	148334	DOR	Wimborne
1850	1890	1700	1850	171980	SOM	Bridgwater
....	....	1700	1780	121592	SOM	Castle Cary
....	....	1600	1992	137588	SOM	Somerton
1800	1900	1700	1800	121592	SOM	Wincanton
....	....	1600	1992	137588	SOM	Yeovil
1841	1861	....	....	138541	STS	Bilston
....	....	....	....	141054	STS	Black Country
1861	1950	....	1861	138541	STS	Walsall
1835	1900	1500	1835	153494	WAR	Warwick
1871	1909	ALL	ALL	143316	WIL	Bishops Cannines
....	....	....	....	141054	WOR	Black Country
DYKES						
....	....	1800	1900	142417	DUR	Jarrow
1853	1992	1600	1992	172863	YKS	York
DYMENT						
....	....	ALL	1800	155470	SOM	Bridgwater
DYMOCK						
1781	1838	1700	1800	163562	LND	Marylebone
DYMOKE						
1300	1900	ALL	ALL	110477	LIN	Scrivelsby
1300	1900	ALL	ALL	110477	LIN	Tetford
DYMOND						
1860	1950	1820	....	126403	CON	Launceston
1851	1868	1800	1900	121541	CON	North Hill
1865	1900	1790	1865	140880	ESS	Theydon Garnon
DYNES						
1864	1873	1800	1864	171662	ARM	Tartaraghan
DYSON						
1620	1900	ALL	ALL	121614	ALL	ALL
....	1823	1750	1850	100048	ESS	Mountnessing
1900	1960	....	....	149721	ESS	Sible Hedingham
1888	1888	1800	1888	108715	LAN	Crompton
1888	1888	1800	1888	108715	LAN	Oldham
1700	1992	....	....	121606	LAN	Oldham
1800	1920	1700	1800	178969	LND	North
1828	1992	....	....	116416	LND	Stepney
1808	1945	1700	1808	109657	SFK	Clare
1560	1900	ALL	ALL	121614	WAR	ALL
1785	1960	ALL	1785	117048	WAR	Birmingham
1540	1992	ALL	ALL	121614	WOR	ALL
1800	1840	1700	1800	110531	WYK	Highburton
1825	1903	....	....	160253	WYK	Holme
1850	1882	1750	1850	110531	WYK	Kirkburton
1360	1800	ALL	ALL	121614	YKS	ALL
1734	1873	1600	1881	166952	YKS	Denby
....	....	1800	1860	102008	YKS	Halifax
1805	1865	1650	1805	168513	YKS	Halifax
1800	1992	1700	1800	132241	YKS	Huddersfield
1799	1900	1650	1824	168513	YKS	Huddersfield
1807	....	1700	1900	174408	YKS	Huddersfield
1800	1992	1800	1820	132241	YKS	Saddleworth
....	....	1901	1925	109657	YKS	Sheffield
1734	1873	1600	1881	166952	YKS	Skelmanthorpe
1805	1954	ALL	1805	158445	YKS	Skidby
1758	....	1730	1750	170348	YKS	Slaithwaite
DYTCH						
?	?	1800	ALL	117919	WAR	Birmingham
DYTE						
1790	1992	....	1790	159972	SOM	Milverton
EACHUS						
....	....	ALL	ALL	121649	ALL	Name Study
EACOTT						
1850	....	1800	1900	142549	WIL	ALL
1779	1828	....	....	124672	WIL	Swindon
EACRET						
....	....	1650	1800	121657	LEX	Bally Brittus
EADE						
1800	1900	1500	1800	136972	CON	Breage
1660	1850	1660	1850	150126	CON	Breage
1800	1900	1500	1800	136972	CON	Germoe
1660	1850	1660	1850	150126	CON	Germoe
1674	1992	ALL	1674	137553	CON	Trigg Minor
1800	1955	....	....	177687	ESS	Colchester
1882	1992	ALL	1882	161608	LND	City
1790	1800	1700	1900	135496	NFK	Norwich
EADE contd.						
1797	1951	....	1797	101761	SFK	Blythborough
1600	1700	ALL	ALL	132276	SFK	Peasenhall
1700	1730	ALL	ALL	132276	SFK	Westleton
1814	1830	1700	1814	150614	SFK	Westleton
1730	1960	ALL	ALL	132276	SFK	Yoxford
1840	1880	ALL	ALL	171301	SRY	West
....	1946	....	1881	119849	SRY	London
1731	1911	ALL	ALL	125873	SRY	Tilford
1820	1960	....	....	122130	SSX	Buxted
1744	1797	?	1744	121665	SSX	Framfield
1820	1960	....	....	122130	SSX	Framfield
1770	1805	1600	1770	147885	SSX	Wnelsfield
EADEN						
1738	1910	1650	1930	112089	CAM	Cambridge
EADES						
1750	1910	ALL	ALL	164143	DBY	Baslow
1750	1910	ALL	ALL	164143	DBY	Calver
1860	1960	....	....	139971	SFK	Ipwswich
1733	1750	1690	1780	160873	STS	Darlaston
1550	1773	1550	1683	102830	STS	Sedgely
1670	1780	1650	1830	160873	STS	Sedgley
EADIE						
1795	1795	1760	1830	141046	LKS	Glasgow
1830	1862	1800	1890	141046	PER	Dunblane
EADON						
1800	1910	1700	1800	121673	WAR	Long Itchington
1662	1800	1660	1800	149152	YKS	Ecclesfield
1800	1900	1800	1992	149152	YKS	Sheffield
1750	1800	....	....	102946	YKS	Welphenley
EADSON						
1770	1860	1800	1900	121460	LND	Westminster
1840	1860	....	....	121444	MDX	London
EADY						
1800	1960	1500	1800	153230	NTH	Barnack
1742	1813	1742	1813	130222	NTH	Burton Latimer
1813	1916	1813	1935	130222	NTH	Little Harrowden
EAGER						
1800	1899	....	....	121835	NFK	Kings Lynn
1805	....	....	....	121835	SSX	Brighton
EAGERS						
1782	....	....	1992	121681	LEI	???
1810	1900	....	1810	114812	MEA	???
1782	....	....	1992	121681	WEM	???
....	1980	1782	1992	121681	???	Sheffield
EAGLE						
1812	1840	1750	1812	147710	KEN	Appledore
1830	1950	1600	1880	101834	NFK	South West
1800	1992	1700	1800	121703	NTH	Desborough
1770	1850	1700	1770	111945	SFK	Peasonhall
....	....	....	....	162744	YKS	Leeds
EAGLES						
....	....	ALL	ALL	121738	ALL	Name Study
1759	1867	1759	1867	121738	BRK	Brightwalton
1936	1992	1936	1992	121738	BRK	Reading
1867	1920	1867	1920	121738	HAM	Winchester
1841	1890	1700	1841	121711	KEN	ALL
1678	....	....	1700	171441	KEN	Hollingbourne
1841	1871	1871	1992	121711	KEN	Loose
1840	1864	1840	1870	154067	LND	Hackney
1896	1992	1840	1896	121711	LND	Lambeth
1825	1840	ALL	1840	154067	LND	Marylebone
1900	1992	1800	1900	121711	LND	Walworth
1794	1841	ALL	1800	154067	LND	Westminster
EAGLESFIELD						
1802	1850	1600	1900	135968	LEI	Great Dalby
EAKIN						
1800	1992	1700	1992	121746	LND	Tirglassan
....	....	ALL	1700	121746	SCT	???
EALES						
....	....	ALL	ALL	171816	BKM	Wolverton
1760	1850	ALL	ALL	171816	NTH	ALL
1737	1900	....	....	153583	NTH	Bugbrooke
1737	1737	ALL	ALL	171816	NTH	Long Buckby
1900	1950	ALL	ALL	171816	WAR	Birmingham
EALEY						
1837	1865	1866	1900	122408	ENG	ALL
1837	1865	1866	1900	122408	WLS	ALL
EAMER						
1862	....	1840	1860	175684	HAM	ALL
EAMES						
1793	1856	ALL	ALL	121754	BKM	Ellesborough
1787	1840	1650	1825	121754	BKM	Stoke Mandeville
1845	1880	ALL	ALL	121754	BKM	Wendover

Known From	To	Researching From	To	Ref	Cty	Place
EAMES contd.						
1850	1992	1800	1992	161640	DEV	Totnes
1763	1846	1700	1763	172871	HRT	Rickmansworth
1800	1858	....	....	162833	LEI	Glooston
1780	1840	1700	1900	135542	SOM	Ilminster
1725	1827	1600	1827	106313	SSX	Midhurst
EARDLEY						
1801	1880	1760	1880	130621	CHS	Bunbury Over
....	....	1750	1781	149977	STS	Central
1781	....	....	....	149977	STS	Sandon
1700	1899	....	....	147575	???	???
EARDNEY						
1300	1400	1250	1400	154881	LAN	Rougham
EARELL						
1772	1823	ALL	1772	114987	DEV	Torquay
EARESS						
1760	1840	ALL	ALL	159107	NFK	Upwell
EARL						
1854	1992	1700	1854	121770	ALL	ALL
1814	....	1700	1814	170321	DEV	Moretonhampstead
1801	....	1700	1801	170321	DEV	Ogwell
1849	1855	1700	1849	170321	DEV	Shaldon
1730	1754	1600	1754	168637	HAM	Kingsley
1792	1875	1790	1875	144355	KEN	South
1736	....	....	1760	171441	KEN	Canterbury
?	?	?	?	166642	KEN	Folkestone
1800	1950	1790	1950	115797	KEN	Mid
1850	....	....	....	153982	LAN	Liverpool
1790	1964	1790	1964	157880	NFK	Norwich
1815	1825	1600	1825	102571	NIR	Clone
1736	1813	ALL	1770	101281	NTH	Towcester
1805	1834	....	....	142077	SOM	Barton St David
1750	1900	1750	1900	142077	SOM	Polden Hills
1834	1900	....	....	142077	SOM	Sutton Mallet
EARLAND						
....	....	ALL	ALL	121789	ALL	Name Study
EARLE						
....	1761	....	....	153176	BRK	Sunningwell
1842	1858	1700	1842	111449	DEV	Plymouth
1850	1860	1860	1880	112569	KEN	Mersham
1650	1750	1630	1750	142018	SOM	Norton St Philip
....	1800	....	....	174564	SSX	Bexhill
1752	1752	....	....	139971	SSX	Eastbourne
1792	1890	1700	1792	132764	YKS	Richmond
EARLES						
1695	1829	1590	1840	160601	BRK	Reading
EARLEY						
1724	1992	1600	1724	119148	HAM	South
EARLEY-COOK						
?	?	?	?	103942	HRT	Cheshunt
1797	....	....	....	103942	HRT	Turnford
1836	....	....	....	103942	LND	???
....	1904	....	....	103942	SRY	Cobham
EARLY						
1850	1890	1840	1920	173452	DBY	Chesterfield
1850	1880	1700	1900	173452	GLS	Cheltenham
1900	1992	ALL	ALL	115002	HAM	Gosport
1810	1815	1780	1815	155691	HAM	Ringwood
....	....	1700	1800	173452	MDX	London
1767	1964	1700	1837	128694	WIL	Earlstoke
1767	1964	1700	1837	128694	WIL	Imber
1870	1960	1850	1920	173452	YKS	Rotherham
EARNSHAW						
1829	1869	1500	1829	137979	DBY	Dronfield
1705	1950	1600	1705	128376	DUR	Stanhope
EARP						
1760	1860	1760	1860	105724	STS	Elford
1600	1800	ALL	ALL	150347	WAR	Birmingham
EARTHY						
1741	1969	1700	1969	159581	SFK	Stowmarket
EARWACKER						
1700	1992	ALL	1992	121797	ALL	ALL
EARWAKER						
1500	1992	ALL	1992	121797	ALL	ALL
1850	1900	ALL	ALL	122866	HAM	East
1850	1900	ALL	ALL	122866	SSX	East
EARWICKER						
....	....	ALL	ALL	121797	ALL	Name Study
1500	1992	ALL	1992	121797	ALL	ALL
EARWOOD						
1700	1750	1600	1900	166804	HAM	North
1719	1719	....	....	115606	HAM	Linkenholt
EASEY						
....	....	ALL	ALL	165034	ALL	Name Study
EASEY contd.						
1574	1980	1500	1920	165034	ALL	ALL
EASHIOTT						
1800	1850	1800	1850	134422	SOM	Bristol
EASINGWOOD						
....	....	ALL	ALL	143340	ALL	ALL
EASLICK						
1810	1834	1750	1810	149004	CON	Fowey
EASON						
1846	1992	ALL	ALL	112240	KEN	Sittingbourne
1788	1806	1550	1800	147265	LIN	South
1875	1992	ALL	ALL	112240	YKS	Middlesbrough
EASSON						
1850	....	ALL	ALL	130508	FIF	St Monance
EAST						
....	....	ALL	ALL	121800	ALL	Name Study
1600	1900	ALL	1600	121800	ALL	ALL
1751	1751	1600	1899	112631	BKM	Amersham
1820	1950	1600	1820	112828	BKM	Chesham
1798	1822	1700	1798	167452	BKM	High Wycombe
1860	1868	1800	1860	117277	ESS	Barking
1796	1856	1700	1860	151106	LAN	Blackburn
1800	1992	....	....	176125	LIN	Asterby
1786	1815	1700	1800	162396	LIN	Fiskerton
1800	1992	....	....	176125	LIN	Goulceby
1800	1860	1800	1860	155764	LIN	Louth
1800	1840	1600	1800	107565	OXF	Benson
1900	1940	1900	1940	176176	OXF	Shiplake
....	1719	ALL	1719	130079	OXF	Somerton
1630	1735	....	1630	136212	OXF	Somerton
EASTAUGH						
1841	1898	1838	1841	121819	LND	East
1851	1900	1850	1900	121827	LND	Deptford
1851	1900	1850	1900	121827	LND	Walworth
1793	1992	1700	1800	121819	NFK	Norwich
1800	....	1800	1900	121827	SFK	Darsham
1826	1851	1795	1826	121827	SFK	Yoxford
EASTAWAY						
1650	1750	1650	1850	147575	DEV	Ilfracombe
1750	1850	1750	1850	147575	SWL	???
EASTER						
....	....	1800	1880	113514	DUR	Ferryhill
1860	1992	....	....	113514	EYK	Hull
1690	1750	....	....	132756	NBL	ALL
1690	1750	....	....	132756	NBL	Hartburn
....	....	1800	1850	132985	NFK	Felmingham
1800	1899	....	....	121835	NFK	Gaywood
1800	1899	....	....	121835	NFK	Kings Lynn
EASTERBROOK						
1873	1992	1700	1873	141143	CON	St Agnes
1785	1860	1700	1785	119164	DEV	Crediton
EASTERLING						
....	....	ALL	ALL	121843	ALL	Name Study
EASTES						
1797	1832	....	1880	171441	KEN	Cheriton
1797	1852	....	1880	171441	KEN	Northbourne
EASTGATE						
?	1759	ALL	1759	171476	NFK	Feltwell
EASTHAM						
1851	1884	1700	1851	141291	LAN	Preston
EASTHO[E						
1722	1823	1750	1823	144460	SAL	Dawley
EASTIN						
1850	1875	1850	1875	107522	WRY	Sheffield
EASTLAKE						
....	....	ALL	ALL	158321	ALL	Name Study
1880	1992	1800	1992	121878	AVN	Bristol
1696	1890	1600	1920	121878	DEV	West
....	....	1700	1825	121886	DEV	Plymouth
EASTLAND						
1718	1718	....	....	121835	LIN	Carlton Le Moorland
....	....	1700	1900	146668	MDX	???
EASTMENT						
1800	1880	....	....	137480	SOM	Bruton
EASTMOND						
1650	1790	1550	1790	166375	DEV	Mariansleigh
EASTON						
1659	1690	1550	1668	118958	CON	???
1900	1950	1800	1900	107530	DEV	Exeter
....	....	1700	1899	174963	DEV	Kingsteighton
1900	....	1871	1920	163775	ESS	Grays
1630	1903	1800	1946	137774	KEN	South East
1780	1800	1700	1780	169749	LIN	Witton
1750	1840	1700	1750	128244	LKS	Lanark

Known From	To	Researching From	To	Ref	Cty	Place
EASTON contd.						
1750	1840	1700	1750	128244	LKS	Lesahagow
1814	1830	1700	1900	149632	MLN	Edinburgh
1800	1900	1800	1900	173533	NTH	South
1826	1877	1780	1877	131792	SCT	???
1800	ALL	....	....	167037	SSX	Hastings
1732	1797	ALL	1800	137774	SSX	Wincelsea
1560	1800	1560	1800	167924	YKS	Pocklington
1835	1992	1804	1992	116319	YKS	Whitby
EASTWICK						
1860	1980	1700	1860	141658	NFK	???
EASTWOOD						
1884	1933	....	....	121894	KEN	Dartford
1840	1904	1800	1840	110515	LAN	Liverpool
1836	1923	1700	1836	126942	LAN	Manchester
1900	1920	1750	1900	147761	LAN	Nelson
1770	1821	1700	....	134686	LAN	Pilkington
1929	1992	1700	1929	121894	SCT	Stenhousemuir
....	1700	....	....	174564	SSX	???
1780	1980	....	1780	121908	WMD	Birmingham
1775	1790	1745	1790	107522	WRY	Todmorden
1780	1900	1780	1900	177288	WYK	Sowerby Bridge
1880	1975	1600	1975	154229	YKS	South
1790	1812	1750	1790	133760	YKS	Huddersfield
1698	1992	1512	1730	170348	YKS	Kirkheaton
....	....	1745	1980	139424	YKS	Saddlesworth
EASUN						
1734	1992	1700	1992	112402	LND	St Pancras
EASY						
1574	1980	1500	1920	165034	ALL	ALL
1800	1822	1750	1850	134627	CAM	Littleport
EATCH						
1870	1992	ALL	1870	136875	YKS	Bradford
EATOCK						
1860	1932	1765	1860	111767	LAN	Westhoughton
EATON						
1728	1750	1700	1775	149152	DBY	Darley Dale
1724	1992	1650	1724	130966	DOR	Wimborne
1849	....	1800	1849	113352	ESS	Pitsea
1811	1815	1780	1810	131245	LEI	Castle Donington
1850	1992	1790	1850	114499	LIN	ALL
....	1895	....	1895	160652	LIN	Grimsby
1800	1980	ALL	ALL	134287	LND	East
1856	....	1700	....	132128	LND	Bethnal Green
1830	....	1700	1850	143693	LND	St Pancras
1780	1840	1780	1840	167924	MDX	Hackney
1764	1840	1764	1840	176958	MDX	London
1830	1870	1830	1870	167924	MDX	Pancras
1836	1902	1750	1836	159158	MDX	Tottenham
1550	1600	1500	1600	154881	SAL	East Aston
1794	1794	1780	1810	131245	STS	Uttoxeter
1764	1840	1764	1840	176958	WLS	Narberth
1800	1900	1700	1800	176516	WYK	Sheffield
EATON-THOMAS						
1812	?	?	?	121916	LIN	???
EATWELL						
....	....	ALL	ALL	176214	ALL	Name Study
1867	1867	1850	1890	152773	WIL	Lyneham
1896	1900	1860	1900	152773	WIL	Swindon
1918	1925	1900	1930	152773	???	Birmingham
1918	1925	1900	1930	152773	???	Ladywood
EAVES						
1794	1800	....	....	129747	ESS	Colne Engaine
1833	1852	....	....	129747	ESS	Great Tey
....	1820	ALL	1820	134511	KEN	Rochester
1870	1910	1800	1870	125350	LAN	Blackpool
1815	1815	1780	1840	118443	LAN	Lytham
EBBINS						
1794	1830	1750	1794	147885	NTH	Luddington
EBBOTT						
....	....	ALL	ALL	121932	ALL	Name Study
1650	1865	1500	1992	121932	CON	Marhamchurch
1650	1865	1500	1992	121932	CON	Morwenstow
1650	1865	1500	1992	121932	CON	Stratton
1650	1865	1500	1992	121932	CON	Tremaine
1650	1865	1500	1992	121932	CON	Tresmeer
EBBUTT						
1610	1992	1800	1992	117110	KEN	Dartford
1850	1992	1600	1850	117110	MID	Bedford
1610	1992	1800	1992	117110	SRY	Epsom
EBDON						
?	?	?	?	100692	DEV	Sidbury
?	?	?	?	100692	GLA	Cardiff
?	?	?	?	100692	MDX	London

Known From	To	Researching From	To	Ref	Cty	Place
EBORALL						
1866	1992	....	....	161284	WOR	Bromsgrove
EBREY						
....	....	1800	1900	144401	SAL	Shrewsbury
ECCLES						
1700	1750	1600	1700	113204	ANT	Belfast
ALL	1880	1250	1900	135429	IRL	Dublin
1750	1900	1750	1900	125237	LAN	Darwen
1800	1880	1880	1992	162256	LAN	Darwen
....	....	1754	1992	121940	LAN	Goosnargh
1843	1894	1700	1992	140066	LAN	Liverpool
1880	1910	1880	1910	135429	LAN	Manchester
ALL	1780	1250	1900	135429	TYR	Ulster
ECCLES-JONES						
....	1944	....	....	173991	CON	Falmouth
....	1944	....	....	173991	CON	Wadbridge
ECCLESHALL						
....	....	ALL	ALL	105260	ALL	Name Study
ALL	ALL	ALL	ALL	105260	ALL	ALL
ECCLESTONE						
1880	1900	1800	1950	135968	LAN	West Derby
ECKERSLEY						
1790	1860	1700	....	162809	LAN	Bolton
1780	1800	1700	1780	155500	LAN	Leigh
1839	1900	....	....	148261	LAN	Manchester
1680	1838	....	....	148261	LAN	Prestwich
1830	1850	1750	1830	123978	LAN	Salford
ECKFORD						
....	....	1750	1900	106607	DUB	ALL
ECLES						
1784	1815	1760	1815	119059	BKM	Brill
ECOPPE						
1550	1700	1550	1800	163015	LIN	Denton
ECRET						
....	....	1600	1800	121657	WAR	???
ECTON						
1800	1900	1800	1900	126640	HAM	New Forest
EDBROOK						
1830	1850	1800	1830	145424	ALL	ALL
EDBROOKE						
1500	1900	1550	1900	153788	ALL	ALL
EDDIE						
1790	1880	1700	1800	106267	KCD	???
EDDISON						
....	....	1700	1885	144452	YKS	Leeds
EDDLESTON						
1867	1960	1867	1878	103586	HAM	Gosport
EDDOLLS						
1780	1960	1600	1780	121959	GLS	South
1850	1920	....	....	121185	WIL	ALL
1720	1770	1700	1800	121959	WIL	West
1878	1970	1800	1891	167045	???	Bristol
EDDOLS						
1800	1900	1760	1900	106801	GLS	St George
EDDY						
1830	1992	1700	1830	129437	CON	Penwith
1834	1992	1834	1992	127248	CON	Penzance
1812	1825	....	....	127248	CON	Sancreed
1700	1726	1600	1700	102571	CON	Zennor
1781	1799	1500	1799	127248	CON	Zennor
1823	1844	1800	1823	128368	DEV	Bickington
1808	....	1600	1835	115525	SOM	Bath
EDE						
1800	1900	1600	1800	158046	CON	East
1674	1992	ALL	1674	137553	CON	Trigg Minor
1895	1988	1850	1895	100943	DBY	Uttoxeter
1807	1807	....	....	152102	SRY	Leigh
....	....	1800	1890	126136	SSX	Bosham
1895	1988	1850	1895	100943	STS	Uttoxeter
EDELSTON						
1800	1900	1700	1800	170739	LAN	Preston
EDEN						
1873	1992	1700	1873	141143	CON	Redruth
1780	1992	1550	1780	151025	GLS	Chipping Campden
1750	1810	1600	1750	108413	GLS	Great Barrington
1780	1850	1780	1850	154377	LND	???
1790	1900	....	1790	159972	WIL	Devizes
1819	1877	1700	1819	171980	???	Bristol
EDENS						
1772	1992	1750	1992	135933	OXF	Charlbury
1772	1992	1750	1992	135933	OXF	Fawler
EDERINGTON						
1799	....	....	....	151351	DBY	St Alkmunds Derby
1802	....	....	....	151351	NTT	Basford

Known From	To	Researching From	To	Ref	Cty	Place
EDEY						
1865	1925	ALL	ALL	102326	SOM	Bath
EDGAR						
....	....	ALL	ALL	147168	ALL	Name Study
1856	1992	1750	1992	176621	DOW	Newtownards
1830	1874	ALL	1885	165301	DUR	South
1861	....	....	....	121851	NBL	Allendale
....	....	ALL	1850	165301	NBL	Newcastle Upon Tyne
1850	1980	1700	1850	150371	ROX	Castleton
EDGCOMBE						
....	....	ALL	ALL	168882	ALL	Name Study
1250	1992	ALL	....	168882	ALL	ALL
EDGE						
1651	1791	....	....	165999	DBY	Derby
1825	1909	1825	1909	173681	DBY	Fough Farm
....	....	1800	1900	101672	DOR	Poole
1850	1858	1800	1850	111821	DUR	Durham
1846	....	1700	1900	152714	LAN	Manchester
1890	1910	1700	1940	152714	NTT	Basford
1897	1910	1700	1940	152714	NTT	Mansfield
....	....	1700	1900	152714	SRY	Carshalton
1869	....	1700	1900	152714	SRY	Southwark
1800	1900	1800	1900	105511	STS	ALL
1900	1950	1700	1900	116777	STS	Stoke On Trent
1839	1900	1839	1900	105511	STS	Waterfall
EDGECOMBE						
1770	1805	1740	1800	124974	BRK	Ashbury
EDGELAR						
1860	1900	ALL	1900	158003	YKS	York
EDGELAW						
1617	1700	ALL	1750	149063	MLN	Newbattle
EDGELEY						
1800	1870	ALL	ALL	106097	NFK	Kings Lynn
....	....	1630	1780	103713	SFK	Wickhambrook
1560	1930	1600	1700	179175	SFK	Wickhambrook
EDGER						
1764	1800	1700	1781	167533	DEV	West Buckland
EDGERLEY						
1750	1992	1700	1800	135496	CHS	Great Budworth
1874	....	1830	1874	128503	STS	Wolverhampton
EDGERTON						
1700	1850	1700	1850	142123	SAL	Baschurch
1650	1750	1600	1750	142123	SAL	Prees
EDGINGTON						
1854	1914	1800	1854	167231	MDX	Westminster
1730	1880	1880	1900	107816	SRY	Guildford
1903	1960	....	....	163287	WAR	Aston Birmingham
1903	1960	....	....	163287	WAR	Erdington
EDGINTON						
1750	1850	1700	1750	171859	WOR	ALL
EDGLEY						
1850	1890	1790	1900	130567	MDX	East London
1790	1840	1790	1900	130567	NTH	Cottingham
EDGWORTH						
1737	1865	1600	1733	100447	GLS	Bibury
EDIE						
1640	1665	1600	1700	153354	CON	Gwennap
EDIS						
1760	1992	1700	1800	115614	GLS	Bristol
1760	1992	1700	1800	115614	GLS	Gloucester
1840	1920	ALL	ALL	162191	NTT	Nottingham
....	....	?	?	148989	???	???
EDITON						
ALL	ALL	ALL	ALL	124206	LND	ALL
EDKINS						
....	....	ALL	ALL	170658	ALL	Name Study
1802	1825	1750	1850	153249	WAR	Alcester
EDLIN						
1860	1890	....	....	162833	LEI	Aylestone Park
1400	1900	ALL	ALL	177571	MDX	ALL
EDLRIDGE						
1788	1826	1700	1850	106313	MDX	Sunbury
EDMANS						
....	....	ALL	ALL	121975	ALL	Name Study
EDMEADES						
1610	1886	1600	1890	174238	KEN	ALL
1771	1886	1600	1890	174238	KEN	Longfield
1820	1860	1800	1900	162345	KEN	Longfieldhill
EDMED						
1836	1859	ALL	1836	146986	KEN	Maidstone
EDMISTON						
1800	1856	1750	1856	148288	FIF	Strathmiglo
EDMOND						
1800	1809	1700	1800	103268	YKS	Bempton
EDMONDS						
....	....	ALL	ALL	159085	ALL	Name Study
1800	1850	1700	1900	138517	BDF	Barton In Clay
1837	1920	1700	1850	135887	BKM	Princes Risborough
1824	1857	ALL	ALL	156884	DOR	Swanage
1837	1881	ALL	ALL	156884	HAM	Sothampton
1847	1929	1700	1847	128465	HEF	ALL
1797	1850	ALL	1797	119105	IRL	Dublin
1880	1950	....	....	124877	KEN	Chatham
1860	....	1860	....	109398	KEN	Milton
....	....	....	1800	121363	KEN	???
1770	1780	ALL	1770	124877	LND	Marylebone
1837	1920	1700	1850	135887	MDX	Holbonr
1780	1850	....	....	124877	SRY	Sutton
1810	1896	1700	1900	125865	STS	ALL
1786	1830	1600	1830	145432	STS	Enville St Mary
EDMONDSON						
1774	1868	1542	1774	141291	LAN	Aldingham
....	....	1650	1750	147613	LAN	Barnoldswick
1820	1854	1800	1820	165026	LAN	Colne
1809	1872	1700	1810	169854	LAN	Furness
1710	1752	1658	1710	141291	LAN	Heysham
....	....	ALL	ALL	178403	YKS	West
....	....	1750	1900	147613	YKS	Skipton
....	....	1720	1800	147613	YKS	Thornton In Craven
EDMONSON						
....	1841	1700	1861	170178	YKS	Giggleswick
EDMUND						
1772	1800	1650	1772	172898	MON	Llanhennock
1828	....	....	....	146536	SCT	???
EDMUNDS						
1760	1830	1700	1850	121274	HAM	Isle Of Wight
1757	1859	1700	1900	111155	LND	Spitalfields
1845	1929	1840	1930	177016	MON	Chepstow
1840	1859	1840	1890	111155	SFK	Sudbury
EDMUNDSON						
1861	1861	1700	1861	170178	CHS	Stockport
EDNAY						
....	....	ALL	ALL	122009	ALL	Name Study
1840	1992	1600	1992	122009	ALL	ALL
EDNEY						
1840	1850	1700	1850	126772	HAM	Havant
EDRIDGE						
1840	1880	?	1840	158569	GLS	???
EDSER						
1600	1800	ALL	ALL	174637	ALL	ALL
....	....	ALL	ALL	174637	SRY	ALL
EDSON						
1843	....	1815	1843	122017	WYK	Leeds
1815	1824	ALL	1815	122017	WYK	Pateley Bridge
....	....	1700	1813	135011	YKS	???
EDWARD						
1802	1909	....	....	135453	ANS	Stracartho
....	....	1780	1850	148210	BAN	Keith
1840	....	1800	1900	139114	WLS	???
EDWARDES						
970	1992	....	....	112445	WLS	Pembroke
EDWARDS						
1821	1821	ALL	1860	132217	AGY	Beaumaris
1802	1909	....	....	135453	ANS	Stracartho
1760	1770	....	....	114723	BDF	Dunstable
1750	1870	1700	1750	133671	BDF	Langford
1750	1850	1850	1960	153486	BDF	Langford
1800	1880	1700	1800	171891	BKM	Chalfont St Peter
1699	1728	1699	1709	107360	BKM	Stony Stratford
1841	1881	1700	1900	122181	BKM	Wendover
1895	....	....	....	136735	BKM	Wolverton
1838	1853	1800	1875	154032	BRE	Brynmawr
1700	1850	....	....	114723	BRK	Lambourne
1806	1806	1750	1820	124974	BRK	Welford
1841	1861	1861	1881	123129	CAE	Aberdaron
1805	1858	1700	1900	145955	CAE	Conwy
1840	1992	1760	1840	138207	CAE	Nefyn
1793	....	1793	1841	123129	CAE	Rhiw
....	....	....	1760	137405	CAM	South
1799	1818	1750	1850	167002	CAM	Cambridge
1850	1900	?	1850	123161	CGN	Aberystwyth
1911	1992	....	....	122157	CGN	Cardigan
1845	1872	1750	1850	179671	CHS	Gt Boughton
1890	1992	1890	1992	122238	CHS	Rockferry
1801	1871	ALL	1800	142034	CMN	Betws
1821	1861	1818	1871	159743	CMN	Myddfai
1788	1812	1780	1815	159743	CMN	Talley
1850	1970	....	....	122165	CON	Bodmin

Known From	To	Researching From	To	Ref	Cty	Place
EDWARDS contd.						
1724	1830	....	....	122165	CON	Breage
1830	1850	....	....	122165	CON	Crowan
1724	1830	....	....	122165	CON	Germoe
1900	1992	?	1900	129615	CON	Pendeen
1776	1776	1700	1776	161837	CON	Redruth
1780	1800	1700	1800	175838	CON	Redruth
1780	1850	1750	1800	117943	CON	Scilly Isles
1840	1850	....	....	122165	CON	St Neot
1827	1895	1700	1857	156051	CON	Uny Lelant
1830	1992	1750	1880	122149	CWD	Llangollen
1698	1968	1500	1698	122092	CWD	Melin Y Coed
1840	1860	1750	1860	139483	DEN	Henllan
1818	1845	1600	1818	118605	DEN	Rossett
1708	1830	1800	1830	170968	DEV	Devonport
....	....	1800	1820	118575	DEV	Instow
1850	1920	1820	1992	175668	DEV	Plymouth
1820	1870	1820	1870	118575	DEV	Tawstock
?	....	1700	1960	123668	DEV	Tiverton
1891	....	....	....	145521	DOR	Bridport
....	....	ALL	ALL	115231	DUR	Jarrow
1890	1992	1890	1992	159689	DUR	Trimdon Grange
1771	1858	ALL	ALL	147621	FLN	Halkyn
1803	1848	....	....	147621	FLN	Holywell
1811	1811	1811	1811	145580	FLN	???
1861	1985	1861	1985	159743	GLA	Aberdare
1785	?	....	....	176559	GLA	Bryncethin
1840	1915	1700	1840	142212	GLA	Merthyr Tydfil
1860	1992	1700	1860	103098	GLA	Swansea
1871	1992	1871	1992	159743	GLA	Swansea
1890	1950	....	....	104272	GLA	Taffs Well
1750	1760	1700	1800	138150	GLS	South
....	....	....	....	141224	GLS	South
1786	1825	ALL	ALL	162434	GLS	Bisley
?	?	....	....	161020	GLS	Bristol
1800	1860	1806	1827	176958	GLS	Bristol
1760	1850	1760	1850	111538	GLS	St Briavles
1830	1900	ALL	ALL	162434	GLS	Tidetiham
1700	....	....	....	176958	GLS	Westbury On Trym
1800	1860	1600	1800	169773	GLS	???
1865	1961	1700	1865	109223	GMP	Newpitsligo
1698	1968	1500	1698	122092	GYN	Melin Y Coed
1804	1992	1800	1992	122122	HAM	Alverstoke
1791	1846	1846	1850	178705	HAM	Swanmore
1800	1950	1800	1950	129151	HEF	Aymestrey
1800	1850	1750	1800	176311	HEF	Hoarwithy
1800	1950	1800	1950	129151	HEF	Pembridge
1800	1950	1800	1950	129151	HEF	Shobdon
1772	1826	1700	1800	102717	HRT	Albury
1791	1855	....	....	116602	HRT	Kelshall
1790	1810	1600	1790	122084	HRT	Rickmansworth
1650	1700	1650	1700	167924	HRT	Willian
1859	....	1700	1992	154474	KEN	Birchington
....	....	1800	1900	166960	KEN	Bromley
1900	1940	1860	1900	139483	LAN	Bootle
1844	1862	....	....	145580	LAN	Liverpool
1750	1800	....	....	129747	LIN	Harmston
1777	....	ALL	....	104515	LIN	Heckington
1700	1992	1600	1700	102342	LIN	South Ormsby
1784	1844	....	....	129747	LIN	Waddington
1861	....	1861	....	135488	LND	South East
1835	1855	1800	1855	160741	LND	Bermondsey
1850	1890	1830	1850	117943	LND	Hackney
1870	ALL	1500	1870	145378	LND	Nunhead
1840	1910	1600	1840	122084	LND	Shoreditch
1850	1890	1830	1850	117943	LND	Stepney
1841	1895	1750	1841	116106	LND	Westminster
1844	....	1700	1992	154474	MDX	Bethnal Green
1830	1992	1800	1830	140317	MDX	Hoxton
1830	1880	1800	1830	140317	MDX	Islington
1815	1850	1750	1850	147958	MDX	Marylebone
1841	1905	1800	1910	155969	MDX	Marylebone
1844	....	1700	1992	154474	MDX	Spitalfields
1843	1854	1800	1860	142921	MGY	Berriew
1840	1915	1700	1840	142212	MON	Cwm
1780	1870	1725	1890	160849	MON	Llandogo
....	1805	1500	1805	175072	MON	Llandrinio
1862	1900	1850	1920	118540	MON	Llantarnam
1784	1924	1700	1784	159735	MON	Shirenewton
....	....	1700	1780	111538	MON	???
....	....	ALL	ALL	133361	NFK	Attleborough
1800	1980	1700	1800	160296	NFK	Coltishall
1850	1900	1850	1992	143529	NFK	Kings Lynn
1800	1980	1550	1800	160296	NFK	Scottow
1700	1850	1780	1850	143529	NFK	Wells Next Sea
1846	1847	ALL	ALL	134120	NFK	Wells
1872	1877	ALL	ALL	134120	NFK	West Lynn
1740	1780	1700	1800	151742	NRY	North York Moors
1810	1810	1790	1840	105120	OXF	Banbury
1911	1992	....	....	122157	PEM	Crymmych
1790	1870	1700	1790	101524	POW	Llanidloes
1700	1905	1500	1992	176877	RAD	Cwmdeuddwr
1860	1900	1860	1900	129151	RAD	Presteigne
....	....	1800	1992	143456	SAL	Cleehill
1747	....	1600	1800	176877	SAL	Clun
1768	....	1700	1800	176877	SAL	Llanfair Waterdine
1840	1870	1800	1860	122238	SAL	Ludlow
1757	1815	1650	1757	139769	SAL	Oswestry
1757	1776	1700	1757	160474	SAL	St Martins
1752	1867	1700	1752	160474	SAL	Welshampton
1820	1848	1600	1848	108197	SFK	Ipswich
....	....	1700	1900	140627	SFK	Sibton
1756	1925	ALL	ALL	153516	SOM	Banwell
1840	1867	1800	1867	151424	SOM	Bath
1756	1925	ALL	ALL	153516	SOM	Wick St Lawrence
1720	1760	1720	1780	159581	SRY	Cranleigh
1896	....	....	....	173932	SRY	Epsom
....	....	1800	1890	155969	SRY	Lambeth
....	....	1800	1890	155969	SRY	Peckham
1910	1940	....	....	122130	SSX	Buxted
1700	1860	1660	1750	103446	SSX	Cuckfield
1750	1900	1650	1750	104914	SSX	East Grinstead
1900	ALL	1500	1900	145378	SSX	Eastbourne
1860	1905	1836	....	145521	SSX	Kymer
....	....	1700	1800	118834	SSX	Pagham
1700	1860	1660	1750	103446	SSX	Pyecombe
1880	1900	....	....	122130	SSX	Ripe
1800	1992	ALL	1800	122130	SSX	Rotherfield
1800	1992	ALL	1800	122130	SSX	Uckfield
1700	1860	1660	1750	103446	SSX	Westmeston
....	1700	....	....	174564	SSX	???
1700	1851	ALL	1700	122106	STS	Newcastle Under Lyme
1750	1992	1558	1750	153427	STS	Stoke On Trent
1782	1877	....	....	138223	STS	Tipton
1752	1867	1700	1752	160474	STS	West Bromwich
1850	1900	....	....	176591	STS	Wolstanton
1772	1992	1700	1772	147850	SXE	Pett
1820	1904	1700	1900	168068	SXW	Horsham
1820	1904	1700	1900	168068	SXW	Roffey
1877	1877	1877	1877	143286	WAR	Aston
1767	1900	1750	1800	102830	WAR	Birmingham
1870	1940	1850	1992	122203	WAR	Birmingham
1800	1900	....	....	112879	WAR	Coventry
1800	1900	1750	1900	112879	WAR	Stoneleigh
1500	1844	1500	1844	102830	WAR	Tanworth
1600	1700	ALL	1700	132950	WIL	Brinkworth
1781	....	1740	1800	155969	WIL	Corsham
1693	1766	1693	1766	131156	WIL	Cricklade
1765	1795	1700	1765	144711	WIL	Hannington
1765	1795	1700	1765	144711	WIL	Highworth
1700	1800	1600	ALL	162434	WIL	Highworth
1816	1850	?	1850	103934	WIL	Trowbridge
1800	....	1800	1850	102016	WLS	North
1853	1900	1700	1853	144614	WLS	Ebbw Vale
1864	1992	1850	1860	140317	WLS	Llangollen
....	?	....	1737	105155	WLS	Llanymynich
1845	1920	1800	1920	133426	WOR	Dudley
1869	1945	1805	1945	122203	???	London
....	....	1800	1850	115142	???	Trevethin
EDWARDSON						
1870	1970	ALL	ALL	122254	LAN	Liverpool
1810	1850	1780	1880	122254	LAN	Newton Le Willows
EDWICKER						
1760	1992	1600	1800	113654	SSX	Lodsworth
1830	1992	1600	1830	113654	SSX	Petworth
EDWORTHY						
ALL	ALL	ALL	ALL	130389	DEV	ALL
1853	1892	1840	1870	131369	DEV	Lampfordcourty
EEDE						
1772	1947	1750	1850	116483	SSX	Bury
EELES						
....	....	ALL	ALL	144770	ALL	Name Study
EELS						
1800	....	1700	....	134589	YKS	Saxton
EELY						
1814	1860	1800	1870	124788	DBY	Wardlow

Known From	To	Researching From	To	Ref	Cty	Place
EFFAMY						
1836	1836	1800	1890	105333	HAM	Isle Of Wight
EFFNER						
1837	1980	ALL	1837	129658	ALL	ALL
EGAN						
....	....	ALL	ALL	122289	ALL	Name Study
1834	....	....	....	144169	IRL	ALL
1840	1875	1800	1900	117781	IRL	Cork
1880	1956	1800	1950	117781	KEN	Greenwich
1880	1956	1800	1950	117781	KEN	Hull
1750	1800	ALL	1992	170909	KIK	Castlecomer
1900	1992	ALL	ALL	122297	LAN	Liverpool
1858	....	....	....	144169	LAN	Liverpool
1876	....	....	....	144169	LAN	Manchester
1900	....	....	....	144169	LAN	Salford
1900	....	....	....	144169	???	Stoke
EGAR						
1648	1940	....	....	128996	CAM	Thornley
EGERTON						
....	....	ALL	ALL	122300	ALL	Name Study
ALL	ALL	ALL	ALL	122300	ALL	ALL
1830	1992	ALL	1830	110000	CHS	Congleton
1725	1890	....	....	132756	OXF	ALL
1725	1890	....	....	132756	OXF	Bicester
1850	1900	1600	1900	142123	SAL	Wem
EGGAR						
1813	1860	1780	1813	162701	HAM	Long Sutton
1780	1806	1806	1813	162701	HAM	Odiham
EGGBEER						
1795	1880	1750	1795	175986	DEV	Ashburton
EGGERS						
1750	1935	1700	1750	165417	???	London
EGGETT						
1760	1895	1770	1992	122319	NFK	Kings Lynn
EGGINS						
1780	1992	ALL	1780	131393	CON	Launceston
1780	1992	ALL	1780	131393	DEV	???
1790	1850	ALL	1850	131393	SSX	Ewhurst
EGGLESTON						
1785	1845	1550	1785	150843	YKS	Ottringham
EGGLETON						
1832	1915	1760	1832	132586	BRK	Buscot
1831	1890	1700	1831	111953	BRK	East Ilsley
1820	1900	1700	1820	113727	HRT	Tring
1815	1870	1600	1900	101834	NFK	West
1750	1846	ALL	1750	167878	WIL	Burbage
....	....	1750	1850	132586	WIL	Highworth
?	?	1650	?	178667	WIL	Marlborough
EGGLISHAW						
1813	1883	....	....	147885	NTT	Selston
EGLESTONE						
1757	....	....	....	151351	NTT	Basford
EGLETON						
1737	1760	ALL	ALL	121754	BKM	Aylesbury
1763	1783	ALL	ALL	121754	BKM	Stoke Mandeville
EGLIN						
1890	1910	1860	1890	142492	LAN	Lancaster
1640	1800	1600	1750	144606	SOM	Odcombe
EGLINTON						
1850	1914	1850	1914	133175	LND	???
1850	1914	1850	1914	133175	???	Easton
EGLISHER						
....	....	1750	1813	147885	DBY	???
EGNY						
....	....	1660	1720	103713	CAM	Waterbeach
EHN						
1781	1992	ALL	ALL	102563	LND	East End
EHRHARDT						
1851	1897	....	....	176125	???	Birmingham
EILES						
1839	1842	1839	1851	147257	SRY	Southwark
EINON						
....	....	ALL	ALL	160857	ALL	Name Study
EITE						
1796	1850	1700	1890	128929	DBY	ALL
1800	1861	1790	1870	122335	NTT	Colston Bassett
1835	1870	1835	1924	122335	NTT	Nottingham
EKINS						
1731	1811	ALL	1992	168718	BDF	North West
1845	1862	ALL	ALL	130664	BDF	Eaton Socon
1845	1862	ALL	ALL	130664	HUN	Eaton Socon
1820	1850	1750	1880	123536	HUN	Great Staughton
1804	1842	ALL	ALL	150886	HUN	Great Staughton

Known From	To	Researching From	To	Ref	Cty	Place
ELAM						
....	....	ALL	ALL	150827	ALL	Name Study
ALL	ALL	ALL	ALL	150827	ALL	ALL
1870	1992	1870	1992	150827	LAN	Liverpool
1867	1923	1697	1900	150827	YKS	Brighouse
1660	1867	1500	1867	150827	YKS	Huddersfield
....	1772	1730	1816	128961	YKS	Leeds
ELAN						
1820	1920	ALL	1900	151017	LND	South
1820	1920	ALL	1900	151017	LND	Hoxton
ELAND						
1100	1910	1670	1850	134007	LIN	Driby
1825	1851	1800	1870	136980	SRY	Bermondsey
1871	1900	1840	1871	142360	YKS	York
ELBOURNE						
1853	1936	....	1853	146072	MDX	Battle Bridge
ELBURN						
1720	1992	1600	1992	112631	BKM	ALL
ELCOAT						
1760	1840	ALL	ALL	106844	DUR	Aycliffe
ELCOCK						
1787	1806	1700	1800	129453	KEN	Woolwich
ELCOMB						
1820	1890	1800	1820	122378	KEN	Hadlow
1820	1890	1800	1820	122378	KEN	Mereworth
1885	1928	....	....	122378	KEN	Ryarsh
ELDEN						
1800	1810	1800	1810	174386	LND	Westminster
ELDER						
1835	1860	1825	1860	122394	ANS	Aberdeen
1825	1900	ALL	1825	117188	ANS	Kingoldrum
1839	1845	ALL	ALL	122386	DUR	Sunderland
1790	1860	1750	1850	122394	FIF	Anstruther
1833	1860	1800	1850	122394	FIF	Pittenweem
1850	1860	1840	1860	122394	MLN	Leith
1826	1992	ALL	ALL	122386	NBL	Newcastle
1836	1992	1836	1893	142840	NBL	Newcastle
ELDERKIN						
1831	1896	ALL	1831	159077	NTH	Oundle
ELDERTON						
1756	1945	....	....	148237	SSX	Chichester
ELDIN						
1786	1851	1700	1786	130990	YKS	Knottingley
ELDRIDGE						
1824	1844	1500	1850	157538	DEV	Plymouth
1830	1880	ALL	1880	100269	KEN	Dover
1850	....	....	1850	164011	KEN	Sheerness
1863	1899	ALL	1899	152641	KEN	Willesborough
1721	1791	1700	1800	105120	MDX	Harmondsworth
....	1884	1858	1884	133639	MDX	Islington
1763	1763	1500	1763	110310	SSX	Battle
1747	1860	1730	1800	177601	SSX	Sedlescombe
ELEMENT						
....	....	1600	1700	149977	HEF	ALL
1813	1916	....	....	136905	HEF	North
1775	1801	....	....	149977	HEF	Eye
1750	1820	....	....	140864	MDX	Edmonton
1750	1820	....	....	140864	MDX	London
....	....	1600	1700	149977	WOR	ALL
1600	1795	1600	1795	136905	WOR	Rochford
1700	1770	....	....	149977	WOR	Rochford
1842	1866	1700	1842	177113	WOR	St Swithin
ELEMES						
1800	1970	1600	1800	160229	WIL	Gastard
ELEMS						
....	....	1750	1850	122661	HAM	Appleshaw
ELENGAM						
1680	1700	1400	1680	178969	HRT	North Church
ELERS						
1700	1740	1700	1992	167592	IRL	Dublin
1680	1690	1650	1992	167592	LND	Fulham
1680	1690	1650	1992	167592	MDX	London
1690	1700	1650	1992	167592	SRY	Vauxhall
1690	1720	1650	1992	167592	STS	Newcastle Under Lyme
1700	?	1650	1992	167592	STS	Uttoxeter
ELEY						
....	....	ALL	ALL	122408	ALL	Name Study
1830	1890	1700	1992	170518	BRK	Coleshill
1537	1900	....	....	122408	DBY	ALL
1812	....	ALL	ALL	138533	DBY	Marston On Dove
1837	1900	1901	1992	122408	ENG	ALL
1870	1950	1840	1900	173630	ESS	Brentwood
1859	1900	1700	1992	170518	WIL	Highworth

Known From	To	Researching From	To	Ref	Cty	Place
ELEY contd.						
1837	1900	1901	1992	122408	WLS	ALL
ELFICK						
1650	1750	ALL	1700	115282	SSX	East
ELFLETT						
1770	1992	1700	1800	138142	NFK	ALL
ELFORD						
1750	1940	1750	1940	173681	BRK	New Hinksey
1767	....	1700	1800	176923	SOM	Kilmersdon
1760	1850	1700	1800	123137	SOM	Limington
ELGAR						
1609	1660	....	....	142522	KEN	Ripple
1713	?	?	?	166642	KEN	Sellinge
ELGIE						
1744	1899	....	....	173916	YKS	Stokesley
ELIAZ						
1897	....	ALL	1897	122572	LND	ALL
ELIMAN						
1734	1788	1719	1800	107360	NTH	Badby
ELIOT						
1460	1560	1400	1580	159581	SRY	Wonersh
1834	1834	1750	1820	102830	WAR	Bickenhill
ELIOTT						
1770	....	....	....	141798	ROX	Stobs
ELISHA						
1756	1824	1824	1851	131768	BRK	Shinfield
ELKIN						
....	....	1851	1871	156833	CHS	Broadbottom
....	....	1851	1871	156833	CHS	Mottram
1860	1992	1700	1870	122424	STS	Stoke Upon Trent
ELKINGTON						
1800	1830	1750	1830	123722	LND	Southwark
1505	....	....	....	101613	OXF	ALL
1882	1960	1800	1882	135364	YKS	Dewsbury
1880	1930	1850	1880	135364	YKS	Tong Street
ELKINS						
1766	....	1600	....	152722	HAM	Breamore
1866	1914	....	....	172871	MDX	Hampstead
1800	1817	1750	1850	144606	MDX	Westminster
1812	1846	1700	1812	172871	WIL	Westbury
ELLA						
....	....	ALL	ALL	122432	ALL	Name Study
1790	1800	1750	1800	169560	YKS	Cottingham
ELLACOMBE						
1800	1900	1750	1992	135429	DEV	ALL
....	....	ALL	ALL	167746	DEV	ALL
ELLACOTT						
1844	....	ALL	ALL	110272	CON	North Petherwin
ELLAM						
1810	1821	....	1810	101761	WRY	Kirkheaton
ELLCOCK						
1800	1880	1800	1880	133086	HRT	???
1650	1800	....	1800	133086	SFK	Barrow
ELLEBY						
1835	1916	1750	1835	178993	DBY	Ashbourne
ELLEN						
1796	....	1700	....	123560	KEN	Bishopsbourne
ELLENDEN						
1775	1825	1800	1825	154903	KEN	Ripple
ELLENGER						
1800	1841	ALL	ALL	111945	SFK	East
ELLERAY						
1701	1992	1701	1992	125172	LAN	Hawkshead
1701	1992	1701	1992	125172	WES	Winster
ELLERBY						
1820	1880	1700	1840	160717	DUR	Sadberge
ALL	ALL	ALL	ALL	160873	NBL	Newcastle On Tyne
1851	1867	ALL	ALL	160873	NBL	Simonburn
1780	1871	ALL	1950	160873	YKS	North Riding
ELLERSHAW						
....	....	1700	1800	147613	YKS	Bentham
1709	1829	....	....	168424	YKS	Bentham
1750	1780	1700	1900	130419	YKS	Clapham
ELLERTON						
1750	1860	1700	1900	178047	LAN	Kendal
ELLERY						
1864	1970	1700	1864	111279	CON	North
1750	....	....	....	114723	CON	Bodmin
1780	....	1700	1992	129348	CON	Egloshayle
1800	1870	1800	1992	129348	CON	Falmouth
1809	1940	?	1809	113360	CON	Perranzabuloe
1800	....	?	?	136999	CON	Quintrell Downs
1777	....	1800	1900	178845	CON	St Breock
1851	1932	1500	1851	173886	CON	St Columb Mincer
ELLERY contd.						
1800	1840	ALL	1850	161292	DOR	Bridport
1826	....	1800	1826	162825	GLA	Swansea
1819	1992	1700	1819	149241	HAM	Southampton
1804	1856	1700	1804	101443	NRY	Lythe
1806	....	1700	1806	101443	NRY	Scalby
1800	1992	1700	1992	177652	WAR	Birmingham
1620	....	1500	....	134589	YKS	Hovingham
ELLET						
1721	1721	....	....	127426	KEN	Canty St Margarets
1840	1916	1800	1930	176982	KEN	Stoke
ELLETT						
1780	1790	1750	1780	133221	DEV	Exeter
1812	1830	....	....	133221	LND	Rotherhithe
ELLEY						
1569	1900	ALL	ALL	134511	NTT	Arnold
ELLICOMBE						
....	....	ALL	ALL	167746	DEV	ALL
ELLICOTT						
1891	1965	ALL	1912	108642	BKM	Amersham
1800	1860	1700	1800	179191	CON	Blisland
1800	1860	1700	1860	179248	CON	Bodmin
1862	1865	ALL	1930	108642	HRT	Northaw
1860	1895	1860	1910	179248	KEN	Plumstead
1860	1900	1860	1920	179191	KEN	Plumstead
1860	1895	1860	1910	179248	KEN	Woolwich
1862	1865	ALL	1930	108642	MDX	Marylebone
1891	1965	ALL	1912	108642	MDX	Southall
ELLIFF						
1850	....	ALL	1880	122459	IRL	ALL
1740	1880	1600	1740	122459	LIN	Boston
ELLIMAN						
1850	1900	1750	1850	146110	WAR	Napton On The Hill
ELLINGFORD						
1800	....	....	....	131822	ESS	Gt Wigborough
ELLINGHAM						
1637	1960	1200	1637	162671	BDF	Egglington
1637	1960	1200	1637	162671	BDF	Stanbridge
1848	....	....	....	140031	WAR	ALL
ELLINGWORTH						
....	....	ALL	ALL	112003	ALL	Name Study
1780	1940	1600	1992	112003	ALL	ALL
1880	....	....	....	133922	KEN	???
ELLINOR						
1899	1950	1832	1992	161861	CAM	Witchford
ELLIOT						
1805	1805	1775	1850	133450	DEV	Plymouth
1805	1810	1750	1841	122483	DOR	Lyme Regis
1850	1910	1750	1850	166294	DUR	Penshaw
1780	1860	....	1780	176516	DUR	Stockton
1764	1806	ALL	1764	165301	DUR	Weardale
1861	1881	1845	1861	122483	GLA	Cardiff
1800	....	....	....	122491	GLS	ALL
1842	....	1842	?	122491	GLS	Bristol
1831	1842	1820	1861	122483	GLS	Bristol
1831	1842	1820	1861	122483	GLS	Clifton
1800	....	1842	?	122491	GLS	Wooten Under Edge
1783	1837	1650	1790	131377	LIN	Corringham
1913	1992	1800	1913	102849	LND	Walthamstow
1891	1965	ALL	1912	108642	MDX	Ealing
1735	....	....	1740	160873	NBL	Haltwhistle
1807	1860	1770	1807	173118	NBL	Kirk Whelpington
1641	....	....	1641	101761	NTT	Barton In Fabis
1780	1860	....	1780	176516	NYK	Yarm
....	....	ALL	1805	122483	ROX	Hawick
....	....	1700	1805	122483	SOM	Ilminster
....	....	1700	1805	122483	SOM	South Petherton
1751	1824	1650	1751	139084	SRY	Chiddingfold
1855	1870	1870	1992	109843	SSX	Fairlight
1830	1855	1855	1992	109843	SSX	Fittleworth
1832	1839	....	....	109819	SSX	Whatlington
1813	1839	1800	1813	109819	SSX	Winchelsea
1850	1870	1800	1900	138878	STS	Tipton
1695	1699	1670	1720	142018	WIL	Malmesbury
1650	1710	1650	1710	142018	WIL	Salisbury
ELLIOTT						
1775	1785	1700	1800	124974	BRK	Leckhampstead
1870	1965	....	....	124974	BRK	Reading
....	....	1700	....	159824	CON	Liskeard
1725	1786	1700	1725	149152	DBY	Baslow
....	1800	....	....	122505	DBY	Cromford
1871	1900	ALL	1871	105481	DBY	Kilburn
1809	1900	1600	1890	165697	DBY	Swanwick
1770	1860	1700	1860	137782	DEV	North

Known From	To	Researching From	To	Ref	Cty	Place
ELLIOTT contd.						
1740	1820	1730	1830	120995	DEV	Kenn
1785	1992	1600	1840	122513	DON	Adara
1785	1992	1600	1840	122513	DON	Killybegs
1880	1960	1800	1880	126675	DOR	Wimbourne
1812	1950	1700	1812	117463	DUR	ALL
1877	1992	....	....	132357	DUR	Bishop Auckland
1758	1800	1600	1800	116637	DUR	Herrington
1758	1800	1600	1800	116637	DUR	Penshaw
1752	1775	ALL	1752	154563	DUR	Ryton
1802	1992	1600	1802	116637	DUR	Sunderland
1800	1820	ALL	ALL	161292	GLS	Owlpen
1800	1900	1700	1800	145017	GLS	Tetbury
1826	1883	1700	1992	126454	GLS	Wootten Under Edge
1800	1875	1800	1900	124974	HAM	Kingsclere
1843	1909	1700	1843	145971	HAM	Portsea
1840	1908	ALL	1840	131881	HAM	Portsmouth
....	....	1809	1892	146706	IRL	Thubber
1700	1893	ALL	ALL	149438	KEN	Gravesend
1700	1893	ALL	ALL	149438	KEN	Milton
1820	1850	1700	1950	122475	KEN	???
1884	1992	1800	1992	116742	MDX	Acton
1838	1888	1810	1838	162523	MDX	Acton
1820	1992	1700	1950	122475	MDX	Poplar
1820	1992	1700	1950	122475	MDX	Stepney
1850	1960	ALL	ALL	162469	NBL	Central
1720	1754	1700	1760	110728	NBL	Edlingham
1804	1863	1800	1900	110728	NBL	Hepple
1772	1804	1760	1810	110728	NBL	Norham
1811	1833	1538	1840	118893	NBL	Spittal
1825	1848	1600	1825	102571	NIR	Fivemiletown
1896	1980	1700	1895	161470	NTH	Daventry
1807	1825	1770	1825	124915	NTT	East Drayton
1808	1877	1808	1877	149403	OXF	Thame
1660	1839	....	....	165999	SSX	West
1550	1992	1550	1992	122521	SSX	Mayfield
1650	1800	1550	1650	154016	SSX	Wisborough Green
1850	....	1850	1930	122505	STS	Newcastle
1879	1992	1838	1893	108901	SYK	Sheffield
1800	1992	....	1848	122467	WIL	Salisbury
1800	1969	1700	1992	122742	WIL	Salisbury
1789	1789	ALL	1789	136875	YKS	Ferry Fryston
1925	1992	....	....	110159	???	ALL
ELLIOTT-WELLS						
1878	....	1878	1992	149055	SSX	Selsybill
ELLIS						
1874	1900	....	....	151238	BDF	Toddington
1790	1850	1700	1830	117005	BKM	Astwood
1820	1878	....	....	146811	BRE	Clydach
1732	1732	....	....	108510	BRK	Barkham
1830	1860	1800	1860	100242	BRK	Reading
1851	1881	ALL	1850	158631	CAE	Glanllyn
....	....	1881	1900	158631	CAE	Morfabychan
1818	1870	1750	1900	113212	CAM	Ickleton
1890	1910	1800	1900	114472	CHS	Runcorn
1800	1992	1700	1992	133450	CON	Paul
1800	1850	1700	1800	128325	CON	St Stephen In Brannel
1850	1992	ALL	1850	122572	DBY	ALL
1800	1860	1700	1992	122602	DBY	Barlborough
1677	1768	ALL	1677	154563	DBY	Barlborough
1808	1930	ALL	1930	175757	DBY	Cheshire Boundary
1677	1767	ALL	1677	154563	DBY	Whitwell
....	....	1780	....	140082	DBY	???
1712	1900	1700	1900	124427	DEN	Corwen
1780	1992	1700	1910	122548	DEV	South
1900	1950	1800	1900	107530	DEV	Exeter
....	....	1600	1992	137588	DEV	Newton St Cyres
1761	1833	....	1900	110132	DEV	Powderham
....	....	1750	1875	163082	DOR	Corscombe
1750	1875	ALL	ALL	101400	DUR	Whickham
1780	1850	1850	1992	156132	ESS	Upminster
1790	1840	1750	1900	152528	ESS	Waltham Abbey
1864	1871	....	....	146811	GLA	Briton Ferry
1873	1956	....	....	102644	GLA	Reynoldston
1850	1992	ALL	1850	140813	GLS	ALL
1750	1881	1720	1900	157171	GLS	Minsterworth
1774	1906	....	....	102644	GLS	Nailsworth
1800	1850	1750	1800	177024	GLS	Newent
1790	1992	....	....	118672	GLS	Tirley
1896	1992	....	....	103330	HAM	Sheet
....	1675	ALL	ALL	129933	HAM	Yateley
1800	1850	1770	1850	126144	KEN	Gillingham
1595	1790	....	....	103330	KEN	Hawkhurst
ELLIS contd.						
1765	1845	1765	1845	107522	KEN	Sittingbourne
1712	1779	....	1712	177504	KEN	Strood
1840	1840	1800	1840	113646	KEN	Swanscombe
1786	1813	1700	1850	120901	LAN	Burnley
....	1913	....	1913	146811	LAN	Liverpool
1800	1843	ALL	1843	173290	LAN	Warrington
1800	1880	1650	1890	154598	LEI	Leicester
1800	1850	1700	1900	100129	LEI	Ullesthorpe
1760	1850	1760	1860	162396	LIN	North
1600	1992	ALL	ALL	150797	LIN	Corby Glen
1600	1992	ALL	ALL	150797	LIN	Cranwell
....	1789	1500	1789	175072	LIN	Kettlethorpe
1830	....	....	1992	151270	LIN	Swinhope
1850	1881	1850	1900	100242	LND	South
1831	1992	1750	1854	122580	LND	Clerkenwell
1782	1883	1782	1883	102806	LND	Hackney
1890	1992	1850	1900	122610	LND	Lambeth
1831	1992	1750	1854	122580	LND	Westminster
1842	1925	1800	1841	170348	LND	Woolwich
....	....	ALL	ALL	178403	LND	???
1880	1888	....	....	146811	LTN	Edinburgh
1769	1771	1650	1768	131245	MDX	Shoreditch
1860	1950	1760	1860	109479	MGY	Church Stoke
1710	1825	1710	1825	109819	MGY	Llandysul
1780	1845	1700	1900	139203	MON	Alberbury
1850	1900	1700	1900	160954	MSY	Liverpool
1854	1870	....	....	146811	NBL	Tynemouth
1832	1860	1700	1832	165867	NFK	Brandon
1800	1992	1700	1800	126063	NFK	Norwich
1800	1900	1700	1800	126063	NFK	Whitwell
1800	1950	1600	1800	122599	NFK	Yarmouth
1850	1992	ALL	1850	122572	NTT	ALL
1569	1900	ALL	ALL	134511	NTT	Arnold
1788	1881	1750	1788	173371	PEM	Haverfordwest
1797	1830	1750	1800	149993	SAL	Madeley
1870	1871	....	....	146811	SAL	Shrewsbury
1772	1794	....	1772	146811	SAL	Wellington
1858	1861	1855	1861	100242	SRY	Godstone
1787	....	....	1800	171441	SRY	Puttenham
....	1870	1700	1870	170178	SSX	Eastbourne
1550	1700	1550	1700	122521	SSX	Mayfield
1790	1896	....	....	103330	SSX	Uckfield
1790	1896	....	....	103330	SSX	Waldron
1846	1874	1846	1874	109819	STS	Bilston
1846	1874	1846	1874	109819	STS	Rowley Regis
1875	....	1800	1875	144711	STS	Tixall
1750	1880	1600	1900	170178	SXE	Chiddingly
1863	....	1800	1992	171875	TYR	Dungannon
1820	1850	1700	1820	167649	WAR	Castle Bromwich
1700	1799	ALL	ALL	146633	WIL	Huish
1740	1920	1600	1930	118281	WIL	Market Lavington
....	1871	1871	1900	178659	WOR	Great Malvern
1753	1830	ALL	1753	161330	WOR	Worcester
1820	1850	1800	1820	147338	WRY	Bradford
1855	1880	1835	1880	107522	WRY	Dewsbury
1880	1980	1700	1880	122556	WYK	Mirfield
1676	1775	1775	1850	149519	YKS	Dennington
1805	1875	1700	1805	173843	YKS	Holmfirth
1843	1992	1700	1863	123951	YKS	Huddersfield
1800	1850	1800	1850	123595	YKS	Huddersfield
1774	1779	?	1774	128910	YKS	Marr
1752	1780	1650	1750	170348	YKS	Mirfield
1870	1985	1800	1992	122602	YKS	Sheffield
1715	1737	1715	1749	108391	???	???
ELLISON						
1767	1794	....	....	138851	CHS	Bartington
1830	1980	1800	1830	127949	CHS	Whitegate
....	....	1700	....	127760	DOR	Bournemouth
1795	1831	1800	1850	163694	IOM	Peel
1809	....	1800	....	104043	LAN	Blackburn
....	....	1750	1840	111503	LAN	Blackburn
1820	1893	1800	1903	115673	LAN	Bury
....	....	1750	1840	111503	LAN	Gt Harwood
1850	1992	1830	1850	141070	LAN	Hindley
1820	1893	1800	1903	115673	LAN	Leigh
1800	1900	1881	1893	149322	LAN	Leyland
1600	1725	1600	1725	109347	LAN	Oswaldtwistle
1806	1992	1500	1806	122629	LAN	West Derby
1841	1851	ALL	1853	162825	LAN	Westhoughton
1850	1992	1830	1850	141070	LAN	Wigan
1800	....	....	....	100536	SCT	???
1810	1845	1750	1810	162396	WES	Appleby

Known From	To	Researching From	To	Ref	Cty	Place
ELLISTON						
1856	1900	ALL	1856	171719	LND	South East
ELLITHORN						
1840	1992	1700	1840	118443	LAN	Preston
ELLORS						
1805	1828	1700	1805	160024	NTT	Newark
ELLOT						
....	1713	....	....	122505	DBY	Morton
ELLOTT						
1650	1800	1650	1820	122505	DBY	Matlock
1650	1800	1650	1820	122505	DBY	Wirksworth
1830	1870	1700	1900	130419	LAN	Sabden
ELLOWAY						
1735	1750	1700	1750	124974	WIL	Ramsbury
ELLSEY						
1641	1803	1550	1830	137359	SSX	Ardingly
1803	1863	1800	1860	137359	SSX	Brighton
ELLSMORE						
1926	1992	1880	1910	122637	HAM	Andover
1918	1926	1900	1918	122637	WIL	Shrewton
ELLSNORTH						
1920	1961	....	....	147702	HUM	Beverley
ELLSOM						
1864	1864	1800	1880	127361	LIN	Grantham
ELLWELL						
1790	1841	....	....	125423	STS	Sedgley
ELLWICK						
1826	1850	....	....	135070	MDX	Stepney
ELLWOOD						
1845	1930	1780	1930	130036	CUL	Cockermouth
1920	1940	1920	1940	130036	CUL	Penrith
1875	1930	1800	1875	122653	LAN	Lancaster
1870	1992	1600	1870	100730	LAN	???
1749	1770	1700	1749	128961	MDX	Tottenham High Cross
1790	1960	1700	1790	125415	WES	Appleby
?	?	....	....	122645	WES	Casterton
1780	1850	1700	1850	143553	WES	Crosby Rav
....	....	?	?	122645	WES	Crosby Ravensworth
?	?	....	....	122645	WES	Hutton Roof
?	?	....	....	122645	WES	Kirkby Lonsdale
....	....	?	?	122645	WES	Middleton
ELMES						
....	....	1700	....	122661	HAM	Isle Of Wight
1753	1845	1700	1750	122661	HAM	Kimpton
....	....	1753	1850	122661	HAM	Ludgershall
1828	....	1750	1828	122661	HAM	Southampton
1840	1992	1800	1900	122688	LND	East
1840	1992	1800	1900	122688	LND	Poplar
1840	1992	1800	1900	122688	LND	Shadwell
1800	1970	1600	1800	160229	WIL	Corsham
1753	1753	1700	1753	122661	WIL	Durrington
ELMORE						
1820	1840	1750	1850	143006	MDX	Pinner
ELMS						
1760	1992	ALL	1760	108502	KEN	Bexley
1755	1992	1720	1992	169250	KEN	Bexley
ELPHICK						
1950	1960	....	....	122718	HAM	Waterlooville
1800	1900	....	....	122718	KEN	Horsmonden
1740	1811	....	....	122718	SRY	Cranleigh
1791	1887	1700	1791	100242	SSX	Barcombe
1738	1841	....	....	144282	SSX	Barcombe
1930	1960	1930	1960	122718	SSX	Chichester
1795	1915	1820	1840	122718	SSX	Craley
1750	1800	1600	1900	171522	SSX	Eastbourne
1816	1831	1700	1900	171522	SSX	Hastings
1767	1817	1667	1797	177490	SSX	Hastings
1750	1900	1750	1900	122521	SSX	Hooe
1820	1840	1750	1825	103446	SSX	Maresfield
1738	1841	....	....	144282	SSX	Plumpton
1790	1850	1650	1790	139106	SSX	???
1690	1778	1500	1800	170178	SXE	Chiddingly
1850	1950	ALL	1900	107948	SXE	Westham
ELPHINSTONE						
900	1900	....	....	122726	ALL	ALL
1570	1900	....	....	122726	OKI	Orkney
1420	1630	....	....	122726	PEE	Henderston
1420	1630	....	....	122726	PEE	Peebles
1470	1800	....	....	122726	SCT	North East
ELRINGTON						
1700	1799	1700	1799	169781	DUR	???
ELSAM						
1890	1916	ALL	1900	115878	LIN	Stamford
ELSDON						
1800	1900	1700	1800	118915	NBL	ALL
ELSE						
1780	1850	1700	1850	117617	CAM	Parson Drove
1794	1850	1700	1794	156698	KEN	Dover
1781	1781	1600	1992	110787	LEI	Cosby
ELSEGOOD						
....	....	ALL	ALL	122750	ALL	Name Study
ELSEY						
1760	1790	1538	1820	118893	NFK	???
ELSING						
1600	1639	....	....	101028	SFK	Lidgate
ELSLEY						
....	....	ALL	ALL	134961	ALL	Name Study
1797	1827	1700	1900	110191	MDX	London
1770	1850	1700	1830	146803	SRY	Frimley
ELSMOOR						
1800	1850	1750	1800	110639	STS	Cheadle
1800	1850	1750	1800	110639	STS	Stone
ELSOM						
1872	1992	ALL	1872	115878	LIN	Morton By Bourne
1842	1992	ALL	1842	115878	LIN	Rippingale
1860	....	ALL	ALL	146145	YKS	Cottingham
ELSOMS						
....	1694	....	1694	108510	LIN	Bassingthorpe
ELSON						
1760	1810	1740	1830	171158	DEV	Halberton
1834	1883	ALL	1906	168696	GLS	Bedminster
1873	1992	1873	1992	122769	LND	Lambeth
1900	1992	1800	1900	152633	SOM	Glastonbury
1845	1992	1821	1992	138312	SRY	Central
1873	1992	1873	1992	122769	SRY	Clapham
1903	1903	ALL	1903	138819	T&W	Newcastle Upon Tyne
ELSTOB						
1730	1910	1700	1900	151742	DUR	South
ELSTON						
1850	....	....	....	145068	DEV	Exeter
ELSWORTH						
1822	1881	1750	1900	118397	DOR	Hazelbury Bryan
ELSWORTHY						
1800	1841	1800	1841	103608	LIN	Spalding
1800	1992	1600	1800	123242	SOM	Selworthy
1818	1992	1800	1992	103608	YKS	Hull
ELTINTON						
1495	1950	1495	1950	128783	LEI	Shawell
ELTON						
1830	1836	ALL	1840	107026	BKM	Denham
1780	1904	1700	1950	119040	DOR	Wimborne
1780	1904	1700	1950	119040	DOR	Witchampton
1836	1930	1800	1950	107026	MDX	Uxbridge
1750	1900	1750	1900	133450	SOM	Clifton
1750	1780	1700	1800	119040	WIL	Idmiston
1800	1809	1500	1810	104825	WIL	Newton Tony
1750	1780	1700	1800	119040	WIL	Porton
ELTRINGHAM						
1800	1912	....	....	100633	DUR	???
1800	1912	....	....	100633	NBL	???
ELVE						
....	....	ALL	ALL	179124	ALL	Name Study
ELVEY						
1871	1871	1800	1900	145955	CMA	Kendal
....	....	1700	1750	154873	KEN	Chatham
1860	1930	1800	1860	104418	LND	Battersea
1871	1871	1800	1900	145955	WES	Kendal
ELVIDGE						
1820	1880	1820	1860	103616	WYK	Tickhill
ELVIN						
1812	....	1700	1812	116637	DUR	Southwick
1812	....	1700	1812	116637	DUR	Sunderland
1850	1950	1800	1900	107417	MDX	St Pancras
1760	1920	1600	1920	160946	NFK	ALL
1767	1992	....	....	122777	NFK	Norwich
ELVIS						
....	....	ALL	1803	152978	???	Birmingham
ELVISH						
....	....	ALL	ALL	151750	ALL	Name Study
ALL	ALL	ALL	ALL	151750	ALL	ALL
ELVY						
1840	1900	1700	1860	139254	KEN	Gillingham
ELWALL						
1790	1841	....	....	125423	STS	Sedgley
ELWAY						
1750	1850	1700	1780	144657	SOM	Wellington

Known From	To	Researching From	To	Ref	Cty	Place
ELWELL						
1850	1911	....	....	131024	BDF	Biggleswade
1600	1683	....	....	142522	DOR	Stoke Abbott
1790	1841	1700	1860	125423	STS	Sedgley
1794	....	....	1817	140767	WAR	Birmingham
1783	1992	....	....	104302	???	Walsall
ELWIG						
1841	....	1830	1851	115886	HUN	St Ives
1862	1865	1851	1871	115886	KEN	North
1881	1894	1870	1992	115886	KEN	Tunbridge Wells
1861	....	1865	1871	115886	SRY	Southwark
ELWORTHY						
1850	1900	1750	1850	128538	ALL	ALL
1734	1855	....	1734	163031	DEV	North
1550	1900	1500	1650	139556	DEV	Witheridge
1400	1600	1400	1700	139556	SOM	Carhampton Hundred
ELY						
1860	1900	1860	1900	135941	CAM	Horseheath
1830	1860	1830	1860	135941	CAM	Linton
1850	1992	1750	1850	170062	LAN	Manchester
1713	1837	....	1713	101761	LIN	West Keal
1813	1830	1800	1880	158658	NFK	Norwich
....	....	1700	1800	140627	NFK	Thurlton
1780	1830	1760	1830	135941	SFK	Thredgell
1760	1800	1690	1850	126276	WIL	Chippenham
ELYOTT						
1559	1559	....	....	127426	WAR	Birmingham
EMANUEL						
1918	1930	1918	1930	138398	MON	Abertillery
EMBER						
....	....	1500	1899	115975	WIL	ALL
EMBERTON						
....	....	....	....	127272	STS	Norbury
....	....	....	....	127272	STS	Stafford
EMBERY						
1800	1981	1700	1799	167118	DEV	Bideford
1713	1878	....	....	122785	WIL	Calne
EMBLETON						
1850	1950	1850	1992	139270	NBL	Embleton
1750	1980	1700	1750	132942	NBL	Long Framlington
EMBLING						
1837	1992	ALL	1937	122793	ALL	ALL
1754	1810	1600	1754	122793	DEV	Plymouth
1823	1992	1700	1823	122793	HAM	Gosport
EMBREY						
1840	1870	1800	1840	134856	MGY	Berriew
1830	1870	1750	1920	131792	MON	Llantilio Perthorley
1593	1674	1593	1674	103977	OXF	Warborough
EMBRIDGE						
1830	1830	1830	1830	145580	LND	Shoreditch
1830	1830	1830	1830	145580	MDX	Shoreditch
EMBRIE						
1621	1640	....	....	122785	WIL	Devizes
EMBRY						
1713	1750	....	....	122785	WIL	Calne
1629	1667	....	....	122785	WIL	Devizes
EMBURY						
1720	1800	1700	1850	152900	BRK	Appleton
1720	1800	1700	1850	152900	BRK	Eaton
1766	1841	1700	1850	152900	BRK	???
1766	1841	1700	1850	152900	OXF	Abingdon
EMENS						
1820	1830	1800	1850	123536	NBL	Glanton
EMENY						
1815	1980	1700	1815	152587	???	Bower Gifford
EMERSON						
1880	1970	1850	1900	128457	ANT	Shankill
1750	1850	1650	1900	127353	BKM	Shendley
1840	1970	1740	1920	128457	DOW	Copeland Island
1725	1950	1600	1725	128376	DUR	Stanhope
1791	1992	1584	1791	122807	HRT	Bishops Stortford
1650	1890	1650	1890	106674	NFK	Hulkham
1836	1884	1781	1983	127353	SRY	Lambeth
EMERTON						
1800	....	....	....	148768	LND	Bethnal Green
....	1826	1750	1840	152129	SRY	Mortlake
1790	1871	1820	1871	152129	SRY	Richmond
1825	....	1820	1830	152129	SRY	Wimbledon
1871	....	1850	1880	152129	SSX	Hastings
EMERY						
....	....	ALL	ALL	122831	ALL	Name Study
1896	1896	1600	1896	144851	BDF	Biggleswade
1700	1925	1600	1930	157023	BDF	Eaton Socon
EMERY contd.						
1800	1850	ALL	1850	105376	CAM	Chatteris
1800	1850	ALL	1850	105376	CAM	March
....	....	1750	1850	105678	GLS	Wotton Under Edge
1682	1844	1600	1682	145459	HAM	Botley
1750	1850	1750	1850	152404	LAN	Eccles
....	....	1843	....	107247	LND	ALL
....	....	1800	ALL	149187	LND	St Pancras
1867	1992	1750	1867	121010	MDX	Bethnal Green
1820	1850	1820	1850	124605	MDX	Bethnal Green
....	....	1700	1899	174963	MDX	London
1810	....	....	....	117579	MDX	Westminster
1676	1806	....	....	135437	NFK	Baconsthorpe
1705	1855	....	....	135437	NFK	Bodham
1719	1792	....	....	135437	NFK	Briston
1786	1786	1754	1812	107360	NTH	Whilton
....	....	1750	1850	105678	SOM	Bath
1743	1904	1600	1743	177164	SOM	Sedgemoor
1828	1970	1790	1860	124028	SRY	U Norwood
1628	1740	....	....	165999	SSX	Tarring
1878	1900	1800	1900	165441	STS	Newcastle
EMES						
1600	1665	1300	1600	144657	HAM	East Tisted
1550	1600	1300	1600	144657	LND	St Dunstans
1814	....	1700	....	123552	NFK	Thrandeston
1814	....	1700	....	123552	SFK	Thrandeston
1550	1650	1300	1600	144657	SSX	Chichester
EMETT						
1795	1850	1700	1800	139092	SRY	Croydon
EMM						
....	....	1600	1992	115975	DOR	ALL
....	....	1600	1992	115975	HAM	ALL
1742	1851	1740	1861	170143	HAM	Buriton
1742	1851	1740	1861	170143	HAM	Petersfield
1580	1992	1320	1580	112747	WIL	ALL
1600	1899	1400	1992	115975	WIL	ALL
1841	1992	1700	1850	171247	WIL	Braod Chalke
EMMANS						
1709	....	1600	1750	143693	BRK	Upton Nervet
EMMENS						
1805	1855	1780	1880	124974	HAM	Kingsclere
EMMERSON						
1755	1800	1700	1850	123536	DUR	Brancepeth
1860	1900	1850	1980	123536	DUR	Shildon
1811	1992	1750	1900	116823	DUR	Stockton
1840	1960	ALL	ALL	132071	DUR	Sunderland
....	....	1700	1901	120278	EYK	???
1800	ALL	1500	1800	145378	KEN	Ramsgate
1800	1850	....	....	124621	LIN	Althorpe
1819	1826	1775	1826	141097	LIN	Haxey
1780	1787	ALL	1780	169730	NFK	Docking
1795	1865	1770	1795	152870	NFK	Toftrees
1780	1840	1750	1850	109525	NYK	Fylingdales
1750	1800	1700	1800	116823	NYK	Middlesbrough
1840	1870	1800	1900	116823	NYK	Stainbridge
1740	1866	....	1740	101761	SFK	Fornham
1910	ALL	1500	1910	145378	SSX	Hastings
EMMETS						
1681	....	1681	1992	131156	WIL	Somerford Keynes
EMMETT						
1826	1915	1795	1826	163686	LAN	Heywood
1863	1992	1800	1863	139777	OXF	Crowell
1800	1881	1700	1900	116742	YKS	Morton
EMMINES						
1873	1992	1873	1992	112534	CAM	Cambridge
1873	1992	1873	1992	112534	LND	ALL
1873	1992	1873	1992	112534	YKS	Leeds
EMMINS						
1800	1828	1700	1800	134384	CAM	Soham
1869	1912	....	....	134384	LAN	Manchester
1803	1869	....	....	134384	LND	Finsbury
1803	1869	....	....	134384	LND	Hoxton
1803	1869	....	....	134384	LND	Islington
1803	1869	....	....	134384	LND	Kensington
EMMONS						
1843	1900	1800	1843	176257	CAM	Soham
1770	1780	1700	1800	166804	HAM	North
EMMOTT						
1804	1826	1750	1804	174211	LAN	Clitheroe
1773	1798	1700	1798	141062	LAN	Manchester
....	....	1860	1960	147613	YKS	Bentham
....	....	1740	1860	147613	YKS	Bolton Abbey
....	....	1850	1950	147613	YKS	Skipton
....	....	1650	1750	147613	YKS	Thornton In Craven

Known From	To	Researching From	To	Ref	Cty	Place
EMMS						
1685	1800	1600	1900	107980	NFK	Arminghall
1730	1850	1730	1992	107980	NFK	Swantonmorley
EMONEY						
1754	1940	....	....	128996	CAM	Thornley
EMORY						
1755	1940	....	....	128996	CAM	Thornley
EMSLEY						
1750	1900	1750	1900	153621	WYK	Queensbury
1791	1839	?	?	176702	WYK	Queensbury
ENDACOTT						
1793	1853	1700	1793	150657	DEV	Chagford
1608	1900	....	1900	123447	DEV	Dartmoor
ENDALL						
1550	1600	1450	1550	174513	OXF	Lower Heyford
ENDERSBY						
1806	1900	ALL	1900	137286	BDF	East
1816	1860	....	1816	108839	BDF	Clifton
ENDERSON						
1670	....	....	1670	101761	LIN	Halton Holegate
ENEVER						
1800	....	1800	....	157848	ESS	Hornchurch
1800	....	1800	....	157848	LND	Whitechaple
1800	1911	1750	1860	113093	LND	???
ENGERT						
....	....	ALL	ALL	122866	ALL	Name Study
1842	1992	ALL	ALL	122866	MDX	Islington
ENGLAND						
1810	1865	1750	1810	115312	CAM	Thorney
1834	1860	1800	1992	118753	DEV	Exeter
1840	1870	1750	1840	135658	DEV	Plymouth
1756	1786	....	....	122106	DOR	Blandford
1650	1650	1550	1700	133450	IRL	Lifford
1843	1992	1800	1992	153133	MDX	London
1842	....	1800	1842	132853	MDX	Shoreditch
1797	1880	ALL	1797	130575	NTH	Harleston
1640	1950	1580	1640	134139	NTH	Harleston
1797	1880	ALL	1797	130575	NTH	Kislingbury
1813	1850	....	....	147885	NTT	Heanor
1600	1900	1558	....	112968	SOM	Crewkerne
1708	1900	1558	....	112968	SOM	Merriott
1650	1854	ALL	1693	122106	SOM	Merriott
1775	1985	1600	1775	169595	WIL	Alderbury
1800	1850	1750	1850	125792	WIL	Westbury
....	....	?	?	134201	WRY	Addingham
1800	1992	1700	1800	160253	WYK	Darton
1800	1992	....	....	160253	WYK	Holmfirth
1860	1900	1800	1992	174335	YKS	Attercliffe
1860	1900	1800	1992	174335	YKS	Handsworth
1836	1859	1800	1859	176885	YKS	Saxton
1860	1900	1800	1992	174335	YKS	Sheffield
1814	1858	1600	1632	174831	???	Pucklechurch
ENGLISH						
1820	1875	1600	1825	153591	CAM	???
1847	1957	ALL	1847	171719	CMA	Burgh-By Sands
1780	1800	ALL	1800	115266	DOR	ALL
?	?	ALL	ALL	174432	DUR	Haughton Le Skerne
1808	1882	1700	1807	132764	DUR	Wearhead
1851	1851	ALL	1851	167959	ESS	Bradwell
....	....	1750	....	113352	ESS	Hutton
1880	1920	ALL	ALL	131490	HAM	Tichfield
1900	1960	1800	1992	157023	LND	Shepherds Bush
1880	....	1860	1880	163775	MDX	Bethnal Green
1790	1970	1700	1850	141402	NFK	Ormesby
1776	1992	1700	1850	175218	NFK	???
1673	1673	1600	1673	155276	SFK	Barking
1815	1913	1750	1815	129712	SFK	Bungay
1866	1950	1800	1950	104574	SSX	Felpham
1790	1840	1500	1880	157929	SSX	Mid
1704	1748	1600	1704	175781	WIL	Bromham
1850	1992	1700	1850	125601	WOR	Redditch
ENIFFER						
....	....	ALL	ALL	122874	ALL	Name Study
ENNALS						
1650	1750	1600	1750	133817	SFK	Hitcham
ENNESS						
1780	1920	1700	1820	122882	ESS	Wooford Bridge
ENNETT						
1831	1871	....	1831	101761	IRL	???
ENNEVER						
1760	1871	1700	1760	114871	SOM	Walcot
ENNEW						
1750	1960	1700	1750	140317	ESS	East Donyland
1750	1960	1700	1750	140317	ESS	West Mersea
ENNIS						
....	....	1830	1890	117137	GLS	Coleford
1820	1840	1820	1840	176494	KIK	Woodstock
ENNOS						
....	....	1800	....	108677	MDX	Willesden
ENOCH						
1780	1810	1780	1810	151297	GLA	Cilybebyll
ENOUF						
ALL	ALL	ALL	ALL	115126	CHI	ALL
ENSBY						
1850	1870	1700	1900	169536	ALL	ALL
ENSOR						
1800	1860	ALL	ALL	143294	LEI	Hinckley
1806	1992	1700	1806	155748	WAR	Birmingham
ENSTONE						
....	....	ALL	ALL	122890	ALL	Name Study
....	....	1600	1992	122890	ALL	ALL
1852	1876	ALL	1852	136875	GLS	Tewkesbury
ENTWHISTLE						
1800	1825	....	....	129747	LAN	Manchester
?	?	....	?	135615	LAN	Waterside
ENTWISLE						
1750	1900	1750	1900	125237	LAN	Darwen
1800	1880	1880	1992	162256	LAN	Darwen
ENTWISTLE						
1750	1830	1750	1830	122254	LAN	Bolton
1830	1950	1700	1992	167673	LAN	Bolton
1893	....	ALL	1893	176842	LAN	Bolton
1802	1874	1500	1874	169439	LAN	Haslingden
1820	1970	1820	1900	122254	LAN	Liverpool
1832	1842	1800	1842	102121	LAN	Over Darwen
1826	1870	1750	1825	118354	LAN	Wigan
EOFORWACER						
1066	1200	ALL	1992	121797	ALL	ALL
EPEY						
1754	1822	1700	1760	103462	CAM	Colne
1754	1822	1700	1760	103462	HUN	Colne
EPLETT						
....	....	ALL	ALL	178845	ALL	Name Study
1832	....	ALL	ALL	178845	CON	St Columb Major
1667	1841	ALL	ALL	178845	CON	St Ervan
1727	1992	ALL	ALL	178845	CON	St Eval
EPOLITE						
1850	1856	1800	1850	178845	LAN	Liverpool
EPPS						
ALL	ALL	ALL	ALL	146080	KEN	ALL
1750	1992	1650	1750	122912	KEN	East
1767	1900	1867	1992	166804	KEN	Maidstone
EPTON						
1875	1992	....	....	160008	EYK	Goole
....	....	1750	1875	160008	LIN	Wainfleet
ERASMUS						
....	....	1825	1992	115142	WLS	ALL
ERBACH						
....	....	ALL	ALL	137138	ALL	ALL
ERINGTON						
1150	1225	1100	1250	154881	ALL	ALL
ERNST						
1824	1904	ALL	ALL	118192	ENG	ALL
ERREY						
1730	1992	ALL	1992	119105	ENG	ALL
1828	1828	1750	1850	121568	SOM	North East
ERRICKER						
1800	1992	ALL	1992	121797	ALL	ALL
ERRIDGE						
1840	1900	1700	1840	134899	KEN	Kingsdown
1840	1900	1700	1840	134899	KEN	Ringwould
ERRINGTON						
1832	1860	1700	1860	179248	CMA	Appleby
1723	1766	ALL	1766	116548	DUR	Ryton
1830	1976	....	....	157988	DUR	Ryton
1830	1976	....	....	157988	DUR	Stanley
1138	1864	1138	1864	119741	NBL	South West
1830	1900	1700	1900	179191	NBL	Appleby
1640	1670	....	....	105759	NBL	Newcastle On Tyne
1860	1992	....	....	179248	WYK	Bradford
ERSKINE						
1673	....	....	....	151351	ANS	Arbroath
1730	....	1730	1845	119458	BEW	Coldingham
....	....	1800	1900	120227	DEV	Stonehouse
1800	ALL	1650	ALL	122939	DFS	ALL
1830	1992	ALL	ALL	142611	DOW	Newry
1704	ALL	1650	ALL	122939	KKD	ALL
1790	1870	1750	1870	155004	MLN	Edinburgh

Known From	To	Researching From	To	Ref	Cty	Place
ERSKINE contd.						
1720	ALL	1650	1720	122939	WIG	ALL
ERSWELL						
1870	1872	1700	1870	148334	HRT	Saffron Walden
ERWIN						
....	....	ALL	ALL	136603	ALL	Name Study
1780	1800	ALL	ALL	130508	DUR	Sunderland
ESARTT						
1778	1809	ALL	ALL	175587	SOM	Martock
ESCOTT						
1944	1992	1850	1944	122947	AVN	Eastville
1804	1829	....	....	101028	DEV	Bampton
1838	1903	ALL	1992	159174	DEV	Bampton
ESCRICK						
1600	1800	ALL	ALL	153192	YKS	Howden
ESCRICKE						
1600	1790	ALL	ALL	153192	YKS	York
ESDAILE						
1800	1850	1700	1800	172898	NFK	Kings Lynn
1881	1900	1870	1910	124001	SSX	East Grinstead
ESHELBY						
1764	1848	1573	1763	117803	NRY	Alne
....	....	1732	1795	117803	NRY	Bagby
ESKDALE						
....	....	1675	1703	117161	YKS	Hawsker
ESKRICK						
1708	1862	ALL	ALL	153192	LAN	Bolton
1678	....	ALL	ALL	153192	YKS	Elland
ESKRIETT						
1820	1992	1700	1820	110442	WYK	Ferrybridge
ESLER						
1800	1980	1750	1850	103756	ANT	Broughshane
ESLIN						
?	1836	ALL	1836	153710	LAN	Liverpool
ESPLIN						
1850	1992	1800	1850	174653	ANS	Forfar
ESSAM						
1880	1992	1600	1880	122963	LND	Marylebone
1880	1992	1600	1880	122963	LND	Paddington
....	....	1851	ALL	122963	SRY	Chertsey
ESSERY						
....	....	ALL	ALL	122971	ALL	Name Study
1837	1985	1625	1837	122971	ENG	ALL
1837	1985	1625	1837	122971	WLS	ALL
ESSEX						
1631	?	?	?	166642	KEN	Woodchurch
1761	1775	1650	1760	131245	WAR	Coventry
ESSLEMONT						
....	....	ALL	ALL	122998	ALL	Name Study
ESTE						
1600	1900	ALL	1600	121800	ALL	ALL
ESTILL						
1703	1808	....	....	117161	YKS	Fylingdales
ESTILOW						
1820	1890	....	....	114545	NTT	Nottingham
ESTLIN						
1550	1800	ALL	ALL	129240	LEI	Hinckley
ESTOP						
1695	1731	1550	1694	102830	STS	Kingswinford
ETCHELLS						
1860	1992	1800	1860	108359	LAN	Patricroft
ETCHES						
1800	1992	1650	1800	123005	YKS	Doncaster
ETHEREDGE						
1632	1900	ALL	ALL	128279	HAM	New Forest
ETHERIDGE						
....	....	ALL	ALL	111414	ALL	Name Study
....	....	1840	1846	166022	BRE	Hay On Wye
1880	1992	ALL	ALL	123048	DUR	Bishopwearmouth
....	....	ALL	ALL	111414	GLS	ALL
1794	1794	1770	1800	111414	GLS	Ashleworth
1780	1820	1700	1840	166022	GLS	Bishops Cleeve
1543	1971	ALL	ALL	111414	GLS	Maismore
....	....	1700	1850	118834	HAM	Beaulieu
1800	1896	1700	1900	177369	HAM	Ringwood
1921	....	ALL	1887	123013	HAM	???
1853	1874	1853	1874	166022	KEN	Ramsgate
1846	1853	1846	1853	166022	LAN	Bolton
1878	....	1870	1880	123013	LND	Islington
1573	1960	....	....	161853	NFK	Stoke Ferry
1910	1910	1900	1915	111414	STS	Pye Green
1877	1881	1877	1891	111414	STS	Tipton
1871	1876	1865	1880	111414	STS	Wednesbury
1874	1874	1871	1881	111414	STS	West Bromwich
ETHERIDGE contd.						
1830	1851	1700	1900	178322	WOR	Halesowen
1896	1955	1885	1955	111414	WOR	Oldbury
ETHERINGTON						
....	1880	1830	1880	151912	LAN	Cottam
1830	1992	1750	1830	121509	LAN	Lancaster
1880	1880	1830	1880	151912	LAN	Preston
1830	1992	1750	1830	121509	LAN	Woodplumpton
....	....	1750	1790	172847	MDX	London
1830	1860	....	....	172847	NTT	Lenton
1807	1842	1700	1807	152056	NTT	Radford
1620	1660	1600	1620	121339	NYK	Wensley
....	....	1750	1790	172847	STS	Stafford
ETHERINTON						
1660	1660	1630	1690	105333	SSX	New Fishbourne
ETTE						
1850	1900	1700	1850	107271	NTH	ALL
EUDEN						
1732	1992	ALL	ALL	118370	KEN	Hackington
EUDY						
1780	1858	1700	1780	176575	CON	Cambrone
EUSTACE						
....	....	ALL	ALL	123056	ALL	Name Study
1550	1992	1066	1992	123056	BKM	Bledlow
1877	1900	1800	1877	139785	CLA	Doonbeg
1660	1992	....	....	123056	CON	Crowan
1300	1992	1300	1992	123056	DEV	Tavistock
1066	1980	1066	1992	123056	IRL	Kildare
1550	1992	1066	1992	123056	OXF	Bledlow
EUSTICE						
1600	1992	1600	1992	143766	CON	ALL
EVA						
....	....	ALL	ALL	123064	CON	ALL
....	....	ALL	ALL	123064	CON	Kerrier
....	....	ALL	ALL	123064	CON	Penwyn
1800	....	....	....	170313	CON	St Erith
1600	....	?	?	136999	CON	St Keverine
....	....	ALL	ALL	123064	DEV	ALL
1880	1992	ALL	ALL	123064	DEV	Tavistock
EVAN						
1792	....	1750	1841	123129	CMN	Llandybie
1730	1900	1730	1900	129054	GLA	Ewenny
1730	1900	1730	1900	129054	GLA	Newton Nottage
1792	1850	1750	1850	118540	PEM	Llandewi Velfrey
EVANS						
1782	1786	....	....	138401	AGY	Aberfraw
1782	1786	....	....	138401	AGY	Llanddaniel Fab
1782	1786	....	....	138401	AGY	Llangadwaladr
1898	1970	1800	1897	151882	AVN	Bristol
1830	1992	1600	1830	149713	BDF	Flitwick
1811	1860	1700	1811	159646	BDF	Pulloxhill
1763	1859	1700	1992	176877	BRE	Llanafanfawr
1848	1958	1600	1848	162035	BRE	Talsgarth
1921	1984	1500	1921	110310	BRK	ALL
1667	1846	1667	1846	104027	CAE	Deganwy
1667	1846	1667	1846	104027	CAE	Glanwydden
....	....	1800	ALL	145939	CGN	Aberystwyth
1750	1903	1770	1903	176958	CGN	Cardigan
1830	1860	1790	1900	162450	CGN	Hawen
1750	1903	1770	1903	176958	CGN	Llangoedmore
1850	1940	1700	1850	155101	CGN	Llangyby
1830	1860	1790	1900	162450	CGN	Troedyrar
1791	....	ALL	ALL	131415	CMN	North
1785	1861	1785	1861	158658	CMN	Carmarthen
1850	1992	....	....	135666	CMN	Garnant
1819	1864	1800	1840	109517	CMN	Llandarrog
1791	1871	1700	1992	176923	CMN	Llandeilo
1811	1817	....	....	129232	CMN	Llandeilofawr
1841	1881	1832	1881	123129	CMN	Llanelly
1815	1992	....	1849	138320	CMN	Llanfynydd
1871	1992	1820	1834	123129	CMN	Llangennech
1787	1826	1745	1787	123129	CMN	Llangyndeyrn
1800	1830	1800	1830	135666	CMN	Llanstephan
1790	1825	1750	1830	158658	CMN	Talley
1900	1992	1600	1900	123242	CON	Perranzabuloe
1900	1992	1600	1900	123242	CON	St Agnes
1759	1891	1700	1795	160474	CWD	Chirk
1795	1880	1700	1795	157147	CWD	Denbigh
1810	1885	1700	1950	159719	DEN	Abergele
1852	1853	1830	1855	132217	DEN	Denbigh
1807	1887	1807	1887	147621	DEN	Denbigh
1700	1800	ALL	1880	132217	DEN	Glan Conwy
1750	1992	....	....	118672	DEN	Henllan
1813	1891	1700	1950	159719	DEN	Llandrillo

Known From	To	Researching From	To	Ref	Cty	Place
EVANS contd.						
1800	1940	1700	1800	157147	DEN	Llangwyfan
....	....	....	....	132217	DEN	Llansanffraid
1775	1825	1820	1835	105694	DEN	Ruabon Rhos Llanerchrigog
1832	1832	ALL	1832	110833	DEN	Wrexham
1780	1870	1700	1900	156531	DEV	Appledore
1832	1900	?	1832	153591	DEV	North Molton
1900	1927	1850	1980	111007	DFD	Pembroke Dock
1785	1860	1770	1860	105333	DOR	Wimborne
1814	1881	....	....	147621	FLN	Cwm
....	1825	1780	1851	135658	FLN	Gronant
1810	1830	1750	1900	129607	FLN	Hope
1850	1992	....	....	135666	FLN	Rhuddlan
1810	1850	ALL	1850	132217	FLN	Tremeirchion
1802	....	ALL	ALL	147621	FLN	Whitford
1875	1910	1875	1910	135666	GLA	Aberdare
....	1884	1600	1992	176990	GLA	Aberdare
1900	....	1750	1900	144150	GLA	Cefn Vaynor
1851	1992	....	....	129232	GLA	Cwmavon
1830	1850	1830	1850	135666	GLA	Dowlais
1845	1992	ALL	1992	125113	GLA	Gelli
1841	1992	....	....	129097	GLA	Llantrisant
1850	1900	1700	1850	131253	GLA	Llanwonno
1900	1901	....	....	135666	GLA	Maerdy
1817	1850	....	....	129232	GLA	Merthyr Tydfil
1860	1913	1700	1860	138525	GLA	Merthyr Tydfil
1850	1910	1850	1910	135666	GLA	Mountain Ash
....	1884	1600	1992	176990	GLA	Mountain Ash
1889	1889	1800	1900	127361	GLA	Neath
?	....	....	....	118508	GLA	Penygraig
....	....	1871	1940	123315	GLA	Pontypridd
1910	1960	1910	1960	135666	GLA	Pontypridd
1892	?	1892	1992	174262	GLA	Pontypridd
1850	1960	1700	1850	123102	GLA	Swansea
1850	1945	1820	1945	123145	GLA	Swansea
1920	1960	1920	1960	135666	GLA	Swansea
1871	1871	1800	1900	136042	GLS	Arlingham
1798	1820	1700	1800	108413	GLS	Bristol
1750	1842	1700	1850	147575	GLS	Cirenchester
1840	1860	1840	1860	126209	GLS	English Bicknor
1745	1778	....	....	135437	GLS	Newland
1767	1855	ALL	1992	159174	GLS	St Aldate
1810	1880	1700	1810	134368	GLS	Winstone
1830	1965	....	....	159301	GNT	Newport
1800	1830	1650	1830	158542	HAM	Boldren
1796	1892	1700	1820	117773	HEF	Marstow
1807	1992	ALL	1807	125210	HRT	Bishops Stortford
1667	1696	....	....	117234	IRL	Carlow
1812	....	....	....	101613	KEN	Etham
1850	....	1830	1890	126144	KEN	Gravesend
1776	1776	1750	1800	122254	LAN	Bolton
1800	1800	1700	1850	126837	LAN	Bolton
1780	1800	1700	1800	126837	LAN	Lancaster
1880	1959	1800	1880	115541	LAN	Liverpool
1800	1855	....	....	140082	LAN	Liverpool
1815	1850	1780	1815	176311	LAN	Liverpool
1828	1937	ALL	ALL	127000	LAN	Manchester
1838	....	....	....	172723	LAN	Manchester
1897	1992	1700	1897	123153	LAN	Oldham
1826	1847	1750	1850	126586	LAN	St Helens
....	1800	ALL	1800	134511	LAN	Toxteth Park
1820	1820	?	1820	123161	LEI	Beeby
1850	1910	1800	1910	142891	LIN	Grimsby
1915	1925	1880	1915	165689	LND	East
1868	1951	1840	1868	153990	LND	Bethnal Green
1850	1992	1700	1850	157449	LND	Camberwell
1867	1880	....	....	132888	LND	Islington
1828	1865	....	1880	171441	LND	Marylebone
1828	1865	....	1880	171441	LND	Paddington
1803	1859	1780	1841	170348	LND	Woolwich
1833	....	1820	1841	176923	LND	???
1880	1880	1880	1880	147575	MDX	Bromley By Bow
1757	1852	1750	1852	130990	MDX	Westminster
1881	1902	1821	1902	159778	MER	Llandrillo
1877	1992	?	1877	156337	MGM	Cwmaman
1874	1881	1750	1900	114456	MGY	ALL
1790	1828	1790	1828	151599	MGY	ALL
1862	1870	1700	1862	111775	MGY	Carno
1851	1890	1600	1851	156914	MGY	Kerry
1800	1900	1800	1900	167924	MGY	Llandiniam
1829	....	ALL	1829	131725	MGY	Manafon
1852	1946	1700	1852	138673	MGY	Welshpool
1850	1909	1700	1900	142212	MON	Brynmawr

Known From	To	Researching From	To	Ref	Cty	Place
EVANS contd.						
1880	1950	1850	1950	123250	MON	Caldicot
1833	....	1820	1841	176923	MON	Penyvan
....	....	1837	1900	123315	MON	Risca
....	....	1750	1850	147613	OXF	Spelsbury
1800	1920	1700	1850	103845	PEM	Bletherston
1750	1903	1770	1903	176958	PEM	Bletherston
1750	1903	1770	1903	176958	PEM	Haverfordwest
1800	1850	1750	1800	177024	PEM	Haverfordwest
....	1745	1650	1745	121010	RAD	Old Radnor
1675	1730	1675	1730	127655	SAL	Bitterley
1808	1881	....	1808	131741	SAL	Broseley
1821	....	ALL	1821	131725	SAL	Dawley
....	1800	....	1800	177695	SAL	Dawley
1789	1815	ALL	1789	131725	SAL	Madley
1801	1861	1500	1801	175072	SAL	Middleton
1820	1880	1700	1820	168785	SAL	Much Wenlock
1867	1900	1700	....	123471	SAL	Pavement Gares
1860	1931	1750	1860	153974	SAL	Pontesbury
1860	1931	1750	1860	153974	SAL	Pontesford
1860	1931	1750	1860	153974	SAL	Shrewsbury
1700	1800	....	1800	177695	SAL	Wellington
1740	1780	1700	1740	155500	SAL	Wistanstow
1860	1910	1869	1889	165840	SOM	Bridgewater
1833	1862	1833	1862	165840	SOM	Cannington
1623	1833	1623	1833	165840	SOM	Weare
1826	1874	....	1826	133566	SRY	Bermondsey
1825	1846	1700	1825	160474	STS	Bilston
1893	1992	....	....	123099	STS	Compton
1828	1937	ALL	ALL	127000	STS	Dudley
1858	1866	1700	1992	110418	STS	Sedgly
1813	1992	1700	1813	123277	STS	West Bromwich
1841	1851	1700	1850	164909	STS	West Bromwich
1841	....	1841	....	123099	STS	Wolverhampton
1797	1947	1797	1920	123285	SYK	Elsecar
1854	1871	1854	1992	156426	WAR	Aston
1850	1880	....	....	123161	WAR	Birmingham
1860	1920	1820	1920	151637	WAR	Ladywood
1845	1992	ALL	1992	125113	WLS	Cardigan
1651	1992	1600	1651	123307	WLS	Llanberis
1850	1992	1700	1850	157449	WLS	???
1939	?	1800	?	116009	WMD	Birmingham
1890	1992	1800	1992	161861	WMD	Blackheath
1848	1892	1700	1850	164909	WOR	Cradley
1858	1866	1700	1992	110418	WOR	Dudley
1848	1892	1700	1850	164909	WOR	Oldbury
1838	1858	....	....	138339	WOR	Worcester
1828	1937	ALL	ALL	127000	WOR	???
1903	1992	1900	1992	123250	YKS	Hull
1930	1980	1850	1950	123293	???	Bristol
1870	....	1800	1870	127787	???	Bristol
1771	1992	....	....	142808	???	Bristol
EVASON						
1790	1992	1790	....	111287	SAL	Kewley
EVATT						
1880	1946	1700	1800	172022	LEI	Leicester
EVE						
1770	1855	1600	1770	108197	ESS	Maldon
....	....	1650	1780	154873	KEN	Canterbury
....	....	1600	1700	154873	KEN	Wye
EVEA						
1639	1780	1500	1650	153591	CON	Camborne
1639	1780	1500	1650	153591	CON	St Just
EVELEIGH						
1805	1992	1600	1805	148040	CON	Launceston
1825	1850	1700	1900	119083	DEV	East
1808	1992	....	1808	103705	DEV	Attery St Mary
1820	1890	....	....	126187	DOR	Bridport
1825	1850	1700	1900	119083	LND	ALL
EVELY						
1795	1830	1750	1795	136220	DEV	Northlew
EVENDEN						
....	....	ALL	ALL	172812	KEN	ALL
1820	1880	1800	1900	144843	KEN	Coxley Heath
1820	1880	1800	1900	144843	KEN	East Farleigh
1820	1880	1800	1900	144843	KEN	Maidstone
1800	1900	ALL	ALL	123323	SSX	East
EVENING						
....	....	1700	1800	171794	CUL	Embleton
EVERARD						
....	....	1830	1890	155039	HAM	Hartley Westpall
....	....	1600	1777	150150	NTH	Naseby
EVERATT						
1700	1900	1600	1900	114383	LIN	Laughton

Known From	To	Researching From	To	Ref	Cty	Place
EVERED						
1778	....	1600	1778	116637	SFK	Barrow
EVEREST						
1862	1940	....	1862	178861	KEN	Farningham
1550	1650	1500	1650	154881	KEN	Penshurst
1850	1950	1800	1850	121053	SRY	Camberwell
1790	1794	1790	1850	100668	SSX	Holtye Common
EVERET						
1786	1790	1700	1800	131377	LIN	Ancaster
1720	1771	....	....	101028	SFK	Barrow
EVERETT						
1779	1992	1700	1779	145823	CAM	Horseheath
1782	....	1700	1782	144746	ESS	Boreham
1737	1877	1600	1737	100013	ESS	Great Waltham
....	....	1866	1992	123331	GLS	ALL
1770	1866	....	....	123331	GLS	Awre
1500	1750	....	....	123331	GLS	Berkeley
1500	1750	....	....	123331	GLS	Dursley
1770	1866	....	....	123331	GLS	East Dean
1840	1885	....	....	100048	KEN	Chatham
....	....	1992	....	123331	LAN	Manchester
1861	1960	....	....	100048	LND	Greenwich
1815	1830	1825	1850	100048	MDX	Bromley By Bow
1780	1800	1800	1825	100048	MDX	Limehouse
?	?	?	?	133361	NFK	Central
1817	1857	1700	1816	131245	NFK	Norwich
1790	1810	1700	1790	112593	NFK	Tharston
1900	1992	1600	1900	105023	NFK	???
1880	1887	1880	1890	100048	SRY	Camberwell
1863	....	ALL	1863	104299	YKS	Thorne
EVERINGHAM						
1745	1765	ALL	1770	113611	EYK	Hull
1320	1400	1250	1400	154881	NTT	Laxton
EVERINGTON						
1877	1992	ALL	1900	113611	EYK	Hull
1778	1860	ALL	1880	113611	LIN	East Keal
1778	1860	ALL	1880	113611	LIN	West Keal
EVERISS						
1880	....	....	....	170313	WAR	Birmingham
EVERITT						
1860	1970	1750	1860	151165	ESS	Rochford
1700	1992	1700	1920	142565	NFK	Hilgay
1841	1851	1840	1860	115193	SOM	Bath
1840	1960	1815	1992	115193	SOM	Bristol
EVERLEY						
1500	1900	1500	1900	170216	WIL	ALL
EVERNDEN						
1697	1757	1600	1800	176672	ALL	ALL
EVERRETT						
1883	1992	1850	1950	144606	MDX	Westminster
EVERS						
1900	1992	1900	1992	134910	YKS	York
EVERSDEN						
1798	1834	....	1798	108839	CAM	Harlton
EVERSFIELD						
1798	1900	1700	1900	172073	KEN	East Malling
EVERSHED						
1843	1853	....	....	147486	LND	Kensington
1800	1843	....	....	147486	SSX	Pulborough
EVERSON						
1860	....	ALL	ALL	157864	LND	Poplar
EVERTON						
1500	1600	....	....	100420	WAR	Coleshill
1500	1600	....	....	100420	WAR	Meriden
EVERY						
1770	1971	1700	1900	100536	CON	???
....	....	1700	1900	135968	LND	Kensington
1800	1922	1700	1799	179612	SOM	Bleadon
1828	1850	1828	1850	159913	SOM	Catcott
EVETTS						
1838	1850	1700	1838	159093	WAR	Birmingham
EVILL						
....	....	1680	1800	108243	SOM	Bath
EVINGTON						
....	....	ALL	ALL	123366	ALL	Name Study
1700	1860	1700	1900	123366	BDF	Luton
1590	1800	1590	1800	123366	HRT	Kimpton
1590	1800	1590	1800	123366	HRT	Kings Walden
1590	1800	1590	1800	123366	HRT	Wheathamstead
1850	1960	....	....	123366	LAN	Manchester
1600	1630	1260	1700	123366	LEI	ALL
1259	1600	1250	1600	123366	LEI	Evington
1259	1600	1250	1600	123366	LEI	Houghton On Hill
1600	1850	1620	1720	123366	LIN	Pinchbeck
EVINGTON contd.						
1600	1850	1620	1720	123366	LIN	Spalding
1550	1630	1550	1800	123366	LND	City
1550	1630	1550	1800	123366	LND	Enfield
1550	1630	1550	1800	123366	LND	Hackney
1550	1630	1550	1800	123366	LND	Stepney
1830	1950	1830	1980	123366	YKS	Hull
EVINS						
1830	1900	....	....	147885	NTH	Luddington
EVISON						
1776	1785	1550	1800	147265	LIN	Coningsby
EVITTS						
1827	1890	1700	1870	117005	WAR	Coventry
EVOMY						
1780	1800	1700	1850	162620	NBL	Newcastle
EVOY						
1840	1850	1837	1900	111090	WEX	???
EVRAT						
1751	1772	1600	1750	101575	YKS	Whitgift
EWARDS						
1822	1908	1820	1910	165441	STS	Newcastle
EWART						
1728	1918	ALL	ALL	145092	DFS	Annandale
1750	1992	1700	1750	171034	YKS	Huddersfield
EWELL						
1675	1696	1600	1675	150894	KEN	Herne
1803	....	ALL	1800	128090	KEN	Sandwich
EWEN						
1820	1992	1700	1820	123374	ABD	Birse
1597	1718	1550	1718	174343	HAM	Bighton
1808	1808	ALL	1808	129283	NFK	Cawston
EWENS						
....	....	ALL	ALL	123382	ALL	Name Study
....	....	1725	1760	132748	HAM	East Meon
1759	1806	1740	1860	132748	HAM	Warblington
1830	1860	1800	1830	125318	SSX	Harting
EWER						
?	?	ALL	1800	117919	MDX	London
EWERS						
....	....	1800	1992	101184	STS	Burton On Trent
EWIN						
1780	1820	1750	1820	135941	ESS	Ashdon
1850	1870	1700	1992	170585	SFK	Haverhill
EWING						
1890	1992	1840	1890	123390	LND	Bow
....	....	ALL	1864	119326	MLN	Edinburgh
1850	1900	1700	1850	123390	STI	Baldernock
EWINGS						
1440	1520	1400	1500	154881	STS	Walsall
EWINS						
1840	1900	1750	1840	168572	SSX	West
EXALL						
1700	1800	....	....	111333	HAM	North West
EXCEL						
....	....	ALL	ALL	132144	ALL	Name Study
EXCELL						
1780	1860	1700	1800	132144	SSX	ALL
EXELBY						
1620	1900	1620	1900	150126	CON	St Keverne
....	....	1859	1880	136913	DUR	Hartlepool
1755	1992	....	....	112380	YKS	Kirby Malzeard
1880	1920	....	....	136913	YKS	York
EXFORD						
1860	1900	ALL	ALL	120650	DBY	Chesterfield
1817	1849	1849	1860	120650	IRL	???
....	....	1750	1817	120650	SCT	???
1841	1841	ALL	ALL	120650	YKS	Hull
EXLEY						
1880	1950	....	....	127744	DBY	Whaley Bridge
1830	1950	....	....	127744	LAN	Gt Harwood
1814	1879	1700	1814	128031	YKS	Sheffield
EXON						
....	....	1800	1850	145688	LIN	Grimsby
....	....	1800	....	145688	YKS	Brigham
EXTON						
1804	1870	....	1880	171441	KEN	Boughton Under Blean
1796	1881	1796	1881	123404	LEI	Bucksminster
1615	1791	1615	1800	123404	RUT	Empingham
1650	1750	1600	1800	174599	WIL	Heytesbury
EYCOTT						
1788	1788	1700	1800	126667	GLS	Cirencester
EYERS						
....	....	1800	ALL	164615	DEV	Chittlehampton

Known From	To	Researching From	To	Ref	Cty	Place
EYERS contd.						
1830	1851	1852	1992	127787	DOR	Wimborne
....	....	1700	1850	101273	WIL	Enford
EYKYN						
....	....	ALL	ALL	173088	SAL	Bridgnorth
EYLES						
1562	1992	....	....	136417	AVN	Yate
1830	1855	1700	1900	136034	GLS	Cirencester
....	....	1850	1890	159573	LND	Kensington
1793	1973	ALL	1793	115126	NTH	Moulton
1776	1880	1700	1800	147397	NTH	Moulton
1792	1837	1750	1791	175846	SSX	Burwash
1560	1810	1600	1830	156930	WIL	ALL
1770	1810	1740	1830	156930	WIL	Aldbourne
EYLEY						
1727	1727	ALL	1727	157902	YKS	ALL
EYNES						
1450	1550	1400	1550	154881	SAL	Church Stretton
EYRE						
1812	....	1750	1825	138185	DBY	ALL
1778	1815	1700	1778	155489	DBY	Castleton
1844	1900	1700	1844	138657	LAN	Lancaster
1840	1960	1815	1840	155489	LAN	Manchester
1850	1992	1700	1850	150886	LIN	North
1811	1938	1700	1900	177369	LIN	Crowle
1781	1829	....	1781	161691	NTT	Southwell
ALL	ALL	ALL	ALL	151416	SSX	Brighton
1788	....	ALL	1788	102350	YKS	Braithwell
1788	1815	1700	1815	141097	YKS	Braithwell
1821	....	ALL	1821	104299	YKS	Cawthorne
1795	1821	ALL	1795	104299	YKS	Ouzelwell Green
1750	1950	1750	1950	114529	YKS	Sheffield
1850	1876	1800	1850	128368	YKS	Sheffield
1788	1815	1700	1815	141097	YKS	Wadworth
1720	1880	1650	1720	109703	YKS	Whitley
EYRES						
1650	1810	....	....	151351	DOR	Child Okeford
1834	....	1800	1900	122688	DOR	Holwell
1810	1881	....	1810	125954	DOR	Sherborne
1500	1900	1500	1900	170216	WIL	ALL
EYTE						
1850	1900	1700	1850	107271	NTH	ALL
EZARD						
1860	....	1700	1860	130435	YKS	Bridlington
FABIAN						
....	....	ALL	ALL	141712	ALL	Name Study
1620	....	1550	1650	122521	SSX	Crowhurst
FACER						
1719	1800	ALL	1800	137286	BDF	Houghton Conquest
1835	1873	1700	1835	156248	NTH	Long Buckby
FACEY						
1832	1992	1700	1832	174041	DEV	Braunton
FAGAIN						
1865	1950	1865	1925	138096	AGY	Holyhead
FAGAN						
1854	1912	ALL	ALL	178152	HAM	Southampton
1840	1982	1800	1840	161195	WEM	Tullystown
FAGG						
1800	1992	ALL	ALL	148520	KEN	ALL
1686	1992	?	1686	139165	KEN	Elham
1737	....	....	1760	171441	KEN	Thanet
?	?	?	?	166642	KEN	Whitstable
FAHERTY						
....	....	ALL	ALL	123412	ALL	Name Study
....	....	ALL	ALL	123412	ALL	ALL
....	....	1840	1880	170348	IRL	???
1874	....	1840	1880	170348	LND	Woolwich
1805	1972	ALL	ALL	123412	WAR	Birmingham
FAHEY						
1840	1960	1700	1840	140260	GAL	Ballymalward
FAIERS						
1867	1992	1600	1867	123420	SFK	Bury St Edmunds
FAIL						
1825	1850	1700	1920	139203	DUR	Sunderland
FAILES						
1700	1900	....	....	169129	CAM	???
1700	1900	....	....	169129	NFK	West
FAILL						
1780	1840	....	....	102741	NBL	Rothbury
FAIR						
1600	1860	ALL	ALL	149063	BEW	Coldingham
1830	1840	1820	1850	149063	ROX	Crailing
1840	1900	1840	1900	149063	ROX	Morebattle
FAIRALL						
1760	1960	1700	1760	167061	SSX	Wartling
FAIRBAIRN						
1798	1900	1500	1800	144347	BEW	ALL
1819	....	ALL	ALL	131415	BEW	South
1890	....	1700	1900	173347	CAV	Cootehill
1720	1900	ALL	ALL	146803	ELN	Innerwick
1810	1970	1700	1810	130885	NBL	Border
1849	1864	ALL	1849	122386	NBL	Kyloe
1798	1900	1500	1800	144347	ROX	ALL
1920	....	ALL	ALL	143758	ROX	Camptown
1850	1992	1850	1992	144347	???	Edinburgh
FAIRBANK						
1760	1992	....	....	110027	YKS	Elland
1841	1841	1800	1841	108715	YKS	Hightown
1760	1992	....	....	110027	YKS	Ripponden
FAIRBRASS						
1890	....	1860	1992	135429	ESS	West Ham
1880	1900	1840	1992	135429	KEN	Eastry
1860	1880	1860	1992	135429	MDX	Poplar
FAIRBROTHER						
1848	1848	ALL	1992	125113	LAN	Ashton Under Lyne
ALL	1850	....	....	110000	LAN	Bolton
ALL	1850	....	....	110000	LAN	Bury
FAIRBURN						
1900	1992	....	....	172235	KEN	Maidstone
ALL	1900	1825	1879	172235	LND	ALL
FAIRCHILD						
....	....	ALL	ALL	123447	ALL	Name Study
....	....	ALL	ALL	130710	ALL	ALL
1500	1900	....	....	130710	CAM	ALL
1560	1992	....	1992	123447	DEV	ALL
1598	1900	1598	1750	130710	DEV	Barnstaple
1901	1901	ALL	ALL	165085	HRT	Hoddesdon
1860	1992	ALL	1850	125504	LIN	Grantham
1789	1860	1789	1860	130710	LND	Lambeth
FAIRCLOUGH						
....	....	1700	1850	105279	DBY	Belper
1798	1823	1775	1798	179523	LAN	Aughton
1780	1951	1700	1780	163783	LAN	Kirkham
1796	1861	1750	1900	169161	LAN	Liverpool
1700	1712	1700	1720	117145	LAN	Manchester
1761	1774	ALL	ALL	141615	LAN	Pilling
1860	1900	1860	1881	119385	LAN	Preston
1800	1867	....	....	171824	LAN	St Helens
1785	1840	1740	1841	119385	LAN	Stalmine
1870	1950	....	....	105279	WAR	Birmingham
FAIREY						
1836	1930	1700	1850	125628	LND	Shoreditch
FAIRFAX						
....	....	ALL	ALL	123455	ALL	Name Study
1190	1992	1190	1992	123455	ALL	ALL
1750	1800	1600	1750	160598	YKS	Whitby
FAIRFAX-CARLISLE						
1800	1934	1700	1800	148865	WYK	Pudsey
FAIRFOOT						
1850	1916	1840	1900	134376	ALL	ALL
FAIRHALL						
1332	1900	....	....	172456	ALL	???
1851	1901	1586	1851	102512	SSX	Brighton
FAIRHEAD						
1810	1992	ALL	ALL	115762	ESS	Kelvedon
FAIRHURST						
1801	1851	1750	1851	157678	LAN	Halsall
1800	1992	1700	1800	146110	LAN	Ormskirk
1786	1992	1786	1992	110396	LAN	Wigan
1780	1820	....	....	126497	LAN	Wigan
1820	1992	1700	1960	149780	LAN	Wigan
FAIRLESS						
1717	1900	1600	1717	178543	NBL	Allendale
FAIRLEY						
1750	1992	1750	1850	123463	LKS	Biggar
FAIRMAN						
1810	1810	1700	1810	170542	KEN	Ash
1860	1960	ALL	ALL	171883	LND	???
FAIRNINGTON						
1900	1992	ALL	ALL	113662	DUR	Gateshead
FAIRS						
1831	1858	1800	1900	118192	SSX	Brighton
FAIRWEATHER						
1874	1992	1700	1874	117595	CAM	Peterborough
1800	....	1741	1800	129895	SFK	Parham
1863	1863	1700	1863	117595	YKS	York

Known From	To	Researching From	To	Ref	Cty	Place
FAITH						
1844	1928	ALL	1844	108553	SSX	Sidlesham
FAITHFUL						
1627	1627	1590	1630	124974	HAM	Kingsclere
1806	1872	ALL	1806	138290	LND	St Clement Danes
1806	1872	ALL	1806	138290	MDX	St Clement Danes
FAITHFULL						
....	....	ALL	ALL	123498	ALL	Name Study
....	....	1580	1842	123501	HAM	ALL
1750	1850	1500	1850	175463	HAM	ALL
1832	1930	ALL	1832	147877	HAM	Binsted
1751	1785	1785	1818	123501	HAM	Kingsley
1830	1860	1800	1860	176648	HAM	Portsmouth
1842	1992	1750	1842	123501	SOM	Bruton
1818	1820	1775	1818	123501	SOM	South Cadbury
1830	1860	1800	1860	176648	SXW	Selsey
....	....	1580	1842	123501	WIL	South
FALAYS						
1250	1311	1312	1800	123544	YKS	Drax
FALCONER						
1858	1878	1830	1992	166782	ABD	Aberdeen
1759	1817	1500	1759	143073	BAN	Cullen
1795	1797	....	....	168203	CAI	Dunbeath
1766	1776	....	....	168203	CAI	Latheron
1820	1856	1700	1900	137855	MOR	Forres
1872	1888	1870	1890	137855	RFW	Greenock
FALDO						
1450	1750	1450	1750	167924	BDF	Bedford
1560	1720	1560	1720	167924	BDF	Biddenham
1700	1760	1700	1760	167924	BDF	Campton
FALEGAS						
1451	1537	1452	1800	123544	LAN	???
FALKE						
1100	1400	....	....	100420	WAR	Meriden
FALKENER						
1713	1814	1814	1992	151688	LIN	Carlby
1725	1824	1824	1992	151688	LIN	Deeping St James
1680	1757	1757	1992	151688	RUT	Essendine
1680	1757	1757	1992	151688	RUT	Tinwell
1587	1727	1727	1992	151688	RUT	Uppingham
FALKINDER						
1820	1840	1600	1850	135275	LIN	Spilsby
FALKINGHAM						
1825	1850	1700	1825	143243	YKS	Harrogate
FALKNER						
1694	1740	1600	1694	150150	NTH	Naseby
FALL						
....	....	ALL	ALL	123528	ALL	Name Study
1654	1940	....	....	128996	CAM	Thornley
1800	....	ALL	ALL	152226	DOR	Kinson
1771	1863	1700	1770	137561	YKS	Beeston
1771	1863	1700	1770	137561	YKS	Hunslet
FALLA						
....	....	ALL	ALL	123536	ALL	Name Study
....	....	ALL	ALL	123536	ALL	ALL
1870	1960	1850	1992	123536	DUR	Darlington
1800	1900	1800	1992	177180	HRT	Bovingdon
1810	1900	1800	1992	123536	NBL	Belford
1770	1812	1700	1850	123536	NBL	Kirknewton
1850	1992	1800	1850	160075	NBL	???
FALLACE						
1869	1879	ALL	ALL	104191	MDX	London
FALLADOWN						
1707	1720	1680	1707	177393	YKS	Owthorne
FALLAS						
1750	1850	1750	1850	122254	LAN	???
FALLER						
1840	1900	ALL	ALL	124605	MDX	St Pancras
FALLOWES						
1327	1719	1199	1776	123544	CHS	Alderley
FALLOWFIELD						
1780	1825	1600	1780	102571	LAN	Preston St John
1735	1800	1700	1735	116114	YKS	Pocklington
1560	1800	1560	1800	167924	YKS	Pocklington
FALLOWS						
....	....	ALL	ALL	123544	ALL	Name Study
1327	1719	1199	1776	123544	CHS	Alderley
1711	1752	ALL	ALL	141615	LAN	Over Kellet
1870	....	ALL	ALL	100390	LAN	???
1774	1872	ALL	1774	142107	SFK	Capel St Mary
1651	1954	1600	1651	173649	STS	Butterton
1527	1800	1800	1837	123544	STS	Newcastle Under Lyne
1586	1851	1750	1800	123544	YKS	Halifax
FALLOWS contd.						
1800	1823	1750	1800	123544	YKS	Stainland
FALOYS						
1216	1276	1276	1800	123544	YKS	Drax
FALWIZ						
1378	1448	1449	1800	123544	CHS	Alderley
FALXMAN						
1770	1820	1700	1992	167592	MDX	London
1750	1760	1650	1992	167592	YKS	York
FAMILTON						
1880	1925	1850	1900	166391	DUR	Sunderland
FANCETT						
....	....	1860	1880	142131	KEN	Paddock Wood
FANCOURT						
....	....	ALL	ALL	144436	ALL	Name Study
FANCY						
1737	1976	1737	1976	173584	DOR	Poole
FANE						
1722	1992	1558	?	112968	SOM	Stoke Sub Hamdon
FANNING						
1900	1992	1800	1900	102873	MDX	Tottenham
FANNIPAT						
1714	....	1500	1840	164879	SOM	ALL
FANSTONE						
1400	1600	1400	1550	167770	SOM	Yeovil
1880	1930	1910	1922	124001	SSX	Brighton
1500	1992	1400	1992	167770	WIL	Downton
FANTHAM						
1830	1880	1830	1880	133515	LEI	Sutton Cheney
1790	1830	1600	1790	133515	WAR	Knowle
FANTHORPE						
?	?	?	?	133728	LIN	Lindsey Villages
FANTOM						
1841	1861	ALL	1841	171468	YKS	Sheffield
FAR						
1750	1800	1600	1900	166804	HAM	Dean
1750	1800	1600	1900	166804	HAM	Vernham
FARBUS						
1793	1992	1650	1992	123560	KEN	Canterbury
FARDELL						
1780	1871	1871	1900	139785	ESS	North West
FARDON						
1677	1769	1600	1750	173983	OXF	North Newington
1851	....	ALL	ALL	118877	WAR	Bourton On Hill
1763	1764	1700	1800	135496	WAR	Sibford
FAREN						
1894	1896	1884	1900	138266	DUR	South Shields
FARENDEN						
1726	1881	....	....	135437	SSX	Eastergate
1832	1832	....	....	135437	SSX	Eatham
1813	1813	....	....	135437	SSX	Sidlesham
1891	1891	....	....	135437	SSX	Yapton
FARGLE						
1860	1885	1700	1860	168246	MLN	Edinburgh
FARGUS						
....	....	ALL	ALL	175331	ALL	ALL
FARINGTON						
1800	1875	1800	1875	133450	LAN	Leyland
FARLAM						
1743	....	1600	1743	116637	NBL	Allendale
FARLEIGH						
1753	1753	1700	1800	105333	DEV	Rattery
1753	1753	1700	1800	105333	DEV	South Brent
1753	1753	1700	1800	105333	DEV	Ugborough
FARLEY						
....	....	1780	1880	108863	CAV	???
1852	1930	1800	1860	177938	DEV	Lydford
1815	1934	1700	1837	176370	DEV	Plymouth
....	....	1650	1750	156795	DOR	East
....	....	1700	1910	123390	HEF	Munsley
1700	1970	1550	1730	123579	KEN	Central
1700	1970	1550	1730	123579	KEN	East
....	....	1700	1850	179531	KEN	Leigh
1780	1864	....	....	116602	KEN	Ramsgate
1700	1970	1550	1730	123579	KEN	Thanet
....	....	1850	1910	102318	LND	ALL
?	?	1600	1860	120723	LND	Bermondsey
1810	1992	1750	1810	123153	SOM	Bath
1700	1820	1600	1992	127833	SRY	Cobham
1819	1840	1700	1819	148334	WIL	Salisbury
1774	1881	1700	1950	159964	WIL	Stockton
....	....	1600	1899	115975	WIL	Wylye Valley
FARLOW						
1822	....	....	1840	171441	WOR	Wrocester

Known From	To	Researching From	To	Ref	Cty	Place
FARMAR						
1600	1699	1600	1699	169781	IRL	???
FARMARY						
1822	1841	1773	1851	108901	LIN	Roxby Cum Risby
FARMER						
1650	1750	1630	1750	118869	BDF	Steppingley
1780	1850	....	....	157724	BRK	Gt Coxwell
1841	....	....	....	157724	BRK	Reading
1831	1850	1750	1900	106941	DUR	Darlington
1780	1805	1750	1810	171158	ESS	Writtle
1828	1851	1750	1828	178381	GLS	Bourton
1853	1964	1700	1853	128937	GLS	Hardwicke
1725	1825	1700	1820	124974	HAM	Kingsclere
1814	1881	1750	1814	149918	HAM	Minstead
....	....	1600	1950	134546	IOW	Sandown
....	....	1600	1950	134546	IOW	Shanklin
1828	1992	1828	....	123609	KEN	Chatham
1750	1800	....	....	124621	LEI	Great Eastern
1744	1923	1600	1800	135968	LEI	Thornton
....	....	1600	1900	179531	LIN	ALL
1830	1992	1800	1885	112143	MDX	London
1800	1850	1800	1850	135607	MDX	Shoreditch
1778	1851	ALL	1778	175994	MON	Penallt
....	....	ALL	1830	112143	NBL	North Newcastle
1650	1690	1600	1690	111538	NTH	Daventry
1720	1950	1700	1900	123595	NTH	Duston
1813	1859	1700	1830	171662	NTH	Kilsby
1856	1871	....	1856	122378	NTT	Nottingham
1650	1720	1600	1720	154881	SAL	Chirbury
1700	1900	1600	1800	143030	SAL	Shrewsbury
1850	1900	1800	1850	168777	SRY	Egham
1800	1992	1700	1800	145017	STS	Lichfield
FARMERY						
....	....	ALL	ALL	149101	ALL	Name Study
1698	1992	1600	1698	102342	LIN	Hardwickhill
1794	1851	1700	1794	115401	LIN	Searby
FARN						
1760	1954	1700	1760	124583	WAR	Long Lawford
FARNAGH						
1812	1911	?	?	123617	LAN	Goosnargh
1812	1911	?	?	123617	LAN	Woodplumpton
FARNARTH						
1812	1911	?	?	123617	DBY	Derby
1812	1911	?	?	123617	NTT	Nottingham
FARNATH						
1812	1911	?	?	123617	DBY	ALL
1812	1911	?	?	123617	NTT	ALL
1812	1911	?	?	123617	STS	ALL
FARNDALE						
1760	1820	1600	1875	123625	NYK	Brotton
FARNELL						
....	....	1800	1895	161659	BDF	ALL
1890	1992	1500	1890	134600	YKS	Halifax
FARNETH						
1812	1911	?	?	123617	LAN	Bury
1812	1911	?	?	123617	LAN	Liverpool
1812	1911	?	?	123617	LAN	Preston
FARNHAM						
....	1823	1790	1823	133639	SOM	Coker
1760	....	....	....	167037	SRY	Haselmere
FARNOL						
....	....	ALL	ALL	101052	ALL	Name Study
1814	1992	1700	1992	101052	STS	???
1814	1992	1700	1992	101052	WAR	???
FARNON						
....	....	1800	1900	145343	NIR	ALL
FARNORTH						
1840	....	....	....	132632	LAN	Middleton
1840	....	....	....	132632	LAN	Oldham
FARNOTH						
1820	1850	1750	1820	132632	DBY	???
1812	1911	?	?	123617	LAN	Liverpool
1812	1911	?	?	123617	LAN	Preston
1812	1911	?	?	123617	LAN	Wigan
FARNS						
....	1700	....	....	174564	LEI	???
FARNSWORTH						
1713	1713	ALL	1713	159077	NTH	Tansor
1862	1910	1750	1960	145858	NTT	Nottingham
1799	....	ALL	1799	102350	YKS	Rotherham
FARO						
1770	1775	1750	1800	133450	CON	Roche
FARQUAR GRAY						
1874	1874	1800	1874	104728	GLS	Bristol

Known From	To	Researching From	To	Ref	Cty	Place
FARQUAR						
1880	?	1750	1992	167592	YKS	Castleford
1860	?	1750	1992	167592	YKS	Whitwood
FARQUHAR						
1860	1920	ALL	ALL	156604	ABD	New Aberbour
1870	1900	1600	....	161268	ABD	New Deer
1868	1906	1800	1868	101427	BAN	Deskford
1750	1800	1750	1992	104671	SHI	ALL
1750	1965	....	....	137820	SHI	Fetlar
1720	1965	....	....	137820	SHI	Mid Yell
1760	1965	....	....	137820	SHI	North Yell
1758	1965	....	....	137820	SHI	Northmavine
1720	1965	....	....	137820	SHI	South Yell
FARQUHARSON						
1700	1960	1750	1960	145467	ABD	Glenbuchat
1820	1900	1800	1992	133450	ABD	Haughton
FARR						
1838	1992	1700	1835	107123	CHS	Congleton
....	....	....	....	107123	CHS	Macclesfield
1780	....	1700	1850	141739	DOR	???
....	....	1600	1660	163562	ESS	Great Burstead
1839	1992	1760	1839	131296	HAM	Portsmouth
1831	1838	1700	1850	131296	HAM	Warblington
1866	1958	1866	1958	156639	LND	ALL
1758	1876	ALL	1876	156582	MDX	Hanwell
?	?	1700	1850	123668	SOM	Frome
1850	1953	....	....	178276	SRY	Byfleet
....	....	1600	1690	163562	SRY	Croydon
1770	1992	1600	1770	178276	SRY	Witley-Godalming
1785	1790	1750	1850	113743	SSX	Rye
1797	1992	1700	1800	153087	WOR	ALL
FARRALL						
1762	1818	1730	1830	134406	CHS	Frodsham
1800	1900	ALL	ALL	123676	LND	East End
1800	1900	ALL	ALL	123676	LND	Poplar
1762	1814	....	....	173932	SSX	Arundel
FARRANCE						
1850	1860	1800	1850	177024	MDX	Westminster
FARRAND						
1565	1637	....	....	168513	YKS	Almondbury
1660	1684	1600	1700	170348	YKS	Kirkheaton
FARRANT						
....	....	ALL	ALL	123684	ALL	Name Study
....	....	ALL	ALL	123692	ALL	Name Study
ALL	ALL	ALL	ALL	123692	ALL	ALL
1729	1734	....	1729	131385	DEV	Aylesbeare
1802	1992	1750	1850	110604	DEV	Chardstock
1720	1860	1700	1900	136980	SFK	Haverhill
1800	1881	1700	1992	170585	SFK	Haverhill
1795	1992	1795	1992	172952	SSX	Framfield
FARRANTS						
1761	1783	1700	1783	123129	SFK	Cavendish
1712	1782	1650	1782	123129	SFK	Hawkedon
1784	1808	....	....	123129	SFK	Horringer
FARRAR						
1871	1992	1800	1900	127361	WRY	Dewsbury
1800	1916	1600	1900	154601	WYK	Batley
1800	1916	1600	1900	154601	WYK	Desbury
1871	1900	1600	1992	172863	YKS	Harrogate
1820	1992	1700	1850	126586	YKS	Leeds
FARRAT						
1700	1739	1550	1699	102830	DBY	ALL
FARRELL						
....	....	ALL	ALL	124850	ALL	Name Study
....	....	ALL	ALL	177466	CHS	???
1826	....	....	....	116750	IRL	Tippary
1801	1926	....	....	173932	SRY	Ashtead
FARREN						
1831	1896	1700	1830	131245	WAR	Coventry
1777	1813	1700	1777	176710	WAR	Coventry
FARRENT						
1900	1950	1500	1980	164992	LND	ALL
1870	1950	1500	1980	164992	SRY	Battersea
1870	1950	1500	1980	164992	SRY	Lambeth
FARRER						
1700	1860	ALL	ALL	118869	BDF	Flitwick
1850	1914	1780	1850	122351	BDF	Oakley
1700	....	1650	....	116920	DUR	???
1750	1850	....	....	125199	MDX	St Pancras
1747	1786	1728	1812	169552	WES	Staveley
1660	1720	1600	1720	111538	WRY	Calverley
1810	1820	....	....	103721	WRY	Leeds
1633	1743	1574	1844	170267	YKS	Pudsey
1700	1850	1700	1920	115363	YKS	Ripon

Known From	To	Researching From	To	Ref	Cty	Place
FARRINGTON						
1702	1772	....	....	138401	CAE	Bangor
ALL	1702	....	....	138401	CHS	Chester
1801	1801	1700	1800	118605	CHS	Plemstall
1822	1992	1640	1822	123706	KEN	Sittingbourne
1844	1870	ALL	ALL	138886	LAN	Preston
1800	1992	....	....	126543	MDX	Brentford
1841	1871	1700	1841	168033	MDX	Chiswick
1858	ALL	ALL	1880	116734	MDX	Old Brentford
1800	1992	....	....	126543	MDX	Turnham Green
1841	1871	1700	1841	168033	MDX	Turnham Green
FARRIS						
1800	....	....	....	132497	KEN	Lydd
1800	....	....	....	132497	KEN	Lyming
1800	....	....	....	132497	KEN	Lympne
FARRO						
1800	1850	1700	1800	168726	DBY	Castleton
FARROW						
....	....	1800	1900	134546	BDF	Yielden
1700	1810	1650	1750	151742	DUR	South
1852	1992	1700	1852	105635	LAN	Whitworth
1790	1966	1837	1966	148067	MDX	Tottenham
1800	1992	....	1800	150851	NFK	Central
1800	1992	....	1800	150851	NFK	North
1835	1920	1800	1950	107980	NFK	Beeston Regis
1805	1992	....	1805	123714	NFK	Diss
1790	1810	1750	1850	174599	NFK	Stanfield
1780	1830	1700	1850	132659	NFK	Swanton Abbott
1731	1779	1700	1800	107980	NFK	Yelverton
....	....	1850	1950	134546	NTH	Ivywell
1700	....	....	....	114642	SFK	West
1830	1889	....	1900	171441	SFK	Bury St Edmunds
1830	1869	....	1900	171441	SFK	Hawstead
1766	....	ALL	1766	133957	SXW	Funtington
1818	1835	1785	1835	119717	YKS	York
FARTHING						
....	....	ALL	ALL	124486	ALL	Name Study
1853	1947	1700	1992	110418	DOR	Peasdown
1853	1947	1700	1992	110418	DOR	Zears
1853	1947	1700	1992	110418	SOM	Bourton
FARWELL						
1864	1992	1700	1864	150223	DOR	Weymouth
FASNACHT						
1910	1930	1860	1940	124737	SRY	Tooting
1860	1910	1850	1950	124737	SRY	Wimbledon
FATHERS						
1740	1750	1700	1740	134627	NTH	Kings Sutton
1749	1850	1740	1850	134627	OXF	Upper Heyford
1851	1880	1700	1851	101389	SOM	Hinton Charterhouse
1855	1890	1850	1930	160067	SSX	Brighton
FATKIN						
1781	....	ALL	1781	164623	DUR	Gateshead
FATOUX						
....	....	1870	1900	106127	ALL	ALL
FAULCONBRIDGE						
1802	1928	ALL	ALL	126721	NTT	Bulwell
FAULDER						
1865	1892	1825	1865	145084	CMA	Heskett
1800	1850	1800	1850	168432	CUL	ALL
FAULDING						
....	....	ALL	1570	176656	IRL	???
1570	1950	1570	1950	176656	LIN	North
1680	1740	....	....	103721	LIN	Wootton
....	....	1750	1830	108510	LIN	???
....	....	1750	1830	108510	YKS	Hull
FAULDS						
1827	1900	1700	1900	144037	LKS	Glasgow
FAULKENER						
....	1754	1600	1900	135968	RUT	Norcott
FAULKNER						
1900	1960	1700	1900	158976	BKM	South
1820	1992	1800	1820	157740	BRK	Abingdon
1839	1886	1700	1839	115185	CHS	Runcorn
1830	....	1750	1830	179140	ESS	St Pancras
1800	1850	1700	1800	171182	HAM	Ham
1860	1992	1800	1860	155691	HAM	Ringwood
....	....	1835	1840	161357	KEN	Westerham
....	....	1870	1920	147613	LAN	Barrow In Furness
1782	1992	1600	1782	123730	LAN	Eccles
1782	1992	1600	1782	123730	LAN	Salford
1850	1900	1600	1850	160784	LEI	Ridlington
1845	1895	1895	1992	151688	LIN	South Somercotes
1770	1796	1796	1992	151688	LIN	Stamford
1799	1856	1856	1992	151688	LIN	Sutterton
FAULKNER contd.						
1750	1900	1700	1900	123722	LND	City
1835	1900	1600	1835	113263	MDX	London
....	....	1750	1870	147613	OXF	Chadlington
1808	1835	1750	1810	162396	OXF	Murcott
1678	1736	1736	1992	151688	RUT	Great Casterton
1733	1773	....	....	160113	RUT	Ryall
....	....	1700	1992	123749	SOM	Isle Abbott
1890	1992	ALL	1890	123749	SOM	Isle Brewers
1813	1836	....	....	161357	SRY	Lingfield
1841	1853	....	....	161357	SRY	Oxted
1790	1850	....	....	118354	STS	Anslow
1803	1900	1600	1800	124176	WOR	Badsey
FAULKS						
1768	1768	1760	1767	159042	LEI	Firsby On The Wreak
1800	....	1750	1992	101656	LEI	Hinckley
1761	1803	1700	1803	170747	RUT	Langham
FAUSETT						
1875	1920	1850	1992	133450	KEN	Broadstairs
FAUTLEY						
....	....	ALL	ALL	123757	ALL	Name Study
1814	1850	1750	1880	152285	LND	Shoreditch
....	....	1750	1992	123757	SRY	Camberwell
....	....	1530	1992	123757	SSX	Hastings
....	....	1530	1992	123757	SSX	Rye
FAUX						
1866	1992	....	1866	129186	LAN	Chorlton On Medwick
1800	1850	1700	1800	118907	NFK	ALL
FAVELL						
1860	1951	....	....	142360	BRK	Slough
1542	1733	1500	1733	102830	STS	Darlaston
1770	1925	1700	1770	165182	YKS	Spennithorne
FAVIER						
....	....	ALL	ALL	120618	IRL	???
1850	1900	ALL	ALL	120618	SRY	London
FAVILL						
1555	1733	1500	1800	160873	STS	Darlaston
FAWBERT						
....	....	1836	1900	131628	YKS	Bradford
FAWCETT						
1694	1792	1600	1694	152196	CMA	Brigham
1824	1824	1790	1824	159905	CUL	Alston
1840	1880	1830	1900	159905	DUR	South Shields
1799	....	....	....	148768	IRL	Dublin
1861	1881	1848	1881	141194	KEN	Chatham
1848	1861	1848	1861	141194	KEN	Gillingham
1879	1887	ALL	1880	160733	LAN	North
1882	1897	1800	1924	146390	LAN	Birkenhead
1855	1930	1800	1900	122653	LAN	Lancaster
1650	1992	1400	1992	123765	LIN	ALL
1691	1912	ALL	1691	100587	NYK	Appleton Wisk
1691	1912	ALL	1691	100587	NYK	Brompton By Northallerton
1691	1912	ALL	1691	100587	NYK	Scorton
1691	1912	ALL	1691	100587	NYK	St Smeaton
1743	1743	1713	1743	139149	WES	Firbank
1684	1714	1600	1684	102571	WES	Ravonstonedale
1800	1900	....	....	134198	WYK	Horsforth
1770	1790	1700	1790	134198	WYK	Tadcaster
1778	1881	....	1778	168424	YKS	North West
1800	1992	1650	1800	175560	YKS	Halifax
FAWCUS						
1700	1840	ALL	1750	142301	NBL	Warkworth
FAWDINGTON						
1710	1841	1710	1900	167002	NYK	Asenby
1705	1716	1650	1716	167002	NYK	Skipworth
FAWKEN						
1500	1600	....	....	100420	WAR	Meriden
FAWKES						
1627	1760	....	....	164631	DBY	Weston On Trent
1712	1992	....	1712	144363	ENG	ALL
1766	1850	....	....	164631	LEI	Castle Donnington
1732	1795	1700	1775	167533	SOM	Bath
1775	1850	ALL	ALL	111511	YKS	West Riding
FAWLK						
....	....	ALL	ALL	147834	ALL	Name Study
FAXON						
1900	1992	ALL	1992	104299	YKS	Penistone
FAYERS						
1821	1900	1821	1900	123773	LND	Bethnal Green
1800	1950	....	....	162914	NFK	Kings Lynn
1792	....	....	....	123773	SFK	Ubbeston
FAYLE						
1825	1992	1700	1992	160385	IOM	???

Known From	Known To	Researching From	Researching To	Ref	Cty	Place
FAYLE contd.						
1850	1880	....	1850	163295	LAN	Preston
FAZAKERLEY						
1864	1992	1700	1864	123943	STS	Woolstanton
FAZAN						
1760	1992	1690	1992	108375	MDX	Wesminster
1760	1992	1690	1992	108375	SRY	Hammersmith
FEAD						
....	1700	1650	1720	162507	LND	ALL
FEAKES						
....	....	ALL	ALL	123781	ALL	Name Study
1700	1780	1650	1800	139386	SFK	Wortham
FEAKINS						
1850	1900	1600	1850	123587	KEN	Maidstone
FEAR						
1810	1992	1810	1992	148156	CAM	North West
1825	1860	1825	1837	157880	GLS	Bristol
1878	....	1850	....	167290	LND	Holborn
1796	1843	1700	1796	123803	MDX	Islington
1581	1992	ALL	ALL	124982	SOM	Chew Magna
1836	1836	ALL	1992	168696	SOM	Kewstoke
1801	1985	ALL	1992	168696	SOM	Weston Super Mare
FEARDON						
....	....	1750	1900	173746	ALL	ALL
FEARING						
....	....	1910	....	124265	LAN	Claughton
FEARMAN						
1880	1992	1700	1880	167916	???	???
FEARN						
1730	1850	1700	1900	156744	DBY	Bonsall
1730	1850	1700	1900	156744	DBY	Derby
1730	1850	1700	1900	156744	DBY	Duffield
1737	1992	1700	1737	130257	SSX	Penworth
FEARNALL						
1840	1880	1700	1992	145432	WOR	Kidderminster
FEARNLEY						
1767	....	....	....	101869	LND	Aldgate
1783	1866	1783	1866	142980	WYK	Bradford
....	....	?	1870	176702	WYK	Bradford
FEARNS						
1710	1840	1700	1860	142174	STS	Yoxall
FEARNSIDE						
1788	1820	1600	1788	175382	YKS	Leeds
FEARON						
....	....	1870	1891	156833	DOW	Newry
....	....	1870	1891	156833	DOW	Rostrevor
....	....	1891	ALL	156833	LAN	Liverpool
FEASBY						
....	....	1760	1820	145211	WRY	Pateley Bridge
FEAST						
1737	1737	1700	1740	102717	HRT	Stocking Pelham
1680	1680	1610	1680	155276	SFK	Claydon
FEATELEY						
1591	1646	1300	1591	132993	LAN	???
1591	1646	1300	1591	132993	OXF	Oxford
FEATHER						
1839	1850	1800	1850	175986	YKS	Bingley
1860	1992	1800	1900	114081	YKS	???
FEATHERBY						
1793	1816	1750	1830	176621	KEN	Chatham
FEATHERS						
....	....	1874	ALL	149187	ANS	Dundee
FEATHERSTONE						
1730	1790	1538	1790	118893	CUL	Alston
1719	1783	1600	1719	147346	DUR	St Johns Chapel
1790	1850	1538	1850	118893	DUR	St Johns
1860	....	1860	....	158011	LEI	Market Bosworth
....	....	1790	1850	103187	NYK	Danby
1600	1900	1600	1900	150932	NYK	Danby
1600	1700	....	....	100420	WAR	ALL
....	....	1500	1700	136298	YKS	ALL
1800	1850	....	....	177393	YKS	Carlton
1680	1780	....	....	140554	YKS	Cawood
1696	1800	1650	1696	177393	YKS	Cawood
1857	1857	1800	1857	163090	YKS	Foxholes
1790	1840	1760	1840	105759	YKS	Whitby
FEATHERSTONE-BECK						
1860	1881	1860	1881	158011	STS	Burton On Trent
FEATHERSTONEHAUGH						
....	....	1750	1850	144045	BKM	Newport Pagnell
1600	1750	1500	1800	144045	CUL	Kirkhaugh
1736	1992	1500	1773	144045	NBL	Hexham
FEATONBY						
1769	1861	1700	1747	150894	DUR	Durham City
FEAVER						
....	....	ALL	ALL	137766	ALL	Name Study
FEAVIOUR						
....	....	1700	1823	129356	NFK	Kirby Bedon
1793	1810	1750	1800	129356	SFK	Reydon
FEBEN						
1790	1880	1700	1950	136840	HAM	Fareham
1830	1880	1830	1950	136840	IOW	Ryde Area
FECHTMAN						
1800	1900	1800	1900	107476	LND	East
1800	1900	1800	1900	107476	LND	City
FEENEY						
1848	1992	1700	1848	109177	IRL	???
FEEST						
....	....	ALL	ALL	123838	SSX	Worthing
FEHNERS						
1868	1881	1881	1992	149357	MON	Newport
FEIST						
1690	1830	....	....	119121	SSX	Horsham
FELKIN						
1754	1880	....	....	103373	WAR	Birmingham
FELL						
....	....	ALL	ALL	123846	ALL	Name Study
1200	1960	1200	1960	123846	ALL	ALL
1768	1826	1730	1770	170348	DBY	Whitwell
1774	1992	1700	1775	116416	ESS	East Horndon
1860	1870	1860	1870	143588	EYK	Hull
....	....	ALL	ALL	123846	GLS	Bristol
....	....	ALL	ALL	123846	GLS	Gloucester
1839	1992	1700	1840	148059	LAN	Preston
1682	1694	ALL	ALL	141615	LAN	Priest Hutton
1811	1832	1700	1900	118168	LAN	Ulveston
1815	1815	1700	1880	156493	NTT	Nottingham
1760	1792	....	....	129747	SFK	Ipswich
?	?	ALL	ALL	123846	WAR	Birmingham
?	?	ALL	ALL	123846	WAR	Yardley
1790	1992	ALL	1790	179345	YKS	Hull
FELLINDER						
1755	1980	1749	1980	145009	GLS	Winchcombe
FELLINGHAM						
1707	1992	1600	1707	105392	NFK	Border
1707	1992	1600	1707	105392	SFK	Border
FELLOW						
1532	1640	1500	1640	102830	STS	Sedgely
1637	1715	1600	1750	160873	STS	Sedgley
FELLOWES						
....	1793	1700	1817	128961	HRT	Hemel Hempstead
1817	1968	1817	1992	128961	HRT	Redbourn
1792	1839	1979	1992	149543	MDX	Hayes
1750	1950	ALL	ALL	114235	NTH	???
FELLOWS						
1915	1992	1890	1992	146625	DBY	Huddersfield
1915	1992	1890	1992	146625	DBY	Leeds
....	....	ALL	ALL	178152	IOW	???
1757	1775	1720	1800	167002	MDX	London
1850	1900	1700	1850	140880	SSX	Hastings
1880	1992	1800	1880	116815	STS	West Bromwich
1768	1768	ALL	1872	143634	STS	Wolverhampton
1950	....	1940	1992	157392	STS	Wolverhampton
1850	1992	ALL	ALL	115002	WAR	Birmingham
FELLS						
1794	1992	ALL	1800	123854	BDF	Marston Mortaine
1794	1992	ALL	1800	123854	NTT	Hucknall
FELMINGHAM						
1936	1992	1860	1936	107301	KEN	Gillingham
?	?	?	?	107301	NFK	ALL
1833	1932	1700	1850	170836	SFK	Beccles
1784	1947	1700	1850	170836	SFK	Bungay
FELPES						
1711	1711	1700	1720	170143	SRY	Horsell
FELSTEAD						
....	....	1720	1790	102717	HRT	East
1745	1854	1700	1870	148121	HRT	Albury
1745	1854	1700	1870	148121	HRT	???
1875	1920	1700	1992	112003	STS	Burton Upon Trent
FELTHAM						
....	....	ALL	ALL	123870	ALL	Name Study
....	....	ALL	ALL	123870	ALL	ALL
1720	1841	ALL	1720	173304	DOR	Cranborne
1816	1908	ALL	ALL	153516	GLS	Stroud
1864	1865	1860	1870	123870	KEN	Lewisham
1830	1890	1830	1890	123870	MDX	London
1816	1908	ALL	ALL	153516	SOM	Failand
ALL	....	....	....	156221	SOM	Stogursey

Known From	To	Researching From	To	Ref	Cty	Place
FELTHAM contd.						
1870	1960	1870	1960	123870	SRY	New Malden
1500	1900	1500	1900	170216	WIL	ALL
1798	1800	1600	1800	123870	WIL	Hilperton
1700	1840	1600	1900	123862	WIL	Stourton
1820	1957	....	....	123862	???	Bristol
FELTON						
1810	1890	1750	1890	106690	SAL	Bridgnorth
1819	1868	1810	1825	149039	SAL	???
....	1939	....	....	123889	STS	Cannock
1828	1857	1858	1900	123889	STS	Codsall
1600	1800	1600	1900	177180	STS	Gnosall
1800	1992	1750	1980	107611	STS	Rugely
1857	....	....	....	123889	STS	Shareshill
1858	1863	1863	1950	123889	STS	West Bromwich
1865	1992	1865	....	160148	WLS	Laudgar
FENBY						
....	....	ALL	ALL	123897	ALL	Name Study
....	....	ALL	ALL	123897	ALL	ALL
1752	1790	1600	1752	175218	EYK	Preston
FENCOTT						
1900	....	1700	1900	144150	GLA	Merthyr Tydfil
....	....	1791	....	123900	HEF	Eardisland
1900	....	1700	1900	144150	HEF	Hereford
....	....	1791	....	123900	HEF	Leominster
....	....	1791	....	123900	HEF	Yatton
FENDER						
1844	....	1700	1850	161721	DUR	South Shields
1800	1992	1700	1800	123919	LAN	Blackburn
1800	1850	1700	1900	123919	NBL	???
FENLEY						
1850	1880	1750	1850	120529	OXF	Cuddesdon
FENN						
....	....	ALL	ALL	123927	ALL	Name Study
1780	1920	1770	1785	138770	BKM	Denham
1450	1800	1400	1500	138770	BKM	Ivinghoe
1545	1830	1500	1830	175218	BKM	Ivinghoe
1450	1800	1400	1500	138770	BKM	Pitstone
1900	1943	ALL	ALL	120057	HRT	Barnet
1595	1806	ALL	ALL	138770	HRT	Berkhampstead
1595	1806	ALL	ALL	138770	HRT	Northchurch
1750	1870	1700	1900	177180	HRT	Redburn
....	1870	1700	1870	178608	KEN	Deptford
1780	1835	1750	1800	177377	KEN	Rochester
1780	1865	1700	1780	141402	NFK	Hedenham
1721	1721	1700	1725	107360	NTH	Northampton
1820	1872	....	....	125202	SRY	???
....	....	....	?	141216	WAR	Birmingham
FENNA						
1550	1560	1550	1560	155020	CAE	Conwy
1600	1992	1600	1930	155020	CWD	Hope
1600	1992	1600	1930	155020	CWD	Wrexham
1762	1828	1700	1992	152692	DEN	Denbigh
1762	1828	1700	1992	152692	DEN	Wrexham
1606	1992	1606	1930	155020	MSY	Liverpool
FENNAH						
1640	1992	1640	1930	155020	CWD	Hawarden
1640	1992	1640	1930	155020	CWD	Wrexham
1606	1992	1606	1929	155020	MSY	Liverpool
FENNE						
1780	1920	1770	1785	138770	BKM	Denham
1450	1800	1400	1500	138770	BKM	Ivinghoe
1450	1800	1400	1500	138770	BKM	Pitstone
1595	1806	ALL	ALL	138770	HRT	Berkhampstead
1595	1806	ALL	ALL	138770	HRT	Northchurch
FENNEL						
....	....	....	1850	116866	ANT	???
1820	1860	1775	1850	116866	MDX	London
FENNELL						
1550	1992	1550	1850	134848	ALL	ALL
1875	1992	1850	1992	126799	ESS	West Ham
1880	1992	1700	1880	177067	GLS	Ampney Crucis
1750	1992	1700	1992	126799	HAM	Abbotts Ann
1835	1860	ALL	1835	111023	LAN	Walkden
1885	1930	....	....	163155	LIN	Sleaford
1580	1800	....	1800	133086	NTH	ALL
....	....	....	1850	133086	OXF	ALL
1750	1850	ALL	1750	115282	SSX	East
1850	1900	1820	1850	116076	SSX	Wadhurst
1680	1900	....	1900	133086	WAR	ALL
1779	1791	1791	?	128910	WAR	Bedworth
....	....	?	1779	128910	WAR	Walsgrave On Sowe
1700	1820	1760	1800	176958	YKS	Harewood
FENNER						
....	....	ALL	ALL	123935	ALL	Name Study
....	....	ALL	ALL	123935	ALL	ALL
1800	1890	ALL	ALL	123935	CAM	Cambridge
1750	1950	ALL	ALL	145726	GLS	ALL
1750	1950	ALL	ALL	145726	HEF	ALL
1680	1875	1775	1875	133450	KEN	Tonbridge
....	....	1750	1850	131962	LND	Stepney
1882	....	1882	1890	165360	SRY	Battersea
1700	1980	ALL	ALL	123935	SSX	ALL
FENNEY						
1864	1992	1700	1864	123943	STS	Woolstanton
FENNIMORE						
1868	1932	....	1992	137642	OXF	Islip
FENNING						
1790	1830	1750	1830	136840	SFK	Finningham
FENSOM						
1840	1870	1540	1870	171379	BDF	Wilden
1811	1992	ALL	1811	105465	HUN	Great Staughton
FENTIMAN						
1756	1790	1756	1800	165360	KEN	Malling
1859	1886	....	1921	165360	MDX	Soho
1886	1896	1886	....	165360	SRY	Clapham
1841	1855	1800	1855	165360	SRY	Egham
1756	1832	1756	1992	165360	SRY	Lambeth
1390	1700	1390	1756	165360	YKS	West Riding
FENTON						
1500	1800	1500	1880	139858	ALL	ALL
....	....	1200	1992	159220	ALL	ALL
1831	1857	1800	1920	119555	DBY	Ilkeston
1876	1876	1500	1876	110310	LAN	Edgworth
1876	1895	1500	1876	110310	LAN	Liverpool
1818	1839	1800	1839	107573	LAN	Manchester
1810	1850	1750	1810	123978	LAN	Manchester
1834	1889	1800	1900	125350	LAN	Warton
1870	1950	1840	1870	123986	LKS	Glasgow
1900	1921	1855	1921	165360	MDX	Twickenham
1700	1992	....	....	105163	NTT	Sturton Le Steeple
1694	1850	ALL	ALL	159220	NTT	Sturton Le Steeple
1800	1850	1750	1800	123986	PER	Crieff
ALL	1850	....	....	114642	SFK	Chevington
1790	1850	1750	1800	141305	STS	Weston On Trent
....	....	1750	1810	123978	STS	???
1830	1850	1800	1850	124974	WAR	Warwick
1770	1992	1700	1800	169528	YKS	Huddersfield
1920	1973	1800	1920	178276	YKS	Leeds
FENWICK						
1780	1900	1780	1900	110396	CUL	Solport
1754	1790	1750	1760	108871	DUR	Stanhope
1780	1900	1780	1900	110396	DUR	Sunderland
1770	1900	1550	1770	150843	LIN	Hogsthorpe
....	....	1620	1750	108871	LND	East
....	....	ALL	1850	178403	LND	???
1885	1935	1800	1885	128406	NBL	ALL
1520	1600	....	....	132756	NBL	ALL
1520	1600	....	....	132756	NBL	Little Harle
....	....	ALL	ALL	166812	NBL	Newcastle
1814	1992	ALL	1814	152439	PER	Clackmannan
1590	1618	....	....	117234	SCT	Glasgow
1869	1920	1800	1869	166723	SSX	Eastbourne
1856	1992	1700	1856	179566	T&W	Gateshead
1820	1888	....	....	117196	YKS	Richmond
1800	1820	1770	1800	117196	YKS	Stanwick St John
FERAN						
....	....	1815	1836	150819	LKS	Glasgow
FERBON						
1750	1800	1600	1700	151769	DBY	Ticknall
FERDINANDO						
....	....	ALL	ALL	123994	ALL	Name Study
FEREBEE						
1816	1840	1816	1992	173096	GLS	Uley
FERGIE						
ALL	ALL	ALL	ALL	166758	ALL	ALL
FERGUSON						
1841	1851	1700	1841	106836	ARL	Easdale
1888	1950	1700	1888	148423	AYR	Dailly
1803	1810	1600	1803	158984	AYR	Old Cumnock
1857	1880	1850	1900	111821	BEW	Duns
1780	1972	1750	1900	124028	BUT	Rothesay
1782	1853	1700	1782	152196	CMA	Egremont
1834	1863	1700	1900	102881	CUL	Holme Abbey
1750	1850	1600	1850	109274	DFS	Kirkconnel
?	?	?	....	100471	DFS	Lockerbie
....	....	....	1992	137014	DNB	Helensburgh

Known From	To	Researching From	To	Ref	Cty	Place
FERGUSON contd.						
1850	1891	1750	1900	176621	DOW	Newtownards
1820	1850	1600	1820	178101	DUR	Chester-Le-Street
1860	1992	ALL	1860	109339	DUR	Langley Moor
1862	1992	1600	1862	178101	DUR	Stockton
1840	....	....	1840	170461	FIF	Dunfermline
1857	1857	ALL	1992	170909	HAM	Atherfield
1801	1830	1750	1992	166049	INV	Inverness-Leachkin
1800	1841	ALL	1800	131571	IRL	Bawnby
1820	1857	1750	1861	160636	KKD	Dundrennan
1870	1916	....	....	170461	LAN	Barrow In Furness
?	?	?	....	100471	LAN	Blackburn
1900	....	1800	1992	154474	LAN	Kirkdale
1900	....	1800	1992	154474	LAN	Liverpool
1851	1899	1790	1813	161667	LAN	Liverpool
1830	1920	1600	1815	132802	LAN	Manchester
1900	....	1800	1992	154474	LAN	Seacombe
1850	1893	1780	1850	105767	LAN	St Helens
1900	....	1800	1992	154474	LAN	Wallasey
1773	1864	....	....	158895	LKS	Dalziel
1841	1851	1851	1992	106836	LKS	Goven
1790	1992	1700	1900	147095	LKS	Hamilton
1773	1864	....	....	158895	LKS	Hamilton
1790	1992	1700	1900	147095	LKS	Motherwell
1773	1864	....	....	158895	LKS	Wishaw
1832	1832	1800	1832	114448	LND	Shoreditch
1880	....	....	....	145068	LND	???
....	....	1800	1900	147613	NIR	Newry
....	....	1750	1790	162361	PER	Monzievaird
1790	1880	....	....	162361	PER	???
1829	1992	1800	1829	124052	RFW	Greenock
1774	1808	....	....	127140	RFW	Greenock
....	....	ALL	ALL	141739	ROC	Arboll
....	....	1600	1900	137014	SCT	Islay
....	....	1600	1900	137014	SCT	Skye
1850	1893	1750	1850	105767	SCT	???
....	....	1600	1900	136905	TYR	ALL
FERGUSSON						
1775	1795	....	....	171654	AYR	Kirkoswald
1851	1876	1700	1850	115967	AYR	Maybole
1700	1830	1700	1880	120219	PER	Balquhidder
FERLY						
1755	....	....	....	142859	GLS	Avening
FERMOR						
1800	1900	1700	1800	173223	HAM	Ashmansworth
1770	1800	1700	1770	173223	SSX	Rotherfield
FERN						
....	....	1815	1836	150819	LKS	Glasgow
1800	1837	1800	1837	131687	LKS	???
FERNANDES						
1814	1840	ALL	ALL	161047	YKS	East Riding
FERNEE						
1850	1936	1850	1936	163600	MDX	North
FERNEHOUGH						
1764	1845	1700	1900	124788	STS	Ipstones
FERNEYHOUGH						
1681	1783	ALL	1681	143278	STS	Uttoxeter
FERRABY						
1795	1850	1700	1795	169730	SRY	Morden
FERRAND						
1550	1992	1500	1850	124079	LND	ALL
1550	1992	1500	1850	124079	YKS	ALL
FERRAR						
1855	1992	1800	1992	118281	LND	???
1780	1880	1650	1780	118281	NTH	Thrapston
FERREDAY						
....	....	1770	1780	131725	SAL	???
FERRERS						
....	....	1066	1235	124974	STS	Tutbury
FERRETT						
....	....	ALL	ALL	129798	ALL	Name Study
....	....	ALL	ALL	129798	ALL	ALL
1705	1804	1600	1730	121932	CON	Jacobstow
1695	1850	....	....	129267	CON	Jacobstow
1705	1804	1600	1730	121932	CON	Treneglos
1765	1992	ALL	ALL	129798	YKS	Drighlington
FERREY						
1737	1806	1650	1800	115681	DOR	Abbotsbury
FERRIDGE						
1806	1950	1650	1805	112569	???	London
FERRIER						
1722	1862	1700	1992	124087	DNB	Cardross
1820	1992	1780	1900	116238	DUR	South Shields
1857	1992	1857	1992	124087	LAN	Blackley

Known From	To	Researching From	To	Ref	Cty	Place
FERRIMAN						
1763	1765	1700	1800	175307	BRK	Newbury
1932	....	1800	1932	101826	OXF	Leafield
FERRIS						
1877	1898	1800	1900	119202	ANT	Belfast
1787	1811	1787	1811	173738	BRK	Newbury
....	....	1750	1841	139432	DEV	Cornworthy
....	....	1750	1841	139432	DEV	Dartmouth
1600	1699	1600	1699	169781	DEV	Exeter
1840	1992	1700	1840	124109	DEV	Plymouth
1730	1800	....	....	165999	ESS	Great Tey
1850	1860	1700	1900	135968	IRL	ALL
1800	1810	1700	1800	148792	KEN	East
1800	1810	1700	1800	148792	KEN	Dover
1841	1900	1841	1900	108952	LND	Shoreditch
1790	1820	....	1790	102822	WIL	Lyneham
1800	1880	ALL	ALL	107352	WIL	Lyneham
1776	1992	1700	1776	124117	WIL	Rowde
1792	1849	1700	1792	159158	WIL	Rowde
1900	1992	ALL	ALL	115002	WOR	???
....	....	....	1610	103624	???	ALL
FERRY						
1797	1913	ALL	ALL	105015	DOR	Burton Bradstock
1770	1900	1700	1850	126268	LND	Spitalfields
1760	1992	1600	1760	176257	MDX	Stepney
FETHERSTON						
1600	....	....	....	131822	DUR	ALL
FEUALL						
1841	1855	1600	1841	156779	ESS	Colchester
1841	1855	1600	1841	156779	ESS	Lexan
1841	1855	1600	1841	156779	NFK	Great Yarmouth
FEVYER						
1800	1950	1750	1900	154881	SFK	Plomesgate
FEW						
ALL	1606	....	....	170178	WIL	Bishops Cannings
FEWEL						
1680	1812	1680	1800	161357	ESS	Dunmow
1700	1800	....	....	161357	ESS	Gt Dunmow
1680	1780	....	....	161357	ESS	Gt Easton
FEWKES						
1878	1901	1878	1930	123404	DBY	Linton
1670	1892	1600	1900	123404	LEI	Swannington
1670	1892	1600	1900	123404	LEI	Whitwick
FEWSTER						
1800	....	1700	1850	120839	EYK	???
?	?	ALL	ALL	174432	YKS	Brompton On Sawdon
1780	1850	1700	1780	177814	YKS	Ebberston
1773	1992	....	....	124168	YKS	Nunnington
FFARNFOULD						
....	....	1400	1580	154873	SSX	???
FFEYETTE						
1680	1700	ALL	ALL	115266	DOR	ALL
FFIDOE						
1715	....	....	....	131229	HEF	North East
FFITZER						
1808	?	1750	1851	173703	WOR	Worcester
FFLETHE						
1580	....	1550	1600	152110	CAM	Swaffham Prior
FFORD						
1695	1715	1600	1700	171182	WIL	South
1695	1715	1600	1700	171182	WIL	West
FFOULKES						
1790	1880	....	....	124133	CHS	Chester
1700	1770	1700	1800	124133	CWD	Llanelian
FIANDER						
....	....	ALL	ALL	120766	ALL	Name Study
FIBCH						
....	....	1750	1900	123862	SRY	???
FICE						
....	....	ALL	ALL	124141	ALL	Name Study
1800	1992	1500	1800	124141	ALL	ALL
FICKLIN						
....	....	ALL	ALL	130524	ALL	Name Study
FICKLING						
1880	1980	....	1880	130524	MDX	London
1780	1860	ALL	ALL	107425	NFK	Diss
....	....	ALL	ALL	130524	NFK	Saham Toney
FIDDES						
....	....	ALL	ALL	135356	ALL	Name Study
1835	ALL	ALL	1992	170909	ABD	Aberdeen
1806	1820	1820	1992	135356	LAN	???
1750	1880	1700	1992	135356	NBL	???
1809	1876	1700	1800	166723	ROX	Lilliesleaf
1750	1800	1700	1992	135356	ROX	???

Known From	To	Researching From	To	Ref	Cty	Place
FIDDY						
1826	1992	ALL	1826	110000	NFK	Haynford
FIDIAM						
1750	1992	....	....	124168	LAN	Manchester
FIDLER						
1724	1847	1650	1725	118958	CHS	???
1793	....	1750	1820	139483	DBY	Brampton
1820	1992	....	....	139483	YKS	Sheffield
FIDLIN						
1774	1992	ALL	ALL	168815	ALL	ALL
FIDO						
....	....	1850	1940	167045	???	Bristol
FIELD BUSS						
1790	1980	....	....	122130	SSX	Rotherfield
FIELD						
1795	1853	1700	1853	116300	BDF	Biggleswade
1844	....	1800	1845	106062	BKM	Edelsborough
1818	....	....	....	170623	DEV	Ashburton
1759	1759	1700	1759	149152	DEV	Broadhempston
1860	1930	1800	1930	169641	DUR	Sunderland
....	....	ALL	....	119237	ENG	South West
1750	1992	1600	1750	124184	HAM	Gosport
1574	1679	1570	1636	176958	HEF	Hereford
1574	1679	1570	1636	176958	HEF	Rudbaxton
1790	1792	....	....	151750	HRT	Hemel Hempstead
1700	1850	1500	1900	177180	HRT	Hemel Hempstead
1780	1801	1700	1801	147575	HRT	St Mimms
1830	1870	1800	1992	176281	KEN	Marden
1775	1890	1775	1890	100382	LIN	Thurlby By Bourne
1835	....	....	....	173932	MDX	Limehouse
1574	1679	1570	1636	176958	MDX	London
1818	1855	1750	1900	142751	MLN	Edinburgh
1700	1992	1700	1992	114790	OXF	Taston
1714	1797	....	....	166723	SRY	Bisley
....	....	ALL	....	119237	SRY	Richmond
1760	1992	1600	1760	118788	SSX	Rye
....	....	1810	1830	156140	SSX	Slaugham
1815	1885	1700	1960	153346	STS	Kingswinford
1785	1992	1600	1785	124176	WAR	Atherstone On Stour
....	....	ALL	ALL	171816	WAR	Birmingham
1600	1700	....	....	100420	WAR	Meriden
1750	1830	1700	1830	119938	WAR	Oxhill
1574	1679	1570	1636	176958	WLS	St Davids
1840	1860	1700	1860	169641	WOR	Lye
1710	....	....	1710	101761	WRY	Cawthorne
1778	1810	1700	1778	108790	YKS	Skelmanthorpe
1612	....	1500	1800	176958	???	Cambridge
FIELDEN						
....	....	ALL	ALL	124192	ALL	Name Study
1520	1880	1520	1880	107522	WRY	Todmorden
FIELDER						
ALL	ALL	ALL	ALL	124206	HAM	ALL
1796	1861	1750	1796	175064	HAM	Beaulieu
1830	1920	1700	1830	100765	HAM	Bramshaw
1623	1730	1600	1800	145459	HAM	Hursley
1882	1971	1800	1900	124206	LND	ALL
1738	1741	....	....	173932	LND	Putney
1711	....	....	....	173932	SRY	Kingston Upon Thames
1752	....	....	....	173932	SRY	Malden
1641	1735	....	....	173932	SRY	Mortlake
1750	1820	1600	1750	142328	SSX	East
FIELDHOUSE						
1820	1825	1600	1820	175382	LAN	Leeds
FIELDING						
1816	1822	1790	1834	159492	CHS	Mottram In Longdendon
1800	1874	ALL	1900	152021	KIK	ALL
1853	1903	1853	1903	122335	LAN	Blackburn
1840	1880	1800	1840	138940	LAN	Manchester
1800	1992	1700	1800	113050	LAN	Salford
1780	1840	1750	1850	166081	LAN	Stanhill
1800	1992	1700	1800	113050	LAN	Whitefield
1735	1876	1700	1735	128368	LIN	Owston
1760	1960	1700	1960	126500	MLN	Edinburgh
1770	1992	....	....	126497	MLN	Edinburgh
1810	1850	1700	1810	101834	NFK	Central
1633	1722	1550	1633	138584	NTT	Kingston On Soar
1800	1850	1700	1800	166561	NTT	West Leake
FIELDS						
1750	1992	1660	1750	124214	LIN	North Willingham
....	....	1750	1890	179361	WIL	North Tidworth
FIELDSEND						
....	....	ALL	ALL	177024	ALL	Name Study
FIELDSEND contd.						
1600	1800	1500	1900	177024	LIN	Central
1586	1743	....	....	121835	LIN	Waddington
1750	1800	1700	1900	177024	YKS	West Riding
FIELDSON						
1800	1900	ALL	ALL	177024	LIN	Central
FIENNES						
1150	1350	1150	1350	154881	ALL	ALL
FIFE						
1746	1862	1700	1900	146536	AYR	Kilbirnie
1810	1840	1700	1810	100846	CLK	???
FIFET						
1730	1760	1550	1730	156795	DOR	East
FIFIELD						
1741	1881	ALL	1890	137774	KEN	ALL
FIGG						
1830	1850	1750	1850	119008	LND	???
FIGGETT						
....	....	1677	1880	101478	GLS	ALL
FIGGURES						
1773	1992	ALL	ALL	111058	GLS	Blockley
FIGURES						
1815	1992	?	1815	136611	STS	Walsall
....	....	ALL	ALL	111058	WAR	ALL
FILBRICK						
1777	1791	1750	1791	113352	ESS	Rivenhall
FILBY						
....	....	ALL	ALL	124222	ALL	Name Study
....	....	1600	1900	124656	NFK	???
FILDER						
1662	1710	1660	1730	142018	GLS	Tetbury
1691	1743	1690	1780	142018	SOM	Rode
1727	1782	1720	1800	142018	WIL	Bradford On Avon
FILDES						
1608	1796	1744	1796	124826	LAN	Eccles
1799	1945	1799	1920	124826	LAN	Newton Heath
1860	1890	1800	1860	106968	LAN	Worsley
FILER						
1775	1900	1700	1992	176923	SOM	Apulton
FILES						
1758	1895	ALL	1870	137774	KEN	Dover
FILEWOOD						
1705	1992	1650	1705	139505	ALL	ALL
FILKIN						
....	1787	1750	1850	126659	CHS	Nantwich
FILL						
1840	?	1700	1840	164925	KEN	Aslford
1840	?	1700	1840	164925	KEN	Westwell
FILLARY						
1700	1800	1600	1700	168777	SSX	Shipley
FILLINGHAM						
1759	1759	1600	1759	170542	KEN	Throwley
....	....	1800	1899	171794	LIN	Blyton
1700	1730	1600	1750	163562	LIN	Haxey
1839	1851	1700	1839	134651	LIN	Market Rasen
1872	....	ALL	1830	120952	NTT	Misterton
FILMER						
1811	....	....	1820	171441	KEN	Ashford
1834	1844	....	1860	171441	KEN	Lenham
1864	....	....	1880	171441	KEN	Milton Regis
FINAN						
1881	....	1881	1992	145041	DUR	Wingate
FINCH						
1781	1848	1700	1780	173630	DEV	Dittisham
1900	....	....	....	170623	DEV	Plymouth
1787	1837	1841	1851	170623	DEV	South Tawton
....	....	ALL	ALL	171158	ESS	ALL
1811	....	ALL	ALL	116416	ESS	Chelmsford
1838	1930	1700	1850	175978	ESS	Felstead
1780	1872	1740	1840	115797	ESS	Margaretting
1778	1992	1770	1900	109827	HAM	Lockerly
1772	1772	ALL	1772	167959	HRT	Stanstead Abbots
1600	ALL	1550	1800	141151	KEN	ALL
?	?	ALL	1900	116203	LAN	Preston
....	....	ALL	ALL	143340	LAN	???
1849	1928	1830	1928	151599	LND	East
1867	1985	1750	1867	173231	LND	Deptford
1935	1992	....	....	151920	LND	Stamford Hill
1856	1921	ALL	ALL	174017	MDX	Brentford
1810	1900	1800	1900	111589	MDX	Stepney
1330	1390	1070	1520	156647	SSX	Netherfield
1755	1841	1730	1850	105333	SSX	Ripe
1829	1871	1825	1925	132845	STS	Burton Upon Trent
1725	1738	....	....	152234	SYK	Darfield

Known From	To	Researching From	To	Ref	Cty	Place
FINCH contd.						
....	....	1738	1780	152234	SYK	Hatfield
1759	1860	....	....	152234	SYK	Wath Upon Dearne
1800	1992	ALL	ALL	115002	WOR	Overbury
1900	1992	....	....	152234	WYK	Hemsworth
FINCHAM						
1567	1582	1530	1570	108510	CAM	Owtwell In Ely
FINCHER						
....	....	ALL	ALL	124230	ALL	Name Study
ALL	1880	....	....	174556	AVN	Bedminster
ALL	1880	....	....	174556	AVN	Bristol
1740	1750	1740	1750	107360	BKM	Stewkley
FINCHETT						
....	....	ALL	ALL	166812	CHS	Kelsal
....	....	ALL	ALL	166812	LAN	Manchester
FINDING						
1816	1816	....	1840	102822	HUN	St Ives
FINDLATER						
1670	1992	....	....	152218	MOR	???
FINDLAY						
1780	1894	1700	1920	124001	ABD	Kennethmont
1780	1894	1700	1920	124001	ABD	New Deer
1794	1878	....	....	117803	ANS	Arbroath
1783	....	1750	1800	159891	ANS	Forfar
1783	....	1750	1800	159891	ANS	Kirriemuire
1720	1940	1690	1720	150029	AYR	Kilmarnock
1720	1940	1690	1720	150029	AYR	Riecarton
....	....	1710	1770	172871	KCD	Benholm
1802	1900	1800	1861	124001	KCD	Nigg
1802	1900	1800	1861	124001	KCD	Stonehaven
1908	1992	1880	1908	100757	LKS	Hamilton
1759	1779	....	....	171654	LKS	Lesmahagow
1825	1992	ALL	1992	100102	LKS	Warrenhill
FINDLAYSON						
1750	1965	....	....	137820	SHI	Fetlar
1720	1965	....	....	137820	SHI	Mid Yell
1760	1965	....	....	137820	SHI	North Yell
1758	1965	....	....	137820	SHI	Northmavine
1720	1965	....	....	137820	SHI	South Yell
FINDON						
....	....	ALL	ALL	124249	ALL	Name Study
1826	....	....	....	124249	LEI	Monks Kirby
1779	1992	....	....	124249	WAR	South
1577	....	....	....	124249	WAR	Bickenhill
1817	....	....	....	124249	WAR	Coventry
1851	1857	....	....	124249	WAR	Nuneaton
1761	1825	1761	1785	124249	WAR	Stretton On Dunsmore
1618	1850	1700	1770	124249	WAR	Warwick
1818	1989	1818	1989	124249	WOR	Alvechurch
1846	1851	....	....	124249	WOR	Bromsgrove
FINEGAN						
....	....	ALL	ALL	115150	IRL	???
FINERON						
1847	1960	1800	1850	124257	GAL	ALL
FINES						
1791	....	ALL	....	104515	LIN	Timberland
FINKLE						
1736	1736	1700	1800	112089	ENG	East Anglia
FINLAY						
1794	1812	1700	1830	149632	ELN	Tranent
1870	....	1700	1930	126160	LAN	Manchester
1822	1895	....	....	171654	LKS	Carluke
1830	1835	1812	1835	149632	MLN	Edinburgh
FINLEY						
1597	1634	ALL	ALL	101370	FIF	Balchristie
1530	?	ALL	ALL	101370	FIF	Cupar Angus
1683	?	ALL	ALL	101370	IRL	Armaugh
FINLINSON						
....	....	ALL	ALL	155969	ALL	Name Study
1700	1900	1650	1950	155969	ALL	ALL
1814	....	ALL	1835	155969	ELN	Haddington
1814	....	ALL	1835	155969	MLN	Edinburgh
1835	1851	ALL	ALL	155969	YKS	Leeds
FINLOW						
1700	1840	ALL	ALL	134759	STS	Stafford
FINMORE						
1490	1670	ALL	1670	132950	BRK	Kingston Lisle
FINN						
....	....	1600	1992	124273	COR	???
1805	....	....	1830	171441	KEN	Denton
1805	....	....	1830	171441	KEN	Dover
1835	1955	....	1930	171441	MDX	Isleworth
FINNEGAN						
1863	....	....	....	151270	MEA	Nobber
FINNEMORE						
1500	1992	ALL	1992	124281	ALL	ALL
FINNERTY						
1823	1992	1823	1992	111201	MAY	???
FINNESEY						
1843	1843	1500	1843	110310	IRL	ALL
1843	1992	1500	1843	110310	LAN	Liverpool
1841	1850	1500	1841	110310	LAN	Manchester
1830	1992	ALL	ALL	124311	LAN	???
FINNEY						
1937	1950	1901	1937	176885	ESS	East Ham
1869	1909	ALL	1869	164623	IRL	Whitegate
1901	....	1850	1937	176885	NBL	Wallsend
1950	1961	....	....	176885	NTT	Mansfield
1937	1981	....	....	176885	NTT	Sutton In Ashfield
1810	....	....	....	175358	STS	Alton
FINNIGAN						
1850	1900	1840	1900	154342	GLS	Birstol
1800	1850	1600	1850	154342	IRL	Cork
FINNING						
1790	1892	....	1790	102601	DEV	Shobrooke
FINNIS						
1700	1900	1600	1900	154903	KEN	Deal
1860	1872	1700	1900	172316	LND	Whitechapel
FINZEL						
1675	1992	1837	....	176958	DEV	Bideford
1675	1992	1837	....	176958	DEV	Ilfracombe
1851	1877	1600	1992	176958	GLS	Clevedon
1675	1992	1837	....	176958	MDX	London
1675	1992	1837	....	176958	SCT	Glasgow
1675	1992	1837	....	176958	SOM	Bristol
FIORINI						
1874	1992	1800	1919	128694	LND	Marylebone
FIRBER						
1738	1850	1700	1750	172642	MGY	Llanyblodwel
1738	1850	1700	1750	172642	MGY	Llanymynech
FIRBY						
1740	1849	1740	1849	161314	YKS	Hudswell
FIRKS						
....	....	1800	....	159824	DEV	???
FIRMAN						
1800	1900	1700	1950	131822	ESS	Colchester
1814	1840	1750	1850	126586	KEN	Woolwich
1830	1880	1700	1900	156442	LND	Stepney
1800	1920	1800	1920	108006	SFK	Nayland
FIRMIN						
1700	1750	....	....	165999	ESS	Colchester
1830	1992	ALL	1830	125210	ESS	Mistley
FIRMSTONE						
1877	1931	ALL	ALL	118885	NRY	Middlesborough
FIRRELL						
....	....	1850	1992	109533	ALL	ALL
1770	1950	1700	1770	109533	SSX	East
FIRTH						
1670	1700	1600	1670	121339	WYK	Heptonstall
....	....	ALL	ALL	111384	WYK	Northowram
1810	1950	1700	1810	124362	YKS	Bradford
1810	1820	1600	1815	175382	YKS	Bradford
1880	1992	....	....	124354	YKS	Halifax
1810	1950	1700	1810	124362	YKS	Halifax
1870	1992	1870	1992	105449	YKS	Hull
1840	....	1840	1992	108367	YKS	Kirkheaton
1780	1830	1750	1780	133760	YKS	Lindley
1850	1880	....	....	139351	YKS	Liversedge
1820	1840	1780	1820	148113	YKS	Sheffield
1830	1880	1770	1900	170038	YKS	Shipley
1812	1821	ALL	ALL	105449	YKS	Tadcaster
1845	1900	1845	1900	105449	YKS	Willerby
FIRTY						
1750	1992	....	1750	133825	YKS	Hatfield
FISE						
1800	1850	1500	1800	124141	ALL	ALL
FISH						
1847	1871	1847	1892	116424	CON	Lostwithiel
1850	1900	....	1850	158585	ESS	Witham
1750	1900	1750	1900	125237	LAN	Darwen
1800	1880	1880	1992	162256	LAN	Darwen
1825	1880	1800	1881	124788	LAN	Oldham
1700	1820	1600	1850	160849	LIN	Owston Ferry
1820	1850	1750	1880	100439	LND	St Giles Cripplegate
1781	1843	1700	1850	117013	NFK	Alby

Known From	To	Researching From	To	Ref	Cty	Place
FISH contd.						
1850	1870	ALL	ALL	106844	NFK	Dickleborough
1797	1851	1700	1797	131660	NFK	Sharrington
1820	1840	....	....	103721	NRY	Topecliffe By Thirsk
1779	1878	1600	1790	101575	YKS	Malton
1779	1878	1600	1790	101575	YKS	Selby
FISHBOURNE						
1848	....	ALL	ALL	112836	NFK	Holkham
1850	....	ALL	ALL	112836	NFK	Wells
FISHBURN						
....	....	1700	1950	178071	DUR	Norton
....	....	1700	1950	178071	DUR	Stockton
1841	1871	1700	1841	100110	NYK	Brompton
1732	1804	1710	1732	101796	YKS	Woolley
1820	....	....	....	165484	YKS	Woolley
FISHENDEN						
....	....	ALL	ALL	158097	ALL	Name Study
FISHER						
....	....	1750	1840	155594	ANT	Lisburn
1878	1992	1871	1878	155594	ARM	Portaadown
1800	1900	1800	1900	113670	AVN	Bath
1800	1950	1700	1800	128376	AVN	Bristol
1890	1992	1890	1992	175196	AVN	Bristol
1880	1880	1880	1880	175196	AVN	Weston Super Mare
1791	1936	1750	1800	144231	AYR	Riccarton
1901	1992	1500	1901	110310	BRK	ALL
1771	1898	1600	1771	149888	BRK	Faringdon
....	....	1750	1840	155594	CAV	Cootehill
1800	1886	....	1800	133434	CHS	Cheadle Hulme
1842	....	?	1802	128910	DBY	North Wingfield
1830	1900	1800	1900	176648	DEV	Exeter
1817	1992	....	1817	124397	DEV	Molland
....	....	1880	1920	109479	DEV	Teignmouth
1782	1815	1815	1850	124397	DEV	Tiverton
1780	1850	1700	1780	124427	DFS	Duncow
1800	1992	1600	1800	156795	DOR	East
1812	....	....	1830	160873	DUR	Chester Le Street
1970	1992	....	....	107255	ESS	Central
1900	1992	1850	1900	107417	ESS	Leytonstone
1810	1841	1750	1850	118575	GLA	Morriston
1810	1841	1750	1850	118575	GLA	Swansea
1750	1800	1700	1820	138150	GLS	South
1632	....	1578	....	142859	GLS	Frampton On Severn
1750	1890	1750	1890	126551	GLS	Olveston
1792	1866	1700	1800	156981	GLS	Olveston
1800	1850	1750	1900	106631	GLS	Stroud
1770	1992	....	....	118672	GLS	Tortworth
1830	1840	1700	1840	148792	HAM	North East
1876	1903	ALL	ALL	149675	HAM	Itchen Stoke
1794	1845	ALL	ALL	149675	HAM	Titchbourne
....	....	1720	1790	102717	HRT	East
1850	1900	1700	1850	154059	HRT	Hitchin
1776	....	....	1776	108839	HUN	Woodhurst
1750	1793	1750	....	144355	KEN	South
1852	1921	1750	1852	110639	KEN	???
1846	1992	....	....	172529	LAN	Altham
1820	1841	1750	1992	137782	LAN	Barrow In Furness
1783	1869	1700	1783	163783	LAN	Fylde
1614	1640	ALL	ALL	141615	LAN	Garstang
1783	1869	1700	1783	163783	LAN	Garstang
1882	1896	1882	1920	126705	LAN	Manchester
1803	....	....	....	136565	LAN	Preston
1861	1882	1700	1882	178233	LAN	Wigan
1730	1860	1600	1730	164844	LEI	North
1728	1747	ALL	1773	168718	LEI	Thrussington
1800	1881	1500	1992	124443	LIN	South
1879	1916	1700	1950	171522	LKS	Hamilton
1865	1992	....	....	107255	LND	ALL
1900	1992	ALL	ALL	127884	LND	South East
1881	1881	1881	1881	175196	LND	Bromley
1850	1900	1700	1850	155950	LND	Hackney
....	....	ALL	1992	112607	LND	???
1819	1847	1750	1819	164321	MDX	East London
1871	....	ALL	ALL	117560	MDX	Pancras
1872	1909	1800	1880	153362	MDX	Stepney
1790	1890	....	....	141909	MDX	Sunbury
1852	1921	1750	1852	110639	MDX	???
1885	1900	1800	1900	114480	NFK	Norwich
1881	1900	1750	1850	148814	NFK	Norwich
1738	1838	1738	1900	107980	NFK	Raveningham
1903	1992	1700	1903	124400	NTH	Wilby
1707	1786	1500	1786	129011	NTT	Nottingham
....	....	1730	1900	135410	NTT	Nottingham
FISHER contd.						
1825	1850	1750	1875	168297	OXF	Milton Under Wychwood
1780	1850	1700	1850	117617	SFK	Aldeburgh
1675	1735	ALL	1675	168602	SFK	Lowestoft
1806	1806	ALL	1835	107255	SOM	Bath
....	....	....	1832	115290	SOM	Taunton
1968	1992	....	....	107255	SRY	East
1800	1992	1800	1992	179000	STI	Kilsyth
1730	....	1730	ALL	146536	STI	Larbert
....	....	1700	1900	179531	STS	Abbots Bromley
....	....	1700	1900	179531	STS	Blithfield
1850	1920	1800	1850	109479	STS	Dudley
1842	1895	ALL	ALL	156256	STS	Leek
1781	1787	1700	1820	101486	STS	Sedgley
1721	1740	1700	1757	101486	STS	Tipton
1782	1953	1782	1900	101486	STS	Wolverhampton
1550	1600	1500	1600	154881	WEX	Tomduff
1835	1862	1806	1835	107255	WIL	Bradford On Avon
1802	....	....	....	117560	WIL	Burbage
....	....	ALL	1810	151602	WIL	Ramsbury
1850	1900	1700	1850	155950	WIL	Swindon
1738	1939	1600	1900	154601	WYK	Horbury
1871	1965	1750	1871	171034	YKS	Huddersfield
1580	1950	....	....	133388	YKS	Snaith
....	1840	1500	1840	154784	YKS	Tankersley
1852	1909	....	....	176613	???	Hemingford Grey
FISHER-ROWE						
1850	1890	1850	1940	117323	MDX	Old Brentford
FISHLEY						
1750	1900	1600	1992	167592	DEV	Fremington
1780	1800	1600	1992	167592	DEV	Muddlebridge
1880	1920	1600	1992	167592	SOM	Baunton
1900	1940	1600	1992	167592	SOM	Clevedon
FISHLOCK						
1700	1799	1600	1850	130621	WIL	Devizes
FISHWICK						
1859	1946	1820	1880	151912	LAN	Bolton
1859	1946	1820	1880	151912	LAN	Chorley
1780	1850	....	....	126497	LAN	Leyland
1928	1940	?	?	124451	LAN	Liverpool
1851	....	1800	1850	137618	LAN	Parbold
1800	1870	1800	1870	126500	LAN	Wigan
FISK						
....	....	ALL	ALL	124478	ALL	Name Study
....	....	1400	1992	124478	ALL	ALL
1800	1992	1750	1900	154881	LND	ALL
1850	1920	....	....	121185	NFK	ALL
1700	1850	1400	1992	124478	SFK	ALL
1800	1992	1750	1900	154881	SFK	ALL
1750	1850	1500	1992	124478	SFK	Badingham
1700	1992	1200	1700	167010	SFK	Dennington
1200	1600	1600	1700	167010	SFK	Lxfield
FISKE						
1900	1948	1700	1900	126292	LND	East End
1800	1818	1700	1800	155276	SFK	Bucklesham
FISON						
1850	1992	1750	1900	176362	SFK	Ipswich
FISSENDEN						
1810	1870	ALL	ALL	159034	KEN	Birling
1831	....	....	....	159034	KEN	Ryarsh
1860	1890	ALL	ALL	159034	KEN	Snodland
FITCH						
1820	....	1700	1820	145718	BRK	Windsor
1871	1875	ALL	ALL	165085	KEN	Deptford
1820	1848	1700	1950	178616	LEI	Leicester
1839	1931	1750	1839	174203	MDX	Islington
....	....	1830	1870	114782	MDX	???
1700	1850	1700	1850	105848	SFK	Woodbridge
1857	....	....	1857	121002	???	London
FITCHET						
1839	1864	1800	1880	123404	DBY	Lullington
1717	1790	1600	1900	170747	MDX	London
FITCHETT						
1880	1900	1800	1900	129496	NTT	Teversal
FITCHEW						
1716	1840	1650	1840	115681	OXF	Bampton
FITNESS						
....	....	ALL	ALL	124494	ALL	Name Study
FITT						
1720	1780	1720	1780	116483	HAM	Hursley
1820	....	....	....	124508	LND	Lambeth
1820	....	....	....	124508	LND	Newington
1784	....	....	....	124508	NFK	Mattishall

Known From	To	Researching From	To	Ref	Cty	Place
FITTON						
1890	1895	1890	1992	166197	CHS	Willaston
1770	1992	1770	1992	110523	LAN	Rochdale
1750	1840	1720	1840	123595	YKS	Holmfirth
FITZ						
1853	1876	1853	1876	139661	CON	Truro
FITZELL						
1840	1900	ALL	ALL	138363	IRL	Kerry
FITZER						
1808	?	1750	1851	173703	WOR	Worcester
FITZGERALD						
....	....	1100	1450	154873	BKM	???
1870	1992	?	1870	124540	IRL	Dublin
....	....	1850	1900	123765	IRL	Meath
1826	1865	....	....	116750	IRL	Tippary
1840	ALL	....	....	153982	KEN	Erith
1842	....	....	1842	129518	KER	Tralee
....	....	1100	1450	154873	LAN	???
1825	1851	1750	1851	155152	LND	Southwark
....	....	1100	1450	154873	MDX	???
1844	1846	1800	1900	155225	TIP	Clonoulty
FITZGIBBON						
1870	1984	ALL	ALL	131121	CHS	Nantwich
....	....	1600	1700	128627	CLA	???
....	1859	ALL	1859	114030	MDX	London
FITZGIBBON-HENCHY						
....	....	1700	....	128627	ESS	???
....	....	1700	....	128627	IRL	Dublin
FITZHERBERT						
....	1775	1814	....	128848	???	???
FITZHUGH						
1781	1900	1781	1900	147486	NTH	Northampton
FITZJAMES						
....	....	1900	....	110183	IRL	???
1896	1992	1838	1992	110183	YKS	Leeds
FITZJOHN						
....	....	ALL	ALL	168939	ALL	Name Study
1700	1895	1500	1900	161489	HRT	Baldock
1800	1850	1800	1850	140864	HRT	Westmill
....	....	1700	1880	153907	NTH	Woodnewton
1894	1949	....	....	153907	WOR	Stourport
1880	1894	....	....	153907	WOR	Wribbenhall
FITZPATRICK						
1894	1924	1800	1924	128449	COR	Ballinavar
1894	1924	1800	1924	128449	COR	Clonakilty
1881	....	1881	1881	116041	IRL	Aghaboe
1881	....	1881	1881	116041	IRL	Borris In Ossory
1900	1992	ALL	1900	155306	IRL	County Mayo
1800	1843	....	....	124575	IRL	Loughmore
1796	1797	1843	1870	124575	IRL	Thurles
1752	?	1700	1752	134732	IRL	???
1809	1811	1750	1810	123978	LAN	Salford
....	....	....	....	124575	TIP	North
FITZSIMMONS						
1810	1874	1750	1810	167398	IRL	Down
1810	1874	1750	1810	167398	WIG	Kirk Maiden
FITZSIMONS						
1851	1992	1790	1851	124583	CMA	Whitehaven
FLACK						
1870	1890	ALL	ALL	171379	CAM	Littleport
....	....	1700	1850	129364	ESS	Stapleford Abbot
1815	1853	1800	1853	155225	LND	Bethnal Green
1815	1827	1750	1815	155225	LND	City
1838	1992	1700	1838	161446	MDX	London
1700	1900	1700	1900	105848	MDX	St Lukes
....	....	1700	1815	155225	SFK	Boxford
....	....	1700	1815	155225	SFK	Groton
FLACKETT						
1640	1770	1640	1830	124737	BRK	South East
FLADGATE						
1640	1860	1640	1850	124737	SRY	West
FLAGGETT						
1640	1770	1640	1830	124737	BRK	South East
FLAHERTY						
1963	....	....	....	173932	WIL	Bradford On Avon
FLANAGAN						
1864	1913	ALL	ALL	169838	DUB	Dublin
1750	1800	ALL	1992	170909	ROS	Elphin
FLANDERS						
1800	1930	....	....	141909	BDF	Eaton Socon
1737	1893	....	1737	177504	CAM	Downham
1856	1904	1700	1856	129364	ESS	Navestock
1856	1904	1700	1856	129364	ESS	Stapleford Abbots
1800	1940	1870	1940	173533	NTH	ALL

Known From	To	Researching From	To	Ref	Cty	Place
FLANN						
1800	1900	1820	1900	164674	DOR	Portland
FLANNIGAN						
....	....	1850	1920	148210	TYR	Stewartstown
FLASBY						
1750	1800	ALL	ALL	173010	LAN	Tunstall
FLASHMAN						
1802	1992	1500	1802	139335	DEV	Modbury
1802	1992	1500	1802	139335	LND	Lambeth
FLATGATE						
1730	1780	1700	1830	124737	HAM	North East
FLATHER						
1647	1682	1600	1690	128449	YKS	Hartshead
FLATT						
....	....	1538	1820	118893	NFK	Fersfield
....	....	1538	1820	118893	NFK	Kenninghall
FLAVELL						
1795	....	....	....	157155	CAM	Coton
1795	....	....	....	157155	CAM	Cottenham
1795	....	....	....	157155	CAM	Histon
1795	....	....	....	157155	CAM	Impington
1795	....	....	....	157155	CAM	Landbeach
1713	1859	ALL	1713	178926	LEI	Little Bowden
1923	....	....	....	157155	LND	Edmonton
1713	1859	ALL	1713	178926	NTH	Little Bowden
1791	1791	1770	1830	152781	STS	Sedgley
1860	1960	1750	1860	167614	WAR	Birmingham
1830	1870	1800	1900	152781	WOR	Northfield
FLAXMAN						
1650	1992	1650	1992	116726	NFK	Trunch
1840	1940	1700	1940	168068	NFK	Trunch
....	....	1750	1870	106607	SFK	Woodbridge
FLAY						
1815	1818	1750	1818	124990	AVN	Bristol
1828	....	....	....	172545	WIL	Calne
FLEAR						
....	....	ALL	ALL	175501	ALL	Name Study
1850	1880	1850	1920	176400	LIN	ALL
....	....	....	....	176400	NTT	ALL
1803	1869	1770	1870	108901	NTT	Newark
FLECK						
1850	1870	1700	1850	100390	AYR	Kilwinning
1870	1881	1870	1881	100390	DEV	Bideford
1881	1887	1881	1890	100390	LAN	Manchester
1870	1875	1870	1875	100390	LKS	Glasgow
FLEEMING						
1720	....	ALL	ALL	130508	FIF	Kilrenny
1855	....	ALL	ALL	150029	SCT	Glasgow
FLEET						
1820	1840	ALL	1820	134058	BKM	Wingrave
1810	1850	1800	1992	131792	CAM	Soham
1885	1992	1800	1885	169722	DEV	Dartmouth
FLEETHAM						
1719	....	....	....	151351	YKS	Hampsthwaite
FLEETWOOD						
1300	1752	....	....	100536	ALL	???
1710	1710	1650	1750	163783	LAN	Goosnargh
1845	1915	1750	1850	125628	LND	Stepney
....	....	1800	1992	105244	MDX	London
1700	1796	1700	1848	179493	SRY	Ashtead
1700	1796	1700	1848	179493	SRY	Dorking
1850	1910	1800	1992	105244	SRY	Wandsworth
FLEMING						
1780	....	1750	1850	159891	ANS	Carmyllie
1759	1800	1700	1759	127590	ANS	Forfar
1780	....	1750	1850	159891	ANS	Forfar
1796	....	1600	1796	116637	ARL	Kintyre
1840	1850	1800	1850	103756	CAV	Woody Hill
1850	1900	1800	1850	174866	CUL	West
1779	....	....	....	124524	ERY	Cottingham
1860	1940	1860	1940	124605	ESS	West Ham
1830	1992	?	1830	111376	FIF	ALL
1835	1927	1835	1927	124613	GAL	Tuam
ALL	1950	....	....	104132	IOW	ALL
1840	1870	1840	1870	124605	IRL	Cork
1927	1992	1835	1992	124613	LAN	Atherton
1580	1992	1580	1992	125172	LAN	Coniston
1775	1920	1775	1920	171654	LKS	Avondale
1773	1980	1814	1960	127418	LKS	Strathaven
1840	1890	1700	1840	159212	LND	Islington
1804	1864	1750	1830	176621	MDX	London
....	....	1850	1950	119970	MEA	???
1700	1992	ALL	ALL	137847	MON	Chepstow
1796	....	1750	1796	116637	NBL	Allendale

Known From	To	Researching From	To	Ref	Cty	Place
FLEMING contd.						
....	?	?	....	134457	OXF	Banbury
....	?	?	....	134457	OXF	Chadlington
1795	1815	?	1795	111376	PER	Glenshee
1400	1778	1400	1750	154881	PER	Moness
....	....	1800	....	176834	PER	Pitlochry
1700	1830	....	....	117064	ROX	Eckford
1897	1920	ALL	1897	101869	SCT	Dundee
1897	1945	ALL	1897	101869	SCT	Edinburgh
1827	1992	1780	1827	174173	WES	Milnthorpe
1580	1992	1580	1992	125172	WES	Rydal
....	1646	ALL	1646	162507	WES	Rydal
1796	1992	1700	1796	150223	WIL	Heytesbury
1796	1871	1700	1950	159964	WIL	Stockton
1814	1870	1770	1870	121126	YKS	Halifax
....	....	1750	1800	176621	YKS	Halifax
FLEMMING						
1792	1825	....	1825	152803	BDF	Bedford
FLESHER						
1632	....	1550	1700	141151	LND	ALL
FLETCHER						
1855	1948	ALL	1855	106860	ARL	Easdale
1778	1800	1778	1800	139971	BKM	Amersham
1764	1810	1700	1820	176621	BRK	Abingdon
1803	....	1803	....	148156	CAM	Eltisley
?	1940	....	....	128996	CAM	Thornley
1800	....	....	....	124664	DBY	Alderwasley
1863	1992	1862	1929	107131	DBY	Burbage
1800	1992	1500	1800	107123	DBY	Burbage
1800	1992	1500	1800	107123	DBY	Buxton
1863	1992	1862	1929	107131	DBY	Buxton
1900	1992	1900	1900	107123	DBY	Chapel En Le Frith
1849	1895	1800	1910	144223	DBY	Repton
1871	1902	1700	1870	132438	DBY	Ripley
1901	1992	1800	1900	107530	DEV	West
1817	1873	1817	1873	149403	DUR	Chester Le Street
1802	1831	1700	1851	171425	DUR	Chester-Le-Street
1802	1831	1700	1851	171425	DUR	Gainsborough
....	....	1600	1900	179531	DUR	Sedgefield
1802	1831	1700	1851	171425	DUR	Stokesley
1793	....	ALL	1793	154946	ERY	Sledmere
1763	1881	1763	1881	119059	GLS	Evelode
1800	1900	1800	1900	177180	HRT	Bovingden
1800	1860	1750	1800	108359	HUN	Ellington
1800	1900	ALL	1900	131059	KEN	Milton
1800	1890	1750	1830	124648	KEN	Sheppey
1808	1920	1800	1880	138363	LAN	Bolton
1733	1850	1700	1900	177636	LAN	Bolton
1610	1810	1610	1810	127655	LAN	Burnley
1733	1850	1700	1900	177636	LAN	Bury
1820	....	....	1820	101761	LAN	Manchester
1764	....	ALL	1764	144053	LAN	Manchester
1800	1850	1700	1850	158216	LAN	Oldham
1806	1825	1750	1830	159964	LAN	Radcliffe
1733	1850	1700	1900	177636	LAN	Warrington
....	....	1600	1900	124656	LEI	???
1762	1830	1700	1830	162396	LIN	North
1760	1840	1600	1840	126837	LIN	Brant Broughton
1767	1773	1000	1850	168149	LIN	Partney
1600	1750	....	....	124621	LIN	Scamblesby
1632	....	1550	1700	141151	LND	ALL
1882	1940	1807	1882	119059	MDX	Chelsea
1810	1883	ALL	1810	164887	NTH	Rugby
1815	1900	1800	1900	118540	NTT	Farnfield
....	....	1694	1828	135003	NYK	Allerston
1790	1840	1750	1790	121339	NYK	Salton
1826	1894	1800	1894	147311	NYK	Thornton
1758	1758	ALL	1800	168696	OXF	Chipping Norton
1880	1904	1700	1950	107530	OXF	Oxfrod
1832	1892	1800	1832	131326	PEM	Milford
1698	1795	1600	1800	162280	SAL	Little Wenlock
1750	1850	1600	1750	169862	SFK	Bury St Edmunds
1730	1730	1680	1730	155276	SFK	Leiston
1750	1992	1558	1750	153427	STS	Grindon
1850	1886	1825	1850	149772	STS	Kingswinford
1750	1992	1558	1750	153427	STS	Rushton Spencer
1853	....	1300	1992	152501	STS	Tividale
....	....	1600	1950	124656	STS	???
1815	....	1775	1815	140309	WAR	Aston Cantlow
....	....	1650	1950	124656	WAR	???
....	....	1800	ALL	118060	WIL	Chilmark
1797	1962	....	....	115606	WIL	East Knoyle
1814	1992	ALL	1814	157066	WMD	Dudley
1814	1992	ALL	1814	157066	WMD	Tipton
FLETCHER contd.						
1815	1850	1815	1850	107522	WRY	Todmorden
....	....	1890	1940	141984	YKS	Altofts
1750	1850	....	....	141984	YKS	Barlow
1850	1930	1830	1890	123595	YKS	Brighouse
....	....	1890	1950	141984	YKS	Castleford
1885	1940	1885	1992	143944	YKS	Dalby
1877	1878	....	....	132179	YKS	Doncaster
1800	....	....	1850	160873	YKS	Egton
1885	1940	1885	1992	143944	YKS	Harrogate
1850	1900	1800	1900	116823	YKS	Malton
1844	1905	1800	1900	120197	YKS	Morley
1780	1910	....	....	141984	YKS	Sherburn In Elmet
1885	1940	1885	1992	143944	YKS	Skipton
1770	1900	1600	1770	170194	YKS	Slaidburn
....	1880	....	1880	119024	???	Birmingham
FLETT						
1900	1992	ALL	1900	104760	ABD	Aberdeen
1839	1986	....	....	135739	CAI	Wick
1795	1855	1600	1855	148482	OKI	Evie
1900	1992	ALL	1900	104760	SRY	Camberwell
FLEURS						
1864	....	....	....	119911	YKS	???
FLEURY						
1835	1850	1840	1860	165034	LAN	Manchester
FLEW						
1800	1850	1700	1850	161950	DOR	Portland
FLEWERS						
1810	1864	1800	1850	110604	MDX	Dalston
FLEWIN						
1840	1992	ALL	1870	162027	KEN	Dartford
1840	1992	ALL	1870	162027	WLS	Forrest Of Dean
FLEXEN						
1880	1930	1700	ALL	159255	LND	Bethnal Green
FLEXMAN						
1820	....	....	....	145068	ESS	Chelmsford
FLEXNEY						
1641	1870	ALL	ALL	112518	OXF	Witney
FLICK						
1782	1842	ALL	ALL	155373	ESS	Burnham On Crouch
FLICKER						
1840	1970	1700	1840	160709	KEN	Erith
FLIDE						
1700	1800	....	....	100420	WAR	Meriden
FLIGHT						
1803	1851	1750	1803	116440	ESS	Wesyt Hamshire
1732	1856	ALL	1900	132217	GLS	Kings Stanley
1670	1823	1670	1992	163600	GLS	Kings Stanley
1787	1992	1787	....	102989	KEN	Deptford
1800	1950	1700	1800	154059	KEN	Deptford
1823	1969	1823	1992	163600	MDX	East
1823	1969	1823	1992	163600	MDX	North
....	....	1760	1787	102989	NFK	Great Yarmouth
....	....	1600	1800	154059	NFK	Yarmouth
1727	1920	1727	1920	149403	OXF	Thame
FLINDERS						
1800	1950	1700	1900	171484	HUN	Great Gransden
1780	1830	ALL	1800	171484	HUN	Waresley
1785	1785	1750	1790	108510	LIN	Bitchfield
1680	1840	1680	1840	133817	LIN	Donington
1600	1700	1550	1700	133817	NTT	Gedling
1600	1700	1550	1700	133817	NTT	Ruddington
FLINN						
1832	1992	....	....	175803	DUR	Winlaton
FLINT						
....	....	ALL	ALL	123196	ALL	Name Study
1767	1792	1700	1767	119555	DBY	Breaston
1770	1823	1770	1841	140813	DBY	Darley Dale
1895	1992	1700	1900	171689	DBY	Dronfield
1419	1700	1400	1700	102830	DBY	Matlock
1770	1823	1770	1841	140813	DBY	Matlock
1780	1931	1586	1780	102512	LAN	Manchester
....	....	ALL	ALL	123196	NTH	Northampton
....	....	1838	ALL	151173	NTT	Budworth
1811	1865	1800	1865	107573	SRY	Epsom
1838	1885	ALL	1838	115010	SSX	Horsham
1876	1876	1800	1876	174807	SSX	Twineham
1500	1700	....	....	100420	WAR	Allesley
1500	1700	....	....	100420	WAR	Great Packington
1500	1700	....	....	100420	WAR	Meriden
1560	1700	1560	1700	167924	YKS	Pocklington
FLINTHAM						
....	....	ALL	ALL	124680	ALL	Name Study

Known From	To	Researching From	To	Ref	Cty	Place
FLINTOFF						
1800	1992	....	....	176125	LIN	Asterby
1800	1992	....	....	176125	LIN	Goulceby
FLINTOFT						
1850	1940	....	....	139351	YKS	Helmsley
FLOCKHART						
1750	1992	1700	1750	169897	KRS	Cleish
1770	1855	1770	1855	130400	PER	Auchterader
FLOOD						
....	....	ALL	ALL	124729	ALL	Name Study
1720	....	....	....	171441	KEN	Cuxton
1892	1923	1891	1920	124710	KEN	Folkestone
1750	1771	....	....	171441	KEN	Strood
?	?	ALL	ALL	100897	LND	???
1800	1850	1700	1850	139068	NTH	Northampton
FLOODGATE						
1802	1860	1750	1850	110604	KEN	Rochester
1660	1890	1660	1870	124737	LND	South
1660	1890	1660	1870	124737	LND	West
1640	1860	1640	1900	124737	SRY	West
FLOOK						
....	....	ALL	1850	141224	GLS	Bristol
1750	1810	1700	1750	124753	GLS	Stapleton
1825	....	....	....	140414	GLS	Stapleton
1805	1868	1805	1992	124753	GLS	Winterbourne
FLORANCE						
1750	1844	1700	1850	161950	DOR	Portland
FLORRY						
1820	1820	1750	1820	155276	SFK	Levington
FLORY						
1754	1888	....	1754	177504	SFK	Clopton
FLOTER						
1786	1861	ALL	ALL	101486	YKS	East
FLOUD						
1800	1840	1750	1992	135429	DEV	Exeter
1800	1840	1750	1992	135429	DEV	St Thomas
1840	1900	1750	1992	135429	GLA	Aberdare
1850	....	1750	1992	135429	MON	Abergavenny
1875	....	1750	1992	135429	MON	Bedwelty
FLOWER						
1700	1750	1700	1750	156930	BRK	ALL
1750	1800	1700	1800	156930	BRK	Leckhampstead
1800	1850	1750	1800	125377	DOR	Lytchett Matravers
1800	1820	1750	1800	125377	DOR	Wimborne
1715	1992	1600	1992	124761	GLS	South
1870	1950	1870	1950	109827	HAM	Southampton
....	....	?	?	110507	LEI	Leicester
1800	1870	1800	1992	133450	LND	St Pancras
1870	1960	1830	1855	109827	MDX	London
1523	1992	1500	1992	124761	SOM	North East
1771	1936	1700	1771	177075	SOM	Chilcompton
1523	1992	1500	1992	124761	SOM	Combe Hay
?	?	ALL	1850	117919	SOM	Kilmersdon
1826	1992	1600	1826	112747	SOM	Litton
....	....	1250	1550	124761	WIL	West
....	....	1750	ALL	118060	WIL	Compton Bassett
1716	1800	1650	1700	125377	WIL	East Knoyle
1770	1885	1765	1885	152102	WIL	Nunton
....	....	1730	1785	133604	WIL	Seend
FLOWERDAY						
1827	1850	1750	1827	152269	ESS	Stratford
FLOWERDEW						
1500	1992	ALL	ALL	104884	ALL	ALL
FLOWERS						
1808	1992	1697	1808	137537	DEV	Plymouth
1933	1933	1600	1992	172146	ESS	Fyfield
1896	1900	1600	1900	172146	LND	East
1830	1900	1700	1830	101834	NFK	East Dereham
1799	1992	....	....	124788	NTH	Braunston
1850	1992	1750	1850	114693	SFK	North
1874	1874	1600	1992	172146	SFK	South
1800	1900	1750	1900	135429	SOM	Bath
FLOYD PRICE						
1858	1881	1820	1880	159700	???	???
FLOYD						
ALL	ALL	ALL	ALL	124796	BKM	Princes Risborough
1640	1721	1640	1721	103977	BRK	Reading
1825	1860	....	....	136964	CON	Staustell
1851	1992	1600	1992	154342	GLS	Bristol
1570	1780	....	....	133361	KEN	Cheveringham
1570	1780	....	....	133361	KEN	Otham
1780	1800	....	....	133361	KEN	Tunbridge
1600	1841	1600	1992	154342	SOM	Porlock
1860	1940	....	....	133361	SRY	ALL
FLOYD contd.						
1800	1880	1700	1800	143014	STS	ALL
1714	1819	1700	1790	102830	STS	Handsworth
1700	1800	....	....	100420	WAR	Meriden
1795	1851	1770	1795	130990	YKS	Castleford
FLOYDE						
1790	1850	1700	1790	160350	SOM	Porlock
FLUCK						
1757	1890	1600	1757	160601	GLS	Tibberton
FLUDDER						
1777	1812	ALL	ALL	129933	SRY	Carshalton
FLUDE						
1830	1840	ALL	1850	107026	LND	???
FLUDGER						
1700	1800	1700	1800	163643	BRK	???
FLURY						
1701	1712	ALL	1712	108642	MDX	Soho
FLUTE						
1810	1879	1700	1810	161225	BKM	Astwood
FLUTTER						
....	....	1700	1840	121886	NTH	Peterborough
1743	1805	1743	1805	114308	SRY	Godalming
FLUX						
1838	1873	1700	1900	166928	IOW	Southampton
FLYN						
....	....	....	1841	168424	IRL	Cork
1841	1861	....	1841	168424	MON	Risca
FLYNN						
1881	1970	1700	1900	159468	CHS	Birkenhead
....	....	1800	1900	154458	DEV	Plymouth
....	....	....	1841	168424	IRL	Cork
1841	1861	....	1841	168424	MON	Risca
1857	1885	1800	1992	139203	WAT	Dungarvan
FOAKES						
1847	1900	1800	1992	169161	MDX	London
1747	1902	1747	1902	169161	WIL	Horningsham
1690	1770	1690	1770	169161	WIL	Maiden Bradley
1866	1992	1700	1900	125385	WOR	Rochford
FOALE						
1790	1992	1550	1850	146587	DEV	Ugborough
FOCH						
1890	1930	1850	1900	108731	LND	East
1800	1860	1800	1992	101532	LND	Bethnal Green
FOCHE						
1580	1630	....	....	142522	KEN	Worth
FODEN						
1823	1881	ALL	1820	149330	CHS	Middlewich
1500	1695	1500	1685	124842	STS	Fulford
1685	1992	1685	1992	124842	STS	Newcastle
FOGARTY						
1830	1920	1840	1941	163848	TIP	Thurles
1790	1860	1790	1860	163848	WIC	Ballinlonty
FOGG						
1843	....	1800	1900	139114	CHS	Stockport
1740	1992	1600	1800	177091	LAN	ALL
1823	1861	1841	1861	159492	LAN	Manchester
1803	1807	1800	1820	159492	LAN	Warrington
1600	1900	....	....	163503	LAN	???
FOGGIN						
1870	1892	1870	1900	151106	YKS	Acomb
FOGWELL						
1739	1925	1600	1738	102598	DEV	Brixham
1700	1850	1700	1900	151475	DEV	Paignton
FOINQUINOS						
....	....	ALL	ALL	164089	ALL	Name Study
FOISTER						
1737	1992	....	....	134619	YKS	Monkfryston
FOLEY						
1880	1940	1850	1950	177938	IRL	Cork
....	....	1700	1992	131903	LAN	Manchester
1800	1880	1700	1850	108677	STS	South
1874	1969	....	....	146811	WYK	Halifax
FOLIOT						
1220	1350	1200	1350	154881	ALL	ALL
FOLKINGHAM						
1650	1700	1650	1992	139203	LEI	Glenfields
FOLLAND						
....	....	1500	1992	124869	DEV	ALL
1748	1880	1880	1992	124869	DEV	Beaford
1640	1900	1900	1992	124869	DEV	Dolton
....	....	1600	1992	137588	DEV	Dolton
1783	1992	....	....	124869	DEV	St Giles
FOLLETT						
1600	....	ALL	ALL	116394	DEV	Sidmouth

Known From	To	Researching From	To	Ref	Cty	Place
FOLLETT contd.						
1700	....	ALL	ALL	116394	DEV	Topsham
1851	1861	1851	1861	174416	DOR	Cerne Abbas
1841	1851	1841	1851	174416	DOR	Charminster
1793	1926	....	1793	142166	LND	Westminster
1825	1880	1700	1850	160350	SOM	Dunster
1870	1920	ALL	....	120626	STS	Walsall
FOLLEY						
1900	1992	1700	1900	170615	CON	ALL
1720	1750	1720	1750	151297	CON	Kilkhampton
1900	1992	1700	1900	170615	DEV	ALL
1700	1830	1700	1830	151297	DEV	Hartland
FOLLON						
....	....	ALL	ALL	165824	ALL	ALL
1900	....	1850	1930	142549	SOM	ALL
1795	1949	1700	1949	165824	SOM	Batheaston
FOLLOWS						
1835	1870	1800	1870	179299	LND	South
1770	1920	1700	1800	166561	NTT	East Leake
FOLLY						
1660	1720	1660	1720	151297	CON	Weeke St Mary
FOLSTER						
1821	1855	1600	1855	148482	OKI	Birsay
FOLTHORPE						
....	....	ALL	ALL	121991	ALL	ALL
FOLWELL						
1800	1870	1700	1787	173460	KEN	Stourmouth
FOMM						
1760	1840	1700	1900	147958	MDX	Harrow
FONE						
1780	1950	....	....	124877	KEN	Chatham
1750	1780	ALL	1750	124877	KEN	Deptford
1627	1992	1558	1800	112968	SOM	Crewkerne
FOOKS						
ALL	ALL	ALL	ALL	124885	ALL	ALL
1810	1861	....	....	127957	DOR	Osmington
1694	1851	....	....	127957	DOR	Preston
1694	1851	....	....	127957	DOR	Sutton Poyntz
FOORD						
1825	1850	....	....	103608	KEN	Borden
1779	1853	1722	1853	116114	KEN	Brabourne
1870	1890	1870	1890	107522	KEN	Cranbrook
1855	....	....	1870	171441	KEN	Ransgate
1600	....	....	....	108146	KEN	???
1841	1881	1830	1992	116114	MDX	Old Brentford
1673	1870	1600	1880	122122	SOM	Blagdon
1841	1895	1790	1895	124915	SSX	Brighton
1800	1800	1770	1820	124915	SSX	Uckfield
1850	1900	ALL	1900	107948	SXE	Westham
FOOT						
....	....	ALL	ALL	155632	CHI	Guernsey
....	....	ALL	ALL	155632	CHI	Jersey
1844	1992	1700	1844	156264	DEV	Plymouth
1626	1960	....	....	151882	DOR	Batcombe
1825	1857	1700	1825	130648	DOR	Blandford
1822	1875	ALL	ALL	124893	DOR	Long Bredy
1745	1880	1700	1745	168777	HAM	Portsmouth
....	....	1700	1960	104523	KEN	Upper Norwood
1870	1929	1300	1950	152501	LND	Battersea
1795	1822	ALL	ALL	124893	NIR	Dublin
1740	1992	1700	1837	158674	NTH	Peterborough
....	....	1800	1850	125393	SOM	Compton Pauncefoot
1800	....	....	....	158747	SOM	???
....	....	1700	1960	104523	SRY	Upper Norwood
1750	1800	1600	1800	154059	SSX	Chichester
1700	....	....	....	158747	WIL	Mere
FOOTE						
1875	1920	ALL	ALL	156604	GLS	Gloucester
1857	1992	1750	1857	130648	MDX	London
ALL	ALL	ALL	ALL	156604	WIL	Mere
FOOTIT						
1750	1850	1600	1850	126845	LIN	???
FOOTITT						
1825	1848	1750	1869	142085	NTT	Bingham
1630	1900	....	....	165999	NTT	Newark
FOOTMAN						
1630	1730	1600	1730	111538	SAL	???
1730	1900	1730	1900	111538	WOR	???
1843	1900	1843	1992	133639	WOR	???
FOOTTIT						
1737	1820	1700	1740	170348	LIN	Marton
FORBES						
1864	1992	1700	1900	124931	ABD	Strathdon
1730	1835	1730	1992	166782	ABD	Strathdon
FORBES contd.						
1847	1850	1822	1857	109142	ANS	Dundee
....	....	1860	ALL	149187	ANS	Dundee
1795	1888	1790	1900	146536	AYR	Beith
....	....	ALL	ALL	104884	BAN	Fordyce
....	....	ALL	ALL	104884	BAN	Rathven
1885	1992	1800	1885	145041	DUR	Trimdons
1901	....	....	....	132616	ESS	East Ham
....	....	1750	ALL	149187	FIF	Abdie
1837	1871	1750	1871	165824	INV	Dores
1811	1811	1700	1811	153605	KCD	Fetteresso
1905	1977	....	....	132616	LND	Fulham
1866	1887	ALL	ALL	151777	LND	Lambeth
1806	1822	1770	1850	109142	MLN	Edinburgh
1804	1848	1700	1848	166049	MOR	Boharm
1804	1848	1700	1848	166049	MOR	Rothes
1822	1915	1400	1822	140678	PER	Glendevon
1750	1965	....	....	137820	SHI	Fetlar
1720	1965	....	....	137820	SHI	Mid Yell
1760	1965	....	....	137820	SHI	North Yell
1758	1965	....	....	137820	SHI	Northmavine
1720	1965	....	....	137820	SHI	South Yell
FORD						
....	....	1930	ALL	149187	ANS	Dundee
1903	1958	1850	1900	124990	AVN	Bristol
1803	1950	1783	1980	125008	AVN	Writhlington
1770	1799	1538	1865	118893	BEW	Polwarth
1839	1872	1700	1872	112615	BKM	Great Marlow
1839	1872	1700	1872	112615	BKM	Woodburn
1715	1851	1700	1850	125032	BRK	Bucklebury
1837	1992	1830	1992	125032	BRK	Hurst
1848	1973	1800	1929	125032	BRK	Reading
1881	1886	1881	1886	125032	BRK	Shinfield
1849	1852	1840	1860	125032	BRK	Spencers Wood
1844	1975	1800	1900	125032	BRK	Tilehurst
1873	1970	1850	1920	125032	BRK	Winnersh
1800	1992	ALL	1800	158437	BRK	???
1890	1900	1700	1890	132179	CHS	Gt Budworth
1885	1992	....	....	104078	DBY	Whittington
....	....	1700	1740	106127	DBY	???
....	....	1600	1800	103667	DEV	South
1300	1800	1300	1992	133450	DEV	South
1830	1970	1830	1970	148873	DEV	Ashburton
1550	1880	1300	1880	105333	DEV	Buckland In The Moor
1784	1796	ALL	ALL	129933	DEV	Cornwood
1838	1992	1750	1838	140473	DEV	Devonport
1764	1992	?	1764	125059	DEV	Ermington
1831	1873	ALL	ALL	129933	DEV	Exeter
1550	1880	1300	1880	105333	DEV	Holne
....	1753	ALL	ALL	129933	DEV	Holne
1550	1880	1300	1880	105333	DEV	Ilsington
1740	1840	1740	1840	106801	DEV	Ilsington
1550	1880	1300	1880	105333	DEV	Lydford
....	....	1800	1868	116165	DEV	Poltimore
1550	1880	1300	1880	105333	DEV	Widecombe In The Moor
1831	1860	....	....	170526	DOR	Canford
1804	1861	1538	1865	118893	DUR	Houghton Le Spring
1842	1909	....	....	148016	ENG	Stephen
1786	1854	1700	1786	113425	ESS	Maldon
1650	1992	ALL	ALL	124982	GLS	South
1820	1878	1600	1850	115525	GLS	Bristol
1830	1936	....	....	135437	GLS	Bristol
1820	1870	1750	1900	136840	GLS	Bristol
1729	1794	....	....	135437	GLS	Coaley
1750	1835	1500	1750	118877	GLS	Farmington
1787	1811	....	....	135437	GLS	Slimbridge
1838	1920	1838	1920	178683	GLS	Taynton
1862	1920	1867	1920	178683	GLS	Upleadon
....	....	ALL	ALL	145343	HAM	ALL
1500	1900	1500	1900	170216	HAM	ALL
1817	1822	1800	1840	125032	HAM	Basing
1820	1865	1800	1840	125032	HAM	Basingstoke
1822	1892	1800	1900	125032	HAM	Baughurst
1845	1900	1844	1910	125032	HAM	Blackmoor
1825	1831	1824	1832	125032	HAM	Empshott
1831	1845	1830	1846	125032	HAM	Greatham
?	?	?	?	150215	HAM	Havant
1830	1866	1810	1880	125032	HAM	Hook
1877	1941	1870	1920	125032	HAM	Kingsclere Woodlands
1883	1942	1870	1920	125032	HAM	Kingsclere
1830	1866	1800	1880	125032	HAM	Nately Scures

Known From	To	Researching From	To	Ref	Cty	Place
FORD contd.						
1812	1840	1800	1900	125032	HAM	Portsea
1700	1940	....	....	127833	HAM	Portsmouth
1845	1900	1844	1910	125032	HAM	Shelbourne
1825	1825	1820	1830	125032	HAM	Sherborne St John
1785	1850	1770	1830	125032	HAM	Worting
1940	1992	....	....	125032	HAM	Yateley
....	....	ALL	1865	119326	IRL	???
1897	1910	1897	1910	124710	KEN	Elham Valley
1820	1850	1650	1820	158232	KEN	Thanet
1734	1763	1500	1850	132055	KEN	Wateringbury
....	1895	ALL	ALL	129933	LAN	Liverpool
1844	1851	1843	1851	154946	LAN	Oldham
1600	1700	1600	1700	133450	LND	Central
1798	1804	1538	1865	118893	MDX	Islington
....	....	ALL	1865	119326	MLN	Edinburgh
1820	1850	1750	1820	112593	NFK	Long Stratten
1820	1850	1750	1820	112593	NFK	St Mary
1837	1844	1835	1845	125032	OXF	Checkendon
1886	1984	1886	1929	125032	OXF	Dunsden
1837	1844	1835	1845	125032	OXF	Hook End
1760	1780	ALL	1760	131059	SFK	Woolverstone
1837	1880	....	....	135437	SOM	Bedminster
1796	1803	1790	1820	125008	SOM	Binegar
1772	1803	1700	1810	125016	SOM	Binegar
....	1881	ALL	ALL	129933	SOM	Bridgewater
....	....	1750	1850	108677	SOM	Bridgwater
1788	1834	....	....	135437	SOM	Chew Magna
1849	1853	1800	1900	125016	SOM	Dunkerton
1847	1868	1800	1890	165824	SOM	Keynsham
1803	1940	1750	1992	125016	SOM	Radstock
1803	1950	1750	1992	125016	SOM	Writhlington
1803	1950	1783	1980	125008	SOM	Writhlington
1580	1700	1500	1992	133450	SRY	Guildford
1750	1992	1750	1992	133450	SRY	Thames Ditton
1775	1992	....	....	139971	SSX	East Hoathley
1775	1992	....	....	139971	SSX	Eastbourne
1800	1840	1700	1950	171522	SSX	Eastbourne
1831	1858	ALL	ALL	130664	SSX	Kirdford
1700	1905	ALL	ALL	113093	SSX	Ninfield
....	1700	....	....	174564	SSX	???
....	....	1700	1740	106127	STS	Burton On Trent
1788	1850	1600	1992	130125	WAR	Tanworth
....	....	1800	1900	169501	WAR	???
1500	1900	1500	1900	170216	WIL	ALL
1783	1822	1700	1822	174300	WIL	Overton
1781	1992	1700	1800	124966	WIL	Teffont
1823	1823	1821	1841	108901	WOR	Bishampton
1855	1871	ALL	1855	154946	YKS	Huddersfield
FORDE						
1880	....	....	1880	103489	GAL	Gort
1893	1992	ALL	1893	174262	GLA	Pontypridd
FORDER						
1796	1796	1768	1796	152943	HAM	Hursley
1800	1820	1800	1820	154210	WIL	Winterslow
FORDHAM						
....	....	ALL	ALL	125067	ALL	Name Study
FORDRED						
1892	1900	1892	1900	124710	KEN	South East
1825	1855	1800	1900	150002	WAR	Birmingham
FORDS						
1729	1760	....	....	135437	GLS	Frocester
1681	1723	....	....	165999	GLS	Gloucester
FORDYCE						
1750	1965	....	....	137820	SHI	Fetlar
1720	1965	....	....	137820	SHI	Mid Yell
1760	1965	....	....	137820	SHI	North Yell
1758	1965	....	....	137820	SHI	Northmavine
1720	1965	....	....	137820	SHI	South Yell
FOREHAM						
1816	1872	1700	1816	176141	SFK	Lackford
FOREHEAD						
1747	1790	1710	1747	173118	CON	Lansallos
FOREMAN						
....	....	ALL	ALL	125075	ALL	Name Study
1733	1940	....	....	128996	CAM	Thornley
1837	1992	....	1992	125075	ENG	ALL
1800	....	ALL	1800	150983	HAM	Portsea
....	....	1700	1900	125091	KEN	Ashford
....	....	1700	1992	125091	KEN	Blean
....	....	1700	1818	125091	KEN	Canterbury
....	....	1793	1818	125091	KEN	Chartham
....	....	1700	1992	125091	KEN	Chilham
1830	1890	1890	1992	166804	KEN	Faversham

Known From	To	Researching From	To	Ref	Cty	Place
FOREMAN contd.						
1790	1992	ALL	ALL	125083	KEN	Minster Ramsgate
1880	1900	1650	1760	141372	KEN	Thanet.
1650	1992	....	1992	125075	KEN	Whitstable
1818	1890	1700	1818	125091	KEN	Wye
1750	1830	1700	1750	166804	KEN	Yalding
1773	1928	....	....	125105	NFK	Great Yarmouth
1792	1866	1700	1792	125105	NFK	Norwich
1750	1851	1600	1750	125105	NFK	Thelverton
1840	....	ALL	1847	121436	NFK	Tunstead
1699	1992	1538	1699	125105	SFK	North Cove
1674	1992	1538	1674	125105	SFK	Pakefield
1780	1803	1700	1780	125105	SFK	Stuston
1837	1992	....	1992	125075	WLS	ALL
FOREMEN						
1769	1992	ALL	1992	125113	KEN	Birchington
1769	1992	ALL	1992	125113	KEN	Minster
FORES						
1810	1920	1700	1810	162876	MDX	Central
FOREST						
1804	1835	ALL	1804	162108	OXF	Burford
FORESTER						
....	....	1700	1800	179574	PER	Scone
....	....	1750	1800	172871	SRY	Godalming
FORFITT						
....	....	1700	1950	143219	DOR	ALL
FORGAN						
1850	....	ALL	ALL	130508	FIF	Leven
FORGIE						
ALL	ALL	ALL	ALL	126896	ABD	Cruden
ALL	ALL	ALL	ALL	126896	ABD	Longside
ALL	ALL	ALL	ALL	126896	ABD	Peterhead
FORKES						
1880	1910	1800	1920	117722	STS	Wolverhampton
FORMAN						
1790	1860	....	....	159883	ANS	Dundee
1900	1945	....	1900	116777	KEN	Whitstable
....	....	ALL	ALL	154970	LIN	Thorpe
1542	1636	1636	1700	125105	SFK	Bramfield
FORREST						
1818	1839	1700	1900	158666	ANS	Montrose
....	1875	1821	1875	166049	AYR	Dalmellington
1470	1800	ALL	ALL	149063	ELN	Haddington
1800	1940	1700	1800	146587	INV	Beauly
1822	1870	1790	1930	166049	INV	Inverness
1840	1880	1840	1880	150797	KCD	Barchary Ternar
....	....	1700	1890	155713	KEN	Wandsworth
1773	1848	....	....	138231	LAN	Manchester
1820	1850	ALL	ALL	138886	LAN	Preston
1807	1925	ALL	1807	139378	LKS	Glasgow
1807	1925	ALL	1807	139378	LKS	Shotts
1786	1894	1786	1900	104663	LND	???
1820	1850	1750	1850	150797	MLN	Musselburgh
1821	1861	1780	1900	166049	MOR	Forres
ALL	ALL	ALL	ALL	177563	SCT	North East
1800	1814	1600	1800	164879	SOM	Wells
1824	1840	1700	1900	153346	WOR	Lye
1872	....	1872	1992	133639	WOR	Malvern
FORRESTER						
....	....	ALL	ALL	125156	ALL	Name Study
1750	1850	1750	1850	120235	CLK	Clackmannan
1780	1810	1700	1900	113492	FIF	???
....	....	1890	1992	147613	LAN	Barrow In Furness
1890	1910	1800	1890	167258	LAN	Liverpool
1846	1880	....	1846	161888	LKS	Glasgow
1801	....	....	....	161888	LKS	Hutchenston
1800	1900	....	....	150371	ROX	Newcastleton
1800	1992	1800	1992	105147	SAL	Madeley
FORRESTOR						
1850	....	1700	1920	126160	CUL	Bewcastle
1850	....	1700	1920	126160	CUL	Seaton
FORRYAN						
....	....	ALL	ALL	125164	ALL	Name Study
1255	1992	1255	1992	125164	ALL	ALL
FORSDICK						
1800	1992	....	....	135232	HRT	Watford
1800	....	....	....	126543	SFK	Otley
FORSEY						
....	....	1650	1800	106461	DOR	Bridport
1790	1850	1700	1900	121762	SSX	West
FORSGATE						
1800	1820	1700	1800	102288	SFK	Otley
FORSHAW						
1830	1900	1580	1830	122238	CHS	Wirral

Known From	Known To	Researching From	Researching To	Ref	Cty	Place
FORSHAW contd.						
1825	1880	1795	1825	164097	LAN	Ormskirk
1714	....	....	....	110167	LAN	Rufford
FORSTER						
1759	1875	ALL	1875	156310	BKM	North
1655	1940	....	....	128996	CAM	Thornley
1780	1865	1780	1900	105732	CHS	Bromborough
1842	1920	1842	1920	147532	CHS	Witton
1822	1830	1780	1840	160873	CUL	Brampton
1821	1889	1821	1889	147532	CUL	Heskett In The Forest
1820	1860	1700	1860	156442	DEV	Dartmouth
1808	1935	1800	1900	163562	DEV	Stoke Dameral
1851	1851	1700	1851	171514	DFS	Langholm
1820	1830	1800	1850	151653	DON	Roshine Lodge
1784	....	1780	1900	130990	DUR	Durham
1840	1860	1700	1840	135275	DUR	Gateshead
....	1800	1850	....	108936	DUR	Usworth
1688	1715	1658	1688	139149	ERY	Southburn
1811	1839	1500	1839	153095	KEN	Central
1753	1992	1700	1753	156264	KEN	???
1750	1910	1690	....	105732	LAN	Liverpool
1750	1910	1690	....	105732	LAN	Prescot
1861	1891	1891	1992	171514	LAN	Salford
....	....	ALL	ALL	156442	LND	Sydenham
1840	1870	1750	1920	145858	MDX	London
1833	1854	1830	1880	160873	NBL	Newcastle On Tyne
....	....	1725	1825	177229	NBL	Newcastle
1833	1871	1700	1833	127116	NFK	Wymondham
1760	1811	ALL	1760	125253	NYK	Acklam
....	....	1590	1700	115142	STS	???
1722	1764	ALL	1722	102350	YKS	Birkin
FORSTERS						
?	....	?	?	177679	SCT	Borders
FORSYTH						
1867	1952	1867	1952	139807	AVN	Bristol
1841	1870	1867	1870	139807	DEV	Monkton
....	....	1700	1820	125180	IRL	Armagh
1840	1900	1870	1992	125172	LAN	Birkenhead
1840	1900	1870	1992	125172	LAN	Liverpool
1830	1845	1830	1850	141283	LAN	Salford
1851	1870	....	....	127140	LKS	New Monkland
1799	1810	....	1799	146811	MOR	Forres
1799	1810	....	1799	146811	MOR	Greens
....	....	....	1900	113514	SCT	???
1861	1903	1855	1900	141283	STS	Fenton
FORSYTHE						
....	....	1740	1800	154873	BEW	Bunkle
FORT						
1805	1830	ALL	ALL	125202	LAN	Lancaster
1830	1992	ALL	ALL	125202	WRY	Bradford
FORTAY						
....	....	1750	1850	114596	WIG	Isle Of Whithorn
FORTEE						
1649	1789	1600	1992	122211	SRY	Lambeth
FORTESCUE						
1735	1820	....	....	100536	ALL	???
1655	1992	ALL	1700	108502	CAM	Little Gransden
1700	1800	1778	?	105694	HAM	Winchester
1655	1992	ALL	1700	108502	NTH	Longstow
1655	1992	ALL	1700	108502	NTH	Thurning
1691	1780	1600	1763	151513	WAR	Mancetter
FORTH						
1800	1992	1700	1800	160075	DUR	Lumley
1731	1878	....	....	169129	NFK	Magdalen
FORTRYE						
....	....	1570	1670	154873	KEN	Greenwich
FORTUNE						
1650	1700	ALL	1725	149063	BEW	Coldingham
1880	1992	1750	1880	125601	LTN	???
....	....	1800	1992	140759	WIL	Avon
....	....	1800	1992	140759	WIL	Chippenham
1818	1992	1700	1818	110019	WIL	Christian Malford
....	....	1800	1992	140759	WIL	Christian Malford
FORWARD						
1850	1872	....	....	130281	DEV	Mouth Molton
1750	1800	1720	1850	125318	DOR	Sutton Waldron
FORWOOD						
1850	1925	1750	1850	110426	DEV	Tiverton
1760	....	ALL	....	150835	HAM	Portsmouth
....	....	1700	1870	119431	KEN	East
1760	....	ALL	....	150835	LND	???
FOSBERY						
1890	1980	1750	1890	166421	HAM	ALL
FOSBROKE						
....	....	ALL	ALL	109428	ALL	Name Study
FOSBROOK						
1561	1695	1500	1695	102830	STS	Sedgely
FOSH						
1800	1860	1800	1992	101532	LND	Shoreditch
1804	1880	1770	1900	163775	MDX	Bethnal Green
FOSS						
1760	....	....	....	109819	DEV	South West
1760	....	....	....	109819	DEV	???
1790	1810	....	....	127957	DOR	Osmington
1803	1806	1790	1803	109819	LND	London
FOSSCROFT						
1787	1795	1700	1787	176451	YKS	Leeds
FOSSETT						
1812	1841	1812	1841	141194	SRY	Camberwell
FOSSEY						
1840	1900	1700	1992	168327	BDF	Ampthill
1800	1900	1800	1900	108693	BDF	Arlesey
1930	1980	1900	1950	168327	LEI	Leicester
FOSTER						
1812	1890	1750	1812	144746	BRK	Binfield
1630	1674	1600	1630	115819	BRK	Radley
1655	1940	....	....	128996	CAM	Thornley
1820	1870	1750	1820	124427	CAV	Ashfield
1800	1850	1700	1800	147494	CON	Truro
1771	1784	1700	1771	112321	DBY	ALL
1800	1850	1500	1800	179396	DEV	Ottery St Mary
1800	1850	1700	1800	147494	DEV	Rattery
1856	1992	....	....	104949	DEV	Stoke Damerel
1800	1850	1700	1800	147494	DEV	Totnes
1600	1900	1568	1900	125326	DOR	East
1734	1986	1606	1910	125326	DOR	Cranborne
1342	1827	ALL	ALL	105015	DUR	Cold Hesledon
1795	1850	....	....	102881	DUR	Elwick
1850	1900	....	....	102881	DUR	Hartlepool
1790	1820	1750	1790	160458	DUR	Pittington
....	....	1700	1820	102881	DUR	Trimdon
1870	....	1870	1900	135658	GLA	Swansea
1879	1992	1700	1700	113530	GLA	Treforest
1810	1900	1700	1900	148792	HAM	North East
1866	....	....	....	153397	HAM	Brockenhurst
1804	ALL	1804	ALL	170968	HAM	Fareham
1796	1796	1765	1840	124974	HAM	Kingsclere
1780	1880	1700	1780	165336	HAM	Kingsclere
....	....	ALL	....	172219	HAM	Porsmouth
1700	1940	....	....	127833	HAM	Portsmouth
....	....	ALL	....	172219	HAM	Southampton
1860	1992	1700	1860	103098	HAM	Sway
1706	1980	1700	1980	171999	HUN	Godmanchester
1798	1818	1760	1830	116114	KEN	Ashford
1724	....	....	1740	171441	KEN	Frinstead
1800	1992	1750	1800	155500	LAN	Bold
1810	1841	1700	1810	135348	LAN	Kirkham
1826	1868	1700	1826	115185	LAN	Manchester
1850	1950	1800	1850	146102	LAN	Prestwich
1851	1890	....	....	135348	LAN	Royton
1867	1955	1800	1900	146102	LAN	Salford
1700	1750	....	....	126497	LAN	Wigan
1771	1784	1700	1771	112321	LEI	ALL
1780	1900	1780	1900	155764	LIN	Great Steeping
1797	1824	1500	1797	175072	LIN	Lissington
....	....	1775	1850	141984	LIN	Waithe
....	....	1825	1860	141984	LIN	Yaddlethorpe
1754	....	....	....	148768	LND	Wesminster
1876	1951	1876	1951	125326	MDX	West London
1830	1900	1750	1900	105422	NBL	Benwell
....	....	1785	1820	110450	NTH	Bugbrooke
1786	1834	1760	1786	149039	NTH	Bugbrooke
1850	1900	ALL	ALL	154970	NTH	Greens Norton
1822	1822	1750	1851	160636	NTT	Bleasby
1850	1992	ALL	1850	125210	NTT	Kneeton
1861	1885	1822	1851	144096	NTT	Nottingham
1750	1790	....	1790	137634	NTT	Osberton
1851	1992	ALL	1800	125261	NTT	Southwell
1830	1950	1700	1830	125253	NYK	Middlesbrough
1650	1676	ALL	1650	114987	SOM	Aller
....	1848	1800	1848	133639	SOM	Coker
1782	1782	1500	1782	174009	SSX	East
1778	1810	1700	1795	165980	SSX	Hailsham
....	1700	....	....	174564	SSX	???
1797	1992	1750	1800	125318	STS	Bilston
1780	1930	1780	1930	100420	STS	Bloxwich
1600	1930	1600	1930	100420	STS	Darlaston

Known From	To	Researching From	To	Ref	Cty	Place
FOSTER contd.						
1532	1700	1500	1700	102830	STS	Darlaston
1880	1992	1880	1992	125237	STS	Darlaston
1560	1700	1500	1750	160873	STS	Darlaston
1826	1861	1790	1890	169323	STS	Darlaston
1569	1596	1500	1595	102830	STS	Ellastone
1844	1844	1700	1844	172049	STS	Hanbury
1810	1840	....	1840	161888	TYR	Omagh
1880	1910	1800	1880	167983	WAR	Birmingham
1800	1900	1500	1850	118907	WOR	South East
1840	1840	1800	1860	135917	WOR	Dudley
1861	1863	1840	1890	135917	WOR	Kidderminster
1863	1870	1860	1890	135917	WOR	Ladywood
1873	1890	1870	1900	135917	WOR	Malvern
1628	1784	1600	1800	135917	WOR	Old Swinford
1843	1964	ALL	1843	115126	WOR	Throckmorton
1867	....	1860	1880	135917	WOR	Worcester
1774	1796	....	1774	101761	WRY	Methley
1730	1870	1730	1870	153621	WYK	Queensbury
1728	1832	1728	1832	125253	YKS	Acklam
1685	1685	1600	1685	141097	YKS	Braithwell
1780	1900	1750	1850	109525	YKS	Brompton By Sawton
1814	1880	1780	1900	160873	YKS	Heslington
1790	1800	1780	1826	169323	YKS	Otley
....	....	1700	1750	177393	YKS	Ottringham
1739	1759	1600	1750	101575	YKS	Pontefract
1650	1750	1600	1750	119717	YKS	Rosby
1800	1910	....	....	177393	YKS	Selby
....	....	1820	1900	158127	YKS	Sheffield
1728	1760	1760	ALL	125253	YKS	Stainton
1690	1800	1650	1690	177393	YKS	Wistow
1860	1900	....	....	141984	YKS	Witherwick
1699	1728	ALL	1699	125253	YKS	Yarm
1757	1851	1700	1900	160873	YKS	York
1921	....	1870	1921	135917	???	Handsworth
1892	1950	1890	ALL	135917	???	Harborne
FOSTON						
1805	1980	1207	1805	125334	LIN	Market Rasen
1805	1980	1207	1805	125334	LIN	Normanby
1805	1980	1207	1805	125334	LIN	Tealby
1805	1980	1207	1805	125334	YKS	Hull
FOTHERBY						
1810	1992	1700	1850	163015	LIN	Lincoln
1890	1930	1750	1900	119180	YKS	Leeds
FOTHERGILL						
....	....	1750	1850	137685	LND	City
....	....	1750	1850	137685	NFK	Gt Yarmouth
1857	1880	ALL	ALL	142492	NYK	Askrigg
1860	1880	1800	1880	142492	NYK	Settle
....	....	1750	1850	137685	SFK	???
1860	1912	1800	1860	125342	WYK	???
FOTHERINGHAM						
....	....	1650	1740	142670	ANS	Powrie
1832	1879	1703	1783	163139	OKI	Sanday
FOTHERLEY						
1625	1650	1600	1625	121339	NYK	Lythe
FOULDS						
1800	1960	1600	1800	152463	LEI	Long Whatton
FOULGER						
1850	1992	....	....	148091	ABD	???
1861	1883	1855	1883	133639	BKM	Whitchurch
....	1897	1880	1897	133639	DBY	Bigger
1865	1895	1860	1895	133639	LAN	Wallesey
1793	1855	1780	1865	133639	MDX	Marylebone
1826	1841	1810	1860	133639	MDX	St Pancras
1672	1931	1672	1931	148091	NFK	Bedingham
....	....	1765	1793	133639	NFK	???
1862	1872	1855	1872	133639	WOR	Malvern
FOULIS						
1855	1902	....	....	170461	LAN	Blackburn
1785	1840	ALL	1785	167878	OKI	Pap Westray
....	....	....	1855	170461	SCT	???
FOULKES						
1820	1860	....	....	118729	DEN	Holywell
1760	1800	ALL	1760	138401	DEN	Llandulas
1800	1865	1700	1800	157147	DEN	Llandyrnog
1760	1800	ALL	1760	138401	DEN	Llanelian
1790	....	1780	1820	175366	DEV	Dawlish
1782	....	ALL	ALL	147621	FLN	Northop
1830	1992	....	....	105139	GYN	Llandrillo
1830	1881	1880	1980	124133	LAN	Southport
1870	1906	1800	1870	106968	SAL	Ellesmere
1830	1992	....	....	105139	SAL	West Felton
FOULSHAM						
1833	1833	1800	1833	127116	NFK	Wymondham
FOULSTON						
1850	1890	1750	1950	122602	LIN	North Kelsey
FOUND						
1740	1840	1740	1840	151297	DEV	Hartland
FOUNTAIN						
1763	1802	1700	1900	178322	BKM	Denham
1826	1854	1800	1900	178322	BKM	Isleworth
1790	1850	1700	1900	106704	HUN	Upwood
1750	1830	1600	1900	106704	HUN	Warboys
1800	1900	1750	1900	106704	HUN	Woodwalton
1778	1837	....	....	116602	KEN	Greenwich
1816	1840	ALL	ALL	155373	LND	East
1845	1930	1750	1845	147826	LND	Bermondsey
1845	1930	1750	1845	147826	LND	City
....	....	1700	1900	140627	NFK	Norwich
....	....	ALL	ALL	135062	NTT	???
1858	1873	1850	1900	178322	WAR	Birmingham
1830	1850	1800	1830	149632	YKS	Wakefield
1800	1850	....	....	144029	YKS	???
FOURACRE						
1885	1940	1885	1900	163406	MDX	London
....	....	?	?	132195	SOM	Hill Farrance
1700	1900	1700	1900	140295	SOM	West Buckland
FOVARGUE						
....	....	ALL	ALL	128570	ALL	Name Study
FOWARD						
1745	1790	1700	1745	173118	CON	Lansallos
FOWELL						
1650	1871	ALL	ALL	159700	CON	South East
1851	1950	1850	1919	159700	DEV	Plymouth
1455	1830	ALL	ALL	159700	DEV	Ugborough
1790	1880	1600	1790	161543	NFK	Thetford
1797	1850	1750	1850	123404	STS	Gnosall
1859	1899	1857	1900	123404	STS	Wednesbury
FOWKES						
1808	1850	ALL	ALL	107255	LND	ALL
1774	1774	ALL	ALL	107255	LND	Westminster
1781	1781	ALL	ALL	107255	MDX	???
....	....	ALL	ALL	114308	NTH	Floore
FOWLE						
1600	1800	....	....	131857	DOR	Berwick St John
1705	1992	ALL	1705	141526	KEN	Egerton
1817	1864	1700	1850	117013	NFK	Hempstead
....	....	1700	1900	141151	SSX	ALL
1577	1992	....	....	130249	WIL	Pewsey
FOWLER						
1828	1840	1830	1930	165034	ABD	Aberdeen
1690	1920	....	....	123374	ABD	Midmar
1870	1870	1870	1870	151599	BDF	Bedford
1650	1750	1600	1800	177180	BKM	Northall
1800	1851	1700	1810	103896	BRK	Hungerford
1792	1840	1700	1792	123307	BRK	Kintbury
1723	1992	1700	1992	148156	CAM	Graveley
1655	1940	....	....	128996	CAM	Thornley
1663	....	ALL	1663	168602	CAM	Witcham
1860	1930	1700	1860	112941	CHS	Biston
1830	1850	1700	1850	158216	CHS	Stockport
1797	1854	1700	1860	167487	DEV	Uplyme
1700	1850	1700	1850	136786	DOR	Uplyme
1899	....	....	1899	169927	DUR	Darlington
1800	1850	....	....	105759	ESS	Berners Roding
1839	....	1750	1839	179140	ESS	St Pancras
1851	....	....	....	135402	EYK	Hull
1720	....	ALL	ALL	130508	FIF	Pittenweem
1748	1992	1748	1992	178683	GLS	Charfield
1807	1992	1807	1992	178683	GLS	Horsley
1803	....	1803	ALL	125148	GLS	Upton On Severn
....	....	1650	1900	106461	GLS	???
1767	1992	ALL	1767	133868	HRT	South West
1770	1773	1770	1773	108251	KEN	Medway
1900	1992	1870	1992	122238	LAN	Earlstown
1780	1800	....	....	126497	LAN	Leyland
1847	1870	1800	1850	125350	LAN	Preston
....	1846	1800	1875	135658	LAN	Preston
1828	1877	1750	1828	160636	LIN	Blankney
1871	1871	1871	1950	106666	LND	ALL
1864	1873	1860	1880	140295	LND	ALL
1860	1920	1800	1900	153931	LND	Stepney
1874	1930	1870	1960	140295	MON	Newport
1754	1915	ALL	ALL	135208	NTH	Eye
1754	1915	ALL	ALL	135208	NTH	Gunsthorpe
1754	1915	ALL	ALL	135208	NTH	Werrington

Known From	To	Researching From	To	Ref	Cty	Place
FOWLER contd.						
1870	1930	1870	1930	151599	NTT	Sneinton
1796	1849	1700	1870	115967	ROC	Logie Wester
1796	1849	1700	1870	115967	ROC	Urquhart
1740	1740	ALL	ALL	124982	SOM	North
1770	1850	1600	1850	154342	SOM	Bristol
1803	1870	1780	1870	151599	SOM	Chard
1800	1800	1750	1850	121568	SOM	Sedgemoor
1803	1870	1780	1870	151599	SOM	Taunton
1750	1781	....	....	165999	SOM	Taunton
....	....	1650	1900	106461	SOM	???
....	....	1746	....	130079	SOM	???
....	....	1850	1900	122238	SRY	???
1700	1800	1800	ALL	145378	SSX	Tortington
....	....	1800	1950	155802	YKS	North
1730	1992	....	....	124168	YKS	Alne
1788	1815	1700	1850	155969	YKS	Armley
1802	1841	1700	1900	177369	YKS	Hemingbrough
1788	1815	1700	1850	155969	YKS	Leeds
....	....	....	1793	134902	YKS	Sheffield
1750	....	1650	1760	119938	YKS	York
1860	1874	1810	1874	140295	???	Bristol
FOWLES						
1861	....	....	1860	149624	CWD	Erbistock
1880	1943	1700	1880	149624	FLN	Threpewood
1703	1796	....	....	117803	GLS	Tetbury
1817	1874	1817	1874	117803	MDX	St Pancras
FOWLIE						
1820	1883	ALL	1820	106909	ABD	Old Machar
FOWLIS						
1766	1805	1700	1805	163139	OKI	Deerness
FOWNES						
....	....	1800	1899	167614	WAR	Birmingham
1751	1916	....	....	163562	WOR	Broughton
FOX						
1832	1992	....	....	125407	AVN	Bristol
1820	1860	1750	1820	147710	BKM	Hedsor
1890	1920	1850	1890	120529	BRK	Maidenhead
1606	1900	....	....	116173	CUL	St Bees
....	....	1700	1850	109290	DBY	North
1670	1720	ALL	1992	179205	DBY	Ault Hucknall
1700	1750	1700	1750	149152	DBY	Eckington
1740	1780	1740	1800	135801	DBY	Hathersage
1804	....	1750	1804	136816	DBY	Matlock
1780	1812	1700	1780	130257	DEV	Holbeton
1730	1800	1600	1790	126772	DEV	Lifton
....	....	1800	1992	137588	DOR	Compton
1840	1992	1700	1840	160458	DOR	Frampton
1860	....	1860	1950	125466	DUR	Hartlepool
1826	1860	1826	ALL	125466	DUR	Sunderland
1688	1779	....	....	165999	ESS	Fordham
1580	1700	1580	1700	142018	HAM	West
1800	1815	ALL	ALL	125466	HAM	Southampton
....	1800	1700	1815	125466	IOW	ALL
1724	1813	....	....	161357	KEN	Ash
1628	1992	1500	1628	171832	KEN	Denton
1800	1820	ALL	1800	145564	KEN	Reculver
1750	....	....	1750	162086	KEN	Romney Marsh
....	....	ALL	ALL	118400	KEN	???
1810	1876	1810	1876	160237	LEI	Market Harboro
1660	1709	ALL	1709	168718	LEI	Thrussington
1700	1800	....	....	124621	LIN	Swineshead
1813	1865	1797	1865	156582	MDX	Hanwell
1840	1880	1840	1880	167924	MDX	Pancras
1780	1860	1780	1860	167924	MDX	Stepney
1854	1855	....	1854	117234	MDX	Westminster
1808	1812	....	....	101028	NFK	Aylmerton
1746	1797	1797	1813	156582	NFK	Corpusty
1763	1763	1650	1763	163953	NFK	Forncett
1746	1797	1797	1813	156582	NFK	Saxthorpe
1800	1800	....	1800	136212	NFK	Snettisham
1763	1763	1650	1763	163953	NFK	St Marys
1670	1700	....	1700	137634	NTT	Sutton Cum Lound
1782	1824	1600	1825	101575	NTT	Worksop
1555	1900	ALL	ALL	166804	OXF	Bampton
1550	1600	1450	1550	174513	OXF	Lower Heyford
1714	1757	1690	1700	135763	SAL	Newtown
1714	1757	1690	1700	135763	SAL	Wem
....	1870	....	1870	110027	SEL	???
1700	1895	....	....	125393	SOM	Compton Pauncefoot
1840	1955	....	....	125393	SOM	North Cadbury
....	....	1600	1992	137588	SOM	Yeovil
1839	1839	1800	1900	148725	SSX	East Grinstead
....	....	1700	1992	170402	STS	South

Known From	To	Researching From	To	Ref	Cty	Place
FOX contd.						
1580	1750	1580	1750	142018	WIL	ALL
1788	1960	1700	1785	125415	WOR	Powick
1770	1800	1770	1800	120472	WOR	Worcester
1870	1992	ALL	1992	179205	WYK	Bradford
1870	1992	ALL	1992	179205	WYK	Rotherham
1777	1992	....	....	109142	YKS	Batley
1840	1860	1700	1900	136034	YKS	Batley
1800	1860	1750	1870	171549	YKS	Bingley
1833	1833	1800	1835	141097	YKS	Braithwell
1680	1850	....	....	140554	YKS	Coxwold
1627	1766	1500	1627	109142	YKS	Dewsbury
1730	1730	ALL	ALL	120650	YKS	Felkirk
1780	1800	1780	1840	149152	YKS	Handsworth
1760	1820	1600	1760	163236	YKS	Saddleworth
1785	1900	1750	....	109290	YKS	Sheffield
1814	1850	1850	1900	120650	YKS	Sheffield
1802	1992	1778	1831	135801	YKS	Sheffield
1660	1715	1600	1660	174858	YKS	Willerby
1775	1814	ALL	ALL	120650	YKS	Worsboro
FOXALL						
....	....	1700	1870	166863	LND	ALL
1812	1815	1800	1900	165093	WOR	Powick
FOXCROFT						
1854	1926	1700	1854	164178	LAN	Melling
FOXEN						
1796	1827	ALL	1796	143278	NFK	Norwich
FOXLEE						
1900	1992	....	....	153397	HAM	Eastleigh
1900	1992	....	....	153397	MDX	London
1930	1992	....	....	153397	SRY	Weybridge
FOXLEY						
1734	1734	1700	1740	131911	CHS	???
1746	1771	1650	1745	131245	DBY	North Wingfield
....	....	1700	1740	131911	FLN	???
....	....	1700	1740	131911	STS	???
FOXLOWE						
1792	1860	1700	1800	163635	DBY	Winster
FOXON						
1828	1900	1700	1850	100129	LEI	Ellesthorpe
1867	1992	1850	1992	100129	LIN	Stamford
1802	....	....	....	120804	WAR	Ullesthorpe
FOXWELL						
1823	1852	1700	1823	104620	DEV	Appledore
1700	1800	1650	1750	144657	DEV	Hemyock
1780	1821	ALL	ALL	124982	GLS	South
1818	1900	1800	1992	128600	LAN	Manchester
1823	1852	1700	1823	104620	SOM	Appledore
FOY						
1850	1880	1800	1992	157651	DUR	Jarrow
1830	1963	1750	1800	174599	LND	Kensington
1858	1921	1800	1858	173339	MAY	???
1850	....	....	....	114642	MDX	London
1830	1860	1860	1900	179604	MDX	Stoke Newington
1790	1830	1750	1800	179604	SRY	Streatham
....	1891	1700	1900	164909	???	Fulham
FOYLE						
1841	1841	ALL	ALL	115126	DOR	Blandford
1550	1900	....	....	131857	DOR	Fontmell Magna
1767	1815	1700	1767	171182	WIL	South
1767	1815	1700	1767	171182	WIL	West
1730	1861	1690	1880	105333	WIL	Tisbury
FOYSTER						
1814	....	1814	1827	136999	CAM	Wisbech
1823	1850	1700	1823	126349	LIN	Thurlby
FOZZARD						
1820	1930	1750	1950	155969	YKS	Dewsbury
1820	1930	1750	1950	155969	YKS	Ossett
FRADD						
1719	1765	1500	1992	140619	CON	Little Petherick
1853	1900	1500	1992	140619	CON	Padstow
1837	1992	1750	1837	156523	DEV	Plymouth
1892	1962	1850	1992	140619	HAM	Portsmouth
FRAGEL						
....	....	1800	1992	125822	DEV	Bovey Tracey
FRAHER						
1857	1890	1800	1992	139203	WAT	Dungarvan
FRAIN						
....	....	1700	1992	102377	CLA	???
1845	1892	....	....	102377	YKS	Selby
FRAINE						
1820	1900	1700	1900	104256	DEV	North
FRAMPTON						
....	....	ALL	ALL	125474	ALL	Name Study

Known From	To	Researching From	To	Ref	Cty	Place
FRAMPTON contd.						
ALL	ALL	ALL	ALL	125474	ALL	ALL
1794	....	....	....	119911	DOR	Portesham
1820	1850	1750	1850	118397	DOR	Witchampton
1810	1845	1800	1845	155691	HAM	Ringwood
1792	1840	1600	1850	132993	IOW	Newchurch
1805	1871	....	....	124672	WIL	Swindon
FRANCE						
1859	....	ALL	ALL	136735	BDF	Turvey
1830	1889	1830	1900	136328	CHS	Hyde
1776	1853	1750	1776	108154	LAN	West Houghton
1710	1992	1500	1599	125504	LIN	North
1787	1823	1780	1825	136328	YKS	Honley
....	....	1700	1860	143359	YKS	Honley
1771	1844	1500	1844	169439	YKS	Mirfield
FRANCES						
1750	1860	1700	1860	139068	BKM	ALL
1800	....	1750	1850	126144	KEN	Wilmington
FRANCIS						
1772	1992	ALL	1772	157791	BDF	Ridmont
1620	....	1620	ALL	153567	BDF	Shillington
1930	1992	ALL	1930	162027	BDF	Stondon
1600	1750	1500	1900	170216	BRK	ALL
1676	1730	1500	1676	138614	CON	Gwennap
1671	1710	1600	1800	153354	CON	Gwennap
1756	1760	1500	1756	138614	CON	Kea
1756	1760	1500	1756	138614	CON	Kenwyn
1830	1900	....	....	147672	CON	St Day
1738	1838	1700	1850	115991	DEV	Crediton
1870	1942	1870	1942	147966	DEV	Exeter
1780	1800	1700	1800	152579	DEV	Stoke Damerel
1829	1880	1700	1942	173584	DOR	Poole
1790	1992	ALL	ALL	131091	ESS	ALL
1847	1847	1847	1900	106666	ESS	Romford
....	1848	1800	1900	135658	GLA	Cwmavon
....	1848	1800	1900	135658	GLA	Michaelston
1720	1800	1720	1800	151297	GLA	Neath
....	....	ALL	1830	141224	GLS	South
1800	1850	1800	1850	124761	GLS	Bitton
1800	1850	1800	1850	124761	GLS	North Stoke
1780	1780	1750	1800	102970	HAM	East Woodhay
1760	1830	1730	1850	105333	HAM	Isle Of Wight
1602	....	1602	ALL	153567	HRT	Hitchin
1789	....	ALL	1789	153567	HRT	Pirton
1632	....	1632	ALL	153567	HRT	St Ippollitts
1801	1870	1800	1880	148121	KEN	Bexley
1870	1910	1837	1910	130036	LAN	Liverpool
1798	1843	1700	1798	152196	LIN	Kirton In Lindsey
1873	1992	1873	....	156639	LND	ALL
1866	1940	1837	1855	156434	LND	East
1834	1871	1830	1900	148121	LND	City
....	....	1800	1840	164615	LND	Kensington
....	....	1800	1870	137618	LND	Lambeth
1870	1910	....	....	137618	LND	Southwark
1793	....	....	1793	142166	LND	Westminster
1860	1870	1800	1860	147966	MDX	Chelsea
1857	1871	....	....	103659	MDX	Fulham
1659	1992	1630	1992	125520	MDX	London
1797	1817	1797	1829	137898	MDX	Whitechapel
1860	1900	1780	1840	159115	MGY	Clun
1870	1940	1870	1940	156930	MON	Llanfrechfa Upper
1790	1940	1790	1940	156930	MON	Llanfrechfa
1750	1810	1538	1810	118893	NFK	Banham
1782	....	1538	1830	118893	NFK	Bressingham
1740	1860	1600	1740	163732	NFK	Diss
....	....	1538	1850	118893	NFK	Fersfield
1750	1850	1700	1850	103055	NFK	Helhoughton
1750	1850	1700	1850	103055	NFK	Ingham
1702	1777	1600	1700	148121	NFK	Norwich
1880	1910	1700	1880	139122	NFK	Oulton Broads
1702	....	1600	1700	148121	NFK	???
1840	1850	1800	....	113212	SAL	South
1825	1825	1820	1835	111414	SAL	Acton Scott
1860	1900	1780	1840	159115	SAL	Bships Castle
1693	1751	1600	1841	176877	SAL	Clun
1825	1845	1790	1871	111414	SAL	Mainstone
1706	1813	1600	1706	118605	SAL	Moore
1868	1868	1861	1871	111414	SAL	Shrewsbury
1800	1860	1850	1900	173665	SAL	Wistanston
1824	....	1822	1830	148121	SFK	Beccles
1800	1900	1700	1992	112402	SFK	Bury St Edmunds
1775	1783	1650	1774	131245	SFK	Hadleigh
1880	1910	1700	1880	139122	SFK	Oulton Broads
1655	1799	1558	1675	112968	SOM	Ansford
FRANCIS contd.						
1767	1992	1650	1767	123153	SOM	Bath
....	....	1800	1880	133604	SOM	Bath
1800	1899	ALL	1800	112968	SOM	Ditcheat
1800	1899	ALL	1800	112968	SOM	East Pennard
....	....	1500	1880	137472	SRY	Dorking
....	....	1500	1880	137472	SRY	Holmwood
1885	1890	ALL	ALL	124346	T&W	Sunderland
1658	1713	1600	1660	170348	WIL	Stanton Fitzwarren
1840	....	1800	1850	119008	WIL	Stourton
1750	1804	ALL	ALL	128449	WOR	Birmingham
1800	1850	1700	1900	138517	???	London
1861	1906	1800	....	116297	???	Newcastle
?	?	ALL	ALL	117390	???	???
FRANCO						
....	1796	....	....	132837	MDX	???
FRANCOMB						
1844	....	....	....	127582	AVN	Bristol
1562	1697	....	....	165999	GLS	Olveston
FRANCY						
....	....	1780	1830	122416	IRL	???
FRANK						
1779	1859	ALL	1779	103039	DUR	Staindrop
1740	1782	ALL	1740	154946	NRY	Lastingham
ALL	ALL	ALL	ALL	105813	YKS	Whitby
FRANKFIELD						
1855	....	?	1860	164976	GLS	Gloucester
FRANKHAM						
1809	....	1750	1850	169218	SOM	Bath
FRANKISH						
1800	1950	....	....	171921	LIN	Cleethorpes
1772	1800	ALL	ALL	171921	LIN	Middle Rasen
1808	1881	1758	1836	116114	YKS	Bridlington
1717	1841	1500	1717	113689	YKS	Hunmanby
FRANKLAND						
1873	1992	ALL	ALL	125547	ALL	ALL
1818	1832	1800	1900	176133	HUM	Sutton In Holderness
1784	1832	1600	1900	176133	LIN	Gainsborough
1691	1823	....	....	135437	NFK	Bodham
1758	1758	....	....	135437	NFK	Briston
1720	1727	....	....	135437	NFK	Fakenham
1758	1758	....	....	135437	NFK	Weybourn
1655	1900	1600	1860	151742	NRY	Egton
1814	1840	1750	1814	118486	NRY	Helperby
1660	1680	1600	1680	121339	NYK	Brotton
1850	1860	1800	1900	162345	YKS	Barnard Castle
1873	1992	ALL	ALL	125547	YKS	Leeds
FRANKLIN						
?	?	?	?	140244	BDF	Hunts Border
1450	1550	1400	1550	154881	BRK	ALL
1815	1837	1780	1850	105120	CLA	Doonas
1740	1992	....	....	116017	ESS	North West
1876	1992	1800	1992	125563	GLA	Cardiff
1876	1893	1893	1992	169935	GLS	Bledington
....	....	1890	1910	122637	GLS	Gloucester
1884	1884	1836	1884	156981	GLS	Olveston
1830	1940	....	....	159301	GNT	Newport
1702	1702	1650	1800	162620	HAM	Portsmouth
1850	1870	1802	1850	140244	HUN	St Neots
1834	1834	1800	1850	126918	IRL	???
1764	1881	1700	1900	178446	LIN	Ruskington
1797	1797	....	....	144568	LIN	???
1834	1834	ALL	1834	126918	LND	Bermondsey
1912	....	ALL	1912	167711	LND	???
1820	1843	1800	1881	167002	MDX	Clerkenwell
1870	1872	ALL	1883	156175	MDX	Hackney
1845	1851	1845	1891	167002	MDX	Hoxton
1841	1920	1800	1841	151327	MDX	Limehouse
1700	1930	....	1700	113913	NTH	Brackley
1595	1700	....	....	132756	OXF	Bicester
....	1700	....	....	174564	OXF	???
1761	1807	1730	1840	177792	SOM	Langport
1930	1940	....	....	113913	SRY	Brackley
1940	1970	....	....	113913	SRY	Weybridge
1805	1947	1700	1960	141569	STS	Burton On Trent
1844	1933	ALL	1944	109258	WIL	Shrewton
1924	1940	....	1924	122637	WIL	Tilshead
1810	1890	1760	1820	170348	WIL	Wootton Bassett
1723	1850	1700	1850	153249	WOR	Blockley
FRANKS						
1600	ALL	....	....	163465	LIN	Morton
1800	1930	....	....	163465	LIN	Rippingale
1800	1900	1700	1992	145661	MDX	London

Known From	To	Researching From	To	Ref	Cty	Place
FRANKS contd.						
....	1760	ALL	1760	134511	NTT	Oxton
....	....	1800	1900	168645	SAL	Newport
1696	1727	1680	1740	170143	SRY	Wanboro
1696	1727	1680	1740	170143	SRY	Worplesdon
1799	1813	1799	1813	145181	WAR	Birmingham
1811	1908	1811	1938	145181	WAR	Warwick
FRANKUM						
1838	1910	1750	1838	164267	BRK	Arborfield
FRANNIE						
1833	....	1830	1840	163775	MDX	Shoreditch
FRAPWELL						
1800	1900	1750	1850	143030	SOM	Rode
1850	1890	....	....	143030	WIL	North Bradley
FRASCH						
1700	1992	1700	1992	167924	ALL	ALL
1750	1920	1750	1920	167924	MDX	Stepney
FRASER						
1759	1800	1700	1759	127590	ANS	Forfar
1831	1877	1700	1992	172243	BAN	Mills Of Gellymill
....	....	1700	1850	113808	BDF	Bedford
1804	1808	1800	1815	177792	CHS	Stockport
1842	....	1842	1992	113808	DBY	Ilkeston
1846	1871	1790	1881	165824	INV	Boleskine
....	....	1800	1900	105457	INV	Inverness
1801	1830	1750	1992	166049	INV	Inverness-Leachkin
1828	1850	ALL	1828	143820	INV	Isle Of Skye
1822	1992	1700	1822	105201	INV	Kirkhill
1813	1858	1813	1870	177792	LAN	Liverpool
1810	1850	1750	1810	159115	LND	St Marylebone
1845	1930	1800	1845	127949	MDX	Kensington
1845	1930	1800	1845	127949	MDX	Willesden
1841	1900	1700	1851	144037	RFW	Bishopton
1880	1900	ALL	1880	147087	ROC	ALL
1873	1992	....	....	152331	ROC	Black Isle
1822	1992	1700	1822	105201	ROC	Kirkhill
1825	1890	1790	1825	131806	SCT	Inverness
1750	1965	....	....	137820	SHI	Fetlar
1720	1965	....	....	137820	SHI	Mid Yell
1760	1965	....	....	137820	SHI	North Yell
1758	1965	....	....	137820	SHI	Northmavine
1720	1965	....	....	137820	SHI	South Yell
1750	1992	ALL	ALL	140902	SUT	North
1780	1799	1700	1799	116300	YKS	Richmond
1850	....	1800	....	131024	???	Kidderminster
1780	1992	ALL	1780	177814	???	Kiltarlity
FRATER						
1690	1730	ALL	1730	149063	MLN	Stow
FRAYN						
1732	1992	1600	1992	119377	CON	Egloskerry
1752	1880	....	....	121932	CON	Egloskerry
1750	1850	1600	1750	119377	CON	North Tamerton
1752	1880	....	....	121932	CON	Trewen
FRAYNE						
1600	1992	1600	1850	127914	WEX	Wexford
1870	1910	1800	1870	152552	???	Plymouth
FRAZER						
....	....	ALL	1800	119326	ELN	Tranent
1820	1871	1700	1880	159379	FIF	Newburgh
1921	1992	1860	1992	126233	LAN	Liverpool
....	....	1800	1992	126233	LND	???
FRAZIER						
1810	....	ALL	1810	151424	YKS	Hull
FREAR						
1740	1940	....	....	128996	CAM	Thornley
FREARSON						
1880	1970	1850	1880	160806	LEI	Leicester
1900	1992	1900	....	125598	LEI	Market Harborough
FREATHY						
....	....	ALL	ALL	170763	ALL	Name Study
FRECKNALL						
1834	1834	....	....	108901	NTT	Clarborough
FREE						
....	....	ALL	ALL	103209	ALL	Name Study
1630	1757	1500	1760	124796	BKM	Princes Risborough
1750	1880	1750	1800	144657	ESS	Loughton
1800	1800	1750	1825	136042	HRT	Little Hadham
1801	1861	1750	1900	136042	HRT	Standon
1689	1689	....	....	127426	STS	Harborne
FREEBORN						
1754	1992	1754	1992	131822	OXF	Oxford
FREEGARD						
....	....	1840	1920	170879	SOM	Bath
FREELAND						
1880	1940	1840	1960	124745	SRY	North
1617	....	....	....	166723	SRY	Pyrford
1801	1850	1700	1800	125628	SSX	Sedlescomb
1875	1885	1860	1900	142174	WRY	Leeds
FREELOVE						
1803	1815	1770	1803	144878	HRT	Hatfield
1800	....	ALL	ALL	152226	SSX	ALL
FREEMAN						
1810	1850	1700	1810	130443	BDF	???
1650	1700	ALL	1650	131059	BKM	Aylesbury
1850	1950	1750	1850	125660	BKM	Chilton
1797	1797	1770	1810	107360	BKM	East Claydon
1851	1881	1800	1900	126470	BRK	Newbury
1700	1900	1700	1900	125679	BRK	Thatcham
....	1740	....	1740	108839	CAM	Sutton
1777	1803	1700	1777	112321	DBY	ALL
1880	....	....	....	153400	DUR	???
1680	1790	ALL	1680	131059	ESS	Bocking
1780	1840	1750	1800	144657	ESS	Loughton
1811	1900	....	1811	108839	ESS	Pitsee
1830	1992	1750	1830	151165	ESS	Rochford
1700	....	....	....	148768	GLS	Adlestrop
1900	1992	1700	1900	125652	GLS	Bristol
1900	1992	1700	1900	125652	GLS	Chipping Sodbury
1780	1860	1600	1780	118877	GLS	Great Rissington
1724	....	1500	1724	118877	GLS	Hazelton
....	....	ALL	ALL	143634	GLS	Lye
1921	....	1921	1992	169730	HAM	Ropley Four Marks
....	....	1750	1805	172871	HRT	North West
1890	1920	1700	1890	169730	HRT	Bushey
1880	....	....	....	153400	KEN	Deal
1787	1872	1700	1787	161225	KEN	Dover
....	....	1700	1992	149969	KEN	Tunbridge Wells
1880	....	....	....	153400	KEN	Walmer
1860	1870	1870	1992	125695	LAN	Salford
1777	1803	1700	1777	112321	LEI	ALL
1880	1992	1700	1880	102148	LEI	Leicester
....	....	1650	1950	124656	LEI	Shepshed
....	....	1600	1900	124656	LEI	???
1814	1819	1800	1814	128368	LIN	Gainsborough
1814	1819	1800	1814	128368	LIN	Onston
1880	....	....	....	153400	LND	???
1745	1745	1730	1770	105120	MDX	Harmondsworth
....	....	1770	1810	172871	MDX	Highgate
1857	1881	1750	1856	131245	NFK	Norwich
....	1800	....	1800	177695	NTH	Irthlingborough
1760	1900	1841	1900	125709	NTH	Sutton Bassett
1615	1818	ALL	1615	143278	NTH	Whilton
1800	1900	1700	1900	125725	OXF	Fyfield Burford
....	1700	....	....	174564	OXF	Hook Norton
1789	1790	1750	1790	162396	OXF	Shifford
1700	1800	....	....	125709	RUT	Uppingham
1799	1847	1750	1780	135763	SAL	Welshampton
1700	1775	1700	1775	133817	SFK	Bildeston
1880	1992	1800	1992	125687	SFK	Cratfield
1870	1890	1700	1870	178136	SFK	Donnington
1830	1900	1700	1880	117129	SFK	Framlingham
1772	1992	1700	1772	176079	SFK	Kelsale
1762	1829	ALL	ALL	107255	SFK	Tuddenham
1700	1850	ALL	ALL	126098	SOM	Road
1700	1760	1700	1760	159581	SRY	Cranleigh
1755	?	?	?	166642	SRY	Richmond
1802	1810	1750	1850	124907	SSX	Ashurst
1735	1820	1650	1860	110906	SSX	Chichester
1811	1950	1700	1811	170178	SSX	Winchelsea
....	....	1840	1891	155683	STS	Wolverhampton
1850	1970	1840	1890	155357	SXW	Itchenfield
....	....	1650	1950	124656	WAR	???
1700	1850	ALL	ALL	126098	WIL	North Bradley
1500	1700	1500	1700	125679	WIL	Ramsbury
1700	1850	ALL	ALL	126098	WIL	Road
1782	1805	....	....	102733	WOR	Feckenham
1910	1992	1900	ALL	143634	WYK	Wakefield
1778	1820	1500	1778	125695	YKS	Kirkhammerton
1820	1860	1820	1992	125695	YKS	Leeds
1869	1905	1850	1992	150835	YKS	Sheffield
FREEMANTLE						
1858	1992	ALL	ALL	108464	HAM	Arlesford
1858	1992	ALL	ALL	108464	HAM	Easton
1858	1992	ALL	ALL	108464	HAM	Etchinswell
1800	1850	1800	1850	147184	HAM	Romsey
1670	1712	1650	1730	142018	WIL	West Wellow

Known From	To	Researching From	To	Ref	Cty	Place
FREER						
....	....	ALL	ALL	125733	KEN	Gillingham
....	....	ALL	ALL	125733	KEN	Gravesend
....	....	ALL	ALL	125733	KEN	Northfleet
1811	1875	1780	1850	132586	WAR	Nuneaton
....	....	ALL	ALL	125733	YKS	Nunburnhome
FREESTONE						
1881	1914	1600	1920	125741	BKM	Waddon
1670	1752	1600	1920	125741	LEI	Great Easton
1700	1992	1600	1700	149713	LEI	Medbourne
1834	1880	1750	1800	176672	MDX	Islington
1914	1943	1600	1920	125741	MDX	London
1842	1992	1700	1842	166804	NFK	Great Yarmouth
1752	1881	1600	1920	125741	NTH	Geddington
1945	1968	1600	1920	125741	SXE	St Leonards
1943	1945	1600	1920	125741	WES	Windermere
FREETH						
1800	1900	1600	1900	112976	LND	ALL
1900	1992	1700	1900	143324	LND	Acton
1858	1866	1700	1992	110418	STS	Sedgly
....	....	....	....	143324	WIL	???
1870	1900	1800	1900	122610	WMD	Birmingham
1858	1866	1700	1992	110418	WOR	Dudley
FREEZER						
?	?	?	?	129658	ALL	ALL
FREKE						
1880	1992	....	....	137693	???	Bristol
FREMLYN						
1400	1650	1400	1650	154881	KEN	Kemsing
FREMONT						
1724	1846	....	1724	164321	MDX	East London
FRENCH						
1740	1992	1500	1900	141720	ALL	???
1878	1915	1700	1915	170356	BRK	Newbury
1815	1890	1815	1920	148474	CUL	Hayton
1775	1810	1775	1810	148474	CUL	Lanercost
1815	1890	1815	1920	148474	CUL	Wetheral
1760	1900	1600	1900	146846	DBY	Dronfield
1600	1860	1400	1870	105333	DEV	Buckland In The Moor
1600	1860	1400	1870	105333	DEV	Holne
1600	1860	1400	1870	105333	DEV	Ilsington
1600	1860	1400	1870	105333	DEV	Lydford
1885	....	1860	....	146900	DEV	Torquay
1600	1860	1400	1870	105333	DEV	Widecombe In The Moor
1700	1837	1300	1837	140392	DEV	Widecombe
....	....	1800	1925	126241	DUR	ALL
1785	1992	1700	1785	157074	ESS	Birch
1760	1880	1600	1760	125784	ESS	Great Chesterford
1768	1788	....	....	171654	ESS	Paglesham
1800	1880	1700	1800	115541	ESS	Wethersfield
....	1862	1803	....	123609	ESS	Wethersfield
1811	1893	....	....	135437	GLS	Bristol
1709	1765	....	....	135437	GLS	Frocester
1791	1897	1791	1897	168165	GLS	Leonard Stanley
1813	....	1700	1850	136891	GLS	Uley
1740	1992	1500	1900	141720	HAM	Winchester
1890	1920	....	....	110159	IRL	Dublin
1682	....	....	1700	171441	KEN	Ash By Wrotham
1800	1900	....	....	104272	KEN	East Farleigh
1400	1920	....	....	136824	KEN	Ripple
1550	1650	1500	1650	154881	KEN	Seal
1835	1942	1750	1835	111848	LKS	Abington
1837	1861	1700	1992	166073	LND	Spitallfields
1774	1874	1700	1874	138088	MDX	London
1711	1782	1660	1782	176672	NFK	ALL
1856	1871	ALL	ALL	107794	NFK	Knapton
1799	1852	ALL	ALL	107794	NFK	Trunch
1891	1903	ALL	ALL	107794	NFK	Walsham
1871	1886	ALL	ALL	107794	NFK	Waxham
1780	1800	1780	1800	127655	NTH	Byfield
1900	1992	1700	1900	173479	NTH	Northampton
1780	1803	1780	1803	130877	NTT	Mansfield
1780	1803	1780	1803	130877	NTT	Nottingham
1720	1780	....	....	119458	OXF	Standlake
1821	1922	1700	1820	169854	OXF	Wardington
1821	1869	1700	1900	178322	OXF	Wardington
1830	1874	1700	1874	138088	SAL	Whittington
1780	1950	1600	1950	125792	SOM	Taunton
1875	....	ALL	ALL	151580	SRY	Godstone
1890	1992	ALL	ALL	125776	SSX	East
ALL	ALL	ALL	ALL	160261	SSX	East
1784	1926	1700	1800	164542	SSX	West
FRENCH contd.						
1756	1969	1542	1992	107166	SSX	Arlington
1890	1992	1700	1890	125768	SSX	Chiddingly
1890	1992	ALL	ALL	125776	SSX	Mid
1760	1900	1600	1800	113654	SSX	Ticehurst
1861	1868	1800	1900	178322	STS	Sedgley
1869	1881	1868	1900	178322	WAR	Aston
1815	....	....	....	120804	WAR	Coventry
1828	1850	1800	1992	114901	YKS	Braham
1858	1920	1850	1992	114901	YKS	Hunslet
1874	1893	ALL	1980	136891	YKS	South Bank
FRESHNEY						
....	....	ALL	ALL	108634	ALL	Name Study
1800	1850	....	....	124621	LIN	Kelstern
FRESHWATER						
1803	1878	1800	1992	156698	BDF	Potton
FRETTS						
1864	1992	ALL	ALL	115762	LND	Bermondsey
1864	1992	ALL	ALL	115762	SRY	Bermondsey
FRETWELL						
1794	1992	1794	....	111287	DBY	Shipley
1830	....	....	....	174793	DBY	Shipley
1794	1992	1794	....	111287	NTT	Eastwood
FREW						
1827	1870	1800	1827	101796	RFW	Tradeston
FREWER						
....	....	1720	1770	172871	SFK	Bury St Edmunds
FREWIN						
....	....	1880	1900	142638	LND	Fulham
FRIAR						
1820	1830	1750	1820	121339	ESS	Romford
1659	1660	1600	1659	127116	HAM	Hursley
1872	1926	....	....	137790	LAN	St Helens
FRIBENS						
1694	1697	1650	1720	176621	WIL	Marlborough
FRICKER						
1879	....	....	....	133922	HAM	Twyford
1830	1860	1800	1850	101931	JSY	St Heliers
....	....	1820	1855	130184	MDX	Shoreditch
1840	1880	1750	1840	146587	SOM	Bath
1500	1900	1500	1900	170216	WIL	ALL
1819	1879	....	....	133922	WIL	Bishopstrow
1819	1879	....	....	133922	WIL	Boyton
1849	....	....	....	133922	WIL	Carton
1849	....	....	....	133922	WIL	Corton
1830	1992	ALL	1850	100536	???	London
FRICKLEY						
1820	1820	....	....	136891	YKS	Sculcoats
1794	....	1700	1840	136891	YKS	York
FRIDAY						
1807	1992	1700	1807	125814	KEN	Lynsted
1807	1992	1700	1807	125814	KEN	Teynham
FRIDDLE						
1800	1830	....	....	159131	OXF	Shiptom
FRIEND						
1740	1760	1720	1740	134627	CAM	Coveney
1765	1786	....	....	159751	DEV	Lydford
1787	1817	1750	1800	136220	DEV	Northlew
1678	1759	1731	1759	147125	DUR	Ryton Parish
....	....	ALL	ALL	153281	KEN	Ringwould
1770	?	?	?	166642	KEN	???
1700	1830	....	....	148261	NBL	Allendales
1750	1770	1650	1750	164860	SFK	Cotton
1700	....	....	....	126543	SFK	Old Newton
1700	1700	1650	1750	133450	SOM	Taunton
FRIENDSHIP						
1837	1860	ALL	ALL	163988	DEV	South Molton
FRIER						
1789	1992	1600	1789	109061	KEN	East
1850	....	....	1850	164011	KEN	Boughton Aluph
1789	1992	1600	1789	109061	KEN	Medway
1840	....	....	1992	164011	KEN	Sheerness
1804	1804	1700	1850	171662	MLN	Edinburgh
1800	1900	?	1800	158569	WOR	ALL
FRIGALL						
....	....	1850	1992	125822	DEV	Kingsbridge
FRINDLE						
1882	1882	....	....	115606	MDX	Kensington
FRISBY						
1830	1835	....	....	133221	ESS	Loughton
....	....	1780	1825	133221	ESS	Romford
1860	1890	1700	1860	123307	KEN	Sheppey
1851	1900	....	....	133221	LND	Southwark
1720	1800	1600	1720	174130	RUT	Prestland

Known From	To	Researching From	To	Ref	Cty	Place
FRISKNEY						
1860	1870	1850	1900	125830	CAM	North
1750	1890	ALL	ALL	125830	LIN	Central
1900	1980	ALL	ALL	125830	NTT	East
FRISON						
....	....	ALL	ALL	125849	ALL	Name Study
FRISTAN						
1774	1794	1700	1820	176621	YKS	Hull
FRITCHLEY						
1791	1809	....	1809	128910	DBY	Duffield
FRITH						
1851	1904	1800	1900	110345	CHS	Stalybridge
1816	1817	1700	1816	126942	DBY	Chapel-En-Le-Frith
1680	1750	1600	1750	154881	KIK	Waterford
1782	1828	1300	1900	152501	LND	Hackney
1850	1992	1700	1850	151084	LND	Westminster
1730	1869	1600	1992	103837	YKS	ALL
FRIZBY						
....	....	1700	1800	159042	LIN	Dowsby
1740	1740	1700	1800	159042	NTH	Etton
FROGATT						
1857	1881	1700	1857	173797	YKS	Ecclesfield
FROGG						
1773	1867	1500	1992	117900	NTT	Stapleford
FROGGATT						
....	....	ALL	ALL	123528	ALL	Name Study
1662	1790	1550	1709	102830	DBY	Ashbourne
1867	1900	1500	1992	117900	DBY	Ilkeston
1812	1850	1750	1812	157775	LND	Hampstead
1857	1881	1700	1857	173797	YKS	Ecclesfield
FROGGETT						
1813	1948	....	1820	134007	KEN	Sydenham
FROGLEY						
1715	1792	1650	1715	141321	BRK	Childrey
1495	1903	....	....	125628	BRK	Denchworth
FROMANT						
1850	1900	1800	1850	176257	CAM	Swavesey
FROOD						
1825	1884	ALL	1825	166847	SFK	Woolpit
FROSDICK						
1724	1941	1700	1950	107980	NFK	Surlingham
FROST						
....	....	ALL	ALL	125873	ALL	Name Study
1632	1992	1837	1907	114359	ABD	Aberdeen
1744	1811	1700	1744	110922	BDF	Barton In The Clay
1790	1805	....	....	153419	BKM	Burnham
1830	1926	....	....	153419	BKM	Slough
1820	1830	....	....	153419	BKM	Stoke Poges
1830	1926	....	....	153419	BKM	Upton Cum Chalvey
1770	1818	1550	1770	139866	CAM	Brinkley
1841	....	1700	1840	135348	CAM	Wisbech
....	....	1750	1900	174696	CON	Launceston
1811	1992	1811	....	118761	DBY	Crich
1750	1780	1700	1800	161292	DEV	Dawlish
1780	1850	1700	1992	114596	DEV	Molland
1800	1840	1700	1800	126772	DEV	Moreton Hampstead
1808	1910	1622	1808	137537	DEV	Plymouth
....	....	ALL	ALL	162329	EAG	ALL
1871	....	ALL	....	119237	ENG	South
1850	1960	ALL	1850	121053	ESS	Tiptree
1821	1841	ALL	ALL	119504	HAM	Gosport
1592	....	....	....	153397	HAM	Milford
1821	1841	ALL	ALL	119504	HAM	Portsmouth
1825	1850	....	....	135070	KEN	Maidstone
1810	1860	1700	1800	160350	KEN	Teynham
1840	1930	1700	1800	106968	LAN	Manchester
1840	1930	1700	1800	106968	LAN	Salford
....	....	1750	ALL	142298	LEI	Groby
?	?	?	?	126306	LIN	Grantham
1780	1880	1792	1900	125865	LIN	Limdsry
1790	1850	1700	1800	113387	LIN	Spilsby
1816	1835	1800	1835	147575	MON	Usk
1831	1860	....	1831	161888	NFK	Norwich
1690	1992	1690	1992	125881	NFK	Walsingham
1745	1846	1650	1744	131245	NTT	Blidworth
1793	1888	1780	1900	108901	NTT	Cuckney
1851	1881	1841	1881	108901	NTT	Langwith
1700	1820	1700	1820	162329	SFK	West
1764	1783	1680	1780	125865	SFK	Bury St Edmonds
1800	1900	....	....	131474	SFK	Great Livermere
1690	1992	ALL	ALL	131091	SFK	Ipswich
....	....	1770	1821	172871	SFK	Nowton
1714	1780	....	....	129747	SFK	Parham
....	....	1860	1933	133604	SOM	Bath

Known From	To	Researching From	To	Ref	Cty	Place
FROST contd.						
1801	1972	ALL	ALL	153516	SOM	South Brent
1887	....	1700	1992	178276	SRY	Byfleet
1871	....	ALL	....	119237	SRY	Richmond
1698	1992	ALL	ALL	125873	SSX	Heathfield
....	....	1750	1800	134317	STS	Leek
1820	1848	1800	1992	146331	WIL	Salisbury
1828	1828	....	....	108901	YKS	Sculcoates
FROSTICK						
1860	1867	1800	1860	103640	MDX	Islington
FROUD						
1785	1852	1700	1785	117714	BRK	ALL
1806	1830	ALL	1830	135208	BRK	West
1767	....	1650	1800	143693	BRK	Aldermarston
1791	....	1650	1800	143693	BRK	Aldworth
1703	1719	1600	1750	143693	BRK	Basildon
1744	1822	1600	1750	143693	BRK	Beenham
1730	1900	1700	1992	102164	BRK	Bradfield
1763	1797	1650	1770	143693	BRK	Bradfield
1840	1980	1600	1680	141321	BRK	Childrey
1824	....	1800	1850	143693	BRK	Little Wittendham
1731	....	1600	1750	143693	BRK	Purley
1769	....	1700	1800	143693	BRK	Upton Nervet
1841	1881	1881	1992	121711	KEN	Loose
1850	1890	1700	1850	121711	KEN	Maidstone
1893	1900	1860	1893	121711	LND	Acton
1830	1852	ALL	ALL	135208	LND	Kensington
1895	1976	1800	1895	121711	LND	Lambeth
1840	1980	1600	1680	141321	OXF	???
FROUDE						
1900	1992	1700	1910	158836	BRK	ALL
1892	1892	ALL	ALL	135208	KEN	Erith Marshes
1900	1992	1700	1910	158836	SRY	ALL
1868	1869	ALL	ALL	135208	SRY	Croydon
FROWEN						
1786	1804	1600	1785	172006	GLS	English Bicknor
FRUDD						
1818	1972	ALL	1992	104299	YKS	Barnsley
FRUEN						
1841	1872	....	....	143480	HAM	Fareham
....	....	1790	1837	143480	SRY	Ash
....	....	1790	1837	143480	SRY	Frimley
FRUSHER						
1840	1880	1800	1840	161810	NFK	Walsolkien
FRUTS						
1738	1750	1700	1738	147885	NTH	Towcester
FRY						
1820	1913	1500	1820	140279	DEV	Ashwater
1824	1932	1600	1824	100579	DEV	Culmstock
1787	1806	1760	1806	162825	DEV	Lynton
1820	1913	1500	1820	140279	DEV	Northdevon
1720	1800	1650	1750	156698	DEV	Thelbridge
1700	1992	1650	1992	156701	DEV	Witheridge
1500	1900	1500	1900	170216	DOR	ALL
1775	1851	1775	1851	125326	DOR	Cranborne
1800	1900	1899	1901	100536	ESS	???
1720	1880	1680	1900	152528	GLS	Bitton
1750	1850	1700	1850	125792	GLS	Bristol
1840	1992	1700	1840	168084	GLS	Oldland
1720	1880	1680	1900	152528	GLS	Siston
ALL	ALL	ALL	ALL	131997	KEN	North
1720	1950	1500	1950	175463	KEN	West
1775	1800	1725	1780	156698	KEN	Dover
1769	1888	1750	1902	131997	KEN	Isle Of Grain
1750	1817	1700	1750	114871	KEN	Penshurst
1814	1834	ALL	1992	119105	KEN	Tonbridge
1776	1796	1600	1796	147125	KEN	Tonbridge
....	....	1828	1871	116912	KEN	Woolwich
1800	1850	....	....	108847	LND	???
....	1757	1600	1757	153591	SOM	ALL
1780	1850	1600	1780	108413	SOM	Banwell
1650	1800	1600	1700	144657	SOM	Banwell
....	1757	1600	1757	153591	SOM	Bath
1850	1900	1700	1850	107719	SOM	Culmstock
1797	1825	....	1825	152803	SOM	Glastonbury
....	....	....	1882	121169	SOM	Midsomer Norton
1816	1855	ALL	1816	178195	SOM	Weston Super Mare
1882	1882	....	1882	121169	SOM	Widcombe
1798	1832	1700	1798	177075	SOM	Worle
1731	1750	1650	1751	108413	SOM	Yatton
....	....	1767	1828	116912	SOM	???
1720	1950	1500	1950	175463	SSX	ALL
1630	1630	1580	1680	105333	SSX	Rogate
1500	1900	1500	1900	170216	WIL	ALL

Known From	To	Researching From	To	Ref	Cty	Place
FRY contd.						
1812	1812	1780	1810	165530	WIL	Bremhill
1814	1846	1750	1814	133671	WIL	Brinkworth
1810	1860	1700	1810	108413	WIL	Longleat
....	....	1700	1871	159808	WIL	Salisbury
1804	1816	ALL	1804	178195	???	Bristol
FRYAR						
....	....	1500	1600	154873	BKM	Beaconsfield
1801	....	....	1840	171441	KEN	Ospringe
1800	1850	1750	1900	135429	SOM	Bath
FRYATT						
....	....	ALL	ALL	155187	ALL	Name Study
FRYDAY						
1756	....	....	1780	171441	KEN	Lynstead
FRYE						
1710	1730	1600	1992	167592	IRL	Dublin
1720	1760	1700	1992	167592	MDX	London
FRYER						
1817	1861	ALL	1817	126918	ESS	Billericay
1857	1883	1800	1857	102849	ESS	Hockley
1770	1830	1650	1770	165018	EYK	Norton
1728	1770	ALL	ALL	124982	GLS	South
1640	1660	1600	1640	108413	GLS	Berkeley
1865	1880	1800	1865	105767	GLS	???
....	....	1860	....	125962	HAM	Alverstoke
1860	1920	....	....	125962	HAM	Gosport
1790	1791	1750	1810	125970	HAM	Titchfield
1871	1900	1871	1900	125970	IOW	East Cowes
1791	1960	1791	1960	125970	IOW	Yarmouth
1890	1950	1950	1992	173673	LAN	Manchester
1776	....	....	1776	133566	LND	Shoreditch
1841	1867	1800	1840	145963	MDX	London
1736	1781	1700	1800	167002	MDX	London
....	1700	....	....	174564	SSX	???
1800	1900	?	1800	158569	WOR	ALL
1817	1880	1700	1817	173673	WOR	Dudley
1865	1880	....	1865	105767	WOR	???
1834	1834	1800	1992	172782	YKS	Leeds
FRYER-KELSEY						
1814	....	....	....	135402	MDX	Islington
FRYERS						
1875	1992	1800	1875	135658	LAN	Lancaster
FRYOR						
1700	1780	1600	1700	148938	GLS	Arlingham
FRYSER						
1727	1787	1727	1787	103977	BRK	Aldworth
1727	1787	1727	1787	103977	BRK	Streatley
FUDGE						
....	....	ALL	ALL	120766	ALL	Name Study
1780	1790	1780	1790	154210	DOR	Woodsford
....	....	1775	1815	159573	DOR	???
1800	1950	1700	1800	143421	GLS	Oldland
....	....	1775	1815	159573	HAM	???
1768	1876	1700	1876	128694	SOM	Ilchester
1858	1888	1700	1888	169676	SOM	Yeovil
....	....	1775	1815	159573	SOM	???
FUELL						
....	1900	....	1900	121053	LND	City
1820	1950	1700	1992	116742	MDX	Wapping
FUGE						
1830	1950	1830	1910	164399	DEV	Peter Tavy
FUGLER						
1800	1900	1750	1900	128708	CON	Probus
FUKES						
1730	1730	1600	1800	133450	KEN	South West
FULBECK						
1780	1800	....	....	129747	LIN	Leasingham
FULBROOK						
1750	1861	1750	1861	138894	HAM	Odiham
1865	1885	1800	1865	177393	LND	City Of London
1865	1885	1800	1865	177393	LND	Shoreditch
1737	1760	1700	1760	119059	OXF	Oxford
FULCHER						
1830	1966	1800	1830	127116	NFK	Norwich
1820	1825	1750	1820	105031	SFK	Charsfield
1700	1735	1650	1700	155276	SFK	Clopton
FULFORD						
1782	1992	1600	1782	148040	DEV	Bideford
1559	1612	1500	1559	102830	WAR	Tanworth
FULIAMES						
1642	1675	....	1642	149888	SOM	Pitminster
FULJAMBE						
1650	1685	1600	1700	166022	DBY	Chesterfield
1650	1700	1600	1750	166022	NTT	Atherstone

Known From	To	Researching From	To	Ref	Cty	Place
FULJAMBE contd.						
1685	1750	1600	1750	166022	YKS	Rotherham
FULKE						
1500	1782	1500	1782	159581	SRY	West Horsley
FULL						
1760	1775	1700	1760	149152	DEV	Wooland
1830	1860	1750	1860	134759	LND	Stepney
FULLAGAR						
1840	1918	1750	1845	163740	KEN	Tenterden
FULLARD						
?	1940	....	....	128996	CAM	Thornley
FULLBRICK						
....	....	....	....	158747	ALL	ALL
FULLELOVE						
1800	1881	1500	1992	124443	YKS	Ecclesfield
1861	1881	1700	1861	173797	YKS	Ecclesfield
FULLER						
....	....	1700	1900	173746	ALL	ALL
1830	1884	1830	1950	171484	BDF	Northill
1757	1900	1600	1757	165697	CAM	Chatteris
....	....	1500	1840	166863	HAM	Basingstoke
1800	1830	ALL	1850	171484	HUN	Great Gransden
1767	1848	1650	1767	120774	KEN	West
1700	1992	ALL	1700	108502	KEN	Ashford
1670	?	?	?	166642	KEN	Canterbury
1880	1962	....	1880	103489	KEN	Charlton
1840	1980	1840	1980	134767	KEN	Sevenoaks
1860	....	1800	1900	139386	KEN	Shoreham
1700	1992	ALL	1700	108502	KEN	Tenterden
1846	1992	1700	1920	126012	KEN	Whitstable
1849	1894	1894	1910	177393	LND	Kensington
1849	1894	1800	1850	177393	LND	Shoreditch
1840	1841	1800	1900	141046	MDX	Stepney
1793	1814	....	....	135437	NFK	Bodham
1730	1774	....	....	135437	NFK	Corpusty
1826	1826	1700	1826	120367	NFK	Norwich
1727	1777	....	....	135437	NFK	Saxthorpe
1825	1825	1750	1850	126799	NFK	Wretton
1832	1912	1600	1832	150398	SFK	Haughley
1832	1912	1600	1832	150398	SFK	Stowmarket
1823	1850	1792	1850	138312	SRY	Dorking
1796	1845	1720	1796	179493	SRY	Leatherhead
1700	1876	1600	1992	101532	SSX	Ditchling
1870	....	1700	1870	145378	SSX	Eastbourne
1800	....	ALL	ALL	114847	???	Bristol
1620	1822	1600	1620	165417	???	???
FULLERLOVE						
1811	....	1700	1850	135348	CAM	Wisbech
FULLERTON						
1792	1909	ALL	ALL	101370	ANT	ALL
....	....	1700	1960	172111	ANT	Port Glenone
1780	1992	1700	1780	153605	KCD	Fetteresso
1816	1992	1700	1816	108316	LKS	East Kilbride
FULLMAN						
?	1800	1700	1800	152900	KEN	Cranbrook
FULLY LOVE						
1798	1803	1750	1900	122327	LEI	Higham On The Hill
FULTHORP						
1660	1812	1590	1660	155489	DUR	Whickham
FULTON						
....	....	ALL	ALL	126039	ALL	Name Study
....	....	ALL	ALL	148407	ALL	Name Study
ALL	ALL	ALL	ALL	148407	ALL	ALL
1811	1935	1783	1811	137383	LND	West End
1752	1783	1700	1752	137383	RFW	Paisley
FULWELL						
1810	1860	....	....	138339	WOR	Defford
FULWOOD						
1865	1953	1643	1865	143146	NTT	Selston
1532	1860	1450	1860	102830	STS	Sedgely
FUNDELL						
1761	ALL	1700	ALL	159255	BKM	Wendover
1847	ALL	1700	ALL	159255	LND	Bethnal Green
1847	ALL	1700	ALL	159255	LND	Hackney
FUNNELL						
....	....	ALL	ALL	161233	ALL	Name Study
1791	1992	1780	1800	166316	ESS	Dowercourt
1850	1960	1812	1834	136921	KEN	Cranbrook
1760	1900	....	....	122130	SSX	Chiddingly
1840	1980	....	....	122130	SSX	East Hoathly
1887	1992	1880	1992	153834	SSX	Eastbourne
1834	1960	1700	1834	136921	SSX	Ticehurst
1910	1950	....	....	122130	SSX	Uckfield

Known From	To	Researching From	To	Ref	Cty	Place
FUNSTON						
ALL	1857	....	....	172693	IRL	Inniskillen
FURBER						
1700	1700	....	....	162620	DOR	Purbeck
1880	1992	1700	1880	126616	HAM	Boldre
1738	1850	1700	1750	172642	MGY	Llanyblodwel
1738	1850	1700	1750	172642	MGY	Llanymynech
1803	1865	1750	1860	135763	SAL	Whixall
1820	1852	1800	1860	177792	SOM	Kingsbury Episcopi
1793	1849	1770	1850	177792	SOM	Langport
FURBISHER						
1700	1850	....	....	125199	YKS	Featherstone
FURBUR						
1810	....	....	....	111856	STS	Adbaston
FURBY						
1818	....	1818	....	145726	GLS	Oxenhall
1790	1834	1700	1850	152285	LND	Shoreditch
FUREY						
1820	1900	1820	1910	126640	CLA	ALL
FURLOW						
1750	1830	1700	1800	144657	SRY	Horley
FURMSTON						
1730	1889	1650	1730	150614	SAL	Ellesmere
FURNACE						
....	....	1680	1750	147613	YKS	Ingleton
FURNANDIZ						
1840	1992	ALL	ALL	161047	ALL	ALL
FURNAS						
1825	1865	1800	1900	161586	DUR	Sunderland
1741	1814	1600	1741	102571	WES	Crosby Ravensworth
FURNEAUX						
1815	1910	1700	1815	132640	LND	Bethnal Green
FURNELL						
....	....	1500	1850	166863	SOM	ALL
1500	1900	1500	1900	170216	WIL	ALL
....	....	ALL	ALL	145343	WIL	Steeple Langford
1707	1924	1707	1924	137898	WIL	Tisbury
1726	1900	1700	1850	150576	WIL	Tisbury
....	....	ALL	1828	175080	WIL	Tisbury
....	....	1500	1880	166863	WLS	ALL
FURNER						
1890	1915	1915	1992	112569	KEN	Folkstone
FURNESS						
1750	1800	....	....	160458	ALL	ALL
1750	1800	....	....	160458	NBL	???
....	....	1700	1850	140627	NFK	Norwich
1823	1882	ALL	1823	160008	WYK	Elland Halifax
1800	1992	....	1826	144363	YKS	Skipton
FURNEVALL						
1741	1858	ALL	1741	146226	SAL	Moreton Say
FURNIS						
1840	1992	1700	1840	106089	WAR	Southam
FURNISS						
1797	1825	1700	1797	130141	DBY	Eyam
FURNIVAL						
1744	....	....	....	121835	CHS	Malpas
1740	1846	1700	1740	117196	CHS	Warrington
1780	1850	1700	1780	117218	CHS	Warrington
FURRELL						
1840	1880	1700	1880	140171	KEN	Rochester
FURRIAN						
1650	1800	1600	1800	142123	HRT	Pirton
FURSE						
1700	1992	1700	1900	123234	CON	Mevagissey
1784	1992	1550	1784	126055	DEV	ALL
....	....	1700	1850	139432	DEV	South Molten
1740	1992	1600	1740	126063	NFK	Norwich
FURSEDON						
1800	1992	....	....	151084	LND	East
FURSLAND						
1600	1800	....	....	177474	DEV	Bickington
FURZE						
1846	1980	1650	1846	120030	CON	Ruan Lanihorne
1817	1951	ALL	1817	100528	DEV	Thornbury
1800	1992	1600	1800	126063	NFK	Norwich
FUSSELL						
1582	1800	1800	1839	126098	SOM	Hemington
1800	1992	1800	1910	126098	SOM	Road
1800	1900	ALL	ALL	126098	WIL	North Bradley
1800	1936	1800	1910	126098	WIL	Road
FUSSEY						
1800	1980	1800	1980	104396	YKS	Holderness
FUTCHER						
....	....	ALL	ALL	171352	ALL	Name Study
FUTCHER contd.						
1785	1992	ALL	ALL	175684	HAM	ALL
FYALL						
1750	....	ALL	ALL	130508	FIF	St Monance
FYFE						
1746	1862	1700	1900	146536	AYR	Kilbirnie
....	....	1700	1842	100846	IRL	???
1794	1815	....	....	127140	RFW	Greenock
FYFFE						
1863	1992	1700	1863	136026	PER	Errol
1863	1992	1700	1863	136026	PER	Glendoick
FYLES						
1698	1925	ALL	ALL	141615	LAN	Ormskirk
FYRTH						
....	1607	1550	1607	138584	YKS	Methley
FYSON						
1730	1872	....	1730	100064	SFK	Newmarket
GABB						
....	....	ALL	ALL	126101	ALL	Name Study
1628	1747	1600	1750	159700	GLS	Coaley
1275	1700	1700	1992	126101	WOR	Ombersley
GABBETT						
1675	1800	1675	1992	133450	IRL	Cork
1485	1550	ALL	1992	133450	SAL	Acton Burnell
GABBITAS						
....	....	1700	1800	134198	NTT	ALL
1800	1850	1800	1850	134198	NTT	Carlton In Lindrick
1850	1880	1850	1900	134198	SYK	Kilnhurst
GABRIEL						
1750	1900	1650	1800	168750	CMN	Llandebie
1902	1948	1600	1902	165697	CON	Camelford
1902	1948	1600	1902	165697	COR	Fermoy
1350	1450	1300	1450	154881	KEN	Edenbridge
GACHES						
1771	1940	....	....	128996	CAM	Thornley
GADBURY						
1700	1765	1700	1765	124796	BKM	Hughenden
1630	1760	1630	1760	124796	BKM	Princes Risborough
GADD						
1800	1879	1800	1879	142360	MDX	Westminster
....	....	1700	1770	163082	SRY	Godstone
....	1896	1700	1930	124907	SSX	Brighton
1874	1896	1700	1874	124907	SSX	Newhaven
....	....	1810	1820	133221	SSX	Uckfield
GADDES						
1880	1992	1800	1880	146587	T&W	Washington
GADSBY						
1793	1835	1793	1793	145580	DBY	Snelston
1766	1859	ALL	ALL	155373	LND	Shoreditch
GADSDON						
1786	1915	1786	1992	108375	MDX	City
GAFFNEY						
1851	1881	ALL	1850	171751	ROC	Keadue
GAGE						
1730	1900	1650	1800	136840	HAM	Fordingbridge
1657	1657	1600	1700	133450	SOM	West
1850	1992	1800	1992	129488	SOM	Bridgewater
1784	1869	ALL	ALL	153516	SOM	Wick St Lawrence
1800	1840	1750	1800	157740	SSX	West Dean
GAGER						
1850	1992	1750	1850	101893	ESS	Chelmsford
GAGNAL						
1930	....	....	....	145742	WAR	???
GAIGE						
1730	1780	1700	1730	161322	KEN	East
GAIN						
1900	1992	1600	1900	127469	ENG	South
1633	1992	ALL	ALL	126152	HAM	Minstead
GAINER						
1800	1876	1780	1992	122416	CAV	Knockbride
GAINES						
....	....	1850	1890	166863	LND	Wandsworth
....	....	1500	1830	166863	MDX	Millbank
GAINFORD						
1750	1992	1600	1920	126160	CUL	Calderbridge
1750	1992	1600	1920	126160	CUL	Ennerdale
GAINS						
....	1850	....	....	114642	HAM	Isle Of Wight
GAINSFORD						
?	?	?	?	138126	MGY	Newtown
GAIR						
1740	1800	....	....	126497	CAI	Olrig
1807	1992	1500	1900	125385	DUR	ALL
1890	1920	1870	....	134686	LAN	Audenshaw

Known From	To	Researching From	To	Ref	Cty	Place
GAISFORD						
....	....	1700	1850	147303	GLS	Cold Ashton
....	....	1700	1850	147303	WIL	Box
1850	1960	1700	1850	147303	WIL	Colerne
....	....	1700	1850	147303	WIL	Devizes
1558	1754	1558	1754	147486	WIL	Potterne
....	....	1700	1850	147303	WIL	Salisbury
1803	1851	1780	1860	165824	WIL	Trowbridge
1725	1910	1650	1730	174599	WIL	Warminster
....	....	1700	1850	147303	WIL	Westbury
GAITSKELL						
1724	1760	1565	1724	141291	LAN	Dalton In Furness
GALBALLY						
1850	1950	ALL	ALL	171859	ALL	ALL
GALBRAITH						
....	....	1650	ALL	125148	BEW	Coldstream
1800	1823	1800	1900	162507	COR	Frankfield
....	1830	1600	1850	147265	IRL	Conaught
....	1800	1700	1850	162507	IRL	Old Derring
1896	1900	1700	1896	170127	LND	Islington
....	....	1860	ALL	125148	T&W	Sunderland
....	....	?	?	179159	???	???
GALBREATH						
....	1750	ALL	ALL	129933	ARL	Campbeltown
GALDSTONE						
1744	1901	1550	1992	114332	BDS	???
GALE						
1800	1850	1700	1850	174610	CON	???
1836	1903	....	1840	178853	DEV	Lustleigh
1629	1873	1620	1873	151858	DOR	West
1750	1850	1750	1850	126187	DOR	Beaminster
1776	1790	1700	1776	175064	DOR	Bradpole
1850	....	1700	1850	126616	DOR	Bridport
....	....	1500	1784	138614	DOR	Bridport
1840	1860	1750	1840	171859	DOR	Powerstock
1787	1850	1787	1850	126187	DOR	South Poorton
1770	1800	1730	1800	174599	DOR	Winterborne Kingston
1831	1901	....	1839	115355	DUR	Sunderland
1854	1920	....	1861	126276	ESS	Plaistow
1752	1794	1730	1819	162825	GLS	Cirencester
1864	1919	....	....	126187	GNT	Newport
1779	1879	1700	1779	127116	HAM	Hurstbourne
1850	1992	1750	1900	133922	HAM	Southampton
1800	1992	....	1800	148571	HAM	Southampton
1851	1857	1833	1857	124915	HUN	Buckden
1778	....	....	1778	108839	HUN	Colne
1850	1870	1850	1870	108839	HUN	Somersham
1882	1886	1886	1992	122580	LAN	Chorlton
1882	1886	1886	1992	122580	LAN	Manchester
1739	1768	ALL	1739	152838	LIN	Keelby
1718	1770	1600	1750	126837	LIN	Woolsthorpe
1785	1850	1750	1785	157775	LND	Berkely Square
1880	1964	1500	1992	175498	LND	Lambeth
1800	1850	1700	1800	172898	LND	Southwark
1860	ALL	ALL	ALL	117935	LND	???
1780	1820	1780	1840	117501	MDX	Enfield
1803	1840	1840	1920	109851	MDX	London
1830	1992	1750	1850	112704	MDX	Uxbridge
1802	1855	1740	1802	165158	SOM	Selworthy
1816	1900	1816	1900	126187	SOM	Yeovil
1852	1852	1852	1852	126276	WAR	Warwick
1828	1992	1700	1828	161446	WIL	All Cannings
1600	1860	ALL	ALL	117935	WIL	Burbage
1750	1851	1690	1850	126276	WIL	Chippenham
1780	1920	1700	1780	126179	WIL	Chippenham
1831	....	1680	1831	177865	WIL	Everley
1836	1992	1700	1836	126020	WIL	Pewsey
1809	....	1750	1900	166197	WOR	Longdon
1840	1880	1700	1840	129534	YKS	Hull
....	1818	ALL	1818	152838	YKS	Hull
1860	1992	1860	1992	126187	???	Bristol
1870	1992	1870	1992	126187	???	Kingswood
1834	1850	1700	1850	174610	???	Weyford
GALES						
1725	1790	ALL	1725	135143	NFK	Tunstead
GALGANI						
1800	1890	1750	1815	123978	HAM	Winchester
GALL						
1800	1880	1700	1800	126357	ABD	Rayne
1745	1992	ALL	1745	126195	BAN	Banff
1778	1885	1700	1885	126209	NBL	North
1854	1980	1800	1992	126632	NBL	Cramlington
1784	1789	1750	1784	138347	SFK	Earl Soham
GALLAFANT						
1800	1914	1700	1800	133582	ESS	Earlscolne
GALLAGHER						
1848	1868	1848	1868	126217	CMA	Maryport
1869	1992	1869	1992	126217	DUR	South Shields
1905	1992	1800	1905	113166	ESS	East Ham
1848	1992	1700	1848	126217	IRL	Ballygolan
GALLAZI						
1955	....	....	....	173932	WIL	Bradford On Avon
GALLEY						
1845	1959	?	1850	164976	GLS	Gloucester
GALLICHAN						
....	....	1800	....	149187	JSY	St Saviour
GALLIERS						
1790	1840	1700	1900	147508	HEF	Pembroke
GALLIFORD						
1716	1871	ALL	ALL	140155	DEV	Puddington
GALLIMORE						
1766	1800	1600	1766	110639	STS	Cheadle
1766	1800	1600	1766	110639	STS	Leek
1775	1840	....	....	132756	STS	Stoke On Trent
1860	1920	1800	1920	168467	STS	Swinscoe
GALLON						
....	....	ALL	ALL	151440	NBL	ALL
GALLOP						
1776	1793	1500	1776	129577	IOW	???
1810	1834	ALL	1810	112887	SOM	Bath
....	1700	....	....	174564	SSX	???
GALLOWAY						
1890	1910	1890	1910	148288	ARM	Newery
....	1840	....	....	161888	AYR	Monkton
1830	1880	....	1830	161888	AYR	Riccarton
1690	1840	1690	1992	126241	FIF	ALL
1847	1992	....	....	170453	FIF	ALL
1750	1920	1700	1992	148288	FIF	Kirkcaldy
1750	1920	1700	1992	148288	FIF	Strathmiglo
1750	1950	1700	1992	173096	KEN	ALL
1753	....	1753	....	164275	KEN	Lydd
1870	1992	1800	1992	126233	LAN	Liverpool
1870	1992	1690	1992	126241	LND	Wandsworth
....	....	ALL	ALL	112860	LTN	Edinburgh
1840	1870	....	....	121037	MDX	Limehouse
1733	1900	1851	1881	128988	PER	Alyth
....	....	1750	1840	121037	SCT	East
1835	1992	1700	1834	105988	YKS	Bowling
GALLOWEY						
1657	....	1657	....	147532	CHS	Sandbach
GALPIN						
1724	1792	1700	1800	167126	SRY	Mitcham
1724	1792	1700	1800	167126	SRY	Putney
GALT						
1771	1853	1600	1771	160342	KKD	Terregles
1827	1885	1800	1900	130427	LKS	Glasgow
1750	1965	....	....	137820	SHI	Fetlar
1720	1965	....	....	137820	SHI	Mid Yell
1760	1965	....	....	137820	SHI	North Yell
1758	1965	....	....	137820	SHI	Northmavine
1720	1965	....	....	137820	SHI	South Yell
GALTRESS						
1830	1910	1500	1890	146722	ALL	ALL
GALVIN						
1820	1860	....	....	114871	AVN	Bristol
1795	1810	1700	1795	114871	IRL	Cork
....	1860	....	....	126276	IRL	Galway
1863	ALL	ALL	1880	116734	LIM	???
1862	1876	1860	1890	126276	STS	Hammerwich
1863	ALL	ALL	1880	116734	TIP	???
1890	1970	1871	1970	126276	WYK	Denaby Main
GALWARD						
....	....	1800	....	128627	ESS	Saffron Walden
GAMAGE						
1413	1520	....	....	124974	GLA	Coity
1413	1520	....	....	124974	GLA	Coyty Castle
1260	1320	1066	1350	124974	GNT	Rogiet
1176	1330	1066	1330	124974	HEF	Dilwyn
1176	1330	1066	1330	124974	HEF	Masell Gamage
1708	1730	....	....	103632	NTH	Whilton
1752	1852	1752	1860	129194	OXF	Steeple Barton
GAMBEL						
1850	1992	1700	1850	126616	MDX	Bethnal Green
GAMBIER						
....	....	ALL	ALL	126284	ALL	Name Study
GAMBLE						
1850	1992	1800	1850	172650	CAV	Cootehill

Known From	To	Researching From	To	Ref	Cty	Place
GAMBLE contd.						
1572	1588	1500	1571	102830	DBY	Darley
1780	1860	1780	1870	108456	ESS	Witham
....	....	ALL	ALL	178152	HAM	Wherwell
1805	....	1829	....	127647	IRL	Ulster
1600	1699	1600	1699	169781	IRL	???
1850	1930	1800	1850	161292	LAN	Manchester
1727	1792	1550	1800	147265	LIN	South
1872	1960	1700	1872	126292	NFK	East Dereham
1783	1881	1770	1900	108901	NTT	Newark
1749	1773	ALL	1749	136875	YKS	Calverley
1719	1814	1600	1720	174858	YKS	Helmsley
1749	1773	ALL	1749	136875	YKS	Leathley
GAMBLING						
1840	1887	1840	1900	173061	SRY	Croydon
1811	1920	....	....	151548	WIL	West Dean
GAMBRILL						
?	?	?	?	126306	KEN	Dover
GAME						
1753	1773	....	1753	142166	HRT	Westmill
1807	1992	1700	1807	162647	LND	City
1807	1992	1700	1807	162647	LND	East End
1788	....	1700	1790	152110	SFK	Glemsford
1807	1992	1700	1807	162647	SFK	Glemsford
GAMES						
1755	1958	1600	1755	162035	BRE	Talsgarth
GAMESON						
1800	1900	1400	1870	179655	WLS	Monmouth
1815	1871	1800	1900	123250	YKS	Beverley
1790	1804	1750	1850	123250	YKS	Hull
GAMLEN						
1780	1810	1750	1800	153451	SOM	Banwell
1810	1860	1800	1850	153451	???	Bristol
GAMLIN						
1577	1610	ALL	1610	114987	SOM	Aller
1800	1820	ALL	ALL	152226	SOM	Milverton
GAMMAGE						
....	....	1700	1900	106607	SFK	Woodbridge
GAMMAN						
1628	1992	....	....	114669	LND	Stepney
GAMMIDGE						
1783	1861	1780	1871	170143	NTH	Scaldwell
1783	1861	1780	1871	170143	NTH	Walgrave
GAMMON						
1856	1992	1500	1856	153095	DEV	North
1791	1843	ALL	1791	169145	DEV	Appledore
1780	1850	1700	1780	101524	HEF	Bredwardine
....	....	1700	1930	100935	KEN	ALL
....	....	ALL	ALL	118400	LND	St Pancras
1628	1992	....	....	114669	LND	Stepney
....	....	1700	1930	100935	SSX	ALL
GAMPBELL						
1821	1841	1700	1821	165859	MOG	Tehillan
GAMSON						
1880	1911	ALL	ALL	120650	YKS	Rotherham
GAMSTON						
1865	1880	ALL	ALL	120650	DUR	Darlington
?	?	ALL	ALL	120650	WOR	Kidderminster
GANDER						
....	....	ALL	ALL	126314	ALL	Name Study
1200	1940	1200	1940	126314	ALL	ALL
1840	1992	1840	1992	126322	CHS	Chester
1818	1850	....	....	126314	LND	City
1850	1920	....	....	126314	SRY	Bermondsey
1780	1791	1750	1791	126314	SRY	Clapham
1752	1780	....	....	126314	SRY	Cranleigh
1550	1600	1500	1992	114901	SRY	Thursley
1846	1846	1800	1992	165603	SSX	Bolney
1643	1980	ALL	1643	110078	SSX	Eastbourne
1643	1980	ALL	1643	110078	SSX	Herstmonceux
1800	1840	1700	1900	126322	SSX	Rye
GANDY						
1771	1890	1750	1800	108774	DEV	Exeter
1594	1992	1500	1992	126330	DEV	Exeter
GANE						
1850	1870	1700	1850	160660	KEN	Bearsted
1700	1750	1690	1770	142018	SOM	High Littleton
1758	1890	1700	1850	138487	SOM	Shepton Mallet
GANGE						
1825	1825	1775	1850	136042	DEV	Beer
1825	1825	1775	1850	136042	DEV	Seaton
GANN						
....	....	ALL	ALL	126349	ALL	Name Study
1780	1950	ALL	ALL	127078	ALL	ALL
GANN contd.						
1646	1723	1723	1837	126349	ESS	Colchester
1663	1992	....	....	126349	ESS	Stamford Rivers
1710	1992	1600	1710	126349	KEN	Canterbury
1622	1622	1622	1837	126349	KEN	Sandwich
1746	?	?	?	166642	KEN	Whitstable
1614	1633	1633	1837	126349	LIN	Pinchbeck
1596	1654	1654	1837	126349	LIN	Stamford
1790	1805	1805	1837	126349	LND	Covent Garden
1682	1719	1719	1837	126349	RUT	Exton
1848	1992	1600	1848	126349	RUT	Manton
1667	1772	1772	1837	126349	RUT	Ryhall
GANNAUAY						
1838	1850	1750	1850	169234	HAM	Damerham
GANNON						
1890	1957	1880	1910	161411	ALL	ALL
1845	....	....	....	160385	DBY	???
1830	1858	1830	1850	159875	IRL	Kildare
GANT						
1831	....	ALL	ALL	166839	NFK	Thetford
1851	1970	1800	....	106488	SFK	Groton
1817	1946	ALL	ALL	118192	SFK	Hadleigh
GARBET						
....	....	1500	1899	115975	DUR	ALL
GARBETT						
1841	1992	....	1841	131741	SAL	Broseley
1710	1914	....	....	132756	SAL	Dawley
1710	1914	....	....	132756	SAL	Madeley
1841	1992	....	1841	131741	SAL	Pontsbury
1710	1914	....	....	132756	SAL	Shiffnal
1710	1914	....	....	132756	SAL	Wellington
1850	1890	1780	1850	108871	STS	South
GARBUTT						
1872	1992	1700	1872	117463	DUR	ALL
1760	1800	1538	1800	118893	NRY	Hawnby
1825	1925	ALL	1825	161330	WOR	Rock
1813	1881	1812	1890	116114	YKS	Bridlington
1799	1851	1740	1851	116114	YKS	Whitby
1665	1721	1600	1670	174858	YKS	Wintringham
GARD						
1804	1992	1804	1992	126365	DEV	Devonport
1804	1992	1804	1992	126365	DEV	Plymouth
1853	1976	1850	....	146900	DEV	Torquay
GARDENER						
1789	1837	1700	1837	126381	ESS	South
1817	1844	1700	1992	159468	LAN	Fylde
1823	1846	1780	1860	118443	LAN	Marton
....	....	1775	1850	147613	LAN	Melling
1869	?	1832	1869	109975	LND	???
....	....	1750	1850	118834	SSX	Apuldram
1748	1992	1700	1800	126454	SSX	Ewhurst
1850	1992	1700	1850	155411	YKS	North
GARDINER						
1805	1919	1780	1920	146536	AYR	Beith
1774	1841	1700	1840	160601	BRK	Tilehurst
1835	1870	1800	1870	128112	ESS	Chelmsford
1822	1992	ALL	1822	175994	GLS	Haresfield
1822	1992	ALL	1822	175994	GLS	Longney
1753	1902	1720	1850	124028	GLS	Stroud
1820	1850	1800	1870	126438	IRL	Dublin
1786	?	?	?	166642	KEN	???
1782	1798	....	....	171654	LKS	Cambusnethan
1850	1860	1800	1850	146587	LND	ALL
....	1753	....	....	147869	LND	???
1800	1900	1800	1900	124761	NFK	Gt Yarmouth
1746	1761	1720	1746	177393	NFK	Pickerham
1689	1786	1600	1689	169935	OXF	Daylesford
?	....	....	....	102733	OXF	Kidlington
1689	1786	1600	1689	169935	OXF	Kingham
1657	1740	ALL	1750	149063	ROX	Stichel
1764	1869	1700	1800	179000	SCT	Abercorn
1776	....	1776	1992	110868	SCT	Ayr
1812	1852	ALL	ALL	121487	SFK	Hadleigh
1760	1800	1680	1760	155276	SFK	Kirton
1750	1992	1700	1992	133450	SOM	West
1897	1901	1800	1837	177113	WOR	St Clements
1734	1992	ALL	1992	126411	YKS	East
GARDNER						
1850	1911	1850	1911	108278	ANT	Ballymoney
1750	1992	1750	1992	166758	DEV	South
1785	1814	....	....	146560	DON	South
1849	1932	....	....	156647	ENG	???
1800	1900	1700	1800	140317	ESS	Wivenhoe
1810	1836	1800	1857	162825	GLS	Cains Cross

Known From	To	Researching From	To	Ref	Cty	Place
GARDNER contd.						
1839	1843	1836	1850	162825	GLS	Cheltenham
1778	1792	1750	1819	162825	GLS	Cirencester
1800	1830	1750	1830	126446	GLS	Lechlade
1700	1900	....	....	152978	HEF	Bishops Frome
....	....	1700	1750	108677	KEN	North
....	....	....	1804	130060	KEN	Dymchurch
1685	1835	1542	1685	141291	LAN	Denron
1880	1992	ALL	1880	108847	LAN	Lancaster
1780	1830	1700	1780	176311	LAN	Lancaster
1825	1900	....	....	159131	LAN	Preston
1789	1825	....	....	159131	LAN	Treals
1879	1899	1899	1992	146560	LKS	Coatbride
1750	1870	1750	1870	126799	LND	Marylebone
1780	1780	1760	1850	168149	MDX	New Brentford
1780	1780	1760	1850	168149	MDX	Old Brentford
1859	1872	1800	1880	129356	MDX	Whitechapel
1789	1992	1600	1789	147729	NTH	Aynho
....	....	1800	1879	152684	NTH	Bugbrooke
1789	1992	1600	1789	147729	OXF	Cropredy
1800	....	....	....	168041	OXF	Oxford
1760	1760	1600	1800	168149	OXF	Thame
....	....	1800	1880	137685	SFK	Goriston With Southtown
....	....	1800	1880	137685	SFK	Gorleston
1815	1820	1790	1820	147974	SFK	Newbourn
1750	1965	....	....	137820	SHI	Fetlar
1720	1965	....	....	137820	SHI	Mid Yell
1760	1965	....	....	137820	SHI	North Yell
1758	1965	....	....	137820	SHI	Northmavine
1720	1965	....	....	137820	SHI	South Yell
1862	1992	1555	1862	126462	STD	Glasgow
1815	1950	1750	1850	131431	WAR	Birmingham
1822	1870	1700	1900	152714	WAR	Birmingham
1875	1900	....	....	168041	WAR	Birmingham
1712	1910	1680	1750	110906	WAR	Honington
1825	1880	1800	1890	126438	WAR	Solihull
1810	1900	1700	1810	163503	WAR	Tanworth
1820	1851	1820	1860	142018	WIL	Highworth
....	....	1850	1930	106127	WMD	Aston
1808	1959	ALL	ALL	168610	WOR	Bewdley
1822	....	1700	1900	152714	WOR	Kidderminster
1857	1959	ALL	ALL	168610	WOR	Kidderminster
GARDOM						
....	....	ALL	ALL	164593	ALL	ALL
1755	1900	ALL	ALL	164593	SRY	Epsom
GARE						
1843	....	....	....	148768	AVN	Bristol
1690	....	1690	1900	106410	SOM	Huish Episcop
1870	....	....	....	148768	SRY	Newington
GAREY						
1897	1897	1800	1992	140147	IRL	???
1897	1897	1800	1992	140147	LND	Battersea
GARFIT						
1830	1880	1700	1900	100129	CAM	Soke Of Peterborough
1830	1880	1700	1900	100129	NTH	Bainton
GARFORTH						
1861	1900	....	1861	114812	LAN	Oldham
GARGANI						
....	....	ALL	ALL	123978	ALL	ALL
GARGETT						
1810	1992	1700	1810	160571	DUR	Crossgate
1800	1890	1700	1800	138258	DUR	Teesdale
GARGRAVE						
1793	1965	1700	1793	154164	YKS	West Riding
GARIS						
1680	....	....	....	137693	CHI	Guernsey
GARKA						
1827	1846	1800	1827	100277	LND	Shoreditch
GARLAND						
1790	1820	ALL	1790	115266	DOR	ALL
1700	1806	ALL	ALL	128449	GLS	Mangotsfield
1773	1830	1600	1773	149888	GLS	Mangotsfield
1870	1992	1800	1900	147079	IRL	Dublin
1837	1992	1750	1837	114464	LAN	Manchester
1721	....	ALL	1992	159174	LEI	Packington
....	....	1800	1870	147079	OFF	ALL
....	....	1800	1900	146110	SCT	ALL
....	1772	1600	1800	153591	SOM	Yeovil
GARLEY						
1822	....	....	....	148156	NTH	Raunds
GARLICK						
1788	1864	1768	1874	134686	DBY	Charlesworth

Known From	To	Researching From	To	Ref	Cty	Place
GARLICK contd.						
1840	1992	1837	1992	177121	GLS	???
....	....	1700	1930	147508	HEF	ALL
1798	1798	1798	1798	139971	WIL	Hilmarton
GARLING						
....	....	1700	1800	150525	ALL	ALL
GARMSTON						
1797	1838	1797	ALL	145386	GLS	Bristol
GARNER						
....	....	1760	1870	103713	BDF	Bedford
1665	1940	....	....	128996	CAM	Thornley
1714	1793	1600	1714	151254	CHS	North East
1714	1793	1600	1714	151254	CHS	North
1763	1843	ALL	1843	157902	CHS	Altrincham
1843	1843	1810	1850	126705	CHS	Chester
1763	1843	ALL	1843	157902	CHS	Dynham Massey
1900	1940	1800	1900	171514	CHS	Stockport
1685	1992	....	....	149896	HAM	Wickham
1685	1992	....	....	149896	HAM	Winchester
1800	1992	ALL	ALL	126497	LAN	Billinge
....	....	1650	1725	116173	LAN	Furness
1810	1980	1800	1900	126500	LAN	Wigan
1734	1766	1700	1790	123404	LEI	Wymeswold
1787	1794	1700	1787	139122	LIN	Gainsboro
1830	1850	1750	1830	172472	LIN	Long Sutton
1830	1992	1800	1900	151017	LND	Bermondsey
1893	....	1880	1906	138142	NFK	Clenchwarton
1880	1992	ALL	1880	126489	NTH	Earls Barton
1732	1756	ALL	1732	115126	NTH	Kingsthorpe
1770	1850	1600	1770	138584	NTT	East Leake
1875	1895	ALL	ALL	125288	STS	Stafford
GARNETT						
1826	1832	1780	1850	127205	CMA	Kendal
1797	1835	1700	1850	112089	IRL	Latchford
1856	1992	1832	1992	127205	LAN	Salford
1797	1978	1700	1992	112089	LAN	???
1866	1992	1820	1866	126519	MDX	Edmonton
1867	1992	1840	1867	126519	MDX	Hackney
1830	1896	1700	1870	163902	YKS	South
1800	....	1800	....	130710	YKS	Bradford
GARNHAM						
1778	1815	....	....	133663	SFK	Bury St Edmunds
1763	1992	1700	1763	126527	SFK	Capel St Mary
1738	1850	....	....	127779	SFK	Gosbeck
1843	1897	1700	1842	106402	SFK	Nacton
GARNIER						
1620	1640	....	....	167037	MDX	London
GARNISS						
....	....	ALL	1841	156833	ESS	Ingatestone
1851	1992	1750	1851	156833	LAN	Liverpool
....	....	1800	1840	156833	YKS	Hull
GARNON						
1881	....	1860	1890	175684	LND	Bethnal Green
GARNSWORTHY						
....	....	ALL	ALL	127574	ALL	Name Study
GARNWSORTHY						
1800	1900	1800	1900	127574	DEV	Starcross
GARRAD						
....	....	1700	1850	157449	CAM	Gt Wilbraham
....	....	1700	1780	145173	ESS	Chelmsford
....	....	1770	1830	145173	ESS	Coggeshall
....	....	1760	1790	145173	ESS	Great Yeldham
....	....	1830	1860	145173	LND	Bethnal Green
GARRARD						
1728	1772	....	....	127779	BRK	Lambourn
....	....	1700	1872	168653	ESS	ALL
....	....	1750	1850	138738	ESS	Ardleigh
1841	1851	1851	1900	138738	MDX	Bedfont
1850	1920	1800	1920	148377	SFK	Ipswich
....	....	ALL	1800	151602	WIL	Ramsbury
GARRAT						
1800	1846	1700	1846	159581	HAM	Crondall
1700	1800	ALL	ALL	131873	HRT	Furneaux Pelham
....	....	ALL	1800	152889	HUN	St Neots
GARRATT						
1804	1940	....	....	128996	CAM	Thornley
1844	1900	ALL	1900	134503	NTH	Peterborough
1780	1992	ALL	1780	158437	NTH	Peterborough
1810	....	....	....	142859	OXF	Oxford
GARRAWAY						
1780	1880	....	1880	174866	DUR	ALL
....	....	....	....	174866	SCT	???
GARRET						
1750	1950	1600	1750	128376	NBL	Horton

Known From	To	Researching From	To	Ref	Cty	Place
GARRET contd.						
....	1668	....	....	128910	WAR	Nuneaton
GARRETT						
1750	1800	ALL	ALL	149632	AYR	Ardrossan
1850	1992	1700	1850	157449	CAM	Gt Wilbraham
1814	1851	1700	1851	178233	CMA	Whitehaven
1814	1931	1750	1850	118397	DOR	Witchampton
1700	1700	1650	1900	141151	ESS	ALL
1860	1868	1800	1860	117277	ESS	Barking
1716	1726	1650	1900	141151	ESS	Romford
1880	1992	1881	1981	126551	GLS	Almondsbury
1880	1992	1881	1981	126551	GLS	Bridgeyate
1828	1829	ALL	ALL	116378	LND	East
....	....	ALL	1765	103284	SAL	Weston
1600	1992	....	....	126543	SFK	London
1600	1992	....	....	126543	SFK	Wickham Market
....	....	1650	1800	147613	STS	Rowley Regis
....	1770	1600	1800	175633	STS	Uttoxeter
....	....	ALL	1765	103284	STS	???
1813	1866	1813	1992	136808	SXE	Hartfield
1612	1752	1612	1752	178705	WIL	Hannington
1820	1900	1750	1900	126551	WIL	Mere
1790	1798	1700	1790	173452	WIL	Winterbourne Stoke
GARRICK						
1745	1906	ALL	1950	123358	LKS	Glasgow
1745	1906	ALL	1950	123358	YKS	Sheffield
GARROD						
....	1878	1800	1900	137685	LND	Islington
1803	1877	1780	1803	161527	LND	Lambeth
1803	1877	1780	1803	161527	MDX	Marylebone
1761	1992	ALL	ALL	131091	SFK	ALL
1800	1830	1700	1800	177490	SFK	Burgate
1863	1885	1800	1992	117609	SFK	Theberton
1750	1775	....	....	129747	SFK	Wattisfield
....	....	1700	1799	173274	SFK	Whatfield
1803	1835	1780	1803	161527	SRY	Lambeth
GARROT						
1700	1740	1600	1740	154342	GLS	Bitton
GARROTT						
1787	....	1780	1800	163775	MDX	Shoreditch
GARROW						
1850	....	....	....	148768	MDX	Monken Hadley
1700	....	....	....	148768	SCT	Banff
GARROW-MONK						
....	....	ALL	ALL	148768	ALL	ALL
GARSDEN						
1885	1914	....	....	164062	LAN	Darwen
GARSIDE						
1829	1929	1800	1829	160741	LAN	ALL
1835	1855	1800	1855	160741	LND	Bermondsey
1850	1992	1600	1992	120677	WYK	Slaithwaite
1694	....	1660	1710	170348	YKS	Almondbury
GARSON						
1650	1875	....	....	153397	SRY	Charlwood
GARSTER						
1750	1965	....	....	137820	SHI	Fetlar
1720	1965	....	....	137820	SHI	Mid Yell
1760	1965	....	....	137820	SHI	North Yell
1758	1965	....	....	137820	SHI	Northmavine
1720	1965	....	....	137820	SHI	South Yell
GARSTON						
1650	1875	....	....	153397	SSX	ALL
GARTH						
1740	1750	1700	1740	121339	NYK	Marrick
GARTHSON						
1750	1965	....	....	137820	SHI	Fetlar
1720	1965	....	....	137820	SHI	Mid Yell
1760	1965	....	....	137820	SHI	North Yell
1758	1965	....	....	137820	SHI	Northmavine
1720	1965	....	....	137820	SHI	South Yell
GARTHWAITE						
1851	1992	1821	1992	104299	YKS	Barnsley
1821	1851	1796	1851	104299	YKS	Cawthorne
1796	....	ALL	1821	104299	YKS	Kilnhurst
GARTLY						
1836	1992	1600	1836	174106	BAN	Glass
GARTON						
1821	1840	1800	1821	147885	BKM	Lutton
1821	1840	1800	1821	147885	BKM	Upwood
1846	1900	1800	1900	129178	CWD	Wrexham
1775	1830	1745	1775	139149	ERY	Nafferton
1900	1992	1800	1900	109576	LAN	St Helens
1671	1992	1600	1671	102342	LIN	Appleby
1746	1746	ALL	1746	122572	NTT	ALL

Known From	To	Researching From	To	Ref	Cty	Place
GARTON contd.						
1750	1900	1600	1750	172901	NTT	???
GARTSHORE						
1749	1751	....	....	127140	DNB	Kirkintilloch
1770	1856	....	....	127140	LKS	Maryburgh
GARTSIDE						
1725	1857	1650	1750	126411	LAN	Butterworth
1632	1992	1537	1900	161985	LAN	Rochdale
GARTZ						
....	1881	1800	1881	177938	WLS	Swansea
GARVETH						
1500	....	1500	....	116920	CON	???
GARVIE						
1835	....	....	....	147672	SCT	Perth
GARVIN						
....	....	ALL	ALL	126578	ALL	Name Study
1800	1900	1800	1992	126578	CAV	???
....	....	....	....	126578	LDY	South
1798	1921	1600	1992	126578	LDY	Castledawson
1800	....	1800	1992	126578	LDY	Coleraine
1800	....	1800	1992	126578	LDY	Garvagh
1800	....	1800	1992	126578	LDY	Limavady
1800	....	1800	1992	126578	LDY	Macosquin
1839	1873	1839	1992	126578	LDY	Magherafelt
GARWOOD						
....	?	?	....	114642	SFK	West
1700	1870	....	....	116505	SFK	Brockley
1810	1810	1810	1810	136808	SFK	Bury St Edmunds
1759	1776	1700	1800	162884	SFK	Hemley
1629	1687	....	....	142522	SFK	Nacton Parish
GASCOIGNE						
1744	1992	1600	1744	111813	NTT	Woodsetts
1800	1914	1750	1790	135763	YKS	Acomb
1866	1930	1920	1992	118354	YKS	Hull
1744	1992	1600	1744	111813	YKS	North Anston
1729	1866	....	....	118354	YKS	Saxby
1800	1914	1750	1790	135763	YKS	Yokr
GASCOINE						
1837	1992	ALL	1837	131784	LND	ALL
1837	1992	ALL	1837	131784	SRY	ALL
GASCOYNE						
1822	1899	1700	1822	101222	LND	Bethnal Green
1794	1992	1700	1794	116440	SRY	Lambeth
GASELTINE						
1850	1870	1600	1870	123587	BRK	Swallowfield
GASGOGNE						
1880	1900	ALL	1920	123048	WAR	Leamington Spa
GASH						
1718	1870	ALL	....	162302	CUL	???
GASK						
....	....	ALL	ALL	173088	LIN	Wainfleet
GASKELL						
1700	1900	1500	1900	114197	ALL	ALL
1790	1800	1750	1900	135771	CHS	Disley
1812	1871	ALL	ALL	106658	CHS	Rainow
1800	1885	1700	1800	160474	LAN	St Helens
1874	1911	1800	1900	126586	LAN	Wigan
1762	1820	1700	1762	168912	LAN	Wigan
GASKILL						
1889	1896	1859	1896	157678	LAN	Liverpool
GASKIN						
1866	1900	....	....	167150	DUR	Etherley
1839	1866	1750	1839	167150	NBL	Matfen
1900	1950	....	....	167150	NBL	Newcastle Upon Tyne
1795	1880	1780	1880	126594	NTT	Nottingham
1839	1849	ALL	ALL	151645	WAR	Harbury
1810	1819	ALL	ALL	151645	WAR	Hatton
1761	1775	ALL	ALL	151645	WAR	Kineton
1777	1905	ALL	ALL	151645	WAR	Newbold Pacey
1872	1960	ALL	ALL	151645	WOR	Bromsgrove
GASKING						
....	....	ALL	ALL	126608	ALL	Name Study
GASKINGS						
ALL	1724	....	....	105368	WOR	Doritwich
GASS						
1800	1900	....	....	150371	ROX	Dumfries
GASSON						
1672	1850	1600	1672	120774	KEN	South West
1890	1912	....	....	177709	LND	London
....	....	1600	1900	108766	SSX	???
GASTER						
1873	1965	....	....	113018	LND	Bow
1873	1965	....	....	113018	LND	Poplar
1860	1992	1700	1860	131830	LND	???

Known From	To	Researching From	To	Ref	Cty	Place
GASTON						
....	....	1700	1850	165239	ANT	Cullybackey
1873	1992	ALL	ALL	115762	HRT	Wheathamstead
1829	1829	1500	1829	174009	SSX	ALL
GATE						
1845	1920	1800	1992	126632	CMA	Rockcliffe
1717	1720	1600	1750	130125	CUL	Thursby
GATEHOUSE						
1896	1992	1800	1992	129984	KEN	???
GATENBY						
1820	1992	1800	1992	139475	LAN	Manchester
1650	1850	1600	1850	139475	YKS	North
1780	1835	1700	1835	116300	YKS	Richmond
GATER						
1633	1825	1500	1825	126659	CHS	Wybunbury
1850	1900	1850	1900	126659	KEN	Medway
1840	1900	1600	1900	126640	LND	ALL
1860	1900	ALL	ALL	126659	LND	???
1825	1860	1800	1900	126659	SAL	Newport
1850	1890	ALL	1900	126659	SRY	Croydon
1805	1850	1500	1950	126659	STS	The Potteries
GATES						
1850	1890	....	....	125962	BKM	Burnham
1878	1960	1800	1878	126675	HAM	Aldershot
1812	1860	....	....	133221	HAM	Boldre
1714	....	1700	1800	157732	HAM	Hawkley
1861	1870	....	....	133221	HAM	Lymington
....	....	1800	1810	133221	HAM	Milford
1700	1900	....	....	153397	HAM	New Forest
1860	1992	1700	1860	103098	HAM	Sway
1800	1900	1750	1900	177180	HRT	Northchurch
1830	1856	1700	1830	174068	LND	Kensington
1837	1992	1700	1837	130257	LND	Kingsland
1780	1822	1700	1900	159956	SFK	Ingham
....	....	1750	1850	174114	SFK	Rougham
1808	....	1750	1850	139386	SRY	Lambeth
1825	1875	1750	1900	155357	SSX	Crawley
1644	1705	1600	1644	174807	SSX	Woodmancote
GATESMAN						
1875	1992	1700	1875	156760	HAM	ALL
GATFIELD						
....	....	ALL	ALL	126683	ALL	Name Study
1771	1992	1600	1900	126683	MDX	Hanworth
GATHERCOAL						
1855	1992	ALL	1855	123749	SFK	???
GATHERCOLE						
....	....	ALL	ALL	126691	ALL	Name Study
1825	1829	1800	1850	105120	CAM	Fordham
1820	1850	1800	1850	150479	LEI	Allexton
1800	1830	1800	....	150479	NFK	Didlington
1777	1840	1760	1822	176184	NFK	Ingoldisthorpe
1830	1865	1750	1830	105392	NFK	Ringstead
1650	1805	1650	1805	135941	SFK	Lakenheath
1850	1970	1850	1970	150479	WAR	Leamington
GATLEY						
1800	1850	1700	1800	114472	CHS	Bollington
1876	1947	1947	....	109967	ESS	Laindon
1795	1827	1827	1900	146609	YKS	North
GATRALL						
1790	1880	....	1790	137227	IOW	Ryde
1787	1930	1500	1800	132993	IOW	St Helens
GATT						
....	1850	....	1850	136085	BAN	Pennan
GATTACRE						
1180	1500	1180	1500	154881	CHS	Sutton
GATTER						
1750	1850	1700	1850	123722	SOM	Pitminster
GATTY						
1621	1992	ALL	ALL	163562	ALL	ALL
1850	1992	ALL	1850	162108	LND	ALL
GAUCHERON						
1750	1770	1682	1750	142166	???	London
GAUDEN						
1682	1711	ALL	1682	154563	DOR	Langton Herring
GAUDIE						
1696	1855	1600	1855	148482	OKI	Birsay
GAUGHT						
1877	1992	....	....	168254	SFK	Bardwell
1851	1992	....	....	168254	SFK	Honnington
1851	1992	....	....	168254	SFK	Spaiston
GAUL						
1790	1830	1700	1800	126772	DEV	Exeter
GAULD						
1850	1920	1750	1992	121746	BAN	Boyndie

Known From	To	Researching From	To	Ref	Cty	Place
GAULDER						
1793	1831	1700	1793	159158	HRT	Whitchurch
GAULER						
1850	1860	1700	1850	171638	AVN	Bath
1837	1862	1770	1837	117471	GLS	Minchinhampton
GAULT						
....	....	1835	....	146706	CAV	Manor Hamilton
1863	1901	1845	1901	108278	LDY	Limavady
GAUNSON						
1750	1965	....	....	137820	SHI	Fetlar
1720	1965	....	....	137820	SHI	Mid Yell
1760	1965	....	....	137820	SHI	North Yell
1758	1965	....	....	137820	SHI	Northmavine
1720	1965	....	....	137820	SHI	South Yell
GAUNT						
1850	1980	1600	1850	112097	BDF	ALL
1754	1992	ALL	1754	126721	BDF	Campton
1830	1840	1700	1992	112097	LIN	Butterwick
1800	1992	1700	1800	164208	STS	Rocester
1830	1880	1780	1830	172510	YKS	Adwalton
1800	1880	....	1992	164984	YKS	Barnsley
1712	1742	ALL	1712	154563	YKS	Calverley
1830	1880	1780	1830	172510	YKS	Pudsey
1780	1850	ALL	1850	173436	YKS	Silkstone
GAUNTLETT						
1775	1900	1700	1900	121762	HAM	East
1700	1940	....	....	127833	HAM	Portsmouth
1580	1700	1580	1700	142018	WIL	ALL
GAVAN						
1881	1891	1880	1950	132454	DUR	Chester Le Street
GAVIN						
1812	1839	1800	1880	159905	NBL	North Shields
1779	1799	1770	1800	159905	???	Edinburgh
GAWARD						
1900	1992	ALL	ALL	106240	ALL	ALL
1650	1800	....	....	106240	ESS	Eoxwell
1845	1900	....	....	106240	ESS	Leyton
1790	1845	....	....	106240	ESS	Norton Mandeville
GAWEN						
1535	1992	ALL	1535	142069	SSX	Hastings
GAWGHT						
1560	1666	1500	ALL	168254	SFK	Troston Honington
GAWLER						
1700	1850	1600	1700	139092	DOR	Stalbridge
1750	1760	1600	1800	162620	DOR	Sturminster Newton
1700	1720	1600	1900	162620	HAM	Portsmouth
1759	1779	1600	1900	162620	HAM	Titchfield
GAWLEY						
1864	1989	1750	1864	159662	SLI	Castleconner
GAWN						
1785	1835	1511	1785	141291	IOM	Rushen
GAWNE						
1785	1835	1511	1785	141291	IOM	Rushen
GAWT						
1588	....	1500	ALL	168254	SFK	Gt Livermere
1589	1613	1500	ALL	168254	SFK	Ixworth
GAY						
....	....	1700	1850	142026	AVN	Siston
1803	1859	1780	1880	176982	DEV	Stoke Damerel
....	....	....	1730	126748	DEV	Totnes
1750	1870	1680	1900	152528	GLS	Bitton
1820	....	1820	1992	151378	GLS	Chippingsodbury
1750	1870	1680	1900	152528	GLS	Siston
1820	1900	?	1820	158569	GLS	Stroud
1708	1793	1700	1800	178004	HAM	Gosport
1833	1856	1800	1875	136042	LND	East
1717	1796	....	1760	136212	NFK	Wells
....	....	1740	1787	172871	SOM	East
1627	1691	1630	1690	142018	SOM	Bath
1811	1811	1750	1820	136042	SRY	Rotherhithe
....	....	1673	1728	115290	WIL	Broughton Gifford
1754	1839	1700	1800	178004	WIL	Sopworth
GAYDEN						
1769	1806	....	....	169099	OXF	North
1807	1902	1807	1902	169099	WAR	Tredington
GAYDON						
1540	1881	1881	1914	155217	DEV	Barnstaple
GAYE						
1733	....	1700	1733	126748	DEV	Wolborough
GAYFORD						
....	....	1700	1899	174963	SOM	Kilmersden
GAYLER						
1810	1852	ALL	ALL	135909	KKD	???

Known From	To	Researching From	To	Ref	Cty	Place
GAYNE						
1829	1868	ALL	1992	112631	SOM	Shepton Mallet
GAYWOOD						
1860	1913	1700	....	155713	NFK	Kings Lynn
GAZE						
ALL	ALL	ALL	ALL	126756	NTT	ALL
1760	1981	ALL	1760	126756	NTT	Normaton
1760	1992	1700	1760	126756	NTT	Sutton Bonington
GAZZARD						
1659	1992	ALL	1992	164739	GLS	ALL
1650	1810	1550	1650	108413	GLS	Berkeley
GEAKE						
1812	1839	1800	1992	133043	CON	Launceston
1770	1812	1750	1900	133043	CON	South Petherwin
1724	1940	1724	1900	109053	CON	St Germans
GEALE						
1725	1790	ALL	1725	135143	NFK	Tunstead
GEALL						
1800	1864	1592	1850	107166	SSX	Ripe
GEAR						
1740	1850	1740	1850	126500	BAN	Olrig
1740	1800	....	....	126497	CAI	Olrig
GEARING						
1902	....	....	1902	103489	BKM	Dorney
1801	1904	1700	1800	173878	OXF	Checkendon
1858	1902	....	....	103489	OXF	Gt Haseley
GEARL						
1785	1853	ALL	ALL	169730	HAM	Holybourne
GEARLE						
1784	1787	ALL	1784	169730	HAM	Basingstoke
GEARY						
?	?	?	?	169064	DBY	Bradley
1830	1992	1700	1830	118532	GAL	Galway
1754	1895	1500	1895	172294	HAM	ALL
1744	1903	1700	1992	168327	LEI	Anstey
1819	1900	ALL	1819	147877	LEI	Groby
1845	1940	1800	1845	128775	LND	East
1800	....	....	....	116416	LND	Stepney
GEBBETT						
1600	1850	1600	1750	139556	DEV	North
1700	1992	....	....	139556	LND	???
GEBLER						
1882	1992	1882	1896	124826	LIN	Grimsby
GEDDAS						
1739	1739	1600	1800	130125	DFS	Canonbie
GEDDES						
1809	1830	1750	1809	118427	ABD	Longside
1760	1800	....	....	126497	BAN	Rathven
1650	1890	1650	1890	105627	CAI	Wick
1852	....	1800	1852	164402	DUR	North Shields
GEDDIE						
1782	1961	....	....	152331	MOR	Kingston On Spey
GEDEN						
1660	1880	1600	1660	140309	WAR	Tysoe
GEDGE						
1828	1851	1700	1828	123307	NFK	Alderford
GEDYE						
1700	1992	1600	1700	126772	ALL	ALL
1837	1992	1837	1992	126780	ALL	ALL
1605	1689	1605	1689	126780	CON	Kea
1605	1689	1605	1689	126780	CON	Kenwyn
1568	1632	1568	1732	126780	CON	Launceston
1584	1789	1554	1789	126780	CON	Meheniot
1673	1850	1549	1850	126780	CON	St Neot
1807	1888	1800	1911	126780	DEV	Devonport
GEE						
1654	1940	....	....	128996	CAM	Thornley
1800	1850	1700	1850	159441	DEV	ALL
1593	1646	1593	1646	106593	DEV	Dunsford
1634	1639	1634	1639	106593	KEN	Tenterden
1820	1850	1750	1850	159166	LAN	South
1800	1940	1700	1992	110477	LAN	Manchester
1800	1940	1700	1992	110477	LAN	Salford
1859	1880	1800	1859	152463	LEI	Market Bosworth
1800	1853	1800	1853	137200	LEI	St Margarets
1853	1883	....	....	137200	LIN	Spilsby
....	1866	1700	1865	153664	LND	???
1778	1860	1850	1992	133043	NTH	Guisborough
1800	1988	ALL	1800	119067	NTH	Werrington
....	....	....	....	152218	STS	???
1790	1825	1750	1795	142395	WAR	Henley In Arden
....	....	?	?	143499	WIL	Preshute
1703	1835	1650	1700	110027	YKS	Scammonden

Known From	To	Researching From	To	Ref	Cty	Place
GEELAN						
1844	1848	1780	1992	116025	LET	Mohill
GEEN						
1820	1841	1820	1841	154040	DEV	Braunton
1816	1820	1816	1820	154040	DEV	West Down
1841	1960	1841	1960	154040	GLA	Cardiff
1841	1960	1841	1960	154040	GLA	Swansea
GEER						
....	....	ALL	ALL	102504	ALL	Name Study
1500	1992	1300	1992	126799	ALL	ALL
1790	1900	ALL	ALL	134503	KEN	Sundridge
GEERE						
1500	1992	1300	1992	126799	ALL	ALL
GEERING						
1690	1710	....	....	119458	BRK	Sutton Courtenay
1815	1845	ALL	....	132349	SSX	Denton
GEES						
1841	....	ALL	....	153214	MDX	Somers Town
GEESIN						
....	....	ALL	ALL	126802	ALL	Name Study
1480	1900	1480	1900	126802	LEI	ALL
GEESING						
1300	1600	1300	1600	126802	NFK	ALL
GEGGIE						
1807	1809	1800	1830	146528	ELN	Haddington
1830	1870	1800	1870	146528	MLN	Edinburgh
GEIR						
1738	1761	1500	1738	138614	DOR	Bridport
GELDART						
....	....	1850	1992	147613	LAN	Barrow In Furness
1800	1900	1700	1900	138967	LAN	Preston
GELDER						
....	....	ALL	ALL	126810	ALL	Name Study
1538	1970	1400	1930	126810	ALL	ALL
1568	1970	1400	1930	126810	LIN	North
1750	1992	1600	1750	102342	LIN	Flixborough
1756	1782	1756	1782	108901	LIN	Flixborough
1797	1970	1400	1930	126810	YKS	West
GELDRT						
1780	1854	1700	1780	133760	YKS	Huddersfield
GELEIT						
1853	1992	1850	1992	108391	MDX	London
GELL						
....	....	ALL	ALL	126829	ALL	Name Study
....	....	ALL	ALL	126829	ALL	ALL
1780	1800	1700	1850	100129	BDF	Tempstead
1500	1750	1500	1650	131911	DBY	Hopton
1822	1970	1777	1970	126829	DBY	Somercotes
1750	1992	1500	1750	124443	DBY	Wirksworth
1822	1970	1777	1970	126829	DBY	Wirksworth
1759	1770	1511	1759	141291	IOM	Rushen
1796	1970	1777	1970	126829	LEI	Shepshed
1750	1800	....	....	124621	LIN	Althorpe
1822	1970	1777	1970	126829	NTT	Nottingham
1800	1850	1600	1800	113263	YKS	???
GELLATLEY						
1899	....	....	....	137936	ANS	Dundee
GELLEY						
1760	1800	1740	1800	147311	NYK	Scarborough
GELLING						
1700	1850	1500	1800	126837	IOM	???
1830	1890	1830	1900	126837	LAN	Liverpool
1840	....	....	....	153982	LAN	Liverpool
GELLY						
1720	1734	1600	1720	102571	CON	Breage
GELSTHORPE						
1862	1957	1830	1862	137944	LEI	Leicester
GELSTON						
1780	1801	1700	1850	159964	KKD	Kirkpatrick Durham
GEMMEL						
1792	1885	1700	1750	150029	AYR	Loudoun
1792	1885	1700	1750	150029	AYR	Newmilus
GEMMELL						
1745	1765	....	....	171654	AYR	Kilmaurs
....	....	1700	1850	169501	AYR	New Cumnock
1780	1864	1600	1900	132977	KKD	Gatehouse Of Fleet
GENDALL						
1600	1992	1500	1992	163252	ALL	ALL
1618	1808	....	....	143596	CON	Madron
1618	1808	....	....	143596	CON	Morvah
GENDERS						
1700	1850	1800	1900	107611	WAR	ALL
GENDLE						
1800	1900	1500	1900	126845	DEV	???

Known From	To	Researching From	To	Ref	Cty	Place
GENESIS						
....	....	1750	1850	163082	LND	Soho
GENN						
1095	1992	1323	1699	126853	ALL	ALL
GENSON						
....	....	1600	....	137456	WAR	Stockton
GENT						
....	....	ALL	ALL	126861	ALL	Name Study
....	....	1750	1910	100358	CHS	Knutsford
1845	1893	....	....	133779	HAM	Portsmouth
1853	1910	1800	1850	173940	LEI	Oakthorpe
1750	1992	ALL	1750	170046	NFK	Clement
1750	1992	ALL	1750	170046	NFK	Terrington
1842	1900	1700	1842	113808	NTT	West Leake
ALL	ALL	ALL	ALL	114502	SOM	ALL
....	....	....	1878	131741	STS	Walsall
1837	1837	ALL	1992	102245	WAR	Polesworth
GENTLE						
1874	1954	ALL	ALL	140821	LEI	Leicester
GENTLEMAN						
1800	1830	ALL	ALL	124605	OXF	ALL
1855	1992	1750	1855	128651	WLN	Torphichen
GENTRY						
1800	1844	1780	1844	100277	ESS	Bocking
1680	1800	ALL	1680	131059	ESS	Bocking
1800	1992	....	....	131059	ESS	Gt Burstead
1850	1992	1700	1850	107840	ESS	Maldon
GEOGHEGAN						
ALL	ALL	ALL	ALL	106674	NIR	ALL
GEORGE						
1740	1822	1700	1850	140783	BKM	North
1800	1920	....	....	125962	BRK	Bray
....	....	1500	1629	138614	CON	Perranuthnoe
1850	1890	1700	1890	162388	CON	Roche
1850	1890	1700	1890	162388	CON	St Austell
1830	1900	1700	1900	134643	CON	St Endellion
1725	1753	1600	1725	102571	CON	St Gluvias
1791	1992	1700	1791	161446	CON	St Keverne
1754	1787	1700	1787	121398	CON	St Levan
1600	....	?	?	136999	CON	Truro
1800	1900	ALL	ALL	111511	DBY	ALL
....	....	1700	1890	121193	DEV	Plymouth
1826	1992	....	1830	178853	DEV	Plymouth
1860	1920	1880	1920	130567	GLA	Hengoed
1800	1850	1750	1800	174513	GLS	Lechlade
1825	1856	1800	1825	157074	HRT	Hertford
1600	1820	1600	1820	127655	HUN	Bythorn
....	....	?	?	149349	IRL	???
1840	1860	1800	1840	113816	KEN	Dover
1805	1905	1770	1805	168912	LAN	Middleton
1805	1905	1770	1805	168912	LAN	Oldham
1709	1778	1665	1709	174211	LIN	Washingborough
1822	1874	1750	1874	100307	MDX	Central
1930	1950	1700	1860	124036	PEM	Solva
1600	1920	1750	1878	176958	SOM	Bristol
1750	1800	1700	1800	154881	SOM	Chard
1790	1814	1700	1814	174300	SOM	Frome
1854	1861	....	....	130958	SOM	Road
1800	1900	ALL	ALL	111511	STS	ALL
1800	1992	1700	1900	107611	WAR	Aston
1600	1700	....	....	100420	WAR	Meriden
1775	1775	ALL	1992	102245	WAR	Tysoe
1703	1784	1600	1703	175781	WIL	Chitterne
1740	1892	1898	1898	107573	WIL	Horningsham
1694	1712	1660	1720	142018	WIL	Malmesbury
1736	1811	1700	1736	115819	WIL	Preshute
?	?	?	?	143294	WLS	Kevin Mawre
1851	1927	1600	1900	176958	???	Stoke Bishop
1730	....	1600	1735	176958	???	Worcester
GEORGESON						
1750	1965	....	....	137820	SHI	Fetlar
1720	1965	....	....	137820	SHI	Mid Yell
1760	1965	....	....	137820	SHI	North Yell
1758	1965	....	....	137820	SHI	Northmavine
1720	1965	....	....	137820	SHI	South Yell
GERARD						
1900	1992	1600	1900	171255	DBY	Matlock
GERAUGHTY						
1849	....	....	....	117560	SRY	Lambeth
GERHARD						
1860	1900	1850	1900	131962	LND	Highgate
1780	1992	1650	1992	140120	LND	St Pancras

Please send in your entry early

Known From	To	Researching From	To	Ref	Cty	Place
GERMAIN						
1778	1830	1700	1800	129453	WRY	Horton In Ribblesdale
GERMAINE						
1770	1820	1730	1870	176206	LND	Westminster
GERMAN						
1700	1992	1600	1992	117609	DEV	Malden
1700	1992	1600	1992	117609	DEV	Plymouth
1700	1992	1600	1992	117609	DEV	Torquay
1881	1885	1860	1992	117609	MDX	Westminster
....	1770	ALL	1700	134511	NTT	Arnold
1730	1757	1600	1730	152196	WES	Lambrigg
GERRARD						
....	....	1450	1630	154873	BKM	???
1850	1870	1800	1890	102164	DBY	Doveridge
1743	1852	....	....	137480	DOR	Chideock
1870	1992	ALL	1870	130575	LAN	St Helens
1800	1900	....	....	171824	LAN	St Helens
....	....	1450	1630	154873	LAN	???
....	....	1450	1630	154873	MDX	???
1815	1900	....	....	132756	STS	Potteries
1900	1930	1600	1900	171255	STS	Uttoxeter
1500	1900	1500	1900	170216	WIL	ALL
GERRETT						
1821	....	1820	1860	142638	WIL	Horningsham
GERRIE						
1845	1866	1700	1845	106887	ABD	Monquhitter
GERRY						
1827	1992	ALL	ALL	108979	ENG	North
GERSHAM						
....	....	ALL	ALL	131253	DEV	Tavistock
GERVES						
1814	....	?	1820	164976	DBY	Stanton
GEST						
1758	1869	1720	1758	136581	WAR	Warwick
GETHIN						
1766	1850	1600	1766	167649	MGY	Tregynon
1840	1880	....	....	138150	PER	Perth
1400	....	1400	....	108294	SAL	Brompton
1400	....	1400	....	108294	SAL	Churchstoke
GETHING						
1740	1850	1740	1860	159743	BRE	Ystradgynlais
1812	....	ALL	1812	139459	SAL	Donington
GETTINGS						
1900	1992	1850	1900	113050	HRT	Aldenham
1877	1900	1850	1877	113050	MDX	Bow
1540	1811	1540	1811	133922	WIL	Urchfont
GETTY						
ALL	ALL	ALL	ALL	124206	IRL	ALL
GHENT						
1737	....	....	....	117196	CHS	Prestbury
1730	1780	ALL	1730	157899	NTT	Sutton In Ashfield
GHEST						
1726	1775	....	....	121835	LIN	Navenby
GIBB						
ALL	ALL	ALL	ALL	126896	ANS	Aberlemno
ALL	ALL	ALL	ALL	126896	ANS	Fofar
ALL	ALL	ALL	ALL	126896	ANS	Guthrie
1808	1869	1750	1808	179116	AYR	Old Cummock
1870	1934	1700	1870	117463	DUR	ALL
GIBBARD						
1720	1749	....	1720	136212	OXF	Bloxham
GIBBENS						
1778	1855	ALL	1778	125121	KEN	Garlinge
1750	1830	1740	1840	120995	SOM	Nunney
GIBBINGS						
1770	1900	1770	1900	110361	DEV	Tavistock
GIBBINS						
1815	1835	1750	1815	132640	LND	Bethnal Green
1740	1740	ALL	1740	115126	OXF	Banbury
1800	1880	1600	1900	120677	SSX	Stoughton
1833	1841	1750	1833	168033	YKS	York
GIBBON						
1600	1820	....	....	102741	DUR	Hamsterley
1820	1880	1750	1992	123536	DUR	Shildon
1730	1860	1700	1900	123536	DUR	St Andrew Auckland
1800	1900	1700	1800	129135	PEM	Llandissilio
GIBBONS						
1865	1992	1865	1992	100242	BKM	Uxbridge
1710	1785	....	....	119458	BRK	Bray
1875	1895	1700	1875	120529	BRK	Cookham
1890	1890	1800	1890	146110	CHS	Lymn
1538	1850	1538	1850	126942	DBY	Rowsley
1847	1849	1814	1849	126942	ESS	Romford

Known From	To	Researching From	To	Ref	Cty	Place
GIBBONS contd.						
1722	1865	1700	1722	100242	HAM	Basingstoke
....	....	1690	1722	100242	HAM	???
1862	1992	....	1862	176532	HMC	???
1800	1843	ALL	1800	163945	KEN	Brenchley
1838	1992	1780	1838	126942	LAN	Manchester
1530	1880	1750	1900	122602	LIN	North Kelsey
1831	....	....	....	118931	LIN	Pickworth
....	....	1700	1870	130931	MAY	Crossmolina
1865	1992	1865	1992	100242	MDX	Heston
1850	1950	1750	1900	112704	MDX	Heston
1865	1992	1865	1992	100242	MDX	Hillingdon
1815	1846	....	....	152870	MDX	Poplar
1849	1890	1800	1875	149446	OXF	King Sutton
1798	1824	1798	1824	139971	OXF	Oxford
1862	1992	....	1862	176532	SRY	???
1532	1700	1500	1700	102830	STS	Sedgely
1800	1920	1700	1800	100978	STS	Wolverhampton
1770	....	1750	1800	133957	SXW	Boxgrove
1871	1881	1871	1881	118931	WAR	Coventry
1917	1945	ALL	1917	126934	WLS	Gilfach-Goch
1899	1992	....	....	137952	???	Coventry
GIBBS						
1700	1992	1500	1700	126969	DOR	West
?	?	?	?	177938	DOR	Beaminster
1787	1831	1600	1850	130125	DOR	Tyneham
1730	1950	1600	1730	173169	GLS	South
1850	....	1800	1900	118877	GLS	Turkdean
1790	1830	1750	1800	136840	HAM	Fordingbridge
1815	1847	1780	1815	104124	HRT	Rickmansworth
1700	....	ALL	1700	179515	KEN	Ashford
1861	1992	1800	1992	117293	KEN	Woolwich
?	?	?	?	166642	KEN	???
1900	1960	ALL	ALL	100137	LEI	ALL
?	....	?	....	104337	MDX	Mile End Old Town
1854	1856	1830	1870	144797	MDX	Shorteditch
1861	1881	....	1992	126950	MDX	Southwark
1750	1992	1600	1750	128848	NFK	Guestwick
1750	1992	1600	1750	128848	NFK	Hickling
1648	1752	1630	1760	142018	SOM	Catle Cary
1860	....	1700	1860	130389	SOM	Wiveliscombe
1745	1800	1700	1850	177938	SOM	Yeovil
1800	1900	ALL	ALL	151998	SRY	Kennington
1837	1851	1837	1900	113743	SSX	Rye
1820	1950	1780	1992	176982	STS	Bentley Hay
1892	1985	1800	1900	132470	WAR	Birmingham
1821	1890	....	....	149527	WAR	Claverdon
1880	1900	....	....	125938	WAR	Coventry
1827	....	1600	1827	118877	WAR	Long Compton
1830	1920	....	....	149527	WAR	Stratford Upon Avon
1780	1857	1748	1780	149527	WAR	Wolverton
1750	1850	1500	1750	118907	WOR	South East
1764	....	....	....	151351	WOR	Evesham
GIBLETT						
1830	1992	ALL	1830	115177	SRY	Mortlake
GIBSON						
1750	1840	1700	1850	154881	ALL	ALL
1863	1863	1750	1900	112089	ABD	???
1730	1800	ALL	1730	143820	ANS	Farnell
1750	1840	1700	1850	154881	ANT	ALL
1860	1871	1864	1950	159379	ARL	Oban
1826	1827	....	....	127140	AYR	Kilmarnock
....	1850	....	1850	161888	BKM	Woburn
1775	1992	ALL	ALL	127000	CAI	Canisbay
1673	1940	....	....	128996	CAM	Thornley
1808	1845	1600	1808	116637	CUL	Croglin
1774	1841	1600	1774	116637	CUL	Cumrew
1824	1825	1800	1850	105120	DEN	Allington Gresford
1852	1956	ALL	1992	174157	DUB	Dublin
1830	....	1800	1830	152110	DUR	Staindrop
1810	....	ALL	ALL	119504	DUR	Stanhope
1800	....	....	....	100633	DUR	???
1870	1900	ALL	ALL	107352	EYK	Great Driffield
1790	1850	1700	1900	130915	FIF	St Andrews
....	....	1826	1851	161667	HAM	Bighton
1805	....	....	....	127140	IRL	???
?	?	?	?	178144	KEN	Maidstone
1750	1840	1700	1850	154881	LAN	ALL
1715	1765	1542	1715	141291	LAN	Aldingham
....	....	1800	1900	146110	LAN	Bolton
1724	1751	1565	1724	141291	LAN	Dalton In Furnes
1583	1797	ALL	ALL	141615	LAN	Priest Hutton
1738	1740	ALL	ALL	141615	LEI	Chadwell
1750	1900	ALL	1750	157899	LEI	Hose
GIBSON contd.						
1750	1900	ALL	1750	157899	LEI	Redmile
1743	1804	1700	1743	174211	LIN	Waddington
1720	....	....	....	126993	LKS	Biggar
1830	1882	....	....	127140	LKS	Glasgow
1777	1777	....	....	121355	LND	Bethnal Green
1830	1899	1899	1914	161888	LND	Harrow
1860	....	1700	1992	160377	MDX	London
....	....	1750	1860	117471	MLN	Edinburgh
1866	....	....	....	152099	MLN	Edinburgh
1870	1950	1700	1870	179329	NBL	Hexham
....	1849	1800	1850	148288	NBL	Newcastle On Tyne
1786	1811	1750	1786	147745	NBL	Wooler
1800	1820	1700	1850	162620	NBL	???
1870	1900	1700	1880	179574	NIR	Belfast
1741	1989	1700	1741	122467	NTH	Denton
1890	1992	1800	1890	145629	NTT	Lenton
1831	1865	....	....	138827	NTT	Nottingham
1820	1846	1820	....	156019	NTT	Nottingham
1720	....	1600	1720	169862	NYK	Flyingdales
1760	1992	ALL	ALL	107352	NYK	Malton
1814	1930	1790	1900	129194	OXF	Steeple Barton
1690	1830	1690	1800	116831	PER	Aberuthven
1860	1871	1864	1950	159379	PER	Perth
1840	1920	1800	1992	177024	RFW	Glasgow
1782	1951	ALL	1782	108537	RFW	Neilston
1785	1805	1750	1850	177024	RFW	Paisley
1860	1870	1700	1870	126977	SCT	South West
....	....	1863	1992	126977	SCT	Govan
1835	1843	ALL	ALL	113743	SSX	Rye
1820	1992	1700	1820	115096	STS	Newton Solney
1848	1920	1700	1848	105562	WAR	Coventry
1770	1800	....	....	100420	WAR	Meriden
1848	1920	1700	1848	105562	WAR	Rugby
1850	1960	ALL	ALL	162469	WIL	South
1890	1992	ALL	ALL	107352	WYK	East Ardsley
1869	1889	1860	1920	121150	YKS	Barnsley
....	....	1710	1750	177393	YKS	Darrington
1819	1843	1815	1845	108510	YKS	Duffield
1920	....	....	1920	126985	YKS	Huddersfield
1870	1910	1870	1910	146145	YKS	Hull
1830	1870	1750	1830	129534	YKS	Humberside
1843	1851	1815	1845	108510	YKS	Leeds
1823	1903	ALL	ALL	103837	YKS	Lund
1840	1870	ALL	ALL	146145	YKS	Patrington
1852	1956	ALL	1992	174157	???	Liverpool
GICHARD						
1562	1992	1035	1992	127019	CON	St Austell
GIDDENCE						
1752	1822	....	....	115606	WIL	Mildenhall
GIDDENS						
1760	1823	1566	1760	108839	CAM	Sutton
1794	1814	1700	1800	168920	ESS	Low Leyton
1780	1900	1650	1780	166804	WIL	Avebury
GIDDINGS						
1760	1815	....	....	148156	CAM	Gamlingay
1792	....	1792	....	148156	CAM	Litlington
1850	1929	1700	1929	157023	CAM	St Ives
1550	1992	1550	1992	127027	ENG	ALL
1750	1820	ALL	1820	151319	LIN	Tydd
1587	1777	1550	1700	102830	NTH	Woodnewton
1550	1992	1550	1992	127027	WIL	Devizes
1538	....	ALL	ALL	116394	WIL	Urchfont
1540	1811	1540	1811	133922	WIL	Urchfont
1825	1861	1750	1825	112747	WIL	Urchford
GIDDINGS-PYLE						
1803	1890	1803	1890	133922	WIL	Nomansland
GIDDINS						
1700	1900	1800	1900	127027	HRT	ALL
....	....	....	1900	137405	HRT	South
....	....	....	1900	137405	MDX	North
1780	1900	1650	1780	166804	WIL	Avebury
GIDDY						
1634	1743	1598	1760	126780	CON	Liskeard
1598	1635	1598	1673	126780	CON	St Cleer
1538	1726	1538	1765	126780	CON	Stoke Climsland
GIDGEON						
1797	....	....	....	148156	NTH	Pattishall
GIDLEY						
1600	1837	1550	1837	140392	DEV	Dean Prior
1800	1853	1700	1992	117609	DEV	Kingskerswell
1787	....	1750	1790	175684	LND	City
1830	1920	....	....	173444	MDX	London
....	....	1790	1815	173444	SRY	Bermondsey

Known From	To	Researching From	To	Ref	Cty	Place
GIDLOW						
1750	....	1750	1992	127035	LAN	Wigan
GIDMAN						
1780	1850	1780	1890	117145	CHS	Astbury
1850	1992	1600	1900	132306	LAN	Liverpool
GIFFORD						
....	....	1700	1790	103713	CAM	Waterbeach
....	....	1800	1840	163694	DEV	Broad Clyst
1856	1860	1850	1860	128449	KEN	Ashford
1850	1860	1800	1860	161292	SOM	Yeovil
GIGG						
1832	1860	1790	1832	149004	DEV	Membury
GIGGINS						
1812	1880	1590	1850	127043	ESS	ALL
1880	1980	....	....	127043	LND	North
GILBARD						
1700	1920	1750	1992	133450	DEV	Stoke Dameral
GILBERT						
1880	1992	....	....	127078	BKM	Amersham
1880	1923	1700	1880	149861	BRK	Windsor
1605	1992	....	1605	151874	CAM	Burwell
....	....	....	1992	127086	CON	South East
1819	1824	1800	1819	128368	CON	Gulval
1840	1900	1800	1840	132942	CON	Illogan
1626	1992	1626	1992	127124	CON	Mullion
1806	1939	1700	1806	139815	DEV	Holworthy
....	....	....	....	127086	DEV	Tavistock
1802	1814	....	....	151351	DOR	Abbotsbury
1800	1820	....	....	151351	DOR	Frampton
1798	....	....	....	151351	DOR	Maiden Newton
1607	1776	1776	ALL	122106	DOR	Portland
....	....	1700	....	141216	GLS	North
1740	1790	1500	1800	175463	HAM	ALL
1800	1850	1750	1820	115681	HAM	Froyle
1681	1992	1600	1681	127116	HAM	Shipton Bellinger
?	?	?	?	109975	HAM	Titchfield
....	....	1750	1992	108502	HUN	Abbotsley
1800	1851	1800	1856	135828	HUN	Abbotsley
1691	1830	ALL	1691	168602	HUN	Abbotsley
1850	1870	1850	1870	126594	IRL	Dublin
1850	1880	....	....	121185	KEN	ALL
....	....	1750	1810	130184	KEN	Ashford
1850	1875	ALL	1850	165263	KEN	Cranbrook
1770	1890	ALL	1890	127094	KEN	Deptford
1742	1783	....	1800	171441	KEN	Milstead
1800	1850	1700	1800	103446	KEN	Tenterden
1854	1930	....	....	121142	LAN	Liverpool
1754	1778	....	....	121835	LIN	Salmonby
1839	1900	1750	1839	130990	MON	Monmouth
1768	1780	1700	1800	162280	SCT	Moray
1842	1992	1800	1842	151874	SFK	Tannington
1858	1877	1800	1900	127051	SOM	Baltonsborough
1800	1860	1750	1870	127051	SOM	Butleigh
1760	1800	1700	1860	127051	SOM	High Ham
1840	1850	1800	1840	121509	SRY	Camberwell
1810	1841	1750	1810	130214	SRY	Wandsworth
1800	1970	1700	1800	142328	SSX	Beckley
....	....	1750	1810	129356	SSX	Heathfield
1794	1899	1700	1794	119512	SSX	Rotherfield
1810	1850	?	1900	131865	STS	Lichfield
1698	....	1698	....	124842	STS	Tixall
1818	....	1818	1900	115142	WAR	Polesworth
....	....	1700	1899	115975	WIL	East
1700	1850	1700	1850	110361	WIL	Great Bedwyn
1700	1780	1680	1800	127051	WIL	Hindon
GILBERTS						
1620	1722	1600	1750	160873	STS	Kingswinford
GILBERTSON						
1750	1965	....	....	137820	SHI	Fetlar
1720	1965	....	....	137820	SHI	Mid Yell
1760	1965	....	....	137820	SHI	North Yell
1758	1965	....	....	137820	SHI	Northmavine
1720	1965	....	....	137820	SHI	South Yell
GILBEY						
1890	....	....	....	152420	ESS	Loughton
1875	....	1875	....	127647	HRT	Benington
1789	1821	1700	1789	178608	HRT	Reed
1875	....	1875	....	127647	HRT	Ware
GILBODY						
1740	1760	1650	1992	167592	LAN	Liverpool
GILBY						
1784	1940	....	....	128996	CAM	Thornley
1787	1817	1700	1787	150150	RUT	Lyddington
GILCHRIST						
1814	1834	ALL	ALL	129933	ARL	Campbeltown
1870	1900	1865	1960	121320	HAM	South
1780	1800	1700	1850	149098	LTN	Inveresk
1818	1992	1700	1818	127132	MLN	Edinburgh
GILDEA						
1693	1886	....	....	131229	MAY	Ballinrobe
1870	1890	1750	1992	167592	STS	Burslem
GILDEN						
1840	1880	1700	1880	177717	DEV	Torquay
GILDER						
1686	1992	1537	1686	165298	ESS	Dunmow
1804	1900	1770	1900	127159	LIN	Holbeach
GILDERDALE						
1817	1835	ALL	1840	113611	EYK	Hull
GILDERSLEEVE						
1789	1849	ALL	1851	156175	SFK	Stutton
GILDERSLEEVES						
1800	1890	ALL	ALL	111155	SFK	Leiston
1800	1890	ALL	ALL	111155	SFK	Saxmundham
GILDING						
....	....	ALL	ALL	127175	CAM	ALL
1530	1992	ALL	ALL	127175	NFK	ALL
1732	1992	ALL	1732	127167	NFK	Sporle
1797	1827	?	1830	164976	NTT	West Bridgeford
....	....	ALL	ALL	127175	SFK	ALL
GILDON						
1810	1810	1750	1850	167002	LIN	Spilsby
1879	1992	ALL	ALL	112240	YKS	Middlesbrough
GILES						
1857	1928	1850	1940	125032	BRK	Bracknell
1720	1877	1700	1900	125032	BRK	Sandhurst
1827	1880	1780	1880	102970	BRK	Speen
1820	1836	1820	1900	125032	BRK	Wokingham
1886	1992	....	....	134856	CHS	Chester
....	1876	ALL	1876	114030	CON	ALL
1910	1958	1910	1992	121932	CON	Camelford
....	....	1750	1770	138339	CON	St Blazey
1910	1958	1910	1992	121932	CON	St Teath
1726	1992	1650	1726	177091	DEV	Modbury
1830	1870	1800	1830	143332	DEV	Plymouth
1830	1845	1800	1850	176982	DEV	Plymouth
1780	1850	1775	1992	133450	DEV	Stoke Dameral
1700	1799	1700	1799	169781	GLS	Bristol
1775	1900	1775	1900	164704`	HAM	Alresford
1799	1836	1750	1850	125032	HAM	Yateley
1879	1904	ALL	ALL	165085	HRT	Hoddesdon
1678	1884	ALL	1842	137774	KEN	South East
1800	1837	1800	1837	144355	KEN	South
1863	....	....	....	132616	KEN	Dover
1750	1800	1600	1850	166804	KEN	Yalding
?	?	?	?	166642	KEN	???
....	....	1800	1840	134856	LND	Marylebone
1860	1870	1700	1900	140171	LND	St Pancras
1786	1885	ALL	ALL	118168	MDX	London
1880	1992	1800	1992	152609	NBL	Blyth
1880	1992	1800	1992	152609	NBL	Easdon
1870	1992	1800	1992	117293	NBL	Newcastle
1880	1992	1800	1992	152609	NBL	S Neasham
....	....	1750	1900	111503	SAL	Pontesbury
1832	1936	....	....	134856	SAL	Shrewsbury
1886	....	....	....	132616	SRY	Southwark
1700	1820	1700	1850	171522	SSX	Hastings
1790	1861	1760	1861	169323	STS	Darlaston
1803	1853	1750	1810	103896	WIL	Froxfield
1824	1825	1800	1850	105120	WIL	Overton
1732	1766	1700	1732	127116	WIL	Preshute
1870	1920	1700	1870	126772	WIL	Warminster
1873	1873	1871	1873	108901	WOR	Old Swinford
1817	1849	ALL	1817	154946	YKS	Huddersfield
GILFOYLE						
....	....	1700	1837	151254	IRL	Wicklow
GILGRAVES						
?	?	....	....	154113	BRK	Wokingham
GILHAM						
1819	....	1700	1819	123307	BRK	Kintbury
1680	1820	ALL	ALL	175943	CAM	Cambridge
1750	1850	1850	1992	139203	KEN	Aldington
....	....	ALL	ALL	172413	SRY	Horsell
GILHESPEY						
1843	1851	?	1843	115169	DUR	Durham
GILKES						
1746	1811	1500	1811	169439	OXF	Adderbury

Known From	To	Researching From	To	Ref	Cty	Place
GILKS						
1873	....	....	....	132381	STS	Wolverhampton
GILL						
....	....	ALL	ALL	111430	ALL	Name Study
1803	1826	ALL	1803	168602	CAM	Littleport
1830	1871	ALL	1871	159077	CAM	Whittlesey
1790	1992	1500	1900	129925	CAM	???
1832	1851	ALL	1850	133159	CMA	Ulpha
1685	1992	....	....	127221	CON	North
1685	1992	....	....	127221	CON	Advent
....	....	1700	1992	109193	CON	Egloshayle
....	....	1700	1850	160997	CON	Egloshayle
1740	1746	1740	1746	141690	CON	Falmouth
1750	1800	1600	1800	146730	CON	Passim
....	....	....	....	127221	DEV	ALL
1880	1992	1800	1880	173770	DEV	South
?	?	?	?	156671	DEV	Kings Nympton
1737	?	1600	1737	126357	DEV	Tavistock
1753	1992	1600	1753	130966	DOR	Abbotsbury
1841	1902	1808	1856	125903	DOR	Wimborn
1847	1900	1750	1846	106607	DUB	ALL
1800	1992	1700	1992	127264	DUB	Dublin
1786	1858	1750	1786	115819	ESS	Colchester
1850	1871	1830	1900	113719	GLS	Bristol
1711	1830	1650	1710	112569	GLS	Stroud
....	....	....	....	127272	IRL	Shinrone
1820	1850	1810	1900	171522	KEN	Maidstone
1840	1845	1800	1850	170852	LAN	Ashton Under Lyne
1798	1832	ALL	1830	133159	LAN	Bardsea
1840	1992	ALL	1850	113476	LAN	Colne
1850	1952	1850	1992	133159	LAN	Liverpool
1896	1899	....	....	151351	LAN	Liverpool
1831	1950	1700	1831	165182	LAN	Tatham
1839	....	....	....	142859	LAN	Warrington
1851	1887	ALL	ALL	151777	LND	Bethnal Green
1874	....	1870	1880	163775	MDX	Bethnal Green
....	....	1870	1890	112569	MDX	Enfield
1908	1920	....	....	151351	MDX	Hampstead
1773	1773	1750	1800	167002	MDX	Shoreditch
....	....	ALL	ALL	135968	NTH	Northampton
?	?	1700	1800	120650	NTT	North
1790	1992	1500	1900	129925	SFK	???
1746	1849	ALL	ALL	153516	SOM	Banwell
1746	1849	ALL	ALL	153516	SOM	Kewstoke
1891	1941	1800	1900	115746	SOM	North Petherton
1867	1900	1800	1867	117633	SRY	Croydon
1793	1793	1750	1800	167002	SRY	Southwark
1750	1850	1600	1750	142328	SSX	Beckley
1623	1625	1600	1650	105120	SSX	Brighton
1700	1800	1600	1810	171522	SSX	East Dean
1784	1848	1770	1890	171522	SSX	Hastings
1800	1829	1780	1900	171522	SSX	Rye
1750	1850	1600	1750	142328	SSX	Udimore
1731	1775	1500	1730	127248	STS	Kingswinford
1644	1699	1600	1720	160873	STS	Kingswinford
1865	1992	1865	1992	127248	STS	Wolverhampton
....	....	ALL	ALL	141747	WES	Kirkby Lonsdale
1778	1842	1778	1842	127248	WOR	Brierley Hill
1772	1870	1725	1800	150002	WOR	Clent
1840	1872	....	....	151351	YKS	Boston Spa
1889	1889	1500	1889	110310	YKS	Cleethorps
....	....	1800	1900	129593	YKS	Featherstone
1633	1653	1500	1992	102520	YKS	Fewston
1850	1890	1840	1900	108952	YKS	Halifax
1719	....	....	....	151351	YKS	Hampsthwaite
1788	1827	....	....	151351	YKS	Harewood
1862	1926	1700	1862	109649	YKS	Huddersfield
1889	1992	1500	1889	110310	YKS	Hull
1770	1925	1700	1770	138584	YKS	Keighley
1832	1838	....	....	151351	YKS	Keighley
1720	1771	....	....	151351	YKS	Kirkby Overblow
1747	1839	1600	1750	101575	YKS	Knottingley
1740	1806	1600	1740	116637	YKS	Long Marston
1726	1992	....	....	134619	YKS	Long Marston
1805	1805	1780	1810	108510	YKS	Mirfield
1652	1788	....	....	151351	YKS	Otley
1747	1839	1600	1750	101575	YKS	Pontefract
ALL	1780	ALL	1780	102350	YKS	Poppleton
1790	1806	....	....	151351	YKS	Saxton In Elmet
1850	1900	1750	1850	177296	YKS	Sheffield
1890	1954	1800	1992	157651	YKS	Sherburn In Elmet
....	....	?	?	115592	YKS	Wakefield
1795	1820	1760	1820	153737	YKS	Wakefield
1923	1992	1900	1992	157651	YKS	York

Known From	To	Researching From	To	Ref	Cty	Place
GILLAIT						
....	....	1790	1820	174602	LIN	Grantham
GILLAM						
1700	1750	1500	1700	174661	BRK	ALL
1906	....	ALL	1906	170666	CAM	Cambridge
1830	1890	1820	1890	127353	DOR	Haydon
1906	....	ALL	1906	170666	LND	Croydon
1782	1785	ALL	ALL	127280	MDX	London
1781	....	1700	1800	131377	NTH	Woodford
1854	1864	1854	1890	133639	SOM	Coker
1780	....	1750	1850	127353	SOM	Hardington
1785	1905	ALL	ALL	127280	SSX	Brighton
1880	1992	1870	1980	127353	WIL	Poulshot
GILLANDER						
1765	1840	1700	1765	147125	DUR	Swalwell
GILLANDERS						
1793	1810	1700	1793	118427	ABD	Glenmuick
1850	1900	1800	1900	137758	MOG	Monaghan
1880	1992	ALL	1880	142263	ROC	Dingwall
GILLARD						
....	....	ALL	ALL	127302	ALL	Name Study
....	....	ALL	ALL	127302	ALL	ALL
1800	1900	1700	1800	146374	DEV	Southpool
1850	1910	1800	1850	161292	SOM	Bristol
1810	1840	1780	1840	168580	SOM	Drayton
1840	1860	1840	1860	128856	WAR	Birmingham
GILLATT						
1650	1800	....	....	129747	DBY	Bolehill
1650	1800	....	....	129747	DBY	Norton
1650	1800	....	....	129747	DBY	Woodseat
1824	1836	1824	1992	131563	LIN	Wroot
1768	1830	1700	1830	131563	NTT	Carlton Lindrick
1765	1880	1765	1992	131563	NTT	Finningley
1768	1830	1700	1830	131563	NTT	Worksop
1830	1860	1830	1992	131563	YKS	Anston
1600	1740	1500	1992	131563	YKS	Barnby Dun
1737	1800	1600	1800	131563	YKS	Harthill
1740	1880	1500	1992	131563	YKS	Hatfield
1850	1880	1850	1992	131563	YKS	Todwick
GILLBERRY						
....	....	ALL	ALL	127310	ALL	Name Study
GILLES						
1730	1770	1730	1770	106305	ARL	Kilmartin
GILLESPIE						
1840	1950	1700	1840	140260	DON	Dungloe
GILLESPY						
1811	1870	ALL	1800	112771	CUL	Stapleton
GILLETT						
....	1950	1800	1940	113174	CAM	Downham
....	1950	1800	1940	113174	CAM	Ely
....	1950	1800	1940	113174	CAM	Littleport
....	1950	1800	1940	113174	CAM	Sawston
1788	1863	1700	1788	176672	GLS	Farmington
1600	1940	1550	1970	127345	KEN	ALL
1650	1900	1550	1950	127345	KEN	Canterbury
1815	....	1815	1900	102083	LAN	Street
1859	1929	....	....	112429	LAN	Westby
1843	1843	ALL	ALL	143537	LND	ALL
....	....	ALL	1833	175331	OXF	Chipping Norton
....	....	1750	1850	101273	WIL	ALL
1866	....	ALL	ALL	125202	???	???
GILLEY						
1808	1992	1600	1808	166650	DEV	Littleham
GILLFEATHER						
1836	ALL	ALL	1836	116734	ANT	Belfast
GILLIANS						
1600	1700	1600	1700	167924	BDF	Campton
1600	1700	1600	1700	167924	BDF	Southill
GILLIAT						
1700	1980	1550	1700	173169	LIN	Horncastle
GILLIATT						
....	....	ALL	ALL	151823	ALL	Name Study
1840	1890	1550	1840	150843	LIN	North Owersby
GILLIE						
1745	1977	1600	1992	112089	BEW	???
GILLIES						
1800	1820	1750	1800	177024	INV	Skye
GILLIGAN						
1861	1890	1800	1861	175595	MAY	???
1815	ALL	ALL	1840	116734	WEM	???
GILLINGHAM						
....	....	ALL	ALL	155829	ALL	Name Study
....	....	ALL	1755	104310	DOR	Beaminster
....	....	1600	1992	137588	DOR	Cerne Abbas

Known From	To	Researching From	To	Ref	Cty	Place
GILLINGHAM contd.						
1900	1992	....	....	153397	DOR	Weymouth
1825	1900	1800	1900	170119	IOW	Mottistone
1895	1895	1870	1875	130559	SRY	Southwark
GILLINGS						
1770	1845	1550	1770	150843	SFK	Lound
GILLION						
1837	1900	ALL	1992	127361	WRY	Pontefract
GILLIOTT						
....	....	1700	1800	178411	NTT	Newark
GILLIVER						
1750	1992	1600	1750	127388	LEI	Ashby
1750	1992	1600	1750	127388	LEI	Sheepy
?	?	1820	1900	127388	LND	Hackney
1786	1992	1600	1786	127388	STS	Gresley
1723	1880	1600	1723	127388	WAR	Polesworth
GILLMAN						
1880	1940	1850	1940	121878	AVN	Bristol
1600	1992	1600	1992	129739	COR	ALL
1790	1860	1750	1860	121878	GLS	Avening
....	....	1830	1850	177725	SFK	Combs
1884	1910	1800	1884	107832	STS	Sheen
GILLOM						
1730	1800	ALL	1750	115266	DOR	ALL
GILLON						
1820	....	....	....	174750	SCT	Edinburgh
GILLOTT						
1766	1791	ALL	1766	169730	YKS	Eccleshall
1816	1816	1750	1816	128368	YKS	Sheffield
1798	....	1750	1820	139483	YKS	Sheffield
GILLOW						
1880	1920	1880	1920	132721	KEN	???
GILLS						
1896	1970	1800	1992	116246	DUR	Bishops Auckland
GILLSON						
1800	1881	....	1900	137405	CAM	East
GILMORE						
....	....	ALL	ALL	152048	ANT	???
1897	1949	1800	1897	159336	IRL	Careck Fergus
1885	1951	ALL	1885	107751	LAN	Liverpool
1652	ALL	....	1652	127396	NFK	Norwich
....	....	....	....	105465	SLI	Ballymote
1855	1992	ALL	1855	105465	SLI	Branchfield
....	....	1500	1730	166863	SOM	ALL
GILMOUR						
1805	1944	ALL	1800	146757	AYR	Kilmarnock
1805	1944	ALL	1800	146757	AYR	Muirkirk
1851	1881	1820	1900	110426	LKS	Langloan
1881	1992	....	....	128643	OKI	ALL
1783	1992	1783	1992	127418	RFW	Eaglesham
1783	1992	1783	1992	127418	RFW	East Kilbride
GILMUIR						
1800	1830	....	....	126497	CAI	Wick
GILMURRAY						
1897	1962	ALL	ALL	150681	FER	Belcoo
GILPIN						
....	....	1700	1830	156140	LEI	Leicester
....	1700	....	....	174564	SSX	???
1833	1881	1800	1833	156140	STS	Wednesbury
1900	1931	1800	1950	122203	WAR	Birmingham
1798	1849	1700	1798	152196	WES	Kendal
1820	1865	1750	1850	103055	WYK	Leeds
1200	1850	....	....	100536	???	???
GILROY						
1984	1984	....	....	127426	DEV	Plymouth
1978	1981	....	....	127426	HRT	St Albans
1968	1974	....	....	127426	LND	St Pancras
1880	1921	....	....	127434	MLN	Edinburgh
1914	1958	....	....	127426	MON	Crosskeys
1909	1909	....	....	127426	MON	Risca
1826	1880	....	1826	127434	NBL	Ford
1921	1992	....	....	127434	ROX	Darnick
1921	1992	....	....	127434	ROX	Melrose
1939	1939	....	....	127426	WAR	Birmingham
1942	1942	....	....	127426	WAR	Handsworth
GILSON						
1830	1905	1750	1830	132640	SFK	Ipswich
GILSTON						
....	....	ALL	ALL	113115	ALL	Name Study
GILTRAP						
1834	1992	1834	....	158011	WIC	Holywood
GIMBERT						
....	....	ALL	ALL	127450	ALL	Name Study
1701	1783	1566	1701	108839	CAM	Sutton

Known From	To	Researching From	To	Ref	Cty	Place
GIMBLETT						
1720	1939	1900	1992	121932	CON	Launceston
1720	1939	1900	1992	121932	CON	North Petherwin
1720	1939	1900	1992	121932	CON	Trenglos
1865	1925	1800	1925	106186	DEV	Holsworthy
GIMLETT						
1751	1800	1600	1751	149888	CON	Landrake
GIMSON						
1793	....	1600	1800	110787	LEI	Cosby
GINDLER						
1800	....	....	....	170313	HAM	Kingsclere
GINGELL						
1700	1900	1600	1992	154342	GLS	Bitton
1800	1992	1600	1800	127469	GLS	Bristol
1700	1750	1600	1750	154342	GLS	Mangotsfield
1822	1822	1750	1822	118192	GLS	Nympsfield
1700	1900	1600	1992	154342	GLS	Oldland
1859	1992	1759	1859	177490	LND	Notting Hill
1800	1992	1600	1800	127469	SOM	Bristol
GINGER						
1800	1960	1750	1850	101664	BDF	ALL
1600	1750	1500	1800	177180	BKM	Wing
GINMAN						
1870	1965	....	....	137030	SSX	Hunston
GINN						
1653	1900	1900	1992	127477	CAM	Kirtling
1780	1840	1750	1992	122416	DON	???
1780	1840	1750	1992	122416	FER	???
1790	....	1780	1818	148121	MDX	Edmonton
1788	1796	1750	1815	148121	MDX	Tottenham
1788	1815	1700	1815	148121	MDX	???
GINNIFF						
1846	1992	1750	1880	103462	DOW	Banbridge
GINSBERG						
1900	1920	....	....	148989	LND	East
GIPPS						
1755	1853	1700	1755	114871	SFK	Kedington
GIRDLER						
1724	1800	1700	1750	108510	BRK	Hurst
1800	....	....	....	170313	HAM	Kingsclere
GIRDLESTONE						
....	....	ALL	ALL	127485	ALL	Name Study
?	1940	....	....	128996	CAM	Thornley
1780	1992	....	....	146870	NFK	Holt
1935	1992	ALL	ALL	127493	SFK	Felixstowe
GIRDWOOD						
1798	1798	1600	1850	130125	KKD	Terregles
1844	1870	1870	1992	146560	LKS	Coatbride
GIRLING						
1780	1800	1700	1900	135496	NFK	Norwich
1850	1920	1800	1920	148377	SFK	Ipswich
1840	1900	1750	1840	138010	SFK	???
GIRVAN						
....	....	ALL	ALL	127507	ALL	Name Study
1732	1900	1600	1732	127507	ANT	Carnmoney
1824	1900	1700	1824	105562	AYR	ALL
1775	1845	ALL	ALL	146757	AYR	Kirkoswald
1824	1900	1700	1824	105562	SCT	Glasgow
GISBORNE						
1770	1830	1700	1770	140309	WOR	Bretforton
GITSOM						
1832	1919	....	....	125407	AVN	Bristol
GITTENS						
1854	1992	....	....	107158	MDX	Shoreditch
GITTINS						
1861	1992	1861	1992	133442	CHS	Birkenhead
1860	1860	....	....	113050	IRL	???
1802	1830	ALL	1830	134058	SAL	Oswestry
1785	1835	1750	1785	113050	SAL	Pentre Coed
1802	1830	ALL	1830	134058	SAL	Welshampton
1850	1860	1800	1850	133442	SAL	Wem
1839	1950	1750	1839	127523	WAR	Birmingham
1820	1920	1790	1820	162361	WAR	Birmingham
GITTUS						
....	....	ALL	ALL	127531	WAR	ALL
1800	1992	....	....	127531	WOR	ALL
1797	1940	1536	1963	127531	WOR	Crowle
GIVEN						
1850	....	ALL	ALL	130508	FIF	Elie
GIVENS						
1795	1854	1750	....	156191	NBL	Berwick On Tweed
GLACEY						
1785	1793	1700	1800	125032	BRK	Reading
1829	1846	1700	1850	125032	BRK	Sonning

Known From	To	Researching From	To	Ref	Cty	Place
GLACEY contd.						
1788	1831	1700	1850	125032	BRK	Wokingham
1801	1853	1700	1860	125032	HAM	Eversley
GLADDEN						
1650	1850	1600	1650	135879	NFK	Marsham
GLADDERS						
1620	1992	1500	1620	167967	DUR	???
GLADDES						
1856	1986	1750	1860	118516	HAM	South Hants
GLADDIS						
1750	1750	1720	1800	166677	IOW	ALL
GLADDLE						
1846	1853	1800	1850	162272	LND	St Pancras
GLADSTONE						
ALL	....	ALL	....	168599	KEN	Erith
1826	1858	1700	1825	131245	MDX	Poplar
GLADWELL						
1884	1992	1700	1884	113166	KEN	???
1800	1900	1650	1800	168653	SFK	ALL
1739	1880	ALL	1891	156175	SFK	Haughley
1739	1880	ALL	1891	156175	SFK	Shotley
GLADWIN						
....	....	1870	1890	133221	LND	Fulham
1803	1884	1700	1884	150150	WAR	Welford On Avon
GLADWISH						
1279	1992	....	....	127558	ALL	ALL
1279	1992	....	....	127558	SSX	ALL
GLAISTER						
....	....	1800	1899	171794	CUL	Holme Cultram
GLANAN						
....	1846	....	....	140767	IRL	???
1876	....	1876	1881	140767	YKS	Leeds
GLANCEY						
1770	1830	1750	1900	152528	GLS	Bitton
1776	1837	....	....	165999	GLS	Bitton
1770	1830	1750	1900	152528	GLS	Siston
GLANDER						
....	....	ALL	ALL	112801	ALL	Name Study
GLANFALE						
1550	1650	1500	1550	132942	CON	St Gluvias
GLANFIELD						
1846	1900	1900	1992	167533	NFK	Yarmouth
1800	1840	1800	1992	135429	OXF	Cuddesdon
1650	1790	1769	1790	111422	SFK	Ipswich
1650	1790	1769	1790	111422	SFK	Melton
GLANISTER						
....	....	1700	1900	117587	NTH	???
GLANLEY						
....	....	ALL	ALL	127884	WLS	ALL
GLANVILL						
1779	1853	1700	1779	107654	DEV	Plymouth
GLANVILLE						
....	1791	1700	1791	104310	CON	Bodmin
1800	1900	ALL	1800	141704	CON	Camborn
....	....	ALL	ALL	147915	CON	Rame Peninsula
1700	1980	....	....	145939	CON	St Newlyn
1857	1880	1820	1900	165034	DEV	Devonport
1815	1880	1700	1880	166650	DEV	Plymouth
1883	1961	1700	1883	115894	MDX	London
GLASBY						
1830	1850	1700	1850	132659	NTT	Finningley
GLASCOCK						
....	....	ALL	ALL	117102	ALL	Name Study
GLASCOTT						
1837	1850	1700	1837	126349	WAR	Coventry
GLASGOW						
1815	1850	1750	1850	103756	ANT	Ballymena
1813	....	1800	1830	163775	MDX	Clerkenwell
1713	1992	1650	1992	176621	TYR	Cookstown
GLASIER						
1588	1890	1533	1900	170291	LIN	Kesteven
GLASPOOL						
....	....	ALL	1800	173614	HAM	South
1670	1800	ALL	1800	173614	HAM	Southwick
GLASS						
1815	1900	1700	1900	103403	ABD	Aberdeen
....	....	1840	ALL	149187	ANS	Dundee
1806	1814	1770	1850	109142	ANS	Forfar
1800	1900	ALL	ALL	122866	BRK	South
....	....	ALL	1791	119326	ELN	Tranent
1863	1876	1876	1992	146560	FIF	Dollar
1800	1900	ALL	ALL	122866	HAM	North West
1769	....	....	1769	117234	IRL	Down
1815	1822	1815	1850	109142	LKS	Glasgow
GLASS contd.						
1830	1869	1800	1890	153257	LND	Lambeth
....	....	1750	ALL	149187	MOR	Duffies
1855	1983	1750	1855	143472	PER	Perth
1890	1900	1890	1900	153052	WIL	Ashton Keynes
GLASSON						
....	....	ALL	ALL	115959	ALL	Name Study
1500	1992	1500	1992	115959	CON	ALL
....	....	1700	1900	135968	CON	ALL
1875	1900	1700	1992	140287	CON	Lelant
1749	1896	1650	1749	127590	CON	Madron
1875	1900	1700	1992	140287	CON	Twoednack
1815	1992	1700	1815	161446	CON	???
GLASSPOOL						
1779	1959	1779	1959	173762	HAM	Owslebury
GLASSPOOLE						
1830	1853	ALL	1830	159204	NFK	Norwich
GLASTONBURY						
1810	1850	1538	1810	154792	GLS	Cotswolds
GLAVE						
1843	1843	1750	1860	146609	YKS	Rotherham
GLAYSHER						
1790	1890	....	....	128759	HAM	Headley
GLAZE						
....	....	ALL	ALL	174033	WAR	Birmingham
GLAZEBROOK						
1746	....	ALL	ALL	151580	HRT	St Amwell
?	?	?	?	120073	SSX	Shoreham
GLAZIER						
1800	1860	....	....	140317	SFK	Bury St Edmunds
1900	1992	1900	1992	124613	SSX	Guestling
GLAZIER-BUSS						
1895	....	1800	1920	153036	SSX	Battle
GLAZING						
1794	1815	1700	1850	126586	SFK	Clare
GLEADHILL						
1590	1647	1590	1647	128449	YKS	Hartshead
GLEADLE						
1647	1700	1590	1700	128449	YKS	Hartshead
GLEDHILL						
1835	1847	ALL	1860	113611	EYK	Hull
1800	1899	....	....	144029	LAN	Birstall
1800	1899	....	....	144029	LAN	Dewsbury
1800	1847	ALL	1850	113611	LIN	Winteringham
1796	1840	1766	1796	139149	WRY	Halifax
1780	1820	1750	1850	127604	WRY	Stainland
1760	1870	1700	1760	110027	YKS	Barkisland
1736	1907	1680	1920	118974	YKS	Batley
1907	1932	1700	1907	109649	YKS	Halifax
1620	1669	1590	1670	128449	YKS	Hartshead
1780	1850	1700	1800	110345	YKS	Huddersfield
1800	1850	1750	1800	123595	YKS	Huddersfield
1760	1870	1700	1760	110027	YKS	Rishworth
1725	1992	1650	1725	110027	YKS	Scammonden
1820	1946	1820	1946	127604	???	Greater Manchester
GLEDSTONE						
1847	....	....	....	130923	YKS	Keighley
GLEED						
1845	1900	....	....	136824	NTT	Nottingham
1839	1900	?	1900	127612	SRY	Chelsea
1756	1820	....	....	115290	WIL	Lydiard Millicent
GLEESON						
....	....	1700	1992	132799	LAN	Manchester
GLEGHORN						
1895	1992	1870	....	106003	DUR	Hebburn
1895	1992	1870	....	106003	DUR	Jarrow
1800	1992	....	....	127124	ENG	ALL
1895	1992	1870	....	106003	NBL	North Shields
GLEIBERMAN						
ALL	ALL	ALL	ALL	138622	ALL	ALL
GLEN						
1820	1849	1790	1849	179000	DNB	Water Of Leven
1860	1992	ALL	ALL	110388	KEN	Deal
1722	1822	....	....	154849	RFW	Lochwinnoch
1800	1810	1800	1900	169404	YKS	Hull
GLENCROSS						
1720	1826	ALL	1992	100536	CON	???
GLENDENNING						
1910	1950	1867	1910	144266	NBL	Newcastle Upon Tyne
GLENDINNING						
1800	1992	1800	1992	160210	NBL	ALL
GLENFIELD						
1862	1992	ALL	1862	139378	ANT	Lisburn

Known From	To	Researching From	To	Ref	Cty	Place
GLENIE						
1810	....	1800	1815	169625	BDF	Bedford
1783	....	1750	1800	169625	SCT	Aberdeen
GLENISTER						
....	....	ALL	ALL	169625	ALL	Name Study
1550	1992	ALL	ALL	127620	ALL	ALL
1550	1899	....	....	127620	BDF	???
1800	1840	1600	1992	112828	BKM	Chesham
1790	....	ALL	ALL	169625	BKM	Wooburn
1550	1992	1730	1880	127620	BKM	???
1790	1835	1700	1900	153826	BKM	???
1835	1856	1800	1900	153826	GLS	Cheltenham
1700	1850	1700	1900	177180	HRT	Bovingdon
1816	....	1790	1820	169625	HRT	Dudswell
1816	....	1790	1820	169625	HRT	Northchurch
1550	1992	1730	1880	127620	HRT	???
GLENISTERS						
....	....	ALL	ALL	127620	ALL	Name Study
GLENN						
1790	1870	....	....	155756	NTH	Hartwell
1756	1790	1700	1756	155756	NTH	Potterspury
1871	1924	....	....	155756	NTH	Yardley Gobion
GLENNERSTER						
1790	1896	1780	1810	176419	HRT	Watford
GLENNIE						
1851	1992	1600	1851	146137	ABD	Tyrie
1811	1811	1700	1811	153605	KCD	Fetteresso
GLENWRIGHT						
1885	....	1850	1992	145041	DUR	Trimdons
1751	1931	ALL	1751	160199	NBL	Haltwhistle
GLEW						
1720	1750	1680	1720	162396	LIN	Belton
1841	1845	1841	1845	163309	LIN	Keadby
1770	1844	1500	1844	157538	LIN	Owston
1770	1844	1500	1844	157538	LIN	West Butterwick
1780	1820	....	....	140554	YKS	Wiston
GLIBBERY						
....	....	ALL	ALL	127639	ALL	Name Study
ALL	ALL	ALL	ALL	127639	ALL	ALL
GLIDDON						
1750	1992	....	1992	123447	DEV	ALL
1780	1880	....	....	141909	DEV	Cummins
GLIDE						
1840	1880	1750	1840	168351	ESS	Harwich
GLINN						
1710	1992	?	1710	147915	CON	Rame Peninsula
GLODE						
1793	1800	1800	1830	177199	LND	Marylebone
GLOSSOP						
1833	1860	1700	1833	120200	DBY	Staveley
GLOSTER						
....	....	1700	1790	118192	MDX	ALL
1850	1992	1700	1850	122114	WAR	Birmingham
GLOUGH						
1824	1963	1700	1824	167541	HRT	Watford
GLOVER						
1900	1992	ALL	ALL	150681	ANT	Crumlin
1750	1800	1750	1800	138878	CUL	Whithaven
1850	1900	1775	1850	172561	DEV	Milton Damerel
1800	1900	1700	1800	116432	DEV	Parkham
1838	1900	....	....	171492	ESS	???
1678	1900	1678	1992	127655	GLS	Stroud
1678	1900	1678	1992	127655	GLS	Tetbury
1584	1657	?	1584	113999	KEN	West
1583	1657	ALL	1583	143278	KEN	Ashford
1830	1900	1750	1830	142328	KEN	Hythe
1809	1809	1780	1992	173096	KEN	Ivychurch
....	....	1800	1900	125660	KEN	Westerham
1880	1970	1820	1880	178675	LAN	Manchester
1843	....	1800	1850	172855	LAN	St Helens
1850	1900	1750	1850	176524	LAN	St Helens
1695	1760	1690	1800	142174	LEI	North
1841	1861	1841	1871	146773	LEI	Chadwell
1799	....	....	1799	101761	LEI	Cossington
1720	1838	....	....	137618	LIN	Wispington
1828	1920	1800	1900	142875	LIN	???
1840	1900	ALL	1840	138169	LND	City
....	?	....	1901	105155	LND	St Olive
1780	1906	1600	1780	153362	NFK	New Buckenham
1660	1690	1640	1700	142174	NTT	South
1817	1900	....	....	113999	OXF	Filkins
1800	1830	1750	1800	177024	RFW	Barrhead
1620	1840	1580	1860	160849	SAL	Broseley
1853	1856	1600	1853	152080	SOM	Somerton
GLOVER contd.						
1878	1992	1700	1878	105201	SRY	Bermondsey
1657	1817	....	....	113999	SRY	???
1700	1890	1650	1900	110906	SSX	Singleton
1840	1930	1840	1992	160849	STS	Norton In The Moors
1865	1880	1865	1880	178675	WAR	Birmingham
1678	1900	1678	1992	127655	WIL	Marlborough
1750	1810	1700	1810	178675	WOR	Kidderminster
GLOYN						
1800	1900	1700	1800	156531	DEV	West
1714	1900	1650	1714	139815	DEV	Dookbury
1950	....	1700	ALL	131253	DEV	Tavistock
GLOYNE						
1793	1841	1793	1851	134880	DOR	Sherborne
1851	1872	1851	1872	134880	MDX	St Pancras
1851	1851	1800	1872	134880	SRY	Lambeth
1889	1944	1889	1952	134880	YKS	Leeds
GLOYNS						
1800	1900	1700	1800	154458	DEV	Plymouth
GLUE						
....	....	ALL	1870	138169	YKS	Bradford
GOACHER						
1750	1926	1746	1926	107166	SSX	Ashurst
GOAD						
1839	1992	1700	1839	118788	KEN	East Malling
1626	1774	1542	1626	141291	LAN	Aldingham
1755	1782	1700	1760	116173	LAN	Furness
1880	ALL	1700	1900	135127	LND	St Mary Newington
1848	1924	ALL	1848	147877	SRY	Sutton
GOAFE						
1790	....	ALL	ALL	131490	HAM	Tichfield
GOAR						
1800	1850	1750	1800	108359	HUN	Spaldwick
GOATCHER						
1750	1850	1700	1992	148784	SSX	Wasington
GOATER						
1825	1831	1700	1825	147346	HAM	St Boorne Mary
1800	1900	1750	1900	154881	LND	ALL
GOATH						
1725	1725	1670	1725	155276	SFK	Newbourn
GOATLY						
1810	1880	1750	1810	143332	LND	Westminster
GOATS						
1681	1761	1566	1681	108839	CAM	Sutton
1770	1775	1700	1770	155276	SFK	Felixstowe
GOBBY						
....	....	....	....	108480	HRT	???
....	....	....	....	108480	LND	Tower Hamlets
GOBEY						
1884	1925	ALL	ALL	168211	BDF	Luton
GOBLE						
1862	1870	ALL	1862	175080	HAM	Wymering
1879	1992	1800	1879	151793	SRY	Reigate
1827	1861	ALL	1827	175080	SSX	Funtington
1660	1872	ALL	1660	114928	SSX	???
GODBER						
....	....	ALL	ALL	127663	ALL	Name Study
1819	....	?	1820	164976	NTT	Stapleford
GODBOLD						
1900	1992	....	....	154261	ESS	Buckhurst Hill
1850	1900	....	....	154261	MDX	Battersea
1850	1900	....	....	154261	MDX	Lambeth
....	....	1200	1850	154261	SFK	Fressingfield
GODDALE						
1742	....	....	....	111856	???	Stow
GODDANEW						
1740	1992	1650	1750	160083	DEV	ALL
GODDARD						
....	....	ALL	ALL	127671	ALL	Name Study
....	....	ALL	ALL	127671	ALL	ALL
1855	1992	1800	1855	164747	BRK	Thrupp
1815	1823	1600	1823	152080	BRK	West Hendred
1740	1940	....	....	128996	CAM	Thornley
1862	1992	?	1862	153613	DBY	Glossop
1877	1915	1850	1971	136719	HAM	Amport
1839	1992	1700	1839	149241	HAM	Southampton
....	1750	1650	1750	121010	HAM	Wootton St Lawrence
1789	1871	....	....	115606	HAM	Yateley
1795	1820	ALL	1820	134503	KEN	Old Romney
1790	1875	1700	1790	170747	LEI	Bushby
?	?	?	?	147400	LEI	Humberstone
1842	1864	1800	1860	103896	LND	Shoreditch
?	?	?	?	127701	LND	???
1850	....	....	....	125199	MDX	Bethnal Green

Known From	To	Researching From	To	Ref	Cty	Place
GODDARD contd.						
1818	1890	1800	1900	172960	MDX	Hackney
1834	1980	1780	1834	107743	MDX	London
1832	1895	1700	1832	103640	MDX	Marylebone
1773	1992	ALL	1773	107239	NFK	Breckles
1773	1992	ALL	1773	107239	NFK	Stowbedon
1873	1992	1600	1875	110795	NTT	Nework On Trent
1890	1900	1850	1920	158623	NTT	Nottingham
1795	1900	1750	1950	158399	SRY	Compton
1720	1815	1700	1815	159581	SRY	Cranleigh
1805	1878	1730	1805	127698	SSX	Angmering
1878	1992	....	....	127698	SSX	Brighton
1562	1992	1654	1992	114308	WAR	Coventry
1844	1877	1820	1900	136719	WAR	Shilton
1810	1890	1700	1900	135968	WIL	Great Bedwyn
1670	1820	1670	1820	127655	WIL	Ogbourne St George
1870	1950	....	....	105651	WOR	Bredon
GODDART						
1750	1850	1700	1850	177377	DUR	Sunderland
GODDEN						
1825	1900	1750	1850	145343	HAM	Clanfield
1630	1733	ALL	1630	173304	KEN	Thurnham
1843	1992	....	....	137952	LND	Limehouse
1801	1851	1825	1900	115886	WIL	Collingbourn Kingston
GODDERIDGE						
....	....	ALL	ALL	104884	STS	ALL
GODDING						
....	....	ALL	ALL	120006	ALL	Name Study
GODENCH						
1800	....	ALL	ALL	172812	KEN	ALL
1800	....	ALL	ALL	172812	LND	ALL
GODFREE						
1615	1804	ALL	1615	143278	NTH	Brockhall
GODFREY						
....	....	1760	1783	133221	BDF	Potton
....	1875	1700	1875	120529	BRK	Cookham
1600	1880	1600	1900	161276	BRK	Cookham
1680	1825	....	1800	137405	CAM	South
1759	1772	....	1759	108839	CAM	Harlton
1740	1940	....	....	128996	CAM	Thorney
1765	....	?	?	108189	ESS	Chelmsford
1740	1840	1700	ALL	113603	ESS	Theydon Garnon
1840	1864	ALL	ALL	134260	GLS	Long Ashton
1805	1805	?	1805	158569	GLS	Pebworth
1600	1650	1600	1650	167924	HRT	Baldock
1851	1992	1700	1851	174378	HRT	Bushey
1780	1800	....	....	171999	HRT	Ippollitts
1779	....	1750	1780	153249	KEN	Ashford
1844	1992	....	1843	129461	LND	???
1840	1900	1840	ALL	113603	MDX	Bow
1824	1992	1824	1992	161705	NFK	???
1750	1850	1600	1850	119172	NTT	Blidworth
1730	1800	1750	1880	130621	NTT	Blidworth
1850	....	1800	1900	102164	NTT	Gedling
1737	....	1700	1750	124796	OXF	Cumnor
1840	1992	1600	1840	121118	OXF	Garsington
1750	1771	1700	....	178020	SOM	Fitzhead
1750	1771	1700	1800	178020	SOM	Lydeard St Lawrence
1800	....	....	....	101613	SRY	Lambeth
GODINCH						
1800	....	ALL	ALL	172812	KEN	ALL
1800	....	ALL	ALL	172812	LND	ALL
GODING						
1894	1924	1800	1900	135763	SOM	Bath
1894	1924	1800	1900	135763	SOM	Twerton
1880	1992	1600	1800	166103	YKS	West Hartlepool
GODKIN						
1830	1864	1780	1864	149632	IRL	Gorey
1830	1864	1780	1864	149632	IRL	Wexford
GODLEY						
1788	1838	1775	1850	136328	CHS	Newton
1805	1860	1700	1805	168033	KEN	Brasted
1805	1860	1700	1805	168033	KEN	Sundridge
1800	1982	ALL	1800	165212	NTT	Worksop
1890	1992	1800	1890	127728	YKS	Sheffield
GODOLPHIN						
1100	1608	....	....	132993	CON	East
GODSALL						
1796	1805	1770	1796	153176	GLS	Forthampton
GODSALVE						
1600	1700	1600	1700	169781	LAN	Yealand Conyers
GODSMARK						
1760	1824	1824	1900	109320	SSX	Cuckfield
GODSMARK contd.						
1800	1840	....	....	127744	SSX	Horsham
GODSMITH						
1815	1870	1870	1992	145564	KEN	Tunbridge Wells
GODSOME						
....	....	....	1950	130168	WAR	Illmington
GODSON						
....	....	ALL	ALL	120162	ALL	Name Study
ALL	ALL	ALL	ALL	120162	ALL	ALL
GODWIN						
....	....	ALL	1850	114308	BDF	Dunstable
1880	1900	1800	1992	102415	DUB	Dublin
1761	1857	1750	1860	103632	GLS	Cirencester
....	....	1700	1900	166863	HAM	South Stoneham
1592	1762	1500	1708	156515	HEF	Titley
1600	1700	1550	1900	177180	HRT	Hemel Hempstead
1830	1917	ALL	1830	172901	OXF	ALL
1834	....	1750	1850	118397	OXF	Henley On Thames
1800	1950	1650	1800	158925	SOM	Batheaston
1770	1992	1580	1770	175870	SOM	Batheaston
....	....	1840	1853	133639	STS	Wolverhampton
....	....	1800	1880	102415	WAR	Birmingham
1800	1870	ALL	ALL	113859	WIL	Coombe Bissett
1795	1992	1795	1925	152102	WIL	Downton
1680	1710	1650	1690	156930	WIL	Hillcutt
1800	?	ALL	ALL	107352	WIL	Lyneham
1780	1882	ALL	ALL	151645	WOR	Bromsgrove
1786	1866	ALL	ALL	151645	WOR	Elmbridge
GODWINE						
1843	1844	1804	1904	167959	LND	City
GOEBLE						
1675	....	ALL	1675	131059	KEN	Cowden
GOFF						
1854	1950	ALL	1854	137553	BRK	Reading
....	....	....	1830	166510	DBY	???
1846	1992	ALL	1900	178632	NFK	Norwich
1850	....	....	....	175587	NFK	Westfield
GOFFE						
1670	1760	1600	1760	136840	HAM	Fordingbridge
1611	1650	1588	1611	174807	SSX	Woodmancote
GOFORTH						
1823	1847	ALL	ALL	114030	ALL	ALL
GOGGIN						
....	....	ALL	ALL	109614	ALL	Name Study
GOGGS						
1550	1830	ALL	ALL	124877	NFK	North West
GOGLE						
1399	1992	1750	1900	164437	NFK	ALL
GOHNS						
1835	1992	1800	1910	162582	LND	Pimlico
GOILLON						
1848	1992	1700	1900	144258	ENG	???
GOING						
1880	1920	1800	1992	145556	ESS	Southend
GOLBY						
1725	....	1700	1750	124796	NTH	Marston St Lawrence
1755	1800	1650	1755	134317	NTH	Middleton Cheney
GOLD						
1777	1870	1770	1900	166685	DEV	Bickleigh
1800	1820	1650	1820	158542	HAM	Ringwood
1740	1800	ALL	ALL	113743	KEN	ALL
1788	1788	1700	1788	113425	KEN	Hinxhill
1740	1800	ALL	ALL	113743	SSX	ALL
1558	1800	1800	1992	127825	SSX	???
1691	....	....	1720	160873	STS	Sedgley
1881	1881	1881	1900	178322	WAR	Birmingham
GOLDBY						
1600	1900	1900	1992	129763	NTH	West
GOLDEN						
1752	1830	....	....	127779	HAM	Ringwood
1800	1850	1700	1800	139092	SSX	Hastings
GOLDER						
....	....	ALL	ALL	127752	ALL	Name Study
1794	1881	1765	1794	163686	WAR	Birmingham
GOLDFINCH						
....	....	ALL	ALL	178454	ALL	Name Study
1700	1900	ALL	ALL	178454	KEN	ALL
1860	1900	1800	1860	154962	KEN	East
1736	1830	1700	1850	173460	KEN	Stourmouth
1784	1915	1680	1784	118079	KEN	Whitstable
1860	1900	1800	1860	154962	KEN	Whitstable
1850	1900	1840	1920	111325	KEN	Woolwich
1700	1900	ALL	ALL	178454	LND	ALL
1772	1866	1740	1866	124028	SSX	Chichester

Known From	To	Researching From	To	Ref	Cty	Place
GOLDIE						
1760	1840	ALL	1992	119105	DFS	ALL
1791	1802	1700	1800	176451	LAN	Manchester
1790	1830	1750	1850	109010	MLN	Edinburgh
?	?	?	?	127760	SCT	Kilmarnock
GOLDING						
....	....	ALL	ALL	159611	ALL	Name Study
1734	1845	....	....	115290	BRK	Waltham St Lawrence
1802	1824	1800	1850	129798	CMA	Drigg
1678	1992	1600	1700	148954	ESS	Colchester
1600	1800	1600	1800	114529	ESS	Tilbury Juxta Clare
1758	1992	....	....	127779	HAM	Ringwood
1847	1992	1800	1847	166855	HRT	Hemel Hempstead
1801	1992	1801	1992	127795	KEN	Bobbing
1841	1900	1700	1900	127108	KEN	Dartford
1788	1823	1700	1788	117927	KEN	St Mary Cray
1746	1748	ALL	1746	175994	MON	Whitchurch
....	....	ALL	ALL	161470	OXF	Boars Hill
1700	1734	....	....	115290	OXF	South Stoke
....	....	ALL	ALL	161470	OXF	Wootton
1600	1800	1600	1800	114529	SFK	Stoke By Clare
1800	1870	....	....	121061	WIL	Charlton
....	....	1800	1900	179361	WIL	Downton
1781	1900	....	....	121061	WIL	Minety
1740	1800	1750	1800	165530	WIL	Sherston
1870	1992	1800	1870	127787	???	Bristol
GOLDINGAY						
1845	1850	1800	1900	123145	WAR	Castle Bromwich
GOLDRING						
1771	1992	ALL	1771	106666	ALL	ALL
1800	1843	1751	1992	127817	HAM	Hayling
1751	1800	1751	1992	127817	HAM	Westbourne
GOLDS						
1558	1992	1558	1992	127825	ALL	???
1794	1830	....	....	145394	SSX	Ashurst
GOLDSACK						
1850	1880	1800	1850	121185	KEN	South
1809	1992	1700	1809	161225	KEN	Northbourne
GOLDSBOROUGH						
1890	1992	....	....	175099	DUR	???
1729	1752	1700	1800	141097	YKS	Bradfield
GOLDSMITH						
1820	1946	1774	1820	123706	IOM	Andreas
1842	1893	....	....	144282	KEN	Dartford
1780	1881	....	....	144282	KEN	Northfleet
1780	1881	....	....	144282	KEN	Ryarsh
1739	1760	1600	1740	101575	NFK	Wells Next The Sea
1720	1820	1600	1992	127833	SRY	Ewell
1770	1992	1500	1950	127868	SSX	East
1815	1834	ALL	....	132349	SSX	East Hoathly
1813	1842	1750	1800	166723	SSX	Hailsham
1660	1960	1600	1960	128856	SSX	Horsham
GOLDSPINK						
1838	1900	1700	1900	178136	YKS	Swinton
GOLDSTON						
1760	1830	1700	1800	162043	SFK	Horringer
GOLDSTONE						
1870	1900	1800	1870	151165	LND	Hackney
GOLDSTRONG						
1855	1900	ALL	1992	146390	LAN	ALL
GOLDSWORTHY						
1880	1883	1880	1883	150355	CAE	Llanegan
1780	1830	1700	1780	142905	CON	West
1928	1928	1750	1950	121568	CON	Carn Marth
1773	1802	1747	1802	150355	CON	Crowan
1851	1992	1700	1851	105635	CON	Gwennad
1800	1878	1700	1800	176575	CON	Gwinear
1825	1834	1825	1834	150355	CON	St Austel
1847	1863	1847	1863	150355	DEV	Bere Alston
1840	1849	1840	1849	150355	GLA	Dowlais
1890	1992	1890	1992	150355	GLA	Llanbradach
1803	1826	....	....	127957	LND	Clerkenwell
1826	1867	....	....	127957	LND	Stepney
1872	1880	1872	1880	150355	MGY	Llanidloes
1750	1775	1700	1750	142905	SOM	Taunton
GOLDTHORP						
....	....	1625	1837	122971	YKS	Barnsley
1725	1802	1625	1837	122971	YKS	Darton
1740	1948	1740	1900	158712	YKS	Rothwell
GOLDTHORPE						
1734	1983	....	....	127876	BDF	Biggleswade
1837	1900	....	....	122971	ENG	ALL
1734	1983	....	....	127876	HRT	Hitchin
1734	1983	....	....	127876	KEN	Beckenham
GOLDTHORPE contd.						
....	....	1855	1900	122971	MDX	ALL
1837	1900	....	....	122971	WLS	ALL
1760	1870	....	....	170798	WRY	Penistone
1760	1870	....	....	170798	WRY	Thurlstone
....	....	1570	1701	127876	YKS	Cawthorne
....	....	1570	1701	127876	YKS	West Riding
GOLDWIRE						
1675	1800	....	....	153397	HAM	Christchurch
GOLDWYRE						
1675	1800	....	....	153397	HAM	Christchurch
GOLES						
1558	1992	1558	1992	127825	ALL	???
GOLIGHTLEY						
1860	1880	1800	1890	139858	ALL	ALL
GOLIGHTLY						
1772	1772	ALL	1772	154563	DUR	Weardale
GOLLAN						
1800	1850	1700	1800	145637	NAI	Nairn
GOLLAND						
1720	1940	....	....	127884	LAN	Manchester
....	....	?	?	118621	LIN	???
....	....	1100	1720	127884	NTT	West Bridgford
GOLLEDGE						
1811	1900	ALL	1811	129658	SOM	ALL
GOLLINGS						
....	....	?	?	118621	DBY	???
....	....	?	?	118621	LAN	Wansford
....	....	?	?	118621	NTT	???
GOLLOP						
1840	1841	1800	1840	116572	DOR	Netherbury
1812	1863	1780	1850	115797	DOR	South Perrott
1883	1992	1840	ALL	105686	WIL	Landford
GOLSTON						
1663	....	....	....	153397	HAM	Boldre
GOM						
....	1799	....	....	130079	OXF	Merton
GOMER						
1807	1837	ALL	ALL	163988	DEV	South Molton
1750	1800	1600	1800	154342	GLS	Yate
GOMERSALL						
....	....	ALL	ALL	127892	ALL	Name Study
1753	1870	....	1753	101761	WRY	Kirkheaton
1830	1911	....	....	148350	WRY	Lightcliffe Halifax
1826	1971	ALL	ALL	143618	WYK	Castleford
GOMM						
1840	1960	1700	1840	139777	LND	South
1850	1890	1700	1900	122475	MDX	Limehouse
1850	1890	1700	1900	122475	MDX	Stepney
GOMME						
1785	....	....	1785	108839	BKM	Chesham
....	1799	....	....	130079	OXF	Merton
GOMPERTZ						
....	....	1700	....	146188	LND	London
GONDERTON						
1881	1883	1856	1950	139173	STS	Pensnett
GONEY						
1843	1860	ALL	1860	165654	SOM	Bath
GOOCH						
ALL	ALL	ALL	ALL	123692	ALL	ALL
1820	1860	1750	1850	174599	ESS	Wix
1778	1832	....	....	178330	LND	Clerkenwell
1805	1840	....	....	160458	LND	???
1805	1840	....	....	160458	NBL	???
1780	1820	1700	1780	102288	SFK	Hemley
....	....	1765	1778	178330	SFK	Stone
1765	....	....	....	100676	SFK	Stoven
GOOD						
1780	1900	1700	1950	124184	DOR	Stoke Abbott
1666	1794	1600	1666	145459	HAM	Hound
1746	1746	1600	1746	170542	KEN	Hythe
1800	1840	ALL	1992	119105	SFK	Bures
1750	....	....	....	157724	SFK	Bures
GOODACRE						
1900	1900	1800	1950	162620	BRK	Wokingham
GOODAGE						
1818	1818	1754	1830	107360	BKM	Stewkley
GOODAIR						
1880	1935	1850	1900	100242	LND	South
1837	1872	....	....	145912	YKS	Wakefield
GOODALE						
1750	1980	1565	1750	103527	NFK	???
....	1700	....	....	174564	SSX	???

Known From	To	Researching From	To	Ref	Cty	Place
GOODALL						
....	....	ALL	ALL	127922	ALL	Name Study
1600	1700	1600	1700	167924	BDF	Shillington
1600	1700	1600	1700	167924	BDF	Upper Gravenhurst
1823	1830	1823	1830	130222	BKM	Wavendon
1650	1750	1550	1700	107697	CON	Fowey
1820	1870	ALL	1900	105376	DBY	Coton In The Elms
1580	1850	1580	1850	127914	DUB	Dublin
1780	1929	1700	1780	167932	FIF	Kilconquar
1683	1730	1680	1750	105325	HAM	Andover
....	....	1683	1780	143480	HAM	Andover
1753	1950	1753	1950	105325	HAM	Fareham
1780	1992	1683	1780	143480	HAM	Fareham
1780	1992	....	....	143480	HAM	Gosport
1846	1954	ALL	1954	109258	MDX	Cowley
1750	1850	1700	1850	101273	SFK	Clare
....	....	1798	1992	161543	SRY	Rotherhithe
1830	1854	1700	1830	141291	STS	Walsall
1675	1992	1675	1940	127914	WEX	Wexford
1808	1839	ALL	1808	167878	WIL	Cholderton
1759	1828	1759	1828	130877	YKS	Garforth
....	....	ALL	ALL	155632	YKS	West ryding
GOODARE						
1750	1992	1500	1992	156183	YKS	ALL
GOODAY						
1730	1930	1730	1930	105317	ESS	ALL
GOODBODY						
....	....	ALL	ALL	127930	ALL	Name Study
1200	1992	ALL	ALL	127930	ALL	ALL
1560	1920	1560	1992	160946	NFK	ALL
GOODBRAND						
1827	1827	1800	1827	149632	ABD	Aberdeen
GOODBUN						
1881	....	ALL	ALL	159026	YKS	Rotherham
GOODCHILD						
1840	1880	....	....	127949	BKM	Bledlow
1756	1776	1650	1800	143693	BKM	Monks Risborough
1590	1840	ALL	1590	127949	BKM	Prices Risborough
1790	....	1700	1850	143693	BKM	West Wycombe
1797	1905	1700	1799	166804	BRK	Brimpton
1870	....	....	....	170313	BRK	Stanmore
1832	....	....	....	124559	BRK	Swallowfield
1800	1875	....	....	153397	BRK	Swallowfield
1711	1887	....	....	127957	DOR	Purbeck
1839	1904	....	....	127957	DOR	Winfrith Newburgh
1700	1875	....	....	153397	HAM	ALL
1748	....	ALL	ALL	169730	HAM	Stratfield Turgis
1740	1761	ALL	ALL	169730	HAM	Weston Patrick
....	....	ALL	ALL	167827	MDX	Stanwell
1882	1882	1700	1882	145718	SRY	Lambeth
1799	1808	1700	1799	150169	SRY	Merstham
1772	1793	1700	1772	176451	YKS	Bradford
1875	1992	1850	1992	159018	YKS	Sheffield
GOODDEN						
1664	1782	1600	1750	129356	SOM	Martock
GOODE						
1654	1940	....	....	128996	CAM	Thorney
1700	1799	ALL	1700	162507	CON	Gwennap
1860	1992	1700	1860	103098	HAM	Portsmouth
1760	1780	1700	1800	123137	LEI	Evesham
1806	1954	....	....	140139	LND	Brockley
1806	1954	....	....	140139	LND	Deptford
1754	1920	1700	1780	127965	MDX	London
1799	1924	1700	1799	129712	SFK	Haughley
1844	1870	1820	1844	139408	WAR	Clifton
1870	1963	1844	1963	139408	WAR	Rugby
GOODEARE						
1691	1732	1600	1750	157716	YKS	Huddersfield
GOODEARL						
1863	1992	ALL	1992	143197	BKM	High Wycombe
GOODEN						
1813	1830	1750	1850	126586	SFK	Hundon
GOODENOUGH						
....	1829	1700	1800	132586	BRK	Buscot
1795	1810	1700	1826	127973	HAM	Old Basing
1826	?	1700	1826	127973	MDX	London
1750	1825	1750	1992	133450	WIL	Swindon
1740	1770	ALL	ALL	107840	???	London
GOODER						
....	....	1700	1850	129046	WYK	Huddersfield
GOODERHAM						
1850	1900	1700	1992	140287	SFK	Debenham
GOODES						
1863	1915	....	....	114545	HUN	Sawtry
GOODEVE						
1567	1698	1567	1698	141259	ESS	Great Waltham
1569	1800	1569	1800	141259	HAM	ALL
1766	1900	ALL	1992	100536	JSY	???
1780	1800	1700	1800	135771	SRY	Hants Border
GOODEY						
1820	1845	1800	1825	149039	BKM	Newport Pagnell
1860	1992	1700	1860	128007	LND	Shoreditch
GOODFELLOW						
1911	1919	....	1911	129518	LAN	Blackpool
1837	1870	1700	1837	173037	MOG	Castle Brayney
1835	1911	1700	1835	155705	ROX	Mertown
1835	1911	1700	1835	155705	ROX	Nenthorn
1824	1992	1814	ALL	118060	WIL	Teffont
1911	1919	....	1911	129518	YKS	Wakefield
GOODHAND						
1790	1992	1600	1900	169560	LIN	North
GOODHEW						
1898	1935	1800	1992	122475	KEN	Lewisham
1898	1935	1800	1992	122475	KEN	Strood
GOODIER						
1850	1910	....	....	137790	CHS	Coppenhall
1850	1950	1837	1850	166464	LAN	Blackburn
1777	1839	1700	1839	141062	LAN	Eccles
GOODILL						
1857	1992	1800	1857	163090	YKS	Driffield
....	....	1700	1857	163090	YKS	Whitby
GOODING						
1700	1871	1871	1992	149357	DEV	Morebath
....	....	1825	1992	162019	GLA	Merthyr Tydfil
1807	1815	1780	1820	166316	MDX	White Friars
....	....	1825	1992	162019	MON	Tredegar
1797	1935	1797	1935	128023	OXF	Marsh Baldon
1830	1992	ALL	ALL	167940	SFK	Ipswich
1840	1902	1815	1840	134082	SOM	Langport
GOODISON						
1750	1940	1500	1940	125725	ENG	ALL
1750	1900	1500	1900	125725	MDX	London
1840	1992	1866	1992	146625	YKS	Huddersfield
1840	1992	1866	1992	146625	YKS	Sheffield
1840	1992	1866	1992	146625	YKS	Stannington
GOODLAD						
1602	1992	1550	1602	128031	YKS	Thorpesalvin
GOODLAND						
1750	1992	1600	1750	101524	SOM	West
GOODLIFFE						
....	....	ALL	ALL	112003	ALL	Name Study
1600	1940	1600	1992	112003	ALL	ALL
GOODMAN						
1750	1992	1500	1992	166758	BDF	???
1803	1992	ALL	ALL	169838	CAE	Pwllheli
1746	1781	ALL	1781	168718	CON	South East
1824	1860	....	....	161489	CON	Phillack
1748	....	....	....	166723	CON	Warbstow
....	....	1600	1824	161489	ENG	South
1750	1992	1500	1992	166758	HRT	???
1816	1833	?	1830	164976	LAN	Oldham
1606	1992	....	....	128058	LEI	Clipston
1606	1992	....	....	128058	LEI	Crick Guilborough
1606	1992	....	....	128058	LEI	London
1606	1992	....	....	128058	LEI	Longbuckby
1606	1992	....	....	128058	LEI	Market Harboro
1791	1861	1700	1791	160024	LEI	Melton Mowbray
1606	1992	....	....	128058	LEI	West Haddon
1796	1828	1750	1830	176621	LIN	Long Sutton
1817	1843	1500	1817	129577	LND	Poplar
1840	....	....	....	129577	LND	Stepney
1911	1939	....	....	161489	MDX	Brentford
1614	1757	....	....	103632	NTH	Great Brington
1606	1992	....	....	128058	NTH	Great Brington
1779	1823	1730	1860	167002	NTT	North Muskham
1800	1855	1851	....	118931	OXF	Burford
?	?	ALL	ALL	100897	SRY	???
....	....	ALL	1606	128058	WAR	Environs
....	....	ALL	1606	128058	WAR	Wormleighitton
1771	1850	ALL	1771	167878	WIL	Easton
1845	1863	1800	1992	167983	WOR	Hartlebury
1840	1900	ALL	1850	106283	WOR	Kidderminster
1840	1900	ALL	1850	106283	WOR	Stourport
GOODRED						
1731	1750	ALL	1992	159174	LIN	Long Sutton
GOODRICH						
1780	1900	....	....	108677	ESS	ALL
1800	1865	1700	1865	104396	LIN	West Keal

Known From	To	Researching From	To	Ref	Cty	Place
GOODRICH contd.						
1780	1900	....	....	108677	WLS	South
GOODRICK						
1813	1921	1750	1813	114545	LIN	East Keel
1813	1921	1750	1813	114545	LIN	Fens
1773	1992	1668	1773	115576	NFK	Swaffham
GOODRIDGE						
1700	1850	1700	1900	151475	DEV	Paignton
1809	1830	1770	1809	173118	DOR	Wyke Regis
GOODS						
1863	1915	....	....	114545	HUN	Sawtry
GOODSELL						
1870	....	....	....	173150	SXE	Brede
1777	1841	1814	1992	140058	SXE	Ewhurst
1800	1875	ALL	1800	173150	SXE	Ewhurst
GOODSHIP						
1770	1920	1700	1992	101273	WIL	ALL
GOODSIR						
1775	1860	....	....	128066	FIF	Abbotshall Kirkcaldy
1861	1992	....	....	128066	T&W	South Shields
GOODSON						
1832	1904	1700	1832	125636	LEI	Harby
1832	1904	1700	1832	125636	LEI	Muston
1837	....	....	....	165387	MDX	Camden Town
1750	1945	1540	1750	154458	SOM	Baltonsborough
GOODVIGHT						
1800	1860	1700	1800	138959	SRY	Chessington
1800	1860	1700	1800	138959	SRY	Ewell
1800	1860	1700	1800	138959	SRY	Hook
1800	1860	1700	1800	138959	SRY	Tolworth
GOODWELL						
....	....	1600	1950	134546	IOW	Brading
GOODWILL						
1780	1851	1800	1851	171166	WRY	Ganthorpe
GOODWIN						
1855	1884	1800	1855	178896	ANS	Dundee
1736	1940	....	....	128996	CAM	Thorney
?	?	ALL	ALL	174432	CAM	Whittlesey
1800	1992	1650	1800	128074	CHS	Macclesfield
1800	1992	1650	1800	128074	CHS	Prestbury
1863	....	1829	....	156191	DBY	Buxton
1818	1867	1700	1818	139386	DBY	Chesterfield
....	....	1700	1760	161357	ESS	Dunmow
1705	1770	....	....	161357	ESS	Great Dunmow
1818	1873	1780	1818	132411	HAM	Ovington
1787	1831	....	....	144355	KEN	East
....	....	ALL	ALL	130524	KEN	Maidstone
....	....	1790	1810	105694	LAN	Manchester
1840	1992	1700	1840	128074	LAN	Manchester
1840	1890	1750	1900	113387	LIN	Welton Le Marsh
1853	1940	1853	1853	133930	LND	ALL
1881	1992	1700	1881	133647	LND	Kensington
1800	1884	1830	?	153990	LND	West Ham
1829	1851	1500	1854	157538	MDX	London
1881	1965	....	1880	130524	MDX	Whitechapel
1840	1880	1750	1850	135496	NTH	Boddington
1740	1871	1700	1740	151300	SAL	Broseley
1740	1871	1700	1740	151300	SAL	Madeley
1831	....	1750	1850	131377	SFK	Hoxne
1850	1900	....	....	132756	SRY	Walton On Thames
1830	1860	....	1860	102822	WAR	Birmingham
1850	1900	....	....	132756	YKS	Leeds
1815	1830	1800	1992	102415	YKS	Sheffield
GOODWORTH						
....	....	ALL	ALL	128104	ALL	Name Study
ALL	ALL	ALL	ALL	128104	ALL	ALL
1596	1792	ALL	ALL	128104	LAN	ALL
1575	1823	ALL	ALL	128104	LIN	ALL
1616	1992	ALL	ALL	128104	LND	ALL
1648	1992	ALL	ALL	128104	YKS	ALL
GOODWYN						
1795	1992	ALL	1795	138126	CMN	Conwyl Elfed
1795	1992	ALL	1795	138126	CMN	Llanddowror
1795	1992	ALL	1795	138126	MGY	Abermule
1795	1992	ALL	1795	138126	MGY	Llanmerewig
1795	1992	ALL	1795	138126	MGY	Newtown
?	?	?	?	138126	SCT	Glasgow
GOODY						
1600	1800	1600	1800	114529	ESS	Tilbury Juxta Clare
1815	....	1780	1820	152110	SFK	Glemsford
1600	1800	1600	1800	114529	SFK	Stoke By Clare
GOODYEAR						
1872	1878	1850	1878	124990	AVN	Bath
GOODYEAR contd.						
1798	1861	....	....	166189	BKM	Boarstall
1857	1877	1857	1877	119202	CON	Bodmin
1739	1820	1500	1860	119202	DEV	South Hams
1815	1870	1815	1900	119202	DEV	Stonehouse
1770	1791	1700	1770	133949	HAM	Christchurch
1831	1886	1831	1886	147486	HAM	Portsea
1870	1900	1870	1900	119202	KEN	Deptford
1870	1900	1870	1900	119202	KEN	New Cross
1640	....	ALL	....	104515	LIN	Heckington
1831	1886	1831	1886	147486	SSX	Felpham
GOODYER						
1814	1950	1810	1992	158399	SSX	Burpham
1810	1810	1650	1890	158399	SSX	Bury
1800	1940	1700	1800	120227	SSX	Prinstead
1754	1792	1700	1800	157716	YKS	Huddersfield
GOOK						
1811	....	....	1811	177504	MDX	London
GOOKE						
1706	1706	ALL	1706	154563	DOR	Osmington
GOOLD						
1859	?	1859	1883	128112	CHS	Wirral
GOOM						
1700	1900	1500	1800	174661	ALL	ALL
GOORE						
1700	1780	ALL	ALL	137987	LAN	Altcar
GOOSE						
1766	1770	1730	1808	169552	LAN	Goosnargh
1750	1770	1750	1800	176281	LIN	Spilsby
1810	1992	1580	1810	175870	NFK	Walsoken
GOOSEMAN						
1835	1921	1800	1925	142891	LIN	Grimsby
GORD						
1860	....	1700	1992	167673	ALL	ALL
GORDEN						
....	....	ALL	1830	140848	DEV	ALL
1789	1802	ALL	ALL	129933	DEV	Exeter
GORDGE						
....	....	1830	1841	138614	AVN	Bristol
....	....	1500	1650	138614	CON	Fowey
1800	1850	....	....	138614	DOR	Bridport
1716	1850	....	....	138614	DOR	Charmouth
1658	1700	....	....	138614	DOR	Whitchurch
GORDON						
1856	....	1700	1856	145718	ABD	Aberdeen
1790	1850	1700	1850	176788	ABD	Aberdeen
1728	1873	1600	1800	162280	ABD	Cabrach
1870	1893	ALL	ALL	129933	ARL	Kirn
1138	1800	1700	1900	159956	BEW	???
1822	1850	1750	1822	146609	CUL	North
1850	1900	1800	1950	178799	DOW	Kilhorne Annalong
1938	1965	1700	1938	115401	DUR	Sunderland
1844	1876	1700	1844	117595	HAM	Portsea
1849	1870	1750	1992	102415	INV	Fastnacyle
1800	1830	1700	1800	100978	KCD	Bervie
1785	1844	1700	1790	134732	LDY	Kilrea
1799	1832	ALL	1799	121525	LIM	Limerick
1849	1922	1800	1900	177970	NBL	South
1780	1992	1740	1780	128139	SCT	???
1792	1992	1770	1792	128139	STS	Brierley Hill
1875	1930	ALL	1900	115045	STS	West Bromwich
1840	1859	1750	1840	136530	WAR	Birmingham
1790	1992	1740	1780	128139	WOR	Dudley
GORE						
....	....	1800	....	137456	BDF	Campton
1800	1860	1750	1900	104868	GLS	Cheltenham
1738	1807	1700	1807	128147	KEN	Challock
1906	1936	....	....	128147	KEN	Folkestone
1851	1861	1851	1945	128147	KEN	Herne Bay
1838	1850	....	....	128147	KEN	Newnham
1803	1812	....	....	128147	KEN	Sheldwich
1827	1828	1778	1828	128147	KEN	Stalisfield
?	....	....	....	169358	LAN	???
1607	1761	....	....	131229	MAY	???
1824	1829	1800	1900	105619	MDX	Ealing
1802	1900	1700	1802	167886	NTT	Nottingham
1817	1880	1600	1817	156914	RAD	Glascwm
GOREHAM						
1835	1960	1700	1834	131245	NFK	Norwich
GORELY						
1700	1992	1700	1992	128163	KEN	ALL
GOREY						
1848	1930	1800	1848	132039	HAM	Southampton

Known From	To	Researching From	To	Ref	Cty	Place
GORICK						
....	....	ALL	ALL	110086	ALL	Name Study
GORING						
1500	1620	1500	1600	144657	HAM	Basingstoke
1500	1600	1300	1600	144657	SRY	Worplespon
....	....	ALL	1992	164879	SSX	ALL
1600	1992	1600	1992	177423	SSX	East
1600	1992	1600	1992	177423	SSX	West
GORMAN						
1750	1992	1600	1750	145017	DEV	ALL
1879	1957	1872	1879	128791	DUR	Consett
1850	1900	1900	1992	145017	GLA	ALL
1860	1890	1890	1992	145017	???	Bristol
GORNAL						
1820	1840	....	....	102741	MGY	Welshpool
1873	1890	....	....	102741	NBL	Newcastle Upon Tyne
1851	....	....	....	102741	STS	Wolverhampton
GORRIDGE						
1800	....	ALL	ALL	172812	KEN	ALL
GORRIE						
....	....	ALL	ALL	102695	ALL	Name Study
1750	1992	1750	1992	156183	PER	ALL
1795	1815	....	....	168203	PER	Aberdalgie
1826	1846	....	....	168203	PER	Monzie
1846	1904	....	....	168203	PER	Pedgorton
GORRINGE						
1778	1826	1600	1778	164879	SSX	ALL
1780	1821	1780	1821	100242	SSX	Barcombe
GORRUM						
1920	1940	1800	1920	101907	KEN	Deal
GORSE						
1796	1860	1796	1860	138703	DBY	Duffield
1815	....	1750	1900	109894	DBY	Mackworth
1796	1860	1796	1860	138703	DBY	Quarndon
1896	1927	....	....	173568	LAN	Blackburn
1815	....	1750	1900	109894	STS	Uttoxeter
GORST						
1796	....	ALL	ALL	141739	ENG	???
1578	1733	1567	1734	169552	LAN	Garstang
1869	1891	1658	1893	169552	LAN	Heysham
GORSUCH						
....	....	ALL	ALL	128198	ALL	Name Study
1786	1992	....	....	128228	ALL	ALL
ALL	ALL	ALL	ALL	128201	ALL	ALL
....	....	1700	1786	128228	ESS	ALL
....	....	1650	1750	128228	HRT	ALL
ALL	ALL	ALL	ALL	128201	LAN	ALL
....	....	....	1650	128228	LND	ALL
GOSBY						
....	....	ALL	ALL	143391	ALL	Name Study
GOSDEN						
....	....	ALL	ALL	128236	ALL	Name Study
1710	1870	1600	1870	129194	HAM	ALL
1599	1992	ALL	ALL	128236	IOW	ALL
1599	1992	1599	1992	129194	IOW	ALL
1550	1900	1550	1900	129194	SSX	West
GOSE						
1775	1820	....	....	151785	HUN	Leighton Bromswold
GOSLETT						
....	....	ALL	ALL	175455	ALL	Name Study
GOSLEY						
1670	1755	....	....	174319	CON	Mevagissey
GOSLING						
1800	1950	1700	1800	142905	CHS	Cheadle
1807	1854	1650	1854	166987	KEN	Margate
1692	....	....	....	171441	KEN	Strood
1839	1841	1800	1930	139203	LND	Lewisham
1837	1842	....	....	101028	MDX	London
1864	....	1800	1992	111201	NTT	Bulwell
1793	1793	1770	1793	161896	SFK	Polstead
1867	1869	1800	1940	139203	SRY	Penge
1800	1930	1800	1930	121533	SRY	Richmond
1800	1850	....	....	142360	WIL	Chiseldon
GOSNALD						
....	....	ALL	ALL	165743	ALL	Name Study
GOSNAY						
....	....	?	....	115592	YKS	Wrenthorpe
GOSNEL						
1715	1715	....	....	127426	STS	Harborne
1715	1715	....	....	127426	STS	???
GOSNELL						
1646	1646	....	....	127426	STS	???
GOSNEY						
ALL	ALL	ALL	ALL	128252	ALL	ALL
GOSNEY contd.						
1843	....	1830	1900	127353	DOR	Stourton Caundle
1784	1851	....	....	133221	HAM	Breamore
1814	1970	1780	1814	153419	HAM	Portsea
GOSNOLD						
1450	1900	ALL	ALL	165743	ALL	ALL
GOSS						
....	....	1600	1800	103667	DEV	South
1800	1840	1780	1992	137448	DEV	Bideford
1881	....	1860	1880	108030	GNT	Newport
1880	1992	ALL	1992	128260	HAM	Soton
1790	....	....	....	117579	KEN	Wilmington
ALL	1860	ALL	1992	128260	LND	ALL
1701	1739	1600	1700	131245	WAR	Leek Wootton
1860	1883	1860	1883	138703	YKS	Sheffield
GOSSE						
....	....	1650	1800	147613	BDF	Flitton With Silsoe
....	....	1650	1800	147613	BDF	Shillington
GOSSELIN						
1600	....	....	....	137693	CHI	Guernsey
GOSSLING						
1800	1900	1900	....	108677	DOR	East
1800	1900	1900	....	108677	HAM	Christchurch
GOSTELOW						
1819	....	....	....	151548	NTH	Preston Capes
1819	....	....	....	151548	WAR	Rugby
GOSTLING						
1779	1992	1700	1779	116440	SFK	Carlton Colville
GOSWELL						
1700	1900	1800	1900	128287	BRK	Finchampstead
1600	1700	....	....	128287	BRK	Pangbourne
1700	1800	1700	1800	128287	BRK	Swallowfield
GOTBED						
1700	1850	....	....	177474	DEV	Combe-In-Teignhead
GOTER						
1740	1770	1700	1740	127116	HAM	Longstock
GOTHERIDGE						
1790	1900	1700	1900	132950	DBY	Church Broughton
1750	1900	1750	1900	160547	DBY	Hartshorne
GOTOBED						
?	?	?	?	168947	???	???
GOTT						
....	....	ALL	ALL	128295	ALL	Name Study
1750	1850	1650	1750	111511	YKS	Bingley
....	1780	....	....	174564	???	???
GOTTERSON						
....	....	ALL	ALL	124338	ALL	Name Study
GOTTLER						
....	....	ALL	ALL	130818	LND	Whitechapel
GOTTS						
....	....	ALL	ALL	128309	ALL	Name Study
1900	1920	1850	1950	100129	GLS	Bristol
1850	1870	1700	1900	100129	NFK	Cromer
GOTYHEIN						
1857	1898	ALL	1857	169730	HRT	Ware
GOUCH						
1840	1910	1790	1910	179000	STI	???
1800	1850	1700	1800	167770	WIL	Calne
GOUCK						
1802	1874	....	....	137936	ANS	Arbroath
GOUDGE						
1775	1992	ALL	ALL	128325	CON	St Stephen In Brannel
1820	1880	1700	1820	165549	CON	St Stephens In Brannel
....	....	ALL	ALL	128325	LND	ALL
GOUDIE						
....	....	1760	1840	111376	MDX	Wapping
GOUGE						
1850	1992	1700	1850	128465	HAM	Gosport
1750	1900	....	....	113093	KEN	Borden
1723	....	....	1800	171441	KEN	Bredgar
GOUGER						
1751	1787	ALL	1787	152838	YKS	Walkington
GOUGH						
1773	....	1773	....	123099	BRK	Easthampstead
1747	....	1747	....	123099	BRK	Warfield
1880	1910	1600	1880	118648	CMA	Whitehaven
1840	1992	1840	1900	149136	DOR	Yetminster
1907	....	....	....	150762	GLA	Cardiff
1767	1851	ALL	1767	116408	GLS	ALL
....	....	ALL	1750	141224	GLS	South
1773	1773	1700	1851	111414	GLS	Ashleworth
1850	1992	1800	1992	129240	GLS	Bristol

Known From	To	Researching From	To	Ref	Cty	Place
GOUGH contd.						
1794	1794	1780	1851	111414	GLS	Maisemore
1860	1900	ALL	ALL	131490	HAM	Tichfield
1786	1825	1500	1825	157538	HRT	Shenley
1786	1825	1500	1825	157538	HRT	Ware
1830	1850	1800	1854	129240	IRL	Cork
1875	1930	1837	1875	166464	LAN	Manchester
1775	1825	1774	1896	172243	LAN	Manchester
1819	1839	?	1819	121665	LAN	Stretford
1774	1856	?	1774	121665	LIN	Deeping St James
1750	1880	ALL	ALL	137987	SAL	Albrighton
1840	1866	1800	1866	108510	SAL	Dawley
....	1600	....	1600	177695	SAL	Stockton
1830	1890	1750	1890	122505	STS	Forsbrook
1851	1900	1850	1992	116408	WAR	Birmingham
1790	1832	1790	1830	150479	WAR	Birmingham
....	....	1550	1650	165042	WIL	ALL
1896	1992	....	....	132462	???	Barton Hill
GOUJON						
1830	1900	ALL	ALL	175943	BDF	Luton
1725	1830	ALL	ALL	175943	LND	???
GOULD						
1840	1900	1700	1900	128341	BRK	Newbury
1840	1897	1700	1900	128341	BRK	Reading
1780	....	1780	1900	106410	DEV	Hockworth
1780	....	....	....	117579	DEV	Hockworthy
1719	....	?	1720	103934	DEV	North Molton
1827	1910	1800	1866	152102	DOR	Whitechurch Canonicorum
....	....	1829	1905	115061	ESS	South West
....	....	1800	1890	142131	HRT	Great Hormead
1788	1788	....	....	144355	KEN	South
1740	1800	ALL	ALL	113743	KEN	Leigh
....	....	1800	1895	115061	MDX	Hackney
1817	1849	1700	1860	148288	PER	Perth
1817	1849	1700	1860	148288	PER	Redgaten
1817	1849	1700	1860	148288	PER	Scone
1825	1871	1700	1825	115185	SAL	Shrewsbury
1800	1950	1600	1800	128376	SOM	Camerton
1796	1980	ALL	ALL	153516	SOM	Kewstoke
1795	1992	1700	1800	145149	SOM	Martock
1800	....	1800	1900	106410	SOM	Pitminster
1810	1861	1700	1861	117579	SOM	Pitminster
1796	1947	ALL	ALL	153516	SOM	Puxton
1800	....	1800	1900	106410	SOM	Trull
1740	1800	ALL	ALL	113743	SSX	ALL
1757	1992	....	1757	138541	STS	Alrewas
1797	1870	1700	1790	128333	STS	Leek
1851	1871	1871	1960	138541	STS	Pelsall
1851	1871	1871	1992	138541	STS	Walsall
1850	1880	1700	1900	128341	WIL	Aldbourne
1790	....	....	....	142158	WIL	Aldbourne
1700	1840	1600	1800	128341	WIL	Chippenham
1752	1866	1700	1752	150150	WOR	Cleeve Prior
1800	1850	1700	1900	138517	WOR	???
1860	1960	1800	1860	128368	YKS	Bowes
1860	1960	1800	1860	128368	YKS	Sheffield
GOULD-BOURN						
1800	1992	1750	1800	128384	LAN	Manchester
GOULDBOURNE						
1864	1888	ALL	1900	146315	LAN	Chorlton
1864	1951	ALL	1900	146315	LAN	Manchester
GOULDEN						
1688	1948	1688	1948	176621	KEN	Canterbury
1810	1840	1700	1840	105759	MDX	Shoreditch
GOULDER						
ALL	ALL	1600	1700	140716	DBY	Derby
1912	1992	1700	1912	173479	NFK	Norwich
GOULDING						
1785	1842	1785	1992	151270	CAM	Whittlesey
1866	1890	1700	1992	121150	GLS	Woodchester
1795	....	....	....	142859	WIL	Minety
1802	1869	1750	1802	103039	YKS	Sheffield
GOULDS						
1750	1880	1880	1920	127825	KEN	Dartford
1750	1880	1880	1920	127825	KEN	Maidstone
1750	1880	1880	1920	127825	KEN	Towbridge
1558	1880	1880	1920	127825	NTT	???
GOULTY						
....	....	ALL	ALL	128392	ALL	Name Study
1550	1992	ALL	1992	128392	ALL	ALL
GOUNDRILL						
1756	1827	ALL	1756	154946	YKS	Eastringham

Known From	To	Researching From	To	Ref	Cty	Place
GOUNDRY						
....	....	ALL	ALL	128414	ALL	ALL
1860	1992	ALL	1860	128414	DUR	Auckland
GOUNDS						
1780	1822	1750	1820	109517	HUN	Ramsey
GOURD						
....	....	ALL	ALL	169447	ALL	Name Study
1729	1800	1729	1820	113085	SRY	Godstone
GOURLAY						
1720	....	ALL	ALL	130508	FIF	Anfield Plain
1770	1860	1700	1800	133787	LKS	Carnwath
GOURLEY						
1870	1900	1700	1870	173037	ANT	South
1709	1848	1600	1700	147346	FIF	Kilconquar
GOUSAL						
1280	1350	1200	1350	154881	KEN	ALL
GOUSHILL						
....	....	ALL	1600	178403	DBY	???
1380	1460	1300	1460	154881	NTT	Hoveringham
....	....	ALL	1600	178403	NTT	???
GOVAN						
1789	1875	1750	1880	177970	???	Glasgow
GOVER						
1765	1830	ALL	ALL	115126	HAM	Fareham
....	....	1700	1850	103667	HAM	Meon Valley
GOVIER						
1737	1855	ALL	1880	104299	SOM	Old Cleeve
GOWAN						
....	....	....	1837	121851	ANT	Belfast
1825	1850	1800	1900	142875	SFK	???
GOWANLOCK						
....	....	1700	1820	117587	DFS	???
GOWANS						
1838	1928	1800	1840	141798	ROX	Galashields
GOWAR						
1810	1861	....	....	178330	ESS	Stratford
1750	1810	....	....	178330	KEN	Greenwich
GOWARD						
1781	1797	1600	1781	156779	NFK	Taverham
GOWEN						
....	....	1700	1850	140627	LND	Cripplewood
1780	1840	1750	1840	124605	NFK	Great Yarmouth
GOWENLOCK						
....	....	ALL	ALL	128422	ALL	Name Study
1747	1803	1700	1803	141062	SEL	Selkirk
GOWER						
1750	1992	ALL	1992	172812	KEN	ALL
1785	1833	....	....	144355	KEN	South
1850	1900	1700	1850	144681	KEN	Maidstone
ALL	1600	....	....	132756	NBL	???
1730	1870	1700	1870	146803	NFK	Redenhall
1775	1883	1700	1775	129356	SSX	Hellingly
1795	1992	1700	1795	159565	WOR	Bromsgrove
ALL	1600	....	....	132756	YKS	???
GOWERS						
1790	1845	1750	1820	171158	ESS	Roxwell
1803	....	1780	1810	152110	SFK	Hartest
GOWING						
1780	1840	1750	1840	124605	NFK	Great Yarmouth
GOWLAND						
1900	1920	ALL	1920	113662	DUR	Rowlands Hill
1715	1796	ALL	1715	154563	DUR	Stanhope
GOWLETT						
....	....	ALL	ALL	128430	ALL	Name Study
1750	1820	1700	1900	162345	MDX	Uxbridge
GOWMAN						
1670	1800	ALL	1670	145017	DEV	ALL
GOWN						
1869	1992	ALL	1900	101362	LND	Central
GOYDEN						
1770	1870	1700	1870	175838	CON	St Agnes
GOYDER						
1800	1992	1700	1992	103292	MDX	Westminster
GOYER						
1787	1992	1787	1992	108278	ANT	Belfast
GOYMER						
....	....	ALL	ALL	155187	ALL	Name Study
1743	1853	1700	1853	124605	ESS	Gt Holland
GOYNE						
1831	1900	1700	1831	149608	CON	St Agnes
GRABHAM						
1850	1972	....	....	105473	DUR	???
1752	1851	1790	1851	160164	SOM	Buckland St Mary

Known From	To	Researching From	To	Ref	Cty	Place
GRACE						
~~1850~~	~~1915~~	~~....~~	~~....~~	~~159131~~	~~BDF~~	~~Bedford~~
1813	1900	1813	1900	130222	BDF	Husborne Crawley
1800	1820	1800	1820	130222	BDF	Leighton Buzzard
1893	1893	ALL	ALL	128449	DBY	Derby
1750	1900	ALL	ALL	128449	ENG	South
1811	1811	ALL	ALL	128449	ESS	Colchester
1820	1900	1720	1900	176524	GSY	St Peter Port
1780	1851	1600	1900	166804	HAM	Clatford
1780	1851	1600	1900	166804	HAM	Goodworth
1851	1880	ALL	ALL	128449	KEN	Ashford
1836	1851	ALL	ALL	128449	KEN	Ramsgate
1595	1796	ALL	1590	120200	LAN	Childwall
1899	1903	ALL	ALL	128449	LAN	Lancaster
1595	1796	ALL	1590	120200	LAN	Prescot
1903	1992	ALL	ALL	128449	WAR	Birmingham
1788	1811	1700	1850	124974	WIL	Britford
1681	1815	1500	1853	169439	YKS	Dewsbury
1863	1890	ALL	ALL	128449	YKS	Doncaster
GRACEY						
1838	1860	1838	1921	128457	ANT	Belfast
1838	1885	....	....	128457	DOW	Belfast
....	....	1700	1812	128457	DOW	Lurgan
1812	1888	1812	1838	128457	DOW	Magheralin
GRADDAGE						
....	....	ALL	ALL	144991	ALL	Name Study
GRADDON						
1799	1826	1799	....	102954	SSX	Winchelsea
GRADIDGE						
1573	1992	ALL	ALL	128473	ALL	ALL
1575	1992	1331	1575	118060	HAM	South
GRADWELL						
1810	1848	....	....	116602	LAN	West
GRADY						
1780	1926	1801	1873	126276	HAM	Portsea
1840	1920	1800	1840	121509	IRL	Cork
1840	1920	1800	1840	121509	IRL	Limerick
1840	1920	1800	1840	121509	IRL	Louth
1899	1966	1800	1899	108405	LAN	Manchester
1899	1966	1800	1899	108405	LAN	Salford
1871	....	....	....	155675	MDX	Shadwell
1871	....	....	....	155675	MDX	Stepney
1822	1992	1700	1830	118532	TIP	New Caste
GRAFHAM						
....	....	ALL	ALL	147206	ALL	Name Study
1689	1754	1660	1754	159581	SRY	Albury
1689	1754	1660	1754	159581	SRY	Cranleigh
?	....	....	?	111104	SRY	Epsom
?	....	....	?	111104	SRY	Ewell
?	....	....	?	111104	SRY	Sutton
GRAFTER						
1834	1856	1500	1856	151483	LND	London
GRAFTON						
1600	1800	1600	1800	140090	DBY	Chesterfield
1820	1850	ALL	1850	142301	DEV	Plymouth
1810	1840	1750	1810	121509	LAN	Liverpool
1735	1812	1735	1812	110361	WIL	Stinchcombe
GRAGG						
1765	1928	1700	1765	169803	SSX	Horsham
GRAGSON						
1680	1705	1500	1992	102520	YKS	Northowram
GRAHAM						
1870	1946	1850	1900	100846	ANS	Lochee
1843	1980	1800	1900	121134	ANT	Carnaughlis
1780	1800	1700	1850	115967	AYR	Kirkoswald
1826	1851	1800	1826	115967	AYR	Maybole
1800	1850	1800	....	175234	BRK	Abingdon
1850	1900	1830	1860	155047	CHS	Liverpool
....	....	ALL	1775	177822	CMA	Longtown
1820	1992	1750	1992	170038	CMA	Workington
1700	1890	1660	1890	148474	CUL	Arthuret
1841	1980	1780	1841	128511	CUL	Carlisle
1700	1890	1660	1890	148474	CUL	Kirkandrews On Esk
1800	1850	1750	1850	122254	CUL	Lazonby
1892	1970	1700	1892	135151	CUL	Penrith
1720	1803	1650	1800	154881	CUL	Whitehaven
1828	1924	1750	1856	142883	DFS	Johnstone
1820	1890	1700	1890	169978	DFS	Lochmaben
1780	1802	1750	1800	154881	DUB	Monkstown
1750	1840	1650	1750	169315	DUR	Aycliffe
1804	1895	ALL	1910	158445	DUR	Durham
1828	1848	1820	1855	130990	DUR	Percymain
1833	1980	1830	1900	119474	DUR	Sunderland
1840	1896	1800	1840	154873	DUR	Sunderland

Known From	To	Researching From	To	Ref	Cty	Place
GRAHAM contd.						
1870	1920	ALL	ALL	169315	DUR	Sunderland
1841	1861	1800	1871	171425	DUR	Sunderland
1800	1857	....	1860	128546	FER	Ballinamallard
1830	1845	1800	1840	128546	FER	Enniskillen
....	....	....	1850	128546	FER	Ulster
1753	1772	....	1800	171441	KEN	Canterbury
1864	1889	....	....	138231	KEN	Deal
1890	1897	1890	1897	100846	KEN	Dover
1864	1889	....	....	138231	KEN	Dover
1873	1955	1700	1873	144754	KEN	Halstead
1861	1951	ALL	1861	107751	LAN	Liverpool
1864	1893	ALL	1864	108537	LAN	Liverpool
1830	1900	1830	1900	122254	LAN	Liverpool
1880	1992	....	1800	115150	LKS	Glasgow
1851	1881	1851	1992	128546	LKS	Glasgow
1860	1913	1840	1860	160741	LND	Bromley
1860	1913	1840	1860	160741	LND	Rotherhithe
1860	1913	1840	1860	160741	LND	Southbank
1784	1824	1750	1900	177822	LTN	Dalkeith
1852	1871	1871	1900	110132	MDX	Islington
1896	1940	1890	1992	137650	MDX	London
1852	1871	1871	1900	110132	MDX	St Pancras
1860	1890	1700	1950	137650	MLN	Edinburgh
1800	1834	ALL	1800	154563	NBL	Allendale
1758	....	1758	....	156892	NBL	Bamburgh
1828	....	....	....	132381	NBL	Haydon Bridge
1816	1844	1700	1851	110132	NBL	Hexham
1816	1844	1700	1851	110132	NBL	Ulgham
1825	1881	ALL	1825	161330	NTT	Awsworth
1818	1992	ALL	1818	146994	PER	St Martins
1824	1992	1700	1861	105899	ROX	Ancrum
1810	1860	1700	1840	106267	ROX	???
1860	1913	1840	1860	160741	SCT	ALL
1820	....	1700	1800	162507	SCT	Glasgow
1790	1992	1650	1790	158992	STS	Burslem
1882	1955	1850	1900	146978	WAR	Birmingham
....	....	ALL	1830	170135	WAR	Birmingham
1805	1850	1750	1850	122254	WES	Askham
1805	1850	1750	1850	122254	WES	Bampton
1860	1933	1860	1992	151378	WYK	Luddenden Foot
1833	1889	1833	1992	151378	WYK	Sowerby
1841	1861	1800	1871	171425	YKS	Bedale
1871	1992	1871	1992	128546	YKS	Doncaster
1680	1800	1600	1850	154016	YKS	E Witton
....	....	1850	1890	173614	YKS	Hull
GRAIEN						
1863	ALL	ALL	1880	116734	LIM	???
1863	ALL	ALL	1880	116734	TIP	???
GRAINGER						
....	....	1823	1875	144738	ABD	Aberdeen
1674	1740	1650	1800	176621	BRK	Speen
....	....	1826	1912	144738	KEN	Gravesend
1840	1873	1700	1840	120367	LND	North East
1861	1951	1861	1951	144738	SSX	Brighton
....	1847	....	1847	140767	STS	Kingswinford
1700	1851	1600	1700	133787	WIL	Calne
....	....	....	1845	140767	WOR	Dudley
1800	1850	1750	1850	116823	YKS	Fylingdales
GRALE						
1650	1812	1813	1992	166804	HAM	Andover
GRAMMER						
1759	1841	1760	1837	150053	NTH	Ailsworth
GRANDIN						
....	....	1800	ALL	149187	JSY	Grouville
GRANEY						
1810	1820	1750	1810	151769	YKS	Sheffield
GRANGE						
1830	1856	1700	1850	153001	DUR	West Hartlepool
1826	1924	1808	1924	136808	HUN	Warboys
1785	1869	ALL	1785	145211	WRY	Pateley Bridge
GRANGER						
1790	1864	1600	1790	148040	CON	Delabole
1733	....	1600	1733	132802	DOR	Sydling St Nicholas
1562	1850	....	....	172987	IOW	Niton Parish
1840	1873	1700	1840	120367	LND	North East
1750	1800	1700	1800	135941	SFK	Poslingford
....	....	ALL	1800	155470	SOM	Bridgwater
....	....	1750	1850	137111	STS	Brierley Hill
1800	1850	1800	1900	177180	STS	Tipton
GRANLEESE						
1822	1992	1650	1822	151092	FER	???
1810	1914	1600	1810	102571	NIR	Henrystuchen

Known From	To	Researching From	To	Ref	Cty	Place
GRANNELL						
1900	1992	1800	1900	128554	LAN	Liverpool
GRANNUM						
....	....	ALL	ALL	128562	ALL	Name Study
GRANT						
1780	1880	1780	1880	113670	AVN	Bristol
1810	1830	1700	1810	179574	AYR	Ayr
1843	....	....	....	167444	BRK	Reading
1742	1800	1600	1800	130125	DFS	Canonbie
1691	1730	1650	1750	126667	DOR	Winfrith Newburgh
1691	1775	....	....	127957	DOR	Winfrith Newburgh
1980	1992	1800	1980	167835	DUR	Ferryhill
....	....	ALL	ALL	101885	GLA	Tonypandy
1650	1750	1650	1750	144657	HAM	Farringdon
1828	1828	1700	1828	100110	HAM	Winchester
1849	1992	1700	1850	148423	INV	Cromdale
1855	1992	ALL	1855	123749	INV	Rothiemurchus
1800	1820	1600	1820	175382	LAN	Leeds
1600	1870	1600	1870	154598	LEI	Kibworth
1785	1844	....	....	171654	LKS	Newmains
1870	1890	1600	1870	122084	LND	Bethnal Green
1800	1820	1760	1864	137057	MOR	Cromdale
1891	?	ALL	ALL	149985	NFK	Leith
1850	1920	1700	1850	146110	SCT	ALL
1871	....	1700	1871	177865	SCT	Glasgow
....	....	?	1790	103934	SCT	Skye
1800	1870	1700	1870	174300	SOM	Bath
1800	1851	1700	....	152722	SOM	Butleigh
1805	1870	1800	1875	154733	SOM	Widcombe
1800	1810	1750	1800	177024	SRY	Merrow
1799	....	....	....	120804	WAR	Withey Brook
GRANT-TAYLOR						
1941	1950	1890	1941	173215	ALL	ALL
GRANTHAM						
1650	1750	1600	1850	177180	BKM	Chetwode
1894	1970	1800	1992	104701	BRK	Cippenham
1894	1970	1800	1992	104701	BRK	Slough
1600	1992	ALL	ALL	137847	HAM	Kingsworthy
1800	1992	ALL	ALL	137847	HAM	Winchester
....	?	?	....	134457	YKS	Leeds
GRANTLIFF						
1847	....	1700	1847	107123	CHS	Macclesfield
GRANVILLE						
....	....	....	....	107433	ALL	???
....	....	1700	1900	122203	DEV	???
1850	....	1700	1992	166073	LND	Hackney
....	....	1800	1900	128597	SOM	Glastonbury
....	....	1700	1900	122203	SOM	???
1829	1850	1700	1992	166073	WAR	Birmingham
GRASBY						
1790	1880	1550	1790	150843	YKS	South Cave
GRASSICK						
1826	1865	1700	1885	131423	ABD	Towie
....	1920	....	1920	136085	MLN	Leith
GRASTON						
1730	?	1600	1992	167592	FLN	Hawarden
GRATTAN						
1810	1840	1750	1810	121509	LAN	Liverpool
1900	1992	1700	1900	165573	LKS	???
GRATTON						
1850	1860	1700	1992	167592	DBY	Derby
1752	1802	1752	1807	148121	DBY	North Wingfield
1674	1752	1600	1755	148121	DBY	Wingerworth
1800	....	1770	1800	174602	DBY	Wingerworth
1695	1862	....	....	108057	DBY	Wirksworth
1835	1900	ALL	1900	173614	DEV	North
1850	1890	1700	1850	139432	DEV	South Molten
1807	....	1805	1810	148121	NTT	Nottingham
1830	1871	1830	1871	174602	YKS	Sheffield
GRAVATT						
1720	1720	1700	1720	170143	HAM	Eat Meon
1720	1720	1700	1720	170143	HAM	Hambledon
GRAVE						
1815	1890	1750	1815	105767	CMA	???
1815	1890	1750	1815	105767	LAN	???
GRAVELEY						
1722	1804	1600	1722	137979	YKS	Barwick In Elmet
GRAVELL						
1800	1992	1600	1992	114596	CMN	Pembray
1800	1880	1600	1880	154342	GLS	Bristol
GRAVENOR						
1838	1920	1730	1830	177164	MON	ALL
GRAVER						
1850	1900	1850	1900	136867	CON	Penzance
GRAVES						
1759	1870	1759	1900	142352	CAM	Toft
1760	1770	1700	1760	151769	DBY	Derby
1800	1872	1760	1850	102717	HRT	East
1829	....	1700	1829	102148	LIN	ALL
1810	1820	1600	1820	149845	LIN	ALL
1788	1798	1700	1815	149098	LIN	Boston
....	....	1800	1930	134503	LIN	Wolds
1795	1811	1650	1850	153079	NFK	Mattishall Burgh
1662	1685	1640	1700	142018	SOM	Chard
GRAVESTOCK						
1800	1850	1600	1900	132403	HRT	Central
GRAVESTON						
1799	1838	ALL	ALL	118168	LAN	Cartmel
GRAVETT						
1876	1950	ALL	ALL	134260	SSX	Billingshurst
GRAVIL						
1731	1992	1600	1731	172332	LIN	Epworth
GRAY						
1820	1870	1700	1820	105457	ABD	Aberdeen
1798	1992	1700	1800	130605	ANS	Arbroath
1874	1874	1850	1874	123358	ANS	Forfar
1820	1840	1700	1830	146714	ANS	Forfar
1868	1920	1600	1868	127507	ANT	Larne
1868	....	1800	1868	101427	BAN	Deskford
1590	1700	1550	1800	177180	BDF	Eaton Socon
1806	1878	1700	1806	145823	BKM	Gt Marlow
....	....	1700	1900	129364	BKM	Uxbridge
1588	1992	1588	1992	128619	CAI	ALL
1780	1800	....	....	126497	CAI	Halkirk
....	....	1800	1880	138940	CON	???
1857	1925	ALL	1857	159077	CUL	Carlisle
1830	1855	1780	1850	126586	DFS	Kirkconnel
1770	1810	1700	1770	156795	DOR	North
1840	1992	1700	1992	150797	DOR	Gillingham
....	....	1840	1950	125342	DUR	ALL
1820	1850	ALL	ALL	130508	DUR	Pittington
1851	1929	ALL	ALL	150401	ENG	???
1800	....	....	....	140317	ESS	Fingerhoe
1770	1790	....	....	157732	ESS	Romford
1860	1927	1860	1927	101877	ESS	Upminster
....	....	1838	1992	136166	GLA	Cardiff
....	....	1750	1840	136166	GLA	St Fagons
1872	1992	1700	1870	103098	IOW	Sandown
1875	1950	1850	1920	133922	JSY	St Helier
....	....	....	....	100838	KCD	Aboyne
?	?	?	?	126020	KKD	Balmaghie
....	....	1886	1940	126713	LAN	Manchester
1806	1976	1700	1992	128600	LAN	Manchester
1875	ALL	ALL	ALL	101648	LIN	Wickenby
1780	1992	1700	1780	102342	LIN	Winterton
1704	1749	1671	1749	122734	LKS	Hamilton
1860	ALL	ALL	....	110388	LKS	Lanark
1790	1900	1700	1850	170488	LKS	Stone House
1740	1865	1700	1740	114871	LND	ALL
1784	1820	....	....	101869	LND	Chelsea
1780	1922	1780	1922	101877	LND	Clerkenwell
1820	1836	1820	1836	101877	LND	Holborn
1850	1920	1850	1920	101877	LND	Islington
1865	1881	1865	1881	101877	LND	Marlylebone
1855	1861	1855	1861	101877	LND	Soho
1855	1861	1855	1861	101877	LND	St Anns
1834	1860	1834	1860	101877	LND	St Pancras
....	....	1700	1800	108677	LND	???
1848	1992	1800	1920	128694	MDX	Barnet
1776	1855	....	....	167533	MDX	Brentford
1763	1783	1760	1800	148121	MDX	Edmonton
1760	....	ALL	1760	142301	MDX	London
1810	1855	1750	1900	176982	MDX	London
1845	1845	1810	1880	105333	MDX	Stepney
....	....	1700	1900	129364	MDX	Uxbridge
1717	1820	1600	1720	177164	MON	Mynyddislwyn
1800	1900	ALL	ALL	101400	NBL	South East
1814	1992	ALL	1814	154520	NBL	Newburn
....	....	1700	1850	140627	NFK	Norwich
....	....	ALL	ALL	104531	NFK	Weston Longville
1860	1992	....	....	128643	OKI	Westray
....	....	1700	1800	162493	OKI	Westray
1918	1992	1850	1918	113050	OXF	Oxford
1850	1992	....	1850	110027	PEE	Peebles
....	....	1700	1900	134546	PER	Abernyte
1860	1880	ALL	ALL	148458	PER	Blairgowrie
1860	1880	ALL	ALL	148458	PER	Eastmill
1800	1850	....	....	117064	ROX	Ancrum

Known From	To	Researching From	To	Ref	Cty	Place
GRAY contd.						
1710	1730	ALL	1730	149063	ROX	Melrose
1850	1950	1800	1900	169404	SCT	Edinburgh
1833	1945	1815	1833	118133	SCT	Glasgow
1850	1992	....	1850	110027	SEL	Selkirk
1500	1900	1500	1900	168882	SFK	ALL
1835	1838	....	....	164232	SFK	Bury St Edmunds
1730	1850	1700	1800	129003	SFK	Campsey Ashe
1750	1965	....	....	137820	SHI	Fetlar
1720	1965	....	....	137820	SHI	Mid Yell
1760	1965	....	....	137820	SHI	North Yell
1758	1965	....	....	137820	SHI	Northmavine
1720	1965	....	....	137820	SHI	South Yell
1900	....	1800	1930	142549	SOM	Batheaston
1835	1890	1800	1900	165824	SOM	Batheaston
1800	1835	1750	1800	121592	SOM	Bourton
....	....	1700	1899	174963	SOM	High Littleton
1840	1992	1700	1992	150797	SOM	Holwell
1768	1812	1738	1768	139149	SOM	Taunton
1840	1992	1700	1992	150797	SOM	Temple Coombe
....	....	1700	1890	158763	SRY	Dulwich
1870	1922	?	1870	124540	SRY	Egham
1729	1770	1600	1729	164879	SSX	New Timber
1812	1832	....	....	168203	STI	Killearn
1832	1884	....	....	168203	STI	Kippen
1790	1992	1790	1992	161705	STS	Harborne
1830	1930	1800	1900	136239	STS	Walsall
1830	1930	1800	1900	136239	WAR	Birmingham
1878	1915	1878	1915	143286	WAR	Edgbaston
1790	1992	1790	1992	161705	WAR	???
1500	1900	1500	1900	170216	WIL	ALL
1785	1785	1755	1785	131342	WIL	Dinton
....	....	1750	1800	121592	WIL	East Knoyle
1826	....	1815	1830	165824	WIL	East Knoyle
1870	1922	?	1870	124540	WIL	Mere
1813	1850	....	....	115606	WIL	Sedehill
1700	1900	1700	1900	110361	WIL	White Parish
....	....	1886	1940	126713	YKS	Bradford
1752	1773	1500	1752	125695	YKS	Kilnwich
....	....	1886	1940	126713	YKS	Leeds
1868	1891	1800	1992	117609	???	Hampstead
GRAYLAND						
....	....	ALL	ALL	162361	ALL	ALL
1800	1987	....	....	162361	WAR	Birmingham
1700	1800	....	....	162361	WOR	Old Swinford
GRAYLIS						
1860	1900	1860	1900	157503	LAN	Preston
....	....	1800	1860	157503	MAY	???
GRAYSON						
1860	....	ALL	....	155713	NYK	Pickering
1815	1950	1750	1850	131431	STS	Brierley Hill
1791	1829	....	....	141097	YKS	Edlington
1836	1880	1836	1880	111457	YKS	Leeds
1801	1860	1700	1992	151521	YKS	Sheffield
GRAYSTON						
1700	1992	1650	1730	162396	SFK	Charsfield
GREASBY						
1861	1872	....	....	163031	SYK	Austerfield
GREASEY						
1787	1962	....	....	128015	LIN	Dunholm
1761	1796	....	....	128015	LIN	Legsby
GREASLEY						
1866	1992	....	....	163155	LEI	Coalville
1846	1992	1750	1846	176257	LEI	Congerstone
1800	1830	1700	1800	126772	LEI	Leicester
GREASON						
1820	1880	1700	1830	146714	NBL	ALL
GREATBACH						
....	....	ALL	ALL	167592	STS	ALL
....	....	ALL	ALL	167592	STS	Newcastle Under Lyme
GREATBATCH						
1853	1860	1700	1900	135623	STS	Stoke On Trent
GREATHEAD						
1690	1800	1600	1800	128708	NYK	Richmond
GREATHOLDER						
1740	1770	1700	1740	101958	LND	Strand
GREATOREY						
1826	1992	?	1826	153613	DBY	Carsington
1826	1992	?	1826	153613	DBY	Matlock
GREAVES						
1790	1992	1700	1790	135747	BKM	Hillesdon
1778	1867	1600	1778	133264	DBY	Boylestone
1813	1867	1867	1966	133264	DBY	Derby

Known From	To	Researching From	To	Ref	Cty	Place
GREAVES contd.						
1813	1836	1800	1900	133264	DBY	Mackworth
1790	1900	....	....	107484	DBY	Shirland
1813	1867	1867	1966	133264	DBY	St Alkmund
1850	1992	ALL	1900	113611	EYK	Hull
1842	1992	1690	1842	138029	LAN	Chorley
1842	1992	1690	1842	138029	LAN	Leyland
1842	1992	1690	1842	138029	LAN	Liverpool
1706	1731	ALL	ALL	141615	LAN	Stalmine
1810	1870	1800	1900	177024	MDX	Soho
....	....	1750	1800	107484	NTT	Hucknall Torkard
1700	1980	1700	1850	173819	NTT	Oxton
1720	1900	ALL	1720	176516	NTT	Sutton Cum Lound
1850	1992	....	....	128716	SAL	Oswestry
1740	1757	1700	1757	148288	YKS	Hemsworth
1740	1820	1710	1820	123595	YKS	Holmfirth
1760	1850	1700	1860	138517	YKS	Holmfirth
1800	1850	1750	1800	173452	YKS	Rotherham
1775	1830	1750	1775	177024	YKS	Rotherham
1831	1870	ALL	1831	154563	YKS	Sheffield
GREEDY						
1880	1992	....	....	125407	SOM	Wiviscombe
GREEN						
1868	....	1800	1950	146978	AVN	Bristol
1600	1700	1600	1700	167924	BDF	Meppersall
1787	1825	ALL	1825	134058	BDF	Oakley
1814	1897	1770	1890	167711	BDF	Oakley
1802	1802	1700	1900	178322	BKM	Denham
1768	1865	1768	1865	107360	BKM	Milton Keynes
1865	1948	1830	1865	113301	BKM	Princes Risborough
1759	1940	1700	1759	105562	BKM	Stoke Goldington
1865	1948	1830	1865	113301	BKM	Wingrave
1800	1890	....	....	114146	BRK	Blewbury
1717	1830	....	....	115606	BRK	Cookham
1717	1830	....	....	115606	BRK	Windsor
1720	1780	....	....	126497	CAI	Olrig
....	....	1500	1750	138614	CAI	Sinnigoe
1851	1887	1700	1851	153079	CAM	Doddington
1826	1992	....	....	103012	CAM	Ely
....	1851	....	1900	137405	CAM	Landbeach
1667	1940	....	....	128996	CAM	Thorney
....	....	1760	1800	103713	CAM	Trumpington
1851	1887	1700	1851	153079	CAM	Wimblington
1806	1901	1800	1900	122351	CHS	Canals
1881	1931	ALL	ALL	118885	CHS	Stalybridge
1861	1940	1700	1861	138983	CON	Penzance
1821	....	1700	1821	138983	CON	St Buryan
....	....	1700	1900	138983	CON	St Paul
1850	1992	1700	1900	122270	DBY	Chesterfield
1789	1906	ALL	ALL	128821	DBY	Denby
1788	1801	1700	1800	138185	DBY	Dore
1788	1801	1700	1800	138185	DBY	Dronfield
1830	1900	1800	1900	176648	DEV	Exeter
....	....	1700	1832	167649	DOR	ALL
1800	1916	1760	1800	131326	DOR	Bothenhampton
1860	?	1800	1860	172251	DOR	Bushey
1832	1839	....	....	167649	DOR	Hinton
1814	....	1814	1850	145726	DOR	Melcombe Regis
1812	....	....	....	119911	DOR	Portesham
1700	1799	1700	1799	169781	DUR	Elwich Hall
1780	1992	ALL	ALL	131091	EAG	ALL
1730	1770	....	....	129747	ESS	Colne Engaine
....	....	1700	1992	140627	ESS	Frinton
1800	1830	1750	1992	177709	ESS	???
1850	1900	1850	1900	145122	FLN	Mold
....	....	1840	1880	111538	GLS	Cheltenham
1880	1884	1855	1880	164917	GLS	Cheltenham
1660	ALL	....	....	142158	GLS	Cromhall
1800	1850	1800	1850	111538	GLS	Great Witcombe
1700	1900	1650	1900	123722	GLS	Pucklechurch
1760	1800	1760	1800	111538	GLS	Westonbirt
1869	1992	ALL	ALL	124893	HAM	ALL
1846	....	ALL	ALL	119504	HAM	Alverstoke
1780	1850	ALL	1780	150983	HAM	Portsea
....	....	1700	1800	128627	HEF	Kilpeck
....	....	1700	1800	128627	HRT	Kilpeth
1849	1869	1800	1900	114405	HRT	Royston
1750	1850	1750	1850	106704	HUN	Alconbury
1800	1900	1780	1900	106704	HUN	Upton
1824	1826	ALL	ALL	119504	IRL	???
?	?	?	?	150215	KEN	Chatham
1800	1900	....	....	104272	KEN	Loose
1870	1925	1830	1900	177989	KEN	Sevenoaks
1810	1880	1780	1880	128740	KEN	Teynham

Known From	To	Researching From	To	Ref	Cty	Place
GREEN contd.						
....	....	1700	1750	154873	KEN	???
1750	1800	1700	1800	155500	LAN	Atherton
1782	1851	....	1820	169412	LAN	Blackburn
1770	1861	1730	1871	174211	LAN	Colne
1800	....	1800	....	147532	LAN	Deane By Bolton
1400	....	1300	1500	176923	LAN	Kendal
1838	1842	1838	1860	126705	LAN	Liverpool
1845	1992	ALL	1845	152315	LAN	Liverpool
1739	....	1650	1750	179078	LAN	Melling
1860	1920	1860	1920	148962	LAN	Pendleton
1773	1809	ALL	ALL	141615	LEI	South
1824	1992	1800	1992	128783	LEI	Birstall
1900	1992	1600	1992	112003	LEI	Osgathorpe
1815	....	....	1815	164321	LEI	Tilton
....	....	ALL	ALL	143340	LEI	???
1755	1760	1720	1760	108510	LIN	Bitchfield
1700	....	....	....	169129	LIN	Deeping
1818	....	....	....	114545	LIN	Fens
1740	1760	1700	1800	120529	LIN	Revesby
1750	1815	....	....	129747	LIN	Scothorne
1818	....	....	....	114545	LIN	Sibsey
1740	1750	1700	1800	177024	LIN	Spridlington
1850	1895	1800	1850	128775	LND	Central
1850	1895	1800	1850	128775	LND	East
?	?	?	?	133418	LND	East
1800	1880	....	....	128759	LND	Bermondsey
....	....	1800	1880	128805	LND	City
1879	1892	1838	1920	128805	LND	Lambeth
1879	1920	1800	1900	128813	LND	Lambeth
1910	1920	1800	1930	128813	LND	Southwark
1832	1832	....	....	121355	LND	Whitechapel
1880	1986	ALL	....	136018	LND	Woolwich
1930	1992	1800	1930	128732	LND	???
1880	1992	1800	1880	149365	MDX	Acton
....	....	1800	1899	174963	MDX	Bethnal Green
1829	1853	1700	1829	118168	MDX	Holborn
....	....	1850	1900	106356	MDX	London
1870	1900	1800	1870	107697	MDX	London
1828	1850	1750	1828	127973	MDX	London
1889	....	1880	1900	163775	MDX	Stepney
....	....	1800	1899	174963	MDX	Tottenham
1800	1850	1800	1850	106631	MDX	Westminster
1739	1992	1538	1839	154792	MON	ALL
1750	1992	1750	1992	111074	NBL	Bedlington
1771	1771	1750	1772	170100	NBL	Hexam
1760	1950	1650	1760	128376	NBL	Wallsend
1700	1800	ALL	ALL	107425	NFK	Diss
1801	1908	1700	1850	117013	NFK	Great Ryburgh
1760	1860	....	....	128759	NFK	Hockwold
1800	1992	1700	1800	128848	NFK	Holt
1750	1830	1750	1830	145122	NFK	Norwich
1780	1970	1700	1970	158054	NFK	Norwich
1800	1860	1700	1800	172022	NFK	Sporle
1820	....	....	....	169129	NFK	Tilney
1807	1881	....	....	125202	NFK	Warhame
....	....	1800	1899	142409	NFK	???
1770	1850	1850	1992	133507	NTH	Greens Norton
1775	1850	1700	1775	147885	NTH	Greens Norton
1800	1861	1700	1800	130990	NTH	Kingscliffe
1828	1850	1828	1850	130222	NTH	Titchmarsh
1860	1890	1860	1890	130222	NTH	Twywell
1850	1950	1800	1900	102164	NTT	Bingham
1850	1992	ALL	ALL	128821	NTT	Kirkby
1825	....	....	....	135518	NTT	Radford
1837	1880	1790	1830	147885	NTT	Selston
....	....	1860	1890	155551	OXF	Chinor
1835	1925	1835	1925	149403	OXF	Oxford
1739	1750	1700	1750	159905	OXF	Shenington
1893	1992	1803	1892	118850	OXF	Swalcliffe
1699	....	1650	1750	124796	OXF	Tetsworth
1835	1925	1835	1925	149403	OXF	Wolvercote
....	....	1700	1800	159042	RUT	Whissendine
1792	1802	1740	1792	170100	SAL	ALL
1792	1802	1740	1792	170100	SAL	Weston Rhyn
1860	1992	ALL	ALL	115762	SFK	Bungay
....	....	1700	1992	140627	SFK	Ipswich
1800	1900	1800	1900	156086	SFK	Kentford
1845	1905	1800	1930	156086	SFK	Lackford
1800	1840	1750	1850	138878	SFK	Lowestoft
1849	1900	1800	1849	128724	SFK	Wetherden
....	....	1750	1900	106356	SFK	???
1800	1830	1750	1992	177709	SFK	???
1750	1965	....	....	137820	SHI	Fetlar

Known From	To	Researching From	To	Ref	Cty	Place
GREEN contd.						
1720	1965	....	....	137820	SHI	Mid Yell
1760	1965	....	....	137820	SHI	North Yell
1758	1965	....	....	137820	SHI	Northmavine
1720	1965	....	....	137820	SHI	South Yell
1819	1819	1750	1850	121568	SOM	North East
1790	1842	....	1850	121169	SOM	Frome
1750	1992	1700	1800	112704	SOM	Holcombe
1840	1992	ALL	ALL	124893	SRY	ALL
1727	1850	1650	1900	156698	SRY	Chertsey
....	....	1803	1851	139831	SRY	Clapham
....	....	1800	1899	174963	SRY	Labeth
1854	1880	1700	1854	134368	SRY	Lambeth
....	....	ALL	1800	103284	SRY	London
....	....	1750	1828	127973	SRY	Southwark
1826	1861	1570	1826	133752	STS	Brewood
1781	1880	1770	1890	160873	STS	Brierley Hill
1826	1861	1804	1826	133752	STS	Coven
1812	1980	1700	1812	176052	STS	Hilltop
1706	1770	1600	1800	160873	STS	Kingswinford
1826	1861	1804	1826	133752	STS	Paradise
1878	1900	1870	1900	134627	STS	Walsall
1860	1878	1800	1860	134627	STS	West Bromwich
1880	1992	....	....	173827	STS	West Bromwich
1840	1890	ALL	1840	176060	STS	West Bromwich
....	....	1800	1902	105562	WAR	Birmingham
1803	1822	1800	1822	128449	WAR	Birmingham
1822	1891	....	....	164062	WES	Grayrigg
1800	1830	1750	1800	136840	WIL	Avon Valley
1819	1891	....	1819	130184	WIL	Calne
1786	1786	....	1850	121169	WIL	Crockerton
1820	....	1820	....	133922	WIL	Nomansland
1849	....	1800	1870	142018	WIL	Salisbury
1780	1790	1780	1790	154210	WIL	Winterslow
1710	1870	1650	1710	168777	WIL	Winterslow
1803	1822	1800	1822	128449	WOR	Harbourne
1788	1872	....	....	138339	WOR	Kempsey
....	....	1700	1900	170313	WOR	Stourport
....	....	1703	1992	121940	WRY	Meerbeck
ALL	1810	....	....	170798	WRY	Penistone
ALL	1810	....	....	170798	WRY	Silkstone
1822	1992	1750	1850	135550	YKS	Dales
1790	1900	1700	1900	135240	YKS	Knottingley
1775	1992	ALL	1800	162027	YKS	Leeds
1755	1780	1700	1800	177024	YKS	Rotherham
1818	1888	1889	1992	175412	YKS	Sculcoates
1800	1841	....	....	102946	YKS	Sheffield
1765	1874	1700	1770	170348	YKS	Sheffield
1781	1992	1500	1781	128872	YKS	Thorner
....	....	1880	ALL	130222	???	???
GREENACRE						
1867	1880	1830	1892	133574	YKS	Leeds
GREENALD						
1800	....	....	....	144029	LAN	Birstall
GREENALL						
1830	1843	1500	1830	110310	LAN	Aighton
1782	1854	1500	1782	110310	LAN	Dutton
....	....	1750	1950	111503	LAN	Lancaster
1900	....	....	....	115371	LAN	Melling
1804	1826	1700	1826	178233	LAN	St Helens
1870	....	....	....	115371	LAN	???
GREENAWAY						
1852	1902	ALL	ALL	118168	CMA	Egremont
1816	....	....	....	124982	GLS	Berkeley
1823	1850	1700	1850	118168	GLS	Hampen
1803	1853	1803	1853	141194	GLS	Northleach
....	?	?	....	134457	OXF	Chadlington
1820	1871	1800	1900	107980	STS	Kingswinford
1790	1820	....	1790	102822	WIL	Cliffe Pypard
1814	....	1780	1830	170348	WIL	Garsdon
....	....	ALL	1820	167029	WIL	Ramsbury
GREENBERRY						
1600	1850	1550	1650	163015	LIN	ALL
GREENE						
1619	....	ALL	1619	153567	DOR	Gillingham
1660	ALL	....	....	142158	GLS	Cromhall
1700	1800	1700	1800	133817	LIN	Spalding
1877	1890	1800	1877	139785	LND	Stepney
1400	....	1300	1500	176923	NTH	Greens Norton
1877	1890	1800	1877	139785	SOM	Bedminster
1500	1700	....	....	100420	WAR	Meriden
GREENER						
1850	1960	1600	1850	128899	DUR	Dunston
1850	1960	1600	1850	128899	DUR	Gateshead

Known From	To	Researching From	To	Ref	Cty	Place
GREENER contd.						
1850	1960	1600	1850	128899	DUR	Lowhand
1850	1960	1600	1850	128899	DUR	Sunderland
1850	1960	1600	1850	128899	NBL	Newburn
1850	1960	1600	1850	128899	NBL	Newcastle On Tyne
GREENFIELD						
1700	1800	ALL	1850	149063	BEW	Coldingham
1790	1800	1700	1790	139092	DOR	Stalbridge
1810	1897	ALL	ALL	108979	ENG	North
1787	1980	1787	1980	163309	LIN	Horncastle
1800	1900	....	....	100633	LIN	???
....	....	1750	1850	147613	OXF	Spelsbury
1880	1900	1800	1900	113646	SRY	Clandon
1837	1879	1700	1837	115185	STS	Kingswinford
GREENGRASS						
1787	1992	ALL	1787	128902	NFK	Great Dunham
1858	1992	....	....	128902	NFK	Norwich
1789	1850	....	....	128902	NFK	Saham Toney
1381	1599	....	....	128902	SFK	Blackbourne Hundred
1787	1992	ALL	1787	128902	SFK	Fakenham Magna
GREENHALGH						
1791	1814	1770	1814	102121	LAN	Bolton
1764	1835	....	....	138851	LAN	Bolton
1800	1850	1700	1992	114596	LAN	Burnley
1780	1850	....	....	100056	LAN	Bury
1722	1841	?	1722	128910	LAN	Bury
1700	1830	1700	1830	152404	LAN	Eccles
1780	1850	....	....	100056	LAN	Elton
1810	1865	1780	1810	164259	LAN	Mancester
1950	1992	1950	1992	133450	LAN	Manchester
1780	1850	....	....	100056	LAN	Tottington
1746	1775	1746	1800	128929	LND	Central
1810	1950	1800	1890	128929	SAL	Dawley
1770	1920	1700	1800	154245	SAL	Dawley
1810	1950	1800	1890	128929	SAL	Madely
1880	1992	1850	1992	128929	WMD	Birmingham
GREENHALL						
1850	....	1850	....	159247	LAN	Wigan
GREENHAM						
....	....	ALL	ALL	150975	ALL	ALL
1837	1920	1700	1837	115444	AVN	Bristol
1875	1940	ALL	ALL	164801	GAL	Tuam
1760	1900	1760	1900	136840	IOW	Ryde Area
....	....	ALL	ALL	164801	LEX	Stradbally
ALL	....	....	....	150975	SOM	Crewkerne
ALL	....	....	....	150975	SOM	Norton Sub Hamdon
1760	1900	1760	1900	136840	SOM	Ryde Area
....	....	....	....	116254	SRY	???
GREENHILL						
....	....	1700	1800	147613	WOR	Old Swinford
GREENHON						
....	1820	1700	1900	126292	SFK	Newmarket
GREENHOOD						
1665	1750	1665	1750	119717	YKS	No Frodingham
GREENHOW						
1697	1973	?	?	104329	YKS	???
GREENING						
1850	1860	1840	1940	142743	AVN	Clifton
1794	....	1700	1850	143693	BKM	Mentmore
1807	1992	1700	1807	144614	GLS	Aston Blank
1700	1837	....	1837	171646	GLS	Aston Blank
1790	....	1700	1790	167649	GLS	Elmore
1774	1992	1650	1774	128937	GLS	Gloucester
1892	....	1850	1992	166197	WOR	Chanceley
GREENLAND						
1841	1845	1830	1845	134252	BKM	Chesham
1857	1921	1700	1857	177865	DEV	???
1700	1740	1690	1770	142018	DOR	ALL
1735	1860	1720	1860	142018	GLS	ALL
1631	?	?	?	166642	KEN	Saltwood
1690	1780	1670	1790	142018	LND	ALL
1600	1750	1600	1750	142018	SOM	ALL
1519	1521	ALL	1567	156175	SSX	???
1634	1850	1650	1800	142018	WIL	ALL
1824	1830	1780	1841	134252	WIL	Devizes
GREENLAW						
1850	1933	....	....	168203	CAI	Lybster
1839	1850	....	....	168203	CAI	Wick
1780	1839	....	....	168203	ELN	Haddington
....	....	1700	1820	142670	MLN	Edinburgh
GREENLEES						
1804	....	?	1825	103934	AYR	???
1817	1858	1750	1800	144606	MDX	London

Known From	To	Researching From	To	Ref	Cty	Place
GREENOP						
....	....	ALL	1880	173045	WES	Troutbeck
GREENOUGH						
1870	1992	1700	1870	118923	LAN	St Helens
1800	1950	1700	1800	120669	LAN	Westleigh
1800	1950	1700	1800	120669	LAN	Wigan
1785	1817	....	....	152234	WYK	Whitkirk
GREENS						
1750	1775	....	1750	176761	NBL	Ancroft
GREENSIT						
1850	1992	1700	1850	100803	WYK	Halifax
GREENSLADE						
1835	1840	1820	1840	134139	DEV	Exeter
1701	1870	1650	1700	119164	DEV	Rose Ash
1795	1871	ALL	1992	159174	DEV	Westleigh
1750	1862	1730	1862	107573	SOM	Winsford
GREENSMITH						
1748	1817	....	....	117374	NTT	South Muskham
GREENSTED						
1745	1806	....	1840	171441	KEN	Borden
1750	1783	....	1800	171441	KEN	Stockbury
GREENWAY						
1830	1860	ALL	1830	122823	CON	Cardingham
1718	1718	ALL	1718	154563	DOR	Portesham
....	....	1800	1890	165824	GLS	Bristol
1780	1840	1700	1850	126268	LND	Finsbury
....	....	1800	1890	165824	SOM	Bristol
GREENWELL						
1820	1992	....	....	175161	DUR	Bishop Auckland
1887	1992	1700	1887	167967	DUR	Stockton
1783	1863	1750	1783	103039	DUR	Wolsingham
1742	1780	1700	1800	123536	DUR	Wolsingham
GREENWOOD						
....	....	ALL	ALL	128953	ALL	Name Study
1550	1980	1450	1550	128953	BKM	Haddenham
1837	1863	1863	1900	128961	BKM	High Wycombe
1750	1980	1650	1750	128953	BRK	Wallingford
1880	1951	ALL	ALL	135224	CHS	Rainow
?	?	?	?	161306	ENG	???
....	....	ALL	ALL	128961	ESS	ALL
1772	1864	1600	1900	128961	ESS	Chelmsford
1729	1820	1600	1900	128961	ESS	Coggeshall
1702	1814	1600	1900	128961	ESS	Colchester
1844	1900	1840	1900	135305	ESS	Colchester
1708	1889	1600	1900	128961	ESS	Halstead
1800	1850	ALL	ALL	124982	GLS	South
1736	1744	1736	1851	128961	HRT	Hatfield
....	1823	1810	1900	128961	KEN	Dover
1792	1885	1792	1900	128961	KEN	Rochester
1800	1860	1750	1900	138517	LAN	Aston Under Lyne
....	....	1750	1860	135410	LAN	Droylesden
1711	1739	1559	1739	141291	LAN	Furness
....	....	....	....	123471	LAN	???
1807	1811	1804	1855	128961	LND	Bethnal Green
1795	1831	1795	1850	128961	LND	City
....	1795	1780	1851	128961	LND	Plaistow
1769	1854	1804	1871	128961	LND	Southwark
1838	1861	1838	1900	128961	LND	St Pancras
1804	1814	1800	1871	128961	LND	Whitechapel
1650	1980	1550	1650	128953	MDX	London
1721	1768	1700	1768	128961	MDX	Stepney
....	....	ALL	ALL	128961	NFK	ALL
1694	1856	1650	1694	147745	NTT	Edwinstowe
1694	1856	1650	1694	147745	NTT	Mansfield
1750	1992	ALL	1750	100803	NYK	Gisburn
1820	1992	1650	1800	173665	NYK	Gisburn
1837	1859	1837	1900	128961	OXF	Chipping Norton
1700	1980	1600	1700	128953	OXF	Wallingford
....	....	ALL	ALL	128961	SFK	ALL
....	1702	1600	1702	128961	SFK	Great Bricett
1734	1761	1600	1733	131245	SFK	Great Yarmouth
1614	1614	1550	1614	155276	SFK	Mendlesham
1600	1775	1600	1775	107522	WRY	Todmorden
1760	1992	ALL	ALL	100803	WYK	Erringden
1845	1992	1845	1992	153621	WYK	Halifax
....	....	1750	1875	100390	WYK	Keighley
1770	1900	1700	1770	175986	YKS	Bingley
1780	1840	1700	1780	160024	YKS	Bradford
1735	....	1700	1750	170348	YKS	Doncaster
1811	1860	1700	1811	175900	YKS	Halifax
1798	1819	1770	1799	128961	YKS	Kildwick
1865	....	1800	1900	119180	YKS	Leeds
1800	1860	1700	1800	108790	YKS	Midgley

Known From	To	Researching From	To	Ref	Cty	Place
GREENYER						
1831	1831	ALL	ALL	132349	SSX	Denton
GREEP						
1841	1880	1840	1880	135429	DEV	Cornwood
GREER						
....	1914	....	....	128988	MLN	Bathgate
GREESON						
....	1822	....	1850	137405	CAM	North
GREEST						
1678	1814	1550	1814	174343	HAM	Hambledon
GREET						
1740	1770	1740	1770	144878	CON	St Just In Roseland
1520	1696	....	1520	161837	CON	St Just Roseland
1869	1982	1600	1992	141100	CON	???
GREETHAM						
1936	1936	1935	1937	127612	KEN	Rochester
GREG						
1898	1992	1890	1900	120286	ESS	Romford
1876	1890	1850	1876	120286	NTT	Nottingham
GREGG						
1840	1884	1700	1884	153826	MDX	London
1834	1877	1800	1900	163317	NIR	Belfast
1626	1907	ALL	ALL	168610	WOR	ALL
GREGGS						
1760	1840	....	....	108871	DUR	Weardale
GREGOIRE						
1836	1907	1836	1907	157244	WAR	Birmingham
GREGOOSE						
1703	1992	1500	1703	139084	ESS	ALL
GREGORY						
1700	1758	1700	....	115576	BRK	Cheveley
1833	....	1800	1833	108391	BRK	Reading
1754	1760	1754	1760	178705	BRK	Reading
1752	1812	ALL	1812	118737	BRK	West Woodhay
1800	1900	1550	1900	149837	CHS	ALL
1848	1908	1750	1848	155845	CHS	Northwich
1790	1885	1780	1900	168947	CHS	Whitegate
1790	1885	1780	1900	168947	CHS	Winsford
....	....	1700	1850	160997	CON	???
1757	1970	ALL	1757	102350	DBY	Baslow
1845	1875	1750	1875	117722	DBY	Belper
1774	1774	ALL	1774	126942	DBY	Darley Dale
1855	....	ALL	ALL	119180	DBY	Duffield
1751	1992	1751	1992	112852	DBY	Ilkeston
1862	1900	1801	1900	112852	DBY	Litchurch
1725	1865	1600	1725	134090	DEV	Colebrook
1725	1865	1600	1725	134090	DEV	Crediton
1899	1960	1870	1899	139130	GLA	ALL
1800	1860	1700	1900	157171	GLS	Hazelton
1740	1825	1700	1900	157171	GLS	Naunton
1815	1835	1700	1850	158399	HAM	Croowham
1800	1880	1600	1900	120677	HAM	East Meon
1904	1992	1904	1992	111600	HAM	Lymington
1904	1992	1904	1992	111600	HAM	Southampton
1850	....	....	....	136565	LAN	Ormskirk
1815	1826	1750	1826	108154	LAN	West Houghton
1800	....	....	....	111570	MDX	Edmonton
1640	1660	1550	1650	111538	MDX	London
1843	1983	1815	1893	107573	MDX	Shoreditch
1810	1959	1700	1810	164070	MON	Trevethin
1780	1850	....	1780	136212	NFK	Wells
1786	....	?	1790	164976	NTT	Bramcote
1850	1992	....	....	177326	NTT	Tuxford
1720	1900	1600	1720	167584	NYK	Stanwick
1860	1992	ALL	ALL	112275	SAL	Central
1725	1750	1700	1800	149993	SAL	Shifnal
....	1900	....	1900	119024	SOM	Corsley
1750	1992	ALL	ALL	113093	SOM	Frome
....	....	1850	1870	139130	SOM	Radstock
1817	1866	1750	1817	159158	SOM	Stowey
1798	1870	1700	1798	169730	SRY	Croydon
1650	1800	1550	1650	147583	SRY	Ockham
1860	1870	1800	1860	171387	SSX	ALL
1852	1992	....	1852	121002	SSX	Brighton
1877	1883	ALL	ALL	119180	STS	Burton On Trent
1638	1749	1600	1770	160873	STS	Kingswinford
....	1900	....	1900	119024	WIL	???
1883	1950	ALL	ALL	119180	YKS	Leeds
1855	1920	1700	1855	165867	???	Myton
GREGREY						
1799	....	....	....	126187	DOR	South Poorton
GREGSON						
1791	1850	ALL	ALL	141615	LAN	East
?	....	....	?	169358	LAN	Bolton Le Moors
GREGSON contd.						
1742	1776	....	....	138851	LAN	Bolton
1836	1855	1800	1870	118443	LAN	Marton
1608	1992	1600	1992	166952	LAN	Penwortham
1800	1880	1880	1992	162256	LAN	Tockholes
?	?	?	?	118044	LIN	Glentham
1759	1828	ALL	ALL	122386	WES	Appleby
1700	1992	1540	1700	129038	WES	Appleby
....	....	1700	1800	147613	WES	Kendal
1700	1750	1600	....	118591	WES	Warcop
1700	1992	1540	1700	129038	WES	Warcop
GREIFF						
....	....	1900	1992	129046	ALL	ALL
GREIG						
1875	1930	1800	1900	106925	ABD	Newhills
1740	....	....	....	126993	ANS	Montrose
ALL	ALL	ALL	ALL	129259	CON	ALL
1755	1835	1755	1835	125598	FIF	St Andrews
1801	1883	1700	1801	102997	GMP	New Deer
1816	1861	1750	1820	117315	KCD	Fordoun
1816	1816	1700	1900	159956	LND	Lambeth
1780	1850	1780	1850	167924	MDX	Islington
1830	1880	1830	1880	167924	MDX	Pancras
1860	1871	1860	1960	171662	MLN	Dalkeith
1830	1857	1750	1860	171662	STI	Larbert
GRELLIS						
1834	1992	ALL	ALL	120057	ALL	ALL
GRENFELL						
1768	1792	....	1772	150320	CON	Madron
1803	1832	....	....	130176	CON	Sancreed
1759	1837	1700	1759	150320	CON	St Ives
GRENVILLE						
....	....	....	1851	145742	LAN	Liverpool
1750	1992	1700	1992	128597	SOM	Edington
GRESHAM						
1810	....	1800	1840	177792	IRL	???
1836	1908	1830	1920	177792	LAN	Liverpool
?	?	?	?	141003	LIN	???
GRESLEY						
1770	1800	....	....	100420	WAR	Meriden
GRESSIER						
1830	1836	1836	?	177156	LAN	Liverpool
1750	1830	1700	1750	177156	LEI	Holt
1800	....	1770	?	177156	LND	Hanover Square
GRESTY						
1500	1980	....	....	129054	CHS	Elesmere
....	....	ALL	1860	146315	CHS	Heaton Norris
1722	1823	....	....	138851	CHS	Weaverham
....	....	1700	1992	178268	LAN	Chorlton
1869	1938	ALL	1900	146315	LAN	Didsbury
GRESWELL						
1750	....	....	1750	162086	CHS	Audlem
GRETTON						
1800	1930	....	....	173827	DBY	Swadlincote
GREVES						
1715	1770	1715	1770	127655	WAR	Ullenhall
GREVILE						
1550	1850	....	....	132837	GLS	???
GREWAR						
1769	1905	1700	ALL	147036	ANS	Glenisla
GREWCOCK						
1735	1992	1570	1992	129410	ALL	ALL
....	....	1750	1900	112879	LEI	Hinckley
GREY						
1600	1800	1600	1800	167924	BDF	Campton
1796	1810	1700	1770	100846	CLK	???
1797	1812	ALL	1797	122572	CON	ALL
1800	....	....	....	100633	CUL	???
1797	1812	ALL	1797	122572	DEV	ALL
1800	1861	1700	1992	101532	DOR	Weymouth
1200	1300	ALL	1300	100536	ESS	???
1828	1849	ALL	ALL	118168	MDX	Shoreditch
1630	1700	....	....	132756	NBL	Bitchfield
1739	....	1700	1800	124796	NTH	Hartwell
1739	....	1700	1800	124796	NTH	Yardley Gobion
1794	1867	....	....	137936	SHI	Unst
GREYGOOSE						
1761	....	1700	1761	123129	SFK	Cavendish
GRIBBIN						
....	....	ALL	ALL	129070	ALL	Name Study
....	....	ALL	1947	129070	ALL	ALL
....	....	1750	1820	129070	CUL	ALL
1880	....	1830	1880	174866	CUL	Whitehaven
1850	....	1750	1850	174866	IOM	ALL

Known From	To	Researching From	To	Ref	Cty	Place
GRIBBIN contd.						
1820	1992	....	....	129070	LAN	Manchester
GRIBESBY						
1818	1818	1790	1850	105333	HAM	Isle Of Wight
GRICE						
1710	1940	....	....	128996	CAM	Thorney
1790	1800	1770	1790	117196	CHS	Frodsham
1740	1900	1600	1900	116173	CUL	West
1765	1900	1700	1900	135968	LEI	Sewstern
....	....	1800	1900	141623	SFK	Lowestoft
1875	1881	1875	1930	159468	STS	West Bromwich
GRIDLEY						
1730	1750	1700	1770	135941	SFK	Glemsford
1700	1899	1770	1840	135941	SFK	Stansfield
1670	1900	1600	1900	125792	SOM	Taunton
GRIER						
....	....	ALL	ALL	129089	ALL	Name Study
ALL	ALL	ALL	ALL	129089	ALL	ALL
1884	1992	1850	1884	100757	DON	Dunfanaghy
1725	1820	1700	1992	133450	LND	Wallbrook
GRIERSON						
1716	1950	1700	1800	144231	DFS	Ruthwell
GRIEVE						
....	....	ALL	1820	156116	BEW	???
1723	1741	ALL	1723	154563	DUR	Lamesley
1720	1800	1700	1900	130915	ELN	Dirleton
1750	1800	1650	1750	170488	NBL	Grievestead
1750	1850	ALL	1992	119105	ROX	Castleton
1690	1780	ALL	1780	149063	ROX	Melrose
1800	1900	....	....	150371	ROX	Newcastleton
GRIEVES						
1780	1780	1750	1800	116386	DUR	Washington
1806	1833	1750	1870	116386	NBL	Newburn
GRIEVESON						
1830	1860	1700	1960	101907	DUR	Bishopswearmouth
1860	1980	1700	1860	101907	KEN	Chatham
GRIFFIN						
1866	1992	?	1866	124540	ARM	Newry
1738	1895	1738	1895	119059	BKM	Brill
1799	1881	1700	1950	159964	BKM	Thornborough
1738	1965	1707	1895	119059	BKM	Waddesdon
1600	1720	1500	1800	177180	BKM	Waddesdon
1818	1830	1780	1830	147885	BKM	Wolverton
1706	1840	1685	1992	118494	CON	Grampound
1913	1992	1685	1992	118494	CON	Liskeard
1913	1992	1868	1913	118494	CON	Pensilva
....	....	1845	1868	118494	CON	St Blazey
1840	1881	1685	1992	118494	CON	Tywardreath
1700	1850	1700	1850	150797	DBY	South
1700	1850	1700	1850	150797	DBY	Derby
1850	1910	1700	1910	104744	DEV	Ulcumbe
1850	1960	1600	1850	131261	ESS	Walthamstow
1888	1940	1940	1992	179140	ESS	Walthamstow
1861	1884	1860	1900	107980	GLA	Cardiff
1838	....	ALL	ALL	121436	GLS	Thornton
....	....	1750	1850	131431	GLS	???
....	1778	ALL	ALL	129933	HAM	Eversley
1786	1873	ALL	ALL	129933	HAM	Yateley
1850	1920	1700	1850	177881	KEN	Queenborough
1830	....	....	....	163392	LAN	Liverpool
1860	....	....	....	165387	LND	Central
1824	1890	....	....	174319	LND	South
1879	....	1837	1900	103608	LND	Fulham
1838	1887	1750	1992	179140	MDX	Bethnal Green
1866	1992	1866	1992	129100	MDX	Whitechapel
1801	1992	ALL	....	116475	NFK	Walpole St Peter
1830	1900	....	....	147885	NTH	Towcester
1864	1892	ALL	1864	165735	SOM	Bristol
1700	1850	1850	1900	120189	SOM	Chew Stoke
1651	1700	1500	1651	120189	SOM	Winford
1844	1865	ALL	1870	118737	SRY	Lambeth
1820	1900	1820	1900	113743	SSX	Brede
1800	1840	....	....	105147	WAR	ALL
1690	....	1650	1720	170348	WIL	Highworth
....	....	1800	1830	159840	WIL	Marlborough
1805	....	....	....	147486	WIL	Potterne
1820	1992	....	....	175161	WOR	Kidderminster
1825	1890	1800	1992	116653	WOR	Worcester
1825	1964	....	....	138118	WOR	Worcester
....	....	1819	1820	175161	WOR	Worcester
GRIFFITH						
1782	1786	1780	....	138401	AGY	Aberfraw
1810	1992	1760	1810	138207	CAE	Llanengan
1841	1881	1816	1841	123129	CAE	Llanfaelrhys
GRIFFITH contd.						
1600	1700	....	....	176958	CGN	Blaenporth
1817	1900	1700	1817	124427	CGN	Llanbadarn Fawr
1767	1889	1700	1767	118605	CHS	Stanney
1779	1779	ALL	1779	154032	CMN	Pembrey
1733	1881	1700	1992	176923	GLA	Llangyfelach
1813	1856	1800	1856	162825	GLA	Swansea
....	....	ALL	ALL	115231	HEF	Ledbury
1830	1857	1700	1860	100439	LAN	Liverpool
1830	1857	1700	1860	100439	LAN	Rochdale
1830	1992	....	....	127779	MDX	London
1600	1700	....	....	176958	PEM	Llangoedmore
GRIFFITHS						
1847	1847	1840	1880	125032	BKM	Denham
1906	1930	1776	1906	129143	BRE	Beulah
1906	1930	1776	1906	129143	BRE	Llanafan
1793	1896	....	....	179523	CHS	Over
1840	1870	1700	1840	138452	CMN	Gwynfe
1813	1896	....	....	129232	CMN	Kidwelly
1800	1900	1700	1800	129135	CMN	Llandeilo
1841	1900	ALL	ALL	114987	CMN	Llandevaelog
1840	1870	1700	1840	138452	CMN	Llangadog
1802	1828	ALL	1850	154032	CMN	Llannon
1825	1851	1800	1861	159743	CMN	Llanwinio
1776	1813	....	....	129232	CMN	St Ishmael
1823	1890	1700	1850	118397	ESS	Rayleigh
1871	1881	1871	1950	159743	GLA	Aberfan
1880	1920	1800	1900	166901	GLA	Cardiff
1812	1920	1800	1992	115673	GLA	Cilybebyll
1870	1992	....	....	129232	GLA	Cwmavon
1775	1900	1750	1900	118540	GLA	Llangynwydd
1835	1992	....	....	142093	GLA	Llwydcoed
1836	1851	1800	1860	154032	GLA	Merthyr Tydfil
1750	1850	1750	1850	151297	GLA	Neath
1850	1992	1800	1992	129240	GLS	Bristol
1821	1901	1750	1821	155225	GLS	Sandhurst
1803	1992	1750	1820	142042	HAM	South Hayling
1872	1992	1800	1872	129186	LAN	Hulme
....	....	1858	1992	121940	LAN	Manchester
1870	1992	1840	1870	129119	MDX	Chelsea
1860	1992	1800	1860	167460	MDX	Clerkenwell
1844	1844	1800	1850	125032	MDX	Westminster
1500	1678	1500	1700	154881	MGY	Montgomery
1915	1980	1900	1980	118540	MON	Pontypool
1871	1881	1850	1910	154032	MON	Rhymney
1826	1880	1750	1826	159735	PEM	Cilgerran
1789	1992	1500	1789	140279	PEM	Milford Haven
1785	1850	1750	1850	118540	PEM	St Dogmaels
1785	1850	1750	1850	118540	PEM	St Ishmaels
1701	1992	1600	1992	141798	RAD	Noth
....	....	1800	1835	142093	RAD	Trewerw
1848	1962	1790	1850	135763	SAL	Baschurch
1789	1815	1600	1789	132802	SAL	Ironbridge
1849	1943	?	1849	136611	SAL	Leebotwood
1860	1890	1800	1900	106968	SAL	Myddle
1790	1951	ALL	1790	158445	SAL	Treflach
....	....	....	1829	140767	WAR	Birmingham
1818	1861	1700	1861	178233	WLS	Denbigh
1836	1909	1700	1836	144614	WLS	Ebbw Vale
1809	1965	1500	1809	176974	WOR	Tenbury
....	....	1820	1880	129208	YKS	Sheffield
1860	1992	1800	1860	167614	???	Llangollen
1894	1917	1850	1894	129208	???	Manchester
GRIGG						
....	....	ALL	ALL	129259	ALL	Name Study
ALL	ALL	ALL	ALL	129259	CON	ALL
1735	1900	ALL	1735	129267	CON	St Stephens By Launceston
1763	1992	1763	1900	106593	DEV	North West
1780	1890	1780	1890	105317	DEV	Exeter
1862	1962	ALL	1862	167959	ESS	Thundersley
1850	1900	1850	1900	108693	HRT	Weston
GRIGGE						
ALL	ALL	ALL	ALL	129259	CON	ALL
GRIGGLESTONE						
1893	....	ALL	ALL	107425	NFK	Norwich
GRIGGOR						
ALL	ALL	ALL	ALL	129259	CON	ALL
GRIGGS						
1801	1803	1700	1850	102938	BKM	Olney
ALL	ALL	ALL	ALL	129259	CON	ALL
1800	1850	ALL	ALL	131873	ESS	Manuden
1800	1850	ALL	ALL	131873	HRT	Ugley
1450	....	1450	1960	119458	KEN	East

Known From	To	Researching From	To	Ref	Cty	Place
GRIGOR						
1775	1959	1800	1959	134686	ROC	Black Isle
1800	1955	1700	....	134686	ROS	Rosemarkie
GRIGS						
ALL	ALL	ALL	ALL	129259	CON	ALL
GRIGSBY						
1880	1943	....	....	122378	KEN	Egerton
1837	1860	....	1837	122378	KEN	Loose
1850	1880	....	....	122378	KEN	Maidstone
GRIGSON						
1550	1992	....	....	130680	NFK	Central
GRILLS						
1540	1800	....	....	129550	CON	Southill
1841	1851	1846	1855	124001	DEV	South East
1850	1900	1800	1992	133450	DEV	Plymouth
....	....	1600	1992	129550	DEV	???
....	....	1600	1992	129550	IRL	???
1861	1910	1846	1863	124001	KEN	Chatham
GRIMBALDESTON						
1740	1770	1650	1820	105333	LAN	Walton Le Dale
GRIME						
1750	1900	1750	1900	125237	LAN	Darwen
1800	1880	1880	1992	162256	LAN	Darwen
1850	1940	1800	1992	166081	LAN	Preston
1660	1992	ALL	1815	142301	LAN	Walmersley
1790	1850	1750	1800	166081	LAN	Wheelton
GRIMES						
1840	....	1840	1880	135429	DEV	Lympstone
1886	1925	1886	1925	129283	ESS	Silvertown
1640	1800	ALL	ALL	172812	GLS	ALL
1840	1860	1500	1992	175498	IRL	???
....	....	1600	1900	179531	LIN	ALL
1840	1860	1500	1992	175498	LND	Blackfriars
....	....	1800	1919	129275	LND	Newington
....	....	1800	1900	129275	LND	Walworth
1797	1992	1797	1992	145238	NFK	North
1795	1820	1795	1850	129283	NFK	East Barsham
1820	1858	1800	1860	129283	NFK	Fakenham
1731	1932	1730	1795	129283	NFK	Felbrigg
1698	1701	ALL	1698	129283	NFK	Knapton
1703	1730	1703	1750	129283	NFK	Sustead
1800	....	....	....	100633	NTT	???
1858	1903	1858	1903	129283	SFK	Lowestoft
....	1790	....	....	128910	WAR	Nuneaton
1814	ALL	ALL	1840	116734	WEM	???
1690	1711	1650	1750	170348	WIL	Puton
GRIMMER						
1883	....	1840	1890	144606	MDX	Westminster
....	1760	....	1760	151688	NFK	Catfield
1823	1861	1861	1992	151688	NFK	East Ruston
GRIMMETT						
1762	1826	ALL	1762	115126	OXF	Great Tew
GRIMMETTE						
1819	1992	....	....	129291	LND	???
GRIMMOND						
1861	1874	1700	1860	129305	ANS	Dundee
1824	1902	1700	1824	178896	ANS	Dundee
1824	1902	1700	1824	178896	ANS	Monifieth
1791	1841	1700	1860	129305	PER	Airntully
GRIMOLDBY						
?	?	?	?	118044	LIN	Keddington
GRIMSDELL						
1765	....	1700	1765	176885	BKM	Great Hampden
GRIMSDITCH						
1811	1853	1600	1811	117730	CAM	Littleport
....	....	ALL	ALL	130850	LAN	Manchester
GRIMSEY						
1821	1880	1750	1850	128732	ESS	Thorrington St Osyth
GRIMSHAW						
1820	1871	ALL	1820	172901	DBY	ALL
1820	1871	ALL	1820	172901	LAN	ALL
1774	1791	1349	1803	147281	LAN	Ashton Under Lyne
?	1771	....	....	138851	LAN	Bolton
....	....	1857	....	106623	LAN	Calsford
1771	1910	1600	1910	129313	LAN	Droylsden
1600	1725	1600	1725	109347	LAN	Oswaldtwistle
1650	1863	1600	1851	170267	YKS	Aire Valley
GRIMSHIRE						
1700	1723	....	1760	171441	BRK	Stanford In The Vale
GRIMSLEY						
1790	....	ALL	1790	130079	OXF	Bicester
GRIMSON						
....	....	1700	1850	140627	NFK	Hales
GRIMSTEAD						
....	....	ALL	ALL	129321	ALL	Name Study
GRIMSTER						
1770	....	1700	1770	101524	SOM	Ilton
GRIMSTONE						
....	....	ALL	ALL	145475	ALL	Name Study
GRIMWADE						
1773	1900	1773	1900	114081	ESS	Burnham
....	....	1600	1800	114081	SFK	Central
GRIMWOOD						
1820	1884	1600	1992	161543	ESS	Colchester
1895	1900	1800	1900	123811	SFK	Ipswich
1700	1800	1700	1800	133817	SFK	Nedging
GRINDALL						
1736	1841	1700	1736	172006	HEF	Goodrich
GRINDLEY						
1762	....	ALL	1839	131725	SAL	Malinslee
1780	1977	1700	1977	138088	SAL	Whittington
1700	1750	1600	1700	173312	STS	Whitmore
GRINDROD						
1815	....	1750	1815	100390	LAN	Manchester
GRINDY						
1800	1840	1800	1840	108510	STS	Tunstall
GRINELL						
1862	....	1700	1992	149659	MDX	London
GRINGLE						
1723	1800	1600	1723	166804	SFK	Kirkley
GRINGLEY						
1800	1900	1800	1900	114529	YKS	Sheffield
1700	1850	1700	1900	114529	YKS	Swinefleet
GRINNEY						
1772	1992	1641	1992	146439	DEV	North
GRINSDALE						
....	1769	ALL	1769	175080	DEV	Beer
....	1769	ALL	1769	175080	DEV	Seaton
GRINSTED						
1820	1900	ALL	1900	118338	KEN	Rochester
1790	1929	....	....	135984	KEN	Sheerness Minster
1790	1929	....	....	135984	LND	Deptford
1790	1929	....	....	135984	LND	Rotherhithe
1775	1992	1775	1992	147001	SSX	Horsham
1745	1851	....	....	144282	SSX	Shermanbury
1785	1897	1700	1785	104922	SSX	Wisborough Green
GRINT						
1823	1882	1800	1850	129356	MDX	St Pancras
....	....	1750	1820	129356	SFK	Wrentham
GRINTER						
1850	1966	1700	1850	171182	DOR	ALL
1879	1900	1700	1879	129364	ESS	Forestgate
1879	1900	1700	1879	129364	ESS	Leytonstone
GRIPTON						
1825	....	....	....	130486	STS	Stafford
GRISBY						
1779	1808	1775	1820	108251	KEN	Maidstone
GRISDALE						
1684	1992	ALL	1684	153729	CUL	ALL
GRISENTHWAITE						
1600	1900	1600	1992	147788	CUL	ALL
1600	1900	1600	1992	147788	CUL	Penrith
GRISSELL						
1770	1837	....	....	160458	ALL	ALL
....	1764	ALL	ALL	129933	LND	Camberwell
1770	1837	....	....	160458	SRY	???
GRIST						
1812	1992	....	....	129372	AVN	Radstock
1800	1850	1770	1860	166677	HAM	Bullington
1730	1812	1600	1734	129372	SOM	Hemington
1779	1781	....	....	112887	WIL	Bradford
1790	1817	....	1817	121169	WIL	Longbridge Deverill
GRISWOLD						
1200	1639	1535	1639	129380	WAR	Kenilworth
1200	1639	1535	1639	129380	WAR	Knowle
1200	1639	1535	1639	129380	WAR	Lapworth
1200	1639	1535	1639	129380	WAR	Rowington
1200	1639	1535	1639	129380	WAR	Snitterfield
1200	1639	1535	1639	129380	WAR	Solihull
1200	1639	1535	1639	129380	WAR	Stoneleigh
1200	1639	1535	1639	129380	WAR	Wootton Wawen
1200	1639	1535	1639	129380	WAR	Wroxall
1200	1639	1535	1639	129380	WAR	Yardley
GROAT						
1720	1750	....	....	126497	CAI	Olrig

Known From	To	Researching From	To	Ref	Cty	Place
GROBITY						
1700	1799	ALL	ALL	146633	HRT	Hemel Hempstead
1700	1799	ALL	ALL	146633	LND	City
1700	1799	ALL	ALL	146633	WIL	Gt Bedwyn
GROCER						
1739	1775	....	....	127426	NTH	Earls Barton
GROCOAN						
1834	1871	ALL	ALL	152919	SOM	Bristol
GROCOCK						
1700	1992	1570	1992	129410	ALL	ALL
1840	1870	1700	1800	155950	LEI	Leicester
GROCOTT						
1817	1900	1850	1871	156574	CHS	Englesea Brook
1780	1900	1780	1900	165441	STS	Stoke On Trent
GROGONO						
1849	1914	1800	1849	109576	MDX	Paddington
GRONOW						
....	....	ALL	ALL	129402	ALL	Name Study
1832	1900	1800	1900	118540	GLA	Llangynwydd
GROOCOCK						
1570	1992	1570	1992	129410	ALL	ALL
GROOM						
1813	1992	1750	1992	102970	HRT	Flamstead
1850	1992	1700	1850	109061	LND	Mile End
1880	1882	1800	1940	151181	LND	Peckham
1850	1992	....	....	143049	MDX	London
1850	1906	1767	1992	129429	NFK	Attleborough
....	....	1600	1700	129429	NFK	Bunwell
1797	1938	1700	1900	156353	NFK	Crimplesham
1850	1906	1767	1992	129429	NFK	Rockland St Peter
1725	1802	1700	1725	168521	NFK	Sculthorpe
....	....	1650	1992	143049	NFK	???
....	....	1780	1820	177393	SAL	Ellesmere
1833	1840	....	....	177393	SAL	Wem
1600	1800	1550	1800	142123	SAL	Weston Under Redcastle
1730	1890	ALL	1730	100536	SFK	???
1858	1858	1820	1880	151181	SRY	Camberwell
1872	1972	1872	1992	165441	STS	Shelton
1863	1900	....	....	177393	YKS	Doncaster
GROOMBRIDGE						
1700	1900	1700	1900	100617	KEN	Shoreham
1800	1899	ALL	ALL	103837	YKS	Hull
GROOME						
1700	1920	ALL	1992	100536	???	Aldburgh
GROSE						
....	....	ALL	ALL	129445	ALL	Name Study
ALL	ALL	ALL	ALL	129445	ALL	ALL
1829	1992	1700	1829	129437	CON	West
1790	1900	1700	1900	142875	CON	Kenwyn
....	1920	....	....	147672	CON	Liskeard
1840	1920	1840	1992	137448	CON	Sancreed
GROSIER						
1730	1800	....	....	102741	DUR	Gainford
GROSS						
1757	1757	1750	1760	107360	NTH	Harlestone
GROSSE						
1799	1925	....	1799	132837	MDX	???
1687	1701	ALL	1687	115126	NTH	Kingsthorpe
GROSSET						
1800	1870	1750	1800	147095	SCT	Edinburgh
GROSSIER						
1600	ALL	ALL	ALL	115126	CHI	ALL
GROSSMITH						
....	....	1790	1870	170437	HAM	Portsmouth
GROSVENOR						
1738	1827	1827	1992	175412	STS	Rowley Regis
GROTRIAN						
....	....	ALL	ALL	103454	???	???
GROTTICK						
....	....	ALL	ALL	112801	ALL	Name Study
GROUCUTT						
1717	1877	1600	1717	120189	STS	Wolverhampton
GROUND						
1654	1940	....	....	128996	CAM	Thorney
GROUNDS						
1792	1874	....	....	176613	CAM	Wisbech
1839	1839	1790	1839	178055	CHS	Thelwall
1830	1890	1750	1830	129453	LAN	Warrington
GROUT						
1800	1810	1750	1810	158658	ESS	Debden
1620	1800	1600	1840	105333	HAM	Portsmouth
1813	1992	....	1812	129461	LND	???
1830	1992	1550	1830	171395	SRY	Great Bookham

Known From	To	Researching From	To	Ref	Cty	Place
GROUT contd.						
1620	1800	1600	1840	105333	SSX	Chichester
GROVE						
1700	1900	1550	1700	148296	BKM	Boundaries
1700	1900	1550	1700	148296	BRK	Boundaries
1870	1992	1870	1992	121738	BRK	Reading
1607	1687	....	....	165999	GLS	Henbury
....	....	1700	1850	152390	HRT	Bishops Stortford
1600	1650	?	1600	158569	HRT	St Albans
1709	....	....	1740	171441	KEN	Bethersden
....	....	1700	1850	152390	LND	Benfleet
1871	1898	ALL	1871	168742	LND	London
....	....	1700	1850	152390	LND	Stratford
1700	1900	1550	1700	148296	LND	???
1870	1890	1800	1950	178799	MDX	Clerkenwell
1870	1890	1800	1950	178799	MDX	Holborn
1742	1791	ALL	1992	119695	SOM	West Pennard
1700	1900	1550	1700	148296	SRY	West
1825	1992	1600	1825	115525	STS	Bilston
....	....	1800	1875	108243	WLS	South
....	1860	....	1950	130168	WLS	Pontypool
GROVEHURST						
....	....	1250	1350	154873	HEF	Horsmonden
GROVER						
1758	1792	1700	1800	157732	HAM	Alton
1788	1850	1700	1788	167711	HAM	Binstead
1650	1850	1600	1750	168343	HAM	???
1890	1925	ALL	ALL	164887	HRT	Watford
1691	1814	1680	1797	170143	SRY	Burpham
1797	1881	1795	1900	170143	SRY	Sutton
1691	1814	1680	1797	170143	SRY	Worplesdon
1757	1860	ALL	1757	136387	SSX	Fletching
1880	1890	....	....	136387	SSX	Lindfield
1890	1971	....	....	136387	SSX	???
GROVES						
1832	1840	1830	1861	115886	BRK	Clewer
1780	....	....	....	151351	DOR	Powerstock
1714	1714	1600	1714	159239	ESS	Colchester
1773	1992	....	....	159387	GLS	Cotswolds
1600	1750	1600	1750	131040	GLS	Gloucester
1673	1896	1600	1773	169242	HAM	Isle Of Wight
1800	1950	1700	1900	170933	HAM	Southampton
1830	....	1830	1940	100307	KEN	Woolwich
1824	1992	....	1824	129518	KER	Tralee
1729	1745	ALL	ALL	141615	LEI	Snarestone
1730	1812	1580	1812	129496	LIN	Colsterworth
1871	....	1861	1992	115886	LND	North
1779	....	ALL	1779	161500	MDX	Chelsea
1779	....	ALL	1779	161500	MDX	Kensington
1850	1900	1850	1950	129496	NTT	Nottingham
1800	1900	1750	1850	168297	OXF	Milton Under Wychwood
1825	1825	1800	1830	111414	SAL	Acton Scott
1799	1799	1750	1851	111414	SAL	Wistanstow
1800	1992	1600	1800	129488	SSX	Steyning
....	1700	....	....	174564	SSX	???
1600	1700	1600	1700	131040	STS	ALL
1600	1700	1600	1700	131040	WOR	ALL
1900	1992	1700	1850	164429	YKS	Whitby
GRUBB						
1810	1850	1700	1810	130443	BDF	???
GRUBY						
1719	1814	1654	....	131210	ESS	Chingford
1719	1814	1654	....	131210	ESS	Waltham Abbey
1750	1800	1700	1800	144657	ESS	Waltham Holy Cross
GRUDGEFIELD						
1590	1674	ALL	1590	168602	SFK	Lowestoft
GRUMITT						
1785	1900	ALL	1785	115843	LIN	Edenham
GRUMMEL						
1764	1766	1720	1800	159905	CUL	Cumwhinton
GRUMMETT						
1900	1934	1800	1900	144630	NFK	Sporle
GRUNDY						
1704	1795	ALL	1795	116548	DUR	ALL
1915	1992	1900	1992	129526	ESS	Chelmsford
....	....	1600	1800	129534	LAN	East
1885	1992	....	1900	147818	LAN	Bolton
1795	1968	....	....	169013	LAN	Bolton
1800	1960	1600	1800	129534	LAN	Bury
1869	1992	1869	1992	115932	LAN	Manchester
1800	1810	1700	1800	121509	LAN	Whalley
1850	1880	1800	1992	129526	LEI	Loughborough
1713	1848	1560	1713	129526	LEI	Wymeswold

Known From	To	Researching From	To	Ref	Cty	Place
GRUNDY contd.						
1817	1819	1800	1840	108510	STS	Harrisea Headh
1836	1880	1800	1900	129526	YKS	Sheffield
1867	1890	1850	1956	129526	???	London
GRUT						
....	....	ALL	ALL	160105	ALL	Name Study
GRUTCHEFIELD						
....	....	ALL	ALL	129542	ALL	Name Study
GRYLL						
1700	1850	....	....	141178	CON	South East
GRYLLS						
....	....	ALL	ALL	129550	ALL	Name Study
1550	1900	ALL	ALL	137286	CON	ALL
1750	1900	....	....	129550	CON	Helston
1600	1750	....	....	129550	CON	Lanreath
GRYME						
1504	1750	ALL	ALL	129283	NFK	North East
GUBB						
1625	1730	1580	1625	102571	CON	Penzance
1540	1950	1700	1890	132721	DEV	North
1800	1992	1700	1800	164798	DEV	Exeter
1893	....	....	....	156639	ESS	West Ham
1890	1900	1800	1890	131350	WLS	Swansea
GUBBINGS						
....	....	ALL	ALL	131253	DEV	Tavistock
GUBBINS						
....	....	ALL	ALL	129569	ALL	Name Study
1680	1992	1300	1680	129577	IOW	???
1759	1759	1755	1765	107360	NTH	Blakesley
GUDE						
1811	1817	ALL	1811	122572	ALL	ALL
GUDERIAN						
ALL	ALL	ALL	ALL	124206	ALL	ALL
GUDGE						
1822	1992	....	1822	151270	SOM	Misterton
1822	1992	....	1822	151270	SOM	South Petherton
GUDGEON						
1826	1826	1500	1826	110310	LAN	Blackburn
1660	1840	ALL	ALL	124311	LAN	Mitton
1713	1843	1500	1713	110310	LAN	Ribchester
GUDGER						
1800	1937	1750	1850	157716	YKS	Huddersfield
GUERIN						
1830	1860	1750	1860	173312	IRL	???
GUERNIERE						
1875	1893	ALL	ALL	106313	ALL	ALL
GUESS						
....	....	ALL	ALL	129585	ALL	Name Study
GUEST						
1747	1757	1738	1900	129607	CHS	Runcorn
1773	1810	1750	1850	129607	DEN	Gresford
1810	1900	1800	1900	129607	FLN	Hope
1722	1737	1700	1750	133280	GLA	Merthyr Tydfil
1772	1992	1700	1800	105201	KEN	Tonbridge
1750	....	ALL	1750	179515	SAL	Telford
1824	1957	1700	1824	137154	SRY	Frimley
1603	1786	1550	1786	102830	STS	Sedgely
1850	1870	1800	1900	107476	STS	Woodsetton
1759	....	....	....	142859	WIL	Leigh
1820	1870	1800	1900	107476	WOR	Dudley
1802	....	....	....	102733	WOR	Redditch
1815	1952	1750	1821	136301	YKS	Barnsley
1950	....	1800	1900	129593	YKS	Featherstone
GUILDFORD						
1500	1600	1450	1600	154881	KEN	Sittingbourne
1906	1960	1850	1960	165824	SOM	Bath
GUILFORD						
1700	1950	1500	1700	153230	LEI	Keyham
GUILFOYLE						
1850	1874	1800	1900	133043	CLA	Scariff
GUILLAUME						
1700	....	....	....	137693	CHI	Guernsey
GUILLE						
ALL	ALL	ALL	ALL	115126	CHI	ALL
1700	1900	....	....	137693	CHI	Guernsey
GUISE						
1770	1800	....	....	100420	WAR	Meriden
GUISELEY						
....	....	ALL	ALL	129623	ALL	Name Study
1417	1992	1400	1992	129623	YKS	???
GUIVER						
1800	1950	1700	1992	162345	ESS	Romford
1750	1900	....	....	129801	HRT	Barkway

Known From	To	Researching From	To	Ref	Cty	Place
GULBY						
....	....	1350	1400	154873	KEN	Orpington
GULL						
1840	1910	....	....	171972	ESS	Colchester
GULLEY						
1879	....	1872	1992	118567	CHS	Birkenhead
1780	1825	1780	1850	118567	DEV	South Molton
1820	1960	1820	1992	118567	GLA	Aberdare
1820	1960	1820	1992	118567	GLA	Neath
1820	1960	1820	1992	118567	GLA	Swansea
GULLICK						
....	....	ALL	ALL	174963	ALL	Name Study
....	....	ALL	ALL	174963	ALL	ALL
1839	1845	1800	1839	155217	CON	St Stephens
1830	1844	....	1830	108839	DEV	Totnes
GULLIDGE						
1745	1900	1600	1745	177164	SOM	Sedgemoor
GULLIFORD						
1861	1940	1850	1992	129631	MON	Blaenavon
1841	1851	1700	1860	129631	SOM	Camerton
1851	1855	1700	1992	129631	SOM	Clandown
....	....	1700	1992	129631	SOM	Midsomer Norton
1800	1870	1770	1870	124761	SOM	Radstock
....	....	1700	1992	129631	SOM	Radstock
GULLIVER						
1861	1881	1850	1992	129631	GNT	Blaenavon
1790	1870	1700	1800	107611	WIL	Wingfield
GULLOCK						
....	....	ALL	ALL	174963	ALL	ALL
GULLY						
....	....	1880	1992	161829	CON	???
1867	1992	?	1867	153613	DBY	ALL
1837	1940	1750	1992	161829	DEV	???
1874	....	....	....	140473	???	???
GUM						
1850	1880	1750	1850	129666	DEV	Berrynarbor
1855	1864	1850	1890	129666	DUR	Auckland
1760	1852	1650	1852	129666	WIL	Seend
GUMBERT						
....	....	1100	1200	154873	NTT	Hockerton
GUMBLETON						
....	....	ALL	ALL	175226	ALL	Name Study
1779	1853	1700	1992	102415	DOR	Poole
1838	1900	1700	1992	102415	WIL	West Grinstead
GUMBLEY						
1874	1992	1980	1992	130311	LAN	Littleborough
1775	1790	1600	1775	130311	WAR	Coventry
1790	1937	1600	1992	130311	WAR	Stoneleigh
....	....	1840	1900	130311	YKS	Hebden Bridge
1851	1851	1852	1900	130311	YKS	Otley
GUMBRELL						
1820	1893	ALL	1913	158070	SSX	Poynings
GUMLEY						
1794	1900	1700	1900	153826	CAV	???
1640	1787	1550	1639	131245	LEI	Countesthorpe
GUMM						
1812	1992	1700	1812	175722	MDX	Brentford
1832	1879	1780	1880	135933	OXF	Charlbury
1832	1879	1780	1880	135933	OXF	Fawler
....	1799	....	....	130079	OXF	Merton
GUMMOE						
1700	....	1600	....	116920	CON	St Ewe
GUMMOW						
1730	1740	1680	1750	168580	CON	Newley East
1760	1770	1750	1800	168580	CON	St Colan
1760	1800	1700	1760	165549	CON	St Columb Major
1760	1770	1750	1820	168580	CON	St Enoder
GUMTER						
1830	1865	ALL	ALL	162434	GLS	Woolaston
GUNBY						
1734	1992	1650	1734	102342	LIN	Scotten
GUNDRILL						
1790	1833	1700	1850	100439	HRT	Weston
GUNESS						
1836	....	1750	....	134589	LIN	Wadingham
GUNHOUSE						
1836	....	1750	1900	134589	LIN	Wadingham
GUNN						
1840	1862	....	....	127140	AYR	Stevenston
1748	1779	....	....	168203	CAI	Latheron
1817	....	....	....	127140	CAI	Thurso
1732	1992	1700	1992	128481	CAI	Watten
1851	1929	ALL	ALL	108979	ENG	North
1806	1808	1750	1830	179140	ESS	Hatfield Broad Oak

Known From	To	Researching From	To	Ref	Cty	Place
GUNN contd.						
1868	....	....	....	127140	LKS	Glasgow
1790	1811	1700	1789	131245	MDX	Whitechapel
1880	1930	....	....	111260	MLN	Newington
1880	1930	....	....	111260	ROX	Kelso
1812	1870	1780	1812	150029	SCT	Edingburgh
1812	1870	1780	1812	150029	SCT	Glasgow
1750	1965	....	....	137820	SHI	Fetlar
1720	1965	....	....	137820	SHI	Mid Yell
1760	1965	....	....	137820	SHI	North Yell
1758	1965	....	....	137820	SHI	Northmavine
1720	1965	....	....	137820	SHI	South Yell
1875	....	ALL	ALL	150681	SLI	???
1817	....	....	....	127140	SUT	Farr
GUNNELL						
1826	1894	ALL	1826	129682	GLS	Cheltenham
GUNNER						
1750	1820	1700	1820	146803	HAM	Crondall
1798	1836	1770	1851	170143	SRY	Send
1798	1836	1770	1851	170143	SRY	Stoke
1764	1929	....	....	115606	SRY	Windlesham
GUNNING						
1881	1909	1500	1881	175072	IRL	???
GUNNINGHAM						
1814	1880	1800	1900	118540	SOM	Wells
GUNSON						
1894	1939	....	....	117196	CHS	Didsbury
1839	1867	1800	1839	117196	DUR	Hetton Le Hole
1839	1940	1750	1839	117218	DUR	Houghton Le Spring
1794	1820	1770	1840	118443	LAN	Blawith
1867	1894	....	....	117196	LAN	Longsight
GUNSTON						
1746	1902	....	1746	103489	OXF	Gt Haseley
GUNSTONE						
....	....	ALL	ALL	129690	ALL	Name Study
GUNTER						
1699	1940	ALL	1940	118737	BRK	Newbury
1825	....	1800	1900	126144	KEN	Wrotham
GUNTHORPE						
....	....	ALL	ALL	124222	ALL	Name Study
GUNTON						
....	1719	....	1719	108839	CAM	Sutton
1774	1793	1700	1774	176885	NFK	Costessey
GUNTRIP						
1745	1850	1650	1850	162043	BKM	Buckingham
1800	1880	1700	1992	116742	OXF	Aston Rowant
GUPPY						
1850	1992	1800	1850	140465	SOM	Bath
GUPWELL						
1500	1992	ALL	ALL	124281	ALL	ALL
GURD						
1700	1750	1550	1700	156795	DOR	East
1869	....	ALL	1992	174157	LEX	Stradbally
1800	1850	ALL	ALL	151998	WIL	Donhead St Mary
1797	1825	1700	1797	150223	WIL	Fonthill Gifford
GURDON						
1850	1992	1850	1992	133450	SFK	Grundisburgh
GURLEY						
1810	....	1780	1880	141739	FIF	???
GURLING						
....	1764	....	1800	137405	SFK	West
GURNETT						
1790	1820	ALL	1992	119105	SSX	ALL
GURNEY						
1755	1851	1600	1755	167355	BKM	Wingrave
1850	1890	1850	1900	148563	CHS	Birkenhead
1787	1865	?	1865	177806	CMA	Wreay
1557	1992	1066	1557	140252	DEV	Dartmouth
....	....	1750	1851	111414	GLS	ALL
1802	1802	1750	1851	111414	GLS	Ashleworth
1760	1830	1750	1830	156930	GLS	Kempley
1802	1858	1750	1861	111414	GLS	Maisemore
1680	1992	1600	1700	129704	HRT	Arnham
1887	1992	1800	1900	149012	KEN	Bermondsey
?	?	?	?	154687	KEN	Herne
....	....	ALL	1890	178195	KEN	London
?	?	?	?	154687	KEN	Reculver
1889	....	1850	1889	151610	LND	Notting Hill
1823	1899	1800	1823	165107	LND	St Pancras
....	....	ALL	1890	178195	MDX	London
1780	1980	ALL	ALL	127884	MDX	Pinner
1776	1992	1700	1776	129712	SFK	Bury St Edmunds
....	....	ALL	1890	178195	SRY	London
1880	1900	1830	1900	122351	WAR	Rugby
GURR						
1822	1900	1700	1900	170054	KEN	Bromley
1837	1859	1850	1860	138312	KEN	Hythe
GURTEEN						
....	....	1600	1992	129720	CAM	Haverhill
1900	1992	....	....	129720	DUR	Houghton Le Spring
....	....	1600	1992	129720	ESS	Great Yeldham
....	....	1600	1992	129720	SFK	???
GURTON						
1823	1864	1750	1823	113352	ESS	Faulkbourne
GUSTARD						
1830	1840	ALL	1830	158577	NBL	Long Framlington
GUSTERSON						
1820	1955	ALL	ALL	133930	LND	ALL
GUSWELL						
1880	1925	1850	1930	157341	DEV	Plymouth
GUTCH						
....	....	ALL	ALL	152285	ALL	ALL
GUTCHER						
1673	1691	....	....	128066	FIF	Pitcruvie
GUTHERSON						
1700	1770	1700	1800	149152	NBL	???
GUTHRIE						
1725	1930	....	1725	160431	ABD	Pitsligo
....	....	1716	ALL	149187	ANS	Monifieth
....	....	1716	ALL	149187	ANS	Murroes
1750	1992	....	1992	129739	BEW	ALL
1780	1840	1750	1840	122416	DON	???
1780	1840	1750	1840	122416	FER	???
....	....	ALL	ALL	125733	KEN	Northfleet
1870	1992	....	1992	129739	SEL	Selkirk
1750	1965	....	....	137820	SHI	Fetlar
1720	1965	....	....	137820	SHI	Mid Yell
1760	1965	....	....	137820	SHI	North Yell
1758	1965	....	....	137820	SHI	Northmavine
1720	1965	....	....	137820	SHI	South Yell
GUTSELL						
1783	1920	1700	1920	113743	SSX	Brede
GUTTERIDGE						
1744	....	....	....	129747	IOW	Brightstone
1804	....	....	....	129747	IOW	Freshwater
1835	....	....	....	129747	IOW	Mottiston
1852	....	....	....	129747	IOW	Newport
1776	....	....	....	129747	IOW	Yarmouth
1750	1840	1700	1900	126799	KEN	Rochester
1840	1992	1800	1992	126799	LND	Lambeth
1850	1869	1775	1850	121037	MDX	Bethnal Green
1869	1954	1550	1868	129763	NFK	Haddon
1840	1860	1800	1860	137111	STS	Sedgeley
GUTTIS						
1830	....	1800	1900	141933	MDX	London
GUY						
1800	1888	1825	1875	172634	ARM	Portadown
1885	1992	....	....	176125	BRK	Newbury
1823	1885	1800	1850	176125	BRK	Reading
1875	1914	1700	1875	111708	CON	Scilly Isles
1700	1740	1650	1700	129445	CON	St Endellion
1700	1740	1650	1700	129445	CON	St Minver
....	....	1550	1700	156795	DOR	East
1800	1992	1700	1992	119040	DOR	Parkstone
1800	1992	1700	1992	119040	DOR	Poole
1819	....	1800	1850	163775	DOR	Shaftsbury
....	....	1700	1992	122009	ESS	East
1780	1808	1780	1851	173703	GLS	???
1580	1580	....	....	153397	HAM	Milford
1809	1871	ALL	ALL	149489	HAM	Portsmouth
1771	1792	1771	1800	126667	IOW	Godshill
1800	1900	1850	1900	121592	IOW	Newport
1845	1992	1800	1845	103322	LAN	Chorley
1770	....	1700	1800	139483	LAN	Melling
1845	1992	1800	1845	103322	LAN	Salmesbury
1840	1900	1800	1840	139483	LAN	Walton
1700	1750	1700	1750	123765	LIN	Orby
1800	1860	1800	1830	161586	SSX	Bosham
1636	1676	....	1636	129771	SSX	Ripe
1830	1871	....	....	118729	STS	Shiffnel
1645	1724	1645	1724	160237	STS	Tamworth
....	....	1670	1800	147613	YKS	Bentham
1743	1856	1700	1900	116742	YKS	Swaledale
GUYER						
1757	1850	1700	1757	133442	KEN	Woolwich
GUYON						
1720	1770	....	....	165999	ESS	Coggeshall

Known From	To	Researching From	To	Ref	Cty	Place
GUYTON						
1817	1838	1700	1816	131245	NFK	Norwich
GUYVER						
....	....	ALL	ALL	129801	ALL	Name Study
1655	1900	....	....	129801	ESS	Broxted
1540	1921	....	....	169188	ESS	Thaxted
1540	1921	....	....	169188	ESS	Tilty
GWATKIN						
1850	1900	....	....	137200	HEF	Goodrich
1850	1900	....	....	137200	HEF	Ross
GWATKINS						
1850	1900	....	....	137200	HEF	Goodrich
1850	1900	....	....	137200	HEF	Ross
GWEAWN						
250	....	....	....	178160	???	Catterick
GWGAN						
....	....	ALL	ALL	178160	WLS	???
GWILLIAM						
1876	1992	....	1876	131741	CHS	Marford
1876	1992	....	1876	131741	DEN	Gresford
GWILLIM						
1719	1761	1600	1861	176877	BRE	Llanafanfawr
1800	....	1860	....	177105	DEN	Hawarden
1691	1760	ALL	1691	158739	GLA	Merthyr Dyfan
1750	1790	1600	1750	123390	HEF	Tarrington
1800	1900	1700	1992	145661	MDX	London
1804	1844	1750	1804	131660	MGY	Newtown
1837	....	1750	1850	177105	MON	Guilsford
1800	1900	1700	1992	145661	WLS	???
GWIN						
1747	1747	....	....	135437	MON	Newchurch
GWINNELL						
....	....	1850	1910	151157	CHS	ALL
GWINNETT						
1777	1992	....	....	129828	GLS	Badgworth
1795	1859	1700	1860	126667	GLS	Gloucester
1604	1730	1730	1777	129828	???	Dudley
1604	1730	1730	1777	129828	???	Wolverhampton
GWINNUTT						
1797	1850	1700	1900	135127	WOR	Dudley St Thomas
GWYLIM						
....	....	1700	1870	142212	GLA	Rhondda
GWYN						
1820	1900	....	....	179396	LND	Paddington
1600	1850	1600	1850	146730	NFK	Passim
GWYNN						
1500	1900	1600	1900	129836	MGY	Llanlais Cearenium
1500	1900	1600	1900	129836	MGY	Welshpool
GWYNNE						
1786	1825	1825	1930	145963	SSX	Lewes
GWYON						
1817	1900	1700	1817	158739	PEM	Cemais Hundred
GYDE						
1812	1851	1772	1812	131342	MDX	London
GYE						
1678	1687	1600	1800	159956	SFK	Woolpit
GYLMAN						
1560	1650	1560	1650	167924	BDF	Shillington
GYNES						
....	....	ALL	ALL	129844	ALL	Name Study
1115	1992	1000	1992	129844	ALL	ALL
GYNGELL						
1834	1847	....	....	129852	BRK	Ashampstead
1822	1828	....	....	129852	BRK	Hurst
1817	1940	1700	1817	129852	BRK	Reading
1828	1833	....	....	129852	BRK	Warfield
H'OULDRIDGE						
1758	1992	1700	1758	102342	LIN	Burton Upon Stather
HABBERLEY						
....	....	1500	1992	129860	ALL	ALL
1609	1743	....	....	129860	HAM	Portsmouth
1856	1881	1700	1950	172316	LND	Bethnal Green
1856	1881	1700	1950	172316	LND	Poplar
1856	1881	1700	1950	172316	LND	Stepney
1837	1985	1500	1837	129860	MDX	London
1837	1985	1600	1837	129860	SAL	ALL
....	1700	....	1700	177695	SAL	Clunbury
1790	1861	1600	1790	176052	SAL	Dawley
HABBUCK						
1789	1791	1700	1850	121746	MDX	Westminster
HABERJAM						
1676	1823	1400	1850	112089	???	???
HABERMEHL						
1871	1877	....	....	135437	MDX	Clerkenwell
HABERMEHL contd.						
1871	1871	....	....	135437	MDX	Finsbury
1890	1890	....	....	135437	MDX	Hoxton
1883	1883	....	....	135437	MDX	Islington
HABERSHON						
1757	1823	1650	1900	112089	YKS	Rotherham
HABGOOD						
....	....	ALL	ALL	123358	ALL	ALL
1750	1825	1700	1900	103993	SSX	Eastbourne
1814	1950	1750	1814	123358	WIL	Cricklade
HABLY						
1754	1826	1600	1754	153001	CON	Gwennap
HACK						
1800	1820	ALL	....	104515	LIN	Baston
HACKELTON						
1870	1983	....	1869	121908	WMD	Birmingham
HACKER						
1878	1940	1878	1950	129879	CMA	Barrow In Furness
1822	1980	1800	1980	129879	CMA	Ulveston
....	....	1750	1800	177725	CON	Poundstock
1869	1986	1750	1850	139777	LND	???
1800	1992	ALL	1800	118060	WIL	Fonthill
1795	1822	?	?	129879	WIL	Swindon
HACKESON						
1850	1992	1500	1850	169986	STS	Bilston
HACKET						
1820	....	....	....	151181	MDX	London
HACKETT						
?	?	ALL	1880	175757	IRL	ALL
1850	1875	ALL	1880	175757	LAN	ALL
1849	1860	ALL	1849	122572	LND	ALL
....	....	1830	....	145688	LND	St Sepulchre
1850	1992	....	....	120472	WAR	Birmingham
1679	1800	....	....	115142	WAR	Bulkington
....	....	1600	....	115142	WAR	Nuneaton
1838	....	....	....	145742	WAR	Nuneaton
1834	1873	1600	1873	153591	YKS	Bradford
1880	1880	....	....	120472	???	Hulme
1880	1880	....	....	120472	???	Manchester
HACKFORD						
1820	1850	ALL	1850	134503	LIN	Wolds
HACKIEY						
1655	1698	....	....	172987	ESS	???
1562	1698	....	....	172987	IOW	Calbourne Parish
1562	1992	1562	1992	172987	IOW	Newport Parish
1562	1992	1626	1653	172987	IOW	Niton Parish
HACKING						
1830	1992	1650	1830	135038	LAN	Accrington
HACKLEY						
1825	1900	....	....	132756	STS	Handford
1825	1900	....	....	132756	STS	Hartshill
1825	1900	....	....	132756	STS	Trentham
HACKNEY						
?	1758	....	....	138851	CHS	Davenham
HACKSHALL						
....	....	ALL	ALL	129887	ALL	Name Study
HACKWELL						
1850	1900	1850	1900	139920	LND	Shoreditch
HACKWOOD						
....	....	ALL	ALL	139092	ALL	Name Study
1650	1840	1840	1992	139092	ALL	???
HACON						
....	....	1100	1992	115975	ALL	ALL
HADAWAY						
1824	1900	1800	1900	166960	KEN	Chart Sutton
1824	1900	1800	1900	166960	KEN	Headcorn
HADDEN						
1838	....	....	1838	153699	BAN	???
....	....	ALL	1772	119326	MLN	Newbattle
1809	1865	....	....	103373	SOM	Bristol
HADDER						
1719	1803	....	1719	108839	CAM	Sutton
HADDERELL						
1780	1850	1780	1850	110361	WIL	Kington Langley
HADDINGTON						
1640	1665	1625	1992	114901	SRY	Thursley
1830	1992	1776	1992	161640	YKS	Tadcaster
HADDOCK						
1783	....	1566	1783	108839	CAM	Sutton
1650	1700	1600	1650	113204	DOW	Purdysburn
1580	1660	1500	1580	178470	DUR	Lamesley
1775	1820	1600	1775	116637	DUR	Penshaw
1775	1820	1600	1775	116637	DUR	Washington
1881	1992	1787	1881	129895	SFK	Thorndon

Known From	To	Researching From	To	Ref	Cty	Place
HADDOCK contd.						
1780	1860	1650	1780	163732	SFK	Thorndon
HADDON						
1859	1881	ALL	1859	115355	CAM	Peterborough
1859	1881	ALL	1859	115355	HUN	Peterborough
1881	1936	ALL	ALL	115355	HUN	Ufford
1881	1936	ALL	ALL	115355	LIN	Ufford
....	....	ALL	1892	178403	LND	ALL
1739	1760	1600	1740	101575	NFK	Wells Next The Sea
1859	1881	ALL	1859	115355	NTH	Peterborough
1895	1939	....	....	129909	NTH	Rushden
1881	1936	ALL	ALL	115355	NTH	Ufford
1922	1992	....	....	129909	NTH	Wellingborough
1810	1904	1750	1900	129909	NTH	Wollaston
1881	1936	ALL	ALL	115355	RUT	Ufford
....	....	ALL	1850	178403	SRY	Ham
....	....	ALL	1840	178403	SRY	???
1838	1857	ALL	ALL	125288	WAR	Birmingham
HADDOW						
....	1870	....	....	120804	LKS	Stonehouse
HADDRELL						
....	....	ALL	ALL	129917	ALL	Name Study
1800	1850	1800	1850	110361	WIL	Kingston St Michael
HADDY						
1754	1800	1600	1754	149888	CON	St Ives
HADEN						
1880	1895	1800	1895	132470	WOR	Dudley
1880	1895	1800	1895	132470	WOR	Sedgeley
HADFIELD						
1750	1802	....	....	129747	CHS	Bosden
1834	1838	1790	1834	159492	CHS	Mottram In Longdendon
....	1881	ALL	ALL	176737	DBY	ALL
1805	1851	ALL	1805	135143	ESS	Harwich
1870	1900	1800	1870	137278	LAN	Newton
1886	1918	1837	1918	173576	LAN	Oldham
1810	1926	1700	1810	112844	YKS	Bradfield
1810	1850	1700	1900	121762	YKS	Sheffield
....	....	1837	1992	135011	YKS	???
HADINGHAM						
....	....	ALL	ALL	164585	ALL	Name Study
HADLAND						
1835	....	....	....	164003	LND	???
1835	1845	1800	1835	134317	NTH	Daventry
HADLER						
....	....	1500	1992	129925	ALL	ALL
1758	1947	1700	1910	120634	KEN	Maidstone
HADLEY						
1897	1943	ALL	ALL	129933	HAM	Southsea
....	1796	ALL	ALL	129933	LND	St Mary Whitechapel
1776	1840	1700	1840	141062	MDX	St Marylebone
1826	1864	ALL	ALL	129933	MDX	St Pancras
1900	1970	1830	1900	114170	MON	Tredegar
1869	1872	ALL	ALL	129933	SSX	Lindfield
1900	1970	1830	1900	114170	WLS	South
HADLOW						
....	....	1500	1840	129925	ALL	ALL
HADMAN						
1737	1737	1600	1737	159239	ESS	Colchester
HADOCK						
1724	1743	....	....	139971	SSX	Arlington
HADWIN						
1660	....	....	1700	171441	KEN	Bicknor
1770	1855	1770	1855	136905	LAN	North
1823	1830	1800	1900	122653	LAN	Liverpool
1749	1880	1700	1749	136905	WES	South
HAFFNER						
....	....	ALL	ALL	129968	ALL	Name Study
HAFIELD						
1679	1750	1600	1750	130125	HEF	Cradley
HAFNER						
....	....	1800	1992	162620	KEN	???
1870	1992	1800	1992	162620	LND	???
HAGAN						
1837	1860	1700	1837	146161	COR	Fermay
1793	1854	1750	1854	132780	LAN	Liverpool
1912	1925	1869	1925	146773	YKS	Hull
HAGAR						
1890	....	....	....	152420	ESS	Loughton
1826	1860	1800	1860	171565	YKS	Hull
HAGART						
1840	1851	1830	1880	170992	SCT	Port Glasgow
HAGEN						
....	1832	1800	1851	128961	SRY	Bermondsey
HAGEN contd.						
....	1834	1800	1851	128961	SRY	East Dulwich
HAGGART						
1779	1839	....	....	121355	LND	City
1779	1839	....	....	121355	LND	Shoreditch
1779	1839	....	....	121355	LND	Stepney
HAGGAS						
....	....	1700	1900	108677	YKS	Keighley
1710	1800	....	....	145688	YKS	Keighley
HAGGER						
1911	1992	1837	1992	129984	ESS	West Ham
1850	1870	1700	1850	167649	HRT	ALL
1790	1890	1700	1790	158208	HRT	Therfield
1858	1871	1800	1900	123811	SFK	Bramford
HAGGERSTON						
1281	1890	1821	....	100536	NBL	???
HAGGETT						
1844	1960	1750	1850	148814	LND	Stepney
HAGGOT						
1665	....	1630	1680	170348	WIL	Swindon
HAGHAN						
1836	1992	1700	1840	161772	IRL	???
HAGTHORPE						
1590	1700	1590	1700	161705	NFK	Little Snoring
HAGUE						
1790	1820	....	....	100056	CHS	Stockport
1850	1900	....	....	100056	LAN	Ashton Under Lyne
1831	1893	1800	1831	134309	LAN	Oldham
1723	1815	1700	1820	151599	LIN	Swinderby
1660	1680	....	....	148261	LND	???
1500	1600	....	....	148261	SCT	Bermerysyde
1890	1893	1879	1902	108901	SYK	Beighton
1907	1907	1905	1908	108901	SYK	Sheffield
HAGUES						
1795	1867	1700	1766	136816	DBY	Chesterfield
1795	1867	1700	1766	136816	DBY	Walton
HAIG						
....	....	1700	1800	130915	BEW	???
1770	1830	1700	1800	130915	ELN	???
1885	1895	1866	1885	106623	MDX	Marylebone
....	....	1700	1900	142670	MLN	Edinburgh
....	....	1840	....	106623	SFK	Brent Ely
HAIGH						
1850	1992	1800	1900	143502	CAM	Castle Camps
1730	1771	ALL	1775	113611	WYK	Almondbury
1861	1992	....	....	115258	YKS	Clayton West
1650	1950	1600	1890	166952	YKS	Cumberworth
1650	1950	1600	1890	166952	YKS	Emley
1892	1935	1800	1892	109649	YKS	Halifax
1850	1992	1800	1900	143502	YKS	Halifax
1805	1843	1680	1870	157716	YKS	Huddersfield
1662	1686	1620	1700	170348	YKS	Huddersfield
1820	1820	1750	1820	128368	YKS	Leeds
1827	1903	1750	1830	169056	YKS	Lepton
1800	1850	1790	1850	123595	YKS	Lindley
1830	....	1850	1950	112615	YKS	Mirfield
1787	....	1760	1800	170348	YKS	Saddleworth
1650	1992	1600	1900	166952	YKS	Shelley
1805	1872	1750	1805	133760	YKS	Staithwaite
1770	1810	1600	1810	156183	YKS	Thornhill
HAILE						
....	....	ALL	ALL	130001	ALL	Name Study
1800	1992	ALL	ALL	140813	ALL	ALL
1733	1992	ALL	1733	129992	CUL	Cumberland
HAILEE						
....	....	1550	1600	156795	DOR	East
HAILES						
1795	1992	1600	1795	105384	DUR	Swalwell On Tyne
1845	1920	....	....	139874	GLS	Cheltenham
1763	1844	....	....	139874	SFK	Woodbridge
HAILEY						
....	....	ALL	ALL	130028	ALL	Name Study
HAILS						
1881	1900	1797	1881	129895	SFK	Debenham
1777	1781	1700	1900	159956	SFK	Hepworth
HAILWOOD						
1895	1992	1895	1992	130036	LAN	Liverpool
HAIMES						
1840	1992	ALL	1840	104442	CON	East
1840	1992	ALL	1840	104442	DEV	Plymouth
HAINE						
1687	1805	1680	1780	142018	SOM	Taunton
HAINES						
1737	....	ALL	1737	139459	BDF	Woburn

Known From	To	Researching From	To	Ref	Cty	Place
HAINES contd.						
1790	1830	ALL	ALL	168912	DEV	Burlescombe
1850	1900	....	....	129151	LAN	Manchester
1753	1754	1650	1752	131245	LEI	Tilton
....	....	1800	1900	176508	LND	Islington
1840	1900	1800	1840	154962	LND	Kilburn
1450	1550	1400	1550	154881	SAL	Church Stretton
1777	....	1713	1777	131210	SRY	Mickleham
1808	1992	1750	1808	176257	SRY	Rotherhithe
1887	1910	ALL	ALL	127280	SSX	Brighton
....	....	1800	1900	105864	WAR	Warwick
1690	1834	1690	1834	107573	WIL	Corsley
1777	1798	1700	1777	179647	WOR	Hanbury
1863	1960	1800	1865	168947	YKS	Stockbridge
HAINING						
1876	1992	1876	1992	112305	LKS	Glasgow
HAINSBOROUGH						
1856	1992	1800	1900	149012	KEN	Bermondsey
HAINSBY						
1800	1920	1700	1900	130044	MDX	Chelsea
1900	1992	1600	1900	130044	MDX	London
1750	1850	1700	1850	130044	MDX	Stoke Newington
HAINSWORTH						
1840	1864	1700	1850	154601	WYK	Denholme
1834	1907	....	....	176702	WYK	Queensbury
1840	1864	1700	1850	154601	WYK	Thornton
1800	1820	1600	1820	175382	YKS	Bradford
1851	....	....	....	127701	YKS	Pateley Bridge
1822	1987	1800	1900	120197	YKS	West Riding
HAIRSINE						
1656	1940	....	....	128996	CAM	Thorney
1741	1992	ALL	1850	176338	EYK	Howden
1850	1992	1850	1992	176338	EYK	Hull
1717	1992	1700	1850	130052	YKS	East Riding
HAISELL						
1896	1992	....	1794	130060	KEN	Dover
1896	1992	....	1794	130060	KEN	Lydd
1896	1992	....	1794	130060	SSX	Icklesham
HAITH						
1700	1800	....	....	124621	LIN	Stallingborough
HAKE						
1770	1790	1700	1900	119083	DEV	East
1823	1833	1800	1840	108251	KEN	Medway
1790	1992	1700	1920	130087	SOM	Minehead
1790	1992	1700	1920	130087	SOM	Taunton
HAKEN						
1827	1830	1800	1830	163201	MDX	St Lukes
HAKES						
1870	1965	1800	1950	135801	NTT	Retford
1866	1900	1850	1950	135801	WMD	West Bromwich
HALAY						
....	1561	1500	1600	138584	YKS	Rothwell
HALBARD						
1800	1970	1800	1970	154598	NTH	Cranford
HALBROOK						
....	....	ALL	ALL	130095	ALL	Name Study
HALCOTT						
1600	1800	....	....	167037	NFK	Hoe Hall
HALCROW						
1830	1850	1750	1830	116572	SHI	Bressay
1750	1965	....	....	137820	SHI	Fetlar
1720	1965	....	....	137820	SHI	Mid Yell
1760	1965	....	....	137820	SHI	North Yell
1758	1965	....	....	137820	SHI	Northmavine
1720	1965	....	....	137820	SHI	South Yell
HALDANE						
1833	1874	1874	1992	146560	LTN	Queensferry
1766	1992	1650	1766	145440	PER	Blackford
HALDEN						
1650	1700	1600	1700	154881	PER	Gleneagles
HALDENE						
1650	1700	1600	1700	154881	PER	Gleneagles
HALDER						
1803	1850	1700	1803	123390	HEF	Dymock
HALDIN						
1772	1871	1700	1800	102717	HRT	Standon
1875	1960	1850	1950	102717	MDX	Enfield
HALDSWORTHE						
1600	....	1600	....	154601	WYK	Horbury
HALE						
1800	1840	1840	1900	149632	BRK	Wokingham
1811	1885	1750	1992	131792	CAM	Melbourn
1814	....	....	1814	167053	ESS	Bulmer
1750	1850	1600	1900	176958	GLS	Bristol
HALE contd.						
1835	1915	1800	1835	118710	KEN	Portsmouth
1700	1760	1700	1780	144657	LIN	Barton St Peters
1800	1992	1650	1800	173665	LND	Islington
1825	1880	1750	1825	132640	LND	London
1902	1905	....	....	132179	LND	Poplar
1830	1856	1700	1856	149632	MDX	Staines
1800	1900	1700	1800	108677	MDX	Willesden
1880	1920	1880	1920	118540	MON	Bedwellty
....	....	1600	1950	149454	NFK	???
1850	1961	1830	1850	115495	NTT	Newark
1882	1992	1880	1992	165824	SOM	Bath
1750	1850	1600	1900	176958	SOM	Bath
1790	1881	1600	1881	165824	SOM	Keynsham
1850	1950	1750	1850	125660	SSX	Withyham
1607	....	....	1630	160873	STS	Pattingham
....	....	1800	ALL	164615	WIL	Dittons Marsh
HALES						
1765	1940	....	....	128996	CAM	Thorney
1800	1890	1800	1900	156744	DBY	Derby
1755	1775	1730	1800	171158	ESS	Felstead
1750	1950	1650	1950	124761	GLS	South
1754	....	....	1760	171441	KEN	Bicknor
1790	1900	1550	1790	127345	KEN	Boxley
1871	?	ALL	ALL	130109	KEN	Boxley
1729	....	....	1760	171441	KEN	Boxley
1848	....	ALL	ALL	130109	KEN	Bredhurst
1724	....	....	1760	171441	KEN	Frinstead
1790	1900	1550	1790	127345	KEN	Hartlip
1794	1802	ALL	ALL	130109	KEN	Hartlip
1798	1873	....	1900	171441	KEN	Hartlip
1856	1954	ALL	ALL	130109	KEN	Medway Town
1876	1895	....	1900	171441	KEN	Newington By Sittingbourne
1824	1834	ALL	ALL	130109	KEN	Stockbury
1757	1783	....	1800	171441	KEN	Stockbury
1871	?	ALL	ALL	130109	KEN	Teynham
1850	1870	1600	1992	159956	LND	Chelsea
1866	1910	1800	1866	166707	NTH	Towcester
1763	1844	....	....	139874	SFK	Woodbridge
1828	1916	1700	1827	131245	SRY	Newington
1800	1890	1800	1900	156744	STS	Uttoxeter
1880	1900	ALL	....	120626	STS	Walsall
1770	....	1770	....	140767	YKS	York
HALEWOOD						
1830	1860	1800	1860	169161	LAN	Liverpool
1830	1860	1800	1860	169161	LAN	St Helens
HALEY						
1831	1861	1861	1900	145262	CHS	Stalybridge
1700	1850	....	....	141178	CON	South East
1800	1880	1750	1992	133450	DEV	Kingsbridge
....	....	1819	1850	116602	MDX	St George In The East
1785	1785	1700	1785	167452	OXF	Emmington
HALFAKER						
1665	....	ALL	1665	131059	KEN	Aylesford
HALFARD						
1806	1884	1840	1992	139602	SOM	Ruishton
HALFHEAD						
1802	....	1750	1850	139386	MDX	Enfield
HALFHIDE						
1674	1757	1600	1800	122211	SRY	Lambeth
HALFORD						
1790	1870	1750	1900	104361	MDX	Clerkenwell
1789	1992	1700	1789	107999	MDX	Finsbury
1774	....	?	1780	164976	NTT	Nottingham
HALFPENNY						
1680	1800	1600	1680	149373	KEN	Deptford
1820	1830	1800	1850	113743	MDX	London
HALFYARD						
....	....	ALL	ALL	130117	ALL	Name Study
1741	1806	ALL	1741	139602	DEV	Exeter
....	....	ALL	ALL	121320	LND	ALL
1806	1884	1806	1992	139602	SOM	North Currey
1806	1870	ALL	1992	139602	SOM	Taunton
HALIFAX						
1900	....	....	....	161136	LIN	Holbeach
1787	1864	1700	1800	162507	???	???
HALKYARD						
1851	1913	1800	1851	108715	LAN	Oldham
HALL						
1781	....	1781	1800	106410	AVN	Henbury
....	1815	....	1820	146811	AYR	Beith
1840	1992	1700	1840	132772	BRK	Newport Pagnell

Known From	To	Researching From	To	Ref	Cty	Place
HALL contd.						
....	....	....	1839	130184	BRK	Reading
1793	1814	1750	1793	164259	BRK	Reading
1720	1750	1700	1750	125032	BRK	Stratfield Mortimer
1600	1650	1580	1650	118338	BRK	Windsor
1698	1720	ALL	1698	168602	CAM	Wentworth
1845	1845	1800	1845	163783	CHS	Birkenhead
1890	1950	ALL	ALL	169838	CHS	Birkenhead
1654	1711	1739	1827	138401	CHS	Chester
1799	1992	1700	1833	138282	CHS	Malpas
1799	1992	1700	1833	138282	CHS	Threadwood
1792	1900	1600	1820	130230	CON	Helston
1853	1893	1800	1853	128368	CON	Penzance
....	....	ALL	1890	178403	DBY	ALL
1300	1992	....	....	137111	DBY	Castleton
1814	1992	1700	1860	113166	DBY	Derby
1690	1957	1690	1857	131709	DBY	Glossop
1800	1992	1700	1800	164208	DBY	Milford
1730	1820	1700	1800	111821	DBY	Shipley
1674	....	....	....	138401	DEN	Ruabon
1702	1702	ALL	1702	154563	DOR	Litton Cheney
1716	....	1716	1992	127035	DOR	???
1880	1992	1800	1992	116246	DUR	North
1730	1780	1600	1730	116637	DUR	Bishopwearmouth
1770	1790	1700	1770	121339	DUR	Darlington
1738	1763	1700	1800	123536	DUR	Hamsterley
....	....	1857	....	112585	DUR	Hartlepool
1730	1780	1600	1730	116637	DUR	Monkwearmouth
....	....	1740	1794	159905	DUR	Stockton
....	....	ALL	1813	175773	DUR	Stockton
1871	1945	1835	1900	112585	DUR	Sunderland
1730	1780	1600	1730	116637	DUR	Sunderland
1726	1745	ALL	1726	154563	DUR	Weardale
....	....	1835	1871	112585	DUR	???
1840	1960	....	....	175773	ERY	Hull
1822	1880	ALL	1822	169145	GLS	Awre
1826	1831	1826	1831	138398	GLS	Barnsley
1800	1850	1800	1850	124605	GLS	Bristol
1826	1826	....	....	135437	GLS	Bristol
1777	1800	1700	1992	116653	GLS	Frampton On Severn
1723	1754	....	....	165999	GLS	Gloucester
1700	1700	1600	1700	174130	GLS	Willersey
1880	1992	....	....	169145	GNT	Newport
1640	1960	1640	1960	118338	HAM	Braemore
1640	1960	1640	1960	118338	HAM	Fordingbridge
1770	1871	1600	1950	158399	HAM	Hartley Wespall
1640	1960	1640	1960	118338	HAM	Ibsley
1730	1770	ALL	ALL	115002	HAM	Micheldever
1770	1940	1700	1770	110116	HAM	Petersfield
1841	1841	1780	1841	133000	HAM	Portsea
1640	1960	1640	1960	118338	HAM	Rockbourne
1839	1992	1714	1839	178578	HEF	Garway
1888	....	1870	1992	151378	HEF	Kington
1818	1881	1700	1899	112615	HEF	Ledbury
1839	1992	1714	1839	178578	HEF	St Weonards
1887	1891	1887	1891	138398	HEF	Welshnewton
1700	1800	1600	1900	177180	HRT	Bovington
1802	1864	1802	1864	148156	HUN	Central
1802	1864	1802	1864	148156	HUN	North
1835	....	1802	....	148156	HUN	Gt Giddings
1760	1770	....	....	140317	HUN	Woodhurst
1778	1778	....	....	144355	KEN	South
....	....	1700	1800	129976	KEN	Folkestone
1766	1766	1700	1900	141151	KEN	Folkestone
1772	1773	1760	1785	130206	KEN	Shorne
1788	1788	1700	1900	141151	KEN	Whitstable
1845	1860	1700	1845	146161	LAN	Ashton Under Lyne
1800	1950	1600	1800	121118	LAN	Great Eccleston
1793	1923	1750	1870	118443	LAN	Inskip
1780	1840	1700	1779	102830	LAN	Manchester
1798	1798	1775	1800	126705	LAN	Manchester
1830	1920	1700	1920	158216	LAN	Manchester
1802	1869	ALL	1869	165654	LAN	Manchester
1616	1985	1616	1985	136328	LAN	Middleton
1830	1920	1700	1920	158216	LAN	Oldham
1819	1992	1819	1992	159492	LAN	Oldham
1864	1892	....	....	164062	LAN	Preston
1702	1789	....	....	165999	LEI	Loughborough
1890	1992	1700	1950	178616	LEI	Shepshed
1750	1800	1700	1800	120529	LIN	Fenton
1800	1860	1700	1860	169560	LIN	Keelby
1893	1918	1918	1992	146560	LKS	Coatbride
1850	1891	1800	1955	146536	LKS	Glasgow
1800	1900	1750	1900	154881	LND	ALL
HALL contd.						
1818	1873	....	....	160776	LND	Bishopsgate
1850	1992	1600	1992	159956	LND	Chelsea
1911	1911	1900	1915	152773	LND	Dulwich
1874	1940	1600	1800	143693	LND	Hammersmith
1865	1878	1750	1900	143693	LND	Islington
1839	1841	1800	1930	139203	LND	Lewisham
1876	1891	1850	1911	152773	LND	Peckham
....	....	1820	....	151610	LND	Poplar
1840	1860	1840	1900	130222	LND	Shoreditch
....	....	ALL	1880	175323	LND	St James
1815	1992	1750	1815	130249	MDX	ALL
1860	1992	1837	1860	166464	MDX	Hackney
1852	1861	1700	1840	168033	MDX	Hampton
1794	....	1700	1850	143693	MDX	Hayes
1830	1870	1800	1900	143693	MDX	Heston
1793	1992	1650	1793	118583	MDX	London
1837	....	1800	1900	143693	MDX	Southall
1838	1992	1838	1992	141267	MDX	Spitalfields
1789	1794	1700	1790	130214	MDX	West Drayton
1828	....	1800	1850	146536	MLN	Roslin
1830	1860	1811	1860	109819	MOG	Drumswords
1836	....	ALL	ALL	172057	MOG	Drumswords
....	....	1750	1890	151203	MON	Abertillery
1900	....	1880	1992	151378	MON	Monmouth
1798	1799	1790	1850	130125	NBL	Alnwick
....	....	1750	1850	112585	NBL	Chatton
1760	1950	1600	1760	128376	NBL	Cramlington
1829	1900	1750	1900	105422	NBL	Earsdon
1718	1722	1690	1720	149152	NBL	Earsdon
1700	1830	1650	1800	170488	NBL	Ford
1804	1810	1800	1900	132454	NBL	Gosforth
....	....	1795	1818	160776	NBL	Hexham
1826	1835	1826	1835	112585	NBL	Holy Island
1856	1900	1850	1950	130125	NBL	Newbiggin Street
....	....	1835	1871	112585	NBL	Newcastle On Tyne
1850	1896	1822	1896	153176	NBL	Newcastle On Tyne
1790	1800	....	1790	157139	NBL	Newcastle
1791	1992	1700	1791	159980	NBL	Newcastle
....	....	1830	1860	175773	NBL	Newcastle
1700	1799	1700	1799	169781	NBL	Ouseburn
1818	1850	1815	1890	130125	NBL	Shilbottle
1770	1780	1600	1800	130125	NBL	Stannington
1798	1826	1750	1800	112585	NBL	Wooler
1900	1992	ALL	1930	111678	NFK	Diss
1824	1943	ALL	1824	103039	NFK	Lynn
1812	1992	1650	1812	118265	NFK	Mattishall
1900	1992	ALL	1930	111678	NFK	Norwich
1820	1880	1820	1880	167924	NFK	Pancras
1780	1850	1780	1850	167924	NFK	St Lukes Finsbury
1600	1700	1600	1700	167924	NFK	Tavenham
1870	1880	1700	1899	112615	NTH	Northampton
1900	1992	....	....	130133	NTT	Long Eaton
1900	1965	1700	1900	148423	NTT	Newstead
1690	1720	....	1720	137634	NTT	Rampton
1813	1946	1750	1813	179663	NYK	Husthwaite
1813	1946	1750	1813	179663	NYK	Malton
1756	1890	1500	1786	168629	NYK	Ryedale
1834	1859	1800	1859	147311	NYK	Wold Newton
1701	1834	....	1700	130133	OXF	Great Tew
1799	1835	1835	1850	178705	OXF	Northmoor
1860	....	1700	1860	144614	OXF	St Ebbes
1850	1855	....	....	130133	OXF	Swerford
....	....	1750	1890	151203	PEM	Rosemarket
1888	....	1870	1992	151378	POW	Presteigne
1770	ALL	ALL	ALL	149063	ROX	Hawick
1896	1940	1896	1940	149063	ROX	Melrose
1863	1992	1863	1992	179116	SAL	Bridgnorth
1781	....	....	1805	171441	SAL	Kinlet
....	....	1800	1900	145688	SAL	Shrewsbury
....	....	....	1850	130060	SCT	???
1805	?	1805	1845	108006	SFK	Ipswich
1837	1992	1826	1992	171581	SOM	Burnham
1726	1750	....	....	135437	SOM	Crowcombe
1826	1992	1800	1992	171581	SOM	Mark
1756	1770	....	....	135437	SOM	Stogumber
1793	1853	....	....	135437	SOM	Stogursey
1759	....	1600	1759	149888	SOM	West Monkton
....	....	1838	1861	130184	SRY	Battersea
1749	1749	1749	1749	170143	SRY	Chobham
1821	1992	1650	1821	118583	SRY	London
1815	1992	1750	1815	130249	SRY	Southwark
....	....	1600	1815	104469	SRY	Wandsworth
1749	1749	1749	1749	170143	SRY	Woking

Known From	To	Researching From	To	Ref	Cty	Place
HALL contd.						
1780	1878	....	....	168777	SSX	Watergate
1741	1896	1710	1750	173649	STS	Abbots Bromley
1822	1822	1790	1820	179116	STS	Handsworth
1750	1780	ALL	ALL	107840	STS	Stafford
1670	1750	1600	1800	177180	STS	West Bromwich
1875	1992	....	1950	130168	WAR	Birmingham
1848	1861	1861	1863	179116	WAR	Birmingham
1850	1914	1850	1992	143650	WAR	Leamington Spa
1806	1863	....	....	102733	WAR	???
1809	1919	ALL	ALL	117307	WIL	Cricklade
1810	1830	1750	1810	140309	WOR	Bretforton
1863	1992	....	....	161284	WOR	Bromsgrove
1624	1658	....	....	164631	WOR	Bromsgrove
1835	1890	1750	1900	133426	WOR	Dudley
....	....	ALL	1600	164631	WOR	Hallow
1805	....	....	1830	171441	WOR	Stourport
....	....	ALL	1600	164631	WOR	Suckley
1890	....	1885	1992	151378	WOR	Tenbury Wells
1597	....	....	....	164631	WOR	Worchester
1813	1830	1750	1813	175773	YKS	North
1767	1795	1700	1850	116386	YKS	Armley
1755	1880	1700	1755	130206	YKS	Craven
1742	1766	1680	1742	116114	YKS	Flamborough
1770	1770	....	....	141097	YKS	Humbleton
1830	1850	1830	1840	176958	YKS	Leeds
1820	1850	1800	1850	136220	YKS	Northallerton
?	?	ALL	ALL	174432	YKS	Norton
1801	1829	1801	1829	136808	YKS	Rillington
1853	1992	ALL	ALL	161047	YKS	Robertown
....	1636	1600	1700	138584	YKS	Rothwell
1771	1790	1750	1992	114901	YKS	Selby
1754	....	....	....	165484	YKS	Woolley
1830	1927	1750	1830	137944	YKS	York
1840	1900	....	....	100536	???	???
HALL-ROBINSON						
1836	1992	....	....	175803	DUR	South Shields
HALLAM						
....	....	ALL	ALL	136425	ALL	Name Study
1860	1885	1860	1885	167924	GLA	Cardiff
1890	1890	....	....	137804	LAN	Haslingden
1819	1992	1700	1819	130257	LEI	Barwell
1877	1901	1800	1877	113050	LEI	Loughborough
1802	1900	1600	1802	152463	LEI	Prestwold
1800	....	1750	?	177156	LEI	???
1750	1992	1750	1992	167924	MDX	ALL
1850	1900	1850	1900	167924	MDX	Hammbersmith
....	1700	ALL	1700	134511	NTT	Calverton
1809	1836	1775	1809	178241	NTT	Clipston
1811	....	....	....	162744	NTT	Cotgrave
1837	1904	1754	1904	178241	NTT	Cotgrave
1855	1943	1851	1943	165441	STS	Newcastle
1817	1992	1700	1816	112844	YKS	Bradfield
1841	1930	ALL	1841	171468	YKS	Sheffield
HALLAS						
....	....	ALL	ALL	130265	ALL	Name Study
1837	1980	1700	1837	130265	YKS	South
1837	1980	1700	1837	130265	YKS	West
1836	1840	ALL	1870	158445	YKS	Huddersfield
HALLATT						
1747	1992	1747	1900	111791	DBY	Barlow
HALLET						
1747	1747	ALL	1747	154563	DOR	Puncknowle
1774	1774	....	....	135437	GLS	Bristol
HALLETT						
....	....	ALL	ALL	135100	ALL	Name Study
1829	1926	1800	1880	124788	CHS	Stalybridge
1790	1890	1400	1900	130273	CON	???
1842	1922	1700	1900	167487	DEV	Thorncombe
1790	1890	1400	1900	130273	DEV	???
1840	1992	1500	1840	126616	DOR	Netherburn
....	....	1800	1900	179361	DOR	Netherbury
1842	1922	1700	1900	167487	DOR	Thorncombe
1750	1900	1750	1900	136484	LND	Marylebone
1750	1900	1750	1900	136484	LND	Shoreditch
1859	1930	1700	1859	152544	SSX	Rotherfield
1500	1636	....	....	148261	???	Weymouth
HALLEY						
1700	1800	1600	1700	132659	ERY	Bubwith
1700	1800	1600	1700	135755	YKS	ALL
HALLGARTH						
1600	1800	1600	1800	124826	LIN	Alford
1838	1862	1838	1881	124826	LIN	Louth
HALLGATH						
1800	1810	1700	1820	149845	LIN	ALL
HALLICK						
1730	1730	1700	1750	136840	HAM	Fordingbridge
HALLIDAY						
....	....	ALL	ALL	130303	ALL	Name Study
1799	1839	1700	1900	139203	DFS	Johnstone
....	....	ALL	ALL	148830	DFS	Johnstone
....	....	1500	1800	138614	DFS	Kirkmahoe
1800	....	1830	1992	130486	DFS	???
....	1850	1750	1850	146927	DFS	???
1795	1890	....	1875	147818	LAN	Worsley
1860	1992	1800	1860	126535	MDX	Holborn
1750	1900	1500	1750	118915	NBL	ALL
1800	1900	....	....	150371	ROX	Newcastleton
1860	1992	1800	1860	126535	SCT	???
1782	1820	1750	1850	157651	YKS	Terrington
1809	1992	1750	1992	157651	YKS	York
HALLIER						
1780	1800	1780	1800	157171	GLS	Arlingham
1810	1900	1800	1930	157171	GLS	Newnham On Severn
1730	....	....	....	118672	GLS	Tortworth
1740	1780	1700	1850	157171	GLS	Wickwar
HALLIFAX						
1800	1840	1700	1800	114871	LND	ALL
HALLILEY						
1800	1850	1850	1992	168408	WYK	Dewsbury
1800	1850	1750	1850	168408	WYK	Huddersfield
1800	1850	1850	1992	168408	WYK	Wakefield
HALLING						
1430	1820	ALL	1820	134538	GLS	Badgeworth
1430	1820	ALL	1820	134538	GLS	Churchdowne
1430	1820	ALL	1820	134538	GLS	Parton
1430	1820	ALL	1820	134538	GLS	Pirton
HALLINGHAM						
1830	....	1750	1800	165476	KEN	Aylesford
1830	....	1750	1800	165476	KEN	Stockbury
HALLINS						
1744	1775	1680	1850	157171	HEF	Weston Beggard
HALLIWELL						
1830	1830	1830	1830	145580	LAN	Bolton
1839	1992	1839	1839	145580	LAN	Liverpool
1850	1910	1800	1992	166081	LAN	Rochdale
1831	1932	1831	1932	148091	LAN	Salford
1849	1849	1800	1900	117668	LAN	Winstanley
1720	....	....	1720	101761	LIN	Lincoln
HALLKINS						
1790	1790	1700	1790	179116	STS	Ipstones
HALLORAN						
1830	1860	....	....	116408	HAM	Alverstoke
HALLOT						
1822	1841	1820	1850	151599	DBY	Derby
1822	1841	1820	1850	151599	NTT	Nottingham
HALLOWAY						
1823	1840	1600	1850	145432	WOR	Worcester
HALLOWES						
1538	1593	1586	1800	123544	YKS	Halifax
HALLOWS						
1620	1850	1550	1992	133450	DBY	Dethick
1680	1800	1650	1992	133450	HRT	Hertford
1715	1740	1650	1800	133450	LAN	Rochdale
HALLPIKE						
1740	1855	1700	1740	128333	YKS	Giggleswick
HALLS						
1781	....	ALL	1781	168602	CAM	Burwell
1902	1992	....	....	126926	CAM	Cambridge
1810	1902	....	....	126926	CAM	Coton
1886	1957	....	....	154814	ESS	Earls Colne
1783	1846	....	....	126926	ESS	Hellions Bumpstead
1890	1982	....	....	154814	ESS	South Ockendon
1877	1963	1700	1877	162000	KEN	Swale
HALLSWORTH						
1820	1840	1700	1820	130346	BDF	Marston Moretaine
1647	1804	1550	1804	102830	DBY	ALL
1840	1992	1800	1840	130346	DBY	Derby
HALLUM						
1800	1820	1700	1800	179574	PER	Kincardine By Doune
HALLYBONE						
1850	1900	ALL	ALL	107417	ALL	ALL
1875	1896	1800	1900	107417	MDX	Limehouse
1825	1896	1800	1900	107417	MDX	Poplar
HALPIN						
1840	1900	?	1840	102512	IRL	Dublin
1873	....	....	....	130354	IRL	Tipperary

Known From	To	Researching From	To	Ref	Cty	Place
HALSAL						
1760	1799	1700	1760	152196	IOM	???
HALSALL						
1500	1700	....	....	100420	WAR	Meriden
HALSE						
....	....	ALL	ALL	130362	ALL	Name Study
ALL	ALL	ALL	ALL	130362	ALL	ALL
....	....	ALL	1800	167029	DEV	Exeter
1800	1900	1800	1900	176281	MDX	Ealing
HALSEY						
1600	....	....	....	103349	BDF	Hemstead
1880	1920	1650	1880	140198	HRT	West
1800	1900	1700	....	111724	HRT	Bushy
1880	1920	1650	1880	140198	HRT	Great Gaddesdon
1880	1920	1820	1880	140198	HRT	Hatfield
1800	ALL	1800	1850	107379	HRT	Hemel Hempstead
1650	1800	1600	1900	177180	HRT	Kings Langley
1880	1920	1650	1880	140198	HRT	Mid
1835	1992	ALL	ALL	115762	HRT	Sandridge
1820	ALL	1812	1850	107379	HRT	St Albans
1880	1920	1650	1880	140198	HRT	St Albans
1820	1880	1650	1880	140198	HRT	Welwyn
1760	1992	1600	1760	148237	SSX	Sidlesham
1890	1900	1800	1890	135496	WIC	Arklow
HALSNODE						
1600	1670	....	....	142522	KEN	Canterbury
HALSON						
1841	1853	1841	1870	130370	ANS	Dundee
1664	1864	1644	1864	130370	FIF	Anstruther
1780	1805	1775	1805	130370	FIF	Wemyss
1809	1884	1809	1884	130370	LAN	Liverpool
1805	1824	1805	1840	130370	MLN	Cockpen
1841	1881	1830	1900	130370	PER	Rattray
HALSTEAD						
....	....	ALL	ALL	142182	ALL	Name Study
1700	1970	1777	1970	153621	LAN	Burnley
1837	1872	1750	1900	116742	LAN	Marsden
....	1726	1600	1726	132209	NFK	Attleborough
?	?	?	?	133957	SXW	Westhampnett
1803	1827	ALL	1827	173290	YKS	Halifax
1700	1970	1777	1970	153621	YKS	Sowerby Bridge
HALSTED						
1290	1992	1290	1992	142182	ALL	ALL
1290	1992	1290	1992	142182	LAN	Burnley
HALTON						
1780	1992	1700	1790	155500	LAN	Great Sankey
1780	1992	1700	1790	155500	LAN	Leigh
1781	....	1766	1781	122572	NTT	ALL
1800	1850	....	....	132756	STS	Potteries
HALWOOD						
1851	1895	1851	1895	130036	CHS	Runcorn
1812	1865	1700	1895	130036	LAN	Manchester
HALYBURTON						
1400	1550	1350	1550	154881	ELN	Dirleton
HAM						
1861	1861	1861	1886	166502	HAM	Southampton
1815	1904	ALL	1850	136700	LND	North
1886	1892	1862	1916	166502	LND	Kilburn
1780	1850	1720	1780	103675	SOM	ALL
1840	1860	ALL	ALL	136700	SRY	Camberly
HAMBLEN						
1818	1992	1700	1818	161446	DOR	Sherborne
HAMBLETON						
1837	1838	ALL	1992	163821	HAM	Portsmouth
1839	....	ALL	1992	163821	SOM	Camerton
1910	....	ALL	1992	163821	SOM	Congresbury
ALL	1837	ALL	1992	163821	SOM	Mells
1845	....	ALL	1992	163821	SOM	Midsomer Norton
ALL	1837	ALL	1992	163821	SOM	Publow
1899	1901	ALL	1992	163821	SOM	Taunton
1720	1992	1600	1800	113654	SSX	Midhurst
1750	1992	1600	1750	113654	SSX	Petworth
HAMBLEY						
1800	1850	1700	1860	179248	CON	Bodmin
1760	1840	1700	1860	179191	CON	Egloshayle
1770	1825	ALL	1925	115347	CON	Lanivet
1800	1850	1700	1860	179248	CON	Wadebridge
HAMBLIN						
1872	1895	....	....	116602	BRK	Maidenhead
1609	1863	ALL	1609	161500	SOM	Castle Cary
HAMBLY						
1200	1992	1200	1992	130478	CON	Central
1700	1839	ALL	1992	168718	CON	South East
1706	1726	1600	1706	102571	CON	Kenwyn
HAMBLY contd.						
1800	1820	ALL	ALL	130389	CON	Padstow
1838	1838	1838	1838	108901	CON	St Budock
1860	1992	1800	1900	127361	CON	St Endellion
1880	ALL	1600	1880	130397	CON	St Endellion
1900	1970	1800	1970	171042	DEV	Plymouth
HAMBRIDGE						
1845	1845	1800	1845	103640	KEN	Gillingham
1893	1897	ALL	ALL	101230	LAN	Leigh
HAMBROGE						
1841	....	1810	1860	149292	DOW	Groomsport
HAMBROOK						
....	....	ALL	ALL	100498	ALL	Name Study
HAMBY						
1650	1790	1744	1757	111422	SFK	Ipswich
1650	1790	1744	1757	111422	SFK	Trimley
HAMER						
1850	1930	1800	1992	150541	LAN	South
1892	1968	1800	1892	108715	LAN	Ashton Under Lyme
1800	1992	1700	1800	132268	LAN	Bury
1808	1835	1780	1820	149772	LAN	Bury
1750	1992	....	....	169226	LAN	Lancaster
1830	1895	1800	1920	126705	LAN	Manchester
....	....	ALL	ALL	166812	LAN	Manchester
1740	1861	1741	1770	108944	WYK	Blackmoor Meltham
1740	1850	1685	1740	110027	YKS	Elland
1750	1992	1600	1750	169226	YKS	Leeds
1740	1850	1685	1740	110027	YKS	Scammonden
HAMERSLY						
1870	1900	1750	1900	178136	STS	Longton
HAMERTON						
1770	1850	1600	1770	139106	LND	London
HAMES						
1801	1815	1700	1800	149098	LEI	Leicester
HAMILL						
1846	1992	....	....	172529	DOW	Clough
HAMILTON						
1800	1831	1800	1850	153354	ANT	Belfast
....	....	1700	1800	167932	ANT	Clandeboyes
1780	1992	1780	1992	113670	AVN	Bath
1780	1992	1780	1992	113670	AVN	Bristol
1725	1755	....	....	171654	AYR	Dunlop
1820	1850	1780	1850	128244	CAV	Bailieborough
1820	1850	1780	1850	128244	CAV	Skeagh
1796	1929	1766	1796	139149	DBY	Bakewell
1800	1820	1750	1850	121274	DFS	Moffat
1816	1881	1750	1881	149292	DOW	Bangor
1695	1799	1650	1850	176621	DOW	Dromore
1816	1881	1750	1881	149292	DOW	Groomsport
1770	1779	1700	1992	168181	DOW	Newry
1900	1992	1600	1900	127469	ENG	South
1844	1930	1844	1992	179183	ESS	Stratford
1885	1992	1750	1885	179140	ESS	Stratford
1899	1970	1800	1899	126225	FER	Irvinestown
1720	1766	1700	1720	158143	FIF	Rhynd
1808	1858	1700	1808	162035	GLS	Bristol
1851	....	1750	1851	179183	HRT	Bishops Stortford
1851	1859	1770	1851	157643	HUM	Hull
1820	1878	1750	1900	158666	IRL	ALL
....	1800	1600	1850	147265	IRL	Conaught
....	....	1860	1992	159964	KKD	ALL
1818	1863	1750	1900	159964	KKD	Dalry
1870	1893	1870	1900	159964	KKD	New Galloway
....	....	1770	1841	157643	LAN	Manchester
1875	....	....	....	106852	LAN	St Helens
1750	....	....	1800	117889	LKS	Boghead
1887	1910	1800	1920	120146	LKS	Carluke
1822	1842	....	....	171654	LKS	Carluke
....	....	1750	1900	110663	LKS	Glasgow
1844	1870	ALL	ALL	129933	LKS	Glasgow
1819	1891	1800	1900	130427	LKS	Glasgow
1850	1950	1850	1920	130400	LKS	Glasgow
1849	1895	1820	1900	166049	LKS	Glasgow
1666	1846	....	....	101621	LKS	Hamilton
1780	1850	1780	1850	130400	LKS	Hamilton
1750	....	....	1800	117889	LKS	Lesmahagow
1812	1818	ALL	ALL	129933	LKS	Lesmahagow
1814	1833	....	....	171654	LKS	Newmains
1833	1870	1833	1870	170623	LND	Pancras
1849	1851	1800	1870	159905	NBL	Earsdon
1810	1928	1750	1870	179000	SCT	Bo'ness
1860	1900	1750	1900	130419	SCT	Creetown
1780	1910	1700	....	130419	SCT	Dalbeattie
1809	....	....	....	170623	SCT	???

Known From	To	Researching From	To	Ref	Cty	Place
HAMILTON contd.						
1819	1902	1819	1992	101621	SRY	Bermondsey
1765	1765	1700	1765	147575	???	???
HAMLET						
1857	1876	ALL	1857	160008	CHS	Stockport
HAMLETT						
1730	1970	ALL	ALL	140740	GLS	Cheltenham
HAMLEY						
1200	1992	1200	1992	130478	CON	Central
1705	1754	1600	1730	121932	CON	Tremaine
1800	1840	1700	1850	155683	DEV	Tavistock
HAMLIN						
1615	1980	1500	1700	144398	BRK	Reading
1765	1992	1600	1765	134430	BRK	Tilehurst
1894	1920	1920	1960	133264	DBY	Borrowash
HAMLYN						
1550	1880	1300	1880	105333	DEV	Buckland In The Moor
....	....	1600	1900	177725	DEV	Clovelly
1550	1880	1300	1880	105333	DEV	Holne
1550	1880	1300	1880	105333	DEV	Ilsington
1550	1880	1300	1880	105333	DEV	Lydford
1550	1880	1300	1880	105333	DEV	Widecombe In The Moor
?	?	?	?	141003	DEV	???
1800	1850	1700	1800	171182	SOM	Chinnock
HAMM						
1881	1938	1700	1881	139203	DUR	Sunderland
HAMMERSLEY						
1750	....	1750	1800	130486	CHS	Bosley
1803	1860	1700	1803	129208	CHS	Macclesfield
1800	1900	1750	1900	130494	MDX	Islington
1845	1896	ALL	1845	105481	NTT	Sneinton
1790	1820	1750	1850	130494	SRY	Rotherhithe
1750	....	1750	1800	130486	STS	Haughton
1800	....	1800	1900	130486	STS	Stafford
HAMMERTON						
1744	1940	....	....	128996	CAM	Thorney
1760	1780	1700	1780	148288	YKS	Wakefield
HAMMETT						
1781	1900	1787	1900	131113	DEV	Wembury
1794	1872	1790	1880	104477	DOR	Wimborne
1842	1910	1840	1910	104477	HAM	Hamble
1889	1945	1880	1950	104477	HAM	Southampton
1860	1880	ALL	ALL	173657	HRT	Kings Walden
1850	1950	1800	1950	126144	KEN	???
1872	1920	1870	1920	104477	LND	Lambeth
1850	1950	1800	1950	126144	LND	???
1779	1854	1749	1779	139149	SOM	Taunton
HAMMON						
1680	1992	1500	1992	135577	ALL	ALL
1850	1900	1850	1900	128740	KEN	Gillingham
HAMMOND						
....	....	ALL	ALL	130540	ALL	Name Study
1819	1896	....	1819	133566	CAM	Ely
1760	1901	....	....	171492	CAM	Linton
....	....	ALL	ALL	141186	CHS	ALL
1850	1992	1880	1960	132683	CHS	Altincham
1817	1900	1700	1817	172588	CHS	Knutsford
1908	1970	....	....	173142	DBY	Derby
1850	1950	1700	1850	121339	DUR	Darlington
1837	1900	....	1837	130524	ESS	North
1780	1880	1700	1780	130680	ESS	Great Warley
1770	1992	....	1770	130680	ESS	Upminster
1700	1992	ALL	ALL	130508	HAM	Andover
....	....	1600	1900	160970	HRT	North
1600	1650	1500	1650	142123	HRT	Pirton
1827	1900	1600	1950	149454	HRT	Ware
1790	1869	1700	1900	178322	KEN	Ash
1700	1900	1700	1900	122521	KEN	Chatham
1777	1857	1750	1900	170143	KEN	Marden
1809	1900	1780	1900	151599	KEN	Swalecliffe
1850	1900	....	....	172588	LAN	Manchester
1792	1818	....	....	121355	LND	Bethnal Green
1870	1920	....	....	130532	LND	Soutwark
1792	1818	....	....	121355	LND	Whitechapel
1850	....	....	....	145068	LND	???
1860	1889	1851	1910	133639	MDX	Islington
1824	1851	1800	1860	133639	MDX	Marylebone
1901	1910	1896	1910	133639	MDX	Shoreditch
1824	1851	1800	1860	133639	MDX	Westminster
1747	1769	1700	1800	117013	NFK	Dersingham
1840	1880	1800	1900	101508	NFK	Kings Lynn
1849	1851	ALL	1872	175080	NFK	Lynn

Known From	To	Researching From	To	Ref	Cty	Place
HAMMOND contd.						
1797	1797	ALL	1752	159077	NTH	Cotterstock
1780	1826	1780	1992	105147	SAL	Worthen
1890	1930	1750	1890	102288	SFK	Ipswich
1853	1992	1750	1853	134015	SFK	Ipswich
1700	1799	1700	1800	135941	SFK	Lakenheath
1853	1992	1750	1853	134015	SFK	Stowmarket
1700	1799	1700	1800	135941	SFK	Wangford
1842	1851	1600	1870	145289	SOM	Sandford Orcas
....	....	1600	1660	130516	SRY	North West
1800	1865	1700	1800	132640	SRY	Bagshot
1730	1800	....	....	130516	SRY	Horsell
1790	1825	1700	1790	132640	SRY	Shalford
1660	1900	1600	1660	130516	SRY	Windlesham
1713	1831	1650	1830	154881	SSX	Battle
1835	1992	1600	1835	164879	SSX	Brighton
1800	1870	ALL	ALL	130664	SSX	Duncton
1572	1635	....	....	165999	SSX	Stopham
....	....	ALL	1850	165263	SSX	Waldron
1780	1800	ALL	ALL	141186	STS	North
1770	1850	1600	1992	178268	STS	Kingsley
1646	1840	ALL	1840	141062	STS	Leek
....	....	1700	1820	130532	WAR	Coventry
1830	1850	1700	1830	130532	WAR	Meriden
1790	1850	1700	1850	130532	WAR	Warwick
1766	1828	1700	1800	179337	WIL	Calne
1775	1816	1740	1840	160873	WOR	Great Witley
HAMMONDS						
1775	1889	?	1775	121665	GLS	Bristol
1831	1851	1820	1861	111414	HEF	Wigmore
....	....	1750	1830	111414	SAL	Lingen
1898	1898	1891	1900	111414	SAL	Shawbury
1868	1868	1861	1871	111414	SAL	Shrewsbury
1869	1872	1861	1881	111414	SAL	Uffington
1929	1935	1900	1935	111414	SAL	Wrockwardine
HAMNET						
1800	1820	1750	1800	172898	LND	Bermondsey
HAMNETT						
1800	1820	1750	1800	172898	LND	Bermondsey
HAMON						
1508	1943	ALL	1508	115126	CHI	ALL
1801	1863	....	....	141356	JSY	Grovville
HAMOND						
1697	1697	1697	1697	170143	SSX	Trotton
HAMOR						
1700	1800	....	....	177318	LAN	Barry
HAMPDEN						
1300	1705	ALL	1705	162507	BKM	Hampden
HAMPSEY						
1845	1992	1845	1992	108278	LDY	Articlave
HAMPSHAW						
1890	1992	ALL	1890	109509	WYK	Holmfirth
HAMPSHIRE						
1823	1830	1700	1850	102520	KEN	Lenham
1826	1890	1780	1860	174912	KEN	London
1865	1897	1800	1865	108715	LAN	Ashton Under Lyme
1780	ALL	....	....	167037	SRY	Haselmere
1826	1890	1780	1860	174912	SRY	London
....	1818	1700	1818	110531	WYK	Ccartworth
HAMPSON						
1800	1930	....	....	135984	CHS	Liverpool
1600	1700	....	....	164038	ESS	Patcham
1868	1992	1700	1868	165581	GLA	Cardiff
....	....	1850	1880	127949	LAN	Aspull
1746	1746	1746	1746	143286	LAN	Bolton
1855	1900	1855	1900	130567	LAN	Manchester
1873	1930	1880	1920	131865	LAN	Manchester
1800	1930	....	....	135984	LND	Islington
1819	1992	1700	1992	130559	SRY	Camberwell
1819	1992	1700	1992	130559	SRY	Lambeth
HAMPTON						
1832	1869	1832	1992	151378	AVN	Clifton
1545	1804	ALL	ALL	132942	CON	ALL
1750	1992	1700	1992	152528	ESS	Waltham Abbey
1924	....	1890	1992	151378	GLA	Aberdare
1893	....	1850	1992	151378	GLA	Pontypridd
1869	1951	1869	1992	151378	HAM	Cheriton
....	....	1800	1940	153931	HAM	Lymington
....	....	1750	1830	102717	HRT	Broxbourne
1825	1830	1800	1830	119059	SRY	Godalming
1862	1992	....	....	165352	SRY	Guildford
1881	....	1882	1992	166197	WOR	Chanceley
HAMS						
1732	....	ALL	ALL	113700	WIL	Bishops Cannings

Known From	To	Researching From	To	Ref	Cty	Place
HAMSHARE						
1842	1842	1750	1842	118192	SRY	ALL
HAMSHER						
1730	1780	1600	1730	115525	SRY	Abinger
HAMSTEAD						
1600	1699	1600	1700	135941	SFK	Wickhambrook
HANBRIDGE						
1920	1923	....	....	101230	LAN	Salford
HANBY						
1830	1992	1700	1900	178136	YKS	Mexborough
1800	1840	1750	1800	161519	YKS	Middleham
1680	1738	1650	1700	170348	YKS	Thornhill
HANCEFORD						
1500	1992	....	....	130834	ALL	ALL
HANCER						
1720	1850	....	....	163465	NTT	Newark
1700	1800	....	....	165999	NTT	Newark
HANCHET						
1650	1850	....	....	138037	HRT	North East
HANCHETT						
1560	1800	1560	1800	167924	ESS	Arkesden
1750	1820	1750	1820	167924	HRT	Datchworth
1750	1850	1750	1850	167924	HRT	Shephall
1740	1760	1740	1760	167924	HRT	Wydial
HANCOCK						
1761	1848	ALL	1848	168718	CON	South East
1753	1960	1600	1760	170607	CON	Altarnun
1640	1900	1500	1640	148598	CON	Cambourne
1600	1850	....	....	103381	CON	Looe
1859	1960	....	....	124567	CON	St Austell
1600	1850	....	....	103381	CON	Stoke Damarel
1740	1740	ALL	1800	173614	DEV	Barnstaple
1780	1850	1750	1992	133450	DEV	Devonport
1836	1836	1700	1836	153605	DEV	Horrabridge
1600	1850	....	....	103381	DEV	Memhemiot
1836	1836	1700	1836	153605	DEV	Plymouth
....	....	1500	1992	130583	GLS	Chipping Campden
1753	1753	1700	1752	102830	GLS	Cirencester
1800	1847	ALL	ALL	152641	GLS	Stinchcombe
1847	1881	ALL	ALL	152641	GLS	Stonehouse
1630	1989	....	....	142522	GLS	Twining
1807	1807	1700	1807	173886	IRL	Dublin
1827	1893	1700	1827	173886	LAN	Manchester
1575	....	1575	....	109347	LAN	Padiham
1803	1803	....	....	159492	LAN	Warrington
1723	1834	....	....	144568	LIN	???
1750	1760	1600	1992	167592	LND	Battersea
1862	....	....	1870	171441	LND	Hanover Square
1840	....	....	1850	171441	LND	Holborn
1883	1945	1500	1992	175498	LND	Lambeth
1770	1865	1600	1770	139106	LND	London
1842	....	....	1870	171441	LND	Southwark
1800	1960	1700	1900	106313	MDX	Brentford
1750	1760	1600	1992	167592	MDX	London
1817	1841	1700	1847	102881	MDX	Shoreditch
1860	1992	ALL	1860	130575	NTH	???
1860	1992	ALL	1860	130575	OXF	???
1770	1800	1750	1992	167592	SAL	Coalbrookdale
1874	1956	1874	1881	104213	SOM	Bath
1900	1982	1881	1992	176923	SOM	Bath
....	....	1559	1700	130591	SOM	Bridgwater
1780	1820	1750	1992	167592	SOM	Brislington
1790	1810	1750	1992	167592	SOM	Bristol
1559	1759	....	....	130591	SOM	Halse
1797	1851	1700	1881	176923	SOM	Kilmersdon
1524	1900	1450	1524	130591	SOM	Lydeard St Lawrence
1559	1870	....	....	130591	SOM	Milverton
....	....	1559	1600	130591	SOM	Nettlecombe
....	....	1559	1700	130591	SOM	Stoke St Gregory
1800	1900	1600	1800	129550	SOM	Wiveliscombe
1464	1900	....	....	130591	SOM	Wiveliscombe
....	....	1348	1559	130591	SOM	???
1800	....	....	....	137693	SOM	???
1841	1917	1791	1992	163813	STS	Etruria
1792	1992	1700	1818	119296	WAR	Birmingham
1740	1750	1700	1992	167592	WAR	Birmingham
1720	1740	1600	1992	167592	WAR	Wolverhampton
1860	1992	ALL	1860	130575	WAR	???
1770	1880	1841	1881	104213	WIL	Box
1730	1992	....	1730	136778	WIL	Corsham
1730	1860	1000	1992	168149	WIL	Corsham
1816	1876	1750	1900	120146	WIL	Edington
1900	1992	ALL	ALL	130583	WOR	Badsey
1750	1770	1700	1992	167592	WOR	Worcester

Known From	To	Researching From	To	Ref	Cty	Place
HANCOCK contd.						
1842	1866	1800	1842	150657	???	Bristol
1829	1829	ALL	1829	119636	???	Holloway
HANCOX						
1838	1899	1750	1900	114456	SAL	ALL
....	....	1600	1850	136379	SAL	???
1840	1920	1700	1920	133426	STS	Coseley
....	....	1700	1900	133426	STS	Sedgeley
1808	1808	1750	1900	114456	WAR	Brandon
1757	1780	1700	1800	176621	WAR	Coventry
1400	1899	1400	1899	125148	WAR	Tysoe
1757	1780	1700	1800	176621	WAR	Wolston
HANCY						
1834	1992	....	1834	100064	SFK	Bungay
HAND						
1598	1859	....	....	135437	CHS	Chester
1800	1880	....	....	141178	CON	South East
1875	....	1875	....	109347	LAN	Haslingden
1825	1848	....	....	135437	LAN	Liverpool
1755	1900	1600	1900	141445	NTT	Nottingham
1755	1900	1600	1900	141445	NTT	Orston
....	....	1700	1800	178411	NTT	Oxton
1830	1950	ALL	1992	102245	STS	Wolverhampton
1811	1834	1700	1850	112216	WIL	Bremhill
HANDCOCK						
1579	1992	1700	1800	130605	DUR	Tanfield
1700	....	....	....	148768	IRL	???
1579	1992	1700	1800	130605	NBL	Hartsburn
HANDCOCKS						
1789	1789	1760	1789	108510	SAL	Wrockwardine
HANDEBO						
1785	ALL	ALL	1836	116734	IRL	Kilbride
1785	ALL	ALL	1836	116734	IRL	Tullamore
1785	ALL	ALL	1836	116734	WEM	???
HANDEL						
1814	....	1300	1992	152501	ALL	ALL
1500	1992	1500	1992	130672	SOM	Taunton
HANDELL						
1500	1992	1500	1992	130672	SOM	Taunton
HANDERIN						
1850	1900	1850	1900	150479	GLS	Cheltenham
HANDFORD						
1541	1769	1500	1650	102830	DBY	Dalbury Lees
1838	1865	1800	1900	105120	DBY	Mugginton
1797	....	1750	1797	103772	DBY	Stanton By Dale
HANDLE						
1500	1992	1500	1992	130672	SOM	Otterford
1500	1992	1500	1992	130672	SOM	Pitminster
HANDLEY						
1880	1924	ALL	ALL	130613	BRE	Builth Wells
1840	1900	1750	1840	172472	ESS	Maldon
1780	1860	1720	1881	130621	HEF	Tenbury
1660	1850	....	....	165999	LEI	Bottesford
1820	1856	1700	1820	148342	LEI	Croxton Kerrial
1660	1850	....	....	165999	LEI	Redmile
1660	1850	....	....	165999	LIN	Barrowby
1824	1992	1700	1824	130648	LIN	Grantham
1837	1992	1700	1837	130648	LIN	Great Gonerby
1660	1850	....	....	165999	LIN	Sedgebrook
1824	1992	1700	1824	130648	LIN	Spittlegate
1800	1970	ALL	ALL	130613	RAD	Aberedw
1780	1860	1670	1870	130621	STS	South
1850	1900	1850	1900	107476	STS	Doxey Wood
HANDO						
1500	1992	1500	1992	130672	SOM	Cannington
1500	1992	1500	1992	130672	SOM	Hutton
1500	1992	1500	1992	130672	SOM	Spaxton
HANDOL						
1500	1992	1500	1992	130672	SOM	Taunton
HANDOLE						
1500	1992	1500	1992	130672	SOM	Creech St Michael
HANDOLL						
1500	1992	1500	1992	130672	SOM	North Curry
HANDS						
1620	1850	1850	....	130680	GLS	Chipping Camden
1768	1788	ALL	1768	115126	NTH	Blisworth
1820	1825	1500	1825	104825	OXF	Cowley
1678	1992	....	....	130680	WAR	Stoneleigh
HANDSCOMB						
1829	1927	ALL	1827	138290	BDF	Ampthill
1871	?	1871	1876	130699	CAM	Mebourne
1876	?	1876	1899	130699	LND	Poplar
HANDSEL						
1708	1738	ALL	1708	169730	NFK	North Elmham

Known From	To	Researching From	To	Ref	Cty	Place
HANDSFORD						
1500	1992	....	....	130834	ALL	ALL
HANDSLEY						
1722	1848	ALL	ALL	154806	LIN	Louth
1722	1848	ALL	ALL	154806	LIN	Spilsby
HANDSON						
1817	1821	....	....	144495	CHI	Guernsey
HANDY						
1817	1904	1750	1950	177970	DUR	Lanchester
1850	1870	ALL	1850	141224	SOM	???
1890	....	ALL	ALL	143758	WAR	Birmingham
1670	1900	ALL	ALL	143758	WAR	Ilmington
1780	1992	1750	1880	162582	WAR	Ilmington
1600	1750	1600	1750	153451	WIL	Great Sumerford
1600	1750	1600	1750	153451	WIL	Rudbourne
HANES						
1866	1880	1865	1992	131865	LIN	Harmston
1744	....	ALL	....	104515	LIN	Irnham
HANGER						
1837	1864	ALL	ALL	135208	NTH	Eye
1837	1864	ALL	ALL	135208	NTH	Gunsthorpe
1808	1830	1790	1830	155683	NTH	Rushden
1837	1864	ALL	ALL	135208	NTH	Werrington
HANHAM						
1810	1880	1800	1900	102970	DOR	Upwey
HANKERD						
1870	1899	1800	1869	151882	KEN	Elham
HANKEY						
1699	1992	ALL	1699	154563	DUR	Weardale
1824	1880	1800	1890	124788	LAN	Manchester
1799	1849	1760	1820	166898	MDX	Westminster
1876	1896	ALL	ALL	169897	YKS	Gisbourne
HANKIN						
1840	....	ALL	1840	142301	MDX	Finsbury
1774	1774	ALL	ALL	126721	NTT	Hucknall
1810	1850	1700	1800	162884	SFK	Ipswich
HANKINS						
....	....	1692	1980	153265	NTH	Central
HANKINSON						
....	....	ALL	ALL	130702	ALL	Name Study
1826	1896	1700	1850	125350	LAN	Lytham
1845	1992	1700	1845	144967	LAN	Martinscroft
1826	1896	1700	1850	125350	LAN	Warton
HANKS						
1720	1820	1600	1850	166804	OXF	ALL
HANLEY						
1863	1900	1863	ALL	145386	EYK	Hull
....	....	....	1820	161667	IRL	???
....	....	1800	1950	134546	NTH	Pytchley
1750	1800	....	....	140554	YKS	Boston Spa
1680	1730	1600	1800	112372	YKS	Nidderdale
HANLON						
1870	1960	1840	1870	111856	COR	???
HANLY						
....	....	1660	1700	111414	MGY	Berriew
HANMER						
1298	1992	1298	1900	130710	CWD	Hanmer
HANN						
1772	1776	ALL	1774	122106	DOR	Bridport
1720	1720	1650	1775	144606	SOM	Montacute
HANNA						
....	....	1750	1820	121479	NIR	Ulster
1190	1992	1190	1992	130753	WIG	Sorbie
HANNAFORD						
1893	....	1893	....	130737	DEV	South
1550	1880	1300	1880	105333	DEV	Buckland In The Moor
1834	1900	1700	1900	141127	DEV	Dartmouth
1550	1880	1300	1880	105333	DEV	Holne
1550	1880	1300	1880	105333	DEV	Ilsington
1550	1880	1300	1880	105333	DEV	Lydford
1785	1785	1700	1820	105333	DEV	Rattery
1785	1785	1700	1820	105333	DEV	South Brent
1893	....	1893	....	130737	DEV	Thurlstone
1785	1785	1700	1820	105333	DEV	Ugborough
1550	1880	1300	1880	105333	DEV	Widecombe In The Moor
1815	1870	1600	1870	166650	DEV	Widecombe
HANNAH						
1850	1992	1750	1850	121479	ABD	Aberdeen
....	....	1066	....	130745	BRK	???
1880	1992	1880	1992	106836	DNB	Dumbarton
1700	1750	....	1750	130745	DON	???
1798	1850	1600	1850	130125	KKD	Terregles
HANNAH contd.						
....	....	1066	....	130745	LIN	???
1807	1833	1770	1820	141046	LKS	East Kilbride
1750	1992	1150	1992	130745	LKS	Kirkfieldbank
1946	1992	1946	1992	130745	LKS	Lesmahagow
1870	1880	1880	1910	106836	LKS	Partick
1828	1970	1828	1970	104027	RFW	Partick
1850	1870	1700	1850	106836	RFW	Port Glasgow
1150	1992	1150	1992	130745	WIG	Sorbie
1190	1992	1190	1992	130753	WIG	Sorbie
1828	1970	1828	1970	104027	???	Glasgow
HANNAM						
....	....	ALL	ALL	130761	ALL	Name Study
1847	1931	ALL	ALL	155373	LND	Islington
1850	1920	1750	1900	145866	SOM	Huish
HANNAY						
ALL	ALL	ALL	ALL	113972	SCT	ALL
1190	1992	1190	1992	130753	WIG	Sorbie
ALL	ALL	ALL	ALL	113972	???	Northumbria
HANNEN						
1750	1780	1700	1800	136840	HAM	Fordingbridge
HANNENT						
1839	1860	1760	1840	167452	MDX	Shoreditch
HANNEY						
1190	1992	1190	1992	130753	WIG	Sorbie
HANNIGAN						
....	....	1840	1875	163791	KID	Kildare
HANNING						
1820	ALL	ALL	ALL	130788	ALL	ALL
HANNINGAN						
1860	1944	1700	1860	128465	KID	Athy
HANNINGTON						
1662	1992	ALL	1700	130796	HAM	South
1662	1992	ALL	1700	130796	KEN	South
1796	1850	1700	1800	172898	LND	Paddington
1796	1850	1700	1800	172898	LND	Soho
....	....	....	....	158763	SRY	???
1662	1992	ALL	1700	130796	SSX	South
HANNON						
1900	1992	....	1992	171131	LND	London
HANNOTE						
1674	1940	....	....	128996	CAM	Thorney
HANRAHAN						
1850	1900	ALL	ALL	128279	LND	Shoreditch
HANSCOMB						
ALL	ALL	ALL	ALL	137243	ALL	ALL
HANSCOMBE						
1560	1700	1560	1700	167924	BDF	Shillington
1665	1731	1600	1750	142123	HRT	Pirton
1776	1846	1776	1846	175420	OXF	Henley On Thames
HANSELL						
1805	1992	1809	1992	130826	NBL	Newcastle
1805	1992	1809	1992	130826	PER	Edinburgh
1805	1992	1809	1992	130826	YKS	York
HANSFARD						
1500	1992	....	....	130834	ALL	ALL
HANSFORD						
....	....	ALL	ALL	130834	ALL	Name Study
1500	1992	....	....	130834	ALL	ALL
1800	1992	1700	1800	177938	DEV	Exeter
1850	1906	1700	1850	177938	DEV	Feniton
1755	1992	1700	1755	130966	DOR	Abbotsbury
1791	1992	1650	1791	130966	DOR	Loders
1800	1835	1700	1800	162884	DOR	Stoke Abbot
HANSHAW						
1860	1992	1500	1860	129577	LND	Stepney
HANSLIP						
1648	1731	1500	1700	100013	SFK	Mildenhall
HANSLOPE						
1066	1150	1066	1160	124974	BKM	Hanslope
HANSOM						
1866	1871	1842	1871	173851	YKS	Scarborough
HANSON						
....	....	ALL	ALL	100382	ALL	Name Study
1840	1870	....	....	102741	DUR	Crook
1840	1870	....	....	102741	DUR	Stanhope
....	....	1827	1873	103187	EYK	York
....	1700	....	....	174564	KEN	???
1806	1992	1700	1992	130850	LAN	North East
1768	1768	1500	1768	169439	LAN	Church
1885	1906	ALL	ALL	130664	LAN	???
1840	1881	1800	1992	144703	LEI	ALL
1749	1976	1700	1976	104396	LIN	ALL
1800	1992	1700	1850	112704	LIN	Saysthorpe

Known Researching
From To From To Ref Cty Place

HANSON contd.
1775 1890 1775 1890 100382 LIN Thurlby By Bourne
1782 1945 1700 1782 129445 LND Westminster
1700 1800 .... 165999 NTT Newark
1871 1881 ALL 1871 161330 NTT Nottingham
1750 1965 .... 137820 SHI Fetlar
1720 1965 .... 137820 SHI Mid Yell
1760 1965 .... 137820 SHI North Yell
1758 1965 .... 137820 SHI Northmavine
1720 1965 .... 137820 SHI South Yell
1815 1830 1700 1850 144703 WAR ALL
1890 1900 ALL ALL 155373 YKS South
1874 1900 1816 1874 102199 YKS Hartshead Moor
1815 .... 123951 YKS Stainland
1801 1820 1750 1801 179086 YKS Wilsden
1712 1788 1600 1765 101575 YKS ???

HANSORD
1819 1830 ALL ALL 134929 ESS Harwich

HANSTEAD
1745 1851 .... 166189 HRT Rickmansworth

HANTON
.... 1911 1918 122963 LND ALL
1791 1992 1600 1791 122963 SFK Wetheringsett Cum Brockford

HANTY
1780 1801 1700 1780 176451 YKS Holbeck

HANWAY
1830 1880 ALL ALL 152021 KIK Kilmacow

HANWELL
1783 1992 ALL ALL 130869 ALL ALL

HAPGOOD
.... 1700 1900 143324 WIL Ashton Keynes

HARADINE
1872 1992 1700 1850 120723 LND Bermondsey

HARAL
1760 1992 1780 1900 176958 LAN Blackburn
1760 1992 1780 1900 176958 YKS Barnsley
1760 1992 1780 1900 176958 YKS Huddersfield
1760 1992 1780 1900 176958 YKS Leeds
1760 1992 1780 1900 176958 YKS Wakefield

HARANETT
1706 1793 1733 1793 104817 WIL Whiteparish

HARBER
1800 ? ALL ALL 166243 DEV St Georges
1800 1900 1700 1900 132950 HEF Norton Juxta Kempsey
1780 1793 1500 1780 129577 IOW ???
1830 ? ALL ALL 166243 MDX Shoreditch
1700 1850 ALL ALL 154830 SSX Worth

HARBERT
1820 1860 1750 1830 170852 YKS Stillingfleet

HARBERTSON
.... ALL ALL 130877 ALL Name Study
1784 1992 1700 1784 130877 NBL ALL

HARBEY
1825 1849 .... 130079 LND Stepney

HARBIRD
1880 1890 .... 162752 ENG South

HARBONE
1815 1825 1800 1880 109371 GLS Preston On Stour

HARBOR
.... 1780 .... 145688 SFK Wortham

HARBORD
1650 1800 1650 1780 168343 NFK ???

HARBOROUGH
1799 1849 1600 1799 108588 BDF Eaton Bray
1598 .... 1500 1600 152110 CAM Haddenham

HARBOTTLE
1462 1657 1600 1640 132837 LIN ???
1650 1650 1590 1640 132837 LND ALL
1777 1951 1550 1777 130885 NBL Morpeth
1399 1487 .... 132837 NBL ???
1462 1657 1600 1640 132837 RUT ???

HARBOUR
1817 .... 117560 MDX Pancras

HARBOURNE
.... ALL 1879 166499 ??? London

HARBRIDGE
.... ALL ALL 126705 ALL Name Study
1722 1992 ALL 1992 126705 CHS ALL
1759 1992 ALL 1992 126705 LIN ALL

HARBRON
1919 1970 1896 1919 130893 DUR Darlington
1660 1821 1660 1830 136328 DUR Haughton Le Skerne

HARBRON contd.
1830 1992 1830 1880 136328 LAN Manchester

HARCOCK
1850 1960 ALL ALL 162469 SFK North

HARCOMBE
1859 1940 1861 1940 133175 GLS Pucklechurch

HARCOURT
.... 1066 1212 124974 LEI Bosworth
1500 1550 1450 1550 154881 LEI Thringston
1160 1234 1120 1212 124974 OXF Stanton Harcourt

HARCUS
1880 1920 1800 1880 165956 CMA Cockermouth
.... ALL 1800 110965 OKI Westray

HARDACRE
1880 1940 1870 1940 114936 LAN High Walton

HARDBOTTLE
1817 1992 ALL 1817 143960 NYK Kilburn

HARDCASTLE
1780 1820 1750 1800 177377 ESS Colcehster
.... ALL ALL 166812 LAN Manchester
1780 1992 1700 1780 127728 YKS Barnsley
1560 1972 1300 1600 112224 YKS Nidderdale
1700 1800 1600 1992 122084 YKS Otley

HARDEMAN
1730 1810 1600 1730 119148 HAM New Forest

HARDEN
1815 1992 1700 1815 130966 DOR Blandford
1849 1918 1800 1849 102849 ESS St Osyth
1760 1934 1700 1992 147982 KEN Dartford
1800 1992 .... 130907 KEN Hamstreet
1750 1773 1750 1773 127183 SSX Balcombe
1736 1800 1066 1736 130907 SSX West Hoathley

HARDESTY
1772 1839 ALL ALL 154067 LND Clerkenwell

HARDEY
1800 1900 1700 1800 105589 DEV Plymouth
1814 1900 ALL 1814 176656 LIN North

HARDGROVE
1700 1810 1800 1830 119903 MOG Monaghan

HARDIE
1800 1870 1700 1900 130915 ABD Daviot
.... 1800 1900 105198 ABD New Machar
1880 .... ALL 1900 145254 LAN Manchester
1788 1832 1700 1850 171662 MLN Dalkeith
.... 1800 1900 143685 MLN Edinburgh
1901 1992 1800 1901 179647 SCT Falkirk

HARDIMAN
1803 1833 1803 1841 153176 GLS Bishops Cleeve
1860 1868 1840 1900 121541 STS Brierlyley Hill
1720 1740 1600 1750 171182 WIL South
1720 1740 1600 1750 171182 WIL West

HARDING
1900 1992 1700 1900 161780 AVN Bristol
1815 1861 1815 1861 117803 BKM Botolph Claydon
1772 1802 1700 1772 172871 BKM Chalfont St Giles
1706 1785 .... 1800 137405 CAM South
1864 1992 .... 130923 CAM Swaffham Bulbeck
? .... 116793 CHS ???
1748 1823 ALL 1823 168718 CON South East
1650 1720 1650 1720 127655 COR Ballydaniel
1650 1720 1650 1720 127655 COR Great Island
1867 1992 1700 1867 130931 COR Millstreet
.... 1770 1870 136166 DEV Marwood
.... 1810 1900 136166 DEV Pilton
1815 1992 1700 1815 130966 DOR Blandford
1896 1992 .... 166855 DUR ???
.... 1780 1870 117137 GLA Newton Nottage
1860 1992 1700 1860 146064 GLS Bristol
1860 1992 1700 1860 146064 GLS Gloucester
? ? ? ? 142018 HAM Petersfield
1840 .... 132888 HAM Southampton
1850 1920 .... 166995 HAM Southsea
1836 1920 ALL 1836 129658 KEN Lewisham
1853 1913 1800 1853 125342 LAN ALL
1890 1950 .... 1900 147818 LAN Huyton
1830 1890 .... 162833 LEI Glooston
.... 1800 1900 156795 LND North
1877 1981 1850 1877 116076 LND Holborn
1853 1963 1700 1853 160709 LND Somerstown
1799 1992 1750 1992 126799 LND St Pancras
1820 1858 1800 1820 161527 LND Westminster
1837 1992 .... 167649 MGY Berriew
.... 1700 1837 167649 MGY Castle Caerinion
1915 .... 150762 MON Ebbw Vale

Known From	To	Researching From	To	Ref	Cty	Place
HARDING contd.						
1870	....	....	....	150762	MON	Sirehowey
1896	1992	....	....	166855	NYK	???
1698	....	1600	1750	143693	OXF	Crowell
1773	1900	....	....	161861	SOM	Writhlington
1800	1850	1800	1850	106631	SOM	Yatton
1707	1707	....	....	115606	SRY	Farnham
....	1785	ALL	ALL	129933	SRY	Godalming
....	....	1800	1900	121592	SRY	Woking
1700	1992	1600	1700	148237	SSX	Sidlesham
1878	1940	1860	1940	165441	STS	Hanley
1820	1867	1820	1867	138118	STS	Madeley
1790	1850	1650	1790	151084	STS	Maer
1500	1600	....	....	100420	WAR	Meriden
1810	1846	1750	1810	133671	WIL	Brinkworth
1800	1880	1800	1880	113670	WIL	Colerne
....	....	1750	1822	101060	WIL	Salisbury
1650	1732	1650	1770	142018	WIL	Salisbury
1859	1897	1700	1859	174831	WIL	Trowbridge
1822	1835	....	....	101060	WIL	Wylye
1850	1877	1850	1877	134767	YKS	Barwick In Elmet
1758	....	ALL	1758	154946	YKS	Coxwold
1730	1764	1700	ALL	146145	YKS	Danby
1780	1870	ALL	1870	146145	YKS	Glaisdale
1730	1764	1700	ALL	146145	YKS	Guisborough
HARDINGTON						
1850	1937	1837	1850	173576	YKS	Sheffield
HARDISTY						
....	....	ALL	ALL	160415	ALL	Name Study
1890	1970	1500	1800	139599	LAN	Colne
1851	1937	1700	1851	130974	YKS	Apperley Bridge
1790	1810	1700	1790	177393	YKS	Barmby Marsh
1740	1760	1700	1800	157651	YKS	Farnham
1585	1773	1400	1992	102520	YKS	Fewston
1770	1790	1700	1800	157651	YKS	Haxby
1600	1900	1200	1900	160415	YKS	???
HARDLE						
1774	1774	ALL	ALL	113360	HAM	Ovington
HARDLEY						
1825	1825	1800	1850	105333	HAM	Isle Of Wight
HARDMAN						
1720	1838	1700	1850	119091	GLS	Dymock
1690	1840	1600	1690	165530	LAN	South East
1810	....	....	1810	157406	LAN	Bolton
1800	1985	1800	1900	171824	LAN	St Helens
1923	....	....	....	158720	LND	Croydon
1848	....	....	....	158720	LND	Greenwich
1898	....	....	....	158720	LND	Lewisham
1827	1895	1800	1895	141283	WOR	Worcester
HARDRES						
1698	1698	....	....	144355	KEN	South
HARDS						
1862	1900	1750	1950	170054	MDX	Islington
1840	1845	1800	1860	142018	WIL	Salisbury
HARDWAY						
....	....	ALL	ALL	127256	ALL	Name Study
HARDWICK						
....	....	ALL	ALL	138541	ALL	Name Study
....	....	ALL	ALL	138177	ALL	Name Study
....	....	1300	1992	138541	ALL	ALL
....	1753	....	....	154024	DBY	Heath
....	....	ALL	1700	178403	DBY	???
1830	1870	1700	1830	139106	LND	???
1836	1958	1700	1836	129712	MON	Monmouth
1824	....	ALL	1824	164623	NTT	Weston
1830	1850	1750	1830	132640	SFK	Bramford
1572	1713	1450	1750	160873	STS	Pattingham
HARDWIDGE						
....	....	ALL	ALL	130982	ALL	Name Study
HARDY						
....	....	ALL	ALL	176761	ALL	Name Study
1900	1992	....	....	104302	AVN	Bristol
1802	1845	1800	1810	130990	CHS	Stockport
1845	1873	1845	1900	130990	CUL	Carlisle
1800	1950	1650	1800	128376	CUL	Hayton
1784	1810	1750	1837	162825	CUL	Kirkoswald
1828	1828	1526	1830	102121	DBY	Ilkeston
....	....	ALL	1850	138169	DEV	Sidmouth
1783	1869	1700	1900	110191	DOR	Broadwey
....	....	1790	1992	140619	DOR	East Stoke
1775	....	1750	1800	148121	DOR	Langton Herring
1800	1900	ALL	1800	138169	DOR	Marshwood
1488	....	1488	1992	127035	DOR	???
1899	1950	....	1899	131008	DUR	Hartlepool

Known From	To	Researching From	To	Ref	Cty	Place
HARDY contd.						
1815	1900	1750	1920	160849	ERY	Hull
1825	1906	1797	1825	120146	ESS	Fobbing
....	....	ALL	1850	133698	ESS	Hornchurch
1672	1753	1600	1672	175218	EYK	Preston
1848	1869	1830	1900	136719	HAM	Abbotts Ann
1800	1870	1775	1870	171549	HAM	Brading
1781	1862	1750	1880	136719	HAM	Hustbourne Priors
1886	1912	1880	1920	102121	LAN	Bolton
1737	1812	1737	1812	159492	LAN	Manchester With Salford
1850	1859	1850	1859	102121	LAN	Manchester
1880	1992	....	1900	147818	LAN	Oldham
1705	1796	1705	1796	159492	LAN	Oldham
1859	1886	1859	1886	102121	LAN	Rochdale
1679	1900	1640	1679	176249	LEI	North West
1850	1883	1500	1992	137626	LEI	Market Bosworth
1768	1925	1500	1992	137626	LEI	Newboldverdon
1736	1811	....	1736	101761	LIN	Friskney
1750	1920	1700	1920	128805	LND	ALL
1770	1854	1700	1870	128813	LND	City
1881	1929	1850	1930	128813	LND	Southwark
1800	....	ALL	1800	108847	LND	???
1847	1850	1847	1850	102121	MON	Tredegar
1746	1992	1600	1746	176761	NBL	Amble
1880	1992	1860	1880	176761	NBL	Blyth
1746	1992	1600	1746	176761	NBL	Broomhill
1746	1992	1600	1746	176761	NBL	Byker
1746	1992	1600	1746	176761	NBL	Chevington
1746	1992	1600	1746	176761	NBL	Norham Ford
1746	1992	1600	1746	176761	NBL	Widdrington
1740	1870	1700	1900	169641	NFK	Marham
1776	1791	1630	1776	138029	NFK	Seringham
1773	1871	....	....	176249	NTT	South West
1798	1900	1600	1900	124834	NTT	East Leake
....	....	1680	1720	177393	NTT	North Wheatley
1700	1790	....	....	176125	SFK	East Bergholt
....	....	1750	1900	101273	SRY	North
....	....	ALL	1750	138169	STS	Wolverhampton
....	1861	....	1861	150495	STS	Wolverhampton
....	....	1806	1930	131032	WES	???
1794	1992	....	1794	101761	WRY	Halifax
1700	1770	1670	1700	122904	WRY	Kildwick
1803	....	....	1803	101761	WRY	Ripponden
1819	1829	1750	1819	128368	YKS	Doncaster
1933	1948	1865	1933	131032	YKS	Doncaster
1871	1980	1600	1980	172863	YKS	Harrogate
1933	1948	1865	1933	131032	YKS	London
1853	1853	ALL	1900	146315	YKS	Long Preston
1659	1715	1600	1660	170348	YKS	Mirfield
1914	1943	1850	1914	158275	YKS	Sheffield
1933	1948	1865	1933	131032	YKS	Thorne
HARDYMAN						
....	....	ALL	ALL	131040	ALL	Name Study
1756	1850	1600	1850	131040	DOR	Thorncombe
HARE						
1770	1850	1700	1850	141410	BKM	Wingrave
1672	1940	....	....	128996	CAM	Thorney
1828	1839	....	....	129232	CMN	Laugharne
1850	1992	....	....	131059	ESS	Chelmsford
1850	1992	....	....	129232	GLA	ALL
....	....	?	?	179159	HRT	???
1840	....	1750	1840	165689	IRL	???
1800	1992	ALL	1800	159441	KEN	Sheppey
1840	1992	1800	1900	111147	LEI	ALL
1840	1920	1930	1992	165689	LND	East
1855	1940	1850	1970	141410	LND	Balham
1864	....	1800	1900	135925	LND	Stepney
1801	1890	1700	1930	144797	MDX	Bethnal Green
....	1834	1700	1834	126292	MDX	Lambeth
1800	1992	1750	1800	168777	MDX	Teddington
1839	1992	....	....	129232	PEM	Saunderfoot
1633	1900	ALL	1663	131059	SFK	Woolverstone
1788	1815	1700	1815	141097	YKS	Braithwell
1602	1716	1500	1720	168920	YKS	Emley
1788	1815	1788	1815	141097	YKS	Wadworth
1730	1791	1650	1730	138584	YKS	Whitkirk
HARES						
1850	1900	1850	1900	124761	GLS	South
1750	1850	1750	1850	124761	SOM	Shipham
1767	1788	1600	1767	164879	SOM	Wells
1872	1880	1800	1872	125342	WLS	Bedwelty
HARESIGN						
1724	1830	?	1800	130052	CAM	Fens

Known From	To	Researching From	To	Ref	Cty	Place
HARESIGN contd.						
1758	1992	1650	1800	130052	LIN	Fens
HAREWELL						
1776	1789	1730	1800	131547	GLS	Long Newnton
HARFIELD						
1720	1992	ALL	1720	131067	SSX	West Thorney
HARFLETE						
1500	1500	....	....	159883	KEN	Wingham
HARFORD						
1750	1800	1600	1800	154342	GLS	Stapleton
1730	1760	1730	1760	163848	WIC	Rathleasty
HARGER						
1775	1870	1740	1780	128333	YKS	Giggleswick
HARGEST						
1780	1992	1700	1780	172642	HEF	Letton
1780	1992	1700	1780	172642	HEF	Norton Canon
1780	1992	1700	1780	172642	SAL	Shrewsbury
HARGRAVE						
1815	1854	ALL	1860	113611	EYK	Hull
1828	1874	1803	1828	149578	LAN	Ashton Under Lyne
1828	1874	1803	1828	149578	LAN	Manchester
1850	1992	1700	1850	118532	MDX	London
1790	1980	1800	1920	161586	YKS	Brotherton
1790	1980	1800	1920	161586	YKS	Knottingley
HARGRAVES						
1815	1854	ALL	1860	113611	EYK	Hull
HARGREAVES						
1728	1926	1700	1800	126411	LAN	South East
1800	1992	1800	1992	109347	LAN	Accrington
1804	1992	....	....	147753	LAN	Adlington
1675	....	1675	....	109347	LAN	Altham
....	....	1700	1992	111503	LAN	Blackburn
1800	1880	1700	1840	131075	LAN	Blackburn
1600	1890	1500	1800	177318	LAN	Blackburn
1825	....	1825	....	109347	LAN	Burnley
....	....	1700	1992	111503	LAN	Chorley
1804	1963	1700	1894	115894	LAN	Chorley
1800	1880	1700	1840	131075	LAN	Clitheroe
1800	....	1800	....	109347	LAN	Haslingden
1830	1934	1700	1830	138304	LAN	Haslingden
1793	1846	1750	1793	178381	LAN	Haslingden
1700	1825	1700	1825	109347	LAN	Huncoat
1845	1920	1840	....	144827	LAN	Lancaster
1846	1851	....	....	178381	LAN	Manchester
1813	1828	1790	1828	108952	LAN	Pendle
1725	....	1725	....	109347	LAN	Sawley
1845	1920	1840	....	144827	LAN	Slyne
1790	1880	1750	1900	131075	LIN	North
1740	1900	1700	1920	160849	STS	Norton In The Moors
1680	1820	....	....	121983	STS	Ruston Spencer
1955	....	....	....	173932	WIL	Bradford On Avon
1625	....	1625	....	109347	YKS	Gisburn
1802	1873	1750	1830	163740	YKS	Hartshead
1840	1935	1800	1992	131075	YKS	Holbeck
1860	1956	....	....	178241	YKS	Leeds
1757	1871	1690	1871	178241	YKS	Tong
1840	1935	1800	1992	131075	YKS	Wortley
HARGROVE						
....	1770	....	....	125954	YKS	Kirkby Malzeard
HARINGTON						
....	....	ALL	ALL	131288	ALL	Name Study
1300	1630	....	....	175439	RUT	Exton
HARIS						
1907	1940	1800	1907	156248	STS	Wordsley
HARISON						
1795	1870	1600	1795	158496	NBL	Alendale
HARKER						
1741	1940	....	....	128996	CAM	Thorney
1850	1992	1650	1850	173665	NYK	Wensleydale
1750	1992	ALL	1750	131091	YKS	North Riding
HARKEY						
1788	1800	1700	1900	135496	CHS	North
HARKNESS						
1817	1890	1700	1817	135151	CUL	Cockermouth
1886	1924	1800	1886	165123	DUR	Consett
HARKNETT						
1850	1875	1800	....	118591	ESS	Epping
1777	....	1700	1780	130214	ESS	Epping
HARLAND						
1762	1788	1600	1762	175218	EYK	Driffield
....	1793	....	1793	146811	NBL	Tynemouth
1835	1900	1550	1835	150843	YKS	Eastrington
1840	1900	1700	1840	167762	YKS	Whitby

Known From	To	Researching From	To	Ref	Cty	Place
HARLE						
1852	1898	1880	1898	165840	SRY	Newington Butts
HARLETT						
....	....	1700	1859	152544	KEN	Chiddingstone
HARLEY						
1766	1790	....	1766	177504	CAM	Littleport
1750	1992	1750	1967	131113	DEV	ALL
1902	....	1902	....	161721	DUR	South Shields
1896	1954	1954	1992	146560	LKS	Coatbridge
1752	1992	1500	1752	164798	SAL	Central
1826	1842	1700	1900	131105	SAL	Cleobury
1752	1992	1500	1752	164798	SAL	Eaton
1060	1370	1000	1280	124974	SAL	Harley
1758	1908	1700	1758	166464	STS	Rugeley
1891	1968	1890	1992	131105	WAR	Birmingham
1913	1992	1900	1992	131105	WAR	Coventry
1851	1851	1820	1853	131105	WOR	Astley
1881	1881	1851	1885	131105	WOR	Bellbroughton
1853	1853	1851	1885	131105	WOR	Lower Mitton
1885	1891	1885	1891	131105	WOR	Stourbridge
1856	1992	1700	1856	123943	YKS	Sheffield
HARLIN						
1780	....	1700	1900	130419	YKS	Giggleswick
HARLING						
1850	1992	ALL	ALL	131121	KEN	???
1800	1974	ALL	ALL	154806	LAN	Rochdale
1800	1974	ALL	ALL	154806	LAN	Wray
....	....	ALL	ALL	131121	LAN	???
1856	1947	1800	1855	171719	LND	St Pancras
....	....	1750	1850	163082	SRY	Godstone
1850	1870	1750	1992	167592	YKS	Castleford
HARLOW						
1770	1992	1770	1992	131156	KEN	Bishopsbourne
1800	1950	1700	1800	158232	KEN	Margate
1882	1887	ALL	ALL	174998	LAN	Longsight
1800	1850	1700	1800	172898	LND	Holborn
1800	1850	1700	1800	172898	LND	Southwark
HARMAN						
....	....	ALL	ALL	131164	ALL	Name Study
1800	1869	1800	1869	176869	BRK	Thatcham
1700	1900	1650	1750	108677	ENG	South
1895	1935	1800	1895	106046	KEN	Bromley
1840	1850	1750	1840	106046	MDX	Feltham
1795	1851	1700	1800	130214	NFK	Gateley
1860	1900	....	1860	153982	SRY	Walworth
1800	1866	1600	1800	164879	SSX	ALL
1774	1835	....	....	144282	SSX	Barcombe
1820	1820	1792	1820	118192	SSX	Brighton
1590	1780	ALL	ALL	131164	SSX	East Grinstead
1763	1835	....	....	144282	SSX	Hamsey
1792	1792	1750	1820	118192	SSX	Westham
....	1600	....	....	174564	SSX	???
1555	1992	....	....	131172	SXE	Rye
1920	....	....	....	131008	YKS	Barnsley
1700	1800	1650	1700	177393	YKS	Owthorne
HARMER						
1540	1992	1400	1992	139068	ALL	ALL
1546	1992	....	....	108502	ESS	Brightingsea
1700	1957	1500	1600	150940	GLS	Kings Stanley
....	....	?	?	179159	HRT	???
1500	1900	....	....	111732	KEN	ALL
1760	1779	1610	1760	138029	NFK	Seringham
1789	1883	1750	1833	100242	SSX	Glynde
....	....	1540	1840	119431	SSX	Heathfield
1750	....	1700	1800	113743	SSX	Hurstmonceiux
1546	1992	....	....	108502	SSX	Lewes
1602	1602	....	....	127426	STS	???
1807	1881	1800	1992	167002	SXE	Warbleton
HARMS						
....	....	1800	1826	154873	KEN	Milton
....	....	1800	1826	154873	KEN	Sittingbourne
HARMSWORTH						
1600	1690	1500	1600	141925	BRK	Sulhamstead Abbott
1750	1900	ALL	1750	111333	HAM	North West
1765	1842	ALL	ALL	129933	HAM	Odiham
1856	1881	ALL	ALL	129933	HAM	Yateley
1840	1872	1800	....	109282	LND	Central
HARNDEN						
1832	1992	1750	1800	172618	DEV	Salcombe
1860	1930	1800	1860	115703	HAM	Portsmouth
1810	1992	1700	1810	108502	KEN	Ashford
1810	1992	1700	1810	108502	KEN	Great Chart
1810	1992	1700	1810	108502	KEN	Mersham
....	....	1700	1850	172618	SSX	Rye

Known From	To	Researching From	To	Ref	Cty	Place
HARNESS						
1720	1900	1650	1720	165018	LIN	Wainfleet
HARNETT						
1820	1871	1800	1871	134880	KEN	Folkestone
1800	1840	1800	1850	170852	KEN	Folkestone
1591	1658	....	....	107085	KEN	Ramsgate
HARNEY						
....	....	ALL	ALL	144002	ALL	Name Study
1920	....	1900	....	109398	LND	Stepney
HARNIESS						
1800	1900	1700	1800	176753	LIN	Binbroke
HARNIMAN						
....	....	ALL	ALL	131180	ALL	Name Study
HARNWELL						
1814	1840	1800	1840	141135	CAM	Cotton
HAROLD						
1880	1900	ALL	ALL	112518	DUB	Dublin
HARPER						
1798	1850	1600	1798	127507	ANT	Carnmoney
1840	1916	1840	1992	140090	ANT	Lisburn
....	....	ALL	ALL	171816	BKM	Wolverton
1786	1805	1786	1805	141690	CON	Bodmin
1830	1945	1700	1830	120944	CON	St Agnes
1717	1719	1600	1719	133000	DEV	Axmouth
1895	1914	1865	1914	102989	ESS	Canning Town
1783	1992	1700	1783	175218	EYK	Hull
1814	1880	1780	1880	128244	GLS	Gloucester
1814	1880	1780	1880	128244	GLS	Newent
1914	1953	1914	1960	102989	KEN	Dartford
1859	1914	....	....	131210	KEN	Plumstead
1887	....	1850	1992	166197	LAN	Blackburn
1874	1992	1800	1874	121673	LND	Kensington
1791	1900	....	....	131210	LND	Shoreditch
1791	1900	....	....	131210	LND	Woolwich
1813	1992	1700	1813	100110	NFK	West Rainham
1840	1880	1800	1840	159115	SAL	Wem
1569	1715	1500	1715	102830	STS	Sedgely
1600	1900	....	....	100420	WAR	Berkswell
1600	1900	....	....	100420	WAR	Meriden
1800	1900	ALL	ALL	171816	WAR	Newbold On Avon
1783	1980	1700	1850	170178	WIL	Ogbourne St Andrew
....	....	ALL	ALL	143014	WYK	ALL
1750	1810	1650	1750	165018	WYK	Swanland
1700	1865	1750	1791	171565	YKS	Hull
1670	1810	1600	1700	174858	YKS	Hunmanby
1882	1941	1864	1882	131326	YKS	Rotherham
1882	1941	1864	1882	131326	YKS	Sheffield
HARPHAM						
1804	1849	1700	1804	139386	NTT	Rampton
HARPUM						
1876	1992	....	1900	137642	KEN	Medway
HARPUR						
1843	1843	....	....	115606	BRK	Denchworth
1794	1822	1600	1794	102571	CON	Kenwyn
1750	1760	1700	1850	176281	MDX	Hatton
1750	1850	1700	1850	176281	MDX	Westminster
HARRAD						
1811	1926	ALL	1992	159174	STS	Burton On Trent
HARRAP						
1839	1992	ALL	1839	160938	YKS	Saddleworth
HARRARD						
1719	....	....	1719	101761	NTT	Nottingham
HARRAS						
1784	1786	1780	1790	170143	HAM	Liss
1807	1807	1807	1807	170143	SSX	Trotton
HARRATAGE						
1715	....	....	....	171441	KEN	Rochester
HARRELL						
1675	1962	1280	1675	131237	WIL	Bulkington
HARRIES						
1750	1850	1650	1900	139866	GLA	Gwenlais
1810	1992	ALL	1810	142034	GLA	Llangiwc
1850	1928	1700	1850	131253	GLA	Llanwonno
1789	1900	1780	1900	118540	MON	Newchurch
1783	1822	ALL	1992	101079	PEM	Eglyscymyn
1852	....	ALL	1852	123013	PEM	Llanwndra
....	....	1700	1799	179612	PEM	Solva
1872	1880	1800	1872	125342	WLS	Mountain Ash
1872	1880	1800	1872	125342	WLS	Penrhiwceiber
HARRIGAN						
....	....	ALL	ALL	143340	ALL	ALL
?	?	?	?	120332	TIP	Carrick On Suir
HARRIMAN						
1801	1869	1700	1950	178616	LEI	Hathern
HARRIMAN contd.						
1801	1980	1600	1801	131261	LEI	Sutton In The Elms
1801	1869	1700	1950	178616	NTT	Nottingham
HARRINGTON						
ALL	ALL	ALL	ALL	131288	ALL	ALL
1802	1885	1700	1802	152196	CMA	Bootle
....	....	ALL	ALL	135062	DOR	???
1765	1765	?	?	108189	ESS	Boreham
....	....	1538	1900	131318	ESS	Finchingfield
1892	....	1850	1950	176885	ESS	Walthamstow
1777	1837	1538	1777	131318	ESS	Wethersfield
1700	1750	1700	1800	111007	ESS	Widford
1800	1920	1750	1935	145572	HRT	Datchworth
1850	1920	1750	1935	145572	HRT	Elstree
1832	1881	1750	1900	126918	IRL	Cork
1832	1881	1750	1900	126918	IRL	Kerry
1795	1920	1750	1935	145572	KEN	Woolwich
1851	1881	1750	1900	126918	LND	Bermondsey
1795	1900	1750	1935	145572	LND	???
1850	1916	ALL	1850	115118	MDX	East London
....	1850	1700	1850	178608	MDX	Limehouse
1837	1913	1750	1837	148709	SRY	Farnahm
1837	1992	1700	1837	131296	SRY	Farnham
....	....	1700	1900	131296	SRY	Frimley
1837	1992	1700	1837	131296	SRY	Hale
1700	1800	....	....	100536	???	Bath
HARRIOTT						
1803	1893	....	....	144282	SSX	Hamsey
1824	1887	1612	1824	127698	SSX	South Heighton
HARRIS						
1880	1962	1980	1992	119016	ALL	ALL
1792	1860	1700	1880	113107	ANS	Arbroath
1831	1831	1831	1831	145580	ANS	Dundee
1860	1870	ALL	ALL	117366	AVN	Bristol
1771	1825	....	....	175102	BDF	Barton Le Clay
1728	1796	1728	1796	103977	BDF	Houghton Regis
1728	1796	1728	1796	103977	BDF	Luton
1788	1806	1800	1900	175102	BDF	Streatley
1530	1620	1400	1600	144657	BKM	Hardwick
1840	1881	1840	1881	125229	BKM	Hazlemere
1829	1851	1829	1851	125229	BKM	Hughenden
1800	1988	1700	1860	129755	BKM	Marlow
1500	1600	1400	1600	144657	BKM	Padbury
1850	1856	1850	1860	142638	BRE	Crickhowell
1920	1930	1884	1992	131458	CON	Charlestown
1826	1838	1826	1992	121932	CON	Jacobstow
1824	1900	1858	1992	131369	CON	Lanlivery
1750	....	1750	1900	116920	CON	Mevagissey
1683	1760	....	....	174319	CON	Mevagissey
1760	1808	1650	1900	146986	CON	Penryn
1638	1992	?	1638	141143	CON	Redruth
1650	....	1650	1750	116920	CON	Roseland Peninsular
1600	1900	1600	1900	131458	CON	St Austell
1676	1734	1600	1676	128082	CON	St Clether
....	....	....	1800	117714	CON	St Just In Roseland
1600	1800	1600	1800	150126	CON	St Keverne
1840	....	....	....	153885	CON	St Mabyn
....	....	1750	1850	117714	CON	St Mawes
1815	1880	1700	1815	161837	CON	St Pinnock
?	?	1780	1816	131733	DBY	Bakewell
1600	1750	1550	1600	131350	DEV	Arlington
1730	1992	....	1730	131385	DEV	Aylesbeare
1736	1800	1580	1736	111031	DEV	Barnstaple
1800	ALL	....	....	103381	DEV	Broadhempston
1832	1900	....	....	131350	DEV	Challacombe
1797	....	ALL	1861	169374	DEV	Charleton
1863	....	ALL	1863	164623	DEV	East Stonehouse
1600	1699	1600	1699	169781	DEV	Exeter
1854	1897	1800	1900	179337	DEV	Exeter
1800	ALL	....	....	103381	DEV	Kingsbridge
1750	1830	....	....	131350	DEV	Loxhore
1830	1884	ALL	ALL	140155	DEV	Plymouth
1820	1900	ALL	1870	142301	DEV	Plymouth
1738	1900	1600	1992	130125	DOR	Chaldon Hg
1871	1992	1871	1992	162124	DOR	Weymouth
1740	1870	1700	1850	136840	DOR	Wool Area
1900	1992	1900	1992	133450	DOR	???
....	....	....	1771	142409	ENG	Midlands
1780	1850	....	....	105759	ESS	Barking
1765	1845	1600	1765	111031	ESS	Mid
1900	1921	1900	1921	123773	ESS	Walthamstow
1850	1860	1860	1950	178845	GLA	Dowlais
1800	1992	ALL	1800	131393	GLA	Loughor
1830	1850	1850	1950	178845	GLA	Merthyr Tydfil

Known From	To	Researching From	To	Ref	Cty	Place
HARRIS contd.						
1762	1992	ALL	1900	131334	GLS	ALL
1850	1874	1600	1850	111031	GLS	East
1700	....	....	....	148768	GLS	Adlestrop
....	....	ALL	1800	141224	GLS	Bitton
1616	1796	1550	1796	102830	GLS	Bouton On The Water
1870	1900	1870	1900	142077	GLS	Cam
1838	....	1841	1887	164895	GLS	Cheltenham
....	....	1700	1835	101478	GLS	Costwolds
1800	1992	1750	1800	116513	GLS	Deerhurst
1800	1890	1800	1890	163287	GLS	Elmstone Hardwicke
1851	1897	1800	1851	155225	GLS	Gloucester
1901	1929	1850	1901	178381	GLS	Gloucester
1780	1850	1600	1850	154342	GLS	Mangotsfield
....	....	ALL	1800	141224	GLS	St George
1803	1881	1800	1881	142077	GLS	Tetbury
1500	1900	1500	1900	170216	HAM	ALL
1700	1800	ALL	ALL	122866	HAM	North West
1858	1992	ALL	ALL	108464	HAM	Burclere
1920	1930	1700	1920	100765	HAM	Lockerly
1812	1992	1812	1862	131342	HAM	Millbrook
1858	1992	ALL	ALL	108464	HAM	Newtown
1792	1992	ALL	1792	178659	HAM	Otterbourne
1856	1896	1856	1950	143715	HAM	Oundle
1896	1950	1889	....	143715	HAM	Peterborough
1780	1992	ALL	1790	150215	HAM	Waterlooville
1816	1852	1800	1852	155942	HAM	???
....	1916	1881	1916	142638	HEF	Ewyas Harold
1860	1881	1850	1900	142638	HEF	Kentchurch
1851	1900	1830	1851	155047	HEF	Leominster
1880	1900	ALL	ALL	173657	HRT	Harpenden
1750	1800	1750	1800	167924	HRT	Ickleford
1847	1933	1980	1992	119016	HRT	Thorley
1826	1900	1750	1891	129984	KEN	South East
1782	1859	1720	1782	154873	KEN	Ashford
1910	1930	1900	1992	123250	KEN	Aylesford
....	1800	....	....	174564	KEN	Bilsington
1797	1992	1700	1797	173231	KEN	Bromley
1841	1897	1840	1910	132497	KEN	Canterbury
1782	1859	1720	1782	154873	KEN	Canterbury
1860	1948	1818	1860	154873	KEN	Faversham
1800	1838	1800	1992	137448	KEN	Folkstone
1810	1885	1700	1800	160350	KEN	Minster In Sheppey
1830	1900	1600	1830	151025	KEN	Sandhurst
1860	1948	1818	1860	154873	KEN	Sittingbourne
1845	1992	1845	1900	111791	KEN	Yalding
1873	1894	ALL	1911	101362	KER	Killarney
1840	1950	1800	1840	111031	LAN	Liverpool
1862	1952	....	....	145580	LAN	Liverpool
....	....	ALL	ALL	100390	LAN	Manchester
1800	1945	?	1900	131458	LAN	Salford
1800	1875	ALL	ALL	106097	LEI	Pickwell
1798	1865	1700	1900	135968	LEI	Wymeswold
1800	1992	1700	1800	102342	LIN	Alkbarough
?	?	?	?	142638	LIN	Cowbit
1850	1880	1550	1850	147265	LIN	Mid
1775	1794	ALL	1775	152838	LIN	Ulceby
1870	1960	1700	1870	117269	LND	Bermondsey
1920	1940	1920	1940	130222	LND	Hoxton
1895	1920	ALL	ALL	120154	LND	Kentish Town
1830	1900	1800	1992	133450	LND	Leytonstone
1884	1942	1500	1992	175498	LND	Poplar
1900	1920	1900	1920	111589	LND	Shepherds Bush
1831	1861	1770	1831	117471	LND	Shoreditch
1823	1839	....	....	160776	LND	Shoreditch
1850	1950	ALL	ALL	157864	LND	Southwark
1870	1992	1870	1992	123773	LND	St Pancras
1818	1831	....	....	111856	LND	???
1874	....	1870	1880	142638	MDX	Haggerstone West
1851	....	1800	1851	100242	MDX	Heston
1818	1935	1700	1992	110191	MDX	London
1843	1900	1800	1900	126586	MDX	London
1850	1870	1750	1850	130044	MDX	London
1899	....	1870	1939	131482	MDX	London
1847	1867	....	....	158747	MDX	London
....	....	1790	1820	160776	MDX	London
....	....	ALL	ALL	156930	MON	Bettws Newydd
1880	1900	1850	1920	123250	MON	Caerleon
1850	1880	1850	1910	156930	MON	Clytha
1780	1880	1780	1880	156930	MON	Llangwn
1800	1900	1700	1900	172561	MON	Trellech
1844	1980	1844	1947	131407	NFK	Ditchingham
1850	1900	1850	1900	173533	NTH	Duston
1800	1850	1750	1800	123595	NTH	Harpole

Known From	To	Researching From	To	Ref	Cty	Place
HARRIS contd.						
1862	1862	ALL	1870	117307	NTH	Northampton
1817	1870	....	....	157724	OXF	Burford
1777	1844	1777	1844	131407	OXF	Chesterton
....	....	1700	1790	137618	OXF	Yarnton
1811	1992	1800	1820	131326	PEM	Milford
1720	1800	1720	1800	167924	PEM	Tenby
1795	1880	ALL	ALL	131415	PER	Dunkeld
1829	....	1829	1850	142638	RAD	Llyswen
1750	1845	1750	1845	148210	RUT	Langham
1780	1780	1780	1780	139971	SAL	Cround
1793	....	1790	1800	178845	SAL	Llanvair Waterdine
1844	1980	1844	1947	131407	SFK	Bungay
1820	1821	1800	1842	170143	SOM	Bath
1843	?	ALL	ALL	153516	SOM	Berrow
1843	?	ALL	ALL	153516	SOM	Congresbury
1841	1851	1841	1992	162124	SOM	Ilminster
1843	?	ALL	ALL	153516	SOM	Lympsham
1800	1840	1750	1840	131431	SOM	Publow
1640	1750	1640	1750	142018	SOM	Rode
1740	1820	1740	1830	138479	SOM	Shapwick
1843	?	ALL	ALL	153516	SOM	South Brent
1756	1992	1745	1755	108227	SOM	White Lackington
....	....	1800	1900	136166	SOM	Worle
1833	1852	1833	1852	155942	SRY	Brixton
1800	1842	1780	1800	102075	SRY	Lambeth
1827	1849	1775	1850	129356	SRY	Southwark
1900	1920	1900	1920	111589	SRY	Wimbledon
1632	1658	....	....	117404	STS	Milwich
1875	1925	ALL	1875	115045	STS	West Bromwich
....	....	1800	1850	149306	STS	Wolverhampton
1843	1843	1820	1851	170143	WAR	Birmingham
1750	1850	1650	1800	177180	WAR	Offchurch
1500	1900	1500	1900	170216	WIL	ALL
1815	1900	1800	1900	170143	WIL	Corsham
1828	1851	1750	1900	113212	WIL	Salisbury
1802	....	ALL	ALL	116394	WIL	Salisbury
1780	1834	1750	1780	131342	WIL	Stockton
1700	1800	1700	1800	142018	WIL	Trowbridge
1800	1840	1800	1850	138479	WIL	Warminster
1790	1812	1760	1790	131342	WIL	Wylye
1833	1860	1700	1850	119849	WMD	Edgbaston
....	....	1800	1840	160601	WOR	Droitwich
....	....	1700	1800	170313	WOR	Stourport
1744	1767	....	1744	101761	WOR	Worcester
1840	1860	1800	1900	143502	WOR	Worcester
1800	1992	1700	1800	131377	WOR	Yardley
1866	1866	1800	1880	127361	WRY	Dewsbury
1897	1910	1750	1896	131245	WRY	Leeds
1903	1992	1900	1992	123250	YKS	Hull
HARRISON						
1850	1890	1800	1850	126225	ARM	Market Hill
1700	1750	1550	1700	145688	BRK	Warfield
1728	....	....	1728	108839	CAM	Coveney
1660	1940	....	....	128996	CAM	Thorney
1744	....	....	....	151270	CAM	Whittlesey
1800	1810	1780	1810	155047	CHS	Liverpool
1800	1830	ALL	ALL	119253	CHS	Stockport
1867	1889	ALL	1867	160008	CHS	Stockport
1852	1992	....	1852	105295	CLV	Hartlepool
1760	1840	1700	1760	152196	CMA	Bridekirk
1871	1871	1700	1900	145955	CMA	Kendal
1931	1992	1852	1931	145084	CMA	Threlkeld
1799	1876	....	....	118354	CUL	Grasmere
1869	1874	ALL	ALL	155608	DBY	ALL
1735	1851	1700	1856	142085	DBY	Chellaston
1600	1860	1600	1860	166952	DBY	Crich
1850	1900	1850	1900	124605	DBY	Derby
1780	1992	1700	1800	124788	DBY	Hope
1770	1857	1700	1770	174602	DUR	Gatehead
1852	1992	....	....	105295	DUR	Hartlepool
1786	1820	1600	1786	115169	DUR	Haughton Le Skerne
1680	1750	1600	1750	154342	GLS	Bitton
1650	1800	1600	1750	144657	HAM	Farringdon
1810	1852	1700	1860	162280	HAM	Portsmouth
1830	....	....	....	151785	HUN	Bluntisham
1806	1840	1800	1840	117668	LAN	Ashton In M
....	....	1890	1992	147613	LAN	Barrow In Furness
1714	....	1714	1770	177768	LAN	Claughton
1786	1900	1600	1992	131601	LAN	Cockerham
1840	1890	1750	1900	157171	LAN	Colne
1861	1881	1700	1992	121215	LAN	Denton
1786	1900	1600	1992	131601	LAN	Forton
1809	1849	1700	1992	159468	LAN	Fylde

Known From	To	Researching From	To	Ref	Cty	Place
HARRISON contd.						
1786	1900	1600	1992	131601	LAN	Garstang
1781	....	1781	1850	177768	LAN	Garstang
1850	1900	1750	1992	150541	LAN	Gorton
1840	1885	1840	1885	117668	LAN	Haydock
1780	1820	1750	1820	152404	LAN	Hulton
....	1850	1500	1850	175072	LAN	Kirkham
1800	1900	1800	1900	177768	LAN	Liverpool
1787	1900	1600	1787	102571	LAN	Manchester
1625	1850	1750	1992	133450	LAN	Manchester
1870	1870	1870	1870	115932	LAN	Oldham
1820	1881	1700	1820	135348	LAN	Oldham
1813	1841	....	....	110167	LAN	Preston
1829	1875	1829	1875	159131	LAN	Preston
1925	1930	1900	1992	127205	LAN	Salford
1670	1992	1781	1992	131504	LAN	Tarleton
1800	1820	....	....	126497	LAN	Wigan
1746	....	1746	1810	177768	LAN	Winmarleigh
....	....	1812	1907	175161	LEI	Leicester
1800	1881	1760	1800	174211	LIN	Blankney
1902	1952	1800	1992	120987	LIN	Great Gonerby
1703	1780	?	1703	128910	LIN	Laughton
1780	1799	1740	1800	174211	LIN	Mid Rasen
1782	1852	1852	1992	128910	LIN	Scotter
1800	1881	1760	1800	174211	LIN	Wellingore
1800	1850	ALL	ALL	114235	LIN	???
1850	1975	....	....	169102	MDX	Acton
1850	1975	....	....	169102	MDX	Ealing
1850	....	....	....	133698	MDX	Fulham
1819	1821	1700	1818	131245	MDX	Hackney
1850	....	....	....	133698	MDX	Hamm
1850	1975	....	....	169102	MDX	Hayes
1864	1992	1700	1900	102326	MDX	Islington
1900	1980	1700	1900	160989	NBL	Seaton Sluice
ALL	1852	....	....	105295	NBL	Stanfordham
1820	1880	1850	1880	174998	NBL	Sunderland
1739	1805	1700	1800	117013	NFK	Edgefield
1775	1873	....	....	157554	NFK	Great Yarmouth
1780	1820	1780	1820	110205	NFK	Norwich
1757	1780	1650	1757	101443	NRY	Hinderwell
1795	1992	1700	1795	105902	NTH	Raunds
1869	1874	ALL	ALL	155608	NTT	ALL
1867	1960	1860	1960	131199	NTT	Bramcote
1785	1860	1800	1900	170348	NTT	East Retford
1870	1881	1881	1992	128910	NTT	Hucknall Torkard
1783	1783	....	....	108901	NTT	Nottingham
1850	1992	1790	1992	131555	NTT	Nottingham
1900	1992	1900	1992	143774	NYK	Middlesborough
1700	1970	ALL	....	134244	NYK	Rillington
1700	1907	ALL	1992	168696	OXF	Enstone
1643	1643	ALL	1750	168696	OXF	Heythrop
....	....	ALL	1822	169102	OXF	Tadmarton
1822	1849	....	....	169102	OXF	???
1790	....	1750	1800	100129	RUT	Bisbrooke
?	?	?	?	138622	SAL	???
1760	....	....	....	129747	SFK	Ipswich
1750	1965	....	....	137820	SHI	Fetlar
1720	1965	....	....	137820	SHI	Mid Yell
1760	1965	....	....	137820	SHI	North Yell
1758	1965	....	....	137820	SHI	Northmavine
1720	1965	....	....	137820	SHI	South Yell
1860	1880	1840	1880	135429	SOM	Bath
1720	1720	1600	1720	144851	SSX	Hastings
1820	1880	1800	1900	111147	STS	ALL
1765	1880	1700	1765	120049	STS	Biddulph
1765	1880	1700	1765	120049	STS	Horton
1853	1915	1700	1992	131601	STS	Maer
1856	1930	1750	1930	131547	STS	Mucklestone
1867	1992	1700	1867	158518	STS	Rowley Regis
1807	1953	1700	1807	156248	STS	Sedgley
1831	1870	1830	1870	143774	SYK	Leeds
1836	1882	ALL	1836	100528	WAR	Leamington
1871	1871	1700	1900	145955	WES	Kendal
1840	1992	ALL	1840	131571	WOR	Evesham
?	?	?	?	138622	WOR	???
1680	1848	1650	1848	153273	WRY	Bentham
1795	1900	1760	1920	147338	WRY	Bradford
1833	1833	1810	1833	147338	WRY	Northowram
1783	1992	....	....	152765	YKS	South
1871	1992	ALL	ALL	107913	YKS	Bradford
1860	1992	1800	1860	131628	YKS	Bradford
....	....	1700	1831	131598	YKS	Egton
....	....	1800	1900	147613	YKS	Giggleswick
....	....	1700	1831	131598	YKS	Glaisdale
....	....	1700	1831	131598	YKS	Green Houses
1850	....	1750	....	134589	YKS	Halifax
1700	1750	1700	1750	167924	YKS	Holtby
....	....	1700	1770	177393	YKS	Howden
1820	1992	1750	1820	128538	YKS	Hull
1860	1992	1800	1860	131628	YKS	Leeds
1738	1804	1700	1800	137561	YKS	Leeds
1850	1960	....	....	136824	YKS	Sheffield
....	....	1700	1800	147613	YKS	Slaidburn
1800	1822	1700	1800	166928	YKS	Speeton
1837	1840	....	1850	147818	YKS	Tholthorpe
1749	1766	1730	1749	101796	YKS	Wakefield
1600	1750	1683	1720	105694	YKS	Wakefield
1690	1800	1690	1800	176958	YKS	Wakefield
1870	1992	1800	1850	167568	YKS	???
HARRISON-CRIPPS						
1878	1960	1700	1960	141550	BKM	Marlow
HARRISS						
1893	1932	1700	1893	142484	IOW	Newport
HARRISSON						
ALL	1850	....	....	133698	SOM	Axbridge
HARRLOD						
1795	1992	1980	1992	114979	LEI	Earl Shilton
HARROD						
....	....	1800	1900	108936	DUR	Wingate
1800	1850	1600	1800	132403	NTT	ALL
HARROLD						
1790	1875	1770	1875	159700	GLS	Dursley
1860	....	....	1860	164011	KEN	Folkestone
1878	1899	ALL	1878	169943	MDX	Bow
1834	1992	1800	1834	144010	OKI	Gairsay
HARRON						
1885	1992	1700	1885	113794	DON	Raforty
HARROP						
1739	....	1687	1739	117196	CHS	Dawsworth
1687	1739	ALL	1739	141062	CHS	Gawsworth
1860	1880	1840	1890	173428	LND	Southwark
HARROW						
1700	1750	....	....	126497	CAI	Olrig
....	....	ALL	1850	131636	ENG	???
1724	1850	1700	1850	157732	HAM	Alton
1850	1900	ALL	1850	131636	LND	Soho
HARROWELL						
1794	1822	1700	1880	124907	HRT	Hemel Hempstead
HARROWER						
....	....	ALL	ALL	131644	ALL	Name Study
....	....	ALL	1850	131644	CLK	Alloa
....	....	ALL	1850	131644	CLK	Tillicoultry
1800	1900	ALL	1850	131644	FIF	Culross
1860	1960	ALL	1960	131644	LAN	Manchester
1600	1700	1550	1650	154881	MLN	Edinburgh
1800	1900	ALL	1850	131644	PER	Torryburn
HARROWING						
1800	1850	1700	1800	107344	NFK	East Walton
HARRUP						
1720	1740	1650	1750	135496	CHS	Gawsworth
HARRY						
1790	1810	1750	1830	158658	CMN	Llandybie
1806	1830	1750	1840	158658	CMN	Llanelli
1702	1896	....	....	143596	CON	Mousehole
1840	1992	1700	1992	117609	DEV	Plymouth
1800	1875	1725	1800	165468	GLA	Loughor
1804	1820	1700	1880	128163	HEF	Kings Caple
....	....	1700	1899	174963	MON	Caldicot
HARRYMAN						
1700	1900	1750	1850	126144	KEN	Boughton
1700	1900	1750	1850	126144	KEN	Mereworth
HARSANT						
1744	1898	....	....	118370	SFK	Woodbridge
HARSE						
1843	1914	ALL	ALL	153516	SOM	Butcombe
....	1766	1500	1766	175072	SOM	Winscombe
HART						
1765	1837	1500	1765	125695	BDF	Potton
1726	1781	ALL	1781	168718	BDF	Riseley
1723	1940	....	....	128996	CAM	Thorney
1850	1992	1700	1992	111147	DBY	ALL
1630	1800	ALL	ALL	141739	DON	???
1900	1992	1538	1900	131318	DOR	South
1910	1992	1850	1992	131679	ESS	Clacton
1757	1776	1700	1800	126586	ESS	Great Yeldham
1700	1780	1600	1800	126586	ESS	Panfield
1790	1865	1850	1992	126799	ESS	West Ham

Known From	To	Researching From	To	Ref	Cty	Place
HART contd.						
1795	1992	1700	1795	158143	FIF	Dunfermline
1815	1992	....	....	131660	GLS	Bristol
1850	1943	1851	1992	101656	GLS	Painswick
1720	....	ALL	1720	179515	HRT	Chishunt
1814	1845	....	....	131210	HRT	Ware
1825	1830	1700	1800	123870	IRL	Desertcreat
1619	1895	ALL	1770	137774	KEN	South East
1849	....	....	....	164631	KEN	Aylesford
1860	....	....	1860	164011	KEN	Folkestone
1826	1851	....	....	164631	KEN	Sittingbourne
1840	1920	1700	1992	131601	LAN	Croston
1840	1920	1700	1992	131601	LAN	Merebrow
1840	1992	1700	1840	158917	LAN	Orford
1840	1920	1700	1992	131601	LAN	Southport
1840	1920	1700	1992	131601	LAN	Tarleton
1830	....	....	1830	111767	LAN	Westhoughton
1800	1900	1700	1850	142204	LAN	Westhoughton
1782	1846	1700	1846	178233	LAN	Wigan
1826	1862	1700	1826	165220	LEI	Leicester
1870	1970	1750	1870	152730	LIN	Bassingham
1717	1747	1700	1747	102830	LIN	Bourne
1866	1992	1700	1866	108316	LKS	Barony
1866	1992	1700	1866	108316	LKS	Parkhead
1875	1925	1875	1992	165603	LND	Croydon
1872	1872	1860	1992	165603	LND	Edmonton
1900	1992	....	1900	159514	LND	Hoxton
1730	1750	1730	1750	174386	LND	Westminster
1839	....	....	....	131210	MDX	Enfield
....	....	1800	1870	176435	MDX	Hackney
1540	1600	ALL	ALL	141739	MDX	Hampton Wick
1853	1992	1800	1900	166960	MDX	London
1780	1786	1750	1850	116386	NBL	Newcastle
1827	1850	1700	1900	158666	NFK	Caister
1770	1992	1700	1992	126799	NFK	Docking
1790	1992	1600	1790	111198	NYK	Lythe
1770	1992	1500	1770	140279	PEM	Dale
1780	1912	1700	1800	119164	SFK	ALL
1800	1900	1600	1900	100927	SFK	Gorleston
....	....	1650	1695	172871	SFK	Rougham
1750	1965	....	....	137820	SHI	Fetlar
1720	1965	....	....	137820	SHI	Mid Yell
1760	1965	....	....	137820	SHI	North Yell
1758	1965	....	....	137820	SHI	Northmavine
1720	1965	....	....	137820	SHI	South Yell
1816	....	....	....	119911	SOM	Wayford
1800	1860	1600	1800	169773	SRY	Ash
1803	1857	1750	1950	158399	SRY	Compton
1764	1796	....	....	115606	SRY	Guildford
1834	1888	1750	1860	163740	SRY	Newington
1809	1809	....	1809	129771	WAR	Birmingham
1800	1992	1600	1992	168327	WIL	Hilmarton
1790	1890	....	....	132225	WIL	Seend
1700	1992	1600	1992	168327	WIL	Seend
1698	1820	1660	1840	160873	YKS	Sutton On Derwent
HARTAS						
1823	1844	ALL	ALL	115967	YKS	Pickering
HARTBURN						
1700	1992	1600	1992	141445	DUR	ALL
HARTE						
1790	1840	1750	1850	174599	ESS	Wix
HARTERY						
1860	1880	1859	1880	109371	GLA	Cardiff
HARTFIELD						
1830	....	....	....	153931	HAM	Portsmouth
HARTHORN						
1691	1701	1600	1700	149098	YKS	Laughton En Le Morthen
HARTILL						
1843	1920	1843	1940	163171	LEI	Snarestone
HARTIN						
1690	1752	1600	1700	134627	OXF	Upper Heyford
1862	1908	....	1862	165484	???	Brighton
1862	1908	....	1862	165484	???	Edmonston
HARTLE						
1750	1870	1750	1870	126209	WOR	Bromsgrove
....	....	1850	1992	147613	WOR	Dudley
HARTLEY						
1827	....	1700	1845	110914	CHS	Bredbury
1815	1842	1770	1881	160636	CHS	Poynton
1800	1860	1750	1800	106194	DBY	Hathersage
1795	1810	ALL	1810	132217	DBY	Norton
1829	1880	1829	1880	132217	DBY	Whitwell
1890	1960	1890	1960	169927	DUR	Darlington

Known From	To	Researching From	To	Ref	Cty	Place
HARTLEY contd.						
1848	1900	1800	1900	117781	EYK	Hull
....	....	1800	1950	167843	LAN	Burnley
1779	1834	1700	1834	141062	LAN	Colne
1825	1850	1750	1850	157171	LAN	Colne
1786	1807	1745	1810	174211	LAN	Colne
1863	1943	1851	1881	160636	LAN	Denton
1785	1868	ALL	ALL	107913	LAN	Downholland
1880	....	1870	1900	144827	LAN	Lancaster
1825	1900	ALL	ALL	169528	LAN	Liverpool
1752	1890	1500	1992	117234	LAN	Trawden
1853	1909	....	1853	149624	LAN	Winewall In Colne
1800	1900	1700	1800	147494	LND	London
1899	....	1870	1939	131482	MDX	London
1880	1940	1880	1940	132217	NTT	Nottingham
1649	1661	1600	1680	105120	SSX	Brighton
1825	1890	1780	1825	173673	WOR	Dudley
....	....	1800	1870	137618	WRY	Stanley
....	....	ALL	ALL	178403	YKS	West
1817	1825	ALL	ALL	169528	YKS	Cargrave
1715	1740	1680	1992	114901	YKS	Castleford
1779	1900	1750	1779	109703	YKS	Ecclesfield
1807	1992	ALL	1800	131695	YKS	Halifax
1865	1880	1850	1890	169927	YKS	Kirk Sandall
1730	1880	1680	1730	162396	YKS	Kirkby Malham
1807	1992	ALL	1800	131695	YKS	Leeds
1750	1800	1700	1900	130419	YKS	Long Preston
1770	1780	1600	1780	175382	YKS	Long Preston
1870	....	1870	1900	169927	YKS	Mexborough
1850	1992	ALL	1850	131172	YKS	Outwood
1803	1888	1750	1900	118443	YKS	Slaidburn
1805	1828	1780	1850	170348	YKS	Warley In Halifax
1780	1850	1700	1780	111511	YKS	West Riding
HARTNELL						
1656	1790	1600	1656	109061	DEV	North
1770	1790	1650	1992	109061	DEV	Plymouth
1815	1992	1815	1992	109061	KEN	Medway
?	?	?	?	132195	SOM	Wellington
HARTNETT						
1920	....	....	....	153397	KEN	Dover
HARTNOLL						
....	....	1600	1992	176990	ALL	ALL
1890	1940	1600	1992	176990	DEV	Plymouth
....	....	....	....	176990	???	London
HARTNUP						
1750	1850	1650	1750	139106	KEN	Goudhurst
HARTOP						
1700	1890	....	....	131555	LEI	Barkby
1810	1912	....	....	130958	MDX	Bethnal Green
HARTOPP						
1600	1890	....	....	131555	LEI	ALL
1826	1834	1700	1825	131245	WAR	Exhall
HARTRIDGE						
....	....	ALL	ALL	135984	KEN	ALL
1800	1900	....	....	104272	KEN	East Farleigh
1800	....	....	....	104272	KEN	Loose
HARTSHORN						
1869	1901	1840	1901	108391	MDX	London
1839	1928	ALL	1899	114030	MDX	London
....	....	1800	....	170313	SAL	Madeley
....	....	1800	1860	161659	STS	Darlaston
1846	....	....	....	170313	STS	Wolverhampton
1878	1957	....	....	139351	YKS	Wakefield
HARTWELL						
1867	1873	1857	1874	124974	BDF	Luton
1865	1945	1860	1920	124974	BRK	Reading
1800	1871	1700	1800	151300	GLS	Chipping Campden
1840	1865	1800	1860	124974	HRT	St Albans
1746	1850	....	....	137111	NTH	Farthinghoe
1855	1940	....	....	103810	NTT	Newark
1871	1878	1878	1992	151300	WOR	Worcester
HARVEY						
1800	1830	1740	1800	101796	AYR	Irvine
1800	1817	ALL	1850	151815	CAM	Bourn
1797	1797	1730	1850	167002	CAM	Cambridge
1803	1839	....	....	148156	CAM	Eltisley
1745	1870	1700	1992	131792	CAM	Fordham
1847	1879	1847	1992	149314	CGN	Aberystwyth
1810	1900	ALL	1900	137286	CON	West
1800	1942	1600	1800	131814	CON	Chacewater
1710	1944	1500	1710	149314	CON	Chacewater
1748	1992	1700	1748	140449	CON	Crowan
1700	1870	1600	1870	143766	CON	Crowan
1700	1870	1600	1870	143766	CON	Gwinear

Known From	To	Researching From	To	Ref	Cty	Place
HARVEY contd.						
1645	1960	?	1645	125059	CON	Illogan
1710	1944	1500	1710	149314	CON	Kenwyn
1800	....	1800	....	134813	CON	Laneast
1700	1784	1500	1784	132993	CON	North Hill
1859	1871	1859	1992	172596	CON	Paul
1720	1992	1600	1840	129437	CON	Penwith
....	....	1600	1800	131814	CON	St Agnes
1710	1944	1500	1710	149314	CON	St Agnes
1715	1735	1600	1715	102571	CON	St Buryan
1794	1860	1740	1790	178845	CON	St Mawgan
1800	....	1800	....	134813	CON	Stoke Climsland
1804	1900	1750	1804	139815	CON	Treleigh
1710	1944	1500	1710	149314	CON	Truro
1700	1856	ALL	ALL	104191	CON	???
....	....	1700	1900	126055	DEV	Bovey Tracey
1837	1992	1750	1809	170968	DEV	Devonport
1743	1754	1700	1743	131660	DOR	Dorchester
....	....	....	1820	160369	DOR	Dorchester
1808	1893	1800	1900	102717	ESS	Grays
1850	1940	1800	1850	119342	ESS	Nazeing
1817	1921	1750	1850	118397	ESS	Rayleigh
1800	1850	1750	1800	119342	ESS	Saffron Waldon
1859	1992	1800	1859	155381	ESS	Southminster
1790	1900	1750	1950	131822	ESS	Wivenhoe
....	....	1800	1860	108030	GLA	Swansea
....	....	1830	....	160369	GLS	Winchcomb
1890	1992	1860	1890	108030	GNT	Newport
1880	1992	1800	1992	114596	HAM	Isle Of Wight
1871	ALL	1871	ALL	170968	HAM	Portsea
1900	1992	1800	1900	155144	HAM	Portsmouth
1791	1841	1750	1841	173622	HRT	Cheshunt
1778	1826	1778	1826	136808	HUN	Warboys
1830	1851	1800	1900	157848	KEN	Erith
....	1800	ALL	1800	152889	KEN	Romsey
1702	....	....	1720	171441	KEN	Wormshill
1817	1836	1800	1850	151599	LEI	ALL
1868	1950	1877	1992	149314	LND	ALL
1870	1900	1840	1870	149373	LND	City
1820	1840	1700	1850	126268	LND	Finsbury
1869	1874	ALL	ALL	101362	LND	Lambeth
1870	1900	1840	1870	149373	LND	Southwark
1860	1992	1800	1992	151459	LND	???
1871	1902	1860	1920	102717	MDX	Edmonton
1860	....	1750	1860	134473	MDX	Islington
1854	1865	1850	1870	102717	MDX	Shadwell
1850	1870	1800	1870	147575	MDX	Stepney
....	....	1750	1800	102717	NFK	Hassingham
1719	1962	ALL	1719	171719	NFK	Wymondham
....	1700	ALL	1700	134511	NTT	East Stoke
1668	....	ALL	ALL	105481	NTT	Nuthall
....	1700	ALL	1700	134511	NTT	Papplewick
1782	1847	1700	1782	141313	SCT	ALL
1858	1992	1800	1858	131806	SCT	Glasgow
1650	1992	1650	1992	166758	SCT	???
1833	1881	1800	1833	129895	SFK	Debenham
1760	1847	....	....	129747	SFK	Ipswich
1884	1992	1750	1884	118265	SFK	Lowestoft
1743	1875	....	....	131660	SOM	Frome
1770	1870	1700	1770	165530	SOM	Keynsham
1782	1860	1808	1992	139602	SOM	Taunton
1782	1860	ALL	1782	139602	SOM	Thornfalcon Trull
1834	1868	ALL	1860	117366	SOM	Weston Super Mare
1800	1850	1800	1850	167924	SRY	Camberwell
1687	1870	1580	1687	143898	SSX	Battle
1687	1870	1580	1687	143898	SSX	Whatlington
1834	1855	ALL	....	150835	STI	Grahamston
1840	1885	ALL	ALL	125288	STS	Aldridge
1662	1881	....	1881	155055	STS	Cannock
1909	1992	1837	1909	165751	STS	Chasetown
1841	1899	ALL	ALL	149489	STS	Dilhorne
1809	1878	1750	1809	125288	STS	Fradley
1762	1837	1720	1762	166464	STS	Longdon
1735	1735	1700	1750	150002	STS	Marchington
1824	1826	ALL	1854	156175	SXE	Ashburnham
1763	1839	1700	1763	125288	WAR	Sutton Coldfield
1933	1948	1800	1942	131032	YKS	Doncaster
1844	1992	ALL	1844	146226	YKS	Doncaster
1750	1850	....	....	124621	YKS	Hull
1933	1948	1800	1942	131032	YKS	Thorn
1807	....	....	....	165484	YKS	Woolley
1920	1992	1700	1920	171913	???	???
HARVEY-ENEVER						
....	....	ALL	ALL	157848	ALL	ALL

Known From	To	Researching From	To	Ref	Cty	Place
HARVIE						
....	....	1500	1830	166863	LKS	East Kilbride
1880	1900	1880	1910	170143	MDX	Ealing
1817	1850	....	....	154849	RFW	???
1841	1860	1820	1840	118133	SCT	Glasgow
1650	1992	1650	1992	166758	SCT	???
1811	1825	1750	1811	126357	STI	Campsie
HARWIN						
1749	1900	ALL	1749	157511	IRL	Stoke Ferry
1749	1900	ALL	1749	157511	NFK	West Dereham
HARWOOD						
1745	1787	....	1800	137405	CAM	South
1866	....	1750	1900	152110	DUR	Southwick
1780	1800	1750	1830	156930	GLS	Kempley
....	....	1800	1992	111503	LAN	Blackburn
1750	1900	1750	1900	125237	LAN	Darwen
1800	1880	1880	1992	162256	LAN	Darwen
1770	1880	1700	1800	102172	LAN	Ramsgreave
1795	1871	1700	1992	116742	LIN	Boston
1820	1870	1700	1900	116742	MDX	Tottenham
1840	1890	....	1840	174025	MDX	Westminster
1774	1795	....	....	135437	NFK	Ditchingham
1748	1992	1700	1992	147311	NYK	Scarborough
1784	....	ALL	1992	159174	OXF	Banbury
1869	1939	1840	1869	116912	PEM	Pembroke Dock
1624	1877	....	....	137030	SSX	Cold Waltham
1890	1938	1885	1947	152781	WAR	Smethwick
1787	1852	1650	1900	146986	WIL	Homington
1851	1881	1831	1891	152781	WOR	Harbourne
1860	1992	1700	1860	131830	YKS	Hebden Bridge
HASBURY						
....	....	1650	1750	147613	WOR	Dudley
HASE						
1875	1915	1870	1920	177024	SRY	Wandsworth
HASELL						
1847	1847	ALL	ALL	124982	SOM	Bishop Sutton
1830	1871	ALL	ALL	153516	SOM	Dundry
HASELTON						
1600	1700	ALL	ALL	124621	IRL	ALL
1600	1700	ALL	ALL	132446	IRL	ALL
1691	1950	1748	1992	110876	SFK	Belstead
1691	1950	1748	1992	110876	SFK	Bentley
HASELY						
1724	1724	ALL	1800	168696	OXF	Charlbury
HASEMAN						
1871	....	....	....	173932	SRY	Ewell
HASKAYNE						
1861	1916	1800	1861	135364	LAN	Aughton
HASKELL						
1500	1900	1500	1900	170216	DOR	ALL
1400	1992	1400	1992	131857	DOR	Cann
1400	1992	1400	1992	131857	HAM	Fontmell Magna
1746	....	....	....	153397	HAM	Milford
....	....	....	....	164968	HAM	Southampton
....	1766	....	....	156671	HEF	Ross On Wye
1890	....	1700	1992	149969	SOM	Bath
1500	1900	1500	1900	170216	WIL	ALL
1400	1992	1400	1992	131857	WIL	Charlton Donheads
HASKETT						
?	?	1600	?	178667	DOR	ALL
?	?	1600	?	178667	WIL	ALL
HASKING						
1670	1809	1500	1670	138614	CON	Perranuthnoe
HASKINS						
1800	1850	1600	1850	154342	GLS	Bristol
1797	1900	1650	1992	170585	GLS	Oldland
HASKOLL						
1776	1992	ALL	ALL	156671	MON	Trostrey
HASLAM						
1769	1890	1600	1769	176249	DBY	East
1830	1870	ALL	1870	175757	DBY	Belper
1620	1992	ALL	1992	157902	LAN	ALL
1850	1992	1850	1992	109347	LAN	Accrington
1850	....	1850	....	109347	LAN	Bacup
1825	....	1825	....	109347	LAN	Blackburn
1780	1850	ALL	ALL	122254	LAN	Blackrod
1850	1918	1890	1920	131865	LAN	Manchester
1800	....	....	....	163910	LAN	Oldham
1800	1850	1700	1800	121509	LAN	St Helens
1800	1850	1700	1800	121509	LAN	Wigan
HASLEGRAVE						
1730	1760	?	1730	128910	YKS	York
HASLEM						
....	....	1700	....	123471	CUL	Bootle

Known From	To	Researching From	To	Ref	Cty	Place
HASLER						
1850	....	....	....	152455	ESS	Little Dunmow
1700	1900	ALL	ALL	131873	ESS	Manuden
1650	1850	....	....	138037	HRT	North East
1700	1800	ALL	ALL	131873	HRT	Albury
HASLETT						
1725	1965	ALL	ALL	131881	HAM	Porstmouth
1830	1850	1700	1992	127299	HAM	???
....	....	1700	1992	127299	LND	ALL
HASSALL						
1500	1600	1450	1600	154881	CHS	Hankelow
1818	1848	1700	1818	150614	CHS	Little Budworth
1713	1920	ALL	ALL	131911	CHS	???
1860	1992	1700	1860	131903	LAN	Manchester
1718	1796	1650	1800	176621	WAR	Coventry
HASSAN						
....	....	....	....	127272	MDX	Marylebone
....	....	....	....	127272	WAR	Birmingham
HASSARD-SHORT						
....	....	ALL	ALL	131938	ALL	Name Study
1794	1930	1886	1930	131938	LIN	Edlington
1794	1930	1886	1930	131938	YKS	Harrogate
1794	1930	1886	1930	131938	YKS	York
HASSELGRAVE						
1710	1762	1650	1800	134589	YKS	Cawood
HASSELL						
1780	1846	1752	1780	178926	LEI	Kilby
HASTE						
1640	1992	....	1640	151874	SFK	Bildeston
1724	1771	1650	1723	131245	SFK	Hadleigh
1850	....	ALL	ALL	125466	SFK	Stutton
1790	1992	1750	1992	170038	YKS	Idle
HASTEAD						
1863	1987	ALL	ALL	107336	CAM	Soham
HASTIE						
....	....	ALL	1704	119326	ELN	Prestonpans
....	....	ALL	1783	119326	MLN	Newbattle
....	1890	....	1890	147818	YKS	Middlesborough
HASTINGS						
1660	1830	1660	1830	127655	CLA	Killaloe
1884	1992	1803	1884	131946	HAM	Portsmouth
1500	1600	1450	1600	154881	LEI	ALL
1706	1800	ALL	1706	149195	LEI	North East
1610	1700	1610	1650	127655	LEI	Humberstone
1869	....	1860	1870	163775	MDX	Poplar
1810	1900	1750	1800	178543	NBL	Newcastle
1820	1870	1820	1880	154598	NTT	Blyth
1670	1720	1600	1670	123102	OXF	Burford
1660	1830	1660	1830	127655	TIP	Fort Henry
HASWELL						
....	....	ALL	ALL	131954	ALL	ALL
1910	1992	....	1910	131954	DFS	Newton Stewart
1910	1992	....	1910	131954	DFS	Wigtown
1700	1799	1700	1799	169781	DUR	Durham
1750	1900	1750	1900	136484	LND	Aldersgate
1750	1900	1750	1900	136484	LND	Shoreditch
1732	1780	1750	1850	130230	SRY	Oxted
HATCH						
1761	1776	1650	1800	143693	BKM	Burnham
1791	1793	1700	1850	143693	BKM	Iver
1790	1840	1750	1850	120472	BRK	Cookham
1605	1826	ALL	1605	168602	CAM	Haddenham
1605	1826	ALL	1605	168602	CAM	Longstanton
1605	1826	ALL	1605	168602	CAM	Stuntney
1772	1870	....	....	135739	DUR	North
1700	1810	1700	1992	111325	ESS	Elmstead
?	?	?	?	145920	ESS	Great Bursted
1735	1818	1735	1818	173851	GLS	Ministerworth
1800	1930	1700	1800	100765	HAM	Bramshaw
1863	1918	ALL	1920	118737	LND	Islington
1740	1770	1700	1800	147958	LND	Wapping
HATCHARD						
1772	1861	1750	1900	123536	HAM	Portsea
1740	1770	1700	1800	123536	HAM	Purbeck
1768	1768	1700	1800	123536	HAM	Wareham
1874	1897	1850	1945	123536	NBL	Newcastle On Tyne
HATCHELL						
....	....	ALL	ALL	131962	ALL	Name Study
....	....	1700	1850	131962	DEV	Cullumpton
1690	1840	....	....	131962	IRL	Wesford
....	....	1840	1900	131962	JSY	???
1670	1860	1670	1860	127914	WEX	Wexford
HATCHER						
1860	?	1800	1860	172251	DOR	Arne
HATCHER contd.						
1819	1862	1700	1900	110191	DOR	Broadwey
1763	1823	1730	1770	149993	HAM	Hursley
1840	1950	1775	1840	103446	KEN	West
HATCHETT						
1734	1734	1734	1734	152943	HAM	Timsbury
1650	1850	....	....	138037	HRT	North East
HATCLIFFE						
1800	1992	....	....	176125	LIN	Asterby
1800	1992	....	....	176125	LIN	Goulceby
HATELEY						
1800	1900	1750	1810	124648	MDX	Bethnal Green
HATELY						
1800	1900	1750	1810	124648	MDX	Bethnal Green
1850	1960	ALL	ALL	162469	NBL	Central
HATFIELD						
1891	1992	ALL	1891	100803	KEN	Bidborough
1791	1992	1750	1850	140473	RAD	Knighton
1870	....	....	1870	162086	YKS	West
HATHAWAY						
1850	1950	ALL	1850	135607	BRK	Mortimer
....	....	1800	ALL	164615	HEF	Hereford
1890	1925	ALL	ALL	164887	HRT	Watford
1700	1960	1500	1700	125415	WAR	Sutton Coldfield
HATHER						
1848	1900	1848	1992	178411	NTT	Nottingham
1672	1848	ALL	ALL	178411	NTT	Oxton
HATHERELL						
1875	1925	1800	1875	106186	GLS	Old Sodbury
HATHERILLO						
....	....	1800	1950	107506	SSX	Brighton
HATHERLEY						
1860	1915	1700	1860	106976	NTT	Keyworth
HATHERLY						
1819	1819	1819	1819	175196	AVN	Bristol
1800	1850	1700	1900	148288	HAM	Portsea
HATHWAY						
....	....	ALL	ALL	131997	GLS	ALL
1775	1789	1762	1789	131997	GLS	Bristol
1825	1837	1825	1874	131997	LND	Hoxton
1825	1837	1825	1874	131997	MDX	London
1854	1945	1854	1945	131997	WAR	Birmingham
1854	1945	1854	1945	131997	WAR	Coventry
HATKILL						
....	....	1300	1992	166081	YKS	ALL
1393	1710	1300	1800	166081	YKS	Slaidburn
HATKINS						
1722	1756	ALL	ALL	175587	SOM	Martock
HATKISS						
1780	1800	1750	1780	125318	STS	Sedgeley
HATLEY						
1778	1992	1700	1777	132004	CAM	Bottisham
1841	1935	1800	1950	141046	KEN	Greenwich
HATRICK						
1860	1860	1800	1860	149632	NIR	Antrim
1860	1860	1800	1860	149632	NIR	Carnlough
HATSWELL						
....	....	ALL	ALL	132012	ALL	Name Study
HATT						
....	....	ALL	ALL	132020	ALL	Name Study
1851	1878	1846	1878	125229	BKM	Hazlemere
1851	1929	1832	1901	125229	BKM	High Wycombe
1823	1948	1771	1949	125229	BKM	Hughenden
1797	1909	1797	1909	125229	BRK	Compton
1758	1773	1758	1780	125229	BRK	Lambourne
1841	1881	1841	1881	116769	HAM	Stoke Charity
1840	1926	1840	1900	127094	KEN	Chatham
1780	1807	ALL	1830	127094	SRY	Rotherhithe
HATTAM						
1797	1855	1600	1797	102571	CON	Kenwyn
HATTEN						
1791	1791	1700	1800	124974	BRK	Ashbury
HATTER						
1806	1850	1750	1806	167711	WIL	Salisbury
HATTERSLEY						
1630	1790	....	....	172286	WYK	Ecclesfield
1790	1900	....	....	172286	WYK	Keighley
HATTLE						
1780	1850	....	....	126497	NBL	Scremerston
HATTON						
1600	1750	....	....	177318	CHS	Great Budworth
1862	1992	?	1862	153613	CHS	???
1862	1992	?	1862	153613	DBY	???
1765	1900	1700	1765	152579	DOR	Whitchurch

Known From	To	Researching From	To	Ref	Cty	Place
HATTON contd.						
1765	1900	1700	1765	152579	DOR	Winterborne
1700	1880	1700	1950	111007	ESS	Barking
1700	1880	1700	1950	111007	ESS	Loughton
1800	1980	1700	1800	124133	ESS	???
1842	1928	1750	1842	128937	GLS	Ruardean
....	....	1694	1820	119431	KEN	East
1764	1877	1877	1992	158704	KEN	???
1800	1940	1700	1992	110477	LAN	Manchester
1756	1949	1600	1756	120200	LAN	Prescot
....	....	1886	1940	126713	LAN	Salford
1756	1949	1600	1756	120200	LAN	Warrington
1800	1980	1700	1800	124133	LND	ALL
1880	1920	1550	1891	104892	STS	West Bromwich
1920	1992	....	....	104892	STS	Wolverhampton
?	?	ALL	1850	117919	WOR	Old Swinford
HAUGH						
1692	1880	1650	1700	178543	CUL	Houghton
HAUGHEY						
1758	1966	1600	1758	132039	IRL	Antrim
HAUGHTON						
1750	1880	1650	1850	139866	CHS	Dukinfield
1816	1816	1816	1881	160636	CHS	Mobberley
1730	1755	1700	1900	151254	LAN	Denton
1730	1755	1700	1900	151254	LAN	Haughton
1821	1860	1700	1821	127116	NFK	Norwich
1772	1824	1650	1771	131245	WAR	Stoke
HAUKES						
1632	1680	1600	1650	170348	WIL	Wanborough
HAUMSHAW						
1670	....	1670	....	154601	WYK	Horbury
HAUNCH						
1805	1900	ALL	1800	115118	ESS	Budbrook
HAUNTON						
....	....	ALL	ALL	132047	ALL	Name Study
HAUXWELL						
1790	1810	1750	1790	118486	NRY	Well
1817	1930	1700	1950	134643	NYK	Leyburn
HAVARD						
1100	1750	....	....	151130	CMN	???
1820	1850	1840	1850	160121	HAM	Portsmouth
1870	1890	1870	1890	160121	NBL	Newcastle
HAVELOCK						
....	....	ALL	ALL	132063	ALL	Name Study
1788	....	1788	1939	132063	CUL	Alston
1729	....	1729	1986	132063	DUR	Sunderland
1838	....	1838	1934	132063	NBL	Castleward
1695	....	1695	1769	132063	NBL	Haltwhistle
1626	....	1626	1988	132063	NBL	Newcastle
1816	....	1857	1970	132063	NBL	Tynemouth
1665	....	1665	1936	132063	NRY	Guisborough
1576	....	1576	1775	132063	NRY	Marske In Cleveland
1876	....	1876	1968	132063	NRY	Middlesbrough
1884	....	1884	1978	132063	SRY	Wandsworth
HAVER						
1879	1992	1879	1992	132071	DUR	Sunderland
1787	1992	1787	1992	132071	NBL	Newcastle
HAVERLAND						
1660	1720	1640	1720	135941	SFK	Lakenheath
HAVERS						
....	....	ALL	ALL	132101	ALL	Name Study
1450	1800	1400	1949	132098	NFK	Diss
1450	1800	1400	1949	132098	NFK	Norwich
1820	1850	1700	1840	106267	SFK	North
1850	1850	1860	1992	132098	SFK	Lowestoft
1850	....	1850	1992	119849	WAR	Birmingham
HAVILLAND						
1450	1992	1100	1992	133450	CHI	Guernsey
1500	1880	1500	1992	133450	DOR	ALL
1500	1880	1500	1992	133450	GLS	ALL
1500	1880	1500	1992	133450	SOM	ALL
HAVIS						
....	....	1600	1900	149128	ALL	ALL
1860	1900	1600	1900	149128	ESS	Great Wakering
1860	1900	1600	1900	149128	ESS	Hadleigh
HAW						
1698	1784	1500	1698	175072	LIN	Belchford
1856	1866	1765	1992	132128	LND	Bethnal Green
1867	1900	1900	1992	132128	LND	St Pancras
1856	1866	1765	1992	132128	MDX	Poplar
1867	1900	1900	1992	132128	MDX	???
....	....	1800	1900	139297	YKS	Birdforth
1780	1810	1700	1850	177970	YKS	Carthorpe
....	....	1800	1900	139297	YKS	Ripon
HAW contd.						
1808	1890	1800	1900	177970	???	Newcastle
HAWARD						
1785	1820	1700	1785	137618	OXF	Bampton
1576	....	....	1580	160873	STS	Walsall
HAWATT						
1802	1827	ALL	1802	106909	BAN	Gamrie
HAWDON						
1811	1825	1800	1900	123536	DUR	Gateshead
1700	1870	1700	1870	105376	DUR	Staindrop
1811	1871	1800	1900	123536	NBL	Newcastle On Tyne
1800	1850	1750	1850	123536	NBL	Wolsingham
HAWE						
1850	1850	1700	1850	178608	MDX	West Hackney
HAWES						
1845	1845	1845	1845	173851	BKM	Great Bradwell
1806	1806	1600	1806	159239	DOR	Kingston
1855	1866	....	....	135070	ESS	West Ham
1679	1722	ALL	1679	141526	HRT	Berkhamstead
1836	1940	1800	1940	153133	HRT	Great Gaddesden
1679	1722	ALL	1679	141526	HRT	Tring
....	1845	1700	1845	144754	MDX	Bethnal Green
1840	1852	....	....	135070	NFK	East Dereham
1870	1992	....	....	132136	OXF	Oxford
1750	1813	1700	1750	158402	SFK	Weybread
HAWFORD						
....	....	1750	1900	115142	WAR	Mancetter
HAWGOOD						
1560	1992	1560	1900	132144	ALL	ALL
HAWICK						
1750	1965	....	....	137820	SHI	Fetlar
1720	1965	....	....	137820	SHI	Mid Yell
1760	1965	....	....	137820	SHI	North Yell
1758	1965	....	....	137820	SHI	Northmavine
1720	1965	....	....	137820	SHI	South Yell
HAWKE						
1700	1992	1590	1930	132152	CON	Helston
1818	....	ALL	ALL	110272	CON	Lewannick
1736	1837	1750	1850	176982	CON	Wadebridge
1812	1860	1700	1812	163953	DEV	Brixham
1820	1880	ALL	ALL	162205	SSX	Lewes
HAWKEN						
1810	1852	1750	1810	149004	CON	Boconnoc
....	....	1750	1992	129429	CON	Camelford
1833	1900	1700	1855	156051	CON	Liskeard
1773	1867	1600	1773	149888	CON	St Breward
1850	1930	1800	1900	129429	LND	Lewisham
HAWKER						
1800	1832	1832	1850	119164	DEV	Exeter
1873	1992	1800	1891	141461	DOR	Poole
1783	1842	....	....	116602	GLS	Coates
1800	1900	1700	1840	134252	LND	Marylebone
1748	1783	1710	1748	139149	SOM	Bishops Hull
1840	1930	1930	1992	105651	WOR	Bredon
1797	1867	1830	1880	177350	WOR	Claines
1858	1910	1800	1992	166197	WOR	Eldersfield
HAWKES						
....	....	ALL	ALL	132160	ALL	Name Study
1650	1881	....	....	132179	BKM	Great Missenden
....	....	1562	1756	132160	DEV	Barnstaple
....	....	1562	1756	132160	DEV	Exeter
1881	....	....	....	132160	DUR	West Rainton
1760	1937	....	....	132160	ESS	???
1630	1800	1630	ALL	125148	GLS	Buckland
1761	1908	1725	1831	132160	GLS	Eastville
1761	1908	1725	1831	132160	GLS	Longley
1843	1846	1652	1846	173851	GLS	Ministerworth
1761	1908	1725	1831	132160	GLS	Quesgley
1913	1933	....	....	132160	GLS	Stapleton
1864	1866	1864	1866	173851	LAN	Liverpool
1913	1954	....	....	132160	LND	Chiswick
1856	....	....	....	156329	LND	Islington
1879	1884	....	....	132179	MDX	Norlands
1880	1985	1880	1985	132160	NBL	Blyth
1890	1935	ALl	ALL	154490	NTH	Culworth
1780	1850	1780	1850	124605	NTH	Kings Sutton
1753	1840	....	....	165514	WAR	Hatton
1697	1762	....	....	165514	WAR	Tanworth In Arden
1811	1853	1811	ALL	125148	WOR	Evesham
1615	....	....	1630	160873	WOR	Old Swinford
1837	1960	1837	1960	155519	YKS	Bickerton
1843	1992	1867	1992	173851	YKS	Hull
1761	1908	1725	1831	132160	???	Birmingham
1846	1992	1841	1992	173851	???	Bristol

Known From	To	Researching From	To	Ref	Cty	Place
HAWKESFORD						
1700	1800	....	....	100420	WAR	Meriden
HAWKESWORTH						
1600	1650	1500	1600	113204	YKS	Hawkesworth
HAWKEY						
1618	1900	....	....	145297	CON	Central
1800	1992	1660	1992	133868	CON	Padstow
1800	1992	1660	1992	133868	CON	St Briock
1650	1800	1670	1750	133450	CON	St Columb Major
1846	1992	....	....	133868	CON	St Issex
HAWKIN						
1790	1800	ALL	1850	173614	DEV	Barnstaple
HAWKING						
1742	1826	1783	1826	131113	CON	Botus Fleming
HAWKINGS						
ALL	ALL	ALL	ALL	132195	ALL	ALL
HAWKINS						
1800	1840	1800	1840	155764	BKM	Aylesbury
1700	1900	1650	1950	177180	BKM	Edlesborough
1800	1820	1700	1800	120529	BRK	Hinton Waldrist
1660	1794	1600	1800	176621	BRK	Newbury
1760	1820	1600	1850	164704	BRK	Padworth
....	....	1600	1850	164704	BRK	Sulhampstead
1775	1835	1700	1745	124974	BRK	Welford
1860	1880	1700	1860	143103	CHS	Stockport
1750	1800	1750	1850	123722	DBY	Duffield
....	....	1562	1756	132160	DEV	Barnstaple
1670	1728	....	....	151475	DEV	Totnes
1720	1860	1680	1880	111759	DOR	Litton Cheney
1910	....	1910	....	157392	GLA	Cardiff
....	....	ALL	1820	141224	GLS	Bitton
1850	....	....	....	137375	GLS	Coaley
1843	1851	1851	1900	159867	GLS	Newland
1800	1830	1750	1830	146803	HAM	Crondall
1570	1570	....	....	153397	HAM	Milford
1874	1950	1700	1874	167819	HAM	Southampton
1816	1851	1700	1850	159867	HEF	Welsh Newton
1800	1850	1700	1840	106267	HRT	Bushey
1847	1992	1500	1847	132233	HRT	Harpenden
1861	1861	1852	1875	132217	HUN	Peterborough
1775	1842	1700	1775	170542	KEN	Lynsted
1820	1860	....	....	132225	KEN	Sandwich
1760	1820	....	....	132225	KEN	Wye
1840	1850	1840	1850	121479	LAN	Liverpool
1700	1950	1700	1992	134422	LAN	Liverpool
1700	1950	1700	1992	134422	LAN	West Derby
1798	1890	1700	1900	135968	LEI	Rothley
1864	1865	1864	1875	168289	LND	Westminster
1815	1860	1750	1860	144797	LND	Whitechapel
1697	1766	ALL	1697	171980	LND	???
1850	1900	ALL	1860	142301	MDX	London
1875	1940	1875	1940	132217	NTT	Nottingham
?	?	?	?	132195	SOM	ALL
1780	1841	....	1841	133825	SOM	West Horrington
....	1771	1600	1771	132209	SSX	Climping
1817	1863	....	....	104922	SSX	Wisborough Green
1714	1992	ALL	1714	171980	STS	Burton On Trent
1813	....	....	....	138541	STS	Cannock
1811	1851	....	....	138541	STS	Penkridge
1861	1900	....	1861	138541	STS	Walsall
1830	1860	1800	1830	133493	STS	Wednesbury
1840	....	ALL	ALL	113581	WAR	Birmingham
....	....	1750	1992	140759	WIL	Avon
....	....	1750	1992	140759	WIL	Chippenham
HAWKINSON						
1794	1992	1650	1794	120200	LAN	Warrington
HAWKS						
1820	....	1800	1820	176885	ESS	Little Dunmow
HAWKSFORD						
1600	1700	1550	1780	160873	STS	Wednesfield
HAWKSHAW						
1836	1836	1836	1992	152943	HAM	Portsea
HAWKSWORTH						
1801	1900	1700	1900	135968	LEI	Belton
1880	....	1880	....	104213	SYK	Sheffield
HAWKYARD						
....	....	ALL	ALL	166057	ALL	Name Study
1860	1992	1700	1860	132241	YKS	Huddersfield
HAWLEY						
....	....	1600	1850	135755	DBY	ALL
1800	1992	1700	1800	164208	DBY	Milford
1784	1855	1740	1784	103004	DBY	Winster
1810	1992	1700	1810	158917	LEI	Melton Mowbray
1830	1940	1830	1940	134767	NFK	Norwich
HAWLEY contd.						
1800	1850	1700	1850	158356	WRY	Swinton
1835	1900	ALL	ALL	120650	YKS	Cawood
1790	1830	1700	1790	120650	YKS	Sherburn In Elmet
1835	1992	1700	1855	174106	???	Birmingham
HAWORTH						
1700	....	1700	....	109347	LAN	Accrington
1800	1940	1600	1900	133833	LAN	Accrington
1670	1830	1670	1830	127655	LAN	Altham
1843	....	1700	1843	128503	LAN	Edgend
1670	1830	1670	1830	127655	LAN	Hapton
1800	1900	1750	1830	138150	LAN	Liverpool
1700	1825	1700	1825	109347	LAN	Owsaldtwistle
1818	....	....	....	151629	LAN	Rochdale
1670	1830	1670	1830	127655	LAN	Shuttleworth Hall
1750	1900	1650	1750	179078	LAN	Shuttleworth
1720	1992	1650	1720	132268	LAN	Turton
1801	1850	1750	1810	169056	YKS	Halifax
1750	1785	1700	1850	144622	YKS	Rawmarsh
HAWS						
1830	1870	1800	1850	109517	CAM	Welney
HAWSE						
1780	1845	1700	1900	124796	BKM	Lacey Green
1845	1847	1840	1850	124796	MDX	Hillingdon
HAWTE						
1450	1550	1400	1550	154881	KEN	Shelvingborne
HAWTEN						
1550	1583	....	1583	103349	OXF	Swalcliffe
HAWTHORN						
1800	1825	....	....	153397	BRK	ALL
1775	1820	1740	1775	122904	LAN	Blackburn
1880	1970	1800	1920	130869	MOR	Peterhead
1768	1859	....	....	160458	NBL	???
1600	1850	1500	1900	134937	STS	???
1700	1764	ALL	ALL	128449	WAR	Birmingham
1700	1764	ALL	ALL	128449	WAR	Bordesley
1700	1764	ALL	ALL	128449	WAR	Deritend
HAWTHORNE						
....	....	ALL	ALL	169765	ALL	Name Study
....	....	1780	1853	100358	LDY	Moghera
HAWXWELL						
1635	1818	....	....	151351	YKS	Well
HAXBY						
1749	1757	1700	1800	123250	YKS	Cranswick
1749	1757	1700	1800	123250	YKS	Hutton
HAXELL						
1650	1675	ALL	ALL	132276	SFK	Bildeston
1800	1970	ALL	ALL	132276	SFK	Ipswich
1550	1720	1550	1650	132276	SFK	Long Melford
1675	1780	ALL	ALL	132276	SFK	Ringshall
1780	1830	ALL	ALL	132276	SFK	Somersham
HAXTON						
1930	1980	1900	1980	135925	HRT	Letchworth
HAY						
1845	1900	1700	1845	106887	ABD	Boharm
1600	1930	1700	1930	145467	ABD	Glenbuchat
1850	1920	1850	1920	137057	ABD	Tarland
1844	1867	....	....	137936	ANS	Dundee
1730	1810	....	....	168203	CAI	Dunbeath
1810	1877	....	....	168203	CAI	Latheron
....	....	ALL	1840	127000	ELN	Garvald
1700	1720	1700	1800	130915	FIF	Leuchars
1799	1820	1750	1800	137057	INV	Abernethy
1849	1863	1800	1900	139114	LKS	Glasgow
1893	1893	1890	1910	151157	LKS	Hamilton New Cross
1799	1820	1750	1800	137057	MOR	Cromdale
1771	1771	1700	1850	159379	PER	Tibbermore
1850	1905	1800	1905	147095	SCT	Edingburgh
1750	1965	....	....	137820	SHI	Fetlar
1720	1965	....	....	137820	SHI	Mid Yell
1760	1965	....	....	137820	SHI	North Yell
1758	1965	....	....	137820	SHI	Northmavine
1720	1965	....	....	137820	SHI	South Yell
1722	1725	1710	1730	159905	???	Edinburgh
HAYBALL						
1850	1900	1750	1850	158925	SOM	Chard
HAYBITELL						
1750	1800	1600	1750	170194	SRY	Ockham
HAYCOCK						
....	1772	1740	1800	128961	ESS	Coggeshall
1870	....	1700	1992	167673	NTH	ALL
1900	1960	....	....	156868	SAL	Dawley
1803	1803	1750	1825	132284	SAL	Oswestry

Known From	To	Researching From	To	Ref	Cty	Place
HAYCRAFT						
....	....	1600	1992	137588	DEV	Shobrooke
HAYCROFT						
1857	1886	....	1857	129518	YKS	Barnsley
1880	1913	....	1880	129518	YKS	Kings Lynn
HAYDEN						
1782	1886	....	1881	137405	CAM	Willingham
1808	1958	1700	1808	169730	ESS	Debden
1831	....	....	....	164968	HRT	???
1788	1875	1750	1788	101427	IOW	Brading
1751	1778	1697	1751	101427	IOW	Newchurch
1838	1838	....	1890	171646	MDX	East London
1500	1900	1500	1900	134759	NFK	Kings Lynn
1500	1900	1500	1900	134759	NFK	Norwich
1870	1950	1800	1880	125938	STS	Walsall
1796	1867	....	1796	144800	YKS	Huddersfield
1796	1867	....	1796	144800	YKS	Wetherby
HAYDON						
....	....	ALL	1785	179477	DEV	???
1930	....	1925	1935	163775	MDX	Paddington
1769	1880	1740	1870	124028	SRY	Mitcham
HAYE						
1881	1900	1863	1881	129895	SAL	Witchurch
HAYES						
1850	1900	....	....	142026	AVN	Kingswood
1770	1873	....	1860	137405	CAM	South
1750	1850	1650	1750	142670	CMA	Kirkhampton
1798	1850	1770	1850	121126	COR	Crohane
1820	1992	....	....	132292	DBY	Belper
1820	1992	....	....	132292	DBY	Holbrook
1758	1930	....	....	132292	DBY	Pinxton
1890	1980	1800	1900	105198	DOW	???
1848	1992	....	1848	166510	ENG	Central
1788	1870	1750	1800	156515	GLS	Bitton
....	....	1700	1800	142026	GLS	Castle Combe
1890	1960	1700	1960	172405	HAM	Hursley
1790	....	1750	1790	119938	HEF	Weston Beggard
1885	1920	....	....	117196	HRT	Aldenham
....	....	....	....	107433	HRT	???
1900	1992	1800	1900	131350	IRL	Ballalonford
....	....	ALL	ALL	143340	IRL	???
1760	1833	....	....	140023	KEN	East
1770	1950	1700	1950	126144	KEN	West
1880	1920	1800	1900	101907	KEN	Strood
1800	1992	ALL	1800	146226	LAN	Ainsworth
1812	1930	1770	1881	174211	LAN	Bury
1837	1900	1800	1837	154024	LAN	Golborne
1840	1865	ALL	1880	175757	LAN	Kirkham
1862	1914	ALL	1862	108537	LAN	Liverpool
1812	1930	1770	1881	174211	LAN	Radcliffe
1870	1992	1800	1870	121509	LAN	St Helens
1850	1921	....	1850	151270	LIM	Doon
1866	1940	?	1866	177806	LIN	Sutton Bridge
1590	1699	1590	1700	162507	LND	ALL
1895	1896	1800	1900	106976	LND	Brentford
....	....	....	....	107433	LND	???
1875	1885	....	....	117196	LND	???
1875	1945	1750	1874	131245	MDX	Bethnal Green
....	....	1800	1899	174963	MDX	Hoxton
1849	1909	1800	1849	117218	MDX	London
1798	1992	....	....	132292	NTT	Ashfield
1810	?	ALL	ALL	107352	NTT	Bulwell
1798	1992	....	....	132292	NTT	Suttone Kirkby
1928	....	1928	1928	116041	OFF	Coolderry
1747	1817	1700	1817	159905	OXF	Shenington
1791	....	1600	1800	145432	STS	Walsall
ALL	1720	....	....	142158	WIL	Aldbourne
1720	1880	ALL	1720	167878	WIL	Great Bedwyn
....	....	1800	1850	142026	WIL	Yatton Keynall
HAYFORD						
1820	1860	1820	1860	130222	LND	Shoreditch
HAYGARTH						
1600	1992	1600	1992	132306	???	???
HAYHURST						
1850	1992	1850	1992	109347	LAN	Accrington
1825	....	1825	....	109347	LAN	Stoneyhurst
1809	....	1750	1850	179078	YKS	Bolton By Bowland
HAYLAND						
1835	1896	1835	1896	132314	LIN	Methringham
1836	1873	1836	1886	132314	NTT	Dunham
1836	1873	1836	1886	132314	NTT	Laneham
1819	1850	1700	1819	132314	SCT	Dumfries
HAYLER						
1800	1830	ALL	ALL	164887	SSX	South

Known From	To	Researching From	To	Ref	Cty	Place
HAYLES						
1798	1992	1700	1798	164267	HAM	Portsmouth
....	....	1600	1950	134546	IOW	Godshill
1736	1795	1500	1736	129577	IOW	???
HAYLOCK						
1820	1900	1800	1900	149853	NFK	West Tofts
1781	1836	1700	1780	100013	SFK	Icklingham
1500	1900	1500	1900	170216	WIL	ALL
HAYMAN						
1748	1939	1700	1748	165123	DEV	Beer
....	....	1720	1850	179213	DEV	Buckfastleigh
1860	1890	1700	1960	172421	DEV	Devonport
1703	1800	1650	1703	141372	DEV	Sandford
1748	1939	1700	1748	165123	DEV	Whimple
1475	1992	ALL	1992	133450	KEN	East
1750	1900	1700	1900	126144	KEN	West
HAYMEN						
1800	1860	1700	....	131253	DEV	West Tiegnmouth
HAYMES						
....	1850	1750	1992	146927	DEV	Alliscombe
HAYNE						
1700	1750	ALL	ALL	131873	DEV	Exeter
1718	1718	ALL	1718	154563	DOR	Long Bredy
1700	1850	1600	1750	132659	NFK	Ruston
HAYNES						
1830	1992	1700	1830	135232	BKM	Aylesbury
1830	1992	1700	1830	135232	BKM	Ford
1830	1992	1700	1830	135232	BKM	Walton
1830	1875	1750	1830	100390	CHS	Chester
....	....	1750	1825	100358	DBY	Derby
1812	1890	....	....	135968	DBY	Wensley
1660	1660	1600	1680	174599	DOR	Shaftesbury
?	1984	1750	1950	153249	GLS	ALL
1820	1900	1800	1890	126438	HAM	Lymington
1780	....	....	....	145920	HAM	Warsash
1590	1753	ALL	1800	153249	HEF	ALL
1890	1940	1890	1940	129151	HEF	Kimbolton
1890	1940	1890	1940	129151	HEF	Pembridge
1800	1940	1890	1895	169668	LAN	Liverpool
1660	1692	ALL	1700	112275	LEI	Sileby
1890	1930	1800	1890	117714	LND	Fulham
1840	1992	ALL	ALL	115762	LND	Marylebone
1835	....	1820	1841	176923	LND	Turnham Green
1793	1910	1650	1800	106313	NTH	Boddington
1786	1973	1650	1786	166111	NTH	Charwelton
1750	1832	1750	1835	103632	NTH	Greens Norton
1800	1875	1750	1800	147885	NTH	Greens Norton
1791	1992	1694	1791	132357	OXF	West
1600	1650	1550	1600	174513	OXF	Upper Heyford
....	....	1700	1766	149977	SAL	ALL
1877	1992	1877	ALL	132349	SFK	Ipswich
1586	1811	1530	1811	147001	SRY	Ockley
1729	1811	....	1729	132837	SRY	Wootton
....	....	1700	1766	149977	STS	West
1766	1850	....	....	149977	STS	Gnosall
1801	1950	1771	1801	173339	STS	Lichfield
1780	1937	1750	1950	153249	WAR	ALL
1812	1923	1750	1812	159158	WAR	Birmingham
....	....	1800	1900	105864	WAR	Warwick
1650	?	ALL	ALL	153249	WOR	ALL
1850	1900	1500	1850	169986	WOR	Old Bury
HAYS						
1742	1797	1700	1820	159042	RUT	Whissendine
HAYSE						
1780	1830	....	....	118729	LAN	Cockerham
HAYSOM						
1550	1688	1550	1688	132365	DOR	Blandford
1680	1980	1680	1980	132365	DOR	Swanage
....	....	1700	1800	171182	HAM	Ringwood
HAYSTON						
1797	1914	1600	1797	173711	CMA	Helsington
HAYTER						
1850	1890	1840	1890	176958	CMA	Whitehaven
1770	1840	1700	1850	136840	HAM	Winchester
1850	1890	1840	1890	176958	MDX	London
1921	1992	1800	1921	121568	SOM	Templecombe
....	....	1750	1860	142549	WIL	ALL
1870	1992	1700	1870	132373	WIL	Devizes
1790	....	?	1800	103934	WIL	Donhead St Mary
HAYTHORNTHWAITE						
1850	1900	ALL	1900	123048	WRY	Skipton
1690	1850	ALL	1850	123048	WRY	Slaidburn
HAYTHORPE						
1778	1810	1700	1778	144711	NFK	Hardingham

Known From	To	Researching From	To	Ref	Cty	Place
HAYTON						
....	....	1870	1915	124265	CMA	Kendal
HAYWARD						
1810	1820	....	....	148415	BKM	Fingest
1830	1888	ALL	1830	148415	DEV	Exeter
1851	....	1851	1992	168572	DEV	Plymouth
1820	1840	....	....	148415	DEV	Topsham
1898	1977	1860	1945	164127	DFD	Llandovery
1850	1900	ALL	1992	128260	DOR	ALL
1520	1900	1500	1900	147214	DOR	Langton Matravers
1775	1810	ALL	1775	148415	ESS	Helions Bumpstead
1816	....	....	....	124982	GLS	Berkeley
1771	1940	1600	1771	155101	GLS	Brockhampton
1760	1825	ALL	1840	132217	GLS	Kings Stanley
1799	....	1750	1790	178845	GLS	Rockhampton
1854	1919	1850	1925	147214	HAM	Gosport
1800	1830	1750	1830	168572	HAM	Gosport
1799	1822	1500	1799	129577	IOW	???
....	....	1600	1670	161357	KEN	Birchington
1820	1844	1700	1900	141151	KEN	Seasalter
1820	1844	1700	1900	141151	KEN	Whitstable
1777	1860	ALL	1800	134503	KEN	Wye
1760	1892	1760	1892	143286	LAN	Liverpool
1819	1992	1750	1819	154024	SAL	Westbury
1900	1992	1800	1900	155780	SFK	Saxmundham
1800	1881	1765	1800	129895	SFK	Wetheringsett
1833	1891	1700	1833	163953	SFK	Wetheringsett
1840	1870	....	....	148415	SOM	Bath
1700	1750	1600	1700	147583	SRY	Woking
1777	1992	1700	1777	170747	SRY	???
1800	1830	1750	1830	168572	SSX	Bexhill
1777	1992	1700	1777	170747	SSX	???
1884	1930	1884	1930	133426	STS	Coseley
1845	1992	....	....	132381	STS	???
1570	1570	1550	1600	167002	SXE	Hailsham
1781	1810	1750	1820	179337	WIL	Chippenham
1838	1970	1700	1838	112283	WIL	Downton
1855	1942	1814	1839	103969	WIL	Hankerton
1854	....	1854	1900	149284	WIL	???
1900	1992	1700	1900	112860	???	London
HAYWELL						
1712	1712	ALL	1712	154563	DOR	Winterbourne Steepleton
HAYWOOD						
....	....	....	1730	137405	CAM	Cambridge
1819	1877	1700	1819	117927	DOR	Beaminster
1786	1786	1700	1786	113425	ESS	Maldon
1755	....	....	....	129747	IOW	Mottistone
1833	1881	1790	1900	165824	LAN	Bolton
1806	1890	1700	1806	117226	LEI	Appleby
1865	....	1760	1865	132438	LEI	Barrow On Soar
1843	1861	ALL	1850	152641	LEI	Castle Donnington
1806	1890	1700	1806	117226	LEI	Loughborough
1800	1850	1700	1900	138517	LEI	???
1813	1837	1780	1850	166316	MDX	St Pancras
1758	1770	....	....	102733	WIL	Latton
1780	1992	1700	1780	173827	WOR	Bromsgrove
1780	1992	1700	1780	173827	WOR	Droitwich
....	1780	1750	1780	109622	YKS	Huddersfield
HAZARD						
1768	....	....	....	117196	DUR	Durham
1906	1946	1906	1992	108979	DUR	Sunderland
?	?	....	....	159069	GLS	Bristol
HAZEL						
1790	1915	1700	1790	158208	CAM	Stretham
....	....	1690	....	151602	WIL	Southbroom St James
HAZELHURST						
1834	1955	1810	1992	116653	STS	Aston
HAZELL						
1814	1902	ALL	1992	112631	BKM	Penn
1809	1900	1700	1851	170178	BKM	Penn
1855	1916	1700	1992	170356	BRK	Newbury
1832	1862	....	1890	171441	BRK	Stanford In The Vale
....	1840	ALL	1840	134511	KEN	Strood
1831	1992	ALL	ALL	115762	LND	Clerkenwell
1860	1924	1850	1950	159964	MDX	Tottenham
1794	1842	1650	1793	131245	NFK	Norwich
HAZELTON						
....	....	ALL	ALL	110876	ALL	Name Study
1600	1900	ALL	ALL	124621	IRL	ALL
....	....	....	....	106372	MDX	Mile End
1840	....	ALL	ALL	106372	MDX	St Georges
....	....	....	....	106372	MDX	Whitechapel

Known From	To	Researching From	To	Ref	Cty	Place
HAZELTON contd.						
....	1812	....	....	106372	NFK	Wells
1652	1691	1652	1748	110876	SFK	Bentley
1844	1885	1700	1850	153001	SFK	Ipswich
1652	1691	1652	1748	110876	SFK	Wherstead
1600	1900	1600	1900	132446	TYR	ALL
HAZELWOOD						
1600	1699	1600	1699	169781	ERY	???
HAZLEHAND						
....	....	ALL	1750	151602	WIL	Woodborough
HAZLEWOOD						
1854	1884	....	....	118729	LAN	Barton
1800	1992	1700	1800	135658	OXF	Banbury
HAZON						
1852	1870	1750	1850	132454	DUR	Durham
1768	1966	1600	1800	132454	NBL	Newcastle On Tyne
HEAD						
1874	1910	....	....	177407	BRK	Reading
1749	1749	1700	1749	153605	CON	Paul
....	....	ALL	1850	166499	CON	St Gluvias
1740	1800	1700	1800	154881	DUB	Dublin
1800	1850	ALL	ALL	130508	HAM	Andover
1784	1861	1700	1784	145971	KEN	Ashford
....	....	1700	1850	102881	KEN	Rochester
1770	1850	1770	1840	178454	KEN	Tonbridge
1875	1930	1800	1900	106925	NFK	???
1780	1850	1700	1992	177636	SOM	Shepton Mallet
....	....	1750	1800	136638	SSX	East Grinstead
1700	1980	....	....	148237	SSX	New Fishbourne
1820	1874	1700	1900	177407	WIL	Ebbesborne Wake
1789	1943	1650	1800	106313	WIL	Milton
HEADDON						
....	....	1850	1900	152285	HAM	Portsmouth
HEADFORD						
....	....	1800	1950	116335	AVN	Bristol
1800	1900	1750	1900	123722	GLS	Bristol
HEADLAND						
1770	1860	ALL	1900	113492	BDF	North
1725	1866	ALL	1725	108642	BDF	Odell
1725	1866	ALL	1725	108642	BDF	Riseley
1725	1866	ALL	1725	108642	BDF	Sharnbrook
1725	1866	ALL	1725	108642	BDF	Souldrop
1857	1900	ALL	ALL	155454	LIN	Lincoln
1857	1900	ALL	ALL	155454	LIN	Sleaford
1850	1870	1750	1900	135925	LND	Islington
HEADLEY						
....	....	ALL	ALL	132462	ALL	ALL
....	1822	1821	1825	132462	LIN	Wainfleet
1700	1892	1600	1700	132462	YKS	Newton On Ouse
HEADON						
1700	1992	1600	1992	132470	DEV	ALL
HEADWORTH						
1817	1929	ALL	1817	171360	LND	Bunds Green
HEAGUE						
1800	1830	1700	1800	154075	GLS	Painswick
HEAL						
1771	1851	1600	1771	145289	HAM	Isle Of Wight
1786	1992	1680	1992	121568	SOM	North East
1871	1992	1800	1871	132489	SOM	Bedminster
1871	1992	1800	1871	132489	SOM	Bristol
1871	1992	1800	1871	132489	SOM	Wells
HEALD						
1700	1900	1700	1900	156744	YKS	Wakefield
HEALEY						
1840	1849	1840	1849	105848	IRL	Cork
1820	1880	1800	1920	106976	LAN	Ashton Under Lyne
1743	1870	1650	1840	115681	OXF	Witney
HEALY						
1884	1992	1800	1884	105392	MAY	Lisenumera
HEAM						
1807	1881	1807	1881	138398	HEF	Orcop
HEAMES						
1807	1881	1807	1881	138398	HEF	Orcop
1851	1859	1851	1859	138398	HEF	Town Garway
HEAND						
....	....	1865	....	149187	FIF	Abdie
HEANES						
1744	1768	ALL	ALL	165972	DEV	Okehampton
HEANEY						
....	1874	1700	1930	124907	IRL	???
HEAP						
1800	1940	1700	1850	130419	LAN	Belthorn
1770	1790	1730	1770	122904	LAN	Colne
1800	1940	1700	1850	130419	LAN	Haslingden

Known From	To	Researching From	To	Ref	Cty	Place
HEAP contd.						
1800	1850	1700	1850	157503	LAN	Haslingden
1860	1923	1850	1923	172855	LAN	Haslingden
1774	1787	....	....	142859	LAN	Heaton
1780	1850	1700	1850	126268	LND	Finsbury
1830	1890	1700	1850	154601	WYK	Denholme
1800	1860	1800	1860	153621	WYK	Queensbury
1830	1890	1700	1850	154601	WYK	Thornton
HEAPS						
1846	1900	1800	1900	100307	LAN	ALL
1815	1897	1750	1900	179078	LAN	Haslingden
1804	1900	1700	1800	138304	LAN	Walton Le Dale
1871	1905	ALL	1871	107964	MDX	Holborn
1871	1905	ALL	1871	107964	MDX	Shoreditch
HEAR						
....	....	1700	1800	172901	SLI	???
HEARD						
1939	1939	1900	1992	121932	CON	Boscastle
1708	1750	1600	1708	126357	CON	St Gennys
1826	1853	1771	1826	135879	DEV	Barnstaple
1846	....	1846	1992	114596	DEV	Cornwood
1856	1890	1800	1890	116297	ESS	Finchingfield
1750	1820	....	....	140317	ESS	Fingerinhoe
1780	1800	1750	1850	171158	ESS	Little Leighs
1856	1890	1800	1890	116297	ESS	Wethersfield
1800	1811	1750	1850	147958	LND	???
1770	1850	1700	1850	136840	SOM	Brendon Hills
HEARDER						
....	....	ALL	ALL	132527	ALL	Name Study
HEARFIELD						
1866	1871	1832	1871	136565	NRY	Hull
HEARLE						
1900	1989	....	....	132535	AVN	Bristol
....	....	1600	1900	132535	CON	ALL
1800	1900	1800	1900	132535	CON	Tregony
1600	1800	1600	1900	132535	NBL	West Kirkharle
HEARN						
1800	1870	1700	1850	152579	BKM	Upton Cum Chalvey
1766	1822	1650	1850	143693	BRK	Beenham
1762	1767	1650	1800	143693	BRK	Bucklebury
1745	....	1700	1800	143693	BRK	Finchampstead
1851	....	1850	1900	143693	BRK	Reading
1734	1739	1650	1800	143693	BRK	Sulhampstead Bannister
1734	1784	1650	1800	143693	BRK	Sulhampstead
1822	1842	1750	1870	143693	BRK	Wollhampton
1877	1907	ALL	1939	118389	DEV	Torrington
1785	1992	1600	1785	132551	HAM	Portsmouth
?	?	?	?	166642	KEN	Godmersham
1780	1890	1750	1780	125318	KEN	Habledown
1800	1900	1700	1800	114871	KEN	Harbledown
1900	1925	....	....	114871	KEN	Tonbridge
1800	1992	....	....	108057	LEI	Leicester
1940	1960	1800	1940	141402	LND	Hampstead
1928	1947	....	....	114871	LND	Southfields
?	?	1600	1700	132551	NIR	???
1725	1881	1700	1881	132543	SFK	Stowmarket
1725	1881	1700	1881	132543	SFK	Stowupland
....	....	ALL	1877	118389	SOM	???
HEARNE						
1786	1874	1700	1786	107344	CAM	Peterborough
1748	1940	....	....	128996	CAM	Thorney
HEARNSHAW						
1826	1922	1826	1922	148091	YKS	Leeds
1826	1922	1826	1922	148091	YKS	Sheffield
HEARSON						
....	....	1860	ALL	115908	ALL	ALL
1670	1780	ALL	....	104515	LIN	South
....	....	ALL	1900	115908	LND	ALL
....	1790	ALL	1790	134511	NTT	Arnold
HEARST						
1830	1920	ALL	ALL	113700	MAY	Castlebar
1830	1920	ALL	ALL	113700	MAY	Westport
HEART						
1850	1852	1750	1850	114693	SFK	North
HEASEY						
1582	1980	1500	1920	165034	ALL	ALL
HEASLER						
1769	1797	1650	1770	100013	ESS	Great Waltham
HEASLETON						
1500	1700	ALL	ALL	132446	ENG	ALL
HEASMAN						
1666	....	1666	....	127035	KEN	Cowden
1666	....	1666	....	127035	SRY	East Grinstead
HEASMAN contd.						
1780	1798	ALL	ALL	132578	SSX	Ardingley
1526	1670	ALL	ALL	132578	SSX	Barcombe
1670	1780	ALL	ALL	132578	SSX	Cuckfield
1900	1917	....	....	132578	SSX	Ditching
1650	1850	1600	1650	104914	SSX	East Grinstead
1839	1860	1800	1839	138347	SSX	East Grinstead
1798	1900	ALL	ALL	132578	SSX	Lindfield
HEASY						
1582	1980	1500	1920	165034	ALL	ALL
HEATH						
1827	1834	1750	1860	152129	BKM	West Wycombe
1833	1992	1825	1900	152129	BRK	Bisham
1707	1927	....	....	124672	BRK	Faringdon
1800	1820	1700	1800	120529	BRK	Hinton Waldrist
1851	1992	ALL	1851	155306	DBY	West Hallam
1814	1814	1700	1814	163953	DEV	Brixham
1780	1870	1700	1870	140392	DEV	Dartmouth
1569	1881	....	....	159751	DEV	South Hams
1842	....	....	....	135771	DEV	Totnes
1850	1878	....	....	132594	DUR	Hetton Le Hole
1849	1890	....	....	132594	DUR	Sunderland
....	....	1778	1838	132594	ESS	Harwich
1860	....	1800	1860	135771	GLS	Bristol
1681	1880	1600	1900	130125	HAM	Hound
....	....	1755	1818	132594	HAM	South Hayling
1803	1803	1750	1830	142042	HAM	South Hayling
1840	1900	1700	1900	158542	HAM	South Stoneham
1690	1880	1600	1800	136840	HAM	Southampton
1730	1800	1700	1800	140864	HRT	St Albans
1700	1850	1650	1900	177180	HRT	Watford
1880	1940	....	....	167304	KEN	Hildenborough
1829	1989	1815	1989	138312	KEN	Riverhead
1810	1900	ALL	ALL	177989	KEN	Riverhead
1800	1940	1700	1992	110477	LAN	Manchester
....	....	1880	1920	124796	LAN	Penketh
1800	1940	1700	1992	110477	LAN	Salford
1914	....	1880	1920	124796	LAN	Warrington
1700	1742	1700	1745	156817	LEI	Sileby
1778	1778	1700	1790	159042	LIN	Careby
1833	1992	1833	1883	152129	LND	Central
....	1875	....	1875	175579	LND	Algate
1833	1839	1700	1832	131245	LND	Christchurch
....	1928	....	1875	175579	LND	Clapham
1800	1880	....	....	167304	LND	Whitechapel
1820	1992	1800	1992	132608	LND	???
1816	1880	1780	1850	141283	MDX	Clerkenwell
1800	1960	....	....	140864	MDX	Edmonton
1800	1960	....	....	140864	MDX	Enfield
1825	....	1825	1850	152129	MDX	Mile End
1776	1778	1700	1776	131245	MDX	St Luke
1800	1900	1700	1992	102164	OXF	Henley
1845	1869	1750	1845	176907	SAL	Shrewsbury
1800	1880	ALL	ALL	154091	SOM	Chelwood
1664	1880	1664	1881	170143	SRY	Stoke
1791	1992	1780	1880	125520	SRY	Wandsworth
1664	1880	1664	1881	170143	SRY	Worplesdon
1860	1890	1800	1860	156957	STS	South
1900	1992	1700	1900	158941	STS	Burslem
1855	....	ALL	ALL	158941	STS	Cheadle
....	....	1750	1880	168645	STS	High Offley
....	....	1870	1992	109894	STS	Newcastle
1899	....	1899	1940	122505	STS	Newcastle
1740	1860	....	....	137111	STS	Norton Cames
1775	1992	1700	1992	167991	WIL	Sutton Benger
1763	1877	1700	1763	159158	WOR	Severn Stoke
HEATHCOTE						
1600	1700	1685	1700	105694	DBY	Chelmorton
?	?	?	?	154687	KEN	Greenwich
?	?	?	?	154687	LND	Golders Green
HEATHER						
....	....	ALL	ALL	132624	ALL	Name Study
1797	1820	ALL	1797	133957	HAM	Portsea
1803	1992	1700	1803	132632	HAM	???
1803	1992	1700	1803	132632	KEN	???
1810	1992	1700	1810	132640	SRY	Lambeth
1803	1992	1700	1803	132632	SRY	???
1797	1820	ALL	1797	133957	SSX	Funtington
1803	1992	1700	1803	132632	SSX	???
HEATHERINGTON						
1725	1797	ALL	1725	165301	DUR	Weardale
HEATHFIELD						
1794	1800	1750	1850	113743	SSX	Rye
1784	1784	1600	1784	144851	SSX	Salehurst

Known From	To	Researching From	To	Ref	Cty	Place
HEATON						
....	....	1800	1900	168815	CHS	ALL
1868	1900	1700	1868	115185	IOM	Onchan
1834	1860	1800	1900	168815	LAN	ALL
1870	1870	ALL	ALL	130575	LAN	Eccleston
1867	1902	1700	1867	130931	LAN	Salford
1870	1870	ALL	ALL	130575	LAN	St Helens
1802	1850	1723	1850	143286	LAN	Westhoughton
1800	1992	....	....	176125	LIN	Asterby
1800	1992	....	....	176125	LIN	Goulceby
1592	1992	1200	1592	159832	LIN	Great Coates
1750	1992	1650	1800	132659	WRY	Bingley
1850	1960	ALL	ALL	132667	WYK	Haworth
HEAUME						
1824	....	1750	1824	131326	GSY	???
HEAVEN						
1670	1700	ALL	ALL	113700	GLS	Cromhall
1837	1992	1700	1837	128465	SOM	Axminster
HEAVENOR						
....	....	ALL	....	150835	ENG	???
1830	1900	ALL	....	150835	LIM	Pallas Kenry
HEAVER						
1900	....	....	....	151416	SSX	Brighton
1826	1826	1600	1826	147885	SSX	East Grinstead
1876	1876	ALL	ALL	132349	SXE	Brighton
1620	1720	....	....	119431	SXE	Dallington
HEAVISIDE						
1730	1790	1538	1790	118893	CUL	Alston
1677	1822	ALL	1677	154563	DUR	Auckland St Helen
HEAZEL						
1780	ALL	....	....	142158	BRK	Reading
HEAZELTON						
1500	1700	ALL	ALL	124621	ENG	ALL
HEBB						
1780	1790	1700	1780	151769	LEI	Knipton
HEBBARD						
1837	1862	1600	1837	141100	CON	Breage
1837	1862	1600	1837	141100	CON	Rinsey
HEBBERD						
1764	1795	1750	1795	107573	HAM	Odiham
HEBBES						
1770	1950	ALL	ALL	137286	BDF	ALL
1838	1931	1780	1838	161225	BDF	Thurleigh
HEBBLETHWAITE						
1890	1992	1890	1960	132683	LAN	Liverpool
1630	1870	1580	1870	132675	WES	Kendal
1817	1946	1790	1900	147338	WRY	Northowram
....	....	1600	1775	134317	YKS	Halifax
1600	1870	1400	1870	132675	YKS	Sedburgh
HEBBLEWHITE						
1750	1812	....	1750	101761	LIN	Normanby Le Wold
1800	1893	1750	1870	108510	YKS	Hull
HEBDEN						
....	....	ALL	ALL	132691	ALL	Name Study
1800	1890	1780	1890	164518	YKS	Wakefield
HEBDITCH						
1860	....	1700	1880	124966	SOM	Yeovil
HEBORN						
?	?	?	?	133418	OXF	???
HEBRON						
1710	1850	1550	1710	108308	YKS	Eskdale
HECK						
....	....	1800	1850	125628	LND	Shoreditch
HECKLES						
....	....	1800	1900	154873	NBL	Newcastle
1760	1910	1700	1760	130877	YKS	Wetherby
HECKS						
....	....	ALL	ALL	164194	ALL	Name Study
1750	....	1750	1900	106410	SOM	Pitminster
HEDDON						
1784	1784	....	1784	131385	CON	Strattum
HEDGE						
1747	1823	....	1747	124524	NTH	Northampton
HEDGECOCK						
1650	1860	....	....	165999	ESS	ALL
1650	1860	....	....	165999	ESS	Maldon
....	....	1750	1825	130184	KEN	Ashford
?	?	....	....	121185	KEN	Dover
1871	1992	....	....	165999	LEI	Leicester
1860	1890	....	....	165999	SSX	Brighton
1880	1900	1800	1880	109746	WOR	Bromsgrove
HEDGER						
1500	1880	1500	1880	132721	ALL	ALL
1760	1800	1680	1760	132748	HAM	East Meon

Known From	To	Researching From	To	Ref	Cty	Place
HEDGER contd.						
1655	1851	ALL	1655	132748	HAM	Emsworth
1850	1950	1850	1950	132721	HAM	Hayling Island
1860	1880	1800	1880	132721	HAM	Portsea
1851	1871	1871	1900	132748	HAM	Portsea
1905	1920	1871	1905	132748	LND	Poplar
....	....	1600	1766	164879	SRY	ALL
1766	1930	1600	1766	164879	SRY	Crawley
1820	1930	1700	1820	164879	SRY	Horley
1788	?	ALL	ALL	166243	SRY	Worplesdon
1500	1880	1500	1880	132721	SSX	West
1650	1700	ALL	1650	132748	SXW	Westbourne
HEDGES						
1737	1737	1710	1750	107360	BKM	Gayhurst
1750	1850	1750	1850	177288	BKM	Stewkley
1640	1850	....	....	132756	BRK	Abingdon
1786	1786	1700	1900	145718	BRK	Cookham
1640	1850	....	....	132756	BRK	Kennington
1640	1850	....	....	132756	BRK	Radley
1640	1850	....	....	132756	BRK	Sunningwell
1759	1771	ALL	ALL	113700	GLS	Ozelworth
1900	ALL	....	....	132756	MDX	Woodford Green
1860	ALL	....	....	132756	OXF	Bicester
1765	1918	....	....	132756	OXF	Headington
1830	1942	1830	1942	149403	OXF	Oxford
1640	1964	1600	1640	165417	???	???
HEDINBURGH						
1860	1992	1800	1860	133027	DUR	ALL
HEDLEY						
1795	1992	1700	1795	132772	DBY	???
1700	1799	1700	1799	169781	NBL	Hedley On The Hill
1800	1850	1850	1992	174149	NBL	Newcastle On Tyne
HEEKES						
1869	....	1865	1900	133639	MDX	Chelsea
HEELEY						
1760	1992	1600	1760	116513	WAR	Birmingham
1830	1900	1800	1830	125393	WAR	Birmingham
1801	1850	1600	1801	132802	WAR	Birmingham
HEELIS						
....	....	ALL	ALL	106631	ALL	Name Study
1800	1890	1780	1920	106631	MDX	Westminster
HEENAN						
1780	1992	1780	1992	106305	DOW	???
HEEPS						
1630	1870	1550	1630	129763	NTH	North
HEEREBERT						
1612	1664	1664	1708	178705	WIL	Hannington
HEFFER						
1700	1860	1500	1700	174661	BRK	ALL
HEFFERNAN						
1820	1870	....	....	136492	IRL	???
1820	1840	1700	1900	153826	TIP	Tipperary
HEFFORD						
....	....	1700	1900	153583	LEI	South
....	....	1800	1870	153583	NTH	Spratton
HEGAN						
1854	1992	1854	1992	132780	WAR	Coventry
HEGBIN						
....	....	ALL	ALL	143510	ALL	Name Study
HEGG						
1882	....	ALL	ALL	140902	DBY	Derby
HEGGIE						
1770	1900	ALL	1770	117188	FIF	Criech
HEGINBOTTOM						
....	....	1700	1980	139424	YKS	Saddlesworth
HEIGHES						
....	....	1700	1992	132799	HAM	Oakhanger
HEIGHINGTON						
1862	1880	....	1862	100064	WIC	Douard
HEIGHWAY						
1616	1830	1385	1830	132802	SAL	ALL
HEIRONS						
1841	?	1800	?	136522	SRY	Streatham
HELGREEN						
1820	1850	1800	1992	133450	OXF	Oxford
HELIE						
1850	1992	1700	1850	148059	ALL	ALL
HELLABY						
1639	1992	1600	1639	172049	DBY	Longford
1639	1992	1600	1639	172049	DBY	Wirksworth
HELLARD						
1816	1992	....	....	175803	WIL	Trowbridge
1700	1735	1600	1700	174858	YKS	Thwing

Known From	To	Researching From	To	Ref	Cty	Place
HELLAWELL						
1861	....	1841	1861	108944	WYK	Blackmoor Meltham
1909	1992	1800	1910	132810	YKS	Huddersfield
HELLENS						
....	....	ALL	1840	132829	CMA	Whitehaven
1870	1992	....	....	132829	T&W	Newcastle Upon Tyne
1840	1870	....	....	132829	T&W	Sunderland
HELLEWELL						
1779	1779	1759	1779	147281	LAN	Rossendale
HELLIER						
1769	1800	1700	1769	138010	DEV	Colaton Raleigh
1800	1850	1700	....	131253	DEV	Ipplepen
1841	1863	1700	1992	170518	DOR	Bellchalwell
1706	1732	ALL	1706	154563	DOR	Osmington
1840	....	1700	1860	105767	GLS	Bristol
1840	....	1700	1860	105767	SOM	???
HELLIN						
....	....	ALL	ALL	134392	ALL	ALL
HELLINGS						
1860	1900	1800	1900	139327	DEV	Melksham
HELLIWELL						
....	1863	....	....	163686	LAN	Todmorden
1813	1861	1750	1875	137782	WYK	Stainland
1839	1907	1800	1839	109649	YKS	Hebden Bridge
1890	1992	1700	1860	131830	YKS	Hebden Bridge
1792	1819	1770	1850	116114	YKS	Heptonstall
1813	1858	ALL	1858	173290	YKS	Hiptonstall
1815	1861	1815	1861	116114	YKS	Sowerby
....	1863	....	....	163686	YKS	Todmorden
HELLYER						
1690	1779	ALL	1690	122106	DOR	Portland
1830	1900	1830	1900	105848	SRY	Bermondsey
HELM						
....	....	1400	....	162930	LAN	Chipping Goosenargh
1770	1992	....	....	162930	LAN	Dalton
1770	1992	....	....	162930	LAN	Rampside
1770	1992	....	....	162930	LAN	Ulverston
....	....	1400	....	162930	LAN	Whittingham
1858	1992	1700	1900	167606	WYK	Sowery Bridge
1750	1894	....	....	162930	YKS	Whitby
HELME						
1580	1604	ALL	ALL	141615	LAN	Warton
HELMORE						
1867	1933	ALL	1867	176419	DEV	Ivybridge
....	....	1600	1992	137588	DEV	Newton St Cyres
....	1847	1700	1847	177938	DEV	St Thomas
HELMOTH						
ALL	ALL	ALL	ALL	147354	ALL	ALL
HELPS						
1900	1992	1900	1992	133450	STS	Nuneaton
1816	....	?	1820	103934	WIL	Trowbridge
HELSOP						
1820	1850	1780	1850	170038	CMA	Penrith
HELSTROP						
1825	1881	1538	1861	118893	DUR	Egglescliffe
1737	1745	1538	1861	118893	NRY	Birkby
1740	1790	1538	1861	118893	NRY	Great Smeaton
1760	1830	1538	1861	118893	NRY	Kirklevington
1825	1841	1538	1861	118893	NRY	Marton
1810	1830	1538	1861	118893	NRY	Yarm
HEMBER						
1840	1940	....	1838	117773	GLS	Bristol
1841	1874	1800	1850	117773	SOM	Taunton
HEMBERY						
1715	1807	1650	1820	113069	SOM	Huntspill
1715	1807	1650	1820	124990	SOM	Huntspill
1807	1883	1700	1883	113069	SOM	Paulett
1807	1883	1700	1883	124990	SOM	Pawlett
HEMBROW						
1817	1839	ALL	1817	139602	SOM	Stoke St Gregory
1818	1844	1844	1992	139602	SOM	Taunton
HEMERS						
1841	1864	1841	1864	173851	AVN	Bristol
HEMINGTON						
....	....	ALL	ALL	132845	ALL	Name Study
1788	1900	ALL	ALL	132845	SRY	Southwark
HEMINGWAY						
ALL	1780	....	....	170798	WRY	Mirfield
1850	1860	1700	1850	145688	YKS	Dewsbury
1602	1940	1600	1881	166952	YKS	Dewsbury
1845	1906	....	....	145912	YKS	Stanley
HEMMANT						
1714	1940	....	....	128996	CAM	Thorney
HEMMING						
....	....	ALL	ALL	132853	ALL	ALL
1844	....	....	....	132853	ESS	Leyton
1730	1820	1700	1850	167126	LND	???
1873	1947	1800	1873	132853	MDX	Bethnal Green
1845	....	....	....	132853	MDX	Stoke Newington
1845	1868	....	....	132853	MDX	Westminster
1830	1831	....	....	132497	OXF	Oxford
1830	1942	1700	1830	124281	WAR	Birmingham
1815	1871	1800	1992	174475	WOR	Alveditch
1815	1871	1800	1992	174475	WOR	Bromsgrove
1857	1883	1800	1992	174475	WOR	Feckenham
1857	1883	1800	1992	174475	WOR	Lickey
1883	1897	....	....	174475	WOR	Stourbridge
HEMMINGS						
1724	1860	1700	1880	113085	BKM	Iver
1740	1780	1700	1750	135496	GLS	Broad Campden
1854	1900	1800	1992	176184	GLS	???
1856	1890	1850	1900	113085	MDX	Uxbridge
1800	1900	1750	1900	170186	NTH	Eydon
1650	1800	1550	1850	170186	OXF	Cropredy
1825	1900	....	....	132756	STS	Pottereis
1825	1900	....	....	132756	STS	Stoke Vale
HEMMINGWAY						
1817	1818	1780	1824	123404	NFK	Great Yarmouth
1851	1914	1849	1992	123404	YKS	Dewbury
HEMPSALL						
1760	1992	1550	1760	128074	NTT	East Markham
1768	1768	1768	1768	108901	NTT	West Markham
HEMPSTEAD						
1837	1872	1800	1871	164259	SRY	Croydon
HEMS						
....	....	ALL	ALL	104434	ALL	Name Study
1764	1992	1764	1992	104434	LND	East
1817	1893	....	1850	152803	LND	Shoreditch
HEMSLEY						
1866	1906	ALL	1866	165263	KEN	Shipbourne
....	....	1821	1841	165263	SSX	Fletching
....	....	ALL	1821	165263	SSX	Isfield
1813	1835	1780	1835	116483	SSX	Maresfield
1851	....	ALL	1861	165263	SSX	Wadhurst
1886	1954	1700	1886	149624	YKS	Bradford
HEMSWELL						
1828	1888	....	....	114545	LIN	Lincoln
HEMSWORTH						
1600	1865	1600	1826	161705	NTT	North
HEMUS						
1800	1900	1700	1900	133876	WOR	Bromsgrove
1800	1900	1700	1900	133876	WOR	Catshill
HENBEST						
1580	1992	1580	1992	141380	ALL	ALL
1819	1843	1800	1851	170526	HAM	Bramshaw
HENCHEB						
1884	1937	1840	1883	167568	LND	Vauxhall
HENCHMAN						
1750	1750	1750	1750	170143	NTH	Wellingborough
HENCY						
....	....	1600	1700	128627	CLA	???
....	....	1600	1700	128627	IRL	Dublin
HENDEBOURCK						
1865	1935	1800	1865	174041	LND	Bow
HENDEN						
1632	1687	ALL	ALL	135208	KEN	Biddenden
HENDERSON						
1770	1980	ALL	ALL	156604	ABD	New Deer
1800	1880	....	....	140864	ABD	Strichen
1785	1816	1750	1820	172162	ANS	Dundee
1760	1890	....	....	126497	CAI	Halkirk
1748	1916	....	....	168203	CAI	Latheron
1770	1890	1700	1890	126500	CAI	Wick Bower
1870	1992	1870	1992	178357	CHS	Wirral
1805	1900	1894	1925	132934	CUL	Maryport
1789	1840	ALL	1885	177695	DUR	Beamish
....	....	1800	1900	142417	DUR	Easington
1798	1908	1798	1908	149403	DUR	Lamesley
1775	1800	ALL	1850	158445	DUR	Monkw'mth
....	....	1800	1850	111732	DUR	Monkwearmouth
1790	1840	1700	1790	133019	DUR	Sadberge
1808	....	1700	1992	107204	DUR	Stockton
1800	1850	1750	1850	123536	DUR	Wolsingham
1850	1929	1850	1902	153176	DUR	???
1740	1768	ALL	1768	149063	ELN	Dunbar
1880	1920	....	....	111732	ESS	Plaistow
1842	1845	1700	1842	122394	FIF	Kennoway

Known From	To	Researching From	To	Ref	Cty	Place
HENDERSON contd.						
1719	....	1700	1800	169218	FIF	St Monance
1850	1992	1850	1992	178357	LAN	Liverpool
1863	1881	1881	1963	153109	LIN	Spittlegate
1780	1900	1760	1900	167088	LND	Marylebone
1835	1855	1835	1855	168289	MLN	Cramond
1775	1907	1850	1910	176982	MLN	Edinburgh
1834	1851	1750	1900	159379	MLN	West Calder
1800	1920	1700	1800	130885	NBL	Bamburgh
1700	1800	1700	1800	160121	NBL	Haltwhistle
1840	1873	ALL	1992	102245	NBL	Newcastle Upon Tyne
1770	1850	1770	1850	160121	NBL	Newcastle
?	1850	....	....	153176	NBL	???
1775	1930	1750	1992	133450	PER	Fossewell Bank
1800	1992	1750	1800	111821	ROC	Urray
1750	1800	1750	1900	119725	ROX	Jeburgh
1760	1874	1700	1820	179000	SCT	Abercorn
ALL	ALL	ALL	ALL	174793	SCT	Edinburgh
....	....	ALL	1850	111732	SHI	ALL
1750	1965	....	....	137820	SHI	Fetlar
1720	1965	....	....	137820	SHI	Mid Yell
1760	1965	....	....	137820	SHI	North Yell
1758	1965	....	....	137820	SHI	Northmavine
1720	1965	....	....	137820	SHI	South Yell
1825	1930	....	....	132896	STS	Birmingham
1825	1930	....	....	132896	WAR	Birmingham
HENDEY						
1748	1790	1500	1748	129577	IOW	???
HENDING						
1850	1920	ALL	1850	141224	GLS	South
HENDON						
1803	1803	ALL	1850	168696	WIL	Dauntsey
HENDRA						
1490	1992	ALL	ALL	132942	CON	ALL
HENDREN						
1794	1920	1794	....	123609	IRL	Caldymore
HENDRICK						
1724	....	1724	1788	156892	LAN	Rainford
HENDRY						
1795	1840	1700	1800	167258	ABD	New Pitsligo
1870	1992	1700	1870	136573	CAI	Latheron
1870	1920	1800	1900	111821	LKS	Govan
....	....	1700	1750	101818	NFK	Burnham Sutton
1792	1866	1700	1850	145750	NFK	Kings Lynn
....	....	1860	1930	101818	NFK	Well Next Sea
....	....	1782	ALL	149187	PER	Perth
1937	....	....	....	136018	SRY	East Molesey
HENDY						
1885	1992	1800	1885	140163	DEV	Plymouth
1850	1920	ALL	1850	141224	GLS	South
1819	1885	1650	1819	166170	WIL	Ramsbury
HENFREY						
1769	1992	1700	1769	100994	LIN	Deeping St James
1820	1900	ALL	ALL	107670	LND	???
1820	1900	ALL	ALL	107670	NTT	???
HENLEY						
1766	1870	1750	1900	118486	BDF	Eaton Bray
1850	1924	1858	1992	131369	DEV	Ellacombe
1725	....	ALL	1725	115282	SSX	East
1750	1773	ALL	....	132349	SXW	Petworth
HENLY						
1527	1992	ALL	ALL	104884	ALL	ALL
1777	1992	ALL	1777	147389	GLS	Bristol
1520	ALL	ALL	ALL	132950	WIL	ALL
HENMAN						
1731	1754	ALL	1731	168602	BDF	Odell
....	....	1750	1800	154873	KEN	Milton
....	....	1750	1800	154873	KEN	Sittingbourne
HENN						
1830	1992	ALL	1830	158437	LND	Chelsea
HENNER						
1893	1992	1500	1893	110310	YKS	Hull
HENNESSEY						
1850	1900	ALL	1850	108812	COR	???
1881	1884	....	....	128015	MDX	Bromley
1900	1992	1900	1992	110825	MDX	London
1909	1958	....	....	128015	NTT	Nottingham
HENNESSY						
1860	1900	1830	1900	113107	GLA	Dowlais
1842	1950	....	....	144673	IRL	???
1842	1950	....	....	144673	LND	East
HENNEY						
....	....	ALL	ALL	132969	ALL	Name Study
HENNIGAN						
1881	1936	1800	1940	164097	LAN	Liverpool
HENNIKER						
1823	1823	1823	1823	108278	KEN	Challock
HENNING						
....	....	ALL	ALL	144959	ALL	Name Study
1908	1992	1600	1908	164240	DOR	Edmondsham
1806	1992	ALL	1800	179167	HAM	Lymington
1814	1992	1750	1814	167436	HAM	Portsea
HENRIQUES						
....	....	ALL	ALL	112070	ALL	Name Study
1808	....	1750	1808	179140	ESS	Shoreditch
1790	1800	1700	1850	126268	LND	Spitalfields
HENRY						
1735	1840	1735	1840	128481	ANS	Montrose
1759	1800	1750	1800	176923	CMN	Talley
1715	1891	1650	1715	159565	DUR	Iveston
1779	1790	....	1779	117234	IRL	Tyrone
1749	1992	1600	1749	132977	KKD	Gatehouse Of Fleet
1874	....	1800	1900	135623	LAN	Liverpool
1820	1910	1700	1850	156442	LDY	Maghera
....	....	ALL	ALL	166812	NBL	Newcastle
1794	1992	1750	1800	140473	PEM	Pembroke
1660	1900	....	....	109304	SHI	Aithsting
1750	1965	....	....	137820	SHI	Fetlar
1720	1965	....	....	137820	SHI	Mid Yell
1760	1965	....	....	137820	SHI	North Yell
1758	1965	....	....	137820	SHI	Northmavine
1660	1900	....	....	109304	SHI	Sandsting
1720	1965	....	....	137820	SHI	South Yell
HENSBERGH						
1690	1790	1790	1900	123102	BKM	Hambleden
1850	1930	1930	1992	123102	DBY	BAKEWELL
1830	1850	1850	1950	123102	GLS	Wickwar
1830	1850	1850	1950	123102	OXF	Burford
HENSBY						
1755	1805	1740	1805	135941	SFK	Lakenheath
HENSELL						
1842	1992	1700	1842	166804	NFK	Great Yarmouth
HENSHALL						
1801	1940	....	....	137790	CHS	Acton
1801	1940	....	....	137790	CHS	Huxley
1825	1992	1700	1825	161446	CHS	Tarpoley
HENSHAW						
1750	1992	1700	1750	155500	CHS	Prestbury
1817	1898	1700	1898	178500	DBY	Ilkeston
1888	1992	ALL	ALL	115762	LEI	Leicester
1825	1950	ALL	1825	112313	LIN	Stamford
1735	1786	1735	1786	147532	SAL	Whitchurch
HENSMAN						
1749	1940	....	....	128996	CAM	Thorney
1851	1984	1851	1900	160237	LEI	Clipston
HENSON						
1830	1945	1770	1830	130346	DBY	Derby
1850	1895	....	....	132985	LIN	Barrowby
1840	....	1750	1850	116432	LIN	Belchford
1845	1890	1800	1850	132985	LIN	Grantham
....	....	ALL	ALL	124613	LND	Twickenham
1850	1940	1870	1940	173533	NTH	ALL
1824	1897	1820	1897	112925	NTH	Passenham
1864	....	1800	1992	111201	NTT	Bulwell
....	....	ALL	1825	114308	OXF	Bambury
1783	1795	....	1783	100064	RUT	Whissendine
1950	1992	....	....	124613	SSX	Hastings
1920	1960	....	....	132985	YKS	Wakefield
HENSTRIDGE						
1770	1930	1700	1770	173223	WIL	South Newton
HENSTUS						
1829	1830	....	....	145394	DEV	East Stonehouse
HENTALL						
1790	1992	1500	1992	102261	???	London
HENTON						
1880	....	1700	1900	166359	???	???
HENTSCH						
1915	1930	ALL	ALL	134929	SRY	New Malden
HENTY						
1837	1872	....	1837	129771	SSX	Hailsham
HENWOOD						
1780	1784	....	1800	171441	BRK	New Windsor
1827	1852	1800	1850	104183	CON	Gwennap
1808	1881	1700	1992	153540	CON	Maker
1694	1694	1650	1725	133450	CON	Roche
1847	1928	1700	1847	153540	DEV	Devonport
?	?	ALL	ALL	172251	DEV	Devonport

Known From	To	Researching From	To	Ref	Cty	Place
HENWOOD contd.						
1820	1881	1800	1821	149489	DEV	Plymouth
1823	1830	1750	1850	172251	HAM	Portsmouth
HENZELL						
1590	1830	1590	1830	156892	NBL	Newcastle
HENZEY						
1724	?	1690	?	156892	LAN	Eccleston
HEPBURN						
1725	1856	1725	1856	171654	AYR	Sorn
1800	1900	1700	1800	118419	BAN	Ordiquhill
1820	1860	1750	1900	176397	KRS	Kinross
HEPPELL						
1790	1800	1700	1790	133019	DUR	Jarrow
1720	1992	1540	1784	133027	NBL	Kirkwhelpington
1790	1992	1650	1790	133019	NBL	Newcastle Upon Tyne
HEPPENSTALL						
1820	1948	....	....	160253	WYK	Hepworth
HEPPETT						
1860	....	1860	1900	178845	GLA	Dowlais
1835	....	1800	1850	178845	NBL	???
HEPPLE						
....	....	1700	1810	155608	DUR	Chester Le Street
HEPPLEWHITE						
1850	1960	1700	1850	133035	BRK	Crowthorne
HEPPOLETTE						
1901	....	1800	1850	178845	LAN	Bolton
HEPPTONSTALL						
1888	?	1700	1900	159336	YKS	Great Ouse Burn
HEPTINSTALL						
1786	1849	1700	....	140783	MID	???
HEPTONSTALL						
1840	1850	ALL	ALL	125202	WRY	Pontefract
1790	1840	1700	1992	114901	YKS	Garforth
1805	1860	1800	1900	141984	YKS	Hillam
1840	1860	1840	1992	114901	YKS	Hunslet
1750	1900	....	....	141984	YKS	Monk Fryston
HEPWORTH						
1600	1830	....	1600	101761	WRY	Emley
1799	1860	1799	1860	138703	YKS	Elescar
1830	1985	1500	1830	110310	YKS	Hull
1830	1830	1500	1830	110310	YKS	Sheffield
1799	1860	1799	1860	138703	YKS	Sportboro
1827	1827	....	....	141097	YKS	Wadworth
HERBERT						
1750	1800	....	....	132837	BDF	Biggleswade
1837	?	1600	1830	168548	BKM	???
1700	1780	1700	1992	142360	BRK	Wargrave
1837	?	1600	1830	168548	BRK	???
1826	1992	1700	1826	152269	CUL	ALL
....	....	1600	1720	116173	CUL	West
1790	1821	ALL	ALL	135909	CUL	Gosforth
....	....	1750	1850	103667	DEV	South
1770	....	1600	1900	162388	DEV	Chagford
1775	1827	ALL	1775	125121	ESS	Maldon
1880	1920	1880	1910	142794	GLA	Mountain Ash
1735	1808	ALL	1735	158739	GLA	St Andrews
1780	1992	1500	1780	114049	GLS	South
1857	1992	1857	1992	165395	GLS	Painswick
1783	1786	1700	1783	178381	GLS	Sevenhampton
1761	1992	1600	1761	110019	GLS	Stanstead
1800	1992	....	....	132837	HUN	Huntingdon
1840	1900	1700	1840	174572	KEN	Sheerness
1878	1950	1850	1992	135933	LND	Southwark
1870	1920	1600	1870	168548	LND	Southwark
1830	1850	1830	1850	174386	LND	Westminster
1863	1951	1797	1863	109975	LND	???
1860	1950	1800	1870	172170	MDX	London
1901	1992	....	1900	166189	MDX	Stockwell
1819	1864	1700	1819	172898	MON	Wyesham
1863	1951	1797	1863	109975	NTH	???
1700	....	....	....	148768	OXF	Pyrton
1700	....	....	....	148768	OXF	Sandford
1812	1871	1841	1871	170623	OXF	Watlington
1775	1827	ALL	1775	125121	SFK	Eye
....	....	1760	1950	136166	SOM	Bridgwater
1863	1951	1797	1863	109975	SRY	???
1300	....	1070	1520	156647	SSX	Netherfield
1756	1800	1700	1756	176710	WAR	Coventry
1790	1992	....	....	104949	WIL	Minety
HERBISON						
1880	1992	1700	1880	165239	ANT	Cullybackey
HERBY						
....	1850	ALL	1850	177695	NTH	???

Known From	To	Researching From	To	Ref	Cty	Place
HERCULESON						
1750	1965	....	....	137820	SHI	Fetlar
1720	1965	....	....	137820	SHI	Mid Yell
1760	1965	....	....	137820	SHI	North Yell
1758	1965	....	....	137820	SHI	Northmavine
1720	1965	....	....	137820	SHI	South Yell
HERD						
1850	1900	1800	1900	123765	CAM	Cambridge
1800	1900	1800	1992	171077	CON	St Breock
....	....	1700	1992	167223	DEV	Crediton
1731	1746	ALL	1746	129283	ESS	Great Braxted
1840	1860	1800	1900	117781	EYK	Hull
1840	1860	1800	1900	117781	SCT	???
1745	1800	1700	1745	111236	YKS	Sedburgh
HERDMAN						
1587	1754	1500	1800	160873	NBL	South West
1735	1857	1700	1890	160873	NBL	Simonburn
HERDSFIELD						
1800	1854	1700	1992	160377	MDX	London
HERETAY						
1840	....	ALL	ALL	113700	MAY	Westport
HEREWARD						
1866	1992	....	....	176125	DOR	Toller Porcorum
HERING						
1806	1876	1806	1876	177199	LND	Marylebone
HERITAGE						
....	....	ALL	ALL	133078	ALL	Name Study
1314	1992	ALL	ALL	133078	ALL	ALL
1790	1800	1750	1800	102970	BKM	Askett
1819	1870	....	1819	176702	BKM	Aylesbury
1800	1850	1800	1850	102970	BKM	Gt Kimble
1869	1896	....	....	153842	LND	Paddington
1896	1927	....	....	153842	SAL	Wellington
1830	1900	1750	1900	107611	WAR	Aston
1785	1869	ALL	1841	153842	WAR	Stratford On Avon
1870	1992	....	....	176702	WYK	Bradford
HERLEY						
1860	1870	1870	ALL	165689	LND	East
HERMAN						
1840	1870	....	1870	109568	BRK	Hanney
1800	1850	1600	1800	154059	LND	St Martins
HERMERY						
1857	....	....	....	144711	LND	Southwark
1788	1813	1700	1788	144711	WIL	Hannington
HERMITAGE						
1827	1835	1550	1827	147265	LIN	South
1818	1818	1500	1818	174009	SSX	East
HERMON						
....	1820	....	1820	133086	BRK	ALL
1820	1880	1820	1880	133086	LND	City
1810	1820	1810	1820	133086	SRY	Weybridge
HERN						
?	?	?	?	100692	DEV	Sidbury
HERNIMAN						
....	....	ALL	ALL	107034	ALL	Name Study
HERON						
....	....	ALL	ALL	100854	ALL	ALL
1778	1810	1750	1850	123536	DUR	Hamsterley
1800	1992	1750	1820	122297	DUR	South Shields
1839	....	....	....	133094	IRL	Cork
1865	1867	....	....	133094	IRL	Kildare
1843	1992	1700	1843	133108	IRL	Limerick
1869	....	....	....	133094	KEN	???
1880	....	....	....	133094	LAN	Mossley
....	....	1500	1992	132551	SCT	ALL
1663	1758	....	....	139483	WIG	Penninghame
HERRATY						
1832	1992	1700	1900	122114	WAR	Solihull
HERRIARD						
1726	1818	1726	1818	161950	HAM	Kingsclere
HERRICK						
1830	1992	1700	1830	165581	LIN	Wickenby
HERRIDGE						
....	....	ALL	ALL	133116	ALL	Name Study
1863	1886	ALL	ALL	119504	DOR	Cuckhorn Weston
1838	....	ALL	ALL	119504	DOR	Kington Magna
1927	....	ALL	ALL	119504	HAM	Portsmouth
HERRIER						
1707	1707	1680	1750	125032	HAM	Tunworth
HERRIES						
1841	1992	1700	1850	155705	ELN	North Berwick
1841	1992	1700	1850	155705	ELN	Terreggles
1841	1992	1700	1850	155705	KKD	Colvend

Known From	To	Researching From	To	Ref	Cty	Place
HERRIET						
1839	1839	1750	1880	176672	SSX	ALL
HERRING						
1800	....	1800	....	134813	CON	Altarnun
1631	1992	1631	1700	165891	LIN	Boston
1823	1895	....	....	114545	LIN	Butterwick
1823	1895	....	....	114545	LIN	Fens
1823	1895	....	....	114545	LIN	Midville
1842	1853	1830	1870	162272	LND	St Pancras
1795	1816	1750	1850	162272	MDX	Southgate
HERRINGSHAW						
1830	1880	1750	1900	109517	CAM	ALL
1830	1880	1750	1900	109517	NFK	ALL
HERRINGTON						
1870	1992	ALL	ALL	161047	DBY	North
....	....	1750	1860	179361	WIL	Bower Chalke
....	....	ALL	ALL	135062	WIL	???
HERRIOTT						
1700	1850	1700	1850	123722	NTT	Sutton
HERRIVEN						
1868	1932	1750	1868	168025	SFK	Lowestoft
HERRON						
1725	1761	ALL	1725	154563	DUR	Weardale
HERRSEIN						
1663	1663	1625	1700	130052	YKS	Sandtoft
HERSANT						
....	....	ALL	ALL	148369	ALL	Name Study
HERSEBERGER						
1878	1992	....	....	133752	LAN	Liverpool
HERSENT						
1560	1660	1550	1660	130052	HAM	Southampton
HERSIN						
1656	1681	1630	1700	130052	CAM	Thorney
HERTZ						
1830	1860	1700	1992	167592	LAN	Liverpool
1830	1860	1700	1992	167592	LAN	West Derby
HERWIG						
1800	1992	....	....	125407	LND	East
HESELTINE						
1844	1895	1600	1850	146676	DUR	Cockfield
1844	1895	1600	1850	146676	DUR	Towlaw
1700	1729	....	....	131660	SFK	Exning
1700	1729	....	....	131660	SFK	Wood Ditton
1759	1900	1700	1800	168424	YKS	Aysgarth
HESELTON						
1850	1850	1750	1900	176672	ALL	ALL
HESELWOOD						
1841	1861	1700	1841	135011	YKS	Pickering
HESFORD						
1800	1818	1750	1818	141062	LAN	Eccles
1833	1863	1800	1863	102075	LND	Westminster
HESK						
1820	1850	....	1820	135089	KEN	???
1820	1850	....	1820	135089	LND	???
HESKETH						
1747	1924	1747	1924	106291	CWD	Abergele
....	....	1750	1900	176117	LAN	Padiham
1170	1992	....	....	100536	LAN	???
HESLEDEN						
1800	1840	1700	1900	130419	YKS	Giggleswick
HESLIN						
1863	1880	1830	1880	150827	YKS	Harrogate
HESLING						
1728	1980	1650	1750	166405	YKS	Leeds
HESLOP						
1760	1841	1700	1760	112585	CUL	Farlam
....	....	1841	1880	112585	DUR	???
1806	1992	1700	1806	160199	NBL	Haltwhistle
1806	1992	1700	1806	160199	NBL	Haydon
....	....	1841	1880	112585	NBL	???
....	1790	....	....	153176	NBL	???
1840	1935	....	....	132829	T&W	Newcastle Upon Tyne
....	....	ALL	1840	132829	T&W	North Sheilds
HESSELGRAVE						
1730	1760	?	1730	128910	YKS	York
HESSELTON						
1500	1700	ALL	ALL	132446	ENG	ALL
HESSEY						
1744	1779	ALL	1744	154946	ERY	Eastringham
HESSION						
1850	1930	1800	1930	118540	WAR	Birmingham
HESSLETON						
1500	1700	ALL	ALL	124621	ENG	ALL

Known From	To	Researching From	To	Ref	Cty	Place
HESSNAN						
1930	1992	1800	1930	178527	MEA	Athboy
1930	1992	1800	1930	178527	MEA	Ballivor
HESTER						
1844	1992	1700	1900	145513	BRK	Cookham
1734	....	1700	1750	124796	OXF	Tackley
1822	1904	ALL	ALL	124176	OXF	Woodstock
?	?	?	?	133418	OXF	???
HESTERMANN						
1828	1960	ALL	ALL	168815	ALL	ALL
HETH						
1711	1711	ALL	ALL	130508	HAM	Clatford
1711	1711	ALL	ALL	130508	HAM	Goodworth
HETHER						
1617	1617	....	....	115606	HAM	Odiham
HETHERINGTON						
1830	1850	1750	1850	122254	CUL	Penrith
1855	1992	1600	1855	133132	CUL	Wetherall
1810	1960	1700	1810	100714	NBL	Hexham
1735	1837	1698	....	120634	WMD	Beetham
HETT						
1731	....	....	....	124524	DUR	High Conniscliffe
1767	1767	ALL	ALL	120650	NTT	Norton Cuckney
HEUDEBOURCK						
....	....	ALL	ALL	136670	ALL	Name Study
HEWARD						
1704	1757	....	....	166723	SRY	Horsell
HEWENS						
1739	1785	ALL	1739	102245	WAR	Tysoe
HEWER						
....	....	ALL	ALL	133140	ALL	Name Study
1750	1900	....	....	152978	GLS	Chalford
....	....	ALL	1800	152978	OXF	Alvescot
HEWES						
1760	1850	1700	1760	110906	BKM	Twyford
HEWETSON						
....	....	1700	1992	168181	KIK	ALL
....	....	1700	1992	168181	TIP	ALL
1830	1935	....	1830	118451	WES	Windermere
....	....	1700	1992	168181	WEX	ALL
HEWETT						
1800	1900	1800	1900	171077	CON	St Breock
1830	1860	1750	1860	118575	DEV	North
1819	1899	ALL	1890	162507	HAM	Gosport
1780	1850	1780	1850	133795	SCT	???
1753	1915	1700	1753	160709	SSX	Lavant
1815	....	1770	1820	145297	WIL	Dilton
HEWGILL						
....	....	1700	1832	131598	YKS	Danby
....	....	1700	1800	131598	YKS	Egton
....	....	1700	1800	131598	YKS	Glaisdale
HEWINGS						
1864	ALL	1840	1864	159654	SOM	Nynehara
1818	1895	1700	1992	166197	WOR	Honeybourne
HEWINS						
1813	1854	1854	1992	102245	GLS	Tredington
1854	1854	....	....	102245	WAR	Birmingham
1871	1879	....	....	102245	WAR	Coleshill
1857	1871	....	....	102245	WAR	Shustoke
1785	1830	1830	1992	102245	WAR	Stretton On Fosse
1740	1850	1775	1840	140309	WOR	Inkberrow
HEWISH						
....	....	1650	1992	114596	DEV	Cheriton Fitzpaine
HEWITON						
1800	1899	....	....	164151	CUL	Wigton
HEWITSON						
1756	1881	1756	1881	110396	CUL	Cocklehill
1864	1900	1750	1864	134651	CUL	Dalston
1819	1845	1700	1819	115169	DUR	Darlington
1860	1950	1750	1860	134473	MDX	Islington
1704	1799	ALL	1704	171573	WES	Ravenstone Dale
HEWITT						
1800	1850	....	....	153397	BRK	Swallowfield
1803	1803	1795	1805	126705	CHS	North East
1818	1822	ALL	1825	133159	CMA	Whitehaven
1900	1930	1850	1900	174335	DBY	Garston
1900	1930	1850	1900	174335	DBY	Liverpool
1704	1980	1704	1980	133175	GLS	Mangotsfield
1704	1980	1704	1980	133175	GLS	Pucklechurch
1800	1850	....	....	153397	HAM	Border
1829	1914	ALL	1830	149446	HAM	Farringdon
1836	1836	1600	1836	152080	HAM	???
....	....	1700	1770	147613	HUN	Great Staughton
1840	....	....	....	117560	KEN	Greenwich

Known From	To	Researching From	To	Ref	Cty	Place
HEWITT contd.						
1800	1870	1538	1800	158232	KEN	Thanet
1847	1905	....	....	164062	LAN	Bolton
....	1835	ALL	1835	153710	LAN	Eccleston
1851	1861	1845	1890	126705	LAN	Hulme
1810	1925	1783	1810	165158	LAN	Lathom
1825	1992	ALL	1825	133159	LAN	Liverpool
1860	....	....	....	163392	LAN	Liverpool
1731	1815	1650	1731	160474	LAN	Prescot
1823	1848	1815	1850	126705	LAN	Stretford
1815	1881	1700	1820	160636	LEI	Sproxton
1848	1894	1800	1848	149578	LND	Finsbury
1874	1935	....	1875	130524	MDX	Hackney
1816	1841	1790	1860	133639	NFK	Banham
1646	1992	ALL	ALL	142565	NFK	St Faiths
....	....	1800	1899	142409	NFK	???
1850	1900	1700	1850	107271	NTH	North East
1800	1950	1800	1950	105511	OXF	Cropredy
1780	1780	1700	1780	155276	SFK	Felixstone
1842	1842	1500	1842	176974	STS	Fenton
1790	1820	1750	1820	128708	STS	Penkridge
1787	1860	1600	1787	133167	WAR	Coventry
1760	1820	1700	1760	172022	WAR	Coventry
....	....	1700	1765	116173	WAR	Leek Wootton
1812	1992	1750	1812	116513	WAR	Yardley
1800	1850	1700	1800	171182	WIL	South
1800	1850	1700	1800	171182	WIL	West
1838	1992	?	?	176702	WYK	Clayton
1827	....	ALL	1827	152234	WYK	Garforth
1650	1650	1600	1650	141097	YKS	Braithwell
1700	1899	1700	1900	163902	YKS	Sheffield
HEWLET						
1645	1700	1600	1645	145459	HAM	Wellow
HEWLETT						
1724	1780	1600	1800	162620	DOR	Dorchester
....	....	1700	1850	118834	DOR	Poole
1841	1841	1800	1900	126799	LND	Shoreditch
1790	1841	1700	1900	126799	MON	Monmouth
1700	1800	1600	1700	174513	OXF	Kencot
1762	1980	ALL	ALL	153516	SOM	Banwell
1834	1850	....	1814	178365	WIL	Overton
HEWSON						
1700	1900	1600	1700	132659	ERY	Aughton
1720	1760	1600	1992	167592	LAN	Liverpool
1825	1955	1800	1992	133450	LIM	???
1700	1900	1700	1900	123765	LIN	ALL
1815	1850	ALL	1850	134503	LIN	Alford
1800	1820	1700	1800	145688	LIN	Grimsby
1680	1760	....	....	145688	LIN	Tetney
1877	1900	ALL	1877	149357	MON	ALL
1717	1726	1690	1730	149152	NBL	Earsdon
1700	1860	1660	1750	160768	SXW	Eartham
1700	1860	1660	1750	160768	SXW	East Dean
1840	1880	....	....	160768	SXW	Oving
1700	1860	1660	1750	160768	SXW	Singleton
HEWTSON						
1695	1716	1600	1700	101575	YKS	Whitgift
HEX						
....	....	1650	1750	153281	SOM	North Petherton
HEXT						
....	....	ALL	ALL	133191	ALL	Name Study
1837	1940	ALL	ALL	133191	ALL	ALL
1500	1970	....	....	100536	CON	???
1550	1850	1300	1880	105333	DEV	Buckland In The Moor
1550	1850	1300	1880	105333	DEV	Holne
1550	1850	1300	1880	105333	DEV	Ilsington
1550	1850	1300	1880	105333	DEV	Lydford
1550	1850	1300	1880	105333	DEV	Widecombe In The Moor
1650	1800	1600	1837	140392	DEV	Widecombe
HEXTALL						
....	....	1300	1420	154873	CHS	Wetenhall
....	....	1100	1300	154873	HEF	Hextall
1687	1761	ALL	ALL	141615	LEI	Barlestone
HEXTER						
....	....	ALL	ALL	133205	ALL	Name Study
....	....	ALL	ALL	133205	DEV	Exeter
HEY						
1821	....	1770	1840	170348	YKS	Warley In Halifax
HEYBYRNE						
1819	1992	1700	1819	133213	IRL	Dublin
HEYDEN						
1786	1800	1786	1800	178705	BRK	Reading

Known From	To	Researching From	To	Ref	Cty	Place
HEYDON						
1848	1992	1700	1848	129984	HRT	???
1855	1964	1855	1964	123404	WOR	Finstall
1810	1870	1780	1870	123404	WOR	Tardebigg
HEYES						
1650	1850	1600	1992	167592	FLN	Buckley
1830	1870	1800	1830	121509	IRL	???
1838	1871	1750	1838	120669	LAN	Bury
1720	1750	1600	1992	167592	LAN	Liverpool
1790	1992	1750	1790	157740	LAN	Widnes
1850	1900	....	....	126497	LAN	Wigan
1850	1920	1850	1900	126500	LAN	Wigan
HEYHOE						
1755	1868	1600	1800	174920	NFK	Swaffham
HEYLER						
1816	....	1800	1840	133639	WOR	Stourport
HEYMAN						
1853	1992	ALL	1853	107239	LND	???
HEYS						
1855	1910	....	....	117196	LAN	Southport
1796	1855	1770	1796	117196	LAN	Whittle Le Woods
1789	1800	1700	1800	162396	LIN	Market Rasen
1784	1820	....	....	133221	WIL	Downton
HEYSETT						
1750	1900	1750	1900	154857	DEV	Bradford
HEYTER						
1500	1625	1500	1800	170216	WIL	ALL
HEYWOOD						
1852	1900	ALL	1900	104531	LAN	Farnworth
?	....	....	....	116092	LAN	Manchester
1812	1840	1770	1812	174211	LAN	Middleton
1880	1900	1800	1880	150061	LAN	Ormskirk
1791	1992	1750	1791	175722	MDX	Brentford
1791	1992	1750	1791	175722	MDX	Chiswick
1850	1860	1800	1900	104868	SOM	Weston Super Mare
1806	1872	1700	1872	136530	WOR	Alcester
HEYWORTH						
1821	1882	1786	1882	141550	LAN	Bacup
1821	1882	1786	1882	141550	LAN	Liverpool
HEZMALHALCH						
1775	1900	1700	1775	176451	YKS	Leeds
HIAM						
1730	1930	ALL	ALL	159107	NFK	Upwell
HIATT						
1775	1830	1775	1830	119091	LND	City
1828	1850	1775	1875	119091	LND	Paddington
1828	1850	1775	1875	119091	LND	St Pancras
1844	1852	....	1844	168890	NTH	Deventry
1780	1850	1780	1850	119091	OXF	Henley
1781	1852	....	....	175587	SOM	Taunton
1785	1820	1785	1820	119091	SRY	Kew
HIBBARD						
1841	1890	1700	1835	124060	NFK	Wells Next The Sea
1650	1870	1650	1900	159468	WIL	Corsham
HIBBERD						
1700	1940	....	....	127833	HAM	Portsmouth
1841	1890	1700	1835	124060	NFK	Wells Next
1550	1800	1550	1800	160849	NTT	Blyth
1780	1850	1600	1850	148288	WIL	Barford
1831	1880	1700	1831	150223	WIL	East Tisbury
1733	1796	1700	1830	105333	WIL	Salisbury
HIBBERSON						
1856	1871	1853	1856	108901	SYK	Sheffield
HIBBERT						
1755	1830	1730	1755	175986	CHS	Plemstall
1711	1730	1650	1711	175986	CHS	Prestbury
....	....	1700	1851	124060	DBY	Kings Mewton
1878	1981	1788	1878	112135	DBY	Litton
....	....	1750	1790	176036	DBY	Mellor
1821	1855	ALL	1992	159174	GLA	Coity
....	....	1790	1850	176036	KEN	Bromley
1836	1870	1790	1836	145424	MDX	Aldgate
1765	....	ALL	1992	159174	MON	Llanllowel Usk
1836	1851	1700	1835	124060	NFK	Holkham
HIBBET						
1825	....	1790	1825	173118	MON	Newport
HIBBETT						
1822	1856	?	1822	121665	LIN	Uffington
HIBBITT						
....	....	ALL	ALL	133256	RUT	ALL
1730	1870	ALL	1992	133256	RUT	Empingham
1730	1870	ALL	1992	133256	RUT	Exton
HIBBS						
1822	1992	1699	1821	118559	BDF	Sandy

Known From	To	Researching From	To	Ref	Cty	Place
HIBBS contd.						
1822	1992	1500	1821	118559	DOR	Corfe
1822	1992	1500	1821	118559	DOR	Wareham
1748	1839	....	....	127957	DOR	Winfrith Newburgh
....	....	....	1830	161667	DOR	???
1851	1992	....	....	118559	GSY	ALL
1851	1992	....	....	118559	JSY	ALL
....	....	ALL	ALL	118559	KEN	Tonbridge
1792	1862	1750	1792	149047	LAN	Manchester
1831	1881	ALL	ALL	141186	STS	Central
1831	1881	ALL	ALL	141186	STS	North
1831	1881	ALL	ALL	141186	STS	Ashton Under Lyme
1877	1877	1800	1900	117722	WAR	Dudley
HIBERNIA						
....	....	ALL	ALL	137006	ALL	Name Study
HIBLET						
....	....	1750	1850	137685	LND	???
....	....	1750	1850	137685	NFK	Gt Yarmouth
HICHCOCKE						
1742	1800	ALL	ALL	106313	OXF	Entstone
HICHENS						
1813	1850	1750	1820	125628	CON	Paul
HICK						
1708	1800	1600	1700	114162	CON	St Minver
1800	1900	....	....	114162	SOM	Bath
1738	1786	1650	1738	177393	YKS	Stillingfleet
HICKEN						
....	....	1600	1992	125857	WAR	Birmingham
HICKERSON						
1736	1758	ALL	1841	156582	MDX	Hanwell
HICKES						
1700	1799	....	....	100536	CON	???
1720	1800	....	....	157724	SFK	Groton
HICKEY						
1800	1835	1800	1850	153354	CLA	???
1881	1903	1800	1881	175722	IRL	Cork
1881	1903	1800	1881	175722	LND	Southwark
HICKFORD						
1613	1682	....	....	133299	ESS	Colchester
1581	....	....	....	133299	ESS	Frating
1572	....	....	....	133299	ESS	Great Bentley
1561	1612	....	....	133299	ESS	Great Bromley
1695	....	....	....	133299	ESS	Great Wigborough
1584	....	....	....	133299	ESS	Lamarsh
....	....	ALL	ALL	133299	HRT	Ickleford
1650	1670	....	....	133299	KEN	Ightham
1835	....	....	....	133299	LIN	Luddington
....	....	....	....	108197	SFK	Clare
1811	1830	1750	1850	126586	SFK	Clare
HICKIN						
1891	1985	....	....	149497	???	Birmingham
HICKISSON						
1880	....	....	....	127078	LND	???
1701	....	....	....	133299	WAR	Barston
HICKLAND						
1818	....	....	....	133299	LIN	Louth
1814	....	....	....	133299	LIN	Sutton St Nicholas
1323	....	....	....	133299	NFK	Hickling
1749	....	....	....	133299	WAR	Birmingham
HICKLENTON						
....	....	ALL	ALL	133299	CAM	Ickleton
1790	1810	....	....	133299	LND	Southwark
1790	1810	....	....	133299	LND	Westminster
1837	....	....	....	133299	MDX	Enfield
1660	1834	....	....	133299	NFK	Norwich
1835	....	....	....	133299	SFK	Beccles
HICKLER						
1841	....	....	....	133299	STS	Aldridge
1810	....	....	....	133299	YKS	Lythe
HICKLES						
....	1992	....	....	133299	NTH	Flore
HICKLETON						
1710	1810	....	....	133299	ESS	White Colne
1641	....	....	....	133299	NFK	Attleborough
1634	1790	....	....	133299	NFK	Great Yarmouth
1778	1850	ALL	1778	161330	NFK	Mileham
1790	1795	....	....	133299	NFK	North Elmham
1600	1823	....	....	133299	NFK	Norwich
1730	1810	....	....	133299	WAR	Southam
1730	1810	....	....	133299	WAR	Warwick
....	....	ALL	ALL	133299	YKS	Hickleton
HICKLEY						
1822	....	....	....	133299	DBY	Heanor
1822	1992	1231	1822	133272	HAM	East
HICKLEY contd.						
1822	1992	1231	1822	133272	HAM	Southampton
1136	1196	....	....	133299	HAM	Southampton
1750	1780	....	....	133299	KEN	Dover
1640	1660	....	....	133299	KEN	Lamberhurst
1630	1660	....	....	133299	KEN	Milton By Gravesend
1755	1776	....	....	133299	LEI	Broughton Astley
1849	....	....	....	133299	LEI	Lutterworth
1827	....	....	....	133299	LEI	Narborough
1792	1843	....	....	133299	LND	Spitalfields
1756	....	....	....	133299	LND	St Katherine Creechurch
1789	1829	....	....	133299	LND	St Marylebone
1828	1832	....	....	133299	LND	St Pancras
1769	....	....	....	133299	MDX	Enfield
1824	....	....	....	133299	NTH	Wollaston
1795	....	....	....	133299	NTT	Nottingham
1770	1840	....	....	133299	WAR	Birmingham
1770	1800	....	....	133299	WAR	Butlers Marston
1830	....	....	....	133299	WAR	Coventry
1830	....	....	....	133299	WAR	Kenilworth
1590	1600	....	....	133299	WAR	Wolfhamcote
1613	1872	....	....	133299	YKS	ALL
1829	....	....	....	133299	YKS	Ainderby Steeple
1796	....	....	....	133299	YKS	Barton St Cuthbert
1830	1840	....	....	133299	YKS	Bedale
1857	....	....	....	133299	YKS	Bulmer
1859	....	....	....	133299	YKS	Coatham
1620	....	....	....	133299	YKS	Easingwold
1775	....	....	....	133299	YKS	Hutton Magna
1824	....	....	....	133299	YKS	Middleton Tyas
1842	....	....	....	133299	YKS	York
HICKLIN						
....	....	ALL	ALL	133299	ALL	Name Study
1332	1992	ALL	ALL	133299	ALL	ALL
1698	....	....	....	133299	CAM	Glinton
1723	1725	....	....	133299	CAM	Northborough
1647	1737	....	....	133299	CAM	Peakirk
1820	1834	....	....	133299	DBY	Allestree
1852	....	....	....	133299	DBY	Ashford
1800	1865	....	....	133299	DBY	Barrow Upon Trent
1822	1832	....	....	133299	DBY	Belper
1770	1860	....	....	133299	DBY	Boylestone
1740	1830	....	....	133299	DBY	Brailsford
1825	1830	....	....	133299	DBY	Chesterfield
1770	1860	....	....	133299	DBY	Church Broughton
1800	1822	....	....	133299	DBY	Derby
1780	1790	....	....	133299	DBY	Doveridge
1850	1860	....	....	133299	DBY	Fairfield
1830	1865	....	....	133299	DBY	Hartshorne
1830	1860	....	....	133299	DBY	Hayfield
1770	1860	....	....	133299	DBY	Marston Upon Dove
1830	1865	....	....	133299	DBY	Newton Solney
1770	1775	....	....	133299	DBY	Sutton On The Hill
1827	....	....	....	133299	DBY	Ticknall
1735	1865	....	....	133299	DBY	Twyford
1392	....	....	....	133299	KEN	Ditton
1392	....	....	....	133299	KEN	Eylesforde
1650	1870	....	....	133299	LEI	Belton
1660	1992	....	....	133299	LEI	Breedon On The Hill
1850	1930	....	....	133299	LEI	Donington Le Heath
1850	1930	....	....	133299	LEI	Hugglescote
1660	1780	....	....	133299	LEI	Kegworth
1650	1775	....	....	133299	LEI	Leicester
1770	1780	....	....	133299	LEI	Market Bosworth
1849	....	....	....	133299	LEI	Orton On The Hill
1815	....	....	....	133299	LEI	Swithland
1600	1610	....	....	133299	LEI	Syston
1730	1780	....	....	133299	LEI	Thrussington
1841	....	....	....	133299	LIN	Louth
1727	....	....	....	133299	LND	Aldgate
1651	....	....	....	133299	LND	Bishopsgate
1640	....	....	....	133299	LND	Chelsea
1665	1820	....	....	133299	LND	Clerkenwell
1760	1768	....	....	133299	LND	Cornhill
1640	1700	....	....	133299	LND	Cripplegate
1660	1800	....	....	133299	LND	Holborn
1700	1710	....	....	133299	LND	Newgate
1620	1700	....	....	133299	LND	Putney
1819	....	....	....	133299	LND	Shoreditch
1760	1765	....	....	133299	LND	Southwark
1730	1871	....	....	133299	LND	Westminster
1700	1710	....	....	133299	LND	Whitechapel
1340	....	....	....	133299	NFK	Norwich

Known From	To	Researching From	To	Ref	Cty	Place
HICKLIN contd.						
1729	1822	....	....	133299	NTT	Burton Joyce
1950	1992	....	....	133299	NTT	Long Eaton
1791	1805	1700	1815	137235	NTT	Nottingham
1948	1975	....	....	133299	NTT	Radcliffe On Trent
1770	1820	....	....	133299	STS	Alrewas
1650	1992	....	....	133299	STS	Burton Upon Trent
1332	1333	....	....	133299	STS	Draycott In The Clay
1750	1960	....	....	133299	STS	Fazeley
1770	1820	....	....	133299	STS	Hamstall Ridware
1740	1820	....	....	133299	STS	Hanbury
1740	1820	....	....	133299	STS	Marchington
1720	1860	....	....	133299	STS	Tamworth
1790	1860	....	....	133299	STS	Tatenhill
1680	1830	....	....	133299	STS	Tutbury
1740	1800	....	....	133299	STS	Uttoxeter
1865	1910	....	....	133299	STS	Walsall
1770	1820	....	....	133299	STS	Wolverhampton
1740	1840	....	....	133299	STS	Yoxall
1800	1860	....	....	133299	WAR	Atherstone
1710	1890	....	....	133299	WAR	Bedworth
1650	1890	....	....	133299	WAR	Birmingham
1650	1850	....	....	133299	WAR	Coventry
1770	1800	....	....	133299	WAR	Kingsbury
1740	1800	....	....	133299	WAR	Mancetter
1740	1835	....	....	133299	WAR	Sutton Coldfield
1740	1890	....	....	133299	WAR	Warwick
1560	1610	....	....	133299	WAR	Wolfhamcote
1590	1620	....	....	133299	WAR	Wootton Wawen
1640	1870	....	....	133299	WOR	Dudley
1810	1860	....	....	133299	WOR	Worcester
1857	1923	....	....	133299	YKS	Shipley
HICKLING						
499	1992	....	....	133299	ALL	ALL
1482	1510	....	....	133299	BKM	Calverton
1482	1510	....	....	133299	BKM	Stoney Stratford
1896	1978	....	....	133299	BRK	Goring
1896	1978	....	....	133299	BRK	Upton
1630	1750	....	....	133299	CAM	Glinton
1742	....	....	....	133299	CAM	March
1629	1870	....	....	133299	CAM	Peakirk
1950	1989	....	....	133299	CMA	Ambleside
1970	1987	....	....	133299	CMA	Kendal
1820	1835	....	....	133299	DBY	Alfreton
1870	1965	....	....	133299	DBY	Allestree
1873	....	....	....	133299	DBY	Ault Hucknall
1849	....	....	....	133299	DBY	Beighton
1780	1992	....	....	133299	DBY	Breaston
1858	1864	....	....	133299	DBY	Codnor
1348	1992	....	....	133299	DBY	Derby
1770	1890	....	....	133299	DBY	Duffield
1900	....	....	....	142085	DBY	Elvaston
1834	1992	....	....	133299	DBY	Ilkeston
1786	1992	....	....	133299	DBY	Long Eaton
1914	....	....	....	142085	DBY	Longeaton
1855	1992	....	....	133299	DBY	Loscoe
1813	....	....	....	133299	DBY	Marston Montgomery
1366	1372	....	....	133299	DBY	Matlock
1816	1870	....	....	133299	DBY	Ockbrook
1348	....	....	....	133299	DBY	Repton
1820	1835	....	....	133299	DBY	Ripley
1786	1992	....	....	133299	DBY	Sawley
1858	1864	....	....	133299	DBY	Smalley
1816	1870	....	....	133299	DBY	Spondon
1813	1814	....	....	133299	DBY	Ticknall
1790	1800	....	....	133299	DBY	Wirksworth
1989	1992	....	....	133299	DEV	Brixham
1920	1992	....	....	133299	DEV	Budleigh Salterton
1373	....	....	....	133299	DEV	Crediton
1379	1395	....	....	133299	DEV	Exeter
1880	1966	....	....	133299	ESS	Hunsdon
1880	1992	....	....	133299	ESS	Ilford
1880	1966	....	....	133299	ESS	Roydon
1920	1992	....	....	133299	GLS	Cheltenham
1960	1992	....	....	133299	HAM	Alton
1930	1988	....	....	133299	HRT	Much Hadham
1800	1992	....	....	133299	HUM	Kingston Upon Hull
1985	1992	....	....	133299	IOW	Cowes
1389	....	....	....	133299	KEN	Ditton
1389	....	....	....	133299	KEN	Eylesford
1389	....	....	....	133299	KEN	Faversham
1550	....	....	....	133299	KEN	Seal
1578	1800	....	....	133299	LEI	Ab Kettleby
HICKLING contd.						
1790	1992	....	....	133299	LEI	Ashby De La Zouch
1770	1800	....	....	133299	LEI	Belgrave
1700	1870	....	....	133299	LEI	Belton
1829	....	....	....	133299	LEI	Blackfordby
1690	1710	....	....	133299	LEI	Branston
1730	....	....	....	133299	LEI	Buckminster
1873	1988	....	....	133299	LEI	Coalville
1660	1830	....	....	133299	LEI	Croxton Kerrial
1823	1835	....	....	133299	LEI	Donington Le Heath
1820	1830	....	....	133299	LEI	East Leake
1822	1830	....	....	133299	LEI	Enderby
1784	1823	....	....	133299	LEI	Frisby On The Wreake
1755	1780	....	....	133299	LEI	Garthorpe
1680	1830	....	....	133299	LEI	Hathern
1680	1872	....	....	133299	LEI	Hoby
1582	1730	....	....	133299	LEI	Hose
1800	1810	....	....	133299	LEI	Hoton
1823	1992	....	....	133299	LEI	Hugglescote
1642	1850	....	....	133299	LEI	Humberstone
1900	1992	....	....	133299	LEI	Ibstock
1630	1992	....	....	133299	LEI	Leicester
1842	....	....	....	133299	LEI	Lockington
1567	1830	....	....	133299	LEI	Long Clawson
1660	1713	....	....	133299	LEI	Long Whalton
1469	1992	....	....	133299	LEI	Loughborough
1827	....	....	....	133299	LEI	Lowesby
1720	1820	....	....	133299	LEI	Market Bosworth
1832	....	....	....	133299	LEI	Markfield
1680	1992	....	....	133299	LEI	Melton Mowbray
1826	1843	....	....	133299	LEI	Mountsorrel
1686	....	....	....	133299	LEI	Muston
1803	....	....	....	133299	LEI	Newbold Verdun
1820	1825	....	....	133299	LEI	Oaks In Charnwood
1832	....	....	....	133299	LEI	Orton On The Hill
1560	1828	....	....	133299	LEI	Prestwold
1761	1835	....	....	133299	LEI	Rotherby
1730	1820	....	....	133299	LEI	Rothley
1555	1678	....	....	133299	LEI	Saxelbye
1730	1820	....	....	133299	LEI	Scalford
1758	1832	....	....	133299	LEI	Seagrave
1598	1835	....	....	133299	LEI	Shepshed
1832	1835	....	....	133299	LEI	Somerby
1828	....	....	....	133299	LEI	Sutton Cheney
1750	1992	....	....	133299	LEI	Syston
1652	....	....	....	133299	LEI	Thornton
1732	1985	1500	1732	107042	LEI	Thrussington
1782	1820	....	....	133299	LEI	Thrussington
1823	1824	....	....	133299	LEI	Tilton On The Hill
1631	1830	....	....	133299	LEI	Twyford Cum Thorpe Satchville
1470	1825	....	....	133299	LEI	Walton On The Wolds
1820	1987	....	....	133299	LEI	Whitwick
1828	....	....	....	133299	LEI	Woodhouse
1560	1920	....	....	133299	LEI	Wymeswold
1680	1872	....	....	133299	LIN	Ancaster
1710	1770	....	....	133299	LIN	Asgarby By Sleaford
1850	1986	....	....	133299	LIN	Billinghay
1700	1992	....	....	133299	LIN	Boston
1800	1820	....	....	133299	LIN	Colsterworth
1650	1800	....	....	133299	LIN	Cowbit
1650	1850	....	....	133299	LIN	Crowland
1640	1992	....	....	133299	LIN	Deeping St James
1872	1890	....	....	133299	LIN	Fleet
1620	1680	....	....	133299	LIN	Gainsborough
1823	....	....	....	133299	LIN	Kirton In Holland
1814	....	....	....	133299	LIN	Legbourne
1385	1992	....	....	133299	LIN	Lincoln
1690	1722	....	....	133299	LIN	Long Sutton
1785	1992	....	....	133299	LIN	Louth
1560	1630	....	....	133299	LIN	Morton By Bourne
1713	1842	....	....	133299	LIN	Moulton Near Spalding
1816	....	....	....	133299	LIN	South Witham
1634	1992	....	....	133299	LIN	Spalding
1770	1992	....	....	133299	LIN	Stamford
1794	1830	....	....	133299	LIN	Weston
1747	1795	....	....	133299	LIN	Whaplode Drove
1817	1827	....	....	133299	LIN	Whaplode
1890	1992	....	....	133299	LIN	Wisbech
1685	1992	....	....	133299	LND	ALL
1700	1850	....	....	133299	LND	Aldgate
1938	1988	....	....	133299	LND	Camberwell

Known From	To	Researching From	To	Ref	Cty	Place
HICKLING contd.						
1852	....	....	....	133299	LND	Charterhouse
1840	....	....	....	133299	LND	Cheapside
1840	....	....	....	133299	LND	Clerkenwell
1730	1768	....	....	133299	LND	Cornhill
1800	....	....	....	133299	LND	Covent Garden
1860	1865	....	....	133299	LND	Garlickhithe
1685	1798	....	....	133299	LND	Holborn
1852	....	....	....	133299	LND	Kennington
1860	1865	....	....	133299	LND	Mounthaw
1803	1804	....	....	133299	LND	Newington
1755	1942	....	....	133299	LND	Shoreditch
1755	1814	....	....	133299	LND	Southwark
1805	1808	....	....	133299	LND	St Martins In The Fields
1834	1871	....	....	133299	LND	St Pancras
1785	1870	....	....	133299	LND	Stepney
1880	1988	....	....	133299	LND	Vauxhall
1868	1871	....	....	133299	LND	Wandsworth
1822	1871	....	....	133299	LND	Westminster
1772	1824	....	....	133299	LND	Whitechapel
1755	1815	....	....	133299	MDX	Enfield
1325	1389	....	....	133299	MDX	Woolwich
1847	1992	....	....	133299	NFK	Buxton
1588	1698	....	....	133299	NFK	Easton
1376	1992	....	....	133299	NFK	Great Yarmouth
1770	1876	....	....	133299	NFK	Hempnall
1402	1534	....	....	133299	NFK	Hickling
1730	....	....	....	133299	NFK	Ludham
1600	1642	....	....	133299	NFK	Mattishall
1487	1992	....	....	133299	NFK	Norwich
1567	1614	....	....	133299	NFK	Spixworth
1430	1441	....	....	133299	NFK	Walsingham
1520	1558	....	....	133299	NTH	Blakesley
1421	1427	....	....	133299	NTH	Clay Coton
1520	1558	....	....	133299	NTH	Cold Higham
1550	1610	....	....	133299	NTH	Greens Norton
1520	1992	....	....	133299	NTH	Northampton
1520	1558	....	....	133299	NTH	Patcote
1520	1558	....	....	133299	NTH	Silverstone
1454	....	....	....	133299	NTH	Whiston
1311	1992	....	....	133299	NTT	ALL
1770	1835	....	....	133299	NTT	Arnold
1814	1866	....	....	133299	NTT	Barton In Fabis
1850	1881	1830	1900	142085	NTT	Barton In Fabis
1829	1980	....	....	133299	NTT	Basford
1598	1780	....	....	133299	NTT	Bingham
1844	1970	....	....	133299	NTT	Bulwell
1800	1860	....	....	133299	NTT	Bunny
1659	....	....	....	133299	NTT	Clifton
1700	1986	....	....	133299	NTT	Cotgrave
1670	....	....	....	133299	NTT	Farndon
1830	1860	....	....	133299	NTT	Gedling
1800	1860	....	....	133299	NTT	Gotham
1680	1857	....	....	133299	NTT	Granby
1670	1992	....	....	133299	NTT	Hickling
1956	1986	....	....	133299	NTT	Hucknall
1770	1845	....	....	133299	NTT	Keyworth
1780	1988	....	....	133299	NTT	Kinoulton
1600	1860	....	....	133299	NTT	Lenton
1790	1830	....	....	133299	NTT	Linby
1398	1455	....	....	133299	NTT	Lindeby
1780	1988	....	....	133299	NTT	Long Eaton
1888	1992	....	....	133299	NTT	Mansfield
1400	1992	....	....	133299	NTT	Nottingham
1900	1988	....	....	133299	NTT	Nuthall
1790	1830	....	....	133299	NTT	Papplewick
1740	1860	....	....	133299	NTT	Plumtree
1750	1992	....	....	133299	NTT	Radford
1800	1940	....	....	133299	NTT	Ruddington
1800	1946	....	....	133299	NTT	Sherwood
1770	1845	....	....	133299	NTT	Stanton
1757	1881	1700	1757	130877	NTT	Sutton Bonington
1600	1988	....	....	133299	NTT	Sutton Bonington
1808	1821	1600	1840	142085	NTT	Sutton Bonnington
1464	1992	....	....	133299	NTT	Sutton In Ashfield
1770	1780	....	....	133299	NTT	West Bridgford
1740	1830	....	....	133299	NTT	West Leake
1900	1988	....	....	133299	NTT	Wilford
1763	1782	....	....	133299	NTT	Willoughby On The Wolds
1770	1992	....	....	133299	NTT	Worksop
1796	1798	....	....	133299	NTT	Wysall
1846	....	....	....	133299	OXF	Charlbury

Known From	To	Researching From	To	Ref	Cty	Place
HICKLING contd.						
1945	1992	....	....	133299	OXF	Oxford
1428	....	....	....	133299	SFK	Friston
1822	1826	....	....	133299	SFK	Gorleston With Southtown
1869	1870	....	....	133299	SFK	Halesworth
1798	1825	....	....	133299	SFK	Walsham Le Willows
1958	1992	....	....	133299	SOM	Pawlett
1960	1992	....	....	133299	SRY	Godalming
1418	....	....	....	133299	SRY	Kingston
1970	1988	....	....	133299	SSX	Chichester
1307	1345	....	....	133299	SSX	Chinting Seaford
1352	1353	....	....	133299	SSX	Horsted Keynes
1890	1992	....	....	133299	STS	Burton On Trent
1851	1930	....	....	133299	STS	Cannock Chase
1880	1950	....	....	133299	STS	Wolverhampton
1956	1992	....	....	133299	SYK	Doncaster
1828	1854	....	....	133299	WAR	Leamington
1950	1992	....	....	133299	WAR	Long Itchington
1414	1430	....	....	133299	WAR	Monks Kirby
1934	1992	....	....	133299	WAR	Sutton Coldfield
1740	1992	....	....	133299	WAR	Warwick
1680	1992	....	....	133299	WMD	Birmingham
1938	1992	....	....	133299	WMD	Coventry
1800	1992	....	....	133299	WMD	Dudley
1932	1992	....	....	133299	WMD	Solihull
1850	1992	....	....	133299	WOR	Malvern
1830	1852	....	....	133299	WYK	Horbury
1820	1992	....	....	133299	WYK	Pontefract
1850	1992	....	....	133299	WYK	Shipley
1800	1850	....	....	133299	WYK	Thornhill By Dewsbury
1950	1992	....	....	133299	YKS	Catterick Garrison
1840	1988	....	....	133299	YKS	Rawmarsh
1392	1992	....	....	133299	YKS	York
HICKLING-BURNETT						
1794	1803	....	....	133299	MDX	London
HICKLINGAM						
1676	....	....	....	133299	LIN	Welby
....	....	ALL	ALL	133299	SFK	Icklingham
1560	1590	....	....	133299	SFK	Melton
HICKMALT						
1863	....	....	....	133299	KEN	Halling
HICKMAN						
....	....	ALL	ALL	126020	BRK	ALL
1796	....	....	....	126020	BRK	Aldworth
1814	1821	....	....	133299	DBY	Belper
1778	1814	....	....	133299	DBY	Chesterfield
1837	1865	....	....	133299	DBY	Norton
1831	....	....	....	133299	DBY	Pentrich
1842	....	....	....	133299	DBY	Ticknall
1563	....	....	....	133299	ESS	Great Bromley
1576	1583	....	....	133299	ESS	Hornchurch
1818	....	....	....	133299	ESS	Saffron Walden
1812	....	....	....	133299	ESS	Woodham Walter
1790	1855	1750	1890	153249	GLS	Chipping Campden
1851	1941	1750	1851	150614	HAM	New Forest
1880	1950	1850	1950	175668	KEN	North
1740	1753	....	....	133299	KEN	Canterbury
1734	....	....	....	133299	KEN	Chevening
1661	....	....	....	133299	KEN	Dartford
1768	....	....	....	133299	KEN	Rochester
1825	....	....	....	133299	KEN	Sheerness
1768	....	....	....	133299	KEN	Strood
1790	1849	....	....	171654	LEI	Catthorpe
1657	1701	....	....	133299	LIN	Alford
1759	....	....	....	133299	LIN	Brant Broughton
1601	1692	....	....	133299	LIN	Gainsborough
1832	....	....	....	133299	LIN	Gedney Hill
1809	....	....	....	133299	LIN	Heckington
1747	....	....	....	133299	LIN	Holbeach
1654	....	....	....	133299	LIN	Louth
1841	....	....	....	133299	LIN	Surfleet
1747	....	....	....	133299	LIN	Trusthorpe
1865	1934	1865	1992	165603	LND	High Barnet
1592	1684	....	....	133299	MDX	London
1790	1831	....	....	133299	NTH	Daventry
1779	....	....	....	133299	NTH	Fawsley
1587	1871	....	....	133299	NTH	Newnham
1796	....	....	....	133299	NTH	Preston Capes
1832	....	....	....	133299	NTT	Colston Bassett
1759	....	....	....	133299	NTT	Gonalston
1825	....	....	....	133299	NTT	Hawksworth
1835	....	....	....	133299	NTT	Hickling

Known From	To	Researching From	To	Ref	Cty	Place
HICKMAN contd.						
1683	1689	....	....	133299	NTT	Kilvington
1674	1813	....	....	133299	NTT	Lowdham
1702	....	....	....	133299	NTT	Misterton
1779	1816	....	....	133299	NTT	Nottingham
1823	....	....	....	133299	NTT	Orston
1786	1800	....	....	133299	SFK	Lavenham
1764	1819	....	....	133299	SFK	Sudbury
1796	1814	....	....	133299	SFK	Wattisfield
1833	1851	1833	1851	160164	SOM	Buckland St Mary
1850	1880	1800	1920	175668	SSX	Hastings
1780	1790	....	....	103764	STS	Penn
1803	1828	1700	1900	178322	STS	Sedgley
1793	1861	....	....	133299	WAR	Birmingham
1738	....	....	....	133299	WAR	Sheldon
1573	....	....	....	133299	WAR	Wolfamcote
1810	1840	1800	1850	103764	WOR	Dudley
1849	1854	....	....	133299	WOR	Dudley
1660	1838	....	....	133299	WOR	Old Swinford
1600	1992	1300	1600	170194	WOR	Oldswinford
1728	1859	....	....	133299	WOR	Worcester
1835	....	....	....	133299	YKS	Ecclesfield
1825	1826	....	....	133299	YKS	Emley
1822	1829	....	....	133299	YKS	Fulford
1822	1858	....	....	133299	YKS	Kingston Upon Hull
1663	....	....	....	133299	YKS	Kirk Deighton
1814	1821	....	....	133299	YKS	Rotherham
1687	1858	....	....	133299	YKS	Sheffield
1795	1859	....	....	133299	YKS	York
1865	1934	1865	1992	165603	YKS	???
1898	1934	....	1934	134724	???	Birmingham
HICKMANS						
1500	1736	1500	1736	102830	STS	Sedgely
1687	....	....	....	133299	STS	Sedgley
1805	1823	1700	1805	149977	STS	Sedgley
1520	1786	1500	1800	160873	STS	Sedgley
1803	1869	1700	1800	169854	STS	Sedgley
1736	1816	1700	1840	160873	STS	Womborne
1868	....	....	....	133299	WOR	Cradley
1598	1783	....	....	133299	WOR	Dudley
1569	....	....	....	133299	WOR	Halesowen
1626	1632	....	....	133299	WOR	Old Swinford
1658	1668	....	....	133299	WOR	Worcester
HICKMAR						
1740	1820	ALL	1740	115282	SSX	East
HICKS						
....	....	ALL	ALL	107409	ALL	Name Study
1767	1767	1690	1800	107360	BKM	Bierton
1802	1857	1760	1860	107360	BKM	Stone
1824	1881	....	....	117374	BRK	Thatcham
1691	1940	....	....	128996	CAM	Thorney
1829	....	....	....	153885	CON	Bodmin
1860	1992	1700	1961	133337	CON	Dobwalls
1860	1992	1700	1961	133337	CON	Falmouth
1860	1992	1700	1961	133337	CON	Fowey
1800	1850	1700	1850	156442	CON	Fowey
1830	1908	....	....	133302	CON	Illogan
....	....	1720	1800	177725	CON	Jacobstow
1772	1824	....	....	147915	CON	Looe
1696	....	....	....	133302	CON	Mawgan In Pydar
1650	1748	1650	1748	133310	CON	Mawgan In Pydar
1862	....	ALL	ALL	110272	CON	North Petherwin
1800	1880	1600	1800	133329	CON	Polperro
1772	1883	1772	1883	133310	CON	Redruth
1795	1800	1775	1825	133450	CON	Roche
1749	1771	1749	1771	133310	CON	St Austell
1642	1860	1600	1860	153591	CON	St Buryan
1660	....	....	....	133302	CON	St Colomb Major
1696	1740	1700	1800	178845	CON	St Ervan
1728	1770	....	....	133302	CON	St Eval
1650	1748	1650	1748	133310	CON	St Eval
1696	1740	1700	1800	178845	CON	St Eval
1800	1900	1800	1900	171077	CON	St Issey
1642	1860	1600	1860	153591	CON	St Just
1798	....	....	....	133302	CON	St Wenn
1854	1917	....	....	133302	CON	Tuckingmill
1690	1890	....	1690	101168	CON	Uskeard
1800	1841	1700	1800	154040	DEV	Berrynarbor
1841	1861	1841	1992	154040	DEV	Combe Martin
....	....	1700	1800	156795	DOR	North
....	....	1880	1914	169722	DOR	Poole
....	....	1870	1992	161489	ENG	South
1744	1947	1600	1744	137553	ESS	North
1770	1850	1600	1800	127833	ESS	West

Known From	To	Researching From	To	Ref	Cty	Place
HICKS contd.						
1898	1952	ALL	ALL	123013	GLA	Cardiff
1820	1992	1650	1820	151092	GLS	Cheltenham
1983	1992	....	....	133302	GLS	Gloucester
1643	1810	....	....	165999	GLS	Henbury
1790	1970	1790	1970	176567	GSY	St Peter Port
1828	1849	1850	1992	161489	HRT	Willian
1820	1850	1800	1900	111325	KEN	Greenwich
1767	1767	....	....	121355	LND	Shoreditch
1883	1920	1883	1920	133310	LND	Southwark
1800	1860	ALL	ALL	149004	LND	Southwark
1816	1891	1700	1992	170054	LND	Southwark
1920	1984	1920	1984	133310	LND	Streatham
1870	1960	1700	1870	149357	MON	Newport
1893	1921	....	....	133302	MON	Sudbrook
1790	1822	1790	1822	108251	NFK	Sea Palling
1847	1848	1847	1848	119636	NFK	Wells
1784	1797	1766	1784	122572	NTT	ALL
1857	....	ALL	1879	123013	OXF	Thrupp
1656	1947	1500	1656	137553	SFK	South
1820	?	ALL	ALL	153516	SOM	Banwell
1829	1900	1700	1829	145459	SOM	Bath
1820	?	ALL	ALL	153516	SOM	Hewish
1800	1881	1700	1800	148997	SOM	Keynsham
....	....	ALL	1850	138169	SOM	Lympsham
1820	?	ALL	ALL	153516	SOM	Wick St Lawrence
1790	1970	1790	1970	176567	SOM	Yeovil
1825	1835	1825	1835	120405	SSX	Ninfield
1782	1826	1700	1826	120405	SSX	Ticehurst
1826	1877	1826	1900	120405	SSX	Wartling
1914	1940	....	....	169722	WIL	West
1879	....	1879	1899	123013	WIL	Wroughton
ALL	ALL	....	....	171972	YKS	North
1923	1983	....	....	133302	???	Bristol
HICKSON						
1770	1810	1700	1850	110906	BKM	Marsh Gibbon
1832	1892	1800	1832	117196	CHS	Congleton
1781	1829	1700	1781	160024	CHS	Great Budworth
1925	1925	1992	1992	149543	SSX	Brighton
HICKTON						
1657	1992	ALL	ALL	133345	NTT	Skegby
HIDE						
1700	1710	1650	1700	108413	GLS	Painswick
1650	1850	....	....	138037	HRT	North East
....	....	?	....	128589	HRT	Hitchin
1850	1900	ALL	ALL	130664	KEN	Bexley Heath
1840	1925	ALL	1850	142301	MDX	London
1735	1992	ALL	ALL	130664	SSX	Easebourne
HIDEN						
1838	1856	1800	1838	108391	MDX	London
HIDER						
1740	1950	1750	1800	103446	SSX	Withyham
HIDSON						
1845	1950	....	....	172170	MDX	London
1800	1845	1750	1800	172170	WAR	Birmingham
HIERON						
....	....	ALL	1800	178403	DBY	???
....	....	ALL	1800	178403	DEV	???
1870	1992	1870	1950	133353	GLS	Bristol
1640	1960	1650	1950	133353	GLS	Minchinhampton
HIGBID						
1896	....	1860	....	167290	MDX	Mary Le Bone
HIGGENBOTHAM						
1700	1800	1700	1800	152404	CHS	Stockport
HIGGENS						
1680	1700	1680	1700	142018	GLS	???
1698	1730	1680	1750	142018	WIL	Salisbury
HIGGESON						
1817	1817	1817	1992	174262	WAR	Birmingham
HIGGIE						
....	....	1850	1950	137685	LND	Sydenham
HIGGIN						
1700	1900	1720	1900	178047	LAN	Lancaster
1580	1750	....	....	133388	YKS	Barnoldswick
HIGGINBOTHAM						
1779	1785	1700	1779	114472	CHS	Pott Shrigley
1750	1821	....	....	138851	CHS	Werneth
HIGGINBOTTOM						
....	....	1700	1992	171689	DBY	Chesterfield
....	....	1920	1932	130036	LAN	Manchester
1837	1910	1800	1910	130036	STS	Blythe
....	1832	....	1850	160873	YKS	York
HIGGINS						
1790	1900	ALL	ALL	133361	BKM	ALL

Known From	To	Researching From	To	Ref	Cty	Place
HIGGINS contd.						
....	....	1780	1880	133388	CHS	Chester
1840	1900	....	....	133388	CHS	Hyde
1797	1830	1760	1800	173118	DOR	Ryme Intrinsica
1881	1992	1500	1881	141089	ESS	Loughton
1581	1607	1574	1646	142859	GLS	Kings Stanley
1900	1992	....	....	133361	HRT	Hemel Hempstead
....	....	1800	1899	104884	IRL	Longford
1698	1874	1678	1874	144355	KEN	South
1845	1992	1800	1845	113964	LEI	Leicester
1640	1723	1640	1690	156817	LEI	Loughborough
1757	....	ALL	ALL	110272	SOM	Baltonsborough
1850	1900	1700	1850	154458	SOM	Baltonsborough
1820	1851	....	....	152722	SOM	Butleigh
1820	....	....	....	152722	SOM	Glastonbury
1804	1824	1700	1992	150835	TYR	???
1800	1992	1700	1992	177652	WAR	Aston
1580	1812	....	....	133388	YKS	ALL
1690	1812	....	....	133388	YKS	Bradford
1690	1812	....	....	133388	YKS	Halifax
....	....	1580	1812	133388	YKS	Leeds
1580	1850	....	....	133388	YKS	Pontefract
1814	1893	1750	1840	163740	YKS	Pontefract
1790	1850	....	....	133388	YKS	Wakefield
HIGGINSON						
1863	....	1863	....	147486	LAN	Crumpsall
1837	....	1837	....	147486	LAN	Preston
1850	1920	ALL	1850	122572	LEI	ALL
1850	1920	ALL	1850	122572	LND	ALL
1840	1875	ALL	1840	102016	MDX	Marlyebone
1713	....	1700	1750	163775	MDX	Stepney
....	....	1700	1850	154458	SAL	???
1850	1950	....	....	154458	WAR	Birmingham
HIGGITT						
....	....	ALL	1875	173177	STS	Rugeley
HIGGLETON						
1826	1960	1700	1826	133582	ESS	Earlscolne
HIGGON						
1850	....	1700	1850	161780	PEM	Haverfordwest
HIGGS						
1800	1900	1800	1900	177571	BKM	Loughton
1725	1825	....	1725	135089	BRK	Basildon
1786	1851	....	1880	171441	BRK	Buckland
1788	1820	....	1820	171441	BRK	New Windsor
1750	1770	1700	1800	136840	HAM	Fordingbridge
1780	1795	1760	1800	142174	KEN	North
....	....	1700	1800	135089	LEI	S Kilworth
1850	1992	....	....	135089	LND	North
1910	1980	1700	1910	112739	LND	Bethnal Green
1794	1992	1600	1794	160342	OXF	South Stoke
....	....	1500	1760	133426	SAL	East
....	....	1500	1760	133426	STS	South
1708	1906	1700	1992	133426	STS	Penn
....	....	1660	1900	133426	STS	Tettenhall
1675	1807	1807	1900	133426	STS	Trysull
1871	1928	1871	1992	133426	STS	Wednesbury
1836	1881	1881	1992	133426	STS	Willenhall
....	....	1600	1900	133426	STS	Wolverhampton
1830	1992	1700	1830	115444	WMD	Wednesbury
1807	1851	1700	1900	178322	WOR	Halesowen
HIGH						
1850	1992	1800	1850	174653	ANS	Dundee
1814	1871	ALL	1814	167878	KEN	ALL
1720	1825	1650	1720	169021	LAN	Torver
1800	1870	1700	1800	117463	NFK	North East
1847	1877	1700	1847	160601	NFK	Hempnall
HIGHAM						
1700	1700	1650	1750	159107	CAM	Elm
1830	1876	....	1830	133434	CHS	Cheadle Hulme
1645	1992	1500	1645	170569	CHS	Cheadle
....	1800	1800	1850	126659	CHS	Gawsworth
1760	1770	ALL	1760	141224	GLS	Westerleigh
1786	1817	ALL	ALL	154067	KEN	Swanscombe
1706	1717	1650	1706	163783	LAN	Goosnargh
1900	1925	1895	1930	129879	LAN	Leyland
1845	1864	1800	1880	120901	LAN	Mawdesley
1920	1992	1900	1992	129879	LAN	Preston
1730	1830	1730	1800	126500	LAN	Wigan
1730	1830	....	....	126497	LAN	Wigan
1780	1800	ALL	ALL	154067	LND	Spitalfields
1775	1800	ALL	ALL	154067	SRY	Christchurch
1781	1804	1781	1804	136808	YKS	Aldbrough
HIGHGATE						
1800	1992	ALL	1800	158445	SSX	Nuthurst
HIGHGATE contd.						
1800	1992	ALL	1800	158445	SSX	Rusper
HIGHLAND						
1930	1992	1500	1930	140279	CON	Bodmin
1834	1992	1700	1840	161772	IRL	???
HIGHLEY						
1851	1915	1841	1950	133442	KEN	Sheerness
1826	1840	1790	1826	133442	MON	Chapel Hill
HIGHT						
1924	....	ALL	ALL	107425	ESS	East Ham
HIGHTON						
1890	....	1850	....	110264	INV	???
HIGHWOOD						
1796	1836	ALL	1836	168696	SOM	Weston Super Mare
HIGMAN						
1550	1992	ALL	1992	133450	ALL	ALL
....	....	ALL	1992	119873	CON	Roche
....	....	ALL	1992	119873	CON	St Austell
HIGNELL						
....	....	1700	1850	133469	GLS	Central
....	....	1700	1850	133469	GLS	South
....	....	1700	1850	133469	GLS	Bristol
....	....	1700	1850	133469	GLS	Cirencester
....	....	1700	1850	133469	GLS	Elberton
....	....	1700	1850	133469	GLS	Old Sodbury
....	....	1700	1850	133469	GLS	Olveston
....	....	1700	1850	133469	GLS	Thornbury
....	....	ALL	ALL	117390	???	???
HIGNETT						
1850	1870	1800	1870	161292	CHS	Runcorn
1746	1992	....	....	133477	SAL	Pontesbury
HIGSON						
1860	....	1840	1890	117145	LAN	Bolton
1800	1850	1700	1850	120219	LAN	Bolton
1804	....	1750	1850	179078	LAN	Bury
1758	1782	....	....	118729	LAN	Leigh
1811	1850	1750	1890	174998	WYK	Waddington
HIGTON						
1705	1900	1600	1700	116408	STS	Wetton
1850	1992	....	....	116408	WAR	Birmingham
HILBERD						
1740	1800	....	....	129747	LIN	Scothorne
HILBORNE						
....	....	ALL	ALL	168866	ALL	Name Study
HILDER						
....	....	ALL	ALL	133485	ALL	Name Study
1300	1992	900	1992	133485	ALL	ALL
1750	1850	1850	1900	143898	SSX	Battle
1714	1952	1500	1714	110310	SSX	Salehurst
1750	1850	1850	1900	143898	SSX	Whatlington
1690	1920	1600	1690	109533	SSX	???
1832	1894	1800	1900	167002	SXE	Salehurst
HILDITCH						
1800	1850	1700	1800	118702	CWD	Llandyrnog
HILES						
ALL	ALL	....	....	153397	ALL	ALL
HILEY						
....	....	1700	1886	120278	EYK	Kingston Upon Hull
1850	1992	1700	1850	123730	LAN	Salford
1750	1810	1600	1800	144657	LIN	Caistor
1780	1840	1600	1800	144657	LIN	Gainsborough
1800	1870	1800	1900	144657	LIN	Lincoln
1800	1880	1700	1900	144657	LIN	Spalding
1850	1960	1700	1850	114685	MON	Llanwenarth
1850	1960	1700	1850	114685	MON	Trevithen
1880	1992	ALL	1880	112771	NTT	East Retford
1800	1992	1700	1800	157708	STS	Burton On Trent
1790	1992	1600	1790	123730	YKS	Honley
HILIER						
1790	1905	1600	1800	112747	WIL	Central
HILL EARLE						
....	....	1750	1840	153923	DEV	Loddiswell
....	....	1840	1895	153923	JSY	St Helier
HILL						
1829	1841	ALL	1829	121827	ALL	ALL
1900	1980	1500	1900	119792	ANT	ALL
1850	1857	1845	1889	108278	ANT	Belfast
1826	1911	1700	1826	134732	ANT	Lough Neagh
1763	1992	ALL	ALL	146366	BEW	Duns
1650	1750	1600	1900	177180	BKM	Chesham
1879	1992	1800	1992	161640	BKM	Little Brickhill
1700	1760	1500	1760	137472	BRK	Compton
1700	1760	1500	1760	137472	BRK	Hampstead Norreys
1700	1760	1500	1760	137472	BRK	Norris

Known From	To	Researching From	To	Ref	Cty	Place
HILL contd.						
1654	1940	....	....	128996	CAM	Thorney
1773	....	ALL	ALL	110477	CAM	Wisbech
1940	1992	1700	1940	105007	CHS	Crewe
1838	1887	?	?	124788	CHS	Dukinfield
1830	1841	1810	1850	126705	CHS	Runcorn
1700	1800	ALL	ALL	172812	CON	ALL
1722	1795	ALL	1795	168696	CON	East
1800	1900	1800	1900	178047	CON	Camelford
1790	1910	1790	1910	110523	CON	Manaccan
1850	1992	1700	1850	160997	CON	Wadebridge
....	....	1900	1992	161829	CON	???
1874	1992	1750	1874	159212	CUL	Camerton
....	....	1700	1992	171689	DBY	Chesterfield
1700	1790	1600	1700	172901	DBY	S Wingfield
1832	1845	?	1832	128910	DBY	Swanwick
1672	1992	1600	1672	133531	DBY	Ticknall
1661	1661	1550	1700	105333	DEV	Buckland In The Moor
1661	1661	1550	1700	105333	DEV	Holne
1661	1661	1550	1700	105333	DEV	Ilsington
1661	1661	1550	1700	105333	DEV	Lydford
1800	....	1750	1800	165689	DEV	Plymouth
1816	1875	1700	1816	165859	DEV	Spreyton
1709	1900	1660	1709	133523	DEV	Tavistock
1661	1661	1550	1700	105333	DEV	Widecombe In The Moor
1730	1850	1600	1800	173223	DOR	???
1770	1970	....	1770	142409	ENG	Midlands
1640	1769	....	....	165999	GLS	Badgeworth
1715	ALL	....	....	142158	GLS	Berkeley
1800	1850	1800	1850	106631	GLS	Bisley
1792	....	....	....	142859	GLS	Bisley
1800	1880	1600	1800	169773	GLS	Cam
1640	1769	....	....	165999	GLS	Charlton Kings
1850	1880	1800	1880	147478	GLS	Coaley
1850	1880	1800	1880	147478	GLS	Dursley
1800	1850	1600	1800	169773	GLS	Dursley
1654	1808	....	....	165999	GLS	Dymock
1700	1700	1650	1700	148938	GLS	Fretherne
1654	1808	....	....	165999	GLS	Hasfield
1794	....	....	1820	171441	GLS	Newnham
1744	1808	1700	1900	157171	GLS	Preston
1800	1840	1750	1992	173096	GLS	Uley
1891	1921	1800	1891	155144	HAM	Portsmouth
1730	1850	1600	1750	127833	HRT	East
1650	1750	1600	1900	177180	HRT	Bovington
1850	1880	1830	1900	111325	HRT	Hertford
1789	1836	....	1789	142166	HRT	Walkern
....	1780	ALL	1780	152889	HUN	St Neots
1860	1900	1860	1900	110523	IOM	Braddan
1867	1992	1800	1900	128384	IRL	Cork
1841	1856	1834	1860	100048	KEN	Chatham
....	....	1759	1992	121940	LAN	Culcheth
1591	1619	ALL	ALL	141615	LAN	Ormskirk
1855	....	ALL	ALL	138533	LAN	Poulton Le Sands
1732	1950	1648	1750	138304	LAN	Rochdale
....	....	1700	1900	130931	LAN	Warrington
1850	1905	1800	1905	122238	LAN	Winwick
1813	1868	1800	1900	116173	LEI	Leicester
1676	1676	1600	1676	174130	LEI	Shearsby
1750	1820	1750	1890	103721	LIN	Belton In Axholme
1780	1870	....	....	103721	LIN	Epworth
1814	1839	1700	1814	139386	LIN	Gainsborough
1790	....	1750	1800	170348	LIN	Marton
1670	1750	....	....	103721	LIN	Owston
1800	1850	1800	1850	123765	LIN	Withern
....	....	1830	....	174963	LIN	???
1877	1901	1901	1992	146560	LKS	Coatbride
1891	1992	?	1891	156337	LND	Fulham
?	1854	ALL	1807	100897	LND	Lambeth
1800	1870	1700	1800	172898	LND	Lambeth
1912	1965	1700	1830	133582	LND	Lewisham
1880	1980	1860	1980	145009	LND	Pacras
1850	1880	1800	1850	113816	LND	Poplar
....	....	1850	1914	173355	LND	Wandsworth
1820	1910	1780	1820	177814	MDX	Shorditch
1842	....	1830	1842	176885	MDX	St Clement Danes
1814	1834	....	....	100048	MIL	Army 46th & 53rd Foot
1809	1812	....	....	100048	MIL	Royal Marines HMS Sceptre
1790	1810	1780	1830	176982	MLN	Edinburgh
1808	1830	1800	1850	178004	MON	Pontypool

Known From	To	Researching From	To	Ref	Cty	Place
HILL contd.						
1660	1992	....	....	104531	NFK	Central
1716	1716	....	....	135437	NFK	N Elmham
1702	1840	ALL	1797	115126	NTH	Kingsthorpe
1840	1890	1830	1900	106569	NTT	Beckingham
1660	1680	1600	1660	121339	NYK	Lythe
1735	1800	....	....	132756	SAL	Madeley
1774	1841	....	....	155055	SAL	Madeley
....	....	1700	1940	105007	SAL	???
1900	....	....	....	151416	SCT	Edinburgh
1688	....	1600	1690	152110	SFK	Glemsford
1855	1866	1800	1900	121568	SOM	North East
1817	....	1800	1842	176885	SOM	Bath
1800	1850	1800	1850	100862	SOM	Bristol
1903	1940	1900	1940	152935	SOM	Compton Dando
1740	1871	1700	1992	178020	SOM	Lydeard St Lawrence
1774	1813	1750	1813	107573	SOM	Wiveliscombe
1740	1871	1700	1992	178020	SOM	Wiveliscombe
1830	1912	1700	1830	133582	SRY	Bermondsey
1810	1835	1700	1810	132640	SRY	Lambeth
1755	1992	....	1755	133566	SRY	Merton
1867	1956	1700	1866	153664	SRY	???
1700	1750	1700	1750	152404	SSX	Rodgwick
1860	1860	1750	1860	171662	STI	St Ninians
....	....	1800	1870	137111	STS	Bilston
1655	1707	1600	1730	160873	STS	Kingswinford
....	....	1750	1874	159212	STS	Netherton
1829	1870	1700	1829	133493	STS	Wednesbury
....	....	1700	1940	105007	STS	???
1888	1992	1700	1888	100110	SYK	Kimberworth
1820	1881	1841	1881	108901	SYK	Sheffield
1890	1898	ALL	ALL	115002	WAR	Birmingham
1800	1937	1800	1937	140724	WAR	Birmingham
1787	....	ALL	1992	159174	WAR	Birmingham
1793	1992	ALL	1793	174262	WAR	Birmingham
1741	1741	1700	1745	124974	WIL	Ramsbury
1689	1709	1670	1720	142018	WIL	Salisbury
1721	1747	1700	1750	159107	WOR	Bellbroughton
1721	....	1690	1730	160873	WOR	Holt
1800	1900	1800	1900	173681	WOR	Lye
1828	1920	....	1920	171441	WOR	Worcester
1750	1900	ALL	1900	151319	WRY	Doncaster
1738	1992	1650	1738	102342	WRY	Snaith
1794	1840	1700	1850	133574	YKS	Barwick In Elmet
1725	1740	1700	1992	114901	YKS	Bilton
1715	1731	....	1731	109622	YKS	Cherry Burton
1851	1871	1840	1880	133574	YKS	Horsforth
1825	1887	1825	1910	130974	YKS	Hunslett
1731	1888	....	....	109622	YKS	Laxton
....	....	1825	1900	141984	YKS	Monk Fryston
1880	1900	1870	1920	133574	YKS	Pool In Wharfdale
1726	1992	....	....	134619	YKS	Poppleton
1792	....	ALL	1792	102350	YKS	Sherburn In Elmet
....	....	1700	1850	141984	YKS	Sherburn In Elmet
1815	1825	1700	1825	130974	YKS	Thornhill
1791	1811	ALL	ALL	159026	YKS	Treeton
1866	1897	1800	1900	160644	???	Bristol
HILL-COTTINGHAM						
1860	1992	1860	1950	171638	ALL	ALL
HILLARY						
....	....	....	....	157368	???	North
HILLAS						
1625	1700	....	....	100099	WRY	???
HILLER						
....	1800	....	....	174564	KEN	???
HILLHOUSE						
1812	1900	1800	1950	144037	DNB	Old Kilpatrick
HILLIAM						
1762	1940	....	....	128996	CAM	Thorney
HILLIARD						
....	....	ALL	ALL	174963	BDF	Shillington
1837	....	....	....	167444	BRK	Basildon
1780	....	....	....	140082	LND	Gunnersbury
1855	....	1537	1619	140082	LND	???
....	....	1854	....	174963	LND	???
1825	1855	....	....	140082	MDX	Holborn
1800	1840	1840	....	147184	SRY	Mortlake
HILLIEAR						
1770	....	....	....	133779	WIL	Fittleton
HILLIER						
1705	1705	1670	1705	108510	BRK	Wokingham
1796	1820	....	....	174319	HAM	Andover
1829	1910	ALL	1830	149446	HAM	Binstead
1895	....	1850	1918	152099	SRY	Battersea

Known From	To	Researching From	To	Ref	Cty	Place
HILLIER contd.						
1500	1900	1500	1900	170216	WIL	ALL
1770	....	ALL	ALL	116394	WIL	Bowood
1903	1992	1648	1903	133604	WIL	Bremhill
....	1910	....	....	126276	WIL	Calne
1813	1859	ALL	1813	167878	WIL	Cholderton
1830	1860	1800	1900	162345	WIL	Devizes
1903	1992	1648	1903	133604	WIL	Foxham
1770	1950	1650	1800	101834	WIL	Marlborough
1800	1992	....	....	122491	???	Bristol
HILLIKER						
....	....	ALL	ALL	133612	ALL	Name Study
HILLING						
1840	....	1770	1840	119938	NFK	Loddon
HILLINGWORTH						
....	....	1800	1900	140236	YKS	Morley
HILLMAN						
1800	1900	ALL	ALL	131873	LND	East
1500	1850	1400	1800	144657	SOM	Banwell
1837	1970	1700	1970	146293	SOM	Bath
1500	1800	1400	1800	144657	SOM	Congresbury
1808	1872	ALL	ALL	153516	SOM	Worle
1800	1850	ALL	ALL	131873	YKS	Sculcoates
HILLMEN						
1847	1847	1800	1900	142921	NTT	Nottingham
HILLS						
....	....	....	1750	137405	CAM	Rampton
1826	1903	ALL	1826	159077	CUL	Carlisle
1880	1920	1800	1992	145556	ESS	Southend
1880	1992	1850	1992	126799	ESS	West Ham
1715	....	ALL	1750	102016	HAM	Southampton
....	....	1820	1824	133620	IRL	Dublin
1851	1900	1780	1992	116297	KEN	Bobbing
1675	1745	ALL	1992	132055	KEN	Canterbury
1784	1830	....	....	133620	KEN	Deal
1775	1950	1775	1992	106798	KEN	Doddington
1577	1815	....	....	133620	KEN	Sandwich
1870	1900	1800	1900	116297	KEN	Sittingbourne
1790	1950	1600	1790	127345	KEN	???
1786	....	?	1790	103934	LND	Edmonton
1835	1875	....	....	133620	LND	Rotherhithe
1875	1900	....	....	133620	LND	Wapping
1800	1900	1800	1900	130044	MDX	London
1826	1887	1800	1900	126799	NFK	Upwell
1770	1826	1700	1900	126799	SFK	Mildenhall
....	....	1600	1900	102318	SRY	East
....	....	ALL	1860	178403	SSX	Pulborough
1800	1900	1800	1992	165603	YKS	Yarm
HILLYARD						
....	....	ALL	ALL	174963	BDF	Shillington
1776	1992	1700	1776	152684	NTH	Central
HILLYER						
1772	1850	1750	1850	159581	SRY	West Horsley
1772	1850	1750	1850	159581	SRY	Worplesdon
HILMAN						
1744	1844	1700	1992	117609	DEV	Torquay
HILSDEN						
1811	1830	....	1811	136212	CAM	Cambridge
HILSON						
1800	1900	1800	1992	110965	ROX	ALL
HILTON						
1780	1825	1720	1850	125032	BRK	Finchampstead
1796	1819	1760	1830	159905	DUR	South Shields
1930	1992	ALL	1930	115428	DUR	???
1800	1855	1750	1860	171549	LAN	Ashton Under Lyne
1700	1750	1600	1700	155500	LAN	Leigh
1850	1900	....	....	122238	LAN	Lowton
1760	1992	....	....	138231	LAN	Manchester
1832	1898	1800	1832	175447	LAN	Middleston
1868	1918	1840	1944	133639	LAN	Oldham
1815	1872	1700	1872	174998	LAN	Preston
1787	1900	1700	1800	159964	LAN	Ringley
1766	1805	ALL	1766	146226	LAN	Whitefield
....	....	1700	1800	110914	LAN	Wigan
1800	1900	1881	1893	149322	LAN	Wigan
1705	1776	1600	1700	118958	LAN	???
1759	....	....	....	127795	SSX	Berwick
....	....	1700	1807	149977	STS	Tamworth
1807	1870	....	....	149977	STS	Wolverhampton
1715	1731	1650	1731	141097	YKS	Braithwell
1831	....	1800	1992	103837	YKS	Hull
HILYEAR						
1820	1820	1750	1820	174599	DOR	Shaftesbury

Known From	To	Researching From	To	Ref	Cty	Place
HIME						
1790	1933	1790	1992	164984	ALL	ALL
1790	1933	1790	1992	164984	LAN	Liverpool
HIMMINS						
....	....	ALL	1900	115908	ALL	ALL
HIMPFEN						
1880	1992	1880	1992	153052	ENG	ALL
HINCE						
1940	1992	1500	1940	119792	SAL	ALL
HINCHCLIFF						
1830	1950	1700	1830	108790	YKS	Skelmanthorpe
HINCHCLIFFE						
1750	1850	1800	1950	135801	YKS	Sheffield
HINCHLIFF						
1759	1802	1700	1900	109290	YKS	Sheffield
HINCHLIFFE						
ALL	1782	ALL	1782	149403	LND	???
1871	1992	1800	1871	109509	WYK	Holmfirth
1860	1992	1700	1850	120596	WYK	???
1830	1900	1830	1900	144290	YKS	Doncaster
1851	1992	1851	1992	104612	YKS	Hinchliffe Mill
1639	1943	1600	1639	133760	YKS	Holmfirth
1851	1992	1851	1992	104612	YKS	Huddersfield
1850	1992	ALL	1850	143022	YKS	Huddersfield
1730	1900	1500	1950	114898	YKS	Meltham
1900	1992	1800	1992	132810	YKS	Meltham
1798	1880	1700	1992	151521	YKS	Penistone
1835	1992	1700	1835	133647	YKS	Pudsey
1730	1900	1500	1950	114898	YKS	Ramsden
1798	1880	1700	1992	151521	YKS	Sheffield
1805	1881	1700	1881	163902	YKS	Sheffield
HINCKINGTON						
1865	1865	1800	1875	136042	HAM	Sopley
HINCKLEY						
1878	1953	....	....	107174	CON	Hayles
HIND						
1731	....	....	1740	171441	KEN	Canterbury
1800	1980	ALL	1900	115347	LAN	ALL
1803	1881	1800	1880	136565	LAN	Preston
1793	1871	ALL	1793	145335	NTT	Eakring
1778	1871	1871	1992	145335	NTT	Farnsfield
1825	1890	1800	1900	103128	NTT	Nottingham
....	....	1750	1855	135410	NTT	Nottingham
1890	1992	....	....	115479	NTT	Selston
1737	1759	1700	1760	170348	NTT	Sturton Cum Fenton
....	1818	?	1818	128910	NTT	Warsop
1600	1652	....	....	115819	SAL	Newport
1639	1796	1600	1992	122211	SRY	Lambeth
1775	1800	1700	1800	136565	WES	Burton In Kendal
....	....	1820	1900	135410	???	London
HINDE						
1830	1900	1700	1900	140171	DOR	Portland
1819	1829	....	....	141097	YKS	Braithwell
HINDER						
1711	1805	1670	1720	170348	WIL	Purton
HINDES						
1797	1830	1700	1900	126586	LAN	???
1806	1992	1800	1992	172995	LND	Hackney
1783	1860	1700	1840	133701	SFK	Eye District
HINDHAUGH						
1660	1812	1660	1992	159980	NBL	Rothbury
HINDLE						
1848	1939	1800	1848	160474	LAN	Blackburn
1750	1900	1750	1900	125237	LAN	Darwen
1800	1880	1880	1992	162256	LAN	Darwen
1575	....	1575	....	109347	LAN	Downham
1800	1900	1700	1800	132268	LAN	Haslingden
1764	1916	1500	1916	169439	LAN	Haslingden
1799	1925	1750	1880	172855	LAN	Haslington
1750	1790	1700	1750	122904	LAN	Padiham
1880	1992	1800	1900	134481	LAN	Stalybridge
HINDLEY						
1800	1820	1700	1850	159964	LAN	Middle Hulton
1870	1960	1700	1992	126349	STS	Hednesford
HINDMARSH						
1850	1930	1850	1992	160156	DUR	Gateshead
1700	1900	....	....	116998	KEN	ALL
1700	1900	....	....	116998	NBL	ALL
1795	1850	1700	1850	160156	NBL	Hexham
....	....	ALL	ALL	178691	NTH	Hexham
HINDS						
1810	1960	1810	1960	161705	DBY	Derby
1865	1952	1800	1865	113352	KEN	Cliffe
....	....	1713	1734	130060	KEN	Hawkhurst

Known From	To	Researching From	To	Ref	Cty	Place
HINDS contd.						
1767	....	1700	1770	130443	MDX	Pinner
1800	....	....	....	152722	NTT	Hockley
1820	1850	1700	1820	133167	WAR	Oldbury
HINDSON						
....	1807	1700	1807	140678	CUL	Culgaith
1774	1992	1700	1800	135550	CUL	Eden Valley
....	1807	1700	1807	140678	CUL	K. Thore
1774	1992	1700	1800	135550	WES	Eden Valley
HINE						
1600	1850	....	....	133698	BRK	Brimpton
1750	1992	ALL	ALL	101281	DEV	ALL
1750	1992	ALL	ALL	101281	DOR	ALL
1700	....	ALL	ALL	126098	DOR	South
1500	1850	....	....	133698	HAM	Kingsclere
....	....	1800	1850	137111	KEN	Woolwich
1850	1950	....	....	133698	MDX	Fulham
1850	1950	....	....	133698	MDX	Hamm
1838	1873	1838	1873	115940	MDX	Islington
1793	1812	1790	1812	115940	MDX	St Luke
1750	1992	ALL	ALL	101281	SOM	ALL
1600	1950	1600	1992	133655	STS	Alstonfield
1700	1950	1600	1806	133655	STS	Flash
1800	1950	1700	1992	133655	STS	Leek
1650	1950	1600	1700	133655	STS	Longnor
1700	1950	1600	1992	133655	STS	Meerbrook
1900	1960	1900	1992	119059	STS	Tipton
1850	1900	1700	1900	141445	WAR	Hilmorton
HINES						
....	....	ALL	ALL	167827	LAN	Manchester
1863	1863	ALL	ALL	143618	MDX	Camden Town
1769	1838	1730	1880	136719	NFK	Seething
1783	1860	1700	1840	133701	SFK	Eye District
1835	1835	ALL	ALL	143618	SFK	Mellis
1800	1854	1760	1861	153508	SOM	Kingston St Mary
....	....	1800	1900	176508	SRY	Southwark
1881	1900	1881	ALL	143618	WYK	Wakefield
HINGLEY						
1780	1860	....	1780	147362	STS	Tutbury
HINKLEY						
1800	1910	1700	1800	130346	DBY	Dalbury
HINKS						
1860	1860	....	....	168564	GLS	Fairford
....	....	1600	1950	134546	HAM	Foreham
....	....	1600	1950	134546	IOW	Brading
....	....	1600	1950	134546	IOW	Sandown
....	....	1600	1950	134546	IOW	Shanklin
1860	1930	1850	1992	168564	KEN	Blackheath
1850	1870	....	....	124672	OXF	Oxford
1789	1850	....	....	124672	OXF	Weston On The Green
1802	1864	ALL	ALL	136735	SAL	Minsterley
1650	1870	1650	1950	127655	WAR	Alcester
1829	1992	1700	1829	164879	WAR	Birmingham
1650	1870	1650	1950	127655	WAR	Hastings
1650	1870	1650	1950	127655	WAR	Leamington
1650	1870	1650	1950	127655	WAR	Wolfhampcote
1945	....	....	....	131008	YKS	???
HINKSMAN						
1300	1992	1300	1992	133744	ALL	ALL
HINSHELWOOD						
1740	....	....	....	126993	ROX	Hobkirk
HINSLEY						
1767	1767	1750	1800	173517	WAR	North
HINSON						
1900	?	?	1900	133728	LIN	North
1850	1914	1850	1992	143650	WAR	Leamington Spa
1900	?	?	1900	133728	YKS	Leed
HINTON						
1840	1895	1881	1992	149659	BRK	Hagbourne
1712	1850	1800	1992	133450	BRK	Reading
1839	1843	1700	1850	164909	BRK	Windsor
....	....	1834	1867	154040	DEV	Exeter
1621	1786	1557	1786	142859	GLS	Avening
1700	ALL	1764	1869	107379	HRT	ALL
1870	?	1870	1920	108006	LAN	Lancaster
?	?	?	?	108588	LAN	Liverpool
1834	....	1750	1900	141151	LND	ALL
1854	1900	1700	1854	160709	LND	Somerstown
1740	1789	....	....	166189	MDX	Harefield
1680	1800	....	....	119458	OXF	South
1550	1600	1500	1600	154881	SAL	East Aston
1748	1992	1700	1900	168785	SOM	Frome
1650	1880	1600	1900	148652	WIL	Wilton
....	....	1700	1899	115975	WIL	Wylye Valley
HINTON contd.						
....	....	1830	1860	138339	WOR	???
1800	ALL	1764	1869	107379	YKS	Middlesborough
HINVEST						
....	....	1700	1785	156760	HAM	Eling
HINWOOD						
....	....	ALL	ALL	138908	ALL	Name Study
1618	....	....	....	133736	WIL	ALL
HINXMAN						
....	....	ALL	ALL	133744	ALL	Name Study
1300	1992	1300	1992	133744	ALL	ALL
HIORNS						
1820	....	1700	1850	145157	LND	Hackney
1820	....	1700	1850	145157	LND	Leabridge
1795	1854	....	....	165514	OXF	Barford St Michaels
....	....	1700	1820	145157	WAR	Warwick
HIPKIN						
1666	1780	ALL	1800	156310	NFK	???
HIPKISS						
....	....	1550	1750	115142	STS	Rowley Regis
1768	1793	1700	1768	133167	STS	Rowley Regis
1840	1930	1600	1900	100013	STS	Wolverhampton
HIPPISLEY						
1750	1970	1750	1970	122122	SOM	Yatton
HIPPOTT						
1815	1837	....	....	133736	HAM	Kingsclere
HIPSEY						
1812	1850	1700	1812	145823	ESS	Maldon
HIPWOOD						
1716	1881	....	....	155055	STS	Brewood
HIRCHBERG						
1878	1992	....	....	133752	LAN	Liverpool
HIRD						
1820	1840	1790	1860	146714	ANS	ALL
1740	1800	1770	1820	160504	NYK	Bedale
1780	1820	1780	1820	160504	SOM	Bristol
1860	1900	1840	1992	146714	T&W	ALL
1780	1810	1700	1850	160504	WLS	ALL
1711	1750	1600	1711	171573	YKS	Arkengarthdale
1711	1750	1600	1711	171573	YKS	Bedale
....	....	....	1900	121363	YKS	Leeds
HIRISON						
1805	1992	1700	1810	161772	NFK	???
HIRON						
1557	1866	ALL	ALL	153249	GLS	ALL
?	?	ALL	ALL	153249	WAR	ALL
1815	1900	1700	1815	162361	WOR	Worcester
HIRONS						
....	....	1800	1850	105198	NTH	Irthlingborough
....	....	1814	1879	118850	OXF	Banbury
....	....	1814	1879	118850	OXF	Wardington
HIRSCHBERG						
1878	1992	....	....	133752	LAN	Liverpool
HIRSHBERG						
1878	1992	....	....	133752	LAN	Liverpool
HIRST						
1838	1923	1838	1923	142069	LAN	Burnley
1854	1870	1870	1900	138584	LAN	Bury
1780	1881	1780	1815	166952	LAN	Liverpool
....	....	1700	1980	163724	LAN	Manchester
1856	1900	1200	1900	163724	LIN	Isle Of Axholme
1721	1804	ALL	ALL	176656	LIN	Skidbrook
1598	....	....	1598	101761	WRY	Horbury
1758	1992	....	1758	101761	WRY	Meltham
....	....	1750	1850	129046	WYK	Huddersfield
1803	1898	ALL	1803	154563	YKS	ALL
1873	1992	....	1873	141968	YKS	Almondbury
1790	1851	1750	1900	157716	YKS	Austonley
1700	1870	1600	1700	129534	YKS	Barnsley
1803	1898	ALL	1803	154563	YKS	Barwick In Elmet
1838	1923	1838	1923	142069	YKS	Burnley
1788	1841	1700	1788	160024	YKS	Clayton
1812	1851	1750	1870	157716	YKS	Holmfirth
1795	1825	....	....	138584	YKS	Horbury
1800	1900	1600	1992	122084	YKS	Huddersfield
1632	....	1600	1650	170348	YKS	Huddersfield
1770	1800	1750	1800	123595	YKS	Mirfield
1740	1871	1700	1871	166952	YKS	Mirfield
1798	1930	1600	1930	150118	YKS	Morley
1768	1795	1700	1768	138584	YKS	Rothwell
1700	1870	1600	1700	129534	YKS	Wakefield
1845	1992	ALL	1845	109320	YKS	???
HISCOCK						
....	....	ALL	ALL	104000	ALL	Name Study

Known From	To	Researching From	To	Ref	Cty	Place
HISCOCK contd.						
ALL	ALL	ALL	ALL	104000	ALL	ALL
1800	1890	ALL	ALL	154970	BRK	Hamstead Norris
1765	1835	1600	1850	133779	HAM	Broughton
1813	1850	1650	1850	133779	HAM	Lymington
....	....	....	1834	121169	KEN	???
1850	1860	....	....	133779	LND	Bermondsey
1840	1904	....	....	133779	LND	Chelsea
1761	1910	1700	1832	133787	MDX	Hounslow
1785	1992	1700	1900	102164	OXF	Henley
1830	1870	ALL	ALL	177989	SSX	Brighton
1760	1790	1700	1800	176672	SSX	Salehurst
1881	1927	1800	1881	120146	WIL	Bishops Cannirks
1770	....	....	....	133779	WIL	Fittleton
1717	....	....	....	115576	WIL	Heddington
1830	1992	ALL	1740	151602	WIL	Wilcot
1740	....	....	....	133779	WIL	???
HISCOCKS						
1800	1897	1600	1800	133825	GLS	Sapperton
1823	1873	1800	1875	154733	SOM	Widcombe
HISCOX						
1770	1875	1700	1770	114871	SOM	Ashwick
1759	1810	....	....	115290	WIL	Corsham
HISCUTT						
1730	1770	ALL	ALL	163562	CON	Central
1687	1717	ALL	ALL	163562	WIL	Longbridge Deverill
HISGROVE						
1750	1992	ALL	1992	156272	ALL	ALL
HISLOP						
1750	1790	....	....	141798	ROX	???
1829	....	....	....	138061	SRY	Egham
HISTED						
1770	1830	1830	1880	102318	SRY	East
1752	1838	1838	1992	139343	SSX	Buxted
HISTON						
1834	....	....	....	129747	SAL	Dawley Magna
HITCH						
1710	1816	ALL	1850	151815	CAM	Haslingfield
1613	1992	1400	1613	133809	CAM	Melbourn
1806	1872	1700	1806	153206	HRT	East Barnet
1774	1793	1700	1793	153206	HRT	Northaw
1774	1774	1700	1774	153206	HRT	???
1814	1860	1800	1860	169323	STS	Darlaston
HITCHCOCK						
1843	1843	....	....	115606	BRK	Kingston Bagpuize
1850	....	1840	1880	135429	DEV	Buldeigh Salterton
1805	1805	1700	1875	107654	DEV	Hemyock
1560	1900	1500	1900	119113	DEV	Thorcombe
1600	1900	1600	1900	119113	DOR	Pitthouse
1560	1900	1500	1900	119113	DOR	Thorcombe
1650	1860	....	....	165999	ESS	ALL
1650	1992	1600	1992	161543	ESS	Dedham
1884	1884	1800	1884	127981	MDX	London
1805	1850	....	....	142360	OXF	Bampton
1700	1800	1600	1700	174513	OXF	Somerton
1877	1904	ALL	ALL	124176	OXF	Spelsbury
1650	1700	1600	1700	133817	SFK	Copdock
1732	1762	ALL	1732	122106	SFK	Lavenham
1680	1730	1650	1750	133817	SFK	Somersham
1600	1900	1600	1900	119113	WIL	Blunts Court
1600	1900	1600	1900	119113	WIL	Maltravers
1600	1900	1600	1900	119113	WIL	Woolcombe
HITCHCOX						
1770	1870	1650	1770	106313	OXF	Ardley
HITCHEN						
1850	1950	1700	1992	121762	ALL	ALL
1810	1921	1770	1820	173649	LAN	Bacup
1840	1890	1800	1900	136034	LAN	Manchester
1700	....	1700	....	109347	LAN	Read
1850	1950	1700	1992	121762	YKS	Sheffield
HITCHENER						
1787	1852	1782	1992	138088	STS	Penkridge
1740	1800	1700	1740	166464	STS	Rugeley
HITCHIN						
1780	1800	ALL	ALL	130508	SAL	Longden Upon Tern
1800	1900	ALL	ALL	130508	WOR	Stourbridge
HITCHINGS						
....	....	1700	1900	136972	CON	Crowan
1803	1839	1775	1803	173118	PEM	Nevern
HITCHINS						
1826	1940	ALL	ALL	171980	ALL	ALL
1830	1840	1790	1850	168580	CON	Gt Blazey
1690	1870	1600	1870	155195	LND	Bethnal Green
1808	1992	1600	1808	133825	LND	???

Known From	To	Researching From	To	Ref	Cty	Place
HITCHMAN						
....	1700	....	1700	177695	NTH	Long Buckby
1880	1950	1750	1880	177237	WAR	Shipston
HITCHMOUGH						
1840	....	1800	1850	126586	LAN	Halewood
HITCHON						
....	....	ALL	ALL	133833	ALL	Name Study
1600	1992	1100	1992	133833	ALL	ALL
HITCHSON						
1800	1880	1700	1800	117218	CHS	Congleton
HITT						
1820	....	1800	1880	135429	DEV	Aylesbeare
HIVES						
1800	1820	1790	1830	124915	NTT	East Drayton
HIXSON						
1800	1992	ALL	ALL	177989	GLA	Swansea
HIZZY						
1790	1992	ALL	1790	177245	BRK	???
HLODERNESS						
1785	1862	....	1785	109622	LAN	Preston
HLOMES						
1679	1742	1650	1800	123536	DUR	Brancepeth
HOAD						
1800	1900	1700	1800	134848	KEN	Wittersham
....	1800	....	....	174564	KEN	Wittersham
1850	1992	ALL	1850	141704	SSX	Thakeham
HOADLEY						
1848	1872	1700	1872	116300	KEN	Maidstone
1869	1871	1800	1930	139203	SRY	Croydon
1860	1992	....	....	122130	SSX	Rotherfield
1800	1900	ALL	1800	122130	SSX	Ticehurst
HOAR						
1829	....	1700	1992	107204	CON	Flushing
1815	....	....	....	153400	CON	Kestle Mill
....	1830	....	....	153400	CON	Linkinhorne
1818	1820	....	....	153400	CON	St Enoder
1860	1992	ALL	ALL	123064	DEV	Tavistock
1764	1792	ALL	ALL	115126	HAM	Bishops Waltham
1759	1992	1600	1760	126063	HAM	Crondall
1822	1955	1800	1992	115991	HAM	Portsnouth
1894	....	....	....	153400	???	Southport
HOARE						
....	....	ALL	ALL	157422	ALL	Name Study
1745	....	1650	1780	143693	BKM	Beaconsfield
1818	1960	ALL	1818	118060	BRK	Reading
1808	....	1700	1850	146978	DBY	Herby
1737	1936	....	....	151238	DEV	Axmouth
1600	1837	1550	1837	140392	DEV	Dean Prior
1780	1870	1600	1780	123390	DOR	Beaminster
1550	1875	1680	1860	172634	DOR	Beaminster
1843	1882	1750	1843	173843	DOR	Beaminster
1780	1860	1600	1780	123390	DOR	Broadwinsor
....	....	1890	1916	123390	GLA	Cardiff
1865	1890	1800	1870	147478	GLS	Cheltenham
....	....	....	....	165255	GLS	Forest Of Dean
1759	1992	1600	1760	126063	HAM	Crondall
1811	....	1750	1811	132853	HRT	Halford
1851	1861	....	....	119334	LND	Hammersmith
1800	1825	?	1800	158569	LND	Westminster
....	....	1800	1830	130184	MDX	Shoreditch
1752	1832	1752	1832	121681	SOM	Curry Rivel
1784	1855	ALL	1784	139602	SOM	Curry Rivel
1900	1925	1800	1890	158836	SRY	ALL
1871	....	1800	1871	132853	SRY	Lambeth
1800	....	1800	1900	139114	SSX	Durringlow
1838	1863	1800	1900	139114	SSX	Worthing
HOATH						
1828	1992	ALL	1828	100803	SSX	Hartfield
HOBBIS						
1750	1784	1700	1800	153249	WAR	Birmingham
1790	1935	ALL	1992	133876	WOR	Kingsnorton
1790	1935	ALL	1992	133876	WOR	Northfield
HOBBS ALABY						
1850	1992	1850	1992	133922	JSY	St Helier
1780	1820	1750	1800	133922	NFK	Clenchwarton
1800	1870	1800	1900	133922	NFK	West Lynn
HOBBS						
1776	1992	1700	1992	101621	AVN	Bristol
1506	1823	1506	1800	133884	BKM	ALL
1890	1970	1500	1890	110310	BRK	Basingstoke
1812	1900	1812	1900	133884	BRK	Thatcham
1877	1960	ALL	ALL	112518	BRK	Woolhampton
1750	1850	1500	1750	133892	CAM	ALL
1772	....	....	1772	146935	CHS	???

Known From	To	Researching From	To	Ref	Cty	Place
HOBBS contd.						
1836	1925	1700	1992	113123	DEV	Exeter
1870	1992	ALL	ALL	133930	DEV	Plymouth
1640	1690	1600	1690	112593	DOR	Cranborne
1742	1900	ALL	1742	165735	GLS	Bristol
1840	1895	1840	1900	157171	GLS	Newnham On Severn
1880	....	ALL	ALL	150681	HAM	Aldershot
ALL	ALL	ALL	ALL	149675	HAM	Bishops Sutton
1690	1900	....	....	112593	HAM	Breamorie
1690	1696	ALL	ALL	149675	HAM	Chilcomb
1835	1876	ALL	ALL	149675	HAM	Church Oakley
1815	1845	ALL	ALL	149675	HAM	Crondell
1772	1922	ALL	ALL	149675	HAM	East Stratton
ALL	ALL	ALL	ALL	149675	HAM	Harestock
1804	1992	ALL	ALL	149675	HAM	Headbourne Worthy
1653	1992	ALL	ALL	149675	HAM	Kings Worthy
1759	1890	1700	1900	112518	HAM	Kingsclere
1758	1950	1758	1823	133884	HAM	Kingsclere
ALL	ALL	ALL	ALL	149675	HAM	Littleton
1797	1896	ALL	ALL	149675	HAM	Long Sutton
1823	1869	ALL	ALL	149675	HAM	Martyrworthy
1721	1907	ALL	ALL	149675	HAM	Micheldever
1836	1874	1600	1836	152080	HAM	Micheldever
1739	....	....	....	153397	HAM	Milford
1830	1848	ALL	ALL	149675	HAM	Nursling
1763	1890	ALL	ALL	149675	HAM	Overton
1798	1802	ALL	ALL	149675	HAM	Ovington
1800	1850	1700	1850	156442	HAM	Porstmouth
1900	1992	1900	1992	133922	HAM	Southampton
1633	1864	ALL	ALL	149675	HAM	Sparsholt
1700	1725	ALL	ALL	149675	HAM	Stoke Charity
1889	1899	ALL	ALL	149675	HAM	Whitchurch
ALL	ALL	ALL	ALL	149675	HAM	Winchester
1736	1841	ALL	ALL	149675	HAM	Wonston
1700	1790	1600	1900	177180	HRT	Bovington
1821	?	?	?	166642	HRT	???
1830	1992	ALL	1830	115177	KEN	Margate
1819	1880	1800	1880	123021	KEN	Rochester
1860	....	1860	....	135488	LAN	Precott
....	....	1874	1930	142654	LND	South East
1853	1915	1853	1915	116831	LND	Hackney
1880	1992	ALL	ALL	155373	LND	Islington
1772	....	1740	1775	124796	LND	Soho
1803	1851	1790	1860	132608	LND	???
1750	1850	1750	1800	140864	MDX	Edmonton
1750	1850	1750	1800	140864	MDX	Enfield
1821	?	?	?	166642	MDX	???
1750	1850	1500	1750	133892	NFK	West
1830	1950	1830	1906	125709	NTH	Cranford
1830	1950	1830	1906	125709	NTH	Woodford
....	....	1600	1992	174963	SOM	Babington
1847	1848	1750	1850	121568	SOM	Bishops Lydeard
....	....	1600	1992	174963	SOM	Coleford
1800	1992	1750	1992	161861	SOM	Hemington
1650	1730	1600	1730	139092	SOM	Henstridge
1650	....	1600	1992	174963	SOM	Kilmersden
1719	1784	1710	1784	107573	SOM	Winsford
?	?	ALL	ALL	100897	SRY	Walworth
1878	1992	1800	1878	166200	WAR	Birmingham
1900	1992	1800	1900	110043	WCY	???
1731	1767	ALL	1731	158445	WIL	Melksham
....	....	1789	1789	114308	WIL	Stert
....	1902	....	1902	133906	???	???
HOBBY						
....	....	1650	1768	133949	DOR	ALL
1600	1745	1500	1600	133949	DOR	Corfe Mullen
1768	1900	1650	1768	133949	HAM	South
HOBDAY						
....	....	1830	1992	132438	DBY	Derby
1755	1958	....	....	139165	KEN	Barham
1762	1800	1700	1800	129984	KEN	Folkestone
1812	....	....	....	167037	SSX	Hastings
1820	1992	1750	1820	115312	WOR	Worcester
HOBDEN						
1850	1992	1850	1950	127868	SSX	East
1784	1806	1750	1850	100242	SSX	Chailey
HOBKYN						
1585	1705	ALL	ALL	141615	LAN	Priest Hutton
HOBLEY						
....	....	ALL	ALL	133965	ALL	Name Study
....	....	ALL	1992	133965	ALL	ALL
HOBLIN						
1600	1690	....	....	174319	CON	Gorran

Known From	To	Researching From	To	Ref	Cty	Place
HOBLYN						
1566	1803	....	....	100536	CON	???
HOBMAN						
1605	....	ALL	....	104515	LIN	Norton Disney
HOBSON						
....	....	ALL	ALL	133981	ALL	Name Study
1790	1940	1880	....	134007	BDF	Eaton Socon
1892	1904	1892	1940	126705	CHS	Wirral
1823	1915	1750	1925	162183	DBY	ALL
1820	1870	ALL	1820	148180	ERY	Newington
1800	1843	1750	1800	149047	LAN	Manchester
1600	1992	1600	1992	135968	LEI	ALL
....	....	1670	1850	134007	LIN	Driby
1850	1917	1700	1992	139270	LIN	Frodingham
1800	1850	1700	1850	100439	LIN	Greetham
1800	1833	1750	1800	102008	LIN	Haxey
1757	1851	1560	1900	134023	LIN	Laughton
1634	....	1600	ALL	134007	LIN	Spalding
1800	1850	1700	1850	100439	LIN	Wrangle
1680	1940	....	....	134007	NTT	East Markham
....	....	ALL	ALL	133973	SYK	Rotherham
1795	1816	1795	1862	108901	SYK	Sheffield
....	....	ALL	ALL	133973	SYK	Sheffield
1895	1992	ALL	ALL	112461	WOR	Stourbridge
1760	....	....	1760	101761	WRY	Honley
1766	....	....	1766	101761	WRY	Meltham
1600	1992	1600	1992	104566	YKS	Copmanthorpe
1860	1900	1800	1900	147788	YKS	Horsforth
1844	1877	1700	1877	138355	YKS	Hunslet
1800	1900	1800	1900	114529	YKS	Sheffield
1830	1870	1800	1900	165662	YKS	Sheffield
1700	1850	1700	1900	114529	YKS	Swinefleet
HOBY						
1750	....	ALL	1785	168718	NTH	Rothwell
HOCHHEIMER						
1900	1914	....	....	136255	LAN	Manchester
1840	?	....	....	136255	LND	???
HOCKADAN						
1878	....	ALL	1878	164755	CMA	Millom
HOCKADAY						
1680	1692	1640	1720	142018	SOM	ALL
HOCKE						
1800	1825	1750	1860	113697	MDX	Hackney
HOCKEN						
1805	1992	1700	1805	164917	CON	South
1800	1880	....	....	174319	CON	Lanteglos By Fowey
HOCKETT						
1770	1810	1700	1850	148725	HRT	Cheshunt
HOCKEY						
1784	1851	1600	1784	149357	DEV	Kilmington
1851	1992	....	....	108030	GNT	Newport
1824	1851	ALL	ALL	141526	LND	???
ALL	....	....	....	150975	MDX	St Pancras
1860	1992	....	....	149357	MON	Newport
1831	1871	1800	1831	149357	SOM	Bridgwater
ALL	....	....	....	150975	SOM	Horsington
1841	1851	1800	1841	108030	SOM	Odcombe
ALL	....	....	....	150975	SRY	Southwark
HOCKIN						
1650	1920	1650	1920	134031	CON	ALL
1851	....	....	....	130656	CON	Calstock
1585	1860	1500	1860	143766	CON	Cambourne
1585	1860	1500	1860	143766	CON	Gwithian
1813	....	....	....	130656	CON	Phillack
1838	1992	1700	1838	161446	CON	???
1750	1850	1750	1850	134031	DEV	ALL
1800	1900	1800	1900	133450	DEV	Dartmouth
1871	....	....	....	130656	GLA	Llwynyppia
HOCKING						
....	....	ALL	ALL	166871	ALL	Name Study
1700	....	....	....	114723	CON	Bodmin
1853	1873	ALL	1853	134058	CON	Camborne
1815	1818	1780	1850	176982	CON	Egloshayle
1750	1900	1650	1900	118818	CON	Illogan
1853	1873	ALL	1853	134058	CON	Illogan
1857	....	....	....	150657	CON	Lanlivery
1850	ALL	ALL	ALL	113093	CON	London
1924	?	1924	1992	172596	CON	Penzance
1780	1992	ALL	1780	129992	CON	Phillack
1850	ALL	ALL	ALL	113093	CON	South Hill
1780	1992	ALL	1780	129992	CON	St Erth
1800	1820	1700	1950	168734	CON	St Ive
....	....	1800	1850	150800	CON	???
1800	1860	1700	1900	168734	DEV	Plymouth

Known From	To	Researching From	To	Ref	Cty	Place
HOCKING contd.						
....	....	1800	1850	150800	DEV	???
HOCKLESS						
....	....	ALL	ALL	134066	ALL	Name Study
HOCKNELL						
1800	....	ALL	1800	104760	CHS	Chester
1884	1992	ALL	1800	104760	KEN	Lewisham
1864	....	ALL	1800	104760	SRY	Walworth
1850	....	ALL	1800	104760	YKS	Sheffield
HOCKNEY						
1880	1960	1700	1850	134074	LIN	Barton On Humber
1780	1920	1700	1780	115401	LIN	Elsham
HOCKRIDGE						
1640	1750	1640	1750	106593	CON	Kilkhampton
HODDELL						
1757	....	?	1760	103934	HUN	Ellington
1800	1850	1600	1800	133892	MDX	London
HODDER						
1875	ALL	1750	1875	104167	DOR	Morcombelake
1725	1810	1700	1810	174599	DOR	Netherbury
1874	1920	ALL	ALL	104167	DOR	Whitchurch
HODDINOTT						
1800	1992	ALL	ALL	158798	SOM	East
1810	1883	....	....	117579	SOM	Keinton Mandeville
HODDS						
1830	1880	1800	1880	158658	NFK	Great Yarmouth
HODDY						
1865	1974	1837	1865	166464	MDX	Paddington
HODENET						
1100	ALL	1100	ALL	108294	???	???
HODGART						
1800	1833	1800	1850	146536	RFW	Paisley
HODGE						
....	....	ALL	ALL	148695	ALL	Name Study
....	....	1847	....	150711	AVN	St Georges
1718	1724	ALL	ALL	174777	AYR	Muirkirk
1830	1870	1780	1830	145858	CON	Camborne
1887	1946	1700	1900	121312	CON	Chacewater
1620	1670	1600	1700	132942	CON	Cubert
1794	....	ALL	ALL	110272	CON	Davidstow
1769	1872	1700	1880	121126	CON	Kenwyn
1833	1992	1700	1883	130257	CON	Manaccan
1860	1880	1700	1914	170615	CON	Probus
1802	1837	1700	1802	161837	CON	St Austell
1863	....	1840	....	173991	CON	St Austell
1860	1946	1860	1992	121312	CON	Twelveheads
1800	1965	1770	1800	128368	DEV	Ipplepen
1800	1840	1800	1840	136239	DEV	Marystone
1800	1992	1600	1800	134090	DEV	Mid And North
1800	1952	1700	1800	161950	DEV	Plymouth
1770	1874	ALL	1874	165654	GLS	St George
1820	1866	....	....	138045	GNT	Chepstow
1800	1900	1800	1900	110523	GNT	Monmouth
1850	....	1800	1900	126144	KEN	Greenwich
....	....	ALL	ALL	118400	KEN	Wateringbury
1850	1890	....	....	122238	LAN	Bootle
1860	1900	1750	1860	109959	LAN	Liverpool
1846	1901	1846	1901	122238	LAN	Liverpool
1869	1880	1869	1880	138045	MON	Monmouth
1880	1948	1880	1948	138045	MON	Rhymney
1866	1869	1866	1869	138045	MON	Usk
HODGEKISS						
....	1800	....	1800	177695	STS	Gt Wyrley
HODGES						
1850	....	....	1921	136964	DEV	Plymouth
....	....	1600	1992	137588	DOR	Dorchester
1876	1906	....	....	134112	GLA	Aberdare
1770	1790	ALL	ALL	113700	GLS	Ozelworth
1906	1992	....	....	134112	GNT	Natyglo
1730	1900	1700	1800	151637	HEF	Withington
1560	1798	....	....	134112	HEF	???
1900	1992	....	....	141267	KEN	Faversham
1839	1992	....	....	163155	LEI	Griffdam
....	....	1800	1860	172871	MDX	Hampstead
....	....	1800	1850	172871	MDX	Highgate
1742	1748	1650	1742	172898	MON	Trelleck
1760	1850	1720	1760	134139	NTH	Haselbeech
ALL	1810	....	....	105368	SOM	Beauchamp
?	?	ALL	1850	117919	SOM	Evercreech
....	1770	1500	1770	175072	SOM	Keynsham
1861	1915	ALL	ALL	140155	SOM	Weston Super Mare
....	....	1800	1899	174963	SRY	Lambeth
1900	1992	1700	1900	126616	SRY	Southwark
1850	....	1700	1850	126616	SSX	Trotton
HODGES contd.						
1643	1749	1600	1780	160873	STS	Sedgley
1852	1852	ALL	ALL	134120	WOR	Great Malvern
1852	1903	ALL	ALL	134120	WOR	Kempsey
1874	1916	ALL	ALL	143529	WOR	Kempsey
....	1852	ALL	ALL	143529	WOR	Severnstoke
1781	....	....	....	145726	WOR	Upton On Severn
1767	....	....	1767	101761	WOR	Worcester
1903	....	ALL	ALL	143529	WOR	Worcester
1798	1876	....	....	134112	???	Forest Of Dean
HODGET						
1773	1795	1600	1800	155152	NTT	Widmerpool
HODGETTS						
1600	....	ALL	ALL	105767	STS	ALL
1816	1902	....	....	112232	STS	Blackheath
1640	....	ALL	ALL	105767	WOR	ALL
HODGKIN						
1600	1900	1600	1900	135968	LEI	Slawston
HODGKINS						
....	....	1850	1992	134546	BDF	Yielden
1861	1926	ALL	1861	171468	YKS	Sheffield
HODGKINSON						
....	....	ALL	ALL	134163	ALL	Name Study
all	ALL	ALL	ALL	134163	ALL	ALL
1798	1814	1650	1797	131245	DBY	Tibshelf
1768	....	ALL	ALL	147621	FLN	Northop
....	....	1756	1992	121940	LAN	Ashton In Makerfield
1820	1900	ALL	ALL	138363	LAN	Chorley
1781	1799	1600	1781	102571	LAN	Preston St John
....	....	1800	1900	134155	LAN	Preston
....	....	1800	1900	134155	LAN	Wigan
....	....	1756	1992	121940	LAN	Winick
1820	1840	1820	1840	178675	LIN	Fulbeck
1600	1992	1600	1900	168467	STS	???
HODGSHON						
1660	1680	1600	1660	121339	NYK	Lythe
HODGSOM						
1856	1992	1700	1992	173053	CUL	Bolton
HODGSON						
1859	1959	1800	1960	136719	ALL	London
1745	1827	1745	1827	149403	CMA	Castle Carrock
1760	1820	ALL	1992	133159	CMA	Whitehaven
1800	....	1600	1800	116637	CUL	Castle Carrock
....	....	1700	1800	116173	CUL	Moresby
1640	1700	1600	1750	138878	CUL	Whitehaven
1845	1950	ALL	ALL	119253	DBY	Bugsworth
1838	1845	ALL	ALL	119253	DBY	Glossop
1780	1992	ALL	1780	134171	DUR	Hamsterley
1730	1780	....	....	108871	DUR	Medomsley
1827	1920	1586	1827	102512	DUR	Newbottle
1748	1831	1600	1748	147346	DUR	St Johns Chapel
1827	1850	1550	1830	147265	DUR	???
....	....	ALL	1765	113611	EYK	Preston
1851	1870	....	....	129232	GLA	Merthyr Tydfil
1870	1883	....	....	129232	GLA	Pontardawe
1899	1939	....	....	129232	GLA	Ruthin
1883	1930	....	....	129232	GLA	Swansea
1860	1905	ALL	1925	147567	HRT	Abbots Langley
1830	1870	ALL	1870	147567	HRT	Redbourne
1821	....	....	1840	171441	KEN	Canterbury
1832	1900	....	1900	171441	KEN	Cheriton
1840	1900	ALL	1840	135062	KEN	Woolwich
1828	1890	1828	1881	102121	LAN	Bolton
1791	1838	ALL	ALL	119253	LAN	Foulridge
1780	....	....	....	125199	LAN	Kirkham
1800	1900	ALL	ALL	154970	LAN	Tunstall
....	....	1800	1850	129232	LIN	Bardney
....	1803	1500	1803	175072	LIN	Tealby
1764	1794	1750	1800	113611	LIN	Winteringham
....	....	1800	....	108677	LND	North
1825	....	1750	1825	121010	NFK	Kings Lynn
1770	1850	1700	1770	121339	NYK	Salton
1827	1850	1550	1830	147265	NYK	???
....	....	1891	1992	134198	SYK	Sheffield
....	....	?	?	134201	WRY	Gisburnforrest
1828	1875	1700	1900	102660	WRY	Idle
1828	1875	1700	1900	102660	WRY	Thackley
1500	1750	1400	1500	134198	WYK	Bradford
1712	1930	1600	1712	134198	WYK	Cleckheaton
1823	1992	ALL	1823	111384	WYK	Leeds
1712	1930	1600	1712	134198	WYK	Scholes
1765	1825	ALL	ALL	119253	YKS	Barnoldswick
1893	1893	1893	1992	174262	YKS	Barnsley

Known From	To	Researching From	To	Ref	Cty	Place
HODGSON contd.						
1784	1784	1740	1790	108510	YKS	Batley
1714	1853	1600	1714	154172	YKS	Bradford
1881	1992	1841	1881	165026	YKS	Bradford
1720	....	1650	....	134589	YKS	Haxby
1838	....	....	....	175587	YKS	Headingley
....	....	1730	1790	175773	YKS	Hull
1785	1992	1785	1992	140767	YKS	Leeds
1790	1825	1700	1840	168297	YKS	Leeds
1720	1760	1680	1720	177393	YKS	Newton Upon Wharf
1732	1770	1600	1800	165190	YKS	Northowram
1733	1750	1700	1733	177393	YKS	Owthorne
1838	1860	1800	1838	177393	YKS	Paull
1800	1860	1500	1800	167843	YKS	Preston Under Scar
1800	....	....	1840	171441	YKS	Richmond
1832	1992	ALL	1811	119504	YKS	Romaldkirk
1650	1700	1600	1700	119717	YKS	Rosby
1882	....	ALL	ALL	176737	YKS	Sheffield
1760	1770	....	....	177393	YKS	Stillingfleet
1760	1780	....	....	177393	YKS	Wheldrake
1785	1992	1785	1992	140767	YKS	York
1811	1832	ALL	1811	119504	???	Grain
HODISON						
1851	1871	1800	1850	108227	DEV	Milton Abbot
HODJINS						
1775	1790	....	....	102946	WAR	Cobington
HODKINSON						
1820	1930	....	....	132225	CHS	Tarporley
1796	1963	1750	1992	127264	LAN	Salford
HODNET						
1100	ALL	1100	ALL	108294	???	???
HODNETT						
1100	ALL	1100	ALL	108294	???	???
HODSDEN						
1860	1905	ALL	1925	147567	HRT	Abbots Langley
HODSDON						
....	....	ALL	ALL	134228	ALL	Name Study
1200	1992	1200	1992	134228	ALL	ALL
1814	1834	1750	1850	100048	MDX	Harrow
HODSKIN						
1700	....	ALL	....	104515	LEI	Burbage
HODSON						
1739	1828	1700	1850	167002	CAM	Cambridge
1800	1881	ALL	ALL	157864	DBY	S Wingham
1790	1800	1640	1790	119385	DBY	South Wingfield
1850	1900	1800	1850	127949	LAN	Westhoughton
1750	1780	....	....	177318	LAN	Wigan
1772	....	1750	1800	170348	LIN	Torksey
ALL	1906	ALL	1906	102334	MDX	Poplar
1910	1980	1875	1992	133450	MDX	Richmond
1810	1844	....	....	119385	NTT	Stapleford
1820	1980	1790	1900	134236	STS	North
1794	1798	1790	1850	134236	STS	Adbaston
1835	1943	1835	....	145807	STS	Birmingham
1840	1900	ALL	1840	135062	STS	West Bromwich
HODY						
1400	1461	1400	1461	135569	DOR	Kyngton
1400	1461	1400	1461	135569	DOR	Stoure
1350	1500	1350	1600	135569	SOM	Bridgwater
1350	1500	1350	1600	135569	SOM	Woolavington
HOEY						
1817	1853	1815	1855	130990	MDX	Westminster
HOFF						
1794	1845	ALL	....	134244	DOR	Weymouth
1845	....	ALL	....	134244	HAM	Portsmouth
1650	1992	ALL	ALL	162620	LIN	???
HOFORD						
1720	1720	1650	1750	144606	OXF	Witney
HOG						
1704	1704	1600	1750	130125	DFS	Canonbie
1749	1751	....	....	112887	ELN	Pencaitland
HOGAN						
1814	1816	1800	1830	105120	COR	Fermoy
1838	1861	1700	1838	109983	IRL	Dublin
....	1500	ALL	1650	162507	LND	Hackney
1780	1900	1780	1840	103845	PEM	Hakin
HOGARTH						
1890	1940	1700	1890	121452	AYR	???
1860	1930	ALL	1940	123048	DUR	Monkwearmouth
1850	....	1750	1992	118532	LND	ALL
....	1787	....	....	153176	NBL	Allendale
HOGBEN						
1832	1872	1600	1832	174548	KEN	Folkestone
1871	1894	ALL	1894	152641	KEN	Minster In Thanet
HOGER						
1791	1817	1750	1800	162396	OXF	Shifford
HOGES						
ALL	1810	....	....	105368	SOM	Shepton
HOGETTS						
ALL	1761	....	....	105368	STS	???
HOGG						
1810	1825	1750	1800	147095	ABD	Fintray
1775	1810	1700	1800	147095	ABD	Skene
1770	1790	ALL	1800	149063	BEW	Ettrick
....	....	1800	1850	134260	DUR	Ryton
....	....	ALL	1715	119326	ELN	Tranent
1820	1840	....	....	137227	ESS	Harwich
1570	1780	1570	1780	127655	GLS	Painswick
1570	1780	1570	1780	127655	GLS	Pitchcombe
1800	1844	1840	1864	157538	HAM	Southampton
1759	....	1700	?	160385	IOM	Andreas
1865	1930	1840	1950	157538	IOW	Ryde
....	....	1700	1899	174963	IRL	Clare
....	....	1700	1899	174963	IRL	Limerick
1833	1908	1750	1925	155969	KEN	Plumstead
1780	1800	....	1780	137227	KEN	Strood
1833	1908	1750	1925	155969	KEN	Woolwich
1770	1820	1700	1820	134252	LND	St Botolph
1820	1840	1750	1840	134252	MDX	Finsbury
1870	....	1840	1910	167932	MDX	Hoxton
1860	1900	1750	1860	134260	NBL	Blyth
1850	1960	ALL	1850	134260	NBL	Tynemouth
....	....	....	1850	134902	NTT	East Drayton
1800	1850	ALL	1992	170909	ROS	Elphin
1781	1857	....	....	127426	SFK	Hadleigh
1750	....	1700	....	134589	YKS	Easingwold
HOGGAN						
1731	1765	....	....	113484	KRS	Backside Of Aldie
HOGGARD						
....	1719	1650	1720	174858	YKS	Helmsley
HOGGART						
1700	1800	ALL	1800	131059	MDX	???
1744	1806	1714	1744	139149	WES	Millthrop
HOGGARTH						
1750	1850	1700	1850	162191	WES	Kendal
HOGGET						
1841	....	1700	1850	161721	DUR	South Shields
1860	1890	1800	1860	100277	LND	Lambeth
HOGGINS						
1773	1807	1740	1807	123404	LEI	Old Dalby
1776	1776	1700	1800	111414	SAL	Westbury
HOGSDEN						
1843	1992	1500	1843	128872	SRY	Ashstead
HOGSFLESH						
?	....	....	?	141941	HAM	Southwick
1805	1852	1750	1861	153508	MDX	Hanworth
HOGTON						
1700	1750	....	....	177318	LAN	Blackburn
HOGWOOD						
....	....	ALL	ALL	128465	ALL	Name Study
1822	1992	1650	1850	128465	ALL	ALL
HOHLAH						
1800	1900	1700	1800	108359	HUN	Ellington
HOILE						
....	....	ALL	ALL	134279	ALL	Name Study
1906	1913	1850	1930	150002	KEN	Elham
HOILES						
1723	....	....	1723	101761	LIN	Leake
1780	1840	1700	1840	139688	LND	East End
HOLAH						
....	....	ALL	ALL	171352	ALL	Name Study
1900	1954	1870	1900	164364	YKS	Doncaster
HOLBECHE						
1500	1700	....	....	100420	WAR	Meriden
HOLBERY						
1840	1900	ALL	1840	178934	NTT	Mattersey
HOLBOURN						
1800	1900	1700	1900	118303	KEN	Dartford
1800	1900	1700	1992	118303	SRY	London
HOLBROOK						
....	....	ALL	1992	131083	AVN	Bristol
....	....	1800	....	113352	ESS	Hutton
1807	1807	ALL	ALL	128449	GLS	Bristol
....	....	1700	1760	166979	IOW	Newtown
....	....	1860	1920	166979	SSX	Rye
HOLBURN						
1780	1850	1750	1880	151742	DUR	South

Known From	To	Researching From	To	Ref	Cty	Place
HOLCRAFT						
1850	1900	1500	1850	169986	WOR	Dudley
HOLCROFT						
....	....	ALL	ALL	173606	ALL	Name Study
1350	1400	1300	1400	154881	CHS	Tabley
1600	1992	1600	1992	134295	STS	North
HOLDAWAY						
1804	1828	1800	1992	167800	HAM	Crondall
1804	1828	1800	1992	167800	HAM	Odiham
1770	1960	1750	1960	110183	HAM	???
HOLDCROFT						
1600	1992	1600	1992	134295	STS	North
HOLDEN						
1814	....	1800	1852	169625	ANT	Ballyedward
1814	....	1800	1852	169625	ANT	Kilwaughter
1810	1850	ALL	ALL	168912	CHS	Gawsworth
1874	1980	1837	1874	105473	KEN	Gravesend
1825	....	1825	....	109347	LAN	Acrrington
1856	1992	....	....	131504	LAN	Banks
....	....	1800	1992	111503	LAN	Blackburn
1810	?	1800	1832	102121	LAN	Bolton
1820	....	1800	1840	117145	LAN	Bolton
1705	1992	1600	1705	119822	LAN	Bolton
1770	1790	1740	1770	132268	LAN	Bolton
1750	1900	1750	1900	125237	LAN	Darwen
1800	1880	1880	1992	162256	LAN	Darwen
1810	?	1800	1832	102121	LAN	Edgeworth
1730	1800	1680	1730	168912	LAN	Great Sankey
1800	1881	1784	1880	136565	LAN	Lower Darwen
1858	1889	1830	1873	134309	LAN	Oldham
1800	1881	1784	1880	136565	LAN	Over
1840	1980	ALL	1840	135062	LAN	Prescott
1841	1871	1800	1891	142204	LAN	Westhoughton
1880	1992	ALL	1880	156078	NFK	ALL
1775	1800	ALL	1775	146226	NFK	Garboldisham
1750	1900	....	....	171824	SCT	Dunbarton
....	....	1842	1992	107999	SSX	Brighton
1780	1860	ALL	1780	119687	SSX	Cuckfield
1871	1900	....	....	119687	SSX	Handeross
1780	1836	ALL	1780	115118	SSX	Northchapel
1850	1900	1700	1850	133892	STS	ALL
1750	1860	....	....	164631	STS	Colwich
1842	1883	1850	1992	109819	STS	Rowley Regis
1850	1900	1700	1850	133892	WAR	ALL
1833	1842	ALL	1833	109819	WOR	Dudley
1617	1646	1500	1992	102520	YKS	Halifax
1750	1900	1650	1750	134317	YKS	Halifax
HOLDER						
1790	1885	1750	1900	157171	GLS	Newnham On Severn
1734	1762	1700	1800	121525	GLS	Painswick
1800	1927	1700	1800	139335	GLS	Painswick
1773	1840	1700	1773	173770	HAM	South
1821	1899	1700	1880	178233	HAM	Petersfield
1813	1813	....	....	127426	HEF	Dorstone
1804	1804	....	....	127426	HEF	Kinnersley
1746	1785	....	....	127426	HEF	???
1866	1887	ALL	1880	118737	LND	St Pancras
1850	1891	1840	1900	105120	WAR	Birmingham
1734	1775	1680	1734	116114	YKS	Barmston
1766	1881	1766	1881	116114	YKS	Bridlington
HOLDERNESS						
1790	1860	1550	1790	150843	YKS	Ottringham
HOLDFORTH						
1794	1834	1770	1850	170143	SRY	Woking
HOLDGATE						
1814	1860	1800	1880	124788	DBY	Bradshaw Edge
HOLDICH						
....	....	ALL	ALL	134325	ALL	Name Study
1735	1940	....	....	128996	CAM	Thorney
HOLDING						
1803	1841	1760	1803	174211	LAN	Bury
1828	1900	....	....	171824	LAN	St Helens
1850	1960	1730	1992	176524	LAN	St Helens
1810	1810	1775	1825	136042	MDX	???
HOLDIP						
....	....	ALL	ALL	134341	ALL	Name Study
HOLDOM						
1860	1890	....	....	111368	BDF	Caddington
1790	1840	....	....	111368	BKM	Great Brickhill
1850	1870	....	....	111368	SRY	Bermondsey
HOLDOWAY						
....	1803	1700	1803	178608	KEN	Greenaythe
HOLDSTOCK						
1772	1869	....	1772	108839	BDF	Datchworth
HOLDSTOCK contd.						
1763	1800	1650	1830	100382	KEN	Appledore
1907	1907	....	....	127426	KEN	Lenham
1874	1992	1600	1874	128465	KEN	Lydd
1830	1960	1830	1960	100382	KEN	Rolvenden
HOLDSWORTH						
1828	....	....	1828	101761	WRY	Leeds
....	1786	1700	1786	160024	YKS	Clayton
1815	1846	1815	1870	123250	YKS	Halifax
....	....	1830	1884	155039	YKS	Halifax
1862	1992	1826	1862	147060	YKS	Leeds
1790	1924	1600	1800	134368	YKS	Ripon
1796	1912	ALL	1796	103004	YKS	Sheffield
HOLDWAY						
1780	1895	1750	1945	124974	HAM	Ashmansworth
1783	1812	1700	1783	127116	HAM	Smannell
460	585	460	585	124974	NFK	ALL
....	....	1825	1895	124974	STS	ALL
HOLE						
1700	1800	1650	1700	106194	DBY	Ashover
1792	1930	1700	1792	139815	DEV	Cookbury
1720	1755	....	....	165999	LEI	Leicester
....	1880	....	1880	119024	SOM	Bruton
1700	1850	1650	1850	123722	SOM	Luxborough
1731	1764	ALL	1992	119695	SOM	West Pennard
1850	1950	1850	1950	154903	SOM	Westbury
1707	1736	1650	1707	174807	SSX	Woodmancote
HOLFORD						
1827	1885	ALL	ALL	110388	HAM	Portsea
1806	1950	1841	1950	100668	SSX	Framfield
1866	1942	1700	1866	170542	WOR	Little Comberton
HOLGATE						
....	....	1800	1900	123765	CAM	ALL
1841	1881	....	....	134384	LAN	Blackburn
1720	1870	1720	1870	127655	LAN	Burnley
1907	1930	....	....	134384	LAN	Oswaldtwistle
1720	1870	1720	1870	127655	LAN	Padiham
1811	1842	1700	1811	134384	YKS	Bolton By Bowland
1811	1842	1700	1811	134384	YKS	Grindleton
....	....	1803	1992	155039	YKS	Halifax
1760	1868	1700	1760	177555	YKS	Hatfield
HOLHURST						
1781	....	1700	1800	168912	CHS	Over Peover
HOLIDAY						
1653	1940	....	....	128996	CAM	Thorney
HOLKYN						
1610	1635	ALL	1635	168718	CON	South East
HOLLAH						
1753	....	....	....	136999	CON	Gulval
HOLLAMS						
1740	1763	1700	1763	148288	KEN	Brookland
HOLLAND						
1715	1940	1650	1800	117005	BDF	Eaton Bray
1800	1900	1750	1900	177180	BDF	Woburn
1865	1900	1750	1850	171891	BKM	High Wycombe
1791	....	....	1791	177504	CAM	Littleport
1840	1866	1758	1840	163686	CHS	Cheadle
1840	1885	1840	1891	134406	CHS	Nantwich
1773	1887	1720	1887	134406	CHS	Tarporley
1773	1887	1720	1887	134406	CHS	Tiverton
1850	1925	1750	1992	162183	DBY	ALL
1775	1861	....	....	173827	DBY	Newhall
1780	1850	1768	1870	117145	DBY	South Normanton
1700	1826	1600	1800	161950	DOR	Portland
1829	1992	ALL	1829	175994	DOR	Weymouth
1754	1795	1754	1795	161950	DOR	Wyke Regis
1897	....	....	....	101869	DUR	City
1798	1964	ALL	ALL	113662	GLS	Newent
1782	1830	1500	1830	175463	HAM	ALL
1740	1860	1700	1850	136840	HAM	Fareham
1800	1830	1700	1830	148792	HAM	Wootton St Lawrence
1780	1858	1700	1780	115460	HRT	Kesworth
1869	1992	1700	1869	103950	KEN	Gravesend
1869	1877	1869	1900	126705	LAN	Chorlton
1769	1992	1650	1769	166138	LAN	Manchester
1786	1844	1756	1786	139149	LAN	Paidham
1820	1875	1800	1820	113050	LAN	Worsley
1799	1865	1799	1865	160504	LND	ALL
1853	1900	1800	1900	134422	LND	Southwark
1870	1992	ALL	ALL	163368	NTT	Gotham
1830	1874	1800	1900	134422	SOM	Bristol
1800	1880	1750	1800	101427	SSX	North
1827	1943	1813	1827	101427	SSX	Horsham
1780	1800	1700	1780	166154	SSX	Lewes

Known From	To	Researching From	To	Ref	Cty	Place
HOLLAND contd.						
1790	?	ALL	ALL	166243	SSX	Nuthurst
1800	?	ALL	ALL	166243	SSX	Shipley
1900	1992	....	....	100536	SSX	???
....	....	1700	1800	126357	STS	Barton Under Needwood
1700	1800	1600	1900	150002	STS	Barton Under Needwood
1845	1953	1700	1845	176052	STS	Birmingham
1878	....	ALL	1900	139459	STS	Cradley
1813	1929	1750	1900	122351	STS	Odd Rode
1878	....	ALL	1900	139459	STS	Tipton
1574	1633	1500	1650	160873	STS	Walsall
1850	1912	1830	1912	177709	STS	Wednesbury
1841	1862	....	....	102733	WAR	Birmingham
....	....	ALL	1700	103284	WOR	Bristol
1816	1900	1700	1900	152714	WOR	Worcester
1870	1890	1800	1890	141496	WYK	Leeds
1820	1865	1700	1820	176516	WYK	Sheffield
1897	....	....	....	101869	???	Berwick On Tweed
HOLLANDS						
1860	1950	1700	1860	141119	KEN	Dartford
1816	1992	1700	1816	134430	SSX	Withyham
1900	1980	1800	1900	174734	SXE	Central
HOLLAWAY						
....	....	1800	1900	129275	KEN	Gravesend
HOLLEBON						
1770	1992	....	1770	152242	SSX	Eastbourne
1770	1992	....	1770	152242	SSX	Seaford
HOLLELY						
1660	1880	1500	1660	170194	DBY	Barlow Lees
1729	1975	1637	....	134449	DBY	Barlow
1567	....	1567	1729	134449	DBY	Beeley
1861	1902	1861	1902	134449	NTT	Edwinstowe
1902	1937	1902	1937	134449	NTT	Matlock
1902	1937	1902	1937	134449	NTT	Worksop
HOLLES						
1770	1770	1750	1800	136840	IOW	Newchurch
HOLLEY						
1860	1881	1800	1960	176869	GLS	Bristol
1850	1992	1700	1850	157449	SOM	Bath
HOLLIBONE						
1725	....	ALL	1725	115282	SSX	East
HOLLICK						
....	....	ALL	ALL	134465	ALL	Name Study
1772	1826	1720	1780	170348	WIL	Wroughton
HOLLIDAY						
1850	1890	1850	1890	134481	CHS	Crew
1730	1803	ALL	1900	131334	CMA	Holmecultram
1800	1830	1700	1830	134481	CUL	Arthuret
1713	1780	1600	1713	140678	CUL	Kirkland
1805	....	1805	....	115576	KEN	???
1830	1850	1830	1850	134481	LAN	Blackburn
1730	1803	ALL	1900	131334	LAN	???
1720	1992	ALL	ALL	172901	LND	ALL
1760	1823	1700	1823	168920	LND	Bermondsey
1800	1900	ALL	ALL	131873	LND	Hackney
1800	1900	ALL	ALL	131873	LND	Islington
1800	1850	ALL	ALL	131873	LND	Lambeth
1850	1915	ALL	ALL	157864	LND	Southwark
1800	1830	1600	1800	134708	MDX	Stoke Newington
1720	1992	ALL	ALL	172901	OXF	ALL
1724	1851	1650	1900	118397	OXF	Bampton
1823	1960	1720	1823	134473	SRY	Islington
1790	1870	1700	1790	137278	YKS	Roecliffe
HOLLIDGE						
1826	1900	1600	1826	146161	NFK	Norwich
HOLLIER						
1796	1796	1760	1830	105333	HAM	Isle Of Wight
1770	1851	1600	1851	145289	HAM	Isle Of Wight
....	....	1750	1870	176125	SOM	Burrington
1700	1871	1700	1861	131024	SRY	Lambeth
1870	1930	....	....	176125	WIL	Devizes
HOLLIES						
1819	1871	1700	1871	121150	WOR	Dudley
HOLLIGRENE						
1620	1660	1600	1680	160873	STS	Sedgley
HOLLIMAN						
1800	....	....	....	112534	BKM	ALL
1858	1992	1858	1992	112534	BKM	Long Crendon
1858	1992	1858	1992	112534	CAM	Cambridge
1887	....	1800	....	162752	HRT	???
1858	1992	1858	1992	112534	LND	Chelsea
HOLLIN						
1844	1851	1844	1992	124087	DNB	Bonhill
1826	1840	1800	1992	124087	LAN	Accrington
HOLLINGDALE						
1780	....	....	....	145920	SSX	Shorham
HOLLINGS						
1900	1992	1700	1900	111066	WRY	ALL
1800	1897	1700	1897	156086	YKS	Hunslet
HOLLINGSBEE						
1680	1900	ALL	ALL	134503	KEN	East
HOLLINGSWORTH						
1771	1817	1600	1771	112321	DBY	Melbourne
1750	1922	1700	1750	167649	HRT	Ashwell
1790	1830	1750	1800	120529	LIN	Grantham
1870	1930	ALL	ALL	167940	SFK	Ipswich
1870	1930	ALL	ALL	167940	SFK	Sudbury
1960	1992	1700	1960	171913	???	???
HOLLINGWORTH						
1412	1992	ALL	ALL	134511	ALL	ALL
1850	1900	....	1850	118451	LAN	Ashton Under Lyne
1790	1830	1750	1800	120529	LIN	Grantham
1800	1860	1750	1861	166952	YKS	Kirkburton
HOLLINPRIEST						
1821	1834	ALL	ALL	168815	ALL	ALL
HOLLINRAKE						
1851	1912	1800	1880	174580	YKS	Bradford
1806	1992	1700	1806	123730	YKS	Todmorden
1832	?	1800	1851	174580	YKS	Todmordon
HOLLINS						
1800	1830	1600	1992	167592	CHS	Manchester
1750	1992	1600	1750	169676	HAM	Portsea
1840	1992	ALL	1992	134538	MON	Chepstow
1720	1760	1600	1992	167592	STS	Hanley
1850	....	1750	1900	109894	STS	Leigh
1800	1816	1800	1816	147532	STS	Litchfield
1760	1800	1600	1992	167592	STS	Shelton
1840	1850	1700	1992	167592	STS	Stoke
1780	1800	1700	1992	167592	STS	Woolstanton
1724	1766	1600	1724	110639	STS	???
1870	1900	1700	1870	121258	WAR	Coventry
HOLLINSHEAD						
1720	1977	....	....	137790	CHS	Church Minshull
HOLLINSON						
1810	1810	1750	1810	121509	LAN	Liverpool
HOLLIS						
....	....	1600	1850	137014	CAM	ALL
1823	....	1823	1935	105996	GLS	Maugersbury
1736	1766	1700	1736	145459	HAM	Fawley
....	....	1600	1850	137014	HUN	ALL
....	....	1800	1900	167045	MON	Caldicott
....	....	1600	1850	137014	NTH	ALL
1704	1729	ALL	1704	115126	NTH	Kingsthorpe
1715	1725	1650	1715	147885	NTH	Towcester
....	1670	ALL	ALL	129933	SRY	Ockham
....	....	1700	1800	126357	STS	Barton Under Needwood
1791	1949	1600	1791	112410	STS	Hanley
....	....	1600	1850	137014	WAR	ALL
HOLLISTER						
....	....	ALL	ALL	160334	ALL	Name Study
1770	1870	1770	1870	120235	WIL	Chisledon
HOLLMAN						
1800	1992	1800	1992	111589	KEN	Ightham
HOLLOBON						
1869	....	....	....	166723	SSX	Eastbourne
HOLLOW						
1665	1685	1600	1665	102571	CON	Zennor
HOLLOWAY						
....	....	1600	1950	134546	BDF	Knotting
....	....	1600	1950	134546	BDF	Melchbourne
....	....	1600	1950	134546	BDF	Yielden
1770	....	1700	1800	143693	BRK	Sulham
1736	1750	1630	1780	143693	BRK	Waltham St Lawrence
1615	1992	1500	1992	136794	DBY	ALL
1851	1881	ALL	ALL	155608	DBY	ALL
1765	1799	1700	1765	128724	ESS	Colchester
1740	1870	1600	1870	154342	GLS	Stapleton
1770	1850	1600	1770	162361	GLS	Wootten Under Edge
1669	1794	ALL	ALL	117307	HAM	South
1780	1900	ALL	ALL	122866	HAM	Andover
1820	1920	1800	1900	136840	HAM	Andover
1805	1820	....	....	133221	HAM	Breamore
1698	1775	1698	1775	104817	HAM	Eling
1710	1780	1650	1780	136840	HAM	Fordingbridge

Known From	To	Researching From	To	Ref	Cty	Place
HOLLOWAY contd.						
1915	1923	1837	1915	171247	HAM	Odiham
1779	1790	1750	1800	100242	HAM	Pamber
1669	1698	1634	1700	104817	HAM	Romsey
1740	1780	1740	1780	114073	HAM	Upper Clatford
1922	1927	1922	1927	171247	HAM	Winchfield
....	....	1870	1920	134546	LND	Balham
....	....	1870	1920	134546	LND	Battersea
1837	1866	1780	1837	162523	LND	St Pancras
1805	....	1805	....	161527	LND	Westminster
....	....	1870	1920	134546	MDX	Ashford
....	....	1805	....	161527	MDX	Marylebone
1820	1992	1750	1820	115312	MDX	???
1722	1745	ALL	1722	115126	NTH	Brafield On The Green
1826	1992	ALL	ALL	155608	NTT	ALL
1870	1954	....	....	106720	OXF	Chadlington
1730	....	1700	....	101966	SSX	Aldingbourne
1826	....	....	....	101966	SSX	Ardingly
....	....	1900	1920	134546	SSX	East Grinstead
....	....	1930	1970	134546	SSX	Hastings
1770	....	1700	....	101966	SSX	Litlington
1840	1980	....	....	120472	WAR	Aston
1790	1850	1650	1790	170194	WAR	Birmingham
1840	1980	....	....	120472	WAR	Yardley
1784	1820	....	....	133221	WIL	Downton
1730	1752	1632	1759	147486	WIL	Potterne
1790	1820	1750	1820	158658	WIL	Westbury
1805	1850	1775	1887	104817	WIL	Whiteparish
1856	1901	1901	1992	145432	WOR	Kidderminster
1770	1992	ALL	ALL	177989	WOR	Oldbury
1780	1980	1538	1980	117617	WOR	Worcester
1825	1830	1700	1850	145432	WOR	Worcester
HOLLOWELL						
1755	1992	1575	1755	134554	NTH	???
1825	1891	1750	1825	174203	SRY	North
HOLLOX						
1830	1870	1830	,870	118206	NFK	Feltwell
HOLLYOAK						
1860	1890	....	....	174815	STS	West Bromwich
HOLLYWOOD						
1895	1992	....	....	112232	DUB	Dublin
HOLMAN						
1700	1723	ALL	1723	168718	CON	South East
1801	1801	1100	1801	117749	CON	Crowan
1700	1850	1600	1850	134562	CON	Lawhitton
1837	1889	1889	1992	162973	CON	Liskeard
1838	1992	1700	1838	130257	CON	South Petherwin
1837	1870	1870	....	162973	CON	St Cleer
1683	1724	1600	1730	134562	DEV	Bradstone
1830	1890	1500	1900	134562	DEV	Lifton
1870	1930	1700	1960	101907	KEN	Strood
1786	?	?	?	166642	KEN	???
1750	1860	1750	1880	118818	NTH	Welford
1711	1733	....	....	171654	SOM	Crewkerne
1750	1800	1700	1900	111589	SRY	Godstone
1700	1750	1700	1750	111589	SSX	Crowhurst
ALL	ALL	ALL	ALL	131164	SSX	Mid
1900	1908	....	....	153982	YKS	Hull
HOLMDEN						
....	....	1800	1992	125660	KEN	Edenbridge
HOLME						
1819	1850	1750	1850	107654	DBY	Tideswell
....	1769	....	1769	128910	LAN	Bury
1800	1900	....	....	146854	LAN	Lancaster
....	....	1740	1850	147613	LAN	Melling
1832	1992	1700	1832	164208	LAN	Morecambe
....	....	1740	1900	147613	LAN	Tatham
....	....	1740	1900	147613	LAN	Tunstall
1820	1900	1600	1820	142646	WES	Crosby
1736	1780	1711	....	138401	WES	Killington
1736	1780	1711	....	138401	WES	Kirkby Lonsdale
1820	1900	1600	1820	142646	WES	Ravensworth
1820	1900	1600	1820	142646	WES	Thrimby
....	....	1800	1950	147613	YKS	Bentham
....	....	1700	1750	147613	YKS	Ingleton
HOLMES						
1880	1941	ALL	ALL	150681	ANT	Aghalee
1858	1927	1850	1930	146536	AYR	Dalry
....	....	1800	1830	117137	BRE	Llangattoch
1720	1760	1670	1720	156930	BRK	ALL
1828	....	....	....	141356	BRK	Ashampstead
1700	1800	1670	1800	156930	BRK	Leckhampstead
1780	1810	1700	1810	124605	BRK	Reading
HOLMES contd.						
1700	....	....	1740	171441	BRK	Shrivenham
1654	1940	....	....	128996	CAM	Thorney
1900	1920	1800	1900	168815	CHS	ALL
1800	1870	ALL	1800	154563	CUL	Alston
1788	....	1788	....	147532	CUL	Carlisle
1829	1992	....	1929	161691	DBY	Derby
1750	1992	....	....	144304	DBY	Twyford
....	....	1800	1850	148113	DBY	???
1818	1881	....	1818	165484	DEV	Plymouth
1784	1816	1770	1820	165972	DEV	Tiverton
1832	1870	....	....	115290	DEV	Totnes
1828	1895	1750	1828	167525	ESS	Halstead
1930	....	....	....	144169	HEF	Much Marcle
1800	1960	....	....	153486	HUN	???
1530	1992	1530	1992	145769	KEN	ALL
1870	1906	....	....	162442	KEN	???
1640	?	?	?	166642	KEN	???
1820	1900	1800	1900	168815	LAN	ALL
1763	1992	1650	1763	163783	LAN	Barton
....	....	1800	1970	111503	LAN	Blackburn
1858	1862	ALL	1862	133159	LAN	Liverpool
1840	1880	1830	1900	158216	LAN	Manchester
....	....	ALL	ALL	166812	LAN	Manchester
1880	1992	1700	1880	138657	LAN	Salford
1832	1848	ALL	1992	133159	LAN	Ulverston
1826	1950	1700	1826	140260	LAN	Wigan
1800	1900	1800	1900	134597	LAN	Worsley
1604	1604	....	....	103632	LIN	Foston
1857	1992	....	1900	178861	LND	Islington
1875	1992	1800	1875	110043	LND	Marylebone
1841	1876	....	1841	142166	MDX	Edeware
1853	1936	1700	1900	126683	NFK	Blakeney
1750	1900	1750	1900	162914	NFK	Burnham Westgate
1750	1900	1750	1900	162914	NFK	Kings Lynn
....	....	1700	1850	140627	NFK	Norwich
1861	1950	1700	1861	179051	NFK	Wareham
1851	1992	1780	1851	118486	NRY	Husthwaite
1933	1933	1858	1933	125717	NTH	???
....	1750	ALL	1750	134511	NTT	Calverton
....	1780	ALL	1780	134511	NTT	Cotgrave
1820	1860	1750	1850	116572	NTT	???
1830	....	1700	1850	158216	NTT	???
1750	1780	....	....	140554	OXF	Mapledurham
....	....	1700	1850	140627	SFK	Raidon
1750	1925	1750	1925	109002	SRY	Bagshot
1750	1925	1750	1925	109002	SRY	Chobham
1880	1910	1840	1880	134139	SSX	Brighton
1845	1860	1800	1900	121541	STS	Brieryley Hill
....	....	....	1832	115290	STS	Stone
1826	1960	1826	1960	105147	STS	Tipton
1802	ALL	1750	1850	134627	STS	Walsall
1500	1800	....	....	100420	WAR	Meriden
1595	1760	1595	1760	127655	WAR	Newham
1595	1760	1595	1760	127655	WAR	Wolfhampcote
1700	1900	....	....	146854	WES	Orton
1848	1972	1700	1848	174335	YKS	Attercliffe
1830	1927	1750	1830	165018	YKS	Beverley
1750	1992	1700	1992	134589	YKS	Bolton Percy
1840	1880	1840	1900	153737	YKS	Leeds
1890	1928	....	1928	113034	YKS	Middlesborough
1830	1927	1750	1830	165018	YKS	Scarborough
1848	1972	1700	1848	174335	YKS	Sheffield
1611	1700	1550	1620	176451	YKS	Skipton
1850	1930	1814	1850	136824	YKS	Stainforth
1790	1835	1750	1850	153737	YKS	Wakefield
1819	1850	1700	1819	171980	???	Bristol
HOLMS						
1670	1720	1640	1720	135941	SFK	Lakenheath
HOLMSTEAD						
1860	1860	1800	1860	176672	ESS	ALL
HOLMWOCD						
1841	1851	ALL	1841	165263	SSX	Rotherfield
HOLNES						
1818	1818	1700	1900	178624	KEN	Folkestone
HOLNESS						
1791	1950	1700	1791	149195	KEN	East
1812	1870	....	....	130281	KEN	Blean
1828	1840	1800	1828	155217	KEN	Dover
1790	1992	1500	1992	129925	KEN	???
HOLNEY						
1400	1600	....	....	164038	SSX	Henfield
HOLROYD						
1815	1900	1800	1900	134643	LAN	Lees

Known From	To	Researching From	To	Ref	Cty	Place
HOLROYD contd.						
1815	1900	1800	1900	134643	LAN	Oldham
1750	1870	1750	1870	153621	WYK	Ripponden
1571	1756	1400	1815	134643	WYK	Rishworth
1815	1860	1800	1900	134643	WYK	Saddleworth
1571	1756	1400	1815	134643	WYK	Stainland
1873	1886	1840	1890	123250	YKS	Brighouse
1842	1873	1840	1880	123250	YKS	Halifax
1887	1992	1870	1992	123250	YKS	Hull
1832	....	....	....	161136	YKS	Sheffield
HOLSWORTH						
1880	1920	ALL	ALL	130508	LND	St Pancras
HOLT						
1800	1992	1700	1800	135747	BKM	Edgcott
....	....	1800	1847	137758	BRK	Abingdon
1673	1940	....	....	128996	CAM	Thorney
1865	1949	....	....	116475	CHS	Altringham
1822	1832	1822	1870	160636	CHS	Mottram In Longdendale
1886	1900	1800	1992	170569	CHS	Stockport
1910	1970	....	....	101176	DBY	Derby
1860	1920	1500	1920	137472	DBY	Derby
1780	1820	ALL	1800	115266	DOR	ALL
1750	1900	1700	1900	123722	DOR	Broadwindsor
1869	....	1850	1870	152110	DUR	Stranton
....	....	1830	1840	152110	DUR	W Hartlepool
1730	1992	1600	1730	166103	ESS	Theydon Mount
....	....	1700	1800	167916	HEF	Bromyard
1737	1764	....	....	138851	LAN	Bolton
1787	1852	ALL	1787	169285	LAN	Bolton
1800	1800	1750	1851	160636	LAN	Brackley
....	....	1700	1992	111503	LAN	Chorley
1865	1927	1865	1927	134686	LAN	Clayton
1866	1957	1866	1957	160636	LAN	Denton
1700	1720	1600	1992	167592	LAN	Liverpool
1755	1860	1755	1860	159492	LAN	Manchester With Salford
....	1836	ALL	1836	127000	LAN	Manchester
....	....	1820	1950	173940	LAN	Manchester
1846	....	....	....	156868	LAN	Oldham
1861	1992	1861	1992	159492	LAN	Oldham
1798	1860	1798	1860	134686	LAN	Pilkington
1809	1851	1750	1851	179078	LAN	Rossendale
1787	1852	ALL	1787	169285	LAN	Upholland
1787	1852	ALL	1787	169285	LAN	Wigan
....	....	1700	1750	115142	LEI	Leicester
1860	1920	1800	1860	132438	LIN	Boston
1800	1865	ALL	1800	120952	LIN	Broughton
1800	1865	ALL	1800	120952	LIN	Frodingham
....	....	....	....	134651	LIN	Louth
1891	....	ALL	1891	120952	LIN	Winterton
1845	1860	ALL	ALL	137758	LKS	Glasgow
1885	....	1885	....	135488	LND	Bermondsey
....	....	1800	1992	101176	MON	ALL
1767	1850	1700	1767	156426	STS	North
1712	1927	....	....	117404	STS	Church Eaton
1850	1880	....	1850	123161	WAR	Birmingham
....	....	1700	1992	101176	WOR	ALL
1800	1992	1700	1900	134678	WYK	Huddersfield
1800	1992	1700	1900	134678	WYK	Lindley
1800	1900	1700	1800	134651	YKS	Mirfield
1915	....	ALL	1915	120952	YKS	Sheffield
1795	1871	1770	1870	121126	YKS	Southowram
1820	....	....	....	120804	???	Halifax
HOLTBY						
....	....	1770	1828	135003	NYK	Allerston
HOLTE						
1752	....	....	1752	101761	LAN	Middleton
1850	1880	....	1850	123161	WAR	Birmingham
HOLTER						
1900	1970	....	....	122130	SSX	Barcombe
1800	1900	....	....	122130	SSX	Westham
HOLTHAM						
1873	1873	1820	1992	131865	WAR	Coventry
1873	1873	1820	1992	131865	WAR	Foleshill
HOLTOM						
1815	1832	1800	1830	171654	NTH	Potterspury
HOLTON						
1780	1875	ALL	ALL	153753	BKM	Bow Brickhill
1770	1800	1600	1770	104469	BKM	Tingewell
HOLTORF						
1854	1854	1700	1854	164879	LND	St George In The East

Known From	To	Researching From	To	Ref	Cty	Place
HOLTUM						
1685	1900	1650	1700	142395	KEN	Preston Wingham
HOLWAY						
....	....	ALL	ALL	155780	ALL	ALL
HOLWELL						
1756	1912	1700	1992	156493	LND	ALL
HOLYER						
....	....	ALL	ALL	134740	ALL	Name Study
HOLYFIELD						
1783	1889	1783	1890	143774	BRK	Appleton
1695	1760	1695	1760	143774	NTH	Kings Sutton
1700	1900	1740	1885	143774	OXF	ALL
1740	....	1740	....	143774	OXF	Northleigh
1671	1740	1670	1750	143774	WAR	Birmingham
HOLYHEAD						
1785	1966	1760	1966	169323	STS	Wednesbury
HOLYOAK						
1880	1992	1700	1880	146064	GLS	Bristol
1801	1850	1600	1805	110787	LEI	Cosby
HOLYOAKE						
....	....	....	1835	178985	WAR	Morton Bagot
....	....	....	1653	178985	WAR	Southam
HOMAN						
1596	1690	1500	1700	176745	KEN	Thanet
HOMBSTRON						
1560	1700	1560	1700	167924	HRT	Bennington
HOME						
1808	1919	?	1808	143324	ANS	Forfar
1867	1929	1867	1929	151599	KEN	Ramsgate
1740	1867	1700	1867	151599	SAL	Bishops Gate
HOMER						
....	....	1790	1992	147613	STS	Rowley Regis
1830	1992	1700	1830	158518	STS	Rowley Regis
....	....	1800	1900	166383	WAR	Birmingham
1840	1880	1800	1900	142174	WOR	Cradley
HOMES						
1600	1992	1600	1992	134759	MDX	London
HOMEWOOD						
1770	1826	1700	1770	166820	KEN	Borden
....	1760	1600	1850	175641	KEN	Eynsford
1770	1880	ALL	ALL	131164	KEN	Tudety
....	....	1830	1860	162647	LND	East End
1600	1992	1600	1992	169250	SRY	Horley
1600	1992	1600	1992	169250	SRY	Pembury
1600	1992	1600	1992	169250`	SRY	Southwark
HOMRETH						
1841	....	1810	1860	149292	DOW	Groomsport
HONE						
1816	1850	1800	1850	178330	KEN	Milton
1800	1900	1800	1850	114405	LND	South
1800	1850	....	....	178330	LND	Hammersmith
1830	1880	....	....	128759	LND	Westminster
1800	1992	ALL	1800	134783	OXF	Goring
1780	1863	1760	1870	159905	OXF	Swalcliffe
1692	1751	1650	1800	159905	WAR	Brailes
1770	1992	1550	1770	134775	WAR	Honington
1816	1869	1816	1900	159905	WAR	Warmington
HONEL						
1841	1950	1750	1840	135658	GLA	Llantwit Major
HONER						
1860	....	ALL	ALL	154091	MDX	Hackney
HONESS						
1794	....	....	....	135402	KEN	Goudhurst
HONEY						
1756	1846	1756	1761	153176	BRK	Sunningwell
1770	1880	1770	1850	138096	CON	Talland
1860	1980	1860	1980	148873	DEV	Plymouth
1743	....	ALL	1743	114987	DEV	Torquay
....	....	1750	1825	151084	LND	East
....	....	ALL	ALL	174033	SRY	Kingston
HONEYBALL						
....	....	ALL	ALL	134791	ALL	Name Study
....	1800	1600	1850	175641	SFK	Denston
HONEYCOMBE						
....	....	ALL	ALL	166758	ALL	Name Study
ALL	ALL	ALL	ALL	166758	ALL	ALL
....	....	1800	1992	122076	CON	St Cleer
HONEYGETT						
1718	1820	1650	1750	165980	SSX	Dallington
HONEYMAN						
1899	1992	....	....	170453	FIF	ALL
HONEYSETT						
1798	1820	1540	1850	176621	SSX	Battle
1800	?	1540	1800	134805	SXE	???

Known From	To	Researching From	To	Ref	Cty	Place
HONEYWELL						
1850	....	1850	1940	150444	DEV	Ashburton
HONEYWOOD						
....	....	ALL	ALL	127337	ALL	Name Study
1800	1900	1800	1942	131407	SFK	Norfolk Border
HONIE						
1672	1694	1550	1672	139084	KEN	Shipbourne
HONNER						
1836	1852	1809	1852	104604	LND	Central
HONNOR						
1650	1760	1600	1900	177180	HRT	St Albans
HONOREE						
1767	ALL	ALL	1770	116734	MDX	Bethnal Green
1767	ALL	ALL	1770	116734	MDX	Shoreditch
1767	ALL	ALL	1770	116734	MDX	St Leonards
HONOUR						
....	....	ALL	ALL	135658	ALL	Name Study
1500	1600	....	....	142425	BDF	Gabriel Honour
1660	1800	1600	1800	142123	BDF	Shillington
1845	1930	1700	1845	171891	BKM	Seer Green
1650	1870	1500	1900	177180	BKM	Wing
1841	1950	1750	1840	135658	GLA	Llantwit Major
....	....	1700	1850	135658	GLS	ALL
1600	1900	....	....	142425	OXF	Bicester
1713	1820	1600	1900	107565	OXF	Charlton On Otmoor
HONY						
1750	1992	1750	1992	134813	CON	Bodmin
1750	1992	1750	1992	134813	CON	Liskeard
HONYBONE						
1833	1851	1500	1833	110310	BRK	Newbury
1827	1851	1500	1827	110310	WIL	Swindon
HOOD GRANVILLE						
....	....	1700	1900	122203	DEV	???
....	....	1700	1900	122203	SOM	???
HOOD						
1840	1900	ALL	ALL	130508	ABD	Aberdeen
1816	1952	1700	1829	163244	ANS	Brechin
1789	....	1770	1841	169625	ANT	Ballynagashel
1789	....	1770	1841	169625	ANT	Larne
1680	1850	ALL	1850	149063	BEW	Bunkle
1680	1850	ALL	1850	149063	BEW	Coldingham
1660	1765	1550	1765	102830	DBY	Alkmanton
....	....	1700	1900	122203	DEV	???
1750	1800	1650	1750	108413	GLS	Hinton
1740	1800	1600	1800	154342	IRL	Waterford
1850	1866	1850	1992	163244	KCD	Nigg
1684	1992	....	1684	144363	LEI	Castledunnington
1805	1870	1770	1805	120286	ROX	Bowden
1809	1828	ALL	1828	156175	SFK	Haughley
....	....	1700	1900	122203	SOM	???
1800	1850	1600	1800	160229	WIL	Lacock
1817	1845	1700	1817	128031	YKS	Sculcoates
HOODINOTT						
....	....	?	?	159069	GLS	Bristol
HOODLESS						
1780	1840	1600	1780	146730	CUL	Passim
1760	1870	1700	1870	107441	MDX	London
HOOK						
1650	1830	1650	1830	138894	BKM	Marsh Gibbon
1712	1992	1580	1712	159239	DOR	Blandford
....	....	1760	1860	131962	DOR	Minterne
1780	1970	ALL	ALL	176907	GLS	West
1802	1848	....	....	144282	KEN	Darenth
1802	1848	....	....	144282	KEN	Dartford
1791	1825	ALL	1791	147877	LEI	Long Whatton
1630	1761	1630	1761	138894	OXF	Piddington
1700	1900	1500	1900	102555	SOM	Spaxton
1820	1870	1820	1900	113743	SSX	Brede
1770	1850	....	....	122130	SSX	Brightling
1860	1890	1800	1950	151246	SSX	Hastings
1880	1970	....	....	122130	SSX	Ripe
1800	1970	....	....	122130	SSX	Rotherfield
1686	1870	1600	1686	165980	SSX	Wartling
HOOKE						
1845	1895	1750	1850	103055	LEI	Leicester
....	....	1870	....	145998	LND	???
HOOKER						
....	....	1870	1880	126675	BDF	Luton
1750	1900	1700	1900	124699	HAM	East
1806	1881	1770	1992	121827	HAM	East Stratton
1723	1770	1680	1722	121827	HAM	Easton
1761	1823	1740	1823	107573	HAM	Odiham
1806	1992	....	1806	103705	HAM	???
....	....	1865	1900	121827	HRT	Hatfield
HOOKER contd.						
1837	1981	ALL	1837	108642	HRT	Hemel Hempstead
1718	?	?	?	166642	KEN	Ashford
1915	1950	1800	1915	126675	KEN	Folkestone
1837	1981	ALL	1837	108642	MDX	Hayes
1837	1981	ALL	1837	108642	MDX	Hendon
1810	1835	1810	1881	136808	SRY	Lingfield
1863	....	....	....	173932	WIL	Sutton Veny
HOOKEY						
1600	1800	....	....	153397	HAM	Christchurch
1795	1940	1700	1795	118834	HAM	Portsmouth
1835	1950	1750	1835	148709	IOW	Gatcombe
HOOKHAM						
1890	1960	1800	1890	128775	LND	South
HOOKINS						
1771	1803	1700	1820	121525	DEV	Broad Clyst
HOOKWAY						
....	....	ALL	ALL	134821	ALL	Name Study
1854	....	....	....	145742	AVN	Bristol
1780	1881	1700	1780	167118	DEV	Monleigh
HOOLE						
1740	1940	....	....	128996	CAM	Thorney
....	....	1700	1800	146110	LAN	Preston
1839	1992	1500	1870	151483	YKS	Shefield
HOOLEY						
1550	1992	1550	1900	134848	ALL	ALL
1700	1850	1700	1850	135755	CHS	ALL
1800	1992	ALL	1800	168955	CHS	ALL
1837	1992	1550	1850	147265	CHS	East
1800	1992	ALL	1800	168955	CWD	ALL
....	....	1750	1850	130443	LEI	???
HOON						
1846	....	....	....	101869	LND	Stepney
HOOPER						
1800	1992	1750	1810	134856	CON	South East
1820	....	....	1890	152064	CON	Calstock
1800	1992	1800	1992	146943	CON	Delabole
1819	1992	1700	1819	140449	CON	Gwennap
1796	1800	1700	1992	146943	CON	Luxulyan
1691	1784	1500	1784	132993	CON	North Hill
1770	1850	ALL	1770	122823	CON	St Austell
1800	1900	1700	1900	162736	CON	St Cleer
1770	1850	ALL	1770	122823	CON	St Mewan
1770	1814	1650	1770	172898	DEV	Chudleigh
....	....	1600	1900	108766	DEV	Hatherleigh
1700	1900	1550	1900	108766	DEV	North Tawton
1779	1780	....	1779	131385	DEV	Topsham
1920	1992	ALL	1992	153311	DEV	Torquay
1800	1900	ALL	ALL	116823	DEV	Totnes
....	....	1800	1865	155551	DEV	Uffculme
1790	1943	1790	1943	176176	DEV	???
1810	1992	1600	1810	168084	DOR	Poole
1720	1720	1700	1720	165530	GLS	North Nibley
1750	1850	1700	1750	165530	GLS	Ozleworth
1750	1800	ALL	ALL	130508	HAM	Andover
1787	1838	1787	1838	103977	HRT	Aldenham
1787	1838	1787	1838	103977	HRT	Bushey
....	....	1780	1890	178284	KEN	Sandwich
1858	1947	....	....	135453	LND	Chelsea
1843	1868	1800	1843	138290	LND	Mary Le Bone
1843	1868	1800	1843	138290	MDX	Mary Le Bone
1706	1712	ALL	1706	159077	NTH	Tansor
1840	1900	1700	1840	167762	SOM	Bath
1838	1838	1838	1838	143286	SOM	Bishops Hull
....	....	1865	1910	155551	SOM	Wellington
1817	1849	1700	1817	127590	WIL	Atworth
1777	1859	1700	1777	145513	WIL	Collingbourne
1597	1725	1575	1785	145300	WIL	Edington
1817	1871	1812	1871	108901	WOR	Claines
1817	1871	1812	1871	108901	WOR	Hindlip
1840	....	....	....	102733	WOR	Malvgrn
1813	1933	1761	1933	108901	WOR	Tibberton
....	....	1750	....	166383	WOR	Worcester
HOOPPER						
1812	....	....	....	117579	DOR	Gillingham
1750	1800	....	....	117579	SOM	Bratton Seymour
HOOSON						
1740	1780	1700	1740	173312	FLN	Cilcain
HOOTON						
1767	1944	1700	1767	119075	BKM	Weston Underwood
1882	1938	1700	1882	174262	ENG	South
1882	1938	1700	1882	174262	ENG	Midlands
1837	1992	1700	1900	119377	NTT	Newark

Known From	To	Researching From	To	Ref	Cty	Place
HOPCRAFT						
1790	1900	1790	1900	131555	NTT	ALL
HOPCROFT						
1850	1992	1500	1850	141720	LND	Lambeth
1850	1992	1500	1850	141720	LND	Stepney
1790	1900	....	....	131555	NTT	ALL
HOPE						
1860	1992	1700	1860	155705	BEW	Maxton
1841	1900	1800	1841	149330	CHS	Nantwich
1814	1846	1555	1814	126462	CMA	Caldbeck
1883	1950	1700	1883	179051	DUR	St Giles
1819	1992	1810	1880	134864	LAN	Bolton
1889	1970	1889	1970	134864	LAN	Bury
1793	....	1745	1810	134864	LAN	Eccles
1793	....	1745	1810	134864	LAN	Manchester
1793	....	1745	1810	134864	LAN	Worsley
1860	1992	1700	1860	155705	ROX	Crailing
1860	1992	1700	1860	155705	ROX	Nenthorn
1761	1839	1700	1850	149098	STS	Burslem
1750	1810	1700	1750	132268	WAR	Burmington
1805	1910	ALL	1992	167878	WIL	Burbage
1864	1880	1888	1992	140635	WOR	ALL
1888	?	1888	1992	140635	WOR	Colwall
HOPELY						
....	....	ALL	ALL	170860	IRL	Wexford
HOPES						
1830	1900	1700	1830	143421	GLS	N Common
1785	1900	1785	1900	178705	OXF	Westwell
HOPGGOD						
1870	1870	1800	1870	177253	WIL	Milston
HOPGOOD						
1754	1835	1600	1753	153958	BRK	Bradfield
1580	1800	1600	1800	145661	WIL	Aldbourne
1580	1800	1600	1800	145661	WIL	Chute
1870	1920	1800	1870	177253	WIL	Durrington
HOPKIN						
1570	1720	1500	1650	101834	CAM	Central
1750	1850	1750	1850	141577	GLA	Llangynwd
1871	1992	1800	1871	178551	LEI	Waltham
HOPKINS						
1600	1850	ALL	ALL	124796	ALL	ALL
1731	1808	1700	1808	119059	BDF	Leighton Buzzard
1761	1837	1650	1800	143693	BKM	Bledlow
1762	1855	1650	1800	143693	BKM	West Wycombe
1800	1930	1820	1925	135925	BRK	Chaddleworth
1802	1939	1700	1802	123307	BRK	Kintbury
1800	1866	1600	1992	166804	BRK	Lambourn
1654	1940	....	....	128996	CAM	Thorney
1811	1952	1700	1811	165859	DEV	ALL
....	....	1700	1808	138614	DOR	Bridport
1790	1851	....	....	117579	DOR	Shaftesbury
1745	1825	1650	1800	139866	GLA	Gorseinon
1880	....	1850	1900	151181	GLA	Swansea
1760	1782	ALL	ALL	124982	GLS	South
1750	1827	....	....	122491	GLS	Berkeley
1607	1768	....	....	165999	GLS	Henbury
1770	1850	1600	1850	130125	GLS	Wickwar
1703	1703	1650	1750	148938	GLS	Wickwar
1800	1988	1700	1800	165271	GLS	Willersey
1840	1865	1760	1880	174599	GLS	Willersley
1830	1850	1750	1900	135925	HAM	Bournemouth
1800	1850	1700	1800	171182	HAM	Havant
1846	....	....	....	153397	HAM	New Forest
1760	1992	1700	1760	175846	HAM	Portsea
1840	1870	1800	1992	139181	HEF	Allensmore
1741	1992	1641	1992	134880	KEN	Elmsted
1860	1870	1860	1992	139181	LAN	Manchester
1856	....	1700	....	132128	LND	Poplar
1850	1960	1850	1850	134872	LND	Wandsworth
1816	1820	1700	1816	172898	MON	Llandogo
1815	1843	1600	1815	175781	SOM	Maiden Bradley
1750	1830	1650	1750	147583	SOM	Martock
1840	1861	1700	1840	138509	STS	Wolverhampton
1780	1992	1720	1780	154318	WAR	Birmingham
1800	1845	1780	1992	122416	WIC	???
1720	1780	....	....	142158	WIL	Aldbourne
1654	1850	....	....	124672	WIL	Swindon
1879	1880	1840	1879	167568	???	???
HOPKINSON						
1809	....	ALL	1992	159174	DBY	Alfreton
1840	1900	1700	1840	167762	DBY	Alfreton
1680	1860	1600	1680	106194	DBY	Ashover
1867	....	1700	1867	139386	DBY	Chesterfield
1778	....	ALL	1992	159174	DBY	South Wingfield
HOPKINSON contd.						
1845	1881	1700	1844	139122	DBY	Tibshelf
....	....	1770	1800	106127	ENG	???
1804	1804	ALL	1804	154563	WES	Kendal
1790	1992	1760	1992	152668	WYK	Birstall
1790	1992	1760	1992	152668	WYK	Huddersfield
1860	1890	1800	1860	150061	YKS	Bradford
HOPLEY						
1700	1992	1700	1992	158038	CHS	Chester
1700	1992	1700	1992	158038	CHS	Malpas
HOPPER						
....	....	ALL	ALL	144517	ALL	Name Study
1702	1800	....	....	134902	CAM	Great Gidding
1650	1900	1600	1992	140287	CAM	Great Gidding
1776	1802	ALL	1776	154563	DUR	Whickham
1647	1647	....	....	127426	KEN	Charing
1791	1808	ALL	1791	175080	KEN	Gravesend
1840	1960	1700	1840	134899	KEN	Kingsdown
1829	1939	1700	1801	104310	KEN	Maidstone
1840	1960	1700	1840	134899	KEN	Ringwould
1829	1939	1700	1801	104310	KEN	Rochester
?	?	?	?	166642	KEN	???
1840	1850	1800	1900	136174	TYR	Ballygawley
1830	1992	1830	1992	148210	TYR	Drumshambo
....	1819	1750	1819	138339	WOR	Ripple
1809	1861	1750	1809	158267	YKS	Wharram
HOPPING						
1795	1830	1700	1900	116742	MDX	Heston
HOPPINS						
1811	1855	1700	1800	173630	DEV	Plymouth
HOPPITT						
1950	1992	1950	1992	134910	CAM	Fulbourn
1775	1950	1775	1950	134910	CAM	Stapleford
HOPPS						
1780	1810	1700	1780	121339	NYK	Richmond
HOPPY						
....	....	1700	....	137456	CAM	Gransden
HOPSON						
1851	1992	1851	1900	103020	DEV	Bideford
1851	1992	1851	1900	103020	GLS	Cheltenham
1637	1992	1637	1900	103020	GLS	Stroud
1804	1839	ALL	1804	175080	GLS	Stroud
1818	1992	ALL	ALL	115762	LND	Holborn
1742	1886	1724	1886	156892	NRY	Overton
1833	1848	ALL	ALL	138223	SAL	Wellington
1799	1987	ALL	ALL	138223	STS	Tipton
1851	1861	ALL	ALL	138223	WOR	Dudley
HOPTON						
1827	1988	1800	1900	116386	YKS	Leeds
HOPWOOD						
1800	1810	1750	1900	113212	CAM	Ickleton
....	....	1764	1992	121940	DBY	Glossop
1780	1820	....	....	126497	LAN	Wigan
1840	1992	1840	1900	123463	LND	Bethnal Green
1820	1822	1700	1819	131245	NRY	New Malton
1752	1777	ALL	1777	127000	SAL	Whitchurch
HORA						
ALL	ALL	ALL	ALL	134929	ALL	ALL
1819	1820	ALL	ALL	134929	ESS	Harwich
1850	1900	ALL	ALL	134929	LND	Camberwell
HORABIN						
1832	1859	1859	1992	117099	LAN	Manchester
HORAM						
1846	1985	1750	1850	118516	HAM	Portsea
HORAN						
1850	1920	....	....	121185	KEN	ALL
1885	1928	1800	1885	174408	OFF	Clayne
HORDEN						
1780	1810	1538	1820	118893	DUR	???
HORDERN						
1500	1992	1200	1992	134937	ALL	ALL
1759	1818	1700	1818	141062	STS	Norton
HORDLEY						
1690	1854	....	....	117404	SAL	Alberbury
HORE						
1851	....	1700	1992	107204	DEV	Plymouth
HORGAN						
1853	1860	1860	1926	134945	SOM	Bristol
HORLER						
1804	1842	ALL	1804	166847	GLS	Bristol
1790	1864	1700	1992	176923	SOM	Holcombe
1741	1825	1700	1851	176923	SOM	Kilmersdon
1841	1861	1835	1861	176923	SOM	Midsomer Norton
1800	1900	1500	1800	179396	SOM	Midsomer Norton

Known From	To	Researching From	To	Ref	Cty	Place
HORLER contd.						
1871	1892	1861	1992	176923	SOM	Paulton
1874	1874	....	1874	121169	SOM	Radstock
HORLINGTON						
1700	1992	....	....	134953	MDX	London
HORLOCK						
1836	1980	ALL	1900	151017	SSX	Brighton
HORLOR						
....	....	1800	1850	113697	SOM	Lydicombe
....	....	1800	1850	113697	SOM	Widdicombe
HORN						
1780	....	....	....	126497	ABD	Forgue
....	....	1700	1950	161268	ABD	Forgue
1826	1881	1750	1826	106062	BDF	Stanbridge
1893	1964	....	1873	163228	CHS	Lancaster
1849	1885	1820	1900	116505	CUL	Penrith
1924	1934	1924	1928	133922	DEV	Exeter
1870	1920	1850	1930	176982	DEV	Plymouth
1780	1900	1780	1900	160814	DEV	Plymstock
1815	1860	1800	1900	155004	DNB	Kirkintilloch
1844	1850	1800	1900	163244	DNB	Kirkintilloch
1791	1900	1739	1925	116580	HAM	Portsmouth
1801	1865	ALL	1992	125113	KEN	Margate
1855	1900	1782	1854	151882	MDX	London
1850	1940	1750	1900	113859	SSX	Westbourne
1735	1757	1680	1780	176621	WAR	Wolston
1703	1820	....	....	116505	WES	Brougham
1650	1992	1500	1992	167843	YKS	Bolton Cum Redmire
HORN-MORGAN						
1830	1992	1500	1853	151483	HAM	Southampton
HORNBUCKLE						
1700	?	ALL	ALL	165646	LEI	Frisby On The Weale
1892	1992	1800	1892	134988	NTT	Bradmore
1892	1992	1800	1892	134988	NTT	Bunny
HORNBY						
1661	1940	....	....	128996	CAM	Thorney
1870	1933	1841	1881	108901	GSY	St Peter Port
1820	1883	....	....	151912	LAN	Clitheroe
1675	1690	1600	1800	141151	LND	ALL
1807	....	....	1820	171441	LND	City
1920	1992	ALL	ALL	134996	LND	Islington
1920	1992	ALL	ALL	134996	T&W	Basford
1830	1880	ALL	ALL	128279	WES	South
1600	....	1600	....	109347	YKS	Gisburn
....	....	1750	1820	151912	YKS	Great Eccleston
1700	....	1650	....	134589	YKS	Hovingham
1820	1883	....	....	151912	YKS	Mitton
1830	1992	ALL	1830	169692	YKS	Newby Whiske
1841	1861	1841	1881	108901	YKS	Rawcliffe
1828	1836	1828	1836	108901	YKS	Sculcoates
HORNCASTLE						
....	....	1830	1870	135151	CUL	Watermillock
1800	1830	1700	1800	135151	DBY	Chesterfield
....	1609	1550	1650	138584	YKS	Badsworth
HORNE						
1797	....	....	....	164968	BRK	Englefield
1743	1855	....	....	168203	CAI	Mid Clyth
1850	1890	1865	1900	126586	CHS	Birkenhead
1860	1992	ALL	ALL	123048	ESS	Harwich
....	....	1800	....	136255	IRL	???
1720	1720	....	....	159883	KEN	Canterbury
1716	1750	1690	1716	155217	KEN	Dover
1750	1800	ALL	1800	131059	KEN	Maidstone
1765	1887	1750	1890	103632	LAN	Manchester
1840	....	....	....	136255	LAN	Manchester
1813	1828	1794	1850	108952	LAN	Padiham
1841	1891	1840	1891	108952	LAN	Rawtenstall
1850	....	ALL	ALL	172057	NFK	Lowstoft
1843	1890	1750	1900	126586	SAL	Bridgnorth
1860	1880	ALL	1880	123048	SFK	Shotley
1821	1992	....	....	112143	SRY	Normandy
1798	1817	....	1798	112143	WIL	Salisbury
HORNEL						
1841	1950	1750	1840	135658	GLA	Llantwit Major
HORNER						
1840	1992	ALL	1850	142301	MDX	London
1768	....	....	1768	101761	WRY	Thornhill
1895	1974	1800	1895	145327	WYK	Bradford
1882	1890	1500	1882	110310	YKS	Hull
1860	1870	ALL	ALL	112496	YKS	Mickley
....	....	1650	1800	135038	YKS	Pateley Bridge
1848	1992	1700	1848	135011	YKS	Ripon
1800	1992	....	....	135038	YKS	Settle
1905	1992	1700	1905	171913	???	???

Known From	To	Researching From	To	Ref	Cty	Place
HORNIMAN						
1680	....	1680	1945	119458	BRK	Abingdon
1500	ALL	....	....	103381	BRK	Reading
1500	ALL	....	....	103381	DEV	Tawton
1500	ALL	....	....	103381	OXF	Abingdon
HORNSBY						
1760	1820	1650	1780	101834	CAM	South West
1774	....	1600	1774	100013	ESS	Pleshey
1742	1742	ALL	1835	113611	LIN	Burton On Stather
1675	1690	1600	1800	141151	LND	ALL
1810	....	....	1810	101761	NRY	Spofforth
1900	1948	1800	1900	143707	SRY	Kingston On Thames
HORNSEY						
1900	1980	ALL	ALL	150932	CLV	Middlesborough
....	....	1800	1900	150932	NYK	Pickering
1851	1855	....	....	141097	STS	Birmingham
1800	1868	1800	1868	141097	YKS	Hull
1738	1860	1700	1900	141097	YKS	North Newbald
HORRELL						
1800	1992	1700	1800	115444	DEV	Morchard Bishop
1750	1837	....	....	165999	GLS	Bristol
HORRIGAN						
1858	1992	ALL	1858	123749	GAL	???
....	....	ALL	ALL	143340	LIM	???
HORRIX						
1783	....	1770	1790	163775	MDX	Shoreditch
HORROCKS						
1776	1791	ALL	1776	146226	LAN	Ainsworth
1802	....	1700	1800	120901	LAN	Aughton
1600	1800	1750	1780	116831	LAN	Preston
1798	1940	ALL	1798	162221	LAN	Ramsbottom
1859	1884	1700	1992	110205	LAN	Salford
....	....	1700	1980	135046	LAN	Wigan
HORROLL						
1868	1871	ALL	ALL	165824	DEV	Plymouth
1873	1881	ALL	ALL	165824	SOM	Bath
HORRY						
1860	1871	1850	1871	168181	LIN	Boston
HORSAM						
1650	1760	1580	1770	105333	DEV	Buckland In The Moor
1650	1760	1580	1770	105333	DEV	Holne
1650	1760	1580	1770	105333	DEV	Ilsington
1650	1760	1580	1770	105333	DEV	Lydford
1650	1760	1580	1770	105333	DEV	Widecombe In The Moor
HORSECRAFT						
1757	1793	....	....	139971	SSX	East Hoathly
1757	1793	....	....	139971	SSX	Uckfield
HORSECROFT						
1700	1800	ALL	1700	115282	SSX	East
HORSEFIELD						
1839	1888	1814	1888	157678	LAN	Manchester
1739	1760	1700	1760	177393	YKS	Beeston
1750	1900	1700	1900	104396	YKS	East Riding
1776	1800	1700	1776	177393	YKS	Felkirk
HORSELL						
....	....	ALL	ALL	135445	ALL	Name Study
HORSEMAN						
1823	1895	1823	1895	173[illegible]62	HAM	West Woodhay
1600	....	....	....	167037	???	Burton
HORSEPOOL						
1802	1940	....	....	128996	CAM	Thorney
HORSEWELL						
1600	1992	1600	1992	155128	ALL	ALL
HORSEWILL						
1600	1992	1600	1992	155128	ALL	ALL
HORSEWOOD						
....	....	1750	1800	148199	LIN	Binbrook
HORSEY						
....	....	1700	1900	156531	DOR	ALL
HORSFALL						
1800	1992	1600	1800	135054	LAN	Formby
1750	1992	ALL	1992	124389	WRY	ALL
1850	....	1875	1968	154695	WRY	Bradford
1850	....	1875	1968	154695	WRY	Leeds
1848	1900	....	1848	176702	WYK	Northowram
1830	1880	1800	1900	123595	YKS	Almondbury
1860	....	1700	1992	124389	YKS	Halifax
1647	....	1620	1680	170348	YKS	Huddersfield
1754	1865	1700	1754	133760	YKS	Staithwaite
1822	....	1700	1822	110914	YKS	Wakefield
HORSFIELD						
1841	1927	1700	1841	153362	DBY	Whitle

Known From	To	Researching From	To	Ref	Cty	Place
HORSFIELD contd.						
1925	1992	....	....	110159	???	ALL
HORSFORD						
?	....	....	....	154296	IRL	Cork
HORSHAM						
1880	1980	ALL	ALL	135062	BKM	???
1880	1980	ALL	ALL	135062	BRK	???
HORSKINS						
1745	1745	....	....	121355	LND	Stepney
HORSLEN						
1700	1810	1650	1800	144657	ESS	Writtle
HORSLEY						
....	....	1800	1840	103713	CAM	Soham
1500	1950	1500	1950	126489	DBY	Denby
1560	1863	ALL	ALL	161411	DBY	Denby
....	....	1875	1930	122343	DUR	Sunderland
1840	1900	1800	1840	105716	LAN	Machester
ALL	1500	....	....	132756	NBL	Horton
1794	1992	1700	1794	121258	WAR	South
1840	1870	1750	1900	135429	YKS	Gate Hemsley
1850	1870	1750	1900	135429	YKS	York
HORSMAN						
1750	1845	1650	1750	167452	BKM	Towersey
1775	1790	ALL	ALL	169528	MDX	London
1790	1848	ALL	ALL	169528	SRY	Camberwell
1790	1848	ALL	ALL	169528	SRY	Clapham
1848	1992	ALL	ALL	169528	YKS	Bradford
1848	1992	ALL	ALL	169528	YKS	Thorne
HORSMEN						
1596	1839	....	1839	109622	YKS	Pateley Bridge
HORSNAILL						
1772	1792	1750	1800	128961	KEN	Strood
HORSNELL						
1850	1950	1750	1850	128007	LND	Bloomsbury
HORSTMAN						
1850	1992	....	....	135089	???	London
HORSUP						
....	....	ALL	ALL	135097	ALL	Name Study
ALL	ALL	ALL	ALL	135097	ALL	ALL
1838	1989	1650	1992	135097	SFK	Ispwich
HORSWELL						
1600	1992	1600	1992	155128	ALL	ALL
HORSWILL						
....	....	ALL	ALL	155128	ALL	Name Study
1600	1992	1600	1992	155128	ALL	ALL
1700	1805	1700	1805	110434	DEV	Plymouth
HORSWOOD						
1800	1992	....	....	134619	LIN	Boston
1771	1837	1771	1837	163309	LIN	Horncastle
HORTEN						
1860	1903	....	....	125962	HAM	Portsea
HORTH						
....	....	ALL	ALL	135119	ALL	Name Study
HORTON						
....	....	ALL	ALL	135135	ALL	Name Study
1850	1900	1800	1992	177180	BKM	Dagnall
1846	1926	1846	1940	140295	GLA	Cardiff
1874	....	1750	1900	109894	GLS	Bitton
1830	1845	1830	1850	140295	GLS	Cheltenham
....	....	1791	1881	104264	GLS	Tetbury
1800	1900	1600	1800	132403	HRT	Central
1810	1880	1500	1880	169439	KEN	Bilsington
1774	....	....	1774	155667	KEN	Elham
....	....	1850	1859	173274	KEN	Snave
1850	1870	1870	1900	106356	KEN	Wateringbury
1840	1868	1840	1870	140295	LND	ALL
1876	1992	1870	1992	111600	LND	Chelsea
1800	1900	1600	1800	132403	MDX	North
1890	1950	1850	1950	101974	MDX	Bethnal Green
1890	1950	1850	1950	101974	MDX	Hackney
1750	1800	....	....	108200	MDX	Hillingdon
1800	1835	....	....	108200	MDX	Uxbridge Moor
1824	....	1700	1992	167800	OXF	Chearsley
1737	1815	1600	1737	132802	SAL	Ironbridge
1863	1992	1700	1863	122467	SRY	Lambeth
1875	....	1875	1950	109894	SRY	Rotherhithe
1876	1878	1876	1878	147257	SRY	Walworth
1858	1992	1600	1858	176915	STS	Bilston
1800	1812	1790	1812	174602	STS	Rowles Regis
....	....	....	1808	145742	STS	Walsall
1881	1918	1700	1881	174297	WAR	Birmingham
....	....	1900	1992	136743	WAR	Coventry
....	....	1791	1881	104264	WIL	Crudwell
1820	1940	1780	1820	106194	WMD	Dudley

Known From	To	Researching From	To	Ref	Cty	Place
HORTON contd.						
1806	1992	1700	1900	135127	WOR	Tardbigge
1783	1824	....	1783	101761	WRY	Kirkheaton
1840	1992	1820	1992	146625	YKS	Sheffield
HORTSEED						
1590	1600	ALL	1590	131059	SFK	Ipswich
HORWOOD						
1830	ALL	....	....	167037	GLS	Stroud
1825	1900	ALL	1930	142301	HAM	Langley
1895	1929	1800	1895	149861	SRY	Woking
HOSEASON						
1750	1965	....	....	137820	SHI	Fetlar
1720	1965	....	....	137820	SHI	Mid Yell
1760	1965	....	....	137820	SHI	North Yell
1758	1965	....	....	137820	SHI	Northmavine
1720	1965	....	....	137820	SHI	South Yell
HOSFORD						
1655	1665	....	....	154296	DEV	Tiverton
1560	....	....	....	154296	DOR	Dorchester
HOSGOOD						
1730	1730	1680	1750	121568	SOM	Brompton Regis
HOSIE						
....	....	ALL	ALL	137243	ALL	Name Study
1750	1900	ALL	ALL	137243	ABD	ALL
1750	1900	ALL	ALL	137243	ANS	ALL
HOSIER						
1818	1850	1818	1850	166898	HRT	Abbots Langley
1710	1797	1700	1720	166898	HRT	Kings Langley
1857	....	1800	....	162752	HRT	???
HOSKEN						
....	....	1500	1992	136972	CON	ALL
1700	1940	1500	1700	136972	CON	Breage
....	....	1800	1950	136972	CON	Crowan
1700	1940	1500	1700	136972	CON	Germoe
1845	1980	1800	1845	150657	CON	Gwennap
1857	1884	....	1857	117951	CON	Linkinhorne
....	....	1800	1992	136972	CON	Madron
....	....	1750	1900	136972	CON	Mawgan In Meneage
....	....	1800	1992	136972	CON	Penzance
1858	1880	1700	1858	162035	GLS	Bristol
1784	1844	1600	1798	115525	GLS	Henbury
HOSKIN						
1847	1931	1847	....	170461	CON	Callington
1823	1911	1700	1823	176575	CON	Gwinear
....	....	1700	1900	136972	CON	Penryn
1800	1940	1800	1940	118818	CON	Perranzabuloe
1600	1700	1550	1600	132942	CON	Perranzabuloe
1788	1992	1788	1992	141267	CON	St Buryan
1787	1863	ALL	ALL	104191	CON	St Just
1819	1892	....	1819	170461	DEV	Tavistock
....	....	1820	1900	108243	WLS	South
HOSKING						
....	....	1500	1900	136972	CON	ALL
1700	1940	1500	1700	136972	CON	Breage
1700	1940	1500	1700	136972	CON	Germoe
1816	1816	1780	1816	108510	CON	Madron
....	....	1800	1992	136972	CON	Madron
....	....	1600	1850	127833	CON	Penzance
....	....	1800	1992	136972	CON	Penzance
1840	1870	1800	1880	137278	CON	Saltash
1900	1992	1750	1900	146374	CON	St Gluvius
1807	1981	1700	1807	110426	CON	St Hilary
1837	1992	1700	1837	140449	CON	St Hilary
1819	1851	1780	1816	108510	CON	St Ives
1754	1826	1600	1754	149888	CON	St Ives
1788	1816	1780	1816	108510	CON	St Just
HOSKINS						
....	....	ALL	ALL	135178	ALL	Name Study
1750	1992	ALL	1750	135143	ALL	ALL
1857	1884	....	1857	117951	CON	Linkinhorne
1800	1800	1700	1950	168734	CON	St Ive
1700	1985	ALL	ALL	135178	DEV	ALL
1700	1985	ALL	ALL	135178	DOR	ALL
1769	....	....	....	151351	DOR	Powerstock
ALL	ALL	ALL	ALL	135178	ENG	ALL
1724	1985	ALL	ALL	135178	MON	ALL
1800	1850	1750	1850	161292	SOM	Crewkerne
1641	....	1600	1680	170348	WIL	Stratton St Margaret
ALL	ALL	ALL	ALL	135178	WLS	ALL
HOSMER						
1900	1992	1700	1900	135542	KEN	Tonbridge
1797	1797	ALL	1797	159077	NTH	Cotterstock

Known From	To	Researching From	To	Ref	Cty	Place
HOSSELL						
1875	1900	1875	1900	161586	YKS	Knottingley
HOSSILL						
1781	1893	1600	1780	101575	YKS	Goole
1781	1893	1600	1780	101575	YKS	Knottingley
1781	1893	1600	1780	101575	YKS	Pontefract
HOSTAGE						
1770	1890	1650	1992	167592	CHS	Chester
1800	1860	1650	1992	167592	CHS	Northwich
1820	?	1650	1992	167592	STS	Potteries
HOTCHKISS						
1900	1980	1600	1900	166766	SAL	Chirbury
1900	1980	1600	1900	166766	SAL	Hockleton
....	....	1700	1800	154458	SAL	???
1800	1900	ALL	ALL	159530	SCT	ALL
HOTFIELD						
1780	1992	ALL	ALL	127078	ALL	ALL
HOTHAM						
1750	1880	1600	1750	133132	LIN	Haxey
1904	1908	1904	1908	138398	MON	Beaufort
1750	1880	1600	1750	133132	YKS	Sheffield
HOTHERSALL						
ALL	1992	ALL	1992	133450	LAN	Ribchester
1575	1700	1550	1992	133450	LND	Central
HOTOFT						
1400	1500	1350	1500	154881	HRT	Knebworth
HOTSON						
1830	1870	1830	1870	118206	NFK	Kings Lynn
1830	1870	1830	1870	118206	NFK	Rougham
1800	1850	1800	1850	173428	SSX	Compton
HOTTEN						
1685	1992	1685	1992	135186	CON	Ladock
1685	1992	1685	1992	135186	CON	Probus
HOUCHELL						
....	....	ALL	ALL	126616	ALL	Name Study
1790	1992	1500	1790	126616	SFK	ALL
HOUDE						
....	....	ALL	ALL	135194	ALL	Name Study
HOUGH						
1728	1793	1600	1793	151254	CHS	Cheadle
1755	1919	....	....	108057	CHS	Middlewich
1728	1793	1600	1793	151254	CHS	Wilmslow
1665	1837	1550	1700	102830	DBY	Bradley
1678	1824	....	....	165999	DBY	Derby
1872	1920	....	....	134430	HAM	Portsmouth
1861	1871	1861	1871	138398	HEF	Llangarren
1830	1992	1700	1830	128074	LAN	Manchester
1799	1851	ALL	1890	129313	LAN	Salford
1881	1891	1881	1891	138398	MON	Blaina
1881	1891	1881	1891	138398	MON	Nantyglo
HOUGHAM						
1540	1540	....	....	159883	KEN	Wingham
HOUGHT						
1798	1818	1750	1818	141097	YKS	North Newbald
HOUGHTON						
1893	....	ALL	1910	170666	CAM	Soham
1800	....	1750	1800	135771	CHS	Central
....	....	ALL	ALL	166812	HAM	Gosport
1716	1830	ALL	ALL	135208	KEN	Ashford
1830	1836	ALL	ALL	135208	KEN	Canterbury
1794	1840	ALL	ALL	135208	KEN	Deal
1794	1840	ALL	ALL	135208	KEN	Dover
1725	....	1725	....	109347	LAN	Accrington
1820	1992	1700	1900	135232	LAN	Bolton
1776	1992	1590	1776	120200	LAN	Childwall
1700	1800	....	....	177318	LAN	Ditton
1800	1958	ALL	ALL	120669	LAN	Hale Bank
1593	1595	1300	1650	132993	LAN	Houghton
1866	1980	1700	1900	140066	LAN	Liverpool
1800	1958	ALL	ALL	120669	LAN	Manchester
1800	1830	1700	1800	155500	LAN	Newton Le Willows
1650	....	1650	....	109347	LAN	Paidham
1776	1992	1590	1776	120200	LAN	Prescot
1823	1850	1823	1850	143286	LAN	Prescot
1800	1851	ALL	ALL	107913	LAN	Scarisbrick
1776	1992	1590	1776	120200	LAN	Warrington
1785	1992	ALL	ALL	135224	LIN	Cleethorpes
1785	1992	ALL	ALL	135224	LIN	Grimsby
1733	1798	1707	1812	107360	NTH	Welton
1900	1992	1800	1900	135216	NTT	Nottingham
1594	1662	ALL	ALL	135208	SSX	Mayfield
1708	1709	ALL	ALL	135208	SSX	Petworth
1880	....	1880	1900	148504	WAR	Studley
....	....	....	....	107433	WAR	???

Known From	To	Researching From	To	Ref	Cty	Place
HOUGHTON contd.						
1790	1848	1720	1790	139149	WES	Kendal
1844	1992	1800	1992	174475	WOR	Cotshill
1842	1908	1815	1908	174475	WOR	Feckenham
HOUHGTON						
1824	1862	1750	1900	114456	LAN	ALL
1790	1900	ALL	1790	117765	LAN	Liverpool
HOULDER						
1841	1992	1700	1850	135240	YKS	Pontefract
HOULDIN						
1850	1950	1850	1950	122238	CHS	Birkenhead
1800	1871	1821	1871	122238	LAN	Liverpool
HOULDSWORTH						
1825	1860	1840	1840	122238	CHS	Higher Bebbington
....	....	1800	1825	122238	YKS	???
HOULKER						
1500	1600	1500	1600	109347	LAN	Read
HOULSBY						
1840	1992	....	....	122297	DUR	South Shields
HOULSTON						
1840	1860	ALL	ALL	161292	SAL	Shifnal
HOULT						
1874	1874	ALL	....	146935	CHS	???
1818	1839	1700	1818	139386	ERY	Balkholme
....	....	1700	1992	111503	LAN	Leyland
....	1700	ALL	1700	134511	NTT	Arnold
HOULTON						
1724	1823	1700	1800	108510	BRK	Wokingham
HOUNSELL						
1850	1929	1700	....	135259	DOR	ALL
1800	1900	1600	1800	110329	DOR	Symondsbury
1760	1806	1700	1760	100277	SSX	Battle
HOUNSOME						
1742	1742	1730	1750	170143	HAM	Petersfield
HOUNTE						
1593	1595	1550	1620	105120	SSX	Lancing
HOURIHAN						
1860	1900	1830	1900	113107	GLA	Dowlais
HOUSDEN						
1842	1900	1770	1850	115681	BDF	Everton
1790	1810	1750	1810	158658	ESS	Debden
HOUSE						
1753	1753	....	....	115606	BRK	Reading
1850	1992	1700	1850	157872	BRK	Welford
1781	....	1700	1850	110205	DOR	Broadwey
1700	1850	1650	1900	111589	DOR	Puddletown
ALL	ALL	....	....	153397	HAM	ALL
....	....	1700	1870	166863	HAM	South Stoneham
1897	1992	ALL	1904	108642	KEN	Dover
....	....	1880	1900	133221	LND	Fulham
1897	1992	ALL	1904	108642	MDX	Hayes
1820	1860	1600	1820	124176	OXF	Spelsbury
1828	1828	1700	1850	121568	SOM	Ash Priors
....	....	1750	1900	109770	SOM	???
HOUSEHAM						
1829	1957	1829	1957	151211	LIN	Louth
HOUSELEY						
1850	1992	....	....	115479	NTT	Kimberley
1850	1992	....	....	115479	NTT	Sutton In Ashfield
HOUSEMAN						
1750	1800	1700	1850	178047	LAN	Lancaster
1728	1850	1700	1900	102563	YKS	Darley
HOUSHAM						
....	....	ALL	ALL	135267	ALL	Name Study
HOUSLEY						
1850	1880	1800	1900	143006	LAN	Ashton Under Lyne
HOUSSART						
1850	1992	1850	1992	155675	ESS	Shoreditch
1850	1992	1850	1992	155675	LND	West Ham
1850	1992	1850	1992	155675	MDX	Hackney
1722	....	....	....	155675	MDX	Westminster
1715	....	....	....	155675	MDX	???
HOUSTON						
1820	1850	....	....	137936	FIF	Kinglassie
1822	....	1800	1850	146536	RFW	Greenock
HOUTON						
1790	1812	1790	1812	103977	MDX	Sunbury
HOVELL						
1860	1950	1860	1890	135275	MDX	Clerkenwell
1860	1950	1860	1890	135275	MDX	Holborn
1671	1700	....	....	129747	SFK	Ipswich
HOVENDEN						
....	....	ALL	ALL	117552	ALL	Name Study
1859	1894	....	1859	137073	KEN	Romney Marsh

Known From	To	Researching From	To	Ref	Cty	Place
HOVENDEN contd.						
ALL	ALL	ALL	ALL	100536	WLS	Ferryside
HOVER						
1880	....	....	....	163392	IRL	???
1880	....	....	....	163392	LND	Canning Town
1681	1716	....	....	139971	SSX	Herstmonceux
1681	1716	....	....	139971	SSX	Wartling
HOVEY						
1800	1900	....	....	171824	LND	Hackney
1837	1992	1837	1992	163643	MDX	London
1760	1900	....	....	177903	NTT	Nottingham
1800	1900	....	....	171824	SRY	Greenwich
HOW						
1828	1852	1800	1850	136042	BDF	Kempston
1746	....	....	....	138401	CUL	Wetheral
1799	1845	1760	1845	135828	ESS	Downham
....	1849	1800	1849	128961	HRT	Abbots Langley
1799	1869	1770	1869	144878	HRT	Sarratt
1863	1870	1850	1900	136042	HUN	Eynesbury
1749	1804	....	....	127426	KEN	Boughton Monchelsea
1835	1929	1830	1850	135828	MDX	South Hackney
1767	1767	1700	1767	172553	SFK	Glemsford
1794	1794	1700	1850	121568	SOM	West
1770	1840	1700	1840	136840	SOM	Brendon Hills
1796	1825	1825	1900	120723	SOM	Shapwick
....	....	....	1890	158763	???	Malvern Wells
HOWARD						
1750	1900	1700	1900	152900	BKM	Eddlesborough
1756	1827	....	1820	137405	CAM	South
1826	1900	1800	1900	124788	CHS	Dukinfield
1756	1833	1500	1756	135291	CHS	Glossop
1796	1855	1750	1851	160636	CHS	Mottram In Longdendale
1756	1833	1500	1756	135291	CHS	Mottram
1756	1833	1500	1756	135291	CHS	Stalybridge
....	....	1700	1890	117854	CHS	???
1803	....	....	....	109347	DBY	Bakewell
1800	1992	1600	1800	135313	DEV	Barnstaple
1757	1785	1789	ALL	164674	DEV	Exeter
1860	1992	ALL	ALL	135321	EAG	Maldon
1698	1815	1690	1815	135305	ESS	Manningtree
1805	1924	1800	1900	135305	ESS	Mistley
1856	1992	1830	1900	135933	ESS	Terling
1850	ALL	....	....	163392	ESS	Wivenhoe
1600	....	1600	1900	106410	GLS	Berkeley
1645	1686	....	....	117579	GLS	Berkley
1600	....	1600	1900	106410	GLS	Tortworth
1746	1780	1600	....	164038	HAM	Wonston
1800	1900	....	....	174556	HRT	St Albans
1807	1850	1600	1807	165697	HUN	Offord Darcy
....	....	1851	1950	178284	KEN	Sandwich
1850	....	1850	....	109347	LAN	Bury
1851	1881	1851	1900	126705	LAN	Cholrton On Med
1855	1898	1800	1855	175447	LAN	Middleston
1866	....	1866	1900	135348	LAN	Oldham
....	....	1866	1900	135348	LAN	Rochdale
1841	1928	1790	1841	178055	LAN	Warrington
1790	1908	1700	1890	117854	LAN	???
1826	....	1700	1800	143448	LIN	Grainthorpe
....	....	1800	1900	109134	LIN	Grimsby
....	....	1700	1840	113697	LND	East
1825	....	1825	....	109347	MAY	???
1820	....	1750	1820	174955	MDX	Brentford
1759	1759	1720	1800	167002	MDX	London
1846	1852	1750	1845	131245	MDX	St Pancras
1750	1840	1750	1840	115614	NFK	Ditchingham
1878	1953	1800	1900	144630	NFK	Docking
1842	1876	ALL	1842	157791	NFK	Kings Lynn
1820	1900	1820	1900	173533	NTH	South
1820	1900	....	....	153583	NTH	Bugbrooke
1750	1992	1600	1900	106569	NTT	Central
1750	1992	1600	1900	106569	NTT	North
1710	1890	1700	1900	106569	NTT	Wigsley
1850	1992	1700	1850	171840	OXF	Oxford
1550	....	....	....	176958	PEM	Flotherhill
1850	1960	ALL	ALL	162469	SFK	North
1850	1900	1700	1850	149705	SFK	Halesworth
1800	1850	1700	1800	139106	SRY	???
1746	1780	1600	....	164038	SSX	Chichester
1764	1873	1750	1900	167487	SSX	Fittleworth
1510	1800	1500	1850	133450	SSX	Lingfield
1800	1833	ALL	ALL	141186	STS	North
1900	1980	1800	1980	135283	WIL	Islington
....	....	1801	1882	141399	WLS	Bassaleg

Known From	To	Researching From	To	Ref	Cty	Place
HOWARD contd.						
1800	1830	1700	1992	102520	YKS	???
1908	1992	....	....	117854	YKS	???
1300	1710	....	....	100536	???	???
HOWARD-OSBORNE						
1855	1875	ALL	1855	166847	LND	Stepney
HOWARTH						
1850	1870	1600	1850	175382	CHS	Hooleyhill
1826	1833	1820	1845	145602	LAN	Haslingden
1800	1850	1790	1800	101796	LAN	Leigh
1802	1851	1700	1802	135364	LAN	Littleborough
1779	1845	ALL	1779	172901	LAN	Manchester
1868	1873	1825	1873	136565	LAN	Newchurch In Rossendale
1872	1992	1800	1872	175447	LAN	Oldham
1798	1844	1841	1844	151750	LAN	Oswaldtwistle
1851	1900	1900	1992	135364	LAN	Rochdale
1779	1992	1700	1779	135372	LAN	Rochdale
....	....	ALL	ALL	141747	LAN	South Manchester
1850	1900	ALL	1900	123048	WRY	Skipton
1880	1992	1780	1880	142697	YKS	Huddersfield
1737	1761	1700	1750	170348	YKS	Rawmarsh
HOWAT AIKMAN						
1900	1992	ALL	1900	100536	SCT	???
HOWAT						
1837	1992	1750	1834	144010	AYR	Newton Upon Ayr
1864	1909	1827	1883	118133	SCT	Bridgeton
HOWATSON						
1754	1992	?	1754	112356	DFS	???
HOWCROFT						
1881	1900	1800	1992	116246	DUR	Hartlepool
1909	1976	1909	....	135380	LAN	???
1851	1855	....	....	141097	STS	Birmingham
1855	....	....	....	141097	YKS	North Newbald
HOWDEN						
1905	1992	1800	1905	177199	LIN	Scampton
1905	1992	1800	1905	177199	LIN	Willoughton
1860	1930	1800	1860	133787	LKS	Motherwell
HOWDON						
....	....	1850	1950	137685	LND	Sydenham
HOWE						
....	....	ALL	ALL	179620	ALL	Name Study
1900	1992	1500	1700	143154	BDF	Bedford
1900	1992	1500	1700	143154	BDF	Blunham
1700	1992	1500	1700	143154	BDF	Flitton
1800	1992	1500	1700	143154	BDF	Gravenhurst
1828	1852	1800	1850	136042	BDF	Kempston
1862	1871	1841	1920	124915	BKM	Missenden
1837	1910	1790	1837	121037	BKM	Tilehurst
1837	1910	1790	1837	121037	BRK	Tilehurst
1810	1880	1700	1820	101834	CAM	South West
1864	1900	1750	1864	134651	CUL	Dalston
1891	1992	1800	1900	173053	DUR	Ferryhill
1770	1950	1650	1770	128376	DUR	Stanhope
1820	1841	....	....	103632	DUR	Sunderland
1880	1951	1860	1992	112585	DUR	Sunderland
1884	1908	1884	1908	123773	ESS	Walthamstow
1826	1871	1800	1871	119059	GLS	Northleach
1710	1722	1600	1900	157147	HAM	Upton Grey
1863	1870	1850	1900	136042	HUN	Eynesbury
1900	1901	1871	1940	124915	IOW	Ventnor
1792	1792	....	....	127426	KEN	Lenham
1820	1950	1780	1820	132268	LAN	Manchester
1830	1910	1750	1830	179140	LIN	Boston
1880	....	1880	1900	123773	LND	Holborn
....	1883	....	....	159999	LND	???
1850	....	....	....	135402	MDX	Islington
1816	1950	....	1816	158585	MDX	Kensington
1797	1797	1750	1820	116114	NFK	Welbourne
1796	1796	1750	1900	126586	NTH	Peterborough
....	....	1800	1900	177776	NYK	Stonegrave
1774	1860	ALL	1774	107255	SFK	Bury St Edmunds
1767	1767	1700	1767	172553	SFK	Glemsford
1800	1930	ALL	ALL	167940	SFK	Preston
1857	1938	1880	1938	123773	SOM	Luxborough
1795	1900	1795	1900	118540	WAR	Birmingham
1830	1830	1800	1850	171662	WIL	Salisbury
1869	1900	1880	1940	171662	YKS	Thornaby
HOWELL						
1850	....	....	....	173932	AVN	Bathampton
1830	1851	....	....	173932	AVN	Bristol
1819	....	....	....	173932	AVN	Widcombe
1584	1638	1560	1625	103349	BKM	Marsh Gibbon
....	1830	....	....	137995	CMN	Llanddensant

Known From	To	Researching From	To	Ref	Cty	Place
HOWELL contd.						
1910	1950	1730	1992	135429	DEV	Alphington
1855	1860	1850	1880	135429	DEV	Countisbury
1780	1800	1730	1992	135429	DEV	Exeter
1870	1920	1730	1992	135429	DEV	Exmouth
1820	1870	1730	1992	135429	DEV	Lympstone
1920	....	1730	1992	135429	DEV	Ottery St Mary
1800	1820	1730	1992	135429	DEV	Topsham
1820	1900	1600	1900	113778	DUR	Sunderland
1798	1811	1790	1830	158658	GLA	Juxta
1798	1811	1790	1830	158658	GLA	Llantwit
1798	1811	1790	1830	158658	GLA	Neath
1804	1900	ALL	1804	158739	GLA	St Andrews
1733	1819	ALL	1733	158739	GLA	St Georges
....	....	?	?	132195	GLS	Bristol
1812	1992	....	....	135437	GLS	Bristol
1800	1920	1750	1840	138150	GLS	Bristol
1800	1860	1600	1800	169773	GLS	Lydney
1772	1902	....	1772	117773	GLS	St Briavels
1780	1992	1740	1992	152447	LAN	Worsley
1818	1915	1700	1818	137383	LND	West End
1800	1900	ALL	ALL	131873	LND	Westminster
1881	1881	....	....	135437	MDX	Ealing
1871	1871	....	....	135437	MDX	Hanwell
1770	1775	1750	1810	105120	MDX	London
1787	1799	....	....	135437	MON	Llangwm
1846	....	....	....	173932	NFK	North Elmham
1799	....	....	....	173932	SAL	Madeley
1866	....	1829	1831	151041	SAL	Shrewsbury
1789	....	....	....	173932	SAL	Wellington
1840	1910	1780	1910	135429	SOM	Bath
1821	1866	....	....	135437	SOM	Bath
1858	....	1850	1880	135429	SOM	Bath
1870	....	1850	1880	135429	SOM	Beckington
1600	1800	1620	1800	142018	SOM	Rode
1858	....	1850	1880	135429	SOM	Woodborough
1825	1850	1800	1825	107093	SRY	Battersea
1845	1950	1840	1950	171522	SSX	Eastbourne
....	1806	....	....	174564	SSX	???
1839	1864	1800	1839	177555	STS	Sedgley
1841	....	1841	1992	140058	SXE	Barcombe
1871	....	1861	1992	140058	SXE	Lewes
1750	1790	1700	1800	174599	WIL	Kilmington
1698	1770	1690	1770	142018	WIL	Mere
1889	....	....	....	173932	WIL	Norton Bavant
1698	1750	1690	1750	142018	WIL	Warminster
1866	....	1829	1831	151041	WLS	Bersham
1827	....	1700	1992	107204	YKS	Whitby
1700	1800	1700	1800	133795	???	???
HOWELLS						
....	....	1800	1830	142093	CMN	Llanboidy
....	....	1830	1880	142093	CMN	Llansadwrnen
1873	1928	1873	1928	142751	GLA	Barry
....	....	1750	1873	142751	GLA	Kenfig Hill
1860	1940	....	....	142093	GLA	Llwydcoed
1800	1992	1700	1800	131083	SAL	Brookhampton
1800	....	....	1800	164011	WOR	Worcester
1864	1962	1700	1900	129623	YKS	Keighley
HOWES						
1788	1828	....	....	142360	BKM	Penn
1811	1811	ALL	1811	151424	HRT	Hemel Hempstead
1860	1870	1840	1900	126144	KEN	Northfleet
1840	....	....	....	130079	LND	Deptford
1840	....	....	....	130079	LND	Greenwich
1781	1992	1700	1815	161446	NFK	Necton
1720	1858	1720	1860	103632	NTH	Greens Norton
HOWETT						
1801	1801	1770	1801	128368	LND	St George Hanover Square
HOWEY						
1819	1850	1600	1850	130125	NBL	Longhorsley
HOWFIELD						
1787	1807	1600	1787	102571	LAN	Blackburn
HOWIE						
1800	1960	1770	1830	144231	AYR	North
1760	1992	1700	1800	167398	AYR	Fenwick
1760	1992	1700	1800	167398	AYR	Mauchline
1816	1992	1600	1816	133132	MLN	Leith
HOWISON						
1798	....	....	....	135453	DFS	Moodlaw
1800	1870	1700	1750	155004	MLN	Edinburgh
1818	1868	ALL	ALL	135453	PER	Rannagulzion
HOWITT						
1850	1940	1800	1850	171891	BKM	Chalfont St Peter
HOWITT contd.						
1815	1881	1700	1820	160636	LIN	Sproxton
....	1849	1750	1850	132586	WIL	Highworth
HOWKINS						
1902	....	1890	1910	163775	MDX	Kensington
....	1800	....	1800	177695	WAR	Braunston
HOWL						
....	....	1750	1850	147613	STS	West Bromwich
HOWLAND						
?	?	?	?	166642	KEN	???
1838	....	1750	1838	108596	YKS	Lockton
HOWLES						
1818	1818	1790	1818	108510	SAL	Shifnal
HOWLETT						
....	....	....	1824	176702	BKM	Aylesbury
1830	1861	....	1870	153818	BKM	Bishopstone
1889	....	1889	....	135488	CAM	Peterborough
1830	1886	1830	1900	142018	GLS	Cheltenham
1730	1750	1700	1730	165530	GLS	Dursley
1850	1890	ALL	ALL	171816	HRT	Hemel Hempstead
1848	1992	ALL	1850	112720	HRT	Tring
1805	1960	1750	1805	135461	LIN	North
1770	1800	1760	1820	142018	LND	ALL
1820	1992	ALL	1820	160938	NFK	North
1845	1890	1813	1900	142840	NFK	Carleton Rode
1830	1895	....	....	122319	NFK	Kings Lynn
1791	1833	1791	1844	142840	NFK	Pulham Market
1550	1992	....	....	129763	NTH	Brixworth
1800	1850	1750	1900	138878	SFK	North
1807	1809	1790	1840	142018	SOM	Bath
HOWMAN						
1793	1828	1700	1800	175218	NFK	North West
HOWSE						
ALL	ALL	....	....	153397	HAM	ALL
1720	1780	....	....	132756	OXF	Bicester
1867	1992	1700	1992	112216	OXF	Shipton On Cherwell
1550	1650	1450	1550	174513	OXF	Upper Heyford
HOWSON						
1720	1850	1700	1900	115681	BRK	Buckland
1770	1831	ALL	1770	154563	DUR	Darlington
1750	1820	1650	1750	168351	LND	Westminster
1795	1930	1700	1795	150096	YKS	Kippax
HOY						
1890	1923	1700	1890	144150	CAM	Fulbourn
....	....	1740	1800	148474	CUL	Carlisle
1825	1874	....	....	116602	HRT	Anstey
....	....	ALL	ALL	130818	LND	Deptford
1785	1807	1750	1850	148288	PER	Tibbermore
HOYES						
1759	1799	1759	....	113875	LIN	Bucknall
HOYLAND						
1850	1850	1700	1900	121762	YKS	ALL
1890	1919	ALL	1890	175080	YKS	Barnsley
HOYLE						
1840	1858	1700	1840	111449	CON	St John
....	....	1700	1740	154873	KEN	Lynsted
1650	1750	....	....	119431	KEN	Walmer
1815	1853	1500	1853	169439	LAN	Haslingden
1840	1880	1800	1840	138940	LAN	Manchester
1857	1912	....	1857	163686	LAN	Wardle
1803	1912	1780	1920	147338	WRY	Huddersfield
1765	1786	....	1765	101761	WRY	Ripponden
1890	1992	1800	1890	135496	YKS	Bradford
1815	1992	....	....	148350	YKS	Brighouse
1819	1992	1700	1819	102199	YKS	Scholes Cleckheaton
1846	1973	1800	1992	103292	YKS	???
HOYLES						
1720	1850	1850	1992	117072	LIN	Wrangle
HOYTE						
1675	1824	....	....	174319	CON	Grampound
HREATHWOOD						
1856	1917	1800	1856	126225	ARM	???
HUBANK						
1695	....	1695	....	139149	WRY	Kirkburn
HUBBALL						
1628	1804	....	....	117404	STS	Baswich
1830	1980	1700	1830	176052	STS	Birmingham
1811	1980	1700	1811	176052	STS	Walsall
HUBBARD						
1843	1881	....	....	102881	DUR	Sunderland
1743	1765	1700	1800	176621	ESS	Dedham
1750	1970	1700	1750	143170	ESS	Witham
1600	1680	1560	1900	173096	KEN	Adisham
1630	1740	1600	1900	173096	KEN	St Lawrence

Known From	To	Researching From	To	Ref	Cty	Place
HUBBARD contd.						
1784	1784	1600	1992	110787	LEI	Gilmorton
1725	1871	1600	1900	126381	LEI	Leicester
1894	1960	....	1894	135518	LEI	???
1756	1900	1550	1800	102830	LIN	Ruskington
1760	1851	....	....	164631	LIN	South Witham
....	....	1750	1843	102881	NFK	Gt Yarmouth
1804	1851	....	....	101028	NFK	Lt Plumstead
1790	1860	1780	1800	161322	SOM	Taunton
1790	1800	1700	1820	131547	SRY	Capel
1805	1848	1700	1805	127590	SRY	Deptford
1750	1925	ALL	ALL	164453	SSX	West
1750	1925	ALL	ALL	164453	SSX	Pulborough
1770	1800	1700	1770	172901	WOR	Dudley
HUBBERT						
1900	1992	1830	1900	128864	CHS	Chester
HUBBLE						
1800	1857	1700	1800	144126	KEN	Sevenoaks
1750	1800	1700	1760	144126	KEN	Wrotham
HUBEN						
....	....	ALL	1810	127094	SSX	Wetham
HUBER						
1905	1992	1800	1930	122610	WMD	Birmingham
HUBERT						
1600	ALL	ALL	ALL	115126	CHI	ALL
....	....	1800	ALL	149187	JSY	St Martin
HUBSDELL						
1828	1886	1800	1900	104922	HAM	Gosport
HUCK						
1750	1781	1500	1750	129577	IOW	???
HUCKBODY						
1767	1786	1650	1766	131245	LIN	Spalding
HUCKEL						
1852	1919	....	1852	165484	HRT	Ashwell
HUCKER						
1840	1930	1800	1870	135534	DEV	Okehampton
1760	1860	1700	1760	135534	DEV	Tiverton
1790	1800	1790	1992	106410	SOM	Somerton
HUCKLEBRIDGE						
1550	1800	1300	1992	135542	SOM	ALL
1794	....	ALL	1794	104299	SOM	Cannington
HUCKLESBY						
1798	1819	1700	1819	128961	BDF	Leadgrave
1895	1911	1840	1992	128961	HRT	Harpenden
1821	1878	1819	1992	128961	HRT	Redbourn
HUCKSTEP						
1711	1992	1556	1711	108502	KEN	Ashford
HUDD						
1800	1860	1800	1880	135429	SOM	Bath
1713	1735	1713	1735	118192	SRY	Farnham
1611	1652	1611	1652	118192	SRY	Guildford
ALL	1840	1800	1850	135429	WIL	Lacock
1800	1850	1600	1800	160229	WIL	Lacock
HUDDART						
1760	1992	1700	1800	135550	CUL	Eden Valley
....	....	1800	1899	171794	CUL	Holme Cultram
1760	1992	1700	1800	135550	WES	Eden Valley
HUDDERSTON						
1814	1829	ALL	ALL	120650	YKS	Cottingwith
1780	1881	ALL	ALL	120650	YKS	Hook
HUDDLESFORD						
1705	....	ALL	....	104515	LIN	Kyme
HUDDLESTON						
ALL	ALL	ALL	ALL	163376	ALL	ALL
1701	1901	1590	1901	153273	LAN	Dalton In Furness
1723	1785	1542	1723	141291	LAN	Furness
1819	1992	1700	1819	152196	LIN	Kirton In Lindsey
....	1750	ALL	1750	134511	NTT	Southall
1800	1820	1700	1992	102377	YKS	Middleton On The Wolds
1802	1850	1700	1802	115967	YKS	Nafferton
HUDDLESTONE						
....	....	ALL	ALL	163376	ALL	Name Study
ALL	ALL	ALL	ALL	163376	ALL	ALL
1865	1956	1752	1865	107247	CAM	Harlton
?	1940	....	....	128996	CAM	Thorney
1594	1810	1550	1725	102830	LIN	Nassington
1729	1992	1600	1729	111198	NYK	Pickering
HUDDY						
1550	1970	1500	1750	135569	CON	Probus
1690	1800	1670	1690	158089	CON	St Michael Penkevil
HUDGELL						
1600	1992	ALL	1992	106739	ALL	ALL
HUDGIN						
1841	1881	....	....	116475	IOM	Lonan
HUDLESTON						
ALL	ALL	ALL	ALL	163376	ALL	ALL
1700	1912	....	....	100536	???	???
HUDSON						
....	....	1800	1900	159840	BDF	Marston Moretaine
1848	1980	....	....	141321	BRK	Abingdon
1760	1854	1760	1854	138894	BRK	Fyfield
1760	1848	1700	1760	141321	BRK	Fyfield
1850	1992	1850	1950	107131	CHS	Macclesfield
1820	1992	1500	1820	107123	CHS	Macclesfield
1746	....	ALL	ALL	131415	CMN	North
1850	1960	ALL	ALL	162469	CUL	North
1790	1852	1790	1852	147532	CUL	Penrith
1851	....	ALL	1992	159174	DBY	Boundary
1867	1992	1650	1767	115096	DBY	Radbourne
1730	1950	1600	1730	128376	DUR	Chester Le Street
1841	1862	1800	1845	154873	DUR	Sunderland
1820	1900	ALL	ALL	130613	GLS	Stowe
1832	1992	1700	1832	150290	KEN	Hendon
1724	1992	1600	1992	135577	KEN	Isle Of Thanet
1851	....	1800	1850	171441	KEN	Ramsgate
1765	1802	....	1850	171441	KEN	Wingham
1860	1992	1750	1860	154415	LAN	Liverpool
1863	1913	1863	....	156892	LAN	Manchester
....	....	1800	....	154377	LEI	Cossington
1799	1822	....	1799	101761	LEI	Hinckley
1782	....	ALL	1992	159174	LEI	Twycross
1770	1980	1600	1900	123293	LIN	Gainsborough
1800	1819	ALL	1800	154563	LIN	Gainsborough
1884	....	1884	....	162663	LIN	Gunby
1778	1850	1550	1800	102830	LIN	Ruskington
1851	1936	1800	1850	167568	LND	Clapham Common
....	1851	1800	1900	175633	MDX	West Hackney
1862	1880	1830	1860	173118	NBL	Gateshead
1850	1992	ALL	1850	160938	NFK	North
1700	1850	1850	1900	142417	NFK	Dereham
1760	1834	ALL	1840	113611	NFK	Watton
1810	1850	1700	1810	130443	NTH	???
1736	1786	....	1736	101761	NTT	Kirton
1808	1808	1700	1808	142085	NTT	Normanton On Soar
?	?	?	?	148288	NTT	Nottingham
?	?	?	?	148288	NTT	Stapleford
1700	1750	1600	1800	166804	OXF	Bampton
1870	1890	1870	1890	138894	OXF	Oxford
1871	1913	1914	1992	108227	SOM	Draycott
1807	....	....	1807	133566	SRY	Southwark
1860	1940	ALL	1860	131849	SSX	East
1860	1940	ALL	1860	131849	SSX	Waldron
1900	1960	1800	1900	173029	STS	East
1840	....	1840	....	104213	SYK	Sheffield
1843	....	1843	....	104213	WAR	Birmingham
....	1869	....	1950	130168	WAR	Birmingham
1874	1874	ALL	1874	119636	WIC	Arklow
1790	1844	....	....	145327	WYK	Fewston
1786	1925	1750	1950	129798	YKS	Birstall
....	1777	1700	1777	138584	YKS	Keighley
1818	1992	1750	1818	150096	YKS	Knarlesborough
1640	1700	1640	1750	117706	YKS	Leeds
1800	1900	1600	1900	147788	YKS	Leeds
1810	1840	1750	1900	171484	YKS	Leeds
1709	1720	....	....	141097	YKS	North Newbald
1816	1841	1800	1816	128368	YKS	Sheffield
1710	1819	1710	1781	146897	YKS	Silkstone
1797	....	1750	....	134589	YKS	Thwing
HUDSON-DAVIES						
1871	....	ALL	ALL	131415	PEM	North
HUDSWELL						
....	....	ALL	ALL	106739	ALL	Name Study
1800	1992	ALL	1992	106739	ALL	ALL
HUDY						
1400	1700	1400	1700	135569	DEV	Kingswear
HUEGDON						
....	....	ALL	ALL	138800	ALL	Name Study
HUEY						
1840	1900	1800	1900	142875	IRL	???
HUFFERDINE						
1840	1900	ALL	1992	102245	STS	Brewood
HUGAL						
1870	1900	1800	1992	162620	DUR	Gateshead
HUGEILL						
....	....	1700	1832	131598	YKS	Danby

Known From	To	Researching From	To	Ref	Cty	Place
HUGGAN						
1621	1640	ALL	ALL	141615	LAN	Warton
HUGGARD						
....	....	ALL	ALL	128090	IOM	???
1870	....	1800	1870	128090	LAN	Manchester
HUGGART						
....	1782	....	1782	146811	AYR	West Kilbride
HUGGETT						
1874	....	1850	1880	163775	MDX	Bethnal Green
1841	1992	1800	1850	173061	SRY	Croydon
1740	1992	1700	1740	128724	SSX	ALL
1796	1796	....	....	139971	SSX	Bishopstone
1792	1856	....	....	139971	SSX	Eastbourne
1859	1921	....	....	145521	SSX	Eastbourne
HUGGETTT						
1791	1878	ALL	1992	125113	KEN	Canterbury
1791	1878	ALL	1992	125113	SSX	Brighton
HUGGILL						
1760	1860	1700	1800	171891	BRK	Didcot
HUGGIN						
1799	1799	ALL	....	115355	NTH	ALL
1799	1799	ALL	....	115355	RUT	ALL
HUGGINS						
....	....	ALL	ALL	135593	ALL	Name Study
1750	1930	1750	1930	135593	ALL	ALL
1720	1920	1700	1992	132799	BRK	Steventon
1857	1883	ALL	ALL	134929	LND	Paddington
1830	1850	1800	1900	127981	MDX	London
HUGH						
1800	1900	ALL	1850	145939	CON	Beryan
HUGHEA						
1860	1992	1830	1860	167363	WOR	Leigh
HUGHES						
....	1824	1500	1824	175072	AGY	Beaumaris
1840	1992	1840	1992	135666	AGY	Llanddona
1800	1900	1700	1980	135631	AGY	Llanrhuddlad
1844	1886	1842	1890	159786	AGY	Llansadwrn
1870	1960	1860	1900	111791	AGY	Llysfaen
1812	1884	1810	1890	159786	AGY	Penrhosllugwy
1840	1920	1800	1920	118540	ARM	Keady
1771	....	1700	1800	143693	BRK	Bray
1846	1992	1700	1846	125024	BRK	Clewer
1757	1804	....	....	115606	BRK	Cookham
1680	1750	....	....	119458	BRK	Newbury
1802	1836	1700	1810	164909	BRK	Oakley Green
1822	1893	1750	1930	143693	BRK	Reading
1855	1868	1700	1850	143693	BRK	Tilehurst
....	....	1800	....	118591	CAE	Aberdaron
1830	....	1700	1830	157147	CAE	Port Dinorwic
....	....	1700	1820	130931	CAR	???
1800	1850	1800	1850	167924	CHS	Farndon
1812	1815	1800	1900	165093	CHS	Great Boughton
1894	1935	....	....	132179	CHS	Hapsford
1877	1877	1980	....	152188	CHS	Seacombe In The Wirral
1843	....	1800	1900	139114	CHS	Stockport
1878	1908	ALL	1878	164755	CMA	Millom
1870	1910	1850	1870	176931	CMN	Lliwdy
1870	1910	1850	1870	176931	CMN	Pontfaen
1840	1992	1800	1900	142778	CWD	Dyffryn Clwyd
1800	1850	1700	1800	118702	CWD	Henllen
1750	1850	1750	1850	135666	DEN	Denbigh
1750	1850	1750	1850	135666	DEN	Henllan
1800	1850	1800	1850	135666	DEN	Llandyrnog
1702	1752	....	....	147885	DEN	Llanfair D C
1780	1992	1780	....	118672	DEN	Llanfair Talharion
1823	1846	1790	1846	174289	DEN	Llangollen
1750	1850	1750	1850	135666	DEN	Llannefydd
....	....	....	1822	154024	DEN	Llanrhaeadr
1830	1950	ALL	1950	132217	DEN	Llanwrst
1800	1850	1800	1850	135666	DEN	Llanynys
1876	1992	....	1876	131741	DEN	Ruabon
1846	1902	1790	1846	174289	DEN	Ruabon
1835	....	....	....	167037	DOW	Bambridge
1760	1880	1760	1850	108456	ESS	Kelvedon
1792	1869	1792	1869	147621	FLN	Caerwys
1850	1992	1750	1850	135658	FLN	Flint
1870	1992	1870	1992	135666	FLN	Greenfield
1870	1992	1870	1992	135666	FLN	Holywell
1850	1992	1750	1850	135658	FLN	Holywell
1830	1870	1830	1870	135666	FLN	Llanasa
1830	1890	1830	1890	135666	FLN	Trelawnyd
1808	1861	1750	1810	155500	FLN	Whitford
1670	1992	....	....	118672	FLN	Ysceifiog
HUGHES contd.						
1718	1869	1718	1869	158658	GLA	Llantrisant
....	....	1780	1820	117137	GLA	Newton Nottage
1908	1925	1908	1925	135666	GLA	Pontlotyn
1925	1939	1925	1939	135666	GLA	Pontypridd
1870	1900	1750	1870	135658	GLA	Swansea
1700	1992	1700	....	118672	GLS	Wotton Under Edge
1830	....	1700	1900	157147	GYN	Rhiwlas
1788	1794	1700	1850	143693	HAM	East Woodhay
1773	1838	1750	1850	136719	HAM	Wooten St Lawrence
1702	1992	ALL	ALL	115762	HRT	Redbourn
1955	1975	1955	1975	135666	IOW	Niton
....	....	1700	1837	146358	IRL	ALL
1851	1919	ALL	1919	106283	IRL	Ireland
1680	1766	....	....	127426	KEN	Harrietsham
1760	1849	....	....	127426	KEN	Lenham
1794	1794	....	....	127426	KEN	Rodmersham
1851	1919	ALL	1919	106283	KEN	Sandwich
1743	1743	1600	1743	170542	KEN	Woodnesborough
1813	1992	1700	1813	125024	LAN	Liverpool
1850	1992	1800	1900	135658	LAN	Liverpool
1877	?	ALL	1877	152188	LAN	Liverpool
1862	1890	1750	1871	163740	LAN	Liverpool
1830	1900	1830	1900	167924	LAN	Liverpool
1871	1900	1871	1900	115932	LAN	Manchester
1824	1992	1700	1864	130931	LAN	Salford
1810	....	....	....	172820	LND	St Marylebone
1844	1992	....	1843	129461	MDX	Bloomsbury
1830	1900	1650	1830	158992	MER	Derwenlas Isygarreg
1808	1992	1700	1808	149241	MER	Llangwm
1849	1871	....	....	154024	MGY	Buttington
1789	1878	1600	1789	156914	MGY	Kerry
1838	1839	1750	1900	114456	MGY	Llanfair
1839	....	....	....	153524	MON	Tredegar
1850	1955	1700	1860	160954	MSY	Liverpool
1841	1881	1700	1890	170518	OXF	Banbury
1846	1899	1700	1846	109223	POW	Llanmerewig
1815	1840	ALL	1840	149063	ROX	Hawick
1849	1849	....	....	154024	SAL	Alberbury
1857	1927	1800	1900	102075	SAL	Bomere Heath
1840	1920	ALL	1840	179612	SAL	Staton Lacy
1860	1874	....	....	118133	SCT	Bridgeton
1860	1920	1800	1945	135429	SOM	Bath
1775	1857	....	....	135437	SOM	Taunton
....	....	ALL	1850	178403	SRY	Bookham
1750	1800	1750	1850	103055	SRY	Lambeth
1840	1933	1790	1839	157619	SSX	Brighthelmstone
1800	....	....	....	174750	SSX	Brighton
1799	....	ALL	1992	159174	SSX	Lyminster
1860	1900	1700	1870	170607	SSX	Sudbury
1840	1864	1840	1992	152943	STS	Brockmoor
1870	....	ALL	ALL	149489	STS	Burslem
1900	1920	ALL	ALL	152641	STS	Walsall
1877	1879	ALL	ALL	152641	STS	Wednesbury
1869	1992	ALL	ALL	150681	TYR	Dungannon
1866	1900	1700	1992	113123	WAR	Birmingham
1800	1903	1800	1903	140724	WAR	Birmingham
1880	1900	1700	1800	142395	WAR	Birmingham
....	....	1800	1900	154458	WAR	Birmingham
1845	1880	1845	1880	146617	WAR	Stratford On Avon
1750	1800	1600	1800	130125	WOR	Alfrick
1821	1992	....	....	134619	WOR	Dudley
....	....	....	1884	140767	WOR	Dudley
1801	1867	1750	1801	179647	WOR	Hanbury
1880	1950	....	....	173827	WOR	Lye
1803	1862	....	....	102733	WOR	Redditch
1860	1905	1750	1860	138339	WOR	Worcester
HUGHESDON						
1784	1838	ALL	ALL	105015	SSX	Horsham
HUGHF						
1700	1940	1550	1700	167584	DUR	Teesdale
HUGHNOWNE						
1560	1600	1560	1600	167924	HRT	Walkern
HUGHSON						
1680	?	1600	1992	167592	CHS	Chester
1750	1840	1700	1800	155500	SAL	Wistanstow
1750	1965	....	....	137820	SHI	Fetlar
1720	1965	....	....	137820	SHI	Mid Yell
1760	1965	....	....	137820	SHI	North Yell
1758	1965	....	....	137820	SHI	Northmavine
1720	1965	....	....	137820	SHI	South Yell
HUGILL						
....	....	1700	1800	131598	YKS	Egton
....	....	1700	1800	131598	YKS	Glaisdale

Known From	To	Researching From	To	Ref	Cty	Place
HUGO						
....	....	1830	1840	130877	CON	Cardinham
1850	1980	1850	1992	171417	DEV	Plymouth
HUISH						
....	....	ALL	ALL	135712	ALL	Name Study
....	....	1864	1992	135712	GLA	Cardiff
....	....	1864	1992	135712	GLA	Swansea
....	....	1650	1900	135712	GLS	Dursley
....	....	1650	1900	135712	GLS	Uley
....	....	1854	1992	135712	MON	Blaenavon
....	....	1854	1992	135712	MON	Newport
1150	1900	1150	1900	135712	SOM	Central
1150	1900	1150	1900	135712	SOM	North
1800	1960	1700	1900	142050	SOM	South
1742	1828	1740	1830	142018	SOM	Ashwick
1703	1837	ALL	ALL	153516	SOM	Congresbury
HUITSON						
1800	1992	1700	1800	135720	DUR	Seaham
1800	1992	1700	1800	135720	T&W	Sunderland
1600	1699	1600	1699	169781	YKS	Throxenby
HUKE						
1823	1823	1800	1823	100277	LND	Shoreditch
HULBARD						
1802	1992	ALL	1802	178926	LEI	Kilby
HULBERT						
1802	1992	ALL	1802	178926	LEI	Kilby
1856	1898	1800	1898	128694	LND	Marylebone
1827	1850	1800	1880	132608	LND	???
1857	1926	1790	1857	111740	SSX	Brighton
HULCUP						
1708	1836	1700	1850	132608	BRK	Lambourn
HULF						
ALL	ALL	ALL	ALL	171964	ALL	ALL
HULHERAN						
1836	....	ALL	ALL	172057	ROS	???
HULL						
....	....	ALL	ALL	135739	ALL	Name Study
....	....	ALL	1900	151815	BDF	Little Barford
1826	1865	ALL	1900	151815	CAM	Bourn
....	....	....	....	135747	DOR	Shaftsbury
1595	1750	1595	1750	135747	DOR	Tolpuddle
1802	1935	1800	1900	135739	DUR	North
1616	1800	1616	1802	135739	DUR	Brancepeth
....	....	ALL	ALL	135739	DUR	???
1780	1829	1730	1780	172871	HRT	Rickmansworth
....	....	ALL	ALL	178152	IRL	???
....	....	ALL	ALL	178152	LAN	Liverpool
1825	1970	1825	1970	100080	LAN	Preston
1790	1850	1790	1850	100080	LAN	The Fylde
1870	1940	1700	1870	121452	LND	East
....	....	ALL	ALL	167827	MDX	Stanwell
1800	1860	1700	1800	107344	NTH	Nassington
1809	1850	1700	1825	166561	NTT	Tollerton
1830	1900	1700	1830	144681	SRY	Dorking
1828	1836	1790	1850	179337	WIL	Lnagley Burrell
1807	1902	1700	1830	109983	WOR	Hillmorton
....	....	?	?	134201	???	London
HULLAND						
1780	1930	1600	1780	145017	DEV	North
HULLAW						
1760	1780	1700	1760	158976	YKS	Hampsthwaite
HULLEY						
....	....	ALL	ALL	135755	ALL	Name Study
1500	1900	1500	1900	135755	ALL	ALL
1370	1900	1450	1900	135755	CHS	ALL
....	....	1600	1900	135755	DBY	ALL
1500	1900	1500	1900	135755	ENG	ALL
1600	1900	1600	1900	135755	LAN	ALL
1580	1900	1580	1900	135755	YKS	ALL
HULLINGHURST						
1780	1820	1750	1890	133442	LAN	Preston
HULLY						
1650	1850	1650	1850	135755	CMA	ALL
HULME						
1759	1992	1700	1800	135763	CHS	Astbury
1728	1807	1600	1793	151254	CHS	Cheadle
1840	1980	1800	1840	149373	CHS	Macclesfield
1759	1992	1700	1800	135763	CHS	Sandwich
1728	1807	1600	1793	151254	CHS	Wilmslow
1860	1992	1840	1880	117145	LAN	Bolton
1748	1856	1700	1840	174211	LAN	Little Heaton
1849	1988	1840	1849	159522	LAN	Manchester
1788	1800	1700	1800	159964	LAN	Ringley
1748	1856	1700	1840	174211	LAN	Unsworth

Known From	To	Researching From	To	Ref	Cty	Place
HULME contd.						
....	....	1800	1845	124796	LAN	Wigan
1909	1936	1700	1909	173797	NBL	Newcastle On Tyne
1822	1880	1880	1992	148180	STS	Fenton
1845	....	1700	1890	110914	WLS	Montgomery
HULSE						
1837	1906	....	....	137790	CHS	Allostock
1704	1909	1700	1930	168947	CHS	Davenham
1704	1909	1700	1930	168947	CHS	Winsford
1830	1900	1750	1830	173029	CHS	Wybunbury
1814	1992	1700	1814	158917	LAN	Manchester
1858	1992	1800	1860	173649	STS	Stoke On Trent
HULSON						
ALL	ALL	ALL	ALL	151750	ALL	ALL
1800	1922	1700	1800	177881	CON	???
1800	1922	1700	1800	177881	DEV	Devonport
HULSTON						
....	....	ALL	ALL	151750	ALL	Name Study
....	1858	....	1950	130168	ENG	Midlands
HUMAN						
1745	1900	ALL	ALL	172103	SFK	East
HUMBER						
1680	1720	1650	1750	149993	HAM	Candovers
1867	1970	ALL	1867	142107	LEI	Leicester
1840	1910	1800	1992	158623	NTT	Central
HUMBERSTON						
1800	1880	1750	....	101923	LIN	Horncastle
1800	1880	1750	....	101923	LIN	Louth
HUMBERSTONE						
1781	1812	1680	1780	153842	BDF	Campton
1500	1600	....	....	167924	HRT	Bennington
1703	....	....	1703	142166	HRT	Walkern
1843	....	1840	1850	153842	KEN	Dover
1837	1910	1725	1837	105503	LIN	East
1890	1930	1890	1930	101877	LND	Islington
1861	1867	1850	1867	153842	LND	Islington
....	....	1830	1840	153842	YKS	Leeds
1838	1948	1800	1900	102164	YKS	Sheffield
HUMBLE						
1843	1914	1700	1843	152269	DUR	ALL
1735	....	....	....	117196	DUR	Durham
....	1850	ALL	1900	177695	DUR	Wickham
1800	1992	1699	1992	143049	NBL	North East
HUMBY						
1730	1992	1700	1900	162582	HAM	West
1731	1880	1700	1890	128783	HAM	Lyndhurst
1800	1910	ALL	ALL	135798	HAM	Portsmouth
....	....	ALL	1800	151602	HAM	Wellow
1800	1810	ALL	ALL	135798	IOW	ALL
1595	1731	1595	1780	128783	WIL	Downton
HUME						
1600	1700	1600	1700	169781	DEV	Milton Abbott
1700	1720	1700	1750	130915	ELN	Dirleton
1850	1900	1750	1850	172472	ESS	Goldhanger
1673	1750	1600	1800	176621	FIF	Aberdour
1812	1922	1922	1992	101427	HAM	Portsmouth
HUMES						
1803	1917	1600	1992	130125	DUR	Chester Le Street
1863	1992	1700	1863	179051	DUR	Cornforth
HUMFORD						
1791	1860	....	....	165514	WAR	Hatton
1747	1808	....	....	165514	WAR	Shipston On Stour
HUMM						
1829	1851	1700	1851	172316	LND	Hackney
1829	1851	1700	1851	172316	LND	Stepney
1950	1992	1790	1950	125555	MDX	Bethnal Green
1883	1986	1700	1883	138436	MDX	Stepney
HUMMERSTONE						
1677	1992	1600	1677	115096	HRT	Cheshunt
HUMPAGE						
1900	1992	ALL	ALL	129240	WAR	Birmingham
1930	....	....	....	145742	WAR	Birmingham
HUMPHREY						
1806	1830	1780	1806	127116	AGY	Llanfaelog
1817	1835	1700	1817	122394	AYR	Craigie
1793	1858	....	1793	163201	BAN	Fordyce
1793	1858	....	1793	163201	BAN	Keith
1820	1840	ALL	1820	134058	BKM	Wingrave
1700	1770	1700	1800	124133	CWD	Llanelian
1718	1982	1718	1982	107379	HRT	Tring
1839	1920	1700	1839	178187	KEN	Hever Castle
1760	1880	ALL	....	104515	LIN	South
1700	ALL	1830	1920	107379	LND	ALL
1820	1850	1815	1870	168920	LND	Battersea

Known From	To	Researching From	To	Ref	Cty	Place
HUMPHREY contd.						
1815	....	1800	1815	168920	LND	Stepney
1850	1980	....	....	147273	LND	???
1700	ALL	1838	1920	107379	MDX	Brentford
1660	1992	ALL	ALL	160873	NBL	Newcastle On Tyne
1773	1992	....	1773	142409	NFK	???
1840	1870	....	....	165948	NTH	Helmdon
1658	1850	1658	1850	140724	NTH	Moreton Pinkney
1735	1800	....	....	132756	OXF	Bicester
1926	....	....	....	133922	SRY	Leigh
1785	1852	ALL	ALL	135909	SRY	Oxted
1852	1982	ALL	ALL	135909	SRY	???
1770	1960	1770	1950	102490	SSX	ALL
1817	1841	1700	1850	117331	SSX	Hartfield
ALL	1642	....	....	170178	WIL	Bishops Cannings
1810	1870	1550	1810	150843	YKS	Easingwold
HUMPHREYS						
1790	1840	1700	1900	153826	CAM	???
....	....	1800	1850	142093	DEN	ALL
1830	1890	ALL	ALL	104191	DFD	Aberystwyth
1772	1800	1750	1772	168777	ESS	Rochford
1850	1992	....	....	142093	GLA	Aberdare
1750	1800	1650	1750	177776	MGY	Llanrhaiadre-Moch-Nant
1800	1900	....	....	177776	MGY	Llanwddyn
1880	1900	1850	1900	131431	MGY	Newtown
1830	1960	....	....	168777	SSX	Firle
1830	....	1830	....	159247	WAR	Coventry
1780	1825	1700	1780	139866	WIL	Salisbury
1856	1928	....	....	161306	WLS	ALL
1830	....	1830	....	159247	???	Manchester
HUMPHRIES						
1829	1851	1750	1850	117315	FLN	Hanmer
1803	1803	1600	1803	112410	FLN	Holywell
1750	1810	1650	1750	135844	GLS	Ampney Crucis
1870	1960	....	....	135844	GLS	Maisey Hampton
1846	1917	....	....	164003	GLS	Wotton Under Edge
1784	1807	ALL	1850	118737	HAM	Old Basing
1726	?	?	?	166642	KEN	Sheldwich
1850	....	....	....	141208	MDX	Isleworth
1890	1992	1800	1900	128732	MGY	???
1850	1985	1700	1870	160954	MSY	Liverpool
1665	1930	....	....	149888	OXF	Great Milton
1766	1817	1766	1817	139971	SAL	Church Pulverbatch
1872	....	1872	....	125563	SAL	Shrewsbury
1734	1779	1600	1800	153591	SSX	Hastings
1734	1779	1600	1800	153591	SSX	Littlehampton
1887	1947	1700	1890	153702	???	Birmingham
HUMPHRIS						
?	....	1700	1960	123668	AVN	Bristol
HUMPHRISS						
1791	1837	1600	1800	118877	GLS	Bourton On Water
HUMPHRY						
1658	1850	1658	1850	140724	NTH	Moreton Pinkney
HUMPLEBY						
1831	1890	1700	1830	126772	YKS	Helmsley
HUMPREY						
....	....	ALL	ALL	100153	SRY	ALL
HUN						
1830	1852	1800	1850	103756	???	Harmondsworth
HUNCKYNGE						
1080	1080	....	....	135852	SAL	Hunkinton
HUNDERWOOD						
....	....	....	....	129577	IOW	???
HUNKIN						
1100	1992	....	....	135852	CON	ALL
1100	1992	....	....	135852	CON	Liskeard
1600	1992	1600	1900	123234	CON	Mevagissey
1833	1920	1600	1833	163112	CON	Mevagissey
1100	1992	....	....	135852	DEV	ALL
1600	1992	....	....	135852	SWL	ALL
HUNKING						
1600	1992	....	....	135852	CON	ALL
....	....	1800	1899	159840	CON	St Germans
1100	1992	....	....	135852	DEV	ALL
HUNKINS						
1100	1992	....	....	135852	CON	ALL
1100	1992	....	....	135852	DEV	ALL
1600	1992	....	....	135852	SWL	ALL
HUNN						
1750	1992	1600	1992	135860	NFK	Fleggburgh
HUNNEYBALL						
1808	1992	1800	1992	172995	ESS	Little Bromley

Known From	To	Researching From	To	Ref	Cty	Place
HUNNISETT						
1750	1900	1700	1750	135879	SSX	Hellingly
HUNT DANIEL						
1783	1816	1750	1800	109819	WOR	Kidderminster
HUNT DAVIES						
1850	1900	1850	1900	129151	RAD	Coombe
1850	1900	1850	1900	129151	RAD	Presteigne
HUNT						
1787	....	1700	1800	143693	BKM	Amersham
1600	1850	1600	1850	135976	BRK	Cholsey
1819	1921	1750	1820	135925	BRK	Lechhampstead
....	....	1700	1750	117714	BRK	Purley
1731	....	1650	1750	143693	BRK	Purley
....	....	1800	1900	117714	BRK	Thatcham
1808	1838	1808	1838	136808	CAM	Elm
1889	1902	....	....	125784	CAM	Newmarket
1859	1881	ALL	1859	115355	CAM	Peterborough
1790	1812	ALL	1812	159077	CAM	Whittlesey
1776	1829	1750	1855	148121	DBY	Denby
1923	1992	1892	ALL	135917	DBY	Mickleover
1817	1818	1812	1818	148121	DBY	South Wingfield
1855	1865	1855	1865	172634	DEV	Exeter
1900	1992	1538	1900	131318	DOR	South
1815	1820	1750	1830	160849	DOR	Shaftsbury
1700	1735	1700	ALL	135917	DUR	Barnard Castle
1769	1815	1732	1831	135917	DUR	Darlington
1799	1811	1776	1811	135917	DUR	Morton Tinmouth
1768	1960	1768	1876	102806	ESS	Laindon
1872	1992	1700	1872	113166	GLS	Bristol
1648	1730	1640	1730	142018	GLS	Bristol
1804	1860	1800	1860	152935	GLS	Bristol
1810	1992	....	....	118672	GLS	Leckhampton
1793	1851	1600	1793	165298	GLS	Stroud
1591	....	....	....	152943	HAM	Awbridge
....	....	1814	1834	143480	HAM	Fareham
....	....	1700	1840	101559	HAM	Gosport
1591	....	....	....	152943	HAM	Michelmersh
1795	1797	ALL	ALL	119504	HAM	Portsea
1780	1900	ALL	1780	150983	HAM	Portsea
1800	1850	1600	1850	130125	HAM	Portsmouth
1810	1840	1750	1840	136840	HAM	Portsmouth
1840	1980	1800	1900	125032	HAM	Southampton
1859	1881	ALL	1859	115355	HUN	Peterborough
1787	1831	1600	1800	132993	IOW	Carisbrooke
1787	1831	1600	1800	132993	IOW	Eatcombe
1811	1841	ALL	1992	125113	KEN	Ash
1884	1917	1880	ALL	135917	KEN	Chislehurst
1700	1900	1600	1700	154016	KEN	Dymchurch
1714	....	....	1714	155667	KEN	Elham
1759	....	1750	1806	148121	KEN	Goudhurst
....	....	1700	1900	129275	KEN	Gravesend
....	....	1800	1900	129275	KEN	Northfleet
1823	1853	1820	1853	148121	KEN	Rochester
1853	1876	1700	1853	173509	KEN	Tunbridge Wells
1750	1900	1750	1900	125237	LAN	Darwen
1800	1880	1880	1992	162256	LAN	Darwen
1871	1900	ALL	ALL	135909	LAN	Leigh
....	....	1800	1992	131504	LAN	Leyland
1820	1843	1800	1900	118168	LAN	Manchester
1794	1805	1731	1805	135917	LAN	Manchester
1749	1992	1749	1890	131504	LAN	Much Hoole
1764	1871	ALL	ALL	135909	LAN	Much Hoole
1700	1992	1600	1850	135968	LEI	Blaby
1823	1872	1800	1900	116173	LEI	Leicester
1700	1992	1600	1850	135968	LEI	Leicester
1750	1790	....	....	165999	LEI	Leicester
1870	1900	1600	1992	109924	LEI	Loughborough
1823	1890	1700	1900	135968	LEI	Mountsorrel
1723	1742	1600	1723	150150	LEI	Whetstone
1822	1850	1750	1850	115681	LIN	Grantham
1811	1829	1780	1850	151599	LIN	Hykeham
1702	1840	....	....	165999	LIN	Swinderby
1702	1840	....	....	165999	LIN	Thurlby
1800	1899	ALL	ALL	146633	LND	ALL
1880	1992	1880	1992	135941	LND	Battersea
....	....	....	1860	110817	LND	Bethnal Green
1880	....	1880	....	123773	LND	Holborn
1854	1992	1800	1992	135933	LND	Islington
1860	1989	1700	1860	136018	LND	Islington
1849	1905	1840	1905	135917	LND	Islington
1790	1992	....	....	135984	LND	Lambeth
1790	1992	....	....	135984	LND	Southwark
1880	1992	1880	1992	135941	LND	Wandsworth
1790	1992	....	....	135984	LND	Westminster

Known From	To	Researching From	To	Ref	Cty	Place
HUNT contd.						
1770	1860	1700	1800	100048	MDX	Harlington
1860	1989	1700	1860	136018	MDX	Islington
....	....	1800	1880	158259	MDX	Kensington
....	....	1800	1880	158259	MDX	London
1819	1851	1851	1870	165298	MDX	London
1826	1900	1826	1992	142735	MDX	Poplar
1855	1912	1750	1860	163740	MDX	Shoreditch
1826	1900	1826	1992	142735	MDX	Stepney
1800	1870	1800	1870	135941	MDX	Westminster
1830	1900	1830	1950	160849	MON	Monmouth
1859	1881	ALL	1859	115355	NTH	Peterborough
1824	1853	....	1800	151688	NTH	Ufford
1702	1840	....	....	165999	NTT	South Scarle
....	....	1680	1713	177393	NTT	Weston
1800	1819	1732	1831	135917	NYK	Barton
1849	1937	1750	1849	166464	OXF	Bladon
....	....	1750	1850	108049	OXF	Epwell
1865	1880	1865	1885	135941	SCT	Glasgow
1800	1830	1780	1900	111325	SFK	Ashbocking
....	....	1740	1790	172871	SFK	Bradfield St George
....	....	1750	1800	174114	SFK	Bradford St George
1880	1992	1700	1880	158755	SFK	Ipswich
1861	1881	1800	1861	154954	SFK	Occold
1850	1901	1700	1850	174114	SFK	Rougham
....	....	1800	1920	174114	SFK	Shelland
1860	1880	1850	1900	109525	SFK	Stowlangtoft
1580	1750	1580	1760	142018	SOM	ALL
1774	1853	ALL	1820	174815	SOM	Banwell
1795	1900	1750	1900	118540	SOM	Cannington
1829	1964	1829	1899	135992	SOM	Clifton
1783	1803	1700	1783	161446	SOM	Misterton
1840	1900	....	1840	125393	SOM	North Cadbury
1854	1859	ALL	1900	168696	SOM	Yatton
1860	1925	ALL	ALL	156558	SRY	Camberwell
1920	1950	....	....	135925	SRY	Farnham
1805	1860	1700	1805	101559	SRY	Lambeth
1800	1899	ALL	ALL	146633	SRY	Richmond
1845	1892	1844	1890	100048	SRY	Southwark
....	....	....	....	164968	SSX	Battle
1720	1740	....	....	103764	WAR	Bidford On Avon
1813	1856	1700	1900	124281	WAR	Birmingham
1876	1960	1700	1876	125415	WAR	Birmingham
1500	1900	1500	1900	170216	WIL	ALL
1716	1747	1716	....	115576	WIL	Bromham
....	....	ALL	ALL	144762	WIL	Marlborough
1806	1896	1700	1896	136530	WOR	Alcester
1826	1992	1800	1992	105147	WOR	Alvechurch
1860	1952	1840	1860	153907	WOR	Bewdley
1863	1992	....	....	161284	WOR	Bromsgrove
....	....	1700	1840	153907	WOR	Churchill
1816	1820	1800	1860	109819	WOR	Dudley
....	1831	....	1831	140767	WOR	Dudley
1816	1820	1800	1860	109819	WOR	Rowley Regis
1700	1730	1675	1992	114901	YKS	Wheldrake
1750	....	1700	....	134589	YKS	Wigginton
1850	1889	....	....	125784	???	Birmingham
1850	1889	....	....	125784	???	Saltley
HUNTBACH						
1576	1603	....	....	117404	STS	Bushbury
HUNTER						
1800	1920	1850	1920	145467	ABD	Cushnie
....	....	ALL	1760	136050	ABD	Fyvie
1762	1992	ALL	1800	136050	ABD	Methlick
1860	1900	....	....	137936	ANS	Dundee
1700	1992	1600	1700	113204	ANT	North
1870	1992	1750	1870	118052	ANT	Ballycastle
1700	1992	1600	1700	113204	ANT	Dunmurry
1869	1920	1600	1869	127507	ANT	Racavan
1835	1875	1800	1835	142360	AVN	Bristol
1790	1850	1700	1900	179574	AYR	Ayr
....	....	1700	1809	136069	AYR	St Quivox
1809	1992	....	....	136069	AYR	Troon
1750	1850	1600	1750	142328	CLK	Alloa
....	....	1700	1733	108510	CLK	Clackmannan
1750	1850	1600	1750	142328	CLK	Tillcoultry
....	....	1700	1733	108510	CLK	Tillicoultry
1850	1870	....	....	161675	CLK	Tillicoutry
1815	1821	1700	1795	100846	CLK	???
1800	1912	1750	1900	179000	CLK	???
1846	1852	1700	1846	122394	DFS	Dunscore
1823	1852	1700	1823	122394	DFS	Glencairn
1855	1867	1700	1883	122394	DFS	Kirkconnel
1858	1883	1700	1929	122394	DFS	Sanguhar

Known From	To	Researching From	To	Ref	Cty	Place
HUNTER contd.						
1868	1883	1868	1883	122394	DNB	Ballock
1850	1930	ALL	1850	178470	DUR	North
1845	1857	1538	1992	118893	DUR	Bishop Wearmouth
1758	....	1600	1758	116637	DUR	Boldon
1840	1910	ALL	ALL	162620	DUR	Burnopfield
1860	1890	1700	1992	162620	DUR	Chester Le Street
1832	1848	1538	1992	118893	DUR	Dawdon
1819	1821	1538	1992	118893	DUR	Haswell
1880	1992	1750	1880	166294	DUR	Houghton
1816	1832	1538	1992	118893	DUR	Houhgton Le Spring
1700	1812	1538	1992	118893	DUR	Lanchester
1600	1700	1600	1700	169781	DUR	Medomsley
1832	1891	1538	1992	118893	DUR	Seaham Harbour
1870	1900	....	....	146870	DUR	South Shields
1840	1949	1800	1840	154873	DUR	Sunderland
1650	1860	1500	1900	114898	ELN	ALL
....	....	1750	1992	107778	ELN	Edinburgh
1650	1860	1600	1900	114898	ELN	Tyninghame
1650	1860	1600	1900	114898	ELN	Whitekirk
1733	1757	1700	1733	108510	FIF	Kincardine On Forth
1823	?	ALL	ALL	101370	FIF	Perth
1823	?	ALL	ALL	101370	FIF	Saline
1733	1757	1700	1733	108510	FIF	Tulliallan
1733	1757	1700	1733	108510	FIF	???
1798	1820	1790	1830	179604	HAM	Gosport
1790	1830	1700	1790	138983	IRL	Dublin
....	....	1700	1820	136034	IRL	Holyhay
1750	1762	1762	1800	179604	KEN	Lamberhurst
1870	1992	ALL	1900	136077	LAN	East
1663	1699	1565	1663	141291	LAN	Furness
....	1862	1759	1862	111767	LAN	Hindley
1820	1870	1700	1819	172006	LAN	St Helens
1908	1932	1880	1970	179000	LKS	Birkwood Square
1880	1941	1840	1880	163694	LKS	Glasgow
....	....	1790	....	138983	LND	ALL
1840	....	1750	1900	152129	LND	Central
1900	1930	1900	1920	116157	LND	South
1820	1850	1700	1930	136034	MDX	London
1830	1855	1800	1875	136042	MDX	Paddington
1920	1920	ALL	1920	179515	MIL	Indian Army
....	....	ALL	1791	119326	MLN	Newbattle
1830	1850	1830	1880	179604	MON	Bedwelty
1830	1850	1830	1880	179604	MON	Tredegar
....	....	ALL	ALL	136085	NBL	ALL
....	....	1780	1820	159905	NBL	Elsingtonhall
1820	1840	1700	1992	162620	NBL	Heddon On The Wall
....	1800	....	1800	136085	NBL	Newbrough
....	....	ALL	ALL	166812	NBL	Newcastle
1820	1992	1700	1992	162620	NBL	North Shields
1800	1890	1800	1890	136085	NBL	Redesdale
....	....	1700	1850	162620	NBL	Tanfield
1851	....	ALL	ALL	105481	NTT	Old Basford
1730	1992	1600	1992	148482	OKI	Orkney
1822	1856	1856	1992	136050	SCT	ALL
1750	1965	....	....	137820	SHI	Fetlar
1720	1965	....	....	137820	SHI	Mid Yell
1760	1965	....	....	137820	SHI	North Yell
1758	1965	....	....	137820	SHI	Northmavine
1720	1965	....	....	137820	SHI	South Yell
1740	1860	1700	1900	139203	SHI	Tingwall
1800	1828	1750	1850	136042	SRY	Lambeth
....	1700	....	....	174564	SSX	???
1770	1850	1700	1850	179000	STI	Muiravonside
....	....	ALL	1840	132829	T&W	Gateshead
1840	1992	....	....	132829	T&W	Newcastle Upon Tyne
1772	1819	ALL	1772	154946	WES	Appleby
1772	....	ALL	1772	154946	WES	Bongate
1700	1850	1650	1850	143553	WES	Milburn
1776	1803	1760	1803	107573	WIL	Chiselton
1850	1900	....	....	177393	YKS	Featherstone
1730	1850	1680	1730	177393	YKS	Ottringham
1490	1750	1300	1500	179604	YKS	Thornton Le Dale
1870	1870	1750	1880	100501	???	Birmingham
HUNTER-GARDNER						
....	....	1800	1900	137685	LND	City
....	....	1800	1900	137685	SFK	Goriston With Southtown
HUNTING						
1865	1986	....	....	136093	WOR	Ashton Under Hill
1807	1863	....	....	136093	WOR	Evesham
1769	1807	....	....	136093	WOR	Pinvin
HUNTINGDON						
1816	1966	1500	1816	114111	HAM	Portsmouth

Known From	To	Researching From	To	Ref	Cty	Place
HUNTINGFORD						
....	....	ALL	ALL	146552	ALL	Name Study
1700	1900	1600	1900	121762	HAM	Bramshot
HUNTINGTON						
1692	1992	1500	1692	136107	CMA	???
1800	1946	1700	1800	169803	HAM	Portsea
1816	1966	1500	1816	114111	HAM	Portsmouth
HUNTLEY						
1780	ALL	....	....	142158	BRK	Reading
1880	1900	ALL	ALL	122866	MON	Ebbw Vale
1849	1870	ALL	1849	166847	SOM	Bath
....	....	1820	1840	117137	SOM	Publow
1820	1850	ALL	1870	132187	SRY	Lingfield
HUNTLEY-THOMAS						
1850	1950	1850	1950	118540	GLA	Lansanor
HUNTRESS						
1920	1985	1650	1985	126241	DUR	ALL
1920	1985	1650	1985	126241	NBL	ALL
HUNTRODS						
1844	1851	1800	1850	144797	DUR	Seaham
1749	1850	ALL	ALL	131199	YKS	Fylingdales
HUPSTON						
1880	1992	1880	1992	120251	WAR	ALL
HUQUENAN						
1800	1900	....	....	153397	HAM	New Forest
HURAM						
1850	1992	1700	1850	148059	STS	Colwich
HURCOMBE						
1812	1813	1750	1813	147575	LND	Shoreditch
1813	....	....	1813	167053	MDX	Paddington
1814	....	....	1814	167053	OXF	Bampton
HURD						
1770	1795	ALL	ALL	149489	HAM	South
1694	1795	ALL	1795	114987	SOM	Somerton
HURDEN						
....	....	ALL	ALL	136123	ALL	Name Study
1811	1955	1810	1980	136123	CON	Bodmin
1655	1934	1570	1812	136123	DOR	Abbotsbury
1690	1743	1570	1746	136123	DOR	Allington
1720	1868	1699	1980	136123	DOR	Chickerell
1685	1853	1682	1980	136123	DOR	Langton Herring
1628	1786	1568	1794	136123	DOR	Portesham
1780	1880	1750	1980	136123	DOR	Stinsford
1767	1799	1767	1801	136123	SOM	Bonham Chapel
1809	1980	1809	1985	136123	SOM	Bruton
1773	1829	1720	1837	136123	SOM	Penselwood
1841	1871	1841	1980	136123	SOM	Wincanton
HURDING						
1800	1992	1700	1992	143014	DOR	ALL
1617	1738	1614	1770	136123	DOR	Litton Cheney
1635	1772	1628	1797	136123	DOR	Long Bredy
1721	1725	1630	1812	136123	DOR	Puncknowle
1662	1677	1546	1731	136123	DOR	Wooton Glanville
1800	1992	1700	1992	143014	SOM	ALL
HURDLESTONE						
1814	1992	1750	1814	176257	SOM	North Cadbury
HURDLEY						
....	....	....	1810	102059	MGY	Montgomery
HURDON						
1802	1833	1800	1980	136123	CON	Egloskerry
1597	1840	1597	1980	136123	CON	Northill
1283	1854	1283	1980	136123	CON	Southpetherwin
HURDUS						
1860	?	1750	1992	167592	YKS	Castleford
1860	?	1750	1992	167592	YKS	Whitwood
HURFORD						
1790	1871	1600	1790	149888	DEV	Tiverton
....	....	1650	1760	153281	SOM	North Petherton
1800	1850	1800	1900	141933	SOM	Taunton
1850	1900	1800	1930	115746	SOM	West Monkton
HURKETT						
1872	1949	....	....	147869	DEN	???
1872	1949	....	....	147869	LND	???
1760	1900	1700	1992	101273	WIL	ALL
HURKS						
1778	....	1700	1778	113352	ESS	Rivenhall
HURLBUT						
1635	1992	1450	1635	159832	WIL	???
HURLE						
1700	1992	1650	1900	130494	ALL	ALL
1810	1880	1800	1900	130494	KEN	Deptford
1750	1810	1710	1810	130494	KEN	Greenwich
1780	1830	1760	1850	130494	MDX	London
....	....	?	?	169358	WIL	Edington
HURLE contd.						
1830	1900	1700	1830	130990	WIL	Trowbridge
....	....	?	?	169358	WIL	Trowbridge
HURLEY						
1831	....	ALL	1900	169374	COR	Monkstown
1817	....	1817	1850	149284	DEV	???
1813	1880	1813	....	123609	KEN	Rochester
1780	....	1780	....	139149	SOM	Bishops Hull
1815	1855	1700	1900	177873	SOM	???
....	....	ALL	1785	179477	SOM	???
1690	....	1600	....	133590	STS	Tipton
HURLINGTON						
1520	1700	....	....	134953	YKS	Slaidburn
HURLOCK						
1764	1992	1644	1764	136158	ESS	East End
1764	1992	1644	1764	136158	LND	Stepney
HURLSTOWE						
1790	1860	....	....	120472	WAR	Packwood
HURMAN						
....	....	1760	1900	136166	SOM	Burnham
....	....	1850	1907	136166	SOM	Worle
HURN						
1786	1874	1700	1786	107344	CAM	Peterborough
1748	1940	....	....	128996	CAM	Thorney
1691	1750	....	....	165999	GLS	Henbury
1813	....	1750	1900	135585	HAM	Alverstoke
1813	....	1750	1900	135585	HAM	Portsmouth
1851	1902	....	....	135585	SSX	Chichester
HURRELL						
1830	1850	1800	1830	145424	ALL	ALL
1850	1900	1800	1992	133450	DEV	Stokenham
1800	1840	1700	1880	177717	DEV	Torquay
1820	1980	1500	1992	124443	ESS	Colchester
1830	1850	ALL	1830	108197	NFK	Heigham
1700	1899	....	....	121835	NFK	Norwich
HURREN						
1800	1860	1500	1860	175463	SFK	ALL
1806	1992	1700	1806	152552	SFK	Chediston
1810	....	ALL	1810	154288	SFK	Easton
HURRY						
1662	1940	....	....	128996	CAM	Thorney
HURSE						
1869	1929	1903	1992	167533	IRL	Dublin
HURST						
....	....	ALL	ALL	136174	ALL	Name Study
....	....	?	?	110507	AYR	Catrine Sorn
1560	1992	1560	1992	136182	BKM	ALL
1765	1799	1700	1850	159964	BKM	Lt Horwood
1868	1951	....	....	154024	CHS	Weaverham
1736	1992	1690	1736	105384	DUR	Winlaton On Tyne
....	....	1800	1900	154261	HAM	New Forest
1830	1992	1750	1900	133922	HAM	Southampton
....	....	1750	1842	147850	KEN	Margste
1695	1889	....	....	109495	LAN	Eccles
1825	1851	....	....	166030	LAN	Heaton Norris
....	....	1600	1700	105384	LAN	Manchester
....	....	1700	1980	163724	LAN	Manchester
1685	1735	1650	1685	118958	LAN	???
1800	1830	1800	1841	164895	LEI	Thurmaston
1800	1900	1800	1900	106577	LIN	Epworth
1856	1900	1200	1880	163724	LIN	Isle Of Axholme
1800	1899	ALL	ALL	146633	LND	ALL
1842	1864	....	....	147850	LND	Mary Le Bone
1870	1930	....	....	154261	LND	St George In East
1881	1884	1700	1992	177733	MDX	Marylebone
1855	1881	....	....	102741	NBL	Newcastle Upon Tyne
1793	1875	1760	1820	170348	NTT	Ordsall
1799	1850	1799	1850	118540	NTT	Upton By Southwell
1524	1992	1500	1992	136182	OXF	ALL
1782	1845	1782	1845	103977	OXF	Ewelme
1782	1845	1782	1845	103977	OXF	Newington
1782	1845	1782	1845	103977	OXF	Warborough
1782	1845	1782	1845	103977	OXF	Watlington
1800	1899	ALL	ALL	146633	SRY	ALL
1820	1992	1780	1900	136174	TYR	Dungannon
....	....	1750	1850	129046	WYK	Huddersfield
1910	1992	1800	1992	132810	YKS	Netherton
HURSTHOUSE						
1580	1840	1500	1588	102830	DBY	ALL
1550	1800	1550	1800	133817	LIN	Maxey
1550	1800	1550	1800	133817	LIN	Morton
1550	1800	1550	1800	133817	LIN	Moulton
1550	1800	1550	1800	133817	LIN	Spalding

Known From	To	Researching From	To	Ref	Cty	Place
HURT						
1660	1720	1600	1660	111236	DBY	North Wingfield
HURTEN						
1850	1900	1800	1992	167592	STS	Stoke
HUSBAND						
1714	1965	1562	1905	109053	CON	Lezant
1724	1724	ALL	1724	131881	FIF	Ceres
1700	1900	1700	1900	130915	FIF	Leuchars
1837	1862	1500	1837	104140	MDX	London
1730	....	....	1730	101761	NTT	Dunham
1811	1835	1800	1850	102881	NYK	Kirby Misperton
1845	1914	1800	1845	102881	NYK	Loftus
1833	1864	1833	1864	137537	WLS	Haverfordwest
1810	1830	1700	1900	158976	YKS	Skelton
HUSKINS						
1700	1858	1700	1880	175633	STS	Tamworth
HUSKISSON						
1835	1992	ALL	ALL	124893	LND	ALL
....	?	....	....	141941	WAR	Birmingham
HUSON						
1700	1760	1600	1992	167592	LAN	Liverpool
HUSSELBEE						
1801	1900	1700	1800	137499	STS	Cannock
1801	1900	1700	1800	137499	STS	Penkridge
HUSSELL						
1747	1960	1747	1900	162825	DEV	North
HUSSEY						
1743	1875	1650	1743	167452	BKM	Bradenham
1900	....	1800	1930	143693	BKM	High Wycombe
1767	1857	1650	1800	143693	BKM	Hughenden
1767	....	1650	1800	143693	BKM	Princes Risborough
1816	1877	1700	1850	143693	BKM	West Wycombe
1300	1400	1250	1400	154881	DBY	Holbrook
1720	1750	1650	1750	174599	DOR	Broadwinsor
1750	1800	1740	1850	174599	DOR	Symondsbury
1800	1825	1750	1800	142905	LAN	Manchester
1870	1900	1850	1920	105333	MDX	London
1838	1992	....	....	175803	SCT	Crammond
1840	1890	....	....	137693	SOM	???
1720	1780	....	....	142158	WIL	Aldbourne
HUSTHWAITE						
....	....	ALL	ALL	103721	ALL	Name Study
HUSTLER						
1609	1972	....	....	100536	SFK	???
1600	1932	....	....	100536	YKS	???
HUSTWAYTE						
....	....	ALL	ALL	103721	ALL	ALL
HUTCHCRAFT						
1790	....	1790	1970	163171	CAM	Cambridge
HUTCHENCE						
1800	....	1600	1800	109967	HAM	Whitchurch
HUTCHEON						
1750	1970	1600	1970	149233	ABD	Fyvie
1800	....	ALL	ALL	130508	ABD	Peterhead
HUTCHESON						
1750	1970	1600	1970	149233	ABD	Fyvie
1724	1739	ALL	ALL	174777	AYR	Muirkirk
1790	1880	1700	1790	118419	MOR	Duffus
HUTCHIN						
....	....	1760	1800	102717	HRT	Albury
1752	1992	1500	1752	132233	HRT	Albury
....	....	1800	1850	102717	HRT	Stanstead
1841	1992	1800	1841	116475	IOM	Lonan
1860	1992	ALL	ALL	115762	NFK	Bungay
1860	1992	ALL	ALL	115762	NFK	Norwich
1700	1800	1600	1800	105333	SSX	Chichester
HUTCHING						
1803	1894	1803	1894	164399	DEV	Shaugh Prior
HUTCHINGS						
1836	1894	....	....	166189	BKM	Gerrards Cross
1843	....	....	....	133922	DEV	Wolborough
....	....	1835	1876	145270	DOR	Swanage
1836	1851	1825	1861	147974	HAM	Southampton
1823	....	....	....	138061	KEN	Lewisham
....	....	1900	1906	145270	LND	St George H Sq
1875	1882	1875	1882	147974	MDX	Bethnal Green
1791	1900	1700	1790	166464	OXF	Bladon
1709	1800	1570	1815	147974	SOM	Crewkerne
1820	1880	1820	1880	133922	SOM	Montacute
ALL	1816	....	....	105368	SOM	Shepton
1660	1760	1650	1800	142018	SOM	Taunton
....	....	1730	1760	142018	SRY	Chirstchurch
1820	1992	1700	1900	160822	SSX	Hastings
1850	1900	1850	1900	100382	SSX	Tortington
HUTCHINS						
1770	1830	1770	1840	140295	DEV	Burlescombe
1803	1803	1750	1803	174289	HAM	Ringwood
1800	....	1600	1800	109967	HAM	Whitchurch
1819	1840	1819	1900	148121	HRT	Furneux Pelham
1710	1856	1700	1856	148121	HRT	???
1783	1816	1780	1820	148121	MDX	Edmonton
1851	....	1820	1851	172588	MDX	St Lukes
1715	1767	....	1715	124524	NTH	Northampton
1800	1860	1750	1900	138517	SOM	East Pennard
1853	1853	1600	1853	152080	SOM	???
1836	1850	1800	1860	131547	SRY	Bethworth
1834	1836	1800	1860	131547	SRY	Reigate
1794	1900	1700	1794	121258	WAR	Snitterfield
HUTCHINSON						
1730	1812	1600	1730	144711	CAM	March
1777	1777	....	....	135437	CHS	Nantwich
1812	1861	1700	1812	117471	CUL	Alston
1800	1950	1700	1800	128376	CUL	Farlam
1869	1980	....	....	132985	CUL	Millom
1876	1881	1868	1882	152110	CUL	Workington
1830	1850	1800	1900	129496	DBY	Loridgehay
1833	1844	....	....	152110	DUR	Hartlepool
1780	1820	1700	1820	116823	DUR	Sedgefield
1830	1833	....	....	152110	DUR	Staindrop
1843	1871	1843	1880	152110	DUR	Stranton
1809	1853	1800	1900	166960	ESS	Chelmsford
1820	1886	1750	1818	160911	HUN	Colne
1855	1867	1850	1875	110051	KEN	Dartford
1889	1992	1800	1940	141461	LAN	Ashton Under Lyne
1827	....	1800	1850	108154	LAN	Bolton
....	1850	ALL	1850	134511	LIN	Denton
1630	1992	....	....	174947	LIN	Gedney
1500	1700	ALL	ALL	110477	LIN	Louth
1859	....	1859	....	158305	LIN	Sleaford
1784	1840	1700	1840	126454	LIN	Springthorpe
1500	1700	ALL	ALL	110477	LIN	Theddlethorpe
....	....	1830	1887	147176	LND	Blackfriars
1866	....	1866	....	147184	LND	Lambeth
1785	1826	1750	1850	130990	NBL	Allendale
1810	1840	....	....	103764	NBL	Newcastle
1804	....	1750	1810	152110	NRY	Forcett
1725	1750	1700	1725	145211	NRY	Masham
1804	....	1750	1820	152110	NRY	Ovington
1988	1992	....	....	133299	NTH	Northampton
1720	1800	....	1800	137634	NTT	East Retford
1826	1840	....	....	163465	NTT	Perlethorpe
....	....	1798	1847	103187	NYK	Egton
1960	1992	....	....	133299	NYK	Middlesborough
....	1700	....	....	174564	SSX	Hooe
1822	1824	1800	1861	110051	STS	Wolverhampton
1877	1992	ALL	....	132349	SXE	Brighton
....	....	....	1806	176702	WES	Kirby Stephen
1790	1850	ALL	1790	145211	WRY	Clint
1806	1940	....	....	176702	WYK	Bradford
1880	1980	1700	1880	122556	WYK	Mirfield
1800	1900	1700	1800	176516	WYK	Sheffield
1788	1860	1750	1790	132985	YKS	Arkengarthdale
1820	1860	1750	1870	109010	YKS	Hawnby
....	....	1700	1850	166960	YKS	Hull
....	....	1700	1760	132985	YKS	Marsk-By-Richmond
....	....	1700	1850	147176	YKS	Newsham
1740	1850	1600	1900	112372	YKS	Nidderdale
1740	1860	1700	1740	136220	YKS	Ovington
1732	1774	1710	1732	101796	YKS	Royston
1750	1770	1600	1750	108308	YKS	Swaledale
HUTCHISON						
1790	....	....	....	167037	SCT	Edinburgh
1840	1880	1800	1880	136239	SRY	Lambeth
HUTHNANCE						
1595	1976	1570	1976	136247	CON	Gwinnear
1345	1976	1570	1976	136247	CON	Helston
1701	1745	1700	1745	136247	DEV	St Giles On The Heath
HUTLEY						
....	....	1700	1896	155713	ESS	Mountfitchet
....	....	1700	1896	155713	ESS	Stanstead
HUTSON						
1775	1800	ALL	1775	131059	ESS	Danbury
....	1878	1700	1878	109223	SOM	Easton
1763	1889	ALL	....	132349	SXE	East Hoathly
1850	1850	1750	1992	100501	???	Dalkeith
1850	1850	1750	1992	100501	???	Haddington

Known From	To	Researching From	To	Ref	Cty	Place
HUTT						
1720	....	ALL	ALL	130508	FIF	St Monance
1815	1840	1750	1850	124311	MDX	Bethnal Green
1922	1970	1880	1922	131733	MDX	Mortlake
?	?	?	?	108758	???	???
HUTTON						
1740	1800	1700	1800	169560	ANS	Kettins
1780	1820	1780	1820	130222	BDF	Aspley Guise
1669	1992	1650	1992	154709	BRK	Reading
1773	1936	1600	1992	145955	CMA	Kendal
....	....	1821	1992	147249	CMA	Penrith
1674	1674	1500	1674	154539	DUR	Barnard Castle
1674	1674	1500	1674	154539	DUR	Gainford
1800	....	ALL	ALL	130508	FIF	Kilrenny
1850	....	ALL	ALL	130508	FIF	Leven
....	1755	1700	1755	148288	FIF	Strathmiglo
1669	1992	1650	1992	154709	HAM	Basing
1500	1524	1500	1580	108510	LAN	Priest Hutton
1500	1524	1500	1580	108510	LAN	Warton
1800	1992	1700	1800	113786	LIN	Somercotes
1871	1893	....	....	101869	LND	???
?	?	?	?	130354	NBL	Throckley
1750	1850	....	....	100099	WAR	Birmingham
1773	1936	1600	1992	145955	WES	Kendal
1789	1886	1700	1900	178322	WOR	Halesowen
1569	1569	1545	1569	108510	YKS	Lockington
1570	1605	1500	1580	108510	YKS	York
HUXAM						
1750	1815	1600	1870	105333	DEV	Rattery
1750	1815	1600	1870	105333	DEV	South Brent
1750	1815	1600	1870	105333	DEV	Ugborough
HUXFORD						
....	....	1570	1850	136263	DOR	ALL
1800	1992	....	....	136263	HAM	???
1697	1820	....	....	136263	IOW	Arreton
1697	1820	....	....	136263	IOW	Brading
HUXHAM						
1849	1888	1750	1841	107662	DOR	Ilsington
1841	1896	1750	1841	107662	DOR	Plymouth
HUXLEY						
1840	1861	1840	1861	159492	LAN	Manchester With Salford
1821	1888	1780	1820	144746	WOR	Ribbesford
1856	1928	1820	1856	144746	WOR	Worcester
HUXTABLE						
1700	1860	1600	1800	166375	DEV	Chittlehampton
HUXTER						
1897	1937	1830	1896	106402	LND	Wimbledon
HUZZARD						
1791	1822	1780	1860	135917	EYK	Beeford
1803	1838	1750	1850	135917	EYK	Brandesburton
1860	1970	1800	1900	135917	EYK	Etton
1766	1789	1750	1800	135917	EYK	Flamborough
1775	1867	1700	1900	135917	EYK	Hull
1826	1830	1800	1850	135917	EYK	N Frodingham
1799	1832	1750	1850	135917	EYK	Sigglesthorne
1760	1809	1700	1850	135917	EYK	Skipsea
1950	1992	1950	ALL	135917	EYK	Walkington
HUZZELL						
ALL	ALL	ALL	ALL	142360	ALL	ALL
HYAMS						
1884	1894	1750	1883	131245	MDX	Bethnal Green
HYATT						
....	....	ALL	ALL	136271	ALL	ALL
1889	1901	1901	1992	122807	LND	Lisson Grove
?	?	?	1838	147400	LND	Soho
1872	....	....	....	171905	LND	Strand
?	?	?	1838	147400	MDX	Soho
1877	1992	1840	1877	126519	SOM	Shepton Mallet
HYDE						
1877	1877	1877	1950	106666	ALL	ALL
1876	1900	1850	1900	107700	AGY	Holyhead
1852	....	1700	1800	107700	ARM	Moy
1722	1941	....	....	116602	BKM	Drayton Parslow
1783	....	1760	1790	163775	BRK	Reading
....	....	?	....	128589	CAM	Weston
1800	1850	1800	1850	144657	COR	???
1840	1992	1500	1840	126616	DOR	Loders
1833	1886	1750	1833	143707	ENG	South Coast
....	....	1700	1900	150762	GLS	Hill
1736	1755	1700	1726	127116	HAM	Longstock
1790	....	1740	1839	142859	LAN	Manchester
1879	1992	1800	1879	122378	NTT	Nottingham
....	....	1780	1850	170313	SAL	Hopton Wafers
HYDE contd.						
1850	1910	1800	1900	144657	SOM	Bristol
1880	1900	1800	1900	160563	SOM	Street
1880	1900	1800	1900	160563	SOM	Walton
1871	1881	ALL	1871	165263	SSX	Rottingdean
1800	1910	1800	1930	105945	WAR	Birmingham
1700	1750	ALL	ALL	147567	WAR	Fillongley
1565	1660	....	....	157120	WIL	ALL
HYDEN						
....	....	1600	1800	136298	CON	ALL
....	....	1600	1992	136298	STS	ALL
HYDER						
1700	1992	ALL	1700	100803	SXE	Rotherfield
HYDES						
1850	1900	1750	1850	112704	LIN	Addlethorpe
1820	1992	1750	1820	136301	YKS	Barnsley
1820	1992	1750	1820	136301	YKS	Dodworth
HYEM						
1770	1992	1700	1800	121703	SFK	Felixstowe
HYETT						
1774	1992	1774	1992	131156	GLS	Huntley
1657	1699	1600	1750	155896	GLS	Westbury On Severn
1826	....	1747	1992	171905	GLS	???
HYLAND						
1841	1992	1700	1841	161772	CAV	???
1890	1890	1500	1890	110310	IRL	Dublin
1920	1920	1500	1920	110310	LAN	Liverpool
1845	1992	1845	1902	136328	LAN	Manchester
1863	1992	....	1863	151270	OFF	Tullamore
1774	1847	1774	1847	136328	SRY	Isleworth
HYLANDS						
....	....	ALL	ALL	136344	ALL	Name Study
1241	1900	1200	1900	136344	ALL	ALL
HYMAN						
1880	....	....	....	114529	LND	???
HYNAFORD						
....	....	1550	1600	130591	SOM	Wilton
HYNARD						
1569	1992	1569	1992	136352	SFK	West
1609	1992	1609	1992	136352	SFK	Mildenhall
1825	1886	1750	1825	126047	SFK	Stoke By Nayland
1569	1992	1569	1992	136352	SFK	Thurston
HYNDMAN						
?	?	?	?	114685	AYR	Muirkirk
HYNER						
....	....	ALL	ALL	136352	ALL	Name Study
1609	1992	1609	1992	136352	CAM	East
1609	1992	1609	1992	136352	SFK	Mildenhall
HYNES						
1861	1900	1800	1900	144037	BDS	Jedburgh
HYSLOP						
1850	....	ALL	1992	150630	HAM	Portsmouth
HYTCH						
....	....	1700	1800	128627	ELN	Haddington
....	....	1800	....	128627	LND	???
I'ANSON						
1700	1800	1760	1800	176281	KEN	Southborough
IAGO						
1760	1820	1760	1810	148377	CON	Saltash
IBBERSON						
1765	1911	1700	1765	109142	YKS	Batley
1820	1860	....	....	102946	YKS	Sheffield
IBBIT						
1840	....	....	....	103225	BDF	Gamlinsay
IBBOT						
1800	1963	1600	1963	106704	HUN	Upton
IBBOTSON						
1830	1850	1800	1880	123048	WRY	Skipton
1840	1880	....	1840	114812	YKS	Sheffield
ICKEL						
....	....	ALL	ALL	133299	ALL	ALL
50	449	....	....	133299	ANGLIA	Schleswig
1782	....	....	....	133299	LND	St Marylebone
499	520	....	....	133299	MCA	East Anglia
ICKELING						
....	....	ALL	ALL	133299	ALL	ALL
680	750	....	....	133299	CAM	Peakirk
697	700	....	....	133299	DBY	Repton
798	807	....	....	133299	KEN	ALL
673	714	....	....	133299	LIN	Crowland
499	850	....	....	133299	MCA	ALL
1208	1301	....	....	133299	NFK	Hickling
1710	....	....	....	133299	NFK	Norwich
1789	1790	....	....	133299	WAR	Aston

Known From	To	Researching From	To	Ref	Cty	Place
ICKELING contd.						
1747	....	....	....	133299	YKS	Cayton By Scarborough
IDDENDEN						
....	....	ALL	ALL	108065	KEN	ALL
IDDESON						
....	....	1680	1790	145211	NRY	Kirby Malzeard
IDE						
1908	1980	....	....	136379	HAM	Southampton
....	....	1800	1850	136379	HAM	Warblington
1780	1840	1700	1850	126268	SSX	West
1800	1932	1600	1800	145165	SSX	Oving
....	....	1590	1650	136379	SSX	Up Waltham
1650	1800	....	....	136379	SSX	West Wittering
IDEN						
1290	1350	....	....	156647	SSX	Netherfield
1800	1850	1750	1800	107611	STS	Rugely
IDENDEN						
1760	1790	1760	1790	153303	KEN	Luddenden
IDIENS						
1800	1840	1700	1800	118486	STS	Trysull
1715	1850	1680	1730	137413	STS	Wolverhampton
....	....	1700	1800	108863	STS	???
IFOULD						
1627	1785	ALL	1627	136387	HAM	Mapledurwell
1815	1917	....	....	136387	HAM	Steep
1917	1970	....	....	136387	SSX	Chichester
1915	1992	....	....	136387	SSX	???
IGGLESDEN						
1713	1780	ALL	1713	119687	KEN	Newenden
1780	1992	....	....	119687	SSX	Rye
IGGULDEN						
ALL	ALL	ALL	ALL	148997	ALL	ALL
1745	1992	1475	1745	148997	KEN	ALL
....	1820	ALL	ALL	152641	LND	Deptford
ILBECHE						
1500	1600	....	....	100420	WAR	Meriden
ILES						
1562	1992	....	....	136417	AVN	Bristol
1820	1850	....	....	110159	FER	Devenish
1867	1992	1841	1867	136409	GLS	Bristol
?	?	?	?	136395	GLS	Bristol
1771	1980	....	....	170623	GLS	Bristol
1759	1761	ALL	1992	163821	GLS	Chipping Sodbury
1850	....	....	....	137693	GLS	Winterbourne
1759	1761	ALL	1992	163821	GLS	Yate
1841	1841	1700	1841	136409	SOM	Bridgwater
?	?	?	?	136395	SOM	Bristol
1760	1820	1740	1760	134139	WIL	Inglesham
1805	1869	1700	1850	160059	???	Bristol
ILETT						
1805	1926	1650	1805	165298	KEN	???
1805	1926	1650	1805	165298	MDX	London
1805	1926	1650	1805	165298	SRY	???
ILIFFE						
1826	1939	ALL	1992	135062	CHI	Guernsey
1560	1800	1800	1992	129763	LEI	Foxton
1592	1748	ALL	ALL	141615	LEI	Hinckley
1750	1850	1750	1850	167924	LEI	Leicester
1826	1939	ALL	1992	135062	STS	West Bromwich
ILINGWALL						
1830	1860	1830	1900	144290	INV	Beaulty
ILLIDGE						
1778	1879	1879	?	158763	MDX	???
ILLINGSWORTH						
1819	....	....	....	142859	LAN	Haslingden
ILLINGWORTH						
1803	1821	1700	1803	100110	WYK	Idle
ILLMAN						
1774	1790	1760	1800	131547	SRY	Capel
1773	1774	1760	1780	131547	SRY	Charlwood
1772	1789	1740	1790	131547	SRY	Newdigate
ILLSLEY						
1792	1942	?	1792	136611	BRK	Bray
....	1830	ALL	1830	134511	LEI	Balckfordby
ILOTT						
1800	1930	1700	1800	105392	HRT	Aston
ILSLEY						
1560	1700	1500	1750	125032	BRK	Burghfield
1818	1889	1700	1818	170356	BRK	Reading
1740	1850	1730	1850	125032	BRK	Stratfield Mortimer
1630	1705	1600	1750	125032	BRK	Tilehurst
1841	....	1700	1840	160601	BRK	Tileshurst
1740	1780	1730	1800	100242	HAM	Basing

Known From	To	Researching From	To	Ref	Cty	Place
ILSLEY contd.						
1700	1800	1680	1800	125032	HAM	Bramley
IMAGE						
1830	1850	1750	1830	172472	LIN	Long Sutton
IMBER						
1860	1992	1830	1900	148083	DOR	Dorchester
1790	1890	1750	1800	174599	DOR	Shaftesbury
1850	....	ALL	ALL	127078	DOR	???
IMBRIE						
1590	1667	....	....	122785	WIL	Devizes
IMESON						
1750	1820	....	....	144568	YKS	???
IMISON						
1875	1885	1837	1885	130036	MDX	London
IMMS						
....	....	1745	1992	144738	SSX	Firle W Ringmer
IMPEY						
1760	1992	1700	1800	158380	BKM	Amersham
1671	1900	....	1860	137405	CAM	South
1759	1850	ALL	1759	162655	CAM	South
IMRIE						
1840	1900	1800	1850	133787	ANS	Dundee
INCE						
1700	1992	1600	1950	154881	LND	ALL
1850	1950	1850	1950	135976	SSX	Newhaven
INCH						
....	....	ALL	ALL	136433	ALL	Name Study
INCHES						
....	....	ALL	1710	119326	PER	Clunie
INCHLEY						
1791	1992	1700	1800	128694	WIL	Urchfont
INCLES						
1750	1850	....	....	124621	NTH	Deene
IND						
1848	1875	1830	1880	142360	GLS	Cirencester
ING						
1823	1854	1700	1823	105775	KEN	Chislet
INGALL						
....	....	ALL	ALL	136441	ALL	Name Study
1816	....	ALL	....	104515	LIN	Corby Glen
1696	1696	1600	1750	149098	YKS	Tickhill
INGATE						
1688	1944	1688	1888	129194	SFK	East
INGE						
1800	1830	1700	1900	108111	KEN	Faversham
1859	1860	1850	1880	105775	KEN	Westbere
INGERSOLE						
1845	1992	1700	1800	172820	ESS	Brentwood
INGHAM						
....	....	ALL	ALL	162159	ALL	Name Study
....	....	1784	1992	121940	LAN	Blackburn
....	....	1784	1992	121940	LAN	Colne
1525	....	1525	....	109347	LAN	Read
1832	....	ALL	ALL	100390	LAN	Rochdale
1880	....	1880	1900	130990	LEI	Leicester
1850	1992	1700	1850	100803	WYK	Halifax
....	....	1700	1760	147613	YKS	Bolton By Bowland
....	....	1750	1800	147613	YKS	Giggleswick
1820	1900	1700	1820	130990	YKS	Leeds
1849	1861	1700	1849	138673	YKS	Oulton
1750	....	1730	1770	170348	YKS	Ovendon
1815	1870	....	....	145912	YKS	Stanley
1828	1871	1870	1900	130990	YKS	Thorne
INGLE						
1873	1992	1700	1873	160911	CAM	Over
1700	1890	....	....	100536	CAM	???
1700	1890	....	....	100536	HAM	???
1870	1980	1500	1870	168017	YKS	North
INGLEBY						
....	....	1800	1900	147613	STS	Rowley Regis
1780	1870	1720	1780	145211	WRY	Pateley Bridge
....	....	1750	1885	128554	YKS	Goole
INGLEFIELD						
1850	1890	1800	1890	153877	CHS	The Wirral
INGLES						
1806	1870	1800	1992	130583	GLS	Willersey
1740	1900	1700	1992	146129	ROX	Castleton Parish
1677	1806	1500	1800	130583	WOR	Bretforton
1870	1992	1500	1992	130583	WOR	Broadway
INGLETHORPE						
1750	1992	1538	1750	154792	LND	ALL
1750	1992	1538	1750	154792	SAL	ALL
1750	1992	1538	1750	154792	SFK	ALL

Known From	To	Researching From	To	Ref	Cty	Place
INGLEY						
....	....	....	1905	147362	DBY	???
....	....	1800	1992	147613	WOR	Cradley Heath
INGLIS						
1704	....	....	....	151351	ANS	St Vigeans
1888	1980	1800	1888	136468	BDS	Ashkirk
1832	1992	1700	1832	108316	LKS	Douglas
1833	1861	1700	1900	169390	LKS	Glasgow
1740	1900	1700	1992	146129	ROX	Castleton Parish
1800	....	....	....	169919	ROX	???
1850	1900	1700	1850	146110	SCT	ALL
1800	1910	1830	1910	166685	SOM	Taunton
INGMAN						
....	....	1750	1900	108812	LAN	Rochdale
....	....	1600	1992	108812	WLS	???
INGOE						
1800	1992	....	....	122297	DUR	South Shields
INGOLD						
1807	1900	1750	1900	136476	ESS	Broadoak
1807	1900	1750	1900	136476	ESS	Hatfield
....	....	1800	ALL	136476	HRT	Bishops Stortford
INGRAM						
1700	1892	1690	1908	124001	ABD	Clatt
1700	1892	1690	1908	124001	ABD	Kennethmont
1767	1992	1700	....	110264	BAN	Gamrie
1855	1992	1854	1992	176958	CMA	Carlisle
1855	1992	1854	1992	176958	CMA	Whitehaven
1640	1800	ALL	ALL	132942	CON	ALL
....	....	1680	1732	145270	DOR	Broadmayne
1860	1860	....	....	159883	DOR	Dorchester
1896	1899	1800	1900	176958	DUR	Jarrow
1855	1992	1854	1992	176958	DUR	South Shields
1890	1974	....	....	144215	GLA	Blaengarw
1643	1880	1648	1880	106410	GLS	Berkeley
1816	....	....	....	124982	GLS	Berkeley
1676	1881	ALL	ALL	117579	GLS	Stone
1645	1700	....	....	117579	GLS	Tortworth
1745	1900	1720	1900	105333	HAM	Isle Of Wight
1854	....	1800	1880	176958	KCD	???
1750	1790	1700	1750	163163	KEN	Bewenden
1815	1840	1800	1850	126144	KEN	Woolwich
1855	1992	1854	1992	176958	LAN	Ashton Under Lyne
1855	1992	1854	1992	176958	LAN	Barton On Irwell
1855	1992	1854	1992	176958	LAN	Eccles
1855	1992	1854	1992	176958	LAN	Leigh
1832	1885	1700	1832	169730	MDX	Hackney
1855	1992	1854	1992	176958	MDX	London
1829	1830	1700	1828	131245	MDX	Spitalfields
1824	1861	1820	1900	117579	MON	Bassaleg
1815	1870	1500	1815	176974	RAD	Llanbadarnfynydd
1732	1745	1700	1780	105333	SOM	???
1614	1672	....	....	165999	SSX	Angmering
1881	1886	1870	1890	124001	SSX	East Grinstead
1899	....	1850	1992	166197	WAR	Birmingham
1800	1992	1700	1992	165344	WAR	Rugby
1541	1824	1200	1824	176923	WAR	Wolford
1500	1900	1500	1900	170216	WIL	ALL
1800	1839	1800	1840	108456	WIL	Dilton Marsh
1780	....	1750	1850	126144	WIL	Fisherton
1770	1800	1770	1800	108456	WIL	Westbury
1790	1810	1700	1790	140309	WOR	Bretforton
1815	1886	1700	1815	156248	WOR	Bromsgrove
1825	1850	1550	1830	147265	YKS	Leeds
1899	1980	1899	1992	176958	YKS	Wakefield
INGROUILLE						
ALL	ALL	ALL	ALL	115126	CHI	ALL
INGS						
....	....	1750	1950	159484	HAM	Fordingbridge
1750	1950	1650	1750	128376	SOM	S Brewham
1880	1932	1800	1880	139963	SRY	Surbiton
1700	....	ALL	ALL	116394	WIL	Semley
INGSLEY.						
....	....	1650	1750	147613	STS	Rowley Regis
INKER						
1750	1800	1700	1800	106631	SOM	Puxton
INKERSOLE						
....	....	1550	1750	174696	LIN	Spalding
INKPEN						
1760	1825	1700	1900	122610	DOR	Sturminster Newton
INKSTER						
1750	1965	....	....	137820	SHI	Fetlar
1720	1965	....	....	137820	SHI	Mid Yell
....	....	1650	1870	143359	SHI	North Mavine
1760	1965	....	....	137820	SHI	North Yell
INKSTER contd.						
1758	1965	....	....	137820	SHI	Northmavine
1720	1965	....	....	137820	SHI	South Yell
INMAN						
1795	....	....	1892	147672	DBY	Hadfield
1800	1900	1800	1900	136484	LND	Shoreditch
1800	1900	1800	1900	136484	LND	Westminster
1780	1850	1750	1992	178020	SOM	Combe Florey
1825	1992	1700	1825	168408	WYK	Dewsbury
1825	1992	1700	1825	168408	WYK	Heckmonike
1825	1992	1700	1825	168408	WYK	Leeds
1825	1992	1700	1825	168408	WYK	Liversedge
1815	1840	1750	1815	175986	YKS	Bradfield
1607	1614	1550	1620	176451	YKS	Embsay
1850	1992	....	....	139351	YKS	Heckmondwike
1890	....	....	....	152420	YKS	Sheffield
INNALL						
1759	1759	....	....	165999	GLS	Bristol
INNES						
1820	1840	1750	1820	144150	ABD	Aberdeen
1850	1870	1800	1920	135429	DEV	Exmouth
....	....	1700	1880	146234	FIF	Burnt Island
1840	1992	....	....	136492	IRL	Aitkenhead
1840	1992	....	....	136492	IRL	Baillieston
1840	1992	....	....	136492	LKS	Coatbridge
1850	1859	1800	1855	119628	MLN	Edinburgh
1771	1992	1700	1841	136506	MOR	Birnie
INNINGS						
1721	1721	....	....	135437	SSX	Chichester
INNOCENT						
1741	1860	1700	1900	129496	NTT	Watton In Vale
1797	1895	1780	1802	156655	WAR	Coventry
1746	1761	1720	1805	156655	WAR	Mancetter
INNOUS						
1830	1935	ALL	ALL	113859	KEN	Lewisham
INNS						
1812	....	1500	1812	145718	BDF	Eversholt
INSCH						
1806	1992	ALL	ALL	146366	MOR	Elgin
1806	1992	ALL	ALL	146366	MOR	St Andrews Llanbryde
INSKIP						
1786	1877	ALL	1786	126721	BDF	Campton
1662	1884	1600	1670	173649	STS	Dilhorne
INSLEY						
1855	1900	1750	1855	120650	DBY	Chesterfield
....	....	1750	1855	120650	NTT	???
1767	1767	1750	1800	173517	STS	South
....	....	1750	1855	120650	STS	???
1767	1767	1750	1800	173517	WAR	North
INSTANCE						
1775	1841	1777	1837	122238	SAL	Bitterley
INSTONE						
1881	1992	1800	1881	174041	GNT	Newport
INSTRELL						
1645	1645	1645	1836	144665	HAM	Elvetham
INVERARITY						
....	....	ALL	ALL	131539	ALL	Name Study
INWARD						
1840	1840	1800	1840	113646	KEN	Swanscombe
INWOOD						
1811	1852	1750	1811	104124	HRT	Rickmansworth
....	....	1880	1900	133221	LND	Lambeth
1876	1992	....	1876	138320	MDX	St Pancras
ION						
1650	1750	1600	....	118591	WES	East Ward
1600	1850	....	....	146854	WES	Orton
IONS						
1850	1900	1700	1850	160725	NBL	ALL
IREDALE						
1747	?	1700	1820	136522	WYK	Birkenshaw
1790	1920	1700	1920	136522	WYK	Birstall
IRELAND						
....	....	ALL	ALL	137006	ALL	Name Study
....	....	1809	ALL	149187	ANS	Dundee
1800	1962	1670	1800	162582	DEV	Ashburton
1800	1850	1700	1900	126586	DEV	Exeter
1786	1799	1700	1799	148288	FIF	Kettle
....	....	1700	ALL	149187	FIF	St Monance
....	....	1750	1850	101478	GLS	Costwolds
1785	1889	1700	1785	128317	GLS	Painswick
1807	1807	1750	1850	159964	KKD	Balmaghie
1843	1847	1840	1900	159964	KKD	Crossmichael
1825	1836	1800	1850	159964	KKD	Kelton

Known From	To	Researching From	To	Ref	Cty	Place
IRELAND contd.						
1838	1840	1800	1850	159964	KKD	Kirkpatrick Durham
1848	1873	1840	1900	159964	KKD	Urr
1800	1848	1750	1800	151912	LAN	Aighton
....	....	1800	1925	122653	LAN	Lancaster
1800	1848	1750	1800	151912	LAN	Ribchester
1700	1800	1700	1800	167924	MDX	Ealing
1913	1980	1700	1913	110108	NTT	Nottingham
....	....	1600	ALL	149187	PER	Murthly
1894	1966	1800	1894	136557	WES	Kendal
1856	1992	1750	1826	136530	WOR	Alcester
IREMONGER						
1700	1898	1680	1900	124974	BRK	Beenham
1563	1669	1550	1680	124974	BRK	Bradfield
1500	1730	1450	1800	124974	BRK	Bucklebury
1602	1661	1580	1670	124974	BRK	Stanford Dingley
1799	1980	1643	1980	163309	LIN	Horncastle
IRESON						
1895	1992	1700	1895	122467	SRY	Lambeth
IRETON						
1165	1900	1165	1900	127329	DBY	???
1684	....	1684	1900	127329	GLS	???
....	....	1765	1900	127329	HRT	???
1572	1849	1572	1900	127329	LAN	???
1561	1829	1500	1900	127329	LIN	???
1628	1900	1628	1900	127329	LND	ALL
1589	1795	1500	1900	127329	NTT	???
1582	1755	1500	1900	127329	SAL	???
1564	1826	1500	1900	127329	YKS	???
IRISH						
1790	1992	....	....	143855	DEV	South
....	....	1700	1790	143855	DEV	Buckfastleigh
1776	1895	1600	1900	105333	DEV	Buckland In The Moor
1776	1895	1600	1900	105333	DEV	Denbury
1776	1895	1600	1900	105333	DEV	Holne
1776	1895	1600	1900	105333	DEV	Ilsington
1776	1895	1600	1900	105333	DEV	Lydford
1776	1895	1600	1900	105333	DEV	Widecombe In The Moor
1776	1895	1600	1900	105333	DEV	Woodland
IRONMONGER						
1550	1750	1500	1750	167088	BRK	Bucklebury
1594	1713	ALL	ALL	141615	LEI	Burton On The Wolds
IRONS						
1838	....	1850	1992	166197	GLS	Forthampton
1800	1992	1800	1992	179302	HRT	Harpenden
1902	....	1880	1910	163775	MDX	Bethnal Green
1847	1992	1800	1992	116742	MDX	Heston
....	1919	1800	1992	166197	WOR	Eldersfield
IRONSIDE						
....	....	ALL	ALL	149403	ALL	Name Study
1770	1895	....	1770	125954	DOR	Castleton
IRONSIDES						
....	....	ALL	ALL	149403	ALL	ALL
1756	1893	1756	1992	149403	DUR	Lamesley
IRTON						
1530	1850	1850	....	134007	CMA	Irton
IRVIN						
1831	1839	....	....	136565	LAN	Manchester
1802	1871	1800	1871	136565	LAN	Prestow
1863	1868	1800	1863	103322	LAN	Wigan
1757	....	1538	1780	118893	NRY	???
IRVINE						
....	....	1797	1875	174319	ANS	???
1804	1992	1500	1804	150991	CMA	Carlisle
1800	1992	1800	1992	106305	DOW	???
1870	1992	1700	1870	136573	FIF	Kirkcaldy
....	1846	....	....	140767	IRL	???
1863	1863	1700	1870	173037	LDY	ALL
1760	1760	....	....	159883	PER	Logierait
1840	1865	ALL	1865	149063	ROX	Melrose
1846	....	1802	....	127647	SCT	Mousewald
1600	1992	1600	1800	104914	SHI	Delting
1750	1965	....	....	137820	SHI	Fetlar
1835	1890	1700	1850	139866	SHI	Lerwick
1720	1965	....	....	137820	SHI	Mid Yell
1760	1965	....	....	137820	SHI	North Yell
1758	1965	....	....	137820	SHI	Northmavine
1720	1965	....	....	137820	SHI	South Yell
IRVING						
....	....	ALL	1890	178403	ALL	ALL
1804	1992	1500	1804	150991	CMA	Carlisle
1797	1992	ALL	1797	179345	CUL	Burgh By Sands

Known From	To	Researching From	To	Ref	Cty	Place
IRVING contd.						
1865	1945	1800	1850	173649	CUL	Carlisle
1851	1851	1800	1851	157651	CUL	Walton
....	....	1700	1820	117587	DFS	Annan
1770	1850	1600	1850	130125	DFS	Hoddom
1717	1801	ALL	1800	162507	DFS	Langholm
....	1846	....	....	140767	IRL	???
1900	1987	....	....	147702	MSY	Chorlton On Medlock
1817	1855	1800	....	109290	YKS	Sheffield
IRWIN						
1800	1950	1650	1800	128376	CUL	Hayton
1812	....	1600	1812	116637	DUR	Sunderland
1888	1992	ALL	1888	105465	ENG	???
....	....	1780	1850	100188	GLA	Moriston
....	....	1847	1875	100188	GLS	Cheltenham
1803	1837	1750	1837	136581	TYR	Ballygawley
1882	1930	ALL	1885	173045	WES	Langdale
ISAAC						
1810	1857	1740	1850	121126	ABD	Udny
1841	....	1819	1841	123129	CMN	Felinfoel
1842	1881	1819	1842	123129	CMN	Llangennech
1771	1900	1600	1771	108286	DEV	Torrington
1880	1940	....	....	175587	GLA	Hafod
1790	1875	1750	1875	118575	GLA	Llangiwg
1889	1920	1800	1965	127361	GLA	Neath
1666	1992	....	....	122777	GLS	Sodbury
1781	1816	1739	1781	103918	HAM	Portsea
1791	1992	?	1791	136611	LIN	Cammingham
1750	1992	1600	1750	102342	LIN	Stallingborough
1870	1920	....	....	131962	LND	Highgate
1850	1870	....	....	131962	LND	Mayfair
1920	1953	....	....	131962	SFK	Brantham
1780	1880	1700	1780	175587	SOM	Martock
....	....	1600	1850	131962	SSX	Bognor
1888	1925	1800	1880	125342	WLS	Mountain Ash
1888	1925	1800	1880	125342	WLS	Penrhiwceiber
ISAACS						
....	....	....	....	123110	CMN	Henllan Amgoed
....	....	....	....	123110	CMN	Llangan
1850	1992	1700	1850	167223	DEV	Crediton
....	....	1500	1850	137502	DEV	Exeter
1850	1890	1850	1890	137502	DOR	ALL
1781	1816	1739	1781	103918	HAM	Portsea
1854	1927	....	....	165727	LND	East
1808	....	1808	....	156027	WOR	???
ISARD						
....	....	ALL	ALL	136638	ALL	Name Study
1800	1992	ALL	ALL	136638	ALL	ALL
1773	1992	1500	1773	136638	SSX	East Grinstead
ISBELL						
1830	1849	1820	1849	140295	LND	ALL
ISBILL						
....	....	1700	1992	140627	NFK	Hockering
ISBISTER						
1891	?	ALL	ALL	149985	NFK	Leith
1750	1965	....	....	137820	SHI	Fetlar
1720	1965	....	....	137820	SHI	Mid Yell
1760	1965	....	....	137820	SHI	North Yell
1758	1965	....	....	137820	SHI	Northmavine
1720	1965	....	....	137820	SHI	South Yell
ISEMONGER						
1780	1820	1700	1850	126268	SSX	West
ISGATE						
1820	1870	1700	1820	101834	NFK	Hilgay
ISGROVE						
....	....	ALL	ALL	156272	ALL	Name Study
1750	1992	ALL	1992	156272	ALL	ALL
ISHAM						
....	....	ALL	ALL	144436	ALL	Name Study
ISHERWOOD						
....	....	ALL	ALL	136646	ALL	Name Study
1866	1895	1850	1950	144908	BDF	Langford
1750	1830	1830	1992	136646	BDF	Southill
1800	1880	ALL	ALL	119253	CHS	Stockport
1835	1862	1800	1900	144908	ESS	Stratford
....	....	1250	1850	136646	LAN	Bolton
1748	1800	ALL	ALL	119253	LAN	Kearsley
1840	1870	....	1875	147818	LAN	Kearsley
1800	1850	1800	1880	120219	LAN	Leigh
....	....	1600	1850	136646	LAN	Manchester
1790	1820	ALL	1820	142301	LAN	Wamersley
1820	1890	....	....	136646	MDX	London
ISLES						
1846	1846	1700	1846	113425	KEN	Bexley

Known From	To	Researching From	To	Ref	Cty	Place
ISLES contd.						
1856	....	ALL	1856	151424	YKS	Bradford
ISLEY						
1776	1810	....	1776	132837	WIL	???
ISLIP						
ALL	1840	....	....	137545	ALL	ALL
....	....	1550	1900	136654	BDF	ALL
....	....	1650	1850	136654	BKM	ALL
....	....	1650	1900	136654	CAM	ALL
1840	....	ALL	ALL	137545	HEF	Colley Western
....	....	1700	1850	136654	HUN	ALL
1870	1992	1600	1992	136654	LEI	ALL
....	....	1600	1992	136654	LIN	ALL
1790	1992	1650	1992	136654	NTH	ALL
1690	1850	1500	1850	136654	RUT	ALL
ISMADE						
1750	1780	1740	1800	138479	GLS	Horfield
ISMAY						
....	....	1650	1790	110671	NBL	Newcastle On Tyne
ISOM						
1801	1830	ALL	1830	168718	LEI	Queniborough
1773	1801	ALL	1801	168718	LEI	Twyford
ISON						
1820	1849	1849	ALL	131571	MDX	Hackney
ISSARD						
1740	1815	1700	1800	131431	MGY	Trefegwlys
1790	1880	1700	1900	131431	SAL	Pontesbury
1790	1880	1700	1900	131431	SAL	Whittington
ISSOTT						
1600	....	1600	....	154601	WYK	Horbury
ISTED						
1770	1830	1830	1880	102318	SRY	East
1694	1750	ALL	1694	139343	SSX	Buxted
ITCHENER						
1740	1787	1700	1800	138088	STS	Penkridge
IVE						
1903	1903	1903	1903	147575	LND	Hammersmith
1850	1950	1850	1900	147575	LND	???
1850	1950	1850	1900	147575	MDX	???
1700	1799	1660	1770	135941	SFK	Wickhambrook
IVENS						
1854	1992	....	....	127701	NTH	Orlingbury
1700	1850	1800	1850	141682	OXF	Swinbrook
IVERSON						
1620	1740	1600	1700	159123	KEN	Canterbury
1861	1909	1860	1920	159123	KEN	Dover
1740	1861	1700	1860	159123	KEN	Folkstone
1867	....	....	....	103233	SRY	Balham
IVES						
1850	1900	1700	1850	112097	BDF	ALL
1762	....	1700	1800	124796	BKM	Princes Risborough
1795	1863	....	....	139866	CAM	Balsham
1849	1888	1800	1888	143448	LIN	Grimsby
1885	1885	1800	1992	117293	MDX	Hammersmith
1648	1675	1550	1700	109290	NFK	Central
1850	1881	ALL	ALL	157864	NFK	Kirby Cane
1814	1900	1800	1900	142875	NFK	Thurlton
1802	1941	1700	1822	101575	NFK	Wells Next The Sea
1600	1992	....	....	109495	NFK	Yarmouth
1700	1750	1550	1700	139866	SFK	Gazeley
1860	1870	1840	1880	116173	SRY	Chertsey
1830	1900	....	....	117560	SRY	Chertsey
1802	1941	1700	1822	101575	YKS	Hull
?	....	....	....	147184	???	London
IVESON						
1812	1886	1700	1812	109657	YKS	Gayle
1812	1886	1700	1812	109657	YKS	Middlesbrough
IVETT						
1750	1830	1750	1830	116831	HUN	Yelling
IVEY						
1819	1903	1700	1800	110701	CON	Camborne
1801	1801	1100	1801	117749	CON	Crowan
1800	1900	ALL	ALL	150169	HAM	Ropley
1829	1929	....	....	144673	LND	East
IVIL						
1800	1860	1800	1860	152404	LAN	Clifton
IVINGS						
....	....	ALL	ALL	124176	OXF	Chipping Norton
IVITT						
1770	1850	1770	1850	116831	CAM	Lolworth
IVORY						
....	....	ALL	ALL	136662	ALL	Name Study
1720	1920	1500	1800	136662	NFK	Norwich
IZARD						
....	....	ALL	ALL	136638	KEN	ALL
....	....	ALL	ALL	136638	SSX	ALL
IZAT						
1850	1874	....	....	132381	FIF	Markinch
IZOD						
1545	1992	ALL	ALL	136689	ALL	ALL
IZZARD						
1810	1892	ALL	1830	123013	GLS	???
....	....	ALL	ALL	136638	KEN	ALL
1740	1790	1700	1740	108448	LND	East
....	....	ALL	ALL	136638	SSX	ALL
JABBETT						
1850	1992	1850	1992	136697	WAR	Birmingham
1790	1992	1790	1992	106305	WAR	Chilvers Coton
JABES						
1772	1803	ALL	1770	142034	GLA	Llangiwc
JACK						
1798	1830	....	....	154849	AYR	???
1800	1852	1500	1800	138614	CAI	Dunnet
ALL	ALL	ALL	ALL	101370	IRL	ALL
1880	1936	1800	1940	164097	LAN	Liverpool
....	....	1860	1900	132381	LKS	Glasgow
1830	1865	1800	1900	146536	LKS	Shotts
....	....	1795	1815	176893	LND	Lambeth
1791	....	1700	1800	115967	ROC	Logie Wester
1791	....	1700	1800	115967	ROC	Urquhart
....	....	ALL	ALL	101370	SCT	ALL
....	....	1795	1815	176893	SRY	Brixton
JACKET						
1770	....	1770	1900	139114	CON	Launceston
JACKLIN						
1758	1871	ALL	1800	136700	CAM	Litlington
1761	....	....	1761	101761	LIN	Stenigot
1872	1992	ALL	1872	136700	SSX	Brighton
1763	1823	1700	1992	151521	YKS	Sheffield
JACKMAN						
1809	1841	1700	1809	170585	DEV	ALL
1836	1940	....	1836	133566	DEV	Devonport
1816	1992	1800	1992	171581	DEV	???
1731	1992	1500	1992	145289	HAM	Isle Of Wight
1780	1820	ALL	1780	150983	HAM	Isle Of Wight
1800	1900	1800	1900	177032	HAM	Lymington
1841	1881	1841	1992	170585	HAM	Portsmouth
1769	1920	ALL	ALL	136719	HAM	Tidworth
1650	1900	1472	1650	102601	IOW	Brightstone
1824	....	1800	1825	174602	KEN	Greenwich
1825	....	ALL	1825	118060	KEN	???
1835	1960	1770	1940	136271	MDX	Willesden
1770	1845	1770	1940	136271	OXF	Thame
1747	1791	ALL	ALL	136719	WIL	Collingbourne Ducie
1834	1881	1780	1834	144746	WOR	Pershore
1719	1830	1700	1800	173290	YKS	Langcliff
1730	1760	1700	1800	166081	YKS	Long Preston
1750	1850	1700	1900	166081	YKS	Settle
1850	1881	1850	1881	174602	YKS	Sheffield
JACKS						
1784	1804	....	....	171654	LKS	Lesmahagow
JACKSON						
1827	1851	ALL	ALL	136735	BDF	Aspley Guise
1889	....	....	....	136735	BDF	Leighton Buzzard
1841	1860	1700	1840	106976	BKM	Hambleden
1840	1880	1840	1880	129925	CAM	Cambridge
1660	1940	....	....	128996	CAM	Thorney
1769	....	1769	....	139149	CHS	Astbury
1797	1861	1700	1797	147885	CHS	Bidston
1736	1823	1700	1736	152196	CMA	Gosforth
1892	1892	1700	1900	145734	CMA	St Bees
1830	1860	1700	1830	132993	CON	Torpoint
1812	1882	1700	1992	153540	CON	Torpoint
....	....	1700	....	108677	CUL	Blencogo
1858	1913	ALL	1858	122823	CUL	Calderbeck
1740	1992	1500	1992	136794	DBY	ALL
1858	1877	1700	1858	138509	DBY	Belper
1700	1710	....	....	103764	DBY	Celmorton
1790	1950	1660	1790	136824	DBY	Dronfield
1830	1860	1700	1830	132993	DEV	Devonport
1851	1881	1700	1900	139254	DOR	Shillingstone
1883	....	....	....	112887	DUB	Dublin
1890	1992	1800	1890	153087	DUR	South
1890	1992	1800	1890	153087	DUR	Mid
1896	1992	ALL	1896	156035	DUR	Stockton
1795	....	1600	1795	116637	DUR	Sunderland
1771	1793	ALL	1771	154563	DUR	Weardale

Known From	To	Researching From	To	Ref	Cty	Place
JACKSON contd.						
....	....	1800	1899	171794	DUR	Willington
1760	1784	1500	1790	161489	ESS	Walthamstow
1750	1900	....	....	100536	ESS	???
1717	1867	1600	1717	175218	EYK	Preston
?	?	....	....	161020	GLS	Bristol
1820	1880	1700	1830	126772	HAM	Ropley
1750	1850	ALL	ALL	131873	HRT	Furneaux Pelham
1820	1992	1750	1820	101893	HRT	???
....	....	1800	1899	104884	IRL	Belfast
1640	1725	....	....	117234	IRL	Cavan
1820	1861	1780	1820	128724	KEN	Charing
....	....	1733	1765	161667	KEN	Crayford
1809	1809	1770	1795	144606	KEN	Woolwich
1950	1992	1930	1992	133450	KEN	???
1794	1888	1750	1800	151912	LAN	Aighton
1800	1817	1600	1800	102571	LAN	Broughton In Furness
1757	1818	1750	1820	126705	LAN	Bury
1706	1935	ALL	1706	175862	LAN	Carmel
1794	1888	1750	1800	151912	LAN	Chipping
?	1923	1800	1880	112879	LAN	Chorlton
1630	....	....	....	117234	LAN	Eccleston
1820	1900	1750	1820	132268	LAN	Farnworth
1880	1992	1870	1992	143065	LAN	Hindley Green
1795	1992	1795	1992	147249	LAN	Liverpool
?	1923	1800	1880	112879	LAN	Manchester
....	....	1700	1900	118923	LAN	Manchester
1900	1900	?	?	121223	LAN	Manchester
1840	1859	ALL	1930	129313	LAN	Manchester
1840	1860	1800	1860	136034	LAN	Manchester
1872	1880	1870	1900	143065	LAN	Manchester
1889	1889	1859	1889	157678	LAN	Manchester
1711	1845	1650	1845	141062	LAN	Middleton
1800	1870	1800	1870	115932	LAN	Oldham
1811	1880	1750	1880	177636	LAN	Ribchester
1808	1857	1808	1870	126705	LAN	Tottington
1780	1840	1700	1850	177636	LAN	Warrington
1785	....	1785	....	139149	LAN	Warton
1581	1622	ALL	ALL	141615	LAN	Warton
1850	1910	1750	1850	152471	LEI	ALL
1841	1992	1700	1841	113808	LEI	Anstey
1841	1992	1700	1841	113808	LEI	Cropston
1794	1992	1700	1900	178616	LEI	Earl Shilton
....	....	1830	1940	136743	LEI	Loughborough
1700	1900	1600	1700	124176	LEI	Saltby
1700	1820	1600	1700	136743	LEI	Saltby
1790	1850	1700	1790	151769	LIN	Barkstone
....	1668	1500	1668	175072	LIN	Billinghay
1850	....	1850	....	136786	LIN	Boston
1660	1716	....	....	129747	LIN	Claypole
1790	1850	1700	1790	151769	LIN	Grantham
1737	....	ALL	....	104515	LIN	Rauceby
1723	1752	1600	1722	131245	LIN	Spalding
....	....	1700	1850	136743	LIN	Stainby
1770	1810	....	....	103721	LIN	Waddingham
1817	1831	ALL	1850	113611	LIN	Winteringham
....	1830	1600	1850	175641	LIN	???
1830	1880	1800	1900	152528	LND	Bethnal Green
1830	1850	1800	1830	113816	LND	Chiswick
1770	1822	1500	1850	161489	LND	Kentish Town
1810	1992	ALL	ALL	157864	LND	Walworth
1750	1900	....	....	100536	LND	???
....	1840	1700	1840	129925	LND	???
1853	1853	1800	1853	174130	MDX	Kensington
1809	1871	1700	1809	110639	MDX	London
1877	1882	1800	1877	167231	MDX	Poplar
1828	1833	1790	1840	155683	MDX	St Pancras
1821	1992	....	....	127779	MDX	Westminster
1769	1927	1750	1800	173428	NBL	Allendale
....	....	1600	1730	154873	NBL	Holy Island
1840	1890	ALL	ALL	101400	NBL	North Shields
1820	1881	ALL	ALL	157864	NFK	Loddon
1837	1858	ALL	ALL	117072	NFK	Methwold
1810	1850	1700	1820	147710	NFK	Norwich
1833	....	1700	1833	101443	NRY	Birdsall
1692	1755	1500	1692	125695	NTH	Harrington
....	....	ALL	ALL	171816	NTH	Heyford
1666	1730	1630	1666	147745	NTT	Greasley
1818	1818	....	....	108901	NTT	Newark
1796	1888	1770	1843	147311	NYK	Scarborough
1595	1830	....	....	132756	OXF	Bicester
1750	1900	....	....	100536	OXF	???
1800	1900	....	....	150371	ROX	Newcastleton

Known From	To	Researching From	To	Ref	Cty	Place
JACKSON contd.						
1820	1840	1700	1820	113697	RUT	Uppingham
1759	1875	1700	1759	160474	SAL	Ellesmere
....	....	1750	1992	143456	SAL	Kynnersley
1840	1851	1830	1880	170992	SCT	Port Glasgow
1826	....	....	1840	171441	SFK	Hawstead
....	....	1825	1827	155683	SRY	Mitcham
....	....	1859	1930	129313	SRY	Southwark
1740	1827	1720	1850	105333	SSX	Chichester
1800	1886	....	....	145394	SSX	Slindon
1835	1900	1800	1950	144037	STI	Baldernock
1850	1850	ALL	ALL	141186	STS	Abbots Bromley
1871	1890	ALL	ALL	149489	STS	Hanley
1800	1870	1800	1870	115932	STS	Wooten
1820	1900	?	1820	158569	STS	???
1759	1992	1600	1759	136727	WAR	Aston
....	....	1750	1850	112879	WAR	Birmingham
1820	1992	1700	1820	124281	WAR	Birmingham
1759	1992	1600	1759	136727	WAR	Birmingham
1860	1880	1800	1875	142395	WAR	Birmingham
1926	1992	....	....	136743	WAR	Coventry
1800	1880	1750	1980	135631	WES	Barbob
1700	1783	1650	1700	135151	WES	Dupton
1751	1754	1558	1751	141291	WES	Kendal
1890	1900	1800	1900	135496	WIC	Arklow
1890	1992	....	1890	136778	WIL	Corsham
1838	1840	1800	1870	176079	WIL	Marlborough
1890	1981	1700	1981	124400	WOR	Worcester
1780	1840	1750	1850	123285	WYK	Kirkburton
1817	1899	1750	1816	115134	YKS	North
1860	1880	1700	1900	136034	YKS	Batley
1800	....	1700	1800	110345	YKS	Braithwell
1780	1890	....	....	118206	YKS	Castleford-Kellington
1862	1890	1700	1857	171662	YKS	Eston
1795	1820	1700	1795	165018	YKS	Everingham
1704	1726	1600	1992	102520	YKS	Fewston
1932	1992	1900	1992	138371	YKS	Huddersfield
1811	1992	....	1811	168521	YKS	Huddersfield
1800	1992	1800	1992	143200	YKS	Hull
1844	1877	ALL	1844	152838	YKS	Hull
1786	1814	1750	1820	148121	YKS	Humbleton
....	....	1700	1800	107018	YKS	Kirkbymoorside
1790	1820	1700	1790	165018	YKS	Leven
....	....	1750	1850	116823	YKS	Malton
1711	1752	1600	1750	101575	YKS	Pontefract
....	....	ALL	1890	173045	YKS	Rotherham
1876	1992	....	1992	130842	YKS	Sheffield
1863	....	ALL	1863	104299	YKS	Thorne
....	....	1700	1770	177393	YKS	Wistow
....	....	1800	1899	125857	???	Birmingham
JACKWAY						
1807	1839	ALL	1807	175080	GLS	Stroud
JACOB						
....	....	ALL	ALL	136832	ALL	Name Study
?	?	?	?	138622	CON	???
?	?	?	?	138622	DEV	???
....	....	1500	1726	138614	DOR	Bridport
1796	1854	ALL	1796	131881	HAM	Brixton
....	....	1600	1950	134546	IOW	Brading
....	....	1600	1950	134546	IOW	Freshwater
1802	1804	....	....	127426	KEN	Stalisfield
1825	1825	....	....	127426	KEN	Wychling
....	....	1800	1850	136832	NFK	ALL
1771	1827	1500	1771	141089	NFK	ALL
1765	1827	1700	1765	175218	NFK	North West
1190	1850	1800	1850	136832	SFK	ALL
1640	1720	1600	1750	154881	TIP	St Johns Town
1901	1907	1901	1907	141097	YKS	Cottingham
1868	1931	1800	1931	141097	YKS	Hull
JACOBS						
1750	ALL	....	....	167037	BRK	Ashbury
1830	1850	ALL	1830	167878	CON	ALL
?	?	?	?	138622	CON	???
?	?	?	?	138622	DEV	???
1776	1989	1660	1775	136859	HAM	Fareham
1878	1900	1878	1992	165727	LND	East
1841	1881	1841	1881	108952	LND	Shoreditch
....	1753	....	....	147869	LND	???
1819	1932	1800	1830	113786	NFK	Holt
1795	1915	ALL	ALL	124982	SOM	ALL
1730	1992	1650	1900	136840	WIL	Avon Valley
JACOM						
1861	....	1600	1861	105023	STS	Bloxwich

Known From	To	Researching From	To	Ref	Cty	Place
JACOM contd.						
1861	....	1600	1861	105023	STS	Walsall
JACOMBS						
1816	1825	ALL	1851	104299	SOM	Shepton Mallet
JACQUES						
1800	1820	1600	1800	146730	CUL	Passim
1881	1992	ALL	1881	136875	DUR	Gateshead
1848	1890	1840	1850	131687	LAN	Manchester
1848	1890	1840	1850	131687	LAN	Salford
1800	1992	1600	1800	166103	LEI	Rothley
1808	1950	1700	1808	165182	NYK	Ebberton
1786	1790	1700	1840	113751	SFK	Southwold
JACQUEST						
1745	....	1700	1745	105457	NTH	???
JAFFRAY						
1760	1882	1700	1760	141798	STI	Bannockburn
JAFFREY						
1750	1800	1750	1800	130915	ABD	Fyvie
1827	....	....	1827	155667	LKS	Glasgow
JAGER						
1880	1920	1850	....	121460	LND	???
JAGGER						
1860	1992	ALL	1900	162027	WYK	Honley
1562	1592	1500	1560	176451	YKS	Kirkburton
1780	1940	1500	1992	170038	YKS	Shelf
JAGO						
1830	1870	ALL	ALL	115266	CON	ALL
1631	1930	ALL	1631	172502	CON	Landrake
1631	1930	ALL	1631	172502	CON	Lantegloss
1760	1820	1760	1810	148377	CON	Saltash
1700	1940	....	....	127833	HAM	Portsmouth
JAKEMAN						
1884	1902	1700	1992	177733	YKS	Leeds
JAKES						
1864	....	ALL	1864	170674	CAM	Willingham
JAMES						
1700	1780	1620	1780	118869	BDF	Northill
1777	1827	1700	1777	125105	BRK	Maidenhead
1840	1923	1750	1840	141321	BRK	Wooton
1749	....	....	1749	177504	CAM	Littleport
1785	1820	1700	1800	160350	CGN	Llanddewibrefi
1800	1900	1800	1900	141577	CGN	Llanilar
1860	1985	ALL	ALL	107182	CMA	Whitehaven
1825	1900	1775	1825	165468	CMN	North
1860	1890	1700	1847	123110	CMN	Abernant
1850	1992	1850	1980	145009	CMN	Llangunnock
1860	1890	1700	1847	123110	CMN	Trelech
1860	1992	1700	1860	109193	CON	Bodmin
1800	1992	1600	1800	136972	CON	Breage
1800	1992	1600	1800	136972	CON	Germoe
1847	ALL	1800	1847	159654	CON	Goonhaven
1690	1890	1690	1900	147419	CON	Gwennap
1800	1992	1600	1800	136972	CON	Helston
1744	1867	1500	....	149314	CON	Kenwyn
1700	1855	1700	1900	100536	CON	Liskeard
1754	1881	1754	1992	172596	CON	Madron
1828	1910	1828	1910	159913	CON	Newquay
1744	1775	1700	1744	153605	CON	Paul
1754	1881	1754	1992	172596	CON	Paul
1744	1775	1700	1744	153605	CON	Penzance
1850	....	1780	1850	159654	CON	Perranzabuloe
1564	1639	1645	1700	153591	CON	Phillack
1850	....	1780	1850	159654	CON	Scorrier
1800	1992	1600	1800	136972	CON	Sithney
....	....	....	1800	114812	CON	St Agnes
1564	1639	1645	1700	153591	CON	St Buryan
1771	....	1700	1771	178845	CON	St Ervan
1564	1639	1645	1700	153591	CON	St Just
1700	1880	....	1880	133086	CON	St Keverne
1600	1992	1600	1992	150126	CON	St Keverne
1769	1964	1769	1964	137324	CON	Towednack
1744	1867	1500	....	149314	CON	Truro
1860	1992	1700	1860	140449	CON	Uny Lelant
1827	1838	1780	1860	155438	CUL	Addingham
1727	1772	1703	1727	141291	CUL	Ulpha
1841	1890	1800	1950	137782	DBY	Glossop
?	?	?	?	136999	DEV	Exeter
1840	1865	1830	1870	136980	DEV	Hennock
1700	1840	1650	1870	121096	DEV	Uffculme
1869	....	....	....	164356	DOR	Wareham
1860	1950	1750	1860	115738	DOW	Portadown
1757	1774	1700	1756	132764	DUR	Weardale
?	?	?	?	136999	ENG	London
1881	1975	1700	1881	102997	ESS	Springfield
JAMES contd.						
1784	1802	1770	1820	136980	ESS	Theydon Garnon
1890	1900	1800	1900	137294	GLA	ALL
1887	1927	1700	1887	105309	GLA	Aberdare
1780	1930	1780	1930	135666	GLA	Capel Llaniltern
1887	1927	1700	1887	105309	GLA	Dinas
1750	1815	....	....	135666	GLA	Drope
1750	1900	1700	1900	118540	GLA	Llangynwydd
1730	1900	1700	1900	118540	GLA	Maesteg
1838	1965	1600	1838	176915	GLA	Merthyr Tydfil
1838	1965	1600	1838	176915	GLA	Neath
1750	1920	....	....	135666	GLA	Pentyrch
1750	1815	....	....	135666	GLA	St Bride
1750	1815	....	....	135666	GLA	St George
1750	1992	....	....	135666	GLA	Vale Of Glamorgan
1869	1983	1700	1869	144614	GLS	Cheltenham
....	....	1800	1850	172871	GLS	Cheltenham
1805	1849	1800	1850	141283	GLS	Forest Of Dean
1754	1906	ALL	1754	175862	GLS	Stow On Wold
1800	1900	ALL	ALL	103152	GLS	Stroud
1708	1877	1550	1708	102830	GLS	Turkdean
....	....	1800	1899	174963	GLS	Woodchester
1890	1940	1870	1980	142549	HAM	Bournemouth
1869	1937	1869	....	133922	HAM	Bramshaw
1790	1840	1600	1840	145289	HAM	Isle Of Wight
1840	1900	1750	1840	146587	HAM	Isle Of Wight
1815	1979	ALL	1979	111600	HAM	Lyndhurst
1815	1979	ALL	1979	111600	HAM	Southampton
1825	1916	1700	1900	177369	HAM	???
1851	1876	1750	1851	148814	HEF	Hereford
1820	1910	ALL	1900	154490	HUN	Godmanchester
1820	1910	ALL	1900	154490	HUN	St Ives
ALL	1960	....	....	104132	IOW	ALL
1750	1992	1650	1750	114693	KEN	Sandhurst
1895	1910	1890	1935	137782	LAN	Barrow In Furness
1815	1890	1815	1890	100080	LAN	Liverpool
1820	1930	1750	1992	137782	LAN	Manchester
1785	1785	1600	1785	172332	LIN	Epworth
1889	1948	1884	1889	126624	LND	East
1749	1816	1730	1850	143774	LND	Shoreditch
1836	1850	1780	1820	165530	LND	St Pancras
1712	1737	....	....	121355	LND	Whitechapel
1856	1992	?	1856	159514	LND	???
1780	1950	1650	1780	177776	MGY	Meifod
1700	1810	....	....	135666	MON	Aberystruth
1750	1900	1750	1900	135666	MON	Bedwellte
1790	1860	1790	1860	139807	MON	Bedwelty
1790	1840	1600	1790	123390	MON	Cresseny
1790	1840	1600	1790	123390	MON	Llantillio
1829	1904	1700	1829	164070	MON	Trevethin
1824	1882	1600	1824	158496	NBL	Newcastle
....	....	1800	1900	147729	NFK	???
....	....	1809	1836	114308	NTH	Rothersthorpe
1810	1960	1700	1810	120081	NTH	Syresham
1818	1992	1700	1818	152056	NTT	Nottingham
1800	1900	1700	1900	142115	PEM	Llangwm
1828	1871	1700	1828	158739	PEM	Manordeifi
....	....	1750	1900	108243	PEM	Solva
1884	....	1700	1884	120030	PEM	???
1880	1958	1500	1880	176974	RAD	Llanbadarnfynydd
1836	1865	1750	1850	118605	SAL	Hopesay
1752	1840	1700	1752	155276	SFK	Walton
1820	1900	1800	1900	112976	SOM	Bath
1882	1933	1880	1902	149314	SOM	Bath
1753	1791	1600	1750	100013	SOM	Binegar
1873	....	1850	1900	142549	SOM	Castle Cary
?	?	ALL	1900	117919	SOM	Croscombe
1907	1910	1910	1992	141771	SOM	Ditcheat
....	....	....	?	132195	SOM	Hill Farrance
?	?	ALL	1900	117919	SOM	Holcombe
ALL	ALL	ALL	ALL	124206	SOM	Shepton Mallet
1840	1960	ALL	1840	178195	SOM	Weston Super Mare
1768	1788	....	....	131210	SRY	Morden
1827	1992	....	....	125105	SRY	Walton On Thames
1768	1788	....	....	131210	SRY	Wimbledon
....	1700	....	....	174564	SSX	???
1627	1794	....	....	117404	STS	Blymhill
1856	1883	1800	1856	105538	STS	Great Bridge
1790	1850	1790	1850	100080	STS	Hanley
1800	1900	1700	1800	169978	STS	Stonnall
1717	1801	....	1717	100900	STS	Walsall
1880	1970	1700	1900	167606	STS	Walsall
1877	1884	1884	1888	126624	WAR	Birmingham
1877	1884	1884	1888	126624	WAR	Edgbaston

Known From	To	Researching From	To	Ref	Cty	Place
JAMES contd.						
....	....	ALL	1860	169919	WEX	Enniscorthy
1844	1908	....	....	149314	WIL	Avebury
1841	1876	1700	1876	162035	WIL	Christian Malford
1869	1937	1869	1937	133922	WIL	Nomansland
1777	1992	1700	1777	141879	WLS	South
1837	1852	1837	1852	174475	WOR	Alvechurch
1840	....	....	....	102733	WOR	Worcester
1805	1832	ALL	1805	178195	???	Bristol
JAMESON						
1792	1796	1792	1840	126705	CHS	Tarvin
1776	1840	1740	1840	113484	LND	ALL
....	....	1700	1750	154873	NBL	Holy Island
1740	1824	1740	1840	113484	NBL	Kirk Newton
....	....	1825	1880	124796	SCT	Edinburgh
1750	1965	....	....	137820	SHI	Fetlar
1720	1965	....	....	137820	SHI	Mid Yell
1760	1965	....	....	137820	SHI	North Yell
1758	1965	....	....	137820	SHI	Northmavine
1720	1965	....	....	137820	SHI	South Yell
JAMIESON						
1795	....	....	....	137936	ANS	Inverkeillour
1890	1992	1700	1890	115738	ANT	Belfast
1841	1881	1841	1881	118974	AYR	Bieth
1790	1810	1700	1850	167398	AYR	Craigie
1790	1810	1700	1850	167398	AYR	Mauchline
1846	....	....	....	127140	DNB	Kirkintilloch
1770	1790	1700	1800	130915	FIF	Forgan
1860	1906	1841	1910	124001	KKD	Carsphairn
....	....	1800	1900	110663	LKS	Glasgow
....	....	1900	1946	110663	LND	???
1770	1832	1841	1891	146560	LTN	Dalmeny
1770	1832	1841	1891	146560	LTN	Leith
1770	1832	1841	1891	146560	LTN	Queensferry
1774	....	....	....	127140	RFW	Greenock
....	....	1800	1992	137014	SCT	Hamilton
....	....	1700	1900	109304	SHI	Aithsting
1750	1965	....	....	137820	SHI	Fetlar
1720	1965	....	....	137820	SHI	Mid Yell
1760	1965	....	....	137820	SHI	North Yell
1758	1965	....	....	137820	SHI	Northmavine
....	....	1700	1900	109304	SHI	Sandsting
1720	1965	....	....	137820	SHI	South Yell
1780	1920	1700	1992	104671	SHI	Yell
JANAWAY						
1835	....	1833	1849	164232	HAM	Wickham
JANDRILL						
1818	1847	1800	1847	108510	SAL	Shifnal
JANE						
1670	1699	ALL	1699	168718	CON	South East
1830	1880	1800	1992	116009	CON	Cawsand
1830	1880	1800	1992	116009	CON	Kingsand
1830	1880	1800	1992	116009	CON	Torpoint
JANES						
1600	1850	ALL	ALL	124796	ALL	ALL
....	....	ALL	ALL	137022	ALL	ALL
1853	1858	1850	1860	137022	BKM	High Wycombe
1748	1953	1664	1950	125229	BKM	Hughenden
1700	1840	1650	1840	124796	BKM	Princes Risborough
1813	1837	1813	1832	125229	BKM	Princes Risborough
1860	1871	1860	1940	137022	BRK	Maidenhead
1807	1830	ALL	ALL	136948	CHS	Cheadle
1709	1709	1650	1709	174289	HAM	Christchurch
1865	1884	1800	1900	127302	HAM	Hythe
1700	ALL	1750	1850	107379	HRT	ALL
1850	1960	1700	1803	136921	KEN	Woolwich
1825	1865	1800	1850	105619	MDX	Marylebone
1733	1733	ALL	1733	108642	MDX	Soho
1733	1733	ALL	1733	108642	MDX	St James
1881	....	1870	1900	137022	MDX	Staines
....	....	1700	1823	174300	SOM	Hewish
JANION						
1854	1881	ALL	1881	175757	CHS	Frodsham
JANMAN						
1966	1992	....	....	137030	BRK	Bracknell
1986	1992	....	....	137030	BRK	Wokingham
1759	1962	....	....	137030	SSX	Bosham
1834	1888	....	....	137030	SSX	Chichester
1593	1814	....	....	137030	SSX	East Dean
1584	1803	....	....	137030	SSX	East Marden
1610	1808	....	....	137030	SSX	Funtington
1578	1655	....	....	137030	SSX	Harting
1836	1992	....	....	137030	SSX	Littlehampton
1612	1833	....	....	137030	SSX	Lodsworth
JANMAN contd.						
1809	1841	....	....	137030	SSX	Lyminster
1763	1852	....	....	137030	SSX	Midhurst
1600	1625	....	....	137030	SSX	North Marden
1642	1780	....	....	137030	SSX	North Mundham
1840	1969	....	....	137030	SSX	Oving
1780	1875	....	....	137030	SSX	Pagham
1810	1860	1700	1810	165867	SSX	Pagham
1871	1911	....	....	137030	SSX	Portfield
1948	1969	....	....	137030	SSX	Rumboldswhyke
1879	....	....	....	137030	SSX	Sidlesham
1566	1809	....	....	137030	SSX	Up Marden
1613	1640	....	....	137030	SSX	West Dean
1854	1867	....	....	137030	SSX	West Lavant
JANNAWAY						
1800	1950	1820	1860	167851	HAM	Stiedfield
1850	1924	1840	1870	167851	MDX	London
JANNEY						
1895	1895	1590	1890	139645	LIN	Conisholme
1800	1900	....	....	177687	LIN	Fulstow Mumby
1761	1886	1742	1886	139645	LIN	Fulstow
1802	1949	1656	1989	139645	LIN	Grainthorpe
1851	1852	1697	1916	139645	LIN	Marshchapel
1862	1862	1800	1889	139645	LIN	Skidbrook With Saltfleet
1813	1910	1813	1910	139645	LIN	Strubby
1820	1830	ALL	ALL	135224	???	???
JANSEN						
1830	1980	1700	1830	137049	MDX	North East London
JANSON						
1818	1850	....	....	156728	CHS	???
JANVERIN						
ALL	1900	....	....	104132	HAM	Hamble
JAPING						
1839	1968	1873	1938	137057	YKS	Bradford
JAPP						
1792	1922	1700	1850	155705	ANS	St Vigeans
1792	1922	1700	1850	155705	KCD	Inverkeillor
1792	1922	1700	1850	155705	KCD	St Vigeans
JAQUES						
1820	1918	1800	1820	137944	LEI	Claybrook
1709	1881	ALL	1760	149195	LEI	Cole Orton
1820	1918	1800	1820	137944	LEI	Desford
1826	1826	....	....	141097	LIN	Wroot
1787	1909	1773	1900	163406	SOM	Bath
1750	1835	1700	1835	119717	YKS	Staithes
JARDINE						
....	....	ALL	ALL	137065	ALL	Name Study
1823	1992	ALL	ALL	120103	CMA	Carlisle
?	?	?	....	100471	DFS	Annan
?	?	?	....	100471	DFS	Dumfries
1825	1888	1750	1900	119725	LKS	Glasgow
1823	1955	1823	1850	120103	SCT	South
1774	1861	1700	1774	157775	SCT	Milnhouse
1823	1992	ALL	ALL	120103	SCT	???
JARLETT						
1750	1880	1600	1880	156280	SRY	Shere
JARMAIN						
1830	1900	....	1830	135844	SRY	Croydon
JARMAN						
1850	1900	ALL	ALL	163368	BDF	Dunton
1770	....	ALL	ALL	116394	KEN	Milton By Gravesend
1700	1850	1700	1850	154377	LND	???
1838	1970	1800	1900	102164	NTT	Carlton
1650	1740	1640	1740	135941	SFK	Glemsford
JARRARD						
1860	1900	1750	1860	171255	DBY	Ashborne
JARRATT						
....	....	ALL	ALL	137138	ALL	ALL
JARRET						
1792	1847	1700	1792	119512	SSX	Mayfield
JARRETT						
....	....	ALL	ALL	137138	ALL	ALL
....	....	ALL	ALL	137138	AVN	ALL
1762	....	1760	1770	161942	BRE	???
....	....	ALL	ALL	137138	BRK	ALL
1797	1852	1797	1992	159875	CAM	Coxton
1871	1872	....	....	151351	DBY	Staveley
....	....	ALL	ALL	137138	GLS	ALL
1840	1870	1800	1870	137111	GLS	Bristol
1800	1992	1500	1992	130583	GLS	Cherington
....	....	ALL	ALL	137138	HRT	ALL
....	....	ALL	ALL	137138	IRL	ALL
....	....	ALL	ALL	137138	KEN	ALL

Known From	To	Researching From	To	Ref	Cty	Place
JARRETT contd.						
1815	1900	1700	1850	135968	KEN	Tunbridge Wells
....	....	ALL	ALL	137138	LAN	ALL
....	....	ALL	ALL	137138	LIN	ALL
....	....	ALL	ALL	137138	LND	ALL
1871	1901	1870	1901	161942	MDX	Hackney
1827	1838	....	....	161942	MDX	London
1838	1848	....	....	161942	MDX	Pimilio
1830	1930	1730	1830	177164	MON	Caerleon
....	....	ALL	ALL	137138	OXF	ALL
....	....	ALL	ALL	137138	SAL	ALL
1880	....	....	....	151351	SCT	Edinburgh
1811	1812	1805	1815	161942	SOM	Bristol
1803	1828	1750	1803	110922	SRY	ALL
1897	1947	....	....	161942	SRY	Mortlake
1820	1850	1820	1850	113743	SSX	Rye
....	....	ALL	ALL	137138	STS	ALL
1820	1900	?	1820	158569	STS	Dudley
1850	1860	ALL	ALL	131172	SXE	Wadhurst
....	....	ALL	ALL	137138	WAR	ALL
1895	1899	ALL	ALL	116378	WAR	Birmingham
....	....	ALL	ALL	137138	WLS	ALL
....	....	ALL	ALL	137138	WOR	ALL
1764	1830	....	....	151351	WOR	Evesham
JARROLD						
1884	1902	1800	1884	102849	HUM	Hull
JARROT						
....	....	ALL	ALL	137138	ALL	ALL
JARVICE						
1660	1700	....	....	119458	BRK	Hurley
JARVIS						
1793	1834	1600	1834	137170	BDF	Luton
1700	1992	1500	1700	137170	BKM	Haddenham
1789	1860	1650	1788	166820	BKM	Penn
1750	1797	?	1750	144800	CAM	Wittlesley
1700	1900	....	....	146870	DBY	Whaley
1856	....	....	1856	117234	DEV	Plymouth
1756	1986	1600	1756	117676	ESS	Central
1900	1920	1900	1920	147575	ESS	Frinton
1817	1883	....	....	140341	ESS	Thaxted
....	....	1800	....	128627	ESS	???
1880	1949	1700	1880	166480	JSY	ALL
1781	1929	ALL	ALL	105015	KEN	Chatham
....	....	1800	1950	162000	KEN	Medway
1830	1897	1795	1830	165107	KEN	Petham
....	....	1800	1950	162000	KEN	Swale
1779	1900	ALL	....	104515	LIN	South
1883	1992	....	....	140341	LND	Stratford
1841	1869	....	1888	120588	LND	???
1700	1950	1700	1950	125881	NFK	North West
1771	....	....	....	121835	NFK	East Dereham
1700	1900	....	....	142530	NFK	East Dereham
1840	1900	1800	1900	123870	NFK	Lowestoft
1800	1899	....	....	121835	NFK	Swaffham
1850	1900	1800	1992	136867	NFK	Swaffham
1800	1860	1800	1860	173533	NTH	South
1830	1900	1700	1830	130990	NTH	Peterborough
1774	1947	1600	1774	123420	SFK	Exning
1875	1900	1800	1970	150703	SRY	Camberwell
1827	1982	1780	1900	102075	SRY	Newington
1770	1850	ALL	ALL	151998	SSX	Bolney
1776	1820	1700	1900	138363	STS	Keele
1883	1900	1850	1900	151637	STS	Tamworth
1888	1895	1869	1888	120588	YKS	Hull
1817	....	....	....	161136	YKS	Sheffield
1780	....	....	....	161136	YKS	Thorpe Hesley
JARY						
1797	1870	1750	1880	158658	NFK	Norwich
1800	1950	1800	1950	162329	NFK	???
1800	1950	1800	1950	162329	SFK	???
JASPER						
1740	1965	1654	1923	109053	CON	Lezant
1760	1781	1700	1800	153354	CON	North Hill
1775	1900	ALL	1775	129267	CON	South Petherwin
1843	ALL	....	....	169897	SAL	Kinnerley
1763	1763	1500	1763	174009	SSX	ALL
1700	1992	ALL	1600	131849	SSX	East
1700	1992	ALL	1600	131849	SSX	Brighton
JAUNCEY						
1800	1900	ALL	ALL	121622	GLS	ALL
1750	1900	ALL	ALL	121622	HEF	ALL
1800	1900	ALL	ALL	121622	WOR	West
JAUNDRELL						
....	....	1750	1850	147613	STS	West Bromwich

Known From	To	Researching From	To	Ref	Cty	Place
JAY						
....	....	1740	1800	103713	CAM	Woodditton
1790	1860	ALL	1860	168718	CON	South East
1880	1992	1800	1992	137294	ESS	Cranham
1880	1992	1800	1992	137294	ESS	Stanford Le Hope
1740	1800	1600	1800	154342	GLS	Bitton
1800	1870	1700	1800	101958	LND	East
1890	1920	1800	1890	153362	LND	Marylebone
....	....	1746	1800	129895	SFK	Framlingham
JAYNE						
1565	1851	1545	1992	123021	GLS	Henbury
1847	1992	ALL	1847	130605	LND	Lambeth
....	....	ALL	ALL	123021	MON	ALL
1847	1992	ALL	1847	130605	SRY	Croydon
1618	1714	ALL	ALL	111295	???	Bristol
JEACOCK						
....	....	ALL	ALL	137189	ALL	Name Study
1640	1820	....	....	121983	NTH	???
1730	1750	....	....	121983	OXF	North
1327	1730	....	....	121983	WAR	East
1327	1730	....	....	121983	WAR	South
1830	1992	1700	1830	176710	WAR	Bubbenhall
JEAGER						
1880	1930	1850	....	121460	LND	Wandsworth
JEAKINS						
1730	1761	1500	1730	125695	BDF	Gamlingay
JEAL						
....	....	ALL	ALL	137197	ALL	Name Study
1836	1920	1750	1992	144525	LND	South
JEANNES						
1837	1897	ALL	ALL	119504	DOR	Lydlinch
JEANS						
1800	....	1720	1800	165158	DEV	Plympton St Mary
ALL	ALL	ALL	ALL	165158	DEV	Uffculme
1823	1850	1800	1880	127353	DOR	Haydon
1793	1823	1780	....	127353	DOR	Hermitage
1804	....	ALL	ALL	110272	DOR	Radipole
1790	1825	1600	1800	105619	DOR	Stalybridge
JEAQUES						
1800	1800	ALL	ALL	171816	WAR	Newbold On Avon
JEARY						
1800	1831	1831	1891	125105	NFK	Great Yarmouth
....	....	1700	1850	140627	NFK	Mattishall
JEAVONS						
1830	1906	ALL	ALL	122386	DUR	Ryton
1830	1906	ALL	ALL	122386	DUR	Winlaton
....	....	1800	1920	133426	STS	South
....	....	1600	1992	147613	STS	Rowley Regis
1800	1992	ALL	1992	107050	WAR	Birmingham
....	....	1600	1992	147613	WOR	Dudley
JEE						
....	....	ALL	ALL	137200	ALL	Name Study
1800	1853	1800	1853	137200	LEI	St Margarets
1853	1883	....	....	137200	LIN	Spilsby
1792	1992	1750	1940	124028	SRY	Croydon
JEENS						
1760	1950	1700	1800	115614	GLS	Gloucester
JEEVES						
....	....	ALL	ALL	138460	ALL	Name Study
JEFCOATE						
?	?	ALL	ALL	100897	LND	???
....	....	1880	1935	137391	WAR	Birmingham
JEFFCOAT						
1786	1855	....	....	163155	LEI	Stanton Under Bardon
JEFFCOATE						
1883	1992	1700	1883	121258	NTH	ALL
JEFFCOCK						
1888	1902	ALL	1980	136891	YKS	Hunslet
JEFFCOTT						
....	....	1840	....	145998	LND	???
1820	1960	1700	1820	151300	WAR	Coventry
JEFFCUTT						
1800	1992	ALL	1800	147087	GLS	ALL
JEFFERIES						
1730	1875	1730	1875	172634	BRK	Shrivenham
1830	1900	ALL	1900	131334	GLS	ALL
1819	1860	1600	1819	115525	GLS	Kingswood
1791	1840	1600	1791	115525	SOM	Cheddar
1763	1992	ALL	ALL	112259	WIL	North
1728	1837	ALL	ALL	117307	WIL	Chiseldon
1740	1752	1700	1800	179337	WIL	Lnagley Burrell
JEFFERS						
....	....	1700	1850	137227	COR	???

Known From	To	Researching From	To	Ref	Cty	Place
JEFFERSON						
1847	1992	ALL	1847	104221	CLV	Middleton
1847	1992	ALL	1847	104221	CLV	Stranton
1779	1779	1750	1779	147311	NYK	Scarborough
1730	1832	1760	1849	168165	YKS	Bentley
1730	1832	1760	1849	168165	YKS	Doncaster
1786	1809	1600	1786	134368	YKS	Seamer
1823	1928	1700	1823	173479	YKS	Sutton On Forest
1770	1825	1700	1830	115967	YKS	Whitby
JEFFERY						
?	....	1700	1960	123668	AVN	Bristol
....	....	1700	1780	103713	CAM	Woodditton
1723	1723	1723	1723	141690	CON	Creed
1636	1900	ALL	1636	122017	CON	Gwennap
1890	1992	1700	1850	143936	CON	Gwennap
1800	1860	ALL	1810	142301	CON	Plackburgh
1770	1791	1770	1793	141690	CON	Probus
1750	1992	1750	1992	164399	DEV	Hartland
1734	1734	?	1734	158569	ESS	Rickling
....	....	1600	1950	134546	IOW	Bembridge
....	....	1600	1950	134546	IOW	Brading
1700	1860	1550	1700	114294	KEN	Brenchley
....	....	1800	1851	115886	KEN	Mid
....	....	1870	1920	141623	LND	Bloomsbury
1838	1992	1700	1838	152552	LND	St Pancras
1900	1992	ALL	1900	111678	NTH	Bugbrooke
1760	1900	1600	1800	141445	NTT	Nottingham
1771	1901	ALL	ALL	124982	SOM	ALL
1840	1970	1840	1970	154938	SOM	Chard
1605	1639	1550	1650	167002	SXE	Southease
1500	1620	1500	1700	170216	WIL	ALL
1800	1860	1800	1860	154210	WIL	Winterbourne Earls
1770	1793	1600	1992	102520	YKS	Fewston
JEFFERYS						
1715	1811	1650	1992	101621	BDF	Bedford
JEFFORD						
1807	1826	1750	1807	115460	BDF	Luton
1743	1747	1600	1830	133000	DEV	Axmouth
1820	1830	1700	1850	142050	SOM	South
JEFFREY						
1811	1902	1700	1811	166723	BEW	Gordon
1773	1829	1773	1837	107360	BKM	Moulsoe
1687	1721	1600	1687	102571	CON	Gwennap
1700	1800	....	....	100633	DUR	???
1652	1696	....	....	165999	ESS	Chelmsford
....	....	1800	1860	167932	NBL	Twizel
....	....	ALL	1800	114308	NTH	Kislingbury
1687	1743	....	....	129747	SFK	Glemsford
JEFFREYES						
1840	1870	1800	1870	114642	MDX	Mile End
JEFFREYS						
1800	....	ALL	1850	174637	GLA	Swansea
JEFFRIES						
1850	1900	....	....	109452	BRK	Wantage
1760	1860	ALL	1800	115266	DOR	ALL
1820	1851	1800	1860	171441	MDX	Isleworth
....	....	ALL	ALL	174033	SRY	Camberwell
....	....	ALL	1811	114308	SRY	Chiddingford
1780	1780	1700	1780	179116	STS	Ipstones
1787	....	....	1820	171441	WIL	Warminster
1760	1770	1700	1760	140309	WOR	Badsey
JEFFS						
1848	1905	1848	1905	164704	GLS	???
1900	1940	1700	1900	173479	NTH	Naseby
1721	1721	1600	1721	110787	RUT	Cottesmore
1842	....	1842	....	164135	???	Birchington
JEKYLL						
1800	1843	1750	1875	141771	SOM	Ditcheat
JELBERT						
1819	1824	1800	1819	128368	CON	Gulval
JELF						
1845	1955	1700	1845	177113	WOR	St Peter
JELFES						
1759	1780	1700	1800	149691	WOR	Bedley
JELKS						
1600	1650	1550	1600	174513	OXF	Oxford
JELLETT						
....	....	1700	1890	121193	HAM	Southampton
JELLEY						
1750	1992	ALL	ALL	137243	ALL	ALL
1600	1992	1600	1992	150479	LEI	Leicester
1800	1831	1800	1831	151599	NTT	Nottingham
1720	1860	1720	1860	150479	NTT	Sutton Bonnington
JELLEYMAN						
1807	1900	1770	1900	127159	OXF	Bloxham
JELLICOE						
1796	1881	1740	1796	179523	CHS	Wirral
JELLIMAN						
1744	1773	1700	1744	178381	OXF	Shilton
JELLIS						
1650	1730	1530	1730	118869	BDF	Central
JELLOWS						
....	....	ALL	ALL	137251	ALL	Name Study
JEMMESON						
1790	1970	1700	1790	137278	YKS	Wold Newton
JEMSOB						
1790	1992	1700	1790	178608	ESS	Southend
JEMSON						
1700	1750	ALL	1700	131059	KEN	East Farleigh
JENKERSON						
1792	1836	1760	1837	150053	SFK	Barnby
JENKES						
1740	1992	1650	1740	137332	???	???
JENKIN						
1690	1885	1740	1885	176958	CGN	Cardigan
?	?	?	?	176958	CGN	Duffryn
1600	1992	ALL	ALL	137286	CON	West
1846	....	....	....	136964	CON	Illogan
1779	....	1740	1780	178845	CON	Illogan
....	....	1700	1900	136972	CON	Isle Of Scilly
1813	1883	1800	1813	128368	CON	Madron
1818	1847	ALL	1818	162108	CON	Mylor
....	....	1850	1970	163791	CON	Newquay
1865	1992	1700	1900	106186	CON	Redruth
1850	1910	1700	1850	120944	CON	St Austell
1599	1620	1500	1600	102571	CON	St Columb
1626	1819	....	....	174319	CON	???
1819	1931	1780	1900	122688	DEV	Totnes
1820	1900	1700	1820	158739	GLA	Caduxton J Neath
1777	1796	1700	1861	176923	GLA	Llangyfelach
1720	1800	1720	1800	151297	GLA	Neath
1690	1885	1740	1885	176958	PEM	Llangoedmore
1690	1885	1740	1885	176958	PEM	Pantirion St Dogmaels
JENKINS						
1800	1992	ALL	1800	138126	BRE	Aberscyr
1800	1992	ALL	1800	138126	BRE	Llandefaelog Fach
1859	1859	1800	1859	156914	CGN	Eglwsfach
....	1835	....	....	177008	CGN	Llabadan Fawr
1850	1910	1700	1860	148563	CHS	Wirral
1798	1803	1700	1825	168149	DEV	Exeter
1819	1931	1780	1900	122688	DEV	Totnes
1800	1850	....	....	131857	DFD	Newport
1800	1850	....	....	131857	DFD	Parrog
1780	1820	ALL	1780	115266	DOR	ALL
1731	1900	1500	1900	170216	DOR	ALL
1814	....	....	....	151351	DOR	Piddletrenthide
1757	1992	1700	1757	130966	DOR	Poole
1880	1992	1870	1992	123250	DUR	Consett
1927	1992	1800	1992	137294	ESS	Stanford Le Hope
1837	1900	1800	1920	140295	GLA	Cardiff
1800	1837	1800	1840	140295	GLA	Cowbridge
....	1850	1800	1900	135658	GLA	Cwmavon
....	....	1640	1780	100188	GLA	Hensol
1785	1910	1750	1910	118575	GLA	Llangiwg
1890	1992	....	1890	138320	GLA	Merthyr Tydfil
1900	1910	1800	1900	158976	GLA	Merthyr Tydfil
....	1850	1800	1900	135658	GLA	Michaelston
1850	1927	1800	1992	137294	GLA	Miskin
1880	1950	....	....	104272	GLA	Taffs Well
1848	1988	1750	1850	165271	GLA	Tenby
1800	1992	ALL	1800	138126	GLA	Treorchy
1800	1992	ALL	1800	138126	GLA	Ynysybwl
1800	1850	ALL	ALL	124982	GLS	South
1816	....	....	....	124982	GLS	Berkeley
1720	1860	ALL	ALL	165255	GLS	Forest Of Dean
1690	1735	....	....	165999	GLS	Henbury
1842	1960	1819	1842	111856	GLS	???
1830	1840	1800	1850	158658	GNT	Blackwood
1851	1871	....	....	129097	GNT	Llangatock
1850	1900	ALL	ALL	122866	HAM	East
1890	1982	1850	1950	130451	HAM	???
1830	1850	1830	1870	111538	HEF	Fownhope
1790	1810	1790	1820	111538	HEF	Leominster
1807	....	....	....	144169	HEF	Michaelchurch-Escley
1881	....	....	....	144169	HEF	Much Birch

Known From	To	Researching From	To	Ref	Cty	Place
JENKINS contd.						
1836	....	....	....	144169	HEF	Pencoyd
....	....	1500	1632	143138	KEN	East Greenwich
1809	....	....	....	103233	KEN	Folkestone
1900	1992	1800	1992	143650	KEN	Gravesend
1730	....	1730	1815	119458	KEN	Selling
....	....	1847	1870	161667	KEN	Whitstable
1851	1853	1841	1859	165255	LAN	Manchester
1745	....	ALL	....	104515	LIN	Creeton
1750	1900	ALL	ALL	131873	LND	Westminster
1828	1865	1700	1825	168149	MDX	London
1827	1851	1790	1827	174955	MDX	Marylebone
....	....	1840	1870	117137	MON	Abertillery
....	....	1820	1840	117137	MON	Blaenavon
1880	1889	1850	1900	123250	MON	Caerleon
1860	1920	1860	1920	116807	MON	Llanover
....	1858	....	1880	161888	MON	???
1760	1760	1750	1770	107360	NTH	Whilton
1800	1826	1800	....	105139	POW	Mochdre Newtown
....	....	1750	1770	111538	SAL	Clun
1830	1992	1700	1830	130257	SOM	ALL
1854	1880	1700	1854	134368	SRY	Lambeth
1850	1920	ALL	ALL	122866	SSX	East
1840	....	....	1840	110027	WLS	Monmouth
1830	1884	1730	1830	145149	WOR	Dudley
....	....	ALL	1850	179477	???	Bristol
JENKINSON						
1810	1850	ALL	ALL	154806	LAN	Caton
1820	1856	....	....	118729	LAN	Glasson
1810	1850	ALL	ALL	154806	LAN	Wray
1830	1890	1800	1900	136174	TYR	Minterburm
1890	1992	1880	1890	161861	???	Liverpool
JENKS						
....	....	....	....	113840	HEF	ALL
1800	1992	?	1800	174181	HEF	Bockleton
1740	1992	1650	1740	137332	SAL	ALL
1775	1992	1721	1775	113840	SAL	Madeley
1538	1721	1721	1775	113840	SAL	Shrewsbury
1783	1845	ALL	1872	143634	STS	Bilston
1768	1822	1700	1768	177555	STS	Sedgley
1768	1768	ALL	1872	143634	STS	Wolverhampton
....	....	....	....	113840	WOR	ALL
1800	1992	?	1800	174181	WOR	Bockleton
JENKYN						
....	....	1500	1620	137340	CON	Breage
1620	1880	ALL	ALL	137340	CON	Crowan
1640	1740	1640	1750	137340	CON	Wendron
JENNENS						
1825	1825	....	....	127426	STS	Handsworth
1715	1715	....	....	127426	STS	Harborne
1851	1851	....	....	127426	STS	Ninevah
1849	1849	....	....	127426	WAR	Aston
1817	1817	....	....	127426	WAR	Birmingham
1851	1992	1650	1851	178985	WAR	Birmingham
1618	1618	....	....	127426	WAR	Shottle
1602	1866	....	....	127426	WAR	???
JENNER						
1800	1992	1650	1992	166758	ALL	ALL
1780	1810	1700	1800	147478	GLS	Hardwicke
1580	1640	ALL	1580	137367	GLS	Kemspford
1600	1850	ALL	1600	137367	GLS	Mesey Hampton
1850	....	....	....	137375	GLS	Standish
1675	1970	1675	1992	137308	KEN	Cranbrook
1819	1850	1800	1880	145602	KEN	???
1850	1992	....	....	137367	LND	North
1818	1880	1818	1890	145602	LND	Camden Town
1585	1650	ALL	1585	137367	LND	City
1871	1900	....	....	130281	LND	Deptford
1900	1920	1800	1900	153362	LND	Marylebone
1818	1880	1818	1890	145602	LND	St Pancras
1830	1887	1800	1900	143677	MDX	Finchley
1803	1850	1780	1850	100242	SSX	Barcombe
1810	1857	ALL	ALL	119105	SSX	Chailey
....	....	1700	1800	100536	SSX	???
1600	1850	ALL	1600	137367	WIL	Marston Meysey
JENNES						
1811	1850	1790	1932	148067	NFK	Carbrook
JENNET						
1788	....	1700	1800	133957	HAM	Petersfield
JENNINGS						
....	....	ALL	ALL	169633	ALL	Name Study
1866	1946	1830	1870	142360	BRK	Chaddleworth
1856	1922	1851	1970	137405	CAM	Newmarket
1822	1851	1800	1860	137405	CAM	Wisbech
JENNINGS contd.						
1841	1861	1840	1880	156833	CHS	Audley
1890	1960	1700	1960	121495	CON	South
1788	1860	1780	1870	143774	DBY	Bradwell
1890	1960	1700	1960	121495	DEV	North
1810	1850	1600	1810	134090	DEV	Honiton
1810	1850	1600	1810	134090	DEV	Uffculme
1670	1885	1650	1992	122319	ESS	South East
1848	ALL	ALL	1992	170909	GAL	Aughrim
1778	1785	1700	1992	116653	GLS	Fretherne
1707	....	1707	1992	139955	HAM	Ringwood
1930	....	....	....	144169	HEF	Brampton Abbotts
1800	1992	1500	1800	114049	HRT	ALL
1874	....	1800	....	162752	HRT	???
1800	1992	1500	1800	114049	HUN	ALL
1800	....	....	1800	117234	KEN	Cobham
1887	1960	1785	1887	134473	KEN	East Wickham
1800	....	....	1800	117234	KEN	Lenham
1787	1787	1700	1800	126837	LAN	Lancaster
....	1688	1650	1750	138584	LEI	Kegworth
1800	1900	1500	1800	114049	LND	ALL
1600	....	1550	1800	141151	LND	ALL
1776	1826	1600	1780	161489	LND	City
1804	1806	....	....	116254	LND	Hammersmith
1900	1992	1800	1935	175684	MDX	ALL
1767	1850	1700	1800	137413	SAL	Baschurch
....	....	1853	....	140767	SAL	Dawley
1767	1850	1700	1800	137413	SAL	Hodnet
1767	1850	1700	1800	137413	SAL	Shrewsbury
1840	1974	1796	1974	137723	SFK	Horham
....	....	1700	1992	140627	SFK	Walton
1830	1840	1800	1900	115746	SOM	Taunton
1851	1953	1700	1851	176052	STS	Birmingham
....	....	1795	1850	115142	STS	Brierley Hill
1727	1754	....	....	127426	STS	Harborne
....	....	1811	....	174602	STS	???
....	....	1815	1859	107247	WIL	Manningford Abbots
1800	1900	1800	1900	106429	WRY	Campsall
....	....	....	1851	137405	YKS	ALL
1850	1900	1700	1992	165255	YKS	Castleford
1600	1800	1600	1800	167924	YKS	Kirby Underdale
1856	1992	1700	1856	123943	YKS	Sheffield
....	....	1750	1850	115142	???	Brierley Hill
JENNINGTON						
....	1751	ALL	1751	152838	YKS	Walkington
JENNINS						
1757	1757	....	....	127426	STS	Harborne
1780	1780	....	....	127426	WAR	Birmingham
1797	1797	....	....	127426	WAR	???
JENNIS						
1679	1729	....	....	101028	NFK	Sheringham
JENNISON						
1800	1850	1700	1800	157708	DBY	Duffield
1790	1833	1700	1790	115967	YKS	Hutton Cranswick
1859	....	1833	1863	115967	YKS	Sinninton
1863	1883	1859	1880	115967	YKS	Whitby
JENNS						
1830	1992	ALL	ALL	137421	WAR	Birmingham
JENSEN						
1850	1920	1800	1920	159220	DUR	Hartlepool
1818	1898	1600	1950	107700	HUM	Hull
1900	1992	1890	1992	107700	LAN	Liverpool
JENSON						
....	....	1600	....	137456	WAR	Stockton
JENVEY						
1800	1840	1600	1840	158542	HAM	Brockenhurst
JEPHCOTT						
....	....	ALL	ALL	137464	ALL	Name Study
1500	1800	1500	1800	137464	WAR	Ansty
JEPMAN						
1700	....	ALL	1800	168696	CON	East
JEPPS						
1600	1992	1600	1992	114790	BDF	Shillington
JEPSON						
1750	1900	1750	1900	125237	LAN	Darwen
1800	1880	1880	1992	162256	LAN	Darwen
1700	1800	1600	1800	132950	LIN	Lincoln
1824	....	1700	....	123552	MDX	London
1806	1900	1750	1806	178993	YKS	Almondbury
1670	1750	1600	1780	166022	YKS	Ecclesfield
1780	1850	1700	1780	149152	YKS	Sheffield
1850	....	1850	1900	168572	YKS	Sheffield
1864	1935	1840	1864	177555	YKS	Wombwell
....	....	1880	1905	100234	???	Stepney

Known From	To	Researching From	To	Ref	Cty	Place
JERAM						
1819	1930	1700	1840	160865	HAM	Porstmouth
1578	1862	1500	1578	173770	IOW	???
JERDAN						
1750	1850	1600	1900	125148	ROX	Kelso
JEREM						
1840	1860	1750	1840	146285	SRY	Brixton
JEREMY						
1823	1826	1820	1823	164577	GLS	Berkely
....	....	1800	1900	110353	MON	Tredegar
1819	1829	1700	1819	164577	WLS	Camarthen
1835	1842	1830	1835	164577	WOR	Worcester
JERIES						
1800	?	....	....	176559	GLA	Penfai
JERMAN						
1825	1870	1780	1860	174912	AGY	Amlwch
JERMY						
....	1901	....	....	153400	LND	St Pancras
1850	1992	ALL	ALL	142565	NFK	Great Yarmouth
1450	1550	1400	1550	154881	NFK	Worstead
1200	....	....	....	100676	NFK	Wroxham
JEROME						
1763	1783	1793	1814	164704	BRK	Sulhampstead
1537	1790	1500	1850	137472	BRK	Yattenden
1800	1992	1700	1800	102873	BRK	Yattendon
1841	1861	1790	1890	137472	OXF	Henley On Thames
1841	1861	1790	1890	137472	OXF	Shiplake
1850	1950	1850	1950	137472	SRY	Dorking
1850	1950	1850	1950	137472	SRY	Kingston
1850	1950	1850	1950	137472	SRY	Richmond
JEROMSON						
1750	1965	....	....	137820	SHI	Fetlar
1720	1965	....	....	137820	SHI	Mid Yell
1760	1965	....	....	137820	SHI	North Yell
1758	1965	....	....	137820	SHI	Northmavine
1720	1965	....	....	137820	SHI	South Yell
JERRAM						
1794	1794	1794	1794	131970	NTT	Sandiacre
JERRAMS						
1841	1855	1841	1855	118931	NTH	Kings Sutton
JERRARD						
1880	1900	1600	1880	171255	DBY	Ashborne
1743	1852	....	....	137480	DOR	Chideock
1800	....	....	....	137480	DOR	Milton Abbas
JERRETT						
....	....	ALL	ALL	137138	ALL	ALL
1810	1900	ALL	ALL	163473	DEV	Lapford
1700	1860	1600	1860	142018	WIL	South East
JERROM						
1854	1874	1800	1890	136719	ALL	London
JERVIS						
1814	1935	?	1900	164976	DBY	Stanton
1800	....	ALL	ALL	130508	FIF	Elie
1880	1920	....	1880	174025	GLS	Maesteg
1804	1850	1600	1804	119822	LAN	Bolton
1887	1903	1903	1960	137499	LAN	Burnley
1804	1850	1600	1804	119822	LAN	Leigh
1774	1874	1700	1874	138088	MDX	London
1699	1742	....	1699	151688	NTH	Etton
1769	1789	1789	1992	151688	NTH	Glinton
1700	1850	1600	1700	147729	NYK	Richmondshire
1830	1874	1700	1874	138088	SAL	Whittington
1802	1880	1700	1900	138878	SFK	Lowestoft
1800	1992	1700	1825	137499	STS	Stafford
1800	1992	1700	1825	137499	STS	Stone
JESNEY						
1800	1992	....	....	176125	LIN	Asterby
1800	1992	....	....	176125	LIN	Goulceby
JESON						
1672	1700	ALL	ALL	141615	LEI	Kings Norton
JESSETT						
....	....	ALL	ALL	124974	ALL	Name Study
....	....	ALL	ALL	124974	ALL	ALL
1861	1917	1855	1917	124974	BDF	Luton
1880	1882	1878	1884	124974	BKM	Aylesbury
1849	1870	1848	1880	124974	BKM	Eton
1865	1867	1863	1869	124974	BKM	Iver
1774	1861	1700	1861	124974	BKM	Lower Winchendon
1870	1884	1800	1900	124974	BRK	Boxford
1681	1687	1650	1700	124974	BRK	Chaddleworth
1600	1620	1595	1625	124974	BRK	Chieveley
1672	1692	1650	1700	124974	BRK	Clewer
1480	1595	1400	1600	124974	BRK	East Ilsley
1882	1885	1880	1888	124974	BRK	East Shefford
JESSETT contd.						
1690	1992	1600	1992	124974	BRK	Eddington
1890	1989	1800	1989	124974	BRK	Hoe Benham
1690	1992	1600	1992	124974	BRK	Hungerford
1560	1992	1500	1992	124974	BRK	Kintbury
1774	1774	1750	1800	124974	BRK	Letcombe Bassett
1817	1906	1800	1920	124974	BRK	Marsh Benham
1820	1992	1600	1992	124974	BRK	Newbury
1843	1910	1700	1992	124974	BRK	Redaing
1885	1905	1850	1905	124974	BRK	Riseley
1604	1653	1600	1670	124974	BRK	Waltham St Lawrence
1617	1712	1600	1750	124974	BRK	West Woodhay
1828	1849	1650	1850	124974	BRK	Windsor
1872	1906	1850	1920	124974	ESS	West Ham
1886	1895	1880	1897	124974	GLS	Cirencester
1843	1992	1800	1992	124974	HAM	Crookham Village
1719	1725	1700	1870	124974	HAM	East Woodhay
1905	1927	1905	1927	124974	HAM	Eversley
1860	1927	1850	1927	124974	HAM	Hartley Wintney
1626	1642	1600	1700	124974	HAM	Quarley
1794	1845	1750	1850	124974	HAM	Winchester
1854	1992	1830	1992	124974	HEF	Ledbury
1867	1869	1860	1875	124974	HRT	Bushey
1863	1926	1850	1926	124974	KEN	Deptford
1861	1946	1850	1946	124974	MDX	Acton
1881	1886	1850	1900	124974	MDX	Edmonton
1869	1873	1865	1875	124974	MDX	Hampstead
1844	1854	1800	1875	124974	MDX	Islington
1855	1903	1840	1920	124974	MDX	Paddington
1880	1964	1850	1965	124974	MDX	Peckham
1920	1954	1910	1954	124974	MDX	Rotherhithe
1852	1941	1830	1941	124974	MDX	Streatham
1888	1919	1850	1919	124974	MDX	Woodgreen
1907	1992	1900	1992	124974	NFK	Norwich
1902	1992	1890	1992	124974	NTH	Helmdon
1735	1790	1710	1800	124974	OXF	Becklay
1648	1729	1620	1740	124974	OXF	Bicester
1631	1798	1605	1810	124974	OXF	Burford
1725	1806	1700	1810	124974	OXF	Caversfield
1568	1620	1540	1630	124974	OXF	Chalgrove
1646	1794	1600	1800	124974	OXF	Charleton On Otmoor
1777	1831	1750	1840	124974	OXF	Chipping Norton
1763	1782	1740	1790	124974	OXF	Headington
1759	1820	1740	1830	124974	OXF	Islip
1773	1839	1750	1850	124974	OXF	Kirklington
1767	1791	1745	1800	124974	OXF	Launton
1824	1992	1600	1992	124974	OXF	Oxford
1708	1784	1680	1800	124974	OXF	Stoke Lyne
1868	1942	1850	1942	124974	SRY	Croydon
1870	1903	1850	1910	124974	SRY	East Molesey
1880	1929	1850	1929	124974	SRY	Egham
1893	1928	1870	1928	124974	SRY	Lewisham
1810	1837	1790	1850	124974	SSX	Slinfold
1788	1886	1727	1890	124974	WAR	Napton On The Hill
1843	1876	1830	1890	124974	WAR	Priors Marsden
1881	1992	1727	1992	124974	WAR	Rugby
1774	1776	1770	1777	124974	WIL	Baydon
1796	1853	1780	1853	124974	WIL	Chisbury
1881	1981	1850	1981	124974	WIL	Marlborough
1895	1905	1890	1910	124974	WOR	Malvern
1841	1924	1820	1924	124974	YKS	Sheffield
JESSMAN						
1890	1930	1800	1890	117714	LND	Fulham
JESSON						
....	....	1860	1992	147613	LAN	Barrow In Furness
1715	1900	1600	1715	164844	LEI	North West
....	....	1800	1860	147613	SAL	Wellington
1836	1878	ALL	1836	100528	WAR	Leamington
JESSOP						
1920	1940	1800	1920	157058	CHS	North East
1858	1905	1700	1900	167606	DBY	Cromford
1858	1905	1700	1900	167606	DBY	Wirksworth
....	1683	1500	1683	175072	LIN	Billinghay
1664	....	ALL	....	104515	LIN	Rauceby
1827	1853	1800	1860	102075	LND	Holborn
1826	1910	....	....	169056	YKS	Halifax
1773	1826	1700	1775	169056	YKS	Lepton
1800	1860	1800	1830	130621	YKS	Ossett
JESSUP						
1861	....	1850	1992	140058	KEN	Pembury
1830	1850	1800	1861	140058	SXE	Hartfield
JEUNE						
1860	1935	....	....	113484	CHI	Jersey

Known From	To	Researching From	To	Ref	Cty	Place
JEVON						
1646	1726	1580	1726	117579	STS	Tipton
JEW						
1790	1984	1750	1790	130877	YKS	Arnold
JEWEL						
1692	1699	1600	1692	164283	CON	Ladock
JEWELL						
1805	1850	1750	....	118591	CON	Davidstow
1765	1992	1500	1780	137502	DEV	St Giles In The Wood
1550	1950	1550	1950	175463	HAM	ALL
1850	1992	1700	1850	157449	LND	Marylebone
1779	1891	1750	1891	132608	LND	???
....	....	ALL	1900	178403	LND	???
....	....	1800	1850	106356	SFK	???
1799	1946	1650	1799	107654	SOM	Curry Rivel
1750	1992	1600	1750	166650	SOM	Curry Rivel
1750	1992	1600	1750	166650	SOM	Whitestaunton
1800	1900	1700	1800	125660	SRY	Lingfield
JEWELS						
1790	1980	1500	1790	130885	CON	Launcells
JEWHURST						
1870	1895	1870	1895	113743	SSX	Rye
JEWITT						
1620	1980	ALL	1620	137510	DUR	ALL
1620	1980	ALL	1620	137510	ENG	North East
1620	1980	ALL	1620	137510	NBL	ALL
1620	1980	ALL	1620	137510	NYK	ALL
JEWKES						
1825	1911	1300	1992	152501	STS	Lower Gornal
1825	1911	1300	1992	152501	WOR	Dudley
JEWSON						
1837	1988	1600	1992	159980	ALL	ALL
1655	1988	1600	1992	159980	NFK	Tilney St Lawrence
1860	....	....	....	153982	SRY	Southwark
JEX						
1874	1892	....	....	176885	ESS	Walthamstow
1867	1871	....	....	176885	MDX	St Georges Hanover Square
1738	1805	1600	1738	176885	NFK	Costessey
1797	....	1750	1797	176885	NFK	North Tuddenham
1807	1861	1861	1867	176885	NFK	Swanton Morley
1795	1802	1700	1795	175722	NFK	Wolferton
1790	1800	1750	1790	176672	NFK	Woodton
JEZARD						
1700	1992	ALL	ALL	107670	KEN	East
JEZZARD						
1660	1992	ALL	ALL	107670	KEN	East
1772	1870	....	....	143898	KEN	Sandwich
JIFFKINS						
1783	1797	1783	1797	126667	OXF	Chinnor
JIFKINS						
1809	1839	1800	1850	126667	BKM	Monks Risborough
JIGGINS						
1786	1953	ALL	ALL	114030	ESS	South East
JILBERT						
....	....	....	....	127086	CON	South East
....	....	....	....	127086	DEV	Tavistock
JILL						
....	....	1840	1895	153923	JSY	St Helier
JILLOTT						
1700	1992	1550	1700	171395	YKS	Kirkburton
JINKENS						
1850	1871	1871	1900	178659	WMD	Wolverhampton
JINKS						
1825	1850	1790	1825	126659	SAL	ALL
JOANES						
1790	1992	1700	1790	165379	WLS	???
JOASS						
1856	1992	1800	1856	126454	LND	???
JOB						
1672	1838	1500	1900	153354	CON	Gwennap
JOBBINS						
1779	....	1700	1992	101656	WIL	Herston Magna
JOBBITT						
1709	1850	1600	1992	136697	STS	Walsall
JOBLING						
1800	1875	1600	1992	174149	DUR	Gateshead
1580	1850	1500	1580	132942	DUR	Whickham
1840	1885	1885	1992	174149	NBL	Newcastle On Tyne
JOBSON						
1851	1861	1780	1881	123536	NBL	Central
1851	1861	1780	1881	123536	NBL	North
1761	1777	1700	1880	159905	NBL	Embleton
JOE						
1832	1921	ALL	1832	115355	ANS	Menmuir
JOHANNES LE CARPENTER						
1303	....	....	1303	112178	CON	Liskeard
JOHN						
1778	1794	1778	1794	158658	CMN	Llanarthne
1670	1702	ALL	1702	168718	CON	South East
....	....	1650	1760	174319	CON	Mevagissy
1629	1635	1500	1629	138614	CON	Perranuthnoe
....	1975	1890	1926	131938	GLA	Aberdare
1780	1848	1700	1780	124036	GLA	Bonvilston
1890	1975	1890	1926	131938	GLA	Britton Ferry
1879	1948	ALL	ALL	123013	GLA	Cardiff
1822	1845	ALL	1822	174777	GLA	Llanrhydian
1784	1942	1750	1942	158658	GLA	Llansamlet
1770	1890	....	....	117137	GLA	Llantrisant
1829	1909	1800	1992	171875	KKD	Auchencairn
1857	....	ALL	1879	123013	PEM	St Nicholas
JOHNCOCK						
1748	1806	1748	1807	144355	KEN	South
1838	1980	1700	1838	158232	KEN	Thanet
JOHNS						
ALL	ALL	ALL	ALL	108480	CON	ALL
1781	1992	1588	1781	137537	CON	Callington
1692	1992	....	1692	160652	CON	Callington
1850	1992	1700	1850	143936	CON	Gweek
1750	1820	1700	1800	107697	CON	Helston
1700	1900	1500	1700	136972	CON	Helston
1827	1890	1750	1900	148652	CON	Launceston
1796	1796	ALL	ALL	113360	CON	Perranzabuloe
1750	1900	1750	1850	160792	CON	Polperro
1650	1650	1670	1750	133450	CON	St Columb Major
1790	1850	....	....	165999	CON	St Ives
1851	....	....	....	168416	CON	St Winnow
1700	1900	1500	1700	136972	CON	Wendron
1850	1992	1700	1850	143936	CON	Wendron
1784	1821	....	....	159751	DEV	Bratton Clovelly
1850	1920	1700	1850	118915	DEV	Plymouth
1800	1900	1800	1850	160792	DEV	Plymouth
1848	1848	1800	1882	127361	DEV	Putford
1784	1992	1700	1784	123803	HAM	Crondall
1814	1841	1785	1992	158399	HAM	Crondall
1785	1874	1650	1950	158399	HAM	Crookham
1766	1800	ALL	ALL	169730	HAM	Dogmersfield
1814	1890	ALL	1992	159174	LND	East
1827	1827	1810	1850	125032	PEM	Lampeter
1782	1925	ALL	1782	137553	PEM	Pembroke Dock
1782	1925	ALL	1782	137553	PEM	Steynton
1700	1725	1750	1992	114901	SRY	Godalming
1675	1830	1675	1830	127655	WAR	Aston Cantlow
1675	1830	1675	1830	127655	WAR	Morton Bagot
1675	1830	1675	1830	127655	WAR	Ullenhall
1675	1830	1675	1830	127655	WAR	Wilmcote
1857	1900	....	....	173827	WOR	Stourbridge
JOHNSON						
....	....	ALL	ALL	137839	ALL	Name Study
1700	1900	1600	1700	113204	ANT	Lisburn
1790	1850	1750	1855	137758	AYR	Cumnock
....	....	....	1800	137456	BDF	Campton
1840	1860	1840	1860	177571	BKM	Upton Cum Chalvey
1730	1871	1650	1900	167002	CAM	Cambridge
1800	....	1750	1850	102016	CAM	Chatteries
1844	....	1775	1844	103772	CAM	Downham
?	?	....	....	159395	CAM	Isleham
1810	....	1750	1850	102016	CAM	Swanesey
1655	1940	....	....	128996	CAM	Thorney
1831	1853	1831	1853	111228	CHS	Ashley
1896	....	1600	1992	137812	CHS	Cheadle
?	?	?	?	137790	CHS	Chelford
1865	1943	....	....	147621	CHS	Everton
1831	1853	1831	1853	111228	CHS	Malpas
?	?	?	?	137790	CHS	Snelson
1884	1936	1884	1936	111228	CHS	Warmingham
1828	1852	1750	1828	118168	CMA	Whitehaven
1732	....	1700	1740	160873	CUL	Arthuret
1812	1860	1800	1900	119725	CUL	Kirkandrews On Esk
1813	....	ALL	1813	137715	CUL	Muncaster
....	....	1500	1900	137472	DBY	Derby
1650	1743	1550	1743	102830	DBY	Matlock
1820	1840	1700	1820	151300	DBY	North Wingfield
1795	1798	....	....	121290	DBY	Repton
1840	1880	ALL	1950	145254	DBY	Repton
1790	1820	1750	1850	111821	DBY	Shipley
1820	....	1800	1820	139483	DBY	Staveley

Known From	To	Researching From	To	Ref	Cty	Place
JOHNSON contd.						
1807	1880	1725	1807	105503	DEV	Brixham
1850	1900	1800	1900	162272	DEV	Torquay
1850	1900	1800	1925	126179	DOR	Corfe Castle
....	....	1700	1800	162620	DOR	???
1875	1911	1700	1875	115169	DUR	Darlington
1843	1850	?	1843	115169	DUR	Durham
1794	1839	ALL	1794	154563	DUR	Durham
1881	1992	ALL	1881	136875	DUR	Gateshead
1870	1900	1800	1992	162620	DUR	Gateshead
1898	....	ALL	1900	155608	DUR	Ryhope
1790	1890	ALL	ALL	122297	DUR	South Shields
1850	1992	1600	1770	132764	DUR	South Tyneside
1725	1755	1650	1725	108871	DUR	Stanhope
1784	1886	1550	1800	147265	DUR	???
1865	1912	....	....	160385	ENG	Birkenhead
1784	1784	1760	1785	147338	ERY	Bishop Burton
1698	1876	1600	1700	148954	ESS	Braintree
1894	1915	1860	1894	126519	GLA	Swansea
1838	1903	?	1838	136611	GLS	Thornbury
1780	1870	ALL	1800	142301	GLS	Upton St Leonard
1881	....	....	....	160385	HAM	Southampton
1792	1875	1812	1875	151750	HRT	Berkhampstead
1750	ALL	1775	1830	107379	HRT	Hemel Hempstead
1801	1865	1801	1880	144878	HRT	Kings Langley
....	....	1740	1830	130184	HRT	Stanstead Abbots
1890	1912	....	....	160385	IOM	Douglas
....	1881	1500	1881	175072	IRL	???
1800	1900	ALL	ALL	165743	KEN	North
1831	1893	1500	1870	157538	KEN	Bersted
1886	1946	ALL	ALL	118168	KEN	Bexley
1831	1893	1500	1870	157538	KEN	Maidstone
1774	1778	....	1774	177504	KEN	Meopham
1600	1992	ALL	ALL	137847	KEN	Minster
1713	1739	1690	1713	128724	KEN	Postling
1764	1838	1700	1764	170542	KEN	Wingham
....	1800	....	....	146811	LAN	Blackley
1833	1880	....	....	166189	LAN	Liverpool
1837	....	?	1840	103934	LAN	Manchester
1800	1850	1700	1800	142905	LAN	Manchester
1873	1899	1550	1880	147265	LAN	Manchester
1857	1945	1800	1857	176907	LAN	Manchester
1741	1789	1741	1789	111228	LAN	Pavyhulme
1870	1992	1870	1992	137804	LAN	Rossendale
1682	1729	ALL	ALL	141615	LAN	Scarisbrick
1750	1870	1536	1780	137804	LAN	Slaidburn
1830	1880	1800	1830	172006	LAN	St Helens
....	....	1700	1817	137626	LEI	Leicester St Mary
1637	1824	....	....	165999	LEI	Leicester
1813	1854	1649	1813	126454	LEX	Killeigh
1799	1833	1800	1840	159042	LIN	Baston
1798	1798	1750	1810	159042	LIN	Bourne
1784	....	....	....	129747	LIN	Claypole
1797	1841	ALL	1797	118362	LIN	Donington In Holland
1769	1836	1830	1992	117072	LIN	Halton Holegate
....	....	ALL	ALL	173088	LIN	Hatcliffe
1870	1904	1870	1904	102296	LIN	Louth
1893	1893	1890	1900	123250	LIN	Skirbeck
1814	1814	ALL	1814	131881	LIN	Sleaford
1800	1875	....	....	145394	LIN	Stamford
1850	1900	1800	1900	123145	LIN	Thornton Le Fen
1840	1880	1830	1900	120529	LIN	Washingborough
1767	1767	ALL	1770	113611	LIN	Winteringham
1845	1900	1845	1920	137758	LKS	Glasgow
1830	1865	ALL	1830	122572	LND	ALL
1873	1987	....	1873	137642	LND	Central
1873	1987	....	1873	137642	LND	North
1861	1900	1900	1992	138738	LND	Battersea
....	....	ALL	ALL	130818	LND	Camberwell
1765	1929	1700	1800	163562	LND	Poplar
1800	1992	1750	1800	122580	LND	Southwark
1800	1830	1700	1850	126268	LND	Stepney
1765	1929	1700	1800	163562	LND	Stepney
1813	....	1790	1820	163775	MDX	Bethnal Green
1860	1940	1860	1940	177571	MDX	Hillingdon
1500	1992	ALL	ALL	119857	MDX	London
1800	1992	ALL	ALL	137847	MDX	Poplar
1824	....	ALL	1824	151424	NBL	Berwick On Tweed
1841	1851	ALL	1841	154946	NBL	Halewhich
1750	1800	1750	1800	160121	NBL	Haltwhistle
1800	1992	1700	1800	160032	NBL	North Shields
1867	1896	1800	1900	144630	NFK	Bircham
1839	1884	1750	1839	137685	NFK	Gt Yarmouth

Known From	To	Researching From	To	Ref	Cty	Place
JOHNSON contd.						
....	....	1800	1850	119008	NFK	Horsey
1790	1900	1600	1790	101834	NFK	Methwold
1600	1992	....	....	169129	NFK	Tilney
1786	1992	1750	1992	148156	NTH	South
1800	1865	1800	1870	112925	NTH	Deasnhanger
1777	1850	1777	1850	135895	NTH	Northampton
1819	1916	1700	1840	117005	NTH	Towcester
1810	1880	1780	1880	130621	NTT	Blidworth
1810	1880	1691	1840	130621	NTT	Nottingham
1900	1992	1880	1930	137472	NTT	Nottingham
1840	1881	1880	1992	151300	NTT	Worksop
1750	1870	1536	1780	137804	NYK	Clapham
1750	1870	1536	1780	137804	NYK	High Bentham
1880	1927	1800	1880	125342	NYK	Masham
1784	1886	1550	1800	147265	NYK	???
1530	1875	1450	1600	137618	OXF	South West
1670	1750	....	....	119458	OXF	Ducklington
1480	1992	ALL	1480	118915	OXF	Standlake
1851	1930	1800	1850	151882	OXF	Thame
1780	1820	....	1820	102822	OXF	Witney
1800	1900	....	....	150371	ROX	Newcastleton
1800	1860	1750	1850	143502	SAL	Central
....	....	1750	1850	143502	SAL	Kinnersley
....	....	1700	1860	138738	SAL	Whitchurch
1680	1740	....	1680	101761	SFK	Bury St Edmunds
1811	1829	1750	1850	137685	SFK	Goriston With Southtown
1811	1829	1750	1850	137685	SFK	Gorleston
1730	1785	1700	1785	135941	SFK	Lakenheath
1750	1965	....	....	137820	SHI	Fetlar
1750	1992	1650	1992	104671	SHI	Lerwick
1720	1965	....	....	137820	SHI	Mid Yell
1760	1965	....	....	137820	SHI	North Yell
1758	1965	....	....	137820	SHI	Northmavine
1720	1965	....	....	137820	SHI	South Yell
1750	1992	1650	1992	104671	SHI	Unst
1750	1992	1650	1992	104671	SHI	Yell
....	....	1700	1831	126357	SLI	???
....	....	1775	....	174963	SOM	High Littleton
1700	1830	1650	1725	144606	SOM	Odcombe
1851	1992	1800	1851	123080	SOM	Radstock
1590	1660	....	....	142522	SRY	Burnham
1810	1834	1750	1860	155969	SRY	Camberwell
....	1920	1880	1950	137685	SRY	Croydon
1784	1809	ALL	1784	169730	SRY	Richmond
1900	1953	1900	1953	176176	SSX	Chichester
....	....	1800	ALL	173835	SSX	Coldwaltham
1760	1955	1736	1925	107166	SSX	Shipley
1750	1913	1650	1750	119164	SSX	Shipley
1750	1992	1700	1800	120049	STS	Audley
1880	1900	ALL	ALL	158941	STS	Burslem
1843	1862	1700	1900	175307	STS	Cheadle
1798	1911	1700	1850	155152	STS	Hanford
1790	1861	1700	1790	179116	STS	Ipstones
1798	1992	....	....	121290	STS	Rolleston
1750	1992	1700	1800	120049	STS	Stoke On Trent
1896	....	1600	1992	137812	STS	Stoke On Trent
1798	1992	....	....	121290	STS	Tutbury
1793	1804	1770	1850	167002	SXE	Burwash
1757	1790	ALL	1992	102245	WAR	Ansley
1834	1937	1800	1937	145807	WAR	Birmingham
1861	1936	1750	1861	153974	WAR	Coventry
1773	....	1600	1773	132802	WAR	Edgbaston
1710	1800	....	....	117560	WAR	Ryton On Dunsmore
1803	1872	1700	1881	165824	WIL	Trowbridge
1753	1810	ALL	1753	145211	WRY	Ferrensby
1750	1992	1600	1750	102342	WRY	Rawcliffe
1734	1775	1600	1700	154601	WYK	Batley
1841	1851	....	....	146811	WYK	Rishworth
1830	1850	1750	1830	151068	YKS	Clapham
1700	1800	....	....	167924	YKS	Crambe
1718	1760	1675	1992	114901	YKS	Garforth
1771	1824	1700	1850	131199	YKS	Hackness
1800	1860	1750	1880	138517	YKS	Halifax
1800	1845	1800	1900	131199	YKS	Harwood Dale
1760	1790	....	....	102946	YKS	Healaugh
1721	1794	1700	1750	173290	YKS	Horton In Ribblesdale
1850	1930	1800	1850	118915	YKS	Hull
1874	1900	1700	1874	115169	YKS	Loftus
1827	1900	1700	1827	178993	YKS	Meltham
1803	1826	....	....	141097	YKS	North Newbald
1845	1992	1845	1992	131199	YKS	Scarborough

Known From	To	Researching From	To	Ref	Cty	Place
JOHNSON contd.						
1818	1992	1700	1818	165379	YKS	Scarborough
1840	....	1800	1840	139483	YKS	Sheffield
1815	1992	1700	1815	111813	YKS	Silkston
....	....	1700	1800	171794	YKS	Sowerby
1840	....	1840	ALL	154946	YKS	Startforth
1760	1790	....	....	102946	YKS	Tadcaster
1815	1992	1700	1815	111813	YKS	Tadcaster
1790	1840	1760	1819	146897	YKS	Wakefield
1660	1702	1600	1660	174858	YKS	Willerby
....	....	1700	1800	171794	YKS	Yarm
1880	1910	1800	1890	146722	YKS	York
1925	1992	....	....	110159	???	ALL
1883	....	....	....	160385	???	Newcastle On Tyne
....	1859	ALL	1859	165263	???	???
JOHNSONS						
....	....	1800	1900	157201	NFK	Martham
JOHNSTON						
....	....	ALL	ALL	137928	ALL	Name Study
1871	1897	1750	1992	137863	ABD	Aberdeen
....	....	1750	ALL	149187	ABD	Lonmay
....	....	1750	ALL	149187	ABD	Old Deer
....	....	1860	ALL	149187	ANS	Dundee
1911	....	1700	1992	137855	ANT	Aghadrumglasny
1839	1992	1600	1839	178101	ANT	Kirkinriola
1815	1902	1700	1815	134732	ANT	Lough Neagh
1820	1850	1690	1850	158313	ARM	???
1868	....	1800	1868	101427	BAN	Deskford
1810	1864	1787	....	138401	CUL	Brampton
1810	1864	1787	....	138401	CUL	Heskett
....	....	1800	1860	148474	CUL	Kirklinton
1750	1800	1650	1750	118958	DFS	???
1911	....	1700	1992	137855	DOW	Aghadrumglasny
1756	1807	1700	1800	154881	DOW	Banbridge
1800	1992	1800	1992	106305	DOW	???
....	1820	1750	1850	138584	FER	Colmon Island
1843	1849	1841	1851	118974	FIF	Markinch
1816	1963	1700	1816	101737	FIF	St Monans
1760	1851	1600	1851	145289	HAM	Isle Of Wight
1861	1911	1838	1992	163244	LAN	Liverpool
1869	1900	1869	1900	177792	LAN	Liverpool
1832	1840	1820	1840	177792	LAN	Manchester
1820	1841	1820	1880	128856	LND	Park Street
1830	1897	1830	1930	160067	MDX	Edmonton
1811	....	....	....	148768	MDX	St Andrews
1800	1813	1800	1900	137898	MDX	St Bartholomew
1600	1800	1550	1800	154881	MLN	Corstorphine
1843	....	ALL	ALL	172057	MOG	Killeevan
1835	1992	1700	1835	169110	NBL	North Shields
1777	1855	1600	1855	148482	OKI	Birsay
1700	1740	ALL	1740	149063	ROX	Stichel
1866	1866	1750	1900	127302	SCT	Edinburgh
1760	1937	....	....	137936	SHI	Unst
1830	1900	1830	1900	146536	STI	Bannockburn
....	....	1700	1900	167223	STI	Falkirk
JOHNSTON-CAMPBELL						
?	?	?	?	147990	CUL	ALL
?	?	?	?	147990	DFS	ALL
JOHNSTONE						
1822	....	1780	1890	111848	AYR	Cumnock
1815	1820	1800	1830	105120	CLA	Doonas
1821	1850	1800	1821	142883	DFS	Hoddom
1769	1805	ALL	1992	119105	DFS	Johnstone
1861	1992	1800	1861	137944	DFS	Kirkton
1821	....	....	1821	148830	DFS	Lochmaben
1830	1940	1700	1900	108618	DFS	Rhonehouse
....	....	?	?	100471	DFS	???
1780	1880	1750	1800	111821	INV	Petty
1871	....	....	....	141267	IRL	Dundalk
1850	1870	1800	1900	111821	LKS	Bothwell
1815	1878	....	....	137952	LND	???
1832	....	....	....	111856	NFK	Stowbridge
....	....	ALL	1784	114308	NTH	Kislingbury
1840	1992	?	1840	111376	PEE	Peebles
....	....	1800	1900	102768	SCT	Oban
1753	1860	1700	1900	146536	STI	Muiravonside
1932	....	1932	....	148830	TYR	Grange School
1876	1950	....	1870	160431	???	Inverness
JOHSTONE						
1756	1864	ALL	1741	138401	CUL	Armathwaite
JOICE						
1860	1992	ALL	1860	130605	DUR	Winlaton
JOINER						
1818	1940	1800	....	109967	BKM	Chesham

Known From	To	Researching From	To	Ref	Cty	Place
JOINER contd.						
1786	1838	1786	1838	136808	HRT	Barkway
1860	1860	1700	1870	173460	KEN	East
JOINES						
1630	1790	1500	1790	138681	WAR	Alcester
JOINSON						
1760	1840	....	....	132225	CHS	Wallasey
JOINT						
1800	1900	1700	1800	101591	DEV	ALL
JOLIFFE						
1745	1780	1700	1750	117773	GLS	Bristol
1759	1786	1750	1800	126667	IOW	Newchurch
JOLIN						
ALL	ALL	....	....	153397	CHI	Jersey
1851	1992	1845	1992	153389	CON	ALL
1851	ALL	....	....	153397	HAM	Lymington
1798	1871	1740	1871	153389	HAM	Southampton
1740	1875	1740	1992	153389	JSY	ALL
1857	1992	1850	1992	153389	MDX	London
JOLLEY						
?	1905	....	....	127582	LAN	Warrington
JOLLIFFE						
1630	1846	....	....	121932	CON	Jacobstow
1670	1720	1630	1750	174599	DOR	Shaftesbury
1767	1838	1767	1930	156647	HAM	Arreton
1570	1795	1550	1800	171549	HAM	Isle Of Wight
1839	1881	1839	1900	147486	HAM	Portsea
1846	....	1840	1850	163775	MDX	Bethnal Green
1870	1870	1840	1900	120243	MON	Bedwellty
JOLLY						
1749	1850	ALL	1749	129062	ANS	Mill Of Aucheen
1870	1992	1750	1870	118052	ANT	Ballycastle
1810	1900	1700	1992	146943	BKM	Central
1841	1870	....	....	161675	CON	Gwennap
1755	1821	....	....	169129	NFK	Swaffham
1764	1764	....	....	135437	NFK	Wells
JONAS						
1785	1858	1700	1785	125458	CON	St Issey
1785	1858	1700	1785	125458	CON	Steval
1800	1899	....	....	137960	NFK	Nolt
JONE						
....	....	1800	1835	110515	WOR	???
JONES						
1835	1992	1700	1835	138355	AGY	Aberffraw
....	....	ALL	ALL	157864	AGY	Amlwch
1751	1880	ALL	ALL	152021	AGY	Brynsiencyn
1830	1885	1800	1900	168947	AGY	Holyhead
1757	1796	....	....	138401	AGY	Llanddaniel Fab
1785	1820	1750	1800	177024	AGY	Llaneillian
1806	1942	1700	1806	127116	AGY	Llanfaelog
1834	1992	1700	1834	138355	AGY	Llaniestyn
1860	1923	?	1860	127612	AGY	Redwharfe Bay
1835	1940	1800	1992	142743	AVN	Bristol
1615	1730	ALL	ALL	118869	BDF	Steppingley
1775	....	1775	....	176176	BKM	Hambleden
1718	1992	1650	1992	110906	BKM	Ludgershall
1810	1848	1700	1848	115681	BKM	Stoke Madeville
1760	1812	1760	1812	176958	BRE	Brecon
....	....	1700	1992	140759	BRE	Brilly
1760	1812	1760	1812	176958	BRE	Broynllis
....	....	1700	1800	179612	BRE	Capel Isaf
1711	1731	....	....	177008	BRE	Cricardan
1838	1851	....	1837	176729	BRE	Cricknowel
....	....	1700	1992	140759	BRE	Hay
1760	1812	1760	1812	176958	BRE	Llanddew
....	....	1700	1992	140759	BRE	Llangattock
....	....	1700	1992	140759	BRE	Llangynydwr
....	....	1700	1992	140759	BRE	Llengenny
1780	1992	1700	1780	118656	BRE	Newbridge On Wye
1841	1841	1800	1851	159743	BRE	Pont Nedd Fechan
....	....	1700	1992	140759	BRE	Pwllywrach
1880	1953	1800	1953	138045	BRE	Talgarth
....	....	1700	1992	140759	BRE	Talgarth
1760	1812	1760	1812	176958	BRE	Talgarth
1835	1938	1930	1938	138053	BRK	Maidenhead
1837	1869	....	....	138339	BRK	Reading
1907	1913	1850	1907	138053	BRK	Wantage
1820	1970	1750	1850	115614	CAE	Aberdaron
....	....	1800	....	118591	CAE	Aberdaron
1855	....	1827	1857	123129	CAE	Aberdaron
1860	1900	1800	1860	138207	CAE	Aberdaron
1840	1920	1800	1840	108448	CAE	Bangor
1890	1930	1700	1890	138207	CAE	Bardsey Isle
1748	1769	1700	1769	132217	CAE	Beddgelert

Known From	To	Researching From	To	Ref	Cty	Place
JONES contd.						
1870	1982	1870	1982	104027	CAE	Bethesda
1890	1940	1820	1890	138207	CAE	Bryncroes
....	....	1800	1880	138614	CAE	Criccieth
1830	....	....	....	152099	CAE	Llandegai
1902	1942	1750	1902	156248	CAE	Llandudno
1870	1982	1870	1982	104027	CAE	Llanfayrfechan
1860	1900	1800	1860	138207	CAE	Llanfimangel
1815	1867	1800	1830	115614	CAE	Nefyn
1830	1920	1700	1830	157147	CAE	Port Dinorwic
1793	1796	1700	1793	123129	CAE	Rhiw
1780	1840	1700	1780	151068	CAE	Tyddynelenddu
1840	....	....	....	146455	CAE	Tyddywhen
1835	1992	1750	1835	130249	CGN	Dihewid
1810	1815	1800	1840	158658	CGN	Llanarth
1770	1960	ALL	1750	179612	CGN	Llanbadarnfawr
1798	1992	ALL	1950	132217	CGN	Llanddewi Aberarth
1871	....	1800	1871	176931	CGN	Llanwenog
1900	1950	1700	1992	157392	CHS	Birkenhead
1750	1782	....	....	135437	CHS	Chester
1760	1775	....	....	135437	CHS	Christleton
1900	1992	1900	1992	138118	CHS	Crewe
1808	1992	1808	1941	163813	CHS	Nantwich
1855	1876	1830	1855	118435	CHS	Tranmere
1891	1939	1800	1900	162450	CMN	Llanartheney
....	....	1790	1845	118575	CMN	Llangadog
1879	....	ALL	1879	123013	CMN	Llangeler
?	?	?	?	138126	CMN	Llanllawddog
?	?	?	?	138126	CMN	Llanpumsaint
1828	1881	1820	1860	159743	CMN	Mydrim Llanwinio
1800	1825	1750	1830	158658	CMN	Talley
1817	1900	1800	1900	118540	CMN	Trelech Ar Bettws
1835	1992	ALL	1835	144053	CMN	???
....	....	1750	1860	143359	CON	Churchtown
1780	1911	1700	1800	176575	CON	Gwinear
1827	1875	1700	1846	156051	CON	St Agnes
1826	1885	1700	1826	133523	CON	St Dominick
1849	1967	1800	1849	160474	CWD	Chirk
1830	1992	1700	1900	142778	CWD	Dyffryn Ial
1790	....	1750	1840	122149	CWD	Llansilin
1772	1772	1700	1771	102830	DBY	Derby
1836	1856	1700	1856	172049	DBY	Derby
1813	....	ALL	ALL	147621	DEN	Bettws-Yn-Rhos
1780	1840	1700	1900	124427	DEN	Cerrigydrudion
1883	....	ALL	1889	147222	DEN	Colwyn Bay
1811	....	1700	1950	159719	DEN	Colwyn
1752	1844	1752	1844	104027	DEN	Glan Conwy
1750	1992	....	....	118672	DEN	Henllan
1700	1752	....	....	147885	DEN	Llanfair D C
1800	1992	....	....	118672	DEN	Llangernyw
1812	1837	....	1840	135275	DEN	Llangollen
1842	1875	1842	1861	102121	DEN	Llanrwst
1795	....	1700	1900	157147	DEN	Llanrwst
1800	1879	....	....	138401	DEN	Llansannan
1775	1992	....	....	138401	DEN	Llysfaen
1730	1880	1730	1880	104027	DEN	Rhyd
1883	....	ALL	1889	147222	DEN	Rhyl
1831	1992	....	1831	138320	DEN	Ruabon
1830	1870	1800	1830	177210	DEN	Ruthin
1800	1844	1800	1900	105732	DEN	Wrexham
1900	1930	1850	1900	150541	DEN	Wrexham
1835	1992	ALL	1835	144053	DEN	???
1726	1900	1600	1900	112976	DEV	Ottery St Mary
1746	1992	1600	1746	158496	DEV	Ottery St Mary
1861	1887	....	1861	145858	DEV	Plymouth
1861	1887	....	1861	145858	DEV	Teignmouth
1813	1880	1813	1880	129054	DFD	Abergwilli
1600	1992	ALL	1800	100536	DFD	Llandeilo
1813	1880	1813	1880	129054	DFD	Llanfihangel-Ar-Arth
1813	1880	1813	1880	129054	DFD	Llanpumpsaint
....	....	1750	1800	176621	DOR	Poole
....	....	ALL	1835	170135	DOR	Weymouth
1887	1960	1850	1887	102881	DUR	Hartlepool
1880	1917	1880	....	140635	DUR	Sunderland
1775	1992	....	....	138401	FLN	Abergele
1850	1992	1800	1850	126322	FLN	Bagillt
1800	1850	ALL	1992	164984	FLN	Bagillt
1700	1880	....	....	147885	FLN	Bodfari
1800	1850	ALL	1992	164984	FLN	Caerwys
1865	1865	1500	1865	110310	FLN	Holywell
1800	1824	ALL	ALL	124982	FLN	Holywell
1780	1830	1750	1900	129607	FLN	Hope
1834	1897	1700	1950	159719	FLN	Llanasa

Known From	To	Researching From	To	Ref	Cty	Place
JONES contd.						
1871	1947	1700	1871	115185	FLN	Mold
1823	....	1700	1900	152714	FLN	Mold
1841	1939	1700	1950	159719	FLN	Rhuddlan
1775	1992	....	....	138401	FLN	St George
....	....	1747	....	138401	FLN	Whitford
1861	1871	ALL	1992	159174	GLA	Aberavon
1824	....	1700	1850	138428	GLA	Aberfan
1855	1861	ALL	1992	159174	GLA	Bridgend Park
1911	1992	1800	1911	164879	GLA	Caerphilly
1820	1900	ALL	1820	135062	GLA	Cardiff
1890	1910	1900	1992	166901	GLA	Cardiff
....	....	1854	1904	140759	GLA	Dowlais
1830	1900	1830	1900	118575	GLA	Godre'r Graig
1861	1881	1841	1881	159743	GLA	Hirwaun
1810	1992	ALL	1810	142034	GLA	Llangiwc
1780	1992	1780	1992	152129	GLA	Llanrhydian
1793	1851	ALL	1992	159174	GLA	Llantrisant Hendy
1830	....	ALL	1992	159174	GLA	Llantwit Fardre
1861	1985	1861	1992	159743	GLA	Llwydcoed
1800	1850	1800	1850	147575	GLA	Lougher
1930	1956	....	....	138215	GLA	Merthyr Tydfil
1850	1992	1700	1850	138525	GLA	Merthyr Tydfil
1802	....	1780	1830	169625	GLA	Merthyr Tydfil
1864	1864	1850	1880	178004	GLA	Merthyr Tydfil
....	....	1800	1900	179612	GLA	Merthyr Tydfil
1730	1992	....	....	129232	GLA	Neath Valley
1824	....	1700	1850	138428	GLA	Neath
1750	1850	1750	1850	151297	GLA	Neath
1840	1915	1800	1900	131431	GLA	Pendoylan
1870	1900	....	....	117137	GLA	Pontlotyn
1890	....	....	....	161136	GLA	Port Talbot
1824	....	1700	1850	138428	GLA	Rheola
1880	1950	1870	1950	138479	GLA	Treorchy
1752	1828	1557	1851	142859	GLS	Avening
1774	1900	1600	1774	149888	GLS	Bitton
1864	1864	ALL	1992	125113	GLS	Bream
1835	1940	1800	1992	142743	GLS	Bristol
1880	1950	1880	1950	162140	GLS	Bristol
1915	1992	....	....	138339	GLS	Cheltenham
1800	1830	1800	1830	147575	GLS	Coleford
....	....	1735	1833	101478	GLS	Deerhurst
1710	1720	1650	1750	155896	GLS	Gloucester
1840	....	1800	1840	147478	GLS	Newnham
1890	1992	1500	1890	134600	GLS	Shirehampton
1880	1992	ALL	1880	160938	GLS	Tetbury
....	....	1855	1865	149187	GNT	Chepstow
1847	....	....	....	129097	GNT	Llanfreckua
1843	1850	....	....	129097	GNT	Llangatock
....	....	1850	1960	133604	GNT	Llantarnam
....	....	1750	1820	117129	GNT	Raglan
1820	1900	1730	1850	176524	GSY	St Peter Port
1830	1992	1700	1830	110701	GYN	Trefrien
1920	1992	1700	1920	118702	GYN	Tremadoc
1807	1871	1700	1807	149918	HAM	Bramshaw
1924	1935	1920	1938	138053	HAM	Dummer
1924	1935	1920	1938	138053	HAM	Odiham
1800	1840	1650	1840	158542	HAM	Ringwood
1600	1900	1600	1900	150479	HAM	Romsey
1818	1850	1700	1850	171182	HAM	Rowner
1851	1992	....	....	176729	HEF	Craswell
1780	1915	1700	1900	131547	HEF	Leintwardine
1880	1890	1800	1890	138045	HEF	Leintwardine
1830	1900	1800	1880	162191	HEF	Madley
1842	1851	....	1837	176729	HEF	Peterchurch
1816	1970	1800	1970	145009	HEF	Walterstone
1780	1850	1780	1992	133450	HRT	Broxbourne
1768	1800	1600	1800	132993	IOW	Carisbrooke
1768	1800	1600	1800	132993	IOW	Eatcombe
1800	1847	1600	1850	147265	IRL	Leitrim
1740	1810	ALL	1810	115282	KEN	East
1830	1992	....	....	118370	KEN	Canterbury
1829	....	....	....	138061	KEN	Lewisham
1891	1992	....	....	121061	LAN	Aldham
1832	1992	1680	1832	138029	LAN	Chorley
1840	....	1820	1900	146102	LAN	Chorlton
1861	1957	1860	1992	144460	LAN	Droylsden
1832	1992	1680	1832	138029	LAN	Leyland
1865	1865	1500	1865	110310	LAN	Liverpool
1851	1861	1750	1900	114456	LAN	Liverpool
1838	1992	1838	1838	145580	LAN	Liverpool
1853	....	1700	1950	159719	LAN	Liverpool
1789	1878	ALL	1789	164623	LAN	Liverpool
1856	1890	1850	....	156019	LAN	Manchester

Known From	To	Researching From	To	Ref	Cty	Place
JONES contd.						
1876	1992	1700	1876	172588	LAN	Manchester
1840	1904	1840	1904	176958	LAN	Manchester
1853	1960	1800	1860	138304	LAN	Preston
1849	1967	1800	1849	160474	LAN	Rainhill
1800	1900	1750	1850	166901	LAN	Salford
1845	1867	1800	1867	178004	LAN	Salford
1850	1960	1730	1992	176524	LAN	St Helens
1895	....	....	....	146455	LAN	Toxteth Park
1860	....	1700	1860	130435	LEI	Wogston
....	....	1845	1992	141399	LND	East
1860	1992	ALL	ALL	157864	LND	Bromley By Bow
1870	....	1850	1900	124796	LND	Peckham
1832	1859	....	1832	142166	LND	Shoreditch
1860	....	ALL	ALL	156558	LND	Shoreditch
1820	1881	1800	1820	169803	LND	St George In East
1870	....	1700	1870	138436	MDX	Bethnal Green
1825	1871	ALL	1825	169730	MDX	Chelsea
1856	1879	1800	1950	160903	MDX	Harrow
1850	1950	1700	1900	138371	MDX	London
1815	1940	1780	1992	173096	MDX	London
1856	1879	1800	1950	160903	MDX	Marylebone
....	....	ALL	ALL	151998	MDX	Paddington
1750	1860	1700	1900	138517	MDX	St Georges Court
1880	1900	1860	1900	124605	MDX	St Pancras
1874	....	1860	1880	163775	MDX	Stepney
1856	1879	1800	1950	160903	MDX	Weald
1800	1870	1800	1870	135941	MDX	Westminster
1810	....	1750	1850	102016	MDX	???
1838	1992	1750	1875	138185	MDX	???
1850	1930	1850	1930	111538	MER	Bala
1829	1829	1820	1850	132217	MER	Dolgellau
1820	....	....	....	167037	MER	Festinog
1799	1992	1700	1800	149241	MER	Gwern Yr Ewig
1799	1992	1700	1800	149241	MER	Llanfor
1799	1992	1700	1800	149241	MER	Llangower
1800	1850	1800	1850	111538	MER	Llanowchllyn
1840	1960	1650	1840	158992	MER	Machynlleth
1920	1992	1700	1920	118702	MER	Maewtwrog
1830	1944	1750	1850	115614	MER	Talsarnau
1872	....	ALL	ALL	138533	MGY	Berriew
1800	1865	....	....	167649	MGY	Berriew
1840	1924	1800	1850	176125	MGY	Gayford
....	....	1700	1800	167649	MGY	Guilsfield
1780	1992	1700	1780	118656	MGY	Llandinam
1820	1874	ALL	1820	158445	MGY	Llanfihangel
1827	1855	1600	1827	156914	MGY	Llanrhaedr
1846	1923	1700	1950	159719	MGY	Mallwyd
1550	1992	1500	1900	154881	MGY	Montgomery
1810	....	ALL	ALL	172057	MOG	???
1720	1800	1650	1992	133450	MON	Abergavenny
1820	1853	1700	1900	164070	MON	Abersychan
1904	1908	1904	1908	138398	MON	Beaufort
....	....	1770	....	174963	MON	Caldicot
1840	1900	1750	1840	105740	MON	Chepstow
1828	1992	....	1828	138320	MON	Llandinam
1810	....	1538	1828	118893	MON	Llanfrechfa
1888	....	1888	....	159913	MON	Monmouth
1780	1827	1827	1900	118583	MON	Newport
1920	....	....	....	138215	MON	Newport
1828	....	1538	1828	118893	MON	Panteg
1900	1980	1900	1980	138045	MON	Rhymney
1855	1890	1850	1900	178004	MON	Risca
....	....	....	....	163775	MON	Swansea
1847	1850	1847	1850	102121	MON	Tredegar
1837	....	1830	1860	169625	MON	Tredegar
1800	1880	1700	1900	156442	MON	Varteg
1750	1840	....	....	101028	NFK	Blofield
1826	1841	....	....	101028	NFK	Lt Plumstead
1861	1992	ALL	1861	115878	NTH	Kings Sutton
1830	1850	1790	1830	149462	NTH	Preston Capes
1737	1797	1710	1800	107360	NTH	Wappenham
1718	1900	1650	1992	110906	OXF	West
1800	1850	1700	1800	174513	OXF	Alvescot
1761	....	1700	1800	143693	OXF	Aston Rowant
1814	....	....	1820	171441	OXF	Headington
1700	1800	1600	1700	174513	OXF	Shilton
1765	1800	1650	1800	143693	OXF	Stokenchurch
1907	1913	1850	1907	138053	OXF	Wantage
....	....	1700	1930	119520	PEM	Lawrenny
....	....	1740	1790	157643	POW	Llangadfan
1785	1992	ALL	1785	100536	POW	Sennybridge
1818	1871	1818	1891	138398	RAD	Abbey Cum Hir
1770	....	1700	1800	176877	RAD	Beguildy

Known From	To	Researching From	To	Ref	Cty	Place
JONES contd.						
1819	1834	1800	1851	176877	RAD	Bleddfa
1789	1880	1600	1789	156914	RAD	Bryngwyn
1780	1806	1700	1841	176877	RAD	Cwmeuddwr
1832	....	....	....	140473	RAD	Knucklas
1861	1961	1600	1861	156914	RAD	Llanbadarn Fawr
1799	1840	1750	1840	160873	RAD	Llangunllo
1776	1825	1700	1800	176877	RAD	Nantmel
1881	1898	1881	1898	138398	RAD	St Harmon
....	....	1500	1992	119792	SAL	ALL
1632	1770	....	....	117404	SAL	Broseley
1758	1852	1700	1758	169021	SAL	Chirbury
1800	1830	1750	1850	131431	SAL	Claverley
1812	1918	1800	1845	108510	SAL	Dawley
....	....	1858	....	140767	SAL	Dawley
1745	1960	1500	1745	125415	SAL	Dudleston
1850	1926	1989	1992	114979	SAL	Hadley
1815	....	1690	1815	132802	SAL	Ironbridge
1825	1992	1800	....	105139	SAL	Linley
....	....	ALL	ALL	138274	SAL	Little Drayton
1820	1953	1760	1800	135763	SAL	Loppington
1835	1944	....	....	110515	SAL	Ludlow
....	....	ALL	ALL	138274	SAL	Market Drayton
1820	1871	....	....	121061	SAL	Oswestry
....	....	1810	1841	111414	SAL	Pontesbury
1790	1840	1790	1840	140724	SAL	Shrewsbury
1825	1940	1800	1885	103128	SAL	Wellington
1950	1992	1600	1950	138274	SAL	Wem
1780	1992	1600	1840	113654	SAL	Wrockwardine
1860	....	....	1860	111767	SAL	???
1835	1835	....	....	135437	SOM	Bath
1830	1870	1830	1870	142018	SOM	Bath
1855	1881	1790	1855	173371	SOM	Bath
1835	1940	1800	1992	142743	SOM	Bristol
1800	1867	1800	1940	166898	SOM	Chilton Upon Polden
1650	1710	1630	1720	142018	SOM	Merriott
1825	1891	ALL	1825	178195	SOM	Nether Stowey
1682	1785	1600	1682	153281	SOM	North Petherton
1600	1900	....	....	108677	SOM	Shepton Mallet
1846	1891	ALL	1846	178195	SOM	Weston Super Mare
1725	1736	1650	1725	108413	SOM	Yatton
1800	1830	1750	1800	132640	SRY	Bagshot
1834	....	?	1840	103934	SRY	Kennington
1841	1964	1700	1841	169730	SRY	Wandsworth
1840	1950	1800	1920	115681	SRY	Woking
1750	1860	1710	1860	105333	SSX	Brighton
1750	1860	1710	1860	105333	SSX	Laughton
1750	1860	1710	1860	105333	SSX	Uckfield
1832	1930	....	....	136824	STS	Bilston
1860	1992	1700	1860	171174	STS	Bloxwich
1846	ALL	ALL	1865	116734	STS	Gomal Wood
....	....	1800	1849	160474	STS	Kingswinford
1919	....	1919	1938	138053	STS	Litchfield
1819	1900	1819	1900	138118	STS	Madeley
1790	1900	1750	1830	138487	STS	Rowley Regis
1846	ALL	ALL	1865	116734	STS	Sedgley
1826	?	....	....	102121	STS	Stafford
1827	1890	1700	1820	133167	STS	Tipton
1820	1850	....	....	156485	STS	Trescott
1820	1870	1820	1870	167924	STS	Wenesbury
1800	1992	1700	1992	165344	WAR	Aston
1800	1950	1750	1890	103721	WAR	Birmingham
1846	ALL	ALL	1865	116734	WAR	Birmingham
1833	1900	1750	1832	131245	WAR	Birmingham
1820	1900	ALL	1820	135062	WAR	Birmingham
1863	1972	1850	1900	163546	WAR	Birmingham
1800	1960	1750	1960	151513	WAR	Grendon
1600	1800	....	....	100420	WAR	Meriden
1830	1960	1700	1830	146110	WAR	Newbold On Avon
1840	1903	1840	1903	140724	WAR	Warwick
1800	1900	....	....	167924	WAR	Yardley
1770	1785	1750	1800	158658	WIL	Bradford Upon Avon
1727	1765	1700	1780	170348	WIL	Broad Blunsdon
1802	1992	ALL	1802	123749	WIL	Cherhill
1776	1880	1700	1900	177210	WIL	Crudwell
1776	1880	1700	1900	177210	WIL	Hankerton
1803	1822	1800	1860	158658	WIL	Holt
1705	1758	1680	1760	142018	WIL	Malmesbury
1800	1875	....	....	110124	WIL	Marlborough
1803	1850	ALL	1850	158445	WIL	Melksham
....	....	1700	1800	110124	WIL	Mildewhall
1766	1883	....	....	115606	WIL	Overton
1875	1960	....	....	110124	WIL	Swindon
1795	1815	1600	1800	153591	WLS	Brymbo

Known From	To	Researching From	To	Ref	Cty	Place
JONES contd.						
1795	1815	1600	1800	153591	WLS	Bwlch
1795	1815	1600	1800	153591	WLS	Denbeigh
1795	1815	1600	1800	153591	WLS	Flint
1795	1815	1600	1800	153591	WLS	Gwyn
1818	1860	....	....	140317	WLS	Llangollen
1868	....	1868	1992	137308	WLS	Treherbert
1802	1908	ALL	ALL	149683	WOR	South
1750	1780	1700	1800	159107	WOR	Chaddesley Corbett
1890	1963	1858	1890	174475	WOR	Cotshill
1900	1992	1500	1900	119792	WOR	Dudley
....	1830	1830	1880	120219	WOR	Kidderminster
1770	....	....	1800	160873	WOR	Martley
1878	1945	1850	1950	177989	WOR	Oldbury
1800	1850	1750	1800	138339	WOR	Pershore
1890	1963	1858	1890	174475	WOR	Ruberty
1830	1870	1800	1850	120286	WOR	St Clement
1822	1900	1780	1820	108103	WOR	Upton On Severn
1772	1800	1700	1772	159158	WOR	Wick
1880	....	....	....	140635	YKS	ALL
1870	1885	1870	1885	135275	YKS	Doncaster
1824	....	1750	1900	159468	YKS	Halifax
1874	1877	1700	1874	138673	YKS	Oulton
1841	1861	ALL	1841	145335	YKS	Sheffield
1870	1950	1750	1950	115622	YKS	West Riding
....	....	ALL	1820	138169	YKS	York
....	....	1852	....	149497	???	Birmingham
1891	1961	....	....	149497	???	Kidderminster
1860	....	....	1860	111767	???	???
JONHES						
1850	1850	1800	1850	126586	MDX	London
JOPE						
....	....	ALL	ALL	101591	DEV	ALL
JOPLEN						
1825	1850	ALL	ALL	143332	BRK	Aldermaston
JOPLING						
....	....	ALL	ALL	157163	ALL	Name Study
1812	1865	1750	1850	141461	DUR	North West
1800	1950	1600	1800	128376	DUR	Stanhope
JORDAN						
1817	....	1700	1750	143693	BKM	Beaconsfield
1784	1789	1700	1800	143693	BKM	Penn
1800	1845	....	1845	171441	BRK	Buckland
1863	....	1840	1870	171441	BRK	Stanford In The Vale
1740	1940	....	....	128996	CAM	Thorney
1802	1890	1750	1802	102598	DEV	Brixham
1857	1881	1700	1857	103411	DEV	North Lew
1832	....	1700	1900	166359	DEV	Starcross
1790	1830	1800	1900	176281	ESS	Stonden Massey
1665	1814	1600	1750	175218	EYK	Grindale
1746	1992	1700	1992	138584	FER	Aghaveagh
1850	1992	ALL	1850	136875	GLS	Sandford
1874	1989	1700	1874	145459	HAM	Southampton
1640	1700	ALL	1640	131059	KEN	Ash By Ridley
1785	1785	1700	1900	178322	KEN	Ash
1750	1850	1750	1850	154903	KEN	Deal
1832	1862	1700	1832	128465	KEN	Gravesend
?	?	?	?	166642	KEN	Mersham
1843	1992	1700	1843	158917	KEN	Milton Next Sittingbourne
....	....	1700	1880	138614	LAN	Blackburn
1793	1839	....	....	121142	LAN	Liverpool
1736	1886	1600	1735	138592	LEI	Groby Cum Ratby
1897	1992	....	....	138592	LEI	Leicester
1800	1860	1650	1890	154598	LEI	Leicester
1862	1992	1862	1992	138606	LND	ALL
1868	?	....	....	120340	LND	Shoreditch
1632	1757	1600	1640	134627	OXF	Lower Heyford
1850	1992	ALL	1850	136875	OXF	Sandford
1632	1757	1600	1640	134627	OXF	Upper Heyford
1798	1900	ALL	ALL	171727	SAL	Bucknell
1845	1958	1820	....	120634	SRY	Lambeth
....	....	ALL	ALL	138576	SYK	Rotherham
1100	1400	....	....	100420	WAR	Meriden
1837	1992	1837	1992	138606	WAR	Wolverhampton
1802	1851	1790	1881	165824	WIL	Keevil
1830	1992	1600	1800	169773	WIL	Semington
1780	1840	1700	1780	156140	WOR	Dudley
1771	1865	1700	1900	135704	WOR	Hampton
1858	1900	1858	1900	145319	WOR	Stourbridge
1850	1900	1700	1992	121762	YKS	ALL
1800	1880	....	....	142522	YKS	Beeford
1890	1950	1600	1890	144045	YKS	York
JORDEN						
ALL	1765	....	....	105368	IRL	Dublin
....	....	ALL	1900	165646	STS	Tipton
JORDON						
1714	1714	....	....	127426	KEN	Lenham
JORY						
1830	1850	1850	1992	133493	CON	Gwennap
1800	1992	1700	1800	133493	CON	Helston
1700	1890	1700	1890	154628	CON	St Kew
JOSE						
1849	1866	1830	1992	117609	CON	Constantine
....	....	1700	1850	147044	CON	Gulval
....	....	1700	1850	147044	CON	Madron
....	....	1700	1850	147044	CON	Paul
....	....	1700	1850	147044	CON	St Just In Penwith
JOSEPH						
ALL	ALL	ALL	ALL	138622	ALL	ALL
1666	....	1660	1700	178845	CON	Stithians
1786	1865	....	....	167533	GLA	Merthyr Tydfil
1720	1957	....	....	138630	HEF	Horsewayhead
1720	1957	....	....	138630	HEF	Staunton On Arrow
1858	1858	1800	1875	178004	WLS	South
JOSEY						
1817	1860	1700	1900	137022	BRK	Inkpen
1867	1884	1860	1940	137022	BRK	Reading
1885	1914	1880	1940	137022	OXF	Sonning Common
JOSLIN						
1700	1850	....	....	156531	DEV	Ashreigney
1860	1992	1700	1860	138649	DEV	Plymouth
1811	1940	1700	1811	107794	ESS	Billericay
1804	1992	1700	1804	138657	ESS	Cressing
1811	1940	1700	1811	107794	ESS	Gt Burstead
1822	1850	1700	1822	118362	NFK	Norwich
JOSLING						
....	....	ALL	ALL	138665	ALL	Name Study
ALL	ALL	ALL	ALL	138665	ALL	ALL
1840	1992	1750	1840	150703	ESS	Little Waltham
1767	....	1650	1767	100013	ESS	Pleshey
JOUCHIN						
....	....	1780	1992	118923	IOM	Douglas
JOULE						
1796	1900	1700	1800	159166	DBY	North
JOULES						
1820	1850	....	....	118354	YKS	Hull
JOUSSE						
1792	1837	....	....	101028	MDX	London
JOUXSON						
1670	1750	....	....	166995	SOM	Thorn Falcon
JOWERS						
1881	1940	ALL	1881	178195	KEN	London
1881	1940	ALL	1881	178195	MDX	London
1881	1940	ALL	1881	178195	SRY	London
JOWETT						
1840	....	ALL	ALL	138533	DBY	Bluntisham
1796	1871	1750	1900	147958	LAN	Cockerham
1796	1871	1750	1900	147958	LAN	Garstang
1792	1857	1600	1805	145971	WYK	Halifax
1770	1981	1700	1770	169935	YKS	Haworth
1805	1870	1750	1805	176451	YKS	Holbeck
JOWITT						
1796	1992	ALL	1796	169943	YKS	Haworth
1849	1992	1700	1849	138673	YKS	Oulton
JOWSEY						
....	....	1836	1838	104442	MDX	St Giles
JOY						
?	?	....	....	154113	BKM	Langley
1790	1900	1700	1900	107352	DEV	Alverdiscott
....	....	1500	1850	166863	DEV	Kingsbridge
1840	1870	1840	1910	135429	ESS	Bethnal Green
1780	1850	1750	1992	135429	KEN	Headcorn
1830	1880	1750	1992	135429	KEN	Linton
1830	1880	1750	1992	135429	KEN	Loose
?	?	?	?	166642	KEN	???
1820	1920	1840	1910	135429	MDX	Islington
....	....	1830	1870	166863	SOM	Bristol
1889	1893	....	1903	153982	SRY	Rotherhithe
1700	1800	....	....	156922	YKS	Arksey
JOYCE						
1745	1940	....	....	128996	CAM	Thorney
....	....	1750	1775	177229	DEV	Kings Nympton
1870	1955	ALL	ALL	178152	HAM	Southampton
1854	1870	ALL	ALL	178152	HAM	Wherwell
1741	1762	....	1741	108839	HUN	St Meots
1798	1889	1700	1798	110639	IRL	Galway

Known From	To	Researching From	To	Ref	Cty	Place
JOYCE contd.						
....	1800	....	1800	108197	LND	Fulham
....	....	ALL	ALL	100153	MAY	Westport
1770	1780	1700	1770	124427	NBL	Newcastle
1550	1700	1550	1700	100927	NTH	Hargrave
1750	1900	1600	1992	167592	SAL	Whitchurch
1754	1856	1730	1880	107573	SOM	Mells
JOYES						
1830	1950	1700	1830	164178	SXW	Central
JOYNER						
1780	1850	....	....	132756	BKM	Worminghall
1750	1870	1700	1900	177180	HRT	Kings Walden
ALL	1755	....	....	132756	OXF	Charlton On Otmoor
ALL	1755	....	....	132756	OXF	Launton
JOYNES						
1665	1840	1500	1840	102830	NTT	ALL
1739	1992	1739	1992	138703	NTT	Newark
1690	1950	1600	1850	160083	NTT	Nottingham
1880	1930	1880	1930	138681	WAR	Kings Norton
1791	1860	1690	1890	138681	WOR	Inkberrow
1840	1950	1800	1900	160083	YKS	Sheffield
JOYNSON						
1790	1805	1700	1790	114472	CHS	Barrow
1830	1860	1800	1830	117196	CHS	Crowton
1840	1930	....	....	132225	CHS	Wallasey
JOYS						
1650	1820	ALL	ALL	106313	BRK	Stanford In The Vale
JUBB						
1793	1992	....	....	160253	WYK	Penistone
1772	1992	1250	1772	138711	YKS	Huddersfield
....	....	....	1830	114812	YKS	Shefield
JUBY						
1810	1860	1700	1810	171859	SFK	Bury St Edmunds
JUDAN						
1860	....	....	....	135488	SSX	Brighton
JUDD						
1848	1874	1818	1992	104299	DUR	Barnard Castle
1700	1992	1600	1992	138746	ESS	ALL
1843	1860	1880	1900	176044	ESS	Havering
1828	1992	1600	1992	138746	HRT	ALL
1818	....	ALL	1848	104299	HRT	Bishops Stortford
1862	1957	1830	1862	137944	LEI	Leicester
1768	?	ALL	1768	171476	LEI	Leire
....	....	1800	....	117714	LND	West
1842	1988	1830	1992	118842	MDX	North
1842	1988	1800	1842	118842	MDX	Tottenham
1760	1801	1650	1760	167533	NFK	Norwich
1842	1919	1700	1842	138568	NFK	Thetford
1799	1841	1799	1841	108251	OXF	Witney
....	....	1550	1800	176230	SFK	Brandon
1815	1963	1600	1815	165697	SFK	Mildenhall
1815	1828	1600	1992	138746	WIL	Salisbury
1881	1920	1880	1920	108251	WIL	Swindon
....	....	1700	1750	168777	WIL	Winterslow
1874	1915	1848	1992	104299	YKS	Hunslet
1793	1900	1700	1800	118516	???	Birmingham
JUDE						
1688	1782	....	1800	137405	CAM	South
1760	1840	1760	1850	169641	NBL	Newcastle
JUDGE						
1700	....	1650	1750	124796	BKM	Hughenden
1800	1900	1700	1900	177180	HRT	Bovingdon
1830	1968	....	....	105759	IRL	Sligo
1851	....	....	1851	146935	IRL	???
1830	1860	1750	1960	100382	KEN	Rolvenden
JUDGES						
....	....	ALL	ALL	138754	ALL	Name Study
JUDKINS						
1824	1824	ALL	ALL	143537	LND	ALL
1840	1992	ALL	1850	111678	NTH	Central
JUDSON						
1841	1841	1600	1841	156914	SAL	Oswestry
1800	1890	1700	1800	116815	YKS	Vale Of Pickering
JUFF						
1830	1992	ALL	1830	111880	MDX	Stamford Hill
JUFFS						
1770	1800	1770	1800	138762	BDF	Chalgrave
1750	1900	1750	1900	138762	BDF	Houghton Conquest
1775	1850	1775	1850	138762	BDF	Steppingley
1830	1900	1830	1900	138762	BDF	Woburn
1689	1750	1650	1750	138762	GLS	Childs Wickham
1725	1750	1700	1800	138762	GLS	Chipping Camden
1850	1900	1850	1900	138762	GLS	Morton In Marsh

Known From	To	Researching From	To	Ref	Cty	Place
JUFFS contd.						
1750	1800	1750	1800	138762	GLS	Stretton On Fosse
1750	1850	1750	1850	138762	HRT	Harpenden
1790	1870	1790	1850	138762	LND	Rotherhithe
JUKES						
1790	1850	1600	1850	110329	DOR	North
1660	1992	ALL	ALL	147133	DOR	Bourton
....	....	1500	1800	166863	DOR	Holwell
....	....	ALL	ALL	108065	LND	Shoreditch
1660	1992	ALL	ALL	147133	LND	???
1915	1965	....	....	150762	MON	Newport
1841	1851	1851	1900	139173	SAL	Hopesay
1813	1813	1813	1840	139173	SOM	Cutcombe
1660	1992	ALL	ALL	147133	SOM	???
1768	1790	....	....	115606	WIL	East Knoyle
1660	1992	ALL	ALL	147133	WIL	???
JULL						
1700	1992	1600	1700	117110	KEN	Canterbury
1834	....	1600	1834	117234	KEN	Lenham
JULYAN						
1850	1900	1850	1900	129151	AYR	???
1850	1900	1850	1900	129151	HEF	Yarpole
1850	1900	1850	1900	129151	YKS	Thirsk
JUMP						
1814	1840	1750	1840	145750	LAN	Tarlton
JUNG						
?	?	?	?	138622	ALL	ALL
JUNIPER						
....	....	ALL	ALL	138770	ALL	Name Study
1500	1992	ALL	ALL	138770	ALL	ALL
1700	....	ALL	1700	131059	ESS	Bocking
JUP						
1600	1700	ALL	ALL	138789	SSX	Nuthurst
JUPE						
1765	1780	1710	1820	178330	DOR	Bourton
1744	....	....	....	129747	IOW	Arreton
1742	1850	....	1850	102601	IOW	Godshill
1771	1774	....	....	129747	IOW	Godshill
1831	1949	1700	1831	100110	KEN	Maidstone
1600	1800	ALL	ALL	138789	SSX	Nuthurst
JUPP						
....	....	ALL	ALL	113468	ALL	Name Study
....	....	ALL	ALL	103543	CAM	Peterborough
....	....	ALL	ALL	103543	CAM	Wisbech
....	....	ALL	ALL	103543	LND	Paddington
1874	....	1870	1880	138797	LND	Westminster
1845	1881	1845	?	110922	SRY	Putney
1874	....	1870	1880	138797	SRY	Southwark
1845	1845	1800	1880	110922	SSX	ALL
1780	1890	1700	1800	176745	SSX	West
1750	1860	1500	1750	138797	SSX	Hurstpierpoint
1600	1940	ALL	ALL	138789	SSX	Nuthurst
1825	1870	ALL	ALL	130664	SSX	Pulborough
JUPPE						
1600	1850	ALL	ALL	138789	SSX	Nuthurst
JURY						
1718	1860	1718	1992	114596	DEV	Ash Regney
JUST						
1732	1772	1700	1732	176885	NFK	North Tuddenham
JUSTICE						
1750	1850	....	....	103764	BKM	Marsh Gibbon
1768	1815	1768	1815	175420	BRK	Padworth
1840	1850	1800	1860	173452	GLS	Cheltenham
1540	1599	1540	1599	143162	KEN	???
JUTSON						
1800	....	1700	1950	141151	KEN	Whitstable
JUTSUM						
1753	1992	1600	1900	151033	DEV	ALL
1810	1860	1600	1992	151033	LND	ALL
JUTTON						
....	....	ALL	ALL	151467	ALL	ALL
KALER						
1885	....	1800	....	119776	???	Leamington
KALEY						
1816	1852	1800	1900	146269	LND	Westminster
KANDOW						
1800	1992	1700	1992	158364	ANS	Aberlemno
KANE						
1816	1992	ALL	1934	138819	T&W	Newcastle Upon Tyne
....	....	1800	1860	161659	WEX	Dunmore
1600	1992	ALL	1992	168696	WIL	ALL
1895	1985	1860	1895	161659	WMD	ALL
KARBY						
1820	....	1700	1820	169935	MDX	Stratford

Known From	To	Researching From	To	Ref	Cty	Place
KARN						
1800	1980	ALL	ALL	140740	GLS	Slimbridge
KARNEE						
....	1813	ALL	1813	175080	DEV	Stoke Damerel
KARSLAKE						
1550	1992	1500	1700	135429	ALL	ALL
KASSELL						
....	....	ALL	ALL	138843	ALL	Name Study
KATES						
....	1817	1600	1850	175641	SFK	Cowlinge
KATLINE						
1710	....	ALL	....	104515	LIN	Grantham
KAVANAGH						
1860	1920	1700	1992	113778	CMA	Egremont
1876	1900	1800	1876	103322	YKS	Tadcaster
KAVANNAGH						
1848	1900	1700	1992	131601	LAN	Liverpool
KAWRDIN						
1230	1394	1230	1400	156809	CHS	Carden
KAY						
1720	1980	ALL	1720	103438	BAN	Fochabers
1810	1992	ALL	1810	110000	CHS	Dukinfield
1820	1960	ALL	ALL	106658	CHS	Macclesfield
1860	1890	1840	1890	117145	CHS	Stalybridge
1800	1840	1780	1800	117196	CHS	Weaverham
1820	1960	ALL	ALL	106658	CHS	Wheelock
1800	1900	1800	1992	139203	ESS	Great Leighs
1882	....	1809	....	127647	KKD	Kelton
1850	1992	1800	1900	108359	LAN	Bolton
1808	1992	ALL	1808	110000	LAN	Bolton
1880	....	....	....	116211	LAN	Bolton
1720	1901	....	....	138851	LAN	Bolton
1872	1940	1860	1940	168947	LAN	Bolton
1779	1992	ALL	1779	110000	LAN	Bury
1938	1992	1875	1938	174998	LAN	Bury
1750	1900	1750	1900	125237	LAN	Darwen
1800	1880	1880	1992	162256	LAN	Darwen
1720	1901	....	....	138851	LAN	Horwich
1840	1910	1900	1930	117129	LAN	Liverpool
....	....	1700	1850	117129	LAN	Preston
1860	1890	1840	1890	117145	LAN	Stalybridge
1775	1820	1750	1775	132268	LAN	Turton
1580	1850	1850	1992	162256	LAN	Turton
1850	1900	....	....	126497	LAN	Wigan
1650	1700	1650	1992	139203	LEI	Glenfields
1890	1992	1700	1992	110663	LKS	Glasgow
1849	1863	1800	1900	139114	LKS	Glasgow
1840	....	1800	1900	139114	PER	Comrie
1800	1850	1813	1850	126276	WRY	Kirkburton
1707	1774	1670	1710	170348	YKS	Doncaster
1750	1800	1700	1800	165662	YKS	Ecclesfield
1800	1900	....	....	131474	YKS	Leeds
1741	....	1600	1741	116637	YKS	Long Marston
1700	1800	1600	1992	139203	YKS	Richmond
1760	1829	1700	1760	156302	YKS	Ripon
1750	1800	....	....	102946	YKS	Thurscoe
1741	....	1600	1741	116637	YKS	York
1800	1900	1800	1992	139203	YKS	York
KAYE						
1856	1900	1820	1900	170992	CHS	Wincham
1804	1919	1700	1805	111198	WYK	Huddersfield
1561	1707	....	....	168513	YKS	Almondbury
1733	1887	1700	1740	170348	YKS	Almondbury
1790	1840	1750	1870	153737	YKS	Dalton
1700	1760	....	....	123595	YKS	Huddersfield
1887	1930	1750	1888	171034	YKS	Huddersfield
1727	1810	1690	1730	170348	YKS	Kirkheaton
1823	....	ALL	1824	151424	YKS	Leeds
KAYLER						
1880	....	....	....	104337	MDX	???
KEADIE						
1723	1723	ALL	1723	131881	FIF	Kirkaldy
KEAL						
1851	1900	....	....	177687	LIN	Withern
KEALING						
1854	....	1750	1900	179078	SAL	Tong Norton
1894	1896	....	....	112909	SRY	Southwark
KEAN						
1848	....	1700	1880	115967	MLN	Edinburgh
KEANE						
....	....	1800	1868	161659	WEX	Dunmore
1873	1900	ALL	ALL	116823	YKS	Boosbeck
KEANEY						
1855	1880	1850	1900	128988	LET	Kiltyclogher
KEAP						
1822	1886	1750	1822	174211	LAN	Briercliffe
1822	1886	1750	1822	174211	LAN	Burnley
KEAR						
1711	1992	1600	1750	163740	GLS	Newland
KEARLEY						
1700	1840	1700	1840	138894	HAM	Sopley
KEARNEY						
1789	1926	1750	1992	127264	LIM	Limerick
KEARSE						
1700	1850	1800	1850	141682	OXF	Witney
KEARSEY						
....	....	ALL	ALL	138908	ALL	Name Study
1827	1992	1700	1827	138916	KEN	Erise
KEARSLEY						
1650	1850	....	....	177318	LAN	Daene
KEARTON						
ALL	ALL	ALL	ALL	105724	ALL	ALL
....	....	1700	1850	101273	WIL	Calne
1659	1659	1600	1700	123250	YKS	Askrigg
KEAST						
1845	1932	ALL	1880	114030	CON	Lanreath
1831	1923	1700	1855	156051	CON	St Neot
KEAT						
1879	1889	1866	1896	108251	KEN	Greenwich
KEATING						
....	1890	?	?	121223	CHS	Birkenhead
1883	1959	1837	1883	173576	CHS	Broadbottom
1830	1935	....	....	135666	GLA	Mountain Ash
KEATINGS						
?	?	?	?	112437	LKS	Shotts
KEATLEY						
1801	1870	1780	1822	147311	NYK	Scarborough
KEATS						
ALL	ALL	ALL	ALL	132330	ALL	ALL
....	....	ALL	1992	104795	LND	Hammersmith
....	....	ALL	1992	104795	LND	Kensington
1844	1844	ALL	1844	108553	SSX	Sidlesham
1770	1820	....	....	113514	WIL	North Bradley
KEATT						
1691	1691	ALL	1691	154563	DOR	Wyke Regis
KEAY						
1780	1830	....	....	132225	CHS	Wallasey
1853	1853	1800	1853	144177	FIF	Ceres
KEBBY						
1807	1850	1807	1850	170119	HAM	Ibsley
1719	1992	1500	....	138134	SOM	Charlton Adam
KEDDIE						
1810	1851	1841	1891	146560	FIF	Auchtermuchty
1785	1785	....	....	168203	FIF	Largo
1785	1809	....	....	168203	FIF	Scoonie
1810	1851	1841	1891	146560	PER	Perth
KEDGE						
1841	1970	ALL	ALL	138924	BDF	Bedford
1790	1930	1790	1930	138924	BDF	Clophill
1851	1900	ALL	ALL	138924	BKM	Chalfont Sr Peter
1570	1904	1570	1871	138924	BKM	Denham
1861	1871	ALL	ALL	138924	BRK	Windsor
1851	1992	ALL	ALL	138924	CAM	Cambridge
1801	1851	1841	1871	138924	ESS	Beaumont
1851	1890	1841	1890	138924	ESS	Colchester
1841	1890	1790	1890	138924	ESS	Gt Oakley
1915	1978	ALL	ALL	138924	KEN	Canterbury
1861	1871	1861	1871	138924	KEN	Romney Marsh
1670	1975	ALL	ALL	138924	LND	ALL
1909	1992	1841	1871	138924	MDX	Brentford
1839	1841	1841	1871	138924	MDX	Hillingdon
1841	1871	1841	1871	138924	MDX	Uxbridge
1840	1871	1800	1871	138924	NFK	Bracon Ash
1801	1841	1841	1871	138924	NFK	Fakenham
1780	1987	1700	1987	138924	NFK	Mulbarton
1861	1952	1780	1960	138924	NFK	Norwich
1861	1987	1841	1944	138924	NFK	Outwell
1861	1987	1841	1944	138924	NFK	Upwell
1820	1841	1841	1871	138924	NFK	Wood Dalling
1766	1981	1750	1871	138924	NFK	Wymondham
1627	1700	1627	1750	138924	SFK	Boxford
1900	1907	1900	1907	138924	SFK	Felixstowe
1841	1861	1841	1861	138924	SFK	Hadleigh
1570	1861	1560	1871	138924	SFK	Kersey
1840	1921	1840	1930	138924	SFK	Layham
1841	1871	1841	1871	138924	SFK	Polstead
1841	1987	1841	1980	138924	SRY	Kingston
1841	1965	1841	1871	138924	SRY	Richmond

Known From	To	Researching From	To	Ref	Cty	Place
KEDWARDS						
1896	1992	1896	1992	101451	WAR	Birmingham
1747	1896	1747	1896	101451	WOR	Evesham
KEEBLE						
1814	1955	1700	1814	145823	ESS	Walton On The Naze
1721	1744	....	....	129747	SFK	Debenham
KEECH						
1798	1798	1700	1800	120081	DOR	South
1811	....	....	....	119911	DOR	Abbotsbury
1811	....	....	....	119911	DOR	Bridport
1783	1825	1700	1785	138932	DOR	Toller Porcorum
1853	1853	1853	1861	138932	DOR	West Knighton
KEEDWELL						
1860	....	....	....	172723	SOM	Dundry
KEEGAN						
1817	1880	1700	1817	120707	DUB	Droghida
KEEL						
1750	1880	1750	1890	120472	BRK	Reading
1812	1812	....	....	120472	BRK	Wokingham
KEELER						
1804	1885	1750	1900	156698	KEN	Elham
1880	1905	....	....	133779	KEN	Wootton
1816	1816	ALL	1816	108197	NFK	Worstead
KEELEY						
1750	1850	1700	1800	120529	BRK	Hurley
1802	....	1802	1871	171905	IRL	Cork
1859	....	....	....	124559	LND	Lambeth
1851	....	....	....	171905	MDX	St Giles
1862	....	....	....	124559	MDX	Westminster
KEELING						
1775	1850	1750	1800	170852	NTT	Worksop
1867	1907	1837	....	120634	SRY	Lambeth
....	....	1740	1780	170852	STS	Colwych
1691	1777	....	....	117404	STS	Ellenhall
1789	1910	1780	1912	165441	STS	Hanley
....	....	1853	1923	173355	WAR	Birmingham
1600	1700	....	....	100420	WAR	Meriden
KEELY						
1720	1760	1650	1800	139386	SFK	Burgate
KEEMISH						
1750	1880	1780	1850	102016	CAM	Cambridge
1710	1750	1650	1710	102016	HAM	Cheriton
1710	1750	1650	1710	102016	HAM	Winchester
....	....	1780	1820	102016	MDX	Marylebone
KEEN						
1739	....	1650	1750	143693	BKM	Radnage
1851	1881	....	....	139157	BKM	Thame
1890	....	....	1890	171441	BKM	West Wycombe
1809	1815	1500	1810	104825	BKM	Wingrave
1710	1780	1650	1710	132268	GLS	Addlestrop
1750	1790	1600	1800	140066	GLS	???
1843	1925	ALL	ALL	151777	LND	Bethnal Green
1829	1834	1750	1900	124907	LND	Camberwell
1791	1870	1790	1870	145238	LND	Holborn
1810	1862	....	1810	101761	MDX	East London
1863	1992	1700	1992	113638	MDX	London
1898	1944	1800	1898	127981	MDX	London
1800	1860	1800	1860	167924	MDX	Pancras
....	....	1590	1823	139157	OXF	Clinnor
1750	1850	1750	1850	167924	PEM	Tenby
1600	1845	ALL	1992	168696	WIL	ALL
....	....	1800	ALL	164615	WIL	Westbury
KEENAN						
1856	1992	1600	1856	131261	DOW	Portaferry
....	....	1800	1900	133043	FER	Enniskillen
....	....	ALL	ALL	115533	LAN	Failsworth
KEENE						
1790	1880	1700	1790	133507	BKM	Dinton
1701	1782	1650	1850	155896	GLS	Gloucester
1800	1850	1700	1800	138959	HAM	Farleigh
1800	1850	1700	1800	138959	HAM	Wallop
1860	....	....	....	165395	LND	ALL
1860	1881	....	....	173932	LND	???
1850	1875	1800	1850	143332	SRY	Chertsey
1890	1992	....	....	138959	SRY	Hook
1890	1992	....	....	138959	SRY	Kingston
1850	1910	1910	1992	138959	SRY	Mainey
1850	1910	1910	1992	138959	SRY	Oatlands
1890	1992	....	....	138959	SRY	Surbiton
KEENS						
....	....	1845	1880	161659	BDF	Everholt
KEEP						
1327	1960	1327	1960	138975	BDF	North
1826	1900	1600	1826	131261	BDF	Marston Moretaine

Known From	To	Researching From	To	Ref	Cty	Place
KEEP contd.						
1270	1412	1270	1450	138975	BKM	East
1820	1900	1800	1930	138967	BRK	ALL
1219	1880	1200	1600	138975	BRK	East
1800	1930	1750	1930	138967	BRK	Hurst
1750	1850	1600	1850	126845	BRK	???
1740	1770	1700	1770	125032	HAM	Kingsclere
1700	ALL	....	....	153397	HAM	Strathfield Saye
1202	1850	1200	1600	138975	LIN	South
1800	1830	1800	1860	144657	LIN	Lincoln
1800	1930	1800	1930	138967	LND	???
1370	1512	1370	1600	138975	NFK	West
1404	1920	1408	1880	138975	NTH	South
1750	1800	1750	1800	144657	NTT	Shelton
KEERS						
1793	1949	ALL	1793	104221	NBL	Wallsend
KEET						
1796	1818	ALL	ALL	170437	HAM	Portsmouth
1830	1884	ALL	ALL	170437	LAN	Liverpool
KEETCH						
1881	1992	....	....	138991	LND	East
....	....	1700	1881	138991	SOM	Staplegrove
KEETLEY						
1819	1860	1815	1870	139017	LIN	Claypole
1830	1992	1830	1992	139017	LIN	Lincoln
1759	1810	1750	1820	139017	LIN	Stapleford
1800	1898	1800	1900	151599	NTT	Nottingham
KEETON						
....	....	1900	1919	111414	CAM	Doddington
1853	1890	1890	1992	139025	YKS	Sheffield
KEEVILL						
1770	1992	1500	1770	139033	SOM	Midsomer Norton
1770	1992	1500	1770	139033	WIL	Beckington
1770	1992	1500	1770	139033	WIL	Holcombe
KEFFORD						
1803	1866	ALL	1900	151815	CAM	Arrington
1872	1932	ALL	1872	100072	CAM	Sawston
KEGGIN						
1800	1850	1700	1800	139106	IOM	???
1800	1850	1700	1800	139106	LAN	Greater Manchester
KEHOE						
1933	....	1925	1935	163775	WEX	Wexford
KEIGHLEY						
1856	1856	1700	1856	100110	WYK	Bradford
1807	1866	1750	1807	179086	YKS	Bradford
1746	1769	1622	1851	170267	YKS	Pudsey
KEIGWIN						
1588	1656	1560	1588	102571	CON	Madron
KEIL						
1780	1801	1780	1801	178357	ROC	Fearn/tain
KEILL						
1900	1992	1900	1992	178357	CHS	ALL
1885	1992	1885	1992	178357	LAN	ALL
1835	1845	1835	1845	178357	LAN	Liverpool
KEILLOR						
1800	1900	1700	1900	138517	???	Carnoustle
1800	1900	1700	1900	138517	???	Forfarshire
KEILOR						
1750	1992	....	....	134805	LND	East
....	....	ALL	1750	134805	YKS	???
KEILTY						
....	....	1800	1900	145343	NIR	ALL
KEIR						
....	....	ALL	1741	119326	PER	Tomtaiwan
KEIRL						
1840	1862	1700	1840	153281	SOM	North Petherton
KEITH						
1860	1992	....	....	151130	ANS	Dundee
1150	1588	1100	1600	154881	AYR	Galstoun
1890	1910	....	....	157937	CMA	Barrow In Furness
....	....	1650	1850	119784	DNB	Cardross
1890	1910	....	....	157937	LAN	Barrow In Furness
1860	1865	ALL	1860	157937	STS	Dudley
KELBRICK						
1690	1800	1600	1850	166081	LAN	Hambleton
1800	1868	1760	1800	128333	LAN	Lancaster
KELCEY						
1677	1900	1550	1677	169676	KEN	Eythorne
KELL						
1875	1930	1600	1875	127507	ANT	Glynn
1820	1992	1700	1820	160571	DUR	Tanfield
1837	1900	1837	1881	175188	DUR	Wingate
KELLAGHER						
1850	1890	....	....	136492	IRL	???

Known From	To	Researching From	To	Ref	Cty	Place
KELLAGHER contd.						
1850	1890	....	....	136492	LTN	Edinburgh
KELLAN						
1814	1814	1700	1850	121568	SOM	Kingston St Mary
KELLAND						
1853	1944	ALL	1867	169374	JSY	St Helier
1825	1860	....	....	165999	LEI	Leicester
1750	1820	....	....	165999	SOM	Taunton
KELLAWAY						
1811	1936	1780	1811	107654	DEV	Bridestow
1840	1880	....	1840	179213	DEV	Bridestowe
1840	1920	....	....	155683	DEV	Bristol
1800	1840	1700	1850	155683	DEV	Tavistock
1860	1960	....	....	164593	???	Bristol
KELLEHER						
....	....	1700	1840	130931	COR	Millstreet
KELLET						
1858	1891	1700	1992	173053	DUR	West Auckland
1858	1891	1700	1992	173053	DUR	Woodland
1691	1843	ALL	ALL	104191	IRL	Clones
KELLETT						
1832	1960	1800	1992	142875	CAV	???
1900	1992	ALL	1900	112771	LAN	Dalton In Furness
KELLEWAY						
1678	1843	....	....	174270	DOR	Hampreston
1678	1843	1650	1678	174289	DOR	Hampreston
1717	1717	1600	1717	174289	HAM	Christchurch
1698	1717	1500	1698	174270	HAM	Christchurch
KELLEY						
1797	1850	ALL	1797	133957	DOR	Poole
1810	1890	1800	1890	139068	LND	ALL
KELLIE						
....	....	1750	ALL	149187	MOR	Urquhart
KELLINGLEY						
1597	1635	1560	1635	160849	LIN	Ulceby
KELLOCK						
1816	?	1700	1900	122394	DFS	Morton
1856	1878	1700	1900	122394	DFS	Sanquhar
1818	1829	1700	1900	122394	DFS	Thornhill
KELLOND						
1797	....	1797	1808	169374	DEV	Charleton
1828	1844	1844	1880	169374	DEV	Sherford
KELLOW						
1844	1844	ALL	1844	109258	WIL	Shrewton
KELLOWAY						
1830	1860	ALL	1830	108197	SRY	Brixton
KELLY						
1865	1865	1800	1865	179116	AYR	Tarbolton
1850	1890	1750	1850	108413	DOW	Downpatrick
....	....	ALL	1808	119326	ELN	Prestonpans
1711	1822	1567	1890	141291	IOM	Rushen
1860	1940	1836	1950	117145	IRL	Kildare
1854	1881	ALL	ALL	106216	IRL	???
1813	1830	1813	1830	171751	IRL	???
1870	1920	1850	1980	135631	LAN	Liverpool
1860	1960	1840	1880	165093	LAN	Liverpool
1850	1868	....	....	166189	LAN	Liverpool
....	....	1835	1880	165093	LAN	Manchester
1861	....	ALL	ALL	172057	LIM	Killglass
1818	1840	1800	1891	115886	LND	St Pancras
1858	1915	1820	1835	133531	LND	Stepney
....	1846	....	....	140767	MAY	Ballina
....	....	1700	1840	130931	MAY	Swinford
1803	1992	1700	1803	101419	MDX	ALL
....	....	ALL	ALL	121363	MON	Newport
1885	1885	1880	1880	171751	NBL	Cullercoates
1840	1884	1940	1992	171751	NBL	Felton
1885	1885	1880	1880	171751	NBL	Tynemouth
....	....	1830	1880	147613	NIR	Newtown Breda
?	1825	1700	1825	134732	NIR	???
1850	1970	1700	1850	112526	OFF	Clonfanlough
1833	1833	1800	1833	179116	RFW	Neilston
1846	....	1850	....	140767	STS	Cheadle
1857	1992	ALL	1857	118362	TYR	Dromore
1870	1930	1800	1992	113123	WAR	Birmingham
1880	1900	1800	1880	100978	WIG	Stranraer
1848	1868	1868	1891	104043	WOR	St Martins
1868	1992	1868	1992	140767	YKS	Leeds
1850	1903	....	....	131717	???	Drogheda
KELMAN						
....	....	ALL	ALL	139076	ALL	Name Study
KELSALL						
1794	1864	?	1794	121665	CHS	Ashton Upon Mersey
1600	1805	1590	1790	112364	CHS	Northenden

Known From	To	Researching From	To	Ref	Cty	Place
KELSALL contd.						
1819	1838	?	1819	121665	LAN	Stretford
KELSEY						
1790	1799	1600	1799	130230	DEV	Plymouth
1760	1826	....	1760	124524	ERY	Cottingham
1820	1850	1700	1790	130230	KEN	ALL
1820	1850	1851	1992	130230	KEN	Deptford
1850	1950	1800	1900	114383	LIN	Gainsborough
....	....	....	1820	156833	YKS	Hull
KELWAY						
1650	1980	1600	1992	104671	CON	Falmouth
KEMBER						
1798	1820	1800	....	156027	HAM	???
KEMBLE						
1616	1680	....	....	142522	BRK	Reading
KEMBREY						
1788	1924	1788	1992	109436	GNT	Wolvesnewton
KEMISH						
1600	1773	1500	1600	127116	HAM	Ampfield
KEMP						
....	....	ALL	ALL	139130	ALL	Name Study
....	....	1100	1900	139130	ALL	ALL
1750	1881	1600	1750	126357	ABD	Rayne
1550	1650	1500	1800	177180	BKM	Swanbourne
1776	1802	ALL	ALL	119253	CHS	Baguley
1650	ALL	....	....	103381	CON	ALL
1843	1870	1750	1843	168173	CON	Camborne
1900	1960	1800	1900	173835	CON	St Ithians
1887	1992	1700	1887	139122	CUL	Workington
1767	1879	1532	1767	139130	DEV	Bampton
1900	....	1850	1910	109363	DEV	Brixham
1650	ALL	....	....	103381	DEV	Tamerton Folliot
1878	1899	ALL	1878	167959	ESS	Prittlewell
1872	1899	ALL	1872	167959	ESS	Romford
1870	1989	1880	1940	139130	GLA	ALL
1808	1896	1808	1896	170143	HAM	Bramshott
1808	1896	1808	1896	170143	HAM	Liss
1920	1945	1530	1992	145769	KEN	ALL
1866	....	....	1866	133434	KEN	Eltham
1794	1881	1750	1794	151327	KEN	Gravesend
1761	1806	1700	1761	137383	KEN	Newington Next Hythe
1756	1872	1650	1756	145823	KEN	Romney Marsh
1552	?	?	?	166642	KEN	Whitstable
1552	?	?	?	166642	KEN	Wye
1815	1930	1815	1850	169528	LAN	Liverpool
1800	1850	ALL	ALL	169528	LAN	Preston
1800	1890	1800	1910	173622	LND	Hackney
1850	1992	1700	1850	157872	LND	Islington
1807	1850	1807	1907	127183	LND	Marylebone
1770	1802	....	1770	142166	LND	Stepney
1830	1906	....	....	127779	MDX	Clerkenwell
1850	1915	1800	1850	174920	MDX	Harlesden
1858	1893	1750	1857	131245	MDX	Poplar
1869	1880	1800	1960	128961	NFK	Great Yarmouth
1814	1839	....	....	151548	NFK	Yarmouth
1745	1884	1700	1745	178500	NTT	Greasley
1809	1861	1800	1900	101508	NTT	Halam
1789	1850	1600	1790	124176	NTT	Kinoulton
1809	1861	1800	1900	101508	NTT	Southwell
1799	....	1800	1900	139114	PER	Locherlour
1773	1836	ALL	1773	129283	SFK	Oulton
1767	1879	1532	1767	139130	SOM	Chipstable
1825	1945	1825	1945	153834	SSX	East
1628	1747	1600	1750	170143	SSX	Chichester
1681	1730	1660	1750	170143	SSX	Heyshott
1763	1791	1500	1763	110310	SSX	Mountford
1726	1900	1726	1900	170143	SSX	Rogate
1750	1850	1700	1900	162736	SSX	Ticehurst
1726	1900	1726	1900	170143	SSX	Trotton
1790	1900	1650	1790	139106	SSX	???
1800	1930	....	....	139130	WLS	Llantwit Major
1841	1992	1700	1841	168408	WYK	Batley
1841	1992	1700	1841	168408	WYK	Dewsbury
1800	1820	1750	1800	119032	YKS	Full Sutton
KEMPSEY						
1685	....	1600	1685	166723	LND	London Wall
KEMPSHALL						
....	....	ALL	ALL	125873	ALL	Name Study
....	....	ALL	ALL	125873	ALL	ALL
1650	1992	1650	1992	141380	ALL	ALL
KEMPSON						
1770	1900	1700	1770	132268	GLS	Addlestrop
1848	1900	1840	1880	155683	SRY	Wonersh

Known From	To	Researching From	To	Ref	Cty	Place
KEMPSTER						
1650	1800	1500	1850	177180	BKM	Wingrave
1750	1820	ALL	1750	125393	HRT	Great Gaddesden
1860	1992	....	....	125393	SOM	Compton Pauncefoot
1860	1992	....	....	125393	SOM	North Cadbury
1841	1890	1700	1992	170518	WIL	Highworth
KEMPTON						
1864	1992	1772	1992	142360	BRK	Maidenhead
1790	1853	1700	1992	142360	CAM	Ely
1836	1940	....	....	128996	CAM	Thorney
1880	1900	....	....	149667	SOM	Shepton Mallett
KEMSLEY						
1805	....	ALL	ALL	151327	KEN	Higham
1880	1992	1700	1880	122963	LND	Marylebone
1880	1992	1700	1880	122963	LND	Paddington
KEN						
1766	1800	1650	1766	138584	LAN	Eccles
KENCH						
1890	1938	1850	1900	108731	LND	West
1830	1850	1830	1850	174386	MDX	Paddington
1779	1862	1770	1865	135933	OXF	Charlbury
1658	1857	1658	1960	132705	WAR	Dunchurch
KENCHINGTON						
....	....	1789	1944	159484	HAM	Fordingbridge
KENDAL						
1760	1820	....	....	140554	DOW	Newcastle
1645	1720	1640	1750	117706	YKS	Leeds
KENDALL						
1750	1850	1600	1750	158046	CON	East
1800	1992	1760	1800	108359	CON	Helston
1777	1814	1800	1900	178845	CON	St Breock
1839	1992	1700	1839	170976	CON	St Clumb Major
1760	1800	1700	1760	108359	CON	St Tudy
1599	1992	....	1599	100900	CON	???
1880	1900	1920	1992	178845	GLA	Mountain Ash
1710	1766	1770	1800	178845	GLS	Cheltenham
1756	1851	1756	1881	139157	HAM	Ringwood
....	....	1850	1880	171948	LAN	Backbarrow
1690	1717	1542	1690	141291	LAN	Gleaston
1790	1836	1790	1850	100862	LND	East
1848	1890	....	....	139157	LND	Kensington
....	1788	ALL	1788	162507	LND	Lincoln Inn Fields
....	....	1850	1900	129275	LND	Woolwich
1200	1900	....	....	108677	WAR	Austrey
....	....	1840	....	174564	WOR	Droitwich
1816	1858	1700	1890	102660	WRY	Idle
1816	1858	1700	1890	102660	WRY	Thackley
1764	1821	1700	1900	167487	YKS	Halifax
1784	1858	1784	1858	150827	YKS	Huddersfield
1877	1881	1800	1900	119008	YKS	Ilkley
1877	1881	1800	1900	119008	YKS	Nessfield
KENDERDINE						
1570	....	....	....	156809	DBY	Aston On Trent
1699	....	....	....	156809	DBY	Shottle
1587	1749	1587	1800	156809	SAL	Lydbury North
1564	1875	1564	1875	156809	STS	Stafford
KENDREW						
1870	1992	1800	1870	110442	WYK	Leeds
1773	1872	1700	1900	116742	YKS	Leeds
KENDRICK						
ALL	1840	....	....	137545	ALL	ALL
1780	1992	ALL	ALL	154806	CHS	Birdenhead
1780	1992	ALL	ALL	154806	CHS	Woodch
1840	....	ALL	ALL	137545	HEF	Pyke Cum Lyde
1900	1950	1900	1980	126144	KEN	Gravesend
1841	1871	1871	1950	138541	STS	Walsall
1911	1944	1874	1944	139173	STS	West Bromwich
1874	1874	1800	1900	139173	WOR	Dudley
1874	1874	1800	1900	139173	WOR	Netherton
1888	1888	1874	1888	139173	WOR	Oldswinford
KENE						
1500	....	....	....	100536	KEN	???
KENELY						
1830	....	....	....	155225	COR	???
1859	....	....	....	155225	LND	Camberwell
1881	....	1861	1886	155225	LND	City
1861	....	....	....	155225	LND	Deptford
KENEWELL						
ALL	....	....	....	123641	NTT	Worksop
KENINGALE						
....	....	ALL	ALL	166464	ALL	Name Study
1761	1953	1700	1760	166464	SFK	Stoke By Nayland
KENLYSIDE						
1841	1881	1841	1941	120987	CUL	Penrith
KENNARD						
1800	1992	....	1900	171441	KEN	Mid
1863	?	ALL	ALL	158070	SSX	Seaford
KENNAUGH						
1877	1932	ALL	1877	111619	IOM	Patrick
KENNEDY						
1800	1992	1700	1992	158364	ANS	Aberlemno
1880	1920	1600	1880	127507	ANT	Rasharkin
1731	1766	....	....	168203	CAI	Latheron
....	....	1780	1820	170348	CHS	Congleton
1835	1992	1700	1835	126985	CLA	Ennistimon
1842	1892	1700	1842	135151	CUL	Dalston
1732	1782	1730	1790	176621	DBY	Bradley
1800	1850	1750	1850	126802	DOR	Wareham
1854	1992	1800	1854	139203	DUR	Sunderland
1711	1711	1650	1750	176621	ESS	Rocheford
1711	1741	1650	1750	176621	ESS	South Ockenden
1860	1933	1800	1992	139181	GAL	Dunmore
1860	1933	1800	1992	139181	GAL	Tuam
....	....	1800	1876	132489	IRL	Cork
1920	1984	1700	1920	115584	IRL	Neenagh
1854	1992	1800	1854	139203	IRL	???
1829	....	1800	1829	139483	IRL	???
1871	1992	ALL	1871	170704	IRL	???
1830	1950	1865	1992	117110	KEN	Canterbury
1789	1830	1770	1830	176621	KEN	Teston
....	....	1831	1869	116912	KEN	???
1880	1930	1850	1880	139483	LAN	Liverpool
1888	1992	ALL	ALL	139181	LAN	Newton
1863	1863	1700	1870	173037	LDY	ALL
1862	1921	....	1862	151270	LIM	Doon
1834	1880	1700	1900	162620	NBL	North Shields
1765	1767	ALL	1790	113611	NFK	East Dereham
1730	1805	ALL	1810	113611	NFK	Watton
1758	1898	1700	1898	108154	PER	Dull
1771	1900	....	....	141798	ROX	Hawick
....	1698	1600	1700	176621	SCT	Edinburgh
1813	....	1813	....	116793	SCT	Glasgow Gorbals
1815	....	....	....	170348	STS	Stone
1849	1900	1700	1849	143812	TIP	Lorrha
1800	1897	1700	1950	118680	TIP	???
1876	1992	1860	1876	132489	???	Bristol
KENNEL						
1803	1992	....	1802	129461	LND	Westminster
KENNELL						
1853	1944	1750	1944	122475	MDX	London
KENNER						
1823	1866	....	....	139211	CON	Lawhitton
1790	1830	....	....	139211	CON	North Hill
1666	1689	....	....	139211	CON	South Petherwen
1583	....	....	....	139211	CON	St Keverne
1683	....	....	....	139211	CON	Tywardreath
1823	1866	....	....	139211	DEV	Brixham
1552	....	....	....	139211	DEV	Parkham
1818	1855	1700	1855	178012	LND	St Pancras
KENNERLEY						
1870	1927	1800	1870	162795	CHS	Northwich
1812	1900	ALL	ALL	127094	KEN	Dartford
KENNETT						
1800	1830	ALL	ALL	139181	HEF	Allensmore
1800	1830	ALL	ALL	139181	HEF	Thruxton
1800	1830	ALL	ALL	139181	HEF	Treville
1628	1814	1600	1820	176621	KEN	Brabourne
1807	1980	....	....	100986	KEN	Broadstairs
1650	1800	1500	1650	175269	KEN	Dover
1680	1755	....	....	119458	KEN	Godmersham
1720	1900	1650	1750	170488	KEN	Herne
1800	1860	1750	1840	123978	KEN	Isle Of Sheppey
1798	1828	....	....	115290	WIL	Lydiard Millicent
KENNINGTON						
1818	1893	....	....	103810	LIN	Gainsborough
KENNISH						
1800	....	....	1800	111767	IOM	Kirk German
1761	1865	1700	1761	135151	IOM	Maughold
KENNISON						
1895	1950	1850	1992	177180	BKM	Ivinghoe
1650	1715	1600	1720	138150	GLS	South
KENNY						
....	....	ALL	1872	104531	IRL	Sligo
....	....	....	....	102946	IRL	???
1872	....	ALL	ALL	104531	LAN	Bolton
1722	1722	....	....	135437	NFK	Fakenham
1861	1920	....	....	102946	YKS	Sheffield

Known From	To	Researching From	To	Ref	Cty	Place
KENSETT						
1841	1928	1500	1900	132977	SSX	West
KENSEY						
1711	....	1650	1750	143693	CON	St Clements
KENT						
1780	1787	1700	1850	169390	AYR	Dunlop
1757	1800	1539	1873	108251	BRK	Langford
1820	....	1613	1831	149640	CAM	Cambridge
1766	1833	1766	1833	157066	CHS	Congleton
1700	1900	1700	1992	151475	CON	South West
1881	1900	1700	1900	175293	CON	Plymouth
1850	1992	1853	1948	123773	CON	St Columb
1780	1824	1650	1780	165549	CON	St Dennis
1738	1789	1700	1800	176982	CON	Truro
1844	1871	1750	1844	170968	DEV	Brixham
1881	1900	1700	1900	175293	DEV	Plymouth
1732	1813	1700	1732	127116	DOR	Tarrant Hinton
1860	1992	1700	1860	139254	ESS	Stock
1867	1900	1841	1887	164895	GLS	Cheltenham
1765	1950	1400	1992	139270	HAM	East Meon
1744	1802	ALL	ALL	129933	HAM	Portsmouth
1740	1800	1650	1740	120685	HRT	Ardeley
1800	1960	1500	1800	125415	HRT	St Albans
1840	1880	1750	1900	118281	HRT	Tewin
1860	1992	1860	1992	133450	KEN	Chatham
1600	....	ALL	1600	131059	KEN	Cowden
1860	1992	1700	1860	139254	KEN	Rochester
1881	....	1850	1992	106739	LAN	Liverpool
1800	1992	1700	1800	119261	LIN	Holbeach
1780	1787	1700	1850	169390	LKS	Glasgow
1780	1787	1700	1850	169390	LKS	Lanark
1866	1866	1866	1900	106666	LND	Hackney
1817	1817	1800	1850	147575	LND	Shoreditch
....	....	1800	1900	117714	LND	St Johns Wood
1844	1861	....	1881	137405	MDX	East
1900	1954	1830	1992	139270	MDX	East
1859	1881	1837	1881	149640	MDX	London
....	....	1700	1864	118168	MDX	Poplar
1850	1992	1700	1850	119261	NFK	Denver
1722	1916	1690	1715	135763	SAL	Fitz
1722	1916	1690	1715	135763	SAL	Preston Gubbalds
....	....	1864	1930	175110	SRY	Farnham
1640	1850	ALL	1860	106739	SSX	Lewes
1765	1790	1600	1765	164879	SSX	Upper Beeding
....	....	1700	1900	179531	STS	Abbots Bromley
1800	1820	1700	1900	179531	STS	Leek
1823	1906	1790	1823	110515	STS	Stoke On Trent
1840	1870	1700	1900	179531	STS	Uttoxeter
1950	1992	1700	1950	171255	WAR	Birmingham
....	....	1780	1860	179361	WIL	Everleigh
1805	1861	1800	1861	108251	WIL	Oaksey
1879	....	1850	1992	106739	WMD	Birmingham
KENTISH						
....	....	1750	1850	146927	ALL	???
KENTLETON						
1824	1869	1800	1900	146269	MDX	Chelsea
KENTWELL						
....	1790	....	1790	161888	MDX	???
KENWARD						
1811	1850	1700	1900	135968	SSX	Lewes
1800	1900	1600	1800	158925	SSX	Lingfield
KENWARDEN						
1481	1516	1481	1516	156809	DBY	Conkesbury
1481	1516	1481	1516	156809	DBY	Over Haddon
KENWOOD						
1570	1970	....	....	129054	DEV	???
1811	1820	1800	1900	151246	SSX	Hailsham
1778	....	....	1800	151246	SSX	Isfield
KENWORTHY						
....	....	1750	1870	112038	CHS	Stockport
1814	1992	....	....	160253	WYK	Holmfirth
....	....	1700	1814	160253	WYK	Saddleworth
KENYON						
1812	1851	1700	1992	160385	IOM	Ramsey
1725	....	1725	....	109347	LAN	Altham
1870	1980	1800	1870	128384	LAN	Manchester
1850	1942	1700	1890	129623	YKS	Huddersfield
KEOGH						
1895	1980	ALL	1895	142107	IRL	Portarlington
KEOUGH						
....	....	1840	1920	139297	DUB	???
....	....	1865	1870	139297	???	Holyhead
1858	1900	....	1870	139297	???	Liverpool

Known From	To	Researching From	To	Ref	Cty	Place
KEPPIE						
1750	1992	1600	1992	139300	ELN	ALL
1860	1992	1800	1992	139300	LAN	Liverpool
1860	1992	1800	1992	139300	LAN	Manchester
1800	1900	....	....	146854	LAN	Southport
1750	1992	1600	1992	139300	SCT	Edinburgh
1860	1910	1800	1992	139300	SCT	Glasgow
1820	1992	1800	1992	139300	SSX	Brighton
1800	1992	1700	1992	139300	WIG	Sorbie
1800	1992	1700	1992	139300	WIG	Whithorn
1860	1900	....	....	139300	WOR	Worcester
KER						
1850	1870	1800	1920	135429	DEV	Exmouth
1400	1520	1350	1600	154881	ELN	Samuelston
....	....	ALL	1741	119326	PER	Tomtaiwan
1740	1801	ALL	1740	110965	ROX	ALL
KERCHEVALL						
1766	1766	1720	1810	167002	NTT	Balderton
KERCHIN						
1703	1800	1600	1702	131245	LEI	Queniborough
KERFOOT						
ALL	1800	1450	1800	116785	ALL	ALL
KERKHOFF						
....	....	ALL	ALL	135704	ALL	Name Study
ALL	ALL	ALL	ALL	135704	ALL	ALL
1762	1798	1700	1800	135704	MDX	London
1806	1992	1800	1992	135704	WAR	Birmingham
KERLE						
1713	1752	1600	1752	113069	SOM	Catcott
1713	1752	1600	1752	124990	SOM	Catcott
1789	1801	1780	1850	113069	SOM	Huntspill
1789	1801	1780	1850	124990	SOM	Huntspill
1756	1763	1756	1800	113069	SOM	Wedmore
1756	1763	1756	1800	124990	SOM	Wedmore
KERLEY						
1861	1876	1800	1891	119199	DOR	Cranborne
KERMODE						
1805	1836	1700	1805	135151	IOM	Maughold
KERN						
....	....	....	1800	114308	SRY	Chiddingford
KERNER						
....	....	ALL	ALL	139327	ALL	Name Study
1793	1992	1500	1992	139327	LND	Lambeth
1793	1992	1500	1992	139327	SRY	Lambeth
KERNEY						
....	....	?	1841	144800	IRL	???
1841	1954	....	....	144800	YKS	West
KERNICK						
1786	1848	ALL	ALL	113360	CON	Perranzabuloe
KERR						
....	....	1750	1900	134546	ANS	Dundee
1790	1992	....	....	144088	AYR	Cauieshill
1840	1860	1700	1840	169501	AYR	New Cumnock
....	....	1808	1850	150029	AYR	???
1836	....	1800	1870	149292	BEW	Berwick
1850	1874	1800	1874	126586	DFS	Kirkconnel
1750	1850	1600	1992	109274	DFS	Sanquhar
1851	1920	1851	1992	153273	FLN	Flint
1800	1850	ALL	ALL	131873	IRL	Londonderry
1860	....	1836	1880	149292	LAN	Liverpool
1860	1992	1700	1860	124931	LKS	Glasgow
1800	1900	ALL	ALL	131873	LND	Westminster
....	....	1808	1850	150029	RFW	???
1800	1890	1800	1890	138894	ROX	Kelso
1900	ALL	ALL	ALL	149063	ROX	Morebattle
1900	1935	1900	1957	162442	SCT	Glasgow
1902	1902	1900	1902	162442	SCT	Greenock
1851	1900	1900	1992	120286	SEL	Slekirk
KERRIDGE						
....	....	ALL	ALL	139351	ALL	ALL
1844	1903	1700	1844	106836	LND	Marylebone
1860	1950	....	....	129895	SFK	Winston
KERRIGAN						
1890	1992	ALL	1890	139378	IRL	???
KERRY						
1780	1880	ALL	ALL	139386	SFK	Wattisfield
KERSEY						
1800	1900	1600	1800	167010	SFK	Bucklesham
1841	1851	1841	1851	130192	SFK	Iken
KERSHAW						
1860	1900	1860	1900	173614	DEV	Barnstaple
1819	....	1750	1850	179078	LAN	Bacup
1740	1860	1740	1900	119385	LAN	Hoole
1810	1905	ALL	1810	172901	LAN	Manchester

Known From	To	Researching From	To	Ref	Cty	Place
KERSHAW contd.						
1865	1887	?	1890	164976	LAN	Oldham
....	....	1750	1860	100390	LAN	Rochdale
1843	1992	1843	....	139416	LAN	Rochdale
1889	1992	1800	1889	139394	LAN	Royton
1800	1880	1880	1992	162256	LAN	Tockholes
1882	1992	1856	1882	111805	LAN	Todmorden
1811	1992	ALL	ALL	140813	NTT	ALL
1757	1850	....	....	151351	NTT	Basford
1836	1836	ALL	1900	173614	NTT	Mansfield
1885	1928	1800	1885	174408	OFF	Clayne
1778	....	1778	....	139149	WRY	Halifax
1725	1860	1725	1860	153621	WYK	Queensbury
1800	1839	1700	1900	102520	YKS	Thornton
1882	1992	1856	1882	111805	YKS	Todmorden
KERSHOPE						
1157	....	....	....	140104	CUL	Kershope
KERSLAKE						
....	....	ALL	ALL	139319	ALL	Name Study
....	....	1700	1850	139432	CON	North Hill
1819	1843	?	1819	136611	DEV	Holcombe Rogus
1880	1980	1750	1880	122556	DEV	Loxbeare
1841	1871	1871	1900	139432	DEV	Tavistock
1750	1780	1750	1755	110159	DEV	Tiverton
1700	1800	ALL	ALL	121436	DEV	Tiverton
....	....	?	?	104310	DOR	Stoke Abbott
1819	1843	?	1819	136611	SOM	Holcombe Rogus
KERSLEY						
....	....	ALL	ALL	139440	ALL	Name Study
1829	1840	....	....	116254	HAM	Aldershot
1760	1818	....	....	145394	HAM	Herriard
1830	1850	1800	1850	130516	HAM	Rotherwick
KERSWELL						
1836	1860	1830	1860	170526	DEV	Aveton Gifford
KERTON						
1830	1850	1830	1992	104140	SOM	Ashwick
1830	1850	1500	1830	104140	SOM	Shepton Mallet
KERVILL						
1790	1992	1650	1790	131067	LND	City
KERVILLE						
1790	1992	1650	1790	131067	LND	City
KERWIN						
1875	1884	1850	1875	109878	IRL	Dublin
1750	1850	1750	1850	167924	KEN	Deal
1820	1860	1820	1860	167924	KEN	Deptford
1800	1850	1800	1850	167924	MDX	Stepney
KERWINY						
1600	1800	....	....	167924	KEN	Walmer
KESBEY						
1828	1853	1500	1853	169439	KEN	Bonnington
KESKET						
1796	1818	1700	1796	152196	CMA	Allonby
KESSELL						
1800	1917	1700	1800	148806	CON	Chacewater
1825	1880	1700	1825	148806	CON	St Austell
1850	1870	1700	1890	162388	CON	St Austell
KESSLEY						
1723	1793	1700	1830	136719	HAM	Winslade
KESTERTON						
....	....	ALL	ALL	139459	ALL	Name Study
1590	1992	ALL	ALL	139459	ALL	ALL
1620	1750	....	....	121983	WAR	Aston
1750	1880	....	....	121983	WAR	Erdington
KESTLE						
1797	1850	1700	1800	142999	CON	Padstow
KETCHER						
1760	1784	....	....	171654	ESS	Canewdon
KETCHIN						
1815	1900	1800	1900	148474	ROX	Castleton
....	....	1700	1850	148474	SCT	South
KETCHINER						
1600	1799	1660	1780	135941	SFK	Mildenhall
KETE						
1760	....	ALL	1760	115282	KEN	East
KETLEY						
1797	1974	1700	1800	175978	ESS	Braintree
1830	1830	1826	1844	124915	ESS	Sandon
KETT						
1795	1844	....	....	135437	NFK	Ditchingham
KETTEL						
1760	1900	1700	1920	111325	ESS	Elstead
KETTER						
....	....	ALL	ALL	139467	ALL	Name Study
KETTERIDGE						
1780	1992	1700	1800	148725	ESS	North West
1800	1860	1700	1800	137421	WAR	Kingsbury
KETTERINGHAM						
1850	1992	1700	1850	139475	NFK	North
1765	1865	1700	1800	112038	NFK	Middleton
KETTLE						
1686	1740	ALL	ALL	175943	CAM	Cambridge
1813	1851	ALL	1860	118737	ESS	Colchester
....	1790	ALL	1790	134511	LEI	Saltby
1825	1890	1500	1992	124443	LIN	South
1834	1875	1800	....	109746	WOR	Bromsgrove
1873	1916	ALL	ALL	151696	???	Aylesbury
KETTLESTRING						
1797	....	1700	....	134589	YKS	Newton On Ouse
KETTLETY						
1780	1920	....	1780	159972	SOM	Bath
KETTLEWELL						
1790	1850	1840	1900	103128	YKS	Whixley
1707	....	1600	1707	116637	YKS	Whixley
1750	....	1700	....	134589	YKS	Wigginton
KETTON						
1776	1806	1776	1812	124915	NTT	East Drayton
KEVAN						
1680	1840	1600	1680	139483	KKD	Kirkcudbright
1840	1870	....	....	139483	WIG	Kirkinner
1870	1930	....	....	139483	YKS	Sheffield
KEVERN						
1760	1864	1750	1900	139491	CON	Ludgvan
1864	1930	....	....	139491	CON	Penzance
1930	1950	....	....	139491	DEV	Exeter
1962	1992	....	....	139491	DEV	Illogan
1921	1950	....	....	139491	DEV	Sidmouth
KEVERNE						
1660	1760	1660	1800	139491	CON	Paul
KEVERYN						
1605	1660	1500	....	139491	CON	St Keverne
KEVIS						
1830	1992	....	1992	103470	LND	Stepney
1880	1992	....	1992	103470	LND	Walthamstow
KEW						
1686	1983	ALL	ALL	136719	HAM	Tadley
1813	1834	ALL	1900	146315	NTH	Northborough
KEWELL						
1742	1800	1700	1900	128163	SSX	West
1500	1992	1650	1992	149802	SSX	Chichester
KEY						
1750	1770	....	....	171654	AYR	Mauchline
1650	1900	1700	1850	115452	CON	Mid
1830	1930	1700	1830	159212	CUL	Whitehaven
1700	1802	1700	1802	151297	DEV	North Huish
1840	1880	1800	1900	138193	HUN	Ramsay
1722	1809	1650	1800	160636	LIN	Hackthorne
....	....	ALL	ALL	177466	LIN	Tattershall
....	....	ALL	1880	161209	MDX	London
1846	1870	1800	1846	123277	NTT	Nottingham
....	....	ALL	1660	103284	SAL	Newport
1600	1900	....	....	176591	STS	Standon
1600	1900	....	....	176591	STS	Weston
1600	1700	....	....	100420	WAR	Meriden
KEYES						
1840	1880	1750	1840	146587	SOM	Bath
KEYS						
1749	1759	....	1780	171441	HRT	Westmill
1880	....	ALL	1992	150630	KEN	Gillingham
....	1600	....	....	174564	LEI	Catsfield
1800	1880	....	....	162833	MDX	???
1798	1815	1700	1798	163953	SFK	Ipswich
KEYSELL						
1620	1750	1600	1800	156515	HEF	Orleton
KEYTE						
1800	1992	1600	1800	120723	GLS	Blockley
1632	1662	1662	1800	120723	GLS	Ebrington
1795	1835	1700	1850	124974	WAR	Barford
KEYWORTH						
1850	1900	1850	1910	123765	LIN	Caistor
1800	1900	1800	1900	123765	LIN	Lincoln
1705	1773	?	1705	128910	LIN	Willingham By Stow
KIBBLE						
1811	1992	1700	1811	118788	KEN	Shorne
1864	....	1864	....	141194	SRY	Bermondsey
KIBBLEWHITE						
1810	1851	1750	1810	178381	WIL	Cricklade

Known From	Known To	Researching From	Researching To	Ref	Cty	Place
KICKIE						
1930	1992	1800	1930	119733	SCT	???
KICKWEED						
1721	1728	....	....	122319	ESS	South East
KID						
1720	....	ALL	ALL	130508	FIF	St Monance
KIDALL						
....	....	1300	1700	139521	YKS	ALL
KIDD						
1847	1871	....	....	168203	ANS	Dundee
1820	1831	1820	1992	168181	ARM	Armagh
1817	1820	1800	1992	168181	ARM	Tanderagee
1800	1850	1700	1900	169978	AYR	Kilwinning
1850	1900	1800	1900	169978	DFS	Lochmaben
....	....	ALL	1830	118362	ESS	Stratford
1550	1850	ALL	1850	151319	LAN	Cuerdley
1862	....	....	....	130923	LND	Holborn
1875	1912	1850	....	167290	MDX	Mary Le Bone
1700	1946	....	....	169129	NFK	East
1833	1934	ALL	1833	118362	NFK	Thornage
1833	1871	....	....	168203	PER	Errol
KIDDALL						
....	....	1600	1850	139521	HRT	ALL
....	....	1300	1700	139521	LIN	North
1500	1610	1500	1610	139521	NTH	Higham Ferrers
KIDDELL						
1796	....	1780	1836	136964	BDF	Radwell
1812	1812	ALL	ALL	106313	ESS	ALL
KIDDLE						
....	....	ALL	ALL	179590	ALL	Name Study
....	....	1300	1992	179590	ALL	ALL
1992	....	....	....	139513	DOR	Poole
1867	1992	....	....	139513	DOR	Southampton
....	....	1600	1850	139521	HRT	ALL
1771	....	....	....	139513	LND	Wigmore Street
....	....	1800	1900	146277	MDX	Shoreditch
1597	1992	1790	1802	139513	SOM	Bayford
1590	1840	....	....	139513	SOM	Charlton
1871	1936	....	....	139513	SOM	Musgrove
1871	1936	....	....	139513	SOM	North Cadbury
1843	1992	....	....	139513	SOM	Somerton
1597	1992	....	....	139513	SOM	Stoke Trister
1729	1992	....	....	139513	SOM	Wincanton
1860	....	....	....	139513	WLS	ALL
KIDDOR						
1743	1770	1500	1743	125695	YKS	Everingham
KIDGELL						
1661	1733	1600	1661	127116	HAM	Abbotts Ann
KIDGER						
1775	1850	ALL	ALL	154008	ALL	ALL
KIDHAM						
1742	1850	1650	1800	129976	KEN	Folkestone
KIDMAN						
1500	1992	ALL	ALL	139548	ALL	ALL
....	....	?	1750	103934	BDF	Biggleswade
1850	1900	1600	1850	113654	LND	ALL
....	....	1880	1940	173355	LND	South
KIDNER						
....	....	ALL	ALL	139556	ALL	Name Study
1500	1850	1500	1850	139556	DEV	North
1600	1992	1600	1900	139556	HMC	London
1166	1992	1500	1900	139556	SOM	West
1770	1860	1770	1860	106801	SOM	North Petherton
KIDNEY						
1799	....	1800	1900	139114	KEN	Leeds
ALL	ALL	1800	1900	139114	KEN	Ulcombe
KIDSON						
1760	1866	1760	1900	157430	WOR	Martley
KIDWELL						
....	....	ALL	ALL	139564	ALL	Name Study
ALL	ALL	ALL	ALL	139564	ALL	ALL
1849	1894	1850	1900	175307	LND	ALL
KIELLOR						
....	....	ALL	ALL	139572	ALL	Name Study
KIELY						
1820	1960	1820	1900	116831	WAT	Clashmore
KIETH						
1765	1795	1841	1891	146560	PER	Perth
KIFF						
1700	1800	1650	1850	152900	BKM	St Albans
1790	1897	1770	1897	144878	HRT	West
1800	1900	1800	1900	152900	MDX	Northolt
KIFFIN						
1880	1950	1880	1950	140422	WAR	Birmingham
KIFFT						
1777	1795	....	....	158895	WIL	Sutton Benger
KIFT						
1825	1850	ALL	ALL	177989	GLA	Oystermouth
KIKKIE						
....	....	1800	1992	146234	ARL	Dunoon
KILBECK						
?	1880	1700	1992	167096	OXF	All Saints
KILBER						
....	1736	1700	1736	128961	HRT	Ickleford
KILBORN						
1700	1946	1700	1992	139580	NTH	Kettering
KILBOURNE						
1800	1992	1200	1800	139599	LEI	Castle Donnington
1793	1830	1500	1800	139599	LEI	Loughborough
KILBURN						
1750	1900	....	....	102741	DUR	Consett
1750	1900	....	....	102741	DUR	Crook
1750	1900	....	....	102741	DUR	Hitton Le Weak
....	....	1800	1870	108936	DUR	Wingate
1826	1871	1841	1871	116114	YKS	Bainbridge
KILBURY						
1820	1931	ALL	ALL	149489	HAM	South
KILBY						
1809	1872	....	....	127426	LND	ALL
1833	1833	....	....	127426	MDX	Balls Pond St Pauls
1872	1872	....	....	127426	SRY	Camberwell
1905	1905	....	....	127426	STS	Handsworth
1914	1914	....	....	127426	WAR	Aston
1855	1939	....	....	127426	WAR	Birmingham
1850	1960	1700	....	148342	WAR	Birmingham
1929	1929	....	....	127426	WAR	Nechells
1949	1949	....	....	127426	WAR	Oscott College
1870	1870	....	....	127426	WAR	St Martins
....	....	1870	1890	164364	WIL	Swindon
1890	1950	....	....	164364	YKS	Balby
1890	1950	....	....	164364	YKS	Doncaster
KILDEA						
1851	1881	ALL	1881	171751	ROC	Keadue
KILDUFF						
....	....	ALL	ALL	139629	ALL	Name Study
....	....	ALL	ALL	139610	ALL	Name Study
KILFOY						
1880	1898	1880	1898	173215	CMA	Cleator
KILGORE						
1660	1843	ALL	ALL	101370	DOW	Donagheady
KILLEEN						
1840	1850	1700	1900	135968	IRL	Athlone
KILLEN						
1750	1820	....	....	165999	SOM	Taunton
KILLENBACK						
1845	....	....	....	176540	MDX	Hackney
KILLER						
1550	1992	ALL	ALL	139637	DBY	Matlock
1750	1850	ALL	ALL	139637	LAN	Manchester
KILLEY						
....	....	1700	1800	147613	IOM	Malew
....	....	1780	1820	121479	IOM	???
KILLICK						
1400	1992	ALL	ALL	106534	ALL	ALL
1840	1916	....	1840	134007	ESS	Manningtree
1828	1851	1700	1828	133582	KEN	Deptford
1800	1840	1700	1800	133493	LND	London
1755	1800	....	....	164593	LND	???
1400	1992	ALL	ALL	106534	SRY	Nutfield
....	....	....	1840	134007	SRY	Wonersh
KILLIGREW						
....	....	1700	1992	146390	IRL	ALL
KILLINGBECK						
1700	1750	....	....	165999	ESS	Alphamstone
1902	1905	....	....	132179	LND	Poplar
1725	1830	1725	1850	122416	YKS	Drax
KILLIP						
1873	1883	1800	1873	160385	IOM	Jurby
1859	....	....	....	156647	IOM	???
KILLON						
....	....	ALL	ALL	139653	ALL	Name Study
KILMINSTER						
1788	1850	ALL	1850	132217	GLS	Uley
1855	1881	?	1855	111155	LND	Bow
1862	1992	....	1862	151270	WIL	Highworth
1828	1881	?	1828	111155	WIL	Westbury
KILMINSTER-BRIND						
1855	1992	1855	1992	111155	LND	Bow

Known From	To	Researching From	To	Ref	Cty	Place
KILMISTER						
1610	1890	1763	1890	178683	GLS	Rodmarton
1610	1890	1789	1878	178683	WIL	Enford
KILNER						
1572	1642	ALL	ALL	141615	LAN	Warton
1800	1850	....	....	135968	SSX	East Grinstead
1650	1850	1600	1650	104914	SSX	West Hoathly
KILOW						
1821	1992	ALL	ALL	139459	IRL	Ulster
KILVINGTON						
1805	1992	1805	1992	139661	YKS	Bagby
1805	1992	1805	1992	139661	YKS	Balk
1760	1890	....	....	102946	YKS	Hunsingore
1828	1881	1881	1992	139661	YKS	Rainton
1841	1880	....	....	102946	YKS	Tockwith
KIMBELL						
....	....	ALL	ALL	124176	OXF	North Leigh
KIMBER						
1820	1900	1750	1950	135925	BRK	Newbury
1765	....	1600	1765	149888	BRK	Radley
1700	1730	ALL	1700	135143	DEV	Bideford
1700	1992	1600	1900	139688	HAM	ALL
1815	1850	1800	1850	176648	HAM	South
....	....	1747	1812	139157	HAM	Andover
1800	....	....	....	152722	HAM	Breamore
1675	1850	1640	1680	149993	HAM	Candovers
1700	1800	1700	1850	145602	HAM	Crawley
1800	....	....	....	152722	HAM	Fordingbridge
1700	1992	ALL	ALL	115002	HAM	Winchester
1780	1847	....	....	133779	HAM	???
1819	1980	1790	1820	116076	KEN	Otford
1819	1980	1790	1820	116076	KEN	Snodland
1819	1980	1790	1820	116076	SRY	Limpsfield
1850	1900	ALL	ALL	166537	WAR	Birmingham
1680	1780	ALL	1800	167029	WIL	Burbage
1744	1829	ALL	1744	167878	WIL	Burbage
1785	1854	1700	1785	145513	WIL	Fosbury
1800	....	....	....	152722	WIL	Salisbury
1850	....	1840	1880	135429	YKS	York
KIMBERLEY						
1825	1826	1800	1830	173452	STS	Swindon
1813	1874	1700	1813	136530	WOR	Coventry
KIMBRELL						
1740	1776	1700	1790	131326	CON	Mevagissey
KIMLIN						
1860	1900	ALL	ALL	145386	LAN	Manchester
....	....	1839	ALL	145386	MAY	Thurlough Park
KIMMER						
1734	1771	1680	1740	103896	WIL	Froxfield
1800	1834	ALL	1790	151602	WIL	Wilcot
1802	1877	1700	1801	166782	WIL	Wilcott
KIMMINGS						
1867	1960	ALL	ALL	139696	IRL	???
KIMMINS						
....	....	ALL	ALL	139696	IRL	???
KIMMONS						
....	....	ALL	ALL	139696	IRL	???
KIMPTON						
ALL	ALL	ALL	ALL	139718	ALL	ALL
KINCH						
1815	1860	1700	1860	108111	HAM	Fareham
KINCHIN						
....	....	1700	1849	166170	LND	Bethnal Green
KIND						
1850	1992	....	....	133515	WAR	Atherstone
1745	1850	....	1745	133515	WAR	Whetstone
KINDER						
1780	1890	1600	1850	137235	CHS	Gt Budworth
1740	1851	1600	1740	123102	DBY	Wirksworth
....	....	1700	1820	132241	YKS	Saddleworth
KINDERSLEY						
1635	1950	ALL	ALL	124893	DOR	ALL
1600	1992	1500	1992	149934	DOR	ALL
KINDLY						
....	....	ALL	1715	119326	ELN	Gladsmoor
KINDRED						
1775	1798	1600	1775	116637	DUR	Edmundbyers
KINDRICK						
1688	1688	....	....	135437	CHS	Chester
KINETON						
1867	1868	1800	1868	114472	CHS	Runcorn
KING						
....	....	ALL	ALL	139742	ALL	Name Study
1800	1950	1700	1800	140864	ABD	Strichen
KING contd.						
1854	1890	1820	1890	107700	AGY	Anglesey
1820	1941	1820	1941	139807	AVN	Bristol
1790	1890	....	....	160806	BDF	Turvey
1779	1860	1725	1880	124796	BKM	Akeley
1700	1800	1650	1800	177180	BKM	Aylesbury
1820	1824	1790	1820	169021	BKM	Chesham
1751	1751	1675	1751	167452	BKM	Monks Risborough
1870	1920	1860	1950	124796	BKM	Tingewick
1878	1890	1860	1900	124796	BKM	Water Stratford
1800	1850	1650	1850	172545	BRK	Harwell
1846	....	1800	1900	108391	BRK	Reading
1860	1992	1800	1860	102253	CAM	Barrington
1801	1946	1700	1801	145823	CAM	Coton
1800	1900	1800	1992	139866	CAM	Newmarket
1715	1940	....	....	128996	CAM	Thorney
1840	1960	1800	1960	105732	CHS	Bromborough
1860	1955	1860	1955	107174	CON	Hayle
....	....	1700	1925	139815	CON	Illogan
....	....	1700	1925	139815	CON	Penzance
....	....	1500	1800	138614	CON	Perranuthnoe
1700	1900	1700	1900	110523	CON	St Hilary
1745	1745	1745	1745	120944	CON	St Hillary
1850	1880	1800	1850	146609	DBY	Matlock Bath
1900	1992	1800	1950	171689	DBY	North Wingfield
1766	1875	....	....	177091	DEV	Buckland
1799	....	1750	1799	164267	DEV	Instow
1766	1875	....	....	177091	DEV	Monachdrum
1817	1992	1650	1817	139769	DEV	Tavistock
1743	1878	1600	1743	172898	DEV	Woodleigh
1600	1900	1600	1900	150797	DOR	Gillingham
1790	1850	1790	1850	154210	DOR	Hampreston
1861	1861	1841	1881	152781	DOR	Horton
....	....	1780	1830	100234	DOR	Poole
1789	1848	ALL	ALL	122106	DOR	Sherborne
1650	1730	1500	1650	113204	DUB	Swords
....	....	ALL	1764	119326	ELN	Tranent
....	....	1750	1800	172871	ESS	Chelmsford
1800	1830	1750	1900	111325	ESS	Colchester
1800	1830	1750	1900	111325	ESS	Greenstead Juxta
1850	1869	1800	1880	105120	ESS	Thorrington
1898	1980	1850	1898	138991	ESS	West Hampshire
1730	1800	ALL	1730	141224	GLS	South
1800	1840	1600	1840	154342	GLS	Bisley
1730	1800	....	....	167037	GLS	Bristol
1855	1866	....	....	167037	GLS	Frampton On Severn
1806	1951	?	1806	176052	GLS	Gloucester
1780	1810	1700	1780	148113	GLS	King Stanley
1809	....	?	1825	103934	GLS	Painswick
1830	ALL	....	....	167037	GLS	Stroud
1720	1770	1770	1992	105651	GLS	Twyning
1880	1925	1880	1992	106186	HAM	Abbotts Ann
1831	1838	....	....	174319	HAM	Andover
1760	1820	ALL	1760	135143	HAM	Gosport
1775	1808	1700	1775	169242	HAM	Hordle
1767	1847	....	1767	143901	HAM	Lymington
1800	1850	1800	1850	106631	HAM	Portsea
1655	1785	1550	1655	114928	HAM	Portsmouth
....	....	1780	1830	100234	HAM	Ringwood
1749	1749	1710	1800	105333	HAM	Ringwood
1795	1830	1700	1850	106186	HAM	Whitchurch
1700	1720	1600	1800	162620	HEF	Leominster
1790	1860	1600	1790	123390	HEF	Tarrington
1829	1854	....	....	172871	HRT	Rickmansworth
1811	1957	1700	1811	150886	HUN	Hail Weston
1881	1910	1910	1992	151688	HUN	Orton Longville
1777	1797	1797	1992	151688	HUN	Warmington
....	1841	1830	1850	142018	IOW	Barisber
1800	1950	1750	1950	126144	KEN	West
1849	1880	1800	1900	131571	KEN	East Malling
1781	1880	ALL	ALL	151327	KEN	Northfleet
....	....	1839	1865	161667	KEN	Ridley
1874	1913	1790	1874	146919	LAN	Austwick
1874	1913	1790	1874	146919	LAN	Clapham
1800	1870	1700	1800	174130	LEI	Bilston
1689	1689	1550	1688	131245	LEI	Cosby
1764	1881	....	....	117560	LEI	Hinckley
1890	1920	1860	1920	138444	LEI	Leicester
1780	1790	....	....	103764	LEI	North Kilworth
1840	1860	1820	1880	122327	LEI	Nuneaton
1900	1992	1600	1992	112003	LEI	Osgathorpe
1800	1870	1700	1800	174130	LEI	Tugby
1603	....	1603	1900	115142	LEI	Twycross
1830	1907	1830	1992	151688	LIN	Crowland

Known From	To	Researching From	To	Ref	Cty	Place
KING contd.						
1846	1931	....	....	169498	LIN	Hagworthingham
1790	....	....	....	129747	LIN	Leasingham
1750	1992	1600	1750	102342	LIN	Messingham
1770	1791	1600	1780	101575	LIN	Tattershall
1860	1928	1928	1992	151688	LIN	Whaplode Fen
1818	1858	1818	1858	149403	LND	ALL
1820	1850	....	....	135089	LND	Bethnal Green
1851	1900	....	....	174319	LND	Chelsea
1794	1850	1750	1850	101060	LND	Marylebone
1867	1992	1800	1867	139785	LND	Mild End
1862	1864	1800	1862	138290	LND	Paddington
1865	1876	1865	1890	167002	MDX	Kentish Town
1754	1827	1700	1851	167002	MDX	London
1760	1800	....	....	167037	MDX	London
1862	1864	1800	1862	138290	MDX	Paddington
1838	1846	1811	1896	167002	MDX	Pancras
1800	1840	1800	1900	107700	MDX	Stepney
1800	1840	1700	1800	171662	MLN	Liberton
1787	1918	1700	1799	139793	MON	Llanvaches
1775	1830	1700	1830	145750	NFK	ALL
1800	1870	1800	1870	124605	NFK	Great Yarmouth
1820	1900	1840	1880	135429	NFK	Great Yarmouth
1800	1900	1800	1900	124761	NFK	Gt Yarmouth
1830	1870	1800	1900	111821	NFK	Norwich
1734	1734	1730	1740	107360	NTH	Badby
1750	1843	1843	1992	151688	NTH	Fotheringhay
1840	1860	1800	1850	137111	NTH	Gt Brington
1753	1842	1842	1992	151688	NTH	Harringworth
1799	1815	1815	1992	151688	NTH	Nassington
1830	1894	1894	1992	151688	NTH	Newborough
1696	1771	....	1696	151688	NTH	Rockingham
....	....	1600	1700	163260	NTH	Rockingham
1725	....	1700	1750	124796	NTH	Sulgrave
1803	1850	....	....	151351	NTT	Basford
1802	....	....	....	151351	NTT	St Mary Nottingham
1614	1645	....	....	151351	NTT	Widmerpool
1820	1860	1800	1860	148377	OXF	Aston Rowant
1797	1868	1750	1880	142360	OXF	Bampton
1697	....	....	....	130079	OXF	Bletchingdon
1833	1992	1750	1833	139777	OXF	Crowell
ALL	1755	....	....	132756	OXF	Launton
1890	1992	1860	1890	177539	OXF	St Clements
1880	1992	1880	1992	135429	PEM	Milford Haven
1842	1861	1800	1842	146358	RFW	Port Glasgow
1760	1775	1700	1800	175684	SFK	ALL
1745	1900	1550	1992	139866	SFK	Gazeley
1860	1870	1840	1880	135429	SFK	Gorleston
1738	1992	1650	1738	155276	SFK	Leiston
1800	1900	1840	1880	135429	SFK	Mutford
1720	....	....	1720	101761	SFK	Pakenham
1600	1800	1600	1800	139688	SFK	Tattingstone
1820	1840	1800	1850	142018	SOM	Bath
1880	1960	1880	....	120103	SOM	Cummidge
1828	1992	1800	1992	171581	SOM	Tickenham
1881	ALL	....	....	117560	SRY	Camberwell
1785	1871	1600	1900	150118	SRY	Chertsey
1783	1851	1600	1900	150118	SRY	Cobham
1850	1860	1830	1870	138444	SRY	Croydon
1807	1869	1750	1807	100242	SSX	Barcombe
1832	1833	1830	....	156019	SSX	Brighton
1697	1742	1650	1800	155896	SSX	Ewhurst
1805	1984	1700	1837	176370	SSX	Hurstpierpoint
1809	1821	1750	1900	174521	SSX	Rye
1790	1880	1700	1790	146285	SSX	Westbourne
1845	1845	ALL	1872	143634	STS	Bilston
1865	1880	ALL	1880	143634	STS	Lucknow
1821	1823	ALL	1872	143634	STS	Tamworth
1700	1900	1800	1992	112062	WAR	Cheshunt
1500	1700	....	....	100420	WAR	Meriden
1823	1845	1800	1823	177555	WAR	Tamworth
1790	1804	1790	1804	139807	WES	Kendal
1500	1900	1500	1900	170216	WIL	ALL
1820	1875	1800	1900	105732	WIL	Netheravon
1685	1712	1660	1740	105333	WIL	Salisbury
1896	1896	1860	1900	152773	WIL	Swindon
1860	1920	1750	1860	156566	WOR	Evesham
1690	1890	ALL	1700	146722	WYK	Barnoldswick
1881	1960	1872	ALL	143634	WYK	Wakefield
1757	1881	....	....	152234	WYK	Whitkirk
....	....	1800	1900	116823	YKS	Middleton
KINGAN						
....	....	ALL	ALL	139882	ALL	Name Study

Known From	To	Researching From	To	Ref	Cty	Place
KINGDOM						
....	....	ALL	1992	122572	ALL	ALL
KINGDON						
1580	1970	....	....	129054	CON	???
....	....	ALL	ALL	139890	DEV	ALL
1800	1880	ALL	ALL	139890	DEV	Bishops Nympton
1730	1800	ALL	ALL	139890	DEV	Rose Ash
....	....	1600	1900	124273	DEV	Silverton
1580	1970	....	....	129054	DEV	???
1750	1930	1800	1992	133450	LND	Deptford
1750	1930	1800	1992	133450	LND	Uxbridge
1880	1992	ALL	ALL	139890	SOM	West
KINGE						
1697	....	....	....	130079	OXF	Bletchingdon
KINGETT						
1828	1992	1296	1828	139912	LND	Clapham
KINGHAM						
1830	1900	1800	1992	177180	HRT	Bovingdon
1700	ALL	1732	1780	107379	HRT	Hemel Hempstead
1796	1847	1745	1800	100277	HRT	Tring
1838	1961	....	....	100277	LND	Lambeth
KINGHCOTT						
1574	1574	1500	1600	142042	WIL	Grittleton
KINGHORN						
1785	1901	1600	1785	167541	FIF	Auchtermuchty
KINGHT						
....	....	....	....	165565	???	???
KINGMAN						
1813	1881	1700	1881	176923	SOM	Easton
1751	1835	1700	1992	176923	SOM	Farrington Gurney
KINGO						
1686	1711	....	....	137936	FIF	Crail
KINGOW						
1686	1711	....	....	137936	FIF	Crail
KINGS						
1697	....	....	....	130079	OXF	Bletchingdon
1750	....	....	....	102733	WOR	Feckenham
....	....	1670	1750	147613	WOR	Old Swinford
KINGSBURY						
1790	1871	1650	1800	109835	DOR	ALL
1815	1815	1700	1814	131245	SFK	Boxford
ALL	1800	....	....	157724	SFK	Edwardstone
1806	1850	ALL	1992	119105	SFK	Groton
1670	1800	....	....	157724	SFK	Lavenham
1780	1850	1700	1830	117005	SFK	Sudbury
1796	1940	1767	1796	175846	SOM	Weston Super Mare
1796	1940	1767	1796	175846	SOM	Worle
KINGSFORD						
1600	1900	1600	1900	134503	KEN	East
1700	1850	1700	1850	154903	KEN	East
....	....	1700	1840	155322	KEN	Dover
1860	1900	1840	1860	155322	MDX	St Pancras
KINGSLEY						
1896	1992	1700	1886	105163	KEN	Dover
1800	1830	1800	1900	176281	NBL	Berwick
KINGSMILL						
....	....	ALL	ALL	139939	ALL	Name Study
KINGSNORTH						
1800	1850	ALL	1850	134503	KEN	Staplehurst
KINGSTON						
1818	1888	1700	1818	163740	BKM	Marlow
1840	1910	1910	1992	111961	CON	Mevagissey
1760	1860	1700	1880	121126	COR	Crohane
....	....	1750	1850	145637	LND	???
....	....	1600	1650	108677	SOM	Bath
KINGSTONE						
1850	1992	1750	1850	176079	CAM	North
1840	1900	1700	1840	174572	KEN	Sheerness
KINGSWELL						
1886	1992	1707	1992	139955	BRK	Maidenhead
1886	1992	1707	1992	139955	HAM	Lymington
1886	1992	1707	1992	139955	HAM	New Milton
1886	1992	1707	1992	139955	HAM	Pilley
1820	1850	1600	1850	132993	IOW	Carisbrooke
1820	1850	1600	1850	132993	IOW	Eatcombe
1729	1781	1500	1729	129577	IOW	???
KINGSWOOD						
1841	1887	1800	1900	129313	LAN	Manchester
KINGTON						
1850	1992	1700	1850	177415	SOM	Bristol
1823	1844	1000	1992	168149	WIL	Corsham
1790	1830	1700	1820	142042	WIL	Grittleton
KINGWELL						
1800	1950	1800	1950	178799	DEV	Plymouth

Known From	To	Researching From	To	Ref	Cty	Place
KINGWELL contd.						
1791	1992	1600	1761	139963	DEV	???
KINKAID						
1830	1840	....	....	130079	SCT	???
KINLAY						
....	....	1850	1992	144738	MDX	London
....	....	1850	1992	144738	SSX	???
KINLEY						
....	....	1750	1850	163082	LND	Stepney
KINLOCH						
1686	1686	ALL	1686	131881	FIF	Kirkaldy
KINMOUTH						
1910	1940	1850	1992	138053	COR	ALL
KINNEAR						
1780	1820	1780	1820	116831	FIF	Moonzie
KINNERSLEY						
....	....	1800	1992	150762	LND	Shoreditch
1794	1820	1770	1860	169323	LND	Spitalfields
KINNEY						
....	....	1760	1860	108863	ARM	Killevy
KINNIBURGH						
1813	1931	1750	1813	140678	LKS	Kirkintilloch
KINNISH						
1830	1992	1806	ALL	123471	IOM	Hales
1806	1992	1700	1992	123471	LAN	Walney
?	?	?	?	123471	SAL	???
KINNISON						
1854	1873	....	....	139971	SCT	Dundee
KINRY						
1759	1780	1700	1759	141291	IOM	Andreas
KINSELLA						
1882	1954	1800	1882	175595	DUB	Dublin
1850	1930	1700	1900	160954	MSY	Liverpool
KINSEY						
1750	1800	1750	1800	177288	LAN	Salford
....	....	1800	1840	153915	MGY	Llanidloes
1851	....	1840	1851	153915	MGY	Welshpool
1848	1992	1700	1825	153915	SAL	Rodington
1746	1841	1746	1992	142735	SFK	Old Newton
....	....	1700	1786	149977	STS	ALL
....	1840	ALL	1840	127000	STS	Dudley
1789	1796	....	....	149977	STS	Ingetre
1798	1836	....	....	149977	STS	Sandon
....	1840	ALL	1840	127000	WOR	???
KINSMAN						
1864	1992	1700	1864	130257	CON	Breage
1864	1992	1700	1864	130257	CON	St Keverne
1850	1923	1850	1970	112399	CON	Truro
KINVIG						
....	....	ALL	ALL	140007	ALL	Name Study
KIPLIN						
....	....	ALL	1890	173045	YKS	Rotherham
....	....	ALL	1890	173045	YKS	Sheffield
KIPLING						
1622	1832	1832	1900	140015	DUR	Barnards Castle
1580	1751	....	....	140015	DUR	Ronaldkirk
1616	1900	1680	1770	147729	DUR	Teesdale
ALL	?	?	?	140015	ENG	ALL
1837	1905	1905	1950	140015	LND	Shoreditch
1616	1900	1680	1770	147729	NYK	Teesdale
1688	1767	1580	1688	140015	YKS	Barningham
1615	1736	1736	1900	140015	YKS	Bowes
1719	1830	1600	1900	140015	YKS	Gilling
KIPPAX						
1800	1850	1800	1850	119091	LAN	Burnley
1780	1780	1740	1780	174211	LAN	Clitheroe
KIPPIN						
1810	1880	1800	1900	123021	SRY	Ewell
KIPPING						
1880	1992	1700	1880	155497	BKM	High Wycombe
KIPPS						
1784	1992	ALL	ALL	140023	ALL	ALL
....	....	ALL	ALL	159840	SRY	Bermondsey
KIRBY						
1800	1850	ALL	ALL	141739	AVN	Bath
1742	1828	1720	1780	108510	BRK	Wargrave
1742	1807	1720	1780	108510	BRK	Wokingham
1720	1940	....	....	128996	CAM	Thorney
1725	1735	1700	1750	171158	DEV	Halberton
1741	1949	ALL	ALL	141615	LEI	Great Glen
1824	1900	1700	1824	104744	LND	Newington
1866	1992	?	1866	156337	MDX	Kensington
1855	1945	ALL	1855	117366	NFK	North Walsham
1800	1900	1750	1800	142913	NTH	Ashley
KIRBY contd.						
1878	1881	ALL	1879	155683	SRY	Lambeth
....	....	1775	1841	130621	STS	Bradeley By Stafford
1612	1693	1550	1693	102830	WAR	Warwick
1870	1890	1800	1920	149691	WIL	Alderbury
1600	1800	1600	1800	167924	YKS	Kirby Underdale
1795	1807	1743	1841	116114	YKS	Ruston
1756	....	1700	....	134589	YKS	Thorner
1790	1820	1770	1790	128368	YKS	Thornhill
1820	....	1750	....	134589	YKS	Westow
KIRCHER						
....	....	ALL	ALL	140074	ALL	Name Study
KIRK						
1800	1900	1700	....	111724	ALL	ALL
1800	1960	1700	1860	127353	BKM	Drayton Parslow
1895	1992	....	1895	105295	CLV	Middlesbrough
....	....	1750	1950	115622	DBY	ALL
1789	1824	1789	1824	136980	DOW	Comber
1811	1865	....	1811	175552	FIF	Ceres
1803	....	1803	1900	167932	KKD	Gatehouse
1788	1788	1750	1788	163783	LAN	Kirkham
1829	1884	1800	1900	125865	LEI	Leister
....	....	1700	1820	113697	LEI	Loughborough
1757	1851	1720	1851	151599	LEI	Thrussington
1920	....	1920	....	162663	LIN	West
1670	1830	1670	1830	103721	LIN	Althorpe
1840	1920	1800	1920	103721	LIN	Belton In Axholme
1800	1830	1800	1830	103721	LIN	Burringham
1740	1819	ALL	1800	152838	LIN	Marshchapel
1667	1700	1600	1667	177393	NTT	Clayworth
1798	1900	1600	1900	124834	NTT	East Leake
1769	1890	....	1769	101761	NTT	Lowdham
1700	1730	....	....	177393	NTT	South Wheatley
1895	1992	....	1895	105295	NYK	Brompton
1895	1992	....	1895	105295	NYK	Thornton Le Beans
1812	....	....	1812	167053	OXF	Checkendon
1797	1852	1841	1891	146560	PER	Perth
1861	....	....	....	127140	RFW	Greenock
1820	1863	1750	1820	113697	RUT	Uppingham
1797	1852	1841	1891	146560	SCT	Edinburgh
1800	1880	1750	1900	112879	WAR	Coventry
1720	....	1650	....	134589	YKS	Haxby
1682	1920	ALL	1730	146145	YKS	Kilburn
1805	1837	1700	1805	166723	YKS	Leeds
1895	1992	....	....	105295	YKS	Middlesbrough
1682	1920	ALL	1730	146145	YKS	Wass
KIRKBANK						
1600	1850	1500	1850	114383	CMA	Whicham
KIRKBRIDE						
1800	1840	1750	1860	137278	YKS	Pateley Bridge
KIRKBRIGHT						
1600	1670	1900	1950	112372	YKS	Nidderdale
KIRKBY						
1350	1400	1300	1400	154881	ALL	ALL
1911	1913	....	1911	129518	ESS	Westham
1546	1652	1300	1600	145459	HAM	Romsey
....	....	1700	1800	118168	LAN	Cartmel
1688	1727	1565	1688	141291	LAN	Dalton In Furness
1844	1893	1800	1840	128333	LAN	Lancaster
1885	1992	1800	1885	135461	LIN	North
1800	1992	....	....	176125	LIN	Asterby
1800	1992	....	....	176125	LIN	Goulceby
1911	1913	....	1911	129518	LND	???
1819	1838	?	1820	164976	NTT	Stapleford
1813	1867	....	....	156418	NYK	Burneston
1779	1992	1500	1779	114588	NYK	Leeds
1742	1916	1700	1742	156418	NYK	Ripon
KIRKE						
1891	1909	....	....	116017	LND	Battersea
1884	1891	....	....	116017	LND	Chelsea
1909	1992	....	....	116017	LND	Tottenham
....	1670	1550	1670	148288	NTT	Clifton
1680	1940	....	....	134007	NTT	East Markham
....	....	1750	1900	115622	YKS	East Riding
KIRKHAM						
1796	....	1650	1796	139386	CHS	Aldford
1743	1890	1680	1850	143286	CHS	Daresbury
....	1855	....	....	139386	CHS	Pulford
1800	1850	1700	1800	140082	DBY	Parwich
1680	1740	1700	1750	161357	ESS	Gt Easton
1750	1900	1750	1900	125237	LAN	Darwen
1800	1880	1880	1992	162256	LAN	Darwen
1800	1852	1700	1992	159468	LAN	Fylde

Known From	To	Researching From	To	Ref	Cty	Place
KIRKHAM contd.						
1800	....	1700	1850	135348	LAN	Kirkham
1813	1992	1790	1851	176109	LND	Marylebone
1765	1821	....	....	173827	WOR	Droitwich
1877	1900	....	....	162833	???	Bradford
1850	....	....	....	140082	???	Manchester
KIRKIN						
1740	1851	1700	1870	173622	HRT	Cheshunt
KIRKLAND						
1861	1992	....	....	121290	DBY	Derby
1835	1840	1800	1850	105120	DBY	Mugginton
1768	1861	....	....	121290	DBY	Spondon Derby
1840	1960	1860	1960	151106	LAN	Rochdale
1905	1992	1700	1900	111694	NTT	Screveton
KIRKLY						
1724	1724	ALL	1724	154563	DUR	Weardale
KIRKMAN						
1771	1789	1650	1770	131245	DBY	Sandiacre
1860	1992	1860	1992	140090	LND	North
1860	1992	1860	1992	140090	LND	South
KIRKPATRICK						
1847	1933	1800	1847	146900	ANT	Belfast
1752	1782	....	....	138851	CMA	Carlisle
1727	1836	1700	1830	162507	DFS	Closeburn
1689	1884	1600	1891	160636	KKD	Dundrennan
1847	1933	1800	1847	146900	LKS	Glasgow
KIRKUP						
1800	1900	1750	1992	108855	NBL	Alnwick
....	....	1700	1850	108855	NBL	Yarm
....	....	1700	1850	108855	YKS	Yarm
KIRKWOOD						
1787	1992	1869	1900	166286	KEN	Deal
1787	1992	ALL	1787	166286	KEN	Walmer
1800	1900	1750	1830	102024	LAN	Manchester
1870	....	ALL	ALL	169897	LKS	Blantyre
1858	1924	....	....	132381	LKS	Glasgow
1850	1970	1830	1955	155004	LKS	Glasgow
1787	1992	1869	1900	166286	LND	East
1787	1992	1869	1900	166286	LND	Deptford
1753	1787	1753	1787	166286	SCT	Paisley
1787	1992	ALL	1787	166286	SSX	Cuckmere Haven
1760	1830	1700	1850	155004	STI	Kilsyth
KIRLEW						
1500	1800	1500	1920	121096	EYK	Hemingborough
1850	1960	ALL	ALL	162469	YKS	North
KIRNUT						
1700	1715	ALL	1700	117994	HAM	Ovington
KIRSOP						
1774	1824	....	....	117625	DUR	Consett
1851	1992	1851	1992	118095	NBL	Newcastle On Tyne
1795	1813	1795	1813	118095	NBL	Simonburn
1698	1774	1600	1698	117625	NBL	Warden
1827	1850	....	....	117625	YKS	Deighton
KIRSOPP						
1875	....	....	....	140104	DUR	Gateshead
1849	1992	....	....	140104	NBL	Hexham
1683	1768	1600	1800	160873	NBL	Simonburn
KIRSTING						
1810	1842	....	....	168041	MDX	Bow
KIRTLAND						
1749	1749	1700	1800	167002	NTH	Haselbech
KIRTLEY						
1723	1858	1820	1850	153842	DUR	Monkwearmouth
1836	1932	....	....	157988	DUR	Stanley
1723	1858	1820	1850	153842	DUR	Tanfield
KIRTON						
1800	1850	1800	1992	119725	ABD	New Deer
1875	1885	1850	1900	123765	DUR	Stockton
1820	1878	1750	1820	107093	MDX	London
1750	1900	....	....	153583	NTH	Bugbrooke
KIRWAN						
1880	1891	1800	1992	139181	LAN	Newton
KIRWOOD						
1600	....	....	....	124508	HEF	Eardisland
1670	....	....	....	124508	LND	Holborn
KISBEY						
....	....	1700	1770	154873	KEN	Sittingbourne
KISBY						
1673	1940	....	....	128996	CAM	Thorney
1633	1748	....	1780	171441	KEN	Borden
KITCAT						
....	....	ALL	ALL	171441	ALL	Name Study
KITCHELL						
1800	1916	....	....	145394	SSX	Chichester
KITCHEN						
1731	....	....	1731	108839	HUN	Godmanchester
1775	....	1775	....	109347	LAN	Goosnargh
1775	....	1775	....	109347	LAN	Stonyhurst
1850	1870	1800	1850	101826	OXF	Burford
1810	1833	1650	1810	139769	OXF	Oxford
1850	1870	1800	1850	101826	OXF	Witney
1666	1747	....	1666	101761	WRY	Whitgift
1738	1786	1700	1738	145327	WYK	Hampsthwaite
1799	1899	1750	1799	138584	YKS	Horsforth
1713	....	1680	1720	170348	YKS	Throapham
KITCHEN-HEDGER						
1788	?	ALL	ALL	166243	SRY	Worplesdon
KITCHENER						
....	....	ALL	ALL	166758	ALL	Name Study
ALL	ALL	ALL	ALL	166758	ALL	ALL
1850	1899	ALL	1992	150630	HRT	Aston
1850	1899	ALL	1992	150630	HRT	Benington
KITCHER						
1860	1992	1830	1992	148083	HAM	Lymington
ALL	ALL	....	....	153397	HAM	New Forest
1861	1992	1861	1871	148083	JSY	???
KITCHIN						
1706	....	1600	1706	116637	DUR	Durham City
1833	1906	....	1992	137642	KEN	Hythe
1856	1877	ALL	ALL	118168	LAN	Manchester
1913	1923	ALL	ALL	118168	SRY	Croydon
1650	1800	1800	1840	148113	YKS	Doncaster
KITCHIN.						
1692	1754	1600	1692	152196	CMA	Irton
KITCHING						
1840	1900	1840	1992	140120	DUR	Auckland
1800	1950	1700	1800	140112	DUR	Auckland
1800	1950	1700	1800	140112	DUR	Shildon
1836	1889	1700	1850	126772	LEI	Thurgarton
1800	1821	1750	1800	161896	LND	Southwark
1787	1860	1780	1860	140120	YKS	North
1757	1780	1600	1757	140120	YKS	West Rounton
KITCHINGS						
1848	....	1800	1992	166197	WOR	Longdon
KITE						
1881	1897	1841	1881	178381	GLS	Naunton
1803	1992	1700	1803	166804	HAM	Andover
1864	1939	1300	1992	152501	KEN	Hoo
1900	1927	1500	1927	164992	KEN	River
1817	1950	....	....	154091	MDX	Islington
1773	1841	1700	1773	178381	OXF	Shilton
....	....	ALL	1817	154091	WOR	Evesham
KITSON						
1719	1787	ALL	ALL	175005	CAM	Bourn
?	?	1500	1992	101303	SAL	ALL
1820	1851	....	....	102741	SAL	Coalbrookdale
1890	1992	1500	1890	101303	SAL	Ironbridge
1700	1800	1700	1800	169781	SOM	Bath
1838	1952	1750	1838	145823	SRY	Lambeth
1850	1992	1800	1992	161640	YKS	Bradford
1734	1760	?	1734	128910	YKS	Knaresborough
1796	1880	1880	1992	128910	YKS	Marr
....	....	ALL	ALL	155632	YKS	West ryding
1760	1782	....	....	128910	YKS	York
KITT						
1847	1992	1700	1847	140147	CON	Saltash
1847	1992	1700	1847	140147	CON	Trematon
1860	1889	ALL	ALL	140155	DEV	Plymouth
KITTERMASTER						
1550	1900	....	....	100420	WAR	ALL
KITTLETY						
1780	1920	....	1780	159972	SOM	Bath
KITTO						
1775	1825	1750	1850	136867	CON	Breage
....	....	1700	1900	136972	CON	Breage
....	....	1700	1900	136972	CON	Germoe
1837	1889	1889	1992	162973	CON	Likeard
1700	....	1700	1850	116920	CON	Mavagissey
1837	1925	1600	1992	104302	CON	Redruth
1650	....	1650	1850	116920	CON	St Ewe
KITTOW						
1837	1889	1889	....	162973	CON	Linkinhorne
1837	1889	1889	1992	162973	CON	Liskeard
KITTRIDGE						
....	....	1830	1880	129313	CHS	Congleton
1880	1992	1750	1880	140163	DEV	Plymouth
1861	1866	1854	1880	129313	LAN	Droylsden
....	....	1800	1880	140163	LEI	???

Known From	To	Researching From	To	Ref	Cty	Place
KITTS						
1893	1900	....	....	135070	LND	Poplar
KLELTY						
1902	....	1900	1910	163775	MDX	Kensington
KLIEN						
1890	1930	1850	1950	133922	JSY	St Helier
KLOODHOUSE						
1903	1910	ALL	ALL	151696	LND	Lambeth
KNAGGS						
1880	1890	1800	1992	135011	YKS	Pickering
1750	1760	1700	1750	158976	YKS	Skelton
KNAPE						
1787	1808	1700	1786	131245	LND	Queenhithe
KNAPMAN						
1756	1992	1600	1756	110752	DEV	Ashburton
?	?	?	?	101591	DEV	South Brent
1780	1871	....	....	159751	DEV	South Hams
KNAPP						
....	....	1800	1910	140198	KEN	Sandwich
1823	1851	ALL	ALL	112275	LEI	North East
1817	1923	1700	1923	174076	NTH	Kettering
....	....	1740	....	174963	SOM	Kilmersden
1663	1992	1500	1663	114588	WIL	Chippenham
KNAPTON						
1687	1782	1600	1687	137979	YKS	Barwick In Elmet
1761	1900	1600	1761	154172	YKS	Pontefract
KNEATH						
1891	....	....	1891	126519	GLA	Swansea
KNEEBONE						
1874	1930	1700	1992	153540	DEV	Devonport
KNELL						
1750	1850	1600	1750	158984	DOR	Cerne Abbas
ALL	ALL	ALL	ALL	166243	KEN	Luddenham
....	1895	1800	1895	140201	LND	Camberwell
KNELLER						
1750	1900	ALL	ALL	152226	HAM	Kings Somborne
KNIBB						
1845	1845	1700	1845	120081	NTH	South
1635	1635	....	....	103632	NTH	Northampton
KNIBBS						
1751	1832	1700	1751	164267	OXF	Witney
KNIFE						
1590	1733	ALL	ALL	107255	BRK	Bray
1617	1729	ALL	ALL	107255	BRK	Wargrave
1729	1825	ALL	ALL	107255	BRK	Winkfield
1851	1851	ALL	ALL	107255	GLS	Bisley
1825	1876	ALL	ALL	107255	LND	Marylebone
KNIFTON						
....	....	1750	1992	160245	LEI	Wymeswold
1815	1914	1650	1815	172448	NTT	East Leake
KNIGHT						
1880	1910	1600	1992	168831	AVN	Easton
....	....	1770	1800	103713	BDF	Elstow
....	....	1650	1700	106127	BRK	Hurst
1567	1567	1530	1570	124974	BRK	Kintbury
....	....	1650	1700	106127	BRK	Shinfield
....	....	1650	1700	106127	BRK	Swallowfield
1839	1992	ALL	1839	146757	CHS	Warrington
1782	1807	1700	1782	152196	CMA	Carlisle
1749	1792	1700	1749	152196	CMA	St Bees
1840	1858	1700	1860	170615	CON	Creed
1630	1649	1600	1630	102571	CON	Gulval
1890	1941	1800	1992	160156	CON	St Agnes
1810	1858	1700	1900	106186	CON	St Austell
1630	1649	1600	1630	102571	CON	Zennor
....	....	ALL	ALL	152226	DEV	Bampton
1815	1860	1765	1815	136220	DEV	Beaworthy
....	....	1600	1992	140279	DEV	Black Torrington
1695	1695	1600	1720	105333	DEV	Buckland In The Moor
1793	1850	1770	1900	142638	DEV	Hatherleigh
1695	1695	1600	1720	105333	DEV	Holne
1695	1695	1600	1720	105333	DEV	Ilsington
1823	1850	1800	1870	142638	DEV	Lamerton
1695	1695	1600	1720	105333	DEV	Lydford
1800	1910	1820	1910	172634	DEV	Sampford Peverell
1695	1695	1600	1720	105333	DEV	Widecombe In The Moor
1590	1854	1854	1992	112941	DEV	Yarcombe
1880	1992	1880	1963	140295	GLA	Cardiff
....	....	1850	1920	106607	GLS	Cheltenham
1800	1840	1750	1992	173096	GLS	Uley
1750	1800	ALL	ALL	130508	HAM	Andover
1780	1800	1750	1850	149993	HAM	Cheriton

Known From	To	Researching From	To	Ref	Cty	Place
KNIGHT contd.						
1400	1700	1400	1700	144657	HAM	Farringdon
1810	1860	ALL	ALL	169730	HAM	Froyle
1790	1880	ALL	1790	150983	HAM	Portsea
1785	1810	ALL	ALL	169730	HAM	Weston Patrick
1710	1710	1650	1750	136840	HAM	Winchester
1793	1853	1757	1793	112364	HRT	Chipping Barnet
1727	1894	1700	1750	169730	HRT	Standon
1686	1686	?	1686	158569	HRT	???
1785	....	....	1785	171441	KEN	Ash
1600	1650	ALL	1600	131059	KEN	Cowden
1727	....	....	1727	177504	KEN	Shorn
1702	1728	....	1740	171441	KEN	Stockbury
1789	1833	....	....	171441	KEN	Wickhambreux
?	?	?	?	166642	KEN	???
1830	....	1700	1947	109223	LAN	Broughton
1836	1860	1700	1860	178233	LAN	Manchester
1830	....	1700	1947	109223	LAN	Urmston
1775	1913	1700	1775	116106	LIN	Blankney
1775	1913	1700	1775	116106	LIN	Martin
1775	1913	1700	1775	116106	LIN	Stapleford
1775	1913	1700	1775	116106	LIN	Washingborough
1850	1920	....	....	143464	LND	Islington
1850	1992	1850	1992	106119	LND	Shoreditch
1809	....	....	1809	133566	LND	St Marylebone
1800	1850	1750	1850	166022	LND	???
1853	1853	1800	1854	174130	MDX	Kensington
1900	1920	1900	1950	135925	MDX	Staines
....	....	ALL	1800	119326	MLN	Duddingston
....	....	ALL	1800	119326	MLN	Newbattle
....	....	ALL	1800	119326	MLN	Newton
1845	1875	1800	1845	155691	NTH	Cosgrove
1815	....	....	....	148156	NTH	Little Billing
1805	1805	1780	1805	103632	NTH	Northampton
1736	1780	ALL	1780	168718	NTH	Sudborough
1810	1850	1850	....	130443	NTH	???
1559	1950	ALL	ALL	164143	NTT	Gunthorpe
1811	1960	ALL	1811	168742	NTT	Worksop
....	....	1650	1700	106127	OXF	Faringdon
1835	1859	1835	1859	178705	OXF	Northmoor
1820	1850	1700	1820	151769	RUT	Oakham
1870	1884	1870	1885	140295	SOM	Bridewater
1730	1890	1700	1900	140295	SOM	Broomfield
1840	1992	1700	1992	152226	SOM	Evercreech
1620	1680	....	....	142522	SOM	Kingsbury
1800	1820	ALL	ALL	152226	SOM	Milverton
....	....	1600	1896	176117	SOM	Taunton
1800	1820	ALL	ALL	152226	SOM	Wiveliscombe
1801	1805	1805	1840	176257	SRY	Addington
1897	1897	1897	1930	174130	SRY	Croydon
1819	1898	....	....	127779	SRY	Egham
1832	1860	ALL	ALL	156558	SRY	Farnham
1850	1900	1850	1950	167401	SRY	Reigate
1770	1940	....	1940	109568	SRY	Shertsey
....	....	1800	1992	163244	SRY	???
1780	1855	1750	1860	116483	SSX	Burton Cum Coates
....	....	1700	1850	167401	SSX	Ifield
1830	1879	1811	1879	138312	SSX	Itchingfield
1800	1850	1600	1900	120677	SSX	Rogate
1765	1780	1700	1800	131547	SSX	Rudgwick
1809	1992	1500	1809	128872	SSX	Slinfold
1810	1858	ALL	1810	115010	SSX	Slinford
1732	1800	1600	1732	133132	STS	Millwich
1810	1835	ALL	....	132349	SXE	Seaford
1769	1769	1700	1800	167002	SXW	Horsted Keynes
1840	....	1750	1840	121010	WAR	Birmingham
1850	1970	1700	1850	140260	WAR	Birmingham
1800	1850	1775	1800	101796	WAR	Solihull
1780	1992	1700	1900	140287	WAR	Stratford On Avon
1745	1798	1650	1744	131245	WAR	Stretton On Dunsmore
1824	1992	1800	1992	161861	WIL	Figheldean
1835	1911	ALL	....	132349	WIL	Wilford
1680	1800	1650	1680	140309	WOR	Badsey
1782	1820	ALL	1782	115126	WOR	Little Comberton
KNIGHT-PITT						
1859	1977	1859	....	148687	LND	Mile End
KNIGHTLEY						
1795	1808	....	1795	164321	MDX	East London
KNIGHTON						
1825	1913	1825	1913	112852	DBY	Cotmanhay
1680	1800	1550	1800	100927	NTH	Raunds
KNIGHTS						
1770	....	1700	1770	140317	ESS	East Donyland

Known From	To	Researching From	To	Ref	Cty	Place
KNIGHTS contd.						
1898	1980	1900	1980	140325	ESS	Kirby Le Soken
1770	....	1700	1770	140317	ESS	Wivenhoe
1881	....	ALL	ALL	155373	LND	Shoreditch
1850	1900	1800	1900	140325	NFK	Carbrooke
1690	1800	1600	1850	140325	NFK	Carleton Rode
1860	1940	1850	1940	140325	NFK	Caston
1841	1992	ALL	ALL	154490	NFK	Crimplesham
....	....	1700	1790	129127	NFK	Forncett St Peter
1620	1900	1600	1900	140325	NFK	Forncett St Peter
1850	1960	1800	1960	140325	NFK	Griston
1800	1850	ALL	ALL	100161	SFK	Kessingland
1726	1992	1700	1900	166960	SFK	Leiston
1726	1992	1700	1900	166960	SFK	Marlesford
KNIPE						
....	....	ALL	ALL	112895	ALL	Name Study
1820	1850	....	1820	169188	LND	Westminster
KNIVET						
1753	1829	1650	1753	118397	SFK	Dennington
KNIVETON						
1287	1693	1550	1693	102830	DBY	Ashbourne
1846	....	1700	1846	140716	LEI	Wymeswold
1904	1960	....	....	121290	???	Derby
KNOPP						
....	....	ALL	1810	155470	ESS	Boxted
1801	1992	1500	1801	128872	ESS	Elmstead
....	....	ALL	1810	155470	SFK	Stoke By Nayland
KNOTT						
1869	1992	1789	1869	107190	CLV	Thornaby On Tees
1810	1900	....	1820	179213	DEV	Buckfastleigh
1840	1872	1800	1840	128368	DEV	Okehampton
....	....	1700	1810	179213	DEV	South Brent
1779	1870	1700	1779	145823	DOR	Sherborne
1800	1899	1800	1899	169781	DUR	Laithkirk
1788	1878	1750	1902	153508	HAM	Kingsley
1858	1992	1800	1992	141046	KEN	Ashford
1854	1854	1820	1870	141046	KEN	Dover
1750	1750	....	....	159883	KEN	Hougham
1780	1803	1780	....	116297	KEN	Lenham
1840	1880	ALL	ALL	117145	LAN	Bolton
1851	1900	....	....	135968	LAN	Bolton
1780	1805	ALL	ALL	124982	LAN	Lancaster
1850	1900	1850	1900	121223	LAN	Manchester
1787	1820	1760	1840	170348	LAN	Rochdale
1866	....	....	1866	126519	MDX	Edmonton
1700	1799	1700	1799	169781	SOM	Dawdrip
1700	1799	1700	1799	169781	SOM	Dinnington
1816	1867	1750	1830	150738	WAR	Cilvers Coton
1780	1805	ALL	ALL	124982	WES	ALL
KNOTTLEY						
1850	1878	ALL	1992	125113	SRY	Clapham
KNOW						
1800	1992	1558	1800	140341	KEN	Hoo
KNOWL						
....	....	1600	ALL	115142	WAR	???
KNOWLDEN						
1880	1920	....	....	121460	LND	???
1600	1850	ALL	ALL	174637	MDX	London
KNOWLER						
1790	1830	1700	1900	166804	KEN	Faversham
1741	1770	1600	1741	170542	KEN	Sandwich
KNOWLES						
1946	....	....	....	145742	AVN	Bristol
1880	1890	1870	1900	149144	CHI	St Peter Port
1812	1840	ALL	1812	146757	CHS	Warrington
1801	1822	ALL	1822	139149	DBY	Bakewell
1559	1749	1550	1633	102830	DBY	Matlock
1772	1957	1700	1804	136816	DBY	Matlock
1772	1957	1700	1804	136816	DBY	Tansley
1860	1880	....	....	140376	DUR	Stockton
1947	1950	....	....	140368	ESS	Upminster
1870	1934	1891	1992	139602	GLA	Cardiff
1760	1769	....	....	135437	GLS	Frampton
1787	1787	....	....	135437	GLS	Slimbridge
1976	1985	....	....	140368	HAM	Basingstoke
1960	1986	....	....	140368	HAM	Farnborough
....	....	1630	1900	166278	HAM	???
1890	1992	1800	1992	127353	HUN	Conington
1879	....	1850	1900	127353	HUN	Gt Whyte
?	?	?	?	154687	KEN	Ashford
1826	1867	1860	1992	172243	KEN	Woolwich
1840	....	....	....	133094	LAN	Denton
1650	1800	....	....	177318	LAN	Horswich
1835	1851	1805	1850	136565	LAN	Manchester
KNOWLES contd.						
1590	1830	1830	1992	162256	LAN	Quarlton
1700	1860	ALL	ALL	173010	LAN	Tunstall
1700	1860	ALL	ALL	173010	LAN	Wigan
1830	1924	1800	1924	133248	LEI	Market Harboro
....	....	....	....	140376	LIN	Dalderby
....	....	....	....	140376	LIN	Haltham
1810	1889	....	....	169498	LIN	Holbeach
....	....	....	....	140376	LIN	Nettleham
1820	1900	....	1820	140376	LIN	Welton
....	....	....	....	140376	LIN	Willingham
1871	1891	ALL	ALL	139602	LND	ALL
1885	....	1881	1885	147257	MDX	Chiswick
1885	....	1881	1885	147257	MDX	Gunnersbury
1840	1858	1750	1900	116106	MDX	Heston
1762	1784	1762	1992	109819	NFK	Hemsby
1821	1861	....	....	140368	NTT	Oldcotes
1957	1960	....	....	140368	RUT	Ketton
1717	....	1660	1730	160873	SAL	Wenlock
1785	1866	ALL	1992	139602	SOM	Langport
1785	1866	1866	1992	139602	SOM	Taunton
1864	1888	1851	1888	147257	SRY	Lambeth
....	....	1790	1890	166278	SRY	???
1700	1750	1600	1700	163015	SSX	West
1766	1890	ALL	1966	149799	SYK	Campsall
1717	1767	1700	1780	160873	WOR	Great Witley
1728	1992	....	....	134619	WOR	Oldswinford
1807	1820	....	....	140368	YKS	Austerfield
1737	1770	....	....	140368	YKS	Batley
1847	1898	....	....	140368	YKS	Bentley With Arksey
1880	1970	1700	1900	167606	YKS	Bradford
1807	1843	....	....	140368	YKS	Cantley
1646	1719	....	....	140368	YKS	Dewsbury
1808	1814	....	....	140368	YKS	Finningley
1700	1861	1650	1880	110728	YKS	Horbury
1877	1947	....	....	140368	YKS	Hull
1860	1930	1860	1992	114901	YKS	Hunslet
1768	1780	1740	1992	114901	YKS	Milford
1683	....	....	....	151351	YKS	Otley
1880	1970	1700	1900	167606	YKS	Ripon
1776	1780	....	....	140368	YKS	Rossington
1800	1828	1800	1992	114901	YKS	Selby
1825	1860	1800	1992	114901	YKS	Thirsk
1829	....	....	....	127140	YKS	???
KNOWLING						
1620	1992	1300	1992	140392	ALL	ALL
1600	1700	1600	1850	177180	HRT	Tring
KNOWLSON						
1760	1840	1680	1760	137278	YKS	Stillington
KNOWLTON						
1785	1869	1785	1869	139971	BDF	Podington
1861	1881	1861	1881	139971	ESS	Aveley
1814	1836	1700	1836	172294	HAM	ALL
KNOWLYS						
1600	1950	ALL	1992	100536	ESS	???
1600	1950	ALL	1992	100536	SFK	???
KNOX						
1820	....	1750	1820	108596	AYR	ALL
1871	1907	ALL	ALL	149004	LDY	Limovady
1630	1803	....	....	131229	MAY	Killala
1630	1803	....	....	131229	MAY	Moyne
1850	1900	1700	1900	160954	MSY	Liverpool
1817	1961	1750	1817	128406	NBL	ALL
1760	1790	ALL	1770	142301	NBL	Warkworth
1798	1881	1790	1900	119725	ROX	Jedburgh
KNUCKEY						
1830	1992	ALL	ALL	111961	CON	St Gluvias
1680	1850	1650	1850	142123	CON	Stithians
KOLTER						
....	....	ALL	ALL	130818	LND	Whitechapel
KOWIESON						
....	....	1700	1830	142670	ROX	Orchard
KRAKER						
1844	1900	ALL	ALL	141704	SRY	Croydon
KRALL						
1800	1960	1700	1800	173223	???	???
KRELLE						
1807	1851	1700	1807	160601	LND	???
KRINKS						
....	....	....	1992	127086	ALL	ALL
KUCK						
1790	1992	....	....	140414	LND	Spitalfield
KURN						
1830	1851	1800	1851	119059	SRY	Godalming

Known From	To	Researching From	To	Ref	Cty	Place
KYBERD						
1854	1874	1800	1854	178608	MDX	Hackney
KYFFIN						
....	....	ALL	ALL	140422	ALL	Name Study
1788	1850	1788	1821	140422	DEN	Llanwryst
KYFFYN						
1856	1900	1856	1992	140422	DEN	Wrexham
KYLE						
1850	1960	1890	1992	150371	CUL	Brewcastle
1750	1992	1780	1992	106305	DOW	???
1860	1960	1700	1850	150371	ROX	Castleton
1850	1992	1750	1850	122513	TYR	Newton Stewart
KYME						
1500	....	....	....	100536	KEN	???
KYNARDSLEY						
1000	1340	900	1340	124974	HEF	Kinnersley
KYNASTON						
1450	1500	1350	1500	154881	SAL	Moreton
KYNE						
....	....	ALL	ALL	121029	ALL	Name Study
1800	1861	1750	1800	103896	DEV	ALL
1784	1992	1684	1784	140430	LND	Central
KYNNERSLEY						
1734	1813	ALL	1734	171980	STS	Uttoxeter
KYNSEY						
1800	1880	1800	1880	177288	CHS	Knutsford
KYTHELL						
1821	1821	1800	1840	177970	PER	???
KYVELYOC						
....	....	1100	1232	124974	CHS	Chester
L ANGLOIS						
....	....	ALL	ALL	155632	JSY	Channel Islands
L'ESTRANGE						
1830	....	1780	1850	119970	DUB	Huntstown
LA COUTURE						
1608	1608	ALL	ALL	115126	CHI	ALL
LA FEUVRE						
1780	1816	ALL	ALL	115126	CHI	ALL
LA ROCHE						
1676	1966	ALL	1731	108642	MDX	Chelsea
1676	1966	ALL	1731	108642	MDX	Soho
LA TOUCHE						
1841	1992	1600	1841	124281	IRL	Ireland
1841	1992	1600	1841	124281	WAR	Birmingham
LA ZOUCH						
1100	1349	1100	1350	154881	LEI	Ashby
LABAT						
1693	1900	1800	1900	119105	IRL	Dublin
LABBETT						
1748	1900	1720	1760	137413	DEV	Crediton
LABBITT						
1790	1828	1700	1830	179337	DEV	Braunton
LABERT						
1850	1900	1860	1900	140422	SRY	Rotherhithe
LABRAM						
....	....	ALL	ALL	140457	ALL	Name Study
LABRUM						
....	....	1700	1899	174963	BDF	Chalgrave
....	....	1700	1899	174963	BDF	Toddington
1864	1885	1840	1885	147486	NTH	Northampton
....	....	1700	1799	174963	NTH	???
1800	1992	1700	1992	165344	WAR	Rugby
LACE						
1650	1815	1600	1851	150304	IOM	Bride
1635	1992	ALL	1635	129992	IOM	Isle Of Man
LACEY						
1807	1825	1807	1825	119059	ALL	ALL
1558	1861	1558	1861	125229	BKM	Great Hampden
1813	1841	1788	1856	125229	BKM	Gt Missenden
1619	1940	1619	1949	125229	BKM	Hughenden
1740	1861	1740	1861	125229	BKM	Princes Risborough
1727	1810	1727	1812	125229	BKM	Saunderton
1784	1871	....	....	172154	BRK	Cookham
1775	1992	1700	1775	140473	DEV	Devonport
1775	1992	1700	1775	140473	DEV	Plymouth
1613	1613	ALL	1620	129283	ESS	Kelvedon
1851	1922	....	....	179108	GLS	Bitton
1876	1945	....	....	179108	GLS	Bristol
1826	1910	....	....	179108	GLS	Oldland
1777	1838	1600	1838	145289	HAM	Isle Of Wight
1840	1992	1800	1840	167568	IOW	ALL
1858	1861	....	....	117374	LIN	Grantham
1807	1820	1780	1860	119059	MDX	Chelsea
1861	1870	1700	1861	172588	MDX	London
LACEY contd.						
1748	1789	....	....	117374	NTT	Nottingham
1850	1992	1800	1850	140465	SOM	Bath
....	....	1749	1833	130079	SOM	Crewkerne
1770	1790	1750	1792	109746	WOR	Bromsgrove
LACK						
1618	1780	1500	1800	143693	BKM	Beaconsfield
1748	1837	....	1851	137405	CAM	Willingham
1770	1845	1700	1770	101958	LND	Shoreditch
1828	1845	1828	1851	156892	LND	Shoreditch
1760	1793	....	1760	151688	NFK	Lessingham
1830	1845	1828	1845	156892	NFK	Walsingham
1700	1992	ALL	ALL	164682	NFK	Wells Next The Sea
1826	1826	1775	1882	107360	NTH	Harlestone
1775	1870	1539	1850	107360	NTH	Kingsthorpe
LACKEY						
1869	1957	1869	1901	129100	MDX	Hoxton
LACY						
1560	1770	1500	1800	142123	BDF	Shillington
1717	1800	1600	1717	158739	GLA	St Georges
1808	1927	1750	1820	173649	SRY	Southwark
1765	1992	1700	1780	140481	YKS	East Riding
LADBROOK						
....	....	1800	1851	111414	ALL	ALL
1842	1842	1841	1851	111414	MDX	Bethnal Green
1812	1877	1500	1812	130583	WOR	Broadway
LADBROOKE						
....	....	ALL	1828	106178	ESS	Colchester
1828	1975	ALL	1828	106178	NFK	Central
1828	1975	ALL	1828	106178	NFK	South
....	....	ALL	1828	106178	SFK	???
LADD						
1600	1670	....	....	142522	KEN	Canterbury
1912	1992	1700	1912	158518	LIN	North Hykeham
....	....	....	1713	140503	SFK	Charsfield
....	....	....	1561	140503	SFK	Coddenham
....	....	....	1708	140503	SFK	Debach
....	....	1620	1780	140503	SFK	Framlingham
....	....	1780	1789	140503	SFK	Halesworth
....	....	1562	1585	140503	SFK	Holton St Peter
....	....	1610	1613	140503	SFK	Parham
1790	1840	....	....	140503	SFK	Southwald
1750	1850	1700	1850	156280	SRY	Shere
1789	1800	1740	1800	145300	WIL	East Coulston
1800	1810	1775	1800	168076	WIL	Edington
LADDS						
1805	1866	ALL	1805	164623	LND	Southwark
LADE						
1819	1912	1800	1992	167002	SXE	Warbleton
LADNER						
1785	1817	....	....	127957	CON	Perranuthnoe
LADWELL						
1768	1900	....	....	139823	NFK	Crostwick
1820	1992	1820	1992	139823	NFK	Oulton
LADYMAN						
1688	1713	1600	1800	130125	CUL	Dalston
LAFFER						
1760	1841	1760	1841	142018	SOM	Bath
LAFFORD						
1750	1992	1700	1750	121509	GLS	Maisey Hampton
1750	1992	1700	1750	121509	GLS	South Cerney
LAFLETT						
1800	1880	1800	1880	105759	MDX	Bethnal Green
LAFLIN						
....	....	ALL	ALL	140538	ALL	Name Study
1525	1992	ALL	ALL	140511	SFK	???
LAGER						
1819	1892	1800	1892	154709	DBY	ALL
LAGLAND						
1814	1960	1814	1992	168971	WOR	Leigh
LAGOE						
....	....	1550	1992	115142	WAR	Mancetter
LAIDLAW						
1871	1992	ALL	ALL	106658	CHS	Macclesfield
....	....	1700	1850	169501	DFS	Sanguhar
1841	1861	ALL	ALL	106658	LAN	Liverpool
1729	....	1700	1850	111848	LKS	Crawfordjohn
1740	1900	ALL	1740	115118	ROX	Cavers
....	....	1795	1830	154512	ROX	Lilliesleaf
LAIDLAW-MCLAUGHLAN						
1863	1871	1700	1920	139203	DUR	Sunderland
LAIDLER						
1550	1900	....	....	100420	WAR	Berkswell
1800	1900	....	....	100420	WAR	Meriden

Known From	To	Researching From	To	Ref	Cty	Place
LAIDMAN						
1760	1783	1600	1770	101575	YKS	Knottingley
1760	1783	1600	1770	101575	YKS	Pontefract
LAIGHTON						
1840	1910	1830	1920	100862	LND	East
LAILEY						
....	....	ALL	ALL	102024	ALL	Name Study
1700	1992	ALL	ALL	102024	ALL	ALL
1866	....	1700	....	132128	LND	Holburn
LAIMBEER						
1800	1992	ALL	ALL	154008	ALL	ALL
LAIN						
....	1780	ALL	1780	134511	LIN	Saltby
LAINCHBURY						
....	?	?	....	134457	OXF	Dean Spelsbury
LAING						
1775	1857	1750	1850	137057	ABD	Logie Coldstone
1798	1851	....	....	127140	ARL	Kintyre
1798	1851	....	....	127140	ARL	Southend
1808	1900	....	....	140554	BEW	Cockburnspath
1795	1888	ALL	ALL	106844	DUR	Central
....	....	1800	1907	125571	DUR	Hartlepool
1793	1927	....	....	127140	LKS	New Monkland
1800	1880	1700	1800	103896	LND	ALL
1860	1930	....	....	111260	LTN	Edinburgh
1860	1930	....	....	111260	MLN	Newington
1850	1992	1750	1850	140546	MLN	Penicuik
1756	1838	ALL	ALL	106844	NBL	Chollerton
....	....	1700	1795	106860	NBL	Chollerton
1850	1960	ALL	1850	156078	SCT	???
1723	1780	....	....	127140	STI	Kilsyth
LAINSTON						
1701	1730	1600	1701	145459	HAM	Hursley
LAIRD						
1750	1780	....	....	126497	CAI	Canisbay
1858	1992	1800	1992	140090	LKS	Glasgow
1820	1852	1700	1829	120367	LND	North East
1854	1992	1854	1992	140562	OKI	Firth
LAIT						
1855	1855	....	....	135437	NFK	E Dereham
LAITY						
1852	1992	1700	1852	101567	CON	Penzance
1852	1992	1700	1852	101567	CON	St Hilary
1700	1900	1700	1900	110523	CON	St Hilary
LAKE						
1815	1815	ALL	1900	112631	BKM	Farnham Royal
1740	1750	1721	1812	107360	BKM	Middle Claydon
1770	1869	1738	1904	107360	BKM	Stewkley
1755	1837	1755	1992	140570	CHS	Chester
1866	1949	1750	1866	107123	CHS	Macclesfield
1755	1837	1755	1992	140570	CHS	Neston
1811	1832	1700	1900	178322	DEV	Ashburton
1800	1992	1800	1960	173614	DEV	Barnstaple
1722	1722	ALL	1722	135143	DEV	Bideford
1786	1826	1650	1786	172898	DEV	Chudleigh
1740	1740	ALL	1800	173614	DEV	Wembworthy
1820	....	....	1820	177504	DEV	Whitestone
1820	1992	1700	1900	177369	DOR	Central
1902	....	....	....	133922	DOR	Cerne Abbas
1850	1992	ALL	1850	100536	ESS	???
1860	1861	1861	1865	140589	GLA	Aberdare
1861	1861	1861	1865	140589	GLA	Britton Ferry
1860	1861	1861	1865	140589	GLA	Merthyr Tydfil
1827	1850	1750	1850	108413	GLS	Bristol
1770	1850	1700	1850	142123	HRT	Pirton
1860	1930	1850	1950	118737	KEN	Chatham
1841	1845	1830	1855	179256	KEN	Deptford
1830	1845	1830	1855	179256	KEN	Greenwich
1768	1944	1500	1800	153230	LIN	Deeping
1790	1860	1700	1850	106313	MDX	Chiswick
1880	1940	1840	1900	172170	MDX	London
1813	1820	1700	1820	117013	NFK	Ingoldisthorpe
1840	1860	1840	1900	117536	NFK	Kings Lynn
....	....	1700	1992	140627	NFK	Norwich
1880	1960	1875	1920	107360	NTH	Roade
1825	1850	ALL	1850	118737	SFK	Toft Monks
1865	1865	1861	1885	140589	???	Bristol
1871	1921	ALL	1871	178195	???	Bristol
1865	1865	1861	1885	140589	???	Clifton
LAKELAND						
1804	1856	1750	1831	151912	LAN	Aighton
1804	1856	1750	1831	151912	LAN	Billington
LAKEMAN						
1720	1837	ALL	1720	102334	CON	Mevagissey

Known From	To	Researching From	To	Ref	Cty	Place
LAKEMAN contd.						
1907	1992	ALL	1907	124346	GLA	Swansea
1837	1992	1837	1992	102334	LAN	Liverpool
LAKER						
....	....	ALL	ALL	140597	ALL	Name Study
1857	....	1300	1992	152501	ESS	East Ham
....	....	1760	1841	130184	KEN	Ashford
1800	1992	ALL	ALL	140597	KEN	Canterbury
1700	1992	ALL	ALL	140597	KEN	Stowting
1558	1992	ALL	ALL	140597	SRY	Nutfield
1700	1992	ALL	ALL	140597	SSX	Billingshurst
1732	1992	ALL	ALL	140597	SSX	Horsham
1510	1730	ALL	ALL	140597	SSX	Loxwood
1591	1992	ALL	ALL	140597	SSX	Shipley
1880	1900	1700	1880	177237	SSX	Shipley
1746	1992	ALL	ALL	140597	SSX	Yapton
LAKEY						
1886	1904	....	....	106747	DEV	Plymouth
1846	1854	....	....	176885	NFK	Great Witchingham
1839	1841	1800	1839	176885	NFK	Lyng
1839	....	1800	1839	176885	NFK	West Bradenham
LAKIN						
1801	1858	ALL	ALL	130575	LEI	Leicester
1750	1837	....	....	122505	STS	Stoke On Trent
LALEY						
....	....	ALL	ALL	102024	ALL	ALL
LALLY						
1793	1816	....	....	131210	GAL	Galway
1852	1852	ALL	1852	119636	NIR	???
1848	1875	1838	1880	131210	OFF	Birr
LALOR						
1880	1883	1800	1900	127523	LEX	Ballyroan
1800	1877	1700	1950	118680	LEX	Rathdowney
1866	1883	1800	1866	127523	???	Abbeyleix
LAMACQ						
....	....	ALL	ALL	140600	ALL	Name Study
LAMB						
1865	1989	1700	1864	136859	ABD	Peterhead
1665	1720	1600	1700	153591	CON	St Columb Major
....	....	1800	1900	137782	CUL	ALL
1880	1914	1700	1880	146021	DBY	Ilkeston
1700	1900	1500	1900	125792	DOR	Sherborne
1690	1700	ALL	1690	131059	ESS	Bocking
1813	1832	1700	1813	120707	HAM	ALL
1851	1960	1800	1850	147907	HUN	Huntingdon
....	....	1770	1830	172871	IRL	Cork
1826	....	1800	1830	153737	IRL	Monaghan
1800	1850	1700	1992	131601	LAN	Cockerham
1800	1850	1700	1992	131601	LAN	Ellel
1800	1850	1700	1992	131601	LAN	Lancaster
1800	1850	1700	1992	131601	LAN	Lydiate
1813	1823	1800	1850	149047	LAN	Manchester
1859	1920	1800	1859	172871	MDX	Hampstead
....	1720	ALL	1720	134511	NTT	Linby
1816	1946	ALL	1816	115126	OXF	Great Tew
1650	1777	1600	1800	173983	OXF	Rolwright
1813	1921	....	....	139874	SCT	Glasgow
1813	1921	....	....	139874	SCT	Paisley
1814	1814	1700	?	125806	WOR	Bromsgrove
1770	....	....	....	131229	WOR	Salwarpe
1846	1980	....	1846	176702	WYK	Bradford
1850	1992	1700	1850	100803	WYK	Halifax
1626	....	....	....	151351	YKS	Kilwick In Craven
1850	1880	1850	1992	153737	YKS	Lleds
1857	1992	1600	1857	160172	YKS	North Rdg
1760	1780	1700	1760	158976	YKS	Skelton
LAMBE						
1500	1648	1450	1650	154881	KEN	Lambden
1830	1992	1292	1992	163945	SSX	Brighton
1830	1992	1292	1992	163945	SSX	Rye
1830	1992	1292	1992	163945	SSX	Wilmington
LAMBERT						
1820	....	1840	1992	151378	AVN	Clifton
1612	1780	ALL	1612	168602	BDF	Biddenham
1612	1780	ALL	1612	168602	BDF	Stagsden
1800	1808	1700	1800	100846	CLK	???
....	....	ALL	1810	147567	DOR	Longham
1720	1780	....	....	151351	DOR	Okeford Fitzpaine
1746	1746	ALL	ALL	130508	DUR	Stanhope
1867	1992	1300	1890	152501	ESS	East Ham
1898	1900	1898	1900	140422	ESS	Forest Gate
1750	1800	1700	1800	154601	EYK	Aughton
1821	1840	1500	1850	140619	HAM	Ringwood
1850	1992	1795	1992	140635	HAM	Southampton

Known From	To	Researching From	To	Ref	Cty	Place
LAMBERT contd.						
....	....	1750	1820	102717	HRT	Ware
....	....	....	....	172987	IOW	???
1845	1871	1800	1871	147575	KEN	Lewisham
1800	1880	1800	ALL	139181	LAN	Earlestown
....	....	1800	1992	147613	LAN	Tunstall
1820	1900	1820	1900	110523	LAN	???
1876	....	1800	1920	152129	LND	Central
1815	....	....	....	135488	LND	East
....	1890	1800	1890	142697	LND	Battersea
1878	1900	1870	1900	140422	LND	City
1890	1900	1850	1992	140619	MDX	Isleworth
1549	1608	1540	1650	107980	NFK	Oxnead
1798	1913	1600	1798	156779	NFK	Plumstead
1766	1933	1760	1992	171654	NTH	Potterpury
1784	1816	1780	1816	108901	NTT	Blyth
1814	1992	ALL	1814	161330	NTT	Nottingham
....	....	1700	1992	140627	SFK	Cookley
1814	1903	1700	1814	129712	SFK	Earl Stonham
1790	1860	1700	1790	163732	SFK	Redgrave
....	....	ALL	1725	103284	SFK	???
1300	1650	1300	1650	144657	SRY	Banstead
1900	1947	1850	1992	140619	SRY	Farnham
1847	1847	1500	1847	174009	SSX	Brighton
1819	1845	1800	1871	147575	SSX	Laughton
1819	1845	1800	1871	147575	SSX	Lewes
1765	1765	1550	1765	102830	STS	Ashbourne
1800	1900	1700	1800	116408	STS	West Bromwich
....	....	1800	1992	147613	YKS	Thornton In Lonsdale
1850	1880	1600	1850	175382	YKS	Wakefield
LAMBIE						
1925	1992	....	....	153397	SCT	Glasgow
LAMBLY						
....	....	1600	1835	137812	WOR	Broadway
LAMBORN						
1778	1846	1700	1850	140783	BKM	Twyford
LAMBORNE						
1820	....	....	....	140082	LND	???
LAMBOURN						
1700	1800	1700	....	175234	BRK	East Ilsley
....	....	1800	1900	164801	BRK	Hungerford
....	....	ALL	1810	147567	DOR	Longham
1690	ALL	....	....	142158	WIL	Aldbourne
LAMBOURNE						
1728	1778	1650	1728	140643	BRK	Hinton Waldrist
1816	1840	1750	1816	140643	BRK	Ilsey
....	....	ALL	ALL	164801	GLA	Cardiff
1883	1920	....	....	164801	HEF	Hereford
1814	1837	1750	1850	113638	WIL	Broad Hinton
LAMBSHEAD						
1755	1934	ALL	1755	177482	DEV	Ilsington
1830	1851	1830	ALL	177482	DEV	Stoke Gabrel
1803	1830	1800	ALL	177482	DEV	West Alvington
LAMBTON						
1600	1992	1500	1600	179051	DUR	Monkwearmouth
....	....	1700	1900	110132	DUR	???
1793	1799	1700	1992	110132	NBL	???
LAMBURN						
1778	1798	1750	1820	119059	BKM	Brill
1841	1992	1841	1916	144878	MDX	St Pancras
LAMDEN						
1777	1923	1777	1923	144525	BRK	Mortimer
1777	1923	1777	1923	144525	HAM	Pamber
LAMEY						
1850	1979	....	....	156671	DEV	Appledore
?	?	ALL	ALL	156671	GLA	Newton
LAMIN						
....	1800	ALL	1800	134511	NTT	Linby
LAMING						
1840	1900	1700	1840	134899	KEN	Kingsdown
1840	1900	1700	1840	134899	KEN	Ringwould
?	?	?	?	157570	LND	Bermondsey
1851	1992	ALL	ALL	103837	YKS	Hull
LAMLEY						
?	?	ALL	ALL	156671	DEV	Appledore
1926	....	1926	1992	137812	KEN	Broadstairs
1871	1888	1600	1871	137812	WAR	Exhall
1871	1888	1600	1871	137812	WAR	Wixford
....	....	1600	1835	137812	WOR	Bretforton
LAMMIE						
1870	1980	1870	1992	146536	AYR	Dalry
1810	....	1700	1850	126772	AYR	New Cumnock
LAMMIMAN						
1824	1992	1600	1992	103837	LIN	ALL
1851	1992	ALL	ALL	103837	YKS	Hull
LAMMIN						
1870	1900	1800	1870	114081	LND	???
LAMMING						
1880	....	1850	1900	109363	LIN	Grimsby
LAMONBY						
1806	....	1700	1900	102881	CUL	Holm Cultram
LAMOND						
1795	1815	?	1795	111376	PER	Glenshee
LAMONT						
1930	1992	1700	1930	115304	AYR	Ayrshire
1807	1867	1790	1880	176982	PER	Perth
LAMPARD						
1834	1914	1800	1900	166960	MDX	London
1834	1867	1834	1867	151424	SOM	Bath
1500	1900	1500	1900	170216	WIL	ALL
1700	1992	ALL	1700	118060	WIL	East Knoyle
LAMPEN						
....	....	ALL	ALL	140651	ALL	ALL
1805	1910	1805	1910	140651	DEV	Dartmouth
1690	1805	1690	1805	140651	DEV	Totnes
1850	1950	1850	1950	140651	DUR	South Shields
LAMPERT						
1771	1790	1700	1771	155217	KEN	Canterbury
LAMPEY						
1808	1937	1572	1808	137537	DEV	Plymouth
LAMPITT						
1841	1992	1700	1841	156264	OXF	Banbury
LAMPKYN						
....	....	ALL	ALL	152595	ALL	Name Study
LAMPLOUGH						
1690	1910	1650	1910	152668	HUM	Garton On The Wolds
1895	1915	ALL	1992	109509	LIN	Helpringham
LAMPLUGH						
1720	1740	1650	1720	121339	NYK	Wensley
1879	1967	1870	1879	158267	YKS	Driffield
LAMPORT						
1888	?	1888	1992	168181	CAM	Cambridge
1800	1880	1800	1900	127051	SOM	Baltonsborough
1680	1840	1650	1850	127051	SOM	West Pennard
LAMPRA						
....	....	1500	1900	136972	CON	ALL
LAMPREY						
1800	1920	1700	1800	139491	SOM	Ashbrittle
....	....	1700	1800	139491	SOM	Taunton
1800	1920	1700	1800	139491	SOM	Wellington
LAMPWRIGHT						
1812	1860	1812	1860	155519	MDX	London
LAN						
1815	1900	ALL	ALL	121428	CHS	ALL
LANCASHIRE						
1700	1945	1600	1900	161411	DBY	Denby
1679	1850	1640	1680	149993	WOR	Bewdley
LANCASTER						
1725	1940	....	....	128996	CAM	Thorney
1700	1992	1600	1992	130125	CUL	ALL
1800	1850	1700	1850	143553	CUL	Addingham
1827	1838	1780	1860	155438	CUL	Addingham
1739	....	1650	1992	103942	CUL	Bridekirk
1700	1992	1480	1700	140678	CUL	Culgairth
1739	....	1650	1992	103942	CUL	Dean
1700	1992	1480	1700	140678	CUL	Edenhall
1825	....	....	1992	103942	HAM	Southsea
1881	1966	1800	1881	162949	LAN	Liverpool
....	1794	ALL	1794	152838	LIN	Grimoldby
1800	1992	....	1800	158305	LIN	Market Rasen
....	1774	ALL	1774	152838	LIN	S Reston
?	?	?	?	154687	LND	Islington
1694	1797	1600	1694	164879	SOM	Wells
1853	1891	....	....	168971	WAR	Birmingham
....	....	ALL	ALL	174033	WAR	Birmingham
1750	1860	1750	1860	145319	WAR	Coverntry
....	....	1400	1700	140678	WES	Barton
....	....	1700	1799	158240	WES	Patterdale
1700	1992	1480	1700	140678	WES	Temple Sowerby
1790	1992	1790	1992	168971	WIL	Earl Stoke
1853	....	....	1992	103942	???	Maidenhead
LANCE						
1814	1866	ALL	1866	108553	DOR	Blandford
1761	1900	1700	1900	130427	DOR	Blandford
LANCEFIELD						
1829	1927	ALL	1829	138290	KEN	Crundale

Known From	To	Researching From	To	Ref	Cty	Place
LANCELEY						
1873	1942	ALL	ALL	131121	IRL	Galway
1873	1942	ALL	ALL	131121	IRL	Kilkenny
LANCUM						
1790	1992	1700	1850	104418	NTH	Kettering
LAND						
1877	....	ALL	ALL	159026	DBY	Derby
1600	1800	1610	1750	172642	DEV	Tiverton
1559	1927	ALL	ALL	175005	DEV	Tiverton
....	....	1700	1799	174963	GLS	Leonard Stanley
1762	1800	....	....	164631	KEN	Greenwich
1762	1800	....	....	164631	KEN	Lee
1600	1930	ALL	ALL	140686	NFK	ALL
1827	1888	1700	1950	136530	NFK	Mattishall
1824	....	1750	1824	132853	SRY	Mortlake
LANDEG						
....	....	ALL	ALL	140694	ALL	Name Study
ALL	ALL	ALL	ALL	140694	ALL	ALL
1600	1992	1450	1992	156515	ALL	ALL
LANDELLS						
1716	....	1650	1800	169218	FIF	St Monance
LANDEN						
1827	1992	ALL	1934	156175	KEN	Northfleet
LANDER						
1878	1911	1875	1925	142506	BDF	Luton
....	....	ALL	ALL	140708	CON	ALL
1800	1992	1600	1800	113654	DBY	Belper
1700	1765	1700	1800	171549	DEV	Buckfastleigh
1760	1800	ALL	1800	115266	DOR	ALL
1674	1929	1538	1992	174521	DOR	Langton Matravers
1525	1738	ALL	ALL	174521	DOR	Piddletrenthide
1777	1992	1650	1777	123153	GLS	Forest Of Dean
....	....	ALL	ALL	140708	LEI	ALL
1830	1900	1830	1900	142506	MDX	Kensal Green
1872	1882	1870	1885	142506	SSX	Worthing
....	....	ALL	ALL	140708	STS	ALL
1785	1850	ALL	ALL	140708	WAR	Birmingham
LANDER-BOYCE						
1986	1992	....	....	133299	LND	Islington
LANDERS						
1930	1950	ALL	ALL	124311	LND	???
LANDERYOU						
1580	1785	1520	1580	102571	CON	Constantine
LANDIMORE						
1750	....	....	....	129747	SFK	Hopton
LANDON						
....	....	ALL	ALL	110493	ALL	Name Study
1700	1900	....	....	108677	HRT	Cheshunt
LANDRETH						
....	....	ALL	ALL	152862	ALL	Name Study
LANDREY						
1752	1992	1980	1992	140139	CON	Sheviock
LANDRUM						
....	....	ALL	ALL	159131	ALL	Name Study
1828	1855	....	....	159131	IRL	???
1855	1900	....	....	159131	LAN	Preston
LANDRY						
....	1843	1800	1843	139491	CON	East
....	1843	1800	1843	139491	CON	Polruan
LANDYMORE						
1750	1775	....	....	129747	SFK	Wattisfield
LANE						
1867	1934	1750	1863	153974	BKM	Butlers Cross
....	....	1840	1900	166448	BKM	Seer Green
1856	1862	1856	1866	170143	BRK	Reading
1877	1992	1700	1877	125024	BRK	Windsor
1695	1850	1600	1900	108510	BRK	Wokingham
1840	1900	1700	1900	156221	CHI	Jersey
1812	1902	1800	1900	167487	DEV	Thorncombe
1731	1900	1500	1900	170216	DOR	ALL
1840	1900	1700	1900	156221	DOR	Broadwindsor
1812	1902	1800	1900	167487	DOR	Thorncombe
1840	1900	1800	1900	128449	GLS	Bristol
1800	1830	1780	1830	126594	GLS	Painswick
1731	1900	1500	1900	170216	HAM	ALL
1831	1992	1700	1831	125024	HAM	Stockbridge
1875	1914	1700	1875	156248	HEF	Broadwas
1800	1900	1750	1850	121703	HUN	Sawtry
1750	1992	ALL	ALL	140740	IOW	Arreton
1828	1900	1800	1839	131369	IRL	Cork-Ross
1837	1992	1750	1840	126535	KEN	Bromley
1884	1992	?	1884	147923	KEN	Frindsbury
1807	1850	1770	1807	176257	KEN	Lewisham
1880	1920	1800	1960	101907	KEN	Strood
LANE contd.						
1900	1961	1800	1900	160474	LAN	Blackburn
....	1790	1500	1790	140716	LEI	???
1819	1873	1700	1818	178500	LIN	Kirkby La Thorpe
1780	1790	1700	1780	151769	LIN	Marston
1894	1992	1700	1894	105309	LND	East
1850	1920	1850	1920	117641	LND	Bethnal Green
1911	1992	ALL	1911	149071	LND	Hackney
1859	1895	ALL	ALL	151777	LND	Lambeth
1852	1859	ALL	1852	168742	LND	London
1870	1872	1869	1874	170143	MDX	Ealing
....	....	ALL	1807	170135	MDX	Greenwich
1802	1868	1779	1870	170143	MDX	Shadwell
1802	1868	1779	1870	170143	MDX	Southall
1787	....	1700	1787	101443	NRY	Lastingham
1794	1820	1750	1794	147885	NTH	Luddington
1821	....	ALL	ALL	105481	NTT	Old Basford
1832	1858	1700	1832	153346	SAL	Cleobury
1832	1887	1831	1890	170143	SOM	Bath
1836	1900	1700	1850	107719	SOM	Wellington
1784	1880	1600	1788	114634	SOM	Wickwar
1859	1895	ALL	ALL	151777	SRY	Camberwell
1858	1878	1700	1858	153346	STS	Kingswinford
....	1860	....	1950	130168	STS	Smethwick
1813	1992	1813	1881	140767	STS	Stourbridge
1900	1961	1800	1900	160474	STS	Wednesbury
1900	1945	1900	1945	128449	STS	West Bromwich
1740	1760	1700	1760	119938	WAR	Atherstone
1900	1992	ALL	ALL	128449	WAR	Birmingham
1850	1980	1840	1903	140724	WAR	Birmingham
1813	1992	1813	1881	140767	WAR	Birmingham
1800	1992	1700	1992	177652	WAR	Ladywood
1813	1992	1813	1881	140767	WOR	Dudley
1780	1900	1600	1900	130125	WOR	Suckley
1842	1845	1842	1845	170143	YKS	Nyton
1834	1840	1834	1840	170143	YKS	Sunderland
....	....	....	....	114545	???	???
LANE-FOX						
1816	1816	1700	1816	179043	YKS	Bramham
LANES						
1611	1611	....	....	127426	KEN	Lenham
....	....	....	1738	130060	KEN	Lydd
LANG						
1891	1992	1891	1992	149276	AVN	Bristol
1881	1935	1881	1906	149276	BRK	Windsor
1800	1900	1650	1800	149608	CON	Alternon
....	....	1700	1899	174963	DEV	Kingsteighton
1773	?	1773	1850	149276	DEV	Newton St Cyres
1799	1849	1700	1799	167118	DEV	Thornbury
1850	1992	1850	1992	149276	DEV	Tiverton
....	....	1882	1992	136166	GLA	Cardiff
1881	1992	1900	1992	149276	KEN	Belvedere
1817	1922	1750	1830	151912	LAN	Blackburn
1840	....	....	....	127140	LKS	New Monkland
....	....	1876	1882	136166	SOM	Bedminster
....	....	1800	1900	136166	SOM	Bridgwater
....	....	1868	1877	136166	SOM	Burnham
....	....	1850	1992	160342	SOM	Taunton
1870	1930	1850	1992	105244	SRY	Wandsworth
1800	1850	ALL	1800	105244	SSX	W Wittering
1803	1840	1700	1900	153826	???	Louth
LANGAN						
1800	1992	....	....	139971	MAY	Ballycastle
LANGBORNE						
1763	1895	....	....	173916	YKS	Whitby
LANGDALE						
1779	1812	1775	1812	154598	YKS	Skirpenbeck
1730	1752	1700	1752	154598	YKS	Thirkleby
LANGDON						
....	....	....	....	151475	AVN	Bristol
1603	1619	1550	1619	102571	CON	St Mabyn
1800	1840	ALL	ALL	151475	DEV	North
1500	1950	1300	1992	105333	DEV	Buckland In The Moor
1800	1992	1700	1800	140775	DEV	Exeter
1500	1950	1300	1992	105333	DEV	Holne
1500	1950	1300	1992	105333	DEV	Ilsington
1500	1950	1300	1992	105333	DEV	Lydford
1500	1950	1300	1992	105333	DEV	North Bovey
1500	1950	1300	1992	105333	DEV	Widecombe In The Moor
....	....	1750	1850	146374	NTH	Little Houghton
1800	1840	ALL	ALL	151475	SOM	North
1820	1875	1700	1820	171182	SOM	Chiselborough

Known From	To	Researching From	To	Ref	Cty	Place
LANGDON contd.						
1650	1730	1630	1750	142018	SOM	Merriott
....	....	....	....	151475	WAR	Birmingham
1850	1992	1850	1992	146374	WAR	Leamington Priors
LANGDON-DAVIES						
1840	1992	....	....	151475	???	???
LANGDOWN						
1795	1821	ALL	1795	112887	DOR	Lytchett Mattravers
LANGFORD						
1690	1870	ALL	1600	130621	ALL	ALL
ALL	ALL	ALL	ALL	157120	ALL	ALL
1629	1851	1550	1851	113069	BRK	W Shefford
1629	1851	1550	1851	124990	BRK	West Shefford
1705	1741	ALL	1705	168602	CAM	Coveneyh
1875	1880	....	....	116408	CHS	Birkenhead
1574	1752	....	....	157120	CHS	Wirral
1409	1628	....	....	157120	CON	ALL
1566	1992	....	....	157120	CON	Bratton Clovelly
1672	1992	....	....	157120	CON	St Austell
1686	1987	....	....	157120	CON	St Clear
1225	1510	....	....	157120	DEV	ALL
1545	1742	....	....	157120	DOR	ALL
....	....	ALL	1850	170135	HAM	Portsea Island
1711	1830	....	....	157120	MDX	Covent Garden
1779	1943	....	....	157120	MDX	Marylebone
1776	....	....	....	150762	MON	Blaenavon
1895	1992	....	....	150762	MON	Ebbw Vale
1605	1710	1605	1710	127655	SAL	Frodesley
1700	1800	1650	1800	142123	SAL	Ightfield
1820	1960	1820	1980	150762	SAL	Little Dawley
1605	1710	1605	1710	127655	SAL	Stanton Lacey
....	....	1600	1992	174963	SOM	ALL
....	....	1700	1799	174963	SOM	High Littleton
1875	1970	1835	1875	140880	SSX	West
1817	1885	1700	1817	145971	SSX	Cowfold
1900	1940	ALL	....	116408	STS	West Bromwich
1542	1594	....	....	157120	WIL	ALL
1405	1752	....	....	157120	WLS	ALL
1740	1992	....	....	126101	WOR	Ombersley
1831	1931	1750	1940	140783	WOR	Pershore
1913	1946	1905	1913	160180	YKS	Bradford
LANGHAM						
1920	1992	1920	1992	120529	BRK	Reading
1770	1800	1700	1770	155500	LAN	Warrington
1630	1812	1770	1812	171654	LEI	Catthorpe
1820	1850	1820	1850	120529	LND	Paddington
1820	1850	1790	1850	129356	MDX	Marylebone
1820	1850	1790	1850	129356	MDX	St Pancras
1823	1850	1785	1825	129356	MDX	Westminster
1850	1920	1850	1992	120529	OXF	Oxford
1800	1820	1700	1850	120529	SFK	Newmarket
LANGHELT						
....	....	ALL	ALL	177024	ALL	Name Study
1830	1890	1800	1900	177024	MDX	St Marylebone
1744	1800	1700	1750	177024	MDX	Westminster
1800	1815	1750	1800	177024	SRY	Guildford
1820	1920	1800	1920	177024	SRY	Southwark
LANGHORN						
1800	1992	1700	1900	140805	CMA	Cotehill
1800	1992	1700	1900	140805	CMA	Wetheral
LANGLEY						
1726	1830	ALL	....	115355	BDF	ALL
1650	1860	ALL	1992	168718	BDF	ALL
1791	1850	1700	1820	117005	BDF	Eaton Bray
1838	1858	....	1880	171441	BKM	West Wycombe
1867	1871	1800	1950	139203	KEN	Beckenham
1820	1860	1500	1880	137472	KEN	Chatham
1838	....	1800	1860	159034	KEN	Deptford
1820	1860	1500	1880	137472	KEN	Gillingham
1820	1860	1500	1880	137472	KEN	Rochester
1820	1860	1500	1880	137472	KEN	Strood
1746	1763	....	....	121355	LND	Bethnal Green
1746	1763	....	....	121355	LND	Stepney
1853	1864	1830	1864	108391	MDX	London
1839	1992	1839	1992	101079	MON	Tredegar
....	....	ALL	ALL	116882	NBL	ALL
1827	1900	1500	1827	141089	NFK	ALL
1728	1850	1600	1850	175218	NFK	North West
1855	1856	1700	1855	154164	NFK	Terrington St Clements
1660	1894	ALL	1992	168718	NTH	ALL
....	....	1820	1830	117137	SOM	Coleford
1770	1992	ALL	1992	101079	SOM	Stratton Fosse
1800	1922	....	....	145394	SSX	Farnhurst
LANGLEY contd.						
1700	1900	1700	1900	125938	WAR	Coleshill
1700	1900	1700	1900	125938	WAR	Netherwhitacre
....	....	1800	1830	117137	WIL	Warminster
....	....	ALL	....	116882	YKS	ALL
1770	1812	1720	1833	170267	YKS	Pudsey
LANGMAID						
....	....	ALL	1900	140848	ALL	ALL
1800	1850	1600	1800	154059	DEV	Plymouth
....	....	1700	1825	154059	HAM	Portsea
LANGMAN						
....	....	1550	1992	143219	BRK	Hurley
1764	1992	ALL	ALL	140821	CAM	Chatteris
....	....	1550	1992	143219	CAM	Downham
....	....	1500	1992	143219	CON	ALL
1810	1872	ALL	1872	168718	CON	South East
1740	1850	1600	1740	126357	CON	Lawhitton
....	....	1550	1992	143219	DEV	South
....	....	1550	1992	143219	DEV	Exeter
....	....	1550	1992	143219	MDX	London
LANGMEAD						
....	....	ALL	ALL	140848	ALL	Name Study
....	....	ALL	1900	140848	ALL	ALL
1833	1851	1800	1833	130184	LND	Southwark
LANGRIDGE						
1811	1835	....	....	140856	AVN	Bristol
1870	1939	1300	1992	152501	ESS	East Ham
1621	....	....	....	133736	HAM	East Tytherley
1817	1859	1715	1880	145149	HAM	Kilmiston
1815	1960	....	....	140856	HAM	Portsmouth
....	....	ALL	1891	178195	KEN	London
1874	1940	1800	1900	163694	LND	ALL
1900	1960	....	....	140864	MDX	Enfield
....	....	ALL	1891	178195	MDX	London
1840	1960	....	....	140864	MDX	North London
....	....	ALL	1891	178195	SRY	London
1750	1830	1750	1800	140864	SSX	East Grinstead
1795	1992	1500	1850	140872	SSX	???
1812	....	....	....	140856	WIL	Salisbury
LANGRISH						
1719	1824	1600	1750	157732	HAM	Chawton
1866	1910	....	1866	142166	SRY	Epsom
LANGSBEAR						
1748	1818	1700	1748	139963	DEV	???
LANGSTAFF						
1609	1874	1580	1900	102881	DUR	Romaldkirk
1855	1880	....	....	102881	DUR	Stainton
1804	....	....	....	148016	ENG	Kendal
LANGSTON						
1833	1926	ALL	ALL	127000	LAN	Manchester
1833	1926	ALL	ALL	127000	STS	Dudley
1833	1926	ALL	ALL	127000	WOR	???
LANGSTONE						
....	....	1700	1850	130931	COR	Millstreet
LANGSTRETH						
1840	1900	1700	1840	134899	LAN	Lancaster
LANGSTROTH						
1750	1850	1600	1800	175382	YKS	K Malham
LANGTHORN						
1880	1920	ALL	ALL	127884	MDX	Pinner
LANGTHORNE						
1850	1870	1800	1850	136220	YKS	Northallerton
LANGTON						
1600	1750	1500	1750	167088	CMA	Whitehaven
....	....	1870	1890	121452	LAN	Oldham
....	....	1823	1850	166960	LIN	Cunningham
1836	1900	ALL	1836	152021	LIN	Louth
1851	1871	....	....	177687	LIN	Louth
....	....	1700	1920	121452	LND	???
1688	1761	ALL	1688	143278	NTH	Muscott
1700	1880	ALL	1700	164887	NTH	Whilton
1860	1860	1800	1860	151300	YKS	Attercliffe
LANGWORTHY						
1550	1660	1300	1700	105333	DEV	Buckland In The Moor
1550	1660	1300	1700	105333	DEV	Holne
1550	1660	1300	1700	105333	DEV	Ilsington
1550	1660	1300	1700	105333	DEV	Lydford
1550	1660	1300	1700	105333	DEV	Widecombe In The Moor
LANHAM						
1818	1843	1818	1843	131970	HAM	Southampton
1850	1900	1800	....	118591	LND	Whitechapel
1786	1850	1720	1875	147001	SRY	South

Known From	To	Researching From	To	Ref	Cty	Place
LANHAM contd.						
1800	1920	1700	1800	118281	WIL	Market Lavington
LANK						
1702	1733	1607	1733	153257	CAM	Oakington
LANKESTER						
1820	1992	1700	1820	164860	SFK	Hasketon
1775	1900	1700	1900	153249	WOR	Ribbesford
LANKEY						
1795	1854	1500	1795	118877	DOR	Gillingham
LANKSBURY						
1778	1900	1600	1778	149608	CON	Redruth
LANKSHEAR						
....	....	ALL	ALL	140899	ALL	Name Study
LANKTON						
1702	1702	1600	1701	131245	DBY	North Wingfield
LANNIN						
1870	1900	1850	1870	106968	NBL	Wallsend
LANNING						
....	....	....	1854	145742	???	Bristol
LANSDALE						
1802	1992	1700	1802	102342	STS	Abbots Bromley
1724	1812	1700	1724	125342	WYK	Keighley
LANSDELL						
1600	1992	1600	1992	140929	ALL	ALL
1626	1992	1600	1797	137308	KEN	Cranbrook
1792	1804	1792	1863	138495	NFK	Hapton
LANSDOWN						
1754	1960	1725	1960	154709	GLS	ALL
1662	1779	1500	1851	176923	SOM	High Littleton
LANSEMAN						
1710	1760	1700	1800	130915	FIF	Forgan
LANTAFF						
1770	1824	1770	1824	148156	CAM	East
1772	1823	1750	1823	148156	HUN	West
LANY						
1825	1992	1700	1825	102997	AYR	Stewarton
LANYON						
1818	1992	ALL	1818	151076	CON	ALL
....	....	....	1750	140937	CON	Gwinear
....	....	1370	1550	174319	CON	Madron
1546	1576	1500	1546	102571	CON	Sithney
1700	1830	1650	1830	121126	CON	St Agnes
1750	1900	....	....	140937	CON	St Allen
....	....	....	1750	140937	CON	St Ives
1776	....	?	1776	155667	???	Devonport
1776	....	?	1776	155667	???	Stoke Damerelin
LAPEYRE						
....	....	ALL	ALL	108170	ALL	Name Study
LAPIDGE						
1692	1891	1600	1750	101575	YKS	Knottingley
1692	1891	1600	1750	101575	YKS	Pontefract
LAPLEY						
1815	1815	1700	1850	172316	SFK	Sudbury
LAPPAGE						
1897	....	....	....	132616	LND	Kennington
1886	1940	....	....	132616	SRY	Southwark
LAPPALE						
1780	1900	1700	1780	156302	STS	Tipton
LAPPAN						
1846	1992	....	....	172529	TYR	Derryloran
LAPPER						
1716	1790	1600	1850	166804	OXF	ALL
LAPPIN						
1870	1983	1870	1915	140945	FIF	???
1858	1867	ALL	....	146935	???	???
LAPPING						
1858	1867	ALL	....	146935	???	???
LAPRAIK						
1775	1830	1600	1775	158984	HAM	ALL
LAPSLEY						
1812	1900	1800	1950	144037	DNB	Old Kilpatrick
1725	1828	....	....	101370	ENG	???
LAPSLIE						
1750	1810	1700	1810	135941	MLN	Stockbridge
LAPWORTH						
1600	1800	....	....	100420	WAR	Meriden
LARARD						
1830	1992	1600	1850	140953	ALL	ALL
LARBY						
1793	1823	1750	1795	172871	SSX	Farnhurst
LARCOMBE						
1769	....	....	....	119911	SOM	Wayford
LARDEN						
....	....	ALL	ALL	140961	ALL	Name Study

Known From	To	Researching From	To	Ref	Cty	Place
LARDEN contd.						
1882	1882	1700	1950	172316	LND	Bethnal Green
LARDUR						
1688	1688	1650	1690	124974	BRK	Binfield
LARGE						
1824	1861	1824	1870	126705	CHS	Tarvin
1869	1869	ALL	1870	146315	LAN	Didsbury
1845	1865	1750	1845	113697	LAN	Oldham
1800	1948	....	....	171824	LAN	St Helens
1800	1950	1700	1800	171921	NFK	Brancaster
....	1700	....	....	174564	OXF	???
1680	1760	1680	1760	127655	WIL	Purton
LARGUE						
1722	1797	1550	1750	147265	ABD	???
1722	1797	1550	1750	147265	BAN	???
1801	1851	1700	1801	102997	GMP	Forglen
LARHAM						
?	?	?	?	129399	ENG	???
LARID						
....	....	ALL	ALL	152048	STI	Falkirk
LARK						
1699	1738	....	1699	108839	CAM	Harlton
1870	1880	1870	1900	136867	CON	Penzance
1860	1992	1700	1992	107301	ESS	ALL
1645	1992	1645	1992	107301	KEN	ALL
1840	....	1800	1840	119938	NFK	Norwich
LARKAM						
1500	1900	1500	1900	170216	BRK	ALL
1802	1823	1500	1802	129577	IOW	???
1500	1900	1500	1900	170216	WIL	ALL
LARKE						
1400	1500	1300	1500	144657	NFK	Thetford
1800	1850	1700	1800	138010	NFK	???
LARKHAM						
....	....	1700	1992	137707	DOR	???
1880	....	ALL	ALL	107948	HAM	Petersfield
1890	1950	ALL	ALL	107948	MDX	Brentford
LARKIN						
1840	....	....	....	175358	GAL	ALL
1840	....	....	....	175358	GAL	Gort
1870	1945	1870	1960	138479	IRL	Cork
1860	1992	1700	1860	109061	KEN	Medway
1797	1992	1600	1797	151092	KEN	Staplehurst
....	....	ALL	ALL	117889	LKS	Cadzow
....	....	ALL	ALL	117889	LKS	Dalziel
1780	1810	1805	1810	110159	LOU	Dundalk
1920	1940	....	....	113743	SSX	Brede
1850	1870	1850	1870	138479	YKS	Doncaster
LARKING						
1839	1850	1750	1839	113182	KEN	Greenwich
1800	1850	1700	1850	133817	KEN	West Peckham
LARKINS						
1737	1992	1600	1737	111198	BDF	Willington
LARKMAN						
1720	1800	1720	1800	161705	NFK	Weybourne
LARKUM						
1820	1876	....	....	140988	CHS	Stockport
LARKWORTHY						
1507	1685	....	....	133299	DEV	Ashwater
1685	1866	....	....	133299	DEV	Exeter
LARNER						
1850	1950	1750	1850	105716	GLS	South East
1792	1843	1650	1795	108413	SOM	Central
1790	1873	....	....	175439	SSX	Chichester
LARNEY						
....	....	1500	1950	166863	ALL	ALL
....	....	1500	1950	166863	IRL	ALL
LAROCHE						
....	....	1500	1750	175269	SRY	Egham
LARRANCE						
1777	1868	1777	1868	159581	SFK	Stowmarket
LARRATT						
....	....	1825	1992	112038	ALL	ALL
1820	1870	....	....	112038	HUN	Maxey
1820	1880	....	....	112038	LIN	Thurlby
1875	1920	....	....	112038	NTT	Nottingham
LARRETT						
1857	1928	1800	1857	116505	LND	Pimlico
1706	1793	ALL	1815	168718	NTH	Kettering
LARTER						
1816	1992	1816	1992	145238	NFK	North
1914	1930	1750	1914	178527	NFK	Norwich
1850	1960	ALL	ALL	162469	SFK	North

Known From	To	Researching From	To	Ref	Cty	Place
LARWARDINE						
1838	1840	1800	1870	176079	WIL	Marlborough
LARY						
1900	1906	1840	1920	149632	MDX	Chelsea
LASBURY						
1796	1870	ALL	ALL	143839	WIL	Bradford On Avon
LASCELLES						
1775	....	1775	1992	127035	DUR	???
1820	1900	1800	1930	111325	KEN	Woolwich
1775	....	1775	1992	127035	YKS	East
1771	1771	1700	1850	107654	YKS	Coverham
LASENBY						
1540	1590	ALL	ALL	141615	YKS	Whitewell
LASHBROOK						
....	....	ALL	ALL	140996	ALL	Name Study
ALL	ALL	ALL	ALL	140996	ALL	ALL
LASHMAR						
1851	....	....	....	144282	DBY	Belper
1865	1989	....	....	144282	SRY	Merstham
1865	1989	....	....	144282	SRY	Reigate
1775	1851	....	....	144282	SSX	Twineham
LASHMORE						
1750	1800	1600	1800	103446	SSX	ALL
LASKEY						
1799	1820	1700	1845	170992	CON	Feok
1829	1942	1700	1992	173053	CON	Perranworthal
....	....	ALL	1800	140848	DEV	ALL
1770	1851	1700	1770	125105	DEV	Cheriton Bishop
1621	1715	1538	1620	150622	DEV	Moreton Hampstead
1836	1992	1750	1835	150622	DEV	Newton Ferrers
1690	1801	1538	1689	150622	DEV	Whitestone
?	?	?	?	141003	DEV	???
1858	1942	1850	1992	173053	DUR	West Auckland
LASLETT						
1680	1940	1680	1940	134287	KEN	???
LASSAM						
1817	1853	1815	1855	130990	MDX	Westminster
1754	1800	1750	1850	130990	SRY	Cranley
1754	1800	1750	1850	130990	SRY	Dorking
LAST						
1840	1992	1500	1840	126616	SFK	Butley
1820	1860	....	....	110159	SFK	Ipswich
1845	1992	1700	1850	156450	SFK	???
LATCH						
1866	1924	....	....	173355	GLS	Chalford Hill
LATCHAM						
....	....	ALL	ALL	141011	ALL	Name Study
1860	1861	1840	1860	140589	GLA	Aberdare
1796	1840	1700	1840	140589	SOM	Wedmore
1743	1953	....	....	147907	SOM	Wells
LATCHFORD						
1846	1992	ALL	1846	141038	HRT	Boxmoor
1846	1992	ALL	1846	141038	HRT	Hemel Hempstead
?	?	?	?	163945	LIM	???
LATE						
1726	1756	1650	1756	167533	SOM	Bath
LATES						
....	....	1820	1900	139297	WAR	Birmingham
LATEWOOD						
1795	1992	1795	1992	110825	SAL	Oswestry
LATEY						
1780	1992	1850	1860	133531	ALL	ALL
LATHAM						
1785	1926	1700	1785	160024	CHS	Northwich
1809	....	1700	1810	107999	DEV	Ilfracombe
?	?	....	....	161020	GLS	Bristol
....	....	1930	1992	173355	GLS	Minchinhampton
1670	1754	1600	1800	155896	KEN	Canterbury
1785	1992	1750	1830	118354	LAN	Leigh
1700	1930	1700	1992	121320	LAN	Liverpool
....	1897	....	1920	159999	LAN	St Helens
....	....	ALL	1850	178403	LND	???
1803	1809	....	1803	164321	MDX	East London
1821	1821	ALL	1992	102245	MDX	Westminster
1764	1832	ALL	1840	113611	WYK	Thorne
1700	1800	1800	1992	156922	YKS	Barnby Dun
1766	1810	1730	1810	149152	YKS	Ecclesfield
1775	....	1775	....	109347	YKS	Slaidburn
LATHBURY						
....	....	?	1788	128910	LEI	Desford
1810	1868	1868	1992	128910	WAR	Chilvers Coton
1788	....	....	....	128910	WAR	Nuneaton
LATHER						
1835	1870	1800	1965	141046	PER	Blackford
LATHLEAN						
1799	1850	....	....	130176	CON	Camborne
1830	1900	1700	1845	156051	CON	Lanivet
LATHLIEFF						
1820	1920	1750	1920	146684	LND	East
LATHOM						
1350	1450	1300	1450	154881	LAN	Knowsley
1840	1861	1813	1840	155810	TIP	Tipperary
LATIE						
1750	1800	1600	ALL	162434	SOM	Bath
LATIMER						
1870	1992	1870	1992	110825	NBL	Sunderland
LATIMORE						
1856	1992	1800	1856	126454	ARM	Belfast
LATTEN						
1746	1801	ALL	1813	156582	NFK	Corpusty
1746	1801	ALL	1813	156582	NFK	Saxthorpe
LATTER						
1864	1864	ALL	1864	120057	ESS	Mile End
1860	1925	....	1860	165484	SSX	Wadhurst
LATTIMER						
1739	1884	....	1739	142166	NTH	Rothwell
LAUDER						
1400	1500	1350	1500	154881	ALL	ALL
1860	1938	ALL	ALL	145092	DFS	Tinwald
1580	1680	ALL	1700	149063	ELN	Tynningham
1800	1950	1650	1800	128376	NBL	Tweedmouth
1770	1965	1730	1965	141046	PER	Auchterarder
LAUGHEAD						
1730	1775	....	....	142522	IRL	???
LAUGHER						
1780	1992	1538	1780	154792	WOR	ALL
LAUGHLAN						
1864	1992	1700	1864	136026	AYR	Galston
LAUGHTON						
1750	1826	1700	1750	144606	DUR	South Shields
1630	1790	1630	1790	127655	HUN	Brington
1730	1870	1650	1750	123293	LIN	Owston
1680	1710	1650	1765	169323	LIN	Scotter
LAUND						
....	....	ALL	ALL	154970	YKS	Addingham
LAUNDER						
1890	1940	ALL	ALL	121398	CON	Redruth
1625	1640	ALL	1640	128082	CON	St Minver
1725	1805	1650	1725	118958	DEV	???
....	....	?	....	142085	LEI	Castle Donington
1804	1883	1700	1912	142085	LEI	Castle Donnington
LAUNDREL						
1715	1740	1690	1992	114901	YKS	Harewood
LAURANCE						
1709	1715	....	....	101028	HRT	Thundridge
1934	....	1800	1970	170674	LND	Islington
1692	1939	1692	1939	139807	YKS	ALL
LAURENCE						
1888	....	ALL	1934	170674	CAM	Cambridge
1600	....	1600	1900	106410	GLS	Berkeley
....	....	1800	ALL	164615	HEF	Hereford
1840	1900	1700	1900	114677	LEI	ALL
1896	1939	1800	1896	172448	???	Liverpool
LAURENCESON						
1750	1965	....	....	137820	SHI	Fetlar
1720	1965	....	....	137820	SHI	Mid Yell
1760	1965	....	....	137820	SHI	North Yell
1758	1965	....	....	137820	SHI	Northmavine
1720	1965	....	....	137820	SHI	South Yell
LAURIE						
1880	1920	1850	1920	177024	DUR	Jarrow
1920	1960	ALL	1920	128171	LAN	Liverpool
....	....	1500	1900	166863	LKS	ALL
....	....	1500	1900	166863	SCT	Glasgow
LAVELLE						
1865	1992	1700	1992	112089	IRL	???
1814	1850	....	....	139971	MAY	Ballycastle
LAVENDER						
....	....	ALL	ALL	141054	ALL	ALL
1707	1772	....	1780	137405	CAM	South
1920	1992	1700	1992	151459	ESS	South
1750	1800	1750	....	106704	HUN	Warboys
1791	....	1791	1992	137308	KEN	Horsmonden
1920	1992	1700	1992	151459	MDX	South
LAVER						
1816	1992	1790	1861	172553	ESS	Great Yeldham
1816	1992	1790	1861	172553	ESS	Little Yeldham
1750	1800	1750	1800	141062	ESS	Walthamstow

Known From	To	Researching From	To	Ref	Cty	Place
LAVER contd.						
1750	1800	1750	1800	141062	LND	St Dunstan In The West
1690	1750	ALL	1750	141062	SOM	Curry Rivel
1780	1960	1700	1780	103675	SOM	Meare
....	....	1700	1900	160342	SOM	Taunton
LAVERACK						
1600	....	ALL	ALL	103837	YKS	Goole
1790	1925	ALL	ALL	103837	YKS	Hull
LAVERICK						
1803	1861	1600	1803	158496	DUR	Great Lumley
LAVERSUCH						
1785	....	ALL	ALL	177547	KEN	Plumstead
LAVES						
1660	1700	1500	1730	105333	DEV	Buckland In The Moor
1660	1700	1500	1730	105333	DEV	Holne
1660	1700	1500	1730	105333	DEV	Ilsington
1660	1700	1500	1730	105333	DEV	Lydford
1660	1700	1500	1730	105333	DEV	Widecombe In The Moor
LAVIES						
1850	1950	1800	1992	133450	ESS	???
LAVINGTON						
1744	....	ALL	ALL	116394	DEV	Exeter
1600	1800	1500	1700	139688	HAM	Micheldever
1720	....	ALL	ALL	116394	LND	Holborn
1790	1820	1790	1820	116831	LND	???
1702	....	....	....	142859	WIL	Crudwell
LAW						
....	....	1530	1992	141240	ALL	ALL
1678	1929	ALL	ALL	101443	ALL	Egton
1605	1718	ALL	1605	168602	BDF	Campton
1776	....	....	....	124524	DUR	Gainford
1770	1865	ALL	ALL	162108	ESS	Clavering
....	....	1800	1865	115517	ESS	Elmdon
1808	1863	ALL	1992	109851	ESS	Hockley
1792	....	....	1800	171441	HRT	Datchworth
....	....	1800	1850	177725	KEN	Great Chart
1859	1883	1800	1850	125350	LAN	Bacup
1815	1860	1750	1900	179078	LAN	Haslingden
1801	1838	1838	1992	151688	LIN	Deeping St James
1825	1851	1851	1992	151688	LIN	Spalding
1807	1850	1750	1850	139378	LKS	Glasgow
1871	....	1700	1900	135968	LND	Kensington
1804	1949	1949	1992	151688	NTH	Crowland
1778	1796	1796	1992	151688	NTH	Duddington
1740	1800	1700	1800	167088	NTH	Hardingstone
1788	1864	1750	1810	141097	NTT	Pleasey Hill
1781	1795	1795	1992	151688	RUT	Essendine
1808	1851	1851	1992	151688	RUT	Exton
1753	1780	1780	1992	151688	RUT	Ketton
1850	1900	ALL	1900	131059	SFK	Woodbridge
1894	1907	1500	1894	141089	SRY	Newington
1894	1907	1500	1894	141089	SRY	Southwark
?	?	1842	1891	117919	STS	???
....	....	1700	1992	122742	WIL	Chippenham
1722	1750	1690	1730	170348	WIL	Lydiard Millicent
?	?	1842	1891	117919	WOR	???
1805	1865	1805	1865	107522	WRY	Todmorden
1814	1868	1750	1850	137782	WYK	Stainland
LAWCOCK						
1847	1860	1847	1900	141097	YKS	Braithwell
1877	1903	1870	1903	141097	YKS	Rotherham
LAWDAY						
1852	1916	1830	1926	163775	MDX	Stepney
LAWER						
1870	1890	1870	1992	121312	CON	Baldhu
1863	1992	1600	1863	141100	CON	St Enoder
1870	1890	1870	1992	121312	CON	Truro
LAWES						
1688	1800	1650	1850	123536	DUR	Wolsington
1860	1930	1700	1860	141119	HAM	ALL
LAWFORD						
1760	1992	ALL	ALL	141127	HAM	West
1816	1861	1816	1861	138398	HEF	Stretton Sugwas
1811	1861	1811	1861	138398	HEF	Yarkhill
1832	1880	1800	1920	126586	LND	Islington
1800	1900	1750	1920	103616	MDX	London
LAWLESS						
....	....	ALL	ALL	141135	ALL	Name Study
1900	1992	1700	1900	141143	IRL	Waterford
1855	1950	1855	1927	141135	LAN	Manchester
1832	1855	1800	1855	141135	LAN	Warrington
LAWMAN						
1794	1849	1750	1850	116505	CUL	Wetheral
LAWN						
1840	....	1800	1900	139114	LND	???
1830	1850	1700	1830	116572	TYR	Strabane
LAWNDY						
1520	1600	1500	1600	154881	KEN	Chiddingstone
LAWRANCE						
1830	1870	1800	1890	138444	LEI	Earl Shilton
1775	1825	....	....	124621	LIN	Pinchbeck
LAWRENCE						
1750	1900	1750	1800	140864	ABD	Longside
1600	1700	1600	1700	167924	BDF	Shillington
1850	....	....	....	141208	BKM	Wooburn Green
1800	1992	....	....	141208	BRK	Bucklebury
1851	1900	ALL	ALL	112518	BRK	Woolhampton
1687	1690	ALL	1687	168602	CAM	Grantchester
1700	1881	1700	1881	141178	CON	South East
1825	1860	1775	1880	132470	DEV	Ashreigney
1825	1860	1775	1880	132470	DEV	Chulmleigh
1786	1811	1700	1786	127116	DOR	Fontmell Magna
1841	1881	1800	1850	101265	DOR	Fontmell
1645	1690	....	....	122106	DOR	Milton Abbas
1801	1891	1801	1891	131970	ESS	Panfield
1893	1893	1860	1910	151157	FIF	Cowdenbeath
1870	1870	1850	1890	151157	GLA	Ystradyfodwg
1645	....	....	....	117579	GLS	Berkley
1716	1916	ALL	1716	149888	GLS	Mangotsfield
1716	1823	1700	1850	102717	HRT	Braughing
1799	1813	1790	1820	138215	HUN	Brington
1830	1880	1721	1970	138215	HUN	Holm
1766	1785	....	1800	171441	KEN	Ash
1865	1892	ALL	ALL	135208	KEN	Belvedere
1831	1992	1700	1830	105988	KEN	Deal
1865	1892	ALL	ALL	135208	KEN	Erith Marshes
1855	1870	1800	1855	146285	KEN	Gravesend
....	1882	1855	1882	133639	LAN	Oldham
1850	1992	1750	1850	118052	LDY	Coleraine
1867	....	....	1867	162086	LND	North
....	....	1830	1860	123390	LND	Bow
....	....	1750	1900	129275	LND	Southwark
....	....	1750	1850	125628	LND	Stepney
....	....	1800	1900	129275	LND	Walworth
1840	....	1800	1840	119938	NFK	Luddon
1850	1870	1850	1900	119938	NFK	Norwich
1833	1850	1830	1890	165093	SAL	Oswestry
1814	1992	1700	1820	106267	SFK	North
1790	....	1750	1840	119938	SFK	Eye
1766	1855	1700	1860	130087	SFK	Withersfield
1818	1880	1800	1900	167487	SOM	Merriot
1646	1831	1558	....	112968	SOM	Merriott
1832	1900	1832	1880	144878	SRY	Lambeth
....	....	1830	1860	123390	STI	Baldernock
1867	1867	1850	1910	151157	STS	Bilston
1871	1871	1850	1910	151157	STS	Wednesbury
1888	1888	1700	1888	174262	WAR	Birmingham
1818	1871	ALL	ALL	141186	WIL	Aldbourne
1790	1970	ALL	ALL	143839	WIL	Bradford On Avon
1717	1717	....	....	115606	WIL	Eisey
1717	1717	....	1717	136212	WIL	Eisey
1818	1871	ALL	ALL	141186	WIL	Ramsbury
LAWRENSON						
1840	1950	1800	1900	141232	DUR	South Shields
1831	1890	1750	1900	118443	LAN	Goosnargh
1760	1800	1600	1992	167592	LAN	Liverpool
1850	1892	1700	1900	157147	LAN	Prescot
1815	1850	1800	1850	141232	SHI	ALL
LAWREY						
?	?	?	?	136999	CON	Gulval
LAWRIE						
1870	1900	1870	1900	172855	LKS	Allanton
1774	1794	....	....	171654	STI	Stirling
LAWRY						
1700	1900	1600	1700	107905	CON	Central
?	?	?	?	136999	CON	St Agnes
1780	1900	1750	1800	168750	CON	St Ives
LAWS						
....	....	ALL	ALL	141240	ALL	Name Study
1838	1847	ALL	1838	165301	DUR	Weardale
1821	1821	1700	1900	105333	HAM	Ellingham
1815	1815	1700	1900	105333	HAM	Portsea
1848	1871	1700	1900	105333	HAM	Ringwood
1786	1889	1700	1900	105333	HAM	Rockbourne
1825	1870	....	....	135070	LND	Shoreditch

Known From	To	Researching From	To	Ref	Cty	Place
LAWS contd.						
1847	1992	ALL	1847	154520	NBL	???
1774	1774	....	1774	100064	NFK	West Tofts
1860	1930	1700	1860	141119	WIL	ALL
LAWSON						
....	....	ALL	ALL	102687	ALL	Name Study
1820	1850	1700	1900	138517	ANS	Barry
1719	1940	....	....	128996	CAM	Thorney
1850	1870	1700	1870	126802	CUL	ALL
1817	....	....	1817	176761	CUL	Brampton
1817	....	....	1817	176761	CUL	Hayton
1800	1854	....	....	159948	CUL	Penrith
1817	....	....	1817	176761	CUL	Scaleby
1677	1799	1600	....	159948	CUL	Wetheral
1885	....	1860	1992	151378	DBY	Chesterfield
1853	....	....	....	135453	DFS	???
1833	1856	1822	1856	122440	DUR	Heworth
1470	1525	ALL	1550	149063	ELN	Haddington
1900	1992	....	....	141267	ESS	Ilford
1800	1862	1800	1860	143774	EYK	Scarborough
1750	....	ALL	ALL	130508	FIF	Pittenweem
1890	1947	1700	1890	169730	HRT	Bushey
1774	1774	1700	1900	141151	KEN	ALL
1774	1774	1700	1900	141151	KEN	Whitstable
....	....	1698	1740	106011	LAN	Ashton In Makerfield
1840	1850	1840	1900	106011	LAN	Bolton
1850	1860	1800	1850	113050	LAN	Bolton
1796	1840	1796	1850	106011	LAN	Chorley
1796	1850	1750	1796	113050	LAN	Chorley
1787	1840	1600	1800	126837	LAN	Lancaster
1840	1880	1840	1900	126837	LAN	Liverpool
1850	1900	1850	1900	106011	LAN	Manchester
1860	1992	1800	1860	113050	LAN	Manchester
1740	1800	1740	1800	106011	LAN	Newton In Makerfield
....	....	1770	1795	106011	LAN	Prescot
....	....	1770	1795	106011	LAN	Upholland
....	....	1770	1795	106011	LAN	Warrington
1800	1875	1600	1800	141275	LIN	North East
1730	1800	....	....	140554	LKS	Glasgow
1837	1889	1750	1837	127590	MDX	London
1890	1929	....	1929	159948	NBL	Newcastle Upon Tyne
1725	1820	1725	1820	122440	NBL	Wylam
1856	1932	1800	1856	118710	NTT	Nottingham
....	....	ALL	1822	111384	NYK	Scarborough
1871	1874	1800	1871	121037	SRY	Southwark
1800	1941	1800	1870	141283	STS	Longton
1766	1800	1700	1766	141283	STS	Stafford
1822	1861	ALL	1822	111384	WYK	Leeds
1890	1920	ALL	ALL	162027	WYK	Shipley
1855	1890	....	....	159948	YKS	Loftus In Cleveland
1837	....	1750	1860	135623	???	West Kirby
LAWSON-FREEMAN						
1930	....	1930	1992	169730	SRY	Kingston
LAWTHER						
....	....	ALL	1830	132071	ALL	ALL
1830	1992	ALL	ALL	132071	DUR	Sunderland
1840	1850	ALL	ALL	132071	NBL	Tynemouth
LAWTON						
1782	1782	1600	1800	117005	BKM	Astwood
1550	1850	ALL	1650	141305	CHS	South East
1843	1843	1790	1850	126705	CHS	Chester
1800	1830	1750	1830	137782	CHS	Stalybridge
....	....	1750	1850	100390	CHS	Warrington
1829	1871	?	?	124788	LAN	Manchester
1850	1870	1800	1850	161292	LAN	Manchester
1800	1830	1750	1830	137782	LAN	Stalybridge
1753	1808	....	1753	101761	NTT	Everton
....	....	1800	1900	146978	STS	Burslem
1900	1950	ALL	ALL	158941	STS	Burslem
1790	1900	1700	1790	156574	STS	Madeley
1831	1878	ALL	ALL	143618	STS	Tunstall
1907	1957	1907	1957	143618	WYK	Castleford
1881	1907	1878	1907	143618	WYK	Knottingley
1791	1861	ALL	1871	143634	WYK	Morley
1871	1984	1865	ALL	143634	WYK	Wakefield
1800	1880	1780	1880	123595	YKS	Cleckheaton
1800	1890	1750	1800	123595	YKS	Huddersfield
1861	1900	1800	1920	107727	YKS	Hull
....	....	1820	....	119768	YKS	Saddleworth
1820	1880	1820	1880	123595	YKS	Saddleworth
1800	1900	1710	1950	131822	YKS	York

Known From	To	Researching From	To	Ref	Cty	Place
LAX						
1750	1808	....	....	141313	CLV	Marton
1890	....	....	....	164275	NBL	Newcastle Upon Tyne
1808	1864	1700	1750	141313	YKS	North
LAXTON						
....	....	1700	1850	179248	LIN	Spalding
1823	1881	ALL	ALL	125202	NFK	Warham
1900	1992	1850	1900	179248	WYK	Bradford
1900	1992	1850	1900	179248	WYK	Keighley
LAY						
1792	1862	ALL	1880	118737	BRK	Abingdon
1787	1876	....	....	125628	BRK	Denchworth
1805	1940	1700	1905	141321	BRK	Dewchworth
1880	1960	1500	1992	175498	LND	Lambeth
....	1891	1800	1900	132586	NFK	Stratton St Mary
LAYBOURNE						
1784	1851	1600	1860	147125	DUR	Winlaton
1817	1850	1750	1850	102881	DUR	Wolviston
LAYCOCK						
1600	1850	....	....	146854	WES	Orton
....	1926	....	1926	111171	WYK	Bradford
1811	1859	1811	1859	141097	YKS	Adwick Le Street
1850	1851	....	....	141097	YKS	Balby
1800	1850	1800	1850	171549	YKS	Bingley
1650	1850	ALL	ALL	134759	YKS	Bolton Percy
1765	1804	ALL	1765	102350	YKS	Braithwell
1751	1871	1650	1875	141097	YKS	Braithwell
1813	1900	1800	1900	141097	YKS	Conisborough
1633	1900	1600	1900	141097	YKS	Doncaster
1813	1813	....	....	141097	YKS	Hooton Roberts
1808	1808	....	....	141097	YKS	Maltby
1750	1815	....	....	141097	YKS	Mexborough
1760	1800	....	....	141097	YKS	Micklebring
1896	1896	....	....	141097	YKS	Rossington
1841	1841	....	....	141097	YKS	Stainton
1812	1839	....	....	141097	YKS	Swinton
1650	1850	ALL	ALL	134759	YKS	Tadcaster
1788	1851	....	....	141097	YKS	Wadworth
1795	1798	....	....	141097	YKS	Womersley
LAYLAND						
1834	1920	ALL	ALL	116416	CHS	Warrington
LAYLEY						
1850	1950	ALL	ALL	102024	ALL	ALL
LAYMAN						
1840	1862	1800	1992	117609	DEV	Kingskerswell
LAYTON						
1820	1865	1700	1800	137421	CAM	Wicken
1660	1992	1660	1992	156515	RAD	ALL
1880	....	1880	ALL	137421	WAR	Birmingham
LAYZELL						
1800	1900	1800	1992	171417	ESS	Great Bentley
....	....	1750	1850	163082	SRY	Godstone
LAZARUS						
?	?	?	?	138622	LIN	Lincoln
LAZENBY						
1800	1860	....	....	162302	DUR	???
1800	1860	....	....	162302	NBL	???
....	....	ALL	ALL	138576	WYK	Halifax
LAZONBY						
....	....	....	....	157368	???	North
LE BRETON						
1550	1992	1450	1888	141348	JSY	Trinity
LE BRUE						
1700	1792	ALL	ALL	115126	CHI	ALL
LE BRUNE						
1200	1350	1150	1350	154881	KEN	Edenbridge
LE CLERCQ						
1838	1963	1820	1838	141356	JSY	Grovville
LE CLERK						
....	....	1066	1280	124974	GNT	Malpas
LE FEUVRE						
1758	1992	ALL	1758	130796	CHI	Guernsey
1758	1992	ALL	1758	130796	HAM	South
1758	1992	ALL	1758	130796	HAM	Southampton
1758	1992	ALL	1758	130796	JSY	St Brelade
LE GASSICK						
1871	1980	1760	1871	112992	DEV	Kingsbridge
LE GEYT						
1806	1806	1600	1992	104302	KEN	Deal
LE HARDY						
1500	1500	ALL	ALL	115126	JSY	St Johns
LE HURAY						
1761	....	1730	1761	131326	GSY	???

Known From	To	Researching From	To	Ref	Cty	Place
LE LACHEUR						
1700	....	1700	1750	131326	GSY	???
LE MAISTRE						
1500	1700	....	....	119105	JSY	ALL
LE MARECHAL						
1685	1920	1685	1820	147974	MDX	East
LE MESSURIER						
....	....	ALL	ALL	141364	ALL	Name Study
1400	1992	1700	1992	141364	ENG	ALL
1400	1992	1700	1992	141364	GSY	ALL
LE MONTAIS						
1770	....	ALL	1770	119105	JSY	ALL
LE PAGE						
1804	1891	ALL	ALL	115126	CHI	ALL
1750	1900	1750	1992	172359	GSY	St Andrew
LE PINE						
1811	1836	ALL	ALL	135208	KEN	Canterbury
LE PLA						
1627	1940	....	....	128996	CAM	Thorney
LE QUEUX						
1843	....	....	....	165808	LND	???
LE RICHE						
1849	1924	1700	1849	166480	JSY	ALL
LE ROY						
1600	1790	1550	1600	159115	GSY	Castel
LE SAGE						
....	1793	1750	1800	176621	MDX	London
LE SEELLEUR						
....	....	ALL	ALL	146099	ALL	Name Study
1463	1992	1600	1992	146099	ALL	ALL
LE TISSIER						
1700	1992	....	....	162590	GSY	ALL
1700	1992	1700	1992	162590	GSY	Catel Parish
LE-FEVRE						
1846	1856	1856	1992	141399	LND	Shoreditch
LEA						
....	....	ALL	ALL	109932	ALL	Name Study
....	....	1750	1850	152684	CHS	Middlewich
1721	1843	....	....	116602	LAN	West
1750	1900	1750	1800	176524	LAN	Billinge
1800	1850	....	....	171824	LAN	St Helens
1730	1950	1600	1730	128376	NBL	Kirkhaugh
....	....	1700	1750	149977	SAL	North East
1830	1860	1700	1960	137731	SAL	Cheswardine
1760	1780	ALL	ALL	130508	SAL	Wrockwardine
....	....	1700	1750	149977	STS	West
1750	1810	....	....	149977	STS	Gnosall
1700	1759	1600	1800	160873	STS	Kingswinford
1853	1992	1700	1853	138673	WAR	Edgbaston
....	....	1600	1900	106461	WIL	ALL
....	....	1600	1900	106461	WIL	Calne
1700	1890	....	....	149764	WOR	Kidderminster
LEABERRY						
1700	1760	....	....	177393	YKS	Stillingfleet
1683	1700	1650	1683	177393	YKS	York
LEACH						
....	....	ALL	ALL	141410	ALL	Name Study
1770	1770	1750	1800	134627	CAM	Chatteris
1771	1953	1760	1900	156353	CAM	Haddenham
1689	1689	1650	1720	167002	CAM	Histon
....	1799	....	1840	137405	CAM	Sutton
1824	1860	1750	1824	137650	DEV	Black Dog
1800	1900	1650	1800	149608	DEV	Newton St Petrock
1600	1700	1580	1600	168777	HAM	Nether Wallop
1669	1930	1600	1950	141410	HRT	Watford
1790	1920	1600	1900	106704	HUN	Upton
1860	1890	1860	1980	141410	KEN	Ashford
1844	....	1800	1900	139203	KEN	Beckenham
1750	1900	1750	1900	125237	LAN	Darwen
1800	1880	1880	1992	162256	LAN	Darwen
1867	1940	1700	1867	104485	MDX	Islington
1862	1880	1830	1860	173118	NBL	Gateshead
1760	1840	1650	1840	141402	NFK	Hedenham
....	....	1750	1850	147613	OXF	Spelsbury
1800	1850	ALL	1992	170909	ROS	Elphin
1696	....	....	1696	101761	WRY	Skipton
1817	....	ALL	ALL	166839	WYK	Haworth
LEACK						
1890	1900	1800	1890	135658	LAN	Lancaster
LEADBEATER						
1756	1791	1650	1791	148288	STS	Lichfield
1756	1791	1650	1791	148288	STS	Stowe
1730	1800	....	....	164631	STS	Stowe
....	....	ALL	1730	164631	STS	Uttoxeter
LEADBETTER						
1561	1992	....	1561	159506	LAN	Ormskirk
1880	1945	1700	1880	157996	LAN	St Helens
1840	1880	ALL	ALL	150347	WAR	Birmingham
LEADBITTER						
1800	1992	1750	1800	168777	DUR	City
LEADER						
1740	1827	1650	1740	106313	BRK	Coleshill
1871	1877	1700	1871	173509	ESS	Bocking
1871	1877	1700	1871	173509	SFK	???
1722	1761	1722	1761	178705	WIL	Highworth
....	....	1800	1992	176184	???	???
LEADLEY						
1790	1840	1760	1790	134139	EYK	Bridlington
1730	....	1550	1730	150843	YKS	Easingwold
LEADNER						
1800	1875	1700	1800	135313	KEN	Ash Nr Sandwich
LEADSTONE						
1616	1950	ALL	ALL	142255	ALL	ALL
LEAF						
1821	1981	1800	1992	144908	HAM	Gosport
LEAFE						
1766	1811	....	....	131210	LND	Covent Garden
1766	1811	....	....	131210	MDX	Isleworth
LEAH						
....	....	ALL	ALL	168920	ALL	ALL
1752	1876	....	....	157465	LND	Various
1685	1797	....	....	157465	YKS	Emley
1716	1850	1685	ALL	168920	YKS	Emley
LEAHY						
1860	1890	....	1860	161888	IRL	Cork
LEAK						
1818	1838	1700	1818	152056	LIN	Aswarby
....	....	1700	1825	141437	NFK	Cromer
1860	1950	....	....	141437	NFK	Gorleston
1825	1880	1825	1880	141437	NFK	Yarmouth
1860	1950	....	....	141437	SFK	Gorleston
1869	1893	1830	1893	107573	SRY	Lambeth
1770	1840	1700	1770	120049	STS	Stoke
LEAKE						
1800	1900	1700	1900	141445	LEI	Barrow On Soar
1790	1992	1790	1910	123145	WAR	Castle Bromwich
1640	1667	1600	1667	148288	YKS	Sheffield
LEAKEY						
1726	?	ALL	ALL	153516	SOM	Axbridge
1766	1826	1740	1826	151599	SOM	Bradford On Tone
1766	1826	1740	1826	151599	SOM	Kingston St Mary
LEALL						
1820	1851	1750	1820	168033	HAM	Gosport
1820	1851	1750	1820	168033	HAM	Isle Of Wight
LEAMAN						
1791	1820	1770	1791	128368	DEV	Ashburton
1790	1992	1790	....	162809	DEV	Ashburton
1781	1841	1700	1841	137901	DEV	Colebrooke
LEAN						
1680	1780	1600	1900	153354	CON	Gwennap
LEANE						
1593	....	1580	1630	114332	CON	Poughill
LEANEY						
....	....	1850	1899	173274	KEN	Snave
LEANING						
1660	1992	1660	1992	171581	LIN	Grasby
1660	1992	1660	1992	171581	LIN	Wrawby
LEAR						
1785	1850	....	....	102946	DEV	Ashburton
1799	1840	....	....	102946	DEV	Buckfastleigh
1760	1790	1650	1840	105333	DEV	Buckland In The Moor
1760	1790	1650	1840	105333	DEV	Holne
1760	1790	1650	1840	105333	DEV	Ilsington
1760	1790	1650	1840	105333	DEV	Lydford
1827	1992	1770	1827	146900	DEV	Torquay
1760	1790	1650	1840	105333	DEV	Widecombe In The Moor
1800	1850	1700	1800	152579	DOR	Gillingham
ALL	1800	ALL	1800	142425	GLS	South
1740	1760	1600	1760	154342	GLS	Bitton
1795	1820	1700	1820	155683	GLS	Bitton
1792	1923	ALL	1792	116327	HAM	Alverstoke
1792	1992	ALL	1792	178659	HAM	Otterbourne
1833	1838	1700	1832	131245	KEN	Deptford
....	....	....	1858	121169	SOM	Midsomer Norton
1800	1950	1700	1800	128376	SOM	Radstock
1858	1858	....	1858	121169	SOM	Shepton Mallet

Known From To Researching From To Ref Cty Place

LEARE
1600 1800 .... 177474 DEV Ilsington
LEARMONTH
1773 1992 ALL 1773 116696 ELN East Linton
LEARMOUTH
1790 1820 1750 1992 114901 DUR Sunderland
1820 1840 1820 1992 114901 YKS Thirsk
LEARNER
1681 1754 ALL ALL 121487 SFK Hessett
LEAROYD
1860 1930 .... 108685 YKS Leeds
1830 1992 .... 145912 YKS Stanley
LEARY
1675 1718 .... 1675 101761 LIN Gayton Le Marsh
LEASK
1850 1960 1700 1850 141453 ABD ???
1750 1965 .... 137820 SHI Fetlar
1720 1965 .... 137820 SHI Mid Yell
1760 1965 .... 137820 SHI North Yell
1758 1965 .... 137820 SHI Northmavine
1720 1965 .... 137820 SHI South Yell
LEAT
ALL ALL .... 153397 HAM Ringwood
1760 1850 .... 150266 WIL Warminster
LEATHAN
1831 1905 1700 1857 156051 CON St Buryan
LEATHER
.... ALL ALL 141488 ALL Name Study
1702 1786 1500 1700 141488 CHS Farnworth
1600 1700 1300 1600 141488 CHS Risley
1865 1900 1700 1900 115894 CHS Stockport
1880 1890 1890 1940 141488 CHS Wirral
1860 1920 1860 1992 141488 HAM Portsmouth
1786 1992 1786 1992 141488 YKS Leeds
LEATHERDALE
1779 1992 ALL ALL 156310 ESS Chapel
1615 1992 ALL ALL 156310 SFK ???
LEATHERLAND
1776 .... ALL ALL 105481 NTT Bilborough
LEATHERS
1845 .... 1845 1900 177768 ??? Glasgow
LEATHES
1770 1900 .... 100536 ??? ???
LEATON
1785 1940 .... 128996 CAM Thorney
LEAVENS
1873 1992 ALL 1873 149071 LND Hackney
1873 1992 ALL 1873 149071 LND Islington
LEAVER
1775 1992 1775 1992 176176 BKM Hambleden
1848 1874 1700 1900 145718 BRK Cookham
1830 1840 ALL 1830 158437 BRK Maidenhead
1912 1932 1912 1930 171247 HAM Hook
1818 1839 1700 1818 152056 NTT Radford
1841 1987 1700 1900 171247 WIL Broad Chalke
LEAVERSUCH
1880 1880 1880 1880 147575 HAM Southampton
1800 1843 1750 1850 147575 WIL Shrewton
1851 1851 1800 1851 147575 WIL ???
LEAVES
1802 1830 1550 1800 177164 SOM Middlezoy
LEBIREL
1694 1745 ALL ALL 115126 CHI ALL
LEBROW
? ? ALL ALL 110515 LAN Liverpool
LEBUTT
.... ALL ALL 141518 ALL Name Study
LECKIE
1761 1790 1720 1770 108510 FIF Auchtertool
1800 .... 141798 PER Carse Of Gowrie
LECONTE
1654 1940 .... 128996 CAM Thorney
LECOTT
1787 1835 1500 1800 157538 DEV ALL
LECOUNT
1822 1992 1700 1822 101540 HRT Hertford
LECYTHWATE
1577 1584 ALL ALL 141615 LAN Ormskirk
LEDDRA
1720 1794 1700 1790 108510 CON St Ives
LEDEUX
1790 .... 1760 1800 163775 MDX Stepney
LEDGAR
.... ? .... 115592 YKS Wakefield
LEDGARD
.... ? .... 115592 YKS South Elmsall
LEDGER
1794 .... 124508 ESS Woodford
1750 1850 1700 1850 126144 KEN West
1715 1992 ALL 1715 141526 KEN Ulcombe
1810 1840 1700 1810 130230 SRY Godstone
1850 1940 .... 1940 109568 SRY Shertsey
1659 .... 124508 SRY West Horlsey
1782 1902 1700 1902 159581 SRY West Horsley
1860 1992 .... 148431 SRY Woking
1809 1860 1700 1809 148431 SRY ???
1696 1696 1650 1750 167002 SXE Heathfield
1870 1870 .... 1890 102059 YKS Barnsley
.... 1750 1790 177393 YKS Fryston
LEDGERWOOD
1848 1992 1700 1848 155136 AYR Kilmarnock
1848 1992 1700 1848 155136 AYR Kilmaurs
.... 1700 1848 155136 IRL ???
LEDINGHAM
1800 1910 .... 1900 174246 ABD ALL
1770 1834 1700 1850 169161 ABD Aberdeen
LEDSTON
1544 1820 ALL ALL 142255 ALL ALL
LEDWELL
1910 1992 .... 141534 IRL Tramore
LEE
1700 1850 1700 1900 177180 BKM Astin Abbots
1800 1992 1700 1992 177652 BKM Bierton
1825 1840 1750 1900 113212 BKM Whaddon
1791 1817 .... 1791 177504 CAM Littleport
.... 1800 1900 141585 CAM Ware
1750 1880 1600 1750 116432 CON Quethiock
1750 1880 1600 1750 116432 CON St Stephens Saltash
1700 1950 1700 1900 130869 CUL Alston
.... 1800 .... 140082 DBY ???
1829 1829 1700 1829 100110 DEV Bradninch
1764 1900 1700 1900 115991 DEV Crediton
1800 1826 1800 1992 117609 DEV Devonport
? ? ? ? 174130 DEV Drewsteignton
1800 1992 .... 137693 DEV Halberton
1600 1900 1600 1900 141577 DEV Halberton
1600 1850 1600 1850 141577 DEV Mid
1600 1960 1820 1960 141577 DEV Tiverton
1672 1712 1650 1720 165972 DEV Totnes
1815 1881 1700 1992 122742 DOR Weymouth
1841 1868 1600 1841 175781 DOR Weymouth
1873 1890 1700 1873 146161 DUR Jarrow
.... 1888 ALL 1925 167878 ENG ALL
1850 1887 1800 1850 169757 ESS ALL
1627 1713 .... 165999 ESS Broomfield
1796 1800 ALL 1800 163341 ESS Colchester
.... 1850 1920 116467 ESS Romford
1821 1939 1600 1821 157953 ESS The Roddings
1740 1940 .... 147621 FLN Whitford
1830 1850 1830 1850 138444 GLS Westbury
.... 1694 1875 175110 HAM Aldershot
1812 1817 .... 1850 171441 HAM Alton
1786 1845 1700 1786 117595 HAM Portsea
.... 1860 1880 124516 HEF ???
1855 1992 .... 172529 HUM Hull
1846 1896 1700 .... 104043 IRL ???
1850 1900 .... 136492 IRL ???
.... 1700 1900 102717 KEN ALL
1800 1850 ALL .... 172812 KEN ALL
1900 1992 1900 1992 141585 KEN Belvede
1866 1866 1500 1900 137472 KEN Chatham
1810 1850 1700 1850 149160 KEN Deptford
1866 1866 1500 1900 137472 KEN Gillingham
1850 1871 1750 1850 168033 KEN Minster
1850 1871 1750 1850 168033 KEN Ramsgate
1866 1866 1500 1900 137472 KEN Rochester
1866 1866 1500 1900 137472 KEN Strood
1820 1992 1820 1992 110825 KEN Thanet
1881 1992 .... 112380 LAN Duckinfield
1841 .... 110167 LAN Preston
1819 1893 1700 1819 120200 LAN Warrington
1825 .... ALL 1825 147877 LEI Evington Lodge
1904 1984 .... 1904 137073 LEI Leicester
1800 1992 1700 1992 177652 LEI Waltham
.... 1850 1900 121673 LIN Grantham
1820 1980 1700 1820 160458 LND ALL
1800 1854 1773 1800 101060 LND Bermondsey
1877 1909 ALL 1700 172316 LND Bethnal Green

Known From	To	Researching From	To	Ref	Cty	Place
LEE contd.						
1699	1751	ALL	1751	162507	LND	Bread Street
1800	1850	1700	1900	152900	LND	St Pancras
1850	1900	....	....	136492	LTN	Edinburgh
1882	1931	ALL	ALL	155454	MDX	Chelsea
1882	1931	ALL	ALL	155454	MDX	Fulham
1840	....	1820	1850	171441	MDX	Heston
1844	....	1840	1880	171441	MDX	Isleworth
1860	1950	1800	1860	172170	MDX	London
1840	1900	1800	1992	177180	MDX	Millwall
1820	1840	1700	1819	131245	MDX	Shoreditch
1857	1857	1850	1900	102717	MDX	Stepney
1898	....	ALL	1898	167711	MDX	Tottenham
1873	....	1840	1880	171441	MDX	Twickenham
1775	1775	1750	1800	144606	MDX	Westminster
1850	1940	ALL	ALL	142719	MDX	???
1860	1870	1800	1880	109010	MOG	Monaghan
1821	1891	ALL	1860	171751	NBL	Allendale
1700	1830	....	....	148261	NBL	Allendales
1741	1760	1700	1800	149152	NBL	Bedlington
1707	1830	1700	1866	150304	NBL	Haltwhistle
1725	1770	1700	1780	149152	NBL	Howick
1773	....	1700	1773	132853	NFK	Besthorpe
1784	1927	ALL	ALL	141569	NTH	Sudborough
1717	1726	....	1717	101761	NTT	Lenton
1790	1830	1830	1880	148113	NTT	Lowdham
1738	1771	1710	1738	147311	NYK	Seamer
1800	1830	1780	1800	103632	RUT	Exton
1800	1820	1700	1800	151769	RUT	Pickworth
....	....	1800	1860	124516	SAL	???
1737	1813	ALL	1737	126942	SFK	Stonham Aspal
1850	1930	1750	1850	145017	SOM	Taunton
1882	1992	?	1882	156337	SOM	???
....	....	1700	1900	102717	SRY	ALL
1880	1992	1700	1880	118788	SRY	Camberwell
1718	1738	1700	1740	159581	SRY	Cranleigh
....	....	1694	1875	175110	SRY	Effingham
1830	1950	1830	1950	110183	SRY	Thames Ditton
1884	1992	1700	1884	125024	SSX	Brede
1700	1800	ALL	ALL	154830	SSX	Cuckfield
1883	1992	1700	1883	125024	SSX	Rye
1837	1967	1837	1881	104213	SYK	Sheffield
1800	1992	1700	1992	177652	WAR	Ladywood
1818	....	....	....	111856	WAR	???
1800	1875	1800	1924	173762	WIL	Devizes
1830	1992	1830	1992	167339	WIL	???
1820	1856	1750	1820	144177	WRY	Calverley
1770	1992	1670	1770	141593	WYK	Sherburn
1850	1890	1850	1890	121223	WYK	Thornhill
1788	1926	....	....	109142	YKS	Batley
1736	1788	1650	1736	109142	YKS	Birstall
1760	1814	ALL	ALL	120650	YKS	Carlton Snaith
1736	1760	1700	1736	120650	YKS	Harewood
1814	1903	ALL	ALL	120650	YKS	Hook
1790	1880	1790	1880	123595	YKS	Kirkheaton
1701	....	ALL	1701	104299	YKS	Lofthouse
1770	1800	1600	1780	175382	YKS	Long Preston
1830	1880	1780	1830	172510	YKS	Pudsey
1799	1860	....	....	102946	YKS	Sheffield
1794	1902	1750	1794	103004	YKS	Sheffield
1673	....	1650	1700	170348	YKS	Thornhill
....	1892	....	1892	134724	???	Birmingham
1900	1965	1800	1900	177717	???	Bristol
....	....	ALL	ALL	132179	???	Travelling People
LEECH						
1790	1838	1700	1790	171514	CHS	Bickley
1790	1838	1700	1790	171514	CHS	Malpas
1700	....	....	....	153117	ESS	???
....	....	1700	1992	122742	GLS	???
1760	1780	ALL	1760	131059	KEN	Ash By Ridley
1820	....	....	1820	101761	LAN	Manchester
1815	1824	1815	ALL	146226	LAN	Manchester
1845	1855	1800	1855	163791	LAN	Manchester
1871	1900	1900	1992	171514	LAN	Manchester
1871	1900	1900	1992	171514	LAN	Salford
1700	....	....	....	153117	LND	East
1850	....	1800	1900	141623	MDX	Hackney
1838	1871	1871	1900	171514	SAL	Whitchurch
1643	1655	1600	1750	159956	SFK	Badwell Ash
1849	1966	ALL	1849	109320	SFK	Bury St Edmunds
1849	1966	ALL	1849	109320	SFK	Eyke
1840	1840	1800	1840	146803	SFK	Redisham
1640	1900	ALL	1700	141305	STS	Newcastle
1760	1870	1700	1760	173452	YKS	Cawthorne
LEECH contd.						
1840	1930	1700	1840	154970	YKS	Wigglesworth
LEEDEN						
....	....	ALL	ALL	143537	ALL	ALL
LEEDHAM						
....	....	1670	1992	165700	DBY	South
....	....	1670	1992	165700	LEI	???
....	....	1800	1900	155543	SRY	Southwark
1797	1929	....	....	145327	WYK	Northowram
1797	1929	....	....	145327	WYK	Queensbury
LEEDS						
1680	1950	1600	1890	141410	CAM	Haddenham
1830	1950	1800	1950	141410	HUN	Bluntisham
1734	1759	1650	1734	144711	HUN	Bluntisham
1734	1759	1650	1734	144711	HUN	Holywell
LEEFARR						
1825	1881	1800	1881	125598	BDF	Studham
1855	1992	1855	1992	125598	HRT	St Albans
LEEK						
1840	1950	1835	1950	107522	LAN	Rochdale
1753	1753	....	....	135437	NFK	Saxthorpe
1780	1880	1750	1800	137413	STS	Wolverhampton
....	....	....	1783	142409	STS	Yoxall
LEEKEY						
1692	1713	ALL	ALL	151394	KEN	Chatham
1746	1929	ALL	ALL	151394	LND	Central
LEEKS						
1700	1920	1600	1900	139688	SFK	ALL
LEEMING						
1700	1920	1700	1930	121320	LAN	Manchester
1700	1920	1700	1930	121320	LAN	Salford
....	....	ALL	1792	119326	YKS	Bilton In Ainsty
LEEPER						
1765	1992	1700	1765	128724	ESS	Colchester
LEES						
ALL	ALL	ALL	ALL	141658	ALL	ALL
1840	1870	1750	1900	126802	AYR	ALL
1800	1850	1600	1800	158984	AYR	ALL
1836	1900	1700	1836	168262	CHS	Reddish
1829	1888	1700	1850	126411	LAN	Crompton
....	....	1851	....	156833	LAN	Liverpool
1810	1878	1750	1878	151432	LAN	Oldham
1780	1860	1750	1790	165530	LAN	Rochdale
1920	1981	....	....	141674	LEI	Appleby Magna
1843	1861	ALL	1850	152641	LEI	Castle Donnington
1744	1870	....	....	164631	LEI	Castle Donnington
1820	1910	1800	1950	135283	LND	Finsbury Park
1905	1960	1800	1905	126519	LND	???
1841	1851	1800	1860	156833	STS	Bradley
1532	1750	1500	1750	102830	STS	Ellastone
1841	1851	1800	1860	156833	STS	Hanley
1841	1851	1800	1860	156833	STS	Penkridge
....	....	....	....	141674	STS	???
LEESE						
1841	1851	1800	1860	156833	STS	Bradley
1820	1880	1880	1992	148180	STS	Foxt
1841	1851	1800	1860	156833	STS	Hanley
1841	1851	1800	1860	156833	STS	Penkridge
1841	1880	1800	1992	142921	STS	Sandon
LEESING						
1726	1789	1650	1800	112526	LIN	Croft
LEESON						
....	....	ALL	ALL	141682	ALL	Name Study
1825	1930	1700	1930	168947	DBY	Shirley
1800	1930	1800	1900	141682	WAR	Coventry
1700	1800	1700	1800	141682	WAR	Kenilworth
1700	1770	1700	1790	127655	WAR	Priors Marston
1887	1978	....	....	140031	WAR	Solihull
LEET						
1770	1820	ALL	1770	119105	IRL	Dublin
LEEVES						
1600	1800	1800	ALL	145378	DOR	Stoke Abbott
....	....	1500	1800	145378	KEN	Cranbrook
1750	1854	1855	ALL	145378	SOM	Wrington
1725	ALL	1500	1725	145378	SRY	Dorking
1670	ALL	1500	1670	145378	SSX	Tortington
1750	ALL	1500	1750	145378	SSX	Uckfield
LEFEAVER						
1850	1920	1800	1850	121185	KEN	ALL
LEFEUVRE						
1881	1992	1871	1925	108901	GSY	St Peter Port
LEFEVER						
1846	1856	1822	1992	141399	LND	Shoreditch

Known From	To	Researching From	To	Ref	Cty	Place
LEFEVRE						
1700	1992	1700	1992	125881	CAM	March
1655	1940	....	....	128996	CAM	Thorney
1700	1992	1700	1992	125881	LIN	March
LEFFIN						
....	....	ALL	ALL	148946	ALL	Name Study
LEFFLER						
1793	1895	1750	1793	174173	LND	Lambeth
LEFTLY						
1921	?	1900	1940	167568	LND	Chelsea
LEGASSICK						
1720	....	1600	1730	179213	DEV	Dean Prior
1714	1939	1600	1714	165123	DEV	Modbury
LEGAT						
....	....	ALL	ALL	141747	ALL	ALL
LEGATE						
....	....	ALL	ALL	141747	ALL	ALL
LEGERTON						
1750	1800	1700	1800	121096	SRY	Bermondsey
LEGEYT						
1730	1800	1650	1730	118745	GLS	Redmarley
LEGG						
1800	1992	1500	1800	141720	ALL	???
1804	1860	ALL	1804	106909	BAN	Cushnie
1790	....	ALL	ALL	120332	BRK	Burford
1708	1882	1700	1882	151858	DOR	West
1855	....	1800	1855	116572	DOR	Bridport
....	....	ALL	ALL	126098	DOR	Cattistock
1760	1840	1700	1890	112712	DOR	Fordington
1850	1900	1850	1900	154210	DOR	Kinson
1650	1992	1500	1650	126969	DOR	Mythe
....	....	....	....	154210	DOR	Poole
1760	1992	1650	1992	112712	DOR	Puddletown
1750	1850	1750	1850	154210	DOR	West Parley
1850	1881	1500	1920	137472	HAM	Alverstoke
1850	1881	1500	1920	137472	HAM	Gosport
1856	1881	1500	1920	137472	HAM	Portsea
1850	1881	1500	1920	137472	HAM	Portsmouth
1800	1992	1500	1800	141720	HAM	Titchfield
1909	1992	1890	1920	137472	KEN	Chatham
1909	1992	1890	1920	137472	KEN	Gillingham
1909	1992	1890	1920	137472	KEN	Strood
1790	1830	1700	1830	133817	NBL	North Shields
1829	1850	1800	1840	109525	NYK	Harwood Dale
1655	1698	ALL	ALL	122106	SOM	Chard
1794	1878	1770	1794	131326	SOM	East Coker
1662	1688	1650	1700	142018	SOM	Taunton
1851	1992	ALL	1851	141704	SRY	Guildford
1850	1930	1800	1930	118540	WAR	Birmingham
LEGGATT						
....	....	ALL	ALL	141747	ALL	ALL
1844	1844	1800	1960	141046	BRK	Wokingham
1823	1842	1700	1900	128163	SSX	Chichester
LEGGE						
1800	1992	1500	1800	141720	ALL	???
1860	1900	ALL	1860	106909	ABD	New Pitsligo
1550	1750	1300	1550	113204	ANT	Belfast
....	....	1700	....	168386	BAN	Boynoie
1779	1779	1770	1780	170143	HAM	Buriton
1655	1655	1620	1700	125032	HAM	Sherbourne St John
1800	1992	1500	1800	141720	HAM	Titchfield
1760	1790	1700	1790	136840	WIL	Avon Valley
LEGGETT						
....	....	ALL	ALL	141747	ALL	Name Study
....	....	ALL	ALL	141747	ALL	ALL
1760	1790	1700	1800	133817	KEN	Elmsted
1800	1921	ALL	1800	118222	NFK	Romburgh
1840	1846	1840	1846	143529	NFK	Wells Next Sea
LEGGO						
1591	1771	....	....	143596	CON	Madron
LEGGOT						
....	....	1800	1876	135011	YKS	???
LEGGOTT						
....	....	ALL	ALL	141747	ALL	ALL
1800	1830	1750	1826	176583	YKS	Beverly
LEGH						
1300	1530	1300	1500	144657	CHS	Adlington
LEGON						
1808	1880	1750	1808	103896	MDX	St George
LEGOOD						
1800	1900	1800	1900	130044	MDX	London
LEGOTT						
1780	1940	....	....	131075	LIN	Blyton
1770	1860	1740	1800	131075	LIN	Haxey
LEGOTT contd.						
1780	1940	....	....	131075	LIN	Scotter
LEGRAINE						
1651	1940	....	....	128996	CAM	Thorney
LEGROVE						
1800	1830	1700	1830	148792	HAM	North East
LEHAIR						
1670	1820	ALL	ALL	166537	CAM	Thorney
LEHAIRE						
1656	1940	....	....	128996	CAM	Thorney
LEHMANN						
....	....	ALL	ALL	127884	ALL	ALL
LEIBORNE						
1607	1709	1607	1709	104817	HAM	Eling
LEICESTER						
1824	1907	1700	1824	167886	LAN	Penketh
LEIGH						
1780	1810	1730	1780	168912	CHS	Over Peover
1150	1550	1100	1550	154881	CHS	Westhall
1550	1808	1500	1808	176923	CMN	Carmarthen
1775	1850	1750	1992	136867	CON	Penzance
1526	1589	1300	1526	174319	DEV	???
1768	1862	1750	1862	176923	GLA	Pontarddulais
1453	1720	1450	1750	171549	HAM	Arreton
1791	1852	ALL	1791	100528	HUN	St Ives
?	?	?	?	142514	KEN	Bromley
1660	1680	1600	1750	155896	KEN	Canterbury
1889	1889	1500	1889	110310	LAN	Liverpool
1800	1880	1880	1992	162256	LAN	Tockholes
1830	1992	1700	1830	130257	SOM	Combwitch
1692	1808	....	....	115290	SOM	Wedmore
1782	1796	1700	1850	149098	STS	Burslem
1500	1550	1400	1600	176923	STS	???
LEIGH-TRAVIS						
1860	1880	1800	1900	158216	LAN	Manchester
LEIGHT						
1856	....	1840	1870	133639	DOR	Melcombe Regis
LEIGHTON						
1815	1890	1900	....	159891	ANS	Airlie
1630	....	....	....	100676	ANS	Dundee
1769	1769	ALL	1769	154563	DUR	Durham
1767	1800	....	....	178330	LND	Brixton
1630	....	....	....	100676	LND	Clerkenwell
1767	1800	....	....	178330	LND	Clerkenwell
1650	1767	....	....	178330	SCT	Aberdeen
1790	1900	1650	1790	170194	WAR	Birmingham
LEIGO						
....	....	1800	1901	168815	ALL	ALL
LEIPER						
....	....	ALL	ALL	115231	NBL	Berwick
LEIR						
1850	1860	1840	1875	141771	AVN	Uphill
1870	1890	1840	1920	141771	AVN	Weston
1880	1885	1780	1885	141771	DOR	Weymouth
1880	1917	1880	1917	141771	GLS	Bristol
1880	1937	1880	1960	141771	HAM	Southampton
1617	1940	1600	1992	141771	SOM	Charlton Musgrove
1617	1940	1600	1992	141771	SOM	Ditcheat
LEISHMAN						
....	....	....	....	171662	MLN	Liberton
LEITCH						
....	....	1700	1800	175889	ARL	Dunoon
1800	1900	1800	1925	144290	INV	Inverness
1805	1850	1780	1850	141798	LDY	???
1850	1992	1800	1850	141798	RFW	Linwood
1833	1849	1800	1900	179116	RFW	Neilston
LEITH						
....	....	ALL	ALL	141801	ALL	Name Study
1840	1900	1800	1875	150312	CAI	Keiss
LEITHAL						
1900	1970	1800	1900	149454	NFK	???
LEIVERS						
1630	1850	ALL	ALL	107352	NTT	Greasley
1800	....	1700	1800	138185	NTT	Selston
LEJEUNE						
1640	1851	1640	1851	116394	HAM	Beaulieu
1640	....	ALL	ALL	116394	HAM	Boldre
LELLIOTT						
1835	1895	1700	1850	152285	SSX	???
LEM						
....	....	ALL	ALL	141828	ALL	Name Study
1800	1880	....	....	102318	HAM	ALL
1765	1859	....	....	141828	STS	Bilstow
1772	1900	1670	1772	141828	STS	Monk Hopton

Known Researching
From To From To Ref Cty Place
LEM contd.
1765 1859 .... 141828 STS Tipton
1525 1925 1550 1725 141828 WMD Bridgnorth
1870 1992 1700 1900 106186 WOR Worcester
1780 1950 .... 141828 WOR Worcester
1864 1950 1700 1864 141828 YKS Sheffield
LEMAN
1682 1736 1600 1682 155276 SFK Grundesburg
LEMEN
1900 1950 1800 1920 130869 MOR Peterhead
LEMERES
1753 1768 1700 1770 144797 MDX Spitafields
1753 1768 1700 1753 179663 MDX Spitalfields
LEMM
1800 1880 .... 102318 HAM ALL
1771 1850 1600 1771 141828 HAM Bedhampton
1780 1950 ALL 1780 141828 ??? London
LEMMENS
1595 1992 1450 1595 141836 ALL ALL
LEMMON
1828 1840 ALL 1828 131881 HAM Portsmouth
.... 1700 1800 163260 NTH Nassington
LEMON
1750 1900 1700 1900 169536 MDX St Pancras
1811 1853 1700 1855 136530 NFK Honingham
LEMONS
1742 1852 .... 1742 151688 RUT Ketton
LEMUNYAN
1725 1992 ALL 1725 165042 ALL ALL
LENAN
1824 .... 1800 1900 139114 CLA Burrin
LENCH
1824 1884 .... 158178 MDX Hackney
.... 1700 1764 149977 WOR ALL
1764 1855 .... 149977 WOR Martley
1624 1848 1538 1624 158178 WOR Worcester
LENG
.... ALL ALL 141844 ALL Name Study
1650 1670 1600 1650 121339 NYK Lythe
1780 1900 1700 1900 165557 YKS
Carlton In Cleveland
LENHAM
.... ALL ALL 141852 ALL Name Study
LENNANE
1842 .... 1700 1880 115967 IRL Clare
LENNEY
1830 1870 ALL 1830 113158 SRY Camberwell
LENNIE
1745 1900 1600 1900 134155 MLN Gorebridge
LENNON
1796 1850 1600 1796 127507 ANT Kilwaughter
1900 1940 1800 1992 106003 ??? Newcastle
LENNOX
1843 1866 1840 1900 146536 AYR Beith
1825 1935 1700 1950 144037 AYR Catrine
1819 1992 1750 1819 144010 PER Perth
1780 1850 1780 1850 116831 PER Trinity Gask
1819 1992 1800 1819 144010 SCT Dundee
LENOX
1725 1744 .... 171654 AYR Sorn
LENTON
1785 1940 .... 128996 CAM Thorney
1825 1992 ALL ALL 154490 HUN Abbots Ley
1713 1814 ALL 1814 111023 LIN Swaton
1866 1925 ALL 1866 108553 NTH Gretton
1828 1904 1750 1828 153974 WAR Coventry
LENTZ
1871 1907 1700 1871 164879 MDX London
LEONARD
.... 1875 ALL 149187 ANS Dundee
1836 1871 .... 152870 BRK Newbury
1840 1850 1750 1900 143502 CAM Cambridge
1812 1812 ALL 1812 164623 DUR Heworth
1810 1880 1700 1810 143421 GLS Kingswood
1735 1755 1600 1735 134090 KEN Romney
1800 1992 .... 176125 LIN Asterby
1800 1992 .... 176125 LIN Goulceby
1880 .... 1800 1950 107891 LND Shoreditch
1849 1901 ALL 1901 116548 MEA ALL
1860 1880 1850 1900 163791 MLN Edinburgh
.... 1626 .... 1650 103349 MON Pontipool
1630 1992 .... 1630 144363 MON ???
1860 1900 1700 1860 149705 SFK West Row
1793 1992 1700 1793 141879 STS Central

Known Researching
From To From To Ref Cty Place
LEONARD contd.
1815 1825 1700 1815 152870 WIL Calne
1828 1992 1700 1828 141879 WLS South
1660 1992 1620 1900 141887 ??? Bristol
LEONARDS
1800 1875 1850 1900 154903 DEV Exeter
LEOPARD
1776 1940 .... 128996 CAM Thorney
LEOPPARD
.... 1870 1880 126675 LND London
LEPLA
1820 1941 1656 1820 126292 CAM ALL
LERICHE
.... 1800 1930 147508 HEF Hereford
LEROY
1654 1940 .... 128996 CAM Thorney
LERRY
1850 1970 1850 1970 157589 WLS ALL
LERWILL
.... ALL ALL 141917 ALL Name Study
LESANT
1766 1850 1650 1800 173983 CON ALL
LESBY
.... 1800 1900 141933 MDX London
LESLIE
1779 1936 1700 1779 119881 ABD Belhelvie
1750 1850 1750 1850 148210 ABD Fyvie
1771 1854 ALL ALL 131415 BEW Duns
.... 1800 .... 149187 FIF Ceves
.... 1800 .... 149187 FIF Kirkcaldy
.... 1844 121169 IRL ???
1870 1930 .... 140317 MDX Hackney
1875 1880 1860 1895 112216 MDX Islington
.... 1700 1992 112216 MLN Edinburgh
.... ALL 1800 110965 OKI North Isles
.... 1750 1900 129275 SCT Peterhead
ALL .... 156221 SOM Bath
LESSON
1803 1841 1841 .... 164895 WAR Coventry
LESTER
1778 1778 1700 1800 140783 BKM ???
1857 1919 1840 1940 144908 CHS Chester
1889 1896 1880 1920 144908 CLV Middlesborough
1660 1800 ALL 1700 115266 DOR ALL
1910 1981 1900 1992 144908 HAM Gosport
1794 1874 1750 1794 166707 LEI Misterton
1794 1874 1750 1794 166707 LEI Walcot
1833 1875 1800 1880 144908 LND West Norwood
1811 1899 1700 1810 131245 MDX Whitechapel
1879 1909 1600 1879 143146 ??? Hanley
LETALL
1643 1940 .... 128996 CAM Thorney
LETCHFORD
1850 1860 1850 1870 113646 KEN Gravesend
1770 1992 1500 1770 141925 KEN Meopham
1850 1860 1850 1870 113646 KEN Muton
1800 1840 1800 1900 141933 LND ???
LETHBRIDGE
1806 1917 1783 1920 141895 DEV Ugborough
LETHERLONG
1811 ALL 1750 1811 171190 WAR Barton On The Heath
LETHIEULLIER
.... 1600 1900 141151 KEN ALL
.... 1600 1900 141151 LND ALL
LETT
1816 1816 1700 1816 170178 LND Lambeth
1800 .... ALL 1900 174637 WOR ???
LETTEN
1855 1992 1700 1855 103950 KEN Gravesend
LETTICE
1870 1907 ALL ALL 168610 WOR Worcester
LETTON
.... 1850 1850 1900 166383 DBY Derby
1840 1992 1750 .... 166383 KEN Greenwich
LEVER
1687 1772 1687 1772 148156 BKM Hanslope
1810 1890 1800 1890 102121 LAN Bolton
1883 1910 ALL 1992 136077 LAN Farnworth
1801 1992 1801 1992 147249 LAN Port Sunlight
1700 1900 1700 1900 105511 OXF ALL
1800 1950 1800 1850 105511 OXF Chesterton
1700 1900 1700 1900 105511 OXF Cropredy
1580 1900 .... 141976 SRY Richmond
ALL ALL ALL ALL 105511 WAR ALL

Known From	To	Researching From	To	Ref	Cty	Place
LEVER contd.						
1800	1900	1800	1900	105511	WAR	Harbury
1792	1852	1787	1870	136980	WIL	Ludgershall
1791	1992	1700	1800	116289	WIL	Tisbury
1780	1992	....	1780	141968	YKS	Ripponden
LEVERETT						
1854	1921	1700	1854	163929	NFK	Diss
1854	1921	1700	1854	163929	NFK	Shelton
1780	1870	1700	1780	115541	SRY	Wandsworth
LEVERIDGE						
1860	1890	1800	1860	134139	LND	ALL
LEVERNS						
....	1750	ALL	1750	134511	NTT	Arnold
LEVERS						
1825	1925	1800	1950	144290	LEI	Branston
1750	1800	1700	1850	144290	NTT	East Bridgford
1800	1900	1750	1900	144290	NTT	Granby
LEVERSUCH						
1823	....	1800	1830	175684	HAM	ALL
LEVETT						
1843	1900	1800	1843	176257	CAM	Soham
1877	1986	1750	1880	139777	NFK	???
1706	1865	1557	1706	164860	SFK	Pettistree
1750	1880	1700	1900	111325	SSX	Wilmington
....	1700	....	....	174564	SSX	???
1838	1900	1600	1900	117862	YKS	East Riding
1819	1900	1700	1820	117862	YKS	Hull
LEVETT-SCRIVENER						
1800	1992	1800	1992	162515	NFK	ALL
1800	1992	1800	1992	162515	SFK	ALL
LEVEY						
1836	1992	1800	1836	179167	HAM	Southampton
LEVI						
?	?	?	?	138622	CON	???
?	?	?	?	138622	DEV	???
LEVICK						
1600	1850	1600	1850	127914	DBY	Dronfield
1830	1880	1830	1880	127914	YKS	Darrington
LEVINS						
1830	1860	1700	1830	174661	IRL	Drogheda
1900	1950	1850	1980	166154	SRY	Mitcham
LEVIT						
1750	....	....	....	130923	CAM	Swaffham Bulbeck
....	....	ALL	1872	146315	YKS	Kexborough
LEVITT						
....	1768	1740	1804	128961	ESS	Coggeshall
1770	1800	ALL	1770	131059	ESS	Tolleshunt D'arcy
1665	1783	1600	1665	175218	EYK	Warter
1765	1900	1700	1765	150096	YKS	Ferry Fryston
1815	1988	....	....	141984	YKS	Monk Fryston
1765	1820	ALL	1765	102350	YKS	Pontefract
1760	1860	....	....	141984	YKS	Pontefract
1790	1860	....	....	141984	YKS	Purston Jaglin
1725	1735	1700	1750	141984	YKS	Womersley
LEVOT						
1622	....	....	....	142859	GLS	Leonard Stanley
LEVY						
?	?	?	?	138622	CON	???
?	?	?	?	138622	DEV	???
1871	1891	1871	....	121495	HAM	Andover
1860	....	1700	1870	124966	HAM	Winchester
LEWARNE						
1580	1992	1650	1992	141992	ALL	ALL
1580	1992	1650	1992	141992	CON	ALL
1838	....	1700	1838	130656	CON	Laneast
....	....	....	....	135488	LND	Bermondsey
LEWENDEN						
1828	1861	ALL	ALL	177989	BRK	Newbury
1800	1820	ALL	ALL	177989	OXF	Whitchurch
LEWER						
....	....	ALL	ALL	171603	ALL	Name Study
1859	1992	ALL	1859	179167	SRY	Godalming
LEWERS						
1871	....	....	....	163910	CHS	Nantwich
1808	1873	1837	1880	163910	LAN	Salford
LEWES						
1600	1780	1500	1800	176958	CMN	Llysnewydd
1720	1750	....	....	176958	PEM	Tredefald
LEWIN						
1800	1866	1700	1900	116742	CAM	Leverington
1864	1969	1700	1864	112283	KEN	Sevenoaks
1753	1889	ALL	1992	168718	LEI	ALL
....	....	1700	1800	136743	LEI	Burton On Wolds
1926	1992	1800	1926	136743	LEI	Loughborough

Known From	To	Researching From	To	Ref	Cty	Place
LEWIN contd.						
....	....	1700	1800	136743	LEI	Prestwood
1841	1880	1800	1835	136743	LEI	Seagrave
1885	1885	ALL	ALL	101486	STS	Stoke Upon Trent
LEWINGTON						
....	....	ALL	1850	111333	BRK	Leckhampstead
....	....	1770	1800	117137	WIL	Marlborough
LEWIS						
....	....	ALL	ALL	102180	ALL	Name Study
1848	1888	1700	1950	159719	AGY	Gaerwen
1830	....	1830	1900	157147	AGY	Llanedwen
1800	....	1700	1860	157147	AGY	Llanfechell
....	....	1700	1900	110353	AVN	Abson
1800	1992	....	....	142026	AVN	Bristol
....	....	1700	1900	110353	AVN	Wick
1830	1874	1825	1890	154032	BRE	Brynmawr
1729	1891	ALL	ALL	154032	BRE	Llanigon
1710	1766	....	1780	171441	BRK	Faringdon
1827	1841	1795	1850	100242	BRK	Reading
....	....	1800	1900	117714	BRK	Thatcham
....	....	1800	1850	147885	CAE	Caernarfon
1830	....	1700	1900	157147	CAE	Llanrug
1820	1944	1700	1820	124427	CGN	Borth
1830	....	....	....	137308	CGN	???
1790	1860	....	....	140570	CHS	Chester
1845	1891	1825	1845	110930	CHS	Nantwich
1830	ALL	ALL	1866	116734	CHS	Sandbach
1890	1915	....	....	147885	CHS	Wallasey
1661	1835	1500	1661	149314	CMN	Carmarthen
1800	1850	1600	1900	120677	CMN	Cliffig
1860	1890	1800	1920	142042	CMN	Dryslyn
1853	1992	ALL	ALL	164550	COR	Aughadown
1845	1992	ALL	ALL	164550	COR	Ballydehob
1845	1992	ALL	ALL	164550	COR	Coomhola
1853	1992	ALL	ALL	164550	COR	Schull
1850	1920	1700	1850	118915	DEV	Barnstaple
1760	1810	1720	1837	140392	DEV	Georgeham
1850	1920	1700	1850	118915	DEV	Plymouth
1835	1871	1800	1875	177393	DEV	Templeton
1825	1850	1825	1850	159131	DFD	Castle Buthe
1735	1830	1830	1992	148415	ENG	South
1804	1810	1750	1815	136042	ESS	Epping
1850	1900	ALL	1950	123048	ESS	Harwich
1650	1700	1600	1650	177024	ESS	High Easter
1879	1879	1700	1879	105163	FLN	Anttani
1830	1860	1700	1900	152714	FLN	Hope
1880	1980	....	....	142093	GLA	Aberdare
1790	1992	1700	1789	172006	GLA	Aberdare
1816	1992	....	....	129232	GLA	Aberdulais
1863	....	1800	1920	138428	GLA	Baglan
1800	1837	1800	1851	140295	GLA	Cardiff
1799	1849	1799	1849	158658	GLA	Coity
1760	?	....	....	176559	GLA	Coity
1766	1855	1700	1860	140295	GLA	Ewenny
1893	1992	ALL	1893	142034	GLA	Glynneath
1858	1932	....	....	175587	GLA	Hafod
....	....	1800	1858	175587	GLA	Llangyfelach
1777	1833	1777	1833	158658	GLA	Llansamlet
1720	1840	1720	1840	151297	GLA	Neath
1863	....	1800	1920	138428	GLA	Pontrhyd-Y-Fen
1870	1952	1800	1992	106488	GLA	Swansea
1790	1992	1700	1789	172006	GLA	Ynyshire
1779	1851	ALL	1992	159174	GLS	Barton St Mary
1660	ALL	....	....	142158	GLS	Cromhall
1853	1992	ALL	1853	148997	GLS	Malvern
....	....	1750	1800	142026	GLS	Nailsworth
1800	1850	1700	1800	148059	GLS	Tidenham
1806	1992	1750	1806	123153	GNT	Abergavenny
....	....	1850	1870	114782	GNT	Ebbw Vale
1842	1992	ALL	1842	142034	GNT	Llandfer
1836	1920	1700	1830	157147	GYN	Caernarvon
1845	1906	1870	1906	151335	HEF	South
1800	1852	1750	1860	148288	HEF	Ayemestry
1808	1812	1780	1808	103918	HEF	Bodenham
1801	1912	1800	1954	142077	HEF	Brilley
1800	1852	1750	1860	148288	HEF	Elton
....	1992	ALL	1992	143197	HEF	Hay On Wye
1800	1852	1750	1860	148288	HEF	Leinthale
1790	1810	1790	1870	153303	HEF	Letton
1853	1992	ALL	1853	148997	HEF	Malvern
1800	1852	1750	1860	148288	HEF	Pipe Aston
....	....	1732	1924	119431	KEN	East
1735	1830	ALL	1735	148415	KEN	Chislehurst
....	....	1500	1632	143138	KEN	East Greenwich

Known From	To	Researching From	To	Ref	Cty	Place
LEWIS contd.						
?	?	?	?	166642	KEN	Mersham
1800	1830	ALL	1800	126322	LAN	Liverpool
1870	1890	....	....	147885	LAN	Liverpool
1808	1873	1837	1880	163910	LAN	Salford
1843	1918	ALL	1843	122858	LAN	Southport
1950	1992	1900	1992	123765	LIN	Grimsby
1860	1900	1700	1900	113387	LIN	Louth
1874	1992	....	1874	137642	LND	North
1869	1992	....	1869	142166	LND	Bethnal Green
....	1934	1850	1935	106402	LND	Childs Hill
1848	1920	1800	1848	159212	LND	Clerkenwell
....	....	1600	1799	115975	LND	London
....	....	1790	1900	142131	LND	Shoreditch
1857	1992	1800	1857	118230	LND	St Saviour
1878	1937	1800	1878	149578	LND	Tottenham
....	....	1700	1877	164178	LND	???
1862	....	....	1862	103489	MAY	Ballina
1862	....	....	1900	103489	MAY	Ross
1800	1860	1700	1800	113816	MDX	Isleworth
1870	1880	1800	1920	142050	MDX	London
1810	1830	1780	1850	176982	MDX	London
1800	ALL	....	....	142158	MER	Barmouth
1787	....	1700	1851	176877	MER	Dolgellau
1721	1721	....	....	135437	MON	Llangwm
1820	1860	1820	1860	156930	MON	Llanhennock
1770	ALL	....	....	142158	MON	Mynnyddislwyn
1864	1971	1835	1864	149314	MON	Newport
....	....	1750	1900	139297	NTH	Burton-Latimer
....	....	1750	1900	139297	NTH	Finedon
1800	1880	1750	1920	142379	NTH	Isham
....	....	1795	1850	100242	OXF	Caversham
1870	1881	1800	1881	162450	PEM	Haverfordwest
1850	1960	1700	1850	114685	PEM	Llanwynda
1850	1890	1850	1890	156744	PEM	Llanychaer
....	....	1850	1880	142093	PEM	Wiston
1726	1754	1600	1800	176877	RAD	Cwmdeuddwr
1809	1983	1800	1992	176877	RAD	Rhayader
1810	1828	1800	1881	160482	SAL	Cockshutt
....	....	1865	1871	116602	SAL	Cressage
1744	....	ALL	1744	131725	SAL	Dawley Magna
1716	1828	1600	1900	144460	SAL	Dawley
1800	1992	1750	1850	122149	SAL	Fitz
1800	1992	1750	1850	122149	SAL	Oswestry
1849	1880	1800	1881	160482	SAL	Whittington
1730	1992	1600	1730	102253	SFK	Brightwell
1730	1810	1650	1730	155276	SFK	Brightwell
1681	1992	ALL	1681	142107	SFK	Stratford St Mary
1700	1736	....	1700	122815	SFK	Tannington
1775	1850	1700	1850	106631	SOM	Bleadon
1800	....	1800	1992	131156	SOM	Farmborough
1815	1860	1780	1880	165980	SSX	Hooe
1837	1900	....	....	100536	SSX	???
1828	1960	ALL	1828	174815	STS	Birmingham
1828	1960	ALL	1828	174815	STS	Handsworth
1794	1865	1750	1870	134627	STS	Rushall
1828	1960	ALL	1828	174815	STS	West Bromwich
1828	1860	1750	1880	100439	STS	Wolverhampton
1826	1960	ALL	1826	117048	WAR	Birmingham
....	....	1800	1900	154458	WAR	Birmingham
1870	1975	1700	1870	146110	WAR	Leamington Spa
....	....	1860	1900	139297	WAR	???
1807	1807	1700	1820	153184	WIL	Lydiard
1680	1720	1670	1750	142018	WIL	Marlborough
1943	1943	1900	1943	174262	WLS	Maesteg
1791	1837	1770	1791	161284	WOR	Alvechurch
1800	1900	1550	1800	169986	WOR	Bromsgrove
1853	1992	ALL	1853	148997	WOR	Malvern
1890	1930	....	1890	102059	YKS	Barnsley
1824	1846	1700	1846	147125	???	Salisbury
1824	1846	1700	1846	147125	???	West Harnham
LEWIS-HOWELL						
....	....	?	....	137995	CMN	Llanddensant
LEWNEY						
1784	....	1700	....	160385	IOM	Braddan
LEWORTHY						
ALL	ALL	ALL	ALL	151750	ALL	ALL
1873	1895	ALL	ALL	161098	DEV	South Molton
1860	1900	1800	1900	139327	DEV	Tavistock
1895	1992	1895	1992	161098	???	Bristol
LEWRY						
1835	1864	1775	1835	129712	SSX	Maresfield
1800	ALL	1500	1800	145378	SSX	Slaugham
LEWSEY						
1948	1992	....	1992	142190	DNB	Alexandria
1790	....	....	....	142190	ESS	Braintree
1758	....	....	....	142190	ESS	Castle Hedingham
1784	....	....	....	142190	ESS	Maplestead
1888	1992	....	....	142190	MDX	London
1787	....	....	....	142190	SFK	Sudbury
LEWTHWAITE						
1600	1992	1500	1900	114383	CMA	Broadgate
....	....	1600	1750	116173	CUL	West
LEWTUS						
1600	....	ALL	ALL	167622	ALL	ALL
LEWTY						
1630	1830	....	....	165999	LEI	Bottesford
LEY						
1920	1920	1900	1992	121932	CHS	Birkenhead
1920	1920	1900	1992	121932	CHS	Wallasey
1860	....	....	1860	164011	DEV	Topsham
1793	1934	....	....	132160	DEV	Werrington
1860	....	....	....	164593	???	Clifton
LEYBOURN						
1700	1710	....	....	103721	LIN	Althorpe
LEYCESTER						
1400	1500	1350	1500	154881	CHS	Tabley
LEYDEN						
1850	1900	....	....	136492	IRL	???
1850	1900	....	....	136492	LTN	Edinburgh
LEYLAND						
1843	1992	1700	1843	173711	LAN	Chorley
1790	1870	1700	1870	151254	LAN	Culcheth
1856	1858	1800	1900	154539	LAN	Eccleston St Helens
1790	1870	1700	1870	151254	LAN	Leigh
1855	1912	1750	1855	154539	LAN	Prescot
1800	1920	1700	1920	157147	LAN	St Helens
1830	1925	1700	1829	172006	LAN	St Helens
1803	1843	1700	1843	173711	LAN	Wigan
LEYSHON						
1868	1992	1700	1868	142212	MON	Bedwellty
LEYSHONE						
1868	1992	1700	1868	142212	GLA	Ynyshir
LIBBETTER						
1812	1823	1700	1825	124907	SSX	Worth
LIBBY						
1814	1814	1700	1814	153605	CON	St Austell
1730	1800	1600	1730	109061	DEV	Stoke Damerel
LICKBARROW						
1600	1700	....	....	146854	WES	Orton
LICKFOLD						
....	....	ALL	ALL	142220	ALL	Name Study
1300	1992	1100	1992	142220	ALL	ALL
1700	1900	1700	1900	142220	HAM	East
1600	1850	1500	1900	142220	LND	City
1803	1828	....	1803	142166	LND	???
1600	1992	1500	1992	142220	MDX	ALL
1700	1992	1600	1992	142220	SRY	ALL
1550	1992	1550	1992	142220	SRY	West
1297	1880	1100	1992	142220	SSX	West
1656	1782	....	....	165999	SSX	Lurgashall
LICKIS						
1780	1992	1600	1992	114197	ALL	ALL
LICKISS						
....	....	ALL	ALL	142239	ALL	Name Study
LICKLEY						
....	....	ALL	ALL	142247	ALL	Name Study
1600	1992	1600	1900	142247	ENG	???
1600	1992	1600	1900	142247	SCT	???
LICRECE						
1870	1948	1700	1992	160377	MDX	London
LIDDALL						
1800	1899	ALL	ALL	146633	HRT	Hemel Hempstead
1800	1899	ALL	ALL	146633	LND	ALL
1700	1800	ALL	ALL	146633	WIL	ALL
LIDDELL						
1761	1765	1700	1760	163562	LND	Stepney
1780	1859	1750	1780	141798	STI	St Ninians
LIDDIARD						
1840	1992	1700	1840	173460	AVN	Bath
1620	1730	1550	1700	124974	WIL	Aldbourne
1650	1820	1600	1700	143030	WIL	Aldbourne
1730	1790	1700	1900	124974	WIL	Ramsbury
LIDDICOAT						
1611	1762	1550	1800	153591	CON	Newlyn East
1611	1762	1550	1800	153591	CON	St Columb Major
1611	1762	1550	1800	153591	CON	St Denys

Known From	Known To	Researching From	Researching To	Ref	Cty	Place
LIDDINGTON						
1851	1854	1700	1850	120081	NTH	South
LIDDLE						
1880	1960	1800	1992	118281	DUR	Witton Le Wear
1897	1960	1800	1896	106402	LND	Wimbledon
1840	1860	1800	1900	142050	LTN	Edinburgh
1770	1800	ALL	1800	149063	ROX	Hawick
1897	1960	1800	1896	106402	SRY	Kingston On Thames
LIDDY						
1853	1992	ALL	1853	107239	MDX	Poplar
LIDGATE						
....	....	ALL	ALL	141747	ALL	ALL
LIDGETT						
....	....	ALL	ALL	141747	ALL	ALL
1782	....	1760	....	130192	CHS	Malpas
LIDSTER						
1900	1928	1928	1941	148903	DEV	Plymouth
LIDSTONE						
....	....	ALL	ALL	142255	ALL	Name Study
1500	1992	ALL	ALL	142255	ALL	ALL
LIDWELL						
1700	1835	1800	1992	163848	TIP	Templemore
LIFECHILD						
1740	1746	1740	1746	141690	CON	Falmouth
1770	1771	1770	1793	141690	CON	Probus
1773	1793	1773	1793	141690	CON	St Enoder
LIFFEN						
....	....	1300	1992	115975	ALL	ALL
LIFFORD						
1815	1900	1750	1815	132640	KEN	Sydenham
1847	1902	ALL	1847	151777	LND	Newington
1847	1902	ALL	1847	151777	SRY	Camberwell
?	....	....	?	111104	SRY	Epsom
LIFLY						
1746	1746	1600	1746	174130	GLS	Burton On The Hill
LIGGAT						
1880	1992	ALL	1880	142263	AYR	Beith
LIGGET						
....	....	ALL	1872	142298	TYR	???
LIGGETT						
....	....	ALL	ALL	142271	ALL	Name Study
....	....	ALL	ALL	141747	ALL	ALL
ALL	ALL	ALL	ALL	142271	ALL	ALL
1870	1893	1700	1992	151521	YKS	Leeds
LIGGINS						
1740	1840	1700	1880	138444	WAR	Church Lawford
LIGHT						
1862	1895	1820	1862	117358	LND	Bermondsey
1740	1992	ALL	1740	142301	MDX	Shoreditch
1819	1851	....	....	135437	NFK	Ditchingham
1730	1832	1700	1890	153877	SAL	Claverley
1804	1804	ALL	ALL	124982	SOM	North
1770	?	ALL	ALL	153516	SOM	Chew Magna
1770	?	ALL	ALL	153516	SOM	Kewstoke
1827	....	....	....	119911	SOM	Pensford
1770	?	ALL	ALL	153516	SOM	Worle
1872	1916	....	....	145394	SRY	Godalming
1824	1916	....	....	145394	SSX	Ditchling
1800	1916	....	....	145394	SSX	Slindon
?	?	?	?	111937	WIL	Market Lavington
1732	1732	....	....	115606	WIL	Ogbourne St Andrew
LIGHTBODY						
1790	1884	1700	1800	167398	WIG	Kirkmaiden
LIGHTBOUND						
1800	1992	1800	1992	109347	LAN	Accrington
1825	....	1825	....	109347	LAN	Darwen
LIGHTBOWN						
1750	1900	1750	1900	125237	LAN	Darwen
LIGHTBROUWN						
1800	1880	1880	1992	162256	LAN	Darwen
LIGHTFOOT						
1790	1850	1700	1810	117005	BKM	Chichley
1816	1840	1800	1840	149330	CHS	Nantwich
1815	1950	....	1815	106917	CHS	Over
1815	1950	....	1815	106917	CHS	Wharton
1860	1992	1700	1860	109193	CON	St Breock
....	....	1700	1992	109193	CON	St Kew
LIGHTNING						
1680	1890	ALL	ALL	103985	NFK	ALL
1680	1890	1600	1680	103985	NFK	Hethersett
1680	1890	1600	1680	103985	NFK	Norwich
LIGHTOLER						
1725	....	1725	....	109347	LAN	Oswaldtwistle
LIGHTON						
1896	1992	....	....	142336	DBY	Chesterfield
1800	1992	1700	1800	142336	LIN	Boston
1815	1900	1770	1815	108103	NFK	Hardwick
1831	1900	1770	1815	108103	NFK	Shelton
1881	1992	....	....	142336	SYK	Sheffield
LIGHTOWLERS						
1770	1808	1700	1770	130206	YKS	Bradford
LIGHTWING						
1880	1900	1750	1880	103985	NFK	Hethersett
1760	1820	1700	1900	106356	NFK	Wymondham
LIHOU						
....	....	1400	1950	125296	GSY	???
LIKEMAN						
1766	1992	1600	1766	164879	SSX	ALL
LILBURN						
1800	1900	1800	1900	123765	LIN	Lincoln
LILE						
1780	1840	....	1780	142344	DEV	Monkleigh
1840	1897	....	....	142344	DEV	Torrington
1840	1992	....	....	142344	GLA	Swansea
LILES						
1867	1891	1840	1867	126519	MDX	Hackney
LILL						
1800	1980	ALL	1800	154059	DOR	Dorchester
1800	1970	1500	1800	154059	KEN	Deptford
1750	1770	1700	1750	121339	LIN	Alford
1780	1820	1500	1780	154059	LND	Westminster
1800	1850	1500	1800	154059	SRY	Wandsworth
LILLEY						
1727	1980	1600	1992	112089	CAM	Cambridge
1871	1945	1871	1945	142352	CAM	Chesterton
1830	1870	1830	1870	142352	CAM	East Hatley
1599	1845	1599	1845	142352	CAM	Guilden Morden
1850	1880	1600	1850	123390	HEF	Asherton
1850	1880	1600	1850	123390	HEF	Munsley
1740	1830	1700	1830	111538	HRT	Much Marcle
1781	1864	1650	1992	159468	KEN	Ashford
1846	....	1700	1900	126012	KEN	Whitstable
1780	1812	1750	1850	123536	NBL	Newcastle On Tyne
1820	1900	1700	1850	160725	NBL	Newcastle Upon Tyne
1830	1900	1800	1900	153931	SFK	Stoke By Nayland
1894	1984	1800	1893	131245	SRY	Camberwell
1787	1861	1700	1881	160636	YKS	Saddleworth
1828	1992	1800	1886	142360	YKS	York
LILLICO						
1900	1930	1700	1800	150371	ROX	Castleton
LILLIE						
1850	....	1700	1850	151440	NBL	ALL
1800	1850	....	....	151440	NBL	Alnwick
1829	1992	1700	1829	170453	ROX	Kelso
LILLIMAN						
1780	1900	1600	1800	142379	NTH	Cransley
1580	1720	1580	1800	142379	NTH	Ringstead
LILLINGTON						
....	....	ALL	ALL	142387	ALL	Name Study
1815	1910	1813	1912	154733	DOR	Winfrith
LILLY						
1760	1773	1760	1790	142352	CAM	Litlington
1786	1786	....	....	103632	LAN	Manchester
1774	1779	1730	1820	167002	NTT	Cromwell
1686	1910	1700	1900	166960	SFK	Polstead
1805	1900	1700	1805	170771	SOM	Marstock
1750	1992	1650	1850	142395	WOR	Bromsgrove
LILLYCRAP						
1885	ALL	1885	ALL	160164	SOM	Buckland St Mary
LILLYWHITE						
1712	1890	1600	1712	157732	HAM	Hawkley
1768	1893	1746	1893	107166	SSX	Findon
LILWALL						
1787	1827	....	....	131229	HEF	ALL
LILY						
1800	1800	1800	1800	139971	BDF	Souldrop
1794	1805	1790	1830	142352	CAM	Abinton Agotts
LIMB						
1714	1769	ALL	1714	126942	DBY	Beeley
1833	1992	1835	....	162744	NTT	Bagthorpe
LIMBOARD						
1750	1778	ALL	1750	152234	WYK	Garforth
LIMBORD						
1750	1813	1790	1813	171166	WRY	Garforth
1750	1800	1700	1992	114901	YKS	Garforth
LIMBREY						
....	....	1700	1900	135968	LEI	ALL

Known From	To	Researching From	To	Ref	Cty	Place
LIMBRICK						
1811	1879	1811	....	129100	MDX	Mary L Bone
LIMER						
1778	1800	1750	1778	155276	SFK	Felixstowe
LIMERICK						
1841	....	1750	1992	160032	DUR	Sunderland
1841	....	1750	1992	160032	IRL	???
LIMESI						
1101	1103	1066	ALL	108294	???	???
LINBERRY						
1840	1900	ALL	ALL	113859	SSX	Bramber
LINCE						
1857	1887	1700	1856	131245	NFK	Norwich
LINCH						
1780	1840	1700	1840	139688	GLS	Bristol
1857	1870	ALL	ALL	117889	LKS	Chapel Hall
LINCOLN						
1697	1992	ALL	1700	108502	BDF	Campton
1755	1900	1700	1900	147958	BDF	Clophill
1800	1850	1800	1850	152528	BDF	Sheppershall
1718	1850	1700	1718	169730	HRT	Standon
1697	1992	ALL	1700	108502	HUN	Abbotsley
1697	1992	ALL	1700	108502	KEN	Bexley
1740	....	....	....	157554	NFK	Attlebridge
1740	1850	1650	1750	142417	NFK	Dereham
1851	1880	1871	1880	142840	NFK	Moulton
1790	1852	1700	1900	136530	NFK	Yaxham
1683	1992	....	1683	142409	NFK	???
LINDAL						
1790	1821	ALL	ALL	135909	CUL	Gosforth
LINDER						
....	....	ALL	ALL	142433	ALL	Name Study
LINDFIELD						
....	....	ALL	ALL	142441	ALL	Name Study
1360	1992	1000	1992	142441	ALL	ALL
LINDGREEN						
....	....	ALL	ALL	160199	ALL	ALL
1886	1913	ALL	1886	160199	DUR	South Shields
LINDGREN						
1800	1900	ALL	ALL	154067	LND	ALL
LINDLEY						
1886	1904	....	....	106747	DEV	Plymouth
1748	1846	1700	1850	159964	LAN	Ringley
1760	1775	1700	1760	114871	LEI	Leicester
1800	1870	1760	1800	114871	LND	ALL
1803	1873	1803	....	163171	YKS	Pontefract
1762	....	....	....	165484	YKS	Woolley
LINDO						
....	....	ALL	ALL	142468	ALL	Name Study
1880	1940	ALL	1992	156078	SUT	Tyne And Wear
LINDOP						
1782	1992	1600	1770	142476	STS	ALL
1820	1900	1600	1800	109304	STS	North
....	....	ALL	1700	142476	YKS	ALL
LINDORES						
1881	1904	1881	1920	126705	LAN	Manchester
LINDRIDGE						
1808	1852	ALL	ALL	125466	KEN	ALL
LINDSAY						
1660	1700	ALL	1660	143820	ANS	Arbroath
?	1843	1800	1843	174955	ANS	Dundee
1869	....	1850	1869	174955	ANS	Forfar
1868	....	....	....	174955	ANS	Montrose
1896	1992	....	....	164151	CUL	Frizington
1868	....	....	....	164151	DUR	Heworth
1800	1820	1750	1850	130915	FIF	Largo
1720	1740	1650	1720	100978	KCD	Kinneff
1861	1881	1861	1881	138401	LAN	Liverpool
1775	1800	....	....	171654	LKS	Avondale
1824	1845	1750	1890	111848	LKS	Crawfordjohn
1825	....	1750	1850	141739	LKS	Glasgow
1770	1789	....	....	171654	LKS	Lesmahagow
1800	1973	1800	1980	146536	LKS	Shotts
1840	1860	....	1860	116866	LKS	???
?	?	?	?	142514	NIR	Belfast
1880	1992	1800	1880	165336	OXF	Brightnell Baldwin
1700	1750	1600	1700	174513	OXF	Broadwell
1843	1992	....	....	172529	SCT	Dundee
1890	1920	1885	1930	142506	SRY	Croydon
1830	1891	....	....	138401	WES	Beetham
1830	1891	....	....	138401	WES	Old Hutton
1809	....	1800	1810	138401	YKS	Dent
LINDSELL						
1750	1837	1650	1750	139084	ESS	Little Canfield

Known From	To	Researching From	To	Ref	Cty	Place
LINDSEY						
1812	1840	ALL	1812	159077	CAM	Whittlesey
1865	?	1830	1900	142506	ESS	Billericay
1685	1875	ALL	1685	172901	OXF	ALL
1779	1794	....	....	124672	OXF	Cogges
1817	1918	....	....	124672	OXF	Oxford
1794	1817	....	....	124672	OXF	Yarnton
LINDSTER						
1800	1992	1800	1992	106305	DOW	???
LINE						
1700	1992	1700	1992	127353	BKM	Drayton Parslow
1700	1992	1700	1992	127353	BKM	Newton Longville
1804	1851	1750	1851	145750	BKM	Sherington
1920	1980	1900	1992	127353	BKM	Stoke Hammond
1739	....	....	....	166723	CON	Stoke Climsland
1729	1829	1650	1729	166111	NTH	Bozeat
1835	1850	1700	1860	168327	NTH	West Haddon
1856	1958	1833	1958	127353	SRY	Lambeth
LINEHAM						
....	....	ALL	1820	167029	HRT	St Albans
LINEKAR						
1872	....	ALL	ALL	140902	CHS	Chester
1903	....	ALL	ALL	140902	CHS	Wirral
LINES						
1820	1900	....	....	101559	BKM	Stony Stratford
1840	1992	1822	1992	112925	BKM	Stony Stratford
1840	1992	1822	1992	112925	BKM	Wolverton
1800	1850	1600	1800	154059	ESS	Chelmsford
1774	1831	1600	1774	149888	GLS	Bitton
....	....	1700	1830	101559	HRT	St Albans
1819	1882	1810	1822	112925	HRT	St Albans
1780	1820	1500	1780	154059	KEN	Deptford
1700	1900	....	....	142530	NFK	East Dereham
1850	1900	1750	1850	160296	NFK	Tunstead
1899	1935	1796	1898	118850	NTH	Chipping Warden
1803	1828	1800	1828	103632	NTH	Hellidon
1899	1935	1796	1898	118850	OXF	Chipping Warden
1800	1900	ALL	ALL	142549	WIL	ALL
1800	1881	1700	1992	122742	WIL	Woodford
LINEY						
1764	1829	1740	1829	107573	HAM	Itchen Stoke
LINFITT						
....	....	ALL	ALL	154067	ALL	Name Study
1850	1887	ALL	ALL	154067	GSY	Peter Port
1775	1866	ALL	ALL	154067	LND	ALL
LINFOOT						
1888	1934	1700	1900	159336	YKS	Spofforth
LINFORD						
1811	1866	1811	1866	138703	HUN	Huntingdon
....	....	1650	1750	115142	???	Mancetter
LING						
....	....	1700	1800	108677	KEN	North
1884	1940	1750	1884	171662	MDX	Hackney
1700	1800	1700	1800	115614	SFK	Campsey Ash
....	....	1800	....	137456	WAR	Napton
LINGARD						
1600	1992	ALL	1992	157902	CHS	Altrincham
1600	1992	ALL	1992	157902	CHS	Bowdon
1788	1878	1500	1878	169439	LAN	Huncoat
1800	1992	....	....	176125	LIN	Asterby
1800	1992	....	....	176125	LIN	Goulceby
1800	1881	1700	1881	101923	LIN	Louth
1780	1851	?	1780	121665	STS	Darlaston
1826	1848	1826	1848	116653	STS	Walsall
1817	1992	1750	1817	103004	YKS	Sheffield
1785	1928	1500	1992	102520	YKS	Thornton
LINGEN						
1400	1550	1400	1550	154881	HEF	Wylton
LINGHAM						
1860	1992	1750	1860	163732	KEN	Chatham
LINGLEY						
1852	1900	1800	1900	124788	LAN	Manchester
1876	....	ALL	ALL	176737	LAN	Manchester
1560	1992	ALL	ALL	142565	NFK	Norwich
LINGS						
1711	1818	1600	1950	169889	LIN	Caistor
LINK						
1860	1880	1860	1930	122343	DUR	Sunderland
1900	1910	1860	1930	122343	GLA	Cardiff
LINKLATER						
1773	1879	1715	1773	163139	OKI	Deerness
1880	1970	1748	1880	142573	OKI	Stromness
LINLEY						
1850	1900	1700	1850	114383	LIN	North Scarle

Known From	To	Researching From	To	Ref	Cty	Place
LINLEY contd.						
1726	1924	1600	1790	101575	YKS	Holbeck
1726	1924	1600	1790	101575	YKS	Leeds
LINN						
1830	1860	....	....	127140	LKS	Glasgow
LINNANE						
1840	1866	1800	1992	172243	CLA	Miltown Malbay
LINNELL						
1775	1880	....	....	151785	HUN	Leighton Bromswold
1850	1900	1800	1850	172898	LND	St Pancras
1700	1830	1600	1830	100927	NTH	ALL
1730	1900	1730	1900	173533	NTH	South
....	....	ALL	1860	114308	NTH	Floore
....	....	ALL	1860	114308	NTH	Kislingbury
LINNETT						
1841	1992	1841	1900	133248	NTH	ALL
1842	1874	1800	1992	124044	NTH	Calycotton
1841	1992	1841	1900	133248	NTH	Rothwell
LINNEY						
1912	1989	1800	1912	170569	CHS	Stockport
1890	1992	....	1900	147818	LND	East
LINNINGTON						
....	....	ALL	ALL	149411	ALL	Name Study
1672	1779	1600	1762	145289	HAM	Isle Of Wight
1795	1819	ALL	1795	106909	IOW	Newport
1770	1820	ALL	1770	145564	KEN	Greeenwich
1820	1850	1850	1992	145564	KEN	Welling
LINOM						
1750	1992	1600	1750	117110	KEN	London
1750	1992	1600	1750	117110	MDX	London
LINSCOTT						
....	....	1600	1992	137588	DEV	Exeter
LINSEY						
1709	1827	1650	1850	118397	OXF	Coggs
LINSLEY						
1797	1992	1770	1900	122440	DUR	North East
1770	1822	1770	1856	122440	NBL	Newburn
....	....	ALL	ALL	172324	SCT	???
LINSTEAD						
1870	1958	1700	1870	132926	MDX	Bethnal Green
LINTER						
....	....	ALL	ALL	142581	ALL	Name Study
ALL	ALL	ALL	ALL	142581	ALL	ALL
LINTOFF						
....	....	1700	....	118532	ESS	???
LINTON						
1800	1828	1700	1900	161950	DEV	Plymouth
1802	1894	1700	1900	177369	LIN	Crowle
1900	1992	1800	1900	142603	LKS	ALL
1900	1992	1800	1900	142603	LKS	Glasgow
1760	1800	1700	1900	168629	NYK	Danby Wiske
1690	1780	1500	1690	168629	NYK	Goathland
1900	1992	1800	1900	142603	RFW	Busby
1830	1992	ALL	1830	112771	ROX	???
1770	1992	1740	1770	161284	STS	Bilston
1830	1880	1750	1830	177296	YKS	Sheffield
1818	1835	1785	1835	119717	YKS	York
LINTOTT						
1826	1992	1800	1992	107980	NFK	Norwich
LINWOOD						
....	....	1760	1820	103713	CAM	Ashley
LION						
1747	1762	1700	1747	126918	ESS	Downham
1658	1660	ALL	ALL	141615	LEI	Hinckley
LIPLEY						
1834	1861	1700	ALL	172316	LND	Bethnal Green
LIPPETT						
1806	1992	1700	1850	123072	GLS	Cheltenham
LIPPITT						
1850	1900	1700	1900	114677	WOR	ALL
LIPSCOMB						
1823	....	....	....	173932	SRY	Leatherhead
LIPSCOMBE						
1754	1800	1725	1992	173096	BRK	Hurley
1904	1904	....	....	127426	KEN	Maidstone
1790	1850	1770	1992	173096	MDX	Harmondsworth
1725	1750	1700	1992	173096	OXF	Merton
LIPTROP						
1760	1800	ALL	1760	175080	DEV	Tavistock
LIPTROT						
1816	1932	1792	1890	102121	LAN	Bolton
1800	1930	....	....	126497	LAN	Wigan
1800	1930	1800	1930	126500	LAN	Wigan
LIQUORISH						
1721	1736	ALL	ALL	141615	LEI	Arnesby
LISE						
1762	1791	1730	1800	136719	WIL	Collingbourne Ducis
LISHMAN						
1713	....	ALL	1713	119326	NRY	Newby Wiske
LISLE						
....	....	ALL	ALL	142611	ALL	ALL
1835	1992	ALL	ALL	142611	NBL	Ancroft
1830	1840	ALL	ALL	142611	SCT	Borders
LISNEY						
....	....	ALL	ALL	142638	ALL	Name Study
1539	1992	ALL	ALL	142638	ALL	ALL
1841	1938	1840	1940	142638	MDX	Cricklewood
1816	1841	1792	1841	142638	MDX	Hendon
LISSAMAN						
1767	1767	1650	1766	131245	WAR	Ryton On Dunsmore
ALL	ALL	....	....	117560	WAR	???
LIST						
....	....	ALL	1825	103284	SFK	???
LISTER						
1850	1917	1850	1974	141895	DEV	Plympton St Mary
1800	1816	1800	1820	110728	DUR	Satley
1841	1881	1841	1881	110728	DUR	Sunderland
1792	1798	1792	1798	110728	DUR	Wolsingham
1732	1830	1730	1870	143774	EYK	Scarborough
1750	1790	ALL	1750	145211	NRY	Welbury
1700	1720	....	1720	137634	NTT	Carlton In Lindrick
1720	1850	1720	1850	137634	NTT	Sturton Le Steeple
1713	....	1650	1713	148288	NTT	Upper Broughton
1700	1810	1600	1850	142123	SAL	Prees
1790	1992	1740	1790	154318	SCT	Leith
1830	....	1800	1900	153931	SFK	Polstead
?	?	?	?	176958	SOM	Bath
1727	....	....	1727	101761	WRY	Flockton
1727	....	....	1727	101761	WRY	Thornhill
1838	1859	ALL	1838	160008	WYK	Elland
1915	1992	ALL	1992	121622	YKS	Doncaster
1820	1960	....	....	148350	YKS	Hipperholme
1915	1992	ALL	1992	121622	YKS	Thorne
1797	1883	1700	1797	166723	YKS	Weardley
....	....	1700	1750	177393	YKS	Wistow
1804	1992	ALL	1804	148172	YKS	York
LITCHFIELD						
1765	1817	ALL	ALL	128449	WAR	Coventry
1693	1992	1670	1992	107573	WAR	Kingsbury
LITHERLAND						
1900	....	....	....	147702	MSY	Chorlton On Medlock
LITHGOE						
1800	....	....	....	171824	LAN	St Helens
LITLEFIELD						
1600	1700	1600	1700	106305	ENG	Titchfield
LITSON						
....	....	1800	1861	108030	DEV	Linton
1861	1992	....	....	108030	GNT	Newport
LITSTER						
1780	1992	ALL	1992	119105	LKS	Glasgow
LITTEM						
1800	1850	1600	1800	162434	WIL	Highworth
LITTLE						
1685	1775	ALL	1685	108642	BDF	Pavenham
1685	1775	ALL	1685	108642	BDF	Sharnbrook
1685	1775	ALL	1685	108642	BDF	Stevington
....	....	....	1800	177822	CMA	???
1784	1992	1550	1784	142646	CUL	North East
1870	1992	1700	1920	126160	CUL	Camerton
1890	1992	1600	1900	134155	CUL	Carlisle
1870	1992	1700	1920	126160	CUL	Frizington
1851	1875	1800	1900	105449	CUL	Longtown
1745	1992	1745	1992	142662	CUL	Longtown
1828	1904	1750	1992	157651	CUL	Walton
1800	1992	1500	1992	175498	CUL	Wandsworth
1704	1800	1600	1850	130125	DFS	Canonbie
1800	1900	....	....	150371	DFS	Castleton
1770	1790	1600	1800	130125	DFS	Hoddom
1850	1992	1800	1850	143189	DUR	Piercebridge
1863	1904	1863	1992	157651	DUR	South Sheilds
1760	1760	ALL	1760	154563	DUR	Weardale
1789	1789	1500	1789	110310	ESS	ALL
1810	1820	1770	1850	168580	ESS	Dunmow
1873	1900	1800	1900	175684	ESS	Ongar
1856	1903	ALL	1880	113611	EYK	Hull
1824	1860	ALL	1860	113611	EYK	Market Weighton
1846	1898	1750	1890	164097	FER	Kesh

Known From	To	Researching From	To	Ref	Cty	Place
LITTLE contd.						
1870	1900	1860	1992	152943	GLS	Bristol
....	....	1700	....	141216	GLS	Mid
1856	1881	1500	1890	137472	HAM	Alverstoke
1856	1881	1500	1890	137472	HAM	Gosport
1856	1881	1500	1890	137472	HAM	Portsea
1870	1900	1860	1992	152943	HAM	Portsea
1856	1881	1500	1890	137472	HAM	Portsmouth
....	....	1750	1900	142670	HRT	St Albans
....	....	ALL	1900	154482	IOM	St John
1820	1890	1790	1940	169323	LND	Spitalfields
1800	1992	1500	1992	175498	LND	Wandsworth
1872	....	....	1872	176761	NBL	Haltwhistle
1872	....	....	1872	176761	NBL	Mickley
1875	1925	1875	1992	105449	NBL	Newcastle
1872	....	....	1872	176761	NBL	Prudhoe
....	....	....	1800	177822	ROX	???
1850	1992	....	....	108898	SCT	Glasgow
?	?	ALL	ALL	100897	SRY	???
1777	....	....	1790	160873	STS	South
1803	1992	ALL	1803	152919	WIL	Chippenham
1749	....	....	....	167037	WIL	Wootton Bassett
1780	1840	1700	1900	143189	YKS	Hutton Magna
LITTLEBOY						
1700	1800	1600	1800	104361	BKM	Iver
1810	1881	1800	1915	104361	MDX	Brentford
1838	1940	1835	1838	110213	MDX	Fulham
LITTLECHILD						
....	....	ALL	ALL	142689	ALL	Name Study
1209	1992	1209	1992	142689	ALL	ALL
1800	1900	1750	1900	147958	HRT	North Mymms
LITTLEDALE						
1600	1800	1500	1800	167088	CMA	Whitehaven
LITTLEDYKE						
1870	1952	....	....	103632	DUR	Seaham Harbour
1740	1800	1600	1740	151769	LIN	ALL
1584	1605	....	....	103632	LIN	Foston
1615	1660	....	....	103632	LIN	Long Benington
1695	1780	....	....	103632	LIN	Stamford
1663	1695	....	....	103632	LIN	Westbough Cum Doddington
1740	1850	1650	1740	151769	RUT	Exton
1782	1875	....	....	103632	RUT	Oakham
LITTLEFARE						
1736	....	1538	1780	118893	NRY	Kirby Ravensworth
LITTLEFIELD						
1770	1837	ALL	1770	173304	HAM	Hambledon
LITTLEFORD						
....	....	ALL	ALL	124923	ALL	Name Study
LITTLEHALES						
....	....	ALL	ALL	175013	ALL	Name Study
LITTLEJOHN						
1760	1800	1700	1800	167258	ABD	Tarves
1832	1860	1700	1880	113107	ANS	Arbroath
1777	1806	1750	1820	109142	ANS	Forfar
1800	....	1800	1900	139114	DEV	Exeter
1782	1849	....	1782	142166	LND	Shoreditch
1782	1849	....	1782	142166	LND	Stepney
1882	1904	1842	1904	162280	MLN	ALL
1556	1583	ALL	1556	161500	SOM	Crewkerne
1846	1866	1700	1846	113425	SRY	Tooting
LITTLEJOHNS						
1850	1992	1700	1850	170739	LND	???
1800	1992	ALL	ALL	139890	SOM	West
LITTLEMORE						
1776	1794	ALL	ALL	149489	CHS	Middlewich
1752	1889	1702	1900	132314	CHS	Newton
LITTLEPAGE						
1603	1751	1550	1750	124796	BKM	Great Hampden
1685	....	1650	1790	124796	BKM	Monks Risborough
1709	....	1680	1720	124796	BKM	Princes Risborough
LITTLETON						
1810	1860	1700	1900	162345	CON	Launceston
1890	1992	ALL	ALL	176222	LND	Bermondsey
1691	1792	1600	1800	162280	SAL	Edgmond
LITTLEWOOD						
1853	1868	....	....	108200	BRK	Datchet
1799	1853	....	....	108200	BRK	Old Windsor
1717	1780	....	....	108200	BRK	Warfield
1736	1992	ALL	ALL	127175	ESS	ALL
1851	1906	1700	1851	153109	NFK	Hemsby
1851	1906	1700	1851	153109	NFK	Martham
1728	1771	....	1728	151688	NFK	South Walsham
1771	1771	ALL	1780	113611	WYK	Almondbury
LITTLEWOOD contd.						
1890	1992	ALL	1900	162027	WYK	Huddersfield
1720	1771	ALL	1775	113611	WYK	Thornhill
1830	1969	1800	1830	174173	YKS	Dewsbury
1880	1992	1800	1880	142697	YKS	Halifax
1800	1900	1650	1900	106933	YKS	Holme Valley
1820	1830	1800	1840	120529	YKS	Leeds
LITTLEWORTH						
1798	1870	1750	1880	110183	SRY	???
LITTON						
1700	....	....	....	124508	DBY	Ashbourne
1790	....	....	....	124508	LAN	Warrington
LIUSEY						
1872	1932	1800	1950	109460	YKS	Golcar
LIVER						
....	....	1800	1825	120049	LAN	Kirkham
LIVERMORE						
1769	1769	1745	1769	165107	ESS	Maldon
1920	....	1920	1992	142719	GLA	Barry
....	....	1910	1945	147613	HAM	Bournmouth
1840	1845	1800	1845	112577	LAN	Manchester
1920	....	1920	1992	142719	LND	Kings Cross
1883	1953	1953	1992	125024	SFK	Ipswich
1880	1910	1790	1960	142719	SSX	Westfield
1881	1992	1700	1881	125024	SXE	Rye
1940	1952	1940	1992	142719	WOR	Bromsgrove
....	....	1890	1910	147613	???	London
LIVERSAGE						
1741	1766	1700	1741	149977	STS	Gnosall
LIVERSEDGE						
....	1770	1700	1800	128961	ESS	Manningtree
1700	1992	ALL	ALL	150347	WAR	Birmingham
1817	1896	1750	1817	174173	YKS	Leeds
LIVESEY						
1867	1985	....	....	166030	LAN	Manchester
1727	1783	1700	1800	170348	YKS	Huddersfield
LIVEYEY						
1600	1800	....	....	177318	LAN	Middleforth
LIVINGS						
....	....	1800	1950	159964	HRT	Ardeley
1849	1989	1800	1950	159964	HRT	Little Munden
LIVINGSTON						
1836	1992	....	....	142727	ABD	Fraserburgh
1765	1787	1750	1800	103632	LAN	Salford
....	1830	1700	1841	142727	STI	Stirling
LIVINGSTONE						
1800	1900	1700	1800	146587	ARL	Mull
1810	1820	1750	1900	135925	BRK	Newbury
....	....	ALL	1799	119326	ELN	Prestonpans
1400	1500	1350	1500	154881	ELN	Saltcoats
....	....	ALL	1800	119326	MLN	Duddingston
....	....	ALL	1800	119326	MLN	Newbattle
....	....	ALL	1800	119326	MLN	Newton
1882	1912	....	....	161306	SCT	Glasgow
1700	1960	1700	1992	142735	SCT	Highlands
LIVOCK						
1840	1992	1750	1940	148660	NFK	East
1774	1992	1650	1790	103462	NFK	Norwich
LIZARS						
1850	1860	1800	1850	158380	MDX	Islington
LLANWARNE						
....	....	ALL	ALL	142743	ALL	Name Study
....	....	ALL	ALL	142743	ALL	ALL
1750	1900	1650	1992	142743	HEF	ALL
1750	1900	1650	1992	142743	MON	ALL
LLEWELLYN						
....	1840	1800	1925	135658	GLA	Cwmavon
1808	1812	1800	1820	158658	GLA	Juxta
1799	1917	1790	1917	158658	GLA	Kenfig
1817	1871	1817	1871	125717	GLA	Llanguick
1808	1812	1800	1820	158658	GLA	Llantwit
1799	1917	1790	1917	158658	GLA	Margam
1769	1789	1700	1800	166898	GLA	Margam
1800	1850	ALL	ALL	112496	GLA	Merthyr Tydfil
....	1840	1800	1925	135658	GLA	Michaelston
1740	1992	....	....	129232	GLA	Neath Valley
1800	1850	ALL	ALL	112496	GLA	Neath
1808	1812	1800	1820	158658	GLA	Neath
1714	1851	1600	1713	172006	GLA	Radyr
1813	1890	1780	1895	174912	GLA	St Fagens
....	1925	1800	1925	135658	GLA	Swansea
....	....	1800	1870	160601	GLA	???
1880	1930	1880	1950	174912	GLS	Coleford
....	....	1855	1880	160601	LND	???

Known From	To	Researching From	To	Ref	Cty	Place
LLEWELLYN contd.						
1789	1805	1770	1810	166898	MDX	Westminster
1871	1881	1840	1900	154032	MON	Rhymney
....	....	ALL	ALL	154032	RAD	ALL
LLEWELYN						
1810	1900	1700	1900	168750	GLA	Sketty
1805	1825	1770	1810	177377	GLA	St Fagans
LLEWHELLIN						
1780	1850	1700	1890	118540	PEM	Marteltwy
....	....	1800	1924	142751	PEM	Narberth
1866	1886	1800	1924	142751	PEM	Pembroke
LLOYD						
1800	1992	....	....	167045	AVN	Bristol
1640	1721	1640	1721	103977	BRK	Reading
....	....	1800	ALL	145939	CGN	Aberystwyth
1772	....	1750	1881	142794	CGN	Caron-Uwch-Clawdd
1790	1940	1776	1890	142794	CGN	Llanddewibreifi
1846	1912	1810	1880	166677	CHS	Birkenhead
1876	1889	1876	....	142832	CLV	Middlesbrough
1827	....	1750	1851	123129	CMN	Llanfihangel Aberbythych
1829	1860	1700	1829	158739	CMN	Llanfihanger-Ar-Arth
1824	1830	1700	1835	142824	CMN	Llangendeirne
1837	1860	1830	1870	123250	CMN	Pembrey
1617	1797	1617	1797	106291	CWD	Abergele
1759	1992	1600	1900	142778	CWD	Dyffryn Ial
1868	1960	1840	1960	150827	CWD	???
1848	1868	1845	1850	151599	DBY	Derby
1831	1951	1840	1910	176958	DEN	Brymbo
1800	1950	1700	1800	142905	DEN	Llanelian
1800	1812	1780	....	138401	DEN	Llansannan
1900	1930	1850	1900	150541	DEN	Wrexham
1831	1951	1840	1910	176958	DEN	Wrexham
1850	1900	1600	1900	132306	DEN	???
1805	1813	....	....	142859	FLN	Holywell
1900	1930	1880	1930	123250	GLA	Cardiff
1841	1871	1800	1880	118575	GLA	Clydach
1800	1900	1800	1900	118575	GLA	Morriston
1880	1908	1880	1910	142794	GLA	Mountain Ash
1841	1871	1800	1880	118575	GLA	Pontardawe
1729	1880	1700	1729	142786	GLS	Mitcheldean
1792	ALL	....	....	117560	HAM	Andover
....	....	1600	1780	123390	HEF	Putley
1875	1992	1700	1992	177733	LAN	Liverpool
1775	1850	1775	1992	133450	LAN	Manchester
1827	1992	1700	1827	140260	LAN	Manchester
1825	1992	1803	1881	142859	LAN	Manchester
1871	1920	1860	1920	169161	LAN	Manchester
1831	1951	1840	1910	176958	LAN	Manchester
1730	1992	1730	1900	142891	LAN	Prescot
1841	1852	ALL	ALL	109266	LND	ALL
1866	1890	1800	1890	121460	LND	Westminster
1860	1880	....	....	121444	MDX	London
1813	1970	1813	1900	141283	MDX	Marylebone
1860	1992	ALL	ALL	169897	MGY	Criggion
1500	1650	1500	1650	154881	MGY	Llandyssil
1798	....	ALL	ALL	174637	MGY	Llandyssil
1800	....	1800	1834	109266	MGY	Llanfaircaerenion
1805	1829	....	....	128082	MGY	Newtown
1700	1992	....	....	160822	MGY	Trefeglwys
....	....	1700	1800	167045	MON	Caldicott
1884	1884	ALL	ALL	124982	MON	Trevethin
1800	1850	1800	1850	140724	PEM	Milford Haven
....	....	1600	1700	142786	RAD	Clyro
1800	1992	1600	1800	156914	RAD	Colva
1790	1860	1750	1800	142395	RAD	Llanbister
1761	1798	1700	1851	176877	RAD	Llanbister
1791	1826	1750	1851	176877	RAD	Llandewi
1846	1881	1500	1846	176974	RAD	Llandrindod
1713	1746	1600	1851	176877	RAD	Nantmel
1776	1851	1750	1851	176877	RAD	Rhayader
1838	1992	1750	1838	140473	RAD	Walton
1850	1960	1800	1842	111856	SAL	Alberbury
1820	1840	1800	1850	169161	SAL	Beckbury
....	....	1750	1818	176125	SAL	Bridgenorth
1901	1927	1840	1927	162450	SAL	Cleobury Mortimer
1790	1813	1750	1813	141283	SAL	Oswestry
1800	1960	1700	1800	125415	SAL	Shrewsbury
ALL	ALL	ALL	ALL	142816	SAL	Shrewsbury
1791	1992	1600	1791	156914	SAL	Trefonen
1820	1841	ALL	ALL	153753	SAL	Wombridge
1878	1900	1700	1878	168653	SFK	ALL
1800	1850	1850	1992	126616	SFK	Burstall
LLOYD contd.						
1834	....	1834	1840	109266	SFK	Horningsheath
1770	1850	1700	1890	168580	SOM	Muchelney
1868	1900	1800	1900	142875	STS	Bilston
1840	1868	1840	1868	147311	STS	Cobridge
1830	1889	1830	1889	142832	STS	Wolverhampton
1850	1900	1830	1988	142840	STS	Wolverhampton
1847	1870	1840	1870	169161	STS	Wolverhampton
1850	1950	1850	1950	140724	WAR	Birmingham
1825	1992	....	....	176125	WIL	Great Bedwyn
....	....	1800	1880	176125	WIL	Staverton
1100	1905	....	....	100536	WLS	???
1780	1880	1780	1880	103764	WOR	Dudley
1800	....	1800	1900	116920	WOR	Kings Norton
1800	1871	1700	1800	117773	WOR	Worcester
1865	1992	1850	1992	123250	YKS	Hull
LLOYD-JONES						
1860	1992	....	....	158348	CAE	???
LLOYDE						
....	....	1500	1992	141720	HAM	???
LOACH						
1840	1870	1750	1970	142913	WAR	Birmingham
....	....	1800	1841	111414	WAR	Stratford Upon Avon
....	....	1830	1851	111414	WOR	Oldbury
LOADEL						
1792	1792	1500	1800	132993	DOR	???
1792	1792	1500	1800	132993	HAM	???
1792	1792	1500	1800	132993	IOW	???
LOADER						
1862	1956	1850	1956	142921	DUR	South Shields
1778	1837	1750	1850	136719	HAM	Basing
1786	1880	1754	1900	145459	HAM	Wellow
1840	1840	1800	1850	142921	NBL	North Shields
LOAKE						
1715	1759	1500	1715	125695	NTH	Desborough
LOAN						
1872	1992	1600	1872	110795	CON	Lostwithiel
1872	1992	1600	....	110795	HAM	Portsmouth
1820	1820	1700	1820	157031	IRL	???
1835	1900	1800	1835	157031	WIG	Wigtown
LOASBY						
1715	1992	ALL	1992	168718	NTH	ALL
LOATON						
1848	1992	1600	1848	179051	DUR	St Giles
LOBB						
1770	1992	1592	1771	171050	CON	North
1770	1992	1592	1771	171050	CON	Mid
....	....	ALL	ALL	147915	CON	Rame Peninsual
1857	1992	1800	1865	127361	CON	St Endellion
?	?	?	?	142948	HAM	Isle Of Wight
LOBBETT						
....	....	ALL	ALL	142956	ALL	Name Study
LOBDELL						
....	....	ALL	ALL	112763	ALL	Name Study
LOBJOIT						
1800	1992	1600	1800	149829	ALL	ALL
LOBLEY						
....	....	ALL	ALL	142964	ALL	Name Study
1740	1832	ALL	1740	154563	LIN	Gainsborough
1845	1923	1780	1845	118 86	NRY	Crayke
1750	1875	1700	1890	108510	YKS	Dewsbury
1760	1878	1760	1900	129798	YKS	Horley
1750	1875	1700	1890	108510	YKS	Morley
LOCH						
....	....	1750	1850	174114	SFK	Thingoe
LOCHORE						
1753	1773	1750	1780	171654	LKS	Lesmahagow
LOCHRIE						
1850	1960	1700	1850	174254	LKS	Bellshill
1900	1992	....	....	142972	STI	Kilsyth
LOCK						
1810	1910	1800	1910	164704	BRK	Reading
1798	1880	1798	1880	142980	CAM	Stretham
1779	1992	1600	1800	146676	CUL	???
1800	1900	1700	1800	116432	DEV	Bishops Tawton
1860	1992	1700	1850	121282	DEV	Broadwoodkelly
1770	1840	1770	1840	124605	DEV	???
1830	1880	1750	1830	171859	DOR	Dorchester
1800	1837	....	1837	171646	GLS	Bourton On The Water
1822	1840	1700	1900	103640	GLS	Brockhampton
1830	1850	....	....	117579	GLS	Stone
1785	1900	ALL	ALL	126071	GLS	Tetbury
1650	1900	1600	1992	130125	HAM	Longparish

Known From	To	Researching From	To	Ref	Cty	Place
LOCK contd.						
1801	1856	1800	1856	154709	HAM	Portsmouth
1801	1856	1800	1856	154709	HAM	Southampton
1805	1861	1750	1880	123536	HAM	Titchfield
1718	1833	1600	1718	170542	HAM	Titchfield
1740	1992	1500	1740	141720	HAM	???
....	....	1750	1850	120456	LND	???
1840	1880	1840	1880	124605	MDX	Bethnal Green
1769	1992	1700	1769	161446	OXF	???
1778	1796	1600	1778	116637	SFK	Barrow
1757	1950	1757	1992	142735	SOM	ALL
1730	1800	1650	1800	136840	SOM	Brendon Hills
1782	1801	1782	1783	114308	SRY	Frensham
1840	1900	ALL	ALL	149004	SSX	Cocking
1500	1900	1500	1900	170216	WIL	ALL
1880	1960	1880	1960	142980	WYK	Bradford
1820	1870	1750	1850	120529	YKS	Pontefract
LOCKE						
1770	1860	....	....	160458	ALL	ALL
1845	1886	1700	1845	149632	BRK	Easthampstead
....	....	1500	1850	166863	DEV	Devenport
....	....	1500	1850	166863	DEV	Plymouth
1650	1650	1600	1700	174599	DOR	Shaftesbury
1789	....	ALL	1789	123013	GLS	???
1650	1840	1600	1840	136840	HAM	Andover
1740	1992	1500	1740	141720	HAM	???
1830	1945	1700	1900	168068	IOW	Brading
1800	1820	1700	1850	143006	IRL	Dublin
1880	1992	1800	1880	143006	LAN	Manchester
1830	1992	1650	1830	137073	NFK	Clippesby
1830	1992	1650	1830	137073	NFK	Repps With Bastwick
1777	1969	1700	1969	159581	SFK	Bacton
1777	1969	1700	1969	159581	SFK	Stowmarket
LOCKER						
1780	1992	1700	1780	157740	STS	Fenton
LOCKETT						
1634	....	1634	....	147532	CHS	Barthomley
1825	1882	1750	1900	114626	CHS	Nether Alderley
1790	1820	1700	1850	149098	STS	Burslem
1800	....	1600	1800	169862	STS	Fulford
LOCKEY						
1730	1820	1730	1820	127655	GLS	Nailsworth
1730	1820	1730	1820	127655	GLS	Tetbury
1769	1900	1700	1992	159980	NBL	Alnwick
1786	....	....	1786	176761	NBL	Ancroft
1866	1873	1700	1866	176761	NBL	???
LOCKHART						
1706	1920	ALL	ALL	145092	DFS	Annandale
1849	1992	1600	1849	100579	LKS	Old Monkland
1820	1860	1820	1860	126500	MDX	London
1860	1920	....	....	126497	NBL	Berwick Upon Tween
1843	1992	1843	1992	111228	SAL	Culmington
1849	1992	1600	1849	100579	SCT	Glasgow
1850	1860	....	....	126497	STS	Stafford
1860	1890	1860	1890	126500	WAR	Birmingham
1800	1820	....	....	126497	???	London
LOCKHEAD						
1782	1782	ALL	1782	108537	RFW	Neilston
LOCKIE						
1831	1896	1822	1839	153176	NBL	Newcastle On Tyne
LOCKIER						
....	....	1650	1750	153281	SOM	North Petherton
LOCKING						
1900	1910	1900	1930	125830	LEI	North
1890	1900	ALL	1960	125830	LIN	Central
1920	1980	1900	ALL	125830	NTT	South
LOCKLEY						
....	....	1700	1800	169056	FLN	???
LOCKTON						
1886	1992	1700	1886	117331	MDX	Fulham
LOCKWOOD						
1817	1850	....	1817	101761	NFK	Croxton
1855	1964	....	....	112232	WOR	Dudley
1777	1843	ALL	1777	126721	WYK	Cumberworth
1800	1850	1600	1992	120677	WYK	Honley
1800	1992	1700	1800	160253	WYK	Huddersfield
1750	1850	ALL	ALL	107352	WYK	Kellington
1871	1893	1066	1900	108669	WYK	Leeds
1734	....	1700	1770	170348	YKS	Almondbury
1740	1880	1700	1790	177814	YKS	Ebberston
1750	1800	1730	1800	123595	YKS	Holmfirth
1800	1827	?	1800	144800	YKS	Holmfirth
1748	1784	1700	1750	170348	YKS	Kirkburton
1864	1888	1700	1864	115401	YKS	Ossett
LOCKWOOD contd.						
1633	1670	1610	1633	101796	YKS	Royston
LOCKYER						
1692	1766	1550	1800	154881	ALL	ALL
1808	....	1700	1900	109894	DOR	Bere Regis
1743	....	1743	1992	127035	DOR	???
....	....	1837	1900	123315	IOW	ALL
1692	1766	1550	1800	154881	KEN	ALL
1782	1992	ALL	1782	152315	SCT	Annan
1813	1836	1700	1900	164070	SOM	Cheddar
1813	1836	1700	1900	164070	SOM	Chedzoy
1770	1950	1600	1770	128376	SOM	Midsomer Norton
LOCOCK						
1786	1839	....	....	175587	SOM	Martock
?	?	1700	1900	120723	SOM	Staywell
LOCOK						
1850	1900	1600	1850	120723	SOM	Staywell
LODDER						
1600	1992	1400	1992	143014	ALL	ALL
LODDIGES						
1700	1860	....	....	165719	MDX	Stoke Newington
LODER						
1503	1857	1711	1835	121681	DOR	Dorchester
1503	1857	1711	1835	121681	DOR	Hazelbury Bryan
1750	1870	1700	1900	116742	OXF	Aston Rowant
1729	....	1700	1740	124796	OXF	Marston
LODGE						
1861	1920	1800	1860	135275	DUR	Gateshead
1881	1925	....	....	101028	ESS	Chingford
1840	1845	1700	1840	110051	ESS	Grays
1797	1956	....	....	101028	ESS	High Easter
1855	1884	ALL	1992	159174	GLS	Gloucester
....	....	1850	....	153931	HAM	Portsmouth
....	....	1750	1900	129275	LND	Stepney
1854	1912	....	....	101028	MDX	Islington
1799	1936	ALL	1799	171573	NYK	Bedale
1799	1936	ALL	1799	171573	NYK	Hornby
1870	1992	1800	1870	167460	SOM	Yeovil
1720	1900	1600	1700	143030	WIL	Corsham
....	1850	1750	1850	110531	WYK	Kirkburton
1750	1850	1700	1850	110612	YKS	North
1857	....	1800	1900	122661	YKS	Bretton
1845	1992	ALL	1845	143022	YKS	Huddersfield
1860	1930	1850	1992	165603	YKS	Yarm
LODWICK						
1798	1992	....	....	132292	DFD	Ammanford
LOESCHER						
1800	1960	1800	1960	128856	ALL	ALL
LOFAS						
....	....	ALL	ALL	109886	LIN	Humberside
LOFT						
1800	1922	1700	1922	170054	LND	Southwark
1840	1950	ALL	1840	143022	YKS	Huddersfield
LOFTHOUSE						
1850	1914	1750	1850	153362	LAN	Ashton-Under-Lyne
1840	1880	1850	1900	175382	LAN	Sabden
1775	1925	1775	1925	109347	LAN	Whalley
1808	1818	1690	1836	133574	YKS	Kirkby Malzeard
1790	1850	1600	1800	175382	YKS	Settle
LOFTS						
....	....	ALL	ALL	172413	CAM	Sawston
1800	1850	1700	1850	118907	LND	???
LOFTUS						
....	....	ALL	ALL	100234	ALL	ALL
1500	1750	1500	1700	133450	IRL	Dublin
LOGAN						
1760	1992	1500	1760	143073	ABD	Cruden
1820	1860	1600	1860	132306	ANS	???
1800	1830	1690	1830	158313	ARM	???
1690	1992	1700	1992	119725	AYR	Kilbirnie
1670	1795	1670	1800	146536	AYR	Kilbirnie
1845	1895	1800	1845	176931	GLA	Cardiff
1756	1870	1650	1756	135151	IOM	Maughold
....	....	1820	1860	121479	LAN	Liverpool
1880	1920	1860	1920	132306	LAN	Liverpool
1850	1900	1850	1900	119725	LKS	Glasgow
1852	1874	1800	1852	174807	WIG	Portpatrick
LOGIE						
1850	1992	....	....	101990	OKI	Stronsay
1850	1992	....	....	101990	OKI	Westray
....	1611	ALL	1611	162507	SCT	Logie
LOGSDON						
1800	1850	1700	1800	171182	HRT	Broxbourne

Known From	To	Researching From	To	Ref	Cty	Place
LOKER						
1745	1787	1745	1787	129283	ESS	Black Notley
1638	1745	ALL	1745	129283	ESS	Great Braxted
1597	1636	ALL	1636	129283	ESS	Langford
LOLE						
....	....	1600	1683	150150	NTH	Cold Ashby
LOLLEY						
1800	1900	1750	1900	134589	YKS	Hemingbrough
LOMAS						
1631	1992	ALL	ALL	143111	CHS	East
1770	1800	1600	1770	137731	CHS	Astbury
1883	1910	1837	1883	173576	CHS	Broadbottom
1800	1992	1800	1992	155993	CHS	Cawsworth
1826	....	1800	1900	131148	CHS	Cheadle
1690	1943	ALL	ALL	143111	CHS	Prestbury
1631	1796	ALL	ALL	143111	DBY	Ashover
1600	1890	1600	1992	124788	DBY	Chapel En Le Frith
1509	1992	ALL	ALL	143111	DBY	Chapel En Le Frith
1700	1730	1700	1730	103764	DBY	Chelmorton
1900	....	ALL	ALL	112275	DBY	Matlock
1759	1920	1759	1992	111287	DBY	Mosborough
....	....	ALL	ALL	143111	STS	ALL
1532	1992	1532	1992	143111	STS	Alstonefield
1659	1992	1600	1659	141879	STS	Elkston
1800	1960	1830	1992	137731	STS	Stafford
1875	1900	1875	1900	146617	WAR	Marton
1853	1875	1853	1875	146617	WAR	Woolscott
LOMAX						
1600	1800	1600	1800	152404	LAN	Bury
1680	1700	1650	1690	165530	LAN	Bury
LOMBARD						
1580	1623	1500	1630	143138	DOR	Thorncombe
1850	1980	1750	1900	116238	DUR	South Shields
1608	1610	ALL	1617	143138	KEN	Tenterden
LOND						
1831	1959	1700	1831	151866	NFK	Great Plumstead
LONDON						
1855	1920	1800	1855	149578	ESS	Barking
1713	1764	ALL	1713	175080	LND	Stepney
1700	....	ALL	ALL	107425	NFK	Diss
LONEY						
1731	1992	1731	1809	114359	HAM	Portsmouth
1848	1848	1848	1848	143286	SOM	Wellington
LONG						
1900	1992	1500	1700	143154	BDF	Bedford
1900	1992	1500	1700	143154	BDF	Rendhold
1835	1878	1700	....	123552	CAM	Cambridge
1821	?	....	....	129100	DEV	Topsham
1860	1902	1860	1878	131938	GLA	Mountain Ash
1816	....	....	....	124982	GLS	Berkeley
1700	1820	1600	1900	154342	GLS	Bitton
1780	1890	1750	1890	131431	GLS	Woodchester
1800	1820	ALL	1860	111732	HAM	Basingstoke
1800	1900	ALL	ALL	122866	HAM	Pamber
1759	1774	1500	1759	129577	IOW	???
1830	1860	1830	1870	110183	IRL	Fermoy
1650	1750	....	....	119431	KEN	Lydden
1689	....	ALL	....	104515	LIN	Heckington
1850	1860	1850	1874	152773	MDX	Bethnal Green
1835	1878	1700	....	123552	MDX	London
1816	1850	1790	1850	152773	MDX	Spitalfields
1800	1850	1600	1850	154342	NFK	Alpington
1840	1860	1780	1850	155764	NFK	Downham Market
1800	1992	1500	1700	143154	OXF	Church Hanborough
1730	1889	....	....	159751	OXF	Hanborough
1700	1992	1500	1700	143154	OXF	Much Baldon
1856	1992	1700	1856	169382	PEM	Rhos Crowther
1760	1780	....	1760	137227	SFK	Nowton
1831	1899	1700	1899	174300	SOM	Bath
1851	1933	1600	1851	143146	SOM	Chard
1925	1967	1900	1925	171247	TIP	Carney
....	....	1847	1869	118850	WAR	Kineton
1500	1900	1500	1900	170216	WIL	ALL
....	1810	ALL	1810	167878	WIL	Burbage
1702	1992	1700	1900	145513	WIL	Great Bedwyn
1670	1700	1650	1680	165530	WIL	Sherston
1843	1992	ALL	1992	143197	WIL	Trowbridge
1603	1960	1600	1902	169900	YKS	Guiseley
LONGBOTTOM						
1870	1890	1870	1890	110159	KEN	Erith
....	....	1886	1940	126713	LAN	Salford
1860	1870	1865	1870	110159	LND	???
1840	1860	1850	1860	110159	SFK	Ipswich
1815	1840	1815	1820	110159	WRY	Bradford

Known From	To	Researching From	To	Ref	Cty	Place
LONGBOTTOM		contd.				
....	....	1886	1940	126713	YKS	Bradford
1775	1851	1750	1775	112364	YKS	Leeds
1760	1800	1550	1800	147265	YKS	Leeds
LONGCAKE						
1763	1810	1700	1763	133019	CUL	Deanham
LONGDEN						
1780	1853	ALL	ALL	106658	CHS	Macclesfield
1805	1830	1700	1900	141569	DBY	Repton
1778	1929	ALL	1778	103004	DBY	Winster
1775	....	1700	1770	178845	GLS	Rockhampton
1800	....	....	....	100633	NTT	???
1800	....	....	....	100633	YKS	???
LONGDON						
....	1850	ALL	ALL	122866	MDX	East
LONGFORD						
1850	1992	1750	1850	167789	DUB	Dublin
1535	1992	....	....	157120	GLS	ALL
1679	1770	....	....	157120	GLS	Sevenhampton
1551	1643	....	....	157120	GLS	Withington
1410	1699	....	....	157120	NTT	ALL
1497	1662	....	....	157120	SAL	ALL
1769	1992	....	....	157120	WAR	Stretton On The Fosse
LONGHORN						
....	....	1500	1899	115975	DUR	ALL
LONGHURST						
1832	1929	1803	1929	138312	SRY	Central
1820	1870	1700	1870	131547	SRY	Betchworth
1780	1820	1700	1800	131547	SRY	Capel
1860	1930	1800	1880	131547	SRY	Dorking
?	?	ALL	1815	117919	SRY	Leatherhead
1614	1769	....	....	139971	SSX	Herstmonceux
1614	1769	....	....	139971	SSX	Wartling
LONGLAND						
1544	1630	ALL	ALL`	113433	BKM	ALL
1837	1838	1838	1861	166502	HAM	Dibden
1775	1799	1592	1837	166502	HAM	Eling
1572	1810	ALL	ALL	113433	HUN	Buckden
1524	1721	ALL	ALL	113433	HUN	Paxton
1841	1972	ALL	ALL	113433	HUN	Ramsey
1674	1782	ALL	ALL	113433	HUN	St Neots
1735	1920	ALL	ALL	113433	HUN	Warboys
1567	1713	1500	1800	113433	LND	ALL
1916	1926	1892	1916	166502	LND	Balham
1804	1930	1700	1900	115207	NTH	Yardley Hastings
1473	1527	ALL	ALL	113433	OXF	Henley On Thames
1399	1610	1300	1610	113433	SAL	Kinlet
LONGLEY						
1874	1953	1840	1890	144746	IOW	Shanklin
1700	1992	1700	1992	143200	KEN	Lydd
1843	....	1800	1890	144746	KEN	Maidstone
1700	1992	1700	1992	143200	SSX	???
1790	1830	1770	1790	128368	YKS	Leeds
LONGMAN						
....	....	ALL	ALL	143219	ALL	Name Study
....	....	1550	1992	143219	CON	ALL
....	....	1750	1992	143219	DBY	Derby
1790	1880	1750	1790	143219	DBY	Elvaston
....	....	1750	1992	143219	DBY	Ilkeston
1550	1690	1880	1992	143219	DEV	North
1550	1880	1500	1992	143219	DOR	East
....	....	1550	1992	143219	GLS	Bristol
1730	1880	1700	1992	143219	GLS	Thornbury
1550	1880	1300	1992	143219	HAM	West
1860	1910	1690	1860	100765	HAM	Southampton
1800	1880	1800	1992	143219	HRT	South
....	....	1750	1992	143219	LEI	Loughborough
....	....	1550	1992	143219	LIN	ALL
1550	1880	1500	1992	143219	MDX	London
....	....	1550	1850	143219	NFK	Norwich
1699	....	ALL	ALL	105481	NTT	Beeston
1550	1880	1550	1992	143219	SOM	East
....	....	1550	1992	143219	SOM	Bath
1730	1985	1730	1985	130451	SOM	???
....	....	1750	1992	143219	STS	Stoke On Trent
....	....	1750	1992	143219	STS	Tipton
....	....	1850	1992	143219	SWL	Cardiff
....	....	1870	1992	143219	SWL	Mountain Ash
....	....	1870	1992	143219	SWL	Swansea
1550	1850	1550	1992	143219	WIL	South
1700	1880	1700	1992	143219	YKS	Holderness
1700	1880	1700	1992	143219	YKS	Hull

Known From	To	Researching From	To	Ref	Cty	Place
LONGMIRE						
....	....	ALL	ALL	143227	ALL	Name Study
LONGMORE						
....	....	ALL	ALL	163457	ALL	Name Study
1800	1992	1600	?	143235	BAN	???
1860	1890	1750	1860	128244	CAV	Bailieborough
LONGMUIR						
1860	1992	1800	1880	163694	LKS	Glasgow
LONGNEY						
1960	1992	1700	1960	171913	???	???
LONGRIDGE						
1680	1850	....	....	160458	ALL	ALL
1680	1850	....	....	160458	NBL	???
LONGSLOW						
1870	1992	1700	1870	121258	LEI	Lutterworth
LONGSTAFF						
1880	1950	....	....	102881	DUR	Hartlepool
1857	1857	1700	1857	100110	DUR	Sunderland
1842	1875	1750	1842	102881	DUR	Sunderland
1709	1743	1600	1709	102571	WES	Brough
1794	1860	1650	1794	135151	WES	Crosby Garrett
1775	....	1600	....	118591	WES	East Ward
LONGSTAFFE						
1700	1900	....	....	146854	WES	Kirkby Stephen
LONGSWORTH						
1869	1923	....	....	166030	LAN	Manchester
LONGTHORN						
1770	1800	ALL	1850	151319	LAN	ALL
1770	1800	ALL	1850	151319	YKS	ALL
LONGTHORNE						
....	1832	....	....	119768	YKS	Coxwold
LONGUEHAYE						
....	....	1750	1850	114308	LND	???
LONGWORTHY						
....	....	1800	1900	167401	SRY	Kennington
LONNEN						
1820	1880	....	....	104817	WIL	Whiteparish
LONNON						
1814	1840	1800	1992	152943	HAM	Portsea
LONSDALE						
1750	1790	1700	1750	162396	LIN	Snitterby
LOOKE						
1561	1642	1561	1642	114987	SOM	Aller
LOOKUP						
1805	1850	....	....	132756	DUR	???
1805	1850	....	....	132756	NBL	???
LOONEY						
....	....	1700	1820	135151	IOM	Maughold
1810	1840	1750	1810	116572	IOM	???
....	....	ALL	ALL	121320	LND	ALL
LOOTES						
....	....	1880	1992	154105	GLS	Morton In Marsh
LORAINE						
1800	1992	1700	1800	178225	NBL	Corbridge
LORD						
....	....	ALL	ALL	157449	ALL	Name Study
1790	1900	1790	1900	130222	BDF	Husborne Crawley
1857	1884	....	1857	117951	CON	Liskeard
1714	1880	1600	1714	167355	ESS	Gt Bentley
1850	1992	1700	1850	157449	GLS	Handborough
1820	1950	1700	1820	160458	LAN	Bacup
1800	1992	1700	1992	179078	LAN	Bacup
1744	1839	1720	1870	108510	LAN	Bolton
1920	1992	1846	1920	162221	LAN	Bury
1816	1992	ALL	1816	162221	LAN	Dean Bolton
1801	1883	ALL	1801	143308	LAN	Hopwood
1757	1968	1700	1940	143286	LAN	Kearsley
1900	1992	1880	1900	143294	LAN	Litherland
1800	1940	1700	1992	110477	LAN	Manchester
1840	1992	1840	1992	110523	LAN	Rochdale
1800	1940	1700	1992	110477	LAN	Salford
1800	1880	1880	1900	143294	LEI	Hinckley
1748	1800	ALL	1748	143294	LEI	Sapcote
1761	1860	1650	1761	163953	NFK	Forncett
1883	1939	....	....	143308	NFK	Norwich
1850	1992	1700	1850	157449	OXF	Handborough
1745	....	1650	1745	152110	SFK	Glemsford
1840	1887	1700	1840	146110	WAR	Long Itchington
1749	1992	....	1749	168521	YKS	Bradford
....	1859	1720	1870	108510	YKS	Leeds
....	1800	....	....	100536	???	???
LORDEN						
1800	1881	ALL	1800	106739	HAM	Southampton

Known From	To	Researching From	To	Ref	Cty	Place
LORENZE						
1894	1992	1880	1992	149098	MDX	London
LORIMER						
....	....	ALL	1840	174777	DFS	Penpent
....	1851	1841	1851	174777	GLS	Cheltenham
....	1871	1861	1871	174777	KKD	Parton
....	1861	1851	1861	174777	MDX	Islington
LORKING						
1780	1880	1780	1880	108006	SFK	Clare
LORMAN						
1786	1992	ALL	ALL	114391	ALL	ALL
LORNE						
....	....	1800	1950	139203	ALL	ALL
1834	....	1800	1940	139203	BRK	Thatcham
1856	1979	1800	1900	139203	SRY	Croydon
LORT						
1750	....	....	....	100099	LEI	???
1500	1900	....	....	100536	STS	???
1785	1900	....	....	100099	WAR	Birmingham
1500	1900	....	....	100536	WLS	???
LOSH						
....	....	ALL	ALL	146544	ALL	Name Study
LOT						
1698	1725	....	....	159751	DEV	Bridestowe
1845	1992	1700	1845	109177	IOW	Whitwhile
LOTHIAN						
1800	1992	1750	1800	144134	BEW	Westruther
1819	1982	1850	1985	169420	SCT	South
LOTON						
1532	1672	1500	1636	102830	STS	Dilhorne
LOTT						
1816	1891	1816	1891	114359	WIL	Manningford
LOTTEE						
1659	1940	....	....	128996	CAM	Thorney
LOUCH						
....	1741	1700	1741	121037	BRK	Sonning
....	1741	1700	1741	121037	OXF	Sonning
1835	?	ALL	ALL	153516	SOM	Weston Super Mare
LOUGH						
1760	1884	ALL	1884	157066	CHS	Chester
1760	1884	ALL	1884	157066	CHS	Liverpool
1760	1884	ALL	1884	157066	CHS	Northwich
1760	1884	ALL	1884	157066	CHS	Witton
1791	1855	1600	1791	139084	ROX	Corby
LOUGHARY						
1850	1899	....	....	142972	LKS	ALL
LOUGHER						
?	?	?	?	176958	GLA	???
LOUGHLIN						
1836	1923	1700	1836	173797	WIC	Rahan Craney
LOUGHRAN						
....	....	ALL	ALL	143340	ALL	ALL
LOUGHRIDGE						
....	....	1800	1900	147613	NIR	ALL
LOUGHTON						
1822	1965	1700	1830	122114	WOR	Droitwich
LOUKES						
....	....	1700	1900	143359	YKS	Sheffield
LOUND						
1729	1785	1600	1800	117463	NFK	Blakeney
LOURIE						
1790	....	....	....	167037	SCT	Lieth
LOUTH						
1818	1919	1700	1818	152056	LIN	Scredington
LOUTHAN						
1871	1881	ALL	1871	168742	LND	London
LOVAT						
1817	1845	ALL	1817	122386	NBL	North Tyne
1880	1900	1800	1880	173029	STS	East
LOVATT						
1915	1992	ALL	ALL	143367	SRY	North
1850	1950	ALL	ALL	143367	STS	Bilston
1740	1850	1670	1740	143367	STS	Burton On Trent
1750	1920	1650	1750	141062	STS	Newcastle Under Lyne
1853	1992	1750	1910	135623	STS	Stoke On Trent
1740	1850	1670	1740	143367	STS	Stretton By Burton
LOVE						
1890	1992	ALL	1890	143383	ANT	Belfast
1770	1820	1600	1770	127507	ANT	???
1760	1828	....	....	148261	ARL	Kilberry
1725	1825	1700	1725	157708	AYR	Dreghorn
....	1741	....	1780	137405	CAM	Haddenham
1730	1760	1700	1730	151866	CAM	Impington

Known From	To	Researching From	To	Ref	Cty	Place
LOVE contd.						
1780	1861	1700	1780	165158	DEV	Axmouth
1862	1992	1750	1870	106844	DON	North
1823	1851	....	1823	143375	DOR	Lyme Regis
1849	1900	....	1849	158585	ESS	Witham
1830	1840	1800	1850	139203	FER	???
1680	1700	ALL	1680	141224	GLS	South
1750	1900	1700	1900	124699	KEN	Central
1750	1900	1700	1900	124699	KEN	East
1738	1879	?	1738	116076	KEN	Birling
1887	1949	1820	1887	146919	LAN	Lancaster
1823	....	1700	1800	143448	NFK	Sheringham
1688	1688	ALL	1688	115126	NTH	Brixworth
1724	1812	ALL	ALL	135968	RUT	Hambleton
1802	1869	1600	1802	133132	SFK	Brampton
1760	1881	1760	1881	170143	SSX	Harting
1760	1881	1760	1881	170143	SSX	Rogate
1851	....	1851	....	143375	STS	Dudley
1830	....	....	....	106852	WIG	Kirkinner
....	1840	....	1992	165484	YKS	Kingston Upon Hull
LOVE;;						
1852	1876	1830	1880	144797	MDX	Stepney
LOVECRAFT						
1816	1851	1750	1816	120146	DEV	Chagford
LOVEDAY						
1832	1832	1800	1832	133000	CAM	Littlington
1690	1791	1570	1690	159158	GLS	Painswick
1841	1944	1841	1944	102954	LND	Lambeth
....	....	1600	1700	154377	NTH	ALL
1856	1856	1820	1860	133000	NTH	Islip
1730	1900	1730	1900	154377	NTH	Islip
1780	1830	1740	1830	135941	SFK	Kedington
1830	1860	1830	1860	135941	SFK	Withersfield
1819	....	1750	1900	139386	SRY	Clapham
1863	1893	1700	1992	102520	YKS	Norwich
LOVEDER						
1792	1851	1700	1850	133957	HAM	Forton
1747	1747	ALL	1747	131881	HAM	Porstmouth
1792	1851	1700	1850	133957	SSX	Westbourne
LOVEGROVE						
....	....	ALL	ALL	143405	ALL	Name Study
....	....	ALL	ALL	143405	ALL	ALL
1752	1766	1700	1800	167002	BKM	Eton
1779	1859	1750	1900	167002	BKM	Upton Cum Chalvey
1800	1866	1600	1870	166804	BRK	East
1800	1870	1600	1992	112828	HAM	Sherbourne St John
1849	1930	1800	1992	149659	MDX	London
LOVELAND						
....	....	1582	1843	175110	SRY	Farnham
1765	1850	1700	1765	132640	SRY	Shalford
LOVELESS						
1780	1840	1780	1840	154210	DOR	Coombe Keynes
1840	1900	1840	1900	154210	DOR	Kinson
1750	1780	1730	1780	154210	DOR	Tolpuddle
1770	1992	....	....	109495	NFK	Bressingham
1630	1770	....	....	109495	SFK	Tostock
LOVELL						
ALL	1560	....	....	143413	ALL	ALL
ALL	1560	....	....	143413	BKM	ALL
1830	1880	1800	1880	148431	DEV	ALL
....	....	ALL	ALL	116394	DEV	Topsham
1845	1875	1750	1900	110191	DOR	Blandford Forum
1798	1881	1760	1887	125903	DOR	Canford Magna
1800	1900	1600	1900	154342	GLS	Bitton
1700	1800	1600	1800	154342	GLS	Mangotsfield
1800	1950	1700	1800	143421	GLS	Oldland
1700	....	....	....	142018	GLS	Wickwar
1700	1900	1650	1900	124699	HAM	Central
1650	1700	1650	1700	144657	HAM	Congresbury
1860	1900	1860	1900	170526	HAM	Portsmouth
1700	....	1650	1700	135771	HAM	Surrey Border
1763	....	....	1780	171441	HAM	Wootton St Lawrence
1765	1834	1700	1850	176788	LND	???
1779	1992	1750	1779	176257	MDX	Stepney
....	....	1700	ALL	154377	NTH	ALL
1600	1992	....	....	153583	NTH	Bugbrooke
1800	1900	1800	1900	154377	NTH	Clapthorn
1680	....	....	....	148156	NTH	Grendon
1560	1992	1560	1992	143413	NTH	Silverstone
ALL	1560	....	....	143413	OXF	ALL
1650	1750	1600	1750	123722	SOM	Nettlecombe
1780	1800	1700	1800	167088	SOM	Shipham
1590	1992	ALL	1590	164879	SOM	Wells
1746	1842	1650	1800	173983	SOM	Wells
LOVELL contd.						
....	....	1750	1850	166995	WIL	Milton
1878	....	ALL	ALL	125202	???	???
LOVELOCK						
1800	1860	1800	1860	124605	BRK	Reading
1801	?	?	1900	136611	GLS	Shipton Moyne
1770	1800	1700	1770	166804	HAM	Banghurst
1780	1800	ALL	ALL	124605	HAM	Baughurst
1780	1800	1700	1780	166804	HAM	Hannington
1750	1800	1700	1750	166804	HAM	Kingsclere
ALL	1714	....	....	170178	WIL	Devizes
LOVELY						
1748	1794	1700	1750	141283	IOM	ALL
1773	1861	1740	1773	174211	LIN	Branston
1773	1861	1740	1773	174211	LIN	Navenby
LOVERHAM						
....	....	1700	1800	129356	MDX	Westminster
LOVERIDGE						
?	?	?	?	177938	DOR	Beaminster
1725	1880	1700	1900	157171	GLS	Churcham
1680	1900	1680	1900	157171	GLS	Newent
....	....	1750	1800	138339	GLS	Norton
1720	1769	1720	1769	157171	GLS	Pauntley
LOVERING						
1822	1872	....	....	142999	CON	Padstow
1707	1900	1500	1707	148679	DEV	East
1797	1797	1750	1800	142999	DEV	Ilfracombe
LOVES						
1783	1788	1750	1793	123404	NFK	North Elmham
LOVET						
1780	1802	1766	1780	122572	NTT	ALL
LOVETT						
1940	1963	1700	1940	103640	ESS	Stratford
1940	1963	1700	1940	103640	ESS	West Ham
1830	1871	1800	1992	143456	GLA	Merthyr Tydfil
1830	1871	1800	1992	143456	GLA	Neath
1785	....	ALL	ALL	112275	LEI	Frisby On Wreake
1827	....	....	....	163155	LEI	Hugglescote
1820	1850	1600	1850	113654	LND	Stepney
1800	1992	1700	1992	143456	SAL	North
1780	1992	1700	1780	108103	SFK	Thorndon
1788	1885	1760	1885	138495	WAR	Coventry
1788	1885	1760	1885	138495	WAR	Withybrooke
LOVEY						
1788	1920	1788	1852	102806	CON	Ponsanooth
LOVICK						
1770	1803	1700	1800	103462	NFK	Norwich
1870	1880	1700	1870	149705	SFK	Botesdale
LOVIE						
1835	1980	1750	1834	168386	ABD	Strichen
LOVIS						
1756	1770	1500	1756	138614	DEV	Tavistock
....	....	1500	1809	138614	DEV	???
LOW						
1823	1944	1700	1823	106887	ABD	Cruden
1800	1920	1800	1950	149233	ABD	Newmachar
1823	1944	1700	1823	106887	ABD	Udny
1806	1953	1800	1866	173428	ESS	Chelmsford
1800	1857	1857	1992	117269	ESS	South Hanningfield
1850	?	?	?	143464	GLS	Bristol
1820	1871	1780	1890	105333	MDX	London
1812	1992	1700	1812	143472	PER	Perth
1600	....	....	1630	160873	STS	Walsall
LOWBRIDGE						
1864	1885	1700	1864	138509	STS	Walsall
LOWCOCK						
1811	1815	....	....	141097	YKS	Adwick Le Street
1750	1850	....	....	141097	YKS	Doncaster
1879	1883	....	....	141097	YKS	Wentworth
LOWDEN						
1845	1880	1750	1850	146285	MDX	Marylebone
LOWDIN						
1750	?	1600	1992	167592	SOM	Bristol
LOWE						
1820	1850	1800	1900	124427	ANS	Montrose
1841	1860	1700	1850	170178	BKM	Hambledon
1795	1850	1700	1850	135496	CHS	North
1718	1859	....	....	108057	CHS	Middlewich
1849	1992	ALL	1849	165212	CHS	Sandbach
....	....	ALL	1800	178403	DBY	Denby
1871	1881	1800	1900	133264	DBY	Quarndon
1755	1775	1700	1800	171158	ESS	Willingale
1769	1992	1769	1992	110396	LAN	Ashton
....	....	1860	1950	147613	LAN	Barrow In Furness

Known From	To	Researching From	To	Ref	Cty	Place
LOWE contd.						
1877	....	ALL	1877	148172	LAN	Manchester
1769	1992	1769	1992	110396	LAN	Wigan
1777	1819	ALL	1819	168718	LEI	Queniborough
1740	1809	1770	1992	117072	LIN	Horsington
1854	....	ALL	ALL	143529	LND	Battersea
1890	1982	1800	1890	174041	LND	Bow
1828	1992	....	1827	129461	LND	???
1890	1940	1700	1980	115894	MDX	London
1810	1880	1700	1992	114596	NTH	Daventry
1836	1844	?	1836	128910	NTT	Skegby
1720	1743	1744	1992	175412	SAL	Lilleshall
1830	1900	1750	1900	143502	SAL	Wellington
1890	1992	....	....	124354	SCT	Glasgow
1637	1679	....	....	142522	SFK	Chelmondiston
1830	....	1600	1830	132802	STS	Bilston
....	1931	1800	1931	109223	STS	Burton On Trent
?	....	....	?	143499	STS	Darlaston
....	....	1750	1850	147613	STS	Darlaston
1822	1865	1790	1880	169323	STS	Darlaston
1821	1950	1750	1900	155152	STS	Hanley
1688	1785	ALL	1688	143278	STS	Uttoxeter
1840	1910	1600	1840	122084	WAR	Birmingham
1845	....	....	....	145742	WAR	Coventry
1861	1983	1800	1861	166707	WAR	Dunchurch
1814	1850	1700	1850	136530	WOR	Alcester
1800	1840	1700	1992	167592	WOR	Worcester
....	....	1800	1900	171794	YKS	Middlesbrough
LOWEN						
1754	1808	1700	1800	101400	HRT	Tewin
LOWER						
1660	1714	ALL	1992	100536	CON	???
....	....	ALL	ALL	135968	SSX	ALL
....	....	ALL	1860	178403	SSX	Brighton
1804	1857	ALL	....	132349	SXE	Newhaven
LOWERY						
1860	1890	1860	1992	137782	CUL	ALL
1822	1844	1800	1850	120146	ESS	West Thurrock
1820	1860	1750	1992	137782	LAN	Barrow In Furness
LOWES						
1642	1666	1666	1700	143545	CMA	Threlkeld
1757	1789	....	....	168521	DUR	Middleston On Teeside
1746	1789	1650	1746	143545	DUR	Stanhope
1753	1823	ALL	1753	154563	DUR	Weardale
....	1723	1650	1723	143545	NBL	Haltwhistle
....	1723	1650	1723	143545	NBL	Hexham
LOWETH						
1741	1834	ALL	1834	168718	NTH	Deene
LOWEY						
1709	1885	1511	1795	141291	IOM	Rushen
LOWIS						
1700	1850	1700	1850	143553	WES	Milburn
1550	1800	1550	1800	143553	WES	Shap
LOWLOW						
....	....	1800	1900	143685	LND	St Pancras
LOWMAN						
1718	1718	1650	1750	124974	BRK	Arborfield
1786	1787	....	....	112968	DOR	Beaminster
1793	1803	....	....	112968	DOR	Bridport
1765	1803	....	....	112968	DOR	Wayford
1800	1850	....	....	112968	SOM	Crewkerne
LOWN						
1640	1640	....	....	127426	KEN	Harrietsham
LOWNDES						
1744	1773	1700	1850	179256	BKM	Wavenden
1769	1992	....	....	138231	LAN	Manchester
1769	1992	....	....	138231	RFW	Paisley
1748	....	....	....	148768	SRY	Camberwell
LOWNEY						
1800	1850	1800	1900	128449	COR	Bantry
1850	1992	1850	1900	128449	COR	Clonakilty
1800	1850	1800	1900	128449	COR	Frilane
LOWREY						
1890	1982	ALL	1982	177695	DUR	Stanley
LOWRIE						
1835	1835	1700	1835	106887	ABD	Peterhead
1850	1932	1800	1850	122882	ARL	Glen Buck
LOWRY						
1833	1992	ALL	ALL	110388	IRL	Belfast
1838	1860	ALL	ALL	145386	LAN	Manchester
1823	1992	1500	1823	114588	LND	Clerkenwell
1803	....	1803	ALL	145386	SCT	???
LOWS						
1778	1879	1600	1900	159956	SFK	Market Weston
LOWSON						
1820	1850	1700	1900	138517	ANS	Barry
LOWTH						
....	....	ALL	ALL	143561	ALL	ALL
1865	1992	ALL	ALL	143561	DBY	ALL
1550	1992	ALL	ALL	143561	LEI	ALL
1700	1992	ALL	ALL	143561	LIN	ALL
1818	1919	1700	1818	152056	LIN	Scredington
1550	1992	ALL	ALL	143561	NTT	ALL
LOWTHER						
....	1730	ALL	1731	153729	CUL	Matterdale
1660	1878	....	....	149616	DFS	Dornock
1730	....	1600	1730	116637	DUR	Wasington
1840	1870	1700	1870	136034	MDX	London
1794	1874	....	....	117803	NRY	Alne
1742	1793	....	....	117803	NRY	Kilburn
1780	1850	1700	1850	126268	SOM	Bath
1291	1430	1066	1120	124974	WES	Lowther
1810	1930	1550	1810	150843	YKS	Ampleforth
1700	....	1650	....	134589	YKS	Hovingham
LOWTHIAN						
....	1805	1769	1805	161527	CUL	Brampton
1805	1851	1769	1851	161527	MDX	Marylebone
LOWTON						
1800	1900	1750	1920	115746	SOM	ALL
LOXLEY						
1841	1945	1776	1841	121924	WAR	Temple Grafton
LOYD						
1771	1771	1750	1770	165530	WIL	Sherston
LOYDE						
1820	1861	1780	1820	108103	SFK	Gislingham
LOYLEY						
1844	1890	1700	1850	178616	LEI	Leicester
LOYNDS						
1818	1992	....	....	172529	LAN	Altham
LOYNS						
1760	1850	1760	1850	140295	SOM	Langford Budville
1830	1900	1830	1900	140295	SOM	West Buckland
....	....	1700	....	137456	WAR	Dunchurch
LUBBOCK						
1800	1900	1700	1900	106674	NFK	Wells
LUCAS						
1852	1852	1850	1855	143618	AVN	Bristol
1818	1842	ALL	ALL	143618	AVN	Keynsham
1800	1807	1810	1890	147826	BKM	Tingewick
1725	....	1650	1780	139386	CAM	Elsworth
....	....	1800	1885	152684	CHS	Congleton
?	?	?	?	111937	CON	Trenarren
1690	1750	1500	1800	133450	DEV	Bampton
1904	....	....	....	161136	GLA	Port Talbot
1855	1855	1852	1870	143618	GLA	Swansea
1700	1992	1700	1992	172359	GSY	Forest
1850	1900	1850	1900	135895	HAM	Curdridge
1795	1840	1750	1800	123978	HAM	Winchester
1754	1814	1700	1850	139386	HUN	Hemingford Abbots
1817	1972	1800	1891	157597	KEN	Gravesend
1820	1830	1800	1850	126217	KEN	Sheerness
1560	1678	ALL	ALL	141615	LAN	Brindle
1756	1756	1700	1756	163783	LAN	Garstang
1785	1802	1760	1802	164097	LAN	Ormskirk
1850	1860	....	1850	102059	LAN	Preston
1838	1992	1770	1920	179299	LND	ALL
1830	1992	1700	1830	155373	LND	East
1800	1807	1810	1890	147826	LND	City
1818	1850	1770	1818	173673	MDX	Finsbury
1784	1843	....	....	124524	NTH	Northampton
1790	1841	1790	1880	118818	NTH	Towcester
1761	1901	ALL	1761	168742	NTT	Askham
1761	1901	ALL	1761	168742	NTT	Worksop
1800	1900	1800	1920	123145	SAL	Church Stretton
1864	1906	1906	1992	103292	SRY	Alfold
1800	1992	1500	1950	137472	SRY	Brockham
1800	1992	1500	1950	137472	SRY	Dorking
1800	1992	1500	1950	137472	SRY	Leigh
ALL	1764	....	....	105368	SRY	New Kingston
....	....	1750	1850	126217	SRY	Rotherhithe
1725	1864	1650	1860	127183	SSX	East Grinstead
1816	....	1816	....	143642	SSX	Tarring
1833	1881	1700	1880	125806	WAR	Birmingham
1500	1650	1500	1900	170216	WIL	ALL
1850	1960	ALL	ALL	162469	WIL	South
1907	1992	1907	ALL	143618	WYK	Castleford

Known From	To	Researching From	To	Ref	Cty	Place
LUCAS contd.						
1869	1992	1865	ALL	143618	WYK	Knottingley
1907	1944	1800	1900	109460	YKS	Milnsbridge
?	?	?	?	147869	???	Dalston
?	?	?	?	147869	???	West Hackney
LUCASSI						
1830	1874	1800	1900	134422	SOM	Bristol
LUCE						
1920	1992	....	....	143650	GLS	Cheltenham
LUCHFORD						
1800	1860	1700	1960	101907	KEN	Snodland
1860	1940	1800	1960	101907	KEN	Strood
LUCK						
1797	1824	1700	1797	148202	ESS	Fyfield
1900	1940	....	....	148202	GLA	Aberdare
1850	....	1850	1900	106410	GLS	Berkeley
....	1893	ALL	1893	165263	KEN	Hawkshurst
1480	1550	1450	1550	154881	KEN	Penshurst
1728	1778	ALL	ALL	141615	LEI	South
1830	1857	....	....	148202	LEI	Sheershead
1849	1849	ALL	1849	167959	MDX	Friern Barnet
1863	1900	....	....	148202	MDX	Islington
....	....	1750	1950	176362	SRY	Merrow
1750	....	1700	1800	113743	SSX	Herstmoncieux
1780	1890	1750	1890	103993	SSX	Warbleton
LUCKES						
1780	1820	1700	1820	161292	DEV	Exmouth
LUCKET						
1820	1846	1780	1820	128724	BKM	Langley Marish
1755	1832	1700	1755	141321	BRK	Childrey
LUCKETT						
1757	1763	ALL	1763	158062	OXF	Adderbury
1794	1878	ALL	1794	158062	OXF	Aston
1757	1763	ALL	1763	158062	OXF	Bodicote
LUCKHAM						
1673	1860	1600	1900	122688	DEV	Marlborough
1673	1860	1600	1900	122688	DEV	South Hams
LUCKHURST						
1825	1870	....	....	114871	KEN	Boxley
1800	1992	1750	1992	110205	KEN	Eythorne
ALL	ALL	ALL	ALL	166243	KEN	Luddenham
LUCKIN						
1861	....	1800	1890	116572	SSX	Steyning
LUCKING						
1685	1992	1500	1992	146846	ESS	ALL
1799	1880	....	....	101028	ESS	Hatfield Peverel
1790	1992	1700	1790	116416	ESS	Little Leighs
1685	1992	1500	1992	146846	ESS	Romford
LUCOCK						
1770	1800	1600	1992	167592	LAN	Liverpool
LUCOP						
....	....	ALL	ALL	149403	ALL	Name Study
....	....	ALL	ALL	149403	ALL	ALL
1834	1957	1834	1957	149403	YKS	Hull
LUCY						
1840	1992	1700	1840	143669	HEF	Colwall
LUDCOCK						
1663	1725	....	....	165999	DBY	Derby
LUDDINGTON						
1830	1843	1500	1830	113689	EYK	Hull
1808	1830	1750	1808	113689	EYK	Willerby
....	....	ALL	ALL	113689	YKS	ALL
1648	1669	1500	1648	113689	YKS	Hotham
LUDFORD						
....	....	1530	1800	115142	LEI	Twycross
LUDFORD-FREEMAN						
?	?	?	?	125652	???	???
LUDGATE						
1837	1839	ALL	1992	159174	KEN	Faversham
1899	....	ALL	1992	159174	KEN	Rochester
1879	....	ALL	1992	159174	LND	Newington
1846	....	ALL	1992	159174	LND	Smithfield
1834	....	ALL	1992	159174	SSX	South Bersted
1864	1885	ALL	1992	159174	STS	Burton On Trent
1739	1809	ALL	1992	159174	WAR	Cubbington
1710	1739	ALL	1992	159174	WAR	Leek Wootton
LUDKIN						
1829	1829	1700	1829	163953	NFK	Fundenhall
LUDLAM						
1797	1860	ALL	ALL	143677	NTT	Lenton
LUDLOW						
1540	1815	1540	1815	127655	GLS	Tetbury
....	....	1800	1925	143685	HAM	Portsmouth
1840	1900	1600	1900	129011	SAL	Wem

Known From	To	Researching From	To	Ref	Cty	Place
LUDLOW contd.						
....	....	1800	1850	143685	SOM	Road
....	....	1650	1800	143685	SOM	Taunton
1540	1815	1540	1815	127655	WIL	Brokenborough
1540	1815	1540	1815	127655	WIL	Crudwell
....	....	1775	1850	143685	WIL	Keevil
1540	1815	1540	1815	127655	WIL	Shipton Moyne
1540	1815	1540	1815	127655	WIL	Tetbury
LUDMAN						
1780	1840	1700	1780	132748	HAM	Blendworth
LUDOVICK						
1822	1856	1856	1992	136050	SCT	ALL
LUER						
1800	1820	1750	1850	151653	SOM	Langport
LUFF						
1800	1870	1700	1900	138517	GLS	Bilton
1750	1920	1850	1900	126640	HAM	South
1765	1780	1730	1765	157775	HAM	Portsea
1850	1950	....	....	126640	LND	Edmonton
1778	1827	....	....	103918	OXF	Oxford
....	....	1720	1778	103918	WIL	Marlborough
LUFFLUM						
1772	1865	1772	1865	103977	MDX	Feltham
1772	1865	1772	1865	103977	MDX	Isleworth
LUFFMAN						
1850	1980	1850	1920	166154	LND	Tooting
1780	1850	1650	1780	163449	WIL	Whiteparish
LUFKIN						
1803	1850	1700	1803	138347	ESS	North East
LUGG						
....	....	1700	1850	109894	DOR	Bere Regis
LUKE						
1959	1961	1950	1970	143693	BKM	High Wycombe
1861	1870	1800	1900	143693	BKM	Slough
1861	1870	1800	1900	143693	BKM	Upton Cum Chalvey
1861	1900	1850	1930	143693	BRK	Reading
1858	1859	1855	1865	143693	BRK	Tilehurst
1984	1992	1980	1992	143693	CHS	Macclesfield
1959	....	1945	1970	143693	CHS	Stockport
ALL	....	....	....	150975	CON	Camborne
1770	1893	1500	1850	143693	CON	Cambrone
1779	....	1600	1850	143693	CON	Crowan
1744	....	1600	1800	143693	CON	Helston
1846	....	....	....	136964	CON	Illogam
1738	1811	1500	1850	143693	CON	Illogan
1632	1835	1500	1900	143693	CON	Redruth
1612	1724	?	?	159913	CON	Redruth
1774	....	1700	1800	143693	CON	St Austell
1697	1803	1600	1697	168173	CON	St Austell
1772	....	1700	1800	143693	CON	St Blaxey
1711	....	1650	1750	143693	CON	St Clements
1735	1759	1550	1820	153591	CON	St Enoder
1800	1850	1750	1850	168750	CON	St Ives
1690	....	1600	1800	143693	CON	Stithians
1838	....	1800	1900	143693	CON	Truro
1987	1992	1960	1992	143693	DBY	Dove Holes
1524	1850	ALL	1700	141305	DEV	Exeter
1847	....	1835	1855	143693	DEV	Exeter
1524	1850	ALL	1700	141305	DEV	South Hams
1855	....	1800	1855	140082	DUR	???
1992	....	1980	1992	143693	ESS	Harlow
1792	1992	....	....	152765	HAM	Gosport
1808	1968	1700	1808	143707	HAM	Portsea
1856	1883	1700	1856	117927	HAM	Southampton
1823	....	....	....	138061	KEN	Deptford
1806	1811	1750	1850	143693	KEN	Dover
1818	....	1810	1830	143693	KEN	Gillingham
1961	....	1930	1980	143693	KEN	Herne Bay
1820	1855	1810	1860	143693	KEN	Woolwich
1929	1950	1900	1970	143693	LAN	Liverpool
1837	1851	1820	1900	143693	LEI	Coalville
1915	1940	1900	1950	143693	LND	Hammersmith
1907	....	1850	1950	143693	LND	Kensal Rise
1893	....	1850	1950	143693	LND	Kensington
1876	....	1800	1950	143693	LND	St Marylebone
1792	1992	....	....	152765	LND	???
1940	1960	1930	1980	143693	MDX	Hounslow
1855	....	1850	1860	143693	SOM	Bristol
1944	....	1930	1980	143693	SOM	Minehead
1849	1853	1835	1860	143693	SOM	Taunton
1845	....	1835	1855	143693	SOM	Wolley
1862	1992	1900	1992	143693	SRY	Godalming
1963	1965	1900	1992	143693	SRY	Haslemere
1816	....	1810	1830	143693	SSX	Eastbourne

Known From	To	Researching From	To	Ref	Cty	Place
LUKE contd.						
1840	....	1800	1850	143693	STS	Wednesbury
1811	1813	1750	1850	143693	TIP	Caher
1811	....	1750	1850	143693	WEX	Enniscorthy
LUKENS						
1640	1800	ALL	ALL	131164	SSX	Burstow
LUKERS						
1786	1840	1786	1840	147575	CAM	Chesterton
LULHAM						
1700	1992	ALL	1700	131091	SSX	ALL
LULY						
1801	1885	?	1801	147915	CON	???
LUMB						
1822	1845	1820	1851	102121	YKS	Dewsbury
1822	1845	1820	1851	102121	YKS	Leeds
....	....	1800	1900	145998	YKS	Mirfield
1770	1992	1537	1770	132179	YKS	Ripponden
LUMBARD						
1650	1700	1650	1700	142018	SOM	Chard
1677	1732	1670	1750	142018	SOM	Taunton
LUMBER						
1794	1842	ALL	1794	166847	BRK	Abingdon
1800	1874	1600	1800	141925	SOM	Batcombe
1719	1823	....	....	165999	SOM	Batcombe
1719	1823	....	....	165999	SOM	Bruton
1719	1823	....	....	165999	SOM	Dinder
LUMBY						
1950	1992	1900	1992	133450	DOR	???
1850	1992	1827	1992	130036	LAN	Liverpool
....	....	1837	1880	130036	WYK	Lumby
1746	1767	1600	1760	101575	YKS	Leeds
1750	1920	1750	1920	161314	YKS	Pudsey
LUMKIN						
1774	1827	1774	1827	164232	SFK	Theberton
LUMLEY						
....	....	ALL	ALL	143723	ALL	Name Study
....	....	1700	1855	177725	EYK	Hull
1800	1900	1700	1800	124427	MER	Llanwrin
1770	1992	1700	1750	138258	NYK	Ravensworth
1651	1881	1600	1900	102563	YKS	Hampsthwaite
LUMMAS						
1759	1920	1759	1992	111287	DBY	Mosborough
1744	1791	1710	1744	149039	NTH	West
LUMMIS						
1650	1992	1500	1650	143731	SFK	Hartismere
LUMMON						
1764	1798	ALL	1764	154563	DEV	Woodbury
LUMMS						
1877	1877	ALL	....	132349	LND	Hackney
LUMSDEN						
1750	....	ALL	ALL	130508	FIF	Kilconquhar
1750	1800	ALL	ALL	130508	FIF	Pittenweem
1820	1860	1800	1900	143758	NBL	Ilderton
1850	1992	1700	1850	174726	NBL	Ilderton
1790	1840	1700	1900	143758	NBL	Nesbit
1850	1992	1700	1850	174726	NBL	Wooler
LUN						
1775	....	....	1775	101761	NTT	Everton
1802	....	....	....	171166	WRY	Swillington
LUND						
1675	1725	1675	1725	109347	LAN	Accrington
....	....	1650	1680	177393	NTT	Weston
1740	1750	1600	1992	167592	SOM	Bristol
1790	1820	1750	1800	119032	YKS	Killinghall
1889	....	....	....	153400	???	Stockport
LUNDE						
1630	1630	1600	1650	141097	YKS	Braithwell
LUNDIE						
1792	1887	1700	1880	113107	ANS	Arbroath
LUNDY						
?	?	?	?	173274	IRL	Antrim
LUNE						
1790	1992	1790	1992	120251	WAR	ALL
LUNN						
1746	1838	ALL	1838	118990	BRK	Wlatham St Laurence
1800	1850	1600	1800	154059	ESS	Chelmsford
....	1785	ALL	ALL	129933	HAM	Nateley Scures
1860	....	....	....	116793	LAN	Failsworm
....	....	ALL	ALL	121991	NFK	ALL
1850	1915	....	....	171891	OXF	Checkendon
....	....	ALL	ALL	121991	SFK	ALL
....	....	1750	1850	171891	SRY	Bagshot
1700	1810	....	....	133221	SSX	Wisborough Green
1718	1804	....	....	152234	WYK	Swillington

Known From	To	Researching From	To	Ref	Cty	Place
LUNN contd.						
1820	1872	1761	1880	129216	YKS	Thorpe Salvin
LUNNON						
1794	1808	1750	1992	114901	BKM	Hedsor
1808	1992	1800	1992	114901	BKM	Wooburn
1895	1962	1842	1875	106402	LND	Childs Hill
LUNT						
1711	1938	1600	1900	145955	CAE	Llanrhos
1893	1992	ALL	1893	109320	WAR	Aston
LUNTLEY						
1854	1930	1854	1900	143774	EYK	Scarborough
1754	1860	1754	1890	143774	???	London
LUNTS						
1750	1850	1750	1850	129836	STS	Audley
LUPTON						
....	1855	....	....	153176	DUR	Consett
1800	1860	1700	1890	105333	IOM	ALL
1800	1860	1700	1890	105333	IRL	ALL
1850	1900	1700	1900	105333	LAN	Liverpool
1850	1900	1700	1900	105333	LAN	Southport
1850	1989	1750	1850	174939	YKS	Harrogate
1880	1992	....	....	102377	YKS	Leeds
1830	1860	1700	1992	102377	YKS	Wakefield
1853	1874	ALL	1874	104299	YKS	Wakefield
LUQUAS						
1760	....	1730	1750	131326	GSY	???
LUSBY						
1949	1992	1850	1949	177199	LIN	Grasby
1804	1854	1804	1881	156639	YKS	Hull
LUSCOMBE						
1605	1650	1575	1675	171549	DEV	Buckfastleigh
1756	1919	1600	1756	124109	DEV	Loddiswell
1790	1850	1790	1850	106801	DEV	South Brent
1700	1800	....	....	160814	DEV	Ugborough
LUSH						
....	....	ALL	ALL	143790	ALL	Name Study
1837	1988	....	....	143782	ALL	ALL
1600	1988	ALL	ALL	143782	BRK	ALL
1843	1911	ALL	ALL	117307	BRK	Wokingham
1600	1988	ALL	ALL	143782	DOR	ALL
1830	1850	1750	1850	156280	DOR	Wimborne
1600	1988	ALL	ALL	143782	HAM	ALL
1776	1842	ALL	ALL	117307	HAM	South
1600	1988	ALL	ALL	143782	MDX	ALL
1600	1988	ALL	ALL	143782	SOM	ALL
1600	1988	ALL	ALL	143782	SRY	ALL
1600	1988	ALL	ALL	143782	SSX	ALL
....	....	1800	1900	142549	WIL	ALL
1600	1988	ALL	ALL	143782	WIL	ALL
1500	1900	1500	1900	170216	WIL	ALL
1710	1720	1650	1750	174599	WIL	Donhead St Mary
1720	1922	....	....	174599	WIL	Kilmington
LUSHER						
1665	1698	....	1665	101761	SFK	Pakenham
LUSHINGTON						
1910	1992	1910	1992	121320	ENG	ALL
1628	1992	1066	1628	163945	KEN	Rodmersham
LUSIGNAN						
1628	1992	1066	1628	163945	KEN	Sittingbourne
LUSKEY						
1670	1728	1500	1800	153354	CON	North Hill
LUSTED						
1520	1800	ALL	1800	156175	SXE	Ninfield
LUTER						
1500	1900	1500	1900	170216	WIL	ALL
LUTHER						
....	1920	....	1920	173533	DOR	ALL
1826	1871	1700	1826	115185	SAL	Shrewsbury
LUTKIN						
....	....	ALL	ALL	117986	ALL	Name Study
....	....	ALL	ALL	117978	ALL	Name Study
LUTLEY						
....	....	ALL	ALL	143804	ALL	Name Study
....	....	....	....	160164	ALL	ALL
1682	1992	1682	1992	160164	DEV	Blackdown
1880	1992	1881	1992	160164	LAN	Manchester
1769	1916	1765	1885	160164	SOM	Buckland St Mary
LUTMAN						
1814	1842	1814	1842	147575	MDX	Parsons Green
LUTON						
1886	....	ALL	1900	104299	SOM	Shepton Mallet
....	....	1800	1900	108723	STS	Birmingham
LUTSKE						
....	....	ALL	ALL	130818	LND	Camberwell

Known From	To	Researching From	To	Ref	Cty	Place
LUTT						
1777	....	....	1777	108839	CAM	Witcham
LUTUS						
1600	....	ALL	ALL	167622	ALL	ALL
LUTY						
1630	1830	....	....	165999	LEI	Bottesford
LUTYENS						
....	....	ALL	ALL	100889	ALL	Name Study
LUTZ						
....	....	1700	1850	131962	LND	Stepney
LUXALL						
....	....	1550	1700	156795	DOR	East
LUXFORD						
....	....	....	1830	175773	ALL	ALL
....	....	ALL	1900	178403	SSX	West
1644	1660	1660	1670	168785	SSX	East Grinstead
LUXMOORE						
ALL	1820	1800	1880	135429	DEV	Bratton Clovelly
1800	1900	1600	1900	112976	DEV	Thorverton
LUXMORE						
1776	1992	1700	1776	156264	DEV	Tavistock
LUXTON						
1600	1992	....	....	143855	DEV	Central
1704	1992	1660	1710	173649	DEV	Clayhanger
1811	1876	ALL	ALL	114987	DEV	Exeter
1844	1992	1750	1844	154415	DEV	Plymouth
....	1858	1500	1858	104825	DEV	Tamerton Folliott
....	....	1800	1992	153540	DEV	Tavistock
1740	1740	ALL	1800	173614	DEV	Wembworthy
LYALL						
1660	1992	ALL	1660	143820	ANS	Farnell
1760	1800	1500	1760	138614	CAI	Dunnet
1740	1800	1600	1740	158143	FIF	Newburgh
1829	1992	1700	1829	160032	NBL	Belford
1829	1992	1700	1829	160032	NBL	Ellingham
LYANT						
1686	1760	1600	1686	145459	HAM	Eling
LYDDIETH						
....	....	ALL	ALL	143839	ALL	Name Study
1849	1870	ALL	ALL	143839	LAN	South
LYDDON						
1732	1992	1154	1732	133914	DEV	Twitchen
1761	1761	1700	1800	121568	DEV	West Anstey
1790	1830	1700	1850	136840	SOM	Brendon Hills
LYDFORD						
1779	1992	1700	1850	116289	DOR	Gillingham
LYDIARD						
1770	1992	1580	1770	175870	SOM	Batheaston
LYDSTON						
1511	1956	ALL	ALL	142255	ALL	ALL
LYE						
1828	1880	1788	1900	121568	SOM	North East
1830	1880	1600	1830	101389	SOM	Bath
1690	1830	1830	1900	101389	SOM	Martock
1788	1788	1700	1800	121568	SOM	Martock
1825	1959	1780	1930	133604	WIL	Market Lavington
1825	1959	1780	1930	133604	WIL	West Lavington
1840	1950	....	....	143847	YKS	Leeds
1800	1880	....	....	143847	YKS	Masham
1851	....	1800	1900	138746	???	Turdsey
LYELL						
1790	1960	....	....	143855	AYR	Mauchline
1750	1880	....	1750	161888	AYR	Mauchline
1595	1730	....	....	159751	DEV	Bradworthy
....	....	1700	1850	143855	FIF	Newburgh
LYES						
1731	1992	1538	1770	143863	GLS	North
1731	1992	1538	1770	143863	WOR	South
LYFORD						
....	....	ALL	ALL	133434	ALL	Name Study
1450	1992	1200	1992	133434	ALL	ALL
1788	1840	ALL	....	172812	BRK	ALL
1698	1820	ALL	1698	120332	BRK	Drayton
1698	1820	ALL	1698	120332	BRK	Steventon
1698	1820	ALL	1698	120332	BRK	Sutton Courtenay
LYGO						
1830	1860	....	....	177326	YKS	???
LYGO-SIMMONS						
1833	1992	ALL	1833	118060	KEN	Rochester
LYLE						
1735	1902	....	....	159751	CON	Launcells
1873	1881	....	....	159751	CON	Liskeard
1868	1992	....	....	159751	DEV	Torquay

Known From	To	Researching From	To	Ref	Cty	Place
LYLES						
1770	....	1550	1770	139866	CAM	Westley
LYLICK						
1698	....	....	....	131326	CON	St Austell
LYLIES						
?	?	....	....	135615	LAN	Grenfields
LYMESEY						
1101	1103	1066	ALL	108294	???	???
LYMESY						
1101	1103	1066	ALL	108294	???	???
LYMN						
1800	1930	1700	1800	172448	DBY	Alfreton
LYNALL						
....	....	ALL	ALL	143871	ALL	Name Study
LYNAM						
1820	1820	1700	1820	112097	DBY	Duffield
LYNAS						
1859	....	1700	1992	107204	DUR	Stockton
....	....	1700	1960	158976	YKS	Skelton
LYNAUGH						
....	....	....	....	169544	IRL	Neath
LYNCH						
1847	1992	....	1847	143901	DUB	Dublin
....	....	ALL	ALL	143340	IRL	Limerick
1910	....	1800	1960	101907	KEN	Strood
1850	1992	....	....	108898	LAN	Liverpool
1800	1897	1700	1950	118680	LEX	???
1915	1917	1917	1992	166073	LND	Letonstone
1893	1909	1700	1916	166073	LND	Stepney
1845	1862	1800	1881	110132	MDX	???
LYND						
1816	1836	1700	1816	149632	MDX	Stepney
LYNDALL						
....	....	ALL	ALL	163562	ALL	ALL
LYNDS						
1600	1799	....	....	143928	KEN	Medway Towns
1727	1992	1700	1987	143928	KEN	Meopham
LYNE						
1775	1934	1700	1950	122688	CON	St Teath
1900	....	....	....	154407	DEV	Plymouth
1841	1851	1800	1851	155225	GLS	Bristol
1850	1992	1700	1850	143936	LIN	Brigg
LYNES						
1812	1992	1790	1812	144223	IRL	Armagh
1860	1992	1700	1860	160571	LEI	Swithland
LYNKHULL						
1250	1350	1200	1350	154881	KEN	Hever
LYNN						
1867	1880	....	....	148202	HAM	Southampton
1884	1885	1885	1900	148202	HAM	Winchester
1884	1901	1800	1884	175595	IRL	Belfast
1891	1891	1880	1900	126705	IRL	Dublin
1865	1890	1890	1992	146560	LKS	Coatbride
1857	1992	1857	1992	112305	LKS	Coatbridge
1810	1918	1810	1918	130710	LND	Mile End
1851	1862	1843	1851	148202	LND	Shoreditch
1800	....	....	....	135488	NFK	Emneth
1831	1843	1700	1831	148202	SSX	Brighton
....	....	1805	1820	136638	SSX	East Grinstead
LYNNE						
1917	ALL	ALL	....	100536	KEN	Dover
1780	1917	ALL	ALL	100536	WLS	???
LYON						
1775	1860	1700	1775	152196	CMA	Gosforth
1747	1762	1700	1747	126918	ESS	Downham
....	....	ALL	ALL	149268	IRL	???
1825	1857	1750	1880	176621	KEN	Canterbury
1813	1866	1750	1866	145750	LAN	ALL
....	....	1700	1992	170402	LAN	South
1841	1893	1750	1841	135364	LAN	Down Holland
1805	1906	1700	1805	123706	LAN	Ormskirk
1830	1992	1700	1992	143944	LAN	Prescot
1830	1992	1700	1992	143944	LAN	Whiston
1830	1992	?	1830	143952	LIN	Gainsborough
....	....	?	1830	143952	PER	ALL
....	....	ALL	ALL	149268	RUT	???
1800	1840	1800	1850	123145	WMD	Birmingham
LYONS						
1250	1400	1200	1400	154881	NBL	Warkworth
1740	1834	1740	1834	158011	ROS	Lyonstown
?	1992	1875	1992	158011	SLI	Heapstown
1871	1881	1800	1940	119008	SRY	Kingston
....	....	1800	ALL	164615	WIL	Westbury

Known From	To	Researching From	To	Ref	Cty	Place
LYST						
1878	1923	1800	1900	164402	NFK	Norwich
LYSTER						
1800	1850	1700	1900	128163	SAL	Brosely
LYTE						
1500	1550	1500	1600	171549	HAM	Arreton
LYTH						
1800	1992	1700	1850	143944	YKS	Hull
1492	1992	1492	1992	162809	YKS	Neton
1492	1992	1492	1992	162809	YKS	Rawcliffe
1800	1992	1700	1850	143944	YKS	Scarborough
LYTHGOE						
1809	1856	....	....	168920	CHS	Wallasey
1800	1840	1700	1840	151254	LAN	Leigh
LYTTON						
....	1850	1850	1900	166383	DBY	Derby
LYUS						
....	....	ALL	ALL	143979	ALL	Name Study
LYVESEY						
1600	1800	....	....	177318	LAN	Middleforth
M'CONNELL						
....	....	1800	1920	113514	IRL	???
M'KENZIE						
1888	1992	ALL	1888	179434	ABD	Kintore
1888	1992	ALL	1888	179434	ABD	Oyne
MABBETT						
1820	1850	ALL	ALL	145386	HAM	Plaitford
MABBOTT						
1817	1841	1800	1817	128368	YKS	Sheffield
MABBUTT						
1803	1992	1770	1992	107514	BRK	Abingdon
1750	1850	1700	1850	147575	CAM	Cesterton
1750	1850	1700	1850	147575	CAM	Hildershem
1840	1930	1840	1930	147575	MDX	Fulham
1803	1992	1770	1992	107514	WIL	Marlborough
MABE						
1717	1738	1700	1750	171549	HEF	Bridstow
MABELL						
1849	1860	?	1849	121665	WOR	Stourport
1750	1821	?	1750	121665	WOR	Worcester
MABEN						
....	....	ALL	ALL	109339	ALL	ALL
MABER						
1717	1992	1600	1730	170607	DOR	Lytchett Matravers
MABEY						
1817	....	1750	1817	116572	DOR	Bridport
1852	1949	1800	1900	136646	MDX	London
MABIN						
1760	1784	....	....	144568	ROX	???
MABLE						
1750	1821	?	1750	121665	WOR	Worcester
MAC DOWELL						
1709	1992	....	....	143987	DOW	Nonaghadee
1709	1992	....	....	143987	NIR	Belfast
MACALLUM						
1830	1960	ALL	1800	156116	ARL	???
MACARTHY						
1812	1866	1787	1866	104604	COR	Blarney Castle
1840	1850	1820	1860	104604	NBL	Newcastle On Tyne
MACAULAY						
1790	1900	1790	1900	144290	ROSS-SHIRE	Stornoway
MACBRYDE						
1854	1992	1600	1850	100730	WIG	Whithorn
MACBURNIE						
1762	1913	1600	1760	156221	DFS	ALL
MACDIARMID						
1817	....	....	....	127140	ARL	Appin
1817	....	....	....	127140	ARL	Ardsheal
1818	1854	....	....	127140	ARL	North Shian
1851	1930	....	....	127140	LKS	Glasgow
1749	1751	....	....	127140	PER	Lochtayside
1875	....	....	....	127140	RFW	Greenock
MACDONALD						
1812	1860	1800	1860	133884	ARL	Balachulish
1846	1878	....	....	127140	DNB	Kirkintilloch
1900	1992	1800	1900	153087	DUR	Mid
1818	1992	....	....	108529	HAR	Kylas
1818	1992	....	....	108529	HAR	Tarbert
1749	1900	1600	1749	142328	INV	Dalville
1830	1871	1790	1900	165824	INV	Dores
1797	1903	1903	1920	110035	INV	Fort William
1840	1848	....	1840	144029	INV	Fort William
1801	1830	1750	1992	166049	INV	Inverness-Leachkin
1865	1925	1865	1925	144290	INV	Isle Of Sky
MACDONALD contd.						
1800	....	....	....	167037	INV	Kilmuir
1800	1960	1600	1960	114898	INV	North Uist
1840	1970	1800	1970	149233	INV	North Uist
1865	1925	1865	1925	144290	INV	Skaebust
1749	1900	1600	1749	142328	INV	Skye
1820	1850	1820	1850	128449	IRL	???
1860	1992	ALL	1860	143324	LKS	Cluland
1860	1992	....	....	113247	LND	???
1823	1992	1823	1992	146366	MOR	Forres
1798	1800	1750	1800	111821	ROC	Contin
1880	1992	ALL	1880	142263	ROC	Dingwall
1840	1900	1800	1900	149233	ROC	Gairloch
1843	1992	1750	1843	144010	SCT	Applecross
1850	....	1700	1850	113247	SCT	Edinburgh
1900	1951	1850	1900	174807	SCT	Edinburgh
1825	1949	1790	1825	131806	SCT	Inverness
1880	1992	....	....	113247	SRY	Woking
1857	1904	ALL	ALL	128449	STS	Black Country
1857	1904	ALL	ALL	128449	STS	Tipton
1919	....	1900	1930	163775	YKS	Barnsley
1902	1904	1850	1920	137944	???	Edinburgh
1817	....	....	....	120804	???	Isle Of Tiree
MACDOUGALL						
1790	1830	1700	1900	144290	ARL	Mingrie
1850	1910	1825	1992	133450	SCT	Edinburgh
MACDOWELL						
1870	1880	1750	1992	167592	YKS	Castleford
MACDUELL						
1829	1864	1700	1864	156582	LND	East
1829	1864	1700	1864	156582	LND	City
1807	....	1700	1864	156582	MDX	Spitalfields
MACE						
1755	1850	1720	1900	110906	BRK	Binfield
1870	1992	....	....	143294	CHS	Bromborough
1870	1992	....	....	143294	CHS	Nenferry
....	....	1750	1900	136476	GLS	Todenham
1850	1857	1800	1860	146803	HRT	Watford
....	....	ALL	1836	143294	LND	Battersea
1800	1920	1800	1920	121207	LND	Minories
1800	1920	1800	1920	121207	LND	Shoreditch
1800	1920	1800	1920	121207	LND	Wanstead
1841	1871	1800	1871	100242	MDX	Hillingdon
1800	1930	1800	1992	110906	MDX	Uxbridge
1890	1960	1890	1960	121207	SRY	Ewell
1833	1992	1820	1833	161284	STS	Checkley
1885	1950	1300	1992	152501	STS	???
1810	1810	ALL	....	132349	SXE	Seaford
1885	1950	1300	1992	152501	WOR	Dudley
MACER						
1718	1914	....	1725	108839	CAM	Coveney
1718	1914	....	1725	108839	CAM	Witcham
MACEY						
....	....	1700	1794	133523	ALL	ALL
1820	1830	1700	1820	132993	CON	Torpoint
1820	1830	1700	1820	132993	DEV	Devonport
1891	1931	1700	1891	142484	HAM	Fyfield
....	....	1700	1794	133523	HAM	New Forest
....	....	1600	1800	124958	SOM	ALL
1873	1875	1700	1873	158976	SRY	Roehampton
1860	1900	1800	1870	101265	WIL	Bishopstrowe
1818	1992	1700	1818	174688	WIL	Chilmark
1840	1992	....	....	124958	???	Bristol
MACFADYEN						
1841	1900	1700	1900	144037	STD	Kilfinichen
MACFARLANE						
1850	1971	1600	1850	176915	ARL	Arrochar
1600	1840	....	....	149764	PER	Port Of Menteith
1750	1900	1750	1900	120235	ROC	Stornoway
1800	1992	ALL	1800	144053	SCT	ALL
1800	1900	1750	1850	124699	SCT	South West
1864	1891	1600	1864	147885	SCT	Glasgow
MACFARLANG						
1851	1992	1700	1887	108316	STI	Balfron
1851	1992	1700	1887	108316	STI	Strathblang
MACGILLIVRAY						
1825	1930	1725	1825	141836	RFW	Greenock
MACGOWAN						
1835	....	ALL	ALL	121754	DOW	Belfast
MACGREGOR						
....	1830	....	1851	103349	PER	???
MACGUIRK						
1880	1920	ALL	1880	141224	GLS	Bristol
....	....	ALL	1880	141224	IRL	???

Known From	To	Researching From	To	Ref	Cty	Place
MACHAM						
....	....	1550	1700	156795	DOR	East
MACHEN						
1737	1992	1700	1737	130257	SSX	Penworth
MACHIN						
....	....	ALL	ALL	159204	NFK	Norwich
1880	1920	1800	....	135860	NTT	Nottingham
1813	1861	1750	1813	167932	STS	Burslem St John
1776	1992	....	....	144088	STS	Horton
1728	1992	....	....	144088	STS	Whitmore
1892	1992	....	1892	163031	SYK	Sheffield
1885	1920	1500	1885	175072	WRY	Sheffield
1885	1920	1920	1992	175072	YKS	ALL
MACHINDER						
1820	....	....	1992	151270	LIN	Sausthorpe
MACINNES						
1840	1940	1800	1950	149233	INV	Plockton
MACINTOSH						
1800	1875	1800	1875	144290	ROSS-SHIRE	Knockbain
MACIVER						
1650	1920	1500	1920	144290	ROSS-SHIRE	Stornoway
1787	1811	1780	1811	151858	SCT	Scoraig
MACK						
1793	1810	1600	1793	147346	DUR	Sunderland
1852	1992	1800	1852	151343	IRL	Sligo
?	?	1850	1875	131733	IRL	???
1841	1905	....	....	164062	LAN	Liverpool
MACKALL						
1782	1785	ALL	ALL	127280	MDX	London
MACKAY						
1780	1890	1700	1890	126500	BAN	Wick
1780	1992	1700	1780	144134	CAI	Thurso
1830	1890	....	....	126497	CAI	Wick
1810	1840	....	....	144126	KEN	Sheerness
1840	1850	1850	1900	144126	KEN	Woolwich
1878	1957	1700	1900	165476	LND	Hackney
1817	1817	1817	1850	146889	NAI	Nairn
1789	1798	1700	1789	144126	PER	Longforgan
1800	1817	ALL	ALL	101370	SCT	Dornoch
1783	1980	1500	1783	138614	SUT	Clyne
1780	1800	....	....	126497	SUT	Farr
1817	1820	1750	1850	146889	SUT	Lairg
1825	1825	1800	1850	146889	SUT	Ospisdale
MACKDOUEL						
1775	1775	....	....	121355	LND	Shoreditch
MACKENDER						
1712	1931	1640	1931	135941	SFK	Lakenheath
MACKENZIE						
1912	....	....	....	144142	AYR	Stevenston
1799	1905	....	....	135453	DNB	???
1800	1850	1800	1860	176982	DOW	Donaghadee
1780	1800	1750	1800	111821	INV	Ardersier
1796	1983	1700	1992	112089	INV	Dores
1900	....	1750	1900	144150	INV	Inverness
1900	....	1700	1900	144150	INV	Kiltarlity
1839	....	....	1839	101761	LND	East
1860	....	ALL	ALL	157864	MLN	Edinburgh
1838	1992	1700	1838	166987	OKI	Stronsay
1880	1992	ALL	1880	142263	ROC	Dingwall
1820	....	1700	1820	115967	ROC	Fodderty
1780	1992	1750	1780	111821	ROC	Logie Wester
1650	1702	1600	1700	154881	ROC	Seaforth
1800	1900	1750	1900	120235	ROC	Stornoway
1780	1992	1750	1780	111821	ROC	Urquhart
1780	1840	1750	1800	111821	ROC	Urray
1790	1960	1750	1800	158828	ROC	???
1801	1888	1800	1888	151858	SCT	Ardindrean Lochbroom
1850	1925	1850	1992	133450	SSX	???
1780	1992	1780	1992	125687	YKS	Barnsley
1780	1992	1780	1992	125687	YKS	Sheffield
MACKERELL						
1800	....	....	....	168041	SFK	Gorleston
MACKERETH						
1800	1900	1750	1800	149373	CUL	Cockermouth
1813	1873	1750	1900	132314	WES	Natland
MACKERNES						
....	....	ALL	ALL	165999	ENG	ALL
1640	1760	....	....	165999	LIN	Bucknall
MACKETT						
1767	1838	1767	1930	156647	HAM	Arreton
....	....	1800	1860	155322	KEN	Dover
MACKEY						
1817	1842	1800	1850	165972	LND	Westminster
MACKIE						
1834	1890	1700	1834	119881	ABD	Aberdean
1880	1900	....	....	148342	ABD	Peterhead
1911	1911	....	....	144177	ANS	Abroath
1910	1910	1891	1910	144177	ANS	Montrose
1853	1891	1800	1853	144177	FIF	Ceres
1790	1992	....	1790	160431	KCD	Benholm
1779	1851	....	1992	143901	LND	Finsbury
1783	....	1783	1992	142735	SCT	???
1793	1856	1650	1793	179043	YKS	Wakefield
MACKIFF						
1856	....	1700	....	132128	KEN	Graves End
1856	....	1700	....	132128	KEN	Wilton
MACKINDER						
1713	1741	1675	1713	174211	LIN	Barkston
....	....	1840	1890	164984	LIN	Boston
1713	1741	1675	1713	174211	LIN	Nocton
MACKINNON						
1840	1859	....	....	127140	RFW	Greenock
1817	....	....	....	120804	???	Isle Of Tiree
MACKINTOSH						
1861	1930	....	....	111260	LTN	Edinburgh
1861	1930	....	....	111260	MLN	Newington
1846	1881	1846	1881	106593	NTT	Nottingham
1895	1913	1830	1895	120561	SCT	Aberdeen
1786	....	....	1786	101761	YKS	Warmsworth
MACKLEM						
1905	....	....	....	123633	IRL	???
MACKLEY						
1971	1992	....	....	144185	ESS	Rayleigh
1926	1992	....	....	144185	ESS	Westcliffe On Sea
1911	1926	....	....	144185	LND	Leytonstone
1851	1923	1600	1850	144185	NFK	Norwich
1800	1890	....	....	118206	YKS	Knottingley
MACKLIN						
1750	1820	1750	1820	126446	BRK	Bradfield
1788	1864	ALL	1788	102385	DEV	???
1800	....	....	....	152722	HAM	Portsmouth
1744	1906	1744	1851	102954	HAM	Winchester
....	....	?	?	118176	HEF	Allensmore
1850	....	....	....	152722	WIL	Salisbury
MACKMAN						
....	....	ALL	ALL	144207	ALL	Name Study
1760	1992	ALL	1760	144207	ALL	ALL
MACKMIN						
1760	1992	ALL	1760	144207	ALL	ALL
MACKNIGHT						
1822	1847	1847	1992	145440	ANT	Belfast
1887	1992	....	....	144215	DUR	Chester Moor
1793	1992	....	....	157988	DUR	Chestermoor
1793	1992	....	....	157988	DUR	Durham
1793	1992	....	....	157988	DUR	Shinriff
1822	1847	1847	1992	145440	STS	ALL
MACKRETH						
1700	1960	1500	1700	107042	ENG	North
MACKRILL						
1787	1860	1700	1787	174688	MDX	London
1755	1771	1700	1755	174688	SRY	Dulwich
MACKWOOD						
1817	1832	1700	1816	115134	YKS	North
MACLAGAN						
1788	1893	ALL	ALL	120219	PER	Perth
MACLEAN						
1799	....	1750	1850	111848	ARL	Ardgour
1806	1992	1750	1800	111821	ROC	Urray
MACLEOD						
1799	1992	....	....	108529	HAR	Kylas
1799	1992	....	....	108529	HAR	Tarbert
....	....	1700	1900	141739	ROC	Tain
1725	1992	1625	1725	141836	SCT	Kershader
1750	1870	1650	1750	141836	SCT	Valtos
1660	1860	ALL	ALL	141739	SUT	Sallachy
MACMILLAN						
1809	1891	1750	1809	111848	ARL	Ardgour
ALL	1700	1749	1873	172235	NBL	Allendale
MACMURRAY						
1970	1992	....	....	131954	DFS	Kirkcudbright
1970	1992	....	....	131954	DFS	Minnigaff
1970	1992	....	....	131954	DFS	Newton Stewart
1784	1837	....	1837	131954	DOW	Bangor
1837	1920	1837	....	131954	LTN	Dalkeith
1837	1920	1837	....	131954	LTN	Edinburgh
1837	1920	1837	....	131954	LTN	Lasswade
1837	1920	1837	....	131954	LTN	Leith

Known From	To	Researching From	To	Ref	Cty	Place
MACMURRAY contd.						
1837	1920	1837	....	131954	LTN	Portobello
1920	1959	1920	1959	131954	PER	Dunblane
MACMYN						
1775	1853	1700	1861	160636	KKD	Dundrennan
MACNALLY						
1851	1903	1700	1900	178322	KEN	Ash
MACNAUGHT						
1771	1819	....	....	127140	ARL	Kintyre
1771	1819	....	....	127140	ARL	Southend
1771	1819	....	....	127140	AYR	Kilmarnock
1771	1819	....	....	127140	AYR	Riccarton
1771	1819	....	....	127140	DNB	Bridgend
1771	1819	....	....	127140	LKS	Biggar
1771	1819	....	....	127140	LKS	Gillespie
1900	....	....	....	127140	LKS	Glasgow
1813	1883	....	....	127140	LND	Hackney
1813	1883	....	....	127140	LND	Stepney
1820	1992	....	....	127140	RFW	Greenock
1900	1992	?	1900	163864	RFW	Greenock
MACNAUGHTON						
....	....	1850	1950	173940	SCT	???
MACPHAIL						
1800	1874	1750	1800	111821	ROC	Logie Wester
MACPHERSON						
1869	1870	1851	1871	134686	HIL	Insh
....	....	?	?	134201	INV	North Uist
1800	1900	1780	1900	160563	PER	Bridge Of Cally
1870	1897	....	....	134686	STD	Glasgow
MACQUEEN						
1820	1910	....	....	116173	CUL	St Bees
MACQUISTEN						
1820	1840	1840	1900	144266	SCT	Glasgow
MACRAE						
1775	1850	1775	1900	144290	INV	Inverness
1787	1992	1700	....	110264	RFW	Greenock
....	....	1600	1900	144274	ROC	Kintail
1750	1850	1700	1900	144290	ROSS-SHIRE	Killearnan
1700	1900	ALL	....	144290	ROSS-SHIRE	Knockbain
1834	1858	ALL	ALL	101370	SUT	Golspie
MACRO						
1730	1811	....	1730	100064	SFK	Barrow
1730	1811	....	1730	100064	SFK	Gareley
MACROFT						
1764	1900	1800	1900	171417	ESS	Gt Baddow
MACROW						
1590	1666	....	1590	101761	SFK	Bury St Edmunds
MADDAFORD						
1828	1919	1750	1828	147907	CON	Callington
1659	1659	1600	1720	105333	DEV	Buckland In The Moor
1659	1659	1600	1720	105333	DEV	Holne
1659	1659	1600	1720	105333	DEV	Ilsington
1659	1659	1600	1720	105333	DEV	Lydford
1659	1659	1600	1720	105333	DEV	Widecombe In The Moor
MADDAMS						
1747	1820	1716	1747	162523	HRT	Ayot St Lawrence
MADDEN						
1870	1960	1840	1870	111856	COR	???
1842	....	....	....	136964	ENG	Watford
1820	1860	....	....	136492	IRL	Aitkenhead
1820	1860	....	....	136492	IRL	Baillieston
1825	1992	1700	1825	149918	LAN	Liverpool
1837	1855	ALL	1830	159875	LDY	Portglenone
1820	1860	....	....	136492	LKS	Coatbridge
1820	1860	....	....	136492	LKS	Shettleston
....	....	ALL	ALL	152048	TYR	???
MADDERN						
1820	1880	1820	1880	150479	AGY	Holyhead
1540	1900	1540	1820	150479	CON	Penzance
MADDERS						
1850	1900	1850	1992	117870	WAR	Birmingham
MADDEVER						
....	....	ALL	ALL	160423	ALL	Name Study
1500	1992	1500	1992	160423	ALL	ALL
MADDICK						
1818	1864	....	....	151548	DEV	Rattray
MADDICKS						
1869	1889	1700	1900	177873	GLS	Bristol
MADDICOTT						
1800	1860	1700	....	131253	DEV	Ipplepen
MADDISON						
1875	1900	1800	1992	128937	DUR	ALL
MADDISON contd.						
....	....	1800	1890	126136	DUR	Chester Le Street
1800	1850	1800	1900	127108	LIN	Boston
1666	1700	1600	1700	127108	LIN	Fulletby
1900	1930	1850	1900	152730	LIN	Holton Le Clay
1695	1720	1695	1750	127108	LIN	Lowtoynton
1730	1785	1700	1850	127108	LIN	Mareham On The Hill
1785	1850	1785	1850	127108	LIN	Nest Keal
1800	1810	1800	1810	127108	LIN	Stickney
....	....	1530	1992	145769	LND	Sydneham
MADDOCK						
1801	1847	1600	1801	152080	CON	Callington
1687	1750	1650	1750	171549	DEV	Buckfastleigh
MADDOCKS						
1778	1877	1750	1877	158658	CMN	Llanarthne
1700	1850	ALL	ALL	150347	DBY	Repton
1750	1875	1700	1900	157171	GLS	Churcham
1710	1720	1700	1725	157171	GLS	Hartpury
1725	1730	1710	1730	157171	GLS	Minsterworth
1680	1700	1660	1725	157171	GLS	Rudford
1790	1810	1790	1850	126594	LEI	Quorndon
1804	1992	1700	1804	116513	SAL	Bridgnorth
1843	ALL	....	....	169897	SAL	Kinnerley
1750	1850	1750	1850	142123	SAL	Knockin
1690	1800	1690	1800	142123	SAL	Oswestry
1640	1650	1600	1700	142123	SAL	Prees
1650	1900	1600	1900	142123	SAL	Wem
1880	1980	1700	1880	129011	STS	Lynn Shenstone
....	....	ALL	1860	129011	STS	Stafford
1700	1850	ALL	ALL	150347	WAR	Birmingham
MADDOR						
?	?	?	?	162728	ROX	Mossburnford
MADDOX						
1840	1840	1800	1850	136840	GLS	Bristol
1746	1862	1746	1862	158658	GLS	St Briavels
....	1844	1844	1861	174777	HEF	Hereford
1861	1881	ALL	1861	174777	HEF	Norton Canon
1733	1930	1700	1960	147508	HEF	Tillington
1900	1992	....	....	165441	LAN	Liverpool
1758	....	ALL	1992	159174	SAL	High Ercall
1739	....	ALL	1992	159174	SAL	Withington
....	....	ALL	1766	103284	SRY	London
1785	....	ALL	1992	159174	STS	Wolverhampton
1808	1824	ALL	1992	159174	WAR	Birmingham
MADDRELL						
1796	1884	1700	1900	141291	IOM	Rushen
MADDY						
1874	?	1830	1992	150355	BRE	Llangynydr
MADELEY						
1800	1900	1600	1800	165247	SAL	ALL
1891	1976	....	1891	165484	SAL	High Ercall
1891	1976	....	1891	165484	SAL	Roden
1800	1900	1600	1800	165247	STS	ALL
MADEN						
1840	1900	1840	1900	110523	LAN	Bacup
1889	1992	1700	1889	105635	LAN	Stacksteads
MADES						
1880	1920	1880	1920	159220	DBY	Bolsouer
1871	1920	1700	1871	105163	NTT	Southwell
MADGE						
1850	1900	ALL	ALL	163473	DEV	Bow
....	....	1500	1812	144312	DEV	Exbourne
....	....	1780	1895	115061	DEV	Exeter
1811	1901	1500	1812	144312	DEV	North Tawton
1838	1925	1500	1812	144312	DEV	Okehampton
1750	1850	ALL	ALL	163473	DEV	Sandford
1907	1992	....	....	144312	DEV	Tiverton
1870	1947	....	....	144312	DEV	Woodbury
1660	1730	1660	1730	163473	DEV	Zeal Monochorum
....	....	1800	1895	115061	ESS	South West
....	....	1795	1895	115061	ESS	West Ham
1830	....	....	....	132888	LND	???
....	....	1800	1912	115061	SOM	Yeovilton
MADILL						
1820	1992	1700	1820	172650	MOG	Drum
MADISON						
....	....	1800	1860	139297	NTH	Irthlingborough
MADLE						
1850	1900	1700	1850	138991	ESS	South West
MADOWDER						
1480	1841	1841	1992	103411	DEV	Central
1480	1841	1841	1992	103411	DEV	South
MADY						
1810	1860	1700	1860	135275	MDX	St Pancrass

Known From	To	Researching From	To	Ref	Cty	Place
MAEER						
1800	1840	1800	1880	135429	DEV	Colaton Raleigh
MAETRIC						
1868	....	1860	1870	163775	MDX	Bethnal Green
MAGEE						
....	1890	1850	1890	148288	ARM	Newry
MAGGS						
....	....	ALL	ALL	152498	ALL	Name Study
1860	1888	1855	1920	165492	LND	Mile End
?	?	ALL	1850	117919	SOM	Holcombe
1741	....	1700	1800	176923	SOM	Kilmersdon
1747	1885	ALL	1992	152498	WIL	Maddington
1684	1703	ALL	1992	152498	WIL	Market Lavington
1800	1860	1750	1800	165492	WIL	Mere
1720	1920	ALL	1992	152498	WIL	Orcheston St George
1722	1850	ALL	1992	152498	WIL	Orcheston St Mary
1780	1850	ALL	1992	152498	WIL	Pottern With Marston
1825	1942	ALL	1992	152498	WIL	Rolleston
1706	1900	ALL	1992	152498	WIL	Shrewton
1732	1758	ALL	1992	152498	WIL	Stanton St Bernard
1827	1836	ALL	1992	152498	WIL	Tilshead
1621	1716	ALL	1992	152498	WIL	West Lavington
1804	1876	1750	1804	159565	???	Bristol
1804	1876	1750	1804	159565	???	St Georges
MAGIN						
1862	1890	ALL	ALL	134996	T&W	Newcastle
MAGINNES						
1870	1900	1870	1900	145122	YKS	Leeds
MAGINNIS						
1803	1846	ALL	ALL	120669	DOW	???
1851	1861	ALL	ALL	120669	LAN	Manchester
MAGLOCHLAINN						
....	....	ALL	ALL	144339	ALL	Name Study
MAGNAY						
....	....	ALL	ALL	134961	ALL	Name Study
MAGNES						
1860	....	....	....	135771	LND	East
MAGRATH						
....	....	ALL	1850	123412	IRL	Waterford
1845	1992	....	....	123412	???	Bristol
MAGSON						
1750	1850	1750	1850	166081	LAN	Manchester
1830	1900	1800	1900	166081	LAN	Preston
....	1645	1600	1675	152560	NTT	???
MAGUIRE						
1864	1992	1785	1992	144355	COR	Dunmanwry
....	....	1850	....	140333	IRL	Skibbereen
....	1855	....	....	128988	LET	Kiltyclogher
1919	....	1919	....	144355	???	Glasgow
MAHER						
1795	1797	1750	1800	105120	COR	Cork City
MAHLER						
....	....	1800	1900	113697	LND	Hackney
MAHON						
1850	1900	ALL	ALL	113581	LND	Shoreditch
MAHONE						
1750	1800	1600	1750	176761	NBL	Ancroft
1757	1842	....	1757	176761	NBL	Norham Ford
MAHONEY						
1800	1900	ALL	1800	108197	IRL	Cork
1871	1890	ALL	ALL	149004	LDY	Limovady
1846	1992	1800	1920	144371	LND	Rotherhithe
1840	1900	....	....	137618	LND	Southwark
1872	1872	1800	1992	108421	MDX	Westminster
1830	1840	1780	1860	151947	PEM	Pembroke Dock
1873	1873	1800	1992	108421	SRY	Wandsworth
MAHONY						
....	....	ALL	ALL	152005	ALL	Name Study
?	?	?	?	152005	COR	Bandon
MAIDEN						
1500	1800	ALL	1800	177695	SAL	Astley Abbots
1800	1899	ALL	1800	177695	SAL	Dawley Parva
1793	1860	1700	1800	138487	WOR	Elmbridge
1844	1992	1700	1844	116165	WOR	Hartlebury
MAIDENS						
....	....	ALL	1796	101761	LIN	South East
1785	1796	....	1785	101761	LIN	Croft
MAILE						
1900	1992	1800	1900	103896	LND	ALL
MAILLEN						
1700	....	1766	ALL	146536	STI	Larbert
MAILLER						
1813	1883	....	....	113484	PER	Dunning
MAIN						
1831	1905	1800	1992	117609	DEV	Kingskerwell
1806	1806	....	....	135437	GLS	Bristol
1674	1980	1600	1700	144398	HAM	Porstmouth
1674	1980	1600	1700	144398	IOW	Cowes
1830	....	ALL	ALL	152226	LND	ALL
1700	1860	....	....	137111	NTH	Gt Brington
1805	1885	....	....	126977	SCT	Stranraer
MAINS						
1812	1820	ALL	ALL	178470	NBL	Hexham
MAINSBRIDGE						
1546	1785	1546	1785	107573	HAM	Eling
MAINSTONE						
....	....	....	....	114847	CON	ALL
1759	....	1700	....	114847	GLS	Dursley
1800	1889	1800	....	114847	GLS	Henbury
1800	....	ALL	ALL	114847	GLS	Iron Acton
1700	1722	1650	1725	108413	GLS	North Nibley
1577	....	1500	....	114847	GLS	North Nibley
....	....	....	....	114847	LND	ALL
1914	1916	1900	1916	114847	SOM	Bridgewater
....	....	....	....	114847	SRY	ALL
ALL	ALL	ALL	ALL	114847	WLS	ALL
....	....	....	....	114847	WLS	Lydney
MAINT						
1663	1663	1630	1730	105333	SSX	Rogate
MAINWAIRING						
1820	1992	1820	1992	116807	GLA	Pont Ar Dawe
MAINWARING						
....	....	1550	1700	144401	CHS	South
1200	1550	....	....	116327	CHS	Over Peover
1768	1817	....	....	129232	CMN	Llanedi
1839	1992	....	....	129232	GLA	Cwmavon
1886	1908	1912	1992	122580	LAN	Chorlton
1886	1908	1912	1992	122580	LAN	Manchester
1600	1891	....	....	144401	SAL	ALL
1800	1960	1550	1700	144401	SAL	North
1850	1950	1600	1850	169862	SAL	Lilleshall
....	....	1550	1700	144401	STS	West
1550	1992	....	....	116327	STS	Whitmore
MAIOR						
....	....	1600	1650	108677	SOM	Bath
MAIR						
1700	1800	1780	1820	121479	ABD	Aberdeen
1755	1815	1700	1850	176788	ABD	Aberdeen
1850	1900	1850	1992	100226	ABD	Woodside
1809	1992	1700	1807	108316	LKS	Ponfeigh
1804	1992	?	1804	177806	PER	Errol
....	....	1750	1850	100226	SCT	North East
?	?	?	?	142247	SCT	???
MAIRIS						
....	....	ALL	ALL	144428	ALL	Name Study
1730	1992	1400	1730	144428	WCY	ALL
MAISH						
1725	1776	1650	1750	177938	DOR	Beaminster
MAISLAND						
....	....	ALL	ALL	143340	LAN	???
MAITHIESON						
1830	1892	1700	1830	119881	ABD	Oyne
MAITLAND						
....	....	1808	1810	155683	ESS	Stratford
1818	1860	1800	1992	119725	LKS	Glasgow
ALL	ALL	ALL	ALL	116270	SCT	ALL
1752	1921	1300	1928	152501	SCT	Aberdeen
MAJOR						
1707	1800	1600	1707	116637	CON	St Ives
1789	1850	ALL	ALL	107352	DEV	Bideford
1840	1900	1750	1900	126586	DEV	Exeter
1755	1915	1700	1930	103144	DEV	Moretonhampstead
1815	1900	1800	1900	118540	GLA	Llangynwydd
1765	1888	1600	1765	135844	GLS	Fairford
1790	1850	ALL	1800	118338	HAM	Alton
1779	1900	1700	1900	177369	LIN	Crowle
1730	1992	1603	1730	102342	LIN	Roxby
1790	....	....	....	163171	LND	Hoxton
1755	1879	....	....	133590	???	Mortonhamstead
MAKEHAM						
1824	1853	1750	1824	161225	BDF	Steppingley
MAKEIT						
1736	....	....	1736	101761	NTT	Weston
MAKEMAN						
1638	1992	ALL	1638	144207	ALL	ALL
MAKEN						
1780	1850	1780	1850	156485	SFK	Stowlangtoft

```
  Known     Researching
  From  To  From  To   Ref   Cty  Place
MAKENDER
  1672 .... ALL  .... 104515 LIN Sedgebrook
MAKENS
  .... .... 1820 1860 142417 NFK ???
MAKEPEACE
  1858 .... ALL  1858 134171 DUR Hamsterley
  1767 1787 1700 1787 133167 WAR Coventry
MAKER
  1833 1848 1700 1833 173797 CON St Austell
MAKIN
  1750 1750 .... .... 138231 LAN Manchester
  1750 1750 .... .... 138231 LAN Salford
  1700 .... ALL  1700 141879 LND ???
  1780 1850 1780 1850 156485 SFK Stowlangtoft
MAKINS
  1800 1851 1750 1800 116505 SFK Lawshall
MAKINSON
  1900 1940 1720 1870 117145 LAN Adlington
  .... 1845 1800 1845 103322 LAN Adungton
  1900 1940 1720 1870 117145 LAN Blackrod
  1869 1930 1600 1869 131261 YKS Sheffield
MAKMAN
  1622 1992 ALL  1622 144207 ALL ALL
MALANDIE
  1852 .... 1830 1860 163775 MDX Bethnal Green
MALBY
  .... .... ALL  ALL  144444 ALL Name Study
MALCOLM
  .... .... 1600 1796 116637 ARL Kintyre
  1849 1992 ALL  ALL  146757 AYR Beith
  .... .... 1700 1850 124931 AYR Poltalloch
  1849 1992 ALL  ALL  146757 AYR Riccarton
  .... .... 1500 1806 138614 CAI Dunnet
  1803 1838 ALL  ALL  135909 CAI Wick
  1860 1885 1700 ?    168246 CHS Tarporley
  .... .... ALL  1849 146757 IRL Derry
  1850 1900 1700 1900 126837 LAN Liverpool
  1847 1901 1700 1850 124931 LKS Glasgow
  1860 1885 1700 ?    168246 MLN Edinburgh
  1796 .... 1750 1796 116637 NBL Allendale
  1700 1800 1600 1800 126802 PER Dunblane
  1800 1900 1850 1900 126802 SCT Glasgow
  1800 1850 1850 1850 126802 STI ALL
MALCOLMSON
  1750 1965 .... .... 137820 SHI Fetlar
  1720 1965 .... .... 137820 SHI Mid Yell
  1760 1965 .... .... 137820 SHI North Yell
  1758 1965 .... .... 137820 SHI Northmavine
  1720 1965 .... .... 137820 SHI South Yell
MALCOM
  1890 1930 1700 1890 121452 AYR ???
MALE
  1820 1850 .... .... 118729 CHS Birkenhead
  1771 1771 1700 1850 176079 HUN Hemingford Grey
  1700 1800 1700 1800 119113 SOM Shipton Beauchamp
  1821 1840 1700 1960 153346 STS Kingswinford
MALES
  1650 1740 1600 1750 142123 HRT St Pauls Walden
  1694 1992 1597 1800 144460 HRT Walden
MALEY
  1870 1910 1850 1910 147311 STS Eccleshall
MALFANT
  .... .... ALL  ALL  144320 ALL Name Study
MALIM
  1808 1845 1700 1808 162248 NRY Aldborough
MALIN
  1850 1900 1850 1900 144479 AVN Bath
  1700 1750 1600 1700 144479 CHS ???
  1875 .... ALL  1875 131059 ERY Sculcoates
  1808 1860 ALL  1870 113611 EYK Hull
  .... .... 1600 1950 137014 NTH ALL
  1749 1870 1700 1749 149039 NTH West
  1861 1992 1700 1861 166111 NTH Nether Heyford
  .... .... 1600 1950 137014 WAR ALL
  1788 1851 1538 1800 144479 WAR Harbury
  1850 1900 1700 1850 144479 WAR Leamington Spa
  1850 1900 1538 1850 144479 WAR Milverton
  1600 1950 .... .... 137014 WAR Napton
  1800 1875 1538 1800 144479 WAR Warwick
MALINS
  1760 1918 1822 1917 178683 WOR Cropthorne
  1770 1869 1814 1917 178683 WOR Pershore
MALIPHANT
  .... .... ALL  ALL  144487 ALL Name Study
```

```
  Known     Researching
  From  To  From  To   Ref   Cty  Place
MALIPHANT contd.
  1520 1992 1200 1520 144487 ALL ALL
MALKIN
  1720 1850 1600 1750 141496 CHS Nantwich
  .... .... ALL  ALL  141534 DUR Murton
  1800 .... 1700 1850 139386 SFK Barningham
MALKINSON
  1850 1992 1600 1992 123765 LIN ALL
  1800 1862 1700 1862 104396 LIN North Cockerington
MALLADEW
  1773 1792 1700 1775 135348 LAN Ashton Under Lyne
  1792 1842 1790 1850 135348 LAN Oldham
MALLALIEU
  1857 1992 ALL  1857 160938 CHS Ashton Under Lyne
  .... .... 1800 ALL  164615 CHS Broadbottom
  1820 1900 1750 1900 107654 YKS Saddleworth
MALLAM
  .... .... ALL  1811 122572 ALL ALL
  1811 1817 1766 1811 122572 LND ALL
  1812 1863 1772 1812 131342 MDX London
MALLARD
  1750 .... .... .... 118672 GLS Wotton Under Edge
  1714 1842 1714 1863 148156 NTH Central
  1714 1842 1714 1863 148156 NTH South
  1707 1842 1707 1842 148156 NTH Wootton
MALLAT
  1550 1650 1500 1800 177180 BKM Swanbourne
MALLCOH
  1861 1992 1861 1951 127418 PER Blairgowrie
MALLEN
  1805 1881 .... .... 144495 CHI Guernsey
  1901 1907 .... .... 144495 ESS Walthamstow
  1881 1901 .... .... 144495 ESS West Ham
  .... .... ALL  1805 144495 IRL ???
MALLERY
  .... .... ALL  ALL  144509 ALL Name Study
  1900 1992 ALL  ALL  144509 HRT Watford
  1790 1830 1780 1860 144509 KEN Chatham
  1973 1992 1936 1992 144509 KEN Woolwich
  1830 1910 1830 1930 144509 SRY Peckham
MALLESON
  1856 1856 .... .... 152943 HAM Central
MALLETT
  .... .... ALL  ALL  144517 ALL Name Study
  1829 1908 ALL  ALL  149004 DEV South Tawton
  1810 1988 1700 1810 144614 GLS Longhope
  1788 1851 1700 1788 148938 GLS Stone
  1800 1950 1800 1980 134422 SOM Abson
  1800 1950 1800 1980 134422 SOM Wick
  1775 1881 1750 1850 124648 SRY Lambeth
  1673 1850 1673 1850 151467 WAR Tysoe
MALLINDER
  1840 1900 1840 1900 123870 LND ???
MALLINSON
  .... .... 1500 1673 127248 CUL Penryth
  1790 1823 .... .... 129747 LAN Ashton Under Lyne
  .... .... 1840 1992 127248 LAN Blackburn
  .... .... 1672 .... 127248 LAN Shap
  1880 1890 1860 1900 142174 WRY Leeds
  1764 1764 ALL  1770 113611 WYK Hatfield
  1681 1785 1650 1700 170348 YKS Almondbury
  1673 1992 1673 1992 127248 YKS Craven
  1775 1901 1901 1992 127248 YKS Kirk By Malham
  1748 1775 1748 1775 127248 YKS Long Preston
  1843 .... .... 1843 146935 YKS Southeram
MALLOCH
  1792 1992 1700 1792 158143 PER Methven
MALLON
  1819 1881 1750 1820 176451 LAN Manchester
MALLORD
  1680 1740 1700 1750 176281 MDX Islington
MALLOTT
  1780 1800 1750 1800 167088 LND Marylebone
MALLOWES
  1539 1612 1500 1650 107980 SFK Eye
MALLOWS
  1836 1930 ALL  1836 146226 NFK Garboldisham
MALONEY
  1838 1896 1800 1900 133043 CLA Whitegate
  1800 1860 1800 1860 121339 IRL ???
  .... .... 1860 1900 125555 LAN Manchester
  1880 1910 ALL  ALL  162620 LND Battersea
  1900 .... 1850 1900 175684 MDX Marylebone
  1859 1992 ALL  1859 153729 MDX Stepney
```

Known From	To	Researching From	To	Ref	Cty	Place
MALONEY contd.						
1847	1900	1800	1992	160156	SOM	Publow
1867	1921	1800	1867	173339	STS	Wolverhampton
MALPAS						
1824	....	....	....	167444	WOR	Claine
MALPASS						
1860	1880	1600	1860	160784	GLS	Leonard Stanley
1821	1992	1776	1821	163813	STS	Madeley
1700	1850	....	....	176591	STS	Madeley
MALPRESS						
1755	1992	1700	1992	144525	ALL	ALL
MALROY						
1800	....	1750	1820	148288	AYR	Ayr
1800	....	1750	1820	148288	AYR	Stewarton
MALT						
....	....	1550	1800	176230	SFK	Brandon
1670	1770	1640	1770	135941	SFK	Lakenheath
1774	1774	1740	1750	124974	WIL	Baydon
MALTBY						
1550	1992	ALL	1992	144533	ALL	ALL
1700	1992	ALL	1700	168955	LIN	ALL
....	....	1600	1750	141275	LIN	North East
1798	1803	....	....	129747	NFK	North Wotton
1758	....	....	....	129747	NFK	Wiggenhall
MALTBYE						
....	1705	?	1705	128910	LIN	Willingham By Stow
MALTSHIRE						
1770	1940	....	....	128996	CAM	Thorney
MALTWOOD						
1857	....	....	....	117579	MDX	Hackney
MALYN						
1598	1599	1500	1600	152110	CAM	Haddenham
MAN						
1600	1900	1400	1900	105333	DEV	Buckland In The Moor
1600	1900	1400	1900	105333	DEV	Holne
1600	1900	1400	1900	105333	DEV	Ilsington
1600	1900	1400	1900	105333	DEV	Lydford
1600	1900	1400	1900	105333	DEV	Widecombe In The Moor
MANCEAU						
1859	1907	ALL	1827	124346	T&W	Sunderland
MANCHEE						
....	....	1700	....	159824	ENG	ALL
MANCHER						
....	....	1660	1690	103713	CAM	Cambridge
MANCHESTER						
1840	1880	1800	1900	111147	LEI	ALL
?	?	?	?	144576	WYK	Huddersfield
?	?	?	?	144576	WYK	Mletham
MANCHETTE						
1867	1909	....	....	121967	LEI	Melton Mowbray
MANCILL						
1773	1796	1700	1800	159905	OXF	Swalcliffe
MANDELLI						
ALL	....	....	....	156221	KEN	ALL
MANDER						
1790	1900	1550	1790	144584	NTH	???
1790	1900	1550	1790	144584	OXF	???
1617	1675	1550	1616	102830	WAR	Aston Cantelow
1790	1900	1550	1790	144584	WAR	Frankton
1790	1900	1550	1790	144584	WAR	Marton
1730	1740	1650	1730	133167	WAR	Wolverton
MANDERS						
1914	1992	1600	1914	108812	KID	Naas
MANDERSON						
....	....	1700	1992	167223	CON	Mawnan
....	....	1700	1900	167223	ELN	Dunbar
1836	1923	1815	1836	118133	SCT	Gorbals
MANDEVILLE						
....	....	ALL	ALL	144592	ALL	Name Study
1800	1840	1700	1800	161365	NTT	Carburton
MANDRY						
ALL	ALL	ALL	ALL	144606	ALL	ALL
1790	1920	....	1790	113891	LND	Westminster
MANE						
1674	1674	1670	1795	150053	NTH	ALL
MANETTE						
....	....	1700	1886	155136	LND	???
MANFIELD						
1788	....	1750	1800	175684	LND	City
MANGALLS						
1820	1850	1800	1870	144622	YKS	Wath On Dearne
MANGHAM						
1860	1910	1850	1915	144622	YKS	Kilnhurst
1750	1810	1650	1850	144622	YKS	Rawmarsh
1860	1910	1850	1915	144622	YKS	Swinton
MANHIRE						
....	?	1700	1900	144347	CON	St Austell
MANHOOD						
....	....	ALL	ALL	154385	ALL	Name Study
....	....	....	....	154385	ESS	Plaistow
MANICOM						
1830	1852	1700	1837	176370	DEV	South
MANIFIELD						
1811	1923	ALL	1811	103039	NTT	Retford
MANIFOLD						
....	....	1800	ALL	164615	CHS	Hyde
1720	1740	1600	1992	167592	FLN	Hawarden
MANION						
....	1890	....	....	126276	IRL	Galway
1849	1871	1851	1881	126276	LEI	Whitwick
1871	1917	1871	1900	126276	WYK	Denaby Main
1871	1871	1871	1881	126276	WYK	Normanton
MANKTELOW						
1794	....	1750	1850	154962	KEN	Whitstable
MANLEY						
1800	1992	1600	1800	144649	CHS	Wrenbury
1680	1870	1600	1992	114596	DEV	Cheriton Fitzpaine
1700	1800	1500	1800	144657	DEV	Hemyock
1791	1850	ALL	1791	126721	DEV	Tiverton
....	....	1751	1851	154040	DEV	Upottery
1851	1871	1851	1871	154040	DEV	Yarcombe
....	....	1810	....	174963	ENG	???
1682	1686	1600	1700	144649	FLN	Erbistock
1885	1933	1885	1933	154040	GAL	Aberdare
....	....	1871	1900	154040	GNT	Blaenavon
1841	....	....	....	144673	LND	East
MANLY						
1747	1768	ALL	1768	127000	CHS	Acton By Nantwich
1650	1800	1650	1800	170488	KID	Timolin
MANN						
1764	1804	1764	1992	172596	CON	Paul
1764	1804	1764	1992	172596	CON	St Buryan
?	?	?	?	141003	DEV	???
1860	1940	1860	1940	119059	DOR	Poole
1850	1992	1750	1992	157651	DUR	Tyneside
1800	1850	1700	1800	167649	GLS	Hartpury
....	....	1780	1849	133604	GLS	Tetbury
1800	1900	....	....	133698	HAM	West Cowes
ALL	1800	....	....	133698	KEN	Chislehurst
1840	1992	1840	1992	144703	LEI	ALL
1872	1931	....	....	144711	LND	Tooting
....	....	1765	1857	144738	MDX	London
1781	1817	....	....	157554	NFK	Swanton Morley
1770	1840	1700	1900	144703	NTH	ALL
....	....	1770	1805	110450	NTH	Weedon Bec
1820	1900	1600	1820	148296	SFK	South
....	....	1700	1850	140627	SFK	Cookley
1800	1900	1800	1870	140236	SFK	Kersey
1750	1965	....	....	137820	SHI	Fetlar
1720	1965	....	....	137820	SHI	Mid Yell
1760	1965	....	....	137820	SHI	North Yell
1758	1965	....	....	137820	SHI	Northmavine
1720	1965	....	....	137820	SHI	South Yell
1736	1966	1700	1900	119059	SRY	Abinger
1800	1900	1700	1800	144681	SRY	Epsom
1766	1893	1799	1893	119059	SRY	Godalming
....	....	1821	1847	114308	SSX	Brighton
....	....	1861	1992	144738	SSX	Brighton
....	....	1765	1805	144738	SSX	Burwash
1787	1871	1800	1900	101508	SSX	Heathfield
....	1700	....	....	174564	SSX	???
1870	1900	1850	1870	176583	STS	Briarly Hill
1880	....	1870	1900	144703	STS	Burton On Trent
1870	1900	1850	1870	176583	STS	Dudley
1870	1900	1850	1870	176583	STS	Quarry Hill
1800	1820	1700	1900	144703	WAR	ALL
1873	1944	1700	1870	122114	WAR	Birmingham
1790	1860	1790	1860	140724	WAR	Birmingham
1790	1850	1650	1800	106313	WAR	Harbury
1757	1822	1650	1756	131245	WAR	Stretton On Dunsmore
....	....	1700	1899	115975	WIL	East
1850	....	1770	1861	170267	YKS	Holbeck
1848	....	1700	1880	109223	YKS	Knostrope
1700	1898	1700	1812	139270	YKS	Leeds

Known From	To	Researching From	To	Ref	Cty	Place
MANN contd.						
1809	1817	1770	1851	170267	YKS	Leeds
MANNAKEE						
....	....	ALL	ALL	136751	ALL	Name Study
MANNERING						
1760	1860	1700	1900	131431	KEN	Bethesden
1800	1850	1800	1850	130400	KEN	Boxley
1850	1920	1850	1900	130400	KEN	Maidstone
1800	1860	1750	1860	131431	MDX	London
MANNERS						
1870	1955	1800	1870	144746	BRK	Windsor
1830	1890	1800	1900	125032	BRK	Woodley
....	....	ALL	1769	119326	MLN	Newbattle
....	....	1000	1992	170232	NBL	ALL
....	1895	1800	1895	144746	NBL	Belford
1802	1992	1700	1802	144754	SSX	Hurstpierpoint
1541	1955	1820	1992	161861	WIL	Heddington
MANNING						
1900	1992	ALL	ALL	135321	CAM	Kings Lynn
1822	1880	?	1822	144800	CAM	March
1892	1992	1850	1892	161861	CAM	Southery
1815	1840	1750	1840	128449	COR	Arcahan
1815	1840	1750	1840	128449	COR	Dunmanway
1693	1743	1600	1743	133000	DEV	Axmouth
1825	....	....	1825	135089	DEV	Exeter
1840	1923	ALL	ALL	121398	DEV	South Molton
1809	1883	1700	1809	167118	DEV	Sutcombe
1800	1840	ALL	ALL	121398	DEV	Swimbridge
1900	1992	....	....	123773	ESS	Walthamstow
1682	1725	ALL	1682	125121	ESS	Wivenhoe
1577	1642	....	1723	142859	GLS	Minchinhampton
....	....	1800	1900	134546	LAN	Heaton
1900	....	1900	....	123773	LND	Bethnal Green
1838	1838	1838	1992	106666	LND	City
1825	1992	1800	1900	144797	LND	Ratcliff
1806	1838	1700	1806	145823	MDX	Bloomsbury
....	....	ALL	ALL	144762	MDX	Hampstead
1806	1838	1700	1806	145823	MDX	Poplar
1854	1992	1700	1854	144762	MDX	St Pancras
1892	1992	1850	1892	161861	NFK	Southery
1757	1783	1750	1790	107360	NTH	Harlestone
1797	1870	ALL	1797	115126	NTH	Moulton
1798	1824	1700	1850	144797	ROS	Kilbride
1680	1780	1600	1680	155276	SFK	Barking
....	1816	1790	1816	128724	SFK	Barrow
1850	1870	1790	1850	128724	SFK	Bury St Edmunds
....	....	1600	1682	172871	SFK	Whepstead
....	....	1750	1820	129356	SFK	Wrentham
1856	1992	1750	1850	135763	STS	Wolverhampton
1819	1850	....	1851	118931	TIP	???
1800	1860	1750	1860	107611	WAR	Aston
1858	1885	1851	1885	118931	WAR	Warick
1880	1992	....	....	144800	YKS	Halifax
MANNION						
1901	....	ALL	ALL	174017	GAL	???
1885	1900	1850	1920	123145	LOG	Longford
1749	1798	1700	1824	144797	ROS	Kilbride
1861	1992	ALL	1861	174017	YKS	Huddersfield
MANNIX						
1850	1905	....	....	144673	IRL	???
1850	1905	....	....	144673	LND	East
MANNS						
1841	1902	1700	1841	139025	SAL	???
1841	1902	1700	1841	139025	STS	???
MANNY						
1300	1400	....	....	128147	KEN	Tunstall
MANOURY						
1600	1699	....	....	137960	MDX	London
MANSBRIDGE						
....	....	ALL	ALL	144819	ALL	Name Study
MANSDEN						
1750	1900	1750	1900	125237	LAN	Darwen
MANSEL						
1040	1908	ALL	ALL	100536	WLS	???
MANSELL						
1825	1980	1800	1950	138096	GLS	Sheepscombe
1662	1662	1650	1700	111414	MGY	Berriew
1850	ALL	....	....	142158	MON	Trevethin
....	....	1750	1850	143502	SAL	ALL
1753	1753	1700	1800	111414	SAL	Asterley
1763	1813	1700	1851	111414	SAL	Pontesbury
1820	1861	1820	1891	111414	SAL	Westbury
1776	1860	....	....	144568	SAL	???
1750	1800	1730	1800	146803	SRY	Farnham
MANSELL contd.						
1855	1917	1800	1855	152463	STS	Burton On Trent
1845	1876	1845	1876	141291	STS	Sedgley
....	....	ALL	1900	165646	STS	Tipton
1825	1845	1700	1876	141291	STS	Wolverhampton
....	....	1882	1904	118850	WAR	Birmingham
1773	1840	1650	1773	150150	WAR	Preston On Stour
MANSER						
1905	1935	....	1930	137642	KEN	West
1850	1930	1850	1930	136484	LND	Shoreditch
MANSERGH						
1670	1900	1600	1670	152196	WES	Kirby Lonsdale
MANSFIELD						
1762	ALL	ALL	1840	116734	CAM	Balsham
1762	ALL	ALL	1840	116734	CAM	Linton
1833	1970	ALL	1833	126942	ESS	Henham
1840	....	....	1840	164011	HRT	Hatfield
1844	....	....	....	133094	IRL	Cork
1727	1865	1600	1865	137626	LEI	Desford
1892	1920	1892	1920	123773	LND	Bethnal Green
1802	1870	ALL	1802	100897	LND	Lambeth
1820	1900	....	....	111368	SRY	Bermondsey
1933	1992	....	....	126187	???	Bristol
MANSLEY						
1824	1960	1750	1900	131709	LAN	Leigh
MANSON						
1780	1905	1700	1800	126500	BAN	Wick Bower
1780	1900	....	....	126497	CAI	Bower
1800	1899	ALL	1850	127000	CAI	Canisbay
1790	1808	1700	1855	166049	CAI	Mey-Canisbay
....	....	1700	1900	164410	CAI	Thurso
1869	1922	1800	1900	105414	CAI	Wick
1836	1869	....	1870	169412	CHS	Over
1900	1992	1850	1900	164410	LAN	Liverpool
1792	1992	....	....	128643	OKI	Westray
1620	1992	1650	1992	104671	SHI	Bressay
1750	1965	....	....	137820	SHI	Fetlar
1720	1965	....	....	137820	SHI	Mid Yell
1760	1965	....	....	137820	SHI	North Yell
1758	1965	....	....	137820	SHI	Northmavine
1720	1965	....	....	137820	SHI	South Yell
1620	1992	1650	1992	104671	SHI	Unst
MANSTONE						
1731	1900	1500	1900	170216	DOR	ALL
MANT						
1860	1900	ALL	1860	135607	SRY	Woking
MANTELL						
....	....	ALL	ALL	144835	ALL	Name Study
1694	1855	ALL	ALL	161551	KEN	ALL
....	....	1800	1900	153281	SOM	Bridgewater
MANTERFIELD						
1752	1780	1700	1900	144843	LIN	Bassingham
1780	1810	1700	1900	144843	LIN	Harmston
1800	1850	1700	1900	144843	NTT	Newark
MANTHORP						
1460	1992	ALL	ALL	129003	SFK	ALL
MANTHORPE						
1802	1910	1600	1802	133132	NFK	Norwich
MANTLE						
....	....	1768	1823	161667	KEN	Dartford
1720	1760	ALL	....	104515	RUT	Market Overton
MANTON						
1705	1768	ALL	1800	173177	CAM	Levrington
....	....	1700	....	137456	NTH	Cottesbrooke
1814	1992	1700	1814	170747	RUT	Market Overton
MANTZ						
1848	1910	1848	1910	144541	KEN	Deptford
1750	1920	1750	1920	144541	MDX	London
MANUEL						
1870	1950	1850	1950	135801	NTT	Kersall
1800	1850	1800	1850	167924	SAL	Owestry
1800	1850	....	....	106674	WLS	Llanidloes
1900	1980	....	....	106674	YKS	Middlesborough
1850	1900	....	....	106674	YKS	Sheffield
1850	1960	1700	1900	135801	YKS	Sheffield
MANUELL						
....	....	1700	1886	155136	LND	ALL
....	....	1700	1886	155136	NTT	Tuxford
MANVELL						
ALL	ALL	....	....	153397	HAM	ALL
ALL	ALL	....	....	153397	SRY	ALL
ALL	ALL	....	....	153397	SSX	ALL
MANZINI						
1870	1890	1850	1992	167592	FLN	Buckley

Known From	To	Researching From	To	Ref	Cty	Place
MANZINI contd.						
1890	1900	1850	1992	167592	LAN	Birkenhead
1900	1910	1900	1992	167592	STS	Potteries
MANZONI						
1890	1900	1800	1992	167592	CHS	Birkenhead
1880	?	1800	1992	167592	FLN	Buckley
MAP						
....	....	ALL	ALL	153761	ALL	Name Study
MAPLE						
1820	....	1730	1880	135429	DEV	Withycombe Raleigh
1791	1825	1790	1820	154873	KEN	Canterbury
1734	1850	1700	1992	120499	KEN	Littlebourne
1791	1825	1790	1820	154873	KEN	Littlebourne
1780	1930	ALL	ALL	113859	SSX	Thakeham
MAPLEDORAM						
1740	1840	1700	1850	126268	DEV	East
MAPLES						
1663	1777	....	....	121835	LIN	Navenby
MAPLESDEN						
....	....	1500	1992	167576	SSX	Maplesden
MAPLETHORP						
1770	1850	ALL	ALL	120529	LIN	Billinghay
MAPLETHORPE						
1770	1850	ALL	ALL	120529	LIN	Billinghay
MAPP						
1820	1860	....	....	164631	STS	Penkridge
MAPPLES						
1813	....	....	....	172820	LIN	New Sleaford
MAPPLETHORP						
1822	1850	....	1850	102822	LND	Central
MAPSTON						
1809	1820	1700	1810	134260	GLS	Bristol
1820	1840	ALL	ALL	134260	SOM	Compton Martin
MAPSTONE						
1867	1980	ALL	ALL	153516	SOM	Bishop Sutton
1800	1850	1600	1800	110329	SOM	Mendip
MAQUAY						
1750	1775	1775	1875	119970	DUB	Dublin
MARA						
....	....	ALL	ALL	158747	ALL	Name Study
MARBECK						
....	....	ALL	ALL	144894	ALL	Name Study
....	....	ALL	ALL	157406	LAN	???
MARCER						
1798	1900	1600	1900	124834	NTT	East Leake
MARCH						
1580	1690	ALL	1700	101079	DEV	Sherford
1679	1705	....	....	151351	DOR	Okeford Fitzpaine
1792	1839	ALL	1792	175080	GLS	Bisley
1838	....	....	....	170623	LND	Marylebone
1860	....	ALL	ALL	156558	LND	Strand
....	....	1700	1799	142409	NFK	???
1700	1800	1600	1700	142670	SOM	Cucklington
1750	1850	ALL	ALL	154830	SRY	Dorking
1754	....	....	....	117579	STS	Sutton Coldfield
1750	1820	1600	1750	106054	WAR	Sutton Coldfield
1769	1830	1600	1790	162507	YKS	Fremington
MARCHAND						
1600	1699	....	....	137960	MDX	London
MARCHANT						
1884	1973	1955	1975	143715	CAM	Peterborough
1789	1940	....	....	128996	CAM	Thorney
1800	1880	1700	1800	165123	DEV	Beern
1846	1855	ALL	1900	143715	GLS	Cirencester
1816	1852	1816	1900	143715	GLS	Stroud
1865	1916	1700	1865	115460	KEN	Edenbridge
1876	1984	1600	1876	174548	KEN	Folkestone
1669	1992	1362	1670	163945	KEN	Rother Valley
1823	1864	ALL	ALL	121754	LND	Eastcheap
1850	1860	1850	1860	152773	MDX	Bethnal Green
1816	1860	ALL	ALL	124311	MDX	Shoreditch
1850	1850	1800	1850	152773	MDX	Spitalfields
1884	1973	1855	1975	143715	NTH	Peterborough
1680	1720	1670	1740	142018	SOM	Shepton Mallet
1800	....	....	....	101613	SRY	Lambeth
....	....	1880	1992	135844	SRY	Lambeth
....	....	1700	1850	121193	SSX	Central
1733	1870	....	....	113093	SSX	Brightling
1790	1870	....	....	135844	SSX	Icklesham
1940	1949	1940	1949	113743	SSX	Peasmarsh
1780	1840	1700	1780	104809	SSX	Westham
1803	1992	1800	1860	162809	YKS	Halifax
MARCHBANKS						
1780	1809	1700	1850	135348	CAM	Wisbech

Known From	To	Researching From	To	Ref	Cty	Place
MARCHE						
1750	1790	1700	1750	159115	GSY	St Peter Port
MARCHMENT						
1810	1869	1700	1810	162035	HAM	Winchester
1835	1840	1700	1840	103268	WIL	Upavon
MARCUS						
1810	1880	1700	1810	109959	LND	Spitalfields
MARDEL						
1890	1992	1890	1992	121320	ENG	ALL
MARDEL-FERREIRA						
1890	1992	1890	1992	121320	ENG	ALL
MARDELL						
1850	?	ALL	ALL	107352	HRT	ALL
MARDEN						
1640	1714	....	....	127426	KEN	Harrietsham
1730	1730	....	....	127426	KEN	Lenham
MARDLIN						
1791	1890	1780	1920	144908	BDF	Blunham
1923	1992	1900	1992	144908	BDF	Great Barford
1832	1850	1820	1870	144908	BDF	Leighton Buzzard
1607	1635	1600	1680	144908	BDF	Lidlington
1754	1780	1720	1800	144908	BDF	Old Warden
1580	1606	1500	1650	144908	BDF	Ridgmont
1850	1923	1830	1940	144908	BDF	Turvey
1684	1714	1650	1750	144908	BDF	Wilshamstead
1840	1880	1800	1840	173444	HRT	Stevenage
MARE						
?	....	....	....	116092	DEV	Exeter
1802	1812	1795	1860	165441	STS	Hanley
1700	1800	1700	1800	146226	STS	Potteries
MARENGO						
....	....	ALL	ALL	147451	ALL	Name Study
MARET						
1650	1800	....	....	119105	JSY	ALL
MARFELL						
....	....	ALL	ALL	144916	ALL	Name Study
MARFLEET						
....	....	ALL	ALL	144924	ALL	Name Study
MARFLITT						
1778	1808	1750	1800	147311	NYK	Hutton Buscel
MARGAM						
....	1908	....	1908	142794	GLA	Mountain Ash
MARGERISON						
1808	1808	1808	1808	143286	LAN	Blackburn
1600	1780	ALL	ALL	144932	LAN	Blackburn
1720	1800	ALL	ALL	144932	LAN	Samlesbury
MARGERSON						
1863	1863	ALL	ALL	143618	MDX	Camden Town
MARGETTS						
1727	1920	ALL	ALL	169528	OXF	Churchill
MARGRAVE						
1604	1810	....	1735	109622	LIN	Crowle
MARGRETT						
....	....	ALL	ALL	144940	ALL	Name Study
ALL	ALL	ALL	ALL	144940	ALL	ALL
MARINER						
1800	1824	ALL	ALL	113360	HAM	Twyford
MARIOTT						
1591	1591	....	....	127426	KEN	Rodmersham
1752	1868	1750	1868	107360	NTH	Blisworth
1763	1763	1740	1765	107360	NTH	Long Buckby
MARIS						
1779	1803	1750	1780	162396	CAM	Linton
MARJESON						
....	....	1700	1740	177393	YKS	Owthorne
MARK						
1815	1839	....	....	146560	ANT	Carnbeg
1800	1900	1600	1992	130125	CUL	Brampton
1761	1814	1730	1814	159905	CUL	Cumwhinton
1713	1725	1600	1992	130125	CUL	Dalston
1746	1850	1600	1992	130125	CUL	Thursby
1860	1890	1830	1992	130125	LAN	Liverpool
1863	1964	1964	1992	146560	LKS	Coatbride
MARKE						
1730	1736	1700	1740	128961	ESS	Coggeshall
MARKEL						
1792	1812	1740	1812	172871	SFK	Beyton
1792	1812	1740	1812	172871	SFK	Tostock
MARKER						
....	....	ALL	ALL	144959	ALL	Name Study
MARKES						
1830	1900	1790	1830	144223	IRL	Armagh
MARKEY						
1838	1870	1800	1870	168920	LAN	Manchester

Known From	To	Researching From	To	Ref	Cty	Place
MARKHAM						
1830	1858	ALL	1830	146986	BDF	Dunstable
1650	1992	1600	1790	124796	BKM	Tingewick
1760	1860	....	....	143030	BKM	Woolstone
....	....	1700	1900	101958	CAM	ALL
1805	1805	1700	1804	131245	LIN	Frieston
1700	1992	1600	1700	102342	LIN	Laughton
....	....	1700	1850	101958	SFK	ALL
1800	1900	1600	1800	168653	SFK	ALL
1789	1806	1789	1832	164232	SFK	Sudbourne
MARKILLY						
1666	1940	....	....	128996	CAM	Thorney
MARKLEW						
1870	1943	1850	1943	165441	STS	Cannock
1640	1960	1550	1640	161853	STS	Lichfield
1840	1890	1837	1900	165441	STS	Lichfield
MARKLEY						
1840	....	....	....	127353	HUN	Stilton
MARKLOVE						
1650	ALL	....	....	142158	GLS	Cromhall
MARKS						
....	1818	ALL	ALL	129933	CHS	Nantwich
....	1818	ALL	ALL	129933	DOR	Poole
1840	....	....	....	175358	DUB	ALL
1750	1800	1700	1775	152579	HAM	Isle Of Wight
1697	1733	1600	1697	145459	HAM	South Stoneham
1754	1772	....	....	127957	IOW	Shalfleet
1900	1910	ALL	ALL	119180	KEN	Bromley
1855	1950	1700	1900	119180	LND	East
....	....	1700	1850	145157	LND	Tottenham
1855	1950	1700	1950	119180	MDX	North
....	1836	ALL	1836	127000	SAL	Tilstock
....	....	1800	1900	146110	WMD	ALL
MARKWELL						
....	....	ALL	ALL	144975	ALL	Name Study
1850	1992	1700	1850	157872	LND	???
1750	1825	1700	1750	154873	NBL	Holy Island
MARKWICK						
1860	....	1860	....	135488	SSX	Brighton
1760	1830	1650	1830	121126	SSX	Hooe
1712	1840	1840	1860	156140	SSX	Ucfield
1600	1950	1700	1890	144983	SSX	Uckfield
MARLAND						
1770	1790	1770	1790	107522	LAN	Ashton Under Lyme
1870	1900	....	1870	118451	LAN	Ashton Under Lyne
1750	1800	1750	1800	152404	LAN	Hulton
....	....	1750	1850	141984	LIN	Alkborough
1790	1885	1790	1885	107522	WRY	Todmorden
MARLBOROUGH						
1830	1909	1770	1880	179256	HRT	Bushey
1830	1909	1770	1880	179256	HRT	Elstree
1844	1980	1800	1980	145009	MDX	Stepney
MARLES						
....	....	1858	1867	154040	DEV	Exeter
MARLEY						
1800	1992	1700	1800	145017	DEV	ALL
....	....	1500	1780	138614	DEV	???
1850	1860	....	....	145025	SOM	Exford
1780	1960	1700	1992	149209	SOM	Exford
1800	1880	ALL	1800	132829	T&W	Newcastle Upon Tyne
MARLIN						
1709	1709	....	....	135437	GLS	Frocester
MARLOR						
1739	1739	....	....	159492	LAN	Oldham
1873	1959	1800	1880	146102	LAN	Salford
1820	1950	1750	1820	146102	LAN	Worsley
MARLOW						
1730	1992	1550	1900	107514	HAM	ALL
1780	1912	1750	1920	136719	HAM	East Oakley
1850	1880	1850	1880	170119	HAM	Ellingham
1771	?	ALL	1771	171476	NFK	Bexwell
1910	1980	1698	1860	145491	NTH	Desborough
....	....	ALL	1800	114308	NTH	Kislingbury
1800	1992	1700	1992	165344	WAR	Willoughby
....	....	1800	1950	122203	WAR	???
1730	1992	1550	1900	107514	WIL	ALL
MARLTON						
....	....	1660	1760	103713	SFK	Wickhambrook
MARNELL						
....	....	ALL	ALL	107956	ALL	Name Study
MARNER						
1760	1833	1720	1880	105333	SSX	Birdham
MAROLLEAU						
....	....	1700	1750	150967	LND	Spitalfields

Known From	To	Researching From	To	Ref	Cty	Place
MARPLES						
1825	1992	1700	1825	120383	DBY	Marsh Lane
1871	1911	....	....	108901	SYK	Sheffield
MARQUAND						
1750	1820	....	....	176583	GSY	St Peterport
1540	1900	1540	1950	125296	GSY	???
MARQUICK						
1490	1710	1440	1500	156140	SSX	Barcombe
MARQUISS						
1849	1932	1700	1849	146072	WIL	Box
MARR						
1766	1860	1700	1860	139378	AYR	Coylton
1620	1650	....	1650	137634	NTT	Blyth
1835	1864	1800	1835	100757	???	???
MARRIAGE						
....	....	ALL	ALL	140228	ALL	Name Study
1650	1992	ALL	ALL	140228	ALL	ALL
....	1830	1800	1900	128961	ESS	Chelmsford
1810	....	....	....	145068	ESS	Hornchurch
MARRIOT						
1600	1850	1600	1850	167924	BDF	Upper Gravenhurst
1758	1776	1700	1758	149195	LEI	Wreak Valley
1740	1800	1740	1800	118540	NTT	ALL
MARRIOTT						
1880	1945	1880	1945	166146	BKM	???
1719	1940	....	....	128996	CAM	Thorney
....	....	1700	1900	101184	DBY	North East
....	....	1700	1800	101184	DBY	Ashover
1850	1992	ALL	1992	179205	DBY	Stretton
....	?	?	?	127442	DBY	???
1784	1915	1784	1915	147621	FLN	Halkyn
1835	1870	1835	1850	106798	KEN	Maidstone
1700	....	1600	1900	131024	MDX	London
1820	1850	1750	1850	122599	NFK	Yarmouth
1790	....	ALL	1790	143278	NTH	Everdon
1748	1809	ALL	1992	115126	NTH	Milton Malsor
....	1800	....	1800	177695	NTH	Wilby
1880	1945	1880	1945	166146	NTH	???
1832	1895	1700	1832	169889	NTT	Bulwell Nottm
1789	....	ALL	ALL	105481	NTT	Bulwell
....	....	....	1814	134902	NTT	Darlton
1814	....	1814	....	160164	NTT	East Bridgeford
....	?	?	?	127442	NTT	Normanton
1850	1860	1700	1900	121762	YKS	ALL
1770	....	1720	1770	108510	YKS	Batley
1770	....	1720	1770	108510	YKS	Dewsbury
....	....	1870	1900	177768	???	Glasgow
MARRIS						
1740	1829	ALL	1850	152838	LIN	Keelby
MARRISON						
1565	1910	1565	1992	145076	ALL	ALL
MARROTT						
....	1700	ALL	1700	134511	NTT	Calverton
MARROW						
1850	1860	1800	1920	105732	LAN	Wigan
1820	1920	1700	1920	149780	LAN	Wigan
MARRS						
1906	1992	1872	1906	145084	CMA	Wigton
1828	1939	ALL	ALL	145092	DFS	South
MARSDEN						
....	....	ALL	ALL	145122	ALL	Name Study
....	....	ALL	ALL	145122	ALL	ALL
1805	1850	....	....	109347	DBY	Bakewell
1810	1880	....	....	132756	DBY	Chesterfield
1870	ALL	....	....	132756	DUR	Hetton Le Hole
1840	ALL	....	....	132756	DUR	New Silksworth
1840	ALL	....	....	132756	DUR	Ryhope
1840	ALL	....	....	132756	DUR	Sunderland
1840	ALL	....	....	132756	DUR	Tunstall
1305	1600	1305	1450	145130	LAN	Alkincotes
....	....	1800	1880	134848	LAN	Birkdale
1850	1992	1700	1850	128554	LAN	Blackburn
1800	1880	1880	1992	162256	LAN	Darwen
1927	1939	ALL	1927	146315	LAN	Great Harwood
1770	1790	1700	1800	120049	LAN	Kirkham
1800	....	1800	....	109347	LAN	Liverpool
1870	1885	1800	1900	145254	LAN	Manchester
1825	1850	1800	1880	137782	LAN	Mawdesley
1508	1800	1508	1633	145130	LAN	Tockholes
1800	1880	1880	1992	162256	LAN	Tockholes
1425	1600	1425	1520	145130	LAN	Whalley
1561	1900	1620	1800	145130	LAN	Wigan
1723	1789	1700	1830	176621	WYK	Farsley
1845	....	1750	1860	100390	WYK	Heaton

Known From	To	Researching From	To	Ref	Cty	Place
MARSDEN contd.						
1853	1873	ALL	1858	146315	YKS	Austwick
1880	1934	1800	1880	135364	YKS	Bradford
1881	1966	....	....	151718	YKS	Emley
1770	1820	1650	1850	171484	YKS	Guiseley
?	?	?	?	119997	YKS	Hudd
1840	1850	1840	1850	145122	YKS	Knaresborough
1780	1880	1775	1780	112364	YKS	Leeds
1850	1950	1850	1900	145122	YKS	Leeds
1675	1992	1500	1992	145114	YKS	Leeds
1810	1854	1750	1900	171484	YKS	Leeds
1853	1873	ALL	1853	146315	YKS	Long Preston
1800	1927	1800	ALL	145122	YKS	Masham
1750	1800	1750	1800	145122	YKS	Middlesmoor
1849	1851	1850	1880	170348	YKS	Rawmarsh
1713	....	1680	1750	170348	YKS	Thryberg
1871	1900	1800	1871	135364	YKS	Tong Street
1675	1992	1500	1992	145114	YKS	Wakefield
MARSDIN						
1820	1910	ALL	ALL	142611	YKS	Thorne
MARSH						
1708	1779	1660	1710	162396	CAM	Linton
1700	1800	....	....	164631	CMA	Linton
1760	1809	1760	1809	129216	DBY	Beighton
1815	1861	1700	1815	139386	DBY	Killamarsh
1800	1889	....	....	108057	DBY	Wirksworth
1729	1992	1700	1800	145149	DOR	Beaminster
1871	1906	ALL	1871	175862	HAM	Bishops Waltham
1871	1906	ALL	1871	175862	HAM	Corhampton
1700	1859	1700	1820	115797	HAM	East Meon
1800	1930	1700	1800	110116	HAM	Froxfield
1792	1851	1700	1792	168033	HAM	Gosport
1886	1928	1886	1968	173762	HAM	Kingworth
1792	1851	1700	1792	168033	HAM	Portsea
1790	1916	ALL	1790	173304	HAM	Soberton
....	....	1760	1900	145173	HAM	Twyford
....	....	1850	1900	145173	HAM	Winchester
1900	....	....	....	144169	HEF	Brampton-Abbotts
1865	....	....	....	144169	HEF	Bridstow
1800	....	....	....	144169	HEF	Hentland
1894	....	....	....	144169	HEF	Hereford
1861	....	....	....	144169	HEF	Hillgates
1871	....	....	....	144169	HEF	Little Bigglestone
1829	....	....	....	144169	HEF	Llanwarne
1863	....	....	....	144169	HEF	Much Birch
1876	....	....	....	144169	HEF	Much-Dewchurch
1881	....	....	....	144169	HEF	Poolsnatch
1777	....	....	....	144169	HEF	Ross On Wye
1777	....	....	....	144169	HEF	Weston
1870	?	1700	1992	167592	HRT	Eastbury
1768	1992	ALL	1992	141585	KEN	Bekesbourne
1768	1992	ALL	1992	141585	KEN	Lymming
1919	1992	1800	1919	145165	KEN	Orpington
1861	1861	1800	1861	105775	KEN	River
1773	1773	1700	1900	141151	KEN	Whitstable
1810	1850	1700	1900	178454	KEN	Woolwich
1820	1861	1820	....	102121	LAN	Bolton
1760	1787	....	....	138851	LAN	Bolton
1812	1992	1850	1912	160911	LAN	Boothstown
1820	1861	1820	1861	102121	LAN	Halliwell
1830	1850	1830	1850	151599	LAN	Liverpool
1800	1900	1600	1799	172006	LAN	St Helens
1841	1992	1700	1841	178233	LAN	St Helens
1800	1900	1800	1900	126500	LAN	Wigan
1800	1850	....	....	126497	LAN	Wigan
1849	1872	1800	1849	153362	MDX	Poplar
ALL	ALL	ALL	ALL	169838	MGY	ALL
1826	1850	ALL	ALL	169838	MGY	Llanfyllin
1930	....	....	....	144169	NFK	ALL
....	....	1800	....	145688	NFK	Bacton
1880	1935	1880	1935	151599	NTT	Nottingham
1905	1992	1700	1905	111694	NTT	Scarrington
1905	1992	1700	1905	111694	NTT	Screveton
1760	1900	1760	1900	118540	NTT	Southwell
1618	1704	1600	1800	159956	SFK	Walsham Le Willows
1738	1799	1707	1799	107573	SOM	Brushford
1810	1830	....	....	150282	SOM	Dulverton
1709	1752	1700	1752	107573	SOM	Elworthy
1800	1820	1750	1820	158658	SOM	Glastonbury
1826	....	....	....	150282	SOM	Harkwell
1845	1865	1800	1870	163775	SRY	Bermondsey
1796	1797	1790	1840	105333	SRY	Guildford
1842	1928	1822	1928	116653	STS	Rushall
1550	1840	1500	1840	102830	STS	Sedgely
MARSH contd.						
....	....	1700	1850	147613	STS	Sedgley
1612	....	....	1640	160873	STS	Sedgley
1880	1910	....	....	120626	STS	Walsall
1700	....	1600	1900	133590	STS	???
1760	1809	1760	1809	129216	SYK	Harthill
1860	1880	ALL	....	120626	WOR	Dudley
....	....	1804	....	170461	WOR	Kidderminster
....	....	ALL	1890	175080	YKS	Barnsley
1849	1860	1849	1860	151599	YKS	Hull
1820	1920	....	1820	134902	YKS	Sheffield
1799	1848	1795	1805	151599	YKS	Sheffield
MARSH-CALDWELL						
1850	?	1800	1992	167592	STS	Audley
1850	?	1800	1992	167592	STS	Newcastle Under Lyme
MARSHAL						
1716	1745	1700	1850	176397	KRS	Kinross
1808	1808	....	....	168203	PER	Muckhart
MARSHALL						
1838	1862	1800	1900	144231	AYR	Neilston
1760	1900	....	....	171891	BKM	West Wycombe
1820	1900	ALL	1820	111333	BRK	Brimpton
1840	1880	....	1840	113891	BRK	Brimpton
1780	1810	1700	1810	124605	BRK	Reading
1843	1845	1843	1845	145181	CAM	Chatteris
1675	1940	....	....	128996	CAM	Thorney
1750	1780	1600	1992	167592	CHS	Northwich
1750	1780	1600	1992	167592	CHS	Weaverham
1750	1780	1600	1992	167592	CHS	Wilbraham
1836	1980	1600	1850	170607	CON	Looe
1710	1710	1650	1775	133450	CON	S Gennys
....	....	1680	1992	173592	CON	St Gennys
1857	1880	1850	1890	151599	DBY	Derby
1772	1806	ALL	ALL	112275	DBY	Melbourne
1800	1900	1700	1800	107484	DBY	Shirland
1878	1881	1850	1884	145181	DBY	Whittington
1737	1764	ALL	ALL	129933	DEV	Cornwood
1795	1850	1760	1820	137413	DEV	Honiton
1825	1875	....	....	160814	DEV	Ugborough
1808	1992	1700	1800	168386	DNB	Cumbernauld
1875	1992	1700	1875	167967	DUR	Stockton
1780	1800	ALL	1780	131059	ESS	Gt Burstead
1830	1951	....	....	137936	FIF	Central
1890	1992	1890	1992	140635	HAM	Southampton
1814	1814	1750	1820	136042	HRT	Knebworth
1700	1850	ALL	ALL	131873	HRT	Little Hadham
1821	1834	1750	1875	136042	HRT	St Pauls Walden
1570	1853	ALL	1853	137774	KEN	South East
1820	1860	1700	1820	146285	KEN	Ashford
1781	1781	1750	1800	116114	KEN	Brabourne
1791	1895	1600	1800	165476	KEN	Great Chart
....	....	1820	1830	126675	KEN	Snargae
....	....	1800	1899	173274	KEN	Snave
1851	1992	1700	1851	162000	KEN	Swale
1880	1900	1800	1880	126675	KEN	Warehorne
1800	1850	....	....	122378	KEN	West Peckham
1845	1918	1750	1900	114456	LAN	ALL
1880	1900	ALL	ALL	177989	LAN	Ashton Under Lyne
1724	....	ALL	ALL	112461	LAN	Birkdale
1807	1830	ALL	ALL	125202	LAN	Lancaster
1855	1930	1800	1900	178489	LAN	Liverpool
1650	1992	1650	1992	152676	LAN	North Meols
1827	1967	1827	1967	124613	LAN	Ormskirk
1650	1992	1650	1992	152676	LAN	Southport
1864	1987	ALL	1864	115355	LEI	ALL
....	1800	....	....	174564	LEI	Egmanton
1860	1960	ALL	1860	166146	LEI	Walton On The Wolds
1780	1992	ALL	ALL	120650	LIN	North
1900	1992	1700	1900	145246	LIN	Alford
1789	1853	ALL	1820	113611	LIN	Barton On Humber
1666	1747	....	1666	101761	LIN	Croft
1700	1730	1650	1700	169749	LIN	Glentham
1772	1850	....	1772	101761	LIN	Market Rasen
1700	1730	1650	1700	169749	LIN	Normanby
1770	1866	....	....	171654	LKS	Cambusnethan
1889	1984	1984	1992	146560	LKS	Coatbride
....	....	1811	1885	132381	LKS	Glasgow
1840	....	1800	1880	141739	LKS	Glasgow
1908	1992	1880	1908	100757	LKS	Hamilton
....	....	1760	1800	161357	LND	Camden
1850	1875	1800	1900	126535	LND	Poplar
....	....	1760	1800	161357	LND	Soho
1850	1928	1800	1992	113123	LND	Tooting

Known From	To	Researching From	To	Ref	Cty	Place
MARSHALL contd.						
1800	1900	1800	1950	134422	LTN	Linlithgow
1730	1820	1700	1750	176281	MDX	Islington
1799	1839	1700	1799	169935	MDX	Mile End
1799	1850	ALL	1799	169943	MDX	Mile End
1713	....	1700	1725	163775	MDX	Stepney
....	....	1820	1900	159840	MDX	Wapping
1806	1851	1600	1806	158496	NBL	Long Benton
1881	....	1840	1881	145041	NBL	Shields
1755	1992	1755	1992	145238	NFK	Bacton
....	....	1500	1800	171891	NTH	Mansfield
1744	1824	ALL	1744	168742	NTT	Egmanton
1813	1980	1782	1900	121134	NTT	Greasley
1790	1840	1790	1840	137634	NTT	Marnham
1630	1790	....	1790	137634	NTT	Rampton
1872	1872	1820	1900	127361	NTT	Southwell
1750	1800	1600	1750	169862	NYK	Flyingdales
1750	1800	1700	1750	121339	NYK	Gilling
1788	1788	1760	1788	147311	NYK	Hinderwell
1630	1660	1600	1630	121339	NYK	Lythe
1800	1840	1750	1800	165468	PEM	Pembroke
1775	1775	ALL	1775	121355	SCT	Dumfires
1780	1992	ALL	1780	152315	SCT	Mouswald
1811	1859	1775	1811	161810	SOM	Axbridge
1815	1847	1847	1900	112364	SRY	Bermondsey
1742	1992	1740	1948	138312	SRY	Dorking
1925	1989	1800	1925	154539	SRY	Wandsworth
1850	1900	1850	1900	113743	SSX	Brede
1660	1800	ALL	ALL	131164	SSX	Hailsham
1750	1820	1700	1850	121274	SSX	Midhurst
1750	1800	1600	1750	158968	STS	Lichfield
1780	?	1700	1992	167592	STS	Newcastle Under Lyme
1803	1992	1600	1803	158968	STS	Wasall
1790	1924	1750	1992	147982	SUT	Durness
....	....	1700	1829	161659	WAR	ALL
1715	1750	1680	1715	110906	WAR	Barcheston
1770	1800	....	....	100420	WAR	Meriden
1841	1916	1700	1992	113123	WAR	St Marys
1700	1823	....	....	128694	WIL	Netheravon
....	....	ALL	1800	151602	WIL	Rasmbury
1851	1851	1851	....	108901	WOR	Claines
1857	1883	1857	1871	108901	WOR	Ombersley
1908	1908	....	....	108901	WOR	Tibberton
1698	....	....	1698	101761	WRY	Emley
1746	1867	....	....	145211	WRY	Ferrnesby
1850	1950	1835	1950	107522	WRY	Todmorden
....	....	1700	1780	145211	WRY	Yeadon
1808	1808	1750	1900	114456	YKS	ALL
....	....	1650	1750	147613	YKS	Bentham
1727	1827	1600	1900	124257	YKS	Cawood
1771	1773	ALL	1860	158445	YKS	Gate Helmsley
1883	1966	1800	1883	151343	YKS	Goore
1770	1850	ALL	1770	143022	YKS	Huddersfield
1775	1805	1700	1775	138584	YKS	Keighley
1833	1877	1795	....	146706	YKS	Kirkby Moorside
1833	1877	1795	....	146706	YKS	Lastingham
1754	....	1700	....	134589	YKS	Nun Monkton
1780	1860	1700	1800	101044	YKS	Pannal
1789	1851	ALL	1789	145203	YKS	Pannal
1727	1827	1600	1900	124257	YKS	Ryther
....	....	1800	1870	147613	YKS	Sheffield
1883	1966	1800	1883	151343	YKS	Snaith
1772	1811	1740	1780	170348	YKS	Sprotborough
1690	....	ALL	ALL	112461	YKS	Tadcaster
1680	1740	1680	1740	167924	YKS	Warthill
1830	1919	ALL	1830	158445	YKS	Westow
1795	1850	1760	1820	137413	???	Bristol
MARSHALSEA						
1827	1827	....	....	152102	DOR	Whitechurch Canonicorum
MARSHAM						
1840	1940	1750	1840	163732	NFK	Norwich
MARSHFIELD						
....	....	ALL	ALL	145270	ALL	Name Study
1850	1992	1500	1992	145289	ALL	ALL
....	....	1591	1650	145270	DEV	Charleton
1734	1766	....	....	145270	DOR	Broadmayne
....	....	1766	1919	145270	DOR	Langton Matravers
MARSHMAN						
1600	1700	1600	1700	142018	WIL	ALL
1760	1900	1760	1900	108456	WIL	Dilton Marsh
1810	1850	....	....	145297	WIL	Dilton
1650	1750	1600	1750	145297	WIL	Warminster
MARSHMAN contd.						
1760	1900	1760	1900	108456	WIL	Westbury Leigh
1760	1800	....	....	145297	WIL	Westbury
1640	1760	1640	1760	108456	WIL	Westminster
MARSIGILL						
1640	1660	1600	1640	121339	NYK	Lythe
MARSLAND						
1803	1825	1770	1825	147338	WRY	Heptonstall
MARSON						
....	....	1700	1780	172847	DBY	Wirksworth
1780	....	?	1780	103934	HRT	Willian
1603	1881	1600	1885	145300	LIN	Stainby
1800	1830	....	....	172847	NTT	Hickling
1750	1820	1650	....	124184	STS	Acton Trussell
1750	1820	1650	....	124184	STS	Bedsall
1750	1820	1650	1900	124184	STS	Checkley
1750	1820	1650	1900	124184	STS	Church Eaton
1588	1674	1550	1587	102830	STS	Sedgely
1700	1771	1600	1800	145319	STS	Wolverhampton
1793	1992	1830	1992	145319	WAR	Birmingham
1793	1862	1750	1900	145319	WAR	Coventry
1715	1763	?	1763	128910	WAR	Nuneaton
MARSTON						
....	....	ALL	ALL	145327	ALL	Name Study
1692	1889	ALL	1992	168718	LEI	ALL
1820	1828	1828	1870	120650	LEI	Humberston
1735	1820	?	1735	120650	LEI	Thrussington
....	1779	....	....	128910	WAR	Bedworth
....	....	1500	1680	145327	WYK	Bilton
1882	1992	....	....	145327	WYK	Bradford
1844	1879	....	....	145327	WYK	Fewston
1677	1992	....	....	145327	WYK	Hampsthwaite
....	....	1500	1680	145327	WYK	Knaresboro
....	....	1500	1870	145327	YKS	???
MARSTONE						
1750	1860	1700	1750	103675	SOM	Wedmore
MART						
1814	1902	1700	....	123560	KEN	Bexley
MARTAIN						
1837	1871	1600	1837	141100	CON	Breage
1837	1871	1600	1837	141100	CON	Rinsey
MARTEL						
1742	?	1722	1742	114073	ESS	Woodham Walter
MARTEN						
1880	1920	ALL	....	145556	GLS	???
1645	1900	ALL	....	145556	SSX	Ringmer
1828	1860	1828	1992	127183	SSX	Rottingdean
MARTHOLM						
....	....	ALL	1800	159441	LAN	???
MARTIN						
....	....	ALL	ALL	145416	ALL	Name Study
1880	1992	....	....	158348	ABD	Aberdeen
1750	1960	1850	1992	145467	ABD	Coull
1832	1919	ALL	ALL	146757	AYR	New Cumnock
1861	....	ALL	ALL	161608	BDF	Woburn
1786	1814	1700	1800	143693	BKM	Great Marlow
1835	....	1750	1850	143693	BKM	Hambleden
1804	1947	1750	1950	136719	BRK	Hannington
1715	1750	ALL	1740	118737	BRK	Purley
1700	1750	1550	1700	145688	BRK	Warfield
1750	1830	ALL	....	145556	CAM	Downham
1750	1930	ALL	....	145556	CAM	Littleport
1857	1857	1811	1860	109819	CAV	Drummartin
....	....	1700	1770	142670	CMA	Kirkhampton
1791	1913	1600	1791	148040	CON	Davidstow
....	....	1800	1900	116335	CON	Helston
1800	1820	ALL	1850	144533	CON	Helston
1808	1868	1740	1800	178845	CON	Illogan
1800	....	?	?	136999	CON	Kenwyn
1850	1870	1870	1910	178845	CON	Lanner
1874	1929	....	....	176109	CON	Launceston
1620	1850	1620	1850	150126	CON	Mullion St Martin In Meneage
1881	1900	1700	1900	175293	CON	Plymouth
1850	1992	1600	1850	123242	CON	St Agnes
?	?	?	?	111937	CON	St Austell
1770	1884	1600	1770	141100	CON	St Martin In Meneage
1500	1950	1700	1980	104183	CON	Stithians
1641	....	1800	1900	178845	CON	Stithians
1734	1750	1700	1734	173118	CON	Talland
1600	1800	1600	1800	116866	CUL	???
1739	1992	1680	1739	145440	DBY	Derby
1764	1841	ALL	1764	145335	DBY	Pentrich

Known From	To	Researching From	To	Ref	Cty	Place
MARTIN contd.						
1836	ALL	?	?	147869	DEN	???
....	....	1600	1992	137588	DEV	Barnstaple
1809	1992	ALL	1855	115177	DEV	Broad Hembury
1600	....	ALL	ALL	116394	DEV	Burrington
1800	1900	1700	1900	118303	DEV	Modbury
....	....	1810	1850	159840	DEV	N Bovey
....	....	1800	1900	116335	DEV	Plymouth
1805	1900	1780	1900	148652	DEV	Plymouth
1881	1900	1700	1900	175293	DEV	Plymouth
....	....	1700	1810	159840	DEV	Spreton
1900	1992	....	1992	171743	DEV	Upottery
1789	1838	....	....	171654	DFS	Dumfries
1836	1900	1600	1836	158984	DOR	Weymouth
1837	....	....	1837	148830	DOW	Ballybrick
1856	1900	1750	1900	176621	DOW	Newtownlands
1790	....	1600	1790	116637	DUR	Chester Le Street
1777	1820	1600	1777	116637	DUR	Monkwearmouth
1905	1920	....	....	136565	DUR	Stockton On Tees
1830	1915	....	....	146447	DUR	Stockton On Tees
1777	1820	1600	1777	116637	DUR	Sunderland
1850	1900	1900	1950	145408	ESS	Colchester
1910	1960	....	....	135437	ESS	Walthamstow
1800	....	1770	....	116866	GLA	???
1800	1850	1750	1850	124761	GLS	South
....	....	ALL	1820	141224	GLS	Bristol
1765	1800	1600	1800	130125	HAM	Bishopstoke
1840	1865	....	....	153397	HAM	Brockenhurst
1807	1992	1600	1807	145459	HAM	Hound
1806	1864	1794	1864	145394	HAM	Preston Candover
1815	1920	1750	1815	101060	HAM	Southampton
1760	1760	1700	1770	136840	HAM	Southampton
1726	1900	1726	ALL	145386	HAM	West Dean
1860	1992	1700	1860	124966	HAM	Winchester
1740	1770	1740	1770	167924	HRT	Shephall
1812	1890	1700	1890	157384	HUN	South Neots
1842	....	....	....	160385	IOM	Douglas
1820	1840	1800	1850	144533	IRL	Cork
1859	1992	1830	1860	145424	IRL	Cork
1845	1992	ALL	ALL	115762	IRL	Dublin
1847	1992	....	1847	115150	IRL	???
1770	1820	1700	1900	171522	KEN	Boxley
1835	1870	1870	1992	145564	KEN	Chiddingstone
1871	1875	ALL	ALL	165085	KEN	Deptford
1810	1835	ALL	1810	145564	KEN	Leigh
ALL	ALL	ALL	ALL	166243	KEN	Selling
1800	1900	1500	1800	132055	KEN	Strood
1871	1950	....	....	100986	KEN	???
1903	1992	1903	1903	145580	LAN	Liverpool
1830	1887	1800	1830	113050	LAN	Manchester
1880	1992	....	....	158348	LAN	Manchester
1900	1992	....	....	149675	LEI	Leicester
1800	1992	....	....	176125	LIN	Asterby
1815	....	1815	....	113875	LIN	Claypole
1800	1992	....	....	176125	LIN	Goulceby
1861	1923	1895	1992	145335	LIN	Lincoln
1850	1900	1750	1850	147494	LND	East
1804	1992	1700	1804	158232	LND	East
1820	1892	1700	1820	104744	LND	Camberwell
1886	1992	....	....	140791	LND	Camden Town
1875	1970	1850	1992	145572	LND	Hackney
1790	1879	1700	1790	137383	LND	Paddington
1875	1970	1850	1992	145572	LND	Shoreditch
1800	1830	1700	1800	172898	LND	Stepney
1826	1826	1700	1900	178322	MDX	Hanwell
1895	1900	....	....	135437	MDX	Islington
1835	1900	1900	1992	133507	MDX	Poplar
1837	1854	....	1837	177504	MDX	St Pancras
1800	1826	1700	1900	153354	MLN	St Cuthbert
1830	1950	1700	1830	171921	NFK	Brancaster
1850	1870	1800	1900	129496	NFK	Ditchingham
1813	1900	1750	1900	146803	NFK	Pulham
1840	1884	....	....	105708	NFK	Stockton
1880	....	....	1880	120596	NFK	???
1900	....	....	....	136565	NRY	Leeds
1770	1912	1770	1900	116661	NTH	South
1795	1861	ALL	1795	164623	NTT	Bulcote
1792	1861	ALL	1792	164623	NTT	Lambley
1875	1900	1800	1900	178136	NTT	Nottingham
1760	1848	....	1760	101761	NTT	Shelford
1754	....	....	....	146447	NYK	Middleton Tyas
1771	1837	1650	1800	112526	OXF	Berrick Salome
1797	1797	1750	1797	147745	PER	Perth
1797	1821	ALL	1796	131725	SAL	Dawley
1797	....	ALL	1797	131725	SAL	Kemberton
1796	....	ALL	1796	131725	SAL	Shifnal
1750	1927	1700	1927	135941	SFK	Withersfield
....	....	ALL	1800	103284	SFK	???
1810	1840	1790	1851	165824	SOM	Bath
1837	1921	ALL	ALL	153516	SOM	Chew Stoke
1790	1850	1750	1860	158658	SOM	Croscombe
1801	1841	ALL	ALL	118389	SOM	Nunney
1790	1850	1750	1880	158658	SOM	Wells
1885	1992	1800	1992	132810	SOM	Yeovil
1875	1992	ALL	ALL	151580	SRY	Godstone
1870	1915	1800	1870	145351	SRY	Lambeth
1871	1879	ALL	ALL	165085	SRY	Newington
1875	1958	ALL	ALL	165085	SRY	Rotherhithe
1840	1960	1700	1840	170801	SSX	Brighton
1800	ALL	....	....	145378	SSX	Eastbourne
1777	1808	1500	1777	144851	SSX	Fairlight
1800	ALL	1500	1800	145378	SSX	Framfield
1800	ALL	1500	1800	145378	SSX	Hailsham
1860	1992	....	1920	151246	SSX	Hastings
1800	ALL	1500	1800	145378	SSX	Heathfield
1648	1812	....	....	139971	SSX	Herstmonceux
1645	1900	ALL	....	145556	SSX	Isfield
1645	1900	ALL	....	145556	SSX	Lewes
1752	1752	1600	1752	147885	SSX	Lindfield
1645	1900	ALL	....	145556	SSX	Little Horsted
1645	1900	ALL	....	145556	SSX	Ringmer
1645	1900	ALL	....	145556	SSX	Ripe
1800	1900	ALL	ALL	151998	SSX	Salehurst
1850	1985	1820	1890	173428	SSX	Wadhurst
1800	ALL	1500	1800	145378	SSX	Waldron
1648	1812	....	....	139971	SSX	Warbleton
....	....	ALL	1870	165263	SSX	Warbleton
1645	1900	ALL	....	145556	SSX	West Firle
1881	....	1851	1881	165263	SSX	Wladron
1887	1949	ALL	ALL	123706	STS	Cannock
....	....	....	1875	145742	STS	Wednesbury
1800	1950	ALL	1992	102245	STS	Wolverhampton
....	....	ALL	1802	145548	SXW	Littlehampton
1850	1900	1850	1992	116408	WAR	Birmingham
1797	1828	1700	1900	178322	WAR	Birmingham
1760	1992	1700	1760	116513	WAR	Solihull
1800	1850	1700	1850	143553	WES	Warcop
1807	1851	1700	1800	169242	WIL	Everleigh
1586	1790	ALL	1820	136719	WIL	Great Bedwyn
1827	....	ALL	1827	116408	WOR	ALL
1863	....	ALL	ALL	161608	WOR	Bredon
1855	1881	1835	1855	134309	WOR	Kidderminster
1700	1992	1700	1992	143014	WSX	ALL
1781	1912	1781	1872	121681	YKS	Hull
1779	1938	1700	1779	171565	YKS	Hull
1904	1975	....	....	176966	YKS	Sheffield
1880	....	....	1880	120596	YKS	???
MARTINDALE						
1620	1670	1620	1670	127655	CUL	Watermillock
1665	1770	1665	1770	127655	GLS	Bristol
1831	1969	1798	1831	116076	YKS	Malton
1831	1969	1798	1831	116076	YKS	York
MARTINELLI						
....	....	ALL	1860	161357	ALL	ALL
1767	1900	....	....	161357	LND	Greater
1810	1832	....	....	161357	SSX	Brighton
MARTINS						
1842	1842	....	....	115258	WIL	Preshute
MARTLAND						
1839	1901	1770	1839	123706	LAN	Ormskirk
MARTYN						
1679	1992	?	1649	145610	CON	Crantock
1600	1992	1500	1600	162507	CON	Gwennap
1663	1816	....	....	145483	CON	North Tamerton
1656	1881	....	....	145483	CON	South Petherwin
1668	1960	1500	1750	163562	CON	St Columb Minor
1600	1992	1500	1600	162507	CON	Truro
1634	1770	....	....	145483	DEV	Lifton
1850	1986	....	....	163562	LND	Kensington
1730	1772	ALL	1730	169730	SRY	Mitcham
1645	1900	ALL	....	145556	SSX	Ringmer
....	....	1326	1743	145483	WCY	???
MARVELL						
1837	1837	1837	1837	113646	LND	Clapton
MARVILL						
1871	1992	....	....	145629	DBY	Derby
1800	1871	1700	1800	145629	LEI	Kibworth Beauchamp

Known From	To	Researching From	To	Ref	Cty	Place
MARVIN						
1800	1900	1700	1800	118214	WIL	Hilperton
MARWOOD						
1790	1992	ALL	....	143944	ALL	ALL
1871	1929	....	....	153176	DUR	???
....	....	1700	1910	156760	HAM	Southampton
1749	1992	1749	1992	151211	LIN	East Marsh
1749	1992	1749	1992	151211	LIN	Wold
1827	1857	1800	....	109282	LND	Central
1807	1871	....	....	153176	NYK	Holtby
MARY						
1821	....	....	....	123633	SCT	Castle Milk Dunn
MARYCHURCH						
1819	1870	ALL	1870	104299	GLS	Bristol
MARYON						
....	....	ALL	ALL	145637	ALL	ALL
1500	1992	ALL	ALL	102202	ESS	Chelmsford
1700	....	....	1700	145637	ESS	Shelley
MASDEN						
1800	1992	1700	1800	102342	LIN	Liddington
MASE						
1820	1910	1700	1820	166804	NFK	Syderstone
MASFORD						
1790	1980	1700	1900	160083	DEV	ALL
MASH						
1746	1780	ALL	1746	168602	CAM	Conington
1820	1992	1700	1820	145645	NTH	East
MASHFIELD						
....	....	1680	1732	145270	DOR	West Knighton
MASHITER						
....	....	1780	1820	147613	LAN	Tatham
MASKELL						
1788	1883	....	....	115606	BRK	New Windsor
1818	1892	1700	1818	176052	BRK	Steventon
1790	1866	1790	1866	134880	ESS	Maldon
1784	1935	1700	1800	103896	OXF	Henley
1780	1899	1700	1900	164305	SXE	Ditchling
MASKELYNE						
1420	1811	1400	1900	176621	WIL	Purton
MASKEW						
1800	1992	....	....	135038	DOR	Dorchester
....	....	1830	1992	135038	LAN	Rochdale
1840	1992	....	....	135038	STS	Bilston
1840	1992	....	....	135038	STS	Stoke On Trent
1700	1800	....	....	135038	WES	Kendal
MASKIL						
1763	1763	1700	1763	165530	WIL	Sherston
MASKRAY						
1800	1900	....	....	146854	LAN	Southport
MASKREY						
1100	1992	1100	1992	102830	DBY	ALL
1100	1992	1100	1992	102830	STS	ALL
MASLEN						
1915	1992	....	....	145653	GLS	Cheltenham
1835	1950	1700	1856	119849	SRY	Southwark
1781	1992	1700	1781	161446	WIL	All Cannings
....	....	ALL	ALL	114308	WIL	Devizes
MASLIN						
1851	1992	1851	1992	175196	AVN	Bristol
1700	1800	1550	1700	145688	BRK	Warfield
1829	1829	1829	1829	175196	CON	Penznace
1850	1871	1700	1871	166928	HAM	???
MASON						
1800	1880	1800	1880	125229	BKM	Gt Missenden
1798	1841	....	....	115606	BRK	Clewer
1778	1930	1700	1930	145750	CAM	Elm
1832	1832	1550	1850	147265	CHS	East
1874	1939	1874	1939	107131	CHS	Macclesfield
1840	1880	1800	1850	135496	CHS	Widnes
1808	1992	ALL	1808	145734	CMA	West
....	1992	....	....	158348	CMA	Kendal
1636	1762	1600	1800	153591	CON	St Just In Penwith
1800	....	....	....	124664	DBY	Belper
1797	1854	....	....	144282	DBY	Belper
1850	1870	1840	1900	143006	DBY	Darley Dale
1797	1854	....	....	144282	DBY	Duffield
1750	1850	1650	1750	118745	DBY	Little Eaton
1780	1900	1700	1850	124788	DBY	New Mills
1797	1854	....	....	144282	DBY	Ticknall St George
....	....	ALL	ALL	169315	DUR	East
1850	....	1750	....	134589	DUR	Darlington
1840	....	1750	....	134589	DUR	Gateshead
1600	1699	1600	1699	169781	ERY	Driffield
1600	1699	1600	1699	169781	ERY	Hull
MASON contd.						
....	....	1800	1860	154261	ESS	Foulness Island
1860	1900	....	....	154261	ESS	Great Wakering
1860	1950	....	....	113514	EYK	Hull
1750	1800	1700	1800	106631	GLS	Dymock
1755	1858	1700	1781	127116	HAM	Longstock
1820	1900	1800	1850	176648	HAM	Southampton
1795	1873	?	1795	158569	HEF	Byton
1650	1800	ALL	ALL	131873	HRT	Little Hadham
1734	1734	1650	1734	178608	HRT	Reed
1820	1850	1700	1900	172421	HRT	St Albans
1840	1880	ALL	1880	112275	HUN	Godmanchester
....	....	1825	1992	108502	HUN	Kimbolton
1840	1880	1800	1850	143006	HUN	Stilton
1910	1992	1530	1992	145769	KEN	Dover
1787	1823	1780	1830	108251	KEN	Medway
1836	1992	1700	1836	145696	LAN	Ashton Under Lyne
1900	1992	....	....	175099	LAN	Liverpool
1804	1804	1750	1804	178004	LAN	Manchester
1836	1992	1700	1836	145696	LAN	Mossley
1840	1880	1800	1850	135496	LAN	Widnes
1850	1930	1850	1930	159247	LAN	Wigan
1900	1992	....	....	113018	LEI	Leicester
1768	1810	ALL	1768	154946	LIN	Luddington
1790	1810	1750	1850	123536	LND	Holborn St Andrews
1819	1872	1700	1850	155152	LND	Newington
1840	1900	1840	1900	119091	LND	Rotherhithe
1851	1948	1700	1851	157767	LND	???
1822	....	....	1822	164321	MDX	East London
1889	....	1870	1889	133639	MDX	London
....	....	1800	1900	176508	MDX	Pancras
1880	1992	1800	1992	152609	NBL	Blyth
1822	1847	1800	1850	152609	NBL	Burradon
1857	1863	1800	1900	152609	NBL	Callaly
1822	1847	1800	1850	152609	NBL	Coltparks
1880	1992	1800	1992	152609	NBL	Easdon
1822	1861	1700	1911	152609	NBL	Eglingham
1852	1855	....	....	152609	NBL	Gt Tosson
1800	1880	....	....	132756	NBL	High Heaton
1880	1992	1800	1992	152609	NBL	Horton
1800	1880	....	....	132756	NBL	Long Benton
1800	1880	....	....	132756	NBL	Newcastle
1822	1861	1700	1911	152609	NBL	Rothbury
1880	1992	1800	1992	152609	NBL	S Neasham
1822	1861	1700	1911	152609	NBL	Whittingham
1823	1824	1700	1845	152609	NBL	Wooperton
1708	1756	1650	1800	109290	NFK	Central
....	....	1740	1780	145211	NRY	Newton On Ouse
1780	1840	1700	1850	162043	NTH	Syresham
1880	1992	1800	1880	156957	NTT	Nottingham
....	....	1530	1992	145769	OXF	ALL
....	....	1803	1843	152684	OXF	North
....	....	1700	1850	152684	OXF	Deddington
....	1700	....	1700	177695	OXF	Shibford
1717	1748	1600	1800	176877	RAD	Beguildy
1800	1840	1700	1850	142174	SAL	Albrighton
1850	1930	1850	1930	159247	SAL	Horsehay
1805	1847	....	....	174319	SRY	Mitcham
1836	1900	1810	1900	148067	SRY	Southwark
1840	1900	1750	1850	105716	SSX	Bosham
1832	1870	1800	1870	126454	STS	Perry Barr
1611	1726	1550	1726	102830	STS	Sedgely
1680	....	....	1700	160873	STS	Sedgley
1790	1861	1760	1870	169323	STS	Wednesbury
1860	1900	1700	1860	171174	STS	Willenhall
1845	1880	1840	1900	142174	STS	Wolverhampton
1651	1716	1600	1800	162280	STS	Wolverhampton
1864	1864	1864	1864	143286	WAR	Aston
1650	1750	1600	....	118591	WES	Brougham
1769	1853	1700	1769	152196	WES	Sedburgh
1748	1830	1700	1830	139483	WIG	???
1720	1775	1700	1790	142018	WIL	Salisbury
1822	1846	ALL	1822	102245	WOR	Alvechurch
1810	1880	....	....	138339	WOR	Hill Croome
1810	1880	....	....	138339	WOR	Ripple
1775	1860	1775	1860	145726	WOR	Upton On Severn
1757	1992	?	1757	113840	YKS	Bramham
1700	1775	1650	1700	111236	YKS	Dent
1635	1635	1600	1650	119938	YKS	York
1850	....	1850	....	117250	???	Lewisham
MASSAM						
1654	1874	....	....	156418	NYK	Melsonby
MASSER						
1800	1992	....	....	134619	WAR	Atherstone

Known From	To	Researching From	To	Ref	Cty	Place
MASSER contd.						
1833	1902	1830	1910	116114	YKS	Leeds
1734	1841	1680	1850	116114	YKS	York
MASSEY TIDSWELL						
....	....	1820	1909	151211	LIN	Louth
....	....	1820	1909	151211	LIN	Surfleet
MASSEY						
....	....	ALL	ALL	145793	ALL	Name Study
1837	1860	ALL	ALL	149004	BKM	Broughton
1780	1992	ALL	ALL	168912	CHS	East
1730	1992	1700	1800	155047	CHS	Alderley
1758	1810	1700	1758	168912	CHS	Alderley
1745	1845	1700	1750	100293	CHS	Rostherne
1650	1770	1650	1992	133450	CON	Liskeard
1550	1750	1500	1750	102830	DBY	ALL
....	1881	ALL	ALL	176737	DBY	ALL
1870	1880	1870	....	145807	DBY	Claycross
1700	1750	1650	1750	169749	DBY	Norbury
1823	1835	1823	....	145807	DEV	Plymouth
1750	1850	1650	1750	132268	LAN	Ainsworth
1861	1950	1832	1861	145785	LAN	Liverpool
1811	1833	1720	1811	155489	NBL	Bedlington
1785	....	1785	....	160164	NTT	Balderton
....	1784	?	1784	128910	NTT	Greasley
1785	1823	1600	....	145807	SAL	Bridgnorth
1550	1750	1500	1750	102830	STS	ALL
1880	1992	1880	1992	145807	WAR	Birmingham
1835	1870	1600	....	145807	WOR	Dudley
1881	1900	....	....	121061	YKS	Bradford
1700	1880	....	....	121061	YKS	Pocklington
1848	1973	1820	1848	162523	YKS	Pontefract
1839	1851	1833	1890	155489	YKS	Rotherham
MASSIAH						
1852	1892	1850	1900	104604	LND	North
MASSIE						
1680	1870	1600	1680	173312	CHS	Nantwich
MASSINGHAM						
....	....	ALL	ALL	145815	ALL	Name Study
1500	1992	ALL	ALL	149721	ALL	ALL
1680	1815	1680	1815	149721	HRT	Broxbourne
1690	1790	1600	1900	149721	HRT	Hoddesdon
1700	1900	1700	1900	149721	MDX	Bethnal Green
1700	1900	1700	1900	149721	MDX	Stepney
1749	1815	....	....	101028	NFK	Aylmerton
1500	1992	1500	1900	149721	NFK	Aylmerton
1816	....	....	....	121835	NFK	Binham
1700	1899	....	....	121835	NFK	Langham
1597	1992	1597	1992	149721	NFK	Langham
MASSOM						
1820	1980	1750	1850	105198	NTH	Irthlingborough
MASSY						
1350	1450	1300	1450	154881	ALL	ALL
MASTER						
1914	....	1850	....	167290	LND	Kilburn
1914	....	1850	....	167290	LND	Mary Le Bone
MASTERMAN						
1866	1992	1700	1866	150223	DOR	Weymouth
MASTERS						
....	....	ALL	1880	138592	DBY	East
1880	1890	....	....	138592	DBY	Alfreton
1890	1910	....	....	138592	DBY	Ilkeston
1732	1992	1500	1750	145831	DEV	South Hams
1680	1710	ALL	1680	115266	DOR	ALL
1700	1730	1550	1700	156795	DOR	East
1860	1920	1800	1860	177253	DOR	Dorchester-Mureton
1831	1992	1700	1831	145823	DOR	Trent
1860	1900	....	....	130281	HAM	Southampton
1787	1923	1600	1787	145459	HAM	Southampton
1815	1860	1815	1860	107522	KEN	Romney Marsh
1832	1890	1800	1870	127981	MDX	London
1788	1788	1700	1800	117013	NFK	Docking
....	....	1750	1780	110450	NTH	Heyford
1910	1946	....	....	138592	NTT	Mansfield
....	....	1795	1858	130079	SOM	Crewkerne
1823	1882	1800	1900	135763	SOM	Huntspill
1831	1992	1700	1831	145823	SOM	Trent
1818	1818	ALL	1850	107026	SRY	Newington
MASTERSON						
....	....	ALL	ALL	120316	ALL	Name Study
1770	1840	1700	1880	150118	NFK	Great Yarmouth
1850	1960	ALL	ALL	162469	SFK	North
1850	1900	1700	1900	106356	SFK	???
MASTIN						
....	....	1700	1900	129275	KEN	Gravesend
MASTIN contd.						
....	....	1800	1900	129275	KEN	Swanscombe
....	....	1800	1900	129275	LND	Woolwich
MASTING						
1756	1756	1550	1755	102830	LIN	Lincoln
MASTON						
1743	1787	1700	1743	148938	GLS	Hardwicke
MAT						
ALL	ALL	ALL	ALL	116432	ALL	ALL
MATCHAM						
1755	1771	1750	1771	148121	DOR	???
1755	1771	1750	1830	148121	WIL	???
MATCHES						
1796	1855	1750	1855	163139	OKI	Deerness
MATCHWICKE						
1674	1707	1650	1707	159581	SRY	Bramley
1674	1707	1650	1707	159581	SRY	Shere
MATES						
1670	1767	....	....	139971	SSX	Herstmonceux
MATHAMS						
1840	1870	1820	1900	111325	LND	Mile End
....	....	1850	....	106356	SFK	Ipswich
MATHER						
1628	1650	1600	1650	145882	CHS	Liverpool
1750	1992	1700	1920	145866	DBY	Derby
1840	1880	1830	1900	117145	LAN	Adlington
1790	1823	....	....	171824	LAN	Billings
1840	1880	1830	1900	117145	LAN	Chorley
1596	1600	1600	1700	145882	LAN	Lowton
1628	1727	1613	1630	118958	LAN	???
1850	1960	1700	1850	145858	NTT	Nottingham
1590	1700	ALL	ALL	137987	SAL	Preston Gubbals
MATHERS						
1874	1924	1700	1874	106887	ABD	New Deer
1922	1925	ALL	ALL	109509	LIN	Gainsborough
1850	1867	1800	1850	128368	YKS	Bowes
MATHESON						
1780	1813	1500	1780	138614	CAI	Canisbay
1820	....	1700	1820	115967	ROC	Ferrintosh
MATHEW						
1821	1992	1600	1821	146137	ABD	Longside
1821	1992	1600	1821	146137	ABD	Peterhead
1830	1839	1700	1992	168181	ARM	Armagh
1650	1700	1600	1700	124974	BRK	Enborne
1887	1887	1800	1992	168181	CAV	Belturbet
1866	1870	1800	1992	168181	FER	Lisnaskea
1740	1992	....	....	118672	FLN	Caerwys
1660	1850	1600	1850	105228	SFK	Ixworth
1804	1804	1700	1992	168181	TIP	ALL
MATHEWS						
1865	1992	1800	1865	155594	ANT	Belfast
1815	1870	1700	1992	133663	BRK	Boxford
....	....	1700	1850	147044	CON	Gulval
....	....	1700	1850	147044	CON	Madron
....	....	1700	1850	147044	CON	Paul
....	....	1700	1850	147044	CON	St Just In Penwith
1800	1886	?	1992	131458	CON	Trywreath
1840	....	....	....	136964	DEV	Plymouth
1790	1844	1790	1992	164984	FLN	Bagillt
1871	1881	1871	1881	143286	GLS	Cheltenham
1798	1851	1798	1850	179337	GLS	Dyrham
1798	1851	1798	1850	179337	GLS	Hinton
1880	1920	1850	1920	141046	MDX	Holborn
1869	1900	1800	1870	172871	MDX	Marylebone
....	....	1700	1850	140627	NFK	St Faiths
?	?	ALL	ALL	160288	OXF	Xofrod
1799	1832	1700	1850	117331	SSX	Withyham
1727	....	1727	ALL	118060	WIL	Maden Bradley
?	?	?	?	108758	???	???
MATHEWSON						
1750	....	ALL	ALL	130508	FIF	Pittenweem
1750	1965	....	....	137820	SHI	Fetlar
1720	1965	....	....	137820	SHI	Mid Yell
1760	1965	....	....	137820	SHI	North Yell
1758	1965	....	....	137820	SHI	Northmavine
1720	1965	....	....	137820	SHI	South Yell
MATHIAS						
1800	1860	1750	1890	118540	PEM	Middle
1750	1850	1600	1750	103845	PEM	Uzmaston Slebech
MATHIESON						
1931	....	....	....	159921	ANS	Glenprosen Kirriemuir
1809	1820	1780	1809	101796	ARL	West Dunulteuh
1792	1819	1750	1820	179000	FIF	Dunfermline

Known From	To	Researching From	To	Ref	Cty	Place
MATHIESON contd.						
1839	....	....	....	159921	INV	Croy
1879	....	....	....	159921	MOR	Edinkillie
1834	....	....	....	159921	ROC	Contin
MATLEY						
1720	1850	1600	1720	170194	DBY	Bakewell
MATLOCK						
1570	1600	ALL	....	104515	LIN	Beckingham
MATON						
....	....	ALL	ALL	145890	ALL	Name Study
1885	1932	1800	1885	153990	KEN	Cooling
1837	1920	1700	1850	135887	WIL	Farley
1837	1920	1700	1850	135887	WIL	Pitton
MATRAVERS						
1879	1992	1800	1920	121568	SOM	Ashill
MATSELL						
1650	1992	1750	1837	164437	NFK	ALL
MATSON						
1745	1762	1745	1762	144355	KEN	South
1720	1775	1700	1730	154873	KEN	Canterbury
1600	1690	....	....	119431	KEN	Thanet
1843	1900	1600	1843	144045	YKS	York
MATTENLEY						
....	....	1650	1852	146048	MDX	Brentford
1837	1852	1650	1836	146048	MDX	Uxbridge
MATTENLY						
1837	1852	1650	1836	146048	MDX	Uxbridge
MATTEWS						
1723	1992	ALL	ALL	115002	HAM	Micheldever
MATTEWSON						
1895	1930	1930	1992	146560	LKS	Coatbride
MATTEY						
1770	1867	....	....	131229	HEF	ALL
MATTHEW						
....	....	1750	1850	134546	ANS	Dundee
1674	1785	1600	1674	102571	CON	Paul
....	....	1700	1850	143359	FIF	???
1729	1756	1600	1861	176923	GLA	Pontlliw
1800	1930	1700	1800	120227	SSX	Prinstead
MATTHEWS						
....	....	1849	1858	143480	AYR	Kirkoswald
1671	1804	ALL	1671	168602	BDF	Odell
1825	1992	ALL	ALL	104183	BKM	Dorton
1850	1936	1800	1850	158402	BKM	Latimer
1700	1900	1700	1900	173738	BRK	Thatcham
1790	1879	....	1880	137405	CAM	Foxton
1888	1992	1750	1888	107123	CHS	Macclesfield
....	....	1500	1900	136972	CON	Breage
1850	1900	1850	1900	147419	CON	Cornelly
....	....	1500	1900	136972	CON	Crowan
1781	1940	1600	1781	148040	CON	Lanteglos
1800	1992	1700	1992	140287	CON	Lelant
1638	1896	....	....	143596	CON	Mousehole
1638	1896	....	....	143596	CON	Paul
1780	1992	1700	1780	129437	CON	Penwith
1775	1798	1700	1775	153605	CON	Penzance
1800	1992	1700	1992	140287	CON	St Hilary
1781	1940	1600	1781	148040	CON	St Kew
1700	1859	1700	1859	178012	CON	St Levan
1788	1825	1700	1788	161837	CON	St Pinnock
1845	1860	ALL	1845	153060	CUL	Crosthwaite
1758	1992	1700	1800	145939	DEV	Bradninck
1785	....	1600	1992	124389	DEV	Broadwidger
1758	1992	1700	1800	145939	DEV	Silvertow
1770	....	1700	1900	106410	DEV	Uppottery
1785	....	1600	1992	124389	DEV	Virginstow
1780	1920	1600	1992	124389	DEV	Werrington
1425	?	....	....	145947	GLA	Llandaff
1822	1951	1700	1822	176052	GLS	Glouster
1837	1965	1700	1992	115991	HAM	Emsworth
....	....	1785	1875	143480	HAM	Itchen
....	....	1785	1875	143480	HAM	Southampton
1786	1786	1786	1800	156485	HRT	St Albans
....	....	1800	1825	137405	HUN	St Ives
1548	1992	1700	....	145998	IOW	???
1835	1935	1835	1920	172634	LAN	Liverpool
1767	1854	....	....	123641	LIN	Frodingham
1800	1850	1550	1800	150843	LIN	Rillingholme
1880	1910	1850	1930	173614	LND	Battersea
1759	1851	....	....	114669	LND	Holborn
1890	1905	1850	1905	166154	LND	Tooting
1854	1930	1750	1880	155152	LND	Walworth
1842	1898	1800	1842	132853	MDX	Bethnal Green
....	....	ALL	ALL	167827	MDX	Stanwell
MATTHEWS contd.						
1810	1870	....	....	101028	NFK	Aylmerton
1819	....	1819	1879	116424	NFK	Bawburgh
1642	1789	....	....	101028	NFK	Sheringham
1750	1900	ALL	....	143944	NTH	ALL
1871	1891	....	....	123641	NTT	Askham
1824	1849	....	....	117374	NTT	Bulwell
1877	1927	....	....	123641	NTT	Chilwell
1856	1992	1700	1856	122378	NTT	Nottingham
1868	1992	1600	1820	124176	OXF	Headington
1750	1850	ALL	ALL	106313	OXF	Little Milton
1850	1905	1550	1891	104892	SAL	Condover
1850	1884	1800	1850	158267	SFK	Haughley
1750	1850	1650	1750	158402	SFK	Weybread
1824	1856	1700	1850	145963	SOM	Bath
1927	1983	1920	1983	165824	SOM	Bath
1869	1951	1800	1869	132489	SOM	Bedminster
1869	1951	1800	1869	132489	SOM	Bristol
1869	1951	1800	1869	132489	SOM	Frenchay
1725	1767	1700	1785	165824	SOM	Pen Selwood
1861	1881	1852	1930	165824	SOM	Saltford
1672	1695	1665	1705	165824	SOM	Wincanton
1910	....	....	....	145920	SRY	Epsom
1802	1978	1700	1800	166723	SSX	Westham
....	1600	....	....	174564	SSX	???
1500	1850	1500	1850	156485	STS	Codsall
1670	1783	....	1670	146013	STS	Pattingham
1500	1992	ALL	ALL	156485	STS	Pattingham
1500	1850	1500	1850	156485	STS	Wolverhampton
1800	1880	1800	1920	177571	WAR	Newbold On Avon
1837	1871	1700	1837	146021	WAR	Solihull
1756	....	ALL	1756	154946	WES	Kirkby Stephens
1763	1992	ALL	1992	146005	WIL	Central
....	1807	....	....	126276	WIL	Chippenham
1814	1860	1500	1815	104825	WIL	Devizes
1790	1851	1780	1881	165824	WIL	East Knoyle
1700	....	ALL	ALL	116394	WIL	Keevil
1768	....	....	....	126276	WIL	Langley Burrell
1708	1880	ALL	1708	158445	WIL	Melksham
1763	1992	ALL	1992	146005	WIL	Patney
1750	....	1700	1750	153249	WOR	Worcester
1860	1992	....	....	145912	YKS	South Leeds
MATTHEWSON						
....	....	1700	1800	148474	CUL	Kirkandrews On Esk
MATTIN						
1795	1861	1700	1800	116378	HUN	Buckden
MATTINGLEY						
1837	1900	1650	1992	146048	MDX	Brentford
1800	1837	1851	1925	146048	MDX	Helston
1850	1870	1750	1900	112704	MDX	Heston
1800	1837	1851	1925	146048	MDX	Southall
1837	1900	1650	1992	146048	MDX	Uxbridge
MATTINGLY						
1100	1992	1100	1992	146056	BRK	Mattingly
1840	1900	1700	1840	167762	BRK	Shellingford
1100	1992	1100	1992	146056	HAM	Mattingly
MATTINSON						
1655	1780	1600	....	118591	WES	Warcop
MATTLE						
1780	1860	1780	1860	126500	NBL	Berwick Upon Tween
MATTLEY						
1770	1780	....	....	103764	LAN	Manchester
MATTOCKS						
1788	1788	?	1850	168149	MDX	Isleworth
MATTS						
1820	1992	ALL	ALL	143537	LEI	ALL
MATYEAR						
1730	1800	1700	1800	167088	LND	Fulham
MAUD						
1816	1914	1600	1816	176915	BRE	Vaynor
1816	1914	1600	1816	176915	GLA	Merthyr Tydfil
1756	1798	....	....	169129	NFK	Thornham
MAUDE						
1850	1890	1800	1900	129496	YKS	Gildersome
MAUDIT						
1150	1268	1130	1268	124974	BKM	Hanslope
1066	1268	1066	1268	124974	HAM	Hartley Mauditt
MAUDSLEY						
1875	1940	1880	1935	122238	LAN	Lowton
1846	1894	ALL	1846	157198	LAN	???
1846	1894	ALL	1846	157198	WES	Kirkby Lonsdale
....	....	1730	1800	147613	YKS	Bentham
1846	1894	ALL	1846	157198	YKS	Bracewell
1850	1875	1851	1851	122238	YKS	Skipton

Known From	To	Researching From	To	Ref	Cty	Place
MAUGHAM						
1800	1992	ALL	1800	134171	DUR	Hamsterley
1800	1900	1600	1900	126845	DUR	???
....	....	1750	1880	166294	NBL	Burradom
1866	....	1830	1890	170348	NTT	Worksop
MAUGHAN						
1848	1925	1926	1992	132934	CUL	Maryport
1800	1950	1700	1800	140112	DUR	Bishop Auckland
1800	1950	1700	1800	140112	DUR	Durham
1835	1850	....	....	139971	MAY	Ballycastle
MAUL						
1800	1992	1700	1800	146064	SOM	Bristol
MAULAM						
1710	....	1600	1710	132802	DOR	Upcerne
MAULE						
1756	1760	1700	1756	177059	BEW	Duns
1760	1992	1760	1786	177059	NBL	ALL
1770	1860	1700	1800	169315	NBL	Alnwick
1497	1731	....	....	100536	SCT	???
1800	1992	1700	1800	146064	SOM	Taunton
MAUN						
1854	1914	1700	1854	146072	LND	Marylebone
MAUND						
....	....	1700	1899	115975	LND	London
MAUNDER						
1590	1800	1500	1992	114596	DEV	Cruwys Morchard
1839	1953	1066	1992	108669	DEV	Exeter
1809	1815	....	1809	131385	DEV	Topsham
1808	1850	1790	1820	109371	DEV	Washfield
MAUNDRELL						
....	....	ALL	ALL	110469	ALL	Name Study
1379	1992	ALL	ALL	110469	ALL	ALL
MAUREWARD						
1350	1450	1300	1450	154881	LEI	Cole Orton
MAURICE						
ALL	1785	....	....	170798	NTT	Sutton Bonnington
1840	1900	1700	1840	129135	PEM	Clydau
MAVIN						
1843	1992	1800	1843	160032	NBL	North Shields
....	....	1500	1800	146099	NBL	Rothbury
1843	1992	1800	1843	160032	NBL	Woodhorn
MAVINS						
....	....	ALL	ALL	146099	ALL	Name Study
1800	1992	....	....	146099	NYK	Guisborough
MAVROCORDATOU						
1600	1950	ALL	ALL	162620	ALL	ALL
MAW						
1700	1791	ALL	ALL	154067	LIN	Haxey
1860	1930	1800	1860	146102	WYK	Leeds
1790	1860	....	1860	113034	YKS	Farndale
MAWANT						
1760	1830	1700	1800	110116	HAM	Headley
MAWBEY						
1729	1800	ALL	ALL	149438	MDX	Fulham
1729	1800	ALL	ALL	149438	NTH	Wilbarston
MAWBY						
1700	1900	1700	1900	135968	LEI	ALL
1800	....	....	....	145750	LIN	Sutton
1860	1992	1700	1860	146110	NTH	Crick
MAWDSLEY						
1750	1866	1700	1866	145750	LAN	Crosby
1801	1896	1800	1854	147281	LAN	Haslingdon
1798	1992	1750	1800	135364	LAN	Ormskirk
1750	1960	ALL	ALL	126977	LAN	Sefton
MAWER						
1790	1860	1550	1790	150843	LIN	Horncastle
1892	1943	1943	1992	176885	NTT	Nottingham
MAWKINSON						
1767	1767	1650	1800	168149	LIN	Partney
MAWSON						
1840	1850	1840	1850	107522	CUL	Workington
1861	1947	1770	1865	146919	LAN	Lancaster
1830	1992	1800	1830	157740	LAN	Nether Kellet
1680	1725	1600	1992	114901	YKS	Harewood
....	....	1800	1899	171794	YKS	Sowerby
1770	1860	1700	1770	111511	YKS	West Riding
MAXALL						
1713	1770	1600	1713	163236	YKS	Saddleworth
MAXFIELD						
1754	1765	1754	1754	145580	DBY	Snelston
1758	1825	....	....	132381	DUR	South Shields
1780	1871	1780	1871	162914	NTT	Nottingham
1780	1907	ALL	1780	102350	YKS	Rawmarsh
1780	1907	ALL	1780	102350	YKS	Wadworth

Known From	To	Researching From	To	Ref	Cty	Place
MAXON						
1751	1804	1804	1992	151688	LIN	Langtoft
MAXSON						
1716	1732	1732	1992	151688	NTH	Etton
MAXTED						
1886	1926	1890	1940	110051	ESS	West Ham
1810	1853	1700	1900	110051	KEN	East
MAXWELL						
1450	1500	1400	1500	154881	ALL	ALL
1641	1641	1600	?	168181	ANT	ALL
1835	1837	1835	1848	168181	ANT	Portrush
?	?	1700	1992	168181	ARM	Armagh
1809	1809	1700	1850	168181	ARM	Keady
1749	1940	....	....	128996	CAM	Thorney
1785	1920	1500	1920	114758	DFS	Moniaive
1770	1809	1700	1992	168181	DOW	Newry
1815	1900	ALL	1815	131059	ESS	West Ham
....	1887	1800	1992	168181	FER	Lisnaskea
1750	....	1700	1850	130419	KKD	Buittle
1830	1845	1800	1992	168181	LDY	Killowen
1775	1800	ALL	1775	131059	LIN	???
1856	1932	1700	1856	102997	LKS	Govan
1819	1831	1819	1844	168181	MAY	Castlebar
1819	1831	1819	1844	168181	MAY	Westport
1794	1887	1750	1795	128333	MLN	Currie
1840	1850	1750	1840	133019	NBL	Newcastle On Tyne
1870	....	....	....	130354	SCT	Motherwell
1755	1788	1700	1755	156302	YKS	Richmond
MAY						
1818	1992	1600	1818	146137	ABD	Lonmay
1818	1992	1600	1818	146137	ABD	Peterhead
1816	1857	1600	1816	115525	AVN	Bristol
1870	1992	1800	1870	168076	AVN	Clifton
1761	....	1650	1750	143693	BKM	Burnham
1764	1820	1750	1860	125032	BRK	Brimpton
1715	1868	1700	1858	125032	BRK	Burghfield
1875	1956	1870	1956	125032	BRK	Earley
1750	1819	1740	1830	125032	BRK	Englefield
1800	1885	1750	1885	125032	BRK	Hurst
....	....	ALL	ALL	125032	BRK	Mid
1760	1844	1750	1850	125032	BRK	Pangbourne
1687	1734	1680	1750	125032	BRK	Reading
1802	1885	1800	1900	125032	BRK	Sonning
1790	1800	1790	1820	125032	BRK	Sulham
1714	1753	1714	1753	125032	BRK	Sulhamstead Abbots
1750	1774	1737	1780	125032	BRK	Theale
1845	1873	1830	1880	125032	BRK	Tilehurst
1864	1870	1850	1870	125032	BRK	Wargrave
1827	1924	1820	1924	125032	BRK	Woodley
1795	1825	1700	1850	133450	CON	Falmouth
1800	....	1700	1800	135771	CON	St Endellion
....	....	1800	1950	171689	DBY	North Wingfield
1831	1890	1800	1831	173118	DEV	Bideford
1800	1900	1600	1800	119954	DEV	Dunsford
1790	1875	1790	1875	133450	DEV	Gittisham
1843	1875	ALL	1843	169145	DEV	Norton
1750	1992	1600	1750	119954	DEV	Rewe
....	....	1700	1900	168653	ESS	ALL
1800	1992	1800	1992	125679	ESS	Rochford
1926	1992	ALL	ALL	146188	FIF	Leuchars
1840	1910	ALL	ALL	143839	GLS	South
1840	1900	1600	1992	112828	GLS	Bristol
1710	1810	1680	1710	165530	GLS	North Nibley
1875	1992	....	....	169145	GNT	Newport
....	....	ALL	ALL	125032	HAM	North East
1640	1845	1500	1850	125032	HAM	Basing
1700	1920	1600	1920	125032	HAM	Basingstoke
1450	1920	1450	1920	167088	HAM	Basingstoke
1737	1809	1720	1837	125032	HAM	Bramley
1894	1973	1800	1992	115991	HAM	Emsworth
1450	1575	1400	1600	125032	HAM	Farringdon
1820	1959	1820	1959	174343	HAM	Hambledon
1500	1605	1500	1620	125032	HAM	Kingsclere
1728	1750	1720	1760	125032	HAM	Long Sutton
1787	1961	?	1787	113360	HAM	Longparish
1752	1828	1710	1830	125032	HAM	Mapledurwell
1670	1880	1600	1880	125032	HAM	Nately Cures
1768	1790	1760	1795	125032	HAM	Newnham
1780	1992	1650	1780	124052	HAM	Odiham
1900	1950	1800	1960	173746	HAM	Portsmouth
1838	1840	1700	1862	105775	HAM	Romsey
1694	1694	1650	1700	125032	HAM	Sherborne St John
1712	1776	1700	1780	125032	HAM	Sherfield On Loddon
1712	1820	1550	1820	174343	HAM	Soberton

Known From	To	Researching From	To	Ref	Cty	Place
MAY contd.						
1706	1712	1700	1715	125032	HAM	Tunworth
1706	1727	1700	1750	125032	HAM	Up Nately
1848	1869	1840	1870	125032	HAM	Winchester
1550	1597	1550	1650	125032	HAM	Wolverton
1770	1792	1760	1800	125032	HAM	Wootton St Lawrence
1550	1725	1500	1750	125032	HAM	Worting
1623	1664	1620	1670	125032	IOW	Newport
1884	1992	1884	1992	105775	KEN	Broadstairs
1895	1930	1800	1899	146161	KEN	Chatham
1860	1875	1850	1950	105775	KEN	Dover
1791	1992	1650	1791	138673	KEN	Dover
1776	....	....	1776	155667	KEN	Elham
1700	1927	....	....	114294	KEN	Folkestone
1860	....	....	1860	164011	KEN	Folkestone
1926	1946	1800	....	146188	KEN	Lee
1700	1850	1700	1850	125679	KEN	Minster In Sheppey
1840	1950	1800	1950	122602	LAN	Liverpool
1900	1930	1900	1992	125032	LAN	Noctorum
1881	1938	1700	1992	112402	LND	Bow
1900	1992	1800	....	146188	LND	Brixton
1714	1714	1700	1730	125032	LND	Houndsditch
1926	....	ALL	ALL	146188	LND	Islington
1825	1830	1700	1850	122602	LND	Lambeth
1881	1992	1800	....	146188	LND	Lambeth
1714	1715	1700	1715	125032	LND	Quenhithe
....	....	ALL	1992	112607	LND	???
1870	1922	1800	1900	146145	MDX	Bloomsbury
1784	1886	1780	1900	108901	NTT	Averham
1835	1845	1830	1870	125032	OXF	Caversham
1924	1987	....	....	125032	OXF	Dunsden
1830	1835	1830	1835	125032	OXF	Mapledurham
1747	1892	ALL	1747	142107	SFK	Capel St Mary
1690	1717	....	....	129747	SFK	Ipswich
1853	1917	1853	1940	125032	SOM	Bath
1733	1842	ALL	ALL	153516	SOM	Puxton
1733	1842	ALL	ALL	153516	SOM	Worle
1733	1842	ALL	ALL	153516	SOM	Yatton
1841	1874	1800	1841	179221	SRY	Aylesford
....	....	....	....	108197	SRY	Egham
1698	1725	1650	1992	114901	SRY	Farnham
1780	1880	1750	1900	146803	SRY	Farnham
1905	1905	1700	1992	177733	SRY	Farnham
1600	1800	ALL	ALL	174637	SSX	???
....	....	ALL	ALL	145343	WIL	ALL
1759	1790	ALL	1759	158445	WIL	Melksham
1847	1903	1847	1903	104604	YKS	Lleds
MAYALL						
1769	1900	ALL	1881	123013	GLS	Cheltenham
1769	1900	ALL	1881	123013	GLS	Prestbury
1845	1865	1750	1845	113697	LAN	Auds
1775	1850	1775	1850	171549	LAN	Manchester
1801	1850	1750	1820	138487	WOR	ALL
1840	1865	1750	1840	113697	YKS	Saddleworth
....	....	?	1859	124540	???	Manchester
MAYBANK						
....	....	ALL	ALL	146196	ALL	Name Study
1859	1861	1862	1890	158526	SRY	Godstone
MAYBERRY						
1750	1820	1750	1820	168750	CMN	Llandilofawr
1750	1820	1750	1820	168750	GLA	Llangefelach
MAYBORN						
1771	1960	1550	1960	100382	KEN	ALL
MAYBURY						
1650	1992	1650	1992	146420	IRL	Cork
1650	1992	1650	1992	146420	IRL	Kerry
MAYCOCK						
1834	1919	1750	1900	149160	LND	Central & East
1765	1865	1707	1865	129909	NTH	Bozeat
1865	1992	1850	1865	129909	NTH	Wellingborough
1810	1820	....	....	103764	OXF	Banbury
1800	1992	1750	1800	125393	WAR	Hunningham
MAYCRAFT						
1789	1860	1500	1800	136204	NFK	???
MAYCROFT						
....	....	ALL	ALL	146218	ALL	Name Study
1587	1992	ALL	ALL	146218	ALL	ALL
1587	1788	1587	1788	146218	GLS	Winchcombe
1800	1850	1800	1850	146218	OXF	Churchill
1800	1992	1800	1900	146218	WOR	Droitwich
MAYE						
1604	1604	....	....	115606	IRL	???
MAYELL						
....	....	1870	1880	126675	SSX	Bramber

Known From	To	Researching From	To	Ref	Cty	Place
MAYELL contd.						
1795	1864	1750	1800	142360	WIL	Broad Blunsdon
MAYER						
1812	1966	1750	1812	173673	LAN	ALL
1808	1865	1750	1865	167002	MDX	London
1800	?	1800	1850	161586	SFK	Sweffling
1837	1907	ALL	ALL	149489	STS	Endon
1770	1880	1760	1900	165441	STS	Newcastle
MAYERS						
1800	1850	1800	ALL	146226	LAN	Manchester
1780	1992	1650	1780	158925	SRY	Godalming
1746	1800	1600	1800	146234	WOR	Worcester
MAYES						
1751	1940	....	....	128996	CAM	Thorney
1825	1867	ALL	1992	168718	LEI	ALL
1813	1851	ALL	1836	129283	NFK	Carlton St Peter
1817	1817	1700	1820	117013	NFK	Cawston
....	1812	ALL	1812	168718	NTH	Slipton
1800	1850	ALL	ALL	157864	SFK	Bungay
....	....	....	1851	137405	SFK	Bury St Edmunds
1750	1900	1600	1750	102288	SFK	Rattlesden
MAYHEW						
....	....	ALL	ALL	146242	ALL	Name Study
1837	1904	ALL	ALL	146242	ALL	ALL
1800	1855	1800	1855	119091	LND	East
1815	1918	ALL	1992	179205	LND	Paddington
1815	1918	ALL	1992	179205	LND	St Pancras
1770	1810	1750	1810	119091	LND	Whitechapel
1820	1924	1800	1850	146269	MDX	Chelsea
1844	1860	1750	1850	148814	MDX	Clerken Well
1834	1854	1800	1854	160903	SEL	Hoxne
1750	1900	ALL	ALL	167940	SFK	South West
1849	1992	1780	1849	176257	SFK	Bruisyard
....	....	1650	1800	146250	SFK	Great Waldingfield
....	....	1650	1800	146250	SFK	Long Melford
1860	1950	1860	1950	146250	SFK	Stowmarket
1800	1890	1800	1890	146250	SFK	Woodbridge
1500	1750	1500	1750	100420	WAR	Berkswell
1480	1600	1480	1600	100420	WAR	Coventry
1590	1660	1590	1660	100420	WAR	Meriden
1500	1900	1500	1900	170216	WIL	ALL
MAYLAM						
1825	1850	1750	1825	108413	KEN	Lynsted
MAYLIN						
1791	1840	1600	1791	177644	CAM	Sutton
....	....	?	....	128589	HRT	Hitchin
MAYLOR						
1787	1815	1700	1800	159964	LAN	Windle
MAYMAN						
1745	1992	....	1745	105295	NYK	Flyingdales
MAYNARD						
1790	1800	1750	1800	102970	BDF	Luton
1833	1853	?	1833	127612	BRK	Reading
1757	1800	1700	1757	173118	CON	Talland
1837	1970	1700	1970	146293	DEV	Devonport
1740	1840	1600	1740	151165	DEV	Okehampton
1674	1703	1600	1750	155896	GLS	Gloucester
1800	1870	1750	1870	126144	KEN	West
1830	1955	....	....	167517	LND	East
1830	1955	....	....	167517	LND	South
1830	1830	....	....	127426	LND	Spitalfields
1670	....	1500	1750	153591	SSX	West
1780	1850	ALL	ALL	126144	SSX	Withyham
....	....	ALL	1880	178403	SXE	Eastbourne
1800	1850	1700	1800	120618	WAR	Coventry
1600	1680	1620	1700	142018	WIL	South East
MAYNE						
....	....	ALL	ALL	128147	ALL	Name Study
1596	1620	....	....	128147	BKM	Creslow
1604	1723	....	....	128147	BKM	Dinton
1620	1767	....	....	128147	BKM	Hoggeston
1550	1980	1550	1900	146307	CON	Constantine
1865	1899	ALL	1865	134058	CON	Illogan
1570	1850	....	....	128147	DEV	Exeter
1720	1890	....	....	128147	DUB	Dublin
1800	1930	....	....	128147	FER	Golan
1630	1992	....	....	128147	FER	Mt Sedborough
1700	1850	....	....	128147	MOG	Cootehill
1720	1770	....	....	128147	MOG	Dromore
1850	1900	....	....	128147	WIC	Bray
1679	1905	....	....	128147	WIL	Teffont
1898	1959	ALL	1960	146315	YKS	Leeds
MAYNEY						
1100	1710	....	....	128147	KEN	Biddenden

Known From	To	Researching From	To	Ref	Cty	Place
MAYNEY contd.						
1580	1660	....	....	128147	KEN	Linton
1100	1200	....	....	128147	KEN	Luddesdown
1376	1600	....	....	128147	KEN	Staplehurst
MAYO						
1780	1840	1700	1800	103896	BRK	ALL
1851	1861	1861	1992	149357	DEV	Honiten
1580	1630	....	....	131857	DOR	Cann
1845	1865	?	1850	164976	GLS	Quedgley
1729	1804	1650	1992	155896	GLS	Westbury On Severn
1850	1880	1880	1950	145254	LAN	Manchester
....	....	1750	1850	145254	LAN	Turton
....	....	....	....	107433	WAR	???
MAYOH						
....	....	ALL	ALL	146323	ALL	Name Study
?	....	....	?	169358	LAN	Bolton Le Moors
1875	1875	ALL	1905	175757	LAN	Manchester
MAYOR						
1806	1992	....	....	131504	LAN	Hoole
1760	1907	1686	1973	132705	NTH	Northampton
MAYOTT						
1509	1702	1509	1702	108375	BRK	Abingdon
1714	1895	1714	1895	108375	ESS	Little Burstead
1700	1895	1700	1895	108375	ESS	Mountnessing
1509	1685	....	1509	108375	OXF	Culham
MAYS						
1760	1790	1700	1760	155276	SFK	Falkenham
MAYSON						
1806	1806	1780	1806	108510	DBY	Glossop
1871	1950	1850	1950	153990	LND	Limehouse
MAYTUM						
1600	1920	ALL	ALL	166154	KEN	ALL
1830	1860	1750	1880	166154	KEN	Maidstone
1630	1740	1600	1880	166154	KEN	Sutton Valence
MC CRACKEN						
1809	1992	1800	1881	130877	YKS	Halifax
MCADAM						
1820	1900	1750	1820	165336	CON	Truro
1740	1870	1740	1870	148210	MOR	Boharm
MCALISTER						
1767	1890	1600	1767	127507	ANT	Carrickfergus
....	....	ALL	1845	175757	IRL	???
1845	1865	ALL	1865	175757	LAN	Manchester
MCALLISTER						
1870	1992	1750	1870	118052	ANT	Ballycastle
1880	1992	1750	1880	118052	ANT	Cushendun
1848	1880	1848	1900	146536	AYR	Kilbirnie
MCALPINE						
1818	1845	1800	1850	119725	LKS	Glasgow
MCAPLIE						
1725	1744	....	....	171654	LKS	Carluke
MCAPLIN						
....	....	ALL	ALL	161152	ALL	Name Study
MCARA						
1787	1948	1680	1992	147036	PER	Monzie
MCARDLE						
1849	1900	1600	1900	113778	ARM	Ballymacnab
1880	1920	1880	1992	113778	CLV	Port Clarence
MCARTHUR						
1800	1835	1750	1850	177024	INV	Skye
1871	1878	....	....	121142	PER	Innercraigie
....	....	1800	1900	146110	SCT	ALL
MCARTHY						
1830	1860	ALL	1850	152021	COR	Clonakilty
....	....	1600	1856	144045	IRL	???
1828	1863	1800	1900	118168	MDX	London
1856	1992	1846	1856	144045	NBL	Morpeth
1910	1920	1800	1920	138371	YKS	York
MCARTNEY						
1824	1835	1780	1840	172162	ANS	Barry
1815	1819	1788	1840	172162	ANS	Dundee
MCASLAN						
....	....	ALL	1865	119326	LKS	Barony
MCAULEY						
1800	1900	1800	1900	146358	IRL	ALL
1849	1911	ALL	1849	146757	IRL	North
1884	1992	1800	1884	146358	RFW	Paisley
MCAVOY						
1910	....	....	....	160385	IOM	Douglas
MCBEAN						
1861	....	1800	....	116297	???	Newcastle
MCBETH						
1770	1820	1750	1820	146803	PER	Kincardine
1793	1992	1600	1793	175889	STI	Stirling

Known From	To	Researching From	To	Ref	Cty	Place
MCBLANE						
1752	1831	ALL	ALL	129933	AYR	New Dailly
MCBRATNEY						
....	....	ALL	ALL	163007	ALL	Name Study
MCBRIAR						
1820	1860	ALL	1880	119369	DOW	Killinchy
MCBRIDE						
1850	1992	1750	1850	118052	ANT	Culfeightrin
1850	1992	1750	1850	118052	ANT	Glenshesk
1886	....	....	....	166723	CUL	Cockermouth
MCBURNIE						
1900	1992	1800	1900	167835	DFS	South West
MCCABE						
1839	....	1800	1850	116572	FER	Enniskillan
....	....	1850	1890	108863	LOU	Dundalk
MCCALL						
....	....	ALL	ALL	146382	ANT	ALL
1680	1992	ALL	ALL	146382	ANT	Lisburn
1856	1992	1700	1856	136026	AYR	Galston
1856	1992	1700	1856	136026	AYR	Hurlford
....	....	ALL	ALL	146382	DOW	ALL
MCCALLAM						
1850	1992	1750	1850	170062	LAN	Manchester
MCCALLUM						
1800	1992	1650	1800	122343	ARL	Loch Fyne
1863	1871	1871	ALL	122483	LAN	West Derby
1872	1992	1700	1872	156493	MLN	Benhar
....	....	1650	1800	122343	PER	Strathfillan
1860	1863	1800	1865	122483	SCT	Renfrew
MCCAMBRIDGE						
1850	1992	1750	1850	118052	ANT	Ballycastle
MCCANE						
1775	1780	1700	1780	119059	LND	Shoreditch
MCCANN						
1874	....	....	1874	146935	IRL	Belfast
....	....	ALL	ALL	167827	IRL	Mount Rath
....	....	1800	1900	166863	KKD	Dalbeattie
1817	1880	1600	1817	151092	LDY	Londonderry
1865	1893	1800	1900	146390	NIR	Belfast
1900	1992	1750	1900	128554	SCT	???
1810	1830	....	....	145688	YKS	Drypool
1810	1830	....	....	145688	YKS	Hull
MCCARDLE						
1925	1992	1800	1925	109398	LND	Stepney
MCCAREY						
1848	....	ALL	ALL	145335	ANT	Belfast
1857	1936	1871	1992	145335	DUR	South Shields
MCCARRY						
1850	1992	1750	1850	118052	ANT	Ballycastle
MCCARTHY						
1800	1880	1800	1880	167924	CMN	Carmarthen
1837	1992	1700	1837	123153	COR	Clonakilty
1750	1830	1750	1830	167924	COR	Cork
1837	1917	1800	1837	127590	COR	Fountainstown
1840	1950	1837	1950	162442	ENG	ALL
....	....	1700	1861	172316	IRL	ALL
1878	1936	....	....	162442	IRL	Waterford
1828	1848	....	....	131210	KEN	Woolwich
....	....	1800	1840	101273	KER	???
1826	1992	1600	1826	123420	LND	East
1861	1902	1700	1950	172316	LND	Bethnal Green
1850	1950	1850	1950	162442	LND	Deptford
1861	1902	1700	1950	172316	LND	Whitechapel
....	....	1830	1850	101273	SRY	North
MCCARTIN						
....	....	1800	1900	128554	IRL	Ballymena
....	....	1800	1900	128554	YKS	Sheffield
MCCARTNEY						
1835	1900	1700	1835	145718	ABD	Aberdeen
1777	....	....	....	106852	WIG	Mochrum
MCCARTY						
1840	1890	1800	1890	155357	MDX	London
MCCAUGHAN						
1800	1850	1750	1850	146927	ANT	Ballycastle
....	....	ALL	ALL	152048	ANT	???
MCCCONNELL						
....	....	1700	1920	118834	NIR	Ballyearl
....	....	1700	1920	118834	NIR	Ballylinney
....	....	1700	1920	118834	NIR	Belfast
....	....	1700	1920	118834	NIR	Carnmoney
MCCGRATH						
1859	1945	....	....	164062	IRL	Fermoy
MCCLARE						
1700	1850	....	1700	132837	???	Musselburgh

Known From	To	Researching From	To	Ref	Cty	Place
MCCLARTY						
1884	1920	....	....	136158	SCT	Greenock
MCCLEAN						
1870	1920	1700	1870	173037	MOG	Glasslough
MCCLELLAN						
1800	1840	....	....	120219	LAN	Liverpool
MCCLELLAND						
1820	1856	1800	1860	146536	DOW	Killyleagh
1880	1930	1850	1900	155047	IRL	Cavan
1854	1911	....	1854	121002	IRL	Londonderry
1858	1888	ALL	ALL	163988	KKD	???
1874	1930	1800	1874	125431	LDY	Port Rush
MCCLINCHEY						
1846	1880	1805	1846	123706	LAN	Liverpool
1846	1880	1805	1846	123706	NIR	???
MCCLOUD						
....	....	1750	1830	142476	ARM	Tartaragahn
MCCLUNG						
....	....	ALL	ALL	146412	ALL	Name Study
MCCLURE						
....	....	ALL	ALL	146420	ALL	Name Study
1600	1992	1600	1992	146420	IRL	???
1925	1935	ALL	ALL	164887	LND	Dulwich
....	....	ALL	ALL	139696	SCT	South West
MCCLUSKEY						
....	....	ALL	ALL	152048	ANT	???
MCCOIG						
1829	1933	1800	1933	178446	LIN	Lincoln
1794	1794	1700	1800	178446	SCT	Paisley
MCCOLGAN						
1890	1992	ALL	ALL	146439	DON	ALL
MCCOLL						
1809	1840	1750	1980	135631	ARL	Appin
1809	1840	1750	1980	135631	ARL	Ballachulish
....	1877	1877	1920	166790	IRL	Dublin
1860	1945	1860	1980	135631	LAN	Liverpool
....	....	1840	1890	137391	LKS	Glasgow
....	1838	1838	1920	166790	LKS	St Enochs
1864	1890	1800	1900	121541	PER	???
MCCOLLAH						
1760	1850	1650	1760	154016	YKS	E Witton
MCCOLLOCH						
1804	1900	1780	1804	158089	LND	Tower Of London
MCCOLLUM						
1860	1860	1800	1860	149632	NIR	Antrim
1860	1860	1800	1860	149632	NIR	Carnlough
MCCOLM						
1852	1852	1800	1852	174807	WIG	Portpatrick
1723	1761	....	....	171654	WIG	Stoneykirk
MCCOLVIN						
1744	1799	1500	1744	113689	DUR	Ryton
MCCOMB						
1847	1872	1600	1847	100579	ANT	Aghalee
MCCOMBIE						
1867	1867	ALL	ALL	115355	LEI	ALL
1543	1992	....	1543	161071	SCT	???
MCCONAGHY						
1850	1992	1750	1850	118052	ANT	Ballycastle
MCCONCHIE						
1749	1831	1600	1749	132977	KKD	Gatehouse Of Fleet
MCCONCHY						
1800	1850	1500	1800	170178	LND	Chelsea
MCCONKEY						
1847	1872	1600	1847	100579	ANT	Aghalee
MCCONNEL						
1694	1992	....	....	104302	SCT	Beoch
MCCONNELL						
1889	1911	1800	1890	175595	ANT	Belfast
1840	....	1800	1840	129186	DBY	Spondon
....	....	1800	1870	175595	SCT	Glasgow
MCCONOCHIE						
1800	?	1830	1857	122483	SCT	Isle Of Gigh
1793	?	1793	1850	122483	WIG	Glenluce
MCCONVELL						
1920	1970	1700	1920	111449	MDX	Twickenham
MCCORD						
1834	1886	1886	1992	146560	LKS	Coatbride
MCCORMICK						
1788	1808	....	....	115606	BRK	Reading
1891	....	....	1891	111767	CUL	Cleator Moor
MCCOWAN						
1760	1880	1700	....	178543	AYR	Cumnock
MCCOY						
1895	1970	ALL	1895	179515	NFK	Kings Lynn
MCCRACKAN						
....	....	1760	1809	130877	NTT	Whithorn
MCCRACKEN						
1830	1850	1830	1850	140724	BDF	Luton
....	....	....	1830	121169	IRL	Newry
1850	1875	1850	1875	140724	WAR	Birmingham
MCCRACKIN						
1830	1850	1830	1850	140724	BDF	Luton
1850	1875	1850	1875	140724	WAR	Birmingham
MCCRARRON						
1820	1900	1800	1900	118540	ARM	Keady
MCCREA						
....	....	ALL	ALL	111716	ALL	Name Study
1740	1992	1650	1740	146498	NIR	Lifford
1830	1992	1830	1992	110825	TYR	Dungannon
MCCREADIE						
1840	....	1820	....	116866	LKS	???
....	....	....	1850	116866	NIR	???
....	....	1750	1850	146358	STD	Glasgow
MCCREADY						
1820	1880	ALL	1820	117765	LAN	Liverpool
1845	1900	1845	1911	108278	LDY	Articlave
MCCREATH						
1700	1880	1700	1880	154512	AYR	Ayr
1700	1880	1700	1880	154512	AYR	Kilmarnock
....	....	1750	1770	129933	AYR	Kirkmichael
1700	1880	1700	1880	154512	AYR	Kirkmichael
1700	1880	1700	1880	154512	AYR	Maybole
MCCREDIE						
1857	1992	1700	1857	146501	WIG	Stranrear
MCCRIRICK						
....	....	1700	1850	169501	DFS	Kirkconnel
....	....	1700	1850	169501	DFS	Sanguhar
MCCROHAN						
....	....	1700	1970	108723	KER	Kilurley
MCCUBBIN						
1860	1950	1800	1950	177180	BKM	Linslade
MCCUBRY						
1750	1790	1750	1790	106305	DOW	???
MCCULLAGH						
1800	1992	1800	1950	119865	TYR	Annaghmore
MCCULLOCH						
ALL	ALL	ALL	ALL	126896	DFS	ALL
1825	1861	....	....	146560	DON	South
1835	1874	....	....	146560	DON	Ballymagretty
1800	1851	1800	1992	102946	DUR	Barnardcastle
1807	1881	1800	1881	146528	MLN	Edinburgh
1675	1835	1600	1880	143251	MOR	Dyke
ALL	ALL	ALL	ALL	126896	RFW	Paisley
....	....	1800	1841	102946	SCT	???
....	....	1800	1899	104884	WIG	ALL
1851	1920	1800	1992	102946	YKS	Liversedge
MCCULLOGH						
1788	1823	1788	....	123609	IRL	Caldymore
MCCULLOUGH						
1818	1992	....	....	144088	AYR	Ochiltree
....	....	ALL	1750	149349	IRL	???
....	....	ALL	1782	149349	SCT	???
....	....	1800	1900	148210	TYR	Drumshambo
MCCULLY						
1804	1846	1700	1850	143251	ANT	Belfast
MCCUMISKEY						
1890	1992	1870	1900	136239	LAN	Liverpool
MCCUNE						
1790	1890	1790	1992	163589	CMA	Furness
1790	1890	1790	1992	163589	LAN	Lancaster
MCCURDY						
1857	1960	1857	1910	162078	LAN	Wigan
MCCURLEY						
....	....	ALL	ALL	118974	ALL	Name Study
ALL	ALL	ALL	ALL	118974	ALL	ALL
1880	1992	1700	1880	178225	LDY	Ballymoney
MCCURLIE						
1895	1992	1700	1895	165239	LKS	Airdrie
MCCURRACH						
1830	....	1800	1830	153699	BAN	Rathven
MCDADE						
1739	1899	ALL	1739	174157	DOW	Dromore
1865	1900	1850	1910	126705	IRL	Dublin
1909	1916	1890	1992	126705	LAN	Manchester
MCDANIEL						
....	....	ALL	1827	167959	COR	Carragaline
MCDANNELL						
1700	1850	ALL	ALL	131873	LND	Central

Known From	To	Researching From	To	Ref	Cty	Place
MCDANNELL contd.						
1700	1850	ALL	ALL	131873	LND	East
MCDEARMID						
1817	1920	ALL	ALL	116033	???	South Shields
MCDERMOTT						
1861	....	1850	1870	104043	IRL	???
MCDONAGH						
1830	1884	1800	1900	136980	FER	Adore
1915	1937	....	....	102946	GAL	Goromna Lettermore
1915	1937	....	....	102946	GAL	Trabane Lettemore
MCDONAL						
1851	1853	1800	1851	151343	NIR	Fermanagh
MCDONALD						
1850	1900	1700	1850	167886	ABD	Aberdeen
1831	1885	1780	1885	126586	ABD	Fyvie
1820	1890	....	....	146595	ABD	Marnoch
....	....	ALL	ALL	152048	ANT	???
1790	1992	1700	1790	146587	ARL	Isle Of Tiree
1835	1987	1835	1992	146536	AYR	Dalry
1785	1980	1780	1992	146536	AYR	Kilbirnie
1840	1880	1860	1992	146595	BAN	Boyndie
1790	1890	1600	1992	161543	BAN	Portsoy
1851	1900	1800	1900	144037	BDS	Hawick
1780	1992	....	....	126497	CAI	Halkirk
1780	1960	1780	1960	126500	CAI	Wick Halkirk
1830	1868	....	....	135453	CUL	Aspatria
1780	1900	1740	1900	118540	DEV	Stoke Damerel
....	....	1700	1800	146595	INV	Daviot
1860	1900	1750	1900	135925	INV	Inverness
....	....	1700	1800	146595	INV	Inverness
?	?	?	?	146862	INV	Inverness
....	....	ALL	....	129577	IRL	???
1795	....	1760	1800	177792	LAN	Liverpool
....	....	ALL	1840	119326	LKS	Barony
1838	....	....	....	148768	MDX	St Pancras
1780	1992	ALL	1780	147087	NAI	Nairn
1839	1878	ALL	1839	166847	NBL	South Shields
1827	1992	1700	1827	148423	PER	Aberfeldy
....	....	1800	1900	146110	SCT	ALL
1911	1984	1870	1984	148490	SCT	Glasgow
1770	1800	1770	1800	106305	SCT	Isle Of Mull
1850	1931	1700	1850	177865	SCT	Isle Of Skye
....	....	?	1780	103934	SCT	Skye
1820	1992	1820	1992	143200	SUT	Brora
1874	1874	ALL	1874	119636	WEX	Gorey
MCDONAUGH						
1841	1856	1841	1856	146617	STS	Wolverhampton
1845	1911	1845	1911	146617	WAR	Leamington Spa
MCDONNELL						
1850	1992	1750	1850	118052	ANT	Ballycastle
1870	1992	1750	1870	118052	ANT	Glenshesk
1830	1840	ALL	ALL	146633	COR	Kinsale
....	....	ALL	ALL	129577	IRL	???
1895	1992	1894	1992	146625	LAN	Liverpool
1892	1992	1880	1992	146625	TYR	Moy
MCDONNOUGH						
1850	1992	1750	1992	139181	MAY	Oory
MCDONOUGH						
1850	1992	1850	1992	139181	LAN	Liverpool
MCDOUGAL						
1795	1864	1700	1800	166723	BEW	Huntlywood
....	....	....	....	178357	DFS	Ruthwell
1804	1819	1700	1834	153842	RFW	Paisley
1804	1819	1700	1834	153842	RFW	Port Glasgow
MCDOUGALL						
1896	1992	....	....	146676	CUL	Brampton
1760	1992	1600	1760	146676	NBL	Newcastle
1760	1992	1600	1760	146676	NBL	Ridley
1740	1964	1740	1964	106305	SCT	Lorn
MCDOWAL						
....	1843	1750	1843	167398	IRL	Down
1843	1920	1750	1843	167398	WIG	Inch
1843	1920	1750	1843	167398	WIG	Stoneykirk
MCDOWALL						
1811	1840	1800	1900	146536	DOW	Killyleagh
1854	1854	ALL	1854	112313	KKD	Creetown
1833	1877	1750	1833	140678	WIG	???
MCDOWELL						
....	1830	....	....	117234	AYR	Colmonell
1835	1858	....	....	153842	NFK	Kings Lynn
MCEACHEN						
1800	1850	ALL	ALL	156604	ARL	???
1860	1880	ALL	ALL	156604	DOR	Portland
1850	1950	ALL	ALL	156604	LND	Woolwich
MCELROY						
1858	1888	....	....	173339	CAV	???
1832	1832	1780	1855	141046	IRL	???
1830	1992	1700	1830	122513	LDY	Limavaddy
1865	1895	1830	1930	141046	LKS	East Kilbride
MCERLAIN						
1870	1992	1750	1870	118052	ANT	Armoy
MCEVOY						
....	1878	1878	1930	166790	HAM	Winchester
1850	1930	1700	1850	146684	KIK	Ballyragget
1850	1930	1700	1850	146684	KIK	Toor
1892	....	ALL	ALL	115533	LAN	Failsworth
MCEWAN						
....	....	ALL	ALL	146692	ALL	Name Study
1800	1854	1750	1800	174319	BAN	???
MCEWEN						
....	....	1802	1869	146706	PER	???
1859	1884	1839	1859	164127	STD	Glasgow
MCEWN						
1823	1823	1780	1860	141046	PER	Dunblane
MCFADDEN						
1874	1930	1800	1874	125431	LDY	Port Rush
MCFARLAN						
1840	....	....	....	127140	DNB	Row
1865	....	....	....	127140	???	Edinburgh
MCFARLAND						
....	....	1600	1841	146730	TYR	Cookstown
MCFARLANE						
1854	1877	1800	1871	110043	CLA	Ennis
....	....	1800	1877	110043	COR	???
....	....	1700	1835	146358	IRL	ALL
1824	1890	1750	1850	137782	LAN	Greater Manchester
1800	1830	ALL	1830	152048	LKS	Glasgow
1812	1992	1750	1865	105422	NBL	Howdon
....	....	ALL	1749	119326	PER	Croftpardon
1810	1831	1750	1810	126357	STI	Buchanan
1798	1890	1750	1890	155004	STI	Kilsyth
1833	1860	ALL	1833	153060	TYR	Newtownstewart
1855	....	....	1855	151270	TYR	Omagh
MCFAWN						
....	....	ALL	ALL	144061	ALL	Name Study
MCFAYDEN						
1789	1841	1700	1789	106836	ARL	Islay
MCGARRY						
1860	1992	1800	1992	132799	LAN	Manchester
MCGAUGH						
1800	1820	....	....	133590	TYR	???
MCGAUGHIE						
1825	1885	1780	1852	122882	AYR	Glasgow
MCGEACHAN						
....	....	1800	1900	146110	SCT	ALL
MCGEE						
1845	1992	ALL	1845	146757	AYR	Loudon
1845	1992	ALL	1845	146757	AYR	Stair
....	....	1900	1950	106518	LAN	Liverpool
1886	1992	....	1886	133434	LAN	Manchester
....	....	1900	1950	106518	MDX	London
MCGEENEY						
1900	1980	....	....	106674	CLV	Hartlepool
MCGEENZY						
1800	1850	....	....	106674	IRL	ALL
MCGEO						
1780	....	1700	1900	130419	KKD	Buittle
MCGEOCH						
1844	1855	1800	1900	166960	MDX	London
MCGEORGE						
....	....	ALL	1870	129119	DFS	Dumfries
?	?	?	?	146749	DFS	Haugh Of Urr
MCGEOUGH						
1760	1992	1700	1760	141879	ARM	Central
MCGHEE						
1840	1900	....	....	136492	IRL	Aitkenhead
1840	1900	....	....	136492	IRL	Baillieston
1840	1900	....	....	136492	LKS	Coatbridge
1840	1900	....	....	136492	LKS	Shettleston
MCGHIE						
1765	1858	ALL	ALL	135909	KKD	New Galloway
1835	1855	1800	1850	175684	LND	ALL
MCGHRAN						
1858	1931	1800	1858	122378	IRL	???
MCGIBBON						
1806	1856	1700	1860	139203	ARL	Bute
1838	....	ALL	ALL	172057	PER	???

Known From	To	Researching From	To	Ref	Cty	Place
MCGIL						
....	....	ALL	1835	170135	KEN	Woolwich
MCGILL						
1837	1900	1837	1900	157880	GLS	Bristol
....	1910	....	....	132500	LAN	Oldham
1824	1843	1800	1850	141283	MDX	Marylebone
1862	1920	ALL	ALL	177466	MOG	Clones
MCGILLEN						
1870	1992	1850	1900	128988	LET	Kiltyclogher
MCGILLICUDDY						
1881	1940	1700	1881	105767	COR	???
1881	1940	1700	1881	105767	KER	???
MCGILLOWAY						
1850	....	....	1850	164011	LDY	Culmore
MCGILLURAY						
1774	1800	1500	1774	129577	SCT	Nairn
MCGLADDERY						
1761	1992	1640	1992	146765	ANT	Templepatrick
MCGLASHAN						
....	....	ALL	ALL	148466	ALL	Name Study
MCGLATHERY						
1761	1992	1640	1992	146765	ANT	Templepatrick
MCGLINCEY						
1891	1948	1891	1948	146773	T&W	Gateshead
MCGLINCY						
1812	1992	ALL	ALL	146773	YKS	Skipton
MCGOLDRICK						
1845	....	....	....	136964	SLI	???
MCGOUGH						
1870	1992	1700	1992	122114	STS	Tunstall
MCGOURTY						
1855	1890	1800	1890	126586	LAN	Sutton
MCGOWAN						
....	....	1500	1850	138614	DOW	Garvaghy
1838	1900	1700	1838	143812	FER	Magheraculmany
1856	1992	1800	1856	152293	LAN	Liverpool
1820	?	1820	1850	161624	LAN	Liverpool
1822	....	ALL	ALL	117889	LKS	Avondale
1690	1800	1650	1800	146803	PER	Kincardine
MCGRAN						
1860	1900	1800	1992	178136	STS	Fenton
MCGRATH						
1890	1930	....	....	104272	KEN	East Farleigh
1890	1930	....	....	104272	KEN	Loose
MCGREAL						
1901	1910	1890	1910	115681	GLS	Bristol
1900	1901	1890	1910	115681	KEN	Gillingham
MCGREAVY						
1871	1881	1600	1992	170704	IRL	???
1820	1881	1800	1900	166081	LAN	Preston
MCGREGOR						
....	....	ALL	ALL	173606	ALL	Name Study
?	?	?	?	162728	ARL	???
1841	1848	1835	1850	146846	AYR	Barrhill
1841	1848	1835	1850	146846	AYR	Colronell
1806	1844	ALL	1844	176419	AYR	Kilmarnock
1820	1992	1600	1992	114596	AYR	Saltcoats
1840	1843	....	1850	146811	CLK	Alloa
1840	1843	....	1850	146811	CLK	Logie
1850	1871	1841	1888	134376	GSY	St Peters Port
1910	1970	1800	1910	141402	HAM	Southampton
1769	1881	1600	1992	146846	INV	Grantown
1861	1900	....	....	146811	KRS	Fossoway
1850	1992	1850	1992	146846	LKS	Govan
1809	1860	ALL	1809	122386	PER	North
1849	1992	1700	1849	148423	PER	Aberfeldy
1575	1992	1500	1992	146846	SCT	ALL
1575	1992	1500	1992	146846	SCT	North
1785	1823	1810	1830	146846	WIG	Mull
1860	1992	1850	1992	114596	???	Glasgow
MCGREW						
1726	1900	1600	1726	165379	TYR	???
MCGRIFFEN						
1830	....	1700	1880	115967	AYR	Maybole
MCGRORY						
1840	1920	1800	1920	118540	ARM	Keady
MCGRUTHER						
1823	....	1800	1823	153699	KRS	Crook Of Devon
MCGUCKIN						
1855	1979	1750	1855	150673	ANT	East
MCGUFFIE						
1860	1900	1700	1860	157031	KKD	Balmaghie
1915	1936	....	....	106852	LAN	Woolton
1876	1992	1850	....	106852	WIG	Glasserton
MCGUFFIE contd.						
1890	1911	....	....	106852	???	Liverpool
MCGUFFOG						
1730	1900	1680	1730	139483	WIG	Kirkinner
MCGUINESS						
....	....	1750	1850	146358	STD	Glasgow
MCGUIRE						
1841	1992	ALL	1841	106909	MON	Panteague
MCGUIRK						
1880	1920	ALL	1880	141224	GLS	Bristol
....	....	ALL	1880	141224	IRL	???
MCGURK						
1864	1992	....	....	118133	SCT	Bridgeton
MCHALE						
....	1846	....	....	140767	MAY	Ballina
1846	....	1850	....	140767	STS	Cheadle
1860	....	1860	....	140767	YKS	Leeds
MCHENRY						
1870	1992	1750	1870	118052	ANT	Ballycastle
1870	1992	1750	1870	118052	ANT	Torr
MCHOUL						
1815	1992	....	....	144088	AYR	Kilmaurs
MCILROY						
1832	1832	1780	1855	141046	IRL	???
1865	1895	1830	1930	141046	LKS	East Kilbride
MCILURIDE						
1820	1960	1700	1900	112372	???	???
MCILWAIN						
1874	....	....	....	151548	NIR	Belfast
MCILWAINE						
1750	1800	1679	1750	127507	LDY	Moneymore
MCILWRAITH						
....	1777	ALL	ALL	129933	AYR	???
MCINALLY						
1821	1876	1850	1876	111074	MOG	???
1821	1876	1850	1876	111074	???	Glasgow
MCINIFF						
....	....	ALL	1865	119326	IRL	???
....	....	ALL	1865	119326	MLN	Edinburgh
MCINLWEE						
1810	1992	1600	1840	122513	DON	Adara
1810	1992	1600	1840	122513	DON	Killybegs
MCINNES						
1847	1871	....	....	168203	ANS	Dundee
?	?	?	?	162728	ARL	Appin
....	....	1800	1900	154334	CHS	Stockport
1850	1900	1800	1950	154334	EYK	Hull
....	....	1880	1925	154334	LIN	Louth
....	....	1840	1890	137391	LKS	Glasgow
1833	1871	....	....	168203	PER	Errol
1808	1808	....	....	168203	PER	Muckhart
1808	1810	....	....	168203	PER	Muirside
....	....	1700	....	167223	STI	Falkirk
....	....	1884	1925	137391	WAR	Birmingham
....	....	1830	1850	154334	WYK	Goole
MCINTOSH						
1815	1900	1700	1900	103403	ABD	Aberdeen
1783	1861	1800	1873	105899	DFS	Dumfries
....	....	1800	1862	137685	DNB	Helensburgh
....	....	1870	1910	137685	FIF	Crail
....	....	1850	1880	137685	FIF	Kirculdy
1769	1911	1769	1992	146366	INV	Ardersier
1905	1992	....	....	146862	INV	Inverness
....	....	1800	1840	146595	KCD	Fordoun
1870	1960	1890	....	146595	KCD	Garvock
1910	1954	1900	1960	137685	KEN	Gillingham
1866	....	ALL	ALL	151777	LND	Lambeth
1870	1900	....	....	177903	MOR	Orton
1796	....	1750	1855	166049	NAI	Edinkillie-Cooperhill
1823	1903	1800	1823	179442	PER	Aberfeldy
1800	1841	1700	1875	167207	PER	Kirkmichael
1809	1992	1809	1900	177288	RFW	Greenock
1835	1992	1700	1835	129062	SUT	Dornoch
MCINTYRE						
1822	1898	1700	1822	119881	ABD	Aberdean
1850	1860	1700	1850	106836	ANT	Port Glenone
1780	1820	....	....	126497	CAI	Canisbay
1860	1992	1860	1992	106836	DNB	Dumbarton
1850	....	....	1992	146870	DUR	Jarrow
1804	1850	1780	1850	141798	LDY	???
1899	1942	1800	1900	105414	NBL	Haydon Bridge
1947	1992	....	....	153397	SCT	Glasgow
1932	....	....	1932	148830	TYR	Donemana

Known From	To	Researching From	To	Ref	Cty	Place
MCINTYRE contd.						
....	....	1620	1825	167398	WIG	Kirkcolm
1825	1850	1620	1825	167398	WIG	Stmeykirk
MCISAAC						
1816	1930	1816	1992	111287	LND	City
1850	1992	....	1850	100315	SCT	Glasgow
MCJANNETT						
1750	1900	1600	1900	130419	ALL	ALL
MCJORE						
1648	1992	ALL	1648	146749	???	Haugh Of Urr
MCKAIN						
1816	1835	1800	1850	146269	SFK	North
MCKAY						
1908	1925	1881	1908	158526	ANS	Dundee
1835	1930	....	....	132756	BDF	Eversholt
1835	1930	....	....	132756	BDF	Woburn
1850	1963	1800	1875	150312	CAI	Keiss
ALL	1900	....	....	132756	DFS	Brydekirk
1807	1824	1750	1850	149292	INV	Kilmorack
1852	1992	1800	1852	151343	IRL	Sligo
1838	1859	1750	1900	149292	LAN	Liverpool
1850	1964	....	....	169013	LKS	Glasgow
1800	1880	....	....	126497	MLN	Edinburgh
1863	1960	....	....	132756	OXF	Bicester
1861	1863	....	....	132756	OXF	Oxford
1815	1842	1800	1920	108510	PER	Aberfoyle
1815	1842	1800	1920	108510	PER	Brig O'michael
1842	....	1800	1920	108510	PER	Brig O'turk
1860	1992	1700	1860	160571	PER	Killin
1856	....	1800	....	110264	RFW	Greenock
....	....	....	....	120219	STI	Falkirk
1860	1900	ALL	ALL	120219	STI	Grangemouth
MCKEAN						
1782	1813	ALL	1855	171530	DNB	Yoker
1803	1862	1790	1900	171530	RFW	Paisley
MCKECHNIE						
....	....	1870	1992	163244	LKS	Bellshill
MCKEE						
1890	1992	1890	1992	178357	CHS	ALL
1838	1863	1750	1880	100439	DOW	Hillsborough
1850	1992	1850	1992	178357	LAN	ALL
MCKELL						
1827	1829	1830	1920	150738	YKS	Bradford
MCKELVIE						
1863	1887	....	....	127140	RFW	Greenock
1800	1850	....	....	127140	???	Stoneykirk
MCKEMMISH						
1830	1900	1800	1900	142875	IRL	Londonderry
MCKENDRY						
1840	1860	1840	1880	122343	DUR	Seaham
MCKENNA						
1887	1992	1850	1887	146900	ANT	Belfast
1887	1992	1850	1887	146900	DEV	Torquay
1897	....	ALL	1897	157066	IRL	County Mao
1887	1914	1700	1887	157112	WAR	Warwick
1897	....	ALL	1897	157066	WAT	???
MCKENZIE						
1845	1885	1700	1845	106887	ABD	Rathven
....	....	1600	1900	134546	ANS	Dundee
1800	1850	1750	1850	146927	ANT	Ballycastle
1840	1890	1750	1840	146927	ANT	Belfast
1823	....	1800	1823	153699	AYR	Ayr
1808	1860	1790	1868	163317	BAN	Aberchirder
1886	1961	1870	1916	134082	ELN	Haddington
1830	....	....	....	127140	INV	Inverness
1794	1802	1760	1811	142751	INV	Petty
1800	1880	1750	1900	177024	INV	Skye
1890	1992	1700	1890	165239	LKS	Airdrie
1859	1865	....	....	127140	LKS	Glasgow
1892	1924	1800	1992	150835	MOR	Elgin
....	....	1700	1800	146927	PER	Perth
....	1860	1800	1860	146927	ROC	Ardross
....	1860	1800	1860	146927	ROC	Dingwall
....	....	1600	....	128627	SCT	West Highlands
MCKEOWN						
....	....	1500	1850	138614	DOW	Garvaghy
1875	....	....	1875	146935	IRL	Dundalk
1965	....	1960	1970	163775	MON	Swansea
1840	1940	1780	1920	136174	TYR	Ballygawley
MCKERCHER						
1820	1850	1800	1870	126438	IRL	Dublin
MCKERETH						
1717	....	1700	1760	141739	CMA	Ambleside
1740	1825	1700	1850	141739	NYK	Thornton Le Dale
MCKERRAS						
1825	1830	1700	1830	109010	ABD	Aberdeen
1820	1825	1700	1830	109010	MOR	Elgin
MCKERRELL						
1400	1992	....	....	146951	AYR	Hillhouse
MCKERROW						
1820	1900	1700	1820	169501	AYR	New Cumnock
1880	1920	....	....	169501	DFS	Lockerbie
MCKEVITT						
....	1932	1700	1932	146978	LOU	Carlingford
MCKIE						
1825	1840	1780	1850	123536	ANT	ALL
1800	1890	1780	1900	148474	CUL	Carlisle
1841	1895	ALL	ALL	157856	KEN	Rochester
1841	1895	ALL	ALL	157856	KEN	Tunbridge Wells
1825	1840	1780	1850	123536	NBL	Alnwick
1800	....	....	....	106852	WIG	Kirkinner
MCKILL						
....	....	1500	1800	138614	DFS	Dunscore
MCKILLOP						
1870	1992	1750	1870	118052	ANT	Loughguile
MCKINDLAY						
1760	1800	1700	1800	124699	SCT	ALL
MCKINLAY						
....	....	ALL	1852	119326	MLN	Newbattle
MCKINLEY						
1850	1992	1600	1850	118052	ANT	Ballycastle
1878	1940	1878	1940	111457	DON	???
1867	1913	1600	1867	178101	DOW	Waringstown
1815	....	ALL	ALL	103837	YKS	Scarborough
MCKINNELL						
1809	1879	1600	1809	132977	KKD	Gatehouse Of Fleet
MCKINNEY						
1854	1986	1750	1854	173231	DON	Killibegs
1900	1992	1750	1900	118052	LDY	Coleriane
MCKINNON						
1800	1852	1800	1852	159875	INV	Kyleaken
1800	1852	1800	1852	159875	INV	Skye
1879	1946	1889	1931	127183	SRY	Greenwich
MCKINSTRY						
1825	1850	1800	1850	103756	ANT	Ballymena
1884	....	....	1884	103489	ANT	???
MCKINTY						
1938	1971	1938	1945	131938	GLA	Pontypridd
MCKISSOCK						
1780	....	1750	1780	146536	AYR	Largs
MCKNIGHT						
1811	1850	1780	1820	130621	DFS	Annan
....	....	1780	1820	130621	KKD	Buittle
MCKUNE						
....	....	ALL	ALL	144932	DFS	Kirkbean
MCLACHAN						
1898	1992	1800	1900	167843	DUR	Wolsingham
MCLACHLAN						
1826	1992	1700	1826	144223	SCT	Stirling
MCLARDY						
1798	1992	1750	?	147028	LAN	Formby
MCLAREN						
?	?	?	?	162728	ARL	Appin
1830	1863	1863	1900	179574	CLK	Alloa
1750	1900	1750	1900	147036	PER	Auchtergaven
1855	1992	1855	1967	127418	PER	Doune
1827	1850	1700	1827	179574	PER	Doune
MCLAUGHLAN						
1810	....	1700	1810	139483	WIG	Inch
MCLAUGHLIN						
1863	1906	1700	1920	139203	DUR	Sunderland
1834	....	ALL	....	149004	NIR	???
MCLAURIN						
1806	1992	1700	1992	139203	ARL	Dunoon
MCLEAN						
1800	1890	1700	1992	175889	ARL	Innellan
....	1890	?	?	121223	CHS	Birkenhead
1900	1983	1800	1900	173770	DEV	Plymouth
1893	1992	ALL	1893	147060	DFS	Dumfries
1835	1900	1800	1992	177024	INV	Skye
....	....	ALL	ALL	129933	IRL	Belfast
....	1871	ALL	ALL	129933	LKS	Glasgow
1874	....	....	....	127140	LKS	South Medrox
....	....	1700	1800	146927	PER	Perth
....	....	1800	1992	175889	RFW	Greenock
1740	1992	1740	1992	106305	SCT	Argyle
1828	1909	1750	1828	153974	WAR	Coventry

Known From	Known To	Researching From	Researching To	Ref	Cty	Place
MCLEAVY						
1890	1992	1800	1890	128864	CHS	Congleton
MCLEISH						
1760	1800	....	....	159883	PER	Little Dunkeld
MCLELLAN						
1720	1800	1500	1720	138614	DFS	Lochmaben
1838	1992	1838	....	106895	MDX	London
1838	1992	1838	....	106895	MDX	Mile End
1838	1992	1838	....	106895	MDX	Whitechaple
MCLELLAND						
....	....	1945	1992	173355	ROX	Melrose
MCLENNON						
1829	1831	....	....	147672	DEV	Plymouth
1849	....	1750	1992	102415	INV	Invercannich
MCLEOD						
1799	1850	1750	1799	101796	ARL	Kilcalmonell
....	....	1700	1850	175889	ARL	Tiree
....	1840	1700	1900	107972	AYR	Dalmelington
1826	....	1600	1826	107921	AYR	Dalmellington
1793	1806	....	....	168203	CAI	Lybster
1784	....	....	....	132381	CAI	???
1875	1992	ALL	1875	147087	INV	ALL
....	....	1750	1810	126357	INV	Kilmuir
....	1852	....	1852	167037	INV	Kilmuir
1830	1865	1780	1835	119628	INV	Skye
....	1852	....	1852	167037	INV	Skye
1800	1880	1750	1900	177024	INV	Skye
1790	1824	ALL	1790	167878	MLN	Edinburgh
1830	1880	1700	1830	118419	MOR	Dyke
1820	?	ALL	ALL	101370	SUT	Clyne
MCLISTER						
1850	1992	1750	1850	118052	ANT	Ballycastle
MCLOED						
1824	?	1700	1824	122394	INV	Gleelg
MCLOUGHLIN						
1880	1992	1700	1880	135313	GLA	Cardiff
1894	1992	....	....	106682	LAN	Accrington
....	....	1875	1992	106682	LAN	Liverpool
MCLUCKIE						
1823	1992	1823	1992	171654	STI	Stirling
MCLURE						
1908	1985	1850	1908	166723	WAR	Coventry
1820	1992	1700	1992	114596	WIG	Isle Of Whithorn
MCMAHON						
1830	1836	1861	1890	111090	CLA	???
1853	....	1853	1992	129216	DOW	Downpatrick
1828	1837	1800	1850	148563	IRL	Monahan
1811	?	1800	1828	148563	KEN	Dover
1848	1851	1800	1848	177393	LND	Islington
1848	1851	1800	1848	177393	MDX	Islington
MCMAIN						
1850	1900	1750	1850	154458	DEV	Plymouth
MCMANUS						
1889	1911	1800	1890	175595	ANT	Belfast
....	....	1750	1840	142476	LAN	Liverpool
1800	1960	1750	1800	107700	MEA	Kells
MCMASTER						
1887	1907	1700	1887	153605	LAN	Liverpool
MCMEEKAN						
1800	1860	1750	1900	144231	DFS	Caerlaverock
MCMEEKIN						
1836	1854	1800	1850	147095	ANT	???
1870	1900	1845	1900	147095	SCT	Edingburgh
MCMICHAEL						
1850	1992	1750	1850	118052	ANT	Ballycastle
MCMIKEN						
1744	1992	1600	1744	132977	KKD	Gatehouse Of Fleet
MCMILLAN						
1780	1790	1770	1780	101796	ARL	Kilean
1849	....	1700	1992	137855	ARL	Skipness
1785	1850	1500	1850	114758	DFS	Carsphairn
1785	1850	1500	1850	114758	DFS	Moniaive
1820	1992	1800	1850	150312	INV	Glenurquhart
1890	1992	1800	1890	147109	LAN	Liverpool
1879	1891	1879	1992	137855	RFW	Greenock
....	....	ALL	1840	147109	SCT	???
MCMILLIAN						
....	....	ALL	1836	119326	LKS	Glasgow
MCMINN						
....	....	ALL	ALL	147117	ALL	Name Study
ALL	ALL	ALL	ALL	147117	ALL	ALL
1840	1845	ALL	1845	134058	SAL	Oswestry
MCMONNIES						
1850	....	....	....	106852	KKD	Gatehouse Of Fleet
MCMONNIES contd.						
1855	1890	....	....	106852	WIG	Whitham
MCMORDIE						
1890	1934	1800	1934	175749	ARM	Darkley Keady
MCMULLAN						
1870	1992	1750	1870	118052	ANT	Ballycastle
MCMULLEN						
1810	1835	1700	1810	134090	ARM	South
1903	1944	1850	1900	125431	DOW	Downpatrick
1840	1850	1750	1850	107697	TYR	Dundalk
MCMULLIN						
1800	....	1800	1900	139114	ARM	???
....	....	1600	1950	149454	HRT	???
MCMURDO						
1870	1900	1840	1992	129119	DFS	Dumfries
1790	1850	1700	1992	144231	SCT	ALL
MCMURRAY						
1970	1992	....	....	131954	DFS	Kirkcudbright
1970	1992	....	....	131954	DFS	Minnigaff
1970	1992	....	....	131954	DFS	Newton Stewart
1784	1837	....	1837	131954	DOW	Bangor
....	....	ALL	1865	119326	IRL	???
1753	1818	1700	1850	159964	KKD	Kirkpatrick Durham
1837	1920	1837	....	131954	LTN	Dalkeith
1837	1920	1837	....	131954	LTN	Edinburgh
1837	1920	1837	....	131954	LTN	Lasswade
1837	1920	1837	....	131954	LTN	Leith
1837	1920	1837	....	131954	LTN	Portobello
....	....	ALL	1865	119326	MLN	Edinburgh
1920	1959	1920	1959	131954	PER	Dunblane
MCMURTREY						
1874	1935	....	....	151548	NIR	Belfast
MCNAB						
1841	1885	....	....	147672	AYR	Kirkoswald
1847	1930	....	....	132896	CLK	Tillicoultry
1881	1911	1870	1880	115495	LAN	Chorlton Upon Medlock
1830	1855	1830	1855	136980	SCT	Port Glasgow
MCNAE						
1764	1827	1700	1764	167932	KKD	Gatehouse
MCNAIR						
1810	1940	....	....	146811	AYR	Fairlie
....	1788	....	1788	146811	RFW	Paisley
....	1788	....	1788	146811	RFW	Stewarton
MCNALL						
1862	1880	....	....	127140	LKS	Glasgow
1840	....	....	....	127140	NIR	Belfast
MCNALLY						
1805	1890	1600	1805	127507	ANT	Carnmoney
1891	....	....	1891	111767	CUL	Cleator Moor
1895	1895	1800	1900	167843	DUR	Darlington
1837	1992	ALL	1837	153729	MDX	Stepney
1800	1992	1700	1992	177652	WAR	Aston
MCNAMARA						
1830	1850	1700	1900	118753	CLA	Ennis
1830	1860	1830	1870	103225	ESS	Walthamstow
MCNAMEE						
1828	1850	1800	1870	148288	NBL	Newcastle On Tyne
MCNARIN						
1775	....	....	1775	120464	WIG	Stoneykirk
MCNARINE						
1775	....	....	1775	120464	WIG	Stoneykirk
MCNAUGHTON						
1847	....	1750	1850	111848	ARL	Acharacle
....	....	ALL	1744	119326	PER	Balledmund
1900	1992	1720	1900	147176	PER	Balquhidder
....	1818	....	1851	103349	PER	???
MCNEAL						
....	....	1800	1880	135046	IOM	Ramsey
MCNEE						
1800	1880	1700	1900	141739	LKS	Glasgow
MCNEIL						
1850	1992	1750	1850	118052	ANT	Ballycastle
1880	1992	1750	1880	118052	ANT	Cushendun
....	....	1824	1888	146358	IRL	ALL
1850	1937	1800	1850	179442	PER	Aberfeldy
1865	1900	1700	1830	129062	SCT	Isle Of Mull
MCNEILL						
1868	1920	1600	1868	127507	ANT	Larne
1820	1992	1820	1992	106569	ARL	Colonsay
1780	1992	1780	1992	106305	DOW	Aughlisnafin
1900	1992	1700	1900	112860	SEL	Selkirk
MCNEILLY						
....	....	1700	1980	172111	ANT	Ahoghill

Known From	To	Researching From	To	Ref	Cty	Place
MCNELLA						
1820	....	ALL	ALL	113700	MAY	Westport
MCNICOL						
....	....	1824	1888	146358	IRL	ALL
MCNIELL						
1805	1992	1871	1992	130826	LTN	Edinburgh
MCNISH						
1800	1950	ALL	1800	100536	SCT	???
MCNULTY						
1840	1992	1700	1840	130931	MAY	Belmullet
MCNURTY						
1851	....	....	1851	146935	IRL	???
MCPAUL						
....	ALL	ALL	....	100153	DON	Kilmacrennan
MCPHAIL						
....	....	1500	1880	166863	ARL	Isle Of Coll
1820	1850	1800	1850	150312	PER	Monzie
1800	1850	....	....	148261	RFW	Bridge Of Weir
MCPHEARSON						
1862	1881	1800	1992	150835	MOR	Forres
MCPHEE						
1837	ALL	ALL	1830	116734	AGY	???
1834	1838	ALL	ALL	129933	ARL	Campbeltown
....	....	ALL	1834	129933	ARL	Carradale
1800	ALL	....	....	169919	ARL	Mull
1864	1898	ALL	ALL	129933	LKS	Glasgow
1872	ALL	1913	1915	116734	MIL	Royal Air Force
....	....	1750	1850	146358	STD	Glasgow
MCPHERSON						
1859	1859	1750	1992	137863	ABD	Aberdeen
1887	1914	1914	1992	146560	LKS	Coatbride
1833	....	?	1840	103934	SCT	Skye
1790	1992	ALL	1790	177814	???	Badenoch
MCPHIE						
1833	1857	1800	1860	169161	ANS	Dundee
1857	1920	1857	1992	169161	LAN	Liverpool
1857	1920	1857	1992	169161	LAN	Manchester
1845	1860	....	....	176540	LDY	Magherafelt
MCQUEEN						
1835	1855	1750	1880	100439	INV	Portree
1740	1925	ALL	1925	100102	LKS	Crawford
1900	1950	1800	1992	110663	LKS	Glasgow
MCQUISTON						
....	....	1700	1820	144266	SCT	Glasgow
MCRAE						
1793	1864	1750	1800	174319	BAN	???
1775	1850	1775	1900	144290	INV	Inverness
1805	1934	1750	1805	140678	PER	Weem
....	....	1600	1900	144274	ROC	Kintail
MCROBERT						
1812	1867	1867	ALL	179310	KKD	Kirkcudbright
1759	1783	ALL	ALL	179310	KKD	Tongland
1854	1854	....	....	179310	LAN	Haslingdon
MCROBERTS						
1960	1992	1760	1899	167835	SCT	Tinwald Dalbeattie
MCROSIN						
....	....	ALL	1800	119326	MLN	Newbattle
MCSHANE						
1900	....	....	....	148768	HAM	Portsmouth
MCSPORRAN						
1900	1992	1800	1900	101788	???	Glasgow
MCSTAY						
1776	1804	1700	1776	137383	BKM	Weston Underwood
MCTAGGART						
1802	....	....	....	127140	ARL	Knapdale
1742	1774	1700	1775	119717	DFS	Galloway
MCTAVISH						
1814	....	....	....	127140	ARL	Kilmartin
1819	1826	1700	1850	131423	INV	Kiltarlity
MCTIGUE						
1840	....	ALL	ALL	113700	MAY	Westport
MCTURK						
1767	....	1700	1850	126772	AYR	New Cumnock
MCVAY						
1820	1870	....	....	136492	IRL	???
MCVEIGH						
1850	1992	ALL	ALL	128821	ANT	Aghalee
1879	1979	1850	1879	150673	ANT	Maghragelt
1820	1950	ALL	1914	119369	DOW	Killinchy
1831	1992	1600	1830	178101	DOW	Magheralin
MCWHOR						
1845	1880	ALL	1992	157066	CHS	???
1845	1880	ALL	1992	157066	MSY	Liverpool
MCWILLIAM						
1765	1900	....	1765	152927	BAN	Keith
1880	1992	....	1920	162949	WIG	Glen Luce
1747	1893	....	....	106852	WIG	Kirknner
MCYLVORREY						
1682	1743	1700	1743	141291	IOM	Rushen
MEABY						
....	1849	....	....	133922	HAM	Bramshaw
1825	1849	....	....	133922	HAM	Eling
MEACHAM						
1875	1875	1800	1900	121568	GLA	Cardiff
MEACHER						
1700	1900	1700	1950	177180	BKM	Ivinghoe
MEAD						
1820	1860	1700	1820	109681	AVN	Bristol
1728	....	1650	1750	143693	BKM	Amersham
1731	1735	1650	1750	143693	BKM	Beaconsfield
1729	1743	1650	1750	143693	BKM	Burnham
1735	1822	ALL	ALL	121754	BKM	Stoke Mandeville
1774	1828	ALL	ALL	121754	BKM	Wendover
1850	1900	1800	1950	177180	BKM	Wigginton
1620	1809	....	....	115495	DBY	Long Eaton
1620	1809	....	....	115495	DBY	Sawley
1719	1858	1700	1900	147214	ESS	Great Burstead
1829	1992	1829	....	106895	ESS	Higheaster
1903	1906	1895	1908	113719	GLS	Bristol
1871	1920	1861	1881	124001	HAM	Portsmouth
1777	1800	1740	1800	102970	HRT	Hemel Hempstead
1700	1708	1650	1750	147214	HRT	Sawbridgeworth
1700	ALL	1770	1819	107379	HRT	St Albans
1800	1850	1800	1850	100862	LND	East
1878	....	1878	1992	101141	LND	North
1828	1871	1750	1828	149578	LND	Fulham
1824	1889	1824	1910	147214	LND	Newington
1824	1889	1824	1910	147214	LND	Southwark
1815	1843	1795	1861	113719	SOM	Frome
1861	1895	1856	1895	113719	WIL	Bradford
1821	1857	ALL	1992	167878	WIL	Tilshead
1855	1992	1800	1992	132810	WIL	Westbury
1753	1844	....	....	173916	YKS	Aislaby
MEADE						
1600	1992	....	....	130249	COR	Kinsdale
1851	1992	1750	1851	101893	ESS	Chelmsford
1870	....	ALL	1992	134376	KEN	Hollingbourne
1845	1900	1845	1900	157503	LAN	Preston
1840	1840	1800	1840	157503	LOU	Maine
1840	1845	1840	1845	157503	NBL	Newcastle On Tyne
1880	1958	1790	1880	174262	WLS	Bridgend
MEADEN						
1830	1850	ALL	....	172812	BRK	ALL
1765	1785	1840	1855	178330	DOR	Bourton
1765	1785	1756	1790	178330	DOR	Gillingham
1790	1825	1790	1825	178330	SOM	Bath
MEADOW						
1735	1806	ALL	ALL	141615	LAN	Selmersdale
MEADOWCROFT						
1824	1886	1700	1824	153109	LAN	Burtonwood
1800	1970	....	....	123102	LAN	Lancaster
1790	1800	1700	1790	123102	LAN	Rochdale
MEADOWS						
....	....	ALL	ALL	171263	ALL	Name Study
1811	1992	1843	1992	147249	CHS	Bebington
1865	1870	1865	1900	120049	CHS	Birkenhead
1890	1944	....	....	164631	DBY	Castle Gresley
1850	1900	1700	1850	144681	ESS	Halstead
1830	1880	1750	1850	137421	GLS	Deerhurst
1830	....	1800	1855	123404	GLS	Gloucester
1830	....	1800	1855	123404	GLS	St Mary De Lode
1827	1870	ALL	1870	147222	LAN	Aintree
1815	1825	1750	1840	120049	LAN	Liverpool
1827	1870	ALL	1870	147222	LAN	Liverpool
....	....	ALL	ALL	105929	LAN	Manchester
1706	1719	ALL	1719	168718	LEI	Queniborough
1820	1830	1700	1900	141569	NTH	Slipston
1789	1855	1600	1855	148482	OKI	Birsay
....	....	ALL	1650	164631	RUT	ALL
1761	1900	....	....	164631	RUT	Brooke
1658	1830	....	....	164631	RUT	Egleton
1500	1992	1500	1992	148210	RUT	Langham
....	....	ALL	1650	164631	RUT	Oakham
1648	1947	1500	1648	154288	SFK	Barking
1648	1947	1500	1648	154288	SFK	Hintlesham
1729	1807	1650	1729	118397	SFK	Monk Soham
1770	1885	1700	1770	164860	SFK	Pettistree

Known From	To	Researching From	To	Ref	Cty	Place
MEADOWS contd.						
1850	1855	1840	1860	120049	STS	Cosely
1840	1860	1840	1880	120049	STS	Stoke On Trent
MEADS						
1641	1891	1566	1900	147257	BKM	Hambleden
1641	1891	1566	1900	147257	BKM	Medmenham
1839	1888	1600	1838	152269	BKM	Taplow
1757	1780	1730	1800	147257	BRK	Cookcham
1757	1992	....	....	115606	BRK	Cookham
1920	1950	....	....	121444	KEN	Maidstone
MEAGER						
1887	1992	....	....	140791	LND	Camden Town
MEAGHER						
....	....	1800	1900	147079	KIK	???
MEAGRE						
1600	1700	1600	1700	167924	HRT	Bennington
MEAKER						
1740	1785	1740	1785	159913	SOM	Edington
1771	1974	ALL	ALL	140155	SOM	Puriton
MEAKIN						
....	....	1800	1846	177393	NTT	Snenton
MEAKINS						
1716	1740	1650	1800	167002	CAM	Cambridge
1793	1843	1790	1850	171654	NTH	Potterspury
MEAL						
1790	1860	....	....	159883	ANS	Dundee
1795	1795	1770	1795	108510	HUN	Huntingdon
1742	1794	1700	1742	151327	KEN	Mereworth
MEALEMOUTH						
ALL	ALL	ALL	ALL	147354	ALL	ALL
MEALING						
1794	1992	1750	1794	147907	GLS	Hawkesbury
1849	....	1800	1900	139114	WLS	???
1716	1890	1650	1760	179647	WOR	Evesham
MEALMOUTH						
ALL	ALL	ALL	ALL	147354	ALL	ALL
MEANEY						
1875	....	1700	1909	156582	WAT	Waterford
MEAR						
1887	1992	....	1887	171743	SOM	Staple Fitzpaine
1750	1850	1750	1850	123595	YKS	Kirkburton
MEARBECK						
1740	1800	ALL	ALL	142611	YKS	Hatfield
MEARE						
1500	1700	ALL	ALL	146226	STS	Morton Le Moors
MEARNS						
1838	1873	1780	1840	172871	ANS	Montrose
1839	1900	1750	1870	135925	BAN	Banff
1758	1758	1700	1758	153605	KCD	Benholm
....	....	1700	1900	129275	SCT	Cruden
MEARS						
1890	1920	1700	1930	172405	HAM	Curdridge
1813	1813	1700	1813	113425	KEN	Boughton Under Blean
1700	1900	1700	1900	123765	LIN	East Side
1820	....	1800	1900	143758	NFK	Guestwick
1800	....	1750	1900	143758	NFK	Reepham
1897	....	....	....	173932	SRY	Epsom
1742	1742	1722	1753	107573	WIL	Warminster
MEASE						
1744	1803	1714	1774	139149	ERY	Lund
MEASEY						
1667	1667	1550	1666	102830	WAR	Aston Cantelow
MEASURES						
1800	1980	....	....	147273	BDF	???
1718	1940	....	....	128996	CAM	Thorney
1800	1980	....	....	147273	HUN	???
1755	1831	1600	1755	137626	LEI	Packington
1830	1900	1550	1830	147265	LIN	South
1850	1980	1500	1850	147273	LIN	???
1850	1880	1550	1850	147265	NTH	North
MEATCHAM						
1869	1896	1793	1832	161667	DOR	Bere Regis
MECHAM						
....	....	ALL	ALL	173525	ALL	Name Study
MECK						
1700	1794	....	....	169129	NFK	North Elmham
1732	1738	ALL	1732	169730	NFK	North Elmham
MECKIFF						
1743	1881	1740	1992	108251	KEN	Medway
MECKLENBURGH						
....	....	1650	1880	146234	CAM	ALL
1850	1900	1800	1850	173428	ESS	Chelmsford
1768	1768	1760	1790	173428	NFK	Old Buckenham
MECROW						
1768	1808	1712	1856	138495	KEN	Wingham
MEDCALF						
1780	1992	1740	1992	108243	HRT	Hertford
1800	1850	1600	1800	145688	LIN	North Coates
1800	1850	1600	1800	145688	LIN	Saleby
1770	1947	1700	1947	135941	SFK	Hundon
1780	1850	....	....	129801	SFK	Stradishall
MEDCRAFT						
....	....	1500	1992	115975	ALL	ALL
MEDCROFT						
1600	1992	ALL	ALL	146218	ALL	ALL
MEDFORTH						
1836	1900	ALL	1836	107964	EYK	Holly
MEDGETT						
....	....	ALL	ALL	127884	KEN	ALL
MEDHURST						
1830	1880	1830	1880	152250	HAM	St Mary Bourne
1820	1860	1820	1860	155764	KEN	North West
1818	1882	....	....	144282	KEN	Northfleet
1818	1882	....	....	144282	KEN	Sutton At Hone
1792	1881	1700	1795	110949	SSX	Mayfield
MEDLAM						
1800	1841	?	1800	121665	WAR	Sutton Coalfield
MEDLAND						
1755	1970	1700	1970	137529	CON	Poundstock
MEDLEY						
1794	1898	1740	1900	105333	HAM	Isle Of Wight
MEDLICOTT						
1760	1790	1700	1850	155896	GLS	Gloucester
MEDLIN						
1837	1895	1837	1895	159913	CON	Falmouth
MEDLOCK						
1790	1820	....	1800	152889	HUN	Gt Staughton
MEDLOCKE						
1800	1900	1700	1930	100129	BDF	Tempsford
MEDNIS						
1900	1992	....	1900	176761	ENG	ALL
MEE						
1856	1992	1700	1856	172049	DBY	Derby
1700	1720	1600	1700	151769	DBY	Ticknall
1690	ALL	....	....	142158	GLS	Gloucester
1790	1860	1750	1850	134597	LAN	Manchester
1733	1800	1600	1733	152463	LEI	Walton On Wolds
1740	1791	....	....	151351	NTT	South Wilford
1856	1992	1700	1856	172049	STS	Lichfield
MEECH						
1816	1900	ALL	ALL	115266	DOR	ALL
1684	1708	1600	1750	177938	DOR	Beaminster
1754	1754	ALL	1754	154563	DOR	Portesham
MEECHAM						
1873	1976	1873	1897	147281	NTH	Kettering
MEEDS						
1768	1935	1768	1992	129216	NTT	Mansfield
MEEHAN						
....	....	ALL	1872	104531	IRL	Sligo
1872	1992	ALL	ALL	104531	LAN	Bolton
1859	....	ALL	ALL	117889	LKS	Newmains
MEEK						
1840	1870	1700	1840	155322	GLS	Gloucester
1881	1915	1872	1915	169323	LEI	Leicester
1806	1896	ALL	ALL	109266	LKS	Dunsyre
1839	1868	1800	1868	153990	LND	???
1769	1836	1750	1860	169323	NFK	ALL
1810	1889	....	....	143308	NFK	Hempnall
1790	1810	ALL	1790	143308	NFK	Norwich
1876	1883	1872	1940	169323	NTT	Nottingham
1850	1900	1800	1850	161349	SAL	Betley
....	....	ALL	ALL	169315	STS	Darliston
1837	1870	1810	1880	169323	WAR	Birmingham
MEEKS						
1768	1780	1700	1768	134627	CAM	Wilburton
MEER						
1850	1950	1800	1900	107417	SOM	Halse
MEERING						
1880	1960	1800	1880	137707	NFK	???
MEERS						
1850	1900	1800	1850	137413	ALL	ALL
MEES						
1850	1960	1700	1850	147303	GLS	Bristol
....	....	1700	1850	147303	WIL	Bradford On Avon
....	....	1700	1850	147303	WIL	Murhill
....	....	1700	1850	147303	WIL	Winsley

Known From	To	Researching From	To	Ref	Cty	Place
MEESON						
1765	1992	1700	1800	152692	DEN	Ruabon
1800	1810	1700	1850	150002	STS	Barton Under Needwood
MEETEN						
1750	1920	ALL	ALL	164453	SSX	West
MEGGINSON						
1700	1992	1600	1992	147311	NYK	Scarborough
MEGGISON						
....	....	1700	1800	116173	YKS	Helmsley
1900	....	....	....	142360	YKS	York
MEGGITT						
1883	....	1880	1992	131563	YKS	Hatfield
MEGGS						
1747	1786	1550	1750	174343	HAM	East Worldham
1760	1813	1700	1813	167533	SFK	Acton
MEGNIN						
1746	1841	1700	1850	144797	LND	Stepney
MEGRATH						
1900	1992	1900	1992	110825	ANT	Belfast
MEGSON						
....	....	ALL	ALL	147338	ALL	Name Study
1365	1992	1365	1961	147338	ALL	ALL
MEHARG						
1850	1992	1750	1850	167789	ANT	???
1850	1992	1750	1850	167789	DOW	???
MEHUISH						
1753	1831	1720	1831	107573	DEV	Bampton
MEIKLE						
1785	1826	ALL	....	155713	LKS	Avondale
1870	....	....	....	106852	LKS	Carluke
MEIKLEHAM						
....	....	ALL	ALL	119679	ALL	Name Study
MEINOLL						
1293	1627	1550	1627	113956	DBY	Youlgreave
MEISLER						
1866	1923	....	....	165727	LND	East
MELBOURNE						
1840	1900	1550	1840	150843	LIN	North Owersby
1816	....	....	....	148768	MDX	St Pancras
1841	1920	1800	1841	124397	SRY	Godstone
MELDRUM						
....	....	1800	1870	124931	ABD	Alford
....	....	1800	1870	124931	ABD	Strathdon
1785	1796	....	ALL	101370	FIF	Limekiln
1722	1763	1700	1800	159905	KRS	Kinross
MELEMOUTH						
ALL	ALL	ALL	ALL	147354	DOR	ALL
MELEN						
1813	1855	1750	1875	153249	WOR	Redditch
MELHUISH						
1729	1856	1680	1780	121568	SOM	West
MELIA						
1800	1870	1800	1870	121339	DUR	Darlington
1800	1860	1800	1860	121339	IRL	???
1890	1992	1850	1920	136239	LAN	Liverpool
MELLARD						
....	....	1600	1806	150150	WYK	Crofton
MELLER						
1790	1840	1800	1900	176281	KEN	Tudeley
MELLERS						
1850	1870	1800	1850	143898	DEV	Tavistock
MELLEY						
1790	1880	1530	1790	169986	WOR	Frankley
MELLING						
1859	....	1859	1992	151378	HEF	Preston On Wye
1770	1830	1770	1840	145602	LAN	Chorley
1850	1920	ALL	1850	144932	LAN	Lathom
1751	1840	1750	1870	118443	LAN	Lytham
1784	1784	1700	1784	163783	LAN	Woodplumpton
MELLINGS						
1850	....	1800	1900	131547	HEF	Leintwardine
MELLIS						
1802	1850	1750	1800	141798	PER	???
MELLISH						
1950	1992	1800	1950	125555	MDX	Finsbury
1950	1992	1800	1950	125555	MDX	Shoreditch
1836	1856	....	....	173932	SRY	Ashtead
1829	....	....	....	173932	SRY	Lambeth
1866	....	....	....	173932	SRY	Long Ditton
1643	....	....	....	173932	SRY	Wotton
MELLMOUTHE						
1592	?	ALL	ALL	147354	DOR	ALL
MELLOR						
1845	1870	1800	1845	151343	CHS	Ancoats
1800	....	....	....	122505	CHS	???
1840	1880	1800	1900	111147	DBY	ALL
1800	1900	1750	1800	165336	DBY	Belper
....	1690	1600	1700	152560	DBY	Idridgehay
1845	1870	1800	1845	151343	LAN	Manchester
1872	1992	....	....	106895	LAN	Oldham
1900	1900	ALL	ALL	127787	LEI	Leicester
1812	1889	1700	1812	110639	STS	Cheadle
1812	1889	1700	1812	110639	STS	Leek
1870	1900	1750	1900	178136	STS	Longton
1900	....	....	....	122505	STS	Newcastle
1820	1870	1800	1820	128333	STS	Sheen
1810	1841	ALL	1810	122017	WYK	Saddleworth
1737	....	1700	1740	170348	YKS	Almondbury
1685	1845	1650	1685	101796	YKS	Darton
1800	1869	1700	1800	102008	YKS	Thurstonland
MELLORS						
1800	1992	ALL	1800	134511	NTT	Arnold
MELLOWS						
....	1804	1700	1804	160024	NTT	Newark
MELLS						
1862	1862	1862	1890	168149	LIN	Spilsby
MELLSOP						
....	....	ALL	ALL	151386	ALL	Name Study
MELMETH						
ALL	ALL	ALL	ALL	147354	ALL	ALL
MELMOTH						
1580	1992	ALL	ALL	147354	ALL	ALL
1885	1939	1880	1992	147354	DEV	Plymouth
ALL	ALL	ALL	ALL	147354	HAM	ALL
MELMOUTH						
....	....	ALL	ALL	147354	ALL	Name Study
1327	1992	ALL	ALL	147354	DOR	Bishops Caundle
MELSOM						
....	....	ALL	ALL	147370	ALL	Name Study
MELSOME						
1887	1915	1887	1915	178683	GLS	Kemble
1800	1927	1800	1992	178683	WIL	Maddington
1800	1874	1800	1874	178683	WIL	Norton Bavant
MELTON						
1820	1844	1700	1850	117013	NFK	Docking
MELVELLE						
1750	1800	ALL	ALL	140902	SUT	Brora
1750	1800	ALL	ALL	140902	SUT	Golspie
MELVEN						
1750	1800	ALL	ALL	140902	SUT	Brora
1750	1800	ALL	ALL	140902	SUT	Golspie
MELVILLE						
1780	1803	1750	1803	148288	FIF	Auchtermuchty
1800	1900	ALL	1800	117188	FIF	Balmerino
1780	1803	1750	1803	148288	FIF	Strathmiglo
1827	1841	1800	1827	146358	KCD	Castletown
1860	1860	1800	1800	146358	KCD	Mary Culter
1862	1992	1800	1862	146358	LTN	Edinburgh
1800	1860	....	....	159883	PER	Drimmie
1700	....	?	?	136999	SSX	Brighton
1750	1992	ALL	ALL	140902	SUT	Brora
1750	1992	ALL	ALL	140902	SUT	Colspie
MELVIN						
1839	....	....	....	120804	LKS	Stonehouse
1750	1770	1750	1770	146536	STI	Larbert
1750	1850	ALL	ALL	140902	SUT	Brora
1750	1850	ALL	ALL	140902	SUT	Golspie
MELWAYE						
1540	1599	1540	1599	143162	KEN	Medway
MEMBREY						
1819	1992	ALL	ALL	147389	DEV	ALL
MEMORY						
1720	1885	ALL	ALL	147397	LEI	Leicester
1695	1720	ALL	1730	147397	LEI	Quarndon
1830	1841	....	....	167517	LND	South
1885	1930	....	....	147397	NTH	Northampton
MENADUE						
1802	1992	1650	1802	114863	CON	South West
1802	1992	1650	1802	114863	CON	Breage
1802	1992	1650	1802	114863	CON	Perranzabuloe
1802	1992	1650	1802	114863	CON	Sithney
MENCE						
1779	1992	....	....	126101	WOR	Ombersley
MENEAR						
1834	1851	1800	1870	127973	CON	St Austell

Known From	To	Researching From	To	Ref	Cty	Place
MENHAM						
1872	1890	ALL	ALL	174505	DUR	Gateshead
MENHENETT						
1881	1956	1800	1950	147419	CON	Rose
1850	1950	1800	1950	147419	CON	St Agnes
MENHENICK						
1600	1800	1800	1840	147419	CON	St Breward
MENHENIOT						
1841	1912	1700	1950	147419	CON	Zelah
MENHENOTT						
1880	1955	1880	1955	147419	CON	Goonhavern
MENNIE						
1760	1900	1500	1760	147427	ABD	Rayne
1850	1960	1700	1780	136921	SCT	Aberdeen
MENNIM						
....	....	ALL	ALL	147435	ALL	Name Study
MENSLEY						
1800	1900	1700	1800	133019	CON	Launceston
1865	1900	1800	1865	133019	MDX	South Hampstead
MENZIES						
1876	1881	1876	1881	145181	DBY	Whittington
1835	1846	1835	1846	145181	HUN	Staunton
1774	1790	1700	1850	159379	PER	Aberfeldy
1820	1840	1800	1820	149632	PER	Weem
1850	1871	1848	1871	145181	WAR	Nuneaton
MEPHAM						
1750	1900	....	....	122130	SSX	Burwash Common
1830	1900	....	....	122130	SSX	Rotherfield
....	....	1900	....	100536	SSX	???
MEPSTED						
1864	1868	1800	1900	164992	KEN	Dover
1800	1900	....	....	109452	KEN	???
1843	1844	1800	1900	164992	YKS	Scarborough
MERCER						
1840	1850	ALL	1840	146757	BEW	Gordon
....	....	....	....	150584	BRK	Chieveley
1640	1913	....	....	150584	BRK	Winterbourne
1692	1692	....	....	135437	CHS	Chester
1817	1817	....	1861	103349	KEN	High Halden
1750	1780	1700	1750	120901	LAN	Burnley
1850	1900	1750	1850	132632	LAN	Heywood
1843	1906	1843	1906	122238	LAN	Liverpool
1855	1992	1500	1890	134600	LAN	Liverpool
1829	1992	1750	1829	176257	LAN	Liverpool
1825	1860	....	....	138231	LAN	Manchester
1825	1860	....	....	138231	LAN	Salford
1804	1871	1750	1890	126586	LAN	???
1680	1705	ALL	1705	149063	ROX	Melrose
....	....	1800	1890	131989	SSX	Blackheath
1809	1860	....	....	160067	SSX	Brighton
1844	1862	1862	1992	107255	WIL	Bradford On Avon
1805	1844	ALL	ALL	107255	WIL	Westwood
1795	1854	1750	1795	149152	YKS	Sheffield
MERCHANT						
....	....	ALL	ALL	125733	BRK	Ashbury
1817	1829	1750	1850	131547	GLS	Cherington
....	....	ALL	ALL	125733	WIL	Swindon
....	....	1800	1880	129445	WIL	???
MERCOTE						
1775	1885	1700	1900	145572	KEN	Woolwich
1775	1885	1700	1900	145572	LND	Edgware Road
MERDLING						
1750	1850	....	....	132756	BDF	Ridgemont
MERDON						
1550	1880	1300	1880	105333	DEV	Buckland In The Moor
1550	1880	1300	1880	105333	DEV	Holne
1550	1880	1300	1880	105333	DEV	Ilsington
1550	1880	1300	1880	105333	DEV	Lydford
1570	1640	1500	1700	151653	DEV	North Bovey
1550	1880	1300	1880	105333	DEV	Widecombe In The Moor
MERE						
1100	1400	1100	1400	146226	STS	???
MEREDITH						
....	....	ALL	ALL	147443	ALL	Name Study
1830	1900	1750	1830	173312	CHS	West
1750	....	1600	1750	129607	DEN	Gresford
1698	1900	....	....	165999	GLS	Bristol
1698	1900	....	....	165999	GLS	Hembury
1698	1900	....	....	165999	GLS	Olveston
1813	1813	....	....	127426	HEF	Dorstone
1818	1836	....	....	127426	HEF	Kinnersley
1852	1852	....	....	127426	HEF	Staunton On Wye

Known From	To	Researching From	To	Ref	Cty	Place
MEREDITH contd.						
1779	1779	....	....	127426	HEF	???
1825	....	ALL	1825	124206	MON	???
1715	1848	1600	1992	176877	RAD	Beguildy
1800	1992	1821	1992	122238	SAL	Broseley
1780	1810	1801	1820	122238	SAL	Willey
1850	1880	....	....	117560	SRY	Chertsey
1594	1814	1550	1610	102830	STS	ALL
1810	1992	1766	1992	145319	WOR	Hagley
1845	1850	1800	1850	138487	WOR	Hartlebury
MEREFIELD						
1765	1866	1700	1765	127116	DOR	Compton Abbas
MERES						
1810	1900	1750	1810	152471	LEI	Leicester
MERNOR						
1902	....	1880	1910	163775	MDX	Chelsea
MERRALL						
1821	1843	ALL	1821	174815	LEI	Leicester
1788	1856	ALL	ALL	141615	NTH	Wilbarston
MERREDEW						
1800	1910	ALL	ALL	134481	ALL	ALL
MERRELEW						
1600	1670	1550	1600	121339	NYK	Lythe
MERRETT						
1812	1992	....	1812	106100	GLS	Arlingham
....	....	ALL	ALL	106100	GLS	Frampton On Severn
1770	1900	1650	1800	147478	GLS	Longney
1770	1900	1650	1800	147478	GLS	Moreton Valence
1770	1900	1650	1800	147478	GLS	Stndish
1747	1840	ALL	ALL	129933	HAM	Portsmouth
1819	1838	1700	1818	131245	KEN	Greenwich
1770	1771	1700	1769	131245	MDX	Brentford
1874	1932	ALL	ALL	129933	SRY	Sutton
1840	1900	1700	1840	164879	SSX	ALL
1700	1900	1600	1900	147486	WIL	Potterne
MERRICK						
....	....	ALL	ALL	100390	CHS	Warrington
1730	1860	1700	1900	157171	GLS	Bulley
1813	....	1800	1850	136905	HEF	Eye
1893	1920	1800	1925	147508	HEF	Hereford
....	....	1750	1830	163201	MAY	Ballindine
1780	1800	....	....	140554	SAL	Bishopscastle
1789	1992	1600	1789	109177	???	London
MERRICKS						
1860	1860	1750	1900	127302	SCT	Edinburgh
MERRIFIELD						
1640	1700	1640	1700	142018	WIL	South East
MERRIGAN						
....	....	ALL	ALL	147524	ALL	Name Study
MERRIKIN						
1700	1950	1760	1992	125881	LIN	Kings Lynn
1700	1950	1760	1992	125881	NFK	Kings Lynn
MERRILEES						
1729	1840	ALL	1729	122386	DUR	Whickham
MERRILL						
1582	1992	1582	1992	147532	CHS	ALL
1580	1890	1580	1890	147532	DBY	ALL
1800	1992	1800	1992	147532	LAN	Liverpool
1800	1992	1800	1992	147532	LAN	Manchester
1730	1820	1600	1750	112704	LIN	Winthorpe
1850	1850	1850	1900	106666	LND	Clapham
1810	1850	1740	1810	134139	NTH	Wilbarston
1886	1980	1700	1886	107301	NTT	Netherfield
1820	1992	1820	1992	147532	SAL	Adderley
1866	1875	1866	1875	147532	SAL	Childs Ercall
1800	1850	1800	1850	147532	SAL	Market Drayton
1800	1992	1800	1992	147532	STS	ALL
MERRILLS						
1722	....	1650	1730	152110	SFK	Glemsford
MERRIMAN						
....	....	ALL	ALL	147540	ALL	Name Study
1867	1885	1800	1950	146978	GLA	Swansea
....	....	1650	1850	115142	LEI	Twycross
1850	1910	1850	1910	117323	MDX	Old Brentford
1867	1885	1800	1950	146978	MON	Newport
1660	1900	1660	1840	128708	WIL	Marlborough
MERRIN						
1850	1992	1750	1850	170062	LAN	Manchester
MERRINGTON						
....	....	ALL	ALL	148326	ALL	Name Study
1679	1757	....	1757	137405	CAM	Haslingfield
MERRIT						
1880	1960	1880	1960	112712	WIL	Chapmanslade
1700	1900	1700	1900	112712	WIL	Market ;avington

Known From	To	Researching From	To	Ref	Cty	Place
MERRITT						
....	....	ALL	ALL	147559	ALL	Name Study
1066	1950	1066	1950	147559	ALL	ALL
....	....	1780	1820	148113	GLS	King Stanley
1820	1845	ALL	ALL	147567	HAM	Clanfield
1830	1920	1830	1920	147567	HAM	East Meon
....	....	1860	1880	148113	STS	Sedgeley
MERRY						
....	....	ALL	ALL	106275	ALL	Name Study
....	....	1700	1850	169501	DFS	Kirkconnel
1866	1887	ALL	1887	175862	OXF	Bucknell
1706	1736	....	....	117404	STS	Kings Bromley
MERRYFIELD						
....	....	ALL	ALL	143502	ESS	ALL
MERRYMAN						
....	....	1800	1900	115142	???	Oakthorpe
MERRYWEATHER						
ALL	ALL	ALL	ALL	147575	ALL	ALL
1905	....	....	....	167444	BRK	Reading
1886	1901	1820	1885	113719	LIN	Lincoln
1850	1895	....	....	173142	LND	Battersea
MERSH						
1790	....	....	1800	171441	HAM	Crawley
....	....	1650	1800	145173	HAM	Morestead
MERVIN						
....	....	1700	1900	106461	WIL	ALL
MERWOOD						
1841	1992	....	....	107158	IOW	Newport
MERYICK						
1810	1992	1500	1853	151483	HAM	Southampton
MESLEY						
1750	1850	1700	1750	147583	SSX	Falmer
1750	1850	1700	1750	147583	SSX	Lewes
MESNARD						
1800	1850	1850	1960	153486	KEN	???
1700	1850	1850	1960	153486	LND	Southwark
MESSAM						
....	....	?	?	143499	WIL	Preshute
MESSENGER						
....	....	ALL	ALL	147591	ALL	Name Study
ALL	ALL	ALL	ALL	147591	ALL	ALL
....	....	ALL	1730	103284	BKM	???
1843	1913	1840	1900	125032	BRK	Hurst
1765	1818	1500	1765	104825	BRK	Waltham St Lawrence
1730	1840	1700	1850	125032	BRK	Waltham St Lawrence
....	....	ALL	1730	103284	BRK	???
....	....	1800	1870	177903	CMA	Moresby
1741	1763	....	....	138401	CUL	Distinction
1900	1940	1890	1940	151181	ESS	Ilford
1840	1880	1700	1840	173835	GLS	Preston
....	....	1700	1820	173835	GLS	South Cerney
1695	....	....	1720	171441	KEN	Lenham
1882	....	1800	1940	151181	LND	Peckham
1862	1868	1830	1862	120731	MDX	Chelsea
1800	1850	1650	1800	139769	MDX	London
1880	....	1860	1900	151181	MDX	Peckham
1780	1837	....	....	127035	MDX	???
....	....	1840	1910	165786	NBL	Newcastle
1773	1800	ALL	ALL	177989	OXF	Holton
1859	1859	1820	1880	151181	SRY	Walworth
1880	1992	....	....	173835	SSX	Brighton
1880	1992	....	....	173835	SSX	Hove
1780	1950	ALL	1820	153184	WIL	Ashton Keynes
....	....	ALL	1800	151602	WIL	Rasmbury
MESSER						
1873	1930	1700	1873	177881	MLN	Edinburgh
1800	1880	1800	1860	119059	OXF	Kingston
MESSETER						
1811	1965	1700	1992	112216	WIL	Calne
MESSETTER						
....	....	ALL	1650	178411	NTT	North
MESTON						
1756	1900	ALL	ALL	169528	ABD	ALL
METCALF						
1870	1980	1870	1992	160849	LAN	Audenshaw
1650	1880	1600	1900	160849	LIN	North
1800	1840	1700	1800	101907	NBL	North Shields
1753	....	....	1753	101761	NTT	Everton
....	....	1750	1800	172871	SFK	Bury St Edmunds
1788	1822	1700	1850	143251	SLI	???
1859	1939	1850	1939	131865	WES	Kirkby Stephen
1810	1860	1750	1810	122343	YKS	Boulby
1820	1865	1865	1992	139351	YKS	Rillington
1818	1820	....	....	139351	YKS	Ripley

Known From	To	Researching From	To	Ref	Cty	Place
METCALFE						
....	....	ALL	ALL	105813	ALL	ALL
....	....	1300	1992	147605	ALL	ALL
1786	1880	1786	1880	162914	CAM	Swavesey
1873	1918	....	....	121142	CUL	Sedburgh
1771	1992	1770	1910	147621	FLN	Whitford
1783	1985	1770	1876	149845	LIN	Brigg
1783	1985	1770	1876	149845	LIN	Caistor
1747	1907	1600	1760	101575	LIN	Elsham
1747	1907	1600	1760	101575	LIN	Wrawby By Briggs
ALL	1600	....	....	132756	NBL	???
1750	1850	1500	1800	168629	NYK	Lockton
....	....	1800	1900	147613	YKS	Burton In Lonsdale
....	....	1750	1800	147613	YKS	Clapham
1840	1860	....	....	102946	YKS	Coxwold
1840	1860	....	....	102946	YKS	Crayke
1820	1860	....	....	102946	YKS	Easingwold
1841	1871	....	....	102946	YKS	Farlington
1908	1935	....	1950	177695	YKS	Great Smeeton
1750	1992	1750	1992	116173	YKS	Helmsley
1747	1907	1600	1760	101575	YKS	Hull
....	....	1725	1770	147613	YKS	Ingleton
1755	1992	1755	1992	173738	YKS	Lockton
1700	1800	....	....	102946	YKS	Middleton On Moor
1790	1820	....	....	102946	YKS	Newton On Ouse
1880	1899	....	....	102946	YKS	Sessy
1770	1820	....	....	102946	YKS	Stillington
....	....	1800	1900	147613	YKS	Thornton In Lonsdale
1670	1730	1600	1700	116173	YKS	Whorlton
1760	1866	....	....	100536	???	???
METCLAF						
1797	1927	1700	1810	118362	LIN	Donington In Holland
METCLAFE						
....	....	ALL	ALL	105813	ALL	Name Study
1827	1982	ALL	ALL	112240	YKS	Aysgarth
1831	1992	1300	1831	100196	YKS	Drighlington
....	....	ALL	1820	178403	YKS	Stainton
1862	1982	ALL	ALL	112240	YKS	Stokesley
METFORD						
1771	1797	1770	1800	151599	SOM	Broadway
METHERELL						
....	....	ALL	ALL	147648	ALL	Name Study
METHERINGHAM						
....	....	ALL	ALL	147656	ALL	Name Study
METHVEN						
1820	1880	1750	1820	176753	LND	Whitchapel
METLAND						
1815	....	1700	1850	151246	KEN	Yalding
METSON						
....	....	ALL	ALL	147664	ALL	Name Study
1849	1877	1700	1849	173509	ESS	Braintree
METTER						
1811	1823	1770	1811	107654	DEV	Bridestowe
METTERS						
1790	1850	1790	1850	143898	DEV	Tavistock
?	?	?	?	157570	DEV	???
MEW						
1890	1890	1890	1950	106666	ALL	ALL
1736	1804	1500	1736	129577	IOW	???
MEWBURN						
....	....	1600	1800	179531	DUR	ALL
....	....	1600	1800	179531	YKS	Stainton
MEWES						
1772	1964	ALL	ALL	147680	ENG	South East
1772	1964	ALL	1773	147680	KEN	ALL
1772	1964	ALL	1773	147680	LND	ALL
MEWETT						
1562	1992	1562	1900	104914	ALL	ALL
1752	1784	....	....	139971	SSX	Eastbourne
MEWHA						
....	....	ALL	ALL	109150	ALL	Name Study
MEWIS						
1819	1992	1700	1819	130257	LEI	Barwell
MEWKILL						
1860	....	....	....	174750	MDX	London
MEWTON						
1800	1992	1600	1800	121118	CON	Central
1851	1992	1600	1851	147699	CON	Allet
1842	1922	1842	1864	170976	CON	Kenwyn Truro
....	....	1600	1800	147699	CON	Kenwyn
1800	1992	1600	1800	147699	CON	Perranzabuloe

Known From	Known To	Researching From	Researching To	Ref	Cty	Place
MEYER						
....	....	1870	1920	100358	LIN	Boston
MEYERS						
1881	1992	1800	1900	105414	LEI	Market Harborough
MEYNELL						
1800	1850	1700	1800	161519	YKS	Crathorne
1840	....	....	....	119911	YKS	Leyburn
MEYRICK						
1828	1860	1800	1831	152943	GLS	Oldbury On The Hill
MIALL						
1668	1813	1600	1813	159581	SRY	East Clandon
1668	1813	1600	1813	159581	SRY	Shere
MICALLEF						
1736	1962	....	....	147702	GLA	Barry
MICHAEL						
1772	1859	....	....	129097	BRE	Llandeffelle
1840	1870	1700	1840	138452	CMN	Gwynfe
1840	1870	1700	1840	138452	CMN	Llangadog
....	1846	....	....	140767	MAY	Ballina
1790	1860	1790	1860	139807	MON	Bedwelty
1846	....	1850	....	140767	STS	Cheadle
1860	....	1860	....	140767	YKS	Leeds
MICHEAL						
1817	1870	1800	1816	172006	GLA	Rhondda
MICHEAU						
1773	....	1700	1800	116432	DEV	ALL
MICHEL						
1787	....	ALL	1787	165263	SSX	Rotherfield
MICHELL						
1625	1935	....	....	174319	CON	Gorran
1690	1992	....	....	109444	CON	Gwinear
1600	1800	1600	1800	132942	CON	Gwinear
1786	1872	....	....	174319	CON	Mevagissey
1621	1763	1580	1621	102571	CON	Morvah
1840	1850	1800	1850	137111	CON	Probus
....	....	1600	1750	130591	SOM	Wiveliscombe
1820	1878	1800	1900	176982	STS	Bentley Hay
MICHELSON						
1767	1819	1750	1800	159042	LIN	Dowsby
1733	1733	1700	1750	159042	RUT	Thistleton
MICKLAM						
1776	1859	ALL	1776	133957	SXW	Funtington
MICKLE						
1857	1880	1850	1900	111821	BEW	Duns
MICKLEBOROUGH						
....	....	1700	1850	117587	NFK	South
MICKLEBURGH						
....	....	ALL	ALL	147710	ALL	Name Study
ALL	ALL	ALL	ALL	147710	ALL	ALL
1821	1846	1760	1850	147214	ESS	Great Baddow
1790	1860	1790	1860	130400	SFK	Lowestoft
MICKLEFIELD						
....	....	1700	1737	172871	SFK	Bury St Edmonds
MICKLETHWAITE						
1890	1899	....	1890	102059	YKS	Barnsley
1831	1992	1750	1831	136301	YKS	Dewsbury
1831	1992	1750	1831	136301	YKS	Thornhill
MICKLEWRIGHT						
1741	1847	....	....	117404	STS	Gnosall
1790	1791	1700	1850	179116	STS	Gnosall
MICKMAN						
1833	1834	1800	1850	129607	DOW	Mourne
....	1846	....	....	140767	IRL	???
1851	1920	1851	1881	140767	YKS	Leeds
1851	1920	1851	1881	140767	YKS	Scarborough
1851	1920	1851	1881	140767	YKS	Whitby
MIDDLEBROOK						
1850	1992	1750	1850	102342	LIN	Isle Of Axholme
1750	1910	1850	1880	129496	YKS	Morley
MIDDLEBROOKE						
1667	1712	....	....	121835	LIN	Waddington
MIDDLEDITCH						
1849	....	ALL	ALL	149438	ESS	Terling Green
1700	1820	1700	1800	115614	SFK	Campsey Ash
....	?	?	....	114642	SFK	Hawkedon
MIDDLEMISS						
1740	1750	1700	1760	130915	ELN	Dirleton
MIDDLEMORE						
1400	1900	1400	1900	100420	WAR	ALL
MIDDLESTON						
1823	....	1823	....	104213	DBY	Hope
....	....	1800	1840	154873	DUR	Sunderland
MIDDLETON						
1740	1960	1600	1992	149233	ABD	Chapel Of Garioch
MIDDLETON contd.						
1790	1862	1700	1790	119881	ABD	Coull
1824	1827	1500	1824	110310	BRK	Newbury
1550	1900	1700	1800	147729	DBY	Chesterfield
1803	1876	1750	1900	124788	DBY	Smalldale
1800	1853	1800	1890	124788	DBY	Thornhill
1863	1884	1600	1910	159042	DUB	Dublin
1810	1992	1700	1810	147737	DUR	ALL
1768	1800	1600	1800	130125	DUR	Chester Le Street
1830	1970	1800	....	119474	DUR	Sunderland
1758	1992	1758	1992	136158	ESS	Terling
1700	1800	1700	1800	116831	HUN	Ramsey
....	....	1700	....	149004	IRL	???
1806	1812	1780	1806	147745	KEN	Brompton
1841	1992	1810	1841	137952	KEN	Minister In Sheppey
1871	1920	1864	1930	159042	LAN	Salford
1750	1850	ALL	ALL	145726	LEI	Hinckley
1830	1880	1800	1992	102407	LEI	Hinkley
1800	1992	ALL	ALL	152226	LND	Deptford
ALL	1850	....	....	114642	MDX	London
1810	1992	1700	1810	147737	NBL	ALL
1841	1841	ALL	1992	102245	NBL	Newcastle Upon Tyne
....	....	1800	1850	146269	NFK	Lynn
1730	1750	1700	1730	121339	NYK	Easington
1875	1939	1700	1875	147761	OXF	???
1762	1790	1740	1790	135828	SFK	Shipmeadow
1733	1733	1680	1750	121568	SOM	West
1764	1840	1700	1840	138487	SOM	Pitminster
1900	1950	....	1900	116777	STS	North
....	....	1600	1780	137014	STS	Polesworth
1790	1803	....	1790	101761	STS	Stoke On Trent
....	....	1600	1780	137014	STS	Tamworth
1814	1824	1750	1814	117625	YKS	Brignall
1784	1900	....	....	118354	YKS	Dent
1828	....	....	....	175587	YKS	Headingley
....	....	1650	1750	131598	YKS	Hutton Bushell
1900	1992	1800	1992	147788	YKS	Leeds
MIDDLETON-SALT						
1832	....	....	....	167444	STS	Tamworth
MIDDLEWICH						
1842	1850	1800	1842	128368	DEV	Ipplepen
MIDDLEWREK						
1842	1850	1800	1842	128368	DEV	Ipplepen
MIDDLEYARD						
....	....	ALL	ALL	147796	ALL	Name Study
MIDELTON						
1764	1840	1700	1840	138487	SOM	Pitminster
MIDGELEY						
1816	1824	ALL	1824	148172	YKS	Wetherby
MIDGLEY						
1843	1992	1800	1860	114464	LAN	Manchester
1750	1800	1660	1750	147583	SSX	Falmer
ALL	1880	....	....	170798	WRY	Calder Valley
1600	1730	1400	1600	147583	YKS	Halifax
1808	1832	ALL	1832	173290	YKS	Halifax
1730	1850	....	1800	147818	YKS	Harewood Estates
1600	1730	1400	1600	147583	YKS	Keighley
1800	1906	1700	1800	112224	YKS	Leeds
1845	1992	....	1845	141968	YKS	Leeds
1821	1900	1800	1992	111821	YKS	North Bierley
1840	1992	1840	1992	147818	YKS	Rufforth
1910	1950	1900	1950	147818	YKS	Shipley
MIDLAM						
1902	1942	1750	1902	156248	CAE	Llandudno
MIDMER						
1820	1992	ALL	1850	131172	SXE	Ticehurst
MIDWINTER						
....	....	ALL	ALL	147834	ALL	Name Study
1900	1992	....	....	147842	LIN	Scunthorpe
....	....	ALL	ALL	147842	WLS	???
MIDWOOD						
1871	1979	1700	1871	138436	YKS	Huddersfield
1871	1979	1700	1871	138436	YKS	Sheffield
MIELL						
1781	1992	1700	1781	161446	WIL	All Cannings
MIEN						
1700	1799	1700	1799	128481	CMA	???
MIERS						
1730	1750	1650	1730	121339	DUR	Staindrop
MIFLIN						
1820	1851	1700	1840	132586	WAR	Rugby
MIGHALL						
1895	1979	1700	1895	107506	SSX	???

Known From	To	Researching From	To	Ref	Cty	Place
MIGHILL						
1700	1750	1560	1750	150517	DOR	North
MIGNON						
1700	1900	ALL	ALL	166022	ALL	ALL
MIHILL						
1650	1700	1560	1750	150517	DOR	North
MIKOSZ						
1892	1920	1890	1980	151742	ESS	London
MILBANK						
1869	1893	1800	1992	116297	ESS	Epping
....	1872	ALL	1872	159204	ESS	Ingrave
1869	1893	1800	1992	116297	SRY	Newington
MILBORNE						
1807	....	ALL	ALL	159034	MDX	Islington
MILBOURN						
1891	1992	1800	1891	147850	DUR	South Shields
1891	1992	1800	1891	147850	LND	Mary Le Bone
MILBOURNE						
1780	1864	1780	1864	149403	CUL	Hayton
MILBURN						
1890	1992	1700	1900	140805	CMA	Cotehill
....	....	1830	1870	150800	CON	St Breock
1740	1820	....	....	102741	DUR	Stanhope
1740	1820	....	....	102741	NBL	Birtley
1784	1900	1750	1992	106003	NBL	Tynemouth
1792	1900	1700	1792	152196	WES	Kendal
1796	1837	1700	1796	125571	YKS	Guisborough
....	....	1700	1770	177393	YKS	Ryther
MILDENHALL						
....	....	1800	1880	142131	BRK	Buckland
1726	1907	....	....	127779	BRK	Lambourn
....	1898	....	....	147869	WIL	???
....	1898	....	....	147869	???	Hungerford
MILDON						
....	....	ALL	1992	164739	DEV	ALL
1798	1840	ALL	1992	164739	DEV	Cullompton
1800	1900	1800	1900	172634	DEV	Tiverton
MILDRED						
....	....	ALL	ALL	118192	ALL	Name Study
1730	1992	ALL	ALL	118192	ALL	ALL
MILEHAM						
1780	1930	ALL	1780	147877	HAM	Bentley
....	1797	1700	1820	176621	LND	???
....	....	1840	1880	150525	MDX	Norwood
1730	1780	1550	1730	150843	NFK	Ludham
....	....	ALL	ALL	102083	SRY	Aldershot
MILEMAN						
....	....	ALL	ALL	143081	ALL	Name Study
1870	1900	....	....	111368	SRY	Southwark
MILES						
1796	1992	1750	1796	147907	GLS	Aldsworth
1820	1890	1820	1890	110523	GNT	Monmouth
....	....	1800	1900	103667	HAM	South East
1795	1800	1700	1900	158399	HAM	Mattingley
1800	1850	1600	1900	120677	HAM	Micheldever
1792	1920	....	....	168777	HAM	Micheldever
1939	....	1939	1992	104876	HAM	Portsmouth
1815	1841	1700	1815	166804	HAM	Quarley
1750	1839	1700	1750	132039	HAM	Winchester
1712	1792	1650	1712	168777	HAM	Winchester
1842	1852	1800	1980	171999	HRT	Ickleford
1790	1880	ALL	1790	131091	KEN	ALL
1830	1870	1700	1830	173460	KEN	East
1718	1750	....	1780	171441	KEN	Borden
1768	1838	ALL	1768	175080	KEN	Eynsford
1768	1838	ALL	1768	175080	KEN	Gravesend
1850	....	ALL	ALL	172057	KEN	???
....	....	1800	1810	129933	LND	Deptford
1811	1891	1811	1891	144541	MDX	London
1825	1855	....	....	127779	MDX	St Pancras
1850	....	ALL	ALL	172057	MDX	???
1796	1973	1920	1925	164070	MON	Trevethin
1700	1850	1650	1850	126799	NFK	Great Bircham
1799	1799	ALL	1799	108197	NFK	Happisburgh
1849	....	1800	1849	128724	SFK	Haughley
1850	1992	1808	1850	129895	SFK	Ipswich
1822	1940	....	1845	166553	SOM	Frome
....	....	1780	1820	177725	SOM	Glastonbury
1798	1871	1700	1798	164267	SRY	Aldershot
1851	1960	1800	1900	113387	SRY	Great Bookham
1850	1900	1700	1900	106755	SSX	Burgess Hill
1785	1863	ALL	1785	158445	SSX	Horsham
....	....	1700	1900	106755	SSX	Hurstpierpoint
1850	1900	1700	1900	106755	SSX	Keymer Clayton
MILES contd.						
1746	1880	1600	1750	147885	SSX	Keymoe
1746	1880	1600	1750	147885	SSX	Lindfield
1850	1900	1700	1900	106755	SSX	Plumpton
1864	1890	ALL	ALL	149004	SSX	Uckfield
1746	1880	1600	1750	147885	SSX	Wnelsfield
1771	1805	1730	1770	103896	WIL	ALL
1650	1950	1600	1700	157287	WIL	Maiden Bradley
....	....	1830	1855	111856	WLS	Paren Pleu
1829	1850	1700	1829	155810	???	Manchester
MILESON						
1700	1912	....	....	171492	CAM	Cambridge
1700	1912	....	....	171492	ESS	???
1700	1912	....	....	171492	KEN	???
1700	1912	....	....	171492	LND	???
1700	1912	....	....	171492	SFK	Norton
MILFORD						
1820	1862	1820	1992	114596	DEV	Ash Reigney
1813	1881	?	1813	147915	DEV	Tedburn St Mary
1685	1788	1600	1685	158402	DEV	Zeal Monackorum
1910	1920	1920	1940	151742	ESS	London
MILGATE						
1666	1844	1600	1900	153591	KEN	Appledore
1666	1844	1600	1900	153591	KEN	Frittenden
1870	1900	1870	1900	113743	SSX	Rye
MILHAM						
1762	1762	1500	1762	110310	SRY	Farnhan
1821	....	ALL	1821	125466	SSX	ALL
MILHENCH						
1821	1992	1426	1821	147931	LAN	Oldham
....	....	1426	1992	147931	WIG	Dumfries
1821	1992	1426	1821	147931	YKS	Saddleworth
1816	1816	1774	1816	159492	YKS	Saddleworth
MILINGTON						
1700	1920	ALL	ALL	148113	ALL	???
MILL						
1841	1866	1837	1870	106321	CON	Illogan
1841	1866	1837	1870	106321	CON	Redruth
1818	1845	....	....	130176	CON	Redruth
1760	1794	1600	1760	102571	CON	Uny Lelant
1869	1927	1866	1927	106321	DBY	Buxton
?	?	?	?	117528	DEV	Newton Tracy
1790	1810	1780	1850	171158	DEV	Uffculme
1926	1992	1926	1992	106321	SFK	Ipswich
MILLAGAN						
1748	1769	1600	1748	145289	HAM	Isle Of Wight
MILLAR						
1850	....	ALL	ALL	117889	ANS	Forfar
1830	1950	1700	1830	155497	ANT	???
1748	1765	1740	1780	146536	AYR	Kilmaurs
1800	1840	1700	1800	146285	CON	Mylor
1787	1825	1650	1850	159956	FIF	Cupar
1770	1880	1600	1770	160342	KKD	Lochrutton
1871	1914	1840	1871	120146	LKS	Dalserf
1841	....	....	1841	148830	LND	Brixton
1710	1710	ALL	1730	129283	NFK	Hales
1811	1992	....	1811	175552	ROX	Gattonside
1779	1841	1779	1840	171654	STI	Stirling
MILLARD						
1850	1992	1700	1850	173460	AVN	Bath
1850	1992	ALL	ALL	164933	BDF	Bedford
1750	1950	1750	1950	114790	BDF	Meppershall
1870	1992	1870	1992	147966	GLS	Cheltenham
1689	1724	....	....	176958	GLS	Shepton Mallet
....	....	1900	1992	109479	LAN	Oldham
1806	1841	1841	1992	135127	LND	Kensington
1811	1881	....	....	103373	PEM	Pembroke
1842	1870	1800	1850	147966	SAL	Sedgley
....	....	ALL	ALL	139033	SOM	ALL
1789	1900	1700	1930	147958	SOM	Batcombe
1789	1900	1700	1930	147958	SOM	Kilmersdon
1729	1743	1729	1760	142018	SOM	Rode
1813	1917	1700	1992	170518	SOM	Taunton
1806	1841	1841	1992	135127	WAR	Ladywood
....	....	ALL	ALL	139033	WIL	ALL
1700	1900	1700	1900	110361	WIL	Nettleton
1830	1870	1700	1992	172421	WIL	Westbury
1815	1844	....	....	121835	???	Walberton
MILLARDS						
1793	1874	ALL	ALL	168009	LND	Islington
MILLEDGE						
1736	1805	1600	1815	147974	DOR	South East
MILLEN						
1798	1874	1700	1920	172073	OXF	Spelsbury

Known From	To	Researching From	To	Ref	Cty	Place
MILLER						
ALL	ALL	ALL	ALL	148180	ALL	ALL
1713	1844	1600	1867	115630	AYR	Dundonald
1700	1890	ALL	ALL	149632	AYR	Saltcoats
1809	1850	ALL	1809	126721	BKM	North Crawley
....	1841	1810	1890	128961	BRK	Newbury
1800	1900	1750	1850	107417	BRK	Windsor
....	....	1500	1786	138614	CAI	Canisbay
1743	1801	....	....	168203	CAI	Dunbeath
1792	....	1700	1992	154474	CAI	Thrumster
1760	1870	....	....	126497	CAI	Thurso
1792	....	1700	1992	154474	CAI	Thurso
1792	....	1700	1992	154474	CAI	Wick
1809	1927	1800	1980	148083	CAM	Cambridge
?	?	....	....	159395	CAM	Cambridge
?	?	....	....	159395	CAM	Fulbourn
1820	1860	1750	1850	126586	CAM	Wisbech
1855	1861	1855	1861	117668	CHS	Antrobus
1790	1855	1700	1860	117668	CHS	Appleton
1871	1937	1861	1937	117668	CHS	Cogshall
1812	1923	1700	1812	141542	CHS	Hooton
1861	1861	1859	1871	117668	CHS	Widnes
1716	1716	....	1716	108510	CLK	Clackmannan
1850	1984	1800	1850	124583	CMA	Whitehave
1722	....	....	1740	160873	CUL	Brampton
1866	1920	1800	1866	159212	CUL	Workington
1832	1839	....	....	151238	DEV	Beer
1561	1827	1827	1992	143901	DEV	Bradninch
1850	1960	1800	1900	122688	DEV	Lostleigh
1850	1960	1800	1900	122688	DEV	Plymouth
....	....	1700	1850	147613	DFS	Lochmaben
....	....	1700	1850	147613	DFS	Tinwald
1820	1860	1780	1833	161357	DOR	West
1580	1892	1500	1850	176621	DOR	Horton
1580	1892	1500	1850	176621	DOR	Knighton
1811	1839	1811	1954	131970	DOR	Poole
1769	1992	1700	1769	130966	DOR	Wimborne
1850	1890	1800	1850	155594	DOW	Downpatrick
1846	1846	1700	1870	159042	DOW	Killyleagh
1802	....	....	....	148016	ENG	Kendal
1774	....	1700	1774	100013	ESS	Great Waltham
1872	1900	1872	1992	168637	ESS	Harwich
1872	1900	1700	1872	168653	ESS	Harwich
1855	1896	1840	1900	104299	GLS	Bristol
1700	1750	1600	1750	154342	GLS	Siston
1600	ALL	....	....	153397	HAM	New Forest
1806	1806	1780	1820	146358	HIL	ALL
ALL	1840	....	....	105368	IRL	Belfast
1802	....	....	....	148016	IRL	???
1800	1850	1700	1800	112569	KEN	Aldington
1500	1550	1480	1550	154881	KEN	Chelsfield
1830	1955	1700	1900	178624	KEN	Folkestone
1811	....	....	1840	171441	KEN	Newington Next Hythe
1849	1912	....	....	148032	KEN	Whitstable
....	....	1700	1992	111503	LAN	Chorley
1831	1856	....	1831	169412	LAN	Halliwell
....	....	1700	1992	111503	LAN	Leyland
1839	1873	1500	1839	110310	LAN	Liverpool
1840	1900	1820	1992	164984	LAN	Liverpool
1847	....	1800	1875	124796	LAN	Pemberton
1804	1831	1600	1831	110787	LEI	Cosby
....	....	1750	1850	115045	LEI	Norton By Twycross
1814	1850	1700	1900	148008	LIN	ALL
1800	1890	....	1800	161888	LKS	Glasgow
1799	1847	1790	1819	171654	LKS	Rutherglen
1900	1986	ALL	....	136018	LND	South West
1844	1865	1800	1865	145602	LND	Bethnal Green
1840	1849	1800	1872	168637	LND	Edgware
1898	1972	1800	1898	103691	LND	Kentish Town
1816	1863	1700	1900	159956	LND	Lambeth
....	1834	1810	1834	128961	LND	Marylebone
1844	1992	1800	1844	120170	LND	Stepney
....	....	ALL	1819	164984	LTN	Leith
1860	1992	1810	1992	105333	MDX	London
1908	1992	1700	1908	149659	MDX	London
1823	1841	....	1823	176761	NBL	Chevington
1688	1730	1650	1750	160873	NBL	Newcastle On Tyne
1845	1863	ALL	1845	122386	NBL	Newcastle
1774	1820	....	1774	100064	NFK	Little Dunham
1766	1845	1650	1850	149160	NFK	Norwich
1800	1830	1700	1830	106976	NTT	Costock
1856	1992	....	....	101990	OKI	Eday
1856	1992	....	....	101990	OKI	Stronsay
MILLER contd.						
....	....	1770	1841	128961	OXF	Dorchester
1883	1883	1884	1992	127787	PEM	Pembroke Dock
1802	1850	1750	1800	141798	PER	Perth
1799	1851	1851	1911	148024	PER	Scone
1821	1992	1700	1820	136026	ROX	Cavers
1821	1992	1700	1820	136026	ROX	Hawick
1821	1992	1700	1820	136026	ROX	Wilton
1920	1932	1850	1945	104531	SCT	Glasgow
1833	1836	....	....	118133	SCT	Glasgow
....	....	1700	1860	123390	SCT	Glasgow
1820	....	1700	1992	154474	SCT	Stornaway
1800	1900	ALL	ALL	100161	SFK	North
1660	1700	1600	1700	144657	SOM	Congresbury
1841	1851	ALL	1855	104299	SOM	Stoke St Gregory
1900	1986	ALL	....	136018	SRY	South West
1838	1890	1810	1960	148067	SRY	Bermondsey
1901	1912	1901	1992	168637	SRY	Great Bookham
1840	1856	1700	1840	146161	SRY	Greenwich
1737	1902	....	....	100536	SRY	???
1890	1980	....	....	122130	SSX	Buxted
?	?	1777	1848	117919	SSX	Chichester
1880	1900	....	....	122130	SSX	Haywards Heath
1790	1790	1500	1770	110310	SSX	Mountford
1840	1945	1750	1840	132640	SSX	Warbleton
1766	1865	1700	1850	122688	SSX	Westbourne
1800	1980	....	....	122130	SSX	Westham
1860	1980	1900	1960	122130	SSX	Willingdon
1737	1902	....	....	100536	SSX	???
1900	1992	1750	1900	148059	STS	ALL
1900	1992	1800	1900	148059	STS	Hednesford
1791	1828	ALL	....	132349	SXE	Buxted
1422	....	1422	1992	115142	WAR	Mancetter
1656	....	1600	1700	170348	WIL	Purton
1840	1890	1800	1900	107417	WIL	Wootton Bassett
1867	....	1844	1900	115630	WOR	Malvern
1737	1902	....	....	100536	???	Croydon
....	....	....	1890	158763	???	London
MILLERCHIP						
1820	1950	1820	1900	125938	WAR	Coventry
MILLES						
1751	1751	....	....	127426	KEN	Rochester St Nicholas
1683	1683	1600	1683	155276	SFK	Wetheringset
MILLETT						
1690	1790	ALL	1790	137286	CON	West
1692	1967	1600	1692	111163	CON	???
1873	1940	....	....	153982	MDX	St Pancras
1803	1992	1803	1992	148091	SOM	Beckington
1803	1992	1803	1992	148091	SOM	Lullington
1815	1868	1790	1815	175951	YKS	Pontefract
MILLFIELD						
1660	1940	....	....	128996	CAM	Thorney
MILLGROVE						
1794	1951	1500	1794	176052	GLS	Blaisdon
MILLHOUSE						
....	....	ALL	ALL	173096	ALL	Name Study
1610	1992	1580	1992	173096	ALL	ALL
....	....	1860	?	170046	LIN	Spalding
1610	1750	1750	1992	170046	LIN	Woolsthorpe
MILLICHAMP						
....	....	ALL	ALL	148105	ALL	Name Study
1856	1992	1500	1856	119792	SAL	ALL
MILLICHIP						
1872	1901	1800	1900	162450	SAL	Wellington
MILLIER						
....	....	ALL	ALL	106631	ALL	Name Study
1800	1900	1700	1900	106631	SOM	Bleadon
MILLIGAN						
1863	1863	1700	1870	173037	ANT	Hillsborough
1830	1992	ALL	1830	112771	DFS	Gatehouse Of Fleet
1740	....	....	....	148644	DFS	Glenmade
1740	....	....	....	148644	DFS	Kirkmahoe
1863	1863	1700	1870	173037	DOW	Lisburn
1800	1850	1750	1850	152404	KKD	Anwoth
MILLINER						
1738	1788	....	....	175587	SOM	Martock
MILLINGTON						
1760	1900	1700	1900	117668	CHS	Antrobus
1860	1880	1860	1880	117668	CHS	Cogshall
....	....	1400	1800	148121	CHS	???
?	?	?	?	172049	DBY	Derby
1900	1992	....	....	162752	HRT	Hemel Hempstead
1790	1820	1800	1820	101796	LAN	Salford

Known From	To	Researching From	To	Ref	Cty	Place
MILLINGTON contd.						
1795	1850	1700	1795	130206	LIN	Saltfleetby
1799	1992	1750	1799	154024	SAL	Melverley
1805	1805	1805	1805	139971	SAL	Shrewsbury
1800	1803	1700	1810	148121	SAL	Whixall
1800	1803	1700	1810	148121	SAL	???
1879	....	1800	1900	175307	STS	Cheadle
1876	1947	1850	1947	148148	WLS	Hawarden
MILLIQUET						
1750	....	1700	1900	141151	LND	ALL
MILLIS						
1891	....	1885	1920	165492	SRY	Kingston On Thames
MILLMS						
1730	1890	....	....	118206	LIN	Marton
1730	1890	....	....	118206	NTT	Retford
MILLNER						
1800	1825	1800	1825	116831	LND	Finsbury
1820	1880	1830	1880	116831	STS	Wednesbury
MILLS						
1834	1992	1800	1834	166855	BKM	Newport Pagnell
....	....	1800	1930	100188	BRE	Talgarth
1800	1860	1700	1800	101834	CAM	Kingston
1800	1854	1500	1992	148164	CON	Gorran
1837	1875	ALL	ALL	163112	CON	Mevagissey
1800	1854	1500	1992	148164	CON	Tregavarras
1750	1850	1700	1850	154881	COR	Cork
1780	1900	....	....	142026	DEV	Clovelly
1800	1850	1800	1850	155764	DEV	Exeter
1752	1792	....	....	161357	DOR	Beaminster
1700	1799	1700	1799	169781	DOR	Beaminster
1686	1729	1600	1700	177938	DOR	Beaminster
1816	1871	1600	1816	116637	DUR	Monkwearmouth
1816	1871	1600	1816	116637	DUR	Sunderland
....	....	1750	1780	142026	GLA	Neath
1750	....	1750	1900	106410	GLS	Berkeley
1590	1736	....	....	165999	GLS	Henbury
1741	1825	ALL	ALL	118192	GLS	Nympsfield
1758	....	....	....	117579	GLS	Stone
....	....	....	1835	112518	HAM	Basingstoke
1766	1841	1766	....	115576	HAM	Clanukke
1785	1992	1700	1785	102342	HAM	Portsea
1787	1992	1700	1787	170542	HAM	Whitchurch
1816	1992	1816	1992	172952	IOW	Newport
1805	1945	1805	1945	107522	KEN	North
1938	1992	1875	1938	174998	LAN	Bury
1750	1869	1700	1900	102660	LAN	Failsworth
1750	1869	1700	1900	102660	LAN	Hollinwood
1850	1900	1600	1992	122084	LAN	Oldham
1893	1910	1890	1900	159492	LAN	Oldham
1876	1900	1800	1876	175447	LAN	Oldham
1860	1992	1800	1992	164518	LAN	???
1740	1800	1740	1800	103721	LIN	Ulceby By Barton
1850	1900	1800	1900	147958	LND	East
1843	1861	1800	?	165808	LND	Hampstead
1806	1867	1750	1806	175064	LND	Holborn
1843	1861	1800	?	165808	LND	St Pancras
1840	1900	....	....	129267	LND	Stoke Newington
1790	1992	1790	1992	148377	MDX	London
1850	1890	1840	1900	177571	MDX	Whitton
1871	....	ALL	ALL	138533	MGY	Berriew
1836	....	ALL	ALL	172057	MOG	Killeevan
1903	1984	ALL	1926	138819	NBL	Clara Vale
1850	1860	1800	1900	123536	NBL	Fenwick
1756	1864	1756	1992	146366	NBL	Wooler
....	....	1800	1890	175773	NFK	ALL
1837	1992	1700	1900	102326	NFK	Wereham
....	....	1800	1890	175773	SFK	ALL
1801	1811	1793	1811	116114	SFK	Drinkstone
1830	1881	1700	1850	131377	SFK	Hoxne
1880	1900	1808	1880	129895	SFK	Ipswich
1910	1963	....	....	106704	SFK	South Cove
1748	1824	1700	1824	159581	SFK	Stowmarket
1871	1891	ALL	1891	112178	SFK	Woodbridge
....	....	ALL	1750	103284	SFK	???
1841	1892	1700	1841	153281	SOM	Chard
1720	1720	1650	1750	136840	SOM	Clewkerne
1817	1992	1600	1817	123242	SOM	Dunster
1700	1850	ALL	ALL	154830	SRY	ALL
1656	1804	....	....	165999	SSX	Angmering
....	....	1835	1876	127698	SSX	East Dean
?	1819	1750	1819	165220	SSX	West Grinstead
1810	1811	1750	1820	142999	SSX	Withyham
....	....	1750	1850	159166	STS	ALL
1850	1891	ALL	1891	155683	STS	Kinver
MILLS contd.						
1790	1851	1700	1992	159468	STS	Tipton
1800	....	....	....	170313	STS	Tipton
1851	1915	....	....	149551	WAR	Alcester
1730	1800	1730	1800	167924	WAR	Bedworth
1810	1992	1750	1813	116513	WAR	Yardley
1860	1910	1800	1992	139203	WAT	Tramore
....	....	1790	1805	115975	WIL	ALL
1848	....	1800	1850	145297	WIL	Dilton
1674	1720	1650	1720	142018	WIL	Marlborough
1710	1844	1600	1710	120189	WLS	Llanidloes
1837	1992	1538	1837	154792	WOR	ALL
1793	1881	1700	1793	149551	WOR	Harvington
1793	1881	1700	1793	149551	WOR	Rous Lench
1842	1927	ALL	ALL	125202	WRY	Halifax
1850	1930	1830	1890	123595	YKS	Brighouse
1770	....	1600	1770	116637	YKS	Guisborough
....	1771	....	1771	144800	YKS	Huddersfield
MILLSON						
1760	1830	1650	1780	101834	WIL	Marlborough
MILLVILLE						
1660	1940	....	....	128996	CAM	Thorney
MILLWARD						
1824	1924	1820	1950	153818	BKM	Newton Blossomville
1900	1992	1600	1992	112003	LEI	Osgathorpe
1760	1760	1760	1760	139971	SAL	Much Wenlock
1492	....	....	1900	120391	SAL	Shrewsbury
1689	1754	....	....	127426	STS	Harborne
?	?	?	?	100692	STS	Smethwick
1879	1992	....	....	152218	STS	???
....	....	1700	1819	161659	WAR	Longbridge
1758	....	....	....	102733	WIL	Latton
MILMINE						
1880	....	ALL	1880	179515	AYR	???
1895	1970	ALL	1895	179515	NFK	Kings Lynn
MILNE						
1800	1850	ALL	1992	170909	ABD	Aberdeen
1793	1926	1700	1793	112844	ABD	Crimond
1789	1992	1650	1789	172944	ABD	Fyvie
1789	1992	1650	1789	172944	ABD	New Deer
1811	1901	1700	1811	166782	ABD	New Machar
1852	1992	1600	1852	146137	ABD	New Pitsligo
1800	1925	1750	1925	147095	ABD	Peterhead
1770	1790	1740	1830	121126	ABD	Premnay
1760	1780	1700	1800	150002	ANS	Forfar
1790	1960	1790	1960	147036	ANS	Glenisla
1774	1792	1730	1774	172871	ANS	Inverkeilor
1851	1899	1750	1851	127590	ANS	Oathlaw
1720	1760	....	....	126497	BAN	Cullen
1831	1871	1800	1871	171425	DUR	Sunderland
1801	1883	1700	1801	102997	GMP	New Deer
1750	1900	1750	1900	110523	LAN	Rochdale
1808	1808	1780	1808	118486	LAN	Staleybridge
1850	1870	....	....	124532	LKS	Glasgow
1870	....	....	....	148768	MDX	St Pancras
1850	....	....	....	148768	SCT	Aberdeen
MILNER						
....	....	ALL	ALL	148180	ALL	Name Study
ALL	ALL	ALL	ALL	148180	ALL	ALL
1727	1785	....	....	138851	CHS	Frodsham
1727	1785	....	....	138851	CHS	Weaverham
1555	1732	1560	1732	102830	DBY	Ashford
1808	1992	1700	1808	163783	LAN	Inskip
1808	1992	1700	1808	163783	LAN	St Michaels
1832	1865	1700	1832	138673	NBL	Newcastle On Tyne
1784	1784	....	....	108901	NTT	Blyth
1700	1794	1500	1700	110639	STS	Cheadle
1739	1765	1700	1765	141062	STS	Kingsley
1700	1794	1500	1700	110639	STS	Leek
1655	1802	1600	1655	135151	WES	Raventonedale
1898	1944	ALL	ALL	169897	YKS	Long Preston
1785	1817	1700	1900	109290	YKS	Sheffield
1880	1992	ALL	1880	112771	YKS	Sheffield
1810	1861	1804	1833	136808	YKS	Sproatley
1816	1824	ALL	1816	148172	YKS	Wetherby
?	1992	....	....	148172	YKS	York
MILNES						
1560	1732	1560	1732	102830	DBY	Ashford
....	....	1803	1992	155039	LAN	Milnrow
....	....	1803	1992	155039	LAN	Oldham
1890	1992	1750	1890	134678	WYK	Huddersfield
1890	1992	1750	1890	134678	WYK	Lindley
1829	1992	1700	1829	105392	YKS	Tickhill

Known From	To	Researching From	To	Ref	Cty	Place
MILO						
1700	1900	1600	1900	126446	MDX	Stepney
MILSOM						
....	....	1700	1900	110353	AVN	Abson
....	....	1700	1900	110353	AVN	Wick
1871	1927	....	....	148202	GLA	Aberdare
1927	1973	....	....	148202	GLA	Trelewis
....	....	1750	1900	109894	GLS	Bitton
1811	1900	ALL	1900	131334	GLS	Bitton
1900	1992	....	....	137200	GLS	Coalpit Heath
1800	1881	1700	1900	110051	GLS	Stapleton
1850	1900	1800	1900	178004	MON	ALL
....	....	1750	1810	148199	WIL	Bradford
1727	1992	1650	1727	164267	WIL	Holt
1777	1871	1700	1777	148202	WIL	Lacock
1754	1870	1700	1900	178004	WIL	Sopworth
1800	1850	1800	1850	148199	WYK	Wakefield
MILSON						
1785	1900	1700	1785	141798	LIN	West Keal
MILTON						
1870	1992	1700	1870	150487	AVN	Bristol
1800	1992	1800	1992	148210	BAN	Keith
1860	1960	1700	1960	172421	DEV	Torquay
....	....	1700	1992	125857	SRY	Guildford
MILWARD						
1764	ALL	....	....	117048	STS	Harborne
MILWAY						
1600	1860	1560	1600	154873	KEN	Milton
1600	1860	1560	1600	154873	KEN	Sittingbourne
MIMMACK						
1690	1750	1600	1850	123293	LIN	Owston
MIMMS						
....	....	ALL	ALL	148229	ALL	Name Study
ALL	ALL	ALL	ALL	148229	ALL	ALL
1760	1992	....	....	148229	BDF	ALL
1910	1992	....	....	148229	ESS	South
1870	1950	....	....	148229	HAM	South
1800	1860	....	....	148229	HRT	Cheshunt
1780	1870	....	....	148229	HUN	St Neots
1870	1940	....	....	148229	MDX	East
1650	1870	....	....	148229	NTH	East Central
1820	1940	....	....	148229	SRY	North
1870	1992	....	....	148229	SSX	South
1880	1992	....	....	148229	YKS	South
MINARDS						
1750	1850	1700	1880	136239	CON	Talland
MINCHER						
1822	1822	ALL	1872	143634	STS	Wolverhampton
MINCHIN						
1790	1895	1750	1895	125032	BRK	Binfield
1830	1863	1800	1870	125032	BRK	Hurst
1575	1693	1550	1692	102830	GLS	Upper Swell
1883	1945	1700	1883	155101	STS	Bilston
1650	1750	1600	1750	154881	TIP	Mobarnane
1800	1830	1800	1830	177350	WIC	Glenealy
ALL	1734	....	....	170178	WIL	Liddington
MINCHINTON						
1859	1927	....	....	154121	MDX	Clerkenwell
?	?	?	?	154121	SOM	Yeovil
MINDELSOHN						
?	?	?	?	138622	ALL	ALL
MINDENHALL						
....	....	ALL	ALL	157260	WIL	Shalbourne
MINERS						
1696	1757	1600	1800	152285	CON	Roseland
MINETT						
1588	1800	....	....	122491	GLS	Berkeley
1588	1800	....	....	122491	GLS	Cam
1588	1800	....	....	122491	GLS	Coaley
1588	1800	....	....	122491	GLS	Slimbridge
1588	1800	....	....	122491	GLS	Wickwar
MINETTE						
....	....	1700	1886	155136	LND	???
MINGAY						
1744	1784	1650	1850	149160	NFK	Norwich
MINIFIE						
1810	1870	1750	1810	143332	LND	Westminster
1850	1992	1700	1850	128074	SOM	Bath
1850	1992	1700	1850	128074	SOM	Norton Fitzwarren
MINIHAN						
1854	1983	1800	1854	160741	LND	Bromley
1854	1983	1800	1854	160741	LND	Leyton
MINIHIN						
1854	1983	1800	1854	160741	IRL	Cork
MINIHIN contd.						
1854	1983	1800	1854	160741	IRL	Kinsale
MINNET						
1729	1850	1650	1729	158739	GLA	Cardiff
MINNEY						
....	....	ALL	ALL	148245	ALL	Name Study
MINNINGS						
1782	....	....	1800	160873	CUL	Arthuret
MINNIS						
1850	1926	1850	1900	128449	COR	Reenascreena
1810	1860	1800	1900	146536	DOW	Killyleagh
MINNS						
1738	1845	....	1800	136212	NFK	Ingoldisthorpe
1699	1699	....	....	135437	NFK	Paston
MINOGUE						
1900	1950	ALL	ALL	170801	YKS	Knaresborough
MINORS						
1800	1900	1750	1992	177180	KEN	Old Charlton
MINSELL						
ALL	1765	....	....	170798	LEI	Breedon On The Hill
MINSHELL						
ALL	1765	....	....	170798	LEI	Breedon On The Hill
MINSHIN						
1662	1727	1667	1727	173851	GLS	Ministerworth
MINSHULL						
1700	1800	1600	1800	148253	BKM	ALL
1200	1800	1700	1800	148253	CHS	ALL
1772	....	ALL	....	146935	CHS	???
1600	1800	1700	1800	148253	LND	ALL
1600	1800	1700	1800	148253	SAL	ALL
1760	1814	1700	1850	106003	SAL	Chester
1760	1814	1700	1850	106003	SAL	Oswestry
1700	1800	1700	1800	148253	STS	ALL
1700	1992	1700	1800	148253	WAR	ALL
1790	1940	1750	1940	170097	WAR	Birmingham
1700	1992	1700	1800	148253	WOR	ALL
MINSLEY						
1800	1900	1700	1800	133019	CON	Launceston
MINSON						
1827	1880	....	....	148261	GLS	Cheltenham
1771	1794	....	....	148261	LND	Chelsea
1796	1798	....	....	148261	SOM	Ilminster
1695	1787	....	....	148261	SOM	Kingstone
1830	1841	....	....	148261	WAR	Leamington
MINTA						
....	....	1700	1900	148296	LIN	ALL
MINTER						
1850	1900	1650	1850	148296	ESS	Colchester
1760	1830	....	....	169137	ESS	Gt Horkesley
1730	1760	1700	1760	169137	ESS	W Bergholt
1750	1890	1650	1900	148288	KEN	Thanet
1790	1978	1700	1790	170542	KEN	Woodnesborough
1862	1884	1862	1900	155918	LND	ALL
1830	1900	1600	1830	148296	NFK	ALL
1824	1900	1770	1820	148296	NFK	Diss
1750	1800	1550	1750	148296	SFK	Central
1750	1800	1550	1750	148296	SFK	North
1827	1876	1600	1900	155918	SFK	Marlesford
1824	1900	1770	1820	148296	SFK	Palgrave
1824	1900	1770	1820	148296	SFK	Wortham
MINTERN						
1790	1790	1790	1790	161950	DOR	Portland
1864	1870	1841	1881	152781	DOR	Toller Porcorum
1881	1932	1700	1932	148318	LAN	Hulm Chorlton
MINTO						
....	....	1538	1992	118893	ALL	ALL
1840	1930	1538	1992	118893	DUR	Spennymoor
1736	1739	1538	1992	118893	NBL	Alwinton
1750	1790	1538	1992	118893	NBL	Rothbury
MINTON						
1812	1812	1750	1812	156914	RAD	Brilley
....	....	1745	1800	161659	SAL	Bishops Castle
1851	1871	1830	1900	123862	???	Bristol
MINTRAM						
1840	1900	1800	1900	176648	HAM	South
MINTRIDGE						
1588	1771	1500	1550	102830	STS	Sedgely
MINTY						
1804	1827	1700	1900	166049	MOR	Boharm
MIRFIELD						
1883	1899	1850	1900	120529	YKS	Leeds
MIRK						
1836	....	....	....	150282	STI	Falkirk

Known From	To	Researching From	To	Ref	Cty	Place
MIRTLE						
1815	....	1700	1815	123307	BRK	Kintbury
MISKIN						
1946	1992	1946	1992	111600	DOR	Beaminster
1850	1920	1800	1850	121185	KEN	ALL
1800	1850	1750	1992	177180	KEN	Woolwich
1850	1900	1850	1992	177180	MDX	Poplar
MISSING						
1621	1621	....	....	127426	KEN	Canty St Margarets
1613	1613	....	....	127426	KEN	Great Chart
1583	1583	....	....	127426	KEN	???
MISSON						
1870	1950	1700	1870	172448	CAM	Stetchworth
MIST						
1835	1992	1700	1835	148334	WIL	Salisbury
MISTOVSKY						
1910	1930	1880	1910	170224	LAN	Manchester
MITCHAM						
1880	1950	1830	1880	155691	LND	North
....	1900	....	1900	119024	SOM	Bruton
MITCHEL						
1729	1760	....	....	154024	DBY	Whittington
1849	....	1849	....	158305	LIN	Freiston
1870	....	....	....	158305	LIN	Roxholme
1792	1800	....	1800	158305	LIN	Wrangle
1860	....	1800	1900	154601	WYK	Mirfield
MITCHELL						
1808	1950	1700	1850	148342	ABD	Aberdeen
1820	1950	1700	1950	109274	ABD	Alford
1862	1862	1800	1900	126586	ABD	Cruden
1850	1860	1750	1900	135925	ABD	Inverury
....	....	1790	ALL	149187	ABD	Old Deer
....	....	1667	....	149187	ANS	Monifieth
1670	1750	1750	1992	148415	ANT	Glenarm
1781	1821	....	....	127140	ARL	Campbeltown
1794	1831	1700	1900	137650	ARL	Lochgair
1750	1812	ALL	1820	118737	BRK	Brightwalton
1788	1829	....	....	115290	BRK	Shrivenham
1575	1760	1575	1760	108839	CAM	Sutton
1837	1861	....	....	135585	CLK	Alloa
....	....	1800	1992	131903	CLV	West Hartlepool
1700	1810	ALL	1810	168718	CON	South East
....	....	1700	1900	136972	CON	Breage
1850	....	1800	1992	129348	CON	Falmouth
1860	1900	....	....	140082	CON	Falmouth
....	....	1700	1900	136972	CON	Germoe
1830	1900	....	....	140082	CON	Gwennap
1750	1850	....	....	145297	CON	Kenwyn
1815	1992	1800	1830	148377	CON	Lelant
1793	1874	1793	1874	102806	CON	Mylor Bridge
1800	1900	1700	1800	116432	CON	North Tamerton
1700	1881	?	1700	123161	CON	Padstow
1790	1828	ALL	ALL	113360	CON	Perranzabuloe
1800	1850	1600	1800	149608	CON	St Agnes
1805	1992	ALL	1805	148385	CON	St Germans
1710	1797	1600	1710	102571	CON	St Gluvias
1700	1864	ALL	1700	148415	COR	Aghadda
1686	1700	ALL	1686	148415	COR	Cork
1751	1773	1700	1773	133000	DEV	Axminster
1760	1800	1760	1800	107352	DEV	Frithelstock
1740	1854	1600	1740	166723	DEV	Holbeton
1740	1813	1700	1740	179663	DEV	Holbeton
1873	....	....	....	150762	DEV	Plymouth
1740	1813	1700	1740	179663	DEV	Stoke Damerel
....	....	1800	1830	140082	DEV	Stokenham
1880	1950	1830	....	146900	DEV	Torquay
1778	1787	ALL	1778	175994	DOR	Blandford
1775	1860	1700	1775	147583	DOR	Toller Porcorum
1700	1750	1750	1992	148415	DUB	Dublin
1817	1861	1654	....	131210	ESS	Waltham Abbey
?	?	?	?	111457	FIF	???
1800	1850	1800	1850	157171	GLS	Cowley
1625	1750	1625	1750	127655	GLS	Harescombe
1625	1750	1625	1750	127655	GLS	Oxlinch
1810	1848	1780	1851	131326	GSY	St Peter Port
1747	1747	1700	1747	174289	HAM	Christchurch
....	....	1700	1800	176621	HAM	Portsmouth
....	....	....	1850	113891	HAM	Southampton
....	1786	1750	1810	176621	HRT	Albury
1782	1791	1699	1800	131210	HRT	Ware
1829	1880	....	....	152889	HUN	Kimbolton
1750	....	1700	....	143502	KEN	ALL
....	....	1750	1840	130184	KEN	Ashford
1590	1913	1568	1967	169552	LAN	Hawkshead

Known From	To	Researching From	To	Ref	Cty	Place
MITCHELL contd.						
1840	1992	1700	1840	158917	LAN	Manchester
1790	1863	....	....	151912	LAN	Pendleton
1750	....	1750	....	109347	LAN	Read
1840	1900	ALL	ALL	154806	LAN	Rochdale
1669	1992	ALL	1800	112275	LEI	North West
1740	1790	....	....	165999	LEI	Hinckley
1740	1790	....	....	165999	LEI	Loughborough
1900	1960	1700	1920	113387	LIN	Louth
1820	....	1800	1900	135968	LIN	Stamford
1802	1870	1700	1802	119369	LND	Bermondsey
1860	1886	1700	1860	167355	LND	Poplar
....	1824	1750	1850	124907	LND	Westminster
1850	1992	1700	1850	148431	LTN	ALL
....	1850	ALL	ALL	122866	MDX	East
1881	....	....	....	135585	MDX	Brentford
1800	1950	1750	1850	157287	MDX	Holborn
1856	1884	1800	1992	117609	MDX	Islington
1850	1900	....	....	111368	MDX	Marlybone
1856	1884	1800	1992	117609	MDX	Pancras
....	1805	ALL	1805	148385	MDX	Westminster
1845	1868	....	....	137936	MLN	Edinburgh
1914	....	....	....	150762	MON	Ebbw Vale
1845	1980	1700	1992	126632	NBL	Cramlington
1841	1851	1841	1851	171166	NBL	North Shields
1750	1850	1700	1750	158402	NFK	Acle
1782	1870	....	....	169129	NFK	Dersingham
1797	1854	....	....	135437	NFK	Gt Ryburgh
1813	1841	....	....	135437	NFK	Lt Ryburgh
1811	1947	1700	1811	120367	NFK	Norwich
1759	1833	....	....	135437	NFK	Wood Norton
1850	1900	ALL	ALL	148458	NTH	Long Buckby
1790	1820	ALL	1790	152889	NTH	Ringstead
1850	1870	1800	1900	148458	NTH	Welford
1852	1932	1800	1850	153656	PEE	Glenholm
1800	1992	1650	1992	166758	RFW	Paisley
1820	1890	1820	1890	135968	RUT	Whitwell
1590	1940	1590	1940	114316	SFK	Alpheton
1750	1880	1700	1750	158402	SFK	Burlingham
1750	1880	1700	1750	158402	SFK	Strumpshaw
1755	1850	1700	1850	144606	SOM	South
....	....	1700	1822	174300	SOM	Bath
1686	1700	ALL	1686	148415	SOM	Bristol
1881	....	1880	1930	133639	SOM	Coker
1870	1890	1870	1900	142018	SOM	Creech St Michael
1650	1750	1500	1650	147583	SOM	Crewkerne
....	....	1500	1830	166863	SOM	Long Ashton
1600	1700	1620	1700	142018	SOM	Merriott
1840	1850	....	....	111368	SOM	Nailsea
1700	1799	1700	1799	169781	SOM	Preston
1775	1830	1775	1830	159913	SOM	???
1880	....	....	....	135585	SRY	Barnes
1830	1900	1750	1850	144398	SRY	Croydon
1700	1850	ALL	ALL	154830	SRY	Dorking
1892	1914	....	....	131210	SRY	Merton
1712	1770	....	1712	163295	SSX	West
1839	1860	1800	1839	138347	SSX	East Grinstead
1910	1992	....	....	122130	SSX	Hadlow Down
1778	1800	1750	1778	156140	SSX	Hamsey
1805	1860	....	....	145394	SSX	Preston
1780	1940	....	....	122130	SSX	Rotherfield
1810	1810	1750	1810	102830	WAR	Solihull
1844	1852	1813	1850	169552	WES	Burton In Kendal
1749	1853	1569	1872	169552	WES	Crosthwaite
1741	1764	1732	1775	169552	WES	Hugill
1558	1802	1558	1803	169552	WES	Kendal
1743	1959	1651	1959	169552	WES	Staveley
1813	1905	1813	1905	169552	WES	Thrimby
1723	1900	1651	1919	169552	WES	Troutbeck
1735	1965	1735	1975	169552	WES	Underbarrow
1614	1966	1612	1966	169552	WES	Windermere
1720	1812	1720	1812	169552	WES	Winster
1744	1798	1600	1744	175781	WIL	Bromham
1829	1904	....	....	115290	WIL	Wroughton
1840	1900	1750	1840	145408	WIL	Wroughton
1920	1940	....	1920	157406	WRY	Halifax
1850	1992	....	....	148350	WRY	Lightcliffe Halifax
1730	1770	1730	1770	107522	WRY	Todmorden
1830	1900	1780	1830	172510	YKS	Elland
1830	1900	1780	1830	172510	YKS	Greetland
1862	1992	1800	1862	130877	YKS	Halifax
1830	1900	1780	1830	172510	YKS	Halifax
1809	1878	1700	1809	173886	YKS	Halifax
1730	1992	1698	1730	165026	YKS	Haworth

Known From	To	Researching From	To	Ref	Cty	Place
MITCHELL contd.						
....	....	1740	1790	151912	YKS	Kelbrook
1900	1960	1700	1920	113387	YKS	Louth
1851	1992	1700	1851	105635	YKS	Morley
1734	....	1700	1760	170348	YKS	Penistone
1870	1880	ALL	ALL	148458	YKS	Settle
1888	1957	1700	1900	163902	YKS	Sheffield
1634	1690	1600	1992	114901	YKS	Sherburn Elmet
1797	1820	1600	1992	102520	YKS	???
MITCHELMORE						
1780	....	....	....	165387	LND	Central
MITCHELSON						
1880	1992	ALL	ALL	105449	YKS	Hull
1800	1900	ALL	ALL	105449	YKS	Malton
MITCHENOR						
1825	1826	1815	1826	124915	SSX	Brighton
MITCHINSON						
....	....	ALL	ALL	148474	CUL	North
1785	1930	ALL	ALL	148474	CUL	Carlisle
MITFORD						
ALL	1480	....	....	132756	NBL	ALL
ALL	1480	....	....	132756	NBL	Mitford
MITHAM						
....	....	ALL	ALL	128686	ALL	Name Study
1570	1992	1550	1992	128678	ALL	ALL
1570	1900	1570	1900	128678	CAM	Swavesey
MITTEN						
....	....	1870	1920	147613	NIR	Belfast
MITTENS						
1813	1838	1812	1992	106666	LND	Shoreditch
MITTER						
1700	1850	1700	1850	154628	CON	St Kew
MITTON						
1845	1890	1800	1860	165093	LAN	Liverpool
1500	1750	....	....	126497	LAN	Wigan
....	....	1600	1880	135046	LAN	Wigan
MIZEN						
1826	1992	1700	1826	132373	WIL	Bradford Leigh
1851	1992	1800	1851	124117	WIL	Rowde
MOAR						
1745	1992	1600	1992	148482	OKI	Orkney
1750	1965	....	....	137820	SHI	Fetlar
1720	1965	....	....	137820	SHI	Mid Yell
1760	1965	....	....	137820	SHI	North Yell
1758	1965	....	....	137820	SHI	Northmavine
1720	1965	....	....	137820	SHI	South Yell
MOAT						
1780	1920	1700	1960	123536	NBL	Newcastle On Tyne
1757	1773	ALL	1757	152234	SYK	Hatfield
MOBBERLEY						
1894	1989	1800	1890	148490	WAR	Stoubridge
MOBBS						
1875	1900	1800	1900	116173	LEI	Leicester
1850	1992	1700	1992	148512	LND	Bethnal Green
1850	1992	1700	1992	148512	LND	Chelsea
1850	1992	1700	1992	148512	LND	Hoxton
1850	....	....	....	117560	MDX	Chelsea
1881	ALL	....	....	117560	MDX	Hoxton
1883	....	1750	1900	116173	NTH	Kettering
1729	1900	....	1729	136212	OXF	North Aston
MOBERLEY						
1732	1796	ALL	ALL	121754	BKM	West Turville
MOBSBY						
1789	....	ALL	ALL	156558	SSX	ALL
MOCK						
....	....	ALL	ALL	148520	ALL	Name Study
ALL	ALL	ALL	ALL	148520	ALL	ALL
1672	1672	1550	1750	133450	CON	Roche
1816	1855	1816	1855	173738	DEV	Barnstaple
1500	1992	ALL	ALL	148520	DEV	Braunton
MOCKETT						
1850	1992	1600	1800	135313	KEN	Deal
MOCKFORD						
1763	1992	1500	1893	174009	SSX	East
1600	1900	1600	1900	157430	SSX	Brighton
MOCKRIDGE						
1780	1992	1600	1992	141585	DOR	East Orchard
1780	1992	1600	1992	141585	DOR	West Orchard
1645	1862	1600	1930	113069	SOM	Pitminster
1645	1862	1600	1930	124990	SOM	Pitminster
MODDY						
1842	1970	1700	1842	167819	HAM	Sherfield English
MODLEY						
1827	1890	1800	1930	115746	SOM	Taunton
MOECKX						
1845	1868	1300	1992	152501	ALL	ALL
MOFFAT						
1850	1992	1800	1850	172650	CAV	Cootehill
1800	1850	1800	?	136522	DFS	Annan
1788	1922	ALL	ALL	145092	DFS	Annandale
1790	1838	....	....	171654	DFS	Dumfries
....	....	1700	1950	143219	MDX	London
ALL	....	....	....	151416	SCT	ALL
MOFFAT-BELL						
?	?	?	?	147990	CUL	ALL
?	?	?	?	147990	DFS	ALL
MOFFATT						
....	....	ALL	ALL	148539	ALL	Name Study
1850	1992	1850	1900	148563	CHS	Birkenhead
1840	1850	1840	1850	148563	CHS	Chester
1796	1837	1700	1837	148563	IRL	Eniskilen
1850	1900	1860	1900	148563	LAN	Liverpool
1780	1820	1750	1850	133787	MLN	Newton
MOFFITT						
1780	....	....	....	146447	DUR	Gateshead
1790	....	....	....	146447	DUR	South Shields
1790	1835	1750	1850	149152	NBL	Alnwick
1754	1770	....	....	146447	NBL	Bellingham
1851	....	....	....	146447	YKS	Tee Side
MOGER						
1867	1992	....	1867	148571	HAM	Eastleigh
1820	1909	....	....	114669	SOM	Bath
MOGFORD						
1800	1992	1500	1800	148598	DEV	Tiverton
MOGG						
....	....	ALL	ALL	179094	ALL	Name Study
....	....	....	1745	142409	ENG	Midlands
MOGGE						
1695	....	1500	1840	164879	SOM	ALL
MOGGERIDGE						
1800	1992	1600	1992	141585	DOR	East Orchard
1800	1992	1600	1992	141585	DOR	West Orchard
MOGGRIDGE						
1764	1783	1764	1820	154733	DEV	Bratton Fleming
MOGGS						
1629	1816	1600	1700	148601	STS	Tamworth
MOGRIDGE						
1800	1992	1600	1992	141585	DOR	Shaftesbury
MOHR						
1886	1992	1886	1992	106747	KEN	Medway
1886	1900	1886	1992	106747	LND	Bow
1886	1900	1886	1992	106747	LND	Poplar
MOHUN						
....	1777	....	....	148636	BKM	Buckland
1600	1777	1600	1777	148636	BRK	???
1600	1777	1600	1777	148636	CON	???
1600	1777	1600	1777	148636	DEV	???
1600	1777	1600	1777	148636	WIL	???
MOIGNE						
1150	....	....	....	148733	ESS	Great Eastou
MOIR						
1753	1992	1730	....	148644	ABD	Aberdeen
1800	1820	1700	1800	100978	ANS	Montrose
1783	1845	....	....	172871	KCD	Bervie
1738	1781	1680	1740	172871	KCD	Catterline
1738	1781	1680	1740	172871	KCD	Kinneff
1848	1850	1840	1850	168181	MLN	Musselburgh
1850	1905	ALL	ALL	106968	NBL	Wallsend
1830	1861	1700	1830	106968	SCT	???
MOISER						
1850	1992	1850	1992	172227	DUR	ALL
MOISEY						
....	....	ALL	ALL	158593	ALL	ALL
MOIST						
....	....	ALL	ALL	174963	ALL	ALL
MOLD						
1777	1777	ALL	....	115355	LEI	ALL
1754	1797	1650	1753	131245	LEI	Tilton
1776	1992	1700	1900	131547	SAL	Clunbury
MOLDICLIFF						
1735	1835	....	1735	101761	WRY	Upperthong
MOLE						
1748	....	?	1760	103934	DEV	North Molton
1800	1900	1700	1950	148652	DEV	Plymouth
1837	1837	1600	1837	152080	ESS	Hadstock
....	....	1500	1900	149934	LND	City
1780	1814	1750	1830	116386	NBL	Belford
1771	1799	1700	1800	159905	NBL	Embleton

Known From	To	Researching From	To	Ref	Cty	Place
MOLE contd.						
1846	1899	1830	1900	116386	NBL	Newcastle
1701	1742	1690	1800	159905	OXF	Alkerton
1787	....	1600	1878	145432	WOR	Clint
MOLES						
1793	1877	1750	1820	131326	GSY	???
1755	1992	....	....	143596	SOM	Exton Winsford
MOLINEUX						
1830	1895	1750	1830	129208	???	Manchester
MOLISON						
1811	1870	1700	1880	169390	ABD	Aberdeen
1811	1870	1700	1880	169390	SOM	Bristol
MOLL						
1866	1992	1866	1992	144355	KEN	South
1866	1992	1865	1992	144355	LND	???
1880	1992	1880	1992	148660	NFK	Great Yarmouth
1775	1901	1700	1950	148660	NFK	South Walsham
MOLLAND						
?	?	?	?	121185	KEN	South
MOLLESON						
....	....	1700	1800	176036	MDX	London
MOLLET						
1764	1865	ALL	ALL	115126	CHI	ALL
MOLLETT						
1700	1820	1700	1820	142565	NFK	East
MOLLISON						
1663	1722	ALL	1722	162507	ABD	???
MOLLOY						
1838	1838	1810	1841	108901	CON	St Budock
1779	ALL	ALL	1836	116734	DUB	Dublin
1857	1881	1851	1881	108901	GSY	St Peter Port
1800	1820	....	....	108901	IRL	Cookstown
1864	1904	1800	1992	150835	IRL	???
1779	ALL	ALL	1836	116734	LEX	Shahbally
MOLONEY						
1815	1840	1851	1880	111090	IRL	Limerick
MOLYNEUX						
....	....	ALL	ALL	148717	ALL	Name Study
1750	1871	1700	1750	160024	CHS	Northwich
....	....	ALL	1822	178942	LAN	Lathom
....	....	1840	1870	165824	LAN	St Helens
1805	1855	1805	1855	170852	NTT	Radford
1840	....	ALL	ALL	135127	WOR	Dudley St Thomas
MOMBRUN						
1829	1844	1781	1992	148067	KEN	Gravesend
1773	1992	1706	1992	148067	MDX	St Pancras
MOMFORD						
1776	1776	....	....	121355	LND	Stepney
MONAGHAN						
1858	1992	1800	1858	159182	LAN	Kirkham
1858	1992	1700	1858	159182	LET	Aughavas
1890	1920	ALL	ALL	113743	NBL	Morpeth
1883	1940	1850	1920	113743	NBL	Newcastle
1885	1992	....	1885	151270	NTH	Newcastle On Tyne
MONCK						
1670	1992	ALL	1670	148733	ESS	Rodings
MONCKTON RUSSELL						
1794	1894	1700	1794	155217	ENG	Home Counties
MONCKTON						
1454	1833	....	....	175439	YKS	Cavil
MONCREIFF						
1550	1666	....	1550	126748	OKI	???
1628	1744	....	1628	126748	PER	Tippermaloch
MONCUR						
1760	1772	1700	1770	130214	ANS	Strathmartine
MONDAY						
1784	1787	1770	1800	127116	HAM	Fawley
1660	1700	ALL	1700	115282	KEN	East
MONDEY						
1805	1841	1760	1860	123536	HAM	Titchfield
MONEY						
....	....	ALL	ALL	148741	ALL	Name Study
1521	1660	ALL	1800	156310	NFK	North
MONGER						
1800	1940	ALL	ALL	122866	HAM	North West
....	1900	ALL	ALL	122866	MDX	East
MONILAWS						
....	....	ALL	1675	119326	ELN	Longniddry
MONIMENT						
1719	1730	ALL	1719	169730	NFK	Hockering
MONK						
....	....	ALL	ALL	148733	ALL	ALL
1745	1840	1600	1800	143693	BKM	Beaconsfield
1768	1836	1740	1836	119059	BKM	Brill
MONK contd.						
1737	1830	1600	1800	143693	BKM	Burnham
1791	1792	1750	1850	143693	BKM	Iver
1839	1931	1700	1950	115517	ESS	Clavering
1700	1718	1650	1750	126586	ESS	Panfield
1800	1850	1600	1850	154342	GLS	Bitton
1792	1845	1700	1792	128317	GLS	Painswick
1750	1800	1600	1750	154342	GLS	Sustib
1864	1920	1700	1864	104620	HEF	Weston Beggard
1771	1820	1720	1771	172871	HRT	Watford
1761	1791	ALL	1800	112275	LEI	Seagrave
1756	....	ALL	....	104515	LIN	Skillington
1828	?	ALL	ALL	129399	LIN	???
1750	....	....	....	148768	LND	Westminster
1800	....	....	....	126543	MDX	Brentford
1850	1960	1700	1850	148776	MDX	Enfield
1750	....	....	....	148768	MDX	Monken Hadley
1770	1822	1760	1837	150053	NTH	Desborough
1700	....	....	....	148768	OXF	Burford
1800	1992	1500	1950	137472	SRY	Dorking
1800	1992	1500	1950	137472	SRY	Holmwood
1800	1829	1800	1829	147486	SSX	Chichester
....	1700	....	....	174564	SSX	???
1828	?	ALL	ALL	129399	YKS	???
MONK-MASON						
....	....	1800	1900	108677	MDX	London
MONKHOUSE						
1824	1856	1500	1870	151483	LND	Hammersmith
MONKMAN						
1574	1952	ALL	ALL	103837	YKS	North
1785	1901	1650	1800	101575	YKS	Malton
1818	1941	ALL	ALL	103837	YKS	Scarborough
MONKS						
1729	1836	1700	1840	128449	GLS	Stapleton
1899	1992	....	....	112232	IRL	???
1840	1992	1700	1840	164208	LAN	Liverpool
MONKSBY						
1770	1800	....	1800	102822	BRK	Cholsey
MONKTON						
1740	1742	1700	1740	127116	DOR	Fontmell Magna
MONNELL						
....	....	1800	1860	116173	YKS	North
MONNERY						
1900	1992	....	....	148784	SSX	Worthing
MONNOX						
....	....	ALL	ALL	159107	ALL	ALL
MONTAGU						
1722	1793	....	....	166189	BKM	Langley
ALL	....	ALL	ALL	123668	SOM	Bath
MONTAGUE						
1722	1793	....	....	166189	BKM	Langley
1580	1600	....	....	145688	BRK	Winkfield
1820	1992	1400	1820	165964	OXF	Shiplake
1650	1720	1600	1700	144657	SOM	Bleadon
MONTGOMERY						
1844	....	1865	1900	110868	IRL	???
1840	1840	1800	1840	132268	LAN	Haslingden
1886	1918	1918	1992	146560	LKS	Coatbride
1780	1870	1780	1870	130400	LKS	Glasgow
1800	1850	1800	1850	148792	MDX	Mile End
1780	1800	1700	1800	148792	MDX	Shoreditch
1790	1992	1600	1790	152633	YKS	Hull
ALL	1100	....	....	132756	???	???
MONUMENT						
1729	1905	....	....	169129	NFK	Central
1729	1905	....	....	169129	NFK	West
1657	1762	ALL	1700	169730	NFK	North Elmham
MOODIE						
1500	1575	1500	1600	154881	LND	ALL
MOODY						
1825	1905	ALL	....	109258	BKM	Freckwell Heath
1780	1780	1700	1780	121509	CUL	Dalston
1760	1992	1700	1760	160075	DUR	Penshaw
1800	1880	1700	1800	113514	EYK	???
1797	....	1700	1900	118753	GLS	Dursley
1789	1789	1700	1900	141151	HAM	ALL
....	....	1800	1900	173770	HAM	South
....	....	1700	1885	166863	HAM	Leeds
1867	1945	1700	1867	167819	HAM	Southampton
1813	1900	ALL	1813	106283	LIN	Croft
1800	1820	1700	1800	145688	LIN	Grimsby
1600	1680	....	....	145688	LIN	North Ormsby
1813	1900	ALL	1813	106283	LIN	Spalding
1872	1946	1860	1946	116548	LND	Islington

Known From	To	Researching From	To	Ref	Cty	Place
MOODY contd.						
....	....	ALL	1800	108812	MAY	???
1725	1760	1700	1770	107360	NTH	Naseby
1750	1965	....	....	137820	SHI	Fetlar
1720	1965	....	....	137820	SHI	Mid Yell
1760	1965	....	....	137820	SHI	North Yell
1758	1965	....	....	137820	SHI	Northmavine
1720	1965	....	....	137820	SHI	South Yell
1801	1847	1780	1870	136980	SRY	Bermondsey
1750	1800	....	1750	110027	WIL	Whiteparish
1790	1840	....	....	103721	WRY	Leeds
1793	1815	ALL	1793	102350	YKS	Sheffield
MOOK						
1860	1870	1800	1900	126586	ALL	ALL
1730	1840	....	....	139351	YKS	Rillington
MOON						
1800	1880	....	....	141178	CON	South East
1705	1800	1600	1850	159646	CON	St Germans
1807	1930	1700	1807	125458	CON	St Winnow
....	....	....	1860	145858	DON	Sheephaven
1820	....	1820	1992	107999	HAM	Carisbrooke
1825	1900	1750	1850	145343	HAM	Hambledon
1782	1860	1700	1785	149993	HAM	Upper Itchen
1786	....	....	1800	171441	KEN	Hoath
1800	1992	1800	1992	110205	KEN	Rolverden
1824	1844	ALL	1900	115347	LAN	ALL
1850	1890	....	....	117765	LAN	Liverpool
1805	1826	1700	1885	131423	PER	Blair Atholl
1793	1864	1735	1864	107573	SOM	Mendip
1800	1870	1680	1870	120308	SSX	Steyning
1757	1837	1650	1850	167002	SXE	Mayfield
....	1822	1700	1800	132586	WAR	Nuneaton
1800	1850	ALL	1800	117765	WES	Heversham
1790	1992	ALL	1790	107840	???	London
MOONE						
....	....	1860	1950	159646	DEV	Plymouth
MOONEY						
1842	1888	....	1842	110515	IRL	Dublin
1873	1960	1850	1865	148814	LND	Stepney
MOONLIGHT						
1800	1850	....	....	140864	ABD	Strichen
MOOR						
1700	1800	1600	1700	135089	LEI	Kilworth
1740	1780	1538	1780	118893	NRY	Kirklevington
1736	1768	1700	1720	149039	NTH	West
1729	....	ALL	1729	168718	NTH	Ringstead
1730	1756	1700	1800	159956	SFK	Walsham Le Willows
1900	1992	1800	1992	113743	SSX	Northiam
1790	1940	1750	1980	113743	SSX	Rye
1881	1921	....	....	121290	STS	Draycott-In-The-Clay
1771	1921	1700	ALL	121290	STS	Hanbury
1743	1921	....	....	121290	STS	Marchington
1793	1798	1770	1798	141097	YKS	Hull
1734	1798	ALL	1734	102350	YKS	Monk Fryston
1750	1992	1600	1992	114596	YKS	Ripon
MOORBY						
....	....	1750	1850	166081	LAN	Darwen
1800	1900	....	....	146854	LAN	Preston
1820	1881	1800	1900	166081	LAN	Preston
1820	1880	1800	1840	130621	YKS	Alverthorpe
....	....	1700	1800	147613	YKS	Giggleswick
MOORCOCK						
1600	1850	1600	1850	148822	BRK	ALL
1700	1750	1560	1870	148822	BRK	Burghfield
1860	1930	1720	1950	148822	BRK	Sulham
1769	1870	1674	1900	148822	BRK	Wokingham
1877	1980	1870	1980	148822	SRY	Streatham
MOORCROFT						
1869	....	1800	1900	139114	LAN	Ormskirk
1824	1869	1824	1992	115355	WAR	Coventry
MOORE						
1800	1850	ALL	1800	135143	ALL	ALL
1832	1992	1750	1832	149004	BKM	Moulsoe
1861	1992	1800	1861	149004	BKM	Newport Pagnell
1820	1851	ALL	1850	127094	BRK	Maidenhead
1800	1936	1700	1800	134015	CHS	ALL
1550	1950	1550	1950	148857	CHS	ALL
1820	1992	1650	1820	173665	CHS	Malpas
1800	1936	1700	1800	134015	CHS	Romiley
....	....	1800	1900	116173	CUL	Egremont
1700	1900	1600	1900	138878	CUL	Gosforth
1700	1900	1600	1900	138878	CUL	St Bees
1830	1860	1850	1860	146897	CUL	Whitehaven
MOORE contd.						
1883	1920	1700	1883	105163	DBY	Bolsover
1850	1920	1800	1920	159220	DBY	Bolsover
1921	1992	....	....	121290	DBY	Boyleston
1825	1875	1775	1825	172901	DBY	Heanor
1921	1992	....	....	121290	DBY	Somersal Herbert
1865	1936	....	1865	146072	DEV	Holsworthy
1672	1705	1660	1720	165972	DEV	Morchard Bishop
1855	1863	1855	1865	114405	DEV	Pinhoe
1850	1850	1800	1992	133450	DEV	Plymouth
1886	1992	1700	1886	148903	DEV	Plympton
1824	1845	1820	1850	114405	DEV	Silverton
1735	1900	1600	1735	133914	DEV	Twitchen
1705	1823	1700	1800	165972	DEV	Witheridge
1830	1970	1830	1970	148873	DOR	Child Okeford
1830	1970	1830	1970	148873	DOR	Shaftesbury
1740	1800	....	....	165999	ESS	ALL
1756	1792	ALL	1756	169730	ESS	Debden
1856	....	1780	....	116297	ESS	Finchingfield
....	1840	1799	....	123609	ESS	Finchingfield
1655	1682	ALL	1700	129283	ESS	Hadleigh
1839	1863	ALL	1839	114030	ESS	Saffron Walden
1691	1728	ALL	1728	129283	ESS	South Benfleet
1703	1780	1700	1800	148938	GLS	Ashcott
1800	1885	....	....	106240	HAM	Gosport
1800	1850	ALL	1800	150983	HAM	Portsea
1850	1854	ALL	1850	131881	HAM	Portsmouth
1875	1945	....	....	121967	HUN	Ramsey
1757	1768	1511	1757	141291	IOM	Arbory
....	....	1700	1900	147613	IOM	Peel
....	....	1905	1992	161829	IOW	East Cowes
1700	1992	1500	1700	129577	IOW	???
1612	1723	....	....	117234	IRL	Antrim
1775	1863	1775	....	123609	IRL	Ballymena
....	....	1868	1992	115517	KEN	East
1875	1905	1700	1875	154539	KEN	Cranbrook
1250	1450	1200	1450	154881	KEN	Cudham
1745	1854	....	....	164631	KEN	Goudhurst
1909	1936	ALL	ALL	137774	LAN	South
1738	1738	1700	1738	163783	LAN	Goosnargh
....	....	1850	1992	147613	LAN	Liverpool
1800	1936	1700	1800	134015	LAN	Rochdale
1700	1800	1600	1700	135089	LEI	Kilworth
1768	1891	ALL	ALL	141615	LEI	Leicester
1823	1855	ALL	1823	161330	LIN	Fulbeck
1781	1789	1700	1800	131377	LIN	Washingborough
1873	1945	1945	1992	146560	LKS	Coatbride
1864	1900	1864	1900	111457	LKS	???
1858	1863	1833	1900	155918	LND	Bermondsey
1870	1950	1700	1900	175056	LND	Holloway
1870	1950	1800	1870	151084	LND	Islington
1870	1992	1700	1870	148865	LND	Lambeth
1889	1901	1901	1992	122807	LND	Lisson Grove
1750	1810	1700	1810	147575	LND	St James
1900	1920	....	....	110159	LND	???
1891	1891	1800	1900	176044	MDX	Islington
1812	1992	1776	1812	167959	MDX	Tottenham
1840	1874	1797	1840	150894	NBL	North Shields
1740	1800	....	....	165999	NFK	ALL
1823	1908	1800	1825	149039	NFK	Kings Lynn
1860	1992	ALL	ALL	115762	NFK	Norwich
1867	....	1750	1867	179183	NFK	Norwich
1847	1912	1750	1847	118710	NFK	Wells Next Sea
1790	1825	1700	1900	135496	NFK	Weybourne
....	....	1800	1868	115517	NFK	???
1700	1992	....	....	153583	NTH	Bugbrooke
1820	1992	1700	1820	149012	NTH	Guilsborough
1770	1881	1700	1900	133248	NTH	Pytchley
1810	1853	1700	1810	131377	NTH	Rothwell
1813	1900	1700	1900	112097	NTT	Arnold
1835	1930	ALL	ALL	113859	NTT	Nottingham
1706	....	ALL	ALL	105481	NTT	Nuthall
1857	1992	1700	1850	148849	NYK	Caterick
1883	1976	1680	1883	148881	SAL	Edstaston
1883	1976	1680	1883	148881	SAL	Wellington
1883	1976	1680	1883	148881	SAL	Wem
1588	1612	....	....	117234	SCT	Glasgow
1850	1900	1750	1850	129895	SFK	Debenham
1806	1850	....	....	127779	SFK	Ipswich
1900	1925	ALL	ALL	119857	SFK	Lowestoft
1790	1992	1700	1790	123153	SOM	Bath
1842	1860	1800	1842	144177	SOM	Blackford
1760	1760	1700	1780	136840	SOM	Brendon Hills
....	....	ALL	1992	123749	SOM	Bridgwater

Known From	To	Researching From	To	Ref	Cty	Place
MOORE contd.						
1671	1695	1600	1700	129356	SOM	Kingsdon
1800	1825	1800	1825	178705	SOM	Pensford
1795	1860	1795	1860	142077	SOM	Polden Hills
1600	1700	1600	1700	169781	SOM	West Cocker
1800	1900	1500	1800	118915	SOM	West Coker
1881	1992	1700	1881	125024	SSX	Rye
1839	1992	1750	1839	178551	STS	Handsworth
1832	1867	1832	1867	162809	STS	Hanley
1780	1810	1700	1780	151769	STS	Kings Winford
1829	1847	1700	1829	160474	STS	Lichfield
1743	1921	....	....	121290	STS	Marchington
1864	1947	1300	1992	152501	STS	Pensnett
1745	1980	1500	1745	129011	STS	Tettenhall
1853	1992	1300	1992	152501	STS	Tividale
1839	1992	1750	1839	178551	STS	West Bromwich
1813	....	1775	1813	149977	STS	Wolverhampton
1793	....	....	1793	148830	TYR	Ardstraw
1864	....	....	1864	148830	TYR	Loughnease
1850	1900	1850	1860	125938	WAR	Bedworth
1802	1841	1600	1802	178985	WAR	Ipsley
ALL	ALL	ALL	ALL	153249	WAR	Redditch
1866	1941	1700	1866	177237	WAR	Stockton
1841	1992	1700	1841	178985	WAR	Warwick
1850	1992	1300	1992	152501	WOR	Dudley
1855	1876	1700	1855	153346	WOR	Lye
1763	1883	ALL	ALL	153249	WOR	Redditch
1690	1850	1775	1875	171549	YKS	Bingley
1857	1992	1700	1850	148849	YKS	Leeds
1734	1798	ALL	1734	102350	YKS	Monk Fryston
1641	1992	....	....	134619	YKS	Monk Fryston
1810	1838	....	....	154024	YKS	Pocklington
1876	1886	1800	1876	171662	YKS	Sheffield
....	....	1680	1727	177393	YKS	Wistow
1765	1846	ALL	ALL	101370	???	???
MOORES						
....	....	ALL	ALL	166812	LAN	Manchester
1860	1900	1800	1992	166081	LAN	Rochdale
1790	1847	....	....	115606	WIL	East Knoyles
MOORFOOT						
1727	1814	1650	1750	131377	LIN	Corringham
MOORHEAD						
1843	1992	ALL	1843	132829	T&W	Newcastle Upon Tyne
MOORHEN						
1912	1992	1800	1850	149098	BKM	Slough
MOORHOUSE						
1710	1749	1700	1749	153273	WRY	Bentham
1687	1763	1757	1800	145327	WYK	Hampsthwaite
1538	1992	1700	1870	149136	YKS	North
1538	1992	1700	1870	149136	YKS	West
1819	1876	1800	1829	128368	YKS	Doncaster
....	....	1700	1820	116173	YKS	Helmsley
....	....	1700	1900	166960	YKS	Huddersfield
1629	1755	1600	1680	170348	YKS	Huddersfield
1790	1851	1750	1900	157716	YKS	Kirkburton
1717	1808	1700	1812	157678	YKS	Skipton
1830	1960	ALL	ALL	142611	YKS	Wakefield
MOORLE						
1850	1934	....	....	156671	SOM	Nailsea
MOORLEN						
1777	1820	ALL	ALL	132845	KEN	Otham
MOORMAN						
1809	1992	1800	1992	149144	CHI	Guernsey
1809	1992	1800	1992	149144	CHI	Jersey
1750	1850	1700	1870	149144	CON	South
....	....	1700	1800	149144	DEV	North Molton
1806	1850	1770	1870	149144	DEV	Plymouth
1834	1875	1750	1834	173886	GLS	Cirencester
1620	1702	....	....	107085	IOW	???
1880	1920	1880	1920	149144	KEN	Ashford
1852	1860	1850	1900	149144	MDX	London
MOORS						
1820	1960	....	....	153796	CHS	Hyde
1845	1964	1850	1950	135925	LND	Shoreditch
1730	1750	1700	1750	139092	SOM	Henstridge
1820	1850	1750	1900	135925	SOM	Mere
MOOTY						
....	....	ALL	1800	108812	MAY	???
MORALEE						
1738	1950	....	....	102741	DUR	Consett
ALL	ALL	ALL	ALL	110671	DUR	Gateshead
1760	1992	1700	1760	160075	DUR	Hougton Le Sp
1738	1950	....	....	102741	DUR	Stanhope
ALL	ALL	ALL	ALL	110671	DUR	Stanhope
MORALEE contd.						
1920	1940	ALL	ALL	110671	DUR	Sunderland
1738	1950	....	....	102741	DUR	Wolsingham
ALL	ALL	1600	1850	110671	NBL	Newcastle On Tyne
ALL	ALL	1600	1850	110671	NBL	Swirle
MORAN						
1849	1878	?	1850	164976	DBY	Derby
1812	....	1800	1812	179256	GSY	ALL
....	....	1600	1850	146099	IRL	ALL
....	1872	....	....	117374	IRL	Dublin
....	1839	....	1839	161888	KID	???
1890	1992	1800	1890	159182	LAN	Kirkham
1890	1992	1700	1890	159182	MAY	Castlebar
1850	1859	1845	1880	179256	SRY	Lambeth
MORCOM						
....	....	1700	1900	149179	CON	Gwenmap
....	....	1800	1850	153745	CON	Gwennap
....	....	1800	1850	153745	CON	Kenwyn
1788	1992	1700	1920	149179	CON	St Gluvias
1830	1900	1700	1860	160865	HAM	Portsmouth
MORCOMB						
1666	1718	1600	1800	153354	CON	Gwennap
MORDECAI						
1780	1960	1780	1960	141577	GLA	Mid
MORDEN						
....	....	ALL	ALL	168939	ALL	Name Study
MORDUE						
1846	1992	ALL	ALL	157090	DUR	Tyneside
1846	1992	ALL	ALL	157090	NBL	Tyneside
MORE						
1753	1992	1730	....	148644	ABD	Aberdeen
1796	....	1700	1992	167800	DEV	Northam
1857	1992	1700	1850	148849	NYK	Stockton
1775	1821	....	....	171654	PER	Kinnoull
1909	....	1879	....	127647	SCT	Firth Of Fourth
1743	1921	....	....	121290	STS	Marchington
MOREHOUSE						
1791	....	1760	1810	176923	CMN	Llandeilo
1770	....	1700	1841	176923	LND	???
MOREL						
1855	1900	1800	1900	129178	MDX	Islington
....	1791	1700	1791	160024	MDX	London
MORELAND						
1852	1890	1886	1968	143065	LAN	Hindley Green
1852	1980	1800	1980	143065	MON	Ebbw Vale
1800	1850	1750	1850	131431	WOR	???
MOREMAN						
....	....	1500	ALL	149144	DEV	Hartland
MORES						
1770	1800	ALL	1770	115266	DOR	ALL
MORETON						
....	....	1800	ALL	149187	ESS	London
....	....	1700	1900	147508	HEF	ALL
1841	1871	1700	1850	164909	STS	West Bromwich
1835	1939	1823	1861	138495	WAR	Birmingham
1881	1912	1700	1890	164909	WOR	Cradley
1881	1912	1700	1890	164909	WOR	Oldbury
MOREY						
1880	1881	1880	1992	149209	DEV	Brier Hill
1783	1992	1700	1992	149209	DEV	???
1760	1860	1700	1760	132748	HAM	Havant
1850	1860	....	....	145025	SOM	Exford
....	....	1880	1992	149209	WMD	???
MORFEE						
1860	1869	1860	1869	113743	SSX	Rye
MORFETT						
1798	1826	1700	1851	110132	DEV	???
MORFORD						
1722	1970	1650	1722	149217	KEN	Folkestone
MORGAN						
1880	1890	1750	1880	144150	ABD	Aberdeen
1880	1890	1750	1880	144150	ANS	Dundee
1875	....	1875	....	149284	AVN	Bristol
1829	1903	1700	1829	102997	AYR	Stewarton
1780	1899	1780	1845	176958	BRE	Bronllys
1740	1881	1600	1992	176877	BRE	Crickadarn
1900	1989	1880	1989	176877	BRE	Cwmbach
1780	1899	1780	1845	176958	BRE	Llandefaelog Fach
1786	1880	1600	1786	162035	BRE	Llandefalle
1800	1992	....	1800	138320	BRE	Llanelli
1720	1850	1720	1850	120235	BRE	Talgarth
1780	1899	1780	1845	176958	BRE	Talgarth
1840	1992	1700	1840	138525	BRE	???
1800	1880	1810	1880	142794	CGN	Llandelewibreifi

Known From	To	Researching From	To	Ref	Cty	Place
MORGAN contd.						
1840	1870	1700	1840	138452	CMN	Gwynfe
1778	1861	1750	1875	118575	CMN	Laugharne
1848	1902	1800	1902	162450	CMN	Llanartheney
1700	1900	1650	1850	168750	CMN	Llandilofawr
1861	1933	1861	1933	125717	CMN	Llandovery
1790	1810	1750	1830	158658	CMN	Llandybie
1827	....	1750	1827	123129	CMN	Llanfihangel Aberbythych
1840	1870	1700	1840	138452	CMN	Llangadog
1778	1861	1750	1875	118575	CMN	St Clears
1830	1860	1790	1992	166901	CON	St Erth
....	....	ALL	1700	149284	CON	???
1730	1755	1700	1760	171158	DEV	Uffculme
1691	1849	1691	1849	149284	DEV	???
1820	1915	1700	1850	145149	DOR	Horton
....	....	ALL	1700	149284	DOR	???
1815	1888	1782	1888	149292	DOW	Groomsport
1794	1881	1600	1794	116637	DUR	Bishopwearmouth
1840	1992	1700	1840	160571	DUR	Hartlepool
1794	1881	1600	1794	116637	DUR	Sunderland
1954	1985	....	....	159743	GLA	Aberdare
1715	1800	1700	1800	167533	GLA	Caer Moel Eglwysilan
1914	1985	....	....	159743	GLA	Cardiff
1914	1985	....	....	159743	GLA	Glynneath
1800	1845	1715	1800	167533	GLA	Graig Abercanaid
1800	1888	1800	1888	158658	GLA	Llanfabon
1809	1843	1809	1843	158658	GLA	Llansamlet
1850	1900	1700	1850	131253	GLA	Llanwonno
1835	1870	1835	1900	178845	GLA	Merthyr Tydfil
1841	1861	1800	1865	118575	GLA	Morriston
1860	1934	1820	1870	131938	GLA	Mountain Ash
1852	1936	1800	1900	127361	GLA	Neath
1834	....	1830	1850	169625	GLA	Pencoed
1720	1808	ALL	1992	159174	GLA	Rhiw Llanilid
1840	1992	1700	1840	138525	GLA	Rhymney Valley
1550	1992	ALL	1550	131393	GLA	Tredegar
1816	....	....	....	124982	GLS	Berkeley
1820	1840	1750	1840	136840	GLS	Bristol
1840	1870	1860	1865	149322	GLS	Bristol
1800	1900	1775	1875	159700	GLS	Dursley
1750	1860	1750	1900	138193	GLS	Dynock
1780	1992	....	....	118672	GLS	Kingswood
1880	1950	1600	1880	158968	GLS	Whitebrook
1850	1850	1700	1992	140147	HAM	Kings Somborne
1893	1970	1800	1893	139777	HAM	Southampton
1822	1930	1700	1822	122793	HAM	West Meon
1819	1992	....	....	157120	HEF	ALL
1783	....	....	....	131229	HEF	Allensmore
1776	....	....	....	131229	HEF	Burghill
1700	1760	ALL	ALL	139181	HEF	Clehonger
1841	1992	ALL	1841	116408	HEF	Hereford
....	....	1700	1820	176621	HEF	Monmouth
....	....	1700	1820	176621	HEF	Ross On Wye
1790	1830	1750	1830	119938	HEF	Weston Beggard
....	....	?	....	128589	HRT	Codicote
1742	1950	....	....	151882	HRT	Royston
1900	....	1800	1900	144150	INV	Inverness
1790	1810	....	....	143502	KEN	ALL
1746	1992	1700	1746	147850	KEN	Deptford
1746	1992	1700	1746	147850	KEN	Eynsford
1844	1890	1800	1900	100307	LAN	Liverpool
1860	1880	1782	1888	149292	LAN	Liverpool
1894	1894	1700	1894	157112	LAN	Manchester
1850	1922	1800	1849	172006	LAN	Toxteth
1881	1959	1881	1959	156639	LND	ALL
1850	1950	1800	1850	108448	LND	East
1800	1945	1700	1992	112402	LND	St Pancras
1840	1870	....	1870	102822	LND	Westminster
1837	1903	1800	1837	166464	MDX	Clerkenwell
1800	1864	1780	1850	176621	MDX	Stepney
1882	1992	?	1882	156337	MGM	Aberdare
1860	1880	1800	1900	156981	MGY	Llanidloes
1806	1900	1800	1900	118540	MON	Abergavenny
1800	1850	1750	1850	147575	MON	Bedwellty
1790	1875	1700	1790	177164	MON	Caerleon
1875	1927	1875	1927	159743	MON	Castleton Marshfield
1800	1850	1750	1850	147575	MON	Llantarnam
1864	....	ALL	ALL	114618	MON	Monmouth
1858	1868	1858	1868	138398	MON	Mynyddyshwyn
1787	1794	1650	1787	118583	MON	Newport
1836	1940	....	....	134430	MON	Newport
1800	1851	1800	1875	159743	MON	Newport
1855	1855	1800	1875	178004	MON	Risca
1780	1826	1700	1780	159735	MON	Shirenewton
1854	1854	1800	1875	178004	MON	Trevethin
1839	1896	1839	1896	111457	MON	???
1885	1885	1800	1900	100307	NWL	ALL
1840	1940	1700	1840	105767	PEM	Haverfordwest
1809	....	1750	1800	178845	PEM	Narberth
1830	1840	1700	1840	174572	PEM	Newport
1806	1820	1770	1806	173118	PEM	St Nicholas
1808	1870	1700	1992	176877	RAD	Beguildy
1876	....	1875	1899	176877	RAD	Llanfaredd
1700	1920	ALL	ALL	137987	SAL	North West
1842	1992	....	....	134619	SAL	Broseley
1689	1853	1600	1992	176877	SAL	Clun
1820	1967	ALL	1820	158445	SAL	Llanymynech
1802	1810	1800	1850	165093	SAL	Sandford
1640	1745	1640	1750	135941	SFK	Lakenheath
....	1900	....	1900	119024	SOM	Corsley
1750	1850	1650	1750	149306	SOM	Frome
1700	1780	1700	1780	142018	SOM	Norton St Philip
1801	1876	....	....	115290	SOM	Wedmore
1850	1874	1850	1874	149284	SOM	???
1808	1827	ALL	1808	175080	SSX	Funtington
1900	1989	1890	1992	133639	STS	Wolverhampton
1768	1900	1740	ALL	145386	WAR	Ansley
1841	1992	ALL	1992	116408	WAR	Birmingham
1800	1992	1700	1800	149241	WIL	Mere
....	1900	....	1900	119024	WIL	???
1905	1992	....	1905	142166	WLS	Ebbw Vale
....	....	ALL	1647	149349	WLS	Newport
....	....	ALL	1700	149284	WLS	???
1815	....	....	1815	111767	???	Berriew
?	?	?	?	115142	???	???
MORGANS						
1770	1880	1811	1880	142794	CGN	Bettws Bledwrs
1800	1992	....	....	135666	CMN	Llanstephan
1811	1854	ALL	ALL	104191	DFD	Aberystwyth
1841	1861	1800	1870	173428	DFD	Nantcwnlle
1850	1880	1700	1850	121886	PEM	Pwllcrochan
MORGER						
1747	1760	1500	1760	170178	SXE	East Dean
MORICKTON						
1200	1870	1870	1992	137707	KEN	Brenchley
MORIER						
....	....	ALL	ALL	171433	ALL	Name Study
MORILLION						
1643	1940	....	....	128996	CAM	Thorney
MORISON						
1865	....	1865	1992	146560	LTN	Edinburgh
MORLANDS						
1770	1790	1700	1770	121339	NYK	Wensley
MORLE						
1880	1992	....	....	108898	PER	Perth
MORLEDGE						
1800	1850	1700	1800	157708	DBY	Ible
MORLEY						
1772	1822	....	1822	137405	CAM	Haslingfield
1700	1750	1600	1750	168750	CMN	Llandebie
1786	1884	1786	1992	149403	DBY	Horsley
1862	1937	1862	1937	149381	DFD	Llanelli
1771	1800	....	....	122491	GLS	Wooten Under Edge
1800	1878	....	....	145394	HAM	Cliddesden
1847	1940	1600	1847	131261	KEN	Tonbridge
1849	1870	1800	1900	178624	NFK	Gorleston
1750	1800	1700	1800	123722	NTT	Calverton
1797	....	....	1797	108839	SFK	Bury St Edmunds
1770	1800	1700	1900	159956	SFK	Bury St Edmunds
1670	1992	1640	1992	135941	SFK	Lakenheath
1800	1936	1750	1814	149373	SSX	Amberley
....	....	1700	....	164038	SSX	Chidam
1756	1879	1756	1879	149381	SSX	Climping
1632	?	1632	....	149381	SSX	Cowfold
1725	?	1725	....	149381	SSX	Edburton
1661	1701	1661	1701	149381	SSX	Pyecombe
1716	1765	1600	1716	164879	SSX	Upper Beeding
1800	1817	....	1800	129771	WOR	Old Swinford
....	....	ALL	ALL	111384	WYK	Rothwell
1794	....	1750	1794	176885	YKS	Doncaster
1794	....	1750	1794	176885	YKS	Ulleskelf
MORLING						
1721	1781	....	1800	137405	CAM	Rampton
1764	1877	ALL	ALL	125873	SSX	Brighton

Known From	To	Researching From	To	Ref	Cty	Place
MORLOCK						
....	1900	....	....	106372	LND	Poplar
MORLYE						
1592	?	1592	....	149381	SSX	Bolney
1560	....	ALL	1560	149381	SSX	???
MORNE						
?	....	?	?	116610	LAN	Blackburn
MORPHETT						
1640	1992	ALL	1640	141909	KEN	Tenterden
MORPHEW						
1791	1805	1650	1791	138673	KEN	Dover
1720	1900	1650	1900	148288	KEN	Dover
1720	1900	1650	1900	148288	KEN	Lewisham
MORPHY						
1794	1827	1700	1794	109533	SSX	Brede
1860	1992	....	....	109533	SSX	Rye
MORRALL						
1643	1992	1400	1900	114952	WAR	Studley
1643	1992	1400	1900	114952	WOR	Redditch
MORRAM						
1876	....	....	....	144169	LAN	Manchester
MORRAN						
1876	....	....	....	144169	LAN	Manchester
MORRANT						
1805	1830	1700	1805	121010	HAM	Abbots Ann
....	....	1700	1900	133493	HAM	Romsey
MORRELL						
....	....	ALL	ALL	154156	ALL	Name Study
1795	1856	1795	1856	149403	DBY	Duffield
1800	1880	1800	1910	173622	LND	Hackney
....	....	1700	1980	172111	WIL	Calne
....	....	1700	1980	172111	WIL	Chippenham
1870	1992	1750	1870	149462	YKS	Knaresborough
1907	....	1700	1900	149454	YKS	???
MORREN						
....	....	ALL	ALL	149470	ALL	Name Study
MORREY						
....	....	1750	1821	149977	SAL	ALL
1821	1841	....	....	149977	SAL	Newport
MORRICE						
1801	1992	1600	1801	146137	ABD	Buchan
1800	1992	1650	1992	104671	ABD	Footdee
1800	1992	1650	1992	104671	KCD	Nigg
MORRILL						
1632	....	ALL	1632	103624	ESS	Broadoak
1632	....	ALL	1632	103624	ESS	Hatfield
MORRIS						
1800	1890	1750	1800	159891	ANS	Forfar
1681	1698	ALL	1698	108642	BDF	Pavenham
1828	1891	1800	1992	117609	BKM	Cookham Dean
1775	1793	1749	1751	138401	CAE	Penmachno
1840	....	....	....	146455	CAE	Tyddywhen
1655	1940	....	....	128996	CAM	Thorney
1868	1880	1800	1900	131792	CGN	Aberayron
1760	1824	....	....	176958	CGN	Bachendre
1790	1841	ALL	ALL	149489	CHS	Middlewich
1814	....	1782	1814	123129	CMN	Llangyndeyrn
1850	1992	1800	1870	109525	CWD	Bangor
1840	1992	1700	1900	142778	CWD	Dyffryn Clwyd
1832	1867	1700	1831	164798	CWD	Ruabon
1846	1873	ALL	1992	125113	DEN	Corwen
1821	1865	....	....	138401	DEN	Llanelian
1832	1867	1700	1831	164798	DEN	Ruabon
1786	1992	1700	1800	152692	DEN	Ruthin
1824	1838	1838	1875	131733	DFD	Trelech Ar Bettws
1770	1820	ALL	1770	115266	DOR	ALL
1744	....	....	....	126187	DOR	Beaminster
1930	1992	1795	1992	126241	DUR	Gateshead
1830	....	....	....	128945	DUR	Murton
....	....	1795	1992	126241	DUR	Trimdon
1800	1900	....	....	116998	ESS	Harwich
1840	....	....	....	151548	ESS	Romford
1838	1900	1700	1838	143812	FER	Magheraculmany
1670	....	....	....	137936	FIF	Crail
1870	1992	1800	1870	124117	GLA	Aberdare
1775	1800	1650	1850	139866	GLA	Llantilot
....	....	1800	1899	179612	GLA	Merthyr Tydfil
1700	1750	1600	1750	174513	GLS	Blaisdon
1730	1760	1700	1800	155896	GLS	Gloucester
1760	1810	1700	1850	177024	GLS	Taynton
1825	1894	1700	1992	122742	GLS	???
1800	1980	1800	1980	129054	GNT	Mynyddislwyn
1776	1861	1720	1870	105333	HAM	Isle Of Wight
1971	....	....	....	173932	HEF	Hereford
MORRIS contd.						
....	....	1700	1947	109215	HEF	Lyonshall
1830	1900	1800	1830	140309	HEF	Lyonshall
1828	1848	1750	1870	131547	HEF	Orleton
1825	1894	1700	1992	122742	HEF	???
1791	1791	1750	1800	102717	HRT	Albury
1830	1992	1750	1992	114596	KEN	Chatham
1800	1992	1600	1800	113654	KEN	Staplehurst
1800	1897	1800	1992	172243	KEN	Woolwich
....	....	....	1900	147818	LAN	Bolton
1906	1992	1800	1906	103322	LAN	Heath Charnock
1904	1992	1875	1904	131733	LAN	Horwich
1700	1800	1700	1800	152404	LAN	Hulton
1835	1855	1800	1855	103632	LAN	Manchester
....	1873	1600	1992	170704	LAN	Manchester
1796	1822	....	....	171824	LAN	St Helens
1815	1880	....	1820	169412	LAN	Wigan
1796	1876	ALL	1796	171476	LEI	Lutterworth
1770	1850	1700	1770	172847	LEI	Market Besworth
1770	1850	1700	1770	172847	LEI	Sutton Cheyney
1783	1880	1700	1880	115681	LIN	Grantham
1870	....	....	1870	162086	LND	North
1830	1992	1600	1800	169773	LND	London
1860	1890	1840	1860	160741	LND	Rotherhithe
1870	1872	ALL	1883	156175	MDX	Hackney
1853	1880	1820	1880	124974	MDX	Islington
1832	1871	1700	1832	110639	MDX	London
1799	1875	1600	1875	129011	MDX	London
1799	1841	1798	1992	142735	MDX	Mile End
1799	1841	1798	1992	142735	MDX	Stepney
1852	1852	1820	1855	124974	MDX	Tottenham
1880	1920	1880	1950	124974	MDX	Walthamstow
1738	1880	1690	1738	172642	MGY	Carreghova
....	....	1600	1830	176893	MGY	Kerry
....	....	1600	1830	176893	MGY	Llanidloes
1738	1880	1690	1738	172642	MGY	Llanymynech
1805	....	1700	1851	176877	MGY	Trefeglwys
1823	1900	1700	1823	149551	MON	Abercarn
1851	1900	....	....	149551	MON	Pontymister
1725	1900	1725	1900	160849	MON	Trelleck
1767	1881	....	....	157554	NFK	Reepham
1760	1940	1784	1861	149594	NTH	Potterpury
1800	1880	1700	1800	121509	NTH	Woodnewton
1880	1900	....	....	172847	NTT	Nottingham
ALL	1785	....	....	170798	NTT	Sutton Bonnington
1880	1900	....	....	172847	NTT	Sutton In Ashfield
1737	1778	1700	1780	124796	OXF	Elsfield
1833	1878	1810	1900	171441	OXF	Headington
1776	1797	....	1840	171441	OXF	Horsepath
1811	....	1795	1840	171441	OXF	Stanton St John
1700	1800	1600	1750	173983	OXF	Witney
1790	1865	1700	1790	158739	PEM	Whitechurch
1826	1869	1820	1881	176877	RAD	Cwmdeuddwr
1789	....	1750	1800	176877	RAD	Llangynllo
1830	1940	1800	1940	155004	RFW	Greenock
1766	1851	ALL	ALL	101486	SAL	Albrighton
1831	1867	1700	1831	164798	SAL	Coton
1820	1992	1700	1820	172642	SAL	Shrewsbury
1770	1852	1700	1770	169021	SAL	Wem
1790	1818	1700	1818	159581	SFK	Fornham
1795	....	....	1825	152803	SOM	Hardington
1810	1850	1780	1810	149462	SRY	Walworth
....	1600	....	....	174564	SSX	Ashburnham
1710	1860	1650	1950	122602	SSX	Ninfield
....	1600	....	....	174564	SSX	Ninfield
....	....	....	....	127272	STS	Bilston
1853	ALL	....	....	117048	STS	Smethwick
1694	1867	....	....	155055	STS	Wolverhampton
1830	1900	1800	1830	140317	WLS	Llangedwin
....	....	1790	1810	138339	WOR	Claines
1750	1850	1700	1750	174513	WOR	Kemerton
....	....	1790	1810	138339	WOR	Tenbury
1783	1849	1600	1783	115525	WOR	Worcester
1780	1847	....	1880	171441	WOR	Worcester
1930	1992	1795	1950	126241	WYK	ALL
....	....	ALL	ALL	121576	YKS	Hessle
1871	1992	1874	1992	173851	YKS	Hull
1820	1895	1800	1900	159220	YKS	Nutton Cranswick
1803	?	1803	?	173851	YKS	Scarborough
....	....	ALL	ALL	121576	YKS	Selby
1899	1972	....	....	149497	???	Birmingham
1744	1837	....	....	107085	???	???
1890	1992	1700	1890	171913	???	???

Known From	To	Researching From	To	Ref	Cty	Place
MORRISBY						
1580	1850	....	....	110221	YKS	Kippax Garforth
MORRISH						
1660	1680	1600	1660	102571	CON	Gulval
1774	1900	1600	1774	149608	DEV	E Putford
1760	1860	1600	1760	134090	DEV	Tedburn St Mary
1840	1870	1600	1840	122084	LND	Shoreditch
MORRISON						
1818	1901	ALL	1818	149632	ABD	Fyvie
1818	1901	ALL	1818	149632	ABD	Tarves
1780	1868	1550	1800	147265	ABD	???
1849	1992	1700	1850	148423	ANS	Kirriemuir
1780	1872	1700	1870	154881	ANT	Belfast
....	1852	ALL	1852	134058	ARL	Tobermoray
1758	1992	....	....	149616	AYR	Craigie
1803	1838	ALL	ALL	158690	BAN	Alvah
1803	1838	ALL	1850	158690	BAN	Foreglen
1800	1900	1700	1800	118419	BAN	Grange
1780	1868	1550	1800	147265	BAN	???
1790	1970	1790	1970	161705	CHS	North
1800	1920	1800	1992	151254	CHS	Hyde
1800	1920	1800	1992	151254	CHS	Werneth
1760	1796	1700	1800	153354	CLK	Alloa
1806	1819	1750	1819	149292	CUL	Whitehaven
1800	1880	1750	1880	154881	DOW	Derryneil
1840	1870	ALL	1950	119369	DOW	Inch
1850	1980	ALL	1960	119369	DOW	Killinchy
....	....	1750	1900	167401	DUR	South Shields
1829	1900	1800	1900	130427	INV	Inverness
1810	?	1700	1830	122394	INV	Isle Of Skye
1798	1806	1750	1819	149292	IOM	Kirk German
1760	1800	1600	1760	151254	LAN	Haughton
1861	1992	ALL	1861	115878	LEI	Melton Mowbray
1797	1850	1700	1797	149004	LKS	Glasgow
1890	?	1850	1900	122394	LKS	Motherwell
1810	1833	1800	1850	163775	MDX	Clerkenwell
1879	1951	1797	1956	149640	MDX	London
1845	1992	1800	1992	149659	MDX	London
....	....	1799	1801	104442	MDX	Poplar
1803	....	1790	1820	163775	MDX	Winchmore Hill
1792	1824	ALL	ALL	174777	MLN	Leith
1780	1800	1750	1800	111821	ROC	Urray
1854	1924	1700	1854	146072	SCT	Mussleborough
1854	1924	1700	1854	146072	SCT	Prestonpaus
1780	1992	1700	1992	104671	SHI	Nesting
1800	1820	1800	1830	146536	STI	Larbert
1868	1921	1800	1868	127590	SUT	Assynt
MORRISS						
1890	1992	....	....	154075	AVN	Bristol
....	....	1850	1890	154075	HEF	Kington
1840	1850	1850	1890	154075	HEF	Westhide
....	....	1750	1820	154075	WOR	Bewdley
....	....	1750	1820	154075	WOR	Orleton
MORRISSON						
....	....	1850	1920	115045	NTT	Nottingham
MORRIT						
1830	1945	....	....	132756	NTT	Bothamsall
1736	?	1700	1800	137561	YKS	Whitkirk
MORRITT						
1873	....	1700	1873	105163	WYK	Little Heck
....	....	1850	1880	159220	YKS	Pontefract
MORROGH						
1750	1835	1750	1992	163848	COR	Cork City
MORROW						
1845	1898	1800	1920	137448	ARM	Belfast
....	1873	1600	1992	170704	LAN	Manchester
1820	1850	1700	1820	161519	MDX	London
MORSE						
1835	1874	1800	1835	165530	GLS	Hawkesbury
?	?	?	?	144282	GLS	Tresham
....	1756	1650	1756	148288	KEN	Thanet
....	1793	1500	1793	175072	LIN	Wickenby
1901	....	....	....	153400	LND	Pancras
....	....	1773	1850	129895	SFK	Mendham
1807	....	....	....	144282	WIL	Lyneham
1807	....	....	....	144282	WIL	Purton
MORSON						
....	....	1600	1880	129763	NFK	Haddon
MORT						
1800	1992	1800	1992	149675	ALL	ALL
1850	1992	1700	1992	138282	CHS	Malpas
1790	1992	ALL	ALL	173010	LAN	Wigan
1820	1850	1790	1860	158658	NFK	Norwich

Known From	To	Researching From	To	Ref	Cty	Place
MORTARA						
1843	1846	ALL	ALL	134929	LND	Kensington
MORTBY						
1823	1912	....	....	116602	SRY	London
MORTER						
1840	1937	1700	1900	168068	NFK	Neatishead
1798	1808	ALL	ALL	149683	NFK	Thursford
MORTIBOY						
....	....	ALL	ALL	149691	ALL	Name Study
MORTIBOYS						
1461	1992	ALL	ALL	149691	ALL	ALL
MORTIMER						
1000	1411	1000	1400	154881	ALL	ALL
1880	1899	1880	1935	136336	CWD	Wrexham
1782	1899	1780	1900	136336	DEV	Bradninch
1684	1738	1660	1711	165972	DEV	Morchard Bishop
1820	1940	1800	1880	136840	DOR	Wool
1864	1911	....	1890	166510	ENG	London
1750	1992	1600	1992	130125	HAM	ALL
1790	1820	1700	1840	136840	HAM	Andover
?	....	....	....	116092	HAM	Portsmouth
1054	1227	1066	1211	124974	HEF	Wigmore
1800	1992	1600	1800	149713	HRT	Tring
....	....	ALL	1860	145548	LEI	Appleby Magna
1728	1758	1600	1727	131245	LEI	Rearsby
1728	1758	1600	1727	131245	LEI	Wanlip
1700	1900	....	....	149721	LND	Bethnal Green
1700	1900	....	....	149721	LND	Stepney
1820	1992	1600	1820	149705	SFK	Wetheringsett
1838	1992	ALL	1838	130605	SRY	Thornton Heath
1500	1900	1500	1900	170216	WIL	ALL
1824	1843	1800	1843	147575	WIL	Broughton Grifford
1824	1938	1750	1950	127353	WIL	Cherhill
1824	1843	1800	1843	147575	WIL	Orcheston
1800	1827	1800	1860	145602	WIL	Warminster
1808	1827	1700	1808	179086	YKS	Bradford
1857	1857	1800	1880	171662	YKS	Danby
1857	1857	1800	1880	171662	YKS	Eston
1100	1235	....	....	100536	???	???
MORTIMORE						
1816	1840	1750	1900	126586	DEV	Collbrook
....	....	1650	1840	146234	DEV	Morchard Bishop
1820	1840	1820	1840	138479	DEV	???
MORTIN						
....	....	1500	1691	138614	CON	Stithian
1782	....	1782	....	139149	DBY	Bakewell
MORTLEY						
1840	1870	1700	1840	134899	KEN	Canterbury
1776	1809	1776	1960	115436	KEN	New Romney
MORTLOCK						
....	....	ALL	ALL	149748	CAM	ALL
....	....	ALL	ALL	149748	ESS	ALL
1816	1856	ALL	1816	162108	ESS	Purleigh
1810	1920	1700	1800	178969	LND	North
....	....	ALL	ALL	149748	SFK	ALL
MORTON						
....	....	1790	1845	132381	ABD	Aberdeen
1856	1992	1700	1800	172820	ANT	Ballymena
1816	1861	1700	1816	168246	AYR	Loudoun
1850	1900	1800	1950	177180	BKM	Dagnall
1764	....	1700	1764	176885	BKM	Great Hampden
1767	1767	1740	1770	125032	BRK	Wokingham
1800	1980	1700	1800	149756	CMA	Addingham
1738	....	1700	....	162825	CUL	Gamblesby
1775	1796	1745	1775	139149	DBY	Bakewell
1816	1816	1600	1816	148954	ESS	Colchester
1700	1880	1600	1880	154342	GLS	Bitton
1700	1850	1600	1850	154342	GLS	Mangotsfield
1835	1870	1810	1992	149772	LAN	Bury
1850	?	ALL	1850	157902	LAN	Liverpool
....	....	ALL	ALL	130850	LAN	Manchester
....	....	ALL	ALL	130850	LAN	Salford
1700	1728	1650	1750	156396	LEI	Swinford
1791	1806	1789	1830	159042	LIN	Barholm
1830	1833	1830	1840	159042	LIN	Baston
1855	1855	1800	1860	159042	LIN	Langtoft
....	....	ALL	ALL	130850	LND	ALL
1861	1900	1700	1900	126918	LND	Clerkenwell
1808	1861	1700	1900	126918	LND	Lambeth
1838	1863	....	....	170623	LND	Marylebone
1808	1861	1700	1900	126918	LND	Southwark
1819	....	1800	1830	163775	MDX	Hackney
1760	1760	1760	ALL	171816	NTH	Bugbrooke
1789	1789	....	....	159042	NTH	Maxey

Known From	To	Researching From	To	Ref	Cty	Place
MORTON contd.						
1860	1866	1750	1850	127302	SCT	Edinburgh
1841	1871	1700	1850	164909	STS	West Bromwich
1881	1912	1700	1890	164909	WOR	Cradley
1800	1950	....	....	149764	WOR	Kidderminster
1600	1850	....	....	149764	WOR	Leigh
1881	1912	1700	1890	164909	WOR	Oldbury
1800	1900	....	....	149764	WOR	Worcester
....	....	1550	1970	131512	WYK	Huddersfield
....	....	1550	1970	131512	WYK	Salendine Nook
1810	1830	1700	1810	108790	YKS	Bradfield
1760	1840	1740	1840	123595	YKS	Holmfirth
1800	1840	ALL	ALL	170801	YKS	Holmfirth
1760	1904	ALL	1904	100102	YKS	Mirfield
1859	1950	....	....	151785	YKS	Rotherham
1809	1820	1700	1850	169978	YKS	Sheffield
MORVAN						
1800	1860	....	....	116157	LND	ALL
MOSCROP						
....	....	1800	1920	118966	LAN	Bolton
MOSELEY						
1750	1840	1750	1840	131709	CHS	Stockport
1736	1800	....	....	105805	DBY	Cubley
1808	....	1700	1992	153672	HRT	Broxbourne
1736	1925	ALL	ALL	127000	LAN	Manchester
1736	1925	ALL	ALL	127000	SAL	Edstaston
1600	1980	1200	1800	139130	STS	Stafford
1699	1706	1673	1736	105805	STS	Tutbury
....	....	1750	1850	147613	STS	West Bromwich
1855	....	1600	1885	132802	STS	Wolverhampton
1900	1950	1800	1900	138649	WMD	Birmingham
....	....	....	?	141216	WOR	Great Barr
1855	1881	1833	1855	134309	WOR	Kidderminster
MOSELY						
1815	1881	1700	1881	116300	BDF	Biggleswade
MOSES						
1806	1850	1700	....	159794	CAE	Eglwys Rhos
1800	1860	1700	1900	129135	CMN	Myddfai
1726	1770	1650	1726	140678	CUL	Culgaith
1600	1900	1600	1900	160814	DEV	Meavy
1750	1860	1700	1860	105422	DUR	Cockfield
1794	1870	1700	1794	159565	DUR	Stanhope
1750	....	....	....	114529	KEN	Dartford
1900	1910	1870	1900	179027	MON	Maesycwmmer
1850	1992	1700	1850	116815	WOR	Dudley
1833	1855	....	1840	169412	YKS	Drypool
MOSEY						
1690	1755	1500	1992	114901	YKS	Thirkleby
MOSLEY						
1850	1992	1750	1850	107484	DBY	Chesterfield
1788	1959	1610	1930	107654	DBY	Tideswell
ALL	ALL	1800	1900	139114	KEN	ALL
1834	....	1800	1900	139114	KEN	Leeds
1816	1896	....	....	105805	LAN	Manchester
MOSS						
1600	1750	1500	1850	177180	BDF	Eaton Socon
1725	1892	1700	1892	154709	BKM	ALL
1803	1822	1750	1803	125105	BRK	Chosley
1820	....	1800	1840	113638	BRK	Hungerford
1795	1795	ALL	1800	147567	BRK	Newbury
....	....	ALL	1796	149950	BRK	Newbury
....	....	1750	1992	178268	CHS	Congleton
1806	1989	1700	1806	174939	CHS	Macclesfield
1811	1841	1811	1850	126705	CHS	Tarvin
1626	1992	1626	1992	149810	CON	ALL
....	....	1800	1870	172154	ESS	???
1851	....	1851	....	165735	GLA	Cardiff
1781	1992	ALL	1731	165735	GLS	Bristol
1791	1891	ALL	1813	143308	GLS	Broadwell
1863	....	1860	1865	171441	GLS	Cheltenham
1840	1870	ALL	ALL	121320	GLS	Duntisbourne Rouse
1844	....	?	1850	164976	GLS	Gloucester
1840	....	....	1840	171441	GLS	South Cerney
1800	1992	1800	1880	147567	HAM	Bramshott
1796	1992	ALL	1796	149950	HAM	Bramshott
1865	1876	1865	1900	171441	KEN	Birchington
1897	....	1876	1910	171441	KEN	Canterbury
1890	1900	1800	1900	101907	KEN	Gravesend
1800	1900	1800	1900	105732	LAN	Bolton
1788	1819	1650	1788	138584	LAN	Eccles
1850	1900	1800	1900	126586	LAN	Farnworth
1800	1900	1851	1881	114529	LAN	Liverpool
1819	1992	....	....	138584	LAN	Manchester
1881	1891	1871	1891	159492	LAN	Oldham

Known From	To	Researching From	To	Ref	Cty	Place
MOSS contd.						
....	....	1700	1800	146110	LAN	Preston
1800	1900	1800	1900	105732	LAN	Wigan
1901	1966	1800	1901	136905	LAN	Wigan
1760	1960	1700	1960	149780	LAN	Wigan
....	....	1700	1800	171794	LIN	Corringham
1800	1900	....	....	100633	LIN	???
1840	1845	1600	1840	148954	LND	East
1880	1950	1851	1881	114529	LND	???
1851	1882	1840	1880	129283	MDX	St George In The East
1844	1912	1600	1844	143146	NTT	Annesley
1800	1900	....	....	100633	NTT	???
1780	1835	1700	1800	162043	SFK	Wetherdon
1749	1791	....	....	117579	STS	Bilston
1866	1882	ALL	1882	138819	T&W	Newcastle Upon Tyne
1700	1850	1700	1850	143553	WES	Crosby Rav
1820	1992	1750	1820	113638	WIL	East
1752	1823	1700	1850	127353	WIL	Cherhill
1850	1880	1750	1880	109010	WIL	Oakhill
1791	1891	ALL	1813	143308	WOR	Evenlode
1750	1992	1600	1992	120677	WYK	Thurstonland
1840	1870	ALL	1840	143022	YKS	Huddersfield
1782	1792	1780	1792	123250	YKS	Hull
....	....	1700	1800	171794	YKS	Laxton
MOSSEY						
1600	1700	1600	1700	167924	YKS	Kirby Underdale
MOSSMAN						
1824	1908	1700	1850	117005	BKM	Stoke Hammond
MOSSOM						
1737	....	ALL	ALL	155608	DUR	Stockton
MOSSON						
1743	....	1743	1992	138495	GLS	Wyck Rissington
MOSSOP						
....	....	1886	1887	145084	CMA	Whitehaven
1685	1860	1600	1900	116173	CUL	West
1835	1950	ALL	ALL	154806	CUL	Whitehaven
1835	1950	ALL	ALL	154806	LAN	Rochdale
MOTH						
....	....	ALL	ALL	120766	ALL	Name Study
1730	1900	1700	1900	146803	SRY	Frimley
MOTHERLOVE						
....	....	ALL	1992	156078	???	???
MOTLEY						
1790	1992	1600	1880	149845	LIN	ALL
MOTON						
1500	1570	1500	1600	154881	LEI	Peckleton
MOTT						
1729	1804	1700	1704	125520	ESS	Rettenden
....	1820	ALL	1820	177695	ESS	Rochford
1815	1815	....	1815	132837	KEN	???
1815	1919	....	....	132837	MDX	???
1794	1794	ALL	1992	125113	NFK	West Lynn
1790	1830	1750	1880	133922	NFK	West Lynn
1790	....	....	1790	101761	SFK	Fornham
....	....	1750	1850	101273	SRY	North
1884	1945	1800	1884	149861	SRY	Wimbledon
MOTTERSHEAD						
1500	1700	....	....	100420	WAR	Meriden
MOTTON						
1760	1860	1700	1850	139866	DEV	Ilsington
MOTTRAM						
1750	1829	1750	1829	131709	CHS	Alderley Edge
1740	1761	....	....	138851	CHS	Davenham
1850	....	1800	1900	166081	DBY	Boundary
1837	1960	1700	....	148342	EYK	Laughton
1880	....	....	....	101990	???	Leeds
MOUAT						
1750	1965	....	....	137820	SHI	Fetlar
1720	1965	....	....	137820	SHI	Mid Yell
1760	1965	....	....	137820	SHI	North Yell
1758	1965	....	....	137820	SHI	Northmavine
1720	1965	....	....	137820	SHI	South Yell
1780	1900	....	....	137936	SHI	Unst
MOUBRAY						
1600	1966	1066	1966	150045	ALL	ALL
MOUL						
1880	1980	1700	1880	138649	DEV	Plymouth
1835	1992	ALL	ALL	153753	STS	Walsall
MOULAND						
1700	1992	1700	1992	141380	ALL	ALL
MOULD						
1832	1992	....	....	167649	DOR	Hinton Martell
....	....	1700	1832	167649	ENG	South

Known From	To	Researching From	To	Ref	Cty	Place
MOULD contd.						
1750	1800	1600	1850	149934	ESS	West
1709	1834	ALL	1820	113611	EYK	Hull
1690	1992	1650	?	149896	HAM	Avington
....	1992	....	....	149896	HAM	Cheriton
1814	1992	1700	1814	149918	HAM	Easton
1690	1992	1650	?	149896	HAM	Easton
....	1992	....	....	149896	HAM	Winchester
1500	1900	1500	1900	149934	LEI	Appleby Magna
....	....	....	1805	142409	WLS	???
1805	1950	....	....	142409	???	Cannock
1805	1950	....	....	142409	???	Sedgley
MOULDEN						
1875	1930	1800	1875	159212	SRY	Merton
....	....	ALL	ALL	114308	WAR	Coventry
MOULDER						
....	....	ALL	ALL	149926	ALL	Name Study
1710	1762	1650	1750	166804	OXF	ALL
MOULDEY						
....	....	ALL	ALL	108960	BRK	ALL
1600	1780	....	....	108960	BRK	Brightwalton
1750	1850	....	....	108960	BRK	Speen
....	....	ALL	ALL	108960	LND	ALL
....	....	ALL	ALL	108960	OXF	ALL
MOULDS						
1834	1890	1700	1890	153079	CAM	March
1776	1798	1760	1820	136980	ESS	Enfield
1890	1960	ALL	ALL	113662	LEI	Licester
1750	1950	ALL	....	104515	LIN	South
MOULE						
....	....	1500	1900	149934	BKM	ALL
....	....	1500	1900	149934	CAM	ALL
....	....	ALL	1800	155470	DEV	Barnstaple
1760	1800	1600	1850	149934	LND	City
....	....	1500	1900	149934	NTH	Culworth
1796	1922	ALL	1796	115126	NTH	Finedon
1790	1870	1790	1870	149934	WIL	Melksham
1600	1940	1500	1992	149934	WOR	Sneads Green
1775	....	....	....	131229	WOR	Worcester
MOULES						
1670	1740	1670	1740	167924	ESS	Wendon Lofts
1822	1992	1700	1822	149942	YKS	Egton
1822	1992	1700	1822	149942	YKS	Middlesborough
MOULT						
1805	1857	1750	1805	141135	CHS	Mobberley
MOULTON						
1822	1822	1700	1822	113425	ESS	Bradwell On Sea
1850	1960	ALL	ALL	162469	SFK	North
....	....	ALL	1800	103284	SFK	???
....	....	....	....	124206	SOM	ALL
MOULTRY						
1786	1807	1750	1807	148288	FIF	Strathmiglo
MOUNCER						
....	....	1700	1800	116823	NYK	Acklann
MOUNCEY						
1831	....	1825	1835	175587	YKS	Bilton In Ainsty
MOUNDSDON						
1664	1900	1650	1800	137413	DEV	Crediton
MOUNSEY						
1881	....	1800	1900	160199	CUL	Walton
1881	....	1800	1900	160199	DUR	South Shields
....	....	1800	1866	149977	LAN	Manchester
1904	1992	....	....	149977	STS	Wloverhampton
1869	1887	....	....	149977	WOR	Dudley
MOUNT						
1784	1900	1500	1784	125415	LAN	Warton
1916	....	1916	....	162663	LIN	Gunby
MOUNTAIN						
1894	?	ALL	ALL	149985	AYR	Dalmellington
....	....	....	1800	176516	MDX	London
1945	?	ALL	ALL	149985	NFK	Holt
1891	?	ALL	ALL	149985	NFK	Leith
1797	1933	1700	1900	126683	NFK	Wiverton
1823	?	ALL	ALL	149985	NFK	Wiveton
1779	?	ALL	ALL	149985	SRY	Shere
1800	....	1700	....	134589	YKS	Poppleton
MOUNTCASTLE						
....	....	ALL	ALL	164631	ALL	Name Study
....	....	1570	1992	164631	ALL	ALL
1570	1800	....	....	164631	LIN	Lincoln
1790	1904	....	....	164631	MDX	London
MOUNTFORD						
....	....	1600	1992	127833	BRK	Newbury
1770	1885	1750	1770	114073	NFK	Fersfield
MOUNTFORD contd.						
1660	1992	1540	1660	149993	SAL	Wyre Forest
MOUNTJOY						
1800	1992	1700	1850	156450	CON	Kilkhampton
1820	1884	1700	1840	156450	CON	Phillack
1777	1992	1650	1777	123153	GLS	Forest Of Dean
MOUNTJOY-LANDER						
1777	1992	1650	1777	123153	GLS	Forest Of Dean
MOUNTNEY						
1695	1710	....	....	145580	DBY	Derby
1738	1800	....	....	145580	DBY	Edlaston
1766	1766	1766	1766	145580	DBY	Snelston
1592	1592	....	....	145580	DBY	West Hallam
1665	1675	1660	1680	145580	LEI	Leicester
1598	1723	....	....	145580	LEI	Neobald Verdon
1480	1480	1480	1480	145580	NFK	???
1481	1481	1481	1481	145580	YKS	???
1443	1443	1443	1443	145580	???	???
MOURANT						
....	....	ALL	ALL	155632	JSY	Channel Islands
MOURILYAN						
1500	1992	ALL	1992	133450	ALL	ALL
MOUSDALE						
1720	1851	1700	1900	126705	CHS	North West
MOVE						
1837	1837	1600	1837	152080	ESS	Hadstock
MOWAT						
....	....	ALL	ALL	150037	ALL	Name Study
1818	1845	1770	1818	150029	ABD	Aberdeen
1842	1856	1800	1842	174955	ABD	Belhelvie
1780	1822	1500	1780	138614	CAI	Canisbay
....	....	1750	1855	166049	CAI	Mey-Canisbay
1730	1840	1650	1730	100978	KCD	Kinneff
1776	1855	1600	1855	148482	OKI	Birsay
1845	1916	1750	1790	150029	SCT	Glasgow
MOWATT						
1870	1873	....	....	174955	ANS	Brechin
1860	1865	....	....	174955	ANS	Dun
1883	1940	....	....	174955	LND	South West
1883	1940	....	....	174955	LND	South
MOWBERRY						
1600	1966	1066	1966	150045	ALL	ALL
MOWBRAY						
....	....	ALL	ALL	150045	ALL	Name Study
1600	1966	1066	1966	150045	ALL	ALL
1721	1902	1700	1800	169854	DUR	Sunderland
1770	1900	....	....	124168	DUR	Witton Gilbert
1744	1820	1700	1820	151599	LEI	Shepshed
1820	1880	1600	1820	116815	LIN	Crowland
1792	1825	1841	1891	146560	LTN	Dalmeny
1792	1825	1841	1891	146560	LTN	Leith
1792	1825	1841	1891	146560	LTN	Queensferry
1749	1868	?	1749	144800	YKS	Huddersfield
1350	1400	....	....	100536	???	???
MOWELS						
....	....	ALL	ALL	107034	ALL	Name Study
MOWER						
1800	1992	....	1800	159972	HAM	Ringwood
1716	1736	1650	1730	172871	SFK	Cockfield
1837	1861	1800	1837	115746	SOM	Bishops Hull
1800	1992	....	1800	159972	WIL	Calne
MOWFORTH						
1560	1700	1500	1800	150061	CMA	Kendal
1720	1992	1550	1900	150061	YKS	East
MOWLES						
1838	1961	?	1838	112356	ALL	???
MOWLING						
1870	1992	1870	1992	155675	ESS	Little Wakering
1806	....	....	....	155675	ESS	Little Wigborough
MOXEY						
....	....	ALL	ALL	150088	ALL	Name Study
1817	1832	....	....	150088	DEV	Brixham
1723	1817	1650	1723	150088	DEV	Whitestone
1832	1871	....	....	150088	KEN	Ramsgate
1873	1873	1700	1873	117730	LND	ALL
1928	1992	....	....	150088	PEM	Milford Haven
1800	1840	1750	1850	170488	SCT	???
1871	1928	....	....	150088	SFK	Lowestoft
MOXHAM						
....	....	1798	1992	121940	LAN	Clifton
1500	1900	1500	1900	170216	WIL	ALL
1770	1770	1720	1840	105333	WIL	Bower Chalk
1770	1770	1720	1840	105333	WIL	Ebbesborne Wake
1796	1796	1720	1840	105333	WIL	Salisbury

Known From	To	Researching From	To	Ref	Cty	Place
MOXHAM contd.						
1821	1821	1720	1840	105333	WIL	Tisbury
MOXLEY						
1850	1880	1825	1900	136867	LND	ALL
MOXON						
1825	1874	1700	1825	156760	HAM	Southampton
1728	1992	1600	1728	150096	YKS	Ferry Fryston
1728	1992	1600	1728	150096	YKS	Pontefract
MOXSY						
1795	....	1750	1830	102016	MDX	???
MOY						
1750	1850	1750	1850	161705	NFK	North East
1690	1730	1600	1730	122920	SOM	Bristol
MOYCE						
1720	1750	1700	1800	144126	KEN	Wrotham
MOYERS						
1750	1960	1700	1750	121509	LAN	Wigan
MOYES						
....	....	1862	....	149187	FIF	Abdie
1860	1930	1800	1900	168998	LAN	Manchester
1880	1992	1700	1880	158755	SFK	Ipswich
1830	1880	1750	1830	110078	SFK	Winston
MOYLE						
1580	1850	1580	1850	150126	CON	Breage
....	....	1600	1850	127833	CON	Penzance
1845	....	ALL	1845	179515	CON	Penzance
1580	1850	1580	1850	150126	CON	Wedron
1820	....	1800	1850	169625	CON	???
MOYSE						
1805	1811	....	1805	133566	CON	Landulph
1841	1992	1700	1840	105635	NFK	Cley
1785	1815	1700	1785	105031	SFK	Woodbridge
MOYSER						
1664	1939	?	?	136301	YKS	Barnsley
1664	1939	?	?	136301	YKS	York
MOYSEY						
....	....	ALL	ALL	158593	ALL	ALL
MOZEEN						
1754	1992	ALL	ALL	150509	ALL	ALL
1754	1765	ALL	ALL	150509	NRY	Sutton On The Fores
MOZIER						
1930	1950	1850	1930	101907	KEN	Cobham
MQUAD						
1870	1920	1800	1870	110639	IRL	???
MRASURRS						
1782	1852	1700	1960	125865	NFK	North Walsham
MRGATROYD						
1831	1940	1800	1831	125342	WYK	Bingley
MUCH						
1802	1869	1750	1820	126586	LAN	???
MUCHMORE						
1700	1805	1700	1805	110434	DEV	Plymouth
MUCKERSIE						
1700	1840	1500	1950	114898	FIF	ALL
MUCKETT						
1798	1992	1700	1798	170542	HAM	Titchfield
MUCKLE						
1700	....	ALL	ALL	116394	KEN	???
MUCKLESTONE						
....	....	1900	1950	137685	LND	???
MUCOCK						
ALL	ALL	ALL	ALL	126373	ALL	ALL
MUDD						
1830	1992	1800	1992	153133	MDX	London
1782	1866	1750	1880	136719	NFK	Hedenham
1810	1900	ALL	ALL	121401	SFK	Pakefield
MUDDIE						
1760	....	1700	1760	100846	CLK	???
MUDDLE						
1738	1873	1650	1738	150894	KEN	St Laurence
1795	1992	1500	1992	140872	KEN	???
1795	1992	1500	1992	140872	SSX	???
MUDDLES						
1729	1992	ALL	1729	100803	SXE	Rotherfield
MUDFORD						
1700	....	1700	....	123609	SOM	Chinnock
MUDGE						
1550	1837	1550	1837	140392	DEV	Dean Prior
1829	1866	1820	1866	152749	DEV	Exeter
1663	1829	1550	1850	152749	DEV	Kingsteignton
1820	1881	1750	1900	126799	ESS	West Ham
1772	1772	1500	1772	110310	KEN	Benenden
1849	1849	1750	1900	126799	KEN	Dartford
1820	1881	1750	1900	126799	LND	ALL

Known From	To	Researching From	To	Ref	Cty	Place
MUDGE contd.						
1645	1820	1645	1820	156930	WIL	Aldbourne
1660	1700	1660	1700	156930	WIL	Marlborough
MUDIE						
1920	....	....	....	160385	IOM	Douglas
1830	1840	1800	1840	126594	LKS	Glasgow
MUDLE						
1830	1992	....	1830	141607	ALL	ALL
MUDWAY						
....	....	1600	1860	158968	GLS	Coldicote
MUER						
1804	1887	1700	1820	117013	NFK	Great Massingham
MUFF						
1782	....	1780	1900	130990	DUR	Durham
MUGFORD						
1777	1992	1600	1777	150142	CON	Kenwyn
1880	1980	1700	1880	138649	DEV	Plymouth
MUGG						
1803	1828	1700	1803	176710	LEI	Hathern
MUGGERIDGE						
....	1860	....	1950	151246	SSX	Robertsbridge
MUGGINSON						
1660	1785	1600	1825	123404	LEI	Great Bowden
1825	1906	1825	1906	123404	LEI	Hugglescote
MUGGLETON						
1822	1992	1822	1992	112534	CAM	Bottisham
1820	....	....	1992	112534	CAM	Grantchester
1714	1992	1600	1714	150150	LEI	Caldecott
1837	1920	1800	1837	149578	LND	Tottenham
MUGGLEWORTH						
1740	1800	1600	1800	154342	GLS	Bristol
MUGRIDGE						
1782	1861	....	....	114731	HAM	Portsea
MUIR						
1800	1875	1700	1800	158143	FIF	Dalgety
1820	1860	ALL	1860	152048	LKS	Cambusnethan
1820	1860	ALL	1860	152048	LKS	Chapel
1840	1861	ALL	1861	152048	LKS	Chaplehall
1800	1900	1700	1800	142670	MLN	Edinburgh
MUIRHEAD						
1690	1992	1680	....	148644	LTN	Edinburgh
1628	....	1620	....	148644	???	Wester Inche Of Bathcall
MULCAHY						
....	....	1800	1887	130141	COR	Boherbur
....	....	1800	1887	130141	COR	Kanturk
MULCOCK						
....	....	ALL	ALL	126373	ALL	Name Study
MULDER						
1860	1940	ALL	ALL	104183	KEN	???
1860	1940	ALL	ALL	104183	LND	ALL
MULDOON						
1861	1890	1861	1890	111090	SCT	Roxborough
MULDOWNEY						
1871	1914	1838	1914	171298	STS	Stoke-On-Trent
MULES						
....	....	ALL	ALL	150177	ALL	Name Study
?	?	?	?	117528	DEV	North West
MULEY						
....	....	1600	....	158240	ENG	ALL
....	....	1600	....	158240	IRL	ALL
MULHAIR						
....	....	ALL	1865	119326	IRL	???
....	....	ALL	1865	119326	MLN	Edinburgh
MULHARE						
1821	1992	1750	1821	157783	GAL	Longford
MULHOLLAND						
....	1775	1777	1992	162426	ANT	???
MULLADE						
1870	1960	1840	1870	111856	COR	???
MULLAM						
1730	1750	ALL	ALL	130508	DUR	Chester Le Street
MULLAN						
1870	1992	1750	1870	118052	LDY	Coleriane
MULLARD						
1700	1710	1550	1700	135771	HAM	Surrey Border
1780	1816	1780	1816	139971	SAL	Cressage
1750	1764	1650	1750	139084	SRY	Puttenham
MULLEN						
....	....	1500	1992	119792	ANT	ALL
1844	1907	1844	....	162175	CAV	???
1810	1830	ALL	ALL	130508	ESS	Sible Hedingham
1840	1940	....	....	136492	IRL	Aitkenhead
1840	1940	....	....	136492	IRL	Baillieston

Known From	To	Researching From	To	Ref	Cty	Place
MULLEN contd.						
1840	1940	....	....	136492	LKS	Coatbridge
MULLENDER						
1910	1910	1850	1910	103640	SFK	Lowestoft
1810	1900	ALL	ALL	121401	SFK	Pakefield
1780	1856	....	....	118354	STS	Wolverhampton
MULLENGER						
1700	1900	1650	1900	124699	NFK	South
1814	1814	....	....	127426	SFK	Hadleigh
1784	1784	....	....	127426	SFK	???
MULLENOX						
1832	1851	1600	1832	165697	CAM	Cambridge
MULLENS						
1770	1992	ALL	1800	115177	DEV	Axminster
1770	....	ALL	ALL	113700	WIL	Bishops Cannings
MULLER						
1880	1950	1865	1950	127361	GLA	Neath
1860	1940	1810	1940	105333	MDX	London
MULLERT						
1636	....	1636	....	132802	SAL	Leighton
MULLET						
1730	1760	ALL	1760	152889	KEN	Folkestone
MULLETT						
....	....	ALL	ALL	150193	ALL	Name Study
....	....	ALL	ALL	143014	DOR	ALL
....	....	1700	1890	121193	HAM	Southampton
1900	1992	?	?	150185	SFK	Ipswich
MULLEY						
....	....	ALL	ALL	150207	ALL	Name Study
1711	1791	1700	1760	179299	ESS	Great Baddow
1841	1964	1841	....	118761	MDX	Stepney
1881	1900	1850	1881	129895	SFK	Melton
1736	1834	1600	1736	154288	SFK	Needham Market
MULLICE						
1780	1992	ALL	1780	150215	DEV	Stoke Damerel
MULLIDGE						
1863	....	....	....	146013	LND	???
MULLIN						
?	?	?	?	152722	IRL	???
1840	....	....	....	152722	LAN	Liverpool
....	....	1700	1899	174963	LND	Westminster
MULLINDER						
1840	1890	1800	1850	166154	KEN	Maidstone
MULLINGTON						
....	....	....	1718	142409	WOR	???
MULLINS						
1750	1790	1700	1800	178020	SOM	Combe Florey
1770	1992	ALL	1800	115177	SOM	Ilminster
1841	1881	ALL	....	153214	WIL	Hatch Tisbury
1820	1992	1700	1820	150223	WIL	Teffont Evias
MULLIS						
1550	1655	1650	1700	128082	CON	Michaelstowe
1722	1992	ALL	1722	150231	WAR	ALL
MULLISS						
1853	1945	1830	1900	116173	LEI	Leicester
1788	1830	1700	1900	116173	WAR	???
MULLONEY						
1800	1829	1800	1850	153354	GAL	???
MULLOY						
1860	....	....	....	172723	IRL	???
1860	....	....	....	172723	STS	???
MULOCK						
1750	1850	1700	1850	154881	DUB	Dublin
MULVANEY						
1850	1870	ALL	1992	136077	CHS	Birkenhead
....	....	ALL	1992	136077	IRL	ALL
1877	1992	1850	1900	136077	LAN	Bolton
MULVEY						
1894	1894	ALL	1894	150258	LAN	Salford
MUMBY						
1840	1992	1840	1992	176338	EYK	Hull
1775	1840	1775	1840	176338	LIN	Boston
1600	1930	1500	1600	124184	LIN	Grainsby
1600	1930	1500	1600	124184	LIN	Lincoln
1600	1930	1500	1600	124184	LIN	N Thoresby
MUMFORD						
....	....	1600	1992	127833	BRK	Newbury
....	....	1800	1900	102318	ESS	West
1910	1992	1700	1910	113530	GLA	Cardiff
....	....	1870	....	145998	IOW	???
....	....	ALL	ALL	152226	SRY	Ashtead
MUMFORTH						
1795	1851	1795	1851	149403	WYK	Pontefract
MUMMERY						
1701	1913	ALL	1858	137774	KEN	South East
1700	1992	1600	1734	145971	KEN	Ashford
1700	1992	1600	1734	145971	KEN	Great Chart
MUNBY						
1670	1790	....	....	113093	EYK	Sutton
MUNCASTER						
1809	1876	1750	1876	141062	CUL	Carlisle
1821	1867	ALL	ALL	135909	CUL	Gosforth
MUNCEY						
1849	1915	....	1849	108839	BDF	Wrestlingworth
MUNDALL						
1790	1790	ALL	1992	119105	DFS	ALL
MUNDAY						
1860	1992	1850	1900	178047	BKM	Aylesbury
1750	1915	ALL	ALL	153753	BKM	Bow Brickhill
....	....	1700	1800	176885	BKM	Buckland
....	....	1750	1800	176885	BKM	North Marston
1860	1880	....	1860	152889	BKM	W Turville
1819	1879	....	....	176885	BKM	Wendover
1859	1992	1700	1859	125024	BRK	Clewer
....	....	1700	1790	159417	DOR	Folke
1815	1927	1783	1927	139408	DOR	Motcombe
1700	1799	1700	1799	169781	GLS	Bristol
....	....	ALL	ALL	145343	HAM	ALL
1860	1992	1850	1992	149128	HAM	ALL
....	1787	ALL	1787	175080	HAM	Catherington
1808	1850	ALL	ALL	177989	HAM	Kimgsclere
1830	1870	1830	1870	132721	HAM	Portsea
1823	1992	1700	1823	125024	HAM	Stockbridge
1782	1830	....	1782	164321	KEN	Deal
1824	1850	1700	1824	130656	KEN	Rochester
1870	1890	....	....	171557	LND	Greenwich
1875	1934	1875	1934	176885	LND	Paddington
1860	1905	ALL	ALL	147567	LND	Poplar
1857	....	....	....	176885	MDX	Kensington
1794	1871	....	....	170623	OXF	Ewelme
1800	1900	ALL	ALL	177989	OXF	Whitchurch
1854	....	....	....	176885	SRY	Christchurch
1853	....	....	....	176885	SRY	Lambeth
1863	....	....	....	176885	SRY	Rotherhithe
1795	1907	1700	1800	160768	SXW	Chichester
1805	1850	1600	1900	149128	WIL	Pewsey
MUNDELL						
ALL	ALL	ALL	ALL	103543	IOW	Cowes
MUNDEN						
1812	1870	1650	1850	115681	DOR	Bridport
....	....	ALL	ALL	103543	DOR	Morden
1780	1834	....	....	153397	HAM	New Forest
1762	1805	1700	1850	156698	KEN	Dover
1750	1992	1700	1992	156701	KEN	Dover
1750	1840	1700	1900	152900	LND	Westminster
1700	1800	1538	1800	152900	MDX	Chelsea
1769	1800	1600	1900	159956	NTH	Mears Ashby
MUNDHAM						
1800	1890	1750	1850	147710	DOR	South
MUNDIE						
....	1889	1800	1920	142727	ABD	Fraserburgh
MUNDY						
1860	1992	1850	1992	149128	HAM	ALL
1884	1992	ALL	1884	179167	HAM	Basingstoke
1870	1890	....	....	171557	LND	Greenwich
....	....	1700	1899	115975	WIL	East
1805	1850	1600	1900	149128	WIL	Pewsey
MUNE						
1841	1841	1800	1841	149632	PER	Weem
MUNFORD						
1770	1814	1750	1814	114073	NFK	Fersfield
1840	1900	1700	1900	139068	NFK	Kings Lynn
1613	1875	ALL	1613	161500	SOM	Crewkerne
MUNGALL						
1633	1992	1600	1992	111074	STI	Avonbridge
MUNINGS						
....	....	ALL	1700	103284	LND	???
MUNN						
1912	1992	1912	1992	150355	GLA	Caerphilly
1855	1904	1855	1904	150355	GLA	Rhondda
1817	1866	1817	1866	138312	KEN	Central
1800	1870	1770	1810	144606	MDX	Westminster
1832	1855	1832	1855	150355	MON	North
MUNNE						
....	....	1600	1670	154873	KEN	Ashford
MUNNERY						
1800	1900	1700	1850	148784	SSX	Henfield

Known From	To	Researching From	To	Ref	Cty	Place
MUNNS						
1860	....	1700	1900	158976	LND	Westminster
MUNRO						
1832	1910	1750	1910	135925	ABD	Inverurie
1765	1961	1750	1850	153656	ARL	Inverary
1750	1780	....	....	126497	CAI	Halkirk
1700	1750	....	....	126497	CAI	Wick
1830	1900	1830	1900	119725	LKS	Glasgow
1910	1950	1910	1950	135925	LND	Harlesden
1815	1835	1730	1850	143251	ROC	Blackisle
1815	1835	1730	1850	143251	ROC	Culbo
1815	1835	1730	1850	143251	ROC	East Culbo
1806	1810	1700	1830	115967	ROC	Kincardine
1815	1835	1730	1850	143251	ROC	Resolis
1790	1830	1800	1850	119725	ROC	Rosskeen
1760	1992	1700	1760	135747	SCT	Cromarty
1800	1900	1800	1900	176524	SCT	Dumbarton
1700	1870	1800	1850	176281	SCT	Novar
....	....	1500	1860	138614	SUT	Clyne
MUNSEY						
1780	1870	1650	1870	173630	NFK	ALL
MUNT						
1700	1900	1700	1900	108693	HRT	Weston
MUNTON						
....	1797	ALL	1797	129658	HUN	Stilton
MURCH						
1700	1850	ALL	1700	124184	DEV	Honiton
1700	1850	ALL	1700	124184	DEV	Plymouth
1811	1814	ALL	1820	104299	GLS	Bristol
MURCHISON						
1835	1992	1520	1835	144010	SCT	Applecross
MURCOTT						
1700	1775	1635	1835	145572	WAR	Coventry
1700	1775	1635	1835	145572	WAR	Stirchall
MURDEN						
1834	1917	1834	1917	151211	LIN	Little Oakley
1834	1917	1834	1917	151211	NTH	Surfleet
MURDIN						
1842	1866	1840	1842	159522	NTH	???
MURDING						
1735	1735	ALL	ALL	171816	NTH	Crick
MURDOCH						
1831	....	1750	1831	108596	AYR	ALL
1818	1961	....	....	135453	RFW	Cathcart
MURDOCK						
1900	1992	1800	1900	172650	MOG	Drum
MURDY						
1822	1960	1700	1822	101842	DUR	Houghton Le Spring
MURFET						
....	....	ALL	ALL	127736	ALL	Name Study
MURFIN						
1825	1850	1750	1850	172901	DBY	???
MURFITT						
1838	1860	....	....	150290	LIN	Sutton St James
1862	1899	....	....	150290	LND	Bermondsey
MURFOOT						
....	....	1700	1792	150290	CAM	???
....	....	1700	1792	150290	NFK	???
MURGATROYD						
1750	1826	1750	1850	127604	WRY	ALL
MURIE						
1800	1992	1500	1900	150312	PER	Perth
MURKETT						
1760	1913	1700	1800	128694	WIL	Devizes
1760	1913	1700	1800	128694	WIL	Enford
MURKIN						
1822	1850	1750	1850	126586	SFK	Hundon
MURLAND						
1800	1880	1700	1800	113204	DOW	Portaferry
MURLEY						
1800	1870	1700	1800	150320	DEV	Ottery St Mary
MUROOCH						
1870	1992	....	....	108898	LKS	Lanark
MURPHEY						
1792	1836	....	....	150290	CAM	Wisbech
1815	1840	1700	1850	100439	COR	ALL
MURPHY						
1829	1992	1700	1829	109177	CAR	???
1840	....	....	....	175358	COR	ALL
1818	1840	1700	1992	140090	COR	Castlemartyr
1850	1992	1850	1880	150347	COR	???
1748	1890	....	1748	102601	DEV	Topsham
1856	....	1850	1856	148121	DUR	Ludworth
1856	1863	1840	1880	148121	DUR	Thornley
MURPHY contd.						
1851	1900	1700	1900	113778	GLA	Merthyr Tydfil
1834	1837	1800	1850	148121	IRL	Down Patrick
1826	....	....	....	116750	IRL	Tippary
1870	1910	1800	1870	166979	KEN	Canterbury
1862	1862	ALL	1862	108537	LAN	Liverpool
1850	....	....	1850	111767	LAN	Liverpool
1894	1894	1700	1894	157112	LAN	Manchester
1850	1900	1800	1992	166081	LAN	Preston
1850	1900	1800	1849	172006	LAN	Toxteth
1800	1900	1870	1900	101877	LND	Bermondsey
1900	1950	1900	1950	101877	LND	Holborn
1800	1900	1870	1900	101877	LND	Southwark
1820	1830	1820	1830	101877	LND	Spittalfields
1825	1845	1825	1845	101877	LND	Stepney
1860	1930	1860	1930	101877	LND	Walworth
1852	1852	1800	1852	174289	MDX	London
1856	....	1838	1900	148121	NBL	Newcastle On Tyne
....	....	?	1874	160180	NIR	Belfast
1825	1880	ALL	1880	138819	T&W	Swallwell
1765	1777	1700	1800	167002	WAR	Old Stratford
1850	1992	1850	1880	150347	WAT	???
....	....	1874	1913	160180	YKS	Bradford
1874	1913	1874	1913	160180	YKS	Keighley
1802	1802	....	....	141097	YKS	Rotherham
MURRAY						
1840	1900	1815	1840	163139	ABD	Aberdeen
1875	1970	1700	1875	148342	ABD	Huntly
1798	1960	1700	1700	167673	ABD	New Deer
1798	1798	ALL	ALL	130508	ABD	Peterhead
....	....	1800	1850	105198	ABD	???
1898	1968	ALL	1898	147060	ANS	Montrose
1890	1925	1750	1890	108413	ANT	Rasharkin
1790	....	....	1790	101761	CAI	Bower
1774	1820	1500	1774	138614	CAI	Dunnet
1854	ALL	ALL	1854	116734	CAV	???
1900	1940	1800	1900	157058	CHS	Stalybridge
1840	1860	....	....	132225	CHS	Tarporley
1790	1820	1790	1820	151297	CMN	Laughan
1841	1929	ALL	ALL	150401	CUL	Bothel
1800	1992	1700	1800	122513	DFS	Canonbie
1810	1950	1700	1840	106267	DFS	???
1869	1954	ALL	ALL	150401	ENG	???
1820	1912	ALL	1880	113611	EYK	Hull
1800	1900	ALL	1800	108197	IRL	Cork
....	....	1700	1820	106682	IRL	Ferbane
1867	1992	ALL	1867	136875	IRL	???
1816	1850	....	1881	153982	IRL	???
1900	1960	1800	1920	152021	KIK	Kilmacow
1820	1992	....	....	106682	LAN	Burnley
1850	1931	....	....	124532	LKS	Glasgow
1700	1860	....	....	157694	LND	???
1758	....	1730	....	148644	MLN	Cranston
1869	1955	....	....	137936	MLN	Edinburgh
....	....	ALL	1800	119326	MLN	Newbattle
1775	1840	1700	1840	135941	MLN	Stockbridge
1700	1800	1850	1900	150371	NBL	Rideeshope
1833	1916	1800	1900	102164	NTT	Gedling
1700	1820	1650	1800	154881	PEE	Cringletie
1801	1801	....	....	168203	PER	Moneydie
1750	1992	1750	1900	146129	RFW	Port Glasgow
1820	....	1700	1992	171875	ROC	Rogart
1800	1830	1750	1850	144290	ROSS-SHIRE	Garrabost
1800	1900	....	....	150371	ROX	All Border
1850	1960	1600	1850	150371	ROX	Bedrule
1750	1992	1750	1900	146129	ROX	Castleton Parish
1860	1985	1700	1860	146110	SCT	ALL
1807	....	....	1807	117234	SCT	Ayr
1700	1860	....	....	157694	SCT	Cowland
1804	1864	1700	1804	134384	SCT	Dumfries
1700	1860	....	....	157694	SCT	Edinburgh
1857	1860	1853	1861	108278	SCT	Galashiels
1750	1810	ALL	ALL	107425	SCT	Kirkliston
1830	1890	1800	1900	169404	SCT	Peebles
1866	1924	1800	1866	132853	SRY	Lambeth
1850	1881	1830	1881	153982	SRY	Walworth
1730	1900	ALL	ALL	167428	SUT	ALL
1800	1850	1700	1850	143553	WES	Warcop
1810	1960	1650	1810	158992	WES	Whitehaven
1925	....	....	....	173932	WIL	Sutton Veny
1867	1992	ALL	1867	136875	YKS	Bradford
MURRAY-ROUCHARD						
....	....	ALL	ALL	176435	ALL	ALL

Known From	To	Researching From	To	Ref	Cty	Place
MURRELL						
....	....	1538	1992	150436	ALL	ALL
1825	1825	1700	1900	158399	HAM	Hawley
....	....	1800	1900	159093	NFK	Swaffham
....	....	1775	1837	143480	SRY	Ash
1772	1820	1750	1820	119059	SRY	Chiddingfold
....	....	1775	1837	143480	SRY	Frimley
MURRELLS						
....	....	ALL	ALL	150436	ALL	Name Study
MURRISH						
1750	1833	1700	1750	130141	CON	St Just In Penwith
MURSELL						
1546	1950	1500	1700	175730	IOW	Newport
MURTELL						
....	....	ALL	ALL	150444	ALL	Name Study
1700	1800	1755	1940	150444	HAM	Chichester
1700	1800	1755	1940	150444	SRY	Witley
1850	1950	1755	1940	150444	SSX	Brighton
MURTON						
1534	1992	1500	1992	137529	CON	Calstock
1534	1992	1500	1992	137529	CON	Launceston
1534	1992	1500	1992	137529	CON	Tithians
1830	1900	1775	1830	172901	NFK	???
MUSCATT						
1827	1841	....	1827	131385	LND	Stepney
MUSCHAMP						
1750	1780	1700	1992	114901	YKS	Harewood
MUSCROFT						
1757	1860	1700	1992	151521	YKS	Rotherham
MUSE						
1900	1992	1760	1899	167835	CMA	Carlisle
1900	1992	1760	1899	167835	CMA	Kendal
MUSGRAVE						
1756	1875	1700	1840	176621	CAM	Cambridge
....	....	1700	1800	148474	CUL	Kirkandrews On Esk
1100	1992	1100	1992	102830	DBY	ALL
1830	1880	....	....	131202	DUR	Bishop Auckland
1857	1917	1800	1858	167711	DUR	???
1800	1880	1700	1890	151947	LIM	Newcasltе West
1800	1830	....	....	131202	NYK	Grinton
1100	1992	1100	1992	102830	STS	ALL
1690	1815	1690	1815	105759	STS	Alton
1825	1875	1700	1900	121762	YKS	ALL
MUSGROVE						
1847	1920	1750	1850	105422	DUR	Sunderland
1784	....	ALL	1784	125121	LND	East
1799	1830	1800	1810	101877	NFK	Burnham
MUSK						
....	....	ALL	ALL	150452	ALL	Name Study
1700	1992	1600	1700	105392	NFK	Border
1700	1992	1600	1700	105392	SFK	Border
MUSKER						
1785	1860	1700	1785	139483	LAN	Bootle
MUSPRATT						
....	....	ALL	ALL	150460	ALL	ALL
1820	1840	....	....	126640	HAM	North
1880	1980	1700	1880	122556	HAM	Winchester
1750	1850	?	?	173185	WYK	Heckmondwike
MUSSEL						
1900	1970	1800	1935	120510	DOR	Morden
1783	1807	1700	1850	118397	WIL	Downton
MUSSELL						
1811	1829	1811	1829	115940	WIL	Downton
MUSSELLWHITE						
1880	1992	1800	1850	175668	KEN	Cliffe
MUSSELWHITE						
1859	1971	1800	1859	139777	HAM	Fawley
MUSSLEWHITE						
1600	1720	1550	1750	174599	WIL	Downton
MUSSON						
1775	1797	ALL	1775	133957	DOR	Canford Magna
1798	1798	1700	1830	159042	LIN	Bourne
1783	....	ALL	....	104515	LIN	Careby
1604	1605	1550	1605	163015	LIN	Stamford
MUSTIN						
1813	1832	1813	1832	108804	WAR	Alcester
1833	1851	1833	1851	108804	WAR	Arrow
1812	1813	1810	1813	108804	WOR	Inkberrow
MUSTOE						
1606	1708	1550	1707	102830	GLS	ALL
1416	1992	1416	1992	150479	GLS	Slaughter
1827	1849	1750	1850	176621	MDX	Kensington
1327	1401	1327	1400	150479	SSX	Henfield
1600	1900	1500	1900	150479	WOR	???

Known From	To	Researching From	To	Ref	Cty	Place
MUSTOE contd.						
1550	1992	1500	....	150479	???	London
MUSTON						
1728	1788	1650	1727	131245	WAR	Woston
MUTBEAN						
1850	1883	....	....	136964	DEV	Plymouth
MUTFORD						
1766	1875	1700	1875	102970	DOR	Dorchester
MUTLEY						
1760	....	1700	1760	119938	WOR	Mathon
MUTLOW						
1600	1992	....	1600	150495	HEF	Ledbury
MUTTER						
1768	1900	1768	1900	163406	DEV	Beer
1780	1790	1780	1800	115193	DEV	Sampford Peverill
1860	1923	1860	1923	176176	DEV	???
1820	1900	1800	1945	115193	SOM	Bristol
MUTTON						
1820	1900	1700	1850	173460	KEN	Dover
MUTUM						
1781	1992	1555	1781	126462	SFK	Brandon
MUXLOW						
1813	....	ALL	....	104515	LIN	Sedgebrook
MUZEEN						
1705	1992	ALL	ALL	150509	ALL	ALL
1705	1900	ALL	ALL	150509	NRY	Hovingham
MYALL						
1750	1992	ALL	ALL	150517	DOR	North
1850	1992	ALL	ALL	150517	SSX	Central
1850	1992	ALL	ALL	150517	SSX	South
MYAS						
1700	1800	1600	1850	177180	BKM	Aston Abbots
MYCOCK						
1900	1992	1850	1900	161349	LAN	Manchester
1906	1965	ALL	ALL	156256	STS	North
MYERS						
1650	1800	1600	1800	154881	CUL	Whitehaven
1700	1800	1700	1800	154881	DUB	Monkstown
1800	....	ALL	1800	152234	EYK	Foxholes
....	....	1800	1850	113514	LIN	???
1829	1867	....	....	162833	LND	???
1790	1830	1770	1790	121339	NYK	K Ravensworth
....	....	1800	1900	154105	STS	Wolverhampton
....	....	1800	1900	154105	WAR	ALL
....	....	1800	1900	154105	WOR	Dudley
1792	1793	1750	1850	100587	WYK	Yeadon
1750	1775	1700	1992	114901	YKS	Adel
1829	1859	1800	1871	136808	YKS	Brompton By Sawdon
1739	1890	1739	1900	149136	YKS	Pateley Bridge
1840	....	1800	1860	115967	YKS	Pickering
1753	1916	1700	1950	150118	YKS	Spofforth
MYERSON						
1852	1949	1750	1851	131245	MDX	St Pancras
MYFORD						
1840	1862	1791	1992	139114	LND	ALL
1830	....	1800	1900	139114	???	London
MYHILL						
1650	1820	....	....	111333	BRK	Brimpton
1650	1850	1600	1850	177288	ESS	Finchingfield
1770	1834	1770	1992	126128	NFK	Norwich
....	....	1700	1900	143219	NFK	Norwich
MYLAM						
1850	1989	1700	1850	150525	ALL	ALL
MYLES						
1840	1992	1700	1840	122513	FER	???
1760	1880	1700	1900	146803	FIF	Cupar
1850	....	ALL	ALL	167622	LAN	Blackpool
1850	....	ALL	ALL	167622	YKS	Sheffield
MYLREA						
1833	1863	....	....	160385	IOM	Lonan
MYNORS						
1170	1217	1066	1220	124974	GLS	Westbury
....	....	1066	1220	124974	HEF	Burghill
MYNOTT						
....	....	ALL	ALL	150533	ALL	Name Study
MYRING						
1836	1871	....	....	161489	DBY	Etwall
1872	1900	1900	1940	161489	MDX	Ealing
....	....	1600	1870	161489	WAR	Kingsbury
MYRRY						
1737	1800	....	1737	136212	OXF	Duns Tew
MYSON						
1850	1900	1600	1850	169862	SFK	Mildenhall

Known From	To	Researching From	To	Ref	Cty	Place
MYTTON						
1600	1900	....	....	152978	SAL	ALL
1783	1950	ALL	1992	102245	STS	Pattingham
1864	ALL	1800	1864	171190	WAR	Aston
NADEN						
1532	1992	1500	1992	150541	ALL	ALL
1748	....	ALL	1992	159174	DBY	Bakewell
1769	1804	ALL	1992	159174	DBY	Derby
NADIN						
....	....	ALL	ALL	150541	ALL	Name Study
1532	1992	1500	1992	150541	ALL	ALL
1804	1822	ALL	1992	159174	DBY	Repton
1837	1897	ALL	1992	159174	DBY	Woodville
1885	1947	ALL	1992	159174	STS	Shobnall
NADON						
1860	1900	1500	1992	150541	ALL	ALL
NAGBY						
....	....	1800	1850	143898	SSX	Arundel
NAGGINSON						
1818	1841	1750	1818	179086	DBY	Glossop
NAGLE						
....	....	ALL	ALL	170364	ALL	Name Study
1830	1870	1800	1830	155691	LND	East
NAIDEN						
1750	1850	1500	1992	150541	ALL	ALL
NAIL						
1732	1861	1700	1810	161357	DOR	West
....	....	1700	1780	161357	SOM	East
....	....	1700	1800	147613	WOR	Halesowen
NAILARD						
1807	1881	....	....	145394	SSX	Brighton
NAILER						
1786	1786	1786	1786	175420	BRK	White Waltham
NAILOR						
1758	1844	1500	1844	157538	LIN	Scotter
NAIRN						
1700	1900	1650	1840	167398	AYR	Stewarton
1792	1992	1650	1792	150568	BEW	ALL
....	....	1650	1792	150568	FIF	Kingdom Of Fife
1800	1850	ALL	1992	102245	YKS	Richmond
NAIRNE						
....	....	1781	....	149187	PER	Collace
1857	....	ALL	1857	179515	PER	Dunsianane
NAISH						
....	....	ALL	1809	114308	WIL	Stert
NALDER						
1630	1992	....	....	150584	BRK	Chieveley
1630	1992	....	....	150584	BRK	Donnington
1630	1992	....	....	150584	BRK	Kintbury
1630	1992	....	....	150584	BRK	Thatcham
NALL						
1725	1842	ALL	1725	110078	DBY	Chesterfield
NAMMOCK						
....	....	ALL	ALL	141429	ALL	Name Study
NANCARROW						
ALL	ALL	ALL	ALL	150592	ALL	ALL
1800	1900	1800	1900	139718	CON	Camborne
1800	1860	1700	1800	175838	CON	Illogan
1766	1950	1700	1950	142875	CON	Phillack
1800	1875	1730	1850	175838	CON	Redruth
....	....	1700	1800	175838	CON	St Agnes
1780	1900	ALL	1780	150983	HAM	Portsea
NANCE						
1775	1886	1700	1775	172561	CON	St Agnes
NANFAN						
....	....	ALL	ALL	176001	ALL	Name Study
NANGLE						
1910	1920	....	....	128635	LKS	Larkhall
1920	1992	1750	1884	128635	LKS	Motherwell
1884	1910	1700	1820	128635	LTN	Corstorphine
1820	1900	1700	1820	128635	LTN	Edinburgh
NANGREAVE						
1847	1878	1844	1926	116653	STS	Tamworth
NANKERUIS						
1865	1992	?	1865	129615	CON	Pendeen
NANKERVIS						
1700	1992	1600	1900	106186	CON	Zennor
NANKEWELL						
1768	1797	1700	1768	145424	MDX	London
NANKIVELL						
1751	1868	1650	1750	168173	CON	Philleigh
1400	1992	....	....	150606	CON	???
NANNON						
1880	1960	1700	1880	162671	LND	Wandsworth

Known From	To	Researching From	To	Ref	Cty	Place
NANSCAWEN						
1700	1992	....	....	109444	CON	Luxulyan
NANSON						
1768	1809	1768	1809	147532	CUL	Carlisle
NAPIER						
....	....	1700	1900	158291	DOR	ALL
....	....	1700	1900	158291	HAM	ALL
....	....	1700	1900	158291	SOM	ALL
NAPP						
1850	1920	ALL	ALL	118869	BDF	Shefford
1710	1860	1700	1840	118869	NFK	Loddon
NAPPER						
1850	1920	1850	1920	156930	BRK	East Hagbourne
1787	1827	1750	1900	113212	SOM	Malmesbury
1830	1900	1800	1950	131822	YKS	Thirsk
NAPTHALY						
1790	1992	1500	1790	151483	LND	Spitafields
NAPTHINE						
1814	1992	1699	1814	150614	SFK	Blythburgh
NARBETT						
1750	1800	1800	1992	129135	PEM	Clarbeston
NARES						
1715	1915	ALL	ALL	175943	ALL	ALL
NARRAMORE						
1780	1792	ALL	ALL	135208	DEV	Dartmouth
1814	1878	ALL	ALL	135208	DEV	Dawlish
1780	1878	ALL	ALL	135208	DEV	???
1871	1890	ALL	ALL	135208	GLS	Cheltenham
NARROWAY						
1841	1914	1800	1841	177555	WOR	Dudley
NARY						
1860	1920	1800	1860	109479	MAY	???
NASH						
1831	1951	1831	1951	139807	AVN	Bristol
1840	....	1800	1992	151378	AVN	Clifton
1638	1715	1590	1730	124974	BRK	Arborfield
1700	1992	....	....	153397	BRK	Beech Hill
1846	1962	1805	1992	124974	BRK	Easthampstead
1626	1850	1500	1626	104825	BRK	Hurst
1580	1875	1530	1900	124974	BRK	Hurst
1844	....	1500	....	110310	BRK	Reading
1700	1992	....	....	153397	BRK	Reading
1700	1992	....	....	153397	BRK	Stratfield Saye
1550	1600	1550	1670	176923	CMN	Carmarthen
1850	1890	1800	1870	156442	COR	Bandon
1880	1918	1850	1920	133922	DEV	Plymouth
1883	1950	1700	1850	106380	DUR	Middlesborough
1750	1950	1600	1800	133892	ESS	ALL
1793	1802	?	?	108189	ESS	Boreham
1841	1898	1800	1992	137294	ESS	Rawreth
1800	1914	....	1800	101168	HEF	Hay On Wye
1830	1950	1830	1992	150630	HRT	Aston
1830	1950	1830	1992	150630	HRT	Benington
1750	1800	ALL	1750	169730	HRT	Benington
1800	1890	1750	1910	140198	HRT	Mid
1800	1890	1750	1910	140198	HRT	Welwyn Garden City
1800	1890	1750	1910	140198	HRT	Wheathampstead
1724	1724	....	....	127426	KEN	Canty St Mary Bred
1900	1950	....	....	135968	LEI	Rothley
1850	1992	1700	1850	170739	LND	North
1855	1890	1800	1855	151882	MDX	London
1836	1900	1836	1938	127183	MDX	Shoreditch
1869	1922	1800	1992	160156	MDX	Staines
1817	1845	ALL	ALL	124176	OXF	Woodstock
1400	1500	1200	1800	176923	PEM	Nash
1590	1968	....	....	100536	SOM	???
1865	1900	ALL	ALL	141704	SRY	Croydon
?	?	ALL	ALL	100897	SRY	Walworth
1819	1923	....	....	135453	STI	Salmannan
1878	....	ALL	ALL	159026	STS	Stourton
1800	1940	....	....	132225	WIL	Marden
1848	1850	1800	1992	146331	WIL	???
....	....	1800	1900	135968	WLS	ALL
1684	....	....	1700	160873	WOR	Droitwich
1800	1914	....	1800	101168	WOR	Feckenham
1590	1968	....	....	100536	???	???
NASON						
....	....	ALL	ALL	150665	ALL	Name Study
NASSAU						
1841	1841	1700	1841	117595	CAM	Thorney Abbey
1815	1940	....	....	128996	CAM	Thorney
1846	1902	1700	1846	117595	CAM	Whittlesey
NATHAN						
1840	1992	1800	1992	114596	KEN	Chatham

Known From	To	Researching From	To	Ref	Cty	Place
NATHAN contd.						
1930	1940	1875	1940	118524	SCT	Glasgow
NATHANIEL						
1835	1886	1800	1886	158658	CMN	Bettws
NATION						
....	....	ALL	ALL	155780	ALL	ALL
NATTERAS						
1698	1698	ALL	1698	154563	DUR	Weardale
NATTRASS						
1840	1880	1750	1992	143189	DUR	Middleton In Teesdale
NAUGHTY						
1738	1784	1600	1738	164577	MOR	Kinloss
NAULTY						
1865	1895	1842	1865	150673	CAV	Blacklion
NAUNTON						
1772	1883	....	....	125105	SFK	Southwold
NAVIN						
1880	1900	ALL	ALL	170801	DUR	Houghton Le Spring
NAWTHORP						
1740	1815	....	1740	176702	WYK	Northowram
NAWTON						
1790	1992	ALL	ALL	143944	ALL	ALL
NAYDEN						
1750	1850	1500	1992	150541	ALL	ALL
NAYLER						
1786	1786	1786	1786	175420	BRK	White Waltham
1843	1844	1800	1843	114472	LAN	Warrington
NAYLOR						
1786	1786	1786	1786	175420	BRK	White Waltham
1760	1880	1700	1800	141496	CHS	Warrington
1902	1992	ALL	ALL	150681	HAM	Aldershot
1845	1860	1800	1860	153990	KEN	Bredhurst
1740	1812	1700	1740	113050	LAN	Eccles
1839	1839	1814	1839	157678	LAN	Manchester
1782	1992	1700	1860	155500	LAN	Newton Le Willows
1877	1891	1877	1891	159492	LAN	Oldham
1830	1910	1700	1860	117129	LAN	St Helens
1800	1900	1800	1900	144290	LIN	Winterton
1900	1925	1800	1900	178136	NTT	Nottingham
1764	1992	1700	1764	138355	RUT	Preston
1720	1745	1650	1750	100013	SFK	Icklingham
1805	1857	ALL	1805	174815	STS	Sedgley
1880	....	1880	....	104213	SYK	Sheffield
....	....	ALL	1819	102199	YKS	Scholes Cleckheaton
1791	1886	1500	1886	169439	YKS	Thornhill
NEACOMB						
1660	1695	1500	1730	105333	DEV	Buckland In The Moor
1660	1695	1500	1730	105333	DEV	Holne
1660	1695	1500	1730	105333	DEV	Ilsington
1660	1695	1500	1730	105333	DEV	Lydford
1660	1695	1500	1730	105333	DEV	Widecombe In The Moor
NEADS						
1770	1900	1770	1880	166685	SOM	Yatton
NEAGUL						
1832	1870	1800	1870	127981	MDX	London
NEAGUS						
1832	1870	1800	1870	127981	MDX	London
NEAL						
1821	1841	1750	1821	167452	BKM	Wycombe
1800	1845	....	....	137618	BRK	Hatford
1774	1836	1500	1800	104825	BRK	Hurst
1802	1802	1770	1780	124974	BRK	Hurst
ALL	ALL	ALL	ALL	124206	GLA	ALL
1790	1970	1500	1800	153230	HUN	Farcet
1837	1857	1830	1870	163775	KEN	Rotherhithe
1805	1876	....	....	166707	LEI	Arnsby
1753	1794	ALL	1794	168718	LEI	Rearsby
1850	1900	1750	1992	118532	LND	ALL
1863	1960	1800	1863	174807	LND	Hampstead
1855	1992	ALL	1855	123749	LND	???
1871	1871	ALL	ALL	167940	NFK	Fulmodeston
1786	1814	1700	1814	100110	NFK	Rainham
1798	1900	1600	1900	124834	NTT	East Leake
1700	1850	1600	1700	137618	OXF	Bampton
1888	?	ALL	ALL	158070	OXF	Bampton
?	?	?	?	142514	T&W	Sunderland
1775	1870	1695	1775	167525	WIL	North West
....	....	1725	1765	130184	WIL	Edington
1800	1900	1750	1810	165530	WIL	Sherston
1824	1860	1800	1992	161861	WMD	Halesowen
....	....	1700	1800	147613	WOR	Halesowen
NEAL contd.						
1825	1870	1800	1854	137057	YKS	Darfield
NEALE						
....	....	ALL	ALL	118125	ALL	Name Study
1796	1992	1700	1796	126020	BRK	Aldworth
1800	1840	....	....	114723	DEV	Exeter
1781	1805	1700	1781	138932	DOR	Toller Porcorum
1840	....	....	....	151548	ESS	Romford
ALL	ALL	ALL	ALL	124206	GLA	ALL
1881	1932	1800	1900	124206	GLA	Cardiff
1850	1900	....	....	150711	GLA	Merthyr Tydfil
1881	1932	1800	1900	124206	GLS	ALL
1855	1906	?	1860	164976	GLS	Gloucester
1715	1775	....	....	150711	GLS	Oldbury On The Hill
1680	ALL	....	....	142158	GLS	Stone
1881	1932	1800	1900	124206	GNT	Newport
1650	1659	1640	1680	142018	HAM	Southampton
1880	1992	ALL	1880	143049	IRL	Southern
....	....	1800	1871	162736	KEN	Borders
1880	1992	ALL	1880	143049	LND	ALL
1850	1871	1800	1900	116742	MDX	Heston
1750	1770	1700	1992	167592	MDX	London
1870	1989	....	....	128910	NTT	Annesley
1860	1870	....	....	128910	NTT	Cinderhill
1722	1722	1600	1722	147885	SSX	Lindfield
1822	1871	1800	1871	162736	SSX	Ticehurst
1770	1790	1700	1992	167592	STS	Hanley
1684	1849	1849	1992	128910	WAR	Bedworth
1690	1860	1690	1860	154210	WAR	Bedworth
1615	1684	?	1615	128910	WAR	Exhall
1815	1853	....	....	150711	WIL	Sopworth
1831	1980	1750	1830	150703	WOR	Feckenham
NEAME						
1743	1800	1700	1800	100129	KEN	Canterbury
NEARY						
1750	1870	1600	1800	132403	BKM	Central
1750	1870	1600	1800	132403	MDX	North
NEAT						
1800	....	1800	1900	106410	AVN	Shirehampton
1800	....	1800	1900	106410	AVN	Westbury On Trym
1820	1900	....	....	117579	GLS	Shirehampton
1706	1815	?	1820	103934	WIL	Bishops Cannings
NEATE						
1794	1870	1750	1900	116173	LND	???
1791	1875	1600	1791	175781	WIL	Bishops Cannings
1791	1882	1750	1882	107514	WIL	Burbage
1791	1882	1750	1882	107514	WIL	Cadley
....	....	1700	1980	172111	WIL	Chippenham
1798	1805	1750	1820	179337	WIL	Langley Burrell
1791	1882	1750	1882	107514	WIL	Milton
....	1748	ALL	1748	167878	WIL	Southbroom
1849	1946	ALL	1849	108553	WIL	Westbury
NEATH						
1778	....	1700	1817	150738	HUN	Morborne
1817	1851	1851	1881	150738	WAR	Nuneaton
NEAVE						
1800	1900	1700	1800	142905	LAN	Liverpool
1800	1900	1700	1800	142905	LAN	Manchester
1790	1900	1700	1820	112038	NFK	Middleton
1800	1916	1700	1800	119164	NFK	Smallburgh
1854	1875	1854	1992	115673	SRY	Norwood
NEAVES						
1854	....	1854	....	112534	CAM	Coton
NEDEN						
1800	1992	1500	1992	150541	ALL	ALL
NEDGE						
1850	1992	ALL	1850	102407	SAL	Hadley
NEECH						
....	....	ALL	ALL	150746	ALL	Name Study
NEED						
1800	1820	1700	1900	138517	???	London
NEEDES						
1800	1850	1800	1850	142018	SOM	ALL
NEEDHAM						
1885	....	1800	1900	138185	DBY	Ashover
1695	1743	ALL	1695	178926	DBY	Beeley
1879	1930	1800	1879	155144	DBY	Derby
....	....	1840	....	157139	DOR	ALL
....	....	....	1845	157139	DUB	Dublin
1808	....	?	1810	164976	LAN	Oldham
1900	1992	1700	1900	131083	LAN	Stockport
1770	1800	ALL	1900	168718	LEI	ALL
1752	....	ALL	1752	112275	LEI	Ratcliffe On Wreake
1754	1850	1675	1754	150754	LIN	Freiston

Known From	To	Researching From	To	Ref	Cty	Place
NEEDHAM contd.						
....	....	1550	1850	150754	LIN	Holland
1947	1973	....	....	173932	WIL	Bradford On Avon
1800	1950	1800	1950	138045	???	Birmingham
NEEDLE						
....	....	1800	1992	150762	LND	Shoreditch
1910	....	....	....	150762	MON	Ebbw Vale
NEEDLER						
1907	1908	....	....	153982	YKS	Hull
NEEDLES						
1752	1808	1750	1808	103632	NTH	Watford
NEEDLEY						
1795	1820	1760	1861	174211	LIN	Binbrook
1795	1820	1760	1861	174211	LIN	West Torrington
NEEDS						
1826	1947	?	1826	158704	GLA	Pontypridd
1790	1900	1600	1992	154342	GLS	Bristol
1885	1936	1850	1992	121568	SOM	West
1750	1790	1600	1800	154342	WAT	Waterford City
NEEL						
1730	....	ALL	1730	119105	JSY	ALL
1800	1818	1800	1920	165034	TYR	Ballinasaggart
NEELAND						
....	....	ALL	ALL	150770	ALL	Name Study
NEESHAM						
....	....	ALL	ALL	150789	ALL	Name Study
....	....	ALL	ALL	150789	ALL	ALL
....	....	1700	1825	150789	DUR	South
....	....	1825	1850	150789	MDX	Brompton
1825	1911	1790	1930	150789	SAL	Central
1910	1992	....	....	150789	STD	Glasgow
1890	1992	....	....	150789	WAR	North
1770	1803	1550	1800	147265	YKS	North
....	....	1700	1825	150789	YKS	North
1904	1988	....	....	150789	YKS	Sheffield
NEESOME						
1770	1803	1550	1800	147265	YKS	North
NEEVE						
1851	1851	....	....	127426	KEN	East Malling
1723	1890	....	....	127426	KEN	Lenham
1913	1913	....	....	127426	KEN	Rochester
1775	1831	....	....	127426	KEN	Wychling
1820	1820	....	....	127426	KEN	???
1845	1992	ALL	1845	109320	YKS	???
NEEVES						
1772	1844	....	1844	137405	CAM	Barrington
NEGONS						
1670	1710	1640	1710	135941	SFK	Lakenheath
NEGROPONTE						
....	....	ALL	ALL	158534	ALL	Name Study
NEGUS						
1600	1992	ALL	ALL	150797	ALL	ALL
1880	?	1700	1890	150797	HAM	Portsea
1890	1992	1880	1992	150797	KEN	Sheppey
....	1800	....	1800	177695	NTH	Northampton
NEIGHBOUR						
....	....	ALL	ALL	150800	ALL	Name Study
....	....	ALL	ALL	150800	ALL	ALL
1600	1700	1500	1800	177180	BKM	Edlesborough
1814	1992	1800	1992	159581	LND	Forest Hill
....	....	....	....	103608	LND	Wandsworth
1791	1862	1770	1900	139114	MDX	London
1888	1975	....	....	169102	MDX	???
1699	1887	....	....	169102	OXF	Lewknor
1814	1992	1800	1992	159581	SRY	Morden
NEIL						
1795	....	1770	1841	169625	ANT	Glenarm
1867	1992	1700	1867	168246	AYR	Galston
....	....	ALL	1751	119326	ELN	Tranent
1830	....	....	1854	160873	IRL	???
1836	1948	....	1835	150819	LKS	Glasgow
....	....	ALL	ALL	129933	LKS	Lesmahagow
1854	1992	1830	ALL	160873	NBL	Newcastle On Tyne
1774	1992	1830	1992	127418	PER	Erskine
1774	1992	1830	1992	127418	PER	Methven
NEILD						
1830	1850	1800	1830	117196	CHS	Crowton
1760	1860	1800	1860	149322	LAN	Liverpool
NEILL						
1880	1920	1850	1950	178799	DOW	Kilhorne Annalong
1828	1992	....	1828	143901	LAN	Manchester
NEILLEY						
1791	1824	ALL	....	150835	IRL	???
NEILSEN						
1860	1992	....	....	178276	YKS	Hull
NEILSON						
1760	1820	....	....	140554	ELN	Dunbar
1941	1941	....	....	127426	MDX	Harefield
1800	1838	....	....	141798	ROX	Galashiels
1840	1870	1780	1840	139483	WIG	Kirkinner
NEISH						
1810	1900	1810	1900	147036	PER	Muthill
NELL						
1890	1992	1600	1890	140953	ALL	ALL
NELLES						
....	1756	....	....	153176	BRK	Radley
NELLIST						
1750	1770	1700	1750	121339	NYK	Whitby
1770	1930	1550	1770	150843	YKS	Danby In Cleveland
NELMES						
1837	1881	1750	1837	155225	GLS	Abenhall
1830	1880	1795	1960	105759	HRT	Cheshunt
NELSON						
1798	1890	1720	1798	167932	ANT	Clandeboyes
1890	1928	ALL	ALL	125466	DUR	Barnard Castle
1790	....	....	....	167037	ESS	Barking
1794	1886	1700	1800	176869	GLS	Bristol
1813	1817	....	....	174955	KEN	Plumstead
1804	....	1775	1804	174955	KEN	Woolwich
1860	1880	ALL	1992	133159	LAN	Liverpool
1850	1900	1800	1850	161292	LAN	Manchester
?	....	....	....	169358	LAN	Manchester
1850	1871	1800	1900	169153	LAN	Preston
1837	1881	ALL	ALL	154806	LAN	Rochdale
1830	1860	ALL	1992	133159	LAN	Ulverston
1770	1900	1600	1770	150886	LIN	Great Limber
1811	1940	ALL	ALL	145092	LKS	Crawfordjohn
1800	1900	1800	1900	134422	LND	Camberwell
1817	1876	....	....	174955	MDX	Chelsea
....	1880	....	....	167037	MDX	Clerkenwell
1740	1800	1600	1800	100536	NBL	Mitford
1800	1992	....	1800	150851	NFK	Central
1800	1890	1700	1800	175218	NFK	North West
1800	1992	....	1800	150851	NFK	North
1629	1862	1750	1840	143308	NFK	Burnham Thorpe
1815	1915	1750	1850	126470	NFK	Foulden
....	....	1700	1992	140627	NFK	Hockering
....	1771	....	....	167037	NFK	Hunstanton
1600	ALL	....	....	167037	NFK	Scarning
....	1831	1811	....	154024	NTT	Flintham
1769	1992	1700	1769	161446	OXF	???
1794	1886	1700	1800	176869	SOM	Bristol
1841	1874	....	....	174955	SRY	Bermondsey
1859	1865	....	....	174955	SRY	Lambeth
1900	1992	1870	1992	165441	STS	Cheadle
1841	....	ALL	1841	125466	WES	Brough
1882	1981	1700	1882	102997	???	Cathcart
....	....	1858	1900	139297	???	Liverpool
NESBIT						
1740	1790	1740	1790	106305	DOW	???
1820	1900	1800	1820	138045	GNT	Chepstow
1780	1860	1700	1800	150916	NBL	Ford
1850	1910	1850	1910	150916	NBL	Newcastle On Tyne
1770	1780	1700	1770	124427	NBL	Newcastle
NESBITT						
1867	....	ALL	1867	150924	ARM	Tanderagee
1700	1900	1600	1900	167134	CAV	Lismore
1829	1829	1800	1829	144177	DOW	Mourne
NESFIELD						
....	....	1300	1900	150932	ALL	ALL
1700	1850	1600	1750	150932	NYK	Eskdaleside
1698	1888	....	....	100536	SFK	???
1698	1888	....	....	100536	YKS	???
NESOM						
1850	1900	1700	1850	108308	DUR	ALL
NESS						
?	?	?	?	167169	FIF	Dairsie
1750	....	ALL	ALL	130508	FIF	Kilrenny
NETCOTT						
ALL	ALL	ALL	ALL	150940	ALL	ALL
1799	1992	....	1799	166553	SOM	Taunton
NETHERCOTT						
....	....	ALL	ALL	150959	ALL	Name Study
NETHERSELL						
....	....	ALL	ALL	110973	ALL	Name Study
NETHERWOOD						
1849	1860	ALL	1849	122572	LND	ALL

Known From	To	Researching From	To	Ref	Cty	Place
NETLEY						
1810	1950	1750	1810	133434	SSX	Pulborough
NETTELL						
1800	1950	1700	1800	142905	CON	Illogan
NETTIN						
1806	1838	1780	1838	145602	HAM	Christchurh
NETTLEINGHAM						
1800	1900	1700	1940	145572	BRK	Ascot
1775	1900	1700	1940	145572	KEN	Gravesend
NETTLESHIP						
1770	1830	1600	1800	171425	DUR	Darlington
1770	1830	1600	1800	171425	DUR	Sunderland
....	....	ALL	1650	178411	NTT	North
1670	1770	....	1770	137634	NTT	Blyth
1770	1830	1770	1830	137634	NTT	East Retford
1800	1864	1850	1900	135801	NTT	Laughten
1770	1827	1670	1770	162396	NTT	Long Collingham
1736	1798	1700	1798	141097	YKS	Braithwell
1764	1776	....	....	141097	YKS	Conisborough
NETTLETON						
1760	1830	....	....	102946	YKS	Hunsingore
1760	1830	....	....	102946	YKS	Walshford
NETTLINGHAM						
1875	1940	1700	1941	145572	ESS	Brentwood
1875	1940	1700	1941	145572	ESS	Loughton
1875	1940	1700	1941	145572	ESS	Woodford
1800	1925	1700	1941	145572	KEN	Chatham
1875	1940	1700	1941	145572	LND	Forest Gate
NEUHOFER						
1890	1992	....	....	150967	LND	Acton
NEVE						
1800	1850	1700	1800	168785	KEN	Benenden
1845	1992	ALL	1845	109320	YKS	???
NEVELL						
1780	1796	1750	1850	105120	CHS	Cholmondely
1750	1778	1750	1800	105120	DEN	Allington Gresford
1624	1721	1600	1750	105120	SSX	Brighton
1495	1617	1400	1620	105120	SSX	Lancing
NEVEN						
1750	1965	....	....	137820	SHI	Fetlar
1720	1965	....	....	137820	SHI	Mid Yell
1760	1965	....	....	137820	SHI	North Yell
1758	1965	....	....	137820	SHI	Northmavine
1720	1965	....	....	137820	SHI	South Yell
NEVES						
1719	1794	....	....	127426	KEN	Lenham
1776	1776	....	....	127426	KEN	Stockbury
NEVETT						
1792	1796	1796	1825	115819	MDX	Highgate
NEVILL						
....	....	ALL	1800	150983	ALL	ALL
1799	1900	....	....	150983	ESS	Manningtree
1824	1852	1800	1900	166960	GLS	Cheltenham
1824	1852	1800	1900	166960	GLS	Uley
....	....	ALL	1812	127094	KEN	ALL
1820	1854	1820	1854	133817	KEN	Sandgate
1700	1812	ALL	1812	127094	KEN	Wrotham
1813	1820	1780	1832	117145	LAN	Tockholes
1860	1992	1800	1992	144525	LND	South
1866	1992	1600	1866	158461	LND	Poplar
1900	1950	....	1900	130524	MDX	Islington
1830	1852	1800	1900	166960	SOM	Bath
1550	....	....	....	156647	WES	???
NEVILLE						
1040	1254	1040	1250	154881	ALL	ALL
1797	1992	1600	1900	114766	AVN	Central
1838	1992	1843	1900	164704	BRK	Reading
1783	1786	1783	1786	133639	DOR	Sherborne
1771	1925	1760	1925	164704	HAM	Hartley Wintney
1858	1925	1760	1925	164704	HAM	Odiham
1870	1900	....	....	150983	HRT	Bishops Stortford
....	....	ALL	1812	127094	KEN	ALL
1800	1850	1600	1850	175641	KEN	Addington
1700	1812	ALL	1812	127094	KEN	Wrotham
1860	1860	....	1860	161888	LND	???
....	....	ALL	1812	151009	NTT	Thorney
1690	1950	1600	1992	133639	SOM	Coker
1826	....	1815	1835	133639	WIL	Sedgehill
?	?	?	?	150975	???	Bristol
NEVILLES						
....	....	ALL	1812	127094	KEN	ALL
1700	1812	ALL	1812	127094	KEN	Wrotham
NEVIN						
1916	1930	1850	1930	135305	LDY	Coleraine
NEVINS						
1792	1863	....	....	132381	DUR	Gateshead
NEVISON						
1855	1920	?	?	176702	DUR	???
NEVITT						
....	....	ALL	ALL	151017	ALL	ALL
1758	1829	ALL	1900	151017	HUN	Huntingdon
1758	1829	ALL	1900	151017	NTH	Yardley Hastings
NEW						
1845	1880	1845	1900	124974	BRK	Welford
1783	1820	ALL	ALL	142719	DOR	Mappowder
....	....	1700	1900	133493	HAM	Eling
1892	1992	1800	1892	125024	KEN	Tenterden
1825	1825	1810	1830	124974	SRY	Lambeth
1883	1992	1700	1883	125024	SSX	Brede
1880	1910	1880	1940	142719	SSX	Westfield
1784	....	1750	1800	170348	WIL	Lydiard Tregoze
1790	1810	1750	1820	108693	WIL	Malborough
1780	1850	1700	1800	101834	WIL	Marlborough
1800	1880	1700	1992	142719	WIL	Urchfont
1700	1900	1550	1700	151025	WOR	Evesham
NEWALL						
1805	1825	1800	1880	165093	CHS	Great Budworth
1280	1900	1700	1860	164488	LAN	Littleborough
NEWARK						
....	....	1600	1992	101494	ALL	ALL
....	....	1600	1992	151033	LND	ALL
1842	1992	1600	1992	151033	WAR	Coventry
NEWBERRY						
1860	1947	ALL	1860	178195	DOR	Thorncombe
1854	1936	1700	1936	116300	HRT	Stevenage
1851	1900	1800	1851	132039	IOW	Shorwell
1830	1858	....	....	140090	SCT	???
1839	1919	1700	1839	178187	SOM	Horton Wilminster
NEWBERY						
1600	1950	....	....	108677	BRK	Waltham St Lawrence
1811	1929	1700	1811	145823	DEV	Kilmington
1858	1858	1500	1860	175463	LND	Holloway
1600	1950	....	....	108677	LND	Inner
1900	1950	1700	1900	125660	LND	St Barts By The Exchange
NEWBOLD						
1850	1923	1800	1900	133531	DBY	Overseal
1808	1835	1780	1820	149772	LAN	Bury
1794	1992	1792	?	166235	YKS	York
NEWBORN						
....	....	1700	1800	171794	LIN	Corringham
....	....	1700	1800	171794	LIN	Haxey
NEWBORNE						
....	....	....	1785	109290	YKS	South
NEWBURGH						
1400	1450	1400	1500	171549	HAM	Arreton
NEWBURY						
1863	1870	ALL	ALL	168211	BDF	Luton
....	....	ALL	1800	141224	BRK	???
....	1914	ALL	ALL	130818	LND	Camberwell
....	....	ALL	1800	141224	WIL	???
NEWBY						
1815	1960	ALL	1815	145734	CMA	West
1764	1800	1720	1764	111236	DUR	Whitburn
1852	?	?	?	147923	KEN	Medway
1812	1992	1700	1900	178616	LEI	Leicester
1845	1950	1800	1900	158658	NFK	Great Yarmouth
1817	1950	1700	1817	109576	NFK	Lowestoft
....	....	1700	1820	147176	YKS	Barningham
NEWCOMB						
1840	1992	1830	1840	151068	LAN	Liverpool
1700	1880	1700	1880	127655	NTH	Byfield
1700	1880	1700	1880	127655	NTH	Lower Bodington
1700	1880	1700	1880	127655	NTH	Priors Marston
1814	1836	1760	1814	151068	SOM	Bristol
1700	1880	1700	1880	127655	WAR	Byfield
1700	1880	1700	1880	127655	WAR	Lower Bodington
1700	1880	1700	1880	127655	WAR	Priors Marston
NEWCOMBE						
1742	1880	1600	1742	125784	DEV	Inwardleigh
1817	1910	....	....	125784	DEV	Oitehampton
1789	1840	....	....	125784	DEV	Sampford Courtney
1769	1828	....	....	125784	DEV	Sourton
1741	1783	1584	1851	149047	DEV	Swimbridge
1772	1947	ALL	ALL	149683	NTT	Shelford
1100	1400	....	....	100420	WAR	Meriden
1750	1850	1650	1750	107905	YKS	York

Known From	To	Researching From	To	Ref	Cty	Place
NEWDICK						
1568	1738	1500	1900	100013	CAM	Isleham
1473	1751	1400	1900	100013	LIN	Whaplode
1731	1992	ALL	1731	100595	SFK	ALL
1576	1900	1500	1900	100013	SFK	Mildenhall
NEWELL						
1867	1890	1700	1867	139122	BDF	Biggleswade
1736	....	1730	1750	124796	BKM	Aston Rowant
1827	1869	....	....	125962	BKM	Bledlow
1887	1992	ALL	1887	151076	DOR	ALL
....	....	ALL	ALL	121991	NFK	ALL
1675	1757	1620	1800	124796	OXF	Adwell
1795	....	1760	1800	124796	OXF	Lewknow
1646	....	1620	1680	124796	OXF	Radnage
1708	....	1700	1750	124796	OXF	Tetsworth
1887	1992	ALL	1887	151076	SOM	ALL
NEWEN						
1726	1758	....	....	156647	HAM	Areton
NEWENS						
....	....	1550	1800	151084	BDF	???
....	....	1550	1800	151084	BKM	???
....	....	1550	1800	151084	HRT	???
1850	1992	1700	1850	151084	LND	West
NEWETT						
1821	....	1800	1850	124796	BKM	Tingewick
NEWHAM						
1740	1740	ALL	1745	113611	LIN	Winterton
1726	1830	1600	1726	151092	YKS	Howden
NEWIN						
1700	1740	1600	1740	145289	HAM	Isle Of Wight
NEWING						
1850	1880	1750	1850	167789	KEN	Gravesend
1760	1992	1600	1760	102210	KEN	Northbourne
NEWINGTON						
1800	1870	1750	1890	129755	KEN	Dover
1810	1812	1770	1850	167002	SXE	Brightling
NEWIS						
ALL	1765	....	....	105368	SOM	Beauchamp
ALL	1765	....	....	105368	SOM	Shepton
NEWLAND						
1835	1890	1800	1835	179604	BDF	Luton
1795	1870	1700	1900	124974	ESS	Roydon
1800	1880	1750	1950	111007	ESS	Waltham Abbey
1800	1900	1700	1850	145343	HAM	ALL
....	....	1800	1835	179604	HAM	Romsey
1880	1960	1880	1960	111007	LND	East
....	....	1850	1900	176435	MDX	Bow
1675	1700	1650	1992	114901	SRY	Farnham
NEWLANDS						
1811	1830	1780	1840	126594	LKS	Glasgow
NEWLIN						
1683	1992	....	1683	144363	TYR	Mountmellick
NEWLING						
1814	1829	1750	1900	113212	CAM	Ickleton
NEWLOVE						
1800	1992	ALL	ALL	107352	EYK	Great Driffield
1800	1830	ALL	ALL	107352	EYK	Harpham
1650	1780	ALL	ALL	107352	EYK	Wetwang
1760	1880	1800	1881	171166	WRY	Bulmer
1650	1800	1600	1850	121096	YKS	Wetwang
NEWMAN						
....	....	ALL	ALL	151157	ALL	Name Study
....	....	ALL	ALL	151114	ALL	Name Study
....	....	ALL	ALL	151157	ALL	ALL
1700	1790	1700	1790	167924	BDF	Campton
1780	1880	1780	1880	167924	BDF	Shillington
1600	1700	1600	1700	167924	BDF	Stevington
1692	1900	....	....	148032	BKM	Grandborough
1890	....	....	1890	175404	CAM	March
1830	....	1830	1992	129348	CON	Falmouth
1600	1900	1600	1850	133450	DEV	Dartmouth
1752	1800	1700	1840	105333	DEV	Rattery
1752	1800	1700	1840	105333	DEV	South Brent
1752	1800	1700	1840	105333	DEV	Ugborough
1696	....	....	....	151351	DOR	Beaminster
....	....	1800	1930	130184	DOR	Poole
1695	1750	ALL	1740	161357	ESS	Dunmore
1827	1858	1700	1827	167355	ESS	Gosfield
1680	1900	1600	1992	154342	GLS	Bitton
1840	1865	1800	1840	147478	GLS	Cheltenham
1700	1900	....	1700	151157	GLS	Cherrington
1850	1895	1800	1900	142115	GLS	Kempsford
1738	....	1728	1741	142859	GLS	Minchinhampton
1796	....	1700	1992	166197	GLS	Newent
NEWMAN contd.						
1545	1728	1545	1728	102830	GLS	Oddington
1820	....	....	....	104213	GLS	Stroud
1773	....	1700	1992	166197	GLS	Upleadon
1850	....	ALL	ALL	115002	GLS	???
1780	1992	1500	1790	125369	HAM	ALL
1750	1900	....	....	133221	HAM	Breamore
1702	1754	1600	1754	174343	HAM	Droxford
1700	1700	1650	1720	136840	HAM	Fordingbridge
1668	1723	....	....	115606	HAM	Froyle
1891	1931	1700	1891	142484	HAM	Fyfield
1760	1840	1600	1840	125369	HAM	Kimpton
1796	1879	1700	1879	125369	HAM	Shipton Bellinger
1899	1945	1700	1899	167819	HAM	Southampton
....	....	1861	1868	109215	HEF	Eardisley
1868	1951	....	....	109215	HEF	Pembridge
1834	....	1834	1958	156647	IOW	Ryde
1787	1810	....	....	144355	KEN	South
1820	1940	1800	1940	134880	KEN	Hythe
1820	....	1800	1850	134481	KEN	Lewisham
1855	1900	....	1855	122378	KEN	Plaxtol
1840	1974	1800	1974	142891	KEN	Plumstead
1820	1900	1820	1900	136484	LND	Clerkenwell
....	1826	ALL	ALL	129933	LND	St George
1813	1830	1700	1875	124907	LND	Westminster
1840	1992	1740	1840	151165	LND	Whitechapel
1855	1865	1830	1900	176648	MDX	ALL
1870	1930	1870	1930	167924	MDX	Finchley
1810	1900	1750	1900	135860	NFK	Fleggburgh
1860	1881	1860	1881	118192	NFK	Norwich
1740	1800	1700	1800	135941	SFK	Withersfield
1842	1920	1842	1881	104213	SOM	Bath
1755	1839	1732	1839	107573	SOM	Bridgwater
1776	1992	1700	1850	151130	SOM	Bristol
1780	1992	1500	1790	125369	WIL	ALL
1776	1800	1500	1776	115134	WIL	Bishopstone
1770	1880	1841	1881	104213	WIL	Box
....	....	1800	1930	133604	WIL	Box
1873	1930	....	1873	136778	WIL	Box
1817	1849	1800	1849	133604	WIL	Bremhill
1820	1992	1820	1992	131156	WIL	Castle Eaton
....	....	1800	1930	133604	WIL	Chippenham
1817	1849	1800	1849	133604	WIL	Christian Malford
....	....	1725	1765	130184	WIL	Edington
1820	1900	1820	1900	136484	WIL	Salisbury
1827	1850	1800	1881	165824	WIL	Steeple Ashton
1850	1851	1850	1900	165824	WIL	West Ashton
1804	1904	1700	1992	166197	WOR	Longdon
1858	....	1800	1992	166197	WOR	Ripple
1880	1992	1700	1910	105899	???	London
NEWMARCH						
....	....	1066	1200	124974	BRE	Brecon
1738	1738	1700	1790	141097	YKS	North Newbald
NEWNES						
1824	1992	1724	1867	151173	SAL	Shrewsbury
NEWNHAM						
1853	....	1800	1877	153257	LND	Westminster
1781	1788	1700	1800	127183	SSX	Horsted Keynes
NEWNS						
1718	....	....	....	121835	FLN	Worthenbury
1800	1899	....	....	121835	SAL	Calverhall
NEWPORT						
1821	1848	1800	1860	161322	KEN	East
1846	....	1846	....	164135	LND	Poplar
NEWSHAM						
....	....	ALL	ALL	176737	CMA	Kendal
....	....	1500	1900	166081	LAN	ALL
1752	1800	1700	1800	166081	LAN	Garstange
1870	1890	ALL	1890	123358	LAN	Liverpool
1800	1992	1650	1850	166081	LAN	Preston
1882	1946	ALL	ALL	176737	YKS	Sheffield
NEWSOME						
1820	1900	1750	1820	168572	YKS	Dewsbury
1804	1876	ALL	1804	102350	YKS	Howden
1760	1800	1600	1760	175382	YKS	Ripon
NEWSON						
....	....	1700	1850	129550	SFK	Bury St Edmunds
1837	1875	1800	1875	146374	SFK	Theberton
NEWSTEAD						
1795	1870	1650	1795	120774	KEN	West
1620	1785	....	....	129747	LIN	Claypole
NEWTON						
1790	....	1700	1790	141402	BKM	Lee
1820	1896	1750	1900	155845	CHS	Great Budworth

Known From	To	Researching From	To	Ref	Cty	Place
NEWTON contd.						
....	1940	....	....	155845	CHS	Northwich
1800	1860	1700	1800	117218	CHS	Weaverham
1833	1853	1600	1833	117196	CHS	Weaverham
1760	1840	....	....	131288	CUL	Carleton
1830	1842	1700	1900	116173	CUL	Millom
1657	1839	....	....	151238	DEV	Beer
1547	1839	....	....	151238	DEV	Colyton
....	....	ALL	1826	170135	DEV	Honiton
1760	1800	1600	1800	130125	DOR	Chaldon Hg
1760	1760	1700	1800	136840	DOR	Wool
1841	....	ALL	ALL	155608	DUR	Bishop Aukland
1700	1799	1700	1799	169781	DUR	Brancepth
1900	1940	1870	1940	151181	ESS	Ilford
1760	1992	1700	1800	133957	HAM	Froxfield
1857	1970	1700	1850	112283	HAM	Lymington
1760	1992	1700	1800	133957	HAM	Petersfield
1800	1840	ALL	1840	147567	HAM	Petersfield
1760	1992	1700	1800	133957	HAM	Portsmouth
1720	1850	1700	1900	141410	HRT	Watford
1840	1900	1840	1906	108952	KEN	Chartham
....	....	1880	1930	151203	KEN	Dartford
1803	1804	1780	1832	151181	KEN	St Mary Cray
....	....	ALL	ALL	115371	LAN	ALL
1820	1992	1650	1820	128074	LAN	Ancoats
1841	....	ALL	ALL	115371	LAN	Crosby
1853	1897	....	....	117196	LAN	Liverpool
1816	1992	1800	1860	124788	LAN	Liverpool
1750	1850	1750	1850	110434	LAN	Manchester
1820	1992	1650	1820	128074	LAN	Manchester
1854	1924	1800	1980	107476	LEI	Leicester
1799	1800	1750	1850	162396	LIN	South
1875	1992	1875	....	151211	LIN	Blyborough
1776	1900	1700	1992	173096	LIN	Colsterworth
1850	1880	1550	1850	147265	LIN	Mid
1875	1992	1875	....	151211	LIN	North Hykeham
1875	1992	1875	....	151211	LIN	Saxilby
....	....	1850	1900	151203	MDX	Hackney
1800	1992	1800	1992	160210	NBL	ALL
1760	1992	1500	1760	144045	NBL	Hexham
....	....	1606	1850	151203	NBL	Ponteland
....	1805	ALL	1805	164623	NBL	Ponteland
1781	1992	1700	1830	113786	NFK	Gt Yarmouth
1760	1800	1700	1760	172898	NFK	Kings Lynn
1854	1924	1800	1980	107476	NTH	Northampton
....	....	1538	1900	144479	NTH	???
1850	1992	1700	1850	112097	NTT	ALL
1799	1800	1750	1850	162396	NTT	South
1730	1769	1700	1730	147745	NTT	Hucknall Torkard
1713	1760	1680	1713	177393	NTT	North Wheatley
1660	1760	1600	1660	121339	NYK	Lythe
1849	1871	1700	1849	173509	SOM	Kingstone
1815	1841	1785	1815	139149	SOM	South Petherton
1800	1820	ALL	ALL	152226	SOM	Wiveliscombe
1780	1876	1700	1992	178020	SOM	Wiveliscombe
1736	1860	1650	1700	108413	SOM	Wraxall
1840	....	1810	1900	151181	SSX	Fairlight
1840	1842	1800	1870	151181	SSX	Hastings
1832	1833	1800	1840	151181	SSX	Winchelsea
1771	1816	1770	1900	121541	STS	Birmingham
....	....	1802	1895	175161	STS	Bobbington
1771	1816	1770	1900	121541	STS	Halesowen
....	....	ALL	ALL	147222	STS	Handsworth
1780	1810	1700	1780	173312	STS	Newcastle Under Lyme
1859	1943	....	....	177334	STS	Stourbridge
....	....	ALL	ALL	147222	STS	Willenhall
1769	1890	1730	1890	157597	SXE	Hartfield
1850	1900	1700	1850	144479	WAR	Leamington Spa
1841	1875	1538	1841	144479	WAR	???
1859	1943	....	....	177334	WOR	Lye
1818	1854	ALL	1841	152838	YKS	Hull
1691	1750	1650	1700	176451	YKS	Ingleton
NEWTON-COOK						
1820	1960	ALL	1820	133361	LND	Hammersmith
1820	1960	ALL	1820	133361	LND	Soho
NEX						
....	....	ALL	ALL	151262	ALL	Name Study
NEYLAN						
1864	1992	....	1864	151270	LIM	Newcastle West
NIALL						
1800	1820	ALL	ALL	113700	LND	Spitalfields
NIAS						
1827	1856	ALL	ALL	106313	MDX	West

Known From	To	Researching From	To	Ref	Cty	Place
NIBB						
1845	1845	1700	1845	120081	NTH	South
NIBBS						
1793	....	1700	1800	124796	BKM	Tingewick
1796	1830	ALL	ALL	106313	MDX	West
NICE						
....	....	ALL	ALL	151289	ALL	Name Study
NICHOL						
1880	1880	1850	1992	133450	KEN	???
1600	1879	1600	1900	146129	ROX	Castleton Parish
NICHOLAS						
1808	....	ALL	1781	168602	CAM	Littleport
1800	1992	ALL	1992	168718	CON	South East
1560	1673	1520	1650	102571	CON	Constantine
1840	1850	1700	1900	177989	GLA	Oystermouth
1890	1992	....	....	135666	GLA	Whitchurch
1880	1910	1700	1992	148512	GLS	Barton Regis
1855	1939	ALL	1992	104299	GLS	Bristol
1800	1900	1700	1800	151300	GLS	Bristol
1700	1980	1700	1850	151297	GNT	Grosmont
1600	1800	1600	1800	119806	GNT	Lansoy
1600	1800	1600	1800	119806	GNT	Llangunnog
1600	1800	1600	1800	119806	GNT	Llanvihangel Tor Y Mynydd
1600	1800	1600	1800	119806	GNT	Trellech Orange
1600	1800	1600	1800	119806	GNT	Wolves Newton
1805	1830	1700	1805	145459	HAM	Exbury
1755	1851	1700	1755	145459	HAM	Fawley
1813	1898	?	1813	127116	HAM	Woodcutt
1835	1940	1700	1880	160350	KEN	Deal
1880	1910	1700	1992	148512	LEI	Leicester
1857	1955	1700	1900	142212	PEM	Haverfordwest
1880	1910	1700	1992	148512	WAR	Coventry
NICHOLES						
....	1799	1740	1800	132586	WIL	Highworth
NICHOLL						
1850	1992	1750	1850	118052	ANT	Ballycastle
1836	1852	....	....	146560	ANT	Clough
1760	1783	1650	1760	139084	ROX	Bedrule
NICHOLLAS						
1755	....	....	1755	133566	SRY	Merton
NICHOLLS						
1891	1891	1887	1895	159905	BDF	Leighton Buzzard
1760	1840	ALL	1840	151319	CAM	Wisbech
1841	1861	1700	1840	123110	CMN	Trefach
1800	1900	1700	1800	108359	CON	Feock
1800	1901	1750	1992	134023	CON	Gulval
1720	1863	ALL	1720	134783	CON	Gwennap
1685	1740	1600	1800	153354	CON	Gwennap
1700	1992	1700	1992	140449	CON	Kenwyn
1837	1992	1837	1992	168416	CON	Lostwithiel
?	?	?	?	159913	CON	Redruth
1679	1880	1880	1950	178845	CON	Redruth
1830	1970	1700	1860	170615	CON	Roches
1829	1939	1700	1992	106186	CON	St Austell
1830	1970	1700	1860	170615	CON	St Austell
1680	1992	1680	1992	150126	CON	St Keverne
1861	1881	1881	1900	178845	CON	Treleigh
1836	1903	1700	1903	156183	CON	Tywardreath
1750	1930	1750	1900	179507	ESS	Burnham On Crouch
1871	1891	1860	1870	123110	GLA	Aberdare
1798	1992	1798	1992	151335	HEF	Garway
....	....	1800	1880	174394	HEF	Hereford
1638	1992	1600	1700	156035	HEF	Longtown
....	....	1800	1820	147176	HRT	Hatfield
1789	1814	....	1789	108839	HUN	Somersham
1700	1790	ALL	1790	151319	HUN	Yaxley
1766	1864	1700	ALL	141151	KEN	ALL
1847	1876	1820	1900	153508	KEN	Canterbury
1700	1992	1797	1992	122467	KEN	Deptford
1708	1772	1700	1775	108251	KEN	Medway
1854	1992	1780	1854	151327	KEN	Medway
1893	1893	1893	1895	159905	LAN	Tydesly
1812	....	....	....	164631	LIN	Surfleet
1874	1992	1861	1874	132357	LND	East End
....	....	1700	1992	122009	NTT	Central
1850	1992	1850	1920	111562	OXF	Banbury
1886	1886	1885	1890	159905	OXF	Banbury
1841	1861	1700	1840	123110	PEM	Llanbedr Felfre
1820	1842	1800	1842	106690	SAL	Bridgnorth
1875	1970	1828	1890	147176	SRY	Bermondsey
....	1857	ALL	1900	127000	STS	Dudley
....	....	1770	1800	147176	STS	Walsall
....	1857	ALL	1900	127000	WOR	???

Known From	To	Researching From	To	Ref	Cty	Place
NICHOLS						
1843	....	....	....	148768	AVN	Bristol
1815	1815	1750	1850	121568	DEV	North East
ALL	ALL	1806	1850	111554	GLS	Eastington
....	....	1700	1800	128627	HRT	Cheshunt
1792	1992	....	....	107158	IOW	Newport
1854	1992	1780	1854	151327	KEN	Medway
1810	1880	1750	1880	157503	LAN	Preston
1850	1880	1800	1900	153877	LEI	Leicester
1745	1773	ALL	ALL	143294	LEI	Sapcote
1830	1880	1700	1950	141151	LND	Battersea
....	....	1700	1882	102148	LND	East End
1830	1880	1700	1950	141151	LND	Wandsworth
....	....	1750	1900	103888	LND	???
....	....	1700	1800	128627	LND	???
1750	1905	1700	1905	118303	MDX	London
1796	1912	1700	1796	166804	NFK	Harlastone
1769	1789	1620	1769	138029	NFK	Seringham
1810	1872	1700	1871	118222	NFK	W Beckham
1731	1750	1700	1800	159905	OXF	Alkerton
1762	1885	1740	1900	159905	OXF	Shenington
1780	1900	ALL	1780	115118	RUT	Ketton
....	1800	....	1800	177695	SAL	Buildwas
1824	....	1750	1850	143693	SOM	Old Cleeve
1819	1841	1750	1850	143693	SOM	Watchet
1746	1800	1600	1800	130125	WAR	Snitterfield
1660	1850	ALL	1850	132950	WIL	Brinkworth
1804	1992	1750	1804	159565	???	Bristol
NICHOLSON						
....	....	1650	1800	178330	CHS	Heaton Norris
1730	1770	1730	1770	178330	CHS	Macclesfield
1750	....	....	....	131709	CMA	Keswick
1830	1890	1700	1830	135151	CUL	North
1794	....	....	....	138401	CUL	Egremont
1756	1793	....	....	138401	CUL	Hesket In The Forest
1794	....	....	....	138401	CUL	St Bees
1800	1899	....	....	164151	CUL	Wigton
1899	1935	....	....	151351	DBY	Chesterfield
1866	1901	....	....	151351	DBY	Staveley
1628	1885	....	....	124524	DUR	High Conniscliffe
1808	1915	1700	1855	155705	FIF	Ceres
1787	1787	1700	1850	105333	GLS	Tetbury
1865	1960	1865	1878	103586	HAM	Gosport
....	....	1600	1750	154873	KEN	Doddington
1700	1700	1600	1700	139084	KEN	Shipbourne
....	....	1600	1750	154873	KEN	Wouldham
1750	....	1750	....	109347	LAN	Whalley
1758	1800	....	....	165999	LEI	Leicester
1758	1800	....	....	165999	LEI	Redmile
1724	....	1600	1724	151343	LIN	Belton
1774	....	....	....	151351	LIN	Blyton
1779	....	....	....	151351	LIN	Carlton
1724	....	1600	1724	151343	LIN	Epham
1800	1855	1855	1890	148199	LIN	Middle
1760	1900	1800	1992	165697	LIN	???
1600	1620	1560	1620	178330	LND	Hackney
1938	1945	....	....	151351	MDX	Osterley
1830	1880	1730	1830	161519	MDX	Oulston
1819	1848	1750	1819	176249	MDX	Teddington
1876	....	1750	1850	139289	NBL	Hexham
....	....	1750	1780	110450	NTH	Denford
....	....	1750	1780	110450	NTH	Raunds
1750	1832	ALL	ALL	155608	NTT	Collingham
1800	1835	....	....	151351	NTT	Newark
1559	1850	....	....	151351	NTT	Southwell
1700	1750	....	....	165999	NTT	Staythorpe
1768	1792	....	....	178330	OXF	Didcot
....	....	?	?	173851	SCT	???
1850	....	1850	....	135968	SRY	Croydon
1750	1836	1700	1750	179663	WES	Barton
1800	1850	1700	1850	143553	WES	Warcop
1808	1915	1700	1855	155705	WLN	Whitburn
1820	1900	1820	1900	153621	WYK	Halifax
1864	....	1860	1992	151378	WYK	Selby
1864	1917	1837	1992	151378	WYK	Sowerby
1798	1992	....	....	124354	YKS	Harworth
1724	1951	1600	1724	151343	YKS	Hatfield
1750	....	1700	....	134589	YKS	Huntington
....	....	1830	....	119768	YKS	Leeds
1930	1980	1800	1930	119784	YKS	Leeds
1902	....	....	....	151351	YKS	Leeds
1700	1750	1600	1890	165697	YKS	North Anston
1650	1700	1650	1700	119717	YKS	Rosby

Known From	To	Researching From	To	Ref	Cty	Place
NICHOLSON contd.						
1784	1827	ALL	1850	152838	YKS	Rotherham
1861	1992	1700	1861	105635	YKS	Sheffield
1724	1951	1600	1724	151343	YKS	Thorne
1757	1780	1700	1757	177393	YKS	Wistow
NICKIN						
1725	1800	1600	1725	170194	STS	Hatherton
NICKLEM						
1731	1900	1500	1900	170216	DOR	ALL
1731	1900	1500	1900	170216	HAM	ALL
NICKLEN						
1700	1890	....	1700	101168	HAM	Damerham
NICKLES						
1875	1903	1875	1903	156183	CON	Calstock
NICKLESS						
....	....	1750	1900	143502	SAL	ALL
1860	1900	1800	1900	143502	SAL	Wellington
NICKLIN						
1837	1850	1837	1850	156892	LAN	Manchester
....	1815	1815	1851	140767	WAR	Birmingham
....	1815	1815	1851	140767	WOR	Dudley
NICKOLDS						
1800	1900	1689	1900	103144	LND	Islington
1862	1992	1800	1900	133590	MDX	Clerkenwell
1900	1992	1689	1900	103144	MDX	Enfield
1860	1992	1850	1992	133590	MDX	Ensfield
1699	1992	1500	1900	133590	STS	Sedgley
1689	1800	1689	1992	103144	STS	Tipton
1699	1992	1500	1900	133590	STS	Tipton
1770	1800	....	....	100420	WAR	Meriden
NICKS						
1789	1789	ALL	1789	159042	NTH	Maxey
NICKSON						
1700	1800	ALL	ALL	137987	CHS	Malpas
1750	1820	ALL	ALL	137987	FLN	Bangor On Dee
1806	1992	ALL	1806	151394	LND	Central
1779	1857	1700	1790	101575	YKS	Malton
1561	1565	1500	1561	138584	YKS	Rothwell
1779	1857	1700	1790	101575	YKS	Selby
1920	1962	....	....	147702	???	Barrow In Furness
NICOL						
1750	1800	....	....	126497	CAI	Thurso
1823	1825	....	....	118133	FIF	Dunfermline
....	....	1747	1806	118133	FIF	Leslie
1879	1911	1911	1992	146560	LKS	Coatbride
....	....	1700	1900	142670	MLN	Edinburgh
....	....	1700	1992	137855	MOR	Kintesack
....	....	1782	....	149187	PER	Perth
1780	1850	1700	1900	124427	PER	Strathard
ALL	ALL	ALL	ALL	151416	SCT	ALL
NICOLL						
1827	1827	1800	1827	149632	ABD	Aberdeen
1792	....	1792	....	177768	ANS	Airlie
1840	....	1840	....	177768	ANS	Littleton
1753	1878	1750	1850	102717	HRT	Ware
1870	1920	1850	1920	102717	MDX	Enfield
NICOLLE						
1500	ALL	ALL	ALL	115126	CHI	ALL
....	....	1760	....	149187	JSY	St Saviour
NICOLSON						
1750	1992	1700	1800	144231	INV	Braes Skye
1830	1865	1780	1835	119628	INV	Skye
1750	1965	....	....	137820	SHI	Fetlar
1720	1965	....	....	137820	SHI	Mid Yell
1760	1965	....	....	137820	SHI	North Yell
1758	1965	....	....	137820	SHI	Northmavine
1720	1965	....	....	137820	SHI	South Yell
1700	1992	1650	1992	104671	SHI	Whiteness
NIELD						
1646	1992	1940	1992	125520	CHS	Bunbury
1785	....	1600	1785	106054	CHS	Macclesfield
1880	1960	1825	1880	151432	LAN	Oldham
1847	1992	ALL	1847	151424	YKS	Leeds
NIEURZYLA						
....	....	ALL	ALL	151440	ALL	Name Study
ALL	....	....	....	151440	ALL	ALL
NIEUZYLA						
ALL	....	....	....	151440	ALL	ALL
NIGHTINGALE						
1792	1877	ALL	1792	168602	BRK	Bray
1830	1860	....	....	159131	BRK	Waltham St Lawrence
1810	1900	1850	1975	138215	CAM	Benwick
1741	1924	....	....	126926	CAM	Girton
1920	1992	....	....	138215	CAM	Peterborough

Known From	To	Researching From	To	Ref	Cty	Place
NIGHTINGALE contd.						
1900	1949	1850	1910	138215	CAM	Whittlesey
1655	1715	1625	1715	125032	HAM	Bramley
1655	1655	1625	1655	125032	HAM	Sherbourne St John
....	....	ALL	ALL	130524	HRT	Hertford
1721	1810	1680	1900	138215	HUN	Ramsey
1866	1992	1800	1992	120014	KEN	Dover
1849	1849	1849	1875	126705	LAN	Bury
1800	1880	1880	1992	162256	LAN	Tockholes
1920	1992	1700	1992	151459	LND	???
1881	1965	....	1880	130524	MDX	Whitechapel
1888	1970	ALL	ALL	105856	MDX	???
1834	1860	1834	1900	151467	OXF	Watlington
1888	1970	ALL	ALL	105856	SRY	???
1663	1870	....	....	174319	SRY	???
1813	1880	1810	1880	123021	SSX	Rudgewick
....	....	1750	1810	151467	WAR	Birmingham
1760	1850	1700	1850	145319	WAR	Coventry
1800	....	....	....	100536	???	???
NIGHTON						
1800	1850	1750	1900	159107	NFK	Upwell
NILES						
1700	1840	1600	1850	126403	CON	Launceston
NIMMO						
1850	1950	1800	1900	126640	DUR	Newcastle
NIMS						
....	....	ALL	ALL	162299	ALL	Name Study
NINCHWORTH						
1830	....	....	....	172723	ALL	ALL
NIND						
....	....	ALL	ALL	115231	ALL	ALL
1685	1992	1650	1992	136719	ALL	London
1850	1970	1700	1850	160660	LND	South
NINEHAM						
ALL	ALL	....	....	153397	HAM	New Forest
NINIAN						
1750	1965	....	....	137820	SHI	Fetlar
1720	1965	....	....	137820	SHI	Mid Yell
1760	1965	....	....	137820	SHI	North Yell
1758	1965	....	....	137820	SHI	Northmavine
1720	1965	....	....	137820	SHI	South Yell
NINNES						
1691	1756	1650	1750	108510	CON	Towednack
NINNIS						
1624	1668	1500	1624	138614	CON	Perranuthnoe
1824	1992	1750	1992	167991	CON	Towednack
1824	1992	1750	1992	167991	GLA	Rhondda
NIPPER						
1800	1920	ALL	1850	138169	SOM	Compton Bishop
NISBET						
....	....	ALL	ALL	151491	ALL	Name Study
1839	....	ALL	ALL	172057	BEW	Ayton
1600	1870	1500	1870	154881	LKS	Bothwell
1850	1860	1800	1860	146536	LKS	Stane
1750	1965	....	....	137820	SHI	Fetlar
1720	1965	....	....	137820	SHI	Mid Yell
1760	1965	....	....	137820	SHI	North Yell
1758	1965	....	....	137820	SHI	Northmavine
1720	1965	....	....	137820	SHI	South Yell
NISBETT						
1600	1870	1500	1870	154881	LKS	Bothwell
NISELL						
1430	1507	1400	1500	154881	KEN	Wrotham
NIVEN						
1788	....	1700	1800	115967	AYR	Kirkmichael
1845	1845	1800	1845	163783	CHS	Birkenhead
1835	1878	1835	1879	118974	FIF	Limekilns
1805	....	1830	1841	118974	KRS	Orwell
1872	1930	1700	1900	156493	MLN	Benhar
1899	1906	1800	1899	179647	SCT	Falkirk
1845	1845	1800	1845	163783	SCT	Glasgow
1857	1900	ALL	ALL	120219	STI	Falkirk
....	....	....	....	120219	STI	Grangemouth
NIX						
1840	1860	ALL	ALL	130508	ABD	Aberdeen
1730	1760	....	1730	108839	CAM	Coveney
1674	1780	ALL	1674	168602	CAM	Coveney
1674	1780	ALL	1674	168602	CAM	Witcham
1768	1834	1700	1800	159042	LIN	Dowsby
1740	1765	1700	1800	159042	NTH	Etton
NIXON						
1790	1811	1500	1790	125695	CAM	Soham
1800	1900	1800	1850	143553	CUL	Penrith
1730	1800	1700	1850	138878	CUL	Rockcliffe

Known From	To	Researching From	To	Ref	Cty	Place
NIXON contd.						
1839	1910	ALL	1839	126721	DBY	Chesterfield
1845	1871	ALL	ALL	151513	DBY	Church Gresley
1730	1800	1650	1730	132942	DUR	Whickham
1753	1777	1700	1757	167533	GLS	Bristol
1666	?	?	?	166642	KEN	Fordwich
?	?	?	?	151505	LAN	Liverpool
1829	1883	1816	1829	156582	LND	East
1829	1883	1816	1829	156582	LND	City
1827	1943	1700	1827	139084	NBL	Bellingham
1700	1850	1700	1850	160121	NBL	Haltwhistle
1763	1816	ALL	1829	156582	NFK	Norwich
1846	....	1800	1900	115967	NTH	Tynemouth
1865	1935	1700	1865	100145	RFW	Glasgow
ALL	ALL	ALL	ALL	150169	SRY	ALL
1810	1880	1750	1880	176621	TYR	Drumquin
1810	1880	1750	1880	176621	TYR	Omagh
1650	1837	1538	1841	151513	WAR	North
1806	....	ALL	1992	159174	WAR	Aston
1778	1960	1750	1960	151513	WAR	Grendon
1720	1992	1720	1800	124168	YKS	Arkengarthdale
1791	1992	1700	1992	151521	YKS	Rotherham
1840	1880	1800	1840	161519	YKS	Sculcoates
1791	1992	1700	1992	151521	YKS	Sheffield
NOAD						
1770	1785	1770	1785	142018	DOR	Poole
1780	1820	1780	1850	116807	LND	London
1680	1800	1680	1800	142018	SOM	ALL
....	....	1800	1899	104884	SOM	Bath
1800	1840	ALL	ALL	124605	SOM	Bath
1850	1870	1820	1900	116807	SOM	Kilve
1700	1950	ALL	ALL	126098	SOM	Road
1700	1800	1700	1800	142018	WIL	ALL
1700	1900	ALL	ALL	126098	WIL	North Bradley
....	1936	ALL	ALL	126098	WIL	Road
1653	1950	....	....	124672	WIL	Swindon
1636	1831	1600	1650	170348	WIL	Swindon
NOAKE						
1645	1735	1600	1670	124974	BRK	Reading
1460	1670	1600	1670	124974	BRK	Shottesbrook
?	?	?	?	117528	DOR	Sherborne
?	?	?	?	117528	SOM	???
1560	1820	1500	1800	133426	STS	South
NOAKES						
1810	1810	....	....	159883	KEN	Deal
1790	1860	1700	1992	133450	KEN	Mongham
1821	1947	1800	1821	168777	MDX	Shoreditch
1827	1827	1800	1860	176672	SSX	ALL
1750	1800	....	1800	109568	SSX	Whatlington
1836	1925	....	....	121290	STS	Checkley
NOALL						
1700	1800	1575	1700	116637	CON	St Ives
1650	1800	1650	1800	168750	CON	St Ives
1820	1900	....	....	116637	DUR	Sunderland
NOBBS						
1750	1850	1750	1850	111589	IOW	Newchurch
1800	1860	1550	1800	150843	SFK	Lound
1876	1992	1800	1876	118710	TYR	Cooktown
NOBLE						
1841	1992	1770	1880	142727	ABD	Broadsea
1841	1992	1770	1880	142727	ABD	Fraserburgh
....	....	1780	1830	172871	ABD	Fraserburgh
1750	1820	1790	1800	133183	AVN	Bristol
1770	1870	1770	1870	151564	AVN	Bristol
....	1795	....	1795	161888	AYR	Mauchline
1725	1900	ALL	1756	108642	BDF	Odell
1725	1900	ALL	1756	108642	BDF	Sharnbrook
1870	1920	....	....	177903	CMA	Maryport
1790	1830	1700	1800	175838	CON	Redruth
1849	1992	1700	1849	118532	CON	Windyer
1850	1960	ALL	ALL	162469	CUL	North
?	?	?	?	151556	CUL	???
1775	1844	1700	1844	121932	DBY	Crich
1776	1870	1700	1900	151599	DBY	Derby
1885	1941	1524	1992	118893	DUR	Aycliffe
1785	1924	1600	1785	116637	DUR	Bishopwearmouth
1858	1875	1524	1992	118893	DUR	Crawleyside
1822	....	1780	....	156191	DUR	Harraton
1785	1924	1600	1785	116637	DUR	Monkwearmouth
1785	1924	1600	1785	116637	DUR	Sunderland
1700	1992	1600	1992	154342	GLS	Bitton
1650	1700	1600	1992	154342	GLS	Siston
1850	1992	ALL	1800	151602	HAM	Sherfield English
1846	1992	ALL	ALL	151580	HRT	Broxbourne

Known From	To	Researching From	To	Ref	Cty	Place
NOBLE contd.						
1826	1992	1700	1857	119296	KEN	Deal
....	....	ALL	ALL	119296	KEN	???
1758	1800	ALL	1758	102350	LAN	Millom
1790	1800	1700	1800	116432	LEI	Burbage
1792	1992	1700	1792	102342	LIN	Fizwingham
1500	1992	ALL	ALL	119857	MDX	London
1700	1922	1780	1840	101001	MLN	Cockpen
1700	1922	1780	1840	101001	MLN	Lasswade
1800	1900	....	....	151572	NBL	???
1803	1890	1524	1930	118893	NFK	Bressingham
1803	1890	1524	1930	118893	NFK	Fersfield
1524	1900	1524	1992	118893	NFK	???
....	....	1700	1831	150150	NTH	Kettering
1820	1850	1850	1950	116432	NTH	Maidwell
1870	1950	1800	1980	151599	NTT	Nottingham
1700	1800	1700	1800	116823	NYK	Whitby
1850	1870	....	....	177903	PEE	???
1524	1700	1524	1992	118893	SFK	???
1767	1793	1650	1766	131245	WAR	Stretton On Dunsmore
?	?	?	?	151556	WES	???
1850	1992	ALL	1750	151602	WIL	Bishopstone
1850	1992	ALL	1800	151602	WIL	Landford
1850	1992	ALL	1800	151602	WIL	Whiteparish
1700	1880	1600	1750	174599	WIL	Whiteparish
1871	1891	1524	1992	118893	WRY	???
....	....	1700	1706	146706	YKS	Ebberston
1798	1876	1500	1798	125695	YKS	Everingham
1823	1980	1700	1823	138355	YKS	Haxby
1692	1718	1660	1730	170348	YKS	Kirkburton
1802	1820	1700	1850	149098	YKS	Woodkirk
?	....	ALL	....	150835	???	???
NOBLES						
1725	1900	ALL	1756	108642	BDF	Odell
1725	1900	ALL	1756	108642	BDF	Sharnbrook
?	....	?	?	177679	SCT	Borders
NOBORY						
....	....	1600	1899	115975	WIL	Wylye Valley
NOCK						
ALL	ALL	ALL	ALL	151610	ALL	ALL
1813	1860	1766	1860	151610	LND	Shadwell
....	....	1800	1841	111414	STS	Rowley Regis
1720	1789	1700	1800	151610	STS	Rowley Regis
1875	1875	1871	1881	111414	STS	Smethwick
1760	1770	1700	1760	156140	STS	Tipton
....	....	1700	1850	147613	WOR	Halesowen
1840	1857	1830	1881	111414	WOR	Oldbury
NOCKELS						
....	....	ALL	ALL	159840	NFK	Cromer
NODDER						
....	....	1800	1992	129348	CON	Truro
NODDINS						
1650	1850	1650	1850	119717	YKS	Rosby
NODES						
....	....	ALL	ALL	156205	ALL	Name Study
NOEL						
1850	1875	....	....	114871	LND	Hampstead
1820	1850	....	....	114871	LND	Holborn
1770	1820	1700	1770	114871	LND	Piccadilly
NOKES						
....	....	ALL	ALL	151645	ALL	Name Study
1790	1948	1700	1790	169935	ESS	Halstead
1798	1890	1740	1798	169943	ESS	Springfield
1830	....	1800	1850	137782	HEF	Bromyard
1778	1851	1778	1825	144355	KEN	South
1830	1900	1800	1900	151637	WAR	Birmingham
1770	1815	ALL	ALL	151645	WAR	Birmingham
....	1813	1700	1820	148288	WIL	???
1760	1960	ALL	ALL	151645	WOR	Bromsgrove
1763	1785	ALL	ALL	151645	WOR	Stoke Prior
NOLAN						
....	....	1800	....	118826	IRL	Carlow
1820	....	1868	1992	130486	IRL	Cork
1924	1960	....	1924	122637	WIL	Shrewton
NOLBLE						
1632	1875	1600	1640	165417	???	???
NOLDA						
1810	1850	1700	1900	129496	MDX	Islington
NOLLER						
1846	1992	....	....	104078	CAM	Littleport
NOLLOTH						
1765	1830	ALL	1765	178934	SFK	Halesworth

Known From	To	Researching From	To	Ref	Cty	Place
NOLSON						
1850	1992	ALL	ALL	107670	LND	East
NOMES						
....	....	1750	1850	146927	ALL	???
NOOKS						
1830	1850	1836	1870	111090	IRL	Ballina
1830	1850	1836	1870	111090	IRL	Killia
NOONE						
1551	1692	1550	1691	102830	DBY	Longford
NOOT						
1700	1850	1700	1850	167924	PEM	Tenby
NOOTH						
1700	1992	ALL	1700	179345	SOM	Wells
NORBURY						
1848	1853	1800	1880	142751	CHS	Macclesfield
....	....	1800	1848	142751	CHS	Tatton
1650	1700	1700	1992	162256	LAN	Turton
NORCOTE						
1725	....	ALL	1725	130079	OXF	Swyncombe
NORCOTT						
1821	1860	1800	1860	119059	BKM	Brill
1846	....	1700	1870	135623	COR	ALL
1725	....	ALL	1718	130079	OXF	Swyncombe
NORDABY						
....	....	1750	1820	175773	YKS	East
NORDEN						
1548	1626	ALL	ALL	122211	MDX	Fulham
1548	1626	ALL	ALL	122211	MDX	Hendon
NORFOLK						
....	....	1700	1797	102148	LIN	ALL
NORGATE						
1750	1830	1800	1850	144657	HAM	Farringdon
1840	1890	1700	1840	124966	HAM	Winchester
NORGROVE						
....	....	1575	1860	140341	SAL	???
NORKETT						
1840	1870	1840	1870	170119	HAM	Portsea
1865	1992	1600	1865	160040	MDX	London
1725	....	ALL	1718	130079	OXF	Swyncombe
NORMAN						
1609	1795	....	....	138630	CAM	Cottenham
1792	1903	....	....	138630	CAM	Haddenham
1814	1851	....	1878	137405	CAM	Rampton
1764	1936	....	....	138630	CAM	Willingham
1798	1992	1798	1861	147621	CHS	Liverpool
1812	1843	1780	1880	159905	CUL	Carleton
1600	1708	1550	1673	102830	DBY	Wirksworth
1850	1870	1800	1914	141933	DEV	Challacombe
1765	1775	1740	1800	171158	DEV	Halberton
1868	1950	1800	1868	174807	DEV	South Molton
1780	1851	....	....	166316	DEV	Thorverton
1615	1680	1600	1800	151653	DEV	Trusham
1811	....	....	....	119911	DOR	Bridport
1750	1850	ALL	ALL	139564	DOR	Swanage
1824	1861	....	....	148016	ENG	Chasel Hill
1875	1992	1850	1992	133450	KEN	Sevenoaks
1864	1891	1855	1891	159492	LAN	Oldham
1769	1900	1700	1900	135968	LEI	Blaby
1826	1920	1700	1950	178616	LEI	Blaby
1723	1957	1700	1723	124583	LEI	Newton Linford
1861	1950	1950	1992	151688	LIN	Gedney Dyke
1834	1923	....	....	151718	LND	Islington
1848	1920	ALL	1992	143049	MDX	London
1791	1840	1840	1992	151688	NFK	Hickling
1782	1800	....	....	157554	NFK	Marlingford
1790	1830	1750	1830	119938	NFK	Norwich
1767	1780	....	1767	151688	NFK	Paston
1840	1861	ALL	1992	151688	NFK	Stalham
1600	1799	1660	1780	135941	SFK	Mildenhall
1740	1790	1740	1820	151653	SOM	Bledon
1640	1710	1640	1800	151653	SOM	Bridgwater
1770	1900	ALL	1900	104299	SOM	Cannington
1706	1880	1700	1900	151653	SOM	Langport
1834	....	....	....	151718	SOM	Midsommor Norton
1885	1979	ALL	ALL	151696	SRY	Battersea
1813	1828	1785	1813	175951	SSX	Falmer
NORMANTON						
1769	1900	1700	1900	135968	LEI	Blaby
1710	1992	1537	1710	132179	YKS	Ripponden
NORMINGTON						
1826	1891	....	1826	125954	YKS	Bradford
NORMINTON						
1840	1850	ALL	ALL	125202	WRY	Halifax

Known From	To	Researching From	To	Ref	Cty	Place
NORRELL						
1630	1992	1630	1992	121533	SSX	Chichester
NORRES						
....	....	1300	1500	154873	LAN	Speke
NORRIE						
1762	1808	1700	1762	172871	KCD	East
NORRINGTON						
....	....	ALL	ALL	151726	ALL	Name Study
ALL	ALL	ALL	ALL	151726	ALL	ALL
ALL	1840	1800	1880	135429	DEV	Ottery St Mary
1777	1777	....	....	144355	KEN	South
1580	?	?	?	166642	KEN	Ashford
1840	1900	1700	1840	158925	KEN	Greenwich
NORRIS						
1734	1847	....	1841	137405	CAM	Rampton
1855	1951	1800	1855	103896	CHS	Heaton Norris
1850	1889	1889	1992	162973	CON	Liskeard
1700	1992	1500	1992	166758	DEV	South
1550	1770	1300	1800	105333	DEV	Buckland In The Moor
1839	1992	1700	1850	167223	DEV	Crediton
1550	1770	1300	1800	105333	DEV	Holne
1550	1770	1300	1800	105333	DEV	Ilsington
1550	1770	1300	1800	105333	DEV	Lydford
1550	1770	1300	1800	105333	DEV	Widecombe In The Moor
1853	1853	ALL	1853	167959	ESS	Southminster
1829	1962	1700	1829	120367	ESS	Walthamstow
1850	1992	....	....	161969	HAM	Exbury
1850	1992	....	....	161969	HAM	New Forest
1837	?	1791	1837	161284	HEF	Holmer
1668	1703	1511	1703	141291	IOM	Malew
1850	1992	....	....	161969	IOW	Cowes
1800	1850	ALL	....	172812	KEN	Sheerness
1853	1910	1840	1920	168947	LAN	Bolton
1580	1870	1580	1870	100080	LAN	Croston
1853	1910	1840	1920	168947	LAN	Salford
1833	1971	1700	1832	172006	LAN	St Helens
1871	1924	1841	1871	165026	LIN	Lincoln
....	....	ALL	ALL	172812	LND	ALL
1830	1960	1830	1960	134767	LND	Stamford Hill
1829	1962	1700	1829	120367	LND	Walthamstow
1855	1875	1840	1900	168947	LND	Woolwich
1843	1940	1843	1940	134767	MDX	Islington
1898	1966	ALL	1898	167711	MDX	Paneras
1819	1992	ALL	1819	154520	NBL	Cramlington
1750	1992	1700	1900	151742	NRY	North York Moors
1840	1870	1800	1840	146110	NTH	ALL
1820	1910	ALL	1820	159077	NTH	Aldwinkle
1811	1909	ALL	1811	152013	NTH	Brackley
1697	1900	1552	1700	101427	SOM	Central
1867	1947	1697	1900	101427	SOM	Burtle
1830	1866	....	....	153176	SRY	Lambeth
1750	1897	1730	1890	105333	SSX	Chichester
1750	1897	1730	1890	105333	SSX	Mundham
1821	1842	ALL	ALL	125288	STS	Gnosall
1832	1899	....	1860	166553	WIL	Mere
NORRISH						
1866	1893	ALL	1893	114030	CON	Stoke Climsland
1815	1820	1800	1850	102717	DEV	Exeter
1857	1907	1850	1920	102717	MDX	ALL
....	....	1820	1860	102717	SRY	North East
NORRY						
1880	1985	1800	1880	173231	SAL	Madeley
NORTH						
1816	1992	ALL	1816	151777	BKM	???
1846	1992	1846	1992	172596	CON	Drift
1881	1992	1881	1992	172596	CON	Newlyn
1846	1992	1846	1992	172596	CON	Sancreed
1846	1992	1846	1992	172596	CON	St Just
1583	1627	1500	1582	131245	DBY	Dronfield
1735	1806	1650	1730	100013	HAM	Odiham
1735	1809	....	....	115606	HAM	Odiham
1728	1793	1728	1793	103977	HRT	Aldenham
1728	1793	1728	1793	103977	HRT	Shenley
1728	1793	1728	1793	103977	HRT	St Stephens
1760	1950	1600	1760	117110	KEN	Lee
1775	1775	1763	1782	124915	LEI	Rothley
1800	1900	1700	1800	151769	LIN	Foston
1750	1800	1650	1750	151769	LIN	Fulbeck
1800	1900	1700	1800	151769	LIN	Leadenham
1805	1820	1790	1805	147745	LIN	Market Rasen
1878	1952	1837	1952	151173	LND	Bermonsey
1878	1952	1837	1952	151173	LND	Rotherhithe
NORTH contd.						
1798	1900	1600	1900	124834	NTT	East Leake
1800	1899	....	....	164151	SAL	Pimley Manor
1769	1780	1803	1900	124915	SOM	Bath
....	1816	ALL	1992	172596	SOM	Stoke
1879	1992	1800	1879	151793	SRY	Reigate
1841	1900	1815	1900	124915	SSX	Brighton
1844	1848	1800	1860	124915	SSX	Westmiston
1688	1908	1500	1992	144460	STS	Trentham
1820	1830	....	....	103721	WAR	Birmingham
1700	1800	1600	1700	157740	WES	Burton In Kendal
1800	1820	1790	1823	124915	WIL	Devizes
1732	1770	1700	1766	127116	WIL	Ogbourne St George
....	....	....	1848	176702	WYK	Bradford
1835	1902	ALL	1835	160008	WYK	Mirfield
1825	1910	....	....	151785	YKS	Chapeltown
1609	1680	1560	1650	170348	YKS	Mirfield
1786	1850	1600	1786	117110	YKS	White Lee
NORTHAM						
1864	1936	1812	1864	117773	DEV	Tiverton
NORTHCOTE						
1838	1875	1700	1900	169536	LND	St Prancras
1725	....	ALL	1725	130079	OXF	Swyncombe
NORTHCOTT						
1810	1900	1800	1900	118540	DEV	Bideford
1737	1867	1600	1750	150320	DEV	Bridford
1708	1853	1600	1708	150657	DEV	Chagford
1828	1865	....	1830	150320	DEV	Coldridge
NORTHERN						
1676	1718	....	....	174319	CON	Gorran
1873	1878	1873	....	151610	YKS	Drypool
NORTHEY						
1860	1870	1800	1860	151807	CON	Creegbrawse
1800	1900	....	....	153745	CON	Gwennap
1800	1900	....	....	153745	CON	Kenwyn
1783	1874	ALL	1830	162507	CON	Truro
1799	1801	....	1900	147672	DEV	Tavistock
1890	1910	1870	1890	151807	DUR	Newcastle
?	?	1870	1890	151807	DUR	Whickham
1920	1920	ALL	1920	179515	IRL	Ulster
NORTHMORE						
....	....	ALL	ALL	132659	ALL	Name Study
?	?	?	?	101214	DEV	Ermington
1813	1834	1811	1834	141895	DEV	Ermington
?	?	?	?	101214	DEV	Plymouth
1700	1900	1600	1900	132659	DEV	Sheepstor
NORTHOVER						
1843	1880	ALL	ALL	119369	HAM	Bitterne
1860	1893	1860	1893	154199	LND	Soho
1859	1936	....	....	126187	???	Bristol
NORTHROP						
1810	1930	ALL	ALL	172103	CAM	South
1750	1900	ALL	ALL	151815	CAM	West
NORTHWOOD						
1100	1272	1100	1272	154881	KEN	Minster
1100	1272	1100	1272	154881	KEN	Sheppey
NORTON						
1842	1992	1842	1907	107131	DBY	Burbage
1800	....	1800	1850	107123	DBY	Burbage
1800	....	1800	1850	107123	DBY	Buxton
1842	1992	1842	1907	107131	DBY	Buxton
....	....	?	?	102229	DEV	Topsham
1898	1928	ALL	1898	156078	DUR	Stockton
1800	1841	1750	1825	175218	EYK	Hull
1400	1600	1400	1600	144657	HAM	East Tisted
1550	1620	1500	1600	144657	HAM	West Worldham
1744	1744	....	....	144355	KEN	South
1750	1775	1700	1775	133817	KEN	Hunton Minor
1820	1861	ALL	1861	173290	LAN	Little Sankey
1799	1992	1980	1992	114979	LEI	Barwell
1800	1841	1750	1825	175218	LIN	Barton
1903	ALL	ALL	ALL	146188	LND	Brixton
1846	1848	....	....	171492	LND	Walthamstow
1890	1915	1755	1890	177237	MDX	London
....	....	1700	1850	140627	NFK	North Tuddenham
1766	....	ALL	1800	104299	SOM	Old Cleeve
1916	ALL	ALL	ALL	146188	SRY	South Croydon
1805	....	?	1825	103934	SRY	???
....	....	?	1782	103934	SSX	Chichester
1690	1830	1650	1830	111538	WRY	Wakefield
NORWAY						
1700	1800	1700	1850	149144	CON	Lostwithiel
NORWELL						
1740	1800	1740	1800	167924	ESS	Chelmsford

Known From	To	Researching From	To	Ref	Cty	Place
NORWOOD						
1812	....	ALL	ALL	121436	BKM	Cholesbury
1750	1860	....	....	102741	DUR	Stanhope
1817	1858	1815	1860	138312	HRT	Berkhamstead
1833	1880	ALL	ALL	121436	HRT	Tring
1895	1988	1750	1895	139777	LIM	Michelstown
1790	1900	1700	1950	144290	LIN	Newton On Trent
1720	....	....	....	102741	NBL	Newcastle
1775	1875	1775	1875	126209	SAL	South
1811	?	1700	1811	120650	YKS	Asselby
1824	1844	ALL	ALL	120650	YKS	Eastrington
1743	1811	1700	1811	120650	YKS	Howden
NOSSETTER						
?	?	?	?	117528	DOR	Sherborne
NOSSITER						
1770	1850	1600	1770	123390	DOR	Beaminster
NOSWORTHY						
1800	1880	1800	1880	135429	DEV	ALL
1550	1730	1300	1760	105333	DEV	Buckland In The Moor
1550	1730	1300	1760	105333	DEV	Holne
1550	1730	1300	1760	105333	DEV	Ilsington
1550	1730	1300	1760	105333	DEV	Lydford
1550	1992	....	....	177474	DEV	Manaton
1550	1730	1300	1760	105333	DEV	Widecombe In The Moor
NOTAS						
1660	....	....	1700	160873	NBL	Newcastle On Tyne
NOTHER						
1817	1862	....	....	169013	CHS	Warrington
NOTLEY						
....	....	1700	1800	117471	DOR	Bishop Caundle
....	....	1700	1800	117471	DOR	Folke
1730	1860	1700	1880	151858	DOR	Osmington
1841	1992	1801	1914	167258	GLS	Bristol
1780	1850	1750	1850	135941	SFK	Clare
1850	1992	1850	1985	135941	SFK	Withersfield
?	?	?	?	142018	SOM	Chard
NOTT						
....	....	?	?	104310	DEV	Beaford
1820	1875	1750	1850	156698	DEV	Chulmleigh
....	....	?	?	104310	DEV	Merton
1760	1850	1700	1890	138444	HEF	Bromyard
1760	1850	1700	1890	138444	HEF	Colwall
1840	1886	1790	1992	132489	SOM	Bedminster
1840	1886	1790	1992	132489	SOM	Bristol
1895	1920	1895	ALL	138363	YKS	Keighley
NOTTON						
1150	1250	1150	1250	154881	ALL	ALL
NOVELL						
1726	1798	1726	1800	170143	SRY	Farnham
NOVELLO						
1893	1951	ALL	1992	159174	GLA	Cardiff
NOWELL						
....	....	ALL	ALL	153311	DEV	???
1744	....	....	1744	101761	WOR	???
1695	1901	1525	1695	111163	YKS	Thornhill
NOY						
1844	1844	1800	1844	159581	SFK	Framlingham
1807	1900	1807	1935	164232	SFK	Theberton
NOYCE						
1769	1819	1750	1850	101060	HAM	Hound
1829	1831	1790	1890	105333	HAM	Ringwood
....	....	ALL	1800	151602	HAM	Wellow
NOYES						
1520	1588	1500	1600	124974	BRK	Frilsham
1647	1842	....	....	124974	BRK	Reading
1545	1711	1520	1720	124974	BRK	Shinfield
1765	1842	1750	1850	124974	BRK	Southcote
1545	1711	1520	1720	124974	BRK	Trunkwell
....	....	ALL	ALL	124974	HAM	North West
1594	1780	1500	1780	124974	HAM	Andover
1545	1590	1520	1600	124974	HAM	Blissimore
1720	1740	1650	1750	136840	HAM	Fordingbridge
1575	1662	1550	1700	124974	HAM	Hatherden
1581	1602	1550	1620	124974	HAM	Ramridge
1545	1666	1500	1700	124974	HAM	Weyhill
1740	1756	1740	1780	142018	WIL	Trowbridge
1540	1540	1500	1580	124974	WIL	Urchfont
NOYSE						
1794	1840	1500	1840	157538	BRK	Greenham
1794	1840	1500	1840	157538	BRK	Newbury
NUBBS						
1797	1859	1797	1885	123404	NFK	Buxton
NUBBS contd.						
1785	....	1750	1797	123404	NFK	North Walsham
NUBY						
1678	1750	....	....	161357	KEN	Birchington
1677	1706	....	....	161357	KEN	Monkton
NUELLE						
1916	1930	1850	1916	178527	LND	Soho
NUGENT						
1790	1964	....	1790	177504	MDX	London
NUNALY						
1670	1730	1670	1730	127655	HUN	Bythorn
NUNES						
....	....	ALL	ALL	112070	ALL	Name Study
NUNN						
1750	1992	1700	1750	151866	CAM	Milton
1800	1820	1800	1830	171158	ESS	Gt Baddow
1730	1890	1750	1800	140864	HRT	Barkway
1826	1900	1750	1850	115681	NFK	Rushall
1850	1900	ALL	ALL	154830	SFK	ALL
....	....	1700	1830	174114	SFK	Great Whelmetham
1768	1784	1700	1768	128724	SFK	Hargrave
1798	1992	1700	1798	151874	SFK	Ipswich
....	....	1700	1850	174114	SFK	Rougham
?	?	?	?	127701	SFK	Shelland
1741	1992	....	1741	151874	SFK	Shotley
NUNNS						
1780	1950	1700	1950	105287	SRY	ALL
1770	1900	1770	1900	153621	WYK	Wakefield
NURCOMBE						
....	....	ALL	ALL	104884	SOM	ALL
NURFUR						
....	....	1700	1799	142409	NFK	???
NURSE						
1850	1932	ALL	1850	119695	SOM	West Pennard
NUTALL						
1868	1870	1868	1900	126705	LAN	South
NUTBEAM						
1880	1992	1600	1880	126616	HAM	Boldre
NUTE						
1729	1940	?	1729	147915	CON	???
1729	1940	?	1729	147915	DEV	???
NUTHALL						
1811	1833	?	1811	128910	NTT	Kirkby In Ashfield
1742	1843	ALL	ALL	141127	SFK	North
NUTLEY						
1851	1881	1810	1851	128724	KEN	Newington
1883	1910	....	1883	127787	WIL	Winchester
NUTSFORD						
....	....	ALL	ALL	151890	ALL	Name Study
NUTT						
....	....	ALL	ALL	151904	ALL	Name Study
1862	1921	1800	1992	134023	BKM	ALL
1782	1851	1624	1851	149047	DEV	South Molton
1800	1892	1755	1854	153176	OXF	Cowley
1854	1879	1700	1900	175307	STS	Cheadle
NUTTALL						
1877	1915	1855	1877	141135	CHS	Stockport
1883	1992	1800	1883	113050	IRL	Connaught
1770	1868	ALL	1851	146226	LAN	Blackburn
1780	1810	1700	1780	165530	LAN	Bury
1770	1868	ALL	1851	146226	LAN	Darwen
1800	1870	1700	1900	130419	LAN	Haslingden
1770	1868	ALL	1851	146226	LAN	Haslingden
1683	1846	1500	1846	169439	LAN	Haslingden
1882	1900	1600	1900	176133	LAN	Mancester
1800	1950	ALL	ALL	129119	LAN	Pilsworth
1770	1868	ALL	1851	146226	LAN	Pleasington
1855	1992	1800	1877	141135	LAN	Radcliffe
1812	1992	ALL	1812	162221	LAN	Ramsbottom
1735	1770	1700	1735	132268	LAN	Turton
1817	1869	1817	1896	172162	MDX	Islington
1800	1840	....	....	140082	???	Farnsworth
NUTTER						
1763	1992	....	....	152765	CAM	Cambridge
1900	1947	....	....	151912	LAN	Clitheroe
1760	1840	1700	1760	160474	LAN	Colne
1870	1890	1850	1870	124605	LAN	Manchester
1500	1600	1500	1600	109347	LAN	Pendle
1695	1900	1650	1800	151912	LAN	Sabden Valley
NUTTING						
1900	....	....	....	151920	HRT	Datchworth
1900	....	....	....	151920	HRT	Stevenage
NYE						
....	....	ALL	ALL	141860	ALL	Name Study

Known From	To	Researching From	To	Ref	Cty	Place
NYE contd.						
....	....	ALL	ALL	151939	KEN	???
1780	1925	1780	1992	143200	LND	ALL
....	....	ALL	ALL	151939	SRY	???
....	....	ALL	ALL	151939	SSX	East
1700	1970	ALL	ALL	151939	SSX	West
1871	1881	?	1992	167576	SSX	Brighton
O DONNELL						
....	....	1800	1870	120332	LIM	Limerick
1881	....	ALL	1900	153214	TIP	???
O GORMAN						
1874	....	....	1874	146935	IRL	Belfast
O HANNON						
....	....	....	1992	171131	IRL	Ross Common
O HARA						
ALL	1814	ALL	ALL	125253	MAY	???
O LOUGHAN						
1836	1923	1700	1836	173797	WIC	Rahan Craney
O SULLIVAN						
1862	1950	1800	1900	152021	COR	Glounbrack
....	....	1850	....	140333	IRL	Skibbereen
O'BASE						
....	....	ALL	ALL	143057	ALL	Name Study
O'BRIAN						
1826	1832	1826	1832	144878	KEN	Faversham
1847	1992	ALL	1847	110000	WIC	Vale Of Avoca
O'BRIEN						
1870	1945	1800	1900	138371	DBY	Derby
1853	1861	1770	1870	122327	DUB	Dublin
1860	1992	....	....	151947	GLA	Cardiff
?	....	....	....	147184	IRL	???
1812	1880	1600	1812	151092	LDY	Londonderry
1825	1992	ALL	1825	152064	LND	City
1839	1900	1700	1838	163201	TYR	Mourne River
1850	1900	1750	1900	138371	YKS	Sheffield
O'BRYAN						
1840	....	1800	1860	115967	IRL	Waterford
O'CALLAGHAN						
1884	1926	1880	1884	138495	WAR	Birmingham
O'CARRAGHER						
....	....	ALL	ALL	112046	ALL	Name Study
O'CONNEL						
1846	....	ALL	ALL	172057	COR	Kanturk
O'CONNELL						
1850	1904	1800	1900	128449	COR	Ballydehob
1864	1992	1700	1864	109177	COR	Laurnagh
1900	1900	....	....	113514	EYK	???
....	1960	....	....	151963	IRL	???
1820	1850	1600	1850	154342	IRL	???
....	....	1850	1900	172928	KER	Killarney
....	....	1850	1900	172928	LIM	Limerick
?	?	?	?	178144	TIP	Ballynhinch
O'CONNER						
1834	1992	ALL	1834	105465	LIM	Devling
O'CONNOR						
1877	1992	1800	1900	113166	LIM	???
1848	1862	1700	1992	125113	WEM	Athlone
O'DONAHUE						
1914	1968	1890	1914	118168	KEN	Bexley
O'DONNEL						
....	1857	1800	1857	103322	YKS	Tadcaster
O'DONNELL						
1841	1876	1841	1876	138894	BRK	Reading
1893	1944	1860	1920	175595	LAN	Liverpool
....	....	1700	1850	130931	MAY	Swinford
1790	1815	1790	1930	177768	TIP	???
O'DONOGHUE						
....	....	ALL	ALL	151971	ALL	Name Study
....	....	1890	1916	159840	KEN	Crayford
....	....	1883	1890	159840	KER	Tarbert
O'DONOVAN						
1800	1840	1750	1840	128449	COR	Clonakilty
1735	1845	1700	1845	128449	COR	Derrylahan
1735	1845	1700	1845	128449	COR	Dunmanway
1800	1840	1750	1840	128449	COR	Shannonvale
O'DOWDE						
1865	1940	....	....	156787	SLI	???
O'FLANAGAN						
....	....	1800	1853	101125	IRL	ALL
....	....	1840	1853	101125	MDX	London
O'FOGARTY						
1820	1930	1885	1992	163848	DUB	Dublin City
O'GANAGH						
ALL	ALL	ALL	ALL	177555	ALL	ALL

Known From	To	Researching From	To	Ref	Cty	Place
O'HAGEN						
1870	....	....	....	156647	IRL	???
O'HARA						
1600	1882	1600	1880	154881	ANT	O'harabrook
1600	1882	1600	1880	154881	CAV	Drummullery
1827	1850	1827	1900	136484	IRL	???
1902	1950	ALL	1902	147060	LKS	Carluke
1827	1850	1827	1900	136484	LND	Whitechapel
1820	1870	....	....	142522	NIR	???
1853	1853	1820	1862	102830	WAR	Birmingham
O'HARE						
1831	1860	ALL	1831	118362	NYK	Whitby
O'KEEFFE						
1850	1880	....	....	136492	IRL	???
1850	1880	....	....	136492	KEN	Dover
O'KELLY						
1850	1903	....	....	131717	???	Drogheda
O'LEARY						
1807	....	....	1807	111767	IRL	???
O'LLARD						
1850	1880	....	1850	135089	HAM	Aldershot
O'LOAN						
1780	1992	1600	1780	118052	ANT	Glenravel
O'LOUGHLIN						
1829	1918	1800	1829	173339	CLA	Kilnona
O'MALLEY						
1840	1992	ALL	1992	157902	CLA	Ennis
O'MARA						
1837	1986	....	....	158747	ALL	ALL
O'NEIL						
1819	1886	1700	1819	165859	IRL	Dublin
1885	....	....	....	110833	LND	Old Kent Road
O'NEILL						
1870	1992	1750	1870	118052	ANT	Portglenone
1905	1992	ALL	1905	152013	AVN	Bristol
1800	1950	1800	1950	128449	COR	Clonakilty
1900	1950	1700	1900	152021	COR	Clonakilty
1800	1950	1800	1950	128449	COR	Reenroe
....	....	ALL	ALL	101370	IRL	Armaugh
1899	1933	ALL	1899	152013	IRL	Kilkenny
1900	1925	1925	1992	117099	LAN	Liverpool
1899	1905	ALL	1899	152013	LAN	Manchester
1930	1930	1930	1992	106666	LND	Bow
1895	1992	ALL	1895	169692	LND	Islington
1853	1853	1853	1853	133280	TYR	???
O'OLLARD						
1850	1880	....	1850	135089	LND	???
O'RAW						
1825	1845	1700	1992	152048	ANT	Glenravel
....	....	ALL	ALL	152048	IRL	ALL
1850	1955	....	....	152048	SCT	ALL
O'REGAN						
....	....	1700	1850	152390	COR	???
O'RIELLY						
1800	1820	1700	1992	166073	COR	Penny Market
O'SHAUGHNESSY						
1850	1877	1720	1950	118680	ROS	???
O'SHEA						
....	....	ALL	1848	155225	KER	???
1861	1871	1871	1881	155225	LND	City
1851	1861	1861	1881	155225	LND	Mile End Newtown
O'SULLIVAN						
1800	1850	1800	1900	128449	COR	Bantry
1828	1910	1828	1870	152099	COR	Dunmanway
1800	1850	1800	1900	128449	COR	Frilane
1850	1900	1800	1900	128449	COR	Whiddy Island
1840	1875	1875	1992	117110	KEN	Canterbury
1929	1929	1900	1930	136042	SRY	Clapham
O'THAM						
....	....	....	....	158747	HAM	ALL
O'TOOL						
1829	1850	....	....	171549	IRL	???
O'TOOLE						
1800	1860	1800	1860	121339	IRL	???
OAK						
1840	1992	1800	1900	101508	DEV	Topsham
OAKDEN						
1750	1850	1600	1750	149306	STS	Dove Valley
OAKE						
1580	1830	1500	1830	121274	SSX	Rye
OAKELEY						
....	....	1100	1600	176923	SAL	???
OAKES						
1833	1842	1820	1860	126705	CHS	Chester

Known From	To	Researching From	To	Ref	Cty	Place
OAKES contd.						
1776	1857	?	?	173282	HAM	Fareham
1856	1926	?	?	173282	HAM	Gosport
1852	1873	....	....	173282	HAM	Warnford
1790	1900	1800	1900	136786	LAN	Manchester
1889	1992	....	....	132500	LAN	Oldham
1871	1900	1871	....	159492	LAN	Oldham
1770	1915	....	....	100536	SFK	Bury St Edmunds
1830	1908	1730	1830	153109	STS	Burslam
1811	....	1700	1850	143693	WEX	Enniscorthy
....	....	ALL	1800	152978	WOR	Bewdley
1750	1900	ALL	1900	151319	WRY	Sheffield
1870	....	....	....	161136	YKS	Sheffield
OAKESHOTT						
1739	1785	1720	1812	170143	HAM	East Meon
1739	1785	1720	1812	170143	HAM	Privett
OAKEY						
1810	1870	1600	1870	175641	CAM	Doddington
OAKFORD						
1840	1920	1750	1840	146463	LND	Holborn
1839	1846	1750	1839	146463	LND	Kensington
1810	1992	1750	1810	165336	NFK	Fakenham
1834	1861	1750	1834	146463	WIL	Devizes
OAKINS						
1750	1992	1700	1992	102970	HRT	Great Gaddesden
OAKLEY						
1920	1930	1800	1920	122947	AVN	Easton
1850	....	1847	1864	145920	BRK	Faringdon
1800	1850	1850	1900	145408	BRK	Swallow Field
1616	1801	1600	1801	176923	CMN	Carmarthen
1830	1891	1780	1830	166464	DBY	Melbourne
1725	1773	1675	1725	174289	DOR	ALL
1887	....	....	....	145920	HAM	Netley Abbey
1800	1850	1300	1992	152501	LND	Westminster
1823	1825	1700	1822	131245	MDX	Clerkenwell
1550	1600	1500	1616	176923	OXF	Chastleton
1850	....	1847	1864	145920	OXF	Faringdon
....	1752	ALL	1752	127000	SAL	Whitchurch
1624	1960	1550	1624	152110	SFK	Glemsford
1558	1960	1400	1700	152110	SFK	???
1809	1992	1600	1800	124176	SSX	Yapton
1637	1738	1600	1760	160873	STS	Sedgley
1880	1900	....	....	136565	STS	Upper Gornall
1546	1740	1400	1800	176923	WAR	Wolford
1681	1822	1606	1681	179647	WOR	Hanbury
OAKS-MONGER						
....	1930	ALL	ALL	122866	MDX	East
OAKSHOTT						
....	....	1600	1850	110795	HAM	Portsmouth
OARE						
1790	1840	1700	1790	133493	SAL	Grinshill
OASTLER						
....	....	ALL	ALL	152137	ALL	Name Study
1730	1740	1700	1750	177024	LIN	Fulstow
OATAWAY						
1854	....	1700	1900	167223	DEV	Barnsataple
OATES						
1576	1992	1500	1992	152145	CAM	ALL
1835	1930	....	....	147672	CON	Gweniap
1628	1854	1500	1600	153591	CON	Illogan
1628	1854	1500	1600	153591	CON	Redruth
1720	....	1600	1720	116637	CON	St Ives
1628	1854	1500	1600	153591	CON	St Just
1680	1687	1550	1679	131245	DBY	Old Brampton
....	....	ALL	1700	152145	ENG	ALL
1592	1910	....	....	173975	HAM	Damerham
1592	1910	....	....	173975	HAM	Fordingbridge
1666	1741	....	....	115606	HAM	Vernhams Dean
1820	1890	1820	1870	151106	KIK	Leinster
1576	1992	1500	1992	152145	NFK	ALL
1739	1807	1700	1739	178500	NTT	Greasley
1592	1910	....	....	173975	WIL	Rockbourne
1805	1871	1750	1900	116386	YKS	Bateley
1721	....	1600	....	134589	YKS	Halifax
1805	1871	1750	1900	116386	YKS	Leeds
OATLEY						
1837	1970	1600	1837	175781	ALL	ALL
1800	1992	....	....	115258	ESS	Tolesbury
1786	1992	1600	1786	175781	WIL	Bromham
OATS						
1815	1992	1815	1992	163147	CON	Boscawell
1794	1842	1600	1794	102571	CON	Gwennap
1819	1821	....	....	112887	CON	Redruth
?	?	?	?	162620	CON	St Just
OATS contd.						
1815	1992	1815	1992	163147	CON	St Just
1826	1880	1700	1900	162620	NBL	North Shields
OBALSTON						
1720	1743	ALL	1720	173304	DOR	Cranborne
OBERY						
1812	1970	1750	1812	173649	STS	Eccleshall
OBORN						
....	....	1800	1992	109770	SOM	???
OBREY						
1650	1710	1650	1710	133817	LIN	Gosberton
OCHTERLONY						
1673	1731	....	....	151351	ANS	Arbroath
OCKENDEN						
1650	1992	ALL	1700	141704	SSX	Albourne
OCKEY						
1600	1992	ALL	1600	152153	ENG	ALL
OCKFORD						
1855	1861	1750	1855	146463	GLS	Stroud
OCKLEY						
1500	1600	1400	1600	144657	SRY	Worplesdon
OCOCK						
1815	1880	1815	1880	116955	DOR	???
1804	1839	1804	1992	116955	SOM	Crediton
1807	1893	1807	1900	116955	SOM	Taunton
1807	1893	1807	1900	116955	SOM	West Monkton
OCRAFT						
1850	1900	1500	1850	169986	WOR	Dudley
OCTON						
1850	1960	ALL	ALL	162469	NBL	Central
ODBER						
1600	1992	1500	1992	142018	ALL	ALL
ODD						
1728	1992	1700	1992	174238	ALL	ALL
ODDY						
1767	....	1650	1800	139386	LND	St Martins In The Field
1790	1820	1790	1850	166022	LND	???
ALL	1790	....	....	170798	WRY	Batley
ALL	1790	....	....	170798	WRY	Birstall
1842	....	....	....	170798	WRY	Huddersfield
1790	1860	....	....	170798	WRY	Spenvalley
1680	1800	1680	1800	166022	YKS	Rotherham
1650	1700	1600	1750	166022	YKS	Tickhill
ODEHAM						
1712	1940	....	....	128996	CAM	Thorney
ODELL						
1769	1871	ALL	1769	126721	BDF	South East
....	....	1800	....	137456	BDF	Campton
1846	1900	1826	1850	122351	BDF	Goldington
1841	1960	1600	1841	162671	BDF	Langford
1787	1844	....	1860	171441	HRT	Thundridge
1850	1947	1700	1850	176753	MDX	Enfield
1815	1935	1700	1815	126292	MDX	Lambeth
ODGERS						
1679	1750	....	....	174319	CON	Crowan
ALL	ALL	ALL	ALL	171093	GLA	ALL
ODHAMS						
....	....	ALL	ALL	167193	ALL	Name Study
ODIE						
1750	1965	....	....	137820	SHI	Fetlar
1720	1965	....	....	137820	SHI	Mid Yell
1760	1965	....	....	137820	SHI	North Yell
1758	1965	....	....	137820	SHI	Northmavine
1720	1965	....	....	137820	SHI	South Yell
ODINGSELLS						
1260	1734	1100	1800	100307	MDX	London
1242	1680	1500	1700	100307	NTT	Central
1653	1686	1600	1700	100307	YKS	Sherburn
ODLIN						
?	1699	1677	1824	141798	LIN	???
ODNEE						
1830	1870	1800	1870	166650	KER	Tarbert
OETLING						
....	....	ALL	ALL	111082	ALL	Name Study
OFFELOW						
1730	1850	ALL	ALL	159107	ALL	ALL
OFFER						
1813	1817	....	....	155756	WIL	Badbury
1791	1801	1700	1810	155756	WIL	Bromham
1820	1992	....	....	155756	WIL	Devizes
1817	1839	....	....	155756	WIL	Rowde
....	....	1800	ALL	164615	WIL	Westbury

Surname	Known From	To	Researching From	To	Ref	Cty	Place
OFFERTON							
	1652	1759	1600	1800	109290	YKS	Sheffield
OFFICER							
	1720	1940	1500	1750	106267	KCD	???
	ALL	1992	ALL	ALL	164518	YKS	ALL
OFFIELD							
	1500	1992	1400	1992	134759	ALL	ALL
OFFILER							
	1780	1992	ALL	ALL	159107	ALL	ALL
	1800	1980	ALL	ALL	152161	NTT	Basford
	1770	1980	ALL	ALL	152161	NTT	Lenton
OFFLEY							
	....	....	ALL	ALL	159107	ALL	Name Study
	1500	1992	ALL	ALL	159107	ALL	ALL
	1761	1802	....	1841	137405	CAM	Over
	1780	1992	ALL	ALL	152161	DBY	Shirley
	1500	1992	ALL	ALL	152161	HUN	ALL
	1770	1992	ALL	ALL	152161	LND	Covent Garden
	1870	1992	ALL	ALL	152161	SRY	Southwark
	1730	1992	ALL	ALL	152161	STS	Colwich
	1440	1900	ALL	ALL	152161	STS	Madeley
	1870	1988	ALL	ALL	152161	WIL	Swindon
OFFORD							
	1828	....	....	....	174750	MDX	Islington
OFIELD							
	1500	1992	1400	1992	134759	ALL	ALL
OFSPRING							
	1600	1659	1659	1992	175412	LND	London Wall
OGDEN							
	1845	1900	1800	1920	108510	CHS	Stalybridge
	1640	1790	1550	1641	102830	DBY	Matlock
	1850	1870	1850	1880	166022	KEN	Orpington
	1836	....	1836	....	168289	LAN	Calyton
	1830	1850	1800	1850	166022	LAN	Manchester
	1816	1816	1816	1826	159492	LAN	Oldham
	1864	1905	1836	1905	168289	LAN	Wigan
	1709	1738	1670	1709	149039	NTH	Central
	1770	1920	1770	1920	107522	WRY	Todmorden
	1812	1848	1800	1890	108510	YKS	Saddleworth
	1833	1948	1800	1833	136824	YKS	Sheffield
OGG							
	....	....	1600	1790	161543	ABD	Kennethnont
	1790	1992	1600	1992	161543	BAN	Portsoy
OGILVIE							
	1796	1814	1700	1796	118427	ABD	Cortachy
OGILVY							
	1790	1790	....	....	159883	ANS	Dundee
	....	....	1890	1899	174963	???	Bristol
OGLE							
	1880	1992	ALL	ALL	135224	CHS	ALL
	1880	1992	ALL	ALL	135224	IRL	???
OGLEBY							
	1799	1855	1700	1850	100439	DUR	Durham St Nicholls
OGLONBY							
	1748	1748	1700	1750	176451	CMA	Kirby Stephen
OGRAM							
	1803	1850	1750	1803	118486	ERY	Millington
OKE							
	1860	1900	1850	1890	164399	DEV	Welcombe
OKEFORD							
	1680	1680	1750	1834	146463	WIL	Headington
OKELL							
	1842	1842	1842	1842	143286	LAN	Liverpool
OKEOVER							
	1900	1992	1000	1992	168467	STS	Okeover
OKES							
	1730	1818	....	....	132837	CAM	Cambridge
OKINES							
	1820	1950	ALL	ALL	173657	LND	ALL
OKINS							
	1820	1830	1750	1850	171484	CAM	Caxton
OLAND							
	1796	....	1796	1900	106410	SOM	Wellington
OLD							
	1820	....	....	1820	164011	BRK	Aston Tirrold
	1630	1716	1500	1800	153354	CON	Constantine
	1726	1894	ALL	1900	111600	DOR	Piddlehinton
	1830	1850	1850	1992	127787	DOR	Piddletrenthide
	1807	....	....	1807	164011	NTH	Northampton
	1645	1850	1645	1850	148156	NTH	Wootton
OLDACRE							
	1825	1875	....	....	106798	LND	Poplar
OLDBURY							
	1800	1900	1800	1900	114197	STS	Wednesbury

Surname	Known From	To	Researching From	To	Ref	Cty	Place
OLDCORN							
	1800	1840	....	....	129038	CUL	South
	1800	1900	ALL	1800	152188	WES	South
OLDEN							
	ALL	1700	1700	1992	152226	ALL	ALL
OLDERSHAW							
	1840	1880	1750	1800	150797	DBY	South
	1840	1880	1750	1800	150797	DBY	Derby
	1750	1810	1810	1860	177199	KEN	Rochester
	1798	1900	1600	1900	124834	NTT	East Leake
OLDFIELD							
	1860	1910	1850	1930	125423	BRK	Reading
	1690	1920	1600	1860	125423	CAM	Whittlesey
	1785	1992	1700	1785	152196	CMA	Whiteheaven
	1820	1992	1700	1900	142778	CWD	Dyffryn Ial
	....	....	1800	1920	176400	DBY	Chesterfield
	1826	1870	1700	1826	140589	EYK	Pocklington
	1773	1834	1650	1773	164178	LAN	East
	1800	1934	1800	1924	102806	LND	Hackney
	1800	1934	1800	1924	102806	LND	Kennington
	1578	1752	....	....	117404	STS	Penkridge
	1773	1834	1650	1773	164178	YKS	West
OLDHAM							
	1732	1940	....	....	128996	CAM	Thorney
	1850	1956	1700	1850	172049	CHS	Denton
	1826	1881	1700	1826	176907	CHS	Hyde
	1670	1992	....	....	152218	CHS	???
	1824	1881	1834	1992	142999	CON	Bodmin
	1791	1992	1700	1790	142999	CON	Padstow
	1756	1850	1756	1850	176958	GLS	Bristol
	1850	1956	1700	1850	172049	LAN	Ashton Under Lyne
	....	....	1800	1920	118966	LAN	Bolton
	1700	1756	1600	1800	176958	LAN	Bolton
	1884	1939	1855	1884	176907	LAN	Darwen
	1830	1992	1700	1830	131989	LAN	???
	1670	1992	....	....	152218	LAN	???
	1796	1992	1700	1796	119261	LEI	Leicester
	1850	1940	1700	1850	155101	NTH	Wakerley
	1815	1971	1600	1815	172022	WAR	Coventry
	1865	1900	1900	1992	142999	WLS	Cardiff
	1871	1881	1871	1881	159018	YKS	Sheffield
	....	....	?	?	178349	???	Birmingham
OLDING							
	ALL	1700	1700	1992	152226	ALL	ALL
	1764	1849	ALL	1764	175994	HAM	Southampton
	1905	1992	....	....	149551	MON	Abertillery
	....	....	1800	1905	149551	SOM	From
OLDRIDGE							
	1800	1880	1600	1800	154172	YKS	Church Fenton
OLDRING							
	1750	1850	1750	1850	133817	SFK	Beccles
OLDROYD							
	....	....	1700	1992	114596	LAN	Dewsbury
	1700	1800	....	....	169129	LIN	Wolds
	1800	1950	....	....	169129	NFK	West
	1720	1830	....	....	145688	YKS	Dewsbury
	1825	1900	1750	1850	106925	YKS	???
	....	....	....	....	172324	YKS	???
OLFE							
	ALL	ALL	ALL	ALL	171964	ALL	ALL
OLFORD							
	1880	1900	....	....	125962	HAM	Portsmouth
OLGAN							
	....	....	1850	1900	147613	STS	Sedgley
OLIPHANT							
	1727	1746	....	....	138401	CUL	Hesket In The Forest
	1550	1680	1500	1680	154881	SCT	ALL
OLIVE							
	....	....	ALL	ALL	152285	CON	ALL
	1775	1775	ALL	1775	122017	CON	Illogan
	1701	1702	1100	1702	117749	CON	St Martin In Meneage
	1735	1830	1670	1735	173703	GLS	Tewkesbury
	1900	1910	ALL	1992	128260	HAM	Soton
	1832	1900	1500	1992	117900	LAN	Radcliffe
	1767	1784	1700	1850	179078	SFK	Sudbury
OLIVER							
	....	....	ALL	ALL	115088	ALL	Name Study
	1900	1980	1600	1800	152269	BDF	ALL
	1732	1835	1732	1835	121681	BDF	Dunstable
	1798	1992	....	....	117374	BRK	Newbury
	1796	1820	1750	1850	108510	BRK	Reading
	1798	1992	....	....	117374	BRK	Reading

Known From	To	Researching From	To	Ref	Cty	Place
OLIVER contd.						
1722	1860	....	1722	152242	CON	West
1766	1880	1700	1800	163562	CON	Bodmin
1700	....	?	?	136999	CON	Breage
1820	1836	1700	1900	102520	CON	Falmouth
1844	1844	1100	1844	117749	CON	Helston
1858	....	1850	1992	162868	CON	Helston
1780	1870	1780	1870	152250	CON	St Blazey
1702	....	1710	1750	178845	CON	Stithians
1800	1860	1800	1900	178799	CON	Truro
1788	....	1700	1800	138185	DBY	Dore
1788	....	1700	1800	138185	DBY	Dronfield
1784	1850	1700	1784	139815	DEV	Bradford
1814	1814	1780	....	126403	DEV	Devonport
1772	1875	1600	1875	130125	DFS	Westerkirk
1630	1650	1550	1630	156795	DOR	East
1729	1900	1538	1900	118893	DUR	Chilton
1729	1900	1538	1900	118893	DUR	Ferryhill
1840	1950	1700	1950	145319	DUR	Gateshead
1729	1900	1538	1900	118893	DUR	Merrington
1729	1900	1538	1900	118893	DUR	Middlestone Moore
....	1841	ALL	1850	127000	ELN	Garvald
1666	1730	....	1666	142409	ENG	Midlands
1870	....	1850	1992	162868	GLA	Pontypridd
1860	1930	1850	1930	109436	GNT	Wattsville
1770	1850	ALL	1800	141305	HAM	The Candovers
1695	1992	1500	1695	152269	HRT	ALL
1768	1809	1700	1768	115460	HRT	Hexton
1850	1880	....	....	121185	KEN	ALL
1690	1825	ALL	1690	131059	KEN	Ash By Ridley
1836	1900	....	....	164631	KEN	Bromley
1800	1900	....	....	131059	KEN	Chatham
1865	1901	1865	1992	122807	KEN	Sheerness
....	1700	....	1700	177695	LEI	Bringhurst
1829	1921	1700	1992	126349	LIN	Long Sutton
1800	1830	1700	1800	121339	LIN	Skirbeck
1880	1992	1820	1992	108510	LND	Camberwell
1860	1992	....	....	152242	LND	???
1863	1992	1863	....	106895	MDX	Bow
1820	1840	1750	1850	108510	MDX	Hanwell
1863	1992	1863	....	106895	MDX	Poplar
1800	1830	1690	1830	158313	MOG	Carrickmacross
....	....	1740	1992	130826	NBL	Newcastle
1840	1950	1700	1950	145319	NBL	Newcastle
1765	1774	1765	1774	130877	NBL	St John Lee
1764	1764	1760	1784	130877	NBL	Wooler
1830	1850	1750	1850	121886	NTT	Ruddington
1900	1992	ALL	ALL	163368	NTT	Ruddington
1810	1880	1800	1992	133450	OXF	Oxford
1833	1950	1800	ALL	145319	ROX	Jedburgh
1775	....	....	1775	175552	ROX	Jedburgh
1880	1985	1800	1880	173231	SAL	Madeley
....	....	....	?	132195	SOM	West
?	?	?	?	165735	SOM	Bristol
....	....	ALL	1809	164631	SSX	Mayfield
1816	....	ALL	ALL	138533	STS	Rolleston
....	....	1700	1850	101273	WIL	Calne
1700	1870	1600	1900	138878	WOR	Pmbersley
1742	....	....	1760	160873	WOR	Rock
1734	1768	1650	1750	163562	YKS	Bridlington
1800	1921	1800	1921	158305	YKS	Hull
1685	1747	ALL	1750	152838	YKS	Skirpenbeck
1643	1797	1747	....	158305	YKS	Skirpenbeck
....	1792	1792	....	158305	YKS	Swanland
1849	1936	1849	1936	158305	YKS	Swinton
OLIVER-BELLASSIS						
1840	1992	1840	1992	133450	BRK	Boxford
OLIVERSON						
1712	1851	1700	1851	157678	LAN	Halsall
OLIVEY						
....	....	ALL	ALL	152285	ALL	Name Study
....	....	ALL	ALL	152285	ALL	ALL
OLLARD						
1850	1880	....	1850	135089	HAM	Aldershot
1850	1880	....	1850	135089	LND	???
OLLASON						
1750	1965	....	....	137820	SHI	Fetlar
1720	1965	....	....	137820	SHI	Mid Yell
1760	1965	....	....	137820	SHI	North Yell
1758	1965	....	....	137820	SHI	Northmavine
1720	1965	....	....	137820	SHI	South Yell
OLLAY						
1762	1855	1600	1875	148482	OKI	Rendall
OLLERTON						
1836	1992	1700	1877	178233	LAN	Blackrod
OLLEVEANT						
1843	1992	1750	1843	152293	YKS	Maltby
OLLEY						
1848	1871	1500	1900	157538	MDX	Hackney
....	....	1750	1840	143308	NFK	North
1759	1849	....	1759	168521	NFK	Great Snoring
1871	1932	1860	1900	157538	SRY	Richmond
OLLIER						
1890	1992	1700	1890	105007	CHS	Crewe
1781	1937	1750	1790	173649	CHS	Haslington
1890	1992	1700	1890	105007	CHS	Nantwich
OLLIFFE						
....	1920	....	....	159999	LND	Fulham
....	1930	....	....	159999	YKS	???
OLLIS						
1720	1944	1700	1720	149373	SOM	Keynsham
OLLIVE						
1841	1891	ALL	ALL	154806	CHS	Birkenhead
OLMSTEAD						
....	....	ALL	ALL	152307	ALL	Name Study
OLNER						
....	....	1860	1900	166456	WAR	Polesworth
OLNEY						
1800	1850	1850	1890	154296	ALL	ALL
....	1915	1700	1920	164909	MDX	Southall
OLORENSHAW						
1817	1920	1700	1817	105562	WAR	Coventry
1817	1920	1700	1817	105562	WAR	Rugby
OLSON						
1881	1992	1800	1880	126535	MDX	Stepney
OLVER						
1670	1800	ALL	1900	168718	CON	South East
1780	1800	1700	1780	133493	CON	Looe
1570	1830	1350	1570	152323	CON	Ludgvan
1800	1960	1800	1960	152323	LND	Marylebone
OLVERSON						
1700	1812	1700	1812	147575	KEN	Sandwich
OLVESON						
1700	1812	1700	1812	147575	KEN	Sandwich
OMAN						
1797	1880	....	....	152331	CAI	Latheron
1880	1992	....	....	152331	ROC	Easter Ross
1790	....	....	....	126497	SCT	???
OMAND						
1750	1965	....	....	137820	SHI	Fetlar
1720	1965	....	....	137820	SHI	Mid Yell
1760	1965	....	....	137820	SHI	North Yell
1758	1965	....	....	137820	SHI	Northmavine
1720	1965	....	....	137820	SHI	South Yell
OMBLER						
1715	1812	1600	1715	175218	EYK	Leven
OMER						
1869	1876	1876	1950	178284	KEN	Sandwich
OMEROD						
....	....	1700	1992	138657	EYK	Hull
ONELY						
....	....	1700	....	137456	BDF	Carlton
ONG						
1755	1813	....	....	101028	ESS	Hatfield Peverel
ONGLEY						
1780	1850	1780	1850	130400	KEN	Boxley
1670	1960	ALL	ALL	171832	KEN	West Peckham
ONION						
....	....	ALL	ALL	152358	ALL	Name Study
1841	1851	1800	1899	123013	GLS	Lechlade
1750	1800	1700	1750	103446	KEN	Goudhurst
....	....	1800	1899	123013	OXF	Harwick
ONIONE						
1860	1992	ALL	ALL	123013	GLS	Cheltenham
ONIONS						
1781	1788	1770	1820	169323	SAL	Bridgnorth
1750	1815	....	....	129747	SAL	Dawley Magna
1763	1773	1720	1820	169323	SAL	Dawley Magna
1850	1992	ALL	1850	102407	SAL	Wellington
1700	1750	....	....	129747	SAL	Wellington
1817	1840	1780	1870	169323	STS	Bilston
1817	1879	1750	1880	133280	STS	Tipton
1817	1879	1750	1880	133280	STS	Wolverhampton
ONN						
1780	1860	1780	1860	155764	LIN	Louth
ONSLOW						
1231	1920	....	....	100536	ALL	???

Known From	To	Researching From	To	Ref	Cty	Place
ONSLOW contd.						
1822	1865	....	....	135437	CHS	Chester
1871	1871	....	....	135437	ESS	E Tilbury
1881	1885	....	....	135437	KEN	Plumstead
1848	1848	....	....	135437	LAN	Liverpool
1861	1861	....	....	135437	MDX	Ealing
1885	1885	....	....	135437	MDX	Hoxton
1895	1895	....	....	135437	MDX	Islington
1892	1892	....	....	135437	MDX	Poplar
1730	....	....	1870	120391	SAL	Ditton Priors
1894	1894	....	....	135437	SRY	Kingston On Thames
1876	1876	....	....	135437	SRY	Lambeth
1877	1877	....	....	135437	SRY	Stockwell
1895	1895	....	....	135437	SSX	Brighton
ONWIN						
1780	1880	1700	1900	147958	ESS	South West
OPENSHAW						
1800	1992	1100	1800	152366	LAN	ALL
?	?	?	?	176842	LAN	Bolton
1814	1960	1700	1800	138304	LAN	Manchester
OPIE						
1843	1889	1889	1992	162973	CON	Liskeard
1843	1860	1860	....	162973	CON	St Cleer
1840	1900	1750	1850	158593	CON	St Stithians
1831	1875	1700	1800	131148	CON	Stithians
1850	1992	1600	1850	123242	CON	Wendron
1820	....	1800	1850	169625	CON	???
OPPEN						
1837	1914	1800	1960	126586	MDX	London
OPPERMANN						
1724	1992	....	....	171360	LND	ALL
ORAM						
1810	1970	1750	1970	130087	DOR	Shaftesbury
1855	1900	1850	1930	156965	LND	Grays Inn
1810	1970	1750	1970	130087	LND	Shaftesbury
1870	1954	....	1870	152242	LND	Wandsworth
1830	1992	1700	1830	148059	STS	ALL
1802	....	....	....	122505	STS	Wolstanton
1730	1790	1500	1790	109274	WIL	Shalbourne
ORANGE						
1500	1900	1850	1992	119105	JSY	ALL
1795	1839	1750	1820	135550	YKS	West Riding
ORANSE						
1800	1825	1750	1825	123102	YKS	Rotherham
ORBELL						
....	....	ALL	ALL	152374	ALL	Name Study
1515	1693	....	....	100536	ESS	???
ORBY						
1650	1724	....	....	167037	LIN	Croyland
ORCHARD						
1637	1654	1600	1637	116637	CON	Poughill
1742	1756	1700	1742	165158	DEV	Beer
1746	1800	ALL	ALL	165158	DEV	Brancombe
1866	....	....	....	164356	DOR	Wareham
1831	1917	1800	1831	152943	GLS	Tebury
1841	?	....	....	122491	GLS	Wooten Under Edge
1712	1881	ALL	1712	157791	WIL	Calne
ORD						
1804	1837	1760	1804	103322	DUR	Aycliffe
1700	....	1700	1900	116920	DUR	???
1819	1992	1800	1819	111201	LAN	Liverpool
ORDERS						
....	....	ALL	ALL	152382	ALL	Name Study
ORE						
1829	1856	1829	1992	105147	SAL	???
OREILLY						
1836	....	1700	1992	166073	IRL	Dublin
ORFORD						
ALL	ALL	....	....	164143	???	East Anglia
ORGAN						
1600	1900	1600	1900	160814	CON	Mevagissey
1725	?	1700	1750	104655	CON	St Austell
1734	?	1700	1750	104655	CON	St Ewe
1810	1943	1750	1890	126551	GLS	North Nibley
1660	1820	1820	....	145858	GLS	North Nibley
1510	1992	1450	1510	170194	GLS	North Nibley
1920	1934	1840	1920	177040	GLS	Wootton Under Edge
1814	1870	1870	....	145858	SOM	Watchet
1818	1861	1881	1930	144495	SRY	Southwark
ORGILL						
1798	1920	....	....	173827	LEI	Measham
ORIEL						
1700	1973	ALL	ALL	172294	ALL	ALL
ORIVER						
1654	1654	1600	1654	155276	SFK	Felixstowe
ORKEY						
1730	1800	1600	1730	164577	BEW	Ayton
ORKNEY						
....	....	1800	1825	124796	CON	Torpoint
ORMAN						
1790	1900	1700	1900	119040	DOR	Verwood
ORMANDY						
1802	1824	1800	1850	129798	CMA	Drigg
ORME						
1612	1840	1840	1992	114472	CHS	Macclesfield
1600	1700	1500	1700	152404	CHS	Macclesfield
1600	1850	1600	1850	152404	CHS	Stockport
ORMEROD						
....	....	ALL	ALL	152412	ALL	Name Study
1740	1770	1700	1740	122904	LAN	Burnley
1290	1992	1290	1992	152412	LAN	Burnley
1786	....	....	....	142859	LAN	Haslingden
1882	1992	1700	1882	117730	LND	ALL
1810	1845	1810	1850	107522	WRY	Todmorden
ORMISTON						
1831	1950	1800	1900	133248	ALL	ALL
1871	1881	1800	1881	133248	PEM	Pembroke Dock
1831	1874	1803	1880	133248	SSX	Horsted Keynes
ORMOND						
1850	1855	ALL	1992	136077	LAN	ALL
1879	1921	1813	1940	169552	LAN	Bolton Le Sands
1751	1890	1741	1900	169552	LAN	Poulton Le Fylde
ORMONDROYD						
1792	....	....	....	146013	YKS	Bradford
ORMROD						
1860	....	1840	1900	117145	LAN	Bolton
1700	1860	1600	1800	152404	LAN	Eccles
1860	1960	1760	1860	109479	LAN	Oldham
ORMSTON						
1890	....	....	....	152420	NBL	Newcastle
ORR						
1890	1980	1700	1890	108413	ANT	Ballymena
1750	1840	1750	1900	146536	AYR	Kilbirnie
....	....	....	1992	137014	DNB	Helensburgh
1842	1843	....	....	127140	DNB	Row
1810	1866	1750	1900	159964	MLN	ALL
....	....	1600	1900	137014	SCT	Skye
ORRAM						
1822	....	....	....	122505	STS	Newcastle
ORRELL						
1850	1960	1840	1960	152447	LAN	Atherton
1100	1600	1100	1992	152447	LAN	Orrell
1400	1992	1200	1992	152447	LAN	Turton
ORRIDGE						
....	....	ALL	ALL	152455	ALL	Name Study
....	....	ALL	ALL	152455	ALL	ALL
ORRIEL						
1746	1800	1600	1755	101575	YKS	Leeds
ORRIS						
1780	1870	1750	1850	103055	NFK	Hindringham
ORTON						
1750	1820	....	....	165999	LEI	Leicester
1800	1880	1700	1800	152463	LEI	Loughborough
1830	1951	1750	1830	146609	LEI	North Kilworth
....	....	1800	1992	131768	NFK	Great Yarmouth
1700	1880	1600	1700	152471	WAR	Bulkington
....	....	1590	1850	115142	WAR	Mancetter
1700	1880	1600	1700	152471	WAR	Nuneaton
ORVIS						
1628	1992	1500	1628	154288	SFK	ALL
ORYS						
1913	1992	1300	1913	152501	ALL	ALL
OSBALDESTON						
1033	1992	1033	1992	108138	ALL	ALL
1800	1850	1750	1800	135771	CHS	North East
OSBALDESTONE						
1033	1992	1033	1992	108138	ALL	ALL
OSBAND						
1711	1833	ALL	1711	122106	SOM	Merriott
OSBORN						
....	....	1500	1992	152528	ALL	ALL
1726	1869	1650	1726	115460	BDF	Kensworth
1873	1881	1870	1920	137782	CUL	South
1670	1992	1600	1670	143170	DEV	Black Torrington
1819	....	....	....	151548	DEV	Broadhempston
1670	1992	1600	1670	143170	DEV	Crediton
1819	1871	ALL	ALL	137782	DEV	South Tawton

Known From	To	Researching From	To	Ref	Cty	Place
OSBORN contd.						
1774	1992	1650	1992	176044	ESS	Havering
1881	1933	ALL	ALL	130664	ESS	Plaistow
1690	1992	1650	1992	152528	GLS	Bitton
1690	1992	1650	1992	152528	GLS	Siston
1767	1767	....	....	151750	HRT	Berkhampstead
1726	1869	1650	1726	115460	HRT	Kensworth
1810	1920	1700	1850	112038	LIN	???
1840	1850	....	1840	135089	LND	Shoreditch
1810	1992	1580	1810	175870	NFK	Upwell
1800	1900	ALL	1839	101281	NTH	Towcester
1826	1931	ALL	ALL	176052	NTH	Weston
1792	1835	1650	1792	165298	SFK	Kersey
1785	1857	ALL	1785	129283	SFK	Oulton
....	....	1770	1830	148113	SRY	Guildford
1500	1880	1500	1900	152536	SSX	Mid
1797	1872	1700	1797	166707	WAR	Grandborough Woolscott
OSBORNE						
1881	1957	ALL	ALL	161411	ALL	ALL
1782	1820	1782	1820	170267	CON	Fowey
1782	1820	1782	1820	170267	CON	Mevagissey
1780	1800	1760	1850	168580	CON	St Enoder
1725	1780	1700	1800	170267	CON	St Ewe
1834	....	1700	1900	102881	CUL	Holm Cultram
....	....	1600	1800	179477	DEV	South
1798	1798	1750	1825	174289	DOR	Kinson
1774	1992	1650	1992	176044	ESS	Havering
1830	1900	1750	1830	132268	ESS	Rickling
1660	1920	ALL	1660	141224	GLS	South
1667	1798	....	....	165999	GLS	Almondsbury
1800	1860	ALL	ALL	128449	GLS	Bristol
1667	1798	....	....	165999	GLS	Frampton Cottrell
1825	1900	1800	1830	174289	HAM	Hodenhurst
1700	1743	1600	1700	139084	KEN	Shipbourne
1839	1900	1700	1900	167673	LKS	Girvan
1840	1850	....	1840	135089	LND	Shoreditch
1813	1881	1700	1813	165859	LND	Shoreditch
1855	1875	ALL	1855	166847	LND	Stepney
1885	1992	1700	1885	130648	MDX	London
....	....	1750	1900	143502	NTT	Nottingham
1779	1872	....	....	101028	SFK	Barrow
1810	1972	1700	1810	164860	SFK	Easton
1820	1885	1700	1820	130648	SOM	Bath
1869	1881	1850	1881	165824	SOM	Bath
1711	1833	ALL	1711	122106	SOM	Merriott
1870	1950	1870	1950	152536	SRY	Croydon
1870	1950	1870	1950	152536	SRY	Godstone
1820	1839	1700	1820	164909	STS	West Bromwich
1500	1900	1500	1900	170216	WIL	ALL
OSBOURN						
1800	1820	1750	1860	111325	ESS	Elmstead
OSBOURNE						
1840	....	1820	1845	176583	LIN	???
1600	1950	1950	1992	129763	NTH	West
1708	1815	1650	1708	174807	SSX	Newtimber
OSCROFT						
1805	1900	1750	1805	169749	DBY	Ashfield
1805	1900	1750	1805	169749	NTT	Kirkby
OSEMAN						
1800	1850	1750	1850	142395	HRT	Bromyard
OSENTON						
1844	1992	1700	1844	103640	KEN	Cliffe At Hoo
1844	1992	1700	1844	103640	KEN	North Aylesford
OSGARBY						
1750	1992	1650	1750	102342	LIN	Searby Cwm Dwmby
OSGODBY						
1600	1930	1300	1600	145408	LIN	North
OSGOOD						
1595	1770	1590	1650	165417	HAM	Cherewell
1760	....	....	....	168092	HAM	Froxfield
1820	1900	1800	1992	133450	LND	Paddington
OSGOODBY						
?	?	?	?	163430	LIN	???
OSHEA						
1870	1900	1850	1900	111732	LAN	Manchester
1920	1992	....	....	111732	SYK	Sheffield
....	....	1800	1880	111732	WAR	Birmingham
OSLAND						
1791	1900	1665	1934	132845	MDX	London
OSLER						
1780	1850	1600	1850	146730	CON	Falmouth
OSMAN						
1756	1831	1700	1756	127116	HAM	Fawley
OSMAN contd.						
1823	1980	1700	1823	145459	HAM	Fawley
1773	1773	1750	1773	107573	HAM	Monk Sherborne
1750	1802	1782	1802	104817	HAM	Soberton
1763	1809	ALL	ALL	169730	HAM	Weston Patrick
1880	....	....	....	133922	HAM	???
1915	1992	1600	1992	138746	HRT	ALL
OSMOND						
ALL	ALL	ALL	ALL	114502	DEV	ALL
1758	1960	1600	1758	158496	DEV	Exeter
1837	....	ALL	ALL	172057	ESS	???
1871	1900	1650	1871	132039	LND	Central
1837	....	ALL	ALL	172057	LND	???
ALL	ALL	ALL	ALL	114502	SOM	ALL
1810	1851	?	1810	121665	SOM	Wellington
1770	1780	1750	1770	155217	SSX	Findon
ALL	ALL	ALL	ALL	114502	WIL	ALL
OSWALD						
....	....	ALL	ALL	152587	ALL	Name Study
?	?	ALL	ALL	174432	DUR	Witton Gilbert
1871	....	....	....	125326	LND	Marylebone
1845	....	....	....	125326	SSX	Ifield
1800	....	1780	1800	146536	STI	Larbert
OSWELL						
1778	1778	1700	1780	176451	SAL	Shrewsbury
OSWIN						
1608	1750	ALL	ALL	141615	LEI	Kibworth
1895	1972	1800	1895	169803	LEI	???
OTHAM						
1730	1750	1700	1800	171158	ESS	Willingale
OTHEN						
....	....	ALL	ALL	124591	ALL	Name Study
1622	1729	ALL	1622	169730	HAM	Weston Patrick
OTLEY						
1751	1875	1500	1900	159956	SFK	Ousden
OTT						
1860	1880	....	1880	153982	SRY	Southwark
OTTAWAY						
1870	....	ALL	1992	134376	KEN	Hollingbourne
1800	1900	1800	1900	164313	KEN	Maidstone
1756	1860	1700	1860	164313	KEN	Pluckly
OTTER						
1760	1918	1700	1850	163473	DOR	Broadway
1825	1980	1650	1900	123293	LIN	ALL
1825	1980	1650	1900	123293	NTT	ALL
OTTERY						
1889	1974	1800	1889	132489	SOM	Bristol
1889	1974	1800	1889	132489	SOM	Langford
OTTEWELL						
1840	1910	ALL	ALL	175757	DBY	Belper
OTTEY						
....	1819	1740	1819	157643	LIN	Stamford
OTTIWELL						
1845	1920	1845	1992	151254	LAN	Tyldesley
1820	1845	1600	1830	151254	SFK	Hadleigh
OTTO						
1700	1800	....	1770	108375	MDX	City
OTTON						
1780	1880	1730	1992	135429	DEV	Exeter
1750	1850	1750	1992	135429	SOM	Pitminster
OTTY						
1714	1992	1714	1992	143588	WYK	Bradford
1714	1992	1714	1992	143588	WYK	Wakefield
OTWAY						
1814	1874	....	....	173932	SRY	Ashtead
1835	1992	1700	1835	105201	SSX	Petworth
OUGH						
1760	1992	1700	1760	140163	CON	Callington
1760	1992	1700	1760	140163	CON	Liskeard
1850	1992	....	....	140163	DEV	Plymouth
OUGHTON						
1750	1820	....	....	165999	LEI	Leicester
1790	1811	....	....	121355	LND	Stepney
1790	1811	....	....	121355	LND	Stratford
OUGHTRED						
1800	1867	ALL	ALL	141313	DUR	ALL
OULD						
1800	1992	ALL	ALL	111961	CON	Falmouth
1846	1846	1100	1846	117749	CON	Helston
1802	....	....	....	120804	LEI	Claybrooke
1802	....	....	....	120804	LEI	Ullesthorpe
OULSNAM						
....	....	ALL	....	148180	STS	North
1860	1890	1700	1992	167592	STS	Burlsem

Known From	To	Researching From	To	Ref	Cty	Place
OULTON						
....	....	ALL	ALL	137138	ALL	ALL
....	....	ALL	ALL	137138	KEN	ALL
....	....	ALL	ALL	137138	LND	ALL
....	....	ALL	ALL	137138	SRY	ALL
OUSEY						
....	....	ALL	ALL	124788	ALL	Name Study
1600	1992	1570	1992	124788	LAN	Golbourne
OUSLEY						
1778	....	1750	1850	169625	SOM	Chard
1778	....	1750	1850	169625	SOM	Thurlbear
OUSTABY						
1482	1640	....	....	102547	YKS	Etton
OUTHART						
1742	1784	1650	1900	152617	YKS	Brompton By Sauldon
OUTHET						
....	....	ALL	ALL	152617	ALL	Name Study
1815	1839	1650	1815	152617	YKS	Rillington
OUTHWAITE						
1816	1900	1700	1800	162248	NRY	Hornby
1750	1770	1538	1820	118893	NRY	???
1671	....	1600	....	134589	YKS	Barwick In Elmet
OUTRAM						
1776	1960	ALL	ALL	131784	ALL	ALL
1400	1992	1400	1992	160083	ALL	ALL
....	....	1600	1800	116173	DBY	Barlow
....	....	1600	1800	116173	DBY	Dronfield
1789	1948	ALL	1948	118990	ESS	ALL
1864	1881	ALL	ALL	175005	KEN	Sevenoaks
1871	1881	ALL	ALL	175005	KEN	Tenterden
1748	1907	1600	1900	116173	NTT	???
1734	1744	ALL	ALL	175005	SRY	Chelsham
1776	1794	ALL	ALL	175005	SRY	Warlingham
....	....	1600	1800	116173	YKS	South
1759	1932	1730	1880	146897	YKS	Penistone
OUTRED						
1788	1849	1650	1788	152617	KEN	Milton By Gravesend
1697	1725	1650	1697	152617	KEN	Norton Kibby
1692	1828	1656	1697	152617	YKS	Filey
OUTWAITE						
1800	1992	1600	1800	175382	YKS	Ripon
OVAL						
1840	1880	1780	1880	120308	SRY	Croydon
OVENDEN						
1750	1960	ALL	ALL	126144	KEN	???
1750	1960	ALL	ALL	126144	LND	???
1750	1960	ALL	ALL	126144	SRY	???
1800	1992	1750	1800	100994	SSX	Fletching
1750	1960	ALL	ALL	126144	SSX	???
OVER						
1650	1800	1650	1800	152404	HAM	Owlesbury
1878	....	1850	1878	140201	MDX	London
1717	1741	1600	1716	131245	WAR	Leamington Hastings
OVERALL						
1783	1917	1600	1783	165697	CAM	Manea
1827	1992	1700	1827	130257	ESS	Maldon
OVERD						
1900	1950	1850	1900	155802	DEV	Plymouth
OVERELL						
1760	1809	1650	1760	103896	ESS	Kelvedon
OVEREND						
1867	1900	1800	1900	138304	LAN	Preston
ALL	ALL	ALL	ALL	111066	WRY	ALL
1839	1891	ALL	ALL	112267	YKS	Farsley
OVERFIELD						
1800	1800	1700	1800	140589	EYK	Melbourne
1825	1825	1825	1830	140589	EYK	Wintringham
OVERILL						
1750	1800	1750	1800	158658	ESS	Great Saling
1800	1860	1790	1880	158658	ESS	Saffron Waldon
1871	1945	1860	1950	158658	NFK	Great Yarmouth
OVERIN						
1620	1800	....	....	133361	YKS	ALL
1790	1920	....	....	133361	YKS	Addingham
OVERINGTON						
....	....	ALL	ALL	152625	ALL	Name Study
1800	1849	1750	1850	110914	LAN	Liverpool
1894	1920	....	....	134430	SSX	Chichester
OVERNELL						
1820	1907	1800	1900	110604	MDX	Enfield
OVERS						
1866	1992	1800	1900	173428	MDX	Hackney
OVERSBY						
1845	1912	1840	....	144827	LAN	Lancaster
OVERSBY contd.						
1845	1912	1840	....	144827	LAN	Slyne
OVERTON						
?	?	ALL	ALL	138037	EYK	Easington
1710	....	1710	....	113875	LIN	Ruskington
1735	....	....	1735	101761	LIN	Stenigot
1788	1992	....	1788	101761	LIN	Wainfleet
1803	1830	1700	1900	177873	LIN	Wrangle
....	....	ALL	ALL	138037	LND	City
1800	1890	....	1800	136212	NFK	Snettisham
1700	1725	1650	1700	156140	STS	Lichfield
1600	1800	....	....	100420	WAR	Meriden
OVINGTON						
....	....	ALL	ALL	147052	ALL	Name Study
OWEN						
1853	1889	1853	1890	146404	AGY	Amlwch
1787	1870	1787	1870	104027	AGY	Penbynydd
1806	1842	1800	1847	159786	AGY	Pentraeth
1810	1860	1791	1809	138401	CAE	Gyffin
1788	1861	1791	1809	138401	CAE	Llangelenyn
1780	....	1700	....	118591	CAE	Llanor
1867	1992	....	....	138401	CAE	Penmachno
1810	1860	1791	1809	138401	CAE	Roewen
1760	1881	ALL	1759	158631	CAE	Tyddynysguborif
1841	1900	ALL	ALL	149489	CHS	Macclesfield
1878	1908	?	?	164755	CMA	Millom
1800	1880	1700	1800	168351	CON	Penzance
....	....	1800	1900	152684	DBY	Buxton
1736	1756	....	....	138401	DEN	Llangernyw
....	....	1800	1860	158259	DEN	Llangollen
1888	1888	1850	1900	136042	DEV	Exeter
1880	1930	1800	1880	142042	DFD	Aberystwyth
1840	1900	1700	1840	174572	DFD	Llanelli
1840	1992	1840	1992	133450	DOR	???
1774	1791	....	....	138401	FLN	St Asaph
1923	1992	1800	1923	128732	GLA	Cardiff
1835	1927	1800	1930	159743	GLA	Cardiff
1900	....	1700	1900	144150	GLA	Cefn Vaynor
1797	....	1797	ALL	175587	GLA	Llandeilo-Talybont
1920	....	1700	1920	144150	GLA	Merthyr Tydfil
1835	1927	1800	1930	159743	GLA	Penarth
1810	1992	1600	1810	152633	GYN	Croesor
1810	1992	1600	1810	152633	GYN	Dolwyddelan
1807	1992	1700	1899	110701	GYN	Llanellgo Llandidona
1812	1870	1700	1812	109061	KEN	Medway
1829	1992	1750	1829	176257	LAN	Liverpool
1865	....	1750	1865	178381	LAN	Salford
1716	1900	1700	1850	177636	LAN	Warrington
1750	1992	1650	1750	135496	LAN	Widnes
1807	1867	1807	1867	102954	LND	Stepney
....	....	ALL	1878	169943	MDX	East London
1849	1954	1700	1849	145823	MDX	Mile End
....	....	ALL	1800	170135	MDX	Whitechapel
....	....	1830	1870	114782	MDX	???
1816	1820	1750	1874	109819	MGY	Berriew
1840	1912	ALL	1840	158445	MGY	Berriew
1874	1935	1850	1950	139173	MGY	Forden
1700	1780	1700	1800	131911	MGY	Llanfihangel
1800	1900	1700	1800	124427	MGY	Llanwrin
1782	1969	1700	1782	169943	OXF	Chipping Norton
1782	1900	1700	1782	169935	OXF	Hook Norton
1807	1851	1800	1860	159743	PEM	Fishguard
1782	1873	1750	1782	173118	PEM	Letterston
1740	1900	1650	1900	113212	SAL	South
1822	....	1822	ALL	131725	SAL	Dawley Bank
1848	....	1848	ALL	131725	SAL	Dawley Brook
1822	....	ALL	1822	131725	SAL	Dawley Magna
....	....	ALL	1822	131725	SAL	Dawley
1791	1992	1749	1992	152706	SAL	Shrewsbury
1800	1850	1700	1800	152579	SOM	Milverton
1810	1862	1861	1900	112364	SRY	Brixton
1877	....	1800	1900	139386	SRY	Wandsworth
1837	1860	1800	1860	147311	STS	Longton
1775	....	ALL	1830	102016	WAR	Aston
1795	1970	....	....	159131	WLS	Brynsoden
....	....	1850	1900	131962	WOR	ALL
1853	1864	....	1860	171646	WOR	Pershore
1673	1992	1640	1992	152668	WYK	Huddersfield
1802	1992	1700	1802	111201	YKS	Sheffield
1729	1982	1650	1750	111163	???	North
1880	1900	1700	1992	107204	???	Lampeter
1898	1992	1881	1898	158631	???	Rhoslan
....	1800	....	....	100536	???	???

Known From	To	Researching From	To	Ref	Cty	Place
OWEN-LEWIS						
....	....	?	....	137995	DFD	Llanddensant
OWENS						
1819	1992	1700	1819	127116	AGY	Amlwch
1884	1908	1800	1888	132543	AGY	Llanerchymedd
1840	1890	....	....	118729	CHS	Birkenhead
1842	1868	ALL	ALL	124982	CHS	Claughton
1784	1815	1700	1900	152714	CHS	Dodleston
1870	1950	1700	1900	152714	FLN	Buckley
1813	1900	1700	1800	138304	FLN	Holywell
1820	1860	1700	1900	152714	FLN	Hope
1820	1950	1700	1900	152714	FLN	Mold
1847	1847	ALL	1847	152021	LAN	Everton
1847	1847	ALL	1847	152021	LAN	Liverpool
1870	1893	ALL	1980	136891	MDX	St George In The East
1838	1862	1800	1838	164259	MEA	Julianstown
1867	1869	ALL	1992	158631	MER	Blaenau
1867	1869	ALL	1992	158631	MER	Bryn Eglwys
1867	1869	ALL	1992	158631	MER	Ffestiniog
1840	1992	1750	1900	114456	MGY	Guilsfield
1841	1861	1820	1881	176877	RAD	Cwmdeuddwr
1774	1886	1700	1900	176877	RAD	Rhayader
1870	1890	1500	1992	119792	SAL	ALL
1783	1870	ALL	1783	158445	SAL	Llansilin
1757	1799	1700	1757	160474	SAL	St Martins
1893	1989	ALL	1980	136891	YKS	Grangetown
OWERS						
1871	....	1800	1871	113352	ESS	Aythorpe Roothing
OWN						
1788	1861	....	....	138401	CAE	Llanddeiniolen
OWST						
....	....	1550	1750	117803	ERY	ALL
1672	1730	....	....	117803	ERY	Bainton
1742	1858	....	....	117803	ERY	Wilberfoss
1870	1970	1750	1870	152730	YKS	Patrington
OWTRAM						
1400	1750	1400	1992	160083	ALL	ALL
OXENBOULD						
....	....	ALL	ALL	152749	ALL	Name Study
1548	1798	1548	1800	152749	SAL	South
....	....	1698	1800	152749	SAL	Great Oxenbold
....	....	1698	1800	152749	SAL	Monkhopton
1826	1856	1800	1880	152749	SRY	Ewell
1805	1870	1780	1920	152749	STS	South
1777	1859	1750	1890	152749	WAR	Birmingham
1677	1830	1559	1835	152749	WOR	North West
OXENHAM						
1780	1830	1700	1830	167088	DEV	Cornwood
OXFORD						
1660	ALL	....	....	153397	DOR	ALL
1600	ALL	....	....	153397	HAM	ALL
1833	1881	....	....	116602	MDX	Chelsea
1770	1960	1700	1770	161896	SFK	Layham
OXLADE						
1789	1870	1700	1899	112615	BKM	Great Marlow
1638	1746	1500	1638	167541	BKM	Great Marlow
1820	1870	1700	1899	112615	BRK	Cookham
OXLEY						
1838	....	1838	....	161721	DUR	South Shields
1800	1892	ALL	ALL	127175	ESS	ALL
1900	1920	1900	1920	147575	ESS	Frinton
1762	1798	1600	1760	147346	NBL	Fourstones
1772	1790	1700	1772	147885	NTH	Towcester
1800	1850	1700	1850	169978	SOM	Wells
1838	1864	1612	1864	107166	SSX	Heathfield
1818	1881	1800	1992	167002	SXE	Warbleton
1632	1666	....	1632	101761	WRY	Emley
....	1881	....	....	146811	WYK	Elland
1864	1870	....	....	146811	WYK	Lindley
1829	1855	....	1830	146811	WYK	Mirfield
....	1720	1680	1750	138584	YKS	Rothwell
1806	1820	1750	1850	144622	YKS	Wath On Dearne
1699	1992	1650	1699	165417	???	???
OXNAM						
1815	1900	1700	1815	143812	CON	Newlyn East
OXNARD						
1800	1870	1700	1840	106267	DUR	South
OXSPRING						
ALL	ALL	ALL	ALL	122246	ALL	ALL
....	....	....	....	143502	ALL	ALL
1766	1810	1730	1770	149152	YKS	Ecclesfield
OZARD						
1735	1791	1730	1791	151858	DOR	Winfrith Newburgh

Known From	To	Researching From	To	Ref	Cty	Place
PACE						
1771	1771	ALL	ALL	130508	DUR	Tanfield
1840	1992	1538	1830	154792	SAL	ALL
1871	1890	1820	1890	176885	STS	Tunstall
1770	....	1700	1780	119938	WAR	Trdington
PACEY						
1810	1858	1750	1950	169889	LIN	Mavis Enderby
1840	1992	1538	1830	154792	SAL	ALL
PACK						
1814	1900	1700	1814	176257	BDF	Pavenham
1740	1992	1650	1740	152757	HAM	Central
1740	1992	1650	1740	152757	HAM	East
PACKARD						
....	....	ALL	ALL	152765	ALL	Name Study
1316	1992	1308	1992	152765	SFK	East
1614	1625	1550	1614	155276	SFK	Mendlesham
PACKER						
1822	1822	1800	1850	152773	BRK	Reading
....	....	ALL	ALL	153311	DEV	Bow
1724	1900	1500	1730	118877	GLS	Aston Blank
1745	1992	1700	1750	117773	GLS	Bristol
1730	1770	1500	1730	118877	GLS	Lower Slaughter
1750	1900	1800	1900	154903	KEN	North
1880	1992	1880	1992	118877	LND	Lewisham
1854	1874	1850	1874	152773	MDX	Bethnal Green
1848	1851	1840	1874	152773	MDX	Stepney
1780	1930	ALL	1780	171719	NTH	Potterspury
1887	1920	1874	1920	152773	SRY	Camberwell
1672	1851	1607	1851	142859	WIL	Minety
PACKHAM						
1844	1851	....	....	174955	KEN	Brenzett
1801	1925	....	1925	152803	KEN	Chatham
1811	1820	1750	1811	174955	KEN	Ivychurch
1840	1890	1760	1840	154873	KEN	Maidstone
1862	1895	....	....	174955	KEN	New Romney
1784	1800	1700	1992	173096	KEN	Newwenden
1840	1890	1760	1840	154873	KEN	Sittingbourne
1784	1850	1750	1992	173096	KEN	Wittersham
1784	1791	1750	1784	174955	KEN	Wittersham
1745	1850	1700	1745	156140	SSX	Cuckfield
1805	1984	1700	1837	176370	SSX	Hellingly
1764	....	1700	1770	156140	SSX	Hurstpierpont
PACKING						
1678	?	?	?	166642	KEN	Woodchurch
PACKMAN						
1870	1992	....	....	135232	BKM	Aylesbury
1820	1870	1750	1900	135232	HRT	Hertford
1820	1870	1750	1900	135232	HRT	Hitchen
1820	1870	1750	1900	135232	HRT	Watford
....	....	1500	1830	166863	KEN	ALL
1861	1941	ALL	ALL	105856	KEN	???
1861	1941	ALL	ALL	105856	SRY	???
PACKNELL						
1800	....	....	1800	101761	MDX	East London
PACKWOOD						
1800	1940	1800	1940	173533	BDF	ALL
1800	1940	1870	1940	173533	NTH	ALL
PACOCK						
1850	1850	1850	1850	141690	CON	Bodmin
PADBURY						
....	....	ALL	ALL	152811	ALL	Name Study
....	....	1800	?	165808	BKM	Bierton
1846	....	1846	?	165808	LND	ALL
1600	1800	1600	1800	168882	OXF	ALL
PADDISON						
1857	....	....	....	151181	GLA	Swansea
1774	1788	ALL	....	152838	LIN	Brigsley
1808	1992	....	....	152838	LIN	Cleethorpes
1819	1900	ALL	1819	152021	LIN	Great Carlton
....	....	ALL	....	152838	LIN	Lindsey
PADDLE						
....	....	ALL	ALL	152846	ALL	Name Study
PADDOCK						
....	....	1700	1800	101478	WOR	Childs Wickham
PADDON						
1600	1992	1700	1800	107530	DEV	North
....	....	1700	1900	124818	DEV	Chudleigh
....	....	1700	1900	124818	DEV	Dawlish
1880	1950	ALL	ALL	107530	DEV	Exeter
1700	....	ALL	ALL	116394	DEV	Exeter
1829	....	ALL	ALL	137545	DEV	Exeter
1744	1992	1740	1992	161640	DEV	Ideford
....	....	1700	1900	124818	DEV	Kenton
1770	....	ALL	ALL	116394	HAM	Fareham

Known From	To	Researching From	To	Ref	Cty	Place
PADDY						
1780	1820	1700	1820	146730	CON	Falmouth
1500	1700	....	....	100420	WAR	Meriden
PADFIELD						
1803	1939	1750	1950	121568	SOM	North East
....	....	ALL	ALL	174963	SOM	Kilmersden
....	....	1600	1992	174963	SOM	Paulton
....	....	1869	1950	170879	SOM	Shepton Mallett
PADGET						
1840	1992	1600	1840	117730	CAM	Littleport
1800	1900	....	....	110124	WIL	Chippenham
....	....	1700	1850	110124	WIL	Kingston St Michael
1825	1887	1825	1910	130974	YKS	Hunslett
PADGETT						
1900	1945	1800	1900	130346	NBL	Newcastle Upon Tyne
1891	1992	ALL	ALL	131121	NTT	Newark
PADLEY						
1790	1800	1790	1800	154210	DOR	Hampreston
1820	1900	....	....	132756	NTT	???
1752	1801	1792	....	108901	SYK	Arksey
1841	1992	1841	1881	108901	SYK	Sheffield
PADMORE						
1878	1889	1871	1992	159468	CHS	Widnes
PADWICK						
1790	1790	....	....	152102	HAM	West Meon
PAGAN						
....	....	ALL	ALL	152862	ALL	Name Study
PAGDEN						
1650	1680	ALL	1680	115282	SSX	East
PAGDIN						
1710	1800	1680	1710	177393	NTT	North Wheatley
1850	1900	1850	1900	141097	YKS	Conisborough
PAGE						
....	....	ALL	1850	152889	BDF	North
1800	1992	ALL	1800	157511	BDF	Blunham
1812	1880	1812	1900	130222	BDF	Hudborne Crawley
1603	1751	1550	1750	124796	BKM	Great Hampden
1685	....	1650	1790	124796	BKM	Monks Risborough
1709	....	1680	1720	124796	BKM	Princes Risborough
1823	1830	1823	1830	130222	BKM	Wavendon
1805	1992	1700	1805	164747	BRK	Littleworth
1782	1864	ALL	ALL	117307	BRK	Shrivenham
1817	1992	ALL	1817	152919	BRK	Shrivenham
1608	1754	....	1608	108839	CAM	Harlton
1854	1855	1700	1855	104965	DBY	Derby
1868	....	....	....	125202	DUR	Gateshead
1822	1846	1700	1822	113425	ESS	Bradwell On Sea
....	....	....	....	112771	ESS	North Weald Bassett
1776	1855	1776	1855	148091	ESS	Radwinter
1830	1920	....	1830	152927	FIF	North West
1800	1820	ALL	1800	145939	GLS	Bristol
1795	1880	1795	1880	127655	GLS	Cheltenham
1812	1872	1750	1900	162507	HAM	Fareham
?	....	....	....	116092	HAM	Portsmouth
1880	1903	1650	1992	162507	HAM	Portsmouth
1900	1992	1750	1900	158275	HAM	Sholing
1840	1992	1700	1870	124966	HAM	Winchester
1847	1860	1840	1860	103144	HRT	Hemel Hempstead
1840	1847	1840	1860	103144	HRT	Hertford
1730	1840	1712	1960	103144	HRT	Ware
1790	1950	ALL	1850	152889	HUN	South
1811	1957	1700	1811	150886	HUN	Hail Weston
....	....	ALL	1900	134503	HUN	Hailweston
1800	1880	1700	1900	108111	KEN	Canterbury
1750	1840	1700	1750	114871	KEN	Canterbury
1730	1896	1700	1900	178322	KEN	Canterbury
....	....	1733	1852	119431	KEN	Dover
1800	1880	1700	1900	108111	KEN	Faversham
1780	1800	1700	1780	152870	KEN	Faversham
1834	....	1810	1840	171441	KEN	Gillingham
1800	1863	....	....	152870	KEN	Ramsgate
1851	1881	1851	1900	110051	KEN	Sheppey
1808	1825	....	1825	152803	KEN	Strood
1725	1816	....	1860	171441	KEN	Strood
1850	1920	1800	1850	156957	LEI	Rothley
1800	1890	ALL	ALL	111155	LIN	Wrangle
....	1912	....	....	137685	LND	East
....	....	ALL	ALL	118400	LND	Cripplegate
1880	1900	ALL	ALL	130508	LND	Marylebone
....	....	1800	1992	105864	LND	Peckham
1623	1665	....	....	142522	LND	St Martins Ludgate
....	....	1800	1840	123870	MDX	London
1795	1980	1700	1795	168726	MDX	Shoreditch
....	....	1480	1580	154873	MDX	Sudbery
PAGE contd.						
....	....	1600	1700	147567	MDX	Wembley
1868	1892	ALL	ALL	125202	NBL	Newcastle
1786	1831	1750	1900	110051	NFK	Ellingham
1818	1851	ALL	ALL	125202	NFK	Yarmouth
....	....	1700	1855	104965	NTT	Stanton On The Wolds
1846	?	?	1900	136611	SAL	Bridgenorth
1900	1992	....	....	115258	SCT	???
1808	....	....	....	129747	SFK	Bricet
1796	....	....	....	129747	SFK	Elmsett
1557	1730	....	....	129747	SFK	Glemsford
1799	1838	1750	1818	118192	SFK	Hadleigh
1738	1855	1600	1800	159956	SFK	Ousden
1690	1740	1690	1750	142018	SOM	Taunton
1745	1882	1700	1745	176249	SRY	Ashtead
1762	1790	1500	1762	110310	SRY	Farnhan
1764	1884	1650	1764	162701	SRY	Frensham
1767	1797	1700	1850	159581	SRY	Wonersh
1730	....	1700	1780	128724	SSX	ALL
1560	1800	....	....	168777	SSX	Donnington
1794	1794	1600	1794	144851	SSX	Hastings
1840	1900	1800	1840	111325	SSX	Wilmington
....	1700	....	....	174564	SSX	???
1700	1750	ALL	ALL	147567	WAR	Fillongley
1680	1900	1600	1900	152900	WAR	Kenilworth
1667	1692	1600	1667	152196	WES	Kirby Lonsdale
1726	1816	....	....	115290	WIL	Alton Priors
1722	1761	1722	1761	178705	WIL	Highworth
1795	1880	1795	1880	127655	WIL	Marlborough
1648	1679	1600	1680	168920	YKS	Emley
1800	1850	....	....	118354	YKS	Market Rasen
1835	1875	1750	1835	102199	YKS	Scholes Cleckheaton
PAGENHAM						
1450	1554	1400	1550	154881	KEN	Penshurst
PAGET						
1750	1992	1750	1992	152935	AVN	Burnett
1807	1815	1807	1814	161942	DUR	Winlaton Mill
1680	1755	1680	1755	152935	GLS	Bristol
1880	1992	1700	1880	177237	GLS	Broadmarston
1690	1890	1660	1992	156515	GLS	Kemble
1880	1992	1700	1880	177237	GLS	Pebworth
....	....	1729	1793	161942	LKS	Glasgow
....	....	1790	1807	161942	MDX	London
1830	1863	1815	1863	161942	MDX	Piccadilly
1750	1800	1700	1800	152935	SAL	Bridgenorth
1750	1992	1750	1992	152935	SOM	Burnett
1790	1800	1700	1850	168734	WAR	Coventry
PAGETT						
1842	1844	....	....	132853	MDX	Kentishtown
1871	1883	1800	1871	132853	SRY	Lambeth
PAGGINTON						
1821	1850	1800	1850	142360	WIL	Hullavington
PAGINTON						
1740	ALL	....	....	142158	WIL	ALL
PAICE						
1772	1772	1750	1800	136719	BRK	Brimpton
1721	1759	1700	1760	100242	HAM	ALL
1757	1826	1700	1757	127116	HAM	Bramley
1734	1857	1734	1857	152943	HAM	Michelmersh
1733	1798	1693	1798	107573	HAM	Upton Grey
1710	1880	1600	1920	157147	HAM	Upton Grey
1830	1875	1830	1950	157147	SRY	Mitcham
1793	1861	1700	1800	115541	SRY	Wandsworth
PAIGE						
1850	1910	1800	1992	133450	DEV	Kingsbridge
PAILLING						
1766	1788	1720	1830	167002	NTT	Cromwell
PAIN						
1742	1762	1500	1742	125695	CAM	Bassingbourn
1944	1955	1850	1944	122947	GLS	Thornbury
1684	1791	1500	1684	115169	GLS	Wilersey
1785	1785	1750	1820	105333	HAM	Isle Of Wight
1748	1992	1500	1748	152951	HAM	Wield
1800	1900	1600	1992	138746	HRT	Stevenage
1800	1900	1500	1950	164992	KEN	ALL
1720	1860	1500	1860	175463	KEN	East
1780	1780	....	....	159883	KEN	Dover
1846	....	1700	1900	126012	KEN	Faversham
1616	1881	1851	1881	118931	NTH	Kings Sutton
1768	1791	1700	1768	155276	SFK	Melton
1755	1825	1825	ALL	145378	SSX	Heathfield
PAINE						
1780	1840	1720	1780	125318	BKM	Wingrave

Known From	To	Researching From	To	Ref	Cty	Place
PAINE contd.						
1812	....	....	....	167037	BRK	Ashbury
....	....	1750	1875	163082	DOR	Corscombe
1777	1795	ALL	1777	169730	HRT	Rickmansworth
1775	1845	....	....	144568	KEN	???
1825	1850	1750	1800	172898	LND	Newington
1848	1856	1800	1848	149578	LND	???
1750	1830	1750	1830	173533	NTH	South
1840	1880	1700	1840	133507	NTH	Greens Norton
1781	?	1750	1770	149039	NTH	Northampton
1755	1804	1740	1855	107360	NTH	Syresham
1797	1828	1774	1860	107360	NTH	Wappenham
1823	1964	1700	1823	169730	SRY	Mortlake
1755	1825	1825	ALL	145378	SSX	Heathfield
1890	1906	1850	1899	119199	SSX	Wadhurst
1760	1804	1760	1804	100277	SSX	Worthing
1600	1700	1600	1850	177180	STS	Gnosall
....	....	1600	1900	115142	WAR	Mancetter
1800	ALL	....	....	167037	WIL	Wootton Bassett
PAINTER						
1775	1960	1780	1900	109452	BRK	Brightwalton
....	....	ALL	1750	152978	CON	???
1840	1873	1873	1880	172006	GLS	Cinderford
....	....	1700	1860	176664	GLS	Miserden
1860	1880	....	1920	176664	GLS	Painswick
....	....	ALL	1900	173614	HAM	South
1723	1754	1600	1754	174343	HAM	Bishops Waltham
1754	1795	1754	1795	174343	HAM	Soberton
1770	1900	ALL	1900	173614	HAM	Southwick
1851	1900	....	....	139971	LND	Peckham
1800	1850	....	....	155683	MDX	Limehouse
1750	1805	....	....	152978	SAL	Farlow
1800	1900	1800	1900	113670	SOM	Ashill
1727	1980	1500	1721	129011	STS	Abbots Bromley
1710	1727	1680	1750	170348	WIL	Broad Blunsdon
1850	1930	....	....	152978	WOR	Kidderminster
PAISEY						
1800	1900	1750	1900	154881	SOM	Bath
PAISH						
1685	1992	1685	1900	138487	GLS	ALL
PAISLEY						
....	....	ALL	ALL	177830	ALL	Name Study
PALEY						
....	....	ALL	ALL	138835	ALL	Name Study
....	....	....	....	153869	YKS	???
PALFREY						
1793	1890	1750	1890	132543	SFK	Bardwell
1790	1827	....	1790	101761	SFK	Fornham
1761	1854	1750	1860	176621	SFK	Langham
....	....	1780	1820	148113	YKS	Sheffield
PALFREYMAN						
1500	1700	ALL	ALL	110477	LIN	Lusby
1500	1700	ALL	ALL	110477	LIN	Theddlethorpe
PALGER						
1764	....	....	....	129747	LIN	Scothorne
PALGRAVE						
....	....	ALL	ALL	152986	ALL	Name Study
1100	1992	1100	1992	111147	NFK	ALL
PALIMG						
1824	1882	1700	1900	125865	LIM	Limdsry
PALIN						
1864	1869	ALL	ALL	115355	LEI	ALL
1824	1882	1700	1900	125865	LIM	Limdsry
1740	1900	1650	1740	172901	NTT	Strelley
1850	1960	1814	1830	111856	STS	Adbaston
PALING						
1810	1840	1840	1880	148113	NTT	Lowdham
....	1750	ALL	1750	134511	NTT	Oxton
PALK						
1850	1992	1692	1900	152994	DEV	Little Hempston
PALKE						
1560	1700	1500	1700	156000	DEV	ALL
1660	1750	1660	1750	156000	LEI	Melton Mowbray
PALLANT						
1666	1992	1600	1690	153001	SFK	???
PALLAS						
1700	1876	1700	1876	103632	DUR	Sunderland
PALLETT						
1870	1980	1700	1870	166421	HRT	Essendon
1768	1820	1752	ALL	145386	WAR	Ansley
PALLISTER						
1843	....	1800	1870	155438	WES	???
PALMBY						
1749	1764	1700	1780	133000	CAM	Caldecote

Known From	To	Researching From	To	Ref	Cty	Place
PALMER						
1865	1880	1800	1865	155594	ANT	Belfast
....	....	1800	....	116335	AVN	Bristol
1650	1800	....	....	114243	BDF	Bedford
1600	1780	....	....	108677	BKM	Devney
1876	1931	1873	1931	153044	BKM	Haddenham
1650	1800	....	....	114243	BKM	Newport Pagnell
1750	1850	1700	1800	137618	BRK	North West
1800	1850	1750	1850	145661	BRK	Hungerford
1774	1900	....	....	115290	BRK	Lambourn
....	....	1800	1900	137405	CAM	Cambridge
1653	1940	....	....	128996	CAM	Thorney
1800	1800	1700	1800	121509	CUL	Dalston
1818	1864	1800	1882	177792	CUL	Dalston
1850	1920	ALL	ALL	154970	CUL	Scaleby
....	....	1800	1841	128082	DEV	ALL
....	1852	1700	1852	177938	DEV	Coleridge
1770	1950	....	....	159751	DEV	Mid
1840	1840	1800	1840	128368	DEV	Okehampton
1834	1992	1700	1835	161772	DEV	Tiverton
1750	1850	1700	1750	116815	DOR	Charlton Marshall
1807	1881	1750	1830	110949	DOR	Powerstock
1730	1820	1538	1820	118893	DUR	Sunderland Bridge
1775	1800	1700	1992	114901	DUR	Sunderland
1720	1740	1538	1820	118893	DUR	Sunderland
1727	1747	1600	1730	164909	ESS	Roxwell
1822	1868	....	....	129801	ESS	Saffron Walden
1880	1920	ALL	1880	141224	GLS	South
1780	1850	1600	1850	154342	GLS	Bitton
1770	1796	....	1796	149055	GLS	Bristol
1795	1871	ALL	1800	165654	GLS	Siston
1802	....	1700	1800	100013	HAM	Alton
1790	1807	ALL	1790	131881	HAM	Porstmouth
1854	1854	1800	1854	103640	HAM	Southampton
....	1878	1878	1930	166790	HAM	Winchester
1700	ALL	1750	1810	107379	HRT	Hemel Hempstead
....	....	1800	1900	117714	HRT	South Mimms
1750	....	....	....	174750	HUN	Stilton
....	....	1800	1850	147613	IRL	Cork
1890	1992	1500	1890	153095	KEN	Central
1670	1750	ALL	1670	131059	KEN	Cowden
1750	1775	ALL	1750	131059	KEN	Dartford
1807	1879	1807	1920	109851	KEN	Isle Of Sheppey
1775	1825	ALL	1775	131059	KEN	West Malling
1600	1780	....	....	108677	KEN	Wingham
1776	1957	1700	1776	149195	LEI	Hugglescote
1850	1900	1800	1900	156280	LEI	Leicester
1800	1992	1700	1992	177652	LEI	Waltham
1776	1957	1700	1776	149195	LEI	Wreak Valley
....	....	1740	1780	145688	LIN	Algarkirk
1852	1859	1700	1852	153109	LIN	Grantham
1797	....	....	....	153117	LND	East
1797	....	....	....	153117	LND	City
1883	1883	1850	1900	134627	LND	East End
1790	1830	....	....	135070	LND	Hackney
1800	1848	1800	1900	134422	LND	Lambeth
....	....	1850	1900	129275	LND	Plaistow
....	....	1800	1950	129275	LND	Stepney
1880	1950	ALL	1880	131849	LND	Tottenham
1828	1992	1750	1828	167711	MDX	Bow
1850	?	?	?	143464	MDX	Islington
1856	1988	1750	1856	165271	MDX	North London
1838	....	....	1873	153044	MDX	St Pancras
1812	1992	ALL	1812	153028	NFK	Colton
1693	1716	....	....	135437	NFK	Gateley
1787	1787	....	....	135437	NFK	Lt Snoring
1716	1745	....	....	135437	NFK	N Elmham
1845	1871	....	....	125202	NFK	Sedgeford
1815	....	....	....	125202	NFK	Stanhoe
1768	1860	....	....	135437	NFK	Stibbard
1808	1880	1750	1880	126470	NFK	Thetford
1767	1902	1650	1950	112089	NFK	Yarmouth
1797	....	....	....	153117	NFK	???
....	....	1770	1950	141151	NTH	Crick
1770	1850	1770	1850	173533	NTH	Hinton
1910	1988	1910	1988	153044	NTH	Rushton
....	....	1780	1802	177393	NTT	Radford
1850	....	....	....	174750	OXF	Woodstock
1873	1992	ALL	1873	142107	SFK	Barham
1890	1972	ALL	ALL	153281	SFK	Blakenham Magna
1890	1972	ALL	ALL	153281	SFK	Bosmere
1890	1972	ALL	ALL	153281	SFK	Claydon
1851	1992	1837	1891	141267	SFK	Ipswich
1750	1992	1600	1750	112704	SFK	Southwold

Known From	To	Researching From	To	Ref	Cty	Place
PALMER contd.						
1815	1840	1770	1815	168912	SOM	Alsholt
1856	1870	1850	1880	115193	SOM	Bath
1800	1810	1700	1850	177024	SOM	Bath
....	....	....	1773	153044	SOM	Bleadon
1850	1992	1790	1850	168076	SOM	Bridgwater
1650	1750	1600	1750	144657	SOM	Congresbury
1861	1871	1820	1890	162450	SOM	Counsbury
1700	1800	1600	1800	174300	SOM	Crewkerne
1782	1836	1782	1836	153044	SOM	Lympsham
....	....	1750	1840	176796	SOM	Stoke Subhamden
1810	1860	1700	1810	108413	SOM	West Huntspill
1807	....	1807	....	153044	SOM	Weston Super Mare
1850	1900	1900	1992	179612	SOM	Weston Super Mare
....	1838	1800	1850	128961	SRY	Dockhead
1600	1780	....	....	108677	SRY	Richmond
1760	1780	1600	1992	167592	STS	Hanley
1750	1974	1750	1974	124842	STS	Newcastle
1830	1992	1700	1830	153087	WAR	ALL
1832	1832	....	....	127426	WAR	Aston
1806	1855	....	....	127426	WAR	Birmingham
1849	1861	ALL	ALL	153753	WAR	Birmingham
....	....	1800	1920	122203	WAR	???
1670	ALL	....	....	142158	WIL	Albourne
1674	1848	1670	1850	115193	WIL	Aldbourne
1700	1770	1670	1700	165530	WIL	Sherston
1650	1738	1650	1750	142018	WIL	West Wellow
1700	....	1600	....	134589	YKS	Cawood
1800	1840	1750	1800	170348	YKS	Sprotborough
1590	1968	....	....	100536	???	???
PALNT						
1783	....	ALL	1800	174815	DBY	Brailsford
PALSER						
1820	1840	1700	1900	167096	GLS	North Nibley
PAMANT						
1820	1992	1851	1992	123021	SFK	Eriswell
PAMLER						
1750	1850	....	....	124168	YKS	Middleton Tyas
PAMMENT						
1840	1870	1600	1870	175641	CAM	Isleham
1703	1992	1700	1992	169005	ESS	Wennington
PAMPHILION						
....	....	?	?	148989	???	???
PAMPHILON						
1850	1900	ALL	ALL	141704	MDX	Haggerston
PAMPHLETT						
1790	1800	....	1790	137227	KEN	Shepherdswell
PAMPLIN						
1750	1810	1700	1850	141496	HRT	Ware
PANCOUST						
....	....	1650	1900	102784	BKM	Filgrave Cum Tyringham
PANKHURST						
....	....	ALL	ALL	153133	ALL	Name Study
1816	1992	ALL	1816	164887	KEN	Cranbrook
1789	1992	1750	1992	153133	KEN	Leigh
1784	1784	1750	1992	173096	KEN	Newwenden
1800	1992	ALL	....	161780	KEN	???
1733	1733	....	....	139971	SSX	Warbleton
1920	....	....	....	131008	YKS	Darfield
?	?	?	?	168947	???	???
PANNEL						
1840	1850	1800	1850	155357	SRY	Ewhurst
PANNELL						
1710	1960	1600	1710	167355	BKM	Aylesbury
....	....	1559	1760	140341	KEN	Thanet
1900	1960	1800	1900	167355	LND	Westminster
1780	1850	1700	1850	146803	SSX	Harting
PANNIFER						
1794	1816	ALL	1794	168602	ESS	???
PANRUCKER						
1767	1992	1767	1992	153141	LND	Central
PANTING						
1833	1853	ALL	1833	175994	HEF	Ledbury
PANTLING						
1840	1870	ALL	1850	147397	NTH	Irthlingborough
1870	1900	ALL	ALL	147397	NTH	Northampton
PAPE						
1850	1992	....	1850	159514	LND	Hoxton
1841	1881	1780	1960	123536	NBL	Newcastle On Tyne
1824	1825	1780	1960	123536	WAT	Waterford
PAPLAY						
....	....	ALL	ALL	177342	ALL	Name Study
PAPPER						
1800	1840	1800	1840	167924	HRT	Holwell
PAPWORTH						
1700	1850	....	....	167924	BDF	Arlesey
1540	1840	1540	1780	116831	CAM	Elsworth
....	....	1760	1890	103713	CAM	Milton
1750	....	ALL	ALL	116394	CAM	Toft
1778	....	....	1778	108839	HUN	Colne
1700	1992	ALL	ALL	164933	HUN	Over
1700	1992	ALL	ALL	164933	HUN	Ramsey
1700	1992	ALL	ALL	164933	HUN	Swavesey
PAQUELIN						
....	....	?	?	179159	???	???
PARBURY						
....	....	ALL	1766	103284	LND	???
PARCELL						
1780	1882	ALL	1900	177571	HRT	Hitchin
PARDEY						
1795	1945	ALL	1795	151424	DOR	Stratton
PARDOE						
1750	1800	1600	1900	169862	SAL	Cleobury Mortimer
1750	1800	1600	1900	169862	SAL	Ludlow
1769	1831	....	....	102733	STS	Brewood
1850	1920	ALL	ALL	112461	WOR	ALL
1752	1992	....	1757	120979	WOR	Harvington
....	....	1650	1800	147613	WOR	Old Swinford
1740	....	1600	1740	115525	???	Old Swinford
PARDOE-MATTHEWS						
1900	1992	1900	1992	121320	HAM	South
PARDON						
1829	1870	....	1830	178853	DEV	Chagford
PARDOW						
....	....	1732	1776	100331	WOR	???
PARDY						
1823	1850	1820	1850	130990	CHI	Guernsey
PAREN						
1655	1940	....	....	128996	CAM	Thorney
PARFETT						
1850	1900	1800	1860	158836	BRK	ALL
1857	1951	ALL	1857	172502	SRY	Kingston
PARFITT						
1893	1992	?	1893	119296	GLA	Aberdare
1871	1953	....	....	170526	HAM	Portsmouth
1852	1992	1750	1992	121568	SOM	North East
1779	....	....	....	176958	SOM	Bristol
1812	1992	?	1812	119296	SOM	Clutton
1838	....	1830	1900	170526	WIL	Barford St Martin
PARGETER						
1500	1900	....	....	107743	BKM	Whaddon
1500	1900	....	....	107743	NTH	Farthinghoe
1800	1840	1700	1900	115517	WAR	Tysoe
1750	1900	?	1750	158569	WAR	Tysoe
PARGITER						
....	....	1500	1750	111538	NTH	Greatworth
PARHAM						
1838	1857	1700	1838	162000	HAM	Portsmouth
1836	1992	1800	1992	115991	HAM	Westbourne
1848	....	1750	1850	156698	SRY	Chertsey
1783	1840	....	....	135437	SSX	Sidlesham
1500	1900	1500	1900	170216	WIL	ALL
PARIS						
1870	1900	1850	1900	172855	LKS	Shotts
1699	1743	1670	1750	142018	WIL	Salisbury
PARISH						
1600	1750	1600	1750	177180	BKM	Northall
....	....	1600	1670	124796	BKM	Princes Risborough
?	?	ALL	ALL	130508	DEV	Ilsington
1782	1813	1754	1813	153176	DEV	Nymet Tracey
1792	ALL	....	....	153397	HAM	Brockenhurst
1850	1890	ALL	ALL	120456	LND	Greenwich
1842	1850	ALL	1866	118737	LND	Hackney
1900	1950	ALL	ALL	130508	LND	St Pancras
1826	1992	....	1825	129461	NFK	Norwich
1718	1812	1700	1800	171654	NTH	Slapton
....	1824	....	1824	151688	NTH	Ufford
....	....	1750	1900	109770	SOM	???
PARK						
....	....	ALL	ALL	153370	ALL	Name Study
1874	1904	1874	1909	121304	CUL	Gosforth
1851	....	....	1851	101761	CUL	Wigton
1841	1869	....	....	121835	DBY	Berby
1740	1786	1740	1792	151858	DOR	Corscombe
1700	1753	1650	1800	144606	DUR	South Shields

Known From	To	Researching From	To	Ref	Cty	Place
PARK contd.						
1819	1902	ALL	1819	102350	LAN	Broughton In Furness
1863	1874	1863	1874	121304	LAN	Broughton
1655	1840	1693	1840	121304	LAN	Coniston
1850	1880	1780	1890	117145	LAN	Furness
1783	1858	1066	1783	122955	LAN	Halsall
....	....	ALL	1906	153184	LAN	Ormskirk
1721	1778	1600	1721	152196	LAN	Torver
....	....	1600	1750	160989	LND	ALL
1880	1960	1800	1880	100412	NBL	Brampton
1750	1965	....	....	137820	SHI	Fetlar
1720	1965	....	....	137820	SHI	Mid Yell
1760	1965	....	....	137820	SHI	North Yell
1758	1965	....	....	137820	SHI	Northmavine
1720	1965	....	....	137820	SHI	South Yell
1842	1906	1482	1920	121304	WES	Windermere
1906	1992	....	....	153184	WIL	Leigh
....	....	1700	1790	133604	WIL	Little Cheverell
1906	1992	....	....	153184	WIL	Minety
1880	1980	1700	1880	160989	YKS	Leeds
1750	1850	....	....	167843	YKS	Redmire Cum Bolton
1880	1980	1700	1880	160989	YKS	Scarborough
PARKE						
1855	1890	1700	1960	172421	DEV	Totnes
1660	1830	1830	1992	174157	WIC	Baltinglass
1650	1800	1800	1830	148113	YKS	Doncaster
?	?	ALL	ALL	174432	YKS	Ebberston
PARKER						
....	....	1700	1850	151033	AVN	Bristol
1777	1863	1700	1777	115460	BDF	Pulloxhill
1720	1800	1650	1850	110906	BKM	Marsh Gibbon
1880	ALL	....	....	163392	BRK	Caversham
1900	1920	1880	1920	170143	BRK	Lambourn
1830	1952	1800	1830	126349	CAM	Wisbech
....	....	1847	1887	145084	CMA	Whitehaven
1630	1900	....	....	116173	CUL	Bootle
1833	1858	1800	1858	129186	DBY	Barrowash
1839	1871	1700	1871	129186	DBY	Spondon
1780	1900	ALL	ALL	153311	DEV	Bow
1921	1992	1600	1900	151033	DEV	Broadwood Kelly
1921	1992	1600	1900	151033	DEV	Iddesleigh
1826	....	1800	1860	162825	DEV	Ilfracombe
....	....	1600	1850	151033	DEV	West Buckland
1865	1900	....	....	126187	DOR	Lyme Regis
1814	....	1750	1900	109894	DOR	Owermoigne
1718	1748	ALL	1730	154563	DOR	Portesham
1812	1907	1750	1812	164224	DUR	Sunderland
1840	1992	1800	1840	122297	DUR	Wincaton
1880	1992	1830	1899	145041	DUR	Wingate
1826	1851	1807	1881	116424	ESS	Bulmer
1807	1875	1762	1875	110043	ESS	Halstead
1769	1769	1700	1769	178608	ESS	Heydon
1848	1916	....	....	116165	FIF	Anstruther
1800	1900	1700	1850	115614	GLS	Bristol
1800	1900	1700	1850	115614	GLS	Gloucester
1820	1860	....	....	105651	GLS	Twyning
1880	1992	ALL	ALL	115002	GLS	Winchcomb
1793	1830	1780	1835	164402	GLS	???
1611	1720	1550	1720	174343	HAM	Bighton
1844	1992	?	1844	113360	HAM	Otterbourne
1844	1992	?	1844	113360	HAM	Twyford
1834	1900	1700	1854	156051	HRT	Barley
1845	1992	....	....	165352	HRT	Welwyn
1845	1992	....	....	165352	HRT	Westmill
1753	1830	....	....	140023	KEN	East
1800	1840	1700	1800	114871	KEN	Ashford
1861	1866	1860	1866	124710	KEN	Littlebourne
1776	1800	1700	1776	137383	KEN	Queenborough
1800	1850	1600	1800	123587	KEN	Sevenoaks
1871	1938	1871	1992	153273	LAN	Blackburn
1790	1851	1700	1790	120669	LAN	Bury
1765	1992	1500	1800	153230	LAN	Kirkham
1815	1920	1700	1881	174998	LAN	Kirkham
1860	1870	1860	1900	129240	LAN	Liverpool
....	....	1700	1864	170437	LAN	Liverpool
1822	1960	....	1822	146013	LAN	Manchester
1815	1920	1700	1881	174998	LAN	Preston
1860	1930	1800	1860	170437	LAN	Waterloo
1820	1828	1800	1820	117196	LAN	West Derby
1800	1827	1750	1800	151912	LAN	Whalley
1800	1855	?	1800	144800	LIN	Boston
1814	1862	1800	1814	171565	LIN	Grimsby
1791	1800	1750	1800	155950	LIN	Irby On Humber
PARKER contd.						
....	....	1600	1850	151033	LND	Brixton
1825	1850	1700	1900	172421	LND	Lewisham
....	....	1800	1860	148113	LND	St James
....	....	1750	1820	106607	MDX	Bethnal Green
1830	1860	1800	1900	115614	MDX	Hammersmith
1800	1823	1780	1992	110205	MDX	London
1893	1930	....	1901	171646	MDX	North London
1835	1947	1835	1900	173339	MDX	St Louk
1789	1871	1800	1871	148067	MDX	St Pancras
1852	1852	1815	1855	124974	MDX	Tottenham
1879	1992	....	....	169013	MDX	Tottenham
1760	1827	1600	1760	116637	NBL	Blanchland
1810	1820	....	....	103764	NBL	Newcastle
1750	1820	....	....	129801	NFK	New Buckingham
1788	1920	1586	1788	102512	NFK	Surlingham
....	....	1750	1950	153265	NTH	North
1751	1793	1725	1812	107360	NTH	Duston
1894	1955	1894	1955	166146	NTH	Holcott
1815	1815	1800	1825	107360	NTH	Scaldwell
1822	1924	1822	1924	148156	NTH	Wellingborough
....	....	1800	1920	166146	NTH	Wilby
1865	1870	1865	1870	122335	NTT	Nottingham
1753	1900	1700	1753	137413	NTT	Nottingham
1837	1850	1700	1837	108413	OXF	Alvescot
1850	1900	1850	1920	120529	OXF	Oxford
....	....	ALL	1600	164631	RUT	ALL
1591	1760	....	....	164631	RUT	Egleton
....	....	1594	1732	153265	RUT	Empingham
1813	1864	....	....	118729	SAL	Madeley
1881	1992	1841	1881	129895	SFK	East Berghot
1770	1900	1500	1770	110647	SFK	Henly
1793	1818	1700	1793	155756	SFK	Mildenhall
1770	1900	1500	1770	110647	SFK	Newbourn
1818	1890	....	....	155756	SFK	Risby
1800	1860	1700	1800	149306	SOM	Central
....	....	1600	1700	108677	SOM	Bath
1711	1992	1600	1711	153281	SOM	North Petherton
1775	1992	1680	1992	121568	SOM	Sedgemoor
1830	1960	1700	1830	103675	SOM	Wedmore
1812	1850	1750	1812	164224	SRY	Walworth
1880	1920	1880	1960	115614	SSX	Hastings
1800	1900	1700	1800	165263	SSX	Rotherfield
....	....	1700	1770	149977	STS	Central
....	....	1800	1850	108723	STS	Chorley
....	1800	....	1800	177695	STS	Gt Wyrley
1776	1992	1750	1800	129240	STS	Handsworth
1770	1848	....	....	149977	STS	Igestre
1590	1925	ALL	1992	133450	STS	Leek
1859	1886	....	....	149977	STS	Stafford
1847	....	....	....	145742	STS	Wednesbury
1891	1952	....	....	149977	STS	Wolverhampton
1805	1832	1600	1805	150150	SYK	Wakefield
1600	1900	....	....	100420	WAR	Meriden
1757	1900	1600	1900	130125	WAR	Studley
1836	....	....	1880	171441	WAR	???
1723	1761	....	....	171654	WIG	Stoneykirk
1738	1783	1666	1812	153273	WYK	Bentham Mewith
....	....	1650	1750	147613	YKS	Bentham
1850	....	1828	1900	152129	YKS	Goole
1845	....	1840	1890	152129	YKS	Leeds
1750	1800	1650	1900	130419	YKS	Long Preston
1840	1845	....	....	144029	YKS	Sheffield
1840	1916	....	....	145912	YKS	Wakefield
1865	1985	1900	1985	126187	???	Bristol
PARKERSON						
1837	1898	1700	1850	135275	NFK	Norwich
PARKES						
....	....	ALL	ALL	147516	ALL	Name Study
1793	1880	ALL	1793	147362	DBY	Dutfield
1861	1992	....	....	153338	DEV	Devonport
1750	1992	1600	1750	125393	STS	Oscott
1750	1992	1600	1750	125393	STS	Perry Barr
1790	1860	ALL	ALL	117870	STS	Rowley Regis
1844	1992	....	....	144088	STS	Rowleyregis
1817	1846	1817	1846	105147	STS	Tipton
1878	1955	....	1878	131741	STS	Walsall
1826	1871	1700	1826	164879	STS	Walsall
1800	1820	1770	1800	125318	STS	West Bromwich
1750	1992	1600	1750	125393	WAR	Birmingham
1803	1830	1750	1800	156140	WOR	Halesowen
PARKHOUSE						
1750	1880	1750	1880	132721	DEV	North
1790	1860	1775	1875	171549	DEV	Ringsash

Known From	To	Researching From	To	Ref	Cty	Place
PARKHOUSE contd.						
1825	1860	....	....	147486	GLS	Bristol
1800	1940	1800	1992	147486	LND	London
PARKHURST						
1795	1980	1700	1900	166375	MDX	Westminster
1571	....	1500	1700	131547	SRY	Shere
PARKIN						
1820	1900	ALL	ALL	155608	DBY	Denby
1700	ALL	1700	ALL	132950	DBY	Kilburn
1820	1900	ALL	ALL	155608	DBY	Loscoe
1828	1860	1750	1828	147362	DBY	Sutfield
1786	1833	1700	1833	164674	DEV	Atherington
1790	1870	ALL	ALL	107352	DEV	Braunton
1811	1892	ALL	1811	166847	DEV	Chalicon
1703	....	....	....	117196	DUR	Durham
1800	1992	1700	1850	116823	DUR	Sedgefield
1820	1840	1800	1900	117781	EYK	Hull
1900	1980	1800	1900	109487	SYK	Barnsley
1729	1834	1600	1900	107565	WES	Bolton
1726	1753	1600	1726	102571	WES	Ravonstonedale
1854	1875	1830	1875	147311	WYK	Marsden
1874	1900	ALL	1874	154946	YKS	Barnsley
1874	....	ALL	1874	154946	YKS	Huddersfield
1796	1824	1700	1900	137561	YKS	Thorner
1730	1759	ALL	1730	136913	YKS	Whitwell
PARKINS						
1747	1747	1600	1747	105252	LIN	Waddington
PARKINSON						
1873	1992	1700	1850	153362	CAM	Hauxton
1708	1880	....	....	147885	CHS	Bidston
1792	1900	1750	1900	105732	CHS	Chester
1820	1850	1750	1850	153354	DUR	Gateshead
1794	1900	1700	1794	160474	LAN	Blackburn
1814	1818	1775	1841	174211	LAN	Colne
1799	1799	ALL	ALL	124982	LAN	Ellel
1682	1829	ALL	ALL	141615	LAN	Garstang
1707	1868	1600	1707	163783	LAN	Garstang
1838	1851	1790	1838	104043	LAN	Goosenargh
1834	1847	ALL	ALL	124982	LAN	Lancaster
1855	1887	1700	1855	146021	LAN	Manchester
1800	1900	1800	1900	167843	LAN	Manchester
1855	1887	1700	1855	146021	LAN	Salford
1707	1868	1600	1707	163783	LAN	Sowerby
1825	1992	....	....	118729	LAN	Thurnham
1800	1850	....	....	126497	LAN	Wigan
1664	1695	....	1664	108510	LIN	Bassingthorpe
1813	1814	1800	1850	141461	NTH	Hexham
1775	1830	1700	1830	168297	WES	Raucndale
1690	1720	ALL	1750	123048	WRY	Slaidburn
1802	1860	1700	1802	111198	WYK	Leeds
1738	1822	1700	1738	174173	YKS	Ardsley
1822	1980	1700	1822	179086	YKS	Bradford
1769	1800	1700	1850	153354	YKS	Danby Wiske
1868	1970	1841	1900	109630	YKS	Doncaster
1750	....	1750	....	109347	YKS	Gisburn
1775	1830	1700	1830	168297	YKS	Huggate Parish
1750	....	....	....	112348	YKS	Leeds
1830	1830	1800	1850	116386	YKS	Leeds
1738	1822	1700	1738	174173	YKS	Leeds
....	1840	ALL	1840	163341	YKS	Wakefield
1800	1900	1800	1992	139203	YKS	York
....	1861	....	....	144029	YKS	???
PARKS						
1820	1860	1800	1840	149373	KEN	Bermondsey
1820	1860	1800	1840	149373	KEN	Deptford
1830	1880	....	....	122378	KEN	Maidstone
1830	1880	....	....	122378	KEN	West Peckham
?	?	?	?	100692	LAN	Eccles
1880	1930	1880	1930	136484	LND	Shoreditch
1790	1810	1790	1810	153303	NTT	Shelford
1832	1913	....	....	148016	SCT	???
....	....	1800	....	154296	SSX	???
....	1800	....	....	174564	SSX	???
1800	1820	1770	1800	125318	STS	West Bromwich
PARLETT						
1620	1900	ALL	1620	114928	SSX	???
PARLEY						
....	....	ALL	ALL	129224	ALL	Name Study
PARLING						
1700	1850	1600	1992	107115	NFK	ALL
PARLOUR						
1871	....	1700	1900	158976	CLV	Coatham
1906	1940	1800	1980	158976	DUR	Chester Le Street
PARMEE						
1632	1837	ALL	ALL	112518	OXF	Witney
PARMENTER						
....	....	1750	1850	118397	OXF	???
PARMENTIER						
1710	1805	1710	1805	176338	EYK	Flamboro
1790	1820	1700	1800	176338	EYK	Hull
1680	1700	1680	1700	176338	MDX	London
1700	1720	1700	1720	176338	YKS	ALL
1700	1720	1700	1720	176338	YKS	Hull
1700	1720	1700	1720	176338	YKS	Leeds
PARNABY						
....	1840	....	....	153176	NYK	Little Holtby
PARNACOTT						
....	....	1600	1900	154431	ENG	ALL
1820	1880	1800	1900	135429	SOM	Bath
1870	1992	1800	1900	135429	SSX	Brighton
PARNELL						
1746	1940	....	....	128996	CAM	Thorney
1860	1890	1840	1890	117145	CHS	Stalybridge
1200	1900	....	....	153397	HAM	ALL
1800	1875	1700	1800	118834	HAM	Portsmouth
1860	....	1850	1900	126144	KEN	Gravesend
1860	1890	1840	1890	117145	LAN	Stalybridge
1815	1871	....	....	121355	LND	Bethnal Green
1850	1900	1875	1900	138142	NFK	Hagdalen
1861	1992	?	1861	105708	SFK	Lowestoft
1200	1900	....	....	153397	SSX	ALL
1770	1900	ALL	ALL	120618	WAR	Coventry
1840	1850	1700	1850	170291	WAR	Minks Kirby
PARNHAM						
1820	1900	1700	1820	112097	NTT	Newark
PAROISSIEN						
1690	1840	....	....	150967	LND	Spitalfields
PARR						
1590	1875	1500	1992	102970	BRK	ALL
1685	1849	1500	1685	141925	BRK	Sulhamstead Abbott
1779	1829	1750	1800	155934	CAM	Cambridge
1832	1850	1800	1900	177873	CAM	Fordham
1847	1851	1847	1880	126705	CHS	Wirral
1796	1992	1600	1796	108286	DEV	North
1600	1850	1700	1850	141577	DEV	Sampford Peverell
1895	1918	1850	1992	117609	DEV	Tamerton Fliot
1800	1900	1800	1900	141577	DEV	Tiverton
1875	1915	1870	1950	145319	DUR	Gateshead
1880	1992	ALL	1880	178659	ENG	Midlands
1600	1700	1600	1700	144657	HAM	Chawton
1828	1900	1750	1840	142042	HAM	South Hayling
1800	1900	ALL	1900	175757	LAN	Blackburn
....	....	....	1900	147818	LAN	St Helens
1847	1875	ALL	1847	162108	LND	???
1875	1915	1870	1950	145319	NBL	Newcastle
1857	1992	ALL	1857	160199	NBL	Newcastle
1857	1992	ALL	1857	160199	NBL	North Shields
1857	1992	ALL	1857	160199	NBL	Tyneside
1746	....	....	1746	101761	NTT	Shelford
1895	1918	1850	1992	117609	NWL	Bangor
1705	1842	1650	1870	145319	SFK	Exning
1705	1842	1650	1870	145319	SFK	Newmarket
1830	1860	1750	1830	149306	SOM	Central
1680	1830	1650	1780	128449	STS	Kinver
1779	1779	ALL	ALL	128449	WOR	Hagley
PARRATT						
1739	1892	1739	1900	127582	LND	Balham
PARREY						
1750	1790	....	....	125423	WOR	Hanbury
1750	1820	....	....	125423	WOR	Stoke Prior
PARRICK						
....	1722	ALL	ALL	129933	HAM	Yateley
PARRINGTON						
1700	1992	1550	1700	153427	YKS	Combriadent
1700	1992	1550	1700	153427	YKS	Garsdale
PARRISH						
1845	1950	1750	1845	128538	ALL	ALL
1679	....	1650	1680	124796	BKM	Saunderton
1852	1917	....	....	123633	ENG	???
1820	1914	1750	1920	130087	KEN	North
1850	1890	ALL	ALL	120456	LND	Greenwich
PARROCK						
1890	1907	1890	....	159034	LND	Bermondsey
1865	....	1865	....	159034	MDX	St Pancras
PARROTT						
....	....	1700	1800	102393	BKM	Aylesbury
1840	1900	ALL	1840	102393	KEN	Beckenham

Known From	To	Researching From	To	Ref	Cty	Place
PARROTT contd.						
1866	1950	1500	1920	137472	KEN	Chatham
1866	1950	1500	1920	137472	KEN	Gillingham
1866	1950	1500	1920	137472	KEN	North Aylesford
1866	1950	1500	1920	137472	KEN	Rochester
1866	1950	1500	1920	137472	KEN	Strood
1746	....	....	....	148156	NTH	Northampton
1845	1992	1700	1845	138657	NYK	Helmsley
1811	1876	....	1811	160652	SOM	Taunton
?	....	....	?	111104	SRY	Banstead
?	....	....	?	111104	SRY	Belmont
1830	1910	1750	1830	176583	STS	Hanford
PARRY						
1878	1901	1830	1880	162396	AGY	???
1700	1880	1700	1880	177008	BRE	Gwenddwr
1841	1881	1800	1841	116173	CAE	Aberdaron
1855	1954	1770	1865	148490	CAE	Bangor
1804	1858	....	....	138401	CAE	Beddgelert
1748	1992	....	....	138401	CAE	Llanrug
1804	1858	....	....	138401	CAE	Yspytty Ifan
1841	....	ALL	1841	144053	CAE	???
1749	1749	....	....	135437	CHS	Chester
1597	1992	1610	1930	177105	CWD	Llandegla
1841	....	....	....	176958	DEN	Brymbo
1790	1840	1700	1900	124427	DEN	Cerrigydrudion
1850	1992	1660	1850	138274	DEN	Glyn Gerrog
1820	1890	1700	1890	153877	DEN	Holt
1597	1992	1610	1930	177105	DEN	Llandegla
1841	....	ALL	1841	144053	DEN	???
1782	1860	1700	1782	147885	FLN	Bodfari
1797	....	ALL	ALL	147621	FLN	Caerwys
1850	1950	1850	1950	135666	FLN	Holywell
1814	1889	ALL	ALL	147621	FLN	Holywell
1200	1992	1200	1992	153435	FLN	Rhuddlan
1900	....	ALL	ALL	107425	HEF	Hereford
1920	1992	....	....	135666	LAN	Bolton
1877	1920	1860	1940	135933	LAN	Everton
1900	1900	1900	1900	145580	LAN	Liverpool
1852	1895	1800	1900	167606	LAN	Oldham
1820	....	....	....	167037	MER	Festinog
1900	1992	1660	1900	138274	SAL	St Martins
1811	1832	1700	1811	153346	STS	Kingswinford
1787	1787	1650	1787	139769	WAR	Birmingham
1750	1790	1700	1820	125423	WOR	Hanbury
1750	1820	1700	1820	125423	WOR	Stoke Prior
1795	1875	1750	1900	167606	???	Llanarmon
PARSABLE						
1730	1765	1500	1800	149934	DUR	Stockton On Tees
1765	1820	1730	1820	149934	LND	City
PARSELL						
1890	1927	1600	1960	153443	PEM	Johnston
PARSHOE						
....	....	ALL	ALL	174033	SRY	Camberwell
PARSLOE						
1650	1992	1600	1750	153451	GLS	Passum
1820	1920	1820	1920	153451	SOM	Bath
1780	1850	1600	1800	153451	WIL	Great Sumerford
1780	1850	1600	1800	153451	WIL	Rodhoune
PARSLOW						
1845	1870	1500	1845	104825	BKM	Amersham
1630	1801	1600	1800	124796	BKM	Princes Risborough
1844	1844	....	1900	171646	BKM	Prisborough
1750	1796	1650	1750	108413	GLS	Dursley
1800	1992	1700	1800	114693	GLS	Kings Stanley
1830	1860	1800	1900	155500	OXF	Milton Under Wychwood
....	....	1700	1900	179477	???	Bristol
PARSON						
1860	....	1700	1860	120596	LAN	???
1860	....	1700	1860	120596	WYK	???
PARSONAGE						
....	....	ALL	ALL	108561	ALL	Name Study
1700	1770	1600	1992	158216	CWD	Holt
1750	1880	ALL	ALL	137987	DEN	Gresford
1750	1880	ALL	ALL	137987	DEN	Holt
1770	1900	1600	1992	158216	LAN	Hollins Green
1800	1880	1540	1800	169986	WOR	Aluechurch
1815	1992	ALL	ALL	109746	WOR	Bromsgrove
PARSONS						
....	....	ALL	ALL	100382	ALL	Name Study
1920	1970	1800	1920	122947	AVN	St Philips
1789	1992	1785	1992	103012	BDF	Harrold
1816	1992	....	....	103012	BDF	Odell
1800	1850	1600	1850	164607	BKM	Mid
PARSONS contd.						
....	....	1700	1800	119784	BRK	Aston
1800	1900	1800	1900	171077	CON	St Breock
1810	1865	1750	1850	177091	CON	Worvelstowe
....	....	1600	1900	157910	CON	???
1794	1824	1700	1900	136581	DBY	Alfreton
1676	1696	1550	1675	131245	DBY	Morton
1810	1992	1700	1810	153540	DEV	Devonport
1890	....	1840	1900	135429	DEV	Exmouth
1860	1950	1780	1860	173770	DEV	Plymouth
1820	1880	1700	1800	157910	DEV	St Giles In The Heath
1600	1980	1600	1900	157910	DEV	???
1754	1875	1754	1875	153524	DOR	North East
1600	1630	....	....	131857	DOR	Motcombe
1865	1932	....	....	165514	DOR	Sturminster Newton
1850	1900	1750	1900	109894	DOR	Weymouth
1851	1992	1800	1851	102849	ESS	Southend
1873	1920	ALL	ALL	153559	GLA	Cardiff
1600	1690	....	....	153397	HAM	Boldre
1833	1918	1833	1918	133922	HAM	Bramshaw
1760	....	1700	1800	133957	HAM	Froxfield
1760	1805	1730	1810	125032	HAM	Worting
1730	1830	1700	1850	142123	HRT	Sandridge
....	....	1700	1880	162000	KEN	Swale
1794	1960	1700	1960	100382	KEN	Warehorn
1875	1893	ALL	ALL	172588	LAN	Manchester
1776	1890	1700	1900	135968	LEI	Braunstone
1801	1885	1775	1900	136581	LEI	Hinckley
1820	1870	ALL	ALL	143294	LEI	Hinckley
1851	1898	....	....	169498	LIN	Holbeach
1820	1860	1600	1850	113654	LND	ALL
1850	1895	1800	1850	128775	LND	East
....	....	1800	1900	117714	LND	Chelsea
1786	1825	1814	1825	116114	MDX	Harrow On The Hill
....	....	1750	1800	108677	MDX	London
1840	1851	1841	1851	116114	MDX	Old Brentford
1808	1898	1872	1992	169498	NTH	Fotheringham
1816	1992	1789	1992	103012	NTH	Irthlingborough
1880	1910	1860	1880	128775	NTT	Nottingham
1775	1846	1700	1846	136581	NTT	Nottingham
1831	1884	1800	1884	159905	OXF	Shenington
1654	1754	1600	1654	155276	SFK	Felixstowe
1770	1919	ALL	ALL	153516	SOM	Axbridge
1800	1850	1700	1850	153486	SOM	Bath
1640	1720	1640	1720	142018	SOM	Bridgwater
....	....	1840	1860	167479	SOM	Bristol
....	1859	1820	1870	133639	SOM	Coker
1795	1876	1750	1795	153559	SOM	Kewstoke
1770	1840	ALL	ALL	153516	SOM	Kingston Seymour
1747	1867	1720	1881	153508	SOM	Kingston St Mary
1825	1900	1800	1900	149160	SOM	Stanton Drew
1738	1820	1650	1850	149160	SOM	Stogumber
1747	1867	1720	1881	153508	SOM	Taunton
1753	1876	1700	1753	153559	SOM	Wellington
1820	1860	ALL	ALL	153559	SOM	Weston Super Mare
1780	1900	1700	1900	170852	SRY	Albury
1700	1800	ALL	ALL	154830	SRY	Charlwood
1780	1820	1750	1780	131342	SRY	Compton
1770	1992	ALL	1800	142301	SRY	Godalming
1721	1900	1600	1721	110183	SSX	Beckley
1721	1900	1600	1721	110183	SSX	Brede
1827	1861	1800	1900	101508	SSX	Heathfield
1825	1920	1700	1837	176370	SSX	Hellingly
1757	1800	....	....	139971	SSX	Horsted Keynes
1757	1800	....	....	139971	SSX	Uckfield
1900	1960	1800	1960	115045	STS	West Bromwich
....	....	ALL	1755	137014	WAR	ALL
1697	1701	1550	1696	131245	WAR	Hampton In Arden
1500	1700	....	....	100420	WAR	Meriden
1755	1900	....	....	137014	WAR	Napton
1812	1992	1500	1812	153494	WAR	Warwick
1798	1992	1700	1798	123153	WIL	Dilton
1820	1900	1780	1900	155357	WIL	Fovant
1812	1818	1800	1850	109363	WIL	Melksham
1833	1918	1833	1918	133922	WIL	Nomansland
1833	1918	....	....	133922	WIL	Salisbury
1750	1870	1650	1950	130419	YKS	Giggleswick
1750	1870	1650	1950	130419	YKS	Slaidburn
PARSUS						
1550	1700	1550	1700	102830	STS	Sedgely
PARTINGTON						
1850	1992	1750	1850	108359	LAN	Farnworth
1720	1800	....	....	153575	LAN	Little Heaton

Known From	To	Researching From	To	Ref	Cty	Place
PARTINGTON contd.						
1800	1895	....	....	153575	LAN	Manchester
1846	....	1750	1846	178381	LAN	Manchester
1646	1720	....	....	153575	LAN	Middleton
1595	1646	....	....	153575	LAN	Radcliffe
1895	1965	....	....	153575	LAN	Urmston
1850	1925	1800	1925	133450	PER	Blairgowrie
PARTLETT						
1900	1989	1700	1900	171913	LIN	Lincoln
PARTLOW						
1650	1960	....	....	115509	OXF	ALL
PARTON						
1800	1840	1700	1800	157708	SAL	Wellington
PARTRIDGE						
....	....	1700	1799	174963	BDF	Milton Bryan
1764	1900	1700	1764	176257	BDF	Sharnbrook
....	....	1700	1799	174963	BDF	Tilsworth
1793	1839	1500	1840	157538	BRK	Farnborough
1793	1839	1500	1840	157538	BRK	Sparsholt
1825	1930	ALL	ALL	119253	CHS	Heaton Moor
1749	1800	1700	1750	156698	DEV	Witheridge
1750	1850	1700	1900	156701	DEV	Witheridge
1658	1705	1580	1837	165972	DEV	Witheridge
....	....	1750	1950	115045	GLA	Cardiff
1840	....	ALL	ALL	119253	GLS	Chalford
1660	1800	ALL	ALL	119253	GLS	Wishanger
....	....	1750	1950	115045	HEF	Llangaren
1870	1900	ALL	ALL	119253	LAN	Manchester
1800	1960	1700	1800	153583	LEI	Mowsley
1880	1900	1800	1880	108448	LND	East
1813	1850	1800	1880	144398	LND	Southwark
1860	1860	1825	1900	136042	LND	Stepney
1749	1934	1650	1749	166111	NTH	Bozeat
1820	1871	1841	1871	130192	SFK	Aldringham
....	....	....	1780	137227	SFK	???
1738	1854	1500	1735	153591	SOM	Hardington Mandeville
1738	1854	1500	1735	153591	SOM	Yeovil
1624	....	....	1640	160873	STS	West Bromwich
1829	1864	ALL	ALL	119253	WAR	Birmingham
1799	1992	....	....	172529	WAR	Birmingham
1692	1802	1650	1692	160474	WES	Elterwater
1702	1841	1600	1702	152196	WES	Grasmere
ALL	1724	....	....	105368	WOR	Doritwich
1793	1915	....	....	173827	WOR	Droitwich
PARVIN						
1819	1878	1776	1819	127698	SSX	Chichester
PASAND						
1722	1746	1670	1746	107573	WAR	Kingsbury
PASCHOUD						
1770	1826	ALL	ALL	163465	NTT	Newark
PASCO						
1761	1795	1700	1761	173118	CON	Talland
....	....	1740	1760	145297	CON	Veryan
....	....	1700	1992	179531	LND	ALL
PASCOE						
1736	1920	....	1736	145858	CON	Camborne
1823	1911	1700	1823	176575	CON	Gwinear
1760	1992	1700	1760	153605	CON	Heiston
1834	1900	1700	1834	165549	CON	Illogan
?	?	?	?	111937	CON	Roche
1785	1809	1600	1785	129305	CON	Sennen
1700	....	?	?	136999	CON	Sithney
1760	1992	1700	1760	153605	CON	Sithney
1834	1900	1700	1834	165549	CON	Sithney
?	?	?	?	111937	CON	St Austell
1775	....	1770	1800	145297	CON	St Goran
1800	1820	....	....	145297	CON	Tregony
1760	1900	1700	1900	142875	CON	Truro
1840	1906	....	....	145297	CON	Truro
1859	1889	1800	1992	117609	MDX	Amwell
1859	1889	1800	1992	117609	MDX	Islington
PASCOVY						
1704	....	....	....	166723	SRY	Horsell
PASH						
1850	....	1800	1900	132659	DEV	ALL
PASHLEY						
1700	1820	ALL	1820	173436	YKS	Silkstone
PASK						
....	....	1700	1900	168653	ALL	ALL
1799	1940	....	....	128996	CAM	Thorney
1816	....	1790	1816	128724	SFK	Bury St Edmunds
PASKENS						
....	....	1709	1806	143480	HAM	Southampton

Known From	To	Researching From	To	Ref	Cty	Place
PASLEY						
1700	1800	....	....	142670	DFS	Langholm
PASS						
1862	1992	?	1862	153613	CHS	ALL
1800	1900	1700	1800	132632	CHS	Sanbach
1862	1992	?	1862	153613	DBY	ALL
1736	....	....	....	138851	LAN	Deane
....	1779	....	....	138851	LAN	Manchester
1800	1840	1700	1800	152587	WAR	Birmingham
PASSEY						
1800	1992	1600	1800	161977	MDX	Hounslow
1857	1903	ALL	1857	107964	MDX	Islington
PASSMOOR						
1800	1992	1700	1800	160075	DUR	Pittington
PASSMORE						
....	....	1500	1900	136972	CON	ALL
1700	1841	1700	1992	141690	CON	Bodmin
1800	1860	1700	1800	136972	CON	Helston
1800	1860	1700	1800	136972	CON	Wendron
1550	1750	1550	1750	135771	DEV	North
1800	1940	1760	1940	106801	DEV	South
1750	1850	1750	1850	123722	DEV	Exeter
....	....	1800	1861	145270	DEV	Morchard Bishop
1750	1800	1750	1880	135429	DEV	North Molton
1689	1721	ALL	1689	154563	DEV	Ottery St Mary
1850	....	1780	1900	135429	SOM	Bath
1867	1992	1850	1957	164127	SOM	Chard
PASSONS						
1700	1750	1700	1800	171077	CON	Padstow
PASTERFUL						
1896	1918	1850	1895	176435	MDX	Hackney
PASTMOOR						
1733	1733	1733	1733	141690	CON	St Mary
PASTON						
1615	1789	....	....	116602	GLS	Horton
PATCHETT						
....	....	ALL	ALL	153621	ALL	Name Study
1350	1992	1538	1992	153621	WYK	Halifax
1841	1992	?	?	176702	WYK	Queensbury
1802	1802	ALL	1802	173290	YKS	Hiptonstall
PATCHING						
ALL	ALL	ALL	ALL	153648	ALL	ALL
1798	1817	ALL	ALL	149489	SSX	Horsham
PATCHOM						
1674	1674	1600	1674	147885	SSX	Ardingly
PATE						
1826	1900	1600	1826	165697	CAM	Little Downham
1860	1900	ALL	ALL	171530	LKS	Blantyre
1835	1940	ALL	ALL	171530	LKS	Hamilton
1782	1992	1700	1790	153656	LKS	Lesmahagow
PATEMAN						
1754	1940	....	....	128996	CAM	Thorney
PATERSON						
1860	1900	1700	1860	100846	CLK	Clackmanan
1803	....	1700	1780	100846	CLK	???
1810	1912	ALL	ALL	145092	DFS	Annandale
1801	1871	1700	1801	100145	DFS	Dumfries
....	....	1500	1773	138614	DFS	Lochmaben
1825	1866	ALL	ALL	135909	KKD	???
1800	1900	1750	1830	179000	LKS	Airdrie
1766	....	....	....	120804	LKS	Strathaven
1805	1823	....	....	161357	LND	Bermondsey
....	....	1810	1820	161357	LND	Camberwell
....	....	1810	1820	161357	LND	Newington
1600	1670	ALL	1670	149063	MLN	Borthwick
1764	1808	....	....	103632	NBL	Newcastle Upon Tyne
1717	1730	....	....	113484	PER	Abernethy
1800	1900	1800	1925	144290	ROSS-SHIRE	Knockbain
1745	1802	1700	1861	153664	SCT	Sutherland
1859	1859	1700	1880	156493	STI	Glasgow
1859	1859	1700	1880	156493	STI	Govan
PATES						
1500	1950	1500	1950	145726	GLS	Charlton Kings
1690	1900	ALL	1940	177571	HRT	Hitchin
PATEY						
1837	1945	ALL	ALL	156175	SRY	Southwark
PATFIELD						
1888	1927	1650	1888	158151	NFK	Kings Lynn
1864	1864	1650	1864	158151	NFK	Little Dunham
1650	1823	1650	1860	158151	NFK	South Creake
PATIENCE						
1853	1894	ALL	1853	101362	KER	Killarney
PATIENT						
1750	1850	ALL	ALL	131873	ESS	Manuden

Known From	To	Researching From	To	Ref	Cty	Place
PATMORE						
1750	1813	....	....	101028	ESS	High Easter
1745	1820	1700	1750	103896	HRT	Sawbridgeworth
1860	1897	1840	1890	161942	KEN	Dover
1837	1992	1700	1838	100110	LND	Battersea
PATON						
1830	1870	1780	1870	146803	ANS	Montrose
1868	1932	1861	....	153680	ANS	Montrose
1755	1861	ALL	1861	153680	ANS	Usan
....	....	1800	1875	119970	ARM	Armagh
1834	1992	....	....	144088	AYR	ALL
1800	1992	1700	1800	139203	AYR	Beith
....	....	?	?	110507	AYR	Sorn
1832	....	1770	1832	153699	FIF	Cupar
1870	1900	1850	1900	131482	LAN	Barrow In Furness
1804	1834	ALL	1992	119105	LKS	Glasgow
1857	1929	....	....	118133	SCT	Bridgeton
....	....	1835	1857	118133	SCT	Glasgow
PATRICK						
1200	1280	1200	1280	154881	ALL	ALL
1756	1880	1750	1900	104361	EAG	Harleston
1800	1830	1700	1850	126586	ESS	Bridbrook
1760	1800	1800	1992	105651	GLS	Twyning
1847	1881	1700	1992	149659	HAM	Binsted
1800	1960	1700	1800	153583	LEI	Mowsley
1870	1925	1850	1900	104361	MDX	Hackney
....	....	1800	1900	166634	MDX	Islington
1813	1891	....	1813	176761	NBL	Spittle
1813	1891	....	1813	176761	NBL	Tweedmouth Ford
1813	1891	....	1813	176761	NBL	Widdrington
1714	1850	1600	1992	159956	NTH	Burton Latimer
....	....	1720	1760	110450	NTH	Rothwell
1850	1900	1800	1900	169404	SCT	Kilmarnock
1790	1858	1500	1790	110310	SRY	Farnham
1830	1940	1750	1830	142972	STI	Kilsyth
1640	1750	1600	1750	119938	YKS	York
PATRICKSON						
1600	1800	ALL	1992	133159	CMA	Ennerdale
1550	1750	1500	1750	167088	CMA	Whitehaven
1730	1900	1500	1730	101842	CUL	Heathersgill
PATT						
1860	1992	1800	1800	153702	DEV	Alverdiscott
1860	1992	1800	1900	153702	DEV	Bideford
1750	1992	1600	1750	153702	DEV	Yarnscombe
PATTE						
1785	....	....	....	124508	KEN	Canterbury
1793	....	....	....	124508	LND	Marylebone
PATTEN						
1681	1871	ALL	ALL	156310	ESS	Wakes Colne
....	....	1500	1880	166863	IRL	ALL
1790	1850	1790	1850	103764	SAL	Benthall
1584	1683	ALL	1700	156310	SFK	South
1700	1992	ALL	1700	153729	SOM	Crewkerne
PATTENDEN						
....	....	ALL	ALL	140910	ALL	Name Study
ALL	ALL	ALL	ALL	167002	ALL	ALL
1829	1900	ALL	ALL	149438	KEN	East Peckham
1829	1900	ALL	ALL	149438	KEN	Hadlow
1764	1920	1700	1764	118079	KEN	Whitstable
PATTERMASTER						
1800	1850	1800	1890	130222	BDF	Husborne Crawley
1810	1810	1810	1830	130222	LND	ALL
PATTERN						
1765	1880	1700	1992	110906	NFK	Terringtons
PATTERSON						
1805	1992	ALL	1805	154520	BEW	Murton
1751	1930	....	....	153745	DEV	ALL
1650	1820	1600	1800	154881	DON	Rathmelton
1751	1930	....	....	153745	DOR	ALL
1840	1851	....	....	131202	DUR	Lanchester
1914	1950	1850	1950	153737	DUR	Sunderland
1740	1825	....	....	131202	DUR	Weardale
....	....	1800	1992	173053	DUR	Wolsingham
1860	....	1700	1860	100846	IRL	???
1841	....	1700	1800	143448	LTN	East
1787	....	1780	1800	163775	MDX	Shoreditch
1850	1920	1870	1900	126500	NBL	Berwick Upon Tweed
1850	....	....	....	126497	NBL	Berwick Upon Tweed
1600	1740	....	....	122297	NBL	Tynemouth
....	....	1700	1850	152390	NFK	Norwich
1841	....	1700	1800	143448	SCT	Dunbar
1820	1880	1800	1900	154881	SLI	Drumcliffe
1750	1846	1600	1775	101575	YKS	Cottingham
PATTINSON						
1772	1890	1700	1771	132764	CUL	Ainstable
1764	1851	1700	1763	132764	CUL	Alston
1550	1900	ALL	....	104515	LIN	South
PATTISON						
....	....	ALL	ALL	153788	ALL	Name Study
1500	1900	1550	1900	153788	ALL	ALL
1900	1980	1700	1900	150371	CUL	Brewcastle
1721	1831	ALL	1721	154563	DBY	Barlborough
1721	1831	ALL	1721	154563	DBY	Whitwell
1830	1880	1700	1900	152110	DUR	Monkwearmouth
1830	1992	ALL	ALL	153753	DUR	Monkwearmouth
1847	1865	1847	1900	152110	DUR	Southwick
1830	....	1780	1830	152110	DUR	Sunderland
1800	1840	1740	1800	137278	DUR	Weardale
1708	1800	ALL	1708	154563	DUR	Whickham
1834	1992	1803	....	175803	DUR	Winlaton
1800	1828	1800	1828	154563	DUR	Wolsingham
....	....	1600	1800	174696	ESS	Maldon
1850	1980	ALL	1850	103438	GMP	Aberdeen
1865	....	....	....	160385	IOM	Peel
1810	1900	1800	1900	118540	KEN	Chatham
1900	1992	....	....	153796	LAN	Ashton
....	....	1700	1800	147613	NBL	Bolam
1761	1784	1600	1761	116637	NBL	Ponteland
1800	1900	....	....	150371	ROX	Newcastleton
1865	....	....	....	160385	SCT	???
1832	1897	....	....	153796	STS	Newcastle Under Lyme
1758	1776	....	....	141097	YKS	Stainton
....	....	1840	1890	139297	YKS	Thrintoft
PATTLE						
1692	1874	1500	1692	128724	SFK	ALL
PATTON						
1800	1815	1780	1992	168181	ARM	Tanderagee
1874	1900	1800	1900	125431	LDY	Coleraine
....	....	1600	1800	179531	YKS	Stainton
PATY						
....	....	ALL	1805	166499	???	???
PAUDON						
1811	....	....	1820	103934	LAN	Eccles
1811	....	....	1820	103934	LAN	Pendleton
PAUK						
1550	1680	1300	1770	105333	DEV	Buckland In The Moor
1550	1680	1300	1770	105333	DEV	Holne
1550	1680	1300	1770	105333	DEV	Ilsington
1550	1680	1300	1770	105333	DEV	Lydford
1550	1680	1300	1770	105333	DEV	Widecombe In The Moor
PAUL						
1700	1722	1600	1700	102571	CON	Paul
1722	1887	1650	1722	150894	CON	St Kew
1840	1865	1800	1870	142042	DEV	Buckerell
1735	1904	1700	1850	161721	DUR	South Shields
1728	1800	1725	1800	142018	HAM	Winchester
1790	1822	1700	1850	154881	LND	ALL
1760	1822	1700	1800	154881	NBL	Ewart
1830	1880	1800	1992	134937	NFK	???
1800	1870	1700	1800	149306	SOM	West
1809	1871	1700	1890	170518	SOM	Barrington
1700	1750	1700	1750	142018	SOM	Merriott
1838	....	....	....	170526	WIL	Barford St Martin
1860	....	1860	1900	177768	???	Glasgow
PAULDING						
....	....	1787	....	109673	SOM	Bath
PAULET						
1650	1650	1600	1700	133450	SOM	West
PAULEY						
1834	1992	....	....	157155	CAM	Cottenham
1834	1992	....	....	157155	CAM	Histon
1834	1992	....	....	157155	CAM	Impington
1923	....	....	....	157155	LND	Edmonton
PAULIN						
1350	1500	1350	1500	154881	KEN	Brasted
1250	1350	1200	1350	154881	KEN	St Pauls Cray
1814	1884	1814	1884	175420	OXF	Henley On Thames
PAULING						
....	....	ALL	ALL	153818	ALL	ALL
1820	1900	1820	1940	153818	BKM	Monks Risborough
1720	1880	....	1880	153818	BKM	Oakley
1800	1860	1700	1900	153826	BRK	Abingdon
1732	1761	1700	1850	118397	OXF	Asthalleigh

Known From	To	Researching From	To	Ref	Cty	Place
PAULL						
1650	1992	1600	1914	118818	CON	Illogan
1820	1854	1750	1820	144177	CON	St Agnes
1780	1849	1750	1900	167487	DEV	Plymouth
1867	1940	1850	1992	164127	SOM	Chard
PAULSON						
1920	1950	1800	1870	146102	LAN	Stockport
1800	1880	1750	1880	173819	NTT	Oxton
PAVELEY						
....	....	ALL	ALL	127272	ALL	Name Study
....	....	....	....	127272	HRT	Sawbridgeworth
PAVELY						
....	....	....	....	127272	ESS	ALL
PAVER						
1858	1929	....	....	171557	LND	Greenwich
?	?	....	....	171557	LND	Nunhead
....	1930	....	....	171557	SSX	Five Oakes
PAVEY						
1786	1992	1700	1992	132187	HRT	East
1786	1992	1700	1992	132187	HRT	Ware
1830	1860	1800	1830	166383	KEN	Deptford
1900	1992	1900	1992	153834	SSX	Eastbourne
1867	1900	1867	1900	153834	SSX	Tunbridge Wells
PAVIOUR						
1890	1992	ALL	1890	102407	WYK	Huddersfield
PAVISS						
....	....	1750	1780	103713	CAM	Ashley
PAVITT						
1783	....	1700	1800	138185	ESS	ALL
....	....	1600	1840	153842	ESS	South
1873	1930	1860	....	116297	ESS	Harlow
1882	1970	....	....	153842	HRT	Barnet
1873	1930	1860	....	116297	LND	Greenwich
1823	1881	1780	1841	153842	LND	St Marylebone
1823	1881	1780	1841	153842	LND	St Pancras
PAVOR						
1854	....	1750	1900	175307	STS	Cheadle
PAVORD						
1792	1878	1700	1972	153281	DOR	Nether Compton
1792	1875	1700	1972	153281	SOM	Chard
PAWLEY						
1715	1992	ALL	1715	153850	CON	Lelant
1715	1992	ALL	1715	153850	CON	Penzance
1550	1595	1500	1550	102571	CON	Uny Lelant
1802	1840	1700	1802	149578	DEV	Plymouth
1802	1840	1700	1802	149578	DEV	Stoke Damerel
....	1750	ALL	1750	134511	LEI	Wigston
1722	1842	1600	1722	175218	NFK	North West
PAWSEY						
1777	....	1700	1790	135941	SFK	Poslingford
1749	1770	1650	1800	126586	SFK	Stansfield
PAWSON						
1838	1838	1800	1992	172782	YKS	Aberford
1656	1679	1600	1992	114901	YKS	Otley
1712	1774	1600	1712	166723	YKS	Pannal
PAWTON						
1696	....	1600	1720	160873	STS	Sedgley
PAXSON						
1650	1992	ALL	1650	127213	BKM	Marsh Gibbon
PAXTON						
1596	1616	....	1616	103349	BDF	Odell
1800	1899	1800	1899	169781	DUR	Lamsley
1800	1899	1800	1899	169781	DUR	Low Fell
1820	....	1750	1820	103772	LKS	Barony
1850	1992	1700	1850	175137	NBL	ALL
1850	1960	1700	1850	174254	SCT	Springburn
PAY						
1730	1850	1700	1900	105287	KEN	East
1850	1940	1700	1890	129755	KEN	Dover
?	?	?	?	166642	KEN	???
1830	1880	1780	1830	161519	SSX	Harting
PAYBODY						
1730	1879	1600	1730	178926	NTH	Welford
PAYE						
1900	ALL	ALL	ALL	130788	MDX	Enfield
PAYLER						
....	....	....	....	153869	YKS	???
PAYLOR						
1780	1850	1780	1850	103721	NRY	Topcliffe By Thirsk
1841	1861	....	....	132462	YKS	Dishforth
1861	1913	....	....	132462	YKS	Thirsk
PAYN						
....	1800	ALL	1800	134511	KEN	Chatham
1851	1894	1700	1851	178985	STS	Handsworth

Known From	To	Researching From	To	Ref	Cty	Place
PAYN contd.						
1851	1894	1700	1851	178985	WAR	Handsworth
PAYNE						
1940	?	ALL	1940	100072	BDF	???
?	?	....	....	159069	BKM	Amersham
1838	1907	ALL	1992	112631	BKM	Chalfont St Giles
1716	1730	1716	1730	178705	BRK	Reading
1830	1853	....	1830	136212	CAM	Cambridge
1840	1950	1700	1840	153893	CAM	Ely
1840	1950	1700	1840	153893	CAM	Guyhirn
1844	1865	1844	1865	136980	CHS	Liverpool
1850	1881	1850	1992	172596	CON	Paul
1830	1830	1750	1860	171662	COR	Cork
1785	....	1760	1785	110043	DEV	Shobrooke
1770	1860	1700	1840	110949	DOR	Chideock
1870	1944	1850	1880	163694	ENG	Nottingham
1761	1992	1700	1992	169005	ESS	High Laver
1860	1980	1750	1860	151165	ESS	Rochford
1834	....	1700	1834	157953	ESS	The Roddings
1845	1935	....	1877	166553	GLA	Cardiff
1850	1992	1750	1992	167991	GLA	Rhondda
1875	1992	1750	1992	167991	GLS	Thornbury
1880	1986	ALL	ALL	126756	HAM	ALL
1815	1815	1780	1830	105333	HAM	Portsea
1790	1841	1700	1800	170968	HAM	Portsea
1800	1900	....	....	153931	HAM	Portsmouth
1919	1992	1919	1960	132551	HAM	???
1872	1992	1700	1870	103098	IOW	Sandown
....	....	1700	1992	122742	IOW	Wroxall
1975	1978	....	....	173932	KEN	Canterbury
1853	1870	1850	1900	171441	KEN	Dover
1875	1881	1870	1900	171441	KEN	Faversham
1867	....	....	....	171441	KEN	Gillingham
1788	1805	....	1820	171441	KEN	Great Chart
1853	1870	1850	1900	171441	KEN	Hougham
1830	1860	1700	1830	141402	KEN	Lee
1841	....	....	....	171441	KEN	Minster On Sheppey
1843	1850	1840	1880	171441	KEN	Tonge
1700	1814	ALL	ALL	106097	LEI	Burton Overy
1731	1885	1700	1731	149195	LEI	Hugglescote
1700	1814	ALL	ALL	106097	LEI	Narborough
1800	1841	1800	1900	153877	LEI	Stanton Under Bardon
1776	1950	1700	1776	107344	LIN	Sleaford
1862	1920	1766	1862	122572	LND	ALL
1815	1847	....	1855	171441	LND	Bethnal Green
1843	....	....	1855	171441	LND	Hackney
1850	....	....	1855	171441	LND	Mile End
1911	1992	1882	1911	167231	LND	Wandsworth
1820	1870	1780	1992	173096	MDX	London
1877	1882	1800	1877	167231	MDX	Poplar
1765	....	ALL	1800	102016	MDX	Stepney
1873	1992	1800	1873	176931	MON	Newport
1863	1950	ALL	ALL	107425	NFK	Norwich
1832	1992	1700	1832	118265	NFK	Norwich
1840	1880	ALL	ALL	107425	NFK	Overstrand
1794	1830	1750	1850	110906	NFK	Walpoles
1770	1850	ALL	1770	156922	NTH	Gayton
1880	1986	ALL	ALL	126756	NTT	ALL
1782	1880	....	1782	100064	SFK	Barrow
1905	1905	1850	1905	103640	SFK	Beccles
1724	1724	1650	1800	159956	SFK	Hargrave
1816	1866	1816	1866	136808	SFK	Rede
....	....	1850	1899	173274	SFK	Whatfield
1600	1992	1300	1900	102555	SOM	Banwell
1803	1871	1700	1820	153923	SOM	Bath
1740	1820	1600	1740	108413	SOM	Cross
1796	....	....	....	112887	SOM	Frome
1818	1832	1800	1840	121169	SOM	Frome
1780	1840	ALL	ALL	106313	SOM	Langport
1796	1818	....	1796	167053	SOM	Langport
....	....	1700	....	124400	SOM	Sparkford
1792	1793	1700	1792	135410	SOM	West Lydford
1876	1992	....	....	153923	SOM	Weston Super Mare
1845	1861	....	....	173932	SRY	Ashtead
1949	....	....	....	173932	SSX	Brighton
1826	1828	1600	1826	147885	SSX	East Grinstead
1930	....	....	....	153931	SSX	Littelhampton
1836	1867	1800	1900	143677	SSX	Steyning
1852	1960	1778	1852	134872	SSX	Warbleton
1865	1910	1700	1865	139122	STS	Willenhall
1862	1920	1766	1862	122572	WAR	ALL
1810	1855	1700	1900	136034	WAR	Birmingham
1820	....	1700	1820	137421	WAR	Birmingham

Known From	To	Researching From	To	Ref	Cty	Place
PAYNE contd.						
1770	1840	1700	1770	132268	WAR	Burmington
1883	....	....	....	173827	WAR	Edgbaston
1731	1885	1700	1731	149195	WAR	Monk's Kirby
1865	1910	1700	1865	139122	WAR	Willenhall
1759	1811	1600	1759	175781	WIL	Chitterne
1700	1840	....	1840	121169	WIL	Longbridge Deverill
1840	1850	1700	1850	126772	WIL	Warminster
....	....	1700	1890	153907	WOR	Bewdley
1890	1960	....	....	153907	WOR	Stourport
....	....	1700	1890	153907	WOR	Wribbenhall
1831	1957	1831	1957	149403	YKS	Hull
PAYNTER						
1830	1980	1700	1800	153958	BRK	???
1725	1760	1700	1760	108510	CON	St Ives
1900	1992	1830	1900	153966	LND	Pancras
1830	1980	1700	1800	153958	NTH	???
PAYNTING						
1870	1970	....	1869	121908	WAR	Warwick
PAYTON						
1820	....	ALL	1820	139459	WAR	Solihull
PAZZERD						
ALL	ALL	ALL	ALL	167096	ALL	ALL
1840	1992	1700	1992	167096	WIL	Wroughton
PCIEKRING						
1830	1992	1750	1830	122297	DUR	South Shields
PCIKERING						
1890	1890	ALL	1960	146315	YKS	Leeds
PEABODY						
1879	1992	....	....	178926	LEI	Wigston
1850	1870	1800	1900	148458	NTH	Welford
PEACE						
....	1765	?	1765	128910	DBY	Church Gresley
1835	1851	1816	1861	136816	STS	Burton On Trent
PEACEY						
1890	1900	....	....	114723	LND	Plaistow
PEACH						
1630	1730	1630	1730	118869	BDF	Millbrook
1741	1940	....	....	128996	CAM	Thorney
1540	1796	1550	1796	102830	DBY	Bradley
....	....	1800	ALL	114022	DOR	???
1851	1890	1850	1890	121177	ESS	Hockley
1670	1780	1670	1780	127655	GLS	Barnwood
1670	1780	1670	1780	127655	GLS	Woodchester
1900	1992	1700	1900	148849	LEI	Shepshed
1850	1900	1700	1850	177296	LIN	Fulbeck
1845	1865	ALL	ALL	156256	STS	Leek
PEACHEY						
1911	....	ALL	1950	170666	CAM	Soham
....	....	ALL	1700	169137	ESS	North
1720	1880	....	....	169137	ESS	Gt Horkesley
1767	1871	....	....	147907	GLS	Chedworth
1800	1900	1700	1800	118745	LND	Southwark
....	....	ALL	1700	169137	SFK	South
1720	....	1650	1720	100013	SFK	West Stow
PEACHMENT						
....	....	ALL	ALL	138002	NFK	ALL
PEACHY						
1700	1900	....	....	142530	GLS	Paxford
PEACOCK						
1790	1918	....	....	100536	ALL	???
1850	1850	1700	1992	112097	BDF	ALL
....	....	1800	1920	103713	CAM	Soham
1856	1881	1830	1890	132675	CAM	Wimblington
1860	....	....	....	128945	DUR	City
1806	1879	1700	1806	129305	DUR	Evenwood
1800	1859	....	....	116637	DUR	Sunderland
1700	1799	1700	1799	169781	DUR	???
1875	....	1750	1900	109894	GLS	Bitton
1860	1992	1700	1860	168084	GLS	Warmley
1748	1828	1748	1828	138703	HUN	Huntingdon
1748	1828	1748	1828	138703	HUN	St Neots
1816	1909	1750	1816	175064	LND	St Pancras
1901	1955	....	1901	153982	LND	Willesdon
1819	1930	1750	1925	144797	MDX	Bethnal Green
1770	1800	1700	1770	121339	NYK	Salton
1790	1992	1700	1850	144231	RFW	Barrhead
1838	1850	1750	1900	114456	SAL	ALL
1806	1879	1700	1806	129305	YKS	Arkengarthdale
1515	1851	ALL	1515	145203	YKS	Malham
1740	1992	1740	1992	167843	YKS	Redmire Cum Bolton
1700	1740	1500	1800	167843	YKS	Skeughead
PEAGAM						
ALL	ALL	ALL	ALL	165735	ALL	ALL

Known From	To	Researching From	To	Ref	Cty	Place
PEAK						
....	....	ALL	ALL	154016	ALL	Name Study
1800	1880	1770	1800	173118	DEV	Appledore
1680	1840	1600	1680	173312	STS	Keele
PEAKE						
1790	1851	1600	1851	158232	KEN	Thanet
1881	....	1750	1881	153109	LAN	Bolton
1770	1992	ALL	ALL	154008	RUT	ALL
1600	1700	ALL	1600	131059	SFK	Westhorpe
1800	1992	1700	1800	154016	YKS	Ripon
PEAKEHEATH						
1900	....	....	....	122505	STS	Newcastle
PEAKER						
ALL	ALL	ALL	ALL	154024	ALL	ALL
1752	1992	1640	1752	154024	YKS	West Riding
PEAL						
....	....	1700	1900	165476	LND	City
1837	1837	1700	1950	165476	LND	Stepney
PEAR						
1750	1875	1600	1992	157023	GLS	Gloucester Down
PEARCE						
1883	1974	1850	1883	154075	AVN	Bristol
1840	1870	1840	ALL	154091	AVN	Clevedon
1800	1850	1800	1992	133450	BDF	Bedford
....	....	1700	1850	113085	BKM	Iver
1775	1855	1855	1992	141402	BKM	Lee
1870	1950	1840	1950	142360	BRK	Chaddleworth
1726	1770	ALL	1800	151815	CAM	Barrington
1830	1845	ALL	1992	168696	CON	East
1811	1821	1811	1821	141690	CON	Bodmin
1865	1992	?	1865	129615	CON	Gwinear
1750	1800	1700	1900	142875	CON	Gwinear
1749	1790	1700	1749	173118	CON	Lansallos
1784	1900	1700	1784	116432	CON	Morval
1660	1683	1600	1660	102571	CON	Perranzabuloe
1818	1824	1800	....	156019	CON	Redruth
1834	1834	1750	1900	133450	CON	Roche
1815	1932	1736	1934	109053	CON	South Petherwin
1769	1800	1650	1769	163759	CON	St Michael Caerhays
1799	1865	....	....	163759	CON	Veryan
1839	....	....	....	136964	CON	???
1880	1900	1880	1900	154040	DEV	Ashreigney
1900	1963	1900	1963	154040	DEV	Barnstaple
1777	1897	1750	1850	110604	DEV	Chardstock
1641	1947	1641	1947	154040	DEV	Georgeham
1841	....	1800	1992	107662	DEV	Selsey
1722	1809	ALL	1992	122106	DOR	Fortuneswell
1853	....	1800	1992	107662	DOR	Portland
1722	1809	ALL	1992	122106	DOR	Portland
1800	1900	ALL	ALL	174637	DOR	Portland
....	1880	ALL	1880	106283	DUR	Sunderland
1810	1880	ALL	1810	112771	ESS	North Weald Bassett
1902	1992	1902	1992	154040	GLA	Neath
....	....	1700	....	141216	GLS	Mid
1750	1805	1700	1850	177024	GLS	Mitcheldean
1779	1992	....	....	140414	GLS	Stapleton
1761	1761	1700	1761	148938	GLS	Tytherington
1860	1920	1800	1860	154075	GLS	Wotton Under Edge
1790	1920	1790	1920	110523	GNT	Monmouth
1830	1850	1700	1850	148792	HAM	North East
....	1880	ALL	1880	106283	HAM	Marchwood
1820	1900	1600	1992	112828	HAM	Mitcheldever
....	....	ALL	1810	123331	HEF	ALL
1810	1900	....	....	123331	HEF	Abbeydore
1810	1900	....	....	123331	HEF	Golden Valley
....	....	1837	1900	162000	KEN	Swale
....	....	1800	1900	117714	LND	Chelsea
....	....	1850	....	117714	LND	Fulham
....	....	1850	....	151610	LND	Notting Hill
1800	1840	ALL	ALL	154067	LND	Westminster
1812	1905	1700	1820	106313	MDX	West
1860	1992	....	1860	101761	MDX	East London
1850	1880	1880	1930	145408	MDX	Laleham
....	....	1700	1800	129356	MDX	Shoreditch
1883	1992	ALL	ALL	105856	MDX	???
1819	1926	1750	1819	127590	NFK	Southney
1817	....	ALL	1992	159174	SAL	Ashford Carbonell
1840	1920	ALL	1840	179612	SAL	Staton Lacy
1715	1765	1650	1725	144606	SOM	South
1790	1813	ALL	ALL	154091	SOM	Burtle
1798	1828	1790	1975	154121	SOM	Creech St Michael
1790	1813	ALL	ALL	154091	SOM	Edington
1825	1870	1800	1825	136220	SOM	North Petherton
1807	1960	1780	1960	170143	SRY	Woking

Known From	To	Researching From	To	Ref	Cty	Place
PEARCE contd.						
1883	1992	ALL	ALL	105856	SRY	???
1700	1750	1600	1700	105716	SSX	Bosham
1790	1992	1790	....	118672	STS	Newcastle Under Lyme
....	....	1840	1860	102318	WIL	ALL
1808	1950	1750	1860	133787	WIL	Calne
1850	1992	....	....	175803	WIL	Devizes
....	....	1740	1800	154075	WIL	Kingswood
1794	1838	1794	ALL	145386	WIL	Salisbury
....	....	1700	1820	148113	WIL	Trowbridge
1874	1875	1800	1900	124044	WIL	Warminster
1820	1848	1800	1992	146331	???	Bristol
1900	1965	1800	1900	177717	???	Bristol
1840	1900	1800	1840	148113	???	Pilning
PEARCE-BACON						
1817	1992	1700	1817	101842	NFK	Hindolveston
PEARCY						
1781	1992	1700	1781	130257	SSX	Hunston
PEARD						
1750	1760	1700	1780	146986	CON	Penryn
1850	....	....	....	136964	DEV	Plymouth
PEARDON						
1665	1800	1630	1800	159700	CON	Kilkhampton
PEARE						
1834	1837	1800	1863	164828	MDX	Bloomsbury
1836	1879	1750	1836	126985	WEX	Kilmallock
PEARMAIN						
1834	1992	1834	1992	137324	LND	Westminster
PEARMAN						
1773	1851	1700	1773	173843	ESS	Ashdon
1700	ALL	1750	1910	107379	HRT	Hemel Hempstead
1770	1900	1700	1900	169641	NFK	Marham
PEARN						
1630	1992	ALL	1992	168718	CON	South East
1730	1992	1700	1925	162582	CON	South
1730	1992	1700	1925	162582	DEV	South
1820	....	ALL	1820	142301	DEV	Stoke Damerel
PEARS						
1656	1940	....	....	128996	CAM	Thorney
1640	1660	1600	1640	102571	CON	St Just In Penwith
1880	1992	ALL	1900	142301	LAN	Barrow In Furness
1760	1992	1700	1992	159107	NFK	Upwell
1830	1870	1830	1870	111457	YKS	Leeds
PEARSE						
1800	1918	1750	1992	121312	CON	St Enoder
1800	1918	1750	1992	121312	CON	Truro
1841	1900	1800	1992	155896	GLS	Cheltenham
....	....	ALL	ALL	178152	IRL	???
1880	1916	ALL	ALL	178152	LAN	Liverpool
1860	1975	....	....	101028	MDX	London
1820	1845	ALL	1860	118737	SOM	Carhampton
1730	1910	....	....	101028	SOM	Dulverton
1810	1814	....	....	131229	WIL	Westbury
PEARSON						
1864	1900	1750	1864	171662	ARM	Tartarghan
1600	1850	1600	1850	152404	CHS	Stockport
1763	1772	1700	1774	100846	CLK	???
1790	1910	1600	1861	171425	CMA	Alston Muggleswick
1796	1992	1700	1796	158062	CMA	Dalston
1837	1845	1845	1870	140015	CUL	Carlisle
1800	1850	1750	1900	138878	CUL	Whitehaven
1750	1930	ALL	1750	122572	DBY	ALL
1832	1939	1760	1803	136816	DBY	Chesterfield
1832	1939	1760	1803	136816	DBY	Cutthorpe
1821	1840	ALL	1821	152641	DBY	Sawley
1790	1910	1600	1861	171425	DUR	Alston Muggleswick
1743	....	1600	1743	116637	DUR	Bishop Middleham
1810	1992	1750	1810	174785	DUR	Hartlepool
1800	1962	1750	1900	154881	DUR	Shincliffe
....	....	1770	1850	154873	DUR	Sunderland
....	....	1810	1820	133221	ESS	Chingford
1830	1835	....	....	133221	ESS	Loughton
1761	1992	1730	1761	170968	HAM	Alverstoke
1847	1876	1750	1850	118516	HAM	Portsea
1761	1992	1730	1761	170968	HAM	Portsea
1884	1992	1800	1884	154164	HAM	Portsmouth
....	....	?	?	110507	KEN	Chart Sutton
1832	1862	1700	1832	128465	KEN	Milton
....	....	....	1859	161667	KEN	Stone
1800	1809	....	1800	146811	KRS	Fossoway
1780	1900	1700	1992	114596	LAN	Dewsbury
1600	1820	1600	1820	152404	LAN	Eccles
....	....	1630	1700	147613	LAN	Lancaster
PEARSON contd.						
....	....	1700	1740	147613	LAN	Melling
1750	1930	ALL	1750	122572	LEI	ALL
1652	1992	ALL	1800	112275	LEI	North East
1750	1930	ALL	1750	122572	LIN	ALL
1890	1992	1800	1890	154180	LIN	Barton On Humber
1829	1855	?	1829	144800	LIN	Boston
1776	1813	1650	1850	168149	LIN	Boston
1798	1798	1550	1800	147265	LIN	Mid
1741	1773	1700	1741	174211	LIN	Navenby
1741	1773	1700	1741	174211	LIN	Nolton
1763	1763	1700	1800	159042	LIN	Stamford
1862	1942	1600	1862	167355	LND	Bermondsey
....	....	1890	1950	140015	LND	Camberwell
1880	1948	1880	1900	154199	LND	Camberwell
1868	1992	1700	1870	154202	MDX	London
1620	1640	1500	1800	162620	NBL	Allendale
1796	....	....	....	132381	NBL	Newcastle
1750	1930	ALL	1750	122572	NTT	ALL
1810	1890	1800	1900	154210	NYK	Bedale
1740	1790	1700	1800	154210	NYK	Hutton Bonville
1790	1810	1750	1820	154210	NYK	Nerthallerton
1887	....	1887	1890	112615	SAL	Coalbrookdale
1840	....	ALL	1850	112615	SAL	Gosty Hill
1890	....	1890	1895	112615	SAL	Shrewsbury
....	....	1880	1885	154199	SFK	Bury St Edmunds
1700	1800	1700	1800	133817	SFK	Long Melford
1800	1830	1750	1840	168750	SFK	Woodbridge
....	....	1800	1868	130184	SRY	Lambeth
1883	1900	1800	1883	121541	STS	Brierley Hill
1750	1750	1700	1750	125806	STS	Bushbury
1849	1870	1800	1870	164259	STS	Tunstall
....	....	1780	1890	108863	STS	Wolverhampton
1624	1748	....	1748	155055	STS	Wolverhampton
1820	1910	ALL	1930	141569	WAR	Birmingham
1850	1992	ALL	1880	111678	WES	Crosthwaite
1880	....	1880	1883	112615	WOR	Birmingham
1850	1876	1800	1880	112615	WOR	Dudley
1841	1871	1800	1900	161861	WOR	Rowley Regis
1883	1885	1885	1887	112615	WOR	Wolverhampton
1828	1900	....	1828	101761	WRY	Leeds
1808	....	1750	1808	179086	YKS	Bradford
1600	1992	1600	1992	147788	YKS	Leeds
....	....	1800	1900	155098	YKS	Mirfield
1660	1830	1660	1851	170267	YKS	Pudsey
....	....	1737	1884	102199	YKS	Scholes Cleckheaton
1793	1992	1600	1793	154172	YKS	Scholes
1710	1840	1680	1720	170348	YKS	Slaithwaite
1700	1731	1600	1992	102520	YKS	Thornton
1780	1850	ALL	1780	123358	YKS	Wakefield
1782	1821	1700	1782	154164	YKS	West Riding
1700	....	1600	....	134589	YKS	Wigginton
1800	1992	1800	1900	166901	???	Bristol
PEART						
1805	1852	?	1860	103934	LND	???
PEARTS						
1731	1992	1700	1992	153672	BDF	Luton
1731	1992	1700	1992	153672	HRT	Hertford
1731	1992	1700	1992	153672	HRT	Hitchin
PEASANT						
1800	1880	1800	1880	173819	LIN	Coningsby
PEASCOD						
1700	1750	....	....	153397	HAM	Boldre
PEASE						
1792	1792	1700	1992	112097	BDF	ALL
1700	1800	1700	1800	169781	DUR	Durham
1792	1792	1700	1992	112097	HUN	ALL
PEASEY						
1820	1979	1700	1820	164860	SFK	Tostock
PEASGOOD						
1840	1850	1800	1840	121037	MDX	Limehouse
PEAT						
1770	1992	1600	1992	154229	DBY	North
1770	1900	1770	1900	118540	DEV	Alwington
1870	1940	ALL	1900	109509	LIN	Helpringham
1840	1960	1840	1930	102490	NTH	East Carlton
1770	1992	1600	1992	154229	NTT	West
1770	1992	1600	1992	154229	YKS	South
PEATCH						
1710	1733	1710	1733	141690	CON	St Mary
PEATE						
1593	1699	....	....	165999	DBY	Wilne
PEATER						
1768	1768	1734	1768	152943	HAM	Michelmersh

Known From	To	Researching From	To	Ref	Cty	Place
PEATFIELD						
1861	1881	1860	1980	124001	ESS	Romford
1841	1851	1830	1860	124001	HRT	Ware
1793	1981	1770	1913	124001	KEN	Chatham
1768	1930	1870	1880	124001	LAN	Central
1768	1930	1870	1880	124001	LAN	South
1841	1989	1779	1881	124001	LIN	Gainsborough
1636	1980	1630	1881	124001	NTT	Central
1636	1980	1630	1881	124001	NTT	South
1900	1970	1925	1951	124001	SRY	South West
1880	1963	1870	1970	124001	SSX	Brighton
1868	1886	1865	1887	124001	SSX	East Grinstead
PEATHYJOHNS						
1700	1900	1700	1900	105759	ALL	ALL
PEATLING						
....	....	ALL	ALL	154237	ALL	Name Study
1790	1992	1690	1880	154237	LND	Spitalfields
PEATY						
1790	1823	1500	1790	129577	DOR	???
PEBERDY						
1490	1992	1490	1992	154253	LEI	South
1709	1900	ALL	1709	174076	LEI	Saddington
PEBODY						
1879	1992	....	....	178926	LEI	Wigston
PECK						
1700	1830	1700	1830	167924	BDF	Shillington
1900	1992	....	....	154261	ESS	Southend On Sea
1880	1920	1880	1920	124605	ESS	West Ham
1763	....	ALL	1763	168602	HUN	Abbotsley
1740	1880	1740	1880	124605	NFK	Great Yarmouth
1814	1853	ALL	1861	158445	NFK	Whitwell
1839	1839	1700	1839	170542	NFK	Woodton
1820	1891	1790	1891	151599	NTT	Sneinton
1820	1891	1790	1891	151599	NTT	Sutton In Ashfield
1600	1940	....	....	121835	NTT	Worksop
1780	1900	1700	1780	154261	SFK	Chediston
1740	1770	1700	1800	159581	SFK	Framlingham
1815	1992	....	1815	175374	SFK	Ipswich
1843	1945	1843	1945	131997	SFK	Stowmarket
1730	1840	1700	1840	124605	SFK	Wenhaston
1880	1992	....	....	154261	SFK	Withersdale
....	....	ALL	ALL	144762	WIL	Marlborough
....	....	ALL	ALL	144762	WIL	Ogbourn St George
1816	1845	1700	1816	153184	WIL	Ogbourne
1845	1900	....	....	153184	WIL	Shaw
1810	1820	....	....	103764	WOR	Oldswinford
PECKET						
1630	1670	1600	1992	114901	YKS	Thirkleby
PECKHAM						
1746	1801	1600	1746	145459	HAM	Lyndhurst
1779	1781	1750	1780	123978	HAM	Southampton
PECKITT						
1810	1820	1700	1950	167940	SFK	Long Melford
PECKOVER						
....	1808	1750	1850	128961	ESS	Chelmsford
....	1808	1750	1850	128961	NFK	Grimstone
PECKSTON						
....	....	ALL	ALL	119938	ALL	ALL
1800	1890	1800	1890	119938	YKS	Scarborough
PEDDER						
....	....	1680	1730	154873	KEN	Deal
1724	1748	ALL	ALL	141615	LAN	Lower Wyresdale
1640	1667	1600	1640	155276	SFK	Hollesley
PEDEN						
1762	1870	ALL	ALL	101370	ENG	ALL
1764	1870	ALL	ALL	101370	SCT	ALL
PEDERICK						
1780	....	ALL	1800	175773	DEV	Bideford
PEDLAR						
1800	1900	1700	1800	133019	CON	???
PEDLER						
1200	1992	1200	1992	130478	CON	Central
1794	1897	....	1794	108839	HUN	Bluntisham
PEDLEY						
1600	1992	ALL	1600	165395	CHS	Crewe
1600	1992	ALL	1600	165395	CHS	Haslington
....	....	1790	1850	103713	HUN	Great Gransden
1891	?	ALL	ALL	158070	LND	Lambeth
1880	1900	1840	1880	113719	STS	Uttoxeter
1787	1881	1850	1960	139173	WOR	Dudley
1806	....	1700	1992	107204	YKS	Reeth
PEDOTT						
?	?	?	?	138622	ALL	ALL
PEDRICK						
1840	1992	1800	1840	128368	DEV	Okehampton
1840	1992	1800	1840	128368	DEV	Teignmouth
PEDVIN						
1925	1950	ALL	ALL	113824	ALL	ALL
PEEBLES						
1850	1992	1800	1850	174653	ANS	Dundee
1780	1809	1755	1830	167932	FIF	Kilconquhar
PEECOCK						
1800	1850	1700	1850	127914	DBY	Eckington
PEEDELL						
1880	1965	1880	1960	108456	BRK	Reading
PEEDLE						
1801	1822	ALL	1992	115126	BKM	Fulmer
PEEL						
1800	1850	1850	1890	154296	ALL	ALL
1800	1950	1650	1800	128376	CUL	Farlam
1745	1820	1650	1745	133019	CUL	Wigton
1843	1900	1843	1873	138215	HUN	Somersham
1887	1992	1700	1890	155713	KEN	Chislehurst
1846	1919	1700	1992	126012	KEN	Faversham
1841	1950	1841	1881	160636	LIN	Cnetral
1841	1876	1841	1881	160636	LIN	Snelland
1750	1880	ALL	ALL	137987	SAL	Hordley
1780	1900	1841	1900	177350	WYK	Newsholme
1746	1749	....	....	151351	YKS	Ripon
1850	1900	1800	1850	168572	YKS	Sheffield
PEEL-SMITH						
....	?	?	....	134457	YKS	Hull
PEEL-STEPHENS						
1787	1809	1770	1851	160636	LIN	Timberland
PEELESS						
1801	1992	1700	1801	156264	KEN	???
PEELING						
1790	1992	1720	1790	154318	ESS	Clacton
PEEN						
1791	1865	1700	1900	174238	KEN	Gravesend
PEENE						
1784	1820	ALL	1800	115282	KEN	East
PEER						
1700	1992	ALL	ALL	164682	LND	ALL
PEERCYE						
1618	....	1500	1650	143693	BKM	Beaconsfield
PEERLESS						
1800	1837	1700	1800	100935	KEN	Cowden
1837	1894	1700	1900	117331	KEN	Cowden
1700	1750	....	....	119431	KEN	Lyming
....	....	1700	1800	119431	SSX	East
....	....	1700	1890	100935	SSX	Withyham
PEERS						
1880	1900	1880	1930	165034	CHS	Latchford
1808	1881	1740	1808	179523	CHS	Wirral
1763	1838	ALL	1763	112313	CWD	Ruthin
1865	1992	1700	1992	177733	STS	Birmingham
PEET						
1800	1900	ALL	1800	122823	CUL	Calderbeck
1800	1992	1800	1900	132632	LND	???
1712	1992	1600	1712	178500	NTT	Newark
1817	1937	1832	1909	138827	NTT	Nottingham
PEGG						
....	....	1800	1920	154334	DBY	Melbourne
1895	1992	1800	1920	154334	EYK	Hull
1702	1722	ALL	ALL	141615	LEI	North
1820	1950	1750	1840	122149	SRY	Lambeth
1811	1933	1811	1933	128783	STS	Lichfield
....	....	1830	1895	154334	WYK	Tickhill
....	....	ALL	ALL	154970	YKS	Kexby
PEGGS						
1809	1992	ALL	1810	108502	ESS	Brightingsea
PEGLAR						
1802	1909	ALL	1900	104299	GLS	Bristol
PEGLER						
1830	1859	1830	1859	131938	GLA	Swansea
1750	1841	1600	1750	154342	GLS	Bisley
1870	1992	1600	1992	154342	GLS	Bristol
1730	1740	1600	1730	108413	GLS	Durlsey
1800	1850	1750	1992	173096	GLS	Stroud
1839	1839	1800	1900	142921	WIL	Britford
PEGLY						
....	1835	1500	1835	175072	GLS	Bristol
PEILE						
1791	1858	1700	1791	152196	CMA	Harris Park
PEIN						
1713	1726	1650	1712	131245	LEI	Countesthorpe

Known From	To	Researching From	To	Ref	Cty	Place
PEIRCE						
....	....	1800	1890	104922	KIK	Castlecomer
1700	1850	....	....	111538	MDX	Chiswick
1816	1839	1813	1826	147486	WIL	Poulshot
PEIRPOINT						
1760	1992	1700	1992	140287	CHS	Sandbach
....	....	1850	....	106623	LAN	Calsford
PEIRSON						
1805	1890	1700	1800	108308	YKS	Westerdale
PEISLEY						
1836	1992	1650	1836	151092	FER	???
PELFORD						
1685	1685	1550	1685	102830	WAR	Tanworth
PELHAM						
1720	1750	ALL	1750	115282	KEN	East
1300	1360	1300	1700	156647	LIN	Brocklesbury
1450	1700	ALL	1992	133450	SSX	Laughton
PELL						
1780	1900	1600	1780	101834	NFK	South West
PELLANT						
1816	1929	1816	1929	107379	HRT	St Albans
1700	ALL	1816	1929	107379	LND	Cripplegate
PELLETIER						
....	....	ALL	ALL	154350	ALL	Name Study
PELLETT						
1861	....	1800	1870	131547	SRY	Dorking
1800	1900	1700	1900	141151	SSX	ALL
1781	....	1750	1800	131547	SSX	Billinghurst
PELLEW						
1807	1830	1600	1807	131814	CON	Wheel Busy
PELLEY						
1740	1790	....	1740	137227	DOR	Swanage
1810	1860	....	....	137227	IOW	Ryde
PELLIN						
1775	1800	1700	1775	103446	SSX	Newtimber
PELLING						
....	1705	1650	1750	124907	SSX	Portslade
1797	1824	1825	1865	124907	SSX	Poynings
1700	1910	1600	1700	118079	SSX	West Tarring
PELLOW						
1725	1897	ALL	ALL	175005	CON	Central
....	....	1600	1834	117838	CON	Redruth
PELLS						
1888	1992	ALL	1888	150231	ESS	ALL
1807	1992	1700	1807	162647	LND	City
1860	1992	1800	1860	162647	LND	Shoreditch
1800	1992	1700	1800	118478	NFK	Langham
1800	1992	1700	1800	118478	NFK	Morston
1807	1992	1700	1807	162647	SFK	ALL
1700	1800	1600	1700	129003	SFK	Wickham Market
PELLY						
1800	1850	ALL	1992	170909	GAL	Aughrim
1600	ALL	ALL	1992	170909	IRL	ALL
PEMBER						
....	....	ALL	ALL	154369	ALL	Name Study
1810	1837	1700	1810	172898	HEF	Weobley
1815	1837	1700	1815	172898	MON	Mansell Gamage
PEMBERTON						
1750	1850	1750	1850	105732	CHS	Coddington
1818	1850	1800	....	105732	DEN	Ruabon
1818	1850	1800	....	105732	DEN	Wrexham
1851	1992	1700	1851	119075	LAN	Blackburn
1840	1900	....	1840	174025	LAN	Leigh
1850	1880	1800	1850	136522	LAN	Prescott
1350	1500	1300	1500	154881	LAN	Wigan
1790	1850	1700	1950	169889	NTT	Norton
1808	1848	1788	1848	153176	SAL	Oswestry
....	....	1650	ALL	115142	WAR	???
PEMBLE						
1786	1868	1750	1850	110604	KEN	Chatham
1815	1870	1750	1815	123978	KEN	Chatham
PEMBRIDGE						
1257	1376	1066	1376	124974	HEF	Clehonger
1257	1257	1066	1376	124974	HEF	Hereford
1200	1376	1066	1376	124974	HEF	Pembridge Castle
1100	1376	1066	1376	124974	HEF	Pembridge
1200	1376	1066	1376	124974	HEF	Welsh Newton
1841	1873	1500	1992	126799	LND	???
1836	....	1800	1836	129712	MON	Monmouth
1841	1851	1841	1851	126799	OXF	St Clements
1800	1851	1500	1992	126799	WLS	ALL
PEMBROKE						
1850	1890	1800	1860	100048	SRY	Lambeth
PENALUMA						
1820	1860	....	....	107174	CON	Sithney
PENBERTHY						
1713	1865	ALL	1713	134783	CON	Lelant
1713	1865	ALL	1713	134783	CON	St Just
1684	1992	1650	1683	105988	CON	Uny Lelant
PENBURY						
1600	1720	1550	1700	154881	SAL	Chirbury
PENCOTT						
1650	1750	1600	1800	166804	OXF	ALL
PENDAL						
1820	1880	1820	1880	123021	ESS	Great Warley
PENDER						
....	....	ALL	ALL	178152	IRL	???
1880	1916	ALL	ALL	178152	LAN	Liverpool
1866	1897	....	....	159506	LAN	Manchester
1866	1897	....	....	159506	LAN	Preston
1824	1836	....	1824	159506	NBL	Alnwick
1824	1836	....	1824	159506	NBL	Felton
PENDERELL						
1650	1800	1500	1650	113204	STS	Boscobel
PENDGEAST						
?	....	....	....	114642	MDX	London
PENDLEBURY						
....	1833	....	1808	154024	LAN	Ashton In Makerfield
1860	1935	1860	1992	109436	LAN	Bolton
1792	1992	1600	1792	119822	LAN	Bolton
1720	1800	....	....	177318	LAN	Horwich
1860	1935	1860	1992	109436	LAN	Manchester
PENDLETON						
1747	....	?	1750	103934	BDF	Biggleswade
....	1740	ALL	1740	134511	DBY	North Wingfield
1861	1945	ALL	ALL	126977	LAN	Litherland
PENDRED						
....	....	1700	1900	154377	ALL	ALL
1800	1900	1800	1900	154377	HUN	Southoe
PENDRILL						
ALL	ALL	ALL	ALL	114960	ALL	ALL
1760	1776	1760	1776	103101	DUB	ALL
1560	1660	1550	1660	103101	LIN	Revesby
1600	1992	1600	1992	103101	LND	???
1755	1800	1755	1800	103101	NTT	Nottingham
1630	1800	1630	1800	103101	SAL	Boscobel
1550	1600	1550	1600	103101	WIL	Gillingham
1710	1790	1710	1790	103101	WOR	ALL
PENDRY						
1788	1850	....	....	176958	SOM	Bristol
PENELLUM						
....	....	ALL	ALL	101591	DEV	ALL
PENFOLD						
....	....	....	....	154385	ESS	Leytonstone
1861	1886	1700	1861	168033	KEN	Ashford
....	....	1871	1938	131768	KEN	Gillingham
1667	1992	ALL	1700	108502	KEN	Goudhurst
1830	1880	1830	1880	152250	KEN	Goudhurst
1812	1852	....	....	173932	SRY	Ashtead
1730	1850	1500	1730	139084	SRY	Puttenham
....	....	ALL	1820	178403	SSX	West
1851	1854	1819	1870	124915	SSX	Brighton
1800	1888	....	....	116017	SSX	Cuckfield
1600	1800	ALL	ALL	154830	SSX	Kirdford
PENFORD						
1808	1830	1700	1800	177989	HAM	Kingsclere
PENFOUND						
1790	1850	ALL	ALL	143332	DEV	Plymouth
PENGELLY						
....	....	1600	1870	154393	CON	ALL
1789	1992	....	....	154407	CON	Liskeard
1800	1929	?	1800	147915	CON	Looe
1781	1992	1700	1781	154415	CON	Plymouth
1765	1850	1700	1765	136220	DEV	Beaworthy
1781	1992	1700	1781	154415	DEV	Plymouth
PENGILLEY						
1808	1992	1600	1850	166650	DEV	East Budleigh
1808	1992	1600	1850	166650	DEV	Littleham
PENGILLY						
1804	1856	....	....	145394	CON	Botus Fleming
....	....	1600	1815	177725	DEV	Colvelly
....	....	1815	1900	177725	DEV	Yarnscombe
PENHALE						
....	....	ALL	ALL	154423	ALL	Name Study
....	....	ALL	ALL	154423	ALL	ALL
....	....	ALL	ALL	154423	CON	ALL

Known From	To	Researching From	To	Ref	Cty	Place
PENHALE contd.						
1630	1840	ALL	ALL	154423	CON	Gwinear
PENHALL						
....	....	ALL	ALL	154423	ALL	ALL
....	....	ALL	ALL	154423	CON	ALL
1630	1840	ALL	ALL	154423	CON	Gwinear
PENHORWOOD						
ALL	ALL	ALL	ALL	116432	ALL	ALL
PENICAD						
....	....	1720	1992	154431	LND	Cripplegate
PENICOD						
1574	1992	1500	1574	154431	SSX	Boxgrove
PENICUD						
1772	1992	....	....	154431	DEV	Stoke Dameral
PENIKET						
....	....	ALL	ALL	154431	ALL	Name Study
1830	1992	1800	1830	154431	WMD	Smethwick
PENIKETT						
1730	1992	....	....	154431	SSX	Henfield
PENISTON						
1828	?	1800	1846	102121	YKS	Leeds
PENKETH						
1839	1839	1800	1860	141046	CHS	Chorlton
1861	1861	1800	1880	141046	CHS	Weaverham
PENKETHMAN						
1790	1860	1800	1992	128384	LAN	Eccles
PENLEY						
....	1930	1890	1992	176532	DBY	???
?	1811	1800	1811	176532	DOR	Sherborne
1795	?	1795	1811	176532	KEN	Sevenoaks
....	1930	1890	1992	176532	NTT	???
1869	1891	....	....	176532	SXE	Hove
....	1930	1890	1992	176532	WAR	???
PENLINGTON						
....	1771	ALL	1771	127000	SAL	Whitchurch
PENMAN						
....	....	1750	1850	126241	DUR	ALL
1795	1900	1700	1795	158143	FIF	Dunfermline
1825	1870	ALL	ALL	125180	LKS	Faskin
1850	1980	1700	1850	150371	MLN	Edinburgh
1830	1910	1700	1860	146714	T&W	ALL
PENN						
1713	1731	ALL	....	115355	BDF	ALL
1780	1780	1700	1800	136840	CON	Maker
1791	1992	1700	1992	172243	KEN	Bromley
1700	1850	ALL	1992	132055	KEN	Canterbury
1700	1992	ALL	1992	132055	KEN	Dover
....	....	1800	1900	136743	LEI	Loughboro
....	....	1600	1790	100447	OXF	Great Milton
1785	1953	1785	1881	143642	SSX	Angmering
1800	1992	1700	1800	154458	WAR	Birmingham
1957	1959	....	....	103772	YKS	Sheffield
PENNACK						
1880	1973	1600	1900	179299	ESS	Great Baddow
PENNALLS						
....	1765	....	....	103144	SSX	East
PENNANT						
....	....	....	1800	151084	WLS	North
PENNEKETT						
1800	1992	....	....	154431	HAM	Portsea
PENNELL						
1665	1830	1665	....	116394	DEV	Topsham
1800	1900	1800	....	116394	LND	Regents Park
1830	1992	1700	1992	107980	NFK	Norwich
PENNELLS						
1900	....	....	....	100536	SSX	???
PENNELS						
....	1700	....	....	174564	SSX	???
PENNES						
1780	1804	1740	1780	128724	KEN	Stouting
PENNEY						
1800	1992	1800	1992	154466	KEN	Sheerness
1700	1992	1700	1992	154466	LND	???
?	?	?	?	138622	SAL	???
1810	1900	1550	1950	170186	SOM	Yeovil
1808	1880	1758	1858	177490	SSX	Hollington
?	?	?	?	138622	WOR	???
PENNICARD						
....	....	ALL	ALL	154431	DEV	Membury
1750	1800	1800	1992	154431	SRY	???
....	....	ALL	ALL	154431	SSX	Kirdford
PENNICEARD						
....	....	ALL	ALL	154431	LND	???
....	....	1794	1992	154431	SRY	Ewell
PENNICK						
1868	1960	1700	1867	139696	ESS	Coggishall
PENNICODD						
1550	1800	1800	1992	154431	SRY	???
PENNICORD						
....	....	1750	1992	154431	ALL	ALL
PENNICOTT						
1086	1200	1200	1450	154431	DEV	Pennycott
PENNICUD						
1550	1980	....	....	154431	SRY	???
1550	1980	....	....	154431	SSX	???
PENNIKETT						
1750	1900	1900	1992	154431	LND	???
PENNILL						
1788	1847	1788	1847	111228	CHS	Dodcutt Cum Wilkesley
1788	1847	1788	1847	111228	CHS	Harthill
PENNIMAN						
....	....	1600	1700	176389	ESS	Chipping Ongar
....	....	1600	1700	176389	ESS	Great Bromley
....	....	1650	1800	176389	EYK	Howden
PENNINGTON						
1820	1880	1820	1881	122238	CHS	Wirral
1827	....	1700	1992	154474	CMA	Colton
....	....	1837	1930	109797	CMA	Dalton In Furness
1827	....	1700	1992	154474	CMA	Finsthwaite
1770	?	1750	1992	167592	DBY	Wirksworth
1860	1946	1500	1992	117900	LAN	Bolton
1866	1992	1790	1866	146919	LAN	Lancaster
1827	....	1700	1992	154474	LAN	Lancaster
1760	1980	1760	1960	132683	LAN	Liverpool
1720	1870	1650	1992	167592	LAN	Liverpool
1827	....	1700	1992	154474	LAN	Warton
1671	1744	1650	1750	107980	NFK	South Lynn
1790	1840	1750	1992	167592	WOR	Worcester
1790	1870	1700	1790	110442	WYK	Brotherton
PENNOCK						
1868	1960	1700	1867	139696	ESS	Coggishall
1719	1765	1700	1746	147311	NYK	Seamer
PENNY						
1786	1992	1600	1796	146137	ABD	East
1774	1798	ALL	1774	106909	ABD	South Mires
1660	1800	ALL	1800	149063	BEW	Coldingham
1740	....	1700	1740	178845	CON	Illogan
1720	1820	....	1750	179213	DEV	Buckfastleigh
....	....	1800	1992	137588	DEV	Exeter
1683	1800	....	....	127957	DOR	East Lulworth
1827	....	....	....	173932	DOR	Handley
1800	1850	1800	1850	154210	DOR	South Holworth
1816	....	....	....	124982	GLS	Berkeley
1820	1900	1750	1900	133922	HAM	Eling
1776	1851	ALL	ALL	156884	HAM	Eling
1600	1700	....	....	153397	HAM	New Forest
1856	....	....	....	173932	HAM	Portsea Town
1768	1865	1650	1768	129984	KEN	Folkestone
1774	1871	....	1774	100900	RAD	Old Radnor
?	?	?	?	138622	SAL	???
1740	ALL	....	....	142158	SOM	Cadbury
?	?	ALL	1850	117919	SOM	Evercreech
1892	....	....	....	173932	SOM	Weston Super Mare
1840	1853	....	....	173932	SRY	Ashtead
1880	1900	1700	1900	126802	WAR	ALL
1500	1900	1500	1900	170216	WIL	ALL
1803	....	....	....	173932	WIL	Bishopstone
1952	1955	....	....	173932	WIL	Bradford On Avon
1750	1992	1600	1850	171247	WIL	Braod Chalke
1825	1833	....	....	173932	WIL	Codford
1761	....	....	....	173932	WIL	Ogbourne St Geroge
1764	....	....	....	173932	WIL	Preshute
1818	1830	....	....	173932	WIL	Salisbury
1820	....	....	....	117579	WIL	Stourton
1914	....	....	....	173932	WIL	Stourton
1857	1892	....	....	173932	WIL	Sutton Veny
1936	1938	....	....	173932	WIL	Upton Scudamore
1853	....	....	....	173932	WIL	Wilton
1829	....	....	....	173932	WIL	Winchester
?	?	?	?	138622	WOR	???
PENNYCAD						
....	....	1816	1992	154431	SRY	Croydon
PENNYCOTT						
1830	1992	....	....	154431	HAM	Southsea
PENNYCUD						
1760	1850	....	....	154431	SSX	Arundle

Known From	To	Researching From	To	Ref	Cty	Place
PENNYCUICK						
1839	1905	1905	1992	146560	LTN	Edinburgh
PENNYEND						
....	....	1775	1992	154431	SRY	Great Bookham
PENNYMAN						
....	....	ALL	ALL	176389	ALL	Name Study
....	....	1700	1800	176389	CUL	Whitehaven
....	....	1700	1850	176389	DUR	Bishop Middleham
....	....	1700	1850	176389	DUR	Bishopwearmouth
....	....	1700	1850	176389	DUR	Monkwearmouth
....	....	1700	1800	176389	NBL	Embleton
....	....	1650	1700	176389	NBL	Longhoughton
....	....	1650	1750	176389	NFK	Lessingham
....	....	1700	1850	176389	NFK	Thrope Next Nortwich
PENNYMON						
....	....	1750	1850	176389	GLS	Bristol
PENPRASE						
1870	1992	ALL	1870	154482	CON	ALL
1870	1992	ALL	1870	154482	CON	Liskeard
1870	1992	ALL	1870	154482	CON	Redruth
....	....	ALL	1945	154482	LAN	Dalton In Furness
PENRICE						
1865	1910	1837	1992	130036	CUL	Maryport
1679	1865	1600	1992	130036	CUL	Skinburness
....	....	1600	1700	130036	GLA	Kilvrough
....	....	1410	1679	130036	GLA	Penrice
....	....	1600	1800	130036	NFK	Great Yarmouth
1300	1400	....	....	100536	???	???
PENROSE						
1770	1900	1700	1770	108359	CON	Kea
1828	1839	1800	1828	158267	CON	Ladock
1790	1851	1851	1950	118583	CON	Redruth
1790	1841	1841	1950	118583	CON	Truro
1770	1800	....	....	177393	YKS	Brayton
1730	1760	1680	1730	177393	YKS	Dray
PENRUDDOCK						
?	1940	....	....	128996	CAM	Thorney
PENRY						
1896	1935	1979	1992	149543	MDX	London
PENSON						
1632	1646	ALL	1700	133876	SAL	Cleobury Mortimer
1632	1646	ALL	1700	133876	SAL	Highley
1670	1800	1600	1800	133876	STS	Enville
1793	1906	ALL	ALL	168610	WOR	ALL
PENSTON						
1767	....	1650	1780	139386	LND	St Martins In The Field
1765	1875	1700	1900	139386	SRY	Kingston
PENTELOW						
1722	1992	ALL	1720	154490	HUN	ALL
1722	1992	ALL	1720	154490	HUN	Abbots Ley
PENTLAND						
1800	1840	1700	1800	171662	MLN	Liberton
PENTLOE						
....	1805	ALL	ALL	129933	SRY	Tooting Graveney
PENTLOW						
1798	1820	....	....	160822	BRK	???
PENTON						
1810	1900	1600	1810	148296	HAM	Basingstoke
1800	1826	1700	1800	121010	HAM	Chilbolton
1810	1900	1600	1810	148296	HAM	Winchester
1810	1900	1600	1810	148296	LND	???
PENVELL						
1700	1980	1550	1700	171409	KEN	Maidstone
PENWARDEN						
1820	1860	....	....	115274	DEV	Milton Combe
PENWARNE						
1660	1760	1660	1992	133450	CON	Liskeard
PENY						
1700	1750	ALL	1700	115266	DOR	ALL
1689	....	....	....	142859	GLS	Leonard Stanley
PENYCATE						
1750	1980	....	....	154431	SRY	???
PENYEAD						
....	....	1730	1992	154431	LND	Cripplegate
....	....	1783	1992	154431	SRY	Kingston On Thames
PENYMAN						
....	....	1558	1600	176389	GLS	Westbury On Severn
....	....	1700	1750	176389	NBL	Lesbury
....	....	1550	1750	176389	NBL	Newcastle Upon Tyne
....	....	1550	1650	176389	NFK	Bacton
PENZER						
1750	1820	ALL	1992	133876	STS	Enville

Known From	To	Researching From	To	Ref	Cty	Place
PENZER contd.						
1800	1920	1810	1992	133876	WOR	Alvechurch
1800	1920	1810	1992	133876	WOR	Bromsgrove
PEPAL						
....	....	ALL	ALL	136131	ALL	Name Study
PEPLER						
1810	1850	1750	1850	120235	MDX	Gt Stanmore
....	....	1800	1850	143685	WIL	Keevil
PEPLOE						
1800	1850	1750	1850	121509	LAN	???
1800	1850	1750	1850	121509	WLS	???
PEPLOW						
1800	1850	1700	1850	143502	SAL	Central
....	....	1750	1830	149977	SAL	Wellington
1870	1900	1700	1900	117870	WAR	Birmingham
PEPPER						
1640	1700	....	....	119458	KEN	Faversham
1900	1992	1600	1992	112003	LEI	Osgathorpe
1699	1850	1600	1900	170291	LIN	Kesteven
1884	....	....	....	112909	SRY	Bermondsey
1837	1860	1700	1837	117633	SRY	Croydon
1761	1776	....	....	152234	SYK	Darfield
1698	1717	....	....	152234	SYK	Maltby
1650	1831	....	....	152234	SYK	Wath Upon Dearne
1787	1794	....	....	152234	SYK	Womersley
1849	1992	....	....	160148	YKS	Selby
PEPPERDINE						
....	....	ALL	ALL	154504	ALL	Name Study
....	....	1566	1985	154504	LIN	ALL
1650	1985	....	....	154504	LIN	Billinghay
1697	1985	....	....	154504	LIN	Blankney
1766	1985	....	....	154504	LIN	Fiskerton
1794	1985	....	....	154504	LIN	Grantham
PEPPERELL						
ALL	ALL	ALL	ALL	166758	ALL	ALL
....	....	1500	1839	126217	DEV	???
1879	1959	1879	1992	126217	MDX	Bow
1839	1879	1700	1839	126217	SRY	Bermondsey
PEPPIAT						
1722	....	....	....	137170	BKM	Great Brickhill
PEPPIATT						
1868	1868	1868	1920	127302	LND	Kensington
PEPPITT						
1723	1803	1500	1803	137170	BDF	Leighton Buzzard
PERCIE						
1761	1761	1600	1850	130125	NBL	Woodhorn
PERCIVAL						
1600	1800	1600	1800	152404	CHS	Stockport
1913	1992	1847	1913	145084	CMA	Wigton
1810	....	1750	1850	102016	GLS	Bristol
1854	1880	1700	1880	116300	HRT	Bennington
1840	1865	1830	1890	142174	LEI	Leicester
1600	1880	ALL	....	104515	LIN	South
1800	1900	1800	1900	147184	NYK	Wensleydale
1695	1730	1650	1740	142174	RUT	Empingham
1705	1735	1650	1700	167533	SRY	Dorking
1835	1855	1780	1855	133280	STS	Coseley
1835	1855	1780	1855	133280	STS	Dudley
PERCY						
1835	....	1750	1850	142352	BDF	Biggleswade
1803	1992	ALL	1803	154520	BEW	Murton
1811	1890	ALL	ALL	119504	DOR	Belchalwell
1850	1903	1820	1855	109878	GLS	Bristol
1800	1900	1700	1800	171182	HAM	Damerham
1783	1851	1750	1900	142352	HRT	Brent Pelham
1851	1871	1850	1900	142352	HRT	Kelshall
1764	1862	1700	1764	120634	LAN	Pilling
1841	....	1800	1850	142352	LND	St George The Martyr
ALL	1600	....	....	132756	NBL	???
1790	1840	1790	1840	154210	WIL	Winterbourne Dauntsey
PERDIKOU						
1957	1957	....	....	159492	LND	London
PERE						
1792	1860	1750	1860	169323	YKS	Hull
PEREGRINE						
1840	1870	1700	1840	138452	CMN	Gwynfe
1840	1870	1700	1840	138452	CMN	Llangadog
PERIAM						
1800	1825	1800	1825	104256	DEV	Alphington
1830	1855	1500	1855	104256	DEV	Exeter
....	....	1700	1800	104256	SOM	Wellington

Known From	To	Researching From	To	Ref	Cty	Place
PERING						
1760	1881	....	....	159751	DEV	South Hams
PERKES						
1776	....	ALL	1776	123013	WOR	Beckford
PERKIN						
1740	....	1730	1740	135771	DEV	North
1871	1919	1871	1919	170631	DEV	Lew Quarry
1791	1911	1600	1791	148040	DEV	Northam
1674	1686	1600	1800	154539	DUR	Barnard Castle
1883	1989	1700	1883	174939	STS	Ruston Spencer
1806	....	....	....	129747	YKS	Kirkstall
PERKINS						
....	....	ALL	ALL	154555	ALL	Name Study
....	....	ALL	ALL	162159	ALL	Name Study
....	....	ALL	ALL	154555	ALL	ALL
....	1700	1880	....	179477	ALL	ALL
1780	1860	1780	1860	113670	AVN	Bath
1800	1880	1700	1800	146587	BKM	Amersham
1800	1872	1800	1872	119059	BKM	Chilton
1820	1820	1765	1900	154539	BKM	Twyford
1713	1940	....	....	128996	CAM	Thorney
1881	1900	1700	1900	175293	CON	Plymouth
1881	1900	1700	1900	175293	DEV	Plymouth
....	....	1700	1750	174289	DOR	ALL
1744	1744	1600	1800	154539	DUR	Barnard Castle
1800	1940	1700	1800	130680	ESS	Barking
1800	1880	1700	1800	154601	EYK	Colton
1800	1880	1700	1800	154601	EYK	Howden
1800	1880	1700	1800	154601	EYK	Skipworth
1750	1992	1600	1900	154628	GLS	Central
1737	1770	1600	1770	145289	HAM	Isle Of Wight
1800	....	1800	....	115576	IOW	Northwood
1890	1992	1850	1900	154598	LEI	Leicester
1790	1828	....	....	128368	LEI	Mountsorrel
1680	1992	ALL	....	104515	LIN	South
1799	1992	ALL	1799	154563	LIN	Gainsborough
1868	1992	1840	....	156191	LND	Islington
1868	1992	1840	....	156191	MDX	Enfield
1800	1992	ALL	ALL	154547	NFK	East
1880	1940	....	....	154571	NFK	Gt Yarmouth
1850	1880	....	....	154571	NFK	North Walsham
1830	1840	....	....	154571	NFK	Roughton
1799	1992	ALL	ALL	154547	NFK	Swaffham
1880	1950	....	....	154571	NRY	Middlesbrough
1834	1930	1700	1834	130257	NTH	Little Addington
1789	1814	1700	1790	131377	NTH	Rothwell
1785	....	1817	....	127647	NTT	Sutton Parish
1650	1725	....	....	132756	OXF	Bicester
1822	1827	1750	1900	154539	SRY	Camberwell
1867	1871	1700	1800	112615	STS	Aston
1787	....	ALL	1992	159174	STS	Ingestre
1719	1992	ALL	1719	154555	WAR	Hillmorton
1860	1980	1860	1900	154601	WYK	Dewsbury
1860	1980	1860	1900	154601	WYK	Mirfield
1867	1871	1700	1800	112615	???	Birmingham
PERKS						
1852	1893	....	....	115495	DBY	Okeover
1960	1992	....	....	154636	ESS	Southend On Sea
1886	1960	....	....	154636	MDX	London
1822	1921	1796	ALL	154652	SAL	Cardington
1796	ALL	1796	ALL	154652	SAL	Longnor
1814	1862	1700	1862	141291	STS	Wolverhampton
1850	1970	1700	1950	122203	WAR	Aston
1850	1970	1700	1950	122203	WAR	Birmingham
1774	1777	....	....	154636	WAR	Stratford On Avon
1777	1854	....	....	154636	WAR	Temple Grafton
1841	1900	1700	1840	104043	WOR	St Martins
1854	1886	....	....	154636	WOR	Worcester
PERMAIN						
....	....	1670	1750	153842	HAM	Greywell
1750	1851	1700	1750	153842	HAM	Wonston
1833	1861	1795	1841	153842	LND	Kensington
PERNELL						
ALL	ALL	....	....	153397	HAM	New Forest
PERRATON						
1580	1860	1540	1580	168777	DEV	South Huish
PERREN						
1800	1828	1700	1900	138746	ESS	Gt Dunmow
1807	1992	1750	1807	176257	KEN	Greenwich
1819	1828	1800	1900	138746	WIL	Whiteparish
1840	1947	1700	1950	106119	WMD	Walsall
PERRETT						
....	....	ALL	ALL	154679	ALL	Name Study
1850	1900	1700	1950	121762	WIL	East

Known From	To	Researching From	To	Ref	Cty	Place
PERRIAM						
1550	1992	ALL	ALL	135429	ALL	ALL
1780	1820	1700	1820	161292	DEV	Exmouth
PERRIDGE						
....	1820	ALL	1820	152889	HUN	Kimbolton
PERRIN						
1868	1992	1868	1992	104027	BDF	Cranfield
1840	....	1841	1861	115886	BRK	Clewer
1804	1808	1797	1814	115886	BRK	White Waltham
1851	1857	1837	1861	115886	BRK	Windsor
1800	1900	ALL	ALL	121401	BRK	Windsor
1715	1736	ALL	1736	127000	CHS	Acton By Nantwich
....	1849	ALL	1849	134058	CHS	Astbury
1695	1735	....	....	161357	ESS	Gt Dunmow
1680	1720	1650	1750	144657	HAM	West Stratton
1891	1933	1800	1891	118230	LAN	Liverpool
1850	1900	1700	1850	133329	LIN	Skegness
1861	1896	1860	1992	115886	LND	North
?	....	....	?	111104	LND	City
?	?	?	?	154687	LND	City
?	....	....	?	111104	LND	Hackney
?	?	?	?	154687	LND	Hackney
?	....	....	?	111104	LND	Islington
1830	1905	ALL	ALL	147567	LND	Islington
?	?	?	?	154687	LND	Islington
1830	1832	1815	1841	115886	OXF	Rotherfield Greys
1851	1909	1850	1910	177016	WAR	Birmingham
PERRING						
1800	1880	1700	1800	114162	DEV	Dartmouth
1800	1850	1700	1800	114162	DEV	Stoke Fleming
PERRINS						
1837	1992	1861	1992	154695	STS	Tipton
....	....	1800	1884	175161	WOR	Kidderminster
PERRIS						
1700	1900	ALL	1900	154709	ALL	ALL
1760	1992	ALL	1930	154709	DOR	ALL
1815	1880	1700	1815	134368	GLS	Gloucester
PERRIT						
1686	1754	1600	1750	175218	EYK	Rudstone
PERRITT						
1630	1931	1863	1992	158704	KEN	Ramsgate
PERRON						
....	....	ALL	ALL	154717	ALL	Name Study
PERROTT						
....	1853	....	1852	174025	MON	Newport
PERROW						
....	....	ALL	ALL	154725	ALL	Name Study
PERRY						
1817	1838	1770	1820	172871	ANS	Montrose
1810	....	....	1850	171441	BKM	Bletchley
1846	1970	1707	1992	139955	BRK	Bray
1846	1970	1707	1992	139955	BRK	Maidenhead
1760	1900	1700	1920	154776	BRK	Sutton Courtenay
1803	1826	1750	1805	162396	CAM	Linton
1890	1918	1800	1918	163635	CHS	Wirral
1822	1844	1700	1900	135968	CON	ALL
1790	1992	ALL	ALL	154806	CON	Fowey
1800	1850	1700	1992	140287	CON	Towednack
1850	1992	1600	1850	123242	CON	Wendron
....	....	1700	1992	136972	CON	Wendron
1879	....	1870	1880	171441	COR	Cork
1855	1875	1700	1855	134899	COR	Skibbereen
1880	....	1870	1880	171441	DEV	Devonport
....	....	1500	1992	148164	DEV	Sidmouth
1892	1971	....	....	154814	ESS	Leaden Roding
1777	1789	1750	1851	116114	ESS	Roxwell
1800	....	ALL	ALL	116394	ESS	Saffron Waldon
1822	1851	1800	1867	116114	ESS	Widofrd
....	....	ALL	1770	141224	GLS	South
1807	1860	1600	1807	149888	GLS	Bristol
1500	1700	1500	1700	144657	HAM	Micheldever
1720	1720	1650	1750	136840	HAM	Portsmouth
1800	1992	ALL	ALL	154768	HEF	Acton Beauchamp
1830	1992	1538	1830	154792	HRT	Albury
1830	1992	1538	1830	154792	HRT	Bishops Stortford
1830	1992	1538	1830	154792	HRT	Thorley
1830	1992	1538	1830	154792	HRT	Widford
1870	....	1800	....	162752	HRT	???
1857	1950	1750	1857	168025	KEN	Chislehurst
1793	1943	?	?	124451	LAN	Liverpool
1859	1931	1800	1830	163635	LAN	Liverpool
1885	....	1880	1890	171441	LAN	Slaford
....	....	ALL	ALL	135526	LEI	Whitwick
1860	1930	1700	1860	124362	LND	ALL

Known From	To	Researching From	To	Ref	Cty	Place
PERRY contd.						
1851	1857	1850	1860	171441	LND	City
1846	1970	1707	1992	139955	LND	Clerkenwell
?	?	?	?	130354	LND	Leyton
1840	1860	1800	1840	172898	LND	St Martins In The Field
....	....	....	1875	147818	LND	???
1844	1849	1840	1850	171441	MDX	Clerkenwell
1849	1992	1700	1849	126527	MDX	London
1730	1900	ALL	ALL	127175	NFK	ALL
1760	1920	1700	1760	159573	NFK	???
1750	1875	ALL	ALL	106097	RUT	Empingham
1840	1860	ALL	1870	120049	SAL	ALL
....	1819	1750	1820	128961	SFK	Woodbridge
1858	1992	1800	1858	123153	SOM	Bath
1941	1954	1941	1954	154733	SOM	Batheaston
1849	1967	1849	1983	154733	SOM	Bishop Sutton
1655	1904	1654	1912	154733	SOM	Camely
1701	1849	1560	1850	154733	SOM	Chew Magna
1702	1972	1690	1972	154733	SOM	Clutton
1846	1970	1734	1978	154733	SOM	Farmborough
1773	1898	1634	1898	154733	SOM	High Littleton
1730	1755	1600	1730	108413	SOM	Hinton Blewett
1877	....	1870	1880	171441	SOM	Kingsdon
....	....	1754	1812	154733	SOM	Queen Charlton
1709	1946	1607	1948	154733	SOM	Stanton Drew
1757	1968	1757	1977	154733	SOM	Stowey
1841	1900	1813	1900	154733	SOM	Timsbury
1921	....	1890	1925	171441	SRY	Farncombe
1862	1920	1860	1925	171441	SRY	Farnham
1923	....	1920	1925	171441	SRY	Godalming
1737	....	....	....	131210	SRY	Southwark
1870	1900	1800	1870	120049	STS	ALL
....	1909	....	1950	130168	STS	Dudley
1627	1728	1600	1760	160873	STS	Kingswinford
....	....	1600	1850	147613	STS	Rowley Regis
1743	1992	1600	1743	174378	STS	Stafford
1800	....	1750	1800	162361	STS	Wilenhall
1800	1850	....	....	162361	WAR	Birmingham
1800	1870	ALL	1830	174556	WIL	Bodenham
1836	1836	1820	1840	168076	WIL	Edington
?	?	?	?	163279	WMD	Bradley
1800	1992	ALL	ALL	154768	WOR	Bishops Frome
1850	1890	1800	1900	177571	WOR	Halesowen
1690	1992	1600	1890	154784	YKS	South
....	....	1700	1880	102148	YKS	Leeds
PERRYMAN						
1819	1842	ALL	ALL	143618	AVN	Keynsham
....	....	1550	1700	176389	HRT	Aldenham
1840	1845	1800	1900	174661	LND	Lambeth
PERSEHOUSE						
1696	....	1600	1720	160873	STS	Sedgley
PERSSE						
1821	1902	1750	1850	103462	GAL	Galway
PERT						
1670	1992	ALL	ALL	137758	ANS	ALL
1800	1880	1700	1800	100978	ANS	Ferryden
1632	ALL	1713	1900	154822	BRK	???
1846	ALL	1846	ALL	154822	HAM	Portsea
1852	ALL	....	....	154822	SSX	???
PERUIM						
1850	1890	1800	1900	167843	YKS	Norton On Tees
1840	1900	1800	1900	167843	YKS	Stokesley
PERYER						
1828	1944	1700	1828	100110	HAM	Winchester
PESCUD						
1805	1881	ALL	ALL	135909	SRY	Leigh
1881	1992	ALL	ALL	135909	SRY	???
PESKETT						
1600	1900	1600	1980	101532	LND	Dulwich
1699	1850	ALL	ALL	154830	SSX	Bosham
1600	1900	1600	1980	101532	SSX	Horsham
PESTER						
1860	1870	ALL	ALL	101400	ESS	Theydon Garnon
1800	1860	ALL	ALL	101400	ESS	West Ham
1860	1870	ALL	ALL	101400	MDX	Whitechapel
1800	....	....	....	133736	SOM	Haselbury Plucknett
PETCH						
1700	1850	1700	1760	177725	NYK	Kirkby Mooreside
1760	1905	1700	1905	159581	SFK	Culford
1820	1870	....	....	165948	SFK	Culford
1840	1870	1800	1900	169404	YKS	Danby
1852	1888	ALL	1888	158445	YKS	Huddersfield
PETEGREE						
1745	1777	....	....	136158	LND	Norton Folgate
PETER						
1808	1822	1750	1822	109142	ABD	North
1553	1992	1553	1900	134562	CON	North Hill
1420	1992	....	....	100536	CON	???
1770	1850	1650	1770	142670	LKS	Glasgow
PETERFIELD						
1751	1800	1600	1751	149888	CON	Landrake
PETERKIN						
1775	1831	....	....	116327	HAM	Portchester
1733	1744	....	....	116327	HAM	Portsmouth
1881	1959	1959	1992	146560	LTN	Edinburgh
PETERS						
ALL	ALL	ALL	ALL	154865	ALL	ALL
1800	ALL	1600	ALL	154857	AVN	Bristol
1920	1992	1800	1920	122947	AVN	Easton
1832	1992	1700	1832	161446	CON	Camborne
1726	1890	1600	1900	141933	CON	Philleigh
1800	1900	1700	1850	132535	CON	Tregony
1726	1890	1600	1900	141933	CON	Tregony
1750	1850	1600	1750	134104	DEN	Wrexham
1860	1900	1700	1950	152714	FLN	Mold
1660	1738	1660	1738	154873	KEN	Canterbury
1820	1850	1700	1820	115541	KEN	Greenwich
1738	1992	....	....	154873	KEN	Sittingbourne
1867	1873	ALL	ALL	124346	LND	Chelsea
1880	1900	1800	1900	124605	MDX	Marylebone
1844	....	1820	1850	163775	MDX	Stepney
1750	1900	1650	1900	132950	SSX	Portslade
1870	1900	1800	1870	137421	WAR	Birmingham
1913	1914	1900	1992	173835	YKS	Brotton
PETERSEN						
1877	1897	1850	1900	142115	CMN	Pembrey
PETERSON						
1750	1965	....	....	137820	SHI	Fetlar
1720	1965	....	....	137820	SHI	Mid Yell
1760	1965	....	....	137820	SHI	North Yell
1758	1965	....	....	137820	SHI	Northmavine
1720	1965	....	....	137820	SHI	South Yell
1750	1992	1700	1992	104671	SHI	Whiteness
1803	1803	1700	1850	139203	SHI	Whiteness
PETFORD						
1750	1850	1650	1750	171859	WOR	ALL
PETHER						
1842	1906	1790	1842	121053	SRY	Walworth
PETHERICK						
1840	1850	1700	1900	103403	CON	North
PETITT						
1840	1890	1750	1840	119164	SSX	West Firle
PETLEY						
1865	1992	1600	1865	163856	KEN	Dover
1250	1480	1250	1500	154881	KEN	Downe
1480	1600	1450	1600	154881	KEN	Halstead
1600	1943	1600	1950	154881	KEN	Sevenoaks
PETMAN						
1700	1750	1600	1700	124699	KEN	East
1678	....	1650	1750	154962	KEN	Canterbury
PETO						
1800	1870	....	....	160458	LND	???
1590	1690	1550	1992	114901	SRY	Thursley
PETRE						
1630	1678	....	....	165999	GLS	Henbury
PETRI						
1860	1940	ALL	ALL	120057	HRT	Barnet
PETRIE						
1770	1840	1750	1840	146803	FIF	Kettle
1797	1849	1700	1797	153605	KCD	Dunnottar
1750	1965	....	....	137820	SHI	Fetlar
1720	1965	....	....	137820	SHI	Mid Yell
1760	1965	....	....	137820	SHI	North Yell
1758	1965	....	....	137820	SHI	Northmavine
1720	1965	....	....	137820	SHI	South Yell
PETT						
1730	....	....	1730	149888	CON	Linkinhorne
PETTER						
1723	1775	1650	1750	165980	SSX	Herstmonceux
1770	1900	1700	1900	121762	SSX	Rogate
PETTET						
1800	1900	1800	1900	154903	HAM	South
1600	1900	1600	1900	154903	KEN	ALL
PETTICAN						
1751	1760	1655	1750	158178	ESS	Birch
1849	1872	1800	1875	118354	ESS	Kirby Le Soken

Known From	To	Researching From	To	Ref	Cty	Place
PETTICAN contd.						
1771	1849	....	....	158178	ESS	Layer Marney
1860	1992	....	....	158178	ESS	Tollesbury
PETTIFER						
1800	....	....	....	112534	ALL	ALL
1796	1850	1700	1796	123307	BRK	Kintbury
1775	1775	1700	1775	154911	MID	South
1775	1775	1700	1775	154911	NTH	Sulgrave
....	....	ALL	....	119237	SRY	Richmond
PETTIFOR						
1792	1814	ALL	1814	112275	LEI	North
PETTIGREW						
1820	1925	ALL	1820	139378	AYR	Coylton
1810	1880	1850	1890	163554	AYR	Gartcosh
1814	....	1750	1814	108596	BUT	Arran
1810	1880	1850	1890	163554	RFW	How Wood
PETTINGER						
1871	1918	ALL	1918	154946	DUR	West Hartlepool
1850	1992	1785	1850	113719	LIN	Louth
....	1872	1872	ALL	154946	YKS	Crayke
1739	....	ALL	1739	154946	YKS	Whitgift
PETTINGILL						
1783	1900	1600	1800	160296	NFK	Filby
1800	1900	1650	1800	160296	NFK	Mautby
1800	1900	1700	1800	160296	NFK	Winterton
PETTIT						
1716	1782	ALL	1716	168602	BDF	Bletsoe
1782	1851	....	....	168602	BDF	Harrold
1716	1782	ALL	1716	168602	BDF	Kempston
1782	1851	....	....	168602	BDF	Odell
1750	1850	....	....	130230	BRK	Lambourne
1866	1900	ALL	ALL	151815	CAM	Bourn
1866	1900	ALL	ALL	151815	CAM	Longstowe
1790	1800	1700	1850	143502	ESS	South East
1609	....	....	....	107085	ESS	Widford
1600	1900	1600	1900	154903	KEN	ALL
1810	1937	1780	1970	115797	KEN	East
1849	1873	ALL	1850	152641	KEN	Deal
1778	....	ALL	ALL	121754	KEN	Yalding
1812	1832	1700	1832	151254	LAN	Manchester
1903	1903	....	1903	171646	MDX	East London
1744	1956	1650	1744	166111	NTH	Bozeat
1795	1850	1700	1795	167541	SFK	Clare
....	....	ALL	ALL	100153	SFK	Framlingham
1822	1838	ALL	1850	151815	SFK	Rattlesden
....	....	ALL	ALL	100153	SFK	Worlingworth
?	?	?	?	166642	SSX	Ninfield
1660	1720	....	....	119431	SXE	Mayfield
?	?	?	?	153885	WLS	Porthcawl
PETTITT						
1847	1877	1847	1877	108839	BKM	Chesham
1825	....	....	1825	108839	SFK	Newmarket
1830	1840	1800	1900	129607	SRY	Bermondsey
1800	1861	....	....	115940	SSX	Hailsham
....	1800	....	....	174564	SSX	Laughton
1802	1802	ALL	....	132349	SXE	Seaford
PETTMAN						
1800	1890	1700	1800	154962	KEN	East
1765	1947	1700	1900	178322	KEN	Ash
1800	1890	1700	1800	154962	KEN	Whitstable
PETTS						
1880	1900	1880	1900	153052	HRT	Hadhams
1828	1884	1700	1828	160709	LND	Hackney
PETTY						
1813	1879	1800	1900	120561	ESS	Mistley
1860	1887	....	....	133922	HAM	Lymington
1887	....	....	....	133922	HAM	Netley Marsh
1850	1880	1700	1850	146285	HAM	Portsmouth
1800	....	ALL	1800	115118	KEN	Orpington
1808	1850	....	....	178640	LIN	Ludford
1813	1879	1800	1900	120561	LND	Stepney
1790	1920	1666	1851	132160	SOM	Langport Pitney
1790	1920	1666	1851	132160	SOM	Somerton
1650	1930	ALL	ALL	154970	YKS	Bolton Abbey
1590	1700	1500	1524	178640	YKS	Brompton By Sawdon
1700	1860	....	....	178640	YKS	Egton
PETVIN						
1880	....	ALL	ALL	118389	MDX	Hackney
1865	....	ALL	ALL	118389	SOM	Street
1843	....	ALL	1843	118389	SOM	Wells
PETYT						
1650	1720	ALL	ALL	154970	MDX	London
1650	1930	ALL	ALL	154970	YKS	Bolton Abbey
....	....	1820	1960	154970	YKS	Bradford

Known From	To	Researching From	To	Ref	Cty	Place
PETYT contd.						
....	....	1820	1992	154970	YKS	Keighley
PEUDU						
1881	....	....	....	144169	LAN	Chorlton-On-Medlock
1881	....	....	....	144169	LAN	Manchester
PEVALIN						
1820	1880	1750	1820	144398	HAM	Porstmouth
PEVEREL						
1066	1220	1066	1250	154881	NTT	Nottingham
PEVERELL						
1066	1220	1066	1250	154881	NTT	Nottingham
PEWES						
1735	1735	1600	1735	102830	STS	Sedgely
PEWSEY						
1821	....	1700	1850	143693	BKM	Wendover
1840	....	....	....	154989	BKM	Wendover
1776	1799	1700	1850	143693	BKM	West Wycombe
1790	1900	ALL	ALL	118818	HAM	Alresford
1797	1992	ALL	1790	179167	HAM	Alresford
1860	1900	ALL	ALL	118818	HAM	Havant
1868	....	1750	1850	143693	LND	Kensington
PEXTON						
1800	1992	1770	....	106003	WYK	Scarborough
1797	1871	1797	1871	173851	YKS	Scarborough
1785	1872	1500	1785	125695	YKS	Seaton Ross
PEYFORER						
....	....	1066	1350	154873	KEN	???
PEYMAN						
....	....	ALL	ALL	154997	ALL	Name Study
PHANCO						
1795	1992	1750	1992	155004	RFW	Greenock
PHAROAH						
1785	1867	1700	1785	169242	HAM	Gosport
1790	1891	1700	1790	173770	HAM	Portsea
1820	1877	ALL	1820	131881	HAM	Portsmouth
1785	1867	1700	1785	169242	HAM	Portsmouth
PHARON						
1767	?	ALL	ALL	166243	SRY	Puttenham
PHARROW						
1708	....	ALL	....	104515	LIN	Creeton
PHAYER						
1850	1930	ALL	ALL	178454	KEN	ALL
1850	1930	ALL	ALL	178454	LND	ALL
PHEASANT						
....	....	1800	1850	145750	LEI	Castle Donnington
PHEASEY						
1840	1871	ALL	ALL	147281	SAL	Shrewsbury
PHEBY						
1800	1899	....	....	114723	LND	East
1890	ALL	1700	ALL	159255	LND	Bermondsey
PHELAN						
1844	1866	ALL	1866	171751	LEX	???
1866	1925	1866	ALL	171751	NBL	Newcastle Upon Tyne
1940	....	1940	1992	171751	WAR	Coventry
....	....	1840	1875	163791	WAT	Killea
PHELPS						
....	....	ALL	ALL	155012	ALL	Name Study
1754	1781	1700	1754	176907	GLS	West
....	1761	1747	1796	153176	GLS	Bishops Cleeve
1736	1766	....	1736	149888	GLS	Bristol
1824	1852	....	....	112968	SOM	East Pennard
1780	1920	1780	1920	127655	WIL	Marlborough
PHENNA						
....	....	ALL	ALL	155020	ALL	Name Study
1600	1863	1600	1863	155020	CWD	Chirk
1667	1775	1600	1800	155020	CWD	Rhabon
1600	1863	1600	1863	155020	CWD	Wrexham
1853	1992	1853	1992	155020	MSY	Liverpool
PHENNAH						
1695	1992	1695	1992	155020	CWD	Chirk
1695	1992	1695	1992	155020	CWD	Hope
1695	1992	1695	1992	155020	CWD	Wrexham
1847	1992	1847	1992	155020	MSY	Liverpool
PHETHEAN						
....	....	1700	1820	159964	CHS	North East
1814	1850	1800	1850	159964	LAN	Kearsley
PHILBIN						
1857	1906	....	....	138827	MAY	Newport
PHILBRICK						
1933	1959	1600	1900	172146	ESS	Thurrock
PHILCOX						
....	....	ALL	ALL	146153	ALL	Name Study
1803	....	....	....	131210	SRY	Southwark
1571	1880	1500	1860	176621	SSX	Battle

Known From	To	Researching From	To	Ref	Cty	Place
PHILCOX contd.						
1571	1880	1500	1860	176621	SSX	Hastings
1830	....	1830	1992	140058	SXE	Hartfield
PHILIP						
1641	1687	1600	1700	165972	DEV	Morchard Bishop
1791	1864	1700	1791	119881	KCD	Maryculter
PHILIPS						
1940	1992	1900	1992	133450	BKM	Gerrards Cross
1840	1860	ALL	ALL	173657	CON	St Austell
1840	1950	1800	1992	133450	DEV	Plymouth
1846	1866	1600	....	135259	DOR	Mosterton
1745	1750	1700	1750	177024	GLS	Mitcheldean
1666	1829	1550	1696	102830	LIN	Bourne
1590	1685	....	....	103632	NTH	Whilton
1792	1855	1600	1855	148482	OKI	Birsay
PHILIPSON						
1769	1843	1700	1769	179663	DUR	Stanhope
1795	1818	1550	1800	147265	LIN	North
PHILLIBROWN						
....	....	ALL	ALL	170011	ALL	Name Study
1800	1900	1800	1900	106674	LND	ALL
PHILLIMORE						
1780	1900	1780	1900	126551	GLS	Henbury
1780	1900	1780	1900	126551	GLS	Olveston
PHILLIP						
1740	1780	....	....	176958	PEM	Llandewi Velfrey
1750	1965	....	....	137820	SHI	Fetlar
1720	1965	....	....	137820	SHI	Mid Yell
1760	1965	....	....	137820	SHI	North Yell
1758	1965	....	....	137820	SHI	Northmavine
1720	1965	....	....	137820	SHI	South Yell
....	....	1747	1992	155039	YKS	Skipton
PHILLIPPS						
1600	1992	1600	1992	176958	CMN	Abergwili
1650	1800	....	....	100536	???	???
PHILLIPS						
....	....	ALL	1820	178403	ALL	ALL
1884	1992	1700	1884	155136	AYR	Kilmarnock
1884	1992	1700	1884	155136	AYR	Kilmaurs
1765	1815	1765	1815	117803	BKM	Adstock
....	....	1790	1830	117137	BRE	Crickadern
1830	1890	....	....	117137	BRE	Llandefalle
1774	1811	1774	....	115576	BRK	Hungerford
1864	1992	1700	1864	155101	CGN	Aberystwyth
1850	1920	1840	1880	155047	CHS	Liverpool
?	?	....	....	178888	CHS	Mobberley
1830	1840	1830	1860	158658	CMN	Kidwelly
1800	1930	....	....	162094	CMN	Llanelly
1790	1860	1700	1790	123102	CMN	St Clears
1780	1920	1780	1970	121096	CMN	Talley
1660	1728	1600	1800	153354	CON	Gwennap
....	....	1800	....	116335	CON	Helston
1760	1848	1785	1841	124001	CON	Marazion
1704	1851	....	....	127957	CON	Marazion
1820	1860	1780	1860	127361	CON	St Endellion
....	....	1870	1900	116467	CON	???
1745	1864	1700	1745	160474	CWD	Chirk
....	....	ALL	1820	178403	DBY	ALL
....	....	1800	....	116335	DEV	Devonport
1800	1850	1800	1850	124605	DEV	Plymouth
1762	1992	1700	1762	123153	DEV	Tiverton
1818	1847	1818	1847	154040	DEV	West Down
1800	1850	....	....	131857	DFD	Prendergast
1877	1992	ALL	ALL	115762	ESS	Great Wakering
1750	1850	ALL	ALL	137987	FLN	Hope
1890	1992	....	....	135666	GLA	Cynon Valley
1860	1890	1860	1992	152943	GLA	Pontypridd
1870	1967	1700	1870	142212	GLA	Troedyrhiw
1850	1946	ALL	ALL	154806	GLS	Barton
1810	1860	1770	1820	158380	GLS	Frampton Cotterell
1730	1757	1600	1730	108413	GLS	Great Barrington
1779	1835	1600	1779	178152	HAM	Beaulieu
1750	1800	1750	1800	174343	HAM	East Meon
1650	1920	1820	1900	126640	HAM	Minstead
1720	1750	1650	1750	174343	HAM	Old Alresford
1800	1900	1750	1800	121762	HAM	Selborne
....	....	1829	1868	143480	HAM	Southampton
1800	1850	1600	1900	120677	HAM	West Meon
....	....	1800	1920	115045	HEF	Hereford
....	....	1800	1930	147508	HEF	Pembroke
1768	1992	ALL	ALL	116408	HEF	Ross
1770	1774	1770	1774	157171	HEF	Weston Beggard
1892	1898	1880	1906	124001	HRT	Codicote
1756	1838	1756	1838	103977	HRT	Shenley
PHILLIPS contd.						
1756	1838	1756	1838	103977	HRT	Wheathampstead
1829	1900	1790	1829	144223	IRL	Antrim
....	....	1700	1884	155136	IRL	???
1874	1899	1860	1920	171441	KEN	Bapchild
1700	1780	....	....	119431	KEN	Buckland By Dover
1851	1876	1849	1881	124001	KEN	Chatham
1851	1867	....	....	127957	KEN	Chatham
1910	1950	1910	1950	171441	KEN	Faversham
1812	1867	....	1880	171441	KEN	Gillingham
1874	1920	....	1920	171441	KEN	Sittingbourne
1692	1845	1800	1850	171441	KEN	Strood
1744	1771	....	1800	171441	KEN	Tunstall
1817	1817	....	....	139971	KEN	Upchurch
?	?	?	?	166642	KEN	???
1790	1870	1700	1992	114596	LAN	Liverpool
1860	1923	1800	1860	151343	LAN	Liverpool
....	1882	1860	1882	133639	LAN	Oldham
1799	....	....	....	148768	LIN	Bourne
1560	1720	....	....	137618	LIN	Wispington
1850	1938	1700	1950	156493	LND	ALL
1860	1944	1700	1992	112402	LND	Clerkenwell
1845	1939	1750	1900	155152	LND	Lambeth
1875	1941	1850	1875	151173	LND	Rotherhithe
1881	....	ALL	ALL	155373	LND	Shoreditch
1865	1893	1800	1900	165972	MDX	East
1805	1936	1800	1940	176672	MDX	Barnet
1870	....	1750	1870	121010	MDX	Chelsea
1814	1992	....	....	127779	MDX	Holborn
1910	1992	1860	1910	155101	MDX	Southall
1840	1900	....	....	157724	MDX	Stepney
1837	1900	1800	1900	118540	MON	Cwmbran
1816	1900	1800	1900	118540	MON	Llanfrechfa
1730	1900	1600	1900	143766	MON	Llanvaches
1857	....	ALL	ALL	172057	NFK	Lowstoft
1736	?	1700	1720	149039	NTH	West
....	....	1860	....	154377	NTT	Langwith
1780	1820	1780	1820	151297	PEM	Begelly
1838	1890	1700	1838	159735	PEM	Cilgerran
....	....	1500	1700	154245	PEM	Haverfordwest
1811	1877	1700	1850	132993	PEM	Hodgeston
1807	1810	1780	1810	158658	PEM	Manordeifi
1790	1850	1750	1790	114928	PEM	Milford
1836	1862	1750	1850	131792	PEM	Narberth
1700	1899	....	....	121835	SAL	Ellesmere
1700	1900	1650	1700	154245	SAL	Shifnal
?	?	ALL	1850	117919	SOM	Dinder
1819	1858	1819	1858	166898	SOM	East Pennard
1782	1813	1750	1858	166898	SOM	Wyke
1857	....	1830	1850	163775	SRY	Bermondsey
1764	1764	1500	1764	144851	SSX	Guestling
1700	1850	1500	1700	139092	SSX	Hastings
....	1700	....	....	174564	SSX	Hastings
1796	1820	1696	1796	177490	SSX	Hastings
1853	1893	1850	1893	165441	STS	Fenton
1759	1857	....	....	155055	STS	Rugeley
1800	1960	1600	1992	168467	STS	Swinscoe
1876	1929	1800	1875	117722	STS	West Bromwich
1870	1940	....	....	116408	WAR	Birmingham
1890	1970	1700	1950	122203	WAR	Birmingham
1780	1850	....	....	164631	WAR	Birmingham
1890	1970	1700	1950	122203	WAR	Coventry
1890	1970	1700	1950	122203	WAR	Kineton
1830	1830	1800	1860	171662	WIL	Farley
1800	1850	1750	1850	101036	WIL	Whiteparish
1830	1890	....	....	140317	WLS	Llangollen
1792	1850	1600	1850	155071	WMD	Birmingham
1816	....	1816	1891	104043	WOR	???
1865	1929	1865	1992	155098	YKS	Batley
1738	1864	1700	1864	155098	YKS	Birstall
1840	1992	1800	1840	101788	???	Glasgow
PHILLIPSON						
1820	1838	1700	1820	117471	CUL	Alston
1787	1992	ALL	1787	126942	YKS	Bentham
....	....	1650	1750	147613	YKS	Ingleton
PHILLISKIRK						
1814	1992	1750	1814	155179	NYK	Stockton
PHILLO						
1869	....	1850	1870	163775	MDX	Poplar
PHILLPOTTS						
ALL	ALL	ALL	ALL	123692	ALL	ALL
PHILP						
....	....	1800	1900	155969	CON	Redruth
1881	1992	ALL	ALL	156671	SSX	Midhurst

Known From	To	Researching From	To	Ref	Cty	Place
PHILPIN						
1840	1900	1840	1900	141577	MON	Newport
PHILPOT						
1600	1970	1538	1800	155209	KEN	East
1807	1992	1650	1854	166987	KEN	Margate
1550	1860	1550	....	155195	KEN	Ramsgate
1860	1992	....	....	155195	LND	Battersea
1784	1880	1650	1784	163163	MDX	London
1850	1960	ALL	ALL	162469	SFK	North
PHILPOTS						
....	....	ALL	1800	142298	SAL	Ludlow
PHILPOTT						
....	....	ALL	ALL	155209	ALL	Name Study
....	....	ALL	ALL	155217	ALL	Name Study
....	....	ALL	ALL	155217	ALL	ALL
....	....	1800	1850	155225	COR	Newmarket
1635	1992	1500	1635	128724	KEN	Crundale
1754	1881	1538	1914	155217	KEN	Dover
1861	1950	1800	1950	129984	KEN	Saltwood
1630	1900	1538	1800	155209	KEN	???
1871	1920	1855	1871	155225	LND	Bermondsey
1871	1920	1855	1871	155225	LND	Rotherhithe
1789	....	1700	1789	118605	SAL	Westbury
1836	1855	....	....	155225	TIP	Cashel
1836	1855	....	....	155225	TIP	Clonoulty
....	....	1850	1900	131962	WOR	Upton On Severn
PHILPOTTS						
1800	1880	1750	1880	119938	HEF	Cradley
PHILSON						
....	....	ALL	ALL	155233	ALL	Name Study
PHIN						
....	....	1800	ALL	149187	ANS	Beuvie
....	....	1800	ALL	149187	ANS	Liff
PHIP						
....	....	1697	1992	108502	HUN	Meppershall
PHIPPARD						
ALL	ALL	ALL	ALL	155241	ALL	ALL
1721	1992	ALL	1721	157511	DOR	???
PHIPPEN						
1635	1750	1580	1635	165042	DOR	ALL
1800	1992	ALL	ALL	158798	SOM	East
1866	1900	1850	1900	165824	SOM	Bath
1769	1954	1769	1954	148091	SOM	Buckland Dinham
1769	1954	1769	1954	148091	SOM	Burrington
PHIPPS						
1860	1961	....	....	155268	DUR	Hebburn
1760	1789	1700	1800	121525	GLS	Painswick
1790	1834	1700	1790	164917	GLS	Whitecliffe
1770	1880	1700	1900	116173	LEI	Rearsby
1870	1890	....	1870	101761	MDX	East London
1760	1860	....	....	153583	NTH	Bugbrooke
1776	1798	1776	1798	178705	OXF	Broadwell
1740	1826	1740	1826	155268	OXF	Hook Norton
....	1700	....	....	174564	OXF	???
1841	?	ALL	1900	165646	STS	Tipton
1790	1850	1790	1910	153303	WAR	Edgbaston
1797	1961	1772	1860	155268	WAR	Shipston
PHIPS						
1768	1805	1700	1850	141569	NTH	Twywell
....	....	1700	1800	163082	SRY	Sutton
PHIPSON						
....	....	ALL	ALL	158909	ALL	Name Study
PHYSICK						
1780	1889	....	1780	125954	DEV	Tavistock
PHYTHIAN						
1820	1921	....	....	159964	LAN	Kearsley
1800	1900	1822	1900	134422	LAN	Liverpool
1800	1900	1822	1900	134422	LAN	West Derby
PIBEL						
1858	1992	1800	1858	131806	CHS	Congleton
PIBWORTH						
1758	1834	....	....	115606	HAM	Hurstbourne Tarrant
PICK						
1800	1870	1600	1870	130125	HAM	Portsea
1675	1764	ALL	ALL	106097	LEI	Great Dalby
1600	1900	1600	1900	135968	LEI	Great Dalby
1790	1992	1790	1992	106305	LEI	Kirkby Malory
?	?	ALL	1800	117919	LEI	Melton Mowbray
1760	1875	ALL	ALL	106097	RUT	Whissendine
PICKARD						
1810	1820	1764	1820	154733	DEV	Bratton Fleming
....	....	1748	1780	154733	DEV	Challacombe
1703	1751	1700	1754	154733	DEV	Chittlehampton
1700	1719	1700	1750	154733	DEV	Kings Nympton
PICKARD contd.						
1766	1899	1765	1988	154733	DEV	Loxhore
1776	1810	1776	1810	154733	DEV	Satterleigh
1637	1821	1624	1830	154733	DEV	Tawstock
1672	1811	1672	1811	154733	DEV	Warkleigh
1880	1960	1700	1880	157996	GLA	Cowbridge
1818	1850	ALL	ALL	141615	LEI	North
1830	1880	1700	1830	157996	LND	Hackney
1775	1825	1700	1800	148806	NYK	Harome
1793	1992	1600	1793	115096	SXW	Ifield
....	....	1800	1900	141984	YKS	Newthorpe
1760	1860	....	....	141984	YKS	Sherburn In Elmet
PICKEN						
1650	1800	1600	1650	173312	SAL	North
1840	1850	1800	1992	115193	SOM	Bath
1840	1850	1800	1992	115193	SOM	Bristol
PICKENGILL						
?	?	?	?	150215	KEN	Chatham
PICKER						
1690	1730	ALL	....	104515	LIN	Heckington
PICKERDEN						
....	....	ALL	ALL	101974	ALL	Name Study
1700	1992	ALL	ALL	101974	ALL	ALL
PICKERDITE						
....	....	1700	1950	143219	MDX	London
PICKERILL						
1854	1876	1854	1876	141291	STS	Dudley
1830	1854	1700	1830	141291	STS	Walsall
PICKERING						
1720	1940	....	....	128996	CAM	Thorney
1729	1729	....	....	135437	CHS	Christleton
1707	1707	....	....	135437	CHS	Plemstall
1746	1855	1600	1746	150614	CHS	Preston On The Hill
1850	1950	1800	1850	174866	CUL	West
1793	1848	1793	1848	147532	CUL	Penrith
1640	1700	1550	1750	138878	CUL	Whitehaven
1700	1906	....	....	100633	CUL	???
....	....	1750	1850	159166	DBY	ALL
1640	1899	ALL	1640	174157	DOW	Magheralid
1733	1806	1650	1733	176907	GLS	West
1690	1784	....	....	117404	GLS	Blockley
1828	1900	....	....	171824	LAN	Liverpool
1850	1960	1800	1992	176524	LAN	Liverpool
1575	....	1575	....	109347	LAN	Read
1809	1850	1600	1809	137626	LEI	Packington
1780	1840	1780	1840	167924	MDX	Marylebone
1800	1900	1500	1750	118915	NBL	ALL
1700	1906	....	....	100633	NBL	???
1560	1750	....	....	153583	NTH	Bugbrooke
1731	1811	1500	1811	168629	NYK	Ebberston
1820	1952	....	....	117404	SAL	Madeley
....	....	1800	1992	155292	SSX	Eastbourne
1751	1824	ALL	ALL	153753	WAR	Bedworth
1850	1870	1800	1850	103292	WAR	Birmingham
1787	1860	1700	1787	164259	WAR	Coventry
....	....	....	1838	145742	WAR	Nuneaton
1835	1889	ALL	1835	165212	WYK	Rotherham
1835	1889	ALL	1835	165212	WYK	Sheffield
1813	1824	1740	1824	141097	YKS	Hotham
1780	1855	1770	1790	108510	YKS	Leeds
1780	1880	ALL	ALL	139351	YKS	Rillington
1790	1880	....	....	118206	YKS	Staxton
PICKET						
1762	1837	1700	1762	123307	BRK	Winterbourne
1826	....	1800	1830	153737	IRL	Fermanagh
1680	....	1680	1900	119458	OXF	Hanborough
1790	1808	1600	1790	100447	OXF	Ibstone
PICKETT						
1800	1899	ALL	ALL	146633	BRK	Chievely
1744	1771	1740	1780	102717	HRT	Standon
1796	1878	....	....	155314	KEN	Sydenham
1835	1907	1800	1835	159158	MDX	Soithall
1851	....	1851	1878	155314	MDX	Southwark
1812	1871	1841	1871	170623	OXF	Watlington
1796	1854	....	1854	155314	SRY	Clapham
1800	1899	ALL	ALL	146633	WIL	Gt Bedwyn
ALL	1805	....	....	170178	WIL	Ogbourne St Andrew
....	....	1700	1800	111538	WIL	Wroughton
1820	1840	1750	1850	126586	YKS	Leeds
PICKFORD						
1770	1992	1770	1865	162582	DOR	Buckhorn Weston
....	1844	....	1960	116777	KEN	Greenwich
1700	1890	1550	1700	129763	NTH	West
1870	....	1800	1900	135429	SOM	Bath

Known From	To	Researching From	To	Ref	Cty	Place
PICKFORD contd.						
1800	1850	1800	1900	135429	SOM	High Littleton
1700	1760	1600	1900	116777	WAR	Ashow
1822	1833	1800	1822	130877	YKS	Penistone
1904	....	1904	....	112534	YKS	York
PICKLES						
1850	1992	1700	1850	100803	WYK	Halifax
1824	....	ALL	ALL	166839	WYK	Otley
1866	....	ALL	ALL	166839	WYK	Shipley
1880	1960	ALL	ALL	170801	YKS	Grange Moor
1752	1992	ALL	1752	165204	YKS	Heponstall
1802	1860	ALL	ALL	173290	YKS	Hiptonstall
1780	1795	....	....	138584	YKS	Horbury
1736	1790	1700	1750	138584	YKS	Kildwick
1770	1780	....	....	138584	YKS	Rothwell
1860	1966	1860	1966	173290	YKS	Todmorden
PICKNELL						
....	....	1830	1900	155322	SSX	???
PICKNOLL						
....	....	1550	1830	155322	SSX	???
PICKSTOCK						
1560	1880	ALL	ALL	137987	SAL	North West
1884	....	....	....	123889	STS	Dilhorne
1800	1856	1856	1992	123889	STS	Lane End
....	1919	1890	1992	123889	STS	Longton
PICKSTONE						
1775	1980	1775	1980	155330	LAN	Prestwich
1775	1980	1775	1980	155330	LAN	Radcliffe
PICKTHALL						
1825	1925	1825	1992	133450	SFK	Chillisford
PICKTON						
1780	1810	1700	1800	146730	KEN	North West
PICKUP						
1800	1890	1750	1850	155357	KEN	Deptford
1825	1880	1750	1880	155357	KEN	Greenwich
1750	1900	1750	1900	125237	LAN	Darwen
1800	1880	1880	1992	162256	LAN	Darwen
1850	....	1850	....	136786	LAN	Manchester
1827	1827	1803	1852	147281	LAN	Rossendale
1704	1846	ALL	1704	102350	YKS	Monk Fryston
PICOT						
ALL	ALL	....	....	153397	CHI	Jersey
PICTON						
1670	1828	....	....	103373	BKM	ALL
1800	....	1800	1900	176958	CMN	???
1700	....	....	....	176958	GLA	???
1860	1900	1840	1920	117501	KEN	Woolwich
1840	....	1700	1840	160660	LND	East
1650	1832	1760	1830	176958	PEM	Haverfordwest
1650	1832	1760	1830	176958	PEM	Poyston
....	1900	1800	1900	117501	PEM	???
1500	1900	1500	1900	168343	WLS	ALL
1817	1864	1801	1817	137537	WLS	Haverfordwest
1600	....	1500	1900	176958	WLS	Haverfordwest
PIDCOCK						
1546	1675	1550	1675	102830	DBY	Ashover
PIDDINGTON						
1844	1992	1700	1900	145513	BRK	Cookham
1868	1873	....	....	136565	LAN	Newchurch In Rossendale
1850	....	....	....	113018	LND	Poplar
1717	1774	1700	1775	103632	NTH	Maidford
PIDDLE						
?	?	?	?	117528	DOR	Puddletown
PIDDOCK						
1803	1818	ALL	1803	143278	WAR	Birmingham
PIDGEON						
1730	1770	1700	1900	119083	DEV	East
1910	....	ALL	1910	177458	LND	East
1910	....	ALL	1910	177458	LND	South
1910	....	ALL	1910	177458	LND	Battersea
PIDGLEY						
1775	1775	....	....	135437	DEV	Exeter
....	....	1800	1992	107506	HAM	ALL
PIDOUX						
1890	1940	ALL	ALL	174505	DBY	Stapenhill
1856	1860	ALL	ALL	174505	MDX	Islington
PIDWELL						
?	?	?	?	155365	CON	???
?	?	?	?	155365	DEV	???
PIE						
1947	1947	1900	1947	174262	WLS	Maesteg
PIEARSON						
1791	1812	1791	1812	155519	MDX	London
PIERCE						
1830	....	1700	1830	175307	CAM	March
1770	1799	1770	1799	147486	HAM	Portsea
1720	1861	1700	1720	127116	HAM	Romsey
....	....	1700	1865	166863	IRL	Cork
1795	1860	1700	1992	146390	IRL	Wexford
....	....	1500	1850	164992	KEN	Ripple
1750	1800	1700	1750	156981	MGY	Macchynlleth
1780	1860	1600	1860	143766	MON	Llanvaches
1780	1860	1600	1860	143766	MON	Undy
1811	....	ALL	1811	158445	SSX	Nuthurst
1831	1948	1776	1948	125717	SWL	Llansaintffraid
1860	1948	1761	1952	125717	WOR	Wolverhampton
PIERCEY						
1859	1864	1800	1860	131369	DEV	Buckland
1859	1864	1800	1860	131369	DEV	Tavistock
PIERCY						
1699	1806	....	....	165999	CON	Stoke Climsland
1750	1850	1750	1992	133450	COR	Tivoli
1810	1830	1785	1820	115886	OXF	Rotherfield Greys
1790	1840	1790	1840	154210	WIL	Winterbourne Dauntsey
1685	1949	1600	1700	112224	YKS	East Riding
PIERPOINT						
1860	ALL	ALL	1866	116734	CHS	Sandbach
1864	1992	1800	1864	179647	WAR	Birmingham
PIERREPOINT						
1550	1650	1500	1650	154881	NTT	Holme Pierrepoint
1833	1911	1911	1992	148865	SSX	Brighton
PIERREPONT						
1846	1866	1700	1846	138029	LAN	Liverpool
1601	1992	ALL	1601	165204	NTT	Southwell
PIERS						
1830	....	....	....	172723	ALL	ALL
PIERSE						
?	?	?	?	152005	KER	Listowel
PIERSON						
1843	1850	1750	1843	155381	KEN	Canterbury
1899	1910	1874	1910	155381	KEN	Ramsgate
1874	1946	1850	1880	155381	LND	North
1946	1985	....	....	155381	SXE	Heathfield
1700	1800	1700	1800	119717	YKS	Hinderwell
PIFF						
1851	1992	1761	1851	155403	GLS	Elmstone
1851	1992	1761	1851	155403	GLS	Hardwick
1851	1992	1761	1851	155403	GLS	Piffs Elm
PIFFE						
1730	1800	1650	1730	118745	GLS	Down Hatherley
PIGANY						
1870	1950	1500	1950	132098	NFK	Aldby
1850	1945	1800	1992	132098	NFK	Burgh St Peters
1850	1870	....	....	132098	SFK	Lowestoft
PIGG						
....	....	ALL	ALL	135739	ALL	Name Study
1803	1861	....	....	135739	DUR	North
1704	1910	1650	1704	118079	ESS	Chrishall
1760	....	....	....	154571	NFK	Skeyton
1687	1763	....	....	117404	SAL	Upton Magna
1750	1850	ALL	ALL	137987	SAL	Upton Magna
PIGGATT						
....	....	1780	1850	118923	IOM	Arbory
PIGGE						
1818	....	1818	....	143529	NFK	Wiveton
PIGGIN						
1838	1897	1838	ALL	110922	LND	ALL
....	1897	1700	1805	110922	OXF	ALL
PIGGINS						
1700	1870	ALL	ALL	150797	LEI	Bottesford
1700	1870	ALL	ALL	150797	LIN	Folkingham
1889	1939	1700	1889	165859	LND	Fulham
1800	1899	....	....	137960	MDX	London
PIGGOT						
1788	1880	ALL	1788	101001	FIF	Dysart
1800	1920	1800	1912	161705	NFK	Salthouse
1700	1850	1700	1790	161705	NFK	Southery
PIGHILLS						
1795	1992	?	?	176702	WYK	Addingham
....	....	....	1795	176702	WYK	Bingley
....	....	....	1795	176702	WYK	Haworth
PIGNEY						
1849	1992	ALL	1849	134171	WES	Appleby
PIGOT						
1612	1850	....	....	175439	CHS	Nantwich
1612	1850	....	....	175439	STS	Patshull

Known From	To	Researching From	To	Ref	Cty	Place
PIGOTT						
1670	1700	1550	1725	133450	SAL	Chetwynd
PIKE						
1660	1992	1760	1992	155446	BRK	Lyford
1840	1880	1780	1840	160822	CON	Saltash
1840	1880	1780	1840	160822	DEV	Devonport
1900	1992	1800	1865	147826	DEV	Exeter
....	....	1800	1900	126055	DEV	Torquay
1804	1856	1750	1860	155438	GLS	Bristol
1787	1806	1600	1830	107565	HAM	Bramdean
1760	1900	ALL	ALL	122866	HAM	Leckford
....	....	1600	1800	142298	LEI	Ratby
1827	1900	1820	1900	132217	LIN	Horncastle
1803	1820	ALL	1820	132217	LIN	Wainfleet
1871	1890	....	....	116505	LND	South East
1863	1870	1800	1863	174807	LND	St Mary Le Bone
1787	1992	1600	1787	155411	NFK	East Norfolk
1817	1851	1800	1851	116505	SOM	Frome
1722	1775	1650	1722	169234	SOM	Greinton
1891	1925	1800	1930	115746	SOM	North Newton
1851	1874	ALL	ALL	138223	STS	Wolverhampton
1860	1910	....	1860	113891	WIL	Ailsbury
....	....	1780	1820	117137	WIL	Warminster
1682	1812	....	....	151351	YKS	Harewood
1852	1856	1852	1856	132217	YKS	Leeds
PIKET						
1821	1826	1700	1992	168181	LIN	Kirton
PIKETT						
1857	1992	ALL	ALL	155454	LIN	Bourn
1857	1992	ALL	ALL	155454	LIN	Sleaford
PILBEAM						
....	....	ALL	ALL	155462	ALL	Name Study
1840	1900	1700	1900	155462	KEN	West
1770	1837	1700	1900	155462	KEN	Biddenden
1778	1871	ALL	ALL	155462	MDX	London
1742	1760	1710	1800	155462	SRY	Chipstead
1744	1893	1700	1900	155462	SRY	Croydon
1560	1900	ALL	ALL	155462	SSX	East
1849	1900	1800	1849	140880	SSX	Hooe
1560	1900	ALL	ALL	155462	SSX	Mid
PILCH						
1518	1725	ALL	ALL	156310	NFK	Central
1825	1833	1700	1825	100110	NFK	Rougham
PILCHER						
1700	1940	....	....	127833	HAM	Portsmouth
1810	1884	ALL	1810	109851	KEN	East
1773	?	?	?	166642	KEN	Ashford
1777	....	....	1800	171441	KEN	Denton
1589	1815	1589	1934	134880	KEN	Elmsted
1743	1777	1743	1992	134880	KEN	Sutton Valence
PILCOCKS						
....	....	1800	1850	138010	ALL	ALL
PILE						
1850	1900	1700	1914	141933	DEV	Challacombe
PILESLY						
1734	1751	1600	1734	158399	DOR	Winterborne Came
PILFORD						
1708	1785	1650	1708	174807	SSX	Henfield
PILGRIM						
1814	1907	1800	1910	176672	ALL	ALL
1734	1777	1714	1777	173851	BKM	Old Bradwell
1850	....	....	....	174750	MDX	London
1833	1844	1790	1833	155489	???	London
PILKINGTON						
?	1847	?	?	147869	ALL	ALL
1600	....	....	....	167037	DBY	Stauton
1826	1832	....	....	142859	LAN	Edgeworth
1786	1819	....	....	142859	LAN	Haslingden
1768	1788	1500	1788	169439	LAN	Huncoat
1840	1918	1796	1900	142859	LAN	Manchester
1850	1992	1700	1850	155497	LAN	Pendle Hill
1864	1884	1864	1884	168289	LAN	Wigan
PILL						
1820	1850	ALL	ALL	173657	BRK	North West
1792	1809	1700	1792	174688	CON	Kingsand Maker
1683	1992	1600	1683	155500	OXF	Shorthampton
PILLAER						
1800	1900	....	....	116998	LND	Bermondsey
1600	1900	....	....	116998	NFK	Great Yarmouth
1600	1900	....	....	116998	NFK	Norwich
PILLAR						
1794	1992	1700	1794	124109	DEV	Crediton
PILLER						
1800	1900	....	....	116998	LND	Bermondsey

Known From	To	Researching From	To	Ref	Cty	Place
PILLER contd.						
1600	1900	....	....	116998	NFK	Great Yarmouth
1600	1900	....	....	116998	NFK	Norwich
PILLING						
1625	....	1625	....	109347	LAN	Altham
1692	1750	1599	1692	141291	LAN	Lancaster
1759	1795	1600	1765	145971	WYK	Otley
1820	1992	1820	1992	155519	YKS	Elland
1871	1900	1800	1870	138738	YKS	Halifax
PILLINGER						
....	....	ALL	ALL	142425	ALL	Name Study
....	....	ALL	ALL	142425	ALL	ALL
1600	1992	ALL	ALL	142425	GLS	ALL
1750	1850	1600	1850	154342	GLS	Bitton
1790	1860	ALL	ALL	113700	GLS	Hasfield
1500	....	ALL	ALL	142425	HEF	ALL
1500	....	ALL	ALL	142425	SOM	Bath
1600	1992	ALL	ALL	142425	WIL	Box
1600	1992	ALL	ALL	142425	WIL	Yatton Keynell
1700	1750	1600	1750	154342	WIL	Yatton Keynell
PILTER						
....	....	ALL	ALL	135704	ALL	Name Study
ALL	ALL	ALL	ALL	135704	ALL	ALL
1771	1805	1750	1850	135704	DUR	Sunderland
1739	1746	1700	1750	135704	YKS	Fylingdales
PIM						
....	....	ALL	ALL	155527	ALL	Name Study
1570	1992	1570	1992	155527	ALL	ALL
1806	1912	ALL	1806	151424	SRY	Bermondsey
PIMBLE						
....	....	ALL	ALL	115320	ALL	Name Study
PIMBLETON						
....	1740	ALL	1740	134511	DBY	North Wingfield
PIMLETT						
1870	1992	ALL	1870	155535	LAN	Liverpool
PIMM						
1400	1850	ALL	ALL	168009	KEN	South East
1500	1850	....	....	125199	KEN	Chilham
1800	1950	ALL	ALL	168009	LND	North
1800	1950	ALL	ALL	168009	LND	City
1800	1900	ALL	ALL	168009	LND	St Pancras
1862	1884	1700	1831	111953	OXF	Stanton Harcourt
PIMPERTON						
?	?	?	?	118044	LIN	Orby
PINCHAM						
1823	1877	1750	1900	136719	HAM	Amport
PINCHBECK						
1878	1992	ALL	ALL	108022	LIN	Grimsby
1851	1881	1750	1850	108022	LIN	Horncastle
1794	1850	1700	1800	100862	MDX	Shadwell
PINCHES						
1815	1842	1750	1842	148288	HEF	Leintwardine
1740	1760	1700	1740	155500	SAL	Wistanstow
PINCHING						
....	....	1600	1850	155543	ENG	South
....	....	1600	1850	155543	ENG	West
1850	1992	....	....	155543	LND	Central
1833	1850	1700	1900	155543	SRY	Lambeth
PINCHON						
1813	1850	....	1813	159506	YKS	Hull
PINCKNEY						
1066	1650	ALL	ALL	165042	WIL	ALL
PINCOCK						
1700	1850	....	....	126497	LAN	Leyland
1780	1870	1780	1870	126500	LAN	Wigan
PINCOMBE						
1700	1858	1600	1850	132470	DEV	Bishops Nympton
1760	1860	1760	1880	106801	DEV	Bishopsteighton
PINCOTT						
1750	1880	1600	1880	154342	GLS	Bristol
PINDER						
....	....	ALL	ALL	136425	ALL	Name Study
1682	1940	....	....	128996	CAM	Thorney
1795	1806	1790	1850	159905	DUR	South Shields
....	....	1740	1794	159905	DUR	Stockton
?	?	?	?	133728	EYK	West Of Hull
1775	....	1775	....	109347	LAN	Great Harwood
1730	1992	1680	1992	114936	LAN	Ribble Valley
1700	....	1700	....	109347	LAN	Ribchester
....	....	1660	1720	155551	LIN	Yarborough
1850	1992	....	1850	162647	LND	???
1705	1733	ALL	ALL	107840	NTT	Retford
1740	1780	1700	1740	121339	NYK	Whitby
1800	1900	ALL	1950	118338	SOM	Weston

Known From	To	Researching From	To	Ref	Cty	Place
PINDER contd.						
1850	1992	....	....	155551	WYK	Bradford
....	....	1780	1850	155551	WYK	Halifax
1702	1817	....	....	155551	WYK	Liversedge
PINE						
1805	1827	1600	1850	107565	DEV	Sidbury
1800	1820	1800	1890	135429	DEV	Topsham
1810	1830	....	....	150282	SOM	Brushford
1680	1730	1680	1740	142018	SOM	Taunton
PINEL						
ALL	ALL	....	....	153397	CHI	Jersey
PINER						
1679	1759	1620	1800	167002	BKM	Wendover
PINFIELD						
1865	1992	1700	1865	105635	STS	Wednesbury
....	....	?	?	134201	WOR	Worcester
PINGHAM						
1765	1910	1600	1837	155578	KEN	North West
1765	1977	1600	1837	155578	LND	???
1765	1910	1600	1837	155578	SRY	North East
PINHAY						
1774	1842	1700	1850	169161	DEV	Harbetonford
PINHEY						
1864	1913	1864	1913	108782	DEV	Plymouth
PINHORN						
....	....	ALL	ALL	155586	ALL	Name Study
1669	1992	1500	1736	145971	HAM	Isle Of Wight
1669	1992	1500	1736	145971	HAM	Portsea
1833	1992	1700	1833	167150	HAM	Portsmouth
PINION						
1850	1992	....	....	155594	ANT	Belfast
1840	1880	1795	1840	155594	DOW	Waringstown
....	....	1800	1900	155594	WEX	Gorey
PINK						
1756	1881	1756	1992	170585	BRK	Basildon
1672	1747	1600	1672	170585	BRK	Bucklebury
1762	1790	1600	1762	168637	HAM	East Meon
1802	....	ALL	1802	175080	HAM	Wymering
1840	1940	1750	1840	163732	KEN	Lee
1780	1847	....	1870	171441	SRY	Puttenham
1700	1775	1700	1992	114901	SRY	Thursley
1710	1800	ALL	1800	115282	SSX	East
1750	1850	1720	1850	105333	SSX	Birdham
1730	1800	1700	1820	105333	SSX	Yapton
PINKET						
1821	1891	....	....	141356	JSY	St Clement
PINKHAM						
1780	1850	1600	1930	162043	DEV	Plympton St Mary
PINKNEY						
1590	1992	1066	1985	155616	DUR	ALL
....	....	1750	1820	102881	DUR	Barnard Castle
1845	1920	ALL	ALL	155608	DUR	Bishops Aukland
1845	1920	ALL	ALL	155608	DUR	Tudhoe
1807	1831	1750	1807	118486	NRY	Boltby
1832	1992	1700	1870	125466	SFK	Ipswich
1798	....	ALL	....	125466	SFK	Stutton
1440	1980	1066	1985	155616	WIL	ALL
1540	1840	1066	1985	155616	YKS	ALL
1750	1992	1600	1750	169862	YKS	Fylingdales
PINLEY						
1711	1779	ALL	ALL	141615	LAN	Ormskirk
PINN						
1750	1837	1750	1837	108251	DEV	Cullompton
1812	....	ALL	ALL	163988	DEV	Kings Nympton
PINNEGAR						
1777	....	1650	1900	106461	LND	ALL
1777	....	1650	1900	106461	WIL	ALL
1777	....	1650	1900	106461	WIL	Calne
PINNEL						
....	....	1683	1812	169471	BKM	North
PINNELL						
1742	1851	1650	1742	148938	GLS	Cromhall
1748	1992	1600	1748	155624	WIL	Brinkworth
1783	1992	1600	1783	155624	WIL	Crudwell
PINNELS						
1773	1849	1750	1850	136719	HAM	Tidworth
PINNER						
....	....	ALL	ALL	171816	NTH	ALL
1750	1784	1650	1784	170291	NTH	Dodford
1790	1820	1760	1900	111325	SFK	Washbrook
PINNEY						
....	....	1800	1900	153281	SOM	Bridgewater
PINNING						
....	....	ALL	ALL	160830	ALL	Name Study
PINNING contd.						
1600	1950	1540	1992	160849	LIN	ALL
1765	1806	1750	1830	105120	LIN	Hemswell
1685	1772	1650	1790	105120	LIN	Scotton
PINNINGTON						
1725	1800	1680	1730	102024	CHS	South
PINNOCK						
1800	1870	1600	1992	101389	NTH	Rothwell
1757	1936	1650	1800	131377	NTH	Rothwell
PINWILL						
....	....	ALL	ALL	155632	ALL	Name Study
....	....	ALL	ALL	155632	ALL	ALL
1794	1926	ALL	ALL	155632	CHI	Guernsey
1794	1926	ALL	ALL	155632	CHI	Jersey
PIOR						
1830	1863	1700	1863	116300	WAT	???
PIPE						
1862	1900	1800	1861	114693	KEN	Lewisham
1540	....	....	1560	160873	LND	???
1830	1870	1830	1870	111589	MDX	Stepney
....	....	ALL	1750	103284	SFK	???
....	....	1600	1900	177725	SOM	Martock
PIPER						
....	....	ALL	ALL	155659	ALL	Name Study
1878	1896	1851	1878	128961	BRK	East Hendred
1750	1992	1750	1992	161276	BRK	Newbury
1750	1841	1700	1780	121932	CON	Jacobstow
1836	1992	....	1836	155667	CON	Launceston
1750	1841	1700	1780	121932	CON	Warbstow
1855	1992	....	....	102881	DUR	West Hartlepool
1877	1890	1852	1930	133876	GLS	Bristol
1814	1932	1700	1850	102881	KEN	Gillingham
1814	1850	ALL	1850	152889	KEN	Hawkhurst
1810	....	1750	1850	102016	LND	Bishopgate
1800	....	....	....	126543	LND	Fulham
1860	1950	1800	1865	155691	LND	Kensington
1843	1852	1820	1877	133876	MDX	Bethnal Green
1843	1852	1820	1877	133876	MDX	London
1812	1852	1750	1852	133876	SRY	Bermondsey
1812	1852	1750	1852	133876	SRY	Camberwell
1875	1900	1875	1950	113743	SSX	Brede
1700	....	....	....	126543	SSX	Brighton
1620	1704	1620	1704	170143	SSX	Coldwaltham
1868	1881	....	....	102881	SSX	Hastings
1620	1704	1620	1704	170143	SSX	Heyshott
1700	1800	1700	1800	152404	SSX	N Stoke
1841	1865	....	....	122157	STS	Birmingham
1841	1865	....	....	122157	STS	Stoke On Trent
1841	1865	....	....	122157	STS	Woolstanton
1916	1992	....	....	122157	WIL	Swindon
1863	1863	1800	1880	127361	WRY	Pontefract
1887	1892	....	....	122157	???	Middlesborough
PIRIE						
1865	1940	....	1865	174246	ABD	ALL
1832	1835	1830	1840	170348	ABD	Aberdeen
1853	1992	1700	1855	155705	ABD	Auchterless
1811	....	1780	1830	170348	ABD	Ellon
1853	1992	1700	1855	155705	ABD	Forgue
1853	1992	1700	1855	155705	ABD	Insch
1779	1790	1750	1840	121126	ABD	Old Machar
1762	1864	1700	1800	174319	BAN	???
1755	1835	1755	1835	125598	FIF	St Andrews
1848	1867	1840	1880	170348	LND	Lambeth
1914	1950	1850	1992	173096	SCT	Aberdeen
PIRT						
1725	....	1725	....	109347	LAN	Downham
PISSEY						
1730	1850	ALL	1850	109851	ESS	ALL
1882	....	1882	....	135488	LND	Camberwell
PITAWAY						
1797	1922	1700	1796	173673	WOR	Dudley
PITBLADDO						
1742	1774	....	....	137936	FIF	Ceres
PITCAIRN						
1200	1992	ALL	ALL	155713	ALL	ALL
1785	1873	1700	1992	114596	PER	Dunbarton
PITCHER						
1837	1920	1700	1850	135887	BKM	Princes Risborough
1780	1860	ALL	1800	115266	DOR	ALL
1860	1909	1800	1860	103985	DOR	Dorchester
1800	1900	1750	1860	103985	DOR	Netherbury
1837	1920	1700	1850	135887	HAM	Ringwood
1800	1992	....	1800	150851	NFK	Central
1800	1992	....	1800	150851	NFK	North

Known From	To	Researching From	To	Ref	Cty	Place
PITCHER contd.						
1670	1750	1650	1750	142018	SOM	South
PITCHERS						
1820	....	ALL	ALL	138533	NFK	Weasenham All Saints
1800	1945	1600	1992	132098	SFK	Carlton Coleville
1850	1945	1600	1992	132098	SFK	Oulton Broad
PITCHES						
1847	1931	1800	1992	105120	CAM	Fordham
1880	1926	1850	1992	105120	LND	Walthamstow
PITCHFORD						
1815	1842	1800	1850	108510	SAL	Dawley
1762	ALL	ALL	1762	131725	SAL	Ketley
1784	....	ALL	1784	131725	SAL	Shrewsbury
1799	1879	ALL	1879	131725	SAL	Wellington
1784	....	1784	1787	131725	SAL	Westbury
1787	....	1787	1799	131725	SAL	Worthen
PITE						
....	....	ALL	ALL	112623	ALL	Name Study
PITHAM						
1844	1869	1844	1869	139408	WAR	Rugby
PITHER						
1800	1850	1500	1800	174661	BRK	ALL
1660	....	1660	1865	119458	BRK	Cholsey
PITHOUSE						
1799	1891	....	....	115606	WIL	Little Bedwyn
PITMAN						
1821	1900	1700	1821	164267	DOR	Yetminster
1787	....	1787	1992	127035	DOR	???
1800	1850	1600	1992	176494	GLS	ALL
....	....	ALL	ALL	124974	HAM	North East
1600	1760	1600	1710	124974	HAM	Basing
1620	1800	1550	1820	124974	HAM	Basingstoke
1550	1710	1590	1635	124974	HAM	Quarley
1750	1860	1700	1750	103675	SOM	Chedzoy
PITT						
....	....	ALL	ALL	139955	ALL	ALL
1720	1850	1707	1992	139955	BRK	Bray
1720	1850	1707	1992	139955	BRK	Maidenhead
1740	1795	1740	1795	148121	DOR	Balchalual
1850	1900	ALL	1850	143022	ESS	Wivenhoe
1830	1992	1700	1830	155748	GLS	Bristol
1885	1900	1700	1950	168734	GLS	Gloucester
1720	1850	1707	1992	139955	HAM	Aldershot
1720	1850	1707	1992	139955	HAM	North Poulner
1705	1760	1675	1992	114901	HAM	Portsea
1720	1850	1707	1992	139955	HAM	Ringwood
1718	1759	1600	1760	110787	LND	St Clement Danes
1820	1820	1700	1890	153001	SFK	Nacton
1761	1817	ALL	1761	161500	SOM	Crewkerne
1720	1850	1707	1992	139955	SRY	Clerkenwell
1730	1900	1600	1900	119938	WOR	Mathon
1785	1815	1780	1860	157171	WOR	Mathon
PITTAM						
1732	1818	1700	1820	107360	NTH	Blakesley
1760	1950	....	....	165948	NTH	Helmdon
1789	1826	....	....	155756	NTH	Lichborough
1811	1869	1780	1880	107360	NTH	Long Buckby
1795	1911	1700	1795	155756	NTH	Potterspury
1785	1792	1780	1800	107360	NTH	Towcester
1780	1840	1700	1992	140287	WAR	Alderminster
PITTAR						
1700	1830	1700	1850	176788	DUB	???
1805	1992	....	1850	176788	LND	???
PITTARD						
1816	1853	1800	1860	166898	SRY	Walworth
PITTILLA						
1743	1992	1835	1980	139874	NBL	Newcastle
1743	1992	1835	1980	139874	NBL	Sunderland
1798	1808	....	....	139874	SCT	Melrose
PITTIPHER						
1790	1900	ALL	1790	167665	WAR	Warwick
PITTMAN						
1842	1860	1842	1860	131970	HAM	Fordingbridge
1830	1850	1700	1830	123102	KEN	Shoulden
1850	1930	1750	1850	176753	MDX	London
PITTOCK						
....	....	ALL	ALL	155772	ALL	Name Study
1450	1992	ALL	ALL	116459	KEN	ALL
1839	1859	ALL	ALL	151777	KEN	Sandwich
PITTS						
....	....	ALL	ALL	155780	ALL	Name Study
....	....	ALL	ALL	155780	ALL	ALL
?	?	?	?	155780	DEV	ALL
PITTS contd.						
1700	1992	1600	1700	177091	DEV	South Hams
1800	....	ALL	1800	179515	DEV	South Tawton
1775	1875	1550	1800	139866	DEV	Teignmouth
....	....	1800	1836	113352	ESS	Broomfield
....	....	....	....	103608	EYK	Eastrington
....	....	1800	1899	171794	LAN	Ashton Under Lyne
1845	1900	1700	1845	106054	NFK	Walpole St Peter
1844	1918	1800	1844	103365	SRY	Lambeth
....	....	1800	1899	171794	YKS	Bradford
1805	1850	1550	1830	147265	YKS	Leeds
PITZ						
1860	1900	1750	1860	149306	MDX	St Pancras
PIXLEY						
1700	ALL	1752	1835	107379	HRT	St Albans
PIZER						
1851	1992	1820	1920	155799	LIN	Great Ponton
1800	1860	....	1800	110027	WIL	Landford
1800	1860	....	1800	110027	WIL	Whiteparish
PIZZEY						
1838	1898	1700	1838	147389	GLS	Bristol
PLACE						
1800	1900	1700	1900	155802	LAN	Over Wyresdale
1790	1828	1750	1790	128368	LEI	Mountsorrel
1719	1764	....	1719	133566	SFK	Mildenhall
1820	....	1800	....	140236	YKS	Batley
1800	1900	1600	1800	135054	YKS	Spennithorne
PLACKETT						
1700	1850	1700	1850	134848	DBY	Breaston
PLAINE						
1689	1936	....	....	138630	CAM	Willingham
PLAISTED						
1700	ALL	1700	ALL	125512	GLS	Newhnam On Severn
1550	ALL	1550	ALL	125512	GLS	Westbury On Severn
1828	1879	1790	1828	178381	GLS	Westbury
1800	ALL	1800	ALL	125512	KEN	Deptford
1800	ALL	1800	ALL	125512	KEN	Woolwich
?	?	?	?	125512	WIL	Castle Combe
?	?	?	?	125512	WIL	Hannington
PLAISTEN						
....	....	1800	1925	115045	HEF	Hereford
PLAISTER						
1848	1877	....	....	116254	LND	Hammersmith
1700	1800	1600	1800	167088	SOM	Churchill
PLAMPIN						
1620	1670	ALL	1740	131067	LND	City
PLANE						
1764	1936	....	....	138630	CAM	Willingham
1830	1880	1800	1830	146587	MDX	Norwood Green
PLANK						
....	....	ALL	ALL	114308	WIL	Etchilhampton
1730	1900	....	....	132225	WIL	Marden
PLANT						
....	....	ALL	ALL	155837	ALL	Name Study
1833	1912	....	....	137790	CHS	Leese
1800	1850	1720	1820	172510	DBY	Chesterfield
1829	1865	1750	1804	136816	DBY	Clowne
1829	1992	1700	1829	137979	DBY	Clowne
1800	1850	1720	1820	172510	DBY	Clowne
1800	1906	....	1800	123358	DBY	Derby
1829	1865	1750	1804	136816	DBY	Staveley
1730	1835	ALL	1730	164364	DBY	Sutton Cum Duckmanton
1830	1880	1800	1880	109436	SAL	Little Dawley
1841	1861	1700	1841	155810	SOM	Bristol
1790	1890	1700	1800	175307	STS	Cheadle
1861	1861	1862	1992	179116	STS	Sedgeley
1790	1813	1760	1813	133280	WAR	Birmingham
1850	1900	ALL	ALL	172510	YKS	Halifax
1850	1900	....	....	172510	YKS	Sheffield
PLANTEROSE						
1850	1960	....	....	155845	LND	ALL
PLASTER						
....	....	1800	1992	150762	GLS	Fishponds
PLATNAUER						
1790	1980	ALL	ALL	166375	ALL	ALL
PLATT						
....	....	ALL	ALL	100854	ALL	ALL
....	....	ALL	ALL	137421	CHS	Acton By Nantwich
1867	1992	1867	1992	138827	CHS	Altrincham
1845	....	ALL	ALL	137421	CHS	Chester
1851	1992	ALL	1849	165212	CHS	Sandbach
1769	1769	1745	1769	165107	ESS	Maldon
1893	1943	1893	1943	156639	ESS	West Ham

Known From	To	Researching From	To	Ref	Cty	Place
PLATT contd.						
1797	1886	1760	1797	103365	FLN	Overton
1852	1921	1750	1852	110639	KEN	???
1880	1930	1800	1880	134848	LAN	Birkdale
1900	1920	1870	1925	130036	LAN	Liverpool
1790	1861	1616	1890	142859	LAN	Manchester
1812	1888	1750	1888	151432	LAN	Oldham
1765	1847	1750	1850	159964	LAN	Ringley
1810	1850	1750	1809	172006	LAN	St Helens
1752	1850	1700	1850	113743	MDX	Harrow
1852	1921	1750	1852	110639	MDX	???
....	....	ALL	ALL	137421	SAL	Market Drayton
1821	1890	1800	1900	146978	STS	Burslem
1821	1890	1800	1900	146978	STS	Stoke On Trent
1834	1857	1730	1830	137421	WAR	Birmingham
1900	ALL	1700	1900	130397	YKS	Kingston Upon Hull
1722	1939	1700	1750	173649	YKS	Saddleworth
PLATTS						
1813	1840	1700	1812	131245	KEN	Chatham
1808	?	ALL	ALL	172251	NTT	???
PLAYDON						
1790	1900	1600	1900	117617	WOR	Peopleton
1790	1900	1600	1900	117617	WOR	Pershore
PLAYER						
1790	1992	....	1790	143901	DEV	Silverton
1720	1780	ALL	1720	115266	DOR	ALL
1772	1818	....	....	176613	HRT	Aldenham
1772	1818	....	....	176613	LND	ALL
1834	1992	1770	....	156191	WIL	Malmesbury
1800	1850	1750	1992	145661	WIL	Salisbury
1787	1818	ALL	ALL	113662	WIL	Sherston Parva
PLAYFAIR						
1780	1870	1700	1900	130915	FIF	Abdie
PLAYFERE						
1612	....	1500	1700	176958	CAM	Cambridge
PLAYFOOT						
1769	1807	1807	1836	166170	KEN	Brenchley
1800	1860	1700	1850	123137	KEN	Lamberhurst
?	?	?	?	133728	LIN	Winterton
1836	1851	....	....	166170	LND	Highgate
PLAYFORD						
1762	1788	1500	1788	153591	SSX	Northiam
PLAYLE						
1780	....	ALL	ALL	141623	ESS	Fyfield
PLAYNE						
....	....	1580	1650	154873	KEN	Faversham
PLEASANCE						
1845	1845	1800	1845	103640	KEN	Gillingham
1750	1900	1700	1800	177377	KEN	Medway
1785	....	....	1785	100064	SFK	Newmarket
1830	1910	ALL	1830	109320	SFK	Newmarket
PLEASANT						
1674	1787	ALL	1674	168602	CAM	Burwell
PLEASANTS						
1830	1910	ALL	1830	109320	SFK	Newmarket
PLEDGER						
....	....	ALL	ALL	155888	ALL	Name Study
ALL	ALL	ALL	ALL	163716	ALL	ALL
1811	1943	1800	1910	156353	CAM	Haddenham
1868	1934	ALL	1992	143049	MDX	London
1800	1900	....	....	111368	MDX	Marylebone
1600	1699	1640	1690	135941	SFK	Glemsford
1786	1992	1700	1786	155888	SFK	Stoke By Clare
1731	1814	1700	1814	170143	SSX	Harting
PLENDER						
1816	1865	1750	1815	162396	ESS	Saffron Walden
PLESTED						
1873	....	....	....	116254	BKM	Aylesbury
1842	1875	ALL	1992	112631	BKM	Chesham
PLETTS						
1820	1880	1700	1840	106267	DUR	South
PLEVY						
1730	1750	1700	1800	157171	HEF	Leominster
PLEWS						
1700	1850	?	?	173185	WYK	Batley
PLEYDELL						
....	....	ALL	ALL	137081	ALL	Name Study
1425	1700	ALL	ALL	155896	BRK	Coleshill
1870	1950	1870	1950	155896	GLA	Cardiff
1800	1950	1800	1950	155896	GLS	Cheltenham
1700	1840	1650	1850	155896	GLS	Gloucester
1632	1650	1632	1650	155896	GLS	Newnham On Severn
1688	1715	1670	1740	155896	GLS	Painswick
1646	1680	1646	1700	155896	GLS	Stroud
PLEYDELL contd.						
1633	1800	1633	1820	155896	GLS	Westbury On Severn
1662	1691	1660	1760	155896	KEN	Hawkhurst
1740	1860	1670	1870	155896	SOM	Bristol
....	1948	1850	1960	155896	SSX	Battle
1690	1727	1690	1740	155896	SSX	Ewhurst
1820	1912	1820	1912	155896	SSX	Hastings
1714	1825	1714	1850	155896	SSX	Warbleton
1600	1770	1550	1770	155896	WIL	Cricklade
1550	1600	1500	1650	155896	WIL	Shrivenham
....	....	1715	1800	155896	WOR	ALL
PLEYDELL-WILTON						
1760	1833	1700	1900	155896	GLS	Gloucester
PLIMLEY						
1720	1903	1700	1930	168947	SAL	Oswestry
PLIMMER						
1823	1861	1770	1823	168645	SAL	Newport
PLOMER						
1620	1630	1600	1650	111538	HRT	Radwell
PLOUGHWRIGHT						
1860	1980	1700	1860	141658	NFK	Castle Rising
PLOWMAN						
1725	1725	ALL	1725	154563	DOR	Portesham
1850	1853	ALL	ALL	115002	LND	London
1780	1919	ALL	1992	115126	NTH	Blisworth
PLOWRIGHT						
....	....	1736	1992	108502	HUN	Houghton
PLOWS						
1860	1880	1800	1860	150096	YKS	Kippax
PLUCK						
1840	1850	1840	1860	135429	ESS	Braintree
1700	1840	1600	1700	148954	ESS	Saffron Walden
ALL	....	1840	1860	135429	ESS	Saffron Waldon
1840	....	1840	1860	135429	MDX	Bethnal Green
PLUCKNET						
1260	1353	1240	1353	124974	HEF	Kilpeck
PLUCKNETT						
....	....	ALL	ALL	147486	ALL	Name Study
ALL	ALL	ALL	ALL	147486	ALL	ALL
1700	1900	1675	1992	147486	HAM	Portsea
1840	....	1800	1900	122688	LND	East
1840	....	1800	1900	122688	LND	Poplar
1840	....	1800	1900	122688	LND	Shadwell
1837	1970	1700	1970	146293	SOM	Bath
1855	1881	1855	1992	147486	SSX	Bognor
1855	1881	1855	1992	147486	SSX	S Bersted
PLUCKWELL						
....	1754	ALL	1754	134511	NTT	???
PLUM						
1871	1881	1796	1992	136808	CAM	Whittlesey
1748	1807	1720	1807	123404	RUT	Whitwell
PLUMB						
1560	1992	1500	1600	155926	BRK	Lambourn
1761	?	1700	1776	155934	CAM	Ickleton
1830	1960	....	....	164720	CAM	Shepreth
1770	1850	1700	1850	126799	CAM	Soham
1850	1880	1750	1850	124605	CAM	West Wratting
1768	1870	1740	1870	102717	HRT	Braughing
1790	1802	1700	1850	159964	HRT	Great Munden
1835	1881	1830	1950	159964	HRT	Little Munden
1814	1871	1814	1950	159964	HRT	Westmill
1726	1814	....	....	101028	SFK	Barrow
1860	1865	1800	1860	177393	SRY	Reigate
1826	1893	1725	1826	134473	STS	Leek
PLUMBE						
1560	1992	1500	1600	155926	BRK	Lambourn
PLUMBER						
1641	1675	1500	1675	153591	SSX	Iford
PLUMBLEY						
1841	1881	....	....	116475	IOW	Whitwell
1700	1700	1650	1700	155276	SFK	Clopton
1784	1866	ALL	ALL	153516	SOM	Chew Magna
PLUMBRIDGE						
1776	1790	1790	1992	166189	BKM	Denham
PLUMLEY						
1568	1635	1400	1568	120189	DEV	Dartmouth
1500	1560	1450	1600	154881	KEN	ALL
1635	1700	....	....	120189	SOM	Locking
1775	1850	1770	1850	166685	SOM	Yatton
PLUMMER						
1879	1918	1800	1918	128694	LND	Marylebone
1870	1992	1800	1992	103292	MDX	Islington
1860	1872	....	1872	130524	MDX	London
1830	1870	1800	1880	124605	MDX	St Pancras

Known From	To	Researching From	To	Ref	Cty	Place
PLUMMER contd.						
....	....	?	....	128589	NFK	Yarmouth
1679	1679	....	....	103632	NTT	Nottingham
1820	1980	1750	1820	110647	SFK	Haughley
1820	1980	1750	1820	110647	SFK	Henley
1807	....	....	1807	133566	SFK	Mildenhall
1761	1789	1600	1800	158399	SSX	Slaugham
PLUMPTON						
1800	1992	....	....	176125	LIN	Asterby
1800	1992	....	....	176125	LIN	Goulceby
PLUMRIDGE						
....	....	ALL	ALL	153532	ALL	Name Study
1910	1992	1800	1915	155691	LND	North
POASCO						
1733	....	1600	1750	100013	SOM	Wells
POBGEE						
1766	1992	1750	1992	169250	SSX	East Grinstead
1766	1992	1750	1992	169250	SSX	Penge
POBJAY						
1630	1760	1630	1760	142018	SOM	Norton St Philip
POBJOY						
....	....	1650	1760	172871	SOM	East
1756	1858	1700	1756	172871	SOM	Norton St Philip
POCHIN						
1600	1850	1550	1700	155950	LEI	Barkby
1600	1850	1550	1700	155950	LEI	Leicester
1600	1850	1550	1700	155950	LEI	Wigston
POCKET						
1762	1787	1700	1761	172006	GLS	Elmore
POCKETT						
1735	1900	1600	1900	131040	GLS	ALL
POCKLINGTON						
1880	1910	1880	1910	105724	STS	Stoke On Trent
1840	1880	1840	1880	105724	YKS	Wakefield
POCOCK						
....	....	1600	1992	127833	BRK	Newbury
1846	1992	1800	1992	108391	BRK	Reading
1870	1992	1841	1919	110094	BRK	Reading
....	....	ALL	ALL	143324	BRK	Stamford Park
1870	1992	1841	1919	110094	KEN	Dartford
1817	1837	1700	1900	141151	LND	Lewisham
....	....	....	....	108340	LND	???
?	?	ALL	1850	117919	MDX	London
1840	1992	1780	1840	176257	MDX	Westminster
1770	1850	1700	1850	136840	SOM	Brendon Hills
....	....	1800	1950	141151	SOM	Wincanton
1812	1900	1700	1812	165980	SSX	Hailsham
1750	....	ALL	ALL	116394	WIL	Melksham
PODD						
....	....	1777	1795	107247	ALL	ALL
PODGER						
1800	1850	1750	1850	106631	SOM	Bleadon
1840	1860	1700	1840	146587	SOM	Curry Rivel
PODMORE						
1800	1810	1770	1800	113050	CHS	Nantwich
1779	1788	ALL	ALL	129933	CHS	Nantwich
1844	1870	ALL	ALL	129933	IOW	West Cowes
1750	1770	1700	1992	167592	LAN	Liverpool
1830	1992	1800	1830	113050	LAN	Manchester
1896	....	1800	1900	123625	LND	Kensington
1750	1900	1500	1900	139807	SAL	ALL
....	....	1750	1850	143502	SAL	ALL
1860	1900	1750	1850	143502	SAL	Central
1670	1840	1600	1670	173312	SAL	North
1700	1853	1700	1992	159468	SAL	Lilleshall
1740	1750	1700	1992	167592	WOR	Worcester
POFFLEY						
1880	1880	1800	1890	148431	WIL	Cricklade
1880	1880	1800	1890	148431	WIL	Highworth
POGMORE						
1753	1900	1600	1753	154172	NTT	Everton
POGSON						
1800	1850	1600	1992	120677	WYK	Slaithwaite
POHL						
1865	1865	1800	1865	103640	MDX	Holborn
POILE						
1770	1780	1700	1800	131431	KEN	???
POINDEN						
1800	1860	ALL	1800	131881	SSX	Westbourne
POINDESTRE						
1656	1714	ALL	ALL	115126	CHI	ALL
POINFON						
1675	....	....	....	155977	NFK	???
POINTER						
1703	1703	1660	1720	111414	GLS	Maisemore
1820	1851	....	1820	133221	HAM	Breamore
1709	1754	ALL	ALL	169730	HAM	Dummer
1701	1716	ALL	1716	169730	HAM	Herriard
1842	1920	1800	1842	108103	KEN	Swanley
1719	1992	1600	1719	155977	NFK	Hempstead By Holt
1770	1900	1770	1850	142565	NFK	St Faiths
1748	1748	1650	1750	117005	NTH	Cosgrove
....	....	1314	....	155977	OXF	???
1800	1820	....	....	133221	WIL	Downton
POINTING						
....	....	ALL	ALL	136883	ALL	Name Study
1800	1860	1750	1900	131431	SOM	Compton
POINTON						
....	....	ALL	ALL	155985	ALL	Name Study
1813	1850	1700	1850	117315	CHS	Sandbach
POINTUR						
....	....	1213	....	155977	CAM	???
POIZER						
1704	1900	1700	1900	155799	LEI	Stathern
POLAND						
....	....	ALL	ALL	150908	ALL	Name Study
1754	1962	1754	1962	107166	SSX	Heene
POLARD						
....	1850	1750	1850	146927	CON	St Just
POLDEN						
1680	1710	ALL	1680	115266	DOR	ALL
1852	1873	1800	1890	136719	LND	Kensington
1772	1824	1700	1772	174688	WIL	Chilmark
POLDING						
1825	1992	1750	1992	173096	MDX	London
POLE						
1802	1837	1825	1870	167533	GLS	Bristol
1733	1785	1650	1733	148938	GLS	Shapwick
1780	1780	1700	1780	121509	LEI	Barrow Upon Soar
1750	1965	....	....	137820	SHI	Fetlar
1757	1992	1720	1757	122734	SHI	Greenbank
1720	1965	....	....	137820	SHI	Mid Yell
1757	1992	1720	1757	122734	SHI	Mossbank
1757	1992	1720	1757	122734	SHI	Nesting
1760	1965	....	....	137820	SHI	North Yell
1758	1965	....	....	137820	SHI	Northmavine
1720	1965	....	....	137820	SHI	South Yell
1670	1794	1640	1670	167533	SOM	Milverton
1840	1860	1700	1900	162345	SOM	Westpenard
POLGLASE						
1811	1992	1700	1811	148687	CON	Helston
POLGREAN						
1809	1992	1700	1809	129437	CON	West
POLHILL						
1422	1650	1350	1650	154881	KEN	Otford
1753	1761	1739	1753	149217	KEN	Woodchurch
1662	1722	1722	1739	149217	SXE	Burwash
POLING						
1799	1820	....	....	104477	SSX	West Tarring
POLKEY						
ALL	ALL	ALL	ALL	156000	ALL	ALL
1750	1860	1660	1992	156000	LEI	Loughborough
POLKINGHORN						
1888	1940	1700	1786	158089	CON	Kenwyn
POLKINGHORNE						
1560	1808	1560	1808	156019	CON	Breage
1813	1815	1813	....	156019	CON	Lelant
1836	....	1836	....	156019	CON	Luxulyan
1690	1815	1820	1900	178845	CON	Redruth
1836	....	1836	....	156019	CON	Tywardreath
POLL						
1831	1860	....	1860	161888	NFK	Norwich
1740	1770	1600	1740	177164	SOM	Shapwick
POLLARD						
1864	1923	ALL	1887	114030	BDF	North West
....	....	1800	1870	103713	CAM	Soham
1718	1992	1700	1992	140449	CON	Gwennap
1599	1810	1540	1820	155616	CON	Redruth
1780	1910	1760	1890	103128	DBY	Staveley
1749	1882	ALL	1749	165735	DEV	Bishops Nympton
1792	1860	1750	1800	137413	DEV	Glittisham
1792	1860	1750	1800	137413	DEV	Talaton
1820	1860	1750	1900	167401	DUR	South Shields
1860	1866	....	....	135070	GLS	Bristol
1775	1980	1725	1775	156035	HAM	South
1713	1713	ALL	ALL	130508	HAM	Clatford
1713	1713	ALL	ALL	130508	HAM	Goodworth

Known From	To	Researching From	To	Ref	Cty	Place
POLLARD contd.						
1898	1992	ALL	1900	156078	IRL	???
1836	....	1700	1888	156582	KEN	Lewisham
1850	1855	1855	1870	175382	LAN	Accrington
....	....	....	1950	110817	LAN	Burnley
1825	....	1825	....	109347	LAN	Paidham
1816	1903	1790	1840	118354	LAN	Whalley
1791	1992	1750	1791	137944	LEI	Braunstone
1688	1737	1600	1688	138584	LEI	Kegworth
1741	1800	....	....	164631	LIN	Market Overton
1888	....	1867	1890	156582	MDX	Southall
1889	1903	....	....	135070	MDX	Stepney
1830	1880	1700	1850	156051	MDX	Stepney
1750	1850	1750	1850	141682	NTH	Northampton
1766	1890	1700	1766	101524	SOM	North Petherton
1864	1867	1830	1888	156582	SRY	Camberwell
1683	1951	ALL	ALL	105015	SSX	Horsham
1700	1800	1700	1850	139920	SSX	Pagham
1700	1800	1700	1850	139920	SSX	Sidlesham
1850	1900	1800	1992	108642	WAR	Solihull
1800	1821	1780	1800	147338	WRY	Southowram
ALL	1760	....	....	170798	WRY	Spenvalley
1760	1765	1600	1760	175382	YKS	Bradford
1750	....	1600	1750	130419	YKS	Giggleswick
1833	1850	ALL	1833	166847	YKS	Leeds
1800	1850	1780	1800	175382	YKS	Settle
1780	1780	1700	1780	121509	YKS	Wensleydale
POLLEN						
....	....	ALL	1766	103284	MDX	London
POLLENDINE						
....	....	1500	1900	166863	IRL	ALL
....	....	1500	1900	166863	KEN	ALL
POLLET						
....	....	ALL	ALL	156108	ALL	Name Study
1694	1992	1500	1900	156108	LAN	South East
POLLETT						
1720	1850	1720	1890	156086	SOM	Butleigh
POLLEY						
1550	1860	....	....	165999	ESS	ALL
1874	1954	ALL	ALL	151580	LND	Marylebone
POLLICOTT						
ALL	ALL	ALL	ALL	156094	ALL	ALL
POLLIKETT						
....	....	ALL	ALL	156094	ALL	Name Study
POLLINGER						
1750	1900	1750	1992	154342	GLS	Bitton
1700	1750	1600	1700	154342	WIL	Yatton Keynell
POLLINGTON						
1720	1960	....	....	122130	SSX	Rotherfield
1900	1992	....	....	122130	SSX	Uckfield
POLLINTINE						
....	....	ALL	ALL	165948	ALL	Name Study
....	....	ALL	ALL	165948	ALL	ALL
1870	1930	....	....	165948	LND	Bermondsey
1930	1980	....	....	165948	NTH	Sulgrave
1770	1870	1700	1780	165948	SFK	Great Barton
POLLITT						
1820	1900	1700	1820	132268	LAN	Bolton
1840	1880	ALL	ALL	100390	LAN	Manchester
1900	1992	....	....	162744	YKS	Leeds
POLLOCK						
....	....	ALL	1890	156116	ARL	???
1850	....	1800	1860	169625	AYR	Maybole
1890	1992	1700	1890	140147	DFS	Wigtown
1830	1850	1800	1900	139203	DON	Castle Fennell
1857	1952	ALL	1857	143960	IRL	???
1750	1810	1720	1750	122904	LKS	East Kilbride
1875	1897	1750	1874	131245	MDX	Bethnal Green
1750	1950	....	.,..	108677	MDX	London
....	....	1800	1992	147613	NIR	Belfast
1838	1900	1700	1838	143812	RFW	Lochwinnoch
1200	1750	....	....	108677	SCT	South
1857	1952	ALL	1857	143960	SFK	Eye
....	....	....	1992	148830	TYR	Killynaught
POLLY						
1769	1769	1740	1769	161896	SFK	Stratford St Mary
POLLYN						
1776	1900	....	....	169129	NFK	Tilney
POLSON						
1769	1794	1700	1770	166723	GLS	Kings Stanley
POLUS						
....	....	ALL	ALL	130818	LND	London
POLWIN						
1630	1992	1650	1992	104671	CON	Falmouth
POLWIN contd.						
1630	1992	1650	1992	104671	CON	Mullion
POMEROY						
....	....	ALL	ALL	156124	ALL	Name Study
1750	1821	....	....	100536	CON	???
1831	1851	1800	1940	133639	DOR	Beaminster
1851	1873	1840	1900	133639	SOM	Coker
1658	1716	....	1658	149888	SOM	Taunton
POMFRET						
1806	1851	1750	1851	126918	ESS	Lambourne
1806	1835	1750	1851	126918	LND	Bermondsey
POMROY						
1614	1992	ALL	ALL	147389	CON	Callington
1826	1900	1800	1839	131369	DEV	Buckland Mar
POND						
1783	1992	1650	1783	130966	DOR	Canford Magna
1750	1992	1550	1750	156132	ESS	Upminster
1822	1845	1780	1822	177393	LND	Shoreditch
1780	1840	1700	1850	126268	LND	Westminster
1834	1851	1800	1853	126470	NFK	Thetford
PONSFORD						
1780	1992	ALL	ALL	143537	ALL	ALL
1757	1823	1700	1850	120146	DEV	Drewsteighton
1786	1856	1600	1786	174130	DEV	Drewsteignton
1830	1830	1700	1992	124044	???	Bristol
PONSONBY						
1678	1702	1600	1678	152196	CMA	Haile
1830	1835	1750	1850	126985	YKS	Pocklington
PONT						
1851	1992	1750	1850	101540	SSX	Seaford
PONTEFRACT						
1840	1950	1750	1890	160083	YKS	ALL
1805	1926	1750	1832	112844	YKS	Kirkburton
PONTER						
....	....	ALL	ALL	156159	ALL	ALL
1870	1945	1800	1870	156159	AVN	Bath
1760	1820	1700	1760	156159	GLS	Sevenhampton
1808	1992	1700	1810	156159	WIL	Highworth
PONTIN						
1812	1992	1600	ALL	112631	BRK	ALL
1812	1992	1600	ALL	112631	MDX	ALL
1768	1992	ALL	1992	112631	SRY	Egham
PONTING						
....	....	ALL	ALL	156167	ALL	Name Study
1687	1742	....	....	165999	GLS	Almondsbury
1770	ALL	....	....	142158	GLS	Berkeley
1687	1742	....	....	165999	GLS	Henbury
1870	1920	1800	1900	165980	LND	Ealing
1814	1820	1750	1814	133671	WIL	Brinkworth
1657	1900	1600	1657	147729	WIL	Marlborough
PONTON						
1800	1840	1750	1840	136840	HAM	Andover
1840	1850	1750	1870	133019	LND	Bermondsey
1750	1831	1700	1830	154881	MLN	Edinburgh
POO						
1560	1700	1560	1700	167924	YKS	Pocklington
POOK						
....	....	ALL	ALL	166227	ALL	Name Study
1838	1839	1800	1838	157619	HAM	Portsea Island
1880	1927	1850	1992	139564	LND	Wandsworth
....	....	ALL	ALL	151998	SSX	Wartling
1558	1992	ALL	ALL	156175	SXE	Ninfield
POOL						
ALL	ALL	1800	1850	111554	GLS	Kings Stanley
ALL	ALL	1800	1850	111554	GLS	Leonards Stanley
1816	ALL	ALL	1816	133183	GLS	Mangotsfield
1756	1783	1650	1780	131377	LIN	Blankney
1767	....	....	....	151351	NTT	South Wilford
1808	....	....	....	133183	SOM	Ashton
1750	1850	1700	1900	177180	STS	Gnosall
....	....	ALL	1790	151602	WIL	Enford
1780	1900	1650	1780	123005	YKS	Driffield
1780	1900	1650	1780	123005	YKS	Honley
1780	1900	1650	1780	123005	YKS	Thornton
POOLE						
1890	1950	....	....	125962	BKM	Burnham
1824	1880	1824	1880	173851	BKM	Great Bradwell
1800	1850	1750	1830	109517	CAM	Witcham
1840	1900	1700	1900	156221	CHI	Gurnsey
?	?	?	?	156221	CHI	Jersey
1600	1992	?	?	114944	CHS	???
1800	1903	1800	1992	163589	CMA	Furness
1733	1822	1667	1733	103918	CUL	Isel
1899	1960	1700	1799	107832	DBY	Heanor

Known From	To	Researching From	To	Ref	Cty	Place
POOLE contd.						
1816	1851	....	....	135437	DEV	Churchstanton
1849	1849	....	....	135437	DEV	Clayhidon
....	....	....	....	156221	DOR	ALL
1850	1868	1800	1900	177938	DOR	Beaminster
1790	1840	1600	1790	162876	DOR	Lyme Regis
....	....	1800	1930	169382	ESS	Maldon
1907	....	....	....	150762	GLA	Cardiff
1800	1900	1600	1900	154342	GLS	Bitton
1862	1893	....	....	135437	GLS	Bristol
1818	1886	1750	1818	128937	GLS	Hartspury
1798	1992	1770	....	156191	GLS	Kingscote
1700	1800	1600	1800	154342	GLS	Mangotsfield
1794	....	....	....	164003	GLS	Tebury
1850	1900	1600	1800	156221	HAM	ALL
1798	1820	1600	1820	174343	HAM	Portsea
1800	1900	1700	1800	126403	HAM	Portsmouth
1866	1992	....	....	107506	HAM	Winchester
1734	1755	1599	1734	141291	LAN	Ulverston
1823	1873	1500	1823	176974	LEI	Leicester
1600	1992	?	?	114944	LND	???
1870	1958	1700	1870	132926	MDX	Bethnal Green
....	....	1861	1871	116602	MDX	Strand
1800	1870	1750	1900	159107	NFK	Upwell
1779	1793	1760	1793	170143	NTH	Barton
1779	1793	1760	1793	170143	NTH	Broughton
1768	1795	....	....	151351	NTT	Bulwell
1767	....	....	....	151351	NTT	Holme Pierrepont
1857	1861	1820	1860	108510	SAL	Shifnal
1821	....	....	....	123633	SCT	Castle Milk Dunn
1846	....	1700	1992	140953	SOM	Bristol
1805	1992	1600	1805	123242	SOM	Luxborough
1662	1768	1600	1700	156221	SOM	Shurton
1662	1768	1600	1700	129356	SOM	Stogursey
1662	1768	1600	1700	156221	SOM	Stogursey
1850	1854	....	....	135437	SOM	Stoke St Gregory
1792	1800	1750	1812	115746	SOM	West Buckland
1850	1900	1800	1992	133450	SOM	Westbury On Trym
1872	1983	ALL	ALL	156256	STS	Leek
1790	1992	1700	1790	156248	STS	Sedgley
1843	1860	1841	1860	165441	STS	Stoke On Trent
1810	1992	....	....	172529	WAR	Birmingham
1798	1992	1770	....	156191	WIL	Malmesbury
....	....	1600	1800	125857	WOR	Beoley
1836	1899	ALL	ALL	175587	YKS	Long Marston
POOLER						
1500	1900	1500	1900	157430	SAL	ALL
1579	1730	....	....	117404	STS	Haughton
1500	1900	1500	1900	157430	WOR	ALL
POOLEY						
1700	1835	1600	1850	143766	CON	Crowan
1809	1992	1700	1809	156264	ESS	Peldon
1798	1803	1700	1802	131245	HRT	Welwyn
1810	1834	1750	1850	126918	LND	Bermondsey
1867	1873	ALL	ALL	124346	LND	Chelsea
1821	1855	....	1855	152803	NFK	Necton
1819	1992	1800	1850	100862	SSX	Catsfield
1810	1834	1750	1850	126918	SSX	Catsfield
POOLMAN						
1740	....	1700	1850	126268	DEV	East
POONEY						
1759	1946	1700	1759	138010	BDF	ALL
POOR						
1788	1868	1700	1900	167487	DOR	Broadwater
1800	1858	1550	1858	174343	HAM	Froxfield
1750	1785	1700	1750	169242	HAM	Gosport
1800	1820	ALL	1800	131881	HAM	Portsmouth
1701	1793	1600	1701	127116	HAM	St Mary Bourne
1850	1992	....	....	140856	LND	???
POORE						
1815	1889	1760	1815	132039	WIL	Salisbury
POPE						
....	....	ALL	ALL	147516	ALL	Name Study
ALL	....	....	....	150975	BDF	Biggleswade
1805	1992	1600	1805	151092	BRK	Aston
1917	?	1917	1992	172596	CON	Penzance
1710	1900	1650	1710	141372	DEV	Morchard Bishop
1857	1918	....	....	147907	DEV	Tawstock
ALL	ALL	ALL	ALL	103543	DOR	Morden
1831	1866	1800	1831	122661	DOR	Wimborne
1646	1870	1646	1870	178683	GLS	Berkley
1820	1906	1820	1906	178683	GLS	Dymock
1580	1595	....	....	142859	GLS	Minchinhampton
1812	1874	1700	1812	148938	GLS	Wraxall

Known From	To	Researching From	To	Ref	Cty	Place
POPE contd.						
1782	1900	1700	1900	127108	HAM	Steventon
1846	1890	1840	1900	135232	HRT	Watford
1725	1800	ALL	1800	115282	KEN	East
1900	1992	1700	1900	148849	KEN	Folkestone
....	....	1750	1992	133361	LND	???
1840	1870	1750	1840	146285	MDX	Islington
1740	....	....	....	117579	SOM	Frome
1825	1992	1600	1825	120723	SOM	Shapwick
1850	1900	1600	1850	120723	SOM	Staywell
1770	1850	....	....	132756	STS	Potteries
1820	1941	1860	1941	178683	WOR	Berrow
1827	1992	1827	1906	178683	WOR	Birtsmorton
1880	1969	1880	1969	178683	WOR	Longdon
1789	1910	1799	1941	178683	WOR	Pendock
POPEJOY						
1837	1920	1700	1850	135887	BRK	Swallowfield
POPELY						
....	....	ALL	ALL	161160	ALL	Name Study
1766	1940	....	....	128996	CAM	Thorney
POPHAM						
1790	1860	1770	1860	118575	DEV	Ashford
1810	1850	1700	1850	166650	DEV	Berry Pomeroy
1810	1850	1700	1850	166650	DEV	Plymouth
1810	1850	1700	1850	166650	DEV	Tavistock
POPKIN						
1860	1910	....	....	148989	LND	East
1860	1910	....	....	148989	LND	North East
POPKISS						
....	....	ALL	ALL	163708	ALL	Name Study
POPLE						
1763	?	ALL	ALL	153516	SOM	Kewstoke
1763	?	ALL	ALL	153516	SOM	Wick St Lawrence
1790	1861	....	....	140090	SOM	???
POPLETT						
1750	1992	1700	1992	156280	KEN	ALL
1800	1900	1700	1992	156280	LND	ALL
1800	1900	1700	1992	156280	MDX	ALL
1600	1992	1200	1992	156280	SRY	ALL
1820	1992	1820	1992	156280	SSX	ALL
POPPINS						
1840	1900	1700	1840	143812	LIM	Limerick
POPPITT						
....	....	1820	1880	171948	SAL	Longdon
POPPLE						
....	....	ALL	ALL	100056	ALL	ALL
1790	1860	....	....	100056	CAM	Thorney
1740	1940	....	....	128996	CAM	Thorney
1842	....	....	1992	151270	CAM	Whittlesey
1790	1860	....	....	100056	NTH	ALL
POPPLESTONE						
....	....	ALL	ALL	156299	ALL	Name Study
POPPLETON						
1765	1800	1800	1830	156302	YKS	Richmond
1670	1765	1600	1670	156302	YKS	Ripon
POPPLEWELL						
....	....	ALL	ALL	155632	ALL	Name Study
....	....	ALL	ALL	155632	ALL	ALL
1800	1950	ALL	ALL	128449	WAR	Birmingham
....	....	1752	1900	155632	WAR	Birmingham
1750	1900	ALL	ALL	128449	WRY	Heckmondwike
1700	1850	ALL	ALL	128449	YKS	Birstall
1790	1836	1720	1790	151068	YKS	Birstall
1854	1969	1750	1854	122661	YKS	Darton
1600	1900	ALL	ALL	128449	YKS	Hartshead
1600	1900	1500	1900	128449	YKS	West Riding
1726	1926	1500	1726	155632	YKS	West Riding
1750	1800	....	....	144568	YKS	???
PORCH						
1780	1820	1750	1840	166685	SOM	Cameley
PORDAGE						
1750	1842	1750	1900	148784	KEN	Rochester
1500	1750	1400	1992	148784	KEN	Rodmersham
POREL D'AGROND						
1881	1894	1850	1881	124095	LND	Kensington
PORKER						
1826	1868	....	....	135437	GLS	Bristol
1786	1797	....	....	135437	SOM	Kilton
1816	1828	....	....	135437	SOM	Stogursey
1834	1857	....	....	135437	SOM	Taunton
1799	1845	....	....	135437	SOM	Wembdon
PORRETT						
1558	1992	ALL	ALL	156310	NFK	???

Known From	To	Researching From	To	Ref	Cty	Place
PORRIT						
1600	1620	1620	1702	109142	YKS	North
1702	1941	1600	1702	109142	YKS	Birstall
PORRITT						
....	....	1820	1870	103187	NYK	Lythe
1620	1780	1550	1620	121339	NYK	Lythe
....	....	1870	1905	103187	NYK	Ruswarp
PORT						
?	?	?	?	154687	KEN	Herne
PORTBURY						
1800	1900	1700	1800	124214	DEV	Rockbeare
1741	1761	1700	1800	110132	DEV	???
PORTCH						
1835	....	....	....	156329	AVN	Bristol
1900	....	....	....	120057	LND	New South Gate
1820	1980	1820	1980	154709	WIL	Bradford On Avon
PORTEOUS						
1712	1880	1600	1712	147346	LTN	Newton
1820	1850	ALL	ALL	142611	NBL	Ancroft
1850	1917	1850	1974	141895	NBL	Hexham
1750	1965	....	....	137820	SHI	Fetlar
1720	1965	....	....	137820	SHI	Mid Yell
1760	1965	....	....	137820	SHI	North Yell
1758	1965	....	....	137820	SHI	Northmavine
1720	1965	....	....	137820	SHI	South Yell
1749	....	....	1749	101761	WRY	Kirkheaton
PORTER						
1776	1992	1500	1766	143073	ABD	Monquitter
1796	1828	1550	1800	147265	ABD	???
1796	1828	1550	1800	147265	BAN	???
1550	1930	1500	1900	156353	CAM	Haddenham
ALL	1828	....	....	105368	CAV	Virginia
1792	1792	1750	1825	133450	CON	S Teath
1780	1860	1700	1780	121509	CUL	Dalston
1827	1900	1750	1900	166952	DBY	Crich
1860	....	....	....	164275	DUR	Sunderland
?	?	?	?	147400	ESS	Barking
1869	1950	1869	1950	131970	ESS	Bocking
1850	1900	1800	1900	155357	ESS	Chelmsford
1824	1836	1824	1836	131970	ESS	Felsted
1870	1940	1800	1900	113859	ESS	West Ham
1874	1992	1861	....	135437	GLS	Bristol
1840	1840	1750	1840	121509	GLS	Quenington
1850	1920	ALL	ALL	122866	HAM	East
1820	1920	1820	1950	142506	HAM	North
1580	1980	1716	1920	156388	HAM	East Wellow
1800	1870	....	....	105759	IRL	Letterkenny
1740	1760	ALL	1740	131059	KEN	Ash By Ridley
....	....	1840	1867	130184	KEN	Greenwich
1500	1642	1450	1650	154881	KEN	Seal
....	....	....	1860	154024	KEN	Tunbridge
1761	....	1700	1761	139483	KKD	Borgue
1768	1830	1761	1768	139483	KKD	Kirkmabreck
1875	....	1875	....	109347	LAN	Accrington
1850	1992	ALL	1850	118117	LAN	Birch
1792	1872	1770	1820	118443	LAN	Poulton
....	....	1800	1992	111503	LAN	Preston
1829	1970	1829	1970	159131	LAN	Preston
1840	1876	1800	1900	122327	LEI	Leicester
1577	1632	1550	1650	156396	LEI	Shawell
1632	1846	1600	1850	156396	LEI	Swinford
1870	1871	1800	1870	154954	LND	Clerkenwell
1820	1860	1750	1820	141372	LND	Cripplegate
....	....	1700	1850	152390	LND	Leyton
....	....	1700	1850	152390	LND	Stratford
1800	....	?	1900	156361	NFK	Central
1800	....	?	1900	156361	NFK	North
1780	1860	....	....	142522	NIR	???
1666	1666	1550	1850	156396	NTH	Stanford
1886	1992	....	....	154024	NTT	Nottingham
1600	1750	1600	1750	142123	SAL	Prees
1923	1923	1888	1923	118133	SCT	Bridgeton
1704	1730	1650	1730	129356	SOM	Chilthorne Domer
1820	1920	1820	1950	142506	SRY	North
1792	1862	1750	1790	112364	SRY	Bermondsey
1850	1930	ALL	ALL	122866	SSX	East
1689	....	1600	1689	143898	SSX	Hastings
1778	1820	1700	ALL	142506	SSX	Rogate
1800	1917	....	....	100536	SSX	???
1847	....	1700	1847	172022	WAR	Birmingham
1580	1620	1500	1650	156396	WAR	Clifton
1580	1620	1500	1650	156396	WAR	Hillmoreton
1740	ALL	....	....	142158	WIL	Aldbourne
1710	1740	1650	1750	136840	WIL	Avon Valley

Known From	To	Researching From	To	Ref	Cty	Place
PORTER contd.						
1790	1850	1700	1790	166804	WIL	Axford
1726	1900	1707	1726	150185	WIL	Great Somerford
1860	1992	1800	1860	176931	WIL	Lea
1725	1800	1725	1800	109347	YKS	Gisburn
1861	1989	....	....	156345	YKS	Kingston Upon Hull
1752	1992	1700	1900	156345	YKS	Thirsk
PORTERIS						
1767	1813	1500	1767	125695	NTH	Boughton
PORTLOCK						
1865	1896	1700	1865	173886	GLS	Cirencester
PORTMAN						
1725	....	1725	....	109347	LAN	Padiham
PORTOR						
....	....	1800	1900	146110	SCT	ALL
PORTREY						
1577	1790	ALL	1577	158739	GLA	Llantwit Major
PORTSMOUTH						
1758	1785	....	....	127779	HAM	Ringwood
....	....	ALL	ALL	170860	SRY	Bookham
PORTUFIELD						
1831	1885	1800	1831	123897	BEW	Spittal
PORTUS						
1737	1981	....	....	156418	AVN	Batheaston
1737	1981	....	....	156418	SOM	Bath
PORTWOOD						
1892	1973	1700	1914	101222	LND	North
POSINET						
1850	1880	1550	1850	147265	LIN	South
POSINETT						
1850	1880	1550	1850	147265	LIN	South
POSNET						
1850	1880	1550	1850	147265	LIN	South
POSNETT						
1850	1880	1550	1850	147265	LIN	South
POSTGATE						
1833	1885	1500	1930	157538	SRY	Richmond
POSTINGS						
1825	1900	1700	1825	153915	SAL	ALL
POSTLE						
1450	1992	....	....	169129	NFK	East
1784	1928	1750	1784	174173	NFK	Felmingham
POSTLES						
1838	1931	1750	1838	154024	CHS	Northwich
POSTLETHWAITE						
1792	1797	....	....	156434	BDF	Elstow
1792	1797	....	....	156434	BDF	Potton
1792	1797	....	....	156434	BDF	Sandy
1800	1992	1800	1992	178357	CHS	ALL
1700	1900	1750	1830	156434	CMA	ALL
1860	1900	1700	....	123471	CUL	Bootle
1819	1890	ALL	1819	105813	CUL	Whitehaven
1800	1992	1800	1992	178357	LAN	ALL
....	....	1700	1780	116173	LAN	Furness
1725	1755	1565	1725	141291	LAN	Furness
1781	1870	....	....	156434	LEI	Fleckney
1802	1992	1835	1992	156434	LEI	Leicester
1858	1928	....	....	156434	LND	East
1924	1960	....	....	156434	MDX	Enfield
1924	1960	....	....	156434	MDX	Southgate
1786	1791	1558	1786	141291	WES	Kendal
POSTLEWAITE						
1780	1889	ALL	1780	129992	LAN	Lancashire
POSTON						
1810	1851	1800	1851	145319	HEF	Brimfield
....	....	1700	1826	101559	HEF	Hampton
....	....	1700	1800	160776	LND	City
1760	1789	1700	1800	160776	LND	St George In The East
1760	....	1700	1800	160776	LND	Stepney
POTINGER						
....	....	ALL	1800	110965	OKI	North Isles
POTT						
....	....	ALL	1900	177822	SCT	Borders
POTTAGE						
1910	1992	1910	1992	112534	YKS	Scarborough
POTTEN						
1868	....	....	1868	114685	SSX	Patching
POTTER						
....	....	ALL	ALL	155063	ALL	Name Study
1800	1893	1750	1800	115460	BDF	Pulloxhill
....	....	1800	1850	103713	BDF	Wilstead
1846	1992	....	....	104078	CAM	Littleport
1750	1837	1750	1837	108251	DEV	Cullompton

Known From	To	Researching From	To	Ref	Cty	Place
POTTER contd.						
1812	1830	1750	1850	132659	DEV	Sampford Courteney
1800	1850	1750	1880	134376	DOR	Charmouth
....	....	1700	1850	143502	ESS	South East
....	....	1780	1825	102717	ESS	South
....	1807	1750	1850	128961	ESS	Chelmsford
1830	1860	1800	1870	101400	ESS	Feering
1812	1860	1750	1800	101400	ESS	Gt Coggeshall
1820	1910	1800	1820	140317	ESS	Wakes Colne
1870	1903	1870	1903	101400	ESS	Witham
....	1846	....	....	140767	GAL	???
1850	1871	1850	1900	134376	GSY	St Peters Port
1904	1992	ALL	ALL	101400	HRT	East
1782	1787	1740	1787	131210	HRT	Ware
1750	1850	....	....	159883	KEN	Shepherdswell
1671	....	....	1700	171441	KEN	Wormshill
1870	1980	1800	1870	133531	LEI	Leicester
1748	1808	1700	1750	162396	LIN	Belton
1820	....	1750	1820	132853	MDX	Soho
....	....	ALL	1812	170135	MDX	Westminster
1600	1860	ALL	ALL	107425	NFK	Diss
....	....	1780	....	170313	SAL	Knighton
1830	1860	ALL	1830	126322	SFK	Ramsholt
1892	1983	....	....	173932	SRY	Epsom
1789	1872	1650	1789	138673	SRY	Horsham
1850	1903	1850	1903	152129	SRY	Richmond
1800	1992	1700	1800	156450	SSX	Lewes
1730	1760	1600	1730	102571	WES	Orton
1800	1900	....	....	146854	WES	Orton
1819	....	ALL	....	152129	WIL	Heytesbury
1600	1850	1600	1850	141577	WIL	Imber
1800	1900	1800	1900	141577	WIL	Norton Bavant
1821	1931	ALL	ALL	168610	WOR	Bewdley
1821	1931	ALL	ALL	168610	WOR	Kidderminster
1829	1829	1800	1829	113050	WOR	Stourbridge
1770	1850	1600	1900	152714	WOR	Worcester
1853	....	1853	....	140767	YKS	Leeds
1800	1850	1750	1800	119032	YKS	Stamford Bridge
1817	1892	1778	1892	141550	YKS	Tadcaster
1670	1670	....	....	159883	YKS	Wakefield
1737	1900	....	....	104302	???	West Hoathly
POTTERTON						
1828	1992	1650	1992	123552	LEI	Leicester
1826	1992	1789	1826	178926	LEI	Oadby
1743	....	1743	....	113875	LIN	Ruskington
1828	1992	1650	1992	123552	MDX	London
POTTICARY						
1500	1900	1500	1900	170216	WIL	ALL
POTTINGER						
1673	1743	1650	1800	176621	BRK	Speen
1734	....	1650	1800	143693	BRK	Sulhampstead Abbots
1723	1728	1600	1750	143693	BRK	Sulhampstead Bannister
1709	1713	1600	1750	143693	BRK	Upton Nervet
POTTINGTON						
1826	1992	1789	1826	178926	LEI	Oadby
POTTLE						
1806	1825	1700	1806	163953	NFK	Fundenhall
POTTOTON						
1784	1838	ALL	1784	178926	NTH	Deenethorpe
POTTS						
1856	1930	1800	1856	178896	ANS	Dundee
1841	1900	....	1841	133825	CHS	Congleton
1870	....	1750	1870	139386	CHS	Dunkinfield
1830	1860	1750	1900	177210	CHS	Macclesfield
1810	1992	....	1992	129739	CUL	Cockermouth
1760	1870	ALL	1760	161330	DBY	Wormhill
1780	1830	1800	1900	156469	DUR	Darlington
1800	1850	ALL	ALL	130508	DUR	Sunderland
?	?	?	?	133728	LIN	Lindsey Villages
?	?	ALL	1800	117919	MDX	London
1819	1830	1800	1851	126209	NBL	North
1755	1780	1700	1800	102415	NBL	Alnwick
1828	1983	1600	1828	147346	NBL	Belford
1742	1836	1700	1850	144037	NBL	Elsdon
....	....	ALL	1780	156469	NBL	Norham
1803	1992	....	....	134619	SAL	Broseley
1812	....	1800	1850	163295	STS	Chorley
1900	1992	1800	1900	178136	STS	Longton
1770	1850	1850	1992	102415	YKS	Hull
1862	1992	....	....	156469	YKS	Leeds
1830	1862	....	....	156469	YKS	Pudsey
1830	1900	1800	1992	102415	YKS	Sheffield
POULDEN						
....	....	ALL	ALL	173096	ALL	Name Study
POULSOM						
....	1900	....	1950	130168	WLS	Pontypool
POULTER						
1740	1770	ALL	1800	118338	BRK	???
1747	1788	1650	1780	100013	ESS	High Easter
....	....	1800	1900	140759	HAM	Aldershot
....	....	1800	1900	140759	HAM	Farnborough
POULTON						
....	....	ALL	ALL	156477	ALL	Name Study
1824	1840	1750	1824	176885	BKM	Wendover
1830	1861	1800	1900	144908	DOR	Poole
1800	1870	1750	1870	128112	ESS	Purfleet
1671	1861	1860	1950	178845	GLS	Stinchcombe
1900	1970	1700	1980	133337	HEF	Hereford
1725	....	1780	1836	136964	HRT	Baldock
1852	1860	1852	1900	128112	LND	Southwark
....	....	1800	1992	140759	WIL	Avon
....	....	1800	1992	140759	WIL	Chippenham
....	....	1800	1992	140759	WIL	Christian Malford
1830	1861	1853	1861	118931	WIL	Corston
1800	....	....	....	118931	WIL	Somerford Parva
1900	1970	1700	1980	133337	WLS	Tonypandy
1880	1950	1700	1950	172405	???	Wrexham
POUNCE						
1746	....	....	....	151351	YKS	Ripon
POUNCEY						
1830	1870	1800	1870	166316	MDX	St Pancras
POUND						
1797	1905	1700	1900	166804	BRK	Brimpton
1827	1844	1500	1827	110310	BRK	Newbury
1850	....	1800	1900	101672	HAM	Portsmouth
1813	1838	1813	1850	123250	KEN	Margate
1800	1850	1800	1850	176281	KEN	Margate
1838	1842	1835	1850	123250	MDX	Poplar
1838	1838	1835	1850	123250	MDX	Shadwell
1650	1732	1650	1740	142018	SOM	Taunton
1853	1855	?	1853	127612	SRY	Chelsea
?	?	1850	1992	158704	SSX	Hastings
1842	1900	1845	1930	123250	YKS	Hull
POUNDER						
1770	1915	1700	1770	176451	YKS	Leeds
POUNDS						
1669	1787	1669	1787	103977	BRK	East Garston
1753	1850	1753	1850	103977	BRK	Hampstead Marshall
1669	1787	1669	1787	103977	BRK	Hungerford
....	....	ALL	1850	167029	BRK	Hungerford
1753	1850	1753	1850	103977	BRK	Kintbury
1669	1787	1669	1787	103977	BRK	Lambourn
1850	1860	ALL	1850	167029	WIL	Ramsbury
POUNTNEY						
1818	....	1700	1900	152714	WOR	Kidderminster
POVEY						
1750	1850	1700	1850	102970	BRK	Speen
1720	1780	1680	1720	165530	GLS	North Nibley
1756	1992	1700	1897	156493	NTT	Nottingham
1870	?	1700	1992	167592	STS	Burslem
1788	1836	1788	1836	105147	STS	West Bromwich
1788	1841	1700	1850	169323	STS	West Bromwich
POW						
1749	1841	1700	1881	176923	SOM	Midsomer Norton
POWDERILL						
1568	....	ALL	ALL	112275	LEI	Kegworth
1550	....	ALL	ALL	112275	NTT	Thrumpton
POWDITCH						
....	....	ALL	ALL	100773	ALL	Name Study
POWDRICH						
1837	1880	1800	1850	118230	LAN	Liverpool
POWDRILL						
....	....	ALL	ALL	151661	ALL	Name Study
1700	1800	1600	1800	163015	DBY	ALL
1750	1992	?	1750	133108	LEI	Glenfield
1750	1992	?	1750	133108	LEI	Leicester
1700	1992	1600	1700	163015	LIN	ALL
1700	1800	1600	1800	163015	NTT	ALL
POWEL						
1675	1685	ALL	1685	161357	ESS	Great Easton
1700	1750	1700	1800	106631	GLS	Dymock
1781	1892	1700	1781	159565	YKS	York
POWELL						
?	?	?	?	138126	BRE	Aberscyr
1850	1928	1750	1900	129143	BRE	Beulah
1780	1845	1770	1850	140295	BRE	Brilley

Known From	To	Researching From	To	Ref	Cty	Place
POWELL contd.						
....	....	1750	1992	140759	BRE	Bwllch
1818	1937	1700	1992	176877	BRE	Crickadarn
....	....	1750	1992	140759	BRE	Cwmddu
....	....	1750	1992	140759	BRE	Devynoch
1690	1880	1600	1992	156515	BRE	Gwenddwr
1813	....	1700	1841	176877	BRE	Gwenddwr
?	?	?	?	138126	BRE	Llandefaelog Fach
....	....	1750	1992	140759	BRE	Llanspydd
....	....	1700	1830	109223	CHS	Birkenhead
1708	1778	1600	1800	176923	CMN	Llanedi
1900	1992	1800	1900	108618	DBY	Ashbourne
1881	1992	....	....	156523	DEV	Uplyme
....	....	1700	1900	156531	DOR	West
1843	1903	1750	1843	168351	ESS	Earls Colne
1750	1773	1650	1750	139084	ESS	Little Canfield
1835	1850	ALL	1870	118338	ESS	Stratford
1841	1871	1830	1890	159700	ESS	West Thurrock
1720	1806	....	....	176958	GLA	Llandough
1784	1816	1700	1800	135658	GLA	Llantwit Major
?	?	?	?	138126	GLA	Merthyr
?	?	?	?	138126	GLA	Penydarren
....	....	ALL	1820	141224	GLS	South
1800	1881	1600	1992	131563	GLS	Coleford
1739	1860	1538	1839	154792	GLS	Forest Of Dean
1850	1923	ALL	ALL	113700	GLS	Gloucester
1800	1881	1600	1992	131563	GLS	Newland
1920	1950	1920	1992	151378	GLS	St Briavels
1870	1992	1750	1870	156566	GLS	???
1820	1950	....	....	101524	GNT	New Tredegar
1700	1900	....	....	153397	HEF	ALL
1765	1850	1600	1850	130125	HEF	Ashperton
1815	1885	1780	1885	159700	HEF	Clifford
1793	?	?	?	138126	HEF	Cradley
1930	1975	1930	1992	151378	HEF	Hereford
1800	....	1750	1800	119938	HEF	Much Marcle
1757	1981	1500	1757	176052	HRT	Bromyard
1845	1900	....	....	110159	IRL	Dublin
1597	1597	....	....	127426	KEN	Bapchild
1876	....	....	1900	171441	KEN	Canterbury
1621	1621	....	....	127426	KEN	Egerton
1884	1911	....	1950	171441	KEN	Faversham
1602	1602	....	....	127426	KEN	Lenham
1591	1602	....	....	127426	KEN	Rodmersham
1834	1992	?	1834	147923	LIN	Lincoln
1795	1860	....	1795	151084	LND	East
1795	1860	....	1795	151084	LND	City
1874	1909	1800	1874	174920	LND	Lambeth
1830	....	ALL	ALL	156558	LND	Marylebone
1804	1820	1800	1830	113743	MDX	Harrow
1891	1891	1880	1930	141046	MDX	Walworth
1500	1650	1500	1650	154881	MGY	Llandyssil
1800	1880	ALL	ALL	156604	MON	Berry Hills
1900	1920	1900	1992	151378	MON	Cross Keys
1820	1850	1700	1850	156442	MON	Garndiffaith
1840	1891	1840	1891	140295	MON	Gilvern
1918	1951	1918	1992	151378	MON	Monmouth
1785	1797	ALL	1785	168602	NFK	Denton
1795	?	1700	1850	162248	NRY	Hornby
1750	1780	1700	1750	121339	NYK	Manfield
1799	1896	ALL	1799	143960	NYK	Tadcaster
1848	1851	1800	1900	100242	OXF	Bucknell
1831	....	1700	1900	166359	PEM	Nash
1720	1806	....	....	176958	PEM	Rudbaxton
1700	....	....	....	153397	POW	ALL
1760	1992	1700	1760	101524	POW	Ystradfellte
1770	1992	1600	1770	156914	RAD	Bryngwyn
1764	1772	1700	1800	176877	RAD	Cwmdeuddwr
1799	1851	....	....	155055	RAD	Knighton
1768	1788	1700	1800	176877	RAD	Nantmel
1860	1992	1750	1860	156574	SAL	Chirk
1835	1939	1700	....	141909	SAL	Heath Hill
1880	1950	....	....	156868	SAL	Wellington
1797	?	ALL	ALL	153516	SOM	Ubley
1845	1863	1845	1850	110159	SSX	Brighton
1790	1992	1600	1790	148237	SSX	New Fishbourne
1873	ALL	....	....	117048	STS	Smethwick
1870	1992	1800	1870	154180	STS	Wednesbury
1876	1876	1800	1890	117722	WAR	Bromsgrove
1700	1850	1700	1850	145661	WIL	Aldbourne
....	....	ALL	1740	151602	WIL	Wilcot
1734	1800	....	....	100536	WLS	???
1800	1850	ALL	ALL	130508	WOR	Amblecote
1804	1813	1750	1815	109746	WOR	Bromsgrove

Known From	To	Researching From	To	Ref	Cty	Place
POWELL contd.						
1860	1870	1860	1870	138398	WOR	Oldbury
1800	1850	ALL	ALL	130508	WOR	Stourbridge
?	?	?	?	138126	WOR	???
1837	1880	1700	1900	151106	YKS	Acomb
1750	1800	....	....	140554	YKS	Clifford
1716	1737	1600	1730	101575	YKS	Pontefract
1750	?	?	?	147923	YKS	Wragby
1781	1892	1700	1781	159565	YKS	York
POWER						
?	?	1800	1900	116009	ANT	Belfast
1820	1992	1700	1820	165123	GLS	Bristol
1820	1992	1700	1820	165123	GLS	Gloucester
1810	1900	1750	1900	123870	IRL	Dungarvan
1905	1960	ALL	1910	152021	KIK	Kilmacow
1835	1880	1840	1930	165034	LAN	Manchester
....	....	....	....	105406	TIP	Tinderry
1860	1910	1800	1992	139203	WAT	Tramore
1875	1891	1700	1909	156582	WAT	Waterford
1840	1880	1700	1992	116009	WAT	???
....	....	....	....	105406	???	Tinderry
POWERS						
....	....	1800	1840	166596	SAL	ALL
1830	1992	1830	1992	166596	WAR	Birmingham
POWIS						
1851	1992	1851	1992	141267	MDX	Spitalfields
1795	1890	....	....	132756	SAL	Buildwas
POWLES						
1726	1787	ALL	1726	168602	SFK	Lowestoft
POWLESLAND						
1826	....	1700	1800	174130	DEV	Dunsford
1820	1871	1750	1920	137782	DEV	South Tawton
POWLEY						
1867	....	1845	1875	163775	MDX	Stepney
1800	1992	1600	1992	135860	NFK	Caister On Sea
1841	1851	1800	1841	124095	NFK	Ormsby
1600	1750	....	....	146854	WES	Orton
POWLING						
....	....	ALL	ALL	156590	ALL	Name Study
1560	1992	1560	1992	156590	ALL	ALL
1745	1992	1700	1992	173096	SFK	Bildeston
POWNALL						
1785	1823	1700	1785	170569	CHS	Bebington
1860	1890	1830	1860	173673	LAN	Hindley
....	....	1700	1920	105007	LAN	???
POWNCEBY						
1750	1850	1750	1992	136867	LND	ALL
POWNEY						
....	....	ALL	ALL	156604	ALL	Name Study
ALL	ALL	ALL	ALL	156604	ALL	ALL
1820	1877	1750	1900	133043	MDX	London
1812	1836	1600	1812	106054	WAR	Birmingham
1690	1930	1500	1700	137502	WIL	ALL
....	....	1779	1841	130958	WIL	Bremhill
1760	1900	1700	1900	166375	WIL	Bremhill
POWRIE						
1767	1845	....	1767	175552	FIF	Moonzie
1715	1970	1715	1944	132918	PER	Errol
POWTER						
....	1819	ALL	1819	162655	SFK	West
POXON						
....	....	ALL	ALL	156612	ALL	Name Study
ALL	ALL	ALL	ALL	156612	ALL	ALL
POXSON						
....	....	....	....	142085	LEI	Castle Donington
POXTON						
....	1992	1838	1948	151173	KEN	Bexley
....	1992	1838	1948	151173	NTT	Blidworth
POYNER						
1715	1880	1700	1900	157171	GLS	Taynton
POYNTON						
1775	1822	1700	1822	102830	WAR	Birmingham
POYNTZ						
1250	1306	1200	1300	154881	ALL	ALL
POYSER						
....	....	1800	1870	173649	DBY	Derby
POYTHRESS						
....	....	ALL	ALL	162337	ALL	Name Study
PRACEY						
1770	1930	1700	1770	124362	LND	City
PRACY						
....	....	ALL	ALL	156620	ALL	Name Study
1880	1992	....	1992	156620	LND	East
1770	1880	1700	....	156620	MDX	Shoreditch

Known From	To	Researching From	To	Ref	Cty	Place
PRACY contd.						
1840	1850	1700	1850	156620	WIL	Downel
PRADIER						
1870	1930	1650	1992	131679	LND	Bloomsbury
PRAED						
1565	1643	1500	1565	102571	CON	Uny Lelant
PRAGER						
1854	1992	ALL	ALL	156639	LND	ALL
1850	1992	ALL	1850	108847	LND	???
1832	1854	....	....	156639	YKS	Hull
PRAGNELL						
1877	1970	1809	1992	156647	HAM	Isle Of Wight
1834	1867	1809	1992	156647	HAM	South Baddesley
PRAIN						
1800	1860	1750	1900	114898	ANS	Dundee
PRAKE						
1750	1992	1600	1992	122122	DEV	Newton Abbot
PRANCE						
....	....	ALL	ALL	177121	ALL	Name Study
1480	1992	1480	1992	177121	ALL	???
PRANGLEY						
1878	....	1750	1800	170348	LND	St Botolph Without Aldersgate
1778	....	1800	1814	170348	YKS	Sheffield
PRANGNELL						
1839	1992	1650	1992	123552	HAM	Isle Of Wight
1706	1769	1650	1706	121010	HAM	Longparish
1770	1835	ALL	1770	156663	HAM	Romsey
1835	1875	....	....	156663	MDX	Belgrave
1839	1992	1650	1992	123552	MDX	London
1835	1875	....	....	156663	MDX	Westminster
1875	1992	....	....	156663	SSX	Eastbourne
PRANKEARD						
1700	1799	1700	1799	169781	GLS	Bristol
PRANKERD						
1794	1992	1794	1992	156671	DOR	Weymouth
1860	1992	ALL	ALL	156671	GLA	Cardiff
1780	1810	1700	1900	151653	SOM	Langport
PRATER						
1689	1754	1650	1923	132608	BRK	Childrey
1754	1923	1650	1923	132608	BRK	Lambourn
1727	1928	1700	1928	136336	BRK	Lambourn
1796	1918	1700	1796	127116	HAM	Kingsclere
1870	1923	1870	1923	132608	LND	???
PRATLEY						
1890	1928	....	....	106720	OXF	Chadlington
PRATT						
1770	1992	1770	1900	138894	BRK	Abingdon
1870	1961	1538	1960	118893	DUR	Spennymoor
1750	1770	....	....	108375	ESS	Woodham Walter
1780	1850	1750	1850	146803	FIF	Kettle
1780	1803	1700	1803	148288	FIF	Pittenween
1780	1803	1700	1803	148288	FIF	Strathmiglo
1825	1880	1820	1890	142018	GLS	Bristol
....	1845	1830	1850	142018	GLS	Cheltenham
1660	1829	1600	1700	169242	HAM	Exton
....	....	....	....	164968	HRT	Hitchin
....	....	....	....	164968	HRT	Letchworth
....	1760	ALL	1760	134511	LEI	Broughton Ashley
1606	1703	ALL	ALL	141615	LEI	Kegworth
....	....	1650	1750	115142	LEI	Sibson
1799	....	....	....	163155	LEI	Thornton
1912	1958	1900	1912	142581	MDX	Enfield
1823	1840	1750	1850	114642	MDX	???
1841	1869	1538	1960	118893	NRY	Ainderby Steeple
1770	1803	1538	1960	118893	NRY	Patrick Brompton
1841	1869	1538	1960	118893	NRY	Thrinton
1770	1770	....	....	127426	NTH	Earls Barton
1742	1742	....	....	127426	NTH	Mears Ashby
1770	1908	1750	1908	159581	SFK	Framlingham
1600	1880	1600	1800	142018	SOM	ALL
1863	1992	ALL	1863	130605	STS	Stoke On Trent
1830	1992	1700	1830	148059	WAR	ALL
....	....	ALL	ALL	114308	WAR	Lighthorn
1800	1992	1700	1800	148059	WAR	Salford Priors
1650	1700	1650	1700	142018	WIL	North
1822	1851	1750	1900	113212	WIL	Malmesbury
1830	1992	1700	1830	148059	WOR	ALL
1681	1881	....	1681	168424	YKS	North West
PRATTEN						
1760	1992	1760	1992	113670	AVN	Bristol
1828	1880	1828	1880	113670	GLS	Bitton
1750	1900	ALL	ALL	158798	SOM	East
1828	1880	1828	1880	113670	SOM	Bitton
PRATTEN contd.						
1850	1890	1740	1900	170038	SOM	Frome
PRATTSON						
1760	1760	1700	1760	152196	WES	New Hutton
PRAYERS						
1250	1380	1200	1380	154881	ESS	Sible Hedingham
PREBBLE						
1880	1992	1800	1900	172170	MDX	London
PRECIOUS						
1861	1872	1872	1900	168033	KEN	Ashford
1850	1900	1800	1850	124699	NFK	Central
1780	....	ALL	1780	102350	YKS	South Milfor
1687	1992	....	....	134619	YKS	Warthill
1830	1870	1800	1900	142360	YKS	York
1841	1860	1700	1841	168033	YKS	York
PRECTER						
....	....	ALL	ALL	145343	HAM	Farlington
PREDDY						
1777	1812	1700	1820	131547	WIL	Brinkworth
1790	1950	1600	1850	153184	WIL	Lydiard
1760	....	1700	1790	131547	WIL	Stratton St Margaret
1876	1909	ALL	ALL	143316	WIL	Wanborough
PREECE						
1820	1880	1600	1820	123390	HEF	Putley
1833	1850	1800	1992	114901	HEF	Wigmore
1881	....	1828	1881	142638	HEF	Wormbridge
1700	1900	1700	1900	151637	HEF	Wormsley
1857	1880	1850	1992	114901	MDX	Hertford
....	1877	1850	1877	126624	WAR	Edgbaston
....	....	ALL	1891	159808	WIL	Swindon
....	....	ALL	1891	159808	WLS	ALL
PREEN						
....	....	ALL	ALL	140538	ALL	Name Study
1826	1876	1800	1850	156728	BKM	Amersham
1800	1819	1700	1819	156728	BKM	Chalfont St Giles
1600	1887	....	1992	131458	CON	St Austell
1882	1900	1850	1920	101044	YKS	Sheffield
PREES						
1841	1937	1800	1900	124281	WAR	Birmingham
PRENDERGAST						
1800	1900	....	....	132756	LAN	Liverpool
1949	1992	1750	1900	156736	LAN	Salford
PRENTICE						
1780	1809	1760	1850	159581	HRT	North Mymms
1900	1992	....	....	153397	NBL	Alnwick
1780	1950	1780	1950	114316	SFK	Ipswich
1700	1900	1600	1700	179043	YKS	North
PRESBURY						
....	....	ALL	ALL	156744	ALL	Name Study
1660	1992	1600	1992	156744	DBY	ALL
1660	1992	1600	1992	156744	STS	ALL
PRESCOD						
1882	1882	1860	1882	174998	NBL	Sunderland
PRESCOT						
1720	1740	ALL	ALL	138363	SAL	Central
PRESDEE						
1840	....	....	1840	164011	WOR	Worcester
PRESELEY						
1789	....	1760	1810	170348	DBY	Bolsover
PRESLAND						
....	....	ALL	ALL	156752	ALL	Name Study
1691	1949	1670	1949	144460	BDF	Arlesey
1766	1992	1600	1766	156779	ESS	Epping
1766	1992	1600	1766	156779	ESS	North East London
....	....	1870	1992	156760	HAM	Southampton
1853	1870	1700	1853	156760	SFK	Lakenheath
PRESLEY						
1840	1850	1800	1840	146587	MDX	Uxbridge
PRESS						
1888	....	1700	1900	113085	BRK	Reading
1857	1950	1799	1900	112585	DUR	Sunderland
1800	1992	ALL	ALL	113093	NFK	Gt Yarmouth
....	....	1750	1806	172871	WIL	West
1792	1992	1750	1792	111813	YKS	Hawkswick
PRESSEY						
1768	1851	1600	1789	145289	HAM	Isle Of Wight
PRESSICK						
....	....	ALL	ALL	101443	ALL	Name Study
1788	1856	ALL	ALL	101443	ALL	ALL
1844	1851	1830	1880	101443	HAM	Droxford
PRESSLEY						
1652	1680	....	....	151351	DOR	Piddletrenthide

Known From	To	Researching From	To	Ref	Cty	Place
PRESSWOOD						
1865	1920	1700	1865	171913	LIN	???
PRESTHOPE						
....	....	1066	1240	124974	SAL	Westhope
PRESTIDGE						
1856	1879	?	1856	158569	???	???
PRESTON						
....	....	ALL	ALL	156841	ALL	Name Study
ALL	ALL	ALL	ALL	156841	ALL	ALL
1837	1854	1750	1837	150614	CHS	Moulton
1886	1992	1881	1925	108901	DBY	Whitwell
1780	1900	ALL	ALL	156795	DOR	East
1800	1850	1700	1850	126845	DUR	Darlington
....	....	1700	1800	128627	ELN	Haddington
1550	1828	1550	1828	102830	GLS	Notgrove
1750	1780	ALL	ALL	156795	HAM	West
1763	1775	1740	1992	114901	HAM	Warblington
1782	....	....	....	164151	LAN	Hutton
1833	1890	1790	1810	158089	LAN	Manchester
1851	....	....	....	164151	LAN	Robert Hall
1833	1890	1790	1810	158089	LAN	Salford
1851	....	....	....	164151	LAN	Tatham
1691	1900	1600	1900	135968	LEI	Rothley
1611	1693	....	....	165999	LIN	Lincoln
1700	1750	1700	1750	123765	LIN	Orby
1816	1908	1810	1908	108901	LIN	West Halton
1782	1992	1700	1782	102342	LIN	Winterton
1782	1805	1780	1810	108901	LIN	Winterton
1731	1820	1650	1731	114928	LND	???
....	....	1800	....	128627	LND	???
1800	1992	1750	1800	168777	MDX	Hackney
1792	....	ALL	ALL	174777	MLN	Craigmillar
1812	1992	1700	1812	166804	NFK	Great Yarmouth
1842	1992	1700	1842	102253	NFK	Kings Lynn
1816	1920	1800	1850	116076	NTT	Nottingham
1816	1920	1800	1850	116076	NTT	Radford
1883	1902	1800	1900	178624	PER	Dundee
....	....	1700	1800	128627	SCT	Edinburgh
....	....	1800	1900	160695	SFK	Glemsford
....	....	1800	1900	160695	SFK	Hartest
1850	....	....	1850	164011	WOR	Worcester
1823	1904	ALL	ALL	103837	YKS	East
1700	1900	1600	1750	130419	YKS	Bolton By Bowland
1680	1800	ALL	1800	119938	YKS	Caster Malbis
1700	1900	1600	1750	130419	YKS	Giggleswick
1724	1764	1700	1720	162396	YKS	Kirkby Malham
1702	....	....	....	151351	YKS	Pannal
1900	1992	1600	1900	166103	YKS	Rotherham
1760	1770	1600	1760	175382	YKS	Settle
1787	1843	....	....	173916	YKS	York
PRETLOVE						
1829	1829	1718	1829	153257	LND	Whitechapel
1928	1972	ALL	ALL	134120	LND	Wood Green
1830	1992	ALL	1830	108847	LND	???
PRETTY						
1700	1790	ALL	1700	168602	ESS	Colchester
1756	1800	1700	1800	154881	SOM	Chard
1720	1744	1680	1780	160873	STS	Lichfeild
PRETTYMAN						
1875	1992	1875	1992	133450	SFK	???
PREW						
1800	1881	?	1800	123161	DEV	Exmouth
1885	1992	....	....	123161	WAR	Brimingham
1784	....	1784	1800	145505	WOR	Shipston On Stour
PREWETT						
1760	1900	ALL	1992	113492	WIL	South
PRGANELL						
1698	1883	1698	ALL	145386	HAM	Lockerley
PRIAL						
....	1846	....	....	140767	MAY	???
1868	....	1868	....	140767	YKS	Leeds
PRIAULX						
1760	1847	1700	1782	131326	GSY	Forest
PRICE						
1870	....	1840	1910	167932	BDF	Leighton Buzzard
1719	1719	1670	1760	167002	BKM	Little Missenden
1800	1900	1750	1950	177180	BKM	Whitchurch
1866	1905	1800	1900	179027	BRE	Aberyscir
....	....	1750	1840	100188	BRE	Builth
1735	1758	....	....	177008	BRE	Cricardan
1708	1862	1600	1881	176877	BRE	Crickadarn
....	....	1750	1870	140759	BRE	Cwmddu
....	....	1780	1860	117137	BRE	Llanafanfawr
1706	1841	1600	1861	176877	BRE	Llanafanfawr

Known From	To	Researching From	To	Ref	Cty	Place
PRICE contd.						
1900	1905	1800	1900	179027	BRE	Llanfihangel
1874	1900	1874	1900	157007	BRE	Llanfihangle Tal Y Llyn
....	....	1750	1870	140759	BRE	Llangorse
1877	1958	1700	1877	178276	BRE	Llangorse
....	....	1750	1870	140759	BRE	Llanvillo
....	....	1750	1890	140759	BRE	Pwllywrach
1900	1905	1800	1900	179027	BRE	Tal-Y-Llyn
....	....	1750	1890	140759	BRE	Talgarth
....	....	....	1900	135844	BRK	Sulhamstead Abbotts
1787	1818	1780	1818	132217	CAE	Beddgelert
1872	1992	ALL	ALL	135224	CHS	ALL
1837	1838	1750	1867	149292	CHS	Birkenhead
1729	1760	....	....	135437	CHS	Christleton
1920	1938	1900	1920	156981	CMN	Llanelli
1871	1958	1700	1858	177237	DEN	Llanefydd
1806	1838	1750	1867	149292	DEN	Wrexham
1890	1920	1830	1870	145041	DUR	Quarrington Hill
1798	1900	1600	1798	168653	ESS	ALL
1750	1900	1700	1750	126322	FLN	Flint
1824	1960	1600	1824	112410	FLN	Halkyn
1851	1881	1800	1851	158739	GLA	Banwen
1804	1883	1800	1883	158658	GLA	Margam
1845	1992	1750	1992	167991	GLA	Vaynor
1870	1890	1870	1890	156930	GLS	ALL
1786	1840	....	....	165999	GLS	Almondsbury
1871	1900	1700	1870	132438	GLS	Berkeley
1786	1840	....	....	165999	GLS	Bristol
1750	1800	ALL	ALL	140740	GLS	Charlton Kings
1740	1992	1650	1740	116513	GLS	Deerhurst
....	....	1700	1900	135844	GLS	Maisey Hampton
1750	1770	1700	1992	167592	GLS	Ponty Pandy
1860	1910	1860	1930	156930	GLS	Tidenham
1740	1992	1650	1740	116513	GLS	Tirley
1809	....	1800	1900	164070	GLS	Westbury
1721	1759	1700	1760	100242	HAM	ALL
1798	....	....	1838	160873	HEF	Brampton Bryan
1810	1885	1780	1885	159700	HEF	Clifford
1788	1818	1700	1789	119296	HEF	Kington
....	1793	1760	1800	176621	HEF	Kington
1880	1910	1820	1950	173746	JSY	ALL
1773	?	?	?	166642	KEN	Kennington
1730	1992	1730	1992	137308	KEN	Sundridge
1814	1890	1814	1890	143286	LAN	Liverpool
1838	....	1750	1867	149292	LAN	W Derby
1810	1830	....	....	103764	LEI	North Kilworth
1862	1874	1800	1900	143693	LND	Hammersmith
1828	1985	1820	1992	156965	LND	Holborn
1836	....	1750	1850	143693	LND	Islington
1880	1940	1840	1940	147958	LND	Islington
1828	1965	1828	1965	156892	LND	Shoreditch
1850	1900	....	....	139971	MAY	Kilfian
1833	1992	1750	1833	156914	MGY	Kerry
1820	1880	1780	1880	156930	MON	Chepstow
1862	1881	1862	1881	159700	MON	Grosmont
1890	1940	1890	1940	156930	MON	Llanfrechfa Upper
1858	1862	1840	1862	159700	MON	Llanvapley
1850	1880	1850	1880	156930	MON	Shirenewton
1690	1715	1600	1720	156957	NTT	Gotham
1770	1992	1710	1870	156957	NTT	Ruddington
1840	1920	1800	1900	103845	PEM	Hakin
1780	1992	1750	1780	141798	RAD	Central
1810	1890	ALL	ALL	130613	RAD	Aberedw
1849	1871	1849	1992	176877	RAD	Beguildy
1841	....	1820	1841	176877	RAD	Bleddfa
1841	1992	1600	1841	156914	RAD	Bryngwyn
1715	1720	1650	1720	121010	RAD	Glascwm
1844	1848	....	....	176877	RAD	Heytop
1749	1918	1670	1881	156949	RAD	Llanbister
1842	1881	1500	1842	176974	RAD	Llanbister
1850	1992	1600	1850	156914	RAD	Llandeilow Graban
1830	1840	1800	1840	160873	RAD	Llangunllo
....	....	....	1813	116092	RAD	Rhayadar
1774	....	1700	1841	176877	RAD	Rhayader
1740	1853	1600	1881	176877	SAL	Llanfair Waterdine
1750	1860	1750	1860	129836	SAL	Mainstone
1800	1919	1808	1919	156973	SAL	Wrockwardine
1821	1992	1500	1821	175072	SOM	Bath
1840	1992	1800	1840	165468	SOM	Wedmore
1600	1800	1600	1800	152404	SSX	Broadwater
1797	1845	1700	1797	149977	STS	South
1803	....	....	....	102733	STS	Brewood
1840	1900	1840	1920	160873	STS	Brierley Hill

Known From	To	Researching From	To	Ref	Cty	Place
PRICE contd.						
1866	1879	1800	1880	178322	STS	Sedgley
1850	1900	1850	1900	103764	STS	Smethwick
1875	1875	1861	1881	111414	STS	Smethwick
1850	1900	....	....	176591	STS	Wolstanton
1820	1850	1600	1890	133590	STS	Wolverhampton
....	....	1841	1916	149586	WAR	Aston
1881	1930	1879	1950	178322	WAR	Aston
1896	1992	1896	1992	160873	WAR	Birmingham
1880	1882	1800	1880	161810	WAR	Birmingham
....	1873	1868	1873	133639	WAR	Leamington Spa
....	....	1800	1850	111414	WAR	Solihull
1820	1910	1700	1920	107115	WIL	Market Lavington
1822	1850	1800	1855	165824	WIL	Tinhead
1783	1783	....	1800	121169	WIL	Warminster
1828	1965	1828	1965	156892	WLS	South
1760	1992	....	....	100536	WLS	Brecon
1789	1885	1500	1789	153591	WLS	Brymbo
1789	1885	1500	1789	153591	WLS	Bwlch Gwyn
1900	1992	1800	1899	156876	WLS	Cwm
1789	1885	1500	1789	153591	WLS	Denbeigh
1789	1885	1500	1789	153591	WLS	Flint
1850	1910	1850	1880	103764	WOR	Dudley
1760	1779	1700	1760	107123	WOR	Old Swinford
1853	1903	1851	1930	111414	WOR	Oldbury
1888	1930	1868	1992	133639	WOR	Worcester
1876	1886	1800	1876	171662	YKS	Sheffield
PRICE-JONES						
....	....	1821	1854	140759	BRE	Pwllywrach
....	....	1821	1854	140759	BRE	Talgarth
300	1992	ALL	300	112313	CWD	Ystytty Ifan
PRICE-WOOD						
1850	1880	1800	1992	167592	SAL	Ludlow
PRICHARD						
1850	1930	1850	1930	135666	FLN	Holywell
1750	1930	1750	1930	135666	FLN	Trelawnyd
1800	1850	1800	1850	135666	LAN	Liverpool
1800	1900	1700	1850	172561	MON	Trellech
1576	1722	....	....	176958	PEM	Llandaff
1576	1722	....	....	176958	PEM	Mathry
1576	1722	....	....	176958	PEM	Poyston
PRICK						
1681	1705	....	....	101028	SFK	Barrow
PRICKETT						
1817	1940	1810	1940	153818	BKM	Hardmead
1790	1848	1600	1860	107565	HAM	Owslebury
1806	1841	1750	1841	141062	LAN	Pendleton
1730	1760	1650	1750	144606	OXF	Bletchingdon
PRICTER						
1766	1790	....	....	115290	WIL	All Cannings
PRIDDEY						
1878	1930	1600	1992	131229	MDX	Islington
....	....	1860	1960	106127	WMD	Birmingham
1658	1992	1600	1992	131229	WOR	Droitwich
PRIDDICE						
1750	1790	1700	1810	171158	DEV	Farway
PRIDDLE						
....	....	ALL	ALL	157015	ALL	Name Study
1500	1992	ALL	ALL	157015	ALL	ALL
1840	1851	1600	1992	145289	DOR	Sandford Cross
1731	1917	1500	1992	110590	SOM	South
1800	1871	1700	1890	170518	SOM	Hambridge
1800	1871	1700	1890	170518	SOM	Kingsbury Episcopi
1840	1851	1600	1992	145289	SOM	Sandford Cross
PRIDDY						
1840	1901	1820	1920	131547	WIL	Little Somerford
1656	1715	1620	1730	170348	WIL	Rodbourne Cheney
PRIDE						
1669	1851	....	....	165999	GLS	Charlton Kings
1632	....	....	....	142859	GLS	Frampton On Severn
1669	1851	....	....	165999	GLS	Hardwicke
PRIDEAUX						
1619	1758	1550	1619	102571	CON	St Issey
1620	1650	1580	1620	158046	DEV	Crediton
PRIDHAM						
1780	....	1700	1992	167800	DEV	Alwington
1754	1808	1700	1760	119164	DEV	Clyst Hydon
1820	1896	....	....	130281	DEV	Holsworthy
1799	1873	1799	1873	102954	SSX	Winchelsea
PRIDIE						
....	....	1750	1800	159840	OXF	Charlbury
PRIDMORE						
1750	1900	1700	1930	157023	BDF	Eaton Socon
....	....	1700	1780	163260	NTH	Tansor
PRIED						
1721	1759	1700	1760	100242	HAM	ALL
PRIER						
1806	1806	ALL	1806	131849	SSX	West
1806	1806	ALL	1806	131849	SSX	Seaford
PRIEST						
....	....	ALL	ALL	103179	ALL	Name Study
1755	1861	....	....	115290	BRK	Hurst
1838	1911	....	....	115290	BRK	Waltham St Lawrence
1800	1851	1700	1800	144754	HAM	Catherington
1720	1820	1600	1720	104469	OXF	Charlton
1867	1893	1867	1992	118192	SRY	Camberwell
1815	1900	1600	1815	104469	SRY	Wandsworth
1830	1888	1700	1830	144754	SSX	Arundel
1500	1900	1500	1900	170216	WIL	ALL
....	....	1700	1900	147613	WOR	Halesowen
ALL	1810	....	....	170798	WRY	Denby
ALL	1810	....	....	170798	WRY	Silkstone
PRIESTLAY						
1710	1805	....	1745	109622	YKS	Ousefleet
PRIESTLEY						
1810	1810	1700	1820	157031	IRL	???
1800	1820	....	....	153796	LAN	Droylsden
1840	1850	1800	1900	143006	LAN	Manchester
1776	1796	1766	1776	122572	NTT	ALL
....	....	?	?	134201	WAR	Birmingham
1835	1900	1800	1835	157031	WIG	Wigtown
1850	1917	?	?	176702	WYK	Queensbury
1805	1845	1775	1805	159573	YKS	Halifax
1822	1830	1700	1825	135348	YKS	Ossett
1665	1789	....	....	153796	YKS	Woolley
1777	1988	1700	1800	135763	YKS	York
PRIESTLY						
1758	1903	1500	1992	102520	YKS	Thornton
PRIESTMAN						
1770	1780	1750	1770	121339	DUR	Heighington
PRIGG						
....	....	1850	1980	135046	AVN	Bristol
1814	1840	1800	1850	176621	NFK	Thetford
1753	1856	1700	1880	176621	SFK	Bardwell
1753	1856	1700	1880	176621	SFK	Gazeley
PRILE						
....	....	1800	1930	147508	HEF	Leominster
PRIM						
1790	1890	1600	1800	126772	SSX	Arundel
PRIME						
1768	1777	ALL	1800	151815	CAM	Barrington
1793	1923	1700	1793	157058	CAM	Swavesey
PRIMMER						
1820	1854	ALL	....	172219	HAM	Bishopstoke
1900	1992	ALL	1900	157066	HAM	Gosport
PRIN						
1865	1941	ALL	1992	143049	CLA	ALL
1812	1861	1812	1880	112364	SRY	Camberwell
PRINCE						
1800	1900	1800	1900	178004	DBY	Derby
1700	1850	1700	1850	123722	DBY	Youlgreave
1847	1924	1700	1847	146072	DEV	Sidbury
1853	1941	1700	1992	110418	DOR	Peasdown
1853	1941	1700	1992	110418	DOR	Waustron
1843	1900	1700	1843	100765	HAM	Newbridge
1700	1900	1890	1950	118907	HAM	Porstmouth
1800	1900	1900	1992	123315	IOW	ALL
....	....	1860	1900	157082	MDX	Hammersmith
....	....	1890	1920	157082	MDX	Norwood
1850	ALL	....	....	117560	MDX	Shoreditch
1700	1850	1600	1700	169862	SFK	Mildenhall
1853	1941	1700	1992	110418	SOM	Cloford
1784	1800	1750	1850	178004	STS	Mayfield
1876	1992	....	1907	166553	WOR	Wolverhampton
....	....	1790	1850	103713	WRY	Whitkirk
1670	1992	1650	1670	157074	WYK	Thorner
1717	1773	1600	1720	174858	YKS	Hunmanby
1733	....	1700	1800	169625	YKS	???
PRING						
ALL	1840	1750	1840	135429	DEV	Awliscombe
1535	1900	1750	1900	171158	DEV	Awliscombe
....	....	1700	1900	106461	DOR	???
....	....	1700	1900	106461	GLS	Bristol
1834	1851	1851	1871	168033	GLS	Cheltenham
1834	1851	1851	1871	168033	GLS	Leckhampton
1780	1860	1700	1780	168033	KEN	Brasted
1780	1860	1700	1780	168033	KEN	Speldhurst
1780	1860	1700	1780	168033	KEN	Sundridge

Known From	To	Researching From	To	Ref	Cty	Place
PRING contd.						
1897	1973	1850	1973	141550	NIR	White Abbey
....	....	1650	1750	130591	SOM	Milverton
1787	1871	1700	1870	121568	SOM	North Petherton
1839	1868	1800	1839	115746	SOM	Upcott
PRINGLE						
1880	1992	ALL	ALL	157090	DUR	Tyneside
1630	1700	ALL	1700	149063	ELN	Haddington
1820	1992	1700	1820	150363	LTN	Stow
1830	1860	1830	1860	160121	NBL	Newcastle
1880	1992	ALL	ALL	157090	NBL	Tyneside
1893	....	ALL	ALL	105481	NTT	Nottingham
1650	1750	....	....	142670	ROX	South
1800	1880	1700	1920	167207	ROX	???
1800	1880	1700	1920	167207	SEL	???
PRINT						
....	....	1750	1850	157104	???	Birmingham
....	....	1750	1850	157104	???	Shipston On Stour
PRINTOFT						
1500	1700	....	....	100420	WAR	Meriden
PRINTUP						
1500	1700	....	....	100420	WAR	Meriden
PRIOR						
1800	1840	ALL	1850	105376	CAM	ALL
1801	1876	1700	1801	145823	CAM	Swavesey
1840	1880	1700	1992	170518	CON	Launceston
1841	1861	1600	1890	170518	DEV	St Giles In The Heath
1800	1840	ALL	1850	107026	ESS	South
1828	....	....	....	140317	ESS	Great Bromley
1879	1879	1860	1890	151181	ESS	West Ham
1747	1992	1680	1740	173703	GLS	Tewkesbury
1600	1720	1500	1700	144657	HAM	Chawton
1690	1700	1650	1720	136840	HAM	Portsmouth
1785	1841	1600	1785	165298	HRT	Widford
1779	1799	....	1779	108839	HUN	Colne
1800	1820	1750	1850	153354	KEN	Maidstone
1857	1900	1600	1900	176133	LAN	Mancester
1742	1803	ALL	ALL	141615	LEI	Leicester
1840	1992	....	....	157120	LND	ALL
1900	1940	1750	1900	119180	LND	East
....	....	1860	1900	177393	MDX	Kensington
1874	1964	1500	....	110310	MDX	South Hackney
1900	1920	ALL	ALL	125202	MDX	Willesden
1800	1899	....	....	121835	NFK	Kings Lynn
1875	1961	....	....	106720	OXF	Blewbury
1800	1900	ALL	ALL	100161	SFK	North
1700	1900	1700	1900	156086	SOM	Crewkerne
1850	1864	1750	1850	112747	WIL	Keevil
PRISK						
....	....	1750	1920	139815	CON	Four Lanes
....	....	1750	1920	139815	CON	Illogan
PRISSICK						
1847	1868	1830	1900	101443	ERY	Hull
PRISTNUM						
1700	?	....	....	138231	LAN	Manchester
PRITCHARD						
1757	....	....	....	138401	AGY	Llanddaniel Fab
1768	1880	1700	1900	157147	AGY	Llanfair P G
1814	1870	1850	1992	178578	BRE	Pencelli
1743	1900	1600	1992	114472	CHS	West
1878	1894	1878	1894	168564	CHS	Warrington
1600	1670	1600	1700	176923	CMN	Carmarthen
1756	1849	....	....	138401	DEN	Llangernyw
1780	1992	1700	1800	149241	DEN	Rhiwlas Llansilin
....	....	1783	....	109673	DEN	Rhosllanurhygoe
1846	1992	....	....	104302	ESS	Arlesford
1850	1940	1800	1850	126322	FLN	Bagillt
1850	1930	1850	1930	135666	FLN	Holywell
1750	1930	1750	1930	135666	FLN	Trelawnyd
....	....	....	1880	157139	FLN	Wrexham
1750	1800	1700	1800	144657	GLS	Gloucester
1755	1755	1700	1800	157171	GLS	Hazelton
1840	1880	1800	1840	148962	HAM	Stockbridge
....	....	1600	1900	123390	HEF	Tarrington
1820	1820	ALL	1992	125113	KEN	Birchington
1840	1950	1800	1840	121053	KEN	Greenwich
1849	1873	ALL	1850	152641	KEN	Margate
1800	1850	1800	1850	135666	LAN	Liverpool
1880	1992	....	1880	157139	LAN	Liverpool
1800	1900	ALL	1800	141526	LND	Marylebone
1889	1901	1901	1992	122807	LND	Soho
1870	1910	1820	....	167932	MDX	Hoxton
1837	....	ALL	ALL	137421	MGY	Buttington
PRITCHARD contd.						
1821	1880	1800	1900	138088	OXF	Lewknor
1700	1725	1600	1700	114472	SAL	Dudleston
1821	1821	1775	1830	174289	SAL	Lilleshall
1800	1900	1700	1900	144657	SOM	Bristol
1841	1879	1800	1860	124648	SRY	Southwark
1906	1992	....	....	161284	STS	Cannock
1858	1938	....	....	173142	WAR	Birmingham
1450	1992	....	....	104302	WLS	Collenna
....	....	....	1883	158763	WLS	???
1811	1992	1841	1930	177350	WOR	Claines
PRITCHETT						
....	....	....	....	174793	DBY	Ilkeston
....	....	1742	1888	130079	OXF	Bicester
....	....	1742	1888	130079	OXF	Kirtlington
....	....	1750	1825	149977	WOR	ALL
1825	1846	....	....	149977	WOR	Martley
PRITTY						
1850	1937	1725	1850	129895	SFK	Framsden
PRIVETT						
1800	1824	1700	1850	145149	HAM	Bighton
....	....	1800	....	140333	KEN	Erith
....	1933	....	....	140333	LND	South East
PROBERT						
1798	1892	1760	1892	119059	BKM	Brill
1886	1886	....	....	127426	GLA	Merthyr Tydfil
1887	1887	....	....	127426	GLA	Penydarren
1790	1890	ALL	ALL	121614	GLS	ALL
1829	1857	ALL	1906	168696	GLS	Bedminster
1774	1774	1700	1850	157171	GLS	Gloucester
1900	1971	1900	1971	157171	GLS	Maisemore
1840	1940	1800	1940	157171	GLS	Newnham On Severn
1790	1827	1700	1790	121010	GLS	Painswick
1776	1862	1700	1900	157171	GLS	Preston
1775	1775	....	....	127426	HEF	Bredwardine
1740	1900	1600	1740	179396	HEF	Breinton
1800	1800	....	....	127426	HEF	Moccas
1805	1805	....	....	127426	HEF	Monnington On Wye
1852	1875	....	....	127426	HEF	Staunton On Wye
1753	1766	1680	1850	157171	HEF	Westhide
1770	1775	1680	1850	157171	HEF	Weston Beggard
1870	1940	1870	1940	157171	LND	Islington
1933	1933	....	....	127426	MON	Bedwellty
1900	1980	1900	1980	157171	MON	Crumlin
1909	1909	....	....	127426	MON	Risca
....	....	1800	1900	132438	STS	Bilston
1804	....	....	....	127140	???	Edinburgh
PROBETTS						
1830	1840	....	....	118281	BKM	Fulmer
1850	1875	1800	1900	118281	MDX	Paddington
1770	1850	1700	1850	118281	OXF	Bampton
PROBY						
1760	....	ALL	ALL	112461	ALL	ALL
PROCTER						
1760	1810	....	....	178330	CHS	Cranage
1880	....	1880	1992	143944	ERY	Hull
1743	1992	ALL	1743	157198	LAN	Chipping
....	....	1720	1760	178330	LAN	Lancaster
1780	1881	1780	1881	171166	WRY	Bordley
PROCTOR						
1888	1989	1750	1887	136859	ABD	Peterhead
1846	....	....	....	127140	ARL	Muchairn
1818	1920	1840	1920	103225	HRT	Puttenham
1766	1766	ALL	ALL	124982	LAN	Ellel
1877	....	1720	1877	177865	LAN	Lancaster
1730	1960	ALL	ALL	141062	LAN	Wheatley Lane
1850	1992	1700	1850	164429	LIN	Tetney
1800	1900	1650	1900	155462	SFK	Mid
1813	....	1700	1900	123277	STS	West Bromwich
....	....	1800	1920	157201	WIL	Swindon
1630	1730	ALL	ALL	141062	YKS	Giggleswick
....	....	1500	1700	157201	YKS	Horton
1630	1730	ALL	ALL	141062	YKS	Long Preston
....	....	1500	1700	157201	YKS	Ribblesdale
PROFFIT						
....	....	ALL	ALL	157228	ALL	ALL
PROFSER						
1703	1806	1703	1806	177008	BRE	Cricadarh
PROLTOR						
1900	1992	1850	1900	121703	YKS	Pontefract
PROOM						
....	....	ALL	ALL	137103	ALL	Name Study
1454	1992	1400	1992	137103	SFK	Stowmarket

Known From	To	Researching From	To	Ref	Cty	Place
PROSS						
1867	1941	1800	1867	118230	LND	Kennington
PROSSER						
1773	1792	1773	1792	177008	BRE	Llandefalle
1700	1920	1700	1992	156515	BRE	Llyswen
1790	1830	1538	1790	154792	GLS	Forest Of Dean
1847	1919	?	?	157236	GNT	Abercarn
1853	1933	?	?	157236	GNT	Crosskeys
?	....	?	....	104337	MDX	Mile End Old Town
1790	1830	1538	1790	154792	MON	ALL
1800	1890	1780	1900	123145	RAD	Clyro
PROSSOR						
1840	1900	1800	1900	142875	IRL	Cork
PROTAT						
1870	?	1800	1992	167592	MDX	London
1850	1870	1700	1992	167592	STS	Hanley
PROTHERO						
....	....	ALL	ALL	118222	ALL	Name Study
PROTHEROE						
1585	1992	1585	1992	118222	ALL	ALL
....	....	1800	1899	179612	GLA	Merthyr Tydfil
PROUD						
1775	1798	1600	1775	116637	DUR	Edmundbyers
1850	1940	....	....	127833	HAM	Portsmouth
1819	1850	1750	1850	152285	KEN	Gillingham
....	....	1600	1850	127833	KEN	???
....	....	1799	1801	104442	MDX	Poplar
....	....	1760	1800	102881	NYK	East Rounton
1733	1795	ALL	1795	104299	YKS	Lofthouse
PROUDE						
1620	1650	....	....	159883	KEN	Ash
1500	1600	....	....	167924	YKS	Terrington
PROUDFOOT						
....	....	ALL	ALL	157252	ALL	Name Study
1780	1992	....	1891	157252	CUL	Carlisle
....	1882	1500	1882	175072	DFS	Dumfries
1736	1750	1700	1736	179663	DFS	Johnstone
1832	1992	....	....	157252	DUR	Shildon
1810	1992	....	....	157252	DUR	Stanhope
1841	1881	....	....	157252	DUR	Sunderland
1933	1992	1829	1992	157244	FIF	Lower Largo
1933	1992	1829	1992	157244	FIF	St Andrews
....	1882	1882	1992	175072	LAN	Liverpool
1720	1841	1200	1891	157252	LND	City
1750	1992	1700	1891	157252	NFK	North Coast
1933	1992	1829	1992	157244	OXF	Oxford
1933	1992	1829	1992	157244	PER	Perth
1774	1841	....	....	157252	WES	Barton
1781	1800	1750	1780	179663	WES	Barton
PROUDLEY						
1851	1881	1700	ALL	119040	DOR	East
1851	1881	1700	ALL	119040	HAM	Lymington
1800	1875	....	....	145394	SSX	???
PROUDLOVE						
1792	1857	1700	1792	176907	CHS	???
....	....	1700	1850	138614	LAN	Blackburn
PROUSE						
1805	1831	1750	1805	173770	DEV	Bovey Tracey
1810	1900	1810	1900	107352	DEV	Buckland Brwer
1770	1810	1770	1810	107352	DEV	Clovelly
?	?	1700	1850	123668	DEV	Clovilly
1800	1900	1700	1850	157287	DEV	Ilsington
1835	1942	1800	1835	107654	DEV	Plymouth
1730	1770	1730	1770	107352	DEV	Wolsery
PROUT						
1760	1992	1700	1992	102970	BRK	Speen
1801	....	1700	1801	149608	CON	Jacobstow
1800	1850	1800	1970	146293	CON	Stratton
1748	1790	?	1800	103934	DEV	North Molton
1800	1840	1700	1800	133493	DEV	Tavistock
....	....	....	....	137375	GLS	Frocester
....	....	ALL	ALL	157260	HAM	North
....	....	ALL	ALL	157260	HAM	Kingsclere
1840	1913	....	....	147672	SOM	Bath
PROVEN						
1785	1840	1785	1840	133795	SCT	???
PROVICE						
1650	1750	1600	1800	177180	BKM	Hardwick
PROVIS						
1881	1933	....	....	107174	CON	Camborne
PROVOST						
1665	1940	....	....	128996	CAM	Thorney
1851	1960	1850	1950	154539	LAN	Liverpool
1842	1845	1838	1860	154539	LAN	Preston
PROVOST contd.						
1825	1826	1700	1840	154539	YKS	Dewsbury
1827	1836	1700	1840	154539	YKS	Knaresborough
1833	1833	1700	1840	154539	YKS	York
PROWSE						
....	....	ALL	ALL	157279	ALL	Name Study
1700	1992	1500	1992	166758	ALL	ALL
....	....	ALL	1800	140848	DEV	ALL
1040	1992	1040	1992	157295	DEV	Chagford
1810	1992	1700	1810	141658	DEV	Crediton
1850	1946	1750	1870	121312	DEV	Exeter
1800	1900	1700	1850	157287	DEV	Ilsington
1670	1920	....	1850	179213	DEV	Loddiswell
1760	1780	1700	1760	118435	DEV	Teignmouth
1860	1923	1860	1992	121312	DEV	Thorverton
1040	1992	1040	1992	157295	ESS	Colchester
1810	1858	1790	1810	118435	LAN	Liverpool
1841	1992	ALL	ALL	143537	LND	ALL
1810	1890	1800	1992	172995	LND	Camberwell
PROWTING						
1857	1970	1700	1850	112283	HAM	Portsea
PROYBN						
1900	1945	?	1992	131458	LAN	Salford
PRUDAMES						
....	....	ALL	ALL	157309	ALL	Name Study
PRUDDEN						
1730	1800	1650	1750	142670	BDF	Luton
PRUDENCE						
1780	1870	....	....	140864	MDX	Edmonton
1780	1870	....	....	140864	MDX	Enfield
PRUDOM						
1740	....	1550	1740	150843	YKS	Danby In Cleveland
PRUEN						
1493	1992	ALL	1493	157317	CAM	Central
1493	1992	ALL	1493	157317	GLS	Central
PRUER						
1797	1850	1700	1850	147575	CAM	Chesterton
PRUSACEK						
1905	1906	1880	1992	121460	???	Hull
PRUST						
1838	1950	1700	1838	169382	DEV	North
1838	1950	1700	1838	169382	GLA	???
PRYAL						
....	1846	....	....	140767	MAY	???
1868	....	1868	....	140767	YKS	Leeds
PRYALL						
....	1846	....	....	140767	MAY	???
1868	....	1868	....	140767	YKS	Leeds
PRYCE						
1750	1860	ALL	1750	179515	HEF	Wigmore
1838	1839	1750	1900	114456	MGY	ALL
1700	1800	1650	1850	149993	MGY	Betws Cedewain
1800	1992	1600	1800	156914	MGY	Kerry
1800	1992	1750	1800	141798	RAD	Llanbister
1880	?	ALL	1900	165646	WLS	Welshpool
PRYDE						
1780	1880	ALL	1780	163341	MLN	Newtongrange
PRYKE						
1803	1828	ALL	1803	131881	SFK	Great Thurlow
PRYOR						
1800	1840	ALL	1850	105376	CAM	ALL
1850	1900	1850	1900	162736	CON	Liskeard
1750	1890	1700	1750	101931	CON	Porthlevan
1776	1900	1700	1776	109983	CON	Wendron
1850	1992	1600	1850	123242	CON	Wendron
1784	1900	1750	1900	157341	CON	Wendron
1790	1840	1700	1900	162736	DEV	Holsworthy
1885	1985	1885	1985	157341	DEV	Plymouth
?	?	?	?	157325	ENG	Wendren
1630	1630	....	....	159883	KEN	Ash
....	....	1860	1900	177393	MDX	Kensington
1850	1900	1800	1850	168750	SRY	Southwark
1640	1720	1640	1750	142018	WIL	Chitterne
PSCINGA						
1871	1888	....	....	109827	HAM	Southampton
1854	1857	....	....	109827	KEN	Brompton
PUCKETT						
1750	1969	1650	1750	143707	DOR	ALL
PUCKEY						
1815	1893	1700	1815	164917	CON	South
PUCKMORE						
....	....	ALL	ALL	106631	ALL	Name Study
1680	1800	1680	1800	106631	GLS	Dymock
1800	1850	1800	1850	106631	GLS	Stroud

Known From	To	Researching From	To	Ref	Cty	Place
PUDDEFOOT						
1836	....	ALL	ALL	116394	LND	Clerkenwell
1800	....	ALL	ALL	116394	LND	Marylebone
PUDDEN						
1854	1881	1854	1992	133639	SOM	Coker
PUDDEPHAT						
1849	1849	ALL	1992	112631	BKM	Leyhill
PUDDEPHATE						
1869	?	....	....	129100	MDX	Hoxton
PUDDEPHATT						
1792	1815	1700	1792	141402	BKM	Lee
....	....	1800	1940	104256	HRT	Chipperfield
1850	1950	1800	1992	177180	HRT	Flaunden
PUDDICOMBE						
1732	1992	....	....	172030	DEV	Crediton
PUDDIFOOT						
1774	1841	1774	1841	124915	BKM	Missenden
1823	1893	1700	1823	113182	HRT	Watford
PUDDING						
....	1780	ALL	1780	163341	ESS	Clavering
1782	....	1760	1782	133639	SOM	Coker
PUDDLE						
1800	1840	1700	1900	138517	SOM	???
PUDDY						
1845	1865	1750	1845	132640	LND	Bethnal Green
1826	1992	1800	1992	171581	SOM	Burnham
PUDNER						
....	....	....	....	157368	ALL	ALL
PUDNEY						
....	....	ALL	ALL	174092	ALL	Name Study
1829	1850	1500	1850	157538	SRY	Newington
1829	1850	1500	1850	157538	SRY	Southwark
PUDWELL						
1877	1901	1841	1910	111600	OXF	Faringdon
PUGH						
....	....	1830	1855	111856	BRE	Brecon
1874	1953	ALL	1898	101281	CAM	???
1850	1860	1700	1950	157392	CHS	Chester
1865	1865	1800	1875	157384	GLA	Bridgend
1872	1873	1875	1880	157384	GLA	Cardiff
1783	1800	1700	1783	155500	GLS	Didbrook
1803	1950	1672	1958	142077	HEF	Brilley
1714	1900	1714	1900	142077	HEF	Eardisley
1830	1951	ALL	ALL	120669	LAN	Bury
1854	1880	ALL	1854	176842	LAN	Castell Y Dail
1830	1951	ALL	ALL	120669	LAN	Radcliffe
1836	1850	1800	1880	157384	LND	Southwark
1836	1836	1800	1850	157384	LND	Stepney
1819	1841	1750	1850	144797	MDX	Bethnal Green
1861	1890	1800	1900	119008	MDX	London
1883	1924	1863	1882	118230	MER	Llanegryn
1910	1930	1700	1950	157392	MGY	Llanfyllin
1815	1992	1815	1900	157376	MGY	Rhayader
1874	1953	ALL	1898	101281	NTH	???
....	....	1794	....	116092	RAD	Llansanfraidcwmtoydowi
1856	1992	1820	1856	161284	STS	Wolverhampton
....	....	....	1900	176702	SWL	Bettws
1901	1930	1800	1900	153915	WAR	Kidderminster
1766	1848	1500	1766	153591	WLS	Brymbo
1766	1848	1500	1766	153591	WLS	Bwlch Gwyn
1766	1848	1500	1766	153591	WLS	Denbeigh
1766	1848	1500	1766	153591	WLS	Flint
1800	1992	ALL	1800	131571	WLS	Gower
1800	1992	ALL	1800	131571	WLS	Llanrhidian
PUGSLEY						
1801	1801	1700	1800	169234	DEV	Harpford
PUINTUR						
....	....	1206	....	155977	BRK	???
....	....	1212	....	155977	KEN	???
PULAR						
1900	1970	1550	1900	157430	STS	Darlaston
PULCHRO						
....	....	1600	1700	177539	OXF	Eynsham
PULE						
1750	1850	1750	1850	106631	GLS	Stroud
PULEE						
1671	....	....	....	130079	OXF	Swyncombe
PULEN						
1800	1860	ALL	1800	145939	SSX	Kindford
PULESTON						
....	....	ALL	ALL	154628	ALL	Name Study
1295	1900	1295	1900	154628	ALL	???
1250	1600	1200	1600	154881	AGY	Emral
PULESTON contd.						
1280	1664	1066	1320	124974	FLN	Emral
PULHAM						
1881	1920	1860	1992	108421	LND	Haggerton
1825	1859	1700	1880	108421	SFK	Ipswich
PULKER						
....	....	ALL	ALL	101699	ALL	Name Study
1858	1870	1850	1870	109371	OXF	Oxford
PULLAN						
1590	1848	....	1590	157406	WRY	Fewston
1848	1880	1880	1900	157406	WRY	Halifax
1590	1848	....	1590	157406	WRY	Pateley Bridge
1850	1865	1800	1900	120529	YKS	Hampsthwaite
PULLAR						
1772	1850	ALL	1772	177814	PER	Perth
PULLEINE						
1700	1803	....	....	100536	YKS	York
PULLEN						
....	....	ALL	ALL	157449	ALL	Name Study
1840	1992	1810	1840	149713	BKM	Linslade
1900	1992	ALL	1992	128260	HAM	Soton
1900	1920	ALL	1992	128260	JSY	???
1840	1920	1920	1992	149713	LND	Wood Green
1699	1847	1670	1847	159581	SRY	Cranleigh
1850	1992	1700	1850	157449	SRY	Guildford
1850	1992	1700	1850	157449	SRY	Kingston
PULLER						
1500	1950	1500	1950	157430	ALL	ALL
PULLEY						
1831	....	1800	1840	124796	BKM	Akeley
1696	1706	1680	1710	124796	BKM	Buckingham
1839	....	1825	1840	124796	BKM	Thornborough
1679	....	1650	1680	124796	NTH	Higham Ferrers
1761	1855	....	....	124524	NTH	Nothampton
1805	....	1775	1830	124796	OXF	Bletchingdon
1763	1814	1750	1815	124796	OXF	Kidlington
1737	1783	1705	1790	124796	OXF	Merton
1820	....	1800	1840	124796	OXF	Weston On The Green
PULLIN						
1788	1815	....	....	157465	GLS	Chipping Sodbury
1815	1850	....	....	157465	GLS	Hawkesbury
1715	1788	....	....	157465	GLS	Tytherington
1892	1895	....	....	157465	LND	Wandsworth
1876	1906	....	....	157465	LND	Westminster
1890	1992	....	....	157465	NFK	Cromer
1861	1862	1863	1891	157465	WIL	Corsham
1851	1860	....	....	157465	WIL	Tytherton
PULLING						
1808	1834	1700	1808	168033	HEF	Bishops Frome
PULLINGER						
1786	1830	1786	1992	167959	SRY	Bermondsey
PULMAN						
1650	1860	....	....	146676	DEV	Beer
1650	1860	....	....	146676	DEV	Colyton
1860	1992	....	....	146676	NBL	Newcastle On Tyne
PULVERTAFT						
....	....	ALL	ALL	157473	ALL	Name Study
1600	1900	1600	1900	157473	COR	Cork
1650	1800	1650	1800	157473	TIP	ALL
PULVERTOFT						
1200	1800	1200	1800	157473	LIN	Boston
PUMPHREY						
1774	1774	ALL	1774	131849	SSX	West Dean
PUNCHARD						
1850	1880	ALL	ALL	139890	DEV	North
PUNE						
1730	1860	1700	1860	171549	DEV	Boconnoc
PUNNETT						
1779	1860	....	1779	146013	KEN	Maidstone
PUNSHON						
1700	....	1600	....	116920	DUR	Sunderland
1850	1902	1850	....	119474	DUR	Sunderland
....	....	1800	1900	166391	DUR	Sunderland
PUNT						
1796	1992	ALL	ALL	113093	ESS	Langford
PUNTER						
1749	1992	1600	1749	179051	BDF	Luton
1825	1838	1780	1815	157481	BRK	Various
1749	1992	1600	1749	179051	HRT	Harpenden
....	1790	....	....	174564	KEN	Woolwich
1795	1809	1725	1820	157481	LND	St Georges Hanover Square
1837	1920	1835	1920	157481	MDX	Chiswick
....	....	1750	1850	101273	SRY	North

Known From	To	Researching From	To	Ref	Cty	Place
PURCELL						
1840	1861	ALL	1900	127000	LAN	Manchester
1850	1900	1850	1900	157503	LAN	Rawtenstall
1840	1861	ALL	1900	127000	STS	Dudley
1818	1850	1750	1850	157503	TIP	Ballingarry
1840	1861	ALL	1900	127000	WOR	???
PURCHALL						
1798	....	ALL	ALL	164291	BKM	ALL
1584	1832	1584	1900	164291	BRK	ALL
1700	....	1700	1900	164291	HAM	ALL
1660	....	ALL	ALL	164291	LND	ALL
1822	1851	ALL	ALL	164291	MDX	ALL
1664	1815	1664	1900	164291	SRY	ALL
1785	....	ALL	ALL	164291	WIL	Chilton Foliat
PURCHASE						
1754	1885	1750	1885	154709	DOR	ALL
1846	....	1730	1900	109894	DOR	Bere Regis
1689	1992	ALL	1689	157511	DOR	Bere Regis
1689	1992	ALL	1689	157511	DOR	Dorchester
1836	....	....	1992	136964	DOR	Puddletown
....	....	1700	1900	154709	SOM	ALL
1689	1992	ALL	1689	157511	SXW	Chichester
PURCHELL						
1770	1864	1700	1780	164291	SRY	Godalming
PURDOM						
1790	1900	ALL	1790	115118	ROX	Castleton
PURDON						
1834	1900	1500	1940	157538	DUR	West Hartlepool
1817	1840	1700	1840	158313	ENG	???
1810	1830	1750	1820	128244	LKS	Glasgow
PURDUE						
1790	1820	1750	1790	133442	BRK	Newbury
....	....	1700	1880	157546	HAM	Overton
1832	1880	1700	1832	114448	LND	Shoreditch
PURDY						
1870	1930	1800	1870	168947	DBY	Ashbourne
1800	1850	1600	1850	154342	NFK	Alpington
1805	1906	....	....	157554	NFK	Stiffkey
PUREFOY						
1700	1723	1600	1850	178659	ALL	ALL
PURFIELD						
1860	....	1800	1860	147478	HAM	Portsea
1850	1860	1800	1860	147478	KEN	Sydenham
PURKESS						
....	....	1750	1850	116262	HAM	Minstead
PURKIS						
1809	1900	1700	1809	100749	HAM	Portsea
1843	1850	....	1843	110027	HAM	Soberton
1791	1882	ALL	1900	111600	HAM	Totton
1770	1850	1700	1850	136840	IOW	Newchurch
1820	1850	1600	1850	175641	SFK	Stradishall
PURKISS						
1840	1900	1800	1840	125318	ESS	Ardleigh
PURNELL						
....	....	1700	1880	132551	AVN	Bristol
1880	1992	1700	1880	132551	GLA	Ferndale
1617	1792	....	....	165999	GLS	Bristol
1617	1792	....	....	165999	GLS	Dursley
ALL	ALL	....	....	153397	HAM	ALL
1790	1830	1770	1850	120995	SOM	Holcombe
1830	1850	1800	1830	101524	WIL	Bradford On Avon
PURRINTON						
1605	....	1550	1640	143138	DEV	Tiverton
PURROCK						
....	....	?	....	141216	GLS	North
....	....	?	....	141216	GLS	Mid
PURSALL						
1819	1992	1750	1819	161284	SAL	Wrockwardine
PURSE						
1880	1885	1860	1885	164852	WIL	Swindon
PURSELL						
1821	ALL	....	....	117048	WAR	Birmingham
PURSER						
1796	1868	1700	1800	156957	GLS	Redmarley
....	....	1750	1833	138339	WOR	Birlingham
1817	1817	1750	....	140783	WOR	Birlingham
....	....	1810	1820	138339	WOR	Claines
1820	1850	....	....	138339	WOR	Kempsey
PURSEY						
....	....	ALL	ALL	157562	ALL	Name Study
....	....	ALL	ALL	157570	ALL	ALL
1852	1992	....	....	128716	SOM	Bridgwater
1790	1850	1790	1850	159913	SOM	Catcott
....	....	?	?	157562	SOM	???

Known From	To	Researching From	To	Ref	Cty	Place
PURSLOW						
1600	1970	1600	1970	157589	ALL	ALL
PURTON						
1840	1860	1700	1992	143189	DOR	Blandford
PURVER						
1824	1846	1800	1870	136719	HAM	Abbotts Ann
PURVES						
1803	1900	ALL	1800	101001	BEW	East
....	....	ALL	ALL	115231	BEW	Duns
1858	1992	1861	1891	157597	KEN	Gravesend
1894	1894	1800	1930	158399	NBL	Berwick Upon Tweed
PURVEUR						
1748	1828	ALL	1748	157600	BRK	Stratfield Mortimer
1828	1851	1851	1900	157600	GLS	Cheltenham
....	....	1851	1900	157600	GLS	Gloucester
1800	1850	1784	1850	157600	MDX	London
PURVIS						
1850	1920	1800	1850	132942	DUR	Monk Hesleden
1800	1900	....	....	124168	DUR	Penshaw
1819	1960	1700	1819	153362	NBL	Etal
1840	1881	....	....	132497	NBL	Hexham
PURYER						
1782	1969	1600	1782	152269	BKM	Newport Pagnell
PUSEY						
1845	1992	1750	1835	157619	HAM	New Forest
PUSHLEY						
1723	1800	1600	1723	166804	SFK	Kirkley
PUSHMAN						
1887	....	....	....	170623	LND	Ealing
PUSS						
1770	1880	1700	1800	110116	HAM	Fareham
PUSSER						
1750	1800	1700	1850	126268	LND	Deptford
PUTLY						
1600	1670	1600	1700	142018	SOM	ALL
PUTNAM						
....	....	ALL	ALL	157627	ALL	Name Study
1740	....	1740	1772	169625	BKM	Amersham
1712	1764	ALL	1770	121754	BKM	Wendover
1717	1746	1717	1800	169625	HRT	Northchurch
PUTT						
1899	1967	1700	1992	153540	DEV	Devonport
PUTTENHAM						
....	....	ALL	ALL	157635	ALL	Name Study
PUTTERGILL						
1770	1800	1600	1800	126837	LIN	Caythorpe
PUTTOCK						
....	1890	....	....	160806	SRY	Carsh Alton
PUTWAIN						
1796	1992	1600	1796	117110	KEN	Seasalter
PUYRAVEL						
1800	1900	1750	1900	167770	HAM	Gosport
PYATT						
....	....	1842	1870	157643	ESS	Manningtree
1857	1900	1830	1857	157643	LND	St Georges In East
....	....	1770	1865	157643	SFK	Ipswich
PYBUS						
1841	?	1800	1850	136522	WYK	Birstall
1830	1850	1700	1992	172782	YKS	Bolton On Swale
1800	1840	1750	1840	167568	YKS	Liverton
PYCROFT						
1761	1825	1700	1900	135968	LIN	Donnington
1715	1842	1650	1850	149160	NFK	Norwich
PYDD						
....	....	1790	1810	174602	LIN	Aslackby
....	....	1790	1810	174602	LIN	Marston
PYE						
1802	1992	1700	1850	105201	KEN	Bredgar
....	....	1600	1850	179531	LAN	ALL
1810	1881	1788	1881	136565	LAN	Billington
1810	1881	1788	1881	136565	LAN	Blackburn
1826	....	....	1826	159506	LAN	Eccles
1773	1851	1750	1851	157678	LAN	Halsall
?	1880	....	....	165158	LAN	Lathom
1851	1927	1800	1851	111163	LAN	Over Wyresdale
1723	1931	....	....	139211	NFK	Coltishall
1723	1931	....	....	139211	NFK	Hainford
1723	1931	....	....	139211	NFK	Norwich
1790	1851	1750	1865	120146	WIL	Woodborough
1750	1978	1720	1920	103616	WYK	Doncaster
PYECROFT						
1827	1846	1846	1900	159212	LIN	Hackthorn
1783	1829	1700	1783	159212	NTT	Walkeringham

Known From	To	Researching From	To	Ref	Cty	Place
PYER						
1890	1988	1863	1890	177539	LND	Woolwich
PYERS						
1547	1600	1600	1992	116149	DEV	Clyst St George
1859	1992	1600	1992	116149	LND	Shoreditch
PYETT						
1700	1920	ALL	ALL	167940	SFK	Witnesham
PYKE						
1801	1851	1750	1780	165530	SOM	Keynsham
1500	1700	1500	1900	170216	WIL	ALL
PYLE						
1690	1992	1450	1690	157686	HAM	Nether Wallop
1690	1992	1450	1690	157686	HAM	Over
1819	....	....	....	125202	NFK	Yarmouth
PYLE-GIDDINGS						
1820	1890	1820	1890	133922	HAM	Bramshaw
1803	1890	1803	1890	133922	WIL	Nomansland
PYLES						
....	....	1840	1900	177776	CLV	Hartlepool
PYM						
1802	1816	....	1802	131385	DEV	Topsham
1890	....	....	1890	164011	DEV	Topsham
1500	1850	....	....	125199	KEN	Chilham
PYMAN						
....	....	ALL	ALL	113832	ALL	Name Study
PYMER						
1684	1738	ALL	1684	154563	DOR	Abbotsbury
PYNE						
....	....	1700	1950	120715	DEV	ALL
1870	1900	1800	1900	129178	MDX	Islington
PYNEN						
1850	1992	....	....	158348	LAN	Knowsley
PYNN						
1801	1992	1750	1992	144797	KEN	Chatham
PYRAH						
1750	1992	....	....	157694	YKS	Bradford
1750	1992	....	....	157694	YKS	Leeds
PYRKE						
?	?	?	?	144673	ESS	Grays Thurrock
1390	1943	....	....	144673	GLS	Forest Of Dean
1750	1880	1500	1750	128317	GLS	Littledean
?	?	?	?	144673	LND	East
1750	1880	1500	1750	128317	MDX	London
?	?	?	?	144673	SRY	St Mary Newington
PYTHIAN						
1822	1900	1800	1900	134422	COR	Kantark
PYWELL						
1740	1792	ALL	ALL	141615	LEI	Smeeton Westerby
PYZER						
1801	1921	1770	1850	155799	LEI	Branston
QUADLING						
....	....	ALL	ALL	121991	ALL	Name Study
ALL	ALL	ALL	ALL	121991	ALL	ALL
QUAIL						
1841	1940	1841	1992	125172	CUL	Cockermouth
1841	1940	1841	1992	125172	CUL	Maryport
QUAIN						
1854	1992	1800	1854	139203	IRL	???
QUAIT						
1560	....	1560	1870	119458	SSX	Horsham
QUAKETT						
1680	1820	1680	1830	117145	LAN	Eccleston
QUALTROUGH						
1712	1783	1650	1712	135151	IOM	Ruchen
QUANCE						
1800	1850	....	....	144371	DEV	Okehampton
QUANTOCK						
1500	1950	1500	1992	110590	SOM	ALL
QUANTRILL						
1848	1900	....	....	116017	LND	East
1848	1900	....	....	116017	LND	City
QUARMBY						
1850	1921	1750	1850	171034	YKS	Huddersfield
1820	1920	1700	1850	157716	YKS	Linthwaite
....	....	1700	1851	157716	YKS	Slaithwaite
QUARRY						
....	....	ALL	ALL	168270	ALL	Name Study
1861	1861	1830	1900	104663	LND	Chelsea
QUARTERMAIN						
....	....	ALL	ALL	157724	ALL	ALL
1693	1707	1650	1710	124796	BKM	Aston Rowant
1721	....	1690	1750	124796	OXF	Chalgrove
QUARTERMAN						
....	....	ALL	ALL	157724	ALL	Name Study

Known From	To	Researching From	To	Ref	Cty	Place
QUARTERMAN	contd.					
....	....	ALL	ALL	157724	ALL	ALL
1800	....	....	....	157724	LND	ALL
1650	....	....	....	157724	OXF	Cowley
1700	....	....	....	157724	OXF	Oxford
1830	1880	1830	1880	100668	SRY	Walton On Thames
QUARTLY						
1821	1851	1680	1871	121568	DEV	North East
1783	1992	1680	1992	121568	SOM	West
QUARTON						
1800	1819	1750	1850	119032	YKS	Full Sutton
QUATERMAINE						
1593	1676	1593	1676	103977	OXF	Chalgrove
QUAY;E						
1800	1834	1700	1800	135151	IOM	Michael
QUAYLE						
1702	1900	ALL	ALL	150304	IOM	ALL
1790	1870	1600	1790	131962	IOM	Grenaby
....	....	1700	1800	147613	IOM	Malew
1850	1930	1750	1850	134848	LAN	Liverpool
QUEENSBOROG						
1770	1820	....	....	165999	LEI	ALL
1770	1820	....	....	165999	LEI	Bottesford
QUELCH						
1820	1841	ALL	1850	118737	BRK	Wasing
1876	1992	?	1930	158704	KEN	Tundbridge Wells
QUENETT						
1880	1930	1600	1992	154229	YKS	South
QUERIPEL						
1900	1992	1700	1900	166480	JSY	ALL
QUESTED						
1750	1992	1700	1750	157740	KEN	Wye
QUIBELL						
1800	1900	1800	1880	173819	LIN	Hackthorn
QUICK						
1787	1830	1700	1835	128961	BDF	Luton
1735	1835	1700	1835	128961	BDF	Milton Bryant
1632	1729	1600	1632	102571	CON	Gulval
1796	1992	1600	1796	105929	CON	St Ives
1722	1722	1700	1722	108510	CON	Towednack
1620	1786	....	....	139491	CON	Towednack
1633	1851	....	....	139491	CON	Zennor
1850	1992	1700	1850	160725	DEV	South Hams
1700	....	ALL	ALL	116394	HAM	Portsea
1842	....	ALL	ALL	116394	HAM	Southampton
1835	1878	1830	1992	128961	HRT	Redbourn
....	....	1700	1800	117587	LAN	South West
1870	1880	1750	1870	121010	MDX	Chelsea
1850	1870	1780	1890	135429	SOM	Claverton
1780	1850	1780	1890	135429	SOM	Norton St Phillip
QUICKE						
1637	1654	1600	1637	116637	CON	Poughill
1679	....	1600	1679	116637	CON	St Ives
1679	....	1600	1679	116637	CON	Towednack
QUICKFALL						
1940	1992	1800	1992	123765	LIN	ALL
QUIDDINGTON						
1808	1833	ALL	1833	156582	KEN	North West
1808	1833	ALL	1833	156582	SRY	North East
QUIG						
1860	1900	1700	1860	157031	KKD	Balmaclellan
QUIGG						
1831	1870	1825	1890	119628	RFW	Greenock
QUIGGAN						
....	....	1750	1850	131962	IOM	Malew
QUILTER						
1820	1920	....	....	131059	ESS	Billericay
1760	1800	1700	1800	175978	ESS	Braintree
1800	1820	ALL	1800	131059	ESS	Tolleshunt D'arcy
QUIN						
1810	1870	1750	1850	155357	MDX	Shoreditch
QUINCE						
1770	1834	ALL	1770	169730	CAM	Thorney
1763	1992	1540	1800	157759	HUN	Conington
QUINCEY						
....	....	ALL	ALL	157759	ALL	Name Study
1743	1940	....	....	128996	CAM	Thorney
1763	1992	1540	1800	157759	HUN	Conington
1780	1870	1700	1900	141410	LIN	Braceborough
1870	1992	1850	1992	141410	NTH	Peterborough
QUINEY						
....	....	1800	1860	149799	LND	Stepney
1860	1960	1600	1900	119202	MDX	East London
1851	1992	....	....	174297	WOR	Bromsgrove

Known From	To	Researching From	To	Ref	Cty	Place
QUINEY contd.						
1816	....	1816	1870	153249	WOR	Tardebigge
QUINLAN						
....	....	1650	1850	119784	LKS	Port Glasgow
QUINN						
1856	1856	1800	1856	103640	ESS	Stratford
1736	1974	....	....	147702	GLA	Barry
1875	....	....	1875	146935	IRL	Dundalk
1880	1950	....	....	114715	IRL	Muligar
1880	1950	....	....	114715	IRL	Sligo
1870	1880	1800	1900	162272	SRY	Walworth
1800	1992	1800	1950	119865	TYR	Arboe
QUINNELL						
....	....	1700	1992	149969	KEN	Tunbridge Wells
....	....	1750	1900	173835	SRY	Betchworth
....	....	1750	1900	173835	SRY	Brockham
1920	1970	1800	1920	173835	SSX	Amberley
QUINNEY						
1693	1823	1690	1825	103632	NTH	Preston Capes
1860	1900	1750	1850	107182	OXF	Great Bourton
QUINTON						
1692	1992	1850	1992	143049	ALL	ALL
....	....	1700	1820	146730	CON	Passim
1846	....	1700	1880	140953	GLS	???
1830	1992	....	....	157805	LND	St Luke
1480	1992	1600	1850	157805	NFK	Norwich
1807	1830	....	1807	125954	SOM	Wells
1846	....	1700	1880	140953	SOM	???
....	....	1600	1785	149977	STS	Cannock
....	....	1600	1785	149977	STS	Rugeley
1786	1900	....	....	149977	STS	Wolverhampton
1780	1804	1700	1850	118397	WIL	Downton
1719	1992	1600	1719	129712	WIL	Downton
1830	1851	1700	1830	174297	WOR	ALL
QUINTRELL						
1783	1809	1750	1820	100749	CON	St Blazey
....	....	1671	1800	100749	CON	St Gerrans
1818	1900	1818	1900	100749	HAM	Portsea
QUIPP						
....	....	1577	1985	154504	ALL	???
1733	1985	....	....	154504	LIN	Gainsboro
1741	1985	....	....	154504	LIN	Lincoln
QUIPPE						
....	....	ALL	ALL	154504	ALL	Name Study
QUIRIE						
1775	1890	1775	1890	138894	ABD	Crimond
QUIRK						
1835	1854	1800	1835	179604	CHS	Bromborough
....	....	1780	1820	131962	IOM	Douglas
1745	1823	1700	1800	163694	IOM	Peel
....	....	1800	1835	179604	IOM	???
1865	1992	1700	1865	103098	IRL	???
QUIRKE						
1880	1992	1876	1992	157821	COR	Cork
QUY						
....	....	ALL	ALL	157848	ALL	Name Study
....	....	ALL	ALL	157848	ALL	ALL
1800	1900	ALL	ALL	157848	ESS	Barking
ALL	ALL	ALL	ALL	157848	ESS	Gosfield
1900	1950	ALL	ALL	157848	ESS	Ilford
1850	1900	ALL	ALL	157848	ESS	Paglesham
1800	1900	ALL	ALL	157848	ESS	Rochford
1750	1800	ALL	ALL	157848	ESS	Witham
1850	....	ALL	ALL	157848	KEN	ALL
1890	....	ALL	ALL	157848	NBL	Blythe
RABBATTS						
1800	1850	1700	1850	126268	LND	Greenwich
1840	1860	1800	1992	165603	LND	Greenwich
RABBETS						
1722	1732	ALL	ALL	157856	DOR	Wimborne St Giles
1875	1992	ALL	ALL	157856	HAM	Portsmouth
RABBETTS						
1829	1875	ALL	ALL	157856	HAM	Cowes
1829	1875	ALL	ALL	157856	HAM	Northwood
1829	1875	ALL	ALL	157856	HAM	Ryde
1829	1875	ALL	ALL	157856	IOW	???
1747	1816	1600	1747	157856	WIL	Tollard Royal
RABBIT						
1870	1886	ALL	1886	118737	IRL	Glendalkin
RABBITT						
....	....	1860	ALL	159727	LAN	Manchester
....	....	1860	ALL	159727	LAN	Salford
RABETS						
1820	1850	1750	1850	118397	DOR	Witchampton
RABIN						
1866	1992	....	....	165727	LND	East
RABJOHNS						
1731	1795	1731	1795	108251	DEV	Cullopnton
RABY						
1790	1826	....	....	105619	CMN	Llanelli
1782	....	ALL	1782	154946	ERY	Howden
1834	1860	ALL	ALL	138886	LAN	Preston
1714	1810	1700	1820	105619	LND	City
....	....	1700	1825	108049	NTH	Great Oakley
1770	1810	1770	1810	105619	SRY	Cobham
1825	1940	....	....	108049	WAR	Southam
RABY-YOUNG						
1840	....	....	....	135402	MDX	Hoxton
RACE						
1813	1840	1750	1820	137278	YKS	Brignall
1859	1954	1700	1954	123005	YKS	Scraborough
RACEY						
1826	1880	1800	1880	166685	AVN	Bristol
RACHANCE						
....	....	ALL	ALL	171638	AVN	Bath
RACHELSON						
1880	....	....	....	114529	LND	???
RACHER						
1760	1920	ALL	ALL	117323	CAM	Bassingbourn
1762	1872	1500	1762	125695	CAM	Bassingbourn
1820	1880	1700	1840	106267	DUR	South
RACKHAM						
1881	1970	?	1881	131032	LND	London
1850	1992	ALL	ALL	157864	NFK	Kirby Cane
1766	....	....	1766	133566	SFK	Frostenden
1800	1875	1700	1800	106607	SFK	Woodbridge
RACKLEY						
1840	1905	1830	1905	168912	SOM	Bishop Lydeard
1800	....	1750	1850	168912	SOM	Tolland
RACKSTRAW						
1778	1890	1700	1900	129755	BKM	Marlow
RADBURN						
1800	1838	....	....	139971	NTH	Kettering
RADCLIFF						
1668	1947	ALL	1668	116025	ANT	Belfast
RADCLIFFE						
1745	1745	1718	1745	141291	IOM	Andreas
....	....	1780	1850	118923	IOM	Arbory
....	....	ALL	1850	115347	IOM	???
1830	1940	1800	1850	115347	LAN	Liverpool
1700	1710	1600	1700	121339	WYK	Heptonstall
RADFORD						
1819	ALL	ALL	1840	116734	CAM	Brinkley
1830	....	....	....	148156	CAM	Graveley
1750	1800	1600	1850	126837	DBY	Alfreton
1750	1850	1700	1900	145866	DBY	Littleover
1759	1908	1700	1950	169889	DBY	Normanton By Derby
1760	1920	1700	1800	107484	DBY	Shirland
1900	1992	1700	1900	157872	DBY	Tibshelf
....	....	ALL	1794	176532	DBY	???
....	....	ALL	1780	178403	DBY	???
1769	1800	1500	1770	138010	DEV	Colaton Raleigh
1830	1850	1700	1900	167096	DEV	Kentisbere
1860	1900	1800	1860	168572	DEV	Plymouth
....	....	1600	1900	124273	DEV	Silverton
?	1893	1800	?	127841	ESS	???
1864	1900	ALL	1864	134260	GLS	Bristol
1829	....	1783	....	127647	IRL	???
1849	....	ALL	1849	149446	LAN	Liverpool
1715	1900	1715	1900	148911	LAN	Manchester
1735	1810	1500	1735	175072	LIN	Potterhanworth
1815	1870	1815	1900	126837	LIN	Woolsthorpe
?	1893	?	?	127841	LND	East Ham
?	1893	?	?	127841	LND	West Ham
1826	1844	....	....	127140	LND	???
1803	1896	1750	1881	160636	NTT	Newark
....	....	ALL	1794	176532	NTT	???
1740	1992	1700	1740	177075	SOM	Winscombe
1794	1900	ALL	1794	176532	WAR	Nuneaton
?	1893	1800	?	127841	WIL	???
1838	....	1838	1992	168572	???	Birkenhead
RADGE						
1732	ALL	ALL	1732	125571	YKS	North And East Riding
RADHORE						
1798	1992	1650	1798	120227	DEV	Stoke Damerel
RADLEY						
1711	1762	1640	1812	131210	SRY	Bletchingley

Known From	To	Researching From	To	Ref	Cty	Place
RADLEY contd.						
1887	1973	....	1973	130842	YKS	Sheffield
RADNAGE						
1860	1910	....	....	157880	WLS	Monmouth
RADNEDGE						
....	....	ALL	ALL	157880	ALL	Name Study
1800	1980	1790	1900	157880	GLS	Bristol
RADNIDGE						
1770	1980	1770	1900	157880	SOM	ALL
1860	1900	....	....	157880	WLS	South
RAE						
1840	1900	ALL	ALL	156604	ABD	Belhevie
1840	1900	1700	1840	118419	ABD	Old Machar
1800	1960	ALL	ALL	156604	ABD	Premnay
1833	1880	1780	1880	155098	AYR	Kilmarnock
1834	1840	1780	1840	155098	AYR	Old Cumnock
1876	1992	1850	1876	120170	DFS	Annan
1770	1810	....	....	138614	DFS	Dunscore
1832	1916	1700	1832	119881	KCD	Fetteressp
....	....	1500	1800	138614	KKD	Irongray
1820	1850	....	....	140082	LAN	Liverpool
1780	1992	1700	1920	158364	LAN	Liverpool
1800	1825	ALL	ALL	149632	LKS	Glasgow
1844	1921	1800	1844	127590	ROC	Lochbroom
1766	1880	1700	1900	146536	STI	Stenhousemuir
RAEBURN						
1800	1900	1700	1800	118419	BAN	Boyndie
RAERDON						
ALL	1878	....	....	105368	KER	???
RAFE						
1817	1831	1700	1900	118168	NFK	Great Yarmouth
RAFFELL						
1860	1940	1860	1980	157910	GLA	???
....	....	1500	1700	157910	LTN	Edinburgh
RAFFERTY						
1882	1992	1800	1882	108715	COR	Cork
1888	1900	1850	1910	123765	DUR	Stockton
RAFFILL						
1740	1840	1500	1800	157910	DEV	???
1840	1992	1860	1980	157910	GLA	???
1800	1900	1700	1800	157910	SOM	???
RAFFILLS						
1850	1880	1850	1992	157910	GNT	???
RAFFLE						
1860	1900	ALL	1860	134260	NBL	Blyth
RAFTER						
1855	1860	1800	1900	113212	IRL	Kilkenny
1760	1992	ALL	1837	158003	YKS	Whitby
RAFTON						
1760	1992	ALL	1837	158003	YKS	Whitby
RAGAN						
1795	1861	1770	1861	144878	CON	St Just In Roseland
RAGG						
1800	1900	ALL	ALL	135062	WAR	Birmingham
....	....	1700	1750	125571	YKS	Nr York
....	....	1830	....	119768	YKS	Sheffield
1690	1815	....	....	129747	YKS	Sheffield
RAGGETT						
1840	....	1780	1900	167932	LAN	Liverpool
1881	1960	ALL	ALL	105856	MDX	???
1885	1920	1500	1992	124443	SRY	Richmond
1881	1960	ALL	ALL	105856	SRY	???
RAGLESS						
1793	1804	1693	1760	101427	SSX	Chichester
1804	1874	1874	1900	101427	SSX	Horsham
RAHR						
....	....	ALL	ALL	175331	ALL	ALL
RAIKES						
1800	1992	1800	1992	133450	BRE	Treberfyd
RAIL						
1796	1848	1300	1992	157929	CON	West
RAILTON						
1910	1960	....	....	157937	CMA	Barrow In Furness
1910	1960	....	....	157937	LAN	Barrow In Furness
1830	1900	1790	1950	157937	NBL	Newcastle On Tyne
RAIMBAULT						
....	....	ALL	ALL	157945	ALL	Name Study
RAIN						
1768	1835	ALL	1768	154563	CUL	Alston
RAINBIRD						
....	....	ALL	ALL	157961	ALL	Name Study
1756	1853	ALL	1756	114030	ESS	North West
1756	1992	1600	1756	157953	ESS	The Roddings
1693	1839	1600	1992	159956	SFK	Walsham Le Willows
RAINBOW						
1910	....	ALL	ALL	164143	GLS	Bristol
RAINE						
1868	1992	ALL	1870	106844	DUR	Spennymoor
1842	1844	ALL	ALL	106844	NBL	West
1842	1844	ALL	ALL	106860	NBL	West
RAINER						
1740	....	1700	1750	152110	CAM	Burwell
....	....	ALL	ALL	111945	SFK	ALL
RAINES						
....	....	ALL	ALL	172081	ALL	Name Study
1690	1992	1500	1950	106445	SOM	ALL
1690	1960	1690	1960	102490	SOM	Banwell
1800	1870	....	....	142522	YKS	Beeford
RAINEY						
1700	....	....	1700	150851	LIN	Boston
1850	1930	1800	1930	136174	TYR	Garvaghey
RAINFORD						
1815	1870	1750	1870	145750	LAN	ALL
1550	1639	ALL	ALL	141615	LAN	Aughton
....	....	1800	1960	104523	LAN	Kirkham
RAINFORTH						
1804	1892	1760	1804	174173	YKS	Hull
RAINS						
1834	1930	1700	1834	130257	NTH	Little Addington
RAINSFORD						
1661	1700	1661	1700	102628	WIC	Butterhill
RAINY-BROWN						
1900	1992	ALL	1900	100536	SCT	???
RAISBECK						
1641	1900	....	....	104302	YKS	Dufton
RAISON						
1778	1778	1600	1778	105252	LIN	Waddington
1850	1900	....	....	126187	SOM	Mudeford
1789	....	....	....	126187	SOM	Wayford
1825	1900	1825	1890	126187	SOM	Yeovil
RAISTRICK						
1809	1840	1750	1875	102660	WRY	Idle
1809	1840	1750	1875	102660	WRY	Thackley
1900	1992	....	1900	171743	YKS	Horsforth
....	....	....	1830	116866	YKS	???
RAIT						
....	1813	....	....	128988	PER	Alyth
1800	1900	1600	1900	160563	TAY	Liff
RALF						
1831	....	1700	1992	107204	CON	St John In Roseland
1819	1992	ALL	1819	125776	SSX	ALL
RALLI						
1500	1950	ALL	ALL	162620	ALL	ALL
RALLS						
1795	....	....	....	126187	DOR	Winfaith
1880	1950	1700	1880	157996	GLA	Cowbridge
RALPH						
....	....	....	1875	173177	CAM	Wisbech
1810	....	1750	1810	142905	CON	Crowan
1800	1992	1740	1800	149462	CON	Marazion
1851	....	1700	1992	107204	DEV	Plymouth
1850	1875	1850	1875	109347	LAN	Accrington
1875	....	1875	....	109347	LAN	Haslingden
....	....	1720	1745	109134	SAL	???
1819	1992	ALL	1819	125776	SSX	ALL
1825	....	1825	....	109347	YKS	Settle
RALPHS						
1860	1900	ALL	ALL	137987	SAL	Welshampton
RAM						
1600	1880	1600	1880	139904	ESS	ALL
1600	?	1600	?	139904	LND	ALL
1880	1900	1880	1900	139904	LND	Holborn
1880	1900	1880	1900	139904	MDX	Islington
1600	1920	1600	1920	139904	WEX	Ballyteen
1600	1920	1600	1920	139904	WEX	Clonatin
1600	1920	1600	1920	139904	WEX	Ramsfort
RAMAGE						
1783	1839	1700	1839	169927	ABD	Aberdeen
1860	....	1860	1992	169927	FIF	Dundee
....	1860	1860	....	169927	LND	Lambeth
RAMBRIDGE						
....	....	ALL	ALL	114308	WIL	Sailsbury
RAMPLING						
....	....	1800	1850	146269	SFK	Bury St Edmunds
RAMSAY						
1820	1830	1750	1820	144150	ANS	Dundee
1806	1820	....	1850	157139	FIF	ALL
1865	1899	1850	1870	157139	MLN	Edinburgh

Known From	To	Researching From	To	Ref	Cty	Place
RAMSAY contd.						
1750	1900	1600	1750	177881	MLN	Leith
1750	1900	1600	1750	177881	MLN	Newhaven
1900	1992	1880	1900	157139	NBL	Newcastle Upon Tyne
....	....	....	1850	157139	PER	ALL
1870	1900	ALL	ALL	120154	SCT	Glasgow
1850	1940	1800	1850	120286	SEL	Selkirk
1750	1965	....	....	137820	SHI	Fetlar
1720	1965	....	....	137820	SHI	Mid Yell
1760	1965	....	....	137820	SHI	North Yell
1758	1965	....	....	137820	SHI	Northmavine
1720	1965	....	....	137820	SHI	South Yell
1750	1850	....	....	154903	SOM	West Pennard
RAMSBOTTOM						
1805	1948	1750	1805	161179	LAN	Blackburn
1790	1841	ALL	1790	145203	LAN	Heyhouses
1737	....	....	1737	101761	WRY	Bingley
RAMSDALE						
1920	1950	1800	1920	101907	DUR	South Shields
1800	1850	1700	1800	112224	YKS	Market Weighton
RAMSDEN						
1849	1992	1700	1849	107123	CHS	Macclesfield
1770	1900	ALL	1800	115282	KEN	East
1848	1851	1851	1891	159492	LAN	Oldham
1782	1866	1700	1782	145424	MDX	London
1784	1885	1784	1841	165026	YKS	Cowling
1792	1817	1792	1817	176958	YKS	Dewsbury
1790	1992	ALL	1837	158003	YKS	Holderness
1800	1880	1750	1820	123595	YKS	Holmfirth
1790	1992	ALL	1837	158003	YKS	Hull
1630	1648	1500	1630	138584	YKS	Methley
1792	1817	1792	1820	176958	YKS	Ossett
1648	1812	....	....	138584	YKS	Rothwell
RAMSELL						
1643	1725	1600	1740	115630	SAL	Broseley
1811	....	1794	1851	115630	SAL	Lilleshall
1740	1794	1725	1820	115630	SAL	Meole Brace
1803	1869	ALL	1803	131725	SAL	Wellington
RAMSEY						
1810	1915	1650	1840	150819	FIF	Auchterderran
1810	1915	1650	1840	150819	FIF	Beath
1810	1915	1650	1840	150819	FIF	Dalgety
1810	1915	1650	1840	150819	FIF	Dunfermline
1810	1915	1650	1840	150819	FIF	Torryburn
1740	1815	1700	1740	124427	FIF	Tulliallan
1920	1951	1880	1951	150819	MLN	Musselburgh
1920	1951	1880	1951	150819	MLN	Prestonpans
1800	1930	ALL	ALL	167940	SFK	Witnesham
RAMSHAW						
1849	1870	1800	1849	177555	DUR	Stockton
1843	1885	1700	1873	129305	DUR	Trimdon
RAMSKER						
1628	1666	ALL	ALL	159026	YKS	Sheffield
RAN						
1667	....	....	1700	171441	KEN	Lenham
RANBY						
1816	1930	1600	1816	131261	LIN	Blyton
1753	1992	ALL	ALL	139386	NTT	North
RANCE						
1700	1992	1700	1992	158038	ALL	ALL
1725	....	1600	1750	143693	BKM	Bledlow
1856	1992	1825	1856	164216	CHS	Whitegate
1706	....	1600	1750	143693	OXF	Crowell
RAND						
1839	1851	1830	1870	142018	ESS	Colchester
1924	1926	ALL	ALL	125288	LND	Camberwell
RANDAL						
1780	1837	1780	....	112518	WAR	Long Compton
RANDALL						
1837	....	1837	1992	168572	BKM	Amersham
1626	1676	1600	1626	148962	BRK	Silchester
1666	1940	....	....	128996	CAM	Thorney
1785	1785	1700	1785	144177	CON	Egloshayle
1880	1930	1700	1880	165549	CON	Illogan
1880	....	....	....	123099	CON	St Columb Minor
1811	1872	1750	1811	144177	CON	St Minver
....	....	1834	1992	117838	CON	Truro
1839	....	....	....	123099	CON	Truro
1880	1930	1700	1880	165549	CON	Truro
1800	1992	1700	1850	116823	DEV	Stradenham
1820	1850	1790	1850	135895	DOR	Abbotsbury
1731	1774	1700	1800	126667	DOR	West Lulworth
1880	1950	ALL	ALL	123048	ESS	Harwich
1750	?	1600	1992	167592	FLN	Buckley

Known From	To	Researching From	To	Ref	Cty	Place
RANDALL contd.						
1830	1850	1700	1830	173223	GLS	Bristol
1720	1740	1600	1720	148954	HAM	Gosport
1760	1865	....	....	145394	HAM	Herriard
1760	1865	....	....	145394	HAM	Lasham
1790	1850	1700	1820	136840	HAM	Winchester
1795	1801	1600	1801	150150	LEI	Whetstone
1850	....	1850	1992	168572	LND	Lee Park
1690	....	ALL	1690	179515	LND	London
1793	1815	....	1840	171441	LND	Stepney
1841	1881	1841	1881	112518	MDX	Hanover Square
....	....	ALL	ALL	174289	MDX	London
1841	1881	1841	1881	112518	MDX	St Georges
1811	1992	1700	1811	105635	NFK	Wighton
1839	1954	....	....	176966	NTT	Mansfield
1774	1875	1774	1875	147001	OXF	Oxford
....	....	1800	1900	148075	SAL	Coalport
....	....	1800	1900	148075	SAL	Madeley
1798	1798	ALL	1800	174637	SOM	Ilminster
....	1642	1620	1690	142018	SOM	Wells
1850	1853	1700	1890	174270	SSX	Fittleworth
1780	1837	1780	1837	112518	WAR	Long Compton
1655	1806	1700	1820	170178	WIL	Little Hinton
1620	1622	1600	1660	142018	WIL	Melksham
1885	1916	1850	1885	174270	???	London
RANDEL.						
1780	1837	1780	....	112518	WAR	Long Compton
RANDELE						
1818	1818	1750	1818	148938	GLS	Kingswood
RANDELL						
....	....	ALL	ALL	160520	ALL	Name Study
1800	1900	1700	1900	158054	CMN	Kidwelly
....	....	1700	1800	158054	DEV	Appledore
1870	1970	1870	1970	158054	GLA	???
1815	1849	....	1815	164321	LEI	Tilton
....	....	1850	1900	164321	MDX	East London
1794	....	1770	1798	131326	SOM	East Coker
ALL	ALL	ALL	ALL	160520	SSX	East
ALL	ALL	ALL	ALL	160520	SSX	West
RANDLE						
1865	1890	1800	1865	113352	KEN	Cliffe
1858	1858	1830	1858	134309	LAN	Oldham
1820	1900	1820	1900	125938	WAR	Bedworth
1826	1856	1700	1825	131245	WAR	Bedworth
1800	1860	1700	1900	148652	WAR	Exhall
1780	1837	1780	....	112518	WAR	Long Compton
1720	....	....	....	120804	WAR	Withey Brook
RANDLES						
1800	1950	1700	1800	160458	DBY	Hayfield
1720	1992	1600	1720	118605	DEN	Gresford
1800	1840	1700	1900	179531	DEN	Gresford
RANDOLPH						
....	....	1066	1240	124974	SAL	Westhope
RANDON						
1800	1900	1800	1980	118818	LEI	Hathern
RANDS						
1815	1856	....	....	158062	SFK	Copdock
1850	1876	....	....	158062	SFK	Freston
1764	1826	....	....	129747	SFK	Parham
1789	1807	ALL	1789	158062	SFK	Woodbridge
RANESLEY						
1830	1860	1750	1850	126586	YKS	Leeds
RANGER						
1749	1832	1719	1832	120634	KEN	Cranbrook
1785	....	ALL	1785	158445	SSX	Horsham
1780	1820	1700	1820	136840	WIL	Avon Valley
1746	1746	1733	1746	107573	WIL	Hindon
RANGLER						
1840	1840	ALL	....	132349	SXE	Framfield
RANGLEY						
....	1700	....	....	174564	KEN	???
RANKIN						
1776	1992	1700	....	110264	BAN	Gamrie
1847	1847	ALL	1847	162108	MDX	???
1830	1855	1830	1855	136980	SCT	Port Glasgow
1700	1757	....	....	127140	STI	Kilsyth
RANKINE						
1800	1992	1800	1992	111074	STI	Avonbridge
RANN						
1792	1850	1700	1900	135127	STS	Rowley Regis
RANNALS						
1760	1800	1500	1800	132993	IOW	St Helens
RANNIE						
1868	....	1800	1868	101427	BAN	Deskford

Known From	To	Researching From	To	Ref	Cty	Place
RANNS						
1780	1880	1750	1900	156086	CAM	Kennett
RANSHAW						
1900	1950	1700	1900	113387	LIN	Spilsby
RANSLEY						
1780	1900	1780	1900	124699	KEN	South East
1750	1850	ALL	1800	131059	KEN	Aldington
1825	1900	ALL	1875	131059	KEN	Ruckinge
1780	1810	1600	1900	166804	KEN	Yalding
RANSOM						
1849	1992	1849	1860	158089	LND	Islington
1848	1992	1820	ALL	158070	LND	Islington
1870	1992	1800	1870	149365	MDX	Acton
1850	1860	....	....	129607	NFK	Norwich
1804	1860	1780	1850	158089	SFK	Bury St Edmunds
1784	1820	ALL	ALL	158070	SFK	Bury St Edmunds
1858	1992	1850	1992	129607	SRY	Walworth
....	....	1800	1899	171794	YKS	North Allerton
RANSOME						
1745	1850	1700	1850	126799	NFK	Great Bircham
RANSTED						
1700	1750	1700	1750	144657	HAM	Alton
RAPER						
1814	1950	1700	1814	107654	YKS	East Witton
....	....	ALL	1800	148172	YKS	Knottingley
....	....	1500	1899	115975	YKS	Whitby
RAPLEY						
1660	1880	1660	1880	128856	SSX	Shipley
RAPPITT						
1500	1800	ALL	1800	177695	NTH	Irthlingborough
1500	1800	ALL	1800	177695	NTH	Rushden
RAPSON						
1800	1850	1800	1850	104183	CON	Perranarworthal
?	?	?	?	117528	DOR	Sherborne
?	?	?	?	117528	SOM	Yeovil
RASBERRY						
1800	1850	1750	1800	143170	ESS	Witham
RASHBROOK						
1761	1800	ALL	1761	142107	SFK	Holton St Mary
RASHLEIGH						
1550	1700	1550	1750	123722	CON	Cury
1550	1600	....	....	174319	CON	Fowey
....	....	1390	1550	174319	DEV	Barnstaple
RASPISON						
1900	....	1880	1900	126144	KEN	Gravesend
RASTALL						
....	....	....	1825	150150	WOR	Evesham
RASTRICK						
1695	1820	....	....	160458	NBL	???
1695	1820	....	....	160458	SAL	???
RATCHESTER						
1750	1778	1700	1800	116386	NBL	Newburn
RATCLIFF						
1745	1792	....	....	101028	KEN	Maidstone
1725	....	1725	....	109347	LAN	Accrington
1725	....	1725	....	109347	LAN	Rishton
1818	....	....	1818	111767	LAN	Wigan
1700	1750	....	....	101028	LEI	ALL
1804	1821	....	....	127957	MDX	Harefield
1833	1855	....	....	127957	MDX	Hillingdon
1784	1964	....	....	101028	MDX	London
1700	1730	....	....	101028	NTH	ALL
1850	1881	1850	1900	129216	NTT	Walesby
1828	1992	1700	1828	138673	SRY	Rudgwick
RATCLIFFE						
....	....	1500	1620	154873	BKM	Langley
1822	1992	ALL	1992	177695	DUR	Beamish
1750	1992	1650	1992	156701	KEN	Dover
1780	1992	1700	1992	156698	KEN	Dover
1751	1800	1700	1751	176451	LAN	Blackley
1804	1827	1700	1827	178233	LAN	Haigh
1820	1960	1850	....	136786	LAN	Manchester
1748	1992	1748	1992	110396	LAN	Shevington
1748	1992	1748	1992	110396	LAN	Worthington
1830	1844	1830	1850	122335	SFK	Woodbridge
1832	1861	1780	1880	169323	STS	Wednesbury
....	....	1845	....	132381	STS	???
....	....	ALL	ALL	114308	WAR	Coventry
1880	....	....	1880	164011	WOR	Worcester
1828	1861	1820	1870	123250	YKS	Halifax
RATEAU						
....	....	ALL	ALL	158119	ALL	Name Study
RATH						
1891	1931	1800	1891	115355	LAN	Liverpool
RATH contd.						
1700	1800	....	....	165999	LIN	Sedgebrook
RATHBONE						
1872	1874	1872	1900	126705	CHS	Mobberly
1833	1871	....	....	112380	CHS	Rudheath
....	....	1820	1850	158127	DBY	Hathersage
....	....	1750	1810	158127	HAM	Southampton
....	....	1780	1830	158127	LAN	Hale Bank
1696	1849	1849	1992	131601	LAN	Lancaster
....	....	1780	1830	158127	LAN	Liverpool
1819	1856	ALL	ALL	118168	LAN	Manchester
1770	1860	....	....	137111	STS	Norton Cames
RATHBOURNE						
1833	....	1750	1833	142905	LAN	Manchester
RATHBUN						
....	....	ALL	ALL	158135	ALL	Name Study
RATHEL						
1684	....	1677	1725	116580	HAM	Ropley
RATHIL						
1690	1800	....	1800	102822	BRK	Cholsey
RATHMELL						
....	....	ALL	ALL	127574	ALL	Name Study
1782	1992	1700	1805	101044	YKS	Stainburn
1850	1930	....	....	127574	YKS	Whitby
RATHWELL						
1819	1843	1800	1850	130974	YKS	Bramley
RATLIEFF						
1800	1820	1700	1800	104310	LND	Clerkenwell
RATTENBURY						
1740	1764	1700	1740	133523	DEV	Tavistock
RATTER						
1750	1965	....	....	137820	SHI	Fetlar
1720	1965	....	....	137820	SHI	Mid Yell
1760	1965	....	....	137820	SHI	North Yell
1758	1965	....	....	137820	SHI	Northmavine
1720	1965	....	....	137820	SHI	South Yell
RATTERY						
1866	1894	1700	1866	142484	FORFARSHIRE	???
1866	1894	1700	1866	142484	IOW	Newport
RATTIE						
1739	1980	1600	1750	170607	CON	Boconnoc
RATTLE						
1691	....	ALL	1691	154288	SFK	Elmsett
1748	1951	1700	1748	177075	SOM	Winscombe
1790	1804	1750	1850	123250	YKS	Hull
RATTRAY						
....	....	1750	ALL	149187	ANS	Dundee
1780	1780	....	....	159883	ANS	Dundee
1780	1850	....	1780	123358	ANS	Forfar
1797	1900	1900	1992	158143	FIF	Dalgety
1797	1900	1900	1992	158143	FIF	Dunfermline
1723	1797	1600	1723	158143	FIF	Dysart
1723	1797	1600	1723	158143	FIF	Pathhead
....	....	1700	....	108677	LTN	ALL
1838	1992	1750	1838	144010	SCT	Dundee
RAVEN						
1704	1865	....	....	158178	ESS	Bradwell
1640	1789	1538	1640	158178	ESS	Rivenhall
1866	1992	....	....	158178	ESS	Tollesbury
1845	1890	1700	1845	159212	LND	Islington
1791	1871	1700	1800	159123	NFK	Shotesham
1790	1900	1600	1790	174572	NFK	Whissonsett
1825	1863	1800	1870	159123	SFK	Bungay
1797	1992	ALL	1880	127523	WAR	Coventry
1762	1874	1650	1762	127523	WAR	Southam
RAVENHILL						
....	....	1827	....	103217	GLS	City
1660	1820	1800	1900	160539	HEF	Hereford
1650	1700	1650	1750	160539	HEF	Homer
1600	1700	1540	1800	160539	HEF	Woolhope
....	....	1800	1900	160539	WIL	Warminster
1790	....	1700	1790	119938	WOR	Mathon
RAVENS						
1600	1700	1600	1700	167924	BDF	Campton
RAVENSCROFT						
1650	1720	1650	1750	142123	CHS	Acton By Nantwich
1730	1875	1600	1730	150614	CHS	Davenham
....	....	1800	1900	133493	LND	London
1790	1808	1790	1812	123404	STS	Wednesbury
1812	....	1790	1830	123404	WAR	Birmingham
RAVENSDALE						
....	....	ALL	ALL	105791	ALL	Name Study
....	....	ALL	ALL	105791	ALL	???
1700	1992	1200	1700	158186	STS	Cauldon

Known From	To	Researching From	To	Ref	Cty	Place
RAVILIOUS						
1900	1940	1700	1992	167592	LND	ALL
RAW						
1750	1860	....	....	167843	YKS	Redmire Cum Bolton
1670	1881	1670	1992	116742	YKS	Swaledale
RAWBONE						
....	....	1950	1970	158194	CAM	Vourne
....	....	1870	1960	158194	HEF	Central
....	....	1870	1960	158194	HEF	North
1761	1851	....	....	124524	NTH	Brackley
....	....	1600	1900	158194	SAL	Shrewsbury
....	....	1750	1920	158194	WAR	East
....	....	1750	1920	158194	WAR	South
1785	1845	1600	1785	150150	WAR	Bishops Tachbrook
....	....	1850	1970	158194	WOR	Central
....	....	1850	1970	158194	WOR	North
....	....	1900	1960	158194	WOR	West
RAWCLIFFE						
1850	1992	1700	1900	158216	LAN	Accrington
1625	1750	1625	1750	127655	LAN	Altham
?	?	?	?	116610	LAN	Blackburn
1625	1750	1625	1750	127655	LAN	Hapton
1625	1750	1625	1750	127655	LAN	Huncoat
1766	1781	1736	1766	139149	WRY	Huddersfield
1840	1900	1700	1840	158208	YKS	York
RAWDING						
1790	1820	1600	1820	178675	LIN	Fulbeck
RAWDON						
....	....	ALL	ALL	158224	ALL	Name Study
1628	1847	1628	1847	158224	HRT	Hoddesden
1789	1868	....	....	158224	LEI	Ashby De La Zouche
1720	1863	1720	1863	158224	LIN	Carlton Le Moor
1640	1826	1640	1826	158224	NIR	Ballynahinch
1640	1826	1640	1826	158224	NIR	Moira
1863	1992	1863	1992	158224	NYK	Middlesborough
1580	....	....	....	158224	YKS	York
RAWES						
....	....	ALL	ALL	158240	ALL	Name Study
1550	1992	....	....	158240	ALL	ALL
1800	1950	1600	1800	105821	CMA	Kendal
1801	1841	ALL	1801	154563	YKS	ALL
RAWKINS						
1500	1900	1500	1900	170216	WIL	ALL
RAWLE						
1840	....	1800	1910	167932	LAN	Liverpool
1900	1988	1800	1900	139327	LND	Lambeth
1900	1988	1800	1900	139327	SRY	Southwark
RAWLEIGH						
....	....	?	?	104310	DEV	Buckland Filleigh
RAWLETT						
1785	1830	1780	1850	123145	ALL	ALL
....	....	1550	1700	151513	WAR	Grendon
RAWLEY						
1790	1810	ALL	ALL	158259	DOR	Bridport
1820	1880	ALL	ALL	158259	MDX	London
1795	1837	ALL	1795	115126	OXF	Chipping Norton
....	....	1700	1800	158259	SOM	Chard
RAWLING						
1820	1830	....	....	103721	WRY	Leeds
1809	1961	1750	1809	158267	YKS	Locton
1835	1875	1700	1850	145882	YKS	Normandy
RAWLINGS						
1732	1768	1500	1732	125695	BDF	Potton
1900	1992	1700	1900	158275	BRK	Basingstoke
1872	1941	1700	1892	156051	CON	St Levan
1900	1992	....	....	109363	DEV	Newton Abbot
1900	1992	1700	1900	158275	HAM	Basingstoke
1733	1756	....	....	131229	HEF	Much Cowarne
1880	1920	1800	1950	126179	HRT	Hereford
1809	1824	....	....	117560	KEN	Bexley
1827	1900	ALL	ALL	141704	LND	Bermondsey
1827	1900	ALL	ALL	141704	LND	Horsleydown
1827	1900	ALL	ALL	141704	LND	Southwark
1827	1900	ALL	ALL	141704	LND	St Olave
1861	1944	1850	1880	114529	LND	???
1841	ALL	....	....	117560	MDX	Holborn
1798	1890	1700	1798	144754	SSX	Slindon
1860	1903	1860	1950	101265	WIL	Bromham
1817	1866	1750	1880	109363	WIL	Calne
1765	1881	1700	1764	108227	WIL	North Bradley
1866	1923	1800	1930	109363	WIL	Slaughterford
RAWLINS						
1599	1659	....	....	165999	GLS	Brockworth
1599	1659	....	....	165999	GLS	Mickleton
RAWLINS contd.						
1800	1820	1700	1800	130044	MDX	Bethnal Green
1769	1851	....	....	124524	NTH	Brackley
1820	1888	ALL	1900	104299	SOM	Stockland Bristol
1718	1718	....	....	135437	SOM	Stogursey
RAWLINSON						
1809	....	....	....	117196	CHS	Gawsworth
1790	1855	1700	1800	135496	CHS	Henbury
1500	1824	ALL	1500	100536	CUL	???
1840	....	ALL	ALL	167622	LAN	Blackpool
1725	1818	1675	1725	122904	LAN	Burnley
1840	....	ALL	ALL	167622	LAN	Poulton Le Fylde
1500	1824	ALL	1500	100536	LAN	???
1811	1901	1783	1811	164364	LIN	Rothwell
1811	1901	1783	1811	164364	LIN	Tealby
RAWLL						
1734	1967	1734	1967	108375	MDX	City
1853	1940	1853	1992	108375	MDX	Stoke Newington
RAWNSLEY						
1890	1992	ALL	1890	102407	WYK	Bradford
1890	1992	ALL	1890	102407	WYK	Calverley
1865	1992	ALL	ALL	112267	YKS	Leeds
1840	1864	1800	1900	155098	YKS	Rawdon
RAWSON						
1840	1850	....	1840	123161	BDF	Northill
1761	....	....	....	151270	CAM	Whittlesey
1530	1992	ALL	1992	158283	ERY	ALL
1530	1992	ALL	1992	158283	ERY	Hull
1846	1861	1842	1861	165441	LAN	Chorton On Medlock
1812	1843	1800	1870	124915	NTT	East Drayton
1819	1992	1700	1820	118532	NTT	Nottingham
1781	....	1700	1850	146978	NTT	Nottingham
1874	1920	1843	1920	124915	SSX	Brighton
1630	1780	1550	1640	121339	WYK	Heptonstall
1840	....	1700	1840	130435	YKS	Bridlington
RAWSTRONE						
1800	1920	1800	1920	134422	LAN	Grimsagh
1820	1895	1820	1900	134422	LAN	Kirkham
RAY						
1841	....	....	1841	163031	BKM	Haddenham
1860	....	1770	1860	130141	DBY	Stoney Middleton
1680	1705	ALL	1700	161357	ESS	Dunmow
1561	1673	1700	1750	161357	ESS	Gt Easton
1680	1749	....	....	161357	ESS	Gt Leighs
1854	1899	1750	1854	148814	ESS	Woodford
1900	1950	....	....	151181	FLN	Prestatyn
....	....	1600	1900	158291	HAM	ALL
1819	....	ALL	ALL	156884	HAM	Michelmarsh
1819	....	ALL	ALL	156884	HAM	Southampton
1780	1992	1700	1920	158364	LAN	Liverpool
1900	1992	1800	1900	108405	LAN	Manchester
1780	1992	1700	1920	158364	LAN	Manchester
1900	1964	ALL	1964	173290	LAN	Manchester
1900	1992	1800	1900	108405	LAN	Salford
1867	1868	....	1867	163031	LND	Notting Hill
1854	1854	1750	1854	148814	LND	Pancras
1854	1854	1750	1854	148814	LND	St Giles
1400	1800	....	....	100536	SFK	Denston
1880	1992	1700	1880	165581	SOM	Portishead
1889	1992	....	1889	163031	SYK	Sheffield
1861	1992	1800	1900	166960	???	Glasgow
RAYBOULD						
1860	1885	1840	1900	121541	STS	Brieryley Hill
1700	1700	1600	1750	125806	WOR	Clent
RAYDEN						
1838	1858	1750	1900	141151	LND	ALL
RAYFIELD						
1850	....	....	....	122319	KEN	Maidstone
RAYLEY						
1730	1770	....	....	141097	LAN	???
RAYMAN						
1811	1851	1811	1859	107573	SRY	Ewell
1800	1850	1800	1850	106631	SRY	Lambeth
RAYMENT						
....	....	ALL	ALL	158321	ALL	Name Study
1840	1992	1700	1840	117242	CAM	Peterborough
1800	1940	1700	1800	107794	ESS	Billericay
1691	1900	ALL	1900	156310	ESS	Great Tey
1800	1940	1700	1800	107794	ESS	Gt Burstead
1800	1940	1700	1800	107794	ESS	Sible Hedingham
1840	1992	1700	1840	117242	LIN	Stamford
1840	1992	1700	1840	117242	NTH	Peterborough
RAYMOND						
....	....	....	1845	121002	GLA	Merthyr Tydfil

Known From	To	Researching From	To	Ref	Cty	Place
RAYMOND contd.						
1880	1992	....	....	158348	LAN	Manchester
1717	1821	....	....	129747	SFK	Ipswich
RAYMONT-BAKER						
1794	1850	1700	1850	115991	DEV	Broadwoodkelly
RAYNE						
1750	....	ALL	ALL	130508	DUR	Chester Le Street
1771	1771	ALL	1771	154563	DUR	Weardale
1798	1857	1740	1860	105333	HAM	Isle Of Wight
1550	1600	....	1600	137634	NTT	Sutton Cum Lound
RAYNER						
1784	1849	1700	1784	115460	BDF	Dunstable
....	....	1800	1900	103713	CAM	Chesterton
1763	1847	....	1763	177504	CAM	Littleport
1745	1868	1740	1868	100277	ESS	Bocking
....	....	1800	1860	118834	ESS	Orset
1821	1900	1600	1992	159956	ESS	Stisted
1750	1780	1500	1750	129577	IOW	???
1780	1900	1750	1800	151467	KEN	East
1804	1857	ALL	1804	119296	KEN	Walmer
1700	1820	ALL	ALL	110477	LIN	Gate Burton
1700	1820	ALL	ALL	110477	LIN	Lincoln
1868	1992	ALL	1900	115282	LND	ALL
....	....	1800	1900	107816	LND	Clapham
....	....	1872	1950	118834	LND	Hackney
1871	1908	1800	1875	100277	LND	Shoreditch
1780	1850	1780	1850	124605	MDX	East London
1874	1900	1800	1900	127981	MDX	London
1791	1925	1700	1791	172553	SFK	Bures St Mary
1870	1890	1890	1992	160458	SRY	Wandsworth
1734	1831	1634	1734	127728	YKS	Wakefield
1812	1870	1750	1812	176451	YKS	Wakefield
RAYNOR						
1784	1849	1700	1784	115460	BDF	Dunstable
1700	1850	1600	1850	158356	DBY	ALL
1924	....	1920	1930	163775	ESS	West Ham
1840	....	ALL	ALL	155608	NTT	Eastwood
1800	1900	1700	1850	158356	NTT	Greasley
1810	....	ALL	ALL	105481	NTT	Old Basford
RAYSON						
1587	1670	ALL	ALL	141615	BRK	???
1787	1850	1787	....	123609	KEN	Rochester
1787	1850	1787	....	123609	KEN	Strood
1587	1670	ALL	ALL	141615	LEI	???
1587	1670	ALL	ALL	141615	LND	???
RAYTON						
....	....	ALL	ALL	175757	ALL	Name Study
1500	1985	ALL	ALL	175757	ALL	ALL
RAZEY						
....	....	ALL	ALL	137642	ALL	Name Study
....	....	ALL	ALL	137596	ALL	Name Study
REA						
1819	1874	1750	1819	155225	GLS	Chrucham
1780	1992	1700	1920	158364	LAN	Liverpool
1691	1803	1650	1830	160873	WOR	Rock
1830	1992	....	1830	170461	YKS	Hull
REACHER						
....	....	1700	1992	102377	ALL	ALL
1782	1880	....	....	102377	YKS	Easingwold
1700	....	....	1730	160873	YKS	Elvington
1717	1782	....	....	102377	YKS	Tadcaster
READ						
1800	1850	1750	1850	111589	AVN	Bath
1780	1992	1780	1992	113670	AVN	Bath
....	....	ALL	ALL	114308	BDF	Dunstable
1734	1880	1650	1750	144398	BKM	Winchendon
1768	1992	1650	1768	160911	CAM	Sutton
1830	1992	1700	1830	121703	CAM	Whittlesey
1850	1992	1800	1850	149462	CMN	Llanelly
1750	....	1750	1900	116920	CON	Falmouth
....	....	ALL	1729	178411	DBY	Clowne
1780	1992	1780	1992	113670	DOR	Buckhorn Weston
1820	1900	1700	1830	142670	DOR	Buckhorn Weston
1840	1850	1800	1840	101389	DOR	Gillingham
1727	1824	1720	1824	151858	DOR	Powerstock
1805	1915	1750	1805	158410	DOR	Verwood
....	....	1795	1837	143480	DOR	Weymouth
1710	1720	1680	1790	105333	HAM	Bisterne
....	....	....	?	141941	HAM	Catherington
1600	ALL	....	....	153397	HAM	New Forest
1749	1775	1680	1800	105333	HAM	Ringwood
1859	1867	1700	1900	158399	HAM	Southampton
1709	....	1700	1750	126667	IOW	Calbourne
1697	1798	....	1900	171441	KEN	Bredgar
READ contd.						
1639	1860	....	1900	171441	KEN	Doddington
1721	1721	1600	1721	170542	KEN	Goodnestone
1632	1695	....	1720	171441	KEN	Lenham
?	?	?	?	158372	LND	ALL
1849	1900	1800	1849	174203	LND	East
1678	....	....	....	173932	LND	Brixton
1880	....	....	....	173932	LND	Kennsington
1826	1832	....	....	173932	LND	Newington
1760	1860	ALL	ALL	166537	MDX	Hampstead
1830	1992	1780	1830	158380	MDX	Islington
1805	1919	1700	1805	123552	MDX	London
1870	1893	1800	1893	127981	MDX	London
1720	1950	1650	1750	124699	NFK	North
1805	1919	1700	1805	123552	NFK	Attleborough
1600	1780	ALL	ALL	107425	NFK	Diss
1846	1905	....	1846	137073	NFK	Stokesby
1785	1992	1700	1785	105635	NFK	Wighton
....	....	ALL	ALL	114308	NTH	Kislingsbury
1820	1900	1700	1820	138010	SFK	???
1800	1850	1750	1850	111589	SOM	ALL
1840	1900	1600	1840	120189	SOM	Blagdon
1816	1859	1700	1816	169242	SOM	Freshwood
1830	1880	1750	1830	108103	SOM	Maperton
1770	1860	1770	1860	138479	SOM	Meare
1800	ALL	....	....	142158	SOM	Wincanton
1860	1920	1700	1860	124966	SOM	Yeovil
1844	1866	....	....	173932	SRY	Abinger Hammer
1826	1862	....	....	173932	SRY	Ashtead
1849	....	....	....	173932	SRY	Croydon
1801	....	....	....	173932	SRY	Ewell
1796	1831	....	....	173932	SRY	Headley
....	....	1800	1900	133493	SRY	Kennington
1793	1838	....	....	173932	SRY	Leatherhead
1671	....	....	....	173932	SRY	Mortlake
1750	....	....	1750	162086	SSX	Lewes
1869	1885	1700	1920	117331	SSX	Withyham
....	....	1700	1799	104884	STS	Wednesbury
1824	1857	ALL	....	132349	SXE	East Hoathly
1761	1992	1680	1761	167932	YKS	Cayton
READE						
1733	1850	1600	1733	149888	GLS	Mangotsfield
1880	1992	1840	ALL	105686	HEF	Holmer
1877	1988	1850	1877	159522	LND	Westminster
1870	1880	1500	1920	164992	MDX	Clerkenwell
READER						
1700	1992	1600	1700	113654	KEN	Brenchley
1850	1882	1700	1850	166170	LND	St George In East
1877	1988	1850	1877	159522	LND	Westminster
READIE						
1800	1860	1700	1900	138517	???	Dublin
READING						
1650	1717	1600	1720	124796	BKM	Princes Risborough
1810	1810	1800	1810	147575	KEN	Ramsgate
1844	1844	1800	1844	147575	LND	Wapping
1862	....	1860	1870	163775	MDX	Hackney
1804	1863	1750	1804	177075	SOM	Aller
1800	1992	....	1800	159514	WAR	ALL
READMAN						
1680	1992	....	....	158429	NYK	Egton
....	....	1700	1850	102393	NYK	Glaisdale
1680	1992	....	....	158429	NYK	Glaisdale
1680	1992	....	....	158429	NYK	Ugthorpe
1680	1992	....	....	158429	NYK	Whitby
READSHAW						
1715	1803	....	....	102741	DUR	Hamsterley
READYHOFF						
....	....	1740	1750	106429	WRY	Campsall
REAH						
1750	1770	ALL	ALL	107352	DUR	Auckland
REAKES						
1800	1805	1750	1805	155691	KEN	Rochester
REAL						
1750	1830	1300	1992	157929	CON	West
1846	1936	....	....	151238	DEV	Axmouth
REALF						
1200	1992	ALL	ALL	158771	ALL	ALL
1819	1992	ALL	1819	125776	SSX	ALL
REAM						
1594	1850	1550	1660	141593	WYK	Kippax
1594	1850	1550	1660	141593	WYK	Sherburn
REAMES						
1805	1840	1700	1900	157171	GLS	Bishops Cleeve
1839	1860	1800	1900	157171	GLS	Churchdown

Known From	To	Researching From	To	Ref	Cty	Place
REAMES contd.						
1675	1715	1675	1800	157171	GLS	Corse
1715	1800	1700	1850	157171	GLS	Staverton
REANEY						
1810	1810	1750	1810	149152	YKS	Doncaster
REAR						
....	....	ALL	ALL	158437	ALL	Name Study
1750	1992	ALL	1750	158437	LEI	???
1750	1992	ALL	1750	158437	LIN	???
1700	1992	ALL	1700	158437	NTT	???
REARDON						
....	....	1700	1850	130931	COR	Millstreet
1884	1992	1800	1884	149365	MDX	Acton
1838	1876	ALL	1838	153729	MDX	Stepney
REASE						
....	1650	ALL	1675	118338	BKM	West Wycombe
REASON						
1700	1850	....	....	157724	BRK	Gt Coxwell
1820	1847	1750	1820	114928	HRT	Broxbourne
1800	....	1750	1800	119938	WAR	Stratford
REAVELEY						
1680	1780	....	....	102741	NBL	Rothbury
REAVELL						
1842	1918	ALL	1842	148997	CAM	Guilden Morden
REAVELY						
1818	1869	1750	1900	177970	DUR	Tanfield
REAY						
1850	1930	ALL	ALL	178470	DUR	North
1798	1992	ALL	1798	158445	DUR	Birtley
1860	1890	....	....	155195	DUR	Sunderland
1758	1893	1700	1800	169854	DUR	Sunderland
1802	1992	ALL	1802	154520	NBL	Stannington
1830	1860	....	....	132225	SAL	Whitchurch
1800	1840	....	....	132225	SAL	Wybunbury
1800	....	ALL	1800	155195	SCT	???
REBBECK						
1799	1936	....	1799	178365	WIL	Beechingstoke
REBOUSE						
1767	1899	....	....	145394	CON	St Minver
REBURN						
1780	1830	1690	1830	158313	MOG	Carrickmacross
RECKERBY						
1600	ALL	....	....	163465	LIN	Brothertoft
1770	1830	ALL	ALL	163465	LIN	Holbeach
RECKLACE						
1744	....	....	1744	101761	LIN	Lincoln
RECKNELL						
1862	1979	1600	1862	123420	LND	East
1862	1979	1600	1862	123420	LND	South East
REDBURN						
1830	1850	1600	1830	118877	MDX	Bethnal Green
REDDALL						
1640	1900	....	....	132756	BDF	Eversholt
1640	1900	....	....	132756	BDF	Ridgemont
1640	1900	....	....	132756	BDF	Woburn
REDDY						
1790	1900	1600	1900	130125	GLS	Wickwar
REDFEARN						
1868	1992	1750	1868	103691	LND	Kentish Town
REDFERN						
1837	1858	1700	1837	138509	DBY	Belper
1772	1981	1772	1947	147621	FLN	Halkyn
1867	1952	1750	1867	109606	LAN	Denton
1800	1920	1750	1820	138150	LAN	Liverpool
....	....	1750	1800	100129	LEI	North East
1660	1845	1600	1700	120049	STS	Wetton
1790	1992	1790	1992	106305	WAR	Kingsvury
REDFOORD						
1740	1801	1550	1750	147265	ABD	???
1740	1801	1550	1750	147265	BAN	???
REDFORD						
1840	1992	1700	1850	124788	LAN	Manchester
1655	1678	1620	1680	170348	WIL	Marlborough
REDGATE						
1776	1992	1700	1950	169889	DBY	Derby
1766	1766	1766	1766	145580	DBY	Snelston
REDGEWELL						
....	....	1800	1900	154261	ESS	Sible Hedingham
REDGWELL						
1810	1815	1790	1890	176672	ESS	Hanningfield
REDHEAD						
1890	1900	ALL	1950	177695	DUR	Stanley
1790	....	1750	1820	116572	IOM	???
1652	1764	1600	1652	155276	SFK	Mendlesham

Known From	To	Researching From	To	Ref	Cty	Place
REDICAN						
1880	1992	1700	1880	178225	LET	???
REDING						
....	1719	ALL	ALL	129933	HAM	Odiham
REDINGTON						
1790	1900	1700	1950	147958	ESS	West
1790	1900	1700	1950	147958	HRT	East
1880	1930	1800	1900	134481	SRY	Wimbledon
REDITT						
1784	1992	1600	1800	174920	NFK	Necton
REDKNAPP						
1700	1850	1500	1700	147583	MDX	Hampton
1700	1850	1500	1700	147583	MDX	Twickenham
REDMAN						
1682	1992	1500	1682	158461	KEN	Ash
1740	1740	....	....	127426	KEN	Aylesford
1782	1810	....	1782	164321	KEN	Deal
1840	1992	1800	1840	157740	KEN	Folkestone
1687	1789	....	....	127426	KEN	Stockbury
1769	1900	1700	1992	161861	WIL	Appleshaw
1793	1818	1700	1793	121010	WIL	Dauntsey
1784	1885	1703	1784	165026	YKS	Cowling
1807	1830	....	1830	113034	YKS	Goathland
REDMANS						
1695	1735	....	1760	171441	KEN	Stockbury
REDMAYNE						
1800	1850	1750	1850	134759	CUL	Penrith
REDMILE						
1873	1954	1873	1954	112852	NTT	Basford
REDMOND						
?	?	....	....	158348	DUB	???
....	1858	ALL	1858	164623	LAN	Liverpool
1807	....	1800	1900	139114	WEX	Newton Barry
REDMORE						
1660	1992	1500	1700	160083	DEV	North
REDPATH						
1801	1823	ALL	1823	101001	BEW	West
1750	1750	1700	1992	177881	MLN	Newhaven
?	?	?	?	175137	NBL	ALL
REDRUP						
....	....	ALL	ALL	179469	ALL	Name Study
1844	1844	....	1900	171646	BKM	Prisborough
REDSHAW						
1793	1992	1600	1793	172049	DBY	Longford
1800	1992	1700	1800	120839	EYK	Bridlington
1580	1620	....	1620	137634	NTT	Sutton Cum Lound
REDSTONE						
1881	1900	1800	1880	175293	CON	Okehampton
?	?	?	?	117528	DEV	South
1727	1751	....	....	159751	DEV	Bridestowe
1881	1900	1800	1880	175293	DEV	Plymouth
REDWOOD						
1700	1900	1750	1890	172634	DEV	Tiverton
1700	1900	1750	1890	172634	DEV	Uplowman
1900	....	1800	1900	126985	LAN	Coastal
1790	1890	1740	1890	105333	MDX	London
1790	1805	1700	1810	162043	SFK	Haughley
1790	1885	....	....	143596	SOM	Brompton Ralph
REE						
1750	1805	1700	1800	158488	HEF	Leintwardine
1844	1992	1800	1844	158488	MDX	Barnet
1884	1992	1884	1992	158488	MDX	Finchley
1820	1900	1800	1900	158488	MDX	Pinner
REECE						
1842	1842	1800	1850	136301	CHS	Dukinfield
?	?	?	?	104205	GLA	Penrhiwceiber
1735	1866	....	....	141798	HEF	Bacton
1851	1992	1750	1850	121673	HEF	Hoarwithy
1756	1800	1756	1800	138703	HEF	Kenchester
1680	1735	....	....	141798	HEF	Llangarren
1756	1800	1756	1800	138703	HEF	Street Sugwass
1800	1855	1800	1855	138703	HUN	Huntingdon
1842	1842	1800	1850	136301	LAN	Dukinfield
1817	1840	1700	1900	119180	LND	East
1850	....	1807	1837	111856	STS	Wolverhampton
1790	1880	1880	1880	174262	WLS	Bridgend
1867	1908	1850	1870	136301	YKS	Barnsley
REECH						
1682	1800	....	....	157724	SFK	Boxford
1660	1760	ALL	1850	119105	SFK	Groton
1700	1800	....	....	157724	SFK	Groton
REED						
1795	....	....	....	148156	CAM	Isle Of Ely
1871	1871	1871	1992	121932	CON	Bodmin

Known From	To	Researching From	To	Ref	Cty	Place
REED contd.						
1730	1756	1700	1800	153354	CON	Lezant
1752	1992	1640	1751	105988	CON	Ludguan
1871	1871	1871	1992	121932	CON	Northhill
1822	....	....	....	112887	CON	Redruth
1800	1992	1700	1992	133450	CON	S Gennys
1870	1880	1870	1900	105449	CUL	Carlisle
1700	1947	1658	....	116394	DEV	Burrington
....	....	1600	1992	137588	DEV	Crediton
1861	1861	1861	1992	121932	DEV	Pyworthy
1820	1900	1700	1820	155780	DEV	Whimple
1860	1880	1800	1900	123048	DUR	Monkwearmouth
1845	1880	1800	1992	116297	ESS	Harlow
1794	1992	1794	....	116394	ESS	Littlebury
1750	1820	?	1750	158569	ESS	Saffron Walden
1891	....	ALL	1891	123013	GLA	Caerau
1872	1992	1700	1872	158518	GLA	Kenfig Hill
1870	1992	1840	1870	130249	GLS	Bristol
1730	1900	1900	1992	158607	HAM	Brading
....	....	....	?	141941	HAM	Catherington
1840	1992	....	1840	158585	HAM	Isle Of Wight
1840	1992	....	1840	158585	HAM	Portsmouth
1914	1920	1800	1992	158542	HAM	Southampton
1857	1857	....	1857	114685	HAM	Steep
1860	?	1800	1860	108359	HUN	Easton
?	1870	ALL	ALL	105449	IRL	???
1802	1802	....	....	127426	KEN	Stalisfield
....	....	1700	1900	162000	KEN	Swale
1775	1790	1700	1775	130206	LIN	Alford
1732	1876	ALL	ALL	117072	LIN	Friskney
1450	1529	1400	1530	154881	LND	ALL
1821	1830	1830	1861	158569	LND	Lambeth
1838	....	ALL	1838	107964	MDX	Bethnal Green
....	....	....	....	154385	MDX	Canning Town
....	....	1830	1900	159840	MDX	Wapping
1810	1840	ALL	1810	158577	NBL	Alnwick
1830	1860	....	....	158577	NBL	Long Framlington
1688	....	....	1700	160873	NBL	Newcastle On Tyne
1881	1904	1900	1992	105449	NBL	Newcastle
1750	1800	1650	1750	159980	NBL	Stamfordham
1720	1950	1650	1750	124699	NFK	North
1766	1792	....	1766	151688	NFK	Mundesley
1780	1980	ALL	ALL	158593	NFK	Northwold
1915	1973	ALL	ALL	118885	NRY	Middlesborough
....	....	1700	1800	115142	NTT	Gotham
1870	1992	1800	1870	130249	SOM	Dulverton
1850	1992	1600	1900	120677	SOM	Frome
1800	1942	....	....	156671	SOM	Kingston St Mary
1800	1942	....	....	156671	SOM	Staplegrove
1830	1855	1800	1860	166685	SOM	Staplegrove
1860	1992	ALL	ALL	156671	SOM	Taunton
1794	1794	1770	1830	170143	SRY	Woking
1810	1815	1700	1900	171522	SSX	Eastbourne
1781	1795	1681	1781	177490	SSX	Hastings
1840	1900	ALL	ALL	170801	SSX	Lewes
1788	1820	1700	1788	115894	WES	Kendal
1747	....	....	....	115576	WIL	Bromham
1820	1840	ALL	1820	134503	YKS	Preston By Hedon
1804	1992	1600	1804	160172	YKS	Ryedale
REEDE						
1700	1947	1658	....	116394	DEV	Burrington
REEDER						
....	....	ALL	ALL	163937	ALL	Name Study
1775	1810	1700	1850	133450	LND	Soho Square
1629	1850	ALL	1850	158615	NFK	Well Next The Sea
1860	1992	1860	1992	158615	SFK	Ipswich
1690	1775	1640	1775	135941	SFK	Lakenheath
1850	1860	1850	1860	158615	SFK	Lowestoft
REEDIE						
1808	....	....	....	137936	FIF	Central
REEDMAN						
1570	1847	1550	1696	102830	NTH	Nassington
1750	1860	1700	1800	168750	NTH	Nassington
REEDSHAW						
1739	1940	....	....	128996	CAM	Thorney
REEKES						
1732	1732	....	1775	174270	DOR	Canford
REEKIE						
1875	1953	1953	1992	146560	LTN	North Leith
REEKS						
1821	1901	ALL	1821	149950	LND	Holborn
1700	1900	ALL	ALL	152226	SOM	Evercreech
1786	1874	1700	1785	121010	WIL	Melksham
1782	1992	1700	1800	173878	WIL	Melksham

Known From	To	Researching From	To	Ref	Cty	Place
REELEY						
....	....	ALL	ALL	136115	LAN	Barton Under Irwell
....	....	ALL	ALL	136115	LAN	Lancaster
....	....	ALL	ALL	136115	LAN	Manchester
....	....	ALL	ALL	136115	SCT	ALL
....	....	ALL	ALL	136115	WAR	Aston
....	....	ALL	ALL	136115	???	Birmingham
REEP						
1650	ALL	....	....	103381	CON	ALL
1736	1781	1600	1736	149888	CON	Altarnum
1650	ALL	....	....	103381	DEV	Tamerton Follott
REES						
1815	1890	1750	1851	135658	CGN	Cardigan
1840	1900	1700	1850	168750	CMN	Golden Grove
1788	1818	1750	1851	176923	CMN	Llandeilo
1841	1992	1790	1851	123129	CMN	Llangennech
1824	....	1700	1851	176923	CMN	Llannon
1842	1992	1700	1840	132373	GLA	Briton Ferry
1808	1812	1800	1820	158658	GLA	Juxta
1800	1992	?	1800	123161	GLA	Llangyfelach
1831	1860	1800	1860	158658	GLA	Llangyfelach
1850	1920	1800	1920	118540	GLA	Llangynwydd
1808	1812	1800	1820	158658	GLA	Llantwit
1775	1992	....	....	129232	GLA	Neath Valley
1808	1812	1800	1820	158658	GLA	Neath
1835	1992	1800	1992	158658	GLA	Rhyd-Y-Fro
1885	1992	1700	1885	103098	GLA	Swansea
....	....	1800	ALL	106488	GLA	Swansea
....	....	1700	1900	129232	GLA	Tonmawr
....	1851	1800	1875	135658	GLS	Bristol
1876	1992	....	....	169145	GNT	Newport
1830	1910	1650	1830	158992	MER	Derwenlas Isygarreg
1750	1992	1700	1880	122149	MGY	Llanfyllin
1841	1912	1700	1841	149357	MON	ALL
1860	1860	1800	1850	131431	MON	Llanover
....	1850	....	1850	161888	MON	???
1697	1931	1600	1850	142891	SAL	Oswestry
....	1827	1700	1930	168424	SWL	???
1816	1992	ALL	1816	169145	WLS	Tenby
1840	1880	....	1840	161888	YKS	Stockton
REESON						
1817	1958	1754	1958	103012	LIN	ALL
REEVE						
1849	1992	1770	1900	127353	BKM	Aston Clinton
1890	1920	1750	1900	127353	BKM	Pitstone
1893	....	ALL	1910	170666	CAM	Soham
1793	1874	1750	1793	113352	ESS	Fyfield
1707	1880	1500	1710	100013	ESS	Great Waltham
1740	....	1700	1800	113662	GLS	Bisley
1735	1807	1700	1900	127353	HRT	Wilstone
1700	1880	1600	1700	163163	KEN	Ashford
1700	1907	1700	1907	143200	KEN	???
1815	1850	1650	1815	141402	NFK	Ditchingham
1796	1812	ALL	ALL	166243	NFK	Garvestone
1812	1867	1700	1992	158666	NFK	North Wold
1886	1886	1800	1900	175722	NFK	Norwich
1800	1930	1700	1800	110116	NFK	Pulham Market
1788	1812	ALL	ALL	166243	NFK	Reymerston
1741	1790	....	....	157554	NFK	Winfarthing
1769	1992	....	1769	101761	NTH	Daventry
1850	1992	1700	1850	149705	SFK	Ixworth
1714	1809	1600	1850	159956	SFK	Market Weston
1740	1800	1700	1800	135941	SFK	Wratting
1700	1907	1700	1907	143200	SSX	???
1650	1870	ALL	1992	124389	WIL	Cleverton
1650	1870	ALL	1992	124389	WIL	Lea
1758	1782	....	....	102733	WOR	Feckenham
REEVES						
1783	1808	1600	1808	144851	BDF	Caddington
1890	1992	1750	1890	102210	BRK	Henley On Thames
1840	....	ALL	ALL	158690	CAM	Cambridge
1795	1854	1795	1854	143286	FLN	Bangor Is Y Coed
1816	....	....	....	124982	GLS	Berkeley
?	?	?	1992	158704	GLS	Tewkesbury
1750	1850	1650	1800	139688	HAM	Eling
1838	1905	1700	1900	133957	HAM	???
1772	1772	ALL	1772	167959	HRT	Stanstead Abbots
1730	1750	1700	1800	158682	KEN	Ahwkhurst
1850	1970	....	....	158682	KEN	Cliffe At Hoo
1750	1850	1800	1900	158682	KEN	Cranbrook
1809	1859	ALL	ALL	118168	KEN	Farnborough
....	....	ALL	1850	145173	KEN	New Romney
1800	1830	1800	1950	164992	KEN	River
1731	?	?	?	166642	KEN	Whitstable

Known From	To	Researching From	To	Ref	Cty	Place
REEVES contd.						
1872	1949	ALL	1872	176060	LAN	Manchester
1800	1900	1800	1900	139688	LND	East End
....	....	1840	1900	145173	LND	Walworth
1787	1992	1600	1787	141925	MDX	Cowley
1870	1925	1846	1950	136271	MDX	Willesden
1890	1992	1750	1890	102210	OXF	Henley On Thames
1800	1908	1780	1910	109371	OXF	Oxford
....	....	1750	1813	149977	SAL	ALL
1813	1851	....	....	149977	SAL	Hinstock
1800	....	....	....	137693	SOM	Cheddar
1787	1992	1600	1787	141925	SRY	Thorpe
1875	1992	1875	1911	114995	SSX	Eastbourne
1788	1821	1700	1788	137383	SSX	Playden
....	....	1730	1800	158682	SXE	Playden
1830	1870	....	....	103721	WAR	Birmingham
1822	1987	1700	1822	173479	WAR	Leamington
1842	1992	1750	1842	101893	WIL	Calne
1733	1867	1650	1850	118397	WIL	Downton
1836	1900	1700	1836	158232	WIL	Downton
1792	1852	1787	1870	136980	WIL	Ludgershall
1801	1842	1800	1850	161861	WIL	Ludgershall
1707	1891	1650	1992	116653	WOR	Powick
REFORD						
1580	1992	....	....	123374	ANT	Ballinderry
REFOY						
....	....	ALL	ALL	165425	ALL	Name Study
1837	1992	1837	1992	165425	ALL	ALL
1750	1930	1837	1930	165425	SSX	Slindon
REGAN						
1861	1960	1700	1861	105767	COR	South
....	....	....	....	171646	LND	South
REID						
....	....	1700	1850	134546	ANS	Dundee
1869	1900	1600	1869	127507	ANT	Racavan
1794	1992	....	....	144088	AYR	Mauchline
1808	1808	1770	1808	179116	AYR	Ochiltree
1800	1952	....	....	135739	CAI	Keiss
1840	1900	1700	1840	173134	CAI	Wick
1782	1782	1700	1782	158739	CUL	Sebergham
1809	1889	1752	1809	158739	CUL	Whitehaven
1772	1800	1600	1800	130125	DFS	Hoddom
1851	1992	1700	1851	158755	DOR	Portland
....	....	1820	1850	174319	ELN	???
1750	....	ALL	ALL	130508	FIF	Abbotshall
1809	1811	....	....	146811	FIF	Dunfermiline
1829	1835	1700	1900	153354	FIF	Dunfermline
1809	1811	....	....	146811	FIF	Saline
1880	....	1880	1950	178845	GLA	Mountain Ash
1895	1968	ALL	ALL	123013	GLA	Pontypridd
1810	1900	1750	1900	123870	IRL	???
....	....	1800	1810	129933	IRL	???
1830	1861	....	....	146811	KRS	Cleish
1830	1861	....	....	146811	KRS	Hardiston
1830	1992	....	....	121479	LAN	Liverpool
1851	1992	1700	1851	158755	LAN	Liverpool
1900	1940	1700	1992	167592	LAN	Liverpool
1851	1992	1700	1851	158755	LAN	Manchester
1872	1895	ALL	ALL	138886	LAN	Preston
1901	1950	....	....	135968	LEI	Rothley
1780	1850	1700	1870	128244	LKS	Shotts
1857	1878	1800	1857	122068	LND	East
1830	1900	1700	1850	132403	MDX	North
1800	1900	1750	1900	152528	MDX	Hadley
1813	1818	1790	1820	156493	MLN	Dundrumble
....	....	1750	1830	121479	NIR	Down
1791	....	....	....	127140	PER	Balquidder
1831	1857	1851	1881	128988	PER	Kirkmichael
1825	1891	1825	1891	104027	RFW	Partick
1807	1840	1750	1810	121479	SCT	Aberdeen
1861	1885	....	....	118133	SCT	Bridgeton
1807	1840	1750	1810	121479	SCT	Edinburgh
1857	1878	1800	1857	122068	SCT	???
1750	1965	....	....	137820	SHI	Fetlar
1720	1965	....	....	137820	SHI	Mid Yell
1760	1965	....	....	137820	SHI	North Yell
1758	1965	....	....	137820	SHI	Northmavine
1720	1965	....	....	137820	SHI	South Yell
1864	1935	1800	1900	154539	SOM	Frome
1864	1935	1800	1900	154539	SOM	Street
1884	1935	1865	1884	154539	SRY	Southwark
1835	1885	1700	1920	167207	STI	Falkirk
1700	1757	....	....	127140	STI	Kilsyth
1830	1850	1830	1992	165603	WIC	Keiss
REID contd.						
1834	?	1800	1853	122483	???	Paisley
1940	1992	ALL	1940	100536	???	???
REIDFOORD						
1740	1801	1550	1750	147265	ABD	???
1740	1801	1550	1750	147265	BAN	???
REILLY						
1800	1900	....	....	126497	LET	???
1876	1992	....	1876	138320	WEM	Mullingar
RELF						
....	....	ALL	ALL	158771	ALL	Name Study
1160	1992	ALL	ALL	158771	ALL	ALL
1688	1992	ALL	ALL	158798	KEN	West
1766	1821	....	....	133736	KEN	Cranbrook
1720	1850	1500	1850	139386	KEN	Cranbrook
1797	1822	1777	1822	114073	LND	All Hallows Staying
1819	1992	ALL	1819	125776	SSX	ALL
1500	1992	ALL	ALL	113093	SSX	Brighling
1828	1992	ALL	1828	125776	SSX	Brightling
1828	1989	ALL	ALL	158801	SSX	Brightling
1500	1992	ALL	ALL	113093	SSX	Burwash
1900	1992	....	....	100536	SSX	???
RELFE						
1819	1992	ALL	1819	125776	SSX	ALL
RELPH						
1830	1992	ALL	ALL	158771	ALL	ALL
REMEVILLE						
....	....	1066	1230	124974	HAM	Botley
....	....	1066	1230	124974	SAL	Condover
REMINGTON						
1879	1919	1919	1950	117269	ESS	Maldon
1790	1890	1750	1890	153133	HRT	Graveley
1660	1694	ALL	ALL	108510	LIN	Bassingthorpe
1695	1731	ALL	ALL	108510	LIN	Bitchfield
1803	1840	ALL	ALL	108510	LIN	Grantham
1850	1926	1850	1992	108510	YKS	Bradford
1850	1926	1850	1992	108510	YKS	Harrogate
1839	1862	1850	1992	108510	YKS	Hull
1582	1625	1500	1650	108510	YKS	Lockington
REMINGTON-SMITH						
1763	1833	1800	1992	103942	LND	City
REMMINGTON						
1807	1877	1700	1810	131377	NTH	Rothwell
REMNANT						
1869	1992	1800	1992	117293	SSX	Kirdford
REMPHREY						
1860	1920	1840	1992	137448	CON	Tremethick Cross
RENALDES						
?	?	?	?	112437	LTN	Faldhouse
RENARD						
1771	1936	1700	1800	112224	YKS	Baildon
RENCHER						
1700	1722	ALL	ALL	141615	LEI	Kibworth
RENDAL						
1802	1860	1700	1802	114081	OKI	Westray
RENDALL						
1840	1950	ALL	ALL	151998	DEV	Tiverton
....	....	1700	1800	162493	OKI	Westray
1750	1965	....	....	137820	SHI	Fetlar
1720	1965	....	....	137820	SHI	Mid Yell
1760	1965	....	....	137820	SHI	North Yell
1758	1965	....	....	137820	SHI	Northmavine
1720	1965	....	....	137820	SHI	South Yell
RENDELL						
1450	1992	....	....	177474	DEV	Combe In Teignhead
RENDER						
1851	1976	1837	1851	166464	MDX	Clerkenwell
RENDERS						
1850	1900	ALL	ALL	130613	RAD	Disserth
RENDLE						
1811	....	....	1811	177504	DEV	Bridford
1800	1992	1600	1800	135313	DEV	Chittlehampton
1719	1865	ALL	1719	165735	DEV	Chittlehampton
....	....	1700	1800	164798	DEV	Exeter
....	....	ALL	....	172219	DEV	Teignmouth
....	....	ALL	....	172219	LAN	Liverpool
....	....	ALL	....	172219	LND	???
?	?	?	?	165735	SOM	Bristol
1730	1760	1600	1760	154342	SOM	Culbone
RENDLES						
....	....	1860	ALL	174963	DEV	Plymouth
RENFREY						
1805	1883	1700	1992	153540	DEV	Devonport

Known From	To	Researching From	To	Ref	Cty	Place
RENNEL						
....	....	1750	1840	135658	CON	ALL
1840	1870	1750	1840	135658	DEV	Plymouth
RENNICK						
1842	1861	1842	1861	112534	YKS	Hull
1842	1861	1842	1861	112534	YKS	York
RENNIE						
1770	1800	1700	1930	103403	ABD	North West
1770	1890	1700	1890	126500	ABD	Fyvie
1770	1890	....	....	126497	ABD	Fyvie
1800	1850	1800	1900	119725	ABD	New Deer
1840	1851	1800	1870	103403	ABD	Strathdon
1800	1856	1750	1800	159891	ANS	Arbroath
1800	1856	1750	1800	159891	ANS	Kinnell
....	....	1870	1900	159964	LAN	Bootle
1820	1992	....	....	136492	LTN	Edinburgh
1820	1992	....	....	136492	LTN	Glasgow
1797	1920	1750	1950	159964	MLN	Edinburgh
1813	1813	1800	1830	159964	MLN	Kirknewton
1830	1874	1800	1900	159964	MLN	Leith
1771	1830	1700	1830	163104	SCT	Alloa
RENNIKER						
....	....	1790	1840	104590	LAN	Golborne
1790	1840	1790	ALL	104590	LAN	Wigan
RENNISON						
....	1839	1500	1839	175072	LAN	Toxteth
RENNOLDS						
1826	1860	1800	1992	152943	GLS	Bristol
RENNOLDSON						
1744	1887	1700	1794	115401	DUR	Lanchester
RENOLDS						
1795	1842	1750	1992	147982	KEN	Folkestone
RENOUF						
....	....	1600	1992	146099	ALL	ALL
1750	....	ALL	1750	119105	JSY	ALL
....	....	1870	ALL	149187	JSY	St Martin
RENOWDEN						
....	....	ALL	ALL	158844	ALL	Name Study
1848	1870	1839	1870	158844	CON	St Just In Penwith
1910	1992	1900	1992	158844	GLA	Cardiff
1918	1992	1755	1992	158844	GLA	Neath
RENSHAW						
1900	....	....	....	161136	YKS	Sheffield
RENTALL						
1819	....	1799	....	102989	ESS	Finchingfield
1840	1861	1725	....	102989	ESS	Halstead
1861	1956	1861	....	102989	KEN	Plumstead
1820	1824	1820	1840	102989	SRY	Bermondsey
RENTMORE						
....	....	1780	1850	143685	SOM	Kilmersdon
RENTON						
1773	1812	1700	1900	149632	ELN	Birsley
1874	1879	1874	1879	138045	ESS	Forest Gate
1703	1757	....	....	152234	WYK	Whitkirk
1800	1840	1800	1900	138045	YKS	Hebden Bridge
1840	1871	1840	1871	138045	???	Westminster
1880	1925	1880	1925	138045	???	Windsor
RENWICK						
1797	1886	1700	1800	155705	BDS	Blackleemouth
1797	1886	1700	1800	155705	BDS	Cavers
1797	1886	1700	1800	155705	BDS	Yarrow
1783	1864	1688	1783	166723	BEW	Lauder
1772	1795	1688	1772	166723	BEW	Smailholm
....	....	ALL	1850	145319	SCT	South
....	....	ALL	1860	178195	YKS	???
REPPIN						
1770	....	1700	1800	175838	CON	St Agnes
REPTON						
1770	1800	....	....	100420	WAR	Meriden
REPUKE						
1800	1850	1700	1850	108618	LND	Islington
RESBURY						
1825	1950	1750	1825	143170	ESS	Witham
RESTORICK						
....	....	ALL	ALL	158852	ALL	Name Study
RETALLACK						
1700	1800	1700	1800	150126	CON	Manaccan
1700	1800	1700	1800	150126	CON	St Keverne
RETALLICK						
1772	1814	1700	1840	121126	CON	Illogan
1780	1830	1720	....	126403	CON	Polhilsa
1800	1869	1650	1800	165549	CON	Roche
RETILLY						
1814	1814	ALL	ALL	115126	CHI	ALL
REUCASSEL						
1710	1900	1650	1950	146846	AYR	Dailly
REVANS						
?	?	?	?	158860	NFK	???
?	?	?	?	158860	SCT	Edinburgh
?	?	?	?	158860	SCT	Glasgow
?	?	?	?	158860	SFK	???
?	?	?	?	158860	???	Gosport
?	?	?	?	158860	???	Portsmouth
REVE						
1616	1658	....	....	152110	CAM	Swaffham Prior
REVEL						
1700	1825	1700	1825	123595	YKS	Emley
REVELL						
....	....	1750	1800	159042	DUB	Dublin
1770	1943	1700	1770	170542	KEN	Ickham
1650	1800	1650	1750	154245	SAL	Shifnal
1838	1872	1700	1838	145823	SRY	Battersea
....	....	1750	1800	159042	WIC	???
1700	1800	1600	1700	169862	WYK	Wath On Dearne
1860	1992	....	....	118370	YKS	Hull
1853	....	....	....	103225	YKS	Sculcoates
REVIE						
....	....	ALL	ALL	158879	LKS	???
REVILL						
1796	1992	1700	1796	127728	DBY	Duck Manton
1861	1960	1800	1860	148199	EYK	Hull
1894	1930	1890	1930	177016	LAN	Morecambe
1790	1930	1700	1790	172901	NTT	Mansfield
1860	1979	1773	1860	129895	SFK	Mendham
1800	1805	1700	1850	173452	YKS	Rotherham
1851	1906	1906	1939	127728	YKS	Sheffield
1860	1900	1800	1900	173630	YKS	Sheffield
REVITT						
1869	1992	1869	1992	115932	LAN	ALL
1866	1896	1896	1992	145335	LIN	Lincoln
1869	1992	1869	1992	115932	NFK	ALL
1687	1866	....	....	145335	YKS	Stannington
REWCASTLE						
1807	1830	1700	1850	139378	AYR	Kirkoswald
1807	1830	1700	1850	139378	AYR	Pailly
REX						
1800	1850	1750	1850	124605	HEF	Hereford
REYBURN						
1805	1861	ALL	1805	146757	AYR	Kilmarnock
REYNER						
1840	1890	1800	1840	158887	LAN	???
1760	1930	1700	1760	158887	NFK	Central
REYNISH						
....	....	ALL	ALL	177741	ALL	Name Study
REYNOLD						
1644	1644	1600	1644	174807	SSX	Woodmancote
1790	....	1700	....	134589	YKS	Long Marston
REYNOLDS						
....	....	1700	....	164038	ALL	Chester
1833	1849	ALL	1992	112631	BKM	Leyhill
1780	1810	ALL	ALL	124605	BKM	Long Crendon
1820	1870	1850	1870	149322	BKM	Stony Stratford
1850	1870	....	....	162841	BRK	Newbury
1754	1854	ALL	ALL	158933	BRK	Sutton Courtney
1800	1824	ALL	1850	151815	CAM	Arrington
1783	1850	ALL	1992	101079	CMN	Marros
1675	1745	1600	1800	153354	CON	Gwennap
1880	1950	1600	1880	158968	DEV	Exeter
1857	....	ALL	1857	179515	DEV	Thorverton
1889	1893	1893	1992	116297	ESS	Barling
1840	1893	1800	1992	116297	ESS	Harlow
1900	1920	1750	1900	158976	GLA	Swansea
1840	1880	1700	1900	166359	GLA	???
1850	1870	....	....	162841	GLS	Gloucester
1720	1992	1600	1720	158984	HAM	South East
1850	1870	....	....	162841	HAM	Andover
1800	1850	1600	1900	120677	HAM	Wonston
1860	....	....	1860	164011	HRT	Hatfield
1880	1930	1830	1900	155047	IRL	Cork
1675	1742	ALL	1700	131059	KEN	Boughton Aluph
....	1825	1790	1851	128961	KEN	Canterbury
1666	?	?	?	166642	KEN	Fordwich
....	1825	1790	1851	128961	KEN	Rochester
1555	1634	....	....	107085	KEN	???
1856	....	....	....	158895	LIN	Grantham
1856	....	....	....	158895	LIN	Luckington
....	1763	1730	1820	128961	LND	City
1906	1992	ALL	1906	170666	LND	Croydon

Known From	To	Researching From	To	Ref	Cty	Place
REYNOLDS contd.						
1765	1822	....	....	133221	LND	Fordingbridge
1900	1923	1850	1923	157023	LND	Shepherds Bush
1874	1875	1871	1891	115886	LND	St Pancras
1881	1886	1871	1891	115886	LND	Westminster
....	1760	1730	1760	128961	LND	Westminster
....	1825	1790	1851	128961	LND	Whitechapel
1870	1992	1800	1870	158925	MDX	Stepney
1840	1840	1800	1861	111414	MGY	Llanlwchaiarn
1819	1850	1772	1819	112720	MON	Chapel Hill
1800	1945	1700	1945	107514	NFK	South East
ALL	1754	ALL	1754	158933	OXF	Banbury
1820	1825	1500	1825	104825	OXF	Cowley
1871	1871	1840	1871	179116	SAL	Bridgnorth
1659	1734	1627	1659	115819	SAL	Childs Ercall
?	?	?	?	143502	SAL	Cleobury Mortimer
1959	1959	1881	1959	111414	SAL	Longdon On Tern
1861	1861	1861	1871	111414	SAL	Shrewsbury
1833	1992	1700	1833	158917	SAL	Sutton Maddock
1864	1877	1861	1881	111414	SAL	Uffington
1909	1962	1900	1962	111414	SAL	Wrockwardine
1830	1870	1790	1830	134139	SFK	Gisleham
....	....	1800	1900	133604	SOM	Bath
....	....	1800	1900	133604	SOM	Keynsham
1830	1890	1750	1840	160083	SOM	Yeovil
1800	1950	1700	1992	121533	SRY	Richmond
1746	1992	1700	1746	158984	SSX	South West
1814	1992	1700	1814	130257	SSX	Chichester
1830	....	ALL	1820	112771	STS	Dudley
1846	ALL	1840	ALL	134627	STS	Walsall
1830	....	ALL	1820	112771	STS	West Bromwich
1748	1992	....	....	140031	WAR	South
1740	1992	1600	1992	130125	WAR	Beausale
1850	1890	?	?	112720	WAR	Birmingham
1844	1992	1800	1844	135461	WAR	Birmingham
1860	1880	1800	1875	142395	WAR	Birmingham
1793	1793	1793	1992	174262	WAR	Birmingham
1600	1700	....	....	100420	WAR	Meriden
....	....	....	....	107433	WAR	???
1770	1850	....	....	158895	WIL	Corsham
1770	1850	....	....	158895	WIL	Devizes
1820	1920	....	....	162841	WIL	Devizes
1770	1850	....	....	158895	WIL	Sutton Benger
1850	1900	....	....	162841	WIL	Swindon
1811	1846	1700	1820	164909	WOR	Dudley
1811	1846	1700	1820	164909	WOR	Sedgley
1820	1851	1750	1900	137782	WOR	Worcester
1840	1870	1750	1850	143502	WOR	Worcester
1845	1845	1800	1860	127361	WRY	Pontefract
1780	1840	ALL	ALL	142611	YKS	Carlton
1890	1912	?	?	112720	YKS	Wakefield
1845	1872	1750	1850	179671	???	Birmingham
....	....	1700	1992	171913	???	???
REYNOR						
1798	....	ALL	ALL	105481	NTT	Bilborough
RHEAD						
1871	1881	1841	1900	149330	STS	Whitmore
RHEAM						
1790	....	1700	....	134589	YKS	Long Marston
RHIND						
....	....	1700	1840	100846	IRL	???
1715	1847	1600	1715	164577	MOR	Kinloss
1847	1874	1874	1900	164577	NBL	North Shields
RHOADES						
....	....	ALL	ALL	110876	ALL	Name Study
1758	1823	1758	1985	110876	LIN	Orby
1824	1960	1824	1985	110876	SSX	Hurst Pierpoint
RHODEN						
....	1880	....	....	154024	LAN	Golborne
1830	....	....	....	171824	LAN	Rainford
1562	1992	1562	1800	160237	SAL	ALL
1536	1992	1536	1800	160237	STS	ALL
1589	1992	1589	1800	160237	WAR	ALL
1580	1992	1580	1800	160237	WOR	ALL
RHODES DENTON						
1824	1871	1871	1950	139025	YKS	Darton
RHODES						
....	....	ALL	ALL	109924	ALL	Name Study
1655	1940	....	....	128996	CAM	Thorney
1753	1804	ALL	1753	178926	DBY	Ashover
1753	1804	ALL	1753	178926	DBY	Peak Forest
1900	1945	1900	1945	149403	DUR	Gateshead
1600	1699	1600	1699	169781	ERY	Beverley
1777	1912	1500	1912	172294	HRT	ALL
RHODES contd.						
1818	1919	1750	1920	103632	LAN	Manchester
1820	1992	1820	1992	152668	LAN	Manchester
1870	1992	1700	1870	171921	LIN	Marshchapel
1550	1650	....	....	124621	LIN	Scamblesby
ALL	ALL	1700	1780	110671	NBL	Ouseburn
1800	1992	1700	1800	105902	NTH	Eye
1767	1790	....	....	177393	NTT	Bawtry
....	....	1700	1750	177393	NTT	Everton
1774	1992	ALL	1774	126721	NTT	Hucknall
1841	1848	1600	1841	132977	SSX	Shipley Parish
1780	....	....	....	126276	WRY	Carlton In Contin
1850	1870	....	....	126276	WRY	Doncaster
1830	....	1830	1900	101761	WRY	Shipley
1800	1840	1730	1849	126276	WRY	Snaith
1847	1850	1835	1858	126276	WRY	Thorne
1896	....	1886	1900	126276	WRY	Thornhill Lees
1880	1900	....	....	126276	WYK	Dewsbury
1840	1900	1850	1881	126276	WYK	Kirkburton
1900	1992	....	....	126276	WYK	Mexborough
1638	1850	1631	1900	126276	WYK	Saddleworth
1705	1765	ALL	1705	126721	WYK	Tankersley
1752	1780	1700	1838	145106	YKS	Bramham
1833	1916	1820	1920	110728	YKS	Dewsbury
1851	1885	1835	1885	145106	YKS	Easingwold
1800	1830	1770	1840	110728	YKS	Ferry Fryston
1780	1792	1780	1792	145106	YKS	Huntington
1737	1806	1600	1750	101575	YKS	Knottingley
1855	1992	....	....	172529	YKS	Knottingly
1764	1790	ALL	1764	102350	YKS	Ledsham
1827	1835	1827	1835	145106	YKS	Leeds
1794	1888	1794	1888	149403	YKS	Pontefract
1737	1806	1600	1750	101575	YKS	Rothwell
1861	1992	....	....	159018	YKS	Rufforth
1828	....	....	....	161136	YKS	Treeton
RHYED						
1870	1895	1700	1870	123110	PEM	St Davids
RIACH						
1749	....	1749	1800	112844	ABD	Lonsmay
1848	1988	1600	1855	166049	ABD	Towie
ALL	ALL	ALL	ALL	164518	MOR	ALL
RIBBINS						
1811	1900	1760	1900	153508	MDX	Heston
RICE						
1800	1992	1600	1800	112097	DBY	ALL
1790	1825	1750	1850	111821	DBY	Derby
1825	1845	1750	1850	111821	DBY	Sawley
1750	1900	1750	1900	118540	DEV	Alwington
1900	1970	ALL	1900	166545	DEV	Buckfastleigh
1830	1870	1770	1830	154962	DEV	Exeter
1881	1900	1800	1900	101265	GLA	Neath
1882	1889	1860	1900	118230	IRL	Donnybrook
1825	....	1825	1992	130486	IRL	Drogheda
1860	1890	1800	1920	142042	LAN	Liverpool
1884	1906	1886	1906	118230	LAN	St Helens
1830	1850	....	1830	163201	LEI	Leicester
1800	1970	ALL	ALL	113700	MAY	Castlebar
1800	1970	ALL	ALL	113700	MAY	Westport
1851	1881	1800	1850	146269	MDX	Chelsea
1873	1908	1800	1873	174920	MDX	Hammersmith
1840	1885	1700	1840	134899	NFK	Diss
1801	1992	1700	1950	136530	NFK	Mattishall
....	....	1800	?	101672	NIR	Belfast
1795	1860	1700	1795	162396	NTT	Burton On Trent
1857	1880	....	....	103810	NTT	Newark
1887	1929	1800	1887	124435	SFK	Ipswich
1895	1950	1800	1895	123811	SFK	Ipswich
1750	1900	1600	1750	102288	SFK	Woolpit
1739	1992	ALL	ALL	120103	SOM	Berrow
1739	1992	ALL	ALL	120103	SOM	Mark
1700	1757	1650	1760	129356	SOM	Martock
1876	1904	ALL	ALL	149489	STS	Newcastle
1679	1992	1650	1700	173649	STS	Rolleston
1953	....	....	....	173932	WIL	Bradford On Avon
1735	1735	ALL	ALL	113700	WIL	Sherston
1800	1870	1800	1870	102490	???	Hotwells
RICH						
1806	1862	1804	1862	124915	BDF	Salford
1838	1964	1800	1840	163694	DEV	Broad Clyst
1770	1920	....	....	144371	DEV	Okehampton
....	....	ALL	1850	133698	ESS	Romford
....	....	1818	1900	136166	GLA	Cardiff
1730	1808	....	....	167037	GLS	Limehouse
1760	....	....	....	167037	GLS	Rotherhithe

Known From	To	Researching From	To	Ref	Cty	Place
RICH contd.						
1829	1992	1700	1829	110019	GLS	???
1783	1868	....	....	135968	KEN	Chelsfield
1890	1890	1870	1925	124915	LND	Clapton
1838	1992	1700	1838	138436	MDX	St Brides
1618	ALL	....	....	167037	NFK	Mulbarton
1838	1992	1700	1838	138436	SOM	Frome
1524	1800	....	....	130591	SOM	Lydeard St Lawrence
....	....	1450	1524	130591	SOM	???
1800	1880	1750	1800	149373	SSX	Brighton
1901	1903	1890	1905	124915	SSX	Washington
1560	1800	1500	1800	160598	WIL	Christian Halford
1829	1992	1700	1829	110019	WIL	???
RICHANS						
1818	....	....	....	167444	HAM	Hurst Bourne
RICHARD						
1550	1600	1500	1600	176923	CMN	Carmarthen
1629	1779	....	....	176559	CMN	Kidwelly
1865	1900	....	....	159131	DFD	Fishguard
1810	1865	....	....	159131	DFD	Llanwnda
1810	1865	....	....	159131	DFD	Puncheston
1732	1732	ALL	ALL	130508	FIF	St Andrews
1732	1732	ALL	ALL	130508	FIF	St Leonards
1790	1830	1750	1790	159115	GSY	Castel
1866	ALL	....	....	117560	MDX	Hackney
1850	1992	1800	1992	133450	SCT	Edinburgh
1800	....	....	....	117560	???	Edinburgh
RICHARDS						
....	....	ALL	ALL	108294	ALL	Name Study
....	....	ALL	ALL	139238	ALL	Name Study
1760	1880	1700	1880	118540	CMN	Cenarth
1890	....	1800	1890	176931	CMN	Conwil Cayo
1870	1890	1800	1870	123110	CMN	Whitland
1790	1992	1700	1790	130257	CON	Breage
1720	1750	1720	1992	133450	CON	Breage
1840	1900	1700	1840	136972	CON	Breage
1836	1992	1700	1836	101567	CON	Camborne
1800	....	1800	1992	129348	CON	Falmouth
1787	1806	1600	1787	102571	CON	Gwennap
1841	1900	1800	1900	118818	CON	Illogan
1758	1818	....	....	143596	CON	Madron
1720	1750	1720	1992	133450	CON	Mardon
1800	1860	ALL	ALL	112496	CON	Mid
1836	1992	1700	1836	101567	CON	Penponds
?	....	?	....	173800	CON	Perranarworth
1817	....	1750	1810	178845	CON	Redruth
1850	1850	1800	1900	133450	CON	Roche
1800	1850	ALL	ALL	100161	CON	St Germans
1827	1863	....	....	136964	CON	St Ives
1820	1870	1700	1900	168068	CON	St Ives
1778	....	1700	1778	130141	CON	St Just In Penwith
1839	1992	1839	....	173266	CON	St Just
1790	1992	1700	1790	130257	CON	St Levan
1701	1701	1100	1701	117749	CON	St Martin In Meneage
1820	1900	1700	1820	165549	CON	St Stephens In Brannel
1697	1813	1600	1697	102571	CON	Uny Lelant
1700	1840	1700	1890	112712	CON	Zennor
1668	1810	1550	1668	118958	CON	???
1825	1860	1700	1850	106976	DEV	Cullompton
1840	1880	1840	1880	135429	DEV	Exmouth
1790	1900	1790	1900	107352	DEV	Langtree
....	....	1700	1850	110914	DEV	Plymouth
1788	1862	1750	1788	124397	DEV	South Molton
1840	1992	1500	1840	129577	DEV	Totnes
1834	1920	1850	1900	159131	DFD	Haverfordwest
1834	1920	1850	1900	159131	DFD	St Davids
1834	1920	1850	1900	159131	DFD	Whitchurch
1841	1881	1700	1992	170518	DOR	E Pulham
1841	1881	1700	1992	170518	DOR	West Pulham
1840	1992	1750	1992	167991	GLA	Aberdare
1750	1915	1650	1950	105767	GLA	Gower
1870	1890	1800	1870	123110	GLA	Llanwynno
1840	1992	1750	1992	167991	GLA	Maerdy
1890	1992	....	1890	138320	GLA	Merthyr Tydfil
1839	1839	1800	1839	156914	GLA	Merthyr Tydfil
1815	....	1800	1850	169625	GLA	Merthyr Tydfil
1830	1900	1750	1850	168750	GLA	Swansea
?	?	....	....	159069	GLS	Bristol
1830	1850	1700	1830	173223	GLS	Bristol
1740	1760	1700	1760	156930	GLS	Kempley
....	....	1700	1850	103667	HAM	South East
1679	1850	1600	1700	149993	HAM	Lower Itchen
RICHARDS contd.						
....	....	1800	1850	110914	HAM	Portsea
1860	1970	1700	1900	159093	HAM	Portsmouth
1830	1841	1821	1853	108901	HEF	Aymestry
....	1800	ALL	1800	152889	HUN	Gt Staughton
1807	....	....	....	129747	IOW	Godshill
1804	....	....	....	129747	IOW	Newchurch
1840	1992	1500	1840	129577	IOW	???
1820	1882	1820	1900	111791	IRL	Galway
1811	1840	1600	1840	158399	IRL	New Ross
1850	1920	1790	1880	166979	KEN	Canterbury
1800	1850	1800	1850	147575	KEN	Deal
1831	1913	1830	1920	159123	KEN	Dover
1797	....	....	1800	171441	KEN	Elham
1766	....	....	1780	171441	KEN	Newington Next Hythe
....	....	1800	1880	166979	KEN	Thannington
1800	1960	1700	1800	121509	LEI	Barrow Upon Soar
1714	1788	1695	1788	156817	LEI	Loughborough
ALL	1830	....	....	170798	LEI	Staunton Harold
1880	1992	1700	1880	171913	LIN	Lincoln
1860	1992	ALL	ALL	115762	LND	Islington
1835	1835	1800	1835	142999	LND	Lambeth
1860	1865	1800	1900	159093	LND	Stoke Newington
1801	1848	1770	1850	144797	MDX	Shoreditch
....	....	ALL	1847	167959	MDX	Shoreditch
1790	1900	1700	1800	124427	MER	Dolgelly
1830	....	1750	1880	102016	MER	Pennal
1830	1860	1750	1830	105740	MON	Chepstow
1888	....	1888	....	159913	MON	Monmouth
1800	1900	1700	1900	172561	MON	Trellech
1706	1947	ALL	1700	159077	NTH	Tansor
1781	1800	1700	1800	131377	NTH	Woodford
1819	1840	....	....	178241	NTT	Colston Bassett
1920	1992	1700	1920	113530	PEM	Angle
1770	1870	1770	1870	167924	PEM	Tenby
1772	1825	ALL	1992	159174	SAL	Ludlow
1808	1890	ALL	ALL	149004	SOM	Ash
1730	1850	1700	1870	136840	SOM	Brendon Hills
1699	....	....	....	117579	SOM	Frome
1543	1804	ALL	1851	104299	SOM	Milverton
1650	1710	1600	1750	144657	SOM	Milverton
1847	1866	1847	1866	147575	SRY	Battersea
1847	1850	1850	1950	167959	SRY	Bermondsey
1838	1838	1838	1838	147575	SRY	Brixton
1750	1860	1700	1900	122688	SSX	South Bersted
1850	1925	1850	1992	133450	SSX	???
1900	1940	ALL	1992	159174	STS	Burton On Trent
1760	1900	1700	1760	159115	STS	Kingswinford
1885	?	....	....	138118	STS	Madeley
1862	1940	1700	1862	129011	STS	Rugeley
1679	1857	1600	1890	123404	STS	St Bartholomew
1679	1857	1600	1890	123404	STS	Wednesbury
1700	1800	1600	1850	177180	STS	West Bromwich
....	....	....	....	115142	STS	???
1880	....	....	....	170313	WAR	Birmingham
1884	1900	ALL	1992	159174	WAR	Bordesley
1828	1884	ALL	1992	159174	WAR	Dibeth
1789	1880	1750	1900	159905	WAR	Warmington
1810	....	1750	1850	102016	WLS	North
....	1917	ALL	1910	168696	WLS	South
1752	1992	ALL	ALL	159107	WOR	Chaddesley Corbett
1796	1992	1700	1796	159158	WOR	Worcester
RICHARDSON						
1800	1850	1600	1992	176494	BDF	ALL
1729	1762	1500	1729	125695	BDF	Gamlingay
1650	1750	1600	1800	177180	BKM	Preston Bissett
1748	1992	1600	1748	149713	BKM	Twyford
1818	1992	1818	1992	167444	BRK	Ham
1818	1992	1818	1992	167444	BRK	Reading
....	1936	....	....	147869	BRK	???
1853	....	1800	1850	140473	CAM	Ely
....	1781	....	1781	108839	CAM	Sutton
1864	1864	ALL	1888	146315	CHS	Heaton Mersey
1830	1851	1800	1830	170569	CHS	Stockport
1734	1811	1700	1734	152196	CMA	Brigham
1793	1851	1700	1851	178233	CMA	Whitehaven
1850	1880	1800	1900	148458	CUL	Brampton
1706	1788	....	....	138401	CUL	Distington
1783	1992	1550	1783	142646	CUL	Kirkland
1540	1800	1500	1850	138878	CUL	St Bees
1690	1900	1650	1905	103128	DBY	Elmton
....	....	ALL	1800	178403	DBY	Smalley
1780	1803	....	....	152870	DEV	Plymouth

Known From	To	Researching From	To	Ref	Cty	Place
RICHARDSON contd.						
1832	1918	ALL	ALL	145092	DFS	Wamphray
1799	1992	ALL	1799	134171	DUR	Hamsterley
1800	1899	1800	1899	169781	DUR	Shotley Bridge
1739	1739	....	....	103632	DUR	Sunderland
1700	1800	1700	1800	169781	DUR	Sunderland
1765	1850	....	....	108871	DUR	Tanfield
1600	1699	1600	1699	169781	ERY	Hull
1916	1950	ALL	1916	159204	ESS	Chelmsford
1861	1900	1800	1900	162450	ESS	Debden
1790	....	ALL	ALL	107255	ESS	Saffron Walden
1842	1900	1700	1842	168653	ESS	Terling
1770	1800	ALL	1770	131059	ESS	Tolleshunt D'arcy
1916	1950	ALL	1916	159204	ESS	Writtle
1679	1992	ALL	1679	115223	HAM	Hartley Wintney
1800	1992	....	....	167444	HAM	Hurst Bourke
....	....	....	....	107433	HRT	???
1825	1917	....	....	116378	HUN	Offord Cluny
1700	1900	1600	1900	159220	HUN	Ramsey
1900	1960	1850	1925	113387	KEN	Canterbury
1800	1992	1800	1992	172952	KEN	Mayfield
1766	1800	1600	1800	130125	KEN	Sevenoaks
1710	1730	1650	1750	136840	KEN	Sevenoaks
1888	1888	ALL	1888	146315	LAN	Chorlton
1824	1870	1780	1870	103616	LAN	Lancaster
1905	1992	1850	1922	146919	LAN	Lancaster
1902	1977	1750	1950	140066	LAN	Liverpool
1800	1860	1800	1900	134597	LAN	Manchester
1845	ALL	ALL	1875	175757	LAN	Manchester
1650	1689	1500	1689	129011	LAN	Pennington In Furness
1826	1856	ALL	ALL	138886	LAN	Preston
....	....	1792	....	121940	LAN	Ringley
1913	1913	1888	1913	146315	LAN	Rusholme
1880	....	1880	....	159247	LAN	Warrington
1888	1906	ALL	1931	146315	LAN	Withington
1790	1848	1750	1900	176672	LEI	Leicester
1808	....	1700	1808	116173	LEI	Rearsby
1786	1817	1700	1786	159212	LIN	North
1730	1731	1700	1735	108510	LIN	Bitchfield
....	....	1500	1910	137472	LIN	Bourne
1750	1850	1750	....	101923	LIN	Horncastle
1805	1949	1700	1857	160636	LIN	Lincoln
1808	1818	1700	1808	126349	LIN	Pinchbeck
1750	1850	1750	....	101923	LIN	Tetford
1760	....	1760	....	111287	LIN	Waithe
1860	1860	1800	1900	178624	LND	Islington
1812	1830	1750	1900	100129	LND	Pancras
1864	1992	1700	1864	156264	LND	Stoke Newington
1810	1885	1700	1920	167177	MLN	Edinburgh
1810	1885	1700	1920	167177	MLN	Leith
1700	1700	1600	1800	162620	NBL	Allendale
1786	1989	1750	1786	147745	NBL	Amble
1856	1856	1845	1860	130877	NBL	Ancroft
1718	1798	1600	1850	130125	NBL	Chatton
1811	1851	1841	1851	118095	NBL	Ford
1660	1863	ALL	ALL	105015	NBL	Newcastle
1861	1881	1861	1886	118095	NBL	Spittal
1786	1989	1750	1786	147745	NBL	Wooler
1800	1870	ALL	....	143944	NRY	Byland
1721	1992	ALL	1721	125210	NTT	East Bridgeford
1800	1900	1700	1800	148806	NYK	Lastingham
....	....	1700	1854	161446	SAL	???
....	....	1700	1900	132276	SFK	East Bergholt
1769	1769	1720	1820	105333	SSX	Arundel
1815	1865	1750	1815	156140	SSX	Clayton
1711	1830	1650	1710	156140	SSX	Hastings
1800	1840	1700	1800	178454	SSX	Maresfield
1790	1890	1750	1992	179000	STI	Bannockburn
1820	1850	1500	1850	170178	SXE	Little Horsted
1888	1888	1700	1888	100110	SYK	Kimberworth
1900	1992	....	....	100536	T&W	Newcastle On Tyne
1807	1893	1800	1900	112879	WAR	Coventry
....	....	....	....	129038	WES	North
1701	1992	1500	1701	159182	WES	Beetham
1701	1992	1500	1701	159182	WES	Burton
1751	1780	1558	1751	141291	WES	Kendal
1650	1850	1650	1850	143553	WES	Long Marton
1700	1760	1700	1800	134597	WES	Warcop
1750	1800	1700	1850	143553	WES	Warcop
1630	1670	1630	1670	142018	WIL	ALL
1760	1760	1700	1780	136840	WIL	Avon Valley
1733	1757	1700	1800	118397	WIL	Downton
1880	1992	....	....	167444	WIL	Gt Bedwyn
1795	1906	ALL	1795	161330	WOR	Epperstone
1750	1992	1650	1750	102342	WRY	Swinefleet
1696	1736	1600	1700	154601	WYK	Batley
1825	1926	1750	1832	112844	YKS	Almondbury
1780	....	1700	....	134589	YKS	Burnby
1854	1992	1700	1854	161446	YKS	Huddersfield
....	1679	1600	1680	174858	YKS	Hunmanby
1950	1980	1800	1950	119784	YKS	Selby
1870	1992	1870	1910	154598	YKS	Sheffield
1820	1871	1700	1900	158666	YKS	Snaith
1820	1910	1750	1820	118478	YKS	Sneaton
1730	1812	1770	1812	154598	YKS	Strensall
1850	....	1750	....	134589	YKS	York
....	....	1830	1900	122114	???	???
RICHBELL						
1818	1870	....	....	140090	LND	South
RICHE						
1764	1952	ALL	1764	173304	OXF	Henley On Thames
RICHELIEU						
1700	1890	....	....	131474	DUR	Bishop Auckland
1600	1700	....	....	131474	NBL	Corbridge
RICHENS						
1818	1992	....	....	167444	BRK	Ham
1818	1992	....	....	167444	BRK	Reading
1850	....	....	....	145920	OXF	Eaton Hastings
....	....	1650	1800	106461	WIL	ALL
RICHES						
1800	1900	1800	1900	133922	ESS	Brightlingsea
1900	1930	1800	ALL	159255	LND	Bermondsey
1852	1875	1820	1890	136719	LND	Kensington
1810	1890	....	....	135984	LND	Woolwich
?	?	ALL	ALL	100897	LND	???
1800	1860	1700	1800	161292	NFK	Briston
1762	1785	ALL	1762	168602	NFK	Denton
1637	....	....	....	168521	NFK	Marsham
1783	1793	1650	1782	131245	NFK	Norwich
1822	1840	....	1822	165484	NFK	Sprowson
1851	1910	1800	1910	156892	NFK	Walsingham
1810	1890	....	....	135984	NFK	Woodton
1870	1890	?	1870	120308	SFK	Hoxne
1700	1800	1700	1850	133922	SFK	Hoxne
1873	1950	1700	1873	102288	SFK	Ipswich
1600	1700	1600	1800	133922	SFK	Redgrave
1575	1750	1500	1750	133922	SFK	Rickinghall Superior
1730	1850	1730	1900	133922	SFK	Worlingworth
....	....	1700	1900	140627	SFK	Wrentham
1857	1900	1700	1900	112143	YKS	North Allerton
RICHFORD						
1860	....	1860	1992	111201	STS	Ednesford
RICHINGS						
1858	1992	1600	1858	159263	AVN	Bristol
1861	1930	1600	1992	170518	BRK	Faringdon
1830	1881	1600	1992	170518	BRK	Longworth
1726	1900	....	....	127043	OXF	South
RICHINS						
1697	1849	1600	1697	128317	GLS	Painswick
1680	1755	....	....	102733	GLS	South Cerney
RICHMOND						
1585	....	1500	1600	152110	CAM	Swaffham Bulbeck
1585	....	1500	1600	152110	CAM	Swaffham Prior
1500	1900	1500	1900	170216	DOR	ALL
1784	1890	1600	1784	163783	LAN	Goosnargh
1798	1992	1700	1992	159271	LND	East
1807	....	ALL	ALL	159034	MDX	Islington
1865	....	1850	1880	159034	MDX	St Pancras
1840	....	ALL	ALL	159034	MDX	Stepney
1847	1900	1800	1992	116246	NYK	Thirsk
1741	1992	1600	1740	124176	WAR	Ullenhall
1500	1900	1500	1900	170216	WIL	ALL
1800	1860	1800	1992	165603	YKS	Sadberge
1860	1900	1800	1992	165603	YKS	Yarm
RICKABY						
1778	1778	....	....	103632	DUR	Sunderland
1700	1800	1700	1800	116823	NYK	Middlesborough
1700	1800	1700	1800	116823	NYK	Stockton
RICKARD						
1862	1884	1600	1862	167355	BKM	Wingrave
1830	1930	1800	1992	177180	BKM	Wingrave
1766	1992	1700	1766	159298	CAM	Cambridge
1600	1790	1600	1800	159328	CON	Brannell
1744	1751	1600	1800	153591	CON	Camborne
1744	1751	1600	1800	153591	CON	Illogan

Known From	To	Researching From	To	Ref	Cty	Place
RICKARD contd.						
1650	1720	1550	1670	159328	CON	St Enoder
1865	1992	1700	1865	103098	CON	???
1810	1880	1860	1930	159328	DBY	Derby
1790	1840	1810	1860	159328	DEV	Devonport
1830	1950	1800	1992	133450	DEV	Plymouth
1830	1992	....	....	159301	GNT	Newport
....	....	1600	1680	154873	KEN	Canterbury
1869	1913	1700	1992	117269	KER	Killarney
1870	1910	1900	1930	159328	NTT	Nottingham
RICKARDS						
1821	1959	?	1821	136611	GLS	Shipton Moyne
....	....	1900	1992	109894	LND	Stoke Newington
1761	1899	1700	1761	160024	MDX	London
1850	1992	....	....	126659	SAL	Shrewsbury
RICKCORD						
1805	1992	1600	1900	159344	ALL	ALL
RICKERBY						
....	....	1800	1900	155543	LND	Hackney
RICKERS						
....	....	ALL	ALL	128880	ALL	Name Study
RICKET						
....	....	ALL	ALL	121630	ALL	Name Study
RICKETS						
1732	....	....	1760	171441	OXF	Bampton
RICKETT						
1851	1936	....	1851	146072	HRT	Bovingdon
1700	ALL	1700	1950	107379	HRT	Hemel Hempstead
1700	ALL	1700	1950	107379	HRT	Tring
1801	1849	1800	1851	174602	LIN	Marston
1700	ALL	1764	1950	107379	LND	ALL
RICKETTS						
1691	1780	1600	1800	130125	DOR	Coombe Kns
1850	....	1700	....	127760	DOR	Lytchett Maltravers
1690	1750	1650	1750	136840	DOR	Wool
1807	1808	ALL	1807	169730	ESS	Debden
1885	1930	1700	1885	123110	GLA	Dowlais
....	....	1600	1700	148792	HAM	North West
1780	1795	1750	1800	142174	KEN	Wilmington
1840	1900	1800	1900	142174	STS	Wolverhampton
....	....	1800	ALL	118060	WIL	East Knoyle
RICKMAN						
1808	1992	ALL	1808	159352	HAM	Milford On Sea
1850	1900	ALL	1992	128260	HAM	Soton
1800	1849	ALL	1849	131571	MDX	Homerton
RICKS						
1842	1842	ALL	ALL	177547	HAM	Winchester
1784	1857	....	....	144282	WIL	Purton
RICKSON						
1800	....	....	....	100536	???	???
RICKWOOD						
....	....	ALL	ALL	106674	ALL	ALL
RICOLFIS						
1525	1983	ALL	ALL	158771	ALL	ALL
RICWULF						
1750	1880	ALL	ALL	158771	ALL	ALL
RIDD						
1600	1850	1800	1840	132721	DEV	North
1813	1992	1700	1813	159360	DEV	Bratton
1813	1992	1700	1813	159360	DEV	Fleming
RIDDEL						
1816	1950	1670	1900	159379	ABD	West
1818	1818	ALL	1818	114707	ENG	???
....	....	?	?	114707	IRL	???
RIDDELL						
1750	1992	1750	1992	145467	ABD	Cushnie
1793	1936	1700	1793	118427	ABD	Glenmuick
1785	1961	ALL	1785	106909	ABD	Kincardine O'neil
1750	1992	1750	1992	145467	ABD	Towie
1700	1800	1700	1800	113204	DOW	Cumber
1802	1992	1555	1802	126462	NBL	Felton
RIDDELS						
....	....	ALL	ALL	159379	ALL	Name Study
RIDDICK						
1776	1992	1725	1776	159387	WIL	South
RIDDIFORD						
1834	1895	....	....	150282	CON	???
....	1850	....	1850	119024	DEV	Brendon
1760	1782	ALL	ALL	124982	GLS	South
1791	1878	1843	1878	178683	GLS	Thornbury
....	1850	....	1850	119024	SOM	Brendon
RIDDING						
1841	....	ALL	ALL	138533	CMA	Kirkby Lonsdale
1840	1992	1700	1840	156914	STS	Walsall
RIDDIOUGH						
1838	1869	ALL	ALL	166839	WYK	Bradford
RIDDLE						
1800	1800	1700	1800	113646	CAM	Catworth
1800	1800	1700	1800	113646	CAM	Spaldwick
1785	1785	1750	1810	141046	LKS	East Kilbride
1815	1863	ALL	1815	122386	NBL	North Tyne
1815	1815	1800	1815	130877	NBL	Whittingham
?	?	1600	?	178667	SAL	ALL
?	?	1600	?	178667	STS	ALL
RIDDLES						
1794	1900	1790	1900	107166	SSX	Sompting
RIDDLESWORTH						
1776	1992	1500	1776	107123	CHS	Congleton
1900	1992	1800	1900	107123	LAN	Manchester
RIDDOCH						
....	....	1821	1850	174319	BAN	???
RIDDY						
1897	....	ALL	1897	176532	BDF	???
1812	....	1800	1880	176532	SRY	Southwark
1881	1905	ALL	1905	176532	SXE	Brighton
RIDEHALGH						
1897	1928	ALL	ALL	142492	LAN	Waterfoot
RIDENTON						
1813	1827	1750	1813	101060	LND	Stepney
RIDEOUT						
1760	1780	1730	1760	131342	WIL	Baverstock
RIDER						
1788	1819	....	1840	171441	BRK	New Windsor
1704	1769	1650	1800	155896	GLS	Westbury On Severn
1700	1870	1600	1900	142123	SAL	Moreton
1837	1837	ALL	ALL	141186	WIL	Froxfield
1840	1865	ALL	1865	131172	YKS	Pudsey
RIDES						
1750	1800	1750	1800	159409	HAM	ALL
RIDETT						
1715	1785	1700	1800	126667	IOW	Shalfleet
RIDGE						
1630	1748	ALL	1630	168602	BDF	Odell
1810	1811	1785	1830	108510	DBY	Glossop
1838	1883	....	....	103373	DEV	West Down
1830	1840	1800	1900	142875	IRL	???
1784	1861	ALL	1784	168602	NFK	Welney
1400	1660	1400	1660	108294	SAL	Chirbury
1740	1992	ALL	ALL	107670	SSX	Horsham
1814	1992	1700	1800	110442	SYK	Armthorpe
RIDGEN						
1861	1870	1800	1900	123811	SFK	Honington
RIDGEON						
?	?	....	....	159395	CAM	Cambridge
RIDGERS						
1750	1800	1750	1800	159409	BRK	ALL
1750	1800	1750	1800	159409	HAM	ALL
1638	1781	ALL	ALL	129933	HAM	Yateley
RIDGEWAY						
1804	1860	1804	1860	129747	CHS	Bosden
1835	1860	1835	1860	129747	CHS	Cheadle
1845	1861	....	....	132179	LAN	Chowbent
RIDGEWELL						
1848	1988	1750	1850	165271	MDX	Chiswick
RIDGLEY						
1765	1928	1765	1949	125229	BKM	Hughenden
1791	1914	1791	1914	125229	BKM	Princes Risborough
1630	1840	1630	1840	127655	HEF	Yarpole
1630	1840	1630	1840	127655	SAL	Richards Castle
RIDGWAY						
1804	1860	1804	1860	129747	CHS	Bosden
1835	1860	1835	1860	129747	CHS	Cheadle
?	1736	....	....	138851	LAN	Deane
1820	....	1700	1820	116181	LEI	Normanton
1780	?	1700	1992	167592	STS	Burslem
1750	1760	1700	1992	167592	STS	Chell
1790	1820	1700	1992	167592	STS	Hanley
1790	1820	1700	1992	167592	STS	Shelton
1780	?	1700	1992	167592	YKS	Leeds
RIDHOLS						
....	....	ALL	ALL	123064	CON	ALL
....	....	ALL	ALL	123064	DEV	ALL
RIDING						
1850	1876	1780	1876	116742	LAN	Burnley
1800	1900	1800	1900	110523	LAN	Rochdale
RIDINGS						
....	....	....	....	119997	LAN	Preston
?	....	?	?	119997	YKS	Hudd

Known From	To	Researching From	To	Ref	Cty	Place
RIDLER						
1800	1850	1750	1850	106631	GLS	Stroud
RIDLEY						
1874	1992	1800	1992	116246	DUR	ALL
1860	1900	1800	1992	162620	DUR	Gateshead
1818	1838	1800	1818	123307	KEN	Deptford
1800	1813	1700	1800	139084	KEN	Wroyham
1777	1777	1600	1992	110787	LEI	Gilmorton
1704	1735	1680	1770	160873	NBL	Chollerton
1725	....	....	1750	160873	NBL	Newcastle On Tyne
1816	1900	1800	1820	127965	NBL	St John Lee
1831	1831	1700	1850	153001	NYK	Appleton Wiske
1800	1900	1600	1800	118486	SAL	Bridgnorth
....	....	?	?	178349	???	Droitwich
RIDLEY-SMITH						
1860	1886	ALL	1860	150924	YKS	Normanby
RIDLINGTON						
1732	1940	....	....	128996	CAM	Thorney
RIDOUT						
....	....	ALL	ALL	159417	ALL	Name Study
....	....	ALL	ALL	159417	ALL	ALL
....	....	ALL	ALL	159417	DOR	North
1728	1800	1600	1900	159417	DOR	Folke
1704	1740	1700	1750	159417	DOR	Minterne Magna
1750	1800	1600	1900	159417	DOR	Sherborne
1740	1750	1730	1800	159417	SOM	Weston Bamfylde
RIDPATH						
1723	1900	ALL	ALL	163562	ALL	ALL
RIDSDILL						
1792	1871	ALL	1792	166847	YKS	Bolton Percy
RIEDER						
1848	1880	ALL	ALL	154067	LND	ALL
RIEDSTRA						
....	....	ALL	ALL	159425	ALL	Name Study
RIGARLSFORD						
1660	1992	1600	1800	159433	SSX	Horsted Keynes
RIGBY						
....	....	1827	1890	129313	CHS	Congleton
1700	1900	1700	1992	133450	CHS	Oldfield
1820	1872	ALL	1880	127094	KEN	Chatham
1778	1992	1750	1992	159468	LAN	Fylde
1700	1870	1680	1890	117145	LAN	Harrock
1782	1992	1600	1782	144967	LAN	Hindley
1791	1851	1700	1800	159441	LAN	Leyland
1811	1836	ALL	1836	173290	LAN	Little Sankey
1825	....	1825	1992	159468	LAN	Liverpool
1620	1720	....	....	177318	LAN	Maudsley
1788	1802	ALL	1802	127094	LAN	Pendlebury
1864	1903	1700	1864	167886	LAN	Prescot
1820	1850	ALL	ALL	138886	LAN	Preston
1791	1851	1851	1992	159441	LAN	Preston
....	....	1800	1860	169056	LAN	Simonswood
1780	1910	1800	1900	126500	LAN	Wigan
1770	1900	....	....	126497	LAN	Winott
1792	1792	1700	1992	112097	LEI	Loughborough
1560	1830	....	....	129763	NTH	Central
1743	1768	1700	1770	107360	NTH	Chapel Brampton
1790	1865	....	....	129747	SAL	Dawley Magna
1700	1790	....	....	129747	SAL	Wellington
....	....	ALL	1890	129313	STS	Mow Cop
1880	1900	1830	1880	176583	STS	Newcastle Under Lyne
1734	1897	ALL	1841	170704	STS	Talke
RIGDEN						
1840	1920	1700	1840	134899	KEN	North
1840	1920	1700	1840	134899	KEN	Dover
RIGERS						
1750	1800	1750	1800	159409	BRK	ALL
1706	1766	ALL	1706	175080	SSX	West Dean
RIGG						
1824	....	1750	1824	179078	LAN	Rossendale
1756	1776	ALL	ALL	124982	WES	ALL
RIGGALL						
....	....	ALL	ALL	159476	ALL	Name Study
RIGGS						
1751	1783	1750	1783	131113	DEV	Ottery St Mary
1783	1909	1783	1909	131113	DEV	Plymouth
1820	1860	1700	1820	116815	DOR	Blandford
1735	1823	1500	1735	129577	IOW	???
....	....	1700	1899	174963	MDX	London
RIGHALL						
1845	1845	1841	1845	136808	CAM	Whittlesey
RIGHTON						
1733	1896	ALL	ALL	104191	MDX	London
RILEY						
1845	1885	1800	1885	155691	DBY	Chesterfield
1827	1860	1700	1827	120200	DBY	Horsley
ALL	1910	....	....	162590	GSY	St Peter Port
1850	1992	ALL	ALL	108464	IRL	Cork
....	....	1700	1800	128627	IRL	Dublin
1844	....	....	....	109347	LAN	Accrington
1825	....	1825	....	109347	LAN	Barrowford
1806	1851	ALL	1806	145203	LAN	Colne
1819	....	....	1819	149624	LAN	Colne
1825	1884	1500	1884	169439	LAN	Haslingden
1824	1929	1800	1824	170569	LAN	Heaton Mersey
....	....	1780	1860	131962	LAN	Liverpool
1876	1992	1800	1876	141135	LAN	Manchester
1860	1992	....	....	159506	LAN	Manchester
1600	1700	1600	1700	109347	LAN	Oswaldtwistle
1849	1857	1700	1848	131245	LEI	Leicester
1853	1943	1825	1943	125717	LEI	St Margarets
1830	1860	....	1830	159506	LIM	Limerick
1730	1740	....	....	103721	LIN	Luddington
1790	1868	1700	1790	168351	LND	Wapping
....	....	1800	1900	128627	LND	???
1760	1821	....	1760	165484	MDX	???
1850	1882	1820	1943	125717	NTH	Northampton
?	?	?	?	127442	NTT	St Marys
1830	1861	1750	1830	138584	NTT	Stapleford
1824	1875	1700	1824	172049	STS	Alrewas
1591	1868	....	....	117404	STS	Penkridge
1884	1992	1800	1884	174041	STS	Walsall
....	....	1829	1900	149799	SYK	Hooton Pagnall
....	....	1829	1900	149799	SYK	Pontefract
1932	....	....	1932	148830	TYR	Grange School
1800	1810	1750	1850	130869	YKS	Hull
1861	1900	1900	1992	138584	YKS	Keighley
1802	1820	1700	1800	149098	YKS	Woodkirk
RIMELL						
1758	1900	1700	1900	125563	GLS	Weston Sub Edge
1840	1918	1700	1840	172588	MDX	St Lukes
1758	1900	1700	1900	125563	WAR	Brailes
1758	1900	1700	1900	125563	WAR	Tysoe
1758	1900	1700	1900	125563	WOR	Bretforton
1758	1900	1700	1900	125563	WOR	Doddenham
1758	1900	1700	1900	125563	WOR	Hallow
1758	1900	1700	1900	125563	WOR	Worcester
RIMER						
....	....	ALL	ALL	105678	ALL	Name Study
....	....	1600	1900	105678	ALL	ALL
1800	1900	1700	1900	105678	HAM	Southampton
....	....	1600	1900	105678	LND	ALL
1792	1803	1700	1900	105678	SOM	Frome
1790	1860	1700	1900	105678	WIL	Trowbridge
....	1757	....	....	154024	YKS	Wakefield
RIMINTON						
1773	1960	....	....	101869	LND	Teddington
1773	1960	....	....	101869	LND	West Norwood
RIMMER						
1868	1913	1868	1920	126705	CHS	Tarvin
1855	1960	1500	1855	134600	LAN	Liverpool
1600	1944	1600	1900	145750	LAN	North Meols
1832	1992	1640	1832	114995	LAN	Southport
....	....	1800	....	118826	LAN	Southport
1861	1881	1821	1861	120588	LAN	Southport
1811	1900	1700	1900	126586	LAN	Southport
RIMMINGTON						
1550	1968	1650	1949	152668	LAN	Burnley
1840	1890	1840	1890	103225	LAN	Liverpool
1731	1862	1700	1890	108510	LIN	Bitchfield
1795	1920	1700	1795	139122	NTT	Worksop
1855	1901	1800	1855	175951	STS	Staveley
1550	1968	1650	1949	152668	WYK	Ingleton
1839	1862	1700	1890	108510	YKS	Hull
RING						
....	....	1800	1887	130141	COR	Boherbur
....	....	1800	1887	130141	COR	Kanturk
1850	1992	ALL	1850	159514	LND	ALL
1841	1881	1780	1980	118931	NTH	Kings Sutton
1880	1992	1700	1880	106186	SOM	Bath
1800	1900	1800	1992	177180	SOM	Bath
1850	1992	1750	1850	159514	WIL	Chippenham
RINGE						
1858	1950	1700	1900	169536	LND	ALL
1858	1950	1700	1900	169536	MDX	ALL
1729	1729	1680	1729	155276	SFK	Bredfield

Known From	To	Researching From	To	Ref	Cty	Place
RINGER						
1753	1907	1700	1907	141062	KEN	Chelsfield
1774	1850	1774	1850	105066	NFK	Bridgham
1400	1885	1400	1900	105066	NFK	Forncett St Peter
1740	1860	1700	1860	105066	NFK	Shotesham
1599	1793	1550	1800	105066	NFK	Tharston
1830	1930	1800	1930	105066	SFK	Mendham
RINGHAM						
....	....	1700	1830	112038	ALL	ALL
1875	1960	....	....	112038	CHS	Stockport
1790	1820	1700	1790	133167	LIN	Stamford
1800	1880	....	....	112038	LIN	Thurlby
1657	1866	....	1657	151688	RUT	Ryhall
1675	1988	1657	1675	159522	RUT	Ryhall
RINGROSE						
1700	1750	1680	1750	127655	CLA	Moynoe House
1735	1807	....	....	152234	EYK	Rudston
1899	1970	1700	1992	160377	NTT	Beeston
RINGSTEAD						
1730	1854	1700	1850	148725	NFK	Little Walsingham
RINGWOOD						
1851	1992	1851	1992	147230	LND	East End
1815	1841	1700	1841	147230	NFK	Hethel
1820	1880	ALL	1992	125113	NFK	Kings Lynn
1820	1880	ALL	1992	125113	NFK	Wells Next To Sea
1725	1802	1700	1850	126381	NFK	Wells
1820	1880	ALL	1992	125113	NFK	West Lynn
1790	1992	1700	1790	147230	NFK	Wreningham
RINNEL						
1840	1870	1750	1840	135658	DEV	Plymouth
RINTOUL						
....	....	1850	1992	158399	LND	ALL
1794	1818	1700	1900	110191	MDX	London
1805	1900	1805	1950	105759	SCT	South
....	....	1850	1940	158399	SCT	Edinburgh
1890	1992	1700	1900	167223	STI	Falkirk
RIORDAN						
1900	1920	1800	1920	150487	COR	Ballymakeera
....	....	1700	1850	150487	IRL	Coolea
RIORDEN						
1819	....	1800	....	168920	LND	Greenwich
RIPLEY						
1906	....	ALL	1910	170674	CAM	Cambridge
1752	1810	ALL	1752	100587	NYK	Ingleby Arnclife
1650	1900	1700	?	173185	WYK	Batley
1650	1900	1700	?	173185	WYK	Heckmon
....	....	1750	1800	147613	YKS	Bentham
....	....	1700	1775	147613	YKS	Kirkby Lonsdale
1820	1877	1820	1992	151521	YKS	Rotherham
1820	1877	1820	1992	151521	YKS	Sheffield
RIPPER						
1845	....	....	....	161136	LIN	Holbeach
1864	....	....	....	161136	LIN	Sutton Bridge
1864	....	....	....	161136	YKS	Sheffield
RIPPETH						
1778	1810	1700	1900	177970	DUR	Ryton
RIPPIN						
ALL	ALL	ALL	ALL	159530	ALL	ALL
RIPPINGALE						
1802	1888	1780	1900	108901	NTT	Newark
1865	1897	1860	1900	108901	NTT	Retford
RIPPINGHAM						
1860	1888	1860	1900	147184	LAN	Ashton Under Lyne
RIPPON						
1796	1832	1700	1796	149942	DUR	Stanhope
1798	....	1700	1798	149942	MDX	London
RISBRIDGER						
1800	1850	1800	1850	131547	SRY	Betchworth
1850	?	?	?	108189	SRY	Charlwood
1790	1906	1700	1900	168068	SXW	Horsham
RISDALE						
1860	1992	1650	1860	159549	LIN	North
1860	1992	1650	1860	159549	LIN	Isle Of Axholme
RISDON						
1493	1820	ALL	1493	104310	DEV	North
1493	1820	ALL	1493	104310	DEV	Black Torrington
RISELEY						
1639	1776	ALL	1639	168602	BDF	Bletsoe
1639	1776	ALL	1639	168602	BDF	Milton Ernest
1639	1776	ALL	1639	168602	BDF	Odell
RISHFORTH						
....	....	1650	1750	147613	YKS	Addingham
RISHTON						
1840	1992	1700	1840	117447	LAN	Haslingden
RISLEY						
....	....	ALL	ALL	128120	ALL	Name Study
RISTED						
1740	1764	1700	1800	118168	KEN	Bromley
RITCHIE						
1800	1920	1700	1800	123374	ABD	Birse
1800	1900	1800	1850	140864	ABD	Pitsligo
1791	1919	1700	1790	178896	ANS	Craig
1791	1919	1700	1790	178896	ANS	St Vigeans
....	....	1800	1875	174319	ANS	???
....	....	ALL	ALL	116823	DOW	ALL
1850	1900	1850	1900	152250	DOW	Bangor
1820	1860	1700	1820	100978	KCD	St Cyrus
1850	1992	1750	1850	173258	LKS	Lanark
1836	1844	....	....	118133	SCT	Gorbals
1916	1992	1700	1916	122114	WAR	Birmingham
RITSON						
1800	1820	1760	1900	139858	ALL	ALL
1844	1864	1800	1940	145734	CMA	Maryport
RIULF						
1250	1850	ALL	ALL	158771	ALL	ALL
RIVER						
....	....	ALL	ALL	166219	ALL	Name Study
RIVERS						
1800	1872	ALL	ALL	114618	BRK	Aldermaston
1665	1877	ALL	ALL	114618	BRK	Great Farrington
1756	1881	1600	1992	149659	BRK	Hagbourne
1450	1500	1400	1500	154881	KEN	Penshurst
1780	....	1750	1850	126144	KEN	Tonbridge
1865	1916	1800	1865	128384	LAN	Salford
....	....	1750	1850	108677	MDX	London
1880	....	1800	1992	143944	NRY	Thirsk
1735	1795	....	....	114618	OXF	Hagbourne
1804	1992	1750	1992	159581	SFK	Framlingham
1740	1811	ALL	1740	131059	SFK	Ipswich
1750	1805	....	....	131822	SFK	Shelly
RIVET						
1700	1724	1690	1724	128724	SFK	Little Saxham
RIVETT						
1600	1760	1710	1760	168467	DBY	???
1868	1892	....	....	115932	LAN	Manchester
1801	1989	1700	1800	159603	NFK	Great Yarmouth
1868	1892	....	....	115932	NFK	???
1955	1961	1930	1955	159603	???	Birmingham
RIX						
....	....	ALL	ALL	159638	ALL	Name Study
1850	1964	1840	1890	167851	MDX	London
1820	1840	1800	1850	167851	NFK	Holt
1817	1817	1800	1900	107980	NFK	Poringland
RIXON						
1851	....	ALL	1851	102334	ESS	Takely
1844	1865	....	....	159964	LAN	Kearsley
1820	1840	1800	1850	159964	LAN	Radcliffe
1936	1950	1700	1936	156221	NFK	ALL
RIXSON						
1797	1850	1600	1850	175641	KEN	Swanscombe
ROACH						
1870	1950	1870	1920	138096	AGY	Holyhead
1868	....	1800	1950	146978	AVN	Bristol
1872	1921	ALL	1872	152013	DEV	Plymouth
1836	1992	ALL	1899	152013	DEV	Stoke Pamerel
1850	1900	....	....	113514	GLA	Cardiff
1816	....	....	....	124982	GLS	Berkeley
1730	1800	1600	1800	154342	GLS	Bitton
1812	ALL	1780	1812	159654	GLS	Hillsley
1812	....	1700	1812	159654	GLS	Winterbourne
1750	1840	1650	1840	123862	GLS	???
1790	1790	1700	1800	136840	IOW	Newchurch
....	....	1820	1850	113514	IRL	Cork
....	....	1840	1870	138096	PEM	Dinas Cross
ROADHOUSE						
1600	1850	1600	1850	119717	YKS	Monkfrystone
ROADS						
1719	....	1650	1725	124796	BKM	Aylesbury
1500	1600	1400	1850	177180	BKM	Middle Claydon
....	....	1600	1992	102776	BKM	Quainton
1800	1850	1800	1850	124605	NTH	Kings Sutton
ROAN						
....	....	....	?	141216	GLS	Ashleworth
ROB						
1830	....	1750	1830	139483	CAE	Llanstumdwy
ROBBENS						
1830	1876	1750	1830	174068	SOM	Langport

Known From	To	Researching From	To	Ref	Cty	Place
ROBBINS						
1885	1915	1885	1930	165956	BRK	Bray
1840	1860	1700	1840	165956	BRK	Brimpton
1905	1992	1850	1905	176435	CON	???
1810	1851	ALL	1810	164623	DEV	Bideford
1802	?	....	....	103373	DEV	Braunton
1800	1885	1700	....	131253	DEV	Buckland Monochrome
1860	1885	....	....	165956	LND	Spitalfields
1850	1850	1700	1850	121568	SOM	Kilmersdon
1692	1820	1600	1820	177202	WAR	Fenny Compton
1820	1870	1820	1870	177202	WAR	Stretton On Dunsmore
ROBERDS						
1799	1799	1799	1799	136808	HUN	Warboys
ROBERT						
1824	1851	1800	1851	159743	BRE	Ystradgynlais
1802	1830	1780	1830	158658	CMN	Pembrey
1742	1790	1700	1841	176923	GLA	Llangyfelach
1790	1992	1750	1992	176923	GLA	Pontarddulais
1800	1992	1700	1800	135747	GSY	St Peter Port
ROBERTON						
1686	1992	ALL	1686	104035	IOW	ALL
ROBERTS						
1814	1877	1700	1814	127116	AGY	Amlwch
1864	1923	1860	1930	159786	AGY	Llaneugrad
1840	1920	1700	1840	169609	AGY	Llanfaethlu
1815	1942	1780	1870	162396	AGY	Llanfairmatha
1890	1992	1890	1992	116009	ANT	Belfast
1792	1858	ALL	....	115355	BDF	ALL
1792	1813	ALL	1813	168718	BDF	North West
1808	1841	1808	ALL	175854	BDF	Luton
1598	1598	1560	1600	124974	BRK	Hurst
....	....	1750	1900	116173	CAE	Aberdaron
1789	1867	1789	1867	104027	CAE	Glanwydden
1882	1912	1851	1882	159778	CAE	Llanarmon
1724	1907	1724	1907	104027	CAE	Llanbedr-Y-Cennin
1900	1930	1850	1900	138207	CAE	Llangnadl
1880	1935	1880	1992	159794	CAE	Llangystenin
1700	1829	1700	1850	132217	CAE	Penmachno
1810	1900	1795	1900	132217	CAE	Porthmadog
1760	1881	ALL	1759	158631	CAE	Tyddynysguborif
1860	1930	1800	1860	138207	CAE	Tydneiliog
1806	1880	....	....	138401	CAE	Yspytty Ifan
1783	1921	1575	1783	108839	CAM	Sutton
....	....	1660	1750	103713	CAM	Waterbeach
1833	1851	1800	1833	127116	CHS	Chester
....	....	1840	1875	174289	CHS	Liverpool
1895	1992	....	....	143294	CHS	Tranmere
1788	1800	....	....	127957	CHS	Wybunbury
1750	1809	ALL	1809	168718	CON	South East
1828	1906	1700	1992	116009	CON	Cawsand
1840	1945	1750	1992	117609	CON	Constantine
1818	....	1818	1992	129348	CON	Falmouth
1806	1806	1700	1806	161837	CON	Gorran
1828	1906	1700	1992	116009	CON	Kingsand
1793	1805	1750	1825	133450	CON	Lostwithiel
1819	?	1819	?	137324	CON	Madron
1852	1992	1700	1852	101567	CON	Penzance
1805	1816	1769	1805	103918	CON	Saltash
1804	1992	1600	1804	150142	CON	St Agnes
1852	1992	1700	1852	101567	CON	St Levan
....	....	1700	....	159824	CON	St Pinnock
1620	1900	1620	1992	127124	CON	The Lizard
1840	1950	1840	1900	147419	CON	Zelah
1649	1740	1600	1649	102571	CON	Zennor
1829	1856	1800	1920	166677	CON	???
1851	1980	1805	1851	162221	CWD	Brymbo
1778	....	?	1800	103934	DBY	Bakewell
1826	1828	1800	1830	102121	DBY	Ilkeston
1844	1878	1700	1900	135968	DBY	Swadlincote
1780	....	....	....	138401	DEN	Abergele
1746	1780	1712	1780	159786	DEN	Abergele
1821	....	1800	1860	149292	DEN	Derwen
1681	1803	1681	1803	104027	DEN	Fforddlas Bridge
1825	1837	1750	1837	121126	DEN	Henllan
1883	1939	1900	1939	159794	DEN	Llanelian
1812	1992	1750	1850	152692	DEN	Llannefydd
1804	1886	....	....	138401	DEN	Llysfaen
1820	1840	1820	1840	102121	DEN	Ysbyty Ifan
....	....	1750	1850	106607	DEN	Yspytty-Ifan
1750	1785	....	....	141798	DEV	Bovey Tracy
1821	1906	....	....	159751	DEV	Bratton Clovelly
1720	1890	....	....	159751	DEV	Bridestowe
1641	1695	....	....	159751	DEV	Crediton
ROBERTS contd.						
1865	1901	....	....	159751	DEV	Lewtrenchard
1818	1820	1786	1800	141798	DEV	Plymouth
1644	1960	....	....	164399	DEV	Thrushelton
1901	1992	....	....	159751	DEV	Torquay
1820	1850	1760	1870	151947	DFD	Brecfa
1830	1850	1820	1850	135895	DOR	Weymouth
1930	1930	1930	1992	166073	ESS	Barking
1782	1829	1700	1782	147885	FLN	Bodfari
1796	1898	ALL	ALL	147621	FLN	Holywell
1835	1954	ALL	1835	147389	FLN	Meliden
1820	1978	1820	1978	124842	FLN	Mostyn
1843	1943	....	....	147621	FLN	Tremeirchion
1805	1992	ALL	1805	162221	FLN	Treuddyn
1830	....	1700	1800	157147	FLN	Whitford
1861	1985	1861	1985	159743	GLA	Aberdare
....	....	ALL	ALL	110388	GLA	Cardiff
1800	1880	1700	1900	156442	GLA	Cardiff
1870	1960	1700	1870	157996	GLA	Cardiff
1862	1910	1750	1900	131792	GLA	Merthyr Tydfil
1684	1712	1650	1684	148938	GLS	Arlingham
1819	1848	ALL	1848	104299	GLS	Bristol
1837	1929	1750	1837	155225	GLS	East Dean
1822	?	1700	1822	176052	GLS	Gloucester
1844	....	....	....	172723	GSY	???
1874	1992	....	1874	125814	GYN	???
1810	1824	1750	1820	159700	HEF	St Margaret
....	....	?	?	179159	HRT	???
1850	1870	1800	1850	108359	HUN	Ellington
1800	....	1700	1800	108359	HUN	Thorney
1850	1992	1800	1850	108359	HUN	Woodwalton
1820	1880	1700	1850	129755	KEN	Goudhurst
1817	1864	....	....	121835	KEN	Strood
1700	1850	1725	1840	127655	LAN	Burnley
1824	1900	1800	1992	167673	LAN	Cliviger
1847	1900	ALL	1847	152021	LAN	Everton
....	....	?	1897	143294	LAN	Hulme
1826	1887	1700	1826	153109	LAN	Leigh
1835	1900	1600	1835	120189	LAN	Liverpool
1855	1860	1800	1855	135658	LAN	Liverpool
1847	1900	ALL	1847	152021	LAN	Liverpool
1855	1930	1800	1850	165093	LAN	Liverpool
1870	1930	1800	1930	167258	LAN	Liverpool
1843	1868	1700	1868	178233	LAN	Liverpool
....	....	ALL	ALL	167827	LAN	Manchester
1700	1850	1725	1840	127655	LAN	Padiham
1700	1850	1725	1840	127655	LAN	Rochdale
1750	1992	....	....	159816	LAN	Wigan
....	....	1650	1950	124656	LEI	Coalville
1816	1928	1780	1992	102407	LEI	Kirkby
1862	1992	1862	1930	169323	LEI	Leicester
1816	1928	1780	1992	102407	LEI	Mallory
....	....	1650	1950	124656	LEI	Shepshed
1878	1950	1700	1900	135968	LEI	Whitwick
....	....	1600	1900	124656	LEI	???
1872	1992	1808	1992	103012	LIN	South
1920	1992	ALL	1920	176656	LIN	Grimsby
1820	....	....	....	157724	LIN	Langtoft
1851	....	1800	1870	149292	LKS	Glasgow
1880	1980	1800	1880	132187	LND	South
....	....	ALL	1900	151602	LND	Battersea
1849	1851	1700	1992	166073	LND	Bethnall Green
1851	1861	....	....	161357	LND	Camberwell
1893	1917	1700	1992	166073	LND	East End
1880	1880	1880	1880	147575	LND	Hackney
1800	1880	1800	1910	173622	LND	Hackney
1840	1850	1700	1992	166073	LND	Limehouse
1792	1850	1750	1850	157732	LND	St Marylebone
1829	1960	1750	1829	134074	LND	???
1846	1866	1800	1866	147575	LND	???
....	....	1870	1955	159840	MDX	Fulham
1840	1870	1750	1840	146285	MDX	Islington
....	....	1840	1899	164801	MDX	Islington
1885	1950	1885	1940	102016	MDX	London
1815	1893	1700	1992	166073	MDX	Mileend
....	....	1820	1860	159840	MDX	Poplar
1880	ALL	....	....	142158	MDX	Popular
1843	1849	1700	1992	166073	MDX	Ratclife Stepney
1811	1840	1700	1992	166073	MDX	St Dunstans
1801	1900	1700	1992	166073	MDX	Stepney
....	....	1700	1950	143219	MER	Gwyddelwern
1860	1910	1860	1992	102016	MER	Llanbrynmair
1800	1992	1700	1800	149241	MER	Llandrillo
1800	1992	1700	1800	149241	MER	Llanfor

ROBERTS contd.

Known From	To	Researching From	To	Ref	Cty	Place
1740	1820	1740	1820	111538	MER	Llangowek
1820	1930	1820	1930	111538	MER	Llanowchllyn
1820	1860	1750	1820	102016	MER	Pennal
1862	1896	ALL	ALL	169897	MGY	Alberbury
1700	1795	1700	1890	161292	MGY	Llanbrynmwr
1851	1918	1820	1880	166677	MGY	Llanfyllin
1776	1992	1600	1776	156914	MGY	Llangyllin
1830	1906	1800	1880	156981	MGY	Macchynlleth
1630	1700	ALL	ALL	161292	MGY	Trefyglys
1810	1881	1750	1840	159700	MON	Grosmont
1840	1900	1840	1900	140295	MON	Newport
1786	1959	1700	1786	159735	MON	St Mellons
1811	1868	1800	1868	147575	MON	Usk
1805	1992	1805	1992	159689	NFK	Copusty
1700	1943	1700	1943	156353	NFK	Crimplesham
1800	1884	1700	1850	120081	NTH	South
1855	1955	1700	1855	166111	NTH	Bozeat
1841	1851	1775	1851	169323	NTH	Guilsborough
1859	1859	1830	1860	169323	NTH	Naseby
1600	1730	1600	1730	127655	NTH	Staverton
....	....	1600	1900	124273	NWL	Carnarfon
1730	1750	1670	1750	144606	OXF	Witney
1813	1877	1700	1813	162035	PEM	St Issels
1843	1854	1817	1900	171530	RFW	Paisley
1840	1865	1760	1880	174599	SAL	Broseley
1813	1891	1700	1813	169021	SAL	Chirbury
1830	1860	....	1880	113034	SAL	Selattyn
1840	1865	ALL	1840	178934	SAL	Sellatyn
1800	1890	1870	1950	108359	SAL	Shrewsbury
1819	1864	....	1819	131741	SAL	Westbury
1819	1864	....	1819	131741	SAL	Worthen
1825	1863	1700	1825	117927	SRY	Lambeth
....	1800	....	....	174564	SSX	Dallington
1767	1781	1600	1767	164879	SSX	Upper Beeding
1800	1818	....	....	127957	SSX	Walberton
1818	1862	....	....	127957	SSX	Worthing
1800	1817	ALL	1850	171530	STI	Alva
1906	1992	....	....	118699	STS	Cannock
1807	1992	ALL	1807	116408	STS	West Bromwich
1807	1992	ALL	1807	116408	WAR	Birmingham
1818	1838	1800	1838	128449	WAR	Birmingham
1835	1880	1775	1835	163201	WEX	Newtown Barry
....	....	1800	1915	159808	WIL	Swindon
....	....	ALL	1891	159808	WLS	ALL
1845	1903	1800	1845	118710	WLS	North
....	1832	1600	1832	153591	WLS	Wrexham
1818	1818	1750	....	140783	WOR	Birlingham
1818	1837	1800	1837	128449	WOR	Birmingham
1830	1988	1750	1830	165271	WOR	Broadway
1784	1809	1750	1992	166197	WOR	Conderton
1831	1910	1800	1992	166197	WOR	Eldersfield
1773	1800	1700	1773	145963	WOR	Kidderminster
1809	1890	1800	1992	166197	WOR	Longdon
1890	1930	1850	1992	166197	WOR	Pendock
1580	1850	....	1580	101761	WRY	Honley
1820	1830	1600	1820	175382	YKS	Bradford
1747	1869	1730	1880	129798	YKS	Farnley
1891	1900	....	....	121061	YKS	Harswell
1780	1810	1750	1820	123595	YKS	Holmfirth
1772	....	ALL	1772	159026	YKS	Hooton Ruberts
1790	1860	1700	1800	112224	YKS	Keighley
1818	1818	....	1818	162825	YKS	Leeds
1868	1918	....	....	145912	YKS	Wakefield
....	....	....	....	164895	???	Birkenhead
1898	1992	1881	1898	158631	???	Rhoslan
....	....	....	....	164895	???	Wirral
?	?	?	?	115142	???	???

ROBERTSHAW

Known From	To	Researching From	To	Ref	Cty	Place
1812	1892	....	1812	176702	WYK	Northowram
1800	1900	ALL	1900	140813	YKS	Halifax
1705	1768	1500	1800	102520	YKS	Thornton
1818	1852	....	1830	169412	YKS	Thronton

ROBERTSON

Known From	To	Researching From	To	Ref	Cty	Place
1800	1856	1700	1992	100226	ABD	Dyce
1850	1992	1800	1850	174653	ANS	Dundee
1851	1901	....	....	137936	ANS	Inverkeillour
1850	....	1750	1850	159891	ANS	Kirriemuir
1819	1820	1800	1850	159964	AYR	Ardrossan
1816	1840	ALL	1816	146757	AYR	Coylton
1822	1888	ALL	1822	146757	AYR	Kilmarnock
1800	1992	1500	1800	176478	AYR	Kilmarnock
1800	1992	1700	1800	157708	AYR	Maybole
1816	1840	ALL	1816	146757	AYR	Tarbolton

ROBERTSON contd.

Known From	To	Researching From	To	Ref	Cty	Place
1781	1871	1700	1900	147958	BDF	Clophill
1800	1850	ALL	ALL	122297	DUR	South Shields
1840	1992	1840	1900	159905	DUR	South Shields
1840	1925	1840	1992	149098	DUR	Sunderland
1890	1992	1800	1890	145041	DUR	Trimdons
1815	1835	1815	1835	159905	ELN	Prestow Pans
1829	1992	1700	1839	170453	FIF	ALL
1845	1883	1700	1845	159867	FIF	???
1820	1852	1820	1852	159875	INV	Elgol
1820	1852	1820	1852	159875	INV	Skye
1910	1992	1900	1992	133450	KEN	???
1789	1992	1500	1789	159956	LKS	Glasgow
1847	1847	1600	1847	100579	LKS	Old Monkland
1820	1860	....	1860	116866	LKS	???
1860	1870	....	....	151238	LND	Aldgate
1900	1992	1900	1992	133450	LND	???
1800	1854	1700	1860	149098	LTN	Inveresk
1860	1992	ALL	1860	102334	MDX	Bethnal Green
1830	1900	1700	1830	118419	MOR	Bellie
1854	1865	1805	1854	119628	NAI	Elgin
1772	1851	1700	1880	159379	PER	Aberfeldy
1805	1826	1700	1885	131423	PER	Blair Atholl
1810	1840	ALL	ALL	171174	PER	Blairgowrie
1760	1840	....	....	159883	PER	Dalguise
1800	1870	....	....	159883	PER	Dalrulzion
....	....	ALL	1785	119326	PER	Dull
1805	1814	1800	1885	131423	PER	Dunkeld
1782	....	1750	1790	159891	PER	Inchture
1782	....	1750	1790	159891	PER	Meigle
....	....	ALL	1805	119326	PER	Moulin
1816	1893	....	....	141798	PER	Perth
....	....	1600	1800	149098	PER	Pitochry
1813	....	1750	1850	141739	PER	Struan
....	....	1700	1992	137855	RFW	Paisley
1810	1838	1800	1838	147575	SCT	???
1881	1936	ALL	1881	106860	SFK	Woodbridge
1750	1992	1650	1992	104671	SHI	Bressay
1770	1875	1737	1900	159948	SHI	Bressay
1750	1965	....	....	137820	SHI	Fetlar
1720	1965	....	....	137820	SHI	Mid Yell
1750	1992	1650	1992	104671	SHI	Nesting
1780	1992	1780	1992	159948	SHI	Nesting
1760	1965	....	....	137820	SHI	North Yell
1758	1965	....	....	137820	SHI	Northmavine
1720	1965	....	....	137820	SHI	South Yell
1762	....	....	....	132381	SHI	Unst
1750	1992	1650	1992	104671	SHI	Yell
1831	1905	1700	1992	167177	SHI	Yell
1800	1880	1800	1880	128856	SRY	Dorking
....	1826	1800	1850	146927	STI	Falkirk
1803	1905	1700	1850	179000	STI	Polmont
1865	1865	1800	1992	175889	STI	Stirling
1840	1860	1800	1900	167088	WIL	Warminster
1850	1992	1650	1850	167789	WLN	Bo'ness
1780	....	1700	1780	124427	???	Holm

ROBEY

Known From	To	Researching From	To	Ref	Cty	Place
1795	1861	1600	1795	169595	BRK	Longcott
....	....	1900	1930	179280	ESS	Leytonstone
....	....	1780	1815	179280	ESS	Stratford
1815	1900	....	....	179280	MDX	Bow

ROBIE

Known From	To	Researching From	To	Ref	Cty	Place
1862	1865	1829	1897	167290	MDX	St Pancras

ROBIN

Known From	To	Researching From	To	Ref	Cty	Place
1550	1992	1400	1950	125296	GSY	???

ROBINET

Known From	To	Researching From	To	Ref	Cty	Place
....	....	1200	1830	124958	ALL	ALL
1740	1850	....	....	124958	CAM	Foulmire
1630	1800	1800	1830	124958	HUN	Yaxley
1843	1992	....	....	124958	???	Bristol

ROBINETT

Known From	To	Researching From	To	Ref	Cty	Place
1900	1992	1700	1900	149705	CAM	Whittlesey

ROBINI

Known From	To	Researching From	To	Ref	Cty	Place
1920	1992	1700	1920	158836	ALL	ALL

ROBINS

Known From	To	Researching From	To	Ref	Cty	Place
1770	1880	ALL	1800	168718	BDF	North West
1824	1906	1700	1845	156051	CON	Kenwyn
1800	1900	1700	1850	107697	CON	Liskeard
1840	1900	1700	1840	165549	CON	St Austell
1820	1900	1800	1900	142875	CON	Truro
1860	1927	ALL	1860	172502	MDX	Isle Of Dogs
1827	1875	1700	1827	167533	MDX	Shoreditch
1680	1840	1480	1840	113646	NTH	Long Buckby
1680	1840	1480	1840	113646	NTH	West Haddon

Known From	To	Researching From	To	Ref	Cty	Place
ROBINS contd.						
1650	1850	....	....	176591	NTH	Yelvertoft
1824	1952	1700	1824	150320	SOM	Chiselborough
1812	1881	1600	....	135259	SOM	Yeovil
1850	1930	....	....	176591	STS	Burslem
1839	1900	?	1839	158569	WAR	Tysoe
....	....	ALL	1740	151602	WIL	Woodborough
1800	1850	ALL	ALL	163252	WOR	ALL
ROBINSON						
....	....	....	1850	116866	ANT	???
1890	1900	1900	1992	104728	AVN	Bristol
1840	1955	1650	1840	114545	BDF	Bedford
1840	1955	1650	1840	114545	BDF	Elstow
1762	1762	ALL	1762	108642	BDF	Riseley
1836	1841	1700	1992	110418	BRK	Bray
1841	1880	1700	1840	160911	CAM	Over
1678	1940	....	....	128996	CAM	Thorney
1850	1900	1700	1850	158216	CHS	Stockport
1820	....	1600	1860	175641	CHS	Wilmslow
1700	1800	1600	1700	173312	CHS	Wrenbury
1673	1747	1600	1673	141313	CLV	Marton
1841	1841	1700	1850	145955	CMA	Kendal
1698	1701	1680	1720	142018	CMA	Little Broughton
1774	1810	1500	1774	103624	CUL	North
....	....	1650	1750	116173	CUL	St Bees
1825	1888	1750	1825	153109	CUL	Whitehaven
1764	1827	ALL	1764	102350	DBY	Baslow
1732	1732	1600	1732	102830	DBY	Mugginton
....	....	1865	1875	154377	DBY	Whaley
1825	....	....	....	151785	DFS	???
1840	1940	1800	1840	101788	DOW	Greyabbey
....	....	1600	1992	108812	DOW	Rathriland
1820	1877	ALL	ALL	106844	DUR	Central
1772	....	1600	1772	116637	DUR	Aycliffe
1820	1900	1800	1900	142875	DUR	Bishop Auckland
1768	1768	ALL	1768	154563	DUR	Durham
1850	1992	1750	1880	112704	DUR	Hartlepool
1831	1856	1800	1992	146331	DUR	Pittington
1850	1930	1700	1850	158208	DUR	Weardale
1857	1870	1800	1858	167711	DUR	???
1757	1992	ALL	1757	160113	ENG	North
....	....	ALL	1700	125679	ESS	Arkesden
1780	1800	ALL	1780	131059	ESS	West Ham
1750	1800	1700	1800	154601	EYK	Catton
1840	1870	1750	1850	103055	FER	ALL
1863	1950	1700	1863	172448	FLN	Flint
1673	1755	1670	1750	142018	GLS	ALL
1846	1992	1700	1846	156264	GLS	Hinton
1807	1814	1750	1870	131547	HEF	Leintwardine
....	....	1780	1820	131962	IOM	Douglas
1831	1853	1791	1900	139114	KEN	Leeds
1820	1900	1820	1900	110523	LAN	Bacup
1700	1800	1700	1800	152404	LAN	Eccles
1760	1850	1600	1800	177318	LAN	Farnworth
1500	1600	1500	1600	109347	LAN	Great Harwood
1710	1740	1710	1740	107522	LAN	Haslingden
1810	1860	1810	1919	110523	LAN	Higham
1921	1969	....	....	159964	LAN	Kearsley
1870	1875	1600	1875	175382	LAN	Leeds
1860	1945	1860	1980	135631	LAN	Liverpool
1800	1822	1790	1992	110205	LAN	Manchester
1870	1960	1870	1960	161705	LAN	Manchester
1750	1880	1880	1920	111511	LAN	Oldham
1780	1992	ALL	1780	110000	LAN	Padiham
1820	1900	1820	1900	110523	LAN	Padiham
1500	1600	1500	1600	109347	LAN	Pendle
1750	1880	1880	1920	111511	LAN	Prescot
....	....	1800	1900	140805	LAN	Preston
1815	1930	....	....	159964	LAN	Ringley
1820	1900	1820	1900	110523	LAN	Rochdale
....	....	1700	1850	130931	LAN	Salford
1827	1960	1827	1960	148091	LAN	Stretford
1841	1992	1700	1841	115185	LAN	Tydesley
1700	1800	1600	1700	157740	LAN	Warton
1787	1909	1700	1909	159964	LAN	Windle
1590	1723	ALL	ALL	141615	LEI	Hinckley
....	....	1700	1825	101834	LIN	South
1850	1880	1550	1850	147265	LIN	South
....	....	1700	1860	141275	LIN	Barnetby Le Wold
....	1672	1500	1672	175072	LIN	Billinghay
1808	1851	1808	1851	160237	LIN	Boston
1808	1851	1808	1851	160237	LIN	Huttoft
1800	1900	ALL	1900	144290	LIN	Messingham
1660	1675	1600	1700	177024	LIN	Spridlington
ROBINSON contd.						
1890	1914	....	....	168106	LND	Bermondsey
1881	1923	1840	1881	143707	LND	Camberwell
1889	1919	....	....	169102	LND	Hammesmith
1875	1900	1800	1970	150703	MDX	Bethnal Green
1750	1840	1700	1750	147710	MDX	Enfield
1820	1870	1775	1890	116866	MDX	London
1850	1920	1800	1992	133450	MDX	Richmond
1844	ALL	ALL	1844	116734	MLN	Edinburgh
1718	1748	1700	1800	123536	NBL	Chatton
1715	1716	1700	1750	123536	NBL	Ellingham
1801	1890	1700	1800	132764	NBL	Newcastle
1717	1992	1660	1717	159980	NBL	Newcastle
1779	1850	ALL	1851	171751	NBL	Raw Green
1886	1893	1893	1992	156426	NBL	Woodhorn
1825	1992	1700	1825	101834	NFK	South West
1750	....	1650	1750	101443	NRY	Pickering
1788	1938	1700	1788	153001	NRY	Stanwick St Johns
....	....	1755	1860	159840	NRY	York
1823	1867	1750	1823	150150	NTH	Denton
1811	1811	....	....	108901	NTT	Langford
1877	1950	1877	1950	154377	NTT	Langwith
1803	1821	1780	1803	130877	NTT	Mansfield
....	....	1750	1840	154377	NTT	Warsop
1725	1815	1600	1992	157023	NYK	Appleton Le Street
....	....	1820	1900	171948	OXF	Stokenchurch
1745	1992	1500	1800	134155	ROX	Lilliesleaf
1844	ALL	ALL	1844	116734	SCT	???
1844	ALL	ALL	1844	116734	SHI	ALL
1865	1881	1855	1945	166898	SRY	Brixton
1730	1896	....	....	175439	SRY	Esher
1870	1982	1800	1870	168777	SRY	Farnham
1840	1992	1750	1840	159972	SSX	Appledram
1822	1992	....	1822	120979	STS	North
1841	1881	1700	1900	160059	STS	Audley
1770	1957	ALL	ALL	138223	STS	Brewood
1838	1868	1838	1868	156426	STS	Dudley
1800	1830	1700	1850	158216	STS	Newcastle
1808	....	....	....	145742	STS	Wednesbury
1841	1861	1790	1870	169323	STS	Wednesbury
1786	1875	ALL	1786	174815	STS	West Bromwich
1770	1957	....	....	138223	STS	Wolverhampton
....	....	ALL	1816	142298	TYR	???
1786	1875	ALL	1786	174815	WAR	Birmingahm
1695	....	ALL	1992	159174	WAR	Shustoke
1800	1880	1750	1980	135631	WES	Barbon
1830	1884	1700	1830	135151	WES	Cliburn
1841	1841	1700	1850	145955	WES	Kendal
1841	1992	1700	1850	119849	WIL	Allcannings
1866	1901	?	?	147869	WIL	Avebury
1691	1703	1680	1730	142018	WIL	Market Lavington
1790	1880	1880	1905	106127	WMD	Birmingham
1721	1730	1700	1730	160873	WOR	Dudley
1800	1811	1500	1800	176974	WOR	Tenbury
1852	....	ALL	ALL	112275	WOR	Wribbenhall
....	....	1730	1992	121940	WRY	Giggleswick
....	....	1730	1992	121940	WRY	Milldam
1814	1992	1600	1814	145971	WYK	Bradford
1814	1992	1600	1814	145971	WYK	Halifax
1840	1992	1750	1840	160008	WYK	Mirfield
1874	1992	1800	1876	116246	YKS	ALL
1790	1847	1790	1850	176958	YKS	Barnsley
....	....	1680	1780	154970	YKS	Bolton Abbey
1850	....	1850	....	109347	YKS	Bradford
1790	1800	....	1992	137634	YKS	Darfield
1779	1865	ALL	1779	154946	YKS	Eastrington
1821	1821	1800	1821	137979	YKS	Elland
1769	1812	1700	1769	117161	YKS	Fylingdales
1827	1960	1827	1960	148091	YKS	Huby
1828	1852	....	....	154024	YKS	Hull
1860	1992	1850	1926	167851	YKS	Hull
1779	1864	ALL	ALL	175587	YKS	Knaresborough
1820	1930	1800	1900	103128	YKS	Leeds
1875	1940	1700	1875	170607	YKS	Leeds
1864	1942	ALL	ALL	175587	YKS	Morley
1850	?	1800	1900	123293	YKS	Nasborough
1790	1847	1790	1850	176958	YKS	Ossett
1756	1758	....	....	151351	YKS	Otley
1740	1793	1500	1800	167843	YKS	Redmire Cum Bolton
1820	1880	1800	1900	169404	YKS	Richmond
1779	1838	1752	1779	117161	YKS	Scalby
1740	1948	ALL	1840	115215	YKS	Sessay
1790	1847	1790	1850	176958	YKS	Thornill
1751	1992	1700	1751	160024	YKS	Thornton

Known From	To	Researching From	To	Ref	Cty	Place
ROBINSON contd.						
1700	....	....	....	176958	YKS	Wakefield
1800	1828	1700	1850	115967	YKS	Whitby
1841	1971	....	1841	125954	YKS	Wilsden
1730	1896	....	....	175439	YKS	Womersley
1792	....	....	....	165484	YKS	Woolley
1762	1854	1730	1780	135763	YKS	York
1864	1926	....	....	120340	???	Carcroft
1864	1926	....	....	120340	???	Doncaster
1864	1926	....	....	120340	???	Owston
ROBJOHN						
1780	1860	1780	1860	110361	DEV	Tavistock
ROBLET						
....	....	?	?	178349	WLS	???
ROBLEY						
1820	1920	1700	1992	114596	CUL	Carlisle
ROBLIN						
1838	1880	1700	1900	166359	GLA	???
ROBSHAW						
1725	1870	1650	1725	137979	YKS	Hosburn
1725	1870	1650	1725	137979	YKS	Osbon
ROBSON						
1723	1885	ALL	ALL	158690	BAN	Banff
1723	1885	ALL	ALL	158690	BAN	Grange
1723	1885	ALL	ALL	158690	BAN	Marnoch
1513	1865	1513	1865	146366	BEW	Auchencraw
1871	1992	....	....	160148	CLV	Middlesborough
1859	1992	ALL	1859	160199	CUL	Alston
1840	1851	1750	1840	114693	DUR	Birtley
1735	1850	1600	1735	147729	DUR	Darlington
1700	1799	1700	1799	169781	DUR	Darlington
1850	1930	ALL	1850	160156	DUR	Gateshead
1898	1921	ALL	ALL	174505	DUR	Gateshead
1870	1871	1800	1891	126381	DUR	Hartlepool
1789	1827	1750	1789	111236	DUR	Monkwearmouth
1789	1852	1761	1789	160148	DUR	Sedgefield
1836	1992	....	....	175803	DUR	Shotley Bridge
1790	1920	ALL	ALL	122297	DUR	South Shields
1815	1840	1700	1800	136891	DUR	Sunderland
1837	1859	ALL	1837	160156	DUR	Sunderland
1739	1820	1680	1739	160598	DUR	Sunderland
1700	1800	1700	1800	169781	DUR	Sunderland
1760	1787	....	1830	171441	DUR	Wolviston
1825	1881	....	....	152234	EYK	Rudston
1832	1920	1800	1930	171441	KEN	Chatham
1770	1800	1760	1900	105759	KEN	Deptford
1810	1870	1780	1900	152528	KEN	Deptford
1880	1917	1860	1930	171441	KEN	Longfield
1930	1960	1920	1970	171441	KEN	Nerne Bay
1770	1880	....	....	131075	LIN	Scotter
1960	1992	....	....	171441	MDX	Hampton On Thames
1807	1830	1700	1806	131245	MDX	Stepney
1869	....	....	....	146447	NBL	Byker
1756	1851	1700	1793	130877	NBL	Chollerton
1760	1790	ALL	ALL	122297	NBL	Earsdon
1817	1864	ALL	1817	122386	NBL	Hexham
1688	1966	1650	1690	150894	NBL	Longhoughton
1869	....	....	....	146447	NBL	Newcastle Upon Tyne
1850	....	1851	....	171166	NBL	North Shields
1730	1760	ALL	ALL	122297	NBL	Shilbottle
1793	1851	1700	1793	130877	NBL	St John Lee
1750	....	....	....	146447	NBL	Stamfordham
1867	1910	ALL	1867	171573	NYK	Thornton Le Moor
1867	1910	....	....	171573	NYK	West Tanfield
1815	1840	ALL	1840	149063	ROX	Jedburgh
1840	1992	1600	1840	160172	YKS	East Rdg
....	....	1680	1710	177393	YKS	Owthorne
1872	1981	1840	1872	167568	YKS	???
ROBY						
....	....	ALL	ALL	113867	ALL	Name Study
1900	1950	1650	1900	113867	CHS	Chester
1800	1992	1700	1992	113867	LAN	Liverpool
1880	1940	....	....	121142	LAN	Liverpool
1840	1992	1800	1840	108359	LAN	Standish
1800	1992	1700	1992	113867	LAN	Wigan
ROCH						
....	....	1816	1869	116912	PEM	Pembroke Dock
ROCHARD						
....	....	1870	1920	176435	CON	???
ROCHE						
1857	1902	ALL	1857	152064	SCT	Glasgow
1835	....	1868	1992	130486	SCT	???
1790	....	1868	1992	130486	WAR	???

Known From	To	Researching From	To	Ref	Cty	Place
ROCHELLE						
1848	....	1750	1900	179078	SAL	Madely
ROCHESTER						
1734	1992	1585	1734	160202	ESS	Highlaver
1734	1992	1585	1734	160202	HRT	Sawbridge Worth
1725	....	ALL	1725	131059	KEN	Snodland
1800	1992	1800	1992	160210	NBL	Matfen
1795	1795	1700	1900	162620	NBL	Wylam On Tyne
1764	1810	1700	1763	132764	T&W	Monkwearmouth
ROCHFORT						
1780	1840	ALL	1800	141305	IRL	ALL
ROCK						
ALL	ALL	ALL	ALL	170909	ALL	ALL
1800	1850	ALL	1992	170909	ARM	???
1700	1805	1700	1805	107360	BKM	Stony Stratford
ALL	1884	ALL	1992	170909	MAY	Dumore
ALL	1884	ALL	1992	170909	MAY	Garryduff
1819	1877	1800	1820	174602	STS	Rowles Regis
1700	1800	1700	1800	123285	SYK	Worsbrough
1819	1877	1800	1820	174602	WOR	Dudles
ROCKCLIFFE						
1800	1850	1700	1800	129003	KEN	High Halstow
1800	1850	1700	1800	129003	KEN	Shorne
ROCKER						
....	....	ALL	ALL	161128	ALL	Name Study
ROCKETT						
....	....	ALL	ALL	152226	DEV	Bampton
1800	1900	1700	1850	152579	DEV	Stoke Damerel
1820	1992	1700	1992	117269	LND	Stepney
ROCKLEY						
1875	1900	1800	1875	135496	NTT	Nottingham
ROCKWELL						
1600	1700	1560	1700	154296	DOR	Dorchester
1650	1700	1560	1700	154296	LND	ALL
1560	1700	1560	1700	154296	SOM	Fitzhead
ROCLIFF						
1841	1852	1841	1992	149098	MDX	London
RODAS						
1712	1733	1600	1725	101575	YKS	Snaith
RODD						
1732	1907	1732	1907	116424	CON	South East
RODDA						
1809	1860	....	....	107174	CON	Breage
1810	1900	1500	1800	136972	CON	Camborne
1810	1900	1500	1800	136972	CON	Crowan
....	....	1700	1800	154261	CON	Gulval
1800	1992	....	....	154261	CON	Newquay
....	....	1800	1900	136972	CON	Penzance
1826	1992	1700	1826	140449	CON	St Erth
RODDAM						
1767	1826	1750	1850	130990	NBL	Allendale
RODDER						
1775	1775	ALL	1775	122017	CON	Illogan
RODDY						
....	....	1800	1879	163090	IRL	Bauaghadereen
1600	1850	1600	1850	163090	IRL	Fenagh
1850	1992	1800	1850	156574	ROS	Laughlyn
1879	1992	1855	1879	163090	STS	Lichfield
RODELL						
1850	1890	1700	1890	168211	BDF	Luton
RODEN						
....	....	ALL	ALL	160237	ALL	Name Study
1562	1992	1562	1800	160237	SAL	ALL
1562	1860	1770	1840	149993	SAL	Sutton Maddock
1536	1992	1536	1800	160237	STS	ALL
1589	1992	1589	1800	160237	WAR	ALL
1580	1992	1580	1800	160237	WOR	ALL
RODENHURST						
1830	1874	1700	1874	138088	SAL	Ellesmere
RODGER						
1702	1807	1600	1702	152196	CMA	Ennerdale
RODGERS						
1850	1926	1800	1992	149772	LAN	Chadderton
1839	1873	1500	1839	110310	LAN	Liverpool
1840	1870	1840	1920	162507	LAN	Liverpool
1871	1900	....	....	160245	LEI	Kegworth
1900	1992	1865	1910	160245	LEI	Loughborough
1800	1992	....	....	160245	LEI	Shepshed
1700	1800	1650	1700	160245	LEI	Wymeswold
1872	1992	ALL	1872	115878	LIN	Morton By Bourne
1813	1868	ALL	1850	162507	NIR	Omagh
....	....	1700	1754	160245	NTT	Costock
....	....	1700	1754	160245	NTT	Rempstone
1720	1780	1650	1720	121339	NYK	Bolton Castle

Known From	To	Researching From	To	Ref	Cty	Place
RODGERS contd.						
1800	1900	1700	1900	124621	TYR	Killyman
1800	1900	1700	1900	132446	TYR	Killyman
....	....	1770	1800	117137	WIL	Marlborough
....	....	1770	1800	117137	WIL	Ramsbury
1759	1780	1700	1800	160253	WYK	Bingley
1759	....	1700	1800	160253	WYK	Halifax
1785	1992	ALL	ALL	160253	WYK	Huddersfield
1833	1952	1700	1833	128031	YKS	Brampton Bierlow
1795	1900	....	....	102946	YKS	Sheffield
1658	1792	1640	1658	101796	YKS	Woolley
RODHAM						
1884	1911	ALL	1950	177695	DUR	Beamish
RODNEY						
1810	1850	1700	1820	160717	CUL	Skelton
1841	1914	1750	1841	160717	IRL	???
RODOCANACHI						
1500	1950	ALL	ALL	162620	ALL	ALL
RODWAY						
1720	1818	ALL	ALL	113662	GLS	Bisley
1760	1850	ALL	ALL	113700	GLS	Hawkesbury
1750	1780	ALL	ALL	113700	GLS	Ozleworth
1680	1750	ALL	ALL	113700	GLS	Wooton Under Edge
RODWELL						
1820	1840	ALL	1840	134058	BKM	Wingrave
1876	1941	1750	1876	168025	KEN	Chislehurst
1750	1920	1700	1920	178047	SFK	Hadleigh
ROE						
1748	1864	1712	1900	107360	BKM	Stewkley
1740	1781	....	....	178330	CHS	Macclesfield
1698	1723	....	....	178330	DBY	Castleton
1768	1820	1820	1992	148180	DBY	Snelston
1900	1992	1880	1992	113778	DUR	Hartlepool
1813	1906	1700	1813	145823	HRT	Eastwick
....	....	1650	1950	124656	LEI	Coalville
....	....	1650	1950	124656	LEI	Shepshed
1704	1748	1600	1748	123404	LEI	Swannington
1704	1748	1600	1748	123404	LEI	Whitwick
....	....	1600	1900	124656	LEI	???
1800	....	....	1800	158305	LIN	Skirbeck
1800	1820	ALL	....	104515	LIN	Stoxton
1500	1600	1450	1600	154881	LND	Wanstead
....	....	ALL	1910	178403	LND	???
1839	1912	....	....	130958	MDX	Whitechapel
1800	1900	....	....	151572	NFK	Norwich
1770	1900	1600	1900	113778	NYK	Egton
1740	1870	1740	1870	148210	RUT	Langham
1605	1679	1580	1605	115819	SAL	Wrockwardine
1700	1800	1600	1750	144606	SOM	South
1775	1825	1700	1850	106631	SOM	Bleadon
1600	1860	1600	1900	154881	TIP	Rockwell
....	....	ALL	1910	178403	YKS	Sheffield
ROE-HUGHES						
1806	1818	....	....	105147	SAL	Bromfield
ROEBUCK						
1837	1980	1837	1864	156892	LAN	Manchester
1801	1883	1749	1846	108391	MDX	Islington
1837	1953	1837	1953	156892	YKS	Huddersfield
1814	1919	1650	1814	168513	YKS	Huddersfield
1794	1840	1700	1820	146897	YKS	Wakefield
ROFEY						
1892	1892	1840	1900	172324	YKS	Frange
ROFFE						
1752	1778	1600	1752	145289	HAM	Isle Of Wight
1820	1905	1780	1905	179256	HRT	Redbourne
1820	1905	1780	1905	179256	HRT	St Albans
ROFFEY						
1900	1920	1850	1900	158976	BKM	South
ALL	ALL	ALL	ALL	160261	SRY	ALL
1750	1830	1700	1800	144657	SRY	Lingfield
ROGAN						
1832	1992	1801	1992	112305	LKS	Coatbridge
ROGER						
1760	1820	1700	1850	176788	ABD	Aberdeen
ROGERS						
1725	1992	1600	1992	164607	BDF	South
1810	1880	1750	1810	133671	BDF	Langford
1823	....	1700	1850	143693	BKM	Bledlow
1801	....	1700	1850	143693	BKM	Chenies
1788	1880	1600	1992	164607	BKM	Mid
....	....	1650	1890	102318	BKM	Monks Risborough
1700	1900	....	....	114243	BKM	Newport Pagnell
1777	1947	1700	1900	126683	BKM	Penn
1700	1900	....	....	114243	BKM	Sherington
ROGERS contd.						
1809	1860	1600	1809	100447	BKM	Stokenchurch
....	....	ALL	ALL	117390	BRK	Reading
1856	1936	1800	1856	172138	CAR	Bagnelstown
1841	1871	ALL	ALL	131415	CMN	Laugharne
1700	1992	ALL	1992	168696	CON	East
1700	1850	1650	1700	132942	CON	Crowan
1865	1992	?	1865	129615	CON	Gwinear
1840	1992	1800	1870	166901	CON	Phillack
1775	1825	1820	1835	105694	DEN	Ruabon Rhos Llanerchrigog
1860	....	1800	1860	140473	DEV	Devonport
1796	1861	1796	1862	141895	DEV	North Huish
ALL	1900	....	....	106747	DEV	Plymouth
1880	1980	1700	1880	138649	DEV	Plymouth
1839	1903	....	....	147672	DEV	Tavistock
1860	1880	1850	1860	133221	DOR	Holdenhurst
1750	1800	1550	1700	147583	DOR	Rampisham
....	....	1700	1900	143359	ESS	Aveley
....	1880	1805	....	123609	ESS	Wethersfield
....	....	1600	1809	100447	GLS	Bibury
1750	1800	1600	1800	154342	GLS	Bisley
1750	1800	1600	1800	154342	GLS	Bitton
1657	....	....	....	176958	GLS	Shepton Mallet
....	....	1700	1899	174963	GLS	Stroud
1809	1809	1700	1809	102830	GLS	Wyck Rissington
1765	1822	....	....	133221	HAM	Fordingbridge
1740	1770	1700	1780	136840	HAM	Fordingbridge
1800	1992	1700	1800	160318	HAM	Portsmouth
1869	1992	1700	1869	160288	HAM	Portsmouth
1840	1930	1750	1900	113859	HAM	Southsea
1717	1748	ALL	1717	169730	HAM	Wootten St Lawrence
1790	1840	1700	1920	147508	HEF	Pembroke
1869	1992	1700	1869	160288	IOW	Newport
1867	1992	ALL	ALL	115762	IRL	Dublin
1790	1800	1700	1790	121339	IRL	Waterford
1856	1856	1700	1900	146234	KRS	Bowhouse
1870	1875	1800	1870	135658	LAN	Liverpool
....	....	1682	1715	160245	LEI	Seagrave
1790	1850	1600	1850	160369	LIN	Grantham
1750	1800	1750	1800	123765	LIN	Louth
1841	1934	....	....	120340	LIN	Thorne
1863	1979	1600	1863	123420	LND	South East
1788	1872	1788	1872	102806	LND	St Pancras
1886	....	1750	1992	179183	MDX	Bromley
1889	1982	ALL	1889	108642	MDX	Ealing
1926	1945	....	....	120340	MDX	Enfield
1814	1844	1750	1881	160636	MDX	Shoreditch
1889	1982	ALL	1889	108642	MDX	Southall
1820	1850	1700	1820	167649	MGY	Berriew
1845	1868	1800	1900	105449	NBL	North Shields
1712	1773	....	....	171654	NTH	Whittlebury
....	....	1600	?	160369	NTT	Newark
1695	1750	....	....	132756	OXF	Bicester
1695	1750	....	....	132756	OXF	Thame
1820	1930	1800	1870	160350	OXF	Witney
1750	1800	1600	1900	120677	PEM	St Florence
1677	1771	....	....	155055	SAL	Boscobel
....	....	1750	1900	165247	SAL	Ironbridge
1771	1992	1700	1771	174378	SAL	Kinnerley
1841	1881	ALL	1841	109797	SAL	Sandford
?	?	?	?	138622	SAL	???
1848	....	1700	1850	115967	SOM	Bath
1742	1742	....	....	135437	SOM	Pilton
1658	....	....	1658	149888	SOM	Taunton
1890	1960	1860	1930	124745	SRY	North
....	....	1700	1800	118834	SSX	Prinsted
1852	1865	ALL	1852	165263	SSX	Rotherfield
....	....	....	?	141216	STS	Leek
1664	1754	?	1664	128910	WAR	Bulkington
....	....	ALL	ALL	117390	WIL	ALL
1500	1900	1500	1900	170216	WIL	ALL
....	....	1750	1900	151084	WIL	Melksham
1840	1860	1700	1992	124966	WIL	Teffont
1840	....	1750	1840	173673	WOR	Dudley
?	?	?	?	138622	WOR	???
1810	1830	1700	1900	121762	YKS	ALL
1800	....	ALL	ALL	114847	???	Bristol
1872	1912	....	....	120340	???	Hull
....	....	1600	1700	160245	???	London
ROGERSON						
....	....	1800	1890	160393	CHS	Canals
1795	1917	1700	1795	170437	LAN	Fazakerley
1871	1881	1850	1871	113050	LAN	Manchester

Known From	To	Researching From	To	Ref	Cty	Place
ROGERSON contd.						
1805	1859	1859	1992	117099	LAN	Manchester
1841	1992	ALL	ALL	160385	LAN	Manchester
1897	1992	1800	....	160393	LAN	Salford
1796	1875	1796	1875	149403	YKS	Royston
ROGGERS						
1595	1614	1560	1595	102571	CON	Constantine
ROKER						
1845	....	ALL	1845	179515	SRY	Godalming
ROLES						
1860	....	ALL	ALL	154091	MDX	Hackney
ROLF						
1819	1992	ALL	1819	125776	SSX	ALL
ROLFE						
1842	1843	1840	1851	123129	CMN	Cynheidre
1871	1992	1871	1992	123129	CMN	Llangennech
1851	1881	1843	1851	123129	CMN	Llannon
1788	1855	ALL	1992	112631	HAM	Andover
1814	1871	ALL	ALL	105015	HAM	Baughurst
1798	1798	1760	1800	116114	KEN	Ashford
1800	1900	ALL	1850	131059	KEN	Maidstone
1737	1812	....	....	133736	KEN	Yalding
1810	1826	1781	1841	123129	SFK	Chevington
1851	1881	1848	1851	123129	SFK	Horringer
1810	1826	1781	1841	123129	SFK	Ickworth
1841	1848	1826	1851	123129	SFK	Rede
1819	1992	ALL	1819	125776	SSX	ALL
1904	1960	1600	1904	169595	WIL	Alderbury
ROLLASON						
1788	1880	1700	1788	156248	STS	Sedgley
1711	1814	1680	1820	160873	WOR	Dudley
ROLLESTONE						
1759	1818	1660	1820	165972	DEV	Morchard Bishop
ROLLINSON						
1774	....	....	....	142859	LAN	Broughton
1870	1950	ALL	1900	152021	LIN	Wainfleet
1750	1780	1700	1800	108111	WOR	Dudley
1760	1900	1700	1900	121762	YKS	Sheffield
ROLLO						
1750	1954	1725	1750	150312	FIF	Leuchars
1801	....	ALL	1801	102350	SCT	St Andrews
ROLLS						
....	....	ALL	ALL	160415	ALL	Name Study
1800	1850	1700	1850	148784	DOR	Weymouth
1700	1900	....	....	160415	DOR	???
1700	1900	....	....	160415	HAM	???
?	?	?	?	168548	LND	Southwark
1850	1900	....	....	160415	YKS	???
ROLPH						
1774	1860	1750	1860	171549	HAM	Brading
1760	1900	1700	1760	157074	HRT	Kings Langley
ROLSON						
1750	1772	ALL	ALL	141615	LEI	Kibworth
ROLSTONE						
1787	1850	....	1787	177504	DEV	Bridford
ROMAIN						
1843	....	1800	1860	109363	LND	Islington East
1823	1843	1750	1880	109363	WIL	Urchfont
ROMAINE						
....	....	1800	1900	109894	DOR	Bere Regis
1871	1881	1830	1871	140880	SSX	Brighton
ROMERIL						
1688	1688	ALL	ALL	115126	CHI	ALL
ROMMANS						
1764	1780	1600	1764	124257	YKS	Acaster
1764	1780	1600	1764	124257	YKS	Bilborough
ROMNEY						
1700	1800	1800	1900	175307	LAN	Furness
1849	1900	1800	1950	175307	LND	ALL
RONALD						
1750	1810	ALL	ALL	107425	SCT	Kirkliston
RONALDS						
....	....	ALL	ALL	120065	ALL	Name Study
1803	1861	1700	1803	150150	LND	Whitechapel
RONKSLEY						
....	....	1890	1992	147613	YKS	Sheffield
RONSON						
1730	1962	ALL	ALL	141615	LAN	Stalmine
ROOF						
1789	1850	ALL	1789	168602	SFK	Blundeston
1798	....	1600	1798	116637	SFK	Thurston
ROOK						
....	....	1700	1800	171794	CUL	Bassenthwaite
1720	1790	1650	1850	174599	WIL	Downton

Known From	To	Researching From	To	Ref	Cty	Place
ROOKE						
1704	1740	1660	1740	119059	GLS	Evenlode
1771	1948	1750	1950	110183	MDX	Ealing
1828	1961	1800	1961	162450	MDX	Ealing
ROOLEY						
1768	1992	ALL	1768	165204	YKS	Huddersfield
1768	1992	ALL	1768	165204	YKS	Thornhill
1768	1992	ALL	1768	165204	YKS	Wakefield
ROOM						
1700	1860	ALL	ALL	165255	BDF	Eaton Bray
....	....	1800	1960	107816	DEV	Exeter
1860	1870	1870	1992	108367	YKS	Dewsbury
1800	1860	ALL	1800	108367	YKS	Leeds
1800	1810	1750	1890	130869	YKS	Storwood
ROOME						
1851	1870	....	....	164631	DBY	Melbourne
1781	1851	....	....	164631	DBY	Mickleover
1760	1760	....	....	135437	NFK	Billingford
ROONEY						
....	....	1850	1890	108863	DOW	Newry
1845	1890	1840	1992	122319	KEN	Maidstone
1836	....	ALL	ALL	172057	ROS	???
ROOT						
1799	1850	1650	1992	101419	ESS	Hadstock
ROOTES						
1820	1900	1600	1820	123587	KEN	Tonbridge
ROOTHAM						
1635	1812	ALL	1800	168718	BDF	North West
ROOTS						
1851	1851	1800	1851	174130	ESS	Honrchurch
1800	1836	1800	1836	174130	ESS	Lambourne
1836	1860	1750	1992	167991	ESS	Rainham
1847	1870	ALL	1849	138290	KEN	Goudhurst
1667	1884	ALL	ALL	105856	KEN	???
1836	1880	1700	1836	174130	SRY	Streatham
1667	1884	ALL	ALL	105856	SRY	???
ROOTSEY						
1650	1963	....	....	138118	LND	???
ROPER						
1800	1992	1700	1800	160458	DBY	South
1800	1900	1600	1992	128279	LAN	Bolton
1885	1894	1875	1894	137715	LAN	Manchester
1800	1900	1600	1992	128279	LAN	Preston
1750	....	ALL	1788	168718	LEI	Thrussington
1874	1961	1700	1874	163929	NFK	Norwich
1854	1961	1700	1854	163929	SFK	Bildeston
1854	1938	1700	1854	163929	SFK	Somersham
1657	1706	ALL	1657	154563	YKS	Calverley
ROSAMOND						
ALL	ALL	ALL	ALL	160466	ALL	ALL
1709	1822	....	1822	151688	BDF	Eaton Socon
ROSBY						
1785	1814	1600	1850	130125	DUR	Washington
ROSCOE						
1822	1992	1750	1822	160474	LAN	Prescot
1796	1836	1750	1836	178489	LAN	Prescot
1822	1992	1750	1822	160474	LAN	St Helens
ROSCOW						
1801	1888	ALL	1801	162221	LAN	Bolton
ROSE						
....	....	ALL	ALL	160490	ALL	Name Study
1841	1900	1700	1851	144037	ABD	Invergordon
1799	1874	1500	1799	117676	BKM	Haddenham
1881	....	1850	1900	127353	BKM	Little Marlow
1850	1876	1700	....	123560	BRK	Reading
....	....	1750	1837	138339	BRK	Reading
....	....	1850	1900	123765	CAM	ALL
1777	1812	1700	1777	151866	CAM	Eltisley
1830	1992	1830	1950	107131	CHS	Macclesfield
1800	1992	1700	1800	107123	CHS	Macclesfield
1854	1871	....	....	160482	CHS	Nether Alderley
1829	1832	ALL	1829	174815	DBY	Derby
1629	....	....	....	124664	DBY	Hilton
1830	1845	ALL	1830	146986	DOR	Chickerell
1820	1830	....	....	133221	DOR	Fitzpaine
1806	....	1700	1806	148121	DOR	Langton Herring
1820	1830	....	....	133221	DOR	Okeford
1687	....	....	....	151351	DOR	Sturminster Newton
1800	1880	....	....	140317	ESS	Tollesbury
1700	1830	1600	1700	147583	GLS	Fairford
1700	1830	1600	1700	147583	GLS	Hampneth
1807	1869	1780	1870	119059	GLS	Oddington
1775	1795	1750	1801	160482	HAM	Micheldever
1747	1834	1650	1747	144711	HUN	Ramsey

Known From	To	Researching From	To	Ref	Cty	Place
ROSE contd.						
....	....	1750	1787	130184	KEN	Ashford
1695	1695	....	....	127426	KEN	East Malling
1792	1975	1600	1792	174548	KEN	Folkestone
1825	1887	1825	1887	141194	KEN	Gillingham
1770	1800	1770	1810	145602	LAN	Salmesbury
1730	1950	1700	1750	160458	LEI	Belton
1873	1992	....	....	174815	LEI	Leicester
1801	1844	1700	1800	143448	LIN	Grimsby
1816	....	ALL	1816	107964	LIN	Thimleby
1827	1900	ALL	ALL	141704	LND	Bermondsey
1827	1900	ALL	ALL	141704	LND	Horsleydown
1861	1890	ALL	ALL	143529	LND	Kensington
1827	1900	ALL	ALL	141704	LND	Southwark
1827	1900	ALL	ALL	141704	LND	St Olave
1880	....	1880	....	135488	LND	Whitechapel
1722	....	ALL	1722	119326	NRY	Kirby Wiske
1722	....	ALL	1722	119326	NRY	York
1828	1870	1870	1992	117269	NTH	Kettering
1760	1840	1760	....	111287	NTT	East Markham
1760	1840	1760	....	111287	NTT	West Markham
1675	1929	....	1700	136212	OXF	North Aston
1790	1827	1500	1790	129577	SCT	Nairn
1800	1900	1800	1925	133450	SCT	Nairn
1835	1880	....	....	139351	SFK	Thorndon
?	....	....	?	111104	SRY	Epsom
?	....	....	?	111104	SRY	Ewell
1850	1876	1700	....	123560	SRY	Greenwhich
....	....	1650	1750	145637	SRY	Pirbright
1801	1814	....	....	160482	SSX	Brighton
1840	....	....	....	174815	STS	Lichfield
1820	1910	1800	1840	161810	STS	West Bromwich
1797	....	ALL	ALL	113700	WIL	Bishops Cannings
1841	1992	1800	1992	161861	WIL	Idmiston
1720	1850	....	....	172286	WYK	Greaseborough
1838	....	1800	1840	153737	YKS	Lleds
1812	1852	ALL	1813	102350	YKS	Sheffield
1850	....	ALL	ALL	167622	YKS	Sheffield
1600	1840	1500	1992	114901	YKS	Thirsk
?	?	?	?	108758	???	???
ROSEBERRY						
1752	1945	1700	1752	115401	DUR	Sunderland
ROSENBERG						
1895	1992	....	....	124354	LAN	Oldham
1830	1992	1750	1992	114596	YKS	Sheffield
ROSENDALE						
1810	1880	1750	1810	133671	CAM	Bassingbourne
ROSENSTRAUGH						
1875	1885	1860	1900	142174	WRY	Leeds
ROSENTHAL						
1810	1890	1800	1900	123870	MDX	London
ROSERS						
1861	1957	1860	1957	144460	LAN	Droylsden
ROSEVEAR						
1540	1880	1540	1900	160547	CON	Luxulyan
1903	1978	ALL	1903	115355	DBY	ALL
1880	1992	1880	1920	160547	DBY	Castle Gresley
1903	1978	ALL	1903	115355	LEI	ALL
ROSEVEARE						
1863	1927	ALL	1863	160733	CON	St Germsn
ROSEWALL						
1706	....	1600	1706	116637	CON	St Ives
1680	1693	1600	1680	102571	CON	Towednack
1642	1760	1760	1900	139491	CON	Towednack
ROSHIER						
1850	1992	1889	1992	158186	SRY	Croydon
ROSIE						
1800	1880	1700	1880	126500	BAN	Wick
1780	1820	....	....	126497	CAI	Canisbay
1790	....	1700	1992	166049	CAI	Mey-Canisbay
ROSKELL						
1850	1910	....	....	159506	LAN	Fleetwood
1718	1850	....	1718	159506	LAN	Hambleton
1730	1850	1600	1800	113654	LAN	St Michaels
ROSON						
1762	....	ALL	1762	139459	BDF	Woburn
ROSS						
1823	1887	1700	1823	106887	ABD	Rathven
....	....	1700	1850	134546	ANS	Dundee
1850	1992	1800	1850	174653	ANS	Dundee
1846	1919	1700	1846	119881	BAN	Keith
1809	1900	1700	1850	117005	BKM	Astwood
1859	1940	....	....	152331	CAI	Latheron
1842	1933	....	....	168203	CAI	Lybster

Known From	To	Researching From	To	Ref	Cty	Place
ROSS contd.						
1846	1899	....	....	168203	CAI	Swiney
1839	1842	....	....	168203	CAI	Wick
1864	....	1864	....	144355	COR	Dunmanwry
1750	1992	1750	1992	143014	DOR	ALL
1800	1992	1700	1800	160571	DUR	Chester Le Street
1700	1900	....	....	124524	ERY	Cottingham
1700	1908	ALL	ALL	113093	EYK	Beverley
1700	1908	ALL	ALL	113093	EYK	Sutton
1820	1870	1700	1850	149322	FER	Clones
1500	1900	1500	1992	156515	HEF	Dilwyn
1860	1900	1700	1860	145904	HEF	Kings Pyon
1741	1841	1741	ALL	146366	INV	Duthil
1760	1880	1700	1880	150797	KCD	Banchary Ternan
1830	1963	....	....	124524	LAN	Hulme
1794	....	1700	1800	143448	LIN	???
1796	1854	1750	1796	101796	LKS	Anderston
....	....	....	1860	116866	LKS	Glasgow
1806	1827	ALL	1806	146757	LKS	Shotts
1850	1908	....	....	113093	LND	Camberwell
1850	1908	....	....	113093	LND	Lambeth
1881	....	....	....	135585	MDX	Brentford
1880	1900	ALL	ALL	141704	MDX	Haggerston
1798	....	1750	1798	101427	MLN	Edinburgh
1826	....	....	....	112887	MLN	Edinburgh
....	....	1870	....	174963	MON	Newport
1780	1835	1700	1850	143251	MOR	Auldearn
1780	1835	1700	1850	143251	MOR	Dyke
1872	....	1870	1890	115967	ROC	Ardross
....	....	1820	1860	142972	ROC	Dingwell
1859	1924	1700	1925	156493	ROC	Gairloch
1830	1891	1700	1992	171875	ROC	Rogart
1818	1992	1700	1818	105201	ROC	???
....	....	ALL	1808	149349	SCT	???
1880	....	....	....	135585	SRY	Barnes
1880	....	....	....	135585	SRY	Kingston On Thames
1805	1815	1790	1860	179604	SRY	Southwark
1860	1960	....	....	142972	STI	Kilsyth
1779	1799	....	....	171654	STI	Stirling
1820	1910	1800	1840	161810	STS	West Bromwich
....	....	1500	1780	138614	SUT	Clyne
1812	1872	1700	1800	115967	SUT	Creich
1842	1914	....	....	144142	SUT	Invershin
1750	1992	ALL	ALL	140902	SUT	Rosehall
1831	1992	1806	1900	160563	TAY	Dundee
1820	1992	1783	1820	164216	WOR	Worcester
1685	1741	1585	1742	170267	YKS	Pudsey
1880	1979	1700	1880	102997	???	Cathcart
1812	1836	1750	1850	177970	???	Glasgow
ROSSALL						
1829	1860	1750	1900	118443	LAN	Medlar
ROSSELL						
1800	1880	1750	1850	162191	LEI	Loughborough
1839	....	....	1839	101761	NTT	???
ROSSER						
1813	1907	1800	1907	158658	GLA	Cilfynydd
1772	1853	1750	1860	118575	GLA	Llansamlet
1791	1850	1760	1820	141283	GLS	Forest Of Dean
1913	1951	1800	1950	160601	MON	???
ROSSINGTON						
....	....	ALL	ALL	160636	ALL	Name Study
1170	1992	1170	1992	160636	ALL	ALL
1861	1888	1849	1861	160628	DBY	Alfreton Shardlow
1666	1849	ALL	1861	160628	LIN	ALL
....	1750	1500	1992	175072	LIN	ALL
1666	1886	1666	1886	160636	LIN	Blankney
1879	1959	1879	1959	160636	LIN	Lincoln
1666	1886	1666	1886	160636	LIN	Scopwick
1861	1992	....	....	160628	SYK	Rotherham
1861	1992	ALL	1666	160628	SYK	Sheffield
ALL	1666	ALL	1666	160636	YKS	Anston
ROSSITER						
1849	1925	1830	1930	160644	DOR	Halstock
....	....	1900	1940	166979	KEN	Ashford
1900	1992	1800	1992	129976	KEN	???
1825	1895	1825	....	162175	SOM	Daulting
1748	1988	....	1748	160652	SOM	Middlezoy
1765	1819	1700	1850	160644	SOM	West Coker
1879	1992	1870	1992	160644	SOM	Weston Super Mare
ROSTELL						
1577	1577	1500	1576	102830	STS	Darlaston
1577	....	1500	1600	160873	STS	Darlaston
ROSTRON						
1820	1845	1810	1841	102121	LAN	Blackburn

Known From	To	Researching From	To	Ref	Cty	Place
ROSTRON contd.						
....	1886	?	1890	164976	LAN	Chadderton
1830	1861	1799	1861	174998	LAN	Haslingden
ROTHERA						
1780	1940	1700	1780	125342	WYK	Halifax
1780	1940	1700	1780	125342	WYK	Keighley
1850	1992	1700	1850	155411	YKS	North
ROTHERHAM						
1800	1992	1700	1800	120383	DBY	Eckington
1682	1722	1682	1722	107573	WAR	Nether Whitacre
ROTHEROE						
1800	1900	ALL	ALL	177989	GLA	Oystermouth
1738	1780	ALL	ALL	177989	GLA	Rhosilli
1800	1900	ALL	ALL	177989	GLA	Swansea
ROTHERY						
1861	....	ALL	1992	159174	DEV	Bampton
1839	....	ALL	1992	159174	LND	Hoxton
ROTHWELL						
1752	1765	1653	1825	116580	HAM	Binstead
1716	1737	1691	1800	116580	HAM	Holybourne
1816	1839	1500	1840	157538	LAN	ALL
1718	1732	ALL	ALL	141615	LAN	Aughton
1772	1831	1700	1772	176451	LAN	Blackley
1651	1811	....	....	138851	LAN	Bolton
1858	1893	1800	1858	135364	LAN	Bury
1798	1992	1798	1992	145238	LAN	Haslingdon
1900	1992	....	....	102059	LAN	Haughton
1790	1811	1700	1790	123102	LAN	Lancaster
1830	1900	....	1830	102059	LAN	Manchester
1811	1851	1811	1851	159492	LAN	Manchester
1789	1810	1582	....	116580	SRY	Milford
ALL	1720	....	....	170798	WRY	Batley
ROTTEN						
1500	1600	....	....	100420	WAR	Meriden
ROUBILIAC						
1720	1760	1700	1992	167592	MDX	London
ROUFFIGNAC						
....	....	ALL	ALL	108081	ALL	Name Study
1685	1992	1685	1992	108081	ALL	ALL
ROUGHEAD						
1800	1863	1700	1875	146536	STI	Larbert
ROUGHLEY						
1750	1880	....	....	171824	LAN	St Helens
ROUGHSEDGE						
1875	1992	1875	1992	109347	LAN	Accrington
1800	....	1800	....	109347	LAN	Liverpool
ROUGHT						
1750	1992	1550	1750	176230	SFK	Brandon
ROUGHTON						
1780	1851	1700	1900	149047	CAM	March
1520	1992	....	....	160660	NTH	Kettering
ROUGIER						
1680	....	....	....	137693	CHI	Guernsey
ROULSTON						
1700	1881	1850	1910	154512	NTT	Nottingham
1700	1881	1850	1910	154512	NTT	Radcliffe On Trent
ROUNCE						
....	....	ALL	ALL	160679	ALL	Name Study
1915	?	?	?	160679	ALL	ALL
1790	....	....	....	151548	NFK	Yarmouth
1837	1960	1700	1850	160679	NFK	???
ROUND						
1815	1930	....	....	132756	SAL	Dawley
1815	1930	....	....	132756	SAL	Hadley
1815	1930	....	....	132756	SAL	Shiffnal
1815	1930	....	....	132756	SAL	Wellington
1830	1870	ALL	1850	118338	STS	Moxley
1810	1840	1810	1900	165093	STS	Old Swinford
1815	1915	....	....	132756	STS	Tipton
1851	1896	1800	1920	133639	STS	Wolverhampton
1828	1900	1750	1828	146110	WAR	Long Lawford
1920	1992	....	....	160687	WMD	???
1820	1840	1700	1870	125423	WOR	Dudley
1860	1900	1800	1900	138878	WOR	Dudley
1920	1992	....	....	160687	YKS	???
ROUNDTREE						
1857	1992	1830	1857	141879	YKS	Maxborough
ROUNSEFELL						
1810	1830	1700	1870	170615	CON	St Columb
1810	1830	1700	1870	170615	CON	St Issey
ROUPELL						
ALL	ALL	ALL	ALL	103160	ALL	ALL
ROURKE						
1850	1940	1700	1850	140260	OFF	Loughmagh
ROUS						
1754	1787	1628	1754	156779	SFK	Cratfield
ROUSE						
1150	ALL	1000	ALL	154857	CON	ALL
....	....	1700	1800	175838	CON	Truro
1829	1881	1829	1992	113956	DBY	Darley
1885	....	....	....	110833	DBY	Matlock
1800	1829	1800	1992	113956	DBY	Matlock
1150	ALL	1000	ALL	154857	DEV	ALL
1650	ALL	1650	ALL	154857	SOM	ALL
1750	1750	1700	1750	119938	WAR	Oxhill
1800	1958	1600	1800	177237	WAR	Pillerton Hersey
1790	1920	1700	1790	132268	WAR	Pillerton
1760	1784	1760	1800	145505	WOR	Alderminster
ROUSSELIN						
1775	1824	1700	1824	102806	LND	Westminster
ROUSSELL						
1750	1850	1750	1850	176567	GSY	St Peter Port
ROUT						
1819	1841	1819	1992	147230	NFK	Diss
1850	1921	1800	1849	157619	SSX	Slindon
ROUTH						
1790	1810	ALL	1800	112313	MDX	Twickenham
ROUTLEDGE						
....	....	1852	ALL	149187	ANS	Dundee
1738	1820	....	....	138851	CMA	Carlisle
....	1818	....	1857	103349	CUL	Bolton
1759	1992	1700	1759	160709	CUL	Carlisle
1850	1860	1780	1880	157929	KEN	Tunbridge Wells
1860	1935	ALL	1900	177571	LAN	Liverpool
1820	1849	....	....	138851	LAN	Manchester
1800	1992	1700	1800	160717	NBL	North Shields
1810	1940	1700	1810	160717	NBL	Wallsend
1859	1892	1800	1900	176672	SSX	ALL
ROUTLEY						
1766	1889	1700	1766	165859	SOM	Nether Stowey
ROUVIERE						
1695	1695	....	....	121355	LND	Stepney
ROUX						
1880	1992	1700	1880	135313	GLA	Cardiff
1866	1881	1866	1992	168637	LND	St Pancras
1839	1866	1700	1866	168637	LND	Westminster
ROW						
1770	1814	1650	1770	172898	DEV	Chudleigh
1794	1916	1700	1793	131245	MDX	St George In East
1712	1992	1600	1992	116882	NBL	ALL
ROWAN						
1850	1920	1850	1920	118540	DOW	Rathfriland
ROWARK						
1861	1862	1851	1871	106569	LIN	Gainsborough
1861	1862	1851	1871	106569	NTT	Worksop
ROWBOTHAM						
1800	1992	1770	1992	178004	CHS	Altrincham
1790	1840	1700	1790	130206	LAN	Manchester
1771	1800	1700	1875	178004	LAN	Manchester
1841	1850	....	....	144096	LEI	Markfield
1895	1895	1880	1895	130206	MDX	Wood Green
1731	1835	1731	1841	144096	NTT	Bunny
1851	1890	1731	1900	144096	NTT	Nottimgham
ROWBOTTAM						
1768	1830	1700	1900	167533	YKS	Anston
ROWBOTTOM						
1814	1850	1750	1814	118435	CHS	Halton
1878	1960	1700	1878	153346	WOR	Wordsey
ROWDEN						
1700	1800	1600	1700	173223	WIL	Wilton
ROWE						
1800	1820	1750	1850	100129	BDF	Tempstead
1730	1763	ALL	1763	168718	CON	South East
....	....	....	....	140139	CON	Bodmin
....	....	1700	1800	136972	CON	Breage
1890	1970	1700	1890	120944	CON	Camborne
1845	1961	....	....	130176	CON	Chacewater
1650	1850	1600	1900	123722	CON	Constantine
1860	....	1800	1992	129348	CON	Falmouth
1841	1861	1700	1841	117676	CON	Fowey
....	....	1830	1870	155691	CON	Fowey
1800	1850	1700	1850	156442	CON	Fowey
1797	1813	1700	1797	161837	CON	Fowey
....	....	1700	1800	136972	CON	Germoe
1764	1893	ALL	1764	134783	CON	Gulval
1700	....	?	?	136999	CON	Gulval
....	....	1700	1850	147044	CON	Gulval
1650	1900	1500	1650	175269	CON	Helston

Known From	To	Researching From	To	Ref	Cty	Place
ROWE contd.						
1785	1825	1650	....	118591	CON	Laneast
....	1862	ALL	1862	134058	CON	Ludguan
1830	1860	1700	1860	107719	CON	Madron
....	....	1700	1850	147044	CON	Madron
1878	1911	1750	1878	177938	CON	Millbrook
....	....	1700	1850	147044	CON	Paul
....	....	1500	1610	138614	CON	Perranuthnoe
1871	....	....	....	173991	CON	St Austell
1829	1829	....	....	136964	CON	St Clements
1871	....	....	....	173991	CON	St Columb Major
....	....	1500	1713	138614	CON	St Hilary
....	....	1700	1850	147044	CON	St Just In Penwith
1821	1890	1700	1800	170976	CON	St Levan
1838	1842	1800	1868	117277	CON	Stratton
1763	1793	ALL	1793	168718	CON	Warleggan
....	....	1600	1700	128627	CON	???
1851	1992	1700	1800	172820	CON	???
1741	1890	ALL	1741	160733	DEV	South
....	....	1700	....	116092	DEV	Alphington
1680	1880	1600	1992	114596	DEV	Burrington
1755	1790	1750	1790	117323	DEV	Crediton
....	....	1741	1749	160733	DEV	Crediton
1777	1992	....	1777	103705	DEV	Ipplepen
1837	1842	1800	1868	117277	DOR	Stratton
....	....	1700	1800	128627	ESS	Saffrom Walden
1833	1851	1750	1833	140589	EYK	Everinham
1850	1960	1700	1850	148776	HAM	Hambledon
1870	1970	1870	1900	155691	HAM	Ringwood
1855	....	....	....	174408	JSY	???
1709	1851	....	....	152870	KEN	Margate
?	....	....	....	116092	LAN	Liverpool
1747	1752	ALL	ALL	141615	LEI	Chadwell
1841	1881	1800	1900	149330	LIN	Bourne
1841	1866	1800	1841	117277	LND	ALL
1883	1930	1850	1883	160768	LND	Bermondsey
1829	1860	1750	1850	126586	LND	Bethnal Green
1853	....	....	....	160776	LND	Shoreditch
1788	1800	1788	1800	117323	MDX	Acton
1861	1861	1800	1900	118192	MDX	Bethnal Green
1856	1861	....	....	130958	MDX	Bethnal Green
1885	....	....	....	160776	MDX	Edmonton
1899	1992	1800	1900	118192	MDX	Islington
....	....	1850	1920	160776	MDX	Islington
1790	1934	1790	1934	117323	MDX	Old Brentford
1778	1881	1650	1778	125105	NFK	Litcham
1863	1936	1800	1936	118192	NFK	Norwich
1637	1679	....	....	142522	SFK	Chelmondiston
....	....	1760	1830	166448	SFK	Peasenhall
1787	1815	1500	1787	129577	SOM	Taunton
1670	1740	1670	1740	142018	SOM	Taunton
1290	1920	....	....	166448	SSX	Duncaton
1680	1780	1640	1780	105333	SSX	Singleton
1760	1900	1700	1900	105333	SSX	Yapton
1732	1858	1700	1860	127604	WAR	ALL
1883	1928	1800	1883	132543	WAR	Birmingham
ROWELL						
1770	1799	1600	1770	116637	DUR	Offerton
1770	1799	1600	1770	116637	DUR	Penshaw
1820	1928	....	....	116637	DUR	Sunderland
1757	1861	ALL	ALL	169730	HAM	Herriard
1788	1861	ALL	ALL	169730	HAM	Holybourne
1775	1992	1600	1775	160784	LEI	Ridlington
1784	1814	1750	1814	123404	LEI	Snarestone
1800	1833	ALL	ALL	154806	LIN	Spilsby
1531	1992	1531	1925	119741	NBL	South West
1720	1850	1650	1900	110884	NBL	South
ROWETT						
1750	1900	1750	1850	160792	CON	Polperro
ROWING						
1810	1855	....	1855	152803	NFK	Wendling
ROWLAND						
1780	1864	?	1864	159794	AGY	Bwlch Coch
1761	1792	....	....	138401	AGY	Llanddaniel Fab
....	....	1400	1580	154873	BRK	Abingdon
1786	1826	1750	1850	171441	BRK	Buckland
1726	....	....	1820	171441	BRK	Kingston Lisle
1759	....	....	1820	171441	BRK	Sparsholt
1841	1918	1783	....	129097	CMN	Llangeitho
1798	1835	1700	1900	127302	DEV	Bradnich
1500	1900	1500	1900	160814	DEV	South Brent
1720	1780	....	....	142158	GLA	Llanfabon
1870	1970	1800	1870	160806	LIN	Boston
1845	1992	1800	1845	115312	LND	South East
ROWLAND contd.						
1807	1828	1790	1828	151599	MGY	ALL
1815	1992	1700	1992	160849	MON	Trelleck
1850	1860	1800	1850	174513	OXF	Langford
1778	1840	1750	1778	173118	PEM	Letterston
1820	1850	1800	1850	122149	SAL	Oswestry
1734	1814	1690	1735	128724	SFK	Hargrave
ROWLANDS						
1800	1870	1800	1870	109525	AGY	Holyhead
1872	1989	1700	1872	138355	AGY	Holyhead
1818	1851	1800	1899	110701	AGY	Llanddona Pentraeth
1796	1992	....	1827	138320	CAE	Llangain
1750	....	1700	1900	129607	CHS	Runcorn
....	....	1850	1873	120588	CHS	???
1873	1930	1870	1879	120588	LAN	South West
1800	1992	1700	1900	160822	MGY	South West
1857	1992	....	....	128716	MGY	Llanfair Caerinion
1841	....	....	....	155993	RAD	Abbycwmhir
ROWLANDSON						
1730	1900	1600	1800	113654	WES	Kirkby Stephen
ROWLATT						
....	....	1750	1850	134546	NTH	Grafton
ROWLAY						
....	....	?	....	128589	HRT	Hitchin
ROWLE						
1700	1911	ALL	ALL	154806	LIN	Alford
1700	1911	ALL	ALL	154806	LIN	Bilsby
ROWLES						
1808	1880	....	1880	102822	BRK	Newbury
1855	....	1855	1900	130990	NTH	Nassington
1807	1820	....	1850	102822	OXF	Witney
1780	1850	ALL	ALL	113700	WIL	Sherston
ROWLETT						
1800	1840	1750	1850	123536	HUN	Brington
1778	1804	1750	1850	123536	HUN	Molesworth
ROWLEY						
1844	1876	1700	1844	138509	BDF	Luton
1770	1992	1700	1770	118605	CHS	Barthomley
1834	1849	1850	1940	110345	DBY	Ilkeston
1870	1890	ALL	ALL	169315	DUR	East
1814	....	....	1814	167053	ESS	Waltham Abbey
1844	1876	1700	1844	138509	HRT	Luton
1890	....	1800	1900	123625	LND	Fulham
1802	1890	1802	1890	138703	NTT	Retford
1800	1860	1800	1880	138479	SOM	Shapwick
1874	1902	1750	1875	117722	STS	Bilston
1686	....	1600	1720	160873	STS	Kingswinford
1800	1992	1800	....	118672	STS	Newcastle Under Lyme
1760	1992	1600	1759	110345	STS	Tipton
....	....	ALL	ALL	169315	STS	Wolverhampton
1790	1960	1500	1790	125415	STS	Yoxall
1810	1816	1770	1810	154024	YKS	Gomersal
1838	1872	....	....	154024	YKS	Pocklington
1700	1800	1700	1800	167924	YKS	Sherriff Hutton
1787	1826	1700	1787	156183	YKS	Thornhill
ROWLING						
....	....	ALL	ALL	160881	ALL	Name Study
1781	1800	1700	1850	126586	SFK	Stansfield
....	1820	1600	1850	175641	SFK	Stradishall
1750	....	1700	1750	160881	YKS	Bradford
1850	1880	1750	1920	160881	YKS	Halifax
ROWLINGSON						
1730	1880	....	....	133361	CAM	Great Shelford
ROWLSTONE						
1577	1810	1550	1810	102830	DBY	Longford
ROWNEY						
1860	1947	1860	1992	149055	CAM	Girton
1866	1992	1750	1865	105988	CWD	Harwarden
1600	1700	....	....	100420	WAR	Meriden
ROWNING						
1749	....	....	....	148156	CAM	Graveley
ROWNSON						
....	....	1700	1799	171794	CUL	Bassenthwaite
ROWNTREE						
1700	1880	1660	1900	148474	CUL	Lanercost
1740	1851	1700	1860	110728	DUR	Sunderland
1857	1872	1830	1992	114057	NBL	North Shields
....	....	ALL	ALL	155373	YKS	Easingwold
ROWORTH						
....	....	ALL	ALL	170798	ALL	Name Study
....	....	ALL	1892	170798	DBY	ALL
ALL	1892	....	....	170798	LEI	ALL
ALL	1892	....	....	170798	LIN	ALL

Known From	To	Researching From	To	Ref	Cty	Place
ROWORTH contd.						
ALL	1892	....	....	170798	NTT	ALL
ROWSE						
1755	1883	1755	1883	131113	CON	Stoke Climsland
1861	1882	1850	1900	170526	DEV	Lydford
1880	1883	....	....	170526	HAM	Portsmouth
ROWSELL						
1750	1900	1800	1900	154903	SOM	Glastonbury
ROWSON						
1914	1992	1850	1914	160911	LAN	Tylsley
?	?	?	?	118044	LIN	Binbrook
ROWTCLIFF						
1668	1801	....	1840	175773	DEV	ALL
ROWTON						
1810	1905	1810	1853	116831	CAM	Cambridge
1872	....	1870	1900	142638	LIN	Cowbit
1588	....	1588	....	132802	SAL	Leighton
ROXBURGH						
1838	1915	1700	1992	167177	AYR	Kilmarnock
ROXBY						
1856	1925	ALL	1856	115355	DUR	Easington
1850	....	ALL	ALL	157864	ESS	Colcehster
ROY						
1870	1920	1840	1992	140090	IRL	Belfast
1780	1992	ALL	1780	160938	NFK	North
1834	1992	ALL	1834	179345	PER	Methven
1700	1992	....	....	125407	PER	Perth
1800	1850	1775	1800	150312	PER	Pitcairngreen
ROYAL						
1750	1790	1700	1800	130494	KEN	Greenwich
1850	1900	1800	1900	130044	MDX	Shoreditch
1826	1870	1800	1880	158658	NFK	Great Yarmouth
ROYALL						
....	....	ALL	ALL	160946	ALL	Name Study
1500	1992	1500	1992	160946	ALL	ALL
ROYAN						
1796	1868	1796	1877	110043	MOR	Duffus
1853	1877	1796	1877	110043	MOR	Elgin
1877	1959	1800	1877	110043	???	Inverness
ROYDEN						
....	....	ALL	ALL	160954	ALL	Name Study
1600	1992	ALL	ALL	160954	ALL	ALL
ROYDES						
1623	1637	1550	1650	128449	YKS	Hartshead
ROYDS						
1840	1860	1750	1840	103896	LAN	Rochdale
ROYEL						
1812	1881	1800	1900	102563	KEN	Canterbury
1785	1785	1780	1790	102563	NFK	???
ROYLANCE						
....	....	1792	....	121940	CHS	Bowdon
....	....	1828	....	121940	LAN	Ardwick
....	....	1828	....	121940	LAN	Manchester
ROYLE						
1870	1945	....	....	115932	CHS	Knutsford
1769	1992	1600	1769	160962	LAN	Eccles
1834	1992	ALL	ALL	155454	LAN	Heatton
1850	1890	1800	1920	117129	LAN	Liverpool
1871	1992	1871	1992	115932	LAN	Manchester
1819	1930	ALL	1819	122858	LAN	Manchester
1855	....	1754	1855	172243	LAN	Manchester
1769	1992	1600	1769	160962	LAN	Salford
1834	1992	ALL	ALL	155454	MDX	Fulham
ROYS						
1748	1992	1700	1748	176257	MDX	Stepney
ROYSTON						
1750	1850	....	1881	137405	CAM	Willingham
1860	1900	ALL	ALL	121428	CHS	ALL
1880	1900	ALL	ALL	121428	LAN	ALL
ROZE						
1761	1782	1730	1761	131326	GSY	???
ROZEE						
1844	....	1830	1850	163775	MDX	Bethnal Green
RUBBATHAN						
1784	....	1784	1992	121940	MGY	Cefnycoed Llandysul
RUBERY						
all	ALL	ALL	ALL	141224	ALL	ALL
....	....	1700	1900	147494	LND	London
RUBOTHAM						
1750	1850	1750	1850	129836	STS	Audley
1820	....	ALL	1820	112771	STS	Dudley
RUBY						
....	....	ALL	ALL	158593	ALL	ALL
RUBYTHON						
1750	1850	1750	1850	125881	BDF	???
1750	1850	1750	1850	125881	BKM	Olney
RUCHBY						
1841	1886	1700	1841	138509	LIN	Louth
RUCK						
1800	1992	ALL	ALL	140813	ALL	ALL
RUDCHESTER						
ALL	1500	....	....	132756	NBL	???
RUDD						
1875	....	1700	1850	161721	DUR	South Shields
....	....	1500	....	160970	HRT	North
1530	1850	....	....	160970	HRT	Kings Walden
?	1801	1700	1801	176141	MDX	Soho
1800	1860	1700	1900	162345	NFK	Illington
1813	1813	1700	1812	131245	NFK	Norwich
1832	1920	....	....	157880	NFK	Norwich
1832	1920	....	....	157880	NFK	Reepham
1790	1937	ALL	1790	158445	NFK	Sparham
....	....	1790	1830	145211	NRY	Ripon
1798	1890	ALL	ALL	174297	SAL	South
1865	1870	ALL	ALL	125288	SAL	Chetton
1905	1907	....	....	112909	SRY	Lewisham
1700	1800	1600	1900	138878	WES	Brough Under Stainmore
1700	1730	ALL	1760	123048	WRY	Slaidburn
RUDDELL						
1840	1910	ALL	1992	174157	DOW	Moira
1750	1850	ALL	ALL	131873	LND	Hackney
RUDDICK						
1900	1992	1700	1890	167835	CMA	Carlisle
1900	1992	1700	1890	167835	CMA	Hayton
1900	1992	1700	1890	167835	CMA	Talkin
1794	1850	1700	1900	142883	CUL	Farlam
RUDDLE						
....	....	1600	1650	151602	WIL	Bishops Cannings
1600	1770	ALL	1600	167029	WIL	Bishops Cannings
1607	1882	ALL	1992	167878	WIL	Bishops Cannings
....	....	1538	1795	160997	WIL	Blackland
....	....	1538	1795	160997	WIL	Bremhill
....	....	1538	1795	160997	WIL	Bromham
1770	1840	1770	1840	167029	WIL	Burbage
1769	1795	1538	1769	160997	WIL	Calne
....	....	1538	1795	160997	WIL	Calstone Wellington
....	....	1538	1795	160997	WIL	Cherhill
....	....	1538	1795	160997	WIL	Chittoe
....	....	1538	1795	160997	WIL	Heddington
....	....	1538	1795	160997	WIL	Melksham
RUDDOCK						
....	....	1800	1899	104884	ALL	ALL
1834	1884	1800	1992	102407	BRK	Reading
1650	1992	1600	1992	129739	ENG	ALL
1650	1992	1600	1992	129739	IRL	ALL
1596	1850	1596	1992	159956	NFK	North Lopham
1840	1866	....	....	104213	SOM	Holcombe
1775	1856	....	....	132837	SOM	???
....	....	1800	1850	104884	STS	???
RUDGE						
1790	1820	1600	1800	146730	NFK	Norwich
1818	1863	ALL	ALL	125288	SAL	Stockton
1844	1863	1800	1844	125288	STS	Wolverhampton
RUDINGS						
1877	1926	ALL	ALL	127205	LAN	Salford
1843	....	ALL	ALL	127205	LEI	Whitstone
1864	1869	ALL	ALL	127205	STS	Tamworth
1871	1875	ALL	ALL	127205	YKS	Sheffield
RUDKIN						
1875	1992	ALL	ALL	149268	ALL	ALL
1865	1890	1850	1900	126586	BDF	Eaton Socon
1827	1992	1980	1992	114979	LEI	Belton
1834	1865	1800	1900	126586	LEI	Sproxton
1814	1834	1750	1850	126586	NTH	Barnack
1750	1875	ALL	ALL	106097	RUT	Empingham
1750	1875	ALL	ALL	106097	RUT	Exton
1706	1706	1600	1992	110787	RUT	Wing
RUDLEDGE						
1876	1992	1700	1876	132373	GLA	Swansea
RUDMAN						
....	....	ALL	ALL	161012	ALL	Name Study
1538	1992	ALL	ALL	161012	ALL	ALL
1901	1902	1700	1980	162035	WIL	Chippenham
RUDSALE						
1670	1700	1650	1992	114901	YKS	Thirkleby

Known From	To	Researching From	To	Ref	Cty	Place
RUFF						
1679	1940	....	....	128996	CAM	Thorney
1900	1919	1800	1900	122351	LEI	Loughborough
1784	1830	1700	1900	141569	NTH	Sudborough
....	....	1800	ALL	173835	SSX	Amberley
RUFFE						
1726	1726	....	....	135437	SSX	Eastergate
RUFFELL						
1840	....	1800	1840	113352	ESS	Writtle
RUFFHEAD						
1790	1956	ALL	ALL	117005	ALL	ALL
RUFFIAT						
1750	....	1700	1750	138185	DBY	South Normanton
RUFFIED						
1701	1701	ALL	1701	169730	HAM	Herriard
RUFFLE						
....	....	ALL	ALL	123269	ALL	Name Study
RUFFLES						
1789	1793	1500	1789	110310	ESS	Wickford
1760	1857	1700	1900	176621	SFK	Bardwell
1760	1857	1700	1900	176621	SFK	Langham
RUFFLEY						
....	....	1860	1900	176117	???	???
RUFUS						
1900	1925	1900	1950	111007	DFD	Pembroke Dock
RUGG						
....	....	ALL	ALL	149888	ALL	Name Study
ALL	ALL	ALL	ALL	149888	ALL	ALL
1747	1781	....	....	135437	DEV	Exeter
1604	1992	1100	1992	149888	SOM	Huntspill
1798	1802	....	....	135437	SOM	Taunton
RUGH						
1540	1760	1540	1760	104027	CAE	Penrhyn
RUGMAN						
....	....	ALL	ALL	161039	ALL	Name Study
?	?	....	....	161020	GLS	Bristol
RULE						
1807	1920	1807	1920	107174	CON	Breage
1837	1889	1889	1992	162973	CON	Liskeard
1837	1870	1870	....	162973	CON	St Cleer
1809	1861	1700	1809	153168	ESS	Sible Hedingam
1833	1912	ALL	ALL	162108	HRT	Great Hormead
1932	1992	1800	1932	131032	LND	Leytonstone
1760	....	1650	1760	146986	NBL	Berwick
1870	1906	1870	1992	146986	SRY	Croydon
1853	1940	1830	1920	153168	SSX	Guildford
RULTON						
1832	1856	1700	1832	118877	ESS	???
1856	1867	1700	1850	118877	MDX	Whitechapel
RUMBALL						
1611	1800	ALL	ALL	163341	ESS	Clavering
RUMBELOW						
1803	1855	1780	1900	177873	CAM	Isleham
1850	1875	ALL	ALL	106097	NFK	Kings Lynn
RUMBLE						
1750	1900	1600	1900	144657	ESS	Chingford
1700	1750	1600	1800	144657	ESS	Epping
1800	1894	1700	1900	145750	NFK	ALL
1830	....	1750	1880	102016	NFK	Carbrooke
1771	1796	....	....	111856	NFK	Outwell
RUMBLELOW						
1885	1950	....	1885	115509	SWL	ALL
1885	1950	1809	1885	115509	WAR	Birmingham
RUMBOL						
1840	1880	1800	1900	128805	LND	ALL
1848	1881	1800	1900	128813	LND	Lambeth
RUMBOLD						
1850	1950	....	....	161055	GLS	Cromhall
1895	1940	1800	1900	113859	SSX	Washington
1870	1940	1800	1900	113859	YKS	ALL
RUMENS						
1766	....	1700	1766	140953	SRY	???
1900	1992	ALL	ALL	113824	SSX	Rye
....	....	1565	1850	173150	SXE	Brede
RUMLEY						
1795	1805	....	....	144568	YKS	???
RUMMERY						
....	....	....	....	135968	KEN	ALL
1811	1834	1811	1834	138312	SSX	Etchingham
RUMMEY						
1720	1760	1650	1800	125032	HAM	Oakley
RUMNEY						
....	....	1810	1992	147613	LAN	Tunstall
RUMSBY						
1745	1915	1600	1745	115304	SFK	North
RUMSEY						
....	....	ALL	ALL	161063	ALL	Name Study
....	....	1800	1992	140759	BRE	Crickhowell
1900	1931	1800	1900	179027	BRE	Llanfihangel
....	....	1800	1992	140759	BRE	Llangattock
1900	1931	1800	1900	179027	BRE	Tal-Y-Llyn
RUNACLE						
1650	1800	ALL	1650	150649	ESS	Cold Norton
1650	1800	ALL	1650	150649	ESS	White Notley
RUNACRES						
....	....	ALL	ALL	112801	ALL	Name Study
1871	1992	?	1871	147923	LIN	Lincoln
1818	1992	?	1818	147923	SFK	Debenham
RUNAGALL						
1800	1992	ALL	1650	150649	ESS	Cold Norton
1800	1992	ALL	1650	150649	ESS	White Notley
RUNCHMAN						
1770	1992	....	1770	161071	LND	???
....	....	....	1770	161071	NBL	Newcastle
RUNCORN						
1850	....	1800	1850	107123	CHS	Congleton
RUNDEL						
1861	1865	1861	1865	161098	CON	St Austell
1841	1861	ALL	ALL	161098	CON	St Mewan
1865	1950	1865	1950	161098	JSY	St Helier
1890	1992	1890	1992	161098	???	Bristol
RUNDELL						
1817	1992	1600	1817	110795	CON	Lostwithiel
1820	1970	1700	1820	156450	CON	Lostwithiel
RUNDLE						
1700	1850	....	....	129267	CON	Jacobstow
1762	1992	1650	1762	168173	CON	Tregony
1772	1857	1700	1772	161837	CON	Tywardreth
1811	1818	1700	1811	133523	DEV	Tavistock
RUNGE						
1879	1879	1879	1879	145580	LAN	Liverpool
RUNNALLS						
....	1805	ALL	1840	114030	CON	St Breward
RUSBRIDGER						
1770	1800	1770	1800	131547	SRY	Capel
1740	1770	1740	1770	131547	SRY	Newdigate
1697	1705	1650	1730	131547	SRY	Okewood
1650	1680	1600	1700	131547	SRY	Wotton
RUSCOE						
1738	1860	ALL	1900	127000	SAL	Edstaston
1738	1860	ALL	1900	127000	SAL	Wem
RUSDEN						
1600	1992	1600	1840	161101	CON	Penryn
RUSEL						
1750	....	1700	1750	138185	DBY	South Normanton
RUSELL						
1750	....	1700	1750	138185	DBY	South Normanton
1800	1900	1700	1900	124621	TYR	Stewartstown
RUSH						
....	....	ALL	ALL	162779	ALL	Name Study
1820	1875	1820	1875	156183	CON	Blisland
1896	1992	1837	1896	166464	MDX	Paddington
1670	1780	....	....	132756	OXF	Bicester
1800	1860	1800	1940	138193	OXF	Thame
RUSHBROOK						
....	....	1700	1890	118923	ESS	???
1846	1884	1800	1846	128724	MDX	London
RUSHENT						
1798	1890	1700	1960	137499	WIL	Great Bedwyn
RUSHFIRTH						
1800	1827	1750	1850	111821	YKS	Bowling
1800	1827	1750	1850	111821	YKS	Leeds
RUSHFORTH						
1625	1800	1600	1800	176621	WYK	Mirfield
1625	1800	1600	1800	176621	WYK	Rastrick
1650	1860	1600	1900	166952	YKS	Horbury
1650	1860	1600	1900	166952	YKS	Mirfield
RUSHTON						
?	?	?	?	100471	LAN	Blackburn
1850	1992	1700	1992	152412	LAN	Blackburn
1850	1900	1800	1950	177032	LAN	Bolton
1863	1992	1750	....	110264	LAN	Eccleston
1875	....	1875	....	109347	LAN	Haslingden
1822	1846	1800	1822	101796	LAN	Manchester
1875	1881	1875	1891	159492	LAN	Oldham
1826	1827	1800	1850	159964	LAN	Pendlebury
1850	1900	1800	1950	177032	LAN	Wigan

Known From	To	Researching From	To	Ref	Cty	Place
RUSHTON contd.						
1800	1850	1700	1900	177032	SAL	Telford
....	....	1790	....	145688	STS	Norton
1800	1992	1700	1800	157708	WAR	Birmingham
1900	....	1900	....	148504	WAR	Studley
1765	1992	1700	1992	179078	YKS	Slaidburn
RUSHWORTH						
1649	1812	1600	1649	125342	WYK	Bingley
1649	1812	1600	1649	125342	WYK	Haworth
1800	1900	1800	1900	153621	WYK	Queensbury
1808	1808	1770	1851	160636	YKS	Emley
1894	1992	1500	1894	134600	YKS	Halifax
....	....	1900	1992	153087	YKS	North Riding
1838	1864	1838	1864	160636	YKS	Saddleworth
RUSLING						
1772	1853	ALL	1772	164364	LIN	Owston Ferry
1825	1890	ALL	1875	113611	WYK	Hatfield
1825	1895	ALL	1875	113611	WYK	Thorne
1881	1981	1855	1881	164364	YKS	Blackburn
1890	....	....	....	161136	YKS	Sheffield
1881	1981	1855	1881	164364	YKS	Sheffield
1800	....	....	....	161136	YKS	Snaith
1800	....	....	....	161136	YKS	Thorne
RUSS						
....	....	1600	1650	151602	WIL	Bishops Cannings
RUSSAM						
1853	1992	1853	1992	161144	WAR	Birmingham
1540	1992	1540	1992	161144	YKS	Bradford
1540	1992	1540	1992	161144	YKS	Leeds
1540	1992	1540	1992	161144	YKS	York
RUSSEL						
1767	....	1600	1800	143693	BRK	Sulhampstead Bannister
1750	....	1700	1750	138185	DBY	South Normanton
1700	1750	1700	1750	144657	HAM	Farringdon
1786	....	....	....	120804	LKS	Stonehouse
1710	1815	....	....	121355	LND	Bethnal Green
1710	1815	....	....	121355	LND	Hackney
1710	1815	....	....	121355	LND	Stepney
1710	1815	....	....	121355	LND	Whitechapel
1865	1875	....	....	110159	SFK	Ipswich
....	1881	....	....	129097	???	Kidwelly
RUSSELL						
1880	1950	1750	1880	125431	ANT	Belfast
1693	1974	....	....	175749	ARM	Aughnagurgan
1693	1974	....	....	175749	ARM	Lurgan
1834	....	ALL	1834	152048	AYR	Prestwick
1732	1811	1500	1732	125695	BDF	Gamlingay
1796	1992	1700	1796	161225	BDF	Milton Ernest
1700	ALL	1716	1756	107379	BKM	Chesham
1720	1940	....	....	128996	CAM	Thorney
....	....	1640	1690	103713	CAM	Waterbeach
1810	1830	1750	1900	134376	CAM	Wisbeach
1839	1933	1700	1839	107123	CHS	Macclesfield
1720	1850	....	....	161187	CON	Porthleven
1750	1992	ALL	1992	163848	COR	Mount Russell
1750	....	1700	1750	138185	DBY	South Normanton
1780	1820	1750	1900	171158	DEV	Awliscombe
1788	1919	1788	1900	163406	DEV	George Nympton
1782	1839	1700	1800	169234	DEV	Harpford
....	....	1780	1900	155780	DEV	Sidmouth
1812	1891	....	....	135453	DNB	???
1826	1840	....	....	161217	DOR	Iwerne Minster
1700	1800	1700	1800	128163	DOR	Poole
1841	1888	....	....	161217	DOR	Shaftesbury
1793	1794	1700	1992	161217	DOR	Spetisbury
1794	1841	....	....	161217	DOR	Stourpaine
1861	1868	1861	1900	147125	DUR	Winlanton
1821	1925	1723	1871	153591	ELN	Dunbar
....	....	....	1817	142409	ENG	Midlands
....	1860	1800	....	123609	ESS	Black Notley
1820	1920	1800	1980	107476	ESS	Leyton
1790	1850	....	....	142360	GLS	Kempsford
1680	1703	ALL	ALL	124982	GLS	Tortworth
1810	1900	ALL	1800	150983	HAM	Portsea
1767	1771	1700	1767	170968	HAM	Portsea
1876	1876	1850	1876	103640	HAM	Southampton
1700	ALL	1716	1756	107379	HRT	Tring
1800	1800	1700	1850	159107	IRL	ALL
1800	1820	1800	1820	123145	IRL	Dublin
1850	....	1850	1900	126144	KEN	Ash
1892	1927	ALL	1892	138290	KEN	Beckindale
1796	1867	1780	1867	151599	KEN	Bishopsbourne
1796	1867	1780	1867	151599	KEN	Canterbury

Known From	To	Researching From	To	Ref	Cty	Place
RUSSELL contd.						
1800	1850	1600	1850	128740	KEN	Cobham
1850	1900	1850	1992	133450	KEN	Deal
1791	1862	....	1862	103349	KEN	High Halden
1841	1900	1750	1960	100382	KEN	Rolvenden
1776	1776	1776	1776	170143	KEN	Sutton Valence
1840	1851	....	....	133221	KEN	Tunbridge Wells
1860	1915	1840	1915	117501	KEN	Woolwich
1750	1992	ALL	1992	163848	LIM	Mount Russell
1723	1795	1500	1723	153591	LKS	Cadder
1885	1992	1820	1992	112305	LKS	Chapelhall
1825	1848	ALL	1848	152048	LKS	Glasgow
1850	1992	1790	1850	161195	LKS	Glasgow
1753	1799	....	....	171654	LKS	Lesmahagow
1786	....	....	....	120804	LKS	Stonehouse
1820	1920	1800	1980	107476	LND	East
1820	1860	....	....	135089	LND	Bethnal Green
?	1920	....	....	171557	LND	Charlton
1897	1992	1850	1897	128368	LND	Chelsea
1870	1938	....	....	171557	LND	Greenwich
1838	1852	1820	....	156191	LND	Lambeth
?	?	?	?	117528	LND	Southwark
1884	1890	1890	1992	146560	LTN	Queensferry
....	....	1700	1900	121258	MDX	St Pancras
1770	1800	ALL	ALL	162620	NBL	North Shields
1700	1992	ALL	ALL	159107	NFK	Upwell
1829	1992	1750	1829	135747	NTH	Deene
1790	....	ALL	1790	147877	NTH	Gt Brington
1730	1880	1600	1730	121339	NYK	Pickering
1740	1770	ALL	1770	126659	SAL	Acton Scott
1765	....	1550	1765	139866	SFK	Cockfield
1805	1843	1800	1850	151599	SOM	Bradway
1805	1843	1800	1850	151599	SOM	Combe St Nicholas
1700	1900	1700	1900	140295	SOM	Uphill
1820	1883	1600	1826	159239	SOM	Wells
1854	....	....	....	173932	SRY	Ashtead
1870	1900	1870	1900	147575	SRY	Battersea
1860	1861	....	....	131229	SRY	Bermondsey
1860	1861	....	....	131229	SRY	Camberwell
1820	1830	1800	1830	147575	SRY	Carshalton
1850	....	....	....	173932	SRY	Chessington
1840	1860	1840	1870	147575	SRY	Croydon
1820	1830	1800	1830	147575	SRY	Guildford
1838	1852	1820	....	156191	SSX	Brighton
1897	1989	ALL	1897	175323	SSX	Brighton
1820	1825	1800	1820	133221	SSX	Uckfield
1850	....	1800	1992	104574	SSX	Westbourne
1840	1880	1840	1880	105724	STS	Burton On Trent
1800	1900	1700	1800	169978	STS	Stonnall
1730	1870	1720	1920	100420	STS	Wednesbury
1870	1960	1870	1960	111457	TIP	???
1800	1900	1700	1900	132446	TYR	Stewarstown
1673	1673	1550	1672	131245	WAR	Kineton
1820	1840	1800	1860	123145	WAR	Leas Marston
1600	1900	....	....	100420	WAR	Meriden
1750	1840	1540	1850	155616	WIL	East
1790	1850	....	....	142360	WIL	Broad Blundsdon
1738	1873	1765	1900	104817	WIL	Whiteparish
1805	1881	1750	1900	102660	WRY	Idle
1805	1881	1750	1900	102660	WRY	Thackley
1882	1976	1800	1880	166588	YKS	Easingwold
1877	1992	....	....	161217	???	Bristol
1790	1992	1600	1790	109177	???	London
RUSSELL-LILLEY						
....	....	ALL	ALL	139998	ALL	ALL
RUSSEN						
1820	....	....	....	136999	MDX	Twickenham
RUSSIAL						
1750	....	1700	1750	138185	DBY	South Normanton
RUSSLAND						
1750	1965	....	....	137820	SHI	Fetlar
1720	1965	....	....	137820	SHI	Mid Yell
1760	1965	....	....	137820	SHI	North Yell
1758	1965	....	....	137820	SHI	Northmavine
1720	1965	....	....	137820	SHI	South Yell
RUSSON						
....	....	ALL	ALL	161241	ALL	Name Study
1850	1992	....	....	160687	LIN	???
?	?	?	?	161241	STS	Wolverhampton
1869	1992	1800	1900	127523	WAR	Birmingham
1850	1992	....	....	160687	WMD	???
1800	....	ALL	ALL	112461	WOR	ALL
1678	....	....	1700	160873	WOR	Dudley

Known From	To	Researching From	To	Ref	Cty	Place
RUST						
1870	1900	1600	....	161268	ABD	Chapel O'garioch
1870	1900	1600	....	161268	ABD	New Hills
1870	1900	1600	....	161268	ABD	New Machar
1777	1781	1700	1850	159956	SFK	Hepworth
RUSTELL						
1886	1896	1886	1896	173762	HAM	Kingsworthy
RUSTON						
1836	1836	1810	1836	133000	HAM	Alverstoke
....	....	ALL	....	172219	HAM	Portsmouth
....	....	1700	1815	123412	WAR	Birmingham
RUTHEN						
1815	1870	1815	1900	111791	SFK	Reydon
RUTHERFORD						
1845	....	1840	1900	143758	BEW	Coldstream
....	....	ALL	ALL	149349	IRL	???
1784	1820	....	....	139971	KEN	Wingham
1816	1832	1700	1816	126357	LET	Manor Hamilton
1823	1907	1790	1823	165107	LND	Highgate
1823	1907	1790	1823	165107	LND	Islington
ALL	1650	....	....	132756	NBL	ALL
1735	1776	1700	1800	160873	NBL	Haltwhistle
ALL	1650	....	....	132756	NBL	Rutchester
1815	1845	1750	1900	143758	NBL	???
1835	1899	1600	1854	100579	NYK	East Cowton
1760	1955	ALL	ALL	116548	PER	Perth
1770	1992	....	....	141798	ROX	Hawick
....	....	1700	1770	141798	ROX	Jedburgh
?	?	?	?	162728	ROX	Mossburnford
1800	1900	....	....	150371	ROX	St Boswell
1800	1900	....	....	150371	ROX	Wilton
1773	1804	1700	1900	106461	WIL	ALL
RUTHVEN						
....	....	ALL	ALL	159034	ALL	ALL
....	....	ALL	ALL	148830	FIF	Torryburn
1881	....	....	....	159034	HAM	Freemantle
1890	1940	ALL	ALL	159034	LND	Bermondsey
1800	1840	ALL	ALL	159034	LND	City
1800	1850	ALL	ALL	159034	LND	Westminster
1855	1895	ALL	ALL	159034	SRY	Lambeth
1784	1900	1700	1784	109142	WLN	Linlithgow
RUTLAND						
1750	1992	1750	1992	161276	BKM	ALL
1750	1992	1750	1992	161276	BRK	ALL
1807	1850	1700	1900	125865	LIN	Limdsry
1800	....	ALL	1900	174637	WOR	???
RUTLEDGE						
1740	1873	1740	1873	176893	DUB	Tallaght
RUTLEY						
1856	1870	ALL	1849	166847	GLS	Bristol
RUTT						
1850	1911	1800	1992	130559	SRY	Peckham
1837	1940	1700	1992	130559	SRY	Southwark
RUTTER						
1740	1800	1650	1780	101834	CAM	Central
1740	1800	1650	1780	101834	CAM	South
1749	1749	1700	1765	133000	CAM	Caldecote
1749	1764	1749	1764	159875	CAM	Caldicote
1770	1992	ALL	1770	140163	CON	Camewith
1770	1992	ALL	1770	140163	CON	Ruanminor
1749	1755	1700	1749	153605	CON	Sithney
....	....	?	?	105961	DOR	Salisbury
1840	1992	ALL	1840	134171	DUR	Evenwood
1787	1859	ALL	1787	154563	DUR	Wolsingham
1826	1866	1866	1992	176931	GLA	Cardiff
1830	1850	1700	1960	141151	HAM	ALL
....	....	?	?	105961	HAM	North West
?	....	?	?	105961	HAM	East Meon
....	....	?	?	105961	HAM	Isle Of Wight
....	....	?	?	105961	HAM	Southampton
....	....	?	?	105961	HAM	Winchester
1860	1900	1800	1860	137278	LAN	Manchester
1843	1855	1820	1855	162450	MDX	Cowley
....	....	?	....	105961	NBL	Durham
1818	1919	1818	1850	143529	NFK	Kings Lynn
....	....	....	?	105961	SSX	Worthing
1800	1900	1800	1900	105724	STS	Stoke On Trent
1841	....	ALL	1841	139459	STS	???
....	....	....	?	105961	WIL	Ramsbury
1826	1866	1750	1826	176931	WIL	Trowbridge
1863	1992	....	....	161284	WOR	Bromsgrove
....	....	....	?	105961	???	London
RUTTERFORD						
1730	1826	1730	1830	135941	SFK	Lakenheath

Known From	To	Researching From	To	Ref	Cty	Place
RUTTLEDGE						
1755	....	....	....	131229	MAY	Cornfield
RUTTLETON						
1848	....	....	....	114545	BDF	Stanford
RUXTON						
1791	1792	1700	1790	178896	ANS	Craig
RYAL						
1500	1992	1500	1992	160946	ALL	ALL
RYALL						
1800	1820	1600	1800	161292	DOR	Thornford
1794	1815	1750	1794	101060	HAM	Southampton
RYAN						
....	....	1800	1860	157503	CAR	???
1716	1750	1680	1716	173118	CON	Talland
1834	1900	1700	1992	139181	DOW	Corrags
1830	1924	1700	1950	118680	IRL	Toomevara
1811	1870	1811	1870	163554	IRL	???
1811	1870	1811	1870	163554	LKS	Glasgow
1863	1992	....	1863	151270	OFF	Tullamore
1820	1861	1800	1911	121746	TIP	Ballycahill
1830	1923	1700	1950	118680	TIP	Latteragh
1819	1916	1710	1950	118680	TIP	Nenagh
RYCROFT						
....	....	ALL	ALL	161314	ALL	Name Study
1671	1940	ALL	ALL	142980	ALL	ALL
1907	1917	?	?	124451	LAN	Liverpool
1465	1532	1465	1532	161314	LND	Kings Household
1705	1725	1705	1725	161314	LND	St Clements
....	....	ALL	ALL	161314	YKS	ALL
1596	1666	1596	1666	161314	YKS	Bradford
1510	1605	1510	1605	161314	YKS	Craven
1654	1766	1654	1766	161314	YKS	East Ardsley
1765	1875	1765	1875	161314	YKS	Gilersome
1548	1688	1548	1688	161314	YKS	Halifax
1520	1650	1520	1650	161314	YKS	Kildwick
1737	1800	1737	1800	161314	YKS	Leeds
1720	1820	1720	1820	161314	YKS	Rothwell
1558	1635	1558	1635	161314	YKS	Tong
RYDER						
1840	1900	1840	1992	126322	CHS	Chester
1850	1880	1850	1880	169420	DEV	Honiton
1820	1840	1800	1850	126322	DUR	???
....	....	ALL	ALL	172324	ENG	North
1800	1950	1750	1850	146587	MDX	Norwood Green
1830	1880	1560	1830	118486	NRY	Coverdale
1830	1880	1560	1830	118486	NRY	Masham
1835	1992	1700	1835	169021	SAL	Hodnet
1800	1924	1750	1800	168777	SAL	???
1881	1981	1880	1985	169420	SCT	South
1800	1960	1700	1800	153346	STS	Kingswinford
1867	1930	1851	1890	118486	WRY	Selby
1851	1925	1840	1950	116114	YKS	Bradford
1850	....	....	....	151351	YKS	Bramham
1732	1788	....	....	151351	YKS	Coverham
1800	1850	1700	1850	171174	YKS	Coverham
1850	1890	1890	1992	171174	YKS	Harrogate
1800	1851	1821	1861	116114	YKS	Kippax
1829	1992	1600	1940	150118	YKS	Leeds
1807	1845	....	....	151351	YKS	Masham
1788	1827	1788	1835	116114	YKS	Pontefract
1830	1860	1800	1900	167843	YKS	Redmire Cum Bolton
1800	1900	ALL	1992	102245	YKS	Richmond
1866	1871	....	....	151351	YKS	Sleby
1843	....	....	....	151351	YKS	Well
RYDING						
1725	....	1725	....	109347	LAN	Padiham
1828	1910	1828	1910	134880	WIC	Wicklow
RYE						
1740	1992	1350	1992	161322	KEN	East
1758	1840	1650	1758	176249	KEN	East
1831	1929	....	1831	137073	KEN	Romney Marsh
1767	1992	ALL	1767	161330	NFK	Mileham
1831	1929	....	1831	137073	SXW	Penshurst
RYLANCE						
1750	1800	1700	1850	141496	CHS	Winwick
RYLAND						
1796	1850	1700	1796	130648	CUL	North
RYLATT						
1750	1850	....	....	124621	LIN	Boston
1800	1850	....	....	124621	LIN	Timberland
RYLEY						
1770	1800	ALL	1770	131059	ESS	Danbury
1700	1800	1650	1850	177180	STS	Checkley
1600	1720	1600	1750	177180	STS	Moreton

Known From	To	Researching From	To	Ref	Cty	Place
RYMER						
1770	1830	....	....	140554	YKS	Coxwold
1755	....	1700	1755	119938	YKS	East Riding
RYNE						
1800	1830	....	....	126497	LET	???
RYSBRUG						
1320	1397	1200	1700	131547	SRY	Wondersh
RYSEBRIGGER						
1490	1650	1200	1700	131547	SRY	Shere
RYSHBRYGGE						
1393	1511	1200	1700	131547	SRY	Albury
RYVES						
1903	1953	1800	1900	106402	HAM	Southampton
1903	1953	1800	1900	106402	HAM	West End
SABAN						
1824	1893	1800	1900	141666	ESS	Epping
1768	1810	1750	1820	141666	ESS	Gt Hallingbury
1817	1898	1750	1817	174203	HRT	Sawbridgeworth
SABELL						
1850	1992	1550	1850	161349	ALL	ALL
SABERTON						
1674	1732	ALL	1674	168602	CAM	Witcham
SABEY						
1700	1992	1700	1992	114790	BDF	Shillington
SABIN						
1626	1730	1626	1750	171654	NTH	Bradden
1670	1906	1670	1906	140724	OXF	Wardington
1800	1820	ALL	1800	154555	WAR	Hillmorton
SABINE						
1744	1953	1700	1748	132039	LND	Central
1700	1800	....	....	100420	WAR	Meriden
SABISTON						
1846	1992	....	....	169110	NBL	Cullercoats
1808	1846	....	....	169110	NBL	Seaton Sluice
1782	1808	....	1780	169110	OKI	Stromness
SABLE						
1795	1873	1750	1900	147958	ESS	West
SACH						
1849	1871	1800	1849	113352	ESS	Buttsbury
SACKER						
1812	1922	1700	1900	126683	LND	Islington
SACKETT						
....	....	ALL	1660	161357	KEN	East
1600	1810	....	....	161357	KEN	Thanet
1700	1900	....	....	161357	LND	Greater
SACKFIELD						
....	....	ALL	ALL	161365	ALL	Name Study
1920	1960	1700	1920	163902	LAN	South
SACKVILLE						
1720	1790	ALL	ALL	161365	FLN	ALL
1792	1992	ALL	ALL	161365	LAN	Swinton
SADDINGTON						
1819	1890	1700	1992	101141	LIN	Stamford
SADDS						
1800	1808	1700	1800	142328	KEN	Chatham
SADE						
1700	1799	....	....	137960	MDX	London
SADGROVE						
....	....	ALL	ALL	161373	ALL	Name Study
SADLEIR						
1649	....	1649	1900	152072	LIM	???
1649	....	1649	1900	152072	TIP	???
SADLER						
1809	1850	1700	1809	111953	BKM	Radnage
....	....	1500	....	161381	DBY	Chesterfield
....	....	ALL	1810	155470	ESS	Colchester
1680	1780	ALL	ALL	169137	ESS	Gt Horkesley
....	....	1500	1900	152072	ESS	???
1779	1830	....	....	148261	GLS	Cheltenham
....	....	1800	1840	160601	GLS	Cheltenham
1841	....	1700	1841	144614	GLS	Gretton
1821	1844	1750	1900	116742	HRT	Walkern
....	....	1500	1900	152072	HRT	???
....	....	1500	1880	166863	KEN	Chatham
....	....	1500	1880	166863	KEN	Medway
1700	1760	1600	1992	167592	LAN	Liverpool
1630	....	1550	ALL	141151	LND	ALL
1841	1992	....	....	118699	MON	Tredegar
1796	1850	1700	1900	178624	NFK	Gorleston
1700	1770	....	....	165999	NTT	Mansfield
1700	1770	....	....	165999	NTT	Newark
1750	1800	1700	1800	116823	NYK	Sandhutton
1809	1850	1700	1809	111953	OXF	Radnage
1768	1880	1700	1768	119512	SSX	Fittleworth
SADLER contd.						
1773	1850	1600	1773	133167	WAR	Oldbury
1700	1741	1660	1700	170348	WIL	Purton
1779	1992	1600	1779	160172	YKS	North Rdg
....	....	1750	....	147613	YKS	Sheffield
....	....	1500	....	161381	???	South
?	?	?	?	108758	???	???
SAFFELL						
1720	1820	1700	1800	158380	ESS	Great Waltham
SAFFERY						
1800	....	....	....	148768	KEN	Bromley
SAFFREY						
1900	1960	1800	1960	101907	KEN	Strood
SAGAR						
....	....	ALL	ALL	161403	ALL	Name Study
ALL	ALL	ALL	ALL	161403	ALL	ALL
1500	1992	1500	1992	161403	CUL	ALL
1300	1992	1300	1992	161403	LAN	ALL
1600	1900	1500	1992	161403	LAN	North East
1700	1900	1500	1992	161403	LAN	Burnley
1850	1992	1500	1992	161403	LAN	Clayton Le Moors
1700	1900	1500	1992	161403	LAN	Cliviger
1700	1900	1500	1992	161403	LAN	Habergham Eaves
1600	....	1600	....	109347	LAN	Simonstone
1700	1900	1500	1992	161403	LAN	Worsthorne
1600	1620	1550	1600	121339	WYK	Heptonstall
1300	1992	1300	1992	161403	YKS	ALL
SAGE						
1881	....	1876	1920	137782	CUL	Millom
1800	1880	1600	1800	169773	ESS	Wrabness
1800	1800	1600	1800	169773	SFK	Bristol
1785	1785	....	....	135437	SOM	Bedminster
1650	....	ALL	1650	117706	???	Cardiff
SAGER						
1600	1785	ALL	1785	141062	LAN	Simonstone
SAGGERS						
1718	1736	1670	1720	162396	CAM	Linton
SAGGERSON						
1780	1875	ALL	ALL	111511	LAN	Prescot
1830	1880	1700	1920	117129	LAN	Prescot
SAICH						
1726	1980	ALL	ALL	177571	MDX	ALL
SAIL						
....	....	1770	1950	141151	NTH	Crick
SAINES						
1700	1940	1700	1900	161411	ESS	Southminster
SAINSBURY						
1838	....	ALL	ALL	121436	GLS	Thornton
1821	1881	1800	1820	108227	SOM	Beckington
1838	1992	....	....	161438	WIL	Devizes
1838	1992	....	....	161438	WIL	Rowde
1810	....	1810	1992	101656	WIL	Salisbury
1790	....	....	....	138061	WIL	Shrewton
1800	1851	1790	1871	165824	WIL	Steeple Ashton
1705	1838	....	....	161438	WIL	West Lavington
SAINT						
....	....	ALL	ALL	109940	ALL	ALL
1800	1850	1750	1850	145866	DBY	Brailsford
1617	?	?	?	166642	KEN	Whitstable
1818	1904	1700	1900	126683	LND	Bethnal Green
1600	1992	1600	1850	161446	SOM	Misterton
SAINTSBURY						
1559	1705	1460	1644	161438	WIL	Urchfont
SAINTSBURYE						
....	....	1580	1648	161438	WIL	Urchfont
SAINTY						
....	....	ALL	ALL	109940	ALL	ALL
SAKER						
1720	1800	1700	1800	126144	KEN	West
1739	1790	1640	....	131210	SRY	Bletchingley
1804	1887	....	....	131210	SRY	Merton
1804	1887	....	....	131210	SRY	Wimbledon
SALADIN						
1920	....	1800	1920	141542	CHS	Chester
SALADINE						
1800	1900	ALL	ALL	137987	CHS	Dodleston
1879	1976	1879	1900	141542	CHS	Hooton
1750	1800	ALL	ALL	137987	FLN	Hope
SALAMAN						
1580	?	....	....	164690	ARM	???
1260	?	....	....	164690	AYR	Largs
850	?	....	....	164690	CON	???
SALAMON						
1835	1900	1800	1850	161527	LND	City

Known From	To	Researching From	To	Ref	Cty	Place
SALE						
1540	1992	1300	1540	170194	DBY	Barrow On Trent
1550	1680	1500	1700	154881	DBY	Weston On Trent
1750	1850	1600	1800	141496	LAN	Horwich
?	?	?	?	165484	SSX	Wadhurst
SALES						
1600	1700	1550	1700	154881	KEN	ALL
1778	1877	ALL	ALL	121754	KEN	Yalding
SALESBURY						
1590	1770	1590	1770	104027	CAE	Glanwydden
1280	1480	1280	1480	104027	DEN	Denbigh
1450	1590	1450	1590	104027	DEN	Ruthin
1100	1250	1100	1250	104027	LAN	Salusbury
SALIS						
1851	1873	1803	1851	145785	AVN	Bristol
1851	1873	1803	1851	145785	AVN	Clifton
SALISBURY						
1880	1910	1800	1880	135364	LAN	Balckburn
1814	1836	ALL	1814	126942	LAN	Kirkham
1880	1934	1800	1880	135364	LAN	Lower Darwen
SALKELD						
1860	1947	1700	1860	179329	NBL	Newcastle
SALLABANK						
....	....	ALL	ALL	165409	ALL	Name Study
SALLETT						
1880	1936	1500	1930	157538	KEN	Gravesend
SALLIS						
....	....	ALL	1900	161470	BRK	ALL
1824	1844	1824	1844	131970	NTT	Sandiacre
1860	1980	ALL	1860	161470	OXF	Boars Hill
....	....	ALL	1900	161470	OXF	Faringdon
1860	1980	ALL	1860	161470	OXF	Wootton
SALLNOW						
1820	1900	1750	1820	126535	LND	Poplar
1820	1900	1750	1820	126535	LND	Spitalfields
SALMON						
....	....	ALL	ALL	161497	ALL	Name Study
1800	1880	1800	1880	113670	AVN	Bath
1694	....	1650	1750	124796	BKM	Crackmore
1650	1992	1750	1900	104981	ESS	Brightlingsea
1724	1850	1700	1800	157732	ESS	Great Oakley
1800	1840	1750	1840	121509	GLS	Horsley
1650	1850	....	....	138037	HRT	North East
1924	1924	ALL	1924	142107	IRL	Portarlington
1828	....	ALL	1828	161500	KEN	Sittingbourne
1781	1841	1700	1841	141062	KEN	St Mary Cray
1830	1860	1700	1992	146943	LND	City
1779	1941	ALL	1779	161500	LND	Greater
1885	1992	1800	1885	110043	LND	???
1847	1851	1847	1861	146528	MDX	Paddington
1801	1992	1400	1801	161489	MDX	West London
1844	1845	1841	1851	146528	NTH	Rushden
1634	1900	1630	1900	128783	NTT	Ollerton
1746	1900	1746	1900	118540	NTT	Upton By Southwell
1804	1804	....	....	140414	PER	Crief
....	....	ALL	1730	164631	RUT	ALL
1730	....	....	....	164631	RUT	Hambleton
1800	....	1775	1800	164232	SFK	Stowmarket
1816	1872	1600	1850	100013	STS	Codsol
1760	1880	1700	1760	161519	YKS	Kilburn
....	....	1810	1913	116424	YKS	Stillington
SALOMON						
1840	1900	....	....	161527	MDX	Holborn
SALT						
1850	1865	1850	1865	136980	CHS	Stocport
....	1929	1850	1890	146919	LAN	Lancaster
1780	1840	1558	1780	153427	STS	Alstonfield
1850	1950	1600	1850	169862	STS	Cheadle
1862	1884	1700	1900	175307	STS	Cheadle
1812	1992	1800	1992	147311	STS	Dilhorne
1760	1860	1760	1860	105724	STS	Elford
1856	1877	....	....	167444	STS	Tamworth
1805	1813	1800	1992	172782	YKS	Hunslet
SALTER						
1829	1863	ALL	ALL	117366	AVN	Bristol
1750	1992	1700	1992	116742	BKM	Amersham
....	....	1725	1775	172871	BKM	Chalfont St Giles
1700	1733	1700	1733	141690	CON	Bodmin
1710	1730	1710	1730	141690	CON	St Mary
1760	1780	1740	1820	171158	DEV	Broadhembury
1860	1880	1700	1900	167096	DEV	Hemyock
1790	1830	1770	1850	174912	DEV	North Tauton
1790	1830	1770	1850	174912	DEV	Ottery St Mary
1882	1974	ALL	1882	177482	DEV	Totnes
SALTER contd.						
1800	1820	ALL	1820	147567	DEV	Uplyme
1758	1758	....	....	103632	DUR	Sedgefield
1776	1817	1750	1820	105333	HAM	Isle Of Wight
1600	1838	1500	1600	129577	IOW	???
1840	1900	1700	1900	128279	LAN	Preston
1844	1883	1800	1850	100862	LND	East
1812	1911	?	1812	111155	LND	Bethnal Green
....	1823	....	....	103144	LND	???
1791	....	1700	1800	125628	NFK	Great Yarmouth
1789	1900	1850	1880	169153	NTT	Nottingham
1755	1811	1714	1755	154024	SAL	Alberbury
1780	1880	1600	1880	177288	SAL	Powys Border
1780	1856	1700	1870	135305	SOM	Compton Bishop
1876	1900	1870	1910	135305	STS	Brierley Hill
1849	1876	1845	1880	135305	STS	Kingswinford
SALTER-BOWEN						
1800	1905	1800	1910	103144	LND	Clerkenwell
SALTHOUSE						
1829	1883	1780	1950	118443	LAN	Great Eccleston
SALTMARSH						
1730	1992	1600	1730	139785	ESS	North West
SALTON						
1700	1833	1650	1830	154881	MLN	Edinburgh
SALTS						
1850	1950	1850	1950	137464	LAN	W Derby
SALTWELL						
....	....	1700	1827	120510	ESS	ALL
1778	1837	1571	1778	165778	ESS	Shoreditch
1778	1837	1571	1778	165778	HRT	Thorley
SALVIN						
1782	1782	ALL	ALL	126721	NTT	Radcliffe
SAMBER						
1780	1800	....	....	153397	HAM	New Forest
SAMBOURNE						
1823	1939	1720	1823	110043	GLS	Bristol
1823	1939	1720	1823	110043	SOM	Bristol
SAMBRIDGE						
1800	1900	ALL	ALL	152285	ALL	ALL
SAMBROOKE						
1700	1700	1600	1800	133450	SAL	ALL
SAMFER						
1870	1870	1800	1880	144630	NFK	Bircham
SAMFORD						
1520	1580	1500	1520	102571	SOM	Combe Florey
SAMMES						
1891	1926	1891	1926	161535	BRK	Windsor
1539	....	....	....	161535	ESS	Canydon
1567	1705	1532	1678	161535	ESS	Goldhanger
1540	1705	....	....	161535	ESS	Gt Totham
1567	1705	1532	1678	161535	ESS	Little Totham
1772	1812	1628	1812	161535	ESS	Maldon
1775	1992	1846	1887	161535	ESS	Ongar
1780	1801	1780	1801	161535	ESS	Stamford Rivers
1742	1762	1722	1742	114073	ESS	Woodham Walter
1887	1932	....	....	161535	HRT	Boxmoor
1932	1975	....	....	161535	MDX	Hendon
1900	1992	....	....	161535	SRY	Reigate
SAMMISH						
1703	1723	1650	1750	105333	WIL	Tisbury
SAMMON						
1862	....	1800	1900	139114	OFF	Kilcummin
SAMPEY						
....	....	ALL	ALL	119245	ALL	Name Study
SAMPHIRE						
1795	1939	1700	1795	168033	HAM	Alverstoke
1795	1939	1700	1795	168033	HAM	Gosport
1795	1939	1700	1795	168033	HAM	Portsea
SAMPLE						
1600	1992	ALL	1992	144533	ALL	ALL
1854	....	1854	....	161721	NBL	Amble
1860	1900	1700	1992	160377	NBL	Berwick
SAMPLES						
1793	1900	ALL	ALL	161551	LAN	Liverpool
SAMPSON						
1683	1992	1600	1992	161578	CON	West
1790	1800	1770	1820	175838	CON	Falmouth
1750	1800	1700	1780	175838	CON	Kenwyn
1750	1825	1750	1825	136867	CON	Penzance
1800	1830	1770	1830	175838	CON	Redruth
1760	1827	1700	1850	156051	CON	St Agnes
1729	1880	1600	1729	102571	CON	Uny Lelant
1660	1700	1660	1750	116025	COR	???
1840	1841	1800	1840	116572	DOR	Netherbury

Known From	To	Researching From	To	Ref	Cty	Place
SAMPSON contd.						
1660	1700	1660	1750	116025	DUB	???
1900	1934	1800	1900	101826	HAM	Stockbridge
....	....	1800	1840	142131	HRT	Buntingford
....	....	1860	1870	142131	LND	Islington
1890	1992	1800	1890	114464	LND	???
1793	1793	1785	1800	108901	NTT	West Markham
1900	1934	1800	1900	101826	OXF	Barrington
1846	1918	1800	1900	150053	SFK	Oulton
1800	1930	1500	1850	118915	SOM	Brympton Yeovil
1878	1958	1800	1900	155152	STS	Stoke On Trent
1897	1992	1850	1897	113719	STS	Uttoxeter
SAMS						
1776	1830	1600	1900	159956	ESS	Tillingham
1830	....	1700	1830	104809	HRT	???
1817	1850	1817	1850	160121	NBL	Newcastle
1615	1800	ALL	....	100536	SFK	???
SAMSON						
....	....	1700	1830	111708	DFS	Kirkconnel
1650	1700	1600	1700	108677	DOR	Sherborne
1840	1840	....	1900	171646	LND	St Pancras
1720	1770	1700	1770	176958	YKS	Wakefield
1900	1992	....	....	100536	???	???
SAMUAL						
1748	?	1740	1820	132217	CAE	Beddgelert
1818	1854	1810	1854	132217	CAE	Treflys
SAMUEL						
1700	1850	ALL	1700	161357	ESS	Dunmow
1561	1683	1700	1800	161357	ESS	Gt Easton
1559	1783	....	....	161357	ESS	Lt Easton
1837	1942	1800	1837	158739	GLA	Glais
1841	1916	1841	1916	125598	HRT	North Mimms
SAMUELS						
1851	1861	....	....	161357	LND	St Pancras
SAMWAYS						
1806	1850	1806	1900	135895	HAM	Hambledon
1820	1920	1750	1900	145866	SOM	Huish
SAMWELLS						
1861	1879	1750	1861	149918	LEI	Leicester
SAMWYAS						
1500	1700	1500	1900	170216	WIL	ALL
SANDALL						
1850	....	....	1850	164011	KEN	Sheerness
1889	1992	1800	1889	139777	OXF	???
SANDARS						
1825	1992	1825	1992	176303	STS	Tamworth
SANDBACH						
....	....	1600	1850	110914	CHS	???
1500	1600	1500	1600	154881	KEN	Shoreham
SANDELANDS						
1850	1992	1700	1920	126160	CUL	Camerton
1850	1992	1700	1920	126160	CUL	Seaton
SANDELL						
1826	1830	1700	1826	120707	ENG	Birmingham
1882	1900	1700	1840	160865	HAM	Isle Of Wight
1882	1900	1700	1840	160865	HAM	Portsmouth
1800	1850	1850	1900	145408	WIL	North
1640	1700	1640	1700	142018	WIL	South West
SANDELLS						
1840	1845	1800	1840	140643	OXF	Chipping Norton
SANDER						
1647	1675	ALL	ALL	141615	LAN	Warton
1750	1805	?	1750	128910	NTT	Watnall
SANDERCOCK						
....	....	1750	1992	173592	CON	St Gennys
SANDERS						
1639	1743	1600	1800	158402	BKM	Chilton
1773	1794	1700	1830	143693	BKM	Mentmore
1800	1860	1750	1840	109517	CAM	Chatteris
1700	1900	1700	1900	142352	CAM	Swaffham Prior
1757	1860	1740	1870	145297	DEV	West
1839	1992	1800	1839	170976	DEV	Barnstaple
1800	1992	1700	1800	124214	DEV	Exter
1828	1839	1800	1828	136220	DEV	Highampton
1879	1992	1850	1992	161640	DEV	Kingssteighton
1771	1822	1700	1992	167800	DEV	Parkham
1800	1860	1700	1800	154458	DEV	Plymouth
1800	1950	1800	1950	141577	DEV	Tiverton
....	....	ALL	ALL	151998	DEV	Tiverton
....	....	1650	1750	174289	HAM	Sopley
1649	....	?	?	161926	HRT	Kings Langley
1804	1992	....	1804	161691	KEN	Whitstable
1856	1881	1700	1856	119075	LAN	Preston
1844	1844	ALL	ALL	128449	LEI	Leicester

Known From	To	Researching From	To	Ref	Cty	Place
SANDERS contd.						
1837	1837	ALL	ALL	128449	LEI	Loughborough
1450	1800	1400	1800	100420	NTH	ALL
1837	1851	1800	1860	142352	SFK	Horningsheath
1837	1888	1800	1900	175307	SRY	Camberwell
1830	1870	1600	1830	169862	STS	Fulford
1450	1800	1400	1800	100420	WAR	ALL
1864	1960	ALL	ALL	128449	WAR	Birmingham
1750	1864	ALL	ALL	128449	WAR	Coventry
1860	1900	ALL	1860	154555	WAR	Coventry
1823	1992	1600	1830	161632	WIL	Westbury
SANDERSON						
1640	1700	1600	1750	138878	CUL	St Bees
1800	1880	1770	1900	103128	DBY	Chesterfield
1840	1860	1840	1850	161705	DUR	Gateshead
1735	1992	1700	1992	161721	DUR	South Shields
1809	1830	1750	1830	152110	DUR	Sunderland
1840	1960	1780	1840	113514	EYK	Hull
1725	1850	1600	1800	177318	LAN	Blackburn
1725	1850	1600	1800	177318	LAN	Leigh
1860	1960	1860	1960	161705	LAN	Manchester
1842	1900	1800	1831	111856	LAN	???
1854	....	1700	1800	143448	LIN	Holton-Le-Clay
1627	1980	1600	1800	142891	LIN	Lindsey
....	....	1800	1850	113514	LIN	Louth
?	1920	....	?	147400	LIN	Sutton On Sea
1889	1963	....	....	151211	LIN	???
1838	1860	1838	1860	147575	LND	???
1860	....	....	....	152722	MDX	London
1780	1800	1780	1850	123536	NBL	Alwinton
1841	1871	1780	1881	123536	NBL	Newcastle On Tyne
1750	1830	ALL	ALL	114235	NTH	???
1840	1900	....	....	152722	NTT	Nottingham
1806	1992	....	....	161748	NTT	Nottingham
1810	1838	1800	1838	147575	SCT	Penicuik
1848	1992	1600	1900	129593	YKS	ALL
....	....	1700	1806	161748	YKS	South
1738	....	ALL	1738	159026	YKS	Aston-Cum-Aughton
....	....	1700	1800	129593	YKS	Blackbush
1778	1880	1700	1880	129593	YKS	Borrowby
1550	1650	1550	1650	110280	YKS	Bradfield
1800	1871	?	1800	144800	YKS	Holmfirm
1580	1900	1580	1850	110280	YKS	Honley
1800	1871	?	1800	144800	YKS	Howley
1820	....	....	....	152722	YKS	Leeds
1830	1930	1830	1930	110280	YKS	Lockwood
1600	1700	1600	1700	110280	YKS	Penistone
....	....	1700	1800	129593	YKS	Staithes
1800	....	....	....	152722	YKS	York
SANDES						
1625	1675	1540	1625	142646	WES	Lowther
SANDFORD						
1720	1740	ALL	ALL	118737	BRK	Beenham
1779	1919	ALL	ALL	118737	BRK	Newbury
1880	1900	1700	1992	167096	BRK	Wantage
1834	1837	ALL	1837	114030	ESS	South East
1770	1800	1700	1770	172898	LND	Aldgate
1798	....	?	1798	103934	LND	???
1066	1992	ALL	ALL	161756	SAL	Isle In Bicton
1840	1883	1790	1992	105147	SAL	Pontesbury
1066	1992	ALL	ALL	161756	SAL	Sandford In Prees
....	....	ALL	1800	167029	WIL	Wootton Rivers
SANDHAM						
1779	1900	1700	1800	110116	HAM	Hartly Manditt
SANDIFORD						
1600	1800	1600	1800	152404	LAN	Radcliffe
SANDILANDS						
1844	....	....	....	137936	ANS	Dundee
SANDISON						
....	....	1500	1800	138614	CAI	Bower
1750	1965	....	....	137820	SHI	Fetlar
1720	1965	....	....	137820	SHI	Mid Yell
1760	1965	....	....	137820	SHI	North Yell
1758	1965	....	....	137820	SHI	Northmavine
1720	1965	....	....	137820	SHI	South Yell
SANDLAND						
1910	1992	ALL	1910	178632	STS	Chasetown
SANDLES						
1766	1955	1700	1766	159565	GLS	Broadwell
SANDOE						
....	....	ALL	ALL	178438	ALL	Name Study
SANDOM						
1913	1945	1900	1992	108979	LND	ALL

Known From	To	Researching From	To	Ref	Cty	Place
SANDS						
1848	1992	1700	1848	109177	DOW	Bainbridge
....	....	1800	1840	159573	HRT	Chipping Barnet
1840	1880	1800	1840	159573	LND	East End
....	....	1800	1840	159573	MDX	Friern Barnet
1791	1870	1650	1791	120774	SSX	East
1680	1989	1500	1680	161764	SSX	Heathfield
1740	1992	....	....	100536	SSX	???
SANDUM						
1726	1852	1600	1800	161950	HAM	Kingsclere
SANDWELL						
1789	1896	....	1789	146013	KEN	Margate
SANDY						
1785	1805	....	....	171654	LKS	Newmains
SANDYS						
1520	....	....	....	156647	HAM	The Vine
SANFORD						
1870	1992	1750	1880	144630	NFK	Bircham
SANGER						
1840	1992	1600	1840	161772	MDX	Marylebone
....	....	1820	1992	161780	SSX	Alfriston
1500	1900	1500	1900	170216	WIL	ALL
1790	1867	....	....	115606	WIL	East Knoyle
1680	1800	1680	1800	142018	WIL	Salisbury
SANGSTER						
1771	1830	1770	1809	118427	ABD	Longside
1840	1860	1700	1840	100978	ABD	Peterhead
SANGWELL						
1775	1860	ALL	ALL	111333	BRK	West
SANHAM						
....	....	ALL	ALL	161799	ALL	Name Study
....	....	ALL	ALL	161799	ALL	ALL
SANIGAR						
1859	1992	1500	1992	126799	LND	???
1840	1840	1500	1992	126799	???	Bristol
SANKEY						
....	....	ALL	ALL	161802	ALL	Name Study
1207	1992	1207	1992	161802	ALL	ALL
1100	1992	1100	1992	133450	CHS	Warrington
1837	1992	1837	1992	161802	DBY	Church Gresley
....	....	1700	1825	156795	DOR	North
1750	1830	1750	1830	154881	DUB	Dublin
1850	1880	1850	1880	154881	FER	Brookborough
1650	1992	1600	1992	133450	KEN	South West
1150	1450	1100	1450	154881	LAN	Southall
1824	1992	1750	1824	144967	LAN	St Helens
1100	1992	1100	1992	133450	LAN	Warrington
....	....	1500	1992	133450	LND	Central
1705	1907	....	....	139971	LND	Fulham
1450	1600	1450	1600	154881	SAL	Hodnet
1705	1907	....	....	139971	SAL	Much Wenlock
1600	1850	1600	1850	154881	TIP	Fethard
....	....	1800	1837	161802	WAR	Birmingham
SANSBURY						
1744	?	1700	1744	168033	MDX	Chiswick
SANSBY						
1820	1940	....	....	128996	CAM	Thorney
SANSOM						
1700	1820	1700	1820	110434	DEV	Bradninch
1757	1833	....	1757	108839	HUN	Needingworth
1800	1890	1700	1800	145629	NTT	Mansfeild
1890	1992	1850	1890	145629	NTT	Nottingham
1840	1900	1700	1840	172901	NTT	Nottingham
1886	1920	1800	1900	122351	WAR	Rugby
SANSOME						
1787	1870	1750	1900	136719	WAR	Shilton
SANSON						
1774	....	1600	1774	132802	DOR	Minterne Magna
1740	1830	1700	1850	146803	ELN	Dunbar
SANSUM						
1823	1931	1750	1823	128317	GLS	Painswick
1761	1852	1650	1761	148938	GLS	Tytherington
?	?	?	?	101214	HRT	Ware
?	?	?	?	101214	LND	City
SANT						
....	....	ALL	ALL	109940	ALL	Name Study
ALL	ALL	ALL	ALL	109940	ALL	ALL
SANTER						
1820	1830	ALL	ALL	113743	SSX	Rye
SANTO						
1766	1850	1650	1800	173983	CON	Sheviock
SANTOS						
1830	ALL	....	....	132756	DUR	Sunderland
ALL	1845	....	....	132756	ENG	ALL

Known From	To	Researching From	To	Ref	Cty	Place
SANTOS contd.						
1845	1925	....	....	132756	LAN	Liverpool
ALL	1866	....	....	132756	SRY	Walton On Thames
ALL	1870	....	....	132756	YKS	Leeds
SANTS						
1810	1930	1810	1930	142018	ALL	ALL
SANTUS						
....	....	1770	1900	135046	LAN	Wigan
SAPSED						
....	....	ALL	1800	155470	ESS	Saffron Walden
SAPSFORD						
1676	1796	1600	1800	165972	ESS	Great Hallingbury
1862	....	....	....	156329	LND	Hoxton
1844	1929	ALL	1845	111155	LND	Limehouse
1844	1929	ALL	1845	111155	LND	Stepney
1820	1883	1809	1900	165972	MDX	East
SARAH						
1600	1992	1500	1600	161837	CON	ALL
SARD						
1800	1992	1800	1992	143014	ALL	ALL
SARDINSON						
1700	1850	1700	1850	112348	NTT	Southwell
SARE						
1817	1837	1837	1842	161845	MDX	St James
SARGARTSON						
1899	1960	ALL	ALL	135224	LIN	Waltham
SARGE						
1799	1822	1750	1822	141097	YKS	Sculcoates
SARGEANT						
....	....	1800	1900	134546	BDF	Yielden
1820	1850	....	....	126144	ESS	Harwich
1840	1870	....	....	126144	KEN	Gravesend
1819	1860	ALL	1819	152021	LIN	Saltfleetby
1786	1880	1550	1786	102830	NTH	Islip
SARGENT						
1800	1840	1700	1900	162345	BRK	Binfield
1830	1900	1800	1850	102024	CHS	Nantwich
1746	1965	1592	1880	109053	CON	Lezant
1760	1800	....	....	159883	DOR	Bere Regis
1770	1850	1600	1770	173223	DOR	???
1840	1960	....	....	156191	ESS	Halstead
1759	1895	1700	1759	167525	ESS	Halstead
1803	1940	....	....	161969	IOW	Cowes
1803	1940	....	....	161969	IOW	Newport
1803	1940	....	....	161969	IRL	Freshwater
....	1740	ALL	1740	152838	LIN	Keelby
1740	1992	1700	1740	171840	LND	Streatham
....	....	1800	1900	166960	NTT	Radford
1766	....	....	....	135844	SSX	Icklesham
1827	1992	ALL	1827	105406	SSX	Northiam
1843	1880	1843	1880	159557	WIL	Alderton
1700	1850	1700	1850	159557	WIL	Castle Combe
1540	1820	1450	1550	142042	WIL	Grittleton
1530	1800	1530	1800	159557	WIL	Grittleton
SARGISON						
1820	1943	1800	1950	167843	YKS	Redmire Cum Bolton
SARGISSON						
1791	1824	1750	1850	156965	LND	Holborn
SARJEANT						
....	....	1800	1840	133493	DEV	Plymouth
1770	1780	1770	1780	175196	MDX	Westminster
SARLING						
1840	1880	1820	1900	142050	MDX	London
SARRAL						
1787	1854	1500	1769	129577	SOM	Nynehead
SARSFIELD						
1851	....	....	....	128945	DUR	City
1860	1910	1800	1860	172006	GAL	Tuam
1600	....	ALL	1900	174637	IRL	???
1880	1946	1870	1880	172006	LAN	St Helens
SARSON						
1695	1870	ALL	1992	168718	LEI	ALL
1734	1734	1600	1733	131245	LEI	Queniborough
SARVIS						
1721	1806	1650	1820	121126	CON	Mylor
SATCHELL						
1815	1846	1819	1992	164798	CON	Maker
1815	1846	1819	1992	164798	IOW	Carisbrooke
1817	1923	1700	1923	174076	NTH	Kettering
SATCHER						
1827	1847	....	....	145394	SSX	Brighton
SATES						
1750	1850	1650	1750	174513	OXF	Kencot

Known From	To	Researching From	To	Ref	Cty	Place
SATHERLEY						
1855	1865	....	....	172634	DEV	Exeter
SATTERLEY						
1835	1904	1800	1860	131369	DEV	Ashton
ALL	ALL	ALL	ALL	103543	HAM	Southampton
SATTERTHWAITE						
1820	1856	ALL	....	152129	LND	Central
1825	1935	1825	1935	152129	MDX	London
....	....	1800	1900	169501	WAR	???
SAUBERE						
1695	1761	....	1695	164321	MDX	East London
SAUIDGE						
1800	1830	1700	1850	100129	LEI	Ashby De La Zouch
1830	1870	1870	1950	100129	LIN	Stamford
SAUL						
1885	1992	1850	1885	161861	CMA	Keswick
1800	1850	1750	1850	152404	KKD	Kirkcudbright
SAUNDERCOCK						
1769	1843	1600	1769	126357	CON	South Petherwin
1800	1947	1700	1992	161888	CON	???
SAUNDERS						
1840	1900	1700	1840	129364	BKM	Iver Heath
....	....	ALL	1890	178403	BKM	Marlow
1640	1700	1600	1700	124796	BKM	Princes Risborough
1800	1850	1700	1800	111953	BKM	Radnage
1865	1992	....	....	161918	BRK	Sandhurst
1759	1798	....	....	138401	CAE	Llanrhos
1820	1992	1700	1820	117242	CAM	Ely
1790	1811	1500	1790	125695	CAM	Soham
1774	1940	....	....	128996	CAM	Thorney
1828	1844	1840	1841	161896	CMN	Llanelly
1760	1840	ALL	1870	168718	CON	South East
....	1880	1700	1880	147230	CON	Hayle
1841	1850	....	1840	145858	CON	Manaccan
1848	1965	1750	1848	137278	CON	Saltash
1787	1854	1750	1850	132470	DEV	Beaford
1840	1862	1650	1840	161918	DEV	Chittlehampton
1737	1775	....	....	135437	DEV	Hemyock
1800	1882	....	....	170526	DEV	Kingsbridge
1787	1854	1750	1850	132470	DEV	Roborough
1851	1880	1850	1900	126217	DEV	Tauton
1792	1871	1750	1861	154040	DEV	Winkleigh
1800	1900	1650	1800	120081	DOR	Corscombe
1812	1812	1760	1815	174289	DOR	Kinson
1760	1992	1760	1904	161950	DOR	Portland
1740	1768	1700	1800	123536	DOR	Wareham
1846	1849	....	....	176885	ESS	Bocking
1810	....	1750	1840	176885	ESS	Braintree
1840	....	1810	1846	176885	ESS	Felsted
1851	1860	1860	1992	176885	ESS	Great Dunmow
1785	1806	ALL	1806	108642	ESS	Takeley
1797	....	ALL	ALL	175587	GLA	Llandeilo-Talybont
1942	1992	1750	1900	156736	GYN	Caenarfon
1836	1871	1786	1992	161861	HAM	Amport
1745	1992	ALL	1749	162507	HAM	Droxford
1756	1831	1700	1756	127116	HAM	Fawley
1832	1963	1750	1832	175846	HAM	Portsea
1840	1880	1860	1992	162507	HAM	Portsmouth
1882	....	1880	1920	170526	HAM	Portsmouth
1871	1992	1800	1871	159808	HAM	Southampton
1668	1780	1600	1800	130125	HEF	Cradley
1807	1871	1750	1890	131547	HEF	Orleton
1788	1874	1500	1874	172294	HRT	ALL
....	....	?	....	128589	HRT	Hitchin
1787	1850	1700	1800	129976	KEN	South East
....	....	1787	1860	107247	KEN	Folkestone
1824	1900	1700	1824	128465	KEN	Gillingham
1880	1992	1850	1992	126217	KEN	Sheerness
....	....	1860	1870	142131	KEN	Swanley
1672	1672	....	....	166642	KEN	???
1750	1800	ALL	1992	170909	KIK	Muckalee
1855	1920	1840	1920	105333	LAN	Liverpool
1850	1900	ALL	1900	146226	LAN	Manchester
1825	1855	1825	1855	156965	LND	City
1895	1907	ALL	ALL	120057	LND	Fortune Green
1876	1879	....	....	168165	LND	Fulham
1858	1900	1800	1900	126586	LND	Islington
....	....	1860	....	142131	LND	St Giles
1795	1835	1700	1860	105333	MDX	Marylebone
1840	1940	1700	1840	151955	MDX	Staines
....	....	ALL	1766	168602	NFK	???
1773	1773	1550	1773	102830	NTH	Nottingham
1766	1894	1766	....	122572	NTT	ALL
1840	1850	1800	1900	177571	OXF	Henley
SAUNDERS contd.						
1766	1940	....	....	168602	SFK	Lowestoft
....	....	ALL	1766	168602	SFK	???
1830	1840	1700	1850	105333	SOM	Thornfalcon
1865	1920	1920	1992	161918	SRY	Camberley
1780	1880	1700	1850	146803	SRY	Farnham
1884	1969	....	....	164232	SRY	Southwark
1850	1992	....	....	100536	SSX	???
1800	1860	1750	1900	138878	STS	Tipton
....	....	1840	1871	159808	WIL	Salisbury
....	....	1828	1840	159808	???	London
SAUNDERSON						
1604	1706	ALL	ALL	141615	LEI	Billesdon
1690	1900	1600	1690	178640	LIN	Grimsby
1627	1750	1600	1800	142891	LIN	Winteringham
SAUNDRY						
1800	1900	1800	1900	171077	CON	St Issey
1746	1782	ALL	ALL	104191	CON	St Just
SAUNT						
....	....	ALL	ALL	109940	ALL	ALL
SAUNTER						
....	....	1860	1943	102989	ALL	ALL
1830	1840	ALL	ALL	113743	SSX	Rye
SAVAGAR						
....	....	1750	1850	123277	HEF	???
SAVAGE						
1650	1880	ALL	1900	113492	BDF	North
1850	1850	1840	1900	107360	BKM	East Claydon
1696	1750	1600	1750	117005	BKM	Haversham
1813	1814	1800	1837	107360	BKM	Waddesdon
1742	1749	ALL	1742	168602	BRK	Bisham
1733	1940	....	....	128996	CAM	Thorney
1830	1930	ALL	ALL	119253	CHS	Adswood
1800	1880	ALL	ALL	119253	CHS	Baguley
1784	1788	ALL	ALL	119253	CHS	Gt Budworth
....	....	1700	1900	162019	CHS	Rocsavage
1788	1795	ALL	ALL	119253	CHS	Styal
1783	....	ALL	ALL	119253	CHS	Winnington
1817	1830	ALL	ALL	119253	CHS	Woodford
....	....	1700	1900	162019	DBY	Macclesfield
1856	1992	1600	1856	131261	DOW	Portaferry
....	....	1700	1850	162000	HAM	Portsmouth
1780	1850	1750	1780	168777	HAM	Portsmouth
1850	1992	1830	1850	103985	HAM	Titchfield
1696	1930	....	1696	142166	HRT	Layston
1530	1930	1530	1992	145769	KEN	ALL
1840	1992	1780	1840	176257	KEN	Lewisham
1837	1900	....	....	162000	KEN	Swale
?	?	?	?	166642	KEN	???
....	....	1700	1900	162019	LAN	Warrington
1800	1900	1800	1900	163511	LND	City
1892	1892	....	....	139971	LND	Wandsworth
1800	1900	1700	1800	166561	NTT	East Leake
1793	1824	1788	1859	107360	OXF	Ambrosden
1811	1831	ALL	1811	115126	OXF	Banbury
1784	1927	....	....	169528	OXF	Chipping Norton
1785	1785	1727	1792	107360	OXF	Horley
1600	1900	1600	1900	114316	SFK	South West
1765	1865	1700	1765	177075	SOM	Paulton
1855	1886	1830	1855	109878	SOM	Wells
1853	1853	1853	1992	174262	STS	West Bromwich
1851	1854	1600	1854	121150	WOR	Broadway
....	....	1800	1950	105864	WOR	Worcester
....	....	1700	1900	162019	???	Manchester
SAVERY						
ALL	1734	....	....	170178	WIL	Liddington
SAVIDGE						
1684	1837	1600	1684	151866	CAM	Chesterton
1780	1870	1780	1870	163317	SOM	Creech St Michael
SAVIGE						
1615	1807	ALL	1615	168602	BDF	Odell
SAVIGNAC						
....	....	ALL	ALL	146641	ALL	Name Study
SAVIL						
1650	1850	ALL	ALL	131873	ESS	Manuden
1650	1850	ALL	ALL	131873	HRT	Albury
SAVILE						
1250	1930	ALL	1930	162027	NTT	Ollerton
1250	1930	ALL	1930	162027	YKS	Mexborough
SAVILLE						
1791	....	1750	1791	148121	AVN	Bristol
1750	1900	1700	1900	158356	ERY	ALL
....	....	1700	1880	129275	ESS	Thaxted
1890	....	....	....	168041	ESS	West Ham

Known From	To	Researching From	To	Ref	Cty	Place
SAVILLE contd.						
1650	1850	....	....	138037	HRT	North East
1800	1900	1600	1900	120677	PEM	St Florence
1550	1900	1550	1900	158356	WRY	ALL
SAVIN						
1836	1859	ALL	1992	125113	KEN	Birchington
1835	1881	1700	1881	162035	WIL	Chippenham
SAVORY						
1690	1840	1650	1840	121738	BRK	Brightwalton
1794	1992	1600	1794	115096	LND	Central
1800	1980	1800	1980	162051	MDX	Bromley
1800	1950	1800	1950	162051	MDX	Hackney
1640	1900	1640	1900	162051	MDX	Hammersmith
1700	1900	1700	1900	162051	MDX	London
1800	1950	1800	1950	162051	MDX	Poplar
1600	1970	1600	1970	162051	MDX	Stepney
....	....	1700	1900	147494	NFK	???
1700	1880	1700	1880	162051	SRY	Beddington
1800	1950	1800	1950	162051	SRY	Camberwell
1700	1950	1700	1950	162051	SRY	Southwark
1680	1900	1680	1900	162051	SRY	Wandsworth
SAVOURS						
1607	1992	1500	1607	164879	GLA	St Marychurch
SAWARD						
1810	1851	1790	1851	115797	ESS	Tillingham
SAWBRIDGE						
....	....	ALL	ALL	162078	ALL	ALL
1650	1800	1500	1750	162078	WAR	Hillmorton
SAWERS						
1849	....	1700	1849	168246	AYR	Loudoun
SAWFORD						
1775	1940	....	....	128996	CAM	Thorney
1842	1862	1750	1842	129445	LIN	Sutton St Edmunds
SAWKILL						
1900	1915	1800	1945	110841	DUR	South Shields
SAWKINS						
1764	1764	....	....	144355	KEN	South
SAWREY						
1708	1790	1680	1708	117196	CMA	Hawkshead
1500	1700	1400	1700	129011	LAN	Furness
SAWYER						
1840	1845	1700	1840	126772	DEV	Torquay
1761	....	1650	1761	100013	ESS	Great Waltham
1870	1900	....	....	162094	GLS	Cirencester
....	....	1608	1719	104264	GLS	Rodmarton
1666	1717	1650	1750	142018	HAM	East Woodhay
1771	1804	1750	1800	145459	HAM	Eling
1770	1992	1600	1770	103098	HAM	Fawley
1896	1920	1800	1896	117153	KEN	Hastings
1800	....	....	1800	162086	KEN	Romney Marsh
1763	1763	ALL	1770	113611	LIN	Winteringham
1740	1763	ALL	1770	113611	LIN	Winterton
1803	1992	....	....	172529	LND	???
1858	1992	ALL	ALL	115762	NTT	Sutton Bovington
1830	1992	1805	1881	111546	OXF	Eynsham
1800	1850	ALL	1850	155853	SFK	Barking
....	....	1665	1730	104264	WIL	Ashley
1765	1867	....	....	115606	WIL	Ogbourne St Andrew
1820	1870	1700	1820	162094	WIL	West Lavington
1728	1820	1700	1840	142018	WIL	West Wellow
1880	1920	1800	1920	150061	YKS	Bradford
SAWYERS						
1855	1860	ALL	ALL	162108	SSX	Balcombe
SAXBY						
1726	1814	ALL	....	104515	LIN	South
1936	1945	1700	1800	125261	LIN	Eagle
1861	1992	1700	1800	125261	LIN	Wisbey
1620	1700	....	....	153583	NTH	Bugbrooke
SAXELBY						
....	....	ALL	ALL	136425	ALL	Name Study
SAXON						
....	....	ALL	ALL	165646	STS	Tipton
SAXTOM						
1800	1950	1700	1890	157384	YKS	Bingley
1812	1950	1800	1890	157384	YKS	Keighley
SAXTON						
1843	1923	ALL	1843	114030	ESS	South East
....	....	1800	1920	131555	LIN	Grantham
1840	1900	....	....	134198	SYK	Catcliffe
1790	1840	1700	1790	134198	SYK	Whistow
SAYCE						
....	....	ALL	ALL	162116	SAL	ALL
1826	1861	1750	1850	117315	SAL	Whixall
SAYELL						
1837	1933	1850	1875	151335	BDF	Leighton Buzzard
1700	1900	1700	1992	127353	BKM	ALL
1880	1900	1750	1900	127353	BKM	Horton
1875	1933	1850	1933	151335	HRT	Watford
SAYER						
1670	1780	....	....	165999	ESS	Broomfield
1822	1919	ALL	1992	125113	KEN	Birchington
1800	1830	1800	1830	108006	KEN	Canterbury
1832	....	1800	1835	155969	KEN	East Wickham
1800	1810	1780	1832	155969	MDX	Holborn
1809	1826	....	1809	161691	MDX	Shoreditch
1797	1844	ALL	1880	104531	NFK	Newton Flotman
1730	1800	1700	1800	115614	NFK	Thwaite By Loddew
1808	1888	1800	1830	138258	NYK	Bowes
1820	1970	1800	1850	115614	SFK	Buneay
1522	1624	1624	1800	161845	SRY	Peckham
1522	1624	1624	1800	161845	SRY	Southwark
SAYERS						
1870	1950	1870	1896	138312	KEN	Central
1840	1866	1840	1896	138312	KEN	Dover
1900	1992	1800	1900	174335	LND	Brixton
1900	1992	1800	1900	174335	LND	Hackney
1900	1992	1800	1900	174335	LND	St Lukes
1813	1992	ALL	ALL	158070	SSX	ALL
1825	1900	1700	1825	133019	SSX	Brighton
1800	1882	....	....	145394	SSX	Pulborough
SAYLE						
1850	1960	1850	1950	132683	LAN	Liverpool
SAYLES						
1841	1868	1800	1841	132853	SRY	Lambeth
1824	....	1800	1824	132853	SRY	Mortlake
1710	1798	....	1710	101761	WRY	Fishlake
SAYNSBURY						
....	....	1460	1644	161438	WIL	Market Lavington
SAYSELL						
1920	1992	....	....	133124	CLV	???
1900	1992	....	....	133124	DBY	Derby
1850	1960	....	....	133124	DEV	Plymouth
1920	1992	....	....	133124	DUR	???
....	....	1880	1992	133124	GLA	ALL
....	....	1880	1992	133124	GLA	Swansea
....	....	1750	1992	133124	GLS	ALL
....	....	1830	1992	133124	GLS	Bristol
....	....	1750	1992	133124	GLS	Forest Of Dean
....	....	1750	1992	133124	GLS	Westbury On Severn
....	....	1855	1992	133124	HAM	Portsmouth
....	....	1600	1992	133124	HEF	South
....	....	1837	1900	133124	LND	???
1880	1992	1837	1880	133124	MON	ALL
1880	1992	1837	1880	133124	MON	Newport
1875	1992	....	....	133124	SAL	Bishops Castle
1920	1992	....	....	133124	YKS	???
SAYWELL						
1660	1992	1600	1992	144908	HUN	Croxton
1859	1934	1700	1858	162000	KEN	Swale
SCADDAN						
1756	1812	ALL	ALL	179116	CON	Scilly Isles
1810	1900	1600	1810	117110	DOR	Corfe Castle
1841	1874	ALL	ALL	179116	SRY	Lambeth
SCADDEN						
1860	1860	1700	1900	162132	CON	Camborne
1700	1820	1600	1890	162132	CON	Gwinear
....	....	....	....	162132	CON	Ludgvan
....	....	....	....	162132	CON	Warbstow
1736	1992	1736	1992	162124	DOR	Bridport
SCADDING						
1700	1970	1600	1700	117110	CON	Ludgvan
1800	1860	1700	1800	145017	DEV	ALL
....	1736	....	....	162124	DEV	Hemyock
1796	1870	1870	1992	117110	KEN	Canterbury
1800	1960	1840	1960	162140	LND	Islington
SCADENG						
1840	....	1840	1992	162124	LND	???
SCADLOCK						
1710	....	1650	....	134589	YKS	Huntington
SCAFF						
1828	1860	1800	1890	116009	CON	Kingsand
?	?	1800	1992	116009	CON	Redruth
SCAID						
1800	1840	....	....	176540	PER	Methven
SCAIFE						
1851	....	ALL	ALL	147281	LAN	Rossendale
1847	1851	ALL	ALL	129933	LND	Whitechapel

Known From	To	Researching From	To	Ref	Cty	Place
SCAIFE contd.						
....	1869	ALL	ALL	129933	SRY	Epson
1830	1835	1750	1850	126985	YKS	Pocklington
SCALE						
1700	1900	1600	1900	103845	PEM	South
1700	1900	1600	1900	103845	PEM	Mid
SCALES						
....	....	ALL	ALL	162159	ALL	Name Study
?	?	....	....	159395	CAM	Cambridge
1829	1977	ALL	1977	118990	ESS	Prittlewell
....	....	1850	....	117714	HRT	South Mimms
....	....	1890	1930	133639	MDX	London
1825	1865	1700	1825	115304	NFK	South
1798	1817	1795	1817	108901	NTT	Newark
SCALING						
1875	1900	ALL	ALL	116823	NYK	Helmsley
SCALLEY						
1876	....	....	....	165387	STS	Walsall
SCAMEL						
1730	1815	1600	1730	171182	WIL	South
1730	1815	1600	1730	171182	WIL	West
SCAMELL						
1850	1890	....	....	121010	HAM	Wherwell
1710	1746	....	....	136263	WIL	Amesbury
1743	1890	1600	1743	121010	WIL	East Knoyle
1775	1992	....	....	136263	WIL	Wishford
1746	....	....	....	136263	WIL	Woodford
SCAMLER						
1560	1713	1560	1713	107980	NFK	Briston
SCAMMEL						
1808	1823	1750	1850	136719	WIL	Tidworth
SCAMMELL						
1895	1970	1700	1800	118214	HAM	Kingston
1895	1970	1700	1800	118214	HAM	Ringwood
1767	....	1767	....	141194	SRY	Caterham
1500	1700	1500	1900	170216	WIL	ALL
SCANDLING						
1773	1940	....	....	128996	CAM	Thorney
1935	1992	1800	1935	162167	WYK	Huddersfield
SCANE						
1713	1713	....	1767	121169	WIL	Hill Deverill
1701	1767	....	1767	121169	WIL	Longbridge Deverill
SCANLON						
....	1846	....	....	140767	IRL	???
1854	....	1854	1881	140767	YKS	Baildon Moor
1854	....	1854	1881	140767	YKS	Leeds
SCANNELL						
1826	1992	1816	1992	171581	IRL	ALL
SCANTLEBURY						
....	....	1800	1850	150800	CON	???
....	....	1800	1850	150800	DEV	???
SCAPENS						
....	....	ALL	ALL	125490	ALL	Name Study
SCAPLAN						
1680	1765	1600	1790	105333	WIL	Salisbury
SCARBOROUGH						
1824	1897	1824	....	162175	LIN	Caistor
1865	1897	1824	....	162175	LIN	Great Grimsby
1800	1860	1800	1860	155764	LIN	Old Bolingbroke
1562	1697	1550	1696	102830	NTH	Nassington
SCARFE						
1819	1866	1800	1866	118192	SFK	Hadleigh
SCARFF						
1787	1833	1765	1833	115797	ESS	Margaretting
SCARGILL						
1687	1809	....	....	168513	YKS	Thornhill
SCARISBRICK						
....	....	1870	1992	147249	LAN	Toxteth
SCARLE						
1878	1992	....	....	162183	DBY	ALL
....	....	1800	1992	162183	LEI	ALL
1785	1992	ALL	1785	114650	SFK	Flixton
SCARLET						
1740	1992	1740	1992	106305	DUB	???
SCARLETT						
....	....	ALL	ALL	162191	DBY	Derby
1788	1832	ALL	ALL	162191	HEF	Leominster
1876	....	1850	1950	133639	MDX	Islington
1825	1830	1700	1825	134058	STS	Harborne
1840	1860	ALL	ALL	162191	STS	Wolverhampton
1830	1841	1700	1830	134058	WAR	Birmingham
1824	....	ALL	ALL	175587	YKS	Gildersome
SCARMAN						
1880	1880	1840	1920	105333	MDX	Deptford
SCARNELL						
1762	1860	1700	1762	167533	NFK	Rockland St Mary
SCARNING						
1676	1725	1650	1725	167533	NFK	Bergh Apton
SCARR						
1720	1992	1720	1992	161276	BRK	Newbury
1720	1992	1720	1992	161276	CAM	Great Shelford
1777	1793	....	1860	137405	CAM	Rampton
....	....	1800	1830	177725	EYK	Hull
1779	1800	1538	1820	118893	NRY	Patrick Brompton
1802	1920	1800	1992	123250	YKS	Beverley
1841	1992	1800	1992	123250	YKS	Hull
1690	1785	1600	1800	123250	YKS	Worton
SCARROW						
....	....	....	....	104396	YKS	Thorngumbald
SCAWIN						
1820	1880	1800	1880	135429	YKS	York
SCHALLER						
1910	1950	1850	1910	165689	ESS	Dagenham
1910	1930	1850	1910	165689	LND	West
SCHAW						
1780	1850	1700	1780	142328	CLK	Alloa
SCHELCHER						
....	....	1810	1830	114308	OXF	Hornton
SCHILDT						
1800	1900	1700	1992	177180	LND	Stepney
SCHOEN						
....	....	ALL	ALL	141151	ALL	ALL
1752	1800	1750	ALL	141151	LND	???
1800	1829	1750	1900	141151	NTH	Crick
SCHOFIELD						
1820	1825	1800	1850	123536	ANT	ALL
1862	1872	1850	1945	123536	DUR	Gateshead
1800	1800	ALL	1850	136077	LAN	ALL
1800	1830	1700	1850	142204	LAN	Astley
1808	1871	ALL	1820	147281	LAN	Bacup
1802	....	1780	1880	110205	LAN	Bury
1858	1900	ALL	1858	162256	LAN	Chorley
1816	1881	1775	1816	174211	LAN	Hopwood
1816	1881	1775	1816	174211	LAN	Middleton
1820	1860	1770	1820	168912	LAN	Oldham
1830	1881	1800	1891	142204	LAN	Westhoughton
1600	1900	?	?	173185	WYK	Heckmondwike
1820	1861	ALL	1992	111384	WYK	Leeds
1798	1992	ALL	1860	178632	YKS	East
1798	1992	ALL	1860	178632	YKS	South
1753	....	1720	1790	170348	YKS	Almondbury
1841	1980	1700	1841	130974	YKS	East Bierley
1785	1935	ALL	1935	100102	YKS	Gomersall
1753	1969	1700	1753	133760	YKS	Huddersfield
1856	1935	1800	1860	173649	YKS	Mirfield
1834	1881	1700	1834	130974	YKS	Tong
SCHOLEFIELD						
1818	1818	ALL	1818	119636	LAN	Rochedale
1782	1782	1760	1782	147338	WRY	Bradford
1728	1743	ALL	1728	122017	WYK	Saddleworth
1660	1992	1400	1660	163236	YKS	Saddleworth
1818	1871	ALL	1818	119636	YKS	Sowerby Bridge
SCHOLES						
1849	1867	1800	1880	162272	LAN	Ancoats
1900	1910	1850	1992	142743	LAN	Bury
1830	1992	1700	1830	135038	LAN	Darwen
1849	1867	1800	1880	162272	LAN	Manchester
?	?	....	....	132500	LAN	Oldham
1742	1992	....	....	132500	LAN	Shaw
1900	1943	1873	1900	162272	LND	Battersea
SCHOLEY						
....	....	....	....	113735	DBY	Bakewell
....	....	....	....	113735	DBY	Buxton
1642	1826	1500	1734	175072	LIN	Billinghay
1850	1992	....	....	113220	LIN	Grimsby
....	....	ALL	1850	113220	LIN	River Bottom
1725	1832	....	....	141593	WYK	Adwick
1757	1799	1600	1775	101575	YKS	Leeds
....	....	1700	1780	177393	YKS	Marr
....	....	1700	1850	113735	YKS	Sheffield
SCHONSTADT						
1859	1865	1859	1900	163317	LAN	Liverpool
SCHOOLAR						
1830	1884	....	....	147672	MDX	???
SCHORAH						
1840	1992	ALL	1840	154563	YKS	Sheffield

Will you use the BGD ?

Known From	To	Researching From	To	Ref	Cty	Place
SCHULTZ						
1854	1921	1700	1854	164879	LND	St George In The East
SCHULZE						
....	....	1850	1992	140759	HAM	Aldershot
....	....	1910	1992	140759	WIL	Swindon
SCHUNTER						
1893	1897	ALL	ALL	124346	T&W	Sunderland
SCHWEITZER						
1775	1830	1750	1850	163562	LND	Westminster
SCLATER						
1699	1700	ALL	ALL	141615	LEI	Leicester
1775	1780	....	....	164631	LIN	Gainsborough
SCOBIE						
1640	1814	1600	1825	108510	CLK	Clackmannan
SCOBLE						
1824	1992	1750	1824	167436	DEV	Woodleigh
1916	1992	ALL	1992	136077	LAN	East
SCOFFERN						
1810	1889	1810	1889	164399	DEV	Stowford
SCOFFIN						
1820	1840	1820	1850	103225	LIN	Ashby
SCOFIELD						
1850	1992	1750	1850	110442	WYK	Morley
SCOLEY						
1642	1826	1500	1734	175072	LIN	Billinghay
SCOLIN						
....	....	ALL	ALL	158879	SCT	ALL
SCOLLAY						
1750	1965	....	....	137820	SHI	Fetlar
1720	1965	....	....	137820	SHI	Mid Yell
1760	1965	....	....	137820	SHI	North Yell
1758	1965	....	....	137820	SHI	Northmavine
1720	1965	....	....	137820	SHI	South Yell
SCOLTOCK						
....	....	ALL	ALL	162310	ALL	Name Study
1597	1992	ALL	ALL	162310	ALL	ALL
1825	....	ALL	ALL	112275	SAL	Wenlock
SCONCE						
....	....	ALL	ALL	131547	ENG	ALL
1786	1858	1700	1992	113476	LAN	Clifton
1828	....	1820	1840	131547	OXF	Balscott
1820	....	1700	1850	131547	OXF	Banbury
1801	....	1700	1850	131547	OXF	Neithrop
1836	1843	1830	1850	131547	OXF	Wroxton
SCONE						
1890	1992	....	1890	134724	CON	???
SCONSE						
....	....	1700	1850	170313	HAM	Burghclere
SCOONES						
1841	1843	1700	1845	170143	KEN	Hunton
SCOONS						
1838	1893	1800	1992	158704	KEN	Flimwell
SCOPES						
....	....	ALL	ALL	135836	ALL	Name Study
SCORER						
1743	1766	ALL	1766	116548	DUR	ALL
1840	1870	1700	1992	167908	DUR	ALL
1775	1992	1700	1775	159565	DUR	Wolsingham
SCOREY						
1820	1854	ALL	....	172219	HAM	Bishopstoke
1760	1880	....	1760	113891	HAM	Eling
1760	1880	....	1760	113891	HAM	Marchwood
SCORGIE						
....	....	ALL	ALL	141801	ALL	Name Study
1800	1868	1750	1800	137057	ABD	Auchendoir
SCORRILL						
1484	1734	ALL	ALL	122106	SFK	Hitcham
1736	1851	ALL	1742	122106	SFK	Ringshall
SCOT						
1707	....	....	....	151351	ANS	Arbroath
1804	1812	1700	1812	116319	YKS	North
SCOTCHER						
1800	1850	1800	1850	111589	ESS	Stock
SCOTCHMER						
1906	1923	1880	1946	102334	MDX	Poplar
SCOTHERN						
1742	1753	....	1742	101761	NTT	Nottingham
SCOTNEY						
1730	1940	....	....	128996	CAM	Thorney
1841	1992	....	1841	151270	CAM	Whittlesey
SCOTSON						
1804	1844	1700	1900	173711	LAN	Chorley
SCOTT						
....	....	ALL	ALL	162337	ALL	Name Study
....	....	ALL	ALL	162353	ALL	Name Study
1760	1815	ALL	ALL	140902	ABD	King Edward
1800	1850	1800	1850	140864	ABD	Pitsligo
1790	1880	ALL	ALL	140902	ABD	Turriff
....	....	1650	ALL	149187	ANS	Balmossie
1850	....	1800	1992	163244	ANS	Brechin
1889	1900	ALL	1920	171530	ANS	Carnoustie
....	....	1750	1900	134546	ANS	Dundee
....	....	1650	ALL	149187	ANS	Dundee
....	....	1840	ALL	149187	ANS	Edzell
1816	1992	1700	1816	178896	ANS	Panbridge
1816	1992	1700	1816	178896	ANS	St Vigeans
1751	1992	1700	1992	112089	BEW	???
1782	1992	1700	1782	135747	BKM	Lillingstone Dayrell
1762	1820	....	....	115606	BRK	New Windsor
1725	1940	....	....	128996	CAM	Thorney
1857	1872	1790	1857	112720	CHS	Birkenhead
1776	....	1776	....	147532	CHS	Wybunbury
1789	....	....	....	117196	CMA	Hawkshead
1850	1920	ALL	ALL	107530	CON	Penzance
1850	1960	ALL	ALL	162469	CUL	North
1830	1890	1780	1830	155810	CUL	Caldbeck
1756	1881	1756	1881	110396	CUL	Cocklehill
1780	1820	1600	1820	146730	CUL	Workington
1819	1870	1750	1819	159212	CUL	Workington
1600	1989	1600	1992	162388	DEV	Chagford
1712	1949	?	1712	136611	DEV	Holcombe Rogus
....	....	1700	1830	111708	DFS	Kirkconnel
1730	1870	ALL	1890	162507	DFS	Langholm
1760	1800	ALL	1760	115266	DOR	ALL
1841	1851	1700	1992	170518	DOR	Bellchalwell
....	....	ALL	ALL	174289	DOR	Hampreston
1845	1863	1700	1992	170518	DOR	Hazelbury Bryan
1713	1713	1650	1800	162620	DOR	Sherborne
....	....	ALL	ALL	174157	DOW	Dromore
....	....	ALL	ALL	169315	DUR	East
1899	1950	....	1899	131008	DUR	Hartlepool
1800	1880	1700	1800	138258	DUR	Houghton Le Spring
1768	1794	1700	1768	138355	DUR	Preston
1823	1863	1700	1823	115401	DUR	Sunderland
1851	1871	....	....	116637	DUR	Sunderland
....	....	ALL	ALL	162329	EAG	ALL
1779	1992	ALL	ALL	131091	ESS	ALL
1815	1925	....	....	101028	ESS	High Easter
1851	1881	1800	1900	162450	ESS	Thorpe Le Soken
....	....	1775	....	170453	FIF	ALL
1830	1860	1830	1900	171530	FIF	Cameron
1780	1870	1700	1900	130915	FIF	Ceres
1800	1881	ALL	1880	171530	FIF	St Andrews
1840	1860	1800	1840	135658	GLS	Bristol
1847	1900	1700	ALL	135127	HAM	Boldre
1734	1778	1700	1865	126667	IOW	Freshwater
1860	1960	....	....	162361	IRL	Dublin
1856	1992	....	....	162477	KEN	Northfleet
1795	1952	1700	1952	113638	KEN	Wye
1850	1860	....	....	162361	KRS	Kinross
1770	1790	....	....	130915	KRS	???
1823	1823	1823	1823	143286	LAN	Farnworth
1785	1805	ALL	ALL	124982	LAN	Lancaster
1857	1867	....	1880	157139	LAN	Liverpool
1800	1900	1700	1800	164844	LIN	South West
1823	....	....	....	161136	LIN	Cowbit
1823	....	....	....	161136	LIN	Moulton
1796	1992	1796	1992	177687	LIN	South Kelsey
1770	1817	....	....	171654	LKS	Carluke
1754	1774	....	....	171654	LKS	Dalserf
1663	....	1600	1750	162477	LKS	Lanark
1833	1904	1833	1850	160741	LND	Bermondsey
1820	1881	1837	1881	154709	LND	Bethnal Green
1800	1848	1800	1900	163171	LND	Cripplegate
1800	1848	1800	1900	163171	LND	Hockley
1820	1870	1840	1870	163171	LND	New Gloucester Street
1820	1825	1800	1830	162485	LND	Rotherhithe
....	....	1860	1900	142131	LND	Southward
....	....	?	1820	103934	LND	Woolwich
1870	1872	....	....	171492	LND	???
1817	1840	1775	1817	121037	MDX	East
ALL	ALL	ALL	ALL	162434	MDX	Emfield
1880	1920	1800	1900	145866	MDX	St Pancras
....	....	....	1860	157139	MLN	Edinburgh

Known From	To	Researching From	To	Ref	Cty	Place
SCOTT contd.						
1820	1850	ALL	1850	149063	MLN	Stow
1843	....	ALL	ALL	172057	MOG	Drumcaw
1860	1962	1800	1860	128406	NBL	ALL
1828	1992	1700	1828	175137	NBL	ALL
1825	1967	1750	1900	177970	NBL	South
1827	1886	ALL	1827	150924	NBL	Berwick Upon Tween
1840	1850	1840	1850	149063	NBL	Carham
1742	1836	1700	1850	144037	NBL	Elsdon
1764	1770	1730	1820	160873	NBL	Hartburn
1875	?	1875	1992	102245	NBL	Newcastle Upon Tyne
1859	1900	ALL	ALL	125202	NBL	Newcastle
1754	1856	....	....	162477	NBL	Sunderland
1758	1992	1700	1758	162485	NFK	North Elmham
1877	1986	1750	1877	139777	NFK	???
1780	1815	1700	1780	162396	NTT	Clayworth
1810	1940	1600	1810	143146	NTT	Mansfield
1750	1830	1700	1850	141739	NYK	Coxwold
1800	1980	1730	1850	162493	OKI	Westray
1815	1815	....	....	168203	PER	Aberdalgie
1836	1850	1830	1860	162361	PER	Auchterader
1780	1850	1700	1900	148288	PER	Errol
1812	....	1795	1830	162361	PER	Fowlis Wester
1790	1840	....	....	176540	PER	Methven
1826	1826	....	....	168203	PER	Monzie
1780	1850	1700	1900	148288	PER	Scone
1780	1850	1700	1900	148288	PER	Tibbermore
1852	1870	....	....	127140	RFW	Greenock
....	....	1770	1795	162361	ROX	Bonjedward
1850	1900	1850	1900	149063	ROX	Linton
1850	1900	1850	1900	149063	ROX	Morebattle
1800	1900	....	....	150371	ROX	Newcastleton
1820	1840	ALL	1840	149063	ROX	Smailholm
1800	1880	1700	1920	167207	ROX	???
1833	1904	1833	1850	160741	SCT	ALL
1800	....	....	....	161136	SCT	Abbotsford
1834	....	1800	1850	169625	SCT	Bonnet Hill
1802	1885	1840	1913	162442	SCT	Greenock
1830	1900	1700	1840	106267	SCT	Hawick
1800	....	....	....	161136	SCT	Melrose
1800	1880	1700	1920	167207	SEL	???
1750	1992	1750	1800	162329	SFK	West
1836	1851	1600	1836	116637	SFK	Herringswell
1712	1949	?	1712	136611	SOM	Holcombe Rogus
ALL	ALL	ALL	ALL	162434	SRY	Redhill
1838	....	1780	....	116297	SRY	St Saviours
1903	1961	1880	1903	105058	SSX	Haywards Heath
1841	....	....	....	170313	STS	Wolverhampton
1880	1992	ALL	1992	158437	WAR	Birmingham
1848	1992	1750	1848	101893	WIL	Cherhill
1775	1917	1600	1775	150185	WIL	Little Somerford
1800	1870	1750	1900	113212	WIL	Salisbury
1756	1847	1650	1756	129453	WRY	Clapham
1830	1873	1810	1873	147338	WRY	Northowram
1847	1881	ALL	ALL	111384	WYK	Leeds
1740	1850	1740	1850	153621	WYK	Queensbury
1830	1870	1870	1992	108367	YKS	Flockton
1848	1890	1891	1992	175412	YKS	Sculcoates
1783	1932	ALL	1783	103004	YKS	Wakefield
1800	1840	....	....	127140	???	Calderbank
1825	1986	1800	1980	177970	???	Newcastle
1894	....	....	....	153400	???	Southport
SCOULAR						
1804	1884	1841	1884	138606	AYR	Fenwick
1759	1861	1759	1884	138606	LKS	Carmunnock
SCOULLER						
1600	1700	1550	1700	154881	MLN	ALL
SCOURFIELD						
1400	....	1300	1500	176923	LAN	Kendal
1450	1500	1300	1800	176923	PEM	New Moat
SCOURSE						
1820	1872	....	....	135437	GLS	Bristol
1785	1802	....	....	135437	SOM	Bedminster
SCOUSE						
....	....	1700	1850	170313	HAM	Burghclere
SCOVELL						
1840	1900	1700	1840	164879	HAM	ALL
1695	1870	1600	1992	145289	HAM	Isle Of Wight
SCOWCROFT						
1825	1900	1750	1825	132268	LAN	Bolton
1825	1900	1750	1825	132268	LAN	Harwood
SCOWEN						
1890	1980	1700	ALL	159255	LND	Hackney
1890	1980	1700	ALL	159255	LND	Walthamstow
SCOWN						
1772	1992	....	....	172529	CON	Lauceston
SCRACE						
....	....	1798	1851	161667	KEN	Dartford
SCRAFIELD						
1801	1807	1700	1830	176621	LIN	Kirton
SCRAFTON						
1770	1800	ALL	1770	131059	ESS	West Ham
SCRAGG						
1818	1825	1790	1850	131547	SRY	Betchworth
1804	1811	1790	1820	131547	SRY	Cranley
1853	1928	1800	1900	131547	SRY	Dorking
1697	1780	1600	1800	131547	SSX	Rudgwich
SCRANAGE						
1800	1810	1810	1900	166383	WOR	Bromsgrove
1790	1850	1850	1900	166383	WOR	Worcester
SCRASE						
1750	1880	1600	1880	154342	GLS	Bristol
1782	1988	1600	1782	162035	GLS	Bristol
SCRATYARD						
1810	1825	....	....	102946	YKS	Rippon
SCREACH						
1835	1900	1700	1900	141127	DEV	Dartmouth
SCREATON						
....	....	1785	1820	116173	LEI	???
....	....	1785	1820	116173	WAR	???
SCREEN						
1856	1992	ALL	1856	147087	GLS	ALL
1776	1880	1880	1992	178845	GLS	Rockhampton
1845	1992	1750	1845	163082	SOM	Bristol
SCRIBO						
1653	1940	....	....	128996	CAM	Thorney
SCRIMGEOUR						
....	....	ALL	1762	119326	PER	Donnievorich
SCRIMSHAW						
1883	1906	1850	1883	126624	LND	East
1900	1992	1800	1900	177199	NTT	Worksop
SCRINE						
1832	1891	....	....	127779	SRY	Kennington
SCRIPPS						
....	....	1800	1900	152684	HRT	Barkway
SCRIVEN						
....	....	ALL	ALL	104558	ALL	Name Study
1800	1900	1600	1900	142050	SOM	South
1776	1830	1750	1900	113212	WIL	Malmesbury
SCRIVENER						
1850	1980	1700	1850	112097	BDF	ALL
1705	1760	1600	1770	137170	BDF	Leighton Buzzard
1891	1912	....	....	118192	ESS	Harwich
1837	....	....	....	103225	LND	St Georges Hanover Square
1841	1881	1841	1881	141267	NFK	Scole
1539	1663	ALL	1539	131059	SFK	Brantham
SCRIVENNER						
1320	1992	1320	1992	162515	SFK	ALL
1320	1992	1320	1992	162515	SFK	Ipswich
SCRIVENS						
?	?	?	?	154687	GLS	Cheltenham
?	?	?	?	154687	GLS	Condicote
?	?	?	?	154687	GLS	Turkdean
1765	1765	1735	1770	107360	NTH	Wappenham
1800	1880	1700	1900	171522	SSX	Hastings
SCROOM						
1830	1870	....	....	117560	HUN	Leigton
SCROWTHER						
1799	1837	1750	1800	174602	NBL	Lowick
SCRUBY						
1848	....	....	....	127701	SFK	Rattlesden
SCRUSE						
1837	....	....	....	168092	HAM	West Meon
1803	1837	....	....	168092	WIL	Stapleford
SCRUTON						
1800	....	1700	....	134589	YKS	Ribston
SCRUTTON						
1881	1992	1700	1881	178225	CHS	Runcorn
SCUDAMOOR						
1850	1973	1850	1920	102806	SCT	???
SCUDAMORE						
1797	1830	1797	ALL	145386	GLS	Bristol
SCUFFHAM						
1700	1992	1738	1911	174556	SFK	Diss
1700	1992	1738	1911	174556	SFK	Wortham
SCUFFLE						
1808	....	1800	1992	167800	HAM	Winchfield

Known From	To	Researching From	To	Ref	Cty	Place
SCULPHER						
1700	1899	....	....	121835	NFK	Castle Acre
1800	1899	....	....	121835	NFK	Rougham
SCURR						
1800	1899	....	....	164151	CUL	Branthwaite
1729	1992	1600	1728	138401	CUL	Dean
1800	1899	....	....	164151	CUL	Dean
1731	1851	1600	1730	138401	CUL	Egremont
1851	1992	....	....	138401	LAN	Liverpool
1867	....	1850	1992	151378	NYK	Thirsk
1874	....	1850	1992	151378	WYK	Ovenden
1876	....	1850	1992	151378	WYK	Sowerby
SCURRAH						
1840	1992	....	....	148350	YKS	Bradford
SCURRILL						
1736	1851	ALL	1742	122106	SFK	Ringshall
SCUTT						
1600	1812	1500	1850	162388	DEV	Chagford
1863	1871	1837	1900	103608	SRY	Chertsey
SCUTTS						
1775	1801	1600	1775	115525	WIL	Sopworth
SEA						
1700	1890	1650	1890	110906	CAM	Chatteris
SEABORN						
1765	1957	1765	1957	102954	GLS	Berkeley
?	1811	1700	1811	176141	HAM	Selbourne
1819	1992	....	1818	129461	SOM	Bristol
SEABORNE						
1810	1992	1700	1810	156213	HEF	Vowchurch
SEABRIGHT						
1856	1958	1700	1856	177237	GLS	Shepscombe
....	....	1500	1850	175072	LIN	ALL
SEABROOK						
1690	1850	ALL	1850	137286	BDF	West
1753	1947	1694	1753	162523	HRT	Shenley
....	....	1700	1900	150800	HRT	???
1860	1992	1750	1860	156132	LND	Bethnal Green
1828	1847	1828	1847	162523	MDX	Islington
1739	1793	....	....	127957	SFK	Barnardiston
1770	1823	....	....	127957	SFK	Stradishall
1860	1920	1837	1992	177121	YKS	???
SEABROOKE						
1530	1700	ALL	1530	131059	BKM	Cheddington
1700	1775	ALL	1700	131059	BKM	Seabrook
1850	1950	....	....	131059	ESS	Grays
1750	1850	ALL	1750	131059	MDX	???
SEACOLE						
....	....	ALL	ALL	162612	ALL	Name Study
1598	1689	1598	1689	162612	BKM	Grendon Underwood
1584	1642	....	....	162612	OXF	Banbury
1565	1653	1559	1840	162612	OXF	Bletchingdon
1591	1795	1591	1795	162612	OXF	Shipton Under Wychwood
SEAD						
1635	1671	....	1720	171441	KEN	Rodmersham
1733	....	....	1750	171441	KEN	Sittingbourne
1702	1712	....	1750	171441	KEN	Wormshill
SEAGE						
1784	1970	ALL	ALL	163988	DEV	South Molton
SEAGER						
1786	1871	1610	1871	148083	DEV	Chardstock
1820	1871	1610	1871	148083	DEV	Offwell
....	....	1750	1800	153486	HAM	Beaulieu
1892	1960	1700	1900	165476	KEN	Canterbury
1765	1793	1750	1800	117323	MDX	Old Brentford
....	....	1700	1750	153486	SOM	Hunstpill
1634	1736	1630	1740	171654	SOM	Norton Sub Hamdon
1628	1690	1600	1800	160873	STS	Kingswinford
1786	1871	1610	1871	148083	WIL	Calne
SEAGERS						
1730	....	....	1780	171441	KEN	Borden
1721	1752	....	1780	171441	KEN	Frinstead
SEAGO						
1804	1879	1750	1804	174203	NFK	Gimingham
SEAGRAVE						
1800	1900	1750	1900	155357	SSX	Horsham
SEAGULL						
1803	1863	....	1863	152803	KEN	Strood
SEAL						
1714	1818	1650	1714	175951	DBY	Duffield
....	1791	ALL	1790	134511	LEI	Packington
SEALE						
1700	1760	....	....	101028	KEN	Maidstone

Known From	To	Researching From	To	Ref	Cty	Place
SEALEY						
1886	1940	....	....	111554	GLS	Shurdington
1886	1992	1770	1850	111554	SOM	Mark
ALL	ALL	1800	1850	111554	SOM	Puriton
1775	1827	....	....	102733	WOR	Freckenham
SEALY						
1773	1871	1750	1871	154709	DOR	ALL
SEAMAN						
....	....	....	....	108340	KEN	???
....	....	....	....	108340	LND	???
1836	ALL	1800	1836	171190	NFK	Bintree
1700	1720	1690	1750	142018	SOM	Taunton
SEAMAR						
1780	1797	1700	1850	123250	YKS	Beverley
SEAMARK						
1857	?	....	....	162558	KEN	Crockham Hill
....	....	1780	1820	110450	NTH	ALL
SEAMONS						
1841	....	....	....	156329	BKM	Aylesbury
SEANOR						
1805	1815	1775	1992	114901	YKS	Aberford
SEAR						
....	....	ALL	ALL	124125	ALL	Name Study
1832	1857	ALL	....	115355	BDF	ALL
1736	1992	1600	1736	144851	BDF	Dunstable
1840	1944	1700	1840	152269	BKM	ALL
1850	1880	1700	1992	146943	BKM	Central
1832	1857	ALL	....	115355	HUN	ALL
1838	1887	ALL	1838	108197	SRY	Brixton
SEARANCKE						
1650	1750	1600	1850	162566	HRT	Hatfield
1750	1850	1700	1900	162566	HRT	St Albans
1800	1850	1800	1900	162566	MEA	Navan
SEARBY						
?	?	?	?	118044	LIN	Grimsby
1721	1970	ALL	ALL	112526	LIN	Mumby Chapel
1822	....	1780	1822	131326	YKS	Hull
SEARCY						
1816	1870	1750	1820	156957	NTT	Ruddington
SEARE						
1670	1710	1560	1710	118869	BDF	Heath & Reach
1602	1678	1500	1650	124796	BKM	Adstock
SEARING						
1860	1930	ALL	ALL	133884	LND	South
SEARL						
....	....	ALL	ALL	162590	ENG	South
SEARLE						
....	....	ALL	ALL	162574	ALL	Name Study
1732	1940	....	....	128996	CAM	Thorney
ALL	1857	....	....	172693	CON	Fowey
1810	1860	....	1860	161888	CON	Probus
ALL	1840	1800	1880	135429	DEV	Awliscombe
ALL	1802	ALL	1802	170968	DEV	Devonport
1790	....	ALL	1790	137545	DEV	Exeter
1790	1992	1750	1900	162582	DEV	Halberton
1839	1867	1850	1900	176982	DEV	Plymouth
1839	1881	1839	1992	114596	DEV	Washfordpyne
1885	1982	1700	1885	100110	DUR	Stockton On Tees
1700	1820	1500	1820	175463	HAM	ALL
1799	1805	ALL	ALL	129933	HAM	Burseldon
1811	1900	1805	1920	170143	HAM	E Tisted
1811	1900	1805	1920	170143	HAM	Froxfield
1824	....	ALL	ALL	129933	HAM	Portsea
1786	1838	1786	1838	136808	HRT	Barkway
1543	1992	ALL	1543	179345	IOW	Stone
1800	1900	1700	1800	125660	KEN	Edenbridge
....	....	1870	1900	146250	LND	Greenwich
ALL	1635	....	....	162590	LND	???
1783	1885	1753	1783	139149	SOM	Bishops Hull
1804	1859	ALL	ALL	175587	SOM	Taunton
1710	1820	1500	1710	139084	SRY	West
1811	....	1800	1820	162590	SRY	Ash
1750	1854	1720	1861	170143	SRY	Farnham
1635	1798	1600	1800	162590	SRY	Frimley
1861	1953	1860	1953	162590	SRY	Long Ditton
1813	1851	1810	1860	162590	SRY	Pirbright
1851	1855	1849	1860	162590	SSX	Crowhurst
....	....	1800	1870	146250	YKS	North
SEARLES						
....	....	1886	....	169102	HRT	Bishops Stortford
1825	1850	1700	1850	108111	MDX	St Margarets
SEARS						
1777	1777	1700	1881	153206	ALL	ALL
1784	1808	1700	1830	143693	BKM	Great Marlow

Known From	To	Researching From	To	Ref	Cty	Place
SEARS contd.						
1802	1875	1700	1802	153206	HRT	Watton On Stone
1771	1771	1700	1771	153206	HRT	???
1794	1850	1650	1794	120774	KEN	South West
1840	1934	1700	1840	153206	LND	Edmonton
1851	1992	....	1850	129461	LND	???
1869	1869	1700	1869	153206	MDX	Ponders End
1762	1834	1700	1762	122580	MDX	Sunbury On Thames
1774	....	....	1774	101761	NTT	Epperstone
1825	....	1750	1850	139386	SRY	Brixton
SEARSON						
....	....	1780	1800	159042	LIN	Aswarby
1823	1896	1800	1900	159042	LIN	Carlby
SEARSTONE						
1841	1992	1800	1851	101044	SYK	Sheffield
SEARY						
1748	1796	ALL	ALL	179116	BRK	Denchworth
1718	1827	ALL	ALL	179116	BRK	Great Coxwell
SEASTON						
1750	1840	ALL	ALL	128449	NTT	Sutton In Ashfield
1844	1860	ALL	ALL	128449	WAR	Birmingham
SEATH						
1863	1872	1837	1863	120731	KEN	Blean
SEATLE						
1830	....	1750	1880	102016	SRY	Lambeth
SEATON						
1800	1940	1700	1800	110477	CAM	Wisbech
1840	1880	1800	1900	111147	LEI	ALL
1700	1750	1700	1750	114529	LIN	Crowle
1750	1992	1650	1750	102342	LIN	Isle Of Axholme
1730	1777	1777	1850	111023	LIN	Langtoft
1800	1880	1800	1880	111023	LIN	Spalding
1690	1707	ALL	1690	111023	NTH	Elinton
1500	1900	....	....	164631	RUT	Egleton
1650	1900	1650	1900	137464	RUT	Seaton
1820	1992	1750	1820	120294	SCT	???
SEATON-BURNHAM						
1862	....	1862	1992	111023	LAN	Manchester
SEATTER						
....	....	1700	1800	162493	OKI	Westray
1760	1840	1700	1840	167703	OKI	Westray
SEAWARD						
1825	1862	1800	1825	174955	MDX	Marylebone
1793	....	1750	1793	174955	MDX	St Giles
1837	1920	1700	1850	135887	WIL	Farley
1837	1920	1700	1850	135887	WIL	Pitton
SEBER						
1790	1992	1670	1820	159786	???	South
SECCAS						
755	1066	....	....	162604	CON	Seccas Combe
SECCOMBE						
1790	1900	1790	1890	162604	CON	Calstock
1630	1900	1630	1900	162604	CON	Creed St Ewe
1580	1860	1580	1860	162604	CON	Lizard
1641	1880	1641	1880	162604	CON	Probus
1200	1992	1066	1800	162604	DEV	Germansweek
1700	1850	1850	1920	129712	MDX	London
SECCULL						
1673	1895	1646	1988	162612	NTH	Aynho
SECHIARIA						
1560	1992	ALL	ALL	162620	ALL	ALL
SECKER						
....	....	1794	1980	168920	LND	ALL
1794	....	1794	1823	168920	LND	Bermondsey
1830	1992	1700	1865	166987	NFK	Derehem
1779	1794	1760	1794	168920	SFK	Layham
SECKINGTON						
1800	1850	1750	1900	177571	BKM	Loughton
SECKOLD						
....	....	ALL	ALL	162639	ALL	Name Study
SECOLL						
....	1526	....	....	162612	OXF	Stanton Harcourt
SEDDING						
1800	1820	1700	1800	172022	SRY	Hersham
SEDDON						
1826	1850	ALL	1826	147222	LAN	Aintree
1820	1840	....	....	118729	LAN	Bolton
1844	1950	....	....	118729	LAN	Eccles
1826	1850	ALL	1826	147222	LAN	Manchester
1800	....	....	....	152218	LAN	Oldham
1873	....	1850	1900	146102	LAN	Salford
1850	1890	1700	1992	139181	LAN	St Helens
1697	1784	1625	1812	169552	LAN	Tunstall
1840	1992	1750	....	110264	LAN	Whiston
SEDDON contd.						
1820	1900	1750	1820	146102	LAN	Worsley
1771	1839	1670	1839	169552	WES	Middleton
1798	1869	1594	1895	169552	YKS	Sedbergh
SEDGBEER						
1738	1870	1738	ALL	175854	SOM	Dulverton
1738	1870	1738	ALL	175854	SOM	Winsford
SEDGEFIELD						
....	1662	1600	1670	174858	YKS	Hunmanby
SEDGELEY						
1810	1916	1700	1960	141569	WAR	Birmingham
SEDGER						
....	....	1826	1881	161667	LND	Bermondsey
SEDGEWICK						
1870	1992	1800	1870	120308	GLA	Cardiff
1744	1830	1700	1744	152196	WES	Underbarrow
1850	1860	1830	1850	131628	YKS	Bradford
1850	1860	1830	1850	131628	YKS	Leeds
SEDGMAN						
1900	1992	1700	1992	114480	CON	???
SEDGWICK						
1816	1987	1600	1816	173711	CMA	Crosbyravenworth
1755	1805	1700	1755	161896	DEV	Plymouth
1757	1898	1700	1757	156698	KEN	Dover
....	1600	....	....	174564	KEN	???
1800	1850	1750	1850	143553	WES	Appleby
1800	1840	1800	1900	140236	YKS	Doncaster
1712	1992	ALL	1712	160016	YKS	Littondale
1712	1992	ALL	1712	160016	YKS	Ribblesdale
1840	1880	1800	1900	140236	YKS	Ripon
1800	1840	1800	1900	140236	YKS	Sheffield
SEDMAN						
1743	1797	1700	1797	147311	NYK	Scalby
1828	1992	1600	1828	160172	YKS	North Rdg
SEDWELL						
1800	1900	1800	1992	177180	HRT	Bovingdon
1800	1930	1800	1930	138967	LND	ALL
SEE						
1752	1836	ALL	1752	168602	NFK	Welney
SEECOMBE						
1791	....	1700	1900	166359	DEV	Petrockstow
SEED						
1783	1783	1500	1783	110310	LAN	Chaigley
SEEDALL						
1865	1871	1750	1890	174998	LAN	Overdarwen
1817	1850	1750	1890	174998	WYK	Waddington
SEEDE						
1678	1720	ALL	ALL	141615	LAN	Brindle
SEELHOFF						
?	?	?	?	160326	ENG	Central
SEENEY						
1850	1928	1700	1850	174076	OXF	ALL
SEEOCH						
1917	1947	....	1947	124842	LAN	Liverpool
SEERS						
1832	1850	1700	1900	135968	LND	ALL
1803	....	....	....	174750	MDX	London
SEEVIOUR						
1824	1854	1800	1900	145149	DOR	Horton
SEFFORD						
....	....	1730	1800	168777	SSX	Shipley
SEFTON						
1729	1772	1690	1729	179523	LAN	Ashton
1772	1819	....	....	179523	LAN	Burtonwood
1729	1772	1690	1729	179523	LAN	Winwick
SEGAR						
1865	1992	ALL	ALL	108464	LAN	Liverpool
SEGRAVE						
1550	1700	1550	1700	168491	BDF	Caddington
1550	1700	1550	1700	168491	HRT	Flamstead
1700	1800	1700	1800	168491	HRT	St Albans
SEGUIER						
1785	1856	....	....	116602	MDX	St Pancras
SEHAN						
1850	1900	1850	1900	107476	STS	Milwich
SEINESBERIA						
....	....	1190	1580	161438	GLS	Saintbury
SELBY						
1770	1850	....	....	140317	HUN	Ramsey
1837	1860	1780	1837	146358	KCD	Maryculter
1808	1910	1710	1808	162663	LIN	Gumby
1839	1992	1700	1850	162663	LIN	Skillington
1850	1870	1800	1900	123536	YKS	Masham

Known From	To	Researching From	To	Ref	Cty	Place
SELDON						
1850	1960	1199	1850	162671	DEV	Bratton Flemming
1779	1897	1700	1779	162698	DEV	Crowys Morchard
1850	1960	1199	1850	162671	DEV	Loxhore
SELF						
1666	1719	....	....	165999	GLS	Westbury On Trym
1868	1914	1914	1992	162701	KEN	Bromley
1849	1849	ALL	ALL	106844	NFK	Dickleborough
1782	1855	1700	1782	162701	NFK	Redenhall
1780	1992	1780	1992	145238	NFK	Shelfanoer
1780	1992	1780	1992	145238	NFK	Tunstead
1832	1840	1840	1900	162701	SFK	Halesworth
1784	1790	1790	1850	162701	SFK	Homersfield
1769	1770	1700	1769	162701	SFK	Ilketshall
1800	1850	1700	1850	132950	WIL	Great Cheverell
....	....	1700	1780	133604	WIL	Little Cheverell
....	....	1750	1900	133604	WIL	West Lavington
1825	1850	1750	1825	172901	WIL	???
SELFE						
1790	1850	ALL	1790	145939	WIL	Trowbridge
1700	1900	1600	1700	173223	WIL	Woodford
SELKIRK						
1821	....	....	....	162728	ARL	Rosneath
1896	....	....	....	162728	DUR	Hebburn
?	?	?	?	162728	DUR	South Shields
1923	1947	1947	1992	146560	LKS	Coatbride
1855	....	....	....	162728	LKS	Glasgow
1726	....	....	....	162728	ROX	Jedburgh
1640	?	ALL	1640	162728	ROX	Mossburnford Mill
1700	?	....	....	162728	ROX	Scraesburgh
SELL						
1800	1850	1780	1870	123676	CAM	Bassingbourne
1886	....	ALL	1886	170674	CAM	Cambridge
SELLAR						
1825	1830	1700	1800	123870	IRL	???
1769	1992	1600	1992	166049	MOR	Boharm
SELLARS						
1811	....	....	....	115576	NFK	Swaffham
1780	1890	1700	1780	121339	NYK	Newton Dale
SELLEN						
....	....	ALL	ALL	136190	ALL	Name Study
SELLENS						
1700	1850	ALL	ALL	143898	SSX	Sedlescombe
SELLER						
1790	1810	1700	1900	171158	DEV	Farway
1770	1850	1700	1770	121339	NYK	Pickering
1830	1910	1750	1830	176583	STS	Stoke
1800	1859	1700	1800	103268	YKS	Bempton
SELLERS						
1837	....	1800	1837	148199	EYK	Hull
1550	....	1550	....	109347	LAN	Whalley
1781	1900	1600	1781	154172	YKS	Scholes
SELLEY						
1820	1874	1818	1887	116424	CON	Torpoint
1740	1992	1600	1740	162736	DEV	Central
SELLICK						
1817	1992	1650	1817	139769	DEV	Tavistock
SELLIN						
1800	1870	1770	1870	126144	KEN	Frindsbury
SELLINGS						
....	1700	....	....	174564	SSX	Burwash
SELLIS						
1820	1880	1800	1820	147885	IRL	Athlone
SELLMAN						
1850	1947	....	1870	178861	LND	Islington
SELLORS						
....	....	....	....	162744	LEI	Market Overton
SELLS						
1870	1992	....	....	162752	HRT	???
1804	....	ALL	ALL	105481	NTT	Old Basford
SELLWOOD						
1780	1900	1700	1900	162760	BRK	Bradfield
....	....	1770	1840	142131	BRK	Oare
1782	1791	1700	1820	142042	WIL	Berwick Bassett
SELMAM						
1723	1791	1700	1850	118397	OXF	Asthall
SELMAN						
1676	1878	1768	1878	178683	GLS	Charfield
1588	1799	1588	1799	178683	GLS	North Nibley
1800	1900	....	....	152978	WIL	Cricklade
1900	1992	....	....	126187	???	Bristol
SELMES						
1800	1973	1750	1800	147907	SSX	Brede
....	....	1750	1850	125628	SSX	Sedlescomb
SELMES contd.						
1590	1786	1500	1800	153591	SXW	Hastings
1590	1786	1500	1800	153591	SXW	Hooe
1590	1786	1500	1800	153591	SXW	Mountfield
1590	1786	1500	1800	153591	SXW	Sedlescombe
SELSBY						
1775	1900	1800	....	109452	SFK	Dennington
SELTH						
1740	1850	1700	1750	124699	ALL	ALL
SELUY						
1645	....	....	1660	171441	KEN	Canterbury
SELWAY						
1839	....	1750	1839	174629	DEV	Talaton
1830	1900	1800	1860	168076	SOM	Bridgwater
1874	1992	1800	1874	140473	SOM	Curry Rival
SELWOOD						
1630	1992	ALL	1630	118184	CON	Cambourne
SELWYN						
1740	1992	ALL	1717	175994	GLS	Newent
1822	1992	ALL	1822	175994	GLS	Pauntley
SELY						
1814	....	ALL	1814	104299	GLS	Birstol
SEMLEY						
1880	1950	....	....	126276	WRY	Barnsley
1900	1992	....	....	126276	WRY	Wath On Dearne
SEMMENS						
1772	1800	ALL	ALL	104191	CON	St Just
1730	1770	1700	1900	118753	CON	St Just
1780	1950	1700	1890	110116	NFK	Moulton
SEMMONS						
1844	1992	1800	1844	179442	CON	Breage
SEMPLE						
1866	1920	1866	1920	114073	LND	St Martins In The Fields
SENDALL						
1775	1833	1750	1833	179337	GLS	Todmarton
SENECHAL						
1655	1940	....	....	128996	CAM	Thorney
SENIOR						
....	....	ALL	ALL	162787	ALL	Name Study
1806	....	ALL	1806	116327	DOR	Stour
1547	1992	....	....	116327	DOR	Swanage
1700	1750	1600	1800	162620	DOR	???
1840	1897	....	....	116327	HAM	Alverstoke
....	....	ALL	1840	116327	HAM	Porchester
1871	1908	1830	1910	127361	WRY	Dewsbury
1737	1763	....	1737	101761	WRY	Flockton
1800	1867	1700	1800	110531	WYK	Farnley
1840	1870	1750	1840	110531	WYK	Wooldale
1850	1860	1700	1850	145688	YKS	Dewsbury
1880	1900	1880	1900	119474	YKS	Loftus
1850	....	....	....	151785	YKS	Thurgoland
1820	1992	1700	1820	127132	YKS	Wakefield
SENNERTH						
1774	1809	ALL	ALL	163562	LND	Westminster
SENNOCK						
1730	1737	1700	1750	126667	DOR	ALL
SENSICLE						
1730	1890	1600	1730	126349	LIN	Dunsby By Bourne
1765	1790	1700	1765	126349	LIN	Thurlby
SENTER						
....	....	ALL	ALL	127809	ALL	ALL
SEPHTON						
1850	1980	1720	1850	162795	LAN	South West
SEPPINGS						
1734	1864	....	....	152765	NFK	Fakenham
SERAGE						
1765	1765	1600	1765	145289	HAM	Isle Of Wight
SERAPHINA						
1830	1992	1830	1992	100978	ANS	Montrose
SERGEANT						
1759	1761	1759	1761	156922	BDF	Bedford
....	....	....	1850	160369	CAM	Peterborough
1740	1812	....	....	151351	DOR	Powerstock
....	....	ALL	ALL	162809	ESS	Braintree
....	....	ALL	ALL	162809	ESS	Felstead
1748	1784	1700	1820	176621	SFK	Gazeley
1882	....	1800	1882	107832	STS	Cheadle
1666	1865	1500	1666	110639	STS	Willwich
1600	1663	....	....	119431	SXE	Northiam
SERGENTSON						
....	....	1830	1992	147613	WES	Casterton
SERJEANT						
1686	1867	....	1800	137405	CAM	Haslingfield

Known From	To	Researching From	To	Ref	Cty	Place
SERJEANT contd.						
1730	1810	ALL	1730	115118	SFK	Great Waldingfield
1745	1745	1650	1744	131245	WAR	Stockton
SERLO						
....	....	ALL	ALL	162590	ALL	ALL
SERMON						
....	....	ALL	ALL	162817	ALL	Name Study
1212	1992	1212	1992	162817	GLS	???
1212	1992	1212	1992	162817	OXF	???
1212	1992	1212	1992	162817	WAR	???
1212	1992	1212	1992	162817	WOR	???
SERREDGE						
1620	1650	1550	1650	177024	ESS	High Easter
SERSHALL						
1850	1992	....	1850	162647	LND	???
SERVICE						
1800	1900	1750	1950	119865	SCT	Drunmore
1800	1900	1750	1950	119865	SCT	Musselburgh
SESSIONS						
....	....	ALL	ALL	139866	ALL	Name Study
1670	1730	1550	1700	139866	OXF	Stanton Harcourt
SESTON						
1844	1860	ALL	ALL	128449	WAR	Birmingham
SETCHEL						
....	....	1800	1900	136743	LEI	Loughboro
SETCHELL						
1757	1854	1700	1854	101621	BDF	Keysoe
1850	1912	1750	1850	107468	HUN	Central
1737	1841	1650	1740	116114	SFK	Mildenhall
SETCHFIELD						
1889	....	1889	....	135488	CAM	Whittlesey
SETH						
1627	1635	....	1660	171441	KEN	Rodmersham
1799	1992	1700	1799	105902	NTH	Stoke Doyle
1813	1992	1700	1850	174459	WLN	Bo'ness
SETHLE						
?	?	?	?	168548	???	???
SETON						
1100	1992	ALL	ALL	105910	ALL	ALL
1350	1450	1300	1450	154881	ELN	Seton
SETON-BURN						
1500	1957	ALL	ALL	105910	ALL	ALL
SETTER						
1800	1900	1800	1900	114405	DEV	Thorverton
SETTERFIELD						
1850	1890	1840	1850	135429	KEN	Eastry
1849	1856	ALL	ALL	152641	KEN	Minster In Thanet
1800	1900	1840	1850	135429	KEN	Thanet
1765	1992	1600	1765	158232	KEN	Thanet
1880	1992	1850	1992	135429	PEM	Milford Haven
SETTLE						
1800	1880	1700	1800	132241	YKS	Saddleworth
?	?	?	?	168548	???	???
SEVERN						
1802	1818	ALL	1838	162825	DBY	Crich
1870	1950	ALL	ALL	174793	DBY	Ilkeston
1891	1892	1872	1893	162825	DBY	Pinxton
1838	1871	1818	1891	162825	STS	Wednesbury
SEVERNE						
1520	1583	1200	1600	176923	WOR	Shrawley
SEVERS						
1700	1799	1700	1799	169781	DUR	Darlington
SEVIAR						
....	1766	1500	1766	175072	SOM	Winscombe
SEVIER						
1750	1900	1600	1850	149691	HAM	Fordingbridge
SEVILL						
1700	1850	1600	1700	109479	LAN	Lees
1700	1850	1600	1700	109479	WRY	Saddleworth
SEWARD						
1900	1992	1800	1992	162620	BRK	Wokingham
1777	1777	1600	1777	174130	DEV	Drewsteignton
1770	1800	1600	1800	154342	GLS	Bristol
1801	1801	1700	1900	178322	GLS	Bristol
1846	1880	....	....	162833	MDX	???
SEWARDS						
1747	....	ALL	....	104515	LIN	Marston
SEWELL						
1800	1867	....	....	128481	CMA	???
1803	1840	1803	1840	161314	DUR	Gainford
1650	1675	ALL	1650	131059	ESS	Copford
....	....	1822	1840	167959	ESS	Crays Hill
....	1742	1700	1742	128961	ESS	Halstead
1840	1850	....	....	129747	LIN	Harmston

Known From	To	Researching From	To	Ref	Cty	Place
SEWELL contd.						
1814	1820	....	....	129747	LIN	Scothorne
1885	....	....	....	125326	LND	Camberwell
1859	....	....	....	125326	LND	Southwark
1833	....	1700	1900	157147	LND	Streatham
1867	1872	1840	1872	128481	NBL	Newcastle
1746	....	....	1770	160873	NBL	Simonburn
1765	1791	1700	1765	125105	NFK	Great Yarmouth
1800	1900	1750	1900	113093	NFK	Gt Yarmouth
1841	1881	1841	1881	116726	NFK	North Walsham
1837	1923	ALL	1837	165212	NTT	Nottingham
1805	1830	1700	1900	100129	RUT	Langham
1882	1882	1850	1882	103640	SFK	Beccles
1800	1826	1700	1992	112402	SFK	Bury St Edmunds
1842	1842	1820	1825	130559	SRY	Southwark
SEWILL						
1800	1900	1851	1881	114529	LAN	Liverpool
1880	1950	1851	1881	114529	LND	???
SEWREY						
1782	....	1500	1800	100013	HAM	Long Sutton
SEXCELLY						
1707	1718	1700	1992	116653	WOR	Powick
SEXEY						
1539	1620	....	....	178330	SOM	Bruton
SEXTON						
....	....	ALL	ALL	123870	ALL	Name Study
....	....	ALL	ALL	123870	ALL	ALL
1783	1802	1760	1783	142360	BKM	Holyport
1870	1992	ALL	1870	156078	IRL	Cork
....	....	1700	1800	123870	IRL	???
1910	1992	1900	1992	141585	KEN	Horton Kirby
1864	1992	....	1864	151270	LIM	Newcastle West
1830	1880	1700	1992	123870	LND	Ilford
1895	1895	1895	1992	105244	LND	New Cross
1830	1870	1700	1992	123870	LND	???
1848	1989	1700	1847	136859	NFK	Ashmanhaugh
1865	....	1830	1865	123870	SRY	Lambeth
SEYFANG						
1797	1824	1700	1880	167002	MDX	London
1771	1777	1700	1880	167002	MDX	Spitafields
1779	1779	1700	1880	167002	MDX	Whitechapel
1831	1850	1700	1880	167002	SRY	Camberwell
1810	1839	1700	1880	167002	SRY	Southwark
SEYLIARD						
1130	1698	1100	1700	154881	KEN	Edenbridge
SEYMORE						
....	....	1500	1992	141720	HAM	???
SEYMOUR						
1863	1992	1600	1863	178101	ANT	Randelstown
1766	1853	ALL	1766	126721	BDF	Shefford
1650	1700	1600	1800	162868	CAM	Histon
1700	1790	1700	1800	162868	CAM	Stretham
1560	1650	1560	1700	162868	CAM	Wimpole
1800	1992	1800	1900	162868	CAM	Witchford
1904	1904	ALL	ALL	176737	CMA	Kendal
1799	1799	1600	1799	131814	CON	St Agnes
1799	1843	1600	1799	131814	CON	Truro
1724	1836	....	....	158747	DEV	ALL
1650	1750	1550	1992	135429	DEV	Berry Pomeroy
1820	1870	1840	1880	135429	DEV	East Stonehouse
1750	1900	ALL	ALL	131873	DEV	Exeter
1750	1800	1550	1992	135429	DEV	Exeter
1820	1870	1840	1880	135429	DEV	Plymouth
1650	1750	1550	1992	135429	DEV	Totnes
1810	1860	1600	1810	162876	DOR	Bridport
1740	1850	1700	1850	174599	DOR	Shaftesbury
....	....	1700	1800	162884	DOR	Swanage
1750	1950	1550	1992	135429	GLS	Bristol
1820	1992	1600	1820	100358	HAM	Ringwood
1823	1823	1700	1823	170542	HAM	Titchfield
1843	1860	1860	1900	162884	HAM	Winchester
....	1829	?	1829	144800	IRL	???
1880	1992	1880	1992	162868	LAN	Manchester
1876	1946	ALL	ALL	176737	LAN	Manchester
1860	1949	1700	1861	101222	LND	North
1910	1930	1550	1992	135429	LND	Hampstead
1810	....	1700	1900	157147	LND	Streatham
1844	....	1844	....	115940	MDX	St Pancras
1824	1872	....	....	139971	OXF	Oxford
1780	1910	1550	1992	135429	SOM	Bath
1850	1870	....	1870	152803	SOM	Yeovil
1800	....	1700	1900	157147	SRY	Lambeth
1624	1698	ALL	1624	161756	SRY	Limpsfield
1624	1698	ALL	1624	161756	SSX	Chichester

Known From	To	Researching From	To	Ref	Cty	Place
SEYMOUR contd.						
1867	1872	....	....	101184	STS	Burton On Trent
....	....	1872	1890	101184	WAR	Birmingham
1798	1812	....	....	139971	WIL	Hilmarton
1829	1882	?	1829	144800	YKS	Bradford
SEYNISBURY						
....	....	878	1190	161438	GLS	Saintbury
SHAA						
1503	1650	1400	1503	120189	ESS	???
1503	1650	1400	1503	120189	LND	???
SHACKEL						
....	....	ALL	1865	123013	SOM	Yeovil
SHACKELL						
1820	1840	1750	1900	116742	MDX	Ruislip
1893	1950	1870	1893	162892	WLS	Cardiff
SHACKLE						
1879	....	ALL	1879	123013	WIL	Swindon
SHACKLEFORD						
1700	1992	1700	1900	161276	BRK	Reading
1700	1992	1700	1900	161276	HAM	Yateley
SHACKLETON						
1819	1925	1750	1900	121134	LAN	Manchester
1850	....	....	1850	162086	LND	Woolwich
1774	1992	1750	1774	165026	YKS	Keighley
1750	1900	1600	1750	111511	YKS	West Riding
SHACKLEY						
1750	1830	1700	1850	138878	CUL	Egremont
SHACKLOCK						
....	....	ALL	ALL	178411	ALL	ALL
....	....	ALL	ALL	178411	CAM	Wisbeach
1600	1992	ALL	ALL	178411	NTT	North
SHADDICK						
....	....	1600	1800	162906	DEV	ALL
....	....	1600	1800	162906	SOM	ALL
1800	1840	....	....	102946	YKS	Hunsingore
1800	1900	1700	1800	162906	???	Bristol
SHADFORTH						
1758	1938	1700	1900	102881	DUR	Hartlepool
SHADWELL						
1774	1800	ALL	1774	158445	WIL	Melksham
SHAFTEN						
1718	1731	1680	1718	177393	NFK	North Pickerham
SHAFTO						
1450	1980	1560	1920	162914	ENG	ALL
1450	1980	1560	1920	162914	NFK	ALL
1450	1980	1560	1920	162914	SFK	ALL
SHAFTOE						
1718	1731	1680	1718	177393	NFK	North Pickerham
SHAILES						
1802	1992	1700	1802	162922	BRK	Hurley
1916	1992	1916	1916	145580	LAN	Liverpool
1889	1992	....	....	162922	MDX	Ealing
SHAKESHAFT						
1700	1900	....	....	162930	CHS	Wirral
....	....	1920	1992	162930	LAN	Barrow
....	....	1774	1992	162930	LAN	Ulverston
....	....	1920	1931	162930	YKS	Huddersfield
SHAKESPEAR						
1835	1890	1750	1900	133426	STS	Kingswinford
1835	1890	1750	1900	133426	WOR	Dudley
SHAKESPEARE						
....	....	ALL	ALL	162957	ALL	Name Study
1649	1992	ALL	ALL	162957	ALL	ALL
1869	1869	1830	1880	162949	GLS	Chipping Camden
....	....	1600	1900	119083	LAN	Oldham
....	....	1700	1870	162949	STS	Brierley Hill
1835	1992	....	1835	162949	STS	Dudley
1717	....	1600	1740	160873	STS	Kingswinford
1825	1911	1300	1992	152501	STS	???
1835	1992	....	1835	162949	WOR	Bromsgrove
1649	1992	ALL	1649	154555	WOR	Feckenham
1880	1989	1800	1880	162949	WOR	Redditch
SHALDERS						
1780	1800	1500	1780	154059	KEN	Deptford
SHALE						
....	....	1800	1900	121673	STS	Brewood
SHALLCROSS						
1800	1833	....	....	138851	CHS	Davenham
SHALLISH						
1842	....	1700	....	123560	???	???
SHAMBROOK						
....	....	ALL	ALL	162965	ALL	Name Study
1870	1992	1700	1870	162973	DEV	Braunton
1806	1847	1780	1806	161896	GLA	Llanshamlet
SHANAHAN						
1867	1992	ALL	1867	123749	TIP	Nenagh
SHAND						
1884	1904	1874	1956	108251	LND	Chelsea
SHANDS						
1844	1871	1700	1850	135623	LND	London
SHANKLAND						
....	....	ALL	ALL	162981	ALL	Name Study
SHANKS						
1883	1992	1700	1883	170453	FIF	ALL
1711	1740	....	....	137936	FIF	Ceres
1826	....	....	....	116750	IRL	Tippary
1883	1992	?	1883	170453	MLN	ALL
1761	1785	1600	1850	130125	NBL	Woodhorn
1725	1992	1600	1750	163015	SCT	Moray
SHANLEY						
1844	....	ALL	1980	136891	IRL	Roscommon
SHANN						
1800	1850	1750	1850	129623	YKS	Staveley
SHANNON						
1900	1950	1850	1900	145408	HAM	Portsmouth
....	....	1600	1800	166863	IRL	Meath
1850	1910	....	....	136492	KEN	Dover
1920	1920	1920	1940	126705	LAN	West Derby
1933	1933	1858	1933	125717	NTH	???
1850	1910	....	....	136492	WLN	Addiewell
1850	1910	....	....	136492	WLN	Edinburgh
SHAPCOTT						
....	....	ALL	ALL	163023	ALL	Name Study
1770	1930	1770	1850	138096	CON	East Looe
1778	....	1596	1808	132160	DEV	Bishops Nympton
1778	....	1596	1808	132160	DEV	Knowstone
1778	....	1596	1808	132160	DEV	South Molton
....	1954	....	....	132160	???	Bristol
SHAPLAND						
1750	1992	....	1750	163031	DEV	North
1700	....	ALL	ALL	116394	DEV	Burrington
SHAPLEY						
1772	1817	1760	1860	163058	DEV	Berry Pomeroy
1569	1637	1500	1650	163058	DEV	Dartmouth
1804	1804	1700	1850	105333	DEV	Denbury
1737	1745	1725	1790	163058	DEV	Malborough
1890	1914	1830	1920	163058	DEV	Tavistock
1580	1711	1550	1725	163058	DEV	Totnes
1804	1804	1700	1850	105333	DEV	Woodland
SHAPTON						
?	?	ALL	1850	117919	DEV	Awliscombe
SHARLAND						
....	....	ALL	ALL	163066	ALL	Name Study
1835	1850	1700	1835	153923	DEV	Upton Pyne
1840	1893	....	....	153923	KEN	Bromley
1875	....	1700	1875	175307	LIN	ALL
1895	1938	1900	1992	153923	SRY	Thursley
SHARMAN						
1780	1880	ALL	1900	137286	BDF	East
1805	1930	1700	1805	111198	BDF	Willington
1792	....	....	1792	177504	CAM	Littleport
1676	1940	....	....	128996	CAM	Thorney
1558	1801	1700	1801	102830	HUN	Orton Waterville
1790	1813	ALL	....	104515	LIN	Sleaford
1669	1751	1600	1669	150150	NTH	Old
1815	1850	1750	1815	129712	SFK	Bungay
1750	1850	1600	1750	145688	SFK	Wortham
1838	1838	1800	1861	170143	SRY	Woking
....	....	1700	....	137456	WAR	Stockton
....	....	1700	1992	171913	???	???
SHARON						
....	....	ALL	ALL	163074	ALL	Name Study
SHARP						
1778	1850	1700	1778	115460	BDF	Caddington
1629	1723	ALL	1629	168602	BDF	Sharbrook
1629	1723	ALL	1629	168602	BDF	Stagsden
1780	1840	ALL	ALL	156604	BKM	Wraysbury
1646	1871	1646	1881	109002	BRK	Waltham St Lawrence
1850	1900	1800	1900	123765	CAM	Cambridge
1724	1940	....	....	128996	CAM	Thorney
1850	1970	1700	1900	148563	CHS	Port Sunlight
1711	1737	1600	1711	152196	CMA	Ennerdale
1787	1861	?	1861	177806	CMA	Wreay
1776	1876	ALL	ALL	135909	CUL	St Bees
1806	1992	1750	1900	122610	DOR	Poole
1790	1815	1538	1830	118893	DUR	Merrington
1830	....	1750	1830	179140	ESS	St Pancras
1817	....	1700	1817	157953	ESS	The Roddings

Known From	To	Researching From	To	Ref	Cty	Place
SHARP contd.						
1798	1909	....	....	171492	ESS	???
1767	1823	1725	1767	157775	HAM	Honeybourne
1800	1900	1800	1900	123765	HRT	Barkway
1650	1750	ALL	ALL	131873	HRT	Furneaux Pelham
1778	1850	1700	1778	115460	HRT	Kensworth
1820	1902	ALL	1820	169730	HRT	Standon
1779	1809	....	1840	171441	KEN	Borden
....	....	1800	1835	147850	KEN	Maidstone
1896	1960	1700	1900	165476	KEN	Rochester
1800	1900	....	....	146854	LAN	Liverpool
1850	1950	ALL	ALL	134996	LAN	Oldham
1810	1880	1550	1810	147265	LIN	South
1689	1696	....	....	151351	LIN	Alford
1878	....	1878	....	129216	LIN	Brigg
1890	1992	1890	1992	123765	LIN	Grimsby
1800	1900	1840	1860	111422	LND	ALL
....	....	....	....	171646	LND	South
1847	1849	....	....	173932	LND	Clapham
1840	1920	ALL	ALL	156604	LND	Deptford
1798	1909	....	....	171492	LND	Harlow
?	1870	ALL	ALL	100897	LND	Lambeth
1870	1960	ALL	ALL	156604	LND	Plumstead
1814	1852	1800	1870	144797	LND	Stepney
1800	1900	....	....	146854	LND	???
1750	1850	1600	1750	174947	NTH	Cranford
1751	1812	ALL	1992	115126	NTH	Milton Malsor
1783	1871	1600	1783	146676	NTT	Newark
1789	....	....	....	113484	PER	Forteviot
1824	....	ALL	ALL	128481	RFW	Paisley
1674	1674	1600	1675	110787	RUT	Wing
1743	1791	....	....	101028	SFK	Chevington
1765	1791	....	....	101028	SFK	Lt Saxham
1694	1745	....	....	101028	SFK	Wickhambrook
1750	1965	....	....	137820	SHI	Fetlar
1720	1965	....	....	137820	SHI	Mid Yell
1760	1965	....	....	137820	SHI	North Yell
1758	1965	....	....	137820	SHI	Northmavine
1720	1965	....	....	137820	SHI	South Yell
1774	1819	....	....	171654	STI	Stirling
....	1863	1820	1871	140767	WAR	Birmingham
1800	1920	1700	1800	152587	WAR	Birmingham
1880	ALL	1850	1880	171190	WAR	Budbrooke
1805	1919	1700	1805	152196	WES	Kendal
1600	1800	....	....	146854	WES	Orton
1840	1915	?	?	176702	WYK	Queensbury
1760	1921	1600	1760	101575	YKS	Goole
1700	1816	....	....	151351	YKS	Harewood
1666	....	....	....	151351	YKS	Horton
1840	1890	ALL	1840	143022	YKS	Huddersfield
1760	1921	1600	1760	101575	YKS	Knottingley
....	....	1861	1875	131628	YKS	Leeds
1760	1921	1600	1760	101575	YKS	Pontefract
1740	1782	1700	1750	170348	YKS	Rawmarsh
1850	1861	ALL	1861	154946	YKS	Richmond
1760	1921	1600	1760	101575	YKS	Selby
SHARPE						
....	....	ALL	ALL	132713	ALL	Name Study
1920	1992	1875	1919	169374	BDF	Bedford
1820	1992	1700	1820	152633	CAM	Wisbech
1879	....	....	....	171441	COR	Cork
1550	1600	1500	1650	138878	CUL	St Bees
1842	1992	1700	1842	117463	DUR	ALL
....	....	1700	1900	140627	ESS	Frinton
1884	1884	1870	1894	151181	ESS	Plaistow
1879	1879	1860	1890	151181	ESS	West Ham
....	....	....	....	127299	HAM	Portsmouth
....	....	....	1920	110817	HRT	Bishops Stortford
1741	1780	1700	1900	159964	HRT	Great Munden
1800	1877	....	1800	151688	HUN	Brampton
1840	1870	1700	1840	160660	KEN	Bearsted
1706	?	?	?	166642	KEN	Woodchurch
1826	1876	1700	1825	131245	LEI	Quorndon
1810	1880	1550	1810	147265	LIN	South
....	....	....	1900	110817	LIN	Bourne
1799	1821	1700	1799	176885	LIN	Grantham
....	....	....	1900	110817	LIN	Raithby
1803	1853	1700	1802	131245	LIN	Spalding
1830	1850	1850	1900	100129	LIN	Stamford
1800	1900	1840	1860	111422	LND	ALL
1849	1992	1750	1850	163082	LND	Islington
1855	1875	1700	1900	177873	MDX	London
1815	1992	1700	1815	145823	MDX	Whitechapel
1750	1992	ALL	1750	135143	NFK	Tunstead
SHARPE contd.						
1855	1930	1750	1900	121886	NTT	Ruddington
1877	....	1870	1890	171441	SOM	Kingsdon
1829	....	....	....	138061	SRY	Egham
1870	1979	....	....	171441	SRY	Farnham
1907	1927	1900	1992	151181	SSX	Brighton
1907	1927	1900	1992	151181	SSX	Portslade
1894	1894	1884	1910	151181	SSX	Shoreham
1620	1644	1500	1992	102520	YKS	Halifax
1857	1900	1800	1992	151181	???	Jarrow On Tyne
SHARPER						
1750	1800	....	1800	147818	YKS	Harewood Estates
SHARPEY						
1815	1840	1750	1815	132640	KEN	Tenterden
SHARPINGTON						
....	....	ALL	ALL	169935	ALL	Name Study
1795	1819	1720	1795	169943	ESS	Braintree
1587	1603	1603	1744	169935	ESS	Colchester
1795	1819	1720	1795	169943	ESS	Springfield
SHARPLES						
1860	1880	1860	1880	163104	DUR	East Central
1826	1826	1800	1826	149772	LAN	Blackburn
1783	1904	1700	1783	161179	LAN	Blackburn
1786	....	1700	1800	113476	LAN	Kirkham
1843	....	1700	1843	128503	LAN	Lowertown
1880	1992	1800	1880	139475	LAN	Manchester
1822	1851	1849	1851	151750	LAN	Oswaldtwistle
1854	1880	ALL	ALL	138886	LAN	Preston
1782	1900	1600	1900	157503	LAN	Preston
1824	1941	1790	ALL	168920	LAN	Tockholes
1756	1860	1585	1992	163104	LAN	Wigan
1874	1992	1700	1850	128503	STS	Wolverhampton
SHARPLIN						
1830	1900	1800	1900	152528	LND	Bethnal Green
SHARPLING						
1745	1910	....	....	174319	LND	???
SHARRATT						
1740	1760	1600	1992	167592	FLN	Buckley
1893	1992	ALL	1893	109320	WAR	Aston
1700	1900	1600	1900	135968	WAR	Baddesley Ensur
SHARROCK						
1820	1880	1750	1850	141496	LAN	Liverpool
SHARWOOD						
1801	1992	1700	1801	176141	MDX	Soho
SHARY						
1802	1992	1823	1992	163600	LND	East
SHAUGHNESSY						
1800	1830	1750	1850	144657	IRL	???
SHAUL						
....	....	1600	1949	163260	NFK	South Creak
SHAVE						
1720	1878	1700	1800	163473	DOR	Winterborne Whitechurch
1765	1867	1700	1819	167533	MDX	Whitechapel
1811	1914	1700	1870	117005	SFK	Long Melford
SHAW						
....	....	ALL	ALL	144886	ALL	Name Study
1897	1898	1880	1900	119202	ANT	Belfast
1856	1940	1850	1950	146536	AYR	Kilbirnie
1800	1830	....	....	127140	AYR	Kilmarnock
1880	1992	1700	1880	105201	BKM	Great Marlow
1756	1756	1750	1760	107360	BKM	Ivinghoe
1875	....	....	1875	162086	BRK	Reading
1789	....	1789	....	139149	CHS	Astbury
1839	1913	....	1839	163201	COR	Bandon
1811	....	1750	1850	138185	DBY	ALL
1840	1870	ALL	1880	175757	DBY	Belper
1850	ALL	1850	ALL	125512	DBY	Derby
1860	1880	1800	1992	120383	DBY	Eckington
1699	1720	1550	1699	102830	DBY	Longford
1790	1800	1700	1790	151769	DBY	Ockbrook
1800	ALL	1800	ALL	125512	DBY	Rosliston
1851	1992	1700	1851	138355	DUR	West Auckland
1847	1868	1800	1847	172251	HAM	???
1811	1965	1770	1811	163139	INV	Inverness
1800	....	1750	1992	163244	KEN	Bexley
1850	....	1850	....	109347	LAN	Accrington
1800	1851	....	....	129747	LAN	Ashton Under Lyne
1848	....	1750	1848	100390	LAN	Ashton
1890	1950	1800	1900	134562	LAN	Colne
1700	1825	1700	1825	109347	LAN	Great Harwood
1925	....	....	....	112429	LAN	Liverpool
....	....	ALL	ALL	166812	LAN	Manchester
1890	1950	1800	1900	134562	LAN	Nelson

Known From	To	Researching From	To	Ref	Cty	Place
SHAW contd.						
1827	1992	1827	1992	159492	LAN	Oldham
1850	1880	....	1850	102059	LAN	Preston
1844	....	ALL	ALL	158690	LAN	Saddleworth
1897	1903	1800	1897	171514	LAN	Salford
1800	1880	1880	1992	162256	LAN	Tockholes
1760	1844	....	....	163155	LEI	Hugglescote
1827	1832	....	....	163155	LEI	Ravenstone
1750	1800	1650	1750	162396	LIN	North
1786	1786	1750	1851	160636	LIN	Algarkirk
1775	1911	1600	1775	165581	LIN	Belchford
1800	....	....	1992	151270	LIN	Harrington
1885	1992	....	1885	151270	LIN	Louth
?	?	?	?	147400	LIN	Well
1749	1800	1700	1850	179000	LKS	Cadder
....	....	ALL	ALL	152048	LKS	Chapelhall
....	....	1750	1900	110663	LKS	Glasgow
1820	1890	1800	1850	173258	LKS	Lanark
....	....	ALL	ALL	152048	LKS	New Monklands
1770	1800	1770	1992	145157	LND	City
1880	1940	1860	....	116297	LND	Greenwich
1801	1841	1842	1992	175412	LND	Shoreditch
1818	1870	....	....	140090	LND	Westminster
1600	1992	?	?	114944	LND	???
1854	1992	1700	1854	126527	MDX	London
1840	1850	1800	1850	146684	MEA	???
1846	1883	1840	....	152099	MLN	Edinburgh
1890	1920	1500	1992	134562	NFK	Little Ellingham
1770	1815	1750	1800	176281	NTT	East Retford
1720	1795	1600	1750	126837	NTT	Egmanton
1894	1964	1700	1894	148423	NTT	Hucknall
1818	1845	1815	1850	146536	RFW	Paisley
1719	1826	....	....	117404	SAL	Cheswardine
1762	1840	....	1762	117234	SCT	Ayr
1880	....	....	....	103934	SCT	???
1784	1791	....	....	173932	SRY	Abinger
1873	1911	1895	....	152099	SRY	Battersea
1756	1799	....	....	173932	SRY	Oakwood
1761	1860	....	....	173932	SRY	Wotton
1750	1800	1650	1750	139106	SSX	???
....	....	ALL	ALL	152048	STI	Falkirk
1825	1848	ALL	1825	174815	STS	Bilston
1815	1825	1750	1850	149098	STS	Burslem
....	....	1790	1900	147613	STS	Rowley Regis
1861	1871	....	....	174815	STS	Sedgley
1849	....	ALL	1825	174815	STS	Willenhall
1868	....	....	....	174815	STS	Wolverhampton
1813	1813	1700	1850	125806	WAR	Birmingham
1792	1835	1700	1900	141569	WAR	Birmingham
1869	1869	1800	1900	127361	WRY	Bradford
1735	....	....	1735	101761	WRY	Honley
1812	1847	....	1812	101761	WRY	Kirkheaton
1803	1861	1803	1861	149403	WYK	Altoft
1823	1881	....	....	160253	WYK	Holmfirth
1882	1992	1600	1882	100579	WYK	Leeds
1800	1850	1600	1992	120677	WYK	Slaithwaite
1758	1758	....	....	141097	YKS	Adwick Le Street
1800	1992	1700	1800	178993	YKS	Almondbury
1766	1856	1700	1770	151912	YKS	Bolton By Bowland
1790	1820	....	1820	137634	YKS	Darfield
1719	1930	1700	1720	109703	YKS	Ecclesfield
1900	1992	....	1900	135674	YKS	Ecclesfield
1840	1870	1840	1870	169900	YKS	Fenay Bridge
1780	1851	1750	1780	165026	YKS	Hebden Bridge
1888	1946	1750	1888	171034	YKS	Huddersfield
1772	1900	1730	1900	169900	YKS	Kirkburton
1732	1871	1675	1900	157716	YKS	Marsden
1802	1845	1700	1850	157716	YKS	Meltham
1795	....	ALL	1795	111201	YKS	Rotherham
1780	1970	1700	1800	126411	YKS	Saddleworth
1844	....	ALL	ALL	158690	YKS	Saddleworth
1816	1820	1816	1820	159492	YKS	Saddleworth
1681	1720	1600	1681	163236	YKS	Saddleworth
1600	1850	1600	1850	172006	YKS	Saddleworth
1870	1890	1870	1890	169900	YKS	Scissett
1795	....	ALL	1795	111201	YKS	Sheffield
....	....	1650	1800	145157	YKS	Sheffield
....	1784	ALL	1784	152838	YKS	Silkslon
1763	1785	1700	1780	146897	YKS	Silkstone
1830	1880	....	1830	114812	YKS	Stannington
1760	1992	1777	1992	146625	YKS	Stannington
1820	1850	....	1850	137634	YKS	Wakefield
1790	1820	1700	1790	118478	YKS	Whitby
1666	....	1600	1666	116637	YKS	Whixley

Known From	To	Researching From	To	Ref	Cty	Place
SHAW contd.						
1705	1758	1685	1705	101796	YKS	Woolley
SHAWCROFT						
1787	1923	1787	1836	122440	CHS	Mollington
1841	1859	1750	1841	157643	HUM	Hull
SHAWCROSS						
1600	1992	ALL	ALL	163252	ALL	ALL
....	....	ALL	ALL	130850	CHS	ALL
....	....	1800	ALL	164615	CHS	Broadbottom
....	....	ALL	ALL	130850	LAN	Manchester
1800	1900	1800	1900	148911	LAN	Manchester
SHAWE						
1601	1644	ALL	ALL	141615	LAN	Ormskirk
1600	1750	....	....	146854	WES	Orton
SHAWLER						
1635	....	ALL	1635	168718	BDF	Riseley
SHAWTER						
1550	1700	1500	1550	132942	DUR	Aycliffe
SHAWYER						
1826	1992	....	....	107158	MDX	Bethnal Green
1826	1992	....	....	107158	MDX	Hoxton
1826	1992	....	....	107158	MDX	Islington
SHAXTED						
1890	....	....	....	156191	NBL	Newcastle Upon Tyne
SHAXTON						
....	....	?	?	104310	DEV	Merton
SHAYER						
1757	1816	ALL	1850	162507	HAM	Droxford
SHAYLE						
....	1766	1731	1766	153176	GLS	Deerhurst
SHAYLER						
?	?	?	?	163279	???	Astley
SHEA						
1848	....	....	....	155225	LND	Bermondsey
1863	1871	1837	1900	103608	LND	Waterloo
SHEAF						
1850	1960	1700	1850	121185	KEN	South
SHEAHAN						
1820	....	....	....	167037	LIM	Limerick
SHEAN						
1770	1797	1650	1770	146986	DOR	Abbotsbury
1810	ALL	....	....	142158	SOM	Sparkford
SHEAR						
1800	1895	1800	1900	163287	GLS	Cheltenham
1850	1945	1850	1950	163287	WAR	Aston Birmingham
SHEARD						
1828	1871	1813	1871	118974	YKS	Batley
....	1903	....	1903	133906	YKS	Halifax
1851	1883	1800	1851	130974	YKS	Hunsworth
1750	1980	1565	1750	103527	YKS	Kirkheaton
1827	....	1780	1840	170348	YKS	Kirkheaton
1810	1851	1700	1810	103268	YKS	Southowram
1765	1813	1740	1813	118974	YKS	Woodkirk
SHEARDOWN						
1767	1980	1582	1980	163309	LIN	Louth
SHEARER						
1760	1800	1700	1992	175889	ARL	Dunoon
1700	1720	....	....	126497	CAI	Watten
SHEARING						
1783	1868	1705	1783	100277	HAM	Ringwood
SHEARMAN						
1880	1897	1850	1890	161861	CMA	Keswick
1773	1851	1735	1773	174211	LIN	Kingerby
1773	1851	1735	1773	174211	LIN	Mid Rasen
SHEARMUR						
....	....	ALL	ALL	145874	ALL	Name Study
1774	1992	1700	1992	145874	ALL	ALL
SHEARN						
1780	....	....	....	121169	SOM	Midsomer Norton
1861	1992	....	....	115258	YKS	Sheffield
SHEARS						
1840	1880	....	....	144371	DEV	Dartington
1784	1992	1785	1992	133868	DEV	Manaton
1784	1992	1785	1992	133868	DEV	North Bovey
SHEARSMITH						
1780	1850	....	....	140554	YKS	Cawood
SHEARWOOD						
1868	1900	....	1950	153818	BDF	Eversholt
SHEASBY						
....	....	....	....	107433	ALL	ALL
SHEAT						
1870	1870	1830	1870	170143	BRK	Lambourn
1838	1839	1838	1839	170143	HRT	Cheshunt

Known From	To	Researching From	To	Ref	Cty	Place
SHEAVES						
1770	1800	....	....	117579	KEN	Sutton At Hone
SHECKELL						
1860	1870	1800	1900	149462	CMN	Gloucester
1809	1816	1770	1809	162892	SOM	Taunton
1822	1893	1816	1822	162892	SOM	Wellington
SHEDD						
1920	1970	1880	1920	158267	DUR	Darlington
SHEDDEN						
1700	1826	....	....	171654	AYR	Beith
1711	1795	1690	1800	146536	AYR	Kilbirnie
1876	1956	1830	1876	179116	RFW	Clarkston
1800	1863	1700	1800	154954	SOM	Bristol
SHEDRICK						
1824	1869	1800	1869	100862	MDX	London
SHEDWICK						
1787	....	1750	1800	170348	LND	St Botolph Without Aldersgate
SHEE						
1790	1856	1790	1856	177199	LND	Marylebone
SHEEHAN						
1860	....	ALL	ALL	104191	GLA	Mountain Ash
?	....	....	....	141941	IRL	???
1863	1992	....	....	172529	KER	???
SHEEHY						
1846	....	ALL	ALL	172057	COR	Kanturk
SHEEL						
1738	1860	ALL	1738	132829	NBL	Longhoughton
1860	1890	1890	1992	132829	T&W	Newcastle Upon Tyne
SHEEN						
1800	1992	1650	1800	151084	LND	East
1891	....	....	1900	171646	LND	South
1819	1905	1700	1819	170542	SOM	Wells
SHEER						
1880	1992	1760	1992	135429	DEV	Bradninch
SHEERS						
....	....	1640	1750	130079	OXF	Kirtlington
SHEFFIELD						
1839	1892	ALL	1839	112313	CUL	Wigton
1820	1900	ALL	ALL	163368	LEI	Castle Donnington
1800	1840	ALL	1992	119105	LEI	Syston
1730	1800	1650	1800	100927	NTH	Rushden
SHEFFORD						
1800	1899	ALL	ALL	146633	WIL	Gt Bedwyn
SHEIDL						
1832	1848	ALL	1832	104299	DUR	Barnard Castle
SHEKELL						
1684	?	1500	1684	115169	GLS	Childswickham
SHELDON						
....	....	ALL	ALL	163384	ALL	Name Study
1830	1900	1750	1830	138258	DBY	Bonsall
1790	1830	1730	1790	168912	DBY	Bonsall
1901	1920	1920	1960	133264	DBY	Derby
1846	1979	1600	1846	167355	NBL	Newcastle
1882	1908	1850	1920	135305	STS	Brierley Hill
1910	1965	ALL	ALL	156256	STS	Leek
SHELDRAKE						
1787	1820	1700	1900	162620	DOR	Piddletrenthide
1800	ALL	....	....	163392	LND	Canning Town
1790	1824	ALL	ALL	162620	LND	???
1856	1928	1700	1856	163929	NFK	Diss Hayward
1770	1900	1700	1992	126799	NFK	Great Bircham
1840	1900	1700	1840	152552	NFK	Harleston
1856	1928	1700	1856	163929	NFK	Shelton
1820	1856	ALL	ALL	157864	SFK	Framlingham
1800	ALL	....	....	163392	SFK	Troston
....	....	1650	1850	129550	SFK	???
SHELDRICK						
....	....	1770	1860	103713	CAM	Trumpington
1778	1900	1700	1900	145750	NFK	Kings Lynn
SHELL						
1646	1768	1600	1850	169218	WIL	Rowde
SHELLABEAR						
1800	1840	1750	1850	171549	DEV	Ashburton
1762	1925	1600	1762	102598	DEV	Brixham
1839	1992	1600	1839	108286	DEV	Torrington
....	....	1600	1839	108286	???	???
SHELLARD						
1812	1992	1812	1920	163406	GLS	Bristol
SHELLEY						
1906	1992	....	....	104264	GLS	Gloucester
1865	1940	....	....	104264	LND	Islington
1865	1940	....	....	104264	LND	St Pancras
1780	1922	ALL	1790	131091	SSX	ALL
SHELLEY contd.						
1800	1840	1700	1800	142913	STS	Croxton
1839	1880	1750	1839	147362	STS	Eccleshall
1819	1841	1700	1840	100013	STS	Hopton
1682	1823	1500	1682	164178	SXW	Angmering
1682	1823	1500	1682	164178	SXW	Ferring
SHELMERDINE						
1753	1850	1700	1850	129496	CHS	Northenden
1770	1992	1600	1770	145696	LAN	Heyrod
1850	1922	1850	1992	129496	LAN	Manchester
1815	1880	1900	ALL	101230	LAN	???
SHELTON						
1783	1794	ALL	1783	168602	CAM	Over
1809	1850	....	....	129216	DBY	Beighton
1770	1840	1700	1992	173096	GLS	Uley
1556	1749	1556	1600	163414	NFK	Shelton
1733	1992	1640	1700	163414	NTH	Bainton
1645	1829	1645	1829	163414	NTH	Maxey
1730	1992	1600	1900	137162	NTT	???
1851	....	....	....	175587	YKS	Buslingthorpe
1829	....	....	....	175587	YKS	Moortown
1816	1872	1780	1890	160873	YKS	Sutton On Derwent
1692	1719	1650	1750	138584	YKS	Wakefield
1838	....	....	....	175587	YKS	Woodhouse Carr
SHELVEY						
....	....	1850	....	117714	LND	Kensington
1881	1885	1860	1925	117609	MDX	Westminster
SHEMMING						
1800	1840	....	....	114723	SFK	Hoxne
SHENNAN						
1806	1900	1700	1992	171875	KKD	Auchencairn
SHENTON						
....	....	1750	1850	110078	CHS	Acton By Nantwich
....	1835	1835	1900	129011	LAN	St Helens
....	....	1750	1910	110078	STS	Cheadle
1843	1863	1820	1840	165441	STS	Leek
1700	1835	1835	1900	129011	STS	Potteries
1840	1970	ALL	ALL	173436	STS	Wolverhampton
1830	1840	1750	1830	151769	WOR	Dudley
SHEPARD						
1620	ALL	....	....	142158	GLS	Stone
1774	1776	1700	1775	123978	HAM	Southampton
1746	1850	1600	1870	105279	SAL	Little Wenlock
1711	1711	1680	1750	105333	SSX	Singleton
1770	1780	1750	1820	158658	WIL	Holt
SHEPERD						
1733	1800	....	....	166723	DEV	Holbeton
SHEPHARD						
1827	....	1700	1827	100846	KEN	Dover
1881	ALL	1800	....	146188	KEN	Lee
1838	....	ALL	1838	147362	LEI	Blackfordby
1817	1866	....	1817	142166	LND	Bethnal Green
1871	1871	....	....	135437	MDX	Clerkenwell
1827	....	....	....	137308	MDX	Sunbury
1801	1801	1700	1800	117013	NFK	Dersingham
1746	1850	1600	1870	105279	SAL	Little Wenlock
1850	1960	ALL	ALL	162469	SFK	North
1790	1992	1700	1790	176257	SOM	Horsington
1850	1886	1825	1850	149772	STS	Kingswinford
1850	1992	1850	1992	105279	WAR	Birmingham
1858	1950	1800	1950	134880	YKS	Leeds
SHEPHER						
1725	1725	?	1725	158569	ESS	Rickling
SHEPHERD						
1750	1992	1750	1992	145467	ABD	Cushnie
1794	1885	1700	1794	118427	ABD	Old Deer
1843	....	....	....	137936	ANS	Dundee
1851	1985	....	....	140791	BKM	Haddenham
1800	1887	1700	1920	172073	BRK	Reading
1860	1920	1860	1920	177016	DBY	Eckington
1817	....	1810	1900	177016	DBY	Killamarsh
1760	1992	ALL	1800	142301	DEV	Modbury
....	....	1600	1992	137588	DOR	Cerne Abbas
1831	1855	1830	1851	173371	DOR	Gillingham
....	....	ALL	ALL	155373	DOR	Piddletown
1853	1922	1700	1853	143448	ESS	???
1810	1840	1800	1850	146803	FIF	Kircaldy
....	....	ALL	1800	141224	GLS	South
1828	1830	1790	1890	105333	KEN	Faversham
1825	1878	1825	1878	143286	LAN	Manchester
1850	1880	ALL	ALL	171948	LAN	Scales
1770	1992	1700	1770	117226	LEI	Gotham
1770	1992	1700	1770	117226	LEI	Rempstone
1700	1800	....	....	129747	LIN	Kettlethorpe

Known From	To	Researching From	To	Ref	Cty	Place
SHEPHERD contd.						
1800	1850	....	....	129747	LIN	Welbourne
....	....	1800	....	117714	LND	Kensington
1871	1871	1840	1910	105333	MDX	Kensington
1839	1992	1700	1839	149659	MDX	London
1797	....	....	....	131210	MDX	Spitalfields
1780	1810	1750	1810	146803	MLN	Preston
1735	....	....	....	101028	NFK	Horstead
1740	....	ALL	1740	154946	NRY	Lastingham
1770	1992	1700	1770	117226	NTT	Hoton
1770	1992	1700	1770	117226	NTT	Leake
1770	1992	1700	1770	117226	NTT	Ratcliffe
1800	1850	1700	1900	152900	OXF	Banbury
1800	1860	....	....	159883	PER	Drimmie
1746	1850	1600	1870	105279	SAL	Little Wenlock
1760	1992	1700	1760	148237	SSX	New Fishbourne
....	....	ALL	1890	178403	SSX	Wisborough Green
1630	1750	1630	1740	156930	WIL	Aldbourne
1660	1750	ALL	1660	163449	WIL	Aldbourne
1770	1800	1770	1800	179337	WIL	Langley Burrell
1819	1854	1700	1819	129453	WRY	North Craven
1701	1720	....	....	141097	YKS	Braithwell
1769	1789	....	....	141097	YKS	North Newbald
SHEPHERDLEY						
1776	1851	....	....	139971	BKM	Amersham
SHEPHERDLY						
1800	1992	1550	1800	146587	BKM	Amersham
SHEPLEY						
1820	....	1800	1820	135771	CHS	North East
1890	....	1800	1900	134481	CHS	Hyde
1804	....	1700	....	134686	DBY	Charlesworth
1690	1824	....	....	131709	DBY	Glossop
1820	1911	1700	1820	105252	LAN	Middleton
SHEPPARD						
1894	1910	....	....	149632	BRK	Binfield
1894	1910	....	....	149632	BRK	Bracknell
1810	1860	ALL	1850	118737	BRK	Leckhampstead
1670	1860	1600	1860	102970	BRK	Speen
....	....	ALL	ALL	160822	BRK	Streatley
1720	1770	1650	1770	163473	DOR	West
1770	1810	1700	1800	163473	DOR	Affpuddle
1810	1937	ALL	ALL	163473	DOR	Bere Regis
....	....	1800	1880	179361	DOR	Bere Regis
....	....	1600	1992	137588	DOR	Cerne Abbas
1757	1786	1700	1757	127116	DOR	Wareham
1855	1914	1800	1855	173371	GLA	Pontypridd
1820	1890	1820	1890	110523	GNT	Monmouth
1812	ALL	1700	1900	135127	HAM	Portsea St Marys
1870	1936	....	....	174815	LEI	Leicester
1619	1742	ALL	1742	174815	LEI	Wick St Lawrence
1820	1992	1700	1825	166561	LEI	Wymeswold
1815	1850	....	....	163465	LIN	Boston
1809	1826	....	....	163465	LIN	Gainsborough
1826	1840	....	....	163465	LIN	Hull
1792	1992	1700	1900	126683	LND	Bethnal Green
1745	1953	ALL	1853	121355	LND	Bromley By Bow
1745	1953	ALL	1853	121355	LND	Hackney
1745	1953	ALL	1853	121355	LND	Limehouse
1745	1953	ALL	1853	121355	LND	Stepney
1745	1953	ALL	1853	121355	LND	Whitechapel
1830	1930	....	....	101869	LND	???
1851	1992	1851	1992	141267	MDX	Bethnal Green
1900	1906	1800	1912	149632	MDX	Chelsea
....	....	1860	1900	177393	MDX	Kensington
1900	1992	....	....	160822	MGY	Welshpool
1845	....	....	....	160385	NTT	Mansfield
1860	1878	....	....	163465	NTT	Mansfield
1680	1992	....	....	163465	NTT	Newark
1740	1830	1650	1740	164860	SFK	Marlesford
1866	....	....	....	174815	SOM	Bristol
1778	1840	1751	1862	154733	SOM	Camely
1781	1781	....	....	135437	SOM	Chew Stoke
1817	1844	1817	1844	154733	SOM	Clutton
1745	1784	1650	1750	100013	SOM	Emborough
1807	1881	1807	1881	138398	SOM	Frome
1742	1851	ALL	1813	174815	SOM	Kewstoke
1870	1894	1800	1912	149632	SRY	Carshalton
1870	1894	1800	1912	149632	SRY	Redhill
1870	1894	1800	1912	149632	SRY	Streatham
1814	1832	1780	1992	122416	TIP	???
1788	1820	1750	1800	147575	WIL	Fisherton Anger
1650	1760	1650	1760	127655	WIL	Purton
1820	1850	1800	1850	147575	WIL	Salisbury
1750	1880	1750	1880	163449	WIL	Winterslow
SHEPPEARD						
1750	1850	1600	1992	138746	CAM	ALL
1760	1850	1600	1992	138746	SFK	ALL
SHEPPERD						
1780	1805	1700	1850	118397	OXF	Coggs
SHEPPEY						
....	....	ALL	ALL	163503	ALL	Name Study
1800	1992	....	....	163503	WAR	???
1680	1800	1550	1680	163503	WOR	???
SHEPSTON						
1866	1877	1841	1866	106062	GLS	Bristol
1877	1885	1885	1992	106062	GLS	Cardiff
SHEPSTONE						
ALL	ALL	ALL	ALL	171093	GLA	ALL
SHERBEY						
1765	1992	1700	1764	108227	SOM	Rodney Stoke
SHERBORN						
1337	1992	....	....	163511	MDX	Bedfont
SHERBORNE						
....	....	ALL	ALL	163538	ALL	Name Study
1690	1850	1650	1720	138150	GLS	South
1707	1943	....	....	132357	OXF	Sarsden
SHERGOLD						
1890	1992	....	....	133671	BRK	Reading
1860	1951	1840	1918	163546	WAR	Birmingham
1810	1900	1700	1810	171182	WIL	South
1810	1900	1700	1810	171182	WIL	West
1791	....	?	1800	103934	WIL	Bishops Cannings
1771	1824	1600	1771	175781	WIL	Bishops Cannings
1660	1800	1600	1660	173223	WIL	Great Wishford
1803	1890	1750	1803	133671	WIL	Yatesbury
SHERIDAN						
1900	1992	....	....	141267	IRL	Kilkenny
....	....	1700	1884	155136	IRL	???
1856	1937	1856	1992	163554	LKS	Glasgow
1800	1850	1800	1850	163554	RFW	Howwood
1800	1850	1800	1850	163554	RFW	Loch Winnoch
....	....	1700	1884	155136	SCT	???
?	?	1750	ALL	117919	STS	Stoke On Trent
1857	1905	1857	1992	163554	TYR	Castlederg
SHERINGHAM						
....	....	1700	1900	147494	NFK	Sheringham
SHERLOCK						
1800	1992	1700	1800	163570	ALL	ALL
1790	....	....	....	152722	HAM	Breamore
1800	1850	1700	1800	103446	SSX	East
SHERMAN						
....	....	1770	1900	159840	BDF	Bedford
1841	1851	1500	1880	137472	BRK	Kintbury
1878	....	1700	1850	170178	BRK	Kintbury
1841	1851	1500	1880	137472	BRK	Newbury
1590	1610	1500	1650	151653	SOM	Huish Champfleur
1840	ALL	....	....	142158	WIL	Aldbourne
SHERRARD						
....	....	ALL	ALL	163120	ALL	Name Study
1550	1992	1550	1992	163120	ALL	ALL
....	....	ALL	ALL	163597	ALL	ALL
1753	1992	ALL	ALL	163597	LEI	ALL
....	....	1700	1800	150150	LEI	Stretton En Le Field
SHERRATT						
1726	1826	1680	1726	177393	NTT	North Wheatley
1875	1992	1750	1875	151084	STS	North
1850	1870	....	....	177393	YKS	Bawtry
1878	1920	....	....	177393	YKS	Doncaster
SHERRELL						
1790	1900	1600	1790	171182	HRT	ALL
1817	1860	1700	1817	171182	LND	ALL
SHERRIES						
1680	1992	1680	1992	164771	CON	Isles Of Scilly
SHERRIF						
1840	1992	1840	1992	144703	LEI	ALL
1784	1840	1700	1992	144703	NTH	South
SHERRIS						
....	....	ALL	ALL	164771	ALL	Name Study
1869	1914	1700	1869	111708	CON	Scilly Isles
SHERRY						
1890	1920	ALL	1920	128171	LAN	Liverpool
1860	1992	1830	1992	163600	LND	North
1860	1992	1830	1992	163600	MDX	East
1860	1992	1830	1992	163600	MDX	North
1823	1896	1750	1900	155969	MDX	Bethnal Green
1790	1900	1700	1950	155969	MDX	Shoreditch
1823	1896	1750	1900	155969	MDX	Stepney

Known Researching
From To From To Ref Cty Place
SHERRY contd.
.... ALL 1920 128171 SAL ???
1877 1954 1700 1877 124400 SOM Glastonbury
SHERVYN
.... 1700 ALL 115142 WAR ???
SHERWELL
.... ALL ALL 163619 ALL Name Study
SHERWEN
.... ALL ALL 163627 ALL Name Study
1724 1759 1600 1724 152196 CUL Bootle
SHERWILL
1791 1791 1700 1840 105333 DEV
Buckland In The Moor
1791 1791 1700 1840 105333 DEV Holne
1791 1791 1700 1840 105333 DEV Ilsington
1791 1791 1700 1840 105333 DEV Lydford
1791 1791 1700 1840 105333 DEV
Widecombe In The Moor
SHERWIN
1745 1754 1550 1754 102830 DBY Darley
1768 .... 1740 1800 170348 DBY Whitwell
1700 1895 1600 1700 163635 DBY Winster
1840 1992 1700 1840 138657 LAN Lancaster
1860 .... 1860 .... 158011 LEI Barton In The Beans
.... 1600 1809 137626 LEI Packington
1700 1834 1650 1834 173622 RUT Langham
1752 1788 .... 149004 SSX Barlavington
1788 1846 .... 149004 SSX East Dean
SHERWOOD
1792 1992 1608 1992 164704 BRK Reading
1800 1920 1700 1950 121762 HAM Central
1793 1992 1700 1870 178489 LAN Prescot
1802 1900 1700 1802 121037 MDX Bethnal Green
1739 1791 .... 166723 SRY Horsell
1813 .... 1700 1813 166197 WOR Fladbury
1829 1850 1600 1829 124257 YKS Lastingham
SHETFER
1755 1810 ALL ALL 121398 CON St Levan
SHEW
1780 1992 1780 1992 163643 ALL ALL
SHEWARD
1813 1992 1768 .... 175803 MDX Harrow
1881 1912 1860 1930 160873 STS Kingswinford
1894 1992 1894 1992 160873 WAR Birmingham
1803 1858 1780 1880 160873 WOR Astley
1780 1841 1800 1880 154512 WOR Dudley
1780 1841 1800 1880 154512 WOR Kidderminster
1880 1894 1870 1900 160873 WOR Oldbury
SHEWELL
1770 1840 1700 1900 157171 GLS Taynton
SHICKLE
1713 1900 1600 1992 159956 SFK Walsham Le Willows
SHIELD
1860 1900 1700 1992 167096 GLS Almondsbury
1820 1900 1700 1820 115444 GLS Chipping Sodbury
1899 1930 1800 1900 167096 GLS Cirencester
1782 1792 1700 1744 168033 HAM Gosport
1550 1750 1500 1992 162620 NBL Allendale
1880 ? 1700 1900 167096 SOM Keynsham
? ? ? ? 167096 WIL Swindon
.... 1870 1930 163791 WOR Kings Norton
SHIELDS
1800 1899 .... 164151 CUL Branthwaite
1851 .... 1851 101761 CUL Caldbeck
1800 1899 .... 164151 CUL Dean
.... 1841 1888 170569 DBY Derby
1851 .... 1851 101761 DUR Easington
1819 1905 1790 1900 179000 STI Airth
SHIELL
1841 1856 1700 1841 103268 NBL Newcast On Tyne
SHIELLAW
1800 1980 ALL ALL 155608 DUR ALL
SHIELS
1843 1875 1750 1900 164097 DOW Kilkeel
1881 1893 .... 110833 LND East
1855 1871 .... 110833 SCT Edinburgh
.... 1800 1930 164097 SCT Motherwell
SHIFLEY
1810 1855 .... 171654 SRY Newington
SHILBURN
1741 .... 1650 .... 134589 YKS Halifax
SHILCOCK
.... 1800 1850 150800 LND ???
.... 1800 1850 150800 NFK ???

Known Researching
From To From To Ref Cty Place
SHILCOCK contd.
.... 1800 1850 150800 SRY ???
SHILDON
.... 1716 1794 167355 DUR Haughton Le Skerne
1794 1896 1600 1794 167355 YKS Welbury
SHILL
1880 1992 1700 1880 177067 GLS Ampney Crucis
1710 1760 1600 1760 154342 GLS Bitton
SHILLABEAR
1800 1925 1600 1800 102598 DEV Sheepstor
SHILLABEER
.... ALL ALL 163651 ALL Name Study
SHILLAKER
1800 1955 1500 1800 153230 LIN Deeping
SHILLAW
1800 1980 ALL ALL 155608 DUR ALL
SHILLING
.... ALL ALL 163678 ALL Name Study
1825 .... 1825 164011 KEN Boughton Aluph
1790 1931 1785 1931 152102 NFK Dereham
SHILLINGLAW
1836 .... 113484 MLN Edinburgh
SHILLITO
1823 1992 ALL 1823 110000 NTT Worksop
1780 1830 1750 1780 128538 YKS Hull
SHILLITOE
1823 1992 ALL 1823 110000 NTT Worksop
SHILSTONE
1600 1800 1500 1900 112976 DEV Dartmoor
1600 1800 1600 1800 135429 DEV Dunsford
SHILTON
1820 1832 1770 1880 122327 LEI Higham On The Hill
1826 1962 1715 1826 163686 WAR Atherstone
1770 1840 1700 1800 162191 WAR Bedworth
SHILVOCK
1500 1992 ALL ALL 128449 ALL ALL
1750 1780 ALL ALL 128449 STS Black Country
1750 1780 ALL ALL 128449 WAR Birmingham
1750 1780 ALL ALL 128449 WOR Birmingham
SHIMELD
1900 1925 1850 1925 165212 WYK Rotherham
1900 1925 1850 1925 165212 WYK Sheffield
SHIMELL
1820 1860 1800 1850 158380 MDX St Lukes
SHIMIELDS
1790 1820 1700 1790 151769 YKS Sheffield
SHIMMIN
1806 1819 1750 1879 149292 CUL Whitehaven
1798 1806 1750 1879 149292 IOM Kirk German
1822 1992 1700 1850 163694 IOM Peel
1819 1879 1750 1879 149292 LAN Liverpool
.... 1700 1800 129593 YKS Tranmire
SHIN
1842 1919 1700 1842 138568 CAM Thetford
1842 1919 1700 1842 138568 NFK Thetford
1842 1919 1700 1842 138568 SFK Thetford
SHINE
1800 1860 1700 1900 138517 KER ???
1871 1891 ALL 1871 112178 SFK Woodbridge
SHINGLES
1868 1921 1820 1868 155438 ESS ???
SHINGLETON
1800 1992 1750 1800 154318 SOM Wells
SHINKFIELD
1850 .... 149446 HAM Southampton
.... ALL 1820 149446 NFK ???
SHINNERS
1842 .... 1700 1880 115967 IRL Limmerick
SHIP
ALL ALL ALL ALL 163716 ALL ALL
.... 163724 HAM Portsmouth
1895 1951 1850 1920 117269 LND Hackney
SHIPGOOD
1781 1879 .... 171492 ESS The Rothings
SHIPHAM
1690 1900 1600 1690 162396 LIN Gainsborough
SHIPLEY
1823 1992 1700 1823 119261 DBY Holloway
1700 1900 1650 1800 139866 STS Uttoxeter
1840 1870 1800 1900 137278 YKS Bridlington
SHIPMAN
1691 1860 1500 1700 164909 ESS Chigwall
1691 1860 1500 1700 164909 ESS Grent Earter
1691 1860 1500 1700 164909 ESS Roxwell

Known From	To	Researching From	To	Ref	Cty	Place
SHIPMAN contd.						
1691	1860	1500	1700	164909	ESS	St James
1886	1890	1800	1930	164909	SRY	Croyden
SHIPP						
1815	1874	1750	1874	141062	GLS	Bitton
....	....	....	....	163724	HAM	Portsmouth
....	....	ALL	ALL	121991	NFK	ALL
....	....	ALL	ALL	121991	SFK	ALL
1690	1992	1600	1690	163732	SFK	Occold
SHIPPAM						
1700	1800	1700	1800	114529	NTT	Mansfield Woodhouse
1750	1930	1750	1940	114529	YKS	Sheffield
SHIPPEN						
1850	1992	....	....	161594	LAN	Liverpool
1850	1992	....	....	161594	LAN	Manchester
....	....	1600	1750	161594	LND	???
1700	1992	1600	1831	161594	YKS	Barwick In Elmet
1850	1992	1850	1960	161594	YKS	Leeds
....	....	1600	1750	161594	YKS	Methley
....	....	1827	1868	161594	YKS	Ravensworth
1700	1992	1600	1831	161594	YKS	Scholes
SHIPPERLEY						
1660	1880	1550	1660	146587	BKM	Brill
SHIPPEY						
1862	1950	1800	1862	167568	YKS	???
SHIPSEY						
1793	....	1750	1850	142549	WIL	ALL
SHIPSTONE						
1755	1992	1871	1992	112852	NTT	Bulwell
SHIPTON						
1691	1799	1500	1700	164909	ESS	Roxwell
1800	1950	1700	1800	118214	HAM	Andover
1744	1992	1600	1750	163740	OXF	Dorchester
1740	1810	1850	1860	159573	WIL	Devizes
....	....	1690	1740	159573	WIL	Easton Grey
1740	1810	1690	1740	159573	WIL	Luckington
SHIPWAY						
1740	....	....	....	118672	GLS	Tortworth
SHIRAFS						
1840	1860	1750	1840	146587	LND	Holborn
SHIRE						
1602	1992	1400	1992	163759	CON	???
1611	1992	1500	1992	163759	DEV	???
1639	1992	1500	1992	163759	DOR	???
....	....	1800	1900	159336	LND	???
1560	1992	1500	1992	163759	SOM	ALL
1750	1800	1700	1850	123722	SOM	Otterford
SHIREWOOD						
1100	1400	....	....	100420	WAR	Meriden
SHIRLEY						
....	....	ALL	ALL	163767	ALL	Name Study
....	....	ALL	1992	122572	ALL	ALL
1600	1750	1600	1750	105511	DBY	Eyam
1700	1940	ALL	ALL	105511	DBY	Hartington
1803	1859	1750	1810	174289	HAM	Ringwood
1912	1950	1912	1950	105511	LAN	Liverpool
1912	1950	1912	1950	105511	LAN	Manchester
1816	1846	1790	1860	163775	MDX	Westminster
1765	1843	....	....	169129	NFK	Hindolvestone
1830	1900	1830	1900	173533	NTH	South
1860	1950	1860	1992	105511	NTT	Beeston
1860	1950	1860	1992	105511	NTT	Chilwell
1780	1850	1750	1850	144843	SRY	Blindley Heath
1780	1850	1750	1850	144843	SRY	Godstone
1650	1850	1600	1650	168777	SSX	Bolney
ALL	1992	ALL	ALL	105511	STS	ALL
1771	1830	1730	1771	111236	STS	Alstonefield
1650	1940	ALL	ALL	105511	STS	Fawfield Head
1650	1940	ALL	ALL	105511	STS	Longnor
1650	1912	ALL	ALL	105511	STS	Marsh House
1650	1940	ALL	ALL	105511	STS	Rewlach
1805	1805	1500	1805	169439	WAR	Shipston On Stour
SHIRREFFS						
1800	1992	....	....	127140	ABD	Huntley
1920	1945	1914	1992	121568	LND	ALL
1876	1950	....	....	127140	RFW	Greenock
SHIRRIS						
....	1865	1700	1865	109223	GMP	Newpitsligo
SHIRT						
....	....	ALL	ALL	157414	ALL	Name Study
1800	1992	1650	1800	157414	ALL	ALL
1700	1870	ALL	1900	177571	DBY	Chapel En Le Frith
1860	1900	1850	1930	177571	DBY	New Mills
....	....	1830	1992	108367	YKS	Woolley
SHOARD						
1500	1799	1100	1799	163805	WIL	ALL
SHOEBRIDGE						
....	....	ALL	ALL	178454	ALL	Name Study
....	....	ALL	ALL	178462	ALL	Name Study
1700	1930	ALL	ALL	178454	KEN	ALL
1600	1900	....	....	167304	KEN	Cowden
1600	1900	....	....	167304	KEN	Leigh
1700	1930	ALL	ALL	178454	LND	ALL
1840	1880	1800	1900	152528	LND	Camberwell
1815	1900	1780	1992	173096	MDX	London
1700	1930	ALL	ALL	178454	SSX	ALL
SHOESMITH						
1826	1992	ALL	ALL	100803	KEN	Penshurst
....	1800	....	....	174564	SSX	Dinfield
SHOLL						
....	....	ALL	ALL	142905	ALL	Name Study
1700	1980	1600	1900	142905	???	ALL
SHONE						
....	....	1830	1855	109134	CHS	Chester
1774	1776	1750	1800	105120	DEN	Allington Gresford
1880	1960	1850	1880	139475	LAN	Liverpool
1785	1800	1750	1800	163791	SAL	Stanton Hine Heath
1850	1860	1800	1880	139475	SAL	Wem
1820	1850	1750	1860	163791	SAL	Whitchurch
SHONROCK						
1750	1900	1750	1900	125237	LAN	Darwen
SHOOBRIDGE						
1780	1855	....	....	141909	KEN	Tenterden
SHOOSMITH						
1797	1815	1750	1820	129356	SSX	Hellingly
1795	1992	1795	1992	172952	SSX	Laughton
SHOOTER						
1887	1897	ALL	ALL	128821	NTT	Edingly
....	....	ALL	ALL	128821	NTT	Kirkby
SHOPPEE						
....	....	1800	1992	168505	LND	Hillingdon
....	....	1764	1800	168505	LND	Kensington
SHOPSTONE						
?	1806	ALL	ALL	153516	SOM	Wick St Lawrence
SHORE						
1732	....	1732	....	147532	CHS	Acton By Nantwich
1841	1881	1841	1881	163813	CHS	Adbaston
1820	1916	1700	1820	137421	CHS	Faddiley
1700	1860	1750	1860	168467	DBY	???
1790	1881	1538	1790	154792	GLS	Cotswolds
1800	1992	ALL	ALL	137847	HAM	Winchester
1800	1992	ALL	ALL	137847	LND	London
1841	1881	1800	1900	132659	NFK	Wells
1500	1899	1300	1799	163805	SOM	ALL
1770	1992	1770	1992	163813	STS	Eccleshall
1794	1851	....	1794	163031	SYK	Wickerlsey
1500	1899	1300	1799	163805	WIL	ALL
SHOREY						
1800	1850	1700	1800	115541	KEN	Sundridge
SHORLAND						
1639	1641	ALL	1992	163821	DEV	Exeter
1639	1641	ALL	1992	163821	DEV	Exminster
1639	1641	ALL	1992	163821	DEV	Teignmouth
1639	1641	ALL	1992	163821	DEV	Topsham
....	....	1880	1992	171085	DOR	Bournemouth
ALL	1640	ALL	1992	163821	KEN	ALL
1682	1742	1630	1750	129356	SOM	Staplegrove
1662	1768	1600	1700	156221	SOM	Staplegrove
....	....	1700	1800	129356	SOM	Yeovil
ALL	1640	ALL	1992	163821	SSX	ALL
....	....	1600	1992	171085	???	Bristol
SHORROCK						
1866	1931	....	....	164062	LAN	Blackburn
1800	1880	1880	1992	162256	LAN	Darwen
1850	1992	1800	1850	108359	LAN	Manchester
1805	1833	1790	1840	126705	LAN	Preston
SHORT						
....	....	1760	1790	115274	CON	South East
1850	1992	1750	1850	100978	CON	Stratton
1810	1894	1700	1810	169889	DBY	Hognaston
1790	1850	ALL	ALL	107352	DEV	Alverdiscott
1780	1900	1750	1900	118540	DEV	Frithelstock
1850	1900	1700	1900	156531	DEV	Hartland
1754	1829	1600	1754	168637	DEV	Woolsery
....	....	ALL	ALL	151998	DOR	Evershot
1857	1901	1700	1857	138355	DUR	Easington
1700	1900	1600	1992	154342	GLS	Bitton
1751	1780	....	....	165999	GLS	Bitton

Known From	To	Researching From	To	Ref	Cty	Place
SHORT contd.						
1841	....	1800	1841	155225	GLS	Bristol
1679	1681	ALL	1992	163821	GLS	Chipping Sodbury
1700	1900	1600	1992	154342	GLS	Oldland
1680	....	1680	1900	106410	GLS	Stone
1679	1681	ALL	1992	163821	GLS	Yate
1826	1992	1700	1826	110639	IRL	Fermanagh
1845	1917	1800	1992	139203	KEN	Beckenham
1840	1992	....	....	172529	LIN	Grantham
1819	1821	....	....	112887	LND	St Pancras
....	....	1800	1812	174602	NBL	Bamburgh
1760	1900	ALL	1800	142301	NBL	Barmoor
1880	1900	1850	1880	160806	NTH	Chelsea
1750	1800	....	....	160806	NTH	Chelveston
1710	1750	1700	1710	160806	NTH	Great Doddington
1850	1950	1800	1850	160806	NTH	Wellingborough
1800	1850	1750	1800	160806	NTH	Wilby
1790	1820	1700	1790	172901	NTT	Mansfield
1859	1861	1800	1920	139203	SRY	Penge
1834	1881	1750	1834	101427	SSX	Central
1800	1950	....	....	138150	STD	Glasgow
1769	....	....	....	102733	STS	Brewood
1878	....	ALL	ALL	159026	STS	Wourston
1741	....	1600	1741	132802	WOR	Dudley
SHORTALL						
1830	1870	1700	1830	143812	???	Portlaoise
1806	1880	1806	1992	163848	???	Rathmore
SHORTCLIFFE						
1789	1892	....	....	135739	DUR	North
SHORTER						
1844	1851	1800	1960	141046	BRK	Wokingham
1800	1840	1700	1900	171522	SSX	Hastings
1836	1890	1800	1900	133426	STS	South
SHORTHOUSE						
1810	1850	....	....	103764	STS	Brierley Hill
SHORTLAND						
....	....	1800	1850	111414	ALL	ALL
....	....	1800	1900	134546	BDF	Yielden
1830	1850	....	1830	125954	DEV	Plymouth
1842	1842	1810	1851	111414	MDX	Bethnal Green
1690	1900	1900	1992	101389	NTH	Rothwell
1690	1810	1600	1700	131377	NTH	Rothwell
1878	?	ALL	1878	100072	NTH	Weedon
1874	1874	1861	1881	111414	STS	West Bromwich
1846	1846	1841	1861	111414	WES	Little Strickland
SHORTMAN						
1897	1992	1600	1897	163856	AVN	Bristol
1816	1892	1810	1900	157171	GLS	Newnham On Severn
1830	1940	1830	1940	142077	SOM	Keynsham
1793	1840	1700	1841	142077	???	Bristol
SHOTTER						
1787	....	....	....	153397	HAM	New Forest
1850	1992	1600	1850	113263	LND	???
1835	1850	1600	1835	113263	SSX	???
SHOTTON						
1870	1900	1800	1870	179671	DUR	South Shields
1723	1734	1700	1800	144037	NBL	Hartburn
1787	1900	?	1787	158569	STS	???
SHOUKSMITH						
?	?	1687	1760	163864	YKS	Bradford
1787	1992	1760	1787	163864	YKS	York
SHOULDERS						
1819	1850	1700	1851	124907	SSX	Brighton
SHRAPNELL						
....	....	ALL	ALL	163872	ALL	Name Study
SHREEVE						
1731	1808	1700	1808	119059	BDF	Leighton Buzzard
1775	1992	1750	1992	144193	DBY	Claycross
1775	1992	1750	1992	144193	LEI	Harthorne
1710	1730	1550	1710	150843	NFK	Caister On Sea
SHREWSBURY						
1772	....	....	1772	177504	CAM	Littleport
1700	1748	ALL	1750	115282	KEN	East
SHRIMPLIN						
1860	1900	1800	1860	141402	NFK	Ormesby
SHRIMPLING						
1831	1861	1731	1831	177490	NFK	Wymondham
SHRIMPTON						
....	....	ALL	ALL	163880	ALL	Name Study
1794	1809	....	1850	152803	LND	Shoreditch
1782	1850	1750	1850	102717	MDX	ALL
1865	1881	1850	1890	102717	SRY	Peckham
SHRIVES						
1853	1874	1800	1874	147486	NTH	Stanwick

Known From	To	Researching From	To	Ref	Cty	Place
SHROFF						
....	....	ALL	ALL	116343	ALL	Name Study
SHROUDER						
....	....	ALL	ALL	169315	DUR	Sunderland
SHRUBB						
1845	1845	1800	1845	103640	KEN	Gillingham
1689	1912	....	....	175439	OXF	Benson
1689	1912	....	....	175439	SRY	Godalming
SHUBOTHOM						
1730	1865	1730	1865	124842	STS	Newcastle
SHUCKBOROUGH						
....	....	1800	1850	124796	ALL	ALL
SHUFFLEBOTHAM						
1887	1960	1868	1960	143065	LAN	Oswaldtisle
1700	1860	1700	1960	137731	STS	Newcastle
SHUFFLEBOTTOM						
....	....	1300	1992	179590	LAN	ALL
SHUGG						
1653	1900	ALL	ALL	118818	CON	Gwinear
SHUKER						
....	....	ALL	ALL	163899	ALL	Name Study
ALL	ALL	ALL	ALL	163899	ALL	ALL
SHUNN						
....	....	ALL	ALL	119849	ALL	ALL
SHUREY						
ALL	ALL	ALL	ALL	156604	ALL	ALL
SHURLOCK						
1777	1992	1700	1992	159581	SRY	Bramley
1777	1992	1700	1992	159581	SRY	Cranleigh
1765	1790	1700	1765	132640	SRY	Shalford
1777	1992	1700	1992	159581	SRY	Wonersh
SHURT						
1740	1770	1600	1770	154342	SOM	Minehead
SHURVIN						
1840	....	1840	1880	135429	KEN	Greenwich
1890	1900	1840	1992	135429	PEM	Harverfordwest
1800	1900	1840	1880	135429	SRY	Guildford
1700	1850	1840	1880	135429	SSX	Petworth
SHUTE						
1839	....	....	....	173266	CON	St Just
1860	1910	1850	1950	178004	DBY	Derby
1728	1850	ALL	ALL	165972	DEV	South
1780	1900	1780	1900	113670	DOR	Buckhorn Weston
1839	1870	ALL	ALL	119504	DOR	Buckhorn Weston
1770	1785	1750	1900	178004	DOR	Poole
1830	1860	....	....	117579	DOR	Shaftesbury
1780	1830	....	....	117579	DOR	Stour Provost
1777	1950	1700	1992	178004	ENG	ALL
1800	1873	1750	1900	178004	HAM	Gosport
1840	1920	1800	1992	178004	KEN	Greenwich
1830	1872	1820	1880	165972	SRY	Lambeth
SHUTER						
1829	1855	1700	1900	172421	GLS	Toddington
SHUTLER						
1851	1957	ALL	ALL	156884	HAM	Southampton
SHUTT						
1800	1930	1700	1800	116432	DEV	Northam
1840	....	ALL	1850	113476	LAN	Colne
1603	1773	....	....	117404	STS	Blymhill
1840	....	ALL	1850	113476	WYK	Brogden
1850	1851	1700	1992	179086	YKS	Bradford
1806	1810	1750	1820	179086	YKS	Harogate
1780	1820	1750	1820	101044	YKS	Pannal
SHUTTE						
1800	1900	1800	1900	110434	HAM	Southampton
SHUTTELWORTH						
....	....	1700	1870	136743	LAN	Halton
1929	1992	1870	1929	136743	WAR	Coventry
SHUTTLE						
....	....	ALL	ALL	141186	ALL	Name Study
1837	1871	ALL	ALL	141186	WIL	Ramsbury
SHUTTLER						
1790	1870	1770	1870	142018	WIL	West Wellow
SHUTTLEWORTH						
1770	1851	1770	1850	154962	BKM	Quainton
1820	1880	1750	1810	154962	HRT	Barnet
1807	1859	1760	1807	151912	LAN	Billington
1807	1859	1760	1807	151912	LAN	Langho
1860	1887	1700	1860	139122	LAN	Manchester
1850	1980	1750	1850	127949	LAN	Tyldesley
1810	1830	1750	1820	130656	LIN	Coningsby
1805	1855	1700	1830	130656	MDX	Tottenham
....	....	1790	1850	137685	NFK	Gt Yarmouth
1790	1850	1750	1900	150002	WAR	Birmingham

Known From	To	Researching From	To	Ref	Cty	Place
SHUTTLEWORTH contd.						
1550	1900	1550	1900	100420	WAR	Great Packington
1550	1900	1550	1900	100420	WAR	Meriden
1718	1969	....	....	114669	WAR	Shustoke
SHUTTLEWORTH-CLIFT						
....	....	1830	1880	137685	NFK	Gt Yarmouth
SIBBALD						
1820	1890	1780	1830	137618	LND	Southwark
SIBBARD						
1650	1895	1550	1650	129763	NTH	South
SIBBEN						
....	....	1750	1860	128961	ALL	ALL
SIBLEY						
1580	1974	1580	1974	130222	BDF	Husborne Crawley
1760	1780	1760	1780	130222	BKM	Wavendon
1840	1886	1830	1992	117609	CON	Constantine
1783	?	1750	1850	127353	DOR	Melbury Osmund
1870	1992	1850	1992	153052	ESS	Ockendon
1800	1850	1700	1800	169242	HAM	Isle Of Wight
1791	1825	1500	1825	157538	HRT	South
1870	1900	1870	1992	153052	HRT	Hadhams
1773	1821	1700	1850	136042	HRT	Kimpton
....	....	1800	1850	124974	HRT	St Albans
1870	1891	1830	1992	117609	LND	Barnsbury
1745	1750	1745	1750	130222	NTH	Higham Ferrers
1879	1900	1800	1879	124095	???	London
SIDAL						
1600	1801	1700	1800	163902	YKS	Sheffield
SIDAWAY						
1848	1870	1700	1870	119849	WOR	Dudley St Thomas
....	....	1860	1992	147613	WOR	Dudley
SIDDAL						
1600	1801	1700	1800	163902	YKS	Sheffield
SIDDALL						
1730	1806	1730	1806	103977	BRK	Aldworth
....	....	1650	1900	101184	DBY	North East
1801	1954	1600	1801	163902	DBY	North
....	....	1800	1992	101184	DBY	Chesterfield
1833	1883	1800	1992	151378	WYK	Halifax
1845	....	....	....	151785	YKS	Handsworth
1863	1900	1863	1900	156183	YKS	Leeds
1801	1954	1600	1801	163902	YKS	Sheffield
SIDDLE						
ALL	ALL	ALL	ALL	164518	ALL	ALL
1700	1950	ALL	ALL	164518	YKS	Wakefield
SIDDONS						
....	....	ALL	1900	127671	LEI	Leicester
1900	1992	1600	1992	112003	LEI	Osgathorpe
SIDDOWN						
1700	1800	....	....	100420	WAR	Meriden
SIDDOWNE						
1600	1700	1500	1800	177180	STS	West Bromwich
SIDEBOTHAM						
1831	1992	1800	1904	163910	DBY	Chapel En Le Frith
SIDEBOTTOM						
1840	1847	1700	1840	103268	CHS	Tintwistle
1802	1872	....	....	141097	YKS	Adwick Le Street
SIDEN						
1800	1840	ALL	1840	131881	SSX	Westbourne
SIDERY						
1719	1988	1665	1736	171506	BRK	East Hendred
1719	1988	1665	1736	171506	BRK	Upton
1802	1884	....	....	171506	KEN	Lee
SIDES						
1748	1748	1500	1748	169439	OXF	Bloxham
SIDLE						
1600	1801	1700	1800	163902	YKS	Sheffield
SIDLEY						
1800	1830	1700	1800	106313	LND	Ealing
SIDNEY						
1835	....	....	....	156329	AVN	Bristol
1860	....	1800	1860	176885	LIN	Grantham
1770	1800	1700	1800	148288	MDX	London
1780	1880	ALL	1780	107840	STS	Stafford
1670	1870	1670	1870	153621	WYK	Wakefield
SIDWELL						
....	....	ALL	ALL	126950	ALL	Name Study
1603	....	ALL	ALL	126950	ALL	ALL
SIDWELLS						
....	....	ALL	1870	163368	STS	???
SIDYE						
1680	1700	ALL	1850	119105	ESS	Great Henny
1690	1750	....	....	157724	ESS	Gt Heny
SIESTER						
1800	ALL	ALL	ALL	112631	HRT	Tring
SIEVEWRIGHT						
1840	....	1750	1900	135925	BAN	Banff
SIGGEE						
1652	1940	....	....	128996	CAM	Thorney
SIGGERY						
1811	1926	1698	1811	175846	HAM	Cove Farnborough
SIGGS						
....	....	1683	1828	119431	SSX	Heathfield
SIGRAVE						
1550	1700	1550	1700	168491	BDF	Luton
1700	1800	1700	1800	168491	HRT	St Albans
SIGROVE						
1700	1800	1700	1800	168491	HRT	St Albans
SIGSWORTH						
1802	1867	ALL	....	155713	NYK	???
1700	1900	1600	1700	161365	YKS	Easingwold
SILCOCK						
1800	1992	ALL	1800	163945	DOW	Ballinahinch
1696	1992	ALL	1900	156310	SOM	Rode
SILCOCKS						
1841	....	ALL	1992	143197	SOM	Road
1841	1930	ALL	1992	143197	WIL	Trowbridge
SILCOX						
1800	1992	....	1800	138320	SOM	Dunkerton
1974	1985	....	....	173932	SOM	Frome
1911	....	....	....	173932	WIL	Stourton
1940	1970	....	....	173932	WIL	Warminster
SILENCE						
1865	1992	1700	1865	103098	GLA	Swansea
SILK						
....	....	ALL	ALL	163961	ALL	Name Study
1754	1800	1550	1754	174343	HAM	ALL
1793	1986	1793	1986	174343	HAM	East Meon
1836	1904	1800	....	109967	HRT	Aldenham
1770	1850	1700	1770	114871	SOM	Bridgwater
1860	1920	1860	1920	124605	SRY	Camberwell
1754	1870	1720	1900	169250	WOR	Kidderminster
SILKSTONE						
....	....	ALL	ALL	164194	ALL	Name Study
SILLARS						
1750	1992	1700	1800	124699	BUT	Isle Of Arran
SILLENCE						
1870	1930	1700	1870	141119	HAM	ALL
1880	1963	....	....	104817	HAM	Gosport
1704	1802	1704	1802	104817	HAM	Lockerley
1847	1877	1650	1847	179272	HAM	Michelmersh
1877	1989	1650	1877	179272	HAM	Mottisfont
1802	1882	1802	1882	104817	HAM	Sherfield English
1802	1882	1802	1882	104817	WIL	Whiteparish
SILLERS						
....	....	ALL	ALL	124699	ALL	Name Study
1768	1992	1700	1992	124699	AYR	Ardrossan
SILLEY						
....	....	1750	1800	119199	HAM	ALL
....	....	1750	1800	119199	WIL	ALL
SILLIFANT						
....	....	ALL	1920	178403	LND	Walthamstow
SILLITTO						
1812	1992	ALL	1812	160008	STS	Burton On Trent
1812	1992	ALL	1812	160008	STS	Checkley
1812	1992	ALL	1812	160008	STS	Stoke On Trent
SILLS						
1777	1847	....	1777	108839	BKM	Chesham
1729	1818	1700	1820	153249	KEN	Ashford
SILSBY						
1741	1801	....	....	144282	SSX	Shermanbury
SILVER						
1650	1725	....	....	119458	BRK	Hurley
1720	1800	1700	1800	115681	HAM	North East
1880	1992	1837	1880	177539	HAM	Hartley Wintney
SILVERLOCK						
1733	1764	....	....	146811	SSX	Westbourne
SILVERSTON						
1830	1850	1750	1850	166375	SSX	Brighton
SILVERTHORN						
....	....	....	....	165433	AVN	???
....	....	....	....	165433	GLS	???
....	....	....	....	165433	GNT	???
....	....	....	....	165433	WIL	???
SILVERTHORNE						
....	....	ALL	ALL	149020	ALL	Name Study
....	....	....	....	165433	GLS	???

Known From	To	Researching From	To	Ref	Cty	Place
SILVERTHORNE contd.						
....	....	....	....	165433	GNT	???
1840	1992	1700	1840	121037	MDX	Shoreditch
....	....	....	....	165433	WIL	???
SILVERWOOD						
1851	1884	1700	1851	141291	LAN	Preston
1730	1850	....	....	173142	LND	Lambeth
SILVESTER						
1838	1898	1700	1898	106836	BRK	Barkham
....	....	1700	1860	136972	CON	ALL
1867	1884	1800	1884	168564	LIN	Croft
1873	1906	1848	1873	116653	STS	Wolverhampton
SIMCOCK						
1770	1824	....	....	138118	SAL	Market Drayton
SIME						
1820	1830	1750	1820	144150	ANS	Dundee
1740	1992	1750	1800	150002	ANS	Dundee
1780	1855	1700	1855	135941	MLN	Portsburgh
1845	....	1800	1860	124796	SCT	Edinburgh
1860	1923	1845	1930	124796	SCT	Greenock
SIMES						
1718	1776	ALL	1718	154563	DOR	Portesham
1803	1884	1700	1803	154164	HAM	Portsmouth
SIMEY						
1934	1992	1820	1880	174998	NBL	Sunderland
SIMISTER						
1795	1930	ALL	ALL	172901	DBY	ALL
1795	1930	ALL	ALL	172901	LAN	ALL
....	....	?	?	134201	YKS	Pudsey
SIMKIN						
....	....	1800	1992	135216	NTT	Nottingham
1737	1817	?	1737	121665	STS	Darlaston
SIMKINS						
1795	1826	1700	1850	136042	HRT	Kimpton
1824	....	1775	1825	175684	LND	ALL
1876	1876	1800	1890	117722	STS	Walsall
SIMLETT						
1800	1830	1700	1800	146285	DFD	Haverfordwest
SIMMERTON						
1871	1891	1891	1992	146560	LKS	Coatbride
SIMMONDS						
1860	1930	1800	1900	114251	ALL	ALL
1802	1820	1750	1820	172871	BKM	Chalfont St Giles
1830	1841	1800	1865	176877	BRE	Brecon
1800	1880	....	....	159131	BRK	Dedworth Green
1843	1992	1843	1992	167444	BRK	Reading
1758	1800	1600	1758	116637	CON	St Ives
1850	1928	1860	1880	172006	GLS	Cinderford
1761	1877	....	....	172006	HEF	Goodrich
1769	1850	ALL	ALL	135909	LAN	Much Hoole
....	....	1750	1850	163996	LND	Brompton
....	....	1750	1850	163996	LND	Chelsea
1822	....	1750	1822	166723	LND	Hoxton
1870	....	....	....	113018	LND	Poplar
....	....	1800	1900	128627	LND	???
1850	1970	....	....	172871	MDX	Hampstead
1850	1918	1800	1920	163996	MDX	Tottenham
1780	1992	....	....	134619	SAL	Jackfield
1800	1900	1800	1950	158399	SRY	Compton
1918	....	1918	1992	163996	SRY	Croydon
1850	1900	ALL	ALL	131490	SRY	Farnham
1860	1900	ALL	ALL	131490	SRY	Godalming
1800	ALL	1500	1800	145378	SSX	Slaugham
SIMMONS						
1826	1900	....	....	139971	BKM	Amersham
1800	1846	1750	1800	107093	BKM	Brill
....	....	1850	1900	174394	BRK	Crowmarsh Gifford
1860	....	....	1860	164011	BRK	Wallingford
1780	1900	1780	1900	110523	CON	St Hilary
....	....	1750	1870	150800	CON	???
....	....	1750	1870	150800	DEV	???
1874	1992	ALL	ALL	112321	GYN	Llithfaen
1690	1850	1690	1850	105848	HRT	Broxbourne
1800	1900	1700	1992	177180	HRT	Radlett
....	....	1600	1800	142026	KEN	Dover
1755	1780	1700	1800	133450	KEN	East Langdon
1865	1923	1764	1825	161667	KEN	Stone
1836	1992	1700	1836	112321	LEI	Mount Sorrel
1826	1900	....	....	139971	LND	Kensington
....	....	1850	1900	174394	OXF	Crowmarsh Gifford
....	1800	....	....	174564	SSX	Hastings
1800	1900	ALL	ALL	151998	SSX	Salehurst
1820	1992	1820	ALL	108995	SSX	Sayers Green
1663	....	....	....	115576	WIL	Calstone
SIMMS						
1850	1992	1850	1920	111562	BRK	Bracknell
1800	1850	1600	1900	120677	HAM	Faccombe
1859	....	ALL	1859	107964	MDX	Bethnal Green
1790	1908	1700	1850	125806	WOR	Bromsgrove
SIMNETT						
1800	1980	1800	1980	114197	DBY	Burton On Trent
1840	1850	1700	1950	145254	STS	Burton Upon Trent
1800	1980	1800	1980	114197	WAR	Birmingham
SIMON						
1779	....	1700	1779	123129	CMN	Llangyndeyrn
1850	1992	1850	1992	135666	FLN	Bagillt
1850	1992	1850	1992	135666	FLN	Holywell
1700	1810	1700	1810	111538	MER	Llangowek
1840	....	....	....	102733	WOR	Feckenham
1860	1950	1800	1900	169404	YKS	Hull
SIMONDS						
1700	1850	1600	1850	167088	BRK	Hurst
1653	1750	1750	1992	127477	CAM	Woodditton
1749	1800	1730	1800	179337	GLS	Westerleigh
SIMONS						
1900	....	1800	1992	164054	CHS	Dukinfield
1900	....	1800	1992	164054	CHS	Hollingworth
1840	....	1840	1992	164054	CON	Plymouth
1840	....	1840	1992	164054	DEV	Plymouth
1710	1960	1710	1750	140317	ESS	East Donyland
1690	1853	1707	1853	164046	ESS	Elmstead
1815	1877	1700	1815	155101	GLS	Southam
1825	1860	1500	1850	157538	KEN	Maidstone
1750	1992	....	....	177687	LAN	???
1720	1820	ALL	....	104515	LIN	Sedgebrook
1750	1992	....	....	177687	LIN	Thathwell
1843	1992	....	1843	159514	LND	St Lukes
1899	1992	1890	1992	144797	LND	Whitechapel
1800	1890	1750	1900	111759	MDX	Soho
1907	1986	....	....	176966	NTT	Hucknall
1700	1770	1700	1800	144657	SOM	Banwell
1840	....	....	....	102733	WOR	Feckenham
SIMPKIN						
1789	1900	....	....	162655	CAM	Gt Wilbraham
1870	1984	1700	1870	108588	HUM	Hull
1810	1992	1780	1810	154024	LAN	Ashton In Makerfield
?	?	?	?	108588	NFK	Martham
....	1681	ALL	1681	162655	SFK	West
1873	?	?	?	108588	YKS	Leeds
SIMPKINS						
1700	1800	1700	1800	167924	BDF	Shillington
1795	1826	1700	1850	136042	HRT	Kimpton
1900	1959	1900	1960	158607	NFK	West Lynn
1763	1992	1700	1992	116963	WIL	Bradford On Avon
1750	1800	1700	1800	179337	WIL	Bremhill
1798	1841	1700	1798	169609	WIL	Chippenham
1650	1992	ALL	ALL	102202	WIL	Pewsey
SIMPSOM						
1900	1950	1800	1900	116823	YKS	Middleton
SIMPSON						
....	....	ALL	ALL	177172	ALL	Name Study
1831	1831	1750	1850	126586	ABD	Fyvie
1850	1900	1850	1900	140864	ABD	Lonmay
1774	1855	1710	1774	172871	ANS	Craig
1774	1855	1710	1774	172871	ANS	Inverkeilor
1780	1880	1780	1880	148210	BAN	Keith
1798	1900	ALL	1900	127000	CAI	Canisbay
....	....	1500	1787	138614	CAI	Canisbay
1828	1992	1700	1828	151866	CAM	Cambridge
1860	1893	1800	1860	152196	CMA	Egremont
1650	1992	ALL	1650	102083	CMA	Grayrigg
1750	1992	1600	1750	164208	CMA	Morland
1817	....	....	....	164151	CUL	Aikton
1705	1875	1875	1992	145335	CUL	Carlisle
1870	1900	1800	1870	126985	CUL	Walton
1817	....	....	....	164151	CUL	Wigton
1780	....	1780	....	115576	DBY	Wirksworth
1850	1875	1825	1950	133450	DEV	Budleigh Salterton
1800	1810	ALL	1800	128414	DUR	Auckland
1560	1650	ALL	1650	149063	ELN	Haddington
1724	1930	1600	1830	175218	EYK	Leven
1853	1932	1800	1932	164097	FER	Kesh
....	....	1818	....	170453	FIF	ALL
1834	1872	1750	1900	174521	FIF	ALL
?	?	?	?	167169	FIF	Largo
....	....	1750	1800	174319	FIF	???
....	....	1720	1850	166448	HAM	East Tisted

Known From	To	Researching From	To	Ref	Cty	Place
SIMPSON contd.						
....	....	1720	1850	166448	HAM	Silchester
1863	1966	1750	1950	112089	INV	???
1870	1875	1780	1850	120707	IRL	Londonderry
1833	1885	1800	1900	170992	IRL	Newton Limavady
....	....	....	1810	130060	KEN	Dymchurch
1827	1860	1700	1827	152196	LAN	Dalton
....	....	1650	1750	116173	LAN	Furness
1839	1839	1839	1839	145580	LAN	Liverpool
1850	1912	....	1912	153982	LAN	Liverpool
1799	1799	1780	1800	126705	LAN	Manchester
....	....	1810	1992	147613	LAN	Tunstall
1844	1850	1818	1940	115797	LEI	Barkestone
1863	1890	1800	1900	123811	LEI	Whetstone
1882	1904	ALL	1882	164186	LIN	Lincoln
1890	1970	1700	1890	171913	LIN	Lincoln
1807	1830	....	1807	101761	LIN	Wainfleet
....	....	1840	....	116866	LKS	???
1830	1880	1800	1900	132950	LND	ALL
1700	1800	ALL	ALL	131873	LND	Hackney
1832	1851	1700	1992	112402	LND	St Pancras
1834	1872	1750	1900	174521	MLN	ALL
....	....	ALL	1771	119326	MLN	Edinburgh
1833	1992	1750	1833	164224	NBL	Tynemouth
1750	1950	1700	1750	142905	NRY	Dales
....	1780	ALL	1780	134511	NTT	Cotgrave
1810	1810	....	....	108901	NTT	Newark
1800	1836	1700	1800	148806	NYK	Helmsley
1700	1750	1600	1700	174513	OXF	Kencot
1869	1916	1700	1900	166359	PEM	Pembroke Dock
1774	1870	1700	1900	108154	PER	Perth
1802	1836	....	....	113484	PER	Perth
1850	1980	....	....	127140	RFW	Greenock
1834	1872	1750	1900	174521	SCT	Edinburgh
1750	1830	1700	1830	139688	SFK	Ipswich
....	....	1680	....	145688	SFK	Maer
1857	....	1850	1860	163775	SRY	Bermondsey
1879	1895	1879	1895	127183	SRY	Greenwich
1808	1864	1750	1875	155969	SRY	Southwark
....	....	1850	1992	166448	SSX	Petworth
1859	1907	1839	1859	164127	STD	Glasgow
1795	1890	1700	1795	134317	STS	Leek
1672	1767	1600	1672	110639	STS	Stoke On Trent
1865	1966	1750	1992	112089	SUT	Golspie
1760	1992	1500	1760	164178	SXW	Littlehampton
....	....	1800	1900	122203	WAR	???
1779	1992	....	....	164062	WES	Burneside
1800	1992	....	....	106852	WIG	Glasserton
1781	1918	1750	1860	128333	WLN	Bo'ness
1871	1927	1927	1992	101842	WMD	Birmingham
1840	1890	1700	1840	153346	WOR	Stourbridge
1675	1730	1600	1675	145327	WYK	Fewston
1800	1900	1800	1900	153621	WYK	Halifax
1829	1920	1780	1829	130877	YKS	Barwick In Elmete
1705	1727	1500	1992	102520	YKS	Fewston
1771	....	ALL	1771	158445	YKS	Gate Helmsley
....	....	1800	1992	135011	YKS	Pickering
....	....	....	1816	134902	YKS	Sheffield
1840	1936	1840	1936	138703	YKS	Sheffield
....	....	1700	1799	171794	YKS	Soerby
1800	1890	1750	1850	169560	YKS	Sutton On Hull
1750	1992	ALL	ALL	103837	YKS	Witherwick
1800	....	....	....	100633	YKS	???
1829	1850	....	....	127140	YKS	???
1857	1922	1857	....	164135	???	???
SIMS						
1770	1830	1700	1900	116742	BKM	Denham
1793	1874	1700	1793	164259	BRK	Reading
1702	1992	1600	1700	161446	CON	Chaceswater
ALL	1852	....	....	132756	CON	Falmouth
1702	1870	1600	1702	164283	CON	Kenwyn
1692	1699	1600	1699	164283	CON	Ladock
ALL	1852	....	....	132756	CON	St Austell
1750	1920	1700	1900	145866	DBY	Stanton By Bridge
1801	1826	1740	1801	117471	DOR	Sutton Waldron
1870	1992	1600	1870	164240	DOR	Verwood
1876	1885	1885	1992	106062	GLA	Cardiff
1820	1850	1820	1900	127914	GLS	Kings Stanley
1873	1992	....	....	142530	HAM	Burley
1745	1851	1851	1910	164291	HAM	Burley
1723	1745	1600	1723	164291	HAM	Hursley
1833	1962	1700	1833	155721	KEN	New Romney
1731	1992	1700	1730	164267	KEN	Wittersham
....	....	1800	1850	159115	LND	Cripplegate

Known From	To	Researching From	To	Ref	Cty	Place
SIMS contd.						
1833	1992	1833	1850	169757	LND	???
1827	1904	1800	1900	128694	MDX	Barnet
1793	1854	....	....	146811	NBL	North Sheilds
1842	....	ALL	ALL	138533	NFK	Thrigby
1823	1848	1700	1823	139122	NTT	Laneham
1870	1992	....	....	164275	NTT	Nottingham
1777	1992	ALL	1777	130575	RUT	Uppingham
1880	....	....	....	164232	SCT	Edinburgh
1966	1992	....	....	164232	SFK	Ipswich
1620	1670	1620	1700	142018	SOM	East
1939	1980	....	....	164232	SRY	Morden
1724	1776	....	....	146811	SSX	Westbourne
1872	1930	....	....	132756	STS	Longton
1872	1930	....	....	132756	STS	Potts
1883	1918	1830	1890	143294	WAR	Coventry
1800	1850	1700	1800	172901	WIL	Bradford
ALL	1839	....	....	170178	WIL	Ogbourne St Andrew
1804	1827	1750	1804	103896	WIL	Ramsbury
1760	1900	....	....	132225	WIL	Rowde
1691	1763	1740	1800	142018	WIL	Salisbury
SIMSON						
1827	1992	ALL	1827	153729	ANS	Dundee
....	....	....	1850	116866	NIR	???
SINCLAIR						
1821	1860	1700	1860	113107	BAN	Port Gordon
1700	1799	ALL	1775	127000	CAI	Canisbay
1800	1830	....	....	126497	CAI	Latheron
1780	1893	....	....	168203	CAI	Lybster
1813	1881	1800	1900	137715	CAI	Wick
1807	1920	1700	1992	126632	CMA	Rockcliffe
1860	1880	1880	1992	115738	DOW	Warrenpoint
1828	1862	1700	1828	101745	DUR	South Shields
1868	1900	1868	1992	108979	DUR	Sunderland
1843	1912	1750	1843	164224	DUR	Sunderland
1878	1992	ALL	1878	179434	KCD	Fetteresso
1796	1914	1700	1820	163740	KEN	Deptford
1800	1860	1750	1800	159891	PER	Auchteraraoer
1800	1860	1750	1800	159891	PER	Errol
1800	1860	1750	1800	159891	PER	Inchture
1800	1860	1750	1800	159891	PER	Perth
1913	1913	1900	1913	162442	SCT	Greenock
1750	1965	....	....	137820	SHI	Fetlar
1720	1965	....	....	137820	SHI	Mid Yell
1760	1965	....	....	137820	SHI	North Yell
1758	1965	....	....	137820	SHI	Northmavine
1720	1965	....	....	137820	SHI	South Yell
1828	1862	1700	1828	101745	SHI	???
1843	1912	1750	1843	164224	SHI	???
1830	1890	1790	1830	142972	STI	Kilsyth
1801	1901	1700	1820	179000	STI	Kilsyth
SINDEN						
1770	....	....	1800	171441	KEN	Bethersden
1800	1900	1800	1900	138045	KEN	Brenchley
1800	1900	1800	1900	138045	KEN	Five Oak Green
1800	1900	1800	1900	138045	KEN	Morden
1800	1940	1800	1940	138045	KEN	Tonbridge
1770	1858	ALL	1770	177490	SSX	Hstings
SINDERSON						
....	1768	1500	1768	175072	LIN	Glentham
SINE						
1593	1746	1500	1790	105333	SSX	ALL
SINETT						
1900	....	....	....	148989	LND	???
SINFIELD						
1715	1992	1600	1715	149713	BKM	Brickhill
1794	1880	1500	1826	137170	BKM	The Brickhills
1820	1830	1750	1850	139688	LND	East End
SING						
1700	1950	1600	1700	108286	DEV	Torrington
....	....	1600	1992	108286	DEV	???
SINGER						
1777	1896	1858	1992	165077	ABD	Aberdeen
1744	1860	1696	1992	116025	ABD	Insch
1720	1870	1720	1870	177032	SRY	Chertsey
1720	1870	1720	1870	177032	SRY	Farnham
SINGLE						
1750	1850	....	1750	130680	SOM	Chard
SINGLEHURST						
?	?	?	?	164348	DEV	Plymouth
SINGLETON						
1686	1729	....	1730	137405	CAM	Foxton
1791	1850	1700	1791	163783	CHS	Birkenhead
1750	1790	....	1790	161888	CHS	???

Surname	Known From	To	Researching From	To	Ref	Cty	Place
SINGLETON contd.							
	1850	1992	1750	1850	167789	DUB	Dublin
	1850	1900	1800	1850	121509	LAN	Burnley
	1811	1881	1811	1886	153273	LAN	Chipping
	1791	1850	1700	1791	163783	LAN	Kirkham
	1800	1820	1700	1800	151769	LIN	Grantham
	1810	1840	1800	1900	101508	NTT	Southwell
	1600	1750	....	....	165999	NTT	Southwell
	1746	1900	1746	1900	118540	NTT	Upton By Southwell
	....	....	1700	1900	122203	SOM	Cranmore
	....	....	1700	1900	122203	SOM	Wensham
	1500	1900	1500	1900	170216	WIL	ALL
	1832	1992	1700	1832	133647	YKS	Wibsey
SINGS							
	....	....	ALL	ALL	118311	ALL	Name Study
SINKER							
	1780	1860	1760	1880	130621	CHS	Bunbury
SINNICK							
	1852	....	....	....	164356	DOR	Wareham
SINNOT							
	1880	1908	ALL	....	145556	ALL	???
SINNOTT							
	1800	1830	1750	1850	144657	IRL	???
	1845	1992	1700	1845	161446	WEX	Wexford
SINTON							
	1790	1871	1880	1900	119725	ROX	Roxburgh
SIPTHORP							
	?	?	?	?	127701	LND	???
SIRED							
	1796	1832	1700	1796	115460	BKM	Eddlesborough
SIRET							
	1796	1832	1700	1796	115460	BKM	Eddlesborough
SIRMAN							
	1880	1900	1800	1900	156221	GLS	ALL
	....	?	?	?	156221	OXF	ALL
SIRRELL							
	1864	....	1700	1864	104620	HEF	Weston Beggard
SISLEY							
	1843	1863	1843	1863	138312	KEN	Tonbridge
SISSON							
	1706	1940	....	....	128996	CAM	Thorney
	1630	1670	ALL	ALL	141615	IRL	Dublin
SISSONS							
	1700	1850	1600	1950	143189	CMA	Sedbergh
	1830	1870	1800	1900	143189	LAN	Manchester
	1784	1881	1700	1784	164364	LIN	Bishop Norton
	1784	1881	1700	1784	164364	LIN	Epworth
	1800	1880	1700	1800	142875	LIN	???
	1871	1871	1871	1950	106666	LND	Lambeth
	....	....	1700	1784	164364	YKS	Anlaby
	1845	1890	1550	1845	150843	YKS	Beverley
	....	....	1700	1784	164364	YKS	Hessle
SITWELL							
	ALL	1900	....	....	135674	DBY	???
SIVETER							
	....	1843	....	1843	140767	WOR	Dudley
SIVEWRIGHT							
	1810	1890	1740	1820	119628	ANS	Arbroath
	1810	1890	1740	1820	119628	ANS	Dundee
	1810	1860	1810	1860	148210	BAN	Rathven
SIVIER							
	1708	1738	1580	1708	159239	SXE	Mountfield
SIX							
	1655	1940	....	....	128996	CAM	Thorney
SIXSMITH							
	1676	1703	1613	1676	118958	LAN	???
SIZELAND							
	....	....	ALL	ALL	133485	ALL	Name Study
	1810	1850	1850	1900	158887	NFK	Central
	1750	1980	1565	1750	103527	NFK	???
SIZER							
	....	....	ALL	ALL	164372	ALL	Name Study
	1819	1915	1800	1920	137405	CAM	Barrington
	1816	1891	1600	1816	146161	NFK	Norwich
	....	1793	....	1820	137405	SFK	Haverhill
SIZMUR							
	1800	1850	....	1850	109568	SRY	Chertsey
SKALES							
	1760	....	ALL	ALL	107425	NFK	Flordon
SKAR							
	1659	1690	1600	1700	123250	YKS	Askrigg
SKARDON							
	1860	1870	1800	1860	147966	MDX	Chelsea
SKARRAT							
	1720	1770	1600	1992	167592	STS	Burslem
SKEA							
	1863	1871	1837	1900	103608	LND	Waterloo
SKEAINES							
	1811	1841	1780	1860	142018	HAM	Southampton
	1832	1890	1820	1900	142018	WIL	Salisbury
SKEATES							
	1720	1992	1700	1992	140287	AVN	Bristol
SKEELS							
	....	....	1850	1992	147613	ALL	ALL
	1780	1890	1700	1840	134597	CAM	Chatteris
	1790	1850	1700	1992	147613	CAM	Chatteris
SKEEN							
	1830	1840	1750	1850	116386	BEW	Jedburgh
	1830	1840	1750	1850	116386	BEW	Kelso
	1867	1992	1840	1900	116386	NBL	Newcastle
	1838	1871	1800	1900	116386	NBL	Wooler
SKEET							
	?	?	?	?	175145	WAR	East
SKEGG							
	....	1779	1720	1820	128961	BDF	Potton
	1560	1650	1560	1650	167924	HRT	Aston
	1560	1650	1560	1650	167924	HRT	Bennington
	....	1779	1720	1820	128961	HRT	St Albans
	1800	1930	....	....	135984	LND	Hackney
	1800	1930	....	....	135984	LND	Islington
	1800	1930	....	....	135984	LND	Stepney
	....	1806	1750	1810	128961	LND	???
SKEGGS							
	1828	1975	1550	1828	146099	HRT	South
	1798	1803	1700	1802	131245	HRT	Welwyn
	1770	1965	ALL	1770	164380	HRT	???
SKELDING							
	1750	1850	1700	1870	126438	WOR	Stourbridge
SKELDON							
	1800	1992	1650	1800	150568	ELN	Innerwick
SKELHORN							
	....	....	ALL	1837	116475	CHS	North
SKELLETT							
	1811	1900	1700	1900	135968	RUT	S Luffenham
SKELLING							
	1700	1799	1700	1799	147575	GLS	Sedbury
SKELLY							
	....	....	ALL	ALL	176761	ALL	Name Study
	1644	1992	1644	1992	164399	DEV	West
	1801	1900	1801	1850	164402	NBL	Alnwick
	1825	1900	....	1825	176761	NBL	Alnwick
SKELT							
	1900	....	....	....	104337	MDX	???
SKELTON							
	1862	1915	1862	1915	108839	BDF	Luton
	1750	1850	1600	1750	158046	CON	East
	1767	1830	....	1767	108839	DEV	Devonport
	1863	....	ALL	1863	164623	DEV	East Stonehouse
	1660	1992	....	1660	100900	DEV	Plymouth
	1800	1840	1840	1950	158046	DEV	Plymouth
	1740	1850	1650	1740	158046	DEV	South Hams
	1830	1844	1830	1844	108839	DEV	Totnes
	1811	1992	1700	1811	118788	KEN	Canterbury
	1840	1992	1700	1840	160660	KEN	Rochester
	1745	1796	ALL	1745	123641	LIN	North Kelsey
	1890	1992	1700	1890	164410	LND	Poplar
	1881	....	....	....	112380	LND	South Hackney
	1657	1725	1600	1657	177393	NTT	Weston
	1845	1973	1845	1973	108839	STS	Stoke On Trent
	1770	1850	....	....	170798	WRY	Illingworth
	1770	1850	....	....	170798	WRY	Ovenden
	1881	1881	ALL	ALL	143618	WYK	Castleford
	1850	1992	1700	1850	100803	WYK	Halifax
	....	....	1760	....	151629	WYK	Northouram
	1887	1939	1800	1887	127728	YKS	Sheffield
	1665	1850	1600	1665	158046	???	London
SKENE							
	1300	1700	....	....	142670	ABD	Aberdeen
SKEPPER							
	?	?	?	?	141003	LIN	???
SKERM							
	1837	1988	ALL	1837	164569	HEF	Various
SKERMAN							
	1850	1927	1850	1927	108839	CAM	Cambridge
	....	....	1800	1940	159840	HRT	Hertford
	1807	1850	....	1807	108839	HRT	Ware

Known From	To	Researching From	To	Ref	Cty	Place
SKERN						
1835	1992	1700	1850	164429	YKS	Hull
SKERO						
....	....	....	....	104396	YKS	Hull
SKERRATT						
1792	1992	1750	1800	173649	CHS	Goostry
....	....	1800	1890	160393	IRL	ALL
1890	....	1800	1890	160393	LAN	Salford
1807	1863	1750	1850	141283	STS	Newcastle
SKERRETT						
1850	1992	1750	1850	169722	DEV	ALL
SKERRITT						
1900	....	ALL	ALL	112275	DBY	Ripley
SKERROW						
1800	1960	1800	1960	104396	YKS	Hull
....	....	....	....	104396	YKS	Tadcaster
SKERRY						
1805	1860	1841	1861	164402	IRL	Tipperary
1600	1992	1700	1840	164437	NFK	ALL
SKERTEN						
1800	1992	....	1800	159972	GLS	ALL
SKERTON						
1800	1992	....	1800	159972	GLS	ALL
SKETCHLEY						
1613	1992	1500	1613	132233	LEI	???
SKEWES						
1700	1992	1700	1992	164534	CON	ALL
1874	....	....	....	123099	CON	Camborne
1769	1970	1700	1769	177520	CON	Kea
1700	....	....	....	136999	CON	Wendron
SKEWIS						
1700	1992	1700	1992	164534	CON	ALL
SKEWS						
1700	1992	1700	1992	164534	CON	ALL
....	....	1900	....	173991	CON	Falmouth
SKEY						
1832	....	1700	1832	150223	GLS	Thornbury
SKIDMORE						
....	....	ALL	ALL	148555	ALL	Name Study
....	....	ALL	ALL	148547	ALL	Name Study
....	....	ALL	ALL	148547	ALL	ALL
1837	1841	1837	1841	108251	GLS	Ashleworth
1797	1830	1797	ALL	145386	GLS	Bristol
1800	1850	1800	1850	108251	GLS	Winterbourne
1796	1831	1750	1830	137413	NTT	Nottingham
1625	1992	1625	1900	148547	STS	South
1625	1665	1600	1750	160873	STS	Kingswinford
1840	....	....	....	170313	STS	Tipton
1740	1992	1740	1900	148547	WAR	Birmingham
1625	1992	1625	1900	148547	WOR	North
1742	1992	....	....	134619	WOR	Oldswinford
....	1780	1700	1780	123102	YKS	Sheffield
SKIGGS						
1789	1828	1700	1789	167649	HRT	Ashwell
SKILBECK						
1790	1811	1770	1811	156892	NRY	Bilton In Ainsty
SKILLER						
1743	1796	....	....	171441	KEN	Strood
SKILLERN						
1650	1992	ALL	ALL	140813	ALL	ALL
SKILLING						
1700	1799	1700	1799	147575	GLS	Ashton Keynes
1700	1799	1700	1799	147575	GLS	Somerford
1700	1799	1700	1799	147575	WIL	???
SKILLINGTON						
1700	1799	ALL	1800	168718	LEI	Rearsby
1840	1850	1700	1900	153877	NTH	Stoke Albany
SKILTON						
1850	1950	1750	1850	102679	DEV	Turnchapel
1830	1847	1500	1860	137472	SRY	Reigate
SKIMMING						
....	....	ALL	ALL	152048	AYR	Stewarton
1820	1861	ALL	1861	152048	RFW	Paisley
1780	1940	....	....	106852	WIG	Kirkinner
SKINGLEY						
1783	1787	1700	1800	138185	ESS	ALL
....	....	ALL	ALL	171158	ESS	ALL
SKINNER						
....	....	ALL	ALL	141755	ALL	Name Study
1771	1800	ALL	1771	106909	ABD	Pitsligo
1896	1992	ALL	1896	147060	ANS	Montrose
1825	1905	1750	1825	114871	AVN	Bristol
1832	1841	1830	1848	135828	BDF	Great Barford
1824	1854	1700	....	123552	BRK	Thatcham
SKINNER contd.						
1832	1875	1787	1832	174688	CON	Kingsand Maker
1700	1850	1600	1992	114596	DEV	Chittlehampton
1774	....	....	....	137936	FIF	Ceres
1831	1836	1790	1839	155438	GLS	Bristol
1795	1795	1795	1795	106704	HUN	Upton
1744	1896	1600	1744	117110	KEN	Canterbury
1853	1871	....	1853	117234	KEN	Maidstone
1853	1871	....	1853	117234	KEN	Tudley
1770	1790	....	....	130915	KRS	???
1700	1770	1600	1900	176656	LIN	North
1615	1640	ALL	....	104515	LIN	Heckington
1847	1992	ALL	....	157791	LND	Bermondsey
1876	1940	1800	1876	156132	LND	Bethnal Green
1847	1992	ALL	1847	157791	LND	Bethnal Green
1847	1992	ALL	....	157791	LND	Rotherhithe
1830	1851	1830	1834	135828	LND	St Georges Hanover Square
1847	1992	ALL	....	157791	LND	Stepney
1847	1992	ALL	....	157791	LND	West Ham
....	....	ALL	1819	164984	LTN	Leith
1824	1854	1700	....	123552	MDX	London
1888	1888	ALL	ALL	105856	MDX	???
1787	1803	1750	1787	177393	NFK	Ingoldisthorpe
1820	1850	1820	1850	108693	NFK	North Creake
1806	1885	....	....	169129	NFK	Walpole St Andrew
1708	1819	1750	1818	102830	NTH	Islip
1850	....	....	....	145920	OXF	Eaton Hastings
1855	1925	1850	1925	151858	SCT	Balintore
1770	1992	1600	1770	164461	SFK	Bungay
1888	1888	ALL	ALL	105856	SRY	???
1845	....	....	....	125326	SRY	???
1620	1992	ALL	ALL	164453	SSX	West
1863	....	....	1863	117234	SSX	Frant
?	1880	1700	1860	164488	SSX	Thakeham
1620	1992	ALL	ALL	164453	SSX	Thakeham
1780	1900	1500	1780	114049	WIL	North
1695	1765	1600	1700	101575	YKS	Whitgift
SKIPBOARD						
ALL	....	....	....	155993	RAD	St Harmon
SKIPP						
1907	1907	1880	1907	117609	MDX	Islington
SKIPPER						
1700	1850	1500	1700	109959	ESS	Frating
1800	1950	ALL	ALL	166537	NFK	Castle Acre
1789	1900	1700	1789	155276	SFK	Falkenham
SKIPPON						
1749	1992	1580	1749	168521	NFK	Sculthorpe
1780	1850	1700	1780	124427	NFK	Snoring
SKIRROW						
....	....	1620	1750	147613	LAN	Melling
....	....	....	....	104396	YKS	Leeds
SKIRTEN						
1800	1992	....	1800	159972	GLS	ALL
SKIRTON						
1800	1992	....	1800	159972	GLS	ALL
SKITCH						
1700	1987	ALL	ALL	159700	CON	North East
1825	1890	ALL	ALL	159700	DEV	West
SKITTRALL						
....	....	ALL	ALL	164496	ALL	Name Study
SKONTS						
1772	....	....	....	129747	NFK	North Wotton
SKORRELL						
1484	1734	ALL	ALL	122106	SFK	Hitcham
SKOTS						
1690	1720	1600	1750	174599	WIL	Downton
SKOYLES						
....	....	ALL	ALL	164526	ALL	Name Study
SKUCE						
1800	1992	1700	1992	131555	IRL	ALL
1750	1900	1750	1900	164534	OXF	Chalbury
SKUES						
1900	1992	1900	1992	164534	CHS	North
1600	1992	1600	1992	164534	CON	ALL
1850	1992	1850	1992	164534	KEN	Dartford
1887	1992	....	....	164542	KEN	Tonbridge
1800	1992	1800	1992	164534	LND	ALL
1874	1882	....	....	164542	MDX	West
....	....	ALL	ALL	164542	WIL	ALL
1850	1992	1850	1992	164534	YKS	West
SKULL						
1550	1750	ALL	1850	132950	WIL	Brinkworth
1838	1920	?	1838	136611	WIL	Dauntsey

Known From	To	Researching From	To	Ref	Cty	Place
SKULL contd.						
1803	1813	ALL	1900	168696	WIL	Dauntsey
?	?	1700	1860	153222	WIL	Wootton Bassett
SKUSE						
1800	1992	1700	1992	131555	IRL	ALL
1850	1992	ALL	1900	153222	WIL	Leigh
....	....	ALL	ALL	153222	WIL	Minety
1605	1881	1600	1900	164534	WIL	Minety
....	....	1895	1897	164445	WIL	Purton
SKUTT						
1700	1861	1700	1866	145602	DOR	Wimborne
1866	1905	1866	1920	145602	WAR	Kenilworth
SKYRM						
....	....	ALL	ALL	164569	ALL	Name Study
1780	1880	1755	1950	164569	PEM	Manorbier
1780	1880	1755	1950	164569	PEM	Penally
1765	1865	1765	1880	164569	PEM	Tenby
SKYRME						
1841	....	1841	1992	129631	GNT	Blaenavon
1700	1880	1660	1880	164569	HEF	Norton Cannon
1837	1988	ALL	1837	164569	HEF	Various
1840	....	1700	1992	129631	HEF	Vowchurch
1903	1940	1760	1900	129143	PEM	Clarbeston
1792	1878	1794	1878	164569	PEM	Llangwm
1713	1823	1653	1956	164569	PEM	Llawhaden
1850	1900	1837	1900	164569	WOR	Worcester
SLACH						
....	....	ALL	ALL	115231	HEF	Ledbury
SLACK						
....	....	ALL	ALL	124370	ALL	Name Study
1790	1790	ALL	1790	154563	CUL	Alston
1606	1992	1606	1851	166952	DBY	Ashover
1890	1992	1850	1900	107484	DBY	Chesterfield
1750	....	....	....	123641	DBY	Chesterfield
1780	1918	1700	1900	166952	DBY	Crich
....	....	ALL	ALL	111384	DBY	Wirksworth
1850	1950	1700	1850	155497	LAN	Manchester
1834	1861	ALL	ALL	111384	LAN	Middleton
1871	1992	1843	1871	178551	NTT	Nottingham
....	....	....	1820	114812	YKS	Bolsterstone
....	....	....	1820	114812	YKS	Bradfield
SLADDEN						
1750	1992	1800	1992	133450	KEN	???
SLADE						
1600	1810	....	....	174319	CON	Gorran
1785	1821	1730	1785	110043	DEV	Shobrooke
1779	1780	....	1779	131385	DEV	Topsham
1800	1840	1800	1840	135429	DEV	Topsham
1840	1880	1840	1880	135429	DEV	Torquay
1847	1959	1800	1891	141461	DOR	Sherborne
....	....	1750	1800	161357	DOR	Walditch
1843	1850	1850	1900	164577	GLS	Cheltenham
1800	1870	1750	1900	109371	GLS	Great Barrington
1850	1915	1820	1855	155691	MDX	Islington
....	1880	1880	1950	106518	MDX	London
1800	....	1800	1900	106410	SOM	Beer Crocombe
1851	....	1851	1890	133639	SOM	Coker
1835	1840	1810	1841	176923	SOM	Farrington Gurney
1850	1900	....	....	164593	SOM	Ilminster
1809	1854	1700	1861	176923	SOM	Midsomer Norton
1750	1820	1700	1750	101524	SOM	North Currey
1800	1900	1700	1800	176796	SOM	North Perrott
1841	1851	1841	1881	176923	SOM	Paulton
1870	1968	1700	1870	155144	SRY	Newlington
1569	1663	....	....	165999	SSX	Farnhurst
1760	1850	1600	1850	132950	WIL	Bremhill
1812	1812	1812	1812	139971	WIL	Bremhill
1823	1866	1600	1823	175781	WIL	Bromham
....	....	1700	1980	172111	WIL	Lacock
....	....	ALL	ALL	144762	WIL	Marlborough
1777	1900	1600	1777	164577	WOR	Worcester
SLADEN						
1874	1900	ALL	ALL	155608	DBY	ALL
1874	1900	ALL	ALL	155608	NTT	ALL
SLADER						
1500	1900	1500	1992	164607	DEV	Molton
SLANEY						
1750	1880	1650	1750	151769	NTT	Mansfield Woodhouse
SLANN						
1790	1850	1700	1900	154776	BRK	Sunninghill
....	....	1840	ALL	164615	BRK	Sunninghill
SLATER						
1755	....	....	....	135771	CHS	Central
1890	1992	....	1890	102059	CHS	Hyde

Known From	To	Researching From	To	Ref	Cty	Place
SLATER contd.						
1816	1861	1700	....	154601	CMA	Kirkby Lonsdale
1693	1765	1550	1693	102830	DBY	Ashbourne
1800	1950	ALL	ALL	156604	DBY	Matlock
1760	1992	1700	1760	121673	DBY	Scropton
....	....	1800	1850	148113	DBY	???
1772	1891	ALL	1772	164623	DUR	Gateshead
1763	1763	ALL	1763	131881	HAM	Porstmouth
1813	1900	....	....	164631	KEN	Deptford
1910	1965	....	....	164631	KEN	Erith
1590	1992	1420	1992	164658	LAN	South East
1853	1918	1853	1918	122335	LAN	Blackburn
1827	1857	1800	1827	108154	LAN	Bolton
1850	1881	....	....	142859	LAN	Manchester
1775	1850	1775	1850	171549	LAN	Mossley
1790	1992	1700	1790	169056	LAN	Ormskirk
1880	1992	ALL	1880	160938	LAN	Salford
....	....	1800	1880	147788	LEI	Leicester
1868	1940	1840	1868	114073	LND	St Martins In The Fields
1860	1870	ALL	ALL	148458	MLN	Dalkeith
1718	1850	....	....	117803	NRY	Coverham
1816	1855	1600	1855	148482	OKI	Birsay
1860	1900	ALL	ALL	148458	PER	Blairgowrie
1724	1740	1680	1723	156140	SSX	Framfield
1862	1930	....	1900	154601	WYK	Denholme
1848	1900	....	....	136824	YKS	Sheffield
1844	1890	....	....	116602	YKS	Whitby
1860	1900	1700	1860	102210	???	???
SLATFORD						
....	....	ALL	ALL	164666	ALL	Name Study
SLATTER						
1816	1844	1700	1860	160601	GLS	Bledington
1885	1885	1800	1950	168734	GLS	Gloucester
1706	1821	1665	1821	100668	SSX	Battle
SLATTERY						
1900	1992	ALL	ALL	156175	GLA	Swansea
1850	1992	....	....	126276	LEI	Whitwick
SLAUGHTER						
....	....	1760	1841	131768	BRK	Arborfield
1841	1881	1841	1881	131768	BRK	Reading
1500	1620	1400	1660	150479	GLS	Slaughter
1876	1914	ALL	1876	152013	MDX	Islington
SLAWSON						
1700	1800	1800	1950	142913	CHS	Bickley
1900	1980	1800	1900	142913	DEN	Wrexham
1900	1980	1800	1900	142913	LAN	Liverpool
1730	1930	1600	1730	142913	LEI	Billesdon
1850	1950	1700	1850	142913	LND	ALL
1850	1950	1550	1850	142913	NTH	Brigstock
SLAYMAKER						
1700	1893	1871	1992	159468	BRK	Bray
1893	....	1871	1992	159468	NFK	Buxton
SLAYMAN						
1640	1860	....	....	164690	IRL	Ulster
1700	1800	....	....	164690	SSX	Petworth
SLEAMAN						
1550	1900	....	....	164690	CON	ALL
1600	1900	....	....	164690	DEV	ALL
1630	1700	ALL	ALL	164690	IRL	Ulster
SLEATH						
1874	1992	ALL	1874	169870	WAR	Birmingham
SLEDGE						
1680	1720	1670	1730	142018	SOM	Batcombe
SLEE						
1890	1910	1700	1960	121495	CON	South
1890	1910	1700	1960	121495	DEV	North
1800	1900	1700	1800	177091	DEV	Holsworthy
1760	1850	1760	1850	164674	DEV	Marwood
1500	1780	1500	1780	164674	DEV	Shirwell
SLEEMAN						
1850	1992	1700	1850	143936	CON	Helston
1850	1992	1700	1850	143936	CON	Illogan
1800	1905	1700	1800	128325	CON	Newquay
SLEEP						
1703	1936	1600	1700	148040	CON	Forrabury
1700	1820	....	....	113093	CON	Menheniot
1703	1936	1600	1700	148040	CON	Menheniot
1781	1992	1700	1781	154415	CON	Plymouth
1700	1820	....	....	113093	CON	South Hill
1781	1992	1700	1781	154415	DEV	Plymouth
SLEEPER						
1880	1952	1876	1952	149640	MDX	London

Known From	To	Researching From	To	Ref	Cty	Place
SLEIGHTHOLM						
1780	1855	1700	1780	148199	NYK	Burniston
SLEIGHTHOLME						
1700	1850	1600	1992	177725	NYK	Kirkby Mooreside
SLEMAN						
1540	1900	....	....	164690	CON	ALL
1650	1950	....	....	164690	IRL	ALL
SLEMANS						
1540	1900	....	....	164690	CON	ALL
1650	1950	....	....	164690	IRL	ALL
1700	1850	....	....	164690	SSX	Petworth
SLEMMINGS						
1700	ALL	ALL	ALL	164682	ALL	ALL
1737	1992	....	....	164682	SSX	Petworth
1700	1920	....	....	164690	SSX	Petworth
SLEMMON						
1630	1880	....	....	164690	IRL	Ulster
SLEMMONDS						
1800	1920	....	....	164690	SSX	Petworth
SLEMMONS						
1630	1880	....	....	164690	IRL	Ulster
SLEMON						
1630	1880	....	....	164690	IRL	Ulster
SLEMONDS						
1700	1992	ALL	....	164682	SSX	Petworth
SLEMONS						
1630	1880	....	....	164690	IRL	Ulster
SLICER						
1750	1800	1700	1850	110906	BKM	Buckingham
SLIGHT						
1750	1850	1750	1850	144290	LIN	Ancaster
1800	1900	1800	1900	144290	LIN	Wilsford
1858	1880	....	....	172871	MDX	Hampstead
....	....	1800	1860	172871	MDX	Paddington
SLIGHTER						
1300	1400	1250	1400	154881	KEN	Penshurst
SLIGO						
1801	1801	ALL	1801	109886	OXF	Burford
SLIM						
1550	1992	1550	1992	141607	ALL	ALL
SLIMAN						
1825	1851	1700	1950	144037	AYR	Catrine
1600	1900	....	....	164690	SCT	Lowlands
SLIMANS						
1600	1900	....	....	164690	SCT	Lowlands
SLIMMANDS						
1700	1900	....	....	164690	SCT	Lowlands
SLIMMING						
1600	1900	....	....	164690	SCT	Lowlands
SLIMMINGS						
1600	1900	....	....	164690	SCT	Lowlands
SLIMMOND						
?	?	?	?	146862	STI	Stenhousemuir
SLINGER						
1786	1846	1750	1800	151912	LAN	Downham
1775	1825	1775	1825	109347	YKS	Giggleswick
SLINGSBY						
1862	1872	1840	1881	152781	NTT	Bole
....	....	1600	1750	115142	WAR	Bulkington
1800	1840	1700	1840	147788	YKS	Bradford
1751	1860	ALL	1751	158445	YKS	N Ferriby
SLINN						
1550	1992	1550	1992	141607	ALL	ALL
SLITE						
1769	1940	....	....	128996	CAM	Thorney
SLOAN						
1841	1992	1600	1841	107921	AYR	New Cumnock
1790	1815	1780	1820	146536	RFW	Lochwinnoch
SLOANE						
1834	1885	1790	1900	146536	LKS	Glasgow
SLOBOM						
....	....	ALL	ALL	164712	ALL	Name Study
SLOCOMBE						
1550	1992	ALL	ALL	104884	ALL	ALL
SLOGGETT						
1790	1824	ALL	1824	168718	CON	South East
SLOMAN						
....	....	1840	1940	136166	DEV	Walkhampton
....	....	1780	1880	136166	DEV	Yealmpton
....	....	1860	1992	136166	GLA	Cardiff
SLOPER						
1836	1847	ALL	ALL	129933	LKS	Glasgow
ALL	1658	....	....	170178	WIL	Bishops Cannings
SLORACH						
....	....	....	....	100838	BAN	Rothiemay
SLOTE						
1750	1950	1700	1800	109517	CAM	Deeping St James
1783	1940	....	....	128996	CAM	Thorney
1750	1950	1700	1800	109517	HUN	Deeping St James
SLOTMAN						
1856	1936	ALL	ALL	164887	LTN	Edinburgh
SLOUS						
1850	1850	1750	1900	136042	SRY	Rotherhithe
SLOW						
1870	1992	....	....	164720	HRT	Barnet
1870	1992	....	....	164720	HRT	Potters Bar
SLUCOCK						
1530	1992	ALL	1992	164739	ALL	ALL
SLUCUTT						
1836	1992	ALL	1992	164739	ALL	ALL
SLUGG						
1730	1850	1600	1900	112976	WIL	Westbury
SLY						
1673	1940	....	....	128996	CAM	Thorney
1887	1992	1868	1886	113530	GLS	Bristol
1807	1992	1700	1807	113530	WIL	Warminster
SLYE						
....	....	1650	1770	156795	DOR	North
SLYFIELD						
1738	1780	1600	1800	130125	DOR	Chaldon Hg
1740	1750	1700	1750	136840	DOR	Wool
SMAIL						
1837	1992	ALL	ALL	170860	DUR	Felling
1880	1992	....	....	108898	LKS	Lanark
1803	1866	ALL	1855	101001	MLN	Cockpen
1803	1866	ALL	1855	101001	MLN	Lasswade
SMAILES						
1756	1940	....	....	128996	CAM	Thorney
1809	1910	1770	1850	110728	NBL	Central
SMALE						
1870	1900	1700	1900	175293	CON	Okehampton
1870	1900	1700	1900	175293	DEV	Plymouth
1910	1989	1700	1910	112739	DEV	Torquay
1830	?	ALL	ALL	166243	MDX	Shoreditch
1839	?	ALL	ALL	166243	SRY	Croydon
SMALES						
1820	1850	1750	1820	137278	DUR	Lumley
SMALFIT						
1830	1992	ALL	....	125946	YKS	Hinderwell
SMALL						
....	....	1820	1860	179361	DOR	Winterbourne Kingston
1744	1803	1700	1744	127116	DOR	Witchampton
1840	1846	1750	1850	171662	FIF	Cupar
?	?	?	?	167169	FIF	St Monans
1810	....	ALL	1840	104299	GLS	Bristol
1530	1680	1530	1680	127655	GLS	Minchinhampton
1800	1920	ALL	ALL	122866	HAM	North West
1650	1700	1600	1700	152404	HAM	Hawkley
1600	1992	ALL	....	129577	IOW	???
1875	1935	1800	1875	126675	KEN	Warehorne
1850	1940	1800	1850	128384	LAN	Manchester
1880	1906	1800	1992	165603	LND	Chelsea
1880	1906	1800	1992	165603	LND	Fulham
1821	1855	1750	1900	159107	STS	Brierley Hill
1850	1900	1750	1850	154458	WAR	???
1880	1900	1750	1880	134651	YKS	Middlesborough
1900	....	1700	....	100536	???	???
SMALLBONES						
1810	1870	1810	1900	139270	BRK	South
1810	1870	1810	1900	139270	HAM	North
1694	1704	1550	1693	131245	WAR	Stockton
1797	....	....	....	158895	WIL	Enford
1797	....	....	....	158895	WIL	Great Bedwyn
SMALLEY						
1750	1900	1750	1900	125237	LAN	Darwen
1750	1800	....	....	126497	LAN	Wigan
....	....	1700	1880	102148	LEI	ALL
....	....	1860	1880	119423	LEI	North
....	....	1720	1860	119423	LEI	Twycross
1789	1894	ALL	1894	122572	NTT	ALL
1885	1992	1880	1920	119423	NTT	Nottingham
1898	1992	1870	1992	131865	STS	Cannock
SMALLFIELD						
....	....	1700	1800	134503	KEN	???
?	?	1829	1915	117919	MDX	London
1797	1820	1700	1900	102415	YKS	Hull

Known From	To	Researching From	To	Ref	Cty	Place
SMALLMAN						
....	....	....	....	155349	DUR	Thornley
....	....	....	....	155349	DUR	Wheatley Hill
1795	1916	1500	1992	132055	KEN	Greenwich
1840	1850	1800	1850	113212	SAL	South
1874	1992	ALL	ALL	112275	SAL	Bridgnorth
....	....	1800	1850	159115	STS	Bushbury
SMALLPAGE						
....	....	1760	....	151629	WYK	Northouram
1771	1900	1700	1992	107654	YKS	Coverham
SMALLPIECE						
1830	1992	ALL	....	125946	YKS	Hinderwell
SMALLS						
1700	1992	1700	1838	165131	NFK	ALL
SMALLSHAW						
....	....	ALL	ALL	164763	ALL	Name Study
1756	1772	ALL	ALL	179116	SAL	Whitchurch
SMALLSHIRE						
1791	1825	ALL	ALL	179116	STS	Eccleshall
1791	1825	....	....	117404	STS	Stafford
SMALLWOOD						
1750	1850	ALL	1800	141305	CHS	South
1810	1880	1750	1810	162361	WAR	Birmingham
1750	1992	1550	1992	164771	WAR	Birmingham
SMART						
1800	1850	1700	1800	156795	DOR	North
1804	1860	1700	1800	118877	DOR	Gillingham
1870	1900	1850	1992	143758	DUR	Gateshead
1840	1860	1840	1900	143758	DUR	Winlaton
1755	....	....	....	137936	FIF	Ceres
1790	1890	1700	1800	128244	GLS	Gloucester
1790	1890	1700	1800	128244	GLS	Hucclecote
1790	1890	1700	1800	128244	GLS	Witcombe
1822	1881	1851	1881	125326	HAM	Andover
1646	1776	1550	1646	102830	HUN	Orton Waterville
1876	1992	....	....	161284	LAN	Worsley
1882	1992	1860	1882	118877	LND	Lewisham
1820	1840	1750	1900	143758	NBL	Ponteland
1797	1830	1750	1797	147885	NTH	Greens Norton
....	....	ALL	ALL	154970	NTH	Greens Norton
1720	1821	ALL	ALL	105481	NTT	Old Basford
1750	1850	1650	1750	174513	OXF	Burford
1869	1875	ALL	ALL	129933	SRY	Epsom
1842	1855	ALL	ALL	129933	SRY	Sutton
1812	1833	ALL	ALL	129933	SRY	Tooting
....	....	1837	1915	105058	SSX	Haywards Heath
....	....	1600	1840	123390	STI	Baldernock
1906	1992	....	....	161284	STS	Cannock
1825	1911	1300	1992	152501	STS	Lower Gornal
....	....	1874	1992	122114	WAR	Birmingham
1600	1700	....	....	100420	WAR	Meriden
1764	1875	1700	1764	169609	WIL	Chippenham
1800	1850	1750	1800	133671	WIL	Minty
1840	1880	1840	1880	167029	WIL	Savernake
1820	1840	ALL	1820	167029	WIL	Wootton Rivers
1825	1911	1300	1992	152501	WOR	Dudley
1865	1905	1700	1865	176575	???	Stourbridge
SMAWFIELD						
1797	1820	1700	1900	102415	YKS	Hull
SMEATON						
....	....	1900	1910	175889	STI	Stirling
SMEDLEY						
1830	....	ALL	ALL	107123	CHS	Macclesfield
1850	1880	1850	1880	107131	CHS	Macclesfield
1820	1856	1790	1900	148121	DBY	Alfreton
1830	1850	1700	1820	164798	DBY	Bonsall
1811	1890	....	....	115932	DBY	Mansfield
1660	1690	....	....	165999	DBY	Melborne
1791	1799	1791	1799	160164	DBY	Melbourne
1721	1992	1600	1720	113395	DBY	Shottle
1850	1992	1500	1850	164798	DBY	Shottle
1721	1992	1600	1720	113395	DBY	Wirksworth
1850	1992	1500	1850	164798	DBY	Wirksworth
1759	1910	ALL	ALL	147621	FLN	Holywell
1800	1900	1800	1900	115932	LAN	Oldham
1819	1879	1819	1879	160164	LEI	Ashby Do La Zouch
1757	....	ALL	ALL	105481	NTT	Bulwell
1730	1767	1650	1767	148288	NTT	Stapleford
1860	1937	1800	1860	135623	STS	Stoke On Trent
SMEDMORE						
1700	1730	ALL	1700	115266	DOR	ALL
SMEE						
1736	....	1650	1750	143693	BRK	Waltham St Lawrence
SMEED						
1800	....	....	....	148768	KEN	Faversham
SMEETON						
1745	1745	1700	1745	174130	LEI	Fleckney
1722	1722	1700	1722	174130	LEI	Shearsby
....	....	1829	1992	164801	LIN	Kirton
1770	1810	1700	1770	151769	LIN	Threckingham
....	....	ALL	ALL	164801	MDX	London
1600	1930	ALL	ALL	164801	NTH	North
SMELLIE						
1845	1876	ALL	1845	146757	AYR	Ardrossan
1720	1760	1700	1720	101796	AYR	Irvine
SMELT						
....	....	ALL	ALL	106550	ALL	Name Study
1400	1992	1400	1992	106550	ALL	ALL
1770	1790	1700	1770	121339	DUR	Darlington
SMERDON						
....	....	ALL	ALL	164836	ALL	Name Study
1550	1880	1300	1880	105333	DEV	Buckland In The Moor
1550	1880	1300	1880	105333	DEV	Holne
1550	1880	1300	1880	105333	DEV	Ilsington
1550	1880	1300	1880	105333	DEV	Lydford
1550	1880	1300	1880	105333	DEV	Widecombe In The Moor
1869	1927	1800	1870	164828	WOR	Worcester
SMETHAM						
1815	....	1815	....	139149	SOM	Taunton
SMETHILLS						
1829	1992	1700	1829	106089	LAN	Barton
SMETHURST						
?	?	....	....	132500	LAN	Oldham
1851	1868	1851	1871	159492	LAN	Oldham
1803	1992	....	....	132500	LAN	Shaw
SMIDDITT						
1737	?	?	?	166642	KEN	???
SMILES						
1805	1992	1700	1805	129992	NBL	Northumberland
?	?	?	?	130354	NBL	Throckley
SMILEY						
1800	1992	1700	1900	143030	DOW	North
1807	....	....	1807	117234	IRL	???
SMILIE						
1888	1992	ALL	1888	105465	IRL	???
SMIRK						
1592	....	....	....	153397	HAM	Milford
SMITH						
1796	....	1700	1796	101443	ALL	Egton
1940	1971	1900	1992	100226	ABD	Aberdeen
....	....	....	....	144029	ABD	Aberdeen
1856	1864	1850	1864	163317	ABD	Aberdeen
1800	1856	1700	1800	100226	ABD	Braemar
1830	1857	1700	1830	106887	ABD	Fraserburgh
1856	1900	1856	1992	100226	ABD	Newhills
1890	1900	1750	1890	144150	ANS	Dundee
....	....	1800	ALL	149187	ANS	Dundee
1835	1907	1700	1835	178896	ANS	Dundee
1787	1813	1700	1787	127590	ANS	Fowlis Easter
1813	1854	1750	1813	127590	ANS	Glamis
1835	1907	1700	1835	178896	ANS	Monifieth
1826	....	....	....	127140	ARL	Knapdale
1803	1858	ALL	ALL	117366	AVN	Bristol
1860	1944	1860	1944	149284	AVN	Bristol
1800	1870	1700	1900	179574	AYR	Ayr
1840	1992	1750	1850	100501	AYR	Beith
1798	1816	ALL	1798	146757	AYR	Mauchline
1869	1910	1800	1869	179116	AYR	Old Cummock
1720	1860	1700	1860	126500	BAN	Cainsbay
1856	1941	....	....	116165	BAN	Findochty
1856	1864	1850	1864	163317	BAN	Marnoch
1800	1840	1750	1840	124605	BDF	Carlton
1810	1860	1750	1810	133671	BDF	Henlow
1800	1940	....	1992	129739	BEW	ALL
1740	1900	1650	1740	158402	BKM	Chilton
1741	1792	1600	1800	143693	BKM	Hughenden
1804	1884	1800	1890	126667	BKM	Saunderton
1880	1950	1800	1992	177180	BKM	Steeple Claydon
1768	1810	1730	1770	102024	BKM	Upton Cum Chalvey
1750	1900	1600	1950	166804	BRK	North West
1804	1898	1750	1911	172162	BRK	Beedon
1835	1840	1750	1835	132640	BRK	Datchet
1838	....	....	1860	171441	BRK	Kingston Lisle
....	....	ALL	ALL	117390	BRK	Reading
1805	1815	1790	1815	125032	BRK	Reading

Known From	To	Researching From	To	Ref	Cty	Place
SMITH contd.						
....	....	1819	1851	131768	BRK	Reading
1846	1887	1887	1920	172073	BRK	Reading
....	....	1790	1819	131768	BRK	Thatcham
1770	1800	1750	1800	167088	BRK	Warfield
1820	....	....	1840	171441	BRK	Westcote
1850	1992	1700	1850	157872	BRK	Wickham Heath
1810	1992	1750	1810	165336	BRK	Winterbourne
1700	1850	....	....	126497	CAI	Canisbay
1712	1811	....	1830	137405	CAM	South
....	....	1860	1900	103713	CAM	Soham
1781	1829	1750	1851	149047	CAM	Swavesey
1654	1940	....	....	128996	CAM	Thorney
1890	1920	1890	1920	139270	CAM	Whittlesea
1890	1923	1800	1890	144150	CAM	Wicken
1845	1910	1750	1950	112089	CAM	???
1650	1900	1500	1650	113204	CAR	Ballykelly
1806	1852	1559	1850	147265	CHS	East
1884	1884	1700	1884	153605	CHS	Birkenhead
1858	1865	1800	1992	103942	CHS	Chester
1881	1992	....	....	153796	CHS	Godley Hyde
1850	....	1820	1850	154946	CHS	Macclesfield
1828	....	....	1828	163228	CHS	Preston
1766	1850	....	....	153796	CHS	Romiley
1915	1952	1900	1952	118524	CHS	Wallasey
1859	1945	....	1859	163228	CMA	Barrow In Furness
1790	1910	ALL	1900	131334	CMA	Whitehaven
1845	....	ALL	1810	168696	CON	East
....	....	1500	1800	136972	CON	Camborne
1890	1992	....	....	145858	CON	Charlestown
1864	1939	1800	1870	170976	CON	Helston
1790	1847	1790	....	115576	CON	Launceston
1816	1833	1750	1820	169234	CON	Tintagel
....	....	1700	1750	116173	CUL	Fordhouse
1850	1883	ALL	1850	176400	DBY	Ashover
1814	....	....	....	109347	DBY	Bakewell
1850	1881	1827	1890	176400	DBY	Brampton
1885	1905	1800	1880	131075	DBY	Chesterfield
1830	1886	1700	1830	146722	DBY	Chesterfield
1845	1985	1800	1845	155691	DBY	Chesterfield
1917	1927	1700	1917	163902	DBY	Chesterfield
1819	....	ALL	ALL	138533	DBY	Colne
1812	1835	1800	1835	178004	DBY	Darley Abbey
1827	1992	?	1827	153613	DBY	Darley
1828	....	1828	1841	176400	DBY	Dronfield
1688	1688	1550	1687	102830	DBY	Edlaston
1768	1768	1700	1768	102830	DBY	Quarndon
1855	1855	1855	1855	145580	DBY	Tissington
1892	1949	1850	1992	117609	DEV	Tamerton Fliot
1845	....	1800	1875	102016	DFS	Dumfries
1800	1900	1700	1900	169978	DFS	Kirkmahoe
1855	1880	....	....	127140	DNB	Row
1800	1870	1870	1900	117714	DOR	Bettiscombe
1780	1841	?	1853	103934	DOR	Fontmell
1780	1841	....	1853	103934	DOR	Pentridge
1856	1900	1700	1850	145882	DOR	Swanage
1806	1830	1800	....	135895	DOR	Weymouth
....	1920	....	1920	173533	DOR	Wimborne
1803	1803	1538	1992	118893	DUR	Cox Green
1800	1992	ALL	1800	165301	DUR	Durham
1852	1856	1538	1992	118893	DUR	Escomb
1836	1845	1538	1992	118893	DUR	Evenwood
1870	1900	1820	1870	177555	DUR	Hartlepool
1835	1860	1780	1835	154873	DUR	Houghton
1845	1851	1538	1992	118893	DUR	Newfield
1881	1881	1800	1918	163244	DUR	Rushyford
1871	1890	1700	1870	132764	DUR	South Tyneside
1869	1900	1538	1992	118893	DUR	Spennymoor
1790	1850	1790	1930	165034	DUR	Stockton On Tees
1835	1860	1780	1835	154873	DUR	Sunderland
1830	1869	ALL	1830	157791	DUR	Sunderland
1820	1890	1750	1850	169315	DUR	Sunderland
1816	1824	ALL	1824	175773	ERY	Hull
1881	1915	ALL	ALL	143537	ESS	ALL
1804	1810	1750	1815	136042	ESS	Epping
1824	1992	1700	1824	164879	ESS	Gt Canfield
1834	1900	1700	1834	144754	ESS	Hatfield Peverill
1826	1992	1700	1826	133647	ESS	Navestock
1790	1819	1600	1790	108197	ESS	Purleigh
1825	1992	1700	1825	132268	ESS	Rickling
1820	1960	1700	1830	140260	ESS	Rochford
1814	1818	1780	1840	102717	ESS	Thurrock
1841	1871	1841	1871	138924	ESS	Wakes Green
1800	1880	1750	1950	111007	ESS	Waltham Abbey

Known From	To	Researching From	To	Ref	Cty	Place
SMITH contd.						
1796	1814	1750	1850	117781	EYK	Hull
1776	1839	1730	1850	148288	FIF	Kettle
1771	1900	1700	1800	144037	FIF	Kilrenny
1769	1930	....	1769	175552	FIF	Moonzie
1776	1839	1730	1850	148288	FIF	Strathmiglo
1860	1920	1860	1920	118540	GLA	Neath
1864	1898	....	....	150762	GLA	Swansea
1848	1988	....	....	165271	GLA	Tenby
1886	1940	ALL	1940	147087	GLS	ALL
1836	1836	....	....	135437	GLS	Bristol
1670	1670	1550	1670	102830	GLS	Broadwell
1900	1915	1750	1900	147761	GLS	Cheltanham
1880	1992	1800	1880	164917	GLS	Cheltenham
1766	....	1770	1850	178845	GLS	Cheltenham
1788	1804	1750	1810	126667	GLS	Cirencester
1787	1838	....	....	135437	GLS	Coleford
1737	1761	1700	1737	102830	GLS	Coln St Denis
....	....	1788	1822	138339	GLS	Dymock
1813	1862	....	1862	155055	GLS	Gloucester
1755	1860	1680	1900	157171	GLS	Hazelton
1750	1820	1600	1750	108413	GLS	Hinton
1764	1859	1600	1764	149888	GLS	Horfield
1830	1900	1830	1900	132217	GLS	Kings Stanley
1800	1850	1750	1800	174513	GLS	Lechlade
1748	1837	....	....	135437	GLS	Newland
1841	1841	....	....	135437	GLS	St Briavels
1803	1822	1700	1850	110051	GLS	Stapleton
1700	1848	ALL	1848	132217	GLS	Stroud
1859	1926	1750	1859	177040	GLS	Tetbury
....	....	1700	1900	150762	GLS	Thornbury
1750	1800	1750	1850	106631	GLS	Uley
1788	1819	ALL	1850	132217	GLS	Uley
1800	1840	1790	1850	157171	GLS	Uley
1730	....	1600	1799	123013	GLS	Upper Swell
1851	1851	....	....	135437	GLS	West Dean
....	....	....	....	165433	GLS	???
....	....	1850	1870	114782	GNT	Pontypool
....	....	....	....	165433	GNT	???
1700	1900	....	....	111333	HAM	North West
1794	1832	1750	1850	136719	HAM	Amport
1795	1950	1790	1900	109827	HAM	Andover
1740	1750	1700	1750	136840	HAM	Andover
1746	1800	1600	1800	130125	HAM	Barton Sty
1878	....	ALL	ALL	114618	HAM	Basingstoke
1792	1851	1750	1790	133221	HAM	Boldre
1817	1992	1817	1900	109827	HAM	Brown Candover
1794	1832	1750	1850	136719	HAM	E Cholderton
1850	1900	ALL	1850	135607	HAM	East Meon
1780	1780	1700	1800	136840	HAM	East Meon
1855	1886	1855	1886	173762	HAM	East Wooday
1840	1988	1700	1840	103640	HAM	Fareham
1700	1750	1700	1750	144657	HAM	Farley
1779	1859	1600	1779	139084	HAM	Farnborough
1851	1861	....	....	133221	HAM	Lymington
1750	ALL	....	....	153397	HAM	New Forest
1600	1600	1560	1600	125032	HAM	Oakley
1780	1900	....	....	104132	HAM	Overton
1766	1800	ALL	ALL	122866	HAM	Overton
1850	1992	1700	1850	157872	HAM	Overton
1800	1850	1700	1800	172898	HAM	Overton
1858	1900	1800	1900	145882	HAM	Portsea
1836	1876	1836	1876	152943	HAM	Portsea
1808	1846	1750	1900	174521	HAM	Portsea
1847	....	1800	1992	103942	HAM	Soberton
1840	1988	1700	1840	103640	HAM	Southampton
1800	1850	1600	1900	120677	HAM	Sparsholt
1747	1859	1747	1861	170143	HAM	Steep
1650	1778	ALL	ALL	102202	HAM	Tedworth
....	....	ALL	....	172219	HAM	Titchfield
1815	1850	1700	1815	169730	HAM	Weston Patrick
1793	....	1793	....	161861	HAM	Wherwell
1706	....	....	....	131229	HEF	Bromyard
1840	1992	1700	1840	164879	HRT	East
1600	1700	1600	1700	167924	HRT	Ardeley
1860	....	....	1860	164011	HRT	Hatfield
1821	1980	1700	1821	169889	HRT	Hitchin
1750	ALL	1800	1870	107379	HRT	St Albans
1700	1750	1700	1750	167924	HRT	Stevenage
....	....	ALL	1900	146315	HUN	Farcet
1762	....	....	1762	108839	HUN	Needingworth
1849	1849	1800	1850	146315	HUN	Stanground
....	1800	ALL	1800	152889	HUN	Tilbrook
1670	1744	1700	1800	176621	IOW	Godshill

Known From	To	Researching From	To	Ref	Cty	Place
SMITH	contd.					
1760	1850	1500	1850	132993	IOW	Ryde
1760	1850	1500	1850	132993	IOW	St Helens
1866	....	....	....	145742	IRL	Dublin
....	....	1800	1899	104884	IRL	Londonderry
1863	1992	1816	1992	138312	KEN	Central
1807	1851	ALL	1807	164623	KEN	Bexley
?	?	?	?	108502	KEN	Brenzett
1720	1795	1795	1992	165255	KEN	Chiddingstone
1770	1794	1700	1794	148288	KEN	Dover
1790	1992	1700	1790	151327	KEN	Gravesend
1770	1820	1750	1850	126144	KEN	Halling
1807	1851	ALL	1807	164623	KEN	Hurst
1784	1784	....	....	139971	KEN	Luddenham
....	....	....	1712	130060	KEN	Lydd
1848	1988	1750	1850	165271	KEN	Margate
1774	....	....	1774	177504	KEN	Meopham
1678	....	....	1700	171441	KEN	Pluckley
1770	1794	1700	1794	148288	KEN	River
1750	1992	1650	1750	102873	KEN	Romney Marsh
1863	1893	1816	1992	138312	KEN	Staplehurst
1715	1715	....	....	127426	KEN	Stockbury
1858	1946	1800	1920	153990	KEN	Upper Higham
1800	1800	....	....	159883	KEN	Wingham
1848	1988	1750	1850	165271	KEN	Woolwich
....	1832	....	....	154024	LAN	Ashton In Makerfield
1790	1910	ALL	1900	131334	LAN	Bacup
1810	1926	1700	1810	160474	LAN	Blakcburn
1709	1771	1709	1771	143286	LAN	Bolton
1799	1844	1700	1800	107654	LAN	Burnley
1830	1860	1750	1830	160458	LAN	Burnley
1810	1872	1700	1900	157147	LAN	Burtonwood
1750	1850	1650	....	165530	LAN	Bury
1871	1992	1841	1871	165026	LAN	Earby
1810	1926	1700	1810	160474	LAN	Flixton
1850	....	1820	1850	154946	LAN	Gorton
1833	1940	....	1835	169412	LAN	Halliwell
1790	1840	1700	1790	155500	LAN	Leigh
1870	1992	1800	1900	102164	LAN	Liverpool
1870	1900	1850	1910	111325	LAN	Liverpool
1860	1890	1830	1860	118435	LAN	Liverpool
1880	1950	1880	1950	143286	LAN	Liverpool
1835	1960	1835	1900	165093	LAN	Liverpool
1800	1822	1700	1800	113425	LAN	Longridge
1798	1897	ALL	1897	165654	LAN	Manchester
1799	....	....	1799	101761	LAN	Middleton
1830	1992	....	....	135348	LAN	Oldham
1804	1890	ALL	ALL	141615	LAN	Over Kellet
1841	1857	1840	....	162809	LAN	Preston
1748	1748	1705	1748	174211	LAN	Prestwich
1760	....	....	1992	165050	LAN	Shaw
1800	1834	....	....	171824	LAN	St Helens
1800	1901	1750	1799	172006	LAN	St Helens
....	1863	....	....	163686	LAN	Todmorden
1870	1900	1850	1910	111325	LAN	West Derby
....	....	1800	1992	147613	LAN	Wray
1783	1802	ALL	....	115355	LEI	ALL
1790	1817	1750	1817	123404	LEI	Buckminster
1817	1934	1700	1815	118710	LEI	Castle Donnington
1870	1992	1500	1870	169986	LEI	Dishley
1725	1728	1650	1724	131245	LEI	Frisby On The Wreak
1794	1846	1770	1820	137413	LEI	Hinckley
1808	1966	ALL	1808	174076	LEI	Kibworth
1790	1870	1700	1790	164844	LEI	Loughborough
....	....	ALL	1800	142298	LEI	Ratby
1770	1822	ALL	1822	168718	LEI	Rothley
1835	1852	1700	1850	122114	LEI	Rutland
1870	1992	1500	1870	169986	LEI	Thorpe Acre
1780	1920	1780	1920	164895	LEI	Thurmaston
1700	1765	1600	1700	174130	LEI	Tugby
1738	1783	ALL	ALL	141615	LEI	Wycomb
1780	1810	....	....	145688	LIN	Appleby
1770	1800	ALL	1770	152021	LIN	Ashby Puerorum
1803	1809	1796	1850	123404	LIN	Bardney
1792	1823	1800	1835	159042	LIN	Carlby
1887	1984	ALL	ALL	135224	LIN	Cleethorpes
1843	1843	1840	1870	102962	LIN	Deeping St James
1750	1780	1700	1750	151769	LIN	Denton
1814	1861	1800	1814	128368	LIN	Gainsborough
1800	1900	1700	1800	162396	LIN	Great Carleton
1779	....	ALL	....	104515	LIN	Great Ponton
1887	1984	ALL	ALL	135224	LIN	Grimsby
1844	1900	1844	1921	101923	LIN	Gt Carlton

Known From	To	Researching From	To	Ref	Cty	Place
SMITH	contd.					
1844	1900	1844	1921	101923	LIN	Legbourne
1720	....	....	1720	101761	LIN	Lincoln
1778	1827	1650	1778	139769	LIN	Long Sutton
1814	1861	1800	1814	128368	LIN	Owston
1732	....	....	1732	101761	LIN	Stenigot
1800	1900	....	....	177687	LIN	Theddlethorpe
1790	1820	....	....	103721	LIN	Ulceby By Barton
1800	1848	ALL	1848	152048	LKS	Glasgow
1750	ALL	1800	1870	107379	LND	ALL
1800	....	ALL	ALL	172812	LND	ALL
1837	1992	1700	1860	165476	LND	Bethnal Green
1800	1881	1700	1992	112402	LND	Clerkenwell
1849	1851	1700	1880	172316	LND	Enfield
....	....	1800	1850	103713	LND	Finsbury
1850	1914	1850	1914	139904	LND	Hackney
1797	1842	1700	1850	143693	LND	Hammersmith
1853	1960	1800	1970	136719	LND	Kensington
1825	1890	1825	1890	101877	LND	Kentish Town
1905	1960	....	1905	136212	LND	Kilburn
1866	1902	1800	1902	128694	LND	Marylebone
....	....	....	1900	110817	LND	Notting Hill
....	....	1815	1830	161357	LND	Paddington
1930	1960	....	....	135925	LND	Palmers Green
....	....	1800	1900	165476	LND	Sommertown
1850	1992	1700	1992	122742	LND	Southwark
1851	1851	....	....	167517	LND	St Georges
1825	1890	1825	1890	101877	LND	St Pancras
1859	....	1851	1891	115886	LND	St Pancras
1850	1860	ALL	ALL	130508	LND	St Pancras
1834	1875	1800	1880	144797	LND	Stepney
1837	1837	1700	1837	165476	LND	Stepney
1914	1935	1914	1935	139904	LND	Stoke Newington
1845	1992	1750	1845	126535	LND	Strand
1845	1992	1750	1845	126535	LND	Wandsworth
....	....	1871	1918	167029	LND	Westminster
....	....	....	1930	147818	LND	Woodford
1900	1992	ALL	1900	100803	LND	???
1820	1865	1700	1820	139106	LND	???
1806	1846	1780	1846	124028	MDX	Bloomsbury
....	1888	1700	1888	106836	MDX	Brentford
1820	1870	1700	1820	158526	MDX	Hackney
1857	1992	1800	1860	166316	MDX	Hackney
1745	1960	1745	1960	166189	MDX	Harefield
1850	1914	1850	1914	139904	MDX	Islington
....	1834	1750	1880	124907	MDX	Lambeth
1818	1846	1846	1846	137898	MDX	London Wall
1840	1880	1840	1880	124605	MDX	Paddington
1795	1835	1750	1800	177024	MDX	St Marylebone
1866	1866	1860	1880	102962	MDX	Stepney
1914	1935	1914	1935	139904	MDX	Stoke Newington
1900	1900	1900	1992	168149	MDX	Uxbridge
1861	1930	....	....	110132	MDX	???
1795	1814	....	....	144568	MLN	Edinburgh
1860	1880	1850	1900	163791	MLN	Edinburgh
1796	1984	....	....	174319	MLN	Edinburgh
....	....	ALL	1772	119326	MLN	Newbattle
1803	1835	1538	1992	118893	MON	Cwmyoy
1904	1911	....	....	150762	MON	Ebbw Vale
1803	1835	1538	1992	118893	MON	Panteg
1803	1835	1538	1992	118893	MON	Pont Newydd
1827	1835	1538	1992	118893	MON	Pontypool
1804	1838	1804	1900	118893	MON	???
....	....	1770	....	149187	MOR	Drainie
....	....	1770	....	149187	MOR	Duffies
1800	1820	1750	1850	123536	NBL	Berwick
1880	1992	ALL	1880	136875	NBL	Newcastle On Tyne
1860	1860	1850	1870	151599	NFK	Banham
1700	1810	....	....	114871	NFK	Beighton
1760	1819	....	....	135437	NFK	Billingford
1800	1950	1700	1800	171921	NFK	Brancaster
1764	1764	....	....	135437	NFK	Fakenham
1727	1845	....	....	135437	NFK	Gt Ryburgh
....	....	1840	1900	137685	NFK	Gt Yarmouth
1827	....	....	....	106836	NFK	Hammerfield
1788	1875	1750	1900	136719	NFK	Hedenham
1770	1850	1700	1750	141402	NFK	Hedenham
1830	1992	1580	1830	175870	NFK	Kings Lynn
1810	1840	....	....	114871	NFK	Moulton
1733	1817	1600	1756	131245	NFK	Norwich
1834	....	1800	1900	115207	NFK	Swaffham
....	....	1700	1800	140627	NFK	Thurton
1844	1899	1800	1880	101923	NFK	Titchwell
1825	1992	ALL	1825	146226	NFK	Wymondham

Known From	To	Researching From	To	Ref	Cty	Place
SMITH	contd.					
1770	1780	....	....	103721	NRY	Topcliffe By Thirsk
1730	1760	....	....	110159	NRY	Yarm
1700	1790	1730	1790	173533	NTH	South
1829	1840	1829	1840	107360	NTH	Chapel Brampton
1823	1823	ALL	ALL	171816	NTH	Flore
1750	1897	1750	1900	171654	NTH	Grafton Regis
1781	1781	ALL	ALL	171816	NTH	Grafton Regis
1826	1879	1826	1889	107360	NTH	Harlestone
....	1600	....	1600	177695	NTH	Irthlingborough
1740	1900	1700	1750	166375	NTH	Kettering
1792	1811	1786	1811	107360	NTH	Kislingbury
....	....	1739	1871	114308	NTH	Kislingbury
....	1600	....	1600	177695	NTH	Long Buckby
1800	1899	1800	1899	169781	NTH	New Castle
1885	1992	....	1885	151270	NTH	Newcastle On Tyne
1700	1800	1700	1800	169781	NTH	Rochester
1739	....	....	1739	142166	NTH	Rothwell
1824	1824	ALL	1824	159077	NTH	Stoke Doyle
....	....	1750	1850	146374	NTH	Thorpe Mandeville
1805	1891	1805	1891	170143	NTH	Thrapston
1766	1781	1594	1812	107360	NTH	Upton
1805	1891	1805	1891	170143	NTH	Walgrave
1824	1824	ALL	1824	159077	NTH	Wigsthorpe
1700	1940	1600	1700	120758	NTT	Barnby In The Willows
1771	1800	....	....	128910	NTT	Beeston
1811	1830	1780	1811	177393	NTT	Bingham
1787	1804	1740	1787	116173	NTT	Coddington
1753	1795	....	1753	101761	NTT	Epperstone
1853	1992	?	1900	164976	NTT	Nottingham
1832	....	ALL	1832	171573	NYK	Hambleton High House
1820	1885	1700	1820	102393	NYK	Lastingham
1820	1885	1700	1820	102393	NYK	Pickering
1840	1950	1700	1840	165182	NYK	Wrelton
1736	1780	....	1820	171441	OXF	Bampton
1700	1750	1600	1700	174513	OXF	Broadwell
1890	1972	1819	1855	147176	OXF	Deddington
1746	....	....	1746	103489	OXF	Gt Milton
1842	1867	1700	1842	111953	OXF	Headington
1798	1798	....	....	139971	OXF	Oxford
1900	1937	1850	1900	179116	RFW	Clarkston
1891	1906	1881	1950	144037	RFW	Johnstone
1790	1960	1790	1960	120235	RFW	Paisley
1770	1785	1538	1992	118893	ROX	Oxnam
1800	1910	1800	1910	148210	RUT	Langham
1770	1992	ALL	ALL	106097	RUT	Oakham
1770	1992	ALL	ALL	106097	RUT	Whitwell
....	....	1700	1800	179612	SAL	Wentnor
....	....	1750	1900	129275	SCT	Peterhead
1750	1830	1750	1830	115614	SFK	Buneay
1816	1852	....	....	166189	SFK	Bury St Edmunds
1800	1880	ALL	1880	123048	SFK	Butley
1590	1921	1590	1992	165360	SFK	Coastal
1762	1777	1600	1672	125784	SFK	Frostendon
1750	1770	ALL	1850	119105	SFK	Groton
1700	1800	....	....	157724	SFK	Groton
1800	1900	1800	1870	140236	SFK	Kersey
1855	1940	1750	1855	164860	SFK	Letheringham
1820	1841	1770	1820	162396	SFK	Little Thurlow
1800	1900	1800	1850	111422	SFK	Melton
1756	1788	1600	1756	125784	SFK	Metfield
1821	1848	1770	1821	172871	SFK	Nowton
1826	1829	....	....	106836	SFK	Rumborough
1800	1900	....	....	125784	SFK	Rumburgh
1823	1875	1700	1890	112216	SFK	Southwold
1720	1720	1660	1720	155276	SFK	Trimley
1726	1824	1650	1726	155276	SFK	Walton
1700	1899	1740	1860	135941	SFK	Wickhambrook
1881	1900	1725	1881	129895	SFK	Winston
1790	1811	....	....	125784	SFK	Wrentham
1750	1965	....	....	137820	SHI	Fetlar
1720	1965	....	....	137820	SHI	Mid Yell
1760	1965	....	....	137820	SHI	North Yell
1758	1965	....	....	137820	SHI	Northmavine
1720	1965	....	....	137820	SHI	South Yell
1700	1820	1700	1820	142018	SOM	Bath
1856	1882	....	....	131024	SOM	Brent
1830	1900	1830	1900	142077	SOM	Chilton Polden
1801	1803	....	....	135437	SOM	Ilton
1891	1891	....	1891	121169	SOM	Midsomer Norton
1745	1830	1700	1750	144606	SOM	Montacute
1813	1877	....	....	135437	SOM	Taunton
1700	1799	1700	1799	169781	SOM	West Cocker
1871	1992	....	....	165352	SRY	Ashstead
1880	1880	1500	1900	137472	SRY	Brockham
1799	1860	....	....	131229	SRY	Camberwell
1871	1992	....	....	165352	SRY	Chertsey
1811	....	1700	1811	174130	SRY	Cuddington
1880	1880	1500	1900	137472	SRY	Dorking
1880	1880	1500	1900	137472	SRY	Holmwood
1858	1858	1830	1992	165603	SRY	Horne
1826	....	....	1826	133566	SRY	Horseleydown
?	?	1800	ALL	117919	SRY	Leatherhead
....	....	....	....	164968	SRY	Puttenham
1787	1806	....	1820	171441	SRY	Puttenham
1742	....	....	1760	171441	SRY	Thursley
1809	1964	1700	1809	169730	SRY	Wandsworth
1800	1880	1860	1880	111422	SRY	Weybridge
1840	1860	1600	1992	112828	SRY	Worplesdon
1855	....	1800	1855	110132	SRY	???
1830	1851	1700	1900	141151	SSX	ALL
....	....	1700	1770	129356	SSX	Battle
....	....	1700	1851	135844	SSX	Bexhill
1776	1814	1700	1776	174807	SSX	Cuckfield
1830	1846	....	1830	117234	SSX	Frant
1808	....	1700	1808	165263	SSX	Hailsham
1800	1870	1750	1900	135925	SSX	Hastings
1848	1992	1800	1848	177601	SSX	Hastings
1777	1834	1770	1840	129356	SSX	Heathfield
1787	1825	1750	1825	138487	SSX	Horsham
1816	1839	1816	1992	138312	SSX	Iden
1850	1925	1750	1874	165220	SSX	Lewes
1875	1992	1850	1992	133450	SSX	Lindfield
1805	1920	1840	1920	100668	SSX	Mayfield
1831	1871	1831	?	165263	SSX	Ticehurst
1861	1881	....	1992	165263	SSX	Tidebrook
1831	1871	1831	?	165263	SSX	Wadhurst
1777	1834	1770	1840	129356	SSX	Warbleton
1808	....	1700	1808	165263	SSX	Wartling
1760	1770	1700	1800	103764	STS	Alstonfield
1890	1970	1700	1890	109223	STS	Biddulph
1768	1992	1700	1768	126454	STS	Coseley
1863	ALL	ALL	1865	116734	STS	Dudley
....	1800	....	1800	177695	STS	Fenton
1863	ALL	ALL	1865	116734	STS	Gomal Wood
....	1800	....	1800	177695	STS	Gt Wyrley
1790	1992	1700	1992	165441	STS	Hanley
....	....	1829	1848	114308	STS	Kingston
1796	1909	1700	1800	165441	STS	Leek
1800	1850	1750	1860	109010	STS	Lichfield
1863	ALL	ALL	1865	116734	STS	Lipton
1813	1837	1780	1813	165093	STS	Longton
1761	1992	1790	1960	165441	STS	Penkhull
1661	1661	1550	1661	102830	STS	Rowley Regis
1863	ALL	ALL	1865	116734	STS	Sedgley
1768	1992	1700	1768	126454	STS	Sedgley
1691	1720	1650	1750	160873	STS	Sedgley
1736	1803	....	....	155055	STS	Shenstone
1830	1930	1800	1850	155047	STS	Stafford
1832	....	ALL	ALL	159026	STS	Stafford
1871	....	1851	1923	159468	STS	Tipton
....	....	1800	1850	165093	STS	Uttoxeter
1650	1860	1600	1900	100420	STS	Walsall
1840	1930	1830	1880	123595	STS	Walsall
?	1951	....	....	161284	STS	Walsall
1850	1992	1500	1850	148598	STS	West Bromwich
?	?	....	....	161284	STS	West Bromwich
1853	1890	1890	1992	174262	STS	West Bromwich
....	....	1800	1881	110132	STS	Wolverhampton
....	....	1700	1800	147613	STS	Wolverhampton
1777	1798	ALL	....	132349	SXE	Laughton
1775	1860	....	....	117560	WAR	Astley
1850	1940	1750	1940	107611	WAR	Aston
1748	1748	1700	1750	128449	WAR	Aston
1840	1936	1700	1890	161411	WAR	Aston
1800	1992	1700	1992	165344	WAR	Aston
1841	1851	1700	1851	151513	WAR	Baddesley Ensor
1760	1950	1750	1992	100420	WAR	Birmingham
1806	1806	....	....	127426	WAR	Birmingham
1748	1748	1700	1750	128449	WAR	Birmingham
1847	....	....	....	163686	WAR	Birmingham
....	1827	1700	1880	124907	WAR	Brimingham
1697	1701	1550	1696	131245	WAR	Hampton In Arden
....	....	1675	1900	115142	WAR	Mancetter
1500	1800	....	....	100420	WAR	Meriden

Known From	To	Researching From	To	Ref	Cty	Place
SMITH contd.						
....	1779	1675	1800	132586	WAR	Nuneaton
1844	....	1800	1900	143758	WAR	Tysoe
1848	....	ALL	ALL	119504	WES	Appleby
1774	1808	1754	....	138401	WES	Selside
....	....	1600	1800	106461	WIL	ALL
1640	1750	1640	1750	142018	WIL	ALL
....	....	1700	1899	115975	WIL	East
1840	ALL	....	....	142158	WIL	Aldbourne
1616	1700	ALL	1616	167878	WIL	Bishops Cannings
1840	1900	1700	1840	148059	WIL	Bradford
1816	1891	1780	1900	120146	WIL	Bratton
1841	1880	1700	1845	112216	WIL	Calne
1789	1856	1750	1800	170348	WIL	Cliffe Pypard
1800	1900	1750	1850	106186	WIL	Manton
1730	1880	1600	1930	118281	WIL	Market Lavington
1800	1830	1750	1830	144657	WIL	Marlborough
1732	1732	....	....	115606	WIL	Ogbourne St Andrew
1800	1850	1750	1850	145661	WIL	Salisbury
1746	1746	1720	1800	136964	WIL	Semley
1880	1920	1780	1880	164852	WIL	Swindon
1783	1801	....	1783	161691	WIL	Tidcombe
1920	1940	1940	1950	164852	WIL	Warminster
....	....	ALL	1740	151602	WIL	Woodborough
1804	1858	1700	1804	166782	WIL	Woodborough
....	....	....	....	165433	WIL	???
....	....	1855	1992	141399	WLS	Monmouth
....	....	....	....	146595	WLS	???
1937	1939	1900	1992	116009	WMD	Birmingham
....	....	1600	1760	111538	WOR	Claines
1782	1922	ALL	1782	115126	WOR	Little Comberton
1820	1918	....	....	138339	WOR	Pershore
1820	1900	1820	1900	111538	WOR	Tibberton
1760	1820	1760	1820	111538	WOR	Warndon
1826	1876	....	1900	171441	WOR	Worcester
1718	1818	....	1718	101761	WRY	Bingley
1660	1843	1500	1875	102660	WRY	Keighley
ALL	1810	....	....	170798	WRY	Kirkburton
1590	1992	1590	1680	164941	WRY	Leeds
1660	1843	1500	1875	102660	WRY	Thackley
1743	1834	1700	1743	125342	WYK	Bingley
1777	1848	1700	1850	176621	WYK	Rastrick
1757	1920	....	....	141593	WYK	Rotherham
1668	1760	....	....	141593	WYK	Saxton
1871	1992	....	1873	165212	WYK	Sheffield
....	....	....	....	150924	YKS	North
1785	1830	1700	1785	177393	YKS	Barlby
1809	1864	ALL	1864	104299	YKS	Barnsley
1712	1792	1650	1800	141097	YKS	Bradfield
1793	1800	1500	1992	102520	YKS	Bradford
1822	1992	....	1830	169412	YKS	Bradford
1593	1674	....	....	167533	YKS	Bramham
1782	1782	....	....	141097	YKS	Briathwell
....	1824	1700	1824	168424	YKS	Brotherton
1888	....	1850	1888	176885	YKS	Castleford
1800	1815	1750	1850	144622	YKS	Darfield
1887	1984	ALL	ALL	135224	YKS	Darnall
1871	1992	1841	1871	165026	YKS	Earby
1803	1992	ALL	1803	165204	YKS	Elland
1765	1835	1750	1765	171565	YKS	Elloughton
1810	1860	....	....	136964	YKS	Halifax
1819	1940	1700	1900	178233	YKS	Halifax
1701	1854	ALL	1701	147877	YKS	Hawnby
1703	1727	1600	1705	174858	YKS	Helmsley
1800	1992	1650	1800	168513	YKS	Huddersfield
1900	1940	....	....	131075	YKS	Hunslet
1857	....	ALL	1857	151424	YKS	Leeds
1850	1900	1800	1850	165468	YKS	Leeds
1855	....	....	....	151785	YKS	Masbrough
1841	1877	1830	1890	116386	YKS	Meanwood
1880	1895	....	1920	147818	YKS	Middlesborough
1756	1779	....	....	141097	YKS	North Newbald
1822	1830	1700	1825	135348	YKS	Ossett
1811	1850	1780	1811	177393	YKS	Paull
1851	1861	ALL	1881	154946	YKS	Richmond
1816	1861	1770	1881	160636	YKS	Saddleworth
1777	1806	1750	1810	116386	YKS	Scarborough
1870	1992	1700	1870	123005	YKS	Sheffield
1887	1984	ALL	ALL	135224	YKS	Sheffield
....	1850	....	....	106682	YKS	Sowerby Bridge
1803	1992	ALL	1803	165204	YKS	Stainland
....	....	1815	1906	116424	YKS	Stillington
1850	....	1750	....	134589	YKS	Stockton On Forest

Known From	To	Researching From	To	Ref	Cty	Place
SMITH contd.						
....	....	1700	1750	147613	YKS	Thornton In Lonsdale
1600	1700	1600	1700	167924	YKS	Thornton
1860	1919	1800	1860	141313	YKS	Thurlstone
....	1863	....	....	163686	YKS	Todmorden
1752	1810	1700	1810	141097	YKS	Wales
1729	....	....	....	151351	YKS	Well
1850	....	1750	....	134589	YKS	York
....	....	1873	....	174963	???	Birmingham
1838	1954	?	1838	136611	???	Bristol
....	....	1700	1800	115142	???	Rowley Regis
1820	1840	1820	1840	138444	???	Wednesbury
1826	1992	1700	1826	169226	???	Wolverhampton
....	....	1851	1992	106682	???	???
ALL	1805	....	....	132756	???	???
SMITH-BAILES						
....	....	1750	1914	102881	DUR	Sunderland
SMITH-BARRY						
....	....	ALL	ALL	167592	CHS	???
SMITHER						
1950	1992	1700	1841	133582	KEN	Maidstone
1912	1960	1700	1912	133582	LND	Lewisham
1841	1913	1700	1841	133582	SRY	Croydon
SMITHERAM						
1860	1950	1700	1860	165549	CON	Camborne
SMITHERS						
1759	1949	1700	1992	104574	HAM	Porstmouth
1850	1960	1750	1850	115649	SRY	Godalming
1850	1960	1750	1850	115649	SRY	Grayswood
1850	1960	1750	1850	115649	SRY	Haslemere
1850	1960	1700	1850	115649	SRY	Witley
1714	1714	1714	1714	170143	SRY	Worplesdon
SMITHFIELD						
1620	1740	1620	1740	142018	WIL	ALL
SMITHIES						
1886	1914	....	1886	149624	YKS	Bradford
SMITHSON						
....	....	1800	1992	149659	CAM	Hinxton
1900	1992	ALL	1900	156078	CLV	Skelton
1871	1881	1800	1992	149659	ESS	Safron Walden
1680	1790	....	....	170798	NRY	Cundall
1680	1790	....	....	170798	NRY	Norton Le Clay
1707	1827	1687	1827	147311	NYK	Scarborough
1650	1810	1650	1810	128708	WEX	ALL
1737	1793	....	1748	101761	WRY	Mirfield
1750	1830	....	....	170798	WRY	Mirfield
1750	1830	....	....	170798	WRY	Spen Valley
1830	1900	1700	1800	167843	YKS	Feetham
SMITHY						
1709	1773	....	1760	137405	CAM	Long Stanton
SMITHYMAN						
....	....	1855	1930	132381	LKS	Glasgow
1890	1950	1800	1890	128775	LND	Central
1890	1950	1800	1890	128775	MID	Stafford
SMITTEN						
1750	1992	ALL	ALL	140031	ALL	ALL
SMOKE						
1733	1792	ALL	ALL	178411	NTT	Nottingham
SMOKER						
1875	1916	ALL	1875	106151	KEN	Southborough
1860	1970	ALL	1860	106151	LND	Camberwell
SMOLLETT						
1750	1965	....	....	137820	SHI	Fetlar
1720	1965	....	....	137820	SHI	Mid Yell
1760	1965	....	....	137820	SHI	North Yell
1758	1965	....	....	137820	SHI	Northmavine
1720	1965	....	....	137820	SHI	South Yell
SMOOTHMAN						
1600	1700	....	....	167924	YKS	Crambe
1600	1700	....	....	167924	YKS	Foston
SMOOTHY						
1870	1900	1800	1870	157058	SFK	Wratting
SMORTHWAITE						
1755	1755	ALL	1755	154563	DUR	Auckland St Helen
SMOULT						
1500	1650	1500	1650	154881	DOR	Burford Castle
SMOWTON						
....	....	ALL	ALL	169080	NFK	Great Yarmouth
SMURFITT						
1780	1900	1700	1900	165557	YKS	Carlton In Cleveland
SMURFOOT						
1830	1992	ALL	....	125946	YKS	Hinderwell

Known From	To	Researching From	To	Ref	Cty	Place
SMURTHWAITE						
1850	1992	1750	1850	129666	SSX	Chichester
1780	1900	1700	1900	165557	YKS	Carlton In Cleveland
1825	1835	1750	1850	129666	YKS	Cleveland
1830	1992	ALL	....	125946	YKS	Hinderwell
SMY						
1873	1900	1700	1873	102288	SFK	Ipswich
SMYTH						
1700	1750	1500	1700	113204	ANT	Lisburn
1765	1843	....	....	176613	DFS	Dumfries
1800	1904	ALL	....	150835	LIM	???
1794	1857	....	1860	176613	LND	ALL
1859	1901	ALL	1901	116548	MEA	ALL
1590	1992	1590	1680	164941	WRY	Leeds
SMYTHER						
....	....	....	1796	130079	SOM	Crewkerne
SNADAN						
1820	1870	1700	1820	100846	CLK	Dover
SNAILHAM						
1750	1900	1750	1900	136786	LAN	Penwortham
SNAILUM						
1700	1760	1680	1760	142018	SOM	Bath
SNAITH						
1800	1950	1650	1800	128376	CUL	Farlam
1763	1763	1600	1992	144703	DUR	ALL
1770	1800	1700	1770	121339	DUR	Darlington
1821	1953	1750	1950	177970	DUR	Wickham
1808	1992	1808	1992	144703	LEI	ALL
1900	....	1880	1992	144703	NTT	Nottingham
1765	1835	1600	1992	144703	YKS	ALL
1781	1800	1550	1800	147265	YKS	North
SNAPE						
1812	1812	1750	1812	178004	DBY	Darley Abbey
1925	1992	....	....	165565	DBY	Stanley
1700	....	1700	....	109347	LAN	Chaigley
1750	1900	1750	1900	125237	LAN	Darwen
1790	1825	1790	1825	125237	LAN	Withnell
1790	1884	ALL	1790	116408	NTH	Northampton
1700	1900	1650	1992	118303	SFK	ALL
1800	1900	1700	1800	118303	SFK	Haverhill
1890	1992	....	....	165565	STS	Walsall
1788	1900	ALL	ALL	171379	YKS	Sheffield
SNAREY						
1826	1880	1846	1880	164704	BRK	Reading
1867	1939	1700	1867	174076	???	Birmingham
SNATCHFOLD						
1841	1848	1600	1841	132977	SSX	Shipley Parish
SNATT						
1780	1810	1600	1900	166804	KEN	Yalding
SNEAD						
1700	....	1700	....	100536	???	London
SNEAZWELL						
....	....	1700	1840	113697	LND	East
SNEDDON						
1803	1885	1803	1885	171654	LKS	Newmains
1828	1900	....	....	128988	MLN	Lasswade
SNEE						
1900	1992	1700	1900	165573	SCT	ALL
1880	1992	1700	1880	165573	SLI	Coolaney
SNEESBY						
1800	1992	?	1800	112356	ALL	???
SNEESTON						
1770	1950	1700	1900	150061	YKS	East
SNEEZUM						
1850	1992	1600	1850	141275	SFK	ALL
SNELGAR						
1800	1840	1800	1900	129607	SRY	Bermondsey
SNELGROVE						
....	....	ALL	ALL	117536	ALL	Name Study
ALL	ALL	ALL	ALL	117536	ALL	ALL
1963	1965	....	....	173932	DOR	Weymouth
1926	1931	....	....	173932	HAM	Amesbury
1965	....	....	....	173932	HAM	Basingstoke
1796	1902	1650	1796	100765	HAM	Bishopstoke
1775	1860	1700	1775	123978	HAM	Southampton
1920	1926	....	....	173932	HAM	Stockbridge
1786	1948	1600	1786	145459	HAM	Wellow
1944	....	....	....	173932	SOM	Bridgewater
1952	....	....	....	173932	SOM	Wincanton
1795	....	....	....	173932	WIL	Bradford On Avon
1851	1903	....	....	173932	WIL	Heytesbury
1799	....	....	....	173932	WIL	Norton Bavant
1899	....	....	....	173932	WIL	South Stoneham
SNELGROVE contd.						
1794	1887	....	....	173932	WIL	Sutton Veny
1922	....	....	....	173932	WIL	Swindon
1893	1895	....	....	173932	WIL	Tisbury
1860	1864	....	....	173932	WIL	Warminster
1888	1889	....	....	173932	WIL	Wilton
SNELHAM						
....	....	ALL	ALL	167142	ALL	Name Study
SNELL						
1763	1992	1600	1763	165581	ABD	Cruden
1700	1845	ALL	1992	168696	CON	East
1720	1886	ALL	1886	168718	CON	South East
1723	1723	1723	1723	141690	CON	Creed
....	....	ALL	ALL	147915	CON	Lansallos
1809	1900	1700	1809	133523	CON	St Dominick
1800	1850	1700	1800	165549	CON	St Stephens In Brannel
....	....	1800	1900	113174	DEV	Stamford Courtney
1800	1900	....	1800	123447	DEV	Tiverton
1842	1927	....	....	148016	DEV	???
1759	1850	1700	1759	111945	SFK	Brampton
1932	1945	1945	1992	164127	SSX	Worthing
1600	1700	....	....	100420	WAR	Meriden
SNELLER						
1850	1850	1800	1850	146803	SSX	Basham
SNELLGROVE						
1820	1899	1750	1820	124397	DEV	Exeter
SNELLING						
....	....	1800	1899	104884	ALL	ALL
....	....	1800	1900	101184	BRK	Windsor
1740	1800	1600	1800	130125	DOR	Winfrith N
1770	1780	1700	1800	136840	DOR	Wool
1796	1833	1750	1810	120146	ESS	Little Burstead
....	....	1700	1890	101184	KEN	East
1800	1840	1780	1992	165603	KEN	Brenchley
....	....	1730	1800	101184	KEN	Chartham
1794	1871	1780	1992	165603	KEN	Horsmonden
....	....	1760	1850	101184	KEN	Ospringe
1800	1900	1750	1992	165603	LND	Croydon
....	....	1800	....	101184	MDX	ALL
1890	1950	1910	1992	101184	NTT	Nottingham
1830	....	....	....	145068	SFK	Rattlesden
1692	1743	1650	1692	167533	SRY	Dorking
1760	....	....	....	167037	SRY	Haselmere
1826	1881	1750	1826	101427	SSX	North
1867	1872	....	....	101184	STS	Burton On Trent
....	....	1872	1890	101184	WAR	Birmingham
SNELSON						
....	....	ALL	ALL	165611	ALL	Name Study
1745	1811	....	....	124524	CHS	Byley
1629	1811	1600	1629	169935	OXF	Great Tew
SNODDEN						
1843	1970	ALL	ALL	119369	DOW	Killinchy
SNODE						
1755	....	....	1780	171441	KEN	Wichling
SNODGRASS						
1850	1992	1866	1992	113786	LND	Danmark Hill
SNOOK						
....	....	ALL	ALL	101389	DOR	???
....	....	....	?	132195	GLS	Bristol
1798	1830	1700	1798	164267	HAM	Portsmouth
1880	1940	1880	1900	126640	LND	Islington
1700	1802	1558	....	112968	SOM	East Pennard
1700	1802	1558	....	112968	SOM	Pylle
1790	1992	....	1790	178365	WIL	East Knoyle
1840	1880	1800	1840	143332	WIL	Hindon
1795	1992	1750	1921	107573	WIL	Maiden Bradley
1717	1815	1717	1815	137898	WIL	Sutton Mandeville
1650	1785	1590	1820	105333	WIL	Tisbury
SNOOKS						
1720	1882	1540	1903	149640	MDX	Hammersmith
SNOOR						
1895	....	1800	1920	153036	SSX	Battle
SNOSWELL						
1750	1900	1750	1900	163643	KEN	East
1780	1940	1775	1992	133450	KEN	Deal
SNOW						
....	....	ALL	ALL	165638	ALL	Name Study
1720	1835	1650	1720	103896	BRK	Newbury
....	....	1500	1700	165638	DEV	North
1694	1860	ALL	1860	165654	DEV	Morchard Bishop
1829	1900	1700	1850	107719	DEV	Sampford Peverell
1810	....	....	....	101028	ESS	Elsenham
1814	1875	....	1874	130524	ESS	Henham

Known From	To	Researching From	To	Ref	Cty	Place
SNOW contd.						
1780	1804	1600	1780	145289	HAM	Isle Of Wight
1732	1790	1500	1732	129577	IOW	???
1500	1900	1500	1900	135968	LEI	ALL
1620	1981	ALL	1620	165646	LEI	Kilby
?	?	1849	1926	127388	LIN	Althorpe
1800	1850	ALL	ALL	156922	LIN	Gainsborough
1840	1910	....	....	101028	MDX	London
1800	1890	....	....	132756	OXF	Headington
1700	1750	1600	1750	154342	SOM	Porlock
....	....	1500	1700	165638	SOM	???
....	....	1500	1700	165638	???	Bristol
SNOWBALL						
1819	1835	1835	1899	169374	DUR	Witton Gilbert
1700	1800	....	1700	176516	NBL	Allandale
1786	1984	1600	1786	158496	NBL	Ovingham
1700	1800	....	1700	176516	NBL	Wallsend
SNOWDEN						
1832	1992	....	....	178942	EYK	Huggate
....	....	ALL	1730	178942	YKS	Healaugh
1750	....	1650	....	134589	YKS	Hovingham
1730	1814	....	....	178942	YKS	Rufforth
1780	1992	1700	1992	165662	YKS	Sheffield
SNOWDON						
1600	1900	ALL	ALL	163252	YKS	North
SNOWLING						
1784	1861	1700	1992	175722	SFK	Toft Monks
SNOWSELL						
1890	1950	1750	1890	102903	GLS	???
SNUSHALL						
1655	1940	....	....	128996	CAM	Thorney
SOADY						
1729	1837	1600	1729	149888	DEV	Oakford
SOAFT						
....	....	1750	1900	129275	LND	Soho
....	....	1750	1900	129275	LND	Westminster
SOAMES						
1690	1800	1500	1800	175463	KEN	East
SOAN						
1820	....	....	....	133922	SSX	Crawley
SOANE						
1885	1950	1880	1992	158399	HAM	Cove
SOANS						
1800	1920	....	....	110124	KEN	Bromley
....	....	1690	1800	110124	KEN	Westerham
....	....	1530	1690	110124	SRY	Limpsfield
SOAR						
1787	1825	1700	1787	136581	DBY	Derby
1880	1890	....	....	130281	LND	Islington
1760	1880	1600	1800	113654	NTT	Greasley
SOBEY						
....	....	ALL	ALL	165689	ALL	Name Study
1800	1850	1700	1800	129445	CON	Menheniot
1880	1886	1750	1880	165689	DEV	Plymouth
1828	1950	1800	1910	165689	LND	East
SOBIE						
....	....	1883	1884	158763	CON	???
SOCKET						
1828	1992	1790	1828	153001	SAL	???
1790	1992	1500	1790	153001	STS	Madeley
SOCKETT						
1615	1771	1600	1615	115819	SAL	Wellington
SODEN						
1793	1861	1793	1861	118931	OXF	Hook Norton
SOFTLEY						
1852	1919	1852	1919	157023	CAM	St Ives
1916	1992	1903	1916	124346	LND	East Ham
1895	1903	1775	1895	124346	T&W	South Shields
SOILLEUX						
1870	1992	1870	1992	111112	LND	South East
1846	1870	1800	1870	111112	MDX	Hackney
1782	1850	1782	1850	111112	MDX	London Spitalfields
SOLE						
....	....	ALL	ALL	165697	ALL	Name Study
....	....	ALL	ALL	165697	ALL	ALL
ALL	ALL	ALL	ALL	166758	ALL	ALL
1600	1750	1600	1750	167924	BDF	Meppersall
1600	1700	1600	1700	167924	BDF	Shillington
1640	1640	1600	1660	105333	SSX	Singleton
SOLES						
1780	1780	ALL	1780	165700	BRK	Reading
....	....	1800	1900	165700	???	Birmingham
SOLICE						
1776	1798	1776	1798	178705	OXF	Westwell
SOLLAWAY						
1757	1794	....	....	171654	NTH	Grafton Regis
SOLLISS						
1857	1869	....	....	135380	SAL	Ludlow
SOLLOM						
1532	1900	....	....	155055	STS	ALL
SOLLY						
1630	1900	....	....	159883	KEN	Ash
1840	1992	1800	1839	103829	KEN	Canterbury
....	....	1770	1800	159840	KEN	Canterbury
1700	1850	....	....	159883	KEN	Sandwich
1500	1750	....	....	159883	KEN	Wingham
1788	....	....	....	133736	KEN	Woodnesborough
SOLOMAN						
1683	1753	1600	1683	102571	CON	Perranzabuloe
....	1858	....	1858	165840	SOM	Cannington
SOLOMON						
1816	1880	?	1890	159794	AGY	Bwlch Coch
ALL	....	ALL	....	168599	CON	South
1600	....	?	?	136999	CON	St Columb
1818	1992	1700	1818	161446	KEN	Sheerness
1770	1820	1700	1992	122149	LAN	Liverpool
1770	1820	1700	1992	122149	LAN	Manchester
....	....	....	1992	165727	LND	East
1878	....	....	....	171905	MDX	Westminster
SOLON						
1900	1910	1800	1992	167592	STS	Hanley
1870	1910	1800	1992	167592	STS	???
SOMERS						
1700	....	....	....	112348	GLS	Cam
1540	1600	ALL	ALL	106054	KEN	Tonbridge
1733	....	1930	1940	163775	WEX	Wexford
SOMERSCALES						
....	....	ALL	ALL	143227	ALL	Name Study
SOMERVILLE						
1820	1860	1820	1860	164704	DEV	Exeter
....	....	1700	1850	142670	FIF	Kirkcaldy
1848	1858	1700	1848	103950	KEN	Gravesend
....	....	1900	1950	101885	LND	???
1820	1940	1800	1940	110183	LND	???
SOMERWELL						
1700	1992	1600	1700	166316	DEV	Tawstock
SOMERWILL						
1555	1992	1550	1992	125520	DEV	Goodleigh
1555	1992	1550	1992	125520	DEV	Tawstock
1875	1955	....	....	120057	LND	???
SOMES						
1800	1992	1600	1800	149713	NTH	Harrowden
SOMIRELL						
1780	1880	1700	1780	143421	GLS	Siston
SOMMERAYNS						
....	1851	1300	1992	152501	ALL	ALL
SOMMERS						
1804	....	....	....	120804	LKS	Stonehouse
SOMMERVILLE						
1810	1852	1810	1852	114359	HAM	Portsmouth
1790	1890	1890	ALL	105813	RFW	Port Glasgow
1854	1854	....	....	139971	SCT	Irvine
1854	1854	....	....	139971	SCT	Port Glasgow
SOMNER						
1827	1845	1827	1845	149063	BEW	Legerwood
1730	1850	ALL	ALL	149063	ELN	ALL
1845	ALL	1845	ALL	149063	ROX	Kelso
SONE						
1850	1936	1850	1992	116955	LND	???
1850	....	1750	1850	165220	SSX	Cuckfield
1773	1835	1750	1773	165220	SSX	Shipley
?	1817	1750	1817	165220	SSX	West Grinstead
SONGHURST						
1886	1955	1800	1992	107891	LND	East
1799	1808	ALL	1799	169730	SRY	Kingston
SONLEY						
....	....	ALL	ALL	171565	ALL	Name Study
1739	1900	1700	1800	171565	YKS	ALL
SOONS						
1790	1793	....	1790	164321	NFK	Norwich
SOPER						
....	....	ALL	ALL	165743	ALL	Name Study
1700	1880	1700	1900	126438	HAM	Kingsclere
1618	....	....	1660	171441	HAM	Wootton St Lawrence
1700	1800	1650	1700	147583	MDX	Hammersmith
1700	1800	1650	1700	147583	MDX	Twickenham
1700	1850	1600	1992	165743	SSX	ALL
1750	1850	ALL	ALL	151998	SSX	Chiddingly

Known From	To	Researching From	To	Ref	Cty	Place
SOQUI						
1760	1780	1700	1992	167592	MDX	London
1770	1780	1700	1992	167592	WOR	Worcester
SORBY						
1900	....	....	....	156868	LAN	Oldham
SORE						
1650	1800	1550	1650	172901	NTT	Strelley
1714	1903	....	1920	137405	SFK	Bury St Edmunds
1780	1973	1550	1780	150398	SFK	Haughley
SORREL						
1743	1755	....	....	101028	ESS	High Easter
SORRELL						
1785	1992	ALL	1785	165751	ESS	Great Waltham
1780	1800	1750	1850	171158	ESS	Little Leighs
1888	1992	1800	1888	147230	LND	East End
SORRILL						
1857	1869	....	....	135380	SAL	Ludlow
SORTON						
1750	?	1700	1992	167592	FLN	Buckley
1809	1868	1790	1845	141283	STS	Newcastle
SORTWELL						
1837	1992	1837	1992	165778	ESS	Harlow
1837	1992	1837	1992	165778	HRT	Harlow
SOTCHER						
1740	1750	....	....	133221	SSX	Wisborough Green
SOTHCOTT						
....	....	ALL	ALL	106003	ALL	ALL
1900	1992	1850	1992	106003	YKS	ALL
SOUCH						
1830	1992	1700	1992	114596	OXF	Hailey
1840	1850	....	1840	174025	OXF	Ramsden
SOULARD						
1700	1799	....	....	137960	MDX	London
SOULBY						
1740	1800	1640	1740	169749	LIN	Horncastle
SOULSBY						
1741	1940	ALL	1741	154563	DUR	ALL
1805	1850	1750	1850	137278	DUR	Chartershaugh
1775	1830	1775	1830	154563	NBL	ALL
....	....	1840	1920	165786	NBL	Newcastle
1690	1826	1650	1850	165786	NBL	Rothbury
SOUNDY						
....	....	1600	1900	124273	LND	Southwark
SOURBUTTS						
1826	1960	ALL	1826	153184	LAN	Ormskirk
SOUTAR						
1835	1835	1700	1850	112089	LTN	???
1835	1924	1780	1950	112089	SUT	Golspie
SOUTER						
1656	1800	1500	1700	122688	SSX	East Lavant
1656	1800	1500	1700	122688	SSX	Westbourne
SOUTER-OSBORN						
1812	1855	1812	1900	152536	SSX	ALL
SOUTH						
1765	1765	1765	1765	136808	HRT	Barkway
1839	1960	1700	1839	174335	HRT	Roegreen
1839	1960	1700	1839	174335	HRT	Sandon
1751	....	1725	1780	170348	YKS	Rawmarsh
SOUTHALL						
1650	1700	1500	1650	113204	STS	Albrighton
1800	1872	1600	1800	106054	WAR	Birmingham
1815	....	1815	....	140767	WAR	Birmingham
1800	1820	1780	1820	148113	WAR	Birmingham
1800	1820	1780	1820	148113	WAR	Dudley
....	....	....	1840	170461	WOR	Bewdley
SOUTHAM						
1650	1992	ALL	ALL	165808	BKM	Waddesdon
1650	1992	ALL	ALL	165808	BKM	Wing
1692	1940	....	....	128996	CAM	Thorney
1700	ALL	1773	1875	107379	HRT	ALL
1803	1992	ALL	ALL	140821	LEI	Narborough
1700	ALL	1773	1875	107379	LND	ALL
1500	1992	ALL	ALL	165808	LND	ALL
1850	1890	1800	1900	134627	OXF	Steeple Aston
1740	1821	1700	1740	134627	OXF	Upper Heyford
1890	ALL	1890	ALL	134627	STS	West Bromwich
1750	1803	ALL	ALL	140821	WAR	Harborough Magna
SOUTHARD						
1590	1881	1590	1881	108251	DEV	Exeter
SOUTHARTH						
1630	1670	1550	1700	105333	LAN	Penwortham
SOUTHCOMBE						
1856	1950	1800	1860	166316	SOM	Lypeard St Lawrence
SOUTHCOTT						
1805	1825	ALL	1825	104299	GLS	Bristol
SOUTHEE						
1640	1940	1600	1992	144843	KEN	East
1640	1940	1600	1992	144843	KEN	Canterbury
1790	1900	1750	1900	144843	MDX	London
SOUTHENWOOD						
1849	?	?	?	108189	ESS	Chelmsford
SOUTHERBY						
1820	1920	1800	1920	138967	SRY	London
SOUTHERD						
1800	1810	ALL	1850	173614	DEV	Barnstaple
SOUTHERN						
1800	1880	....	....	141178	CON	South East
1823	1909	1750	1950	177970	DUR	Lanchester
1800	1992	1700	1871	165824	LAN	Bolton
1765	1900	1700	1833	136824	YKS	Sheffield
SOUTHERNDEN						
1764	1764	....	....	127426	KEN	Boxley
SOUTHERTON						
1766	1802	1766	1802	139971	SAL	Church Pulverbatch
SOUTHEY						
1590	1780	1590	1800	165832	DEV	Culmstock
1590	1780	1590	1800	165832	DEV	Exeter
....	....	ALL	1780	167029	DEV	Exeter
1614	1850	1614	1850	165832	KEN	Canterbury
1795	1824	1759	1824	165832	KEN	Dover
1830	1900	....	....	155640	SRY	Croydon
1810	1830	1810	1830	155640	SRY	Lambeth
1792	1830	1750	1830	155640	SRY	Newington
SOUTHGATE						
1840	1880	1600	1840	169773	ESS	Bradford
1770	1820	1650	1770	168351	ESS	Kirby Le Soken
1800	1900	1700	1850	174599	ESS	Wix
1900	1992	1800	1950	125385	KEN	ALL
1800	....	....	....	126543	SFK	Bacton
1801	1851	1700	1860	159123	SFK	Claydon
1894	1897	1894	1900	159123	SFK	Colchester
1840	1880	1600	1840	169773	SFK	Harksted
1840	1860	1780	1840	105031	SFK	Ipswich
1871	1891	1890	1895	159123	SFK	Ipswich
1800	1880	1700	1800	132640	SFK	Sproughton
1860	1865	1860	1890	159123	SFK	Stowmarket
1700	....	....	....	126543	SFK	Stowupland
SOUTHILL						
1450	1530	1400	1530	154881	RUT	Exton
SOUTHIN						
1714	1992	1700	1714	165867	SRY	???
1714	1992	1700	1714	165867	SSX	???
SOUTHORN						
1650	1900	1650	1900	105511	NTH	ALL
1650	1950	1650	1950	105511	WAR	ALL
SOUTHWARD						
1870	1950	1840	1870	177903	CMA	Distington
....	....	1640	1840	177903	CMA	Whitehaven
1800	1900	1600	1800	113654	LAN	Inskip
1820	1867	1700	1819	172006	LAN	St Helens
SOUTHWELL						
....	....	ALL	ALL	165875	ALL	Name Study
1748	1940	....	....	128996	CAM	Thorney
1880	1992	1850	1880	173614	HAM	Portsmouth
1800	1992	....	....	176125	LIN	Asterby
1800	1992	....	....	176125	LIN	Goulceby
1840	1900	ALL	1840	157899	YKS	Bradford
SOUTHWICK						
1841	?	ALL	1841	129658	KEN	Woolwich
SOUTHWOOD						
?	?	?	?	150975	DEV	Sidmouth
1790	1890	1650	1900	123293	SOM	ALL
SOUTHWORTH						
1846	1895	1700	1960	137901	CHS	Stockport
1823	1850	ALL	ALL	138886	LAN	Preston
1858	....	....	....	110167	LAN	Tarleton
1823	1992	ALL	1800	165883	???	???
SOUTTER						
....	....	1750	1870	165905	ANS	Brechin
1820	1900	1700	1820	100978	KCD	Fetteresso
1870	1900	ALL	ALL	165905	TAY	Dundee
SOWDEN						
1728	1898	1728	1980	116424	CON	South East
1725	1746	1600	1750	143693	CON	Camborne
....	....	1700	1880	171085	CON	???
1833	....	....	....	148768	SCT	Aberdeen
....	....	1700	1940	171085	SOM	???

Known From	To	Researching From	To	Ref	Cty	Place
SOWDEN contd.						
....	....	1800	ALL	171085	YKS	ALL
....	....	1700	1800	107018	YKS	Kirkbymoorside
SOWDON						
1880	1980	1600	1880	122556	DEV	Witheridge
SOWELL						
1765	1791	1700	1765	125105	NFK	Great Yarmouth
SOWERBUTTS						
1820	1850	ALL	ALL	138886	LAN	Preston
SOWERBY						
....	....	1820	1840	177792	CUL	Dalston
....	....	1800	1880	137618	DUR	Gateshead
1800	1850	1750	1850	144290	LIN	Messingham
1700	1760	....	....	108375	MDX	Minories
1787	1871	....	....	116602	SRY	London
1807	1810	1750	1810	162396	WES	Appleby
1793	1848	1700	1793	117625	WES	Soulby
SOWTEN						
....	....	1500	1980	164992	SRY	North
SOWTER						
....	....	ALL	ALL	165913	ALL	Name Study
SPACKMAN						
1842	1992	ALL	1842	107239	LND	Kennington
1762	1992	1660	1762	165921	WIL	North
SPAIN						
....	....	1850	1900	106356	KEN	Boxley
....	....	1750	1900	106356	KEN	Elham
1860	....	1860	1900	106356	KEN	Newington
1826	1992	1750	1845	142042	KEN	Walmer
SPAINSWICK						
1815	1905	....	1815	167878	WIL	Burbage
SPALDING						
1765	....	1700	1765	105457	DFS	???
1889	1963	....	....	144215	DUR	Chester Le Street
1869	....	1800	1900	102164	LAN	Liverpool
1782	1921	....	....	149616	PER	Kirkmichael
SPALL						
1841	1856	1800	1860	102075	LND	Shoreditch
....	....	....	....	164461	SFK	Woodbridge
SPALTON						
1750	1992	1650	1750	118745	DBY	ALL
1897	1910	1897	1960	133264	DBY	Derby
SPANSWICK						
1706	1806	1690	1806	132608	BRK	Lambourn
SPANTON						
1760	1800	....	....	154571	NFK	Tunstead
1810	1992	1700	1810	166804	NFK	Tunstead
SPARGO						
1550	1992	1550	1992	141607	ALL	ALL
1831	1992	ALL	1831	154555	CON	Gwennap
1750	1760	....	....	139491	CON	Illogan
....	....	1700	1760	139491	CON	Penryn
1850	1960	1700	1850	114685	CON	Sithney
1850	1960	1700	1850	114685	CON	Wendron
SPARHAM						
1900	1930	1900	....	125598	LEI	Market Harborough
SPARHAWKE						
1700	....	1600	1750	169862	SFK	Mildenhall
SPARK						
1780	1992	1780	1992	131156	ANS	Dundee
1780	1992	1780	1992	131156	ANS	Montrose
1772	1772	1680	1772	121568	SOM	Ash Priors
SPARKE						
1580	1690	1500	1992	162620	NBL	Allendale
SPARKES						
1840	1873	1700	1840	111449	BDF	Stagsden
1820	1960	1700	1820	112410	SAL	Blackoe
1851	1861	1810	1890	162450	SOM	Bridgewater
1891	....	....	....	153885	SSX	Hove
1750	1920	1600	1992	117609	WAR	Maxstoke
1600	1900	....	....	100420	WAR	Meriden
1840	1900	1800	1920	170038	YKS	Bradford
SPARKS						
1700	1900	....	....	165999	GLS	ALL
1795	1841	1700	1795	168033	HAM	Alverstoke
1838	1975	1700	1838	167886	LAN	Liverpool
1831	1831	....	....	121355	LND	Bethnal Green
1850	....	....	....	148768	MDX	Marylebone
1880	1980	1800	1880	162485	NFK	Norwich
1880	1900	1860	1880	162485	SFK	Bury St Edmunds
1782	1803	ALL	1782	131881	SFK	Great Thurlow
1870	1870	1850	1870	105775	SFK	Otley
1825	1850	1800	1870	105775	SFK	Wortham
1700	1900	....	....	165999	SOM	ALL
SPARKS contd.						
1851	1900	1700	1851	101389	SOM	Twerton
SPARLING						
1800	1900	1700	1900	140325	ESS	Clacton
1700	1850	1700	1900	140325	ESS	Colchester
1600	1900	1700	1900	140325	ESS	Holland
1846	1920	1830	1920	140325	ESS	Kirby Le Soken
1837	....	ALL	ALL	172057	ESS	???
1740	1843	1650	1740	163783	LAN	Bolton Le Sands
1740	1843	1650	1740	163783	LAN	Goosnargh
1837	....	ALL	ALL	172057	LND	???
SPARNON						
1550	1850	1550	1850	165166	CON	Breage
1650	1800	1650	1800	165166	CON	Illugan
1800	1992	1800	1992	165166	GLA	ALL
SPARROW						
1780	1845	1740	1845	135941	ESS	Belchamp Water
1770	1900	1700	1900	171417	ESS	Gt Baddow
....	1729	1700	1740	128961	ESS	Halstead
1873	1899	ALL	1899	114030	MDX	London
1816	1867	1700	1816	160601	NFK	Attleborough
1692	1699	1620	1692	128724	SFK	Chevington
1835	....	1750	1840	100013	SFK	West Stow
1784	1873	1700	1873	113069	SOM	Frome
1784	1873	1700	1873	124990	SOM	Frome
1780	1914	1700	1780	165956	SRY	Ewell
1825	1880	1800	1890	126438	WAR	Solihull
1770	1810	1700	1770	133671	WIL	Poolkeynes
SPARRY						
1701	1744	1701	1744	155071	STS	Kinver
1845	1900	1845	1900	145319	WOR	Lye
1500	1560	1500	1600	160873	WOR	Old Swinford
1744	1898	1744	1898	155071	WOR	Oldswinford
1645	1701	....	....	155071	WOR	Pedmore
1845	1900	1845	1900	145319	WOR	Stourbridge
SPARVILLE						
1692	1719	ALL	ALL	115126	HAM	Fareham
SPASFORD						
1843	1870	1800	1843	129712	ESS	Hatfield Broad Oak
SPAUGHTON						
....	....	ALL	ALL	165972	ALL	Name Study
1766	1800	ALL	ALL	165972	LND	City
1811	1940	ALL	ALL	165972	SRY	Lambeth
1730	1940	ALL	ALL	165972	SRY	Southwark
SPAULL						
1880	1924	1800	1924	139327	LND	Battersea
SPAVOLD						
1818	1911	1700	1818	172448	NTT	East Retford
SPAWL						
1700	1700	1650	1700	155276	SFK	Walton
SPAWTON						
1550	1900	....	....	165999	NTT	ALL
1650	1700	1650	1710	133817	NTT	Gedling
SPEAIGHT						
1830	1880	ALL	ALL	119180	LND	East
1830	1880	ALL	ALL	119180	MDX	North
SPEAK						
1855	1948	ALL	ALL	131121	LAN	Chorley
1800	1992	ALL	1800	100803	WYK	Erringden
1860	1982	1830	1992	151378	WYK	Halifax
SPEAKE						
....	....	ALL	ALL	166006	ALL	Name Study
1860	1960	1800	1960	166006	BRE	ALL
1875	1950	1800	1992	166006	GLS	ALL
1620	1940	1600	1940	166006	HEF	ALL
1500	1900	1500	1900	166006	MGY	ALL
1580	1900	1800	1880	166006	RAD	ALL
1380	1992	1380	1992	166006	SAL	ALL
1590	1850	....	....	137413	SAL	Fitz
1590	1850	....	....	137413	SAL	Montford
1300	1880	1450	1550	166006	SOM	ALL
1600	1992	1800	1992	166006	STS	ALL
1580	1992	1800	1992	166006	WAR	ALL
1870	1950	1700	1960	166006	WOR	ALL
SPEAKMAN						
1827	1850	1800	1850	118443	LAN	Churchtown
1753	1830	1650	1753	118958	LAN	???
1872	1889	1800	1872	130877	SAL	Oswestry
SPEAR						
1800	1900	1700	1800	166022	CON	East
1630	1750	....	....	149888	CON	Alternun
1700	1900	1600	1900	108766	CON	Padstow
1750	1890	....	....	149888	CON	St Ives
1800	1900	1700	1800	166022	DEV	West

Known From	To	Researching From	To	Ref	Cty	Place
SPEAR contd.						
1850	1960	1700	1850	168734	DEV	Tamerton Foliot
1870	1900	ALL	ALL	166022	GLA	Cardiff
1852	....	1852	1992	157813	???	Bristol
SPEARING						
1750	1840	1700	1800	142670	DOR	Cukhorn Weston
1775	1844	1775	1844	147001	OXF	Oxford
1822	1992	....	1822	151270	SOM	Crewkerne
SPEATE						
1802	1851	1802	1851	166030	LAN	Heaton Norris
SPEDDING						
....	....	ALL	ALL	114596	ALL	Name Study
1837	1955	ALL	ALL	114596	ALL	ALL
1700	1725	1650	1725	135550	WES	North
1750	1992	1600	1992	114596	YKS	Dewsbury
SPEECHLEY						
1701	1940	....	....	128996	CAM	Thorney
1750	1800	1700	1750	155950	CAM	Whittleby
1842	1992	....	1842	151270	CAM	Whittlesey
1750	1800	1700	1750	155950	NTH	Peterborough
SPEECHLY						
1565	1850	1850	1980	107344	CAM	Whittlesey
1800	1860	....	1800	136212	CAM	Whittlesey
SPEED						
....	....	....	1867	163155	ESS	???
1815	1840	ALL	1992	125113	GLS	Westbury
1840	1870	....	....	114723	KEN	Whitstable
1850	1910	1600	1850	160784	LEI	Oakham
1850	1860	....	....	114723	LKS	Glasgow
1860	1926	....	....	131024	SCT	???
1815	1840	ALL	1992	125113	SOM	Wells
1839	1882	1750	1839	121053	STS	Tipton
SPEEDY						
1800	1992	1800	1992	126241	NBL	Berwick Upon Tweed
SPEER						
1872	1992	1700	1872	145823	MDX	Stepney
SPEERSHOT						
1768	1768	1600	1768	170542	HAM	Titchfield
SPEET						
1802	1992	1802	1851	166030	LAN	Failsworth
SPEIGHT						
1796	1838	1700	1796	152196	CMA	St Bees
1725	1804	ALL	ALL	141615	LAN	North
1820	1850	1700	1900	118753	WYK	Bradford
1890	1900	1800	1890	135496	YKS	Bradford
1804	1926	1500	1804	125695	YKS	Campsall
1792	....	1770	1810	176958	YKS	Dewsbury
1840	1880	1830	1900	144622	YKS	Kilnhurst
1739	1776	1600	1750	101575	YKS	Pontefract
1638	1719	1550	1638	138584	YKS	Rothwell
1754	1799	1754	1799	166030	YKS	Rothwell
1792	....	1770	1810	176958	YKS	Thornhill
1850	1855	1750	1850	144622	YKS	Thrybergh
1789	1830	1750	1850	144622	YKS	Wath On Dearne
SPEIRS						
1818	1841	....	....	127140	AYR	Dalry
1850	1992	....	....	117765	LAN	Liverpool
....	....	1750	1860	100390	LKS	West Kilbride
1750	1880	1700	1750	117765	RFW	Bridge Of Weir
SPELLER						
1800	1900	1850	1900	162140	ESS	Blackmore
1536	1837	....	....	148733	ESS	Hatfield
1770	1900	1750	1980	171417	HUN	Huntingdon
1800	1900	1840	1960	162140	LND	Islington
1837	....	....	....	165387	MDX	Camden Town
SPELT						
1668	....	....	....	153397	HAM	Milton
SPENCE						
1778	....	1750	1860	114332	ABD	Huntly
....	....	1700	1980	172111	ANT	Port Glenone
1860	1992	ALL	ALL	153753	DUR	Stockton On Tees
1772	1953	1650	1772	165018	EYK	Beverley
1867	1927	?	1867	125059	LAN	Liverpool
1790	1992	1650	1790	111465	LAN	Tarleton
1850	1980	1750	1850	145645	LEI	East
1850	1980	1750	1850	145645	LEI	North
1869	1946	1946	1992	146560	LKS	Coatbride
1730	1750	1700	1730	121339	NYK	Pickering
1860	1940	1860	1992	178357	RFW	Greenock
....	....	1800	....	149187	SFK	Woodbridge
1750	1965	....	....	137820	SHI	Fetlar
1720	1965	....	....	137820	SHI	Mid Yell
1760	1965	....	....	137820	SHI	North Yell
1758	1965	....	....	137820	SHI	Northmavine
SPENCE contd.						
1720	1965	....	....	137820	SHI	South Yell
1555	1845	ALL	ALL	105015	YKS	Hampsthwaite
1860	1900	1700	1860	108308	YKS	Masham
?	?	?	?	167932	YKS	???
SPENCELAGH						
1766	1780	1790	1850	118737	YKS	East
SPENCELEY						
1793	1851	....	....	124524	ERY	Hull
1830	1921	1790	1900	118737	KEN	Chatham
SPENCER						
1791	1807	1791	1807	156027	AYR	Newmilns
1793	1923	1700	1793	166111	BDF	Harrold
1847	1992	....	....	167444	BRK	Reading
1800	1910	....	....	132179	CHS	Appleton
1834	....	....	....	150282	CON	???
1675	1880	1600	1900	142085	DBY	Elvaston
....	....	?	....	142085	DBY	Ewaston
1841	1861	1800	1841	124095	DBY	Middleton
1841	1861	1800	1841	124095	DBY	Wirksworth
1749	1812	....	....	151351	DOR	Okeford Fitzpaine
1871	1970	1750	1875	112526	DUB	Balbriggan
1790	1850	1700	1900	162620	DUR	Ryton
1810	1992	1600	1810	166103	ESS	Epping
1730	1992	1600	1730	166103	ESS	Theydon Mount
1700	1992	1700	....	118672	GLS	Wotton Under Edge
1793	1801	1754	1801	106747	HAM	Andover
....	1788	ALL	ALL	129933	HAM	Eversley
1790	1913	1700	1800	126772	HAM	Petersfield
1718	1754	1600	1754	174343	HAM	West Tisted
1795	1992	ALL	1794	167444	HEF	Bromyard
1730	1890	1750	1800	140864	HRT	Barkway
1821	1900	1700	1821	103195	IOW	Freshwater
....	....	1700	1992	122742	IOW	Newport
1830	1980	1750	1830	160458	LAN	Burnley
1840	1880	1750	1840	132268	LAN	Bury
1836	1881	1795	1841	174211	LAN	Bury
1740	1814	ALL	ALL	135909	LAN	Croston
1760	1814	ALL	ALL	135909	LAN	Mcuh Hoole
1600	1800	1450	1850	166081	LAN	Newchurch In Pendle
1767	1840	1700	1800	135348	LAN	Oldham
1784	1784	1745	1784	174211	LAN	Prestwich
1840	1880	1750	1840	132268	LAN	Radcliffe
1835	1992	1835	1992	166081	LAN	Rochdale
1780	....	....	....	110167	LAN	Tarleton
1790	1992	1650	1790	111465	LAN	Tarleton
1890	1992	ALL	1890	166146	LEI	Burton On The Wolds
1826	?	ALL	1840	166146	LEI	Hose
1855	1890	1855	1898	163171	LEI	Thringstone
....	....	1500	1992	161470	LEI	Widmerpool
....	....	1800	1880	145173	LND	East
1850	1900	1850	1900	118907	LND	Battersea
1841	1992	1841	1943	130079	LND	Bermondsey
1855	1865	1830	1880	106747	LND	Bow
1799	1992	ALL	ALL	151580	LND	Clerkenwell
1902	1992	1700	1923	166073	LND	Hampstead
1895	1895	1895	1944	104663	LND	Kensington
1875	....	....	1900	171441	LND	Lambeth
1799	1992	ALL	ALL	151580	LND	Marylebone
1855	1865	1830	1880	106747	LND	Poplar
1870	1900	1800	1870	107697	MDX	London
1863	1863	1860	1895	104663	NFK	Norwich
1885	1930	ALL	ALL	147397	NTH	Northampton
1780	1840	....	1840	137634	NTT	Clarborough
1840	1992	....	1992	137634	NTT	East Retford
1844	1992	1844	1992	157813	NTT	Nottingham
1829	1879	....	....	128910	NTT	Sutton In Ashfield
1851	1895	....	....	166146	NTT	Willoughby On The Wolds
1750	1860	1600	1750	118907	NTT	???
1809	....	....	....	167444	SAL	Ludlow
1730	1738	ALL	1730	169730	SRY	Mitcham
1766	1770	1766	1770	108375	SRY	Streatham
1795	1992	ALL	1794	167444	STS	Tamworth
1800	1851	1600	1800	106054	WAR	Birmingham
1795	1992	ALL	1794	167444	WAR	Birmingham
1550	....	1550	1900	115142	WAR	Kingsbury
1759	....	ALL	1759	154946	WES	Appleby
1759	....	ALL	1759	154946	WES	Bongate
1795	1992	ALL	1794	167444	WOR	Claines
1795	1992	ALL	1794	167444	WOR	Powick
....	....	....	1882	176702	WYK	Bingley
....	....	....	1882	176702	WYK	Keighley
1882	1900	1750	1882	102199	YKS	Bingley

Known From	To	Researching From	To	Ref	Cty	Place
SPENCER contd.						
1550	....	1550	....	109347	YKS	Gisburn
1791	1836	1720	1836	175153	YKS	Halifax
1800	1992	1800	1900	145122	YKS	Leeds
1737	1851	1600	1850	166081	YKS	Slaidburn
1791	1836	1720	1836	175153	YKS	Sowerby
1892	1973	1864	1892	124095	???	London
SPENDELOW						
1736	1845	1730	1845	171654	ESS	Great Stambridge
SPENDER						
1620	1720	1620	1720	142018	WIL	ALL
SPENDLEY						
1784	1913	....	....	134007	ESS	Manningtree
1890	1890	1790	1910	118737	YKS	East
SPENDLOVE						
....	....	ALL	ALL	166162	ALL	Name Study
SPENS						
1797	1825	1600	1797	139084	ROX	Craigsanquar
SPENSE						
1790	1992	1650	1790	111465	LAN	Tarleton
SPENSER						
1790	1992	1650	1790	111465	LAN	Tarleton
SPERLING						
1861	1861	1820	1900	162876	ESS	Halstead
SPERNON						
1550	1992	1620	1800	133450	CON	Breage
1550	1850	1550	1850	165166	CON	Breage
SPERRIN						
1889	1947	1800	1950	137685	LND	Canning Town
....	....	1870	1900	137685	LND	Hornsey
....	1889	1820	1950	137685	LND	Islington
SPERRING						
1790	1808	1600	1790	115525	SOM	Litton
1750	1950	1650	1750	128376	SOM	Midsomer Norton
1722	1992	ALL	ALL	158798	SOM	Midsomer Norton
1796	....	ALL	1796	139602	SOM	West Hatch
SPERRY						
1787	1858	1700	1787	178926	LEI	Bagworth
SPIBY						
1838	1860	1700	1900	178233	LAN	ALL
SPICE						
1787	1811	....	....	168041	KEN	Dover
1860	1940	1750	1900	109398	KEN	Sittingbourne
1854	1878	ALL	1854	131881	LND	Shoreditch
SPICER						
1700	1992	....	1700	166189	BKM	Langley
1820	1830	1800	1850	124648	BRK	Reading
1840	1880	1800	1900	126179	DOR	Affpuddle
1782	1804	1600	1782	166170	DOR	Hazlebury Bryan
1593	1947	1500	1593	127116	DOR	Iwerne Courtney
1851	1886	1800	1851	128724	KEN	Guston
?	?	?	?	154687	KEN	Herne
....	....	ALL	ALL	120790	NTT	Earls Barton
1845	1992	1845	1992	120790	NTT	Nottingham
1860	1897	1860	1910	168165	WAR	Leamington Spa
1740	ALL	....	....	142158	WIL	Aldbourne
SPICKETT						
1850	1992	1700	1850	149659	BRK	Hagbourne
1868	1893	1800	1868	122483	WLS	Cardiff Area
SPIELMAN						
....	1890	....	....	159999	HAM	Andover
....	1890	....	....	159999	LND	Battersea
....	1925	....	....	159999	OXF	Oxford
SPIER						
1650	1680	....	....	103764	BKM	Marsh Gibbon
....	....	1750	1850	120472	BRK	Reading
SPIERS						
....	....	ALL	ALL	166219	ALL	Name Study
1850	1950	1750	1850	125660	BKM	Long Crendon
1790	1870	....	....	133361	BKM	Shenley
1846	1875	1875	1992	166197	GLS	Aston Under Hill
1871	....	1871	1992	166197	GLS	Whittingham
1650	1717	1600	1800	133450	IRL	Baggotstown
1829	1859	1750	1829	176907	NTH	???
1842	1900	1750	1900	106941	SSX	Highbrook
1881	1915	1800	1992	166197	WAR	Birmingham
1750	1820	1700	1820	166197	WAR	Haselor
1780	1992	1538	1780	154792	WOR	ALL
1789	1867	1700	1789	166197	WOR	Bishampton
1788	1992	1700	1818	166200	WOR	Bishampton
1788	1992	1700	1818	166200	WOR	Cropthorne
1871	1896	1881	1992	166197	WOR	Eldersfield
SPIKESMAN						
1818	1867	....	....	173932	SRY	Ashtead
SPIKESMAN contd.						
1869	1940	....	....	173932	SRY	Epsom
SPILBURY						
1654	1768	....	....	164631	WOR	Bromsgrove
1694	1759	....	....	164631	WOR	Kidderminster
1628	....	....	....	164631	WOR	Ribblesford
SPILLANE						
1909	1976	1880	1909	124095	IRL	Fermoy
1909	1976	1880	1909	124095	MDX	Hounslow
SPILLER						
....	....	1700	1900	135968	DEV	ALL
1846	1846	....	....	151238	DEV	Amouth
1780	1820	1600	1820	167649	DEV	Yarcombe
1849	1871	1700	1849	173509	SOM	Braodway
1870	1870	1840	1870	168076	SOM	Bridgwater
1780	1820	1600	1820	167649	SOM	Otterford
1790	1900	1700	1790	130257	SSX	Chichester
SPILLET						
1876	1890	....	....	127426	KEN	Aylesford
1647	1647	....	....	127426	KEN	Charing
1851	1851	....	....	127426	KEN	East Malling
1824	1871	....	....	127426	KEN	Lenham
1797	1801	....	....	127426	KEN	Ulcombe
1825	1889	....	....	127426	KEN	Wychling
SPILLETT						
1764	1764	....	....	127426	KEN	Boxley
1816	1900	1787	1816	165107	KEN	Chartham
1730	1836	....	....	127426	KEN	Lenham
1740	1740	....	....	127426	KEN	Wychling
SPILLING						
....	....	ALL	ALL	152986	ALL	Name Study
SPILLSBERY						
1860	1880	....	....	121185	KEN	ALL
SPILLSBURY						
1787	....	1600	1800	145432	WOR	Feckinham
SPILSBURY						
1787	1852	1600	1800	145432	WOR	Bromsgrove
SPINDLER						
1740	1770	ALL	1800	118338	BRK	Abingdon
1740	1770	ALL	1800	118338	BRK	St Helens
1691	1700	1650	1700	173630	SFK	South Elmham
SPINK						
1790	1850	1700	1790	102016	CAM	Cambridge
1730	1821	1600	1821	166243	NFK	Barnhambroom
ALL	ALL	ALL	ALL	166243	NFK	Brandon Parva
1729	1800	ALL	ALL	166243	NFK	Colton
1796	1812	ALL	ALL	166243	NFK	Garvestone
1705	1812	ALL	ALL	166243	NFK	Hardingham
1789	1830	ALL	ALL	166243	NFK	Hockham
1770	....	1700	1800	102016	NFK	Roydon
1818	1821	1600	1821	166243	NFK	Runhall
1656	1672	ALL	ALL	166243	NFK	Weeting
1785	1811	ALL	ALL	166243	NFK	Wilton
....	....	....	1835	160601	NFK	???
1845	1900	ALL	1992	127361	WRY	Pontefract
....	....	1700	1800	142670	YKS	Northallerton
1729	1992	1729	....	166235	YKS	West Riding
SPINKS						
1850	1900	....	....	177326	DBY	???
1750	1815	ALL	1815	113611	EYK	Hull
1826	1871	ALL	1826	126918	LND	Lambeth
1730	1992	ALL	ALL	166243	NFK	Barnhambroom
ALL	ALL	ALL	ALL	166243	NFK	Brandon Parva
1796	1910	1750	1950	107980	NFK	Norwich
1821	1900	1600	1821	166243	NFK	Runhall
1760	1831	1600	1760	156779	NFK	Taverham
SPIRES						
1810	1850	1700	1992	166197	GLS	Aston Under Hill
1880	1890	1850	1992	166197	WOR	Stoulton
SPIRING						
1748	1759	1759	1992	168637	CON	Stratton
1722	....	1600	1748	168637	DEV	Crediton
1748	....	1722	1748	168637	DEV	Stoke Damerell
SPITTAL						
....	....	1790	1850	132381	LKS	Glasgow
1300	1667	1530	1667	166251	STS	Enville
1635	1970	1635	1812	166251	STS	Wednesbury
1604	1992	....	....	166251	WOR	Old Swinford
SPITTLE						
?	?	?	?	163279	WMD	Bradley
1805	1844	ALL	ALL	135127	WOR	Dudley St Thomas
SPITTLEHOUSE						
1790	1810	....	....	145688	LIN	South Kelsey

Known From	To	Researching From	To	Ref	Cty	Place
SPITTLES						
1815	1910	1800	1910	107522	KEN	ALL
SPIVEY						
1700	1904	1700	1800	173185	WYK	Heckmondwike
1650	1942	1650	1942	152668	WYK	Huddersfield
1874	....	ALL	ALL	155373	YKS	South
SPIVIE						
1824	1882	1850	1900	170348	YKS	Almondbury
SPIVY						
1701	....	1670	1720	170348	YKS	Almondbury
SPLAINE						
1870	....	....	....	152455	LND	Hackney
SPLEEN						
1800	1819	1700	1819	156728	BKM	Chalfont St Giles
SPLINGARD						
1830	1950	ALL	ALL	156604	LND	Woolwich
SPOARD						
1864	1992	1864	1886	160237	MDX	Uxbridge
SPODE						
....	....	ALL	ALL	160237	ALL	Name Study
1572	1886	1572	1886	160237	CHS	South East
1593	1880	1593	1886	160237	LAN	South
1636	1886	1636	1886	160237	LEI	Hinckley
1562	1992	1562	1886	160237	STS	Potteries
SPOFFORTH						
1600	1900	1500	1900	138487	YKS	ALL
SPOKES						
ALL	ALL	ALL	ALL	131083	ALL	ALL
....	....	1850	1992	131083	AVN	Bristol
1700	1850	1600	1700	131083	BRK	Abingdon
SPONDER						
1822	1889	1700	....	151831	HAM	Portsmouth
ALL	ALL	ALL	ALL	151831	KEN	Ramsgate
1822	1830	1700	1900	151831	SCT	ALL
SPONG						
....	....	ALL	ALL	166278	ALL	Name Study
....	....	1790	1980	166278	BRK	???
....	....	1795	1980	166278	HAM	???
1642	1934	ALL	1642	173304	KEN	The Weald
....	....	1830	1980	166278	KEN	???
....	....	1870	1980	166278	LEI	???
....	....	ALL	ALL	166278	MIL	ALL
1850	1960	1750	1850	134473	SRY	Brixton
1850	1960	1750	1850	134473	SRY	Lambeth
....	....	1598	1980	166278	SRY	???
....	....	1870	1980	166278	SSX	???
....	....	ALL	1642	173304	YKS	???
SPOONER						
1790	1845	1755	1850	135828	ESS	Great Burstead
1842	1943	....	....	130958	MDX	Bloomsbury
1712	1729	ALL	1730	129283	NFK	Hales
1639	1792	1600	1800	123404	NFK	North Elmham
1807	1856	1700	1807	119512	SSX	Kirdford
1660	1940	ALL	1992	135062	STS	Wednesbury
SPOONLEY						
1800	1850	1800	1850	167924	MGY	Llandiniam
SPOOR						
1811	1851	1711	1811	157988	DUR	Whicham Swalwell
SPOORS						
1780	1860	ALL	ALL	122386	DUR	Ryton
1750	1810	1600	1750	166294	DUR	South Shields
1780	1860	ALL	ALL	122386	DUR	Whickham
1760	1810	1600	1760	166294	NBL	North Shields
1760	1810	1600	1760	166294	NBL	Tynemouth
SPOSITO						
1873	1920	1920	1992	123080	GLS	Bristol
1873	1920	1920	1992	123080	SOM	Bristol
SPOTTISWOODE						
....	....	ALL	ALL	120359	ALL	Name Study
SPOWAGE						
1782	1848	1650	1781	131245	NTT	Blidworth
SPRACKLING						
....	....	ALL	ALL	104000	ALL	Name Study
ALL	ALL	ALL	ALL	104000	ALL	ALL
1766	....	ALL	ALL	110272	DOR	???
SPRAGG						
1775	1820	1750	1820	154709	NFK	ALL
1830	1921	....	....	147672	SOM	Bath
1880	....	....	....	170313	WAR	Birmingham
SPRAGGON						
1666	1772	1600	1772	116637	NBL	Whalton
SPRAGGS						
....	....	1800	....	145998	IOW	???
SPRAGUE						
1780	1992	1600	1780	145017	DEV	ALL
1740	1810	1700	1850	171158	DEV	Uffculme
1820	1900	1750	1850	176524	GSY	St Peter Port
1600	1780	1500	1700	144657	SOM	Wellington
SPRAKE						
1786	1840	1700	1810	107565	SOM	Chard
SPRAKES						
1780	1790	....	....	103721	ERY	Thorne
1820	1850	1800	1890	103721	LIN	Belton In Axholme
SPRANG						
1720	1846	1600	1900	152714	WOR	Evesham
1800	1846	1600	1900	152714	WOR	Worcester
SPRANGE						
....	....	ALL	ALL	156507	ALL	Name Study
SPRANKLING						
....	....	ALL	ALL	175617	ALL	Name Study
SPRATLEY						
1809	1845	1500	1810	104825	BKM	Amersham
1750	1992	ALL	1750	115177	BRK	Finchampstead
1767	1992	ALL	1992	166308	HAM	Southampton
1767	1992	ALL	1992	166308	LND	St Pancras
1767	1992	ALL	1992	166308	LND	Wandsworth
1767	1992	ALL	1992	166308	SSX	Hurstpierpoint
SPRATT						
1817	1844	1700	1817	172898	DEV	Devenport
1837	1992	1780	1850	166316	MDX	St Pancras
1770	1861	1711	1992	126128	NFK	Norwich
1600	....	1500	1600	160873	WOR	Old Swinford
SPRATTON-KNIGHT						
....	....	....	....	165565	???	???
SPRAY						
1794	....	ALL	ALL	151327	KEN	ALL
1700	1950	1700	1890	144983	SSX	Ninfield
1701	1992	ALL	1855	156175	SXE	Ninfield
SPREAD						
1780	1846	1750	1846	116025	LIM	???
SPREADBURY						
1750	1900	1600	1900	120677	HAM	Compton
SPRECKLEY						
1789	1860	....	1789	100064	LEI	Wymondham
SPREEN						
1826	1876	1800	1850	156728	BKM	Amersham
SPRENT						
1550	1992	ALL	ALL	106240	ALL	ALL
1700	1980	1600	1700	124184	HAM	Fareham
1760	1860	....	....	106240	HAM	Gosport
1700	1980	1600	1700	124184	HAM	Gosport
1764	1992	....	....	106240	HAM	Overton
1700	1760	....	....	106240	HAM	Petersfield
1700	1980	1600	1700	124184	HAM	Petersfield
SPRIDDLE						
1840	1900	1700	1900	147958	CON	Cawsand
1750	1750	1700	1760	136840	CON	Maker
SPRIDGEN						
1774	1857	1857	1980	165891	LIN	Creeton & Wigtoft
1774	1857	1857	1980	165891	LIN	Edenham
1774	1857	1857	1980	165891	LIN	Gosberton
SPRIET						
....	....	ALL	ALL	166324	ALL	Name Study
SPRIGGS						
ALL	ALL	ALL	ALL	165824	ALL	ALL
1837	1902	1750	1850	121703	CAM	Peterborough
1829	1992	1600	1829	110795	HAM	Portsmouth
1825	1850	1700	1850	176710	LEI	Hathern
1852	1890	....	....	135070	LND	Bromley
1784	1910	1700	1930	141569	NTH	Weldon
1829	1992	1600	1829	110795	NWL	Ruthin
1877	1879	ALL	ALL	165824	STS	Wolverhampton
1869	....	ALL	ALL	165824	YKS	Barnsley
SPRIGINGS						
1800	1992	1850	1992	125172	CHS	Merseyside
1850	....	....	....	125172	HAM	Portsea
1800	1992	1850	1992	125172	HMC	ALL
SPRIMONT						
1730	1770	1700	1992	167592	MDX	London
SPRINAGE						
....	1820	1800	1820	121037	MDX	Finsbury
SPRING						
1843	1875	....	....	117803	KER	Fieries
1813	1992	ALL	ALL	111058	LIN	ALL
SPRINGALL						
1790	....	....	....	151548	NFK	Yarmouth

Known From	To	Researching From	To	Ref	Cty	Place
SPRINGATE						
....	....	ALL	ALL	166332	ALL	Name Study
....	....	1500	1795	177261	KEN	Central
....	....	1500	1795	177261	KEN	North
....	....	1793	1801	177261	KEN	Capel
1802	1808	....	....	177261	KEN	Deptford
....	....	1785	1792	177261	KEN	Tonbridge
....	....	1793	1801	177261	KEN	Tudeley
1812	1845	....	....	177261	SRY	Rotherhithe
1846	1914	....	....	177261	SRY	Southwark
SPRINGAY						
1870	....	1750	1870	179183	MDX	Shadwell
SPRINGETT						
1878	1937	ALL	1878	169943	ESS	West
1878	1929	1800	1878	169935	ESS	Borders
1836	1872	ALL	1916	146390	ESS	Fordham
1878	1929	1800	1878	169935	MDX	Borders
1859	....	ALL	ALL	121487	SFK	Hadleigh
SPRINGFORD						
....	....	ALL	ALL	166340	ALL	Name Study
SPRINKS						
1750	1900	1600	1760	168572	SSX	West
SPRMCRR						
1866	1920	1700	1992	125865	LEI	ALL
SPROD						
1770	1830	1770	1850	138479	SOM	Butcombe
SPROT						
1800	1885	1700	1885	126209	NBL	North
SPROTT						
1799	1864	....	....	171654	LKS	Hamilton
1800	....	....	....	133590	WLS	???
SPROULL						
1810	....	....	....	132381	IRL	Antrim
SPRUCE						
1850	....	1800	1900	106356	NFK	Wymondham
SPRULES						
1829	1889	1800	1837	156434	LND	East
SPRUSEN						
1833	1833	ALL	1833	126942	ESS	Henham
SPRY						
1700	1799	1700	1799	169781	BRK	West Hendred
1816	1905	ALL	1816	116408	CON	Torpoint
1833	1888	1800	1900	166359	DEV	Ashwater
1600	1700	1600	1700	169781	DEV	Exeter
1816	1905	ALL	1816	116408	DEV	Stoke Damerel
1683	1737	1600	1800	166359	DEV	Tetcott
1880	1905	....	....	116408	HAM	Aldershot
1700	1800	1700	1800	169781	SOM	Bath
SPUR						
1717	....	....	1717	101761	WRY	Horbury
SPURDEN						
1787	1832	ALL	1787	168602	SFK	Lowestoft
SPURGE						
1870	1940	1800	1950	106976	SSX	Bognor
SPURGEN						
1596	1607	1596	1700	159956	NFK	Noth Lapham
SPURGEON						
1570	1929	ALL	1570	157511	ESS	Halstead
1775	1830	1700	1775	167525	ESS	Halstead
1698	1718	1650	1718	119717	MDX	London
1845	1876	ALL	1845	168602	NFK	Norwich
SPURGIN						
1773	1796	....	....	101028	ESS	Hatfield Peverel
SPURLE						
....	....	ALL	ALL	114987	ALL	Name Study
1676	1992	ALL	1676	114987	SOM	ALL
1685	1711	1600	1685	153281	SOM	North Petherton
SPURLING						
1745	....	ALL	1745	125121	MDX	Shoreditch
1716	1747	1600	1747	124435	SFK	Ufford
1894	1970	1800	1894	104701	T&W	Sunderland
SPURR						
....	....	ALL	ALL	166367	ALL	Name Study
....	1600	....	1650	158305	DBY	Heanor
1817	1940	1817	1940	109053	DEV	Walkhampton
SPURWAY						
1100	1786	....	....	172030	DEV	???
SQUANCE						
1772	1840	1750	1850	171549	DEV	West Putford
SQUARE						
1550	1992	1500	1992	133450	DEV	Kingsbridge
SQUAREY						
1715	1775	1650	1800	139866	DEV	Teignmouth

Known From	To	Researching From	To	Ref	Cty	Place
SQUIBB						
1600	....	1600	ALL	145378	DOR	Stoke Abbot
SQUIBBS						
1900	1992	1900	1992	133450	KEN	Gillingham
SQUIBS						
1840	....	....	1840	164011	DOR	Blandford
SQUIER						
1622	1697	....	....	131210	SRY	Carshalton
1700	....	....	....	167037	WIL	Wootton Bassett
SQUINCE						
1846	1914	1700	1846	167355	DUR	Bishop Auckland
1829	1914	1700	1829	167355	YKS	Bradford
1829	1914	1700	1829	167355	YKS	Leeds
SQUIRE						
1870	1910	1700	1960	121495	CON	South
1870	1910	1700	1960	121495	DEV	North
1700	1850	1600	1750	166375	DEV	North
1708	1850	....	....	129267	DEV	Abbots Bickington
1790	1930	1700	1790	116432	DEV	Lifton
1725	1750	1725	1775	171549	DEV	West Putford
1667	1840	....	....	167053	DOR	???
1695	1723	1665	1695	139149	ERY	Southburn
1800	....	....	....	131822	ESS	Wivenhoe
1754	....	1780	1836	136964	HRT	Baldock
1811	1847	ALL	1811	126721	NTT	Radcliffe
1800	....	....	....	131822	SFK	Lowestoft
1700	....	1724	1900	106410	SOM	Long Sutton
1720	....	1650	....	134589	YKS	Haxby
....	....	....	1848	102199	YKS	Scholes Cleckheaton
1650	1730	1600	1800	166081	YKS	Skipton
1700	1750	1700	1800	166081	YKS	Slaidburn
SQUIRES						
1800	1800	1750	1850	178004	CHS	Altrincham
1852	1992	1700	1852	174041	DEV	Braunton
?	?	1700	1900	153222	DOR	Kinson
....	....	1800	1900	166383	MDX	London
1700	1750	ALL	ALL	107425	NFK	Brockdish
1750	1880	ALL	ALL	107425	NFK	Fundenhall
1770	1780	1750	1800	178004	STS	Shutend
1800	1860	1750	1860	110906	SXW	Boxgrove
1700	1860	1700	1860	130621	???	Cledbury Mortimer
SQUIRRELL						
1484	1734	ALL	ALL	122106	SFK	Hitcham
1736	1851	ALL	1742	122106	SFK	Ringshall
1750	1850	1750	1850	133817	SFK	Ringshall
SQUORRELL						
1484	1734	ALL	ALL	122106	SFK	Hitcham
SQURIEL						
1736	1851	ALL	1742	122106	SFK	Ringshall
ST CLAIR						
1812	1820	1790	1822	104604	IRL	???
ST CLARE						
1874	1911	1850	1875	120286	CON	???
1840	....	....	....	175358	SRY	Guildford
ST CLERE						
1864	....	....	....	175358	SRY	Nunhead
ST GEORGE						
....	ALL	ALL	ALL	100153	KIK	Kilkenny City
ST PIER						
ALL	ALL	....	....	153397	ESS	ALL
ST PIERRE						
1750	1780	....	....	153397	ESS	Dagenham
1910	1992	....	....	153397	HRT	Coldicote
ST VALORY						
1066	1211	1066	1160	124974	OXF	Becklay
STABBINS						
....	....	ALL	1820	141224	GLS	South
1796	1861	ALL	ALL	153516	SOM	Kewstoke
STABLE						
1722	1769	1600	1722	152196	CUL	Nether Wasdale
STABLER						
1700	1950	1600	1950	166391	DUR	ALL
1831	1850	ALL	ALL	106941	DUR	Darlington
1700	1950	1600	1950	166391	YKS	ALL
1740	1800	1740	1800	119717	YKS	No Frodingham
STABLES						
1803	1915	1750	1915	155004	BAN	Aberchirder
STACE						
1870	1980	1850	1900	125032	HAM	Southampton
1800	1800	1790	1810	125032	NBL	Newcastle
....	....	1750	1850	163082	SRY	Kingston
1860	1875	1855	1880	125032	SSX	Brighton
1825	1872	1800	1880	125032	SSX	Newhaven
1867	1894	1700	1867	166723	SSX	Piddinghoe

Known From	To	Researching From	To	Ref	Cty	Place
STACE contd.						
1819	1825	1800	1850	125032	SSX	Seaford
STACEY						
1800	1900	1750	1920	128805	BKM	Marlow
1850	1881	1800	1920	128813	BKM	Marlow
1810	1853	1810	1853	166413	CAM	Whittlesey
1853	1890	1853	1890	166413	CAM	Wisbech
1801	1841	1750	1801	177091	DOR	Little Henge
....	....	1800	1930	147508	HEF	Hereford
1886	1915	1860	1992	151378	HEF	Hereford
1510	1730	1510	1730	166413	HUN	Bythorn
1685	1790	1685	1790	166413	HUN	Godmanchester
1728	1751	1728	1751	166413	HUN	Gt Stukeley
1660	1685	1660	1685	166413	HUN	Houghton
1510	1730	1510	1730	166413	HUN	Molesworth
1775	1992	1775	1992	166413	HUN	Ramsey
1870	1992	ALL	ALL	125083	KEN	Ashford
1840	1922	1800	1840	149578	LND	Clerkenwell
1840	1922	1800	1840	149578	LND	Holborn
1800	1950	1750	1850	146587	MDX	Norwood Green
1910	1969	1910	1992	151378	MON	Monmouth
1800	1850	1750	1900	128805	OXF	ALL
1860	1900	1800	1900	130427	OXF	Burcot
1841	1871	1700	1850	128813	OXF	Stokenchurch
1846	?	1700	1846	120871	PEM	Pembroke
1832	1838	1830	1992	101516	SAL	Gravenhanger
1832	1838	1830	1992	101516	SAL	Muclestone
1759	1974	1700	1759	164917	SOM	Curry Rivel
1880	1963	1685	1992	105171	SOM	Weston Zoyland
1850	1900	ALL	ALL	139890	SOM	Westonzoyland
1808	....	1750	1850	139386	SRY	Lambeth
1693	1900	....	....	166448	SSX	Fernhurst
1930	1992	....	....	101516	STS	Cannock
1860	1992	1860	1992	101516	STS	Lichfield
1850	....	1700	1849	136735	WAR	Birmingham
....	....	ALL	1826	152978	WIL	Devizes
....	....	ALL	1826	152978	WIL	Potterne
....	....	ALL	1740	151602	WIL	Wilcot
1880	1917	1880	1917	166413	YKS	Halifax
STACK						
....	....	ALL	1860	166456	LND	City
1836	1847	ALL	1860	166456	MDX	London
....	....	ALL	1860	166456	MDX	Shoreditch
....	....	ALL	1860	166456	MDX	Westminster
....	....	1850	1900	166456	SOM	Bedminster
....	....	1750	1850	166456	SRY	Bermondsey
1861	1992	1860	1900	166456	WAR	Birmingham
....	....	1850	1900	166456	???	Bristol
STACKHOUSE						
1840	1900	1700	1840	134899	LAN	???
1770	1950	1600	1770	158968	STS	Pelsall
STACY						
1837	....	1600	1800	149608	CON	Launceston
1726	1763	1700	1726	127116	HAM	Longstock
STADDON						
1832	1949	1832	1992	132519	DEV	Bampton
1688	1750	1626	1750	132519	DEV	Colebrooke
1805	1857	1804	1860	132519	DEV	Cullompton
1772	1802	1775	1804	132519	DEV	Poltimore
1743	1770	1740	1775	132519	DEV	Whitestone
1843	1860	1842	1875	132519	LND	Clerkenwell
1861	1892	1892	1992	132519	LND	Islington
STADHAM						
1819	....	....	....	176885	BKM	Wendover
STADON						
1820	1980	1800	1900	138444	???	Bristol
STAFF						
1795	1828	1700	1900	118168	NFK	Great Yarmouth
1850	1940	ALL	ALL	107425	NFK	Norwich
STAFFORD						
1650	1650	1500	1800	133450	DBY	Botham Hall
1750	1800	ALL	ALL	130508	DUR	Sunderland
1700	1810	1760	1810	166472	ESS	Barking
1700	1800	1700	1800	166472	ESS	Coggleshall
1800	1870	1800	1870	166472	ESS	Dagenham
1700	1770	1700	1770	166472	ESS	Romford
1811	1951	1811	1951	102954	ESS	Walthamstowe
1796	1825	1796	1825	166472	ESS	West Ham
1700	1800	1700	1800	166472	ESS	Witham
....	....	ALL	ALL	127884	LAN	Liverpool
1850	1900	1800	1930	100129	LIN	Stamford
1802	1992	ALL	1802	171719	LND	Marylebone
1802	1992	ALL	1802	171719	LND	Westminster
1811	1831	1811	1841	166472	MDX	Hackney
STAFFORD contd.						
1820	1845	1820	1860	166472	MDX	Islington
1845	1860	1845	1860	166472	MDX	Kensington
1826	1870	1826	1870	166472	MDX	Pentonville
1885	1992	1800	1885	166855	NTH	Ravensthorpe
1800	1835	1750	1800	100277	SSX	Worthing
....	....	1800	1900	129593	YKS	ALL
?	....	?	?	119997	YKS	Dewsbury
1800	1830	1800	1900	161586	YKS	Pontefract
STAGG						
1795	1822	1600	1822	174343	HAM	Boarhunt
1795	1881	ALL	ALL	149489	HAM	Portchester
1500	1820	1500	1820	125679	SOM	South East
....	....	1800	1900	133639	SOM	Coker
....	....	1700	1800	131652	WMD	???
STAGGS						
1840	1900	1700	1840	144681	HRT	Bishop Stortford
STAHL						
1830	1860	1860	1920	145858	MDX	London
STAINER						
1880	1992	1600	1992	154229	DOR	South
1849	....	1600	1849	132802	DOR	Leigh
1880	1992	1700	1880	166480	DOR	Wimborne Minster
1880	1992	1700	1880	166480	GSY	West Parley
1880	1992	1700	1880	166480	HAM	Hurn
STAINES						
1824	1867	1800	1900	142360	CAM	Ely
1914	1992	1806	1914	111805	CAM	Little Gransden
1841	1900	1600	1900	132497	KEN	Canterbury
....	1740	1650	1750	176621	KEN	Canterbury
STAINFORTH						
1667	1684	1645	1667	101796	YKS	Darfield
STAINSBY						
1838	1865	1800	1890	116386	YKS	Darlington
STAINTON						
....	....	1800	1992	104701	CMA	Sedbergh
1846	....	1813	1850	169552	WES	Burton In Kendal
1758	1779	1727	1779	169552	WES	Killington
1792	1825	1633	1812	169552	WES	Troutbeck
1641	1644	1612	1668	169552	WES	Windermere
1780	1800	....	....	177393	YKS	Birkin
1812	1919	1774	1919	169552	YKS	Howgill
1760	1780	1700	1780	177393	YKS	Kellington
1783	1893	1594	1893	169552	YKS	Sedbergh
STAIR						
1780	1803	1780	1803	114073	HAM	Upper Clatford
STAIRE						
1655	1700	1600	1655	148962	BRK	Silchester
STAIRS						
1845	1870	1800	1870	155691	BKM	North
STAITE						
1750	1800	1700	1750	171859	GLS	Winchcombe
STAKER						
1850	1900	1750	1850	176753	MDX	Enfield
STALEY						
....	....	ALL	ALL	100854	ALL	Name Study
....	....	ALL	ALL	100854	ALL	ALL
1559	1760	1500	1760	102830	DBY	ALL
1837	1900	....	....	173827	DBY	Newhall
1730	1760	1700	1800	137278	DBY	Peak Forest
1750	1850	1600	1850	119172	DBY	Stapenhill
1760	1840	1840	1992	137278	DUR	Teesdale
1750	1850	1700	1900	177180	STS	Tipton
STALHAM						
1900	1992	ALL	ALL	135321	NFK	Wiggenhall
STALKER						
1761	1988	1700	1761	160474	LAN	Blackburn
1800	1800	....	....	168203	PER	Methven
1761	1988	1700	1761	160474	WES	Killington
STALLAN						
....	....	ALL	ALL	172413	CAM	Sawston
STALLARD						
1722	1756	1500	1722	129577	IOW	???
ALL	ALL	ALL	ALL	103543	LND	Stoke Newington
....	....	ALL	ALL	103543	SOM	Bath
STAMFORD						
1770	1780	1700	1992	167592	CHS	Nantwich
1720	1780	1600	1992	167592	DBY	Derby
1595	1800	1550	1850	160849	LIN	Brigg
1790	1830	1700	1992	167592	STS	Audley
1790	1830	1700	1992	167592	STS	Newcastle Under Lyme
STAMMERS						
1836	1889	1700	1836	113425	ESS	Tillingham

Known From	To	Researching From	To	Ref	Cty	Place
STAMMERS contd.						
....	....	1850	1900	129275	LND	Woolwich
1820	?	1820	1920	108006	MDX	ALL
1859	1882	1837	1921	149640	MDX	London
1825	1855	ALL	1825	178934	SFK	Ellough
1805	....	1700	1860	149640	SFK	Long Melford
1860	1900	ALL	1860	134783	SFK	Martismere
1805	....	1700	1860	149640	SFK	Sudbury
STAMP						
1730	1890	1550	1992	168726	DEV	East
....	....	1800	1950	178799	DEV	Brixham
1787	1807	1550	1810	147265	DUR	???
1768	1841	1700	1850	100242	HAM	Bramley
1835	1920	1700	1835	120081	LIN	North
1805	1921	ALL	1921	106283	LIN	Barton On Humber
1780	1857	....	....	126276	LIN	Barton On Humber
1805	1921	ALL	1921	106283	LIN	Brigg
1848	1992	1848	1900	111791	LIN	Louth
1802	1805	1800	1815	108901	LIN	Roxby Cum Risby
1800	1992	1700	1800	102342	LIN	Roxby
1817	1827	1810	1830	108901	LIN	Winterton
1880	1920	1850	1920	166154	LND	Tooting
1880	1950	....	....	126276	WRY	Dewsbury
1857	....	....	....	126276	WRY	Doncaster
....	1897	....	....	126276	WRY	Goole
1874	....	....	....	126276	WRY	Roystone
1795	1822	1750	1850	157651	YKS	East Cowton
1769	1803	ALL	1820	152838	YKS	Hothay
1822	1900	1750	1992	157651	YKS	York
STAMPER						
1623	1890	1623	1992	163589	CMA	Furness
1623	1890	1623	1992	163589	CMA	Rusland Valley
1623	1890	1623	1992	163589	LAN	Dalton
STAMPERS						
1721	1754	ALL	1721	169730	KEN	Margate
STANAWAY						
1830	1850	1800	1850	132659	CON	Calstock
STANBRIDGE						
1650	1750	1600	1992	177180	BDF	Eaton Bray
1775	1820	1700	1775	123978	HAM	Southampton
1835	1853	....	....	117234	KEN	Flimwell
1835	1853	....	....	117234	KEN	Hawkhurst
STANBROOK						
1828	ALL	....	....	117560	HAM	Andover
STANBROOKE						
1751	1785	?	1751	113360	HAM	Longparish
STANBURY						
1873	1914	1870	1992	137782	CUL	South
....	....	1700	1950	120715	DEV	ALL
1813	1871	1750	1820	137782	DEV	South Tawton
STANCOMB						
1550	1880	1300	1880	105333	DEV	Buckland In The Moor
1550	1880	1300	1880	105333	DEV	Holne
1550	1880	1300	1880	105333	DEV	Ilsington
1550	1880	1300	1880	105333	DEV	Lydford
1550	1880	1300	1880	105333	DEV	Widecombe In The Moor
1810	1850	1815	1848	127655	GLS	Bristol
1810	1850	1815	1848	127655	WIL	Trowbridge
STANDEAVEN						
1825	1900	1700	1825	109479	YKS	Almondbury
STANDEN						
1850	1980	1650	1850	171409	KEN	Cranbrook
STANDEVEN						
....	....	ALL	ALL	159697	ALL	Name Study
1781	1840	1751	1781	139149	WRY	Halifax
STANDFORD						
1770	1825	1700	1770	149217	KEN	Lyminge
STANDFORTH						
1804	....	ALL	1804	158445	DUR	Durham
STANDING						
1774	1992	....	....	147850	KEN	Brenchley
1801	1890	1700	1900	178624	KEN	Folkestone
1774	1992	....	....	147850	KEN	Woolwich
1750	1850	1600	1850	132950	SSX	Pulborough
STANDISH						
1697	....	1640	1700	124796	BKM	Great Hampden
STANDLEY						
1835	....	ALL	1992	159174	DBY	Woodville
1725	....	....	....	171441	KEN	Rochester
....	1820	ALL	1820	134511	LEI	Narborough
1760	1786	ALL	1992	159174	LEI	Packington
1800	1900	1700	1800	101834	NFK	Central
STANDLEY contd.						
1820	1910	ALL	ALL	162205	NTH	Geddington
1830	1860	....	1860	102822	WAR	Birmingham
STANDRING						
....	....	ALL	ALL	166529	ALL	Name Study
1789	1830	1750	1900	110205	LAN	Bury
1770	1880	1770	1850	146897	LAN	Rochdale
STANES						
1670	....	ALL	1670	131059	ESS	Bocking
STANESBY						
....	....	ALL	ALL	149535	ALL	Name Study
ALL	ALL	ALL	ALL	149535	ALL	ALL
STANFEILD						
1910	1992	....	1920	134007	YKS	Sheffield
STANFIELD						
1818	?	ALL	ALL	129399	LIN	???
1780	1810	1600	1850	169862	YKS	Ackworth
1818	?	ALL	ALL	129399	YKS	???
STANFORD						
1716	1768	....	1768	137405	CAM	Rampton
1781	1851	ALL	1900	131334	CMA	Himbleton
1841	1992	....	....	129232	GLA	Cwmavon
1795	1835	....	....	129232	GLA	Southerndown
1830	1851	1820	1861	106747	HAM	ALL
1800	....	....	....	169129	IRL	???
1300	1400	1250	1400	154881	KEN	Hever
....	....	ALL	ALL	118400	KEN	Westwell
1871	1875	1830	1900	115207	LAN	Ardwick
1781	1851	ALL	1900	131334	LAN	Stockport
1892	....	....	1892	118400	LND	Shoreditch
1880	....	....	....	169129	NFK	West
1817	....	....	....	172820	SRY	Pirebright
1796	1796	1550	1796	102830	STS	Sedgely
1830	....	....	....	106747	WIL	Whaddon
STANFORTH						
1540	1560	....	....	126497	LAN	Wigan
STANGER						
1874	1992	1800	1992	103314	KEN	Snodland
1880	1913	....	1880	129518	NFK	Kings Lynn
1772	1855	1600	1855	148482	OKI	Orkney
STANGMORE						
1500	1900	1500	1900	170216	HAM	ALL
1500	1900	1500	1900	170216	WIL	ALL
STANGRAVE						
1250	1350	1200	1350	154881	KEN	Edenbridge
STANGROOM						
1796	1796	....	1796	136212	NFK	Wells
STANHAM						
1740	1900	1600	1900	117617	NFK	Shouldham
STANHOPE						
....	....	1700	1850	170976	DEV	Holsworthy
1850	1881	1500	1850	175072	LAN	Kirkham
1850	....	1750	1850	103772	RUT	Whissenden
STANIDGE						
1724	....	1630	1730	170348	YKS	Huddersfield
STANIER						
1843	....	....	....	102733	WAR	Birmingham
....	....	ALL	1850	154075	WAR	Birmingham
1800	1992	ALL	ALL	166537	WAR	Birmingham
1900	1992	....	....	154075	???	Newcastle On Tyne
STANIFORTH						
....	....	1500	1600	120855	DBY	Norton
....	....	1870	1992	120855	YKS	Darnall
STANILAND						
1760	1891	1841	1891	157252	BRK	Abingdon
1750	1891	1750	1891	157252	ENG	Midlands
1862	1862	....	....	108901	NTT	Ordsall
1693	1900	ALL	ALL	169528	YKS	Thorne
STANLAKE						
1789	1855	1700	1860	143251	CON	Bodmin
1789	1855	1700	1860	143251	CON	Lanhydrock
1789	1855	1700	1860	143251	CON	St Kew
1840	....	1840	1880	135429	DEV	Tavistock
STANLEY						
1816	1852	....	1852	137405	CAM	Long Stanton
1719	1719	1660	1718	102830	DBY	Carsington
1900	1992	1700	1900	157872	DBY	Pilsley
1806	1836	ALL	1836	108642	ESS	Takeley
1664	1992	ALL	ALL	166596	GLS	Chipping Campden
1760	1992	ALL	ALL	166596	GLS	Snowshill
1830	....	1850	1992	130486	IRL	Cork
1716	1992	....	1716	159506	LAN	Ashton Under Lyne
1908	1992	....	1908	166553	LND	Croydon
1820	1910	ALL	ALL	162205	NTH	Geddington

Known From	To	Researching From	To	Ref	Cty	Place
STANLEY contd.						
1780	1780	....	....	103632	NTH	Preston Capes
1770	1992	1700	1800	166561	NTT	Ratoliffeon On Trent
1815	1992	1815	1992	166596	OXF	Chipping Norton
1700	1899	1640	1820	135941	SFK	Lakenheath
1872	1940	1800	1870	166588	SRY	Newington
1749	1860	....	....	164631	STS	Colwich
1867	1880	....	....	164631	STS	Stafford
1749	1860	....	....	164631	STS	Stowe
....	....	1800	1850	145688	STS	Whittington
....	....	ALL	ALL	155632	WAR	Birmingham
1825	1880	1800	1825	162361	WAR	Birmingham
1848	1992	1848	1992	166596	WAR	Birmingham
1750	1840	1700	1850	146684	WIC	Cookstown
1803	....	1770	1840	170348	WIL	Wootton Bassett
1869	1992	1700	1869	172448	WOR	Clapton
1774	1827	1770	1830	103632	WOR	Overbury
1860	1890	....	1860	162949	WOR	Redditch
1908	1922	1879	1922	139645	WYK	Bradford
1908	1922	1879	1922	139645	WYK	Eccleshill
1898	1992	ALL	ALL	143634	WYK	Wakefield
1800	1850	1750	1850	138517	YKS	Holmfirth
....	....	ALL	1900	163368	YKS	Keighley
STANMORE						
1765	1992	ALL	ALL	160288	HAM	Andover
....	....	1200	1992	115975	WIL	ALL
STANNANOUGHT						
1746	....	....	....	131504	LAN	Hoole
1746	1776	ALL	ALL	135909	LAN	Much Hoole
STANNARD						
1887	1920	1900	....	109967	BKM	Chesham
1800	1870	1700	1870	124605	ESS	Beaumont
....	....	1900	....	109967	SSX	Crowborough
STANNIFORTH						
1615	1633	1575	1633	141097	YKS	Braithwell
1712	1841	1600	1765	101575	YKS	Howden
1712	1841	1600	1765	101575	YKS	Snaith
STANNING						
1590	1850	1590	1850	171549	DEV	Buckfastleigh
1725	....	1725	....	109347	LAN	Downham
STANROYD						
1750	1800	....	....	134007	CAM	Wisbech
STANSBIE						
1783	1992	1700	1800	140287	WAR	Birmingham
STANSBURY						
1790	1820	1600	1790	108413	SOM	Banwell
STANSBY						
ALL	ALL	ALL	ALL	149535	ALL	ALL
STANSFIELD						
1829	1992	1700	1829	160962	CHS	???
1870	1960	ALL	ALL	169315	DUR	Sunderland
1829	1992	1700	1829	160962	LAN	North
....	....	ALL	ALL	169315	LAN	South
1885	1992	....	....	162264	LAN	Blackpool
1780	1992	1700	1780	162264	LAN	Heptonstall
1929	1992	....	....	162264	LAN	Manchester
....	....	1850	1890	159573	LND	Kensington
1580	1625	1580	1625	107522	WRY	Todmorden
1800	1850	1840	1880	177350	YKS	Brighouse
1833	1891	....	....	162264	YKS	Stansfield
1885	1929	....	....	162264	YKS	Upper Eastwood
1829	1992	1700	1829	160962	YKS	???
STANT						
1750	1880	1750	1880	130567	FLN	Bettisfield
STANTON						
1847	1888	1800	1847	146900	ANT	Belfast
1855	1920	ALL	ALL	149268	CAM	March
1868	1992	....	....	166626	DUR	Winston
1750	1800	1650	1850	133892	LEI	ALL
1825	1840	ALL	1825	122823	LEI	Claybrook
1847	1888	1800	1847	146900	LKS	Glasgow
1789	1920	1750	1860	147974	MDX	Bethnal Green
1765	1840	....	....	160458	NBL	???
....	....	ALL	1870	166626	NTH	Northampton
1700	1880	....	....	121983	NTH	Radstone
1940	1992	1640	1992	148156	NTH	Wootton
1700	1800	....	1800	177695	OXF	Banbury
....	....	1700	1860	153184	SOM	ALL
....	....	1850	1860	153184	SOM	Marlow
1800	1800	....	1800	177695	STS	Gt Wyrley
....	....	1800	1840	163791	WOR	Birmingham
1800	1870	1700	1800	134104	WOR	Warndon
....	....	ALL	1870	166626	???	Newcastle
STANWARD						
1650	1667	1600	1650	155276	SFK	Mendlasham
STANWAY						
1810	1960	1700	1860	122424	STS	North
1750	1830	1700	1850	122505	STS	Audley
1790	1830	1700	1850	122505	STS	Wolstanton
1810	1823	....	....	122505	YKS	Swinton By Sheffield
STANWELL						
1825	1853	1700	1824	131245	LIN	Spalding
STANWORTH						
1625	....	1625	....	109347	LAN	Whalley
STANYON						
1799	1992	ALL	ALL	158585	HUN	Little Stukely
STAPLE						
1799	1910	ALL	ALL	162108	CON	Mylor
?	?	?	?	177938	DOR	Beaminster
....	....	1750	....	108677	LND	St George In The East
1770	1818	ALL	1770	161500	SOM	Crewkerne
STAPLEFORD						
1737	1992	ALL	ALL	168742	LEI	East
....	....	1800	1900	101273	WIL	ALL
STAPLEHURST						
1800	1880	ALL	ALL	131164	SSX	Fletching
STAPLES						
1790	1809	....	1770	108839	CAM	Soham
1837	1900	1837	1900	156388	HAM	East Wellow
1840	1992	1700	1840	166634	KEN	Knockholt
1901	1992	1700	1901	122963	MDX	Willesden
....	....	1800	1992	122556	WIL	Devizes
1809	1992	1700	1809	114464	WIL	Frome
STAPLETON						
1781	1940	....	....	128996	CAM	Thorney
1846	1943	ALL	ALL	151580	HRT	Pirton
1840	1880	1721	1970	138215	HUN	Holme
....	....	1700	1900	147494	LND	London
1624	1900	1790	1900	162914	NTT	Basford
1749	1851	....	....	130877	NTT	Greasley
1624	1900	1790	1900	162914	NTT	Greasley
1801	1848	ALL	1848	178411	NTT	Nottingham
1834	1860	1820	1860	125970	SRY	Southwark
STAPLEY						
1788	?	?	?	166642	KEN	Ashford
1570	1992	1400	1700	166650	SSX	Buxted
1570	1992	1400	1700	166650	SSX	Rotherfield
1824	....	1700	1900	151246	SSX	Wadhurst
STAPOL						
....	....	1748	....	130079	SOM	???
STAPYLTON						
1290	1800	....	....	131229	YKS	North Riding
STAR						
1801	1801	1780	1830	173428	ESS	Chelmsford
1780	1950	1650	1780	128376	SOM	Batcombe
STARBUCK						
1730	1850	1700	1900	119008	LEI	Harby
1695	1730	....	....	119008	NTT	Bramcote
1700	1725	1600	1700	172901	NTT	???
STARES						
1930	1992	ALL	1930	159808	HAM	ALL
STARK						
....	1794	ALL	ALL	129933	DEV	Culmstock
....	....	1820	1825	129933	DEV	Tiverton
1881	1919	1881	1919	124826	LAN	Manchester
1838	....	1838	....	124826	LKS	Glasgow
1863	1869	1863	1871	124826	LTN	Musselburgh
1750	1980	1600	1870	123293	SOM	ALL
1841	1883	ALL	ALL	129933	SOM	Bridgewater
STARKEY						
....	....	ALL	ALL	166669	ALL	Name Study
1750	1901	1534	1750	113050	CHS	Agden
1765	1782	?	1765	128910	DBY	Church Gresley
1785	1815	....	....	165999	GLS	Bedminster
1665	....	ALL	1665	131059	KEN	Leybourne
1857	1906	1906	1920	113050	LAN	Irlam
1815	1871	1855	1900	164321	MDX	East London
1790	1793	....	1790	164321	NFK	Norwich
1811	1818	1818	1992	128910	NTT	Brinsley
1785	1815	....	....	165999	SOM	Stapleton
1790	1992	1750	1820	173649	YKS	Birstall
1876	1988	1850	1876	128368	YKS	Doncaster
1876	1988	1850	1876	128368	YKS	Sheffield
1600	1840	1840	1992	172782	YKS	Wakefield

Known From	To	Researching From	To	Ref	Cty	Place
STARKS						
1831	1879	1800	1880	166677	HAM	Downton
1831	1879	1800	1880	166677	HAM	Hordle
STARLEY						
1615	1907	ALL	ALL	150517	SSX	Central
1615	1907	ALL	ALL	150517	SSX	South
1870	1992	ALL	ALL	150517	WAR	???
STARLING						
1926	1926	1850	1926	103640	ESS	West Ham
1897	....	ALL	ALL	115533	LND	???
1926	1926	1850	1926	103640	MDX	Poplar
1800	1840	1750	1840	158658	NFK	North Walsham
1851	1900	1820	1900	158658	NFK	Norwich
1819	1992	1650	1819	137073	NFK	Stokesby
1800	1840	1750	1840	158658	NFK	Tuttington
1800	1830	ALL	ALL	154008	SFK	ALL
1816	1900	1750	1900	110906	SFK	Hawkendon
1700	1800	1600	1800	105333	SSX	Chichester
1721	1800	1600	1800	130125	WOR	Alfrick
1780	1834	1700	1780	142883	WOR	Bushley
STARMAR						
1801	1801	1700	1800	102830	HUN	Orton Waterville
STARMER						
1800	1830	1650	1800	103888	CAM	Cambridge
1600	1930	1850	1930	125709	NTH	Kettering
STARMORE						
....	1708	1500	1708	175072	LIN	Belchford
STARNELL						
1680	1720	1600	1680	151769	LIN	Fulbeck
STARR						
1673	1718	....	....	117234	IRL	Meath
1781	1781	ALL	ALL	126721	NTT	Bulwell
1800	1850	1845	1860	166685	SOM	Nunney
1830	....	1800	1950	146978	STS	Burslem
STARSMORE						
....	....	ALL	1880	156663	ALL	ALL
....	....	ALL	1880	156663	LEI	ALL
1820	1848	ALL	1820	118222	NTH	Fotheringay
....	....	ALL	1880	156663	SSX	Brighton
START						
....	1851	1700	1851	159271	LND	East
1750	1800	1700	1800	115614	NFK	Gissing
....	....	1841	ALL	175625	NTT	Long Eaton
STARTUP						
....	....	ALL	ALL	166693	ALL	Name Study
1800	1850	1700	1800	143170	KEN	Maidstone
1853	....	1700	1853	173509	KEN	Tunbridge Wells
STATHAM						
1851	1992	1810	1860	173649	DBY	Melbourne
1850	1992	ALL	1850	165751	DBY	Swadlincote
1750	1880	1750	1880	130567	STS	Audley
STATHAMS						
1764	1794	1700	1764	176885	BKM	Great Hampden
STATHERS						
1850	1900	1750	1850	176753	YKS	Cowden
STATTERS						
1805	1927	ALL	1805	158445	YKS	Patrington
STATTON						
1800	....	....	....	136964	BKM	Ivinghoe
STAUNTON						
1821	1992	1750	1821	157783	GAL	Ballenasloe
1880	1992	1600	1880	136638	IRL	Mayo
1811	1992	1700	1811	130931	MAY	Swinford
STAVELEY						
....	....	ALL	ALL	100854	ALL	ALL
STAVERT						
....	....	ALL	ALL	177822	LAN	Manchester
....	....	ALL	ALL	177822	LIN	Liverpool
1695	1900	ALL	ALL	177822	ROX	Newcastleton
1812	1975	1700	1812	115894	WES	Kendal
STAVOLD						
1960	1992	....	....	144215	LAN	Morecambe
STAWELL						
ALL	ALL	1200	1992	167738	ENG	ALL
STAWPERT						
1679	1877	....	....	132381	NBL	???
STAYNES						
1634	1696	ALL	1696	168718	NTH	Irthlingborough
STAYT						
1420	1914	....	....	109991	GLS	Bledington
1780	1900	1500	1900	125725	OXF	Bledington
STEAD						
1841	1860	ALL	1992	133159	HEF	Ford
1680	1720	1650	1720	160849	HEF	South Kelsey
STEAD contd.						
1880	1979	ALL	1880	133159	LAN	Liverpool
1911	....	....	....	150762	MON	Ebbw Vale
....	....	1750	1800	142298	SAL	???
1790	1866	1700	1866	116300	YKS	Easingwood
1826	1854	....	1826	176761	YKS	Holbeck
1826	1854	....	1826	176761	YKS	Howden
1826	1854	....	1826	176761	YKS	Hunslet
1790	1795	1700	1800	168297	YKS	???
STEADMAN						
1820	1992	1700	1820	102342	AVN	Clifton
1784	1834	ALL	1784	152315	SCT	Annan
....	....	1750	1820	147176	YKS	Barningham
STEANE						
1853	1953	1853	1953	143286	WAR	Edgbaston
1701	1920	1500	1700	166707	WAR	Harborough Magna
STEAR						
1688	1735	1550	1700	100013	SRY	Farnham
STEARN						
1780	1851	ALL	1851	118990	ALL	ALL
1806	1870	1700	1806	116440	ESS	West Hamshire
1700	1992	1750	1770	162329	SFK	West
STEARS						
1782	1930	1740	1782	101427	HAM	Portsmouth
1737	1752	1664	1737	101427	SOM	South Petherton
STEBBENS						
1870	1870	1870	1870	166715	DUR	Hartlepool
1839	1857	1839	1857	166715	ESS	Chelmsford
1769	1992	1769	1992	166715	ESS	Maldon
1897	1988	1897	1988	166715	HAM	Portsmouth
1907	1992	1907	1992	166715	KEN	North
1857	1901	1857	1901	166715	LND	North
1870	1923	1870	1923	166715	LND	Bermondsey
1858	1935	1858	1935	166715	LND	Deptford
1821	1850	1821	1850	166715	LND	Stepney
1803	1803	1803	1810	166715	NBL	Newcastle
1844	1868	1840	1870	166715	NFK	Depwade
1791	1805	1791	1805	166715	NFK	Thetford
1842	1992	1842	1992	166715	NFK	Yarmouth
1792	1888	1792	1888	166715	SFK	Hartismere
1824	1842	1824	1842	166715	SFK	Hone
1796	1889	1796	1889	166715	SFK	Mutford
1851	1992	1845	1992	166715	YKS	Bradford
1895	1895	1895	1895	166715	YKS	Halifax
1892	1908	1845	1908	166715	YKS	Wharfedale
STEBBING						
1697	1890	1600	1800	157732	ESS	Springfield
1780	1880	1780	1880	140295	???	London
STEBBINGS						
1851	1881	1700	1851	123307	NFK	Garbolisham
1770	1992	1700	1770	174378	SFK	Otley
1770	1992	1700	1770	174378	SFK	Thorndon
STEBBINS						
1800	1880	1700	1800	104744	ESS	Maldon
STEDFORD						
1778	1818	....	....	144282	SSX	Chailey
STEDMAN						
1740	1740	....	....	127426	KEN	Aylesford
1621	1721	....	....	127426	KEN	Canty St Margarets
1621	1621	....	....	127426	KEN	Egerton
1563	1843	....	....	127426	KEN	Lenham
1685	1685	....	....	127426	KEN	Otterden
1751	1789	....	....	127426	KEN	Stockbury
1775	1816	....	....	127426	KEN	Wychling
1500	1873	1200	1873	113484	KRS	Kinross
1870	1880	1880	1992	148415	LND	Peckham
1818	1841	1200	1873	113484	NFK	East Rudham
1776	1857	1200	1873	113484	SFK	Packenham
1665	1980	1550	1665	166723	SRY	Bisley
1792	....	....	....	173932	SRY	Bramley
1759	1829	1730	1830	159581	SRY	Cranleigh
1793	....	....	....	173932	SRY	Cranley
1791	....	....	....	173932	SRY	Horsell
1806	1881	1700	1806	117676	SSX	Lindfield
STEED						
1880	1980	1200	1880	166731	KEN	Canterbury
....	....	1700	1899	174963	SOM	Kilmersden
....	....	1700	1899	174963	SOM	Mells
STEEDEN						
1770	1992	1700	1950	124796	BKM	Tingewick
1770	....	1700	1800	124796	NTH	Charleton
STEEDMAN						
1755	1770	1716	1983	113484	KRS	Fossoway
1844	1875	1716	1983	113484	KRS	Kinross

Known Researching
From To From To Ref Cty Place

STEEDMAN contd.
1800 1873 1716 1983 113484 KRS Milnathort
1850 1877 1716 1983 113484 MLN Edinburgh
1699 1782 1716 1983 113484 PER Abernethy
1726 1800 1716 1983 113484 PER Baulk Of Struie
1716 1800 1716 1983 113484 PER Forteviot
1827 .... 1716 1983 113484 PER Longforgan
1802 1850 1716 1983 113484 PER Perth
1765 1790 1716 1983 113484 PER Pitwhanatrie
1786 1868 .... 113484 SAL Shrewsbury
1594 1741 .... 117404 STS Penkridge
1593 .... ALL 1600 139459 STS Walsall
1770 1800 .... 100420 WAR Meriden
1860 1992 1700 1860 123307 ??? Edinburgh
STEEDS
1850 1992 1700 1849 156876 ??? Bedminster
STEEL
1818 1860 ALL 1818 149632 ABD Fyvie
1818 1860 ALL 1818 149632 ABD Tarves
1748 1870 1740 1870 171654 AYR Kilmaurs
1793 1857 1700 1900 168246 AYR New Cumnock
1770 1785 1700 1800 145149 DOR Verwood
1792 1792 1700 1800 153001 DUR Eglescliffe
1830 1938 1700 1830 118834 HAM Portsmouth
1840 1900 1800 1840 166804 LND Whitechapel
1737 1825 1700 1860 157503 PER Auchterarder
1650 1992 1650 1992 166758 SCT ???
1810 1850 1700 1900 166804 SFK ALL
STEELE
1836 1992 1700 1836 166782 ABD Old Machar
.... 1800 1850 111708 AYR New Cumnock
1780 1871 ALL ALL 106658 CHS Macclesfield
1780 1871 ALL ALL 106658 CHS Partic Sutton
1565 1668 1565 1668 147532 CHS Wybunbury
1861 1940 ? 1861 177806 CMA Carlisle
1650 1850 1550 1650 103055 CUL West
1730 1771 1650 1800 153354 DUR Gateshead
1610 1780 ALL 1780 111538 GLS North West
1800 1850 1700 1800 118915 HAM ALL
1740 1910 1740 1930 111538 HEF Ross
1766 1992 1766 1992 112305 LKS Coatbridge
1920 1992 .... 1920 113530 PEM Angle
.... 1650 1750 117803 WRY Marton Cum Grafton
STEELEY
1800 1825 1700 1800 110477 CAM Wisbech
1800 1825 1700 1800 110477 NFK Upwell
STEELS
.... 1800 1850 137618 ERY Selby
1800 1992 ALL ALL 105902 NTH Eye
1813 1925 ALL ALL 135208 NTH Eye
1864 .... 163155 YKS Bradford
1870 1910 1700 1900 135127 YKS Pocklington
STEEN
1895 1910 ALL 1895 179515 NFK Kings Lynn
STEENTON
.... 1840 1900 165093 SAL Ludlow
STEEPLE
1882 1992 ALL 1882 160938 LAN Oldham
STEER
.... 1760 1800 165794 DEV Stoke Damerel
1558 1735 .... 115606 HAM Odiham
1700 1911 1500 1700 166804 HAM Odiham
1803 1900 1700 1803 166804 HRT Aldenham
1690 1760 1760 1850 130230 KEN Westerham
1836 1970 1700 1970 152536 SRY Croydon
1730 1900 ALL 1730 135607 SRY Horsell
1754 1876 .... 127957 SRY Limpsfield
1740 1850 1851 1992 130230 SRY Limpsfield
1866 1866 ALL 1866 108642 SRY Lingfield
1600 1659 1500 1700 131547 SRY Ockley
1761 1817 .... 127957 SRY Tandridge
.... ALL ALL 133868 SSX Horsham
1836 1970 1700 1970 152536 SSX Kirdford
1824 1936 1700 1824 119512 SSX Petworth
1810 1810 1600 1810 147885 SSX West Grinstead
1866 1866 ALL 1866 108642 SSX Westhoathly
STEERS
1737 1752 1664 1737 101427 SOM South Petherton
STEEVENS
1700 1850 1600 1690 166979 DEV Tiverton
1849 1891 1830 1922 163317 LND Central
.... 1779 ALL 1779 134511 NTT Trowell
STEFENS
1780 1800 1600 1780 148792 HAM North West

Known Researching
From To From To Ref Cty Place

STEFFEN
.... 1800 .... 137456 BDF Campton
STEGER
1800 1870 1800 1870 138193 SOM Kelston
STEGGALS
1803 1860 1800 1860 119091 NFK Northwold
1764 1803 1750 1810 119091 SFK Gt Finborough
1680 1760 1650 1800 119091 SFK Haughley
STEGGLES
1850 1992 .... 120057 ENG South East
1753 1837 ALL 1752 166820 SFK Brome
STEIL
.... 1600 1680 154873 NBL Holy Island
STEILL
1617 1650 ALL 1650 149063 MLN Newbattle
STELL
1750 1992 1300 1750 100803 WYK Heptonstall
1640 1700 .... 145688 YKS Keighley
STEMP
1800 1850 ALL ALL 107336 DEV Dartmoor
1850 1889 ALL ALL 107336 HAM Crondall
STENLAKE
1817 1992 1650 1817 139769 DEV Tavistock
STENNER
.... 1500 1900 166863 DEV ALL
.... 1500 1900 166863 LND ALL
.... 1500 1900 166863 SOM ALL
STENNETT
1700 ALL .... 163465 LIN Rippingale
.... 1850 1600 1850 175641 LIN ???
STENNING
1698 1724 1670 1770 159581 SRY Cranleigh
STENNITT
1759 1871 .... 1800 109622 YKS Rawcliffe
STENSON
.... 1900 ALL 174963 BKM ???
1780 1890 1750 1992 160458 GLS Coleford
.... 1700 1899 174963 IRL Clare
.... 1700 1899 174963 IRL Dublin
.... 1700 1899 174963 IRL Limerick
.... 1900 ALL 174963 KEN ???
1860 1890 1830 1860 177393 NTT Eastwood
1890 1960 .... 177393 YKS Doncaster
STENT
1777 1851 1770 1861 170143 HAM Buriton
1700 1800 1600 1700 163015 SSX West
STENTIFORD
1760 1850 ALL ALL 162205 DEV Buckfastleigh
STEP
1763 1810 1730 1770 170348 WIL Broad Blunsdon
STEPEHENSON
1754 1754 1538 1780 118893 NRY Great Broughton
STEPHEN
1800 1868 1750 1850 137057 ABD Auchendoir
1850 1900 .... 126497 ABD Forgue
1850 1992 1850 1992 145467 ABD Glenbuchat
.... 1760 .... 149187 ABD Old Deer
1820 1870 .... 148342 ABD Peterhead
.... 1800 1840 172871 ABD Peterhead
1855 1903 .... 172871 ANS Craig
1800 1900 .... 126497 BAN Grange
1800 1900 1750 1900 126500 BAN Grange
1807 1883 1700 1807 102997 GMP New Deer
1803 .... 1700 1803 160385 IOM Lezayre
.... 1780 1820 121479 IOM ???
? 1850 1500 1850 105333 IOM ?????
1654 1992 1858 1992 104302 KCD Kinneff
1880 1930 1800 1920 130869 MOR Peterhead
STEPHENS
? .... 118508 CMN Llanelli
1837 1881 1800 1837 130877 CON Callington
1795 1875 1700 1795 176575 CON Gwinear
.... 1800 1881 139491 CON Liskeard
1834 .... 1834 152242 CON Marazion
1825 1851 1800 1900 121541 CON North Hill
.... 1881 1881 1900 139491 CON Penzance
1841 1871 1800 1881 165824 CON Redruth
1840 1992 .... 109444 CON St Agnes
.... 1700 1900 136972 CON St Angnes
1833 1847 1600 1833 152080 CON St Cleer
1829 1932 ALL 1837 101362 CON St Columb
1830 1940 1760 1830 158267 CON St Enoder
1818 1844 1800 1860 108510 CON St Ives
1772 1850 1600 1772 149888 CON St Ives

Known From	To	Researching From	To	Ref	Cty	Place
STEPHENS contd.						
1862	....	1800	1800	139114	DEN	Ruabon
1839	1871	1800	1940	158399	DEV	Brixham
1740	1780	1690	1890	166979	DEV	Tiverton
1795	1992	ALL	1795	119105	GAL	Galway
1890	1992	1840	1900	166901	GLA	Cardiff
1750	1870	1700	1750	171859	GLS	Alderton
1847	1880	1700	1847	155225	GLS	Bulley
1820	....	....	....	101613	GLS	Cheltenham
1847	1880	1700	1847	155225	GLS	Churcham
1675	1850	....	....	167053	GLS	Cirencester
1787	1787	1730	1890	176672	GLS	Farmington
1880	1923	....	....	155225	GLS	Gloucester
1787	1972	1700	1800	176672	GLS	Sherborne
....	....	1770	1824	101478	GLS	Snowshill
1781	1915	ALL	1781	143960	HAM	Chale
1810	1810	1600	1850	145289	HAM	Isle Of Wight
1800	1900	1800	1900	177032	HAM	Lymington
1795	1992	ALL	1795	119105	KER	Blennerville
1881	1957	1875	1950	165824	LAN	Bolton
1841	1992	1500	1841	110310	LAN	Liverpool
1787	1809	1770	1851	160636	LIN	Timberland
1800	1985	....	....	135984	LND	Clerkenwell
1800	1985	....	....	135984	LND	Islington
1800	1850	1800	1850	124605	MDX	Bethnal Green
1760	1895	1700	1895	166898	MDX	Westminster
1804	1804	1800	1804	147575	MON	Penallt
1800	1850	1700	1850	132993	PEM	Cosheston
1884	....	1700	1884	120030	PEM	Pembroke Dock
1817	1941	1700	1817	164917	SOM	Bath
1790	1800	1800	1900	162876	SOM	Clifton
1786	1826	1760	1850	133639	SOM	Coker
1800	1820	1500	1820	175463	SSX	East Grinstead
1850	1859	1800	1899	113743	SSX	Newhaven
1850	....	1800	1899	113743	SSX	Rye
1835	1881	1800	1890	135763	STS	Wombourne
ALL	1681	....	....	170178	WIL	Bishops Cannings
1800	1860	ALL	1800	167029	WIL	Ramsbury
1740	....	....	1770	160873	WOR	Old Swinford
1841	1841	1500	1841	110310	YKS	Scarborough
STEPHENSON						
....	....	1800	1900	139114	ARM	???
1734	1856	1600	1734	173711	CMA	Milburn
1781	1871	ALL	1781	154563	CUL	Alston
1784	1851	....	....	138401	CUL	Brampton
1784	1851	....	....	138401	CUL	Lamercost
1678	1810	1646	1678	138401	CUL	Penrith
1871	1992	1871	1992	154563	DUR	ALL
1800	1824	1824	1859	117625	DUR	Heworth
1940	1992	ALL	1940	111678	DUR	Wingate
1858	1900	1800	1858	167711	DUR	???
1739	1739	ALL	1745	113611	EYK	Hull
1799	1831	ALL	ALL	124982	LAN	Lancaster
1850	1900	1800	1901	117145	LAN	Ulverston
1700	1789	1700	1992	101087	LIN	South
1800	1992	....	....	176125	LIN	Asterby
1700	1789	1700	1992	101087	LIN	Boston
1800	1992	....	....	176125	LIN	Goulceby
1805	1830	ALL	1850	132217	LIN	Wainfleet
1751	1871	....	....	145335	NBL	Knarsdale
1720	1800	....	1720	176516	NBL	Newcastle
1780	1992	1700	1780	160458	NBL	Ovingham
1774	....	1770	1800	117625	NBL	Shotley
1760	1992	....	....	160458	NBL	???
1851	1851	....	....	108901	NTT	Ordsall
1670	1720	1600	1670	121339	NYK	Lythe
1800	1845	1750	1800	138347	SRY	Beddington
1739	1772	ALL	ALL	124982	WES	Heversham
1785	1810	1755	1785	139149	WES	Kendal
1773	1821	1765	1795	139149	WRY	Burton Leonard
1785	1814	....	1785	101761	WRY	Thornhill
1735	1780	1750	1780	108510	YKS	Batley
....	....	1700	1992	166936	YKS	Batley-Morley
1778	1803	1600	1803	166928	YKS	Brompton By Sawdon
1790	1986	1760	1986	129798	YKS	Farnley
1806	1871	1700	1806	166928	YKS	Flixton
....	....	1800	1992	166936	YKS	Gildersome
1816	1846	1770	1851	170267	YKS	Holbeck
1770	1870	1700	1900	138517	YKS	Holmfirth
1867	1946	....	....	166928	YKS	Hunmanby
1809	1825	1700	1809	137650	YKS	Seamer
1854	1920	1700	1854	116351	YKS	Whitby
1824	1992	....	....	117625	???	Darlingotn

Known From	To	Researching From	To	Ref	Cty	Place
STEPNEY						
1897	1989	ALL	1897	175323	LND	ALL
1897	1989	ALL	1897	175323	SSX	Brighton
STEPTOE						
ALL	ALL	ALL	ALL	166944	BKM	ALL
1877	....	....	....	142360	BRK	Purley
ALL	ALL	ALL	ALL	166944	OXF	ALL
STEREWOOD						
1600	1624	ALL	1600	131059	KEN	Cowden
STERLAND						
1795	1800	1770	1800	174602	DBY	Wingerworth
STERN						
....	....	ALL	ALL	162329	EAG	ALL
1830	....	....	1830	161071	HRT	St Albans
STERNE						
....	....	1707	1804	111805	CAM	Granchester
STERREY						
1600	1992	ALL	ALL	112674	GLS	ALL
STERRY						
....	....	ALL	ALL	159670	ALL	Name Study
1685	1900	1560	1900	166952	GLS	Longhope
1585	1992	1585	1880	166952	SFK	Bury St Edmunds
1585	1992	1585	1880	166952	SFK	Lowestoft
STEVANS						
1575	1710	1575	1992	133450	CON	Bodmin
1600	1680	....	....	139491	CON	Towednack
1600	1680	....	....	139491	CON	Zennor
STEVENS						
1834	1930	1834	1930	113670	AVN	Bath
1750	1800	1700	1820	167088	BKM	Amersham
1741	1770	1600	1750	143693	BKM	Bledlow
1769	....	1700	1780	124796	BKM	Hughenden
1751	1752	1700	1850	156698	BKM	Marlow
1770	1800	1650	1800	143693	BKM	Princes Risborough
1739	....	1600	1750	143693	BKM	Radnage
1776	....	1650	1800	143693	BKM	West Wycombe
1815	1915	1800	1915	170143	BRK	Eastbury
1761	....	....	1780	171441	BRK	Faringdon
1768	1875	1750	1880	136719	BRK	Hampstead Norris
1815	1915	1800	1915	170143	BRK	W Shefford
1786	1992	1600	1865	151033	CON	Duloe
1800	1850	1700	1800	166995	CON	Falmouth
1720	1760	1600	1720	116637	CON	St Ives
1840	1992	1700	1900	168068	CON	St Ives
1750	1900	1700	1800	168750	CON	St Just In Penwith
1816	....	1800	1830	124796	CON	Torpoint
1706	1881	1600	1706	102571	CON	Zennor
1805	....	1850	1992	151378	DBY	Chesterfield
1893	....	1700	1893	116181	DBY	Derby
1820	1850	1850	1950	166979	DEV	Cadbury
1799	1992	1700	1799	167118	DEV	Milton Damerel
1790	1850	1600	1992	167096	DEV	Sheldon
1864	1934	1800	1864	128368	DEV	Teignmouth
1835	1871	1800	1875	177393	DEV	Templeton
1700	1850	1600	1650	166979	DEV	Tiverton
1903	1914	1870	1930	166979	DEV	Torquay
1827	1890	1800	1930	133639	DOR	Abbotsbury
1785	....	1770	1790	133639	DOR	Chelborough
1820	1930	1820	1930	148873	DOR	Hamoon
1856	1910	1850	1950	133639	DOR	Melcombe
1800	1906	ALL	1800	151424	DOR	Stratton
1750	1890	1700	1800	144657	ESS	Chingford
1800	1850	1790	1900	156698	ESS	Chingford
1878	....	1875	1880	163775	ESS	Forestgate
1880	1910	1875	1915	163775	ESS	Leyton
1740	1800	ALL	1740	131059	ESS	West Ham
1820	1850	1790	1900	156698	ESS	Woodford
1762	1762	1500	1762	109274	HAM	Combe
1682	1736	1660	1760	159581	HAM	Crondall
1757	1992	ALL	1757	141526	HRT	Tring
1900	1950	1900	1992	156698	IOW	???
1874	1903	1850	1920	166979	KEN	Canterbury
....	....	1890	1960	166979	KEN	Dover
1819	1870	1700	1819	171182	KEN	Faversham
1843	1868	1830	1870	163775	KEN	Plumstead
....	....	1920	1960	166979	KEN	Tunbridge Wells
1850	?	?	1850	128112	LND	Aldersgate
....	....	1862	1900	151602	LND	Battersea
1835	1850	1800	1850	126586	LND	Shoreditch
1865	....	ALL	ALL	118389	LND	Spitalfields
1850	1960	1850	1850	134872	LND	Wandsworth
1857	....	....	....	156329	LND	West End
1751	1992	1700	1900	156698	LND	???
1840	1861	1800	1880	118192	MDX	Bethnal Green

Known From	To	Researching From	To	Ref	Cty	Place
STEVENS contd.						
1800	1850	1800	1850	124605	MDX	Bethnal Green
?	?	?	?	127701	MDX	Bromley
1853	1906	1800	1860	166316	MDX	Chelsea
1851	1919	1841	1930	167002	MDX	Clapton
1805	1805	1745	1805	107573	MDX	Feltham
1880	1893	ALL	1880	118389	MDX	Hackney
1850	1880	1850	1880	124605	MDX	Hackney
1874	1877	1871	1900	167002	MDX	Islington
1873	1878	1870	1880	163775	MDX	Limehouse
....	....	1800	1900	166960	MDX	London
1851	1860	1800	1900	156698	MDX	New Hampton
1869	....	1845	1875	163775	MDX	Poplar
1828	1875	1800	1900	167002	MDX	Shoreditch
1819	1856	1750	1900	167002	MDX	St Luke
1880	1930	1880	1930	167002	MDX	Stoke Newington
1920	1992	1700	1920	167010	NFK	Thetford
1880	1992	1750	1880	128732	NTH	Northampton
1917	1950	1900	1992	151378	NTT	Mansfield
1679	1992	ALL	1679	110000	NTT	Papplewick
1839	1839	1800	1870	159581	SFK	Stowmarket
1817	1890	1700	1820	121568	SOM	West
1826	1869	1800	1900	121568	SOM	Ash Priors
1813	1992	ALL	ALL	115762	SOM	Bath
1880	?	1800	1992	167096	SOM	Huish-Ch
1841	....	ALL	1880	118389	SOM	Nunney
1795	....	1795	1900	106410	SOM	Pitminster
1860	1930	1850	1920	138479	SOM	Redhill
1843	....	ALL	1907	118389	SOM	Wells
1880	?	1800	1992	167096	SOM	Wiveliscombe
1815	1876	....	....	173932	SRY	Ashtead
1871	....	1870	1873	163775	SRY	Bermondsey
1776	1812	1700	1812	167002	SRY	Camberwell
1840	1900	....	....	117560	SRY	Chertsey
1829	1992	ALL	1829	107239	SRY	Chobhay
1600	1992	1600	1992	139912	SRY	East Clandon
1828	1828	1780	1830	142999	SRY	Godalming
1835	1841	1800	1850	102717	SRY	Lambeth
1792	1818	....	....	173932	SRY	Lambeth
1805	1851	....	....	173932	SRY	Pirbright
1874	....	1871	1881	115886	SRY	Wandsworth
1788	1960	1700	1788	167061	SSX	Bexhill On Sea
1850	ALL	....	....	167037	SSX	Hastings
1800	....	....	....	167037	SSX	Ringmer
1744	1770	1600	1744	147885	SSX	Westmeston
1816	1840	1700	1900	171522	SSX	Willingdon
....	....	ALL	1820	178403	SSX	???
....	....	1792	1870	115142	STS	Central
1802	1939	ALL	....	132349	SXE	Seaford
1740	1987	ALL	....	132349	SXE	Southease
1685	1885	ALL	....	132349	SXE	West Firle
1811	1834	1811	1834	113670	WIL	Etchilhampton
....	....	ALL	1825	151602	WIL	Hindon
1823	1896	1795	1881	115886	WIL	Pewsey
1840	1992	ALL	1992	143197	WIL	Trowbridge
....	....	1700	1800	147613	WOR	Dudley
1860	....	1860	1992	151378	YKS	Ecclesall Bierlow
....	....	1800	1870	169056	YKS	Leeds
STEVENS-DARVELL						
1800	1900	1750	1900	156701	ALL	ALL
STEVENSON						
1778	1830	1700	1778	105457	ABD	Aberdeen
1761	1761	....	....	151351	ANS	Arbroath
1783	1825	....	....	151351	ANS	St Vigeans
....	....	1780	1870	155098	AYR	Kilmarnock
....	....	1750	1770	129933	AYR	Kirkmichael
1840	1860	1800	1850	144231	AYR	Muirkirk
1842	1992	1800	1842	113395	BRK	Hagbourne
1820	1850	1725	1900	133450	CON	Falmouth
1799	....	1700	1800	143243	DBY	Chesterfield
1834	1857	....	1834	161691	DBY	Spondon
1790	1850	1725	1900	133450	DEV	Plymouth
1738	1738	ALL	1738	154563	DUR	Weardale
1850	....	ALL	ALL	155373	KEN	Deptford
1600	1800	1550	1600	173169	LEI	Banbury
1695	1725	1600	1694	131245	LEI	Loughborough
1842	1875	1800	1875	146374	LIN	Gosberton
1801	1807	1730	1830	176621	LIN	Kirtinholme
1780	1870	1750	1992	122416	LKS	Darony
1850	1920	ALL	ALL	110388	LKS	Lanark
1769	?	?	?	152897	MDX	West
1809	1840	1780	1820	128724	MDX	London
1742	1830	1650	1742	175218	MDX	???
....	1900	....	1900	136085	MLN	Leith
STEVENSON contd.						
1770	1891	1700	1890	167703	OKI	Westray
1770	1992	1700	1770	143855	RFW	Kilbarchan
1790	1930	1700	1790	150029	RFW	Lochwinnoch
1813	1813	ALL	1813	108537	RFW	Neilston
1769	?	?	?	152897	SRY	West
1763	1900	1763	1900	167134	SSX	Hastings
1763	1900	1763	1900	167134	SSX	Winchelsea
1702	1812	1600	1702	112410	STS	Croxden
1863	1887	1800	1992	171875	TYR	Dungannon
1740	1791	....	....	171654	WIG	Stoneykirk
1923	....	....	....	173932	WIL	Sutton Veny
1863	1883	ALL	1883	104299	YKS	Kirk Sandall
1804	1826	1800	1826	126705	YKS	Sedbury
STEVENTON						
1853	1992	....	....	128716	SAL	Wellington
STEWARD						
1749	1749	1600	1749	159239	ESS	Colchester
....	....	1700	1900	158054	GLA	Taffs Well
....	....	1800	1830	168777	HEF	Stoke Edith
1700	1850	1750	1850	154377	NFK	Barton Bendish
1817	1851	1700	1851	153079	NFK	Carbrooke
1780	1860	1780	1860	154377	NFK	Stoke Ferry
1800	1860	1800	1860	154377	NFK	Wretton
1837	1980	1837	1980	154377	NTH	Peterborough
1804	1804	1760	1800	158089	SFK	Bury St Edmunds
1685	....	....	1685	101761	SFK	Ickworth
1400	1600	1400	1600	144657	SRY	Bansted
....	....	ALL	1809	152978	WOR	Tenbury Wells
STEWARDSON						
....	....	1700	1800	167258	ALL	ALL
1799	1826	1764	1830	169552	LAN	Cartmel Fell
1762	1777	1724	1794	169552	LAN	Cartmel
1735	1813	1725	1840	169552	LAN	Finsthwaite
1757	1770	1732	1974	169552	WES	Hugill
1780	1858	1780	1858	169552	WES	Selside
1750	1807	1728	1812	169552	WES	Staveley
1770	1850	1700	1850	167258	YKS	West Heslerton
STEWART						
....	....	ALL	ALL	169633	ALL	Name Study
1825	1900	1800	1900	120146	ANS	Montrose
1700	1775	1600	1700	174149	ANS	Montrose
1870	1992	1750	1870	118052	ANT	Armoy
1600	1850	1000	1600	113204	ANT	Ballydrain
1900	1992	1900	1992	110825	ANT	Belfast
1870	1992	1750	1870	118052	ANT	Benbane
1836	1852	....	....	146560	ANT	Clough
....	....	1700	1850	165239	ANT	Cullybackey
1818	....	1800	....	156027	AYR	Ayr
1737	....	....	....	127140	AYR	Irvine
1802	1842	ALL	1887	146757	AYR	Kilmarnock
1838	1890	1830	1992	164984	AYR	Kirkmichael
1890	1992	1890	1992	178357	CHS	Wirral
....	....	1700	1960	136972	CON	Penzance
1800	1992	1800	1992	167215	CON	Penzance
1846	....	1802	....	127647	DFS	Torthornwold
?	?	?	?	167169	FIF	Kilconquhar
?	?	?	?	167169	FIF	St Monans
1790	1810	1700	1800	136840	HAM	Portsmouth
....	....	1750	1900	122742	HAM	Southampton
1800	1900	1600	1800	121118	INV	Kingussie
1830	?	ALL	ALL	101370	IRL	???
1825	1838	1780	1850	131547	KCD	Tulliallan
1850	1900	1850	1900	177288	LAN	Liverpool
1850	1992	1850	1992	178357	LAN	Liverpool
....	....	ALL	1865	119326	LKS	Barony
1840	....	....	1840	161888	LKS	???
1880	1992	ALL	1880	142263	LTN	Edinburgh
1890	1930	ALL	ALL	113743	NBL	Bedlington
1775	1850	1850	1992	174149	NBL	Newcastle On Tyne
1879	1980	1850	1980	113743	NBL	Newcastle
1860	1900	ALL	1860	132829	NBL	Westmoor
1700	1850	1750	1850	154377	NFK	Barton Bendish
1780	1860	1780	1860	154377	NFK	Stoke Ferry
1800	1860	1800	1860	154377	NFK	Wretton
1830	1850	1830	1850	177288	NIR	Londonderry
1800	1850	1780	1800	160806	NTH	Castle Ashby
1843	1932	1750	1850	153656	PER	Aberfoyle
1835	1870	1700	1900	167207	PER	Blair Atholl
1757	1795	....	....	116602	PER	Crieff
1820	1849	1780	1849	148288	PER	Crieff
....	....	ALL	1749	119326	PER	Croftpardon
....	....	ALL	1741	119326	PER	Dull
1841	1861	1750	1841	140678	PER	Dull

Known From	To	Researching From	To	Ref	Cty	Place
STEWART contd.						
1841	1861	1750	1841	140678	PER	Foss
1800	1850	1700	1900	167207	PER	Kirkmichael
1841	1861	1750	1841	140678	PER	Moulin
1820	1849	1780	1849	148288	PER	Scone
1800	1830	....	1851	103349	PER	???
1900	1980	1800	1900	119784	SCT	Anderston
....	....	ALL	1820	171751	SCT	Edinburgh
1736	1855	1600	1855	118680	SCT	Glasgow
1800	1830	1750	1850	116386	SCT	Kelso
....	....	ALL	ALL	149349	SCT	???
1800	1992	1800	1992	167215	SCT	???
1880	1992	1800	1880	142603	STI	Stirling
1880	1900	1800	1880	142603	???	Edinburgh
STEWARTSON						
1870	1930	1900	1970	167258	ABD	Fraserburgh
STIBBLES						
1590	1992	1773	1992	167266	ANS	Dundee
1626	1754	....	....	167266	ANS	Kettins
STIBLIS						
1460	1561	1468	1561	167266	ANS	Couper Angus
STICHBURY						
....	....	ALL	ALL	167274	ALL	Name Study
STICKALORUM						
1750	1830	....	1750	132837	LND	???
STICKLAND						
....	....	ALL	ALL	167282	ALL	Name Study
1778	1841	1778	1841	162825	DEV	Budleigh Salterton
....	....	1750	ALL	170968	DEV	Corfe Castle
1778	1860	1700	1778	139963	DEV	???
1760	1800	ALL	1800	115266	DOR	ALL
1838	1900	1500	1838	167282	DOR	ALL
1500	1900	1500	1900	170216	DOR	ALL
1840	....	....	1840	164011	DOR	Blandford
1720	1992	1600	1992	119040	DOR	Cranborne
1743	1761	1719	1778	162825	DOR	East Stoke
1790	1850	1790	1850	154210	DOR	Hampreston
1753	1830	1700	1753	139963	DOR	???
1806	1860	1750	1806	170968	HAM	Portsea
1850	1880	ALL	1850	148180	SRY	Guildford
1754	1770	1727	1992	140058	SSX	East Grinstead
1650	1727	1727	1992	140058	SSX	Frant
1500	1900	1500	1900	170216	WIL	ALL
STICKLER						
1740	1855	1600	1855	148482	OKI	Birsay
1750	1850	1700	1800	174599	SOM	Witham Friary
STICKLEY						
1792	....	....	....	140856	WIL	Salisbury
STIDARD						
1780	1992	....	1780	159972	GLS	Bristol
STIDDARD						
1780	1992	....	1780	159972	GLS	Bristol
STIDOLPH						
1490	1830	1490	1992	172243	KEN	Bromley
STIDWELL						
1890	1910	1700	1960	121495	CON	South
1890	1910	1700	1960	121495	DEV	North
STIDWORTHY						
1550	1992	1550	1880	135429	DEV	ALL
1787	1950	ALL	ALL	158585	DEV	Southpool
1800	1900	1550	1880	135429	SOM	Bath
1800	1900	1550	1880	135429	SOM	Lidcombe
STIFF						
1539	1900	1539	1992	158550	SFK	Central
1539	1900	1539	1992	158550	SFK	West
1700	1799	1700	1760	135941	SFK	Wickhambrook
STILES						
....	....	1750	1850	173835	GLS	Ampney
....	....	1750	1850	173835	GLS	Crucis
1890	1935	1890	1910	172634	LAN	Liverpool
1836	1992	1700	1992	167991	SRY	Camberwell
STILL						
1570	1775	ALL	1570	131059	KEN	Cowden
1800	1840	1800	1840	107522	KEN	Hever
STILLMAN						
1800	1992	1800	1992	167339	BRK	???
1800	1800	1750	1850	136840	HAM	Andover
1500	1700	1500	1992	167339	SOM	???
1460	1992	1460	1992	167339	WIL	???
STILLWELL						
1800	1900	1840	1860	111422	LND	ALL
STIMPSON						
1804	1992	1700	1804	169757	RUT	Langham

Known From	To	Researching From	To	Ref	Cty	Place
STIMSON						
1720	1875	ALL	ALL	106097	RUT	Braunston
1720	1875	ALL	ALL	106097	RUT	Whissendine
STINCHCOMBE						
1750	1810	1700	1760	138150	GLS	South
1841	1900	1700	1841	148997	WIL	Corsham
STINJEMOR						
1808	1810	1780	1830	150576	WIL	Alvediston
STINSLEY						
1800	1900	1800	1900	173681	WOR	Lye
STINSON						
1800	1876	1780	1992	122416	CAV	Knockbride
1720	1900	1600	1720	173169	LEI	North West
....	....	1700	1799	142298	LEI	Ashby De La Zouch
STINTON						
....	....	1860	1900	157082	MDX	Hammersmith
STIRGIS						
1720	1720	1600	1720	174130	LEI	Tugby
STIRK						
1790	1820	1700	1790	121509	YKS	Wensleydale
....	....	1600	1800	128627	???	Birmingham
STIRLAND						
1871	1972	?	?	104329	YKS	???
STIRLING						
1858	1992	....	....	149616	AYR	Symington
1790	1850	1700	1750	130915	ELN	Gladsmuir
1795	1992	1700	1992	167177	ELN	???
....	1745	1600	1800	153591	LKS	???
1860	1915	1850	1992	167177	MLN	Edinburgh
1860	1915	1850	1992	167177	MLN	Leith
....	....	1700	1790	130915	MLN	???
1300	1400	1250	1400	154881	SCT	ALL
1797	....	....	1992	151270	SOM	Crewkerne
1829	1965	....	....	135453	STI	Denny
STIRRAT						
1791	1841	ALL	ALL	169919	AYR	Dalry
STIRRUP						
1870	ALL	....	....	165158	???	Liverpool
STIRZAKER						
1800	1850	1700	1850	141496	LAN	Fylde
1568	1734	1567	1734	169552	LAN	Garstang
1771	1772	1730	1808	169552	LAN	Goosnargh
1836	1837	1658	1873	169552	LAN	Heysham
1820	....	1820	1910	154474	LAN	Lancaster
1888	....	1800	1900	134651	YKS	Middlesborough
STITT						
1871	1890	1700	1871	140147	DFS	Wigtown
1750	1850	1600	1750	113204	DOW	Comber
STOAKES						
1926	1930	1900	1992	164992	KEN	River
STOAKLEY						
1760	1820	1650	1760	144711	HUN	Holywell
1760	1820	1650	1760	144711	HUN	Somersham
STOBBART						
1800	1880	1860	1910	139858	DUR	Darlington
STOBBIE						
....	....	ALL	1875	127000	ELN	Garvald
STOBBO						
1820	....	ALL	ALL	130508	FIF	Auchtermuchty
STOBBS						
1861	....	....	....	121851	NBL	Allendale
1787	1902	1787	1831	153176	NBL	Allendale
1800	1852	ALL	1827	171751	NBL	Allendale
1770	1800	....	....	172286	NBL	Allendale
1710	1770	....	....	172286	NBL	Hexham
1797	1870	....	....	172286	YKS	Pateley Bridge
STOBIE						
....	....	ALL	ALL	159085	ALL	Name Study
....	....	ALL	1875	127000	ELN	Garvald
1835	1992	1700	1920	167177	MLN	Edinburgh
1835	1992	1700	1920	167177	MLN	Leith
STOBO						
1753	1820	1700	1753	158739	CUL	Whitehaven
STOCK						
1792	1792	1700	1792	112097	BDF	Bedford
1776	1880	1600	1776	167355	ESS	Gosfield
1780	1814	1500	1780	139084	ESS	Takeley
1861	1992	....	....	110957	GLS	Lydney
1766	1839	1600	1766	160601	GLS	Rudford
1836	1836	1600	1836	152080	HAM	Micheldever
1880	1960	1700	1880	167355	LND	Poplar
1830	1900	ALL	1840	142301	MDX	Finsbury
....	....	1700	1860	110957	SOM	Shipham
1860	1950	1850	1960	138479	???	Bristol

Known From	To	Researching From	To	Ref	Cty	Place
STOCKBRIDGE						
1881	1957	ALL	ALL	161411	ALL	ALL
....	....	1800	1850	101125	KEN	Canterbury
1790	1881	1700	1900	161411	KEN	Canterbury
STOCKBURN						
1710	1980	ALL	ALL	166375	ALL	ALL
1700	1800	1600	1700	167584	DUR	Teesdale
STOCKDALE						
1731	1992	1630	1730	167312	CMA	Blindcrake
1804	1980	1700	1804	173029	SAL	Shrewsbury
....	....	....	1855	134902	YKS	Doncaster
1800	1850	....	....	102946	YKS	Felixkirk
1740	1840	1600	1900	130419	YKS	Giggleswick
1783	1783	ALL	1783	145203	YKS	Kirkby Malham
1857	1992	1700	1857	123943	???	East Thorpe
STOCKDILL						
1830	1850	1800	1900	129496	YKS	Morley
STOCKER						
1800	1992	ALL	1800	144053	BRK	???
1864	1875	1800	1864	167363	CAM	Cambridge
1841	1843	1800	1841	167363	CAM	St Ives
1800	1992	ALL	1800	144053	HAM	???
1800	1900	1800	1850	114405	LND	South
....	....	1750	1850	154458	WAR	???
STOCKHALL						
1889	1889	ALL	ALL	171816	WAR	Birmingham
STOCKHAM						
....	1885	1800	1950	146978	MON	Newport
....	1885	1800	1950	146978	MON	Usk
1770	1890	1770	1890	156930	MON	Usk
STOCKLEY						
1701	1883	1700	1883	151858	DOR	Corfe Castle
1890	1992	ALL	ALL	164887	HRT	Watford
1826	1850	1800	1875	155969	MDX	Marylebone
....	....	1800	1870	155969	SRY	Camberwell
....	....	1800	1870	155969	SRY	Peckham
STOCKMAN						
....	....	1700	1800	122688	DOR	Chardstock
1760	1830	1760	1850	122688	DOR	Honiton
....	....	1700	1800	122688	DOR	Wambrook
1850	1953	1850	1992	122688	HAM	Portsea
....	....	1650	1750	153281	SOM	North Petherton
STOCKS						
1800	1830	1700	1850	126268	LND	Stepney
1813	1992	ALL	1813	110000	NTT	Retford
1820	1930	1700	1820	124362	YKS	Dewsbury
1820	1930	1700	1820	124362	YKS	Halifax
STOCKTON						
....	....	ALL	ALL	167371	ALL	Name Study
1850	1992	1850	1992	178268	CHS	Congleton
1750	1850	1600	1850	178268	CHS	Tattenhall
1800	....	....	....	103837	LIN	Alford
1828	1864	1700	1828	153001	SAL	Bridgenorth
1809	1889	1809	1889	149403	YKS	Malton
STOCKWELL						
....	....	1600	1992	149225	ALL	ALL
1825	....	1700	1825	101443	ALL	Marlton
1845	1865	1775	1875	136042	HAM	Portsea
1795	1838	1700	1795	127973	KEN	Ashford
1825	....	1700	1825	101443	NRY	Birdsall
1866	1939	1866	1939	115460	OXF	Oxford
....	....	1600	1992	149225	WIL	Seend
....	....	1600	1992	149225	WIL	Uley
1781	1799	1700	1820	176621	WYK	Clifton
STODDARD						
1888	1964	1700	1888	109223	STS	Biddulph
STODDART						
1829	1940	1700	1850	167398	DFS	Sanquhar
1800	1890	1700	1800	106267	DUR	South
1700	1800	1600	1700	167584	DUR	Teesdale
1818	1827	1700	1818	147346	NBL	Newcastle
1808	1808	1750	1900	100501	PER	Perth
STODGELL						
1800	1900	1750	1900	167770	HAM	Gosport
STOGDEL						
1723	1800	1650	1730	103462	NFK	Norwich
STOKE						
....	....	1700	1899	174963	SOM	Farmborough
STOKER						
1720	1790	1700	1900	167401	DUR	Chester Le Street
1838	....	1800	1860	118753	DUR	Durham
1820	1860	1800	1900	167401	DUR	Houghton Le Spring
....	....	1500	1700	167401	DUR	Whickham
1840	1882	1840	1992	102245	NBL	Newcastle Upon Tyne
STOKER contd.						
1765	....	1600	1765	116637	NBL	Whalton
1800	1880	ALL	1800	165212	WYK	Rotherham
1800	1880	ALL	1800	165212	WYK	Sheffield
STOKES						
1857	1857	1800	1992	137863	BDF	Sunden
1841	1888	1800	1888	139661	BKM	Barton Hartshorn
?	?	?	?	167436	DBY	Chesterfield
1834	1841	1750	1875	136042	DEV	Aylesbeare
....	....	1750	1800	113042	DEV	Modbury
1793	1820	1500	1793	104140	DEV	Talaton
1832	1890	1700	1832	167460	ESS	Chipping Ongar
1630	1750	1550	1700	177024	ESS	High Easter
1780	1880	1750	1900	177024	ESS	High Ongar
....	1840	1800	1850	135658	GLS	Bristol
1780	1839	1750	1820	109517	HUN	Ramsey
1730	1740	1650	1800	133450	KEN	West
....	....	1800	1830	154873	KEN	Dover
1838	1838	....	1838	171646	KEN	Eastry
1871	1900	1871	1889	139661	LAN	Oldham
1865	1945	1865	1992	177024	LND	Catford
1800	1850	1700	1992	146943	LND	City
1850	1900	1850	1992	146943	LND	Shoreditch
1791	1992	1650	1790	167452	MDX	Bethnal Green
1792	1861	1700	1861	147958	MDX	Marylebone
1819	1886	?	?	106259	MOG	???
1814	1870	....	1814	176516	PEM	Haverford West
1830	1992	1750	1830	167436	RUT	Drayton
1850	1992	....	....	128716	SAL	Wem
....	....	1700	1799	174963	SOM	ALL
1783	1832	1700	1851	176923	SOM	Farrington Gurney
....	....	1800	1830	114782	SRY	???
1603	1660	1600	1700	160873	STS	Kingswinford
1750	1850	1750	1900	145319	WAR	Coventry
1826	1861	....	....	151548	WAR	Coventry
1867	1951	1700	1860	122114	WAR	Handsworth
....	....	1750	1800	113042	WIL	Bradford On Avon
....	....	1800	1850	113042	WIL	Trowbridge
STOKOE						
1800	1992	1800	1992	160210	NBL	ALL
1839	1900	1800	1840	127965	NBL	Warden
STOLLARD						
....	....	1700	1800	101478	GLS	ALL
STOLLERY						
1830	1930	1700	1830	102253	SFK	Brightwell
1800	1925	1600	1800	167010	SFK	Kirton
STONAGE						
1782	....	....	1800	171441	HAM	Cheriton
STONAH						
1800	1850	1750	1992	140236	YKS	ALL
STONE						
1748	1748	1650	1748	167452	BKM	Radnage
1800	1850	1750	1800	133671	CAM	Bassingbourne
....	....	1700	1992	167223	DEV	Crediton
1954	1992	....	....	167495	DEV	Dawlish
....	....	1600	1992	137588	DEV	Newton St Cyres
1780	1820	1700	1820	161292	DEV	Stokenham
1808	1992	....	....	112941	DEV	Yarcombe
....	....	1800	1870	135208	DEV	???
1790	1870	1700	1800	156795	DOR	North
1800	....	ALL	1900	174637	DOR	Portland
1809	1830	1770	1809	173118	DOR	Wyke Regis
1820	1822	1800	1850	105333	ESS	Shalford
1841	1881	ALL	ALL	141704	GLA	ALL
1820	1820	....	....	135437	GLS	Bristol
1841	1866	1820	1841	167479	GLS	Bristol
....	....	1830	1860	167479	GLS	???
1828	1849	1828	1849	131970	HAM	Andover
1850	1992	1820	1950	135895	HAM	Fareham
1880	1920	1800	1940	173746	HAM	Portsmouth
1854	1854	1800	1854	103640	HAM	Southampton
....	....	1500	1992	141720	HAM	???
1800	1848	1700	1800	133493	HRT	Rickmansworth
....	....	1830	1852	172162	KEN	Canterbury
1854	1854	1820	1870	141046	KEN	Dover
1843	1863	....	1880	171441	KEN	Ramsgate
1786	1870	1700	1786	126454	KIK	Thomastown
1860	1926	ALL	1860	167495	LND	ALL
1876	....	....	1880	171441	LND	Battersea
1827	1869	....	1827	142166	LND	Bethnal Green
1712	....	....	....	173932	LND	Cripplegate
1926	1954	....	....	167495	MDX	Ickenham
1902	1930	....	1950	171441	MDX	Isleworth
1852	1868	1830	1852	172162	MDX	Islington

Known From	To	Researching From	To	Ref	Cty	Place
STONE contd.						
1840	1850	1800	1880	105333	MDX	London
1860	1926	ALL	1860	167495	MDX	Paddington
1860	1871	....	....	167479	MDX	Pancras
1860	1926	ALL	1860	167495	MDX	St Pancras
1820	....	?	?	136999	MDX	Twickenham
1860	1926	ALL	1860	167495	MDX	Wembley
1760	1800	1700	1810	100048	MDX	West Drayton
1641	1748	....	1641	101761	NTT	Barton In Fabis
1797	1891	ALL	1797	103896	SOM	ALL
1730	1900	1700	1900	118540	SOM	Cannington
1680	1825	1825	1992	112941	SOM	Chipstable
1798	1835	1750	1798	167479	SOM	Kingston
1773	1803	....	....	135437	SOM	Shepton Mallet
1603	1825	....	....	115290	SOM	Wedmore
1807	1877	....	....	173932	SRY	Ashtead
1867	....	....	....	173932	SRY	Cheam
1738	1848	....	....	173932	SRY	Chessington
1743	1825	1700	1825	159581	SRY	Cranleigh
1879	1880	....	....	173932	SRY	Epsom
1869	1871	....	....	173932	SRY	Ewell
1894	1900	1840	1893	167568	SRY	Godalming
1851	....	....	....	173932	SRY	Leatherhead
1752	....	....	....	173932	SRY	Malden
1786	....	....	....	173932	SRY	Walton On The Hill
1819	....	....	....	173932	SRY	Wotton
1724	....	....	....	173932	SSX	Aldingbourne
1754	1825	1500	1754	110310	SSX	Mountford
1841	1885	1700	1841	106054	STS	Sedgley
1500	1600	....	....	100420	WAR	Fillongley
1500	1600	....	....	100420	WAR	Meriden
1800	1860	1700	1800	162884	WIL	Whiteparish
1746	1832	1600	1746	128082	WOR	Ombersley
1880	1900	ALL	ALL	112674	???	Bristol
STONEHAM						
....	....	1800	....	140333	KEN	Frith
1945	....	....	....	140333	LND	South East
....	1934	....	....	140333	SOM	Weston Super Mare
1862	1900	1700	1862	144754	SRY	Peckham
STONEHEWER						
1809	1992	1700	1809	129208	CHS	Macclesfield
STONEHOUSE						
....	....	ALL	1771	119326	MLN	Newbattle
1725	1795	1700	1800	131199	YKS	Fylingdales
1848	1992	1800	1992	161640	YKS	Hunmanby
....	....	1700	1899	174963	YKS	Hunmanby
....	....	1790	1835	146706	YKS	Kirkby Moorside
....	....	1790	1835	146706	YKS	Lastingham
1790	1818	1750	....	162825	YKS	Leeds
....	....	1700	1899	174963	YKS	Scalby
STONEMAN						
1771	1902	ALL	ALL	121398	CON	Illogan
1730	1730	ALL	1800	173614	DEV	Coldridge
1750	1850	ALL	ALL	107352	DEV	Frithelstock
1797	1900	1700	1797	139815	DEV	???
STONER						
1832	1969	....	....	127779	SRY	Lambeth
1837	1992	1837	1992	167576	SSX	Brighton
....	....	1500	1992	167576	SSX	Midhurst
....	....	1500	1992	167576	SSX	Petworth
....	....	1840	1992	167576	SSX	Shoreham
....	....	1840	1992	167576	SSX	Southwick
1797	1826	....	1797	167576	SXW	Easebourne
1830	1890	1750	1850	126586	YKS	Pateley Bridge
STONES						
1480	1992	ALL	ALL	102202	CMA	Cartmel
1800	1822	1780	1850	117145	DBY	South Normanton
1480	1992	ALL	ALL	102202	LAN	Cartmel
1825	1920	1650	1825	120081	LIN	East
?	?	?	?	118044	LIN	Wragby
1825	1910	1750	1900	123293	NTT	Misterton
1790	1800	1750	1790	121339	NYK	Marrick
1862	....	ALL	ALL	159026	STS	Gnosall
1791	1814	1750	1850	109290	YKS	Sheffield
STONESBRIDGE						
1769	1890	1607	1890	153257	CAM	Girton
STONESTREET						
1823	1891	....	....	115606	MDX	Hillingdon
1823	1823	....	1823	136212	SRY	???
STONEY						
1800	1992	1750	1992	140236	YKS	ALL
1701	1956	1600	1970	112372	YKS	Nidderdale
STONIER						
1790	1992	1700	1790	156574	CHS	Odd Rode

Known From	To	Researching From	To	Ref	Cty	Place
STOODLEY						
1700	1992	1530	1700	117447	DEV	Chardstock
STOODLY						
1770	....	....	....	119911	SOM	Wayford
STOOKE						
....	....	1600	1900	126055	DEV	ALL
STOOKES						
1713	1770	ALL	1770	168718	BDF	Riseley
STOPPANI						
ALL	ALL	ALL	ALL	149535	ENG	ALL
STORAR						
1780	1850	1600	1780	108413	LND	Lambeth
STORER						
1824	1870	1824	1870	149403	DBY	Crich
1857	1906	1750	1857	167606	DBY	Cromford
1857	1906	1750	1857	167606	DBY	Wirksworth
?	?	?	?	108391	DUR	West Auckland
1885	1905	1860	1885	167606	LAN	Oldham
1630	1730	1600	1630	169749	LEI	ALL
....	....	1600	1797	137626	LEI	Desford
....	....	1710	1820	115142	LEI	Packington
?	?	?	?	136999	LND	Lambeth
1826	1890	1826	1889	144878	MDX	St Pancras
1712	1800	1680	1770	110728	NBL	Rothbury
1796	1843	1796	1843	144878	WAR	Birmingham
....	....	1750	....	154377	WAR	Seckington
1892	1992	1892	1992	146625	YKS	Huddersfield
STORES						
1860	1992	ALL	ALL	123048	DUR	Monkwearmouth
STOREY						
1741	1741	1700	1741	133000	CAM	Arrington
1847	1881	1847	1893	102482	CMA	Carlisle
1844	....	ALL	1900	134503	DUR	Hartlepool
1851	....	1700	1850	106380	DUR	South Shields
1784	1784	1550	1800	147265	DUR	???
1814	....	1701	1784	131210	HRT	Ware
1791	1858	1791	1880	159875	HUN	Abbotsley
1741	1791	1741	1791	159875	HUN	Arrington
1741	1791	1741	1791	159875	HUN	Bourne
1791	1858	1791	1880	159875	HUN	Croxton
....	....	1700	1839	100447	HUN	Offord
1847	1881	1825	1893	102482	LAN	Machester
1852	1992	1800	1920	178446	LIN	Lincoln
1800	1900	ALL	ALL	141704	LND	Shoreditch
....	....	1700	1850	106380	NBL	Rothbury
1680	1700	1600	1680	121339	NYK	Bolton Castle
1800	1900	....	....	150371	ROX	Newcastleton
1800	1900	1600	1800	172022	SRY	London
1821	1942	1821	1909	121304	WES	Kendal
1592	1894	1500	1900	176362	WES	Troutbeck
1838	1860	1700	1840	126772	YKS	Nunnington
1890	1919	1800	1890	127728	YKS	Sheffield
STORIE						
1793	1812	....	....	171654	LKS	Carluke
STORK						
1780	....	1700	....	134589	YKS	Burnby
STORM						
1662	1743	ALL	1750	113611	LIN	Burton Upon Stather
1740	1817	ALL	1825	113611	LIN	Winteringham
1540	1992	1600	1992	167630	NYK	Robin Hoods Bay
STORMONT						
1850	1992	1700	1850	167649	ALL	ALL
STORR						
1760	1840	1700	1760	168785	MDX	???
1800	1992	1650	1800	173665	NYK	Pickering
STORRAR						
1837	1992	1780	1992	167657	ENG	ALL
1820	1865	....	1820	152927	FIF	Falkland
1855	1920	1700	1992	167657	SCT	ALL
1837	1992	1780	1992	167657	WLS	ALL
STORRES						
1860	1900	ALL	1900	123048	DUR	Bishopwearmouth
STORRIE						
....	....	1867	....	149187	ANS	Dundee
STORROW						
1854	1976	1700	1854	142883	CUL	Carlisle
1878	....	1555	1878	126462	DUR	Piercebridge
STORRS						
1730	1820	1730	1820	137634	NTT	Sturton Le Steeple
1520	1730	....	1730	137634	NTT	Sutton Cum Lound
STORTON						
1769	1783	1769	1783	107360	BKM	Fenny Stratford
1766	1865	1766	1865	107360	BKM	Stony Stratford

Known From	Known To	Researching From	Researching To	Ref	Cty	Place
STORY						
1847	1881	1847	1893	102482	CMA	Carlisle
1755	1790	1755	1790	121304	CUL	Wetheral
1744	1787	....	1820	171441	KEN	Tunstall
1847	1881	1825	1893	102482	LAN	Machester
1794	1913	1794	1913	151211	LIN	Bourne
STORZAKER						
1725	....	1725	....	109347	YKS	Gisburn
STOTE						
1540	1900	ALL	ALL	167665	ALL	ALL
STOTEN						
1863	1933	1700	1863	108588	HRT	Therfield
1780	1880	1750	1900	152528	MDX	Enfield
STOTHARD						
1750	1992	1700	1750	114693	DUR	Monkwearmouth
1830	1830	ALL	ALL	135224	???	???
STOTT						
....	....	ALL	ALL	167681	ALL	Name Study
1850	1980	....	1850	174246	ABD	ALL
1800	1900	1700	1992	156280	BEW	ALL
1848	....	1750	1848	100390	LAN	Ashton
1900	1992	ALL	ALL	117145	LAN	Bolton
1781	1992	1700	1780	142700	LAN	Burnley
1827	1950	1700	1827	167673	LAN	Burnley
1851	1871	1851	1891	159492	LAN	Oldham
1780	1970	1700	1830	126411	LAN	Rochdale
1700	1867	ALL	1700	171573	NYK	Carlton In Cleveland
1700	1867	ALL	1700	171573	NYK	Kirklington
1700	1867	ALL	1700	171573	NYK	Pickhill
1860	1920	....	1900	176702	SWL	Bettws
1838	1863	1800	1863	147338	WRY	Huddersfield
1798	1799	1780	1850	147338	WRY	Leeds
1790	1830	1700	1790	124362	YKS	Dewsbury
1780	1960	1780	1850	123595	YKS	Huddersfield
1737	1816	1650	1737	176451	YKS	Otterburn
1814	....	....	....	123951	YKS	Stainland
STOUT						
1775	....	1775	....	109347	LAN	Simonstone
1832	1992	1735	1992	167703	OKI	Westray
1756	1832	1700	1756	167703	SHI	Fair Isle
STOVE						
1750	1965	....	....	137820	SHI	Fetlar
1720	1965	....	....	137820	SHI	Mid Yell
1760	1965	....	....	137820	SHI	North Yell
1758	1965	....	....	137820	SHI	Northmavine
1720	1965	....	....	137820	SHI	South Yell
STOVEY						
1882	1882	1860	1882	174998	NBL	Sunderland
STOW						
1714	1844	1580	1714	159239	ESS	Colchester
1912	1992	1800	1912	167711	MDX	Hornsey
STOWE						
1793	....	1793	....	113875	LIN	Ruskington
....	....	....	1700	130133	OXF	Great Tew
STOWELL						
....	....	ALL	ALL	167738	ALL	Name Study
ALL	ALL	1200	1992	167738	ENG	ALL
1580	1850	1850	1992	167738	IOM	ALL
STOYLE						
....	....	ALL	ALL	167746	DEV	ALL
1820	1877	ALL	ALL	177482	DEV	Chudleigh
1867	....	....	....	153885	DEV	Crediton
1842	1905	ALL	1905	177482	DEV	Totnes
STRACHAN						
1811	1870	1700	1950	169390	ABD	Aberdeen
1850	1950	1800	1850	105198	ABD	New Machar
1780	1920	1780	1920	148210	ABD	Old Meldrum
1678	1732	....	....	151351	ANS	Arbroath
1791	1992	1760	1945	167754	LND	North & East
1791	1830	1700	1875	124907	LND	Westminster
1760	1843	1760	1870	167754	MDX	Westminster
1861	1940	1750	1861	105767	NBL	Tyneside
STRACHEY						
1700	1799	....	....	147575	???	???
STRADLING						
1840	1900	1700	1840	167762	SOM	Wellington
STRAHORN						
....	....	ALL	ALL	125644	ALL	Name Study
STRAIGHT						
1700	1725	1650	1700	145297	CON	St Allan
1729	1900	1680	1729	160598	ESS	???
STRAIN						
1740	1860	1740	1860	106305	DOW	???

Known From	Known To	Researching From	Researching To	Ref	Cty	Place
STRAIN contd.						
1817	1825	1750	1850	159964	KKD	ALL
STRAKER						
1806	1898	1808	1880	108944	DUR	Barnard Castle
1846	1846	1800	1900	116386	NBL	Newcastle
1744	1768	1720	1744	108944	NBL	Newton In Forest
STRALEY						
1900	1960	1900	1960	167770	HAM	Southampton
STRANACK						
1810	1985	1680	1992	142867	ALL	ALL
1688	1936	....	....	142867	KEN	Margate
1750	1900	....	....	142867	LND	???
STRANG						
1828	1860	1750	1860	120243	CLK	Clackmannan
1725	1992	1500	1725	140279	PEM	Dale
1800	1850	1700	1992	114596	RFW	Eaglesham
....	....	1830	....	123633	SCT	???
1855	1880	1855	1992	120243	STI	Muiravonside
STRANGE						
1800	1820	1750	1800	172898	HAM	Overton
1781	1808	1781	1808	100242	HAM	Pamber
1750	....	ALL	ALL	116394	KEN	Milton By Gravesend
1682	1943	....	....	130958	WIL	Bremhill
1854	....	1854	1900	149284	WIL	???
STRANGER						
1880	1900	1750	1880	134651	YKS	Middlesborough
STRANGEWAYS						
1837	1900	ALL	ALL	109797	ALL	ALL
1630	1750	1630	1992	133450	CON	Lostwithiel
1630	1750	1630	1992	133450	DEV	Colyton
1700	1880	ALL	ALL	109797	NBL	Berwick Upon Tweed
....	....	1700	1799	174963	YKS	Scarborough
STRANKS						
1800	1920	1700	1992	177180	BKM	Aston Abbots
STRAPP						
1750	....	....	....	126993	ALL	ALL
1750	1850	1600	1890	127108	BDF	ALL
STRATFIELD						
1700	1810	....	....	167797	BKM	Marsworth
1700	1810	....	....	167797	HRT	Tring
STRATFORD						
1846	1881	ALL	ALL	119504	HAM	Alverstoke
1846	1881	ALL	ALL	119504	HAM	Portsmouth
1805	1992	1700	1805	167789	LND	???
1821	1822	ALL	ALL	119504	WIL	Cricklade
STRATH						
....	....	ALL	ALL	121126	ALL	Name Study
....	....	ALL	ALL	121126	ALL	ALL
1700	1875	1650	1950	121126	ABD	???
STRATHAM						
?	?	ALL	ALL	172251	NTT	???
STRATHCARN						
....	....	1800	1900	110663	LKS	???
STRATHEARN						
....	....	ALL	ALL	152048	RFW	Paisley
....	....	ALL	ALL	152048	SCT	ALL
STRATHERN						
1840	1954	....	....	127140	LKS	Carmunnock
1840	1954	....	....	127140	LKS	Glasgow
1858	....	1835	....	132381	LKS	Glasgow
STRATTON						
1847	1868	1700	1992	170356	BRK	Spely
1700	1799	1700	1799	169781	GLS	Bristol
1905	1930	1700	1905	167819	HAM	Bishops Waltham
1850	1880	1850	1880	170119	HAM	Ellingham
1694	1700	1600	1800	144460	HRT	Codicote
1600	1720	1600	1720	142123	HRT	Graveley
1790	1870	1800	1900	130567	NFK	Swaffham
....	....	1600	1992	125857	STS	ALL
1836	....	....	....	126020	WIL	ALL
....	....	1600	1992	125857	WIL	ALL
1650	1992	ALL	ALL	102202	WIL	Pewsey
1910	1918	1910	1992	165603	YKS	Yarm
STRAUGHAIR						
1837	1850	1770	1992	167908	DUR	ALL
STRAUGHAN						
1849	1890	ALL	1849	122386	NBL	Wooler
STRAW						
1817	1922	1700	1992	123552	MDX	London
1874	1992	1800	1900	102164	NTT	Gedling
1874	1992	1800	1900	102164	NTT	Lambley
1890	....	....	....	152420	YKS	Sheffield
STRAWSON						
1794	1831	ALL	1835	113611	NTT	Misterton

Known From	To	Researching From	To	Ref	Cty	Place
STREATER						
1500	1650	1400	1650	144657	HAM	Bramshott
1770	1900	1600	1800	144657	HAM	Farringdon
1650	1780	1600	1780	144657	HAM	New Alresford
1720	1860	1600	1860	137359	SSX	Shipley
STREATFEILD						
1514	1718	1450	1750	154881	KEN	Chiddingstone
STREATFIELD						
....	1909	1850	1960	137685	ESS	Southend
1760	....	1760	1803	116297	KEN	Chiddingstone
....	1910	1750	1890	137685	KEN	Chiddingstone
....	1860	1800	1900	137685	KEN	Hever
1780	1992	1700	1900	116297	KEN	Sittingbourne
....	1912	1850	1960	137685	KEN	Sydenham
1910	1952	1860	1960	137685	LND	Edmonton
STREDDER						
1858	1992	1700	1858	179051	BDF	Caddington
1858	1992	1700	1858	179051	BDF	Luton
1858	1992	1700	1858	179051	HRT	Flamstead
1821	1869	1869	1950	118583	MDX	London
STREET						
1880	1930	1880	1930	176176	BKM	Hambleden
1832	1906	1800	1906	142360	BRK	Blewbury
1810	1833	1775	1810	175951	CHS	Nantwich
1900	1960	ALL	ALL	100137	DBY	ALL
1880	1960	1700	1880	158453	DBY	Central
1880	1960	1700	1880	158453	DBY	South
1600	1900	1600	1900	160547	DBY	Newhall
1655	1757	1650	1760	151858	DOR	Corfe Castle
1787	1851	1787	1851	125326	DOR	Cranborne
1700	1750	1700	1750	147575	DOR	Motcombe
1790	1800	1750	1790	133221	HAM	Boldre
1759	1810	1754	1810	125326	HAM	Fording Bridge
....	....	1750	1850	118834	HAM	Portsmouth
1830	1850	ALL	ALL	162280	HAM	Portsmouth
1780	1860	1700	1800	155500	LAN	Lowton
1767	1992	ALL	1767	120022	LEI	Loughborough
1600	1735	ALL	1735	120022	LEI	Wymeswold
....	....	1800	1900	166960	MDX	London
1786	1795	....	....	173932	SRY	Abinger
1811	1859	....	....	173932	SRY	Ashtead
1845	....	....	....	173932	SRY	Chessington
1868	1871	....	....	173932	SRY	Epsom
1820	....	....	....	173932	SRY	Leatherhead
1846	....	....	....	173932	SRY	Richmond
1761	1819	....	....	173932	SRY	Wotton
1900	1960	ALL	ALL	100137	STS	Burton On Trent
STREETER						
1790	1860	1700	1790	177490	SSX	Hollington
1780	1840	1600	1780	107565	SSX	Pulborough
STREETFIELD						
1840	1890	1890	1992	116297	KEN	Hoo
STREETING						
1855	1992	1600	1855	163856	KEN	Canterbury
STREETON						
1792	1904	1700	1792	167533	MDX	Shoreditch
STREETS						
1869	1992	1800	1869	178551	NTT	Lenton
STREIGHT						
1726	1785	....	....	145297	CON	St Erme
STRETCH						
....	....	ALL	ALL	137790	ALL	Name Study
1770	1992	1580	1770	175870	BKM	Wendover
1657	....	ALL	ALL	137790	CHS	Tatton
1840	1900	1700	1840	167762	CLA	Ennis
1879	1899	1658	1899	169552	LAN	Heysham
1841	1984	1722	1984	169552	LAN	Overton
1685	1772	1600	1900	106461	WIL	ALL
STRETTON						
ALL	ALL	ALL	ALL	167827	ALL	ALL
1660	1760	1650	1800	118338	BRK	Cookham
1780	1980	1600	1780	128317	DBY	Breadsall
1842	1992	....	1842	129518	KER	Tralee
1600	1660	ALL	1660	118338	LEI	Claybrook
ALL	ALL	ALL	ALL	167827	NTT	Nottingham
1750	1900	1700	1800	142395	STS	Derby Border
STREVENS						
1757	1992	....	....	107158	KEN	Margate
STRIBLEY						
1850	1900	1850	1900	110361	DEV	Plymouth
STRIBLING						
1850	1883	1800	1890	152285	DEV	???
1851	1881	....	....	106488	SFK	Groton
1744	1921	1700	....	120634	SFK	Groton
STRICK						
1700	1992	....	....	157570	CON	Mylor
STRICKLAND						
1900	1992	1800	1900	167835	CMA	North
....	....	1819	1845	145084	CMA	Wythburn
1782	....	?	1785	103934	DOR	Pentridge
1801	1863	1750	1801	151912	LAN	Clitheroe
1801	1863	1750	1801	151912	LAN	Goosnargh
1738	....	ALL	1738	119326	NRY	Coxwold
1740	1880	1700	1830	151742	NRY	North York Moors
1815	1851	1700	1815	103268	WOR	Claines
1738	....	ALL	1738	119326	WRY	Gt Ouseburn
STRIDE						
1792	1854	1750	1860	165972	HAM	South
1839	1862	....	1880	171441	SOM	Witham Friary
1740	1850	1700	1800	174599	SOM	Witham Friary
STRIGHT						
1790	1801	....	....	145297	CON	St Allen
STRIKE						
1800	1900	1500	1800	136972	CON	Breage
1700	1992	....	....	157570	CON	Mylor
1800	1890	1700	1800	101931	CON	Porthlevan
1800	1900	1500	1800	136972	CON	Sithney
STRINGER						
....	1700	ALL	1700	134511	DBY	Tibshelf
1841	1992	ALL	1850	108502	KEN	Hythe
1841	1992	ALL	1850	108502	KEN	Romney
1700	1799	1700	1799	169781	SOM	Ilchester
1700	1799	1700	1799	169781	SOM	Somerton
1814	1814	1750	1814	118192	SSX	Brighton
1590	1992	....	1590	120979	STS	Hamstall Ridware
1827	1827	1827	1992	174262	WAR	Birmingham
1804	1900	....	....	121924	WAR	Coventry
....	....	1720	1850	115142	WAR	Mancetter
1800	1830	1780	1850	142174	WOR	Cradley
1800	1992	1700	1800	109703	YKS	Ecclesfield
1850	1992	1850	1992	131199	YKS	Scarborough
1796	1958	....	....	145912	YKS	Wakefield
1789	1992	1500	1790	167843	YKS	Wensleydale
STRINGFELLOW						
1936	....	....	....	173932	WIL	Upton Scudamore
STRIPE						
1860	1960	1860	1980	149144	HAM	Portsmouth
1860	1900	1800	1900	149144	HAM	Soberton
....	....	1860	1900	149144	SSX	Chichester
STRITCH						
1840	1900	1700	1840	167762	CLA	Ennis
STRIZAKER						
1795	1817	1700	1992	113476	LAN	Kirkham
STROBRIDGE						
1559	1603	ALL	1660	167851	CON	North
1450	1992	1400	1750	167851	DEV	South West
1450	1992	1400	1750	167851	DEV	Ashburton
1450	1992	1400	1750	167851	DEV	Colyton
1450	1992	1400	1750	167851	DEV	Exeter
1450	1992	1400	1750	167851	DEV	Modbury
1600	1771	ALL	1720	167851	DOR	Stockland
1578	1700	1550	1700	167851	IRL	Northern
1778	1992	1750	1892	167851	KEN	Maidstone
1850	1992	1872	1960	167851	LKS	Glasgow
1539	1992	ALL	ALL	167851	MDX	London
1568	1600	ALL	1720	167851	SOM	Wellington
STROHLE						
1880	1912	1865	1920	167770	LND	Fulham
STRONACH						
1820	1960	1700	1820	167886	ABD	Glass
1846	1885	1824	1992	167878	MDX	London
1790	1824	ALL	1790	167878	MLN	Edinburgh
STRONG						
1886	1931	ALL	1886	117897	BKM	ALL
1804	1847	....	....	115606	BRK	Bray
1834	1834	1800	1870	137413	DEV	Bradwood
1863	1886	1800	1900	136042	DEV	Exeter
1756	1853	....	....	112968	DOR	Melbury Sampforde
1650	1830	ALL	ALL	119040	DOR	Poole
1870	1880	1880	1920	162361	IRL	Dublin
1840	1872	1870	1920	162361	MLN	Edinburgh
?	?	?	?	167894	NBL	Wooler
1886	1931	ALL	1886	117897	OXF	ALL
1750	1840	1700	1750	162361	PER	Moulin
1756	1853	....	....	112968	SOM	Melbury Osmond
1808	1890	1700	1810	131377	WAR	Aston
1670	1770	1640	1770	156930	WIL	Aldbourne

Known From	To	Researching From	To	Ref	Cty	Place
STROOD						
1750	1930	1750	1930	124761	KEN	North East
STROPES						
....	1621	1500	1621	175072	LIN	Billinghay
STROPHAIR						
1840	1992	1750	1840	167908	DUR	ALL
STROUD						
1750	1900	ALL	ALL	122866	BRK	South
....	1800	1600	1800	131040	BRK	Speen
1810	1836	1700	1810	130648	DEV	Exmouth
1800	ALL	1815	1900	107379	DEV	Honiton
1800	ALL	1860	1900	107379	DOR	Weymouth
....	....	1700	1900	145882	DOR	???
1760	1880	1750	1900	152528	ESS	Waltham Abbey
....	1800	....	....	174564	GLS	Cheltenham
1800	1900	ALL	ALL	122866	HAM	North West
1852	....	ALL	ALL	172057	HAM	Southampton
1750	1790	1700	1790	148288	IRL	Dublin
1820	1880	....	....	149764	KEN	Hawkhurst
1827	1833	1820	1835	155969	KEN	Shorne
1620	1860	....	....	121983	KEN	Whitstable
1840	1940	1800	1840	114448	LND	Westminster
....	....	1750	1827	155969	MDX	Holborn
1881	1885	1862	1992	133639	MDX	Islington
1857	1900	1810	1992	130648	MDX	London
....	....	1750	1827	155969	MDX	Marylebone
1800	1900	1800	1900	131040	WIL	Marlborough
STROUDLEY						
1758	1782	1758	1782	103977	OXF	Ewelme
1758	1782	1758	1782	103977	OXF	Warborough
STROUGHAIR						
1840	1860	1750	1840	167908	DUR	ALL
1840	1860	1750	1840	167908	YKS	ALL
STROWGER						
1843	1887	1785	1948	136158	SFK	Southwold
1843	1887	1785	1948	136158	SFK	Westleton
STRUDWICK						
1765	1920	1700	1765	157074	KEN	Eynsford
1712	1785	1700	1800	170143	SRY	Stoke
1712	1785	1700	1800	170143	SRY	Worplesdon
1700	1730	1720	1750	142018	WIL	Seend
STRUGNEL						
1690	1740	1650	1750	136840	HAM	West Meon
STRUGNELL						
....	....	....	....	143480	HAM	Fareham
1805	1987	1790	1987	132608	LND	???
STRUTHERS						
1822	1925	....	....	132381	DNB	???
STRUTT						
....	....	1700	....	145998	ESS	???
1880	....	....	....	136565	NRY	Leeds
1750	....	1700	1750	152110	SFK	Glemsford
STRUTTON						
1800	1858	1700	1900	128163	KEN	ALL
STUART						
1857	1871	1700	1857	106887	ABD	Cruden
1790	1890	....	....	126497	ABD	Forgue
1800	1840	1600	1800	146730	BAN	Keith
1850	1900	1825	1992	133450	KEN	Deal
....	....	1800	1875	135658	LAN	Bleasdale
1800	1960	....	....	132756	LAN	Liverpool
1895	1905	1850	1895	107182	LAN	Southport
1850	1930	1700	1850	100714	ROC	Black Isle
....	1690	1650	1750	135658	SCT	ALL
1750	1820	1650	1750	135658	YKS	Bentham
STUART-COLE						
1864	1865	1860	1870	124753	GLS	Bristol
1890	1900	1890	1900	124753	LAN	Ashton Under Lyne
1871	1992	1871	1992	124753	LAN	Manchester
1864	1865	1860	1870	124753	SOM	Bristol
STUBB						
1836	1861	....	....	115495	YKS	Heckmondwicke
STUBBIN						
1845	1845	1830	1992	137863	LND	Bethnal Green
1864	1864	1830	1992	137863	LND	Mile End
1790	1879	1700	1992	137863	SFK	Ipswich
1838	1838	1700	1992	137863	SRY	Farnham
STUBBING						
1819	1840	....	....	127779	SRY	Egham
STUBBINGS						
....	....	ALL	ALL	137677	ALL	Name Study
....	....	1600	1880	167916	CAM	Igileton
1880	1992	....	....	167916	CAM	Sawston
1910	1992	....	....	113018	LND	West Ham
STUBBINGTON						
1813	1857	1700	1813	154164	HAM	Portsmouth
STUBBINS						
1900	1992	1700	1900	122009	NTT	Central
STUBBLES						
1764	1992	1764	1992	120014	BRK	Sonning
1626	1661	....	....	167266	FIF	St Andrews
STUBBS						
1755	1940	....	....	128996	CAM	Thorney
1634	1843	ALL	ALL	130370	CHS	Gawsworth
1837	1980	1770	....	132136	CHS	Lower Peover
1856	1900	1820	1900	170992	CHS	Northwich
1856	1900	1820	1900	170992	CHS	Wincham
1820	1992	1730	1825	167932	DEV	Brixton
1839	1871	1818	1871	173371	DUR	Darlington
1871	1881	1818	1871	173371	DUR	Tanfield
1770	1795	1760	1800	167924	ESS	Chelmsford
1938	....	....	....	151181	FLN	Prestatyn
1900	1992	1700	1900	160725	HAM	South
1880	1992	1700	1992	114596	HAM	Isle Of Wight
1880	1905	1880	1910	167924	KEN	Dover
1720	1800	1600	1992	167592	LAN	Liverpool
1675	1735	....	....	165999	LEI	Leicester
1820	1850	1820	1880	167924	MDX	Chelsea
1850	1900	1850	1910	167924	MDX	Hampstead
1760	1800	1700	1992	167592	MDX	London
1780	1880	1750	1900	167924	MDX	Whitechapel
1740	1770	1700	1790	167924	NFK	Tavenham
1770	1780	1700	1992	167592	STS	Audley
1770	1850	1700	1992	167592	STS	Burslem
1850	1880	1700	1992	167592	STS	Hanley
1770	1780	1700	1992	167592	STS	Newcastle Under Lyme
1770	1780	1700	1992	167592	STS	Stoke
1770	1780	1700	1992	167592	STS	Woolstanton
1818	1850	1700	1898	115894	WES	Kendal
1818	1870	1818	1870	139807	YKS	ALL
1802	1874	1700	1802	156183	YKS	Holbeck
1850	1850	1750	1850	145858	YKS	Knaresborough
1750	1760	1700	1992	167592	YKS	Leeds
1778	1838	....	....	154024	YKS	Pocklington
STUBLEY						
1825	1860	1750	1825	126535	LND	Southwark
STUCKEY						
1642	1768	1642	1768	165840	SOM	Cheddon Fitzpaine
1804	1830	1750	1804	121568	SOM	Durston
?	....	....	....	162418	SOM	Kingston Seymour
....	?	....	....	162418	SOM	Weston Super Mare
STUDDS						
1783	1900	1700	1783	176257	BKM	Great Brickhill
1800	1850	ALL	ALL	125318	MDX	???
STUDDY						
....	....	1800	1900	131962	ALL	ALL
STUDLEY						
1796	1832	1700	1850	124907	LND	Holborn
STUDT						
1900	1940	1800	1900	111686	WLS	South
STUMP						
1630	1650	ALL	ALL	124982	GLS	Stone
....	1891	1800	1900	132586	WIL	Blunsdon
STUMPE						
1530	1630	1530	1630	111538	WIL	Malmesbury
STURDY						
1821	1860	....	....	117803	NRY	Claxton
1753	1783	....	....	117803	NRY	Easingwold
1718	1750	1583	1718	117803	NRY	Kilburn
1791	1822	....	....	117803	NRY	Stockton On The Forest
1568	1720	1568	1720	117803	NRY	Sutton On The Forest
1830	1900	1800	1900	102164	NTT	Gedling
1750	1992	1750	?	166235	YKS	York
STURGEON						
1665	1774	1600	1665	155276	ESS	Braintree
1823	....	1750	1840	175684	LND	City
1650	1667	1600	1650	155276	SFK	Mendlesham
1620	1719	....	1620	101761	SFK	Whepstead
STURGES						
....	....	ALL	ALL	167940	OXF	ALL
STURGESS						
1797	?	1777	1797	114073	LND	All Hallows Staying
....	....	1700	1830	159808	WIL	Salisbury
STURMAN						
1700	1850	1700	1850	167924	BDF	ALL

Known From	To	Researching From	To	Ref	Cty	Place
STURMAN contd.						
1700	1800	1700	1800	167924	BKM	ALL
....	....	1700	1850	147613	HUN	Great Staughton
....	....	1700	1850	147613	HUN	Woodwalton
1850	1940	1850	1940	167924	MDX	St Pancras
1810	1860	1810	1860	167924	MDX	Stepney
STURMY						
1700	1800	ALL	1700	115266	DOR	ALL
STURROCK						
....	1854	ALL	1854	153729	ANS	Dundee
1840	....	1800	1840	174955	ANS	Mains
1840	....	1800	1840	174955	ANS	Strathmartine
1841	1843	ALL	1841	167959	SRY	Southwark
STURT						
1800	1899	1800	1899	121827	SRY	Chobham
1641	1758	1600	1760	170143	SRY	Farnham
1565	1992	1500	1565	167967	SSX	West
STUTELEY						
1826	....	1750	1826	174955	KEN	Stone In Oxney
STUTLEY						
1780	1900	1700	1992	133450	LND	St Martin In The Field
STUTT						
....	....	ALL	ALL	168122	ALL	Name Study
STUTTLE						
....	....	ALL	ALL	167975	ALL	Name Study
STYLE						
1840	1850	1750	1840	167983	MDX	London
1850	1992	1850	1992	167983	WAR	Coventry
STYLEMAN						
1747	1794	1700	1900	159956	ESS	Tillingham
1500	1700	1500	1700	167339	SOM	???
1460	1992	1460	1992	167339	WIL	???
STYLES						
1870	1953	1800	1870	113352	ESS	Great Waltham
1836	1992	1700	1992	167991	GLA	Rhondda
....	....	1750	1900	108677	KEN	Gravesend
1782	1950	1782	ALL	168009	LND	Islington
1800	1840	ALL	ALL	168009	LND	Shoreditch
1899	1956	1899	1956	132314	MDX	Brentford
1813	1900	1750	1900	132314	MDX	Norwood
1800	1850	ALL	ALL	168009	NFK	Diss
1734	1784	1600	ALL	168009	SFK	Thrandeston
1888	1888	1700	1888	174262	WAR	Birmingham
STYRING						
1801	1878	....	1801	125954	YKS	Doncaster
SUCKLING						
1825	1850	1800	1825	135879	LND	Central
1850	1992	1700	1850	103926	NFK	Hunstanton
1850	1992	1700	1850	103926	NFK	Kings Lynn
SUCKSMITH						
1886	1918	1837	1992	173576	LAN	Oldham
1886	1918	1837	1992	173576	LAN	Preston
SUDBURY						
1800	1950	1700	1900	114383	LIN	North Scarle
1800	1992	1700	1900	114383	NTT	Newark On Trent
SUDDARDS						
1900	1970	1700	1900	168017	ALL	ALL
SUDELL						
1800	1992	ALL	ALL	112461	LAN	Fylde
1800	1850	1600	1800	104469	LND	Wandsworth
SUDEN						
1250	1350	1200	1350	154881	ALL	ALL
SUDERY						
1730	1769	1600	1730	175781	WIL	Chitterne
SUDLOW						
?	?	?	?	110183	CHS	???
SUFF						
1760	1800	1760	1800	151297	GLS	Ruardean
SUFFIELD						
1754	1839	....	....	101028	NFK	Hemblington
SUGARS						
1750	1880	....	....	169129	NFK	???
SUGDEN						
1894	1899	....	....	129232	BRE	Brecon
1902	1992	....	....	129232	GLA	ALL
1858	1874	....	....	129232	WOR	Kidderminster
1880	1894	....	....	129232	WOR	Malvern
....	....	1800	....	118826	YKS	Halifax
....	....	1800	....	118826	YKS	Hull
....	....	1790	1810	116114	YKS	Hunslet
....	....	1780	1835	129232	YKS	Keighley
1610	1640	....	....	145688	YKS	Keighley
1887	....	....	....	161136	YKS	Sheffield

Known From	To	Researching From	To	Ref	Cty	Place
SUGG						
....	....	ALL	ALL	165670	ALL	Name Study
1801	1837	ALL	1801	167878	SOM	Shapwick
SUGGATE						
1750	1950	1700	1750	111945	SFK	Brampton
1750	1950	1700	1750	111945	SFK	Yoxford
SULLEFUN						
1744	1812	ALL	1766	116025	CON	St Erney
SULLIVAN						
1840	1913	....	1840	175579	COR	Clonakilty
1919	1992	1700	1919	179329	DUR	Blaydon On Tyne
1850	....	1800	1850	128724	IRL	Cork
1800	1850	1750	1850	144657	IRL	Cork
1876	1900	1800	1876	168025	IRL	County Clare
1840	1875	1875	1992	117110	KEN	Canterbury
....	....	1800	1869	110132	KER	???
1903	1992	1860	1935	174998	LAN	Bolton
....	1920	ALL	1920	128171	LAN	Liverpool
1867	1895	....	....	116912	LIM	Caherconlish
1880	1992	1880	1992	147230	LND	East End
....	....	ALL	ALL	130818	LND	Greenwich
....	1913	....	1840	175579	LND	Lambeth
1795	1836	....	1795	101761	MDX	East London
1885	1900	1850	1885	128724	MDX	London
1842	1851	1750	1851	166928	MDX	North London
1868	1941	1800	1950	139203	SRY	Croydon
SULLY						
1862	1892	....	1920	171441	MON	Newport
1840	1870	1870	1880	114871	SOM	Bridgewater
1735	1840	1700	1735	114871	SOM	St Decumens
SULMAN						
1781	1950	1780	1940	156353	CAM	Wilburton
SUMERTON						
1607	....	1550	1607	116637	YKS	Whixley
SUMMERELL						
1880	1900	1900	1992	133507	MDX	Kensington
SUMMERFIELD						
1800	1850	1600	1992	176494	BDF	ALL
1783	1912	ALL	1786	108642	BDF	Odell
1783	1912	ALL	1786	108642	BDF	Sharnbrook
1751	1777	....	....	115606	BRK	Bisham
1846	....	1846	1992	168572	DBY	Belper
....	....	1800	1900	177822	LAN	Manchester
1850	1992	1700	1850	168084	LIN	???
....	....	ALL	ALL	127787	LND	Peckham
1783	1912	ALL	1786	108642	NTH	Woolaston
1846	....	1846	1992	168572	NTT	Mount Sorrell
1800	1992	1700	1900	168068	SXW	Horsham
1800	1992	1700	1900	168068	SXW	Roffey
SUMMERHAYES						
1720	1900	1600	1700	167649	DEV	Otterford
1720	1900	1600	1700	167649	SOM	Otterford
SUMMERHILL						
1600	1900	1600	1900	157430	GLS	ALL
1680	1880	....	....	133507	GLS	Siston
SUMMERILL						
ALL	1800	ALL	1800	142425	GLS	South
1856	1992	1800	1856	114464	GLS	Bristol
SUMMERLAND						
?	?	?	?	143359	???	???
SUMMERS						
1800	1850	1700	1860	125423	CAM	Ramsey
1829	1859	1700	1900	158666	CON	Falmouth
1744	1890	ALL	1744	134783	DEV	Cotleigh
1704	?	....	....	168106	DOR	Studland
....	1800	....	1800	177695	ESS	Rochford
1834	1858	1700	1837	162035	GLS	Bristol
1770	1992	1770	....	118672	GLS	Dursley
1880	1992	1775	1992	145505	GLS	Dursley
1776	1825	1700	1850	126667	GLS	Gloucester
1840	1860	1800	1860	167401	HAM	Sopley
1793	....	1700	1850	128805	HAM	Southampton
....	....	1790	1830	128813	HAM	Southampton
1760	1820	ALL	1820	134503	KEN	Sundridge
1825	1925	1800	1950	128805	LND	ALL
1800	1900	1700	1875	154881	LND	ALL
1832	1950	1800	1950	128813	LND	Islington
1906	1985	1870	1950	124796	LND	Leyton
1871	....	1850	1900	124796	LND	Peckham
1888	1980	ALL	ALL	105856	MDX	???
1888	1980	ALL	ALL	105856	SRY	???
1780	1820	1750	1850	144657	SSX	Frant
1820	1850	....	....	138339	WOR	Birlingham
1820	1850	....	....	138339	WOR	Pershore

Known From	To	Researching From	To	Ref	Cty	Place
SUMMERSCALES						
1800	1875	1800	1875	153621	WYK	Halifax
SUMMERTON						
....	....	1800	1830	172073	WAR	Chadshunt
1856	1860	1835	1856	172073	WAR	Stratford On Avon
SUMMONS						
1800	1850	....	1800	100064	NFK	South
1800	1850	....	1800	100064	SFK	North
SUMNER						
....	....	....	1860	157139	CHS	ALL
1889	1900	ALL	1889	147222	LAN	Everton
1889	1900	ALL	1889	147222	LAN	Kirkdale
1850	1992	....	1850	157139	LAN	Liverpool
....	....	....	1840	157139	LAN	Lydiate
1800	1880	1880	1992	162256	LAN	Tockholes
1786	1851	1700	1800	125628	NFK	Great Yarmouth
1643	1643	ALL	1750	168696	OXF	Heythrop
1800	1845	1700	1800	132640	SSX	Rotherfield
1814	1821	1750	ALL	125288	STS	Walsall
1809	1857	ALL	ALL	125288	WAR	Birmingham
1752	1992	1600	1752	163422	WAR	Kenilworth
1825	1992	....	....	163422	YKS	Southam
SUMPTON						
1809	1861	1700	1900	118168	LAN	Ulveston
SUMSION						
1789	1871	ALL	1789	115010	WIL	Colerne
SUNDERLAND						
1600	1677	1600	1700	154601	WYK	Horbury
1860	1992	1750	1860	110442	WYK	Morley
1778	1880	1740	1880	170348	YKS	Ovendon
1850	1992	1600	1850	131172	YKS	Pudsey
SUNLEY						
1833	1881	....	....	156418	NYK	Bilsdale
1804	1867	....	....	156418	NYK	Colo Kirby
1767	1829	....	....	156418	NYK	Hawnby
SUNNUCKS						
1830	....	1750	1900	139386	KEN	Rochester
SURCH						
1811	ALL	1750	1811	171190	WAR	Little Compton
SURFLEET						
1850	1880	1550	1850	147265	LIN	North
1860	1992	1800	1900	101133	LIN	Louth
SURGEY						
1733	....	1700	1850	129011	LND	Chelsea
SURMAN						
....	....	ALL	ALL	168114	ALL	ALL
1750	1780	....	....	168114	GLS	Ashchurch
1780	1871	1795	1817	168114	GLS	Overbury
1543	1739	....	....	168114	GLS	Tredington
1212	1992	1212	1992	162817	GLS	???
1212	1992	1212	1992	162817	OXF	???
1886	1992	1895	1906	168114	WAR	Birmingham
1212	1992	1212	1992	162817	WAR	???
1875	1886	....	....	168114	WLS	Rossett
1780	1871	1795	1817	168114	WOR	Becford
1546	1600	1300	1546	168114	WOR	Eldersfield
1831	1870	1500	1860	157538	WOR	Whittington
1212	1992	1212	1992	162817	WOR	???
SURREY						
....	....	1700	1760	143502	ESS	South East
1670	1790	1600	1950	177180	HRT	Kings Langley
1868	1900	1840	1900	130559	SRY	Lambeth
SURRIDGE						
1840	1861	1800	1840	124990	AVN	Bristol
1813	1944	1700	1790	172553	ESS	Rivenhall
....	....	1700	1850	129364	ESS	Stapleford Abbot
1853	1881	1700	1992	176044	ESS	Stapleford Abbotts
....	....	ALL	1785	179477	SOM	???
....	1850	....	1850	174025	SRY	Clapham
SURTEES						
1750	1815	1700	1850	138878	NBL	Corbridge
SUSAN						
....	....	ALL	ALL	168130	ALL	Name Study
1534	....	....	....	168130	CON	Merther
1327	....	....	....	168130	CON	???
1200	....	....	....	168130	DBY	Chesterfield
1511	....	....	....	168130	DEV	Bideford
1528	....	....	....	168130	KEN	Langdon East
1504	....	....	....	168130	NTH	Peterborough
1194	....	....	....	168130	SFK	???
1200	....	....	....	168130	SOM	Middletown
1420	....	....	....	168130	SSX	Alciston
1540	1992	....	....	168130	SSX	Berwick
1552	1992	....	....	168130	SSX	Hellingly
SUSANS						
....	....	ALL	ALL	168130	ALL	ALL
SUSSEX						
....	....	1700	1992	168157	CON	ALL
1850	1965	1700	1850	168157	DEV	ALL
1670	....	1600	1700	135771	DEV	North
1670	1987	1600	1700	168157	DEV	North
....	....	1700	1992	168157	HMC	ALL
1850	1965	1700	1850	168157	WLS	South
SUTCLIFFE						
1751	....	....	1751	149624	LAN	Colne
1850	1920	1780	1850	105716	LAN	Manchester
1848	1848	1800	1900	151254	LAN	West Manchester
1840	....	ALL	ALL	100390	LAN	???
1600	1902	ALL	1992	124389	WRY	Haworth
1675	1745	1675	1745	107522	WRY	Todmorden
1860	1890	1800	1860	150061	YKS	Bradford
1813	....	1700	1800	120901	YKS	Halifax
1820	1900	1750	1820	172510	YKS	Halifax
1800	1992	1700	1800	168173	YKS	Heptonstall
1840	1992	1838	1895	122440	YKS	Horsforth
1827	1872	ALL	1827	154946	YKS	Huddersfield
1840	1992	1838	1895	122440	YKS	Leeds
1805	1845	1805	1860	155969	YKS	Midgley
1820	1900	1750	1820	172510	YKS	Pudsey
1820	1900	1750	1820	172510	YKS	Shelf
1740	1805	1680	1805	155969	YKS	Stansfield
SUTEHALL						
1910	1992	1900	1992	133450	KEN	???
SUTER						
1812	1992	1800	1992	153834	SSX	East
1910	1992	1910	1992	153834	SSX	Eastbourne
SUTERS						
1780	1880	1780	1880	133817	KEN	Dover
SUTHERLAND						
1834	1851	1700	1860	159379	CAI	Berriedale
....	....	1760	1780	138614	CAI	Canisbay
1801	1865	....	....	168203	CAI	Dunbeath
1800	1900	1700	1800	173134	CAI	Dunbeath
1800	1900	1700	1800	173134	CAI	Houstry
1780	1860	....	....	126497	CAI	Latheron
1780	1965	....	....	168203	CAI	Lybster
....	....	1750	1855	166049	CAI	Mey-Canisbay
....	....	1500	1770	138614	CAI	Olrig
1860	1900	1850	1992	165603	CAI	Reay
1800	1900	1700	1800	173134	CAI	Reay
....	....	1500	1800	138614	CAI	Sinnigoe
1800	1880	1700	1880	126500	CAI	Wick Latheron
1820	1850	1780	1900	135429	IRL	???
1875	1896	1896	1992	146560	LKS	Coatbride
1849	1869	1824	1900	166049	LKS	Glasgow
1817	1950	ALL	ALL	101370	LOU	Mid Garty
1885	1900	1800	1885	142786	MLN	Cockpen
....	....	1826	....	149187	MOR	Drainie
....	....	1826	....	149187	MOR	Elgin
1782	1786	1700	1992	137855	MOR	Kintesack
1823	1901	....	....	132381	MOR	???
1800	1817	ALL	ALL	101370	SCT	Dornoch
1750	1965	....	....	137820	SHI	Fetlar
1720	1965	....	....	137820	SHI	Mid Yell
1760	1965	....	....	137820	SHI	North Yell
1758	1965	....	....	137820	SHI	Northmavine
1720	1965	....	....	137820	SHI	South Yell
1783	1867	....	....	137936	SHI	Unst
1850	1900	1780	1900	135429	SOM	Claverton
....	....	1500	1821	138614	SUT	Clyne
1700	1950	ALL	ALL	101370	SUT	Golspie
....	....	1500	1810	138614	SUT	Rogart
1860	1870	1850	1992	165603	WIC	Keiss
1911	1950	1900	1911	142786	YKS	Sheffield
1823	1824	1823	1850	166049	???	Edinburgh
SUTHERLANDS						
....	....	ALL	ALL	159379	ALL	Name Study
SUTHERS						
....	....	1600	1900	168017	LAN	ALL
....	....	1600	1900	168017	YKS	Todmorden
SUTTCLIFFE						
1787	1789	....	....	142859	LAN	Heaton
1791	1810	....	....	142859	LAN	Prestwich
SUTTERBY						
....	....	ALL	ALL	158593	ALL	ALL
1750	1850	1750	1850	123765	LIN	Gainsby
SUTTIE						
1860	1943	1700	1860	155705	BDS	Leith

Known From	To	Researching From	To	Ref	Cty	Place
SUTTIE contd.						
1860	1943	1700	1860	155705	BDS	Yarrow
1860	1943	1700	1860	155705	???	Edinburgh
SUTTLE						
1800	1829	1600	1830	168548	SFK	Ipswich
....	....	1600	....	168548	YKS	???
SUTTLEWOOD						
1841	1900	1700	1841	113808	LEI	Walton On The Wolds
SUTTON						
1745	1992	1700	1745	151866	CAM	Longatanton
....	....	....	1810	137405	CAM	Over
1762	1800	1575	1800	108839	CAM	Sutton
1800	....	1750	1850	102016	CAM	Swavesey
1714	1940	....	....	128996	CAM	Thorney
1768	1768	1750	1800	134627	CAM	Wilburton
1900	1992	1800	1900	107123	CHS	Macclesfield
1819	1992	1700	1840	168262	CHS	Stockport
1849	1992	1700	1850	118532	CON	???
1702	1702	1660	1700	102830	DBY	Derby
1700	....	1600	1700	135771	DEV	Mid
1800	1870	1700	1800	146285	DFD	Haverfordwest
1708	....	....	....	151351	DOR	Netherbury
1865	1868	....	....	125202	DUR	Hartlepool
1722	1901	1550	1722	150398	ESS	Hatfield Peverel
1722	1901	1550	1722	150398	ESS	Kelvedon
1722	1901	1550	1722	150398	ESS	Rivenhall
1815	1888	1700	1815	145823	ESS	Woodford
....	....	1700	1850	121193	HAM	Portsmouth
1800	1810	1750	1810	178004	HRT	Layston
1815	1825	1750	1861	178004	HRT	Watford
1784	1825	1680	1777	116114	KEN	Brabourne
1820	1875	1875	ALL	131059	KEN	Chatham
1800	....	ALL	1800	131059	KEN	East Farleigh
1762	1762	1700	1800	173460	KEN	Eastry
1776	1992	....	....	131504	LAN	Hoole
1784	1822	ALL	ALL	141615	LEI	Barrow Upon Soar
1800	1850	ALL	ALL	125253	LIN	Ashby
1775	1800	ALL	ALL	125253	LIN	Bilsby
1829	1850	ALL	ALL	125253	LIN	Louth
1800	1850	ALL	ALL	125253	LIN	Partmey
1736	1793	....	....	168238	LIN	South Hykeham
1709	1777	....	....	168238	LIN	Thorpe On The Hill
1767	1844	....	....	168238	LIN	Wragby
1831	1833	1831	1843	168289	LND	Bermondsey
1775	1850	1700	1775	135879	LND	Shoreditch
1825	1860	1800	1860	178004	MDX	Enfield
1850	....	....	....	133698	MDX	Fulham
1850	....	....	....	133698	MDX	Hamm
1845	....	....	....	125202	NFK	Branthill
1873	1876	....	....	125202	NFK	Stiffkey
1879	1881	....	....	125202	NFK	Warham
1797	1840	ALL	1797	115126	NTH	Blisworth
....	....	1787	1787	114308	NTH	Rothersthorpe
....	....	1600	1700	168238	NTT	ALL
1875	1875	....	....	141097	NTT	Asby De La Zouche
....	....	1660	1720	168238	NTT	Besthorpe
1699	1742	ALL	1699	168238	NTT	Coddington
....	....	1550	1640	168238	NTT	Gunthorpe
....	....	1660	1720	168238	NTT	South Scarle
1795	1799	1700	1900	168734	SAL	Chetwynd
1778	1900	1700	1992	168734	SAL	Hinstock
ALL	1850	....	....	133698	SOM	Axbridge
1849	1992	1700	1850	118532	SOM	???
1702	1775	....	....	117404	STS	Basworth
1792	1916	1792	1916	153273	STS	Darlaston
1580	1656	....	....	117404	STS	Rugeley
1792	1916	1792	1916	153273	STS	Stone
1750	1850	1500	1992	177180	STS	Tipton
1753	....	1700	1800	122661	WIL	Durrington
1840	1890	1850	1900	155357	WIL	Pitton
1864	1926	1750	1870	136530	???	Aston
SUZAN						
....	....	ALL	ALL	168130	ALL	ALL
SUZANS						
....	....	ALL	ALL	168130	ALL	ALL
SWABEY						
1800	1865	1700	1870	123870	LND	Olave
1638	1800	1500	ALL	122211	SRY	Lambeth
1800	1865	1700	1870	123870	SRY	Lambeth
SWABY						
1520	1880	ALL	1900	152838	LIN	Marshchapel
1820	1992	1650	1850	131067	MDX	Camden Town
1882	1908	1882	1920	152838	YKS	Rotherham
1854	1926	1854	1950	152838	YKS	Skidby
SWADLING						
1625	1820	....	....	168300	BRK	Radley
1450	1680	....	....	168300	BRK	Sunningwell
1610	1850	....	....	168300	OXF	Oxford
1670	1810	....	....	168300	OXF	South Hinksey
1729	1830	1600	1850	170178	SXE	Udimore
SWAEN						
1680	1780	1600	1700	144606	DUR	South Shields
SWAFFER						
1790	1856	1700	1770	114871	KEN	Canterbury
SWAFFIELD						
....	....	ALL	ALL	140511	ALL	Name Study
1755	1961	1700	1755	104310	DOR	Beaminster
1600	1992	ALL	ALL	140511	DOR	Dorchester
1600	1992	ALL	ALL	140511	SOM	Mid
....	....	ALL	1755	104310	SOM	???
1877	1880	1800	1877	102288	SRY	Norwood
SWAFFIN						
1810	1885	1750	1810	179019	DEV	Brixham
SWAIN						
....	....	ALL	ALL	168319	ALL	Name Study
ALL	ALL	ALL	ALL	168319	ALL	ALL
1750	1830	1750	1830	167924	COR	Cork
1851	1936	1700	1851	105252	DBY	Derby
1780	1800	1600	1780	148792	HAM	North West
1851	1871	....	....	132497	KEN	Canterbury
....	....	1750	1850	151084	LND	East
1834	ALL	ALL	....	111295	LND	London
1800	1900	1800	1900	167924	MGY	Carmarthen
1830	....	ALL	1850	174637	MGY	???
1935	1950	ALL	ALL	164887	SOM	Frome
1890	1992	1890	1992	153834	SSX	Eastbourne
1890	1992	1890	1992	153834	SSX	Hastings
1880	....	ALL	1900	139459	WAR	Birmingham
1880	....	ALL	1900	139459	WAR	Saltley
1880	....	ALL	1900	139459	WAR	Small Heath
1803	1889	....	....	140384	WMD	Birmingham
1803	1889	....	....	140384	WMD	Dudley
1803	1889	....	....	140384	WMD	Oldswinford
1803	1889	....	....	140384	WMD	Yardley
SWAINE						
....	....	1500	1716	138614	DOR	Lyme Regis
1900	1940	1800	1900	170801	SSX	Worthing
SWAINSON						
1800	1850	1700	1900	126802	CUL	ALL
....	1850	ALL	ALL	122866	MDX	East
SWAINSTON						
1850	1900	1700	1850	127299	LND	???
SWAISLAND						
1771	1865	1550	1771	150398	KEN	Bexley
1771	1865	1550	1771	150398	KEN	Crayford
1771	1865	1550	1771	150398	KEN	Dartford
1828	1896	1600	1828	150398	LND	Bermondsey
1828	1896	1600	1828	150398	LND	Woolwich
1828	1896	1600	1828	150398	SRY	Camberwell
1828	1896	1600	1828	150398	SRY	Walworth
SWALE						
1833	1980	1600	1992	172863	YKS	North
1833	1980	1600	1992	172863	YKS	West
SWALES						
....	....	ALL	ALL	136948	BKM	High Wycombe
1850	1920	....	....	103845	PEM	Haverfordwest
1891	1992	1890	ALL	143618	WYK	Castleford
1857	1888	ALL	ALL	143618	WYK	Wakefield
1700	1840	1600	1700	103845	YKS	Dent
1750	1800	....	....	102946	YKS	Gillin
1848	....	ALL	ALL	155373	YKS	Guisborough
1710	1790	....	....	145688	YKS	Keighley
....	....	....	1850	147818	YKS	Lower Wharfedale
1810	....	1800	1900	139114	???	Hartlepool
SWALLOW						
....	....	ALL	ALL	100056	ALL	ALL
....	....	1820	1900	166448	BKM	Beaconsfield
1825	1940	1700	1825	171891	BKM	Chalfont St Peter
1860	1900	....	....	100056	LAN	Ashton Under Lyne
1820	....	....	....	100056	LND	Marylebone
1750	1760	1600	1800	154601	WYK	Batley
1874	....	ALL	ALL	155373	YKS	South
1800	1980	1565	1800	103527	YKS	Almondbury
1818	1992	1700	1818	178993	YKS	Almondbury
1900	1950	1850	1992	174335	YKS	Attercliffe
1722	1821	1675	1851	157716	YKS	Austonley
1690	1760	1650	1690	177393	YKS	Birkin
1750	1980	1750	1980	104612	YKS	Holme

Known From	To	Researching From	To	Ref	Cty	Place
SWALLOW contd.						
1750	1980	1750	1980	104612	YKS	Huddersfield
1900	1950	1850	1992	174335	YKS	Sheffield
SWAN						
1775	1855	....	1855	137405	CAM	South
1680	1780	1600	1700	144606	DUR	South Shields
1807	1992	1600	1807	151092	KEN	Marden
1688	1749	ALL	ALL	141615	LEI	Burton Overy
1870	1902	1800	1870	174068	LND	Lambeth
1803	....	?	1850	103934	LND	???
1500	1992	ALL	ALL	119857	MDX	London
1836	1868	....	....	113484	MLN	Edinburgh
1806	1806	1750	1850	149152	NBL	Alnwick
1600	1900	1600	1900	168343	NFK	ALL
1788	1923	1700	1850	110922	NFK	Great Yarmouth
1815	1832	1832	1992	166804	NFK	Great Yarmouth
1720	1940	1720	1992	168327	NTH	Lowick
1640	1800	1600	1850	168327	NTH	Titchmarsh
1842	1861	1800	1842	146358	RFW	Port Glasgow
1788	1850	1700	1850	110922	SFK	Gorleston
ALL	ALL	ALL	ALL	137731	STS	Mucklestone
SWANKIE						
....	....	1830	ALL	149187	ANS	Dundee
SWANN						
1830	1890	1700	1830	153230	LIN	Deeping
1600	1900	1600	1900	168343	NFK	ALL
1826	1936	ALL	1826	159204	NFK	Norwich
1770	1835	1700	1770	100129	RUT	Barrowden
SWANNELL						
1830	1858	ALL	1830	146986	BDF	Dunstable
....	....	1650	1900	102784	BDF	Felmersham
....	....	1650	1900	102784	BDF	Pavenham
1720	1825	....	....	118354	BDF	Sharnbrook
1807	1839	....	1807	104124	BKM	Newport Pagnell
....	....	1800	1900	102784	BKM	Weston Under Wood
SWANNOCK						
1780	1803	1650	1780	162396	LIN	North
SWANSBOROUGH						
1836	1992	....	1836	136778	WIL	Chippenham
SWANSON						
1742	1877	....	1742	101761	CAI	Bower
....	....	1828	1900	170437	CAI	Wick
1668	1749	1600	1668	150150	RUT	Caldecott
1825	1900	1825	1992	133450	SSX	???
SWANSTON						
1801	1965	ALL	1800	146757	BEW	Duns
1801	1965	ALL	1800	146757	BEW	Gordon
SWANWICK						
1853	1992	1750	1855	135496	NTT	Nottingham
1779	1874	1700	1779	125288	STS	Ashley
SWARBRICK						
1705	1900	1540	1900	100080	LAN	The Fylde
SWARBROOK						
1760	1850	1700	1760	134317	CHS	ALL
SWASH						
1806	1869	1800	1869	154709	GLS	Bristol
SWATMAN						
1862	1941	1750	1862	168025	NFK	Wymondham
SWATTON						
....	....	ALL	ALL	126764	ALL	Name Study
SWAYNE						
....	....	1800	1900	168386	GLS	Painswick
1760	1900	1700	1900	168378	WIL	Boyton
1760	1900	1700	1900	168378	WIL	Corton
1760	1900	1700	1900	168378	WIL	Durnford
1760	1900	1700	1900	168378	WIL	Heytsbury
1760	1900	1700	1900	168378	WIL	Little Langford
1760	1900	1700	1900	168378	WIL	Little Wishford
1760	1900	1700	1900	168378	WIL	Salisbury
1760	1900	1700	1900	168378	WIL	Stapleford
1760	1900	1700	1900	168378	WIL	Upton Lovell
1760	1900	1700	1900	168378	WIL	Wilton
SWAYSLAND						
1796	1798	1790	1850	167002	MDX	London
1769	1776	1730	1800	167002	SXW	Horsted Keynes
SWEAINE						
1711	....	1545	1711	117196	CHS	Gawsworth
1566	1711	ALL	1711	141062	CHS	Gawsworth
SWEBY						
1679	1679	1630	1720	167002	BKM	Wendover
1817	1900	1700	1817	176257	HRT	Hemel Hempstead
SWEET						
....	....	1790	1860	135046	CON	Chacewater
1732	1776	1500	1776	132993	CON	Meheniot
SWEET contd.						
1732	1776	1500	1776	132993	CON	Sheviock
?	?	?	?	111937	CON	St Austell
?	?	?	?	111937	CON	St Ewe
....	....	1790	1860	135046	CON	St Neot
....	....	1700	1800	108677	DEV	Tawton
1713	1819	1600	1713	149888	GLS	Bitton
1820	1830	1700	1820	173223	GLS	Bristol
....	....	1600	1960	149454	LND	???
1774	1820	1700	1780	168033	MDX	Chiswick
1840	1992	1700	1840	168084	SOM	Crewkerne
1820	....	....	....	147672	SOM	Martock
1850	1880	1800	1880	156566	SOM	Merriot
....	....	1650	1720	116173	YKS	Swainby
1819	1870	....	1820	166510	???	Bristol
SWEETAPPLE						
....	....	ALL	ALL	110744	ALL	Name Study
1500	1900	1500	1900	170216	DOR	ALL
1500	1900	1500	1900	170216	WIL	ALL
SWEETING						
....	....	ALL	ALL	168394	ALL	Name Study
1760	1870	1760	1870	127655	GLS	Stroud
1760	1870	1760	1870	127655	GLS	Tetbury
....	1850	ALL	ALL	122866	MDX	East
ALL	....	ALL	ALL	123668	SOM	Congresbury
SWEETLOVE						
1750	1800	1700	1850	121274	KEN	East
1693	1850	1600	1800	133817	KEN	Leeds
1693	1850	1600	1800	133817	KEN	Maidstone
SWEETMAN						
1879	1992	ALL	ALL	164550	COR	Schull
1893	1944	ALL	ALL	106216	WLS	Cardiff
SWENY						
1500	1992	ALL	ALL	105333	ALL	ALL
SWIFFEN						
1775	1775	1720	1820	167002	MDX	St Luke
SWIFT						
1813	1980	1783	1980	125008	AVN	Writhlington
1830	1850	1700	1960	101907	KEN	Boxley
1851	1992	1851	1992	141267	KEN	Sheerness
1829	1851	1806	1851	157678	LAN	Halsall
?	1880	....	....	165158	LAN	Skelmersdale
1826	1829	1700	1825	131245	LEI	Quorndon
1858	1881	1800	1858	157856	MDX	Bethnal Green
1858	1881	1800	1858	157856	MDX	Bow
1858	1881	1800	1858	157856	MDX	Shoreditch
1856	1912	1600	1856	143146	NTT	Farnsfield
1856	1912	1600	1856	143146	NTT	Southwell
....	....	1800	1900	168645	SAL	Wellington
....	....	1750	1850	147613	SAL	Wrockwardine
1813	1992	1800	1992	125016	SOM	Writhlington
1813	1980	1783	1980	125008	SOM	Writhlington
1775	1795	1700	1775	132640	SSX	Rotherfield
1850	1992	1700	1850	168408	WYK	Dewsbury
1800	1850	1600	1992	120677	WYK	Slaithwaite
1824	1992	?	1824	144800	YKS	Halifax
1824	1992	?	1824	144800	YKS	Henley
1824	1992	?	1824	144800	YKS	Huddersfield
1805	1880	1700	1805	102148	YKS	Leeds
....	....	1700	1805	102148	???	Liverpool
SWIGGS						
1824	1870	1824	1870	168416	CON	Lanteglos By Fowey
1625	1805	1625	1777	168416	CON	Menheniot
1599	1612	1599	1612	168416	CON	St Germans
1708	1800	1738	1801	168416	CON	Talland
SWINBANK						
1578	1614	1500	1800	168424	WES	Ravenstonedale
1611	1950	1500	1800	168424	YKS	North West
SWINBURN						
1800	1910	1750	1900	130036	CUL	ALL
1600	1850	1600	1850	168432	CUL	ALL
1820	1992	1700	1820	107298	DUR	Derwentside
1850	1992	1850	1950	168432	LAN	Manchester
1550	1967	1550	1967	168432	NBL	ALL
1820	1992	1700	1820	107298	NBL	Shotleyfield
SWINBURNE						
1851	1992	....	....	132357	DUR	Bishop Auckland
ALL	1350	....	....	132756	NBL	???
1790	1902	1790	1992	165603	YKS	Yarm
SWINCKFIELD						
1653	1826	1500	1860	137170	BKM	Little Brickhill
SWINDELL						
1810	1851	1750	1881	142204	LAN	Leigh

Known From	To	Researching From	To	Ref	Cty	Place
SWINDELLS						
1739	1800	1700	1800	135496	CHS	Gansworth
1745	1788	1720	1745	117196	CHS	Gawsworth
1600	1764	ALL	1764	141062	CHS	Rainow
SWINDEN						
1825	1886	1700	1825	149918	LAN	Liverpool
1800	....	1800	....	116793	YKS	Sheffield
SWINDLEHURST						
1851	1965	1851	1960	104612	YKS	Huddersfield
1851	1965	1851	1960	104612	YKS	New Mill
SWINERD						
?	?	?	?	166642	KEN	Ashford
SWINFIELD						
....	....	ALL	ALL	168440	ALL	Name Study
1836	1875	1700	1836	126772	NTT	Nottingham
SWINN						
1840	1860	1840	1860	143588	EYK	Hull
1840	1860	1840	1860	143588	EYK	Whitby
SWINNARD						
1800	1910	1700	1800	146285	KEN	Ashford
SWINNERTON						
....	....	ALL	ALL	168459	ALL	Name Study
SWINNEY						
1840	1992	1750	1840	160075	DUR	Lumley
SWINSCOW						
1800	1930	....	....	135984	LND	Islington
1800	1930	....	....	135984	LND	Stepney
SWINSON						
1837	1903	ALL	1837	155306	DBY	Holbrook
SWINTON						
....	....	ALL	ALL	168475	ALL	Name Study
1790	....	1780	1800	130915	FIF	St Andrews
SWINYARD						
ALL	ALL	ALL	ALL	137243	ALL	ALL
SWIRE						
1854	....	....	....	120804	???	Manchester
SWIRREL						
1732	1758	ALL	ALL	130508	FIF	Cameron Bowlong
SWITHINBANK						
1706	1769	ALL	1706	154563	YKS	Calverley
SWITZER						
1763	1778	1740	1790	163775	BRK	Reading
SWOFFER						
1780	1800	1780	1900	153303	KEN	Throwley
SWORD						
1812	1844	1600	1812	160342	DFS	Ewes
SWORDS						
....	....	ALL	ALL	168483	ALL	Name Study
SWORTON						
1665	1710	1600	1750	133450	LAN	Warrington
SYDDALL						
1840	1992	ALL	ALL	117145	LAN	Little Lever
SYDER						
1750	1860	1700	1860	125881	NFK	???
1750	1860	1700	1860	125881	SFK	???
SYDNEY						
....	....	1800	1900	150800	LND	???
1400	1600	1350	1600	154881	SRY	Stoke D'abernon
....	....	1800	1900	150800	SRY	???
SYER						
1654	1680	1600	1850	159956	SFK	Walsham Le Willows
SYFLEET						
1759	1783	....	1820	171441	KEN	Stockbury
SYGR						
1654	1677	1620	1690	123404	NFK	North Elmham
SYGROVE						
1745	1992	1500	1745	132233	HRT	Harpenden
1800	1900	1800	1900	168491	HRT	Harpenden
1800	1900	1800	1900	168491	HRT	Redbourn
1750	1850	1750	1850	168491	HRT	Wheathampstead
1870	1920	1870	1920	168491	YKS	Huggate
SYKES						
1820	1900	1700	1850	120839	EYK	???
1824	1858	1800	1824	170569	LAN	Heaton Mersey
1876	1898	1800	1900	149500	LIN	Louth
....	1850	....	....	114642	MDX	London
1827	1850	....	1830	146811	WYK	Huddersfield
1825	1900	1800	1950	123285	WYK	Shelly
1850	1992	1700	1992	120677	WYK	Slaithwaite
1740	1800	1740	1800	119717	YKS	Almondbury
1555	1992	....	....	168513	YKS	Almondbury
1770	1800	1750	1770	123595	YKS	Almondsbury
1817	1842	1780	1817	137057	YKS	Greetland
1750	1950	1700	1880	123595	YKS	Holmfirth
SYKES contd.						
1818	1992	1700	1818	123951	YKS	Huddersfield
1790	1810	ALL	ALL	170801	YKS	Huddersfield
1804	1947	1750	1804	133760	YKS	Linthwaite
1769	1794	1730	1769	133760	YKS	Netherthong
1825	1827	1800	1860	148121	YKS	Sheffield
1709	1763	....	1763	109622	YKS	Snaith
1735	1760	1700	1992	114901	YKS	Thornhill
1780	1841	1600	1992	102520	YKS	Whitley
1825	1827	1790	1860	148121	YKS	???
SYLVESTER						
1720	1746	1700	1760	168556	BRK	???
1896	1992	1896	1992	168564	DEV	Plymouth
1720	1746	1700	1760	168556	HRT	Whitchurch
1783	1843	1783	....	163171	LEI	Snarestone
1746	1992	ALL	ALL	154806	LIN	Alford
1867	1884	1800	1884	168564	LIN	Croft
1746	1992	ALL	ALL	154806	LIN	Spilsby
1834	1992	1800	1850	116815	LND	St Luke
1560	1800	....	....	168556	NTT	Mansfield
1500	1900	....	....	168556	OXF	Burford
1809	1940	....	....	148237	SSX	Chichester
1760	1912	....	....	168556	WIL	Trowbridge
1746	1766	....	....	168556	WIL	Warminster
SYME						
....	....	ALL	1791	119326	ELN	Tranent
....	....	....	....	120219	STI	Falkirk
1500	1610	1500	1700	170216	WIL	ALL
SYMES						
1809	1885	1760	1885	102970	DOR	Burton Bradstock
1850	1860	ALL	1992	160199	DOR	Coastal
1890	1900	1800	1890	148385	DUB	Dublin
....	....	?	....	141216	GLS	Mid
1810	1870	1800	1900	152528	KEN	Deptford
1850	1860	ALL	1992	160199	NBL	Coastal
1600	1750	1600	1750	142018	SOM	Bridgwater
SYMINGES						
....	....	1500	1600	154873	LND	???
SYMMONS						
1730	1870	1730	1870	129054	AVN	Bristol
1730	1870	1730	1870	129054	GLA	Ewenny
1730	1870	1730	1870	129054	GLA	Newton Nuttage
SYMON						
?	?	?	?	108588	LAN	Liverpool
SYMOND						
1709	1732	....	....	138401	CUL	Dean
SYMONDS						
1700	1810	1600	1700	158739	DEV	Braunton
....	....	1800	1850	142026	DEV	Sidmouth
....	....	ALL	ALL	141216	GLS	North
1750	....	....	....	174564	HEF	Ledbury
1842	1900	....	....	103373	MON	Abergavenn
1600	1750	....	ALL	116866	SAL	???
1549	1920	ALL	ALL	114642	SFK	Debden
1568	1624	....	....	129747	SFK	Glemsford
1679	1699	1600	1800	159956	SFK	Market Weston
1730	1787	1700	1790	105333	SSX	Rodmell
1600	1750	....	ALL	116866	WAR	???
....	....	ALL	ALL	141216	WOR	South
....	1840	....	....	174564	WOR	Droitwich
1868	1940	1700	1868	155101	WOR	Strensham
SYMONS						
1600	1992	?	?	114944	CON	ALL
1792	1992	ALL	1992	168718	CON	South East
1790	1992	1700	1790	130257	CON	Breage
....	....	1500	1900	136972	CON	Breage
....	....	1500	1900	136972	CON	Germoe
1810	1848	1800	1850	168580	CON	Hankervis
1770	1850	1750	1850	168580	CON	Indian Queens
1690	1730	1600	1750	168580	CON	Ladock
?	?	?	?	168599	CON	Linkinhorne
1778	1992	1500	1778	150142	CON	Liskeard
ALL	ALL	....	....	168599	CON	St Cleer
1810	1848	1800	1850	168580	CON	St Enoder
1780	1805	1770	1820	168580	CON	St Wenn
1780	1805	1770	1820	168580	CON	Tregolls
1786	1820	1700	1820	119202	DEV	Devonport
1865	1992	....	1865	150495	DEV	Devonport
1816	1900	ALL	1816	149950	DEV	Luppitt
1525	1580	....	....	142522	SRY	West Clandon
SYMPSON						
1688	1908	1500	1908	144460	STS	Trentham
SYMS						
1880	1992	1800	1992	139475	LAN	Liverpool

Known From	To	Researching From	To	Ref	Cty	Place
SYMS contd.						
....	....	1800	1900	122203	???	London
SYRE						
1730	1746	1680	1730	155276	SFK	Otley
SYRETT						
1730	1730	1670	1730	155276	SFK	Brightwell
TABBAT						
1746	1765	ALL	1746	168602	CAM	Conington
1795	1873	ALL	1746	168602	HUN	Bluntisham
1795	1873	ALL	1746	168602	HUN	Needingworth
TABBENER						
1800	1812	1800	1812	120472	WOR	Alvechurch
TABERT						
1800	1930	1700	1800	139491	SOM	Taunton
TABINER						
1900	1920	1900	1992	168181	LIN	Grantham
TABOR						
1747	1940	....	....	128996	CAM	Thorney
....	....	1895	1954	137391	WAR	Birmingham
1670	1870	1870	1992	168726	WIL	Warminster
TABRETT						
1820	1880	ALL	ALL	113700	KEN	Ashford
TACON						
1920	1992	1800	1920	107999	MDX	Acton
TADMAN						
1720	1831	ALL	1840	113611	EYK	Hull
TAFT						
1765	1800	1700	1900	159107	STS	Tettenhall
1784	1814	....	....	117560	WAR	???
....	....	1700	1880	102148	YKS	West
TAGG						
....	?	?	?	127442	DBY	Derby
....	?	?	?	127442	NTT	Alfreton
1763	....	?	1770	164976	NTT	Nottingham
....	....	1550	1600	170313	WOR	Hartlebury
TAGGART						
1892	1982	1850	1980	168629	LAN	Liverpool
1825	1861	1700	1825	145971	LAN	Manchester
TAILBOYS						
1066	1150	1066	1200	154881	ALL	ALL
TAILOR						
1814	....	1750	1851	176877	RAD	Knighton
TAINTON						
1840	1900	1800	1850	156957	GLS	Redmarley
TAIT						
1820	1850	ALL	ALL	130508	ABD	Aberdeen
1845	1900	1800	1900	146536	AYR	Kilbirnie
1847	1891	1800	1992	168637	CUL	Brampton
1827	....	1800	1861	168637	CUL	Kirkandrews On Esk
1890	1895	1850	1900	102717	ESS	Thurrock
1800	1850	1800	1851	126209	NBL	North
1795	1845	1700	1795	128406	NBL	Bamburgh
....	....	1800	1850	102717	ROX	ALL
1600	1650	ALL	1650	149063	ROX	Smailholm
1750	1965	....	....	137820	SHI	Fetlar
1720	1965	....	....	137820	SHI	Mid Yell
1760	1965	....	....	137820	SHI	North Yell
1758	1965	....	....	137820	SHI	Northmavine
1720	1965	....	....	137820	SHI	South Yell
1800	1992	1700	1992	104671	SHI	Tingwall
1803	1803	1700	1850	139203	SHI	Weisdale
1898	....	1898	1992	168637	???	Liverpool
TAKEL						
1700	1800	ALL	ALL	131873	DEV	Exeter
TALBART						
....	1820	....	....	174564	LEI	???
TALBOT						
1086	1086	1066	1150	124974	BDF	Battlesden
1810	1846	1780	1810	128724	BKM	Langley Marish
1833	1884	....	....	123641	DBY	Dronfield
1885	....	....	....	163155	DBY	???
1804	1812	....	....	101028	DEV	Bampton
1691	?	ALL	1691	157511	DOR	Bere Regis
1776	1865	ALL	1776	154563	DOR	Weymouth
1875	1935	1800	1875	160717	DUR	Durham
1850	1900	1800	1850	160717	DUR	South Shields
1390	1453	1200	1500	176923	ENG	???
1830	1992	1650	1830	168653	ESS	ALL
....	....	1700	1850	132276	ESS	Wigboroughs
1801	1832	1700	1801	154164	HAM	Portsmouth
1130	1346	1100	1306	124974	HEF	Eccleswall
1130	1346	1100	1306	124974	HEF	Linton
....	....	1820	1840	177725	LIN	Holton Beckering
....	....	ALL	1573	123641	LIN	Thoranby
TALBOT contd.						
1893	1992	ALL	ALL	120057	LND	Bow
1866	....	ALL	ALL	120057	LND	Limehouse
1865	....	ALL	ALL	120057	MDX	Poplar
1843	1992	1700	1843	138355	NBL	Newcastle
1730	1874	....	....	123641	NTT	Askham
1757	1776	....	....	123641	NTT	E Markham
1601	1714	....	....	123641	NTT	Laxton
1675	1815	....	....	123641	NTT	Ordsall
1820	1970	1750	1820	168645	SAL	Newport
1797	1841	1600	1881	115630	SAL	Sheriffhales
1740	1866	....	....	101028	SFK	Barrow
1810	1893	....	1810	101761	SFK	Brandon
1797	1992	1800	1992	111074	SSX	Horsham
1820	1881	ALL	ALL	141186	STS	Abbots Bromley
1800	1850	1700	1850	114383	STS	Breewood
1840	....	1810	1840	149195	STS	Dudley
1768	1868	1700	1800	160768	SXW	Climping
1790	....	1700	1850	102016	WAR	Moreton Morrell
1810	1880	ALL	1900	102016	WAR	Stratford On Avon
....	1804	1750	1804	128961	WES	Kendal
1843	1887	1843	1887	138398	WIL	Westbury Leigh
....	....	1870	1992	147613	WOR	Dudley
1774	1799	....	1774	101761	WRY	Flockton
1700	1861	1600	1700	154601	WYK	Batley
1746	1900	1600	1746	109142	YKS	Batley
1885	....	....	....	163155	YKS	???
TALBOTT						
1620	1660	ALL	1650	115266	DOR	ALL
1600	1699	1650	1730	135941	SFK	Mildenhall
TALL						
1724	1795	....	1750	137405	CAM	Long Stanton
....	....	....	1750	137405	CAM	Willingham
TALLAND						
1774	1788	ALL	1774	161330	NTT	Nottingham
TALLANT						
1850	1960	ALL	ALL	162469	SFK	North
TALLANTIRE						
1919	1989	....	....	168661	CHS	Cheadle Hulme
1550	1992	1200	1992	168661	CMA	East
1550	1992	1200	1992	168661	CMA	North
1550	1992	1200	1992	168661	CMA	West
1850	1919	....	....	168661	LAN	Manchester
TALLENT						
1657	1849	1650	1800	129194	SFK	East
TALLENTINE						
1768	1796	1700	1768	169935	LAN	Cockerham
TALLING						
....	....	1700	1899	174963	DEV	Kingsteighton
TALLIS						
1600	1700	1728	1992	151475	WAR	Snitterfield
?	1690	....	1690	151475	WAR	Solihull
TALLISS						
1600	1992	1066	1992	168688	ALL	ALL
TALMAGE						
1830	1870	....	1870	109568	BRK	Hanney
1791	1911	1750	1791	113395	BRK	West Hanney
1800	1870	1650	1800	148792	HAM	Whitchurch
TALMEY						
1700	1820	....	....	121983	SSX	Hurspierpoint
TAMBLIN						
1730	1992	ALL	1992	168718	CON	South East
TAMBLINSON						
1674	1833	ALL	1992	168718	CON	South East
TAMBLYN						
1761	1871	1761	1871	123773	CON	St Enoder
TAME						
1500	1900	1550	1900	153788	ALL	ALL
TAMES						
1550	1992	1500	1992	168726	STS	North
TAMKIN						
1800	1870	1800	1900	177571	ESS	Waltham Abbey
1841	1881	1700	1841	119075	KEN	Faversham
TAMLIN						
1839	1891	1800	1900	126470	DEV	Newton Abbott
TAMLYN						
....	....	ALL	1866	114030	CON	Lanreath
TAMPIN						
....	....	ALL	ALL	104973	ALL	Name Study
TAMPLIN						
1816	....	1800	1850	159034	LND	City
1850	1950	....	....	100536	???	???
TAMS						
1860	1880	....	....	121185	KEN	South

Known From	To	Researching From	To	Ref	Cty	Place
TAMS contd.						
1876	1877	1800	1900	113476	LAN	Burnley
1880	1958	1700	1880	132926	MDX	Bethnal Green
1825	1865	1750	1825	135461	STS	Stone
TAMSETT						
1797	1992	....	....	172529	SSX	Battle
TANCARVILLE						
1100	1130	1100	1130	104736	LEI	ALL
1100	1130	1100	1130	104736	LIN	ALL
TANCOCK						
1750	1900	....	....	143855	DEV	Central
1840	1890	1770	1900	102970	DEV	Bondleigh
1783	1834	1700	1992	167800	DEV	Newton St Cyres
TANDY						
1784	1851	ALL	ALL	113662	GLS	Tresham
....	....	1750	1800	138339	KEN	Ashford
1800	1870	....	....	138339	WOR	Kempsey
1900	....	1800	1950	116920	???	Handsworth
TANFIELD						
1452	1639	1639	1792	154911	NTH	Gayton
1840	1860	1800	1840	116572	NTT	???
....	....	1639	1792	154911	YKS	Ripon
....	....	1639	1792	154911	YKS	Thirsk
TANKARD						
1782	1919	1700	1950	147338	WRY	Bradford
1850	1880	1740	1850	149462	YKS	Haddlesey
TANKESLEY						
1725	1794	1600	1750	101575	YKS	Whitgift
TANN						
1852	1992	ALL	ALL	168742	LND	London
....	....	1700	1850	140627	SFK	Cookley
TANNAHILL						
1670	1992	....	1760	150428	AYR	Kilmarnock
1750	1992	1670	1992	150428	RFW	Paisley
TANNATT						
1700	1800	1600	1800	142123	MGY	Llansantfraid-Ym-Mechain
TANNER						
1300	1992	ALL	1992	133450	ALL	ALL
1780	1900	1750	1780	168750	CON	St Ives
1815	1992	1500	1815	110310	ESS	Wickford
1610	1670	1600	1700	159557	GLS	Ablington
1650	1690	1650	1690	159557	GLS	Burton Hill
1780	1850	1780	1850	159557	GLS	Charlton
1900	1977	....	....	104264	GLS	Gloucester
1851	1871	....	....	142859	GLS	Minchinhampton
....	....	1706	1881	104264	GLS	Rodmarton
1680	1750	1680	1750	159557	GLS	Shipton Moyne
1875	1921	....	....	104264	GLS	Siddington
....	....	1715	1881	104264	GLS	Tetbury
1770	1800	1600	1800	130125	GLS	Wickwar
1700	1900	ALL	ALL	122866	HAM	North West
1650	1900	1600	1650	168777	HAM	Nether Wallop
1816	1840	1700	1815	131245	KEN	Chatham
1845	1992	1800	1845	115312	KEN	Maidstone
1861	1881	1840	1861	168785	LND	Hampstead
1820	1900	1700	....	118591	LND	Mile End
1650	1992	1650	1800	168769	POW	Newtown
1830	1992	1830	1992	168769	SAL	Shrewsbury
1700	1730	1700	1760	142018	SOM	Tellisford
1740	1840	1750	1850	121096	SRY	Banstead
1825	1850	1750	1900	139386	SRY	Brixton
1672	1833	1640	1900	168785	SSX	Ditchling
1750	1833	1833	1861	168785	SSX	Wivelsfield
1827	....	....	....	142859	WIL	Charlton
1828	1834	1828	1834	142859	WIL	Leigh
1712	....	1680	1750	170348	WIL	Purton
TANNOCK						
1799	1857	1700	1850	144231	AYR	Tarbolton
TANSEL						
1804	1825	....	....	102733	WOR	North Piddle
TANSER						
1840	1870	1800	1900	116173	LEI	Rearsby
1803	1992	1700	1900	154881	WAR	Rugby
TANSLEY						
1560	ALL	1560	ALL	167924	BDF	ALL
1740	1800	1740	1800	167924	BDF	Shillington
1700	1800	1700	1800	167924	BDF	Southill
1760	1820	1760	1820	167924	BDF	Stotfold
1787	1940	....	....	128996	CAM	Thorney
1780	1922	1700	1780	138347	ESS	North East
1830	1890	1830	1890	167924	HRT	Bladock
1800	1992	1824	1914	168807	HRT	Codicote
1803	1857	....	1803	142166	HRT	Hitchin
TANSLEY contd.						
1800	1992	1824	1914	168807	HRT	Hitchin
1800	1850	1800	1850	167924	HRT	Ickleford
1850	1930	1850	1930	167924	MDX	Finchley
1800	1946	1700	1800	169889	NTT	Sneinton Nottingham
TAPE						
....	....	ALL	ALL	124419	ALL	Name Study
TAPHOUSE						
....	....	ALL	ALL	157260	HAM	Basingstoke
TAPLEY						
1685	1808	1600	1685	166723	LND	Cripplegate
1737	1800	1700	1737	179663	MDX	London
1783	....	1760	1790	163775	MDX	Shoreditch
TAPLIN						
1783	1802	....	....	142360	BKM	Bray
1807	1819	1800	1850	142360	BKM	High Wycombe
....	....	1832	1855	130079	KEN	Byfleet
1828	1915	1796	1920	142360	OXF	Thame
TAPP						
1650	1940	1600	1650	143170	DEV	Sandford
1650	1940	1600	1650	143170	DEV	Shobrooke
1786	....	1786	1992	139602	DEV	South Molton
1760	1860	....	1760	137227	DEV	Teignmouth
TAPPENDEN						
1882	1992	1800	1992	129976	KEN	Canterbury
TAPPER						
1750	1797	1790	1816	126403	DEV	Devonport
1560	1950	1560	1950	177032	DOR	Blandford
TAPPING						
....	....	1650	1890	102318	BKM	Monks Risborough
TAPSELL						
....	....	ALL	ALL	155373	KEN	Deptford
TAPSON						
1815	1992	1700	1885	168823	DEV	Bridestowe
1815	1992	1700	1885	168823	DEV	Lamerton
1815	1992	1700	1885	168823	DEV	Lydford
TARBERT						
1778	1840	....	1782	146811	AYR	West Kilbride
TARBIT						
1839	1839	1750	1839	176486	NBL	Belford
TARBUCK						
1796	....	1796	1815	157740	CHS	Aston By Sutton
TARGETT						
1800	1850	1780	1800	145939	WIL	Bower Chalke
1715	1907	1715	1862	115797	WIL	Tisbury
TARLING						
....	....	1500	1992	168831	ALL	ALL
1700	1850	1600	1992	168831	GLS	ALL
1851	1860	1600	1992	168831	WIL	ALL
1800	1870	1600	1992	168831	WLS	ALL
TARLINGTON						
1801	1837	1700	1900	105023	STS	Lichfield
TARN						
1775	1810	1750	1820	123536	DUR	Middleton In Teeside
TARPLEE						
1834	1889	1800	1900	153249	WAR	Alcester
1795	1832	1700	1850	153249	WOR	Inkberrow
TARR						
1828	1866	1750	1828	121568	SOM	Ash Priors
TARRANT						
1810	1992	1700	1810	124109	DEV	Topsham
1850	1992	ALL	1850	169692	HAM	Barton Stacey
1850	1992	ALL	1850	169692	HAM	Portsmouth
1840	1920	....	....	117137	MON	Abertillery
....	....	1820	1840	117137	SOM	Kilmersdon
....	....	1600	1650	151602	WIL	Bishops Cannings
....	....	1720	1820	117137	WIL	Mildenhall
TARRAT						
1662	1746	1550	1681	102830	DBY	ALL
TARREL						
1788	1884	1780	1884	151858	SCT	Hilton Of Cadboll
TARRY						
1850	1940	1810	1850	166855	BKM	Emberton
1870	1992	1870	1992	132799	BRK	Hanney
1790	1870	1700	1870	132799	BRK	Steventon
1740	1823	1720	1850	107360	NTH	Harlestone
TART						
1900	1992	ALL	ALL	131121	CMA	Barrow In Furness
1900	1992	ALL	ALL	131121	LAN	Barrow In Furness
....	....	1800	1900	103667	SAL	Much Wenlock
TASH						
1710	1800	1710	1800	161705	NFK	Great Cressingham

Known From	To	Researching From	To	Ref	Cty	Place
TASKER						
1700	1850	1600	1992	167592	CHS	Chester
1870	....	....	....	179701	CHS	Upton
1787	1810	1730	1787	149152	DEV	Wooland
1850	1960	1600	1850	131261	ESS	Walthamstow
1700	1758	1600	1800	175633	LIN	Horncastle
1800	1850	1700	1992	167592	MDX	London
....	1700	....	....	174564	SSX	???
....	....	ALL	1850	114308	WIL	Allcanings
1800	1830	1750	1992	167592	WOR	Worcester
1820	1880	1700	1992	114596	YKS	Leyburn
1763	1992	ALL	1992	164739	???	Bristol
TASSELL						
1500	1900	1500	1900	126659	KEN	ALL
TASWELL						
1722	1992	1650	1870	169234	SOM	Greinton
TATCHELL						
....	....	ALL	ALL	168858	ALL	Name Study
TATE						
1812	1835	ALL	1812	122483	CUL	Arthuret
1850	1900	1750	1850	164224	DUR	Sunderland
1874	1874	1870	1900	150568	DUR	Thornley
1835	1866	1800	ALL	122483	IOM	Douglas
....	....	1870	1992	147613	LAN	Barrow In Furness
1817	1839	?	1817	144800	LAN	Manchester
ALL	1736	....	....	132756	NBL	ALL
1934	1992	1890	1934	150568	NBL	Blyth
ALL	1736	....	....	132756	NBL	Chollerton
1778	1833	1750	1900	116386	NBL	Newburn
1778	1833	1750	1900	116386	NBL	Walbottle
1850	1900	1750	1850	164224	SHI	???
....	....	1700	1900	147613	STS	Sedgley
1790	1790	ALL	1790	115282	TAY	ALL
TATHAM						
....	....	1797	?	109975	BDF	Elstow
TATLER						
....	....	ALL	ALL	168874	ALL	Name Study
....	....	ALL	ALL	168866	ALL	Name Study
TATLOW						
1825	1850	1770	1825	151912	LAN	Blackburn
TATNALL						
1846	1879	1846	1900	126705	CHS	Holmes Chapel
TATTER						
1787	1798	1787	1798	124826	WRY	Holmfirth
TATTERSALL						
1575	1700	1575	1700	109347	LAN	Downham
1826	1833	1820	1845	145602	LAN	Haslingden
1839	....	....	....	144169	LAN	Liverpool
TATTERSHALL						
....	1830	....	1830	152838	NTT	Nottingham
1619	....	ALL	1619	153567	WIL	Salisbury
1841	1882	ALL	1882	152838	YKS	Rotherham
TATTERSON						
1850	1945	1850	1945	125741	WES	Kendall
1850	1945	1850	1945	125741	WES	Windermere
TATTESHALL						
1896	....	1700	1900	135968	LAN	Bolton
TATUM						
1800	....	....	....	148768	LND	Bethnal Green
TAUBMAN						
1757	1851	1731	1757	141291	IOM	Arbory
1703	1755	1611	1755	141291	IOM	Malew
TAUERNER						
1752	1885	1600	1900	179299	DEV	Moreton Hampstead
TAUNT						
1602	1992	1500	1992	115460	OXF	Cowley
1602	1992	1500	1992	115460	OXF	Oxford
TAUNTON						
1640	1850	1640	1992	133450	CON	???
TAVENDER						
1780	1950	1700	1780	165530	GLS	South
TAVERNER						
1820	1849	....	1820	177504	DEV	Whitestone
1862	....	1700	1862	113123	SRY	???
TAVNER						
1881	1923	1700	1881	102997	ESS	Springfield
TAWS						
1792	1850	1700	1830	170178	ABD	Kinellar
1830	1850	1850	1950	170178	???	Manchester
TAYLER						
1717	1753	1650	1717	178381	GLS	Sherborne
1780	1915	1780	1915	175420	OXF	Henley On Thames
1800	1900	1700	1800	174513	OXF	Upper Heyford
1838	1958	1700	1992	170054	SRY	Deptford

Known From	To	Researching From	To	Ref	Cty	Place
TAYLOR						
1843	1919	ALL	1843	106909	ABD	Cuminestown
1790	1890	1841	1891	124001	ABD	New Deer
1859	1992	1750	1992	112089	ABD	???
1881	1965	1800	1851	178896	ANS	Dundee
1858	1880	1858	1880	175196	AVN	Weston Super Mare
1830	1900	1700	1830	145017	AYR	Ardrossan
1800	1992	1780	1920	155004	BAN	Findochty
1620	1777	ALL	1620	168602	BDF	Odell
1871	1972	....	....	169013	BDF	Sutton
1839	1842	1820	1839	169021	BKM	Chesham
1824	1910	1750	1900	113212	BKM	Whaddon
1920	1992	1500	1920	110310	BRK	ALL
1881	1992	1800	1881	149004	BRK	Clewer
1900	1940	1900	1940	167924	BRK	Crowthorne
1784	....	1700	1800	143693	BRK	Great Marlow
1800	1850	1750	1850	145661	BRK	Hungerford
1745	1760	1700	1800	124974	BRK	Inkpen
1815	1815	1750	1815	102970	BRK	Leckhampstead
1780	1850	1780	1850	121738	BRK	Peasemore
1900	1992	1900	1992	121738	BRK	Reading
1850	1900	1850	1900	121738	BRK	Winterbourne
1750	1860	....	....	126497	CAI	Bower
1750	1860	1700	1860	126500	CAI	Wick Bower
1702	1774	....	1774	137405	CAM	Foxton
1579	1617	....	1580	108839	CAM	Harlton
1760	1860	1760	1900	136980	CAM	Little Wilbraham
1750	1992	1700	1750	112208	CAM	Lt Downham
1787	1940	....	....	128996	CAM	Thorney
1822	1839	1700	1850	135348	CAM	Wisbech
1790	1860	1790	1860	152250	CAM	Wisbech
1750	1800	1700	1750	135496	CHS	North
1598	1598	....	....	135437	CHS	Boughton
1900	1985	....	....	165441	CHS	Chester
1900	1930	1800	1992	121215	CHS	Hyde
....	....	1810	1850	129313	CHS	Stockport
1800	1992	1700	1925	137901	CHS	Stockport
1882	....	1882	1940	154474	CMA	Kirby Lonsdale
1771	1824	1700	1800	128082	CON	Falmouth
1695	1875	1600	....	118591	CON	Laneast
1771	1824	1700	1800	128082	CON	North Petherwin
1849	....	1800	1992	168637	CUL	Walton
1677	1992	1650	1677	113395	DBY	Ashleyhay
1789	1870	ALL	1870	175757	DBY	Belper
1677	1992	1600	1650	113395	DBY	Crich
1749	1825	ALL	1749	126942	DBY	Darley Dale
1500	1500	1500	1500	145580	DBY	Delahey
1858	....	ALL	ALL	105481	DBY	Derby
1800	1880	1800	1880	124605	DBY	Derby
1836	1950	1700	1836	124214	DBY	Matlock
1830	1960	1700	1830	168947	DBY	Osmaston
1855	1870	ALL	1900	132217	DBY	Whitwell
1838	1878	ALL	1838	168742	DBY	Whitwell
1850	1940	1700	1850	160725	DEV	North
1850	1992	1800	1850	174041	DEV	Bishops Tawton
1542	1800	1542	1800	169161	DEV	Fremington
1786	1840	....	....	169102	DEV	Lympstone
1841	1861	1700	1890	170518	DEV	St Giles In The Heath
1790	1915	1650	1800	156795	DOR	North
1750	1776	1700	1800	136786	DOR	Ryme In Trinseca
1870	1992	....	....	162124	DOR	Weymouth
....	....	1500	1992	141720	DOR	???
1796	1948	1750	1900	177970	DUR	Lanchester
1855	....	1800	1855	140082	DUR	Seaham
1860	1992	1700	1860	160571	DUR	Sunderland
1815	1830	1700	1815	113425	ESS	Abberton
....	....	1750	....	149187	FIF	Abdie
1650	1793	1650	1850	169218	FIF	St Monance
1740	1828	....	....	176958	GLA	ALL
1887	1912	1840	1900	131792	GLA	Cefn-Coed-Y-Cymmer
1871	1871	1800	1900	136042	GLS	Arlingham
1840	1851	1800	1900	178322	GLS	Ashton Under Hill
1550	1711	1550	1612	102830	GLS	Aston Blank
1743	1883	1766	1883	153176	GLS	Beckford
1813	1813	1700	1900	178322	GLS	Longborough
1810	1850	1600	1850	154342	GLS	Mangotsfield
1810	1992	1700	1900	126551	GLS	Olveston
1870	1992	1850	1900	125032	GSY	St Peter Port
1815	1850	1815	1900	102970	HAM	Burghclere
1820	1920	1820	1992	166804	HAM	Burghclere
1700	1820	1650	1992	166804	HAM	East Woodhay
1749	1851	1600	1851	174343	HAM	Hambledon
1784	1784	1500	1784	110310	HAM	Odiham

Known From	To	Researching From	To	Ref	Cty	Place
TAYLOR	contd.					
1780	1800	1780	1800	178705	HAM	Odiham
1814	1850	1790	1850	133000	HAM	Portsea
?	?	?	?	150215	HAM	Romsey
1800	1909	....	....	145394	HAM	Southampton
1830	....	ALL	ALL	156884	HAM	Southampton
1835	1870	....	1835	169188	HAM	Winchester
1761	....	....	....	131229	HEF	Bromyard
1750	1850	1700	1850	119938	HEF	Cradley
1800	....	....	....	144169	HEF	Hereford
1750	1850	1700	1850	119938	HEF	Mathon
1868	....	....	....	144169	HEF	Netherton
1868	....	....	....	144169	HEF	Pencoyd
1700	1800	1700	1950	177180	HRT	Abbots Langley
1800	1880	1700	1850	159107	HUN	Somersham
1711	1715	1511	1715	141291	IOM	Rushen
1840	1940	1700	1900	168068	IOW	Brading
1730	1861	1700	1890	126667	IOW	Calbourne
1809	....	ALL	1809	119687	IOW	Freshwater
1840	1900	....	....	136492	IRL	Aitkenhead
1840	1900	....	....	136492	IRL	Baillieston
1900	1920	1700	1910	135887	KEN	Blean
1764	1839	....	1850	171441	KEN	Borden
1793	1858	1780	1793	117269	KEN	Brenchley
1600	1800	....	....	167924	KEN	Deal
1820	1850	1850	1950	130230	KEN	Deptford
1795	1919	1600	1795	174548	KEN	Folkestone
1752	....	....	1790	171441	KEN	Frinstead
1783	1816	1700	1800	128163	KEN	Hythe
....	....	....	1859	130060	KEN	Lydd
1811	1895	1750	1850	110604	KEN	Medway
1978	1980	....	....	173932	KEN	Pembury
1759	1861	1600	1757	147346	KEN	Rainham
1835	1870	....	1835	169188	KEN	Ramsgate
1864	1983	1800	1992	147982	KEN	Sheerness
1800	1992	1800	ALL	113093	KEN	Sittingbourne
1750	1820	....	....	113093	KEN	Thanet
1600	1800	....	....	167924	KEN	Walmer
1800	1865	....	....	146811	KRS	Cleish
1800	1865	....	....	146811	KRS	Fossoway
1797	1835	1750	1797	147745	KRS	Kinross
....	....	ALL	1920	168955	LAN	Accrington
1860	1891	1860	1891	166952	LAN	Barrow In Furness
1892	1940	1700	1992	150118	LAN	Bolton
1879	....	1820	ALL	168920	LAN	Darwen
1851	1890	1850	1930	129313	LAN	Droylsden
1812	1900	1700	1900	135968	LAN	Great Ecclestone
1791	1870	1768	1870	147281	LAN	Haslingdon
1750	....	1750	....	109347	LAN	Huncoat
1810	1822	1700	1850	135348	LAN	Kirkham
1765	1765	1700	1765	163783	LAN	Kirkham
1851	1974	1500	1851	175072	LAN	Kirkham
1620	1720	1500	1740	105333	LAN	Kutton
1882	....	1882	1940	154474	LAN	Lancaster
1907	?	?	?	108588	LAN	Liverpool
1900	1992	1800	1920	113867	LAN	Liverpool
1830	1850	....	....	147885	LAN	Manchester
1861	1861	1837	1861	157678	LAN	Manchester
1825	1860	....	1870	168424	LAN	Manchester
1800	....	1700	1850	135348	LAN	Oldham
1808	1920	1741	1878	151432	LAN	Oldham
1709	1881	1709	1891	159492	LAN	Oldham
1779	....	?	1800	164976	LAN	Oldham
1850	1900	1700	1850	130419	LAN	Oswaldtwistle
1800	1880	1750	1870	166952	LAN	Preston
1800	1824	1780	1824	102121	LAN	Rochdale
1845	1875	1835	1880	107522	LAN	Rochdale
....	....	ALL	1835	129313	LAN	Rochdale
1840	1900	1800	1992	166081	LAN	Rochdale
1814	1816	1750	1815	123978	LAN	Salford
1589	1758	1759	1992	162256	LAN	Turton
1620	1720	1500	1740	105333	LAN	Walton Le Dale
....	....	1800	1920	135046	LAN	Wigan
1828	1908	....	....	147621	LAN	???
1834	1992	1700	1992	130257	LEI	Croft
1841	1986	1800	1986	128783	LEI	Sileby
1600	1700	1550	1700	154881	LIM	Ballynort
1750	1775	1700	1992	114901	LIN	Avarepark
1800	1825	1700	1800	162396	LIN	Barrowby
1666	....	....	1666	101761	LIN	Croft
1890	1992	1700	1890	161772	LIN	Horncastle
1762	1782	....	1762	101761	LIN	Maltby Le Marsh
1798	1829	1700	1798	160024	LIN	Scremby
1776	....	ALL	....	104515	LIN	Sedgebrook

Known From	To	Researching From	To	Ref	Cty	Place
TAYLOR	contd.					
ALL	....	....	1846	140716	LIN	Swinderby
1750	1850	....	....	124621	LIN	Walcot
1760	1800	....	....	169129	LIN	Wolds
1841	1859	1750	1860	177970	LKS	North
1800	1992	1800	1900	168882	LKS	Airdrie
1840	1900	....	....	136492	LKS	Coatbridge
....	....	....	....	161888	LKS	New Prestwick
1840	1900	....	....	136492	LKS	Shettleston
....	....	1800	1900	156795	LND	North
1847	1847	1750	1870	171662	LND	Chelsea
1818	1873	1800	1992	165603	LND	Deptford
1870	....	1800	1870	154954	LND	Finsbury
1932	1992	1800	1932	131032	LND	Leytonstone
1850	1860	1800	1850	177199	LND	Marylebone
1753	1800	1700	1810	159441	LND	Shoreditch
1840	1859	1700	1840	113425	LND	???
1820	1850	1820	1880	145602	LND	???
1858	1885	....	....	169102	LND	???
1770	1790	1841	1891	146560	LTN	Dalmeny
1770	1790	1841	1891	146560	LTN	Leith
1770	1790	1841	1891	146560	LTN	Queensferry
1900	1978	1900	1992	163600	MDX	North
1899	1901	1800	1898	131245	MDX	Bethnal Green
1820	1850	1850	1950	130230	MDX	Deptford
1825	1874	1750	1825	113697	MDX	Hackney
1847	1900	1800	1992	169161	MDX	London
1820	1960	1700	1820	176516	MDX	London
1841	1881	1880	1992	116114	MDX	Old Brentford
1857	1885	1857	1885	136980	MDX	Paddington
1800	1900	1800	1900	167924	MDX	Paddington
1800	1900	1800	1900	167924	MDX	Pancras
1840	1847	1780	1840	112364	MDX	South Mimms
1844	1844	1700	1846	113425	MDX	St Pancras
1775	1787	1740	1820	167002	MDX	Whitechapel
1885	1975	....	....	169102	MDX	???
....	....	ALL	ALL	165069	MON	Treowen
1854	1865	1805	1854	119628	NAI	Elgin
1647	1789	....	....	169110	NBL	Cresswell
1789	1992	1611	1789	169110	NBL	Cullercoats
1668	1992	1650	1992	111074	NBL	Hanley
1794	1818	1600	1900	130125	NBL	Longbenton
1824	....	....	....	112909	NBL	Newcastle
1760	1800	1500	1760	144045	NBL	Slaley
1735	1800	ALL	1800	142301	NBL	Warkworth
1790	1894	ALL	1790	143308	NFK	Hindolveston
1880	....	....	....	169129	NFK	Magdalen
1800	1900	1800	1992	120499	NFK	Munford
1850	1960	1700	1850	162671	NFK	Olb Bockenham
1804	1804	1700	1804	100110	NFK	Shereford
1820	....	....	....	169129	NFK	Walpole
1800	....	....	....	169129	NFK	West Walton
1750	1992	1700	1750	173878	NTH	Grendon
1830	1860	1820	1850	112925	NTH	Harpole
1817	1847	....	....	171654	NTH	Yardley Gobion
1880	1890	1880	1960	104612	NTT	Alfreton
?	?	1700	1800	120650	NTT	Carburton
1913	1992	1700	1913	110108	NTT	Nottingham
1800	1860	ALL	ALL	120650	NTT	Welbeck
....	....	ALL	ALL	111384	NYK	Scarborough
1770	1855	1600	1855	148482	OKI	Birsay
1744	1744	1740	1750	107360	OXF	Alkerton
1750	1830	....	....	124672	OXF	Ambrosden
1800	1900	....	....	102296	OXF	Headington
1745	1785	1727	1792	107360	OXF	Horley
1830	1860	....	....	124672	OXF	Oxford
1860	1929	1700	1860	144614	OXF	St Ebbes
1700	1800	1700	1800	167924	PEM	Tenby
1830	1850	1700	1850	179191	PER	Blairingone
1807	1807	....	....	168203	PER	Crieff
1810	1992	1700	1810	123374	PER	Gask
1820	1900	1750	1992	110663	PER	???
1821	1821	1800	1840	177970	PER	???
1860	1900	1860	1900	129151	RAD	Coombe
1860	1900	1860	1900	129151	RAD	Presteigne
1770	1800	1700	1770	100129	RUT	Barrowden
?	?	?	?	165484	SAL	Upton Magna
1830	1830	1800	1830	108510	SAL	Wellington
1729	?	ALL	ALL	101370	SCT	ALL
1841	1850	1700	1890	102520	SCT	Fife
1840	1900	1800	1992	131571	SCT	Leith
....	....	1790	1830	147885	SCT	???
1760	1830	1680	1830	135941	SFK	Mildenhall
....	....	1700	1831	126357	SLI	???

Known From	To	Researching From	To	Ref	Cty	Place
TAYLOR contd.						
1697	1854	1500	1850	153591	SOM	Bath
1810	1870	ALL	1880	165654	SOM	Bath
1795	1900	1700	1900	174300	SOM	Bath
1836	1952	1813	1952	115193	SOM	Bristol
1890	1910	1840	1900	156981	SOM	Bristol
1740	1828	....	....	176958	SOM	Bristol
1850	1880	1800	1850	121592	SOM	Chard
1841	....	....	....	162124	SOM	East Coker
1697	1854	1500	1850	153591	SOM	Frome
1782	1900	....	....	161861	SOM	Kilmersdon
1833	1877	1800	1900	104299	SOM	Old Cleeve
1697	1854	1500	1850	153591	SOM	St Petherton
1812	1823	ALL	1841	104299	SOM	Timberscombe
1900	1920	1800	1900	158976	SRY	Ash
1819	1983	1800	1992	147982	SRY	Chertsey
1800	1841	1700	1800	116114	SRY	Kew
....	....	1750	1850	113697	SRY	Mitcham
1776	1801	1770	1801	170143	SRY	Stoke
1776	1801	1770	1801	170143	SRY	Woking
1851	1901	1586	1851	102512	SSX	Brighton
1870	1992	....	....	122130	SSX	Buxted
1920	1992	....	....	122130	SSX	Crowborough
1850	1992	....	....	122130	SSX	Framfield
1952	....	....	....	173932	SSX	Horsham
1800	1992	....	....	122130	SSX	Maresfield
1750	1840	ALL	ALL	162191	SSX	Stanmer
1870	1992	....	....	122130	SSX	Uckfield
1823	1835	....	1823	169188	SSX	Worthing
1800	1917	....	....	100536	SSX	???
....	....	1700	1900	167223	STI	Falkirk
1700	....	1700	....	168882	STI	Muiravonside
1790	1891	1770	1900	168998	STS	Biddulph
1790	1891	1770	1900	168998	STS	Bilston
1850	1992	1750	1850	156574	STS	Burslem
....	....	1830	1860	161659	STS	Darlaston
1790	1891	1770	1900	168998	STS	Mowcop
1790	1850	....	....	132756	STS	Potteries
1800	....	....	....	130486	STS	Stafford
1845	1880	1830	1890	125032	STS	Stoke On Trent
1870	1950	1870	1950	133426	STS	Wednesbury
1800	1850	1750	1800	101524	STS	West Bromwich
1790	1891	1770	1900	168998	STS	Wolstanton
1795	1820	1750	1795	126454	STS	Wolverhampton
1717	1826	ALL	....	132349	SXE	Glynde
....	....	1830	1860	113514	SYK	Barnsley
1860	1870	1800	1850	146722	SYK	Sheffield
1920	1992	ALL	1920	168955	TIP	Nenagh
1788	1904	ALL	1788	103004	WAR	Birmingham
1839	1992	1700	1839	105899	WAR	Birmingham
1870	1930	1700	1870	125415	WAR	Birmingham
1824	1861	ALL	ALL	153753	WAR	Birmingham
....	....	1750	1850	154458	WAR	Birmingham
1880	1992	....	....	158348	WAR	Birmingham
....	....	1800	1840	135089	WAR	Dudley
1600	1800	....	....	100420	WAR	Meriden
1790	1972	1770	1881	157597	WAR	Stratford On Avon
1670	1914	ALL	ALL	169099	WAR	Tredington
1825	1841	ALL	ALL	124176	WAR	Walsgrove
....	....	....	1806	176702	WES	Kirby Stephen
1754	1851	....	....	100951	WIL	North West
1880	1992	1800	1880	176931	WIL	Ramsbury
1780	1830	1700	1992	140090	WIL	Winsley
1880	1992	1800	1880	176931	WIL	Wroughton
1800	1918	1790	1820	128333	WLN	Bo'ness
1780	1880	1750	1780	137413	WOR	Blebroughton
1780	1880	1750	1780	137413	WOR	Clent
1862	1906	1700	1862	178993	WOR	Dudley
1760	1775	1700	1760	140309	WOR	Inkberrow
1855	1880	1880	1992	133507	WOR	Worcester St Martin
1800	1870	1600	1800	122084	WOR	Worcester
1804	....	....	1804	101761	WRY	Honley
1800	1850	1800	1850	136522	WYK	Batley
1830	?	ALL	ALL	107352	WYK	Knottingley
1800	1950	....	....	113514	WYK	Leeds
1800	1900	1800	1900	153621	WYK	Ripponden
1824	1896	1700	1824	163902	YKS	South
1803	....	1700	1900	174408	YKS	Almondbury
1820	1900	....	....	121061	YKS	Bamby Moor
1830	1880	1700	1900	136034	YKS	Batley
1822	1894	ALL	ALL	112631	YKS	Bingley
1822	1822	ALL	1992	112631	YKS	Bradford
1920	1992	....	....	121061	YKS	Bradford
1900	1992	1800	1900	116823	YKS	Catton

Known From	To	Researching From	To	Ref	Cty	Place
TAYLOR contd.						
1860	1891	ALL	ALL	120650	YKS	Cawood
1790	1820	....	....	121061	YKS	Dunnington
1750	....	1650	1850	130419	YKS	Giggleswick
1865	1913	1700	1905	109460	YKS	Golcar
1810	1910	1760	1810	169056	YKS	Halifax
1840	1880	1800	1900	144622	YKS	Kilnhurst
1820	1847	1700	1820	128031	YKS	Kimberworth
1732	1992	1650	1732	168513	YKS	Kirkheaton
1607	1612	1550	1612	138584	YKS	Methley
1844	1992	ALL	1844	169692	YKS	Stockton
1760	1992	1700	1992	169005	YKS	Swinton
1823	....	1750	....	134589	YKS	Wilberfoss
TAYSPILL						
1713	1767	1700	1800	128961	ESS	Colchester
TAYTON						
1789	1992	1700	1789	169226	LIN	Boston
1789	1992	1700	1789	169226	LIN	Leake
1700	1800	1600	1800	170291	LIN	Tattershall
TEA						
1713	1847	1700	1814	102830	WAR	Edgbaston
TEAGLE						
....	....	ALL	ALL	104884	WIL	ALL
TEAGOE						
1782	1801	....	....	129747	SFK	Parham
TEAGUE						
1680	1992	1640	1992	169250	CON	Falmouth
1680	1992	1640	1992	169250	LND	Southwark
1800	1992	1600	1800	169862	SAL	Church Stretton
1800	1992	1600	1800	169862	SAL	Onibury
TEAL						
1720	1752	1700	1800	166804	OXF	ALL
TEALE						
1800	1870	1870	1992	105651	GLS	Twyning
1816	1929	1700	1816	100110	YKS	Knaresborough
TEALL						
1745	1860	1645	1745	165018	EYK	Holme On The Wolds
TEARE						
1910	1912	ALL	1910	107751	LAN	Leigh
TEARLE						
....	....	ALL	ALL	169269	ALL	Name Study
1867	1880	ALL	ALL	138886	LAN	Preston
TEARNAN						
1822	1850	....	....	156728	MDX	???
TEASDALE						
1800	1900	1700	1800	142417	CMA	Alston
1750	1781	ALL	1750	154563	CUL	Alston
1840	1860	1700	1840	139122	LAN	Manchester
1754	1812	1720	1812	123536	NBL	Allendale
1750	1900	....	....	142417	NBL	Haltwhistle
1740	1822	1538	1840	118893	NRY	Grinton
1740	1822	1538	1845	118893	NRY	Marrick
1750	1770	1700	1750	121339	WYK	Heptonstall
1849	1971	1820	1849	164364	YKS	Sheffield
TEBAY						
1800	1900	1750	1830	123137	KEN	North
1900	1992	1700	1900	169285	LAN	Bolton
1881	?	?	?	151505	LAN	Cunsey
1900	1992	1700	1900	169285	LAN	Wigan
1790	1800	1700	1800	123137	LND	ALL
TEBB						
1820	1931	1750	1850	109835	LIN	ALL
1831	1852	1790	1831	154024	LIN	Besthorpe
1851	1886	....	....	154024	NTT	Nottingham
TEBBETT						
1772	1817	ALL	1772	178926	LEI	Enderby
TEBBIT						
1600	1780	1500	1600	169293	CAM	Soham
1780	1855	....	....	169293	CAM	Wicken
1855	1900	....	....	169293	ESS	Hatfield Broad Oak
TEBBLE						
....	....	ALL	ALL	169307	ALL	Name Study
TEBBS						
1861	1900	ALL	ALL	103152	LND	Southwark
TEBBUT						
1657	1760	....	....	165999	DBY	Sawley
1657	1760	....	....	165999	DBY	Wilne
1742	1742	....	....	127426	NTH	Earls Barton
TEBBUTT						
1886	....	ALL	ALL	112275	LEI	North West
1750	1800	1650	1750	169749	LEI	Coalville
1700	1900	ALL	ALL	114235	NTH	ALL
1839	....	....	....	172723	NTH	???
1750	1800	1650	1750	169749	NTT	Normanton

Known From	To	Researching From	To	Ref	Cty	Place
TEBBUTT contd.						
1930	1992	ALL	1930	142263	SRY	Guildford
TEDD						
....	....	ALL	ALL	169323	ALL	Name Study
1700	1863	1700	1863	105147	ALL	ALL
1327	1992	1327	1992	169323	ALL	ALL
1500	1800	....	....	100420	WAR	Meriden
TEDDER						
1855	1910	....	....	159131	BRK	New Windsor
1730	1992	1650	1730	114928	HRT	???
1832	1850	....	....	159131	MDX	???
TEDHAM						
1880	1980	1750	1880	122556	SSX	Warbleton
TEDMAN						
1800	1850	....	....	128759	GNT	Llanarth
1570	1620	....	....	128759	KEN	Dover
TEE						
1870	1900	1700	1900	178136	YKS	Mexborough
TEECE						
....	....	ALL	ALL	169331	ALL	Name Study
1560	1992	ALL	ALL	169331	ALL	ALL
1880	1980	1800	1980	135283	WIL	Finchley
TEED						
1840	....	1800	1900	135429	DEV	Exeter
1840	....	1800	1900	135429	DEV	St Thomas
TEESDALE						
1744	1860	1600	....	103837	LIN	Boston
1753	1860	....	....	103837	LIN	Sibsey
TEETON						
1830	1840	ALL	1850	107026	NTH	Northampton
TEFT						
....	....	1700	1880	102148	YKS	Hull
TEGARDINE						
1655	1940	....	....	128996	CAM	Thorney
TEGGIN						
1807	1864	1864	1880	169366	SAL	Ellesmere
1742	1767	1767	1782	169366	SAL	Whittington
TEGIN						
1640	1712	....	....	169366	SAL	Ellesmere
TEGNER						
....	....	ALL	ALL	146544	ALL	Name Study
TEITYEN						
?	....	?	?	104337	MDX	Mile End Old Town
TELFER						
....	1812	ALL	ALL	129933	LKS	Lesmahagow
TELFORD						
1766	1833	ALL	1892	108642	BDF	Farndish
1766	1833	ALL	1892	108642	BDF	Sharnbrook
1800	1900	1700	1900	126802	DUR	ALL
1839	....	1810	1839	117196	DUR	Hetton Le Hole
1848	1936	1700	1917	153001	DUR	Monkwearmouth
1859	1992	1759	1859	157988	DUR	Stanley
....	1872	....	....	117374	IRL	Dublin
1872	1926	....	....	117374	LAN	Liverpool
1853	1881	....	....	130621	LAN	Preston
1844	1890	1840	1900	135933	NBL	Haltwhistle
1800	1870	1780	1870	130621	SCT	Dumfries
1800	1870	1780	1870	130621	SCT	Glasgow
1879	1879	1800	1900	146358	STD	Glasgow
TELLWRIGHT						
....	....	1600	1900	116777	STS	North
TELSTON						
....	....	1700	1860	146021	LAN	Salford
TEMPERLEY						
1762	1877	1600	1760	147346	NBL	Hexham
TEMPERLY						
1620	....	1600	1620	101524	CON	Manaccan
TEMPEST						
1816	1851	1700	1816	175900	YKS	Halifax
1820	1840	1800	1860	124648	YKS	Huddersfield
1560	1580	1400	1992	102520	YKS	Rylstone
TEMPLE						
1705	....	1690	1710	124796	BKM	Great Hampden
1670	1750	1650	1750	124796	BKM	Princes Risborough
1861	1900	1901	1945	169374	DUR	Sunderland
....	....	ALL	ALL	130818	LND	London
1817	1992	1750	1817	176257	MDX	Shoreditch
1857	1992	1700	1857	169382	NFK	North
1779	1813	1760	1813	147311	NYK	Scarborough
1811	1944	ALL	1811	169374	ROX	Hawick
1820	1830	1800	1992	165603	YKS	Newsham
TEMPLEMAN						
1840	1918	1700	1850	112038	LIN	South
1850	1920	1700	1850	112038	RUT	???
TEMPLEMAN contd.						
....	....	ALL	1992	123749	SOM	Capland
1558	1893	1550	1870	171654	SOM	West Chinnock
TEMPLER						
1820	1850	1700	1850	171212	DEV	Alphington
1835	1900	1835	1992	171212	LND	Marylebone
....	....	1700	1824	160601	OXF	Cassington
TEMPLETON						
....	....	ALL	ALL	169390	ALL	Name Study
1815	1878	1700	1800	169390	AYR	Dunlop
1800	1837	1700	1800	168904	CUL	Workington
1846	....	1846	....	127647	DFS	Torthornwold
1815	1878	1700	1800	169390	LKS	Glasgow
1870	1992	1850	1870	120286	SEL	Selkirk
TENANT						
1790	1900	?	1790	158569	WAR	Brailes
TENNANT						
....	....	ALL	ALL	135739	ALL	Name Study
1830	1926	1800	1830	135739	DUR	North
1880	1900	1800	1900	129496	NTT	Teversal
1803	1821	ALL	1803	111988	NTT	Upton By Southwell
TENNENT						
1769	1992	1745	1992	112305	LKS	Coatbridge
TENNET						
1860	1992	1800	1900	169404	YKS	Richmond
TERHEAGUE						
1770	1800	....	....	100420	WAR	Great Packington
1770	1800	....	....	100420	WAR	Meriden
TERNENT						
1800	1860	....	1800	100064	NBL	Alnwick
TERRAS						
....	....	1850	1900	129275	LND	Woolwich
TERRELL						
1802	1850	1830	1850	169420	DEV	Plymouth
1886	1992	ALL	ALL	169420	SCT	South
TERRETT						
....	....	1700	....	141216	GLS	North
TERREY						
1778	1808	1770	1910	128783	HAM	Beaulieu
TERRIDGE						
1770	1800	....	....	100420	WAR	Meriden
TERRY						
1815	1815	ALL	1900	112631	BKM	Farnham Royal
1750	1890	ALL	1750	118060	BRK	Reading
1800	1950	1700	1800	107530	DEV	West
1791	....	1700	1800	179019	DEV	Marldon
1758	1992	1600	1758	166804	HAM	Odiham
1830	1835	1530	1992	145769	KEN	ALL
1670	?	?	?	166642	KEN	Canterbury
....	....	....	1746	130060	KEN	Hawkhurst
....	....	....	1746	130060	KEN	Lydd
1860	1891	1800	1891	169439	KEN	Mersham
1805	1861	1750	1805	130184	KEN	Pluckley
1818	1844	1700	1850	105775	KEN	Wingham
1850	1900	1700	1900	128163	KEN	Wye
1880	1992	....	....	135089	LND	Hackney
1850	1880	1829	1850	135089	LND	Shoreditch
1830	....	....	1850	113581	LND	???
1900	1992	....	1900	177601	LND	???
1787	1800	1750	1825	155969	MDX	Paddington
1758	1790	1600	1800	165190	NRY	Askrigg
1850	1900	1850	1900	148601	OXF	Great Haseley
1670	1731	1670	1750	170143	SSX	Harting
....	....	1700	1900	166448	SSX	Midhurst
1550	1693	1500	1700	154881	SSX	Wedhurst
1735	1992	ALL	1850	151319	YKS	ALL
TESCH						
1871	1992	1871	1992	173851	YKS	Hull
TESKEY						
....	....	ALL	ALL	146579	ALL	Name Study
TESSIER						
1700	1780	....	....	108448	LND	East
TESTAR						
1843	1889	1843	1889	144878	MDX	St Pancras
1756	1842	1800	1843	144878	WAR	Birmingham
TESTER						
....	1800	....	1800	177695	LEI	Leicester
....	1800	....	1800	177695	NTH	Northampton
1815	1900	1750	1800	103446	SSX	Buxted
1800	1900	1750	1800	104914	SSX	East Grinstead
1851	1900	....	....	153397	SSX	Portslade
TETHER						
ALL	ALL	ALL	ALL	150940	ALL	ALL
....	1830	1500	1992	175072	LIN	ALL

Known From	To	Researching From	To	Ref	Cty	Place
TETLOW						
....	....	ALL	ALL	120537	ALL	Name Study
1846	1966	....	....	156868	LAN	Oldham
TETSER						
....	....	ALL	ALL	170402	ALL	ALL
TETT						
1735	1837	....	1735	131385	DEV	Aylesbeare
....	....	1700	1880	102148	YKS	Hull
TEULON						
1689	1992	1689	1992	169455	ALL	ALL
TEVENDALE						
1822	1992	ALL	1800	169463	KCD	ALL
1822	1992	ALL	1800	169463	LKS	ALL
TEVLEN						
1869	1871	1869	?	127612	SRY	Chelsea
TEW						
....	....	1700	1830	169471	BKM	North
1783	1875	1700	1992	174378	BKM	Shalstone
....	....	1480	1750	169471	NTH	South
....	....	1480	1750	169471	NTH	Mid
....	....	1800	1850	169471	OXF	North
1860	1900	1820	1860	106194	STS	Brownhills
1800	1950	1800	1950	114790	WAR	Harbury
1763	1800	ALL	1763	154555	WAR	Hillmorton
TEWKESBURY						
1819	1840	1760	1819	151068	DBY	Baslow
TEWLEY						
....	....	1700	1775	136905	BDF	Houghton Regis
TEWSON						
1845	1900	1750	1845	177296	LIN	Ancaster
1813	1813	1770	1800	108510	LIN	Bitchfield
THACKER						
1802	1940	....	....	128996	CAM	Thorney
1800	....	....	....	148768	IRL	Dublin
1864	....	1300	1992	152501	KEN	Hoo
1856	1992	1820	1855	113719	LIN	Waddington
1850	....	....	....	148768	MDX	St Pancras
THACKERAH						
1800	1992	1694	1800	148865	WYK	Pudsey
THACKERY						
1752	1836	1700	1850	105732	LAN	Liverpool
THACKRAY						
1800	1980	1750	1980	129798	YKS	Batley
1798	1868	ALL	1798	151424	YKS	Bramley
1840	1890	....	1890	113034	YKS	Pateley Bridge
....	....	1700	1750	177393	YKS	Ryther
THACKREY						
....	....	?	....	115592	YKS	Leeds
THACKWAY						
1890	....	1750	1890	144150	HEF	Yatton
THACKWRAY						
....	....	?	....	115592	YKS	Leeds
THAIN						
....	....	ALL	ALL	126500	ALL	Name Study
1808	1900	ALL	ALL	169528	ABD	ALL
1815	1900	....	1815	152927	ABD	Logie Coldstone
1690	1820	ALL	ALL	126497	BAN	Cullen
1856	1956	....	....	116165	BAN	Findochty
1680	1820	ALL	ALL	126500	BAN	Rathven
1820	1960	ALL	ALL	126500	CAI	Wick Ackergill
1820	1980	ALL	ALL	126497	CAI	Wick
THAKE						
....	....	ALL	ALL	150339	ALL	Name Study
THARALD						
1670	1680	....	....	145688	LIN	Great Coates
THARBY						
1791	1930	ALL	ALL	102326	HRT	Hunsdon
THARP						
1670	1823	....	....	175439	CAM	Chippenham
1841	1992	ALL	1866	108642	ESS	Upminster
1841	1992	ALL	1866	108642	HRT	Watford
1790	....	1600	1790	164879	LND	ALL
1841	1992	ALL	1866	108642	SRY	Lingfield
1841	1992	ALL	1866	108642	SSX	Westhoathly
THATCHER						
1807	1871	....	1807	178365	BRK	Uffington
1800	1843	1800	1850	138479	GLS	Bristol
1864	1886	1800	1864	101826	OXF	Burford
1757	1799	1700	1850	169536	SAL	Alverley
1824	....	1750	1860	137782	SAL	Hopton Wafers
1830	1920	1700	1920	169536	SAL	Worfield
1810	1831	1600	1810	145432	STS	Enville St Mary
THAXTER						
1800	1900	1600	1800	155411	NFK	East Norfolk
THAYRE						
1700	....	....	....	114642	SRY	Alfold
THEAKER						
1860	1900	1860	1992	126837	LAN	Liverpool
1738	1900	1500	1738	127388	LIN	Axholme
1738	1900	1500	1738	127388	LIN	Belton
1790	1860	1700	1860	126837	LIN	Leadenham
?	?	?	?	169544	LIN	Leadenham
1750	1817	1730	1817	147311	NYK	Hinderwell
1858	1920	ALL	1880	158003	YKS	York
THEAKSTONE						
1860	1930	1860	1930	143588	WYK	Bradford
1860	1930	1860	1930	143588	WYK	Ripon
THEEBLE						
1760	....	....	....	129747	SFK	Ipswich
THEEDAM						
1700	1720	....	....	165999	ESS	Great Birch
THEOBALD						
1657	1760	....	....	165999	DBY	Sawley
1657	1760	....	....	165999	DBY	Wilne
1300	1550	1300	1550	154881	KEN	Seal
THETFORD						
....	....	ALL	ALL	107980	ALL	Name Study
1874	1992	1800	1992	107980	LAN	Salford
1430	1992	1200	1992	107980	NFK	ALL
1575	1665	1500	1700	107980	SFK	Cavendish
1689	1766	1650	1800	107980	SFK	Long Melford
THEW						
1770	1841	1700	1780	132764	NBL	Eglingham
THEWLIS						
1835	1989	1500	1835	103624	NBL	ALL
1800	1817	....	1800	144800	YKS	Holmfirth
1738	1780	1700	1740	170348	YKS	Kirkburton
1780	1855	....	....	170348	YKS	Kirkheaton
1790	1850	1750	1850	123595	YKS	Shepley
THEXTON						
....	....	ALL	ALL	169552	ALL	Name Study
1850	1869	1687	1869	169552	CUL	Beckermet St Bridget
1813	1884	1813	1884	169552	CUL	Bootle
1813	1854	1813	1854	169552	CUL	Cockermouth
1559	1871	1559	1871	169552	CUL	Dacre
1863	1867	1837	1867	169552	CUL	Egremont
1568	1812	1568	1812	169552	CUL	Great Orton
1559	1757	1559	1757	169552	CUL	Greystoke
1700	1837	1690	1837	169552	CUL	Krikland
1581	1812	1581	1812	169552	CUL	Lamplugh
1666	1837	1666	1837	169552	CUL	Lanercost
1813	1886	1813	1886	169552	CUL	Matterdale
1813	1941	1813	1941	169552	CUL	Millom
1585	1837	1585	1837	169552	CUL	Muncaster
1661	1886	1661	1886	169552	CUL	Penrith
1580	1812	1580	1812	169552	CUL	Skelton
1810	1960	1726	1975	169552	CUL	Thwaites
1868	1888	1862	1889	169552	CUL	Torpenhow
1689	1867	1689	1867	169552	CUL	Ulpha
1579	1852	1579	1852	169552	CUL	Watermillock
1829	1858	1694	1876	169552	CUL	Whitehaven
1813	1855	1813	1855	169552	CUL	Workington
1900	1905	1855	1905	169552	DUR	Aukland
1922	1962	1888	1963	169552	LAN	Allithwaite
1868	1935	1861	1964	169552	LAN	Barrow In Furness
1728	1837	1728	1837	169552	LAN	Blawith
1815	1956	1634	1961	169552	LAN	Broughton In Furness
1840	1865	1811	1865	169552	LAN	Bury
1861	1916	1860	1947	169552	LAN	Carnforth
1776	1782	1754	1870	169552	LAN	Cartmel Fell
1724	1869	1660	1879	169552	LAN	Cartmel
1849	1854	1585	1954	169552	LAN	Caton
1831	1840	1831	1840	169552	LAN	Chipping
1701	1862	1701	1862	169552	LAN	Claughton
1781	1868	1623	1908	169552	LAN	Colton
1732	1881	1565	1883	169552	LAN	Dalton In Furness
1829	1862	1810	1873	169552	LAN	Dendron
1818	1960	1818	1960	169552	LAN	Field Broughton
1812	1824	1725	1970	169552	LAN	Finsthwaite
1828	1974	1828	1974	169552	LAN	Flookburgh
1660	1734	1660	1734	169552	LAN	Garstang
1639	1753	1639	1753	169552	LAN	Goosnargh
1857	1895	1857	1895	169552	LAN	Grange Over Sands
1676	1812	1676	1812	169552	LAN	Gressingham
1592	1941	1592	1941	169552	LAN	Halton
1833	1868	1832	1888	169552	LAN	Haverthwaite

Known From	To	Researching From	To	Ref	Cty	Place
THEXTON contd.						
1851	1872	1568	1928	169552	LAN	Hawkshead
1658	1812	1658	1812	169552	LAN	Heysham
1868	1876	1742	1876	169552	LAN	Hornby
1916	1940	1865	1940	169552	LAN	Ireleth With Askham
1781	1963	1681	1963	169552	LAN	Kirkby Ireleth
1601	1653	1601	1653	169552	LAN	Kirkham
1759	1908	1599	1908	169552	LAN	Lancaster
1774	1842	1754	1965	169552	LAN	Lindale In Cartmel
1881	1977	1866	1977	169552	LAN	Low Wray
1710	1837	1710	1837	169552	LAN	Lowick
1792	1812	1792	1812	169552	LAN	Pilling
1816	1864	1813	1867	169552	LAN	Preston
1852	1889	1852	1889	169552	LAN	Rusland
1879	1943	1870	1943	169552	LAN	Sawrey
1773	1812	1684	1812	169552	LAN	Seathwaite With Dunnerdale
1588	1812	1588	1812	169552	LAN	Tatham
1662	1812	1662	1812	169552	LAN	Torver
1706	1755	1625	1874	169552	LAN	Tunstall
1809	1913	1697	1972	169552	LAN	Ulverston
1811	1826	1796	1870	169552	LAN	Urswick
1781	1876	1538	1876	169552	LAN	Whittington
1820	1852	1820	1854	169552	PER	Kincardine
1872	1913	1724	1977	169552	WES	Ambleside
1875	1888	1813	1888	169552	WES	Appleby
1932	1934	1866	1934	169552	WES	Arnside
1700	1836	1657	1836	169552	WES	Asby
1793	1933	1566	1941	169552	WES	Askham
....	....	1813	1975	169552	WES	Barbon
1867	1871	1666	1877	169552	WES	Barton
1823	1829	1797	1835	169552	WES	Beathwaite Green
1611	1889	1604	1923	169552	WES	Beetham
1740	1878	1740	1878	169552	WES	Bolton
1860	1927	1662	1927	169552	WES	Brough Under Stainmore
1815	1820	1813	1979	169552	WES	Brougham
1758	1950	1717	1971	169552	WES	Burnside
1658	1850	1653	1949	169552	WES	Burton In Kendal
1837	1975	1837	1975	169552	WES	Casterton
1916	1979	1565	1979	169552	WES	Cliburn
1874	1941	1761	1964	169552	WES	Clifton
1713	1927	1673	1978	169552	WES	Crook
1600	1874	1559	1874	169552	WES	Crosby Garrett
1872	1896	1568	1896	169552	WES	Crosby Ravensworth
1811	1895	1755	1979	169552	WES	Crosscrake
1588	1886	1570	1956	169552	WES	Crosthwaite And Lyth
1813	1862	1813	1862	169552	WES	Dufton
1753	1771	1746	1812	169552	WES	Firbank
1804	1935	1676	1941	169552	WES	Grasmere
1710	1959	1730	1978	169552	WES	Grayrigg
1766	1769	1665	1868	169552	WES	Great Musgrave
1931	1984	1931	1984	169552	WES	Great Strickland
1840	1847	1813	1907	169552	WES	Helsington
1716	1880	1605	1958	169552	WES	Heversham
1870	1906	1842	1928	169552	WES	Holme
1732	1832	1732	1974	169552	WES	Hugill
1732	1832	1732	1974	169552	WES	Ings
1853	1950	1850	....	120103	WES	Kendal
1558	1979	1558	1980	169552	WES	Kendal
1747	1766	1701	1974	169552	WES	Kentmere
1779	1824	1662	1969	169552	WES	Killington
1563	1948	1538	1972	169552	WES	Kirkby Lonsdale
1797	1912	1647	1957	169552	WES	Kirkby Stephen
1813	1912	1813	1912	169552	WES	Kirkby Thore
1827	1921	1827	1921	169552	WES	Langdale
1871	1913	1836	1979	169552	WES	Levens
1813	1978	1813	1978	169552	WES	Long Marton
1736	1776	1670	1861	169552	WES	Longsleddale
1960	1965	1540	1965	169552	WES	Lowther
1927	1977	1927	1977	169552	WES	Lupton
1588	1886	1570	1956	169552	WES	Lythe
1714	1882	1714	1882	169552	WES	Mallerstang
1813	1943	1813	1943	169552	WES	Mansergh
1831	1836	1633	1983	169552	WES	Martindale
1759	1771	1670	1834	169552	WES	Middleton
1679	1888	1679	1888	169552	WES	Milburn
1869	1938	1837	1963	169552	WES	Milnthorpe
1832	1985	1813	1985	169552	WES	Morland
1838	1839	1777	1898	169552	WES	Natland
1747	1931	1741	1976	169552	WES	New Hutton
1571	1875	1571	1875	169552	WES	Newbiggin
1793	1961	1686	1982	169552	WES	Old Hutton
THEXTON contd.						
1771	1936	1813	1972	169552	WES	Orton
1852	1893	1653	1895	169552	WES	Patterdale
1756	1850	1703	1976	169552	WES	Preston Patrick
1803	1925	1571	1980	169552	WES	Ravenstondale
1826	1979	1826	1979	169552	WES	Rydal
1725	1896	1753	1947	169552	WES	Selside
1765	1788	1559	1948	169552	WES	Shap
1899	1939	1871	1979	169552	WES	Skelsmergh
1836	1975	1813	1975	169552	WES	Soulby
1753	1913	1651	1959	169552	WES	Staveley
1813	1881	1813	1881	169552	WES	Temple Sowerby
1879	1955	1813	1986	169552	WES	Thrimby
1811	1932	1811	1932	169552	WES	Troutbeck
1781	1907	1735	1925	169552	WES	Underbarrow
1833	1934	1597	1934	169552	WES	Warcop
1613	1950	1613	1985	169552	WES	Windermere
1756	1811	1720	1812	169552	WES	Winster
1819	1940	1671	1942	169552	WES	Witherslack
1732	1785	1666	1812	169552	YKS	Bentham
1852	1867	1852	1867	169552	YKS	Burton In Lonsdale
1854	1856	1850	1856	169552	YKS	Darton
1814	1848	1813	1848	169552	YKS	Dent
1789	1919	1693	1919	169552	YKS	Garsdale
1774	1941	1774	1941	169552	YKS	Howgill
1776	1862	1776	1862	169552	YKS	Ingleton Fells
1695	1792	1695	1792	169552	YKS	Ingleton
1755	1895	1594	1946	169552	YKS	Sedbergh
1857	....	1676	1857	169552	YKS	Thornton In Lonsdale
THICKBROOM						
1810	1836	1700	1810	164909	WOR	Handsworth
1810	1836	1700	1810	164909	WOR	Sutton Colefield
THICKET						
1776	1801	1700	1775	110345	WRY	Barnborough
THICKNESSE						
1450	1550	1400	1550	154881	STS	Edmunds
THIEFFRIES						
....	....	1550	1650	154873	LND	???
THIRKILL						
all	ALL	ALL	ALL	177628	YKS	ALL
THIRLWELL						
1920	1992	ALL	1992	177695	DUR	Stanley
1740	1856	1500	1740	113689	DUR	Tanfield
THIRNBECK						
1672	1812	1670	1812	169552	WES	Middleton
THIRP						
1841	1992	ALL	1866	108642	ESS	Upminster
1841	1992	ALL	1866	108642	HRT	Watford
1841	1992	ALL	1866	108642	SRY	Lingfield
1841	1992	ALL	1866	108642	SSX	Westhoathly
THIRSK						
1879	1928	1879	1930	126705	LAN	Chorlton
1790	1992	1600	1992	169560	YKS	East Riding
THIRST						
1720	1728	....	1720	151688	NFK	Gimmingham
THIRWALL						
1871	1881	1837	1881	175188	DUR	Hartlepool
1300	1750	....	....	175188	NBL	Haltwhistle
THISLETON						
1770	1931	1700	1931	141097	YKS	Sculcoates
THISTLETHWAITE						
1849	1956	1790	1874	146919	LAN	Austwick
THISTLETON						
1782	1830	1810	1830	151211	LIN	Bourne
1751	1774	1700	1751	102830	LIN	Deepings
1782	1830	1810	1830	151211	LIN	Pinchbeck
THISTLEWOOD						
....	....	ALL	ALL	169579	ALL	Name Study
....	....	1547	1992	169579	ALL	ALL
1655	....	1600	1700	152110	SFK	Glemsford
1655	....	1550	1700	152110	SFK	Sudbury
THODAY						
....	....	ALL	ALL	169587	ALL	Name Study
1600	1992	ALL	ALL	169587	CAM	West
THODY						
1500	1992	ALL	ALL	169587	HUN	ALL
THOM						
1750	1800	ALL	1992	170909	ABD	Aberdeen
1849	1890	1700	1910	139378	AYR	???
1852	....	1830	1850	139483	LAN	Liverpool
1790	1850	1700	1790	139483	LAN	Prescot
1881	1992	1860	1992	112305	LKS	Coatbridge

Known From	To	Researching From	To	Ref	Cty	Place
THOMA						
1851	1900	1800	1880	165441	STS	Hanley
THOMAS						
1859	1871	1859	1881	159778	AGY	Llechgynfarwydd
1850	1900	1850	1992	169668	AGY	???
1820	1920	1750	1850	112704	BRE	Llanelly
1850	1881	1850	1881	138398	BRE	Llangattock
1800	1860	1813	1860	177008	BRE	Talaccddu
1840	....	1800	1900	136891	BRE	Vaynor
1790	1830	....	1830	102822	BRK	Cholsey
1871	1881	ALL	1870	158631	CAE	Glan Gors
1748	1992	....	....	138401	CAE	Llanddeiniolen
1820	....	1755	1820	123129	CAE	Llangaelrhys
1830	1912	1800	1840	115614	CAE	Llithfaen
1800	1950	ALL	1950	132217	CAE	Penmachno
1950	1992	1881	1950	158631	CAE	Tanrallt Llanllyfni
1851	1992	1800	1851	164917	CGN	Llandygwydd
1800	....	1700	....	118591	CGN	Llanwenog
1851	1861	1800	1900	162450	CGN	Troedyrar
1823	1850	1820	1850	130990	CHI	Guernsey
1833	1834	1820	1840	159964	CHS	Stockport
1500	1900	1500	1900	139718	CMN	ALL
1793	1992	1790	1992	158658	CMN	Carmarthen
1793	1992	1790	1992	158658	CMN	Glynneath
1803	1852	1700	1803	158739	CMN	Llanddarug
1800	1955	1750	1800	165468	CMN	Llanelli
1821	1842	1797	1841	123129	CMN	Llangennech
1841	1883	1809	1841	123129	CMN	Llwynhendy
1790	1850	1700	1790	123102	CMN	St Clears
1790	1830	1790	1830	134813	CON	Bodmin
1768	1800	1600	1900	102520	CON	Crowan
....	....	1600	1900	136972	CON	Helston
1790	1830	1790	1830	134813	CON	Lanivet
1876	....	1876	....	168416	CON	Lanlivery
1828	1992	1700	1828	101567	CON	Ludevan
1828	1992	1700	1828	101567	CON	Penzance
1810	1940	1700	1810	136972	CON	Porthlevan
1750	1875	1700	1750	172561	CON	Porthleven
1800	1900	1650	1800	165549	CON	Roche
1810	1940	1700	1810	136972	CON	Sithney
1829	1992	ALL	1829	118184	CON	St Austell
1820	1964	1851	1964	107174	CON	St Erth
1662	1757	1500	1800	153591	CON	St Just In Penwith
....	....	1600	1900	136972	CON	Wendron
1688	1767	1600	1688	102571	CON	Zennor
1830	1992	1600	1830	112003	DBY	Newhall
1846	1846	1800	1850	174289	DEN	Llangollen
1860	1880	1860	1900	117668	DEN	Llysfaen
1800	1850	1700	1800	142905	DEN	Old Colwyn
1859	1885	1859	1881	159778	DEN	Pentrecristionydd
1700	1799	ALL	1799	132217	DEN	Tal-Y-Cafn
....	....	1600	1992	169692	DEV	Babbacombe
1800	1992	1700	1800	104418	DEV	Crediton
1826	1826	ALL	1826	131881	DEV	Devonport
1815	1860	1750	1815	159441	DEV	Devonport
....	....	1650	1685	176893	DEV	Dunchidoeck
....	....	1650	1685	176893	DEV	Exminster
1805	1840	1700	1900	146668	DEV	Honiton
1882	1929	....	....	159913	DEV	Plymouth
1820	1880	1750	1880	102970	DEV	Roborough
1821	1879	1821	1879	129100	DEV	Topsham
1740	1860	1740	1880	169641	DEV	Witheridge
1780	1992	1780	1992	129054	DFD	Rhydcymerau
1896	1992	1750	1896	158275	DOR	Hampreston
1896	1992	1750	1896	158275	DOR	Wimborne
1885	1945	1800	1935	106488	DOR	???
1794	1905	1650	1800	169714	DUR	Bishop Monkwearmouth
1895	1992	1800	1900	167843	DUR	Darlington
1890	1915	1800	1900	113859	ESS	Leyton
1720	1992	....	....	118672	FLN	Llanasa
1800	1850	1750	1830	138150	FLN	Mostyn
1805	....	1800	1880	165093	FLN	???
1887	1927	1700	1887	105309	GLA	Aberdare
1820	1880	1800	1900	157430	GLA	Aberdare
1834	1864	1700	1900	166359	GLA	Abersychan
1775	1841	1700	1775	158739	GLA	Barry
1755	1835	....	....	176559	GLA	Bryncethin
1750	1992	ALL	1750	131393	GLA	Colwinston
1850	1950	1850	1950	157430	GLA	Cwmbach
1887	1927	1700	1887	105309	GLA	Dinas
1796	1846	....	....	176559	GLA	Ffordd Yeyfraith
....	....	1780	1820	117137	GLA	Llansamlet
....	....	1800	1840	117137	GLA	Llantrisant
THOMAS contd.						
1750	1992	....	....	135666	GLA	Llantrisant
1840	1915	1800	1840	131431	GLA	Maesteg
1780	1992	1780	1992	129054	GLA	Margam
1923	1992	1800	1923	128732	GLA	Merthyr Tydfil
1800	1820	1800	1820	156930	GLA	Merthyr Tydfil
1818	....	1800	1850	169625	GLA	Merthyr Tydfil
?	?	?	?	104205	GLA	Penrhiwceiber
1780	1992	1780	1992	129054	GLA	Pontypridd
1750	1992	....	....	135666	GLA	Rhiwbidwal
1746	1958	1700	1745	172006	GLA	Rhondda
1885	1992	....	....	106488	GLA	Swansea
1700	1992	....	....	135666	GLA	Vale Of Glamorgan
1792	1882	1700	1792	134732	GLA	???
1700	1750	1700	1750	156930	GLS	ALL
1783	1840	1700	1783	148938	GLS	Arlingham
1720	1980	1710	1900	138479	GLS	Horfield
1740	1830	1700	1830	156930	GLS	Kempley
1800	1880	1700	1900	138517	GLS	Severn
1870	1940	1840	1900	169706	GLS	Westbury On Severn
1615	1704	....	....	165999	GLS	Westbury On Trym
1800	1880	1700	1900	138517	GLS	Westbury
1840	1900	1800	1992	169668	GYN	Caernarfon
1872	1927	1800	1927	172294	HAM	ALL
1786	1874	ALL	ALL	155632	HAM	Buealieu
1700	1940	....	....	127833	HAM	Portsmouth
1852	1967	ALL	1852	131881	HAM	Portsmouth
1816	1816	1800	1816	152943	HAM	Romsey
....	....	1700	1750	156930	HEF	ALL
1762	1783	?	1762	119296	HEF	Titley
1792	1882	1700	1792	134732	HEF	???
1819	1828	....	....	169692	IOW	Freshwater
1840	1926	1800	1840	128724	KEN	Bredgar
1790	1893	1700	1900	134880	KEN	Bredgar
1818	1986	1818	1986	110175	KEN	Chipstead
1840	1850	1835	1850	107522	KEN	Romney Marsh
1863	1870	1750	1900	114456	LAN	Liverpool
1835	1900	1600	1900	176133	LAN	Manchester
1900	1992	1800	1900	114693	LND	ALL
1875	1992	1800	1875	159212	LND	Hackney
1818	1986	1818	1986	110175	LND	Lewisham
1782	1861	1780	1861	130192	MDX	Brentford
1794	1894	1700	1794	145459	MDX	Hammersmith
1859	1861	1859	1900	167002	MDX	Holborn
1875	1880	1850	1895	112216	MDX	Islington
1855	1911	1855	1911	128740	MER	Blaenau Festiniog
1800	....	1750	1850	102016	MER	Towyn
1796	1918	1750	1900	114456	MGY	ALL
....	....	1820	....	176893	MGY	Bryn Coch
1680	1752	1650	1750	154881	MGY	Llanberewig
1750	1850	1700	1800	112704	MGY	Llangurig
1851	1893	1851	1893	176893	MGY	Llanidloes
1841	1847	1840	....	176893	MGY	Newtown
1850	1900	1850	1992	169668	MON	Aberffraw
1880	1890	1850	1900	123250	MON	Caerleon
1780	1830	1790	1830	156930	MON	Caerwent
1830	1900	1830	1910	156930	MON	Llandenny
....	....	1805	....	174963	MON	Magor
1818	....	....	....	150762	MON	Monmouth
....	....	1840	ALL	174963	MON	Newport
....	....	1805	....	174963	MON	Redland
1750	1850	1750	1850	157430	MON	Risca
1820	1900	1820	1900	156930	MON	Shirenewton
....	....	1805	....	174963	MON	Undy
1900	1992	....	....	135666	MON	Usk
1830	1930	1830	1930	156930	MON	Usk
1794	1905	1650	1800	169714	NBL	North Shields
1794	1905	1650	1800	169714	NBL	Tynemouth
1859	1859	1830	1860	127361	PEM	Fishguard
1813	1913	1700	1813	162035	PEM	Harroldstone
1826	1830	1826	1830	138398	PEM	Letterson
1880	1890	1800	1900	132217	PEM	Llanfyrnach
1730	1900	1730	1900	156744	PEM	Llanychllwydog
1804	1820	1770	1804	173118	PEM	Nevern
1840	1900	1700	1840	174572	PEM	Newport
1826	1826	ALL	1826	131881	PEM	Tenby
1715	....	1600	1750	176877	RAD	Beguildy
1845	1881	1500	1845	176974	RAD	Llanbadarn
1796	1900	1796	1900	129836	SAL	Cumlington
1830	1870	1600	1830	132802	SAL	Ironbridge
1853	1927	1820	1880	166677	SAL	Moreton
1820	1871	1750	1820	155500	SAL	Worthen
1690	1880	1690	1880	102490	SOM	Wick St Lawrence
1788	1989	1700	1788	169730	SRY	Croydon

Known From	To	Researching From	To	Ref	Cty	Place
THOMAS contd.						
1870	1900	1800	1900	113859	SRY	Walworth
1767	1780	1710	1767	128724	SSX	ALL
1670	1800	....	....	168777	SSX	Aypton
1780	1880	ALL	ALL	131164	SSX	Westfield
1830	1838	1820	1900	134376	STS	Newcastle Under Lyme
1830	1842	ALL	1992	134376	STS	Stoke On Trent
....	....	1895	1944	106488	STS	Wolverhampton
1869	1989	1700	1869	155101	STS	Wolverhampton
1750	1975	1650	1750	142395	WAR	Atherstone
1838	1902	1700	1838	126349	WAR	Coventry
1720	1773	....	....	115606	WIL	Eisey
1717	1751	....	1717	136212	WIL	Eisey
1756	1992	1600	1756	169595	WIL	Salisbury
1810	1870	....	....	140317	WLS	Llangedwin
?	?	?	?	152900	WLS	???
....	....	1796	1822	109134	WOR	Stourbridge
1789	1808	1770	1800	170348	YKS	Ovendon
....	....	1870	1929	169722	YKS	South Elmsall
1840	1900	1700	1840	108790	YKS	Sowerby
....	1850	....	1850	119024	???	Bristol
THOMASON						
1812	1880	1800	1900	165093	CHS	Ellesmere Port
1750	1965	....	....	137820	SHI	Fetlar
1720	1965	....	....	137820	SHI	Mid Yell
1760	1965	....	....	137820	SHI	North Yell
1758	1965	....	....	137820	SHI	Northmavine
1720	1965	....	....	137820	SHI	South Yell
1730	1875	1700	1750	150002	WOR	Chaddesley
THOMASSON						
1650	1750	1750	1992	162256	LAN	Edgworth
THOMERSON						
....	....	ALL	ALL	140783	ALL	Name Study
1700	1800	ALL	1992	140783	ESS	South
THOMOS						
1830	1930	1800	1830	138207	CAE	Llanengan
THOMPSETT						
1787	1992	ALL	1787	112178	SSX	Plumpton
THOMPSON						
1820	1900	1700	1820	100978	ABD	Peterhead
1800	1851	1775	1851	173622	ANT	Ballinderry
....	....	ALL	ALL	150924	ARM	???
1765	1765	ALL	1765	126721	BDF	Campton
....	....	1700	....	137456	BDF	Cardington
1727	1771	1650	1800	143693	BKM	Hughenden
1820	1890	....	....	162841	BRK	Wargrave
1843	1897	ALL	1897	127000	CAI	Keiss
1900	....	1880	1920	127353	CAM	Cottingham
1753	1992	1700	1752	132004	CAM	Swaffham Bulbeck
1676	1940	....	....	128996	CAM	Thorney
1913	1992	ALL	ALL	169838	CHS	Birkenhead
1821	1872	1791	1821	139149	CHS	Macclesfield
1725	1812	1700	1725	152196	CMA	Bridekirk
1712	1738	....	....	138851	CMA	Carlisle
1735	1807	1700	1735	152196	CMA	Carlisle
1797	1861	1700	1797	152196	CMA	Whiteheaven
1709	1777	1650	1710	135151	CUL	Addingham
1812	1843	1750	1992	168637	CUL	Brampton
1790	1848	....	....	117625	CUL	Dacre
1717	1794	1600	1800	130125	CUL	Thursby
1840	1870	1840	1992	165697	DBY	Derby
1774	1992	1660	1926	169889	DBY	Derby
1724	1800	1650	1724	163163	DBY	Ellastone
1818	1899	1818	1899	173681	DBY	Harpur Hill
1725	1992	1700	1725	169897	DBY	Heath
....	....	1790	1992	165565	DBY	Stanley
1816	1823	1816	1823	160164	DBY	Ticknall
1858	1900	1837	1858	155381	DEV	Appledore
1831	1851	1750	1992	139203	DFS	Kirkpatrick-Fleming
1913	1992	1860	1992	158755	DOR	South
1608	1834	1565	1815	142530	DOR	Christchurch
1608	1834	1565	1815	142530	DOR	Poole
1808	....	....	....	119911	DOR	Portesham
1870	1895	1700	1870	103462	DOW	Banbridge
1867	1913	ALL	ALL	169838	DUB	Dublin
1750	1795	1600	1750	116637	DUR	Auckland St Andrew
1712	1712	ALL	1712	154563	DUR	Auckland St Helen
1800	1851	1800	1992	102946	DUR	Barnardcastle
1700	1799	1700	1799	169781	DUR	Elwich Hall
1688	1688	1650	1750	144606	DUR	South Shields
1796	1796	1760	1800	159905	DUR	South Shields
1880	1900	ALL	1900	144533	DUR	Stockton
1795	1860	....	....	116637	DUR	Sunderland

Known From	To	Researching From	To	Ref	Cty	Place
THOMPSON contd.						
1880	1900	ALL	ALL	120154	DUR	Sunderland
1800	1920	1800	1930	141232	DUR	Sunderland
1730	1785	ALL	1730	154563	DUR	Teesdale
1730	1785	ALL	1730	154563	DUR	Weardale
1881	1966	1800	1881	111163	ENG	Midlands
1732	....	1732	....	139149	ERY	Holm In The Wolds
1800	1866	1800	1866	100862	ESS	Colchester
1795	1847	....	1795	177504	ESS	Mistley
1899	1950	1800	1899	126225	FER	Irvinestown
1850	....	....	....	133175	GNT	Newport
....	....	1860	1992	158755	HAM	ALL
1825	1825	1780	1830	174289	HAM	Christchurch
1784	1792	1750	1784	127116	HAM	Fawley
1893	1923	ALL	ALL	110388	HAM	Soberton
1812	1852	1500	1852	132993	HAM	Southampton
1800	1899	....	....	165999	HEF	Hereford
1800	1992	1700	1800	169803	HRT	Chorleywood
....	....	1881	1992	158755	IOW	ALL
1729	1802	1500	1729	129577	IOW	???
1830	....	1810	....	127647	IRL	Mayo
....	....	....	1830	121169	IRL	Newry
1812	1840	1700	1812	109061	KEN	Cobham
1860	1890	ALL	ALL	163341	KEN	Folkestone
1818	1992	1800	1932	142891	KEN	Lewisham
1600	1785	1550	1800	154881	KEN	Seal
1870	1992	ALL	ALL	156175	KEN	Swanscombe
1750	1900	1750	1900	125237	LAN	Darwen
1800	1880	1880	1992	162256	LAN	Darwen
1870	1992	1800	1870	122149	LAN	Eccles
1880	1890	1880	1890	160164	LAN	Heaton Norris
1841	1871	ALL	1871	156175	LAN	Liverpool
1842	1890	1750	1850	165654	LAN	Liverpool
1793	1937	1500	1992	175072	LAN	Liverpool
1875	1928	1875	1928	160164	LAN	Manchester
1767	1820	1737	1767	139149	LAN	Padiham
1890	1927	1791	....	160164	LAN	Salford
1750	1800	....	....	126497	LAN	Wigan
1847	1876	1847	1876	160164	LEI	Ashby De La Zouch
....	1866	ALL	ALL	169838	LIM	Limerick
1670	1680	....	....	103721	LIN	Althorpe
1830	....	....	....	126276	LIN	Barton On Humber
....	1668	1500	1668	175072	LIN	Billinghay
1700	1720	1600	1700	151769	LIN	Fulbeck
1761	1992	1700	1761	160024	LIN	Scremby
1783	1800	1550	1800	147265	LIN	Tattershall
1805	1826	1700	1805	137650	LIN	Winterton
1750	1900	1750	1900	122521	LND	Camberwell
1872	1913	1800	1900	127302	LND	Islington
1847	1860	1800	1860	126586	LND	Shoreditch
1820	1950	....	1820	132837	LND	???
1882	....	1862	1892	163775	MDX	Bethnal Green
1789	1809	1750	1850	178004	MDX	London
1775	1840	ALL	....	152129	MDX	Mile End
....	....	1790	1820	132837	MDX	???
1840	1843	1700	1843	138355	NBL	Byker
1847	1992	ALL	1847	154520	NBL	Cramlington
1724	1760	1700	1800	123536	NBL	Elingham
1811	1811	ALL	1811	154563	NBL	Hexhamshire
1840	1870	1800	1850	137278	NBL	Long Benton
....	....	ALL	1800	158445	NBL	Midforth
1850	1865	....	....	125202	NBL	Newcastle
....	....	ALL	1860	158577	NBL	Newtown
1857	1992	1800	1992	165786	NBL	Tynemouth
1790	1871	1700	1790	117463	NFK	North East
1868	1916	1750	1868	168025	NFK	Costessy
1794	1804	....	....	135437	NFK	Gt Ryburgh
1794	1992	1650	1794	118265	NFK	Harlingford
....	....	1700	1920	118834	NIR	Ballyearl
....	....	1700	1920	118834	NIR	Ballylinny
....	....	1700	1920	118834	NIR	Belfast
....	....	1700	1920	118834	NIR	Carnmoney
1746	....	ALL	1746	119326	NRY	Kilburn
....	....	1740	1840	175773	NRY	Northallerton
1818	1844	1844	1992	143944	NRY	Terrington
1830	1910	1830	1910	173533	NTH	South
1840	1960	1800	1850	158380	NTH	Peterborough
1720	1850	ALL	ALL	114235	NTH	???
1818	....	1818	....	156019	NTT	Nottingham
1850	1850	1700	1992	112097	NYK	Edstone
1710	1920	1600	1710	150932	NYK	Farndale
1760	1992	ALL	1800	155713	NYK	Gillamoor
....	....	ALL	ALL	111384	NYK	Scarborough
1828	1863	ALL	1869	127000	OKI	Flotta

Known From	To	Researching From	To	Ref	Cty	Place
THOMPSON contd.						
1828	1863	ALL	1869	127000	OKI	Walls
....	....	1700	1800	162493	OKI	Westray
1760	1992	ALL	1800	155713	SCT	Kirkbymoorside
1700	1800	1700	1800	133817	SFK	Sproughton
....	....	1700	1832	126357	SLI	???
1700	1900	1500	1700	169773	SRY	Esher
1700	1900	1500	1700	169773	SRY	Hersham
1793	1875	1761	....	116254	SRY	Tonghah & Seale
1790	1850	1750	1800	137111	STS	Brierley Hill
1700	1840	1600	1800	165697	STS	Ellastone
1770	1852	1700	1800	169854	STS	Harborne
1800	1992	1700	1800	169854	STS	Sedgley
1796	1861	1700	1900	178322	STS	Sedgley
....	....	1800	1900	149799	SYK	Darrington
1775	1825	1700	1850	143251	TIP	Tullahorton
1870	1887	1861	1900	178322	WAR	Aston
1819	....	1600	1815	106054	WAR	Birmingham
1870	....	ALL	ALL	137421	WAR	Birmingham
1771	1771	1700	1796	178322	WAR	Harborne
1740	1840	1650	1750	137421	WAR	Lea Marston
1820	1850	1650	1950	123145	WAR	Leas Marston
....	....	1860	1992	158755	WIL	ALL
1820	1890	....	....	162841	WIL	Devizes
1762	....	....	....	171166	WRY	Kirk Fenton
1800	1925	1800	1925	139270	YKS	Central
1805	1890	1700	1805	173452	YKS	South
1750	1775	1700	1992	114901	YKS	Askham
1822	1943	ALL	1822	158445	YKS	Beverley
1876	1900	1739	1900	158712	YKS	Bossall
1791	....	1791	1880	169749	YKS	Bradford
1715	1751	1700	1751	141097	YKS	Braithwell
1839	1882	1835	1900	133574	YKS	Bramley
1700	1800	1700	1800	167924	YKS	Bulmer
1838	1992	ALL	1838	136875	YKS	Calverley
1834	1882	1720	1836	137057	YKS	Cleckheaton
1813	1850	....	1850	147818	YKS	Dunnington
1820	1830	1700	1820	151769	YKS	Ferry Fryston
1739	1860	....	....	117161	YKS	Fylingdales
1850	1856	1856	1900	117625	YKS	Guisborough
1814	1960	....	1814	176761	YKS	Holbeck
....	....	....	....	171743	YKS	Horsforth
1650	1750	1650	1800	158712	YKS	Hovingham
1814	1960	....	1814	176761	YKS	Howden
1750	1802	1750	1802	161314	YKS	Hudswell
1735	1791	....	....	141097	YKS	Hull
1814	1960	....	1814	176761	YKS	Hunslet
....	1640	1600	1670	138584	YKS	Kippax
1851	1920	1800	1992	102946	YKS	Liversedge
....	....	1827	1881	158755	YKS	Pickering
....	1797	1750	1797	154024	YKS	Pontefract
1791	....	1791	1880	169749	YKS	Rothwell
1670	1800	1740	1800	158712	YKS	Sheriff Hutton
1731	1850	1600	1730	108308	YKS	Swaledale
....	....	?	....	115592	YKS	Wakefield
1750	1992	1600	1750	169862	YKS	Wath On Dearne
1850	1870	1800	1880	135429	YKS	York
1790	1840	....	....	144568	YKS	???
1600	1700	1600	1700	169781	???	Nottingham
THOMPSTONE						
....	....	ALL	ALL	141062	ALL	Name Study
....	....	ALL	ALL	141062	ALL	ALL
1786	1832	1685	1786	117196	CHS	Gawsworth
1765	1992	1700	1770	135496	CHS	Gawsworth
THOMSOM						
1800	1830	1750	1850	177024	AYR	Ballantrae
THOMSON						
1805	1883	1700	1804	166782	ABD	Auchterless
1850	1960	1850	1960	145467	ABD	Cushnie
1832	1855	1750	1832	144177	ANS	Kirriemuir
1796	1800	ALL	1800	169919	AYR	Ballamtrae
1759	1811	1750	1815	146536	AYR	Dalry
1824	1841	1800	1824	169919	AYR	Dalry
1812	1923	1812	1980	146536	AYR	Kilbirnie
....	....	1780	1870	155098	AYR	Kilmarnock
1800	1850	1700	1900	148288	AYR	Stewarton
1700	1748	1700	1800	169927	BDS	Ednam
1780	1850	1750	1850	146803	BEW	Lauder
1789	1975	....	....	168203	CAI	Dunbeath
....	....	1500	1760	138614	CAI	Dunnet
1789	1951	....	....	168203	CAI	Latheron
1832	1870	....	....	169927	CLV	Guisborough
1816	1837	....	....	169927	CLV	Ormesby
1812	1900	1800	1900	119725	DFS	Cannonbie
THOMSON contd.						
1845	....	1800	1875	102016	DFS	Dumfries
1779	1873	1800	1873	105899	DFS	Dumfries
1837	1895	....	....	169927	DUR	Norton
....	....	ALL	1770	119326	ELN	Aberlady
1730	1750	1700	1750	130915	ELN	Dirleton
1800	1869	1750	1799	108227	FIF	Arngask
....	....	1800	ALL	149187	FIF	Ceres
....	....	1800	ALL	149187	FIF	Diarsie
1799	1860	ALL	ALL	135127	HAM	Christchurch
....	....	1770	1900	168386	KCD	Tulliallan
1800	1992	....	....	176125	LIN	Asterby
1800	1992	....	....	176125	LIN	Goulceby
1850	1943	....	....	124532	LKS	Glasgow
1802	....	....	....	120804	LKS	Strathaven
1880	1992	1840	1900	129976	LND	???
1599	1620	1550	1750	169927	LTN	Rousland
1752	1992	1752	1839	169900	MDX	London
1850	1881	1700	1900	148288	MLN	Edinburgh
1713	1752	1670	1752	169900	MLN	Edinburgh
....	....	1650	1770	147613	NBL	Berwick On Tweed
....	....	1650	1770	147613	NBL	Morpeth
1790	1800	....	....	169927	NBL	Nunriding Hall
1713	1755	1713	1800	169927	NBL	Stamfordham
1828	1863	ALL	1869	127000	OKI	Flotta
1828	1863	ALL	1869	127000	OKI	Walls
1750	1800	....	....	127140	PER	Killin
1827	1992	1700	1827	158143	PER	Meiklour
1655	1713	1600	1713	169900	PER	Perth
1815	1886	....	....	127140	RFW	Greenock
1770	1992	1700	1770	144134	RFW	Langside
1770	1992	1770	1992	167215	ROC	Ross & Cromarty
1815	1910	....	1815	175552	ROX	Jedburgh
1805	1895	1985	1992	114979	SAL	Shrewsbury
....	....	1750	1900	129275	SCT	Cruden
....	1723	....	....	118680	SCT	Glasgow
1775	....	1700	1850	141739	SCT	???
1803	1860	1700	1992	139203	SHI	Tingwall
1840	1840	1750	1850	171662	STI	St Ninians
1670	1760	1640	1760	156930	WIL	Aldbourne
....	....	1760	1800	147613	YKS	Skipton
....	1840	1700	1900	148288	YKS	Wakefield
....	....	1750	1837	155381	???	???
THOMSONE						
1665	1746	1500	1665	143073	BAN	Grange
1665	1746	1500	1665	143073	BAN	Keith
THONE						
1753	1765	....	1753	117234	SSX	Frant
THORBURN						
1756	1992	....	1756	100315	PEE	Eddlestone
1734	1829	1600	1734	169951	ROX	Hawick
THORCKMORTON						
1600	1631	....	1631	103349	MON	???
THORINGTON						
1760	1800	1750	1850	143502	ESS	South East
THORLBY						
1800	1850	1700	1900	100129	LIN	Helpingham
THORLEY						
....	1804	ALL	1804	127000	CHS	Sandbach
THORN						
1600	1700	1500	1900	177180	BKM	Bierton
1753	1935	1592	1753	137537	DEV	Plymouth
1766	1783	1750	1800	149047	DEV	Swimbridge
1700	ALL	....	....	153397	HAM	Lymington
1847	1900	....	....	101060	HAM	Southampton
1750	ALL	1767	1871	107379	HRT	ALL
1855	1860	1800	1900	113212	IRL	Kilkenny
1784	1871	1784	1871	123404	LEI	Sheerply Magna
1719	1787	1680	1787	123404	LEI	Sibson
1664	1762	....	....	171654	LIN	Hareby
1856	1856	1820	1860	133000	NTH	Thrapston
1826	1871	1750	1830	121568	SOM	Bishops Lydeard
1750	1800	1750	1800	144657	SOM	West Buckland
1740	1790	1740	1790	179337	WIL	Chippenham
1847	1930	....	....	147672	WLS	Doormouth
THORNBORROW						
1590	1992	1500	1590	129038	WES	North
1700	1850	....	....	146854	WES	Orton
THORNDIKE						
1830	1940	1700	1840	106267	SFK	North
THORNE						
....	....	1828	....	109673	DEV	Awliscombe
1800	1830	1750	1840	123145	DEV	Bideford
1800	1900	1800	1900	172634	DEV	Tiverton

Known From	To	Researching From	To	Ref	Cty	Place
THORNE contd.						
1729	1800	1600	1850	134643	DOR	Cerne Abbas
1729	1800	1600	1850	134643	DOR	Sherborne
1820	1889	1700	1820	162035	GLS	Bristol
1700	ALL	....	....	153397	HAM	Lymington
1870	1890	1870	1890	134643	LAN	Liverpool
1841	....	1840	1870	134643	LND	Lambeth
1700	1899	....	....	121835	NFK	Norwich
1798	1820	1750	1850	134643	SOM	Frome
1800	....	1750	1800	169625	SOM	Orchard Portman
1840	1890	1750	1890	169978	SOM	Sampford Brett
1789	1789	1600	1789	144851	SSX	Etchingham
1950	1992	1700	1950	171255	WAR	Birmingham
1826	1826	ALL	ALL	171816	WAR	Birmingham
1830	1850	1800	1830	149632	YKS	Wakefield
THORNELL						
1734	1940	....	....	122777	GLS	Frampton Cotterell
THORNELY						
1600	1889	....	....	138851	CHS	Newton Dukinfield
1600	1889	....	....	138851	DBY	Chisworth
1600	1889	....	....	138851	DBY	Glossop
THORNER						
1700	1850	1800	1850	154903	DOR	South
1668	1734	ALL	1668	154563	DOR	Puncknowle
1875	1992	1850	1992	154903	SOM	Pretleigh
THORNETT						
1820	1860	1750	1820	172898	HAM	Whitchurch
1870	1992	1500	1870	169986	LEI	Mt Sorrell
1870	1992	1500	1870	169986	OXF	Chipping Norton
THORNHILL						
1750	1860	1600	1750	172006	DBY	Hope
1841	1881	1700	1840	169994	DBY	Ilkeston
1730	1992	1700	1900	111821	DBY	Shipley
1735	1983	ALL	1735	135062	DBY	Stanton By Bridge
1870	1870	1850	1870	113611	EYK	Hull
1770	1800	1700	1992	118753	GLS	Bisley
1810	1880	1700	1825	166561	LEI	Wymeswold
1871	1992	1700	1992	112445	LND	ALL
1735	1983	ALL	1735	135062	NTT	Beeston
1841	1992	1700	1840	169994	NTT	Beeston
1799	1847	ALL	1870	113611	NTT	Stockwith
1740	1956	ALL	1740	126721	WYK	Tankersley
THORNICROFT						
1767	....	....	....	148156	NTH	Central
1767	....	....	....	148156	NTH	South
1831	1950	1700	1831	146110	WAR	Napton On The Hill
THORNLEY						
1860	1988	....	....	167150	HAM	Portsmouth
1840	1870	1750	1850	134848	LAN	Bury
1841	1860	1750	1841	167150	LAN	Preston
1800	1950	ALL	ALL	174505	LEI	Ashby De La Zouch
THORNS						
1800	1850	1700	1800	152587	ESS	Stanford Le Hope
THORNTHWAITE						
1500	1850	1700	1850	170003	CMA	Allonby
1500	1850	1700	1850	170003	CMA	Aspatria
1500	1850	1500	1800	170003	CMA	Bolton
1700	1900	1500	1992	170003	CMA	Brampton
1700	1900	1500	1992	170003	CMA	Carlisle
1600	1800	1600	1992	170003	CMA	Cockermouth
1600	1800	1700	1850	170003	CMA	Crosthwaite
1880	1900	1880	1992	170003	CMA	Keswick
1500	1850	1500	1800	170003	CMA	Maryport
1800	1992	1890	1992	170003	CMA	Uldale
1770	1850	1800	1992	170003	CMA	Workington
1800	1992	1800	1992	170003	DUR	Sunderland
1800	1900	1800	1992	170003	NBL	Newcastle
THORNTON						
1808	1850	1700	1800	106968	CHS	Runcorn
1749	1749	ALL	1749	122572	DBY	ALL
....	....	1750	1810	118834	DOR	Devonport
....	....	1750	1810	118834	DOR	East Stonehouse
1760	1800	1700	1850	143502	ESS	South East
....	....	1810	1900	118834	HAM	Portsmouth
....	....	1730	1775	172871	HRT	West
1580	1992	ALL	1600	170046	LAN	Caton
1861	1992	1700	1861	105635	LAN	Cliviger
1814	1814	1775	1814	174211	LAN	Colne
1860	1900	1800	1900	106968	LAN	Liverpool
1742	1801	....	....	138231	LAN	Manchester
1860	1900	1800	1900	106968	LAN	Salford
1742	1801	....	....	138231	LAN	Salford
1873	1893	1873	1894	157112	LAN	Simsx Widnes
1850	1850	1750	1880	176672	LEI	ALL
THORNTON contd.						
1910	1992	1750	1910	124931	LND	Deptford
1811	1876	?	1811	109975	LND	Islington
1787	1900	1300	1992	152501	LND	Marylebone
1825	1850	1750	1850	100439	LND	Shoreditch
1650	1840	1550	1650	129763	NTH	South
1700	1880	1700	1880	127655	NTH	Byfield
1749	1749	ALL	1749	122572	NTT	ALL
1800	1860	1800	1860	126594	NTT	Nottingham
1875	1970	1800	1875	156957	NTT	Nottingham
1763	....	?	1770	164976	NTT	Nottingham
....	....	ALL	1800	151602	WIL	Landford
1787	1848	1700	1850	176621	WYK	Rastrick
1746	1783	1740	1790	175153	YKS	Bradford
1822	1822	ALL	1992	112631	YKS	Calverley
1718	1760	1675	1992	114901	YKS	Garforth
1840	1890	1800	1840	123595	YKS	Huddersfield
1790	1900	1650	1992	170038	YKS	Huddersfield
1776	1841	1750	1776	101796	YKS	Woolley
THORNWELL						
1829	1850	1700	1850	131377	STS	Burton On Trent
THOROGOOD						
1880	1980	1600	1880	136638	ESS	ALL
1890	1900	1800	1900	116297	ESS	Braintree
1804	1992	1700	1880	138657	ESS	Cressing
1800	1863	1800	1863	108456	ESS	Faulkbourne
1776	1812	....	....	101028	ESS	Little Hallingbury
1847	1890	1700	1890	116297	ESS	Wethersfield
THOROWGOOD						
1765	1992	1600	1765	170054	LND	East
THORP						
1700	1900	1600	1900	160563	CHS	Manchester
1700	1900	1600	1900	160563	ESS	Colchester
1741	1763	1741	1763	154946	NRY	Lastingham
1800	1820	1750	1850	157171	SFK	Aldburgh
1812	1992	ALL	1812	100803	WYK	Sowerby
1775	1900	1700	1900	154881	YKS	ALL
1740	1870	1700	1740	177393	YKS	Ferrybridge
1812	1857	1700	1812	130990	YKS	Knottingley
THORPE						
....	....	ALL	ALL	154083	ALL	Name Study
....	....	1750	1850	134848	DBY	Barrow
....	....	1750	1850	134848	DBY	Trent
1841	1992	ALL	1866	108642	ESS	Upminster
1880	1940	1850	1940	157171	GLS	Newnham On Severn
1826	1886	1826	1886	164704	HAM	Alton
1841	1992	ALL	1866	108642	HRT	Watford
1822	1865	ALL	....	115355	HUN	ALL
1100	1992	....	....	168882	KEN	ALL
1815	1849	1800	1850	176982	KEN	Isle Of Grain
1817	1868	1700	1817	110914	LAN	Bury
1850	1992	1750	1850	170062	LAN	Manchester
1885	1912	....	....	138827	LAN	Stalybridge
1700	1780	1600	1992	132403	LIN	North
1822	1865	ALL	....	115355	LIN	Bourne
1780	1800	1700	1800	120529	LIN	Coningsby
1850	1870	1850	1880	157171	LND	Chelsea
1844	1869	1800	1850	163295	MDX	Hampstead
1930	....	....	....	144169	NFK	ALL
1822	1865	ALL	....	115355	NTH	ALL
1700	1780	1600	1992	132403	NTT	North
1822	1865	ALL	....	115355	RUT	ALL
1861	1870	1800	1900	123811	SFK	Honington
1100	1992	....	....	168882	SRY	ALL
1841	1992	ALL	1866	108642	SRY	Lingfield
1100	1992	....	....	168882	SSX	ALL
1841	1992	ALL	1866	108642	SSX	Westhoathly
1800	1871	1860	1992	140058	SXE	Lewes
1908	1985	1800	1908	166723	WAR	Coventry
1800	1920	1600	1900	175382	YKS	Bradford
1740	1870	1700	1740	177393	YKS	Ferrybridge
1812	1857	1700	1812	130990	YKS	Knottingley
....	....	1700	1850	110914	YKS	Silkstone
1800	1900	1800	1900	105546	YKS	Wooldale
THORRINGTON						
1777	1992	1777	1992	127035	MDX	Ealing
1780	1860	1700	1780	125318	MDX	London
1777	1992	1777	1992	127035	MDX	New Brentford
THORROLD						
?	1646	1550	1646	171476	NFK	Hackford
THOULD						
1616	1623	....	....	170070	LND	Clerkenwell
1584	1992	1584	1900	170070	WOR	ALL

Known From	To	Researching From	To	Ref	Cty	Place
THOYTS						
1735	1910	....	....	124974	BRK	Sulhamstead
1673	1773	....	....	124974	KEN	Crayford
THRALE						
....	....	?	?	179159	HRT	???
THRALL						
1910	1947	1910	1992	151378	CON	Truro
1947	....	1900	1992	151378	HAM	Southampton
1885	....	1850	1992	151378	NTT	Mansfield
THRASHER						
1790	1880	1500	1900	132055	KEN	Strood
THREADER						
....	....	1796	1847	116912	KEN	Deptford
1847	1941	....	....	116912	KEN	Woolwich
THREADGOLD						
1700	1745	1600	1750	134589	YKS	Cawood
THRELFALL						
1738	1838	....	1738	109622	LAN	St Michaels
THRELKELD						
all	ALL	ALL	ALL	177628	CMA	ALL
THRESHER						
1830	1900	1700	1830	120081	DOR	South
THRIFT						
1830	1900	1800	1992	100129	LIN	Stamford
1591	1650	1300	1600	132993	OXF	Oxford
1795	1820	1700	1850	100129	RUT	Bisbrook
THROSSELL						
....	....	1800	1850	117250	BDF	???
1873	1933	....	....	117250	CAM	Cambridge
1852	1942	....	1852	117250	HUN	St Marys
....	....	1870	1900	117250	YKS	???
THROWER						
1800	1900	1800	1900	124761	NFK	Gt Yarmouth
THRUSSELL						
....	....	1600	1800	147613	BDF	Shillington
THUBRON						
1798	1992	1080	1798	170089	ALL	ALL
THULBORN						
1750	1960	1600	1770	101834	CAM	ALL
THUNDER						
....	....	ALL	ALL	105228	ALL	Name Study
1470	1985	1200	1992	105228	ALL	ALL
THURBON						
1796	1988	1678	1796	159522	CAM	Comberton
THUREY						
1820	1825	1780	1840	105333	MDX	London
THURGOOD						
ALL	ALL	ALL	ALL	133256	ESS	ALL
1590	1670	1670	ALL	133256	ESS	Roxwell
1795	1950	1795	1950	127868	ESS	Terling
1588	1980	1588	1992	133256	ESS	Terling
1800	1900	1800	1900	162140	HRT	Albury
1737	1841	1500	1841	132233	HRT	Furneux Pelham
1830	1900	1800	1900	162140	HRT	Furneux Pelham
THURKETTLE						
....	....	ALL	ALL	119229	ALL	Name Study
THURLBY						
....	1850	ALL	1850	134511	LEI	Saltby
1830	1870	1800	1830	175986	LIN	Leasingham
THURLEY						
1749	1850	ALL	1900	151017	HUN	ALL
THURLOW						
1797	1849	1700	1849	159271	LND	East
1820	1880	1700	1830	106267	SFK	North
THURMAN						
1830	1881	....	....	176966	NTT	Mansfield
THURNALL						
1740	1820	1650	1740	173444	CAM	South
THURNTON						
1790	1860	1600	1790	154172	YKS	Wyke
THURSBY						
1799	1825	1650	1799	138029	NFK	Seringham
THURSFIELD						
?	?	?	?	165395	CHS	Audlem Buerton
1800	1880	1700	1800	143014	STS	ALL
....	....	1700	1767	149977	STS	ALL
1730	1870	ALL	ALL	170097	STS	South
1767	1800	....	....	149977	STS	Gnosall
1760	1992	ALL	ALL	170097	WAR	Birmingham
THURST						
1773	....	1773	1992	151688	NFK	East Ruston
THURSTAIN						
1805	1879	1805	1958	173762	HAM	East Woodhay
THURSTON						
1750	1800	1750	1850	106631	GLS	Dursley
1763	1842	ALL	1763	126721	HUN	???
....	....	1800	1900	106356	NFK	???
1765	1786	1730	1775	162396	SFK	Dallinghoo
1840	1849	1840	1849	105848	SFK	Plomergate Hundred
....	....	1800	1900	106356	SFK	???
THURTLE						
1840	1845	1500	1845	104825	OXF	Oxford
THUSTIN						
1800	1850	1750	1850	158488	BKM	Farnham Royal
THWAITE						
1746	1746	1700	1746	155276	SFK	Falkenham
1687	1881	....	1687	168424	YKS	North West
THWAITES						
1790	1900	ALL	1790	157791	LND	Stepney
1850	1992	1700	1850	155144	MDX	London
1753	1811	ALL	1753	168602	NFK	Elsing
1841	1851	1851	1861	154946	NRY	Richmond
THYER						
1820	1840	1750	1820	132640	LND	London
THYNNE						
1800	....	ALL	1900	174637	IRL	???
....	....	ALL	1889	178659	LTN	Edinburgh
TIBBETT						
....	....	1840	1870	114782	BDF	Eaton Bray
TIBBIT						
1859	1884	ALL	1884	114030	BDF	North West
TIBBLE						
1859	1874	1600	1859	152080	HAM	???
TIBBLES						
1810	1920	....	....	125962	HAM	Portsea
1800	1890	ALL	1800	152064	KEN	Greenwich
1800	1890	ALL	1800	152064	LND	Deptford
1810	1810	....	....	125962	WIL	Lyneham
TIBBS						
1673	1797	ALL	1673	154563	DOR	Puncknowle
1797	1830	1770	1780	154563	DOR	Wyke Regis
....	....	1750	1845	146730	NFK	Drayton
1556	1992	....	....	153583	NTH	Bugbrooke
TICEHURST						
1500	1900	1500	1900	170119	SSX	ALL
1880	1980	1700	1880	170127	SSX	Battle
1700	1823	....	....	139971	SSX	Bishopstone
1880	1980	1700	1880	170127	SSX	Brighton
1700	1823	....	....	139971	SSX	Eastbourne
....	....	....	....	170127	SSX	Sedlescombe
1586	1992	1500	1992	153591	SXW	Ewhurst
1586	1992	1500	1992	153591	SXW	Hastings
1586	1992	1500	1992	153591	SXW	Hooe
1586	1992	1500	1992	153591	SXW	Ore
1586	1992	1500	1992	153591	SXW	Warbleton
TICKLE						
1700	1760	1600	1700	152196	CMA	Great Broughton
1825	1850	1750	1825	108413	GLS	Bristol
1780	1940	....	....	126497	LAN	Wigan
1780	1940	1780	1940	126500	LAN	Wigan
TICKLER						
1738	1780	....	1738	101761	LIN	Hogsthorpe
TICKNER						
....	....	ALL	ALL	170135	ALL	Name Study
1332	1660	1300	1600	170143	ALL	ALL
ALL	ALL	ALL	ALL	170135	ALL	ALL
1813	1850	1700	1850	148288	HAM	Portsea
1830	1860	1800	1850	166022	KEN	Orpington
1850	....	ALL	ALL	174637	SRY	ALL
1694	1900	ALL	ALL	123323	SRY	North West
1614	1632	1600	1632	159581	SRY	Bramley
1653	1855	1646	1855	170143	SRY	Chobham
1700	1850	ALL	ALL	154830	SRY	Dorking
1570	1767	....	....	166723	SRY	Horsell
1653	1855	1646	1855	170143	SRY	Horsell
1570	1765	1550	1765	170143	SRY	Ockham
1570	1765	1550	1765	170143	SRY	Send
1813	1911	1800	1911	170143	SRY	Westfield
1748	1911	1730	1911	170143	SRY	Woking
1825	1860	....	....	172073	SSX	Kirdford
TIDBOULD						
1821	1844	....	....	143596	SOM	Winsford
TIDCOMB						
1650	....	1600	1680	170348	WIL	Chisledon
1680	1720	....	....	170348	WIL	Wanborough
TIDD						
1750	1810	1720	1770	177377	KEN	Gillingham

Known From	To	Researching From	To	Ref	Cty	Place
TIDD contd.						
1850	1870	1850	....	133515	LEI	Somerby
1760	1850	....	1850	133515	RUT	Oakham
TIDEY						
1816	1839	1700	1816	124907	SSX	Shermanbury
TIDMAN						
1805	1900	1805	1992	136646	HAM	Chawton
1790	1850	....	....	102946	LEI	Burbage
....	....	ALL	ALL	178152	LND	???
1821	1871	1800	1900	124788	NTH	Braunston
1750	1805	....	....	136646	WIL	Wilton
TIDMARSH						
1867	1950	....	....	161306	HAM	Aldershot
1793	1874	ALL	ALL	168009	LND	Islington
TIDMAS						
....	....	ALL	ALL	135968	ALL	ALL
TIDSALL						
....	....	ALL	ALL	170151	ALL	Name Study
TIDSER						
....	....	ALL	ALL	170402	ALL	ALL
TIDSWELL						
1858	1992	1700	1900	167606	WYK	Sowery Bridge
TIDY						
1845	1992	1750	1845	178551	NTT	Lenton
1831	1850	ALL	1850	134503	SRY	Caterham
1800	1900	ALL	1900	141704	SRY	Croydon
TIDYMAN						
1736	1755	....	....	138401	CUL	Egremont
TIERNAN						
1830	....	1830	1992	130486	IRL	Drogheda
1880	1910	ALL	ALL	170801	LAN	Manchester
1930	1950	ALL	ALL	170801	YKS	Huddersfield
TIERNEY						
1900	1925	ALL	ALL	120154	DUR	Sunderland
....	....	1750	1850	147613	IRL	???
1861	1925	1700	1900	178616	IRL	???
....	....	1870	1890	147613	LAN	Barrow In Furness
1861	1925	1700	1900	178616	LAN	Blackburn
TIFFANY						
1799	1851	1700	1799	100110	WYK	Farsley
TIFFEN						
1771	1960	....	....	111856	???	Stow
TIFFIN						
1840	1900	1750	1840	172472	ESS	Stow Maries
TIGGALL						
1538	1900	1538	1900	170186	BRK	ALL
1538	1900	1538	1900	170186	HAM	ALL
TIGHE						
1824	1893	1807	1881	160636	CHS	Dukinfield
ALL	1824	1770	1824	160636	IRL	Cork
1852	1992	1790	1852	144223	IRL	Mayo
1885	1902	ALL	ALL	106216	IRL	???
....	....	....	1850	170178	IRL	???
....	....	1850	1992	125555	LAN	Manchester
....	....	1850	1992	125555	LAN	Salford
1850	1992	1800	1880	170178	???	Manchester
TIGWELL						
1538	1900	1538	1900	170186	BRK	ALL
1538	1900	1538	1900	170186	HAM	ALL
TILBERRY						
....	1787	1700	1787	148288	HAM	Portsea
....	1787	1700	1787	148288	HAM	Portsmouth
TILBIE						
1584	1671	....	....	127426	KEN	Lenham
TILBROOK						
1867	1871	1800	1950	139203	KEN	Beckenham
TILBURY						
1819	1864	1700	1819	163740	BKM	West Wycombe
1734	1780	1650	1740	103896	ESS	Hatfield Heath
1830	1992	1600	1830	170194	ESS	???
1700	1850	1600	1700	121010	HAM	Ellisfield
1837	1992	1650	1830	170194	MDX	Central
1850	1860	1750	1850	121010	MDX	Islington
TILBY						
1685	1685	....	....	127426	KEN	Canterbury
TILDEN						
1625	1646	....	....	127426	KEN	Harrietsham
TILDESLEY						
1840	1856	1840	1856	175196	AVN	Bristol
1850	1900	1850	1900	138193	LAN	Leigh
1713	1740	ALL	1713	126659	SAL	Curch Pulverbatch
TILER						
1725	1748	1650	1724	131245	LEI	Frisby On The Wreak
TILL						
1841	1861	....	....	170208	DBY	Newhall
....	....	ALL	1830	140848	DEV	ALL
....	....	ALL	ALL	172413	DEV	East
1700	1800	....	....	165999	LIN	ALL
1700	1800	....	....	165999	NTT	ALL
1800	1992	1500	1800	151483	SAL	Iron Bridge
1675	1675	1600	1675	155276	SFK	Newbourne
1650	1766	1600	1800	105333	SSX	Bosham
1650	1766	1600	1800	105333	SSX	Chichester
1707	1755	ALL	ALL	149004	SSX	Graffham
1650	1766	1600	1800	105333	SSX	West Stoke
1705	1730	....	....	156140	STS	Brewood
1823	1992	1700	1823	161446	STS	Penkridge
1730	1885	....	....	156140	STS	Tipton
1795	1875	ALL	ALL	151513	WAR	Baddesley Ensor
TILLCOCK						
1800	1930	1700	1992	108618	HRT	Ware
1889	1973	ALL	1889	167711	MDX	Chiswick
TILLER						
1500	1900	1500	1900	170216	HAM	ALL
1854	1899	1800	1854	103640	HAM	Southampton
1500	1900	1500	1900	170216	WIL	ALL
TILLEY						
1889	1959	ALL	1992	171751	DUR	Gateshead
1830	1830	1700	1900	173460	KEN	East
1810	1850	1600	1810	170224	LEI	ALL
....	....	1774	1867	175315	LEI	Thorpe Langton
1885	1885	1880	1880	171751	NBL	Cullercoates
1885	1885	1880	1880	171751	NBL	Tynemouth
1785	....	ALL	1812	168718	NTH	Rothwell
1813	1881	....	....	115290	SOM	Wells
1725	1851	1700	1851	170143	SRY	Stoke
1725	1851	1700	1851	170143	SRY	Worplesdon
1685	1705	1650	1685	156140	STS	Caverswall
....	....	1850	1895	170224	WAR	Birmingham
TILLIE						
1750	1800	1650	1750	107697	CON	Pillaton
TILLIN						
1762	1992	....	....	115606	BRK	New Windsor
TILLMAN						
1737	1819	1500	1819	153591	SXW	Peasmarsh
1737	1819	1500	1819	153591	SXW	Rye
1854	1910	ALL	1992	125113	???	???
TILLMUTH						
1960	1989	1500	1989	170232	???	London
TILLOT						
1790	1850	1600	1850	105627	NFK	Garboldisham
1590	1790	1500	1800	105627	SFK	Roudham
TILLOTSON						
1834	1897	1800	1840	136301	YKS	Skipton
1782	1783	....	....	130877	YKS	Swillington
TILLS						
1761	1761	1700	1761	127116	NFK	Norwich
TILLY						
1700	1800	....	....	165999	GLS	ALL
1700	1800	....	....	165999	SOM	ALL
....	....	ALL	1770	141224	SOM	North
1731	1827	ALL	1731	139602	SOM	Langport
1791	1797	1750	1850	173517	STS	South
1791	1797	1750	1850	173517	WAR	North
1770	1800	1640	1800	130621	WIL	All Cannings
TILMOUSE						
....	....	1650	1850	170232	WAR	Berkswell
TILMOUTH						
....	....	ALL	ALL	170232	ALL	Name Study
1655	1989	1500	1989	170232	ALL	ALL
TILNEY						
1700	1992	1700	1838	165131	NFK	ALL
1787	1817	....	1817	101761	SFK	Brandon
TILSED						
1812	1921	1700	1812	155144	DOR	Wincanton
1812	1921	1700	1812	155144	SOM	Wincanton
1812	1921	1700	1812	155144	WIL	Wincanton
TILSTON						
....	....	ALL	ALL	154326	ALL	Name Study
1700	1750	1800	1900	129607	DEN	Gresford
TILT						
1700	1992	ALL	ALL	150347	WAR	Birmingham
TILY						
....	....	ALL	ALL	170240	GLS	ALL
TIMBERDEN						
1150	1250	1100	1250	154881	KEN	Brasted

Known From	To	Researching From	To	Ref	Cty	Place
TIMBERLAKE						
....	....	ALL	ALL	144789	ALL	Name Study
....	....	ALL	1900	177822	HRT	ALL
TIMBERRY						
1816	....	ALL	1816	104299	SOM	Shepton Mallet
TIMBERS						
....	....	ALL	ALL	170259	ALL	Name Study
TIMBRELL						
1800	1900	....	....	121061	WIL	Kemble
1877	1992	....	....	121061	WIL	Minety
TIMBRELL-ROBINSON						
....	?	....	....	162418	GNT	Cardiff
....	?	....	....	162418	YKS	Dewsbury
TIMMES						
1600	1700	1500	1600	174513	OXF	Upper Heyford
TIMMINS						
1776	1992	1776	....	173266	CON	St Gluvias
1872	....	....	....	145742	IRL	Dublin
1815	1865	1750	1900	126586	SAL	Bridgnorth
1836	1836	1800	1861	152781	STS	Sedgley
1785	1870	1700	1785	126411	STS	Tipton
1834	1851	1800	1866	176885	WOR	Dudley
TIMMIS						
1801	1919	1801	1919	153273	STS	Eccleshall
TIMMONS						
1850	1900	1850	1900	148911	ANS	Dundee
TIMMS						
1900	1992	1800	1992	102032	ENG	South East
1953	....	1950	1960	163775	KEN	Woolwich
1700	1752	....	....	127043	OXF	Ascott Under Wychwood
1790	1800	....	....	127043	OXF	Asthall
1800	1950	....	....	127043	OXF	Brize Norton
TIMOTHY						
....	....	ALL	ALL	142158	ALL	Name Study
1770	....	....	....	142158	MON	Bettws
TIMPERLEY						
....	....	ALL	ALL	170275	ALL	Name Study
....	....	ALL	ALL	170275	ALL	ALL
1751	1772	ALL	1751	154563	LIN	Coningsby
TIMS						
1800	1992	1700	1992	170283	OXF	Barford St Michael
1825	1992	1700	1992	170283	OXF	Hook Norton
1788	1850	1600	1850	130125	WAR	Tanworth
TINCKNELL						
1800	1900	1850	1900	154903	SOM	Godney
TINDAL						
1692	1827	1650	1840	151599	LIN	Coleby
TINDALE						
1600	1992	ALL	ALL	150797	LIN	Coleby
1600	1992	ALL	ALL	150797	LIN	Sleaford
....	....	1837	1872	103187	NYK	Whitby
TINDALL						
1820	1900	1750	1820	174211	LAN	Burnley
1860	1890	ALL	1890	104299	LIN	Belton
1820	1900	1750	1820	174211	LIN	Snelland
1890	1992	1890	1992	104299	YKS	Barnsley
1850	1900	1700	1850	118915	YKS	Beverley
TINDELL						
....	1832	1813	1837	153176	NBL	Longbenton
TINDLE						
1878	....	1700	1850	161721	DUR	South Shields
TINDSLEY						
1610	1698	ALL	1610	168602	BDF	Stagsden
TINGAY						
1737	....	....	1737	177504	CAM	Downham
TINGLE						
1800	1850	1750	1850	145750	DBY	Wilne
1750	1880	1650	1750	109703	YKS	Grenoside
TINGLEY						
1820	1850	1800	1850	155357	SXW	Crawley
TINKER						
1800	1900	1800	1900	161705	CHS	North
1772	1772	ALL	1772	126721	WYK	Cumberworth
1841	1841	1800	....	122661	YKS	Cawthorne
TINKLER						
1696	1724	....	....	103632	DUR	Sedgefield
1774	1774	....	1774	136212	NFK	Ingoldisthorpe
TINLEY						
1627	1992	1533	1992	170291	NTT	North
1820	1992	1750	1820	105031	SFK	Ipswich
TINLINE						
1645	1992	1500	1992	139084	ALL	ALL
TINMOUTH						
1660	1992	....	....	122297	DUR	South Shields
TINN						
1861	1891	1891	1900	104728	GLS	Bristol
1837	1841	1700	1837	104728	NBL	ALL
1873	1907	1885	1960	104728	SOM	???
TINNAMS						
1700	1800	....	....	157805	WIL	Bratton
1780	1880	....	....	157805	WIL	Imber
TINNEY						
....	....	ALL	ALL	170305	ALL	Name Study
TINSLEY						
1880	1950	....	1880	161292	CHS	Runcorn
....	....	1750	1850	142670	HUN	Keyston
1820	1840	1820	1840	147532	LAN	Burtonwood
1839	1900	1800	1839	154318	STS	Sedgley
1800	1900	1800	1900	173681	WOR	Lye
TINSON						
....	....	1700	1800	172871	GLS	Lechlade
1847	1851	1810	1847	172871	MDX	Marylebone
1821	1821	1600	1850	168149	WIL	Box
1803	1821	....	1803	136778	WIL	Corsham
1821	1821	1000	1992	168149	WIL	Corsham
TINWELL						
1850	1992	1800	1900	164275	NBL	Newcastle Upon Tyne
TIPLADY						
1837	1904	ALL	1864	108642	HRT	Hemel Hempstead
1829	1867	1800	1829	164291	LAN	Manchester
1837	1904	ALL	1864	108642	MDX	Hendon
1760	1850	1760	1850	117803	NRY	Buttercrambe
1660	1800	1630	1800	117803	NRY	Crambe
....	....	1800	1837	164291	YKS	ALL
1750	1850	ALL	ALL	154970	YKS	Bolton Abbey
1759	1847	....	....	136913	YKS	Buttercrambe
1790	1820	....	....	177393	YKS	Ottringham
1760	1770	....	....	177393	YKS	Patrington
1740	1760	1700	1740	177393	YKS	Welwick
1723	1800	1630	1723	136913	YKS	Whitwell
TIPLER						
1800	1992	1760	1800	166855	NTH	Ecton
1696	1819	ALL	1696	115126	NTH	Kingsthorpe
TIPPER						
1700	1900	1500	1992	136794	DBY	ALL
1784	1851	1624	1851	149047	DEV	South Molton
1870	....	....	....	170313	DEV	Winkleigh
1700	1900	1500	1992	136794	STS	ALL
1841	....	....	....	170313	STS	Wolverhampton
1600	....	1660	1800	170313	WOR	Stourport
TIPPET						
1820	1840	1840	1992	109681	CON	Truro
TIPPETT						
1820	1850	1700	1850	156442	DEV	Dartmouth
1850	1920	1750	1860	112038	LIN	Lincoln
1700	1850	....	....	113093	SSX	Brightling
TIPPING						
....	....	1500	1800	124974	BKM	West
1550	1703	1540	1703	124974	BKM	Ickford
1560	1798	1550	1798	124974	BKM	Shabbington
1600	1738	1580	1738	124974	BKM	Stokenchurch
1591	1798	1591	1798	124974	BRK	Cadmore End
1550	1800	1500	1800	124974	BRK	Chaddleworth
1591	1798	1591	1798	124974	BRK	Fingest
1640	1680	1620	1680	124974	BRK	Kintbury Eagle
1623	....	1623	....	147532	CHS	Barthomley
....	....	1830	1930	168920	CHS	Wallasey
1821	1871	1500	1821	125695	HUN	???
1790	1870	....	....	132225	LAN	Liverpool
1835	1860	1790	1860	168920	LAN	Liverpool
1746	1992	ALL	1746	118117	LAN	Sawley
1465	1525	1420	1530	124974	LAN	Tipping Hill
....	....	1400	1800	124974	OXF	East
1550	1717	1530	1717	124974	OXF	Draycote
1510	1560	1500	1570	124974	OXF	Merton
1585	1725	1575	1725	124974	OXF	Wheatfield
1727	1980	....	1700	134724	WAR	Wootton Wawen
1840	1870	1800	1900	138193	WOR	Malvern
1880	1890	....	....	132225	YKS	York
TIPSON						
1806	1940	1600	1806	110019	LND	City
TIPTAFT						
1725	1992	ALL	1725	157198	LEI	Lyddington
1725	1992	ALL	1725	157198	RUT	Braunston
TIPTOFT						
1400	1500	1350	1500	154881	ALL	ALL

Known From	To	Researching From	To	Ref	Cty	Place
TIPTON						
1770	1936	1700	1900	131547	HEF	Leintwardine
....	....	1700	1800	111414	SAL	ALL
1841	....	1700	1840	136735	SAL	Minsterley
1816	1863	....	....	105147	SAL	Pontesbury
1720	1992	1690	1720	159115	SAL	Westbury
TIPTUN						
1847	1881	1700	1847	150738	SAL	Cleobury Mortimer
TIQUET						
1600	1699	....	....	137960	MDX	London
TIRRELL						
1813	1880	1813	1880	130222	NTH	Wilbarston
1689	1709	1550	1688	131245	WAR	Lighthorne
TISDALL						
1820	....	1700	1820	170321	ESS	Woodford
1840	1863	1700	1840	170321	LND	Golden Square
1808	1814	1700	1808	170321	LND	Greenhill Rents
TISER						
1800	1837	1800	1837	109746	WAR	Stratford Upon Avon
TISSER						
....	....	ALL	ALL	130818	LND	Mile End
TISSINGTON						
1822	1992	1778	1909	163910	LAN	Manchester
1800	....	....	....	163910	YKS	Darton
TITCOMBE						
1818	1835	1750	1850	126470	BRK	Coleshill
1650	1906	ALL	1650	175862	WIL	North
1715	1920	....	....	170348	WIL	Rodbourne Cheney
TITCUMB						
1860	1881	1700	1860	170356	BRK	Great Coxswell
1886	1891	1892	1930	170356	WIL	Chisledon
TITE						
....	....	ALL	ALL	170364	ALL	Name Study
1780	1816	ALL	1992	134376	LND	St Bartholemew
1760	1850	ALL	1992	134376	NTH	Henley In Arden
TITFORD						
1745	1820	....	....	170372	KEN	Cranbrook
1709	1745	....	....	170372	KEN	Hawkhurst
1790	1992	....	....	170372	LND	???
1625	1850	....	....	170372	SOM	Frome
1540	1620	....	....	170372	WIL	Bratton
1600	1640	....	....	170372	WIL	Corsley
1560	1620	....	....	170372	WIL	Steeple Ashton
1600	1992	....	....	170372	WIL	Warminster
1600	1820	....	....	170372	WIL	Wylye
TITHER						
1896	1992	....	....	170380	DUR	South Shields
1704	1741	1670	1720	174289	SAL	Lilleshall
TITHERADGE						
....	....	ALL	ALL	170399	ALL	Name Study
....	....	ALL	ALL	170399	ALL	ALL
1670	1992	ALL	ALL	170399	HAM	???
1835	1992	ALL	ALL	170399	MDX	London
TITLEY						
1710	....	....	....	174750	RUT	Cottesmore-Cum-Barrow
1730	1777	ALL	1730	143278	STS	Uttoxeter
TITMUS						
....	....	ALL	1869	175323	DBY	Derby
....	....	1800	1900	169501	WAR	???
TITSALL						
....	....	ALL	ALL	170402	ALL	ALL
TITSHALL						
....	....	1650	1880	146234	SFK	Farnham
TITT						
1545	1900	ALL	ALL	165654	ALL	ALL
1768	1826	ALL	ALL	165654	WIL	Chitterne
TITTENSOR						
....	....	ALL	ALL	170402	ALL	Name Study
....	....	ALL	ALL	170402	ALL	ALL
1780	1820	1700	1992	167592	STS	Hanley
1710	1992	1710	....	118672	STS	Newcastle Under Lyme
1750	1820	1700	1992	167592	STS	Shelton
1780	1800	1700	1992	167592	STS	Stoke
TITTERINGTON						
1870	1944	1800	1870	162264	LAN	Blackpool
1870	1944	1800	1870	162264	LAN	Marton Moss
TITTERTON						
....	....	ALL	ALL	170410	ALL	Name Study
1863	1900	1750	1900	106941	DBY	Derby
1800	1870	1750	1810	106194	DBY	Longford
1725	1765	1700	1775	149152	DBY	Wirkworth
1758	1773	1773	1850	149152	NTT	Nottingham

Known From	To	Researching From	To	Ref	Cty	Place
TITTERTON contd.						
1799	1833	1700	1799	164674	SAL	Kemberley
1799	1833	1700	1799	164674	SAL	Strickley
....	....	1500	1900	148598	STS	???
TIVENDALE						
1400	1985	?	?	169463	ENG	ALL
1400	1985	?	?	169463	FIF	ALL
TIVER						
....	....	1650	1760	153281	SOM	North Petherton
TIVEY						
1850	1900	1700	1950	141445	DBY	ALL
1793	1992	1700	1950	178616	LEI	Shepshed
1850	1900	1700	1950	141445	NTT	ALL
TIZARD						
ALL	....	ALL	ALL	152285	ALL	ALL
TIZZARD						
1820	1974	1820	1974	148873	DOR	Osmington
1863	1992	1863	1992	172952	HAM	Bitterne
1800	1900	1700	1992	118303	SRY	ALL
1700	1900	1700	1900	118303	SRY	London
TOAKLEY						
1647	1727	1560	1647	155276	SFK	Falkenham
TOASE						
1830	1900	1800	1900	106429	WRY	Campsall
TOATTERSALL						
1780	1806	1700	1780	139483	LAN	Downholland
TOBB						
1760	1820	1700	1750	119938	WAR	Atherstone
TOBIN						
1850	1992	....	....	170437	LAN	Liverpool
....	....	1800	1870	100358	MOG	Castle Blaney
1870	1941	ALL	1906	106968	NBL	Wallsend
TOBY						
....	....	ALL	1800	165042	ALL	ALL
1668	1789	ALL	1668	122106	DOR	Portland
1700	1765	1700	1800	161950	DOR	Portland
TOCKLEY						
1840	1920	1700	1840	138657	ESS	Witham
TOCOCK						
....	....	ALL	ALL	141224	ALL	Name Study
all	ALL	ALL	ALL	141224	ALL	ALL
TOD						
1793	1992	1674	1793	170453	FIF	ALL
1750	....	1700	1750	130915	FIF	Elie
....	....	....	1805	130060	SCT	Peebles
1716	1800	1700	1761	170445	WYK	Leathley
TODD						
1841	1870	1800	1880	116386	BDF	Henlow
1841	1870	1800	1880	116386	BDF	Luton
1809	1900	1700	1850	117005	BKM	Newport Pagnell
1850	1930	1850	1930	167924	CHS	Birkenhead
1807	....	....	....	109673	CHS	Ince
1786	1864	ALL	1786	174777	DFS	Penpont
1700	1800	1650	1800	154881	DON	ALL
1852	1920	1800	1852	164402	DUR	North Shields
1880	1930	1800	1880	123625	DUR	South Shields
....	....	....	1850	170461	ENG	???
1793	1992	1674	1793	170453	FIF	ALL
1750	....	1750	1992	106798	KEN	Rochester
1850	1950	1750	1850	134651	LIN	Boston
1530	1992	1530	1992	146129	LKS	Baromy Parish
1700	1750	1650	1750	170488	NBL	Ancroft
1785	1982	1758	1785	156418	NYK	Brompton By Northallerton
1780	1800	1700	1780	121339	NYK	Gilling
1633	1633	1590	1680	167002	NYK	Wath
1700	1800	1700	1800	116823	NYK	Whitby
1853	1909	....	1853	170461	RFW	Renfrew
1716	1800	1700	1761	170445	WYK	Leathley
1740	1850	1740	1850	167924	YKS	Bulmer
1800	1860	1700	1800	116815	YKS	Huddersfield
1800	1860	1700	1800	116815	YKS	Leeds
1920	1950	1920	1950	167924	YKS	Milnsbridge
1750	1900	1750	1900	167924	YKS	Pocklington
1720	1755	1650	1720	138584	YKS	Rothwell
1700	1750	1700	1750	167924	YKS	Terrington
1740	1850	1740	1850	167924	YKS	Welburn
1750	1900	1750	1900	167924	YKS	Wilberfoss
TODER						
1850	1870	1600	1850	171255	NTT	Newark
TODHUNTER						
1800	1900	1700	1800	132632	CMA	???
1800	1900	1700	1800	132632	LND	???
1800	1900	1700	1800	132632	SSX	???

Known Researching
From To From To Ref Cty Place
TODMAN
1850 1888 1850 1888 140058 SSX East Grinstead
1820 1840 1750 1825 103446 SSX Horsted Keynes
1889 1934 1889 1992 140058 SXE Lewes
1889 1934 1889 1992 140058 SXE Portslade
TOE
1800 1810 .... 103721 WAR Birmingham
TOFFTS
.... 1800 1750 1800 121037 MDX Whitechapel
TOFIELD
1737 1737 1735 1745 107360 BKM Gayhurst
1740 1765 1700 1750 124796 BKM Hughenden
1753 1839 1712 1840 107360 BKM Stewkley
TOFT
1826 1992 1550 1826 138266 DUR ???
1820 1850 1750 1900 164607 MDX Holborn
1826 1992 1550 1826 138266 NBL ???
.... 1600 1992 132403 NTT North
1674 1750 1550 1674 139084 SRY Godalming
1674 1750 1550 1674 139084 SRY Puttenham
1640 1700 1500 1992 167592 STS Burslem
1820 1890 1750 1850 141283 STS Hanley
1780 1840 1500 1992 167592 STS Hanley
1660 1700 1500 1992 167592 STS Shelton
1640 1700 1500 1992 167592 STS Stoke
TOGHILL
1840 1992 1700 1840 168084 GLS Marshfield
1830 1880 1800 1900 132950 LND ALL
1874 1986 1719 1874 170879 SOM Bath
1874 1986 1719 1874 170879 SOM Saltford
TOIN
.... ALL ALL 102296 ALL Name Study
.... 1800 1900 102296 LIN North
1769 1776 1679 1890 102296 LIN Boston
1791 1807 1730 1881 102296 LIN Partney
1809 1887 1746 1992 102296 LIN Spilsby
1825 1869 .... 102296 MDX Isleworth
TOINE
.... 1800 1900 102296 LIN North
1769 1776 1679 1890 102296 LIN Boston
1791 1807 1730 1881 102296 LIN Partney
1809 1887 1746 1992 102296 LIN Spilsby
1825 1869 .... 102296 MDX Isleworth
TOINTON
1785 1869 1700 1900 175307 LIN Fleet
TOKINS
1850 1900 ALL 1850 129658 CAM St Neots
TOLADY
.... 1790 1820 170526 LIN Holbeach
TOLAND
1830 1848 1700 1850 100439 DON Ramelton
TOLCHER
1672 1992 1672 1900 163406 DEV South
TOLE
1740 1992 1500 1992 170496 BDF ALL
1740 1992 1500 1992 170496 BKM ALL
1670 1992 1670 1992 170496 DEV ALL
1670 1992 1670 1992 170496 LAN ALL
TOLEMAN
1854 1854 1800 1860 110922 LND City
TOLFREE
1550 1992 1500 1992 109738 HAM Central
1700 1850 1700 1900 109738 STS Central
TOLHURST
1700 1760 1600 1730 166154 KEN Cranbrook
1700 1760 1650 1740 166154 KEN ???
TOLL
.... ALL ALL 170496 ALL Name Study
1750 1970 1500 1992 170496 BDF ALL
1750 1850 1700 1992 170496 CON ALL
1750 1992 1700 1992 170496 DEV Bere Ferrers
1750 1970 1500 1992 170496 HRT ALL
.... ? ? .... 134457 OXF Charlbury
TOLLADAY
1800 1901 1800 1910 170526 DUR Chester Le Street
1800 1901 1800 1910 170526 DUR Lanchester
1800 1901 1800 1910 170526 DUR Langley Park
1764 1844 1700 1850 125865 SFK Bury St Edmunds
TOLLANDS
1794 1795 1550 1800 147265 LIN North
TOLLER
1760 1765 1700 1760 102784 BDF Everton Cum Tetworth
.... 1820 1840 102784 HUN Fenstanton
TOLLER contd.
1789 1813 1813 1820 102784 HUN Kings Ripton
1847 1992 1700 1890 170518 SOM Taunton
TOLLEY
.... ALL ALL 153311 DEV Bow
1800 1992 1700 1800 121673 SAL Cleobury Mortimer
.... 1815 1600 1815 106054 WAR Aston
1645 1830 1600 1860 150002 WOR Hartlebury
1815 .... 1750 1815 123870 ??? ???
TOLLIDAY
1886 1900 .... 170526 HAM Christchurch
1900 1988 .... 170526 HAM Portsmouth
TOLMAN
1813 1930 ALL ALL 147389 DEV South
1855 1949 .... 145580 LAN Liverpool
1830 1850 1830 1830 145580 LND Shoreditch
1830 1850 1830 1830 145580 MDX Shoreditch
TOLMIE
1865 1870 1800 1900 137650 BAN Aberlour
1794 1802 1750 1824 142751 INV Petty
1885 1900 1800 1950 137650 MDX London
TOLSON
1543 1708 .... 167533 CUL Bridekirk
1833 1881 1833 1881 175188 DUR Darlington
1871 1881 1861 1881 175188 DUR Hartlepool
1870 1992 ALL 1870 143022 YKS Huddersfield
TOLTON
1714 1714 1650 1750 159956 NTH Burton Latimer
TOM
1726 1726 1700 1750 133450 CON Lanivet
.... 1600 1700 174319 CON Tywardreath
TOMAS
1790 1992 1760 1992 125520 WIL Broad Hinton
TOMBLESON
1750 1790 1700 1790 170534 CAM Mainea
1800 1860 1700 1800 110477 CAM Wisbech
1800 1860 1700 1800 110477 NFK Downham Market
TOMBLISON
1778 1992 1650 1850 172928 STS Sedgley
TOMBS
1816 1913 1796 1913 176044 BRK Longworth
1790 1796 1700 1800 176044 BRK Wast Hanney
1790 1796 1700 1800 176044 BRK West Hanney
1800 1830 .... 147486 NTH Northampton
1581 1722 1500 1722 102830 WAR Snitterton
1804 1992 1700 1804 170542 WOR Eldersfield
1871 1900 1850 1900 176044 ??? East Barnet
TOMKIES
1822 1828 1700 1860 167002 MDX Hackney
1852 1859 1700 1860 167002 MDX Islington
1804 1827 1700 1860 167002 MDX London
1791 1828 1700 1860 167002 MDX Shoreditch
TOMKIN
1840 1870 1870 1992 137707 KEN Boughton
.... 1700 1840 137707 KEN Monchelsea
TOMKINS
1770 1830 ALL 1770 154563 DOR Puncknowle
.... 1700 .... 1700 177695 LEI Bringhurst
1820 1900 1820 1950 135968 LEI Leicester
1797 1844 ALL 1841 112518 MDX Hanover Square
1797 1844 ALL 1841 112518 MDX St Georges
1789 1850 1700 1900 135968 NTH Kettering
1826 1826 ALL ALL 128449 WAR Coventry
1857 1933 1800 1857 113352 ??? ???
TOMKINSON
1800 .... ALL 1800 138169 NTT Greasley
1800 1850 .... 138169 NTT Nottingham
TOMLEY
1802 1802 .... 135437 CHS Chester
TOMLIN
1700 1800 1600 1850 177180 BKM Bletchley
1862 1882 1843 1992 138606 KEN Gillingham
1843 1862 1843 1992 138606 KEN West Malling
1904 1956 1843 1992 138606 LND Charlton
1890 1940 ALL ALL 120456 LND Greenwich
1770 1830 1770 1830 173533 NTH South
1770 1800 1500 1700 167843 YKS Preston Under Scar
TOMLINS
1885 ALL ALL 1885 116734 GLS White Cliff
1870 .... 1830 1870 159115 SAL Minsterley
1809 1988 1700 1809 165271 SAL Shrewsbury
1885 ALL ALL 1885 116734 STS Lipton
TOMLINSON
1841 1900 1841 1992 170585 BRK White Waltham

Known From	To	Researching From	To	Ref	Cty	Place
TOMLINSON contd.						
1830	1866	....	....	138118	CHS	Cuddington
1831	1860	1800	1831	149047	CHS	Grappenhall
1700	....	1860	....	165395	CHS	Liverpool
1700	....	1860	....	165395	CHS	Tarporley
1460	1686	1460	1683	102830	DBY	Bradbourne
1820	1900	1800	1900	156744	DBY	Duffield
1763	1992	1750	1763	115495	DBY	Long Eaton
1763	1992	1750	1763	115495	DBY	Sawley
?	?	?	?	170550	ESS	Southend On Sea
1914	1930	1875	1992	138363	HRT	Bushey
....	....	....	....	123471	LAN	???
ALL	1790	....	....	170798	LEI	Breedon On The Hill
1733	1881	1650	1992	170585	LEI	Castle Donnington
1800	1992	....	....	176125	LIN	Asterby
1800	1992	....	....	176125	LIN	Goulceby
?	?	?	?	170550	LND	???
1809	1992	1809	1916	115495	NTT	Keyworth
1834	1929	....	....	112232	STS	Cradley Heath
1900	1992	1700	1900	170577	WYK	Leeds
....	....	1730	1870	147613	YKS	Bentham
1806	....	ALL	1806	154946	YKS	Bubwith
1850	1992	1600	1850	131172	YKS	Carlton
?	?	?	?	170550	YKS	Leeds
1770	1850	1650	1900	130419	YKS	Long Preston
TOMLISON						
1760	1850	ALL	1760	162256	LAN	Walton Le Dale
TOMLYN						
1400	1700	1300	1850	177180	BKM	Winslow
TOMPKIN						
....	....	1600	1769	178411	DBY	Clowne
TOMPKINS						
1774	1992	ALL	1774	130575	BDF	Clifton
1796	1992	1600	1796	110019	BKM	Gt Missingdon
1890	1992	ALL	ALL	113662	LEI	Licester
1753	1829	1700	?	170593	LIN	Walcott
1860	1890	1800	1860	174203	SRY	Newington
TOMPSETT						
1777	1830	1750	1992	151246	KEN	Horsmonsden
1850	1900	1800	1992	151246	KEN	Yalding
1700	1992	ALL	ALL	115282	SSX	ALL
1700	1860	1500	1900	151246	SSX	Wadhurst
TOMPSON						
1675	1693	1640	1750	144606	DUR	South Shields
1850	1885	1841	1860	165441	SAL	Market Drayton
TOMS						
1797	1900	1700	1797	176257	BDF	Leighton Buzzard
1880	1992	1700	1880	167223	CON	Falmouth
1750	1805	1750	1850	171549	CON	Lanteglos By Fowey
1844	1992	1700	1844	145033	CON	Liskeard
1809	1850	1700	1850	104256	CON	Morval
1666	1992	1500	1670	170607	CON	Polperro
1865	1948	1700	1865	149608	CON	St Anns Chapel
1725	1769	1700	1725	173118	CON	Talland
1833	1842	1750	1850	169234	CON	Tintagel
1819	1821	1700	1820	165794	DEV	Bideford
....	....	1700	1992	167223	DEV	Plymouth
1853	1913	1700	1920	165794	DEV	Stoke Damerel
1830	1875	1750	1830	165794	DOR	Lyme Regis
1852	....	ALL	ALL	172057	HAM	Southampton
TOMSETT						
1799	1900	1650	1799	163163	KEN	Staplehurst
1753	1867	....	1753	117234	SSX	Frant
1700	1840	....	....	121983	SSX	Lewes
TOMSON						
1742	1742	....	....	115606	HAM	Odiham
TOMSONE						
1615	1718	1600	1725	141097	YKS	Braithwell
TONDRA						
1826	1881	1700	1826	120707	MAY	Westport
TONERY						
1898	1992	1836	1897	118850	STS	Birmingham
1898	1992	1836	1897	118850	STS	Wolverhampton
TONG						
1808	1832	1780	1840	151599	LEI	Wymeswould
1828	1870	1828	1992	172545	LND	Holborn
1866	....	1700	1900	132128	LND	Holburn
1828	1870	1828	1992	172545	LND	St Pancras
TONGE						
1920	....	1780	1992	135429	DEV	Beer
1780	1840	1780	1992	135429	LIN	Stockwith
1780	1840	1780	1992	135429	NTT	Misterton
1880	1900	1780	1992	135429	YKS	Guisborough
1840	1850	1780	1992	135429	YKS	High Catton
TONGE contd.						
1860	1890	1780	1992	135429	YKS	Huntington
1860	1890	1780	1992	135429	YKS	York
TONGUE						
1899	1926	1900	1992	129984	ESS	West Ham
1822	1892	1750	1822	113050	LAN	Eccles
1684	....	....	....	129747	LIN	Claypole
TONKE						
1532	1590	1500	1589	102830	STS	Darlaston
1590	....	1500	1620	160873	STS	Darlaston
TONKENS						
....	....	ALL	ALL	113115	ALL	Name Study
TONKES						
....	....	....	1785	145742	STS	Wednesbury
TONKIN						
....	....	ALL	ALL	173002	ALL	Name Study
1837	1992	?	1860	170615	CON	North
1710	1870	ALL	1870	137286	CON	West
1650	1750	1650	1992	133450	CON	Lostwithiel
1837	1992	?	1860	170615	CON	Mid
1715	1741	....	1715	153605	CON	Paul
1831	1839	1830	....	156019	CON	Paul
1797	....	1800	....	156019	CON	Penzance
1860	1880	1700	1860	131350	CON	Saint Ive
1834	....	....	....	136999	CON	St Agnes
1820	1820	1750	1820	144177	CON	St Agnes
1800	1825	1700	1800	148806	CON	St Agnes
1704	1826	1650	1700	168173	CON	St Agnes
1812	1860	1700	1810	165549	CON	St Austell
1615	1725	....	....	174319	CON	St Austell
1819	1852	1600	1819	129305	CON	St Just
1704	1826	1650	1700	168173	CON	Tregony
1650	1750	1650	1992	133450	CON	Truro
1817	....	....	....	170623	DEV	Tavistock
1840	1992	1841	1881	170623	GLS	Birstol
1770	....	....	....	142158	MON	Hnllys
TONKS						
1809	1883	1700	1900	136034	SAL	Dawley
1798	1992	1880	1992	145807	STS	Birmingham
1800	1992	1700	1992	177652	STS	Harborne
1840	1840	1800	1840	156914	STS	Walsall
1800	1950	1700	1850	114383	STS	Wolverhampton
1800	1992	1700	1992	177652	WAR	Birmingham
1790	1862	1862	1900	179647	WOR	Evesham
1880	1950	....	....	173827	WOR	Stourbridge
TONKYN						
1721	1771	1500	1800	153591	CON	St Just In Penwith
TONRY						
1898	1992	1836	1897	118850	STS	Birmingham
1898	1992	1836	1897	118850	STS	Wolverhampton
TOOBY						
1800	1860	1750	1850	166081	STS	Burton On Trent
1860	1930	1800	1992	166081	YKS	Wakefield
TOOD						
1716	1800	1700	1761	170445	WYK	Leathley
TOOGOOD						
1830	1910	1700	1930	114677	DEV	ALL
1744	....	1730	?	136964	DOR	Gillingham
1800	1850	1600	1800	154059	ESS	Brentwood
1787	1926	1750	1790	135763	SOM	Huntspill
1821	1837	1813	1855	170267	SOM	Shepton Mallet
1787	1926	1750	1790	135763	SOM	Wedmore
1792	1938	ALL	ALL	153516	SOM	Wedmore
1799	1815	1810	1830	170267	SOM	West Camel
1764	1851	1760	1850	131911	SOM	???
1791	1841	1750	1790	143898	SSX	Arundel
1800	1860	1700	1800	113816	WIL	Stourton
TOOK						
....	....	ALL	ALL	170658	ALL	Name Study
1640	1680	ALL	1700	149063	BEW	Coldingham
1793	1920	1793	1920	170631	DEV	Lewtrenchard
TOOKEY						
1750	1992	1600	1750	134090	KEN	Romney
TOOLADAY						
....	....	1790	1820	170526	LIN	Holbeach
TOOLE						
1840	1900	1800	1850	127523	STS	Brierley Hill
1874	....	1750	1875	128007	WIC	???
TOOLEY						
1807	1992	1807	1992	145238	NFK	North
TOOLY						
1690	1750	1600	1700	122920	LIN	Boston
TOOMBS						
1810	1846	1780	1810	128724	BKM	Langley Marish

Known From	To	Researching From	To	Ref	Cty	Place
TOOMBS contd.						
1819	....	ALL	1840	170674	BKM	Wolverton
1875	1992	1850	1875	170674	CAM	Cambridge
1840	....	ALL	1850	170674	DBY	Chesterfield
1849	....	1840	1875	170674	GLS	Gloucester
....	....	ALL	1840	170674	NTH	ALL
TOOMER						
1692	1992	1690	1992	176621	BRK	Newbury
1880	1986	....	....	133922	HAM	Beaulieu
1880	1986	1880	....	133922	HAM	Houghton
1880	1986	....	....	133922	HAM	Lyndhurst
1880	1986	....	....	133922	HAM	Romsey
1830	1880	1750	1900	148652	HAM	Romsey
1850	1992	ALL	ALL	131164	MDX	Enfield
1850	1992	ALL	ALL	131164	MDX	Holborn
1750	1850	ALL	ALL	131164	SOM	Glastonbury
1800	1950	1700	1800	128376	SOM	S Brewham
1463	1478	1300	1690	176621	WIL	Yeovil
TOOMS						
1780	1992	1600	1992	114596	LEI	Market Harborough
TOON						
....	....	ALL	ALL	150266	ALL	ALL
1791	....	1791	....	160164	DBY	Melbourne
....	....	1700	1799	142298	LEI	Ashby De La Zouch
1784	....	1700	1806	123404	LEI	Culverton
1774	1861	1700	1900	116173	LEI	???
1764	1803	ALL	1764	159042	LIN	Stamford
1797	1797	1700	1800	159042	RUT	Oakham
1710	1855	....	1710	100064	RUT	Whissendine
1741	1841	1700	1900	116173	WAR	North
TOONE						
1820	....	1750	1820	105457	LEI	???
1815	....	....	....	173932	SRY	Abinger
1809	1873	....	....	173932	SRY	Ashtead
....	....	1650	1750	115142	???	Mancetter
TOOP						
....	....	ALL	ALL	170690	ALL	Name Study
1721	1832	1558	....	112968	DOR	Beer Hacket
1700	1800	....	....	170682	DOR	Beer Hackett
1721	1832	1558	....	112968	DOR	Hermitage
1721	....	....	....	170682	DOR	Hermitage
1721	1832	1558	....	112968	DOR	Trent
1850	1971	....	....	170682	MDX	Enfield
1800	....	....	....	170682	NTH	Far Cotton
1849	....	....	....	170682	SOM	Dundry
....	1865	....	....	170682	SOM	High Ham
....	1887	....	....	170682	SOM	Long Ashton
1750	1850	....	....	170682	SOM	Trent
TOOTELL						
1774	1992	1600	1841	170704	LAN	Whittle Le Woods
TOOTH						
1880	1900	1700	1900	109924	BKM	ALL
....	....	ALL	ALL	151998	MDX	Paddington
1745	1770	1700	1800	127183	SSX	East Grinstead
....	....	1700	1830	176710	WAR	Stoneleigh
TOOTHILL						
1880	1970	1870	1900	117145	LAN	Bolton
TOOTILL						
1776	1791	ALL	1776	146226	LAN	Ainsworth
TOOVEY						
1892	1905	ALL	1892	108642	HRT	Watford
1892	1905	ALL	1892	108642	MDX	St Pancras
1604	1628	1500	1650	143693	OXF	Chinnor
TOPCLIFF						
1709	1735	1687	1735	147311	NYK	Scarborough
TOPE						
1500	1992	ALL	ALL	150274	ALL	ALL
TOPHAM						
1698	1729	1650	1750	149152	DBY	Pentrich
1600	1992	1500	1850	124079	YKS	ALL
1711	1754	?	1711	128910	YKS	Knaresborough
1730	1800	1600	1890	112372	YKS	Nidderdale
TOPLADY						
1790	1800	1700	1790	121339	IRL	Waterford
TOPLEY						
1896	1967	ALL	ALL	150681	KEN	Rochester
TOPLIS						
1800	1880	ALL	1800	138169	NTT	Nottingham
TOPLISS						
1700	1750	1600	1700	151769	DBY	Ticknall
1800	1992	ALL	1850	118338	STS	Whittington
TOPP						
1814	1856	1814	1856	174343	HAM	Hambledon
1886	1984	1700	1886	124400	SOM	Sutton Montis

Known From	To	Researching From	To	Ref	Cty	Place
TOPP contd.						
....	....	1700	1814	174343	WIL	ALL
TOPPE						
1500	1800	1500	1900	170216	WIL	ALL
TOPPEN						
....	....	1800	1900	129275	LND	Southwark
TOPPER						
1650	1785	1650	1785	127655	LAN	Burnley
1650	1785	1650	1785	127655	LAN	Marsden
TOPPIN						
1723	1752	....	....	138851	CMA	Carlisle
TOPPING						
1816	1817	1750	1850	167002	CAM	Ely
1800	1880	....	....	171824	LAN	St Helens
1700	1720	1700	1720	167924	YKS	Kirby Underdale
TOPPS						
1864	1878	1800	1900	127361	LIN	Grantham
TORBIT						
1868	1992	?	1868	163864	LND	Islington
TORDOFF						
1810	1869	ALL	ALL	166839	WYK	Bradford
1600	1992	1400	1700	145971	WYK	Wibsey
TORKINGTON						
1800	1992	1700	1850	168262	CHS	Stockport
TORLEY						
1880	1924	1880	1924	140945	FIF	???
TORRANCE						
1834	1877	....	....	135453	LKS	Airdrie
1780	1800	1780	1800	146536	LKS	Carluke
1830	1850	1500	1992	164992	MDX	Clerkenwell
TORRIE						
1775	1795	....	....	171654	PER	Kinnoull
TORSNEY						
....	....	1700	1905	152048	SLI	???
TOSELAND						
1700	1970	1700	1970	154598	NTH	Grafton Underwood
TOSPELL						
1848	1855	1800	1900	153354	MDX	London
TOTEN						
1747	1774	1680	1747	101222	LND	East
TOTNAM						
1702	1702	1680	1720	102717	HRT	Great Hormead
TOTNEY						
1816	1992	1816	1992	112232	STS	Netherton
1816	1992	1816	1992	112232	WOR	Netherton
TOTO						
1500	1650	1500	1700	114383	CMA	Millom
1500	1650	1500	1700	114383	GLS	Winchcombe
TOTTEM						
1788	1992	ALL	ALL	170712	MDX	London
TOTTENHAM						
1825	1826	1800	1900	159964	HRT	Braughing
TOTTERDELL						
....	....	ALL	ALL	170720	ALL	Name Study
TOTTLE						
....	....	1750	1860	164992	KEN	River
1840	1920	1840	1920	142018	SOM	Burrowbridge
TOTTMAN						
....	....	?	....	128589	HRT	Buntingford
1850	1992	1700	1850	105988	KEN	Canterbury
TOTTY						
1787	1817	ALL	ALL	149489	CHS	Middlewich
1855	1900	1800	1900	145319	YKS	Bradford
TOUCHARD						
1730	1826	1700	1730	179663	MDX	Bethnal Green
TOUCHET						
1100	1992	ALL	1992	133450	ALL	ALL
TOUGH						
1871	1992	1800	1870	156523	ABD	???
TOULMIN						
1800	1992	1600	1850	170739	LAN	North
1899	....	ALL	ALL	138533	LAN	Poulton Le Sands
1700	1992	1600	1800	170739	LND	???
1700	1750	1600	1800	170739	WES	???
TOULSON						
1850	....	....	....	145068	KEN	Gravesend
1815	1850	1815	1992	114901	YKS	Alverthorpe
1760	1790	1760	1992	114901	YKS	Birstall
1850	1919	1850	1992	114901	YKS	Hunslet
1690	1780	1600	1992	114901	YKS	Thornhill
TOURNEFORTE						
ALL	ALL	....	....	153397	HAM	Boldre
TOUT						
1868	1899	1800	1868	170747	CON	???

Known From	To	Researching From	To	Ref	Cty	Place
TOUT contd.						
1868	1899	1800	1868	170747	DEV	???
TOVELL						
1780	1992	1600	1900	139688	SFK	ALL
TOVEY						
ALL	ALL	ALL	ALL	170755	ALL	ALL
1663	1754	....	....	165999	GLS	Almondsbury
1663	1754	....	....	165999	GLS	Henbury
1780	1992	1680	1780	177253	SOM	Bedminster
1630	1760	1630	1700	142018	SOM	Norton St Philip
TOWARD						
1800	....	....	....	100633	DUR	???
TOWELL						
1792	1860	1792	1845	122106	MDX	London
1792	....	ALL	ALL	122106	NFK	Diss
1790	1992	1750	1992	110205	NTH	Geddington
1794	1992	1600	1794	178225	NTH	Kettering
TOWERS						
1684	1704	....	....	115606	BRK	Cookham
1860	....	....	....	128945	DUR	Darlington
1650	1780	1500	1700	144657	HAM	Froyle
1797	1830	ALL	ALL	138886	LAN	Kirkham
1810	1850	ALL	1810	135143	OXF	Oxford
1830	1880	ALL	ALL	128279	WES	South
TOWERS-PIERCE						
1800	1850	1700	1800	175307	LIN	Holbeach
TOWERSON						
....	....	1600	1650	170852	NBL	Newcastle
TOWILLS						
1700	1992	1650	1992	111759	DOR	Weymouth
TOWLE						
1782	....	ALL	1782	151009	DBY	Burrowash
1630	1992	1530	1630	151009	DBY	Wilne
1440	1895	?	1870	164976	NTT	Stapleford
TOWLER						
1820	1992	1750	1820	170771	NFK	Sivaffham
1764	1992	1700	1764	127116	WIL	Collingbourne Ducas
TOWLSON						
1900	1912	ALL	1992	128260	LAN	Liverpool
TOWN						
....	....	ALL	ALL	150266	ALL	ALL
1600	1992	ALL	ALL	137847	KEN	Margate
1719	1752	1600	1722	131245	LIN	Spalding
ALL	1880	....	....	170798	WRY	Calder Valley
1860	....	....	....	170798	WRY	Denby
1860	....	....	....	170798	WRY	Huddersfield
TOWNDROW						
1461	1839	1460	1674	102830	DBY	ALL
1865	....	ALL	ALL	105481	DBY	Belper
TOWNE						
1830	1840	1800	1992	167592	CHS	Birkenhead
1780	1800	1700	1992	167592	CHS	Manchester
1760	1840	1700	1992	167592	LAN	Liverpool
1740	1760	1700	1992	167592	LAN	Wigan
1780	1800	1700	1992	167592	MDX	London
TOWNEND						
1825	....	1825	....	109347	LAN	Accrington
1637	1800	....	....	152234	SYK	Wath Upon Dearne
1600	1902	ALL	1992	124389	WRY	ALL
1700	....	ALL	1992	124389	WRY	Cullingworth
1700	1900	....	....	157694	YKS	Bingley
1700	1900	....	....	157694	YKS	Hannorth
1840	1900	ALL	ALL	170801	YKS	Huddersfield
1825	....	1825	....	109347	YKS	Liversedge
1700	1900	....	....	157694	YKS	Thornton
TOWNER						
....	....	ALL	ALL	170828	ALL	Name Study
....	....	ALL	ALL	170828	ALL	ALL
TOWNHILL						
?	?	?	?	118044	LIN	Lincoln
TOWNLEY						
1714	....	....	....	117196	CHS	Prestbury
1846	1932	1800	1846	134384	LAN	Blackburn
1772	....	1730	1808	169552	LAN	Goosnargh
1614	1859	1599	1859	169552	LAN	Lancaster
1841	1851	1700	1840	135348	LAN	Littleborough
1790	1871	1790	1871	169161	LAN	Manchester
1724	1852	1724	1867	169552	LAN	Over Wyresdale
1786	1969	1722	1970	169552	LAN	Overton
1851	1881	1850	1900	135348	LAN	Royton
1790	1871	1790	1871	169161	LAN	Wigan
1760	1844	1740	1870	107360	NTH	Whilton
TOWNROW						
1832	1992	ALL	1832	170836	BDF	Luton
TOWNROW contd.						
....	....	1700	1850	170836	LND	Hackney
....	....	1700	1850	170836	LND	Shoreditch
1809	1992	ALL	1809	165204	NTT	North
1865	1865	....	....	108901	NTT	Ordsall
1809	1992	ALL	1809	165204	NTT	Southwell
1750	1900	1600	1900	117617	SFK	Campsea Ash
TOWNSEND						
....	....	ALL	ALL	123870	ALL	Name Study
....	....	ALL	ALL	123870	ALL	ALL
1885	1962	1800	1900	106186	AVN	Bristol
1600	1700	1600	1700	167924	BDF	Campton
1780	1900	1650	1780	154016	BKM	Marlow
1861	1992	ALL	1861	115878	BKM	Old Bradwell
1697	....	....	1697	149888	BRK	Faringdon
....	....	1800	1900	113174	BRK	Maidenhead
1819	1850	1700	1818	172006	BRK	Windsor
....	....	1700	1850	170887	CAM	Whittlesey
1844	1846	1844	1846	119385	DBY	Derby
1700	1810	1700	1800	119385	DBY	Tideswell
1800	1900	....	....	142077	GLS	Coaley
1828	1891	1700	1900	126683	GLS	Henbury
1750	1812	1750	1812	110361	GLS	Nympsfield
1750	1800	1750	1800	110361	GLS	Stinchcombe
....	....	1550	1635	170844	HAM	Hinton In The Hedges
1758	1775	?	1758	158569	HRT	Abbott Langley
1797	1880	....	....	116378	HUN	Buckden
1850	1900	1700	1850	170887	HUN	Ramsey
1810	1850	ALL	1810	109851	KEN	Isle Of Sheppey
1796	1918	1700	1800	125350	LAN	Blackpool
1869	1900	1869	1900	119385	LAN	Preston
1757	1950	1650	1992	179078	LAN	Townsendfold
1634	1700	1570	1650	170852	LEI	Buckmaster
1640	1992	....	1640	170860	LEI	Buckminster
1868	1992	ALL	ALL	108022	LIN	Grimsby
1817	1900	1750	1840	122149	LND	ALL
1859	1921	1700	1859	150398	LND	Newington
....	....	1800	1900	113174	LND	???
1630	1992	1595	1630	170844	NFK	Bracon Ash
1630	1800	1590	1640	170844	NFK	Norwich
1861	1992	ALL	1861	115878	NTH	Kings Sutton
1638	1915	1550	1650	170852	NTT	Lenton
1810	1840	1800	1841	119385	NTT	Stapleford
1816	1852	ALL	1816	162108	OXF	Aston Bampton
....	....	ALL	1825	114308	OXF	Bambury
1703	1780	....	1800	171441	OXF	Bampton
....	1822	ALL	1849	134058	OXF	Chipping Norton
1773	1920	....	1773	136212	OXF	East Lech
1840	1870	....	....	144371	OXF	Garsington
1850	1960	ALL	ALL	162469	OXF	Garsington
1830	....	....	....	174750	OXF	Oxford
....	....	1600	1630	170844	SFK	Gedding
1890	1950	ALL	1890	110639	STS	Milwich
1788	1842	ALL	1788	123412	STS	West Bromwich
1743	1760	ALL	ALL	153249	WAR	Alveston
....	....	1872	1883	114308	WAR	Coventry
1600	1780	1600	1780	127655	WAR	Lighthorne
1684	1742	1550	1683	131245	WAR	Lighthorne
1743	1760	ALL	ALL	153249	WAR	Snitterfield
1590	1900	ALL	ALL	107352	WAR	Tysoe
....	....	1825	1872	114308	WAR	Warwick
1760	1900	1750	1900	125563	WIL	Bremhill
1773	1891	....	....	115606	WIL	Eisey
1739	1739	1700	1740	124974	WIL	Ramsbury
1818	1925	1780	1891	116114	YKS	Halifax
....	....	1800	1900	108022	YKS	Sheffield
....	....	1612	1630	170844	???	London
TOWNSHEND						
1770	1890	1770	1890	121177	ESS	Tolleshunt D'arcy
1700	1850	ALL	ALL	142565	NFK	Norwich
1750	1850	1750	1850	139068	SSX	ALL
1820	1922	1700	1837	176370	SSX	Lewes
TOWNSIN						
....	....	1700	1860	134546	NTH	Cranford
TOWNSON						
1790	1870	1750	1850	118443	LAN	Coniston
1739	1992	1559	1739	141291	LAN	Furness
1700	1850	....	1700	130680	LAN	Ulverstone
....	....	1650	1900	147613	YKS	Bentham
TOWSE						
1813	1992	1700	1813	174351	EYK	Middleton
TOWSEY						
1850	....	....	....	174750	ENG	???

Known From	To	Researching From	To	Ref	Cty	Place
TOY						
1787	1811	ALL	1811	168696	CON	East
1817	1838	1800	1838	155438	GLS	Bristol
1863	1915	....	....	114545	HUN	Sawtry
TOYE						
1800	1852	1790	1870	163775	MDX	Bethnal Green
TOYER						
1860	1900	1850	1900	118540	BDF	Luton
TOYLOR						
1781	1849	?	1781	121665	WOR	Stourport
TOYN						
....	....	1800	1900	102296	LIN	North
1769	1776	1679	1890	102296	LIN	Boston
1791	1807	1730	1881	102296	LIN	Partney
1809	1887	1746	1992	102296	LIN	Spilsby
1825	1869	....	....	102296	MDX	Lsleworth
TOYNE						
....	....	1800	1900	102296	LIN	North
1769	1776	1679	1890	102296	LIN	Boston
1760	1780	1000	1850	168149	LIN	Boston
1854	1941	ALL	1854	165891	LIN	Lusby
1791	1807	1730	1881	102296	LIN	Partney
1780	1850	1780	1992	168149	LIN	Partney-Spilsby
1809	1887	1746	1992	102296	LIN	Spilsby
1825	1869	....	....	102296	MDX	Isleworth
1820	1890	1820	1920	168149	MDX	Isleworth
1830	1900	1818	1992	168149	MDX	London
TOZER						
....	....	ALL	ALL	170895	ALL	Name Study
1844	1917	....	1845	178853	DEV	Devonport
....	....	1600	1992	137588	DEV	Moreton Hampstead
1745	1992	1700	1992	175609	DEV	Plymouth
TRACE						
1850	1923	1850	1923	168564	DEV	Exeter
1788	1827	1788	1827	168564	DEV	Spreyton
TRACEY						
1850	1940	ALL	ALL	135062	WAR	Knowle
1850	1940	ALL	ALL	135062	WAR	Packwood
1840	1924	1840	1924	122335	WES	Kilbeggan
TRACHAN						
1854	1880	....	....	116165	ABD	Inverallochy
TRACY						
1825	1893	1710	1950	118680	ROS	???
TRAFFORD						
1700	1870	1600	1992	167592	CHS	Chester
1700	1740	1600	1992	167592	CHS	Nantwich
1650	?	1600	1992	167592	CHS	Northwich
1800	1992	....	....	176125	LIN	Asterby
1700	1875	1600	1992	165697	LIN	Frodingham
1800	1992	....	....	176125	LIN	Goulceby
1877	1878	....	....	132179	YKS	Doncaster
TRAHER						
1690	1690	1650	1720	168580	CON	Newlyn East
TRAHERNE						
1600	1970	1600	1970	157589	ALL	ALL
1550	1900	....	....	157589	CMN	ALL
1550	1900	....	....	157589	CON	South Hill
1550	1900	....	....	157589	GLA	ALL
1550	1900	....	....	157589	GLS	Gloucester
1550	1900	....	....	157589	HEF	Hereford
1550	1900	....	....	157589	HEF	Ledbury
1550	1900	....	....	157589	MON	ALL
1550	1900	....	....	157589	WLS	Brecon
TRAIL						
ALL	ALL	ALL	ALL	126896	ABD	ALL
1876	1992	1800	1876	118710	ABD	Ballater
1860	1960	1750	1860	140864	ABD	Fraserburgh
1840	1923	1700	1840	157996	ABD	Glenbervie
1758	1758	1700	1758	153605	KCD	Benholm
1804	....	....	....	140414	PER	Crief
TRAILL						
1940	1992	1700	1940	113786	LKS	Glasgow
TRAINOR						
1815	1839	....	....	146560	ANT	Carnbeg
....	....	....	....	102946	IRL	???
1861	1899	....	....	102946	YKS	Sheffield
TRAMPLERIA						
1750	1816	1700	1750	101524	CON	Redruth
TRANAH						
1720	1992	1720	1992	127795	KEN	Strood
TRANMER						
1650	1750	1500	1650	109959	NYK	Wykeham
1702	1762	1600	1750	174858	YKS	Willerby
TRANTER						
....	....	1800	....	137456	SAL	Dawley
1790	1849	1600	1911	121746	STS	Uttoxeter
1894	1918	1850	1894	175951	YKS	Bradford
TRAPNELL						
....	....	ALL	ALL	102555	ALL	Name Study
1150	1980	ALL	ALL	102555	ALL	ALL
TRASH						
1836	1875	1700	1950	158399	HAM	Hawley
TRASK						
....	1717	1690	1720	133639	SOM	Coker
1670	1808	1558	....	112968	SOM	Merriott
1850	1920	1800	1900	145866	SOM	Yeovil
....	....	1700	1900	145998	SOM	???
TRASLER						
1800	1900	1780	1850	123595	NTH	Duston
....	....	1750	1830	128732	NTH	Nothampton
TRATHAN						
1832	1833	1800	1832	113751	LND	???
TRATHEN						
1798	1888	1700	1800	107719	CON	Bere Ferrers
1800	1900	1600	1800	149608	CON	Redruth
1795	1799	ALL	1860	107719	SOM	Nether Stowey
TRATMAN						
1800	1890	1650	1900	153877	SOM	Bristol
TRATTAN						
....	....	1650	1815	146234	CON	ALL
1815	1815	1650	1840	146234	DEV	Bere Ferrers
TRAVELER						
....	....	ALL	ALL	108588	ALL	ALL
TRAVERS						
1840	1992	1500	1840	126616	DOR	ALL
1850	1900	ALL	1992	128260	DOR	ALL
1868	1957	1800	1870	177938	DOR	Beaminster
1785	1785	1725	1800	174599	DOR	Bridport
1860	1870	1800	1900	110949	DOR	Dorchester
1663	1820	1600	1850	170933	DOR	Loders
1877	1900	....	....	139823	DOR	Longfleet
1877	1900	....	....	139823	DOR	Poole
1868	1880	1850	1920	170933	DOR	Weymouth
....	....	1500	1900	126616	HAM	ALL
1850	1880	ALL	ALL	150347	MDX	London
....	1853	....	1852	174025	MON	Newport
TRAVES						
1809	1845	....	....	139823	DOR	???
TRAVESS						
1881	1992	1851	1992	139823	DOR	Mid & East
TRAVIS						
1581	1869	ALL	1900	141062	LAN	Blackley
1710	1780	1700	1800	151653	SOM	???
TRAWLEY						
1756	1800	1700	1800	115681	BDF	Eaton Socon
TRAYHERN						
1750	....	....	....	142158	GLS	Oldbury
TRAYHURN						
1810	1840	....	1992	161888	GLS	???
TRAYLEN						
1850	1980	1850	1992	156965	LND	City
TRAYTON						
1750	1770	1700	1800	105333	SSX	Laughton
1750	1770	1700	1800	105333	SSX	Lewes
1750	1770	1700	1800	105333	SSX	Ripe
1750	1770	1700	1800	105333	SSX	Rodmell
TREACHER						
1650	....	1600	1838	165131	BKM	Amersham
1650	....	1600	1838	165131	BKM	Berkhampstead
1650	....	1600	1838	165131	BKM	Chesham
1650	....	1600	1838	165131	BKM	Tring
1700	1840	1600	1838	165131	BRK	Beech Hill
1650	1840	1600	1838	165131	BRK	Sonning
ALL	ALL	ALL	ALL	160261	HAM	ALL
1880	1940	1700	1940	172405	HAM	Fareham
1840	1992	1800	1900	165131	HAM	Gosport
1880	1940	1700	1940	172405	HAM	Gosport
1870	1992	1800	1900	165131	HAM	Isle Of Wight
1650	1992	1600	1838	165131	MDX	London
1700	1800	1600	1838	165131	OXF	Statfield Saye
1944	1950	ALL	ALL	164887	SRY	Frimley
TREACY						
1835	1915	1760	1920	118680	TIP	???
TREADAWAY						
1832	1873	....	....	127957	LND	Paddington
1732	1815	....	....	127957	MDX	Harefield
1855	1893	....	....	127957	MDX	Uxbridge

Known From	To	Researching From	To	Ref	Cty	Place
TREADGOLD						
....	....	ALL	ALL	170941	ALL	Name Study
1784	1992	1784	1992	170291	LIN	Kesteven
1759	1784	1600	1784	170291	NTH	South
TREADWELL						
1743	1992	1687	1743	151327	KEN	ALL
1743	1992	1687	1743	151327	LND	ALL
1814	1944	1750	1814	170968	LND	Islington
1853	1900	1700	1853	160709	LND	Southwark
TREAGUS						
1729	1992	....	....	148237	SSX	Chichester
TREAGUST						
1827	1922	1827	1899	127817	HAM	Westbourne
1700	1850	ALL	ALL	154830	SSX	Fishbourne
TREASURE						
?	?	?	?	132195	SOM	ALL
1850	1992	1700	1849	156876	SOM	Coleford
TREASURER						
1831	1900	1831	1900	160563	TAY	Dundee
TREBILCOCK						
1852	1880	?	1852	113360	CON	Perranzabuloe
1564	1890	ALL	ALL	121398	CON	St Columb Minor
1888	1913	ALL	1940	113611	CON	St Columb
....	1984	....	....	129615	???	Bodmin
TREDGET						
1565	1850	ALL	ALL	126381	CAM	South
TREDGETT						
....	....	1600	1720	137316	CAM	Wickham
TREDINNICK						
1680	1970	1400	1680	178969	CON	West
....	....	1800	1992	122076	CON	St Austell
TREDWELL						
1691	1800	1691	1800	143774	BRK	Appleton
TREE						
1817	1843	1700	1817	172898	DEV	Thornerton
TREEN						
1770	1786	....	....	171654	LEI	Catthorpe
1772	1857	1772	1857	114308	NTH	Paulersbery
TREFOR						
925	925	800	1066	124974	FLN	ALL
1880	1992	1700	1880	152633	GYN	Clegir
TREGARTHEN						
1870	1992	1700	1870	170976	CON	Penzance
TREGELLAS						
1600	1900	....	....	160814	CON	St Agnes
TREGEMBO						
....	....	1700	1900	136972	CON	Breage
....	....	1700	1900	136972	CON	Germoe
....	....	1600	1900	136972	CON	St Hilary
TREGENNA						
1780	....	ALL	ALL	168718	CON	Lansallos
TREGENZA						
....	....	ALL	ALL	170984	ALL	Name Study
....	....	ALL	ALL	170984	ALL	ALL
1600	....	1600	1850	170984	CON	St Stephens In Brannel
TREGILGAS						
1723	1823	....	....	174319	CON	Mevagissey
TREGILGUS						
1750	1800	1600	1850	154342	CON	???
TREGLOAN						
1808	....	1750	1805	178845	CON	Illogan
TREGLOWN						
1820	1992	1700	1820	171271	CON	ALL
TREGONING						
1770	1830	1650	1770	165549	CON	Roche
1695	....	1700	1750	178845	CON	Stithians
TREGONNING						
....	....	1500	1708	138614	CON	Gwennap
1700	1759	1600	1800	153354	CON	Gwennap
....	....	1891	1964	149497	CON	Redruth
TREGURTHA						
1871	....	1800	1992	116009	CON	Kingsand
1700	?	1700	1992	116009	CON	Paul
1760	1914	1760	1992	172596	CON	Paul
1840	1855	1800	....	116009	KER	Dingle
TREHARNE						
1778	1861	1750	1875	118575	CMN	Laugharne
TREHERNE						
1793	1881	1764	1879	169099	HEF	Ledbury
TREIN						
1807	1898	1700	1807	173770	DEV	Bovey Tracey
TRELEAVEN						
....	....	1600	1900	179531	CON	Lanlivery
TRELEGGAN						
1643	1673	1600	1643	102571	CON	Constantine
1673	1673	1100	1673	117749	CON	Constantine
TRELEVAN						
1735	1775	1725	1800	171549	CON	Boconnoc
TRELEVEN						
....	....	ALL	ALL	171018	ALL	Name Study
TRELISSICK						
1610	1726	ALL	....	168718	CON	South East
TRELLEGAN						
1713	1760	1600	1900	153354	CON	Constantine
TRELOAR						
1749	1749	1700	1749	153605	CON	Sithney
1800	1992	1500	1800	136972	CON	Wendron
TREMAIN						
1657	1992	ALL	1657	137553	CON	Padstow
1720	....	....	....	164968	CON	Padstow
1657	1992	ALL	1657	137553	CON	St Minver
1720	....	....	....	164968	CON	St Minver
1657	1992	ALL	1657	137553	CON	St Teath
1822	1992	1500	1822	141089	MDX	Stepney
TREMAINE						
1600	1724	1500	1800	153354	CON	Constantine
TREMAN						
1700	1770	1700	1750	144657	SOM	Wellington
TREMAYNE						
1400	1820	ALL	1992	133450	CON	Helston
TREMBATH						
1778	1886	1700	1778	130141	CON	St Just In Penwith
1828	1883	1800	1992	137448	CON	St Just
....	....	1700	1792	139491	CON	St Just
1889	1920	1850	1992	117609	DEV	Tamerton Foliot
TREMBLETT						
1798	1906	ALL	ALL	147389	DEV	Central
1800	1820	1770	1850	174912	DEV	North Tauton
TREMLETT						
1844	1863	1700	1844	172898	DEV	Exeter
1731	1770	1670	1770	165972	DEV	Totnes
TREMLIN						
1850	1940	1800	1900	126640	AVN	Bristol
TRENBATH						
....	....	ALL	ALL	175331	ALL	ALL
TRENBERTH						
1806	1975	1600	1806	102571	CON	Gwennap
TRENCH						
1790	1870	1750	1870	146803	ELN	Garvald
TRENCHARD						
1872	1992	....	....	144053	DEV	ALL
1872	1992	....	....	144053	SOM	ALL
TRENDER						
1860	1992	1650	1850	131067	LND	City
TRENEMAN						
1750	1820	....	....	165999	CON	St Mellion
TRENHOLME						
....	1968	ALL	1968	177695	YKS	???
TRENT						
1600	1992	1500	1992	143014	ALL	ALL
TRENWITH						
1770	1792	1700	1770	153605	CON	Penzance
....	1926	....	....	147672	CON	Redruth
TREPAS						
1642	1651	1620	1700	171026	WAR	Itchington
TREPASSE						
1642	1651	1620	1700	171026	WAR	Itchington
TREPES						
....	....	1500	1800	171026	WAR	ALL
TREPESS						
1793	1989	1500	1800	171026	WAR	Warick
TREPPASS						
....	....	1500	1800	171026	WAR	ALL
TREPPESS						
....	....	1500	1800	171026	WAR	ALL
TREPUS						
1586	?	1550	1610	171026	WAR	Barcheston
TRESCOWDRICK						
....	....	1800	....	159824	CON	???
....	....	1800	....	159824	DEV	???
TRESEDER						
1200	1992	1600	1900	171042	CON	ALL
....	....	1600	1890	176117	CON	Redruth
1790	1820	1750	1992	171042	DEV	West
1790	1820	1750	1992	171042	DEV	Plymouth
....	....	ALL	ALL	171042	WLS	ALL

Known From	To	Researching From	To	Ref	Cty	Place
TRESIDDER						
....	....	1700	1900	136972	CON	Sithney
....	....	1700	1900	136972	CON	Wendron
TRESILLIAN						
1470	1540	1470	1540	137340	CON	East Newlyn
1540	1700	1540	1800	137340	CON	St Buryan
TRESIZE						
1807	1855	1700	1900	178322	GLS	Bristol
TRESSIDER HALL						
....	....	ALL	1882	140163	CON	St Keverne
TRESTON						
1800	1850	1800	1850	106631	MDX	London
TRETHAKE						
1680	1811	ALL	1811	168718	CON	South East
TRETHEWEY						
....	....	ALL	ALL	175668	ALL	ALL
1740	1900	ALL	ALL	175668	CON	ALL
1820	1870	1700	1820	165549	CON	St Dennis
1820	1870	1700	1820	165549	CON	St Stephen In Brannel
?	....	?	....	173800	CON	St Stephen In Brannel
1677	1992	1351	1677	171050	CON	St Stepmen
?	....	?	....	173800	CON	St Wenn
TRETT						
....	....	?	....	128589	NFK	Yarmouth
TREVAIL						
1683	1865	ALL	ALL	175005	CON	Central
TREVALSCUS						
....	....	1500	1600	174319	CON	Gorran
TREVANION						
....	....	ALL	ALL	171069	CON	ALL
TREVANNION						
1869	1909	1869	....	162175	CON	Renrhyn
1869	1909	1869	....	162175	HAM	Alton
TREVARTON						
1791	....	1750	1791	120030	CON	Tregony
TREVASKIS						
1858	1944	....	....	107174	CON	Penwith
TREVATHAN						
1700	1900	1600	1992	171077	CON	???
TREVEAL						
1683	1865	ALL	ALL	175005	CON	Central
TREVEALE						
1683	1865	ALL	ALL	175005	CON	Central
TREVELYAN						
1773	1940	1773	1940	143286	DEV	Burlescombe
TREVENA						
1770	1870	ALL	1770	145564	SRY	Southwark
TREVENEN						
1700	1950	ALL	ALL	137286	CON	ALL
TREVETT						
1850	1992	1750	1992	106763	DOR	ALL
1805	1881	ALL	ALL	105015	DOR	Long Bredy
TREVIGAN						
1700	....	1750	1850	158925	CON	Landrake
TREVIS						
1580	1650	ALL	ALL	137987	CHS	West
1801	1866	1780	1872	162825	DOR	Portland
TREVISS						
1820	1920	ALL	ALL	156604	LND	Kilburn
TREVITT						
1856	1905	1800	1905	120510	DOR	Morden
TREVOR						
1774	1813	ALL	1850	139459	SAL	Donington
TREVORROW						
1800	....	1700	1850	116335	CON	Lelant
TREVYLLIAN						
....	....	1700	1940	171085	CON	Camborne
TREW						
1833	1880	1750	1840	116815	ESS	Shenfield
1903	1992	ALL	ALL	135224	LIN	Cleethorpes
1903	1992	ALL	ALL	135224	LIN	Grimsby
1850	1902	ALL	1902	101362	LND	Central
TREWARTHA						
ALL	ALL	ALL	ALL	171093	CON	ALL
ALL	ALL	ALL	ALL	171093	DEV	ALL
ALL	ALL	ALL	ALL	171093	GLA	ALL
ALL	ALL	ALL	ALL	171093	GNT	ALL
ALL	ALL	ALL	ALL	171093	SCT	ALL
TREWAVAS						
1680	1992	1550	1680	129437	CON	???
TREWEEK						
1640	1717	1600	1800	153354	CON	Gwennap
TREWEEK contd.						
1855	1992	1700	1855	167223	CON	Mawnan
TREWEEKS						
1690	1716	1600	1720	121932	CON	Jacobstow
1690	1716	1600	1720	121932	CON	Week St Mary
TREWELLA						
1686	1854	1500	1854	153591	CON	Camborne
1686	1854	1500	1854	153591	CON	Illogan
1686	1854	1500	1854	153591	CON	Redruth
TREWICK						
....	....	1100	1992	115975	ALL	ALL
TREWIN						
1740	1992	1700	1740	133493	CON	Kilkhampton
TREWOLLA						
1700	1860	1600	1900	162043	CON	ALL
TREWREN						
1600	1992	1600	1992	146404	ALL	ALL
1614	1820	ALL	1820	137286	CON	Constantine
TREZISE						
ALL	ALL	1700	1992	151475	CON	South West
1830	1850	1700	1992	140287	CON	Lelant
1820	1860	ALL	ALL	112496	CON	Mid
1799	1843	....	....	130176	CON	Sancreed
TREZONA						
1805	1827	ALL	1827	134058	CON	Illogan
1800	1914	1700	1800	150320	CON	Illogan
TRIBE						
....	....	ALL	ALL	171107	ALL	Name Study
....	....	ALL	ALL	171115	ALL	Name Study
....	....	1700	1800	171115	HAM	ALL
1805	1845	ALL	1850	147567	HAM	Langrish
1840	1900	1800	1880	130516	KEN	South
....	....	1700	1900	171115	LND	ALL
....	....	1700	1900	171115	SRY	ALL
1613	....	....	....	164968	SSX	ALL
....	....	1650	1850	171115	SSX	ALL
TRIBECK						
....	....	ALL	ALL	166812	HAM	Gosport
TRICE						
....	....	ALL	ALL	128430	ALL	Name Study
1856	1885	ALL	ALL	110388	KEN	Deal
TRICK						
1800	1846	....	1800	163031	DEV	North
TRICKER						
1883	1911	ALL	1883	176419	MDX	Barnet
TRICKET						
1777	1861	1750	1770	147281	LAN	Bacup
TRICKETT						
1881	1988	1879	1907	115495	LAN	Rochdale
....	1850	ALL	1850	134511	NTT	Newark
1821	1884	ALL	1821	168742	NTT	Newark
1750	1900	1750	1900	179701	SAL	Woore
1800	1900	1800	1900	179701	STS	Madeley
1650	1750	1600	1800	179701	STS	Shropshire Border
1809	1864	1760	1809	103004	YKS	Sheffield
1831	1989	1800	1831	115495	YKS	Wardle
TRICKEY						
1850	1992	1700	1850	161772	DEV	Cullompton
TRICKLEY						
1818	....	ALL	1980	136891	YKS	Bridlington
TRICKLEY-COWARD						
1818	....	ALL	1980	136891	YKS	Bridlington
TRICKS						
1796	....	ALL	1796	137545	DEV	Exeter
1770	1802	ALL	1800	167029	DEV	Exeter
1820	1870	1800	1890	167029	LND	ALL
TRIDHOOK						
1900	1992	1700	1900	122114	LND	???
TRIGG						
....	1789	1700	1800	176621	BRK	Hurst
1847	1887	1790	1847	178381	GLS	Westbury
1850	1992	1750	1850	111929	GLS	???
....	....	1800	1850	121185	HAM	ALL
1846	1861	ALL	1846	171468	IRL	Waterford
1861	1902	1902	1992	171468	YKS	Sheffield
TRIGG-SCRIVENER						
1800	1900	1800	1900	162515	SFK	ALL
1800	1900	1800	1900	162515	SFK	Hadleigh
TRIGGS						
1800	1870	1700	1900	168068	CON	Lelant
TRIM						
....	....	1500	1765	166863	DOR	ALL
1760	1920	1500	1760	110329	DOR	North
1740	1820	1740	1820	154210	DOR	Puddletown

Known From	To	Researching From	To	Ref	Cty	Place
TRIM contd.						
1800	1860	1600	1860	154342	GLS	Bristol
TRIMBLE						
1816	....	1700	1816	126357	LET	Manor Hamilton
TRIMBY						
1500	1900	1500	1900	170216	SOM	ALL
1500	1900	1500	1900	170216	WIL	ALL
TRIMMER						
ALL	ALL	ALL	ALL	172324	ENG	South
TRINDER						
1910	1992	1910	1992	161276	BRK	Maidenhead
1821	1992	1700	1821	125024	HAM	Stockbridge
1750	1992	1750	1992	161276	OXF	Bicester
1700	1836	ALL	1836	168696	OXF	Stanton Harcourt
TRINDLER						
1800	1836	1800	1836	147575	SRY	Putney
TRING						
1848	1883	1700	1848	169730	LND	Bromley By Bow
TRIP						
....	....	ALL	ALL	119547	ALL	Name Study
TRIPCONY						
1600	1992	1600	1992	150126	CON	St Keverne
TRIPLETT						
....	1700	....	....	103349	???	Dublin
TRIPP						
1862	1914	1828	1862	117358	LND	Bermondsey
1789	1899	1750	1790	162396	OXF	Shifford
1800	1900	1800	1900	105945	SOM	Shepton Mallett
TRIPPICK						
1754	....	1754	....	153524	DOR	Sixpenny Handley
TRIPPIOCK						
1563	1740	1563	1740	153524	HAM	Rockbourne
TRIPPITT						
1804	1900	1770	1804	118486	WRY	Womersley
TRIPTREE						
1861	1881	1800	1860	131245	MDX	Bethnal Green
1805	1807	1700	1804	131245	SRY	Camberwell
TRISTRAM						
1550	1750	1550	1750	133450	DEV	Bampton
1750	1800	1600	1800	151637	HEF	Pembridge
....	....	ALL	1802	142298	SAL	Ludlow
....	....	ALL	1700	133450	WOR	Belboughton
TRITHALL						
1837	1992	1700	1837	130257	CON	Camborne
TRITT						
....	....	ALL	ALL	171123	ALL	Name Study
TRITTON						
?	?	?	?	166642	KEN	Chislet
TRIVELLI						
....	....	ALL	ALL	152641	ALL	ALL
TRIVETT						
1708	1760	ALL	1708	147362	LEI	Hose
TRIZISE						
1810	....	....	....	136999	CON	St Agnes
TROBE						
1700	1992	1600	1700	160075	NBL	Warwick
TROBRIDGE						
1750	1846	1600	1749	156779	DEV	Crediton
1750	1846	1600	1749	156779	DEV	Exeter
1750	1846	1600	1749	156779	DEV	Kenn
TRODD						
1870	1883	ALL	ALL	175862	HAM	ALL
....	....	ALL	ALL	157260	HAM	Basingstoke
1841	1925	1780	1840	157619	HAM	Gosport
TROLLOPE						
1700	1992	1600	1700	160075	NBL	Warwick
TROSSE						
....	....	1500	1800	179531	ALL	ALL
TROTH						
1832	1896	....	1832	165484	WAR	Birmingham
TROTMAN						
1730	1800	1600	1730	138150	GLS	Berkeley
....	....	1700	1992	150762	GLS	???
1769	1792	....	....	102733	OXF	Kidlington
TROTT						
....	....	ALL	ALL	123218	ALL	Name Study
....	....	ALL	ALL	123226	ALL	Name Study
....	....	ALL	ALL	141631	ALL	Name Study
....	....	ALL	ALL	171158	ALL	Name Study
ALL	ALL	ALL	ALL	123226	ALL	ALL
....	....	ALL	ALL	171158	ALL	ALL
1754	1992	....	1754	171131	DEV	Great Torrington
1825	....	....	....	151785	DFS	???
1900	1920	....	....	153923	KEN	Erith
TROTT contd.						
1895	1900	....	....	153923	LND	Lee
1840	1992	1840	1992	171131	LND	London
1849	....	1765	1840	161527	LND	Strand
1849	....	1765	1840	161527	LND	Westminster
1840	....	1800	1840	161527	MDX	Strand
....	....	1600	1650	130591	SOM	Bradford On Tone
1820	1950	1700	1820	153923	SOM	Drayton
....	....	1450	1600	130591	SOM	Staplegrove
1840	1841	1750	1840	115746	SOM	Taunton
1920	1961	....	....	153923	SOM	Weston Super Mare
TROTTER						
1680	1950	1600	1680	128376	DUR	Stanhope
1840	1890	1750	1850	103055	FER	ALL
1700	1992	1775	1992	133450	GLS	???
1763	....	....	1763	176761	NBL	Byker
1851	....	....	....	171166	NBL	Ford
1773	....	ALL	1773	154946	NRY	Barforth
TROTTLE						
....	....	1680	1730	174289	HAM	Chirstchurch
TROUGHT						
1830	1992	ALL	1830	176656	LIN	North
TROUGHTON						
1846	1957	1700	1846	137154	CMA	Kendal
1815	1861	1750	1900	167002	MDX	Clerkenwell
1852	1878	1800	1900	167002	MDX	Islington
1862	1908	1862	1908	167002	MDX	Tottenham
TROUNCE						
1800	1900	ALL	1800	145939	CON	Beryan
....	....	1700	1850	170313	CON	St Erith
TROUNSON						
1632	1700	1500	1632	138614	CON	Perranuthnoe
TROUP						
1800	1850	1700	1800	171174	ABD	Coull
1816	1841	1750	1816	118427	ABD	Glenmuick
1800	1850	1850	1900	171174	ELN	Haddington
1845	1900	....	....	171174	NYK	Skelton
TROUT						
1805	1805	1700	1805	121568	DEV	North East
1802	1816	....	1802	131385	DEV	Topsham
TROWBRIDGE						
....	....	1500	1650	171182	DEV	Crediton
....	....	1600	1750	171182	DOR	ALL
1780	1790	....	....	133221	DOR	Belchalwill
1765	1775	....	....	133221	DOR	Caundle Marsh
1800	1860	ALL	ALL	162205	DOR	Child Okeford
1800	1866	....	....	133221	DOR	Fitzpaine
1800	1866	....	....	133221	DOR	Okeford
ALL	ALL	....	....	153397	HAM	New Forest
....	....	1600	1750	171182	SOM	ALL
1750	1960	1600	1750	171182	WIL	South
1750	1960	1600	1750	171182	WIL	West
1818	1892	1600	1818	169595	WIL	Salisbury
1805	1863	1775	1860	159700	WIL	Tollard Royal
TROWELL						
1780	1820	1700	1900	141569	NTH	Fortheringhay
TROWER						
1887	1907	1887	ALL	145386	SRY	Croydon
....	....	1750	1950	176362	SRY	Redhill
1887	1960	1750	1890	119164	SSX	Brighton
TROWNSON						
1870	1920	1800	1992	173096	CON	Truro
1900	1920	1800	1992	173096	DEV	Dartmouth
TROWSDALE						
1780	1992	1760	1780	136468	NYK	Gilling
TRUBEY						
1750	1881	1820	1881	144606	SOM	Taunton
TRUBODY						
1783	1903	1700	1903	141062	SOM	Keynsham
TRUBSHAW						
1130	1992	1285	1992	158038	ALL	ALL
1750	....	....	....	130486	STS	Haughton
TRUCKEL						
1780	1800	....	....	135089	HAM	Monxton
TRUCKELL						
1780	1800	....	....	135089	HAM	Monxton
1800	1880	....	....	135089	IOW	Newchurch
1800	1880	....	....	135089	IOW	Ryde
TRUCKELLS						
1780	1800	....	....	135089	HAM	Monxton
1800	1880	....	....	135089	IOW	Newchurch
1800	1880	....	....	135089	IOW	Ryde
TRUCKELS						
1780	1800	....	....	135089	HAM	Monxton

Known From	To	Researching From	To	Ref	Cty	Place
TRUCKLE						
1900	1940	ALL	ALL	175536	SSX	Central
TRUDE						
1900	1900	1790	1890	147826	DEV	Crediton
TRUDGEON						
....	....	1840	....	173991	CON	St Stephen
1781	1992	1500	1781	150142	CON	Veryan
TRUDGETT						
1760	1886	....	....	137316	CAM	Great Shelford
....	....	1720	1760	137316	CAM	Stapleford
1793	1848	1700	1793	173843	SFK	Ingham
TRUE						
1800	1992	....	....	176125	LIN	Asterby
1800	1992	....	....	176125	LIN	Goulceby
1777	1800	1700	1800	150223	WIL	Fonthill Gifford
TRUEBODY						
1550	1800	1675	1775	133450	CON	Lostwithiel
TRUEFITT						
1750	1992	1700	1860	147311	NYK	Hinderwell
TRUELL						
1845	1912	....	....	100536	ALL	???
TRUELOVE						
1754	....	....	....	168920	LND	Hackney
1785	1826	1500	1785	125695	NTH	Overstone
1800	....	ALL	ALL	152226	SSX	ALL
1755	1825	1700	1800	144622	YKS	Barnsley
TRUEMAN						
1816	1851	1816	1851	109002	BRK	Easthampstead
1816	1851	1816	1851	109002	BRK	Wokingham
1800	1830	1700	1800	143243	DBY	Ilkeston
1765	1800	1538	1830	118893	NRY	Bilsdale
1753	1803	1538	1830	118893	NRY	Hawnby
1861	1956	ALL	ALL	109002	SRY	Bagshot
1826	1900	....	....	102733	WAR	Birmingham
TRUGIAN						
....	....	1450	1550	174319	CON	Madron
TRUIN						
1786	1812	1550	1786	166170	BDF	Sandy
1836	1912	....	....	166170	LND	Highgate
TRULL						
1820	1880	1820	1992	173096	GLS	Uley
TRULOCK						
....	....	1538	1992	131318	BRK	North
TRUMAN						
....	....	1800	1992	149225	ALL	ALL
1860	1992	1700	1860	117242	LIN	Grantham
1860	1992	1700	1860	117242	NTT	Nottingham
....	....	1800	1900	166960	NTT	Radford
1800	1920	1800	1920	164895	WAR	Birmingham
....	....	1750	1820	179361	WIL	Seend
TRUMP						
1620	1900	1620	1900	138487	DEV	ALL
TRUMPER						
1736	1760	....	....	166189	MDX	Harefield
1961	1992	?	?	173355	SOM	Clevedon
1962	1992	?	?	173355	WIL	Devizes
TRUMPETER						
1830	1840	1830	1840	101877	SFK	Blaxhall
1780	1800	1780	1800	101877	SFK	Leiston
1810	1845	1810	1845	101877	SFK	Snape
1845	1870	1845	1870	101877	SFK	Tunstall
TRUMPLET						
1750	1820	1500	1850	137472	BRK	Chieveley
1750	1820	1500	1850	137472	BRK	Compton
1750	1820	1500	1850	137472	BRK	Hampstead Norreys
TRUNKS						
....	....	ALL	ALL	171204	SOM	Bridgwater
TRUSCOTT						
1850	1900	1800	1900	137529	CON	Padstow
1882	1950	1870	1910	137529	CON	St Breock
1800	....	1700	....	116920	CON	St Ewe
1780	1850	1770	1890	137529	CON	St Stephen In Brannel
1772	1861	1693	1772	103918	CON	St Stephens In Brannel
1820	1870	1700	1820	165549	CON	St Stephens In Brannel
TRUSLER						
1800	1850	1750	1850	112704	SOM	Mells
TRUSLOVE						
1797	1855	1747	1920	122327	LEI	Burbage
TRUSS						
....	....	ALL	ALL	168939	ALL	Name Study

Known From	To	Researching From	To	Ref	Cty	Place
TRUSSLER						
1660	1720	1600	1750	171212	HAM	Binstead
1745	1900	1745	1992	171212	SRY	ALL
1720	1850	1720	1800	171212	SRY	Frensham
TRY						
1715	1715	1680	1715	153605	CON	Paul
TRYNER						
1750	1900	1650	1750	151769	LIN	Denton
TUBB						
1848	1880	1750	1850	118516	HAM	Portsea
1791	1941	1700	1992	167800	HAM	Rotherwick
1850	1980	ALL	1850	156078	HAM	???
TUBBS						
1876	1951	....	....	171905	MDX	St Giles
TUBBY						
....	....	ALL	ALL	104884	NFK	ALL
TUCK						
1834	1849	ALL	ALL	105015	BRK	Hurley
1850	1900	1800	1900	142875	DEV	Teignmouth
1807	1830	1800	1830	148156	HUN	East
1837	1859	ALL	ALL	118168	LAN	Feltwell
....	....	1890	1992	171239	MDX	Fulham
1850	1885	....	....	117560	MDX	Hoxton
1820	1830	1800	1830	124427	NFK	Briston
1722	1767	....	....	135437	NFK	Fakenham
1783	1850	....	....	169129	NFK	Kings Lynn
1800	1880	1880	1992	171239	NFK	Thetford
1800	1936	....	....	100536	NFK	???
1900	1950	ALL	ALL	131121	SFK	Ipwsich
1776	1850	ALL	1776	158445	WIL	Melksham
TUCKER COOMBES						
1854	....	1800	1900	122688	DEV	Plymouth
TUCKER						
....	....	ALL	1876	114030	CON	ALL
1811	1846	1800	1870	124796	CON	Torpoint
1790	1800	1790	1870	177199	CON	Trematon Castle
1500	1900	1500	1900	132721	DEV	North
1780	1880	1780	1880	106801	DEV	Bishopsteighton
1813	1813	1700	1813	163953	DEV	Branscombe
1810	1892	1810	1892	154040	DEV	Braunton
1840	1860	1700	1900	143189	DEV	Cullompton
1600	1950	....	....	108677	DEV	Exeter
....	....	1535	1810	154040	DEV	Georgeham
1823	1855	ALL	1823	165735	DEV	South Molton
1750	....	ALL	ALL	116394	DEV	Upton Helions
1861	1992	1861	1992	154040	DEV	West Down
....	....	?	?	104310	DOR	Beaminster
1718	1992	ALL	ALL	119504	DOR	Lydlinch
....	....	ALL	1853	170135	DOR	Poole
1800	1840	1800	1840	178705	DOR	Shaftesbury
1568	1666	ALL	ALL	119504	DOR	Stock Gaylard
....	....	ALL	1853	170135	DOR	Weymouth
1600	1950	....	....	108677	DOR	Woolland
1850	1873	1700	1850	109576	ESS	West Ham
1850	1873	1700	1850	109576	GLS	Bourton
1791	1844	1700	1791	148938	GLS	Chilton Polden
....	....	ALL	1800	103284	GLS	???
1851	1891	1800	1900	106577	KEN	Sheerness
1840	1992	1700	1930	105775	KEN	St Lawrence
1820	1850	1750	1820	147745	KEN	Stodmarsh
1820	1910	....	....	112038	LIN	South
1775	1836	....	....	121355	LND	Bethnal Green
....	....	1800	1850	159115	LND	Holborn
1874	....	ALL	ALL	151580	LND	Marylebone
1775	1836	....	....	121355	LND	Shoreditch
1775	1836	....	....	121355	LND	Stepney
1775	1836	....	....	121355	LND	Whitechapel
1884	....	....	....	164003	LND	???
....	....	ALL	1890	178403	LND	???
1820	1992	1820	1908	163600	MDX	East
1820	1992	1820	1908	163600	MDX	North
1857	....	....	....	117579	MDX	Hackney
....	....	1750	1900	112038	MDX	London
1789	1791	1600	1911	121746	MDX	Old Bailey
1710	1830	1650	1760	112038	RUT	???
1864	1881	1845	1900	124796	SCT	Greenock
1858	1992	1800	1858	123153	SOM	Bath
1681	1741	....	....	135437	SOM	Stogursey
1783	1850	1750	1800	138487	SOM	Wells
1687	1852	1650	1852	166898	SOM	Westbury Sup Mendip
1832	1852	....	....	127779	SRY	Kennington
1800	1950	ALL	ALL	154008	WIL	Devizes
1855	1860	1855	1992	165735	???	Bristol

Known From	To	Researching From	To	Ref	Cty	Place
TUCKERMAN						
1819	....	1750	1992	101656	DEV	Kingsbridge
TUCKEY						
1841	1930	1800	1850	133426	STS	West Bromwich
TUCKWELL						
1620	1828	....	....	131660	GLS	Eastleach Turville
1781	1858	1700	1781	163740	OXF	Drayton St Leonards
TUCKWOOD						
1805	1851	ALL	1851	166146	LEI	Burton On The Wolds
1778	....	ALL	ALL	112275	LEI	Frisby On Wreake
1829	1851	ALL	1851	166146	NTT	Willoughby On The Wolds
TUDGAY						
....	....	ALL	ALL	112674	ALL	ALL
1930	....	ALL	ALL	112674	GLS	ALL
TUDGE						
1813	1900	1813	1900	119563	WAR	Birmingham
TUDGEY						
....	....	1700	1950	139254	WOR	Martley
TUDOR						
1850	1900	1700	1850	171255	NTT	Nottingham
1850	1960	1600	1850	166766	SAL	Chirbury
TUDRIE						
1821	1879	1800	1879	119059	HAM	New Alresford
TUDWAY						
....	....	ALL	ALL	171263	ALL	Name Study
TUER						
1755	1784	1600	1755	179043	WES	ALL
1755	1945	1600	1755	179043	YKS	West
TUESHAW						
1725	1737	1700	1770	144797	MDX	Spitafields
TUFF						
1800	1866	1750	1800	171298	CUL	Carlisle
1823	1901	1800	1823	171298	NBL	Tynemouth
1834	....	....	....	151718	SOM	Midsommor Norton
1700	1860	....	....	167037	WIL	Wootton Bassett
1880	1992	1800	1866	171298	YKS	York
TUFFEY						
1940	1960	ALL	ALL	161292	DEV	Brixham
TUFFIN						
....	....	ALL	ALL	170925	ALL	Name Study
1700	1829	1600	1700	127116	DOR	Sutton Waldron
1786	1846	ALL	1992	109851	DOR	???
1800	1850	1600	1900	120677	HAM	Twyford
TUFFNELL						
....	....	ALL	ALL	166022	ALL	ALL
1814	1870	ALL	ALL	168211	BDF	Barton
1870	....	ALL	ALL	168211	BDF	Luton
1790	1830	....	....	166022	LND	???
TUFFS						
1841	1877	1700	1840	135348	CAM	Wisbech
1850	1920	ALL	ALL	171301	NFK	West
TUFIREY						
1700	1839	1650	1750	144606	OXF	Witney
TUFTON						
1698	1698	....	....	139971	SSX	Eastbourne
TUGGEY						
1800	1850	1700	1800	176753	GLS	Bristol
1841	1842	1800	1841	157619	HAM	Portsmouth
TULEE						
1671	....	....	....	130079	OXF	Swyncombe
TULETT						
1850	1950	1750	1850	125660	SRY	Lingfield
1745	1965	ALL	1745	179221	SSX	Worth
TULEY						
....	....	ALL	ALL	171328	ALL	Name Study
1799	1894	1799	1894	136905	OXF	South
TULIP						
1800	1851	1760	1851	174602	DUR	Gateshead
1845	1992	ALL	ALL	170860	DUR	???
1800	1851	1760	1851	174602	NBL	Ovingham
TULK						
1680	1780	1650	1800	167126	DOR	Cann
TULL						
1800	1850	1750	1850	164704	BRK	Padworth
....	....	ALL	1890	171336	BRK	???
1820	1836	....	....	142360	GLS	Kempsford
?	....	....	....	141941	HAM	Alverstoke
?	?	?	?	120073	HAM	Bishops Waltham
?	....	....	....	141941	HAM	Portsmouth
....	....	ALL	1890	171336	HAM	???
1860	1930	....	....	171336	LND	???
TULLEY						
1693	1693	ALL	ALL	130508	DUR	Gateshead
TULLOCH						
1737	1900	1700	1900	169250	LND	Camberwell
1737	1900	1700	1900	169250	SHI	Bressay
1750	1965	....	....	137820	SHI	Fetlar
1720	1965	....	....	137820	SHI	Mid Yell
1760	1965	....	....	137820	SHI	North Yell
1758	1965	....	....	137820	SHI	Northmavine
1720	1965	....	....	137820	SHI	South Yell
TULLY						
1850	1950	1850	1950	148911	ANS	Dundee
1800	....	....	....	126993	ROX	Jedburgh
1800	1860	1600	1830	166154	SSX	Bolney
TUMBELTY						
1890	1950	....	....	131016	LAN	Urmston
TUNBRIDGE						
1850	1980	1850	1992	153249	GLA	Swansea
1540	1855	ALL	ALL	153249	KEN	ALL
1799	1900	ALL	ALL	105015	KEN	Chatham
1855	1870	1850	1900	153249	SRY	Peckham
1900	1965	1900	1970	153249	WAR	ALL
1880	1903	1850	1970	153249	WOR	Redditch
TUNE						
....	....	ALL	ALL	150266	ALL	Name Study
....	....	ALL	ALL	150266	ALL	ALL
1690	1740	....	....	103721	ERY	Adlingfleet
1818	1839	ALL	1818	154946	ERY	Bubwith
1740	1790	....	....	103721	LIN	Belton In Axholme
1730	1740	....	....	103721	LIN	Luddington
1840	1930	ALL	ALL	171379	YKS	Sheffield
1839	....	ALL	1839	154946	YKS	Spaldington
TUNGATE						
1877	1992	1877	1992	115460	NFK	Norwich
....	....	....	....	153869	NFK	???
1850	1860	1850	1992	129607	SRY	Walworth
TUNKS						
1793	1855	....	....	169528	SOM	Bridgwater
1830	1845	....	1850	152803	WOR	Worcester
TUNN						
1816	1830	1750	1900	146331	BDF	Shadforth
TUNNA						
....	....	ALL	ALL	171344	ALL	Name Study
TUNNADINE						
1600	1700	....	....	100420	WAR	Meriden
TUNNAH						
1810	1925	ALL	ALL	101001	BEW	ALL
1809	1839	ALL	1800	101001	ELN	Oldhamstocks
TUNNARD						
1790	1850	1600	1850	175641	LIN	Skirbeck
TUNNELL						
1880	1880	1800	1880	149365	MDX	Acton
TUNNEY						
1840	1900	....	....	136492	IRL	???
1840	1900	....	....	136492	LKS	Coatbridge
1840	1900	....	....	136492	LKS	Shettleston
TUNNICLIFF						
....	....	ALL	ALL	171352	ALL	Name Study
1784	....	ALL	1992	159174	DBY	Hartshorne
TUNNICLIFFE						
1780	1820	1700	1850	151653	DBY	Ilkeston
1801	1970	1700	1800	166464	STS	Yoxall
TUNSTALL						
1800	1825	1750	1800	155500	LAN	Burtonwood
1556	1992	ALL	1556	171360	LAN	Flasby
1830	1900	1800	1900	142875	LAN	Haydock
1747	1992	1700	1747	163783	LAN	Parbold
1590	1992	ALL	1590	171360	LAN	Tunstall
?	?	?	?	130354	LND	Leyton
TUNSTILL						
....	....	ALL	ALL	171360	ALL	Name Study
1556	1992	ALL	1556	171360	LAN	Colne
1556	1992	ALL	1556	171360	LAN	Nelson
1590	1992	ALL	1590	171360	LAN	Preston
1590	1992	ALL	1590	171360	YKS	Skipton
TUNWELL						
1786	1790	1700	1785	131245	MDX	Shoreditch
TUPHOLME						
1540	1850	ALL	ALL	171379	LIN	ALL
TUPLIN						
1796	1881	1700	1796	116432	DEV	Northam
TUPLING						
1700	1992	1500	1900	120596	LIN	???
TUPPEN						
1792	1872	1650	1792	138673	SRY	Wooton
1840	1992	1400	1840	171387	SSX	ALL

Known From	To	Researching From	To	Ref	Cty	Place
TUPPEN contd.						
1718	1718	....	....	139971	SSX	Rottingdean
TUPPEN-LASHMAR						
1850	....	1800	1900	171387	SSX	ALL
TUPPER						
1600	1992	1550	1600	171395	KEN	Maidstone
1827	1849	....	....	145394	SSX	Slindon
TUPPYN-SCRASE						
1616	1630	1580	1680	171387	SSX	ALL
TURBERFIELD						
1890	1910	1880	1950	157937	NBL	Newcastle On Tyne
1810	1850	1600	1850	157937	WOR	Worcester
TURBERVILL						
1707	1992	1750	1992	176958	GLA	Ewenny
1707	1992	1750	1992	176958	GLA	Sutton
TURBERVILLE						
1215	1365	1066	1370	124974	GAL	Bridgend
1091	1365	1066	1370	124974	GAL	Coity
1094	1365	1066	1370	124974	GAL	Coychurch
1094	1365	1066	1370	124974	GAL	Coyty Castle
1281	1365	1066	1370	124974	GAL	Llanharry
1215	1365	1066	1370	124974	GAL	Newcastle
1091	1365	1066	1370	124974	GAL	Newland
1810	1810	1750	1810	126454	STS	Coseley
1760	1850	1700	1760	148059	WAR	Slaford Priors
1150	1435	....	....	100536	WLS	???
TURK						
1841	1851	1841	1881	113719	SOM	Frome
1698	1900	1500	1700	170178	SXE	Iden
TURLAND						
1600	1992	....	....	153583	NTH	Bugbrooke
TURLEY						
1800	1992	....	....	149764	GAL	Newbridge
1765	....	1700	1800	139386	KEN	Headcorn
1845	1992	1700	1845	161772	KEN	Stapleland Marden
1930	1992	1750	1930	154105	WOR	Dudley
TURLEY-SMITH						
1795	1796	1780	1800	105120	DUB	Dublin
TURNAGE						
1817	1923	1550	1817	150398	ESS	Hatfield Peverel
1558	1992	1500	1992	171417	ESS	Stapleford Tawney
TURNBULL						
....	....	ALL	ALL	171433	ALL	Name Study
1840	1900	1800	1840	169501	AYR	New Cumnock
1804	1805	1800	1820	148121	CUL	Penrith
....	....	1700	1850	169501	DFS	Sanquhar
1847	1884	1800	1900	125342	DUR	ALL
1790	1992	1700	1800	160075	DUR	Chester Le Street
1850	1992	1700	1850	135690	DUR	Crook
1860	1982	1800	1890	171425	DUR	Gateshead
1796	1850	1885	1992	131571	DUR	Jarrow
1840	1992	1800	1840	154873	DUR	Sunderland
....	....	1700	1850	135690	DUR	Washington
1824	1873	1800	1873	104604	DUR	???
1800	1890	1750	1800	128244	FIF	Cupar
1800	1890	1750	1800	128244	FIF	Dundee
1800	1890	1750	1800	128244	FIF	Saline
1800	1890	1750	1800	128244	FIF	St Andrews
1830	1870	ALL	1850	118338	NBL	Hexham
....	....	ALL	ALL	178691	NBL	Kirkwhelpington
1730	1790	1885	1992	131571	NBL	Longbenton
1855	1992	1750	1992	117293	NBL	Newcastle
1830	1870	ALL	1850	118338	NBL	Warden
1824	1873	1800	1873	104604	NBL	???
1730	1770	ALL	1770	149063	PEE	Innerleithen
1780	1870	1720	1870	148474	ROX	Castleton
1776	1992	1750	1830	129062	ROX	Lilliesleaf
1650	1670	ALL	1670	149063	ROX	Melrose
1755	1987	1650	1987	179000	SCT	Carriden
1751	....	....	....	130923	???	Newcastle
TURNELL						
1745	1940	....	....	128996	CAM	Thorney
TURNER						
1825	1892	1700	1825	105457	ABD	Peterhead
....	....	1700	1800	175889	ARL	Uig
1828	1861	1700	1860	113107	BAN	Port Gordon
1749	1808	1720	1808	119059	BDF	Leighton Buzzard
1740	....	1650	1800	143693	BKM	Hughenden
1740	1740	1650	1740	167452	BKM	Hughenden
1756	1756	1756	1779	107360	BKM	Ivinghoe
1758	1802	1779	1847	107360	BKM	Stone
1784	1831	1700	1992	167800	BKM	Waddesdon
....	1863	1830	1870	128961	BKM	Wycombe
1810	....	....	1810	164011	BRK	Blewbury
TURNER contd.						
1852	1970	1700	1992	112089	CAM	???
1800	1853	....	....	108057	CHS	Sandbach
1700	1890	1650	1890	138096	CON	Talland
1853	1854	ALL	1854	159077	CUL	Carlisle
1782	1850	1700	1782	133523	CUL	Whitehaven
1755	1856	?	1860	103934	DBY	Bakewell
1770	....	1700	1800	131148	DBY	Chesterfield
1687	1716	1550	1686	131245	DBY	Hathersage
1839	1857	1800	1861	124788	DBY	Little Longstone
1850	1880	1800	1850	146609	DBY	Matlock Bath
1885	1992	1885	1992	171689	DBY	North Wingfield
1755	1856	?	1860	103934	DBY	Upper Haddon
1770	1850	1500	1770	107972	DBY	???
1800	1851	1600	1860	132470	DEV	Ashreigney
1800	1900	1800	1900	154040	DEV	Ashreigney
1644	1825	1600	1850	171549	DEV	Buckfastleigh
1800	1851	1600	1860	132470	DEV	Burrington
1800	1870	1830	1992	176281	DEV	Exeter
1851	....	1700	1851	170321	DEV	Teignmouth
....	1886	ALL	1960	177695	DUR	Croxdale
1770	1790	....	1770	142409	ENG	Midlands
1700	1800	ALL	ALL	131873	ESS	Manuden
1795	1795	?	1795	158569	ESS	Rickling
1650	1800	ALL	ALL	131873	ESS	Stanstead
....	....	ALL	1740	141224	GLS	South
1740	1840	1700	1850	126667	GLS	Cirencester
1800	1992	1800	....	118672	GLS	Wotton Under Edge
1849	1900	ALL	ALL	122866	HAM	East
1764	1906	1750	1906	170143	HAM	Liss
1850	....	1800	1850	128724	IRL	Cork
1860	1930	1700	1860	141119	KEN	ALL
1747	1918	....	1930	171441	KEN	South East
1748	1748	....	....	127426	KEN	Aylesford
1719	....	....	1740	171441	KEN	Bredgar
1896	....	1895	1905	171441	KEN	Chatham
1907	1944	1900	1940	171441	KEN	Faversham
1831	1900	1831	1910	171581	KEN	Forest Hill
1780	1840	1700	1850	129755	KEN	Gravesend
1755	1801	....	....	127426	KEN	Harrietsham
1714	1912	....	....	127426	KEN	Lenham
1793	1793	....	....	127426	KEN	Otterden
1770	1800	1700	1850	120839	KEN	Penshurst
1751	1751	....	....	127426	KEN	Rochester St Nicholas
1940	1973	....	....	171441	KEN	Whitstable
1756	1756	....	....	127426	KEN	Wormshill
1816	1816	....	....	127426	KEN	Wychling
?	?	?	?	166642	KEN	???
1700	1920	1500	1920	105333	LAN	Brownedge
1825	1992	1700	1825	165239	LAN	Bury
1700	1920	1500	1920	105333	LAN	Chorley
1806	1900	1750	1806	135364	LAN	Clegg Hall
1883	1974	1841	1974	164097	LAN	Liverpool
1876	1956	1800	1876	108715	LAN	Oldham
1831	1831	1808	1831	159492	LAN	Oldham
1700	1920	1500	1920	105333	LAN	Preston
1700	1920	1500	1920	105333	LAN	Samlesbury
1700	1920	1500	1920	105333	LAN	Walton Le Dale
1700	....	1700	....	109347	LAN	Whitewell
1891	1916	1850	1930	124796	LAN	Wigan
1805	1992	ALL	1805	174874	LEI	Thorpe
1740	1840	1740	1840	131075	LIN	Kirton Lindsey
1760	1992	1740	1840	131075	LIN	Scotter
?	?	?	?	135224	LIN	???
1830	1992	1800	1992	135860	LND	ALL
1856	1992	....	1900	171646	LND	South
1762	1840	1762	1980	171581	LND	East End
....	....	1800	1900	117714	LND	Kensington
1850	1900	1800	1900	132950	LND	London
1846	1926	....	....	148881	LND	Paddington Green
1874	1992	ALL	ALL	113700	LND	Southwark
1780	1810	1780	1992	176281	LND	Southwark
1798	1799	1760	1800	148121	LND	Spitalfields
....	....	1750	1900	129275	LND	Walworth
1874	....	....	....	150010	LND	???
1846	1926	....	....	148881	MDX	ALL
....	....	ALL	ALL	171638	MDX	Brentford
1865	1865	ALL	ALL	120057	MDX	Limehouse
....	....	1700	1800	106356	MDX	London
1829	1854	1750	1900	110191	MDX	London
1850	1900	1850	1885	128724	MDX	London
1800	1900	1800	1900	144657	MDX	Marylebone
1865	1865	ALL	ALL	120057	MDX	Poplar

Known From	To	Researching From	To	Ref	Cty	Place
TURNER contd.						
1840	1900	1750	1850	112704	MDX	Uxbridge
1798	1799	1760	1800	148121	MDX	???
1725	1820	1725	1992	109819	MGY	Pennarth
1865	1920	....	....	117137	MON	Abertillery
1880	1992	ALL	1880	136875	NBL	Newcastle On Tyne
1841	1873	1800	1900	144037	NBL	Newcastle On Tyne
1816	1900	1700	1816	165182	NBL	Newcastle Upon Tyne
1791	1811	1750	1850	176621	NFK	Croxton
1850	1992	1600	1850	123420	NFK	East Dereham
1797	1851	....	....	131660	NFK	Norwich
1828	1851	1700	1827	131245	NFK	Norwich
1900	1930	1860	1900	162485	NFK	Norwich
1854	1992	?	1854	147923	NFK	Yarmouth
1856	1888	1700	1900	135968	NTT	Nottingham
1764	1900	1764	1900	162914	NTT	Nottingham
1770	1850	1500	1770	107972	NTT	Upper Langwith
1777	1820	1600	1777	107565	OXF	Finstock
1906	....	ALL	ALL	143758	ROX	Camptown
1700	1750	1600	1750	144657	SFK	Hadleigh
1797	1819	1750	1797	155276	SFK	Hemingstone
1750	1850	1700	1850	135941	SFK	Hundon
....	....	ALL	ALL	171638	SFK	Ipswich
1649	1720	....	....	101028	SFK	Lidgate
....	....	1700	1800	171638	SFK	Nayland
1800	....	1770	1820	135941	SFK	Stoke By Clare
1600	1799	1680	1780	135941	SFK	Wickhambrook
1840	1900	1800	1900	171638	SFK	Woodbridge
1830	1850	1800	1850	168076	SOM	Bridgwater
....	....	1855	1865	117137	SOM	Siglestell Willow
1824	1992	ALL	1824	107239	SRY	Chobham
....	....	1795	....	145688	SRY	Epsom
1855	1868	1750	1855	149918	SRY	Lambeth
1818	1992	1818	1992	171654	SRY	Newington
1850	1900	ALL	ALL	122866	SSX	East
1799	1992	1600	1900	135968	SSX	Alfriston
1830	1980	1700	1850	171484	SSX	East Grinstead
1855	1943	1800	1943	127183	SSX	Fletching
1900	1921	1850	1900	174807	SSX	Laughton
1825	1943	1819	1943	127183	SSX	Lindfield
....	....	....	....	171492	SSX	Ringmer
....	1600	....	....	174564	SSX	???
1572	1711	....	....	117404	STS	Blymhill
1891	1930	1700	1900	102326	STS	Chasetown
1854	1966	1740	1854	138223	STS	Gornal
1800	1992	1700	1992	177652	STS	Harborne
1717	1820	1700	1850	160873	STS	Kingswinford
1813	....	ALL	ALL	126098	STS	Madeley
1674	1733	1640	1733	123404	STS	St Bartholomew
1785	1992	ALL	1785	171611	STS	Stourbridge
1683	1717	1650	1750	160873	STS	Walsall
1790	1992	1700	1790	116513	STS	Wednesbury
1674	1733	1640	1733	123404	STS	Wednesbury
1700	1800	1600	1850	177180	STS	West Bromwich
1606	1675	1580	1700	160873	STS	Willenhall
1805	1890	ALL	ALL	124176	WAR	Alcester
1800	1992	1700	1992	177652	WAR	Birmingham
1548	?	1500	1548	171476	WAR	Coleshill
....	1743	....	1743	128910	WAR	Nuneaton
1800	....	ALL	ALL	143758	WAR	Packwood
1800	....	ALL	ALL	143758	WAR	Solihull
1702	1775	1672	1702	139149	WES	Middleton In Lonsdale
....	....	1700	1850	101273	WIL	Enford
1760	1851	....	....	128694	WIL	Netheravon
....	....	1800	1850	117137	WIL	Warminster
1899	1992	1700	1899	150010	WLS	Wrexham
1797	....	....	....	145726	WOR	Queenhill
1839	1861	1802	1861	147338	WRY	Northowram
1793	1835	1770	1839	147338	WRY	Ripponden
1732	1761	ALL	1732	126721	WYK	Tankersley
1701	1701	1600	1701	137979	YKS	Barwick In Elmet
1900	1947	ALL	ALL	135224	YKS	Darnall
1857	1890	1700	1857	171662	YKS	Eston
1700	1900	1700	1900	106674	YKS	Grinton
1850	1890	1800	1910	145858	YKS	Harrogate
1760	1976	1700	1976	104396	YKS	Holderness
1650	1730	1730	1800	174947	YKS	Holderness
1850	1890	1800	1910	145858	YKS	Huddersfield
1790	1969	1700	1800	112224	YKS	Hull
1791	1933	1700	1791	171565	YKS	Hull
1855	1905	1850	1992	171549	YKS	Keighley
1860	1865	1800	1900	144622	YKS	Kilnhurst
1850	1890	1800	1910	145858	YKS	Leeds

Known From	To	Researching From	To	Ref	Cty	Place
TURNER contd.						
1701	1751	ALL	1751	104299	YKS	Lofthouse
1785	1992	ALL	1785	171611	YKS	Rotherham
1900	1947	ALL	ALL	135224	YKS	Sheffield
1870	1992	1840	1992	171670	YKS	Sheffield
1800	1900	1700	1880	173630	YKS	Sheffield
1747	1980	1700	1800	171670	YKS	Wakefield
1884	1992	1700	1900	171689	YKS	Wortley
1808	1850	1800	1900	177873	YKS	???
1914	1918	ALL	ALL	148881	???	Devonport
1939	1992	ALL	1800	165883	???	Walton Le Dale
....	....	ALL	ALL	150401	???	???
TURNERS						
1750	1799	ALL	ALL	138126	GLA	Penarth
TURNESS						
1720	1850	1600	1850	113654	SSX	Barcombe
TURNEY						
1815	1902	....	....	101869	LND	Camberwell
1815	1902	....	....	101869	LND	Dulwich
TURNHAM						
1750	1800	1700	1780	117005	BDF	Tottenhoe
TURNHILL						
1740	1773	ALL	1740	110965	ROX	ALL
TURNOCK						
1791	1848	1700	1850	176451	LAN	Manchester
TURNPENNY						
....	....	ALL	ALL	133701	ALL	Name Study
1860	1890	1700	1860	171174	STS	Bloxwich
1840	1850	1700	1850	133701	YKS	Bardsey
TURNROSS						
1896	1981	....	....	171697	CON	Falmouth
TURP						
....	....	ALL	ALL	165328	ALL	Name Study
TURPIN						
1600	1700	1600	1800	177180	BKM	Waddesdon
1880	1980	1850	1950	157341	DEV	Plymouth
1790	1850	1790	1850	116831	LND	Spitalfields
1855	1969	....	....	164003	SRY	Bermondsey
1855	1969	....	....	164003	SRY	Rotherhithe
1679	1850	....	....	141593	WYK	Sherburn
....	....	1700	1740	177393	YKS	Wistow
TURRALL						
1774	....	ALL	1992	159174	WAR	Newbold On Avon
TURTLE						
1725	1765	1700	1800	167126	OXF	Charlbury
1725	1765	1700	1800	167126	OXF	Enstone
TURTON						
1760	1784	....	....	154024	DBY	Whittington
1881	1891	ALL	ALL	121495	HAM	Andover
....	....	1550	1700	129763	HRT	North Church
....	....	1550	1700	129763	STS	Central
1635	....	1635	....	124842	STS	West Bromwich
1805	1905	....	....	160628	SYK	Ackworth
1909	1945	....	....	160628	SYK	Rotherham
....	....	ALL	1803	160628	SYK	Sheffield
1855	....	....	....	151785	YKS	Handsworth
1775	1785	1750	1992	114901	YKS	Rothwell
1914	1943	1800	1914	158275	YKS	Sheffield
1684	1716	1600	1684	150096	YKS	South Kirkby
1786	1840	ALL	ALL	159026	YKS	Thrybergh
1737	1788	1717	1737	101796	YKS	Woolley
....	....	....	1830	116866	YKS	???
TURVEY						
1870	1921	1830	1921	151599	NFK	Banham
1794	....	1700	1850	139386	SRY	Lambeth
1827	1862	1500	1860	157538	WOR	Whittington
TURVILL						
1550	1960	ALL	ALL	171727	ENG	South
1066	1900	ALL	ALL	171727	ENG	Midlands
1800	1992	ALL	1800	171719	HAM	Alton
TURVILLE						
1806	1992	1067	1806	171735	LEI	Cold Overton
1806	1992	1067	1806	171735	LEI	Sapcote
TUSHINGHAM						
1850	?	1800	1992	167592	STS	Stafford
1880	?	1700	1992	167592	STS	Woolstanton
TUSISE						
....	....	1700	1850	125628	CON	Madron
TUSTIN						
1764	....	1700	1764	139386	NTT	Marnham
TUTCHER						
1853	1992	....	1853	171743	SOM	Nitaunton
TUTHILL						
1835	1900	1700	1835	111945	SFK	Uggleshall

Known Researching
From To From To Ref Cty Place
TUTHILL contd.
1835 1900 1700 1835 111945 SFK Wenhaston
TUTT
1880 .... 1700 1880 124966 HAM Winchester
1750 1982 ALL ALL 137774 KEN ALL
1793 .... 1992 126950 KEN Brabourne
1698 1712 .... 139971 SSX Eastbourne
1728 1750 1680 1728 156140 SSX Warbleton
1615 1652 1550 1800 167002 SXE Chiddingly
1566 1680 1550 1800 167002 SXE Hailsham
1679 1736 1550 1800 167002 SXE Warbleton
TUTTEN
1740 1740 1680 1800 174599 IOW Godshill
TUTTERIDGE
1710 1763 1700 1800 167126 MDX Westminster
TUTTLE
1786 1793 ALL 1786 125121 CHS Middlewich
TUTTON
1800 1850 1750 1800 103675 SOM Wedmore
TUTTY
1761 1901 1700 1900 125865 LIN Limdsry
TUVEY
ALL ALL ALL ALL 167924 ALL ALL
1700 1820 1820 1900 167924 MDX Ealing
1820 1930 1820 1930 167924 MDX Finchley
1800 1860 1800 1860 167924 MDX Hackney
1820 1900 1820 1900 167924 MDX Pancras
TUXFORD
1716 1720 .... 129747 LIN Skellingthorpe
TUXWORTH
1800 1992 .... 176125 LIN Asterby
1800 1992 .... 176125 LIN Goulceby
1740 .... 1740 1845 119458 LIN Louth
TWADDLE
1867 1992 ALL ALL 178373 LKS Carluke
1815 1900 1700 1992 178373 LKS Lesmahogow
TWAITE
1800 1820 1750 1800 115312 NFK Norwich
TWAITES
1831 .... 176885 NFK East Bradenham
1797 1839 1700 1797 176885 NFK West Bradenham
TWAITS
1776 1850 ALL 1776 142107 SFK Washbrook
TWAMLOW
1700 1851 ALL ALL 159492 ALL ALL
1793 1812 .... 159492 LAN Manchester
TWEDALE
1784 1800 1500 1850 168629 NYK Danby Wiske
TWEDDLE
1750 1881 ALL 1880 171751 CUL Bewcastle
1694 1881 ALL 1880 171751 CUL Stapleton
1846 1897 1881 ALL 171751 NBL Raw Green
1891 1986 .... 171751 NBL Stocksfield On Tyne
1916 1992 1916 1992 171751 NBL Wideopen
TWEED
1754 1992 1500 1754 138347 ESS North East
1775 1992 1700 1775 102342 LIN Frodingham
1870 1910 .... 133515 WAR Atherstone
.... 1870 133515 WAR Coventry
TWEEDALE
1815 1937 ALL ALL 120669 LAN Bury
.... 1700 1900 155497 LAN Manchester
1815 1937 ALL ALL 120669 LAN Rochdale
TWEEDY
1770 1805 1700 1770 133019 NBL Elsdon
TWELFTREE
1832 1950 ALL ALL 115177 LND Enfield
TWELLS
1700 1992 1500 1700 171778 LIN ALL
1688 1794 1600 1688 138584 NTT Kingston On Soar
TWELVES
.... ALL ALL 171786 ALL Name Study
? ? .... 121185 KEN Dover
TWELVETREE
1793 1822 ALL ALL 135208 HUN ???
1851 1868 ALL ALL 135208 KEN Lee
1871 1892 ALL ALL 135208 NTH Dogsthorpe
1822 1915 ALL ALL 135208 NTH Eye
1839 1847 ALL ALL 135208 NTH Werrington
TWENTYMAN
.... 1700 1900 171794 CUL Bridekirk
.... 1700 1900 171794 CUL Harrington
.... 1700 1900 171794 CUL Wigton
1800 .... 176788 LND ???

Known Researching
From To From To Ref Cty Place
TWIDDY
ALL ALL ALL ALL 171808 ALL ALL
ALL ALL ALL ALL 171808 NFK Briston
1745 1850 1700 1850 110906 NFK Walpoles
TWIDLE
1837 1856 ALL 1860 113611 LIN Barton On Humber
1793 1837 ALL 1840 113611 LIN Winteringham
TWIGG
1800 1940 1800 1940 154466 KEN Sheerness
1810 1890 1810 1881 106569 LIN Cabourne
.... 1700 1850 152390 ??? Birmingham
TWIGGE
1586 .... 1550 1630 170348 YKS Kirkburton
TWIGGER
1875 1940 1700 1992 178136 NTT Nottingham
TWINEHAM
.... 1874 .... 105899 ENG ???
1857 .... 156329 LND Islington
TWIST
1750 1850 1750 1850 110434 LAN Salford
1750 1992 1750 1900 171824 LAN St Helens
.... ALL ALL 171816 WAR ALL
1800 1900 ALL ALL 171816 WAR Birmingham
TWITCHIN
1560 1619 .... 151408 BKM Tingewick
1860 1915 ALL ALL 151408 BKM Wolverton
1800 1919 ALL ALL 151408 BRK Newbury
1840 1920 ALL ALL 151408 HAM Alton
1586 1875 .... 151408 HAM Andover
1586 1875 .... 151408 HAM Holybourne
1736 1946 ALL ALL 151408 HAM Kingsclere
1819 1840 ALL ALL 151408 HAM Micheldever
TWITE
1750 1992 1700 1837 164437 NFK ALL
1700 1950 1700 1950 125881 NFK North West
TWOCOCK
1881 1992 1800 1992 174238 KEN Gravesend
1828 1881 1700 1900 174238 SRY Bermondsey
1828 1881 1700 1900 174238 SRY Southwick
TWOHEY
1815 1913 1750 1992 156698 MDX ???
TWORT
.... ALL ALL 171832 KEN ALL
1770 1780 1600 1800 151246 KEN Horsmonsden
1833 1881 .... 1881 153982 SRY Old Kent Road
1534 1960 ALL ALL 171832 SSX Frant
TWOSE
1750 1830 1750 1900 106410 SOM Wellington
1790 1810 .... 117579 SOM Wellington
1600 1860 1500 1800 144657 SOM Wellington
TWYCROSS
1621 1737 1500 1621 132993 OXF Oxford
TWYFORD
1852 1950 ALL 1900 131334 CHS ALL
1852 1950 ALL 1900 131334 LAN ALL
TWYMAN
1841 1992 1700 1841 115517 KEN East
1780 1900 1700 1780 124699 KEN East
.... 1992 1873 1900 151173 KEN Bexley
TWYNAM
1630 1700 ALL 1700 158283 ERY ALL
TWYNHAM
1770 .... ALL ALL 116394 HAM Fareham
TWYNING
1653 1876 1600 1992 118222 WLS ALL
TYACK
1669 1719 1600 1669 102571 CON Uny Lelant
TYAS
1850 1881 ALL ALL 103152 KEN Folkestone
1673 1712 1640 1680 170348 YKS Kirkheaton
TYASS
1733 1992 .... 134619 YKS Kellington
TYBBOT
1849 1849 1700 1849 156914 MGY Llanbrynmair
TYE
.... ALL ALL 117811 ALL Name Study
1863 1915 .... 114545 HUN Sawtry
1797 1992 .... 172529 KEN Rolveden
1830 1940 1700 1830 106267 SFK North
1870 1992 .... 1870 120979 WAR Birmingham
TYERMAN
1776 1992 ALL 1776 100587 NYK
Brompton By Northallerton

Known From	To	Researching From	To	Ref	Cty	Place
TYERS						
1825	1992	1700	1825	169889	RUT	Uppingham
....	....	1862	....	149497	???	Birmingham
....	....	1880	1992	149209	???	Birmingham
TYHURST						
1500	1851	1500	1900	170119	SSX	Eastbourn
1500	1851	1500	1900	170119	SSX	Rinsear
TYLDESLEY						
1740	1860	ALL	ALL	173010	LAN	Wigan
TYLEE						
1700	1720	1680	1750	142018	GLS	Bristol
1690	1760	1670	1760	142018	SOM	Bath
TYLER						
1580	1785	1550	1785	124796	BKM	Great Hampden
1770	1875	1750	1850	124796	BKM	Lossely Row
1863	1902	1902	1992	151688	CAM	Trumpington
1800	1900	....	....	117196	DUR	Durham
1815	1835	1700	1820	164909	ESS	Good Easter
1765	1780	1740	1765	117196	ESS	Great Dunmow
1815	1835	1700	1820	164909	ESS	High Easter
1786	1861	ALL	1786	108642	ESS	???
1799	1979	ALL	1799	103004	GLS	Bristol
1700	1725	....	1700	108413	GLS	Withington
1750	1850	1700	1750	143170	KEN	Central
1818	....	....	....	103233	KEN	Marden
1722	1830	1650	1750	103462	LEI	Exton
1722	1830	1650	1750	103462	LEI	Rutland
1803	....	1700	1800	125628	NFK	Norwich
1773	1783	....	1773	151688	NFK	South Lopham
1926	1992	....	....	151688	NTT	Carlton
1800	1845	1800	1900	159018	OXF	Bloxham
1799	1992	1700	1799	171840	OXF	Oxford
1800	1850	1700	1800	108413	SOM	Banwell
1799	1870	1831	1918	144878	SRY	Lambeth
1861	1948	1861	1900	101486	STS	Wolverhampton
1790	1830	1750	1800	109746	WAR	Stratford
1775	1992	1500	1775	154008	WIL	Calne
1890	1975	1700	1920	153222	WIL	Wootton Bassett
TYLLEMUTHE						
....	....	1000	1500	170232	NBL	North
TYM						
1800	1992	1750	1850	139475	DBY	Castleton
TYMBERDEN						
1150	1250	1100	1250	154881	KEN	Brasted
TYNAN						
....	1905	1300	1992	152501	NIR	North
....	1905	1300	1992	152501	STS	Pensnett
TYNDALL						
1760	1900	1500	1900	131431	GLS	Dursley
....	....	1800	1900	151998	SRY	Kennington
TYRER						
1860	1970	1700	1860	137162	LAN	Warrington
TYRRELL						
....	....	ALL	ALL	171867	ALL	Name Study
....	....	ALL	ALL	171891	ALL	Name Study
....	....	1500	1992	171891	ALL	ALL
1579	1880	....	....	171891	BRK	Didcot
1545	1730	1500	1800	171891	BRK	Hagbourne
1617	1830	1830	1950	171891	BRK	Reading
1800	1867	1770	1820	118354	CUL	Embleton
1777	1858	1600	1950	158399	SRY	East Horsley
TYSON						
1820	1880	1700	1820	130230	CMA	Millom
1798	1842	1700	1798	152196	CMA	Whiteheaven
1820	1880	1700	1820	130230	LAN	Broughton
1792	1792	1770	1850	149772	LAN	Colton
1780	1890	1890	1920	171948	LAN	Dalton In Furness
1780	1860	1740	1900	117145	LAN	Furness
1770	1860	1600	1850	171948	LAN	Walney Island
1850	1900	1700	1850	171921	LIN	Cuxwold
1724	1802	1600	1724	152196	WES	Low Meathrop
1865	1992	1700	1865	171913	???	???
TYSSEN						
1700	1799	1700	1799	147575	LND	Shadwell
TYTE						
1760	1992	1600	1760	115525	SOM	Hinton Blewett
TYZACK						
....	....	ALL	ALL	156892	ALL	Name Study
1724	1935	1690	1935	156892	LAN	Eccleston
1730	1935	1690	1935	156892	NBL	Howden Pans
?	?	?	?	156892	STS	Oldswinford
UDALE						
....	....	1600	1812	160342	CUL	???
1812	1859	....	....	160342	DFS	Langholm
UDALL						
1806	1806	1780	1830	133000	DOR	Whichurch Canonicorum
1800	....	....	....	135860	NTT	Nottingham
UDELL						
1750	1900	1600	1850	123293	SOM	???
1750	1900	1600	1850	123293	WIL	???
UDEN						
....	....	ALL	ALL	118370	ALL	Name Study
1732	1850	ALL	ALL	118370	ALL	ALL
UDY						
1870	1960	1700	1870	128325	CON	St Columb Major
UELLOR						
1766	1881	ALL	1992	111023	LAN	Manchester
UGLOW						
1854	1992	1600	1854	118648	CON	Jacobstow
1670	1844	1500	1700	121932	CON	Jacobstow
1545	1678	1400	1560	121932	CON	Marham
1670	1844	1500	1700	121932	CON	Otterham
1632	....	1620	1640	114332	CON	Poughill
1670	1844	1500	1700	121932	CON	St Gennys
1854	1992	1600	1854	118648	???	Marhamchurch
UHRMACHER						
1868	1876	1876	1992	155470	ESS	Colchester
ULF						
ALL	ALL	ALL	ALL	171964	ALL	ALL
ULFE						
ALL	ALL	ALL	ALL	171964	ALL	ALL
ULLATHORNE						
....	....	ALL	ALL	171956	ALL	Name Study
ULLEY						
1750	1850	1700	1850	135755	YKS	ALL
ULPH						
....	....	ALL	ALL	171964	ALL	Name Study
ALL	ALL	ALL	ALL	171964	ALL	ALL
ULYAT						
ALL	ALL	....	....	153397	ALL	ALL
ULYATT						
1785	1940	....	....	128996	CAM	Thorney
UMPELBY						
1795	1992	....	....	156191	LND	Lambeth
UMPLEBY						
1768	1819	1740	....	156191	NYK	Yarm
1837	1932	1600	1837	160172	YKS	North Riding
UNCLES						
1776	1800	1690	1850	126276	WIL	Chippenham
UNDERDOWN						
1820	1880	1700	1820	177881	KEN	Queenborough
1820	1880	1700	1820	177881	KEN	Upnor
UNDERHAY						
1600	1992	ALL	ALL	171972	ALL	ALL
UNDERHILL						
1780	1940	1760	1940	106801	DEV	South Tawton
1834	....	1834	....	156027	LND	Kensington
1640	1700	1640	1700	142018	SOM	ALL
1100	1400	....	....	100420	WAR	ALL
1620	1700	1620	1700	142018	WIL	ALL
UNDERLINE						
1796	....	1720	1986	136964	BDF	Radwell
UNDERSHILL						
1808	....	1808	....	156027	WOR	???
UNDERWOOD						
1840	1860	1800	1880	168076	AVN	Bristol
1809	1886	1750	1850	144231	DFS	Ruthwell
1800	1992	ALL	1800	108502	ESS	Brightingsea
1840	1840	1790	1840	168076	GLS	Eastington
....	....	1790	1840	168076	GLS	Uley
1621	1650	1600	1621	127116	HAM	Romsey
1790	1830	1750	1850	171999	HRT	Ippollitts
1700	1848	1500	1700	129577	IOW	???
1887	1992	1850	1890	155543	LND	Islington
1839	1842	1839	1880	126705	LND	St Martin In The Fields
1800	1850	1800	1900	141933	MDX	Westminster
1830	1992	1700	1830	155411	NFK	North
1730	1837	1680	1760	149039	NTH	West
1656	1992	ALL	1656	171980	NTH	Braybrooke
1813	1930	1700	1813	167533	SFK	Acton
1794	1869	1700	1794	172553	SFK	Bures St Mary
1794	1869	1700	1794	172553	SFK	Polstead
1745	1850	1500	1850	155543	SOM	Butleigh
1720	1992	1500	1750	112704	SOM	Evercreech
1745	1850	1500	1850	155543	SOM	Street

Known From	To	Researching From	To	Ref	Cty	Place
UNGLESS						
1826	....	1815	1864	164232	SFK	Stowmarket
UNICOMB						
1816	1851	1816	1992	126454	SSX	Ewhurst
UNICUME						
1803	1890	1750	1920	165492	KEN	Cranbrook
UNITT						
1730	....	1700	1730	119938	HEF	Coddington
UNSWORTH						
1698	1718	1650	1728	151912	LAN	Chatburn
1698	1718	1650	1728	151912	LAN	Downham
1746	1942	1746	1942	124613	LAN	Leigh
1746	1942	1746	1942	124613	LAN	Lowton
1745	1950	ALL	ALL	173290	LAN	Penketh
1860	1950	1700	1870	172006	LAN	St Helens
1850	1992	1700	1850	172014	LAN	Warrington
1728	1992	1728	1992	110396	LAN	Wigan
1810	1810	1750	1810	121509	LAN	Wigan
1850	1992	1850	1920	111562	OXF	Banbury
UNTHWAITE						
1600	1900	1600	1900	135968	LEI	ALL
UNTON						
1604	1769	....	1580	136093	WOR	Upton Snodsbury
UNWIN						
....	....	ALL	ALL	171263	ALL	Name Study
1787	1985	....	....	162655	CAM	Gt Wilbraham
1810	1862	1780	1810	147745	DBY	Pleasley
1775	1790	....	....	152870	DEV	Stoke Damerel
1885	....	....	....	141208	ESS	Grays
1669	1727	ALL	1669	162655	ESS	Radwinter
1880	....	....	....	141208	MDX	Hayes
1790	1900	....	....	152870	SRY	Lambeth
1890	....	....	....	141208	WLS	Pennal
UPCHER						
1727	1772	1580	1727	159239	ESS	Colchester
UPEX						
1800	1900	1800	1900	108693	NTH	Baunton
UPHAM						
1739	1940	1600	1992	158399	DEV	Brixham
....	....	1850	1950	178799	DEV	Brixham
1663	1992	....	....	172030	DEV	???
1850	1870	1850	1870	101877	LND	Bermondsey
1780	1790	....	....	101877	LND	Holborn
1750	1780	....	....	101877	LND	St Pauls
1750	1780	....	....	101877	LND	Westminster
1820	1840	....	....	101877	SSX	Chichester
UPHILL						
1700	1750	1700	1750	147575	DOR	Motcombe
1700	1800	1600	1700	160598	SOM	East Lydford
1840	1903	ALL	1840	160156	SOM	Radstock
1700	1800	1700	1800	147575	WIL	Salisbury
UPPERDINE						
1600	....	1600	1850	115142	STS	Cannock
1840	1930	ALL	1992	102245	STS	Coven
UPPERTON						
1600	1750	1600	1750	152404	SSX	Burpham
UPPINGTON						
1839	1992	1839	1992	101079	MON	Tredegar
1604	1992	ALL	1992	101079	SOM	Withycombe
UPSTONE						
1650	1860	ALL	1650	142069	OXF	???
UPTON						
1867	1875	....	....	163155	ESS	Saffron Walden
1871	1970	1871	1891	157597	KEN	Bexley
1790	1930	1790	1992	125970	KEN	Bromley
1790	1930	1790	1992	125970	KEN	Lee
1853	1992	1700	1853	172049	LEI	Oakthorpe
1795	1822	ALL	1795	161330	NTT	Nottingham
1673	1881	1650	1900	159905	OXF	Shenington
1853	1992	1700	1853	172049	STS	Alrewas
1694	1900	1837	1900	171727	STS	Hanbury
1821	1860	1800	1992	131865	WAR	Coventry
UPWOOD						
....	....	ALL	ALL	171441	ALL	Name Study
....	....	ALL	ALL	171441	ALL	ALL
URCELL						
1880	....	....	....	116211	LAN	Bolton
1851	1880	1880	....	116211	LAN	Darwen
URCH						
1830	1992	1830	1992	113670	AVN	Bath
1830	1992	1830	1992	113670	AVN	Bristol
1846	....	....	....	145742	AVN	Bristol
1857	1880	1857	1880	113670	GLS	Bitton
URE						
....	....	1600	1732	118834	SCT	???
....	....	1732	1800	118834	SSX	Eastbourne
UREN						
....	....	ALL	ALL	104108	ALL	Name Study
1840	1870	....	....	172065	CGN	Rheidol
1717	1750	1500	1717	138614	CON	Gwennap
1800	1992	1700	1800	116335	CON	Helston
1800	1890	1800	1900	105945	CON	Illogan
....	....	1600	1840	172065	CON	Illogan
1800	1992	1700	1800	116335	CON	Lelant
1769	1800	1500	1800	132993	CON	Ludgvan
....	....	1600	1840	172065	CON	Redruth
1781	1842	1741	1781	129305	CON	Sennen
1870	1883	....	....	172065	LAN	Liverpool
URLWIN						
1685	1685	ALL	1685	115126	BKM	Langley Marrish
URQUARTH						
1750	1965	....	....	137820	SHI	Fetlar
1720	1965	....	....	137820	SHI	Mid Yell
1760	1965	....	....	137820	SHI	North Yell
1758	1965	....	....	137820	SHI	Northmavine
1720	1965	....	....	137820	SHI	South Yell
URQUHART						
1800	1939	1700	1939	100307	ALL	ALL
1819	1835	1800	1850	134880	KEN	Canterbury
....	....	1700	1992	137855	MOR	Dyke
1834	1873	1600	1873	153591	YKS	Bradford
URQUHARY						
1853	?	ALL	ALL	101370	SUT	Brora
URRY						
1715	1778	1715	1992	156647	HAM	Calbourne
1780	1890	ALL	ALL	152285	HAM	Gosport
1778	1799	1720	1830	105333	HAM	Isle Of Wight
1700	1742	1600	1700	145289	HAM	Isle Of Wight
1802	1992	1750	1802	176257	IOW	Shalfleet
URSELL						
1920	1992	1850	1992	151459	ESS	South
1851	1880	1880	....	116211	LAN	Darwen
URWICK						
....	....	ALL	ALL	163562	ALL	Name Study
....	....	ALL	ALL	163562	ALL	ALL
URWIN						
1814	1880	1600	1900	130125	DUR	Washington
....	....	1800	1860	122343	NBL	Newcastle
1861	1900	ALL	1840	160199	NBL	Newcastle
USBORNE						
1500	1900	1500	1900	126659	KEN	ALL
USHER						
1854	1886	1700	1854	100110	GNT	Newport
1768	....	1720	1820	171441	HAM	Bradley
1688	1821	....	1780	171441	HAM	Monk Sherborne
1789	....	1770	1820	171441	HAM	Woodmancot
1861	1868	1850	1900	172073	KEN	Wormshill
1889	1896	....	....	172073	KEN	Wrotham
1830	1848	1800	1900	172073	KEN	Wychling
1674	1704	1600	1674	101575	LIN	Thrulby By Bourne
1800	1900	ALL	ALL	131873	LND	East
1600	1852	ALL	ALL	149063	ROX	Melrose
1875	1875	1875	1891	169609	WIL	Chippenham
1835	1874	1700	1835	169609	WIL	Corsham
USSHER						
1400	1780	1000	1400	113204	TYR	Coagh
USTICK						
1612	1682	1500	1700	153591	CON	Madron
1612	1682	1500	1700	153591	CON	Sancreed
1612	1682	1500	1700	153591	CON	St Just In Penwith
UTLEY						
1760	1866	1700	1760	130877	YKS	Wetherby
UTTERIDGE						
1780	1992	ALL	ALL	172103	CAM	West
1809	1885	....	1809	151688	CAM	Trumpington
UTTING						
....	....	1855	....	109290	LND	ALL
....	....	1830	....	109290	NFK	Kings Lynn
....	....	1700	1800	129356	NFK	Kirby Bedon
....	....	1700	1800	140627	NFK	Seething
....	....	1700	1800	129356	SFK	Sotterley
UTTLEY						
1855	1871	....	....	125202	WRY	Bradford
UTTON						
1823	....	1790	1823	149942	NFK	Aldeby
UZZELL						
ALL	ALL	ALL	ALL	142360	ALL	ALL

Known From	To	Researching From	To	Ref	Cty	Place
UZZELL contd.						
1790	1960	1560	1992	142360	GLS	Kempsford
1849	1904	1700	1849	161683	WIL	Mintey
1849	1904	1700	1849	161683	WIL	Oaksey
1849	1904	1700	1849	161683	WIL	Poole Keynes
VACHER						
1755	1820	1580	1755	159239	DOR	Milton Abbas
1897	1932	1850	1932	159905	DUR	South Shields
VAGUE						
1800	1970	1980	1992	140139	CON	Lanivet
1830	1900	1700	1845	156051	CON	Lanivet
1830	1900	1700	1845	156051	CON	Lanlivery
1640	1850	....	....	145858	CON	Manaccan
VAILE						
....	....	ALL	ALL	176605	ALL	Name Study
VALE						
1759	1759	1750	1800	113751	ESS	Canewdon
1805	1887	1750	1805	178381	GLS	Newnham
1818	1915	1818	1915	127655	HEF	Coddington
1818	1915	1818	1915	127655	HEF	Mathon
1730	1780	1730	1780	127655	HEF	Sutton St Nicholas
1730	1780	1730	1780	127655	HEF	Yarpole
1800	....	....	....	126497	IRL	???
1830	1850	....	....	126500	IRL	???
1760	1820	1760	1820	127655	MDX	Marylebone
1760	1820	1760	1820	127655	MDX	Paddington
1794	1822	1700	1794	161225	MDX	Westminster
1671	1763	1700	1760	142018	WIL	West
1830	....	....	....	126497	???	Birmingham
VALENCE						
1738	1763	ALL	1738	154563	DOR	Burton Bradstock
VALENDER						
1755	1980	1749	1980	145009	GLS	Snowshill
VALENS						
....	....	1700	1770	176036	LAN	Liverpool
VALENTINE						
....	....	ALL	....	172219	DEV	Teignmouth
1799	1820	....	1850	102601	DEV	Topsham
1905	1992	1600	1910	172146	ESS	Thurrock
1795	....	....	....	171824	LAN	Billings
1882	1950	1700	1882	178233	LAN	Blackrod
1820	1992	ALL	1820	117765	LAN	Liverpool
1891	1965	1800	1891	172138	LAN	Preston
....	....	1895	1930	142654	LND	South East
1810	1840	1700	1850	126268	LND	Finsbury
VALENTINEY						
1835	1916	1700	1992	108421	MDX	Covent Garden
VALLANCE						
1741	1769	1700	1770	174289	HAM	Holdenhurst
1741	1800	1500	1800	174270	HAM	Holdenhurst
1850	1905	1850	1900	111791	LAN	Everton
VALLAR						
1791	1856	1700	1900	178233	HAM	Petersfield
VALLE						
1798	1890	1798	1976	148067	MDX	London
VALLENCE						
1840	1886	1700	1900	150797	DEV	Wiveliscombe
1840	1886	1700	1900	150797	SOM	Wiveliscombe
VALLER						
1788	?	ALL	ALL	166243	SRY	Wanborough
1788	?	ALL	ALL	166243	SRY	Worplesdon
VALLEY						
1841	1992	1874	1992	175072	ALL	ALL
VALLIS						
1841	1861	1840	1870	172154	BKM	High Wycombe
1861	1900	....	....	172154	BKM	Slough
1777	1807	1700	1840	172154	HAM	Cliddesdon
1812	1860	1770	1812	172154	OXF	Headington
1825	1847	1700	1825	131660	SOM	Frome
VALPY DIT JANVRIN						
1750	....	ALL	1750	119105	JSY	ALL
VALPY						
?	?	?	?	144258	ENG	???
1500	1800	1800	1900	144258	GSY	???
1500	1800	1800	1900	144258	JSY	???
VAN VAULKENBURGH						
1653	1694	....	1694	109622	YKS	Thorne
VANDERAVORT						
....	....	ALL	ALL	172189	ALL	Name Study
VANDERPLANK						
1818	1852	1700	1818	145971	HAM	Alverstoke
VANDERSTEGEN						
1795	1840	1840	1940	141739	OXF	Cane End

Known From	To	Researching From	To	Ref	Cty	Place
VANN						
1820	1825	1700	1820	164844	LEI	Central
....	....	1600	1992	177725	MDX	Bethnal Green
1828	1943	1700	1828	169803	NFK	Carlton
1888	1980	1700	1888	107301	WAR	Birmingham
VANNER						
1740	1923	1650	1740	132039	IOW	Shorwell
....	....	1600	1992	177725	MDX	Bethnal Green
1840	1930	1840	1992	153133	MDX	London
VANSTONE						
....	....	1600	1992	172197	CON	ALL
1626	1986	1600	1992	172197	DEV	ALL
1783	1986	1600	1992	172197	DEV	Langtree
VANT						
1840	?	1700	1840	164925	KEN	Ashford
1820	1920	1700	1992	170496	YKS	ALL
VARCOE						
1650	1992	1550	1992	133450	CON	Roche
1600	1870	1600	1992	172200	CON	Roches
1600	1870	1600	1992	172200	CON	St Dennis
VARDY						
1796	1992	1720	1796	132357	DUR	Durham
....	....	1500	1750	175269	???	London
VARE						
1791	1851	ALL	ALL	106658	CHS	Rainow
VARLEY						
1799	1851	1700	1890	119555	DBY	Heanor
?	?	?	?	128910	DBY	Heanor
1500	1600	1500	1600	109347	LAN	Downham
1821	1846	1846	1992	117099	LAN	Manchester
1725	....	1725	....	109347	LAN	Padiham
ALL	1800	1780	1992	135429	LIN	Gainsborough
1850	1870	1800	1900	142050	LIN	???
1931	1952	1931	1952	117323	MDX	Acton
1952	1992	1952	1992	117323	MDX	Brentford
1785	1838	1838	1992	128910	NTT	Brinsley
1759	1965	1730	1759	169846	WYK	Bramham
1759	1965	1730	1759	169846	WYK	Chapel Allerton
1759	1965	1730	1759	169846	WYK	Leeds
1837	1992	1837	1890	155519	YKS	Bramham
1500	1600	1500	1600	109347	YKS	Gisburn
1825	1934	....	....	145912	YKS	South Leeds
VARNDELL						
1730	1880	1650	1800	139688	HAM	Bishops Waltham
VARNEY						
1794	1850	1790	1860	160482	GLS	Cheltenham
1700	1850	1600	1950	177180	HRT	Hemel Hempstead
1865	1940	1800	1900	122610	LND	Bermondsey
?	1930	ALL	ALL	151696	LND	???
1890	....	ALL	ALL	105481	NTT	Belper
1880	1890	....	....	121126	WAR	Leamington Spa
VARNHAM						
....	....	1700	1850	179531	KEN	Hever
VARO						
....	....	1740	1880	103713	CAM	Ashley
VART						
1700	1840	....	....	102741	DUR	Cockfield
1700	1840	....	....	102741	DUR	Staindrop
1720	1950	1550	1720	167584	DUR	Teesdale
VARTY						
ALL	1700	....	....	172235	CUL	Aspatria
1700	1992	1780	1992	172235	NBL	Allendale
VARVILL						
1717	1845	1500	1717	125695	YKS	Seaton Ross
VASEY						
1843	1900	1750	1843	172472	LND	Shoreditch
1798	1834	1800	1992	172782	YKS	Leeds
VASS						
1824	1951	1750	1824	175846	BRK	Finchampstead
1822	1858	1858	1992	124559	LND	Lambeth
VASSAR						
....	....	1840	1992	143626	HMC	ALL
....	....	1840	1992	143626	LND	ALL
....	....	1560	1992	143626	NFK	ALL
1837	1925	ALL	1837	159204	NFK	Norwich
VASSE						
1882	1909	....	....	141356	GSY	St Peter Port
VASSIE						
1840	1890	1750	1840	149004	STI	Stirling
VATCHER						
1926	1970	1700	1926	120510	DOR	ALL
1774	1839	ALL	ALL	141127	HAM	Ringwood
VAUGHAN						
1830	1980	1750	1830	172308	AVN	Bristol

Known From	To	Researching From	To	Ref	Cty	Place
VAUGHAN contd.						
1620	1800	1580	1850	172278	BKM	Burnham
1790	1880	1790	1880	172278	BKM	Eton
1820	1838	1700	1992	142212	BRE	Llaneighn
1880	1992	....	....	172278	BRK	Reading
1708	1933	1700	1708	165867	CAE	Llanfarth
....	1900	1700	1900	172405	CHS	Chester
....	....	1800	1851	142093	CMN	ALL
1851	1889	1700	1851	123110	CMN	Newcastle Emlyn
1851	1889	1700	1851	123110	CMN	Trelech
1850	1920	1850	1992	133450	DEV	Braton Flemming
1762	1845	1580	1762	159239	ESS	Copford
1880	1900	1850	1880	156302	HEF	Much Birch
1835	1992	1100	1992	172294	HRT	ALL
1960	?	....	....	172278	KEN	Bexleyheath
1880	1960	....	....	172278	LND	Battersea
1900	1960	....	....	172278	LND	Camberwell
1930	1940	....	....	172278	LND	Fulham
1880	1960	....	....	172278	LND	Wandsworth
1830	1880	ALL	ALL	156558	MDX	Brentford
1765	1789	1700	1800	141798	MDX	St Marylebone
1855	1861	1700	1855	156914	MGY	Llanmerewig
1740	1760	1700	1760	139203	MON	Alberbury
1805	1850	1700	1850	132993	PEM	Cosheston
1838	....	1800	1850	140473	RAD	Old Radnor
1810	1846	....	....	172286	RFW	Paisley
1811	1933	1750	1811	154024	SAL	Alderbury
....	1770	ALL	1770	126659	SAL	Monkhopton
1797	1803	....	....	151351	WOR	Bengeworth
1865	1960	....	....	172286	WYK	Bradford
1890	1992	1700	1890	123005	YKS	Barnsley
VAUSE						
1850	1992	1750	1850	102342	LIN	Isle Of Axholme
1800	1826	....	....	171166	WRY	Bulmer
VAUX						
1740	1840	ALL	1740	164887	NTH	Crick
1740	1840	ALL	1740	164887	NTH	Whilton
VAVASOUR						
1100	1200	1100	1200	154881	ALL	ALL
VAZIE-SIMONS						
1897	1909	ALL	ALL	134929	NFK	North Walsham
VEAL						
1660	1820	....	....	172359	CON	St Columb Major
1800	1962	1650	1850	162582	DEV	Holbeton
1816	....	ALL	1840	174815	DEV	Uffculme
1592	1773	....	....	153397	HAM	Barton
1800	1850	1700	1800	171182	HAM	Havant
1792	1992	1600	1792	172332	LIN	Ashby De La Launde
1720	1785	1640	1785	135941	SFK	Lakenheath
1841	1867	ALL	1841	174815	SOM	Bristol
VEALE						
1800	1992	1700	1800	172340	AVN	Chew Magna
1908	1992	....	1908	121002	CON	Islington
1790	1820	1600	1790	134090	DEV	Germansweek
....	....	ALL	1791	159441	DEV	Holbeton
1780	1913	1500	1780	140279	DEV	Holesworthy
1790	1820	1600	1790	134090	DEV	Okehampton
1780	1913	1500	1780	140279	DEV	Pyworthy
1700	1900	1500	1700	101591	DEV	South Brent
1895	....	1900	1992	126950	LND	Bow
1800	1992	1700	1800	172340	SOM	Bristol
1850	1900	1800	1900	174815	SOM	Bristol
1850	1900	1800	1900	174815	SOM	Weston
1766	1780	1600	1992	140953	SRY	Petersham
VEALL						
1895	1900	....	....	172359	CAE	Llanelly
1805	1808	....	....	172359	CON	St Mary
1805	1808	....	....	172359	CON	Truro
1920	1992	....	....	172359	HAM	Southampton
1992	1992	....	....	172359	HAM	Wellow
1979	1979	....	....	172359	HAM	Winchester
1949	1949	....	....	172359	IOW	East Cowes
1971	1971	....	....	172359	LND	Bromley
1968	1968	....	....	172359	LND	Lambeth
1845	1857	....	....	172359	LND	St Thomas Charberhouse
1887	1893	1700	1992	172359	MON	Newport
VEAR						
1790	1835	1790	1835	114073	HAM	South Stoneham
1790	1992	1700	1992	177687	LIN	Maltby Le Marsh
VEARING						
1790	1850	1790	1860	138479	SOM	Meare
VEARNCOMBE						
1650	1980	....	....	172367	DEV	ALL

Known From	To	Researching From	To	Ref	Cty	Place
VEARNCOMBE contd.						
1650	1980	....	....	172367	HAM	ALL
1650	1980	1650	1750	172367	SOM	ALL
VEARO						
....	....	1740	1880	103713	CAM	Ashley
VEASEY						
1936	1983	1900	1992	110388	KEN	Deal
1887	1887	1850	1887	152781	LIN	Lincoln
1789	1850	1750	1900	113212	SOM	Brewham
1789	1850	1750	1900	113212	SOM	Nunney
....	....	1800	....	137456	WAR	Dunchurch
VEASY						
1853	....	1700	1992	110418	SOM	Cloford
VEECOCK						
....	....	ALL	ALL	172375	ALL	Name Study
VEEL						
1750	1800	....	....	137693	GLS	Wootten Under Edge
VEITCH						
1825	1829	ALL	1829	134058	DEV	Stoke Damerell
1900	1907	ALL	1907	134058	DEV	Torquay
1768	1800	ALL	1800	149063	ELN	Dunbar
1768	1800	ALL	1800	149063	ELN	Haddington
1786	1872	1700	1780	153656	PEE	Drumeizier
VELERS						
....	....	ALL	1800	103284	BRK	Wargrave
VELLEMOUTH						
1820	1840	1820	1820	130222	CON	???
1820	1850	1820	1850	130222	LND	Shoreditch
VELVIN						
?	?	?	?	101214	DEV	Ermington
?	?	?	?	101214	DEV	Ugborough
VENABLES						
....	....	ALL	ALL	172383	ALL	Name Study
1060	1992	1060	1992	133450	CHS	ALL
....	....	1067	1698	172383	ENG	ALL
....	....	1700	1935	156639	ESS	Barking
1768	1809	1698	1768	172383	LND	East
1848	1965	....	....	172383	LND	North
1809	1848	....	....	172383	LND	City
VENESS						
1770	1830	....	1830	113034	KEN	???
1840	1960	1800	1992	165980	SSX	Hooe
1775	....	1740	1780	156140	SSX	Lewes
1750	1960	1650	1992	165980	SSX	Wartling
VENICE						
1750	1960	1650	1992	165980	SSX	Brightling
VENIMORE						
1750	1820	ALL	ALL	106097	LIN	Stamford
VENIN						
1643	1940	....	....	128996	CAM	Thorney
VENING						
....	....	ALL	ALL	172391	ALL	Name Study
VENN						
....	....	ALL	ALL	172413	ALL	Name Study
....	....	ALL	ALL	172413	ALL	ALL
1850	1992	....	1850	150495	DEV	Exeter
1775	1870	1700	1775	155322	GLS	Stonehouse
....	1836	1700	1850	172405	LAN	Liverpool
1789	1812	ALL	1812	104299	SOM	Timberscombe
....	....	1800	1920	102768	???	Ogmore Vale
1880	1992	1700	1900	172405	???	Wrexham
VENNELS						
1770	1850	1700	1850	120235	KEN	Wilmington
VENNER						
1750	1900	1700	1750	172561	CON	Lelant
1720	1750	ALL	1740	115282	KEN	East
....	....	1800	1910	118834	LND	???
1822	1834	1800	1822	137057	SOM	Dulverton
VENNERS						
1859	1900	1850	1900	133280	DUR	Bishop Auckland
1859	1900	1850	1900	133280	DUR	Spennymoor
1823	1855	1800	1855	133280	STS	Tipton
1823	1855	1800	1855	133280	STS	Wednesbury
VENNIMORE						
1650	1750	1550	1650	174513	OXF	Hampton Poyle
VENNING						
1628	?	1600	1900	146668	CON	Altarnun
1800	ALL	....	....	103381	CON	Broadhempston
1700	?	1600	1900	146668	CON	Laneast
....	....	1600	1900	146668	CON	St Cleer
1700	?	1600	1900	146668	CON	St Clether
1835	1860	....	1835	178853	DEV	ALL
VENOY						
1712	1940	....	....	128996	CAM	Thorney

Known From	To	Researching From	To	Ref	Cty	Place
VENSON						
1793	1793	1100	1793	117749	CON	Mawgan In Meneage
VENTERMAN						
1500	....	1500	....	165360	KEN	Canterbury
VENTON						
1700	1760	1600	1700	134090	DEV	Colebrook
VENTRESS						
1600	1835	1600	1835	119717	YKS	Loftus
VENUS						
1800	1910	1600	1800	158984	SSX	South West
VERCOE						
?	?	?	?	168599	CON	St Goran
VERDON						
1817	1817	1750	1817	112593	SFK	Southwold
1817	1817	1750	1817	112593	SFK	Wangford
VERINDER						
1750	1900	1750	1992	176567	GLS	Chalford
1750	1900	1750	1992	176567	GLS	Painswick
1700	1992	1700	1980	176567	GLS	Stroud
1750	1900	1750	1992	176567	GLS	Winchcombe
1830	1992	1830	1992	176567	KEN	Anerley
1700	1992	1700	1980	176567	KEN	Sidcup
1830	1992	1830	1992	176567	LND	Angel
1830	1992	1830	1992	176567	LND	City
....	....	1750	1850	146277	MDX	Bishopgate
....	....	1750	1850	146277	MDX	Shorditch
VERIOD						
1780	1980	1700	1800	106925	ALL	ALL
VERIT						
1773	1992	ALL	1773	179345	OXF	Wheatfield
VERITY						
1674	1774	1674	1800	163317	YKS	Bradford
VERLANDER						
....	....	ALL	ALL	159050	ALL	Name Study
VERMUYDEN						
1620	1700	1620	1700	151653	SOM	Sedgemoor
VERNALL						
....	....	ALL	ALL	172421	ALL	Name Study
1811	1880	1500	1992	172421	ALL	ALL
VERNEY						
1790	1880	1790	1992	162809	BKM	Claydon
1790	1880	1790	1992	162809	BKM	Winslow
1798	1868	1650	1798	166170	WIL	Marlborough
VERNON						
1723	....	....	....	148156	CAM	Graveley
1060	1992	1060	1992	133450	CHS	ALL
1817	1892	1750	1817	167932	CHS	Audlem
1843	1843	1810	1850	126705	CHS	Chester
1762	1932	1650	1762	150614	CHS	Over
1774	1808	1774	1850	126705	CHS	Tarporley
1700	1830	1650	1700	106194	DBY	Ashover
....	....	ALL	1700	178403	DBY	???
1887	1900	ALL	ALL	125202	LND	Paddington
1902	....	ALL	ALL	125202	MDX	Hendon
1900	1992	ALL	1900	123854	NTT	Hucknall
1780	1810	1700	1900	171522	SSX	East Dean
1800	1900	1700	1950	171522	SSX	Eastbourne
1801	....	....	1820	160873	STS	South
1845	1992	1700	1845	172448	WIL	Ramsbury
VERRAL						
1750	1860	1750	1860	152536	SSX	Lewes
VERRALL						
....	....	ALL	ALL	172456	ALL	Name Study
1332	1900	....	....	172456	ALL	???
1800	1900	1900	....	116297	SSX	Rotherfield
VERRAN						
1829	....	1700	1992	173053	CON	Perranarworthal
1820	1850	1790	1850	168580	CON	Veryan
VERRANT						
1850	1900	1800	1900	149144	CHI	Guernsey
....	....	1800	1900	149144	DEV	Plymouth
VERRIER						
?	?	?	?	142018	GLS	Bristol
1750	1850	1700	1992	133450	KEN	Deal
1800	1900	1800	1900	142018	SOM	Stoke St Gregory
1850	1932	1800	1850	122882	SOM	Taunton
VERRILL						
1686	1937	1600	1700	118362	NYK	Staithes
VERRINDER						
....	....	ALL	ALL	172464	ALL	Name Study
1756	1992	1560	1900	140066	GLS	???
VERTIGAN						
1600	1992	....	....	168521	NFK	Norwich
VERYARD						
....	....	ALL	ALL	160555	ALL	Name Study
VESEY						
1600	....	ALL	1900	174637	IRL	???
VESSEY						
1680	1720	1650	1720	160849	LIN	South Kelsey
1628	1720	1560	1628	155276	SFK	Trimley
VESTER						
1750	1830	....	....	144568	YKS	???
VESTRY						
1778	1842	1600	1900	135968	LEI	ALL
VEVIAN						
1669	1669	1600	1725	144606	SOM	Odcombe
VEY						
1884	1915	1850	1950	144908	SSX	Hove
VEYSEY						
1858	1876	1835	1858	155381	DEV	Torrington
VIALLS						
....	....	ALL	ALL	172480	ALL	Name Study
VIALS						
....	....	....	....	102946	NTH	???
1851	1900	....	....	102946	YKS	Liversedge
VIAR						
1700	1799	....	....	137960	MDX	London
VIBERT						
1684	1706	1600	1684	102571	CON	Gulval
1820	1860	1800	1920	133922	JSY	St Helier
VICARIS						
1650	1681	....	....	164631	WOR	Kidderminster
VICARS						
1675	1700	1600	1675	128724	KEN	Waltham
1792	....	....	....	124524	NTH	Brackley
VICARY						
1820	1860	1750	1820	137650	DEV	Black Dog
1700	1940	1600	1700	156531	DEV	Great Torrington
1860	1920	ALL	ALL	113700	DEV	Honiton
....	....	1600	1992	137588	DEV	Newton Abbot
1860	1920	ALL	ALL	113700	DEV	Ottery
1500	ALL	....	....	103381	DEV	Tawton
1832	1852	1750	1875	107654	DEV	Thorn Falcon
1800	1877	1700	1800	148938	GLS	Puriton
1743	1992	1700	1743	172502	SOM	Bury
....	....	1833	1877	172499	SXW	Styning
....	....	1850	1942	172499	YKS	Sheffield
VICCARS						
1809	1838	ALL	1809	152013	NTH	Great Harwood
VICE						
1500	1880	1200	1800	124141	ALL	ALL
VICK						
1895	....	....	....	137375	GLS	Whitminster
1820	1880	1720	1820	172510	GLS	Wotton Under Edge
VICKARS						
1710	1765	1600	1710	152196	CMA	Muncaster
1770	1780	1700	1780	162396	LIN	South
VICKARY						
1818	?	?	1818	136611	DEV	Burliscombe
1760	1770	1700	1770	136840	SOM	Brendon Hills
VICKERAGE						
....	....	ALL	ALL	178179	ALL	Name Study
VICKERMAN						
1814	....	....	1814	101761	WRY	Almondbury
VICKERS						
1759	1811	1759	ALL	175854	BKM	Aston Chinton
1839	1992	1759	ALL	175854	BKM	Linslade
1795	1822	1760	1830	159905	CUL	Alston
1839	1871	1818	1871	173371	DUR	Staindrop
1743	1860	ALL	1743	138290	EYK	Beverley
1860	1890	1800	1992	140058	KEN	Bromley
1855	1871	1855	1900	159964	LAN	Clifton
1820	1850	1820	1900	159964	LAN	Farnworth
1814	1814	1814	1850	126705	LAN	Manchester
1800	1825	1700	1850	159964	LAN	Middle Hulton
1760	1820	....	....	118206	LIN	Louth
1884	1930	....	....	177687	LIN	Louth
1760	1820	....	....	118206	LIN	Mablethorpe
1560	1800	1560	1760	118206	LIN	Market Rasen
1820	1890	....	....	118206	LIN	Marshchapel
1795	1900	1750	1900	106011	LND	ALL
1795	1900	1750	1900	106011	LND	Strand
1795	1900	1750	1900	106011	LND	Westminter
1795	1900	1750	1900	106011	MDX	ALL
1860	1992	....	....	115479	NTT	Brinsley
....	....	1750	1900	106011	SRY	ALL
1904	1970	1904	1970	140058	SRY	Croydon

Known From	To	Researching From	To	Ref	Cty	Place
VICKERS contd.						
....	....	1750	1900	106011	SRY	Wandsworth
1813	1870	1800	1930	165034	YKS	Whitby
1775	1992	1750	1775	178209	YKS	Yeadon
VICKERY						
1910	1989	1700	1910	112739	DEV	Torquay
1764	1992	1600	1764	166804	HAM	Odiham
1825	1870	1790	1950	118737	SOM	Dunster
1800	1830	1700	1800	157708	WAR	Birmingham
VIDGEN						
1770	1791	1750	1830	167126	SOM	Bath
VIDLER						
1838	1981	ALL	1838	157791	HAM	Shipton Bellenger
....	....	1830	....	159824	KEN	???
1910	1925	1914	1933	124435	LND	???
....	....	1830	....	159824	SXW	???
VIDLES						
1840	1850	1600	1850	146684	SSX	Hastings
VIERS						
....	....	1600	ALL	115142	WAR	???
VIGAR						
1770	1779	....	....	112968	SOM	Barton St David
1832	1850	....	....	112968	SOM	Mudford
1724	1992	....	....	112968	SOM	Pitney
VIGERS						
1820	1920	1750	1850	170488	ENG	???
1822	1873	1700	1821	131245	MDX	St Lukes
VIGIS						
1830	1992	....	....	161969	ESS	Chelmsford
1830	1992	....	....	161969	ESS	Romford
1830	1992	....	....	161969	ESS	Tendring
1830	1992	....	....	161969	LND	West Ham
VIGURS						
1845	1992	1700	1845	117846	???	???
VIGUS						
1822	1873	1750	1900	148725	HRT	Hatfield
VILDAY						
1776	1900	ALL	ALL	120774	DEV	South East
VILLAGE						
1888	....	ALL	1900	139459	WAR	Birmingham
1888	....	ALL	1900	139459	WAR	Saltley
1888	....	ALL	1900	139459	WAR	Small Heath
VILLER						
1890	1896	1860	....	167290	MDX	St Pancras
VILLERS						
1400	1712	....	....	172537	LEI	Brooksby
1506	1741	....	....	172537	LEI	Hoby
1465	1814	....	....	172537	SOM	Cannington
1530	1783	....	....	172537	STS	Hanbury
1640	1972	....	....	172537	WAR	Coventry
1614	1694	....	....	172537	WAR	Hampton In Arden
VILLIERS						
1700	1800	1700	1800	154881	KIK	Waterford
1600	1700	1600	1700	154881	LEI	Brokesby
1815	1820	1815	1840	155918	LND	Lambeth
1500	1600	1500	1600	154881	STS	Hanbury
VILLIS						
1780	1780	1700	1800	174599	IOW	Godshill
VINALL						
1848	....	....	1848	167053	ESS	Tendring
1850	1881	1850	1992	172545	KEN	Goudhurst
1820	1920	1760	1992	172545	MDX	London
1820	1920	1760	1992	172545	MDX	St Pancras
1680	1880	ALL	ALL	131164	SSX	Fletching
1760	....	1760	1992	172545	SSX	Laughton
1820	....	1760	1992	172545	SSX	Wartling
VINCE						
1790	1860	1700	1790	168351	ESS	Brightlingsea
1737	....	....	1770	171441	HAM	Brown Candover
1758	1881	1700	1758	169730	HAM	Crondall
1827	1860	1780	1880	171441	HAM	Kilmeston
1843	1865	1750	1900	136042	HAM	Sopley
1789	....	1760	1830	171441	HAM	Woodmancot
1764	1853	1700	1764	168777	HAM	Woodmancott
1762	1765	1740	1800	171441	HAM	Wootton St Lawrence
1913	....	1900	1992	117609	LND	Kensington
1750	1850	ALL	ALL	154830	SFK	ALL
....	....	1810	....	106623	SRY	Woking
1800	....	1700	1820	110914	YKS	Garforth
VINCENT						
?	?	?	?	147869	ALL	ALL
1750	1900	1700	1750	172561	AVN	Bristol
1700	1850	1600	1900	153354	CON	Gwennap
1770	1795	1770	1795	144878	CON	St Just In Roseland
VINCENT contd.						
....	....	1500	1713	138614	CON	Stithians
1835	1915	....	....	151351	DOR	Dorchester
1670	1840	....	....	151351	DOR	Piddletrenthide
1840	1960	....	....	171182	HAM	Rockbourne
1773	1799	1750	1810	105120	KEN	Chatham
1819	1878	1790	1881	124001	KEN	Chatham
1829	1940	1700	1829	110019	LND	Islington
1842	1964	1842	1964	155918	LND	Lambeth
1800	1992	....	....	132179	LND	Stepney
1837	1840	1800	1840	155918	MDX	London
....	....	1700	1800	140627	NFK	Norwich
1800	1850	1700	1800	154458	SOM	Glastonbury
1877	....	....	1880	171441	SOM	Kingsdon
1847	....	....	1860	171441	SOM	Langport
1690	1900	1690	1900	155357	SOM	South Petherton
1760	1820	1760	1820	132721	SSX	Stoke
1790	1840	1700	1790	171182	WIL	Salisbury
1689	....	....	....	131229	WOR	Stoke Prior
VINCER						
1745	1845	1700	1900	134880	KEN	Wye
VINCETT						
1685	1685	....	....	127426	KEN	Otterden
1648	1666	....	....	127426	KEN	Ulcombe
VINDEN						
....	....	ALL	ALL	146781	ALL	Name Study
ALL	ALL	ALL	ALL	146803	ALL	ALL
VINE						
1751	1940	....	....	128996	CAM	Thorney
....	....	1850	1915	158410	HAM	Christcurch
1753	1871	1600	1753	172588	SFK	Bury St Edmunds
1791	1846	ALL	1791	158445	WIL	Potterne
VINECOMBE						
1834	....	1800	1838	116572	CHI	Guernsey
VINES						
1850	1992	1780	1850	111554	GLS	Randwich
1850	1992	1800	1850	111554	GLS	Stroud
....	....	1700	1800	140627	NFK	Norwich
1840	1870	....	....	164593	SOM	Christian Malford
VINEY						
1853	1870	1700	1992	176044	ESS	Havering
1894	1992	1900	1930	176338	EYK	Hull
1827	1957	1700	1827	106054	LND	ALL
....	....	ALL	1823	176338	NYK	Welbury
1806	1856	1806	1860	150576	WIL	Ansty
1836	....	1800	1850	119776	WIL	Donhead St Mary
1848	1917	1824	1950	150576	WIL	Tisbury
1827	1894	ALL	1894	176338	WYK	Tadcaster
1836	1880	1800	....	119776	???	Southampton
VINGOE						
1600	1992	1600	1992	172596	ALL	ALL
1797	1992	ALL	1992	172596	CON	Paul
1711	1746	ALL	ALL	104191	CON	???
VINT						
1700	1800	....	....	100633	DUR	???
VINTEN						
1832	1860	1832	1860	125970	KEN	Bromley
1850	1903	....	....	173142	KEN	Eltham
1832	1860	1832	1860	125970	KEN	Lee
VINTER						
1530	1850	1530	1800	108839	HUN	Godmanchester
VINTERS						
1796	1870	1700	1870	145750	CAM	ALL
VINTON						
1825	1825	ALL	1825	106909	KEN	Blean
1825	1825	ALL	1825	106909	KEN	Boughton
VIOLETT						
1735	1799	1735	1799	160164	SOM	Buckland St Mary
VIPAN						
1851	1900	1500	1818	177644	CAM	Mepal
1840	1900	1500	1757	177644	CAM	Sutton
1840	1900	1500	1757	177644	???	Isle Of Ely
VIPOND						
....	....	ALL	ALL	124389	ALL	ALL
1100	1860	ALL	1992	124389	CMA	Alston
1100	1860	ALL	1992	124389	CMA	Garrigill
1720	1815	1680	1720	122904	WRY	Ingleton
VIPONT						
1254	1291	1200	1300	154881	ALL	ALL
VIRENDER						
....	....	....	1794	130184	WIL	Calne
VIRGEN						
....	....	1830	1880	114782	SOM	South Petherton

Known From	To	Researching From	To	Ref	Cty	Place
VIRGIN						
1800	1826	1800	1826	166685	AVN	Bristol
VIRR						
....	....	ALL	ALL	112119	ALL	Name Study
VITTERY						
1764	1830	1710	1764	102598	DEV	Brixham
VITTLE						
....	....	1750	1800	108243	WLS	Fishguard
VIVASH						
1860	....	1500	1900	153036	HAM	???
1723	1768	1700	1723	115819	WIL	Compton Bassett
1860	....	1500	1900	153036	WIL	???
1860	....	1800	1900	153036	WMD	Birmingham
1860	....	1800	1900	153036	WMD	Edmonton
VIVERS						
....	....	1850	1950	160342	BDF	Bedford
VIVIAN						
....	....	ALL	ALL	172626	ALL	Name Study
1573	1933	1100	1992	172626	CON	Constantine
1800	....	1800	....	134813	CON	Roskear
1700	1900	?	1992	131458	CON	Trywreath
1785	1820	1650	1785	165549	CON	Withiel
....	....	1500	1600	174319	CON	???
1800	1992	1600	1800	172618	DEV	Malborough
1800	1992	1700	1800	172618	DEV	Salcombe
1670	1700	1640	1670	177555	DOR	South
1100	1992	....	....	172626	ENG	ALL
VIVIEN						
1800	1808	1600	1800	152080	CON	Callington
VIVYAN						
1810	1900	1600	1850	159166	CON	ALL
VIZARD						
1737	1757	ALL	ALL	124982	GLS	Dursley
1700	1780	ALL	ALL	124982	GLS	Wotton Under Edge
1780	....	....	....	167037	WIL	Brinkworth
1760	1812	ALL	1812	168696	WIL	Brinkworth
1786	....	1740	1800	170348	WIL	Brinkworth
1780	....	....	....	167037	WIL	Wootton Bassett
VIZE						
1800	1820	1750	1850	126217	SRY	Rotherhithe
VIZER						
1822	1992	....	....	156191	WIL	Easton Grey
VOAK						
1790	1790	1700	1800	136840	HAM	Portsmouth
VOAKE						
1835	1850	1850	1870	114871	AVN	Bristol
1770	1838	1700	1770	114871	SOM	Street
VOCE						
1897	1992	ALL	1897	157066	CHS	???
1600	1992	1700	1940	172634	LAN	Liverpool
1897	1992	ALL	1897	157066	LAN	Warrington
1600	1992	1700	1940	172634	LAN	Warrington
VOCKINS						
1835	1974	1812	1835	164003	MDX	St Sepullhre
1851	....	1812	1851	164003	WIL	Marlborough
VODDEN						
?	?	?	?	117528	DEV	North West
1780	1870	1750	1870	118575	DEV	Tawstock
VODEN						
1783	1784	1700	1800	172197	DEV	Buckland Filleigh
1783	1827	1700	1830	172197	DEV	Langtree
VOGAN						
1800	1872	1690	1800	172650	ARM	Armagh
1825	1992	1800	1825	172650	CAV	Cootehill
....	....	1690	1720	172650	DUB	Dublin
VOGHAN						
....	....	1500	1690	172650	GLS	Westbury On Severn
....	....	1500	1690	172650	HEF	Yarkhill
VOGLER						
1868	1906	1700	1868	103640	MDX	Poplar
VOICE						
....	....	ALL	ALL	172669	ALL	Name Study
1717	1765	1717	1765	151750	HRT	Harpenden
1717	1765	1717	1765	151750	HRT	Northchurch
VOILETT						
1735	....	1735	....	160164	SOM	Crewkerne
VOISEY						
1856	1922	1830	1922	170631	DEV	Stowford Quarry
VOKES						
1843	1992	1700	1843	158917	KEN	Milton Next Sittingbourne
1827	1850	1827	1992	114901	SRY	Chiddingfold
1787	1820	1750	1992	114901	SRY	Godalming
VOKINS						
1774	....	1700	1774	105457	KEN	???
1780	....	....	....	142158	WIL	Aldbourne
VOLLANDS						
1900	1950	1600	1900	172677	ENG	North
....	....	ALL	ALL	172685	YKS	ALL
1900	1950	1600	1900	172677	YKS	Wakefield
VOLLER						
....	....	ALL	ALL	145343	HAM	ALL
1787	1809	ALL	1787	175080	HAM	Hambledon
VON BARGEN						
1802	1897	1897	ALL	171360	???	Manchester
VON HUTON						
1250	?	....	....	147249	YKS	Goldsborough
VON OPPEN						
1837	1890	1800	1900	126586	MDX	London
VOOGHT						
1850	1992	1688	1992	152994	DEV	Central
1673	1840	1673	1992	176893	DEV	Dunchidoeck
1673	1840	1673	1992	176893	DEV	Kenn
1840	1914	1840	1992	176893	LND	ALL
VORCE						
1800	1860	1700	1900	138517	LAN	Lancaster
VORLEY						
1800	1940	1870	1940	173533	NTH	ALL
1750	1830	ALL	ALL	114235	NTH	???
VORST						
1890	1905	ALL	ALL	125318	LND	Stepney
VOSS						
1840	1900	1700	1840	174572	DFD	Llanelli
1750	1880	1720	1750	140317	HUN	Upwood
1826	1826	ALL	1826	115126	LIN	Skirbeck
1838	1899	ALL	1992	115126	NTH	Milton Malsor
VOTIER						
....	....	ALL	ALL	172707	ALL	Name Study
VOUGHTON						
1535	1826	1644	1716	160237	STS	Tamworth
VOUNG						
1800	1992	1800	1992	142662	AYR	Sornhill
VOUSDEN						
1760	1992	ALL	1760	141526	KEN	Brenchley
VOWLES						
1770	1870	ALL	1770	141224	GLS	South
1772	1875	....	....	165999	GLS	Almondsbury
1801	1992	....	1801	172715	GLS	Filton
1850	1960	1781	1860	126551	GLS	Henbury
1808	1828	ALL	ALL	124982	SOM	North
....	....	ALL	1770	141224	SOM	North
1705	1800	....	....	165999	SOM	Abbotsleigh
1863	1873	ALL	ALL	174017	SOM	Bedminster
?	?	?	?	172715	SOM	Dundry
1705	1800	....	....	165999	SOM	Long Ashton
1810	1970	1751	1870	126551	SOM	Whitchurch
1831	1874	ALL	ALL	153516	SOM	Wraxall
1831	1874	ALL	ALL	153516	SOM	???
1873	....	....	....	174017	???	Pontypool
VOYCE						
1400	1730	1350	1400	168777	SSX	Horsham
VOYEZ						
1760	1780	1700	1992	167592	MDX	London
1750	1800	1700	1992	167592	STS	Potteries
VOYSEY						
1871	1899	1871	1895	170631	DEV	South Sydenham
....	1858	1500	1858	104825	DEV	Tamerton Folliott
VSTEISON						
1599	1644	ALL	ALL	141615	LAN	Whittington
VULLIAMY						
1750	1950	....	....	108677	MDX	London
VYAN						
1776	1881	1713	1776	131326	CON	Mevagissey
VYE						
1670	1733	1670	1733	147974	DOR	Corfe Castle
1731	1789	1700	1800	126667	DOR	West Lulworth
1831	1859	1750	1831	143707	DOR	Weymouth
VYSE						
1882	1883	1882	....	172731	LND	Camberwell
1868	1892	....	....	172731	MDX	Holburn
1792	1868	1740	1792	172731	NFK	Diss
1841	1992	1841	1881	104396	YKS	Paull
WABY						
1700	1880	1700	1980	173819	LIN	Hackthorn
WACKETT						
1668	1992	ALL	ALL	101400	HRT	East

Known From	To	Researching From	To	Ref	Cty	Place
WADDELL						
1861	1992	1700	1861	150363	LTN	Stow
WADDELOW						
....	....	ALL	ALL	168939	ALL	Name Study
1730	....	....	1730	108839	CAM	Coveney
1600	1992	ALL	ALL	168939	CAM	Isle Of Ely
1600	1992	ALL	ALL	168939	CAM	Littleport
1880	1992	ALL	ALL	168939	LND	ALL
1528	1992	ALL	ALL	168939	NFK	ALL
WADDING						
1876	1932	1758	1876	175846	IOW	Ryde
WADDINGTON						
....	....	ALL	ALL	152412	ALL	Name Study
....	....	ALL	ALL	172758	ALL	Name Study
1865	1900	ALL	ALL	107182	CUL	ALL
1525	1700	1525	1700	109347	LAN	Altham
1560	1992	1560	1992	152412	LAN	Burnley
1807	1874	1750	1875	147214	LAN	Liverpool
1525	1700	1525	1700	109347	LAN	Padiham
1525	1600	1525	1600	109347	LAN	Wiswell
1762	1778	1730	1800	123404	LIN	Leake
1764	1776	1730	1800	123404	LIN	Lissington
1800	1992	1800	1900	173428	LND	Southwark
1865	1900	ALL	ALL	107182	WES	ALL
1800	1992	1700	1850	172774	YKS	Boltby
1800	1992	1700	1850	132810	YKS	Elland
1775	1992	1600	1775	159360	YKS	Halifax
1777	1951	1600	1777	151343	YKS	Huddersfield
1777	1951	1600	1777	151343	YKS	Normanton
WADDUP						
1801	1851	1760	1801	103365	KEN	Chatham
1841	1851	1851	1992	103365	KEN	Sheerness
WADDY						
....	....	1700	1755	116173	YKS	Helmsley
WADE						
?	?	?	?	131024	BDF	Biggleswade
1635	....	1600	1700	124796	BKM	Princes Risborough
1811	1844	1750	1900	116742	CAM	Leverington
1800	1992	1700	1800	110477	CAM	Wisbech
....	....	1700	1870	110914	CHS	???
....	....	1800	....	118591	CON	Calstock
1811	1831	....	....	112887	CON	Phillleigh
....	....	1700	1820	169234	CON	???
1796	1841	1790	1850	173428	ESS	Chelmsford
1872	1992	1600	1880	172146	ESS	Thurrock
1880	1900	1700	1880	149705	HUN	Stilton
1592	....	....	....	153397	IOW	Carisbrooke
1700	1800	1700	1800	109347	LAN	Accrington
1670	1931	1600	1800	125350	LAN	Blackpool
1700	....	1700	....	109347	LAN	Hapton
1670	1785	....	....	112429	LAN	Lytham
1670	1931	1600	1800	125350	LAN	Lytham
1670	1931	1600	ALL	125350	LAN	Warton
....	....	1800	1840	118591	LND	ALL
1830	1851	....	....	135437	NFK	Bodham
1826	1837	....	....	135437	NFK	Foulsham
1789	1977	....	....	135437	NFK	Stibbard
....	1570	....	....	115819	SAL	Lilleshall
1750	1810	1650	1750	150614	SFK	Blythburgh
1600	1700	ALL	1600	131059	SFK	Ipswich
1852	1867	1822	1852	162523	YKS	Brodsworth
1650	1830	1750	1850	172782	YKS	Burnsall
1807	1907	1750	1807	169056	YKS	Halifax
....	....	1700	1870	110914	YKS	Kilnsey
....	....	1750	1850	169056	YKS	Kirkheaton
1894	1983	1860	1894	147060	YKS	Pontefract
1576	1703	1575	1851	170267	YKS	Pudsey
WADEL						
1780	1875	1780	1875	133795	SCT	Cumbernauld
WADESON						
1700	1800	....	....	146854	LAN	Holme
1800	1900	....	....	146854	LAN	Lancaster
1800	1900	....	....	146854	LAN	Southport
WADHAM						
....	....	ALL	ALL	162531	ALL	Name Study
....	....	....	1992	148679	AVN	Bristol
....	1742	ALL	ALL	129933	DOR	Poole
1713	1767	1545	1855	116580	DOR	Tarrart Hinton
1756	1900	1538	1920	116580	IOW	ALL
1764	1786	ALL	ALL	129933	LND	Whitechapel
WADHAM-WILLIAMS						
1850	1855	1855	1940	141771	SOM	Taunton
WADHAMS						
....	....	1800	1900	174319	MLN	???
WADKINS						
1924	....	....	....	172790	MDX	Lower Edmonton
1878	1951	....	....	172790	MDX	Twickenham
WADLEY						
1800	1880	....	....	140317	ESS	East Donyland
WADLOW						
?	?	ALL	ALL	168939	LND	ALL
?	?	ALL	ALL	168939	NFK	ALL
?	?	ALL	ALL	168939	SAL	ALL
WADMAN						
....	....	ALL	ALL	172804	ALL	Name Study
WADMORE						
1797	1797	....	1797	143901	LND	Finsbury
WADSWORTH						
1900	1931	1800	1992	110418	FER	Enniskillen
....	....	1850	....	106623	LAN	Calsford
1765	1800	1700	1800	147958	LAN	Cockerham
1830	1992	1700	1800	172820	LAN	???
1766	1788	1709	1800	107360	NTH	Badby
1790	1862	1712	1880	107360	NTH	Harlestone
1787	1787	1750	1812	107360	NTH	Welton
1811	1890	....	1811	163031	SYK	???
1877	1882	....	....	146811	WYK	Elland
1884	1912	....	....	146811	WYK	Halifax
1841	1900	....	1841	146811	WYK	Rishworth
1835	1835	1700	1992	102377	YKS	Holme On The Wolds
1836	1836	1800	1836	141097	YKS	Wadworth
1830	1992	1700	1800	172820	YKS	???
WADWORTH						
1772	1992	1700	1772	161446	WIL	Devizes
WAEICK						
1807	1841	1700	1850	160601	LND	???
WAFFORNE						
1690	1747	1707	1812	107360	NTH	Welton
WAFORD						
....	....	ALL	1760	151602	WIL	Ramsbury
WAGER						
1600	1850	ALL	1992	172812	GLS	ALL
WAGG						
1835	1992	1800	1835	154318	NFK	East Dereham
....	1750	ALL	1750	134511	NTT	Papplewick
WAGGOTT						
1800	1865	1750	1800	136220	SOM	Stoke St Gregory
WAGHORN						
....	....	ALL	ALL	172839	ALL	Name Study
1798	1859	1700	1800	130656	KEN	Chatham
1819	1929	1700	1819	122378	KEN	Plaxtol
1854	....	1700	1854	130656	KEN	Strood
1800	1800	....	1800	113034	KEN	???
1867	....	1700	1867	130656	SRY	Redhill
WAGSTAFF						
....	....	ALL	ALL	139262	ALL	Name Study
1600	1992	ALL	ALL	139262	ALL	ALL
....	....	1800	1950	134546	BDF	Sharnbrook
....	....	1800	1950	134546	BDF	Yeilden
1790	1909	1700	1790	163635	DBY	Winster
1750	1830	1650	1750	118958	LAN	???
1808	1913	1765	1808	147850	LND	Hackney
1808	1913	1765	1808	147850	LND	St Pancras
1808	1913	1765	1808	147850	LND	Whitechapel
1839	1992	1700	1839	105392	YKS	Holmfirth
WAGSTAFFE						
1672	1741	1550	1696	102830	DBY	Ashbourne
1826	1860	1750	1860	126586	ESS	Colchester
1810	1870	1810	1870	154598	WAR	Bedworth
1800	1830	1700	1800	163902	YKS	Sheffield
WAILS						
1849	1851	1820	1870	159905	NBL	Earsdon
WAIN						
1750	1900	1750	1900	173681	DBY	Longor
?	?	ALL	1900	117919	KEN	Chislehurst
1910	1992	1800	1992	121215	LAN	Denton
1783	1828	1600	1783	152463	LEI	Barrow Upon Soar
1807	1900	1600	1807	152463	LEI	Long Whatton
1770	1960	1700	1770	172847	NTT	Basford
1770	1960	1700	1770	172847	NTT	Bulwell
1770	1960	1700	1770	172847	NTT	Nottingham
WAIND						
....	....	ALL	....	155713	NYK	Gillamoor
WAINE						
1830	....	1800	1840	172855	LAN	Farnworth
1840	....	1800	1850	172855	LAN	Prescot
1851	1940	1851	1940	118931	OXF	Burford
1831	....	....	....	118931	OXF	Shilton

Known From	To	Researching From	To	Ref	Cty	Place
WAINE contd.						
1868	1992	ALL	1868	154482	RFW	Greenock
WAINEMAN						
1641	1685	1565	1641	141291	LAN	Dalton In Furness
WAINES						
1880	1918	ALL	ALL	118885	NRY	Scarborough
?	?	?	?	169064	YKS	Flamborough
WAINMAN						
1614	1806	1614	1806	117803	NRY	Buttercrambe
1850	1900	1750	1850	167398	YKS	Doncaster
1850	1900	1750	1850	167398	YKS	Hatfield
WAINWRIGHT						
1740	1850	ALL	1850	115347	CHS	Dodleston
1841	1960	1800	1900	149330	CHS	Nantwich
1820	1850	1800	1820	101796	DBY	Belper
1760	1870	ALL	1760	161330	DBY	Wornhill'
....	....	1870	1930	179280	LAN	Great Crosby
1830	1850	1830	1900	115347	LAN	Liverpool
1778	1839	1700	1778	156051	LAN	Rishton
1637	....	1600	1660	160873	STS	Sedgley
1780	1820	1700	1992	102520	YKS	Calverley
....	....	1750	1850	147613	YKS	Hemsworth
WAIT						
1730	1800	1600	1730	164577	BEW	Ayton
1865	1880	1800	1865	172154	BKM	Slough
1763	1825	1700	1780	163740	BRK	Sparsholt
1578	1884	....	1580	108839	CAM	Harlton
1750	1795	....	....	165999	GLS	Henbury
1800	1900	1800	1900	164577	NBL	North Shields
WAITE						
1779	1859	1790	1830	118737	BRK	Beenham
1760	1782	....	1800	171441	BRK	Kingston Lisle
1800	1919	1750	1800	168777	BRK	Reading
1788	1814	....	....	138401	CUL	Distington
1861	....	....	....	165387	MDX	Camden Town
1841	1851	1800	1900	162450	MDX	Ealing
1942	....	1940	1950	163775	MON	Swansea
1850	1870	1800	1900	162620	NBL	North Shields
1892	....	....	1920	171441	SOM	Shepton Mallet
1828	1849	1800	1850	176125	WIL	Easton Royal
1918	....	1890	1930	171441	WRY	Epsom
1703	1792	....	....	151351	YKS	Kirkby Overblow
1850	1880	ALL	1860	142301	YKS	Leeds
1883	1961	1800	1883	125350	YKS	Ripon
WAITES						
1850	....	....	....	142158	MON	Trevethin
WAITHMAN						
1800	1860	1800	1900	168734	WAR	Coventry
WAITMAN						
1770	1834	1600	1992	159956	SFK	Barningham
WAITON						
1825	1846	ALL	1825	154563	DUR	Sadberge
WAKE						
1100	1349	1100	1349	154881	ALL	ALL
1790	1798	1600	1798	155608	DUR	Seahouses
1834	1948	1830	1950	104477	HAM	Bitterne
1840	....	....	....	104477	HAM	Eling
1790	1810	1750	1840	160504	HAM	Eling
1805	1863	1620	1867	149640	HAM	Winchester
1817	....	....	....	104477	KEN	Chatham
1787	1798	1700	1787	129453	KEN	Woolwich
1809	....	....	....	104477	LND	Marylebone
1810	1870	1810	1870	160504	LND	Marylebone
1854	1992	1503	1854	158461	LND	Poplar
1800	1815	1800	1820	160504	LND	Southwark
1780	1850	1700	1800	118303	MDX	London
1720	1740	....	....	105759	NBL	Bamburgh
1808	1898	....	....	162914	NFK	West Winch
1823	1854	....	1823	100064	SFK	Corleston
1868	1980	ALL	1963	138819	T&W	Hebburn
WAKEFIELD						
1670	1730	1670	1730	156930	BRK	ALL
1850	1920	1850	1920	156930	BRK	East Hagbourne
1815	1860	1815	1860	156930	BRK	Greenham
1710	1820	1720	1730	156930	BRK	Leckhampstead
1815	1860	1815	1860	156930	BRK	Newbury
1810	1830	1750	1810	132640	CAM	Wisbeach
....	....	....	....	130842	CMA	Kendal
1783	1820	1700	1783	155500	GLS	Cirencester
1790	1810	1700	1810	148288	HAM	Portsea
1788	1789	1745	1788	165107	LND	Bloomsbury
1860	1870	1860	1870	156930	MON	Llanfrechfa
1780	1965	....	1965	130842	WAR	Central
1780	1965	....	1965	130842	WAR	North

Known From	To	Researching From	To	Ref	Cty	Place
WAKEFIELD contd.						
1700	1830	ALL	1830	168696	WIL	Dauntsey
1882	....	1800	1900	129593	YKS	ALL
1854	1992	1600	1854	104612	YKS	Huddersfield
1854	1992	1600	1854	104612	YKS	New Mill
WAKEFORD						
1796	1814	ALL	1796	108553	HAM	Portsea
1896	1970	1890	1930	166154	LND	Fulham
1772	1825	1700	1772	172871	SRY	Godalming
1840	1870	....	....	172871	SRY	Ripley
1890	1930	1600	1900	166154	SSX	Brighton
1840	1920	1780	1920	166154	SSX	Petworth
WAKEHAM						
1712	1743	1600	1712	172898	DEV	Kingsbridge
1811	1992	1770	1992	125520	HAM	Hamble
WAKELAM						
....	....	ALL	ALL	172901	ALL	Name Study
1750	1992	ALL	ALL	172901	ALL	ALL
1778	1900	1650	1850	172928	STS	Kings Winford
1778	1992	1650	1850	172928	STS	Sedgley
1810	1920	1700	1800	172928	WOR	Dudley
WAKELEY						
1740	1980	ALL	1740	103438	KEN	Rainham
WAKELIN						
1878	1900	1800	1900	118222	LND	Mayfair
1851	....	1800	1851	131806	SCT	Auckinleck
WAKELING						
....	....	ALL	ALL	172936	ALL	Name Study
1820	1825	1790	1850	118737	KEN	Chatham
....	....	ALL	1880	161608	LND	East
1858	ALL	ALL	1858	116734	MDX	Old Brentford
1739	1946	1700	1739	138347	SFK	Haverhill
WAKELY						
1761	....	1700	1900	166359	DEV	Whitstone
....	....	ALL	1850	101036	DOR	Lyme Regis
....	....	?	?	104310	DOR	Stoke Abbott
....	....	?	?	104310	DOR	Swyre
1806	1806	1780	1830	133000	DOR	Whichurch Canonicorum
WAKEM						
1791	....	1700	1800	125628	CON	Manaccan
WAKEMAN						
1882	1992	1700	1882	172944	KEN	Swanscombe
1100	1992	1832	1900	173320	WOR	Beckford
1792	1822	ALL	1992	102245	WOR	Wychbold
WAKERLEY						
....	....	1220	1700	142859	ALL	ALL
1825	1861	1700	1825	112321	LEI	Hoton
1825	1861	1700	1825	112321	LEI	Loughborough
1757	1852	1852	1888	167231	LEI	Melton Mowbray
1888	1914	1850	1888	167231	MDX	Westminster
WAKLEY						
....	....	1327	1700	142859	ALL	ALL
1800	1900	1900	1992	168572	HAM	Gosport
WAKSTEAD						
1744	....	ALL	1744	139459	WAR	Aston Juxta Birmingham
WALBANK						
....	....	1598	1740	145211	WRY	Barnoldswick
1764	1860	1740	1764	145211	WRY	Keighley
1700	1992	1600	1992	129623	YKS	Keighley
WALBRAN						
1824	1846	1820	1880	167002	MDX	London
1698	1836	1650	1900	167002	NYK	Topcliffe
1828	1831	1820	1880	167002	SRY	Camberwell
WALBURN						
1633	1760	1550	1800	167002	NYK	Wath
WALBY						
1600	1800	1600	1800	167924	HRT	Aston
1560	1800	1560	1800	167924	HRT	Walkern
WALCH						
1800	1850	1800	1850	140864	DEN	Ruabon
WALCRAFT						
1740	1800	1600	1850	166804	OXF	ALL
1760	1848	1650	1760	166804	OXF	Bampton
WALDEGRAVE						
1691	1926	ALL	1691	108553	HAM	Portsmouth
1600	1800	ALL	ALL	110477	LIN	Fotherby
WALDEN						
1825	1846	1820	1875	118354	BKM	Chalfont St Peter
....	....	1790	1820	177725	CAV	Killashandra
1790	....	ALL	1790	125121	ESS	???
1845	1980	1700	1845	144754	MDX	Bethnal Green
....	....	1747	1899	139831	NTH	Haselbech

Known From	To	Researching From	To	Ref	Cty	Place
WALDEN contd.						
....	....	1849	1889	139831	NTH	Northampton
WALDIE						
1822	....	1800	1850	169625	ROX	Ashkirk
WALDING						
1746	1890	1746	1890	104817	NTH	Haselbech
WALDOCK						
1700	1992	1700	1992	166758	BDF	???
1700	1992	1700	1992	166758	HRT	???
WALDON						
1800	1808	1800	1820	102717	ESS	Horndon
WALDRAM						
1840	1860	1810	1840	130443	LEI	Belton
1817	1840	1750	1817	130443	LEI	Osgathorpe
WALDREN						
....	....	1600	1778	174130	DEV	Drewsteignton
1777	1872	1750	1900	136719	HAM	Deane
WALDRON						
....	....	ALL	ALL	120057	ALL	ALL
1900	1940	....	....	177407	HAM	Eastleigh
1773	1900	1700	1900	177407	HAM	Kingsclere
1800	1899	1800	1899	143537	LEI	ALL
1895	1925	ALL	ALL	120057	LND	Fortune Green
1840	1900	1800	1840	166464	SRY	Walworth
1888	1980	....	....	104892	STS	Wolverhampton
1887	1887	1700	1900	153222	WIL	Cricklade
....	....	1700	1900	153222	WIL	Leigh
1790	1790	1750	1790	133671	WIL	Ogbourne St Andrews
1870	1879	1750	1820	109746	WOR	Bromsgrove
ALL	1870	....	....	126101	WOR	Bromsgrove
1715	1900	1550	1891	104892	WOR	Clent
1815	1837	1815	1837	174475	WOR	Clent
1915	....	....	....	170313	WOR	Droitwich
1700	1850	1850	1992	126101	WOR	Stoke Prior
WALE						
1807	1992	1807	1992	172952	IOW	ALL
WALES						
1845	1992	....	....	112380	DUR	Sunderland
1818	1867	....	....	135070	MDX	Stepney
1818	1875	1818	1875	172960	NFK	Burnham Market
1731	1810	1731	1810	172960	NFK	Waverney Valley
....	....	1700	1820	163260	NFK	Worm E Gay
....	1841	1841	....	112380	SCT	Edingburgh
1849	1900	1800	1849	128724	SFK	Ixworth
1760	1828	1700	1850	105775	SFK	Mellis
1760	1828	1700	1850	105775	SFK	Pakenham
1731	1810	1731	1810	172960	SFK	Waverney Valley
....	....	1800	1992	128600	SRY	Horley
1850	1940	1850	1920	172960	SRY	Southwark
1800	1850	1700	1800	177296	YKS	Doncaster
1800	1992	....	....	177296	YKS	Sheffield
WALESBY						
1701	1725	....	....	121835	LIN	Legsby
1772	1802	....	....	121835	LIN	Market Stainton
1725	1772	....	....	121835	LIN	Snelland
WALFORD						
1638	....	1638	....	147532	CHS	Macclesfield
1830	1920	1700	1830	172979	STS	Penkridge
WALHOUSE						
1700	1799	....	....	147575	???	???
WALKCUP						
1866	1992	1866	1992	173738	NBL	South Shields
WALKER						
1690	1980	1600	1992	149233	ABD	Chapel Of Garioch
1690	1980	1600	1992	149233	ABD	Fyvie
1799	1931	1700	1799	118427	ABD	Old Deer
1853	1901	1700	1853	106887	ABD	Ordiquhill
1800	1880	ALL	1800	117188	ANS	Inverkeillor
1783	1900	1700	1790	173037	ANT	Hillsborough
1797	1880	1786	1900	146536	AYR	Beith
1765	1775	1720	1815	146536	AYR	Dreghorn
1830	1847	1700	1830	168246	AYR	Galston
1790	1855	1790	1900	119725	AYR	Kilbirnie
1784	1905	1700	1950	146536	AYR	Kilbirnie
1800	1850	1700	1800	158143	AYR	Maybole
1767	1807	1700	1850	143693	BKM	Great Hampden
1801	1956	....	....	176125	BRK	Faringdon
1808	1890	ALL	ALL	149004	BRK	Warfield
1778	1795	ALL	1778	168602	CAM	Littleport
1875	1992	1875	1992	142352	CAM	Shelford
1843	1843	1810	1850	126705	CHS	Chester
1785	1850	1700	1790	118958	CHS	???
1700	1850	1600	1850	167088	CMA	Whitehaven
....	....	1700	1850	116173	CUL	West
WALKER contd.						
1729	1797	....	....	138401	CUL	Branthwaite
1729	1797	....	....	138401	CUL	Dean
1740	1900	1700	1900	150797	DBY	South
1532	1828	1550	1671	102830	DBY	Alkmanton
1765	1792	1700	1765	119555	DBY	Breaston
1770	1850	1810	?	105694	DBY	Buxton
....	....	ALL	1820	126721	DBY	Chesterfield
1853	....	1700	1900	138185	DBY	Chesterfield
1871	1900	1750	1870	178993	DBY	Darley Moor
1828	1857	1828	1920	119555	DBY	Ilkeston
1702	1702	1550	1701	102830	DBY	Matlock
1790	1840	ALL	ALL	173010	DBY	South Wingfield
1770	1920	1700	1992	129496	DBY	Turnditch
1860	1900	ALL	ALL	139890	DEV	East
1783	1900	1700	1790	173037	DOW	Lisburn
1900	1970	1700	1900	104701	DUR	ALL
1820	....	....	1992	146870	DUR	Boldon
1836	1836	....	....	103632	DUR	Colliery Row
1922	1960	1901	1960	115967	DUR	Hartlepool
1789	1841	ALL	1789	100528	DUR	Ingleton
1875	1893	1875	1893	103632	DUR	Seaham Harbour
1703	1775	ALL	1703	171573	DUR	Startforth
....	....	ALL	1886	116351	DUR	Sunderland
1774	1830	ALL	1774	154563	DUR	Weardale
1837	1860	1780	1900	118486	ERY	Flaxton
1804	....	1804	....	139149	ERY	Nafferton
1600	....	....	....	164038	ESS	Wilmington
1754	....	1712	1791	168637	HAM	East Worldham
1791	....	1791	1814	168637	HAM	Petersfield
1712	....	1600	1712	168637	HAM	Sheldon
1548	1992	....	....	175714	HRT	Baldock
1700	ALL	1744	1780	107379	HRT	Hemel Hempstead
1874	1875	1874	1875	142352	HRT	Kelshall
1852	1874	1850	1875	142352	HRT	Reed
1759	....	1700	1800	142352	HRT	Therford
1797	1797	1700	1797	153605	KCD	Dunnottar
1818	1852	1745	1816	173029	KCD	Dunnottar
1867	1898	ALL	1992	125113	KEN	Birchington
1808	1917	....	1920	171441	KEN	Border
1804	....	....	1820	171441	KEN	Charing
1770	1790	ALL	1770	162256	KEN	Darenth
1869	1992	....	1869	141968	KEN	Greenwich
1845	....	1800	....	109967	KEN	Gt Chart
1789	1789	....	....	127426	KEN	Harrietsham
1867	1898	ALL	1992	125113	KEN	Margate
1846	1866	1820	1846	101796	LAN	Ashton Under Lyne
....	1816	1700	1825	135658	LAN	Barnacre
1855	1857	1700	1870	135658	LAN	Barton
....	1809	1700	1860	135658	LAN	Bleasdale
....	1851	1700	1860	135658	LAN	Church Town St Helens
1813	1819	1700	1860	135658	LAN	Goosnargh
1700	1706	1600	1700	163783	LAN	Goosnargh
1913	1992	....	1913	118117	LAN	Manchester
1850	....	1850	....	136786	LAN	Manchester
1860	1900	1800	1870	143006	LAN	Manchester
1700	1992	....	....	157805	LAN	Prescott
....	1846	1700	1870	135658	LAN	Preston
1875	1992	1700	1875	176516	LAN	Preston
1860	1910	1860	1992	135658	LAN	Scotforth
1818	1992	1700	1800	162256	LAN	Turton
....	1825	1700	1860	135658	LAN	Walton Le Dale
1896	1992	....	....	173010	LAN	Wigan
1700	1992	1550	1700	173169	LEI	North West
1745	1790	1700	1745	174130	LEI	Goadby
1758	1900	....	1900	135968	LEI	Great Dalby
1860	1992	1860	1992	122769	LEI	Osgathorpe
....	....	ALL	ALL	104531	LIN	South
....	1738	ALL	1738	152838	LIN	Keelby
1880	1930	1750	1880	173088	LIN	Wainfleet
1896	1992	ALL	ALL	104531	LIN	Whaplode
1765	1794	1764	ALL	104310	LND	Bethnal Green
1859	1861	1700	1992	166073	LND	Bethnall Green
1858	1880	1750	1858	102903	LND	Bloomsbury
1859	1861	1700	1992	166073	LND	Dalston Hackney
1909	1930	1800	1992	166073	LND	Hackney
1858	1880	1750	1858	102903	LND	Islington
1914	1914	1700	1992	177733	LND	Islington
1909	1930	1800	1937	166073	LND	Leabridge
1829	1851	1800	1829	128368	LND	Marylebone
1806	1992	1800	1992	172995	LND	Rotherhithe
1846	1861	1700	1992	166073	LND	Shoreditch
1833	1861	1700	1992	166073	LND	Spitailfields

Known From	To	Researching From	To	Ref	Cty	Place
WALKER contd.						
1790	1800	1800	1817	162256	MDX	Bethnal Green
1842	1885	1800	1885	173061	MDX	Clerkenwell
1810	1829	1800	1829	107573	MDX	Harmonsworth
1891	1944	1800	1900	127981	MDX	London
1756	1756	1700	1850	167002	MDX	London
1821	1992	1780	1992	173096	MDX	London
1860	....	1831	1860	168637	MDX	Marylebone
1838	....	1800	....	109967	MDX	Shoreditch
1817	1851	1775	1875	167002	MDX	St Luke
1791	1992	1750	1791	176257	MDX	Stepney
1895	1895	1895	1930	141046	MDX	Tooting
1870	1930	1800	1870	127949	MDX	Willesden
....	....	1840	ALL	104310	MON	Newport
....	....	ALL	1886	116351	NBL	Annitsford
1914	1965	1872	1992	105449	NBL	Newcastle Upon Tyne
1868	?	1843	1880	105449	NBL	North Shields
1866	1890	1830	1865	173118	NBL	Seaton Delaval
1843	1868	ALL	ALL	105449	NFK	Great Yarmouth
1717	....	ALL	1717	119326	NRY	Maundby
1812	1844	1800	1830	168777	NTH	Badby
1717	1743	1694	1750	107360	NTH	Chapel Brampton
1845	1901	1700	1960	115967	NTH	Tynemouth
1808	1921	1700	1921	125865	NTT	Bummy
1780	1785	1730	1780	162396	NTT	Clayworth
1792	1851	1851	1851	119555	NTT	Greasley
1860	1992	1860	1992	122769	NTT	Nottingham
1703	1775	ALL	1703	171573	NYK	Barnard Castle
1800	1835	1800	1850	102881	NYK	Danby In Cleveland
1730	1770	1700	1730	121339	NYK	K Ravensworth
1823	1873	1800	1823	179663	NYK	Stonegrave
1750	1820	1750	1820	154210	NYK	Thirntoft
1867	1872	....	....	168637	OXF	Aston
1758	1830	ALL	1758	115126	OXF	Great Tew
1861	1918	1861	1992	168637	OXF	Oxford
1785	1992	1851	1881	128988	PER	Alyth
....	1798	1700	1850	148288	PER	Tibbermore
1700	....	....	....	127140	RFW	Greenock
1800	1820	....	....	146870	ROX	Roxburgh
1820	1992	1750	1820	144134	ROX	Sprouston
1851	1881	1840	1992	173010	SAL	Shrewsbury
1770	....	....	....	100676	SAL	Wenlock
1797	1815	1750	1815	173622	SCT	Endinburgh
1843	1861	1861	1992	167576	SOM	Bath
....	....	1750	1850	163082	SOM	Bristol
1806	1892	ALL	ALL	153516	SOM	Chew Magna
1806	1892	ALL	ALL	153516	SOM	Kenn
1806	1892	ALL	ALL	153516	SOM	Wick St Lawrence
1800	....	1750	1850	102016	SRY	Bermondsey
1850	1900	1800	1850	168750	SRY	Southwark
1818	1860	1818	1992	168637	SRY	Witley
....	....	1700	1765	129356	SSX	Arlington
1843	1843	....	....	167576	SSX	Brighton
1883	1900	....	....	158941	STS	Burslem
1875	1900	....	....	173177	STS	Burton
....	....	....	1825	173177	STS	Penkridge
1840	1975	....	....	173177	STS	Rugeley
1767	1800	1700	1767	110639	STS	Stoke On Trent
1855	....	ALL	ALL	158941	STS	Wolstanton
1853	1872	1820	1880	133639	STS	Wolverhampton
1727	1823	....	1823	155055	STS	Wolverhampton
1823	1890	1800	1900	123285	SYK	Elsecar
1849	....	1849	....	104213	SYK	Sheffield
1800	1850	1800	1850	154210	WAR	Bedworth
1850	1880	....	....	120472	WAR	Birmingham
1783	1783	ALL	ALL	125288	WAR	Birmingham
1800	1860	1750	1900	129240	WAR	Birmingham
1820	1870	1800	1830	125938	WAR	Coleshill
1820	1870	1800	1830	125938	WAR	Netherwhitacre
1675	1867	1700	1870	150479	WAR	Radford Semele
1834	1892	1700	1841	156051	WEM	Drumcree
1882	....	1882	1992	168637	WIL	Marlborough
1700	1760	1660	1700	122904	WLN	Torpichen
1687	1992	....	1687	144363	WLS	Redstone
1758	1992	1700	1758	142883	WOR	Bredon
1846	1846	1800	1870	127361	WRY	Dewsbury
1801	1861	1700	1801	100110	WYK	Yeadon
1822	1898	1700	1822	145327	WYK	Yeadon
1800	1900	1800	1920	149136	YKS	North
1805	1890	1700	1810	173452	YKS	South
1834	1912	1800	1834	177555	YKS	Batley
....	....	1700	1825	135658	YKS	Bentham
ALL	ALL	ALL	ALL	105813	YKS	Birstall
ALL	ALL	ALL	ALL	105813	YKS	Bradford

Known From	To	Researching From	To	Ref	Cty	Place
WALKER contd.						
1910	....	....	....	165484	YKS	Bretton
1895	1905	....	....	141984	YKS	Castleford
1829	1851	1800	1829	128368	YKS	Doncaster
1880	1895	....	....	141984	YKS	Grosmont
1800	1850	....	....	125199	YKS	Halifax
1808	1860	....	....	136964	YKS	Halifax
1822	1870	1750	1870	155969	YKS	Halifax
1828	1878	1800	1900	170348	YKS	Halifax
1725	1800	1700	1992	114901	YKS	Harewood
1780	....	ALL	1800	136786	YKS	Harrogate
1820	....	1700	....	134589	YKS	Hemingbrough
1760	1880	1700	1880	123595	YKS	Holmfirth
1820	1860	1775	1871	157716	YKS	Honley
1800	1840	1790	1850	123595	YKS	Huddersfield
1860	1861	1800	1992	146331	YKS	Huddersfield
1820	1851	1700	1870	157716	YKS	Huddersfield
1819	1866	1750	1900	130974	YKS	Hunslet
1881	....	1800	1890	110183	YKS	Keighley
1819	....	....	....	165484	YKS	Kingston Upon Hull
1831	1851	1831	1881	139661	YKS	Leeds
1782	1872	1872	1900	149519	YKS	Leeds
1840	1874	1750	1840	168513	YKS	Mirfield
1784	1970	1700	1784	127728	YKS	Normanton
1700	1950	1600	1992	122084	YKS	Otley
1871	1950	1600	1950	172863	YKS	Otley
1776	1810	1776	1810	149403	YKS	Pickering
1750	1850	....	....	167843	YKS	Redmire Cum Bolton
1730	1780	1700	1730	156302	YKS	Ripon
....	....	1750	1840	147613	YKS	Rotherham
1800	1900	1800	1920	149136	YKS	Scarcroft
1750	1950	1750	1950	114529	YKS	Sheffield
1843	1992	1700	1843	146609	YKS	Sheffield
....	....	1830	1992	147613	YKS	Sheffield
1800	1860	1750	1860	166081	YKS	Slaidburn
1800	....	1750	1850	179078	YKS	Slaidburn
1700	1800	1700	1800	167924	YKS	Thornton
1870	....	1852	1870	176958	YKS	Wakefield
1828	1878	1800	1900	170348	YKS	Warley
1836	1992	....	1836	135674	YKS	Whiston
....	....	1780	1825	173177	???	Birmingham St Martins
1600	1992	....	....	100633	???	Newcastle Upon Tyne
WALKERDINE						
1894	1970	ALL	ALL	101338	ALL	ALL
WALKERLEY						
....	....	1563	1700	142859	ALL	ALL
WALKEY						
....	....	1460	1992	142859	ALL	ALL
1862	....	....	....	173991	CON	Charlestown
WALKINSHAW						
1779	1854	1720	1854	153273	LKS	Carnwath
WALKLATE						
....	....	ALL	ALL	173193	ALL	Name Study
1700	....	?	....	173193	CHS	Astbury Prestbury
1700	1992	ALL	1700	173193	DBY	Derby
1700	1992	ALL	1700	173193	DBY	Ludworth
1700	1992	ALL	1700	173193	DBY	Matlock
1700	1992	ALL	1700	173193	DBY	Mellor
1700	1992	ALL	1700	173193	DBY	Worksworth
1640	1800	ALL	1640	173193	GLS	Fairford
1640	1800	ALL	1640	173193	GLS	Lechlade
1780	1850	?	....	173193	HRT	St Albans
1800	....	?	....	173193	LAN	Manchester
1650	1820	ALL	1650	173193	LND	Stepney
1650	1820	ALL	1650	173193	LND	Westminster
1566	1615	?	....	173193	NTT	Worksop
1700	1850	ALL	1700	173193	STS	Stoke Upon Trent
WALKLEY						
....	....	1570	1700	142859	ALL	ALL
1704	1830	1460	1841	142859	GLS	Kings Stanley
1825	1894	1700	1825	126454	GLS	Kingswood
1600	1694	1537	1791	142859	GLS	Leonard Stanley
1760	1851	1630	1851	142859	GLS	Minchinhampton
1851	1900	1700	1851	155101	WAR	Birmingham
WALKLIN						
1674	1737	1674	1737	103977	OXF	Benson
1674	1737	1674	1737	103977	OXF	Newington
1674	1737	1674	1737	103977	OXF	Warborough
WALL						
1780	1940	1780	1940	113670	AVN	Bath
1806	1900	1700	1850	121312	CON	Padstow
1806	1900	1700	1850	121312	CON	Truro
1760	1940	ALL	ALL	156604	DBY	Ashover

Known From	To	Researching From	To	Ref	Cty	Place
WALL contd.						
1700	1900	ALL	ALL	156604	DBY	Darley
1800	1980	ALL	ALL	156604	DBY	Matlock
....	....	1700	....	141216	GLS	North
1800	1860	1600	1800	173223	GLS	Iron Acton
....	....	1700	....	141216	GLS	Mid
1800	1800	1700	1800	147575	GLS	Tytherington
1880	1970	1870	1970	145009	HEF	Abbey Dore
1827	1841	1825	1900	139173	HEF	Leysters
1860	1875	1800	1890	165093	HEF	Little Hereford
1825	1825	ALL	1825	139173	HEF	Middleton On The Hill
1800	1820	1750	1820	123870	HEF	???
1785	1863	1600	1865	175641	IRL	Wicklow
1840	1864	1700	1840	115517	KEN	East
1817	1840	1600	1840	156183	LND	East
1871	1992	1750	1871	173231	LND	Mile End
1800	1992	1600	1800	173207	SAL	South
1850	1992	ALL	1850	146994	SAL	Albington
1840	1875	1800	1890	165093	SAL	Ashford Carbonel
1725	1852	1650	1890	160849	SAL	Highley
1800	1860	1800	1992	152943	SOM	Bridgwater
1780	1850	....	....	138134	SOM	Taunton
1792	1900	1600	1792	114634	SOM	Wickwar
1847	1992	1700	1847	173215	STS	ALL
1840	1864	1840	1992	152943	STS	Kingswinford
1550	1860	1500	1860	102830	STS	Sedgely
....	1843	....	1843	140767	STS	Sedgley
1800	1914	1700	1800	123870	STS	???
1835	1840	1800	1835	123870	WOR	???
1881	1901	1861	1881	164364	YKS	Sheffield
WALLACE						
1826	1850	1800	1900	119725	ABD	New Deer
1747	1975	1740	1975	175153	ABD	???
1860	1911	1800	1911	108278	ANT	Ballymoney
?	?	?	?	166642	AYR	???
1820	1860	1750	1900	138878	CUL	Whithaven
1806	1869	1700	1800	111031	DFS	Morton
....	....	ALL	ALL	106844	DON	North
1872	1992	1700	1880	106844	DON	Glenalla
1872	1992	1700	1880	106860	DON	Glenalla
1903	1916	1850	1900	125431	DOW	Downpatrick
....	....	ALL	ALL	106844	DOW	Newry
....	....	1800	1899	142298	DOW	???
1752	1752	ALL	1752	131881	FIF	Burntisland
1861	1883	....	....	175080	HAM	Widley
1860	1930	1860	1992	169161	LAN	Liverpool
1789	1807	1760	1820	141046	LKS	East Kilbride
1799	1819	....	....	171654	LKS	Rutherglen
1851	1898	ALL	1851	172901	LND	ALL
1865	1954	1866	1954	176540	LND	Camberwell
....	....	1850	1859	173274	MDX	London
1820	1910	ALL	1820	125148	NBL	Howtel
1800	1834	1600	1840	118877	NBL	Tweedmouth
1850	1860	....	....	169161	OKI	???
1820	1992	1820	....	173266	PEM	Wales
1716	1729	....	....	113484	PER	Forteviot
....	1801	....	....	146811	RFW	Mearns
....	....	1700	1799	125148	ROX	Kelso
1860	1860	ALL	ALL	120057	SCT	Edinburgh
1747	1975	1740	1975	175153	SCT	Old Deer
1730	1800	1730	1800	133795	SCT	???
1780	1900	1730	1900	135941	SFK	Hundon
....	....	1850	1859	173274	SFK	Ipswich
1800	1919	1750	1800	177075	SOM	Kewstoke
1850	1900	1800	1900	145866	SRY	Bermondsey
1856	1992	....	....	125148	T&W	Sunderland
....	....	1800	1899	142298	TYR	???
1734	....	1700	1734	139483	WIG	Kirkinner
1830	1900	1830	1900	102490	WIL	Purton
WALLAGE						
1818	1835	1700	1840	160601	ESS	Steeple Bumpstead
1770	1850	1600	1850	175641	SFK	Denston
WALLAKER						
1880	1980	1750	1880	151165	ESS	Rochford
WALLATOR						
1800	....	....	....	100676	SAL	Cardington
WALLBANK						
....	....	1750	1850	115142	STS	Wolverhampton
1810	1840	1750	1810	151068	YKS	Clapham
WALLBRIDGE						
1770	1770	ALL	1770	154563	DOR	Puncknowle
....	....	1790	1840	132489	DOR	???
....	....	ALL	ALL	173282	HAM	ALL

Known From	To	Researching From	To	Ref	Cty	Place
WALLBRIDGE contd.						
1880	1900	....	....	173282	HAM	Portsmouth
1868	1986	1868	1940	138606	HAM	Southampton
....	....	1790	1840	132489	SOM	Bristol
WALLDER						
1750	1900	1650	1950	122688	SSX	Elsted
1750	1900	1650	1950	122688	SSX	Harting
WALLDUCK						
1850	1870	ALL	ALL	123676	BKM	Stewkley
WALLE						
1885	1992	1860	1890	155691	DOW	Newry
WALLER						
....	....	ALL	ALL	143014	ALL	ALL
....	....	ALL	ALL	175943	BDF	Luton
....	....	1550	1670	154873	BKM	Beaconsfield
1600	1699	1183	1699	162507	BKM	Beaconsfield
1876	1961	....	....	146676	CUL	Isel
1810	1900	1790	1880	103128	DBY	Swanwick
1800	1850	1800	1920	115363	DUB	ALL
1810	1920	1750	1900	110728	DUR	Sunderland
1810	1920	1810	1992	106798	ESS	Colchester
1930	1980	1800	1930	109576	GLS	Bourton On Water
....	....	1570	1600	154873	HAM	Hartley
1844	1876	1600	1900	146676	HRT	???
....	....	1800	1860	171638	HUM	Easterington
....	....	1300	1530	154873	KEN	Groombridge
....	....	1500	1580	154873	KEN	Leigh
1183	1600	1183	1699	162507	KEN	Speldhurst
1876	1877	1800	1900	113476	LAN	Burnley
1889	1901	1901	1992	122807	LAN	Wigan
1790	1925	1725	1790	105503	LIN	Donington On Bain
1850	1900	ALL	1850	152021	LIN	Wainfleet
1690	1790	ALL	ALL	175943	LND	???
1800	1838	....	....	168041	NFK	Great Yarmouth
....	....	1100	1350	154873	NTT	Hockerton
1861	1876	....	....	146676	NTT	???
1750	1860	1700	1900	121762	SSX	Rogate
1802	....	1750	1800	165220	SSX	Shipley
1718	1760	ALL	ALL	173290	YKS	Clapham
1760	1830	ALL	ALL	173290	YKS	Giggleswick
1830	1861	ALL	ALL	173290	YKS	Sowerby Bridge
1861	1986	ALL	ALL	173290	YKS	Todmorden
WALLETT						
1845	1871	1800	1892	168289	STS	Sedgley
WALLEY						
1600	1992	ALL	1600	165395	CHS	Tarporey
1780	1992	1660	1780	173312	SAL	North
WALLEYS						
1300	1400	1300	1400	154881	KEN	Cowden
WALLIN						
1670	1711	ALL	ALL	141615	LEI	Leicester
1869	1904	1600	1908	137812	WAR	Leamington Spa
WALLING						
1620	1674	....	....	142522	ENG	???
....	....	1820	1992	147613	LAN	Tatham
WALLINGER						
1797	1825	1797	1825	107360	BKM	Milton Keynes
WALLINGTON						
1805	1840	1770	1830	110906	MDX	Uxbridge
WALLIS						
....	....	1650	1730	106127	BRK	???
1700	1800	....	....	141178	CON	South East
1847	1947	1770	1847	173339	CON	Luckett
1820	1880	1820	1900	131113	CON	St Cleer
1715	1784	1715	1784	131113	CON	St Just In Penwith
1804	1841	1600	1804	129305	CON	St Just
1781	1992	1565	1780	105988	CON	Towednack
?	....	....	....	169064	DBY	Ashbourne
1824	1928	1500	1850	153230	DBY	Hartshorne
....	....	1650	1730	106127	DBY	???
1803	1938	1700	1850	118397	HAM	Southampton
1780	1860	ALL	1780	175080	HAM	Wymering
1300	1400	1300	1400	154881	KEN	Cowden
1865	1885	ALL	ALL	120154	LND	Kentish Town
1820	....	1750	1820	106127	LND	Shoreditch
1750	1992	1600	1750	174947	LND	St Peters Yard
1800	1825	1750	1800	130214	MDX	Cripplegate
1806	1841	1750	1806	107093	NFK	Norwich
1650	1992	....	....	174947	NTH	Barton Seagrave
1910	1992	1696	1850	145491	NTH	Desborough
1910	1992	1696	1850	145491	NTH	Kettering
1562	1758	1562	1758	103977	OXF	Warborough
1780	1900	1730	1900	135941	SFK	Hundon
1688	1688	1600	1688	155276	SFK	Kirton

Known From	To	Researching From	To	Ref	Cty	Place
WALLIS contd.						
1795	1950	ALL	ALL	153516	SOM	Kewstoke
1795	1950	ALL	ALL	153516	SOM	Kingston Seymour
1850	1900	1600	1900	119083	STS	Chasetown Avon
1867	1936	....	....	121290	STS	Marchington
?	....	....	....	169064	STS	Stramshall
....	....	1650	1730	106127	STS	???
1900	1950	ALL	ALL	119083	WAR	Kenilworth
1677	1841	1500	1850	109274	WIL	Shalbourne
?	....	....	....	169064	YKS	Sheffield
WALLNUTT						
....	....	1750	1900	106607	DUB	ALL
WALLOP						
....	....	1600	1800	159573	HAM	???
1680	1800	1600	1680	159573	WIL	Castle Combe
WALLS						
1830	1871	1830	1900	109142	ABD	Aberdour
1801	1813	1750	1830	109142	BAN	Gamrie
1732	1762	....	....	139971	SSX	Hastings
WALLWORK						
1650	1850	1600	1850	152404	LAN	Clifton
1846	1914	1770	1846	151432	LAN	Manchester
1872	1988	1812	1872	112135	LAN	Oldham
WALLWORTH						
1800	1840	1750	1800	135771	CHS	Stockport
1811	1857	?	1860	103934	LAN	Eccles
1811	1857	?	1860	103934	LAN	Manchester
1811	1857	?	1860	103934	LAN	Pendleton
WALMSLEY						
1900	1960	1700	1900	173347	DOW	Mourne
1819	1923	ALL	1819	122858	LAN	Ashton In Makerfield
1880	1930	1880	1930	114936	LAN	Bamber Bridge
1766	1872	1700	1766	161179	LAN	Blackburn
1750	1900	1750	1900	125237	LAN	Darwen
1800	1880	1880	1992	162256	LAN	Darwen
....	....	ALL	ALL	143340	LAN	???
1882	1992	1880	1992	161640	YKS	Leeds
WALPOLE						
1730	1992	ALL	1730	122696	DBY	Derby
....	....	1881	1915	170569	DBY	Derby
1760	1840	1700	1800	121509	LEI	Barrow Upon Soar
1813	1900	1700	1900	114480	NFK	Antingham
1783	1897	ALL	1897	129283	NFK	Chedgrave
1705	1836	ALL	1705	129283	NFK	Haddiscoe
1735	1788	ALL	1735	129283	NFK	Hales
1710	1945	ALL	1710	129283	NFK	Norton Subcourse
1679	1679	ALL	1679	129283	NFK	Seething
1810	1850	1750	1810	110906	NFK	Terringtons
WALROND						
....	....	ALL	ALL	173363	ALL	Name Study
1200	1992	ALL	ALL	173363	DEV	South
1553	1750	ALL	ALL	173363	SOM	Ilminster
1835	1992	ALL	ALL	173363	SOM	Pitney
1562	1700	ALL	ALL	173363	SOM	Wells
1189	1945	ALL	ALL	173363	WIL	???
WALSH						
1835	1900	1835	1900	129054	AVN	Bristol
1835	1900	1835	1900	129054	COR	Cobh
1835	1900	1835	1900	129054	COR	Youghal
1835	1900	1835	1900	129054	GLA	Cowbridge
....	....	ALL	ALL	143340	IRL	???
1816	1860	....	1816	161888	KID	Castledermot
....	....	1820	1860	159840	KIK	Three Castles
1797	1992	1700	1797	160474	LAN	Blackburn
1750	1900	1750	1900	125237	LAN	Darwen
1800	1900	1700	1900	162256	LAN	Darwen
1850	1911	1850	1930	126705	LAN	Hulme
1847	1850	1840	1850	126705	LAN	Stetford
1861	....	ALL	ALL	172057	LIM	Killglass
1890	1992	1930	1992	158607	LND	ALL
1820	1930	ALL	ALL	113700	MAY	Castlebar
1820	1930	ALL	ALL	113700	MAY	Westport
1839	1870	1830	1880	148067	MDX	St Clement Danes
1867	1876	1835	1900	112216	OXF	Kidlington
1871	1881	1840	1870	148199	SLI	???
1692	1720	1600	1700	176451	YKS	Embsay
1900	....	1750	....	116920	???	Birmingham
WALSHAW						
1808	1844	1700	1910	139203	DUR	Sunderland
WALTER						
1880	1980	1800	1880	173371	GLA	Ponty Pridd
1690	1700	ALL	1690	131059	KEN	Aylesford
1884	1992	1700	1884	132551	KEN	Erith
WALTER contd.						
....	1800	?	1992	163945	KEN	Horsemonden
1640	1850	1640	1850	103993	KEN	Marden
1730	1825	1700	1730	154873	KEN	Marden
1730	1825	1700	1730	154873	KEN	Tonbridge
1804	....	1700	1900	118168	LAN	Great Yarmouth
1800	1852	1852	1900	107964	LIN	Horncastle
1858	1883	1700	1858	150398	LND	Newington
1840	1992	1600	1840	115525	SOM	Bristol
1860	1940	1750	1860	154075	SOM	Shepton Mallett
1770	1915	1700	1770	132640	SSX	Rotherfield
1694	1704	1550	1693	131245	WAR	Stockton
1700	1992	1822	1992	131571	WLS	Gower
1700	1992	1822	1992	131571	WLS	Nicholaston
1823	1900	1760	1800	158089	???	Bristol
WALTERS						
1865	1981	1756	1881	173851	BKM	Great Bradwell
1865	1981	1756	1881	173851	BKM	Old Bradwell
1840	1870	1750	1870	173576	CHS	Macclesfield
?	....	....	....	118508	CMN	Llanelli
1687	1900	1600	1800	173983	CON	Crowan
1850	1950	1600	1850	115134	DBY	Pentrich
1782	1880	1880	?	128910	DBY	Pentrich
1841	1861	1800	1870	118575	GLA	Llangyfelach
1859	1952	1817	1952	125717	GLA	Llangyfelach
1841	....	1830	1861	118575	GLA	Merthyr Tydfil
1850	1992	1700	1992	114596	HAM	Southampton
1869	1924	1802	1992	122238	HEF	Brimfield
1800	1953	1832	1992	115673	HEF	Ledbury
1800	1953	1832	1992	115673	HEF	Yarkhill
1789	1811	1811	1992	176532	KEN	Rotherhithe
1906	1950	1800	1992	122475	KEN	Woolwich
1877	1992	?	1877	156337	MGM	Aberdare
1877	1992	?	1877	156337	MGM	Cwmaman
1803	....	1700	1800	118877	NBL	Tweedmouth
1720	1850	1600	1720	170194	NTT	East Markham
1840	1992	1802	1992	122238	SAL	Bitterley
1814	1992	1814	1992	131156	SOM	Farnborough
1765	1837	1765	1850	165441	STS	Checkley
1824	....	ALL	1824	174815	STS	Willenhall
....	....	1700	1800	147613	STS	Wolverhampton
WALTHAM						
1843	1899	1800	1920	136646	MDX	London
WALTHEW						
1817	1915	1500	1817	122629	LAN	Rainhill
WALTHOE						
1815	1838	1700	1815	110639	STS	Cheadle
WALTON						
1620	1910	....	....	121983	CHS	Alderley
1812	1843	....	....	171824	CHS	Ulkington
1863	1992	1780	1863	173428	CMA	Alston
1750	1992	1600	1750	164208	CMA	Appleby
1863	1992	1780	1863	173428	CMA	Nenthead
1800	1825	1780	1861	123536	CUL	Alston
1700	1930	1600	1900	130869	CUL	Alston
1830	1865	1700	1850	146714	CUL	Alston
1814	1992	1700	1850	124788	DBY	Bradshaw Edge
1870	1910	1860	1910	144541	ESS	East
1550	1833	....	....	100536	ESS	Little Burstead
1737	1800	1600	1737	145459	HAM	Lyndhurst
1843	1900	1700	1843	115185	IOM	Onchan
....	....	....	1875	147818	LAN	Bolton
1750	1940	1500	1950	134562	LAN	Colne
1833	....	1750	1833	108596	LAN	Manchester
1750	1940	1500	1950	134562	LAN	Nelson
1865	1891	1860	1891	159492	LAN	Oldham
1777	1790	1777	1790	111228	LAN	Rosterne
1867	....	....	....	171824	LAN	St Helens
1814	1841	....	....	173401	LIN	Carlton Scroop
1770	1851	....	....	173401	LIN	Fenton
1846	1891	1891	1992	173401	LIN	Foston
1878	1891	ALL	ALL	173401	LIN	Grantham
1878	1891	1891	1992	173401	LIN	Spittlegate
....	....	1700	1850	154458	LIN	???
1840	....	1809	1840	153257	LND	Westminster
1818	1884	1800	1900	108391	MDX	London
1800	1850	1800	1850	106631	MDX	Westminster
1700	1830	....	....	148261	NBL	Allendales
1807	1860	1770	1807	173118	NBL	Kirk Whelpington
1841	1861	1780	1880	123536	NBL	Newcastle On Tyne
1770	1850	1770	1850	160121	NBL	Newcastle
1818	1818	ALL	1818	162825	NTH	Paston
1879	1984	1750	1879	166707	NTH	Yelvertoft
....	....	ALL	ALL	173401	NTT	Newark

Known From	To	Researching From	To	Ref	Cty	Place
WALTON contd.						
1760	1800	1700	1760	164860	SFK	Pettistree
1844	1871	1800	1881	165824	SOM	Bath
1850	1992	1850	1992	133450	SRY	Walton On Thames
1770	....	ALL	ALL	143758	WAR	Alderminster
1850	1880	....	....	120472	WAR	Birmingham
1760	1780	1700	1800	149993	WAR	Solihull
1812	1831	1700	1811	131245	WAR	Wyken
1790	1817	....	....	126276	WRY	Carlton In Contin
1765	1825	1765	1825	107522	WRY	Todmorden
1795	1975	1700	1795	100110	WYK	Claverley
1800	1840	1700	1800	108790	YKS	Heptonstall
1760	1800	....	....	129747	YKS	Leeds
1770	1860	ALL	1992	173436	YKS	Silkstone
1784	1943	1600	1784	179043	YKS	Thirsk
1780	1860	....	1780	114812	YKS	Wortley
WANER						
1848	1929	1800	1890	134082	GLS	Eastington
WANKLIN						
1750	1810	1500	1750	173444	HEF	North
1750	1830	1600	1750	122084	HEF	Leominster
1840	1870	1600	1840	122084	WOR	Worcester
WANKLING						
1880	1930	....	....	173444	WAR	Coventry
WANSBROUGH						
....	....	ALL	ALL	103748	ALL	Name Study
WANSTALL						
1851	1992	1700	1992	173460	KEN	East
WANT						
....	....	ALL	ALL	141496	ALL	ALL
1816	1992	1700	1816	173479	NFK	Broome
WARBLETON						
1734	1773	1650	1800	109290	YKS	Sheffield
WARBOYS						
1761	1992	1600	1761	173487	CAM	Oakington
WARBURTON						
1690	1830	1690	1838	131709	CHS	Hale
1795	1992	1600	1755	119822	LAN	Bolton
1850	1992	ALL	ALL	131121	LAN	Bolton
1790	1880	1790	1880	153621	LAN	Bury
1780	....	....	....	126497	LAN	Leyland
1785	1992	1760	....	112348	LAN	Warrington
....	....	1800	1992	135127	LND	???
1790	1880	1790	1880	153621	YKS	Summerbridge
WARCUP						
1784	1863	1784	1863	173738	NBL	Dinningtoe
....	....	1700	1992	173738	YKS	ALL
1770	1794	1770	1794	173738	YKS	Broughton
1770	1821	1770	1821	173738	YKS	Swinton
WARD						
1749	....	ALL	1800	168718	BDF	North West
1800	1900	1750	1850	107417	BDF	Sharnbrook
1857	1857	1800	1992	137863	BDF	Sunden
1811	1855	1750	1811	174688	BKM	Aylesbury
1807	....	1700	1850	143693	BKM	Great Hampden
1800	1950	ALL	ALL	173657	BKM	Hughenden
1767	1809	1650	1850	143693	BKM	Princes Risborough
1800	1950	ALL	ALL	173657	BKM	Princes Risborough
1765	1806	1700	1800	103896	BRK	Hungerford
1797	1838	1600	1797	152080	BRK	Sutton Courtenay
1795	ALL	ALL	1840	116734	CAM	Balsham
1700	1800	....	....	167924	CAM	Fowlmere
1795	ALL	ALL	1840	116734	CAM	Linton
1820	1850	1800	1850	134627	CAM	Littleport
1760	1820	1740	1760	134627	CAM	March
....	....	ALL	ALL	155632	CHI	Guernsey
....	....	ALL	ALL	155632	CHI	Jersey
1798	1860	1750	1798	173576	CHS	Blackden
1798	1860	1750	1798	173576	CHS	Peover
....	....	1700	1992	173592	CON	St Gennys
1817	1930	....	1817	176761	CUL	Brampton
1817	1930	....	1817	176761	CUL	Hayton
1817	1930	....	1817	176761	CUL	Scaleby
1900	1950	....	....	162183	DBY	ALL
1815	1992	1750	1870	173649	DBY	Derby
1830	1900	1830	1900	118540	DEV	Bideford
1847	1870	1066	1870	108669	DEV	Exeter
1733	1765	1700	1733	179663	DEV	Hobeton
1733	1765	....	....	166723	DEV	Holbeton
1790	1815	1750	1820	173630	DEV	Swimbridge
1783	1807	1807	1817	173541	DEV	Torrington
1817	1930	....	1817	176761	DFS	Cananbie
1800	1850	1600	1950	133590	DUR	???
?	?	?	?	169781	DUR	???

Known From	To	Researching From	To	Ref	Cty	Place
WARD contd.						
1878	1900	1700	1878	168653	ESS	ALL
1750	1830	1700	1850	143502	ESS	South East
....	1867	1808	....	123609	ESS	Braintree
1740	1766	....	....	129747	ESS	Colne Engaine
....	....	1860	1884	130184	ESS	Leytonstone
1891	....	ALL	1890	123013	GLA	Caerau
1600	1700	....	....	176958	GLS	Brislington
1757	1837	1700	1757	167533	GLS	Bristol
1900	....	....	....	173282	HAM	Portsmouth
1750	1890	....	....	164143	HAM	Ringwood
1780	1910	1600	1950	118281	HRT	Tewin
1606	1823	ALL	1793	137774	KEN	ALL
1733	1734	....	1770	171441	KEN	Bethersden
1767	1802	1730	1840	171441	KEN	Charing
1820	1850	1600	1850	113654	KEN	Chatham
1880	1900	1600	1880	103314	KEN	Chelsfield
1816	1845	....	....	139971	KEN	Upchurch
1826	....	1800	1840	171441	KEN	Wichling
1824	1897	1600	1850	165476	KEN	Willsborough
1760	1800	1750	1820	117145	LAN	Bolton
1896	1947	....	....	112429	LAN	Kirkham
1690	1720	1650	1690	155500	LAN	Leigh
ALL	ALL	ALL	ALL	101648	LAN	Manchester
1835	1883	ALL	ALL	146226	LAN	Manchester
1863	1956	1700	1888	178233	LAN	Manchester
1827	1850	1780	1850	118443	LAN	Myerscough
1808	1992	1750	1808	101893	LAN	Salford
1874	1900	ALL	ALL	101648	LAN	Urmston
1882	1992	1700	1992	173517	LEI	ALL
1721	1736	ALL	ALL	141615	LEI	Hinckley
1759	1770	ALL	1759	171476	LEI	Hinckley
1891	1992	1871	1899	173517	LEI	Leicester
1770	1864	1750	1864	151599	LEI	Shepshed
1755	1778	1650	1754	131245	LEI	Tilton
1850	1881	1850	1940	101923	LIN	Aby
1837	1992	1700	1837	165581	LIN	Alford
1800	1850	....	....	124621	LIN	Claxby
1820	1992	1700	1820	122513	LIN	Crowle
1700	1800	1700	1800	133817	LIN	Donington
1850	1881	1850	1940	101923	LIN	Saltfleet
1700	1850	1800	1820	111422	LND	ALL
1830	1870	1800	1900	152528	LND	Holborn
1877	1902	1850	1900	135925	LND	Islington
1902	1986	1900	1960	135925	LND	Palmers Green
1898	....	....	....	175919	LND	Poplar
1752	1833	....	....	161357	LND	Southwark
....	1800	1700	1800	146927	LND	Westminster
1827	1992	1700	1827	105902	LND	???
1840	1890	1860	1890	110159	LND	???
1800	1850	1800	1850	124605	MDX	Bethnal Green
1832	1913	1800	1950	160903	MDX	Hackney
1830	1888	....	....	162914	MDX	London
?	....	?	....	104337	MDX	Mile End Old Town
1832	1913	1800	1950	160903	MDX	Newington
1832	1913	1800	1950	160903	MDX	Stoke
1760	1800	ALL	1800	131059	MDX	???
1817	1930	....	1817	176761	NBL	Haltwhistle
1817	1930	....	1817	176761	NBL	Mickley
1817	1930	....	1817	176761	NBL	Prudhoe
1830	1992	1800	1992	148660	NFK	South East
1850	1920	1700	1850	164860	NFK	Filby
1830	1888	....	....	162914	NFK	Kings Lynn
1711	1836	1600	1710	131245	NFK	Norwich
1733	1992	1600	1773	173495	NFK	Old Buckenham Lodden
1842	1867	ALL	1842	118222	NFK	Saxlingham Nethergate
1822	1850	1750	1822	127590	NFK	Southney
1815	1992	1788	1815	161446	NFK	Sporle
1600	1992	1700	1992	173533	NTH	South
....	....	1800	1900	116173	NTH	Kettering
1846	1900	ALL	1860	101281	NTH	Northampton
1763	1819	ALL	ALL	141615	NTH	Wilbarston
1750	1830	1750	1800	144657	NTT	Nottingham
1870	1900	1800	1900	178136	NTT	Nottingham
....	....	1850	....	154377	NTT	Shirebrook
....	....	1800	....	154377	NTT	Skegby
1850	1992	1700	1850	154741	NTT	Sutton In Ashfield
1730	1770	....	1770	137634	NTT	Worksop
1780	1992	1750	1850	109525	NYK	Fylingdales
1850	1950	1650	1850	173665	NYK	Pickering
....	....	1750	1850	108049	OXF	Banbury
1850	1900	1700	1850	118915	OXF	Oxford

Known From	To	Researching From	To	Ref	Cty	Place
WARD contd.						
1815	1989	1815	1989	149403	OXF	Oxford
....	....	1850	1880	114782	OXF	???
1829	1880	....	....	128082	RAD	Knighton
....	....	ALL	1600	164631	RUT	ALL
1540	1669	....	....	164631	RUT	Egleton
....	....	1750	1821	149977	SAL	ALL
1820	1920	1750	1850	143502	SAL	Central
....	....	1700	1801	128082	SAL	Munslow
1821	1841	....	....	149977	SAL	Newport
1814	....	1814	....	164232	SFK	Battisford
1871	1880	1800	1900	123811	SFK	Bildeston
1812	....	1750	1812	174955	SFK	Brandon
1830	1840	....	....	110159	SFK	Ipswich
1810	1935	1700	1810	138010	SFK	???
1770	1830	1760	1830	142018	SOM	Bath
1815	1898	ALL	ALL	153516	SOM	Chew Magna
1900	1974	....	....	151920	SRY	Ascot
1889	1956	1800	1889	123803	SRY	Camberwell
1892	1921	1800	1891	131245	SRY	Dulwich
1835	1880	1800	1880	102717	SRY	Lambeth
1833	1873	1700	1832	131245	SRY	Lambeth
1880	1900	1870	1920	102717	SRY	Peckham
1776	1843	1700	1776	174807	SSX	Worth
1750	1797	1700	1992	173517	STS	South
1801	1840	1780	1850	160873	STS	Bilston
1801	1871	1760	1900	160873	STS	Brierley Hill
1713	1762	1680	1800	160873	STS	Pattingham
1777	1797	1750	1820	160873	STS	Penn
1800	1850	1700	1800	100978	STS	Wolverhampton
1825	1845	1700	1825	141291	STS	Wolverhampton
1798	1992	1700	1992	173517	WAR	North
1767	1857	1700	1845	102830	WAR	Birmingham
1880	1904	1865	1905	100218	WAR	Coventry
....	....	1576	1900	115142	WAR	Mancetter
?	?	?	?	102245	WAR	Shipston On Stour
....	....	1700	1850	154458	WAR	???
1725	1771	1600	1725	102571	WES	High Ewebank
1730	1992	1700	1730	139149	WES	Middleton In Lonsdale
1735	....	1700	1750	142018	WIL	Salisbury
1820	1930	1700	1800	107611	WIL	Wingfield
....	....	1700	1760	149977	WOR	West
....	....	1700	1850	167916	WOR	Knighton On Teme
1760	1855	....	....	149977	WOR	Martley
1851	1900	1845	1930	160873	WOR	Oldbury
1871	1960	....	....	167916	WOR	Stourbridge
1831	1878	1700	1831	100110	WYK	Calverley
1786	1812	....	....	152234	WYK	Methley
1800	1885	1700	1800	125458	WYK	Pudsey
1569	1812	....	....	152234	WYK	Rothwell
1826	1836	....	....	152234	WYK	Whitkirk
1796	1821	....	....	141097	YKS	Dirtcar
1845	....	....	....	136565	YKS	Hull
1832	1886	....	1850	169412	YKS	Hull
1890	1992	1850	1930	173614	YKS	Hull
....	....	ALL	1847	114308	YKS	Leeds
1870	1900	1700	1870	136905	YKS	Leeds
1830	1920	1700	1830	108308	YKS	Newton Le Willows
....	....	1800	1900	129593	YKS	Pinchinthorp
1852	....	1800	1900	129593	YKS	Pinchinthorpe
?	1840	ALL	ALL	131172	YKS	Pudsey
....	1735	1650	1735	174858	YKS	Reighton
1801	1980	ALL	1850	142506	YKS	Rothwell
1678	....	1600	1678	117234	YKS	Settle
1821	1821	....	....	141097	YKS	Wakefield
1869	1937	1869	....	164135	???	???
WARDAL						
....	....	ALL	ALL	172812	KEN	ALL
....	....	ALL	ALL	172812	YKS	ALL
WARDALE						
1800	1850	1700	1800	148806	NYK	Pickering
1799	1799	1743	1851	116114	YKS	Whitby
WARDEL						
....	....	ALL	ALL	172812	KEN	ALL
....	....	ALL	ALL	172812	YKS	ALL
WARDELL						
1750	1850	1600	1750	161519	DUR	Fishburn
1798	....	1700	1800	115967	YKS	Malton
WARDEN						
....	....	1832	ALL	149187	ANS	Dundee
1800	....	....	....	114723	DEV	Plymouth
1765	1855	....	....	127140	DNB	Cumbernauld
1851	....	....	1851	167053	ESS	Chelmsford
WARDEN contd.						
1670	1670	....	....	166642	KEN	???
....	....	1700	1850	106356	SFK	???
....	....	1700	1800	154458	WAR	Birmingham
1850	1940	1800	1850	104124	WAR	Coventry
WARDER						
....	....	ALL	ALL	106224	ALL	Name Study
1561	1992	ALL	ALL	106224	ALL	ALL
1831	1992	1831	1992	172952	IOW	ALL
WARDIELL						
1796	1837	1700	1795	166820	STS	Sedgley
WARDLE						
1881	1966	1800	1881	117943	CHS	Congleton
1800	....	1750	ALL	177466	CHS	Marple
1604	1992	1604	1992	173681	DBY	Earl Sterndale
1800	1860	1700	1800	165662	DBY	Whittington
....	....	ALL	ALL	172812	KEN	ALL
1763	1992	1700	1800	159964	LAN	Ringley
1786	1992	ALL	ALL	115762	LEI	Diseworth
1700	1992	1700	1992	113786	LIN	Grimsby
1829	1840	?	1829	112356	LND	London
1800	1850	1770	1800	128333	STS	Leek
....	....	ALL	ALL	172812	YKS	ALL
WARDLEY						
1828	1933	1841	1933	108901	NTT	Elmton
1633	1812	....	....	129747	SFK	Glemsford
1822	1850	....	....	129747	SFK	Ipswich
1825	1936	ALL	1825	102350	SRY	Westminster
WARDMAN						
1861	1989	1700	1861	174939	YKS	Ripley
WARDNER						
1500	1900	1500	1900	170216	BRK	ALL
1500	1900	1500	1900	170216	DOR	ALL
1500	1900	1500	1900	170216	WIL	ALL
WARDON						
1820	1860	1800	1900	153877	LEI	Leicester
WARDROP						
1800	1900	1800	1900	105848	SCT	Edinburgh
WARDROPER						
1814	1905	....	....	139874	YKS	Fairley Tyas
1814	1905	....	....	139874	YKS	Slaithwaite
WARE						
1849	1948	1800	1960	141046	BRK	Wokingham
1774	1850	1500	1850	157538	DEV	Honiton
1705	1788	?	1790	103934	DOR	Pentridge
1863	1942	1863	1942	161306	HAM	Aldershot
1750	1900	1600	1900	120677	HAM	Wonston
1750	1850	1700	1950	177180	HRT	Bovingdon
1770	1825	1700	1770	162396	LIN	South
....	....	1800	1900	166960	MDX	London
1817	1881	1750	1850	144606	SOM	Taunton
?	?	?	?	166642	SSX	West Firle
1850	....	1840	1880	135429	YKS	Scarborough
1850	....	1840	1880	135429	YKS	York
1860	1889	....	....	161306	???	St Brides
WAREHAM						
....	....	....	1801	115290	BKM	Datchet
1788	....	1700	1788	118605	CHS	Barthomley
1822	1914	1700	1900	177369	DOR	Central
1780	1820	1550	1630	156795	DOR	East
....	....	1850	1880	133221	DOR	Holdenhurst
1790	1850	1700	1850	145661	DOR	Longham
1700	1770	1700	1770	171549	HAM	Brixton
1760	1930	1700	1890	110116	HAM	Petersfield
1806	1840	....	....	115290	MDX	Cowley
1866	1881	ALL	ALL	149489	MDX	Twickenham
WARES						
1650	1890	1650	1890	105627	CAI	Canisbay
WARHAM						
1839	1839	1790	1845	178055	CHS	Thelwall
....	....	1780	1898	147826	GLS	Tiddington
1815	1947	1790	1815	178055	LAN	Warrington
....	....	1780	1898	147826	LND	Bermondsey
....	....	1780	1898	147826	WAR	Welford
WARHURST						
1781	1840	ALL	1781	161330	DBY	Peak Forest
1848	1992	1797	1848	112135	LAN	Manchester
1848	1992	1797	1848	112135	LAN	Shaw
WARIN						
....	....	....	1992	105295	NYK	Catterick
1895	1992	....	1895	105295	NYK	Thornton Le Beans
WARING						
1700	1740	1600	1700	113204	ANT	Derriaghy
1797	1848	1750	1900	127353	BKM	Buckland

Known From	To	Researching From	To	Ref	Cty	Place
WARING contd.						
1890	1947	....	....	151912	LAN	Blackburn
1825	....	1825	....	109347	LAN	Liverpool
....	....	1900	1992	147613	LAN	Liverpool
1790	1837	1790	1837	119385	LAN	North Meols
1883	1933	1883	1933	119385	LAN	Preston
1856	1890	1800	1880	151912	LAN	Preston
1845	1845	1800	1875	178004	LAN	Salford
1815	....	....	....	109347	LAN	St Helens
1837	1881	1837	1881	119385	LAN	Ulnes Walton
1850	1880	....	....	137618	WRY	Ledsham
1800	1850	....	....	137618	WRY	Thornhill
1750	1800	1600	1900	120677	WYK	Thurstonland
1834	1848	1700	1900	149098	YKS	Leeds
1875	....	....	1910	165484	YKS	Woolley
WARLAND						
....	....	1600	1992	173746	ENG	ALL
1750	1800	1730	1850	173746	OXF	Charlton On Otmoor
1750	1760	1650	1760	173746	OXF	Fencot
1750	1760	1650	1760	173746	OXF	Murcott
WARLOW						
1741	1872	1741	1850	176958	PEM	Haverfordwest
1800	1850	....	....	176958	PEM	Steynton
WARLTERS						
....	....	ALL	ALL	154067	ALL	Name Study
1615	1800	ALL	ALL	154067	HEF	ALL
1800	1905	ALL	ALL	154067	LND	ALL
1841	1868	ALL	ALL	154067	SRY	Addington
1819	1900	ALL	ALL	154067	SRY	Old Malden
1775	1800	ALL	ALL	154067	WOR	ALL
WARLTIER						
1810	1896	1700	1992	125865	STS	ALL
WARLTIRE						
1810	1896	1700	1992	125865	STS	ALL
WARMBY						
1804	1871	1700	1900	173711	LAN	Chorley
WARMOLL						
1760	1892	1700	1900	176672	NFK	ALL
WARMOUTH						
1670	1720	1650	1720	142018	SOM	Taunton
WARN						
....	....	ALL	ALL	173754	ALL	Name Study
?	?	?	?	136395	GLS	Bristol
ALL	ALL	....	....	153397	HAM	New Forest
1800	1850	1700	1800	119164	SFK	Framsden
?	?	?	?	136395	SOM	Bristol
WARNE						
1853	1884	1853	1884	173762	BRK	Newbury
ALL	1853	....	....	172693	CON	Wadebridge
1650	....	....	1680	103349	DEV	Plymouth
1800	1880	....	....	113417	DEV	Plymouth
1787	1805	1700	1800	145459	HAM	Exbury
1809	1810	1780	1850	127116	HAM	Hursley
ALL	ALL	....	....	153397	HAM	New Forest
1869	1992	1700	1869	173770	HAM	Portsea
1869	1992	1700	1869	173770	IOW	ALL
1850	1900	....	....	113417	LND	Stepney
....	....	ALL	1778	103284	MDX	London
1839	1992	....	....	144495	SFK	Ipswich
1683	1700	....	1700	103349	???	Dublin
WARNER						
1799	1992	1700	1799	126527	BKM	Winslow
1741	....	1650	1750	143693	BRK	Basildon
1793	....	1700	1850	143693	BRK	Bradfield
1809	....	1809	1992	101656	BRK	Reading
1822	....	1750	1850	143693	BRK	Reading
1787	1940	....	....	128996	CAM	Thorney
1845	1992	ALL	ALL	164550	COR	Bantry
1845	1992	ALL	ALL	164550	COR	Coomhola
1816	1905	1837	1992	128961	ESS	Chelmsford
1820	1900	....	....	157724	ESS	Lexden
1843	....	1840	1900	101656	GLS	Eastington
1847	....	1840	1943	101656	GLS	Painswick
1740	1820	1740	1820	127655	GLS	Stroud
1802	1856	1700	1800	100013	HAM	Alton
1708	1753	1708	1753	153508	HAM	Alton
1810	1830	1750	1850	126586	HAM	Bentley
1721	1760	1600	1800	126586	HAM	Binsted
1899	1899	1870	1912	107255	HAM	Southsea
1600	1850	....	....	127833	HRT	East
1850	....	ALL	1992	150630	HRT	Aston
1850	....	ALL	1992	150630	HRT	Benington
1674	1812	....	1674	142166	HRT	Walkern
1822	1992	1700	1825	161772	HUN	Brampton
WARNER contd.						
1933	1945	....	....	107255	KEN	Whitstable
1912	1933	1870	1912	107255	LND	Hackney
1800	1860	1750	1850	174386	MDX	Roxeth
1770	1968	ALL	ALL	100919	OXF	Henley On Thames
1870	1870	ALL	1870	107255	SOM	Bristol
....	....	1730	1795	172871	SRY	Godalming
1800	....	....	....	130486	STS	Stafford
1840	1849	1700	1911	121746	STS	Uttoxeter
1795	....	....	....	140031	WAR	South
....	....	1600	....	137456	WAR	Stockton
1820	1881	1815	1881	152102	WIL	Redlynch
1760	1820	1800	1992	172782	YKS	Peckfield
1792	1838	1830	1992	172782	YKS	Ryther
WARNES						
1810	....	ALL	ALL	138533	NFK	Billockby
1790	1992	1550	1800	150843	NFK	Burgh St Margaret
1700	1908	1530	1992	139270	NFK	Gt Dunham
1841	1851	1700	1841	148024	NFK	Norwich
....	....	....	1800	177695	NFK	Norwich
1821	....	1750	1992	171875	NFK	???
....	1800	....	1800	177695	NTH	Northampton
WARNHAM						
1400	1992	1400	1992	178918	ALL	ALL
1400	1992	1400	1992	178918	BRK	ALL
WARNOCK						
1790	1860	1700	1900	144290	LKS	Barony
1850	1900	1800	1925	144290	LKS	Cadder
1820	1900	1820	1900	130400	LKS	East Kilbride
1800	1900	1700	1900	132446	MOG	ALL
1800	1900	1700	1900	132446	TYR	ALL
1800	1900	1700	1900	124621	TYR	Cookstown
WARR						
ALL	ALL	ALL	ALL	173789	ALL	ALL
1811	1864	1811	1949	173789	BKM	Buckingham
1700	1770	1650	1800	177024	GLS	Dymock
1695	1715	1650	1750	177024	GLS	Pauntley
1900	1901	1895	1905	142352	LIN	Bourne
1811	1921	1811	1949	173789	LND	City
1877	1949	1811	1949	173789	MDX	Holborn
1919	1922	1900	1922	142352	STS	West Bromwich
1900	1925	1900	1925	142352	WAR	Stratford On Avon
1820	1835	1820	1835	142352	WOR	Brierley Hill
1870	1880	1870	1880	142352	WOR	Cradley
1800	1820	1790	1820	142352	WOR	Kingswinford
WARRAD						
1898	1911	1898	1911	166715	WAR	Solihull
WARRE						
1557	1683	ALL	ALL	122106	DEV	Woodbury
WARREN						
1920	1992	1900	1992	152935	AVN	Compton Dando
1650	1800	1650	1800	173819	BRK	Uffington
....	....	ALL	1840	103284	BRK	Wargrave
1760	1860	1700	1760	176311	CAM	Burwell
1760	1806	1700	1760	151866	CAM	Cottenham
1720	1940	....	....	128996	CAM	Thorney
1780	1961	1760	1940	156353	CAM	Wilburton
1863	....	1800	1863	156221	CHI	ALL
....	....	1800	1900	173835	CHI	Jersey
1830	1989	1700	1830	174939	CHS	Macclesfield
1790	1992	1700	1790	173878	CON	Falmouth
....	....	1700	1850	147044	CON	Gulval
....	....	1700	1850	147044	CON	Madron
....	....	1850	ALL	173835	CON	Mylor
....	....	1700	1850	147044	CON	Paul
1797	1867	1700	1880	173835	CON	Perranarworthal
1858	1888	1888	1930	173835	CON	Redruth
1788	1992	1788	1992	141267	CON	St Buryan
....	....	1700	1850	147044	CON	St Just In Penwith
1800	1920	....	....	113093	CON	St Stephens
1750	1992	1700	1750	173827	DBY	Newhall
1826	1830	1790	....	146900	DEV	Ipplepen
1850	....	1840	1880	135429	DEV	Lymptstone
1890	1904	1850	1904	152935	DEV	???
1860	1880	....	....	131717	DUB	Dublin
1798	1798	1750	1850	179140	ESS	Gosfield
1810	1992	1800	1992	152528	ESS	Lofts
1815	1845	1770	1845	124974	ESS	Roydon
1603	1992	....	....	174106	ESS	Stambourne
....	....	1750	1850	130680	ESS	Upminster
1814	1814	1780	1814	133000	HAM	Portsea
?	....	?	....	173800	HAM	Portsmouth
1747	1844	ALL	1747	175080	HAM	???
1850	1940	1700	1850	125601	HRT	Hitchin

Known From	To	Researching From	To	Ref	Cty	Place
WARREN contd.						
1800	1850	1700	1950	171522	KEN	Greenwich
1884	1950	ALL	ALL	156868	LAN	Oldham
1786	1815	1750	1815	151599	LEI	Ashby De La Zouch
1815	1897	1815	1897	151599	LEI	Loughborough
1751	1850	1700	1900	135968	LEI	Slawston
....	1818	ALL	1819	134511	LEI	Syston
1853	1992	ALL	ALL	115762	LND	Marylebone
1820	1992	1800	1992	152528	LND	???
1848	1988	1750	1850	165271	MDX	Chiswick
....	....	1775	1785	110450	NTH	Kingsthorpe
1810	1924	1700	1810	166111	NTH	Naseby
1803	1803	1550	1803	102830	NTT	Nottingham
1831	1871	1800	1880	151599	NTT	Nottingham
1808	1852	....	....	129747	SFK	Ipswich
1824	1847	1700	1824	159212	SFK	Ipswich
1881	1881	1881	1881	173851	SFK	Lawshall
1814	....	1700	....	123552	SFK	Thandeston
1838	1992	1700	1838	154415	SOM	Churchstanton
1920	1992	1900	1992	152935	SOM	Compton Dando
ALL	1730	....	....	105368	SOM	Ilminster
1830	1900	1750	1850	144398	SRY	Croydon
1739	....	1700	1750	170348	WIL	Wroughton
1800	....	1800	....	100536	WOR	???
1850	1880	1800	1900	129623	YKS	Staveley
1881	1992	1881	1992	173851	???	London
WARRENDER						
1597	?	ALL	ALL	101370	FIF	Balchristie
1889	1960	1700	1889	173886	STS	Breewood
WARRENER						
1818	1830	1800	1850	162345	SSX	Hamsey
1818	1830	1800	1850	162345	SSX	Lewes
WARREY						
1617	1678	ALL	ALL	122106	DEV	Colaton Raleigh
1557	1683	ALL	ALL	122106	DEV	Woodbury
1535	....	ALL	ALL	122106	ESS	Ardleigh
1654	....	ALL	ALL	122106	KEN	Hythe
WARRIAN						
....	....	ALL	ALL	115010	ALL	ALL
1805	1860	ALL	1805	115010	CON	Charlestown
....	1859	1850	1992	115010	MDX	London
WARRICK						
1812	1870	1750	1920	120472	BRK	Reading
1804	1941	1780	1941	164704	BRK	Reading
1812	1812	....	....	120472	BRK	Wokingham
WARRIE						
1577	....	ALL	ALL	122106	ESS	Harwich
1598	....	ALL	ALL	122106	SFK	Falkenham
1528	1585	ALL	1585	122106	SFK	Shotley
1530	1700	ALL	1530	122106	SOM	Chard
1723	1820	....	....	122106	SOM	Cricket Malherbie
1793	1874	....	....	122106	SOM	Merriott
WARRILOW						
1801	1877	1801	1881	153273	STS	Stone
WARRINER						
1703	1832	1691	1832	169552	LAN	Hawkshead
1595	1801	1569	1812	169552	WES	Crosthwaite
1750	1850	....	....	167843	YKS	Redmire Cum Bolton
1643	1721	1600	1643	165417	???	???
WARRINGTON						
....	....	....	1823	134902	CAM	March
1818	....	1800	1900	139114	CHS	Stockport
1770	1992	1700	1770	160458	DBY	Hayfield
1750	1992	ALL	1750	115355	LEI	ALL
....	....	1800	1840	172154	LND	Southwark
1822	1992	....	....	100986	STS	Leak
....	1851	1800	1900	175633	WOR	Sedgeberrow
1805	1805	....	....	141097	YKS	Braithwell
1805	1920	1750	1805	162523	YKS	Leeds
1797	1805	....	....	141097	YKS	Sheffield
WARRLOW						
1890	1992	1500	1890	134600	GLS	Shirehampton
WARRY						
....	....	ALL	ALL	173894	ALL	Name Study
1647	1744	ALL	ALL	122106	DEV	Axminster
1617	1678	ALL	ALL	122106	DEV	Colaton Raleigh
1682	1766	ALL	ALL	122106	DEV	Otterton
1557	1683	ALL	ALL	122106	DEV	Woodbury
1817	1850	1700	1817	173908	DOR	Evershot
1520	....	ALL	ALL	122106	ESS	East Donyland
1788	1817	....	....	173908	HAM	Winchester
1567	1620	ALL	1674	122106	SFK	Great Wenham
1606	....	ALL	ALL	122106	SFK	Holbrook
1607	....	ALL	ALL	122106	SFK	Ipswich
WARRY contd.						
1567	1620	ALL	1674	122106	SFK	Little Wenham
1530	1700	ALL	1530	122106	SOM	Chard
1570	1863	1530	1863	151599	SOM	Chard
1723	1820	....	....	122106	SOM	Cricket Malherbie
....	....	1700	1788	173908	SOM	Knowle St Giles
1793	1874	....	....	122106	SOM	Merriott
1830	1932	....	....	122106	SOM	Shapwick
1656	1797	....	....	122106	SOM	West Coker
1570	1863	1530	1863	151599	SOM	Winsham
1894	1907	1500	1894	141089	SRY	Newington
1894	1907	1500	1894	141089	SRY	Southwark
1825	1872	....	....	173908	WIL	Christian Malford
WARRYE						
1547	1558	ALL	ALL	122106	KEN	Sellinge
WARSOP						
1711	1821	1550	1710	102830	LIN	Aubourn
WARTER						
1562	1697	1500	1684	102830	STS	Sedgely
WARTH						
....	....	ALL	ALL	173924	ALL	Name Study
WARTNABY						
1600	1830	1600	1800	126837	LEI	ALL
1600	1900	1600	1900	135968	LEI	Great Dalby
1790	1870	1790	1870	126837	LIN	Woolsthorpe
1600	1830	1600	1800	126837	NTT	ALL
WARTON						
1764	1820	1700	1790	163562	LND	Stepney
WARWICK						
....	....	ALL	ALL	173940	ALL	Name Study
1823	....	1700	1823	101443	ALL	ALL
1767	....	1700	1767	105457	BDF	???
1767	....	1700	1767	105457	BKM	???
1801	....	1801	....	173940	CUL	Glasonby
....	....	ALL	1850	142298	DOW	???
1750	1800	1750	1800	162140	ESS	Farnham
1650	1800	....	....	153397	HAM	New Forest
1800	1840	1750	1900	162140	HRT	Albury
1840	1900	1750	1900	162140	HRT	Furneux Pelham
1700	1800	1700	1800	162140	HRT	Little Hadham
1700	1800	1700	1800	162140	HRT	Much Hadham
1700	1800	1700	1800	162140	HRT	Puckeridge
....	....	?	1930	109584	LAN	Lancaster
1930	1938	1900	1950	173940	LAN	Liverpool
1849	1992	1700	1992	177733	LAN	Liverpool
1917	....	....	....	173932	LND	Greenwich
1926	....	....	....	173932	LND	Hackney
1854	....	....	....	173932	LND	Hyde Park Gardens
1870	1900	1870	1900	162140	LND	N Kensington
1873	....	....	....	173932	LND	South Norwood
1850	1900	1850	1900	162140	LND	Strand
1860	1920	1750	1992	144525	LND	???
1712	....	....	....	173932	MDX	Hampton
1750	1870	1720	1750	134139	NTH	Collingtree
1747	1779	1707	1812	107360	NTH	Welton
1779	1851	1851	1870	107123	SAL	Oswestry
1832	....	....	....	173932	SFK	Stradbroke
1826	1883	....	....	173932	SRY	Ashtead
1809	....	....	....	173932	SRY	Clapham
1851	1921	....	....	173932	SRY	Epsom
1782	1816	....	....	173932	SRY	Thames Ditton
....	....	ALL	1850	142298	TYR	???
1801	....	....	....	173940	WES	Appleby
1871	....	....	....	173932	WIL	Melksham
1890	....	....	....	173932	WIL	Sutton Veny
1881	1900	ALL	ALL	112259	WIL	Swindon
WARWICKS						
?	?	?	?	151556	CUL	Dacre
WARWICKSHIRE						
1807	1992	1750	1807	176257	ALL	ALL
WARWOOD						
1726	1770	1726	1770	166715	WAR	Birmingham
WASE						
1600	1800	1550	1992	173959	LEI	ALL
1600	1800	1550	1992	173959	NTT	ALL
WASHBAND						
1863	1863	1600	1863	152080	WAR	Bedworth
WASHBOURN						
1757	1992	1700	1757	156035	WIL	Somerford Keynes
WASHBOURNES						
1500	1934	1500	1934	152536	WOR	Various
WASHER						
1815	1917	ALL	1917	104299	GLS	Bristol
1850	1880	1800	1850	168076	SOM	Bridgwater

Known From	To	Researching From	To	Ref	Cty	Place
WASHER contd.						
1832	1859	1800	1832	175951	SSX	Newick
WASHFORD						
1800	1836	ALL	1850	134503	KEN	Ashford
1800	1851	....	1850	160601	KEN	???
WASHINGTON						
....	....	....	1823	134902	CAM	March
1811	1837	1550	1850	147265	CHS	East
1764	....	1700	1764	118605	CHS	Barthomley
1880	1992	1500	1992	175498	LND	Lambeth
1600	1873	ALL	ALL	118958	OXF	???
WASKETT						
1560	1850	1560	1850	114146	ESS	High Roding
1850	1890	....	....	114146	ESS	Walthamstow
WASLEY						
1850	1860	1850	1992	121312	CON	Chacewater
1840	1880	1800	1890	118346	CON	Deay
WASS						
1806	1840	1700	1840	113808	DBY	Shirland
1770	1860	1750	1900	151742	DUR	South
....	....	ALL	1810	155470	ESS	Colne
....	....	1650	1793	178411	LIN	Swinehead
1583	1992	1583	1992	173959	NTT	ALL
1841	1874	1700	1841	113808	NTT	Arnold
1866	1992	....	....	113808	NTT	East Leake
WASSALL						
....	....	ALL	ALL	125873	ALL	Name Study
....	....	ALL	ALL	125873	ALL	ALL
WASSE						
1583	1992	1583	1992	173959	NTT	ALL
WASSELL						
1778	1828	1720	1828	149640	HAM	Titchfield
1789	1845	1700	1845	154881	SLI	ALL
WASSON						
1850	1992	1700	1850	122513	TYR	Newton Stewart
WASTELL						
1659	1970	1600	1900	154709	DUR	ALL
1800	1874	1700	1799	131245	MDX	Spitalfields
1659	1970	1600	1900	154709	YKS	Whitby
WASTFELDE						
1550	1700	1550	1992	100951	WIL	Chippenham
WASTFIELD						
1733	1760	1733	1810	100951	GLS	Miserden
WATCHAM						
....	....	ALL	ALL	124591	ALL	Name Study
WATCHCORN						
1890	1920	ALL	ALL	176222	IRL	ALL
WATCHMAN						
1886	1992	ALL	1992	177695	DUR	Croxdale
1740	1992	....	....	124168	DUR	Lanchester
WATERAGE						
1756	1756	ALL	1850	173614	HAM	Southwick
WATERFIELD						
....	....	1800	1899	124796	LAN	???
....	....	ALL	1800	142298	LEI	Quorondor
1810	1820	1700	1810	173452	LEI	Worthington
....	....	ALL	ALL	173975	WMD	ALL
WATERHOUSE						
1650	1670	1400	1700	129011	CUL	Tallentire
1854	1928	1700	1854	176052	WOR	Dudley
1770	1775	1750	1770	177393	YKS	Barmby Marsh
1770	1801	ALL	1770	154563	YKS	Otley
WATERLAND						
....	....	ALL	ALL	152277	ALL	Name Study
....	....	1500	1992	152277	ALL	ALL
1540	1992	1540	1992	152277	LIN	Isle Of Axholme
1600	1900	1600	1992	152277	YKS	???
WATERLOW						
1634	1700	1634	1850	113484	KEN	Canterbury
1700	1850	1634	1850	113484	LND	ALL
WATERMAN						
1756	1777	1700	1756	127116	DOR	Sutton Waldron
1865	1875	1865	1871	128287	ESS	Shoreditch
?	1860	1858	1870	128287	ESS	Stratford
1687	1807	1600	1687	173770	HAM	South
1770	1840	1700	1840	136840	HAM	Fordingbridge
1907	1929	1870	1929	133000	HAM	Portsmouth
1780	1850	1700	1960	172421	HAM	Rockbourne
1600	1992	ALL	ALL	137847	HAM	Winchester
1770	1830	1700	1830	108111	KEN	Boughton
1600	1700	1600	1700	133817	KEN	Leeds
1600	1700	1600	1700	133817	KEN	Maidstone
1840	1890	1750	1840	146285	LND	Westminster
WATERS						
1801	....	....	....	138126	BRE	Llandefaelog Fach
1813	1823	1600	1813	149888	BRK	Abingdon
1812	1894	....	....	135739	CAI	Dunnet
1810	1850	1700	1900	142875	CON	Breage
1687	1900	1600	1800	173983	CON	Crowan
1732	1992	ALL	ALL	121398	CON	St Levan
1786	....	1700	1800	110132	DEV	???
1832	1840	1799	1880	136980	KEN	Bethersden
1740	1882	1700	1936	134880	KEN	Bodsham
1832	1992	....	....	145777	KEN	Cranbrook
ALL	ALL	ALL	ALL	166243	KEN	Selling
....	....	....	....	142085	LEI	Belton
1847	1853	1800	1853	124435	LND	Bethnal Green
1851	....	1851	1992	176893	LND	Islington
1815	1851	1851	1992	176893	LND	Lambeth
1800	1840	1800	1840	156930	MON	Basseueg
1750	1800	1600	1750	172561	MON	Llanishen
1830	1930	1820	1930	156930	MON	Usk
1840	1992	1840	1992	147966	NFK	Norwich
1741	....	ALL	1741	168718	NTH	Kettering
1782	1992	1500	1867	174009	SSX	East
1700	1800	1650	1800	154881	SSX	Battle
1802	....	....	....	145777	SSX	Iden
1700	1950	ALL	1700	154555	WAR	Coventry
1550	1992	1550	1992	110361	WIL	Woodford
1620	1840	1600	1890	105627	WLS	Haverfordwest
1618	1739	1618	....	131229	WOR	ALL
WATERSFIELD						
1705	1705	1650	1750	105333	SSX	Chichester
WATERSON						
....	....	1900	1992	147613	LAN	Barrow In Furness
1740	1770	1700	1740	121339	NYK	Salton
WATERWORTH						
1800	1880	1800	1880	142980	LAN	Foulridge
1800	1820	....	....	126497	LAN	Wigan
1850	1926	1850	1926	142980	WYK	Bradford
....	....	ALL	ALL	178403	YKS	West
WATFORD						
1839	1992	1750	1840	101540	LND	St Giles
1770	1820	1600	1770	130230	SRY	Godstone
1663	1666	1660	1670	131547	SRY	Ockley
1650	....	1620	1670	131547	SRY	Shere
1652	1660	1630	1670	131547	SRY	Wotton
WATHAM						
1805	1848	1780	1857	173851	GLS	Ministerworth
WATHEW						
....	....	1700	1850	154458	LIN	???
WATKIN						
?	?	1750	1900	114456	GLA	ALL
1804	1860	ALL	ALL	124176	LEI	Whyfordby
1800	1876	1750	1900	114456	MGY	ALL
1801	1992	....	1801	138320	MON	Llanbrynmair
1735	1896	1700	1740	178543	NTT	Sturton Le Steeple
1840	1860	ALL	1870	120049	SAL	ALL
1870	1900	1800	1900	120049	STS	Stoke
1696	1740	....	1696	101761	WRY	Fishlake
WATKINS						
1798	1940	1700	1798	105457	ABD	Aberdeen
....	....	1800	ALL	135917	BRE	Abergavenny
1871	1928	1800	1928	132543	BRE	Brecon
1867	1992	ALL	ALL	115126	DOR	Cranbourne
1750	1950	1500	1750	107042	DOR	???
1700	1738	ALL	ALL	124982	GLS	Charfield
....	....	1800	1890	143715	GLS	Eastington
1610	1686	....	....	165999	GLS	Henbury
1785	1992	....	1785	138320	GLS	Newland
1757	1862	....	....	165999	GLS	St George In East
1861	1992	ALL	ALL	140740	GLS	Upleaden
1811	1830	1750	1811	148938	GLS	Westbury On Severn
1720	1850	....	....	128759	GNT	Llantilis Crossenery
1890	1900	1700	1890	125415	GNT	Pontypool
1794	....	....	....	131229	HEF	Hampton Bishop
....	1912	1850	1960	137685	KEN	Sydenham
1812	1992	1700	1812	171980	LAN	Prescot
....	....	ALL	ALL	130818	LND	Greenwich
1879	1884	1840	1884	135917	LND	Hampstead
1835	1879	1800	1900	135917	LND	Holborn
1855	1908	1800	1850	174920	MDX	Harlesden
1891	1992	1800	1900	176044	MDX	Islington
....	....	1800	1920	137685	MGY	Welshpool
1874	1992	ALL	1900	174017	MON	Cwmbran
1721	1797	....	....	135437	MON	Llangwm

Known From	To	Researching From	To	Ref	Cty	Place
WATKINS contd.						
....	....	1800	ALL	135917	MON	Monmouth
1874	1992	ALL	1900	174017	MON	Nantyglo
1874	1992	ALL	1900	174017	MON	Pontypool
1850	1920	1700	1850	138525	MON	Rhymney
1754	1846	1777	1846	104817	NTH	Haselbech
1888	1992	1800	1888	174041	OXF	Abingdon
1771	1842	1750	1842	159905	OXF	Shenington
1780	1830	1780	1830	151297	PEM	Pembroke
1800	....	ALL	1800	174033	SFK	Monewden
1845	1945	1800	1845	107042	SFK	???
1750	1950	1500	1750	107042	SOM	???
1800	1850	1800	1850	144657	SRY	Kennington
1796	1950	1773	1796	107042	SRY	Southwark
1785	1785	....	....	139971	SSX	Framfield
1850	1900	1700	1850	107042	SSX	Horsham
1728	1871	ALL	1728	174157	WEX	Dublin
1728	1871	ALL	1728	174157	WEX	Wexford
1867	1992	ALL	ALL	115126	WIL	Cranbourne
1904	1992	1700	1904	150487	WLS	Abercrave
WATKINSON						
1850	1992	1700	1900	122270	DBY	Chesterfield
....	....	ALL	ALL	147222	LAN	Southport
1850	1860	1700	1850	145688	LIN	Grimsby
1680	1750	....	....	140554	YKS	Aberford
1797	1883	1700	1797	159565	YKS	Doncaster
1622	1658	....	....	151351	YKS	Kilwick In Craven
1780	1816	ALL	ALL	159026	YKS	Thrybergh
WATKISS						
ALL	ALL	ALL	ALL	137243	ALL	ALL
1805	1853	1800	1900	136034	SAL	Dawley
WATLING						
1819	1860	1750	1819	103772	CAM	???
1790	1810	1700	1800	129356	NFK	Kirby Bedon
1710	1730	1700	1800	129356	SFK	Bramfield
1730	1750	1700	1800	129356	SFK	Linstead Parva
1760	1790	1700	1800	129356	SFK	Sotterley
1850	1900	1750	1850	105031	SFK	Wangford
WATMER						
1590	1660	1590	1660	175471	KEN	Canterbury
WATMORE						
1500	1992	1500	1992	175463	BRK	ALL
1500	1992	1500	1992	175463	HAM	ALL
1500	1900	1500	1900	175471	SAL	Stottesdon
WATMOUGH						
1450	1700	1450	1700	175471	LAN	Eccleston
1590	1660	1590	1700	175471	YKS	Halifax
WATNEY						
1780	1992	....	1780	174084	SRY	Wimbledon
WATSON						
1947	1948	1947	1960	115932	ALL	???
1770	1980	ALL	ALL	156604	ABD	Aberbour
1800	1810	1750	1850	179671	ABD	Aberdeen
1750	1950	1700	1950	149233	ABD	Auchterless
1700	1800	ALL	ALL	156604	ABD	Pitsligo
1761	....	....	....	151351	ANS	Arbroath
1763	1800	1700	1763	127590	ANS	Forfar
1840	1992	1700	1840	148423	ANS	Forfar
1839	1948	....	....	135453	AYR	Kilmarnock
1868	1886	....	....	146757	AYR	Kilmarnock
1790	1900	1700	1790	133507	BKM	Cuddington
1795	....	1700	1850	143693	BKM	Mentmore
1828	1880	1750	1900	143693	BKM	West Wycombe
1858	1866	ALL	....	109258	BRK	East Locking
1775	1850	ALL	1850	151319	CAM	Littleport
1810	1950	1790	1840	109517	CAM	Nordelph
1654	1940	....	....	128996	CAM	Thorney
1720	1886	1650	1720	135151	CUL	Addingham
1810	1810	ALL	1810	154563	CUL	Alston
1865	1890	....	....	141984	CUL	Cleator Moor
1750	1800	1700	1800	143553	CUL	Kirkland
1776	1809	ALL	1876	102350	DBY	Baslow
1848	1913	1800	1870	135763	DBY	Chesterfield
1870	1935	....	....	151351	DBY	Chesterfield
1730	1845	....	....	164631	DBY	Mickleover
1783	1783	1700	1820	105333	DEV	Rattery
1783	1783	1700	1820	105333	DEV	South Brent
1783	1783	1700	1820	105333	DEV	Ugborough
1812	1900	1800	1950	144037	DNB	Old Kilpatrick
....	....	ALL	ALL	146757	DOW	Downpatrick
1759	1797	1700	1838	153842	DUR	Bishopwearmouth
1860	1871	1800	1900	123536	DUR	Gateshead
1838	1860	1850	1860	153842	DUR	Houghton Le Spring
1840	1850	....	....	116637	DUR	Monkwearmouth
WATSON contd.						
1870	1932	ALL	ALL	122386	DUR	Ryton
1755	1862	1700	1755	103039	DUR	Stanhope
1840	1850	....	....	116637	DUR	Sunderland
1842	1866	1800	1850	154873	DUR	Sunderland
1698	1797	ALL	1698	154563	DUR	Weardale
1870	1932	ALL	ALL	122386	DUR	Winlaton
....	....	1750	....	148644	ELN	Haddington
1810	1810	1775	1810	147338	ERY	Beverly
1737	1866	1707	1737	139149	ERY	Nafferton
1797	1899	1700	1900	118397	ESS	Hockley
1881	1992	1700	1881	105163	EYK	Hull
1797	1812	1750	1800	108510	FIF	Kincardine On Forth
....	1780	1700	1800	130915	FIF	Largo
1797	1812	1750	1800	108510	FIF	Tulliallan
1687	1762	1600	1732	174130	GLS	Burton On The Hill
1705	1875	1700	1900	174238	HAM	Isle of Wight
1680	1838	1680	1992	136808	HRT	Barkway
1790	1930	1700	1790	158208	HRT	Therfield
1750	1950	1700	1950	149233	KCD	Fordoun
1776	1835	....	....	164631	KEN	Bromley
1875	1992	1800	1992	174238	KEN	Gravesend
1685	1776	....	....	164631	KEN	Orpington
1810	1890	1700	1810	142379	KEN	Rochester
1800	1992	1800	1992	110205	KEN	Rolverden
....	....	1700	1850	176397	KRS	Kinross
1785	1850	....	....	125997	LAN	Blackburn
1810	1841	1700	1810	160474	LAN	Blackburn
1733	1806	1733	1806	143286	LAN	Bolton
1749	1992	1660	1750	174211	LAN	Burnley
1749	1992	1660	1750	174211	LAN	Colne
1750	1900	1750	1900	125237	LAN	Darwen
1800	1880	1880	1992	162256	LAN	Darwen
1800	1815	1750	1800	155500	LAN	Penketh
1860	1992	ALL	1992	104590	LAN	Rochdale
1616	1811	ALL	ALL	141615	LAN	Warton
1840	1916	1780	1980	131709	LEI	Narborough
1790	1900	1700	1790	164844	LIN	South West
1756	1860	1700	1830	174165	LIN	Boothby
1883	1904	ALL	1904	138819	LIN	Holbeach
1740	1892	1700	1900	104396	LIN	Isle Of Axholme
1850	1992	....	....	174122	LIN	Lincoln
1800	1850	1750	1800	169749	LIN	March
1838	1886	1886	1992	146560	LKS	Coatbride
1816	1881	1800	1800	120146	LKS	Crawford John
1760	1790	1720	1760	122904	LKS	East Kilbride
1780	1900	1750	1900	133787	LKS	Glasgow
1782	1826	....	....	171654	LKS	Lesmahagow
1855	1992	1700	1855	161772	LND	Clerkenwell
1858	1992	1700	1858	171840	LND	Holborn
1837	1930	1800	1900	126586	LND	Shreditch
1800	1860	1800	1860	167924	MDX	Chelsea
....	....	1850	1900	167401	MDX	Highbury
1737	1796	1650	1800	126586	MLN	Dalkeith
1660	1836	ALL	ALL	105015	NBL	Allendale
1765	1827	1732	1765	116637	NBL	Allendale
1700	1730	1600	1800	162620	NBL	Allendale
1880	1928	1850	1920	105732	NBL	Gateshead
....	....	1768	1800	154873	NBL	Longframlington
1827	1992	1600	1827	174149	NBL	Newcastle On Tyne
1722	1911	ALL	ALL	105015	NBL	Newcastle
1870	1923	1700	1870	179329	NBL	Newcastle
1750	1875	....	1750	176516	NBL	Wallsend
1810	1950	1790	1840	109517	NFK	Nordelph
1804	1842	....	1804	136212	NFK	Wells Next Sea
1854	1867	1700	1860	112216	NFK	Witton
1830	1880	1538	1880	118893	NRY	Thrintoft
1577	1696	ALL	1577	143278	NTH	Staverton
1850	1950	1800	1900	145866	NTT	Basford
1883	1904	ALL	1904	138819	NTT	East Retford
1807	1887	1700	1807	174122	NTT	Newark
1800	1850	1750	1800	169749	NTT	Sutton St Edmund
1680	1720	1600	1680	121339	NYK	Catterick
1826	1826	1800	1826	147311	NYK	Thornton
1861	1992	1700	1861	150363	ROX	Teviothead
1870	1870	1700	1870	104728	SCT	Edinburgh
1846	1895	ALL	ALL	158690	SCT	Kirkcudbright
1780	1992	ALL	1780	100528	SCT	St Vigeans
1797	1992	1700	1797	150363	SEL	Commomside
1797	1992	1700	1797	150363	SEL	Selkirk
1816	1841	1780	1816	128724	SFK	Barrow
1830	1930	1800	1850	115614	SFK	Buneay
1790	1790	1750	1800	136840	SFK	Finningham
1819	1919	....	....	117196	SFK	Ipswich

Known From	To	Researching From	To	Ref	Cty	Place
WATSON contd.						
1820	1880	1750	1820	117218	SFK	Ipswich
1800	1830	1800	1830	115614	SFK	Mettingham
1750	1820	ALL	1800	158798	SOM	Frome
?	?	?	?	166642	SRY	Ash
1752	1793	1752	1793	127183	SSX	East Grinstead
1800	....	ALL	1800	112771	STS	Rowley Regis
1871	1930	ALL	1871	176060	STS	Tividale
1851	1901	1841	1901	108901	SYK	Sheffield
1799	1819	1770	1841	124788	WAR	Wolfhamcote
1845	1860	1800	1900	141984	WES	Ambleside
1715	1800	1700	1800	127604	WRY	Adlinfleet
1887	1930	....	....	174165	WYK	Birkenshaw
1820	1880	1720	1820	160253	WYK	Snaith
1812	1903	1812	1977	116114	YKS	Acaster Selby
1694	1694	1670	1700	141097	YKS	Braithwell
1840	....	....	....	103837	YKS	Brotherton
1820	1830	1750	1850	120529	YKS	Ferry Bridge
1855	1876	....	....	141097	YKS	Haley Hill
1830	1880	1700	1850	126772	YKS	Helmsley
1823	....	1750	....	134589	YKS	Kirby Grindalythe
....	....	ALL	ALL	158445	YKS	Kirk Ella
1800	1940	1750	1850	108510	YKS	Leeds
1900	1992	1500	1900	126616	YKS	Leeds
1842	1894	1700	1842	156183	YKS	Leeds
1770	1992	1740	1770	174173	YKS	Leeds
1814	1824	....	1814	176761	YKS	Leeds
1890	1900	....	....	141984	YKS	Micklefield
1791	....	....	1791	158305	YKS	North Ferriby
1850	1900	1800	1850	174203	YKS	Oldmalton
1732	1771	1600	1732	116637	YKS	Romaldkirk
1861	....	....	....	103837	YKS	Scarborough
1765	1860	1765	ALL	104590	YKS	Todmorden
1704	1767	1690	1704	101796	YKS	Woolley
1810	1840	1750	1850	105767	YKS	York
1810	1820	....	1992	137634	YKS	York
1820	1890	1700	1820	158208	YKS	York
WATT						
1800	1980	1700	1910	174246	ABD	Aboyne
1840	1992	ALL	1840	179434	ABD	Echt
1805	1992	1700	1810	155705	ANS	Barry
1730	....	....	....	126993	ANS	Montrose
1780	1800	1700	1850	174246	ANS	???
1850	1960	1700	1850	174254	AYR	Glagow
1806	1840	1700	1992	137855	DNB	New Kilpatrick
....	....	1850	1907	125571	DUR	Hartlepool
....	....	1700	ALL	149187	FIF	St Monance
1805	1992	1700	1810	155705	KCD	Inverkeillor
1860	1900	1900	1992	123374	KCD	Laurencekirk
1840	1992	ALL	1840	179434	KCD	Mary Culter
1805	1992	1700	1810	155705	KCD	St Vigeans
1800	1992	1900	1992	127418	LKS	East Kilbride
1850	1903	ALL	ALL	110388	LKS	Glasgow
1740	1830	1714	1830	174386	LND	Westminster
1851	1992	....	....	160148	YKS	York
WATTAM						
....	....	ALL	ALL	125245	ALL	Name Study
WATTERS						
1766	1871	1600	1871	141100	CON	Breage
1847	1992	....	1847	115150	IRL	???
1855	1900	1850	1920	123145	STS	Cradley Heath
1800	1900	1700	1900	124621	TYR	Stewartstown
1800	1900	1700	1900	132446	TYR	Stewartstown
WATTERSON						
1780	1847	1511	1847	141291	IOM	Rushen
WATTHEW						
1834	1834	ALL	ALL	120650	NTT	Nottingham
WATTHEWS						
....	....	ALL	ALL	139750	ALL	Name Study
WATTHEY						
1800	1900	1700	1950	141445	DBY	ALL
1800	1900	1700	1950	141445	NTT	ALL
WATTIS						
1830	1992	1700	1830	134775	WAR	Birmingham
WATTMORE						
1600	1800	1600	1800	175471	WOR	Bewdley
WATTON						
1590	1925	1500	1992	174270	DOR	ALL
....	....	ALL	ALL	174289	DOR	ALL
1590	1925	1500	1992	174270	HAM	ALL
....	....	ALL	ALL	174289	HAM	ALL
1760	1790	1700	1850	159107	NFK	Upwell
1750	1850	1650	1750	174297	WOR	Tardebigge
?	?	?	?	138681	???	???
WATTS						
....	....	ALL	ALL	100854	ALL	ALL
1758	....	ALL	1758	139459	BDF	Woburn
1756	1817	....	1840	171441	BRK	Buckland
1849	1881	1700	1849	123307	BRK	Kintbury
1738	1860	1700	1900	102970	BRK	Speen
1800	1992	1700	1800	174335	CAM	Orwell
1800	1992	1700	1800	174335	CAM	Wimpole
1849	....	1800	1849	120030	CON	St Mawes
1600	1900	....	....	174319	CON	???
....	?	ALL	?	100153	COR	???
1743	1744	1740	1750	142018	DEV	Exeter
....	....	1700	1800	156795	DOR	North
....	....	1600	1860	123390	DOR	Beaminster
1820	1850	1750	1900	118397	DOR	Hazelbury Bryan
1720	1820	1700	1900	143502	ESS	South East
1848	1913	1820	1900	135763	GLA	Cardiff
....	....	1700	....	141216	GLS	South
1700	....	....	....	142158	GLS	Berkeley
1800	1850	1600	1850	154342	GLS	Bitton
1850	1878	1830	1895	166898	GLS	Cheltenham
....	1840	....	1840	161888	GLS	Stroud
1705	1875	1700	1900	174238	HAM	Isle of Wight
1800	1850	....	....	154059	HAM	Titchfield
1834	....	....	....	148156	HUN	Bluntisham
1823	1861	1750	1871	148156	HUN	Hemingford Grey
1784	1992	1600	1784	139785	KEN	Marden
1784	1992	1600	1784	139785	KEN	Staplehurst
1850	1900	1900	1992	120618	LAN	Manchester
1870	....	1700	1950	126160	LAN	Manchester
....	....	1700	1880	102148	LEI	ALL
1706	1734	1680	1750	123404	LEI	Wymeswold
?	?	1809	1869	117919	LEI	???
1900	1900	1800	1900	124206	LND	ALL
1860	....	....	....	148156	LND	South
....	....	1750	1880	147826	LND	Bermondsey
1868	....	....	....	120340	LND	Hackney
1868	....	....	....	120340	LND	Shoreditch
....	....	1750	1880	147826	LND	Stepney
1700	1742	1680	1750	142018	LND	Whitechapel
1894	1950	....	....	120340	MDX	Enfield
1850	1880	1850	1910	174386	MDX	Marylebone
1874	1992	1700	1874	174351	NFK	North Walsham
1871	1880	1840	1873	139831	NFK	Norwich
1800	1880	1800	1900	142565	NFK	Norwich
....	....	1807	1839	139831	NFK	Yarmouth
1825	1871	1825	1871	107360	NTH	Blisworth
1673	1757	ALL	1757	168718	NTH	Kettering
1678	1678	ALL	1678	115126	NTH	Pitsford
1813	1880	1813	1950	130222	NTH	Stoke Albany
?	?	1809	1869	117919	NTH	???
1860	1890	....	....	167479	OXF	Witney
1830	....	....	....	145068	SFK	Bury St Edmunds
....	....	1750	1814	172871	SFK	Hawstead
1750	1900	1700	1750	140465	SOM	Bath
1700	1780	1700	1780	142018	SOM	Bath
....	....	1700	1992	149969	SOM	Bath
1870	1980	1870	1980	174300	SOM	Bath
1800	1870	1700	1870	174300	SOM	Crewkerne
....	....	1801	1886	130079	SOM	Haslebury Plucknett
1810	1911	1780	1920	160644	SOM	Monksilver
1752	1792	1740	1800	160644	SOM	Nettlecombe
1673	1696	1600	1673	153281	SOM	North Petherton
1742	1773	....	....	135437	SOM	Pilton
1770	1850	1760	1850	142018	SOM	Shepton Mallet
1825	1857	1750	1825	121568	SOM	Stoke St Gregory
....	1744	1740	1750	142018	SOM	Wells
1745	1946	....	....	145394	SSX	Arundel
1750	1900	1600	1750	154059	SSX	Chichester
....	....	1800	1992	164054	STS	Cradley Heath
1800	1900	ALL	ALL	120618	WAR	Coventry
1838	1860	1800	1838	167479	WAR	Hill Wootton
1861	1992	1700	1880	174378	WAR	Tysoe
1870	1980	1850	1890	164852	WIL	Corsley
1632	....	1600	1670	170348	WIL	Wanborough
1800	1860	1800	1860	138479	WIL	Warminster
....	....	1750	1850	174394	WIL	Westbury
1600	....	1800	1992	164054	WRY	Wortley
WAUD						
ALL	ALL	ALL	ALL	164143	ALL	ALL
WAUGH						
1758	1955	1700	1758	142883	CUL	Farlam
1796	1851	ALL	1800	171751	NBL	Allendale
1800	1850	1750	1850	105422	NBL	Billy Mill

Known From	To	Researching From	To	Ref	Cty	Place
WAUGH contd.						
1824	1871	1800	1870	154873	NBL	Cornhill
1824	1871	1800	1870	154873	NBL	Holy Island
1800	1900	....	....	150371	ROX	Newcastleton
1749	?	1700	1800	179000	STI	Muiravonside
....	....	1700	1899	174963	YKS	Scalby
WAVELL						
1780	1847	1750	1850	171549	HAM	Brading
1800	1992	1800	1992	172952	IOW	ALL
WAVERS						
1846	1992	....	....	118699	BRE	Brynmawr
WAY						
1697	1776	1660	1850	165972	DEV	Morchard Bishop
1763	1811	1760	1820	174416	DOR	Askerwell
1777	1900	1670	1800	101265	DOR	Beaminster
1852	1861	1851	1861	174416	DOR	Cerne Abbas
1841	1851	1841	1851	174416	DOR	Charminster
1811	1823	1804	1837	174416	DOR	Fordington
1810	....	1810	....	174416	DOR	Litton Cheney
1729	1742	1725	1750	174416	DOR	Loders
1762	....	1762	....	174416	DOR	Shipton Gorge
1841	1851	1841	1851	174416	DOR	Winfrith Newburgh
1861	1864	1861	1871	174416	DOR	Wyke Regis
1705	1740	1705	1740	127655	GLS	Bristol
1800	1930	1800	1930	119091	LND	East
1800	1930	1800	1930	119091	LND	South East
1800	1930	1800	1930	119091	LND	West
1880	1924	1880	1924	174416	LND	Camberwell
1830	....	1700	1850	145661	MDX	London
1750	1800	1750	1800	144657	SOM	Wellington
WAYCROFT						
1800	1840	1750	1800	121509	NTH	Woodnewton
WAYE						
1795	....	....	....	170623	DEV	South Tawton
1840	1870	....	....	144371	DEV	Sticklepath
WAYLETT						
1757	1793	ALL	1793	129283	ESS	Hawkwell
WAYLING						
1842	1984	ALL	1842	109320	SRY	Kenley
WAYMAN						
1795	1992	1795	1992	148156	CAM	Isle Of Ely
1700	1870	1600	1900	166391	DUR	ALL
1766	1890	....	....	127140	LIN	???
1827	1878	....	....	127140	LKS	Glasgow
1877	1895	....	....	127140	RFW	Gourock
1797	1895	....	....	127140	RFW	Greenock
WAYMOUTH						
1709	1900	ALL	1709	114987	DEV	Torquay
1850	1920	ALL	1850	141224	GLS	Bristol
WAYNESS						
1830	1880	1830	1880	131938	ROX	Galashields
1830	1880	1830	1880	131938	SEL	Selkirk
WAYTE						
1838	1992	1700	1838	126772	LEI	Thringstone
1847	1847	ALL	1847	119636	NFK	Wells
1832	1880	1600	1832	133132	STS	Burton On Trent
WAYTH						
1685	1992	1685	1992	136158	SFK	Southwold
WEAD						
1700	1725	1700	1725	156817	LEI	Syston
WEAKFORD						
1744	1844	....	....	127957	SSX	Walberton
WEAKLEY						
....	....	1630	1700	142859	ALL	ALL
1800	1900	1900	1992	168572	HAM	Gosport
WEAKLIM						
1811	....	1700	1816	126357	LET	Manor Hamilton
WEALAND						
1800	1825	1800	1850	161586	DUR	Sunderland
WEALE						
1690	1992	ALL	ALL	118656	BRE	Gwenddwr
1690	1992	ALL	ALL	118656	RAD	Disserth
1880	1890	1800	1900	135496	SAL	Ludlow
1800	1900	....	....	151572	SRY	Guildford
WEALLENS						
1790	1860	....	....	160458	NBL	???
WEAR						
1807	....	....	....	150398	KEN	Canterbury
1858	1870	1600	1858	150398	LND	Walworth
1840	1860	1700	1850	179191	ROX	Hawick
....	....	1800	1900	179248	SCT	Hawick
1858	1870	1600	1858	150398	SRY	Camberwell
WEARE						
....	....	ALL	ALL	174424	ALL	Name Study
WEARE contd.						
1821	1839	1839	1891	169374	SOM	Pill
1816	1818	ALL	1841	169374	SOM	Portbury
WEARMOUTH						
?	?	ALL	ALL	174432	DUR	Billingham
1800	1950	1600	1800	128376	DUR	Stanhope
WEARNE						
1846	1846	1100	1846	117749	CON	Helston
1805	1890	1700	1810	101931	CON	Wendron
....	....	1500	1890	136972	CON	Wendron
WEARS						
1787	1787	ALL	1787	154563	DUR	Weardale
WEARY						
1680	1770	1680	1750	143367	CON	Duloe
1680	1770	1680	1750	143367	CON	Kilkhampton
1815	1890	ALL	ALL	143367	CON	Roche
1750	1815	ALL	ALL	143367	CON	St Austell
1845	1910	ALL	ALL	143367	LND	Camberwell
1845	1910	ALL	ALL	143367	LND	Clerkenwell
1845	1910	ALL	ALL	143367	LND	Shoreditch
WEATHERALL						
....	....	ALL	ALL	174440	ALL	Name Study
1831	1874	1810	1900	170992	IRL	Belfast
WEATHERBURN						
1746	1992	....	....	160458	NBL	???
WEATHERCUP						
1869	1900	ALL	ALL	169838	DUB	Dublin
WEATHERDONE						
1815	1860	1750	1820	119164	DEV	Highweek
WEATHERHEAD						
1824	1981	ALL	1981	146226	DBY	Harrogate
1840	1880	1880	1900	114871	LND	Marylebone
1700	1825	1650	1700	114871	WRY	Hunslet
1775	1815	1600	1992	102520	YKS	Flockton
1764	1925	1764	1925	161314	YKS	Keighley
1558	1750	1558	1750	161314	YKS	Pately Bridge
WEATHERHOGG						
1750	1860	....	....	176591	LIN	Algarkirk
1880	1992	....	....	176591	STS	Stoke On Trent
WEATHERILL						
1817	1896	1790	1846	147311	NYK	Hinderwell
1845	1992	1700	1845	138657	WRY	Bilsdale
WEATHERLAY						
1827	....	1700	1826	136735	WAR	Aston
WEATHERLEY						
1810	1860	1700	1810	133523	ALL	ALL
1760	1860	1700	1900	147958	MDX	Harrow
1743	1800	1700	1850	113743	MDX	Ruislip
WEATHERSBEE						
....	....	1750	1850	155322	LND	City
....	....	1850	1880	155322	MDX	St Pancras
WEAVER						
....	....	1500	1900	166863	BRK	ALL
1734	....	1700	1734	113352	ESS	Rivenhall
1796	1821	1769	1821	153176	GLS	Twyning
1884	1984	1884	....	133922	HAM	Eling
1884	1984	1884	....	133922	HAM	Totton
1566	1587	ALL	ALL	141615	LEI	North
1880	1950	1800	1900	135542	LND	Bermondsey
1700	1800	ALL	ALL	174637	MGY	???
....	....	....	1860	168424	MID	Bilston
1780	1850	1821	1821	122238	SAL	Broseley
1850	1875	ALL	ALL	124982	SOM	North
1800	1992	1770	1800	161322	SOM	North
1849	1900	1800	1850	122351	SRY	Deptford
1809	1893	1750	1809	126454	SSX	Bodiam
1834	1955	1810	1992	116653	STS	Aston
1705	1720	1650	1720	120049	STS	Biddulph
1700	1705	1650	1700	120049	STS	Caverswall
1800	1992	1600	1800	152366	WOR	ALL
1871	1992	1816	1992	174475	WOR	Cotshill
1860	....	....	1992	168424	YKS	Barnsley
1869	1930	1600	1869	131261	YKS	Sheffield
WEAVERS						
....	....	ALL	ALL	174483	ALL	Name Study
1861	1900	1825	1861	157465	ESS	Braintree
....	....	1900	1950	157465	LND	Various
1823	1992	1823	1992	174483	WOR	Kidderminster
WEAVING						
ALL	ALL	ALL	ALL	165824	ALL	ALL
1803	1900	ALL	ALL	112259	GLS	ALL
1844	1871	1840	1881	165824	SOM	Bath
1820	....	1800	1840	165824	WIL	Pickwick

Known From	To	Researching From	To	Ref	Cty	Place
WEAVIS						
1850	1960	ALL	ALL	162469	SFK	North
WEBB						
....	....	ALL	ALL	174491	ALL	Name Study
ALL	ALL	....	....	174556	AVN	Bedminster
ALL	ALL	....	....	174556	AVN	Bristol
1800	....	1800	1900	106410	AVN	Henbury
1800	....	1800	1900	106410	AVN	Shirehampton
1820	1950	1600	1820	112828	BKM	Chesham
1800	1900	ALL	ALL	130613	BRE	Llangarten
1751	1885	1790	1950	118737	BRK	Beenham
1737	1910	....	....	177776	BRK	Beenham
1750	1850	1700	1992	149632	BRK	Binfield
1538	1737	....	....	177776	BRK	Bucklebury
1700	1750	1600	1750	167088	BRK	Hurst
1852	1852	1820	1880	136719	BRK	Tadley
1811	1886	1750	1820	129712	BRK	Wallingford
1750	1992	1600	1750	174572	CAM	Balsham
....	....	ALL	ALL	115533	CAM	Gazely
1850	1992	1700	1850	157449	CAM	Gt Wilbraham
....	....	1700	1900	127477	CAM	Kirtling
1760	1780	1740	1790	124605	CAM	Westley Waterless
1755	1826	1755	....	140570	CHS	Chester
1860	1880	1800	1900	117668	CHS	Davenham
1885	1930	1885	1930	117668	CHS	Grappenhall
1796	1992	....	....	169013	CHS	Knutsford
1740	....	1700	1740	131326	CON	Mevagissey
1770	1806	1750	1770	138339	CON	St Blazey
1860	1992	1750	1992	167991	CON	St Just
1800	1888	1700	1800	177091	CON	Stratton
?	?	?	?	142018	DEV	Exeter
1799	1850	1799	1850	175366	DEV	Exeter
....	....	1500	1741	138614	DEV	???
....	....	1700	1900	149454	DEV	???
1870	1920	ALL	1880	106844	DUR	Spennymoor
1790	1820	1750	1850	177024	ESS	Epping
....	1790	....	....	174564	ESS	Grays
1635	1797	ALL	ALL	101400	ESS	Kelvedon
1797	1870	ALL	ALL	101400	ESS	Rivenhall
1867	1900	1870	1915	101400	ESS	Witham
1810	1854	1750	1900	174521	GLS	Bristol
1800	1900	ALL	ALL	130613	GLS	Chastleton
1790	1919	1700	1992	124281	GLS	Elmore
1780	1850	ALL	ALL	117579	GLS	Henbury
1679	1760	1546	1875	142859	GLS	Minchinhampton
1850	1920	1820	1910	117579	GLS	Shirehampton
1794	1992	1700	1794	165921	GLS	Stroud
1796	1860	ALL	1860	132217	GLS	Uley
1800	1870	1800	1870	110523	GNT	Monmouth
1820	1900	1750	1950	133922	HAM	Eling
1903	1920	....	....	173282	HAM	Emsworth
1820	1900	1750	1950	133922	HAM	Forest
1886	1992	1800	1900	155144	HAM	Gosport
1769	1769	1730	1770	124974	HAM	Kingsclere
....	....	1750	1850	118834	HAM	Portsmouth
1854	1920	....	....	173282	HAM	Portsmouth
1920	1920	....	....	173282	HAM	Redding
1852	1950	1500	1852	132993	HAM	Southampton
1798	....	....	....	144169	HEF	Hentland
1798	....	....	....	144169	HEF	Llanwarne
1915	1921	....	....	101400	HRT	Sandridge
1880	1880	1700	1880	121150	HRT	Ware
1899	1944	1860	1944	102989	KEN	Deptford
1810	1851	1750	1860	174599	KEN	Deptford
1905	1992	....	1905	137642	KEN	Hythe
1750	1900	1600	1750	144681	KEN	Petham
1738	1761	1600	1738	139084	KEN	Shipbourne
1850	1900	1600	1850	123587	KEN	Tonbridge
1700	1790	1740	1800	175366	LND	Bishopsgate
1910	1958	1940	1958	137685	LND	Canning Town
1863	1931	1800	1863	174580	LND	Clerkenwell
....	....	1870	1940	137685	LND	Fulham
1800	1900	ALL	ALL	141704	LND	Lambeth
....	....	1780	1830	161187	LND	Strand
1800	1900	ALL	ALL	141704	LND	Wandsworth
?	?	?	?	169064	LND	???
1860	....	1800	1900	134481	MDX	All Souls
1580	1750	1550	1800	175366	MDX	Clerkenwell
1830	1860	....	....	161187	MDX	Dalston
1831	1926	1700	1950	116742	MDX	Harefield
1875	1909	1851	1909	174521	MDX	Kensington Town
1780	1790	1700	1800	175366	MDX	Westminster
1850	1940	1700	1860	160954	MSY	Liverpool
1870	1880	ALL	1880	106844	NFK	East

Known From	To	Researching From	To	Ref	Cty	Place
WEBB contd.						
1740	1890	ALL	1740	108197	NFK	Cromer
1750	1800	1600	1750	160296	NFK	Cromer
....	....	1600	1950	149454	NFK	???
1830	1930	1830	1930	100420	NTH	Daventry
1780	1860	ALL	1835	101281	NTH	Towcester
1880	1992	1500	1920	137472	NTT	Nottingham
?	1880	1880	1900	167096	OXF	All Saints
1840	1900	1700	1840	174513	OXF	Kencot
1782	1782	1700	1782	179116	OXF	Stanton Harcourt
1800	1900	ALL	ALL	130613	OXF	???
1800	1900	ALL	ALL	130613	RAD	Llangarten
1660	1700	1640	1700	135941	SFK	Glemsford
1800	1846	1770	1850	135941	SFK	Hawkedon
1786	1786	1700	1786	155276	SFK	Nacton
1758	1764	1700	1758	155276	SFK	Tuddenham
1700	1899	1740	1850	135941	SFK	Wickhambrook
1700	1800	1700	1820	140295	SOM	Brewham
1600	1750	1600	1750	142018	SOM	Chard
1800	1992	1700	1799	156876	SOM	Coleford
1800	1900	....	....	171824	SRY	Greenwich
1839	1839	1750	1880	176672	SSX	Brighton
1853	1880	....	1853	129771	SSX	Chiddingly
1870	....	....	....	103233	SSX	Ripe
1889	1965	1800	1889	170569	STS	Cannock
1532	1614	1500	1613	102830	STS	Codsall
1830	1930	1830	1930	100420	STS	Lichfield
1673	1851	....	1851	155055	STS	Stone
....	1782	1600	1782	153591	SXW	Winchelsea
1840	1890	1600	1840	122084	WAR	Birmingham
1800	....	....	....	148504	WAR	Feckinham
1840	1850	1800	1840	146110	WAR	Priors Marston
1800	1900	ALL	ALL	130613	WAR	Whichford
ALL	ALL	ALL	ALL	153184	WIL	ALL
1500	1700	1500	1900	170216	WIL	ALL
1840	1940	ALL	ALL	153222	WIL	Brinkworth
1800	1970	ALL	1850	153184	WIL	Brinkworth
1940	1992	....	....	153222	WIL	Hook
1925	1940	....	....	153184	WIL	Minety
1480	1650	1480	1700	175366	WIL	Old Sarum
1855	1860	1860	1992	166197	WOR	Chaceley
1790	1919	1700	1992	124281	WOR	Elmore
1848	1959	ALL	ALL	105996	WOR	Stoke Bliss
....	....	1700	1992	170402	WOR	Tenbury Wells
....	1800	ALL	ALL	174521	WOR	Worcester
?	?	?	?	169064	YKS	Bridlington
1835	1850	1700	1900	158666	YKS	???
WEBBAR						
....	....	1450	1650	130591	SOM	Clatworthy
WEBBER						
1806	1828	1800	1828	144878	CON	St Just In Roseland
1593	....	1500	1593	174629	CON	St Kew
....	....	1860	1992	132438	DBY	Derby
....	....	1750	1820	179604	DEV	North
1830	1871	1860	1880	165441	DEV	Bradminch
1743	1850	1730	1830	137413	DEV	Challacombe
1837	1960	1700	1837	148814	DEV	Chulmleigh
....	....	?	1702	129046	DEV	Crediton
1806	1846	1600	1805	156779	DEV	Exeter
....	1832	ALL	1832	175080	DEV	Exeter
1787	1822	?	1825	103934	DEV	North Molton
1800	1830	1600	1800	134090	DEV	Plymouth
1838	1967	1800	1838	157619	DEV	Plymouth
1820	1880	1820	1992	114596	DEV	Rose Ash
1837	1960	1700	1837	148814	DEV	Roseash
1677	1756	....	....	129046	DEV	Sandford
1825	1843	1750	1825	119164	DEV	South Molton
1880	1960	....	....	113514	GLA	Barry
1794	....	1750	1800	175684	LND	City
1881	1900	1862	1920	148814	LND	Pancras
1823	1881	1800	1900	113751	LND	???
1790	1841	1750	1860	105333	MDX	London
1808	1827	1700	1890	170518	MLN	Edinburgh
1770	1900	1730	1900	118540	SOM	North
1575	1900	1500	1900	133450	SOM	West
1837	1870	1830	1870	121177	SOM	Bridgewater
1805	1848	1805	ALL	175854	SOM	Dulverton
1841	1890	1827	1992	170518	SOM	Taunton
1840	1900	1700	1840	167762	SOM	Wellington
....	....	1800	1920	104256	SOM	Yatton
1800	1861	1862	1900	132438	SSX	Brighton
1867	1915	1700	1867	107506	SSX	???
1830	1871	1860	1880	165441	STS	Stoke On Trent
....	....	ALL	ALL	104884	WIL	Wiveliscombe

Known From	To	Researching From	To	Ref	Cty	Place
WEBBERLEY						
1643	1875	ALL	ALL	135062	DBY	Ashbourne
1875	1992	1750	1875	143855	HMC	ALL
WEBBY						
....	....	1790	1820	123870	WIL	Ironbridge
....	....	1790	1820	123870	WIL	Shropshire
WEBDAY						
1820	1875	1600	1823	153591	CAM	???
WEBLEY						
....	....	ALL	ALL	174637	ALL	Name Study
1600	1800	ALL	ALL	174637	ALL	ALL
WEBSTER						
1830	1992	1700	1830	145017	ABD	Aberdeen
1812	1900	1700	....	148342	ABD	Peterhead
1725	1750	1660	1800	150002	ANS	Dundee
1850	1992	1750	1850	174653	ANS	Dundee
1841	1980	1700	1841	168386	BAN	Grange
1665	1851	....	1900	137405	CAM	Over
1904	....	1904	1920	151041	CHS	Wallasey
1880	1971	1880	1992	140635	CLV	Sunderland
1830	1860	ALL	1830	122823	CON	Bodmin
1730	1732	1600	1900	102520	CON	Crowan
1820	1870	ALL	1880	175757	DBY	Belper
1833	1871	1800	1837	129186	DBY	Spondon
1885	1971	1885	1992	140635	DUR	Sunderland
1895	....	1875	1895	102989	ESS	Canning Town
1894	1950	1850	1890	109398	ESS	Islington
1724	1779	ALL	1724	131881	FIF	Ceres
1750	1850	1500	1850	142069	FIF	Ceres
1881	1920	....	....	143480	HAM	Alverstoke
1881	1920	....	....	143480	HAM	Fareham
....	....	1750	1800	112038	HUN	Maxey
1810	1850	ALL	ALL	159034	KEN	East Malling
1810	1860	ALL	ALL	159034	KEN	Ryash
1850	1900	1800	1900	142875	LAN	Ashton
1755	1807	1600	1755	119822	LAN	Bolton
1892	1992	ALL	ALL	133345	LAN	Bury
1790	1830	1650	1790	146102	LAN	Chorlton
1800	1825	1712	1869	142859	LAN	Manchester
1820	1824	1790	1820	155489	LAN	Manchester
1830	1856	....	....	118729	LAN	Thurnham
1755	1807	1600	1755	119822	LAN	Wigan
1867	1950	1867	1992	115355	LEI	ALL
....	....	ALL	1740	142298	LEI	Ashby De La Zouch
1650	1706	1600	1650	174130	LEI	Houghton On The Hill
1717	1981	1600	1717	102342	LIN	Alkborough
1850	1980	ALL	1850	176656	LIN	Stamford
1900	....	1900	....	123773	LND	Bethnal Green
1840	1870	1800	1900	135283	LND	Marylebone
1880	1931	1850	1930	105333	MDX	Deptford
1808	1808	ALL	ALL	171816	NTH	Bugbrooke
1840	1992	1700	1840	174645	NTH	Hartwell
1876	1992	1700	1906	155101	NTH	Wakererley
....	....	1750	1900	129275	SCT	Peterhead
1831	1831	1750	1831	156914	STS	Aldridge
1900	1980	1800	1900	109487	SYK	Barnsley
1880	1971	1880	1992	140635	T&W	Sunderland
....	....	1838	1845	143480	WAR	Barford
....	....	1838	1845	143480	WAR	Leamington
....	....	ALL	1880	161209	WAR	Warwick
1860	1900	1700	1890	133701	WOR	Hull
ALL	1810	....	....	170798	WRY	Birstall
ALL	1810	....	....	170798	WRY	Drighlington
....	....	ALL	ALL	143014	WYK	ALL
1800	1820	1700	1800	110531	WYK	Kirkburton
1810	1992	ALL	1810	100803	WYK	Sowerby
1800	1911	1800	1911	161314	YKS	Armley
1790	1860	....	....	141984	YKS	Hambleton
1800	1850	1750	1850	116823	YKS	Harone
1838	1947	1800	1870	106003	YKS	Hunslet
1830	ALL	1700	1830	130397	YKS	Kingston Upon Hull
....	....	ALL	ALL	133345	YKS	Pudsey
1848	1882	1824	1848	155489	YKS	Rotherham
1800	1874	ALL	1800	171468	YKS	Sheffield
1800	1840	1750	1840	121509	YKS	Wensleydale
1752	1841	1650	1790	162507	YKS	Whitby
1838	1947	1800	1870	106003	YKS	Wortley
WEDD						
1757	1870	1800	1992	174718	CAM	Bassingbourn
1680	1750	1750	1800	174718	CAM	Fowlmere
1560	1800	1450	1560	174696	CAM	Fowlmere
1757	1992	1800	1992	174718	CAM	Melbourn
1800	1900	....	....	174696	ESS	Great Wakering

Known From	To	Researching From	To	Ref	Cty	Place
WEDD contd.						
1721	....	....	1800	171441	KEN	Bicknor
1695	....	....	1800	171441	KEN	Hucking
1720	1850	....	....	174696	LIN	Boston
1820	1920	....	....	174696	LND	Bayswater
WEDDALL						
1600	1900	1400	1992	126985	YKS	Pocklington
WEDDELL						
1747	1815	....	1747	120464	NBL	Alnwick
WEDGE						
1710	1820	1600	1710	148792	HAM	St Mary Bourne
1700	1750	1700	1750	173819	SAL	Wellington
1700	1815	....	....	164038	SSX	Bosham
WEDGER						
1794	1812	....	....	129747	SFK	Ipswich
WEDGEWOOD						
1400	1600	....	....	100420	WAR	Meriden
WEDLAKE						
....	....	ALL	ALL	173398	ALL	Name Study
1711	1870	ALL	ALL	173398	DEV	North
1780	1830	1700	1800	158925	DEV	Chagford
1875	1992	ALL	ALL	173398	YKS	Middlesborough
WEDLOCK						
....	....	ALL	ALL	100919	ALL	ALL
1816	1874	ALL	ALL	100919	BKM	Hambleden
1800	1860	1700	1860	159441	CON	Helston
1837	1837	1800	1837	128368	DEV	Bickington
1814	1968	ALL	ALL	100919	OXF	ALL
WEDMORE						
1750	1850	1620	1750	167533	SOM	Nailsea
WEED						
1750	1820	ALL	ALL	114235	NTH	???
WEEDALL						
1780	1820	1700	1780	155500	LAN	Wigan
WEEDEN						
1858	1913	1700	1858	147761	LND	Camberwell
WEEDON						
1877	1880	1877	1904	138312	BDF	Leighton Buzzard
1844	1876	1700	1844	138509	BDF	Luton
1786	1839	....	....	108200	BKM	Aston Clinton
1777	1786	....	....	108200	BKM	Hardwick
1802	1904	1802	1904	138312	HRT	South West
1844	1876	1700	1844	138509	HRT	Luton
....	....	1800	1900	115649	LND	Bloomsbury
1834	1992	....	....	108200	SRY	Kingston
....	....	ALL	ALL	101885	YKS	???
WEEKES						
1638	....	....	....	153397	HAM	Westbourne
1804	1851	1700	1803	131245	MDX	Bethnal Green
1785	1908	1750	1784	108227	SOM	Rodney Stoke
1877	1977	1700	1877	174734	SXE	Central
WEEKLEY						
1765	1992	1765	1900	174742	AVN	Bristol
1765	1992	1765	1900	174742	GLS	Bristol
1765	1992	1765	1900	174742	SOM	Bristol
WEEKLY						
1792	1970	1750	1980	169250	KEN	Erith
1792	1970	1750	1980	169250	LND	Lambeth
WEEKS						
....	....	ALL	ALL	160555	ALL	Name Study
1800	1992	1798	1992	161640	AVN	Bath
....	....	1700	1850	133493	CON	Lewannick
1858	1992	1850	1936	126403	DEV	Devonport
1796	1802	....	1796	177504	DEV	Stoke Fleming
1813	1882	1700	1800	131148	DEV	???
1795	1900	ALL	1900	165654	GLS	Bitton
1828	1830	1813	1839	160555	GLS	Compton Greenfield
1800	1870	1762	1879	160555	GLS	Henbury
1894	1956	....	....	160555	GNT	Llantrissant
....	....	1500	1992	153095	KEN	Central
1856	1960	1700	1856	139335	KEN	Woolwich
1825	1853	1825	1853	125717	LEI	St Margarets
1856	1960	1700	1856	139335	LND	Woolwich
1894	1914	....	....	160555	MON	Chepstow
....	....	1600	1830	166863	SOM	Bristrol
....	....	1600	1830	166863	SOM	Long Ashton
1700	1827	1700	1830	115193	SOM	Queen Charlton
1845	1862	ALL	1992	125113	SOM	Wells
....	....	ALL	1810	164631	SRY	Ewell
1800	1840	1750	1800	133671	WIL	Minty
1770	1830	1700	1770	133671	WIL	Poolkeynes
WEEMES						
1800	....	ALL	ALL	112275	HUN	Godmanchester

Known From	To	Researching From	To	Ref	Cty	Place
WEETMAN						
1754	1800	1600	1800	130125	NBL	Lesbury
1871	1992	....	....	118699	STS	Cannock
1619	1723	1626	1723	160237	STS	Hints
WEIGHELL						
1800	1805	....	....	117196	YKS	East Cowton
1695	1887	1600	1695	154164	YKS	West Riding
WEIGHT						
....	....	ALL	ALL	174769	ALL	Name Study
WEIGHTON						
....	1783	1700	1783	148288	PER	Scone
WEIGTMAN						
1889	....	ALL	ALL	105481	NTT	Heage
WEINSTEIN						
?	?	?	?	138622	WMD	???
WEIR						
1805	1960	....	....	127140	ARL	Kilmun
1735	1992	1603	1735	174785	ARL	Lochgiolhead
1855	1965	....	....	174777	AVN	Bristol
....	....	1820	1854	142751	AYR	Ayr
1790	....	ALL	1790	174777	AYR	Glenbuck
1790	....	ALL	1790	174777	AYR	Muirkirk
1850	1900	1800	1850	111708	AYR	New Cumnock
1790	1855	ALL	1790	174777	AYR	Sorn
1874	....	....	....	106852	LKS	Carluke
....	....	1820	1992	112305	LKS	???
?	?	?	?	160091	NBL	Scremerston
1854	1867	1820	1854	142751	RFW	Glasgow
1775	1887	....	....	127140	RFW	Greenock
1825	1847	ALL	1825	108537	RFW	Neilston
ALL	ALL	ALL	ALL	174793	SCT	Glasgow
1894	1931	ALL	1992	159174	STS	Burton On Trent
1826	1960	1750	1826	174807	WIG	Stoneykirk
WELBOURNE						
....	....	1600	1700	136743	LEI	Saltby
....	1790	....	....	128910	LIN	South Kelsey
WELBROCK						
1800	1871	....	1784	133566	MDX	Bethnal Green
WELBY						
....	....	ALL	ALL	174823	ALL	Name Study
1606	1992	1606	1900	126454	LIN	Rauceby
WELCH						
1767	....	1650	1800	143693	BKM	Hughenden
1808	1965	1600	1808	117676	CON	Penryn
1771	1792	1600	1771	116637	DUR	Sunderland
1859	....	....	....	174750	ENG	???
1860	1860	1860	1880	103225	ESS	Walthamstow
1800	1880	1600	1880	154342	GLS	Bristol
....	....	1835	1900	141151	HAM	ALL
....	....	1600	1850	127833	HAM	East
1810	1845	1800	1960	103586	HAM	Emsworth
1700	1940	....	....	127833	HAM	Portsmouth
1760	1850	1700	1760	147575	HRT	St Mimms
1702	1992	1700	1992	171581	IOW	Chale
1859	1880	ALL	ALL	138886	LAN	Preston
1837	....	ALL	1800	165883	LAN	Preston
1700	1805	1700	1805	145602	LAN	Walton Le Dale
1832	1992	ALL	1832	174874	LEI	Broughton On Astley
1832	1992	ALL	1832	174874	LEI	Sutton On The Elms
1750	1795	1700	1750	137383	LIN	Revesby
1855	1992	....	....	175803	LND	Greenwich
1899	1942	1800	1874	174831	LND	Newingham
1928	1928	ALL	ALL	134120	LND	Wood Green
1820	1910	1820	1910	177814	MDX	ALL
1814	1911	1750	1813	167452	MDX	Hackney
1760	1850	1700	1760	147575	MDX	Monken Hadley
1850	1900	....	....	126497	NBL	Berwick Upon Tweed
1820	1940	1820	1900	126500	NBL	Berwick Upon Tween
1823	1992	ALL	1823	129992	NFK	Norfolf
1725	....	1725	....	148156	NTH	Wootton
1875	1992	....	....	106720	OXF	Ilsley
1830	....	....	....	126497	SCT	???
1813	1850	1700	1813	111945	SFK	Covehithe
1813	1850	1700	1813	111945	SFK	Kessingland
1871	1881	1881	1960	174831	SOM	Bath
1500	1840	1500	1900	119113	SOM	Chard
1870	1896	....	....	133922	SOM	Hinton St George
1830	1850	1800	1900	129607	SRY	Camberwell
....	....	1600	1850	127833	SSX	West
WELCHMAN						
....	....	ALL	ALL	174882	ALL	Name Study
WELCOME						
1760	1900	1700	1760	130257	SSX	Chichester
WELDISH						
....	1769	ALL	1769	129658	KEN	Harrietsham
WELDON						
....	....	ALL	ALL	174890	ALL	Name Study
1312	1980	1538	1992	174890	ALL	ALL
1800	1908	1700	1800	174599	DOR	Shaftesbury
1730	1900	1600	1900	117617	RUT	Whitwell
1760	1992	1600	1760	128031	YKS	Sessay
WELDONE						
1864	1864	1800	1875	171662	KIK	Kilkenny
WELFARE						
....	....	....	1900	110817	SSX	East Grinstead
1770	1850	1650	1770	118745	SSX	Hastings
WELFOOT						
1600	1700	1600	1700	169781	DUR	St Helen Auckland
WELFORD						
1737	1933	1737	1884	119059	BKM	Brill
1770	1992	1700	1770	133507	BKM	Dinton
1700	ALL	1787	1880	107379	BKM	Haddenham
1750	1800	ALL	ALL	107352	DUR	Auckland
1758	1779	ALL	1758	132829	DUR	Barnard Castle
1779	1840	....	....	132829	DUR	Durham
1840	1843	1700	1992	164992	DUR	Durham
1881	1881	1700	1992	164992	MDX	Limehouse
1840	1992	....	....	132829	T&W	Newcastle Upon Tyne
1700	ALL	1787	1900	107379	YKS	Middlesborough
1800	ALL	1800	1950	107379	???	Newcastle On Tyne
WELHAM						
1840	1900	1700	1800	168653	SFK	ALL
WELLAND						
1880	1900	1880	1900	120529	LND	Bethnal Green
WELLARD						
1780	1805	1750	1800	177377	KEN	Dover
1800	1900	1750	1820	177377	KEN	Medway
1811	1819	1811	1819	126667	OXF	Crowell
WELLAVIZE						
1713	1832	1713	1832	178705	WIL	Hannington
WELLAWYSE						
1713	1832	1713	1832	178705	WIL	Hannington
WELLER						
1754	1992	....	....	168890	BKM	Amersham
1749	1992	1800	1992	127795	BKM	High Wycombe
1754	1992	....	....	168890	BKM	High Wycombe
1749	1992	1800	1992	127795	BKM	West Wycombe
1877	1881	1850	1950	178799	DOW	Annalong
1860	1860	1800	1900	178624	KEN	Folkestone
1876	1992	1800	1876	108022	KEN	Sittingborne
1850	1992	1500	1850	141720	LND	Lambeth
1850	1992	1500	1850	141720	LND	Stepney
....	....	1820	1900	125555	MDX	Bethnal Green
1830	1878	1830	1950	178799	MDX	Feltham
1542	1750	....	1542	168890	OXF	Berrick Salome
1542	1750	....	1542	168890	OXF	Warborough
1820	1860	1820	1860	176745	SRY	Carshalton
1800	1830	1750	1800	176745	SRY	Oxted
1866	1970	1800	1992	129488	SSX	Buxted
....	....	ALL	1800	173150	SXE	ALL
1800	....	ALL	1800	173150	SXE	Brede
WELLESLEY						
....	....	1800	1900	109677	MDX	London
WELLHAM						
....	....	1750	1900	129275	KEN	Gravesend
....	....	1700	1900	129275	KEN	Swanscombe
WELLING						
1850	1980	ALL	1850	141526	HRT	Aldbury
1811	1860	1800	1900	179256	HRT	Aldbury
WELLINGS						
1743	1743	1600	1743	164879	SRY	Leigh
1820	1980	....	1820	123161	WAR	Birmingham
WELLINGTON						
1850	1900	1850	1900	149144	CHI	Guernsey
1890	1992	1800	1890	169722	DEV	South
WELLMAN						
1792	1852	1700	1791	166820	BRK	Hurst
WELLMANN						
1760	1800	ALL	1760	115266	DOR	ALL
WELLOCK						
....	....	1830	1900	160776	HAM	ALL
....	....	1881	1895	160776	SRY	Bermondsey
....	....	1798	1833	160776	YKS	East Witton
1777	1817	1730	1780	162396	YKS	Kirkby Malham
WELLON						
1798	1798	1700	1798	167452	BKM	High Wycombe

Known From	To	Researching From	To	Ref	Cty	Place
WELLS						
....	....	ALL	ALL	174971	ALL	Name Study
1748	1850	?	1850	103934	BDF	Biggleswade
1690	1992	ALL	1690	131067	BDF	Shefford
1772	1800	1750	1800	119059	BKM	Brill
1736	1756	....	1780	171441	BRK	Buckland
1814	1815	1700	1842	176885	BRK	Clewer
1815	....	1700	1842	176885	BRK	New Windsor
....	....	1780	1833	161357	DOR	West
1733	1844	....	....	161357	DOR	Walditch
....	....	1600	1850	127833	HAM	East
1830	1875	1700	1830	100765	HAM	Christchurch
1742	1851	1740	1861	170143	HAM	East Meon
1690	1825	1650	1690	168777	HAM	Hunton
1810	1900	ALL	1800	150983	HAM	Portsea
1700	1940	....	....	127833	HAM	Portsmouth
1742	1851	1740	1861	170143	HAM	West Meon
1820	1900	1700	1820	173223	HRT	???
1760	1802	ALL	1810	154490	HUN	Abbots Ley
1650	1750	1650	1750	127655	HUN	Bythorn
1791	....	?	1800	103934	HUN	St Neots
....	1846	....	....	140767	IRL	???
1840	1900	1700	1840	102393	KEN	Beckenham
1784	1851	1784	1851	102989	KEN	Knockholt
....	....	1740	1920	166634	KEN	Knockholt
1800	1992	1700	1800	102873	KEN	Penshurst
....	....	1832	1861	155381	KEN	Strood
1845	1851	....	....	133221	KEN	Tunbridge Wells
....	....	ALL	1992	112607	LAN	Bolton
1800	1860	1750	1820	151912	LAN	Chipping Stonyhurst
1825	....	1825	....	109347	LAN	Stonyhurst
1812	1840	1700	1812	172022	LEI	Newtown Linford
1676	1676	1600	1676	174130	LEI	Shearsby
1887	1960	1700	1900	112038	LIN	South
....	....	1810	1830	177393	LIN	Epworth
1840	1900	1700	1840	102393	LND	South
1885	1930	....	....	133221	LND	Old Kent Road
1861	1885	....	....	133221	LND	Shepherds Bush
1820	1825	....	....	133221	LND	St Georges Hanover Square
1822	1851	1750	1851	155152	LND	Stepney
1850	1900	1800	1850	149365	MDX	Acton
....	....	1800	1899	174963	MDX	East London
1847	1870	1853	1870	176885	MDX	Holborn
1876	1879	....	....	176885	MDX	Kensington
1874	....	....	....	176885	MDX	Kentish Town
1870	....	1800	....	123560	MDX	Leytonstone
1881	1896	....	....	176885	MDX	Paddington
1813	1831	1813	1871	167002	MDX	Pancras
1842	....	....	....	176885	MDX	St Clement Danes
1820	1891	1750	1850	122882	MDX	St Mary Le Bone
1824	1992	1700	1824	127132	MLN	Edinburgh
1802	1934	1700	1850	117013	NFK	Dersingham
1728	....	ALL	ALL	107425	NFK	Pulham Market
1786	1920	....	....	166707	NTH	Haselbech
1730	1992	1600	1730	174947	NTH	Kettering
1730	1992	1600	1730	174947	NTH	Thrapston
1730	1992	1600	1730	174947	NTH	Woodford
1800	....	1770	1840	169625	NTT	Nottingham
1800	1892	1700	1840	106267	SFK	North
1690	1750	....	....	129747	SFK	Wattisfield
1845	....	....	....	176885	SRY	Lambeth
1861	1925	1850	1913	155381	SRY	Mitcham
1800	1875	1800	1875	128856	SRY	Westcott
1780	1992	1775	1886	152102	SRY	Wonersh
1840	1900	1700	1840	102393	SRY	???
....	....	1600	1850	127833	SSX	West
1850	1875	1850	1900	161586	SSX	Brighton
1830	....	1830	ALL	145378	SSX	Heathfield
1861	....	1800	1860	116572	SSX	Horsham
1878	....	1878	1992	149055	SSX	Selsybill
1735	1851	1700	1735	133221	SSX	Wisborough Grren
1798	1798	....	....	127426	STS	Handsworth
1857	1900	1800	1992	155152	STS	Walsall
1555	1870	1550	1845	102830	WAR	Birmingham
1820	1840	1820	1840	103721	WAR	Birmingham
1817	1817	....	....	127426	WAR	Birmingham
1847	1851	....	1851	163686	WAR	Birmingham
1795	1795	....	....	127426	WAR	Edgbaston
1750	1790	1700	?	142360	WIL	Broad Blunsdon
1768	1800	1700	1768	129445	WIL	Chippenham
1680	1717	1660	1730	142018	WIL	Marlborough
1846	1869	1641	1869	147486	WIL	Potterne
1768	1800	1700	1768	129445	WIL	Trowbridge

Known From	To	Researching From	To	Ref	Cty	Place
WELLS contd.						
....	....	1894	ALL	174963	WLS	???
1680	....	1650	1700	142018	WOR	Bengeworth
1805	1989	1700	1805	174939	YKS	Easingwold
1740	1800	1700	1750	135763	YKS	Long Marston
....	....	1700	1799	174963	YKS	Scarborough
1775	....	1775	....	109347	YKS	Slaidburn
1699	1900	ALL	ALL	146145	YKS	Wigginton
1699	1900	ALL	ALL	146145	YKS	York
....	....	1894	ALL	174963	???	Bristol
WELLSFORD						
1850	1860	1800	1850	112593	ESS	Witham
WELLSTEAD						
....	....	1820	1880	179361	DOR	Winterbourn Kingston
WELLSTED						
....	....	1777	1882	103217	GLS	City
WELMOTH						
ALL	ALL	ALL	ALL	147354	ALL	ALL
WELSBY						
1903	1992	1850	1930	174998	LAN	Bolton
1813	1871	1700	1813	155500	LAN	Warrington
WELSFORD						
1702	1763	ALL	ALL	175005	DEV	Crediton
1770	1881	ALL	ALL	175005	DEV	Exeter
1863	....	1863	1895	135488	LND	South East
WELSH						
1803	1804	1775	1825	133450	CON	Roche
1800	1800	1800	1860	140864	DEN	Ruabon
1760	1850	1700	1760	147575	HRT	St Mimms
1860	1920	1860	1930	147575	KEN	Frant
1860	1920	1860	1930	147575	KEN	Tunbridge Wells
1760	1850	1700	1760	147575	MDX	Monken Hadley
1856	1930	1800	1880	132470	MON	Caldicot
1856	1930	1800	1880	132470	MON	Newport
1790	1863	ALL	ALL	153516	SOM	Puxton
1790	1863	ALL	ALL	153516	SOM	Sandford
1860	1898	1800	1860	118958	WEX	???
1700	....	ALL	ALL	116394	???	???
WELTDEN						
1100	1500	1100	1500	174890	ENG	North East
1452	1720	1452	1870	174890	LND	ALL
WEMYSS						
1380	1480	1300	1480	154881	SCT	ALL
WENBORNE						
1704	1880	1704	1800	116831	KEN	Plumbstead
WENDEN						
....	....	ALL	ALL	175021	ALL	Name Study
WENHAM						
1770	1820	1700	1830	121126	SSX	Catsfield
WENLOCK						
1750	1912	1700	1770	135763	SAL	Ellesmere
1500	1600	....	....	100420	WAR	Meriden
WENMAN						
1565	1887	1700	1800	117110	KEN	Benenden
WENMOTH						
1600	1800	1400	1600	152323	CON	Lansallos Pelynt
1800	1900	1800	1900	152323	LND	Marylebone
1800	1850	1800	1850	152323	LND	Whitechapel
WENN						
1803	1959	....	1870	152803	KEN	Chatham
1533	1589	ALL	1800	156310	NFK	East Dereham
WENS						
1845	1900	1869	1900	100668	SSX	Eastbourne
WENSLEY						
1700	1750	1600	1992	114596	DEV	Poughill
WENT						
1800	1830	1800	1830	124605	CAM	Brinkley
1800	1830	1750	1830	124605	CAM	Westley Waterless
1730	1900	ALL	ALL	129003	ESS	ALL
1830	1992	1700	1830	178578	HEF	Garway
1806	1992	ALL	ALL	175048	HEF	Pencombe
1830	1992	1700	1830	178578	HEF	St Weonards
WENTWORTH						
1650	1700	1650	1750	133450	KEN	Sarre
1860	....	....	....	172723	LAN	Manchester
1789	1789	ALL	ALL	171816	WIL	Bishopstone
WERE						
1590	1800	1550	1800	165492	SOM	Wellington
WERNHAM						
1400	1992	1400	1992	178918	ALL	ALL
1400	1992	1400	1992	178918	BRK	ALL
1890	1992	?	1890	124540	BRK	Chieveley
1740	1800	1500	1830	137472	BRK	Chieveley

Known From	To	Researching From	To	Ref	Cty	Place
WERNHAM contd.						
1890	1992	?	1890	124540	SRY	Egham
WERRELL						
1808	1934	....	....	115606	WIL	Aldbourne
WERRY						
1720	1900	1660	1950	175056	CON	ALL
1850	1992	1700	1850	140775	CON	St Austell
1800	1900	1700	1950	175056	LND	London
1528	1585	ALL	1585	122106	SFK	Shotley
WESCOMBE						
1830	1850	ALL	ALL	177989	DEV	Cullompton
1890	1920	1880	1950	177989	SSX	Threeoaks
WESELBY						
1780	1840	1780	1820	103616	WYK	Doncaster
WESLEY						
1846	1900	1800	1846	176257	BKM	Slapton
1818	1867	1790	1890	162825	DEV	Budleigh Salterton
1817	1841	1790	1817	144223	LIM	Adare
1850	1900	1700	1900	160954	MSY	Liverpool
1872	1924	1750	1872	118516	???	Berkhampstead
WEST						
....	....	1780	1830	172871	ANS	East
1802	1811	ALL	ALL	117366	AVN	Bristol
....	....	1650	1800	147613	BDF	Flitton With Silsoe
1833	1899	....	....	175102	BDF	Holwell
....	....	1650	1800	147613	BDF	Shillington
....	....	1770	1837	175102	BDF	Shillington
1806	1816	....	....	175102	BDF	Streatley
1762	1794	1650	1762	167452	BKM	Hughenden
1820	1865	1700	1800	171891	BKM	West Wycombe
1800	1830	1700	1900	142875	CON	Breage
1800	1830	1700	1900	142875	CON	St Hilary
1770	....	1500	1890	107972	DBY	Elitton
1786	....	1700	1850	173452	DBY	Netherseal
1757	1854	ALL	1757	175080	DEV	Beer
1757	1854	ALL	1757	175080	DEV	Colyton
1815	1850	1750	1830	115681	DEV	Seaton
1757	1854	ALL	1757	175080	DEV	Seaton
....	....	1854	1880	175080	DEV	Tavistock
....	....	1765	1802	161667	DOR	Poole
1800	1900	1750	1900	138584	FER	Clonelty
1760	1835	1760	1835	178705	GLS	Coln St Aldwyn
1820	1920	ALL	ALL	122866	HAM	North West
1786	1857	1700	1860	162507	HAM	Fareham
1728	....	....	....	153397	HAM	Milford
1800	1992	ALL	1800	150983	HAM	Portsea
1875	1992	1850	1900	175102	HRT	Hitchin
1850	1992	....	....	175099	HUM	Hull
1897	1973	1840	1896	167568	IOW	Ryde
1760	1992	1650	1760	117153	KEN	Deptford
1912	....	....	1920	171441	KEN	East Peckham
1850	1929	1750	1850	165018	LAN	Liverpool
1798	1803	1750	1900	122327	LEI	Higham On The Hill
1820	1855	1800	1860	138444	LEI	Leicester
1800	1850	1700	1880	173452	LEI	Wrothington
1750	1800	1750	1800	123765	LIN	East
1800	1992	....	....	176125	LIN	Asterby
1709	1883	1500	1708	175072	LIN	Billinghay
1800	1992	....	....	176125	LIN	Goulceby
1858	1930	1830	1992	141585	LND	Kensington
1780	1920	ALL	ALL	129933	LND	St Mary Whitechapel
....	....	1600	1900	124656	LND	???
1800	1850	....	....	125709	LND	???
....	....	1800	1830	141585	MDX	Hampton
1614	1725	1500	1614	148962	MDX	Twickenham
1756	1805	1700	1756	114928	MDX	???
....	....	1600	1750	124656	MDX	???
1800	1850	....	....	125709	MDX	???
1849	1851	ALL	1872	175080	NFK	Lynn
1720	1900	1500	1720	179396	NFK	Runcton Holme
1790	1856	ALL	1790	158445	NFK	Sparham
1912	1964	1700	1912	173479	NFK	Thorpe Abbotts
1740	1992	1700	1992	175145	NTH	West Haddon
1746	1746	1500	1746	169439	OXF	Adderbury
1733	1850	ALL	ALL	106313	OXF	Cuddesdon
1814	1839	....	1842	121169	SOM	Bath
1828	1992	....	....	175803	SOM	Broomfield
1811	1872	1750	1811	144711	SOM	Camerton
1811	1872	1750	1811	144711	SOM	High Littleton
1920	1920	1850	1920	121568	SOM	Langport
1765	1800	1700	1800	152579	SOM	Langport
1797	1992	1760	1992	159581	SRY	Albury
....	....	1851	ALL	122963	SRY	Chertsey
....	....	1752	1992	175110	SRY	Frensham
WEST contd.						
1797	1992	1760	1992	159581	SRY	Guildford
1776	1872	1776	1880	136328	SRY	Wallington
1560	1620	....	....	142522	SRY	Waybridge
1800	1992	1800	1992	175196	SSX	Broadwater
1720	1760	1720	1760	116483	SSX	Burpham
1765	1799	1765	1799	175196	SSX	Lancing
1760	1810	1760	1810	116483	SSX	Lindfield
1820	1860	1750	1825	103446	SSX	Maresfield
1800	1820	1800	1820	175196	SSX	West Tarring
1740	1765	1710	1790	105333	SSX	Wollavington
1841	....	1841	....	104213	SYK	Sheffield
1800	1992	1700	1992	165344	WAR	Dunchurch
1500	1900	....	....	100420	WAR	Meriden
1696	1737	1660	1740	142018	WIL	Ashton Keynes
1800	?	?	1900	136611	WIL	Brinkworth
....	....	....	1810	129313	WIL	Wilton
1750	....	1600	1750	106054	WMD	Birmingham
1710	....	....	1710	101761	WRY	Cawthorne
1883	1949	1883	1992	175072	YKS	ALL
1874	1945	....	....	132462	YKS	Full Sutton
1786	1831	1786	1831	139661	YKS	Leeds
1820	1992	1700	1820	102342	???	Bristol
WESTACOTT						
1860	1900	1800	1860	143294	DEV	South Molton
WESTALL						
1700	1830	1600	1900	175234	BRK	East Ilsley
1900	1992	ALL	1800	151602	WIL	Ramsbury
WESTAWAY						
....	....	ALL	ALL	175242	ALL	Name Study
1759	1798	1740	1800	175242	DEV	Broadwoodkelly
1540	1825	1350	1825	175242	DEV	Sampford Courtenay
1600	1992	....	....	172030	DEV	???
WESTBROOK						
1750	1900	ALL	ALL	158593	HAM	ALL
1834	1909	ALL	....	111295	LND	London
WESTBROOKE						
1750	1900	ALL	ALL	158593	HAM	ALL
WESTBURY						
1846	1902	1700	1992	112216	OXF	North
1800	1830	1800	1830	178705	OXF	Broadwell
1840	1850	....	....	103764	STS	Handsworth
WESTCOMBE						
1842	1863	....	....	147486	NTH	Northampton
WESTCOTT						
1730	1880	ALL	ALL	161292	DEV	Dawlish
1840	1850	1840	1950	135925	LND	Kensington
1680	1730	1730	1860	142018	SOM	South
1830	1850	1750	1900	135925	SOM	Mere
WESTERDALE						
....	....	ALL	ALL	100927	ALL	Name Study
1750	1992	1460	1992	100927	RUT	Clipsham
WESTERMAN						
1835	1992	1830	1992	175250	LIN	North
1700	1830	1760	1992	175250	YKS	East
1700	1830	1760	1992	175250	YKS	Hull
1795	1812	1705	1880	137979	YKS	Rothwell
WESTERN						
1858	....	1700	1992	154474	LAN	Caton
1882	....	1700	1992	154474	LAN	Kirby Lonsdale
1858	1925	1700	1858	154474	LAN	Lancaster
1858	1925	1700	1858	154474	LAN	Warton
WESTFIELD						
1773	....	1650	1800	143693	BKM	Princes Risborough
?	1694	....	....	100951	WIL	Salisbury
WESTGARTH						
1753	1810	1650	1753	135151	CUL	Addingham
1756	1798	1700	1756	130877	NBL	Tyneside
WESTGATE						
1810	1898	1810	1898	100668	SSX	East
WESTHEAD						
1690	1850	1590	1850	100080	LAN	Crosby
1800	1860	....	....	126497	LAN	St Helens
WESTLAKE						
1854	....	1700	1900	167223	DEV	Bideford
1847	1899	1820	1899	170631	DEV	Bridestowe
1847	1899	1820	1899	170631	DEV	Lewtrenchard
1841	1881	1851	1880	170631	DEV	Marystowe
ALL	1755	....	....	105368	SOM	Compton Dundon
1781	1815	1700	1780	172871	SOM	Norton St Philip
WESTLAND						
1681	1699	....	....	112887	LND	???
WESTLEY						
1750	1850	ALL	ALL	112496	CAM	South

Known From	To	Researching From	To	Ref	Cty	Place
WESTLEY contd.						
....	....	1760	1790	103713	CAM	Ashley
1750	1850	ALL	ALL	112496	ESS	North West
1806	1860	ALL	1806	131881	SFK	Great Wratting
WESTMACOT						
....	....	ALL	ALL	175277	ALL	ALL
WESTMACOTE						
....	....	ALL	ALL	175277	ALL	ALL
WESTMACOTT						
....	....	ALL	ALL	175277	ALL	ALL
1750	1850	1500	1850	109274	WIL	Shalbourne
1700	1950	1500	1700	175269	WOR	Bredon Hill
WESTMANCOAT						
....	....	ALL	ALL	175277	ALL	ALL
WESTMANCOTT						
....	....	ALL	ALL	175277	ALL	ALL
WESTMORE						
1700	1900	ALL	ALL	175285	IOW	ALL
1841	1881	....	....	116475	IOW	Godsill
WESTMORLAND						
1530	....	....	....	156647	WES	???
1709	1881	1680	1851	170267	YKS	Patrick Brompton
WESTNACOTT						
....	....	ALL	ALL	175277	ALL	ALL
WESTOBY						
....	....	ALL	ALL	175293	ALL	Name Study
....	....	ALL	ALL	175293	ALL	ALL
1858	1992	1750	1850	102342	LIN	Flixborough
1600	1850	1600	1850	175293	LIN	South Humberside
1830	1870	1830	1900	175293	NFK	Great Yarmouth
1884	1992	1880	1992	175293	SFK	Kessingland
1884	1992	1880	1992	175293	SFK	Lowestoft
1806	1890	1700	1900	175293	YKS	ALL
1806	1890	1700	1900	175293	YKS	Hull
WESTON						
....	....	ALL	ALL	175323	ALL	Name Study
1760	1830	1600	1760	173223	BRK	Newbury
1870	1950	1750	1870	153893	CAM	Guyhirn
1870	1950	1750	1870	153893	CAM	Wisbech
1743	1992	1600	1743	155306	DBY	Denby
1851	1880	?	1851	128910	DBY	Heage
1792	1810	....	....	128910	DBY	Horsley
1874	1992	ALL	ALL	174793	DBY	Ilkeston
1720	1800	1700	ALL	175366	DEV	Kenton
1815	1870	....	....	131660	GLS	Bristol
1850	1992	1800	1900	166960	GLS	Bristol
....	....	1761	1992	140619	HAM	Basingstoke
1770	1900	1770	1850	145343	HAM	Hambledon
1834	1890	1790	1992	140619	HAM	Monk Sherbourne
1761	1820	1500	1992	140619	HAM	Pamber
1822	....	....	....	138061	HAM	Portsea
1860	1960	....	....	133361	HRT	Aylesbury
1810	1850	1750	1850	151467	KEN	East
1692	1851	ALL	ALL	161551	KEN	Cranbrook
....	1834	1800	1900	128961	KEN	Dover
....	1834	1800	1900	128961	KEN	Folkestone
1769	1912	ALL	ALL	161551	KEN	Tenterden
....	....	1634	1700	175315	LEI	Eastwell
1740	1820	....	....	103764	LEI	North Kilworth
1900	1992	ALL	ALL	134996	LND	Islington
1816	1992	ALL	ALL	115762	LND	Lambeth
1855	1891	ALL	ALL	105856	MDX	???
1816	1992	ALL	ALL	115762	SRY	Lambeth
1855	1891	ALL	ALL	105856	SRY	???
1863	1935	1863	1935	161551	SSX	Brighton
1758	1839	1700	1757	175846	SSX	Burwash
1851	1989	ALL	1851	175323	SSX	Fletching
1584	1660	ALL	ALL	161551	SSX	Mayfield
1851	1989	ALL	1851	175323	SSX	Mayfield
1684	1986	1600	1986	173339	STS	Alston
1879	1900	1700	1900	175307	STS	Cheadle
1824	1992	1700	1824	115096	STS	Darlastan
1879	1890	1780	1850	107832	STS	Weton
1725	1770	1600	1750	145343	WIL	ALL
....	1842	1750	1842	101893	WIL	Calne
1748	1783	1700	1750	170348	WIL	Purton
1760	1780	ALL	1780	167029	WIL	Shalbourne
?	?	?	?	163279	WMD	Wolverhampton
?	?	?	?	126942	???	???
WESTOVER						
1800	1873	....	....	117579	DOR	Gillingham
1795	1807	....	....	117579	SOM	Bratton Seymour
1787	....	....	....	117579	SOM	Wincanton

Known From	To	Researching From	To	Ref	Cty	Place
WESTREN						
1700	1800	....	1700	175374	DEV	Bow
1800	1832	....	....	175374	DEV	Merton
1700	1800	....	1700	175374	DEV	Nymet Trace
1832	1886	....	....	175374	DEV	Prixford Barton
1886	1992	....	....	175374	SFK	Elmsett
WESTWELL						
1800	1992	1600	1992	175382	LAN	ALL
1810	1881	1750	1891	142204	LAN	Culcheth
WESTWOOD						
....	....	ALL	ALL	123870	ALL	ALL
....	....	....	....	127272	ESS	Manuden
1757	1832	1600	1757	157953	ESS	The Roddings
....	....	1700	1800	123870	IRL	???
1800	1845	1800	1845	123870	LND	Southwark
1831	1992	....	....	132381	SCT	Glasgow
1850	1880	1700	1850	173452	STS	Dudley
1823	1871	1750	1823	149977	STS	Sedgley
1800	1900	1700	1992	177180	STS	Smethwick
1800	1900	1750	1992	177180	STS	Tipton
1850	1880	1700	1850	173452	WMD	Wolverhampton
1885	1920	....	....	149977	WOR	Dudley
1800	1900	1800	1900	173681	WOR	Old Swinford
1797	1813	1750	1797	154024	YKS	Pontefract
WETENHALL						
....	....	1200	1400	154873	CHS	Wetenhall
....	....	1400	1520	154873	KEN	East Peckham
WETHERAL						
1744	1784	1700	1840	160873	NBL	Chollerton
1700	1830	1680	1830	160873	NBL	Kirkwhelpington
WETHERALD						
1826	1851	1700	1871	116114	YKS	Askrigg
WETHERALL						
1739	ALL	ALL	1765	116734	CAM	Balsham
WETHERELL						
1786	....	ALL	ALL	110272	SOM	Horsington
1776	1777	ALL	ALL	124982	WES	ALL
WETHERLY						
1608	1781	....	....	165999	GLS	Henbury
1608	1781	....	....	165999	GLS	Thornbury
WETMOTH						
1604	1619	1558	1698	142859	GLS	Frocester
WETTER						
1819	1819	1700	1819	149314	DEV	Barnstaple
1845	1897	1820	1992	149314	MON	Newport
WETTON						
....	....	....	1992	175404	ALL	ALL
1800	1992	1750	1992	175404	WAR	Coventry
WEYMAN						
1786	1992	1786	1992	175420	BRK	White Waltham
WEYMARK						
1732	1958	1700	1958	100668	SSX	East
WEYMOUTH						
1828	1992	1600	1828	104930	CUL	Arthuret Longtown
1850	1920	ALL	1850	141224	GLS	Bristol
....	....	1600	1828	104930	KEN	Woolwich
....	....	1600	1828	104930	LAN	Manchester
1700	1800	....	....	151475	WOR	Bedminster
....	....	....	....	151475	WOR	Brislington
1700	1800	....	....	151475	WOR	Bristol
WEYMSS						
1779	....	1775	1804	148121	CUL	???
1779	....	1775	1804	148121	SCT	???
WHAITES						
1785	1825	1700	1785	100110	NFK	Rougham
WHALE						
1694	1864	ALL	ALL	131415	BEW	Earlston
1795	1860	1700	1900	166804	HAM	Highclere
1847	1959	1800	1992	176982	HAM	Romsey
1840	1862	....	1862	178861	KEN	Farningham
1770	1860	1700	1900	138878	SFK	North
1844	1860	ALL	....	120626	STS	Walsall
1900	1980	1800	1900	174734	SXE	Central
1803	1924	....	....	121924	WAR	Coventry
....	....	ALL	ALL	104884	WIL	ALL
1770	1850	....	....	159972	WIL	Brinkworth
1850	1992	1650	1850	167789	WIL	???
1851	1876	....	....	138223	WOR	Dudley
1800	1825	1750	1800	172901	WOR	Dudley
WHALEBONE						
1800	1940	1800	1940	154466	KEN	Sheerness
WHALES						
1710	1810	1810	1820	159573	NFK	Beeston
....	....	1810	1820	159573	NFK	Castle Acre

Known From	To	Researching From	To	Ref	Cty	Place
WHALESBY						
1837	1992	1700	1992	146293	ALL	ALL
WHALEY						
....	....	ALL	ALL	175439	ALL	Name Study
1787	1879	....	....	175439	LAN	Wigan
1612	1730	1485	1992	149098	YKS	Laughton En Le Morthen
1778	1813	1775	1992	149098	YKS	Sheffiled
1808	1858	1808	1992	149098	YKS	Thorne
WHALLEY						
1772	1795	ALL	ALL	136948	CHS	Astbury
1841	1871	ALL	ALL	136948	CHS	Chelford
1845	1905	1800	1930	156086	CHS	Handforth
1797	1851	ALL	ALL	136948	CHS	Macclesfield
1865	1930	1750	1865	142646	CUL	Newlands
1791	1830	1750	1900	114456	DOW	Belfast
1841	1992	1750	1900	114456	LAN	ALL
1794	1794	1750	1794	151912	LAN	Aighton
1837	1954	1837	1992	173568	LAN	Blackburn
1800	1845	1800	1930	156086	LAN	Darwen
1860	1895	....	....	136948	LAN	Manchester
1839	1976	1839	1976	136336	LAN	Preston
1830	1830	ALL	1830	126942	YKS	Bentham
1794	1794	1750	1794	151912	YKS	Great Mitton
....	1880	....	....	110183	YKS	???
WHARRAD						
1903	1918	1900	1920	166715	DEV	Plymouth
1900	1992	1900	1992	166715	GLA	Cardiff
1839	1992	1839	1992	166715	WAR	Redditch
1898	1911	1898	1911	166715	WAR	Solihull
1871	1992	1870	1992	166715	WMD	Birmingham
1839	1992	1839	1992	166715	WOR	Redditch
WHARREY						
1729	....	....	1729	101761	ERY	Howden
WHARRY						
1530	1700	ALL	1530	122106	SOM	Chard
1723	1820	....	....	122106	SOM	Cricket Malherbie
1793	1874	....	....	122106	SOM	Merriott
WHARTON						
1816	1896	1793	1949	125229	BKM	Hughenden
1787	1841	1787	1841	125229	BKM	Radnage
1820	1890	1850	1890	159247	CHS	Birkenhead
1765	1775	....	....	108871	DUR	Stanhope
1790	1830	....	....	108871	DUR	Tanfield
1820	1890	1850	1890	159247	LAN	Manchester
1670	....	....	....	156647	LIN	Brocklesbury
1292	1989	1292	1989	135399	WES	North
1796	1811	1766	1796	139149	WES	Kendal
1764	1851	....	1764	109622	WES	Orton
1800	1960	1700	1800	135151	WES	Ravenstonedale
1770	1820	....	....	140554	YKS	Aberford
WHASSALL						
1789	1845	1700	1845	154881	SLI	ALL
WHATCOCK						
1500	1600	....	....	100420	WAR	Fillongley
1500	1600	....	....	100420	WAR	Great Packington
1500	1600	....	....	100420	WAR	Meriden
WHATCROFT						
1840	1992	1500	1840	138266	DUR	???
1840	1992	1500	1840	138266	NBL	???
WHATELEY						
1680	1740	1600	1800	149691	WOR	Bedley
WHATLING						
1900	1960	1800	1900	167010	SFK	Stradbroke
WHATMORE						
....	....	ALL	ALL	175471	ALL	Name Study
1500	1992	1500	1992	175463	BRK	ALL
1500	1992	1500	1992	175463	HAM	ALL
1800	1920	1800	1920	175471	WMD	Birmingham
WHATMOUGH						
1830	1841	1750	1830	144177	WRY	Idle
WHATTON						
1840	1992	....	....	149586	STS	Dudley
WHAYMAN						
1870	1890	1770	1870	105031	SFK	Charsfield
WHEADON						
1811	....	....	....	119911	DOR	Allingtion
1860	1992	1800	1992	152943	GLA	Pontypridd
WHEAL						
1793	1992	....	....	156191	GLS	Kempsford
1793	1992	....	....	156191	WIL	Brinkworth
WHEALE						
....	....	ALL	ALL	118656	ALL	Name Study
WHEARE						
1861	1910	1910	1927	169374	GLS	Abbots Leigh
WHEATCROFT						
....	....	1700	1850	176400	DBY	North
1641	1706	1650	1827	176400	DBY	Ashover
....	....	1700	1850	176400	DBY	Wessington Matlock
1710	1780	1650	1710	132268	GLS	Addlestrop
1818	1861	1818	1899	145505	GLS	Stretton On Fosse
1837	1839	1800	1839	176419	MON	Chepstow
1784	1992	....	....	145505	WOR	Blockley
1784	1868	1784	1800	145505	WOR	Shipston On Stour
WHEATER						
....	....	ALL	ALL	175528	ALL	Name Study
1809	1859	1700	1809	111198	WYK	Leeds
1760	1800	1700	1760	130877	YKS	Spofforth
1760	1800	1700	1760	130877	YKS	Wetherby
WHEATLEY						
1810	1850	1750	1810	133671	BDF	Northill
1850	1914	ALL	ALL	120650	DBY	Chesterfield
1600	1900	ALL	1600	154563	DUR	ALL
1805	1890	ALL	1805	128414	DUR	Durham
....	....	1750	1860	145319	DUR	???
1940	1992	....	....	175544	HRT	Barnet
1802	1864	1700	1900	126586	HRT	???
1825	1940	1800	1940	117501	KEN	ALL
1850	1900	1850	1900	175536	KEN	Tunbridge Wells
1784	1871	ALL	ALL	141615	LEI	Barrow Upon Soar
....	....	1750	1850	142298	LEI	Markfield
1865	1975	1700	1865	171913	LIN	Lincoln
1864	1880	1800	1900	126586	LND	Bethnal Green
1880	1978	....	....	175544	LND	Finchley
....	1825	1800	1825	117501	MDX	???
....	....	1750	1860	145319	NIR	???
1782	1798	?	1800	164976	NTT	Gedling
1650	1992	ALL	ALL	175536	SSX	Central
1760	1850	ALL	ALL	120650	WAR	Chilvers Coton
1851	1992	1841	1851	165026	YKS	Harewood
1851	1992	1841	1851	165026	YKS	Ulleskelf
WHEATON						
1782	1806	1700	1782	102598	DEV	Paignton
1792	1992	1700	1792	100900	DEV	Winkleigh
WHEBLE						
1854	1908	1600	1854	164879	SRY	Camberwell
WHEELBAND						
1822	1864	1800	1822	159042	LIN	Stamford
WHEELDON						
....	....	1650	1800	175560	CHS	South
....	....	1650	1800	175560	DBY	ALL
1850	1992	1600	1992	164518	LAN	Liverpool
....	....	1650	1800	175560	LEI	ALL
1796	1880	....	....	175560	NTT	Balderton
1796	1880	....	....	175560	NTT	North Muskham
....	....	1700	1900	110108	NTT	Nottingham
....	....	1650	1800	175560	STS	ALL
....	....	1650	1800	175560	WAR	ALL
....	....	1700	1923	110108	WOR	Worcester
1910	1992	....	....	175560	YKS	Halifax
WHEELER						
1868	1992	1707	1992	139955	BKM	Bourne End
1867	1970	1700	1867	120510	BRK	Hurst
1868	1992	1707	1992	139955	BRK	Maidenhead
1820	1840	ALL	1860	167029	BRK	Newbury
1800	1850	1800	1850	178705	BRK	Reading
1736	....	?	1740	103934	DOR	Iwerne Minster
1900	1920	1850	1900	179671	ESS	Ilford
1806	1814	ALL	1814	126918	ESS	Lambourne
1800	1860	1700	1800	138150	GLS	South
1791	1839	ALL	1791	175080	GLS	Bisley
1637	1637	....	....	115606	HAM	Binstead
1800	1900	1700	ALL	135127	HAM	Bransgore
1830	1908	1869	1908	142530	HAM	Bransgore
1775	1783	....	....	156647	HAM	Lymington
1811	1880	1811	1910	156647	HAM	South Baddesley
1814	1936	....	....	156647	HAM	St Helens
1750	1825	1600	1850	162620	HEF	???
1849	1905	....	1849	175579	HRT	Harpenden
1750	1780	1500	1750	129577	IOW	???
1812	1891	1300	1992	152501	LND	Chelsea
1863	1992	ALL	ALL	154806	LND	Holborn
1833	1840	....	....	130281	LND	Marylebone
ALL	1850	....	....	114642	LND	Soho
1821	1866	1750	1880	155152	LND	Southwark
1803	1851	1800	1992	142735	MDX	London
1790	1850	1700	1880	134252	OXF	Enstone

Known From	To	Researching From	To	Ref	Cty	Place
WHEELER contd.						
1780	1900	1600	1780	173207	SAL	South
1812	1891	1300	1992	152501	SCT	Glasgow
1823	....	1800	1823	174955	SRY	Camden Town
1790	....	1700	1820	131547	SRY	Capel
1845	1912	1600	1845	141925	SRY	Tooting
1708	1992	1600	1708	149012	SSX	Horsted Keynes
1808	1871	1750	1808	110639	SSX	???
1850	....	....	....	148504	STS	West Bromwich
1900	1930	1700	....	113123	WAR	Birmingham
1800	....	....	....	148504	WAR	Feckinham
1770	1900	1700	1775	149993	WAR	Solihull
1880	1900	....	....	148504	WAR	Studley
1905	1992	....	1849	175579	WIL	Bradley
1786	1814	....	....	170348	WIL	Brinkworth
1685	1758	1680	1760	142018	WIL	Devizes
1725	1900	1700	1900	145300	WIL	Erlestoke
1788	1843	1700	1843	107573	WIL	Maiden Bradley
1693	1732	1680	1760	142018	WIL	Salisbury
1684	1760	1650	1690	170348	WIL	Sutton Benger
WHEELEY						
1852	....	1800	1875	155969	MDX	Bethnal Green
1800	1850	1750	1875	155969	???	London
WHEELHOUSE						
....	....	ALL	ALL	125539	ALL	Name Study
WHEELTON						
....	....	ALL	ALL	147141	ALL	Name Study
1820	1992	ALL	1820	110000	CHS	Macclesfield
WHELAN						
....	....	ALL	ALL	143901	ALL	Name Study
1880	1980	....	....	175587	GLA	Swansea
....	....	1850	1880	175587	IRL	???
1847	....	....	1847	143901	LEX	???
WHELLER						
1790	1860	1790	1992	106410	SOM	Currey Rivel
1790	1870	....	....	117579	SOM	Curry Rivel
WHENT						
....	....	1800	1920	116467	SFK	???
WHEREAT						
1853	1929	1790	1853	145963	SOM	Bristol
WHERRY						
1780	1992	1700	1992	175609	CON	Central
WHERTY						
....	....	ALL	ALL	178152	IRL	???
1873	1882	ALL	ALL	178152	LAN	Liverpool
WHETLY						
1815	....	....	....	129747	LIN	Wellingore
WHETSTONE						
1871	1920	1862	1920	144703	LEI	Leicester
1794	1881	1700	1992	144703	WAR	ALL
WHETTER						
1838	1958	ALL	ALL	173657	CON	St Austell
WHETTING						
1687	....	....	....	176958	SOM	East Pennard
WHETTON						
....	1800	ALL	1800	134511	LEI	Ashby De La Zouch
WHEWELL						
1832	1980	1700	1822	113425	LAN	Ribchester
WHIBLEY						
1889	....	1850	1900	122661	LND	Brentford
1890	....	1850	1900	122661	LND	Wandsworth
WHICHCOTE						
1770	1800	....	....	100420	WAR	Meriden
WHICHER						
1629	1800	1550	1750	122688	SSX	Racton
1629	1800	1550	1750	122688	SSX	Westbourne
WHICK						
1800	1820	ALL	....	156140	STS	Sedgley
WHIELDON						
1740	1780	1600	1992	167592	STS	Fenton
1711	1775	1650	1711	111236	STS	Ipstones
WHIFFEN						
ALL	ALL	ALL	ALL	115126	DOR	Stoborough
1868	....	ALL	ALL	116394	LND	St Pancras
WHIFFIN						
....	....	ALL	ALL	175668	ALL	ALL
1773	1992	....	1773	103489	KEN	North
1773	1992	....	1773	103489	KEN	Meopham
1760	1992	ALL	ALL	175668	KEN	Strood
WHIGHAM						
1848	1975	1700	1850	155705	MLN	Kirknewton
1848	1975	1700	1850	155705	MLN	Ratho
1848	1975	1700	1850	155705	???	Glasgow

Known From	To	Researching From	To	Ref	Cty	Place
WHILDE						
....	....	ALL	ALL	116823	DBY	Alfreton
WHILE						
....	....	1800	1880	100188	MON	Ebbw Vale
WHILEY						
1844	1844	1700	1850	178616	LEI	Leicester
1876	1900	1700	1876	135011	YKS	South Cave
WHILLANCE						
1818	1840	ALL	ALL	157139	NBL	Newcastle
WHILLIER						
1680	1726	1600	1680	115525	HAM	Thorley
WHINCOP						
1800	1860	ALL	1800	178934	SFK	Heveningham
WHINCUP						
1748	1887	....	1748	133566	SFK	Redisham
WHINHAM						
....	....	ALL	ALL	175676	ALL	Name Study
1840	1992	1840	1992	175676	CLV	Stockton
1750	1940	1750	1940	175676	DUR	Sunderland
1830	1871	1830	1871	175676	LAN	Manchester
1740	1900	1740	1900	175676	NBL	Alnwick
1750	1850	1750	1850	175676	NBL	Hartburn
1740	1900	1740	1900	175676	NBL	Morpeth
1750	1900	1750	1900	175676	NBL	Newcastle
1735	1830	1735	1830	175676	NBL	Rothbury
1830	1900	1830	1900	175676	WYK	Leeds
1808	1992	1808	1992	175676	YKS	Hull
WHINYARD						
....	1672	ALL	ALL	129933	SRY	Ockham
WHIP						
1781	....	....	....	132500	LAN	Shaw
WHIPP						
1825	1899	1750	1900	167711	LAN	Burnley
WHIRK						
....	....	1750	1850	126977	SCT	???
WHISKARD						
1700	1799	....	....	121835	NFK	Castle Acre
WHISKIN						
1805	1905	ALL	ALL	175684	MDX	St Lukes
WHISSON						
1727	1727	ALL	1727	129283	NFK	Hautboys
....	....	1780	1858	103187	NFK	Wells
....	....	1858	1880	103187	NYK	Whitby
WHISTLE						
1830	1900	1700	1900	125725	SFK	Bury St Edmunds
WHISTLER						
1875	1912	1850	1950	113611	EYK	Hull
1773	1875	ALL	1875	113611	NFK	Hockwold Cum Wilton
WHISTON						
1813	1953	1750	1813	164321	MDX	East London
1800	1900	1558	1800	153427	STS	Norton In The Moors
1870	1900	1800	1900	138371	YKS	Sheffield
WHITAKER						
1830	1854	1800	1854	165441	CHS	Prestbury
1850	1992	1840	1920	176958	DUR	Hartlepool
1807	1888	?	1807	121665	GLS	Bristol
....	....	1600	1790	100447	HAM	Portsmouth
1500	1800	1500	1800	127655	LAN	Burnley
1795	1992	1600	1795	110914	LAN	Rossendale
1830	1850	1700	1900	130419	LAN	Sabden
1640	1680	1640	1700	142018	SOM	ALL
1830	1854	1800	1860	165441	STS	Stoke On Trent
1800	1890	1700	1800	143243	YKS	Leeds
1850	1992	1840	1920	176958	YKS	Leeds
1850	1992	1840	1920	176958	YKS	Lofthouse
1820	1881	1820	1900	160180	YKS	Oxenhope
1850	1992	1840	1920	176958	YKS	Scarborough
1850	1992	1840	1920	176958	YKS	Sharlston
1902	1913	1902	1992	160180	YKS	Wilsden
WHITBREAD						
1775	1896	1700	1819	117005	BDF	Aspley Guise
WHITBURN						
1655	1905	?	1800	162507	CON	Kea
WHITBURNE						
1630	1695	1600	1700	153354	CON	Kea
WHITBY						
1850	1992	1850	1992	125881	CAM	March
1617	1986	....	....	155055	CHS	Ince
1747	1992	....	....	175714	HRT	Buckland
1747	1992	....	....	175714	HRT	Therfield
1850	1992	1850	1992	125881	HRT	???
1810	1810	1750	1810	121509	LEI	Barrow Upon Soar
1653	1770	....	....	113808	LEI	Wymeswold
1706	1765	1670	1765	123404	LEI	Wymeswold

Known From	To	Researching From	To	Ref	Cty	Place
WHITBY contd.						
....	....	1600	1900	124656	LEI	???
1745	1772	ALL	1745	169730	LND	St Andrew Undershaft
1800	1879	1750	1800	175722	NFK	Kings Lynn
1785	1785	....	1785	136212	NFK	Wolferton
1770	1926	....	....	113808	NTT	Sutton Bonington
1755	1880	1600	1755	163562	SOM	Yeovil
1809	1848	1700	1809	169730	SRY	Putney
WHITCHELO						
1800	1920	ALL	ALL	124605	ALL	ALL
WHITCHER						
1853	1893	....	1850	149950	HAM	Lymington
1500	1900	1500	1900	170216	WIL	ALL
WHITCHURCH						
1850	1992	1800	1900	131040	GLS	Bristol
1718	1767	....	....	165999	GLS	Henbury
WHITCOMB						
1822	1822	1750	1822	103640	HAM	Gosport
1772	1792	1650	1792	174343	HAM	Hambledon
1874	....	ALL	ALL	127205	HEF	Hereford
1902	1992	ALL	ALL	127205	LAN	Salford
WHITCOMBE						
1811	1862	ALL	1862	132217	GLS	Uley
1802	1992	1600	1802	151092	SOM	Pilton
1776	1776	ALL	1810	132217	WIL	Trowbridge
WHITE						
1840	1900	1800	1840	172642	ANT	Ballymena
1840	1900	1800	1840	172642	ANT	Broughshane
1800	1860	....	....	174556	AVN	Bedminster
1810	1992	1910	1992	106186	AVN	Bristol
1820	1825	1800	1830	166685	AVN	Bristol
1694	1992	....	....	175854	BDF	Leighton Buzzard
....	....	ALL	ALL	175943	BDF	Luton
1830	1844	1800	1830	174688	BKM	Ashendon
1866	1920	1800	1866	174688	BKM	Aylesbury
1799	1883	1771	1849	107360	BKM	East Claydon
1839	1839	....	....	148334	BKM	Eton
1792	1919	1600	1792	117676	BKM	Haddenham
1680	1700	....	....	103764	BKM	Marsh Gibbon
1700	1800	1650	1850	177180	BKM	Meadle
1827	1827	1771	1849	107360	BKM	Stone
1813	1814	1800	1837	107360	BKM	Waddesdon
1871	1872	1865	1910	137472	BRK	Kintbury
1871	1872	1865	1910	137472	BRK	Newbury
1871	1872	1865	1910	137472	BRK	Reading
1759	1759	1790	1800	118737	BRK	Speen
1680	1820	ALL	ALL	175943	CAM	Cambridge
1820	1900	1700	1900	122181	CAM	March
1655	1940	....	....	128996	CAM	Thorney
1850	1880	1850	1880	152099	CHS	Birkenhead
1813	1853	1813	1853	134406	CHS	Nantwich
1788	1797	1730	1797	134406	CHS	Runcorn
1797	1811	1797	1819	134406	CHS	Tarporley
1630	1656	ALL	1656	168718	CON	South East
1715	1850	1700	1850	171549	CON	Lanteglos By Fowey
1800	1840	1700	1820	175838	CON	Redruth
1600	1900	1600	1900	175897	CON	St Just In Pewith
1650	....	ALL	1650	153850	CON	St Just
1791	1809	1750	1850	178004	DBY	Baslow
1740	1806	1700	1900	139858	DBY	Chesterfield
1841	....	1770	1841	130141	DBY	Eyam
....	1766	?	1766	128910	DBY	Headnor
1680	1791	1550	1679	131245	DBY	Old Brampton
1734	1768	1650	1733	131245	DBY	Wirksworth
1860	1881	1852	1881	140295	DEV	East Stonehouse
1600	1733	....	....	106240	DEV	Exeter
1790	....	ALL	1790	142301	DEV	Modbury
1600	1630	....	....	106240	DEV	Newton Poppleford
1730	1855	....	....	106240	DEV	Plymouth
1880	1992	ALL	1880	142263	DFS	Lockerbie
1630	1650	1550	1630	156795	DOR	East
1695	1891	ALL	1695	122106	DOR	Fortuneswell
1796	1859	1796	1960	115436	DOR	Portland
1830	1880	1820	1880	140295	DOR	Stallbridge
1825	1843	1700	1890	112216	DOR	Winterborne Whitchurch
1700	1799	1700	1799	169781	DUR	Bishops Auckland
1831	1992	....	....	175803	DUR	Blaydon
1807	1807	ALL	ALL	105015	DUR	Hopewell
1789	1992	ALL	1789	100528	DUR	Ingleton
1800	1899	1800	1899	169781	DUR	Ryton
1840	1992	....	....	113220	DUR	South Shields
1850	1992	1750	1900	116238	DUR	South Shields
WHITE contd.						
1730	1770	1700	1730	121339	DUR	Staindrop
1800	1900	1600	1900	126845	DUR	???
1770	1800	ALL	1770	131059	ESS	Danbury
1800	1850	1770	1850	168580	ESS	Great Leighs
1750	1840	1700	1800	144657	ESS	High Ongar
1900	1960	1750	1900	175978	ESS	Prittlewell
1800	....	....	....	135488	ESS	???
1881	1926	1881	1926	140295	GLA	Cardiff
1780	1992	1600	1992	154342	GLS	Bristol
1800	1910	1700	1880	106186	GLS	Old Sodbury
....	....	1750	1900	147826	GLS	???
1881	....	1780	1992	129631	GNT	Blaenavon
....	....	1750	1800	153486	HAM	Beaulieu
1887	....	1850	1940	142549	HAM	Christchurch
1810	1850	1700	1850	133957	HAM	East Meon
....	1830	ALL	ALL	129933	HAM	Hawley
1803	1880	ALL	ALL	152226	HAM	Houghton
1746	1971	ALL	1746	175862	HAM	Michelmersh
1850	1900	1700	ALL	135127	HAM	Milton
1810	1850	1700	1850	133957	HAM	Petersfield
1894	1980	ALL	1894	109320	HAM	Portsmouth
1800	1992	1600	1992	130125	HAM	Portsmouth
1810	1992	1750	1950	136840	HAM	Portsmouth
1840	1875	1800	1845	155691	HAM	Ringwood
1831	1927	1800	1831	127116	HAM	Romsey
?	?	?	?	159999	HAM	Upper Clatford
1851	....	1800	1850	101524	HEF	Bredwardine
1730	1820	ALL	ALL	175943	HRT	Broxbourne
1730	1820	ALL	ALL	175943	HRT	Hoddesden
1780	1984	1750	1984	152668	HUM	Driffield
1847	1872	ALL	1847	146315	HUN	Farcet
1847	1872	ALL	1847	146315	HUN	Stanground
1699	....	1660	1700	126667	IOW	Freshwater
1608	1900	ALL	1608	129992	IOW	Freshwater
1814	1841	1814	1841	152943	IOW	Ryde
1860	?	?	?	116793	IRL	Dublin
1840	1870	1840	1870	124605	IRL	???
1740	1831	1700	1900	118168	KEN	Bromley
1556	1900	1556	1900	132497	KEN	Canterbury
1604	....	....	1640	171441	KEN	Canterbury
....	....	1850	1881	130184	KEN	Greenwich
1738	1738	....	....	127426	KEN	Lenham
1900	1908	ALL	1908	146315	LAN	Gt Harwood
1900	1908	ALL	1908	146315	LAN	Hartshead
1907	?	?	?	108588	LAN	Liverpool
1832	1900	1700	1900	151254	LAN	Manchester
1797	....	ALL	ALL	143294	LEI	Hinckley
....	....	1735	1850	115142	LEI	Witherley
1785	1785	1550	1800	147265	LIN	South
1821	1841	ALL	1850	113611	LIN	East Keal
1802	1885	1700	1802	165891	LIN	North Hykeham
1785	1788	1550	1800	147265	LIN	Wahplode
1821	1841	ALL	1850	113611	LIN	West Keal
1690	1850	ALL	ALL	175943	LND	City
1830	1850	1800	1900	150002	LND	Lawyers
....	....	1750	1900	129275	LND	Stepney
1690	1850	ALL	ALL	175943	LND	Westminster
1880	....	....	....	163392	LND	???
1900	1992	ALL	1900	106984	MDX	Ealing
1881	1930	1650	1881	175811	MDX	Harlington
1881	1930	1650	1881	175811	MDX	Harmondsworth
1804	1900	1750	1900	113743	MDX	Harrow
1844	1900	ALL	ALL	143839	MDX	Hoxton
1810	1908	ALL	ALL	175943	MDX	Islington
1830	1851	1830	1851	140295	MDX	London
....	....	ALL	ALL	151998	MDX	Paddington
....	....	1800	1855	110132	MDX	St Giles In The Fields
1845	1845	ALL	....	109258	MDX	Yiewsley-Hillingdon
1816	....	1740	1830	135941	MLN	Tollcross
1580	1680	1500	1900	139858	NBL	Hedley In Ovingham
1873	1882	....	....	139874	NBL	North Sheilds
....	....	1840	1992	113220	NBL	North Shields
1715	1930	....	....	169129	NFK	Central
1715	1930	....	....	169129	NFK	West
1780	1856	1700	1780	111953	NFK	Great Snoring
....	....	1700	1850	140627	NFK	Toft Monks
1898	1978	ALL	ALL	118885	NRY	Middlesborough
1750	1750	1700	1750	103632	NTH	Preston Capes
1810	1834	ALL	1900	146315	NTH	Thorpe
1699	1806	1650	1900	139858	NTT	Nottingham
....	1710	ALL	1710	134511	NTT	Papplewick
1650	1788	1600	1900	139858	NTT	Tuxford

Known From	To	Researching From	To	Ref	Cty	Place
WHITE contd.						
1800	1900	1600	1992	113778	NYK	Egton
1761	....	1650	1800	143693	OXF	Aston Rowant
....	....	1800	1900	115517	OXF	Banvury
....	....	1700	1800	147613	OXF	Chadlington
1860	1900	1800	1900	115517	OXF	Shutford
1598	1837	1500	1992	166804	OXF	Stockenchurch
1800	1850	1700	1850	117455	PER	Killen
1710	1740	ALL	1740	149063	ROX	Ancrum
1710	1740	ALL	1740	149063	ROX	Melrose
1855	1900	1850	1900	135941	SCT	Glasgow
1761	1843	1700	1761	157775	SCT	Milnhouse
1910	1910	1800	1910	103640	SFK	Beccles
....	....	1820	....	145688	SFK	Metfield
1890	1992	1800	1890	140465	SOM	Bath
1700	1850	1700	1850	140295	SOM	Brewham
?	?	?	?	154342	SOM	Bristol
1800	1880	....	....	137480	SOM	Bruton
1870	1891	1870	1891	140295	SOM	Glastonbury
....	....	1700	1800	153486	SOM	Huntspill
....	....	1800	1850	133493	SOM	Ilminster
1825	1992	1794	1825	175846	SOM	Weston Super Mare
1825	1992	1794	1825	175846	SOM	Worle
1825	1925	1800	1925	166685	SOM	Yatton
1856	1883	1800	1883	167231	SRY	Addlestone
1864	1900	ALL	ALL	141704	SRY	Battersea
1833	1917	1830	1992	129607	SRY	Bermondsey
1795	1797	ALL	ALL	129933	SRY	Godalming
1855	....	1830	1855	110132	SRY	Lambeth
....	....	1800	1992	163244	SRY	???
1793	1811	1750	1793	175951	SSX	Barcombe
1759	1992	1759	1992	127795	SSX	Berwick
1735	1758	ALL	1735	175080	SSX	Easebourne
1600	1900	1550	1900	105228	SSX	Hastings
1825	1840	ALL	1825	113220	SSX	Hastings
1825	1830	1825	1860	147567	SSX	Henfield
1750	1820	ALL	1820	147567	SSX	Woodmancote
1880	1960	1800	1880	126675	SSX	Worthing
....	....	1700	1860	175889	STI	Airth
1787	1992	1700	1787	174378	STS	Audley
1836	1900	1800	1836	121053	STS	Darlston
....	....	1700	1860	125806	STS	Lichfield
1860	1900	1600	1900	129011	STS	Potteries
1823	1850	1820	1850	152099	STS	West Bromwich
1800	1900	ALL	ALL	154806	STS	West Bromwich
1810	1900	1780	1900	155357	SXW	Cowfold
1800	1850	1800	1850	123285	SYK	Dodworth
1812	1903	1800	1910	123285	SYK	Wentworth
1860	1860	1700	1860	125806	WAR	Birmingham
1826	1992	1800	1992	170976	WAR	Coventry
1762	1851	1600	1762	175781	WIL	Chitterne
ALL	1797	....	....	170178	WIL	Cliffe Pypard
1726	1868	1726	1868	107573	WIL	Hindon
1833	1895	1700	....	135259	WIL	Longbridge Deveril
1814	1986	1804	1814	103969	WIL	Malmsbury
....	....	1700	1850	101273	WIL	Pewsey
1600	1870	1870	1992	168726	WIL	Warminster
1824	1843	1843	1900	175781	WIL	Warminster
1800	1992	1800	1880	123145	WMD	Birmingham
1781	....	....	....	102733	WOR	Tardebigge
1805	1852	....	1810	178853	WOR	???
1815	1890	1750	1920	102660	WRY	Habberley
1815	1890	1750	1920	102660	WRY	Idle
1838	1992	1800	1838	155551	WYK	Allerton
1827	1992	1700	1827	116181	YKS	Handsworth
1891	1891	1870	1894	146315	YKS	Kexborough
1891	1930	1700	1891	111775	YKS	Sheffield
1820	1900	1820	1900	120499	???	Birmingham
1863	....	....	....	126187	???	Bristol
WHITEACRE						
1800	1850	1760	1850	135941	SFK	Hundon
WHITEBREAD						
1795	1837	1700	1837	166782	???	Easton Royal
WHITECROFT						
1840	1900	1700	1900	114677	LEI	ALL
WHITECROSS						
1780	1820	....	....	140554	ELN	North Berwick
WHITEFOORD						
1810	1992	ALL	ALL	124877	ALL	ALL
1500	1750	....	....	124877	AYR	???
1750	1830	....	....	124877	LND	???
1286	1500	....	....	124877	RFW	???
WHITEFORD						
1797	1850	1780	1850	146536	AYR	Beith
WHITEHAD						
1786	1972	1700	1960	107654	YKS	Saddleworth
WHITEHALL						
1815	1860	1790	1860	127604	WAR	ALL
WHITEHEAD						
....	....	1800	1900	160563	CHS	Manchester
1780	1840	ALL	ALL	161551	CHS	Northwich
?	1805	?	1805	130885	GMP	Peterhead
1836	1858	1800	1839	131369	IRL	Cork
1690	1992	ALL	1690	179345	KEN	Ash
1830	1900	1700	1950	170054	KEN	Bromley
1840	1850	1840	1850	107522	KEN	Sittingbourne
1832	1832	1750	1832	113425	KEN	Stowting
1810	....	1810	1839	178381	LAN	Ainsworth
1850	1940	1700	1850	118915	LAN	Ashton Under Lyne
1793	1805	....	....	178381	LAN	Bolton
1743	1880	1650	1750	126411	LAN	Butterworth
1850	1890	1800	1850	172510	LAN	Denton
1800	1820	1790	1800	101796	LAN	Leigh
1841	1860	....	....	124788	LAN	Leigh
1861	1934	1700	1793	178381	LAN	Manchester
....	....	1620	1700	147613	LAN	Melling
1825	1883	1800	1825	134309	LAN	Oldham
?	1880	1700	1900	164488	LAN	Oldham
1839	....	1839	1861	178381	LAN	Pendleton
1800	1992	1800	1992	110523	LAN	Rochdale
1819	....	1800	1830	170348	LAN	Rochdale
1749	1814	ALL	1820	113611	LIN	Wrawby
1831	1892	....	....	127779	MDX	Holborn
1840	1910	1700	1840	130885	NBL	Border
1700	1992	1550	1700	168726	NFK	Upwell
1758	....	....	....	129747	NFK	Wiggenhall
1870	1992	1840	1870	166855	NTH	Cottesbrooke
1790	1992	....	....	130133	NTT	Chilwell
1798	1900	1750	1800	138487	NTT	Worksop
1853	1992	ALL	1853	107239	SRY	Wandsworth
1838	1867	1700	1838	138673	SSX	Horsham
1770	1800	....	....	100420	WAR	Meriden
1818	1918	1750	1825	163740	YKS	Ackworth
1828	....	....	....	109673	YKS	Almondbury
1829	1851	1700	1881	168424	YKS	Bentham
1754	1815	1700	1900	123250	YKS	Beverley
1780	1851	1700	1870	133574	YKS	Guiseley
1830	1992	1700	1830	132241	YKS	Huddersfield
1880	1900	1600	1880	175382	YKS	Leeds
1830	1992	1700	1830	132241	YKS	Marsden
1850	1890	1800	1850	172510	YKS	Sheffield
1794	1805	1750	1794	130885	???	Newcastle
WHITEHORN						
1856	1916	1800	1920	100307	ALL	ALL
1800	1860	1700	1800	130230	BRK	Stanford In The Vale
WHITEHOUSE						
....	....	ALL	ALL	154512	ALL	Name Study
1761	1881	ALL	ALL	154512	ALL	ALL
1600	1900	....	1900	177695	STS	Gt Wyrley
1760	....	1600	1900	133590	STS	Sedgley
1681	1752	1600	1800	160873	STS	Sedgley
1836	1875	1700	1836	126772	STS	Smethwick
....	....	1700	1800	147613	STS	Tipton
1781	1820	1600	1781	158968	STS	Walsall
....	....	ALL	ALL	135062	STS	West Bromwich
1760	1860	1650	1760	151769	STS	West Bromwich
1843	1992	ALL	1843	176060	WAR	Birmingham
1826	1976	1600	1826	176052	WAR	Warwick
1800	1992	ALL	ALL	166537	WOR	Dudley
1800	1960	1700	1800	153346	WOR	Oldswinford
1800	1850	ALL	ALL	130508	WOR	Stourbridge
WHITEHURST						
1685	1730	1730	1870	116777	CHS	Congleton
1650	1800	....	1650	116777	STS	Dilhorne
....	....	1600	1992	178268	STS	Dilhorne
....	....	1600	1992	178268	STS	Kingsley
WHITEING						
1617	1652	....	....	176125	BRK	Hanney
WHITELAW						
1780	1840	1700	1780	128244	PER	Cargill
1780	1840	1700	1780	128244	PER	Lethendy
WHITELEY						
....	....	ALL	ALL	133558	CHS	ALL
1834	1911	1720	1834	136824	DBY	Dronfield
1698	1799	1660	1800	165972	DEV	Down St Mary
....	....	ALL	ALL	133558	DUR	ALL
1860	1992	....	....	107158	KEN	Ashford

Known From	To	Researching From	To	Ref	Cty	Place
WHITELEY contd.						
1850	1992	1700	1850	168408	WYK	Batley
1850	1992	1700	1850	168408	WYK	Dewsbury
1890	1936	1860	1889	108944	WYK	Golcar
1840	?	ALL	ALL	133558	WYK	Huddersfield
1850	1992	1700	1850	168408	WYK	Huddersfield
1850	1992	1700	1850	168408	WYK	Leeds
....	....	ALL	ALL	111384	WYK	Rothwell
1845	1869	1870	1920	108944	WYK	Wakefield
1835	1992	1700	1835	123951	YKS	Halifax
....	....	1753	1992	155039	YKS	Halifax
1800	1850	1750	1800	123595	YKS	Huddersfield
1668	1780	1630	1780	107654	YKS	Northwram
1830	1914	ALL	1830	176656	YKS	Settle
1807	1899	1700	1807	128031	YKS	Sheffield
1835	1992	1700	1835	123951	YKS	Stainland
WHITELOCK						
1800	1900	1750	1900	126446	MDX	Clerkenwell
1845	1845	1840	1992	172782	YKS	Leeds
WHITEMAN						
1760	1992	1600	1760	176079	MDX	Holborn
1700	1992	1600	1700	176079	SSX	Clayton
WHITEOAK						
1900	1966	1880	1885	132659	???	???
WHITEROD						
1821	1840	1700	1850	126586	CAM	Ashley
WHITESIDE						
....	....	ALL	ALL	176087	ALL	Name Study
WHITESTONE						
....	....	ALL	ALL	176095	ALL	Name Study
1710	1992	ALL	ALL	176095	ALL	ALL
WHITEWAY						
....	....	ALL	ALL	176001	ALL	Name Study
1690	1870	1650	1690	168777	DEV	Bickington
1620	1837	1600	1837	140392	DEV	Staverton
1920	1992	1700	1920	126616	SRY	Kingston
1780	1830	1700	1810	106313	WIL	ALL
WHITEWOOD						
1740	1880	1700	1740	134139	HAM	Isle Of Wight
1703	1703	....	....	144355	KEN	South
1840	....	1800	1850	123870	KEN	???
1845	1992	ALL	1850	176656	LND	South
WHITFIELD						
1801	1992	....	1801	178365	BRK	Uffington
1757	1940	....	....	128996	CAM	Thorney
1700	1800	....	....	148261	CUL	Alston
1760	1930	1500	1760	104140	DEV	Chagford
1700	1950	1600	1700	167584	DUR	South
1768	1800	1600	1800	130125	DUR	Chester Le Street
1882	1992	1850	1900	105414	DUR	Hartlepool
1782	1802	1740	1782	177393	FLN	Hanmer
1801	1883	1700	1861	115894	LAN	Chorley
1826	1911	1750	1900	126586	LAN	St Helens
1700	1820	....	....	148261	NBL	Allendale
1650	1710	....	....	148261	NBL	Haydon Bridge
....	....	1750	1800	147613	YKS	Giggleswick
WHITFORD						
1860	1900	1860	1992	121312	CON	Chacewater
1803	1992	1781	1851	176109	CON	Falmouth
1715	1781	....	....	176109	CON	St Just In Roseland
1887	1946	1700	1900	121312	CON	Truro
WHITHAM						
1710	1766	1600	1710	144711	CAM	Whittlesey
....	....	ALL	ALL	176117	LAN	Central
....	....	1880	1950	176117	LAN	Earby
1860	1880	1880	1992	176117	LAN	Great Harwood
1685	1860	ALL	ALL	176117	LAN	Whalley
WHITHILL						
1480	1480	1480	1480	145580	LEI	Shepey
WHITING						
1722	1931	....	....	176125	BRK	Buckland
1699	....	....	....	176125	BRK	Ginge
1805	1867	....	1805	178365	BRK	Sutton Courtenay
1867	1992	1867	1992	112534	CAM	Trumpington
ALL	....	ALL	....	168599	CON	ALL
1707	1992	1600	1750	175218	EYK	Leven
1806	1826	1750	1900	135127	GLS	Painswick
1880	1980	1800	....	135860	KEN	Dartford
....	....	1800	1880	147788	NFK	Diss
....	....	1600	1818	150150	NTH	Brafield On The Green
1880	1896	1850	1896	147788	NTT	Walkeringham
1931	1992	....	....	176125	OXF	Oxford
1753	1840	1700	1840	144606	OXF	Witney
WHITING contd.						
1867	1992	1867	1992	112534	SFK	Haverhill
1819	1870	1800	1920	119091	WAR	Aston
1824	1903	1780	1824	174173	YKS	Hull
WHITINGE						
1617	....	....	....	176125	BRK	East Hendred
WHITLAMB						
....	....	ALL	ALL	172618	DEV	ALL
1900	1992	....	....	172618	DEV	Salcombe
WHITLEY						
1780	1830	1700	1900	105287	CHS	ALL
1730	1900	1600	1780	106313	CHS	Frodsham
?	1890	1850	1890	176141	DEV	Holcombe Burnwell
1850	1950	1750	1850	125660	HRT	Hoddeston
1920	1920	1700	1950	105287	LAN	ALL
?	?	1700	1850	176141	WRY	Sandal
1850	1960	1760	1850	176141	WRY	???
....	....	....	1860	176702	WYK	Bradford
....	....	1700	1850	108510	YKS	Batley
1870	1992	1870	1992	108510	YKS	Bradford
1750	1847	1700	1850	108510	YKS	Dewsbury
1850	1883	1700	1992	108510	YKS	Heckmondwike
1850	1960	1760	1850	176141	YKS	Sheffield
WHITLOCK						
....	....	ALL	ALL	176168	ALL	Name Study
....	....	1700	1825	156795	DOR	East
1883	....	1800	1883	127787	HAM	Fareham
1795	1850	1700	1800	120529	OXF	Witney
WHITLOW						
1780	1830	1700	1800	135496	CHS	Great Budworth
WHITMAN						
....	....	1800	1840	154873	SSX	Rye
....	....	1800	1840	154873	SSX	Udimore
1879	1900	1800	1879	124095	???	London
WHITMARSH						
1560	1950	1560	1950	177032	DOR	Blandford
1770	1824	1700	1770	109983	DOR	Kinson
1709	1840	1650	1709	127116	HAM	Nether Wallop
1920	1992	1920	1992	176176	LND	ALL
1830	1850	1830	1880	100862	LND	Clerkenwell
?	?	?	?	100862	SOM	Bath
WHITMORE						
1840	1870	ALL	1900	145254	DBY	Findern
1657	1807	ALL	ALL	156310	ESS	North East
1760	1900	1700	1992	176184	NFK	Ingoldisthorpe
1890	1970	1800	1890	168645	SAL	Newport
1800	1850	1700	1900	177032	SAL	Stockton
1686	1840	ALL	1900	156310	SFK	South
1775	1891	1820	1920	161586	SFK	Chillesford
1775	1891	1820	1920	161586	SFK	Iken
1800	1900	1600	1800	125660	SRY	Horley
1757	1769	1700	1800	176621	WAR	Coventry
1795	1871	1750	1900	154881	WAR	Rugby
1825	1992	1700	1825	153915	WOR	Stourport
WHITNEY						
....	....	ALL	ALL	176222	ALL	Name Study
....	....	1700	1850	176192	CHS	Acton
1874	1960	1700	1850	176192	CHS	Widnes
1889	....	....	....	131229	ESS	Leyton
1800	1850	1500	1820	176206	GLS	Bristol
1776	1861	1600	1992	131229	HEF	ALL
1770	1850	1200	1800	176206	HEF	ALL
....	....	1740	1965	176192	HEF	Hereford
1850	1850	1800	1900	131431	HEF	???
1840	1871	1840	1950	157538	IOW	Ryde
1840	1900	1700	1900	176206	LND	Westminster
1890	....	....	....	131229	MDX	Clerkenwell
1837	....	....	....	147621	MDX	Edmonton
....	....	1750	1900	176206	NTH	ALL
1798	1843	1840	1850	157538	OXF	Drayton
1674	1740	1500	1700	156515	RAD	Clyro
1400	1520	1350	1520	154881	SAL	ALL
1808	1860	1770	1900	176206	SOM	Bath
....	....	1750	1900	176206	WOR	Ombersley
WHITOAKS						
1762	1770	1700	1800	125903	HRT	Westmill
WHITROD						
1550	1960	1500	1960	109738	EAG	Central
1550	1960	1500	1960	109738	EAG	South
WHITTA						
1800	1992	1550	1800	176230	PEM	???
WHITTACKER						
1800	1992	....	....	122467	LAN	Bury

Known From	To	Researching From	To	Ref	Cty	Place
WHITTAKER						
1900	1992	1500	1900	110310	BRK	ALL
1694	1724	1650	1770	176249	DBY	South East
....	....	1700	1750	102172	LAN	Blackburn
1770	1850	....	....	102172	LAN	Darwen
1807	....	1750	1850	179078	LAN	Haslingden
1773	1773	1745	1773	174211	LAN	Marsden
1735	1774	1735	1774	159492	LAN	Oldham
1841	1851	1750	1900	137782	LAN	Radcliffe
1850	1877	ALL	1850	162221	LAN	Ramsbottom
1815	....	1750	1900	179078	LAN	Ramsbottom
....	....	ALL	ALL	129119	LAN	Rochdale
1824	1845	ALL	1900	165654	LAN	Stockport
....	....	....	1900	147818	LND	East
1759	1921	1840	1891	176249	NTT	South West
1747	1840	1500	1800	155152	NTT	Nottingham
1800	1850	1760	1850	135941	SFK	Hundon
1800	1880	1750	1800	128538	YKS	ALL
WHITTAL						
1850	1960	1600	1856	162671	BDF	Bedford
WHITTALL						
....	....	ALL	ALL	176265	ALL	Name Study
WHITTAM						
1721	1940	....	....	128996	CAM	Thorney
1850	1992	....	....	132500	LAN	Kirkham
1850	1992	....	....	132500	LAN	Oldham
1850	1992	....	....	132500	LAN	Preston
1850	1950	ALL	ALL	134996	LAN	Saddleworth
1850	1950	ALL	ALL	134996	YKS	Saddleworth
WHITTAMORE						
....	....	1760	1840	103713	BDF	Elstow
WHITTARD						
....	....	ALL	ALL	176273	ALL	Name Study
WHITTEM						
1770	1800	....	....	100420	WAR	Coventry
1770	1800	....	....	100420	WAR	Meriden
WHITTEMORE						
1854	1900	....	1854	157406	BDF	???
WHITTENBURY						
1500	1992	1500	1992	175498	ALL	ALL
WHITTENHAM						
....	....	1750	1850	103667	HAM	South East
WHITTICKS						
1790	1851	1700	1850	125903	HRT	Bennington
WHITTING						
1840	1930	1750	1840	114251	ALL	ALL
1697	....	....	....	176125	BRK	Hanney
WHITTINGHAM						
1860	1900	1860	1940	171417	ESS	???
....	....	1859	....	106623	LAN	Calsford
1690	1780	1600	1780	108111	SAL	North East
1882	1903	ALL	ALL	118885	STS	Bilston
WHITTINGTON						
1738	....	1979	1992	149543	BKM	Iver
1850	1970	1250	1850	146838	GLS	Bristol
1850	1970	1250	1850	146838	GLS	Forest Of Dean
1740	1768	1600	1992	145289	HAM	Isle Of Wight
1819	1890	1600	1820	132993	IOW	Carisbrooke
1819	1890	1600	1820	132993	IOW	Eatcombe
1805	....	....	....	141798	LDY	???
1660	1992	1979	1992	149543	MDX	Hayes
1660	1992	1979	1992	149543	MDX	Hillingdon
1717	1846	1650	1830	110728	MGY	Cemmaes
1777	1992	1600	1777	151092	SOM	???
1900	1992	1900	1992	176303	STS	Walsall
1756	1889	1756	1889	176303	WAR	Preston Bagot
1756	1889	1756	1889	176303	WAR	Wootton Wawen
1783	1992	ALL	1783	171468	YKS	Greasebrough
1783	1992	ALL	1783	171468	YKS	Rotherham
WHITTLE						
1750	1800	1700	1750	176311	DOR	Burton Bradstock
....	....	?	?	104310	DOR	Dorchester
1779	1835	1750	1850	148121	DOR	Langton Herring
1848	1992	1848	1992	176338	EYK	Hull
1713	1739	ALL	1739	176338	LAN	Bolton
1804	1910	1750	1830	108154	LAN	Leigh
1841	1851	ALL	1853	162825	LAN	Over Hulton
1739	1848	....	....	176338	LAN	Wigan
1732	1864	ALL	1864	168718	LEI	Queniborough
1853	1870	....	....	162825	LIN	Boston
1770	1992	....	1770	100064	LIN	Casthorpe
1853	1870	....	....	162825	LIN	Spalding
1823	1836	1700	1823	156183	LND	???
1800	1910	....	....	176311	MDX	Twickenham

Known From	To	Researching From	To	Ref	Cty	Place
WHITTLE contd.						
1871	1889	....	....	162825	NTH	Peterborough
....	....	1850	1859	173274	SFK	Hadleigh
....	....	1790	1799	173274	SFK	Whatfield
1655	1700	1630	1700	142018	SOM	Merriott
1750	1992	1750	1900	127914	WIC	Dunlavin
WHITTLES						
1800	1850	1750	1800	175986	YKS	Leeds
1806	1962	ALL	1806	103039	YKS	Sheffield
WHITTME						
1760	1800	ALL	1800	151319	CAM	ALL
1760	1800	ALL	1800	151319	HUN	ALL
1760	1800	ALL	1800	151319	NTH	ALL
WHITTOCK						
1550	1992	1500	1992	142018	SOM	ALL
WHITTOME						
1880	1890	1890	1900	144711	BRK	Newbury
1700	1834	1600	1700	144711	CAM	Whittlesey
1870	1890	1890	1900	144711	HAM	Kingsclere
1834	1874	....	....	144711	HUN	Ramsey
WHITTON						
1800	1840	1700	1900	138517	ANS	Barry
....	....	1810	ALL	149187	ANS	Dundee
1300	1450	1300	1450	154881	OXF	Nethercote
1815	1880	1700	1815	176346	SFK	Denham
1800	1960	1560	1800	152730	YKS	Bedale
WHITTRED						
1700	1800	....	....	100536	CAM	???
WHITTWELL						
1800	1900	1700	....	111724	ALL	ALL
WHITTY						
1851	1860	1825	1850	138932	DOR	Cheddington
1763	1992	....	1763	120979	WEX	Duncormick
WHITWELL						
1835	1880	....	....	176354	SAL	Shrewsbury
1771	1838	....	....	167479	YKS	Dunnington
1760	....	....	1760	158305	YKS	Haxby
1760	1835	....	....	176354	YKS	Haxby
WHITWORTH						
1796	1992	1750	1796	176362	BRK	Newbury
1800	1850	1780	1810	106194	DBY	Heath
1890	1921	1921	1970	141046	KEN	Bromley
1750	1790	1725	1750	101796	LAN	Ashton Under Lyne
1826	1843	1810	1850	126705	LAN	Bury
1849	1992	1700	1849	158917	LAN	Bury
1780	1992	1780	1992	145238	LAN	Haslingdon
1870	1960	ALL	1870	129119	LAN	Heywood
1880	1890	1840	1915	141046	LAN	Manchester
1800	1880	1775	1900	101923	LIN	Horncastle
1800	1880	1775	1900	101923	LIN	Louth
1770	1992	1700	1770	102342	LIN	Wrawby
....	....	1750	1796	176362	MDX	London
1700	1940	1700	1940	153621	WYK	Sowerby Bridge
1810	1870	1700	1810	108790	YKS	Sowerby
WHOLEY						
1830	1930	ALL	1850	131059	ERY	Sculcoates
1870	1890	1870	1900	113611	EYK	Hull
1815	1870	ALL	1870	113611	LIN	Louth
WHOMES						
....	....	ALL	1841	159441	LND	???
WHORLEY						
1634	1940	1500	1837	176370	HAM	Southampton
1650	1800	1500	1837	176370	WAR	ALL
1741	1940	1500	1837	176370	YKS	North Riding
WHORLOW						
1735	?	?	?	166642	KEN	Whitstable
WHORRALL						
1791	1805	1805	1826	178926	DBY	Ashover
WHORWOOD						
1826	1833	1826	1833	166715	WAR	Bedworth
1819	1824	1819	1824	166715	WAR	Berkswell
1726	1770	1726	1770	166715	WAR	Birmingham
1839	1992	1839	1992	166715	WAR	Redditch
1784	1809	1784	1809	166715	WAR	Sutton Coldfield
1685	1727	1650	1750	166715	WOR	Bromsgrove
1839	1992	1839	1992	166715	WOR	Redditch
WHOWELL						
1710	1992	1640	1710	162256	LAN	Bolton
WHURR						
?	?	1600	?	178667	NFK	ALL
WHY						
1811	....	ALL	ALL	137421	CAM	Wicken
WHYARD						
1770	1992	1770	1837	175765	SFK	???

Known From	To	Researching From	To	Ref	Cty	Place
WHYBROW						
1854	1876	1800	1854	128317	NTH	Weedon
WHYLEY						
1792	1992	1700	1792	123277	LIN	Grantham
WHYMAN						
1804	1820	1790	1810	108510	NTH	Peterborough
WHYSALL						
1754	1900	ALL	1754	115843	DBY	Belper
....	....	1830	1855	148121	DBY	Ripley
WHYTE						
1732	1930	....	1732	160431	ABD	Aberdour
1839	1964	1700	1839	106887	ABD	Gamrie
1840	1880	1840	1900	171530	ANS	Arbroath
1894	1930	1855	1900	171530	ANS	Carnoustie
1800	1860	ALL	1800	171530	ANS	Kirriemuir
1866	1869	1800	1891	144177	ANS	Monikie
1840	1843	....	1840	146811	CLK	Alloa
1840	1843	....	1840	146811	CLK	Logie
1776	1809	1750	1820	108510	FIF	Auchterderran
1860	1900	1830	1900	113107	GLA	Dowlais
1820	1870	1750	1900	176397	KRS	Kinross
1858	1868	....	....	116602	LKS	Glasgow
1800	1850	1700	1850	117455	PER	Killen
WHYTINGE						
1623	....	....	....	176125	BRK	East Hendred
WHYTTYNG						
1568	1613	1500	1600	176125	BRK	Hanney
WIARD						
1550	1992	1550	1837	175765	SFK	???
WIBBERLEY						
1643	1875	ALL	ALL	135062	DBY	Ashbourne
1749	....	?	1750	103934	DBY	Bakewell
1850	1900	1800	1900	145866	NTT	Basford
WIBERD						
1750	1850	1750	1900	162140	ESS	Farnham
1750	1850	1750	1900	162140	HRT	Albury
WIBLING						
1760	1820	1700	1760	155500	GLS	Westcote
WIBROW						
1750	1790	1700	1790	135941	ESS	Radwinter
WICK						
1780	1800	ALL	....	156140	SAL	Claverley
WICKARDS						
1750	1800	1700	1800	154903	KEN	Worth
WICKENDEN						
1850	1910	1600	1850	123587	KEN	Tonbridge
1680	1850	1680	1850	164313	KEN	Tonbridge
?	?	?	?	100692	MDX	London
1785	1850	1650	1785	172472	SRY	Crowhurst
1904	....	ALL	1900	165263	SSX	Wadhurst
WICKENS						
1770	1850	ALL	ALL	122866	BRK	South
1650	1850	....	....	111333	BRK	Brimpton
1800	1900	ALL	ALL	122866	HAM	North West
1755	1804	ALL	ALL	129933	HAM	Yateley
1850	1900	1600	1850	121118	LND	???
1712	1742	1700	1742	128724	SSX	ALL
1765	1836	1700	1765	174807	SSX	East Grinstead
WICKERS						
1750	1800	1700	1800	154903	KEN	Worth
1819	1881	1750	1819	166723	LND	Shoreditch
WICKES						
1740	1740	....	....	159883	KEN	Dover
WICKET						
....	....	?	?	134201	WOR	Bromsgorve
WICKETT						
1650	1650	1600	1700	133450	CON	S Gennys
1939	1939	1900	1992	121932	CON	St Austell
WICKHAM						
1790	1992	1600	1830	147192	KEN	North
1800	1880	1750	1900	145319	NFK	Chedgrave
1811	1836	ALL	1811	108197	NFK	Claxton
1865	1992	....	....	145319	NFK	Loddon
1792	1880	1700	1800	172782	NTH	Oundle
1835	1902	1700	1835	109983	SOM	Widcombe
1890	1939	1800	1890	143707	SRY	Egham
WICKINGTON						
1850	1870	1829	1992	127183	MDX	Bethnal Green
WICKINS						
1820	1960	....	....	129801	SRY	Barnes
WICKLIN						
1860	1870	1851	1861	130192	STS	West Bromwich
WICKS						
1795	1890	1750	1900	123145	BRK	Reading
WICKS contd.						
1775	1810	1750	1900	123145	BRK	Stratfield Mortimer
1800	1885	ALL	1885	118990	BRK	Waltham St Laurance
1800	1900	1700	1900	177997	BRK	Windsor
1808	1857	ALL	1808	119296	KEN	Deal
1853	1950	ALL	ALL	176419	KEN	Greenwich
....	....	1890	1992	147613	LAN	Barrow In Furness
1901	1947	1850	1901	119008	LEI	Stathern
1754	1797	1700	1800	109290	NFK	Central
1700	1800	ALL	ALL	177997	NFK	Cressingham
....	....	ALL	ALL	177997	SFK	ALL
1800	1916	1750	1800	129712	SRY	Leigh
1736	1813	1700	1820	176621	SSX	Battle
WICKSTEAD						
....	....	ALL	ALL	176427	ALL	Name Study
WIDCOMBE						
....	....	1600	1899	174963	SOM	Kilmersden
WIDDOCKS						
1845	1992	1840	1900	125903	BDF	Luton
WIDDOWS						
1688	1753	1680	1770	142018	BRK	ALL
1786	1847	1066	1800	122955	DEN	Llangollen
1622	1725	1680	1770	142018	WIL	Marlborough
WIDDOWSON						
1783	1818	1700	1783	139386	DBY	Chesterfield
....	....	1800	1860	132985	LIN	Grantham
WIDDRINGTON						
ALL	1680	....	....	132756	NBL	ALL
WIDER						
1735	1800	1700	1800	110434	CON	St Germans
1800	1900	1780	1880	110434	DEV	Plymouth
1880	1920	1880	1920	110434	YKS	Marsden
WIDGER						
1730	1842	ALL	1836	168696	CON	East
WIDGOOSE						
....	1750	ALL	1750	134511	NTT	Arnold
WIDLAKE						
ALL	ALL	ALL	ALL	123692	ALL	ALL
1711	1870	ALL	ALL	173398	DEV	North
1740	1820	ALL	1850	173614	DEV	Barnstaple
WIDMORE						
1590	1650	1560	1700	124974	HAM	Kingsclere
WIDOWS						
1708	....	ALL	ALL	113700	WIL	Bishops Cannings
WIDOWSON						
1800	1890	1700	1800	101958	LND	Stepney
WIEBKIN						
ALL	ALL	ALL	ALL	114642	ALL	ALL
WIELD						
1872	1900	ALL	ALL	166596	HAM	ALL
WIESEN						
1860	1960	....	....	130230	MDX	London
WIGELSWORTH						
1830	1880	....	....	147265	LIN	North
....	....	1550	1830	147265	YKS	West
WIGFULL						
1897	1933	1871	1897	117358	YKS	Sheffield
WIGG						
1909	1981	1850	1900	142360	BRK	Cookham
1642	1716	ALL	ALL	169730	HAM	Church Oakley
WIGGAN						
1750	....	1750	....	109347	LAN	Whalley
WIGGIN						
1870	1992	ALL	1870	176435	SAL	???
1860	1880	1850	1900	129240	WAR	Birmingham
1680	1770	1600	1992	114901	YKS	Harewood
WIGGINS						
1810	1845	....	....	127779	BRK	Buckland
1833	1912	1800	1833	108391	BRK	Reading
1805	1984	1780	1825	163635	GLS	Cheltenham
1803	1803	1760	1803	174211	LAN	Bury
1839	1910	1800	1910	144460	LAN	Droylsden
1792	1900	1700	1992	144703	LEI	Leicester
....	....	ALL	ALL	115533	LIN	Spalding
1850	1992	1700	1900	160954	MSY	Liverpool
1790	1850	....	1790	174025	OXF	Blackthorn
1835	1847	1750	1835	155500	OXF	Milton Under Wychwood
1810	1850	1760	1810	165530	SOM	Keynsham
?	?	ALL	ALL	100897	SRY	???
WIGGINTON						
....	....	ALL	ALL	176443	ALL	Name Study
WIGGLESWORTH						
1769	1992	1700	1769	176451	YKS	West Marton

Known From	To	Researching From	To	Ref	Cty	Place
WIGGOT						
1762	1762	1762	1762	161950	DOR	Portland
WIGGS						
1500	....	1500	1700	176478	BKM	Ledhurn
1500	....	1500	1700	176478	BKM	Mentmore
1500	....	1500	1700	176478	BKM	Skewkley
1789	1900	1700	1900	162442	HRT	ALL
1800	1992	1600	1800	176478	HRT	Hitchin
1800	1992	1600	1800	176478	HRT	St Albans
WIGHAM						
1864	1927	1820	1864	145084	CMA	Keswick
1634	1900	ALL	ALL	105015	NBL	Coanwood
WIGHT						
1780	1810	1700	1850	130915	ABD	Old Heldrum
1716	1860	1600	1716	163163	MLN	Edinburgh
1839	1992	1750	1839	176486	NBL	Lowick
1815	1980	1815	1992	110965	ROX	ALL
WIGHTMAN						
....	....	1700	1790	130338	LEI	Earl Shilton
....	....	1840	1957	130338	LEI	Loughborough
....	....	1790	1840	130338	LEI	Shepshed
1860	1992	1700	1992	140090	LND	East
....	1620	ALL	1620	134511	NTT	Annesley
....	....	1700	1753	178411	NTT	Oxton
WIGLEY						
1730	....	ALL	ALL	105481	NTT	Nuthall
1835	1960	1835	1992	103810	SAL	Longden
1840	1851	ALL	1840	174815	STS	Handsworth
1840	1851	ALL	1840	174815	STS	West Bromwich
1811	....	ALL	1840	174815	STS	Wolverhampton
WIGMAN						
1783	....	....	....	172820	SRY	Pirebright
1783	....	....	....	172820	SRY	Worplesdon
WIGMORE						
1625	1890	1600	1850	127655	COR	Ballymona
1840	1940	1840	1930	127655	GLS	Cheltenham
1080	1630	1500	1630	127655	HEF	Lucton
1080	1630	1500	1630	127655	HEF	Wigmore
1840	1940	1840	1930	127655	IOW	Carisbrook
1840	1940	1840	1930	127655	IOW	Ryde
?	?	?	?	166642	KEN	Canterbury
1625	1890	1600	1850	127655	WAT	Lismore
1840	1940	1840	1930	127655	WIL	Trowbridge
WIGNALL						
1870	1895	1850	1895	120901	LAN	???
1880	1898	1800	1898	139327	LND	Wandsworth
WIGNEY						
1650	1850	ALL	ALL	134996	SSX	Brighton
WIGZELL						
....	....	ALL	ALL	176508	ALL	Name Study
....	....	ALL	ALL	176508	ALL	ALL
WIILIAMS						
1831	1838	1780	1841	176877	RAD	Bleddfa
1841	....	1840	1881	176877	RAD	Llangynllo
WILBORN						
1790	1835	....	....	133221	HRT	Bishops Stortford
1753	1755	1740	1760	159042	LIN	Careby
1802	1802	1797	1810	159042	RUT	Tinwell
1718	1753	1700	1753	159042	RUT	???
....	....	1800	1810	133221	SFK	Ipswich
WILBOURNE						
1780	1837	1756	1792	136816	DBY	Chesterfield
1780	1837	1756	1792	136816	DBY	Hasland
1817	1992	1700	1817	159158	HRT	Ware
WILBRAHAM						
1794	1800	?	1800	128910	DBY	North Wingfield
1808	1851	1851	?	128910	DBY	Somercotes
1830	1930	1830	1930	167924	LAN	Liverpool
1851	1877	1877	?	128910	NTT	Kirkby In Ashfield
1720	1850	1720	1850	167924	SAL	Whitchurch
1871	1890	ALL	ALL	149489	STS	Hanley
WILBRO						
....	....	ALL	1880	178403	LND	???
WILBURN						
1822	1864	1830	1860	159042	LIN	Stamford
WILBY						
1800	1992	1700	1800	176516	WYK	Sheffield
1681	1863	1600	1681	109142	YKS	Batley
1801	....	....	....	129747	YKS	Horsforth
1750	1890	1700	1890	153737	YKS	Kirkheaton
1829	1834	1829	1834	129747	YKS	Leeds
WILCOCK						
1700	1750	1700	1750	171549	CON	Lanteglos By Fowey
1807	1862	ALL	ALL	149772	FLN	Holywell
WILCOCK contd.						
....	....	1090	1260	124974	GLA	ALL
1858	1992	1700	1857	110345	LAN	Liverpool
1760	1800	1690	1800	139483	LAN	Liverpool
1825	1842	1800	1860	147214	LAN	Liverpool
1750	1992	1730	1992	176524	LAN	St Helens
....	....	1830	1992	147613	LAN	Ulverston
1800	1840	ALL	ALL	123048	WRY	Horton In Ribblesdale
1750	1850	1750	1850	129747	YKS	Barnsley
....	....	1700	1900	147613	YKS	Bentham
....	....	1700	1800	147613	YKS	Ingleton
1744	1823	1500	1823	169439	YKS	Mirfield
WILCOCKS						
1907	....	1800	1907	173770	DEV	South
1550	1930	1300	1992	105333	DEV	Buckland In The Moor
1550	1930	1300	1992	105333	DEV	Holne
1550	1930	1300	1992	105333	DEV	Ilsington
1550	1930	1300	1992	105333	DEV	Lydford
1550	1930	1300	1992	105333	DEV	Widecombe In The Moor
1681	1820	ALL	ALL	165972	DEV	Witherdige
1800	1860	1700	1800	114871	KEN	Canterbury
WILCOX						
1818	1874	1790	1920	113069	AVN	Bristol
1818	1874	1790	1920	124990	AVN	Bristol
1774	1940	....	....	128996	CAM	Thorney
....	1829	ALL	1829	134058	KEN	Ashford
1845	1992	1800	1845	115312	LND	South East
1857	1871	....	....	103659	MDX	Fulham
1887	1900	....	....	103659	MDX	Paddington
1790	1840	1750	1840	156930	MON	Shirenewton
1795	1837	ALL	1795	147877	NTH	Paulerspury
1786	1992	ALL	1786	134783	SOM	Berkley
1777	....	1700	1790	127604	STS	Burton On Trent
1595	1992	ALL	1595	170704	STS	Maer
1600	1700	....	....	100420	WAR	Meriden
1806	1830	1790	1830	179337	WIL	Kingston St Michael
1777	1854	1770	1854	127604	YKS	South
WILCOXON						
1759	1992	1700	1992	134716	CHS	ALL
WILD						
1800	1837	....	....	138851	CHS	Bredbury
1850	1880	ALL	ALL	173010	CHS	Disley
1820	1856	....	....	176559	CMN	Kidwelly
1730	1760	1650	1730	151769	DBY	Derby
1790	1820	1750	1790	160458	DBY	Pinxton
1790	1850	ALL	ALL	173010	DBY	Taxal
1790	1850	ALL	ALL	173010	DBY	Whaley Bridge
1767	....	1767	1850	117625	DUR	Auckland
1774	1856	1700	1856	176559	LAN	Ashton
1825	1935	1700	1825	165239	LAN	Bury
1850	1992	1850	1900	173010	LAN	Leigh
1800	1890	1700	1800	135348	LAN	Oldham
1836	1836	1836	1871	159492	LAN	Oldham
1750	1900	1750	1900	110523	LAN	Rochdale
1774	1856	1700	1856	176559	LAN	Shaw
1850	1992	1850	1900	173010	LAN	Wigan
1817	1846	1700	1817	176575	LEI	Seagrave
1857	1881	1881	1992	143944	NRY	Henderskelfe
1800	1840	....	1840	102822	NTT	Nottingham
1670	1727	....	1690	176540	SAL	Alberbury
1890	....	....	....	176958	WRY	Lofthouse Gate
1890	....	1700	1992	176958	WRY	Stanley
1677	1940	?	1677	125342	WYK	Bingley
1677	1940	?	1677	125342	WYK	Keighley
1800	1992	ALL	1800	131172	YKS	Outwood
1877	1992	1850	1920	176958	YKS	Stanley Outwood
1800	1992	ALL	1800	131172	YKS	Stanley
1877	1992	1850	1920	176958	YKS	Wakefield
WILDASH						
1820	1844	....	....	139971	KEN	Selling
1820	1844	....	....	139971	KEN	Upchurch
WILDBLOOD						
1813	1992	....	....	167932	SAL	Loughton
1750	1992	1600	1750	163503	STS	???
WILDBORE						
1750	1992	1750	1992	176567	LEI	Hinckley
1632	1700	....	1632	108375	NTH	Kings Cliffe
WILDE						
1800	1992	1750	1800	113050	CHS	Macclesfield
1755	1797	1797	1830	145262	LAN	Oldham
1780	....	1830	1992	130486	LAN	Warrington

Known From	To	Researching From	To	Ref	Cty	Place
WILDE contd.						
1761	1788	1700	1900	125865	LIN	Habrough
1838	1992	1830	1838	145262	LND	Cripplegate
1880	1900	1860	1880	103985	LND	Highgate
1830	1910	1750	1830	176583	STS	Congleton
1830	1910	1750	1830	176583	STS	Norton
1830	1910	1750	1830	176583	STS	Ridgeway
1770	1840	1600	1770	134104	WOR	Himbleton
1800	1992	ALL	1800	131172	YKS	Outwood
1800	1992	ALL	1800	131172	YKS	Stanley
1800	1900	1800	1992	139203	YKS	York
WILDER						
1715	....	1700	1800	175307	BRK	Brightwalton
1880	....	....	....	142360	BRK	Newbury
1792	1900	1750	1900	175307	LND	Lambeth
WILDERSPIN						
1720	1992	1720	1992	138142	CAM	Swavesey
1812	1841	1812	1841	108839	HUN	Bluntisham
1789	1851	....	1789	108839	HUN	Needingworth
1853	1877	1853	1877	108839	HUN	Somersham
WILDEY						
1807	ALL	ALL	ALL	112275	NTT	Beeston
WILDGOOSE						
1802	1802	ALL	1802	162825	DBY	Crich
1797	1818	1750	1797	128368	YKS	Sheffield
WILDIG						
....	....	ALL	ALL	176591	ALL	Name Study
1800	1900	....	....	176591	SAL	Woore
1900	1950	....	....	176591	STS	Keele
1600	1800	....	....	176591	STS	Mucklestone
1950	1992	....	....	176591	STS	Newcastle Under Lyme
WILDIN						
1790	1992	1650	1790	110957	GLS	Forest Of Dean
WILDINA						
1820	1841	1750	1900	118443	LAN	Much Hoole
WILDING						
1841	1881	1882	1930	130184	KEN	Ashford
1660	1675	....	1700	171441	KEN	Bicknor
1851	1851	1774	1865	179523	LAN	Liverpool
1800	1881	1700	1800	125105	LND	Shreditch
1732	1800	1700	1732	167541	LND	Westminster
....	....	....	1850	130184	MDX	???
WILDISH						
1800	1992	....	....	154466	KEN	Sheppey
WILDMAN						
1740	1870	1740	1870	118869	BDF	North
1837	1900	ALL	1837	109797	LAN	Bolton Le Sands
1880	1992	....	1880	159514	LND	Hoxton
....	....	1700	1800	106356	NFK	Wymondham
1678	....	1600	1678	117234	YKS	Settle
WILDRIDGE						
1826	1869	1825	1870	113611	NYK	Hull
1777	1809	ALL	1830	113611	NYK	Whitby
WILDSIMTH						
1690	1850	1900	1950	123285	SYK	Worsbrough
WILDY						
....	....	ALL	ALL	176605	ALL	Name Study
WILEMAN						
1848	1992	1980	1992	114979	LEI	Earl Shilton
1880	1900	1800	1992	167592	STS	Burslem
1860	1880	1800	1992	167592	STS	Stoke
WILES						
1705	1739	1700	1750	176613	CAM	Cambridge
1729	1800	....	....	176613	CAM	Chesterton
1856	....	....	....	176613	GLS	Moreton In The Marsh
1781	1856	....	1860	176613	HRT	Hitchin
1822	1837	1750	1850	176621	KEN	St Nicholas At Wade
....	....	1800	1850	163260	NFK	Downham Market
1650	1780	1600	1780	100927	NTH	Rushden
1740	1850	ALL	1740	158445	YKS	South Cave
WILEY						
1835	1890	....	....	123633	DOW	???
1870	1900	ALL	ALL	116823	DUR	Hartlepool
1780	1900	1700	1860	173622	TYR	Drumskinny
1800	1992	....	....	139351	YKS	Stillington
WILFINSON						
1830	1919	1919	1992	100196	YKS	Lindley
WILFORD						
?	?	ALL	1930	117919	LEI	Melton Mowbray
?	?	ALL	1930	117919	STS	Wolverhampton
WILGRESS						
1680	1780	ALL	1680	163449	NFK	Blofield
WILKENS						
1757	1800	1590	1850	108251	BRK	Langford
WILKERSON						
1786	1850	1540	1860	155616	ESS	North
WILKES						
....	....	ALL	ALL	176648	ALL	Name Study
1600	1750	1500	1800	177180	BKM	Little Horwood
1900	1930	1900	1992	168688	DOR	Bournemouth
1815	1840	1700	1815	134368	GLS	Longhope
1729	1729	1700	1729	103632	GLS	Teddington
1818	1883	1750	1950	122688	HAM	Fareham
1800	1992	1750	1900	176648	HAM	Portsmouth
1821	1860	1700	1900	169536	HAM	Romsey
....	....	1850	1900	119083	LAN	Oldham
1847	1992	1847	1992	155993	MGY	Forden
1880	1900	1880	1900	168688	SAL	Bridgnorth
1845	1853	1800	1845	105538	SAL	Ketley
1850	1900	1800	1900	119083	STS	Chasetown
....	....	1800	1850	137111	STS	Darlaston
1859	1900	1700	1859	129011	STS	Tettenhall
1813	1833	1780	1840	169323	STS	Tipton
1853	1992	....	....	105538	STS	Walsall
....	....	1840	1900	137111	STS	Wolverhampton
1794	1850	ALL	ALL	135127	WAR	Birmingham St Martins
1812	1812	1780	1812	128449	WAR	Birmingham
....	....	ALL	ALL	155632	WAR	Birmingham
1910	1992	1910	1992	168688	WAR	Warwick
1800	1992	1600	1800	166103	WOR	Crowle
WILKIE						
....	....	ALL	ALL	104884	BAN	Rathven
1880	1943	1800	....	164275	DUR	Sunderland
1790	1830	1700	1800	169560	FIF	Tayside
....	....	ALL	1864	119326	MLN	Edinburgh
1805	1880	1750	1805	132640	SCT	Dundee
WILKIN						
1757	1864	....	....	138630	CAM	Barrington
1757	1864	....	....	138630	CAM	Croydon Wilds
1757	1864	....	....	138630	CAM	Longstowe
1757	1864	....	....	138630	CAM	Shepreth
1757	1864	....	....	138630	CAM	Thriplow
1806	1830	1750	1840	158658	CMN	Llanelli
1710	....	1500	1710	107972	DBY	Eckington
....	....	ALL	ALL	176656	HUM	Holderness
1560	1992	ALL	ALL	176656	LIN	North
....	1760	1500	1800	107972	SYK	???
WILKINGSON						
1870	1925	1870	1992	139270	BRK	Central
WILKINS						
....	....	ALL	ALL	176680	ALL	Name Study
1850	1900	1700	1850	173460	AVN	Bath
1850	1974	1700	1850	124397	CAM	Over
1812	1992	1600	1812	115096	DEV	Stoke Damerell
1784	1810	1700	1784	148938	GLS	Arlingham
1809	1832	1700	1900	178322	GLS	Bristol
1826	1835	1750	1900	135127	GLS	Stonehouse
1800	1900	1800	1900	176648	HAM	Portsmouth
1788	?	?	?	166642	KEN	Ashford
1850	1850	1830	1890	176672	LEI	Leicester
1815	1992	1700	1815	176672	LEI	Thorpe Acre
....	1887	1850	1900	120529	LND	Bethnal Green
1800	1850	1800	1850	167924	MDX	Chelsea
1790	1880	....	....	137111	NTH	Farthinhoe
1880	1890	1850	1920	176672	NTH	Northampton
1660	1800	....	....	137111	NTH	Syresham
1731	....	1650	1750	143693	OXF	Fulbrook
1820	1859	1795	1820	161810	SOM	Axbridge
1825	1835	1800	1860	124648	SOM	Bridgewater
1882	1992	....	1882	171743	SOM	Buckland St Mary
1770	1881	1700	1930	176664	SOM	Cheddon Fitzpaine
1770	1830	1770	1850	138479	SOM	Compton Martin
....	....	1500	1900	176664	SOM	Pitminster
1892	1922	ALL	1892	152641	STS	Burton On Trent
1750	1992	?	1992	133078	WAR	Kineton
1717	1741	1600	1716	131245	WAR	Leamington Hastings
1710	1825	1710	1825	127655	WAR	Wormleighton
1500	1900	1500	1900	170216	WIL	ALL
....	....	1650	1780	156795	WIL	South
....	....	1760	1812	172871	WIL	West
1759	1841	ALL	ALL	106313	WIL	Lacock
1641	1754	1600	1650	170348	WIL	Stanton Fitzwarren
WILKINSON						
1820	....	1750	1820	108596	BUT	Arran
1766	....	....	1766	177504	CAM	Littleport

Known From	To	Researching From	To	Ref	Cty	Place
WILKINSON contd.						
1653	1940	....	....	128996	CAM	Thorney
?	?	?	?	153079	CAM	Thorney
1810	1960	1700	1810	171832	CAM	Welney
1820	1992	1700	1850	128503	CHS	Acton
1784	1830	ALL	ALL	138363	CHS	Chester
1859	1881	....	....	169013	CUL	Egremont
1697	1770	1600	1800	116173	CUL	St Bees
1871	1915	1771	1871	153958	DBY	Broad Marsh
....	....	1880	1930	176400	DBY	Chesterfield
1775	1824	1700	1800	121932	DBY	Crich
1870	1934	1700	1870	117463	DUR	ALL
1794	1885	1885	1992	131571	DUR	Lamesley
1814	1888	1600	1814	116637	DUR	Monkwearmouth
1728	1728	1650	1750	144606	DUR	South Shields
1814	1888	1600	1814	116637	DUR	Sunderland
1814	....	1750	1830	155969	ELN	Haddington
1758	1787	....	....	156647	HAM	Shalfleet
1844	1992	ALL	1844	176729	LAN	Clitheroe
....	1880	....	1860	154024	LAN	Golborne
1829	1861	ALL	1829	145203	LAN	Higham
1900	....	....	....	136255	LAN	Manchester
1716	1792	1500	1716	110310	LAN	Ribchester
1821	1992	1700	1821	176710	LAN	Rochdale
1792	1860	1700	1900	126586	LAN	Tealby
1550	1992	1550	1992	176699	LIN	ALL
1800	1881	ALL	1881	119067	LIN	Horncastle
1840	1840	....	....	152102	LIN	Saltfleet
1755	1765	....	....	144568	LIN	???
1800	1992	ALL	ALL	152226	LND	Deptford
1809	....	....	1809	101761	LND	Stoke Newington
1892	1992	1700	1892	176710	LND	Tottenham
....	....	1789	1791	104442	MDX	London
1861	....	....	....	112909	MDX	Ratcliffe
1807	1890	1700	1807	159212	NBL	Hexham
1695	....	....	1720	160873	NBL	Newcastle On Tyne
1810	1960	1700	1810	171832	NFK	Halgay
1600	1680	1600	1680	117803	NRY	Claxton
....	....	1750	1803	166189	NTH	Wooten
1800	1850	1700	1900	102164	NTT	Bulwell
1884	1961	....	....	176966	NTT	Hucknall
1690	1920	....	1920	137634	NTT	Littleborough
1700	1920	....	1920	137634	NTT	Osberton
1670	1700	1600	1700	170852	NTT	Radford
1677	....	1550	1677	148288	NTT	Stapleford
1800	1920	....	1992	137634	NTT	Sturton Le Steeple
1841	1870	1700	1841	100110	NYK	Brompton
1750	1860	....	....	132225	SAL	Elsmere
1783	....	....	....	121835	SAL	Prees
1770	1860	....	....	132225	SAL	Wem
1884	....	....	....	112909	SRY	Bermondsey
1820	1870	....	1820	158526	SRY	Christchurch
....	....	1871	1881	116602	SRY	Newington
1776	1862	1700	1776	174807	SSX	Laughton
1800	1870	1800	1870	154210	WAR	Bedworth
1880	1942	1700	1880	105023	WAR	Birmingham
1770	1800	....	....	100420	WAR	Meriden
1700	1900	ALL	ALL	128279	WES	South
1650	1900	1600	1800	162191	WES	Garsdale
1700	1770	1670	1700	122904	WES	Kendal
1698	1992	1600	1700	129038	WES	Warcop
ALL	1760	....	....	170798	WRY	Penistone
ALL	1760	....	....	170798	WRY	Thurlstone
1822	1992	....	....	176702	WYK	Bradford
....	....	....	1822	176702	WYK	Methley
....	....	1500	1870	168017	YKS	North
1885	1992	ALL	ALL	164518	YKS	Aberford
....	1845	1800	1870	120529	YKS	Bagby
1800	1880	....	1992	164984	YKS	Barnsley
1600	1800	....	....	167924	YKS	Bossall
1850	1915	1750	1850	176753	YKS	Doncaster
1725	....	1725	....	109347	YKS	Gisburn
1840	1992	1700	1840	138738	YKS	Halifax
1800	1900	1780	1890	123595	YKS	Huddersfield
....	....	1690	....	145688	YKS	Keighley
1885	1992	ALL	ALL	164518	YKS	Lotherton
1850	1900	1750	1850	177296	YKS	Sheffield
1690	1770	1600	1690	158976	YKS	Skelton
1730	1769	1700	1769	176451	YKS	Skipton
1737	1836	1700	1850	155969	YKS	Slaidburn
1800	1960	1700	1800	108790	YKS	Sowerby
1600	1800	....	....	167924	YKS	Terrington
1770	1800	1600	1992	102520	YKS	Thornhill
1770	1790	1770	1800	171670	YKS	Wakefield
WILKS						
1650	1992	1750	1900	104981	ESS	North East
....	....	1700	1870	146978	GLA	Cowbridge
....	....	1700	1870	146978	GLA	Swansea
1620	1820	....	....	121983	GLS	Berkeley
1840	1900	....	1840	169188	LND	Westminster
1847	1992	1847	1992	155993	MGY	Forden
1720	1760	1700	1800	151742	NRY	North York Moors
1822	....	1750	1992	174408	SSX	???
....	....	1750	1800	176796	WAR	Birmingham
....	....	ALL	1880	161209	WAR	Warwick
1794	....	....	....	151351	WOR	Evesham
1832	1839	1750	1831	131245	WOR	Worcester
1780	1814	1780	1814	154563	YKS	Clapham
1750	1776	ALL	1750	154563	YKS	Hampsthwaithe
WILLAM						
....	....	ALL	ALL	154970	LAN	Tunstall
WILLAN						
1807	1834	1750	1807	176451	CMA	Kirby Lonsdale
1835	1850	....	1850	152803	SRY	Croyden
WILLANS						
1820	1930	ALL	1840	142301	MDX	Harrow On The Hill
WILLAVISE						
1713	1832	1713	1832	178705	WIL	Hannington
WILLCOCKS						
....	....	1800	1900	156795	LND	North
WILLCOX						
1860	1900	1700	1900	171638	AVN	Bath
1750	1850	1650	1750	156795	DOR	East
1800	1860	1700	1960	109894	DOR	Bere Regis
1730	1880	1700	1900	112976	GLS	Bristol
1755	1992	1600	1755	150150	NTH	Towcester
1796	1837	ALL	ALL	124982	SOM	Frome
WILLERTON						
....	....	ALL	ALL	176818	ALL	Name Study
1820	1845	....	....	177725	LIN	Great Carlton
....	....	1845	1900	177725	LIN	Louth
WILLET						
1703	1854	1700	1745	134430	SSX	Cowfold
WILLETS						
1877	1962	ALL	1877	117048	STS	Smethwick
WILLETT						
1580	1693	1693	1992	142409	ENG	Midlands
1790	1900	1650	1790	139106	KEN	???
....	....	1800	....	137456	NTH	Northampton
1726	1950	ALL	ALL	108413	SOM	North
1790	1900	1650	1790	139106	SSX	???
1822	1950	ALL	1822	106909	STS	Madeley
WILLEY						
....	....	....	....	143499	CON	Mullion
1839	1839	1066	1839	108669	DEV	Exeter
....	1810	1500	1860	175072	LIN	ALL
1801	1871	1871	1891	108022	LIN	Baroney
1865	1992	ALL	ALL	108022	LIN	Grimsby
1770	1820	1663	1850	108022	LIN	Normandy By Spittal
....	....	1700	1992	122742	LND	Bermondsey
1840	1900	1650	1840	170194	NTT	Nottingham
1780	1820	ALL	1850	144533	NYK	Acklam
1750	1820	1700	1800	144657	SOM	Bristol
1880	1900	1870	1900	142050	SOM	Yeovil
1843	1851	ALL	1843	124346	T&W	Sunderland
WILLFORD						
?	?	ALL	1930	117919	LEI	Melton Mobray
1800	1992	ALL	ALL	115002	LIN	Sleaford
?	?	ALL	1930	117919	STS	Wolverhampton
WILLGRESS						
1770	1960	1770	1960	163449	NFK	Upton
WILLIAM						
1768	1800	1700	1800	132217	CAE	Treflys
1570	1620	1550	1650	176923	CMN	Carmarthen
1792	....	1750	1792	123129	CMN	Llandybie
1752	1789	1700	1800	176923	CMN	Talley
1780	1820	1780	1820	151297	GLA	Cadoxton Juxta Neath
1831	1878	1800	1878	158658	GLA	Llansamlet
1723	....	1600	1800	176923	GLA	Pontlliw
1805	1876	ALL	1805	100528	IRL	Cockford
WILLIAMS						
1824	1827	1800	1824	127116	AGY	Amlwch
1820	1992	1700	1820	110701	AGY	Bangor
1904	1914	1900	1914	159786	AGY	Benllech
1811	1851	1700	1811	169609	AGY	Bodedern
1851	1927	....	....	169609	AGY	Holyhead
1892	1916	1881	1916	159786	AGY	Llanallgo

Known From	To	Researching From	To	Ref	Cty	Place
WILLIAMS contd.						
1790	1977	1750	1850	162396	AGY	Llanddyfrian
1865	1900	1800	1865	148490	AGY	Llandegfan
1795	1816	1795	1816	159786	AGY	Llanedwen
1824	1881	1500	1824	175072	AGY	Llanedwen
1780	1860	1700	1800	177024	AGY	Llaneilian
1824	1827	1800	1824	127116	AGY	Llanfaelog
1870	?	1850	1900	127612	AGY	Llanfair Mathafarn
1790	1876	1700	1790	157147	AGY	Llanfair P G
1820	1992	1700	1820	110701	AGY	Llanfihangeleseogiog
1800	1870	1600	1980	135631	AGY	Llangoed
1759	1823	1700	1823	113069	AVN	Bristol
1759	1823	1700	1823	124990	AVN	Bristol
1850	1992	1700	1850	131083	AVN	Bristol
1780	1950	1650	1780	128376	AVN	Long Ashton
1650	1750	1600	1850	177180	BKM	Waddesdon
1816	1816	1880	1940	177008	BRE	Brecon
1812	1896	1600	1900	176958	BRE	Brecon
....	....	1750	1850	140759	BRE	Brilley
1760	1992	1750	1920	176958	BRE	Bronllys
1864	1992	1800	1864	118656	BRE	Gwenddwr
1760	1992	1750	1920	176958	BRE	Llanddew
....	....	1780	1850	117137	BRE	Llandefalle
1760	1992	1750	1920	176958	BRE	Llanvihangel Nant Bran
1864	1992	1800	1864	118656	BRE	Llysdinam
....	....	1750	1850	140759	BRE	Talgarth
1760	1992	1750	1920	176958	BRE	Talgarth
1773	1773	1735	1775	124974	BRK	Kingston Lisle
1821	1855	ALL	1821	141526	BRK	Newbury
1875	1992	1820	1992	172545	BRK	Reading
1881	1992	1881	1992	148490	CAE	Bangor
....	....	1750	1850	116173	CAE	Bardsey
1830	1870	1830	1870	115614	CAE	Caerhun
1841	1861	1813	1841	138401	CAE	Caerhun
1909	1980	1850	1909	148490	CAE	Caernarvon
1858	1875	1800	1858	161810	CAE	Caernarvon
1800	....	....	....	142158	CAE	Clynog
1860	1992	1800	1900	177210	CAE	Dwygyfylchi
1700	1864	1700	1864	104027	CAE	Llanbedr-Y-Cennrn
1800	1992	1700	1800	138207	CAE	Llaniestyn
1816	1872	1810	1880	159786	CAE	Llanrug
1870	1992	1870	1960	115614	CAE	Llithfaen
1830	1900	1700	1800	157147	CAE	Rhiwlas
1840	?	1800	1860	120650	CAM	March
1860	?	1800	1860	177253	CGN	Cardigan
1846	1992	1800	1846	176931	CGN	Llanwenog
1900	1970	....	....	142093	CGN	Llwydcoed
....	....	1850	1900	142093	CGN	Rheidoc Valley
1873	1893	ALL	1873	176842	CHS	Birkenhead
1893	1900	1875	1910	126705	CHS	Chester
1692	1731	....	....	135437	CHS	Chester
1869	1962	....	1870	169412	CHS	Witton
1833	....	1800	1850	158658	CMN	Bettws
1850	1900	....	....	156744	CMN	Carmarthen
1770	1851	1750	1860	118575	CMN	Gwynfe
1770	1851	1750	1860	118575	CMN	Llandeilo
1728	1992	....	....	144304	CMN	Llandeilo
1755	1880	1700	1992	176923	CMN	Llandeilo
1848	1900	1800	1900	118540	CMN	Red Roses
1880	1920	1700	1992	107204	CMN	Rhydargeau
....	....	1820	1865	118575	CMN	Talley
1821	1880	1821	1880	141690	CON	Bodmin
1760	1900	1760	1992	133450	CON	Breage
....	....	1600	1900	136972	CON	Breage
1810	1850	1700	1900	142875	CON	Breage
....	....	1600	1900	136972	CON	Germoe
1680	1796	....	....	174319	CON	Grampound
1745	1775	1700	1800	153354	CON	Gwennap
....	....	1740	1820	129992	CON	Gwiwear
1858	1944	....	....	107174	CON	Hayle
1721	1818	1600	1721	102571	CON	Kenwyn
1780	1824	ALL	1824	168718	CON	Liskeard
1790	1850	1790	1992	119873	CON	Luxulyan
1864	1992	1700	1864	130257	CON	Manaccan
....	....	1600	1900	136972	CON	Manaccon
1760	1900	1760	1992	133450	CON	Mardon
1797	1850	1700	1800	142999	CON	Padstow
1740	1821	1740	1880	141690	CON	Probus
1790	....	....	....	172030	CON	Redruth
....	....	1700	1900	136972	CON	Sithney
1818	1863	1700	1818	153605	CON	St Austell
1802	1905	ALL	ALL	121398	CON	St Buryan

Known From	To	Researching From	To	Ref	Cty	Place
WILLIAMS contd.						
1674	1700	1600	1800	102520	CON	St Erth
1800	1800	1700	1800	161837	CON	St Ewe
1684	1824	1684	....	115576	CON	St Issey
1864	1992	1700	1864	130257	CON	St Keverne
....	....	ALL	1992	119873	CON	Tywardreath
1809	1992	1750	1800	176982	CON	Wadebridge
....	....	1600	1900	136972	CON	Wendron
1930	1992	1800	1930	177199	CUL	Barrow In Furness
?	?	1853	1875	131733	CWD	Llangollen
1780	1900	1600	1780	155608	DBY	Heage
1920	....	1800	1920	176834	DEN	Clwyd Valley
1846	1846	ALL	1992	125113	DEN	Corwen
1823	1851	1770	1825	174289	DEN	Erbistock
1836	1880	ALL	1880	132217	DEN	Glan Conwy
1829	1862	1680	1865	176893	DEN	Llanarmon In Ial
1780	1800	1700	1780	147885	DEN	Llanfair D C
1840	....	1830	1940	177016	DEN	Llanfair
1760	1992	....	....	118672	DEN	Llangynhafal
....	....	1700	1950	143219	DEN	Llanrhaiadr In Kinmerch
1810	1860	1760	1840	121126	DEN	Llanrhaiadr
....	....	....	....	132217	DEN	Llansanffraid
1851	1870	?	1851	171298	DEN	Llansanfraid
1860	1880	1860	1980	135631	DEN	Rhuddlan
1800	1800	1800	1860	140864	DEN	Ruabon
1861	1875	1850	1900	174289	DEN	Ruabon
1893	1953	1800	1953	176869	DEN	Ruthin
1868	1964	....	....	147621	DEN	Trefnant
1866	....	1850	1960	177016	DEN	Trefnant
....	....	1800	1860	108030	DEV	Appledore
1770	1820	1700	1770	158739	DEV	Appledore
1800	1870	1700	1870	166650	DEV	East Stonehouse
1788	1826	1737	1847	154040	DEV	Georgeham
1792	1815	ALL	1800	175773	DEV	Plymouth
1850	1950	1750	1850	102679	DEV	Plymstock
1824	1845	1800	1824	145297	DEV	Tavistock
1776	1881	1776	1881	170623	DEV	Teigngrace
1836	....	....	1992	157244	DEV	Totnes
1665	1720	ALL	1700	115266	DOR	ALL
1515	1992	ALL	ALL	124893	DOR	ALL
1750	1829	1700	1749	175846	DOR	Beaminster
1856	1903	....	1856	165484	DOR	Sturminster Marshall
1742	1765	ALL	1742	154563	DOR	Swyre
1880	1900	1870	1920	177024	DUR	Jarrow
1868	1950	1700	1867	177237	FLN	Aberwheeler
1700	1800	....	....	100536	FLN	Boddleweather
....	....	....	1890	129313	FLN	Gorsedd
1871	1932	1700	1871	115185	FLN	Mold
1794	....	ALL	ALL	147621	FLN	Ysceifiog
1905	1918	1905	1958	176893	GLA	Abercave
....	1911	1600	1992	176990	GLA	Aberdare
1883	1938	....	....	144215	GLA	Blaengarw
1803	1936	1800	1936	159743	GLA	Cardiff
1860	1932	1800	1860	177253	GLA	Cardiff
1841	1992	1800	1841	158739	GLA	Dulais Valley
1788	1862	1700	1799	139793	GLA	Eglwysilan
1833	1883	1800	1883	158658	GLA	Eglwysilan
....	1912	1600	1992	176990	GLA	Ferndale
1822	1888	1750	1822	139793	GLA	Lisvane
1800	1870	1800	1870	118575	GLA	Llangiwg
1869	1920	1850	1920	118540	GLA	Llangynwydd
....	....	1800	1830	117137	GLA	Llansamlet
....	....	1800	1840	117137	GLA	Llantrithyd
1800	1815	1750	1830	158658	GLA	Lougher
1800	1870	1800	1870	118575	GLA	Maes Iago
1850	1870	1850	1870	163449	GLA	Maesycwmma
1700	1809	....	....	167533	GLA	Merthyr Tydfil
....	1914	1600	1992	176990	GLA	Mountain Ash
1847	1992	1600	1847	176915	GLA	Mountain Ash
1847	1992	1600	1847	176915	GLA	Neath
1925	1958	....	....	176893	GLA	Pen Y Cae
1750	1900	1750	1900	141577	GLA	Peterston-S-Ely
1812	1841	1780	1850	158658	GLA	Pont-Neath Vaughan
1880	1970	1860	1992	176923	GLA	Pontlliw
1870	1925	....	....	145319	GLA	Rhonnda
1920	1925	....	....	176893	GLA	Ystalyfera
1785	1840	1700	1810	138150	GLS	South
1850	1860	1800	1900	167096	GLS	Almondsbury
1848	1992	1700	1848	137219	GLS	Barton St Mary
1800	1900	1750	1900	138479	GLS	Bristol
1900	1932	1850	1992	173096	GLS	Bristol
1843	....	1820	1992	151378	GLS	Chipping Sodbury

Known From	To	Researching From	To	Ref	Cty	Place
WILLIAMS contd.						
1861	1878	?	1880	164976	GLS	Prestubry
1861	1861	ALL	ALL	140740	GLS	Upleaden
1780	1810	1810	1840	148113	GLS	Westerleigh
1836	1930	1750	1836	105740	GLS	Woollaston
1900	1992	....	....	132357	GNT	Abersychan
1757	1889	1700	1800	109819	GNT	Cwmyoy
1841	1992	1800	1992	122122	GNT	Monmouth
1827	1859	1700	1827	100110	GNT	Newport
1890	1900	1700	1890	125415	GNT	Pontypool
?	?	?	?	169668	GYN	Bangor
?	?	?	?	169668	GYN	Caernarfon
1787	1933	1700	1787	118230	GYN	Llandudno
1870	1980	1750	1900	115215	GYN	Llanwrst
1788	1851	....	....	156647	HAM	Arreton
1829	1870	1750	1828	175846	HAM	Portsea
....	....	ALL	....	119237	HAM	Southampton
1877	1960	1700	1877	147893	HAM	Southampton
1714	1802	....	....	131229	HEF	Bromyard
1851	1881	1800	1900	167983	HEF	Hereford
1800	1850	....	....	144029	HEF	Leominster
1800	1800	....	....	127426	HEF	Moccas
1800	1850	1700	1850	107611	HEF	Prestiegn
1790	1830	1790	1830	153303	HEF	Staunton On Wye
1750	1800	1750	1800	151637	HEF	Wormsley
1777	1777	....	....	127426	HEF	???
ALL	1841	....	....	172693	IRL	Enniscorthy
1841	1851	ALL	1841	100528	IRL	???
1780	....	....	....	139165	KEN	Barham
1817	....	1700	....	123560	KEN	Bexley
1720	1750	1700	1720	154873	KEN	Canterbury
1826	1913	ALL	1890	127094	KEN	Chatham
1862	1862	....	1862	171646	KEN	Folkestone
....	....	1810	1820	138339	KEN	Gillingham
1882	1882	1862	1904	171646	KEN	Greenwich
1750	1770	1700	1800	164992	KEN	Hollingsbourne
1760	1880	ALL	1880	152889	KEN	Hythe
1862	1863	ALL	ALL	114693	KEN	Lewisham
1774	1798	....	1820	171441	KEN	Milstead
1826	1913	ALL	1890	127094	KEN	Rochester
1672	1694	1550	1672	139084	KEN	Shipbourne
1750	1800	1600	1750	117110	KEN	West Malling
1910	1992	ALL	ALL	105856	KEN	???
1939	1992	1875	1939	131733	LAN	Bolton
1900	1930	1850	1900	119318	LAN	Liverpool
1840	1870	1800	1850	138150	LAN	Liverpool
1835	1973	1835	1835	145580	LAN	Liverpool
1856	1881	1800	1855	154539	LAN	Liverpool
1874	1913	1800	1874	118230	LAN	Manchester
1842	1855	1807	1855	129313	LAN	Manchester
1844	1900	1800	1844	136220	LAN	Manchester
1841	1900	1600	1900	176133	LAN	Manchester
1836	....	1800	1880	176885	LAN	Manchester
....	1880	ALL	1880	134511	LAN	Toxteth Park
1900	?	....	....	147893	LND	Colindale
1811	1835	1700	1850	143693	LND	Hammersmith
1845	....	....	....	124559	LND	Newington
1825	1870	1750	1800	172898	LND	Newington
1870	1900	1800	1870	172898	LND	Southwark
1750	1780	1750	1780	127655	LND	St Clement Danes
1841	....	1841	....	123773	LND	Whitechapel
1846	1873	1800	1873	128694	MDX	Barnet
1860	1880	1840	1900	140864	MDX	Islington
1830	1992	1800	1942	105333	MDX	London
1841	1861	....	....	177229	MDX	New Brentford
1792	?	1700	1840	132217	MER	Llanfrothen
1840	1960	1650	1840	158992	MER	Machynlleth
1807	1869	1700	1807	118605	MGY	Forden
1750	1799	ALL	1800	138126	MGY	Kerry
1871	1876	1865	1905	176893	MGY	Llanidloes
1750	1799	ALL	1800	138126	MGY	Vaynur
1858	1928	1800	1850	139793	MON	Bedwas
1790	1840	1790	1840	156930	MON	Caerleon
1814	....	....	....	131229	MON	Chepstow
1800	1850	ALL	ALL	122866	MON	Ebbw Vale
1850	1900	1850	1900	156930	MON	Llanbadoc
1770	1800	1770	1800	156930	MON	Llantarnam
1835	1850	1800	1835	163449	MON	Mynyddslwyn
1840	1900	1840	1900	141577	MON	Newport
1800	1860	1800	1860	156930	MON	Penrhos
1860	1910	1850	1992	178578	MON	Trelleck
1840	1860	1840	1860	156930	MON	Usk
1850	....	1800	1860	120650	NFK	ALL
....	....	1700	1840	177229	NFK	ALL

Known From	To	Researching From	To	Ref	Cty	Place
WILLIAMS contd.						
1793	1805	1700	1900	118168	NFK	Blackney
1820	1900	1700	1820	144681	NFK	Diss
1804	1881	1800	1900	107891	NFK	Tottenhill
1760	1840	1750	1780	127655	NTH	Great Houghton
1750	1825	....	....	118354	NTH	Greens Norton
1760	1840	1750	1780	127655	NTH	Northampton
1824	1908	1700	1840	117005	NTH	Towcester
1900	1979	....	....	176966	NTT	Hucknall
1820	1880	1820	1992	172545	OXF	Abingdon
1823	1992	1700	1823	161446	OXF	Middleton Cheney
1786	1900	1700	1920	172073	OXF	Spelsbury
1813	1850	1700	1820	132993	PEM	Bosherton
1815	1900	1700	1815	129135	PEM	Marros
1774	1992	1500	1774	140279	PEM	Pwllecrochan
1841	1900	....	....	155993	RAD	Abbycwmhir
1865	1896	1850	1950	176958	RAD	Glasbury
1760	1992	1750	1920	176958	RAD	Llandeilo Graban
1850	1900	1600	1850	156914	RAD	Llandewy
....	....	1830	1858	104884	RAD	???
....	....	ALL	....	119237	RAD	???
1662	1772	1600	1881	176877	SAL	Clun
1811	1881	1750	1890	174289	SAL	Donnington
1740	1773	1730	1881	176877	SAL	Llanfair Waterdine
....	....	1800	1900	135496	SAL	Ludlow
1770	1870	1700	1900	142123	SAL	Prees
1770	1870	1700	1900	142123	SAL	Wem
1779	1829	1600	1779	156914	SAL	West Felton
1800	1860	1780	1900	168947	SAL	West Felton
....	....	1740	1840	177229	SFK	ALL
1787	1816	1650	1780	100013	SFK	Mildebhall
1803	1864	1800	1870	164232	SFK	Stowmarket
1820	1860	1700	1900	142050	SOM	South
1841	1857	....	....	131229	SOM	Bath
1826	1905	1800	1920	119091	SOM	Bristol
1826	1905	1800	1920	119091	SOM	Keynsham
1677	1708	1650	1730	142018	SOM	Rode
1686	....	....	1686	149888	SOM	Taunton
1800	1847	1800	1847	140295	SOM	Uphill
1840	1919	1840	1919	140295	SOM	Weston Super Mare
1897	1946	1845	1897	109878	SRY	Ewell
1882	1882	1862	1904	171646	SRY	Greenwich
1869	....	1700	1900	152714	SRY	Southwark
1850	1868	1840	1870	108251	SRY	Wandsworth
1794	1885	1700	1794	119512	SSX	Ardingly
1813	1908	1760	1813	123412	STS	Birmingham
1830	1871	....	....	118729	STS	Brierly Hill
1650	1750	1500	1800	177180	STS	Forton
1650	1800	1600	1900	177180	STS	Gnosall
....	....	1700	1800	147613	STS	Kingswinford
1865	....	ALL	1865	112771	STS	Rowley Regis
....	....	1500	1850	115142	STS	Rowley Regis
1829	1882	....	1829	163228	STS	Tipton
1770	1850	1700	1992	177180	STS	Tipton
1866	1918	1850	1918	176885	STS	Tunstall
1858	1921	....	....	104884	STS	Walsall
1815	1838	ALL	1815	162825	STS	Wednesbury
1858	....	1858	....	104884	WAR	Aston
1780	1820	1600	1820	130125	WAR	Bearley
1813	1908	1760	1813	123412	WAR	Birmingham
1871	1992	1811	1992	168971	WAR	Birmingham
1829	1992	....	1829	143901	WAR	Coleshill
1864	....	....	....	145742	WAR	Coventry
1833	1851	1833	1851	146617	WAR	Ilmington
1698	1728	1550	1697	131245	WAR	Rowington
1800	....	....	....	148504	WAR	Stratford
1850	1960	ALL	ALL	162469	WIL	South
1827	1845	1800	1850	147575	WIL	Salisbury
1840	1880	....	....	129747	WLS	Amlwch
1836	1854	ALL	1836	176842	WLS	Brymbo
1848	....	....	....	129747	WLS	Llandyfrydog
1805	....	....	....	129747	WLS	Llaneilian
1947	1947	1900	1947	174262	WLS	Maesteg
1904	1904	ALL	....	132349	WLS	Treorcy
1836	1854	ALL	1836	176842	WLS	Wrexham
1855	1900	1800	1900	135968	WLS	???
....	....	1600	....	170313	WOR	Stourport
1800	1992	1811	1992	168971	WOR	Worcester
1900	1930	ALL	ALL	143618	WYK	Castleford
1918	1953	....	....	176885	YKS	Castleford
1928	1992	....	....	126187	???	Bristol
1826	....	....	....	165735	???	Bristol
1878	1878	1870	1890	105333	???	Sunderland

Known From	Known To	Researching From	Researching To	Ref	Cty	Place
WILLIAMSON						
1800	1880	1700	1800	100978	ANS	Montrose
1770	....	....	....	126993	ANS	Montrose
1700	1900	1650	1900	139068	BKM	ALL
1770	....	....	1770	101761	CAI	Bower
1853	1986	....	....	135739	CAI	Wick
1720	1750	1700	1750	103764	CHS	Prestbury
1834	....	?	1840	103934	CHS	Warrington
1750	1992	ALL	1750	134511	DBY	Tibshelf
1870	1915	ALL	ALL	106844	DON	North
1780	....	ALL	ALL	130508	DUR	Sunderland
1838	1857	1700	1837	162000	HAM	Portsmouth
1802	1802	1802	1802	148156	HUN	Sawtry All Saints
1790	1862	1700	1720	146358	KCD	Maryculter
1731	1794	1700	1800	162507	KEN	Lewisham
1731	1794	1700	1800	162507	KEN	Plumstead
1731	1794	1700	1800	162507	KEN	Woolwich
1840	....	1750	1900	130419	KKD	???
1800	1910	1700	1910	158216	LAN	Heaton Mersey
....	1866	....	1866	146919	LAN	Lancaster
1833	....	1833	1920	154474	LAN	Lancaster
1889	1939	ALL	1889	108537	LAN	Liverpool
1775	1796	1700	1800	176451	LAN	Manchester
1813	1861	1750	1813	155500	LAN	Newton Le Willows
1800	1910	1700	1910	158216	LAN	Salford
1833	....	1833	1920	154474	LAN	Warton
1800	1900	1700	1900	135968	LEI	Leicester
1832	1870	1870	1992	128910	LIN	Brattleby
1813	....	ALL	....	104515	LIN	Lenton
1700	1950	....	....	163465	LIN	Rippingale
1787	1832	?	1787	128910	LIN	Willingham By Stow
1870	1920	1500	1920	179655	LND	Kensington
1822	1831	1800	1847	133639	MDX	Marylebone
1827	1895	....	....	132381	MLN	Edinburgh
1795	1851	ALL	1820	129283	NFK	East Barsham
1810	1832	1810	1851	170143	NTH	Thrapston
1823	1992	1800	1900	177326	NTT	Eastwood
1870	1900	1900	1992	128910	NTT	Hucknall Torkard
1790	1841	1650	1790	139386	NTT	Rampton
1807	1850	1700	1807	169757	RUT	Langham
1750	1965	....	....	137820	SHI	Fetlar
1720	1965	....	....	137820	SHI	Mid Yell
1760	1965	....	....	137820	SHI	North Yell
1758	1965	....	....	137820	SHI	Northmavine
1720	1965	....	....	137820	SHI	South Yell
1850	1930	....	....	177334	STS	Tamworth
1832	....	....	....	106852	WIG	???
1780	1860	1841	1920	177350	WYK	Marton
....	....	ALL	ALL	103837	YKS	East
1901	....	....	....	177334	YKS	Bolton On Dearne
1790	1790	....	....	141097	YKS	Elloughton
1790	1852	....	....	103837	YKS	Hull
1817	....	....	1817	158305	YKS	Hull
1772	1844	1750	1772	175951	YKS	Warmfield
1754	1992	1700	1900	177369	YKS	York
WILLIM						
1650	1850	1600	1850	139068	HEF	ALL
WILLING						
1775	1850	1750	1850	177377	DEV	Plymstock
WILLINGHAM						
1860	1914	1860	1880	113611	EYK	Hull
1803	1857	ALL	1875	113611	EYK	Preston
1800	....	....	....	177687	LIN	Yarborough
....	....	1869	1892	145270	LND	Westminster
1800	....	....	....	177687	YKS	Ottringham
WILLINGTON						
....	....	ALL	ALL	177385	ALL	Name Study
1800	1850	1800	1850	113670	AVN	Bristol
ALL	1100	ALL	ALL	150347	DBY	Repton
1820	1850	1700	1820	100978	STS	Wolverhampton
1815	1879	....	1879	130842	WAR	North
1100	1992	ALL	ALL	150347	WAR	Birmingham
WILLIS						
1860	1992	1800	1860	161195	ARM	Mullabrack
1820	1992	1750	1992	161276	BRK	Maidenhead
1600	1600	1570	1625	125032	BRK	Oakley
1795	1795	1600	1850	158399	BRK	Shinfield
....	....	1800	1900	125628	BRK	Stanford In The Vale
1681	1681	1500	1699	174270	DOR	Kinson
1681	1681	1600	1700	174289	DOR	Kinson
1900	1930	ALL	ALL	119180	DUR	North
1700	1800	1700	1800	169781	DUR	Redmarshall
1869	....	1700	1850	161721	DUR	South Shields
WILLIS contd.						
1803	1830	1803	1900	149942	DUR	Stanhope
1724	1810	ALL	1724	154563	DUR	Wolsingham
1800	1899	1800	1899	169781	ERY	Goodmanham
1775	1940	1700	1940	177407	ESS	Billericay
1800	1826	1800	1826	145106	ESS	Burnham On Crouch
1788	1920	1650	1992	140120	ESS	Great Bardfield
1800	1850	1750	1850	131431	GLS	Bristol
1850	1861	1750	1850	155942	HAM	Havant
1850	1861	1750	1850	155942	HAM	Hayling Island
1837	1900	1750	1837	150614	HAM	New Forest
1808	1846	1808	1846	103977	HRT	Kensworth
1843	1864	1843	1900	155942	KEN	Deal
....	....	1770	1870	147613	LAN	Tatham
1896	1992	1860	1895	177393	LND	Hammersmith
1844	1924	1800	1844	169803	LND	Wandsworth
1820	1992	1750	1992	161276	LND	???
1830	1900	1700	1900	113859	MDX	Fulham
1843	1895	1700	1920	164909	MDX	Fulham
1880	1930	1900	1970	138932	MDX	Hammersmith
1843	1895	1700	1920	164909	MDX	Hammersmith
1874	1973	1874	1973	103977	MDX	Hampton Hill
1806	1836	1750	1900	155942	MDX	???
1823	1992	1700	1823	176710	NTH	Wellingborough
1763	1763	1740	1763	147311	NYK	Scalby
1880	ALL	....	....	163392	OXF	???
....	....	1750	1900	165247	SAL	ALL
1900	1950	1900	1950	162515	SFK	Ipswich
1833	1843	1810	1836	155942	SRY	Brixton
1820	1992	ALL	ALL	152226	SSX	ALL
....	....	1750	1900	165247	STS	ALL
1664	1708	1600	1750	160873	STS	Tipton
1835	1900	1700	1835	100978	STS	Wolverhampton
1800	1871	1700	1900	116742	WAR	Fenny Compton
1730	1800	1618	1800	130621	WIL	All Cannings
1762	1806	1700	1762	133604	WIL	Bremhill
1850	....	ALL	1850	106984	WIL	Overton
....	....	1750	1900	165247	WOR	ALL
1776	1860	ALL	1799	123013	WOR	Beckford
1885	....	1885	1992	143944	YKS	ALL
1878	1900	1750	1900	119180	YKS	Keighley
WILLIS-FLEMING						
1611	1949	....	....	104132	HAM	North Stoneham
WILLMAN						
....	....	1750	1850	147613	YKS	Clapham
WILLMORE						
1650	1718	1600	1750	160873	STS	Sedgley
1770	1890	1600	1890	117617	WOR	Spetchley
WILLMOT						
?	?	....	....	177431	BRK	Cookham
?	?	....	....	177431	BRK	Early
?	?	....	....	177431	BRK	Reading
1120	1770	....	....	177431	BRK	Wraysbury
1833	1902	ALL	1833	146226	NFK	Garboldisham
1801	1870	1500	1801	132802	WAR	Birmingham
1800	1880	....	....	177431	WAR	Birmingham
WILLMOTT						
1913	1968	....	1913	166189	BKM	Garrads Cross
1700	1992	1600	1992	154342	GLS	Bitton
1769	1830	1700	1830	148288	HAM	Portsea
1769	1992	ALL	1769	177458	HAM	Portsea
1760	1820	1700	1840	136840	HAM	Portsmouth
1769	1830	1700	1830	148288	HAM	Portsmouth
1871	1992	ALL	1871	177458	LND	East
1860	1875	1800	1900	142999	LND	Southwark
1780	1800	1780	1800	174386	LND	Westminster
1741	1909	1730	1897	150053	NTH	Cotterstock
1740	1770	1740	1770	166596	STS	Dudley
1770	1908	ALL	ALL	166596	WAR	Birmingham
1945	....	1850	1950	157201	WIL	Swindon
WILLMOTT-WOOD						
1900	....	ALL	ALL	112275	DBY	Ripley
WILLN						
1849	1896	....	....	163155	WAR	Hartshill
WILLNER						
1741	1919	1630	1741	160474	LAN	Liverpool
1741	1919	1630	1741	160474	STS	Lichfield
1741	1919	1630	1741	160474	STS	West Bromwich
WILLOCK						
1828	1906	1800	1828	101796	LAN	Ashton Under Lyne
WILLOOUGHBY						
1769	1800	ALL	1769	147362	DBY	Barlborough
1769	1800	ALL	1769	147362	DBY	Duffield

Known From	To	Researching From	To	Ref	Cty	Place
WILLOTT						
1812	1992	ALL	1812	169692	CHS	Macclesfield
....	....	1770	1830	179213	CHS	Macclesfield
WILLOUGHBY						
1400	1500	1350	1500	154881	ALL	ALL
1700	1906	1650	1720	178845	CON	Illogan
1847	1992	1800	1846	129062	IRL	Down
1879	1963	ALL	1880	160733	LAN	North
1620	....	....	....	156647	LIN	Brocklesbury
1860	1928	1800	1992	165603	SRY	Limpsfield
WILLOWS						
....	1790	1500	1860	175072	LIN	ALL
1835	....	1750	....	177466	LIN	Billinghay
....	....	1600	1900	177725	LIN	Hannah
WILLOX						
1880	1992	1600	1880	146137	ABD	Buchan
1799	1964	ALL	1799	106909	ABD	Coldhome
WILLRING						
1765	1820	1650	1750	171891	BKM	West Wycombe
WILLS						
1754	1861	1754	1992	172596	CON	Paul
1900	1992	1750	1900	146374	CON	St Hilary
1783	1834	1700	1783	174688	CON	St Mellions
....	....	1700	1799	171794	CUL	Holme Cultram
1856	1889	....	....	177482	DEV	Brixham
1650	1740	1580	1760	105333	DEV	Buckland In The Moor
1650	1740	1580	1760	105333	DEV	Christow
1820	1910	1700	1820	104418	DEV	Dartmouth
....	....	1700	1840	101931	DEV	Devonport
1830	1860	1800	1900	136905	DEV	Dunsford
1650	1740	1580	1760	105333	DEV	Holne
1650	1740	1580	1760	105333	DEV	Ilsington
1558	1992	....	....	177474	DEV	Ilsington
1700	1900	1700	1900	114790	DEV	Kenton
1450	1992	....	....	177474	DEV	Lustleigh
1650	1740	1580	1760	105333	DEV	Lydford
....	....	1600	1730	161543	DEV	Ottery St Mary
1796	1992	1700	1850	122688	DEV	Plymouth
1755	1820	1700	1755	161896	DEV	Plymouth
1796	1992	....	1796	177504	DEV	Slapton
1800	1934	....	....	177482	DEV	South Brent
1796	1992	1700	1850	122688	DEV	South Ham
1734	1881	ALL	1850	177482	DEV	South Milton
1767	1823	?	1767	136905	DEV	Tedburn St Mary
1850	1900	1800	1900	162272	DEV	Torquay
1921	1934	1900	1934	177482	DEV	Torquay
1650	1740	1580	1760	105333	DEV	Widecombe In The Moor
....	....	1870	1920	110329	DOR	Dorchester
1579	1689	....	....	165999	GLS	Brockworth
....	1846	....	....	140767	IRL	???
1751	1751	1725	1812	107360	NTH	Duston
1798	....	....	....	148156	NTH	Upper Heyford
1849	....	ALL	ALL	158690	NTT	Radcliffe
1830	1900	....	....	141798	RFW	Linwood
1895	1992	1700	1895	111775	SOM	Merriot
1650	1761	1650	1770	171654	SOM	West Chinnock
1865	1900	1800	1950	112089	???	???
WILLSON						
....	1798	1700	1800	177938	DEV	Crediton
1700	1750	1600	1700	113204	DOW	Purdysburn
1799	1906	ALL	1799	177512	HRT	Watford
1765	1900	1765	1900	135968	LEI	Slawston
1646	1765	1600	1700	101575	LIN	Castle Bytham
1646	1765	1600	1700	101575	LIN	Thurnby By Bourne
....	1765	1600	1765	135968	NTH	Cottingham
1790	1870	1600	1790	111198	NYK	Thornton Dale
WILLSTEAD						
1795	1810	ALL	ALL	149489	HAM	Portsmouth
WILLY						
....	....	1740	1760	159115	DEV	Kentisbeare
1830	1840	ALL	1830	141224	SOM	Bath
WILMER						
1750	1880	1700	1750	140317	HUN	Little Raveley
WILMHURST						
1651	1718	1600	1750	167002	SXE	Warbleton
WILMINGTON						
1880	1890	1840	1880	135429	DEV	Exmouth
1880	1890	1840	1880	135429	DEV	Littleham
WILMOT						
1700	1780	1600	1700	155500	DBY	Repton
1812	1856	ALL	1874	126918	LND	Holborn
1812	1856	ALL	1874	126918	LND	Lambeth

Known From	To	Researching From	To	Ref	Cty	Place
WILMOT contd.						
1758	1805	1700	1805	156582	MDX	Hanwell
1840	1860	1600	1992	112828	SOM	Congresbury
WILMOTT						
1775	1775	ALL	1800	151815	CAM	Barrington
WILMSHURST						
1808	1808	....	....	144355	KEN	East
1800	1840	....	....	122130	SSX	Brighton
1800	1900	....	....	122130	SSX	Buxted
1880	1950	....	....	122130	SSX	Rotherfield
1930	1992	....	....	122130	SSX	Wadhurst
WILSDON						
1851	1950	1700	1900	119040	GLS	Clapton
1773	1955	....	....	178381	GLS	Clapton
1844	1992	1690	1844	177539	OXF	Eynsham
1749	....	1650	1749	178381	OXF	???
WILSHAW						
....	....	....	1910	163031	SYK	Sheffield
WILSHER						
1820	1880	1700	1900	138517	HEF	???
1760	1800	1760	1800	126276	WIL	Chippenham
WILSHERE						
1750	1900	1700	1800	168750	HRT	Hitchin
WILSHIN						
1800	1940	....	....	127884	MDX	Pinner
WILSHIRE						
1753	....	ALL	1753	158445	WIL	Melksham
WILSON						
1843	1919	1700	1843	157996	ABD	Glenbervie
....	....	1700	1850	165239	ANT	Cullybackey
....	....	ALL	ALL	126098	ANT	???
1800	1992	1500	1900	159956	AYR	Ayr
1809	1830	1700	1900	179574	AYR	Ayr
1750	1810	1750	1810	177768	AYR	Beith
1837	1900	1700	1837	111708	AYR	Cumnock
1825	1845	....	....	171654	AYR	Kilmarnock
1865	1930	1800	1865	179116	AYR	Mid
1798	1963	ALL	ALL	106860	AYR	Monkton
1890	1920	1850	1950	126586	AYR	Muirkirk
1765	1992	1500	1765	143073	BAN	Cullen
1782	1840	1650	1750	114545	BDF	Cardington
1852	1898	....	1852	165484	BDF	Edworth
1782	1840	1650	1750	114545	BDF	Elstow
1903	1956	1880	1903	124095	BDF	???
1850	1920	1850	1900	177660	BEW	Greenlaw
1800	1830	1700	1830	115681	BEW	Paxton
1840	1870	1800	1880	145300	BKM	Tingewick
1867	....	1700	1992	149659	BRK	Hagbourne
1810	....	....	....	132381	BUT	Ruthesay
....	1749	....	1749	137405	CAM	Barrington
1654	1940	....	....	128996	CAM	Thorney
1811	1867	1700	1810	135348	CAM	Wisbech
1865	1900	1865	1930	114472	CHS	Runcorn
?	....	?	?	177679	CMA	ALL
1850	1900	ALL	1992	133396	CMA	???
1847	....	....	....	131288	CUL	Carlisle
1880	1930	1856	1873	135410	CUL	Carlisle
....	1688	1600	1688	117234	CUL	Eglisfield
1849	1909	1800	1900	102962	CUL	Egremont
1875	1885	1850	1885	130036	CUL	Maryport
1788	1870	....	....	164151	CUL	Thackthwaite
1788	1870	....	....	164151	CUL	Westward
1692	1845	ALL	1900	165654	DBY	Little Hucklow
1700	1884	1600	1890	124788	DBY	Thornhill
....	....	ALL	1780	178403	DBY	???
1860	1890	1700	1940	177717	DEV	Torquay
1721	1747	ALL	1721	154563	DEV	Woodbury
1685	1992	?	1685	177806	DFS	Glenvernock
....	....	1700	1830	111708	DFS	Kirkconnel
....	....	1500	1750	138614	DFS	Lochmaben
1775	1981	ALL	1981	153680	DFS	New Abbey
1708	1732	ALL	1708	154563	DOR	Wyke Regis
1804	1920	ALL	1900	174157	DOW	Tullynasoo
1740	1790	1740	1790	106305	DOW	???
1850	1900	1800	1850	121339	DUR	Darlington
1827	1852	1800	1900	132454	DUR	Gateshead
1860	1900	1800	1992	162620	DUR	Gateshead
1853	1881	1600	1853	169595	DUR	Gateshead
1841	....	1700	1850	161721	DUR	South Shields
1728	1864	ALL	1728	154563	DUR	Teesdale
1728	1864	ALL	1728	154563	DUR	Weardale
1790	1830	1790	1830	177660	ELN	Prestonpans
1800	1899	....	1800	177695	ESS	Rochford
1810	1870	1700	1810	107344	ESS	Widdington

WILSON contd.

Known From	To	Researching From	To	Ref	Cty	Place
1778	1932	1750	1900	117781	EYK	Cherry Burton
....	1830	....	1851	103349	FER	Enniskillin
1800	1992	1700	1800	154016	FIF	Cupar
1750	....	ALL	ALL	130508	FIF	St Monance
1719	1758	1700	1800	169218	FIF	St Monance
1851	1856	1845	1851	135410	GLS	Bristol
1850	1900	ALL	ALL	140740	GLS	Charlton Kings
1700	1735	ALL	ALL	154067	GLS	Stanton
1830	1861	1800	1992	144908	HAM	Gosport
1826	1864	1780	1826	170968	HAM	Portsea
1820	1830	1820	1900	109533	HAM	Portsmouth
1860	1987	1843	1987	177547	HAM	Portsmouth
1880	1987	ALL	ALL	177547	HAM	Southampton
1800	1880	1790	1900	142360	HRT	Rickmansworth
1766	1924	1750	1924	159581	HRT	Shenley
1725	1810	1700	1850	139386	HUN	Hemingford Abbots
....	....	....	....	177628	IOM	???
1715	....	1600	1715	117234	IRL	Antrim
1740	1800	1600	1800	154342	IRL	Waterford
1790	1820	1790	1820	121339	IRL	???
1899	1992	1800	1950	129976	KEN	Ashford
1800	1834	1800	1834	108251	KEN	Faversham
....	....	1830	1841	115886	KEN	Tonbridge
1841	1894	1850	1992	115886	KEN	Tunbridge Wells
1799	1992	1770	1798	108227	KRS	Portmoak
1850	....	1850	....	109347	LAN	Accrington
1860	1992	1841	1992	177636	LAN	Balckburn
1920	1926	1863	1926	151041	LAN	Bootle
1856	1958	1837	1856	166464	LAN	Bowick
1844	1917	1700	1844	173711	LAN	Chorley
1790	1860	1600	1790	102571	LAN	Dalton
1721	1798	1600	1721	151254	LAN	Kirkby Laythorpe
1851	1861	ALL	ALL	126098	LAN	Liverpool
1804	1842	1750	1850	178004	LAN	Manchester
1800	1850	1750	1800	114472	LAN	Penketh
1790	1860	1600	1790	102571	LAN	Pennington
1854	1930	1700	1854	134015	LAN	Preston
1830	1881	1800	1900	166081	LAN	Preston
1784	1841	1700	1841	177636	LAN	Ribchester
1920	1926	1863	1926	151041	LAN	Seaforth
1845	1869	1845	1900	165654	LAN	Stockport
1673	1690	1599	1673	141291	LAN	Ulverston
....	....	1800	1880	135410	LAN	Walton Le Dale
1806	1850	1700	1812	149098	LEI	Leicester
1798	1852	1798	1992	151254	LIN	Blankney
1814	1851	1780	1814	177555	LIN	Dunsby
1801	1992	1801	1992	177687	LIN	Louth
1750	....	1600	1800	162620	LIN	Spilsby
1841	1883	1700	1841	134732	LIN	Thorganby
....	....	1800	1860	114782	LIN	Wellingore
1850	1980	1600	1850	112097	LIN	???
1780	1840	1750	1992	122416	LKS	Barony
1760	1780	....	....	171654	LKS	Cambusnethan
1801	1848	....	....	127140	LKS	Douglas
....	....	ALL	1836	119326	LKS	Glasgow
1848	1909	....	....	127140	LKS	Glasgow
1840	....	....	....	132381	LKS	Glasgow
1720	1780	1680	1740	128244	LKS	Lesmahagow
1830	1992	ALL	1900	155713	LKS	Stonehouse
1820	1860	....	1860	116866	LKS	???
1859	1875	1858	1891	115886	LND	Central
1861	1876	1858	1891	115886	LND	South
....	....	ALL	ALL	118400	LND	Bow
1861	1924	1800	1900	153990	LND	Limehouse
1840	1950	1700	1840	165182	LND	Poplar
....	....	1800	ALL	149187	LND	St Pancras
1800	1850	1700	1800	139092	LND	Stepney
1861	1944	1850	1880	114529	LND	???
....	....	?	?	179159	LND	???
1851	1885	1885	1992	146560	LTN	Edinburgh
1861	....	1850	1870	163775	MDX	Bethnal Green
1862	1900	1700	1900	177717	MDX	Bloomsbury
1903	1956	1880	1903	124095	MDX	Hounslow
1850	1850	1800	1850	126586	MDX	London
1920	1960	....	....	130230	MDX	London
1881	1992	1700	1992	177733	MDX	Marylebone
1857	1885	1857	1885	136980	MDX	Paddington
1805	1880	1750	1900	148652	MDX	Westminster
....	....	ALL	1828	119326	MLN	Craighall
1869	....	1860	1900	115967	MLN	Edinburgh
1832	1835	....	....	149632	MLN	Edinburgh
....	....	1730	1810	166294	MLN	Edinburgh
1778	1789	1700	1800	171662	MLN	Edinburgh

WILSON contd.

Known From	To	Researching From	To	Ref	Cty	Place
....	....	ALL	1828	119326	MLN	Inveresk
....	....	ALL	1828	119326	MLN	Newton
1825	....	....	....	175358	MOG	New Bliss
1828	....	1700	1885	131423	MOR	Duffus
1710	1743	1670	1710	160458	NBL	Bywell
1780	1876	....	....	146676	NBL	Chatton
1839	1878	ALL	1839	166847	NBL	South Shields
1790	1940	1600	1800	101834	NFK	West
1800	....	....	....	135488	NFK	Emneth
1778	1850	1600	1778	156779	NFK	Flitcham
1819	1895	1700	1850	125628	NFK	Norwich
....	....	1750	1850	106356	NFK	???
1881	1911	ALL	ALL	118885	NRY	Middlesborough
1730	1760	....	....	110159	NRY	Yarm
1600	1850	1850	1992	129763	NTH	North
1770	1796	....	1770	175404	NTH	Maidford
1800	1900	....	1800	177695	NTH	Northampton
1660	1750	1640	1800	168327	NTH	Titchmarsh
1804	1865	1750	1865	145300	NTH	Towcester
1800	1850	ALL	1850	177571	NTH	Winwick
1850	1980	1600	1850	112097	NTT	Cossall
1750	1846	ALL	1800	178411	NTT	Shelford
1790	1840	1780	1840	154210	NYK	Bedale
1820	1880	....	....	177776	NYK	Coverdale
1780	1810	1700	1780	121339	NYK	Felixkirk
1700	1850	....	....	177725	NYK	Kirkby Mooreside
1740	1800	1650	1740	121339	NYK	Manfield
1690	1800	1600	1690	177776	NYK	Marske In Swalesdale
1750	1800	....	....	177725	NYK	Nunnington
1786	1786	1780	1800	141046	PER	Kinloch
1786	1786	1780	1800	141046	PER	Lethendy
....	....	....	1860	116866	RFW	Paisley
1870	1890	1820	1870	150029	RFW	Pollok
1850	1900	1700	1850	150371	ROX	Annan
1700	1900	....	....	150371	ROX	Castleton
1750	1770	1700	1750	178470	ROX	Eccles
1775	1841	1770	1850	119725	ROX	Hownam
1880	1920	1900	1920	177660	ROX	Kelso
1810	1860	ALL	1860	149063	ROX	Sprouston
1770	1880	1770	1880	133795	SCT	Cumbernauld
....	....	ALL	1890	173045	SCT	Dunfermline
1820	1900	1820	1900	177814	SCT	East Kilbridge
1920	1926	1863	1926	151041	SCT	Glasgow
1817	1860	1750	1860	149632	SEL	Selkirk
1830	1992	1750	1830	179140	SFK	Chelmondiston
1832	1903	1700	1832	179183	SFK	Chelmondiston
1822	1888	1700	1822	165298	SFK	Hadleigh
....	....	1796	1837	137723	SFK	Horham
1686	1750	....	....	129747	SFK	Ipswich
1822	1888	1700	1822	165298	SFK	Washbrook
1864	....	....	....	175358	SRY	Nunhead
1830	1881	1800	1992	115681	SRY	Woking
....	....	1740	1835	115886	SSX	East
1760	1977	....	....	127698	SSX	Brighton
1776	1826	1740	1830	115886	SSX	Guestling
1820	1992	1700	1820	177601	SSX	Guestling-Ore
1871	1891	1891	1940	109533	SSX	Rye
1737	1769	1567	1737	127698	SSX	Shoreham By Sea
1750	1850	1750	1850	129836	STS	Audley
1822	1874	1800	1874	125288	STS	Stone
1730	1770	1650	1730	149977	STS	Stowe By Chartley
1840	1992	ALL	1846	176060	STS	Tamworth
1841	1992	1800	1900	166960	TYR	Kilskeery
1819	....	1800	1841	169625	TYR	Moorefield
1813	1829	....	....	117560	WAR	Birmingham
1800	1992	1700	1992	177652	WAR	Birmingham
1800	1992	1700	1992	177652	WAR	Bordesley
1796	1992	1750	1796	175404	WAR	Dunchurch
1815	1825	1800	1840	154067	WAR	Edgbaston
1740	1861	ALL	ALL	154067	WAR	Shipston
1840	1992	ALL	1846	176060	WAR	Tamworth
1783	1817	1700	1783	135151	WES	Dufton
1825	....	1825	....	109347	WES	Kendal
1786	1791	1558	1786	141291	WES	Kendal
....	....	1700	1750	158240	WES	Longsleddale
1625	1782	1600	1761	102571	WES	Orton
1870	1992	....	1870	100064	WIC	Glen Of Imaal
1850	1992	1750	1850	167398	WIG	Kirk Maiden
1850	1992	1750	1850	167398	WIG	Stoneykirk
1852	1970	1850	1970	145009	WOR	Conderton
1860	1880	ALL	....	120626	WOR	Dudley
....	....	1700	1800	170313	WOR	Stourport

Known From	To	Researching From	To	Ref	Cty	Place
WILSON contd.						
ALL	ALL	ALL	ALL	111066	WRY	ALL
1796	1836	1796	1836	149403	WYK	Crofton
1850	1992	1700	1850	100803	WYK	Halifax
....	....	ALL	1842	111384	WYK	Hunslet
....	....	ALL	1842	111384	WYK	Rothwell
....	....	ALL	1842	111384	WYK	Wakefield
....	....	....	....	177628	YKS	ALL
1819	1970	....	....	168424	YKS	Ackworth
....	....	ALL	1850	146315	YKS	Austwick
1795	1939	ALL	1830	115215	YKS	Bransdale
....	1824	1700	1824	168424	YKS	Brotherton
1800	1851	1835	1841	158712	YKS	Ecclesfield
1825	1861	1820	1870	123250	YKS	Halifax
1850	1860	1600	1930	172863	YKS	Harrogate
1830	1860	1700	1850	126772	YKS	Helmsley
1800	1980	1750	1800	128538	YKS	Hull
1800	1860	1800	....	152021	YKS	Hull
1801	....	....	....	177687	YKS	Hull
1809	1891	ALL	1809	158445	YKS	Humbleton
1863	1992	1700	1833	135011	YKS	Kirbymoorside
1888	1888	ALL	1925	146315	YKS	Leeds
1846	1888	1800	1850	175587	YKS	Morley
1793	1800	1700	1800	132454	YKS	Old Malton
1760	1992	....	1760	144363	YKS	Ripon
1780	1860	1700	1780	123102	YKS	Rotherham
1843	1843	1800	1851	160636	YKS	Rotherham
....	....	1820	1992	106003	YKS	Scarborough
1809	1891	ALL	1809	158445	YKS	Selby
1848	1880	1800	1848	177393	YKS	Selby
1780	1860	1700	1780	123102	YKS	Sheffield
1819	....	....	....	161136	YKS	Sheffield
1753	1787	1720	1800	160873	YKS	Sutton On The Forest
....	....	1800	1820	177393	YKS	Sutton Upon Forest
1823	....	ALL	1823	150924	YKS	Thirsk
1800	1841	....	....	102946	YKS	Tockwith
1800	1877	1790	1805	171670	YKS	Wakefield
1791	....	1791	....	140767	YKS	York
1810	1840	1700	1810	158208	YKS	York
1850	1860	1600	1930	172863	YKS	York
....	....	1700	ALL	111724	???	Arbroath
?	?	?	?	165484	???	Bigglesworth
1820	1860	1820	1860	177768	???	Bothwell
1790	1916	1790	1916	177768	???	Glasgow
1899	1923	1899	1923	111546	???	Liverpool
1850	1900	ALL	1992	133396	???	Newcastle
?	?	?	?	103772	???	???
WILTCHER						
1874	1992	ALL	ALL	170860	DUR	Sunderland
WILTON						
....	....	ALL	ALL	177849	ALL	Name Study
....	....	1700	1770	171638	AVN	Langridge
....	....	1770	1820	171638	AVN	Swanswick
1680	1750	....	1680	149888	CON	Linkinhorne
1700	1860	1860	1900	177849	CON	North Petherwyn
?	?	?	?	136999	CON	St Columb Minor
1820	1850	1700	1850	103772	DBY	Horsley
1700	1860	1860	1900	177849	DEV	North Petherwyn
1730	1760	1700	1850	155896	GLS	Gloucester
1835	....	....	....	153885	HAM	Michelmersh
1766	1984	1700	1900	122610	LND	Stratford
....	....	ALL	1880	178403	LND	???
1802	1832	....	....	112887	WIL	Bradford On Avon
1802	1832	....	....	112887	WIL	Warminster
WILTSHIRE						
1807	1825	1780	1850	171441	BRK	Buckland
1752	1879	....	1920	171441	BRK	Stanford In The Vale
1775	1850	1600	1850	130125	DOR	Chaldon Hg
1770	1800	1750	1800	136840	DOR	Wool
1720	1760	1675	1740	138150	GLS	South
1854	1938	1862	1938	133175	GLS	Bristol
1780	1900	1700	1780	163449	HAM	Romsey
1748	1992	ALL	1748	111155	LND	East
1901	....	1895	1905	171441	MDX	Greenford
1700	1850	....	....	152978	WIL	Calne
1760	1800	1760	1800	126276	WIL	Chippenham
1827	1867	1800	1867	128694	WIL	Devizes
1700	1850	....	....	152978	WIL	Swindon
....	....	1766	....	109673	WIL	Woodborough
....	1852	ALL	ALL	143529	WOR	Severnstoke
WIMBOW						
1804	1828	....	....	131229	GLS	Hawkesbury

Known From	To	Researching From	To	Ref	Cty	Place
WIMPENNY						
....	....	1500	1700	133760	ALL	ALL
1759	1992	1700	1759	133760	YKS	Holmfirth
WINBORN						
....	1700	....	....	174564	SSX	Bexhill
WINCH						
1700	1760	1600	1760	109061	DEV	North
1811	1899	1700	1811	177881	KEN	Queenborough
1772	1853	....	....	101028	SFK	Ickworth
1670	1755	....	....	119431	SXE	ALL
WINCHCOMB						
....	....	ALL	ALL	152285	ALL	ALL
WINCHCOMBE						
1880	1992	....	....	132136	OXF	Winchcombe
WINCHESTER						
1868	1992	1600	1700	177938	CON	Millbrook
1790	1794	....	1790	164321	KEN	Ashford
1818	1857	....	1818	164321	KEN	Dover
1815	1881	ALL	ALL	177903	MOR	St Andrew Lhanbryde
1850	1992	....	....	177911	OXF	???
1780	1895	1800	1950	104914	SHI	Delting
1750	1965	....	....	137820	SHI	Fetlar
1720	1965	....	....	137820	SHI	Mid Yell
1760	1965	....	....	137820	SHI	North Yell
1758	1965	....	....	137820	SHI	Northmavine
1720	1965	....	....	137820	SHI	South Yell
1833	1920	1830	1920	142018	SOM	Stoke St Gregory
1885	1885	1885	1885	175196	SRY	Godstone
1600	1992	1700	1830	100536	SSX	???
WINCHWORTH						
1610	1686	ALL	1610	169730	HAM	Church Oakley
WINDEBANK						
....	....	ALL	ALL	161063	ALL	Name Study
1829	1992	ALL	ALL	172219	ALL	ALL
1763	....	....	1780	171441	HAM	Wield
WINDER						
....	....	ALL	ALL	177954	ALL	Name Study
1720	1992	1320	1720	177954	CMA	ALL
1720	1992	1320	1720	177954	LAN	ALL
1850	....	1850	1900	129712	MDX	London
....	1830	1750	1850	177946	SRY	Horsleydown
WINDLE						
1820	1930	1788	1930	129313	LAN	Manchester
1801	1967	1750	1801	128368	LND	St George Hanover Square
1801	1967	1750	1801	128368	NTT	East Retford
....	....	1700	1820	129313	WIL	Wilton
1787	1825	1730	1790	162396	YKS	Kirkby Malham
....	....	1700	1860	129364	YKS	???
WINDLEY						
1717	....	....	1717	101761	NTT	Nottingham
WINDMILL						
1760	....	1730	1800	124796	BKM	Leckhamstead
1600	1700	1500	1850	177180	BKM	Northall
1774	....	1700	1800	124796	NTH	Yardley Gobion
WINDON						
1790	1992	1500	1790	174467	ALL	ALL
WINDOW						
1800	1860	1538	1800	154792	GLS	Cotswolds
WINDOWS						
1850	1860	1820	1841	133175	GLS	Pucklechurch
1850	1950	1750	1850	114383	STS	Wolverhampton
WINDRAM						
....	....	1790	1820	132241	SCT	???
1820	1840	1700	1820	132241	YKS	Saddleworth
WINDRIDGE						
1640	1992	ALL	ALL	170097	ALL	ALL
1700	1850	1850	1930	154644	GLS	Cheltenham
1700	1850	1850	1930	154644	GLS	Gloucester
WINDROSS						
?	....	....	....	169358	LAN	Leigh
?	....	....	....	169358	YKS	???
WINDSOR						
....	....	1830	1900	109894	DOR	Bere Regis
1858	1895	1750	1858	163740	SRY	Southwark
1871	1958	1066	1992	108669	WYK	Leeds
WINES						
1848	1881	1800	1890	144797	SOM	St Petherton
WINFIELD						
....	....	....	....	142085	LEI	Castle Donington
1825	1856	?	1856	164976	NTT	Burton Joyce
1901	1960	1800	1901	109649	YKS	Huddersfield
WINFREY						
1774	1818	....	1774	101761	YKS	Tickhill

Known Researching
From To From To Ref Cty Place

WING
1723 1940 .... 128996 CAM Thorney
1796 1896 1796 1896 103977 HRT Ridge
1796 1896 1796 1896 103977 HRT Shenley
1796 1896 1796 1896 103977 HRT South Mimms
.... 1550 1632 143138 KEN Sandwich At Hamburg
.... 1834 1830 1840 128961 LND ???
.... ALL ALL 121991 NFK ALL
1700 1945 1700 1840 164437 NFK ALL
.... ALL ALL 121991 SFK ALL
.... 1550 1632 143138 ??? Fleisching
WINGAT
1778 1841 1700 1850 177970 RFW Glasgow
WINGATE
1864 1865 1800 1900 177970 AYR Dalry
1950 1992 .... 177970 CON ???
1800 1850 1700 1800 145017 DEV ALL
1840 1900 1800 1992 133450 DEV Kingsbridge
1845 1854 1700 1900 177970 DNB Glasgow
.... 1860 ALL 175625 GLS Burton St Michael
1844 1952 1700 1900 177970 LKS North
1870 1992 1865 1992 177970 NBL Ashington
1778 1841 1700 1900 177970 RFW Glasgow
.... 1700 1860 119369 SOM Bridgewater
1862 1866 1700 1900 177970 STI Slamanan
1925 1992 .... 177970 YKS ???
WINGFIELD
.... 1750 1880 162361 NFK Old Buckenham
.... 1600 1880 162361 NFK ???
.... 1700 1770 178411 NTT Oxton
1400 1500 1400 1500 154881 SFK Letheringham
.... 1750 1880 162361 SFK Metfield
1800 1860 .... 162361 SFK Wingfield
WINGHAM
1870 1900 ALL ALL 177989 LND East
1870 1900 ALL ALL 177989 LND North
1830 1900 ALL ALL 177989 SSX Brighton
WINGRAVE
1901 1907 .... 132616 LND Fulham
WINGROVE
.... ALL ALL 177997 ALL Name Study
.... ALL ALL 177997 ALL ALL
1716 1850 1716 1800 148601 WIL North Bradley
WININGHAM
.... 1780 1850 113514 EYK Beverley
WINKLE
1850 1880 1850 1880 163449 GLA Swansea
1820 1880 1700 1820 163449 STS Burslem
1882 1920 1850 1930 165441 STS Hanley
WINKWORTH
? ? .... 169544 HAM Basingstoke
1821 1841 1821 1841 173762 HAM Brown Candover
1583 1663 ALL 1633 169730 HAM Church Oakley
WINN
1790 1860 ALL 1835 113611 EYK Hornsea
1835 1860 1835 1860 113611 EYK Hull
.... 1770 1820 147079 LIN ALL
1820 1980 1750 1900 147079 LND ALL
1846 1869 1800 1846 107093 LND Shoreditch
? .... ? .... 104337 MDX Mile End Old Town
1856 1926 ALL 1856 151424 YKS Bradford
1893 1975 ALL 1893 147060 YKS Castleford
1764 1775 .... 173916 YKS ???
WINNALL
1700 1880 1700 1880 139807 ALL ALL
WINNE
1820 1840 1700 1840 106313 BRK Wantage
WINNELL
1812 1992 1500 1890 151483 YKS Shefield
WINNER
.... ALL ALL 173398 NFK Sporle
1901 1992 ALL ALL 173398 YKS Middlesborough
WINNEY
1820 1840 1700 1840 106313 BRK Wantage
1810 .... 1750 1850 102016 SFK Assington
WINNING
1850 1920 1750 1850 173258 LKS Lanark
WINNISTER
1837 1986 .... 158747 ALL ALL
WINROW
.... ALL ALL 170151 ALL Name Study
WINSCOM
1700 1992 ALL 1700 107050 HAM Winchester
1700 1992 ALL 1700 107050 IOW ALL

Known Researching
From To From To Ref Cty Place

WINSER
1750 1850 .... 141909 KEN Tenterden
.... 1890 158763 SRY London
WINSHIP
1720 1830 1500 1800 108618 HAM Portsea
WINSKILL
1768 1768 ALL 1768 154563 CUL Alston
WINSLAIDE
.... 1840 1869 168777 MDX Hampton
WINSLOW
1777 1808 1750 1992 156698 LND Aldersgate
1750 1950 1700 1900 156701 LND London
1850 1870 1800 1880 135429 SOM Bath
1810 1992 .... 115258 WIL Trowbridge
WINSOR
1750 1939 1750 1900 163406 DEV Broadhempston
1840 1880 1700 1840 133493 DEV Stoke Damerel
.... 1750 1970 178004 MON ALL
1805 1965 1800 1965 178004 MON Pontypool
.... 1800 1900 153281 SOM Bridgewater
1775 1775 1700 1775 147575 SOM Broadway
.... 1750 1850 178004 SOM Nailsea
1830 1992 ALL 1830 171468 SOM Yeovil
WINSPEAR
1872 .... 127701 YKS Guisborough
WINSPER
1817 1992 1740 1817 161284 STS Bilston
1500 1800 1500 1800 100420 WAR ALL
WINSTANLEY
1820 1850 1600 1992 176494 LAN ALL
1720 1950 ALL ALL 126497 LAN Wigan
1750 1960 1700 1900 126500 LAN Wigan
.... 1760 .... 112429 LAN ???
.... ALL 1800 164631 MDX London
WINSTER
1733 1812 1670 1812 169552 WES Middleton
WINSTONE
1800 1850 1750 1850 106631 GLS Stroud
1806 1870 ALL ALL 153516 SOM Failand
1806 1870 ALL ALL 153516 SOM Wick St Lawrence
ALL 1797 .... 170178 WIL Wanborough
WINTER
1700 1860 .... 102946 DEV Buckfastleigh
1750 1880 1500 1750 104140 DEV Ugborough
1800 1900 ALL ALL 174637 DOR Portland
1816 1820 1816 1825 115797 ESS Pagusham
1750 1800 1775 1800 153249 GLS Bristol
1850 1870 1850 1945 138193 GLS Dymock
1835 1875 1800 1835 155691 KEN Dover
.... 1860 1950 147613 LAN Barrow In Furness
1825 1956 1700 1825 165581 LIN Fulbeck
1716 1716 1550 1715 102830 LIN North Scarle
1880 1900 1800 1930 135542 LND Southwark
1845 1992 .... 152218 NBL Berwick On Tweed
1835 1856 ALL 1835 166847 NBL Berwick On Tweed
1815 1835 1700 1900 158666 NFK North Wold
1804 1889 1700 1900 107980 NFK Norwich
.... 1700 1900 140627 NFK Norwich
1800 1881 1750 1880 158658 NFK Norwich
1830 1861 1700 1830 102393 NYK Glaisdale
1830 1861 1700 1830 102393 NYK Lythe
.... 1800 1992 147613 OXF ALL
.... 1700 1800 147613 OXF Chadlington
1845 1992 .... 152218 SCT ???
1730 1894 1700 1851 129194 SFK East
ALL ALL ALL ALL 178020 SOM ALL
.... 178020 SOM ???
1841 1970 1800 1900 101508 SSX Brighton
1841 1970 1800 1900 101508 SSX Denton
1713 1880 1550 1712 156140 SSX Hastings
1876 1948 1800 1876 174807 SSX Twineham
1860 1900 .... 102946 YKS Bradford
1815 1853 1700 1853 178012 YKS Leeds
1750 1800 1750 1800 167924 YKS Nunburnholme
1750 1900 1750 1900 167924 YKS Pocklington
ALL ALL .... 137332 ??? ???
WINTERBOTTOM
1780 1812 ALL ALL 117145 LAN Bolton
1780 1812 ALL ALL 117145 LAN Oldham
1805 1843 1785 1805 134309 LAN Oldham
WINTERBOURN
1750 1800 1700 1800 144657 NTT Thorpe
WINTERBOURNE
.... ALL ALL 167827 LAN ALL

Known From	To	Researching From	To	Ref	Cty	Place
WINTERS						
1850	1900	....	....	139971	MAY	Ballycastle
1795	1971	1895	1992	140635	WAR	Leamington Spa
1000	1971	1000	1992	140635	WAR	Stratford On Avon
WINTERSON						
....	....	1800	1900	132489	SOM	Bristol
....	....	1800	1900	132489	SOM	Fishponds
WINTERTON						
1764	1992	ALL	1992	100102	CAM	Whittlesey
1714	1832	....	....	139831	LEI	Barrow Upon Soar
WINTHROP						
1755	1825	1700	1755	152196	WES	Witherslack
WINTINOR						
....	....	1760	1790	103713	BDF	Elstow
WINTLE						
1760	1800	1700	1850	155896	GLS	Westbury On Severn
1840	1845	1750	1850	163244	MDX	London
1870	1992	1800	1900	122610	WMD	Birmingham
WINTOM						
1851	1899	1800	1920	146358	STD	Glasgow
WINTOUR						
1830	1860	1800	1992	172782	NTT	Barton
ALL	ALL	....	....	137332	???	???
WINTRIP						
1870	1900	1800	1870	123625	DUR	South Shields
WINUP						
1881	1881	ALL	ALL	105856	MDX	???
1881	1881	ALL	ALL	105856	SRY	???
WINWARD						
1934	1992	1800	1934	116823	YKS	Middlesbrough
WINWICK						
1800	1876	....	....	137936	SHI	Unst
WINWOOD						
1861	1881	1841	1861	116637	DUR	Monk Heseldon
1733	....	....	....	131229	SAL	Alverley
1731	....	....	....	131229	SAL	Chelmarsh
1799	1841	1600	1799	116637	SFK	Lackford
1827	1841	1600	1827	116637	SFK	West Stow
1735	1808	....	....	131229	WOR	Ombersley
1825	1866	....	....	131229	WOR	Worcester
WINYARD						
....	....	ALL	ALL	178039	ALL	Name Study
WINZAR						
1749	1834	1700	1950	110205	DOR	Broadwey
WIRE						
1843	....	1843	....	102954	LND	Leyton
WIRNHAM						
1400	1992	1400	1992	178918	ALL	ALL
WIRONAM						
1400	1992	1400	1992	178918	BRK	ALL
WISBY						
1840	1880	1750	1840	151165	ESS	Rochford
....	....	ALL	ALL	106526	LND	Fulham
WISDOM						
....	....	ALL	ALL	178047	ALL	Name Study
1750	1992	1720	1920	178047	SSX	Glynde
WISE						
....	....	1810	....	174963	ENG	???
1758	1859	....	....	120278	EYK	Beeford
1830	1992	1700	1850	142042	HRT	St Albans
1653	1730	1600	1675	101575	LIN	Thurlby By Bourne
1740	1837	1700	1992	168327	NTH	Brigstock
1814	1916	1700	1847	117005	NTH	Wellingborough
1838	1851	1841	1851	170623	OXF	Britwell Prior
1800	1940	1800	1940	176176	OXF	Henley On Thames
1780	1790	1750	1900	113212	SOM	Brewham
....	1850	....	1850	119024	SOM	Frome
1780	1790	1750	1900	113212	SOM	Nunney
?	?	1830	1868	109975	SRY	Southwark
....	....	ALL	1750	151602	WIL	Woodborough
1879	1973	1861	1973	111414	WOR	Oldbury
1820	1900	1800	1900	101044	YKS	Arkendale
?	?	1830	1868	109975	YKS	Richmond
WISEDALE						
1856	1888	1800	1856	178055	WAR	Birmingham
WISEMAN						
1700	1988	1500	1700	165379	ENG	???
1800	1820	ALL	ALL	130508	ESS	Sible Hedingham
1809	1883	1650	1920	158542	HAM	Ringwood
1890	1980	1890	1980	163600	MDX	North
1700	1797	1650	1800	154881	MLN	Edinburgh
1620	1840	1500	1620	110329	SOM	Mendip
1740	1800	1650	1800	138878	WES	ALL
1750	1900	ALL	ALL	163252	YKS	North

Known From	To	Researching From	To	Ref	Cty	Place
WISEMAN contd.						
1890	?	1870	1900	163600	YKS	Tadcaster
WISH						
1697	1900	1650	1800	138487	DEV	ALL
WISHAM						
1664	....	1640	1700	171441	HAM	St Mary Bourne
1701	1727	1680	1700	171441	HAM	Steventon
1596	1636	....	1660	171441	HAM	Wootton St Lawrence
WISHART						
1220	1992	1220	1992	178063	ALL	ALL
1787	1900	ALL	ALL	125180	FIF	Abbotshall
1848	1992	1780	1847	157619	MDX	Westminster
1750	1965	....	....	137820	SHI	Fetlar
1720	1965	....	....	137820	SHI	Mid Yell
....	....	1650	1870	143359	SHI	North Mavine
1760	1965	....	....	137820	SHI	North Yell
1758	1965	....	....	137820	SHI	Northmavine
1720	1965	....	....	137820	SHI	South Yell
WISKEN						
....	1837	ALL	ALL	175684	CAM	ALL
....	1837	ALL	ALL	175684	ESS	ALL
WISKIN						
1785	1835	ALL	ALL	175684	LND	City
....	1837	ALL	ALL	175684	SFK	ALL
WISSON						
....	....	1700	1950	178071	SFK	Great Cornard
....	....	1700	1950	178071	SFK	Little Conrard
....	....	1700	1950	178071	SFK	Sudbury
WISTON						
....	....	ALL	1851	175323	SSX	Wiston Manor
WITARD						
1857	1887	1700	1856	131245	NFK	Norwich
WITCH						
1740	1814	ALL	1740	114987	SOM	Somerton
1817	1871	1750	1816	175846	SOM	Stogursey
WITCHELL						
1800	1900	1700	1800	162884	WIL	Charlton
WITCHER						
1850	....	....	....	145068	MDX	Turnham Green
WITCOMBE						
1741	1992	1700	1900	113212	SOM	Langport
1800	1870	1770	1870	124761	SOM	Radstock
WITHALL						
1784	1804	1784	1804	103977	MDX	East Bedfont
1784	1804	1784	1804	103977	MDX	Feltham
WITHAM FOSTER						
....	....	1800	1900	122203	???	London
WITHAM						
1921	1992	ALL	ALL	144762	LND	Islington
1800	1820	1790	1820	151599	NTT	Sutton In Ashfield
1880	1920	1850	1920	118540	SSX	West Hampnett
1797	1867	1700	1797	100110	WYK	Eccleshill
WITHE						
....	....	1800	1900	117714	BRK	Beenham
....	....	1800	1900	117714	BRK	Thatcham
WITHELL						
....	....	ALL	ALL	175706	ALL	Name Study
WITHERIDGE						
....	....	ALL	ALL	178098	ALL	Name Study
WITHERLEY						
1608	1781	....	....	165999	GLS	Henbury
1608	1781	....	....	165999	GLS	Thornbury
WITHERS						
....	....	1700	1900	106755	BKM	Cheshunt
1869	....	ALL	ALL	136735	BKM	Radnage
1770	1980	1700	1950	124974	BRK	Enborne
1823	1992	1700	1823	140260	BRK	Greenham
1697	1802	....	....	115290	BRK	Lambourn
1771	1807	1700	1870	140260	BRK	Lambourn
1812	1905	1700	1950	124974	BRK	Newbury
1810	1820	1750	1900	135925	BRK	Newbury
1771	1807	1700	1870	140260	BRK	Thatcham
....	....	....	1676	142409	CHS	???
1743	1854	1600	1992	170585	DEV	Bishopsteignton
1831	1992	1600	1830	178101	DOW	Magheralin
1676	1992	....	....	142409	ENG	Midlands
1651	1704	....	....	122319	ESS	South East
1900	1960	1700	1900	106755	ESS	Waltham Cross
....	....	1700	1992	150762	GLS	???
1806	1812	....	....	124974	HAM	Baughurst
1840	1880	1800	1880	167568	LND	???
1820	1830	1800	1850	162620	NBL	North Shields
1800	1853	1800	1853	121223	NFK	Holts
1800	1853	1800	1853	121223	NFK	Saxlington

Known From	To	Researching From	To	Ref	Cty	Place
WITHERS contd.						
1790	1921	ALL	ALL	171883	OXF	Great Rollright
1797	1992	1700	1797	123153	SOM	Bath
1820	1900	1800	1900	120995	SOM	Wells
....	....	1800	1992	109770	SOM	???
1800	1935	1800	1935	105945	STS	West Bromwich
1500	1851	ALL	ALL	171883	WAR	Barton On Heath
....	....	1500	1899	115975	WIL	Wylye Valley
WITHERSPOON						
....	....	ALL	ALL	178128	ALL	Name Study
WITHERWICK						
1720	1992	1600	1720	128538	ALL	ALL
WITHEY						
1850	1900	1700	1950	175056	LND	ALL
1801	1850	1700	1800	124281	WOR	Worcester
WITHINGTON						
....	....	....	1830	129313	LAN	Droylsden
1780	1800	....	....	177318	LND	???
1780	1800	....	....	177318	SRY	Sruthworle
1900	1992	1700	1900	178136	STS	Fenton
WITHNELL						
1800	1850	1700	1900	138517	DUR	Newcastle
1848	1992	1700	1848	138029	LAN	Chorley
WITHRY						
1740	1760	ALL	ALL	107840	???	London
WITHY						
?	?	?	?	178144	???	Birmingham
WITNEY						
1834	....	1700	1834	157953	ESS	The Roddings
1860	....	ALL	ALL	154091	MDX	Hackney
1829	1910	ALL	1829	159077	NTH	Aldwinkle
WITT						
1800	1830	1750	1850	113212	HAM	Breamore
1918	1992	ALL	ALL	178152	HAM	Ellingham
1712	1900	1550	1900	107514	HAM	Fordingbridge
ALL	ALL	....	....	153397	HAM	New Forest
1770	1840	1700	1770	135879	HAM	Ringwood
1816	1840	ALL	ALL	159034	MDX	Stepney
1712	1900	1550	1900	107514	WIL	Salisbury
1820	1900	1800	1900	113212	WIL	Salisbury
1840	1910	1800	1950	135283	WIL	Salisbury
1841	1871	1820	1880	142018	WIL	Salisbury
WITTAM						
....	....	1600	1700	144711	CAM	Whittlesey
WITTED						
1814	1930	1800	1980	156965	LND	Shoreditch
WITTER						
1719	1933	ALL	ALL	105554	CHS	Christleton
1768	1851	ALL	ALL	105554	CHS	Clotton
1800	1877	1800	1900	105554	LAN	Liverpool
WITTING						
1700	1900	1700	1900	116726	NFK	Cromer
WITTLETON						
1841	1879	1800	1992	126098	LAN	Liverpool
1850	1860	1840	1992	126098	MDX	London
1825	1861	1750	1825	146609	MDX	London
1790	....	ALL	ALL	126098	NFK	Great Yarmouth
1825	....	ALL	ALL	126098	RFW	Port Glasgow
WITTOCK						
1827	1833	1690	1880	125903	HRT	Walkern
WITTON						
1785	1829	1775	1830	175153	NFK	Winfarthing
WITTS						
1770	1850	1770	1992	133450	GLS	Upper Slaughter
1800	1920	1800	1920	124605	GLS	???
1815	1851	1750	1815	133736	HAM	Kingsclere
ALL	ALL	....	....	153397	HAM	New Forest
....	....	1764	1838	175080	LND	Blackfriars
1880	1944	....	....	164720	LND	Dalston
1744	1764	ALL	1764	175080	OXF	Chipping Norton
1620	1900	....	....	104132	WIL	Aldbourne
WITTY						
1743	1816	1600	1700	174858	YKS	Hunmanby
1700	1742	....	....	174858	YKS	Thwing
WIX						
1750	1770	1750	1800	102717	HRT	Layston
WOBBS						
1788	1992	ALL	1992	125113	NFK	Clenchwarton
1788	1992	ALL	1992	125113	NFK	Kings Lynn
1788	1992	ALL	1992	125113	NFK	West Lynn
WOBY						
....	....	ALL	ALL	162329	EAG	ALL
1800	1950	1800	1950	162329	SFK	East
WOFFENDEN						
1750	1800	ALL	ALL	171379	YKS	Almondsbury
WOFFINDEN						
1753	1805	1600	1753	124257	YKS	Huttons Ambo
WOFFINDIN						
1698	1737	....	1698	170429	YKS	Barnsley
1710	1797	....	1710	170429	YKS	High Hoyland
1809	1842	....	....	170429	YKS	Mexborough
1837	1900	1881	1894	170429	YKS	Rotherham
1906	1976	....	....	170429	YKS	Sheffield
WOGAN						
....	....	ALL	ALL	178160	DUB	???
1902	....	1922	1992	178160	LAN	Oldham
....	....	ALL	ALL	178160	LAN	Wigan
1400	....	1280	1600	176923	PEM	???
....	....	ALL	ALL	178160	PEM	???
1700	....	1700	....	100536	SFK	???
....	....	ALL	ALL	178160	YKS	Bradford
WOHLGEMUTH						
1841	1911	1800	1900	122610	LND	ALL
WOLFE						
1695	....	ALL	ALL	141739	DON	???
....	....	1700	1890	118923	DUR	Bishop Wearmouth
....	1793	1600	1800	147265	IRL	Conaught
1862	....	....	....	103659	KEN	???
1750	1800	1700	1992	167592	LAN	Liverpool
1887	1900	....	....	103659	MDX	Paddington
1791	1992	1700	1791	171662	NTH	Kilsby
1690	1720	1650	1700	173630	SFK	Darsham
1740	1758	1720	1760	131547	SRY	Newdigate
1720	1800	1700	1992	167592	STS	Stoke
....	....	....	....	175404	WAR	ALL
WOLFENDALE						
1786	....	ALL	1786	111023	LAN	Manchester
WOLFENDEN						
1700	1800	1500	1700	113204	ANT	Lambeg
1883	1926	1797	1883	151432	LAN	Oldham
1765	....	1700	1800	179078	LAN	Oldham
WOLFORTH						
1640	1992	ALL	1640	178195	ALL	ALL
WOLGER						
1874	1992	1750	1900	135623	ALL	ALL
WOLLACOTT						
1715	1800	ALL	1715	160733	DEV	Chagford
1824	....	....	1850	171441	LND	St Martin In The Fields
WOLLAND						
1714	1992	1500	1714	103195	DEV	Cullompton
1717	1788	1600	1717	103195	DEV	East Teignmouth
1816	1992	1700	1816	103195	DEV	Exeter
WOLSEY						
1770	1992	1600	1770	124397	SFK	Woolpit
WOLSTENCROFT						
1790	1851	1750	1851	174211	LAN	Bury Ringley
1700	1750	1700	1800	152404	LAN	Clifton
1790	1851	1750	1851	174211	LAN	Ringley
WOLSTENHOLME						
1780	1830	ALL	1800	142301	LAN	Bury
1820	1912	1800	1820	101796	LAN	Clifton
1530	1992	1500	....	178209	LAN	Middleton
1530	1992	1500	....	178209	LAN	Oldham
WOLVERSON						
1800	1900	....	....	177903	YKS	Belper
1800	1900	....	....	177903	YKS	Ripley
WOMBWELL						
1918	....	....	....	178217	BRK	Reading
1949	....	....	....	178217	BRK	Wokingham
1851	1986	....	1811	178217	ESS	Arkesden
1861	1936	ALL	1774	178217	ESS	Braintree
1887	1951	....	....	178217	HRT	Bishops Stortford
WOMERSLEY						
1827	....	ALL	1827	154946	WRY	Huddersfield
WONES						
1785	1809	ALL	ALL	174815	SAL	Minsterley
1817	1938	ALL	ALL	174815	STS	Sedgeley
1817	1938	ALL	ALL	174815	STS	West Bromwich
1769	1816	ALL	ALL	174815	YKS	North West
WONNACOTT						
1800	1851	....	1992	146870	DEV	Kingsnympton
WONTNER						
1761	1992	ALL	ALL	162620	HEF	Leominster
1800	1900	ALL	ALL	162620	LND	???
1800	1900	ALL	ALL	162620	SRY	???

Known From	To	Researching From	To	Ref	Cty	Place
WOOD						
....	....	1700	1880	135046	AVN	Bristol
1870	....	....	....	178357	AYR	Genenal
1800	1840	?	1800	111376	BAN	Fordyce
1800	1840	?	1800	111376	BAN	Portsoy
1746	1849	....	....	165050	BDS	???
1830	1950	1700	1830	140112	BEW	Swinton
1841	1870	1841	1900	178012	BKM	Gerrards Cross
1830	1840	1800	1992	167592	CAM	Cambridge
1850	1992	ALL	1850	108847	CAM	Ely
1850	1930	1850	1950	119865	CAM	Warboys
1870	1880	....	....	139386	CHS	Dunkinfield
1826	1992	....	....	153796	CHS	Dunkinfield
1841	1916	ALL	ALL	106658	CHS	Macclesfield
1590	1850	1620	1670	178330	CHS	Macclesfield
1800	1850	1700	1992	167592	CHS	Northiwch
1840	....	....	....	139386	CHS	Stockport
1700	1800	1700	1800	152404	CHS	Stockport
1750	1800	1600	1992	167592	CHS	Weaverham
1814	1840	1700	1814	139386	CHS	Werneth
1800	1850	1700	1992	167592	CHS	Winnington
1900	?	1800	1992	167592	DBY	Buxton
1771	1886	1600	1770	172006	DBY	Buxton
1485	1743	1450	1700	102830	DBY	Darley
1800	1860	1700	1800	129046	DBY	Denby Dale
1881	1908	....	....	173142	DBY	Derby
1823	1841	ALL	ALL	106658	DBY	Flash
1825	1845	1750	1850	111821	DBY	Sawley
1830	1860	1750	1992	167592	DBY	Wirksworth
....	....	1700	1880	135046	DEV	Culmstock
1850	1992	1700	1850	160725	DEV	South Hams
1867	1883	1800	1867	177393	DEV	Tiverton
1863	1863	....	....	103632	DUR	Houghton Le Spring
1747	1770	1700	1750	178454	ESS	ALL
....	....	1700	1992	122009	ESS	East
1860	1900	1800	1992	167592	ESS	Ingatestone
1843	1895	1700	1920	164909	ESS	Roxwell
1773	1900	1700	1800	144037	FIF	Kilrenny
1800	1992	1700	1992	169560	FIF	Tayside
1900	1970	....	....	178276	GLA	Mountain Ash
1800	1830	1800	1830	126594	GLS	Hempstead
1724	1724	1650	1724	102830	GLS	Naunton
1877	1900	1700	1877	178276	GLS	Ruardean Hill
1786	1880	1700	1785	172006	GLS	Westbury On Severn
1700	1940	....	....	127833	HAM	Portsmouth
1890	1910	1800	1992	167592	HEF	Ledbury
1822	1822	1700	1822	123390	HEF	Tarrington
1840	1860	1800	1992	167592	HRT	Aldbury
1866	1900	1800	1992	167592	HRT	Berkhamstead
1874	1875	1874	1905	178314	IOW	ALL
1792	1880	ALL	1850	115282	KEN	East
1784	1893	1790	1950	118737	KEN	Cillingham
1836	1932	1700	1836	113425	KEN	Deptford
....	....	1700	1900	129984	KEN	Dover
1780	1800	1750	1800	154873	KEN	Faversham
1830	1900	1800	1850	176745	KEN	Hadlow
....	....	....	1760	130060	KEN	Hawkhurst
1800	1804	1700	1900	102520	KEN	Hothfield
1805	1823	1700	1805	113425	KEN	Lydd
....	....	....	1826	130060	KEN	Lydd
1770	1850	ALL	ALL	178454	KEN	Milton
1840	1840	1775	1900	133450	KEN	Sandwich
1500	1611	1600	1930	178284	KEN	Sandwich
1770	1850	ALL	ALL	178454	KEN	Sheerness
1800	1885	1885	1930	178284	KEN	Stonar
....	....	1760	1890	178284	KEN	Thanet
1696	1800	1801	1850	178284	KEN	Wingham
1845	1860	1700	1845	146161	LAN	Aston Under Lyne
1823	1830	1600	1825	175382	LAN	Brighouse
1840	1880	1750	1840	132268	LAN	Bury
1746	1849	....	....	165050	LAN	Delph
1776	1790	1750	1776	147745	LAN	Flixton
1820	1860	1800	1992	167592	LAN	Liverpool
1834	1992	1779	1885	142859	LAN	Manchester
1745	1810	1735	1810	178330	LAN	Manchester
1850	1930	....	....	178381	LAN	Manchester
1600	1742	....	....	159492	LAN	Oldham
1826	1992	1700	1863	178233	LAN	Radcliffe
1820	1860	1700	1992	110205	LAN	Rimington
1840	1850	1821	1840	178381	LAN	Rochdale
1826	1992	1700	1863	178233	LAN	Salford
1840	1880	1800	1840	138940	LAN	Turton
1830	1890	....	1830	163201	LEI	Leicester
1717	1798	1650	1800	156396	LEI	Swinford
WOOD contd.						
1810	1992	1700	1825	166561	LEI	Wymeswold
....	1775	ALL	1775	152838	LIN	North
1730	1890	1700	1890	151599	LIN	Hykeham
....	1787	....	....	128910	LIN	Willingham On Stow
1868	1875	1800	1900	163244	LKS	Motherwell
1890	1890	1800	1992	163244	LKS	Uddingston
....	....	ALL	1810	151602	LND	ALL
1780	1860	1700	1780	172898	LND	Bermondsey
1872	1872	1800	1800	127302	LND	Islington
1860	1950	....	....	164003	LND	New Cross
1791	....	1770	1900	139114	LND	Spitafields
1867	1920	....	....	177393	LND	Westminster
....	....	1780	....	174963	LND	???
1747	1770	1700	1750	178454	MDX	ALL
1830	1903	1650	1830	139769	MDX	London
1826	1992	1790	1826	178365	MDX	St Lukes
1800	1843	1750	1800	121037	MDX	Whitechapel
1738	1992	ALL	1738	159441	MGY	Machynlleth
1633	1992	1500	1633	178225	NTH	Burton Latimer
1850	1992	ALL	1850	125210	NTT	East Bridgeford
....	1680	ALL	1680	134511	NTT	Radford
1748	1809	1700	1748	130877	NTT	Thurgarton
....	....	1700	1810	178411	NTT	Woodborough
1598	1861	ALL	ALL	178292	NYK	Bilsdale
1861	1992	ALL	ALL	178292	NYK	Stokesley
1794	1855	1600	1875	148482	OKI	Rendall
1850	1960	1850	1960	178357	RFW	Greenock
1830	1950	1700	1830	140112	ROX	Kelso
1760	1790	1700	1760	178470	ROX	Kelso
1703	1703	1600	1992	110787	RUT	Wing
1750	1900	ALL	ALL	137987	SAL	Grinshill
1820	1880	1800	1992	167592	SAL	Henley
1820	1880	1800	1992	167592	SAL	Ludlow
1663	1780	....	....	100536	SAL	???
1780	1880	1650	1780	164860	SFK	Copton
1710	1710	1650	1710	155276	SFK	Parham
?	?	?	?	130354	SRY	Camberley
1898	1900	1850	1920	102717	SRY	Camberwell
....	....	ALL	1900	178403	SSX	West
1858	1860	1825	1925	178314	SSX	Buxted
1739	1992	....	....	139971	SSX	Eastbourne
1854	1882	....	1882	127183	SSX	Fletching
1739	1992	....	....	139971	SSX	Hastings
1835	1841	1835	1841	115940	SSX	Southease
....	1700	....	....	174564	SSX	???
1610	1800	1600	1800	103764	STS	Alstonfield
1830	1860	1700	1992	167592	STS	Bignal
1750	1820	1600	1992	167592	STS	Brownhills
1680	1880	1500	1992	167592	STS	Burslem
1879	1970	ALL	1879	109320	STS	Burton On Trent
1814	1920	....	....	121290	STS	Burton On Trent
1840	1900	1850	1992	178268	STS	Cheadle
1700	1750	1600	1992	167592	STS	Chedleton
1793	1947	1750	1850	121053	STS	Darlston
1600	1850	1600	1850	178268	STS	Dilhorne
1850	1992	1850	1992	178268	STS	Kingsley
....	....	1830	....	145688	STS	Kingston
1823	1841	ALL	ALL	106658	STS	Leek
1700	1750	1600	1992	167592	STS	Leek
1860	1930	1800	1992	167592	STS	Newcastle Under Lyme
1823	1841	ALL	ALL	106658	STS	Quarnford
1700	1750	1600	1992	167592	STS	Shelton
1780	1780	ALL	ALL	107840	STS	Stafford
1900	1992	ALL	1900	165646	STS	Tipton
1780	1840	1700	1992	167592	STS	Tunstall
1800	1900	....	....	135968	WAR	Baddesley Ensur
1830	1900	1800	1992	167592	WAR	Coventry
1860	1972	1840	1900	163546	WAR	Dudley
1830	1900	1800	1992	167592	WAR	Newbold Revel
1820	1888	1700	1900	178322	WOR	Halesowen
1884	1900	1800	1884	121541	WOR	Worcester
1818	1818	1800	1818	147338	WRY	Clayton
1843	....	....	1843	101761	WRY	Huddersfield
1760	1830	....	....	126276	WRY	Saddleworth
1800	1860	1700	1800	129046	WYK	Denby Dale
1842	1966	1750	1842	160008	WYK	Goole
1871	1920	1800	1871	109509	WYK	Holmfirth
1795	1930	1600	1992	172863	YKS	North
1795	1930	1600	1992	172863	YKS	West
....	....	1780	1815	177393	YKS	Bardsey
1737	1795	1650	1737	109142	YKS	Birstall
1812	1826	1780	1880	170348	YKS	Bradford

Known From	To	Researching From	To	Ref	Cty	Place
WOOD contd.						
1820	1850	1700	1992	167592	YKS	Castleford
1814	1821	1700	1814	178381	YKS	Elland
1730	1958	1700	1958	175153	YKS	Halifax
1685	1700	1600	1992	114901	YKS	Harewood
1636	1717	1620	1740	170348	YKS	Huddersfield
1870	1992	1700	1870	178276	YKS	Hull
....	....	1700	1800	107018	YKS	Kirkbymoorside
1827	....	ALL	ALL	175587	YKS	Knaresborough
1656	1706	1600	1700	149098	YKS	Laughton En Le Morthen
1800	?	1700	1992	167592	YKS	Leeds
1873	1900	1850	1900	178446	YKS	Mexborough
1739	1750	1600	1740	101575	YKS	Pontefract
1850	1900	1800	1992	167592	YKS	Rippon
1851	1992	1700	1992	134589	YKS	Selby
1870	1992	1700	1870	178276	YKS	Selby
1785	1871	1780	1871	175153	YKS	South Kilvington
1788	1859	1700	1800	102008	YKS	Southowram
1730	1958	1700	1958	175153	YKS	Southwram
1820	1992	....	....	124168	YKS	Terrington
1866	1963	1612	1964	178306	YKS	West Riding
1820	1853	1750	1850	172642	YKS	Yeadon
1837	1847	....	1837	117234	YKS	???
1746	1849	....	....	165050	YKS	???
WOODALL						
1650	1830	ALL	ALL	119253	CHS	Ashton On Mersey
1775	1850	ALL	ALL	119253	CHS	Baguley
1850	1975	ALL	ALL	119253	CHS	Bramhall
....	....	1700	1860	148474	CUL	ALL
1810	1860	1780	1860	148474	CUL	Carlisle
1825	1850	ALL	ALL	119253	LAN	Chorlton Cum Hardy
1809	1809	1770	1856	160636	LIN	Lincoln
1832	1861	ALL	ALL	147281	SAL	Shrewsbury
1806	1845	1700	1806	176907	SAL	Shrewsbury
1750	1775	1700	1750	172901	WOR	???
1900	1992	1750	1900	163082	YKS	North Stainley
1600	1880	1500	1880	150797	YKS	Wistow
WOODBINE						
1760	1820	1700	1900	106356	NFK	Wymondham
1873	....	1800	1900	123277	???	Birmingham
WOODBRIDGE						
1804	1900	1750	1900	133787	MDX	Brentford
1805	1924	....	1805	166189	MDX	Uxbridge
....	....	ALL	ALL	121576	YKS	Hessle
....	....	ALL	ALL	121576	YKS	Selby
WOODBURN						
1816	1861	1700	1816	168246	AYR	Loudoun
1815	1830	1750	1850	122254	WES	Ambleside
WOODCOCK						
1812	1890	1750	1850	131792	CAM	Melbourn
1735	1940	....	....	128996	CAM	Thorney
....	....	1840	1900	111708	CON	Scilly Isles
....	....	1600	1700	178497	DEV	Exeter
1710	1992	1600	1710	178497	DON	Isle Of Scilly
1796	1853	....	....	129801	ESS	Ugley
....	....	1800	1900	117714	LND	West
1869	1871	1800	1950	139203	LND	Catford
1824	1848	1750	1824	116440	MDX	Shoreditch
1800	1855	1800	1853	121223	NFK	Holts
1800	1855	1800	1853	121223	NFK	Saxlington
1703	1992	ALL	ALL	142565	NFK	St Faiths
1813	1880	1813	1950	130222	NTH	Stoke Albany
1812	1859	1650	1812	139769	OXF	Bicester
1812	1859	1650	1830	139769	OXF	Oxford
1780	1992	1700	1780	165891	RUT	Uppingham
1691	1733	?	1691	128910	WAR	Nuneaton
1700	1800	....	....	167924	YKS	Crambe
1747	1843	1700	1747	133760	YKS	Holmfirth
1835	1851	1800	1835	177555	YKS	Liversedge
1817	....	....	....	161136	YKS	Sheffield
....	....	1800	1900	117714	???	Manchester
WOODCOCKE						
1600	1700	1550	1700	154881	KIK	Kilcregan
WOODCOX						
1700	1785	....	....	148261	LND	???
WOODCRAFT						
1853	1992	1800	1992	144908	BDF	Langford
WOODCROFT						
1804	1933	1804	1992	115460	BDF	Studham
1804	1933	1804	1992	115460	BDF	Whipsnade
WOODDEN						
1799	1921	....	....	121355	LND	Haggerston
1799	1921	....	....	121355	LND	Shoreditch
WOODDEN contd.						
1800	1850	1800	1850	140724	WAR	Birmingham
WOODDILL						
1750	1860	1700	....	100536	???	London
WOODDIN						
1800	1850	1800	1850	140724	WAR	Birmingham
WOODDISS						
1624	....	....	....	178586	DBY	Kirksworth
WOODEN						
....	....	ALL	ALL	178519	ALL	Name Study
1740	ALL	1700	1749	110922	NFK	Great Yarmouth
1740	1992	1600	1740	166804	NFK	Great Yarmouth
WOODEY						
1750	1850	1700	1850	123722	GLS	Pucklechurch
WOODFIELD						
....	....	1780	1850	147826	GLS	Tiddington
1849	?	1700	1859	117722	SAL	Clun
1900	1992	1700	1900	117722	STS	Wolverhampton
....	1833	....	....	163686	WAR	Barford
....	....	1780	1850	147826	WAR	Welford
WOODFIN						
1879	1987	1700	1879	123919	SAL	Ellesmere
WOODFORD						
....	....	....	1870	176702	BKM	Aylesbury
1800	1850	1750	1860	152285	HAM	Gosport
1718	1899	1700	1900	171549	HAM	Kingston
1699	....	1660	1700	126667	IOW	Freshwater
1600	1992	1500	1600	129577	IOW	???
1750	1992	1600	1750	121118	OXF	Steeple Aston
....	....	1800	1900	153281	SOM	Bridgwater
1500	1620	1500	1700	170216	WIL	ALL
1632	1668	1630	1680	142018	WIL	South East
1722	....	?	1725	103934	WIL	Tollard Royal
1870	1951	....	....	176702	WYK	Shelf
WOODGATE						
1400	1600	1350	1600	154881	KEN	Chiddingstone
1600	1700	1600	1700	154881	KEN	Edenbridge
1700	1800	1800	1900	163163	KEN	Hawkhurst
1845	1986	....	....	138630	KEN	Paddock Wood
1700	1839	1700	1850	154881	KEN	Tonbridge
1845	1880	1800	1992	151246	SSX	Robertsbridge
1870	1900	ALL	ALL	115002	WAR	Birmingham
WOODGATES						
?	?	ALL	ALL	100897	SRY	Bermondsey
WOODGER						
....	....	ALL	ALL	178535	ALL	Name Study
....	....	1500	1825	166863	KEN	ALL
1930	1992	1830	1930	140546	KEN	East Malling
1690	1950	1650	1950	115797	KEN	Mid
1849	1992	1750	1992	122068	SRY	Godalming
1849	1992	1750	1992	122068	SRY	Guildford
WOODGETT						
1920	ALL	ALL	ALL	135240	LND	London
WOODHALL						
1825	1881	1800	1860	124028	SRY	Carshalton
1755	1956	....	....	114669	STS	West Bromwich
WOODHAM						
1761	1800	1761	1800	179337	GLS	Marshfield
1800	1809	1700	1800	139084	SRY	Compton
WOODHAMS						
1838	1870	1870	1992	102210	KEN	Ashford
1843	?	?	?	166642	KEN	Ashford
1843	?	?	?	166642	KEN	Canterbury
....	....	1750	1850	142999	KEN	Edenbridge
1860	1940	....	....	133361	KEN	Groombridge
1840	1900	1800	1900	142999	SRY	Croydon
1885	1992	1850	1992	130559	SRY	Lambeth
WOODHATCH						
1740	1850	....	1740	110027	HAM	Bishop Waltham
WOODHEAD						
1850	1908	1837	1908	173576	LAN	Oldham
1860	1917	ALL	ALL	152226	LND	???
1601	1992	1500	....	178543	NTT	Edwinstowe
1699	1710	....	1699	101761	WRY	Almondbury
1873	1965	1870	1965	147338	WRY	Halifax
1829	....	....	1829	101761	WRY	Kirkheaton
1810	1873	1780	1880	147338	WRY	Shelf
1715	1755	1715	1755	107522	WRY	Todmorden
1780	1800	1750	1800	109517	WRY	Wooldale
1750	1900	1600	1992	120677	WYK	Meltham
1853	1896	1800	1850	117862	YKS	Sculcoates
1861	1992	....	....	132462	???	Bedminster
WOODHOUSE						
1902	1964	1700	1900	158836	BRK	ALL

Known From	To	Researching From	To	Ref	Cty	Place
WOODHOUSE contd.						
....	1792	?	1792	128910	DBY	Denby
1867	1992	?	1867	153613	DBY	Matlock
1800	....	....	....	170313	HAM	Kingsclere
1730	1992	1600	1730	178578	HEF	Garway
1730	1992	1600	1730	178578	HEF	St Weonards
1851	1861	1861	1992	171514	LAN	Droylsden
1800	1992	1700	1800	164208	LAN	Morecambe
1820	1992	1780	1820	158380	MDX	Clerkenwell
1793	1992	1793	1992	145238	NFK	North
1851	1992	1700	1851	123307	NFK	Norwich
....	....	1800	1992	143456	SAL	Cleehill
1760	1992	ALL	ALL	117870	STS	Rowley Regis
....	....	1650	1750	147613	STS	Rowley Regis
1620	1992	1550	1620	171395	WAR	Tanworth
1851	1851	1700	1850	171514	YKS	Holmfirth
WOODHURST						
1718	1850	1600	1850	170178	SXE	Fairlight
WOODIFIELD						
1710	1992	1600	1710	178527	DUR	City
WOODING						
1800	1854	1770	1860	124648	BKM	Olney
1829	1834	ALL	1829	131725	MGY	Manafon
1880	1954	ALL	1992	131725	SAL	Dawley
1865	1899	ALL	1992	131725	SAL	Ketley
1905	1910	ALL	1992	131725	SAL	Market Drayton
WOODIS						
1549	?	?	?	178586	DBY	Morley
WOODISE						
1686	....	....	....	178586	STS	Grindon
WOODISS						
1780	1850	1700	1780	147583	SRY	Wandsworth
WOODIWISS						
....	....	ALL	ALL	178594	ALL	Name Study
1860	1992	1700	1860	145246	DBY	Duffield
1750	1880	1750	1880	178586	YKS	Barnslet
1855	1992	1855	1992	178586	YKS	Doncaster
1750	1820	1750	1820	178586	YKS	Hartwich Cum Wibsey
WOODIWISSE						
1607	....	....	....	178586	DBY	Church Broughton
WOODLAND						
1795	1852	1700	1820	117005	BDF	Aspley Guise
1594	1599	ALL	ALL	141615	LEI	Hinckley
WOODLEY						
1786	1880	ALL	1992	172812	BRK	ALL
1787	1900	ALL	1900	158798	BRK	Central
1790	1861	1500	1880	137472	BRK	Compton
1790	1861	1500	1880	137472	BRK	Hanpstead
1839	....	1700	1900	166359	DEV	Whitstone
1883	....	ALL	ALL	158879	DEV	???
1775	1800	ALL	1775	131059	ESS	Danbury
1851	1861	1500	1870	137472	OXF	Henley On Thames
1740	1792	1740	1800	103632	WOR	Worcester
WOODLIFF						
1789	1794	1785	1800	108901	LIN	Corringham
WOODLIFFE						
1700	1992	1600	1700	102342	LIN	Aisby
WOODLING						
1793	1870	....	....	145394	HAM	Southampton
1793	1992	ALL	ALL	156884	HAM	Southampton
WOODMAN						
1900	1992	1700	1900	166480	DOR	Bridport
1750	1800	ALL	ALL	130508	HAM	Andover
1747	1857	1700	1881	107573	HAM	Upton Grey
1900	1992	1700	1900	166480	JSY	ALL
ALL	1450	....	....	132756	NBL	Horsley
WOODMANSEE						
....	....	1800	1870	172154	ESS	???
WOODMANSEY						
1750	1924	ALL	1900	173436	YKS	East
WOODMORE						
1732	1813	1500	1732	129577	IOW	???
WOODRIDGE						
?	?	?	?	118044	LIN	Metheringham
WOODROFF						
1690	1860	1580	1890	130621	WIL	Bishops Cannings
1690	1860	1580	1890	130621	WIL	Devizes
WOODROFFE						
....	....	ALL	ALL	125032	HAM	North East
1640	1800	1650	1850	125032	HAM	Basingstoke
1600	1620	1550	1630	125032	HAM	Church Oakley
1710	1785	1710	1850	125032	HAM	Sherfield On Loddon
1620	1645	1620	1650	125032	HAM	Steveton
1782	1807	1775	1820	125032	HAM	Stratfield Turgis

Known From	To	Researching From	To	Ref	Cty	Place
WOODROFFE contd.						
1888	1910	1865	1992	122807	LND	Kensal Green
1798	1900	1600	1900	124834	NTT	East Leake
WOODROW						
....	....	1700	1900	146668	DEV	Honiton
1800	1840	1800	1900	126179	DOR	Affpuddle
1835	1884	....	....	135437	DOR	Turners Puddle
1871	1872	....	....	135437	GLS	Clifton
1832	1832	....	....	135437	SSX	Eatham
WOODRUFF						
....	....	1860	1870	133221	HAM	Portsmouth
1881	1984	1881	1984	108952	SSX	Brighton
....	....	1800	1930	141402	SSX	Hastings
1881	1895	....	....	133221	WIL	Devizes
WOODRUP						
1730	1810	1600	1900	112372	YKS	Nidderdale
WOODS						
....	....	1600	1992	134546	BDF	Bletsoe
....	....	1600	1992	134546	BDF	Sharnbrook
....	....	1600	1992	134546	BDF	Souldrop
1840	1873	1700	1840	111449	BDF	Stagsden
....	....	1600	1992	134546	BDF	Thurleigh
1750	1800	1700	1800	124796	BKM	Great Hampden
....	....	1650	1850	119784	BKM	Penn
1880	1970	1700	1880	149519	BKM	Quainton
1766	1804	1700	1766	149004	BRK	Warfield
1750	1880	1700	1992	131792	CAM	Melbourn
1825	1850	1800	1900	142352	CAM	Swaffham Prior
1871	1900	ALL	ALL	146757	CHS	Warrington
1765	1825	1750	1850	171549	CON	Boconnoc
1741	1741	1700	1750	174289	DOR	West Parley
1710	1715	1650	1720	174289	HAM	Sopley
1800	1950	1700	1800	124133	HRT	Royston
....	....	1800	1900	134546	HUN	St Neots
1758	....	1720	1800	126667	IOW	Shalfleet
1807	1888	1750	1900	174521	IRL	Cork
1863	1902	1700	1950	178616	LAN	Blackburn
1866	....	1800	1866	139483	LAN	Bottle
1750	1800	1600	1800	177318	LAN	Childwall
1875	1900	....	....	122238	LAN	Earlstown
1841	1872	1794	1872	174998	LAN	Kirkham
1836	1878	....	....	116602	LAN	Liverpool
1800	1831	....	....	171824	LAN	Prescot
1863	1902	1700	1950	178616	LAN	Preston
1800	1934	....	....	171824	LAN	Rainford
1750	....	1700	1800	179078	LAN	Tatham
1850	....	....	....	159247	LAN	???
1790	1830	ALL	....	104515	LIN	South
1900	1992	1870	1900	178640	LIN	Grimsby
1800	1860	1700	1800	178640	LIN	Sibsey
1855	1875	1830	1900	120243	MDX	London
1806	1896	1700	1900	178624	NFK	Gorleston
1738	1798	ALL	1738	135143	NFK	Great Yarmouth
1803	1992	ALL	1890	178632	NFK	Gt Melton
1790	1790	1750	1820	174599	NFK	Stanfield
1850	....	1750	1850	164267	NTH	Werrington
1703	1703	1600	1992	110787	RUT	Wing
1885	1912	1860	1920	120243	SFK	Beccles
1710	1721	1600	1800	159956	SFK	Elmswell
1856	1881	1700	1856	113425	SFK	Ipswich
1780	1845	1700	1900	120243	SFK	Lowestoft
....	....	1800	1912	115061	SOM	Yeovilton
1700	1742	....	....	166723	SRY	Horsell
....	1873	1800	1900	124907	SSX	West
1500	1899	1400	1992	115975	WIL	ALL
WOODSBY						
....	....	ALL	1803	152978	WOR	Bewdley
WOODVILLE						
1350	1500	1300	1500	154881	ALL	ALL
1905	1909	1905	1940	126705	CHS	Birkenhead
1897	1972	1870	1897	117358	YKS	Sheffield
WOODWALL						
1842	1886	1700	1842	146978	GLA	Cowbridge
1842	1886	1700	1842	146978	GLA	Swansea
WOODWARD						
1621	1709	ALL	1621	168602	BDF	Biddenham
1621	1709	ALL	1621	168602	BDF	Kempston
1750	1800	....	....	145297	CON	Newlyn
....	....	1700	1730	145297	CON	St Allen
1796	1826	1700	1992	168181	DBY	Littleover
....	1737	ALL	ALL	129933	DEV	Cornwood
....	....	1700	1800	146110	GLS	ALL
1793	1843	1700	1793	127590	GLS	Cam
1856	1896	1856	1950	143715	HAM	Oundle

Known From	To	Researching From	To	Ref	Cty	Place
WOODWARD contd.						
1896	1950	1889	1960	143715	HAM	Peterborough
1854	1992	....	1854	121002	HEF	???
1843	1932	1700	1843	126349	LEI	Leicester
1756	1992	1724	1992	103012	LIN	ALL
1750	1834	1600	1750	126349	LIN	Pinchbeck
1769	1811	ALL	1769	111023	LIN	Scunthorpe
1800	1840	ALL	ALL	154806	LIN	Spilsby
....	....	ALL	ALL	103543	LND	Islington
1890	1970	ALL	ALL	120154	LND	Kentish Town
1760	1950	1760	1950	112925	NTH	Potterspury
....	1750	ALL	1750	134511	NTT	Bleasby
1810	....	....	....	162744	NTT	Kinoulton
1791	1992	1700	1790	166464	OXF	Handborough
1850	1910	1700	1850	155101	STS	West Bromwich
1760	....	1600	1900	133590	STS	Wolverhampton
1783	1783	ALL	ALL	125288	WAR	Birmingham
1819	1840	1840	1992	174262	WAR	Birmingham
1790	1992	1790	1992	106305	WAR	Kingsbury
1800	1850	1700	1900	177210	WIL	Charlton
1639	1992	?	1639	150185	WIL	Claverton
1639	1992	?	1639	150185	WIL	Lea
1798	1987	1813	1902	178683	WOR	Upton On Severn
1843	1916	1700	1843	126349	YKS	South
WOODWARDS						
1803	1841	1600	1803	164879	GLS	ALL
1803	1874	1700	1803	164879	WIL	Cricklade
WOODWIS						
1663	1992	1771	1992	178586	DBY	Bonsall
1663	....	....	....	178586	DBY	Kirksworth
WOODWISE						
1672	....	....	....	178586	DBY	Bonsall
1595	....	....	....	178586	DBY	Longford
WOODWISS						
1732	....	....	....	178586	DBY	Duffield
WOODYER						
1898	1904	1870	1898	113050	LAN	Manchester
WOOF						
1850	1992	ALL	ALL	178691	CUL	Brampton
1890	1992	ALL	ALL	178691	WES	???
....	....	ALL	ALL	178691	WRY	???
WOOKEY						
1860	1950	1860	1950	138479	SOM	???
WOOLARD						
1815	1992	1700	1815	147737	ESS	Gt Bardfield
....	....	1600	1660	154873	KEN	Sittingbourne
WOOLASTON						
1775	....	1700	1860	131547	HEF	Leintwardine
1585	1742	1550	1675	102830	WAR	Tanworth
WOOLCOCK						
1740	1778	1700	1800	104183	CON	Feock
1750	1800	1700	1750	142905	CON	Gwinear
1840	1861	ALL	1861	114030	CON	St Breward
WOOLCOMBE-ADAMS						
1780	1940	1800	1992	133450	DEV	???
1780	1940	1800	1992	133450	WAR	???
WOOLCOTT						
1800	1900	1700	1800	158925	SOM	Chard
WOOLDER						
1822	1850	1780	1822	177393	NTT	Radford
WOOLDRIDGE						
1066	1992	1066	1992	106291	ALL	ALL
1800	1992	1800	1992	178705	DOR	Shaftesbury
1750	1992	1600	1850	124699	HAM	East
1850	1900	1750	1920	133922	HAM	Southampton
?	?	ALL	1900	117919	STS	Wolverhampton
1759	1759	1500	1759	109274	WIL	Shalbourne
?	?	ALL	1900	117919	WOR	Old Swinford
1826	1850	1700	1826	153346	WOR	Old Swinford
1650	1950	1600	1930	126438	WOR	Stourbridge
WOOLERTON						
1680	1940	....	....	128996	CAM	Thorney
1635	1835	1600	1850	142174	LEI	North
WOOLEY						
1715	1750	1660	1715	149039	NTH	Northampton
1844	1946	1844	1881	104213	SOM	Holcombe
1787	1832	ALL	1992	102245	WAR	Coleshill
WOOLF						
1733	1798	ALL	ALL	125466	SFK	Stutton
WOOLFE						
1717	1807	1600	1810	160601	BRK	Reading
....	....	1800	1899	179612	SOM	Wedmore
WOOLFENDEN						
1790	1940	1780	1830	131687	LAN	Rochdale
WOOLFENDEN contd.						
1826	1992	1700	1826	178713	LAN	Rochdale
WOOLFORD						
1770	1820	1770	1992	172545	BRK	Stratfield Saye
1840	1880	1791	1992	172545	DOR	Shaftesbury
1788	1880	1700	1788	163163	WIL	Ramsbury
1784	1835	1700	1850	136034	WIL	Wotton Bassett
WOOLFREY						
1811	1840	1700	1811	167541	LND	Lambeth
WOOLFRIES						
1766	1900	ALL	ALL	115266	DOR	ALL
WOOLFRY						
1800	1880	1600	1900	130125	DOR	Corfe
1800	1820	1750	1820	136840	DOR	Wool
WOOLGAR						
....	....	ALL	ALL	178721	ALL	Name Study
WOOLHOUSE						
1790	1800	1700	1790	151769	NTT	Mansfield Woodhouse
1703	1992	1605	1703	141593	WYK	Rotherham
1750	1900	1650	1750	109703	YKS	Ecclesfield
WOOLISON						
1870	1920	1830	1870	104124	WAR	Leamington
WOOLLACOTT						
1820	1992	1820	1992	114596	DEV	High Bickington
WOOLLAMS						
1727	1948	....	1727	133566	MDX	Aldgate
WOOLLAN						
....	....	ALL	ALL	178748	ALL	Name Study
WOOLLAND						
1817	1863	1600	1817	103195	DEV	Drewsteington
1803	1992	1600	1803	103195	DEV	Moretonhampstead
WOOLLARD						
1803	1846	1770	1870	150002	LND	East
1860	1950	1860	1950	155853	NFK	Walsingham
1590	1850	1850	1900	155853	SFK	Barking
1804	....	1790	1810	152110	SFK	Haverhill
1718	1850	1700	1820	152110	SFK	???
WOOLLER						
1784	1914	1700	1784	178756	SSX	ALL
....	....	1700	1756	178756	YKS	Birstall
WOOLLETT						
1850	1980	1700	1850	171409	KEN	Maidstone
WOOLLEY						
....	....	ALL	ALL	178764	ALL	Name Study
1871	1895	1837	1931	147257	BKM	Wingrave
....	1850	....	1950	130168	ENG	Midlands
1810	1860	1700	1810	174068	KEN	Doddington
....	....	1800	1850	174947	LIN	Blyth
1718	1992	....	....	152765	LND	???
1750	1992	1650	1750	123196	NTH	Northampton
1830	1992	1700	1824	130648	NTT	Basford
....	....	1700	1992	130648	NTT	Codnor
1844	1946	1844	1881	104213	SOM	Holcombe
1771	....	1740	1800	123404	STS	West Bromwich
WOOLLINGS						
....	....	ALL	ALL	178780	ALL	Name Study
WOOLLISCROFT						
1800	1860	1700	1960	137731	STS	Cheadle
WOOLMAN						
1713	1728	1660	1770	167002	BKM	Eton
WOOLMER						
....	....	ALL	1992	122572	ALL	ALL
1350	1992	1775	1992	133450	DEV	ALL
1670	1800	ALL	1670	131059	ESS	Bocking
?	?	?	?	142514	HRT	Benged
1870	1890	1800	1920	148377	MDX	London
WOOLNER						
1800	1860	1800	1992	141933	CON	Paul
1825	1880	1820	1900	178799	CON	Paul
1800	1900	1750	1800	155276	ESS	Colchester
1800	1877	1800	1950	178799	ESS	Plaistow
1800	1877	1800	1950	178799	ESS	West Ham
1779	1828	1700	1779	116440	SFK	Carlton Colville
WOOLNOUGH						
....	....	1750	1950	176362	GLS	Didmarton
1722	1827	1700	1851	129194	SFK	East
1860	1880	1860	1880	101877	SFK	Blaxhall
1800	1900	1850	1860	101877	SFK	Fressingham
1746	1900	1746	1900	101877	SFK	Grundisburgh
1820	1882	1750	1820	155276	SFK	Ipswich
1770	1857	....	1770	122815	SFK	Kelsale
1800	1960	1750	1880	115614	SFK	Leiston
....	....	1750	1950	176362	SFK	Leiston
....	....	1790	1820	160776	SFK	Rendham

Known From	To	Researching From	To	Ref	Cty	Place
WOOLNOUGH contd.						
1786	1800	1786	1800	101877	SFK	Snape
1780	1880	1750	1880	115614	SFK	Snape
....	....	1790	1820	160776	SFK	Swefling
1835	1863	1800	1992	117609	SFK	Theberton
1812	1900	1812	1900	101877	SFK	Tunstall
1800	1900	1850	1870	101877	SFK	Wangford
WOOLRICH						
1800	1992	?	1800	178802	DEN	Marford
1800	1992	?	1800	178802	DEN	Rossent
WOOLTON						
1870	....	1800	1960	101907	KEN	Strood
WOOLTORTON						
1800	1850	1750	1850	146803	NFK	Pulham
WOOLVEN						
ALL	ALL	ALL	ALL	178810	SSX	ALL
1825	1879	1800	1890	110949	SSX	Bramber
1825	1879	1800	1890	110949	SSX	Henfield
1896	1910	1890	1930	110949	SSX	Horsham
WOOLVETT						
....	....	ALL	ALL	178829	ALL	Name Study
WOOLVIN						
ALL	ALL	ALL	ALL	178837	ALL	ALL
1600	1800	ALL	ALL	178837	AVN	Bristol
1670	1992	ALL	1992	178837	GLS	Winchcombe
ALL	ALL	ALL	ALL	178837	SSX	ALL
WOOLWARD						
1649	1735	1600	1649	155276	SFK	Barking
1780	1800	1700	1900	127582	SFK	Ipswich
WOOLWAY						
1750	1970	1600	1992	114596	DEV	Burrington
WOOMANS						
1860	1900	1800	1900	109746	WOR	Bromsgrove
WOON						
1700	1992	....	1700	178853	CON	Roche
WOONE						
1698	1719	....	....	131326	CON	Gorran
WOONTON						
....	....	ALL	ALL	152854	ALL	Name Study
WOOR						
1730	1880	1670	1992	165255	GLS	Forest Of Dean
1730	1880	1670	1992	165255	HEF	South
WOOSMAN						
1812	1838	1700	....	123552	NFK	Attleborough
WOOSNAM						
1806	1866	1600	1806	120189	WLS	Llanidloes
WOOTEN						
1700	1850	ALL	ALL	131873	ESS	Manuden
1650	1850	ALL	ALL	131873	HRT	Furneaux Pelham
WOOTON						
1769	1820	1739	1769	139149	CHS	Congleton
1841	....	ALL	ALL	155373	DEV	ALL
1798	1900	1600	1900	124834	NTT	East Leake
1872	....	ALL	ALL	155373	YKS	North
WOOTTON						
1845	1877	ALL	1877	108197	BKM	ALL
1690	1992	?	1690	129046	BKM	Buckingham
?	?	....	....	178888	CHS	Bebington
1860	1992	....	1896	178861	KEN	Dartford
1752	1881	....	....	124524	NTH	Brackley
....	....	1700	1992	122009	OXF	???
1804	1829	ALL	ALL	101486	STS	Willenhall
1711	1900	1600	1711	175781	WIL	Bromham
....	....	ALL	1790	151602	WIL	Ramsbury
1855	1881	ALL	ALL	143529	WOR	Kempsey
WOOZLEY						
1839	1842	ALL	1839	170917	GLA	Aberdare
1809	1839	ALL	1809	170917	GLA	Merthyr Tydfil
WORALL						
1791	1805	1805	1826	178926	DBY	Ashover
1714	1774	1753	1791	178926	DBY	Beeley
WORBEY						
....	....	....	....	164968	HRT	Hitchin
1749	1783	ALL	1749	169730	HRT	Standon
WORBOYS						
1826	1890	....	....	147907	HRT	Baldock
....	....	....	....	164968	HRT	Hitchin
1850	1900	1700	1950	107727	LND	London
WORBY						
1800	1900	1800	1900	108693	HRT	Weston
WORDEN						
1805	1850	1750	....	118591	CON	Otterham
1841	1881	1841	1881	170631	DEV	Bridestowe
1620	1800	1500	1850	105333	LAN	Brownedge

Known From	To	Researching From	To	Ref	Cty	Place
WORDEN contd.						
1620	1800	1500	1850	105333	LAN	Chorley
1620	1800	1500	1850	105333	LAN	Penwortham
1620	1800	1500	1850	105333	LAN	Preston
1620	1800	1500	1850	105333	LAN	Samlesbury
1620	1800	1500	1850	105333	LAN	Walton Le Dale
WORDINGHAM						
1800	1890	1700	1800	118478	NFK	Stiffkey
WORDLEY						
1841	1900	1700	1840	110051	SFK	Cavendish
WORDLY						
1660	1720	1650	1720	135941	SFK	Glemsford
WORDSWORTH						
1776	1840	1720	1780	109517	WRY	Penistone
1730	1762	1700	1730	133760	YKS	Holmfirth
WORGER						
1783	?	?	?	166642	KEN	Ashford
1796	1853	1700	1796	104310	KEN	Kennington
WORKMAN						
1700	1800	1700	1800	141305	CHS	South East
1870	1992	1750	1870	173770	DEV	Plymouth
1750	1850	1700	1750	101524	GLS	Bisley
1702	1847	ALL	ALL	107255	GLS	Bisley
1760	1800	1760	1800	118540	GLS	Bristol
1702	1847	ALL	ALL	107255	GLS	Chalford Hill
1770	1930	1720	1900	159700	GLS	Dursley
1703	1740	1680	1710	165530	GLS	North Nibley
1744	1815	1700	1744	128317	GLS	Painswick
1765	1871	1870	1992	178845	GLS	Slimbridge
1823	1829	ALL	1850	132217	GLS	Stroud
1833	1858	1750	1900	141151	LND	Chelsea
....	....	1750	1870	173770	NIR	Belfast
1749	1966	1500	1966	169439	OXF	Adderbury
1890	1890	1890	1900	174262	WLS	Maesteg
1857	1900	1857	1943	178683	WOR	Evesham
1765	1918	1790	1917	178683	WOR	Pershore
WORLAND						
1800	....	ALL	ALL	116394	CAM	Whimple
WORLEDGE						
1770	1850	1600	1850	175641	SFK	Denston
WORLIDGE						
1800	1850	ALL	1800	150983	HAM	Portsea
WORLLEDGE						
1780	1784	1700	1850	159956	SFK	Ingham
WORLLIDGE						
1770	1830	1750	1830	135941	ESS	Hempstead
WORLOCK						
1600	1900	1500	1600	173169	GLS	Wotton Under Edge
WORMALD						
1625	1769	1696	1713	109142	YKS	Birstall
1885	....	....	....	154296	YKS	Elland
1885	....	....	....	154296	YKS	Halifax
1790	1810	1750	1800	149152	YKS	Wakefield
WORMALL						
....	....	ALL	ALL	173401	LIN	Grantham
WORMINGTON						
1810	1820	1790	1830	103764	WAR	Alcester
WORMS						
....	....	ALL	ALL	172170	ALL	Name Study
1798	1950	1770	1860	172170	MDX	London
1846	1890	....	....	172170	WAR	Birmingham
WORMSLEY						
1865	1874	1800	1874	131563	LIN	Croft
WORN						
1792	1992	....	....	116505	SFK	Ipswich
1792	1992	....	....	116505	SFK	Orford
WORNHAM						
1400	1992	1400	1992	178918	ALL	ALL
1400	1992	1400	1992	178918	BRK	ALL
WORRAD						
1839	1992	1839	1992	166715	WAR	Redditch
WORRALL						
....	....	ALL	ALL	178942	ALL	Name Study
....	....	ALL	1674	178942	CHS	Neston
1774	1808	1750	1850	126705	CHS	Tarporley
1700	1823	....	....	178942	CHS	Woodchurch
1791	1805	1805	1826	178926	DBY	Ashover
1714	1774	ALL	1714	178926	DBY	Beeley
....	....	1841	1854	178942	HAM	Southampton
1823	1881	....	....	178942	LAN	Liverpool
1826	1992	....	....	178926	LEI	Hoby
1790	1839	1700	1790	169730	LND	City
1800	1992	1700	1800	178934	SAL	Lilleshall
1881	1916	....	....	178942	STS	Hanley

Known From	To	Researching From	To	Ref	Cty	Place
WORRALL contd.						
1800	1992	1700	1992	165344	WAR	Rugby
1850	1870	1700	1850	167649	???	Birmingham
WORRALLO						
1880	1882	1800	1880	161810	WAR	Birmingham
WORRELL						
1850	1900	1800	1920	174386	KEN	Canterbury
WORROD						
1839	1992	1839	1992	166715	WOR	Redditch
WORROLL						
1834	1857	?	1860	103934	CHS	Warrington
WORSDELL						
....	....	ALL	ALL	178950	ALL	Name Study
1700	1992	1600	1700	178950	CON	South
1760	1992	1600	1760	178950	KEN	Lewisham
1750	1950	1800	1950	178950	LAN	Bolton
1600	1980	1600	1980	178950	LEI	ALL
1600	1980	1600	1980	178950	LIN	ALL
1760	1992	1600	1760	178950	LND	Greenwich
1600	1980	1600	1980	178950	RUT	ALL
1750	1850	1750	1850	178950	WES	Kendal
1715	1992	1580	1715	178950	WIL	Devizes
1715	1992	1580	1715	178950	WIL	Enford
1750	1992	1580	1750	178950	WIL	Lugershall
1715	1992	1580	1715	178950	WIL	Pewsey
1750	1992	1580	1750	178950	WIL	Upavon
1750	1980	1750	1980	178950	YKS	Sheffield
WORSEY						
....	1700	....	....	174564	STS	Penkridge
WORSFOLD						
1813	1841	....	....	100668	KEN	Dover
1800	1992	1800	1992	107980	MDX	Hackney
1543	1702	1500	1750	159581	SRY	ALL
?	?	ALL	1770	117919	SRY	Abinger
1702	1741	1660	1741	147001	SRY	Abinger
1543	1702	1500	1750	159581	SRY	Cranleigh
WORSLEY						
1500	1800	....	....	108677	IOW	ALL
1839	1839	1500	1860	137472	KEN	Chatham
1839	1839	1500	1860	137472	KEN	Gillingham
1839	1839	1500	1860	137472	KEN	Rochester
1675	....	1675	....	109347	LAN	Blackburn
1770	1851	1600	1870	105333	LAN	Brownedge
1770	1851	1600	1870	105333	LAN	Chorley
1708	1849	....	....	156418	LAN	Lowton
1740	1850	1650	1740	155500	LAN	Lowton
1860	1910	1800	1910	106429	LAN	Newton
1770	1851	1600	1870	105333	LAN	Preston
1770	1851	1600	1870	105333	LAN	Samlesbury
1800	1880	1880	1992	162256	LAN	Tockholes
1770	1851	1600	1870	105333	LAN	Walton Le Dale
1810	1828	1810	1992	126454	SSX	Ewhurst
1696	....	1500	1696	132802	WOR	Chaddesley Corbett
WORSNIP						
....	....	ALL	ALL	155632	YKS	West Riding
WORSNOP						
1814	1871	1700	1814	145971	WYK	Wyke
1840	1920	ALL	ALL	142611	YKS	Bradford
1700	1900	....	....	131474	YKS	Leeds
WORSTER						
1660	1970	1450	1660	178969	HRT	North West
....	....	1700	....	137456	NTH	Cottesbrooke
1692	1692	1650	1750	167002	NTH	West Haddon
1822	....	1822	....	156027	SRY	Lambeth
WORSWICK						
1860	1900	1800	1860	129003	LAN	Liverpool
WORT						
1830	1850	....	....	153397	HAM	New Forest
WORTH						
....	....	ALL	ALL	178977	ALL	Name Study
1696	1815	1650	1773	107654	DEV	North Lew
WORTHEN						
....	....	ALL	ALL	134597	ALL	Name Study
ALL	ALL	ALL	ALL	134597	ALL	ALL
1760	1850	1760	1900	134597	CHS	Wrenbury
1790	1850	1700	1800	134597	STS	ALL
WORTHINGTON						
1750	1830	1750	1958	131709	CHS	Cheadle
1879	....	1840	1880	154024	LAN	Altrincham
1800	1992	1700	1800	123730	LAN	Eccles
1790	1950	1750	1790	123595	LAN	Manchester
1800	1900	1800	1900	167843	LAN	Manchester
1871	1992	1800	1871	144967	LAN	St Helens
1840	1992	1750	1840	108359	LAN	Standish
WORTHINGTON contd.						
1592	1863	ALL	1992	168718	NTH	ALL
1790	....	ALL	1830	154091	SAL	Madeley
1790	....	ALL	1830	154091	SAL	Shifnal
1717	1769	....	....	117404	STS	Seighford
1800	1950	1800	1880	123595	YKS	Huddersfield
1850	1992	1700	1850	178993	YKS	Huddersfield
....	....	ALL	1790	154091	???	Birmingham
WORTHYLAKE						
1800	1800	....	....	160814	DEV	Chudleigh
1600	1890	1650	1875	172634	DEV	???
1875	1878	1875	1878	172634	MON	Rhymney
WORTLEY						
1765	....	....	....	163155	LEI	Shepshed
1750	1950	1700	1750	152587	SRY	Merstham
WORTLEY-HEPWORTH						
1830	1830	1500	1830	110310	YKS	Wortley
WORTON						
1737	1992	1717	1992	112232	WOR	Oldswindford
WORWOOD						
1811	1837	ALL	ALL	113360	LND	South
WOSONCROFT						
1731	1875	1680	1731	160474	SAL	Clunbury
WOSTEAR						
....	....	1600	1915	123390	LND	London
WOTHERSPOON						
1723	1766	1760	1992	179000	LKS	Craigiemuir
1889	1932	1889	1932	179000	LKS	Kirkmuirhill
1883	1890	1876	1893	179000	LKS	Maryhill
1811	1961	1801	1961	179000	SCT	Linlithgow
1766	1791	1791	1992	179000	SCT	Torphichen
WOTTLEY						
1810	1864	ALL	ALL	149489	WIL	Donhead
WOTTON						
1850	1900	1600	1850	158046	DEV	South
....	1832	....	1830	179019	DEV	Brixham
1791	....	1700	....	179019	DEV	Marldon
1888	1992	1888	1992	174238	KEN	ALL
1450	1550	1450	1550	154881	KEN	Boughton Malherbe
1250	1450	1200	1450	154881	LND	ALL
WRAGG						
1800	1840	1800	1920	173819	DBY	Bolsover
1850	1861	1770	1850	173371	DBY	Heath
1676	1695	1550	1676	102830	LIN	Bourne
1680	....	1500	1680	179035	NFK	Burston
1800	1900	ALL	ALL	135062	NTT	Radford
1500	1600	1600	1700	179035	SFK	Bury
....	....	1850	1880	106429	WRY	Sheffield
1800	1880	....	....	129747	YKS	Barnsley
....	....	1800	1900	158127	YKS	Sheffield
WRANGHAM						
1737	....	1737	....	139149	ERY	Nafferton
WRANN						
1850	1920	1650	1900	158542	HAM	Fawley
WRATH						
1700	1800	....	....	165999	LEI	ALL
1700	1800	....	....	165999	LEI	Bottesford
1880	1992	ALL	1992	105643	LIN	Upton
WRATHALL						
1756	1760	1720	1760	162396	YKS	Kirkby Malham
WRATTEN						
1845	1900	1800	1900	123021	KEN	Sittingbourne
WRAY						
1811	1850	1700	1811	116637	DUR	Bishopwearmouth
1811	1850	1700	1811	116637	DUR	Sunderland
1820	1992	1700	1820	158364	IRL	???
1799	1850	1775	1799	101796	LAN	Leigh
....	....	1860	1992	151041	LAN	West Derby
....	....	1845	1855	149187	MON	???
1760	1992	1600	1760	179043	YKS	West
1770	1850	1700	1820	138487	YKS	Hull
....	....	1700	1800	159166	???	Glasgow
WRAYER						
....	....	1680	1900	117714	BRK	Basildon
WRAYFORD						
1600	1900	1400	1900	105333	DEV	Buckland In The Moor
1600	1900	1400	1900	105333	DEV	Holne
1600	1900	1400	1900	105333	DEV	Ilsington
1600	1900	1400	1900	105333	DEV	Lydford
1600	1900	1400	1900	105333	DEV	Widecombe In The Moor
WRAYLER						
1703	....	1600	1750	143693	BRK	Basildon

Known From	To	Researching From	To	Ref	Cty	Place
WREFORD						
1470	1782	1470	1800	115991	DEV	South
WREN						
1795	1910	1750	1930	123145	BRK	Reading
1844	1863	1600	1873	159042	DUB	Dublin
1780	1825	1750	1830	151742	DUR	Stockton
1768	1792	1760	1792	110728	DUR	Wolsingham
....	....	1700	1992	126950	ENG	South
1750	1800	1538	1750	154792	GLS	Cotswolds
1872	1872	1872	1900	126705	LAN	South
1894	1932	....	....	159042	LAN	Oldham
1873	1891	....	....	159042	LAN	Salford
1800	1850	1750	1850	116823	NYK	Sketton
1800	1900	1750	1850	116823	NYK	Whitby
1693	1695	1650	1750	167002	SXE	Hailsham
1899	1992	1700	1992	113123	WAR	Aston
1899	1992	1700	1992	113123	WAR	Deritend
WRENCH						
1860	1920	....	....	134007	DBY	Baslow
1750	1800	1700	1800	144657	GLS	Bitton
1650	1875	....	....	134007	LND	London
1780	1860	1740	1880	103616	SSX	Salehurst
WRENN						
1750	1800	1538	1750	154792	GLS	Cotswolds
WRENSTED						
1876	1925	1876	1925	167002	MDX	Stoke Newington
WRENTMORE						
1808	1992	1700	1808	161446	SOM	Wrington
WRESSEL						
1603	1850	....	1630	109622	YKS	Ousefleet
WREYFORD						
1800	1840	1600	1840	154342	DEV	Teignmouth
1840	1880	1600	1880	154342	GLS	Bristol
WRIGGLESWORTH						
....	....	ALL	ALL	176435	ALL	Name Study
....	....	ALL	ALL	176435	ALL	ALL
1690	1700	1600	1690	151769	LIN	Threckingham
1830	1950	1700	1830	176435	MDX	Hackney
1875	1890	1850	1900	161586	YKS	Knottingly
1828	1837	....	....	106100	YKS	Leeds
1826	....	....	....	106100	YKS	Sherburn In Elmet
WRIGHT						
....	....	1700	1980	172111	ANT	Port Glenone
....	1769	1730	1780	128961	BDF	Ampthill
1830	1992	1700	1830	105902	BDF	Bedford
1710	1820	ALL	ALL	118869	BDF	Flitton
1770	1828	1762	1850	179256	BDF	Harrold
1780	1850	ALL	ALL	118869	BDF	Shefford
1851	1851	1801	1851	124915	BKM	Chesham
1744	1765	1700	1800	179256	BKM	Wavenden
1600	1650	....	....	145688	BRK	Winkfield
1852	1873	1800	1850	117250	CAM	Cambridge
1850	1900	1700	1850	127477	CAM	Kirtling
1775	1841	ALL	ALL	151815	CAM	Little Gransden
1653	1940	....	....	128996	CAM	Thorney
1815	1960	1780	1992	114898	CHS	ALL
1800	1840	1700	1992	114472	CHS	Bollington
1830	1992	....	....	138118	CHS	Cuddington
1799	1838	1780	1850	126705	CHS	Kelsall
1800	1840	1700	1992	114472	CHS	Macclesfield
1800	1919	1700	1800	129208	CHS	Macclesfield
....	....	1800	1900	110930	CHS	Nantwich
1700	1748	....	....	138851	CHS	Rostherne
1700	1748	....	....	138851	CHS	Tabley
1843	....	....	1843	146935	CHS	???
1794	1857	1700	1810	100846	CLK	Dover
1764	1992	ALL	1764	179345	COR	Skibbereen
1788	1870	ALL	1992	179205	DBY	Codnor
....	....	1800	1850	103713	DBY	Derby
....	....	1500	1910	137472	DBY	Derby
....	....	1800	1900	166383	DBY	Derby
1788	1870	ALL	1992	179205	DBY	Heanor
1788	1870	ALL	1992	179205	DBY	Loscoe
1680	1788	ALL	1992	179205	DBY	Pentrich
1680	1788	ALL	1992	179205	DBY	Ripley
1680	1788	ALL	1992	179205	DBY	Shirland
....	1898	....	....	117250	DEV	Torquay
1862	1992	1855	1960	112216	DOR	Corfe Castle
1852	1917	....	....	105473	DUR	Beamish
1835	1992	1820	1900	159905	DUR	South Shields
1680	1950	1600	1680	128376	DUR	Stanhope
1765	1843	1600	1765	138673	EAG	???
1811	....	....	....	167037	ENG	???
1558	1806	ALL	1806	107255	ESS	Debden

Known From	To	Researching From	To	Ref	Cty	Place
WRIGHT contd.						
1798	1800	1750	1800	179140	ESS	Gosfield
1780	1800	1700	1800	177024	ESS	High Ongar
1551	1835	1500	1550	165417	ESS	Kelvedon
1806	1904	ALL	1806	107255	ESS	Saffron Walden
....	1649	1600	1650	128708	ESS	Saffron Walden
1914	1918	....	....	153885	ESS	Southend
....	....	1750	1900	129275	ESS	Thaxted
1835	....	1835	1850	138584	FER	Clonelty
1776	1781	1760	1785	108510	FIF	Auchterderran
....	....	1700	1780	148113	GLS	Haresfield
1790	1839	1600	1790	162035	GLS	Kemerton
1606	1606	1550	1605	102830	GLS	Whittington
1900	1924	....	....	153885	HAM	Yateley
1798	1838	1782	1840	179256	HRT	Aldbury
1850	1930	1800	1950	119040	HRT	Aston Clinton
....	1759	....	1759	137405	HRT	Barkway
1750	1840	1750	1850	142123	HRT	Pirton
....	1769	1730	1780	128961	HRT	Royston
1730	1780	1730	1780	167924	HRT	Stevenage
1850	1930	1800	1950	119040	HRT	Tring
1880	1992	1800	1880	152471	HRT	Tring
....	....	ALL	1800	151815	HUN	Abbotsley
1826	....	1850	1992	130486	IRL	???
1804	1846	....	1850	152803	KEN	Chatham
1880	1903	1880	1992	129607	KEN	Lewisham
1910	....	....	....	153885	KEN	Sevenoaks
1720	1840	1600	1800	175382	LAN	Barnoldswick
1838	1920	1900	1992	179132	LAN	Bolton
1866	1866	....	....	179310	LAN	Bolton
1894	1899	....	....	179310	LAN	Burnley
1751	1811	1565	1751	141291	LAN	Dalton In Furness
1740	1760	1650	1740	155500	LAN	Lowton
1894	1992	1870	1894	113050	LAN	Manchester
1921	1992	....	....	179310	LAN	Middleton
1875	1904	1825	1875	131733	LAN	Pendleton
1856	1861	1861	ALL	179310	LAN	Rawtenstall
1800	1880	1800	1880	110523	LAN	Rochdale
1800	1992	1600	1992	114596	LAN	Southport
?	1881	....	1881	158011	LAN	Stretford
1841	1966	1771	1845	163686	LAN	Todmorden
1767	1843	ALL	1767	179310	LAN	Waddington
1865	1992	1800	1865	174572	LAN	Walton Le Dale
1854	....	1854	....	179302	LAN	West Derby
1820	1920	ALL	1992	156078	LAN	???
1626	1667	1626	1667	158011	LEI	Cadeby
1774	1795	1766	1800	122335	LEI	Long Chawson
....	1629	....	1629	158011	LEI	Market Bosworth
....	....	1752	1812	179264	LEI	Measham
1898	1964	1812	1898	179264	LEI	Moira
1833	1837	1600	1875	110787	LEI	???
1800	1992	....	....	176125	LIN	Asterby
1865	1940	1860	1940	131865	LIN	Bootby Pagnell
1767	1796	1700	1800	112526	LIN	Croft
1830	1853	ALL	1830	159077	LIN	Crowland
1800	1900	1800	1900	123765	LIN	East Coast
1800	1992	....	....	176125	LIN	Goulceby
1852	1992	1600	1852	102148	LIN	Grantham
1750	1777	ALL	1777	152838	LIN	Maltby Le Marsh
1817	1853	1700	1813	164259	LIN	Moulton
1797	1992	1600	1797	102148	LIN	Spalding
1864	1883	....	....	129909	LIN	Spalding
1891	1891	1700	1891	117730	LND	ALL
1815	1992	1750	1880	179299	LND	South
1830	1831	....	....	153885	LND	Camberwell
1680	1880	....	....	155195	LND	City
1700	1850	ALL	ALL	131873	LND	Hackney
1881	1992	1854	1992	179302	LND	Hackney
1884	....	....	....	151718	LND	Islington
1856	1859	....	....	153885	LND	Newington
1807	....	ALL	1841	164623	LND	Newington
1832	1832	1800	1832	165107	LND	Paddington
1867	1895	....	....	179221	LND	Shoreditch
1850	1882	1700	1850	166170	LND	St George In East
1810	1940	ALL	ALL	110477	LND	St Pancras
1700	1750	ALL	ALL	131873	LND	Westminster
1808	....	....	1825	152803	LND	Whitechapel
1750	1800	1750	1800	167924	MDX	Ealing
1850	1890	1750	1850	146285	MDX	Islington
1830	1904	1790	1830	179140	MDX	Mile End Old Town
1868	....	1750	1868	121010	MDX	Shoreditch
1822	1835	1750	1850	138584	MOG	Tydavnet
1761	1820	1700	1880	159905	NBL	Embleton
1917	....	1870	1917	179329	NBL	North Sheilds

Known From	To	Researching From	To	Ref	Cty	Place
WRIGHT contd.						
1771	1800	1700	1800	129194	NFK	Hemsby
1852	1892	ALL	1852	114030	NFK	Horstead
1770	1992	1580	1770	175870	NFK	Kings Lynn
1792	1984	1750	1822	118362	NFK	North Walsham
1750	1851	1700	1750	158402	NFK	Pulham St Mary
1830	1880	1800	1850	109517	NFK	Upwell
1843	1908	1700	1900	102326	NFK	West Dereham
1814	1814	1700	1814	163953	NFK	Yarmouth
....	....	1850	1900	103713	NRY	Scarborough
1819	1825	1780	1830	179280	NTH	Castor
1787	....	....	1787	101761	NTH	Everdon
1829	1829	1700	1992	112216	NTH	Great Billing
1724	1724	....	....	103632	NTH	Great Brington
1765	1765	1760	1770	103632	NTH	Greens Norton
....	1700	....	1700	177695	NTH	Long Buckby
1829	1829	1700	1992	112216	NTH	Nothampton
1901	1954	....	....	129909	NTH	Wellingborough
1900	1930	1900	1930	134910	NTH	Wood Newton
1772	1781	....	....	151351	NTT	Nottingham
1956	1992	....	....	179310	NTT	Nottingham
1866	....	ALL	ALL	105481	NTT	Radford
1763	....	?	1770	164976	NTT	Stapleford
1820	1885	1800	1900	170348	NTT	Worksop
1819	1850	1700	1900	166561	NTT	Wysall
1757	1757	1710	1800	167002	NYK	Topcliffe
1800	1900	....	1800	174025	OXF	Ramsden
1750	1861	1750	1992	179132	SAL	Coalbrookdale
1780	....	ALL	1780	179515	SAL	Coalbrookdale
1859	1992	....	1859	179221	SCT	Burntisland
1770	1830	1770	1830	133795	SCT	???
....	....	1650	1730	172871	SFK	Cockfield
1848	1892	1800	1900	123811	SFK	Copton
1787	1811	1666	1841	116114	SFK	Drinkstone
1754	1871	1700	1754	172553	SFK	Glemsford
1822	1992	1700	1860	129194	SFK	Halesworth
1840	1992	1700	1840	152633	SFK	Ipswich
1712	1787	....	....	101028	SFK	Lidgate
1781	1850	1700	1850	179078	SFK	Sudbury
1628	1628	1580	1628	155276	SFK	Trimley
1755	1790	1700	1755	128724	SFK	Wickhambrook
1808	1992	1750	1900	144606	SOM	South
1740	....	....	....	142158	SOM	Cadbury
....	....	1870	1917	179329	SRY	Guildford
1861	1878	....	....	153885	SRY	Richmond
....	1750	1800	....	166022	SSX	Hastings
1800	1850	1800	1850	166022	SSX	Ticehurst
....	1700	....	....	174564	SSX	???
1785	1885	1700	1920	167207	STI	Falkirk
1797	1992	1797	1992	158011	STS	Burton On Trent
1887	1950	....	....	173827	STS	Coseley
1888	1987	1867	1881	179116	STS	Coseley
1804	1887	1700	1800	179116	STS	Penkridge
1624	1681	1600	1720	160873	STS	Sedgley
1709	1867	....	....	117404	STS	Seighford
1887	1887	1865	1992	179116	STS	Stafford
1870	1920	....	....	156485	STS	Wolverhampton
....	....	....	1790	142409	STS	Yoxall
1790	1802	1750	1900	122327	WAR	Nuneaton
1822	1943	1800	1881	157597	WAR	Stratford On Avon
1762	1872	1762	1888	145181	WAR	Warwick
1650	1800	1650	1800	128708	WEX	ALL
1770	1900	1760	1800	179213	WIL	Bishopstone
1767	1992	1650	1765	179272	WIL	Bishopstone
1765	1992	1650	1765	179272	WIL	Braodchalk
1770	1992	1730	1780	150002	WOR	Bewdley
1785	1895	1700	1850	138487	WOR	Chaddesley Corbet
1826	1920	1800	1826	154318	WOR	Dudley
1799	1876	1750	....	140783	WOR	Pershore
1800	1992	1750	1800	145440	WOR	Pershore
1839	1992	ALL	1839	111384	WYK	Leeds
1839	1992	ALL	1839	111384	WYK	Scholes
....	....	1750	1772	177393	YKS	Atwick
1800	1860	1700	1900	130419	YKS	Barnoldswick
....	....	1800	....	118826	YKS	Beverley
1841	1871	1841	1871	116114	YKS	Bingley
1841	1871	1841	1888	139661	YKS	Bingley
1798	1820	1750	1820	156027	YKS	Fulstone West
1725	....	1725	....	109347	YKS	Giggleswick
1750	....	1650	....	134589	YKS	Hovingham
1793	?	ALL	ALL	119253	YKS	Keighley
....	....	?	....	115592	YKS	Leeds
1885	1930	1700	1885	144452	YKS	Leeds
1797	1992	1797	?	166235	YKS	Nun Monkton

Known From	To	Researching From	To	Ref	Cty	Place
WRIGHT contd.						
1615	1992	ALL	1615	179345	YKS	Royston
1872	1930	....	....	145181	YKS	Sheffield
1841	1966	1771	1845	163686	YKS	Todmorden
1885	1930	1700	1885	144452	YKS	Wakefield
1900	1992	1900	1992	134910	YKS	York
1830	1900	1750	1900	144622	YKS	York
1750	1800	....	....	156485	???	Llangyllin
1900	1980	....	....	100536	???	???
WRIGHTON						
1820	1840	1700	1992	140953	EYK	???
1900	1920	ALL	ALL	171816	STS	Aldridge
WRIGLEY						
1776	....	1700	1800	110205	LAN	Bury
....	....	1750	1820	151912	LAN	Chipping Stonyhurst
1820	1883	....	....	151912	LAN	Clitheroe
1820	1883	....	....	151912	LAN	Stonyhurst
1788	1861	1650	1788	120200	LAN	Warrington
1707	....	1640	1740	170348	YKS	Huddersfield
1862	1862	1750	1862	107654	YKS	Saddleworth
1755	1800	1600	1755	163236	YKS	Saddleworth
1834	1903	1800	1834	175447	YKS	Saddleworth
1823	....	ALL	1823	104299	YKS	Wakefield
WRIXON						
....	....	1800	1900	179361	DOR	Netherbury
WROE						
1750	1770	1720	1750	177393	YKS	Lomersley
WROOT						
1710	1750	1650	1750	151467	LIN	Belton
1710	1750	1650	1750	151467	LIN	Isle Of Axholme
1750	1900	1750	1900	151467	LIN	Long Sutton
WRYGHT						
1500	1550	....	....	142522	SRY	Wandsworth
WYARD						
....	....	ALL	ALL	175765	ALL	Name Study
1550	1992	1550	1837	175765	SFK	???
WYATT						
1865	1900	....	....	124524	BKM	Newport Pagnell
1836	1841	1700	1992	110418	BRK	Bray
1872	1992	1700	1850	168262	CHS	Stockport
1750	1880	1750	1880	160547	DBY	Appleby
1800	1900	1500	1800	179396	DEV	Burlescombe
1752	1752	1700	1800	105333	DEV	Rattery
1752	1752	1700	1800	105333	DEV	South Brent
1752	1752	1700	1800	105333	DEV	Ugborough
1623	1695	1695	1800	110051	GLS	Bristol
1840	1930	1750	1940	169706	GLS	Westbury On Severn
1747	1800	1600	1750	145459	HAM	Dibden
1700	1992	ALL	ALL	179418	HAM	Eling
1747	1992	1600	1747	103098	HAM	Fawley
1700	1992	ALL	ALL	179418	HAM	Fawley
1720	1800	1720	1800	139688	HAM	New Forest
1700	1992	ALL	ALL	179418	HAM	New Forest
1860	1992	ALL	ALL	179418	LND	South
....	1815	1700	1815	117927	LND	St Magnus The Matyr
1781	1781	....	....	121355	LND	Whitechapel
1820	1890	1820	1890	132721	LND	???
1674	1746	1600	1850	141569	NTH	Fotheringhay
1720	1871	....	....	124524	NTH	Northampton
1700	1872	1700	1872	168262	NTT	Wirksworth
1800	1900	1800	1900	115614	SFK	Leiston
1640	1688	1600	1800	159956	SFK	Woolpit
1844	1851	1844	1851	160164	SOM	Ashbrittle
1770	1992	ALL	1770	114987	SOM	Buckland St Mary
1719	1881	1719	1881	160164	SOM	Buckland St Mary
1735	1737	....	....	160164	SOM	Crewkerne
....	1938	1852	1938	160164	SOM	West Monkton
1572	1992	1500	1850	150002	STS	Architects
1808	1992	1700	1810	161772	WAR	???
1780	1850	1780	1850	103993	WIL	Donhead St Mary
1600	1720	1600	1720	139688	WIL	Downton
1580	1700	ALL	1580	179418	WIL	Downton
WYBORN						
....	....	ALL	ALL	179426	ALL	Name Study
1862	1939	ALL	1862	117692	KEN	Deal
WYBRON						
1806	?	1806	1860	122483	DEV	Georgeham
WYBROW						
1810	1910	1750	1992	118281	SRY	Lambeth
WYCH						
1890	1920	....	1890	102059	CHS	North
1892	....	1800	1892	103322	LAN	Wigan
WYCHERLEY						
1770	1888	1740	1810	135763	SAL	Hodnet

Known From	To	Researching From	To	Ref	Cty	Place
WYCHERLEY contd.						
1770	1888	1740	1810	135763	SAL	Wem
WYE						
....	....	1800	1850	163260	CAM	Wisbech
WYER						
1840	1880	1800	1840	143332	WIL	Hindon
1800	....	ALL	1800	179515	WOR	Kidderminster
WYERS						
1700	1850	1600	1700	170194	BRK	Kingston Lisle
WYETH						
1796	....	1700	1992	167800	BRK	Shinfield
....	....	1780	1870	143480	HAM	Sarisbury
....	....	1780	1870	143480	HAM	Sherbourne
1873	1992	....	....	143480	HAM	Southampton
1873	1992	1780	1870	143480	HAM	St Mary Extra
1800	1825	1700	1800	132640	SFK	Sproughton
....	....	1835	1861	143480	WAR	Caldecote
....	....	1835	1861	143480	WAR	Coventry
....	....	1835	1861	143480	WAR	Nuneaton
WYKE						
1820	1900	....	....	141909	SAL	Shrewsbury
1800	1850	....	....	144029	YKS	???
WYKEE						
1860	1992	....	1860	120979	LEI	Long Clawson
WYKES						
1828	....	1700	....	123552	LEI	Leicester
1828	....	1700	....	123552	MDX	London
WYKINGE						
1200	1300	1200	1300	154881	KEN	Cowden
WYLAM						
1700	1750	....	....	108871	DUR	Washington
WYLDE						
1700	1810	ALL	1900	113492	BDF	North
1746	1831	1650	1745	131245	LEI	Quorndon
ALL	1820	....	....	134708	SAL	Broseley
1880	1890	1850	1900	134708	WOR	Cradley
1850	ALL	....	....	134708	WOR	Stourbridge
WYLEY						
1574	....	....	1600	160873	STS	Walsall
WYLIE						
1796	1830	....	....	127140	AYR	Kilmarnock
....	....	1800	1850	134317	RFW	Paisley
WYLLIE						
....	....	ALL	ALL	179442	ALL	Name Study
1847	1992	ALL	1847	179434	KCD	Dunnottar
1739	1992	1650	1739	179442	KCD	Fordoun
1739	1992	1650	1739	179442	KCD	Stonehaven
1739	1902	1900	1992	179442	PER	Aberfeldy
WYMAN						
....	....	1700	....	141216	GLS	North
WYN						
1718	....	ALL	1718	122017	CON	Mabe
WYNN						
1881	1992	1800	1900	110701	AGY	Llanfihangeleseoging
....	....	?	?	134201	LAN	West Berby
1814	1850	1814	1850	127183	SSX	West Hoathly
WYNNE						
1820	1992	1800	1900	142778	CWD	Dyffryn Clwyd
1789	1873	1722	1788	138401	DEN	Llangermyw
1801	1881	....	....	147621	FLN	Holywell
....	....	1850	1992	138053	LND	Balham
WYNNE-YORKE						
1860	1992	1860	1992	106291	CWD	ALL
WYNTER-BLATHWAYT						
ALL	ALL	....	....	137332	???	???
WYRDENHAM						
1400	1992	1400	1992	178918	BRK	ALL
WYRESDALE						
1700	1914	1660	1900	125938	WAR	Maxstoke
1700	1914	1660	1900	125938	WAR	Shustoke
WYRNHAM						
1400	1992	1400	1992	178918	BRK	ALL
WYTHE						
1850	1960	ALL	ALL	162469	SFK	North
WYVERTON						
1300	1400	1300	1400	154881	ALL	ALL
YABSLEY						
....	....	1600	1992	179477	DEV	ALL
....	....	1600	1813	179477	DEV	Plymouth
1839	1992	1800	1839	150657	DEV	Torquay
1813	1992	....	....	179477	???	Bristol
YALDEN						
1837	1900	ALL	ALL	142638	ALL	ALL

Known From	To	Researching From	To	Ref	Cty	Place
YALDEN contd.						
1900	1960	ALL	ALL	142638	SRY	Wimbledon
YALE						
....	....	ALL	ALL	179485	ALL	Name Study
1600	1992	ALL	ALL	179485	SAL	ALL
YALLOP						
1751	1764	....	1751	151688	CAM	Elm
1781	1826	1826	1992	151688	NFK	Outwell
....	....	1700	1850	152390	NFK	Rockland St Mary
YALLUP						
1860	1898	1898	1992	151688	LIN	Geney Dyke
1828	1873	1873	1992	151688	NFK	West Walton
YANDLE						
1700	1899	1700	1992	178020	SOM	Wiveliscombe
YAPP						
1770	1810	1700	1830	160849	SAL	South
YARBOROUGH						
1800	1900	....	....	124621	LIN	Boston
YARD						
1850	1920	1850	1920	138479	SOM	Athelney
YARDLEY						
1700	1860	1700	1860	179507	ESS	West
1850	1930	1850	1900	179507	ESS	Burnham On Crouch
1650	1860	1600	1860	179507	HRT	???
YARE						
1898	1898	1800	1900	167843	DUR	Wolsingham
1745	1830	1700	1745	152196	WES	Ormside
YARHAM						
1811	1992	1700	1811	105635	NFK	Foulsham
YARNEY						
1805	1865	1750	1900	128155	HAM	Itchen
1788	1810	1700	1840	128155	HAM	Martyr Worthy
1880	....	1880	....	128155	SRY	Farnham
YARRANTON						
....	....	1500	1600	164631	WOR	Astley
YARRINGTON						
1840	1860	1800	1860	137111	WOR	Worcester
YARWOOD						
1880	1900	1800	1900	150541	CHS	Macclesfield
YATE						
1750	1860	ALL	1750	179515	KEN	Gravesend
1634	1759	....	....	175439	SAL	Whitchurch
YATES						
1773	1833	1700	1860	179558	ABD	???
1705	1850	ALL	1850	173177	CAM	Levrington
....	....	ALL	1800	173177	CAM	Wisbech
1800	1850	1650	1900	179531	CHS	Astbury
1841	1930	....	....	179523	CHS	Runcorn
1840	1870	?	1840	144800	CHS	Stockport
....	....	1800	1825	179523	CHS	Stockton Heath
1775	1795	1700	1775	127116	HAM	Abbotts Ann
1780	1850	1750	1850	136840	IOW	Newchurch
1854	1918	1700	1854	162000	KEN	Swale
1794	....	....	1794	111767	LAN	Bolton
1797	1814	....	....	109622	LAN	Broughton
1865	1942	1832	1930	174998	LAN	Chorleton
1843	1900	1750	1843	135364	LAN	Down Holland
1720	1797	....	1751	109622	LAN	Goosnargh
1842	1880	1800	1842	135364	LAN	Halsall
1630	1992	1630	1992	124613	LAN	Leigh
1798	1949	1755	1798	174211	LAN	Little Heaton
1630	1992	1630	1992	124613	LAN	Lowton
1798	1949	1755	1798	174211	LAN	Middleton
1828	1886	....	....	109622	LAN	Preston
....	1684	....	....	117234	LAN	Walton
1879	1921	1600	1879	123420	LND	East
1896	1992	1700	1896	179566	LND	Acton
?	?	?	?	179558	LND	???
1833	1951	1813	1917	135828	MDX	Chelsea
1820	1881	....	....	117560	MDX	Pancras
1850	1930	1850	1992	143944	NRY	ALL
....	....	1740	1830	145211	NRY	Langthorpe
....	1799	1700	1800	148288	NTT	Costock
1842	1925	....	....	114545	NTT	Nottingham
1791	1992	....	....	134619	SAL	Broseley
?	?	?	?	179558	SHI	???
1858	?	?	?	130354	SRY	Camberley
1808	1992	1770	1820	173649	STS	Abbots Bromley
1631	1743	....	....	117404	STS	Church Eaton
1860	1900	1800	1992	179531	STS	Wolstanton
....	....	1620	1700	115142	STS	???
1842	....	ALL	1842	139459	WAR	Aston Juxta Birmingham
1800	....	1750	1800	140309	WAR	Dorsington

Known From To | Researching From To | Ref | Cty | Place

YATES contd.
.... ALL ALL 172413 WIL Dinton
1811 1874 .... 1811 125954 YKS Arksey
1800 1992 ALL .... 125946 YKS Harewood
1840 .... 1800 .... 140236 YKS Spofforth
YATMEN
1704 1704 1650 1750 144606 OXF Alscot
YAUGHAN
1844 .... 1800 1844 132853 ESS Leyton
YAXLEY
1800 1900 1700 1800 171859 NFK Barton Turf
1800 1861 .... 139351 SFK Smallburgh
YEADON
1808 1837 1700 1808 152196 WES Kendal
1805 1939 1700 1805 111198 WYK Leeds
YEAMANS
1600 1680 1600 1680 127655 GLS Bristol
YEANDLE
1790 1920 1700 1800 119164 SOM Treborough
YEARBY
1692 1992 .... 1692 179582 LEI Leicester
YEARDLEY
1868 1885 1500 1868 175072 YKS ALL
1799 1836 ALL 1799 102350 YKS Rotherham
1796 .... 1700 1800 173452 YKS Rotherham
YEARLE
.... ALL ALL 166618 ALL Name Study
YEARNSLEY
1797 1850 .... 135968 SRY Croydon
YEAT
1720 .... 1750 171441 BRK Stanford In The Vale
YEATES
1807 1807 1760 1810 125032 BRK Waltham St Lawrence
.... ALL 1800 140848 DEV ALL
1779 1779 1750 1779 163783 LAN Cockerham
1680 1812 ALL ALL 173010 LAN Tunstall
1850 1930 1850 1992 143944 NRY ALL
1859 ? ALL ALL 153516 SOM Congresbury
1796 1860 1700 1800 115541 SRY Bermondsey
1791 1880 1791 1880 137898 WIL Dinton
1880 1930 1850 1992 166197 WOR Chaceley
1850 .... 166197 WOR Conderton
YEATMAN
1790 1884 .... 115606 WIL East Knoyle
1862 1992 .... 1862 151270 WIL Swinton
YEATS
1780 1820 1650 1780 106313 WIL Milton Lilbourne
1780 1900 1780 1900 154210 WIL Winterslow
1720 1847 1650 1720 168777 WIL Winterslow
1913 1930 .... 156787 ??? Liverpool
YEEND
.... ALL ALL 122173 ALL Name Study
YELF
1841 1851 1700 1841 120871 IOW Newport
1500 1900 1500 1900 170216 WIL ALL
YELLAN
1710 1710 1675 1750 133450 CON St Stephen
YELLAND
1880 1903 1700 1880 177881 CON Plymouth
1800 1890 1700 1800 128325 CON Roche
1639 1850 1500 1650 179604 CON St Stephen In Brannel
1850 1915 1850 1992 179604 CUL Millom
1793 1833 .... 170623 DEV Ashburton
1880 1903 1700 1880 177881 DEV Plymouth
YELLOLY
1750 1790 1700 1750 170488 NBL Holy Island
YELLOWLEY
1808 1992 ALL 1808 154520 NBL Lynemouth
YENDALL
1800 1900 ALL ALL 163252 CON ALL
1880 1914 1850 .... 167320 ESS Canning Town
1880 1914 1850 .... 167320 ??? West Ham
YEO
1540 1890 1700 1790 132721 DEV North
1650 1800 1500 1820 105333 DEV Buckland In The Moor
1650 1800 1500 1820 105333 DEV Christow
1650 1800 1500 1820 105333 DEV Holne
1650 1800 1500 1820 105333 DEV Ilsington
.... 1700 1800 179612 DEV Inwardleigh
1842 1992 1700 1842 156264 DEV Lifton
1650 1800 1500 1820 105333 DEV Lydford

Known From To | Researching From To | Ref | Cty | Place

YEO contd.
1850 1900 1775 1850 172561 DEV Milton Damerel
1650 1800 1500 1820 105333 DEV Widecombe In The Moor
1774 1992 1774 1859 137952 DEV ???
1860 1890 .... 179612 SOM Weston Super Mare
1700 1800 1700 1800 151653 SOM ???
YEOMAN
.... ALL ALL 165816 ALL Name Study
1731 1770 1600 1800 137170 BDF Leighton Buzzard
1800 1992 1650 1992 104671 CON Budock
1820 .... ALL 1992 160199 CON Coastal
1840 .... 1800 1992 129348 CON Falmouth
1820 .... ALL 1992 160199 DEV Coastal
1540 1872 1500 1950 122688 DEV Marlborough
1540 1872 1500 1950 122688 DEV South Hams
1800 1900 1800 1900 138045 ??? York
YEOMANS
1783 1840 ALL 1840 174815 DBY Brailsford
1829 .... 174815 DBY Derby
1830 1960 1700 1830 168947 DBY Wynaston
1790 1992 1750 1900 121096 HAM Cove
1663 1792 .... 131229 HEF North East
YERBURY
1713 1884 1600 1720 177164 SOM Frome
YETMAN
1850 1900 .... 122718 HAM Portsea
1850 1900 .... 122718 HAM Southsea
1900 1910 .... 122718 SRY Horley
1750 1950 1750 1992 122718 SSX Birdham
1750 1950 1750 1992 122718 SSX Bosham
1750 1950 1750 1992 122718 SSX Brighton
1750 1950 1750 1992 122718 SSX Crawley
1750 1950 1750 1992 122718 SSX Wittering
YETTS
1780 1830 1750 1850 109010 MLN Edinburgh
YEWDALL
1929 .... ALL ALL 175587 YKS Moortown
YEWENS
1700 1800 1650 1800 123722 SOM Bradford On Tone
YIELDING
1800 ALL .... 167037 SSX Hastings
YOCKNEY
? ? ? ? 143499 WIL Warminster
YOLE
1850 .... ALL 1850 134171 CON Calstock
1850 .... ALL 1850 134171 CON Tavistock
YON
1700 1799 .... 137960 MDX London
YONGE
1800 1930 ALL ALL 122866 MDX Islington
YOOLE
.... 1676 .... 128910 LIN Laughton
YORE
1863 1992 .... 1863 151270 MEA Nobber
YORK
ALL 1800 1450 1600 116785 ALL ALL
1780 1861 .... 124524 DUR High Conniscliffe
1815 1992 1600 1815 150150 LEI Cosby
1830 1880 1750 1992 173819 LEI Cosby
ALL 1800 1500 1800 116785 NTH ALL
1865 1900 .... 124524 NTH Hardingstone
1790 1810 ALL .... 132349 NTH Hargrave
1750 1880 1750 1992 173819 NTH Kilsby
1750 1890 1700 1992 167940 SFK ALL
1747 1992 1747 1992 100668 SSX East
YORKE
ALL 1800 1450 1600 116785 ALL ALL
.... 1700 1820 179639 BDF ALL
1743 1891 1743 1891 106291 CWD ALL
.... 1700 1820 179639 HUN ALL
ALL 1800 1500 1800 116785 NTH ALL
.... 1700 1820 179639 NTH Central
1786 1820 1770 1841 170143 NTH Walgrave
.... 1700 1820 179639 SAL South
1820 1992 1700 1820 179639 STS South
1820 1992 1700 1820 179639 WAR North
1820 1992 1700 1820 179639 WMD Birmingham
1820 1992 1700 1820 179639 WOR North
YORKE-LODGE
1865 1992 1865 1992 106291 CWD ALL
YORSTON
1828 1925 .... 114731 LND Lambeth

Known From	To	Researching From	To	Ref	Cty	Place
YOUELL						
1843	1850	1800	1950	128961	NFK	Great Yarmouth
YOUINGS						
1785	1830	1830	1992	102245	WAR	Stretton On Fosse
YOULDON						
1850	1900	1800	1900	176648	DEV	Exmouth
YOULTON						
1850	1900	1800	1900	149144	CON	Tintage
YOUNDELL						
1800	1800	1800	1800	107573	WIL	Maiden Bradley
YOUNG LEVEN						
1831	1900	....	....	157724	LND	Stepney
YOUNG						
1790	1790	....	....	159883	ANS	Dundee
1817	1843	1817	1843	164186	AVN	Bath
....	....	....	1992	148679	AVN	Bristol
1756	1777	....	....	171654	AYR	Fenwick
1800	1899	1700	1850	169390	AYR	Saltcoats
1775	1800	1700	1800	106976	BRK	Shiplake
1851	1992	1849	1960	137405	CAM	Cottenham
1850	1992	1840	1992	103225	CAM	Gamlingay
1748	1851	....	1850	137405	CAM	Rampton
1835	1840	....	....	141798	CLK	Alloa
?	1812	....	....	138851	CMA	Carlisle
1828	1909	1800	1838	119059	DOR	Bloxworth
1871	1909	1850	1870	119059	DOR	Glanvilles
1880	1992	1800	1880	112593	DOR	Parkstone
1871	1909	1850	1870	119059	DOR	Wootton
1792	1992	1600	1792	116637	DUR	Bishopwearmouth
1792	1992	1600	1792	116637	DUR	Monkwearmouth
1840	....	....	....	128945	DUR	New Cassop
1780	1850	1650	1900	118281	DUR	Sedgefield
1792	1992	1600	1792	116637	DUR	Sunderland
1850	1900	1850	1900	139920	ELN	Edinburgh
1840	1900	ALL	1840	141224	GLS	South
1795	1871	1700	1795	128937	GLS	Churchham
1763	1942	1700	1763	178381	GLS	Gloucester
1700	1860	1700	1860	171549	HAM	Brixton
1741	1774	1650	1774	121010	HAM	Chilbolton
1722	1742	1600	1722	115525	HAM	Freshwater
1820	1850	1700	1900	135968	HAM	Isle Of Wight
1590	1900	ALL	ALL	128279	HAM	New Forest
1891	1934	1800	1891	155144	HAM	Portsmouth
1708	1758	1500	1708	129577	IOW	???
1805	1862	....	1810	178853	IRL	???
1831	1853	1700	1900	178322	KEN	Ash
1500	1650	1500	1650	179698	KEN	Canterbury
1862	1992	1750	1862	121010	KEN	Chatham
1500	1650	1500	1650	179698	KEN	Chislet
1500	1650	1500	1650	179698	KEN	Herne
1858	1930	1800	1858	139785	KEN	Mid
1760	1783	1700	1783	148288	KEN	Molash
1760	1783	1700	1783	148288	KEN	Thanet
1550	1880	1550	1880	179698	KEN	Thanet
....	....	....	1810	114812	LEI	Oakham
1750	1880	1720	1860	167851	LIN	Barrow On Humber
1750	1880	1720	1860	167851	LIN	Barton
1850	1900	ALL	ALL	154970	LIN	Butterwick
1800	1899	1700	1850	169390	LKS	Glasgow
1880	1935	1850	1900	100242	LND	South
....	....	1800	1900	129275	LND	Rotherhithe
....	1900	....	....	106372	LND	West Ham
....	....	1600	1900	124273	LND	???
1720	1832	1720	1860	118931	MDX	Holborn
1876	....	....	....	135402	MDX	Islington
1830	....	....	....	140317	MDX	Islington
1838	1861	1800	1868	123870	MDX	London
1874	1900	ALL	1874	167878	MDX	London
1720	1832	1720	1860	118931	MDX	St Antholin
1720	1832	1720	1860	118931	MDX	Whitechapel
1789	1869	1750	1789	101427	MLN	Lasswade
1769	1900	1700	1900	118540	MON	Tintern Parva
1744	1753	1700	1780	123536	NBL	Bamburgh
1755	1850	1700	1850	123536	NBL	Belford
1851	1906	1600	1841	158496	NBL	Newcastle
....	....	1890	1992	147613	NIR	Belfast
....	....	1850	1890	147613	NIR	Newry
....	....	1804	1833	135003	NYK	Allerston
1865	1885	1865	1885	118931	OXF	Banbury
1865	1885	1865	1885	118931	OXF	Neithrop
1790	1850	1700	1800	179671	PER	???
1700	1850	1700	1850	144290	ROSS-SHIRE	Knockbain
....	....	ALL	ALL	146390	SAL	ALL
1783	1926	ALL	1800	131695	SCT	Glasgow
YOUNG contd.						
1800	1850	1750	1900	119865	SCT	Inverness
?	1812	....	....	138851	SCT	???
1750	1965	....	....	137820	SHI	Fetlar
1720	1965	....	....	137820	SHI	Mid Yell
1760	1965	....	....	137820	SHI	North Yell
1758	1965	....	....	137820	SHI	Northmavine
1720	1965	....	....	137820	SHI	South Yell
1875	1948	1830	1875	177040	SOM	Bath
1790	1861	1600	1900	149047	SOM	Butcombe
1780	1992	1500	1850	179655	SOM	Pitcombe
1900	1960	1900	1960	138479	SOM	Worle
....	....	1750	1830	123870	SOM	???
1867	1924	1700	1867	117633	SRY	Croydon
1760	1900	1600	1950	171522	SSX	Eastbourne
....	1700	....	....	174564	SSX	???
1700	1730	....	....	127140	STI	Kilsyth
1850	1926	1700	1850	179671	TAY	???
1800	1900	1700	1900	132446	TYR	Dungannon
1800	1900	1700	1900	124621	TYR	Killymaddy
1821	....	1800	....	131865	WAR	Coventry
1500	1900	1500	1900	170216	WIL	ALL
1801	1992	1750	1801	123153	WIL	Chapmanslade
1796	1796	1750	1800	179337	WIL	Yatton Keynell
1717	1743	1717	1743	123404	WOR	Inkberrow
1821	....	1750	1900	137782	WOR	Kempsey
1850	1980	1800	1980	127361	WRY	Dewsbury
1795	1890	....	....	102946	YKS	Bickerton
1795	1890	....	....	102946	YKS	Bilton
1900	1950	....	....	102946	YKS	Bradford
1805	1875	1800	....	112348	YKS	Bramley
1750	1830	1650	1900	130419	YKS	Giggleswick
1800	1885	1600	1800	108308	YKS	Great Langton
1873	1992	1700	1873	179647	YKS	Ouzeburn
1807	1989	1700	1807	174939	YKS	Sessay
1890	1900	....	....	102946	YKS	Wetherby
1846	1875	....	....	106852	???	Liverpool
YOUNGASH						
?	....	....	....	143499	BRE	Hay On Wye
?	....	....	....	143499	HEF	Kingsland
YOUNGER						
....	....	1750	1850	151084	LND	East
1881	....	1860	1992	118877	LND	Lewisham
1754	1780	1538	1780	118893	NBL	Grindon
1766	1863	1600	1770	118877	NBL	Tweendmouth
YOUNGMAN						
1820	1992	1820	1900	155519	MDX	London
1820	1856	1800	1900	121312	SFK	Friston
1860	1992	1800	1992	121312	SFK	Goodmayes
1860	1992	1800	1992	121312	SFK	Hazelwood
1820	1856	1800	1900	121312	SFK	Thorpe
YOUNGS						
1763	....	....	1763	177504	CAM	Littleport
1812	....	....	....	134007	ESS	Manningtree
1792	1792	1700	1800	117013	NFK	Flitcham
YOUNGSON						
1780	1910	....	1900	174246	ABD	ALL
YOXALL						
1780	1900	1700	1900	111589	CHS	Nantwich
YSERBY						
1654	1940	....	....	128996	CAM	Thorney
YUILL						
1792	1992	ALL	ALL	128481	RFW	Paisley
YULE						
....	....	ALL	ALL	157333	ALL	Name Study
1800	....	....	....	131822	CON	ALL
1550	1600	ALL	1600	149063	ELN	Haddington
1740	1810	1700	1810	135941	MLN	Edinburgh
1700	1800	1700	1992	139203	PER	Errol
ZACHARIAH						
....	....	ALL	1870	120480	ENG	ALL
ZACHARY						
1800	1820	1775	1840	159700	MDX	Marylebone
ZANKER						
....	....	ALL	ALL	179728	ALL	Name Study
....	....	ALL	ALL	179728	ALL	ALL
1730	1980	1700	1980	179728	LEI	Billesdon
ZEDDI						
1863	1920	1839	1920	173851	YKS	Scarborough
ZEDY						
1831	1841	1831	1839	173851	YKS	Hull
ZILLWOOD						
1775	1865	1850	1900	161586	SSX	Bosham
ZUPPINGER						
1882	1891	1813	1992	167002	MDX	Islington

SECTION D
INTRODUCTION

This section is arranged both alphabetically, and in reference number order.

An index by maiden name can be found in Section E.

Names are presented in the same way as submitted, but in order to save space, letters after the name, both as membership of institutes or honours have not been printed. Titles such as military rank, Doctor or Professor have been included, except where military or other people have asked for them not to be, for security or other reasons. A name in brackets after the name, shows the maiden name of a married lady.

The entry form gave the option to have the telephone number printed or not. The only change we have made is to represent it as a STD number rather than listing the exchange. Numbers starting with a plus (+) are numbers outside Britain, and you need to add the international prefix in front of this. In the UK this is 010, from the USA and Canada it is 011, and from Australia 00 11. To dial UK STD numbers from other countries drop the first zero of the STD code and start with the international prefix, followed by 44 for Britain for example (0443) 478754 is:-

00 11 44 443 478754 from Australia
010 44 443 478754 from Canada or the USA.

Following the name and address you will find a list of the names contained in the information provided. These are in alphabetical order. Names in capitals (ie SKUSE) shows that an entry exists in the interests section under that name for this individual, while a name in lowercase, starting with a capital (ie Skuse), shows that this is a variant known of, but there are no entries under this name for this individual. There may be for others. This can help you in many ways:-

i) If you can see two or more names you are researching, it may indicate that you are both searching on the same path. Look up the entries to see if they are in similar areas.
ii) By using the variant section, and following variants through section C, to this section you may find your variant listed here as a known alternative. Particularly where information is known from an early time, it is likely that the family over the generations will have been known by several variants of the name. Often the person submitting the information will have given the earliest known name and later variants. If you have not got so far back, you may be classifying the name under one variant only.
iii) The provision of this information, also allows you to see if the person is researching information under their own surname. One objection to presenting the names in alphabetical order is that people will be pestered, with inappropriate inquiries because of their current name. This overcomes the problem. Some women, particularly divorced women, are not interested in their husbands or ex-husbands family.

Name studies in Section C are not capitalised under the name in this section unless there are other entries relating to the name. It is therefore essential to use Sections B and C to find this most valuable contact.

The last item in the entry is a number starting with a letter F. This is the file number of the information submitted, and allows us to get back to the source information. If it is your entry, and you wish to provide updated information, or a change of address it is helpful if you can quote this number. Likewise, if you have written to this individual and your letter is returned, you will find this a convenient way to ask us for any later information we have. Please, however, always give a name as well as a form number. In later editions the reference numbers will change as more peoples entries are put into alphabetical order, but the file number will remain constant.

On some letters sent to you, you may see another number above and to the right of your name, but showing through the window of a window envelope or on a label. Some people have quoted this as a reference number in correspondence. This is, in fact, a mailsort code, which either identifies the office that delivers your mail, or if it has 2 zeros at the end is a residue code for mail in your area. We generate this number with a collection of special programs from the postcode using a database provided by the Post Office. While postcodes stay the same, mailsort codes may vary from time to time. By computer sorting the letters prior to printing into mailsort code order, we can put area letters directly into post office sacks and label them for direct delivery to your local delivery office. This helps the post office, and we get a discount on our mailings. We have done many large mailings while building this directory each of about 120 sacks. If you watch your mail you will see others also using this system, it is called Mailsort and this is sometimes shown on the postage impression. It makes financial sense for all Clubs and Societies to use this for mailings of over 1000 magazines, but few are sufficiently organised. As the programming to achieve this is complex, we will Mailsort code and sort address lists for other Clubs and Societies in order to help them also make the considerable financial saving. If your local Society is not using Mailsort, please bring this to their attention.

100005 ABBOTT Mr E N V. 96 Wattleton Road, Beaconsfield, Bucks, HP9 1RS.
Abbet Abbot Abbott Abbotts BUTTERWORTH F7081

100013 ABBOTT Mrs Elizabeth. (Newdick) Great Acres, Fletchers Lane, Sidlesham, Chichester, Sussex, PO20 7QG. Tel:0243-641448
BAKER BARRACK BASSETT BIRD BLACKER CLIFT COMPTON DAY DISBROW DOWSETT EVERETT HANSLIP HAYLOCK HEASLER HIPKISS HORNSBY JAMES JOSLING MILLER NAYLOR NEWDICK NORTH PALMER PEACHEY POASCO POULTER REEVE SALMON SAWYER SEWREY SHELLEY SHEPPARD SPARROW STEAR WARNER WILLIAMS F5634

100021 ABEL Mr John Roughead. 84 Bennochy Road, Kirkcaldy, KY2 5TR. Tel:0592-263555
ABEL Abell F3909

100048 ABRAHAM Mrs Doreen. 22 Hillford Place, Redhill, Surrey, RH1 5AU. Tel:0737-769639
ABRAHAM ANDREWS BARRINGER BENNETT CAPPER Combes COOK COOMBES Coombs DYSON Everet EVERETT Everitt Evert HILL Hodesdon Hodeson Hodgeson HODSDON Hodson HUNT PEMBROKE STONE F1587

100056 ABRAHAM Mrs Marion. (Walker) 1 Stirling Crescent, Totton, Southampton, Hants, SO4 3BN.
ASH BLANCHER BRADSHAW CARTWRIGHT CASH GREENHALGH HAGUE POPPLE SWALLOW F3789

100064 ABRAHAM Mr Tim. Bakers Cottage, Bovingdon Green, Bovingdon, Herts, HP3 OLF.
ABRAHAM BONE CHANDLER CORNELL DORR DUNTHORN FYSON HANCY HEIGHINGTON HENSON LAWS MACRO MILLER PAYNE PLEASANCE SPRECKLEY SUMMONS TERNENT TOON WAKE WHITTLE WILSON F6050

100072 ABRAM Miss Toni. 28 Langport Drive, Vicars Cross, Chester, CH3 5LY.
ABRAM BOWERS BROOKER BUGG CLARKE DARTS KEFFORD PAYNE SHORTLAND F1876

100080 ACKERS Mrs J S. Thimble Hall, Scorton, Preston, Lancs, PR3 1AY.
HULL JAMES NORRIS SWARBRICK WESTHEAD F2091

100099 ACKROYD Dr J F H. 113 Rr 1, Campbell River, British Columbia, V9W 3S4, CANADA. Tel:+1-604-923-6636
ACKROYD COWLING HILLAS HUTTON LORT F5535

100102 ACKROYD Dr Louis W. 57 Lucknow Avenue, Mapperley Park, Nottingham, NG3 5AZ.
ACKROYD AULD BARRY BEATTIE BROWN FINDLAY MCQUEEN MORTON SCHOFIELD WINTERTON F5954

100110 ACKROYD Mrs Susan. 25 Dorset Avenue, Diggle, Saddleworth, Oldham, OL3 5PL.
ACKROYD Akeroyd Akroyd ALLEN BROWN BRYANT CANTRELL DAVIES Davis DRUMMOND FISHBURN GRANT HARPER HILL ILLINGWORTH JUPE KEIGHLEY LEE LONGSTAFF NEAL Neville-Ussher PATMORE Perryer PERYER PILCH RICHARDSON SEARLE TAYLOR Teal TEALE TIFFANY USHER Ussher WALKER WALTON WARD WHAITES Whitam Whitham WILKINSON WILLIAMS WITHAM Witton F4627

100129 ACRES Mrs R A. 53 St Saviours Road, Kettering, Northants, NN15 5EL.
ACRES BAILEY BAMBER BELLAM BLAUNT BRIERHURST COLE COOK Downes DOWNS ELLIS FOXON GARFIT Garfoot GELL GOTTS HARRISON MEDLOCKE NEAME REDFERN RICHARDSON ROWE SAUIDGE SEWELL SHARPE STAFFORD SWANN TAYLOR THORLBY THRIFT F6252

100137 ACTON Mrs D. (Dicken) 31 Spring Lane, Erdington, Birmingham, West Midlands, B24 9BP.
ACTON ASHLEY BATES CAUSER COULTON DICKEN GIBBS STREET F5598

100145 ADAM Mr David W. 28 Lawrence Close, Charlton Kings, Cheltenham, Glous, GL52 6NN. Tel:0242-570434
ADAM AGNEW NIXON PATERSON F3159

100153 ADAMS Mrs Barbara. 52 Wheelers Lane, East Dubbo, NSW 2830, AUSTRALIA.
ADAMS BANFORD BARNES CANNING CARVER CURTIN CURTIS DIVER HUMPREY JOYCE MCPAUL PETTIT ST GEORGE WATTS F6521

100161 ADAMS Miss Clare. 85 Wollaston Road, Lowestoft, Suffolk, NR32 2PE.
ADAMS BLOWERS COWLES CROUCH KNIGHTS MILLER PRIOR RICHARDS F2777

100188 ADAMS Mr Irwin Lloyd. 7 Hound Road, Netley Abbey, Southampton, Hants, SO3 5FZ. Tel:0703-456019
ADAMS BATEMAN BEVAN BICKERTON-PRATT IRWIN JENKINS MILLS PRICE WHILE F1564

100196 ADAMS Mr J E & Mrs V. (Metcalfe) 2 Moorland Terrace, Garforth, Leeds, West Yorks, LS25 1EJ. Tel:0532-868850
ADAMS ALLUM BRADLEN METCLAFE WILFINSON F5752

100218 ADAMS Ms J M. 12 Homestead Drive, Wigston, Leicester, LE8 2HN.
Bagley Bayley BECK BEGLEY BIRCHALL Birk BURKE DAVIES Davis WARD F643

100226 ADAMS Mr James. 1 Rosemary Gardens, Blackwater, Camberley, Surrey, GU17 0NE. Tel:0276-35198
ADAMS BENNS MAIR ROBERTSON SMITH F6248

100234 ADAMS Mrs Lynn. (Dorey) Cartref, West Rounton, Northallerton, N Yorks, DL6 2LW.
DEIGHTON Doary Dooray Doorey Dore Doree DOREY Dorrey Dorry Dory Doury JEPSON KING LOFTUS F3919

100242 ADAMS Mrs M. (Churcher) 7 Wordsworth Avenue, Eaton Ford, St Neots, Huntingdon Cambs, PE19 3RA.
BLAKE CHURCHER Croxsen CROXSON Croxton Dairey Dairy DAREY Darley DIPLOCK Elfick ELLIS ELPHICK GIBBONS GOODAIR GORRINGE HARMER HARRIS HOBDEN HOLLOWAY ILSLEY JENNER KING LEWIS MACE PAICE POWELL PRICE PRIED STAMP Strainge STRANGE YOUNG F3015

100250 ADAMS Mr Norman. 34 Sweet Briar Grove, Edmonton, London, N9 9NE. Tel:081-803-6790
Donmawe Donmo Donmoe Donmow Donmowe Dunmawe Dunmo Dunmoe DUNMOW Dunmowe F4159

100269 ADAMS Mr Perry R. 2 Tulip Lane East, San Carlos, CA 94070-1551, USA. Tel:+1-415-592-1651
ADAMS ELDRIDGE F7452

100277 ADAMS Mr R H. 7 Wordsworth Avenue, Eaton Road, St Neots, Huntingdon Cambs, PE19 3RA.
ADAMS ANDREWS ATTWOOD BURCHETT CHAPMAN CHEAL CHURCHER CONNOR CROCKETT DAW GARKA GENTRY HOGGET HOUNSELL HUKE KINGHAM PAINE RAYNER SHEARING STAFFORD F3008

100285 ADAMS Mr William Thomas. Brookdale, Mill Road, Whitfield, Brackley, Northants, NN13 5TQ. Tel:0280-850683
ADAMS F5137

100293 ADDERLEY Mrs M J. 13 Musbury Avenue, Cheadle Hulme, Cheshire, SK8 7AT. Tel:0644-853287
MASSEY F3662

100307 ADDINSELL Mr Anthony Guy. 1 Broad Lane, Grappenhall, Warrington, Cheshire, WA4 3ER. Tel:0925-61890
Addinsall ADDINSELL Addlesea Adinsall Adlesay CHEETHAM De Odingsells DIGNALL Doddingsheles GEORGE GROVES HEAPS MORGAN ODINGSELLS URQUHART WHITEHORN F1723

100315 ADDIS Mr Charles. Seaford House, 37 Belgrave Square, London, SW1X 8NS.
ADDIS MCISAAC THORBURN F3346

100323 ADDIS-SMITH Mr John V. Cross End House, Thurleigh, Bedford, MK44 2EE.
Addes Addice Addies ADDIS Addiss Addyes Addys Ades Adice Adis Adiss Adyes Adys Butlen BUTLIN Butling Buttlen Buttlin Buttling F6869

100331 ADE Ms June A. 5536 Newburg Road, Durand, MI 48429, USA. Tel:+1-517-288-3617
PARDOW F5588

100358 ADIN-ATHERTON Mr P D. The Sycamores, 4 Leafield Road, Fairford, Glos, GL7 4LL.
ADIN ATHERTON BYRON GENT HAWTHORNE HAYNES MEYER SEYMOUR TOBIN F4041

100366 ADLAM Mr G J. Border Bridge, Wookey, Wells, Somerset, BA5 1LQ.
ADLAM F6868

100374 ADRIAN Mr R H. Ravensbrook, 12 Snatts Hill, Oxted, Surrey, RH8 0BN.
Adraen Adrain ADRIAN Adrien Adryan Edrain Odrien F6954

100382 ADSETT Mr Roy. 7 Winterstoke Crescent, Ramsgate, Kent, CT11 8AQ. Tel:0843-591183
ADSETT Adshead Adshed Atset Briant BRYANT FIELD Fields HANSON HOLDSTOCK HUTCHINGS JUDGE MAYBORN Maybourn Maybourne PARSONS RUSSELL F1968

100390 AFFLECK Mr & Mrs A. 3 Bessacarr Lane,

Doncaster, South Yorkshire, DN4 7PQ.
AFFLECK BURTON Callum CULM DAWSON DENTON DONALDSON DUNN FALLOWS FLECK GREENWOOD GRINDROD Hains HARRIS HAYNES INGHAM KERSHAW LAWTON MARSDEN MERRICK Politt POLLITT SHAW SPEIRS STOTT SUTCLIFFE Sutliff F4170

100404 AGAR Mr Robert Leslie. 6 Chatford House, The Promenade, Clifton Down, Bristol, BS8 3NG. Tel:0272-237500
AGAR F2107

100412 AGER Mr John. 7 Burton Villas, Hove, E Sussex, BN3 6FN. Tel:0273-773961
AGER ASTELL PARK F3189

100420 AGUTTER Mrs Doreen M K. 263 Station Road, Balsall Common, Coventry, W Midlands, CV7 7EG. Tel:0676-33378
ADAMS ADCOCK Aggutters AGUTTER ALDRIDGE ALSAGER ALSPATH ARMFIELD BAGOT BARFOOTE BARFORD BARNET Barnett BASSETT BEAUFOY BEDSON BELLISSON BERRY BETSON BINT BLISS BODDINGTON BONAKER BOSWORTH BOTILER BROME BRYNKENELL BUNN BURROWS BUTLER CHAPLIN CHETWYND CLARKE COKKES COOK COOKE COOKSON COWDALL COX CROW CUDD DALE DARLINGTON DEVELL DIGBY DODWELL EVERTON FALKE FAWKEN FEATHERSTONE FIELD FLIDE FLINT FLOYD FOSTER GEORGE GIBSON GREENE GRESLEY GUISE Gutter Gutters HALSALL HARDING HARPER HAWKESFORD HOLBECHE HOLMES ILBECHE JONES JORDAN KEELING KEY KING KITTERMASTER LAIDLER LAPWORTH MARSHALL MAYHEW MIDDLEMORE MOTTERSHEAD NEWCOMBE NICKOLDS OVERTON PADDY PARKER PARSONS PRINTOFT PRINTUP REPTON REYNOLDS ROTTEN ROWNEY RUSSELL SABINE SANDERS Saunders SHIREWOOD SHUTTLEWORTH SIDDOWN SMART SMITH SNELL SPARKES STEEDMAN STONE TAYLOR TEDD TERHEAGUE TERRIDGE TUNNADINE UNDERHILL WEBB WEDGEWOOD WENLOCK WEST WHATCOCK WHICHCOTE WHITEHEAD WHITTEM WILCOX WILKINSON WINSPER F1298

100439 AGUTTER Mrs Karen. 40 Warranoyte Road, Research, Victoria, Australia 3095.
BRENNAN BROWN BULMAN BUTTERS CHOWN DUFFIN FISH GRIFFITH GUNDRILL HOBSON LEWIS MCKEE MCQUEEN MURPHEY OGLEBY THORNTON TOLAND F2411

100447 AIKEN Mr Arthur. 6 Burleigh Way, Cuffley, Hertfordshire, EN6 4LT. Tel:0707-872117
AIKEN BARKER BAXTER BIRD EDGWORTH PENN PICKET ROGERS STOREY WHITAKER F5393

100455 AINSLIE Mr C M. 12 The Park, Cumnor, Oxford, OX2 9QS. Tel:0865-863102
Ainsley AINSLIE Aynesley F1832

100463 AINSWORTH Revd Mark J. 13 Cedar Lawn Avenue, Barnet, Herts, EN5 2LW.
AINSWORTH F3007

100471 AIREY Dr George O. 10 Barclay Hall, Mobberley, Knutsford, Cheshire, WA16 7DZ. Tel:0565-873419
AIREY FERGUSON JARDINE JOHNSTONE RUSHTON F4918

100498 AITKEN Mr K G. 2426 E Dewdney Avenue, Regina, Saskatchewan, S4N 4V5, CANADA.
Hambroke HAMBROOK Hembrook F6669

100501 AITKEN Mrs M. Bridgepark, New Abbey, Dumfries, DG2 8HH.
BALLANTINE BARCLAY DODDS HUNTER HUTSON SMITH STODDART F6061

100528 AKED Mrs Cynthia. (Watson) 48 Sandhurst Road, Wokingham, Berks, RG11 3JD. Tel:0734-788412
ARMSTRONG BIGGS FURZE HARRISON JESSON LEIGH WALKER WATSON WHITE WILLIAM WILLIAMS F1963

100536 AKEHURST Mrs M Morwenna L. Little Melbreck, Lilystone Close, Stock, Ingatestone, Essex, CM4 9BY. Tel:0277-841126
Ackhurst Ackurst AIR AKEHURST Akurst AMYS BALFOUR BALFOUR-OGILVY BARWICK BASSETT BASSETT-SMITH BAYTUP BEAUCHAMP BEAUFORT BEECHER BOLD BOND BONES BOSWELL BROOKER BRYANT CAMPBELL CARBIS CAREY Cary COATES COPPARD COXE CRADOCK DACRE Dakins DAKYNS DALES DAY De Heskayte De Heskayth De Ondeslowe DOW ELLISON EVERY FLEETWOOD FORTESCUE FRICKER FRY GILPIN GLENCROSS GOODEVE GREY GROOM GROOME Hagardston Hagarston Hagerston Haggarston HAGGERSTON Hagreston HALL Hardageston Hardargeston HARRINGTON Heskayte Heskayth HESKETH HEXT HICKES HOBLYN HOLLAND HOVENDEN HOWARD HOWAT AIKMAN HUDLESTON HUSTLER INGLE JACKSON JAMES JENNER JONES KENE KNOWLYS KYME LAKE LEATHES LEWIS LLOYD LORD LORT LOWER LYNNE MANSEL Mansell Manxell MAULE Mauncell Maunsell MCNISH MEPHAM METCALFE MILLER MORTIMER MOWBRAY NASH NELSON NESFIELD NIGHTINGALE OAKES Ondeslowe ONSLOW ORBELL OWEN Owgan PALMER PEACOCK PENNELLS PENRICE PETER Petre Philipps Philips PHILLIPPS Phillips POMEROY PORTER POWELL PRICE PULLEINE RAINY-BROWN RAWLINSON RAY REID RELF RICHARDSON RICKSON SAMS SAMSON SANDS SAUNDERS SMALL SNEAD TAMPLIN TAYLOR TRUELL TUCK TURBERVILLE WALTON WARREN WHITTRED WILLIAMS WINCHESTER WOGAN WOOD WOODDILL WRIGHT F5401

100544 AKERS Miss A. Po Box 484, Dee Why 2099, AUSTRALIA.
ACRES F7223

100552 AKISTER Mr Edward. Akehurst Ladywood, Bridge Bank, Iron Bridge, Shropshire, TF8 7JT. Tel:0952-884422
AKISTER F6362

100560 ALBANY Mr C P. Field House, Newbiggin, Stainton, Penrith, Cumbria, CA11 0HT. Tel:07684-83779
ALBANY F4655

100579 ALBUTT Mrs Margaret. (Shaw) 43 High Meadows, Greetland, Halifax, W Yorks, HX4 8QF. Tel:0422-373711
AITKEN ALBUTT BEST CRAWFORD DIXON FRY LOCKHART MCCOMB MCCONKEY ROBERTSON RUTHERFORD SHAW F6419

100587 ALDAM Mrs Susan. 9 Rokesly Avenue, Crouch End, London, N8 8SN. Tel:081-348-3524
BROWN DOLPHIN FAWCETT MYERS RIPLEY TYERMAN Tyreman F5325

100595 ALDEN-MONTAGUE Mrs G. 19 Longdon Wood, Keston Park, Kent, BR2 6EN.
ALDEN-MONTAGUE BRITEE NEWDICK F4508

100609 ALDERMAN Mr Barry. 29 Stanway Road, Waltham Abbey, Essex, EN9 3HU.
ALDERMAN F3625

100617 ALDERMAN Mr R J. Ashley Leigh, Ashley, Box, Corsham, Wilts, SN14 9AJ. Tel:0225-742696
ALDERMAN CORRY GROOMBRIDGE F1980

100625 ALDERSON Mr Godfrey. 12 Masham Road, Harrogate, N Yorks, HG2 8QF.
ALDERSON Aldersonne Anderson Auderson Aulderson F7225

100633 ALDERSON-WALKER Mrs G M. Burnt Walls, Greenhead, Northumberland, CA6 7HX. Tel:06977-47272
AFFLECK ALDERSON BREWIS COOPER CROSS DAVISON ELTRINGHAM GIBSON GREENFIELD GREY GRIMES JEFFREY LONGDEN MOSS PICKERING SIMPSON TOWARD VINT WALKER F2153

100641 ALDERTON Hugh. 16 Woodfield Drive, Gidea Park, Romford, Essex, RM2 5DH.
Alberton Alderten ALDERTON Aldirton Allderton Halderton F2142

100668 ALDERTON Mr K S. 95 Moy Avenue, Eastbourne, E Sussex, BN22 8UQ.
ALDERTON CORNWALL CORNWELL DEWIRD EVEREST HOLFORD QUARTERMAN SLATTER SMITH Wenns WENS WESTGATE WEYMARK WORSFOLD YORK F2665

100676 ALDOUS Mr Douglas E W. The House, The Street, Weybread, Diss Norfolk, IP21 5TL. Tel:037986-751
ALDHOUSE ALDIS ALDOUS BARKLEY GOOCH JERMY LEIGHTON WALKER WALLATOR F619

100684 ALDREN Mr Stephen. 59 Seward Road, Badsey, Evesham, Worcs, WR11 5HQ. Tel:0386-833143
ALDREN F249

100692 ALDRIDGE Mr Vernon. 23 Hansom Avenue, Shipston On Stour, Warwickshire, CV36 4HS. Tel:0608-62721
AGAR ALDRIDGE BRADLEY COTTERILL EBDON HERN MILLWARD PARKS WICKENDEN F1453

100706 ALEFOUNDER Mr P R. 99 Barton Road, Cambridge, CB3 9LL.
ALEFOUNDER Alfounder F3770

100714 ALEXANDER Mrs Alexandra. Robinsfield, Edenhall, Penrith, Cumbria, CA11 8SR. Tel:0768-81449
HETHERINGTON STUART F1643

100722 ALEXANDER Mr George Anthoney. 23 Lodore Drive, Carlisle, Cumbria, CA2 7SG.
ANTHONEY F1132

100730 ALEXANDER Mr Leslie W M. 15 Grasmere House, Gorselands Park, Mossley Hill Drive, Liverpool, L17 1AJ.
ALEXANDER COLE ELLWOOD Macalexander MACBRYDE Mcalexander Mcbryde F5348

100749 ALEXANDER Mrs Mary. (Purkis) 12 Hill Crescent, Honiton, Devon, EX14 8HY. Tel:0404-42656
Purcas Purcass Purchas Purchase Purchass Purches Purckis Purckuse Purkas Purkass Purkes Purkess Purkies PURKIS Purkiss Quinterle Quintral QUINTRELL F5386

100757 ALEXANDER Mrs Ruth. (Marshall) 2/68 Hoteo Avenue, Papatoetoe, NEW ZEALAND.
ASHURST BREARLEY CULPAN FINDLAY GRIER MARR MARSHALL F5490

100765 ALFORD Mr G A. Brackenway, Furzley, Bramshaw, Lyndhurst, Hants, SO43 7JJ.
ALFORD CROOK CROUCHER FIELDER HARRIS HATCH LONGMAN PRINCE SNELGROVE WELLS F4681

100773 ALGAR Mr J C. 5 Southgate Road, Gower, Swansea, W Glamorgan, SA3 2BT.
Poudich Powdich POWDITCH F6982

100781 ALLABY Mrs A S. 2 Miles Close, Aylesbury, Bucks, HP21 2JH.
ALLABY Allobie BARCHARD F6854

100803 ALLAN Mrs Anne. 96 Willowfield Road, Halifax, W Yorks, HX2 7NF.
ALLAN ARDERSLEY AYRTON CARD CLARK CLAY CLEGG COATES CROSSLEY GREENSIT GREENWOOD HATFIELD HOATH HYDER INGHAM LAMB MUDDLES PICKLES SHOESMITH SKELTON SMITH SPEAK STELL THORP WEBSTER WILSON F2903

100811 ALLAN Miss Frances E. 17 Leigh Park, Datchet, Bucks, SL3 9JP.
ALLAN F3262

100838 ALLAN Mr I E. Meiros Farm, Ashington, W Sussex, RH20 3AS.
ALLAN BROWN GRAY SLORACH F3731

100846 ALLAN Mr Richard. 107 Sinclair Drive, Cowdenbeath, Fife, Scotland, KY4 9RG. Tel:0383-510967
ALLAN BOYD CLARK COOK FIFE FYFE GRAHAM Gray GREY HUNTER LAMBERT MUDDIE Mudie PATERSON PATTERSON PEARSON RHIND SHEPHARD SNADAN Snedan WRIGHT F1194

100854 ALLANSON Mrs S. 63 Forester Road, Crawley, W Sussex, RH10 6EL.
HERON PLATT Stailey STALEY Staly Starley Stauelley Stauley STAVELEY Stayle Stayleigh Stelly Sterley Stoyle Tally WATTS F1201

100862 ALLARS Mrs Edna. (Crome) 190 Gossops Drive, Gossops Green, Crawley, Sussex, RH11 8LD. Tel:0293-529172
ALID ALLARS BOCKING CROME DAILLEY HILL KENDALL LAIGHTON MEAD PINCHBECK POOLEY SALTER SHEDRICK THOMPSON WHITMARSH F1326

100870 ALLBERRY Mr S. Flat 1, 113 Victoria Park Road, London, E9 7JJ.
Albery Albray Albury ALLBERRY F7000

100889 ALLCOTT Mr G D. 6 Fratley Avenue, Pakuranga, Auckland, NEW ZEALAND.
BEART LUTYENS F7231

100897 ALLEN Mr Alfred. 29 Greenlea Court, Greenlea Crescent, Swaythling, Southampton Hants, SO2 2PG.
ALLEN BIRCH BLACKMORE BRADSHAW COOK COOKE FLOOD GOODMAN HILL HOBBS JEFCOATE LITTLE MANSFIELD NASH RICHES SHARP WIGGINS WOODGATES F3319

100900 ALLEN Mrs B. 752 Walsall Road, Great Barr, Birmingham, B42 1EX.
ALLEN DAWKINS JAMES KENDALL PENNY SKELTON WHEATON F3819

100919 ALLEN Mr Collin. 128 Bush Road, Cuxton, Rochester, Kent, ME2 1HA. Tel:0634-718607
ALLEN CRESSWELL WARNER WEDLOCK F2734

100927 ALLEN Mr Derek J. 12 Cote Park, Bristol, Avon, BS9 2AD. Tel:0272-687017
ANGUISH Causebrook CODGBROOK Codgbrooke Codgebrook Codgebrooke Cosbrook Cosbrooke Cotesbrook Cotesbrook Cotsbrook CRANE HART JOYCE KNIGHTON LINNELL SHEFFIELD WESTERDALE WILES Wyles F2334

100935 ALLEN Miss I A. 13 Chilston Close, Tunbridge Wells, Kent, TN4 9LS.
ALLEN AVIS CROWHURST GAMMON Pearless Peerles PEERLESS F4689

100943 ALLEN Mrs Jennifer H. (Ede) 15 Recreation Street, Long Eaton, Nottingham, NG10 2DW. Tel:0602-727088
EDE F938

100951 ALLEN Mrs Joyce. (Banks) 6 Potters Way, Reigate, Surrey, RH2 7PF.
BANKS BURDETT TAYLOR WASTFELDE WASTFIELD WESTFIELD F2198

100978 ALLEN Mrs Karen. 136 Carmia Road, Munroe Falls, Ohio, 44262, USA.
BROWN CARGILL COULL COUTS DAVIDSON DONALDSON DUNCAN GIBBONS GORDON KELLY LINDSAY MOIR MOWAT PERT RITCHIE SANGSTER SERAPHINA SHORT SOUTTER THOMPSON WARD WILLIAMSON WILLINGTON WILLIS F5523

100986 ALLEN Mr Kenneth. 74 Leatherhead Ropad, Chessington, Surrey, KT9 2HY. Tel:081-397-7765
ALLEN CANTRILL KENNETT MARTIN WARRINGTON F5890

100994 ALLEN Mrs Linda. 55 The Generals Wood, Washington, Tyne & Wear, NE38 9BN.
Henfree HENFREY OVENDEN F588

101001 ALLEN Mr Maurice D. 48 The Green, Bathgate, West Lothian, EH48 4DB.
ALLAN BOWMAN DOLLERY NOBLE Pegget Picket PIGGOT Pigot PURVES REDPATH SMAIL Smaill Smeill Tunna TUNNAH Tunney Tunnie Tunno F2357

101028 ALLEN Mr Maurice W. 5 Dell Close, Haslemere, Surrey, GU27 1ES.
ABBOTT ADAMS ALLEN BIRD BLUET BONNY BRUNGAR CAMP CHALK COLE COPPING COPSEY DOUCE DURBAN ELSING ESCOTT EVERET FOX GOSLING HUBBARD JENNIS JONES JOUSSE LAURANCE LODGE LUCKING MASSINGHAM MATTHEWS ONG OSBORNE PATMORE PEARSE PLUMB PRICK Radciff Radcleff Radcleife Radcliff Radcliffe Radclyff Radclyffe Raddlyff Ratckif Ratclif RATCLIFF Ratcliffe Ratclifft Ratclift Ratclyffe Ratleff Ratley Ratlieff Ratlif Ratlife Ratliff Ratliffe Ratly Ratlyff Rattcliffe Rattlif Rattliff Retcliffe SCOTT SEALE SHARP SHEPHERD SNOW SORREL SPURGIN SUFFIELD TALBOT THOROGOOD TURNER WINCH WRIGHT F2670

101036 ALLEN Mr Maurice. 25 St Annes Gardens, Woolston, Southampton, Hampshire, SO2 9FJ. Tel:0703-440620
ALLEN BRIDLE PHILLIPS WAKELY F843

101044 ALLEN Mr Richard. 18 Rencliffe Avenue, Rotherham, S Yorks, S60 2RP. Tel:0709-366726
ALLEN Allin BENSON Darbishire DARBYSHIRE Derbyshire MARSHALL PREEN Raffmel Rafmel RATHMELL Rathnell Searston SEARSTONE Seaston Shearston SHUTT WISE F6335

101052 ALLEN Ms Scilla. 23 Ravens Road, Shoreham By Sea, Sussex, BN4 5AJ. Tel:0273-462557
Fairnill Farnal Farnall Farnell Farnill FARNOL Farnoll F50

101060 ALLEN Mrs Wendy. (Martin) 31 Sackville Gardens, Leicester, LE2 3TH. Tel:0533-702786
BACON HARDING KING LEE MARTIN NOYCE RIDENTON RYALL THORN F1610

101079 ALLEN Mr William. 4883 Delevan Drive, Lyndhurst, OH 44124-1015, USA. Tel:+1-216-382-0863
ALLEN BOYD DUNHAM HARRIES LANGLEY MARCH REYNOLDS UPPINGTON F5542

101087 ALLETT Mr John. 31 Kingsley Avenue, Hillmorton, Rugby, Warks, CV21 3JY. Tel:0788-535381
Allatt ALLETT Allitt Allott STEPHENSON F844

101095 ALLISON Ms Diana. 40 Chingford Avenue, Chingford, London, E4 6RP.
ALLISON F7427

101109 ALLISON Mrs J M W. Penvose House, Park Road, Lostwithiel, Cornwall, PL22 0BU.
CLUB Clubb F6623

101117 ALLISTONE Mr John M. 157 Verity Crescent, Canford Heath, Poole, Dorset, BH17 7TX.
ALLISTONE F7058

101125 ALLRIGHT Revd E A J. Each End Cottage, Ash,

Canterbury, Kent, CT3 2BZ. Tel:0304-813040
ALLRIGHT ALLWRIGHT BLAXLAND DREW O'FLANAGAN STOCKBRIDGE F4622

101133 ALLWOOD Mr Robert George. High Banks, Longlands Lane, East Coker, Yeovil, Somerset, BA22 9HN. Tel:0935-862118
ALLWOOD SURFLEET F5406

101141 ALLWRIGHT Mr Keith. 17 Kings Road, Wood Green, London, N22 5SN.
ALLISTON Allright ALLWRIGHT Alright Alrite Alwright Alwrite COE MEAD SADDINGTON F5118

101168 ALMOND Mrs S. (Hicks) 12 Wear Drive, Chelmsford, Essex, CM1 5PT.
ALMOND BAKER HICKS NASH NICKLEN F4823

101176 ALSBURY Mr A. 63 Mill Road, Higher Bebbington, Wirral, L63 5PA.
Ailesberry Ailesbery Ailesbry Ailesbury Ailsberry Ailsbery Ailsbry Ailsbury Alesberry Alesbery Alesbry Alesbury Allsberry Allsbery Allsbry Allsbury Alsberry Alsbry ALSBURY Aylesberry Aylesbery Aylesbry Aylesbury Aylsberry Aylsbery Aylsbury HOLT F1676

101184 ALSOP Mrs Pamela J. 74 Brandish Crescent, Clifton, Nottingham, Notts, NG11 9JX. Tel:0602-211685
ALLSOP ALSOP EWERS MARRIOTT SEYMOUR SIDDALL SNELLING F1312

101192 ALTON Mr John. 6 Church Lane, Amesbury, Salisbury, Wiltshire, SP4 7HA. Tel:0980-622047
ALTON F1799

101206 ALVEY Mr J A. 11717 Bunker Hill Court, Union Bridge, Maryland, 21791, USA.
ALVEY F6805

101214 AMAND Mr G. Highcliffe, Ledbury Road, Ross On Wye, Herefordshire, HR9 7AU.
BOULTON NORTHMORE SANSUM VELVIN F3848

101222 AMANET Mr A V. 155 Gallants Farm Road, East Barnet, Herts, EN4 8EL. Tel:081-368-7847
AMANET Amanethe Amanett Amanez Amaret Amenet Amenete Ammanet Ammenet Ammonet Ammonett Ammonette Ammonnet Amonest Amonet Amonette Amonnet Amonnett Amonret Amonuett Amouet Amounet Cackbread CAKEBREAD DUPRE GASCOYNE Hammanett Hammonet Hamonett Ominett PORTWOOD SEYMOUR TOTEN F3846

101230 AMBRIDGE Mrs Pauline. 18 Kenilworth Close, Macclesfield, Cheshire, SK11 8PF. Tel:0625-431739
AMBRIDGE BONSALL HAMBRIDGE HANBRIDGE SHELMERDINE F854

101249 AMESBURY Mr Bryan. 36 Hencliffe Way, Hanham, Bristol, BS15 3TH.
Aimsbury Ainsbury AMESBURY Amsburie Amsbury DONE DRAKE F4793

101257 AMEY Mr Michael J. Garnetts Wood, Bishops Green, Great Dunmow, Essex, CM6 1NF.
Aime Ame AMEY Amie Amy AMYE F471

101265 AMOR Mr Cecil F. 22 Fox Close, Bradpole, Bridport, Dorset, DT6 3JF. Tel:0308-56876
AMOR CREW LAWRENCE MACEY RAWLINGS RICE WAY F3472

101273 AMOR Mr Stewart. 40 Dolphin Road, Slough, Berks, SL1 1TA. Tel:0753-574525
Amer AMOR Amore Amour Ayers Ayres Cotrel Cotrell Cotterel COTTERELL Cottrel Cottrell DEAN EYERS Eyres Gillet GILLETT Goodale GOODALL GOODSHIP HARDY Holcut Holcutt Hulcut Hulcutt Hurcot Hurcott Hurcut Hurcutt Hurket HURKETT Hurkitt KEARTON Keinton Kerton Kincton Kington Kinton Kirton MCCARTHY MOTT OLIVER Olliver Olyver PUNTER STAPLEFORD TURNER WHITE F4308

101281 AMOS Mr A C. 53 Victoria Street, Wolverton, Milton Keynes, MK12 5HQ.
AMOS BOUNDS BROWN DOWNING EARL Earle HINE OSBORN Osborne PUGH WARD WEBB F3853

101303 AMOS Mrs A. (Butler) 118 Alfreton Road, Sutton-In-Ashfield, Notts, NG17 1FQ.
AMOS BUTLER CLIFFE KITSON F6505

101311 AMPHLETT Mr Walter T. 3 Heath Terrace, Hallow, Worcester, WR2 6LN.
Amfleete Ampfleet Amphlet AMPHLETT Anfleet Anfleete Anflet Anflete F4961

101338 AMSDEN Mr Peter C. Oakbank, Southwaite, Carlisle, Cumbria, CA4 OEW.
Amesden Amisden AMSDEN Amsdon Amysden Amysdon Armsden De Ambrosdon WALKERDINE F1623

101346 AMY Mr Arthur. 17 Charnhill Drive, Mangotsfield, Bristol, BS17 3JR. Tel:0272-562672
AMEY Amie AMY AMYE F747

101354 ANCOCK Mr J F. 51 Oxford Road South, Chiswick, London, W4 3DD.
Alcock Ancock AUCOCK Aucott Aukett Awcock COURT F1958

101362 ANDERSON Mrs C. 8 Bath Road, Bitton, Bristol, Avon, BS15 6HZ.
BAKER BLACK BRENTON DUFTY GOWN HARRIS HARVEY PATIENCE STEPHENS TREW F1245

101370 ANDERSON Miss Carole E. 5527 Saltsburg Road, Verona, PA 15147-3254, USA. Tel:+1-412-793-1809
ANDERSON ANDREWS BLACK Broun BROWN CALHOUN CARNEGIE CRAIGIE DAVIS FINLEY FULLERTON HUNTER JACK KILGORE LAPSLEY MACKAY MACRAE MCLEOD MELDRUM MOORE O'NEILL Paden Peadon Peagan Pedan PEDEN Pedin Pedion Pedon STEWART SUTHERLAND TAYLOR URQUHARY WARRENDER F6507

101389 ANDERSON Mrs Edna. 31 The Greenway, Daventry, Northants, NN11 4EE.
COLEMAN FATHERS LYE PINNOCK READ SHORTLAND SNOOK SPARKS F2093

101397 ANDERSON Mr John. 3 Tower Road, Darwick, Melrose, Roxburghshire, TD6 9AX. Tel:089682-2687
ANDERSON F6456

101400 ANDERSON Mrs Kathleen. 279 Knella Road, Welwyn Garden City, Herts, AL7 3NS. Tel:0707-329896
ANDERSON BURROWS ELLIS GRAY JACKSON LOWEN PESTER POTTER WACKETT WEBB F1547

101419 ANDERSON Mr Peter. 8 Leybourne Road, Strood, Kent, ME2 3QG.
ABERY ANDERSON BECK BEDWELL BROWNE CLARGO COTTER COWLEY KELLY ROOT F403

101427 ANDERSON Mrs Sheila. 9 Westfield Close, Uphill, Weston Super Mare, Avon, BS23 4XQ. Tel:0934-620111
ADAMS ANDERSON COOMBES CUSENS DELACOURT DENMAN DICK DOWN DURSTON FARQUHAR GRAY HAYDEN HOLLAND HUME JOHNSTON NORRIS RAGLESS RANNIE ROSS SHORT SNELLING STEARS STEERS YOUNG F2920

101435 ANDREW Mr B C. Penderel, Middletown, Studley, Warks, B80 7PJ.
ANDREW F1075

101443 ANDREW Mr J W. 26 Hurst Rise Road, Botley, Oxford, OX2 9HQ. Tel:0865-862126
ANDREW BALMER Brakan Brecan Breckaw BRECKON Broccon Ellarby Ellerbie Ellerby ELLERY HARRISON Herrison JACKSON LANE LAW Pressic PRESSICK Preswick Prissic PRISSICK Prisswick ROBINSON SMITH STOCKWELL WARWICK F6254

101451 ANDREW Mrs M J. Penderel, Middletown, Studley, Warks, B80 7PJ.
KEDWARDS F1073

101478 ANDREW Mrs Phyllis Jean. 37 Deacle Place, Evesham, Worcs, WR11 5DD.
ANDREW BOULTON CARTER FIGGETT HARRIS IRELAND JONES PADDOCK STEPHENS STOLLARD F1310

101486 ANDREWS Mrs Marguerite. 22 Parc Y Llan, Hanllan, Denbigh, Clwyd, LL16 5AS.
ANDREWS BOOTH CAUSER Cawser COOPER Corser CROWTHER DAVIS DAVIS-ISAAC FISHER FLOTER LEWIN Morrice Morrifs MORRIS Morriss TYLER Wooten Wooton WOOTTON F963

101494 ANDREWS Mr Robert Newark. 24 Savill Road, Lindfield, West Sussex, RH16 2NX. Tel:0444-482053
ANDREW ANDREWS BRENTLEY Colthurst Coulthirst COULTHURST NEWARK F4901

101508 ANGEL Mrs Angela. The Cottage, Blundel Lane, Stoke D'abernon, Cobham Surrey, KT11 2SF. Tel:0932-863190
ANGEL BASTON HAMMOND KEMP MANN OAK PARSONS SINGLETON WINTER F1519

101516 ANGELL Lord Of Cannock Granville. 34 Manor Avenue, Cannock, Staffs, WS11 1AA. Tel:0543-503764
ANGEL ANGELL STACEY F2458

101524 ANGOVE Mrs W. (Powell) 21 Bryn Siriol, Ty Isaf Estate, Caerphilly, Mid Glamorgan, CF8

2AH. Tel:0222-882005
Angoffe ANGOVE Angowgh Angrosse Angrove Ap Howell CLISSOLD COLES DAVIES DAY EDWARDS Engoffe Engove Engrosse GAMMON GOODLAND GRIMSTER Howell POLLARD Pollett POWELL PURNELL SLADE TAYLOR TEMPERLY TRAMPLERIA WHITE WORKMAN F1613

101532 ANNETT Mr Albert Edward. Comforts Farm, Pallance Road, Northwood, Cowes Isle Of Wight, PO31 8LS. Tel:0983-293888
ANNETT BARRETT DARIDGE FOCH FOSH FULLER GREY PESKETT F3079

101540 ANNETTS Mrs Margaret A. 9 Brand End Road, Butterwick, Boston, Lincs, PE22 0ET. Tel:0205-760311
AKERS DORRINGTON LECOUNT PONT WATFORD F1369

101559 ANSELL Mrs Doreen. (Dolling) 189 Westwood Lane, Welling, Kent, DA16 2HR.
DIBLEY Dolin Doling Dollen Dollin DOLLING Dollings Dollins HUNT LINES POSTON F4345

101567 ANSELL Mrs Jane Elizabeth. 65 Churchtown, Gwinear, Hayle, Cornwall, TR27 5JL. Tel:0736-850878
LAITY RICHARDS ROBERTS THOMAS F2395

101575 ANSON Mr Geoff. 9 Ferndale Drive, Kenilworth, Warks, CV8 2PF.
ANSON BATES BENNISON BILBROUGH BLANCHER BLAZE BLOOM BRADLEY BURRILL CAWTHORN COATSWORTH DAVISON DAWSON DRAKE EVRAT FISH FOSTER FOX GILL GOLDSMITH HADDON HANSON HEWTSON Horshill HOSSILL IVES JACKSON Kime KING LAIDMAN LAPIDGE Lapish LINLEY LUMBY METCALFE MONKMAN NICKSON Orrell ORRIEL PATTERSON POWELL RHODES Roads RODAS SCHOLEY SHARP SKINNER SPEIGHT Stainforth STANNIFORTH TANKESLEY USHER WILLSON Wilson WISE WOOD F6498

101583 ANSTEY Mr Mark Ronald. 129 Beechen Drive, Fishponds, Bristol, BS16 4BX.
ANSTEY F5687

101591 ANSTIS Mr Ray. Little Basing, Vicarage Walk, Bray On Thames, Berks, SL6 2AE. Tel:0628-27127
Anstice ANSTIS Anstiss JOINT JOPE KNAPMAN PENELLUM VEALE F2286

101605 ANTELL Mr John. 11 Portman Road, Pimperne, Blandford, Dorset, DT11 8UJ. Tel:0258-453052
Antel ANTELL Antil Antle F780

101613 ANTROBUS Mrs E L. 69 Malmains Way, Parklangley, Beckenham, Kent, BR3 2SB. Tel:081-650-3015
APPERLEY BUTLER CHARD CHARLETT CHASLEY ELKINGTON EVANS GODFREY MARCHANT STEPHENS F573

101621 APPLEBY Mr Arthur Hamilton. 3 West Park, Hyde, Tameside, SK14 5ER. Tel:061-368-1789
APPLEBY CARR HAMILTON HOBBS JEFFERYS SETCHELL F5910

101648 APPLETON Mr Peter. 12 Blair Avenue, Flixton, Urmston, Manchester, M31 3JS. Tel:061-747-5345
Apelton Apleton Aplton Appelton APPLETON Applton Appulton CHEETHAM GRAY WARD F4217

101656 APPS Mrs Lurline. (Warner) Ms 1197, Yandina, Queensland, 4561, AUSTRALIA.
Ape Appes Appos APPS Apt AULIFF BARBER Davies DAVIS Faulkes FAULKS Fawkes HART Jobb Jobbens JOBBINS SAINSBURY TUCKERMAN Warne WARNER Warren F4602

101664 APTHORP Miss Jan. 241 Walton High Street, Felixstowe, Suffolk, IP11 9DU.
APTHORP COPPING COTTON DOVE GINGER F6384

101672 ARABIN Mrs Shirley. (Rice) 114 Maeroa Road, Hamilton, NEW ZEALAND. Tel:+64-7-839-2164
ARABIN EDGE POUND RICE F5451

101680 ARCH Mr W H. 60 The Bury, Pavenham, Bedford, MK43 7PY.
ARCH Arche De Arches F6604

101699 ARCHER Dr W H. The Old Nursery, Pump Lane North, Marlow, Bucks, SL7 3RD.
PULKER F6553

101702 ARCHIBALD Mr Douglas. Caledon, Auldgirth, Dumfries, DG2 0XP. Tel:0387-74419
ARCHIBALD F3665

101710 ARKLE Mr H J. 12 Woodford Close, Witherwack, Sunderland, SR5 5SA.
ARKLE F6770

101729 ARKWRIGHT Mr Thomas. Ivy Cottage, Limbrick, Chorley, Lancs, PR6 9EE.
ARKWRIGHT Arthright Arthwright Atrick Atricks Atrix Attrick Attricks Harkwright F7226

101737 ARMATAGE Mrs Ann. Ruahine, Kenley Road, Headley Down, Hants, GU35 8EJ. Tel:0428-712657
JOHNSTON F212

101745 ARMATAGE Mr John Sinclair. Ruahine, Kenley Road, Headley Down, Hants, GU35 8EJ. Tel:0428-712697
ARMATAGE ARMITAGE SINCLAIR F213

101753 ARMIN Mr K K. 5 Kings Drive, Bishopston, Bristol, BS7 8JW. Tel:0272-245591
Airmin Airmine Airming Airminge ARMIN Armine Arming Arminge Armyn Armyne Armyng Armynge Ayrmin Ayrmine Ayrming Ayrminge Ermyn F6414

101761 ARMITAGE Mr D. 24 Lynwood Avenue, Felixstowe, Suffolk, IP11 9HS.
Albeson Albinson Albinston Albison ALBISTON ALGAR ANDREW ANDREWS ARMITAGE ASHTON BACON BAMFORD BARNSLEY BATLEY Battlay Beaken Beakon BEAUMONT BELLAMY BERRY BOLT BOWMAN BRADLEY BRISTOL BROADHEAD BROOK BROOKE BROWN BRUCE BYROM CADMAN CALVERT CARTER Cashe CASS CASTLE CHAPMAN CHILD CLARK CLARKSON CLOUGH COOK Cooke COPPING CORBLE COULT COX DAWSON DICKISSON DURRANS EADE Eley ELLAM ELLIOT ELY EMMERSON ENDERSON ENNETT FIELD FLETCHER FOSTER GLOVER GOMERSALL HALLIWELL HARDY HARRARD HARRIS HEBBLEWHITE HEPWORTH HIRST HOBSON HODGES HOILES HOLDSWORTH HOLTE HORNER HORNSBY HORTON HOYLE HUDSON HUSBAND JACKLIN JOHNSON KEEN KING KIRK KITCHEN LAWTON LEACH LEARY LEE LEECH LISTER LOCKWOOD LUN LUSHER MACKENZIE MACKINTOSH MACROW MAIDENS MAKEIT MARSHALL MARTIN METCALF MIDDLETON Modicliff Modicliffe MOLDICLIFF Moldicliffe Moodycliff Moodycliffe MOTT Mouldercliff Mouldercliffe Mouldeycliff Mouldeycliffe Mouldicliff Mouldicliffe MURRAY NOWELL OVERTON OXLEY PACKNELL PALFREY Parfrey PARK PARR PEARCE PEARSON PHIPPS Pocknell PORTEOUS RAMSBOTTOM RECKLACE REEVE RHODES ROBERTS Rossall ROSSELL SAYLES SCOTHERN SEARS SENIOR SHAW SHIELDS SIMPSON SMITH SMITHSON SPUR STEPHENSON STEWARD STONE STURGEON SULLIVAN SWANSON TALBOT TAYLOR TICKLER TILNEY VICKERMAN WATKIN WEST WHARREY Whinfrey WILKINSON WILLIAMSON WINDLEY WINFREY WOOD WOODHEAD WRIGHT F2487

101788 ARMOUR Mr Alexander Eric. 65 Mandarin Way, Wymans Brook, Cheltenham, Glos, GL50 4RS. Tel:0242-582314
ARMOUR DUNN MCSPORRAN PHILLIPS ROBINSON F797

101796 ARMOUR Ms Elizabeth. 11155 Citrus Drive, #60, Ventura, CA 93004, USA. Tel:+1-805-659-5292
ADDY ALLAN ARBUTHNOT ARMOUR ASHTON CAMPBELL CHAMBERLAIN CLARKSON DAWSON DEANS DOW DUGGETT FISHBURN FREW HARRISON HARVEY HOWARTH HUTCHINSON KNIGHT LOCKWOOD MATHIESON MCLEOD MCMILLAN MELLOR MILLINGTON RODGERS ROSS RUSHTON SHAW SMELLIE STAINFORTH THORNTON TURTON WAINWRIGHT WALKER WATSON WHITEHEAD WHITWORTH WILLOCK WOLSTENHOLME WRAY F5529

101818 ARMSTRONG Dawn. 6 The Willows, Sedlescombe Road, St Leonards, E Sussex, TN37 7PE. Tel:0424-752474
DICKINSON HENDRY F1368

101826 ARMSTRONG Mrs Dulcie. (Sampson) 20 Homewaters Avenue, Sunbury On Thames, Middlesex, TW16 6NS. Tel:0932-783304
ARMSTRONG CAWTE FERRIMAN KITCHEN SAMPSON THATCHER F4310

101834 ARMSTRONG Mr Michael J. 1 St James View, East Hanney, Wantage, Oxon, OX12 0HT. Tel:0235-868608
Arber Arbor ARBOUR ARMSTRONG BARTON BELL BLAND BUCKENHAM CARR CHANDLER CHURCHMAN CROSS CURTIS EAGLE Eastgate EGGLETON Esgate FIELDING FLOWERS HILLIER HOPKIN HORNSBY HOWE ISGATE JOHNSON MILLS MILLSON NEW PELL ROBINSON RUTTER STANDLEY Stanley THULBORN Thurborn Thurlborn WILSON F5278

101842 ARMSTRONG Mrs Muriel. The Coach House, Hampton Lucy, Warwickshire, CV35 8BE. Tel:0789-842085

ARMSTRONG BARSTED MURDY PATRICKSON PEARCE-BACON SIMPSON F1507

101850 ARNISON Mrs Janet. Jack Dike, Cliburn, Penrith, Cumbria.
Arnason Arneson ARNISON Arnisson F7172

101869 ARNOLD Mr David. 439 Tachbrook Road, Leamington Spa, Warks, CV31 3DQ. Tel:0926-425115
ARNOLD FEARNLEY FLEMING GRAY HOLLAND HOON HUTTON RIMINTON SHEPPARD TURNEY F1063

101877 ARNOLD Mr Edmund F. 58 Coningsby Road, High Wycombe, Bucks, HP13 5NZ. Tel:0494-28611
Arnald Arnall ARNOLD Arnolde BISHOP BURMAN CAPES Ernald GRAY HUMBERSTONE MURPHY MUSGROVE SMITH TRUMPETER UPHAM WOOLNOUGH F245

101885 ARNOLD Mrs L E. 98 Garratts Way, Downley, High Wycombe, Bucks, HP13 5XZ.
ARNOLD GRANT SOMERVILLE WEEDON F7444

101893 ARNOLD Mrs Leonie. (Jackson) 123 Lynnbrooke Avenue, Blackhouse Bay, Auckland, NEW ZEALAND. Tel:+64-6-266-222
Barnes Barns Burnes BURNS CLAYDON DUNN GAGER Gaiger Gaugeor Gauger JACKSON MEADE REEVES SCOTT WARD WESTON F4687

101907 ARNOLD Mr Philip. 4 Briarwood Drive, Bangor, Co Down, N Ireland, BT19 6UW.
ALEXANDER ARNOLD BARKER BODKIN CLASPER COOPER CRACKNELL GORRUM GRIEVESON HAYES HOLMAN LANE LUCHFORD LYNCH METCALF MOSS MOZIER RAMSDALE SAFFREY SWIFT WOOLTON F1155

101915 ARNOLD Ms S M. 31 Southview Road, Marlow, Bucks, SL7 3JR. Tel:0628-482182
ARNOLD F2501

101923 ARQUATI Mrs Sylvia. (Ward) 56 Shakespeare Avenue, Arnos Grove, New Southgate, London, N11 1AY.
ATKINSON BULLOCK DOWSE HUMBERSTON Humberstone LINGARD RICHARDSON SMITH WARD WHITWORTH F6197

101931 ARSCOTT Mr Norman. 32-2070 Amelia Avenue, Sidney, British Columbia, V8L 4X6, CANADA.
ARSCOTT BATH FRICKER PRYOR STRIKE WEARNE WILLS F5448

101958 ARTER Mr Herbert E G. Conifers, Moor End, Stibbard, Fakenham Norfolk, NR21 0EJ. Tel:032878-325
ABBEY ARTER ARTHUR ATTER BIRD GREATHOLDER JAY LACK MARKHAM WIDOWSON F2871

101966 ARTHUR Mrs Jean. 37 West Avenue, Stockton Heath, Warrington, Cheshire, WA4 6HU. Tel:0925-61674
HOLLOWAY F559

101974 ASH Mr H J. Cedar Lodge, 39 Church Road, Newick, East Sussex, BN8 4JX.
AISH AISHE ASH ASHE HORTON PICKERDEN F1707

101982 ASHBRIDGE Mr D G. 8 North Royd, Hipperholme, Halifax, W Yorks, HX3 8LA.
ASHBRIDGE F7386

101990 ASHBY Mr Brian Edwin & Mrs Betty. Sixpenny Jacks, Yetholm, Kelso, Roxburghshire, TD5 8RU. Tel:057382-232
ALLAN ASHBY BRASS LOGIE MILLER MOTTRAM F1911

102008 ASHBY Mr F W. 8 High Street, Solihull Lodge, Solihull, West Midlands, B90 1EZ.
ASHBY BATES DYSON HOBSON MELLOR WOOD F4933

102016 ASHCROFT Mrs Brenda. Coopers, 12 Downside Close, Shoreham-By-Sea, W Sussex, BN43 6AF.
Aitken AITKIN ANSON ARNOLD ASHCROFT BARTLETT BIRCHALL CLARK CLAYTON COX CRESSWELL CRITCHETT DAVIS DEARSLEY DUDLEY DUNSBEE Dunsby EDWARDS HIGGINSON HILLS JOHNSON JONES KEEMISH Kemish MOXSY OWEN PAYNE PERCIVAL PIPER RICHARDS ROBERTS RUMBLE SEATLE SMITH SPINK SUTTON TALBOT THOMAS THOMSON WALKER WINNEY Winny F750

102024 ASHDOWN Mrs E I. Tan Y Graig, Graig, Glan Conwy, Colwyn Bay, Clwyd, LL28 5TW.
ANDREWS COTTON CURTIS KIRKWOOD LAILEY LALEY LAYLEY PINNINGTON SARGENT SMITH F3199

102032 ASHE Mr Richard. 5 Adcocks Yard, High Street, Measham, Swadlincote Derbyshire, DE12 7JA. Tel:0530-271173
Aishe Aisshe ASHE Asshe Aysshe CHATTEN Chatton De Esse Esse TIMMS F227

102040 ASHFIELD Mrs A R. 65 Denison Road West, Weston, Ontario, M9N 1B9, CANADA.
Aschfeilde ASHFIELD F6779

102059 ASHFORD Dr Ken. 66 Hunters Road, Leyland, PR5 2TT.
ASHFORD AXON BARDSLEY BASHFORD BOWERS HURDLEY LEDGER LEWIS LUCAS MICKLETHWAITE ROTHWELL SHAW SLATER WYCH F2759

102067 ASHFORD Mr L. 149 Manor Way, Crewe, Cheshire, CW2 6JS.
ASHFORD F6308

102075 ASHLEY Mrs Jean. (Bell) 10 Hall Close, Mill End, Rickmansworth, Herts, WD3 2US. Tel:0923-777602
ASHLEY BELL BRAY DEVEREUX HARRIS HESFORD HUGHES JARVIS JESSOP SPALL F4591

102083 ASHTON Mr Geoffrey B. Brockhurst Farm, Wem, Shropshire, SY4 5SB. Tel:0939-32425
ASHTON BARNETT BLUETT COURTNEY DEAKIN GILLETT MILEHAM SIMPSON F1258

102091 ASHTON Mr I B. 7 Woodview, Sprotbrough, Doncaster, S Yorks, DN5 7QS.
ASHTON F6346

102105 ASHTON Mr Mark. Cedar House, Soulton, Wem, Shrewsbury, SY4 5RS.
ASHTON DEAKIN F3269

102113 ASHWOOD Dr John R. White Cottage, Vicarage Lane, Capel, Dorking Surrey, RH5 5LL. Tel:0306-711067
ASHWOOD F2064

102121 ASHWORTH Mr Alf. 84 Seaford Road, Harwood, Bolton, Lancs, BL2 4BU. Tel:0204-593078
ASHWORTH BISSET CRABTREE Entwisle ENTWISTLE GREENHALGH HARDY HODGSON Hodson HOLDEN JONES LEVER LIPTROT Liptrott LUMB MARSH PENISTON ROBERTS ROSTRON TAYLOR F1831

102148 ASKEW-WERE Mrs Stephanie. 1 Harrison Court, Grimsby Road, Cleethorpes, DN35 7EN. Tel:0472-344526
ANDREWS CHURCH CODLING DENTON FREEMAN GRAVES NICHOLS NORFOLK PERRY SMALLEY SWIFT Taff TAFT Tate Tatt Teatt TEFT TETT WATTS WRIGHT F5391

102156 ASLETT Mr William. 12 Kedale Road, Seaford, East Sussex, BN25 2BY. Tel:0323-893437
Acelin Adsett Aislet Allett Alote Anslett Arselet Arselott Arslet Arslett Arsolot Arthlote Arthlottes Artolatt As Ascelin Ascelot Ase Aseelina Aselett Aseplet Ashleat Ashlet Ashlett Ashlott Aslaf Aslat Aslate Aslatt Aslet Aslete ASLETT Asletts Asliate Aslit Aslitt Asllatt Asllett Aslot Aslote Aslott Aslotte Aslut Aslute Aslutt Asplaiet Asplet Asse Asselet Asselett Asselot Asselote Asset Assett Asslade Asslat Asslet Asslett Asslot Asslott Asstlat Ast Astbatt Astelat Astelet Astelot Astlat Astlatt Astlet Astlett Astlott Astolina Asttlet Atelett Atte Lote Attlet Auselett Auslet Auslett Awnsellet Aylett Ayslett Aze Azlack Azlitt Azo Azor De Aisse Haislett Harselett Harset Harslat Harslet Harslett Haselett Haselette Haslat Hasle Haslet Haslett Haslit Haslitt Haslot Haslott Haslotte Hassett Hasslat Hasslett Hastlet Hayslett Hazlett Hazlitt Heaslett Heazlett Hesellette Hoselett Hosleed Huslett Le Asplott F2213

102164 ASLIN Mrs Janice Froud. White Talbots, Miles Lane, Cobham, Surrey, KT11 2ED.
ASLIN AVERN BRAMWELL FROUD GERRARD GODFREY GREEN HEATH HISCOCK HUMBERSTONE JARMAN MURRAY SMITH SPALDING STRAW STURDY WILKINSON F2076

102172 ASPDEN Mr Raymond. 3 Argyll Avenue, Luton, Beds, LU3 1EG.
ASPDEN Aspin Bertwell BERTWISTLE Birtwell Birtwistle DAWSON DOBSON DUXBURY HARWOOD WHITTAKER F3854

102180 ASPELING Mr R L. Po Box 6994, Piscataway, New Jersey, 08855-6994, USA.
ASPELING BLACK LEWIS F7209

102199 ASQUITH Mr Anthony. 57 Queenswood Avenue, Utton, Brentwood, Essex, CM13 1HU. Tel:0277-210023
ASQUITH HANSON HOYLE NAYLOR PAGE PEARSON SPENCER SQUIRE F3195

102202 ASSHETON-STONES Mr Christopher John. The Lane Hall, Weasdale, Newbiggin-On-Lune, Kirkby Stephen, Cumbria, CA17 4LY.
ASSHETON ASSHETON-SMITH DEIGHTON MARYON SIMPKINS SMITH STONES STRATTON F4640

102210 ASSINDER Mrs Freda J. (Newing) 9 Stone Court Lane, Pembury, Tunbridge Wells, Kent, TN2 4DF.
ALLARD ARCHER ASSINDER BRIGGS CHINN COPPINS NEWING REEVES SLATER WOODHAMS F5734

102229 ASTBURY Mrs I M. (Norton) 13 Arrowcroft Road, Guilden Sutton, Chester, CH3 7ES. Tel:0244-300423
NORTON F4566

102237 ASTELL Mr T. 11 Childwall Priory Road, Childwall, Liverpool, L16 7PA. Tel:051-737-2193
ASTELL Asthill Astill F4282

102245 ASTLEY Mrs Mary E. (Cliff) 1 Kington Cottages, Kington Lane, Claverdon, Warks, CV35 8PW. Tel:0926-842061
Agtley Alen ALLEN ARNOLD Ashley Astely Asterley Astle ASTLEY BATCHELOR BEVAN Bevin Bevins CLADERWOOD CLIFF Cliffe Clift DAVISON DIXON DUNMORE Ewings Ewins GENT GEORGE Ghent HAND HENDERSON Hevens Hewen HEWENS Hewigns Hewing Hewings HEWINS Hewons Howins HUFFERDINE Huings Huins JOHNSON LATHAM MARTIN MASON MIDDLETON Mitton MYTTON NAIRN Rider RYDER SCOTT STOKER UPPERDINE WAKEMAN WARD Wholley WOOLEY Woolley YOUINGS F4465

102253 ASTWICK Mrs Deborah. (Neale) 30 Radcot Close, Nine Elms, Swindon, Wilts, SN5 9UY.
KING LEWIS PRESTON STOLLERY F5805

102261 ATHERSUCH Dr John. The Bothy, 16 Ottershaw Park, Chobham Road, Ottershaw Surrey, KT16 0QG. Tel:0932-873033
ATHERSICH ATHERSUCH ATHERSYCH HENTALL F366

102288 ATHROLL Mrs C A. (Riches) 15 Wilshere Close, Kirby Muxloe, Leicester, LE9 9DN.
Atherol Atherold Atheroll Athrol Athrole ATHROLL Athrowl BANIARD CLOVER Earthroll Earthrowl FORSGATE GOOCH HAMMOND MAYES RICE RICHES SMY SWAFFIELD F6212

102296 ATKIN Miss Wendy J. 19 Wesley Close, Sleaford, Lincs, NG34 7LX. Tel:0529-303740
ADKIN ATKIN BOCK JOHNSON TAYLOR TOIN TOINE TOYN TOYNE F344

102318 ATKINS Mr D. 14 Ryde Place, Lee On The Solent, Hants, PO13 9AU.
ABEL ALLWOOD ATKINS BRETTON FARLEY HILLS HISTED ISTED LEM LEMM MUMFORD PEARCE ROGERS TAPPING F1111

102326 ATKINS Mrs Mary Anne. (Mills) 70 Blenheim Chase, Leigh On Sea, Essex, SS9 3BH. Tel:0702-710210
ADAMS ATKINS BILLINGS BOWERS EDEY HARRISON MILLS THARBY TURNER WRIGHT F2462

102334 ATKINS Miss S. 19 Elm Road, Seaforth, Liverpool, L21 1BJ.
BARSBY BURGESS DOWNING HODSON LAKEMAN RIXON ROBERTSON SCOTCHMER F6049

102342 ATKINSON Mr Alfred John. 2 Royal Walk, Appley, Ryde, Isle Of Wight, PO33 1NL.
ATKIN ATKINS ATKINSON BAITSON BINGHAM BOND BOOKER BOUND BROWN BRUMBY BURN CHAPMAN COCK CODLING COGGAN COOKE DINSDALE Drewry DRURY EDWARDS Farmerie FARMERY GARTON GELDER GRAY Grey GUNBY H'OULDRIDGE HARRIS HILL ISAAC JOHNSON KING LANSDALE MAJOR MARKHAM MASDEN MIDDLEBROOK MILLS NOBLE OSGARBY PRESTON RICHARDSON SEATON STAMP STEADMAN TWEED VAUSE WEBSTER WEST WESTOBY WHITWORTH WOODLIFFE F4379

102350 ATKINSON Mrs Barbara. (Maxfield) Burton Common Farm, Burton Salmon, Leeds, LS25 5NB. Tel:0977-672117
AINSWORTH ANDERSON ANDREWS ATKINSON AUSTICK BEACHELL BUTCHART CLEGG COCKBURN COWARD CRAVEN DIXON DOWNS DRABBLE DRAPER EYRE FARNSWORTH FORSTER GILL GREGORY HILL LAYCOCK LEVITT MAXFIELD MOODY MOOR MOORE NEWSOME NOBLE PARK PICKUP PRECIOUS RHODES ROBINSON ROLLO ROSE WARDLEY WATSON YEARDLEY F6026

102369 ATKINSON Mrs Brenda Lucy. Forest Side, Exbury Road, Blackfield, Southampton, SO4 1XD. Tel:0703-891732
ATKINSON BLEWETT CROMPTON F1184

102377 ATKINSON Dave. 23 Delabere Road, Bishops Cleeve, Cheltenham, Glous, GL52 4AN. Tel:0242-674169
ATKINSON BRITTON BUCKLEY CUTHBERT FRAIN HUDDLESTON LUPTON REACHER WADSWORTH F601

102385 ATKINSON Mr J Howard. C4 Keeuilrd, Rr +4, Armstrong, B C, V0E 1B0, CANADA. Tel:+1-604-546-9542
MACKLIN F5184

102393 ATKINSON Miss Jennifer. 3 Allerton Grange Croft, Leeds, LS8 1RN.
ATKINSON BRISBY BRUSBY PARROTT READMAN SMITH WELLS WINTER F5403

102407 ATKINSON Mr John. 7 Fleet Avenue, Dartford, Kent, DA2 6NL.
AITKEN ALLATT BARACLOUGH BRAY MIDDLETON NEDGE ONIONS PAVIOUR RAWNSLEY ROBERTS RUDDOCK F356

102415 ATKINSON M. Terenure, 116 Queens Road, Llandudno, Gwynedd, LL30 1TY. Tel:0492-860688
ATKINSON BLADES GODWIN GOODWIN GORDON GUMBLETON MCLENNON POTTS SMALLFIELD SMAWFIELD F2880

102423 ATTREE Mr Brian. Johanna Westerdijklaan 4, 2104 T T Heemstede, HOLLAND.
Atree Att Ree Atte Ree Attre ATTREE Tree F7389

102431 ATTWELL Mr William. Netherton, 2 Torkington Road, Wilmslow, Cheshire, SK9 2AE. Tel:0625-523205
Atterwell Attewell Attewill ATTWELL Atwell Atwells Atwill Ottewell Ottwell F4213

102458 ATTWOOLL Miss H J. Whitminster Lodge, Whitminster, Glous, GL2 7PN.
Attwoll ATTWOOLL Atwool F6694

102466 ATTWOOLL Ms Heather. Puckpool House, High Street, Arlingham, Glous, GL2 7JN.
Attwool ATTWOOLL Atwool Atwooll F49

102474 ATYED Mr Michael A. 33 St Johns Road, Ipswich, Suffolk, IP4 5DF.
Attyoe ATYED Atyeo F7067

102482 AUCKLAND Ms Mary. 10 Rookery Close, Hatfield Peveral, Essex, CM3 2DF. Tel:0245-381592
ARMSTRONG BECK STOREY STORY F1054

102490 AUDCENT Mr Geoffrey. 33 Chatsworth Road, Brislington, Bristol, BS4 3EX. Tel:0272-721334
ALSOP BAILES BOWN COTTRELL HUMPHREY PEAT RAINES RICE THOMAS WALLACE F2030

102504 AUGUST Ginger M. 32 Stetson Way, Princeton, NJ 08540, USA.
GEER F7284

102512 AULDIS Mr Peter. 83 Anfield Road, Liverpool, Merseyside, L4 0TJ.
ACHILLES Aldhouse Aldis Aldiss ALDOUS Aldus Alldis Audas Audiss Audus Auldis Braizier Brasher Brasier Brayser BRAZIER CUSTARD FAIRHALL FLINT HALPIN Hodgens Hodgeon Hodgin Hodgins Hodgshon HODGSON Hodson Oldis PARKER TAYLOR F3325

102520 AUSEUGA Mrs Kelly. (Raven) Po Box 200, Croydon, Victoria, 3136, AUSTRALIA. Tel:+61-3-726-9695
BAKES BERRY BLACKWELL BOTEREL BOURNE BRAYSHAW CARR COATES CROSLEY DAYE GILL GRAGSON HAMPSHIRE HARDISTY HOLDEN HOWARD JACKSON JEFFERY KERSHAW LINGARD LOVEDAY MITCHELL OLIVER PEARSON PRIESTLY ROBERTSHAW SHARPE SIMPSON SMITH SYKES TAYLOR TEMPEST THOMAS WAINWRIGHT WEATHERHEAD WEBSTER WILKINSON WILLIAMS WOOD F5430

102539 AUST Mr Sidney. 2 Highfield Close, Pembury, Tunbridge Wells, Kent, TN2 4HQ.
Aeste Asst Ast Aste Astes Astte AUST Auste Awst F3451

102547 AUSTERBERRY Revd David. The Rectory, Kinnerley, Oswestry, Shropshire, SY10 8DE.
AUSTERBERRY OUSTABY F149

102555 AUSTIN Mr Brian. 11 Alma Street, Weston Super Mare, Avon, BS23 1RB.
AUTIN HOOK PAYNE TRAPNELL Tratnell Tropinel Trumpmell F14

102563 AUSTIN Mr Edward. 6 Rostherne Avenue, Lowton, Warrington, Cheshire, WA3 2QD.
APPLEBY Austen AUSTIN CARL Downes DOWNS EHN HOUSEMAN LUMLEY Royal Royall ROYEL Royle F3726

102571 AUSTIN Mrs M P. 15 Moffat St, Brighton Beach, VIC 3186, AUSTRALIA.
ALDERSON Alston Alstone ASKEW ATKINSON AUSTIN

Baragwanath BARAGWANNAH BARTELL Bartle BATT BATTEN BAWDEN Beetham BENNETTS BERRIMAN BETHAM BORLASE BORROWLONG BOSCAWEN Bray BREA CARTER CHEKEMBRA CHELEW Chillew CHRISTOPHER CROSS CROWGIE CURNOW DAIN DANIEL DENNISON Dickson DIXON EARL EDDY ELLIOTT FALLOWFIELD FAWCETT FURNAS Furness Furnis GELLY GEORGE GRANLEESE GUBB HAMBLY Harper HARPUR HARRISON HARVEY HATTAM Hattem Hewsdon HODGKINSON HOLLOW HOWFIELD JACKSON JEFFREY JENKIN KEIGWIN KNIGHT Landeriowe LANDERYOU LANGDON LANYON Lenderyou LONGSTAFF MATTHEW MICHELL MILL MITCHELL MORRISH NICHOLAS Oates OATS Ostin PARKIN Parkyn PAUL PAWLEY PEARCE PEARS POTTER PRAED PRIDEAUX QUICK RICHARDS ROBERTS Rogers ROGGERS ROSEWALL SAMFORD SAMPSON SOLOMAN STEVENS THOMAS TRELEGGAN TRENBERTH Trenbirth TYACK VIBERT WARD WILLIAMS WILSON F4412

102598 AUSTIN Mr Malcolm Paul. Lelica, 32 Pettingale Road, Croesyceiliog, Cwmbran, Gwent, NP44 2NZ. Tel:0633-862089
AUSTIN CHANT FOGWELL JORDAN SHELLABEAR SHILLABEAR VITTERY WHEATON F6099

102601 AUSTIN Mrs Valerie. (Chiverton) 7 Chiltern Way, Tonbridge, Kent, TN9 1NQ.
BISHOP Bishopp Bisshop Cheverton Chiferton CHIVERTON Churton Chyfertun DAY Dupe Fenning Fenwich FINNING JACKMAN Jakeman Jakman JUPE Jupp MURPHY VALENTINE F4611

102628 AUSTIN-COOPER Mr Richard A. Butterhill House, 6 Woodside East, Northorpe, Bourne, Lincs, PE10 0HT.
Astin Augustin Augustine AUSTIN COOPER DODSON RAINSFORD F681

102636 AUSTRIDGE Mr P E. 4 Commercial Road, Devizes, Wiltshire, SN10 1EH. Tel:0380-725548
ASTRIDGE AUSTRIDGE F2587

102644 AUTHERS Mr Ellis William. 19 Chase Green Avenue, Enfield, Middlesex, EN2 8DX. Tel:081-366-0777
Arter ARTHUR Arthurs AUTHERS Authurs CLARKE ELLIS F5059

102652 AVENS Mr R B. Ashvale, 9 Harewood Drive, Cold Ash, Berks, RG16 9PF.
AVENS F6596

102660 AVERN Mrs Jocelyn. Unit 5, 201 Gladstone Road, Highgate Hill, Brisbane, Queensland, 4101, AUSTRALIA. Tel:+61-7-844-2997
BRAYSHAW BROWN HODGSON KENDALL MILLS RAISTRICK RUSSELL SMITH WHITE F5582

102679 AVERY Mr John. 2 Beech Court, Beech Avenue, Southampton, Hants, SO2 4TS.
AVERY SKILTON WILLIAMS F6193

102687 AVIS Mr J O. Po Box 9221, Albuguerque, New Mexico, 87119, USA.
LAWSON F7189

102695 AYLER Miss Jean P. 146 Tadcaster Road, Dringhouses, York, YO2 2QW.
Gorie GORRIE F7099

102709 AYRES Mr John. 19 Pittsfield, Cricklade, Wiltshire, SN6 6AW. Tel:0793-750626
AYRES CHICK F4221

102717 AYRES Mrs Leigh. 67 Manchester Drive, Leigh On Sea, Essex, SS9 3EZ.
BRETT Brian BRYAN BUTLER COKER COOK CROCKETT EDWARDS FEAST FELSTEAD FISHER GRAVES Halden HALDIN Hallden HAMPTON HARVEY HUTCHIN Hutchins LAMBERT Larance Laurence LAWRENCE LEE MORRIS Nichol Nicholl Nicholls NICOLL Nicolls NORRISH PICKETT PLUMB POTTER SHRIMPTON SMITH Stephens STEVENS TAIT TOTNAM Tottenham WALDON WARD WIX WOOD F1984

102725 AYTON Mrs B J. 22 The Row, Shireoaks, Worksop, Notts, S81 8LP.
AYTON F2506

102733 AYTON Mrs Denise M. 37 Oyster Row, Cambridge, CB5 8LJ. Tel:0223-316361
BARLOW BARTLETT BIRCH BUCKINGHAM CLARK COOLE COX CRADDOCK DANKS DAY DOBSON DUNN FREEMAN GARDINER GUEST HALL HAYWOOD HOLLAND HOOPER HUGHES JAMES KINGS MILLWARD PARDOE PRICE REEVE RICHINS SEALEY SHORT SIMON SIMONS STANIER TANSEL TROTMAN TRUEMAN WHITE F5630

102741 AYTON Mr John. 37 Oyster Row, Cambridge, CB5 8LJ. Tel:0223-316361
AYTON COLLINGWOOD DAVISON DOWSON FAILL GIBBON GORNAL Grocier GROSIER HANSON Hirst HURST KILBURN KITSON MILBURN MORALEE Morrowlee NORWOOD READSHAW REAVELEY VART F5629

102768 AZE Mr Peter. 31 Castle Road, Pucklechurch, Bristol, BS17 3RF. Tel:0272-372693
Aas Ace Ase AZE Azo Azzo JOHNSTONE VENN F4146

102776 BABER Mrs Vera. 14 Branksome Close, High Street Green, Hemel Hempstead, Herts, HP2 7AG. Tel:0442-64649
Babar BABER Babor Beaver ROADS F1204

102784 BACK Mr J E. 59 Derwent Close, Cambridge, CB1 4DY. Tel:0223-246206
BACK PANCOUST SWANNELL TOLLER F1460

102792 BADBY Mr A J. 5 Woodpeckers Drive, Winchester, Hants, SO22 5JJ.
BADBY F6554

102806 BADCOCK Mr Julian K. Abington Orchard, Leigh Place, Cobham, Surrey, KT11 2HL. Tel:0932-862969
BADCOCK BARTLETT CRUMP ELLIS HUNT LOVEY MITCHELL OLDFIELD ROGERS ROUSSELIN SCUDAMOOR F2661

102814 BADGERY Mr Thomas. 54 Upper Way, Upper Longdon, Rugeley, Staffs, WS1 1QA. Tel:0543-490594
Badgary Badgeary Badgerry BADGERY Badgeworthy Bagery Bagworthy Bajurey Bargery Budgery F5318

102822 BADHAM Mr Peter E H. Beardsland, Lewes Road, Ditchling, W Sussex, BN6 8TZ. Tel:07918-5184
Ab Adam Ab Adham Ap Adam Ap Adham Badam Baddam Baddames BADHAM Badhams BAKER BOOTH BOULCOTT COX DIXON FERRIS FINDING GOODWIN GREENAWAY JOHNSON MAPPLETHORP Mongsby MONKSBY MORGAN Rathel Rathell RATHIL Rathill ROWLES STANDLEY THOMAS WILD Wrathel F2425

102830 BAGGALEY Mrs Sheila J. (James) 1 Salisbury, Pointe Claire, Quebec, H9S 3Y9, CANADA. Tel:+1-514-426-0029
ALEXANDER Allsworth ALSOP ALTON Apperby Applebee APPLEBY Appulbee ASHTON Baddarley BADGLIE Bageley Bagelie Baggaley Baggalow Baggeley Baggerley Baggiley Bagguley Bagilye Baglay Bagley Baglie Bagly Bagney Bagueley Baguely BAGULEY Baines BANES BARKER Barnard BARNET BARNETT Barrow Beatrice Beddows BEDHOUSE Bedhows BENNET Bennett Bernard Betteridge BETTRIDGE Billinge BILLINGS Blackwell BLAKEWELL BRADLEY Breton BRIDGES Briggs Britain Brittan Britten BRITTON BROCKHURST BROOKS BUNNING Burroughs BURROWS BURTON BUSBY Carden CARDIN Carding Cheetam CHITTAM Coal COATES Coke COLE COLUMBELL COOK COOKE CORFIELD Cotes COTTEREL CURTIS DIDCOAT DILLINGHAM EADES EDWARDS ELIOT ESTOP Fallow Farrant FARRAT FAVELL FELLOW Flavell FLINT Flinte FLOYD Flynt Flynte Forster FOSBROOK FOSTER Foy FROGGATT FULFORD Fullard Fullwood FULWOOD GAMBLE Gast GIBBONS GIDDINGS Gittings Gittins GUEST HALL HALLSWORTH HANCOCK HANDFORD Hanford HARPER HARRIS HART Hawlsworth Hebert Hickens HICKMANS Hickmas Hode HOOD Horstus Hosbrook HOUGH Howlesworth HUBBARD Hubbart Hubert Hudd Huddleston HUDDLESTONE HUDSON Hurlstone HURSTHOUSE Hursthowse JAMES JOHNSON Joins Joint JONES Joy JOYNES Joyns Joynt KIRBY Knifeton Knifton Knighton KNIVETON Knollis Knollys KNOWLES LAMBERT Lawson Lawton Lee LEES Leighton Lloyd LOTON Mace Macey MANDER March Mars MARSH MARSON Mascry Masery Masgrave Masgreave Masgreve Masgrove Maskerie Maskery Maskerye MASKREY MASON MASSEY Masson MASTING Maunder MEASEY MEREDITH MILNER MILNES MINCHIN MINTRIDGE MITCHELL Moss Mosse MUSGRAVE Musgrove Mussegreffe MUSTOE NEWMAN NOONE NORMAN O'HARA OGDEN PARSUS PEACH PELFORD Persehouse Pethridge PEWES PHILIPS PIDCOCK POYNTON PRESTON Ragg Ralston REEDMAN ROBINSON ROGERS Rollston ROSTELL Rowlestone ROWLSTONE Sanders SARGEANT Sarjeant SAUNDERS SCARBOROUGH Sclater Sergeant Serjeant SHARMAN SHAW Sherman SHERWIN SKINNER SLATER SMART SMITH STALEY Stally Standford STANFORD Staniford STANLEY Starman STARMAR Staveley

Stavely Stayley SUTTON Tailor Tarrant TARRAT Tay TAYLOR TEA Tee THISTLETON Thomas Thombes Thoms Tombes TOMBS TOMLINSON TONKE Tonks TOWNDROW Townerowe Townrow Toy WAGSTAFFE WALKER WALL WARD WARREN WARSOP WARTER WEBB WELLS WINTER Woddwys Wollaston WOOD Woodis Woodwis Woodys WOOLASTON WRAGG WRIGHT F4162

102849 BAGGALLAY Mr C R. 174a Lonsdale Road, Southend On Sea, Essex, SS2 4LH. Tel:0702-617551
BAGGALLAY BRAND BROWN BUGNIO CUNDY ELLIOT FRYER HARDEN JARROLD PARSONS F5345

102857 BAIGENT Mrs A. The Badgers, 65 Horley Road, Earlswood, Redhill Surrey, RH1 5AL.
BAIGENT F6881

102865 BAIGENT Mr Jim. 109 Badminton Road, Coalpit Heath, Bristol, BS17 2SY. Tel:0454-778406
BAIGENT F2203

102873 BAIGENT Mr Peter. Edge O'Common, 14 Barnfield Road, Riverhead, Sevenoaks, Kent, TN13 2AY.
BAIGENT DRAPER FANNING JEROME SMITH WELLS F5732

102881 BAILES Mr James H. 22 North Close, Elwick, Hartlepool, Cleveland, TS27 3EQ. Tel:0429-267301
ALDER ARCHER ARMSTRONG BAILES DAVIDSON DENT FERGUSON Forster FOSTER HANCOCK Handcock HEAD HUBBARD HUSBAND JONES LAMONBY LANGSTAFF LAYBOURNE LONGSTAFF OSBORNE PINKNEY PIPER PROUD SHADFORTH SMITH-BAILES WALKER F3499

102903 BAILEY Mr Ernest. Newhaven, 7 Woodbank, Glen Parva, Leicester, LE2 9QP. Tel:0533-773345
BAILEY BELCHER COLLIER SNOWSELL WALKER F786

102911 BAILEY Mr Keith. 17 Hay Street, Kadina, SA 5554, AUSTRALIA. Tel:+61-88-211924
BAILEY F4235

102938 BAILEY Mr M. 14 Ainsty Grove, York, YO2 2HQ.
ASHPOLE BAILEY BAILEY-CHURCHILL GRIGGS F6351

102946 BAILEY Mr M. 19 Birch Grove, Bankfoot, Bradford, W Yorks, BD5 8HU.
ARSCOTT AUDAS AUDUS AWDAS BAILEY BOWDEN BUTTON CASTE CLARK COWLEY CRAGGS CROSBY DAVIS DAWSON EADON GREEN HODJINS IBBERSON JOHNSON KAY KENNY KILVINGTON LEAR LEE MCCULLOCH MCDONAGH METCALFE NETTLETON RODGERS SCRATYARD SHADDICK STOCKDALE SWALES THOMPSON TIDMAN TRAINOR VIALS WILSON WINTER YOUNG F1824

102954 BAILEY Mrs P D. 4 St Johns Close, Goring By Sea, Worthing, Sussex, BN12 4HX.
BAILEY GRADDON LOVEDAY MACKLIN OWEN PRIDHAM SEABORN STAFFORD WIRE F1185

102962 BAILEY Mrs Pearl. Po Box 479, Englehart, Ontario, P0J 1H0, CANADA.
Bailey BAILLIE Bailly Baily Cousens COUSINS SMITH WILSON F5173

102970 BAILEY Mr Ron. 4 Shakespear Road, Popley, Basingstoke, Hampshire, RG24 9DH. Tel:0256-471725
BAILEY BOWLES BROWN CARTER DEANE DIFFEY FRANCIS GILES GROOM HANHAM HERITAGE MAYNARD MEAD MUTFORD OAKINS PARR POVEY PROUT SHEPPARD SYMES TANCOCK TAYLOR THOMAS WATTS F1622

102989 BAILEY Mrs Vera. (Webb) 58 Clarendon Gardens, Stone, Dartford, Kent, DA2 6EZ.
BAILEY BALLINGER BELCHAMBER Belchambers Bellchamber Bellchambers CABLE FLIGHT HARPER RENTALL SAUNTER WEBB WEBSTER WELLS F3614

102997 BAIN Mrs Margot. The Bothy, Ardenrun, Tandridge Lane, Lingfield, Surrey, RH7 6LN. Tel:0342-834389
ATHERTON BAIN CLARK CRUICKSHANK Delaney GREIG JAMES LANY LARGUE MAXWELL MILNE MORGAN NELSON ROSS STEPHEN TAVNER F3657

103004 BAINBRIDGE Mrs A J. (Lingard) 37 Moseley Wood Avenue, Leeds, LS16 7HL. Tel:0532-671940
BARKER BISHOP HAWLEY HOLDSWORTH LEE LINGARD LONGDEN SCOTT TAYLOR TRICKETT TYLER F3887

103012 BAINBRIDGE Mrs Ann. 45 Carlton Road, Boston, Lins, PE21 8PA. Tel:0205-368226
Bedall BEEDALL Bidle GREEN PARSONS REESON Rightson ROBERTS WOODWARD F711

103020 BAINBRIDGE Mrs B L. Barn Farm, Ketford, Dymock, Glos, GL18 1LP.
HOPSON F5806

103039 BAINBRIDGE Mr John. 37 Moseley Wood Avenue, Leeds, West Yorkshire, LS16 7HL. Tel:0532-671940
BAGSHAW BAINBRIDGE FRANK GOULDING GREENWELL HALL MANIFIELD WATSON WHITTLES F3886

103047 BAINES Mr Charles Philip. 32 Wat's Dyke Avenue, Mynydd Isa, Mold, Clwyd, CH7 6UL. Tel:0352-4229
Bain BAINES Bains DENTON F89

103055 BAIRD Mr A. Coopersfield, 28a Kennylands Road, Sonning Common, Nr Reading, Oxon, RG4 9JT. Tel:0734-722052
BAIRD Beaird Beard BROWNE CAREY FRANCIS GILPIN Hook HOOKE HUGHES Kilpin ORRIS Robertson ROBINSON Steel STEELE Stiel TROTTER F4594

103063 BAIRD Miss E D. 18 Dairymoor, Wickham, Fareham, Hants, PO17 5JR.
BAIRD Beard F3607

103071 BAKE Mr Gavin. 42 Locomotive Street, Darlington, Co Durham, DL1 2QF. Tel:0325-486035
BAKE F1991

103098 BAKER Mr Charles. 3 Coniston Road, Ringwood, Hants, BH24 1PF. Tel:0425-475354
ARTHUR BAKER COOPER DIXON EDWARDS FOSTER GATES GOODE GRAY PAYNE QUIRK REES RICKARD SAWYER SILENCE Sillence WYATT F4291

103101 BAKER Mr Chris. 18 Gaialands Crescent, Lichfield, Staffs. Tel:0543-263502
Penderel Pendrell PENDRILL F762

103128 BAKER Mr Damian. 22 Hucklow Avenue, Inkersall, Chesterfield, Derbyshire, S43 3EX. Tel:0246-473846
COTTRELL DABLE HIND JONES KETTLEWELL POLLARD RICHARDSON ROBINSON SANDERSON WALLER F1730

103136 BAKER Mrs F. 40 Mornington Crescent, Hadleigh, Benfleet, Essex, SS7 2HP.
DEARLOVE F3265

103144 BAKER Mrs G E. 30 Horam Park Close, Horam, Heathfield, Sussex, TN21 0HW. Tel:04353-2717
AVIS BARNDEN CAPP DANIELS DENIELS MAJOR NICKOLDS PAGE PENNALLS SALTER SALTER-BOWEN F2500

103152 BAKER Mrs Jacqueline K. 68 Beechcroft Road, Longlevens, Gloucester, GL2 9HF. Tel:0452-525436
DAVIS JAMES TEBBS TYAS F4855

103160 BAKER Ms Jane. 17 Gorse Hill, Fishponds, Bristol, BS16 4EG.
BAKER BRAND CRUDGE DANBY DAVIES ROUPELL F3748

103179 BAKER Mrs L C M. 905 Wall Road, Hastings, NEW ZEALAND.
Preist Prest PRIEST F6771

103187 BAKER Mrs L J. (Porritt) 18 Bronzewing Terrace, Glenfield 10, Auckland, NEW ZEALAND.
ADDY FEATHERSTONE HANSON HUTCHINSON PORRITT TINDALE WHISSON F4466

103195 BAKER Mr Leslie D. 33 Skipper Way, Lee On Solent, Hants, PO13 9EU. Tel:0705-551573
BAKER CHIDWICK COOMBES DOHERTY SPENCER WOLLAND WOOLLAND F3586

103209 BAKER Miss M. 4 Pennyfields, Brentwood, Essex, CM14 5JP.
FREE F6710

103217 BAKER Mrs O M. Pineholm, High Close, Bovey Tracey, Devon, TQ13 9EX.
ATKINS RAVENHILL WELLSTED F4624

103225 BAKER Mrs S M. 2 Furnival Close, Virginia Water, Surrey, GU25 4HR. Tel:0344-843675
ADAMS BAKER BEAN BLYTON CROOT Hibbit IBBIT MCNAMARA PROCTOR REVELL RIMMINGTON SCOFFIN SCRIVENER WELCH YOUNG F2199

103233 BAKER Mrs Shirley M R. (Iverson) 12 Downs Road, Folkestone, Kent, CT19 5PW. Tel:0303-255136
IVERSON Iveson JENKINS TYLER WEBB F5960

103241 BAKER Mr Stuart Malcolm. 78 Collyer Avenue, Bognor Regis, W Sussex, PO21 5JT.
BAKER F670

103268 BAKER Mrs Wendy. 103 Rattray Road, Montmorency, Victoria, 3094, AUSTRALIA. Tel:+61-613-435-2997
COATES Coats Cotes DAFFERN Dafforn DAVIDSON EDMOND Edmonds Edmund Edmunds MARCHMENT Marchmont Marshment Marshmont Sellar Sellars SELLER Sellers SHEARD Sheil Sheill Shiel Shields SHIELL SIDEBOTTOM STRICKLAND F5544

103276 BAKES Mrs M. 278 Thornton Road, Thornton, Bradford, BD13 3AB.
Bake BAKES F7110
103284 BALABANOV Olive. 24-6700 Rumble Street, Burnaby, B C, V5E 1P5, CANADA.
BROWN CRECHLO CRESWICKE DAY DEANE GARRETT GREEN HOLLAND KEY LAMBERT LIST MADDOX MARTIN MESSENGER MILLS MOULTON MUNINGS PARBURY PIPE POLLEN TUCKER VELERS WARNE WARREN F5628
103292 BALCHIN Mr Michael. 40 Green Lane, London, SE9 2AG.
Balchen Balchild BALCHIN DICKER GOYDER Gwydyr HOYLE LUCAS PICKERING PLUMMER F3358
103306 BALCHIN Mr Nigel. 4 Fairfields, Sawston, Cambridge, CB2 4DA. Tel:0223-832439
Bachin BALCHIN Baulchen Baulchin Bolchen Bolchin F4773
103314 BALDOCK Mrs B G. (Ward) Roseway Cottage, Butts Green, Lockerley, Romsey, Hants, SO51 0JG.
CRACKNELL STANGER WARD F1750
103322 BALDWIN Mrs D. (Calderbank) 46 Arlington Drive, Leigh, Lancs, WN7 3QP.
BALDWIN BLINKHORN BROWN CALDERBANK CAVENEY COCKER GUY IRVIN KAVANAGH MAKINSON MORRIS O'DONNEL ORD WYCH F5374
103330 BALDWIN Mr David. Orchard House, 107 Andover Road, Winchester, Hants, SO22 6AX.
BALDWIN ELLIS F4099
103349 BALDWIN Mrs Dorothy. 6603 Kensington Avenue, E Richmond Hieghts, CA 94805-2054, USA.
BAKER BARNES COOPER DOUGLAS HALSEY HAWTEN HOWELL LEONARD MACGREGOR MCNAUGHTON MERCER PAXTON ROUTLEDGE RUSSELL STEWART THORCKMORTON TRIPLETT WARNE WILSON F4478
103357 BALDWYN Mr Stephen. Ambleside, 5 Alveston Grange, Mickleton, Chipping Campden, Glos, GL55 6RT. Tel:0386-438829
BALDWYN F330
103365 BALE Mr J E. The Gables, Lines Hill, Aston Abbotts, Bucks, HP22 4NG.
BALE BRIDE DIGGLE PITTS PLATT WADDUP F4166
103373 BALE Mr Robert W. 89 Melfort Road, Newport, Gwent, NP9 3FR. Tel:0633-255008
BALE CAMFIELD Campfield CHIVERS FELKIN HADDEN Haddon Haden Hadon MILLARD Pickthorn Pickton PICTON RIDGE ROBBINS Robins SYMONDS F5023
103381 BALKWILL Mr Jan. 60 Newbury St, Wantage, Oxon, OX12 8DF.
BALKWILL CRIMP DEBELL HANCOCK HARRIS HORNIMAN KEMP REEP VENNING VICARY F5787
103403 BALL Mr G N. Schoolings, Howlett End, Wimbish, Saffron Walden, Essex, CB10 2XW.
BALL DOWNING DUNCAN GLASS MCINTOSH PETHERICK Raeny Rainne Rainnie Rainy Raney Rany RENNIE Renny Reny F3825
103411 BALL Miss J. Crossing, Mary Tavy, Devon, PL19 9QD.
BALL JORDAN MADOWDER F188
103438 BALL Mr M D. 4-351 Military Trail, West Hill, Ontario, Canada M1e 4e5. Tel:+1-416-386-3283
BALL DOWLER KAY PATTISON WAKELEY F443
103446 BALL Mr Nicholas. C/o 12 Asher Reeds, Langton Green, Tunbridge Wells, Kent, TN3 0AL.
ALFREY EDWARDS ELPHICK GILBERT HATCHER HIDER Hyder LASHMORE ONION Pellen PELLIN Pelling SHERLOCK TESTER TODMAN WEST F1480
103454 BALL Mr Ronald H. Barncrosh, Castle Douglas, Kirkcudbrightshire, DG7 1TX. Tel:0556-68216
BALL GROTRIAN F6058
103462 BALL Dr Sheila. 18a Knighton Park Road, Leicester, LE2 1ZA.
DIXON DUNCAN EPEY GINNIFF LIVOCK LOVICK PERSSE STOGDEL THOMPSON TYLER F220
103470 BALLAM Mr David Bower. 13 Woolifers Avenue, Corringham, Stanford Le Hope, Essex, SS17 9AU. Tel:0375-672449
BALLAM BOWER F280
103489 BALLANGER Mr Raymond. Haseley, Reading Road, Woodcote, Reading, Berks, RG8 0QY. Tel:0491-681512
Ballanger BALLINGER DENNEY FORDE FULLER GEARING Gonstone Gunson GUNSTON Gunstone LEWIS MCKINSTRY SMITH Whiffen WHIFFIN Whiffyn Whyfyn F1793
103497 BALLANTYNE Mr John H. 6 Mansfield Place, Edinburgh, EH3 6NB. Tel:031-556-5453
BALLANTYNE F2579
103500 BALLARD Mr Paul. 120 Haygate Road, Wellington, Telford, Shropshire, TF1 2BU. Tel:0952-242417
Balhevd Ballad BALLARD Ballarde F187
103519 BALM Mr David H. 25 Parnell Street, Lower Hutt, NEW ZEALAND.
BALM Balme F7023
103527 BAMBER Mr G. Ash Cottage, 3 Gothic Close, Lincoln, LN6 3LN. Tel:0522-691770
BAMBER Baumber GOODALE SHEARD SIZELAND SWALLOW F6192
103535 BAMBER Mr Richard N. 64 Lancaster Road, Garstang, Preston, Lancs, PR3 1JA. Tel:0995-604812
BAMBER F3943
103543 BAMBROUGH Mrs Edna Frances. 6 Thorndike Close, Maybush, Southampton, Hants, SO1 6FL. Tel:0703-772744
ANDOW BAILEY BAMBROUGH BARNES BIRT DIXON JUPP MUNDELL MUNDEN POPE SATTERLEY STALLARD WOODWARD F2437
103551 BAMENT Miss Sarah J. 15 Malvern Court, Malvern Road, St George, Bristol, BS5 8JP.
BALMENT BAMENT F6501
103578 BAMKIN Mr Keith. 18 Pelham Street, Oadby, Leicester, LE2 4DJ. Tel:0533-717086
BAMPKIN BANKIN BARGER DUGGAN F6256
103586 BAND Mr A D. 14 Hill Top Road, Loughborough, Leics, LE11 3LW. Tel:0509-212748
BAND EDDLESTON NICHOLSON WELCH F1624
103594 BANGAY Mrs A J. 93 Lime Grove, New Malden, Surrey, KT3 3TR.
BANGAY Bangey Bangy F6826
103608 BANGS Mrs Judith. (Smith) Stannington, 56 Whitton Close, Bessacarr, Doncaster, South Yorks, DN4 7RD. Tel:0302-539474
BANG Bange Banges Bango BANGS BRIDGLAND CRANFIELD DEATH DENNY DONNELLY DOUGLAS ELSWORTHY FOORD GRIFFIN NEIGHBOUR PITTS SCUTT SHEA SKEA F6217
103616 BANISTER Mr J M. 102 Ladbrook Road, Solihull, W Midlands, B91 3RW. Tel:021-705-3332
BANISTER DAWSON DRAKE ELVIDGE LAWFORD PYE RICHARDSON WESELBY WRENCH F1856
103624 BANKS Mrs Beth. 124 Greenacres, Wetheral, Carlisle, CA4 8LD. Tel:0228-561189
BANKS COLE COULSON FERRIS MORRILL ROBINSON THEWLIS F2308
103632 BANKS Mr Frederick. 58 Rydal Road, Haslingden, Rossendale, Lancs, BB4 4EF.
Acerley ACKERLEY Ackersley Ackley Adthy Akeley Akerly Atey Athe Athee Athew Athey Athie Aththe Aththew Aththy Athy Athye Attay Atte Attee ATTEY Attha Atthe Atthers Atthew Atthey Atthie Atthy Atti Atty Attye Authey Banckes Bank Bankes BANKS BLAKEY Blencow BLENCOWE Blinco Blincow Bloomfield BLUMFIELD Boleyn Bollen BOYS BULL BULLEN Bullin BURNELL Careless Carles CARLESS Carlos Cayes CHARLTON CHRYSTAL Chrystell Clark CLARKE Clerk Cordner CORNER Crystal Currey CURRY Dickson DIXON Dunkerley DUNKLEY GAMAGE Gammidge Godin GODWIN Godwine Godwyne GOODMAN Goodwin Goodwyn Hackersley Haines Hains Hathey HAYNES Heynes HOLMES Horan Horn HORNE HOWE HOWES KNIBB KNIGHT Lea LEE Leigh Leverston Leverton Levingston Levington Lilley LILLY Lily LINES Litldik Littdike Litteldyke Littledick Littledike Littledyck LITTLEDYKE LIVINGSTON Livingstone Lytledikes Lytledycke MORRIS NEEDLES PALLAS PATERSON PHILIPS PIDDINGTON PLUMMER Queney Quiney QUINNEY Quyney Rhoades Rhode RHODES RICHARDSON RICKABY Rickerby Roades Rodes Roode Roodes SALTER STANLEY TINKLER WALKER WHITE Wilce WILKES Wilks Willetts Willkes Wilts WOOD WOODLEY WRIGHT F627
103640 BANKS Mr Michael John. 28 Hilsea Crescent, Hilsea, Portsmouth, Hampshire, PO2 9SN. Tel:0705-669950
ABBOTT AHLERS Assenden Assendon BANKS BROOKES Brooks BUSBY CALLOW COOPER Couper COWARD Cowper Froslick FROSTICK GODDARD HAMBRIDGE LOCK Locke LOVETT MULLENDER Osenten OSENTON

PALMER PAYNE PLEASANCE POHL QUINN RUSSELL SEWELL SHRUBB SMITH STARLING STONE TILLER VOGLER Whitchomb WHITCOMB Whitcombe WHITE Whittcomb F4621

103659 BANNERMAN Lady Joan. (Wilcox) 73 New Causeway, Reigate, Surrey, RH2 7PP. Tel:0737-221560
FRANCIS WILCOX WOLFE F6166

103667 BANTING D R. 16 Vale Drive, Findon Valley, Worthing, W Sussex, BN14 0DD. Tel:0903-872807
BANTING BLAGG FORD GOSS GOVER HERBERT MILES RICHARDS TART WHITTENHAM F812

103675 BANWELL Mr Eric. Brinton Lodge, 37 Milton Lane, Wells, Somerset, BA5 2QS.
BAKER BANWELL DUCKETT DURSTON HAM LAVER MARSTONE PARKER PITMAN TUTTON F6464

103683 BANYARD Mr Irvine John. Newstead, Coopersale Common, Copersale, Epping Essex, CM16 7QS. Tel:0378-73648
Baignard Bainard Baineard Bangiard Baniard Banniard BANYARD Benyeard Bunyard Bunyeard F1740

103691 BANYER Mr William F. 52 Belmont Gardens, Hartlepool, Cleveland, TS26 9LT.
BANYER MILLER REDFEARN F6531

103705 BARBER Mrs C Y Dawn. (Hooker) 12 Rhodanthe Road, Shorton Valley, Paignton, Devon, TQ3 1RD. Tel:0803-525771
Evelegh EVELEIGH Eveley Evely HOOKER Roe Row ROWE F4184

103713 BARBER Mr Denis. 32 The Fairway, Flackwell Heath, High Wycombe, Bucks, HP10 9NF. Tel:06285-28151
ABBET BARBER BARLEY BARTON BENTLEY BETTLES BOWLER BURLING BUTCHER CAPLE CAWOOD CHAPMAN CLARK CONSTABLE CORNEY CROWLSEY CUDWORTH DAY DIZON EDGELEY EGNY GARNER GIFFORD GREEN HORSLEY JAY JEFFERY KNIGHT LINWOOD MANCHER MARLTON PAPWORTH PAVISS PEACOCK PEDLEY POLLARD POTTER PRINCE RAYNER ROBERTS RUSSELL SHELDRICK SMITH Vara Vard Varer VARO Varow Varrd Varrde Varrow Vear Veara Veard Vearer VEARO Verer WESTLEY WHITTAMORE WINTINOR WRIGHT F158

103721 BARBER Mrs Dianne L. 138 Oak Tree Lane, Selly Oak, Birmingham, B29 6HU. Tel:021-472-0114
ARMITAGE BAYLEY BROOKS CHAPMAN COLINSON COPLEY FARRER FAULDING FISH HILL HUSTHWAITE HUSTWAYTE Hustwick Hustwit Hustwitt JACKSON JONES KIRK LEYBOURN MILLS MOODY NORTH PAYLOR RAWLING REEVES RILEY SMITH SPRAKES THOMPSON TOE TUNE WELLS F2615

103748 BARBER Mrs G. 5 Archers Close, Hertford, SG14 3BD.
Wansborough WANSBROUGH F6750

103756 BARBER Mr Geoff. Sylvanham, Merriwagga, NSW 2652, AUSTRALIA.
BARBER ESLER FLEMING GLASGOW HUN MCKINSTRY F4206

103764 BARBER Mr Jonathan E. 138 Oak Tree Lane, Selly Oak, Birmingham, B29 6HU. Tel:021-472-0114
ARCHER BARBER BENNETT BERISFORD BOND BOSWARD BROWN CANTRELL COX DIXON DURRANT HICKMAN HUNT HUTCHINSON JACKSON JUSTICE KING LLOYD LOMAS MATTLEY MAYCOCK PARKER PATTEN PECK PRICE SHORTHOUSE SMITH SPIER WESTBURY WESTON WHITE WILLIAMSON WOOD WORMINGTON F2614

103772 BARBER Mrs Nellie. Box 272, Carnduff, Sask, S0C 0S0, CANADA.
ALLOTT DICKINS HANDFORD JOHNSON PAXTON PENN STANHOPE WATLING WILSON WILTON F4454

103780 BARDSLEY Mr Alan. Cartref, Church Lane, Gawsworth, Macclesfield, Cheshire, SK11 9QY. Tel:0625-422382
Bardesley Bardley Bardsea Bardsey BARDSLEY Barseley Barsley Barsly F4297

103799 BARK Miss K P. 17 Restrop Road, Purton, Swindon, Wiltshire.
BARK F2305

103802 BARK Miss T. 23 Dauntsey, Chippenham, Wiltshire, SN15 4JE.
BARK F2548

103810 BARKER Florian. 1 East Avenue, Stoke Park, Coventry, Warks, CV2 4DJ.
BARKER BINNEY HARTWELL KENNINGTON RICE WIGLEY F294

103829 BARKER Frances. 19 The Close, Radlett, Herts, WD7 8HA.
SOLLY F2854

103837 BARKER Mrs J. 39 Dunvegan Road, Spring Cottage, Hull, East Yorkshire, HU8 9JD.
BALLANCE BARKER BRISTOW BUTTON CLARKSON DIXON FRITH GIBSON GROOMBRIDGE HILTON LAMING LAMMIMAN LAVERACK MCKINLEY MONKMAN PRESTON SIMPSON STOCKTON TEESDALE WATSON WILLIAMSON F4223

103845 BARKER Mrs Pat. (Swales) 71 Waterloo Road, Hakin, Milford Haven, SA73 3PD. Tel:0437-762059
ADAMS BARKER EVANS HOGAN MATHIAS PRICE SCALE SWALES F2774

103853 BARKER Mr Robin. 38 Pryor Road, Baldock, Herts, SG7 6LH. Tel:0462-490523
Barcker BARKER Brind Brindad Brinded Brindley BRINDY BURKE Chalkeley CHALKLEY Chalkly DALE DAVIDSON F6043

103861 BARLEY K G. 80 George Street, Maulden, Bedfordshire, MK45 2DD.
Barelegge Barlee Barleigh BARLEY Barlie Barly F7092

103888 BARLTROP Mr Roger. Avalon, 1 Glendale Road, Burgess Hill, W Sussex, RH15 0EJ. Tel:0444-232856
ALEXANDER BAKER Balthrop Baltrop Baltrope BARLTROP Barthrop Barthropp Bartrip Bartrop BRAY CARPENTER NICHOLS STARMER F3688

103896 BARNARD Mr Walter. 2a St James Avenue, Marden Ash, Chipping Ongar, Essex, CM5 9EL. Tel:0277-363871
BARNARD BARTHOLOMEW BASSINGHAM Bateson Batson BLACK BURFIELD BUTSON Chappel CHAPPELL Chapple CLEGG COLLINS COXHEAD FOWLER GILES GODDARD Kimber KIMMER Kymer KYNE LAING LEGON MAILE MASKELL MAYO MILES NORRIS OVERELL PATMORE ROYDS SIMS SNOW STONE TILBURY WARD F912

103918 BARNES Mr Andrew. 9 Kindersley Close, East Grinstead, W Sussex, RH19 3NJ.
BARNES DRIVER ISAAC ISAACS LEWIS LUFF POOLE Pooley ROBERTS TRUSCOTT F867

103926 BARNES Mr Bill. 64 Salisbury Road, Werrington, Peterborough, Cambs, PE4 6NW. Tel:0733-576191
BARNES SUCKLING F2910

103934 BARNES Mrs C June. (Buchanan) 50 St Helens Park Road, East Sussex, TN34 2DN. Tel:0424-420065
Armantage ARMITAGE ARMSTRONG BALLS BARNES BENNETT BRODIE BRUNT BUCHANAN COOPER Dickenson DICKINSON DUCKWORTH DUNKLEY EDWARDS GOULD GRANT GREENLEES HAYTER HELPS HILLS HODDELL JOHNSON JONES KIDMAN KING Marsom MARSON MCDONALD MCPHERSON MOLE NEAT Neate NORTON PAUDON PEART PENDLETON PROUT ROBERTS SANDFORD SCOTT SHAW SHERGOLD SMITH STRICKLAND SWAN TURNER WALLWORTH WARE Weare WEBBER WELLS WHEELER WIBBERLEY WILLIAMSON WOODFORD WORROLL F3320

103942 BARNES Lady C M R. Hampton Lodge, Hurstpierpoint, Sussex, BN6 9QN. Tel:0273-833247
AWDREY BURN BURNE EARLEY-COOK LANCASTER REMINGTON-SMITH SMITH F3524

103950 BARNES Cecil Holland. Contracts, Salisbury Gardens, Buckhurst Hill, Essex, IG9 5ER. Tel:081-505-6472
BARNES HOLLAND LETTEN SOMERVILLE F904

103969 BARNES Miss D. 32 Pembroke Green, Lea, Malmesbury, Wiltshire, SN16 9PB. Tel:0666-824794
BARNES HAYWARD WHITE F6078

103977 BARNES Mr Douglas R. 4 Harrowby Road, Leeds, W Yorks, LS16 5HN.
BARLOW BARNES BURGEN Collier COLYER DODSON EMBREY FLOYD FRYSER HARRIS HOOPER Houghton HOUTON HURST LLOYD LUFFLUM NORTH PHILLIPS POUNDS QUATERMAINE Shroudley SIDDALL Sidwell STROUDLEY Wakelyn WALKLIN WALLIS WILLIS WING WITHALL F3252

103985 BARNES Mrs Joan. (Burnett) 81 Stanley Avenue, Baffins, Portsmouth, Hants, PO3 6PL.

BARNES BATES BRACE BURNETT CARDY Lighting LIGHTNING LIGHTWING Lightwyn Lightyn PITCHER SAVAGE WILDE F862

103993 BARNES Mr John D. 19 Avon Crescent, Stratford Upon Avon, Warwickshire, CV37 7EX.
BARNES COPPARD COX DAVIS DENLEY Denly HABGOOD LUCK WALTER WYATT F5744

104000 BARNES Mr Russell M. 42 St Leonards Avenue, Blandford Forum, Dorset, DT11 7NY. Tel:0258-452109
BARNES DOVER HISCOCK SPRACKLING F6013

104019 BARNHURST Mr A. 40 Woodstone Avenue, Stoneleigh, Epsom, Surrey, KT17 2JR.
Barnehurst BARNHURST F6895

104027 BARNSDALE Mr Robert David. 33 Roumania Drive, Craig-Y-Den, Llandudno, Gwynedd, LL30 1UY. Tel:0492-874590
BARNERDSHIL BARNEYSDALE BARNSDALE COLLICK DAVIES EVANS HANNAH JONES OWEN PERRIN Pue Pugh REID ROBERTS RUGH SALESBURY Salisbury Salusbury WILLIAMS F3663

104035 BARON Mrs Joyce E. (Roberton) 6 Waverley Avenue, Kenley, Surrey, CR8 5BE.
ROBERTON F6116

104043 BARON Mr Thomas. 45 Bristol Street, Barrow In Furness, Cumbria, LA14 3LA.
BARON Beron CLINTON ELLISON KELLY LEE MCDERMOTT PARKINSON PERKS PHILLIPS F4662

104051 BARR Mr G A D. 282 Dickson Drive, Irvine, KA12 9HG.
BARR F3630

104078 BARRACLOUGH Ms M. 25 Elmfield Avenue, Longwood, Huddersfield, W Yorks, HD3 4SQ.
BARRACLOUGH BERRY FORD NOLLER Nolly POTTER F3893

104086 BARRANCE Mr John D. Awelfryn, Pentre, Tregaron, Dyfed, SY25 6NF. Tel:0974-298377
BARRANCE F1284

104094 BARRAT Mr George Reginald. 31 Mendip Road, Chelmsford, Essex, CM1 2HN.
BARRAT F2499

104108 BARRETT Mr C L. 15 Limes Road, Folkestone, Kent, CT19 4AU.
U'ren UREN Urin Urine Yorren F6619

104116 BARRETT Mr D E. 24 Old Mill Road, St Catherines, Ontario, L2N 6X2, CANADA.
Barratt BARRETT Berrett F6626

104124 BARRETT Mr Michael. 10 Wellhead Lane, Westbury, Wiltshire, BA13 3PW. Tel:0373-822458
BAILEY BARRETT BRAIN COCKERILL DUNKLEY GIBBS INWOOD SWANNELL WARDEN WOOLISON F4133

104132 BARRETT Mr Robert. Pulteney Cottage, Lower Buckland, Lymington, Hampshire, SO41 9DQ.
BARRETT Bridgeman BRIDGMAN FLEMING JAMES JANVERIN SMITH WILLIS-FLEMING WITTS F3247

104140 BARRETT Mr Stephen. 94 Lockington Avenue, Hartley, Plymouth, Devon, PL3 5QQ. Tel:0752-778781
ALLEN BARRETT BASTIN BICKFORD DAWSON HUSBAND KERTON STOKES WHITFIELD WINTER F5869

104159 BARRINGTON . 50 Upper Park, Loughton, Essex, IG10 4EQ.
ANNING BARRINGTON CLULOW DANCE F900

104167 BARROW Mr Anthony. 38 East Approach Drive, Pittville, Cheltenham, Glos, GL52 3JE. Tel:0242-239777
ATHERTON BARROW HODDER F378

104175 BARROW Mr G. 51 Turpins Way, Baldock, Herts, SG7 6LW.
Abarrow Baro Barro Barrough BARROW Barrows F7230

104183 BARRY Mrs Joan. (Dingle) Tye House, Gedding, Bury St Edmunds, Suffolk, IP30 0QF. Tel:0449-737906
COX CRAWLEY Dingel DINGLE Dingley HENWOOD MARTIN Martyn Mathews MATTHEWS MULDER RAPSON WOOLCOCK F3158

104191 BARRY Mrs Lynne. 23 Church Road, Abertridwr, Caerphilly, Mid Glamorgan, CF8 2DL. Tel:0222-830004
ADDICOAT BARRY CAIGER CHAPPLE CORRIE FALLACE HARVEY HOSKIN HUMPHREYS KELLET MORGANS RIGHTON SAUNDRY SEMMENS SHEEHAN VINGOE F5330

104205 BARTER Mrs Glenys Rhoswen. 1 Birkdale Avenue, Werrington, Peterborough, Cambs, PE4 6RW.
DAVIES REECE THOMAS F3296

104213 BARTHOLOMEW Mrs M E. 16 Nursery Gardens, Purley On Thames, Reading, Berks, RG8 8AS.
BARTHOLOMEW DAVIES DEVONALD HANCOCK HAWKSWORTH HUDSON LEE MIDDLESTON NAYLOR NEWMAN RUDDOCK WALKER WEST WOOLEY WOOLLEY F1506

104221 BARTLE Mr James. 14 Marx Crescent, South Stanley, Co Durham, DH9 6JZ.
Bartel BARTLE BOWMAN JEFFERSON Keears KEERS Keirs Ker Kiers F6463

104248 BARTLETT Mr Raymond Harry. Monks Walk, Quarr Road, Binstead, Rye, Isle Of Wight, PO33 4EL. Tel:0983-64257
BARTLETT F3645

104256 BARTLETT Mr Steve. 3 Delamere Road, Nantwich, Cheshire, CW5 7DR.
BARTLETT FRAINE Perham PERIAM Perriam Peryam PUDDEPHATT TOMS WEBBER F502

104264 BARTLETT Mrs V M. 50 Gloucester Road, Stratton, Cirencester, Glous, GL7 2LA.
HORTON SAWYER SHELLEY TANNER F2161

104272 BARTON Mr Ifor. The Old Vicarage, Station Road, Grasby, Barnetby, Lincs, DN38 6AP. Tel:065262-391
BARTON BEDFORD COLEBROOK DRUST EDWARDS FRENCH GREEN HARTRIDGE JENKINS MCGRATH F1724

104280 BARTON Major John. 21 Avenue Road, Hunstanton, Norfolk, PE36 5BW. Tel:0485-532129
BARTON F1012

104299 BARTON Mr Philip & Mrs Kathryn. 19 Mountbatten Rise, Little Sandhurst, Camberley, Surrey, GU17 8LS. Tel:0344-777259
AMOS ARTLEY ASQUITH AXON BARTON BATES BOOTH BOY Boys CAVELL Cavil Cavill CHARLESWORTH Collumbine COLUMBINE CRAWSHAW Cullumbine DAVY DREW DUNN DURSLEY EVERETT Everitt Everrit EYRE FAXON FRUDD GARTHWAITE Girthwaite GOVIER Hartley HUCKLEBRIDGE JACKSON JACOMBS JUDD LEE LUPTON LUTON MARYCHURCH Merrychurch Millar MILLER MURCH NICHOLAS Nichols NORMAN NORTON PEGLAR Pegler PROUD Rawlen Rawlens Rawlin Rawlings RAWLINS RICHARDS ROBERTS Rollings SELY SHEIDL Shield Shields SMALL SMITH Southcote SOUTHCOTT STEVENSON TAYLOR TIMBERRY TINDALL Tindel Tindle TURNER VENN WASHER WRIGLEY F4181

104302 BARTON Mr Richard Giles. Mulberries, Badingham Road, Framlingham, Suffolk, IP13 9HS. Tel:0728-723615
ALDERSON BARTON DANFORTH ELWELL HARDY KITTO LE GEYT MCCONNEL POTTER PRITCHARD RAISBECK STEPHEN F5035

104310 BARTRON Mrs Audrey. (Swaffield) 7 Dove House, St Marys Court, Peterborough, PE1 1UR. Tel:0733-63702
ASKEW BACKAULLER Backoller BETTY BLINSHAM BROAD CANTERBURY GILLINGHAM GLANVILLE HOPPER KERSLAKE NOTT RATLIEFF RAWLEIGH RISDON Shaxon SHAXTON SWAFFIELD TUCKER WAKELY WALKER WHITTLE WORGER F4827

104329 BARUGH Mr Denis. 16 Stamford Street, Middlesborough, Cleveland, TS1 3EW. Tel:0642-230014
BARFF BARGH Barghe BARK BARR BARROW BARUGH BOWKER BROUGH GREENHOW STIRLAND F3754

104337 BASE Mr Robert. 15 Appleford Close, Hoddesdon, Herts, EN11 9DE.
ADAMS BASE CANHAM DIGBY-GREEN DOBSON GIBBS KAYLER PROSSER SKELT Teitgen TEITYEN Tietgen WARD WINN F5813

104345 BASKER Mr Joe. 20 Maxwell Street, Breaston, Derby, DE7 3AH. Tel:03317-2358
BASKER F3101

104353 BASKERVILLE Mr G. 25 Manor Avenue, Caterham, Surrey, CR3 6AP.
Bascavill Baskavil Baskavill Baskaville Baskcavill Baskerfeelde Baskerfield Baskervil Baskervile BASKERVILLE Baskevile Baskevill Baskeville Baskvyle Beskerville Bnascaville F6250

104361 BASLEY Miss Pamela. 27 Canberra Road, Christchurch, Dorset, BH23 2HN.
BASLEY CRITCHELL HALFORD LITTLEBOY PATRICK F4756

104388 BASLINGTON Mr Colin E. 10 Honeypot Lane, Brentwood, Essex, CM14 4QT. Tel:0277-225613
BASLINGTON Basslington Bazlington Bazlinton F278

104396 BASLINGTON Mrs G M. (Hanson) 10 Honeypot Lane, Brentwood, Essex, CM14 4QT.
BOOTHBY BRUNYEE Cocksworth COXWORTH FUSSEY GOODRICH HANSON HORSEFIELD Horsfield MALKINSON SCARROW SKERO SKERROW SKIRROW TURNER VYSE WATSON F279

104418 BASS Mrs Mary. 55 Newbury Gardens, Stoneleigh, Epsom, Surrey, KT19 0NY.
Alvey ELVEY Elvy Lanckum Lancomb Lancome Lancon LANCUM THOMAS WILLS F5003

104426 BASSENDEN Mr Robert. Starkers, Wray, Lancaster, Lancs, LA2 8QP. Tel:05242-21836
BASSENDEN F1821

104434 BASSIL Miss Barbara. 12 College Rise, Maidenhead, Berks, SL6 6BP.
HEMS F2324

104442 BASSINGTON Mr Geoffrey. The Breezes, Lydney Road, Bream, Glos, GL15 6EW.
ADAMS BASSINGTON DANN HAIMES JOWSEY MORRISON PROUD WILKINSON F5121

104450 BASTON Mr J. 22 Greystones Road, Bearsted, Maidstone, Kent, ME15 8PD.
ASBY BASTON BRUFF CHADD F4226

104469 BATCHELER Mr Stan. 10 Homefield, Child Okeford, Blandford Forum, Dorset, DT11 8EN.
ATKINS BATCHELER CHAPMAN CUPITT DAVIES HALL HOLTON PRIEST SUDELL F642

104477 BATCHELOR Mrs Beryl. (Hammett) 4 Gainsborough Crescent, Lower Hillmorton, Rugby, Warwickshire, CV21 4DQ.
BIRD COLLINS HAMMETT POLING WAKE F1434

104485 BATCHELOR Mr Kenneth. Uganizam, 3 Elven Lane, East Dean, Eastbourne E Sussex, BN20 0LG. Tel:0323-423046
BATCHELOR BOYELL LEACH F433

104493 BATELLE Mr A E. 321 Tring Road, Aylesbury, Bucks, HP20 1PJ.
BEDWARD Bedwood F6959

104507 BATEMAN Mr Roger. 21 Elizabeth Avenue, Hove, Sussex, BN3 6WA.
BATEMAN F1815

104515 BATES Mrs Beryl. (Perkins) 435 Brant Road, Lincoln, LN5 9AL. Tel:0522-722661
BAILIE BARTTRAM BASETON Beacham BEDFORD BEECHAM BISHOP BOOTHBY BRADFORD BRIGGES BRISTOW BROWN BUSH Campain CAMPION CAUNT CLARKSON Clarkstone COTTAM CROPLEY DAVIE Davies Davy DEWY DURHAM EDWARDS Farrow FINES GOODYEAR HACK HANES HEARSON HOBMAN HODSKIN HUDDLESFORD HUMPHREY INGALL JACKSON JARVIS JENKINS JESSOP KATLINE LONG MAKENDER MANTLE MATLOCK MONK Mould MOULDS MUSSON MUXLOW Parkins PATTINSON PERCIVAL PERKINS PHARROW PICKER Pirkins ROE Row Rowe SAXBY Saxilby SEWARDS SHARMAN Simon Simonds SIMONS SKINNER SMITH Symon TAYLOR WILLIAMSON WOODS F5028

104523 BATES Mr George. 8 Levens Drive, Leyland, Lancs, PR5 2SS.
BATES FOOT RAINFORD F195

104531 BATES Mr Robert M. 99 Bournville Lane, Bournville, Birmingham, B30 1LH.
Bate BATES Beats Betts BUCK CARBUTT CHADWICK CROWSON Donning Dunell Dunhill Dunil Dunnel DUNNELL GRAY Haywood HEYWOOD HILL KENNY Meakin MEEHAN MILLER O'meehan SAYER Sayr WALKER F3312

104558 BATH Miss P C. 17 Eastcourt Road, Gloucester, GL1 3LU.
BATH Bathe SCRIVEN Scrivens F6911

104566 BATMAN Mr Philip. 7 Albany Walk, Ilkley, W Yorks, LS29 9LZ. Tel:0943-600447
ALLINSON BATMAN HOBSON F5850

104574 BATT Miss Diana. 21 Highland Road, Northwood Hills, Middx, HA6 1JP. Tel:09274-26054
BATT ENGLISH RUSSELL SMITHERS F2446

104582 BATTEN Mr K. 3 Slains Road, Bridge Of Don, Aberdeen, Scotland, AB2 8TT.
BATTEN Battin Batton Battyn F6916

104590 BATTERSBY Rita. (Astley) 84 Old Clough Lane, Walkden, Worsley, Manchester, M28 5HG. Tel:061-790-5042
Asley Asteley Astle ASTLEY Brearley Briarley BRIERLEY RENNIKER WATSON F2089

104604 BATTY Miss P. 3 Ridgeway House, The Ridgeway, Tarvin, Cheshire, CH3 8JW.
CHAMBERLAINE HONNER MACARTHY MASSIAH MAY ST CLAIR TURNBUKK TURNBULL F6412

104612 BATTYE Mr Colin. Greystones, 62 Miry Lane, Thongsbridge, Huddersfield W Yorks, HD7 2SB. Tel:0484-687594
BAILEY BATTYE CALVERT HINCHLIFFE SWALLOW SWINDLEHURST TAYLOR WAKEFIELD F3088

104620 BAUGH Mr Stanley. 7 Maes Yr Afon, Pontyclun, Mid Glamorgan, CF7 9DL. Tel:0443-225916
BAUGH Boff Bough FOXWELL MONK SIRRELL F1286

104639 BAUGHEN Mr C R. 4 Harewood Close, Reigate, Surrey, RH2 0HE.
Baffin Bauffin Baugham Baughan BAUGHEN Boffin F6654

104647 BAXTER Mrs A. 9 Wendouree Street, Busby, NSW 2168, AUSTRALIA.
Beverlee BEVERLEY Beverly F7202

104655 BAXTER Mr Daniel John. 143 Elizabeth Avenue, Clontarf, Queensland, 4019, AUSTRALIA. Tel:+61-7-284-3842
ORGAN F5148

104663 BAXTER Miss Mary E A. 86 Aspley Way, Peterborough, Cambs, PE3 9PF. Tel:0733-332163
BAXTER CHAMP DADE FORREST QUARRY SPENCER F1218

104671 BAXTER Mrs Rosemary. (Johnson) 647 King Street, Aberdeen, Scotland, AB2 1SB.
ANDERSON BAIRNSON BAXTER BLAIR CAIE COLENSO DU PAY FARQUHAR JAMIESON JOHNSON KELWAY MANSON MORRICE MORRISON NICOLSON PETERSON POLWIN ROBERTSON TAIT YEOMAN F3215

104698 BAYLES Mr John. 22 Arnhem Way, Woodhall Spa, Lincolnshire, LN10 6TJ.
BAYLES F5996

104701 BAYLES Mr Maurice E. 47 Surrey Avenue, Slough, Berks, SL2 1DS. Tel:0753-535609
BAYLES CRAGGS GRANTHAM SPURLING STAINTON WALKER F4814

104728 BAYLEY Ms Merrill. 2nd Floor Flat, 106 Baker Street, London, W1M 1LA.
ARROWSMITH ATKINSON BAYLEY COOMER CULVERWELL FARQUAR GRAY ROBINSON TINN WATSON F5682

104736 BAYLEY Miss P M. Russells Farm, Buckland St Mary, Chard Somerset, TA20 3QF.
CHAMBERLAIN CHAMBERLAYNE TANCARVILLE F889

104744 BAYLISS Mrs P A. (Martin) Garden Cottage, Sweeps Lane, Burford, Oxon, OX18 4NB. Tel:0993-823531
GRIFFIN KIRBY MARTIN STEBBINS F5971

104752 BAYNTON Mr T. 38 Woodside, Leigh On Sea, Essex, SS9 4QU.
BAYNTON F7409

104760 BAZELY Mrs Jill. (Dalton) 161 Farnaby Road, Shortlands, Bromley, Kent, BR2 0BA. Tel:081-460-6019
Ailesbury Albury Alesbury Alsbury AYLESBURY Baseleigh Baseley Basely Bazeley BAZELY Bazley Beazley Bezley DALTON Elsbury FLETT Hocknall HOCKNELL Ocknall Ocknell F2391

104779 BAZLEY Mr Chris. 149 Pah Road, Cockle Bay, Hawick, Auckland New Zealand. Tel:+64-534-5530
BAZLEY F1169

104787 BAZZONE Mr J M. 15 Fraser Close, South Street, Romford, Essex, RM1 2DF.
Bazoni BAZZONE Bazzoni F6676

104795 BEACHAM Mr Ronald. 33 Tattenhoe Lane, Bletchley, Milton Keynes, Bucks, MK3 7AD. Tel:0908-371037
BEACHAM Beachamp Beauchamp Beecham KEATS F4633

104809 BEADLE Mr N. 32 Buckland Rise, Pinner, Middlesex, HA5 3QS.
BEADLE BEDELL MARCHANT SAMS F6261

104817 BEAL Mrs Celia. 50 Brooklands Road, Bedhampton, Havant, Hants, PO9 3NT.
ANGELL BARRETT CHAPMAN CLEVERLEY DRIVER HARANETT HOLLOWAY Leabourn Leabourne Leborne Lebourn LEIBORNE Leyborne Libourn Lonen LONNEN Lonnon Lybourn OSMAN RUSSELL Selance Selence Sellen Sellence Sellens Silence SILLENCE Sillince Sillins Sillons Sollons Sullence Sullens Sullince Sullins Walden

Waldin WALDING WATKINS F2698
104825 BEAL Dr John F. 4 North Park Road, Leeds, LS8 1JD. Tel:0532-661158
ATTWOOD Atwood BEAL Beale Blacknee BLACKNEY Blakeney Boarder BORDER CORNMELL COSTIN COX ELTON HANDS KEEN Keene LUXTON MATTHEWS MESSENGER NASH NEAL PARSLOW REYNOLDS SPRATLEY Thurkle THURTLE VOYSEY F4035
104833 BEAMISH Mr Charles. 1 Pencreber Road, Horrabridge, Yelverton, Devon, PL20 7SF. Tel:0822-852693
Bamis BEAMISH Beaumes Belmeis Bemayes Bemis Bemysh Bewmays F182
104841 BEAN Mr C T. 1 Woodhouse Close, Hove, E Sussex, BN3 5LS. Tel:0273-424815
BEAN Beane Been F2139
104868 BEARD Mr David. 59 Fossdale Moss, Leyland, Lancs, PR5 3WS.
BEARD BOYLES GORE HEYWOOD F5405
104876 BEARD Jane. 35 Portsmouth Road, Surbiton, Surrey, KT6 4QH.
BEARD MILES F734
104884 BEARD Mrs P S. (Henley) The Anchorage, Port E Vullen, Maughold, Isle Of Man. Tel:0624-813576
AMOR BEARD BRIDGEMAN Bridgman Burgeman Burgman CALDERWOOD Davies DAVIS DONALD Flowdie Flowdy Flowerday FLOWERDEW FORBES GODDERIDGE Hendley Hendlie Hendly Henley Henlie HENLY HIGGINS JACKSON MCCULLOCH NOAD NURCOMBE READ RUDDOCK Sloacomb Sloacombe Slockem Slockham Slocomb SLOCOMBE Slocome Slocum Slocumb Slocumbe Slokeham Slowcomb Slowcombe SMITH SNELLING Stockham Stocombe Tachell Tackel Tackle Tagle Tague Teag Teage TEAGLE Teagse Teague Teakle Teaqu Teege Tegel Tegle TUBBY WEBBER WHALE Whales Whayle Wheal Wheale Wheall Whoal WILKIE WILLIAMS F5761
104892 BEARDSMORE Mr Clive. 108 Rotton Park Road, Edgbaston, Birmingham, B16 0LH.
BEARDSMORE HATTON MATTHEWS WALDRON F5729
104906 BEATSON Mr B L. 441 Beechcroft Place, Port Perry, Ontario, L9L 1N5, CANADA.
Bason Bate Bates BEATSON F7168
104914 BEATTIE Dr Alan. 9 Bruntwick Drive, Lower Halstow, Sittingbourne, Kent, ME9 7DX. Tel:0795-843095
ARTHUR BEATTIE BLANCE EDWARDS HEASMAN IRVINE KILNER MEWETT TESTER WINCHESTER F1356
104922 BEATY Mrs Jane V. (Hawkins) 6 Chalet Close, Berkamsted, Herts, HP4 3NR.
BOSTRIDGE GRINSTED HAWKINS HUBSDELL PEIRCE F687
104930 BEATY Mrs Mary. (Weymouth) 45 Broomfallen Road, Scotby, Carlisle, Cumbria, CA4 8DE.
WEYMOUTH F4200
104949 BEAUCHAMP Mrs Brenda M. (Foster) 62 Balliol Road, Wyken, Coventry, CV2 3DS.
FOSTER HERBERT F338
104957 BEAUCHAMP Mr Paul. 62 Balliol Road, Wyken, Coventry, W Midlands, CV2 3DS.
Beacham Beaucham BEAUCHAMP Beecham F164
104965 BEAUFOY Miss C M. 202 Kahutia St, Gisborne, NEW ZEALAND.
BEAUFOY PAGE F4367
104973 BEAUMONT Mrs B. 37 Sheridan Avenue, Caversham, Reading, Berks, RG4 7QB.
Tampen TAMPIN Tampion Tempan F6846
104981 BEAVEN Mr R. 32 Pitchers Hill, Wickamford, Evesham, Worcs, WR11 6RT.
BEAVEN SALMON WILKS F771
105007 BEBBINGTON Mrs Brenda. (Bibby) Merlins Spoke, Sun Hill, Calbourne, Isle Of Wight, PO30 4JA. Tel:0983-78520
BIBBY HILL OLLIER POWNALL F5110
105015 BECK Mr B S. 87 Naseby Tower, Desmond Street, London, SE14 6JT.
BAGGS BECK BINNS BOURNE CREED FERRY FOSTER HUGHESDON JARVIS POLLARD RICHARDSON ROLFE SPENCE TREVETT TUCK TUNBRIDGE WATSON WHITE WIGHAM F142
105023 BECK Mr Derek. 25a Longwood Avenue, Bingley, W Yorks, BD16 2RX. Tel:0274-567343
Bec BECK Becke Bek Bonser BONSOR EVERETT JACOM Jacomb TARLINGTON WILKINSON F1395
105031 BECK Mr K G G. 3 Mount Pleasant Avenue, Hutton, Brentwood, Essex, CM13 1PW. Tel:0277-223248
BECK BOTWRIGHT CATCHPOLE CURTIS FULCHER MOYSE SOUTHGATE TINLEY WATLING WHAYMAN F4711
105058 BECK Mr Kenneth. 29 Osprey Close, Bicester, Oxon, OX6 0YH. Tel:0869-248731
BECK SCOTT SMART F1322
105066 BECK Mrs Sarah. (Ringer) 29 Osprey Close, Bicester, Oxon, OX6 0YH. Tel:0869-248731
RINGER F1323
105074 BECKENHAM Mr Brian. 697 Great West Road, Osterley, Isleworth, Middx, TW7 4PS.
BECKENHAM CALLIS CROMWELL F2005
105082 BECKERLEG Mr John. Jigglers Cross House, 57 High Street, Meppershall, Beds, SG17 5LX. Tel:0462-816547
BECKERLEG CARLION F4288
105090 BECKERLEGGE Mr Philip. Standswell, 36 Cheltenham Road, Cirencester, Gloucestershire, GL7 2HX. Tel:0285-658390
BECKERLEG BECKERLEGGE F3574
105104 BECKETT Eugene. Po Box 502, Cambria, Illinois, 62915, USA.
Beckett Becquet Bequet BEQUETTE F7236
105112 BECKHAM Mr Tom L. 33 Eleanor Road, Bowes Park, London, N11 2QS. Tel:081-889-6380
BECKHAM F2160
105120 BECKINGHAM Mrs Fiona. 28 Esrom Street, Bathurst, 2795, AUSTRALIA. Tel:+61-63-319317
Aldridge AYERS Backingam Backinggam Backinggame BACON BEARD BECKINGHAM Berkingham Bickingham CAN Castell Castelle CASTLE Castles CLARKE COLE DUNN EDWARDS ELDRIDGE FRANKLIN FREEMAN GATHERCOLE Gibbson GIBSON GILES GILL HANDFORD HARTLEY HOGAN HOLDER HOUNTE HOWELL Johnson Johnston JOHNSTONE KING KIRKLAND MAHER NEVELL Nevil Nevill Neville Penney Penning PINNING PITCHES SHONE Smith Thurleigh-Smith Thurley-Smith TURLEY-SMITH Tyrley-Smith Vinceant VINCENT F4202
105139 BEDDOES Mrs Theadora Margaret. 16 Ebnal Road, Shrewsbury, Shropshire, SY2 6PW. Tel:0743-52465
FOULKES JENKINS JONES F914
105147 BEDENHAM Mrs Maureen. 19 Radford Close, Yew Tree Estate, Walsall, W Midlands, WS5 4HW.
ASHCROFT ATKINS BACH BALLUER BEDENHAM BOTT CALLINSWOOD CALLOWAY FORRESTER GRIFFIN HAMMOND HOLMES HUNT ORE PARKES POVEY ROE-HUGHES SANDFORD TEDD TIPTON F2051
105155 BEDFORD Mrs A Patricia. (Glover) 16 Jordan Avenue, Chatham, Ontario, N7M 1A2, CANADA. Tel:+1-519-354-2986
BEEDLE EDWARDS GLOVER F5443
105163 BEDFORD Mrs D B. (Ball) 7 Sunny Hill, Kirton In Lindsey, Gainsborough, Lincs, DN21 4ND.
ARROWSMITH BALL BEDFORD BUTCHER FENTON KINGSLEY LEWIS MADES MOORE MORRITT WATSON F5854
105171 BEDFORD Mr Denis. 5 Orchard Hill, Exeter, Devon, EX2 9ND. Tel:0392-55302
BEDFORD STACEY F2936
105198 BEDFORD Mr J G. 14 Castle Park, Belfast, N Ireland, BT15 5FF.
BALSHAW BEDFORD CAULFIELD CHALMERS HARDIE HAYES HIRONS MASSOM MURRAY STRACHAN F1903
105201 BEDFORD Mr John. 20 Keppel Court, Robina, Queensland, 4226, AUSTRALIA. Tel:+61-75-722410
BEDFORD BONNY CORK FRASER GLOVER Guess GUEST OTWAY PYE ROSS SHAW F4180
105228 BEDINGFIELD Mrs G M. The Barn, Silver Street, Congresbury, Bristol, BS19 5EY.
Beddingfeld Beddingfield Bedinfield Bedingfeld BEDINGFIELD Beningfield Bennifield Benningfield Le Thundre MATHEW Mathews Matthew Matthews Thonder Thondir Thondyer Thondyr Thondyrr Thounder THUNDER Thundere Thundir Thundre Thundyr Tunder Tundur WHITE Whyte F2181
105236 BEDROCK Mr Ronald. 408 Hoylake Road, Moreton, Wirral, L46 6DG.
BEDROCK F3985
105244 BEDSER Mr D S. 6 Tanglewood, Wokingham, Berks, RG11 3PR.
ALLWOOD BEDSER Bedster BERWICK Betser

FLEETWOOD LANG SEXTON F3989
105252 BEE Mr Walter. 72 Newstead Road, Urmston, Manchester, M31 1GL. Tel:061-748-6766
BEE PARKINS RAISON SHEPLEY SWAIN F5908
105260 BEECH Mr Bernard. Ludlow Villa, 3 Station Road, Newport, Shropshire, TF10 7EN. Tel:0952-812139
Eccleser ECCLESHALL Eckleshall F100
105279 BEECH Mr Norman. 28 Ferndale Road, Balsall Common, Solihull, W Midlands, CV7 7AH.
BEECH FAIRCLOUGH SHEPARD SHEPHARD SHEPHERD F584
105287 BEECHING Dr N J. 37 Eshe Road, Blundellsands, Merseyside, L23 8UE.
Beacham Beachen Beaching Bechan Beechen BEECHING BEVAN Comfort Cornfoot CORNFORD NUNNS PAY Whitely WHITLEY Whittley Wittley F1424
105295 BEEDLE Mr L A. 4 Ravensworth Avenue, Normanby, Middlesbrough, TS6 0EE.
Bedell Bedil Beedale Beedel Beedele BEEDLE HARRISON KIRK MAYMAN WARIN F238
105309 BEESON Mr Harry T. 533 Okeefe Court, Kelowna, B C, V1X 6B1, CANADA. Tel:+1-604-765-5814
BEESON JAMES LANE THOMAS F4599
105317 BEETON Mr Philip T. 5 Beaconsfield Avenue, Colchester, Essex, CO3 3DH. Tel:0206-43197
BEETON BRUCE GOODAY GRIGG F2027
105325 BEEZLEY Mr C J. 19 Beech Avenue, Claverton Down, Bath, Avon, BA2 7BA.
BEAZLEY BEEXLEY GOODALL F4786
105333 BELAM Miss C F. Fore Stoke Farm, Holne, Newton Abbot, Devon, TQ13 7SS.
ABBOT Abbott AHLERS Ailing ANDREW Andrews ANSELL APTOR ARCHER AYLING Baalaam BACON Balaam BALAM Balan Balem Balen Balham Ballam BALLARD BARNES BARNET Barnett BARRINGTON BARTLET Bartlett BATTY Baylam Baylham BEALE Beavis BEE BELAM Belan Belane Belem Belen Belham Bellam Bellham BEVIS Blandford BLANFORD BREWER BROOKING BURTE CARTHEW Cauker Caulker CAUNTER CHARD CHATFIELD CHENNELL CHOWN CLEAVE Cleeve COAKER Cocker COKER Coleman COLMAN Cooker COTTELL Cottle CROWCHER CUMMING Davies DAVIS DEACON Dearling DERLING DOWNER DUNNING Durling EFFAMY Ensign ETHERINTON EVANS FARLEIGH Farley FINCH FORD FOYLE FRANCIS FRENCH FRY GRAY Gregsby Grey GRIBESBY GRIMBALDESTON Grimbaldestone GROUT Hamlin HAMLYN HANNAFORD HARDLEY HEXT HIBBERD HILL Hixam HOLLIER HORSAM Horsham Hosam Hossam Hursam Hursham HUSSEY HUTCHIN Hutching Hutchings Hutchins HUXAM Huxham INGRAM IRISH JACKSON JONES KING KNIGHT Landon LANGDON Langworthie LANGWORTHY Lavers LAVES Lawes LAWS LEAR Leer LOW Lowe LUPTON MADDAFORD MAINT Mainte MAN Mann Mardon MARNER Marriner MARSH MEDLEY MERDON MILLER MORRIS Moxem MOXHAM MULLER NEACOMB Neacombe NEWMAN NICHOLSON Noice NORRIS Norrish Norsworthy NOSWORTHY NOYCE Orchard PAIN Palk PAUK PAYNE PINK Raine Raines RAYNE Raynes READ REDWOOD RICHARDSON Roe Row ROWE SALTER SAMMISH SAUNDERS SCAPLAN Scapland Scapslan Scapsland SCARMAN Searman SHAPLEY SHEPARD Sheperd SHEPHERD SHERWILL Sign Simmonds Simonds SINE Smardon SMERDON SNOOK SOLE SOUTHARTH STANCOMB Stancombe STARLING STEPHEN Stephens STONE Sweeney Sweeny Sweney SWENY Swiney Swiny Swiyny SYMONDS TAYLOR Thory Thure THUREY Thurley TILL TRAYTON TURNER URRY WATERSFIELD WATSON WEBBER WEBSTER Werden Wersley WEST Wherden Whorden WILCOCKS Wilcox Willcocks Willcox WILLIAMS WILLS WORDEN WORSLEY WRAYFORD Wreford Wreyford WYATT YEO F2545
105341 BELBIN Mr T C. 42 Fullers Close, Kelvedon, Colchester, Essex, CO5 9JX. Tel:0376-571497
BELBIN F7232
105368 BELCHER Mr Harry G. 17 Millcan Street, Wavell Heights, Brisbane, 4012, AUSTRALIA. Tel:+61-7-266-8175
BELCHER BUTLER CHAD CRANSTON CROWLEY DAVEY DICKSON DUNSTER GASKINGS HODGES HOGES HOGETTS HUTCHINGS JORDEN LUCAS MILLER NEWIS PARTRIDGE PORTER RAERDON WARREN WESTLAKE F6069
105376 BELCHER Mr R. 417 Harborne Road, Edgbaston, Birmingham, B15 3LB.
BARNES BELCHER COTTERALL COTTERILL EMERY GOODALL HAWDON PRIOR PRYOR F6454
105384 BELL Mrs Betty. 3 Ennerdale Walk, Whickham, Newcastle Upon Tyne, NE16 5SW. Tel:091-488-1531
HAILES HURST F325
105392 BELL Mr C R. 79 Dukeswood Drive, Dibden Purlieu, Southampton, SO4 5NH. Tel:0703-842352
Alott Aylett Aylott BELL BOOTH Briant BRYANT Crosbie CROSBY Felingham FELLINGHAM Felmingham Gathercoal GATHERCOLE Healey HEALY Ilet ILOTT Millns MILNES Milns MUSK Muske Wagstafe WAGSTAFF Wagstaffe F6294
105406 BELL Mr David. Po Box 2164, Griffith, NSW 2680, AUSTRALIA. Tel:+1-6-963-0545
BELL POWER SARGENT F5454
105414 BELL Mr David. 9 Nelson Avenue, South Shields, Tyne & Wear, NE33 2NJ. Tel:091-456-0674
BELL BLACK CLARK MANSON MCINTYRE MEYERS WHITFIELD F5713
105422 BELL Mr Edward. 3051 Country Club Drive, Nanaimo, B C, V9T 3G6, CANADA. Tel:+1-604-758-2505
BELL CHAPMAN Forster FOSTER HALL MCFARLANE MOSES MUSGROVE WAUGH F5186
105430 BELL Mr Irving. Po Box 451, Springfield, VT 05156, USA.
BELL F7233
105449 BELL Mrs Julia. 143 Ringinglow Road, Sheffield, S11 7PS.
BELL Dun DUNN Dunne FIRTH LITTLE Mitchellson MITCHELSON REED Reid Rodgers ROGERS WALKER F2495
105457 BELL Mrs M A. (Watkins) 6 Owain Close, Cyncoed, Cardiff, CF2 6HN.
ASHWELL ATKINSON BELL BILLINGHAM BURNELL FRASER GRAY JACQUEST SPALDING STEVENSON TOONE TURNER VOKINS WARWICK WATKINS F4704
105465 BELL Mrs Nolene. (Adams) Po Box 2164, Griffith, NSW 2680, AUSTRALIA. Tel:+61-6-963-0545
ADAMS ALLEN BOWER FENSOM GILMORE IRWIN O'CONNER SMILIE F5455
105473 BELL Mrs Yvonne. 11 Oak Avenue, Gillingham, Kent, ME7 2NS. Tel:0634-54413
ALLAN ATHERFOLD BELL CLARK GRABHAM HOLDEN WRIGHT F1554
105481 BELLABY Mr Arthur. 69 Belper Lane, Belper, Derbyshire, DE5 2UQ.
BARKER BEATON BELERBY BELLABE BELLABEE BELLABEY BELLABIE BELLABY BELLARBE Bellarbey BELLARBIE BELLARBY BELLARBYE BELLEBY BELLERBIE BELLERBY BELLERBYE BELLIBIE BELLOBIE BELLOBYE BLACKWELL BROWN BRYAN BURTON CASTLEDOWN CHAMBERS CHARLESWORTH COLLINS COURTBIE DENNIS ELLIOTT HAMMERSLEY HARVEY HUNTER LANE LEATHERLAND LONGMAN MARRIOTT MOORE PRINGLE RAYNOR REYNOR SELLS SMART SMEDLEY TAYLOR TOWNDROW VARNEY WEIGTMAN WIGLEY WRIGHT F3165
105503 BELLAMY Mr D A. 24 Chruch Avenue, Humberston, Grimsby, DN36 4DL.
ADLARD APPLEBY BANNISTER BELLAMY BLOW BROOMHEAD CHAMP HUMBERSTONE JOHNSON WALLER F2402
105511 BELLAMY Mr David T. 45 Crossdale Drive, Keyworth, Notts, NG12 5HP.
BARTLE BELLAMY EDGE HEWITT LEVER SHIRLEY SOUTHORN F3820
105538 BELLAMY Mrs Vera. (Aston) 145 North Walk, New Addington, Surrey, CR0 9ET. Tel:0689-841435
ASTBURY ASTON BOWDLER JAMES WILKES F5102
105546 BELLINGHAM Mr Roger A. 27 Garths End, Pocklington, York, YO4 2JB.
BELLINGHAM CHARLESWORTH THORPE F2424
105554 BELLWOOD Mr David R. 41 Lingwell Gate Lane, Lofthouse, Wakefield, W Yorks, WF3 3JL. Tel:0924-828893
ASHWORTH BELLWOOD Belwood WITTER F2800
105562 BELMAN Mr Michael & Mrs Marion. Anchorage, 9 Viscount Drive, Pagham, Bognor Regis W Sussex, PO21 4PE.
Bellman BELMAN CHAPMAN COOK Cooke Dainton

Dayton Deaton Deighton DENTON GIBSON GIRVAN GREEN Greene Olerenshaw OLORENSHAW F1614
105570 BELTZUNG Mr Charles. 15 Rue Jean Claude Ponsard, 57518 Montigny-Les-Metz, FRANCE.
BELTZUNG F7235
105589 BENBOW Mr William. 43-933 Admirals Road, Victoria, British Columbia, V9A 2P1, CANADA. Tel:+1-604-388-4173
BENBOW HARDEY F6191
105597 BENDING Mr J H. 5 Uppingham Close, Leicester, LE5 6HT.
BENDING F6943
105600 BENFIELD Baron Kenneth Bertram. 30 Harpenden Drive, Park Hill, Allesley, Coventry, CV5 7QF.
BENFIELD F4966
105619 BENIANS Mr Peter R. 305 Mountnessing Road, Billericay, Essex, CM12 0ER. Tel:0277-652892
Benian BENIANS Benion Benions Benyan Benyans Benyen Benyon Benyons CARTER GORE JANES JEANS RABY F462
105627 BENJAFIELD Mrs Gail. (Darroch) 83 Glenridge Avenue, St Catharines, Ontario, L2R 4X2, CANADA.
BENJAFIELD BROOKS GEDDES TILLOT Tillott WARES WATERS F6132
105635 BENNETT Mrs Barbara. (Bennington) 2 Greave Close, Constablelee Park, Rawtenstall, Rossendale Lancs, BB4 8JT. Tel:0706-228561
Benets Bennets Bennett BENNETTS BENNINGTON FARROW GOLDSWORTHY MADEN MITCHELL Moyce Moyes MOYSE NICHOLSON PINFIELD Randal RANDALL Randell READ THORNTON YARHAM F4101
105643 BENNETT Mrs Deborah. (Wrath) 21 Briar Close, Horndean, Waterlooville, Hants, PO8 9ED. Tel:0705-598078
WRATH F6516
105651 BENNETT Mr F C F. 21 Dene Way, Upper Caldecote, Biggleswade, Beds, SG18 9DL. Tel:0767-314236
BENNETT GODDARD HAWKER KING PARKER PATRICK TEALE F3596
105678 BENNETT Mr Graham. 60 The Avenue, Fareham, Hants, PO14 1NZ. Tel:0329-287112
BENNETT EMERY Rimel RIMER Rimmer Rymel Rymer F2928
105686 BENNETT Mrs H E. 43 Cimla Crescent, Cimla, Neath, W Glamorgan, SA11 3NN.
GOLLOP READE F5959
105694 BENNETT Mrs J. 3 Kokoda Avenue, Mail Service 1536, Bli Bli, Queensland, 4560, AUSTRALIA.
ARCHER EVANS FORTESCUE GOODWIN HARRISON HEATHCOTE ROGERS WALKER F5158
105708 BENNETT Ms Janet. 147 Bullard Road, Norwich, Norfolk, NR3 3RA. Tel:0603-400186
BUTCHER MARTIN Parnall Parnel PARNELL F3372
105716 BENNETT Mr John. 23 Glenfield Road, Brockham, Betchworth, Surrey, RH3 7HR. Tel:0737-843177
ASH BENNETT HORSLEY LARNER MASON PEARCE Pearse Peers Peirce Pierce SUTCLIFFE F1909
105724 BENNETT Mr M A. 46 Grice Road, Hartshill, Stoke On Trent, Staffs, ST4 7PJ. Tel:0782-623208
BENNETT EARP KEARTON POCKLINGTON RUSSELL RUTTER SALT F3931
105732 BENNETT Mrs M F. Brook View House, Walshes Road, Crowborough, E Sussex, TN6 3RE.
COMER FORSTER JONES KING MARROW MOSS PARKINSON PEMBERTON THACKERY WATSON F6114
105740 BENNETT Mr Nigel F. 48 Homeground, Clevedon, Avon, BS21 5AL. Tel:0934-876444
BEVAN JONES RICHARDS WILLIAMS F3926
105759 BENNETT Mr Peter. 35 Westover Road, Fleet, Hants, GU13 9DB. Tel:0252-625015
AYTON BAKER BENNETT ERRINGTON FEATHERSTONE FOWLER GOULDEN HARRIS JUDGE LAFLETT MUSGRAVE NELMES PEATHYJOHNS PORTER RINTOUL ROBSON WAKE F1464
105767 BENNETT Mr Richard. Ael Y Castell, Porth Y Green Close, Cowbridge, South Glamorgan, CF7 7JR.
BELCHER BENNETT BEVAN BEYNON Bynon FERGUSON FRYER GRAVE HELLIER Hodget Hodgets Hodgett HODGETTS MCGILLICUDDY MORGAN REGAN RICHARDS STRACHAN WATSON F459
105775 BENNETT Mrs Yvonne. (May) Arch View, Roxby Road, Thornton Le Dale, Pickering, N Yorks, YO18 7SX.
BOBBY DANTON DUNK ING INGE MARSH MAY Sparkes SPARKS TERRY TUCKER WALES F4340
105783 BENNEWITH Ms G. 7 Endfield Cloisters, Fanshaw Street, London, N1 6LD.
Benewith BENNEWITH Benneworth F7144
105791 BENNY Mrs Kathleen. (Ravensdale) 19 Mary Vale, Godalming, Surrey, GU7 1SW. Tel:0483-415796
Rainesdale Rainsdale Ramsdale Ranesdale Ranesdall Ransdale Ransdall Ravenesdale RAVENSDALE Revenedale F6260
105805 BENSON Mr B. 8 Kitchener Close, Barham, Canterbury, Kent, CT4 6QN. Tel:0227-831591
BENSON MOSELEY MOSLEY F5884
105813 BENSON Mrs Nina E. 29 Skelton Road, Langthorpe, Boroughbridge, North Yorks, YO5 9GD. Tel:0423-324018
BENN BENSON CARTER FRANK Metcalf METCALFE METCLAFE POSTLETHWAITE SOMMERVILLE WALKER F2212
105821 BENTLEY Mr John. Corrin House, 8 Halifax Road, Briercliffe, Burnley, Lancs, BB10 3QH. Tel:0282-25410
Benteley BENTLEY Bently Bentlye BROTHERTON RAWES Raws Rowes Rows F5617
105848 BENTON Mr Anthony. 46 Waldegrave Gardens, Upminster, Essex, RM14 1UX.
BENTON DEATH FITCH FLACK HEALEY HELLYER Simmonds SIMMONS THURSTON WARDROP F5923
105856 BENTON Mr E H. 99 Little Pynchons, Harlow, Essex, CM18 7DF. Tel:0279-420827
BENTON NIGHTINGALE PACKMAN PEARCE RAGGETT ROOTS SKINNER SUMMERS WESTON WILLIAMS WINUP F2712
105864 BENTON Mr Peter T. 40 Walkerscroft Mead, Dulwich, London, SE21 8LJ. Tel:081-670-9757
BENTON BIDWELL BROUGHTON HAINES HAYNES PAGE SAVAGE F625
105872 BENTOTE Mr Malcolm David. 25 Chestnut Drive, Pinner, Middx, HA5 1LX. Tel:081-866-1365
Benetot Bentole Bentot BENTOTE F2484
105880 BERESFORD Mr D K. Rozel Downesway, Alderley Edge, Cheshire, SK9 7XB.
BERESFORD Berisford Berresford F6613
105899 BERG Mrs Joanne. Box 298, Central Butte, Saskatchewan, S0H 0T0, CANADA. Tel:+1-306-796-2148
BAXTER BEGGS BLYTHE CROWLEY GRAHAM MCINTOSH NEWMAN TAYLOR THOMSON TWINEHAM F5465
105902 BERNARD Mrs Joan M. 93 Kidmore Road, Caversham, Reading, Berks, RG4 7NH. Tel:0734-477369
BILLINGS BOTTOMLEY CLARK COGGINS COX CRAXFORD DELL HARRISON RHODES SETH STEELS WARD WRIGHT F2106
105910 BERRIDGE Mr Anthony. Marston, 26 Eglise Road, Warlingham, Surrey, CR6 9SE.
Beridge Berig BERRIDGE SETON SETON-BURN F3447
105929 BERRIDGE Mrs Barbara. 8 Ros Lyn, Carbis Bay, St Ives, Cornwall, TR26 2QE. Tel:0736-794529
BERRIDGE MEADOWS QUICK F2476
105937 BERRY Mr A W. 10 Blackheath, Colchester, Essex, CO2 0AA.
BERRY F3938
105945 BERRY Miss Helen M. 64 Selly Wick Drive, Selly Park, Birmingham, B29 7JH. Tel:021-472-8339
BERRY DOBSON HYDE TRIPP UREN WITHERS F2538
105953 BERRY Mrs Joyce. 1 High Street, Timsbury, Bath, Avon, BA3 1HT.
Aishley ASHLEY BAKER BERRY Burry F2236
105961 BERRY Mrs Judy. 5 Hambling Close, Bulwell, Nottingham, NG6 7DX. Tel:0602-754941
RUTTER F282
105988 BERRY Mrs Naomi B. 11 Callender Place, Cockle Bay, Auckland, NEW ZEALAND.
BERRY BRIGGS CHESTERS GALLOWAY LAWRENCE PENBERTHY REED ROWNEY TOTTMAN WALLIS F5449
105996 BERRY Mrs Patricia. (Webb) 4 Greenway Close, Shipston On Stour, Warks, CV36 4EB. Tel:0608-63878
BALDWYN BERRY HOLLIS WEBB F384
106003 BERRYMAN Mrs Joan. (Peyton) 19 Westfield Avenue, Scarborough, North Yorkshire, YO12

6DG. Tel:0723-362345
GLEGHORN LENNON MILBURN MINSHULL PEXTON SOTHCOTT WEBSTER WILSON F4994

106011 BERTHELOT Mr D R. 2 Hipperson Close, North Walsham, Norfolk, NR28 0SU.
LAWSON VICKERS F4374

106038 BESFORD Mr Anthony Downes. Conifers, 2a Halt Road, Caister On Sea, Gt Yarmouth, Norfolk, NR30 5NZ.
Basfor Besfor BESFORD Bestford DOWNES F5982

106046 BEST Mr David Ian. Lucas Cottage, Beechenlea, Swanley, Kent, BR8 7PR. Tel:0322-667045
BEST HARMAN F594

106054 BEST Dr Nigel. The Lodge, Les Varendes, St Andrews, Guernsey. Tel:0481-55788
BARNSBY BARRICK BEST BROWNE CANNON CORBETT CROSS DEWES MARCH NIELD PITTS POWNEY SOMERS SOUTHALL SPENCER STONE THOMPSON TOLLEY VINEY WEST F3949

106062 BEST Mrs Valerie. 76 Newton Street, Broken Hill, NSW 2880, AUSTRALIA.
BRACEY DICKENSON FIELD HORN SHEPSTON SIMS F5636

106070 BESWETHERICK Mr Anthony. 107 Brighton Road, Newhaven, Sussex, BN9 9NP. Tel:0273-5155471
Beswatherick Beswathick BESWETHERICK Bosvathic Bosvathick Boswatherick Boswathick F891

106089 BESWICK Mrs Ann. 110 Stour Road, Astley, Manchester. Tel:0942-883617
Furness FURNIS SMETHILLS F2134

106097 BESWICK Mrs Elizabeth. 10 Lonsdale Way, Oakham, Rutland, Leics, LE15 6LR. Tel:0572-755210
EDGELEY HARRIS PAYNE PERRY PICK RUDKIN RUMBELOW SMITH STIMSON VENIMORE F2713

106100 BETHEL Dr David. 48 Holmfield Road, Leicester, LE2 1SA. Tel:0533-704921
Abethell Ap Ithel Bathal Bathel Beathel Beathell Beathelle Beathil Beathill Beethell Bethall Betheall BETHEL Betheldo Bethele BETHELL Bethelle Bethill Bethold Bethole Betholl Bettell Beythell Bithel Bothell BREWER Bythall Bythel Bythell COSSINS Ithell MERRETT WRIGGLESWORTH F1758

106119 BETSER Mr Robin. 23 Mount Pleasant Close, Hatfield, Herts, AL9 5BZ.
BATSER Beazer BEDER BEDESOR BEDESTER Bedger BEDR BEDSAR BEDSER BEDSIR BEDSOR BEDSTER BEDSUM BELSER Besser BETCHAR Betcher BETR BETSAR BETSEN BETSER BETSHER BETSHUR BETSO BETSOR BETSTER BETSWORTH BETTSER BETTSOR BETZAR BETZER Bezer Bezoar BLUNT Bodser BODSOR BROAD BUTSER Butzer BUTZOR CLIFT DABORNE KNIGHT PERREN F2887

106127 BETTERIDGE Dr H T. 29 South Street, Elie, Fife, KY9 1DN. Tel:0333-330717
BETTERIDGE FATOUX FORD GARDNER HOPKINSON KNIGHT PRIDDEY ROBINSON Wallace WALLIS F4104

106135 BETTISON Mr J C. Washdyke Cottage, Hackthorn, Lincoln, LN2 3PE.
Bettenson BETTINSON F6618

106143 BETTRIDGE Mrs L J. 34 Wells Road, Chilcompton, Somerset, BA3 4EX.
Beteridge Betridge BETTERIDGE BETTERRIDGE BETTRIDGE F292

106151 BETTS Mrs Marian. (Smoker) 520 Old Bedford Road, Luton, Beds, LU2 7BY.
BATES BETTS SMOKER F6426

106178 BETTS Mr Rodney. Gouray, 39 Hazel Road, Purley On Thames, Reading, Berks, RG8 8HR. Tel:0734-417143
BETTS Calton Carleton CARLTON Ladbroke Ladbrook LADBROOKE F3932

106186 BEVAN Mrs Grace. 114 Inchbonnie Road, South Woodham Ferrers, Essex, CM3 5ZW.
BEAVAN Beaven Bevan Bevin Colet Collect COLLETT Collick GIMBLETT Gimlett Hatharal HATHERELL Jenken JENKIN Jenkyn KING KNIGHT LEM Lemm Lemme NANKERVIS NICHOLLS RING Ringe SMITH TOWNSEND WHITE Wring F5937

106194 BEVAN Mr Philip. 19 Tegfynydd, Swiss Valley, Llanelli, Dyfed, SA14 8HL. Tel:0554-750948
BEVAN HARTLEY HOLE HOPKINSON HORTON TEW TITTERTON VERNON WHITWORTH F4500

106208 BEVAN Mr R J. 7 Rectory Road, Sutton, Surrey, SM1 1QW.
Beavan BEVAN Bevin Buckel Buckell Buckle BUCKNELL F6407

106216 BEVERLEY Mrs Joan. (Burns) 56 Broadbottom Road, Mottram In Longdendale, Hyde, Cheshire, SK14 6JA.
BURNS Byrne Byrnes Byrns DUDDRIDGE KELLY Sweatman Sweatnam SWEETMAN Sweetnam TIGHE F4911

106224 BEVIS Miss F E H. Shalom, 650 Wilmslow Road, Disbury, Manchester, M20 0DE.
ANDREWS BEVIS WARDER F621

106232 BEVIS Ms K V P. 36 Catisfield Road, Catisfield, Fareham, Hants, PO15 5LP. Tel:0329-47258
Beavis Beves BEVIS Bevys BULL F620

106240 BEWES Mr David. Beaumont, 22 Stafford Road, Petersfield, Hants, GU32 2JG. Tel:0730-64744
ANSTIS BAKER BAZELEY BENNETT BEWES BRENT GAWARD MOORE SPRENT WHITE F1487

106259 BEWGLASS Mr Ian R. 30 Hutchins Avenue, Dubbo, NSW 2830, AUSTRALIA.
BEWGLASS STOKES F6492

106267 BEWICK Mrs Pauline. 12 Offa Lea, Newton, Cambridge, CB2 5PW.
BAKER BARLEY BEWICK COLLIE EDDIE GRAHAM HAVERS HAWKINS LAWRENCE MURRAY OFFICER OXNARD PLETTS RACHER SCOTT STODDART THORNDIKE THURLOW TYE WELLS F1236

106275 BHAR Mrs Jill. 8 Hobbs Avenue, Nepean, Ontario, K2H 6W9, CANADA.
MERRY Vineyard Winyard F7038

106283 BIBB Mr Eric. 65 Endcliffe Avenue, Bottesford, Scunthorpe, S Humberside, DN17 2RB. Tel:0724-861196
BAGIER BIBB COAKLEY DRURY GOODMAN HUGHES MOODY PEARCE STAMP F6365

106291 BIBBY Mr Morton. Dyffryn Aled, Llansannan, Denbigh, Clwyd, LL16 5LB.
COCHRANE HESKETH LLOYD WOOLDRIDGE WYNNE-YORKE YORKE YORKE-LODGE F636

106305 BICKNELL Dr Gordon H. 3524 Military Ave, Los Angeles, CA 90034, USA. Tel:+1-310-839-8511
AUSTIN BICKNELL CAMPBELL CANNEY CROW CULBERT GILLES HEENAN IRVINE JABBETT JOHNSTON KYLE LINDSTER LITLEFIELD MCCUBRY MCDONALD MCDOUGALL MCLEAN MCNEILL NESBIT PICK REDFERN SCARLET STRAIN WILSON WOODWARD F5639

106313 BIDDLE Mrs Enid. 44 Rosslyn Avenue, Feltham, Middx, TW14 9LQ.
BEDFORD BERRY BIDDLE EAMES EDLRIDGE GUERNIERE HANCOCK HAYNES HEAD HICHCOCKE Hitchcock HITCHCOX JOYS KIDDELL LAKE LEADER MANN MATTHEWS Nease NIAS NIBBS Nyers PAYNE PEARCE SIDLEY WEST WHITEWAY WHITLEY WILKINS WINNE WINNEY YEATS F2843

106321 BIDDLE Dr Tony. 4 Dale Hall Lane, Ipswich, Suffolk, IP1 3RX. Tel:0473-254808
BALLARD BIDDLE MILL F1379

106348 BIDDULPH Mr Joseph. 32 Stryd Ebeneser, Pontypridd, Mid Glamorgan, CF37 5PB.
BIDDULPH F25

106356 BIDEWELL Mr William H. 2208 Hants Road, Kelowna, British Columbia, V1Z 2L1, CANADA.
Biddel Biddle BIDEL Bidell BIDEWELL Bidle Bidwell Bidwill BONNEY BOTWRIGHT BUTLER Bydall Bydewell CURTIS DADE GREEN HORTON JEWELL Lietwin Lightwin Lightwine LIGHTWING Lytewing MASTERSON MATHAMS SPAIN SPRUCE THURSTON TURNER WARDEN WILDMAN WILSON Wodebine Woodbin WOODBINE Woodbyne F4122

106364 BIDWELL Frank. 1755 Trinity Avenue, Apt 1, Walnut Creek, CA 94596, USA.
Biddle BIDWELL F6946

106372 BIDWELL Valerie. Tomari, Hook End Lane, Hook End, Brentwood Essex, CM15 0HG.
HAZELTON MORLOCK YOUNG F902

106380 BIGLIN Mrs B E. (Nash) 119 Longfield Road, Darlington, Co Durham, DL3 0HS. Tel:0325-284331
BIGLIN BLAIR BRYANT DAVIS NASH STOREY F985

106399 BIGLIN Mrs Cynthia. (Best) 18 Mortimer Road, Filton, Bristol, Avon, BS12 7LF. Tel:0272-698632
BEST F1387

106402 BIGNELL Mrs Esme. 30 Capon Close, Swaythling,

Southampton, Hants, SO2 2LH. Tel:0703-552210
Bignall BIGNELL Bignoll BROWNING GARNHAM
HUXTER LEWIS Liddell LIDDLE LUNNON Lyddel
RYVES F921

106410 BIHAN Ann. 15 Staddlestones, Midsomer Norton, Bath, Avon, BA3 2PP. Tel:0761-419145
BENNET BRADBEER BURNARD CRABB CULLIFORD GARE GOULD HALL HECKS HOWARD HUCKER INGRAM LAURENCE LUCK MATTHEWS MILLS NEAT OLAND SHORT SLADE SQUIRE STEVENS TWOSE WEBB WHELLER F393

106429 BILBROUGH Mr Peter. 6 The Strand, Goring, Worthing, W Sussex, BN12 6DN. Tel:0903-504987
BATTY Bilborough BILBROUGH Bilbruck Bilbruff COLLARD DOWNING JENNINGS READYHOFF TOASE WORSLEY WRAGG F133

106437 BILLETT Mr Michael Charles. The Haven, Keyford Terrace, Frome, Somerset, BA11 1JL.
F1540

106445 BILLING Mr Philip G. 17 Sycamore Drive, Yeovil, Somerset, BA20 2NQ.
BILLING BILLINGE BILLINGS RAINES F1888

106453 BILLINGS Mr A M. 37 Camp Road, St Albans, Herts, AL1 5DX.
Belinus Bellin Belling Bellinge Bellinger Bellings Bellins Billa Billin BILLING Billinge Billinger BILLINGS Billyng Billynge Billynges Bylling Byllinge Byllinges Byllyng Byllynge Byllynges F2188

106461 BILLINGSLEY Mrs G. 1420 South 640 East, Orem, Utah, 84058, USA.
BEAVAN BREWER DAVIS FORSEY FOWLER LEA MERVIN PINNEGAR PRING RICHENS RUTHERFORD SMITH STRETCH F5163

106488 BILLMAN Miss J. 7 Burns Way, St Ives, Hunts, Cambs, PE17 4TS.
BILLMAN GANT LEWIS REES STRIBLING THOMAS F4712

106496 BILNEY Mr M P. 73 Amberley Road, Abbey Wood, London, SE2 0SG. Tel:081-310-5515
BILNEY F6124

106518 BINDING Mr E H D. 100 Eversleigh Road, Scarborough, Queensland, 4020, AUSTRALIA.
BINDING CROOK MCGEE SLADE F5143

106526 BINDING Mrs S. 7 Bondfields Crescent, Havant, Hants, PO9 5EP.
WISBY F3287

106534 BING Mrs Madie. (Killick) Driftwood, 3 Cranbrook Close, Cliftonville, Margate Kent, CT9 3YD. Tel:0843-227241
BING Binge Byng Bynge Carlick Kallock Keilock Keleg KILLICK Killik Killok Killoke Killuck Killucke Kyelyche Kyllyk Kyllyke Ping F407

106542 BINGHAM Mr Donald. 49 Southway, Carshalton Beeches, Surrey, SM5 4HP. Tel:081-643-3135
Bigham Bingam Bingeham BINGHAM Binghame Bingum Binham Byngham Bynghame F3921

106550 BINGHAM Mrs Dorian M. (Smelt) 12 Gossips Wood Road, Rawcliffe Bridge, Goole, N Humbershide, DN14 8PA.
SMELT F2606

106569 BINGHAM Mr Oscar W. 142 Western Boulevard, Nottingham, NG8 3NW. Tel:0602-292998
BINGHAM CLARK CLARKE HILL HOWARD MCNEILL ROWARK TWIGG F840

106577 BINGLEY Mr Randal. 10 Recreation Avenue, Corringham, Essex, SS17 9BZ.
BINGLEY HURST TUCKER F5775

106585 BINLEY Mr R C. 238 Studfall Avenue, Corby, Northants, NN17 1LQ.
Bindley Bingley BINLEY F3278

106593 BIRCH Mrs Ida. 37 Homewood Avenue, Cuffley, Potters Bar, Herts, EN6 4QQ. Tel:0707-873075
ANDREW BIRCH BRAUND BURROW CORY DAVEY GEE GRIGG HOCKRIDGE MACKINTOSH F1518

106607 BIRCH Mr R G. Kyrenia, 2 The Firs, Whitchurch, Shropshire, SY13 1NL.
Tel:0948-3859
BIRCH ECKFORD FLAXMAN GAMMAGE GILL KNIGHT PARKER RACKHAM ROBERTS WALLNUTT F5998

106615 BIRCHENOUGH Mrs F J. 6 Cheyne Walk, Bramblesfield Estate, Longfield, Dartford Kent, DA3 7RN.
Birchenall Birchenhough BIRCHENOUGH Birchinall Birchinhough Byrchenhaughe F6758

106623 BIRD Miss D F. 32 Ambleside Road, South Reddish, Stockport, Cheshire, SK5 7EL.
BIRD DUDMAN GRIMSHAW HAIG PEIRPOINT VINCE WADSWORTH WHITTINGHAM F6141

106631 BIRD Mr Graham. 44 Ravensmede Way, London, W4 1TF.
BATTALIA BENNETT BIRD BOLEY CASTELL CROOK DANIELS FISHER GREEN HARDING HEELIS HILL INKER KING LEWIS MASON MILLIER PODGER POWEL PUCKMORE PULE RAYMAN RIDLER ROE SMITH THURSTON TRESTON WALTON WINSTONE F3811

106658 BIRD Mrs Margaret. 3 Woodside Cottages, Halton, Chirk, Clwyd, LL14 5BL.
Tel:0691-778254
CORBISHLEY GASKELL KAY LAIDLAW Laidley Laidlow LONGDEN STEELE VARE Vear Veire WOOD F1581

106666 BIRD Mrs P. (Goldring) 49 Oakhurst Grove, East Dulwich, London, SE22 9AH.
COLLINS CUFF FOWLER FRANCIS Godring Goldering GOLDRING Goldringe Golering Goleringe Golring Gooldringe Gooldryng Goulderinge Gouldring Gouldringe Gowdringe Gowdringes Gowldring Gowring HYDE KENT MANNING MERRILL MEW MITTENS O'NEILL SISSONS F6020

106674 BIRKBECK Mrs Josi. Fintys Cottage, Creaden Head, Dunmore East, Waterford, IRELAND.
Birbeck Birchbeck BIRKBECK Burkbeck CHERRY EMERSON GEOGHEGAN LUBBOCK MANUEL MCGEENEY MCGEENZY PHILLIBROWN RICKWOOD TURNER F2125

106682 BIRKETT Mrs Sheila. 22 Walpole Street, Burnley, Lancs, BB10 1SW.
BIRKETT DEVEREUX MCLOUGHLIN MURRAY SMITH F6131

106690 BIRKMIRE Mr David. 6 Pickering Close, Urmston, Manchester, M31 3DB.
BIRKMIRE Birkmyer BIRKMYRE FELTON NICHOLLS F1339

106704 BIRRELL Mrs Brenda A. Corner Bungalow, Upton, Huntingdon, Cambs, PE17 5YF.
FOUNTAIN GREEN IBBOT LAVENDER LEACH MILLS SKINNER F2352

106712 BIRT Mr Graham. 24 Avon Way, Thornbury, Bristol, BS12 2DF. Tel:0454-417271
BIRT F4257

106720 BIRTCHNELL Mrs Sheila. 226 Windsor Lane, Burnham, Slough, Berks, SL1 7HN.
BIRTCHNELL HOLLOWAY PRATLEY PRIOR WELCH Welsh F875

106739 BIRTWHISTLE Mrs Betty. 53 Sunningdale Road, Cheam, Surrey, SM1 2JU. Tel:081-641-0533
Bertwisle Bertwistle Birkwistle Birthwistle Birtwell BIRTWHISTLE Birtwisle Birtwistle Birtwizle Burtwistle BYATT CHRISTMAS Hoodswell Huddeswell HUDGELL Hudgle Hudgwell Hudsell HUDSWELL KENT LORDEN Udgell F2430

106747 BISBY Mr & Mrs G D. 16 The Parklands, South Cave, Brough, E Yorks, HU15 2EL.
BISBY COLE DOBSON LAKEY LINDLEY MOHR ROGERS SPENCER STANFORD F1158

106755 BISHOP Mrs Brenda. (Miles) 8 Elizabeth Crescent, East Grinstead, West Sussex, RH19 3JA. Tel:0342-327395
MILES WITHERS F5689

106763 BISHOP Mr David. Pettys Fold, Caraway Close, Ulverston, Cumbria, LA12 9NF. Tel:0229-54578
BISHOP TREVETT F181

106771 BISHOP Mrs Gwyneth. 49 West Street, Pontypridd, Mid Glamorgan, CF37 4PS.
BISHOP F154

106798 BISHOP Mr Peter. The Old Malthouse, Brimpsfield, Gloucester, GL4 8LD.
BISHOP BROADWOOD COOKSLEY HILLS MARRIOTT OLDACRE TODD WALLER F1773

106801 BISHOP Mrs W M. 11 Challoner Court, Bristol, Avon, BS1 4RG.
BRYANT COLLARD EDDOLS FORD KIDNER LUSCOMBE PASSMORE PINCOMBE TUCKER UNDERHILL F836

106828 BLABER Mr A S. 158 Fronks Road, Harwich, Essex, CO12 4EF. Tel:0255-502699
BLABER Blabir Blabour F3489

106836 BLACK Mr Alexander. 4 Rockburn Drive, Clarkston, Glasgow, G76 7PE. Tel:041-638-4604
BLACK FERGUSON HANNAH KERRIDGE MCFAYDEN MCINTYRE SILVESTER SMITH F1711

106844 BLACK Mrs Eraine. Glenalla, 37 Castle Avenue, Balloch, Alexandria Dumbarton, G83 8HU.
ELCOAT Ellcoat FISH Hailcoat Hailcot Helcoat

Hellcoat Hilcoat Hilcot Hilcote Hillcot LAING LOVE RAINE ROBINSON SELF WALLACE WEBB WILLIAMSON F3230

106852 BLACK Mrs Frances. Braeside Of Lindores, Newburgh, Cupar, Fife, KY14 6HU. Tel:0337-40351
BARR BLACK CARNOCHAN CHALMERS CLOCKIE DONALD DOWELL HAMILTON LOVE MCCARTNEY MCGUFFIE MCKIE MCMONNIES MCWILLIAM MEIKLE SIMPSON SKIMMING WEIR WILLIAMSON YOUNG F1239

106860 BLACK Mr R. 37 Castle Avenue, Balloch, Alexandria, Dunbartonshire, G83 8HU. Tel:0389-52214
BLACK BROWNLIE COWAN FLETCHER LAING RAINE ROBERTSON WALLACE WILSON F3229

106879 BLACK Mr W W. 10 Southfield House, South Walks Road, Dorchester, Dorset, DT1 1AD. Tel:0305-268502
BLACK F4253

106887 BLACK Mr William. Dalgetty House, High Street, Ayton, Berwickshire, TD14 5QN. Tel:08907-81427
BLACK BORDON CRUICKSHANK DAVIDSON DEY DUNCAN GERRIE HAY LOW LOWRIE MATHERS MCKENZIE ROSS SMITH STUART WALKER WHYTE F3664

106895 BLACKALL Mr J Mclellan. 49 Primrose Hill, Chelmsford, Essex, CM1 2RH.
BLACKALL BRIGHT MCLELLAN MEAD MELLOR OLIVER F4642

106909 BLACKBURN Ms Catherine. 25 Algonquin Avenue, Kirkland Lake, Ontario, P2N 1C1, CANADA. Tel:+1-705-567-7065
BAILEY BLACKBURN BONNY CARTLIDGE COLE CRAVEN DIACK FOWLIE HAWATT LEGG LEGGE LINNINGTON MCGUIRE PENNY RIDDELL SKINNER TAYLOR VINTON WILLETT WILLOX F7430

106917 BLACKBURN Mr Derek. Mariteau Court, Back Lane, Winchelsea, East Sussex, TN36 4EU.
BLACKBURN LIGHTFOOT F3176

106925 BLACKBURN Mr H R. 38 Hawthorn Drive, North Harrow, Middx, HA2 7NX. Tel:081-868-8760
Ambage Ambidge Ambige Ambrage AMBRIDGE Bambridge BLACKBURN GREIG Hambridge HEAD OLDROYD Rambridge Umbrage VERIOD Veriot F128

106933 BLACKETT Dr Tony. 27 Woodbridge Gardens, Leeds, W Yorks, LS6 3LW.
BLACKETT LITTLEWOOD F1855

106941 BLACKLOCK Miss Audrey. 1 Bell View Close, Windsor, Berks, SL4 4EX. Tel:0753-864315
BLACKLOCK CALVER CLARKE FARMER SPIERS STABLER TITTERTON F3425

106968 BLACKLOCK Mrs June. (Moir) 8 Marsh Street, Walkden, Worsley, Manchester, M28 5HP. Tel:061-799-3209
BANCROFT BARLOW BLACKLOCK DAULBY DODD FILDES FOULKES FROST GRIFFITHS LANNIN MOIR THORNTON TOBIN F1252

106976 BLACKMORE Mr William E. 12 Conisboro Avenue, Caversham, Reading, Berks, RG4 7JB. Tel:0734-470988
BLACKMORE HATHERLEY HAYES HEALEY JACKSON MILLER RICHARDS SPURGE YOUNG F1649

106984 BLACKMUN Mr Arthur. 2 White Butts Road, South Ruislip, Harrow, Middx, HA4 0NB. Tel:081-845-3962
BLACKMAN Cleverley CLEVERLY WHITE WILLIS F6279

106992 BLACKSTONE Mr D. Toad Hall, 60 Torquay Drive, Leigh On Sea, Essex, SS9 1SE.
BLACKSTONE F3376

107018 BLACKWELL Mr Ken. 8 Cliff Mews, Paignton, Devon, TQ4 6DJ.
BICKERDIKE BLACKWELL JACKSON SOWDEN WOOD F5725

107026 BLACKWELL Mr R M. Pevensey, 48 Kit Hill Avenue, Walderslade, Chatham Kent, ME5 9EX. Tel:0634-861802
BALDWIN BLACKWELL COLLINGS ELTON FLUDE MASTERS PRIOR TEETON F1260

107034 BLACKWELL Mr W. 25 Barons Way, Egham, Surrey, TW20 8EA.
HERNIMAN MOWELS F7320

107042 BLACKWOOD Mrs Angela. 7 College Hill, Bargate Wood, Godalming, Surrey, GU7 1YA. Tel:0483-429795
ARNOLD BLACKWOOD DAVISON HICKLING MACKRETH WATKINS F256

107050 BLADON Miss Helena. 34 Warwick Street, Derby, DE24 8WN.
Bladen Bladin BLADON Blayden Blaydon Jeavon JEAVONS Jevon Jevons WINSCOM Winscomb Winscombe Winscome Winskum F3535

107069 BLAGROVE Mr Ian. 57 St Andrews Crescent, Windsor, Berks, SL4 4EP.
BLACKGROVE BLAGRAVE BLAGROVE F6481

107077 BLAIN Mrs Y. 6 Moorhead, Preston Village, Telford, Shropshire, TF6 6DL.
BENTING F7234

107085 BLAIR Mr Mac. 720 Northwood Drive, Huntingdon, TN 38344, USA. Tel:+1-901-986-3924
BULKELEY CANDLER CROOME HARNETT MOORMAN MORRIS PETTIT REYNOLDS F6128

107093 BLAKE Mr Jeff. 17 Chapel Row, Clandown, Radstock, Bath Avon, BA3 3BP. Tel:0761-433427
BLAKE COLES DAY HOWELL KIRTON SIMMONS WALLIS WINN F258

107107 BLAKE Mr P A. 18 Rosevine Road, London, SW20 8BR.
Black BLAKE Blek Leblake F6726

107115 BLAKE Mr Reginald Walter. 1 Longford Gardens, Sutton, Surrey, SM1 3DR. Tel:081-644-0274
BAKER BLAKE PARLING PRICE F4895

107123 BLAKELEY Mr David. 67 Ferrers Way, Ripley, Derbyshire, DE5 3GZ. Tel:0773-744703
Blackeley Blackley BLAKELEY Blakely Blakley FARR FLETCHER GRANTLIFF HUDSON LAKE MATTHEWS NORTON PRICE RAMSDEN RIDDLESWORTH ROSE RUNCORN RUSSELL SMEDLEY SUTTON WARWICK F326

107131 BLAKELEY Mrs P M. 67 Ferrers Way, Ripley, Derbyshire, DE5 3GZ. Tel:0773-744703
BULLOCK FLETCHER HUDSON MASON NORTON ROSE SMEDLEY F327

107158 BLAKEMAN Mrs Marian. (Nichols) 3 Chesham Crescent, Anerley, London, SE20 7RL.
CHESLETT GITTENS MERWOOD NICHOLS SHAWYER STREVENS WHITELEY F2643

107166 BLAKER Mr Roger F. 9 Nelson Road, Hastings, E Sussex, TN34 3RX. Tel:0424-720980
BARON BLAKER FRENCH GEALL GOACHER JOHNSON LILLYWHITE OXLEY POLAND RIDDLES F2316

107174 BLAMEY Mr Arthur. 42c Lime Grove, Bideford, Devon, EX39 3JN. Tel:0237-472912
BLAMEY HINCKLEY KING PENALUMA PROVIS RODDA RULE THOMAS TREVASKIS WILLIAMS F1627

107182 BLAND Mr Malcolm H. Post Office Cottage, Airton, Nr Skipton, N Yorks, BD23 4AE.
BLAND BOARDMAN JAMES Quiney QUINNEY STUART WADDINGTON F2278

107190 BLAND Mrs Muriel. (Knott) 5 Cherrytree Way, Barrow In Furness, Cumbria, LA13 0LG. Tel:0229-828156
BLAND KNOTT F3364

107204 BLAND Mr Tim. 21 Meredith Road, North End, Portsmouth, PO2 9NL.
BLAND BOWEN HENDERSON HOAR Hoare HORE HOWELL LYNAS Lynass OWEN Owens PEDLEY RALF RALPH WILLIAMS F452

107212 BLANDFORD Mr Michael. 6 Rochester Road, Southsea, Hants, PO4 9BA. Tel:0705-736464
BLANDFORD F4632

107220 BLANN-FRY Mrs L. (Blann) 4 Coronation Cottage, Routs Way, Rownhams, Southampton Hants, SO1 8JG.
BLANN F6215

107239 BLATCHLEY Miss Joanna. 115 Kay Street, Darwen, Lancashire, BB3 3EL. Tel:0254-774631
BANNELL BLATCHLEY CHALLANDS Garrard GODDARD Gorrard HEYMAN LIDDY SPACKMAN STEVENS TURNER WHITEHEAD F5307

107247 BLAY Mrs Mary. 26 Bourne Close, Broxbourne, Herts, EN10 7NE. Tel:0992-463622
ATKINSON BAKER BROCKWAY CHAMBERLAIN DEWEY EMERY HUDDLESTONE JENNINGS PODD SAUNDERS F1625

107255 BLAYDON Mrs Angie. 2 Elm Close, Send Marsh, Ripley, Woking Surrey, GU23 6LE. Tel:0483-224511
ADAMS Bladen Bladon Blaiden Blaidon BLAYDON Bleadon BUCKLE DAVIES FISHER FOWKES FREEMAN HOWE KNIFE Kniffe Knyf Knyfe Knyff Knyffe

MERCER Nif Nife Niff Niffe Nyfe Nyffe RICHARDSON WARNER Workeman WORKMAN Wourkman WRIGHT F846

107263 BLEEK Mr Anthony Russell. The Willows, Cretingham, Woodbridge, Suffolk, IP13 7BL. Bleak BLEEK Blleck Blsack F6684

107271 BLENCOWE Mr Roy. Netherfield House, Stanwick, Wellingborough, Northants, NN9 6QF. Tel:0933-622124 BLENCOWE ETTE EYTE HEWITT F1851

107298 BLENKINSOP Mr Roy. 19 Conniscliffe Road, Hexham, Northumberland, NE46 2LW. Tel:0434-605354 SWINBURN F5791

107301 BLETSO Mr David. 27 Arundel Road, Bath, Avon, BA1 6EF. Tel:0225-314085 FELMINGHAM LARK MERRILL VANN F4601

107328 BLEWETT Mrs Anne. 32 Milton Crescent, Godalming, Surrey. Cansdale Cansdell CANSELL F7031

107336 BLIGH Mr Eric G. 59 Thelma Avenue, Canvey Island, Essex, SS8 9AN. Tel:0268-682396 BENFIELD BLIGH DEE HASTEAD STEMP F1211

107344 BLIGH Mrs Irene Sheila. (Speechly) 4 St James Avenue, Hampton Hill, Middx, TW12 1HH. Tel:081-979-0874 BANKS BRADFIELD DEWEY DOLBY HARROWING HEARNE HULL HURN PAYNE SPEECHLY WILSON F5828

107352 BLIGHT Mr Raymond. 74 Haywards Road, Haywards Heath, W Sussex, RH16 4JB. Tel:0444-414957 BLASDON BLIGHT Boils Boyels Boyle BOYLES Boyls Bridden BRIDDON BRIGHT Bryden CHITTY FERRIS GIBSON GODWIN HAYES JOY Leevars LEIVERS Levers LOCKWOOD MAJOR MARDELL MITCHELL NEWLOVE PARKIN PROUSE Prowse REAH RICHARDS SHORT STONEMAN TAYLOR TOWNSEND WELFORD Wellford Wilford F6499

107360 BLINCOW Miss F. 38 Ashby Drive, Rushden, Northants, NN10 9HH. ANDREW Baucot Bawcut BAWCUTT BENT Blencow Blencowe Blinco Blincoe BLINCOW Blincowe BRADSHAW BRIGHTMAN Britman Bryghtman BURBIDGE CARR COX CUTLER DAWSON DIMMOCK DOD DODD Dunckley DUNKLEY EDWARDS ELIMAN EMERY FENN FINCHER FREEMAN GOODAGE GREEN Groce Grose GROSS GUBBINS HEDGES HICKS HOUGHTON JEFFREY JENKINS JONES KING LACK LAKE MANNING MARIOTT Marriott Moodie MOODY Pain PAINE PARKER Payne Pitham PITTAM Pittum RIGBY ROCK ROE Row Rowe SAVAGE SCRIVENS SHAW SMITH STORTON Tailor TARRY TAYLOR TOFIELD Topfield TOWNLEY TURNER WADSWORTH WAFFORNE WALKER WALLINGER WARWICK Wats WATTS WHITE WILLS F1528

107379 BLINCOW Mrs M N. 10 Hartwell Road, Roade, Northampton, NN7 2NT. BAYMAN Beaman Beamond Beamont Beaumont BRADSHAW BURT BUTLER CLARKE Coaney CONEY Darlet DARLETT Darlot Darlott DAVEY HALSEY HINTON HUMPHREY JANES JOHNSON KINGHAM MEAD PALMER PEARMAN PELLANT Pellen Pellent PIXLEY RICKETT RUSSELL SMITH SOUTHAM STROUD THORN WALKER WELFORD F1602

107387 BLISS Mr R H. 201 Uxbridge Road, Mill End, Rickmansworth, Herts, WD3 2DP. Blie Blis Blise BLISS Blisse Blys Blyse Blyss F6691

107395 BLISSITT Mr R F. 43 Servite Close, Overpool Road, Ellesmere Port, South Wirral, L65 1RP. BLISSITT F3066

107409 BLOCK Mr S. Spring Farm, Spout Hill, Groton, Suffolk, CO6 5AH. BLOCK HICKS F6878

107417 BLOCKLEY Mr E G. 27 Laugherne Road, Worcester, Worcs, WR2 5LP. Alleybone Allibone Allybone Blockey BLOCKLEY Blockly Blookley Brockley CAPLEHORN CAPLEHORNE Disdal Disdale Disdall Disdel DISDELL Disedale ELVIN FISHER Hallabone Halleybone Hallibone HALLYBONE MEER Millard MILLER WARD F1512

107425 BLOIS Mr Peter. White House Cottage, Low Street, Tasburgh, Norwich, Norfolk, NR15 1LP. BARBER BIRD Bloice BLOIS Bloise Bloss Blosse Bloy Bloyce Bloye Bloys Bloyse BROWN Browne Burd BUSSEY FICKLING GREEN Greene GRIGGLESTONE HIGHT LONDON MURRAY Paine PARRY PAYNE POTTER READ Reed Reid RONALD Scales SKALES Squire SQUIRES STAFF WELLS F5699

107433 BLOMFIELD Mr P H. Buckland Wood Farm, Buckland Common, Tring, Herts, HP23 6PB. BLOMFIELD BOOT Boote Bootes Boots BOSWELL BROOK BROOKE DEWES GRANVILLE HAYES HOUGHTON MAYO REYNOLDS RICHARDSON SHEASBY F5846

107441 BLOTT Mrs Sylvia. (Hoodless) 127 Langley Crescent, Southway, Plymouth, PL6 6ES. HOODLESS F3724

107468 BLOUET-SMITH Mr J D. Waverley, Rosemount Lane, Honiton, Devon, EX14 8RG. Tel:0404-41293 BLOUET SETCHELL F444

107476 BLOUNT Revd Cyril D. 34 Barnsley Road, Dodworth, Barnsley, S Yorks, S75 3RN. Tel:0226-205240 ANSPACH ATKINS BARKER BLOUNT BLUNT BUGLASS CRADDOCK CUTLER FECHTMAN GUEST HANDLEY NEWTON RUSSELL SEHAN F2557

107484 BLOUNT Mr Graham. Rosslyn, 53 Birkinstyle Lane, Shirland, Derbyshire, DE5 6BS. Tel:0773-832534 BLOUNT BUSWELL GREAVES MARSHALL MOSLEY RADFORD SLACK F4805

107492 BLUNDELL Mr Colyn. 33 Sway Gardens, Bournemouth, Dorset, BH8 0PG. Tel:0202-533671 BLUNDELL F1636

107506 BLUNDEN Mr Barry W. 9 Shelldale Avenue, Portslade, East Sussex, BN41 1LH. HATHERILLO MIGHALL PIDGLEY POOLE WEBBER F4032

107514 BLUNDY Mr Robert William. Garmon Mill, Llanarmon, Mold, Clwyd, CH7 4QW. Tel:08243-631 ASTRIDGE BEAVAN BECKINGHAM Bivyen BLUNDY BRACEY Hockett MABBUTT MARLOW NEATE REYNOLDS Vivian WITT F1708

107522 BOARDMAN Dr Geoffrey. 11 School Lane, Castle Donington, Derby, DE7 2RT. AVERY BAKER BARON BOARDMAN BOCKING BOOTH BOURNER CARTER CROSSLEY CROWTHER EASTIN EASTWOOD ELLIS FIELDEN FLETCHER FOORD GREENWOOD LAW LEEK MARLAND MARSHALL MASTERS MAWSON MILLS MITCHELL OGDEN ORMEROD ROBINSON SPITTLES STANSFIELD STILL SUTCLIFFE TAYLOR THOMAS WALTON WHITEHEAD WOODHEAD F2504

107530 BOASE Miss H. 40 Rosehill, St Blazey, Par, Cornwall, PL24 2LG. BOASE CARTER CHELLEW COLLICK EASTON ELLIS FLETCHER PADDON SCOTT TERRY F1130

107549 BOATER Mr Malcolm Charles. 10 St Matthews Cout, Feltham Road, Ashford, Middx, TW15 2ED. BOATER F7416

107557 BOBIN Mrs Winifred. (Dillingham) 8 Dawlish Crescent, Rayleigh, Essex, SS6 9PN. Baubin BETON Bobain BOBIN Bobine Bobing Boubine Bowbin DILLINGHAM F5296

107565 BOCKETT Mrs Christine. (Blunden) 5 Ruxley Close, West Ewell, Epsom, Surrey, KT19 9ND. BARNES Barns Bennet BENNETT BLUNDEN Blundon BOND Bunson BUNSTON Bunstone COX EAST Est Este Honner Honnour Honor HONOUR PARKIN PIKE PINE PRICKETT Pyke SPRAKE Streater STREETER Streter Strether TURNER F2701

107573 BODDY Mrs Valerie. 15 Mersey Road, Durrington, Worthing, W Sussex, BN13 3NF. AMES BANGER BRADLEY BROCK BROWN CARPENTER CHALCROFT CHINNOCK CHRISTIE COLLIAR COSHILL COULSON CROWCOMBE CULLIFORD DEAN DEER FENTON FLINT GEORGE GREENSLADE GREGORY HAINES HEBBERD HILL HOBBS HOOKER HUNTER JOYCE LEAK LINEY LITCHFIELD MAINSBRIDGE MARSH MEARS MEHUISH MOON NEWMAN OSMAN PAICE PASAND RANGER RAYMAN ROTHERHAM SNOOK STEVENS WALKER WHEELER WHITE WOODMAN YOUNDELL F2400

107581 BODEN Mrs Lilian. 24 Adswood Grove, Meole Braze, Shrewsbury, SY3 9QG. BODEN F448

107603 BODFISH Miss M C. 47 Talbot Road, Wmthwick, Warley, W Midlands, B66 4DX. BODFISH Botfish F6634

107611 BODMAN Mr Paul. 70 Dilmore Avenue, Fernhill Heath, Worcester, WR3 7XA. BODMAN Bodmin BRADFORD CARLIN CASHMORE CHETWIN COLE CROOK CROSSWELL CRUMP DAY FELTON GENDERS GEORGE GULLIVER HERITAGE IDEN MANNING

SMITH WARD WILLIAMS F4

107638 BODY Miss Susie. Hazelmere, Lower Flat, Station Road, Woolacombe Devon, EX34 7AW. BELLAMY BODY COTTON F508

107646 BOFF Mr K J. 21 St Johns Court, Beaumont Avenue, St Albans, Herts, AL1 4TS. BOFF F764

107654 BOGDANOVIC Mrs Anne. (Whitehead) 113 Okehampton Road, St Thomas, Exeter, Devon, EX4 1EP. Tel:0392-57552 CANN GLANVILL HITCHCOCK HOLME JEWELL KELLAWAY LASCELLES MALLALIEU METTER MOSLEY PROUSE RAPER SMALLPAGE SMITH VICARY WHITEHAD WHITELEY WORTH WRIGLEY F1485

107662 BOIS Mrs E M. (Pearce) Alphington House, Grands Vaux, St Saviour, Jersey, JE2 7HG. BISHOP COLEMAN HUXHAM PEARCE F4903

107670 BOLDEN Mrs Joyce. (Ridge) 107 Military Road, Rye, East Sussex, TN31 7NZ. Tel:0797-227150 BOLDEN HENFREY JEZARD JEZZARD NOLSON RIDGE F2311

107689 BOLITHO Mr Paul. 17 Oken Court, Theatre Street, Warwick, CV34 4DF. Tel:0926-401301 BOLITHO F299

107697 BOLITHO Mr Richard T A. 106 Eastbourne Avenue, Toronto, Ontario, M5P 2G3, CANADA. Tel:+1-416-485-6856 Allan ALLEN Belither Blitha Bolitha BOLITHO Bolithoe BORLASE BOWMAN Goodale GOODALL Gooddall GREEN JOHNS MCMULLEN ROBINS SPENCER Tilley TILLIE Tilly F4409

107700 BOLITHO Ms S J. 2 Crendon Close, Studley, Warwickshire, B80 7DB. CONNOLLY HYDE JENSEN KING MCMANUS F314

107719 BOLT Miss B. 15 Bonnington Grove, Heavitree, Exeter, Devon, EX1 2QY. BACK BARBER BOLT COUNTER DUKE FRY LANE ROWE SNOW TRATHEN F276

107727 BOLTON Mr J. 42a Gunton Lane, Cotessey, Norwich, Norfolk, NR5 0AG. CARY DODD LAWTON WORBOYS F6372

107735 BOND Mr A. Guys Cliff Villa, Windermere Road, Lightwater, Surrey, GU18 5TH. Tel:0276-73285 BOND F6207

107743 BOND Mr Egbert. The Hundreds, Cow Lane, Tring, Herts, HP23 5NS. BOND CHEVILL GODDARD PARGETER F5992

107751 BOND Dr P. 42 The Avenue, Alverstoke, Gosport, Hants, PO12 2JR. Tel:0705-581304 BOND GILMORE GRAHAM TEARE F3575

107778 BONE Mr Garry. 19 Foyle Park, Basingstoke, Hants, RG21 3HD. Tel:0256-52862 BONE Bowen Bowun HUNTER F3473

107786 BONE Mr Peter. 17 Fir Tree Gardens, Horndean, Waterlooville, Portsmouth Hants, PO8 9HF. BONE F2481

107794 BONGILLI Mrs Joan. (Joslin) Abonnema, High Street, Lower Brailes, Banbury, Oxon, OX15 5AQ. FRENCH JOSLIN RAYMENT F1527

107808 BONIFACE Mr H J. 5 The Whimbrels, Porthcawl, Mid Glamorgan, CF36 3TR. Boneface BONIFACE Bonneyface Bonniface Bonnyface Bonyface F7237

107816 BONNELL Mrs Marjorie. 1 Berrystead, Hartford, Northwich, Cheshire, CW8 1NG. BALKWILL BEMBRICK EDGINGTON RAYNER ROOM F1890

107824 BONNIN Mrs Jane. (Dossor) Church Path Cottage, Newnham Road, Hook, Basingstoke Hants, RG27 9LY. Tel:0256-763287 BONNIN Dosser DOSSOR F3428

107832 BONSALL Mr Robert. 16 London Road, Flat 2, Buxton, Derbyshire, SK17 9NX. BONSALL CRITCHLOW GILLMAN POOLE SERGEANT WESTON F710

107840 BONSOR Mr John. Lambrigg Foot, Grayrigg, Kendal, Cumbria, LA8 9BL. Tel:0539-84202 BONSOR GENTRY GOODENOUGH HALL MOON PINDER SIDNEY WITHRY WOOD F580

107859 BONTHRONE Mr Mark. 29 Henslowe Road, East Dulwich, London, SE22 0AP. Bontavern Bontawern Bonthorn Bonthorne BONTHRON Bonthrone Bunthorn F85

107867 BONTOUX Mr Raymond. Residence Olympia, Avenue Olympia, 06300 Nice, FRANCE. Bonthoux BONTOUX Bontus F7239

107875 BONWELL Mr Les. 107 Greenways, Eaton, Norwich, Norfolk, NR4 6PD. Tel:0603-55918 BONWELL F6374

107883 BOOCOCK Mr John. 15 Kings Grove, Barton, Cambridge, CB3 7AZ. Tel:0223-262845 Bawcock Beaucock Bocock Bococke Bocoke BOOCOCK Boococks Bookcok Bookecocke Boolcock Boulcock Bowcoc Bowcock Bowcocke Bowcoocke Bowkoke Buckoke BULCOCK Bulcocke Bulcok Bulcoke Bulkok Bulkoke Bullcock Bullock F4700

107891 BOON Mr John M. 12 Blackhorse Lane, North Weald, Epping, Essex, CM16 6EP. Tel:0992-522663 AKERS BLUMSOM Blumson Blumsum BOON Boone LEONARD SONGHURST WILLIAMS F1777

107905 BOOTH Dr David L. Pound Cottage, West End, Combe, Witney, Oxford, OX8 8NP. BOOTH Dalgliesh DALGLISH Dolgleish LAWRY NEWCOMBE F438

107913 BOOTH E J. 22 Newlands Road, St Helens, WA11 9AU. ACKERS BURROWS CHEETHAM HARRISON HARTLEY HOUGHTON F1287

107921 BOOTH Mrs Isabella. 2 Northwood Street, Stapleford, Nottingham, NG9 8GH. Tel:0602-395024 BOOTH MCLEOD SLOAN F2884

107948 BOOTH Mrs Jacqueline E. (Rigden) 16 Sewell Avenue, Bexhill On Sea, East Sussex, TN40 2BH. COLBRAN Colbrand Colbrun Colebran Colebrand Colebrun Collbran DAWES ELPHICK FOORD Foorde Ford Forde LARKHAM F6147

107956 BOOTH Mrs M E. 7 Woodlands Avenue, Water Orton, Birmingham, B46 1SA. MARNELL F6912

107964 BOOTH Mr Ronald G. Clevedon, The Broadway, Woodhall Spa, Lincs, LN10 6SQ. Tel:0526-53701 ASHTON BLAND HEAPS MEDFORTH PASSEY REED ROSE SIMMS WALTER F5916

107972 BOOTH Mr Stanley Austin. 2 Northwood Street, Stapleford, Nottingham, Notts, NG9 8GH. Tel:0602-395024 BAGSHAW BOOTH MCLEOD TURNER WEST WILKIN F2383

107980 BOOTY Mr David. 2 Heather Close, Attleborough, Norfolk, NR17 2PA. Tel:0953-456158 BLAKE BOOTY BROMLEY BURNHAM BUSTON CATT DENNY EMMS FARROW Fetford FISHER FROSDICK GREENAWAY GRIFFIN LAMBERT LINTOTT MALLOWES PENNELL PENNINGTON RIX SCAMLER SPINKS Tedford Tetford Tetforde Tettford Thadford Thalford Thatfoord Thatford Thatfur Theckford Thedford Thedforde Thefford Theford Thelfar Thelford Theoford Thetfer Thetfird Thetfor THETFORD Thetforde Thetforth Thetfur Thettfford Thettforthe Thiford Thitford Thotford Thutfer Titfoord Titford Tytford WINTER WORSFOLD F73

107999 BOOTY Mr Harold. Apt B, St Marks Apartments, St Marks Street, Peterborough, PE1 2TU. Tel:0733-65712 HALFORD HOLDEN LATHAM MOON TACON F4183

108006 BORER Mr Tony. 25 Stretton Road, Addiscombe, Croydon, Surrey, CR0 6EQ. Tel:081-656-5736 BONDS BUNTON FIRMAN HALL HINTON LORKING SAYER STAMMERS F2702

108014 BORLAND Mr Robert E. 2 Hill View, Wimbledon, London, SW20 0TA. Tel:081-947-2724 Barland Boarland Boland Bordland BORELAND Borland Bourland Burland F3217

108022 BORRILL-TOWNSEND Mr Richard. 7 Oak Road, Healing, S Humberside, DN37 7RJ. Tel:0472-882406 PINCHBECK TOWNSEND WELLER WILLEY F6378

108030 BORTHWICK Mrs G. (Harvey) 24 Carfrae Road, Blackhall, Edinburgh, EH4 3QQ. CARD GOSS HARVEY HOCKEY LITSON WILLIAMS F5773

108049 BOSS Mr Raymond H. 11 Cockermouth Close, Leamington Spa, Warks, CV32 6NZ. Basse Boos Boose Bos BOSS Bosse HUNT Rabey RABY WARD F383

108057 BOSSON Mr Allen. 16 Cunningham Park, Mabe, Burnthouse, Cornwall, TR10 9HB. Tel:0326-374461 BAKER BOSSON COOKE GRATTON HEARN HOUGH LOWE MARSH TURNER F2367

108065 BOTTELL Mr Dennis R L. 9 Abridge House, Abridge Close, Waltham Cross, Herts, EN8 8QT.
BOTTELL BOTTLE BROWN IDDENDEN JUKES F3487

108073 BOTTERILL Mr D. 308 Lower Road, Great Bookham, Leatherhead, Surrey, KT23 4DW.
BOTTERILL F6730

108081 BOTTLE Mr John. 20 Stone Lane, Yeovil, Somerset, BA21 4NN.
BOTTLE DE ROUFFIGNAC ROUFFIGNAC F4772

108103 BOUCHER Mrs C. (Lovett) 1 Ivinghoe Close, Chiltern Park, St Albans, Herts, AL4 9JR.
BLAND CHAMBERLAIN CHRISTIAN JONES LIGHTON LOVETT LOYDE POINTER READ F5019

108111 BOULDEN Mr Jim. C/o Vis, Cumberland Avenue, Park Royal, London, NW10 7EH.
Bolden Bolding Bolling Bollyng BOULDEN Boulding CASTLE Hinge INGE KINCH PAGE ROLLINSON Searle SEARLES WATERMAN WHITTINGHAM F3828

108138 BOULDERSTONE-SALTHOUSE Mr Joseph Edward. Green End, 24 Villdale Avenue, Offerton, Stockport Cheshire, SK2 5SQ. Tel:061-456-9138
BALDERSTONE BOLDERSTONE BOULDERSTONE OSBALDESTON OSBALDESTONE F1841

108146 BOULDING Mr D R B. Temple House, 54d Mount Ephraim, Tunbridge Wells, Kent, TN4 8BB.
Balden Balding Baulden Bolden Boldin Bolding Bolling Bollyng Bolynge BOULDEN Bouldin BOULDING Bowlden Bowldinge BOWLING FOORD F5623

108154 BOULTON Ms Mary M. (Simpson) 55 Harbour Lane, Milnrow, Rochdale, Lancs, OL16 4EL. Tel:0706-58833
ALLAN BOULTON BROMILEY FRANCE GREGORY HUTCHINSON KENNEDY SIMPSON SLATER WHITTLE F5230

108162 BOUNDY Mr G C. 73 Churchill Road, Thetford, Norfolk, IP24 2JZ.
Bound Boundry BOUNDY Bownd F3840

108170 BOUREE Alain Et Nicole. 20 Rue De La Belle Epine, 78650 Beynes, FRANCE.
BOURREE LAPEYRE F7241

108189 BOURNE Mrs Judith. (Godfrey) Yew Tree Cottage, Frankton, Rugby, Warwickshire, CV23 9NZ. Tel:0926-632526
BROOKER GODFREY HARRINGTON NASH RISBRIDGER SOUTHENWOOD F4904

108197 BOURNE Mrs Linda. Newland, Landkey, Barnstaple, Devon, EX32 0NL. Tel:0271-830137
ALLCORN ALLEN Bones Borne Bourn BOURNE CALLACK CRASKE CUNNINGHAM DUNHAM EDWARDS EVE HICKFORD HURRELL JOYCE KEELER KELLOWAY MAHONEY MAY MILES MURRAY SEAR SMITH WEBB WICKHAM WOOTTON F244

108200 BOURNE Mrs Pat. (Weedon) 9 Meadows End, Sunbury On Thames, Middx, TW16 6SP. Tel:0932-786713
BARTLETT BOURNE BUTLER HORTON LITTLEWOOD WEEDON F1553

108219 BOURNER Mrs Sheila. 52 Comeytrowe Lane, Taunton, Somerset, TA1 5HY.
Carpender CARPENTER Carpinter F7163

108227 BOURTON Mr J. Flat D, 44 Westbourne Gardens, London, W2 5NS.
BARRIE BOURTON BROUGH DALLY HARRIS HODISON HUDSON RAWLINGS SAINSBURY SHERBEY THOMSON WEEKES WILSON F4145

108235 BOUSFIELD Mr M V F. 3 Eskdale Drive, Formby, Liverpool, L37 2YQ.
Bousefield BOUSFIELD F6704

108243 BOUTAL Mr Chris & Mrs Helena. 42 Charwood Road, Wokingham, Berks, RG11 1RY. Tel:0734-787243
APPLIN BENNETT BOUTAL Boutall Boutel Boutell Boutle BOWTAL Bowtall Bowtel Bowtell Bowtle COX DIXON EVILL GROVE HOSKIN JAMES MEDCALF VITTLE F850

108251 BOVIS Mr Colin. 92 Larkfield Road, Belfast, N Ireland, BT4 1QF.
BARRET BEAR BOVIS BROWN FOWLER GRISBY HAKE HICKS JUDD KEAT KENT MASON MECKIFF NICHOLLS PINN POTTER RABJOHNS SHAND SKIDMORE SOUTHARD WILKENS WILLIAMS WILSON F817

108278 BOVIS Mrs Hilary. 92 Larkfield Road, Sydenham, Belfast, N Ireland, BT4 1QF.
AGAR AUSTEN BLAIR BRYDEN CAMPBELL GARDNER GAULT GOYER HAMPSEY HENNIKER HILL MCCREADY MURRAY WALLACE F818

108286 BOWDEN Mr John. Quoits, Walditch, Bridport, Dorset, DT6 4LD.
BOWDEN ISAAC PARR SHELLABEAR SING F6034

108294 BOWDLER Mr John C A. 33 Glenleigh Park Road, Bexhill On Sea, East Sussex, TN39 4EE. Tel:0424-221968
Boelare Boudelers Boudlers Bowdle BOWDLER Cethin CLEGG De Boeles De Bollers De Boulers De Budlers De Bullers De Buthley GETHIN Gethine Gethyn HODENET HODNET HODNETT LIMESI LYMESEY LYMESY Redge Reg RICHARDS RIDGE Rydge F103

108308 BOWE Revd Kathleen. Cartref, Cliff Lane, Curbar, Sheffield, Yorks, S30 1XD. Tel:0246-582490
ATKINSON Bow BOWE CLARK COOPER HEBRON HUTCHINSON NESOM PEIRSON Pierson SPENCE THOMPSON WARD YOUNG F4125

108316 BOWEN Mrs J. Flat 11, 10 Riverview Gardens, Glasgow, G5 8EL.
COUPER FULLERTON HART INGLIS MACFARLANG MAIR F5837

108324 BOWER Mr Hedley. Milton House, La Haule, St Brelade, Jersey, JE3 8BF. Tel:0534-43167
BOWER F6533

108332 BOWER Mrs M J. 8 Victoria Close, Bramhall, Stockport, Cheshire, SK7 2BZ.
ALDERSLEY Oldersley F6921

108340 BOWERMAN Miss Bev. 33 St Ursula Road, Southall, Middx, UB1 2TH.
BOWERMAN DULING POCOCK SEAMAN F1223

108359 BOWERS Mrs Glenys Penrose. Hilltop Farm, By Pass Road, Davenham, Northwich, Cheshire, CW9 8JU.
CROSS DAVIES ETCHELLS FLETCHER GOAR HOHLAH KAY KENDALL NICHOLLS PARTINGTON PENROSE REED ROBERTS ROBY SHORROCK WORTHINGTON F4963

108367 BOWERS Mrs M. 31 Kings Head Road, Mirfield, W Yorks, WF14 9SJ.
CLARKSON DICKENSON DUFFY FIRTH ROOM SCOTT SHIRT F5862

108375 BOWERS Mr Ron. Road End Cottage, Stockland, Honiton, Devon, EX14 9LJ.
ABBOT BOWER Bowere BOWERS CLANFIELD CUPER Fashion FAZAN Frassan Frazan GADSDON Maote Mayot Mayots MAYOTT OTTO PRATT Rall Rawel Rawl Rawle RAWLL Rorel Rorell Rorle SOWERBY SPENCER WILDBORE F547

108383 BOWES Mrs M E. 21 Carlton Street, Blyth, Northumberland, NE24 2DT.
CARMICHAEL F7083

108391 BOWIE Mrs Miranda. (Geleit) 94 Auckland Road, Potters Bar, Herts, EN6 3HS. Tel:0707-54893
Batchelor BATCHELOUR BROCKBANK BROOKS BUTLIN COAD DENMAN DREDGE ELLIS GELEIT Gelert Gelleit Gileit Gillett GREGORY HARTSHORN HIDEN KING LANGLEY POCOCK ROEBUCK STORER WALTON WIGGINS F6176

108405 BOWKER Mr Eric. 4 Meads Grove, Astley, Tyldesley, Manchester, M29 7HE. Tel:0942-873779
BOWKER DONALDSON GRADY RAY F2878

108413 BOWL Mr David. 52 Derlyn Road, Fareham, Hants, PO16 7TJ. Tel:0329-283764
ARENY Balinger BALLINGER BARWELL Bollinger BOWL Bowld Bowle CARTER Coombes COOMBS DANDO DAVIS Eaden EDEN EVANS FRY FRYER Gasard Gassard Gazard GAZZARD HIDE HOOD JONES KELLY LAKE LARNER MAINSTONE Manstone MAYLAM MURRAY NEWTON ORR Pain PALMER PARKER Parsley Parsloe PARSLOW PAYNE PEGLER PERRY PHILLIPS SMITH Stanbury STANSBURY STORAR Storer TICKLE TYLER Wilet Willet WILLETT Wylett F2187

108421 BOWLER Mr A G. 19 Estella Mead, Newland Spring, Chelmsford, Essex, CM1 4XH.
BOWLER CANNELL MAHONEY PULHAM VALENTINEY F3743

108448 BOWMAN Mrs Dorothy. 43 The Scarr, Newent, Glous, GL18 1DQ.
AUVACHE BOWMAN Charretier CHARTIER CLEMENTS Isard Issard Izard IZZARD JONES MORGAN PARTRIDGE Teisser TESSIER F968

108456 BOWMAN Mrs Edna. 24 Polehampton Court,

Polehampton Close, Twyford, Reading Berks, RG10 9RR. Tel:0734-343858
CURTIS GAMBLE HUGHES INGRAM MARSHMAN PEEDELL THOROGOOD F3132

108464 BOWNESS Miss V K. Northolt, Northcroft Lane, Newbury, Berks, RG13 1BQ. Tel:0635-35377
ASHCROFT BOWNESS DREW FREEMANTLE HARRIS RILEY SEGAR F2617

108472 BOWRING Mr Robert W. 19 Lower Golf Links Road, Broadstone, Dorset, BH18 8BQ. Tel:0202-692374
Bouring BOWER BOWERING Bowers Bowring F1783

108480 BOWTELL Mr & Mrs. 61 Hanson Drive, Fowey, Cornwall, PL23 1ET. Tel:0726-832108
Bartell Boatell Botel Bottell Boughtell Boutell BOWTELL Bowttell Buddell GOBBY JOHNS F823

108499 BOWYER Mr D. Conkers, Hurst Green, Etchingham, Sussex, TN19 7QD.
BOWYER F501

108502 BOWYER Mrs Jill. (Huckstepp) 17 Langton Close, Selsey, Chichester, W Sussex, PO20 0JZ.
BOOTH BOWYER CARTWRIGHT ELMS FORTESCUE FULLER GILBERT HARMER HARNDEN HUCKSTEP Huckstepp LINCOLN MASON PEGGS PENFOLD PHIP PLOWRIGHT SMITH STRINGER UNDERWOOD F2237

108510 BOWYER Mrs Rosemary. Moorfield, Causey Hill, Hexham, Northumberland, NE46 2DW. Tel:0434-602856
AIKEN Aitken ARNOT ARNOTT Atkin Atkine BAILEY BIDDULPH Boucher BOUCHIER BOWYER BROOK CARPENTER CHARLESWORTH CHATTERTON CLAYTON COOK COOPER COUTTS COX CURNOW DEAN DUNCANSON DUNNING ELLIS Elsams ELSOMS FAULDING FINCHAM FLINDERS GIBSON GILL GIRDLER GOUGH GREEN GRINDY GRUNDY HANDCOCKS Hebblethwaite HEBBLEWHITE Hellis HILLIER HODGSON Hollier HOSKING HOULTON HOWLES HUNTER HUTTON Jandrell JANDRILL Jaundrell Jaundrill JONES KIRBY LANE Leacky Leakey Leakie LECKIE LEDDRA LOBLEY LORD Male MARRIOTT MAYSON MCKAY MEAL MILLER NINNES Ninnis OGDEN OLIVER PARKINSON PAYNTER PICKERING PITCHFORD POOLE QUICK REMINGTON RICHARDSON RIDGE RIMMINGTON SCOBIE STEPHENS STEPHENSON Stevens TAYLOR TEWSON WATSON WHITLEY WHYMAN WHYTE WRIGHT F3045

108529 BOYD Revd Dr Donald M. 11 Auldcastle Road, Inverness, IV2 3PZ.
BOYD MACDONALD MACLEOD F3044

108537 BOYD Mr Harold. 23 Millfield, Thornbury, Bristol, BS12 1JL. Tel:0454-412313
BOYD CAREY DANIEL GIBSON GRAHAM HAYES LOCKHEAD MURPHY STEVENSON WEIR WILLIAMSON F1105

108545 BOYD Mr Henry F. 5200 Brittany Drive South #1301, St Petersburg, FL 33175, USA.
BOYD F7242

108553 BOYD Mrs Margaret. (Waldegrave) 23 Millfield, Thornbury, Bristol, BS12 1JL. Tel:0454-412313
CONSTANT FAITH KEATS LANCE LENTON NEATE WAKEFORD WALDEGRAVE Walgraur Walgrave Walgrove Walsgrave Walsgrove F1104

108561 BOYD Nina. 91 Tinshill Road, Leeds, Yorks, LS16 7DN.
Parsnage PARSONAGE Pasnage F7157

108588 BOYD Ms Tricia. (Clews) 39 Holgate Drive, Luton, Beds, LU4 0XD. Tel:0582-596919
ALLEN BARRETT BEEBY CLEWS COX DEARMER HARBOROUGH HINTON SIMPKIN STOTEN SYMON TAYLOR TRAVELER WHITE F2540

108596 BOYD-RUSH Dr Dorothy Ann. 1044 Meadowlark Drive, Harrisonburg, Virginia, 22801, USA. Tel:+1-703-434-6677
BOYD BUTTLE DARLINGTON DEMPSTER HOWLAND KNOX MURDOCH PETTIGREW WALTON WILKINSON F4375

108618 BOYES Dr Alison. 5 March Street, Peebles, EH45 8DF.
BALL BELL BOYES BROCKBANK CLIBBON COPE CORNES DUNKLEY JOHNSTONE POWELL REPUKE TILLCOCK WINSHIP F3889

108626 BOYES Mr Malcolm. 80 Howe Road, Norton, Malton, N Yorks, YO17 9BL.
BOIES BOISE BOYCE BOYES BOYS BOYSE F1508

108634 BOYLEN Mr Jan. 15 Bowden Wood Road, Sheffield, S9 4EJ.
FRESHNEY F7281

108642 BOYLES Mr Richard. 9 Narvik Road, Corby, Nothants, NN18 9DW.
ALLEN ARTLETT BALL BLOOR BOILES BOYLES BRACKER BREWER BROMLEY CARTER COOPER CORNEY CRIPPS DUNBARTON ELLICOTT ELLIOT FLURY Hadland HEADLAND HOOKER HOUSE JANES LA ROCHE LITTLE MORRIS NOBLE NOBLES POLLARD ROBINSON ROGERS SAUNDERS STANLEY STEER SUMMERFIELD TELFORD THARP Tharpe THIRP Thirpe Thorp THORPE TIPLADY TOOVEY TYLER F382

108650 BOYLETT Mr John Edward. 6 Wheat Hill, Letchworth, Herts, SG6 4HJ.
Baylet Baylett Boilet Boilett Boylet BOYLETT Bylate Bylet Bylett Bylot F3071

108669 BOYS Mr Derek J. 97 Lyndale Avenue, Edenthorpe, Doncaster, South Yorks, DN3 2LB.
ATKIN BATH BOYS COOK LOCKWOOD MAUNDER WARD WILLEY WINDSOR F6536

108677 BOYS Mr J V. 21 Moor Road, Broadstone, Dorset, BH18 8BA.
BAILEY BASTARD BOWER BOYS Boyse BRIGG BROWNE CHAFFIN CLOUGH COLE COLLIER COWLEY CROOME DAVIS De Boys De Boyse DOBBIE Dobie ENNOS FOLEY FORD GARDNER GOODRICH GOSSLING GRAY HAGGAS HALE HARMAN HODGSON JACKSON JONES KENDALL KINGSTON LANDON LING MAIOR MONK-MASON NEWBERY PALMER PARKER PARSONS POLLOCK RATTRAY RIVERS Sampson SAMSON Sansom STAPLE STYLES SWEET TUCKER VULLIAMY WELLESLEY WORSLEY F2054

108685 BRACEWELL Mr Sidney Albert. 75 Chetwynd Drive, Whitestone, Nuneaton, Warwickshire, CV11 4TJ. Tel:0203-340667
BRACEWELL LEAROYD F727

108693 BRACEY Mr I D. 1 Speed House, Barbican, London, EC2Y 8AT. Tel:071-628-8835
ALLMAND ANDREWS BASKETT BENNION BRACEY CHAPMAN COPPS DANGERFIELD DEAR FOSSEY GRIGG MUNT NEW SKINNER UPEX WORBY F662

108707 BRACKPOOL Mr & Mrs C. 370 Chipstead Valley Road, Coulsdon, Surrey, CR3 3BF.
Brackpole BRACKPOOL Brappole F6671

108715 BRADBURY Miss Christine A. 1 Bradbury Street, Ashton Under Lyne, Lancs, OL7 9BZ. Tel:061-330-6247
BRADBURY BROADBENT DRONSFIELD DYSON FAIRBANK HALKYARD HAMER HAMPSHIRE RAFFERTY TURNER F1629

108723 BRADBURY Mr Michael. 5 Kilburn Road, Belper, Derby, DE5 1HA.
BRADBURY DAVENPORT LUTON MCCROHAN PARKER F4551

108731 BRADBURY Mr Ralph H. 19 White Lodge Close, Tilehurst, Reading, RG3 6YT.
BRADBURY Fausch FOCH KENCH F4309

108758 BRADFIELD Ms Edna. 76 Chesswood Road, Worthing, Sussex, BN11 2AG.
BARNETT BRADFIELD COVEY HUTT MATHEWS Matthews ROSE SADLER F2895

108766 BRADFORD Mr Benjamin H. 56 Waverley Lane, Farnham, Surrey, GU9 8BN. Tel:0252-715646
ABELL BATCHELOR BOURN BRADFORD GASSON HOOPER SPEAR F4977

108774 BRADFORD Mr Norman. Cherry Cottage, Hulland Village, Derby, DE6 3EP.
GANDY F2497

108782 BRADFORD Mr Richard. 23 Dale Street, Clontarf, Redcliffe, Queensland, 4019, AUSTRALIA. Tel:+61-7-284-7860
BRADFORD PINHEY F5152

108790 BRADLEY Mr A C. 8 Dorset Close, Congleton, Cheshire, CW12 1LU. Tel:0260-274122
BRADLEY DIXON FIELD GREENWOOD HINCHCLIFF Hinchcliffe Hinchliff Hinchliffe Hinschliffe Inchliffe MORTON THOMAS WALTON WHITWORTH WILKINSON F1784

108804 BRADLEY Mr A J. 51 Southcrest Road, Lodge Park, Redditch, B98 7JH.
BRADLEY MUSTIN F1074

108812 BRADLEY Mr Eric. Knightswood, 17 Mullaghmarget Road, Dungannon, Co Tyrone, BT71 6QX, NORTHERN IRELAND.
AVERALL BRADLEY CARTER CORNWALL HENNESSEY INGMAN MANDERS MOODY MOOTY ROBINSON F4930

108820 BRADLEY Mrs J M. Flat 2, 17 Fitzalan Road, Littlehampton, West Sussex, BN17 5JR.

Dudgen DUDGEON Dudgon F7194
108839 BRADSHAW Mr Maurice. 38 Hamilton Road, Scunthorpe, DN17 1BB. Tel:0724-850067
ABBOTT ALLEN ANFEYLD BARTON BEAUMONT BENNETT BESWORTH Bosworth BRACE BRADSHAW CAVE CHAMBERS CHEVELEY CHILDS COWDEREY DENNIS ENDERSBY EVERSDEN FISHER FREEMAN GALE GIDDENS GIMBERT GOATS GODFREY GOMME GULLICK GUNTON HADDER HADDOCK HARRISON HOLDSTOCK JOYCE KITCHEN LARK LUTT MACER MITCHELL MORLEY MUNCEY Munsey NICHOLLS NIX PAGE PAPWORTH PEDLER Petit Pettit Pettit PETTITT PRIOR RICHARDSON ROBERTS SANSOM SILLS SKELTON SKERMAN SMITH STAPLES SUTTON TAYLOR VINTER Vynter WADDELOW WAIT Whyat Whyatt Wiat Wiatt Wiatte WILDERSPIN Wyat Wyatt F4185
108847 BRADSHAW Mrs Valerie. (Pretlove) 247 Kingsbridge Road, Morden, Surrey, SM4 4PX.
BRADSHAW CAPEWELL CORNWELL DAWSON FRY GARDNER HARDY PRAGER PRETLOVE WOOD F4155
108855 BRADY Carol A. 1 Sleepers Delle Gardens, Winchester, Hants, SO22 4NU. Tel:0962-869944
BRADY KIRKUP F23
108863 BRADY Mr L W. 16 Leopold Road, Waterloo, Liverpool, L22 6QZ.
BRADY FARLEY Farrally IDIENS KINNEY MCCABE PEARSON ROONEY F5815
108871 BRAIDFORD Miss Marion C. 11 Falcon Way, Esh Winning, Durham, DH7 9JW.
BAINBRIDGE BRAIDFORD COULTHARD CROXTON FENWICK GARBETT GREGGS HODGSON JOHNSON RICHARDSON WHARTON WYLAM F253
108898 BRAIDWOOD Mr John A H. 44 Plessey Crescent, Whitley Bay, Tyne & Wear, NE25 8QL. Tel:091-252-9950
BRAIDWOOD BROWNER CLARKSON DOWNIE LITTLE LYNCH MORLE MUROOCH SMAIL F290
108901 BRAILSFORD Mr & Mrs A. 65 Charnock Dale Road, Gleadless, Sheffield, S Yorks, S12 3HQ. Tel:0742-658349
ASHLEY BINGHAM BLAGG BRAILSFORD BUTTERWORTH CHEATTER CLEWER COCK COLE COWLISHAW DARWIN DUFTY ELLIOTT FARMARY Farmery FLEAR FORD FRECKNALL FROST GAMBLE GELDER GILES HAGUE HAMBLY HARRISON HEMPSALL HIBBERSON HILL HOBSON HOOPER HORNBY JACKSON LAMBERT LEFEUVRE MARPLES MARSHALL MAY MILNER MOLLOY PADLEY PRESTON RICHARDS RIPPINGALE ROBINSON SAMPSON SCALES SIMPSON STAMP STANILAND STEPHENSON TOWNROW WARDLEY WATSON WOODLIFF Woodliffe F2955
108928 BRAIN Mr Arthur M. 33 Embassy Road, Whitehall, Bristol, BS5 7DZ. Tel:0272-516668
BRAIN Braune F6363
108936 BRAMFITT Mr Guy. 4 Newall Road, Andover, Hants, SP11 8HP.
BRAMFITT FORSTER HARROD KILBURN F4850
108944 BRAMHAM Mr Gordon. 28 Dale Road, Darlington, Co Durham, DL3 8LZ.
BRAMHAM HAMER HELLAWELL STRAKER WHITELEY F4231
108952 BRANDON Mrs Carol. (Horne) 21 Ashcroft Close, Shoreham By Sea, W Sussex, BN43 6YR.
BRANDON CATLOW FERRIS GILL HARGREAVES HORNE JACOBS NEWTON WOODRUFF F2738
108960 BRANDON Mrs Janet. (Mouldey) 50 College Gardens, North Chingford, London, E4 7LG.
BLAND BRANDON MOULDEY Mouldie Mouldy F2317
108979 BRANFOOT Mr D W V. 89 Hutton Avenue, Hartlepool, Cleveland, TS26 9PR. Tel:0429-269379
BASSETT BRANFOOT DALES GERRY GREENFIELD GUNN HAZARD SANDOM SINCLAIR F2714
108987 BRANFOOT Mr J S C Standish. 6a Ashdown Road, Epsom, Surrey, KT17 3PL. Tel:0372-724265 F2121
108995 BRANSON Dr J E. Po Box 191, Yarra Glen, Victoria, 3775, AUSTRALIA. Tel:+61-59-652249
BRANSON SIMMONS F3858
109002 BRANT Mrs Jean. 21 Owlsmoor Road, Owlsmoor, Camberley, Surrey, GU15 4SD. Tel:0344-771091
BRANT CHEESEMAN COCK COX DRAPER HOLMES SHARP TRUEMAN F1308
109010 BRANT Mrs Jeannette. 41 Regent Street, Papatoetoe, Auckland, 1701, NEW ZEALAND.
DANCE GOLDIE HUTCHINSON LEE MCKERRAS MOSS SMITH YETTS F4377
109029 BRANT Miss Ruth J. 25 Hurst Park, Pershore, Worcs, WR10 1PF.
BRANT F2652
109037 BRASS Mr J O L. Ridgeway, Windmill Lane, Ashbourne, Derbyshire, DE6 1JA.
Bras BRASS Brasse F6636
109045 BRAVIN Mr J. 91 Penn Hill Road, Weston, Bath, Avon, BA1 3RT.
Brabant Braben BRABIN Brabing Braven BRAVIN Braving F6278
109053 BRAWN Mr L R. 7 Lorne Court, Lorne Close, Slough, Berks, SL1 2TL.
BARTLETT BATE BRAWN DOWN GEAKE HUSBAND JASPER PEARCE SARGENT SPURR F773
109061 BRAY Mr Donald. 32 Osward, Forestdale, Croydon, Surrey, CR0 9HA. Tel:081-657-7271
BRAY Friar FRIER Fryer GROOM Hartknoll HARTNELL Hartnoll Hurtnoll LARKIN LIBBY OWEN THOMPSON WINCH F2074
109088 BRAY Mr Harry Layton. 16469 Upper Beach Road, White Rock, British Columbia, V4B 5A8, CANADA. Tel:+1-604-536-4928
BRAY F7397
109096 BRAZELL Mr Glyn. 167 Gravelly Lane, Erdington, Birmingham, B23 6LT. Tel:021-382-1340
Brasel Brasell Brashell Brasil Brassel Brassell Brassil Brazel BRAZELL Brazil Brazzille F3465
109118 BREARLEY Lionel. Gateholm, 115 Stocksway, Shepley, Huddersfield W Yorks, HD8 8DN. Tel:0484-603727
BREARLEY F3095
109126 BREEZE Mr Peter. 3 Heather Bank, Billericay, Essex, CM11 2BJ.
Brees Breese BREEZE F3280
109134 BRELLISFORD Mr George. 98 Greenhill Road, Liverpool, L18 7HN.
Boaler Boler Bouler BOWLER Brailesford Brailsford Brailsforth Braylesford BRELLISFORD Brelsford BRILLISFORD HOWARD RALPH SHONE THOMAS F3897
109142 BREMNER Miss Ann. 6 Leeward Gardens, Wimbledon, London, SW19 7QR.
BENNET Bennett Blacklay Blakalay Blakelah Blakelay BLAKELEY Blakely Blakey Blaklah Blaklay Brebner BREMNER FORBES FOX GLASS IBBERSON LEE LITTLEJOHN Pallet Perrett PETER Pollet Pollett Pollitt Porret Porrett PORRIT Porritt RUTHVEN Talbirt TALBOT Talfirth WALLS WILBY WOOD WORMALD Wormall Wormeald Wormeall F6332
109150 BREMNER Mrs J M. 40 Mclennan Avenue, Po Box 2190, Whyalla Norrie, SA 5608, AUSTRALIA.
Mcwha MEWHA F7080
109169 BRENCHLEY Mr T F. 19 Ennismore Gardens, London, SW7 1AA. Tel:071-584-7981
BRENCHLEY BRENCHLY F671
109177 BRENNAN Mrs Kathleen. (Merrick) 12 Caroline Avenue, Lithgow, NSW 2790, AUSTRALIA. Tel:+61-6-351-4391
BARRY BRENNAN BULL FEENEY LOT MERRICK MURPHY O'CONNELL RUSSELL SANDS F5486
109185 BREWARD Mr M J. Hillside Cottage, Upper Church Lane, Hutton, Weston Super Mare, BS24 9SH.
Breewood BREWARD Brewood F6903
109193 BREWER Mr Collin. Lower Town, Egloshayle, Wadebridge, Cornwall, PL27 6HU. Tel:0208-812414
AVERY BREWER BRYANT CLEAVE COLLIN GILL JAMES LIGHTFOOT F5076
109207 BREWER Miss Jennifer Ann. 50 Dorville Road, Lee, London, SE12 8EB.
BONES BREWER BUTCHER F651
109215 BREWER Mrs W V. (Newman) 50 Foley Street, Hereford, HR1 2SQ.
MORRIS NEWMAN F4650
109223 BREWERTON Mrs J S. (Knight) 46 Fountains Avenue, Simonstone, Lancashire, BB12 7PY.
BAKER BISSETT BREWERTON BURDETT DOVE DYCHE EDWARDS HUGHES HUTSON KNIGHT LOWE MANN POWELL Pownall SHIRRIS SMITH STODDARD F5939
109231 BREWIN Mr Sydney. 23 St Catherines Road, Hayling Island, Hampshire, PO11 0HF.

BRAMMAGE BREWIN F6555

109258 BREWSTER Mrs Audrey. 9 Julian Road, Ivybridge, Devon, PL21 9BU.
BISHOP BROWN BULLOCK DAVISON FRANKLIN GOODALL KELLOW MOODY WATSON WHITE F1569

109266 BREWSTER Miss Doris. 49 West Savile Terrace, Edinburgh, Midlothian, Scotland, EH9 3DP.
BREWSTER COSSAR LLOYD MEEK F784

109274 BRIANT Mr Peter. 12 Wyneham Road, Herne Hill, London, SE24 9NT. Tel:071-738-3263
BRIANT Brind Brine DOUSE Dowse FERGUSON Ker KERR MITCHELL ORAM Orum STEVENS Walles WALLIS WESTMACOTT WOOLDRIDGE F6167

109282 BRIDGES Mrs B E. 49 Birchmead Avenue, Pinner, Middx, HA5 2BQ.
ALLEN BOYD BRADLEY HARMSWORTH MARWOOD F5672

109290 BRIDGES Mr D H. 49 Birchmead Avenue, Pinner, Middlesex, HA5 2BQ.
BARTHOLOMEW BILBY BRIDGES Briges Brigis Burdakin BURDEKIN Burdikin CARR Clemens Clement CLEMENTS CURLINGTON Donthon Dunthon Dunthorn Dunthorne DUNTON FOX Hinchcliff Hinchcliffe HINCHLIFF Hinchliffe Irvin Irvine IRVING IVES MASON MILNER NEWBORNE OFFERTON STONES UTTING Warberton WARBLETON Warburton Wickes WICKS Wix F4071

109304 BRIDGWOOD Mr John L. 46 Roewood Lane, Macclesfield, Cheshire, SK10 2PQ. Tel:0628-424647
Bidgood Biggott Bigwood Bregewood Bridewood Bridgewood Bridgewoodde Bridgood BRIDGWOOD Bridgwoode Bridwood Brigoods Brigwood Broodgwood HENRY JAMIESON LINDOP Lindup F1454

109312 BRIERLEY Mr J B. 117 Station Road, Fenay Bridge, Huddersfield, HD8 ODE. Tel:0484-602880
BRIERLEY F6446

109320 BRIGDEN Mrs Lorna. 71 Wroxham Road, Sprowston, Norwich, Norfolk, NR7 8TW.
BRIGDEN GODSMARK HIRST LEECH LUNT NEEVE NEVE PLEASANCE PLEASANTS SHARRATT WAYLING WHITE WOOD F1188

109339 BRIGGS Mrs Elizabeth. 24 Lawrence Street, Darlington, Co Durham, DL1 4EE. Tel:0325-288762
BRIGGS FERGUSON MABEN F4073

109347 BRIGGS Mrs Enid. 85 Plantation Street, Accrington, Lancs, BB5 6RT.
AINSWORTH BAGGLEY BALDWIN BAXTER BENTLEY Brearley BRIERLEY BRIGGS BRINING BROMERLEY BROWN Bryning BULCOCK BUTTERWORTH DUCKWORTH DUXBURY ELLISON GRIMSHAW HANCOCK HAND HARGREAVES HASLAM HAWORTH HAYHURST Herst Heyhurst HINDLE Hirst HITCHEN Hitchon HOLDEN HORNBY HOUGHTON HOULKER HOWARD Hurst INGHAM KENYON KITCHEN LATHAM LIGHTBOUND Lightbown LIGHTOLER LOFTHOUSE Loftus LUND MARSDEN MITCHELL NICHOLSON NUTTER PARKINSON PICKERING PILLING PINDER PIRT POLLARD PORTER PORTMAN RALPH RATCLIFF Riding RILEY ROBINSON ROUGHSEDGE RUSHTON Ryden RYDING Ryley SAGAR SELLERS SHAW SLINGER SMITH SNAPE SPENCER STANNING STANWORTH Stirzaker STORZAKER STOUT TATTERSALL TAYLOR TOWNEND TURNER VARLEY WADDINGTON WADE WARING WELLS WIGGAN WILKINSON WILSON WORSLEY WRIGHT F2976

109355 BRIGHT Mr D. Pondside, Upham Street, Upham, Southampton, Hants, SO3 1JD. Tel:04896-343 F3839

109363 BRIGHT Mrs Marianne Romaine. (Glover) 26 Eagle Close, Kingsteignton, Newton Abbot, Devon, TQ12 3PF. Tel:0626-66227
CARTER COOK KEMP LAMMING PARSONS RAWLINGS ROMAIN Romaine F3330

109371 BRIMSON Mr David P. 84 Dene Road, Headington, Oxford, OX3 7EG. Tel:0865-64026
BRIMSON Brinson CARTER HARBONE HARTERY Hartrey MAUNDER PULKER REEVES SLADE F3584

109398 BRISCOE Mrs Irene. (Dee) 6 Hawthrons, Leigh On Sea, Essex, SS9 4JT. Tel:0702-527649
BRISCOE DAVIES DEE EDMONDS HARNEY MCCARDLE SPICE WEBSTER F7433

109401 BRISON Mr Robert I. 34 Bridge Terrace, Bedlington, Northumberland, NE22 7JT.
Brason Brayson BRISON Brisson F6884

109428 BRISTON Miss M E. 85 Welland Close, Peterborough, Cambs, PE1 3SB.
Boresbroke Fausbrook Fausbrooke Faustbrook Faustbrooke Foosbrooke Forcebrok Forcebroke Forcebrook Forcebrooke Foresbrok Foresbrook Foresbrooke Forsbroock Forsbrook Forsebrook Forsebrooke Forstbrook Forstbrooke Forstebrook Forstebrooke Fosbrock FOSBROKE Fosbrook Fosbrooke Fossbrook Fossbrooke Fostbrook Fostbrooke Frossbrook Frostbrook Fursbrook Fushbrook Fussbrook F6644

109436 BRIXTON Mrs I. 2 Camfield Close, Basingstoke, Hants, RG21 3AQ.
BOYD BRACKSTONE Braxston Braxstone Braxton Braxtone Breckston Breckstone Brexston Brexton Brickston Brickstone BRIXTON Cambrey Cambry KEMBREY OLIVER PENDLEBURY PLANT F700

109444 BROAD Miss Gwen. Hill Place, East Grinstead, Sussex, RH19 4LX.
BOWDEN BROAD DANIEL MICHELL NANSCAWEN STEPHENS F409

109452 BROAD Mr L W. Walnut Tree Cottage, Woolage Green, Canterbury, Kent, CT4 6SF.
BROAD BUTTI JEFFRIES MEPSTED PAINTER SELSBY F1825

109460 BROADBENT Mrs Joan. 19 Heeble Mount, Meltham, Huddersfield, W Yorks, HD7 3HG.
DAWSON LIUSEY LUCAS TAYLOR F3085

109479 BROADBENT Keith. Fairwinds, 5 Tandlewood Park, Royton, Oldham, OL2 5UZ. Tel:061-624-2278
BROADBENT DARNBROUGH ELLIS FISHER MILLARD Narey NARY Neary ORMROD Savil Saville Sevil SEVILL Seville STANDEAVEN Standeven Standhaven Standheaven Standiven F566

109487 BROADBENT Mr Kenneth. 19 Hebble Mount, Meltham, Huddersfield, W Yorks, HD7 3HG.
ANTROBUS BROADBENT PARKIN WEBSTER F3087

109495 BROADBENT Prof Leonard. Junipers, Manorial Road, Parkgate, South Wirral, L64 6QW.
BROADBENT HURST IVES LOVELESS F3307

109509 BROADBENT Ms Susan. (Hinchliffe) Wits End Cottage, 1 Ropery Walk, Keadby, Scunthorpe, South Humberside, DN17 3EB. Tel:0724-783752
BALMFORTH CHARLESWORTH HAMPSHAW HINCHLIFFE LAMPLOUGH MATHERS PEAT Peet WOOD F3381

109517 BROADHEAD Mr Matt. Bethesda, Thornley Drive, Teignmouth, Devon, TQ14 9JH.
BOOTHROYD BROADHEAD BUTCHER BUTTERWORTH COULSON EVANS GOUNDS HAWS HERRINGSHAW POOLE SANDERS SLOTE STOKES WATSON WOODHEAD WORDSWORTH WRIGHT F945

109525 BROADHEAD Mrs Rus. Bethesda, Thornley Drive, Teignmouth, Devon, TQ14 9JH.
BOOTH BRAZELL COX DENNISON EMMERSON FOSTER HUNT LEGG MORRIS ROWLANDS WARD F946

109533 BROADLEY Mrs Deborah. 29 Conifer Close, Church Crookham, Fleet, Hants, GU13 OLR.
BUSBY Ceiling CELLING CHILDERLEY Childrey CHILLERY CURD DINNER Ferral Ferrul FIRRELL Furrel HILDER Morfee Morfey Morphew Morphey MORPHY Selin Verral WILSON F3777

109541 BROATCH Mr J M. Perry Vale, 64 Gatton Road, Reigate, Surrey, RH2 OHL.
Broach BROATCH F6749

109568 BROCK Mr Robert H. 5 Ashridge Road, Wokingham, Berkshire, RG11 1PP.
BAVRIDGE BROCK HERMAN KNIGHT LEDGER NOAKES SIZMUR TALMAGE F3891

109576 BROCKMAN Mrs Y. (Stafford) 4 Holland Place, Holland Road, Frinton On Sea, Essex, CO13 9ES.
BROCKMAN CURTIS GARTON GROGONO NEWBY TUCKER WALLER F849

109584 BROKENSHA Mr David Warwick. Tanrhocal House, 86 Newland, Sherborne, Dorset, DT9 3DT. Tel:0935-817125
BROKENSHA Brokenshaw Brokenshire WARWICK F5257

109592 BROMELL Mrs C R. 156 The Drive, Rickmansworth, Hertfordshire, WD3 4DH. Tel:0923-778560
Bramall Brambel Brambell Bramble Bramel Bramell Bramhill Brammal Brammall Brammell Bramwell Bremall Bremble Bremboll Bremel Bremhall Bremhill Bremil Bremmel Bremmell Bremwell Brimbel Brimble Brimel Brimhall

Brimhill Brimmell Brimwell Bromble Bromehill Bromel BROMELL Bromelle Bromhall Bromhill Bromil Bromill Brommel Brommell Brommelle Bromwell Bromyl Bromyll Broomall Broomell Broomhall Broomhill Broomill Broomville Broomyll Brumble Brumel Brumell Brumhall Brumhill Brummell F6729

109606 BROMLEY Mr Stewart. 1 Andrews Close, Haughton Green, Denton, Manchester, M34 1QZ.
BROMLEY REDFERN F2681

109614 BROOK Mrs D. 7 Werfa Street, Roath Park, Cardiff, South Glamorgan, CF2 5EW.
Gogan Goggan GOGGIN Gogin F6893

109622 BROOK Mr Edward. 59 Ingle Head, Fulwood, Preston, Lancs, PR2 3WS. Tel:0772-716102
Allman ALMOND BARNES BENNETT BROOK BUTLER BUTTERWORTH CLIFF CULSHAW DOGOOD HAYWOOD HILL HLODERNESS HORSMEN MARGRAVE PRIESTLAY STENNITT SYKES THRELFALL Van Vaulconburgh VAN VAULKENBURGH WHARTON WRESSEL YATES F4759

109630 BROOK Mrs Hilary. (Parkinson) 91a Wellhouse Lane, Mirfield, W Yorks, WF14 0NS.
BIRCH BROOK Burch PARKINSON F5739

109649 BROOK Mrs Louise. (Carter) 1 Cosmur Close, London, W12 9SF. Tel:081-740-0164
ARUNDEL CARTER CUNLIFFE GILL GLEDHILL HAIGH HELLIWELL WINFIELD F5129

109657 BROOK Mrs Margaret. (Dyson) Merryhills, Church Lane, Grayshott, Hindhead, Surrey, GU26 6LY.
DYSON IVESON F4059

109665 BROOKBANK Mr M R. 4 Millview Gardens, Upper Shirley Road, Croydon, Surrey, CR0 5HW.
BROOKBANK Brookbanks F7220

109673 BROOKE Miss E W. Anscot, The Highcroft, Bebington, Wirral, L63 7PY.
BROOK BROOKE PAULDING PRITCHARD THORNE TODD WHITEHEAD WILTSHIRE F2472

109681 BROOKE Justin. Chymorvah Vean, Marazion, Cornwall, TR17 0DQ. Tel:0736-710468
BROOKS MEAD TIPPET F578

109703 BROOKES Mr Stanley. Walton Manor, Walton On The Hill, Tadworth, Surrey, KT20 7SA. Tel:0737-813383
BOULDEN BOULDING BRIERS BROOK BROOKE BROOKES Brooks DISNEY EYRE HARTLEY SHAW STRINGER TINGLE WOOLHOUSE F445

109711 BROOKING Mr R H. 37 Churchmead, Keymer, Hassocks, W Sussex, BN6 8BW.
Brookin BROOKING Brookings F6839

109738 BROOKS Mr J W. Halcyon, Boyndon Road, Maidenhead, Berks, SL6 4EU. Tel:0628-33300
Tolefree TOLFREE Tolfrey Tollfrey Tolvery Whiterod WHITROD Whitrood Witrod F470

109746 BROOMFIELD Mr Alan. 14 Holmes Drive, Rubery, Birmingham, B45 9ED. Tel:021-453-7994
Bloomfield Bramfield BRATFIELD Bromfield BROOMFIELD Brounfield Brownfield Brumfield COTTON HEDGECOCK KETTLE LACEY Lasey Parsnage PARSONAGE Pasnage POWELL TISER TYLER WALDRON WOOMANS F3047

109754 BROOMING Miss J M. 36 Lindisfarne Close, Cosham, Portsmouth, Hampshire, PO6 2RD.
BROOMING F3847

109762 BROSCOMBE Mr K. 20 Park Avenue, Mirfield, West Yorks, WF14 9PB.
Broscom Broscomb BROSCOMBE Broskam Broskham F4999

109770 BROSNAN Miss Annie. 2 Low Road, Debenham, Suffolk, IP14 6QU. Tel:0728-860680
BROSNAN CLOTHIER HOUSE OBORN PARISH WITHERS F2892

109789 BROTHERHOOD Mrs B H. 219 Humberston Road, Cleethorpes, South Humberside, DN35 0PH.
COOL Coole F6698

109797 BROUGH Mrs Frances. (Strangeways) 13 Winston Avenue, Bamford, Rochdale, Lancs, OL11 5JA. Tel:0706-59603
BROUGH PENNINGTON ROGERS Strangeway Strangewayes STRANGEWAYS Strangway Strangways WILDMAN F1319

109800 BROWELL Mr Bertram. 261a Park Road, Hartlepool, Cleveland, TS26 9NL. Tel:0429-276888
BROWELL Browl BRUEL BRUELL BRUYLL F3721

109819 BROWN Mrs A L. (Hall) Po Box 1437, Griffith, NSW 2680, AUSTRALIA. Tel:+61-6-962-4858
ADAMS ANGEL BROWN CORBETT CROSIER CROW CRUICKSHANK ELLIOT ELLIS FOSS HALL HOLDEN HUNT HUNT DANIEL KNOWLES MARTIN OWEN TURNER WILLIAMS F5473

109827 BROWN Mrs A M. 42 Whartons Lane, Ashurst, Southampton, Hants, SO4 2EF.
BATCHELOR BROWN FINCH FLOWER PSCINGA SMITH F1448

109835 BROWN Mr A. 9 Wyndham Road, Taunton, Somerset, TA2 6DX.
BROWN KINGSBURY TEBB F1950

109843 BROWN Mrs Betty. (Backler) 3 Perth Court, Upper Avenue, Eastbourne, East Sussex, BN21 3XW. Tel:0323-34927
APPS BACKLER CHATFIELD ELLIOT F6493

109851 BROWN Ms Carol. 32 Burrill Avenue, Porstmouth, Hants, PO6 2EA.
ARNOLD BRIGHTMAN COPLAND GALE LAW PALMER PILCHER PISSEY TOWNSEND TUFFIN F4000

109878 BROWN Mrs Cheryl. 41 Hikurangi Street, Whakatane, Bay Of Plenty, 3400, NEW ZEALAND.
BARRACLUFF BARTON BETTELHEIM BROTHERTON CAPSTICK DAVIES KERWIN PERCY SAVAGE WILLIAMS F5156

109886 BROWN Miss D M. 8 Buckhurst Grove, Wokingham, Berks, RG11 2JR.
BROWN LOFAS SLIGO Slingo F3864

109894 BROWN Mr David. 25 Richards Close, Wellington, Somerset, TA21 0BD. Tel:0823-664553
ACKERMAN BERESFORD Berisford Berresford Berrisford BREWER BROWN CLARKSON COOPER CRISPIN DAY DENNIS DUROSE GORSE HEATH HOLLINS HORTON LOCKYER LUGG MILSOM PARKER PARSONS PEACOCK PURCHASE RICKARDS ROMAINE Wilcock Wilcocks Wilcox Willcock Willcocks WILLCOX WINDSOR F2250

109908 BROWN Mrs Dorothy. 6 Misbourne Drive, Great Missenden, Bucks, HP16 0BL. Tel:02406-5955 F2454

109916 BROWN Mrs E M. 3024-14th Avneue S W, Calgary, Alberta, T3C 0X1, CANADA.
BRATLEY F6774

109924 BROWN Mr & Mrs E R. Huntley, West End, Silverstone, Towcester, Northants, NN12 8UY.
AIRNS BROWN CANNELL HUNT RHODES TOOTH F373

109932 BROWN Mrs E. 11 Wild Raddish Close, Mulbarton, Norwich, Norfolk, NR14 8DB.
LEA F7116

109940 BROWN Mr George W. 2 Rusland Crescent, Ulverston, Cumbria, LA12 9LT.
SAINT SAINTY SANT SAUNT F2297

109959 BROWN Mr H J. Luckhurst, Mayfield, East Sussex, TN20 6TY.
ACKLAM BROWN COLE HODGE MARCUS SKIPPER TRANMER F5789

109967 BROWN Mrs J. Maybank, Rd2, Te Awamutu, Waikato, NEW ZEALAND.
ATKINSON BOWLEY CARTER DAYER GATLEY HUTCHENCE HUTCHINS JOINER SILK STANNARD WALKER F5171

109975 BROWN Mrs Jacqueline. (Gardener) Quinta Terceira, Kiln Lane, Cores End, Bourne End, Bucks, SL8 5JE. Tel:0628-520513
BRAMWELL DE CLIFFORD THORNTON GARDENER GILBERT HERBERT TATHAM THORNTON WISE Wyse F4370

109983 BROWN Mrs Joan. (Hull) 9 Randolf Court, Lower Templestowe, VIC 3107, AUSTRALIA.
ADAMS CADDY HOGAN HULL PRYOR WHITMARSH WICKHAM F5450

109991 BROWN Miss Joan. 8 Green Lane, Rainbow Hill, Worcester, WR3 8NY.
Bailey Baily Baylie BAYLIS Bayliss Bayly STAYT Steyt F3317

110000 BROWN Mr John D. 15 Dorset Avenue, Sunfield Park Estate, Diggle Saddleworth, Oldham Lancs, OL3 5PS.
BOLTON BRIAN BROOKS BROSTER BROWN EGERTON FAIRBROTHER FIDDY KAY O'BRIAN ROBINSON SHILLITO SHILLITOE STEVENS STOCKS WHEELTON F736

110019 BROWN Mrs June W E. (Herbert) 69 Crumpsall Street, Abbeywood, London, SE2 0LR.
BOTELER CASTLE FORTUNE HERBERT RICH TIPSON TOMPKINS VINCENT F5115

110027 BROWN Mrs Kathleen. (Jenkins) 21 Stanley Road, Lindley, Huddersfield, HD3 3LU. Tel:0484-658651
BERRY BRIDGES BRIDLE BROWN BULLAS CLEGHORN CRABTREE FAIRBANK FOX GEE GLEDHILL GRAY HAMER JENKINS MOODY PIZER PURKIS WOODHATCH F5053

110035 BROWN Mrs Lilian F. 143 Napier Road, Glenrothes, Fife, Scotland, KY6 1AX. Tel:0592-754187
COOPER MACDONALD Macdonnell F1615

110043 BROWN Mrs Pamela. 123 Manor Lane, Sunbury On Thames, Middx, TW16 6JE. Tel:0932-787198
COSTELLO HOBBS HOLMES MCFARLANE PARKER PAYNE ROYAN SALMON SAMBOURNE SLADE F298

110051 BROWN Miss Pamela. 14 Field Close, Bromley, Kent, BR1 2SF.
ALLEN BAILEY BRIGGS BROWN Cassey CATER CHANDLER COSSEY Cossi Cossie Cossy COVENEY Covenny Coveny Covney COWLEY CUPHIS HUTCHINSON Koveney LODGE Macksted Macstead Maxstead Maxtead MAXTED Mexstead MILSOM Milson PAGE SMITH Wardley Woodley WORDLEY Wordly WYATT F1904

110078 BROWN Mrs Ruth. (Davis) 17 Greenloons Drive, Formby, Liverpool, L37 2LX. Tel:07048-77626
BLAKE CRAWSHAW DAVIS GANDER Moise MOYES Moyse Moyses NALL Naul Naule Nawle SHENTON F5347

110086 BROWN Miss S. 25 Homecroft Drive, Packington, Leicester, LE6 5WG.
CANFANY GORICK F6556

110094 BROWN Mrs S. 146 Timbeb Bank, Vigo Village, Meopham, Kent, DA13 0SW.
CURD POCOCK F1154

110108 BROWN Mr Stanley. Trewen, Tregrill, Menheniot, Liskeard, Cornwall, PL14 3PL.
BARKER BROWN DUDLEY IRELAND TAYLOR WHEELDON F3340

110116 BROWN Mr Stephen. 34 Elmhurst Road, Gosport, Hants, PO12 1PG.
ALDRED CHRISTMAS HALL MARSH MAWANT PUSS REEVE SANDHAM SEMMENS WAREHAM F4577

110124 BROWN Mrs Valerie. 90 Devon Road, Luton, Beds, LU2 0RL.
Beamish BEAMS Bristoe BRISTOW Bristowe Creek CREW CRICK JONES PADGET Soane Soanes SOANS Sone F4792

110132 BROWN-LEE Mrs Gillian. (Smith) 47 Calbourne Drive, Calcot, Reading, Berks, RG3 7DB. Tel:0734-417368
BACKHOUSE BELL DANIEL DANIELL DRISCOL Driscoll ELLIS Ellise Elliss Graeme GRAHAM Grahme Grayham LAMBTON LYNCH Moffet Moffett Morfat Morfet MORFETT Murfitt Portbery Portbeurye PORTBURY Potberie Potbeury Potbury SMITH SULLIVAN WATERS WHITE F4160

110140 BROWNBILL Mr Tom. Fernlea, 94 Brook Lane, Newton, Chester, CH2 2EU.
BROWNBILL F4760

110159 BROWNE Mr F. 10 Milroy Avenue, Gravesend, Kent, DA11 7AY.
BAIN Bane BARRETT BROWN BROWNE BURKE CARVER CONSTANTINE ELLIOTT FRENCH HORSFIELD ILES JOHNSON KERSLAKE Larken LARKIN LAST LONGBOTTOM MOORE POWELL RUSSEL SMITH WARD WILSON F2825

110167 BROWNE Miss F. 104 Wilson Street, Brunswick, Victoria, 3056, AUSTRALIA.
COOBIN FORSHAW HARRISON LEE SOUTHWORTH SPENCER F5508

110175 BROWNE Ms Gloria. 73a Church Road, Hadleigh, Benfleet, Essex, SS7 2DW.
BASSETT DENCH THOMAS F1737

110183 BROWNE J P. (Fitzjames) The Oak House, 14 Homelands, Leatherhead, Surrey, KT22 8SU.
CLARKE COCKSHOTT COE FITZJAMES HOLDAWAY LEE LITTLEWORTH LONG PARSONS ROOKE SOMERVILLE Sommerville SUDLOW WALKER WHALLEY F1153

110191 BROWNE Mrs Kay. 14 Brunton Street, Wanniassa, ACT 2903, AUSTRALIA.
BARNETT CHAMBERS CRISP ELSLEY HARDY HARRIS HATCHER LOVELL RINTOUL TURNER F3996

110205 BROWNE Mr T A. 14 Brunton Street, Wanniassa, ACT 2903, AUSTRALIA.
BENJAMIN BROWNE BUTTERWORTH CROSS Damen DAMMON Ellsley Elsey Elsley HARRISON HORROCKS Horrox HOUSE LUCKHURST MOON PARKER Rentoul Rentroul Rintoul ROBINSON SCHOFIELD STANDRING TOWELL WATSON Winsar Winsor WINZAR WOOD WRIGLEY F3997

110213 BROWNING Mr Bernard George. 14 Highfield Avenue, Waterlooville, Hants, PO7 7PX. Tel:0705-262408
BROWNING CLOWES DEAVILLE LITTLEBOY F3179

110221 BROWNRIDGE Mr Stan. 98 Hadham Road, Bishops Stortford, Herts, CM23 2QF. Tel:0279-653801
Brownbridge BROWNRIDGE Brownrigg Moresby MORRISBY Mosby F4597

110248 BROWNSEY Mr P W. 9 Louise Avenue, Mangotsfield, Bristol, Avon, BS17 3JF. Tel:0272-563367
ANGEL Angell Brownsea BROWNSEY F4436

110256 BRUCE Major Hugh Glenrinnes. The Coach House, Blofield, Norwich, Norfolk, NR13 4RG. Tel:0603-713784
Brice Broase Brois Broise BRUCE Bruice Bruis Bruisone Bruisson Brus Bruse Brussee Brussoun Brussoune Brys Bryson F6225

110264 BRUCE Dr James Henry Ian. 972 Holderness Road, Hull, HU9 4AB. Tel:0482-74455
ALEXANDER BRIDGE BRUCE HIGHTON INGRAM MACRAE MCKAY RANKIN RUSHTON SEDDON F5876

110272 BRUCE Mrs Joan. (Dennis) 972 Holderness Road, Hull, North Humberside, HU9 4AB. Tel:0482-74455
BOUNDY CROWELL DAW DENNIS ELLACOTT HAWKE HICKS HIGGINS HODGE JEANS SPRACKLING WETHERELL F5379

110280 BRUCE Mr S F. 216 Somerset Road, Almondbury, Huddersfield, W Yorks, HD5 8LP. Tel:0484-548089
BATES BRUCE SANDERSON F3143

110299 BRUDENELL Mr Derry. 36 Eastfield Road, Wellingborough, Northants, NN8 1QY. Tel:0933-278921
BRUDENELL F3774

110302 BRUNDISH Mrs I C. 703 Foxhall Road, Ipswich, Suffolk, IP4 5TB.
Brandish BRUNDISH Brundishe F7123

110310 BRUNSDON Mr & Mrs G. 207 Boothferry Road, Hessle, East Riding, Yorkshire, HU13 9BB.
ATTWOOD BEACH BISHOP BROOKS BRUNSDON CHAMPION CONDON COOK CRUMBLE DAVIES DEWHURST ELDRIDGE EVANS FENTON FINNESEY FISHER GILL GREENALL GUDGEON HENNER HEPWORTH HILDER HOBBS HONYBONE HORNER HYLAND JONES KEMP LEIGH LITTLE MIDDLETON MILHAM MILLER MUDGE NASH PAGE PATRICK POUND PRIOR RODGERS RUFFLES SEED STEPHENS STONE TANNER TAYLOR WHITTAKER WILKINSON WORTLEY-HEPWORTH F2814

110329 BRUNT Mr Graham George. 4 The Rise, Weymouth, Dorset, DT4 0TD. Tel:0305-786932
ANTELL BRUNT COOMBS DAMPNEY HOUNSELL JUKES MAPSTONE TRIM WILLS WISEMAN F804

110337 BRUTON Mr Roger. 15 Adrian Road, Abbots Langley, Herts, WD5 0AG.
BRUTON F7244

110345 BRYAN Mrs Marjorie. (Gledhill) 2 Belgrave Terrace, Lower Brimley, Teignmouth, Devon, TQ14 8LJ. Tel:0626-774767
BLIGHT BOWDEN BRYAN CHARLESWORTH CHESTER DRAKE FRITH GLEDHILL JACKSON ROWLEY THICKET Thickett WILCOCK Willcock F3187

110353 BRYANT Miss Gillian. 20 Heol Llanishen Fach, Rhiwbina, Cardiff, CF4 6LD.
BIGGS Bryan BRYANT JEREMY LEWIS MILSOM F1912

110361 BRYANT Mrs Marjorie. Elmers, Hackthorn, Durrington, Salisbury Wilts, SP4 8AS. Tel:0980-52442
ADAMS BLAKE BRYANT BUCKLE CLARK GIBBINGS GILBERT GRAFTON GRAY HADDERELL HADDRELL Hatherell MILLARD ROBJOHN STRIBLEY TOWNSEND WATERS F3140

110388 BRYCE Mr Robert. 9 Robina Close, Evesham, Worcestershire, WR11 6EZ. Tel:0386-41907
BANTING BRYCE CHISHOLM GLEN GRAY HOLFORD LOWRY ROBERTS STEVENSON THOMPSON TRICE VEASEY WATT F3999

110396 BRYDEN Mrs A M. 27 St Annes Road, Eastbourne, E Sussex, BN21 2DJ.
ATHERTON Briddon Briden Bridon BRYDEN Brydon BULMAN FAIRHURST FENWICK HEWITSON LOWE RATCLIFFE SCOTT UNSWORTH F1069

110418 BUCHANAN Mr J R. 19a Maxton Road, Dover, Kent, CT17 9JL.
BUCHANAN CHURCHILL EVANS FARTHING FREETH PRINCE ROBINSON Vazy VEASY WADSWORTH WYATT F5821

110426 BUCHANAN Mrs Phyl M. (Connell) 259 Mahurangi East Road, Snells Beach, Warkworth, NEW ZEALAND.
ANDERSON BUCHANAN CONNELL DEMPSEY FORWOOD GILMOUR HOSKING F5496

110434 BUCK Mr Colin. 36 Kirkwood Way, Cookridge, Leeds, LS16 7EX. Tel:0532-676417
BLIGHT BLORE BUCK HORSWILL MUCHMORE NEWTON SANSOM SHUTTE TWIST WIDER F1987

110442 BUCK Mr Jonathan. 14 Holgate Road, Pontefract, West Yorks, WF8 4ND. Tel:0977-790120
BARRATT BARTON BUCK BUTLER ESKRIETT KENDREW PENNINGTON RIDGE SCOFIELD SUNDERLAND F6517

110450 BUCKBY Mr James. 15 Winchester Road, Rushden, Northamptonshire, NN10 0HW. Tel:0933-53177
BLACKWELL Bucby Buckbee BUCKBY Buckbye Buckley Buckly Bugbee Bugby Buglee Bukby CURTIS FOSTER MANN MASTERS NICHOLSON PATRICK SEAMARK WARREN F336

110469 BUCKERIDGE Mr John Maundrell. 147 Herrick Road, Loughborough, Leicestershire, LE11 2BS. Tel:0509-212515
BUCKERDIGE Manderell Mandral Mandrell Mandril Maudrell Maunderell MAUNDRELL Maundrill Monderel Monderell Mondrell Mounderell Moundrell Munderell Mundrell F1797

110477 BUCKINGHAM Mrs Dorothy. (Wade) 17 Gloria Way, Grimsby, South Humberside, DN37 9SW. Tel:0472-883018
ALLENBY AUSTWICK D'aubney Daubeney Daubeny DAUBNEY Dimmock DOBSON Dymock Dymok DYMOKE GEE HATTON HEATH HILL HUTCHINSON LORD PALFREYMAN Rainer Rainor RAYNER Raynor SEATON STEELEY TOMBLESON WADE WALDEGRAVE Waldgrave Walgrave WRIGHT F3504

110485 BUCKINGHAM Mr Richard. 53 Oakfield, Goldsworth Park, Woking, Surrey, GU21 3QS.
BUCKINGHAM F887

110493 BUCKLEE Miss B M. 174c Woodcote Road, Wallington, Surrey, SM6 0PD.
Lagnden Landen LANDON Lanedon Llanden F7215

110507 BUCKLEY Mrs Dorothy. (Pearson) 4 Wyandra Crescent, Port Macquarie, NSW 2444, AUSTRALIA. Tel:+61-65-836105
BARDEN BERRY BUCKLEY CALLAGHAN COWARD CURTIS FLOWER HURST PATON PEARSON F4214

110515 BUCKLEY Mr John. 100 Isham Road, Norbury, London, SW16 4TF.
BUCKLEY BURFORD EASTWOOD JONE JONES KENT LEBROW MOONEY F6060

110523 BUCKLEY Ms Pamela J. (Fitton) 76 Greenbank Road, Syke, Rochdale, Lancs, OL12 0EN.
ALLAN Allen BAMFORD BARNACOTT BINNS BLEE BRIERLEY COURTIS CURTIS FITTON HILL HODGE KING LAITY LAMBERT LORD MADEN MILES MILNE PEARCE RIDING ROBINSON SHEPPARD SIMMONS WEBB WHITEHEAD WILD WRIGHT F1072

110531 BUCKLEY Mr Richard H. 243 Bailbrook Lane, Batheaston, Bath, Avon, BA1 7AA.
BAILEY Beley BUCKLEY DENNISON DYSON HAMPSHIRE LODGE SENIOR WEBSTER F1866

110558 BUCKLEY Mr Sidney C. 11 Mainson Dieu Place, Dover, Kent, CT16 1DX. Tel:0304-214304
Buckland Buckle BUCKLEY Buckly F3391

110566 BUCKMASTER Mr Anthony Michael. 109 The Pyghtle, Wellingborough, Northants, NN8 4RR. Tel:0933-678598
Buckemaister Buckmaister BUCKMASTER Buckmayster Buckminster Buckmuster F1281

110574 BUCKOKE Mrs Irene. 49a Emmanuel Road, Balham, London, SW12 0HN.
BUCKOKE F2847

110582 BUDD Mr Bill. 45 Richards Avenue, Forrest Hill, Aukland 9, NEW ZEALAND. Tel:+64-9-410-9576
BUDD F4204

110590 BUDGE Mr Dudley J. 120 Chesterfield Road, Lichfield, Staffs, WS14 0AA.
BUDGE PRIDDLE QUANTOCK F2304

110604 BUDGE Mrs J. (Clarke) 8 Alma Road, Orpington, Kent, BR5 4PT.
BRIGHTWELL BROCKWELL BUDGE FARRANT FLEWERS FLOODGATE OVERNELL PEARCE PEMBLE TAYLOR F2332

110612 BUDGETT Mr David. 40 Bodmin Avenue, Macclesfield, Cheshire, SK10 3JU. Tel:0625-431606
BLADES BROGDEN BUDGETT CAMBAGE LODGE F933

110620 BUDWORTH Mr Foster. 26 Camlet Way, St Albans, Herts, AL3 4TL.
Becket BECKETT Boddeworth Boddeworthe Boddewurth Bodeworth Bodeworthe Bodewurth Buddeworth Buddeworthe Buddewurth Budeworth Budeworthe Budewurth BUDWORTH Budworthe Budwurth Cobley COOLEY F702

110639 BUDZIK Mrs Sylvia. (Barker) 128 Chetwynd Street, Smallthorne, Stock On Trent, Staffs, ST6 1PT. Tel:0782-835256
BARKER BOURNE BROWN BUSHBY CAPEL Cappel Cappell Cartlech Cartlege CARTLICH ELSMOOR FISHER GALLIMORE HOLLINS JACKSON JOYCE MELLOR MILNER MORRIS MQUAD Mquaid PLATT Sarjeant SERGEANT Serjant SHORT SIMPSON TOWNSEND WALKER WALTHOE WHEELER F3952

110647 BUGG Mr Dennis. 31 Stockton Close, Hadleigh, Ipswich, Suffolk, IP7 5SH.
ABBOTT BUGG PARKER PLUMMER F3417

110655 BUIST Mr & Mrs A S. Skips Old Hall Park, Seething, Norwich, Norfolk, NR15 1DW.
Boist BUIST Busst Buste F6633

110663 BULCH Mrs Helen. (Kay) General Delivery, Stella, Ontario, K0H 2S0, CANADA. Tel:+1-613-389-3411
BULCH HAMILTON JAMIESON KAY MCQUEEN SHAW STRATHCARN TAYLOR F4362

110671 BULL Mrs R E. 11 Torbay Road, Urmston, Manchester, M31 1LH. Tel:061-748-2441
BLACK CHIPCHASE ISMAY MORALEE Moraley Moralie Morallie Morelee Morrale Morraley Morralle Morrerley Morrilee RHODES F5286

110698 BULLOCK Mrs K G. 101 Ditton Hill, Long Ditton, Surbiton, Surrey, KT6 5EJ.
ASHBY F6602

110701 BULT Mrs Rebecca. (Williams) 803 Vance Street, Lakewood, Colorado, 80215, USA. Tel:+1-303-237-6344
IVEY JONES OWEN ROWLANDS WILLIAMS WYNN F4234

110728 BUNDRED Mr William. Batenbush Farm Bungalow, Longtown, Carlisle, Cumbria, CA6 5NW. Tel:0228-791258
ANNAN ATKINSON Blundred Bondred Brundred BUNDRED COOK Elliot ELLIOTT Ellot KNOWLES LISTER RHODES ROWNTREE SMAILES Smiles STORER WALLER WHITTINGTON WREN F1415

110736 BUNDY Mrs A. (Angell) 52 Belmont Road, Wealdstone, Harrow, Middlesex, HA3 7PN.
ANGELL F5001

110744 BUNGEY Mr & Mrs R P. 2 Green Close, Headbourne Worthy, Winchester, Hants, SO23 8JZ.
BUNGAY Bungey Bungy SWEETAPPLE F6827

110752 BUNKHAM Mrs B M. (Birmingham) 4 Pullfields, Chesham, Buckinghamshire, HP5 2RB. Tel:0494-785866
BIRMINGHAM Buncombe Bunkam BUNKHAM Bunkum COPELAND KNAPMAN F3519

110760 BUNNETT Mrs S A. 608 Arroyo Seco, Santa Cruz, California, 95060, USA.
BUNNETT F6597

110779 BUNNEY Mr K. 10514 Huntington Wood, Houston, Texas, 77088, USA.
Bonney Buney BUNNEY Bunny F7204

110787 BUNNING Mr L W. 19101 Sierra Majorca Road, Irvine, CA 92715-3939, USA.
BALL BROWN BUNNING BUXTON CLARK COLLIN COLLINS ELSE GIMSON HOLYOAK HUBBARD JEFFS MILLER PITT RIDLEY RUDKIN SHARP WOOD WOODS WRIGHT F5670

110795 BUNT Mr John. 935 Van Nuys Street, San Diego, CA 92109, USA. Tel:+1-619-488-6750
Bundt BUNT Bunte BURR GODDARD LOAN OAKSHOTT Rundeel Rundeil RUNDELL Rundiel Sprigg Sprigge SPRIGGS Sprydge F5020

110809 BUNTING Mr R M & Mrs Y J. Firgrove, Horseshoe Lane, Ash Vale, Aldershot Hants, GU12 5LL. Tel:0252-25644
Bunten Buntin Buntine BUNTING Buntinge Bunton

Buntynge F7149
110817 BUNYAN Mr R. 10 Eastways, Bishops Waltham, Southampton, Hants, SO3 1EX.
BAXTER BUNYAN HUNT POLLARD SHARPE SMITH WELFARE F2646
110825 BUNYAN Mr Terry. 10 Kenton Close, Bracknell, Berks, RG12 3AZ. Tel:0344-50517
Bunion Bunnion Bunnyon BUNYAN Bunyon HENNESSEY LATEWOOD LATIMER LEE MCCREA MEGRATH STEWART F63
110833 BURCH Mr Peter J. 5 Torquay Avenue, Burnley, Lancs, BB10 2NW. Tel:0282-30604
Birch Bramah BRAMALD BRAMALL Bramar Brameld Bramhall Brammer BURCH DRISCOLL EVANS O'NEIL ROUSE Sheils Shields SHIELS F1178
110841 BURCHETT Mr R M G. 25 Mount Road, Mount Pleasant, Newhaven, E Sussex, BN9 OLT.
BIRCHETT BURCHETT SAWKILL F2585
110868 BURDEN Mrs Enid. 34 Inner Crescent, Lithgow, NSW 2790, AUSTRALIA.
BENNETT BURDEN GARDINER MONTGOMERY F5552
110876 BURDGE Mrs Carol. 84 Medworth, Orton Goldhay, Peterborough, Cambs, PE2 ORY.
BROWN BURDGE HASELTON HAZELTON RHOADES F3056
110884 BURDON Dr Douglas. 186 Rosemary Hill Road, Sutton Coldfield, West Midlands, B74 4HP.
BAMLETT BURDON CLAUGHAN DINNING ROWELL F3694
110892 BURFOOT Mr Keith R. 59 Hall Road, Northfleet, Kent, DA11 8AN.
BURFOOT F1085
110906 BURGESS Mrs Beryl. (Jones) 228 Chipstead Way, Woodmansterne, Banstead, Surrey, SM7 3LQ.
ANDREW Benet Benett Benit Benitt Bennet BENNETT Bennitt FREEMAN Gardener Gardiner GARDNER GLOVER HEWES HICKSON Hughes Joanes Johnes JONES MACE MARSHALL Pain Paine Pane PARKER Patten PATTERN PAYNE SEA See SLICER Squire SQUIRES STARLING Tweddy TWIDDY WALLINGTON WALPOLE F2638
110914 BURGESS Mrs Brenda M. (Whitaker) Derby Villa, 11 West Street, Prescot, Lancs, L34 1LE. Tel:051-480-7924
ANSDELL BALLARD BATTERSBY BOLTON BULLOCK BURGESS Carnochan CARNON COPLEY HARTLEY HILTON HORSFALL HULME Hurstfield OVERINGTON Ovington RICHARDS SANDBACH THORPE VINCE WADE WHITAKER Whitechar Whittaker F2923
110922 BURGESS Mr David. 228 Chipstead Way, Woodmansterne, Banstead, Surrey, SM7 3LQ.
Bergis Birges BUNN Burges BURGESS Burgis Burgiss Burigges CANNING Cannings Cannon CARDEW CREED Davice Davies DAVIS FROST Garrett Jarratt JARRETT Jerratt JUPP Pigeon PIGGIN Pigin SWAN Swann TOLEMAN Wodin Woodden Wooddin WOODEN Woodin F2639
110930 BURGESS Miss P. 50 Nicholls Ct, 1 Noblet Street, Findon, SA 5023, AUSTRALIA.
BURGESS DAWSON LEWIS WRIGHT F5627
110949 BURGESS Miss S A. 10 Southgate House, The Drive, Walthamstow, London, E17 3DU. Tel:081-509-3258
Berrey BERRY Burey Burges BURGESS Bury MEDHURST PALMER PAYNE TRAVERS WOOLVEN Woolvin F4193
110957 BURGHAM Mr R S. Red Roof, 38 Holywell Crescent, Abergavenny, Gwent, NP7 5LH. Tel:0873-853995
Burgam BURGHAM Burgum DAVIES STOCK WILDIN Wilding F6010
110965 BURGHER Mr Michael H R. Waverley Lodge, Kelso, Roxburghshire, TD5 7BB. Tel:0573-23326
BROCK BURGAR Burger Burghar Burgher Burghes DRAVER HARCUS HILSON KER LESLIE POYINGER TURNHILL WIGHT F6432
110973 BURGOYNE Mr E G V. 159 Tudor Way, Rickmansworth, Herts, WD3 2HN.
Burgoin BURGOYNE NETHERSELL F6794
110981 BURGUM Mr Doug. 26 Furze Platt Road, Maidenhead, Berks, SL6 7NN.
Bergam Bergham Bergum Burgam Burgham BURGUM F2972
111007 BURMAN Mrs Elaine. (Evans) 4 St Gabriels Court, Pitsea, Basildon, Essex, SS13 2NY. Tel:0268-584069
BURMAN COLEMAN DAVIDGE EVANS HARRINGTON HATTON NEWLAND RUFUS SMITH F2542
111015 BURNETT Mr Thomas R. 3891 Commander Dr, Chamblee, GA 30341-0016, USA.
BURNETT F7246
111023 BURNHAM Mr Charles Seaton. 24 School Lane, Broomfield, Chelmsford, Essex, CM1 5DN.
BURNHAM FENNELL LENTON SEATON SEATON-BURNHAM UELLOR WOLFENDALE WOODWARD F5724
111031 BURNHAM Mrs L M. (Harris) 24 School Lane, Broomfield, Chelmsford, Essex, CM1 5DN.
HARRIS WALLACE F4548
111058 BURNISTON Mrs C M. 40 Beach Road, Weston Super Mare, Avon, BS23 1BG.
BURNISTON FIGGURES FIGURES SPRING F3040
111066 BURNS Mrs Amanda. (Busfield) 1530 Oakridge Road, Kelowna, B C, V1W 3A9, CANADA.
BURNS BUSFIELD CHAPLYN COOPER HOLLINGS OVEREND WILSON F5607
111074 BURNS Mrs Diana. 17 Winton Drive, Glasgow, G12 OPZ. Tel:041-334-2167
BURNS GREEN MCINALLY MUNGALL RANKINE TALBOT TAYLOR F707
111082 BURNS Guenter A. Alsterweg 41, D-2000 Hamburg 63, GERMANY.
OETLING F7335
111090 BURNS Miss Iris. 486 Kings Hwy, Wyandotte, MI 48192, USA. Tel:+1-313-282-0247
BARNES BIRRANE BURNES EVOY MCMAHON MOLONEY MULDOON NOOKS F4652
111104 BURNS Mrs Margaret J. (Perrin) 15 Harcourt Drive, Herne Bay, Kent, CT6 8DJ. Tel:0227-369365
BURNS GRAFHAM LIFFORD PARROTT PERRIN ROSE F5784
111112 BURR Mr Michael John Soilleux. 9 Westland Drive, Hayes, Bromley, Kent, BR2 7HE.
Bere Bire Bur Burgh BURR Burre Soileux SOILLEUX F4785
111120 BURREE Mr John P. Clayhanger House, Clayhanger, Chard, Somerset, TA20 3BJ.
BURREE F3832
111147 BURRELL Mr I S. 15 Cob Place, Godmanchester, Huntingdon, Cambs, PE18 8XD. Tel:0480-451120
Ashmale Ashmall Ashmele Ashmell Ashmenall ASHMOLE Ashmoll BURCHETT BURRELL HARE HARRISON HART MANCHESTER MELLOR PALGRAVE SEATON F374
111155 BURROWS Mrs Elaine. (Wiltshire) 12 The Poplars, Woodbine Close, Waltham Abbey, Essex, EN9 3RL.
BRACKENBURY BRIND BURROWS De Vignes DESVIGNES Devigne Devine Divine EDMUNDS Gildersleaves GILDERSLEEVES Gilersleeves KILMINSTER KILMINSTER-BRIND PAGE SALTER SAPSFORD Wilshere Wilshire Wiltsheir WILTSHIRE F3810
111163 BURROWS Mrs Jill. (Bernard) Orchard Farm, 41 Blackpool Road, Carleton, Poulton Le Fylde, Lancashire, FY6 7QB. Tel:0253-890046
BERNARD BURROW COOKE COOPER MILLETT NOWELL OWEN PYE THOMPSON F4203
111171 BURTON Colonel Richard Michael. Briar Close, 16 Latchmoor Avenue, Gerrards Cross, Bucks, SL9 8LJ. Tel:0753-886979
BURTON LAYCOCK F5808
111198 BURTON Mrs Hazel Jean. (Hart) 102 Ashgrove, Greengates, Bradford, West Yorkshire, BD10 OBP. Tel:0274-616056
ALLBONE BAKER BOAK CHILDS COCKEROM DOBSON HART HUDDLESTONE KAYE LARKINS Larkinson PARKINSON SHARMAN WHEATER WILLSON YEADON F3559
111201 BURTON Mr John. 409 Retford Road, Woodhouse Mill, Sheffield, S13 9WA. Tel:0742-699266
BURTON FINNERTY GOSLING HENSON ORD OWEN RICHFORD SHAW F5814
111228 BURTON Mrs Julie E. Lower Bank, Mellington, Church Stoke, Powys, SY15 6HX. Tel:058862-385
AUSTIN BURTON JOHNSON LOCKHART PENNILL WALTON F2806
111236 BURTON Nigel & Alwyn. Nad Palatou 30, Prague 5, CZECHOSLOVAKIA. Tel:+42-2-524564
AIREY BOSWORTH BURTON HERD HURT MASON NEWBY ROBSON SHIRLEY WHIELDON F6190
111244 BURVILLE Dr Peter J. Sea Gate, Goodwin Road, St Margarets Bay, Dover, Kent, CT15 6ED.
Bervil Bervill Berville Berwill Berwille Burvill BURVILLE Burwill Burwille F7064

111252 BURWOOD Dr Les R V. 1 Sleepers Delle Gardens, Winchester, Hants, SO22 4NU. Tel:0962-869944 BURWOOD F22
111260 BURWOOD Mr P F. 9 Park Drive, Morpeth, Northumberland, NE61 2SY. Tel:0670-513865 BROWN BRYCE GUNN LAING MACKINTOSH F1397
111279 BUSCOMBE Mr Anthony. Trepenpol, 17 Ocean View, Polruan, Fowey, Cornwall, PL23 1QJ. Biscomb Biscumb Boscumb BUSCOMBE Buscumb BUTTERS CALLAWAY Calloway CARDEW Cardue Cargenven CURGENVEN Curvengen ELLERY F5056
111287 BUSH Mrs Aileen. 8 Row Hill, Addlestone, Weybridge, Surrey, KT15 1DL. Tel:0932-852239 BUSH EVASON FRETWELL LOMAS LUMMAS MCISAAC RICHARDSON ROSE F2601
111295 BUSH Mr Milton W. 205 Tri-Mountain Road, Durham, CT 06422, USA. ACHESON ADAMS Atcheson DEJEANNE JAYNE SWAIN WESTBROOK F6522
111309 BUSHBY Mr Keith. 51 St Martins Street, Hereford, HR2 7RD. Bushay Bushbee Bushbie BUSHBY Bushbye F2166
111317 BUSHELL Ms V. 67 Smythe Road, Henderson, Auckland 8, NEW ZEALAND. COTTEE F7259
111325 BUTLER Mr Clive N. 2 Rye Close, Stanway, Colchester, Essex, CO3 5YP. ALEXANDER ATKINS BUTLER BYGRAVE CHRISMAS DAY GOLDFINCH HATCH HICKS HILL HUNT KETTEL KING LASCELLES LEVETT MATHAMS OSBOURN PAGE PINNER SMITH F2624
111333 BUTLER Miss Doris. 16 Manor View, Brimpton, Reading, Berks, RG7 4SJ. Armsworth BUTLER CULLUM Exal EXALL Excel Excell Harmswood HARMSWORTH Lewingden Lewingdon LEWINGTON MARSHALL Mial Miall Myal MYHILL SANGWELL SMITH WICKENS Wiggens Wiggins F2749
111341 BUTLER Mrs Ethel. 289 Timberlog Lane, Basildon, Essex, SS14 1NX. DUNN F3263
111368 BUTLER Miss Helen. 50 Oak Grove Road, Anerley, London, SE20 7RQ. BUTLER CREASEY Creasy Drummey DRUMMY HOLDOM MANSFIELD MILEMAN MITCHELL PLEDGER F1114
111376 BUTLER Mrs Jeanne. (Fleming) Caerlee Hillhead, Forres, Moray, Inverness, IV36 0QT. BUTLER FLEMING GOUDIE JOHNSTONE LAMOND WOOD F4151
111384 BUTLER Mrs Jennifer. (Balmforth) 189 Greenhill Road, Bramley, Leeds, W Yorks, LS13 4JY. Tel:0532-639540 BALMFORTH BENNION BERESFORD Berisford Berrisford BOLTON Boulton BURTON Calverley Calverly CARVELEY Caverly CHARLESWORTH FIRTH HODGSON LAWSON MORLEY SCHOFIELD Scholefield SCOTT SLACK TAYLOR THOMPSON WHITELEY Whitley WILSON WRIGHT F4357
111392 BUTLER Mrs Joan. 84 Abbey Road, Torquay, Devon, TQ2 5NP. Boteler Botelier Botteler BUTLER Buttlar Buttler F3248
111406 BUTLER Mrs Kathleen E. (Murgess) 6 Ives Close, West Bridgford, Nottingham, NG2 7LU. Tel:0602-844609 BONNETT BURGESS F5004
111414 BUTLER Mrs Nora. (Reynolds) Kimbolton House, 9 High Street, Kimbolton, Huntingdon, Cambs, PE18 0HB. BETTON BRUNT CARTWRIGHT DAVIES Eltheridge Etheridg ETHERIDGE Etherig FRANCIS GOUGH GROVES GURNEY Gurny Hammond HAMMONDS HANLY HOGGINS Itheridge JONES KEETON LADBROOK LOACH Mansel MANSELL NOCK POINTER PRICE REYNOLDS SHORTLAND TIPTON WISE F4925
111422 BUTLER Mr R H. 41 Collingwood Road, Hillingdon Heath, Middx, UB8 3EJ. BUTLER BUTTON Collen Collin Collings COLLINS Colyn GLANFIELD HAMBY SHARP SHARPE SMITH STILLWELL WARD F1128
111430 BUTLER Mrs W M. 6 George Street, Stilton, Peterborough, PE7 3XX. GILL F6776
111449 BUTLER Miss Winifred. 112 Quarry Road, Witney, Oxon, OX8 5JJ. BUTLER EARLE HOYLE MCCONVELL SPARKES WOODS F5192
111457 BUTT Mrs V. (Pears) 29a Kauika Road, Whangabei, NEW ZEALAND. Tel:+64-9-438-6689 ANDERSON CAMP CROTTY DAVIS GRAYSON MCKINLEY MITCHELL MOORE MORGAN PEARS RUSSELL F4450
111465 BUTTERFIELD Mrs Gillian. 14 Station Road, Croston, Preston, Lancs, PR5 7RJ. Tel:0772-600583 SPENCE SPENCER SPENSE SPENSER F1303
111473 BUTTERISS Mr J M. 210 Victoria Drive, Eastbourne, E Sussex, BN20 8QN. Bottreaux Buteraus Buttarass Buttaress Butteris BUTTERISS Buttery BUTTRESS Buttrey Buttries Buttriess Buttriss F2867
111481 BUTTERWORTH Mr Alan. 3 Fir Tree Avenue, Boothstown, Worsley, Manchester, M28 4LP. Tel:061-790-4152 BUTTERWORTH F5925
111503 BUTTERWORTH Mrs June. Walkden Barn Farm, Duckworth Hall, Oswaldtwistle, Lancs, BB5 3RQ. Tel:0254-53784 BUTTERWORTH CATON CHARNOCK ELLISON GILES GREENALL HARGREAVES HARWOOD HOLDEN HOLMES HOLT HOULT MILLER PORTER F1608
111511 BUTTERWORTH Mrs P C. 5 Sheppenhall Grove, Aston, Nantwich, Cheshire, CW5 8DF. BUTTERWORTH CALVERT FAWKES GEORGE GOTT HARTLEY MAWSON ROBINSON SAGGERSON SHACKLETON F4900
111538 BUTTREY Ms Pamela. 2 Charles Court, 89 Selsdon Road, South Croydon, Surrey, CR2 6PZ. AUBREY Batrie Botrey Botry Botterel Bottrel Bottris Butterick Butteries Butteris Butteriss Buttery Buttree Buttres Buttress BUTTREY Buttrie Buttriss Buttry Buttrye DOD Dodd EDWARDS FARMER Farra Farrar FARRER Fermer Ferrer FOOTMAN GREEN GREGORY JENKINS JONES LILLEY Lilly Lily NORTON PARGITER Pearce PEIRCE PICKETT PLOMER ROBERTS SIMON SMITH Steel STEELE Stile Stump STUMPE F4313
111546 BUTTRICK Mrs Jean. (Sawyer) 46 Evans Road, Eynsham, Oxford, OX8 1QS. Tel:0865-881447 SAWYER WILSON F6206
111554 BUXTON Mrs Angela Susan. (Vines) 2 Flint Road, Up Hatherley, Cheltenham, Glos, GL51 5JE. Tel:0242-242733 DUCKETT NICHOLS POOL SEALEY VINES F3917
111562 BUZZARD Mr A W. 19 Springfield Avenue, Banbury, Oxon, OX16 9HS. Tel:0295-258817 BARNARD BLENCOWE BUZZARD NICHOLLS SIMMS UNSWORTH F2455
111570 BYE Mr Malcolm. 11 Caddington Close, New Barnet, Herts, EN4 9QH. Tel:081-440-2361 BYE GREGORY F3123
111589 BYFORD Mr Peter G. 24 Heath Drive, Ware, Herts, SG12 0RE. Tel:0920-463804 BAKER Beeford Beeforth Beford BERGIN Biford Burgin BYFORD FINCH HARRIS HOLLMAN Hollyman HOLMAN Holmwood Holyman Homard Homewood HOUSE Howse Hulse NOBBS Olman Oman PIPE READ Reed SCOTCHER Yocksall YOXALL F1798
111597 BYLES Mr G W. 1 Nursery Close, Chineham, Basingstoke, Hants, RG24 0TA. BYLES F4758
111600 CADDY Mr Ian. 32 Esmond Road, London, W4 1JQ. ATTEWELL Caddey Caddie CADDY Cady COLE COTTON GREGORY HORTON JAMES MISKIN OLD PUDWELL PURKIS F5202
111619 CAINE Mr Ronald. Apothecary House, 8 Church Street, Eyemouth, Berwickshire, TD14 5DH. CAINE CLAYTON KENNAUGH F3295
111627 CAINS Mr Keith. 127 Upper Wickham Lane, Welling, Kent, DA16 3AQ. Caines CAINS Canes Caynes Kaines Kains Kaynes Keynes F4658
111635 CAKE Mr A. 22 Clyst Valley Road, Clust St Mary, Exeter, Devon, EX5 1DD. CAKE Kaake Kake F6894
111643 CAKEBREAD Mr G J. 6 Chirton Grove, Leeds, LS8 2SS. CAKEBREAD F7248
111651 CALBERSON Marcel. Gewad 48, 9000 Gent, BELGIUM. CALBERSON F7249
111678 CALDERWOOD Mr J H. 39 Upper High Street, Harpole, Northampton, NN7 4DJ.

BINKS BOWNAS CALDERWOOD HALL JEFFERY JUDKINS PEARSON STEPHENSON F596

111686 CALDON Mr Michael. 1 Yare Close, Great Yarmouth, Norfolk, NR30 1QT. Tel:0493-842787
CALDON STUDT F406

111694 CALDWELL Mrs Dorothy. (Kirkland) 3 Coverdale Avenue, Cooden, Bexhill On Sea, E Sussex, TN39 4TY.
KIRKLAND MARSH F5402

111708 CALDWELL Mrs Thelma. (Wilson) Box 427, Central Butte, Sask, SOH OTO, CANADA.
DUNCAN Duncen GUY Guye Sampson Samsen SAMSON Scot SCOTT Sherries SHERRIS Sherry Steel STEELE Stele Vere Vilsone WEIR Wier Willson WILSON Wilsone WOODCOCK Woodcocke Wulson F5461

111716 CALL Mr D F. 1 Powell Street, Burnley, Lancs, BB11 4JL.
CALL Caul MCCREA F7250

111724 CALLAGHAN Mr Brian J. 10 Burnside Street, Rosytm, Fife, KY11 2NX. Tel:0383-416435
ALCOCK BRUTON CALLAGHAN COWLAND CRANSTON CROCKFORD HALSEY KIRK WHITTWELL WILSON F1272

111732 CALLAGHAN Mrs Sue. 279 Ringinglow Road, Sheffield, S Yorks, S11 7PZ.
BEAR COMPLIN HARMER HENDERSON LONG OSHEA F2911

111740 CALLAN Coral. 8 Brook Street, Hazelbrook, NSW 2779, AUSTRALIA.
CALLAN CHARLES HULBERT F4390

111759 CALLCUT Mr John. Wirmwood, Village Street, Newdigate, Surrey, RH5 5DH. Tel:030677-600
CALLCUT HAWKINS SIMONS TOWILLS F6342

111767 CALLISTER Mrs Sybil. (Eatock) 23 Oakfield Crescent, Aspull, Wigan, Lancs, WN2 1XJ.
BENYON BLOCKLEY CALLISTER CREER CRELLIN CROMPTON EATOCK HART HUNTER JONES KENNISH MCCORMICK MCNALLY MORGAN MURPHY O'LEARY RATCLIFF YATES F5113

111775 CALOW Mr Andrew. 53 Cammell Road, Firth Park, Sheffield, S5 6UW. Tel:0742-441767
CALOW CHESHIRE DAVIES EVANS WHITE WILLS F6070

111783 CALROW Mr Peter James. 2 The Crescent, Newcastle Upon Tyne, NE7 7ST.
Tel:091-266-1171
CALROW F869

111791 CALVER Mrs Pat. 53 London Road South, Lowestoft, Suffolk, NR33 0AS. Tel:0502-563985
BERESFORD BICKERS BURGESS CALVER HALLATT HARRIS HUGHES RICHARDS RUTHEN STAMP VALLANCE F434

111805 CAMB Mrs Brenda. 9 Scarsdale Avenue, Blackpool, Lancs, FY4 2PB.
CAMB DEARDEN KERSHAW STAINES STERNE F3256

111813 CAMBERS Mrs Alleyne. (Atkinson) Greenacres, Lower End, Hartwell, Northamptonshire, NN7 2HS. Tel:0604-862161
ATKINSON CAMBERS CARTER CHARNEY GASCOIGNE JOHNSON PRESS F4673

111821 CAMERON Mr Alistair. 32 Cobran Road, Cheltenham, Nsw 2119, Australia.
ARNOLD CAMERON CARSON CLARKE CLYDE DUNN EDGE FERGUSON HALL HENDERSON HENDRY JOHNSON JOHNSTONE KING MACDONALD MACKENZIE MACLEAN MACPHAIL MICKLE MIDGLEY MORRISON RICE RUSHFIRTH THORNHILL WOOD F1230

111848 CAMERON Mr James D. Kings Fold, Pope Lane, Penwortham, Preston, Lancs, PR1 9JN.
Tel:0772-742236
CAMERON CURRIE FRENCH JOHNSTONE LAIDLAW LINDSAY MACLEAN MACMILLAN MCNAUGHTON F4763

111856 CAMILLERI Mrs Jenny. 75 Pell Street, Broken Hill, NSW 2880, AUSTRALIA. Tel:+61-080-881321
ADDISON FURBUR GODDALE HANLON HARRIS JENKINS JOHNSTONE LEE LLOYD MADDEN MILES MULLADE PALIN PUGH REECE RUMBLE SANDERSON TIFFEN F4341

111864 CAMMIES Mr William Paul. 31 Rockmead Avenue, Kingstanding, Great Barr, Birmingham, B44 9DR.
CAMICE CAMIES CAMISH CAMISHE CAMMIES CAMMIS CAMMISH CAMMISHE CAMMISSE F252

111872 CAMMISH Mr R B. 12 Melrose Street, Scarborough, VO12 7SH.
CAMMISH F6767

111880 CAMPBELL Mrs J C. 50 Imperial Drive, Warden Bay, Isle Of Sheppey, Kent, ME12 4SD.
JUFF F3298

111899 CAMPBELL Mr James. 44 Leven Court, West Bridgend, Dumbarton, G82 4BX. Tel:0389-64311
CAMPBELL F1080

111902 CAMPER Mr Walter John. 21 Norton Crescent, Towcester, Northants, NN12 7DW.
CAMPER F6557

111910 CAMPION Mr L. 74 Ballards Way, South Croydon, Surrey, CR2 7LA.
CAMPION F6662

111929 CAMPKIN Mr D V. 109 Devonshire Road, Weston Super Mare, Avon, BS23 4NY.
CAMPKIN TRIGG F4435

111937 CANN Mrs Shirley. At Last, Hexton Hill Road, Hooe, Plymouth Devon, PL9 9RD.
BOND CANN LIGHT LUCAS MARTIN PASCOE SWEET F540

111945 CANNELL Mrs P. 8 Fiske Gardens, Oulton Broad, Lowestoft, NR32 4RS.
ALIBASTER BARNES Dugdale DUGDELL EAGLE ELLENGER RAINER SNELL Snelling SUGGATE TUTHILL WELCH F4012

111953 CANNON Mr E H. 25 Jessop Avenue, Bridport, Dorset, DT6 4AT.
BLACKALL Blay BLEAY Bley CANNONS CASEY CLARK Drewett Drewit Drewith DREWITT EGGLETON PIMM SADLER SAUNDERS SMITH WHITE F1093

111961 CANNON Mrs M I M. 38 Keith Road, Bournemouth, Dorset, BH3 7DU.
CANNON KINGSTON KNUCKEY OULD F514

111988 CANT Mr & Mrs R A. 3 London Road, Baldock, Herts, SG7 6LE. Tel:0462-892682
Blaiklock BLAYLOCK CANT Cante Cantt Canty Chapel Chapell Chapels Chappel Chappell CHAPPELLS Kant Tenant TENNANT F2119

111996 CANTELLO Mrs Veronica. (Drew) 39 Sarum Avenue, Melksham, Wilts, SN12 6BN.
Tel:0225-702331
CANTELLO Cantelo Canteloe Cantelow Cantelowe Cantle Kantelo F6053

112003 CANTRILL Mr John. Cornerways, 51 Gresley Wood Road, Church Gresley, Swadlincote Derby, DE11 9QP.
ALLARD BILLINGS BRYANT Cant Canter Canterall Canterel Canterell Canterelle Canterhill Canterhulle Cantlen Cantrall Cantrel Cantrell Cantrelle Cantril CANTRILL Cantrille Cantrul Cantrule Cantwall Cantwell Caunton Chanterall Chanterel Chanterell Chanterelle Chantrel Chantrell Chantrelle Chantril Chantrill CLYNICK Cointerel Cointerell Coynterel Cuinterel Cuinterell Cuonterel Elingworth ELLINGWORTH Ellinworth FELSTEAD Getlife Gettlif Gettliffe Goddlife Goddliffe Godeleif Godeleive Godeleve Godileif Godileive Godleif Godleive Godlif Godlife Godliffe Godlyf Goodleuf Goodlif GOODLIFFE Goodlyf Goodyer GREEN Ilingworth Illingworth Illinworth Kanterall Kanterell Kanterill Kantrall Kantrell Kantrill KING MILLWARD PEPPER Quantrell Quantrill Quarntrill Queinterell Quintrell Quyntrel SIDDONS THOMAS F1591

112011 CAPON Mr John W. 15698 Broome Road, White Rock, British Columbia, V4A 5E2, CANADA.
Capan Capen Capin CAPON Cappen F6955

112038 CAPPITT Mr Ewan N. 317 Eastfield Road, Peterborough, Cambs, PE1 4RA. Tel:0733-343474
ALLEN ASPITAL Aspitall BLOODWORTH BURTON Capet Capett Capit Capitt Cappet Cappett Cappit CAPPITT CORBY DAWSON KENWORTHY KETTERINGHAM LARRATT Larrett Larritt NEAVE Neeve OSBORN Osborne Osbourn Osbourne RINGHAM TEMPLEMAN TIPPETT TUCKER WEBSTER WELLS F4686

112046 CARAHER-MANNING D. Po Box 129, Sisterville, VA 26175, USA.
O'CARRAGHER F7333

112054 CARCAS Mr Anthony. 14 Coed Yr Eos, Caerphilly, Glamorgan, CF8 2RS.
Tel:0222-867501
CARCAS Carcass Carcasse Carcus Carkasse F4093

112062 CARDEN Mr A E. 20 Wodehouse Terrace, Falmouth, Cornwall, TR11 3EN.
CARDEN CARWARDEN CARWARDINE Cawarden KING F2223

112070 CARDOZA Mr W Henriques. 13 Rydal Way,

Enfield, Middx, EN3 4PQ.
CARDOZA HENRIQUES NUNES F6773
112089 CARE Mr Ian. 8 Kings Drive, Littleover, Derby, DE3 6EU. Tel:0332-46089
ALLMAN BANNERMAN BLACK CALDER CARE DELLCHAR EADEN FINKLE GARNETT GIBSON GILLIE HABERJAM HABERSHON LAVELLE LILLEY MACKENZIE PALMER SCOTT SIMPSON SMITH SOUTAR TAYLOR TURNER WILLS F4514
112097 CARELESS Mr Leonard. 61 Lilac Crescent, Beeston, Nottingham, Notts, NG9 1PX.
BRYAN CARELESS Carelesse Carless Carlis Carriss COOPER CRAGG DICKONSON GAUNT IVES LYNAM MOORE NEWTON PARNHAM PEACOCK PEASE RICE RIGBY SCRIVENER STOCK THOMPSON WILSON F5083
112100 CAREY Mr J P. 170 Arle Road, Cheltenham, Glous, GL51 8LR.
CAREY F3284
112119 CAREY Tony. 18 Hanger Hill, Weybridge, Surrey, KT13 9XR.
VIRR F7169
112127 CARLAW Mrs P J. (Bentall) 27 Abbots Close, Ramsey, Huntingdon, Cambs, PE17 1UZ. Tel:0487-813463
BENTALL Benthall CARLAW F4346
112135 CARLIN Mrs Linda. 67 Binley Close, Shirley, Solihull, W Midlands, B90 2RB.
ABREY HIBBERT WALLWORK WARHURST F317
112143 CARMICHAEL Mrs June M. (Farmer) 38 Foxearth Road, Selsdon, South Croydon, Surrey, CR2 8EE. Tel:081-657-6866
Cudden CUDDON CUTTER CUTTING FARMER HORNE RICHES F6110
112151 CAROLAN Miss M B. Flat 2, 2 Ashburton Road, Alverstoke, Gosport Hants, PO12 2LJ.
Amflet Amflit Amphlet AMPHLETT F6822
112178 CARPENTER Mr Alexander. 68 Huntsmoor Road, Tadley, Hants, RG26 6DQ. Tel:0734-816877
CAPELIN CARPENTER CHAMPION JOHANNES LE CARPENTER MILLS SHINE THOMPSETT F3339
112186 CARPENTER Mr Barry T. 165 King George Close, Sidemoor, Bromsgrove, Worcs, B61 8SN.
CARPENTER F5382
112194 CARPENTER Mr Charles. 16 Banbrook Close, Solihull, W Midlands, B92 9NE.
CARPENTER F2407
112208 CARPENTER Mr F. 50 Arbury Road, Cambridge, CB4 2JE.
BECK Beek BRUMBY CARPENTER COVENTRY TAYLOR F3734
112216 CARPENTER Miss Niki. 12 Drayton Close, Bracknell, Berks, RG12 3AY.
ANTHONY CARPENTER COLLIER Crocket CROCKETT DAVIS DEAN HAND HOWSE LESLIE Mesceter Meseter Mesiter MESSETER Messiter SMITH THOMAS WALSH WATSON WESTBURY WHITE WRIGHT F4098
112224 CARPENTER Dr Norman. 6 Rooksway, Heswall, Wirral, Merseyside, L60 9JR.
BRACEWELL CARPENTER Cheeseman CHEESMAN Hardcastell HARDCASTLE Herdecastell MIDGLEY Pearcey Pearcy Pearsey PIERCY RAMSDALE RENARD Rennard Rennerd Reynard ROBERTS TURNER F3530
112232 CARR Mr D W. 15 Emmanuel Road, Wylde Green, Sutton Coldfield, W Midlands, B73 5LY. Tel:021-350-0684
BILLINGHAM CARR COONEY HODGETTS HOLLYWOOD LOCKWOOD MONKS TOMLINSON TOTNEY WORTON F2163
112240 CARR Mrs Eileen. (Eason) 27 The Avenue, Healing, Grimsby, DN37 7NB.
CARR EASON GILDON METCLAFE F4044
112259 CARRIER Mr F John. 2 Derwent Close, Leamington Spa, Warwickshire, CV32 6PA. Tel:0926-427451
Carriar CARRIER Carryer Caryer JEFFERIES Jeffries WARWICK Weaven WEAVING F1384
112267 CARRIER Marjorie. (Rawnsley) 2 Derwent Close, Leamington Spa, Warwickshire, CV32 6PA. Tel:0926-427451
ALDERSON OVEREND RAWNSLEY F1385
112275 CARRINGTON Mr David R. Cherry Trees, Wenlock Road, Tasley, Bridgnorth Shropshire, WV16 4QB.
ABBOTT BARKER BODEN BREW CARRINGTON CHESTER DAVIES GREGORY HAYNES KNAPP LOMAS LOVETT MARSHALL MASON MITCHELL MONK NEEDHAM PEARSON PETTIFOR Poudrel Poutrell POWDERILL Powdril Powtrell Pultrel Putel Putrel Putrell ROBINSON SCOLTOCK SKERRITT Smaleman SMALLMAN Smalman TEBBUTT TUCKWOOD WEEMES WILDEY WILLMOTT-WOOD F21
112283 CARROLL Mrs Diana. Gang Warily Farm, Newlands Road, Fawley, Southampton Hants, SO4 1GA. Tel:0703-893147
HAYWARD LEWIN NEWTON PROWTING F2209
112291 CARROLL Miss Kathleen. 12 Summer Gardens, East Molesey, Surrey, KT8 9LT. Tel:081-398-7620
BODGER F2302
112305 CARSON Mr Robert. Kirklea, Symington, Biggar, ML12 6LJ. Tel:08993-516
CAMPBELL CARKWOOD CARSON CUTHBERT HAINING LYNN ROGAN RUSSELL STEELE TENNENT THOM WEIR F1702
112313 CARSON Miss S K. 18 St James Road, Hereford, HR1 2QS.
BEAVER BENNER CARSON HENSHAW MCDOWALL PEERS PRICE-JONES ROUTH SHEFFIELD F466
112321 CARSWELL Mrs M. (Owen) Sainthill, Kingsland Road, Shrewsbury, Shropshire, SY3 7AF.
FOSTER FREEMAN HOLLINGSWORTH SIMMONS WAKERLEY F6455
112348 CARTER Mr David G S. Chandlers, Turners Hill Road, Crawley Down, W Sussex, RH10 4EY. Tel:0342-714660
ASHLEY CARTER CLARKE PARKINSON SARDINSON SOMERS WARBURTON YOUNG F2105
112356 CARTER Mrs G. 12 Windmill Lane, Castlecroft, Wolverhampton, West Midlands, WV3 8HJ. Tel:0902-761170
ANDERSON DANIELLS HOWATSON Movels Mowels MOWLES Sneesbie SNEESBY Snesbie Snezby WARDLE F5363
112364 CARTER Mrs Jennifer. (Marsden) 29 Charteris Drive, East Ivanhoe, Victoria, 3079, AUSTRALIA. Tel:+61-3-499-2076
CATHARDINE KELSALL KNIGHT LONGBOTTOM MARSDEN MARSHALL OWEN PORTER PRIN TAYLOR F4361
112372 CARTER Mrs Linda. 4 Newland Avenue, Harrogate, N Yorks, HG2 8IP. Tel:0423-885138
BLACKBEARD COWLING CROUCHLEY HANLEY HUTCHINSON KIRKBRIGHT MCILURIDE STONEY TOPHAM WOODRUP F1030
112380 CARTER Miss Pamela. 15 Addison Road, Hartlepool, Cleveland, TS24 8DQ.
BILES CARTER DIXON EXELBY LEE RATHBONE SKELTON WALES F4723
112399 CARTER Mrs Paula. 19 Langham Drive, Narborough, Leics, LE9 5EY. Tel:0533-867987
Chegwgen Chegwidden CHEGWYN Chegwyne Chegwynne Chigwin Chigwydden Chuckweedon Chygin Chygwen Chygwin DE MASKELL Keigwin KINSMAN Sugweeden F6227
112402 CARTER Mr W. 24 Meadow Gardens, Crediton, Devon, EX17 1EJ. Tel:0363-773808
ARBON CARTER EASUN FRANCIS MAY MORGAN PHILLIPS SEWELL SIMPSON SMITH F6135
112410 CARTLIDGE Mrs J. (Bennett) 125 Paris Avenue, Newcastle, Staffordshire, ST5 2QP.
ANGEL BATH BENNETT CARTLIDGE COOPER HOLLIS HUMPHRIES PRICE SPARKES STEVENSON F3714
112429 CARTMELL Mr John Edward. Westville, Flaxton, York, YO6 7RJ. Tel:0904-86473
BAILEY BARNES BONY CARTMELL COOKSON GILLETT SHAW WADE WARD WINSTANLEY F2103
112437 CARTY Mr Bernard. 71 Northmuir Drive, Cambusnethan, Wishaw, Lanarkshire, ML2 8NS.
BRANNAN CARTY KEATINGS RENALDES F1358
112445 CARVER Mrs Christine. 2 The Vineyard, Yarmouth, Isle Of Wight, PO41 0XE. Tel:0983-761216
BUTCHER CARVER EDWARDES THORNHILL F3178
112453 CARVETH Mr J H A. 8 Lyme Crescent, Highcliffe, Christchurch, Dorset, BH23 5BJ. Tel:0425-272351
BICE CARVETH F1999
112461 CARYSFORTH Mr Robert. 70 Priory Lane, Penwortham, Preston, Lancs, PR1 0AS. Tel:0772-745931
BEDDARD BENNETT BLUNDELL BUCK CARYESFORD CARYSFORTH HOBSON MARSHALL PARDOE PROBY RUSSON SUDELL F3510
112488 CASBOLT Mr George. 26 Mount Park, Carshalton,

Surrey, SM5 4PS.
CASBOLT F3716

112496 CASBOLT Mr Richard. 3 Kilburn Street, Corinella 3984, Via Lang Lang, Victoria Australia.
BULLOCK Casbold CASBOLT Casbould HORNER LLEWELLYN RICHARDS Tresize TREZISE Wesley WESTLEY F2995

112518 CASEY Mrs Geraldine. 69 Rivermead, Wilford Lane, West Bridgford, Nottingham, NG2 7RE. Tel:0602-817778
BENNETT BLACKWELL CASEY DIX FLEXNEY HAROLD HOBBS LAWRENCE MILLS PARMEE RANDAL RANDALL RANDEL. RANDLE TOMKINS F125

112526 CASHELL Mr T Spencer. 101 Parkside, Kendal, Cumbria, LA9 7LG. Tel:0539-733565
ADAMS APPLEYARD CASEY CASHELL KELLY LEESING MARTIN SEARBY SPENCER WRIGHT F543

112534 CASPER Mr Ronald. 8 Rosevale Terrace, Falsgrave Road, Scarborough, Yorks, YO12 5EN.
BOUTLE CASPER EMMINES HOLLIMAN MUGGLETON NEAVES PETTIFER PICKFORD POTTAGE RENNICK WHITING F528

112542 CASSIDY Mr Raymond. Fernside, Copthall Green, Upshire, Waltham Abbey Essex, EN9 3SZ. Tel:0992-711191
DOCKREE F16

112550 CASTELLO Mr M. 63 Keswick Road, Solihull, W Midlands, B92 7PL. Tel:021-743-0302
CASTELLO F1692

112569 CASWELL Mrs Beulah. (Ferridge) 1276 Irwin Drive, Swift Current, Sask, S9H 1Z7, CANADA.
ANDREWS AUSTEN COLOGNE CRANTON EARLE Farage Farrage Farrige Ferige FERRIDGE Ferrige FURNER GILL MILLER F5497

112577 CATCHESIDE Mr Paul R. 10 Elm Road, Hollins Green, Warrington, WA3 6LP.
CATCHESIDE LIVERMORE F3703

112585 CATHERALL Mrs J M. 6 Blake Close, Bramley, Rotherham, South Yorkshire, S66 0UN.
Catheral CATHERALL Cathral Catral Catrow Catteral Catterall Cattral HALL HESLOP HOWE Hyslop PRESS F6422

112593 CATTELL Mr Stephen C. 2 Congleton Close, Minstead, Lyndhurst, Hants, SO43 7GS. Tel:0703-813574
CATTELL DALBY EVERETT FORD HOBBS VERDON WELLSFORD YOUNG F6083

112607 CATTERALL Mr Roger Wells. 94 Alkincoats Road, Colne, Lancs, BB8 9QQ. Tel:0282-870049
CATTERALL FISHER MAY WELLS F5293

112615 CATTON Miss Christine Elizabeth. 18 Kenwood Drive, Copthorne, Shrewsbury, Shropshire, SY3 8SY.
BISHOP CATTON FORD HAIGH HALL OXLADE PEARSON PERKINS F5853

112623 CATTY Mrs M. 4 Alexandra Close, Chadwell St Mary, Grays, Essex, RM16 4TT.
PITE Pyte F6658

112631 CAUDERY Mrs Susan Alethea. (Elburn) Woodville, New Cut, Green Lane, Redruth, Cornwall, TR15 1AF. Tel:0209-218308
BATCHELOR CAUDERY CYSTER Dorsett DOSSET EAST ELBURN Elburne GAYNE HAZELL LAKE PAYNE PLESTED Ponten PONTIN PUDDEPHAT REYNOLDS ROLFE SIESTER TAYLOR TERRY THORNTON F3130

112658 CAUDLE Mr Brian. 15 Lincolns Close, St Albans, Herts, AL4 9YQ.
CAUDLE F3982

112666 CAULEY Mrs Linda. 34 Aintree Road, Calmore, Southampton, Hants, SO4 2TL.
CAULEY F1060

112674 CAVE Major G P H. 4 Beeching Cottages, Bullo Pill, Newnham On Severn, Glous, GL14 1EB.
ALLISON CAVE Ceave STERREY Sterry Stirri Stirrie Stirry STONE TUDGAY F1869

112682 CAVE Mr H. 1 The Precinct, Cotesbach, Lutterworth, Leic, LE17 4HY. Tel:0455-552994
CAVE F2468

112690 CAVE Mr Hugh. 1 Stratfield Court, Great Holm, Milton Keynes, Bucks, MK8 9EU. Tel:0908-568022
CAVE F6485

112704 CAVELL Mr David A. 205 Woolaston Avenue, Lakeside, Cardiff, CF2 6EX. Tel:0222-753643
ALDRICH ARKLESS CAVELL COLEMAN DAVIES GALE GIBBONS GREEN HANSON HYDES MATTINGLEY MERRILL PALMER ROBINSON THOMAS TRUSLER TURNER UNDERWOOD F3871

112712 CAVETT Mrs Denise B. (Legg) 28 Braemar Court, 40 Ashburnham Road, Bedford, MK40 1DZ. Tel:0234-273109
CAVETT CURNOW DAVIS LEGG MERRIT RICHARDS F4752

112720 CAWTE Mr E C & Mrs C E. 51 Station Road, Ibstock, Leics, LE6 1JL. Tel:0530-60525
Bachelor Batchelder Batcheldor Batcheler Batchellor BATCHELOR Caut Caute Cawt CAWTE CROCKETT-SCOTT HOWLETT REYNOLDS SCOTT F5812

112739 CAWTHORNE Mr Alan. Cliff Lodge, Old Teignmouth Road, Dawlish, S Devon, EX7 0NJ.
CAWTHORNE HIGGS SMALE VICKERY F3009

112747 CAWTHORNE Mrs Nancy. (Emm) 47 London Road, Camberley, Surrey, GU15 3UG. Tel:0276-63271
ATKINS EMM FLOWER GIDDINGS HILIER PRIOR F5057

112755 CESAR Mr N J I. 25 Davidson Road, Addiscombe, Croyden, Surrey, CR0 6DL.
Caesar Ceasar CESAR F6696

112763 CHADDERDON Helen. R D 1 Box 153, La Vernon Center, NY 13477, USA.
CHADDERDON LOBDELL F7252

112771 CHADDERTON Mr Jack. Windrush, 6 Peppers Lane, Burton Lazars, Melton Mowbray Leics, LE14 2XA. Tel:0664-63750
BRADLEY CHADDERTON CHARNLEY DAVENPORT DAVIDSON GILLESPY HILEY KELLETT LINTON MILLIGAN MILNER PAGE PEARCE REYNOLDS RUBOTHAM WATSON WILLIAMS F1307

112798 CHADWICK Mr P. 208 Bedford Street, Crewe, Cheshire, CW2 6JL.
Chaddock CHADWICK F6663

112801 CHADWICK Mr & Mrs R. 75 Laburnum Avenue, Wickford, Essex, SS12 0DB.
CHADWICK Chadwicke Chadwyck GLANDER GROTTICK Runacles Runacre RUNACRES Runacus Runagall Runagle Runeckles Runicles Runnacre Runnacres Runnacus Runnagall Runnalces Runnegar Runnicles Runnigar F6723

112828 CHADWICK Mrs Valerie. 55 Goddard Avenue, Swindon, Wiltshire, SN1 4HS. Tel:0793-523829
CALLINGHAM CHIVERS EAST GLENISTER LOVEGROVE MAY PEARCE SMITH WEBB WILMOT F3119

112836 CHALK Capt Norman. Willow Farm, White Horse Lane, Briggate, North Walsham Norfolk, NR28 9QZ. Tel:0692-536759
CHALK Chalke Chaulk Chok Choke Fishbone FISHBOURNE Fishburne F3323

112844 CHALMERS Mrs Helen. (Mangan) 80 Shakespeare Drive, Cheadle, Cheshire, SK8 2DA.
ADAMSON ALLAN CHALMERS DICK HADFIELD HALLAM MILNE PONTEFRACT RIACH RICHARDSON F4748

112852 CHAMBERLAIN Mrs Elizabeth. (Gregory) 24 Appleton Road, Beeston, Nottingham, NG9 1NE. Tel:0602-251971
GREGORY KNIGHTON REDMILE SHIPSTONE F6439

112860 CHAMBERLAIN Mr Peter James. School House, Bowden, Melrose, Roxburghshire, TD6 0ST. Tel:0835-22309
CHAMBERLAIN GALLOWAY HAYWARD MCNEILL F1952

112879 CHAMBERS Mr John P. 36 Coventry Road, Warwick, CV34 4LJ. Tel:0926-491405
CHAMBERS CHINN COOPER CROFTS EDWARDS GREWCOCK JACKSON KIRK RICHARDSON F6293

112887 CHAMP Mr Peter. 45 Plenty River Drive, Greensborough, VIC 3088, AUSTRALIA. Tel:+61-3-432-1996
ALLEN ANDERSON BARTLETT BLACKALLER BOWLER BRISBANE BROWN BULGIN BURNS CHAMP DARLINGTON GALLOP GRIST HOG JACKSON LANGDOWN OATS PAYNE REED ROSS SHORT WADE WESTLAND WILTON F4699

112895 CHAMPAGNE Mr Warren. 2731 S Place, Tucson, AZ 85713, USA.
KNIPE F7307

112909 CHANDLER Miss Beryl. 49 Station Road, Romsey, Hants, SO51 8DP. Tel:0794-522848
ANGUS CHANDLER KEALING PEPPER RUDD TAYLOR WILKINSON F4293

112917 CHANDLER Mr Robert W. Veris, Cockshot Lane, Dormston, Worcs, WR7 4LB.
CHANDLER F2891

112925 CHANDLER Mrs S K. (Lines) 1 The Lynch Field, Wanborough, Swindon, Wiltshire, SN4 0DA.

ADKINS COMPTON DRUCE HENSON JOHNSON LINES TAYLOR WOODWARD F5991

112933 CHANDLER Mr Tony. 6 Westgate Drive, 6 West Gate Drive, Shropshire, WV16 4QF.
Chandeler CHANDLER Chanler Chaundler F6000

112941 CHANT Mrs Carol. (Foster) 27 Exe Vale Road, Countess Wear, Exeter, Devon, EX2 6LF.
AXTELL CHANT CROSS FOWLER KNIGHT STONE F5779

112968 CHANT Mr David E J. Hamdon, 49 Kings Drive, Eastbourne, E Sussex, BN21 2NY. Tel:0323-22544
BRAKE BULL CHANT COTTLE COX ENGLAND FANE FONE FRANCIS LAWRENCE LOWMAN PHELPS SNOOK STRONG TOOP TRASK VIGAR F2123

112976 CHANTREY Mrs Denise. (Willcox-Jones) 118 Wellsway, Bath, Avon, BA2 4SD. Tel:0225-313270
CHANTREY DENMAN FREETH JAMES JONES LUXMOORE SHILSTONE SLUGG WILLCOX F4590

112984 CHAPLIN Ann T. Snackerty Enterprises, Rfd 2 Box 668, Centre Barstead, NH 03225, USA.
DUNBAR F7267

112992 CHAPLIN Mr Brian. 22 Ambleside Close, Thingwall, Wirral, L61 3XQ. Tel:051-648-3508
BLACKMORE CHAPLIN LE GASSICK F1431

113018 CHAPLIN Ms Carol Rose. 166 Beechcroft Road, London, SW17 7DG.
BEVAN BRICKELL CHAPLIN GASTER MASON PIDDINGTON SIMMONDS STUBBINGS F7441

113026 CHAPLIN Mrs Margaret. 22 Ambleside Close, Thingwall, Wirral, L61 3XQ. Tel:051-648-3508
BOARDMAN F1432

113034 CHAPMAN Mr C J. 3 Broadmere Close, Dursley, Glous, GL11 6PU.
CHAPMAN COX DUNNING HOLMES MAW REDMAN ROBERTS THACKRAY VENESS WAGHORN F2682

113042 CHAPMAN Mr D S. 18 Bescot Drive, Walsall, W Midlands, WS2 9DF. Tel:0922-647687
CHAPMAN STOKES F499

113050 CHAPMAN Mr David. 4 Lockton Close, Vale Park, Reddish, Stockport Cheshire, SK5 7SU. Tel:061-476-3224
BOOTH CHAPMAN DANIELS FIELDING GETTINGS GITTINS GRAY HALLAM HOLLAND LAWSON MARTIN NAYLOR NUTTALL PODMORE POTTER ROGERSON STARKEY TONGUE WILDE WOODYER WRIGHT F1927

113069 CHAPMAN Mrs E F. (Mockridge) 13 Green Lane, Lower Broadheath, Worcester, WR2 6SH. Tel:0905-640131
BOARD BOONE CARTER HEMBERY KERLE LANGFORD MOCKRIDGE SPARROW WILCOX WILLIAMS F789

113077 CHAPMAN Mrs M J. 13 Northleigh Close, Loose, Maidstone, Kent, ME15 9RP.
Cuffe Dob DUFF Duffy Kilduff Mcduff Mcduffey Mcilduff O'diff O'duffy F7266

113085 CHAPMAN Mr R. 44 Swallow Street, Iver Heath, Iver, Bucks, SL0 0HG.
BROOKS CHAPMAN GOURD HEMMINGS PEARCE PRESS F2392

113093 CHAPMAN Dr Stephen. Hope House, Winterbourne Zelston, Blandford, Dorset, DT11 9EU.
BUSS CHAPMAN ENEVER Foord FORD GOUGE GREGORY HOCKING MARCHANT MUNBY PRESS PUNT RELF ROSS SEWELL SLEEP TAYLOR TIPPETT WARREN Warring F2024

113107 CHAPMAN Mr William. 9062 Angell Street, Downey, CA 90242, USA. Tel:+1-310-869-6623
BINNEY BROWN CHAPMAN CONNELLY Connolly COUL HARRIS HENNESSY HOURIHAN LITTLEJOHN LUNDIE SINCLAIR TURNER WHYTE F4119

113115 CHAPPLE Mr R E. Hydecrest, Cirencester Road, Hyde, Chalford Glous, GL6 8PE.
BALDWINSON GILSTON TONKENS Tonkins F6700

113123 CHARD Mrs Vera. (Wren) 18 Whitefield Road, Holbury, Southampton, Hants, SO4 1HS.
HOBBS HUGHES KELLY MARSHALL TAVERNER WHEELER WREN F200

113131 CHARITY Mr John. 55 Hollytree Avenue, Swanley, Kent, BR8 7BB.
CHARITY F1552

113158 CHARLES Ms G. 68 Greenway Close, Friern Barnet, London, N11 3NT.
BRADBURY CHARLES LENNEY F5867

113166 CHARLES Mrs Kaylene. 11 Robyn Crt, Irymple, Victoria, 3498, AUSTRALIA. Tel:+61-5-024-5942
BROADWAY CHARLES COX DWYER GALLAGHER GLADWELL HALL HUNT O'CONNOR F4641

113174 CHARLES Ms P A. 4 Meadow Close, Moulsford, Wallingford, Oxon, OX10 9JL.
CHARLES GILLETT SNELL TOWNSEND F858

113182 CHARLETON Mrs Heather. (Donaldson) 10 Georgeham Road, Owlsmoor, Camberley, Surrey, GU15 4YR. Tel:0344-761086
CHARLETON LARKING PUDDIFOOT F6082

113190 CHARLETON Mr Paul. 10 Georgeham Road, Owlsmoor, Camberley, Surrey, GU15 4YR. Tel:0344-761086
CHARLETON F2918

113204 CHARLEY Lt Col W R H. 16 Ballyblack Road, Newtownards, Co Down, BT22 2AP.
AGAR ASHALL BLACK CHARLEY CORLETT CRAIG CROSS ECCLES HADDOCK HAWKESWORTH HUNTER JOHNSON KING LEGGE MURLAND PENDERELL RIDDELL SMITH SMYTH SOUTHALL STEWART STITT USSHER WARING WILLSON WOLFENDEN F546

113212 CHARLTON Mr Doug. 26 Cumberland Road, Camberley, Surrey, GU15 1AG. Tel:0276-29124
ATTRILL BUTT CHARLTON ELLIS FRANCIS HARRIS HOPWOOD Lea LEE Ley NAPPER NEWLING OWEN PRATT RAFTER SCOTT SCRIVEN SMALLMAN TAYLOR THORN VEASEY Whitcombe WISE Witcom Witcomb WITCOMBE WITT F5062

113220 CHARLTON Mr G E. 15 Weardale Avenue, Forest Hall, Newcastle Upon Tyne, NE12 0HX. Tel:091-266-1581
BELLHOUSE Charlcton CHARLTON SCHOLEY Scolcy WHITE F3941

113239 CHARMAN Mr John Charles. 66 Sunnywood Drive, Haywards Heath, West Sussex, RH16 4PB.
CHARMAN F763

113247 CHARRETT Dr Macdonald A. 33 Denham Lodge, Oxford Road, New Denham, Uxbridge Middx, UB9 4AB. Tel:0895-234840
BAVERSTOCK Charot Charratt CHARRETT Charrot MACDONALD Mcdonald Stock F2378

113255 CHATFIELD Mr C J. Killdoman Courtyard, Barrhill, South Ayreshire, KA26 0PS.
Chatfeild CHATFIELD Chetfield F6835

113263 CHATTERTON Mr M T. Maryvale, Catherine Road, Benfleet, Essex, SS7 1HY.
ALLBROOK CALVERT CHATTERTON FAULKNER GELL SHOTTER F2944

113271 CHEKE Mr D J. Honey Farm, Bramley, Basingstoke, Hants, RG26 5DE.
Cheak Cheake Cheek Cheeke CHEKE F6558

113298 CHENEY Mr Roger. 39 Birch Barn Way, Northampton, NN2 8DT.
Caisned Caisnei Caisneto Casneto Chainey Chainy Chana Chanee Chaner Chaney Channer Chany Chaune Chauner Chauney Chauneys Chaunies Chauny Chawner Chawney Chawny Chayney Chaynye Cheaney Cheany Cheene Cheenei Cheeney Cheeny Cheine Cheiney Cheiny Chenduit Chenduyt Chene Chenea Cheneiy CHENEY Chenie Chenney Chenny Chensy Cheny Chesnei Chesneto Chesney Chesneye Cheyne Cheyney China Chiney Chinney F2008

113301 CHENNELL Mr Paul. 5 Dunstan Road, Golders Green, London, NW11 8AG.
ADLINBTON CHENNELL GREEN F6085

113328 CHERRY Mr Christopher. 26 Foxhope Close, Walkers Heath, Kings Norton, Birmingham, B38 0AR.
CHERRY F6502

113336 CHERRY Mr Peter. 40 Whites Lane, Kessingland, Lowestoft, Suffolk, NR33 7TG. Tel:0502-740229
CHERRY F3817

113344 CHESCOE Mr Nigel. 10 Littlecote Drive, Reading, Berks, RG1 6JD. Tel:0734-598220
Chescae Chescal CHESCOE Chescoll Chescow Chesko Chesso Chessoe Chexo Chisco Chisso Tescoe F3502

113352 CHESTER Mrs Brenda N. (Claydon) 110 Swiss Avenue, Chelmsford, Essex, CM1 2AF.
Bail BALE BREWER BUTLER CHESTER Claden Clayden CLAYDON Clayton COPSEY DALBY Dolby EATON ENGLISH FILBRICK GURTON Halbrook HINDS Hines HOLBROOK HURKS OWERS Philbrick PITTS Randall Randell RANDLE REEVE Reeves RUFFELL Ruffle SACH Saich Stiles STYLES TOMKINS Tompkins WEAVER F4616

113360 CHILD Jill. Sunnyside, Lyme Road, Axminster,

Devon.
BALL BAVERSTOCK BOND CARD CHILD COOKE ELLERY HARDLE JOHNS KERNICK MARINER MAY MITCHELL PARKER STANBROOKE TREBILCOCK Warwood WORWOOD F1036

113379 CHILTON Mr D. 13 Salmond Road, Andover, Hants, SP11 8HF.
CHILTON F6891

113387 CHIMLEY Mr John L. 29 Hartsdown Road, Margate, Kent, CT9 5QS.
CHIMLEY Chimney FROST GOODWIN LEWIS MILES MITCHELL RANSHAW RICHARDSON F5883

113395 CHIPPERFIELD Miss Marlene Y. 7 Sandringham Road, Springfield Park, Sandiacre, Nottingham, NG10 5LD.
ATKINSON Chapper Chipperfeald Chipperfelde CHIPPERFIELD Chipperfold Chipperville SMEDLEY STEVENSON TALMAGE TAYLOR F6237

113409 CHISLETT Mr S. 96 East Street, South Molton, Devon, EX36 3DF.
Cheslade Cheslate Chislet CHISLETT Chisslet Chisslett Chizlet Chizlett F7380

113417 CHISWELL Mrs Ann V. 96 Beaumont Street, Milehouse, Plymouth, Devon, PL2 3AQ.
CHISWELL WARNE F6300

113425 CHITTENDEN Mr W H. 99 The Street, Latchingdon, Chelmsford, Essex, CM3 6JS.
ASKEW BARTON CHURCH DAY DRURY FORD GOLD HAYWOOD Hiles ISLES LITTLEJOHN MEARS MOULTON PAGE SMITH STAMMERS TAYLOR WHEWELL WHITEHEAD WOOD WOODS F743

113433 CHORLEY Mr & Mrs L G. (Longland) 26 Lynton Close, Ely, Cambs, CB6 1DJ. Tel:0353-662087
CHORLEY Langland Langlande Longelande LONGLAND Longlond F1814

113441 CHOULS Mr William H M. 55 Mill Farm Drive, Paganhill, Stroud, Glous, GL5 4JZ. Tel:0453-758031
Choul Chould Chouler Choules CHOULS Chowler Chowles F2948

113468 CHRISTENSEN Dr P. 11 Quesnell Road, Edmonton, Alberta, T5R 5N1, CANADA.
Bricket BRICKETT Briket Brikett Brycket Bryckett Chowin Chowing CHOWINGS Chowins Dartnail Dartnal Dartnale Dartnall Dartnel DARTNELL DASHWOOD Daswood Durtnal Durtnall Durtnel Durtnell Dutnail Dutnal Dutnale Dutnall Gup Gupp Guppe Gupps Jup Jupe Jupes JUPP Juppe Juppes Jups F6915

113476 CHRISTIAN Mrs Jean. (Burrows) 49 Coverside Road, Great Glen, Leicester, LE8 0EB. Tel:0533-592010
BROOK BURROWS DANSON GILL SCONCE SHARPLES SHUTT STRIZAKER TAMS WALLER F4197

113484 CHRISTIE Mrs Jean. Seahaven, Albert Street, Nairn, Scotland, IV12 4HF. Tel:0667-54487
Bartan Bartane BARTON Bartone Bartoun Bartrahame Bartram Bartrem Bauerton Bertane Berton Bertoun Bertown Bertowne Bertram Betan Beton Biron Biroun Birun Bortane Bouerton Bourton Bramall BRAMWELL Braton Breton Bretun Burntoun Buron Burton Burun Byron De Barton De Berton De Beton De Birton De Bret De Briton De Burton De Burun DE GRUCHY HOGGAN JAMESON JEUNE Le Bret Le Bretun Le Burone MAILLER PATERSON SHARP SHILLINGLAW SIMPSON Steadman STEDMAN STEEDMAN Steidman Stidman Stiedman Stoodman Studman SWAN WALLACE Waterlo WATERLOW F1096

113492 CHRISTIE Mr Michael A. 13 Rural Way, Redhill, Surrey, RH1 4BT.
ANNALL Annel BRAZIER CHRISTIE COLEMAN Darnel DARNELL Forester FORRESTER HEADLAND PREWETT Pruet Pruett Pruitt SAVAGE Savidge Savige Wildes Wilds Wiles Willes Wyld WYLDE Wyldes Wylds Wyles F1792

113506 CHRISTMAS Mr Brian W. 74 Oakwood Road, Maidstone, Kent, ME16 8AL.
CHRISTMAS Cristmas F6712

113514 CHURCH Mr D. 2 Wessex Place, Barry, South Glamorgan, CF6 8SP.
A'court Accott Acot ACOTT Acourt Aecot Aecott Aecourt ALLEY ASHTON Bagan Baggaley Baggalin Baggan Bagge Baggen BAGGIN Bagin BALLARD Biggin Bigin Boucher Bouchoer Boutcher Boutchoer BRADFORD BROWN Buggins BUTCHER CHURCH DEVONSHIRE Eastaugh EASTER FORSYTH KEATS M'CONNELL MASON MOODY MYERS O'CONNELL ROACH SANDERSON Saunderson TAYLOR WEBBER WININGHAM F4803

113522 CHURCH Mr Richard. 65 Harrison Drive, High Halstow, Kent, ME3 8TF.
CHURCH F7182

113530 CHURCHILL Mr Brian. 48 Caerleon Road, Dinas Powys, South Glamorgan.
BUSHROD CHURCHILL FOSTER MUMFORD RICHARDS SLY STEELE F3582

113549 CHURCHWARD Mr B G. 38 Longhouse Barn, Penperlleni, Pontypool, Gwent, NP4 0BD.
CHURCHWARD F6609

113557 CLAMP Mr John. 26 Victoria Square, Clifton, Bristol, BS8 4EW. Tel:0272-736222
CLAMP F1765

113565 CLAPHAM Miss E B. 60 Courtfield Gardens, London, SW5 0NF.
CLAPHAM F6012

113573 CLAPP Mrs Cynthia Violet. (Bowdler) 21 Dronsfield Road, Fleetwood, Lancs, FY7 7BW. Tel:0253-771598
CHESTERS F5619

113581 CLARE Mr Peter. 111 Carnarvon Road, London, E18 2NT. Tel:081-505-2278
BUCKTHORPE CHRISTMAS CLARE COPESTAKE HAWKINS MAHON TERRY F898

113603 CLARIDGE Mrs Jennifer. 15 Devonport Gardens, Ilford, Essex, IG1 2QQ.
BLISS CLARIDGE COULSON COULSTON GODFREY F386

113611 CLARK Mr Brian Latham. 102 Murrayfield Road, Hull, HU5 4DU.
AINLEY Allsop ALSOP Alsopp ANDERTON Aneley Anley BAILEY BARTON Boothby BOUTHBY BROWN Browne BULLOCK CASSON Clark CLARKE Clerk COLBRIDGE COOKSON COXON CROFT D'ARCY DALE DALES Darcey Darcie Darcy Darsey Dun DUNN Dunne Etherington EVERINGHAM EVERINGTON Everinton Everton Evrington GILDERDALE Gleadhill GLEDHILL Graves GREAVES Greeves Grieves Hague HAIGH HARGRAVE HARGRAVES Hargreave Hargreaves HODGSON HORNSBY HUDSON Hutson JACKSON JOHNSON KENNEDY Laitham LATHAM Laythum Leetham Letham LITTLE LITTLEWOOD MALIN Mallin MALLINSON Marshal MARSHALL Mold MOULD MURRAY Murrey Murry NEWHAM Ruslin RUSLING Rustling SAWYER Spinck Spincks Spink SPINKS STEPHENSON STORM STRAWSON TADMAN Thornell THORNHILL Thornill TREBILCOCK Trebilcook Twidal Twidale Twidel Twidell TWIDLE Twydale Twydle Whinn Whisler WHISTLER WHITE WHITEHEAD WHOLEY Wilderidge Wildredge WILDRIDGE WILLINGHAM Win WINN Wisler Wistler Wynn Wynne F1658

113638 CLARK Mrs Catherine. (Keen) Arlington, Gairdner River, WA 6337, AUSTRALIA.
BOYDEN BRIGHT BROWNING CLAYTON KEEN LAMBOURNE MOSS SCOTT F4670

113646 CLARK Mrs Elizabeth. (Bullen) 6 Aylward Drive, Stevenage, Herts, SG2 8UR.
BULLEN COOPER DAY ELLIS GREENFIELD INWARD LETCHFORD MARVELL RIDDLE ROBINS F5608

113654 CLARK Mr Ian. 4 The Crest, Surbiton, Surrey, KT5 8JZ.
BAMFORTH BEE BOOTH BOULDEN BOXALL BRIGGS CLARK DUNDERDALE EDWICKER FRENCH HAMBLETON JONES KIDMAN LANDER LOVETT MORRIS PARSONS READER ROSKELL ROWLANDSON SOAR SOUTHWARD TURNESS WARD F1626

113662 CLARK Ian. 10 St Helens Close, Grantham, Lincs, NG31 7EE.
Aldridge ALLDRIDGE BROWN CLARK Clarke Cleark Clerc Clerke Cocks Collings COLLINS COX DICKES Dicks Dickson Dix DIXON Dixson FAIRNINGTON GOWLAND HOLLAND Hollands MOULDS PLAYER Radway REEVE Reve Roadway RODWAY TANDY Tomkins TOMPKINS F1275

113670 CLARK Mrs M F. (Urch) 1 King Alfred Way, Winsley, Bradford On Avon, Wiltshire, BA15 2NG.
BOND CLAY FISHER GRANT HAMILTON HARDING PAINTER PERKINS PRATTEN READ SALMON SHUTE STEVENS URCH WALL WILLINGTON F2314

113689 CLARK Mrs N J L. 18 Marsland Road, Solihull, West Midlands, B92 7BU.

BARKUS FRANKISH LUDDINGTON MCCOLVIN THIRLWELL F3821

113697 CLARK Mrs Shirley C. (Cartwright) 71 Seaview Road, Castor Bay, Auckland 9, 1309, NEW ZEALAND.
CARTWRIGHT CLARK HOCKE HORLOR HOWARD JACKSON KIRK LARGE MAHLER MAYALL Snazel Snazwell SNEAZWELL TAYLOR F4199

113700 CLARK Timothy. 2 Rosemary Close, Abbeydale, Gloucester, GL4 9TL.
ANDREWS ARNELL ASHBY BENNETT CANNON DARN DESLANDES HAMS HEARST HEAVEN HEDGES HERETAY HODGES MCNELLA MCTIGUE MULLENS NIALL PILLINGER POWELL RICE RODWAY ROSE ROWLES TABRETT TURNER VICARY WALSH WIDOWS F1273

113719 CLARKE Mrs C M. 35 Lydd Close, Doddington Park, Lincoln, Lincs, LN6 0NZ.
BREWER BROOKS BUNNEY CLARK Clarke COCKING COLE Coles COTTINGHAM GILL MEAD MERRYWEATHER PEDLEY PETTINGER SAMPSON THACKER TURK F6221

113727 CLARKE Mr C S. 16 Garden Road, Heringham, Norfolk, NR26 8HT.
CLARK Clarke EGGLETON F1309

113735 CLARKE Mrs Catherine. (Allsop) 21 Longmeadows, Darras Hill, Northumberland, NE20 9DX.
ALLSOP BATEMAN BOWLER SCHOLEY F5824

113743 CLARKE Miss Collette. 19 Orwell Court, Brocklesbury Close, Watford, Herts, WD2 4GR.
ALMOND APPS ASHDOWN BATCHELOR BELLCHAMBER BUGBEARD Bugberd BUGBIRD BURR BUTCHERS CATT COGHAN COOK CORNFORD COSTELLO FARR GIBBS GIBSON GOLD GOULD GRIFFIN GUTSELL HALFPENNY HARMER HEATHFIELD HOOK JARRETT JEWHURST LARKIN LUCK MARCHANT MARSHALL MILGATE MONAGHAN MOOR Moore MORFEE PIPER PLATT POWELL SANTER SAUNTER STEPHENS Stevens STEWART WEATHERLEY WHITE F2333

113751 CLARKE Mr G D. 31 Crutchfield Lane, Walton On Thames, Surrey, KT12 2QY. Tel:0932-222695
CHEEPER Chipper JACQUES TRATHAN Trathen VALE WEBBER F6306

113778 CLARKE Miss J. 20 Rushleigh Avenue, Acklam, Middlesborough, Cleveland, TS5 8PF.
BINNS Blumell BLUMER Blummel Clark CLARKE DAY DONOGHUE Donohoe Donohue HOWELL KAVANAGH MCARDLE MURPHY O'day Raw Rawe ROE Rowe WHITE F6325

113786 CLARKE Mrs Janet Y. 9 Fairfield Road, Scartho, Grimsby, Lincolnshire, DN33 3DR. Tel:0472-826841
ALLENBY BASKCOMB CHARTERS CLARKE HUTTON JACOBS NEWTON SNODGRASS TRAILL Wardale WARDLE F3356

113794 CLARKE Mr Joe. 7 Hardwick Crescent, Sheffield, S11 8WB. Tel:0742-666775
CLARKE HARRON F139

113808 CLARKE Miss L. 301 Walton Lane, Walton On The Wolds, Nr Barrow On Soar, Leics, LE12 8JX.
CLARKE FRASER GENT JACKSON SUTTLEWOOD WASS WHITBY F4355

113816 CLARKE Mrs M. 12 Grosvenor Crescent, Hillingdon, Uxbridge, Middx, UB10 9ER. Tel:0895-52964
GEORGE HILL JACKSON LEWIS TOOGOOD F2090

113824 CLARKE Mrs Marina Ann. (Rumens) 35 Bond Street, Bury, Lancs, BL9 7BE.
PEDVIN RUMENS F4084

113832 CLARKE Mrs N J. 5 Pintail Road, Woodford Gree, Essex, IG8 7DX.
PYMAN F6853

113840 CLARKE Mr Philip. Wolverton, 1b Fairfield, Flookburgh, Grange Over Sands Cumbria, LA11 7NB. Tel:05395-58907
CAMBRAY Ginks Jenckes Jenkes JENKS Jinks MASON F302

113859 CLARKE Mrs Sylvia. 49 Furners Mead, Henfield, W Sussex, BN5 9JA.
Clark CLARKE CRAMPTON Durant Durent DURRANT Durrent GODWIN HORN Horne INNOUS LINBERRY Linbery Linbry Linbury Mapel Mapil MAPLE Mappel Mappil Mapple Moor MOORE PORTER ROGERS RUMBOLD THOMAS Wilis Wiliss WILLIS Williss F3203

113867 CLARKE Mr W L. Wych Elms, White Lane Close, Sturminster Newton, Dorset, DT10 1EJ. Tel:0258-72627
CLARKE ROBY TAYLOR F695

113875 CLARRICOATS Mr James Henry. 52 Newton Road, Tilbury, Essex, RM18 8YB. Tel:0375-846699
BARRETT BECKETT BENSTEAD CLARRICOATES HOYES MARTIN OVERTON POTTERTON STOWE F174

113883 CLARRIDGE Mr Nigel. 92 Pontywindy Road, Caerphilly, Mid Glamorgan, CF8 3HA.
CLAKE CLARIDGE CLARRIDGE CLEAK CLICK F1076

113891 CLASBY Mrs Valerie. (Pike) 25 Ravine Road, Boscombe, Bournemouth, Dorset, BH5 2DT.
BURGESS CLASBY MANDRY MARSHALL MITCHELL PIKE SCOREY F369

113905 CLATWORTHY Mr Gordon Seymour. Crantock, 88 Sherford Road, Taunton, Somerset, TA1 3QY. Tel:0823-276634
CLATWORTHY CLOTWORTHY F2771

113913 CLATWORTHY Mrs Margaret Mary. Crantock, 88 Sherford Road, Taunton, Somerset, TA1 3QY. Tel:0823-276634
FRANKLIN F2772

113921 CLAUGHTON Mr Keith W J P. Po Box 400, Dromana, Victoria, 3936, AUSTRALIA.
CLAUGHTON Clauton Clawton F6902

113948 CLAXTON Mr J C. 38 Barton Drive, Newton Abbot, Devon, TQ12 1PD.
CLAXTON Claxtone Claxtonn F6809

113956 CLAY Mr D M. 30 Mill Street, Mansfield, Notts, NG18 2PQ. Tel:0623-648236
BRADSHAW BURN CLAY MEINOLL ROUSE F561

113964 CLAY Mr Geoff. 47 Greengate Lane, Birstall, Leicester, LE4 3JF. Tel:0533-671234
CLAY COOKE CUTTIFORD HIGGINS F1706

113972 CLAY Mrs Jane. 7 Oxted Close, Cramlington, Northumberland, NE23 9YE.
HANNAY F3297

113980 CLAYBURN Mr Rod. 4 Winnham Drive, Fareham, Hampshire, PO16 8QE.
Claspar CLASPER Claybon Clayborn Clayborne Claybourn Claybourne CLAYBURN Claybyn F80

113999 CLAYTON Mrs Joan. (Glover) Mill Farm, West Hendred, Wantage, Oxon, OX12 8RJ.
GLOVER F6096

114006 CLAYTON Mr R. 17 2nd Avenue, Ravenswing, Aldermaston, Berks, RG7 4PU.
Claden Cladon Claiden Claidon Claiton Claton Clayden Claydon CLAYTON Cleydon F4113

114014 CLEAK Mr E R. Tree Stumps, Down Ampney, Cirencester, Glos, GL7 5QR. Tel:0793-750495
Claik Clake CLEAK Cleake Cleek Cleeke Cleik Cleike Clek Cleke Click Clike Klaik Klake Kleek Kleike Kleke F4336

114022 CLEAL Mr R C. 2 Smythe Grove, Warwick, CV34 5SE.
BAKER CLEAL Cleall PEACH F7420

114030 CLEAVE Mr Mark. 11 Chantrell Road, West Kirby, Cheshire, L48 9XR. Tel:051-625-6191
ABLE AVERY BUSH CATON CHALLICE CLEAVE FITZGIBBON GILES GOFORTH HARTSHORN JIGGINS KEAST MOORE NORRISH POLLARD RAINBIRD RUNNALLS SANDFORD SAXTON SPARROW TAMLYN TIBBIT TUCKER WOOLCOCK WRIGHT F3162

114049 CLEETON Mrs J. 3 Bader Gardens, Cippenham, Slough, Berks, SL1 9DJ.
CLEETON HERBERT JENNINGS SKINNER F3866

114057 CLEGHORN Mr Newton. 14 Alfred Street, Newcastle Upon Tyne, NE6 2RA. Tel:091-265-1678
CLEGHORN CORBITT ROWNTREE F5880

114065 CLEMAS Mr Mike. Dunstall House, Earls Croome, Worcester, WR8 9DF. Tel:0905-67488
CLEMAS F1864

114073 CLEMENTS Mrs Joan. 3 Orchard Rise, Groombridge, Tunbridge Wells, Kent, TN3 9RU. Tel:0892-764633
Bundick BUNDOCK Bundwick CROKER HOLLOWAY MARTEL MOUNTFORD MUNFORD RELF SAMMES SEMPLE SLATER STAIR STURGESS Vare VEAR F2801

114081 CLEMENTS Mr Keith. 20 Wantage Road, Irchester, Wellingborough, Northants, NN9 7HE. Tel:0933-59166
CHENNELLS CLEMENTS FEATHER GRIMWADE LAMMIN RENDAL F5601

114103 CLEMETT Mr C J. 7 Brookmead Way, Havant, Hants, PO9 1RT.
Clemet CLEMETT F6650

114111 CLEWS Mrs C J B. Flat 1, 20 Clifton Crescent, Folkestone, Kent, CT20 2EP.
HUNTINGDON HUNTINGTON F5338

114138 CLIFFORD Mr R N. The Stables, 2 Southbank Road, Hereford, HR1 2TJ.
CLIFFORD F6643

114146 CLINCH Mr James. 3 Upper Street, Leeds, Maidstone, Kent, ME17 1SL.
CHRISTOPHER CLINCH Clynch GREEN Wasgate Wasket WASKETT Wosket Woskett F1562

114154 CLINGAN Mr Ian. 11 Savernake Avenue, Melksham, Wilts, SN12 7HB. Tel:0225-706775
Cligand CLINGAN Clingand Clingane Clingen Clingham Clingin Clinging Clingon Clingzean Clinzeand Klingan Klingen Klingham Macclengen Macclingan Macclingand Macclingen Mcclengen Mcclingan Mcclingand Mcclingen F4240

114162 CLINTON Mrs Margaret. (Cawse) 7 Park Close, Burgess Hill, Sussex, RH15 8HL.
Tel:0444-232479
Cause Cauws Caux Caws CAWSE Cawsse CLINTON Clynton HICK Peren Perin Pering Perren Perrin PERRING Perringe Perryn Perrynge Peryn F5225

114170 CLIPPERTON Dr R D J. 8 Netherton Drive, Frodsham, Cheshire, WA6 6DG. Tel:0928-35837
AMOS BISHOP Cleperton Cliperton CLIPPERTON Clippington Clippiton Clipton Clyperton Clyppington HADLEY F4675

114189 CLIVELY Mr F H T. 16 Abbotsmount, St Johns Road, St Helier, Jersey, JE2 6SP.
Tel:0534-25907
CLIVELY F1353

114197 CLIVES Mr S W. 42 Frith View, Chapel En Le Frith, Derbyshire, SK12 6TT.
CARRINGTON CLEAVE CLIFFE CLIVE CLIVES Clyve GASKELL LICKIS OLDBURY SIMNETT F194

114200 CLOTHIER Mr Norman. 91 Silverdale Avenue, Ashley Park, Walton On Thames, Surrey, KT12 1EJ.
CLOTHIER F7133

114219 CLUARD Mr David. 38 Fisher Road, Stoke, Plymouth, Devon, PL2 3BB.
Cleward Cloward CLUARD Cluart Clueard F3634

114227 CLUTTERBUCK Mrs Y E. 173 Leigh Sinton Road, Malvern Link, Worcs, WR14 1LB.
Boure BOWER Bowers Bowre Bowry CLUTTERBUCK F6315

114235 COALES Mr Anthony G. Crossways, Sudborough, Kettering, Northants, NN14 3BX.
Tel:08012-3212
ALLEN BUSWELL CHAPMAN CHEW COALES DRAGE FELLOWES HARRISON SANDERSON TEBBUTT THOMPSON VORLEY WEED F3149

114243 COALES Mr John. The Mount, Parsonage Hill, Somerton, Somerset, TA11 7PF. Tel:0458-72545
BATEMAN BULL COALES PALMER ROGERS F2426

114251 COARE Mr C J. 41 Elm Park Avenue, Elm Park, Hornchurch, Essex, RM12 4SP.
BARNBY Coar COARE SIMMONDS WHITTING F11

114278 COATH Mr W E. 14 Belmont, St Georges Avenue, Weybridge, Surrey, KT13 0BY.
COATH Coeth Coth Cothe Couth F6867

114286 COBB Mr Dave. 32 Sussex Road, Ickenham, Uxbridge, Middx, UB10 8PN. Tel:0895-637495
COBB F3148

114294 COBB Mr David. Sinodun, Shalford, Braintree, Essex, CM7 5HN. Tel:0371-851097
Cob COBB Cobbe Coobe Gefferie Geffry Jefferey Jefferie JEFFERY Jefferye Jeffre Jeffrey Jeffrie Jefrie Jeofrey MAY F565

114308 COBBETT Mr Peterson. 13 St Andrews Road, Earlsdon, Coventry, CV5 6FP. Tel:0203-674900
AGER AMBLER BALDWIN BARNEY BASTOCK BILLINGHURST BRADEN BUTCHER CHURCHER Cobbatt COBBETT Cobbit Cobbitt Cobbutt Cobert Cobet Cobit Cobitt COLLINS CORPES CROSS DEW DODD DUE FLUTTER FOWKES GODDARD GODWIN HENSON HOBBS JAMES JEFFREY JEFFRIES JOHNSTONE KERN LINNELL LOCK LONGUEHAYE MANN MARLOW MASLEN MOULDEN NAISH PLANK PRATT RAMBRIDGE RATCLIFFE READ SCHELCHER SMITH SUTTON TASKER TOWNSEND TREEN WARD F101

114316 COBBIN Mr P F. 11 First Avenue, Dovercourt, Harwich, Essex, CO12 3SH.
BARNES BLOOMFIELD CHATTERS CHILVERS COBBIN MITCHELL PRENTICE SAVAGE F2298

114324 COBBING Mr Bob. 89a Petherton Road, London, N5 2QT.
Cobbin Cobbine Cobbines COBBING Cobbings Cobbins Cobin Cobine Cobines Cobing Cobings Cobins F7134

114332 COBELDICK Mr Trevor M. Po Box 13-320, Johnsonville, Wellington, 6004, NEW ZEALAND.
ALLEN BUES Cobbeldick Cobbeldicke COBBLEDICK Cobeldeke COBELDICK Cobeldycke Cobledick Copledike Copledyke CUPPLEDITCH DAVIE De Cobeldyk GALDSTONE LEANE SPENCE UGLOW F5166

114359 COCKADAY Mr Peter. 1 Keble Close, West Meads, Bognor Regis, Sussex, PO21 5SD.
Cocadee COCKADAY Cockade Cockady Cockeday Cockerdee Cocqidez Coquide Coquidee FROST Kokedes LONEY LOTT Somerville SOMMERVILLE F1812

114367 COCKBURN Mr Andrew. 50 Hillview Crescent, Edinburgh, EH12 8QG.
COCKBURN F5948

114375 COCKBURN Mr R W. 31 Ellen Street, Whitburn, West Lothian, EH47 0HJ.
Coburn COCKBURN Cockburne Cokburn Cokburne F7390

114383 COCKERILL Mr T J. Old Mill House, Weston Colville, Cambridge, CB1 5NY.
COCKERILL CRAGG EVERATT KELSEY KIRKBANK LEWTHWAITE LINLEY SUDBURY TALBOT TONKS TOTO WINDOWS F1871

114391 COCKINGS Mr John R. 12 Lincoln Street, Norwich, Norfolk, NR2 3LA.
Cockain Cockaine Cockaines Cockains Cockan Cockayn Cockayne Cockaynes Cocking COCKINGS Cockins Cokain Cokaine Cokaines Cokains Cokan Cokayn Cokayne Cokaynes Cokin Cokings Cokins Cokyn Lawman Lohrman Lohrmann LORMAN Lormann F2790

114405 COCKRAM Mr Roy. 77 Holly Hill, Bassett, Southampton, Hampshire, SO1 7ES.
Tel:0703-768129
COCKRAM GREEN HONE MOORE SETTER STOCKER F3922

114413 CODD Mr Malcolm. 26 Gladstone Street, Mountain Ash, Mid Glamorgan, CF45 3BT.
CODD F3270

114421 CODD Mr Robert. 17 Ashwell Close, Walcot, Swindon, Wiltshire, SN3 1DY.
Cod CODD F7073

114448 CODLIN Mrs Elfriede. 88 The Fairway, Dymchurch, Kent, TN29 0QP. Tel:0303-872891
BOWLER CODLIN COLLINS COOPER FERGUSON PURDUE STROUD F5964

114456 COE Mrs Carol June. (Owens) 8 Flag Lane North, Upton Heath, Chester, Cheshire, CH2 1LE. Tel:0244-381400
BEMAND DANILY EVANS HANCOX HOUHGTON HUGHES JONES MARSHALL OWENS PEACOCK PRYCE THOMAS WATKIN WHALLEY F5731

114464 COE Mrs Eileen G. (Midgley) 18 Hartley Park Gardens, Hartley, Plymouth, Devon, PL3 5HU.
Tel:0752-661102
BARNES Co COE Cooe GARLAND MIDGLEY SAMPSON STAPLES Sumerhill Sumeril Sumerill Summerhill Summeril SUMMERILL F3767

114472 COE Mr John Sydney. 8 Flag Lane North, Upton Heath, Chester, Cheshire, CH2 1LE.
Tel:0244-381400
BARKER COE DIDSBURY DOD ELLIS GATLEY HIGGINBOTHAM JOYNSON KINETON NAYLER ORME Prichard Prichit PRITCHARD Pritchet WILSON WRIGHT F4612

114480 COFELL Mrs Donna J. (Sedgman) Rr7, Blenheim, Ontario, NOP 1A0, CANADA. Tel:+1-519-676-8223
CLEMENTS COFELL Coffell COLEMAN FISHER SEDGMAN WALPOLE F5178

114499 COFFEY Mr Phillip. 19 Clos Des Pas, Green Street, St Helier, Jersey, JE2 4PW.
Tel:0534-25658
BUTTERFIELD COFFEY EATON F6357

114502 COGGAN Mr Patrick. Parsonage Farm, Stratford Sub Castle, Salisbury, Wilts, SP1 3LH.
BARNARD BARTLETT BOWDITCH CHARD CHUBB COGAN COGGAN GENT OSMOND F106

114510 COGHILL Mr R F. Invertiel, 41 Chalton Road, Bridge Of Allan, Stirlingshire, FK9 4EF.
COGHILL Cogle F7201

114529 COHEN Mrs Patricia A. The Anchorage,

Portscatho, Cornwall, TR2 5HE.
AARONS ARGENT BRETT BRUTY CANTRELL COCKING COHEN EYRE GOLDING GOODY GRINGLEY HOBSON HYMAN MOSES MOSS RACHELSON RAWLINGS SEATON SEWILL SHIPPAM WALKER WILSON F3038

114537 COLAM-JOHNSON Mrs J. Marlow Lodge, Downdyke Road, Sutterton, Boston, PE20 2LB.
COLAM Collam Coulam Coulhame Cowlam F7137

114545 COLBECK Mr John. 7 English Street, Dumfries, DG1 2BU.
ALLISS BATES BOWERING BRACKENBURY COLBECK DAWSON DERBYSHIRE DEVONSHIRE ESTILOW GOODES GOODRICK GOODS GREEN HEMSWELL HERRING LANE ROBINSON RUTTLETON TOY TYE WILSON YATES F5305

114553 COLDWELL Mr John K. 21 Rosemary Lane, Rowledge, Farnham, Surrey, GU10 4DB.
AVISON BEECROFT BOWER COLDWELL CROFTS F3001

114561 COLE Mrs Anne. (Duncalf) 174 Doddington Road, Lincoln, LN6 7HF.
Doncalf DUNCALF Duncalfe Duncaph Duncaulf Dunceph Duncoff Duncroft Duncuff Duncuft F4945

114588 COLE Canon Peter G L. East Worldham Vicarage, Alton, Hants, GU34 3AS.
Coale COLE Coles Coule Coulle KIRKBY Knap KNAPP LOWRY F3905

114596 COLE Mr Charles H B. Southfields, Sandford St Martin, Oxon, OX7 7AG.
BEEDLE BETTS BOLT BOLTON BOSWORTH BOUNDY BROCKELL CALLARD CLAPP CLARKE COHEN COLE DIXON DORE DRANSFIELD FORTAY FROST GRAVELL GREENHALGH HARVEY HEARD HEWISH JURY LOWE MANLEY MAUNDER MCGREGOR MCLURE MILFORD MOOR MORRIS NATHAN OLDROYD PEARSON PHILLIPS PITCAIRN ROBLEY ROSENBERG ROWE SEARLE SKINNER SOUCH SPEDDING STRANG STUBBS TASKER TOOMS WALTERS WEBBER WENSLEY WOOLLACOTT WOOLWAY WRIGHT F1202

114618 COLE Mrs Enid. (Hockley) 40 Wesley Way, Devauden Green, Chepstow, Gwent, NP6 6PG.
MORGAN RIVERS SMITH F3966

114626 COLE Mr Frank. 12 Newbarns Road, Barrow In Furness, Cumbria, LA13 9SF. Tel:0229-828514
COLE DRAKE LOCKETT F3791

114634 COLE Mr George. 63 Castle Rising Road, South Wootton, Kings Lynn, Norfolk, PE30 3JA.
BARRINGTON COLE COLLARD CRAMPTON LANE WALL F2220

114642 COLE Mrs Jennifer. (Symonds) Watkins Lodge, Green Lane, Burnham On Crouch, Essex, CM0 8PU. Tel:0621-782574
ALTHOFF AUSTEN BLANKING BOREHAM BUNTING CAMPION COLE Colven COLVIN DRINKWATER DRUCE FARROW FENTON FOY GAINS GARWOOD JEFFREYES Jeffries Jeffrys MIDDLEDITCH MIDDLETON PENDGEAST PRATT Simonds SYKES SYMONDS THAYRE Webkin WHEELER Wibkin WIEBKIN Wiebking F77

114650 COLEBY Mr G. 329 Long Road, Lowestoft, Suffolk, NR33 9DG. Tel:0502-583768
COLBY COLEBY SCARLE F6269

114669 COLEBY Mrs Rosemary. (Garran) Woodruff Farm, Debden Green, Saffron Walden, Essex, CB11 3LZ.
BENCE BOULD BREWER COLEBY GAMMAN GAMMON MATTHEWS MOGER SHUTTLEWORTH WOODHALL F5384

114677 COLEMAN Mrs C A. (Babb) 100 Knightlow Road, Harborne, Birmingham, B17 8QA.
BABB BISHOP LAURENCE LIPPITT TOOGOOD WHITECROFT F4070

114685 COLEMAN Mr Eric. Maes Yr Hendre, Forge Road, Machen, Newport Gwent, NP1 8PH. Tel:0633-441196
COLEMAN CROWFOOT HILEY HYNDMAN LEWIS POTTEN REED SPARGO F1574

114693 COLEMAN Mr Ken. 75 Sycamore Drive, East Grinstead, W Sussex, RH19 3UL. Tel:0342-317279
COLEMAN FLOWERS HEART JAMES PARSLOW PIPE ROBSON STOTHARD THOMAS WILLIAMS F2561

114707 COLEMAN Lois. Rd #2, Box 258j, Ligonier, PA 15658, USA.
RIDDEL Riddell Riddle F7403

114715 COLEMAN Mr Robert. 3 Woodland Grove, Woodthorpe, Nottingham, NG5 3FX. Tel:0602-624202
BULLOCK BURNETT CLEAVER COLEMAN QUINN F5119

114723 COLEMAN Mr Ronald. 61 Marshall Close, New Southgate, London, N11 1TE. Tel:081-368-7210
COLEMAN EDWARDS ELLERY HOCKING NEALE PEACEY PHEBY SHEMMING SPEED WARDEN F2640

114731 COLES Mr Laurence Christopher. 4 Buckingham Close, Alton, Hants, GU34 1QZ. Tel:0420-89501
COLES MUGRIDGE YORSTON F301

114758 COLEY Mr John. 40 Peewit Road, Evesham, Worcestershire, WR11.
Cawley Cawly Coahley Coale Coalee Coaley Coaleys Coalie Coalle Coalley Coally Coaly Coawly Coeley Coely Cohley Cohleye Coiley Cole Colee Colei Coleley Colely COLEY Coleye Coleyis Coli Colie Coliye Coll Collay Colle Collee Colles Colley Colleye Colli Collie Colliy Colly Collye Coly Colye Cooaly Coole Coolee Cooley Cooleye Coolie Coolley Coolly Coollye Cooly Coolye Corley Coulah Coulay Couley Coulley Couly Couolley Coweley Cowely Cowlay Cowlaye Cowlee Cowleige Cowley Cowleye Cowli Cowlie Cowllay Cowllea Cowllie Cowly Cowlye Coyleie Coyley Coyly Culey Culley De Culegh MAXWELL MCMILLAN F3150

114766 COLFER Mr Neville. Christian Lodge, Church Road, Rudgeway, Bristol, BS12 2SH. Tel:0454-418025
COLFER Colfor NEVILLE F1446

114774 COLK Mr Stanley. 40 Crockett Gardens, Penicuik, Mid Lothian, EH26 9BB.
COLK F5416

114782 COLLEDGE Mrs Valerie. (Stokes) 6 Watson Street, Clontarf, Queensland, 4019, AUSTRALIA. Tel:+61-7-284-8150
COLLEDGE FITCH LEWIS OWEN SMITH STOKES TIBBETT VIRGEN WARD WILSON F5146

114790 COLLETT Mr Neil. 3 Manor Court, Manor Road, Kenilworth, Warwickshire, CV8 2GJ. Tel:0926-512850
BRIMFIELD BROMFIELD CARDALL CASHMORE COLLETT FIELD JEPPS MILLARD SABEY TEW WILLS F490

114804 COLLEY A G. 1b Victoria Road, Chingford, London, E4 6BY.
COLLEY F7421

114812 COLLEY Mrs Barbara. (Bagshaw) 12 Greenfield Crescent, Stonesfield, Witney, Oxon, OX8 8EH.
ATKINSON BAGSHAW BARRON BENNETT CHAPMAN COULSON EAGERS GARFORTH IBBOTSON JAMES JUBB SHAW SLACK WALTON YOUNG F6281

114820 COLLICOTT Mr Mervyn. 22 Parklands Road, Chichester, W Sussex, PO19 3DT.
COLLICOTT DONEY F6337

114839 COLLIER Mr M E. 120 N Schifferdecker, Joplin, Missouri, 64801, USA.
COLLIER F6798

114847 COLLINGS Mrs Julie. 47 Thornpark Road, St Austell, Cornwall, PL25 4DP. Tel:0726-64270
BASKERVILLE FULLER Madestone Maidstone Mainestone Mainston MAINSTONE Manestone Manston Manstone Mayneston Maynestone Maynston Maynstone ROGERS F638

114855 COLLINGS Mr Paul John. The Lancastrian Public House, Scale Hall Farm, Morecambe Road, Lancaster, Lancs, LA1 5JB. Tel:0524-381141
Colins Collin Colling Collinge COLLINGS Collins F4027

114863 COLLINS Ms E C. 6 Crescent Place, Pendeen, Penzance, Cornwall, TR19 7SJ.
Menadew Menadu MENADUE Menardea Minidue F2555

114871 COLLINS Mr E J. 1 Larch Close, Chestnut Avenue, Summersdale, Chichester, PO19 4UE.
BISHOP Bran BRAND Brann BUNN CHANDLER Clayden CLAYDON COLLINS CREASEY Creasy Cresst CRONIN ENNEVER FRY GALVIN GIPPS GRAY Grey Halifax HALLIFAX HEARN Hearne HISCOX LINDLEY LUCKHURST NOEL PAGE PARKER SILK SKINNER SMITH Sulley SULLY SWAFFER Voak VOAKE Vouk Vouke WEATHERHEAD Wetherhead Wetherherd Whetherherd WILCOCKS Wilcox Willcocks Willcox Zolie Zullie F2389

114898 COLLINS Mr Ewen K. 24 Beveridge Road, Kirkcaldy, Fife, Scotland, KY1 1UX. Tel:0592-269209
BRUCE COLLINS CONSTABLE HINCHLIFFE HUNTER MACDONALD MUCKERSIE PRAIN WRIGHT F1077

114901 COLLINS Ms Gail. 508.5 Niagra Street, St Catharines, Ontario, L2M 3P5, CANADA.

Baccus BACKHOUSE BARKER BEAN BELL BENNETT BOSWELL BOULBY Bowlby CALLINGHAM CARR CATHERY Caundrel CHILDS CHITTY COLLINS COOPER Cousens Cousins COUZENS CRAVEN CROSSFIELD CUTLER Cuzens DAY DELL Denier Denyare DENYER DUNN DUTTON FRENCH Gandar GANDER HADDINGTON HALL HARTLEY Heartley HEPTONSTALL HILL HUNT JOHNS JOHNSON KNOWLES LAUNDREL LEARMOUTH Limbart Limbert LIMBORD Limbort LUNNON MAWSON MAY MITCHELL MOSEY MUSCHAMP MYERS NEWLAND PALMER PAWSON PECKET PETO PINK PITT PREECE PRESTON ROSE RUDSALE Seamor SEANOR SYKES TAYLOR THOMPSON THORNTON Tolson TOULSON TURTON Voakes Voaks VOKES WALKER WIGGIN WOOD F7396

114928 COLLINS Mr John H. 50 Tavistock Gardens, Ilford, Essex, IG3 9BE.
BEDFORD CAVE COLLINS Cubbadge CUBBAGE Gobel GOBLE KING PARLETT PHILLIPS PRESTON REASON TEDDER WEST F4651

114936 COLLINS Mr John. 15 Woodstock Crescent, Blackburn, Lancs, BB2 5AZ. Tel:0254-208479
BALDWIN COLLINS HARDACRE PINDER WALMSLEY F1917

114944 COLLINS Mrs Lyn. (Cullen) 26 Hurrell Court, Kingsbridge, Devon, TQ7 1HT.
AUGARDE BRUCE BUCK COLE COLLINE CULLEN POOLE SHAW SYMONS F5404

114952 COLLINS Mr P J. 86 Crossfields, Tarvin, Chester, Cheshire, CH3 8LQ.
MORRALL F4663

114960 COLLINS Mr Peter. 15 Hudsons, Tadworth, Surrey, KT20 5TZ.
PENDRILL F3288

114979 COLLINS Mr Reginald Godfrey. 25 Albert Road, Harlescott, Shrewsbury, Shropshire, SY1 4JD.
COLLINS HARRLOD JONES NORTON RUDKIN THOMSON WILEMAN F3198

114987 COLLINS Mrs S. 3 Alum Way, Bitterne, Southampton, Hants, SO2 5NL.
BALE BERRY BILLING BLACKMORE CORDWENT CULVERWELL DANIEL DAVIES EARELL FOSTER GAMLIN GRIFFITHS HONEY HURD LOOKE LUXTON SPURLE WAYMOUTH WITCH WYATT F3986

114995 COLLINSON Mrs Linda. (Rimmer) 26 Seaford Road, Eastbourne, Sussex, BN22 7JG. Tel:0323-21712
CHAPMAN COLLINSON REEVES RIMMER F4286

115002 COLLIS Mrs Diana. The Strawberry Fields, Pitt, Winchester, Hants, SO22 5QW. Tel:0962-860015
ADAMS ATKINS BARTON COLLIS EARLY FELLOWS FERRIS FINCH HALL HILL KIMBER MATTEWS NEWMAN PARKER PLOWMAN WILLFORD WOODGATE F4736

115010 COLLYER Mrs Ann. 370 Collangatta Road, Tugun, Queensland, 4224, AUSTRALIA. Tel:+61-75-342650
BERGER CHARLWOOD COLLYER FLINT KNIGHT SUMSION WARRIAN F4247

115029 COLSON Mr Stan. Po Box 1837, Leesburg, VA 22075, USA.
Colson CORSON F7258

115037 COLTHUP Miss Joan. 5 Church Lane, Rickmansworth, Herts, WD3 2PS. Tel:0923-774660
COLTHUP Coltrip Coltrup Coultrope F5678

115045 COLVER Mr Philip L. 52 Temple Meadows Road, West Bromwich, W Midlands, B71 4DG.
Calver Clover COLVER CRESSWELL Culver GORDON HARRIS Miler MILLER Morrison MORRISSON PARSONS PARTRIDGE PHILLIPS PLAISTEN F798

115053 COLWELL Mr Eugene A. Penn Lodge, 1 Hanley Terrace, Malvern, Worcs, WR14 4PF. Tel:06845-75819
Colewelle Colwall COLWELL F183

115061 COMBES Mrs Alison. (Renwick) Greensleeves, The Drive, Chichester, Sussex, PO19 4QB. Tel:0243-527323
DURELL GOULD MADGE WOODS F7443

115088 COMEADOW Mrs L. 21 Raymond Street, Noble Park, VIC 3174, AUSTRALIA.
OLIVER F7336

115096 COMER Mrs E. (Hummerstone) Flat 4, 67 Silverdale Road, Eastbourne, East Sussex, BN20 7EU.
BRAGG CAINES COMER GIBSON HUDSON HUMMERSTONE PICKARD SAVORY WESTON WILKINS F6331

115118 COMPER Mrs J. Elmtree Farm, Eastgate, Cawston, Norfolk, NR10 4HQ. Tel:0603-871236
BRINDELL Brindle CAIRNS COMPER COOK Cooke Cumber Cumper DAY DOUGLAS Hance Hanch HARRINGTON HAUNCH HOLDEN LAIDLAW NICHOLS Petit Pettit PETTY PURDOM SERJEANT F2780

115126 CONDUCT Mr Brian V. 35 Fourth Avenue, Denvilles, Havant, Hants, PO9 2QU. Tel:0705-473638
ALLEN AYRES BAILEY Baines Bains BAKER Banns BARBER BAYNES BEESON BLOXHAM BOBIN Boise Boyce BOYES Boys Boyse BRIGGS BRONSON Candlewick CARRE CHAMBERS CLARIDGE CLARKE CLAYSON Conchect Condie Conduc Conduck CONDUCT Condue Conduet Conduett Conduit Conduitt Condy CRIBB Cunditt CURTIS DE CARTERET DE GRUCHY Drelaud Drellet Drellett Drilliot Drilliott DRILLOT DUNKLEY DUREL ENOUF EYLES Foil FOSTER FOYLE GARNER GIBBINS GOVER GRIMMETT GROSSE GROSSIER GUILLE Hammond HAMON Hamptonne HANDS Haore HILL HOAR HOLLIS HOLLOWAY Hor Hore HUBERT INGROUILLE KNIGHT LA COUTURE LA FEUVRE LAMB LE BRUE LE HARDY LE PAGE LEBIREL LOVE MANNING MARRIOTT Mold Mole MOLLET Mould MOULE Moules NICOLLE PEEDLE PLOWMAN POINDESTRE RAWLEY RETILLY ROMERIL SAVAGE SHARP SMITH SPARVILLE SUTTON TIPLER URLWIN Vauss VOSS WALKER WATKINS WATTS WHIFFEN Whoore Whor Whore Wifen Wiffen F4604

115134 CONEY Mr Alan. Cheystone, Wick Road, Milborne Port, Sherborne, Dorset, DT9 5HG. Tel:0963-250475
BARNETT BULLIVANT COLLARD CONEY CROSSLAND JACKSON MACKWOOD NEWMAN WALTERS F6033

115142 CONGRAVE Mr Paul. 29 Prescelly Close, Nuneaton, Warks, CV10 8QA. Tel:0203-346197
ALLSOP ARGYLE ATHERLEY BAKER BARNETT BARRATT BARWELL BAXTER BAYLEY BILLIN BIRD CHAPMAN CLARKE CLAY CONGRAVE DAWSON DRAYTON EDWARDS ERASMUS FORSTER GILBERT HACKETT HAWFORD HIPKISS HOLT JENNINGS KING KNOWL LAGOE LINFORD LUDFORD MERRIMAN MERRYMAN MILLER MORGAN ORTON PAINE PEMBERTON PRATT REED RICHARDS ROBERTS SHERVYN SLINGSBY SMITH SPENCER STEVENS STORER STRINGER TOONE UPPERDINE VIERS WALLBANK WARD WHITE WILLIAMS YATES F1212

115150 CONNER Mr James. 9 Falstaff, Calderwood 15, East Kilbride, G74 3RL. Tel:03552-41179
Barrat Barratt Barret BARRETT BROWN CONNER Connor Conor FINEGAN Finnegan Graeme GRAHAM Grahame Grayme MARTIN O'conner O'connor O'conor Waters WATTERS F3637

115169 CONNOR Miss Diane. 29 Kings Road, Evesham, Worcs, WR11 5BP.
BURN COURT GILHESPEY HARRISON HEWITSON JOHNSON PAIN SHEKELL F2439

115177 CONSTABLE Mr W H. 62 Lyndhurst Avenue, Pinner, Middx, HA5 3XA.
CANNIFORD CONSTABLE CROCKETT DONOVAN GIBLETT HOBBS MARTIN MULLENS MULLINS SPRATLEY TWELFTREE F1498

115185 CONSTANTINE Mrs Ivy. 21 Newbold Avenue, Chesterfield, Derbyshire, S41 7AT.
CONSTANTINE COWERN FAULKNER FOSTER GOULD GREENFIELD HEATON JONES LUTHER ROBINSON WALTON WILLIAMS F4877

115193 CONWAY Mrs B. (Everitt) 6 Fairfield Place, Southville, Bristol, BS3 1LH.
BUTLER EVERITT MUTTER PALMER PICKEN TAYLOR WEEKS F2053

115207 CONWAY Dr Duncan. 36 Torrington Drive, Potters Bar, Herts, EN6 5HS. Tel:0707-52061
CONWAY DOVE LONGLAND SMITH STANFORD F3192

115215 COOK Mr Alexander. 21 Over Links Drive, Poole, Dorset, BH14 9QU. Tel:0202-700283
BUNTING COOK ROBINSON WILLIAMS WILSON F4382

115223 COOK Mrs Annette. (Richardson) Oakdale, Hazeley Heath, Hartley Wintney, Hampshire, RG27 8LS.
COOK RICHARDSON F1187

115231 COOK Mrs Annisabella. 110 Calf Close Lane, Jarrow, Tyne & Wear, NE32 4BS.
BRAY CARSON COOK CROSSLAND EDWARDS GRIFFITH LEIPER NIND PURVES SLACH F3427

115258 COOK Mrs Audrey. (Haigh) 16 Kensington Road,

Morecambe, Lancs, LA4 5LX.
BEEVER BENNET COLLEY COOK HAIGH MARTINS OATLEY PAGE SHEARN WINSLOW F4295

115266 COOK Mrs Jean M. (Rolland) 8 Regents Park Road, Southampton, Hants, SO1 3PN. Tel:0703-782061
Bascomb BASCOMBE Bascum Belet Belett Bellett BILLETT Billot BOWER BUNN BUSH CALLONS Catcut Catcute CATCUTT Childes CHILDS CHINCHEN Chinchin CHURCHILL Collins DARK Durant DURRANT ENGLISH FFEYETTE GARLAND Gilham Gilhem Gilhom Gillam GILLOM HOLT JAGO Jeffereys Jeffreys JEFFRIES JENKINS Kitkat LANDER Lesster LESTER MASTERS MEECH Moores MORES MORRIS Penney Penny PENY PITCHER PLAYER POLDEN SCOTT SMEDMORE STICKLAND STURMY Talbot TALBOTT WELLMANN WILLIAMS Wolfreys Wolfries Woolfreys WOOLFRIES F2247

115274 COOK Mrs M. 42 Whitham Park, Tavistock, Devon, PL19 9BP. Tel:0822-613888
BARTLET COOK PENWARDEN SHORT F4369

115282 COOK Mr Richard. 8 Regents Park Road, Southampton, Hants, SO1 3PN. Tel:0703-782061
AVARD BAKER BASS BURGESS BUTLER COCK COOK Cosham Coshum COSSAM Cossom Cossum DUKE ELFICK Elphick Elphicke Fennall Fennel FENNELL Fennil Funnell Hallibon HENLEY Hickman HICKMAR Hickmett Hickmore HOLLIBONE Holybone Horsecraft HORSECROFT Hoscroth JONES KETE MONDAY Pagdan PAGDEN PEENE PELHAM Pinck PINK Pinke POPE RAMSDEN RAYNER SHREWSBURY Shrosbury Shroseberie TATE Thompset Thompsett Thomsat Thomsett Tompset TOMPSETT Tomsat Tomsatt Tomset Tomsett Vennal VENNER Vinell WOOD F2246

115290 COOK Mr Robert. 105 Portland Road, London, W11 4LN. Tel:071-229-8272
ALLEN BADMAN Bodman CADELL Cadle CLEVERLY Codry COLES COOK Cowdery Cowdrey COWDRY DUCKETT FISHER GAY Gaye GLEED Golden GOLDING Goulding HISCOX Hitchcock HOLMES Kennet KENNETT LEIGH Lygh MITCHELL MORGAN PAGE PALMER Preest Prickter PRICTER Prictor PRIEST STONE TILLEY Tilly WAREHAM Wearham WITHERS F6098

115304 COOK Mr Stanley C. 4 Newark Road, Lowestoft, Suffolk, NR33 0LY. Tel:0502-569638
COOK LAMONT RUMSBY SCALES F6297

115312 COOKE Mr Anthony. 7 Ravenscourt Road, Canterbury, Kent, CT2 9DH. Tel:0227-761089
BROWN CLABON COOKE ENGLAND HOBDAY HOLLOWAY ROWLAND TANNER TWAITE WILCOX F3782

115320 COOKE Mr G. North Cottage, Monmouth Road, Longhope, Glos, GL17 0QF.
Pemble PIMBLE Pimblett Pymble F7203

115339 COOKE Mr Michael F. 21 Georges Hill, Widmer End, High Wycombe, Bucks, HP15 6BE.
COOKE F3423

115347 COOKE Mrs S C. 40 Greenfield Road, Little Sutton, South Wirral, Cheshire, L66 1QR.
BEAMAN BLEWART CLUCAS HAMBLEY HIND Hinde MOON RADCLIFFE WAINWRIGHT F4581

115355 COOKE Mrs Valerie Jayne. (Warrington) 13 Granary Close, Kibworth Beauchamp, Leicester, LE8 0HZ. Tel:0533-793008
ADAMS ALLEN BALFOUR BARNETT BARWELL BASS BETTLES BILLINGS BLOCKLEY BLOODWORTH CORKER DAWSON DUNNET GALE HADDON HUGGIN HUNT JOE LANGLEY MARSHALL MCCOMBIE MOLD MOORCROFT PALIN PENN RATH ROBERTS ROSEVEAR ROXBY SEAR SMITH THORPE WARRINGTON WEBSTER F424

115363 COOKSEY Dr Christopher. 7 The Leys, Basildon, Essex, SS16 4BN. Tel:0268-286125
COOKSEY FARRER WALLER F2795

115371 COOKSON Mr Edward A. 16 Windsor Road, Liverpool, L23 7TR. Tel:051-931-2152
ALCOCK ASHCROFT BUCKLEY BUDWORTH COOKSON GREENALL NEWTON F2578

115398 COOKSON Dr John. 13203 Heritage Woods Pl, Midlothian, Virginia, 23112, USA.
COOKSON F7088

115401 COOLEY Mr John. 10 Stockers Avenue, Winchester, Hampshire, SO22 5LB.
CLARKSON COOLEY FARMERY GORDON Hocknell HOCKNEY LOCKWOOD RENNOLDSON ROSEBERRY SCOTT F4810

115428 COOMBE Revd M T. 8a Furze Road, Maidenhead, Berks, SL6 7RY. Tel:0628-21434
HILTON F3546

115436 COOMBES Mrs Loveday. (White) Summerhayes, 31 Essa Road, Saltash, Cornwall, PL12 4EE. Tel:0752-843580
ARSCOTT COOMBES MORTLEY WHITE F6119

115444 COOMBS Mr Brian. 12 Gorway Road, Walsall, W Midlands, WS1 3BB.
COOMBS GREENHAM HIGGS HORRELL SHIELD F2745

115452 COON Mr George Vernon. Pendower, Knowle Close, Ashburton, Devon, TQ13 7RA. Tel:0364-52987
BULLOCK COON Coone Coun Coune Cune Kewn KEY F635

115460 COONEY Mr Steve John. 73 Station Road, Tempsford, Sandy, Beds, SG19 2AX.
BARON BARRY BINGHAM CLARK COONEY DELLAR DELLER DIXON HOLLAND JEFFORD MARCHANT OLIVER OSBORN PARKER POTTER RAYNER RAYNOR SHARP SIRED SIRET STOCKWELL TAUNT TUNGATE WOODCROFT F6067

115479 COOPER Mr A T R & Mrs A M. 81 Kirkby Folly Road, Sutton In Ashfield, Notts, NG17 5HP. Tel:0623-555287
ALLCOCK COOPER DEWICK HIND HOUSELEY VICKERS F3438

115487 COOPER Mr A. 8 Fishponds Road, Kenilworth, Warwickshire, CV8 1EX.
DADLEY Dadleye Dadlie Dadlye F6899

115495 COOPER Mrs Anne. 14 Mayfield Drive, Morecambe, Lancashire, LA4 6EP. Tel:0524-413964
ARCHER BROOKE DERRICK DISNEY HALE MCNAB MEAD Meads PERKS STUBB TOMLINSON TRICKETT F2533

115509 COOPER Mr C. 8 Adams Crescent, Torpoint, Cornwall, PL11 2DP.
COOPER PARTLOW RUMBLELOW F6452

115517 COOPER Ms Carol. (Twyman) 130 Rusthall Avenue, Chiswick, London, W4 1BS.
CLARINGBOLD LAW MONK MOORE PARGETER TWYMAN WALL WHITE F6056

115525 COOPER Mrs Grace. (Walker) 10 The Crescent, Sea Mills, Bristol, BS9 2JR.
ASHMAN COOK COOPER COX CROSS DEACON EDDY FORD GROVE HAMSHER HOSKEN JEFFERIES MAY MORRIS PARDOE SCUTTS SPERRING TYTE WALTER WHILLIER YOUNG F4287

115533 COOPER Mrs Iris. (Mcevoy) 23 Gibson Crescent, Elworth, Sandbach, Cheshire, CW11 9HW.
KEENAN MCEVOY STARLING WEBB WIGGINS F4301

115541 COOPER Mrs Janet. 78 Selwyn Crescent, Welling, Kent, DA16 2AN.
ANDERSON CARDER COOPER EVANS FRENCH LEVERETT PAICE PETERS SHOREY YEATES F4770

115568 COOPER John. 59 Ghyllside Avenue, Hastings, East Sussex, TN34 2QB.
Bog BOGG Bogge Boggs Bogs F7165

115576 COOPER Mrs M. 366/2 Taylor Avenue, Te Awamutu, Waikato, NEW ZEALAND.
BRAZIER CLARK COLLEDGE COOPER CROME DAVIS GOODRICK GREGORY HISCOCK HOLLIDAY HUNT MILLS PERKINS PHILLIPS REED SELLARS SIMMONS SIMPSON SMITH WILLIAMS F5172

115584 COOPER Margaret. 30 Crosland Hill Road, Crosland Hill, Huddersfield, W Yorks, HD4 5NU. Tel:0484-654585
CRAMPTON KENNEDY F3091

115592 COOPER Mrs Margaret. (Thompson) 81 Burniston Road, Newby, Scarborough, N Yorks, YO12 6PH.
APPLEYARD BRIGGS GILL GOSNAY LEDGAR LEDGARD THACKREY THACKWRAY THOMPSON WRIGHT F3805

115606 COOPER Mrs Myrtle. 33 Cross End, Wavendon, Milton Keynes, Bucks, MK17 8AQ.
ALDRIDGE ANDREWS ANNETTS ATKINS BABYSTOCK BAILY BALDWIN BANBURY BARNETT BOLTER BOWLEY BURNINGHAM BUTCHER CANON CHURCH COOK CROOK DALY EARWOOD FLETCHER FRINDLE GIDDENCE GODDARD GRAY GREEN GUNNER HARDING HARPUR HART HETHER HITCHCOCK HOUSE HUGHES JONES JUKES LAWRENCE LIGHT MASKELL MASON MAYE MCCORMICK MEADS MOORES NEWMAN NORTH OATES PIBWORTH PITHOUSE SANGER SAWYER SCOTT SMITH STEER STONESTREET STRONG SUMMERFIELD THOMAS TILLIN TOMSON TOWERS TOWNSEND WERRELL WHEELER YEATMAN F1019

115614 COOPER Mr Nigel J. 13 Wroxham Drive, Upton, Wirral, Merseyside, L49 0TS.
BALDWIN CLUTTON COOPER DAVIES EDIS HOWARD JEENS JONES LING MIDDLEDITCH PARKER SAYER SMITH START THOMAS WATSON WILLIAMS WOOLNOUGH WYATT F5247

115622 COOPER Mr Peter F. 68 Eastfield Drive, Pontefract, West Yorks, WF8 2EZ. Tel:0977-700702
BARR BILLANY COPLEY JONES KIRK KIRKE F4565

115630 COOPER Mr W. Lydebrook, Malthouse Bank, Little Wenlock, Salop, TF6 5BN. Tel:0952-505442
COOPER Couper Cowper Millar MILLER Ramsel RAMSELL Romsel Romsell Rumsel Rumsell TALBOT F418

115649 COOPEY Mr Ronald Henry. 68 Tredegar Road, Wilmington, Dartford, Kent, DA2 7AZ.
Coopay Coopee COOPEY Coupey CRAY SMITHERS WEEDON F1138

115657 COOPS Mr Philip. 4 Lakeside, Betley, Crewe, Cheshire, CW3 9AH. Tel:0270-820600
COOPES COOPS COUPES COUPS COWPES COWPS F328

115665 COOTER Mr Stephen. 20 Pine Road, Strood, Rochester, Kent, ME2 2HX. Tel:0634-710009
Cootar COOTER Cootter Coutar Couter Coutter F6073

115673 COOZE Mr Reeve & Mrs Nola. (Clarke) 193 Kiripaka Road, Tikipunga, Whangarei, NEW ZEALAND. Tel:+64-9-437-0284
BOOKER CLARKE Coose COOZE Couse CUNNINGHAM ELLISON GRIFFITHS Knef Knieve Knife Kouse NEAVE Neeve WALTERS F4458

115681 COPE Mr & Mrs E F. (Dimes) 19 Highmead Avenue, Newton, Swansea, SA3 4TY.
ABBOTT Aley BODGENER BULL CARTER CASE COPE CROCKER Dimers DIMES Dimmes Dismes Dymes Eley Ely FERREY Fichaw Fichew Fishaw Fishew Fishugh FITCHEW Fitzhugh GILBERT Hailey Haley Haly HEALEY HOUSDEN HOWSON HUNT JONES MCGREAL MORRIS MUNDEN NUNN SILVER TRAWLEY Trolley Trolly WEST WILSON F2666

115703 COPE Mr M E W. 66 Cranwells Park, Bath, Avon, BA1 2YE. Tel:0225-310083
Coap Coape COPE Copp Harden HARNDEN Hernden F2839

115711 COPELAND Mr Douglas Bruce. 8 Upper Park, Loughton, Essex, IG10 4EW. Tel:081-508-4053
COPELAND Coupland Kaupaland F5783

115738 COPELAND Mr Robert D. 33 Westfield Avenue, Ashton-In-Makerfield, Wigan, Lancs, WN4 9RH.
COPELAND JAMES JAMIESON SINCLAIR F3384

115746 COPHAM Mr Michael. 37 Crowcombe Road, Taunton, Somerset, TA2 7NH.
CAPON CHAMBERLAIN CHOPEN COBHAM COLES COPHAM GILL HURFORD JENNINGS LOWTON MODLEY MOWER PIKE POOLE PRING TROTT F4251

115754 COPPARD Mr D. Chez La Coude, Le Compas, 23700 Auzances, FRANCE, FRANCE.
COPPARD F6559

115762 COPPEN Mrs Christine. The Vicarage, St Mary Bourne, Andover, Hampshire, SP11 6AY.
BARKER BOREHAM CHAMBERLAIN CHAPMAN COLLEN COOKE COPPEN FAIRHEAD FRETTS Fritz GASTON GREEN HALSEY HAYNES HAZELL HENSHAW HOPSON HUGHES HUTCHIN MARTIN MOORE PHILLIPS RICHARDS ROGERS SAWYER STEVENS WARDLE WARREN WESTON F2693

115770 COPPING Mr Roy. 158 Shoebury Road, Thorpe Bay, Essex, SS1 3RL. Tel:0702-587882
Cabourne Caffyn Capan Capen Capin Capon Caponere Caponn Caporn Capoun Capping Cappinger Capyn Caupen Caupin Caupion Cawpen Chapyn Choping Choppen Choppin Chopping Choppinge Chopponn Choppyn Choppynge Chopyn Cobben Cobbin Cobbing Cobin Cobyn Cobynge Coffen Coffeyn Coffin Coffing Coffinge Coffyn Cofin Cofyn Coopene Cooping Coopinge Cooppin Cooppyn Coopppyng Coopyne Cop'yn Copan Copeians Copein Copeing Copen Copenal Copenger Copens Cophaen Cophen Cophin Cophynn Copians Copiens Copin Copine Copiner Coping Copinge Copinger Copingers Copings Copini Copinne Copins Copion Copon Copons Coppain Coppan Coppege Coppeinge Coppejans Coppen Coppener Coppengar Coppenger Coppenianssn Coppens Coppent Coppenzans Coppeynge Coppian Coppidge Coppien Coppims Coppin Coppine Coppiner Coppines COPPING Copping' Coppinge Coppinger Coppingers Coppinges Coppingg Coppings Coppinn Coppins Coppner Coppon Coppoyn Coppum Coppyn Coppynat Coppyne Coppyng Coppynge Coppynger Coppyngg Coppynggs Coppynn Coppyns Copyance Copyans Copyinge Copyn Copyne Copyng Copynge Copynger Copyns Copynson Copynyns Copyunore Cupen Cupenes Cupin Cuppeynge Cuppin Cuppyn Cuppyng De Coppinis De Coppum De Copun Keoppen Kipping Koppang Koppeians Koppeinge Koppen Koppin Kopping Koppyn Kopyn Kuping Kypping Kyppyng F1450

115789 COPPOCK Mr David F. 78 Broadmead Road, Blaby, Leicestershire, LE8 3AB. Tel:0533-772179
Cappock Cappocke Cappuch Cappuck Cobbet Cobbett Cobbick Cobbit Cobbitt Cobbut Coboke Cobot Cobut Cooppock Copack Coperoak Cophack Cophacke Copheick Cophocke Cophook Copock Copocke Copot Coppach Coppache Coppack Coppacke Coppaick Coppak Coppatk Coppeck Coppecke Coppert Coppick Coppicke Coppict Coppoch Coppochs COPPOCK Coppocke Coppocks Coppoe Coppok Coppoke Coppook Coppott Coppowe Coppuck Coppucks Copuch Corbet Corbett Corbit Cowpoke F5392

115797 COPSEY Mr David. Anstey Cottage, The Green, Catsfield, Battle, E Sussex, TN33 9DJ. Tel:0424-892516
Beamon BEAUMONT CLEVERLY COLVERSON Colverstone COOPER COPSEY Coverson Culverson EARL FINCH GOLLOP MARSH PETTIT SAWARD SCARFF SIMPSON TARGETT WINTER WOODGER Woodgier Woodier F2704

115800 COPSEY Mr J P. 86 Scrub Rise, Billericay, Essex, CM12 9PE.
Copsay COPSEY Copsie Copsy F7054

115819 CORBETT Mrs Grace E. 2240 Wilson Avenue, Salt Lake City, Utah, 84108, USA. Tel:+1-801-581-1418
ALLEN BLOODWORTH BRACKSTONE BROOKS CORBETT CRAIG CULLIS DAWES DREW FOSTER GEORGE GILL HIND NEVETT REYNOLDS ROE SOCKETT VIVASH WADE F4401

115827 CORBIN Mr Kenneth. 10315 Lagrange Road, Louisville, KY 40223-1226, USA.
CORBIN F7255

115835 CORBISHLEY Mr George. 25 Sandy Brook House, Off Tower Lane, Fulwood, Preston Lancs, PR2 4FT. Tel:0772-713206
CORBISHLEY F767

115843 CORBLE Mr Dennis George. 82 Winchester Court, Vicarage Gate, London, W8 4AF.
CORBLE GRUMITT WHYSALL F2006

115851 CORBY Mr Edward Walker. 21 Durham Terrace, Framwellgate Moor, Durham, DH1 5EH.
Corbey Corbie CORBY Korby F6873

115878 CORBY Mrs Joan. (Elsom) 41 Sanderson Close, Whetstone, Leicester, LE8 3ER. Tel:0533-848173
DALE ELSAM ELSOM JONES MORRISON RODGERS TOWNSEND F3395

115886 CORCORAN Mr Charles. 25 Hydethorpe Road, London, SW12 0JE.
CORCORAN Covernan CROUCH CULLEY Cully Elving ELWIG Elwigg GODDEN Grove GROVES JEFFERY KELLY PERRIN PIERCY REYNOLDS SMITH STEVENS WILSON F1283

115894 CORDING Mr R. 30 Leach Street, Blackburn, Lancs, BB2 3SE. Tel:0254-679803
BEAL CORDING GLANVILLE HARGREAVES LEATHER LOWE REED STAVERT STUBBS WHITFIELD F4326

115908 CORDWELL Dr John. 13 Haw Street, Wotton-Under-Edge, Glous, GL12 7AG. Tel:0453-842439
Cadel Candle Cardwell Caudell CAUDLE Caule Cawdle CORDWELL HEARSON HIMMINS F941

115916 CORFIELD Justin. 37 Miriam St, Rosanna 3084, AUSTRALIA.
CORFIELD F7256

115924 CORKE Miss Brenda. 42 Thistledown Grove, Hampton Dene, Hereford, HR1 1AZ.
BUNGAY CORKE F2102

115932 CORNALL Mrs Sue. (Royle) 45 Plumpton Avenue,

Blackpool, Lancs, FY4 3RB.
ANKERS BARDSLEY Barratt BARRET Barrett Corna CORNAH CORNALL Corner Gorna Gornah Gornall Gorner GRUNDY HARRISON HUGHES JACKSON Revit REVITT Rivet RIVETT Royal ROYLE SMEDLEY WATSON F2977

115940 CORNELIUS Mrs Pat. 32 East Holme, Erith, Kent, DA8 3NR.
CABLE CORNFORD HINE MUSSELL PETTITT SEYMOUR WOOD F1228

115959 CORNEY Mr David. 27 Woodside Road, Plaistow, London, E13 8RX.
Glasan Glasen Glason Glassan Glassen GLASSON Glazan Glazen Glazon Glazzon F91

115967 CORNFORTH Mrs Margaret. (Burns) 13 Spencer Terrace, Takapuna, Auckland, 1309, NEW ZEALAND. Tel:+64-9-486-3415
BEERE BENNAS Bennis BLANCHARD BRACKENRIDGE Brackenrig BRIGGS CARR CORNFORTH DICKSON DOUGLAS Ferguson FERGUSSON FOWLER GRAHAM HARTAS Hartass Harters Hartis Hartiss Hoddles Huddleson HUDDLESTON Huddlestone JACK JEFFERSON Jeneson Jennerson JENNISON KEAN Lenane Lennan LENNANE Lennon MACKENZIE MATHESON MCGRIFFEN MUNRO MYERS NIVEN NIXON O'BRYAN ROBINSON ROGERS ROSS SHINNERS WALKER Wardele WARDELL Wardill WILSON F5495

115975 CORNISH Miss A. 70b King Henrys Walk, London, N1 4NJ.
Braikway Brakway BROCKWAY Brokeway Brokway CHIPCHASE COLLETT CORNISH DALBY Dobey Dolby Em EMBER EMM Emme FARLEY GARBET GILBERT HACON Haken Haking Hakon HINTON Leffin Leffing LEWIS LIFFEN Liffin Lifton Loffen LONGHORN Lyffin Lyffing Lyfton Madcalf Madcalfe Man MANN Mans MAUND MEDCRAFT Medcroft Metcalf Metcalfe MILLS Mitcraft Monday Munday Mundey MUNDY Newberry Newbery Newbory Newbury NOBORY Nuberry Nubory RAPER SMITH Standmore Stanmer STANMORE Stansmore Towick Trevick TREWICK Truick Tyrwhitt WITHERS WOODS F6076

115983 CORNISH Mr David. 21 Farfield Place, Newquay, Cornwall, TR7 1NY. Tel:0637-874823
CORNISH Cornys Cornysh F4469

115991 CORNISH Revd Roger. 216 Outland Road, Peverell, Plymouth, PL2 3PE. Tel:0752-773518
CLAYTON CORNISH Cornishe Cornisshe Cornysh Cornyshe Cornysshe FRANCIS HOAR LEE MATTHEWS MAY PARHAM RAYMONT-BAKER Wrayforde WREFORD F6246

116009 CORRY Mr Dominic. 1 Mount Pleasant, Lower Tremar, Cornwall, PL14 5HQ.
BEATTIE BENSON BUTLER CORRY EVANS JANE POWER ROBERTS SCAFF SMITH TREGURTHA F5615

116017 COSGROVE Mrs Janet. Lanes End, 6 Roundwood Grove, Hutton Mount, Brentwood Essex, CM3 2NE. Tel:0277-222387
BRUCKER CHAMBERLIN FRANKLIN KIRKE PENFOLD QUANTRILL F772

116025 COSGROVE Mr & Mrs Travers. (Davidson) 118 Kidmore End Road, Emmer Green, Reading, Berks, RG4 8SL.
Cooper Cosgrave COSGROVE COWPER DAVIDSON GEELAN RADCLIFF Radcliffe SAMPSON SINGER SPREAD SULLEFUN F4841

116033 COSKER Mrs Eveline Mavis. 9 Crossgate, Durham City, Durham, DH1 4PS.
MCDEARMID F4583

116041 COSS Mr Martin. 32 Rushton Road, Thronbury, Bradford, W Yorks, BD3 8JQ.
ANDERTON COSS FITZPATRICK HAYES F1661

116068 COSSAR Miss A. 49 Hendham Road, London, SW17 7DH.
Crossar CROSSER Crozar Crozer F7210

116076 COSSINS Mrs Mary. (Harding) Steeple Hay, Westwood Close, St Ives, Huntingdon, Cambs, PE17 4DQ.
CAMM Cofsins Cossens COSSINS Cousins Cufsons Cussons FENNELL HARDING KIMBER LOVE MARTINDALE PRESTON F4892

116084 COSSUM Mr Jeffrey K. Po Box 568, Sunbury, Victoria, Australia 3429. Tel:+61-03-744-4245
Cossam Cossom COSSUM F1186

116092 COTSELL Mrs Maureen. (Rowe) 6 Hailsham Road, Polegate, Sussex, BN26 6NL. Tel:0323-482686
ARMSTRONG COTSELL HEYWOOD MARE MORTIMER PAGE PRICE PUGH ROWE F1767

116106 COTTERELL Mrs Pamela. (Bidgood) 76 Butts Hill Road, Woodley, Reading, Berks, RG5 4NR.
BIDGOOD DRAKE DUNN EDWARDS KNIGHT KNOWLES F4532

116114 COTTON Mrs C. (Dunn) 38 Ashfield Road, Stoneygate, Leicester, LE2 1LA.
ANTHONY BRIDGE CLEGG DUNN FALLOWFIELD FOORD FOSTER FRANKISH GARBUTT HALL HELLIWELL HOLDER HOWE KILBURN KIRBY MARSHALL MASSER MILLS PARSONS PERRY Rider ROLFE RYDER Setchall SETCHELL SUGDEN SUTTON TAYLOR TOWNSEND WARDALE WATSON Weatherald WETHERALD WRIGHT F6112

116122 COTTON Mr Michael. Willow Green, The Warren, Ashtead, Surrey, KT21 2SG. Tel:0372-275553
BLANTACH BLUNTACH BLUNTISH COTTON-BLUNTISH F1198

116130 COTTON Mr Ross G H. 673 George Street, Burlington, Ontario, L7R 2V8, CANADA.
COTTON F7016

116149 COUCH Mrs Tracey. 11 Thornton Road, Girton, Cambridge, CB3 0NP.
PYERS F1269

116157 COUGHLAN Mr Brian. Halstead Place School, Church Road, Halstead, Sevenoaks, TN14 7HQ. Tel:0959-32429
CLAMP CLARK COUGHLAN COUGHLIN HUNTER MORVAN F1932

116165 COULL Mr Fraser. 12 Carbery Lane, Southbourne, Bournemouth, Dorset, BH6 3QG. Tel:0202-424152
BRADFORD BUCHAN COULL FORD MAIDEN PARKER SMITH THAIN TRACHAN F2269

116173 COULTHARD Mrs Jill. (Mulliss) Millbrook, Station Road, Verwood, Dorset, BH31 7PU.
AERAY ASKEW BASSETT BENSON BRIGGS Brockbank BROCKLEBANK CASE CHAMBERS Colthart COOPER COULTHARD Coulthart COWARD FOX GARNER GOAD GRICE HERBERT HEWITT HILL HODGSON HUNT IVES LEWTHWAITE MACQUEEN MEGGISON Mennill METCALFE Meynell Minnell MOBBS MONNELL MOORE MOORHOUSE MOSSOP MULLISS NEATE NEWTON OUTRAM Owtram PARKER PARRY PHIPPS POSTLETHWAITE RICHARDSON ROBERTS ROBINSON SCREATON SIMPSON SMITH SWEET TANSER TOON WADDY WALKER WARD WILKINSON WILLIAMS F1350

116181 COUPE Mr C F. 4 Aldersley Close, Findern, Derby, DE6 6QD. Tel:0283-702730
BURBIDGE BURGESS Coop Coope Cope Coup COUPE Cowp Cowpe RIDGWAY STEVENS WHITE F4433

116203 COUPE Mr Raymond R. 8 Brockham Lane, Betchworth, Surrey, RH3 7EL. Tel:0737-843141
Coup COUPE Cowp Cowpe FINCH F4249

116211 COURT Mrs Jean. 31a Little Stoke Lane, Little Stoke, Bristol, BS12 6HS. Tel:0272-759301
COURT KAY URCELL URSELL F324

116238 COURT Mrs Pauline A. (White) 53 Heath Court, Leighton Buzzard, Beds, LU7 7JR. Tel:0525-376883
CATER CHICK COURT FERRIER LOMBARD WHITE F2239

116246 COURTNAGE Mrs Sylvia. (Hall) 59 Davison Drive, Cheshunt, Herts, EN8 0SX.
GILLS HALL HOWCROFT RICHMOND RIDLEY ROBINSON F5599

116254 COUSINS Mrs Eileen. 23 Colne Avenue, West Drayton, Middlesex, UB7 2AJ.
BIGGS GREENHAM JENNINGS KERSLEY PLAISTER PLESTED THOMPSON F5326

116262 COUTTS Mr Alec. Kenneggy House, Rosudgeon, Penzance, Cornwall, TR20 9AR.
COATES COUTTS DONNELLY PURKESS F3913

116270 COVENTRY Mr Charles S. 27/1 Jamaica Mews, Edingburgh, Scotland, EH3 6HL. Tel:031-225-9414
MAITLAND F553

116289 COWARD Mr Maurice. 117g Rowley Way, Abbey Road, London, NW8 0SP.
CHUBB COWARD LEVER LYDFORD F552

116297 COWDREY Mrs Enid A. (Streatfield) 129 Hurst Road, Sidcup, Kent, DA15 9AQ.
BAKER BUCKSEY BUXEY COOK CORDELL Cowdery Cowdray COWDREY Cowdry CRABB DADSWELL FRANCIS HEARD HILLS KNOTT MCBEAN MILBANK Millbank MOORE PAVITT REED REYNOLDS SCOTT SHAW

Streatfeild STREATFIELD STREETFIELD Streitfield THOROGOOD VERRALL F3626

116300 COWELL Mrs Sally. 1 Mulgen Crescent, Bomaderry, NSW 2541, AUSTRALIA. Tel:+61-4-421-3275
DONNELLY FIELD FRASER GATENBY HOADLEY MOSELY NEWBERRY PERCIVAL PIOR STEAD F5479

116319 COWEN Mr Michael Easton. 30 Nab Wood Terrace, Shipley, W Yorks, BD18 4HU. Tel:0274-593937
EASTON SCOT F2473

116327 COWIE Mrs Vera. (Senior) Leighswood, Headley Fields, Headley, Bordon, Hants, GU35 8PT.
LEAR MAINWARING PETERKIN SENIOR F5891

116335 COWLEY Mrs J. Rosentithon, 6 Katherines Walk, Lechlade, Glous, GL7 3DA. Tel:0367-52016
CLEAVES COWLEY HEADFORD MARTIN PALMER PHILLIPS TREVORROW UREN F1206

116343 COWLEY Mrs L. Bywater, 12 Duval Place, Bagshot, Surrey, GU19 5LP.
SHROFF F6657

116351 COWLEY Mrs Margaret. 25 Foxford Crescent, Aldermans Green, Coventry, Warks, CV2 1QB. Tel:0203-663465
CALVERT CURRY DAVISON STEPHENSON WALKER F6408

116378 COWLING Mr Bryan. 18 Hydehurst Close, Crowborough, E Sussex, TN6 1EN.
BATES CHAPMAN COOMBER COWLING GARRETT JARRETT MATTIN RICHARDSON TOWNSEND F2003

116386 COWLING Miss Jennifer. 7c Irvine Place, Stirling, FK8 1BZ.
APPLEYARD BATTERSON BENN BRIGGS Buttery BUTTRY CLIFF COWLING GRIEVES HALL HART HOPTON MOLE OATES PARKINSON RATCHESTER SKEEN SMITH STAINSBY STEWART STRAKER TATE TODD F3670

116394 COX Brenda M. 52 Penn Hill Avenue, Lower Parkstone, Poole, Dorset, BH14 9NA. Tel:0202-746063
BARNES BARNEY BATES BEALE BLAKE BLANCHARD CARRINGTON CARVER CHAPPLE COURTIES COX CROKER FOLLETT GIDDINGS HARRIS HILLIER INGS JARMAN LAVINGTON LEJEUNE LOVELL MARTIN MATTHEWS MUCKLE PADDON PAPWORTH PENNELL PERRY POCOCK PUDDEFOOT QUICK REED REEDE SHAPLAND STRANGE TUCKER TWYNHAM WELSH WHIFFEN WORLAND F613

116408 COX Mrs Christine A. (Morgan) 22 Richard Cooper Road, Shenstone, Staffordshire, WS14 0NL. Tel:0543-480640
Bach BACHE COX DAVIDSON Davison GOUGH Halleren Halleron HALLORAN Halloron Higdon Highton HIGTON Holloran LAMBERT Lampert LANGFORD MARTIN MORGAN Philipps Philips PHILLIPS ROBERTS SNAPE SPRY F450

116416 COX Mrs H M. 11 Queens Road, Enfield, Middx, EN1 1NE.
ABBOTT BARRETT CAWLEY DYSON FELL FINCH GEARY LAYLAND LUCKING F2023

116424 COX Mrs Jan. 100 Fiddlers Folley, Fordham Heath, Colchester, Essex, CO3 5UF.
ALSTON Aston Austen CAREY Cary FISH MATTHEWS PARKER Rod RODD SALMON Sawden SELLEY SMITH SOWDEN F3170

116432 COX Mrs Margaret. 25 Trent Close, Higher Compton, Plymouth, Devon, PL3 6PB. Tel:0752-709573
BELLEW BENNETT BLIGHT BOWLEY Cock Cocks COX Coxe DEACON DINGLE Dolan DOLIN Doolen Doolin GLOVER HENSON LEE LOCK MAT Mats Matt Matts MICHEAU MITCHELL NOBLE Nobles PEARCE Pearse Pellew Penharood Penharwood Penhorad PENHORWOOD Shoot Shute SHUTT Squier SQUIRE Squires TUPLIN Tupling F4980

116440 COX Miss Marjorie. 41 Vincent Close, Hainault, Ilford, Essex, IG6 2SZ.
Ashin ASHLING BASEY Bassey COCK Cox FLIGHT Gascoigne Gascoine GASCOYNE Gosling Goslon GOSTLING STEARN Stern WOODCOCK WOOLNER Woolnough F4856

116459 COX Mr Michael G. 48 Evans Avenue, Allestree, Derby, DE3 2EN. Tel:0332-558450
COX PITTOCK F4657

116467 COX Miss Nancy. La Sagesse Convent, Abbey House, Romsey, Hants, SO51 8YB.
COX DENYER LEE PHILLIPS WHENT F3013

116475 COX Mrs Pauline. 38 Graylands, Woking, Surrey, GU21 4LS.
CHICK COWIN GRIFFIN HOLT HUDGIN HUTCHIN PLUMBLEY SKELHORN WESTMORE F6253

116483 COX Mr Peter. 37 Dickins Way, Horsham, Sussex, RH13 6BQ.
BUNN CLAY COOPER COX EEDE FITT HEMSLEY KNIGHT WEST F1901

116491 COX Mr R L D. 2 Thornleigh Road, Woolston, Southampton, SO2 9DH. Tel:0703-446111
COX F6754

116505 COX Mr Stanley. 43 Stanwell Way, Wellingborough, Northants, NN8 3DF. Tel:0933-278948
ADDISON BACKHOUSE BAKER BEVAN Brook Brooke Brookes BROOKS COCK Cocks Cox GARWOOD HORN Horne Larratt LARRETT LAWMAN Lowman Making Makings MAKINS Meaking Meakings Meeking Meekings PIKE Pyke Warn Warne WORN Worne F5008

116513 COX Mrs Thelma. 28 Laurelwood Road, Droitwich, Worcs, WR9 7SE.
ASHMORE BUTT COX HARRIS HEELEY HEWITT MADDOCKS MARTIN MILLS PRICE TURNER F2983

116521 COXALL Mr Peter. 51 Hardenhuish Road, Brislington, Bristol, Avon, BS4 3ST. Tel:0272-771434
COXALL F3632

116548 COXON Mr Peter. 11 The Pastures, Dringhouses, York, YO2 2JE.
BOURNE COXON ERRINGTON GRUNDY LEONARD MOODY RUTHERFORD SCORER SMYTH F2351

116556 COYNE Mr S. 449 Beake Avenue, Coventry, CV6 2HR.
COYNE F251

116564 COZENS Mr E D. 316 Gladstone Road, Barry, South Glamorgan, CF6 6NH.
COZENS F6857

116572 CRABB Mrs Beverley. (Looney) Matai Road, R D 2, Matamata, 2271, NEW ZEALAND.
BARRY BROUGHTON CHAMPION CRABB CRESSWELL GOLLOP HALCROW HOLMES LAWN LEGG LOONEY LUCKIN MABEY MCCABE REDHEAD SAMPSON TANFIELD VINECOMBE WELLS F5499

116580 CRABBE Mrs Annce C. (Wadham) 119 Wilderness Road, Earley, Reading, Berks, RG26 2RD. Tel:0734-874098
COLE COOPER Cowper Hearn Hern HORN Horne RATHEL Rathill Rathwell Rothell Rothill ROTHWELL Waddam Waddams Waddan Wadden Waddon WADHAM Wadhams Wadim Wadman Wrathwell Wrothall Wrothel Wrothwell F4782

116599 CRABBE Mr John. 2 Field End, Stourport On Severn, Worcs, DY13 8UD. Tel:0299-823248
CRAB Crabb CRABBE Craib F2448

116602 CRABTREE Mr N F. 28 Summerville Gardens, Cheam, Surrey, SM1 2BX.
AINSCOUGH ALLEN ASHURST ATTRYDE BOULDERSTONE BRIERLEY CAMPBELL CAUNCE CHADWICK CLAYTON COLE CORNER CRABTREE CREWE CULSHAW DE CARLE EDWARDS FARLEY FOUNTAIN GRADWELL HALEY HAMBLIN HAWKER HOY HYDE LEA LEWIS MORTBY OXFORD PASTON POOLE SEGUIER SLATER SOWERBY STEWART WHYTE WILKINSON WOODS F1817

116610 CRACKNELL Mrs Julie. 55 Hertford Road, Stevenage, Herts, SG2 8SE.
ALMOND CONLAN CRACKNELL MORNE RAWCLIFFE F1619

116629 CRAFER Mr L R. 40 Ashridge Gardens, Palmers Green, London, N13 4LA.
Crafar CRAFER Craffer Crapher F6991

116637 CRAGGS Mrs K E. (Young) 2 Buckland Rise, Pinner, Middlesex, HA5 3QR.
ACOMB ADKIN ATKINSON AVES BARNETT CARR CHARLTON CRAGGS CRISP DANIEL DAWSON DENT DODSWORTH ELLIOTT ELVIN Elwin EVERED Fairlamb FARLAM FLEMING GIBSON GILL HADDOCK HALL HODGSON HUNTER Irvin IRWIN JACKSON KAY KETTLEWELL KINDRED KITCHIN LOCK LOWTHER MAJOR MALCOLM MARTIN MILLS MORGAN NOALL NOBLE OATES ORCHARD PARKER PATTISON PEACOCK PEARSON PROUD QUICKE ROBINSON ROOF ROSEWALL ROWELL SCOTT SHAW SIMMONDS SPRAGGON STEVENS STOKER SUMERTON THOMPSON WATSON WELCH WILKINSON Windwood WINWOOD WRAY YOUNG F3975

116645 CRAGO Mr William John. 9 Pennor Drive, St Austell, Cornwall, PL25 4UW. Tel:0726-73605
CRAGO F4372

116653 CRAIG Mrs Carole. (Silvester) Rt 2, Vaughan Road, Canton, Georgia, 30114, USA.

Tel:+1-404-345-5330
ANDREWS ARMSTRONG COOPER COPNER COWPER DACBY DANCE DOKE GRIFFIN HALL HAZELHURST JENNINGS LINGARD MARSH NANGREAVE REEVES SEXCELLY SILVESTER WEAVER F3935

116661 CRAIG-MAIR Mrs V. Boundary House, Stodmarsh Road, Canterbury, Kent, CT3 4AH.
ADAMS BRIGSTOCK MARTIN F2343

116688 CRAIGHEAD Dr I B. 13 The Dorkings, Great Broughton, Middlesbrough, TS9 7NA. Tel:0642-712634
Craghead Cragheid CRAIGHEAD Craigheid F577

116696 CRAIGIE Mrs Stella. Craigielea, Finstown, Orkney Isles, Scotland, KW17 2EG.
LEARMONTH F1492

116718 CRAM Mr Nicholas S F. Flat 3, 7 Oak Terrace, Beach Street, Liverpool, L7 0HJ.
CRAM Cramb Crame Cramm F6885

116726 CRANE Mr Herbert F. 4 South Way, Holtspur, Beaconsfield, Bucks, HP9 1DE. Tel:0494-675160
BAKER CRANE FLAXMAN SEWELL WITTING F6348

116734 CRANE Mrs Marcia. (Weiss) 21 Oxford Street, Charters Towers, Queensland, 4820, AUSTRALIA.
BEMI BRADY BRIMMICOMB BURT BUTCHER CERNAN CHAPMAN COLLINS CRANE CUSHWAY DANFORD DOBBINS FARRINGTON GALVIN GILLFEATHER GILLIGAN GRAIEN GRIMES HANDEBO HONOREE JONES LEWIS MANSFIELD MCPHEE Mcphie MOLLOY MURRAY PIERPOINT RADFORD ROBINSON SMITH TOMLINS WAKELING WARD WETHERALL F5501

116742 CRANFIELD Ms J L. Rose Cottage, Church Street, Fenny Compton, Warks, CV33 0YE.
ABERY AXUP BATCHELOR BICKERTON BURGESS CALTHROP CALVERT Chickall CHICKLE COATES COOPER CRANFIELD CROSSLEY DAVIS ELLIOTT EMMETT FUELL GUNTRIP GUY HALSTEAD HARWOOD Haxup HOPPING IRONS KENDREW LEWIN Loader LODER NEALE RAW RIDING SADLER SALTER SHACKELL Shackle SIMS WADE WEBB WILLIS F722

116750 CRASE Mrs Denise. 125 Mcculloch Street, Broken Hill, New South Wales, AUSTRALIA. Tel:+61-8-088-1713
CRASE FARRELL FITZGERALD MURPHY SHANKS F5637

116769 CRATE Mr Paul. 8 Rosemary Terrace, Blyth, Northumberland, NE24 3DS.
CRATE HATT F2060

116777 CRAVEN Mr Maxwell. 19 Carlton Road, Derby, DE3 6HB. Tel:0332-255582
BURDETT EDGE Foreman FORMAN MIDDLETON PICKFORD TELLWRIGHT WHITEHURST F6265

116785 CRAWFORD Mr John. 368 Abergele Road, Old Colwyn, Clwyd, LL29 9LU.
CAREFOOT CARFOOT CRAFFORD CRAFORD CRAWFORD CRAYFORD CROFFORD CROFOOT Crofut CROWFOOT CROWFORD CROWFORTHE Crowfrothe KERFOOT YORK YORKE F291

116793 CRAWFORD Mrs Maureen. 4 Blythe Avenue, Cleveleys, FY5 2LL.
CRAWFORD HARDING KENNEDY LUNN SWINDEN WHITE F3303

116807 CRAWFORD Mrs S M. (Cross) Flat 1, Royal Jersey Golf Club, Grouville, Jersey.
CROSS JENKINS MAINWAIRING NOAD F6068

116815 CRAWFORD Mrs Susan. (Riggs) Southcott, 13 Loxford Road, Caterham, Surrey, CR3 6BH.
CRAWFORD FELLOWS JUDSON MOSES MOWBRAY PALMER RIGGS SYLVESTER TODD TREW F6198

116823 CREE Mrs A J. (Douglas) 104 Harbourne Gardens, West End, Southampton, Hants, SO3 3LZ.
ADAMS ANDERSON ATKINSON BARNARD BLACKLOCK BURROWS CHAPPLE CLOUGH CLUBLEY CREE CUMMINGS DIXON DOBSON DOUGLAS EMMERSON FLETCHER GRAINGER HOOPER HUTCHINSON JACKSON KEANE KING MOUNCER NOBLE PARKIN RANDALL RICKABY RITCHIE SADLER SCALING SIMPSOM TAYLOR TODD WEBSTER WHILDE WILEY WINWARD WREN F6448

116831 CREED Mr Philip T. 156 Hackthorne Road, Christchurch 8002, NEW ZEALAND.
CLACK COCK CREED DESBOROUGH GIBSON HOBBS HORROCKS IVETT IVITT KIELY KINNEAR LAVINGTON LENNOX MIDDLETON MILLNER PAPWORTH ROWTON TURPIN WENBORNE F1701

116858 CREEK Mr M L. 17 Bertram Drive North, Meols, Wirral, Merseyside, L47 0LN.
Creak Creake CREEK Creeke Creyke Crick Criyk F3738

116866 CRESSWELL Mr P S A. 28 Monreith Road, Glasgow, Scotland, G43 2NY. Tel:041-632-1990
ALEXANDER ANDERSON ARCHBELL BROWNLIE CHASSELS CHATAWAY COOK CRESSWELL DOUGLAS FENNEL LINDSAY Maccreadie Macready MARTIN Mccraddie Mccradie MCCREADIE Mccready Mccreddie Mccreddy Mccredie Mccredy Mcgraddy Mcgrady RAISTRICK ROBERTSON ROBINSON ROSS SIMPSON SIMSON SYMONDS TURTON WILSON F1582

116874 CRESWELL Mr Norman W. 5 Shelley Grove, Loughton, Essex, IG10 1BY. Tel:081-508-1157
CRESWELL F901

116882 CREWE Ms Anne. (Row) 11 Wrenswood, Wildwood, Stafford, ST17 4HT. Tel:0785-665400
CREWE LANGLEY ROW F6550

116890 CREWS Mr A J. 106 Ridgeway Road, Rumney, Cardiff, South Glamorgan, CF3 9AB.
Crew CREWS Crewys Cruse Cruyes F7174

116904 CRICHTON Mr A W. 17 The Summit, Baldwins Hill, Loughton, Essex, IG10 1SW. Tel:081-508-6197
CRICHTON F4087

116912 CRICHTON Mr Douglas. 45 Knockside Avenue, Paisley, Renfrewshire, PA2 8LP. Tel:041-884-2272
ALLEN Creichton Creighton CRICHTON Crighton CULVER DIVER FRY HARWOOD KENNEDY O'sullivan Roach ROCH Roche SULLIVAN THREADER Thredder Treader Tredder F5349

116920 CRICHTON-HARRIS Ms Ann. Po Box 219, Columbia Falls, Maine, 04623, USA. Tel:+1-207-483-4009
AKERS ALLEN BELL BROCKBANK BURNS CHRISTOPHERSON CLOAK CLOKE COPELAND DAVIES DENTON FARRER GARVETH GUMMOE HARRIS KITTO LLOYD ORD PUNSHON READ TANDY TRUSCOTT WALSH F5481

116939 CRICK Mr Derek. 33 Meadows Road, Heaton Chapel, Stockport, SK4 5DN.
CRICK F86

116947 CRICKMAY Mr R J. 1 Henley Road, Sandford On Thames, Oxford, OX4 4YN.
CRICKMAY F1124

116955 CRIGHTON Mrs C. (Sone) 21 Davies Street, Charters Towers, Queensland, 4820, AUSTRALIA. Tel:+61-7-787-3379
OCOCK SONE F5459

116963 CRIGHTON Mr G. 68 Stamford Avenue, Springfield, Milton Keynes, Bucks, MK6 3NH. Tel:0908-666047
Creighton Crichton CRIGHTON Criton Cryton Simcens Simkin Simkins Simpkin SIMPKINS Sympkins F605

116971 CRIPPEN Mr John. 4 Whitethorne Avenue, Coulsdon, Surrey, CR5 2PP. Tel:081-660-6909
CRIPPEN F6436

116998 CRISFIELD Mrs Jean. (Piller) 87 Downsview, Luton Village, Chatham, Kent, ME5 0AL. Tel:0634-408752
CHRISFIELD CRISFIELD DUVAL DYER HINDMARSH MORRIS PILLAER PILLER F5264

117005 CRISP Mrs Betty U. 16 Agars Place, Datchet, Slough, Berks, SL3 9AH. Tel:0753-40784
ALLEN BACCHUS BILLINGTON BLACKSHAL BROWN CLARK COX DEWICK ELLIS EVITTS HOLLAND JOHNSON KINGSBURY LANGLEY LAWTON LIGHTFOOT MOSSMAN POINTER ROSS RUFFHEAD SAVAGE SHAVE TODD TURNHAM WHITBREAD WILLIAMS WISE WOODLAND F3142

117013 CRISP Mrs G R. 16 Agars Place, Datchet, Slough, Berks, SL3 9AH. Tel:0753-40784
ADCOCK ALDERSON AMOS BALDING BELL BRIDGES BULLOCK CHURCH CLARK COOPER CRISP DANIEL DAW FISH FOWLE GREEN HAMMOND HARRISON LAKE MASTERS MAYES MELTON MUER SHEPHARD WELLS YOUNGS F2804

117021 CRITCH Mr J. 119 Battenhall Road, Worcester, Worcs, WR5 2BU. Tel:0905-351737
Chreche Chretche Chriche Chritch Chryche Crich Criche CRITCH Crych Cryche Crytche F3226

117048 CROCKETT Mr Jack A H. 28 Bilbrook Grove, Weoley Castle, Birmingham, B29 5RN. Tel:021-427-7050
ADKINS Crockat Crockert Crocket CROCKETT Crockhett Crockit Crockitt DAY DYSON LEWIS

MILWARD MORRIS POWELL PURSELL WILLETS F316

117056 CROCOMBE Mr David. 29 Bury Road, Epping, Essex, CM16 5ET. Tel:0992-576720
Crockham Crocomb CROCOMBE Crocome Crocumb Crowcombe De Craucombe DE CRAUCUMBE De Crawecumbe De Crewecombe F1108

117064 CROFTON Mr C Robin. 8 Wynbury Drive, Totteridge, High Wycombe, Bucks, HP13 7QB. Tel:0494-533775
AGAR BEST BOWDEN BUCKHAM CROFTON DAVIDSON FLEMING GRAY F2743

117072 CROFTON Mrs Carol T. (Hodge) 8 Wynbury Drive, Totteridge, Hihg Wycombe, Bucks, HP13 7QB. Tel:0494-533775
ALLEN CHEFFINS COTMAN HOYLES JACKSON JOHNSON LOWE REED F3566

117080 CROME Mr Geoffrey F. 6 Rutherford Road, Cambridge, CB2 2HH. Tel:0223-841331
CROME F4685

117099 CROMPTON Mr F. 118 Saddle Mews, New Castletown Road, Douglas, Isle Of Man. Tel:0624-661519
BANKS CLARKE CROMPTON DIMELOW HORABIN O'NEILL ROGERSON VARLEY F6181

117102 CROMPTON Mrs J A. 1 Pegelm Gardens, Hornchurch, Essex, RM11 3NU.
GLASCOCK Glasscock F7048

117110 CRONIN Mrs Teresa. (Ebbutt) 78 Central Treviscoe, St Austell, Cornwall, PL26 7QP. Tel:0726-823855
AMIES BANGHAM BEASLEY BEER BERRY CARTER Ebbatt Ebbert Ebbet Ebbetts Ebbit Ebbitt Ebbot Ebbott Ebbut EBBUTT Ebert Ebet Ebott Ebottes Ebytt Hibbit Hibbitt Hibbot Ibbet Ibbett Ibbitt Ibbot Ibbott Ibet Ibot Ibott JULL KENNEDY LINOM NORTH O'SULLIVAN Piotvain Podevin Poitvine Pordvine Portwine Potisain Potvine PUTWAIN SCADDAN SCADDING Scaddon Scadeng SKINNER SULLIVAN WENMAN WILLIAMS F4802

117129 CROOK Mr B. Village Fold, Kirkby Fleetham, Northallerton, N Yorks, DL7 0TX.
CROOK FREEMAN JONES KAY NAYLOR ROYLE SAGGERSON F5248

117137 CROOK Mr Gwyn. 10 Brookside, Tonteg, Pontypridd, Mid Glamorgan, CF38 1PB. Tel:0443-202215
ARTHUR BADGER BALL BARTLETT BODYCOMBE CARTER CROOK DAUGHTON DAVID DODD ENNIS HARDING HOLMES HUGHES HUNTLEY JENKINS JOHN JONES LANGLEY LEWINGTON PHILLIPS PIKE PRICE RODGERS TARRANT THOMAS TURNER WILLIAMS F4335

117145 CROOK Mrs Sheila. (Stones) 109 Crossdale Road, Breightmet Fold, Bolton, Lancs, BL2 5ND.
BANKS BESWICK BIBBY BOW CROOK DAVIDSON FAIRCLOUGH GIDMAN HIGSON HOLDEN HOLLAND HULME KAY KELLY KNOTT MAKINSON MATHER NEVILL ORMROD PARK PARNELL QUAKETT RIGBY STEPHENSON STONES STOTT SYDDALL TOOTHILL TYSON WARD WINTERBOTTOM F1918

117153 CROOM Mrs Janis. 59 Redditch Road, Stoke Heath, Bromsgrove, Worcs, B60 4JP.
BREWIN CROOM DAVIDSON DODDS SAWYER WEST F1902

117161 CROSBY Mr Dennis. 4 Parkside Close, Cottingham, N Humberside, HU16 5PH. Tel:0482-846334
BEEDLE CLARK COLLINSON CROSBY ESKDALE ESTILL ROBINSON THOMPSON F4248

117188 CROSS Craig. 72/4 Rose Street, Edinburgh, EH22 3JG.
CROSS DUCAT ELDER HEGGIE MELVILLE WALKER F1320

117196 CROSS Mr David A. 75 Crosslands Park, Barrow In Furness, Cumbria, LA13 9LB. Tel:0229-822694
ALCOCK ASHWORTH BAKER BINKS BROWN CALDCLEUGH CHORLEY CHURCHYARD COCKBAIN COOK CROSS DODGSHON DRINKWATER FENWICK FURNIVAL GHENT GRICE GUNSON HARROP HAYES HAZARD HEYS HICKSON HUMBLE Joinson JOYNSON KAY NEILD NEWTON PARKER PARKIN RAWLINSON SAWREY SCOTT SWEAINE SWINDELLS TELFORD THOMPSTONE TOWNLEY TYLER WATSON WEIGHELL F488

117218 CROSS Mr David. West Wing, Isel Hall, Cockermouth, Cumbria, CA13 0QG.
ASHWORTH BINKS CALDCLEUGH CROSS FURNIVAL GUNSON HAYES HITCHSON NEWTON WATSON F5719

117226 CROSS Miss E. 31 Abbotsbury Road, Broadstone, Dorset, BH18 9DB.
CROSS HAYWOOD SHEPHERD F4080

117234 CROSS Mrs Marilyn. Rr#8, Brantford, Ontario, N3T 5M1, CANADA. Tel:+1-519-753-6914
BAKER BANNISTER BENNETT BIGGAR BROWN CARNOCHAN CORNWELL CROSS EVANS FENWICK FOX Glaize GLASS HARTLEY HENRY JACKSON JARVIS JENNINGS JULL MCDOWELL MOORE MURRAY SHAW SKINNER SMILEY SMITH STANBRIDGE STARR Thompsett THONE Tompsett TOMSETT WARD WILDMAN WILSON WOOD YATES F4479

117242 CROSS Mr Norman. 285 Wollaton Road, Wollaton, Nottingham, NG8 1FS. Tel:0602-281734
Crofs CROSS DAY RAYMENT SAUNDERS TRUMAN F6285

117250 CROSS Mrs Rosemary Ann. (Burton) Alveare, Bridgewater Road, Dundry, Bristol, BS18 8JP.
BEADLE BURTON MASON THROSSELL WRIGHT F4511

117269 CROSS Mr William. 6 King Henrys Drive, Rochford, Essex, SS4 1HY. Tel:0702-542131
ARCHER CROSS HARRIS LOW REMINGTON RICKARD ROCKETT ROSE SHIP TAYLOR F6144

117277 CROSSLAND Mrs N J. 35 Sherwood Road, Grimsby, South Humberside, DN34 5TG.
CROSSLAND DINGMAN EAST GARRETT ROWE F3910

117285 CROSSWELL Mr Michael. Appletree Cottage, Wyeford Avenue, Charter Alley, Basingstoke Hants, RG26 5PZ. Tel:0256-850206
CARSLAKE Crasswell Craswell Crofswell CROSSWELL Croswell F1399

117293 CROUCH Mrs Linda. (Ballard) 286 Grange Road, Guildford, Surrey, GU2 6QZ. Tel:0483-233863
BALLARD BRYANT CROUCH GIBBS GILES IVES REMNANT TURNBULL F6364

117307 CROUCHER Mrs Eileen. 11a Burney Bit, Bamber Heath, Basingstoke, Hants, RG26 6TJ.
BUNCE CLEVERLY CROUCHER HALL HARRIS HOLLOWAY JEFFERIES LUSH PAGE F1383

117315 CROUCHLEY Mr R W. 6 Lambourn Gardens, Harpenden, Herts, AL5 4DQ. Tel:0852-713059
BRAND Critchley CROUCHLEY Crutchley GREIG Humfreys Humfries HUMPHRIES POINTON Sais SAYCE Sayse F2085

117323 CROUCHMAN Mr Ted. 95 Allenby Road, Southall, Middx, UB1 2EZ. Tel:081-578-2948
BERRY BRIGGS CROUCHMAN CUNNINGTON-CROSS FISHER-ROWE MERRIMAN RACHER ROWE SEAGER VARLEY F391

117331 CROWHURST Mr Leslie J. 11 Grasmere Close, Dunstable, Beds, LU6 3AP.
BARDEN CROWHURST HUMPHREY LOCKTON MATHEWS PEERLESS READ F486

117358 CROWLEY Mr D D. St Judes, Mill Lane, Shoreham By Sea, W Sussex, BN43 5AG. Tel:0273-455256
COX DICK LIGHT TRIPP WIGFULL WOODVILLE F2683

117366 CROWLEY Mrs Kathleen. (Smith) 10 Church Hill, Wroughton, Swindon, Wiltshire, SN4 9JR. Tel:0793-814363
BURRY CODDINGTON CROWLEY HARRIS HARVEY KIRBY SALTER SMITH WEST F2592

117374 CROWLEY Mrs Sheila. 53 Boxted Road, Hemel Hempstead, Herts, HP1 2QL. Tel:0442-60923
BYE GREENSMITH HICKS LACEY MATTHEWS MORAN OLIVER TELFORD F395

117382 CRUDGE Mr W. 35 Saskatoon Place, East Kilbride, Strathclyde, G75 8LP.
CRUDGE F3272

117390 CRUMP Mrs Alma J. 10 Riverside Drive, Wilmington, Delaware, 19809, USA.
CRUMP FRANCIS HIGNELL ROGERS SMITH F6361

117404 CRUMP Mrs Jose. 11 Newquay Road, Park Hall, Walsall, W Midlands, WS5 3EL. Tel:0922-32274
ADDISON Addisonne ATKINS Bailey BARKER BAYLEY COOPER HARRIS Hirdley Hoardley HOLT HORDLEY Hubard HUBBALL Hubberd Huberte HUNTBACH Hurdley Hurlye JAMES JONES KEELING MERRY Mickelwricht MICKLEWRIGHT Micklwright OLDFIELD Ouldfield PICKERING PIGG POOLER Pouler RILEY Ryley SHAW SHUTT SMALLSHIRE Steadman STEEDMAN SUTTON TURNER WORTHINGTON WRIGHT YATES F1637

117412 CRUMPTON Mr Michael. 17 Wragg Court, Cam, Dursley, Glos, GL11 5PN. Tel:0453-548613
CRUMPTON F5762

117420 CRUTTENDEN Mr Ian. 43 Eastcote Drive, Harpenden, Herts, AL5 1SE.
Crittenden CRUTTENDEN F7085

117439 CRUXTON Mr P. 73 Brown Avenue, Church Lawton, Stoke On Trent, ST7 3ER.
Crackstone Craston Crastone Craxton Crokson Croston Croxom Croxon Croxson Croxstone Croxton Cruckston Cruckton Cruston Cruxden Cruxen Cruxon Cruxsonne Cruxston Cruxstonne CRUXTON Cruzston F733

117447 CRYER Revd Mr Neville. 14 Carmires Avenue, Haxby, York, YO3 8NN. Tel:0904-763371
BARKER CRYER DUCKWORTH RISHTON STOODLEY F4929

117455 CRYSLER Mrs Ethel. (Fortier) 1319 Pingree, Lincoln Park, MI 48146, USA.
Tel:+1-313-386-1491
CAMPBELL WHITE WHYTE F5626

117463 CUBITT Mr W H. 14 Church Rise, Ryton, Tyne & Wear, NE40 3DW.
BISHOP CUBITT ELLIOTT GARBUTT GIBB HIGH LOUND SHARPE THOMPSON WILKINSON F713

117471 CUFF Mr David. 44 Pennington Walk, Retford, Notts, DN22 6LS.
BUGG CADDIE Caddy Cadie Cady COOMBES COX CRUMP CUFF Cuffe DYER GAULER GIBSON HARRIS HUTCHINSON NOTLEY Nottley PHILLIPSON SIMS F932

117498 CUFFE Mr J G. 16 Ty Yr Sarn Road, Rumney, Cardiff, CF3 8BD.
Cuff CUFFE Cuffey Culf F6871

117501 CUFLEY Mr David R. 55 Broomhill Road, Dartford, Kent, DA1 3HT. Tel:0322-223292
COCKE COCKS Couffley Coufley CUFFLEY Cuffly Cufflye CUFLEY Cufly Cuflye GALE PICTON RUSSELL WHEATLEY F7

117528 CULLEN Joan. South West Barn, Crowlink, Friston, E Sussex, BN20 0AY. Tel:0323-422318
BARTER Bowden BUSHROD COE COUCH CULLEN MILL MULES Noak NOAKE Nocetter Nocyter Noke NOSSETTER Nossiter Peddle Piddell PIDDLE Pydele Pydell Rapsey Rapsin RAPSON Rapsyn REDSTONE RUSSELL Voaden VODDEN Voddon Voden Vodin Vouden Vousden Vowden Wrapson F3194

117536 CULLEN Mrs Joanne. Charteris, 30 Daltons Fen, Pitsea, Essex, SS13 1JF. Tel:0268-727765
COOKE CROWDER LAKE Snelgar Snelger Snelgrau Snelgrave SNELGROVE Snellgrove F2486

117544 CULLEN Mr Michael. 9 Decoy Drive, Eastbourne, E Sussex, BN22 0AB.
CULLEN CULLING F526

117552 CULLEN Zenda. 6 Ahmell Road, East Tamaki, Auckland, NEW ZEALAND.
HOVENDEN F7296

117560 CULLEY Mrs Carole. (Fisher) 46 Brook Road, South Benfleet, Essex, SS7 5JF.
ALEXANDER ANDERSON CANDLER CASTLE COLLINS COOK Cooke CRAWLEY DREW DUDLEY FISHER GERAUGHTY HARBOUR HEWITT IVES JOHNSON KING LISSAMAN LLOYD MEREDITH MOBBS PRINCE RAWLINGS RICHARD SCROOM SMITH STANBROOK STEVENS TAFT TUCK WILSON YATES F2350

117579 CULLIFORD Mr J R. 34 Meadowland Road, Henbury, Bristol, BS10 7PP. Tel:0272-501963
ABBOT ALLARD AYLES BENISON BEST BRADBEER COURTNEY CRABB CULLIFORD DAUNCEY DEWES DRURY EMERY GOSS GOULD HODDINOTT Hooper HOOPPER HOPKINS HOWARD INGRAM JEVON LAWRENCE LOCK MALTWOOD MARCH MILLS MOSS NEAT PENNY POPE RICHARDS Shade Shares Shaves SHEAVES SHUTE Tooze TUCKER TWOSE WEBB WESTOVER WHELLER F261

117587 CULLING Mr H. 11 Lisburn Lane, Tuebrook, Liverpool, L13 9AE. Tel:051-228-7771
BEESLEY BROWNBILL CHAPMAN Cooling Cullin CULLING DACK GLANISTER GOWANLOCK IRVING MICKLEBOROUGH QUICK F3745

117595 CULLINGHAM Mr G G. 54 Alma Road, Windsor, Berks, SL4 3HA. Tel:0753-863951
APPLETON BRANNEN CULLINGHAM FAIRWEATHER GORDON LEE NASSAU F222

117609 CULLIS-DIXON Mrs Margaret L. (German) 4 Gard Close, Barton, Torquay, Devon, TQ2 8QU.
Tel:0803-312411
APTER BRADY BROWN BULLOCK BURTON COLE COLLINS CULLIS DRAKE GARROD GERMAN GIDLEY GRAY HARRY HILMAN JOSE LAYMAN LEE MAIN MITCHELL MORRIS PARR PASCOE ROBERTS SHELVEY SIBLEY SKIPP SMITH SPARKES TREMBATH VINCE WOOLNOUGH F4887

117617 CULYER Mr J M. 84 Marlpit Lane, Old Coulsdon, Surrey, CR3 2HD.
BUTCHER COUSINS CULYER CUTMORE ELSE FISHER HOLLOWAY PLAYDON STANHAM TOWNROW WELDON WILLMORE F685

117625 CUMBOR Miss M A. 39 Newton Road, Great Ayton, Middlesborough, Cleveland, TS9 6DT.
Tel:0642-722274
BRADLEY Comber Crysoppe Cumber CUMBOR DUR Kersop Kersoppe KIRSOP Kirsopp Kirsoppe MIDDLETON SOWERBY STEPHENSON Stevenson THOMPSON WILD Wilde F5090

117633 CUMMINGS Mr B K. 209 Bierley Lane, Bradford, West Yorks, BD4 6DN.
BANTIN BURNETT CAWTHRA CLEGG CUMMINGS GILL PEPPER YOUNG F6460

117641 CUMNER Mrs Janet. (Lane) 32 Cove Road, Fleet, Hants, GU13 8RN.
BULL BURN BURNS CALLOWAY CUMNER CUSHWAY DULIEU LANE F4524

117668 CUNLIFFE Mr Ian. 3 Blackbridge Court, Blackbridge Lane, Horsham, W Sussex, RH12 1RH. Tel:0403-56598
BUCKLEY Conliffe Cunclife Cuncliff Cuncliffe Cunclyfe Cunclyffe Cundeclif Cundeclyve Cundliff Cundliffe Cunliff CUNLIFFE Cunteclyve HALLIWELL HARRISON Millar MILLER MILLINGTON Milner THOMAS WEBB F3421

117676 CUNLIFFE-JONES Mrs Gillian. (Jarvis) 43 Spalt Close, Hutton, Brentwood, Essex, CM13 2UN.
COOK Cooke Coot COOTE Gervase Gervis Jarves Jarvice JARVIS Jarviss Jervis ROSE ROWE STEDMAN WELCH Welsh WHITE F4438

117684 CUNNINGHAM Mr John A. 13 Waldegrave Gardens, Strawberry Hill, Twickenham, TW1 4PQ.
BAZLEY CALDWELL CARLIN CUNNINGHAM F6504

117692 CUNNINGHAM Mrs M. 10 Little Larkins, Mayhill Road, Barnet, Herts, EN5 2NS.
CUNNINGHAM WYBORN F3261

117706 CUNNINGHAM Mrs Sandra. (Bainbridge) 21 Fitzjohns Avenue, London, NW3 5JY.
Tel:071-794-8536
BAINBRIDGE Bainbrig Bainebrigge Bambrig Bambrigge Banbrig Baynbrig Baynbrigge Baynebrigge Beanbrig BELL Bembrig Bembrigge Benbridge Benbrig Benbrigge Beynbrig Brainbridge CLOWES HUDSON KENDAL SAGE F3816

117714 CURANT Mr R. 105 Harewood Road, Isleworth, Middx, TW7 5HN. Tel:081-560-1896
BRAY COWLEY CROCKER CROXALL CURANT FROUD HARRIS HAYNES HUNT JESSMAN JUDD KENT LEWIS PALMER PARSONS PEARCE SCALES SHELVEY SHEPHERD SMITH TURNER WITHE WOODCOCK WRAYER F1732

117722 CURETON Mr R. 44 Margaret Road, Wednesbury, West Midlands, WS10 7QT. Tel:021-502-0237
BATE BIRCHER BIRD CURETON FORKES GREGORY HIBBS PHILLIPS POWELL ROWLEY SIMKINS WOODFIELD F5840

117730 CURLE Mr & Mrs P. (Harris) 6 Kevin Close, Barnwood, Gloucester, GL4 7JA.
CURLE DENNIS GRIMSDITCH MOXEY ORMEROD PADGET WRIGHT F5707

117749 CURNOW Mrs Ann. (Burke) 755 Gold Street, Redding, CA 96001, USA. Tel:+1-916-243-2001
BATHY Bethy Bothy BOWDEN BURKE Chegwidden CHEGWIN CURNOW HOLMAN IVEY Old OLIVE OLIVER OULD RICHARDS TRELEGGAN VENSON Warne Wearn WEARNE F4649

117757 CURNOW Mrs E S. 200 Hill Street, Richmond, Nelson, NEW ZEALAND.
Bringloe BRINGLOW Brinklo F6742

117765 CURRAN W J. 73 North Linkside Road, Liverpool, L25 9NS.
BARR CHESWORTH Cullan Cullen Cullin CURRAN Curren Currin HOUHGTON Maccready Macready MCCREADY Mcready MOON Spear Spears Speer Speers Speir SPEIRS Spier Spiers VALENTINE F442

117773 CURRELL Mrs Jennifer. 13 Coombe Lane, Westbury On Trym, Bristol, BS9 2AB.
ADAMS Ambery AMBREY Ambrey-Evans Ambury BRANCH Branche Currall Currel CURRELL DAVIS DOWNES EVANS Evans-Ambrey HEMBER Hemborough HOWELL Howells Joleffe Jolife JOLIFFE LLOYD NORTHAM PACKER F2852

117781 CURRY Mr James. 17 Charlton Avenue, Filton Park, Bristol, BS12 7QX. Tel:0272-755529
COPELAND Corry Currey Currie CURRY DRUMMOND Dunell DUNHILL Dunnill Dunning EGAN HARTLEY HERD PARKIN SMITH WILSON F4727

117803 CURRY Mrs Jane. (Campbell) 3 Alleyne Court, Brown Owl, Upper Hutt, 6401, NEW ZEALAND. Tel:+64-4-526-9522
ARMSTRONG Ashelby BEAL Beale Beall BRASELL Brassel Brassell Brazel Brazell Brazil Brazill Brosnahan Brosnahen BROSNAN CAMPBELL COATES Curray Currey Currie CURRY DAWSON DIXON Eshelbey Eshelbie ESHELBY Eshellby Eshlebie Essebie Esselbie Esselby Exelby Exilbie Exilby Finday FINDLAY Finlay Finley Foule Foules Fowle FOWLES HARDING Lowder LOWTHER Ous Oust Owest Oweste OWST PHILLIPS SLATER SPRING STEELE Sturde Sturdie STURDY Sturdye TIPLADY Typlady Typladye Waindman Waineman WAINMAN Wayneman Waynman WILKINSON F4477

117811 CURTIS Mrs E. Baltana, London Road, Barkway, Royston Herts, SG8 8EY.
Tighe TYE F6924

117838 CURTIS Miss Elizabeth. Trewidden, Church Cove, The Lizard, Helston, Cornwall, TR12 7PH.
BLACKMORE CURTIS PELLOW RANDALL F4623

117846 CURZON Mrs Beryl C. 31 Victoria Road, Colchester, Essex, CO3 3NT.
CLEMENTS Courson CURSON Curzon Vigues VIGURS F3498

117854 CUSHING Mrs I P. (Howard) 28 Whitedown Lane, Alton, Hants, GU34 1PT.
BRENCHLEY HOWARD F6259

117862 CUSHION Mrs B R. (Levett) 42 Links Drive, Radlett, Herts, WD7 8BE.
CUSHION Levet LEVETT Levitt Levvett WOODHEAD F5310

117870 CUSSONS S A. Old Sodbury Cottage, Cotswold Lane, Old Sodbury, Avon, BS17 6NE.
BENNETT BISHOP CARTER CHAPMAN COOMBES CUMMINGS DAVIES MADDERS PARKES PEPLOW WOODHOUSE F880

117889 CUTHBERTSON Mrs Mary F. (Hamilton) 82 Mill Road, Stock, Ingatestone, Essex, CM4 9LN.
ALLAN Allen BERRY BRYCE CUMBERTON HAMILTON LARKIN Larkins LINCH Lynch MCGOWAN Mechan Meechan MEEHAN Michan MILLAR Miller F6545

117897 CUTLER Mr Arthur John. 43 Styles Hill, Frome, Somerset, BA11 5JG. Tel:0373-463352
CUTLER Cuttler STRONG F455

117900 CUTLER Mrs Pauline. (Froggatt) 4 Wyvern Way, Carleton, Poulton Le Flyde, Lancs, FY6 7LR. Tel:0253-885960
BEARDSLEY CRANSHAW FROGG FROGGATT OLIVE PENNINGTON F5054

117919 CUTTEN Mr David J W. St Pancras, 26 Cornel, Amington, Tamworth Staffs, B77 4EF. Tel:0827-58202
ANDREWS ARABIN BELLAMY BLUNDELL BROOKES BROOKS BULL CLISBY Cotten CUTTEN Cuttin Cutting Cutton DAYSH DEELYE DUNN DYTCH EWER FLOWER HATTON HODGES JAMES Kutten LAW LONGHURST MAGGS MILLER PENNY PHILLIPS PICK POCOCK POTTS SHAPTON SHERIDAN SMALLFIELD SMITH WAIN WATTS WILFORD WILLFORD WOOLDRIDGE WORSFOLD F122

117927 DABBS Mrs Brenda. (Luke) 4 Wendron Terrace, Sanctuary Lane, Helston, Cornwall, TR13 8UE.
AGLAND BIBBY COFFEE DABBS DYE GOLDING HAYWOOD LUKE ROBERTS WYATT F3946

117935 DACK Mrs Jean. 52 Greenways Crescent, Shoreham-By-Sea, W Sussex, BN43 6HS. Tel:0273-465640
CULLUM DACK GALE F3408

117943 DAFFORNE Mr John F. 31 Waingap Rise, Syke, Rochdale, Lancs, OL12 9TZ.
CRICHTON Daferon Daffarn Daffarne Daffern Dafferne Daffon Dafforn DAFFORNE Daffron EDWARDS WARDLE F1259

117951 DAGLISH Mr Gordon. 95 Hilda Park, Chester Le Street, Co Durham, DH2 2JS. Tel:091-388-6300
DAGLISH HOSKEN HOSKINS LORD F3736

117978 DAGLISH Mrs T J. A Block, C.a.t.s, Raf North Luffenham, Oakham, LE15 8RL.
Ludkin Lurkin Lurkins LUTKIN F7052

117986 DAGLISH Mrs T. 17 Mottershead Drive, Innsworth, Glos, GL3 1EQ.
LUTKIN F7309

117994 DAGWELL Mr David. 10 Daen Ingas, Danbury, Chelmsford, Essex, CM3 4DB.
Dackwell Dagweell Dagwel DAGWELL Dagwol Dakwell Gagwell KIRNUT F774

118001 DAINTON Revd M B. 10 Tern Grove, Loggerheads, Shropshire, TF9 4DZ.
DAINTON F6063

118028 DAINTY Mr Peter John. 20 Cedarwood Drive, Firwood Park, Tuffley, Gloucester, GL4 0AG. Tel:0452-526395
DAINTY F1867

118036 DAKEYNE Mr Christopher W. 12 Highgate, Beverley, N Humberside, HU17 0DN. Tel:0482-870497
Dakaine Dakayne Dakeyn DAKEYNE Dakeyns Dakin Dakyn Daykin Dukeyne F2404

118044 DALES Miss Jill. 32a Churchfield Avenue, North Finchley, London, N12 0NT.
BILTON DALES GREGSON GRIMOLDBY PIMPERTON ROWSON SEARBY STONES TOWNHILL WOODRIDGE F2744

118052 DALLAT Mr Cahal. Drimargy, 9 Atlantic Avenue, Ballycastle, Co Antrim, BT54 6AL. Tel:02657-62467
BLACK BOYD BUTLER DALLAT DARRAGH DEVLIN DONNELLY DUNCAN HUNTER JOLLY LAWRENCE MCALLISTER MCBRIDE MCCAMBRIDGE MCCARRY MCCONAGHY MCDONNELL MCERLAIN MCHENRY MCKILLOP MCKINLEY MCKINNEY MCLISTER MCMICHAEL MCMULLAN MCNEIL MULLAN NICHOLL O'LOAN O'NEILL STEWART F2147

118060 DALLEY Mr A B. 42 Linden Grove, Chandlers Ford, Eastleigh, Hants, SO5 1LD. Tel:0703-261020
CONEY COOL DALLEY FLETCHER FLOWER GOODFELLOW GRADIDGE HACKER HOARE JACKMAN LAMPARD LYGO-SIMMONS MATHEWS RICKETTS TERRY F480

118079 DALLING Mrs Vivien. (Brand) 38a Chase Green Avenue, Enfield, Middx, EN2 8EB. Tel:081-366-3075
BEVAN BOWYER BRAND BURCHER CREEK GOLDFINCH PATTENDEN PELLING PIGG F1151

118087 DALLISON Mr Malcolm. 45 Leigh Close, Walsall, West Midlands, WS4 2DY. Tel:0922-35551
D'alenston Dalason Dalison Dallaston Dallinson DALLISON Dallisson F6437

118095 DALRYMPLE Mrs Ivy. 9 Broomwood Court, Prudhoe, Northumberland, NE42 6RB.
BOWRING DALRYMPLE KIRSOP RICHARDSON F2405

118109 DALRYMPLE Mr R A. Hornby Castle, 7 Blacksmiths Lane, Hockley Heath, Solihull, B94 6QP. Tel:0564-783736
DALRYMPLE Derumple F229

118117 DALTON Mrs A J. 5 Boshaw Farm, Hade Edge, Holmfirth, Huddersfield, HD7 1RS. Tel:0484-684924
BAYLEY DALTON PORTER TIPPING WALKER F3780

118125 DALTON Mr M N. 2 Harewood Close, Reigate, Surrey, RH2 0HE.
DALTON NEALE F6560

118133 DALY Mr K. 15 Ambleside, Newlandsmuir, East Kilbride, Glasgow, G75 8TX.
CADGINE DALY DUNN GRAY HARVIE HOWAT HUGHES MANDERSON MCGURK MILLER NICOL PATON PORTER REID RITCHIE F5256

118141 DAMPIER Mr Lawrence. Po Box 41 Seacrest, Nanoose Bay, B C, V0R 2R0, CANADA.
DAMPIER DAMPIERRE DAVENPORT F7445

118168 DAMYON Mrs Wendy K. Greenaway, Norrels Drive, East Horsley, Surrey, KT24 5DL.
ALLCOCK ANDERTON ARNELL ASHBURNER BALDWIN BIRDBRIDGE CANN CARVER CHURCH CLARK DAMYON FELL GILES GRAVESTON GREEN GREENAWAY GREY HUNT JOHNSON KENT KIRKBY KITCHIN MCARTHY O'DONAHUE RAFE RATHBONE REEVES RISTED STAFF SUMPTON TUCK WALTER WHITE WILLIAMS F2290

118176 DANCE Mr. 20 Penllyn Avenue, Pontnewydd, Cwmbran, Gwent, NP44 1RD.
DANCE MACKLIN F5958

118184 DANIEL Mr Ian. 60 Yathong Road, Caringbah, NSW 2229, AUSTRALIA.
DANIEL DOIDGE SELWOOD THOMAS F5519

118192 DANIEL Mr Jeremy. 23 Gilda Crescent,

Polegate, E Sussex, BN26 6AW. Tel:0323-486460
AISLABIE Aisleby BARNEY BISHOP BREEZE CLASBY COLLIS Dalamer Dalamore Dalemore Dalimere Dalimore Dallamore Dallemore Dallemory DALLIMORE DANIEL Delamere DORE DREDGE ERNST FAIRS GANT GINGELL GLOSTER HAMSHARE HARMAN HUDD Meldread Mellrid Mildread MILDRED Mildredge Mildrett Milldred MILLS Milred Milridge Mylrede NEWMAN PAGE PRIEST ROWE Scarf SCARFE Scarff Scarffe SCRIVENER STEVENS STRINGER F2809

118206 DANIEL Mr Robert. 11a Pierce Crescent, Warmington, Peterborough, PE8 6UG.
ATKINSON Danel Danels DANIEL Daniell Daniells Daniels Dannel Dannels Danyell Danyells HOLLOX HOTSON JACKSON MACKLEY MILLMS PICKERING VICKERS F4567

118214 DANIELL Mr Peter. 58 East Lodge Oak, Farlington, Portsmouth, Hants, PO6 1AG.
COLE DANIELL MARVIN SCAMMELL SHIPTON F2148

118222 DANIELS Mrs Janet. 26 Arden Mhor, Pinner, Middx, HA5 2HR.
Bick Bickes Bicks BIX BIX Bixe Bixx BLYTH Byx Byxe CAINAN Canaan Cannon LEGGETT NICHOLS Prethero Pretheroe Prethro Prethroe Prithro Prithroe PROTHERO PROTHEROE Protherough Prothro Prothroe Prydderch Prytherch Prythro Prythroe STARSMORE Twining Twiny TWYNING Twyny Wakelen WAKELIN Wakeling WARD F3642

118230 DANIELS Mrs Jean. (Williams) 31 Trinity Close, Pound Hill, Crawley, Sussex, RH10 3TW.
LEWIS PERRIN POWDRICH Powdridge PROSS PUGH RICE WILLIAMS F3532

118249 DANIELS Mr L. Flat 2 40 Georges Road, Kemptown, Brighton, E Sussex, BN2 1EF.
BABER Babre Babur F6639

118257 DANKS Mr T. Golygfa Afon, 3 Caerffynnon, Tolsarnau, Gwynedd, LL47 6TA.
DANKS F6632

118265 DANN Mr Cedric & Mrs Margaret. 125 George Borrow Road, Norwich, Norfolk, NR4 7HX. Tel:0603-53179
BROWNE CRICKMORE DANN HALL HARVEY PAYNE THOMPSON F3337

118273 DARBY Mr N W. 281 Westmount Road, Eltham, London, SE9 1NR. Tel:081-856-7584
DARBY F1717

118281 DARBYSHIRE Mr Leslie. 74 Red Rose, Binfield, Bracknell, Berks, RG12 5LD. Tel:0344-420791
BELL BIRD BROCKWELL CALVERT Darbishire DARBYSHIRE Derbishire Derbyshire ELLIS Farra Farrah Farrar Farrer FERRAR Ferrer KENT LANHAM LIDDLE Probart Probets PROBETTS Probits SMITH WARD Whybrow Widbrow Wyborn Wybrew Wybroo WYBROW Wyburn YOUNG F4697

118303 DARE Mrs B. (Nichols) 8 Holland Road, Oxted, Surrey, RH8 9AU. Tel:0883-712304
Dair Dar DARE Dear Deer HOLBOURN MARTIN NICHOLS SNAPE TIZZARD WAKE F1041

118311 DARNES Mrs J. 31 Gerald Road, Worthing, W Sussex, BN11 5QQ.
Sing Singe Singes SINGS Sinns Sins Syng Synge F7015

118338 DARVALL Mr T R. 17 Granville Road, Limpsfield, Oxted, Surrey, RH10 0BX.
BATES BUSAIN CLIFFORD COLBOUNRE DARVALL Darvoll Dorvold GRINSTED HALL MAJOR PINDER POULTER POWELL REASE ROUND SPINDLER STRETTON TOPLISS TURNBULL F3134

118346 DATSON Mr Peter W. 2 Wakanui St, Northcote, VIC 3070, AUSTRALIA. Tel:+61-3-489-9028
DATSON WASLEY F4455

118354 DAVEY Mr Brian. 13 Osborne Road, Morecambe, Lancs, LA4 4LS.
ACKERMAN Akerman ARMER BARROW BATES BENTHAM BLOWFIELD BOLTON BROUGHTON CHRISTOPHER CROSSLEY CROWTHER DAVEY DEAN DICK ENTWISTLE FAULKNER GASCOIGNE Gascoine Gascoyne Gasken Gaskin Gasking HARRISON JOULES Jowles LATHAM MIDDLETON MULLENDER Mullinder Mulliner PAGE PETTICAN POLLARD Swanel Swanil SWANNELL Swannil Turrell Tyrell Tyrrel TYRRELL WALDEN WILLIAMS F2179

118362 DAVEY Mrs K. (Kelly) 20 Hinkley Close, Harefield, Middlesex, UB9 6AA.
BARBER JOHNSON JOSLIN KELLY KIDD METCLAF O'HARE VERRILL WRIGHT F4982

118370 DAVEY Mrs Pauline. (Revell) 85 Radnor Park Road, Folkestone, Kent, CT19 5BU.
DEVANNEY DRYLAND EUDEN HARSANT JONES REVELL UDEN F4076

118389 DAVEY Mr R R. 10 Switchback Road South, Maidenhead, Berks, SL6 7QR.
DAVEY HEARN MARTIN PETVIN STEVENS F2180

118397 DAVEY Mrs S A. Hayesfield, Pioneer Avenue, Combe Down, Bath, BA2 5QX.
ADKINS BUNDY COOPER DAVEY Davy ELSWORTH FRAMPTON GARRETT GODWIN GRIFFITHS HARVEY HOLLIDAY KNIVET Kniyvet Lindsey LINSEY MEADOWS MUSSEL PARMENTER PAULING Pauwling QUINTON RABETS REEVES RICHARDSON SELMAM SHEPPERD Silmam WALLIS WATSON WATTS F4586

118400 DAVID Miss S P. Foxhill, Priest Weston, Montgomery, Powys, SY15 6DF.
BALL BROCKMAN BROOKER COOKE CUMMING DAVID FOX GAMMON HODGE PAGE STANFORD WILSON F861

118419 DAVIDSON Mr Alan. 43 Mount Street, Aberdeen, AB2 4QX.
BROWN DAVIDSON DONALDSON HEPBURN HUTCHESON MCLEOD MORRISON RAE RAEBURN ROBERTSON F4688

118427 DAVIDSON Mrs B. 1 Towers Avenue, Jesmond, Newcastle Upon Tyne, NE2 3QE.
CATANACH Cattanach DUNCAN GEDDES Gilanders GILLANDERS OGILVIE Riddel RIDDELL SANGSTER SHEPHERD TROUP WALKER F3073

118435 DAVIES Revd Alexander Richard. 9 Glan Gors, Harlech, Gwynedd, LL46 2NJ. Tel:0766-780639
BIRCHALL BURKE CLARK DAVIES JONES PROWSE ROWBOTTOM SMITH F3692

118443 DAVIES Mrs Anne. 11 Lowther Drive, Garforth, Leeds, LS25 1EW.
CAPSTICK CROFT EAVES Elethorn Elithorn Ellethorn ELLITHORN Ellithorne Elythorn GARDENER GREGSON GUNSON HALL HARTLEY Laurenson LAWRENSON MELLING PORTER ROSSALL SALTHOUSE SPEAKMAN TOWNSON WARD WILDINA F5657

118451 DAVIES Mrs B. 44 High Street, Gatehouse Of Fleet, Castle Douglas, Kirkcudbrightshire, DG7 2HP. Tel:0557-814482
Cliffeton Cliffton CLIFTON Clyfton DAVIES Davis Hewertson HEWETSON Hewitson Hewittson Hollingsworth HOLLINGWORTH Hollingworthe Hollyngeworth Hollyngworth Marlan MARLAND Marlande Marlin F5357

118478 DAVIES Mr Brian. 6 Cheadle Avenue, Cramlington, Northumberland, NE23 9YT.
BONE BURTON PELLS RICHARDSON SHAW WORDINGHAM F5909

118486 DAVIES Mr C R. 11 Lowther Drive, Garforth, Leeds, LS25 1EW.
ABRAHAM DAVIES FRANKLAND HAUXWELL HENLEY HOLMES Iddens IDIENS LOBLEY MILNE OGRAM PINKNEY Rider RIDLEY RYDER TRIPPITT WALKER F4324

118494 DAVIES Mrs C. (Griffin) Gunwen Farm, Luxulyan, Bodmin, Cornwall, PL30 5DS.
BROWNING CARKEEK GRIFFIN F2110

118508 DAVIES Mr D G. Hafan, 10 Heol Yr Ysgol, Coety Penybont Ar Ogwr, Mid Glamorgan, CF35 6BL.
DAVIES EVANS STEPHENS WALTERS F2452

118516 DAVIES Mrs Danise. (Collins) 4 Stonechat Close, Petersfield, Hants, GU31 4RE.
BARNSLEY COLLINS DAVIS GLADDES HORAM JUDD PEARSON TUBB WESLEY F5267

118524 DAVIES Mr David. 16 Wallacre Rd, Wallasey Village, Wirral, Merseyside, L44 2DY. Tel:051-691-2078
DAVIES NATHAN SMITH F3348

118532 DAVIES Mrs Dulcie. 1035 Great Western Highway, Lithgow, NSW 2790, AUSTRALIA. Tel:+61-63-513915
BAGNELL CHILDS CONNOR DAVIES GEARY GRADY HARGRAVE HOGARTH LINTOFF NEAL NOBLE RAWSON SUTTON F5176

118540 DAVIES Frank T. 3 Main Avenue, Peterston Super Ely, Cardiff, South Glamorgan, CF5 6LQ. Tel:0446-760436
BEER BENNET BRIGGS BUNCHAM CHAPPEL CLARIDGE CLARKE COLWILL COOPER CRABTREE CREED CULLEN DAVID DAVIES DEVONALD DIMMOCK EDWARDS EVAN FLETCHER GRIFFITHS GRONOW GUNNINGHAM HALE HARRIES HESSION HOWE HUGHES HUNT

HUNTLEY-THOMAS HURST JAMES JONES LEGG LLEWHELLIN MAJOR MARRIOT MARSH MATHIAS MCCRARRON MCDONALD MCGRORY MORGAN NORTHCOTT PATTISON PEAT PHILLIPS REES RICE RICHARDS ROWAN SALMON SHORT SINGLETON SMITH STONE TOYER WARD WEBBER WILLIAMS WITHAM WORKMAN YOUNG F2109

118559 DAVIES Mrs Gillian. (Hibbs) La Roche Posay, St Brelade, Jersey, JE3 8FE. Tel:0534-44693
BOWER Eb Ebb Ebbe Ebbes Ebus Hebb Hib Hibb Hibbes HIBBS Hybys Ibbes Ibbs Ibs F4987

118567 DAVIES Mr Howard. 20 Pine View Close, Haslemere, Surrey, GU27 1DU.
GULLEY Gully F5313

118575 DAVIES Mr Hywel G. 75 Maes Iago, Pontardawe, Swansea, SA8 4LR.
Ahterton ATHERTON Courtenay Courtnay COURTNEY DAVIES DELL Delph DELVE EDWARDS FISHER Hatherton HEWETT ISAAC Jenkin JENKINS JONES LLOYD MORGAN POPHAM ROSSER Traharne Treharn TREHARNE Vauden Vawden VODDEN Voden Vowden WALTERS William WILLIAMS F5978

118583 DAVIES Mr Ivor L. 513 Lees Lane, Oakville, Ontario, L6L 4T5, CANADA. Tel:+1-416-845-7520
BICKNELL DAVID HALL JONES MORGAN PENROSE STREDDER F4173

118591 DAVIES Mr J Owen. 10 Beckenham Road, West Wickham, Kent, BR4 0QT.
ABRAM CLOSE DAVIES GREGSON HARKNETT HUGHES ION JEWELL JONES LANHAM LONGSTAFF MASON MATTINSON OWEN ROWE TANNER TAYLOR THOMAS WADE WORDEN F2752

118605 DAVIES Mrs Joan. 24 Caughall Road, Upton Heath, Chester, CH2 1LS.
BENNETT DAVIES EDWARDS FARRINGTON FRANCIS GRIFFITH JAMES Philpot PHILPOTT RANDLES ROWLEY WAREHAM WASHINGTON WILLIAMS F2360

118613 DAVIES Mr John. The Briar, Bergholt Road, Bentley, Ipswich Suffolk, IP9 2DH. Tel:0473-311633
ALDEN F102

118621 DAVIES Mrs L R. (Gollings) 24 Hawkins Road, Shoreham, W Sussex, BN43 6TJ. Tel:0273-594179
GOLLAND GOLLINGS F6137

118648 DAVIES Mr Llewelyn B & Mrs Elizabeth R. (Uglow) 30-6245 Sheridan Road, Richmond, British Columbia, V7E 4W6, CANADA.
CROSS GOUGH UGLOW F4137

118656 DAVIES Mrs M I Dawn. 760 Old Lode Lane, Solihull, W Midlands, B92 8NH. Tel:021-743-0840
DAVENPORT JONES Weal WEALE Wheal WHEALE Wheel WILLIAMS F2549

118664 DAVIES Mrs Muriel. 2 Windermere Road, Parkside, Hereford, HR4 9PR.
BOWEN F2926

118672 DAVIES Mr P. 67 North Denes Road, Great Yarmouth, Norfolk, NR30 4LU.
BALDWIN BULKLEY DAINTON DAVIES ELLIS EVANS FISHER HALLIER HUGHES HUNT JONES MALLARD MATHEW MORGAN PEARCE ROWLEY SHIPWAY SPENCER SUMMERS THOMAS TITTENSOR TURNER WILLIAMS F5372

118680 DAVIES Mrs Rene. 45 Montrose Road, Montrose, Victoria, 3756, AUSTRALIA. Tel:+61-3-728-4136
BROPHY CONWAY CRAW KENNEDY LALOR LYNCH O'SHAUGHNESSY RYAN STEWART THOMSON TRACY TREACY F5160

118699 DAVIES Mrs Ruth. (Sadler) 50 Brynteg Avenue, Pontllanfraith, Gwent. Tel:0495-226352
ROBERTS SADLER WAVERS WEETMAN F5282

118702 DAVIES Mr Stan. Gwyndy, 3 Cysgod Y Craig, Denbigh, Clwyd, LL16 3TD. Tel:0745-816125
DAVIES HILDITCH HUGHES JONES F3233

118710 DAVIES Mrs V K. 10 Rangiora Avenue, Matamata, 2271, NEW ZEALAND.
CHARMAN CHAWNER DAVIES HALE LAWSON MOORE NOBBS ROBERTS SMITH TRAIL F5562

118729 DAVIES Mr W H. 65 Moughland Lane, Runcorn, Cheshire, WA7 4SF. Tel:0928-564303
BLEARS BUDGE CONEYBEARE COOPER CURWEN DAVIES DAWSON DOUGHTY FOULKES GUY HAYSE HAZLEWOOD HIGSON JENKINSON MALE OWENS PARKER PARKINSON SEDDON WEBSTER WILLIAMS F2631

118737 DAVIS Mrs Anne. 15 Woodward Close, Winnersh, Wokingham, Berks, RG11 5NW.
ALDRIDGE BARNETT BECKET BIDMEAD CURR DAVIS DUNN DUNNE GREGORY GRIFFIN GUNTER HATCH HOLDER HUMPHRIES KETTLE LAKE LAY MARTIN MITCHELL PARISH PEARSE QUELCH RABBIT SANDFORD SHEPPARD SPENCELAGH SPENCELEY SPENDLEY VICKERY WAITE WAKELING WEBB WHITE WOOD F845

118745 DAVIS Mr Anthony G. 4 Mount Pleasant, Weybridge, Surrey, KT13 8EP. Tel:0932-844261
BRYER BYRAM Byrom CARWARDINE COATES DAVIS LEGEYT Legeytt Leggett Legyett Legytt Leygett MASON PEACHEY PIFFE SPALTON Spaulton Spawlton Spawton WELFARE Welfer F6271

118753 DAVIS Mr Brian A. Po Box 194, Byron Bay, NSW 2222, AUSTRALIA.
CAMBOURN DAVIS ENGLAND MCNAMARA MOODY SEMMENS SPEIGHT STOKER THORNHILL F7392

118761 DAVIS Mr Douglas. 5 Alder Grove, Stapenhill, Burton On Trent, Staffs, DE15 9QR. Tel:0283-40168
ASHTON DAVIS DERBYSHIRE FROST MULLEY F334

118788 DAVIS Mrs Ethel. (Byford) Berkeley Lodge, Kenegie Hill, Gulval, Penzance Cornwall, TR20 8YN. Tel:0736-63864
Biford BYFORD CURD DAVIS FIELD GOAD KIBBLE LEE Skelleton SKELTON Skilton F3033

118796 DAVIS Mrs G. 5 Oldbury Grove, Beaconsfield, Bucks, HP9 2AJ.
Apgenti Argant ARGENT F6716

118818 DAVIS Mrs Hilda G. 21 Warren Road, Narborough, Leicester, LE9 5DR.
COBB HOCKING HOLMAN HOSKIN LUCAS PAULL PEWSEY RANDON RICHARDS SHUGG F2881

118826 DAVIS Mrs J M. 24 Dunkirk Road, Southport, Lancs, PR8 4RQ.
DAVIS NOLAN RIMMER SUGDEN WRIGHT F2730

118834 DAVIS Mrs M. 303 Rayleigh Road, Eastwood, Leigh On Sea, Essex, SS9 5HX.
ADAMS BAILEY BALLS BATE BENFIELD BLACKLEY COLLINGS COPE DAVIS DEAR EDWARDS ETHERIDGE GARDENER HEWLETT HOOKEY MCCCONNELL PARNELL RAYNER ROGERS STEEL STREET THOMPSON THORNTON URE VENNER WEBB F3058

118842 DAVIS Mrs Nita. (Burgh) 17 Broadwater Rise, Tunbridge Wells, Kent, TN2 5UE.
BARNARD BURGH JUDD F1933

118850 DAVIS Mrs Pamela. 41 Bills Lane, Shirley, Solihull, W Midlands, B90 2HR.
ALLIS BODFISH BURTON COSIER GREEN HIRONS LINES LONG MANSELL TONERY TONRY F318

118869 DAVISON Mr Colin. 66 Sudeley Walk, Putnoe, Bedford, MK41 8JH.
CRAWLEY DAVISON DENTON FARMER Farrar FARRER Gelles Gellis Gelly JAMES Jealys Jeles Jelleys JELLIS Jelly Jellys Jolys JONES Knapp NAPP PEACH Peets Perts Petts Potts SEARE Seayre Seer WILDMAN WRIGHT F525

118877 DAVISON Mrs Elsie. (Smart) 20 Blackbrook Lane, Bromley, Kent, BR2 8AY.
Colett Collet COLLETT COOPER Cowper DERRY FARDON FORD FREEMAN Freman GIBBS Humphreys Humphries Humphris HUMPHRISS Humphrys LANKEY PACKER Parker Radburn Railton Ralton Redbourn REDBURN Relton Rodbourn Rodbur RULTON SMART WALLACE WALTERS Waters Watters YOUNGER F3755

118885 DAVISON Mrs Kim. 32 Morgan Crescent, Theydon Bois, Epping, Essex, CM16 7DX. Tel:0992-813033
BARKER CRANE FIRMSTONE GREEN REED WAINES WHITE WHITTINGHAM WILSON F1699

118893 DAVISON Mr P R D. 27 Fryup Crescent, Guisborough, Cleveland, TS14 8LG. Tel:0287-635316
AITCHISON BELL BINKS BOOMER BROWN BULMER CATLING DAVISON DAWSON DIXON DOVE ELLIOTT ELSEY FEATHERSTONE FLATT FORD FRANCIS GARBUTT HEAVISIDE HELSTROP HORDEN HUNTER IRVIN JONES LITTLEFARE MINTO MOOR NOBLE OLIVER OUTHWAITE PALMER PRATT SCARR SHARP SMITH STEPEHENSON TEASDALE TRUEMAN WATSON YOUNGER F3202

118907 DAVISON Dr W H T. 81 Little Sutton Road, Four Oaks, Sutton Coldfield, W Midlands, B75 6PT. Tel:021-308-0224
AYTON BRUMFIELD COE CRASKE Davidson Davieson DAVISON Davisson Davyson FAUX FOSTER GIBBS LOFTS PRINCE SPENCER F2433

118915 DAVY Mrs Christine. Ladymere Cottage,

Twitchell Road, Gt Missenden, Berks, HP16 0BQ.
BEACHAM BOLTON BOOTH BURCHALL BUSH CHAFFEY DAVY DIXEY DOWNE ELSDON HALLIDAY JOHNS JOHNSON LEWIS MOORE PICKERING SAMPSON STEELE TINDALL WARD WHITEHEAD F1476

118923 DAWES Mrs Esme June. (Bradshaw) 4 Ash Grove, Rainford, St Helens, Merseyside, WA11 8DU.
BRADSHAW BROWNE BUTTERFIELD CROSSLEY DAWES GREENOUGH JACKSON JOUCHIN PIGGATT RADCLIFFE RUSHBROOK Rushbrooke WOLFE F3903

118931 DAWKINS Mrs Susan. Downedge, 110 Romsey Road, Winchester, Hants, SO22 5PJ.
Beadnall BEDNELL BROWN BURCHELL GIBBONS GOODMAN JERRAMS MANNING Mannion PAIN Payne POULTON RING SODEN WAINE YOUNG F2619

118958 DAWSON Mr Harry B. 7625 S Lk Stevens Road, Everett, WA 98205-2811, USA.
ASTLEY BAKER BARLOW BARNSLEY BARRETT DAWSON EASTON FIDLER HILTON HURST JOHNSTON Johnstone LAUNDER MATHER RICHARDS SIXSMITH SPEAKMAN WAGSTAFF WALKER WASHINGTON WELSH F5963

118966 DAWSON Mr James. 3 Levant Street, Padiham, Burnley, Lancs, BB12 7AS. Tel:0282-72474
MOSCROP OLDHAM F5781

118974 DAWSON Miss Jean. 273 Queens Road, Halifax, W Yorks, HX1 4NS. Tel:0422-346367
DAWSON GLEDHILL JAMIESON JOHNSTON Makerly Mccorley MCCURLEY NIVEN SHEARD F2485

118982 DAWSON Mr L. 5 Marian Close, Hayes, Middx, UB4 9DA. Tel:081-841-6771
AUBERT COOK DAWSON F6368

118990 DAWSON Mrs Sandra. 9 Central Avenue, Ashingdon, Rochford, Essex, SS4 3BQ.
ASHWELL BENIAMS BISHOP CHANCE DINES LUNN OUTRAM SCALES STEARN WICKS F2676

119008 DAY Mrs Angela. (Alsford) 37 The Street, Manuden, Bishops Stortford, Herts, CM23 1DF.
ALSFORD BOSWORTH CHALONER COLDWELL FIGG FRANCIS JOHNSON KENDALL LYONS PUGH STARBUCK WICKS F1335

119016 DAY Mrs C R M. 91 Roosevelt Court, Stonehouse Drive, St Leonards On Sea, E Sussex, TN38 9DJ.
HARRIS F397

119024 DAY Mr D H. Aldrans, Church Hill Wroughton, Swindon Wiltshire, SN4 9JR. Tel:0793-812323
DAY DOSWELL FLETCHER GREGORY HOLE MITCHAM MORGAN RIDDIFORD THOMAS WISE F664

119032 DAY Mr George Walpole. 22 Humber Gardens, Wellingborough, Northants, NN8 5WE. Tel:0933-676559
DAY KEMP LUND POTTER QUARTON F1172

119040 DAY Mrs Judy A. (Guy) 10 Lancaster Drive, Broadstone, Dorset, BH18 9EJ.
Addis Addy ADEY Adie Ady Adye Armen Armon BEST CARTER CHARD Croutcher Crouter Crucher CRUTCHER DAY Eddy ELTON Forman GUY Norman ORMAN Ormen PROUDLEY STICKLAND STRONG Willsden Willsdon Wilsden WILSDON WRIGHT F3661

119059 DAY Mrs Nancy H. (Mann) 47 Pine Avenue, Hastings, E Sussex, TN34 3PP.
ADNAM Adnams Adnum Adnums BAILEY Baillie Baily BAKER BARFOOT BARNES Barns BENHAM BIRD BLISS Bonham BROWN BULPITT BUNYAN COLSTON CORBY ECLES Falbrook Flecher FLETCHER Flicher FULBROOK Fulbrooke GRIFFIN Hadnam Hadnams Hadnum HAMPTON Hind HINE HOPKINS HOWE KURN LACEY Lacy LAMBURN Lasy Man MANN Mans MCCANE MESSER Messom MONK MURRELL Murrells Murrill NORCOTT PERKINS Philbrook PROBERT Proberts Probet Probets Probett ROOKE ROSE SHREEVE TUDRIE TURNER WELFORD Welfords Welfors WELLS Wilford YOUNG F248

119067 DAY Mr Ronald James. 70 Westwood Road, Tilehurst, Reading, Berks, RG3 5PP. Tel:0734-427261
DAY DIGBY GEE WILKINSON F6283

119075 DAY Mrs Valerie. (Pemberton) Newlands, Middle Street, Nazeing, Waltham Abbey, Essex, EN9 2LH.
Artar Arter ARTHUR Bromidge BROMWICH Brumidge Brummage BUSWELL CALVERT CLARKSON COOPER HOOTON PEMBERTON SANDERS TAMKIN F4321

119083 DAYMOND Mr David W. 11 Alcester Road, Wootton Wawen, Henley In Arden, Warwickshire, B95 6AY. Tel:0564-793476
ANDREWS DAYMAN Dayment DAYMOND Dement Diamond Diment Dimond Dyment Dymond EVELEIGH Eveley Evely HAKE PIDGEON SHAKESPEARE WALLIS WILKES Wilks F6549

119091 DE ATH Mr Peter. 7 The Birches, Mannings Heath, Horsham, W Sussex, RH13 6JT.
Daeth Darra Darragh DARRAH DEATH Deathe Deeth Deith Hardiman HARDMAN HIATT Hiett Hyatt Hyett KIPPAX MASON MAYHEW Steggall Steggalls STEGGALS Steggells Steggels Stiggles Stiggold WAY Whiteing WHITING Whitting WILLIAMS Witting F1217

119105 DE CAEN Mr & Mrs R F B. 3822 Sixth St Sw, Calgary, Alta, T2S 2MB, CANADA. Tel:+1-403-243-1637
ANDERSON BALLANTYNE BALLEINE BELL BLAKENEY DE CAEN EDMONDS ERREY FRY GOLDIE GOOD GRIEVE GURNETT JENNER JOHNSTONE KINGSBURY LABAT Labatt LE MAISTRE LE MONTAIS LEET LITSTER MARET Marett MUNDALL NEEL ORANGE PATON REECH RENOUF SHEFFIELD SIDYE SMITH STEPHENS VALPY DIT JANVRIN F4028

119113 DE CARTERET Mr Michael. Batu Tegar, Delancey Lane, St Sampsons, Guernsey. Tel:0481-44203
DE CARTERET HITCHCOCK MALE WELCH F3560

119121 DE DULIN Mr Peter L K. Tudor Lodge, 12 Hazeldene Road, Weston Super Mare, BS23 2XL.
DE DULIN DULIN Feast FEIST Fiest F4680

119148 DE GROEN Mr A R G. 663 Portswood Road, Portswood, Southampton, SO2 3SQ.
EARLEY Early HARDEMAN Hardeyman Hardiman Hardyman Wardeman Yearley Yearly F4574

119156 DE GRUCHY Mr Michael. 7 Le Bel Estur, Rue Des Pres, St Saviour, Jersey, JE2 7RB. Tel:0534-24047
CULLINANE DE GRUCHY F5874

119164 DE VIELL Mr Wilfred H. 7 Falcon Way, Kenton, Harrow, Middlesex, HA3 0TW. Tel:081-204-9388
BARKER CLAYDON DALLIN Davil De Vial DE VIELL Deaville Devile Deville Divel Divell Duvall EASTERBROOK GREENSLADE HART HAWKER JOHNSON NEAVE Petit PETITT Pettet Pettit Pettitt PRIDHAM TROWER WARN WEATHERDONE WEBBER YEANDLE F4988

119172 DE VILLE Sir Oscar H G. 18 Pound Lane, Sonning On Thames, Berks, RG4 0XE. Tel:0734-693253
ATHERTON BRIDGETT Bridgewood Daville DE VILLE Deavell Deaville Devell Devoll Deyville GODFREY STALEY F71

119180 DE-VILLE Mrs Dorothy. (Marks) 40 Kingswear Crescent, Whitkirk, Leeds, Yorkshire, LS15 8PH. Tel:0532-643204
ACKROYD BIRKELMANS BURTOFT DE VILLE Deaville Devile Devill Deville FOTHERBY GREENWOOD GREGORY Mark Markes MARKS PRIOR Pryor REECE SPEAIGHT WILLIS F2440

119199 DEACON Mr Andrew. 78 Northcroft, Slough, Berks, SL2 1HP. Tel:0753-651787
APPS CORBIN DEACON KERLEY PAINE SILLEY F4512

119202 DEACON Mrs Frances. 10 Pilton Street, Barnstaple, Devon, EX31 1PE.
BROOKS FERRIS GOODYEAR QUINEY SHAW SYMONS F4819

119210 DEAN Mr Albert. 39 Starmead Drive, Wokingham, Berkshire, RG11 2JA. Tel:0734-786297
AMOS DEAN DEAN F3112

119229 DEANE Mrs P M. 183 Long Lane, Tilehurst, Reading, Berks, RG3 6YW.
Thirkettle THURKETTLE F6799

119237 DEANS Mrs Marianne. (Field) 55 Weybridge, Woodside, Telford, Shropshire, TF7 5QA. Tel:0952-583081
DEANS FIELD FROST PETTIFER WILLIAMS F4951

119245 DEAR Ms Frances. 12 Upper Berkeley Street, London, W1H 7PE.
SAMPEY F7035

119253 DEARDEN Mrs Patricia. (Ardern) Wishanger, One Oak Lane, Wilmslow, Cheshire, SK9 2BL.
Arden ARDERN BENTHAM BENTLEY DAVENPORT DEARDEN Harden HARRISON Hodgen HODGSON ISHERWOOD KEMP PARTRIDGE SAVAGE Savidge WOODALL Woodhall WRIGHT F1795

119261 DEAS Mrs Christine. (Ball) 2 Carlogie Farm

Road, Carnoustie, Angus, DD7 6LD.
Tel:0241-53265
APPLEGATE BAILEY BALL KENT OLDHAM SHIPLEY
F5756

119288 DEBNEY Mr & Mrs C. 8 Hucklebury Close, Purley On Thames, Reading, Berks, RG8 8EH.
Tel:0734-413223
Debeny DEBNEY Debny F6641

119296 DEELEY Mrs P M. (Hancock) 36 Falfield Road, Tuffley, Gloucester, GL4 ONE.
APPLETON BURVILL BUSHELL COOK DEELEY HANCOCK NOBLE PARFITT PRICE RAYNER THOMAS WICKS F4344

119318 DEHANY Dr William. 11 Pennyman Green, Maltby, Middlesbrough, Cleveland, TS8 0BX.
Tel:0642-596207
DEHANY WILLIAMS F1213

119326 DEIGHTON Mr Edgar. 34 Spottiswoode Road, Edinburgh, EH9 1BL.
ALLAN ANDERSON ARCHIBALD BELL BICKERDIKE BIRD BLACK BRUNTON BUCHAN CADDALL CALDER CATLEY CHALMERS CHARLES COATES CORNWELL COWFIELD CUNNINGHAM DEIGHTON DICKSON DUNCAN DUNNING EWING FORD FRAZER GLASS HADDEN HASTIE HOGG HUNTER INCHES KEIR KELLY KER KINDLY KING KNIGHT LEEMING LISHMAN LIVINGSTONE MANNERS MCASLAN MCDONALD MCFARLANE MCINIFF MCKINLAY MCMILLIAN MCMURRAY MCNAUGHTON MCROSIN MONILAWS MULHAIR MURRAY NEIL ROBERTSON ROSE SCRIMGEOUR SIMPSON SMITH STEWART STONEHOUSE STRICKLAND SYME THOMPSON THOMSON WALKER WILKIE WILSON F1542

119334 DEIGHTON Mr Ernest P. 61 Gainsborough Drive, Ascot, Berks, SL5 8TA. Tel:0344-25674
CHAMBERLAIN COX DEIGHTON Dighton Diton Ditton Dyton HOARE F3232

119342 DELLAR Mr John. 7 Station Road, Whittlesford, Cambs, CB2 4NL. Tel:0992-837019
DELLAR HARVEY F2523

119350 DELLER Mr J. 22 Lodge Avenue, Elstree, Herts, WD6 3ND.
DELLER F6901

119369 DELVE Mr John R. 149 Woodyates Road, Lee, London, SE12 9JJ.
DELVE MCBRIAR MCVEIGH MITCHELL MORRISON NORTHOVER SNODDEN WINGATE F1612

119377 DEMAINE Mrs Lynne. (Frayne) 33 Daleside, Cotgrave, Nottingham, NG12 3QN.
Tel:0602-894942
DEMAINE FRAYN HOOTON F3788

119385 DEMPSEY Mrs Margaret J. 4 Hall Drive, Caton, Lancaster, LA2 9QE. Tel:0524-771053
DEAN FAIRCLOUGH Hodgen Hodgin Hodshon HODSON Hudson KERSHAW TOWNSEND Wareing WARING Wearing F1957

119393 DENDLE Mr P G. 17 Winchester Road, Dunscroft, Doncaster, S Yorks, DN7 4NB.
Dendal Dendall Dendell DENDLE F7069

119407 DENNETT Miss Maureen. 134 Ditchfield Road, Hough Green, Widnes, Cheshire, WA8 8HZ.
Tel:051-424-4718
Danat Danet Danett Dannet DENNETT F2222

119415 DENNING Mr P. 8 Hastings Terrace, Marshfields, Bradford, W Yorks, BD5 9PL.
Dening Deninge DENNING Dinning F7012

119423 DENNING Mr Richard. 22 Low Wood Road, Erdington, Birmingham, W Midlands, B23 6HD.
Tel:021-373-8522
DENNING Dennings Smaley Smalie SMALLEY Smallie Smally Smaly Smalye F918

119431 DENNIS Mrs A. 62 Archers Court Road, Whitfield, Dover, Kent, CT16 3HU.
ALLEN CHANDLER DRAWBRIDGE FORWOOD HARMER HATTON HEAVER HOYLE LEWIS LONG MATSON PAGE PEERLESS PETTIT PHILLIPS SERGEANT SIGGS WINCH F3017

119458 DENNIS Mr F H. 62 Archers Court Road, Whitfield, Dover, Kent, CT16 3HU.
BAYLEY COLLIER ERSKINE FRENCH GEERING GIBBONS GRIGGS HINTON HORNIMAN HUGHES JARVICE JENKINS JOHNSON KENNETT PEPPER PICKET PITHER QUAIT SILVER TUXWORTH F3018

119466 DENNIS Ms Judy. Po Box 2, Ballarat 3350, AUSTRALIA.
DENNIS F7261

119474 DENNISON Mrs Jean. 8 Scheuchan View, Stranraer, Wigtownshire, DG9 7TA.
BARNES CRESWICK DENNISON GRAHAM MIDDLETON PUNSHON SENIOR F288

119482 DENNISTON Mrs M. 92 Darraghs Road, Otumoetai, Tauranga, NEW ZEALAND.
Denison Dennison DENNISTON F7075

119490 DENNY Mr R M. 31 Arbutus Road, Meadvale, Redhill, Surrey, RH1 6LJ.
Denney DENNY F7164

119504 DENT Ms C L. 25 Woodsedge, Waterlooville, Hants, PO7 8ER.
ALDERSON ALLISON BELCHER BEWICK BRUNSKILL BYTHEWAY CLEASBY DENT DODDS FROST GIBSON GREEN HERRIDGE HODGSON HUNT JEANNES PERCY SHUTE SMITH STRATFORD TUCKER F4230

119512 DENTON Mrs Judy. (Harwood) 27 Melrose Gardens, Hersham, Walton On Thames, Surrey, KT12 5HF. Tel:0932-220523
BOTTING CHEWTER CROUCHER DAWES GILBERT JARRET SADLER SPOONER STEER WILLIAMS F5002

119520 DENZEY Mr Frank J. Amberley, Spittal, Haverfordwest, Dyfed, SA62 5QP.
CHILDS Denesey Densey Densi Densy Denze DENZEY Denzi Denzy Dinze Dinzey Dinzi Dinzy JONES F3580

119539 DERBY Mr Matthew. 42 Edinburgh Road, Dumfries, DG1 1JQ. Tel:0387-51076
DERBY F5221

119547 DERUSETT Mr John Oodeen. 6 St Peters Court, St Peters Road, Byker, Newcastle Upon Tyne, NE6 2XH.
DERUSETT Tipp TRIP Tripe Tripp F6976

119555 DESAI Mrs Desre. (Walker) 7 Dunedin Avenue, Hartburn, Stockton On Tees, Cleveland, TS18 5JD.
FENTON FLINT VARLEY WALKER F6415

119563 DESBOUGH Mrs Audrey. 52 Ashfield Crescent, Billinge, Wigan, WN5 7TE. Tel:0744-894749
DESBOUGH TUDGE F217

119571 DESFORGES Mr A N. 21 Jenks Avenue, Kinver, Stourbridge, West Midlands, DY7 6AQ.
Tel:0384-872421
Deforge Deforges DESFORGES Difirjis Fergis Forges-De F6004

119598 DEVALL Mr R E. 6 Valley View, Prudhoe, Northumberland, NE42 5BL.
Davall Deavalle DEVALL F6718

119601 DEVITT Dr Thomas O. 146 Hampton Road, Twickenham, Middx, TW2 5QR.
Davitt DEVITT Dewitt Macdavitt Macdevitt F7262

119628 DEVLIN Mr Graham. 21 Union Street, Kendal, Cumbria, LA9 4RR.
CARLIER DAVIES DEVLIN INNES Macleod MCLEOD Nicholson NICOLSON QUIGG ROBERTSON SIVEWRIGHT TAYLOR Twigg F2445

119636 DEVLIN Mrs Rae. (Hancock) 16 Fairway Avenue, Southport, 4215, AUSTRALIA.
Tel:+61-7-531-4313
CASEY DEVLIN HANCOCK HICKS HUDSON LALLY MCDONALD SCHOLEFIELD WAYTE F5659

119644 DEVONISH Mr Lionel A. 118 Dugdale Hill Lane, Potters Bar, Herts, EN6 2DJ.
Davenish Davenishe Davenyshe Davenysshe Daynish Debnish DENNISH DEVENISH DEVONISH Dovnish F3207

119652 DEWELL Mr J. 37 Kirkley Cliff, Sth Loewstoft, Suffolk, NR33 0DB. Tel:0502-574094
ALDRIDGE DAWSON DEWELL F1764

119660 DEWEY Mr Paul. Meadow Rise, Ashley Barn, Briantspuddle, Dorchester, DT2 7HL.
DEWEY Dewy F5907

119679 DIACK Mrs L. 41 Middleton Circle, Bridge Of Don, Aberdeen, Scotland, AB2 8LF.
Mciwham Mclquham MEIKLEHAM F6929

119687 DIBLEY Mr John D. 34 Sadlers Way, Ringmer, Lewes, East Sussex, BN8 5HG.
BATHOLOMEW BOURNE BURGESS DIBLEY HOLDEN IGGLESDEN TAYLOR F1827

119695 DICKENSON Mrs Doris. (Malson) Po Box 2054, Guerneville, CA 95446, USA.
Tel:+1-707-869-3215
APPLEBY CARTER CARY COCK COWARD DUNKERTON GROVE HOLE NURSE F5692

119709 DICKENSON L W. 39 The Meadway, Cuffley, Potters Bar, Herts, EN6 4ET. Tel:0707-872106
DICKENSON F7410

119717 DICKEY Dr Gary Alan. West Hills, 22167 Bryant Street, Canoga Park, CA 91304-2306, USA. Tel:+1-818-712-0208
BOOTH BRIGGS CHAPMAN COATES CRESSEY FARROW FOSTER GREENHOOD HODGSON JAQUES LINTON MCTAGGART NICHOLSON NODDINS Pearson PIERSON Rhodus ROADHOUSE SPURGEON STABLER SYKES VENTRESS F4445

119725 DICKEY Mrs Margaret L. Dove Cottage, Outwoods Lane, Anslow, Burton On Trent Staffs, DE13 0AB.
AULD Beaton BETHUNE Betton COWAN HENDERSON JARDINE JOHNSON Johnston KIRTON KNOX LOGAN MAITLAND MCALPINE MUNRO RENNIE SINTON Thompson THOMSON WALKER WALLACE WILSON F1278

119733 DICKIE Mrs Barbara. 28 Boothroyd Drive, Crosland Hill, Huddersfield, W Yorks, HD4 5QH.
DENHAM DICKIE KICKIE F3092

119741 DICKINSON Major Robert H. 5 Crescent Avenue, Hexham, Northumberland, NE46 3DP.
Caras CARIS Carous Carus Deconson Dicisson DICKINSON Dikison Dixson ERRINGTON Eryngton ROWELL Rowle Rowley F5268

119768 DICKINSON Mr Walter R. 12 Parkstone Mount, Leeds, West Yorks, LS16 6ES. Tel:0532-679171
BELLERBY CUTHBERT DICKINSON LAWTON LONGTHORNE NICHOLSON RAGG F4870

119776 DICKMAN Mrs Jenny. (Viney) 5 Douglas St, Waikari, Nth Canterbury, 8276, NEW ZEALAND. Tel:+64-3-314-4059
KALER VINEY F4482

119784 DIDCOCK Mr Ernest. 27 Balgreen Road, Edinburgh, EH12 5TY. Tel:031-337-3015
BEAL BEALE BLACK DIDCOCK KEITH NICHOLSON PARSONS QUINLAN RICHARDSON STEWART WOODS F576

119792 DIDLICK Mrs P. 15 St Mawes Drive, Broadsands Park, Paignton, Devon, TQ4 7NR.
4502 BRIDGEWATER Bridgwater DAVIES Davis DIDLICK Didlock Didluck HILL HINCE Hines Hints Ince Innes JONES MILLICHAMP Millichap Millichope Mullan MULLEN Owen OWENS F4502

119806 DIEDERICH Mr J W. 3751 Little Neck Point, Virginia Beach, VA 23452, USA. Tel:+1-804-486-7905
NICHOLAS F216

119814 DIEDRICHS Tanis. 2804 Walnut Street, Cedar Falls, Iowa, 50613, USA.
BARNELL Barnhill F7229

119822 DIGGLE Mrs Iris. (Pendlebury) 12 West Park Avenue, Leeds, LS8 2HG.
BARROW BROOKS BUCKLEY COLLINGE CROMPTON HOLDEN Holding JERVIS PENDLEBURY WARBURTON WEBSTER F4274

119830 DIGGORY Mr J F. 4 Woodland Place, Boxmoor, Hemel Hempstead, Herts, HP1 1RD.
Diggery DIGGORY F7007

119849 DIGNEY Mr Ernest F. Rr7 Siza C24, Vernon, British Columbia, V1T 7Z3, CANADA.
BROOKES Choun Chun DIGNEY EADE HARRIS HAVERS MASLEN ROBINSON Shun SHUNN SIDAWAY F4196

119857 DILWORTH Mr William. 51 Chester Road, Walthamstow, London, E17 7HP. Tel:081-520-0235
Delworth Dillsworth Dillworth Dilsworth Dilsworthy Dilwart Dilwarth Dilwert Dilwerth Dilwort DILWORTH Dylworth JOHNSON MOORE NOBLE SWAN Swann F3311

119865 DINEEN Mr Desmond. 10 Harland Square, Wantirna, VIC 3152, AUSTRALIA. Tel:+61-3-801-4250
BROWN COLLINS COMBELLACK DEVLIN MCCULLAGH QUINN SERVICE WOOD YOUNG F4456

119873 DINGLE Mr Donald Frederick. 8 Penwithick Road, Penwithick, St Austell, Cornwall, PL26 8UG.
Dingel Dingell DINGLE Dingley Dinglye Dyngell Dyngle HIGMAN WILLIAMS F632

119881 DINGWALL Mr Robert. 50 North Deeside Road, Bieldside, Aberdeen, AB1 9DR.
ALLAN DINGWALL LESLIE MACKIE MAITHIESON MCINTYRE MIDDLETON PHILIP RAE ROSS F4733

119903 DINSDALE Mr Keith J. 823 Schneider Place, Peterborough, Ontario, K9H 5S6, CANADA. Tel:+1-705-745-6941
DINSDALE HARDGROVE F6229

119911 DINSDALE Mrs Pamela. (Keech) 60 Eastfield Avenue, Weston, Bath, BA1 4HJ.
BAGG BILES BIRCH DAMEN DEACON DINSDALE FLEURS FRAMPTON GREEN HART KEECH LARCOMBE LIGHT MEYNELL NORMAN STOODLY THOMPSON WHEADON F4750

119938 DINSDALE Mr Richard. 47 Eastcote Avenue, Bramcote, Beeston, Nottingham, NG9 3FF.
BAKER BISHOP BRAMHAM CLARK DINSDALE DOWSLING FIELD FOWLER HAYES HILLING LANE LARK Larke LAWRENCE MASON MORGAN MUTLEY NORMAN PACE PATRICK PECKSTON Pexton PHILPOTTS PITT POWELL PRESTON RAVENHILL REASON ROUSE RYMER TAYLOR TOBB UNITT F3711

119946 DINWOODIE Mr D. Applegarth, 31 Glendale Close, Carlton, Nottingham, NG4 4FD.
Denwoodie Dinwiddie Dinwiddy Dinwood Dinwoodey DINWOODIE Dinwoody Dunwiddie Dunwood Dunwoodie Dunwoody F6919

119954 DISMORE Mrs D A. (May) 5a The Broad Walk, Northwood, Middx, HA6 2XF.
MAY F6105

119962 DISNEY Mr Edward. Hillside House, Port Navas, Falmouth, Cornwall, TR11 5RQ.
DISNEY F787

119970 DISNEY Mr Hugh. 121 Cumnor Hill, Oxford, OX2 9JA. Tel:0865-863778
BARLOW BARNARD DISNEY FLEMING L'ESTRANGE MAQUAY PATON F4147

119989 DISS Mr G D. Donibee, 369 Abbey Road, Barrow In Furness, Cumbria, LA13 9JS. Tel:0229-822157
BROSCH DISS Disse Dysse F69

119997 DITTY Mrs Beatrice. (Marsden) Po Box 355, Rio Linda, CA 95673, USA. Tel:+1-916-991-4566
BLAKELEY CLAFTON MARSDEN RIDINGS STAFFORD F6224

120006 DIVER Mrs S J. 100 Studley Avenue, Holbury Soton, Hants, SO4 1PP.
Godden GODDING F7025

120014 DIXON Mr C. 40 Norset Road, Fareham, Hants, PO15 6SS.
DIXON NIGHTINGALE STUBBLES F4797

120022 DIXON Mrs E. 95b Bedford Court Mansions, Bedford Avenue, London, WC1B 3AE.
BRUCE DARBY DIXON STREET F5833

120030 DIXON Mrs Feona. (Furze) The Corner House, 27 Tilmire Close, York, YO1 4NG.
Colet COLLET Collett Furs Furse FURZE JAMES STEPHENS TREVARTON WATTS F4062

120049 DIXON Mr J A. 22 Redwood, Burnham, Bucks, SL1 8JN.
BIRCH BROWN BURSLEM DARWEN DIXON DOXEY HARRISON JOHNSON LEAK LIVER MARSDEN MEADOWS PERRY REDFERN WATKIN WEAVER F4220

120057 DIXON Mrs J A. (Grellis) 25 Salway Drive, Salway Ash, Bridport, Dorset, DT6 5LD.
BARNARD BYRNE COVENTRY DIXON DOUST FENN Grelis GRELLIS LATTER PETRI PORTCH SAUNDERS SOMERWILL STEGGLES TALBOT TURNER WALDRON WALLACE F4081

120065 DIXON Mrs J E. 11 Stanbury Crescent, Folkestone, Kent, CT19 6PB.
RONALDS F7383

120073 DIXON Mrs Margaret. 73 Pasture Hill Road, Haywards Heath, W Sussex, RH16 1LY. Tel:0444-456859
GLAZEBROOK TULL F1943

120081 DIXON Mr Richard. 19 Oakwood Road, Boldmere, Sutton Coldfield, W Midlands, B73 5EH. Tel:021-355-3334
CHURCHILL DIXON JAMES KEECH KNIBB LIDDINGTON NIBB ROBERTS SAUNDERS STAMP STONES THRESHER F1570

120103 DOBSON Mr Duncan Jardine. Low Hurst House, Wreay, Carlisle, Cumbria, CA4 ORH.
CLAPHAM DOBSON JARDINE KING RICE THEXTON F2184

120111 DOBSON Mr E F. 1469 Burnamthorpe Rd W, Mississauga, Ontario, L5C 2S7, CANADA.
DOBSON Dopson F6697

120138 DOBSON Earle. 26 Kenninghall Blvd, Mississauga, Ontario, L5N 1J4, CANADA.
DOBSON Dobston Dopson Dotson F7263

120146 DOCHERTY Mr C J. 12 Windermere Gardens, Alresford, Hants, SO24 9NL.
BATTEN BENNET BLACK BLEWER BROWN BROWNING

DOCHERTY HAMILTON HANCOCK HARDY HISCOCK LOVECRAFT LOWERY MILLAR PONSFORD PYE SMITH SNELLING STEWART WATSON F5872

120154 DOCTOR Mr Mark. 1 Cloverland, Hatfield, Herts, AL10 9ED.
BOYD COOPER CREIGHTON DOCTOR HARRIS RAMSAY THOMPSON TIERNEY WALLIS WOODWARD F2741

120162 DODD Mrs C J. (Godson) 19 Godmans Lane, Marks Tey, Colchester, Essex, CO6 1LU.
GODSON F42

120170 DODD Mr P R. 45 Round Hill Meadow, Great Boughton, Chester, CH3 5XR. Tel:0244-340759
DENTITH DODD MILLER RAE F3305

120189 DODDRELL Mr Vernon James Somerset. The Coach House Of Oakland, Ambleside Road, Windemere, Cumbria, LA23 1AR. Tel:09662-4238
BOUCHER DODDRELL GRIFFIN GROUCUTT MILLS PLUMLEY READ ROBERTS SHAA WOOSNAM F3350

120197 DODSON Mr Michael. 64 Stoneleigh Road, Solihull, West Midlands, B91 1DQ. Tel:021-705-3744
CUTLER DODSON FLETCHER HAINSWORTH F4153

120200 DOLAN Mr John. 5 Brackley Street, Stockton Heath, Warrington, WA4 6DY. Tel:0925-601614
Berkinhead Birchinhead BIRKENHEAD Birkinhead DOLAN GLOSSOP GRACE Grase Grease HATTON Haughton HAWKINSON HOUGHTON LEE Leigh RILEY WRIGLEY F4578

120219 DOLLAR Mrs Jan. 30 Woodlands Drive, Bo'Ness, West Lothian, EH51 0NT. Tel:0506-823380
BROOM Broome DOLLAR FERGUSSON HIGSON ISHERWOOD JONES MACLAGAN MCCLELLAN MCKAY NIVEN SYME F998

120227 DOMMETT Revd Richard R. 14 Norwich Road, Halesworth, Suffolk, IP19 8HN.
DOMMETT ERSKINE GOODYER MATTHEW RADHORE F6086

120235 DONALD Mr Alastair. Rose Cottage, High Street, Widdington, Saffron Waldon Essex, CB11 3PG.
BAKER DONALD FORRESTER HOLLISTER MACFARLANE MACKENZIE MORGAN PEPLER SMITH VENNELS F2169

120243 DONALDSON Mr Alex. Lincoln Lodge, 151 Grenfell Road, Maidenhead, Berks, SL6 1EY.
DAMEREL DONALDSON JOLLIFFE STRANG WOODS F4709

120251 DONE Mr Peter D. 638 Birmingham Road, Lydiate Ash, Bromsgrove, Worcs, B61 0QB.
BLAKEWAY DONE HUPSTON LUNE F1056

120278 DONKIN Miss Anne. 35 Marfleet Lane, Marfleet, Kingston Upon Hull, North Humberside, HU9 5RJ.
ANDREWS ARMSTRONG BALK DONKIN Emerson EMMERSON Highley HILEY WISE Wyse F4267

120286 DONN Mrs Audrey. 18 Nelson St, Ashburton, NEW ZEALAND.
CALDER CAMPBELL CLARKE COX CRAIGIE GREG Gregg HOOD JONES KERR RAMSAY ST CLARE TEMPLETON F4368

120294 DONNE Sir John. The Old School House, Acton Burnell, Shrewsbury, Salop, SY5 7PG. Tel:06944-647
Don Done Donn DONNE Dun Dunne SEATON F1134

120308 DONNELLY Mrs Lorna. (Casban) 60 Crookham Road, Crookham, Fleet, Hants, GU13 0NH.
BISHOP Casball CASBAN Casbard Casbell Casben Casbill Casbolt Casbolte Casbon Casborn Casborne Casboult Casbourn Casbourne Casbull Casburn Casburne DONNELLY MOON OVAL Ovel Ovell RICHES SEDGEWICK Sedgwick F4660

120316 DONOVAN Mrs M E. 42 Kings Road, Fleet, Hants, GU13 9AQ.
MASTERSON F6561

120324 DOO Mr Alfred George. 38 Selborne Road, Sidcup, Kent, DA14 4QY.
Doe DOO Dooe F4875

120332 DOOLEY Mrs M. (Harrigan) 1 Myrtle Terrace, Mumbles, Swansea, SA3 4DT.
BATEMAN DOOLEY HARRIGAN LEGG LYFORD O DONNELL F4832

120340 DORAN Mrs Joan. 25 Langdon Shaw, Sidcup, Kent, DA14 6AX. Tel:081-300-8674
ANDERSON JORDAN ROBINSON ROGERS WATTS F2264

120359 DORE Mrs D. 79 Chatworth Road, West Bridgford, Notts, NG2 7AE.
Spettiswood SPOTTISWOODE F6638

120367 DOREY Miss G E. 5 Rodinghead, Kings Lynn, Norfolk, PE30 4TQ.
BOLTON BOULTON DRAKE FULLER GRAINGER GRANGER LAIRD MITCHELL NORRIS F6451

120375 DORMER Mr E S. 18 Balmoral Court, Dunblane, FK15 9HH. Tel:0786-822571
DORMER F482

120383 DORR Mrs Enid Eileen. (Rotherham) 8 Church Street, Bingham, Notts, NG13 8AL. Tel:0949-837143
BOOTH MARPLES ROTHERHAM SHAW F3914

120391 DORRELL Mr Edward Henry. 2 Ainslie Close, Aylestone Hill, Hereford, HR1 1JH.
CARTER D'raoul Dairel Darell Darral Darrell Dayrell Dorel Dorill Dorrall Dorrel DORRELL Dorril Dorrill DUCE Durrell MILLWARD ONSLOW F30

120405 DORWARD Mr Mike. 27 Buttenshaw Close, Arborfield, Reading, Berks, RG2 9LX. Tel:0734-760786
Debrick Dederich Dederick Dedlick DEDRICK Dedvick Deidrick DORWARD Dorwood Durward Hickes HICKS F2120

120413 DOUBT Mrs J E. 29-931 Gleneagles Drive, Kamloop, British Columbia, V2E 1K4, CANADA.
DOUBT Doupt Dout Doute Dowt F6874

120421 DOUGHERTY Mr Patrick. O'Dochartaigh, Ar Nductas, Inch Island, Co Donegal, IRELAND.
DOHERTY F7264

120448 DOUGHTY Mr Clarence E. Po Box 203, Mays Landing, NJ 08330, USA.
Daughty Dawdy Doten Doty DOUGHTY Dowty F7265

120456 DOUGHTY Mr Kenneth A. 47 Harrow Road, Barking, Essex, IG11 7QZ. Tel:081-594-6229
BARRETT BRIGHT CORBYN DOUGHTY LOCK PARISH PARRISH TOMLIN F497

120464 DOUGLAS Mr James R. Fourways, The Leys, Witney, Oxford, OX8 7AR. Tel:0993-778430
DOUGLAS MCNARIN MCNARINE WEDDELL F518

120472 DOUGLAS Mrs Susan E. (Holloway) 71 Burn Foot Avenue, Fulham, London, SW6 5EB.
BEASLEY BENHAM FOX HACKETT HATCH HOLLOWAY HURLSTOWE KEEL SPIER TABBENER WALKER WALTON WARRICK Warwick F5926

120480 DOUST Mrs S B L. 121 Warren Drive, Hornchurch, Essex, RM12 4QU.
DOUST ZACHARIAH F6606

120499 DOVE Mr Brian Arthur. Druidstone Cottage, Newlands, Balcombe, Sussex, RH17 6JA. Tel:0444-811320
ALLARD COOK DOVE MAPLE TAYLOR WHITE F669

120502 DOW Mrs Eileen M S. Sgeir Dhubh, Shieldaig, Strathcarron, Ross-Shire, IV54 8XS. Tel:05205-272
DOW F3413

120510 DOW Mr Peter J. Branmin (the Pink Bungalow), Flowers Drove, Lytchett Matravers, Poole Dorset, BH16 6BX. Tel:0202-631653
DOW MUSSEL SALTWELL TREVITT VATCHER WHEELER F1193

120529 DOWD Mr Kevin. 56 Peterborough Road, Farcet, Peterborough, PE7 3BN.
BARKS BARTLE CADE CARSLEY CARTER CLARK CLARKE CLEAR COWLING COXHEAD CRESSEY DOWD FENLEY FOX GIBBONS GODFREY GREEN HALL HAWKINS HEATH HOLLINGSWORTH HOLLINGWORTH JOHNSON KEELEY LANGHAM LITTLEWOOD LOCK MAPLETHORP MAPLETHORPE MIRFIELD PARKER PULLAN THORPE WATSON WELLAND WHITLOCK WILKINS WILKINSON F6263

120537 DOWDELL Mr William L. 39 Napier Avenue, Blackpool, Lancs, FY4 1PA.
TETLOW Tettlow Tettlowe F7093

120545 DOWDESWELL Mr David. The Meadows, Hewshott Lane, Liphook, Hants, GU30 7SS. Tel:0428-722117
DOWDESWELL F725

120553 DOWDING Mr John. 300 Rickstone Road, Rivenhall, Witham, Essex, CM8 3HQ. Tel:0376-512374
Doudgen Doudin Dowden Dowdin DOWDING F3809

120561 DOWNES Mr Clive. 21 Hare Lane, Farncombe, Godalming, Surrey, GU7 3EE. Tel:0483-414507
BRIDGER DOWNES DRAGE MACKINTOSH PETTY F2144

120588 DOWNES Mrs H. (Jarvis) 44 Clarence Road, Southport, Merseyside, PR8 4BH.
DOWNES Downs DRITTLER JARVIS Jervis RIMMER Rowland ROWLANDS Rymer Rymmer Trischler F3796

120596 DOWNING Mrs Anne. 18 Worcester Close, Bottesford, Scunthorpe, Humberside, DN16 3TL. Aslin Astlin ASTLING COOLING Hinchcliffe Hinchliff HINCHLIFFE MARTIN PARSON Taplin Tapling Tuplin TUPLING F4968

120618 DOWNS Mrs Kate. (Parnell) 45 The Pastures, Westwood, Bradford On Avon, Wilts, BA15 2BH. DRUMMOND FAVIER MAYNARD PARNELL WATTS F5829

120626 DOYLE Mrs Wendy. (Arm) 65 Station Road, Histon, Cambridge, CB4 4LQ. Tel:0223-232070 ARM Arme Armes Arms BAILEY BOOKER BRAMALL FOLLETT HALES Harm MARSH WHALE WILSON F4572

120634 DRACOS Mrs Elizabeth. 30 Coombe Gardens, London, SW20 0QU. BAGOT BOND CASSON HADLER HETHERINGTON JORDAN KEELING PERCY RANGER STRIBLING F6023

120642 DRAKE Miss P J. 13 Roundmead Road, Basingstoke, Hants, RG21 1TR. CHAFFIN Chafyn F6659

120650 DRAKE Mrs S. (Marshall) 388 Ashgate Rpad, Chesterfield, Derbyshire, S40 4DD. BUTTERFIELD DOWNEY DRAKE EXFORD FOX GAMSON GAMSTON GILL HAWLEY Hecksford HETT Hexford Hinsley HUDDERSTON Illsey Incley INSLEY LEE MARSHALL MARSTON Matthew NORWOOD TAYLOR WATTHEW WHEATLEY WILLIAMS F6484

120669 DRAKE Mrs Sheila. 20 Walker Close, Glusburn, Keighley, W Yorks, BD20 8PW. BAMFORD GREENOUGH HEYES HOUGHTON MAGINNIS Mcinnis PARKER PUGH TWEEDALE F3111

120677 DRANSFIELD Mr Chris. 8 Dunstone Park Road, Paignton, Devon, TQ3 3NG. BAMFORTH BRAKE BRIANT BROWN CLAY DRANSFIELD GARSIDE GIBBINS GREGORY KNIGHT LEWIS LOCKWOOD MILES MOSS PHILLIPS POGSON REED REYNOLDS ROGERS SAVILLE SHAW SIMMS SMITH SPREADBURY SWIFT SYKES TUFFIN WARE WARING WOODHEAD F3020

120685 DRAPER Mr Frank. 124 Lord Street, Hoddesdon, Herts, EN11 8NP. Tel:0992-460117 DRAPER KENT F1045

120693 DRAPER Mrs P A. 65 Hillcrest Road, Frankston, Victoria, 3199, AUSTRALIA. DRAPER F7212

120707 DRAPER Mrs Violet T. 14 Wrights Road, Lithgow, NSW 2790, AUSTRALIA. Tel:+61-6-352-2088 COX DAWKINS DRAPER KEEGAN LAMB SANDELL SIMPSON TONDRA Tonra F5549

120715 DRAYTON Mrs R. (Buckler) 36 Coronation St, Barnstaple, Devon, EX32 7BA. BUCKLER PYNE STANBURY F6423

120723 DRENNAN Mrs Elsie F. (Pope) 105 Bute Road, Wallington, Surrey, SM6 8AE. CAFFIN FARLEY HARADINE HOW KEYTE LOCOCK LOCOK POPE F6491

120731 DREWE Mr G A. 6 Treve Avenue, Harrow, Middlesex, HA1 4AJ. AMES BALLETT BERRIFF BRIDEN DREWE MESSENGER SEATH F6233

120758 DREWERY Mr Carl. 32 Hawksbury Close, Redditch, B98 9JR. Tel:0527-592168 DREWERY Drewry Drury SMITH F4205

120766 DREWETT Mrs L C. 31 St Catherine Street, Ventnor, Isle Of Wight, PO38 1HG. FIANDER FUDGE Fyander MOTH Mothe Phyander F6966

120774 DREWRY Mr Peter. 142 Timberbank, Vigo, Gravesend, Kent, DA13 0SW. Callender COTTENDEN CURD DAVIS Drewry DRURY Filday FULLER GASSON Gaston NEWSTEAD SANDS SEARS VILDAY Vildey F1357

120782 DRING Mr Christopher. 96 St Giles Avenue, Sleaford, Lincs, NG34 7JD. Tel:0529-306322 Caldren Caldron Cauldren Cauldron Coldren COLDRON Couldren Couldron DRING F1050

120790 DRINKWATER Mr Geoffrey. 41 Gwenbrook Avenue, Chilwell, Nottingham, NG9 4BA. Tel:0602-250681 DRINKWATER SPICER F6466

120804 DRISCOLL Mrs Diane. C/o Melvin, 51 Searing Avenue, Harrison, New Jersey 07029 Usa. AITON BROWN COOPER CURE FOXON FRENCH GRANT HADDOW HOLT MACDONALD MACKINNON Melville MELVIN OULD Oulds PATERSON Randal Randall Randel Randell RANDLE RUSSEL RUSSELL SOMMERS Summers SWIRE Swyre THOMSON F1648

120812 DRURY Mr Derek. 67 Borstal Hill, Whitstable, Kent, CT5 4WU. Tel:0227-274162 DRURY F2574

120820 DRURY Mr Henry W. 20 Burford Road, Stratford Upon Avon, Warwickshire, CV37 7ET. Tel:0789-293507 DRURY F421

120839 DRY Mr J D. 5 Midland Road, Stonehouse, Glos, GL10 2DQ. Tel:0453-826718 BEESLEY BLOWMAN BURGESS CORK CORKE DEAKIN DRY FEWSTER REDSHAW SYKES TURNER F5249

120847 DRYHURST Mr Glen. 8 Doulton Way, Ashingdon, Rochford, Essex, SS4 3BX. Tel:0702-544972 Drayhurst Drihurst Drihurste Drwyherst Dryas Dryasse Dryerre Dryers Dryerst Dryess Dryherst Dryhirst Dryhirste Dryhorst Dryhouse DRYHURST Dryhurste F2844

120855 DU-CANE Mrs R A. Forest Cottage, Pilley Bailey, Lymington, Hants, SO41 5QT. CARNALL STANIFORTH F2534

120863 DUBB Mr Leonard. 32 Gorley Court, Woolston Road, Leigh Park, Havant Hants, PO9 4JN. Tel:0705-455817 DUBB F1126

120871 DUCK Mr Ivan. Chenies, Loudhams Wood Lane, Chalfont St Giles, Buckinghamshire, HP8 4AR. DUCK STACEY YELF F6496

120898 DUCKETT Mr R S. Outwood Hills Farm, Lower Outwoods Road, Burton On Trent, DE13 0QX. Duccoths Duckat DUCKETT Duckitt F3948

120901 DUCKWORTH Mr Sydney. Andersons Cottage, Canal Bank, Pygons Hill Lane, Lydiate, Merseyside, L31 4JE. Tel:051-520-1033 CLEGG CULSHAW DUCKWORTH ELLIS HIGHAM HORROCKS MERCER SUTCLIFFE WIGNALL F2319

120928 DUDBRIDGE Mr B J. Red Rock Bungalow, Elm Grove Road, Topsham, Exeter, EX3 0EJ. Tel:0392-874468 DUDBRIDGE F3109

120936 DUDBRIDGE Mrs E J. (Blencowe) 16 Darwin Court, Gloucester Avenue, London, NW1 7BG. Blencko Blenckoe Blenckow Blenco Blencoe Blencow BLENCOWE Blenko Blenkoe Blenkow Blincko Blinckoe Blinckow Blinco Blincoe Blincow Blincowe Blynchoo Blyncko Blynckoe Blynckow F3658

120944 DUDLEY Mrs Elizabeth. Rosemundy Villa, St Agnes, Cornwall, TR5 0DU. Tel:087255-2380 DUDLEY HARPER JENKIN KING ROWE F853

120952 DUDMAN Mrs Mavis. (Holt) 8 Spreighton Road, East Molesey, Surrey, KT8 0JF. FILLINGHAM HOLT Hought Hoult F5277

120960 DUFALL Mr A. 12 Watcombe Road, Bournemouth, Dorset, BH6 3LT. Davol Davole Davoll Davolle Devol Devole DEVOLL Devolle Dival Divale Divall Divalle Divol Divole Divoll Divolle DUFALL Dyval Dyvale Dyvall Dyvalle Dyvol Dyvole Dyvoll Dyvolle F4272

120979 DUFFILL Mr Peter. 30 Park Hill Road, Harborne, Birmingham, B17 9SL. Tel:021-427-2106 DUFFILL PARDOE ROBINSON STRINGER TYE WHITTY WYKEE F2860

120987 DUFFIN Mr Kenneth. 44 Bewcastle Grove, Mowmacre Hill, Leicester, LE4 2JW. Tel:0533-358979 CRAMP DALBY DUFFIN HARRISON KENLYSIDE F6226

120995 DUFFY Ms Ellen. 9 Brine House, St Stephens Road, Bow, London, E3 5PG. ALSOP BARTLETT BEAR BEARD BREEN BUTLER ELLIOTT GIBBENS PURNELL WITHERS F964

121002 DUGGAN Mrs Carol. 1 Dobson Road, Shepparton, Victoria, 3630, AUSTRALIA. BEARDSLEY BINKS DUGGAN FITCH GREGORY MCCLELLAND RAYMOND VEALE WOODWARD F4446

121010 DUGGAN Mr Peter. 75 Alexandra Road, Reading, Berks, RG1 5PS. Tel:0734-663220 ALLDAY ANDERSON BAKER BATT BEALE BOWRING BRACHER BURNETT CHILDEROY COLE COMPTON DEXTER DUGGAN DUNN EMERY EVANS GODDARD HODGSON KNIGHT MORRANT PENTON PHILLIPS PRANGNELL PRICE PROBERT QUICK REDMAN REEKS SCAMELL TILBURY WRIGHT YOUNG F2215

121029 DUJARDIN Mr Edward. Bowood, 30 Beech Hill, Hadley Wood, Barnet, Herts, EN4 0JP.

Dujarden DUJARDIN KYNE Kynne F7213
121037 DULLEY Miss Thelma. Hawkwood, 46 Hillview Road, Chislehurst, Kent, BR7 6DS. Tel:081-857-6010
BAKER BROOKS Doyley Doylye Duley Dullee DULLEY Dyllie Dylly GALLOWAY GUTTERIDGE HOWE LAWSON LOUCH PEASGOOD SCOTT SHERWOOD SILVERTHORNE SPRINAGE TOFFTS WOOD F3014
121045 DUMARESQ Mr Michael. 60 Forest Gate, Evesham, Worcs, WR11 6XY.
DUMARESQ F2162
121053 DUMBLETON Dr Michael. 25 Warfield Road, Bracknell, Berks, RG12 2JY. Tel:0344-427492
BADDLEY BLAKEMORE DUMBLETON EVEREST FROST FUELL PETHER PRITCHARD SPEED WHITE WOOD F3301
121061 DUMONT Miss Sharon. 20 Olympia Street, Norton, Mass 02766, USA.
BASKERVILLE CHEETHAM CLAYTON GOLDING JONES MASSEY ROBERTS TAYLOR TIMBRELL F1028
121088 DUMPER Mr Steve. 5 Elder Grove, Crediton, Devon, EX17 1DE. Tel:0363-775365
DUMBER DUMPER F834
121096 DUNCAN Mr C J. 3 Eddisbury Road, West Kirby, Wirral, Merseyside, L48 5DR.
BURNETT DUNCAN JAMES KIRLEW LEGERTON NEWLOVE PHILLIPS TANNER YEOMANS F5897
121118 DUNCAN Mr Jeremy. 10 Kincarrathie Crescent, Perth, PH2 7HH. Tel:0738-33470
BARROW BUGGINS CUMMING DUNCAN GODFREY HALL MEWTON STEWART WICKENS WOODFORD F4118
121126 DUNCAN Mrs M. (Straith) 802 Michaux Lane, Grosse Pointe Shores, MI 48236, USA. Tel:+1-313-884-0039
CLARK Clarke Clerk DUNCAN FLEMING Flemming HAYES Hays Heys Hodg HODGE HOLT ISAAC Isaak Isaake KINGSTON LANYON MARKWICK Markwicke Marquique Mill Miln MILNE Perie PIRIE Retallic RETALLICK Rettalack ROBERTS SARVIS Service Servis Straith STRATH Stroath VARNEY WENHAM Whenham Whonham WILLIAMS Wonham F4490
121134 DUNCAN Mrs Norma. Malone, 19 Netherton Drive, Frodsham, Cheshire, WA6 6DG.
ALISTER BONNER GRAHAM MARSHALL SHACKLETON F2569
121142 DUNCAN Mr Robert James. 13 Leyland Road, Rainford, Lancashire, WA11 8HF.
DUNCAN GILBERT JORDAN MCARTHUR METCALFE ROBY F954
121150 DUNCLIFFE Mrs Susan. (Gibson) 4 Farm Grove, Rugby, Warks, CV22 5NQ.
ANDREWS BRAYN BROWN GIBSON GOULDING HOLLIES SAVAGE WEBB F6359
121169 DUNFORD Mr Fraser. 1148 Milne Avenue, New Minas, Nova Scotia, B4N 4J2, CANADA. Tel:+1-902-681-7863
BOLTON COOPER CURTIS DUNFORD FRY GREEN GRIST HISCOCK HORLER LEAR LESLIE MCCRACKEN PAYNE PRICE SCANE SHEARN SMITH THOMPSON WEST F5590
121177 DUNFORD K E. Rowans, 4 Lansdowne Avenue, Winchester, Hants, SO23 9TJ.
CAESAR CAMPBELL DUNFORD PEACH TOWNSHEND WEBBER F2999
121185 DUNFORD Mrs Sylvia. 140 Crabble Hill, Dover, Kent, CT17 0SA.
AMOS Brownjohn BROWNON Burkinshaw BURTENSHAW COCKBURN Cockburne Cockeburn Cockeburne COCKS Danford Danforde Darneford Darneforde Darnford Darnforde Denford Denforde DENNE Derneford Derneforde Dernford Dernforde Donford Donforde Dorneford Dorneforde Dornford Dornforde DREW DUNFORD Dunsford DURNFORD Eddells Eddels Eddol EDDOLLS Eddols Edels Edgcock Edgcocke Edgecock Edgecocke Edols FISK Fiske GILBERT GOLDSACK Hedgcock Hedgcocke HEDGECOCK Hiscock Hiscocke HORAN Horen Horon Iddol Iddolls Iddols Idol Idols LEFEAVER Lefevre MISKIN MOLLAND OLIVER SHEAF Sheaff SPILLSBERY Spilsbery Spilsbury TAMS Trig TRIGG Trigge Triggs Twells TWELVES F2958
121193 DUNGATE Mr Brian. 21 Varndean Drive, Brighton, E Sussex, BN1 6RS. Tel:0273-506824
Dengate Dingate DUNGATE Dungett GEORGE JELLETT MARCHANT MULLETT SUTTON F591
121207 DUNHAM Mr Melvyn Alma. 27 Northacre, Banstead, Surrey, SM7 2EG. Tel:07373-58059
DENHAM DENMAN DUNHAM MACE F3236
121215 DUNKERLEY Mr David J. 39 Town Lane, Denton, Manchester, M34 1AF.
BEALE DIGGLE DUNKERLEY HARRISON TAYLOR WAIN F4077
121223 DUNKERLEY Mr John. 73 Sunningdale Avenue, Marton, Blackpool, Lancs, FY4 4HU. Tel:0253-696533
DUNKERLEY JACKSON KEATING KNOTT LEE MCLEAN WITHERS WOODCOCK F6057
121231 DUNKLEY Mrs Enid. 20 Overstone Court, Ravensthorpe, Peterborough, Cambs, PE3 7JE.
BAKER F1690
121258 DUNKLEY Mrs Kay. 20 Donnington Avenue, Coventry, CV6 1FN. Tel:0203-595653
BODDINGTON CLARKE DRAKEFORD DUNKLEY Hollings HOLLINS HORSLEY Hutchings HUTCHINS JEFFCOATE LONGSLOW RUSSELL F2829
121266 DUNMORE Mr Terence L. 19 Cornwallis Grove, Edmonton, London, N9 0TR.
Dunmawe Dunmoore DUNMORE Dunmorr Dunnamore Dunnomore Dunsemore Dunsmore F5
121274 DUNN Mr Chris. 217 Sandpit Lane, St Albans, Herts, AL4 0BT.
DUNN EDMUNDS HAMILTON MARSHALL OAKE SWEETLOVE F4605
121282 DUNN Mr Christopher. 1 Trewithen Terrace, Ashton, Helston, Cornwall, TR13 9TQ. Tel:0736-762502
DUNN LOCK F5075
121290 DUNN Mrs E. (Moore) 14 Princess Drive, Barrowash, Derby, DE7 3LQ. Tel:0332-668844
BRATBY BRETBY BURFORD DUFFIELD JOHNSON Kerkland Ketland KIRKLAND KNIVETON Kyrkeland Kyrkland Kyrklande MOOR MOORE MORE NOAKES WALLIS WOOD F967
121304 DUNN Mrs Eleanor J. Langtree, Hollins Lane, Arnside, Carnforth Lancs, LA5 0EG.
DICKINSON PARK STOREY STORY F223
121312 DUNN Mr Richard J (Jack). 1 Penhaven Court, Island Crescent, Newquay, Cornwall, TR7 1DZ. Tel:0637-850221
BULLOCK CARPENTER DUNN HODGE LAWER PEARSE PROWSE WALL WASLEY WHITFORD YOUNGMAN F1774
121320 DUNN Mrs Sally. The Grange, Roslyn Road, Levin, New Zealand.
BELL BOND DUNN GILCHRIST HALFYARD LATHAM LEEMING LOONEY LUSHINGTON MARDEL MARDEL-FERREIRA MOSS PARDOE-MATTHEWS F2708
121339 DUNNE Mrs Janet. (Wilson) 27 Marshall Street, Crossgates, Leeds, LS15 8DY. Tel:0532-607927
ADDISON Adison ALDERSON ASH Ask Aske ATKINSON BALMFORTH Balmforthe Bamforth Bamforthe BARBER Bolton BOULTON BOWER BOYES BRAMPTON Broton BROTTON BURTON CALBERRY CARLING CARLTON CARR CHESTER CORNER COWLING Crudas CRUDDAS DALES Dolfin DOLPHIN DUCK Ducke DUNNE ETHERINGTON FIRTH Firthe Flecher FLETCHER FOTHERLEY FRANKLAND FRIAR Frier GARTH HALL HAMMOND Hetherington HILL HODGSHON HODGSON Hopes Hoppes HOPPS LAMPLUGH LENG LILL MALONEY MARSHALL MARSIGILL MELIA Merelelew Merelewe MERRELEW Merrelewe MIDDLETON MIERS Moreland Morelands Morland MORLANDS MYERS Nellis NELLIST NEWTON O'TOOLE OLIVER PEACOCK PINDER Porit Poritt Porrit PORRITT Powel POWELL PRIESTMAN RADCLIFFE Rauson Rausone RAWSON Rawsone Rawsonne RODGERS ROGERS Roussel Roussell Rusell Russel RUSSELL Russells SAGAR Sellar SELLARS SELLER Sellers SMELT SNAITH SPENCE STEPHENSON STONES STOREY TEASDALE TODD TOPLADY WALKER WATERSON WATSON WHITE WILSON Wilsone Wilsonne F3526
121347 DUNNICLIFFE Mr R. 15 Hillsway, Chellaston, Derby, DE7 1RN.
Dunnicliff DUNNICLIFFE F6956
121355 DUNPHY Mrs Daisy. (Marshall) 27 Hillingdon Avenue, Sevenoaks, Kent, TN13 3RB. Tel:0732-460980
CARE CARPENTER CARTER CHAPMAN COGAN DAVISON Delieu DULIEU Duliu GIBSON GREEN HAGGART HAMMOND HICKS HORSKINS JAMES LANGLEY MACKDOUEL MARSHALL MOMFORD OUGHTON PARNELL ROUVIERE RUSSEL Russell Shepard Shepheard SHEPPARD SPARKS TUCKER WOODDEN Wooding WYATT F4303
121363 DUNSCOMBE Mr P. 58 Brookmead Drive,

Wallingford, Oxon, OX10 9BJ.
BROWN DUNSCOMBE EDMONDS HIRD KELLY F2597

121371 DUNSTALL Mrs Thelma. 32a Bollard Avenue, Auckland 7, NEW ZEALAND.
ANNETT DUNSTALL Tunstall F6926

121398 DUNSTAN Mrs Beverley. (Trebilcock) West Langarth Farm, Penstraze, Chacewater, Truro Cornwall, TR4 8PH. Tel:0872-560836
BARNES Chadford GEORGE LAUNDER MANNING Sheetford Shetfar Shetfard SHETFER Shetfor Shethford Shitford Shittford Shudford Shutford Shutforth STONEMAN TREBILCOCK WATERS WILLIAMS F2992

121401 DUNVILLE Mrs Jane. Lord Harris Home, St Stephens House, Mole Road, Sindlesham, Wokingham Berks, RG11 5EA. Tel:0734-789769
MUDD MULLENDER PERRIN F5665

121428 DUNVILLE Mr Tony. Lord Harris Home, St Stephens House, Mole Road, Sindlesham, Wokingham Berks, RG11 5EA. Tel:0734-789769
DUNVILLE LAN ROYSTON F5664

121436 DURANT Mrs Sylvia. 17 Hibbert Avenue, Watford, Herts, WD2 4HB. Tel:0923-32825
Booking BROOKING Carslack Carslake CHESHIRE DARKE Dumbleton DUMPLETON FOREMAN GRIFFIN KERSLAKE Keslake NORWOOD SAINSBURY F1754

121444 DURHAM Mr Gordon. 64 Blackbush Spring, Harlow, Essex, CM20 3DZ.
BUGDEN CHAPPLE DURHAM EADSON LLOYD MEADS F1150

121452 DURHAM Mr Ian. 9 Tunbridge Close, Chew Magna, Bristol, BS18 8SU. Tel:0275-332712
BARKER DURHAM HOGARTH HULL LANGTON MALCOM Malcome F4553

121460 DURHAM Mr William. 70 Richmond Crescent, Highams Park, London, E4 9RU.
BEACHAM COLLINS DRAKE DURHAM EADSON JAGER JEAGER KNOWLDEN LLOYD PRUSACEK F221

121479 DURHAM Mr William. 32 Spinnells Road, Harrow, Middx, HA2 9RA. Tel:081-866-3493
ANSELL COGAN DURHAM HANNA HANNAH HAWKINS KILLEY LOGAN MAIR REID STEPHEN F1928

121487 DURRANT Mr Brian. 23 Upper Moors, Great Waltham, Chelmsford, Essex, CM3 1RB.
BAKER BRADSTREET CHAPLIN CHILDS COOPER DRAKE DURRANT GARDINER LEARNER SPRINGETT F4724

121495 DUTCH Mr A. 2 Salisbury Street, Barton Hill, Bristol, BS5 9UD.
DUTCH JENNINGS LEVY SLEE SQUIRE STIDWELL TURTON F3068

121509 DUXBURY Mr Stephen. 4 Frensham Walk, Chatham, Kent, ME5 9DU. Tel:0634-862125
ALDERSON BRADSHAW COTTAM DEWHURST DINSDALE DRUCE DUGDALE DUGGAN DUXBURY ETHERINGTON GILBERT GRADY GRAFTON GRATTAN GRUNDY HASLAM HAYES HEYES HOLLINSON LAFFORD MOODY MORRIS MOYERS Myers PALMER PEPLOE POLE POLLARD PORTER RICHARDS SALMON SINGLETON STIRK UNSWORTH WALPOLE WAYCROFT WEBSTER WHITBY F1840

121517 DUXBURY-COLLIER Mr Clifford. 402-100 Maitland Street, Toronto, M4Y 1G2, CANADA.
DUXBURY F7270

121525 DWYER Mrs Beverley. Box 34, Post Office, Miami, Queensland, 4220, AUSTRALIA.
BALDCOCK BROWNING CAMPBELL CLARKE DEARDEN DUFFIELD GORDON HOLDER HOOKINS PHIPPS F5669

121533 DYER Mr Dave. The Firs, Amberstone Corner, Hailsham, E Sussex, BN27 1PJ. Tel:0323-845107
DYER GOSLING NORRELL REYNOLDS F1769

121541 DYER Mrs Dorothy. (Wood) 6 Patterson Avenue, Brantford, Ontario, N3S 6W9, CANADA.
DYER DYMOND HARDIMAN HOLMES MCCOLL NEWTON PEARSON RAYBOULD STEPHENS WOOD F4381

121568 DYER Mr Malcolm. 81 Padiham Road, Sabden, Nr Blackburn, Lancs, BB6 9EX.
ALLEN BAKER BALL BOND BROWNSELL BUCK Burson BURSTON Burstone Busson CHILCOTT Cockerham COCKRAM Cockrem COLES COLLING COMER COTTLE Crewes CREWS CRIPPS Cruse CRUWYS Cruze DREW DYER ERREY Erry FOWLER GOLDSWORTHY GREEN Hale HAYTER HEAL Heale HILL HOBBS Hosegood HOSGOOD HOUSE HOW Howe KELLAN Kelland Kellane LYDDON LYE MATRAVERS MEACHAM Medleton Melhish MELHUISH Mellish Melluish MIDDLETON NEEDS NICHOLS Nickells Nickels Nickols PADFIELD Parfet Parfett Parfit PARFITT PARKER PRING Quarterly Quartley QUARTLY ROBBINS SHIRREFFS SPARK STEVENS STUCKEY TARR THORN TROUT Urry WATTS WEST F4665

121576 DYER Ms P. 20 Gideons Way, Stanford Le Hope, Essex, SS17 8ED.
DYER MORRIS WOODBRIDGE F3286

121584 DYER Mrs V. (Thorp) The Shaefers, Kelland Hill, Lapford, Crediton, Devon, EX17 6AF. Tel:0363-83469
DAWE DIER DYER F961

121592 DYKE Miss Susan. 29 Westby Road, Boscombe, Bournemouth, Dorset, BH5 1HA.
BAKER COBBETT DYER DYKE GRAY GUY HARDING TAYLOR F454

121606 DYSON Mr K. 49 Stalyhill Drive, Mottram Rise, Stalybridge, Cheshire, SK15 2TT. Tel:0457-764107
DYSON F491

121614 DYSON Mr M R. Melmar, 38 Rosebery Road, Dursley, Glos, GL11 4PU.
DETHICK Dionysia Dison Disun Dyotson DYSON Dysone PROBERT F185

121622 DYSON Mrs M. Melmar, 38 Roseberry Road, Dursley, Glos, GL11 4PU.
Coltas Coultas COULTOUS Cultas Jancey Jauncee JAUNCEY Jauncy Jaunsey LISTER F184

121630 DYSON Mrs S A. Waterlilly Cottage, 8 Water Lane, Richmond, Surrey, TW9 1TS.
RICKET F6562

121649 EACHUS Mr B. 35 Mount Road, Alkrington, Middleton, Manchester, M24 1DY.
Eachewes Eachowes EACHUS Etchewes Hatchous F7046

121657 EACRETT Mrs Joyce. 72 Cayuga Street, Brantford, Ontario, N3S 1W5, CANADA.
EACRET ECRET F5512

121665 EADE Mrs Rosemary. (Kelsall) 58 Quinton Lane, Quinton, Birmingham, B32 2TS.
BEVAN COX DEAN EADE GOUGH HAMMONDS HIBBETT KELSALL LINGARD MABELL MABLE Mables MEDLAM OSMOND SIMKIN Simpkin TOYLOR WHITAKER Whittaker F6494

121673 EADON Mrs B. 10 School Lane, Chase Terrace, Walsall, WS7 8LD.
ADEY EADON HARPER LEE REECE SHALE SLATER TOLLEY F6405

121681 EAGERS Mrs K M. (Sprenger) 282 Duffield Road, Darley Abbey, Derby, DE3 1EP.
ARNOLD DEAN EAGERS Egars Eggars HOARE Loader LODER MARTIN OLIVER F4636

121703 EAGLE Mr Derek C. 1 Forest Gardens, Stamford, Lincs, PE9 2FL. Tel:0780-63316
CRICK Eagel Eagele Eagelle EAGLE Eagles Egel Egle Egles Heigham Higham Hyam HYEM LANE PROLTOR READ Reade Reed SPRIGGS F3895

121711 EAGLES Mrs Pamela. Aquila, New Barn Road, New Barn, Longfield, Kent, DA3 7LG.
EAGLES FROUD F925

121738 EAGLES Mr Stuart. The Eyrie, 90 Water Road, Tilehurst, Reading, Berks, RG3 2NN. Tel:0734-594664
DREWEATT DREWETT EAGLES GROVE SAVORY TAYLOR F4426

121746 EAKIN Mr Terry. Po Box 1699, Mount Isa, 4825, AUSTRALIA. Tel:+61-7-743-8201
BANNON BATHEN EAKIN GAULD HABBUCK RYAN TRANTER TUCKER WARNER F6163

121754 EAMES Mr A J (Tony). Tyes Farm House, Green End Lane, Plymtree, Cullompton Devon, EX15 2JR. Tel:08847-489
Ayers AYRES BENTLEY CHITTENDEN DAVEY Davie Davy EAMES Eams Eemes EGLETON Emes Eyers Heames Imms MACGOWAN MARCHANT MEAD Mobberley Mobberly MOBERLEY Moberly Mobley PETTIT PUTNAM Puttenham Sale SALES Searle F3106

121762 EARDLEY Mr Graham. 40 Nuns Road, Winchester, Hants, SO23 7EF.
ASHTON CARROLL COUTNAGE FORSEY GAUNTLETT HADFIELD HITCHEN HOYLAND HUNTINGFORD JORDAN MARRIOTT MUSGRAVE PERRETT PETTER PHILLIPS ROGERS ROLLINSON SHERWOOD WALLER F665

121770 EARL Mr George. 18 Calway Road, Taunton, Somerset, TA1 3EQ.
EARL Earle F3753

121789 EARLAND Mr R W. Mayns Lane, Burton Overy,

Leicester, LE8 0DP.
EARLAND Erland F7078
121797 EARWICKER Mrs Maureen. 34 Marisfield Place, Selsey, W Sussex, PO20 0PD.
ARREQUER ARRIKER ARWAKER Arwicker EARWACKER EARWAKER EARWICKER EOFORWACER ERRICKER F3818
121800 EAST Mrs Andree L. Bainton Farm House, Bainton, Bicester, Oxon, OX6 9RL.
De L'est EAST Est ESTE F7070
121819 EASTAUGH Mr A S. 70 Bishopton Lane, Ripon, North Yorks, HG4 2QN. Tel:0765-606159
Eastale EASTAUGH Eastaw Easthaugh Eastho Easto Eastoe Eastoll Eastough Eastow Eastowe Eastugh Eatole Estaugh Estaughe Esto Estow F6503
121827 EASTAUGH Ms M. 8 Foalhurst Close, Tonbridge, Kent, TN10 4HA. Tel:0732-350147
ALLEN ANDREWS BECKET BIRKS CLARKE DREW EASTAUGH HILL HOOKER STURT F2711
121835 EASTER Mrs Margaret. (Newns) 23 Wroxham Way, Harpenden, Herts, AL5 4PP.
BARKER BARNES BARWICK BEE BOSWELL BRADLEY CABON CLARKE DAVIS EAGER EASTER EASTLAND FIELDSEND FURNIVAL GHEST GILBERT HURRELL JARVIS MAPLES MASSINGHAM MIDDLEBROOKE MILLARD NEWNS PARK PECK PHILLIPS PRIOR ROBERTS SCULPHER THORNE WALESBY WHISKARD WILKINSON F4754
121843 EASTERLING Mr D W. 14 Brunswick Close, Biggleswade, Bedfordshire, SG18 0DA.
EASTERLING Easterlinge F6979
121851 EASTERLY Mrs Grace. (Edgar) 1710 Hawthorne Drive, Trenton, Michigan, 48183, USA. Tel:+1-313-676-6543
EDGAR GOWAN STOBBS F4483
121878 EASTLAKE Miss Celia. 42 Manor Road, Teddington, Middx, TW11 8AB.
BARRETT EASTLAKE GILLMAN F1360
121886 EASTLAKE Miss S. Belle Vue House, 9 Crackwell Street, Tenby, Dyfed, SA70 7HA. Tel:0834-2686
BOWEN BRAY DOMLEO EASTLAKE FLUTTER MORGANS OLIVER SHARPE F5126
121894 EASTWOOD Mrs Ann. 14 Holly Avenue, Stenhousemuir, Larbert, Scotland, FK5 4DN.
EASTWOOD F2642
121908 EASTWOOD Mr Edgar. Burfield House, Bishampton, Pershore, Worcs, WR10 2LX.
DARK EASTWOOD HACKELTON PAYNTING F2613
121916 EATON-THOMAS Mrs Marion. (Eaton) Post Office, Frankville, Ontario, K0E 1H0, CANADA. Tel:+1-613-275-2920
EATON-THOMAS F5541
121924 EAVES Mrs Sheila. 109 Hinckley Road, Walsgrave, Coventry, CV2 2ES. Tel:0203-615786
LOXLEY STRINGER WHALE F257
121932 EBBOTT Mrs Elizabeth. 409 Birchwood Avenue, White Bear Lake, MN 55110, USA. Tel:+1-612-426-3643
ANSTIS BAKER BLAKE BLUETT BONE BUNTING CRADOCK DENNIS DODGE Doidge Doodge Ebbett Ebbot EBBOTT Ebot FERRETT FRAYN GILES GIMBLETT Hambley Hambly HAMLEY Hamly HARRIS HEARD Ibbott JOLLIFFE LEY NOBLE PIPER REED TREWEEKS UGLOW WICKETT WILKINSON F5179
121940 ECCLES Mrs Mavis. 235 Branch Road, Blackburn, Lancs, BB2 4JZ.
AIRTON ARROWSMITH AVISON Ayrton BATE BENNET BLAKEY Blessard BLEZARD Duckett DUCKIT ECCLES GREEN GRIFFITHS HILL HODGKINSON HOPWOOD INGHAM MOXHAM RICHARDSON ROBINSON ROYLANCE Royle RUBBATHAN F3146
121959 EDDOLLS Mr David. 157 Ryeland Road, Duston, Northampton, NN5 6XJ. Tel:0604-751852
Eadall Eddells Eddels EDDOLLS Eddols Edolls Edols Iddolls Iddols F1886
121967 EDEY Mrs Barbara. (Cox) 5 Delph Street, Whittlesey, Peterborough, Cambs, PE7 1QQ. Tel:0733-202838
COX DOLBY MANCHETTE MOORE F2073
121975 EDMANS Mr C V. 33 Bonaly Gardens, Edinburgh, EH13 0EX.
EDMANS F7119
121983 EDMOND Mrs M E. 3 Hillside, Market Hill, Maldon, Essex, CM9 7QL.
HARGREAVES JEACOCK KESTERTON STANTON STROUD TALMEY TOMSETT WALTON WILKS F3797
121991 EDMONDS Miss Jenifer A. 51 Horns Lane, Norwich, Norfolk, NR1 3ER. Tel:0603-611700
Felthorpe FOLTHORPE LUNN NEWELL QUADLING SHIPP WING F4353
122009 EDNAY Mr Peter. 37 Kingfisher Close, Carisbrooke, Newport, Isle Of Wight, PO30 5XS. Tel:0983-523991
AGER DYER EDNAY Edney GUY NICHOLLS Nichols STUBBINS WOOD WOOTTON F3940
122017 EDSON Miss Dorothy. 4 Blundell Avenue, Cleethorpes, S Humberside, DN35 7PT. Tel:0472-690592
BRADBURY CALLENDER EDSON JEFFERY MELLOR OLIVE RODDER SCHOLEFIELD WYN F2157
122025 EDWARDS Mrs A S. 98 Hempstalls Lane, Newcastle, Staffs, ST5 0SE.
Bibbel Bibble Bibel BIBLE F6674
122033 EDWARDS Miss Angela. Briar Cottage, Church Road, Shedfield, Southampton Hants, SO3 2HW. F1181
122041 EDWARDS Mr & Mrs D. 7 Petworth Close, Wivenhoe, Essex, CO7 9NR.
BERJEW F7219
122068 EDWARDS Mrs Daphne. (Woodger) 22 Etherstone Green, Streatham, London, SW16 2QZ. Tel:081-677-2160
ARSLETT DAVISON REID WOODGER F5319
122076 EDWARDS Mr David. 177 Barlaston Old Road, Trentham, Stoke On Trent, Staffs, ST4 8HJ. Tel:0782-641780
COAD DUNSTAN HONEYCOMBE TREDINNICK F923
122084 EDWARDS Mr Douglas William. 90 Birkenhead Road, Hoylake, Wirral, Merseyside, L47 0LB. Tel:051-632-4600
AMBLER BOYLIN EDWARDS GRANT HARDCASTLE HIRST LOWE MILLS MORRISH TAYLOR WALKER WANKLIN WEBB F474
122092 EDWARDS Mr H W. 7 Erw Wen, Llanddulas, Abergele, Clwyd, LL22 8JN. Tel:0492-517002
EDWARDS F4043
122106 EDWARDS Miss Jean M. 47 Stag Leys, Ashtead, Surrey, KT21 2TQ.
ANGELL BARNES BOWERS BUTTS CHURCHILL COOPER COX EDWARDS ENGLAND GILBERT HANN HELLYER HITCHCOCK KING LAWRENCE LEGG OSBAND OSBORNE PEARCE SCORRILL SCURRILL SKORRELL SQUIRRELL SQUORRELL SQURIEL TOBY TOWELL WARRE WARREY WARRIE WARRY WARRYE WERRY WHARRY WHITE F523
122114 EDWARDS Mrs Kathryn. (Herraty) 16 Hatchford Avenue, Solihull, West Midlands, B92 9AQ. Tel:021-743-3569
BAINES BOWLES BUTLER COPE GLOSTER HERRATY LOUGHTON MANN MCGOUGH RICHARDSON RITCHIE SMART SMITH STOKES TRIDHOOK F6424
122122 EDWARDS Mr Kenneth. 401 Portway, Shirehampton, Bristol, BS11 9UF. Tel:0272-822305
AYERS BAGGS BOUGH BUTT EDWARDS FOORD HIPPISLEY PRAKE WILLIAMS F6172
122130 EDWARDS Mr N D. 24 Harcourt Road, Uckfield, E Sussex, TN22 5DU. Tel:0825-763202
DURRANT EADE EDWARDS FIELD BUSS FUNNELL HOADLEY HOLTER HOOK MEPHAM MILLER MITCHELL POLLINGTON TAYLOR WILMSHURST F1203
122149 EDWARDS Mr N O. 1 Broad Leys, Princes Risborough, Aylesbury, Bucks, HP17 9BJ.
BOHLING EDWARDS JONES LEWIS PEGG REES ROWLAND SOLOMON THOMPSON TOWNSEND F3739
122157 EDWARDS Mrs Normar. 2 Montrose Close, Moredon, Swindon, Wiltshire, SN2 2JS. Tel:0793-642902
BERRY BIZLEY EDWARDS PIPER F1200
122165 EDWARDS Mr P F. Oaklands, Tedburn St Mary, Exeter, Devon, EX6 6EB.
EDWARDS F1986
122173 EDWARDS Mr Peter B. 117 Airdrie Road, Toronto, Ontario, M4G 1M6, CANADA.
BONSER YEEND F7238
122181 EDWARDS Mr Peter. 22 Etherstone Green, Streatham, London, SW16 2QZ. Tel:081-677-2160
BICKNELL DURRANT EDWARDS WHITE F5320
122203 EDWARDS Mr Ray. 16 Hatchford Avenue, Solihull, West Midlands, B92 9AQ. Tel:021-743-3569
ARNOLD Braen Brain Braine Brane BRAYNE DENSHAM EDWARDS GILPIN GRANVILLE HOOD HOOD

GRANVILLE MARLOW PALMER PERKS PHILLIPS Shingelton Shingleton SIMPSON Singelton SINGLETON SYMS WITHAM FOSTER F5099

122211 EDWARDS Mr Roy. 12 Blacklands Drive, Hayes, Middx, UB4 8EU.
BATHMAKER BETHWIN Bisacker BISSACRE Blackden Blagden BLAGDON BRAYNE BROOKES BURROWS CAULKINS Forte FORTEE Fortey HALFHIDE HIND Hinds Hynd Hyndes NORDEN SWABEY F2655

122238 EDWARDS Mr S Clive. 22 Woodlands Road, Parkgate, S Wirral, Cheshire, L64 6RT. Tel:051-336-1190
BROWN DAVIS EDWARDS Forshall FORSHAW FOWLER HILL HILTON HODGE HOULDIN HOULDSWORTH INSTANCE MAUDSLEY MERCER MEREDITH PENNINGTON WALTERS WEAVER WOODS F3100

122246 EDWARDS Mrs Vera. (Oxspring) 68 Mill Hill Lane, Winshill, Burton On Trent, Staffs, DE15 0BB. Tel:0283-43187
OXSPRING F3483

122254 EDWARDSON Mr Stanley. 182 Wilton Road, Shirley, Southampton, Hants, SO1 5HZ. Tel:0703-771683
ANDERSON EDWARDSON ENTWISTLE EVANS Falla Fallah FALLAS Fellows GRAHAM HASLAM HETHERINGTON WOODBURN F2249

122262 EDY Mr G M. 8 Lavender Walk, East Malling, Kent, ME19 6EW.
CHIFNEY F2901

122270 EFFNERT Mrs Rita. Zum Holzle 6, W-7170 Schwab Hall-tungental, Germany.
DIMBERLINE GREEN WATKINSON F1667

122289 EGAN Dr M J S. 10 Rathdown Crescent, Terenure, Dublin 6w, IRELAND.
Eagan Eagen Eagin EGAN Egin Eighan Keegan Macaodhagain Macaogain Mcegan Mckeegan F6860

122297 EGAN Mr Mark. 34 Harton House Road, South Shields, Tyne & Wear, NE34 6EE.
Baines BAINS BEDLINGTON CLEET Colt COULT DRYDEN EGAN HERON Herron HOULSBY Ingo INGOE JOHNSON PARKER PATTERSON Pattison PCIEKRING ROBERTSON ROBSON Tinmoth TINMOUTH Tynemouth Tynmouth F3389

122300 EGERTON Mr Michael J. 8 Odlehill Grove, Abbotskerwell, Newton Abbott, Devon, TQ12 5NJ. Tel:0626-65891
Edgerton EGERTON Eggerton F151

122319 EGGETT Miss M K. 67 Goring Road, Ipswich, Suffolk, IP4 5LR.
Bales Balls BEALES COTTON DUFFIELD EGGETT HOWLETT JENNINGS KICKWEED RAYFIELD ROONEY WITHERS F479

122327 EITE Mrs Nina. 10 Vernon St, Clontarf, Queensland, 4019, AUSTRALIA.
BAILEY BROOMFIELD FULLY LOVE KING O'BRIEN PORTER SHILTON TRUSLOVE WEST WRIGHT F5452

122335 EITE Mr Vivian. 10 Vernon Street, Clontarf, Queensland, 4019, AUSTRALIA.
BEHAN CROYDEN Eit EITE Elte Eyde Eyt Eyte Eytt Eytte FIELDING PARKER RATCLIFFE SLATER TRACEY WRIGHT F5453

122343 EKEBLAD Miss C. 13 Hungate, Pickering, North Yorks, YO18 7DL. Tel:0751-77105
CHORLEY CRAIG HORSLEY LINK MCCALLUM MCKENDRY METCALF URWIN F5085

122351 EL-AHWANY Mrs Doreen. 20 Fern Close, Middleton, Manchester, M24 2FZ.
BRADDOCK COX FARRER GREEN GURNEY HOLLAND ODELL RUFF SANSOM WEAVER F2514

122378 ELCOMB Mrs Audrey. (Hyde) 22 Rosehill Avenue, Brantford, Ontario, N3T 1R8, CANADA.
BALCHIN Balshin BATTY BEAVAN Belshim Bevan Beven Bevin CARTWRIGHT COOMBER ELCOMB FARMER GRIGSBY HYDE M'garran MARSHALL MATTHEWS MCGHRAN Mghren NEWMAN PARKS WAGHORN F5191

122386 ELDER Mrs Anne. 1 Esk Road, Lowry Hill, Carlisle, Cumbria, CA3 0HN. Tel:0228-29491
BELL BURGESS Burrgiss CHILTON CRAWFORD DAVISON DIXON Doglas Dooglesh Dooglesse DOUGLAS Douglesh Douglis Dougliss Dowglles Duglas ELDER FAIRBAIRN Gevans Gillins Givens Gragson GREGSON Grigson Javins Jeavins JEAVONS Jevins Jevons Jillins Jyvins LOVAT MCGREGOR MERRILEES MILLER Moraly Morraleez RIDDLE ROBSON Spoor SPOORS Spours STRAUGHAN Strofen WATSON F550

122394 ELDER Mrs Catherine M. (Hunter) 46 Dunvegan Drive, Chatham, Ontario, N7M 4Z8, CANADA. Tel:+1-519-354-3975
ALLAN BODDAN Bodden Boden Bowden COLLIS CORNFOOT ELDER HENDERSON HUMPHREY HUNTER Kellick KELLOCK Killick MCLOED MORRISON F5587

122408 ELEY Mr Christopher M. Blaen-Y-Wern, Llangyndeyrn, Kidwelly, Dyfed, SA17 5ES.
EALEY Ealy Eele Eeley Eely Eieley Eile Eiley Eilley Elay Elea Elee ELEY Eleye Eli Elie Elley Ellie Elly Ely Elye Eyeley Eyely Eyle Eyley Eyly Eylye Heeley Heely Hele Heley Hely Iley F3792

122416 ELIAS Mrs Joyce. (Stevenson) Rr 1 Gr 2, Box 10, St Norbert, Manitoba, R3V 1LS, CANADA. Tel:+1-204-269-1774
BENNIE BLACKWELL FRANCY GAINER Gaynor GINN GUTHRIE HOPKINS KILLINGBECK SHEPPARD Shepperd Stenson STEVENSON STINSON WILSON F5673

122424 ELKIN Mr John. 4 Quintilis, Bracknell, Berks, RG12 7QQ.
BRAMMAR DARLING DUTTON ELKIN STANWAY F1914

122432 ELLA Mr R E O. 12 Sycamore Green, Gorleston On Sea, Norfolk, NR31 8EW.
Aella Aelle ELLA Ellah Ellar Ellay Elle Eller Elley Ellire Ellor F6765

122440 ELLEFSEN Mrs I M. (Linsley) 121 The Furlongs, Ingatestone, Essex, CM4 0AL.
BOOTH LAWSON LINSLEY Shalcroft Shallcroft Shallcross SHAWCROFT Shawcrosse Shorecroft SUTCLIFFE F1346

122459 ELLIFF Mr P C. 12 Hoylake Avenue, Fixby Park, Huddersfield, W Yorks, HD2 2NJ.
ELLIFF F6438

122467 ELLIOTT Mrs B. 190 The Mallards, Leominster, Herefordshire, HR6 8UJ.
COOMBES CUCKOW ELLIOTT GIBSON HORTON IRESON NICHOLLS WHITTACKER F3324

122475 ELLIOTT Ms C A. 26 Ferris Town, Truro, Cornwall, TR1 3JH. Tel:0872-75438
BRENNAN ELLIOTT GOMM GOODHEW KENNELL WALTERS F3208

122483 ELLIOTT Miss D Anne. 2a Cashiobury Terrace, Southend On Sea, Essex, SS1 1EZ. Tel:0702-345130
ALSTON ELLIOT MCCALLUM MCCONOCHIE REID SPICKETT TATE WYBRON F6544

122491 ELLIOTT Mr David George. 194 High Street, Hanham, Bristol, BS15 3HJ. Tel:0272-615365
BULL ELLIOT HILLIER HOPKINS MINETT MIWETT MORLEY ORCHARD F4878

122505 ELLIOTT Mr James Philip. Hideaway, Rowan Lane, Ashley Heath, Market Drayton Salop, TF9 4PT.
AMOR ELLIOTT ELLOT ELLOTT GOUGH HEATH LAKIN MELLOR ORAM ORRAM PEAKEHEATH STANWAY F917

122513 ELLIOTT Mr John. Rr 5, Petitcodiac, New Brunswick, E0A 2H0, CANADA. Tel:+1-506-485-2033
BIDEN COATES ELLIOTT KYLE MCELROY MCINLWEE MURRAY MYLES WARD WASSON F5574

122521 ELLIOTT Mr V P. 12 Ryecroft Drive, Horsham, Sussex, RH12 2AP.
COOK CRAMP ELLIOTT ELLIS ELPHICK FABIAN HAMMOND THOMPSON F2409

122548 ELLIS Mr A B E. 8 Hillcrest, Mayland, Chelmsford, Essex, CM3 6AZ. Tel:0621-740608
CUTCLIFFE ELLIS F3517

122556 ELLIS Mr Colin J. 98 Wonford Street, Exeter, Devon, EX2 5DF.
DILLOW ELLIS HUTCHINSON KERSLAKE MUSPRATT SOWDON STAPLES TEDHAM F2890

122564 ELLIS Mrs Joan S. (Brett) Iceni, 34 Crosstead, Gt Yarmouth, Norfolk, NR30 4AP. Tel:0493-844981
BRETT F5981

122572 ELLIS Mrs Joan. 22 Stoke Lane, Gedling, Nottingham, NG4 2QP. Tel:0602-878522
BAKER BESTWICK BODYCOT BOWEN CLEWER COUCHE CULLIS Dakin DAYKIN DOREY Eliag Eliaj Eliay ELIAZ ELLIS GARTON GREY GUDE HACKETT HALTON HICKS HIGGINSON JOHNSON KINGDOM Lovatt LOVET MALLAM NETHERWOOD PAYNE PEARSON PRIESTLEY SAUNDERS SHIRLEY SMALLEY THORNTON WOOLMER F1694

122580 ELLIS Miss P. 21 Kennedy Close, Croston Lane,

Orpington, Kent, BR5 1HP.
CRESSWELL ELLIS GALE JOHNSON MAINWARING SEARS Seeres Seers F6299

122599 ELLIS Mr Richard M. End Cottage, Bilhams Hill, Whitwell Street, Reepham Norfolk, NR10 4RB. Tel:0603-871872
ARCHARD BEAZOR ELLIS MARRIOTT F3399

122602 ELLIS Mr Richard. 155 Arthurton Road, Spixworth, Norwich, Norfolk, NR10 3QY.
BOTTOMS BRAY ELLIS FOULSTON GIBBONS MAY MORRIS F5065

122610 ELLIS Mrs S. (Booth) 39 Lacy Drive, Wimborne, Dorset, BH21 1DG.
BOOTH ELLIS FREETH HUBER INKPEN SHARP VARNEY WILTON WINTLE WOHLGEMUTH F5945

122629 ELLISON Mr Thomas Blair. 6 Ruthen Court, Hunter Street, Shrewsbury, Shropshire, SY3 8QN. Tel:0743-353754
BATTERSBY BLADES ELLISON WALTHEW F2570

122637 ELLSMORE Mr Stephen Alan. 204 Weyhill Road, Andover, Hants, SP10 3BG. Tel:0264-358064
Elesmore Ellesmore ELLSMORE Elsemore FRANKLIN NOLAN F3641

122645 ELLWOOD Gladys. 31 Hall Drive, Burley In Wharfedale, Ilkley, W Yorks, LS29 7LR. Tel:0943-862439
DEAN ELLWOOD F129

122653 ELLWOOD Mr William. 6 Scarisbrick Road, Levenshulme, Manchester, M19 2BS. Tel:061-224-8848
CLOSE DACRE ELLWOOD FAWCETT HADWIN IRELAND F5337

122661 ELMES Mr James. Pookeezows, 10 Farnham Avenue, Keymer Hassocks, W Sussex, BN6 8NS. Tel:0273-845020
BUTT DENTON Elemes ELEMS ELMES LODGE POPE POPPLEWELL SUTTON TINKER WHIBLEY F5236

122688 ELMES Mr Peter V. 2 Ramsdale Avenue, Havant, Hants, PO9 4DZ. Tel:0705-474063
BULGER COBBLEDICK ELMES EYRES JENKIN JENKINS LUCKHAM LYNE MILLER PLUCKNETT RICHARDS SOUTER STOCKMAN TUCKER COOMBES WALLDER WHICHER WILKES WILLS YEOMAN F5212

122696 ELMS Mrs Lucille. Queenhill Manor, Upton On Severn, Worcester, WR8 0RD. Tel:06846-2341
WALPOLE F498

122718 ELPHICK Mr John Yetman. Zephyr Cottage, Clay Lane, South Nutfield, Surrey, RH1 4EG. Tel:0737-765776
ELPHICK YETMAN F3152

122726 ELPHINSTON Mr Colin A J. Edrington House, Berwick Upon Tweed, Northumberland, TD15 1UF.
Elphinston ELPHINSTONE F1924

122734 ELPHINSTONE Mrs Barbara. 9 Leslie Road, Lerwick, Shetland Isles, Scotland, ZE1 0QQ.
De La Pole GRAY Grey POLE Poolley Powell F2289

122742 ELSAM Mr Jim. 38 Green Walk, Timperley, Cheshire, WA15 6JN. Tel:061-980-3853
ADAMS BOND BRETT Britt BRYANT COLLINS CROSS DICE Elliot ELLIOTT LAW LEE LEECH LINES MORRIS Pain PAYNE SMITH SPENCER STEWART WILLEY F3701

122750 ELSEGOOD Mr R E. Ninepins, Back Lane, Scoulton, Norwich, NR9 4AQ.
ELSEGOOD Elseygood Elsigood F7009

122769 ELSON Mrs Joyce E. (Walker) The Dial Cottage, 8 Christchurch Bay Road, Barton On Sea, New Milton, Hants, BH25 7NU.
BETTERIDGE BUTTRIDGE CRACKNELL Elsam Elsom ELSON WALKER F5207

122777 ELVIN Mr Ernest H. 25 St Annes Crescent, Bannockburn, Stirling, FK7 8JL. Tel:0786-811363
ELVIN ISAAC THORNELL F1929

122785 EMBERY Mr O F. 12 Parkside Avenue, Winterbourne, Bristol, BS17 1LU. Tel:0454-773029
EMBERY EMBRIE EMBRY Emery IMBRIE F4882

122793 EMBLING Mr John P. 6 Fairthorne Gardens, Alverstoke, Gosport, Hants, PO12 3PU.
ALLEN BROADBANK BULLOCK EMBLING MORGAN F4742

122807 EMERSON Mr Stephen. Apt 8, 4303 27th Avenue, Vernon, B C, V1T 6L2, CANADA. Tel:+1-604-549-2314
BIRD DINGLE EMERSON HYATT MOORE OLIVER PRITCHARD WALLER WOODROFFE F5661

122815 EMERTON Mrs Jackie. 3 Seymour Road, Upper Shirley, Southampton, Hants, SO1 6RH. Tel:0703-701842
BARHAM BARROM CHURCH LEWIS WOOLNOUGH F975

122823 EMERY Mrs Ann. (Blythe) 6 Trojan Close, Busselton, WA 6280, AUSTRALIA. Tel:+61-9-752-2070
BLYTH BRITTAIN COLLINGTON COPPIN GREENWAY HOOPER JACKSON PEET STANTON WEBSTER F4468

122831 EMERY Dr Ashton. Po Box 55322, Northlands 2116, SOUTH AFRICA.
Amery Amory EMERY Imrie F7273

122858 EMMERSON Mrs Joan. 55 Moss Lane, Hesketh Bank, Preston, Lancs, PR4 6AA. Tel:0772-814656
ALTY DISLEY DUGDALE LEWIS ROYLE WALMSLEY F1823

122866 ENGERT Mr J F. Lundy, 31 Tennyson Road, Eastleigh, Hampshire, SO5 5FS. Tel:0703-614616
ASLETT BARRETT BROADHURST CARPENTER CULLUM DOE EARWAKER Enger Engers ENGERT Engerth GLASS HARRIS HOLLOWAY HUNTLEY JENKINS LONG LONGDON MITCHELL MONGER OAKS-MONGER PIKE PORTER SMALL SMITH Stroad STROUD Stroude Strowd SWAINSON Swainston Swanson Swanston Sweetange Sweeteing SWEETING Sweeton Swetinge Swetten TANNER Tannors Tanor TURNER WEST WICKENS Wickince Wickins Wikins WILLIAMS YONGE F2171

122874 ENIFFER Mr D M. 7 Puffinsdale, Clacton On Sea, Essex, CO15 4JG.
Enefer Enever ENIFFER Ennever F7091

122882 ENNESS Mrs Edna. (Lowrie) 38 Murrumbidgee Avenue, Griffith, NSW 2680, AUSTRALIA. Tel:+61-6-962-4237
BLACKMORE CURRIE ENNESS LOWRIE MCGAUGHIE VERRIER WELLS F5434

122890 ENSTONE Mr B W. 43 Winchester Road, Northampton, NN4 9AZ. Tel:0604-761739
Enston ENSTONE Henston Henstone F2322

122904 EOYANG Ms Sarah. 1313 Lincoln #403, Eugene, OR 97401, USA.
Baroman BARROWMAN Boroman Borrowman BOYLE CLELLAND Cogell Coghell Cowell COWGILL CRAIG CRAWFORD CROSLEY Dewherst DEWHIRST Dewhurst DONALDSON Duhirst HARDY HAWTHORN HEAP HINDLE ORMEROD POLLOCK RAWLINSON Rolison Rollinson Rowlinson Vepon Veppon VIPOND Vipont Vippan WALKER WATSON WILKINSON F4244

122912 EPPS Mr E H T. 1 The Green, Charlbury, Oxford, OX7 3QA. Tel:0608-810573
EPPS F2742

122920 ERBEN Mr Michael. Dept Adult Education, School of Education, The University, Southampton Hants, SO9 5NH.
AMHURST DRY MOY TOOLY F79

122939 ERSKINE Mr John Slade. 53 St Andrews Avenue, Prestwick, Ayrshire, KA9 2DZ. Tel:0292-76130
ERSKINE F6487

122947 ESCOTT Mr Terence Adrian. 107 Watleys End Road, Winterbourne, Bristol, BS17 1PW. Tel:0454-772551
ESCOTT OAKLEY PAIN PARSONS PETERS F1939

122955 ESPLEN Mr Ronald S. 12 Townfield Road, West Kirby, Wirral, Greater Liverpool, L48 7EZ. Tel:051-625-8266
BANNING PARK WIDDOWS F5795

122963 ESSAM Mrs Pamela. 127 Shenley Road, Bletchley, Milton Keynes, MK3 7AS.
ATKINS BRAZIER Effam Efsam ESSAM HANTON Hearnton KEMSLEY STAPLES WEST F3244

122971 ESSERY Mr Clive. 12 Old Charlton Road, Shepperton, Middx, TW17 8AT. Tel:0932-241141
ARCHDEACON BOSHARDE Esewyre Essary ESSERY Essewyre Essiry Essory Essury Gawthorp Gawthorpe GOLDTHORP GOLDTHORPE Goldthrop Goldthrope Golthorp Golthorpe Gouldthorp Gouldthorpe Gowthorp Gowthorpe F2069

122998 ESSLEMONT Mr P. 16a Cadogan Square, London, SW1X 0JU.
ESSLEMONT F6563

123005 ETCHES Mr Peter Marcus. 10 Springwood Hall Gardens, Huddersfield, W Yorks, HD1 4HA.
CALVERT ETCHES POOL RACE SMITH VAUGHAN F2931

123013 ETHERIDGE Mrs C S. (Onione) 673 Filton Avenue, Filton, Bristol, BS12 7LA.
BETTERIDGE COMPTON COPNER COTTON ETHERIDGE HARRIES HICKS IZZARD JOHN JONES LOCKE MAYALL ONION ONIONE PERKES REED REID SHACKEL SHACKLE SMITH WARD WILLIS F3197

123021 ETHERIDGE Mrs Judith. The Vicarage, St Johns Road, Oldbury Warley, W Midlands, B68 9RP.
BROCKWELL BURTON HOBBS Jaine Jane JAYNE Jeaine Jeine Jeyne KIPPIN NIGHTINGALE PAMANT PENDAL WRATTEN F2556

123048 ETHERIDGE Mr Mark. 5 Sherborne Avenue, Cyncoed, Cardiff, S Glamorgan, CF2 6SJ.
ADAMSON BRENNAND CLARK ETHERIDGE Ethridge GASGOGNE Hathornthwaite Hawthornthwaite HAYTHORNTHWAITE HOGARTH HORNE HOWARTH IBBOTSON LEWIS PARKINSON RANDALL REED RUDD SMITH STORES STORRES WILCOCK F1915

123056 EUSTACE Mr Donald W. 13 Staveley Road, Chiswick, London, W4 3HU. Tel:081-994-3060
EUSTACE Eustice Eustis Hewstice Stace Stacey Ustis F6

123064 EVA Mr Leonard. 32f West End House, Tavistock, Devon, PL19 8JY.
EVA HOAR RIDHOLS F1336

123072 EVANS Mrs A P. (Lippett) 1a Jessie Road, Bedhampton, Havant, Hants, PO9 3TH. Tel:0705-451776
Lipet LIPPETT F6541

123080 EVANS Mrs Anne. 50 Fouracre Road, Downend, Bristol, BS16 6PH.
COLLIER JOHNSON SPOSITO F2353

123099 EVANS Mrs Daphne. (Bray Collins) Buddlehayes, Southleigh, Colyton, Devon, EX13 6JH. Tel:029780-255
BRAY COLLINS DANZEY EVANS GOUGH RANDALL SKEWES F569

123102 EVANS Mr Derek O. Laurel House, Cowan Bridge, Carnforth, Lancs, LA6 2HS. Tel:05242-71251
COCKERILL DAVIES EVANS Hansborough Hansbrow HASTINGS Hensberg HENSBERGH Hensborough Hensbrow Hinsbergh KINDER MEADOWCROFT ORANSE PHILLIPS PITTMAN ROTHWELL SKIDMORE THOMAS WILSON F5388

123110 EVANS Mrs Eiryl Margaret. (Thomas) 4 Maindy Croft, Ton-Pentre, Rhondda, Mid Glamorgan, CF41 7ET.
BOWEN DAVIES ISAACS JAMES NICHOLLS Rhyad RHYED RICHARDS RICKETTS VAUGHAN F4954

123129 EVANS Mr Esmor. Aelybryn, 51 Heol Troserch, Llangennech, Llanelli, Dyfed, SA14 8AX. Tel:0554-820244
DADE David DAVIES Deed EDWARDS EVAN EVANS Farrance FARRANTS Farrents GREYGOOSE GRIFFITH ISAAC JONES LLOYD MORGAN MORRIS Pharrance REES ROLFE SIMON THOMAS WILLIAM Williams F3437

123137 EVANS Mrs Gillian F. (Parkes) Greenvale, Southdown Road, Millbrook, Torpoint, Cornwall, PL10 1EH.
BLAGDON BURFIELD CHAMBERLAIN Chamberlayne Chamberlen Delnot Dillnutt DILNOT Dilnott DILNUTT Dylnet Dylnot Dylnott ELFORD Good GOODE Goud Platfoot PLAYFOOT Playford Splayfoot Teaby TEBAY F6433

123145 EVANS Mr J M. 396 Sarehole Road, Hall Green, Birmingham, B28 0AJ. Tel:021-777-4780
BANKS BARNSLEY BROCKLESBY BUSHELL CHANDLER CLARK COLLINS CROSBIE CROWTHER DARBY EVANS GOLDINGAY JOHNSON LEAKE LUCAS LYON MANNION PROSSER RAWLETT RUSSELL THOMPSON THORNE WATTERS WHITE WICKS WREN F2507

123153 EVANS Miss Jacqueline. 69 Wellsway, Bath, Avon, BA2 4RT. Tel:0225-310620
ADAMS BULLOCK EVANS FARLEY FRANCIS LANDER LEWIS MCCARTHY MOORE MOUNTJOY MOUNTJOY-LANDER PARSONS PERRY PHILLIPS TUCKER WITHERS YOUNG F1761

123161 EVANS Mrs Jan. (Rees) Oakfield House, Calverton, Milton Keynes, MK19 6EQ.
EDWARDS EVANS HOLT HOLTE MITCHELL PREW RAWSON REES WELLINGS F1148

123188 EVANS Mrs Jean N. 5 Beaufort Drive, Kittle Gower, Bishopston, Swansea, SA3 3LD.
COOLING F7405

123196 EVANS Mrs Jean. 12 Hadleigh Gardens, Boyatt Wood, Eastleigh, Hants, SO5 4NP.
CRADDOCK FLINT WOOLLEY F3660

123218 EVANS Mrs L. 6 Downside, East Isley, Newbury, Berks, RG16 0LD.
Tratt TROTT F7442

123226 EVANS Mrs Lynne. 22 Church Side, East Ilsley, Newbury, Berks, RG16 0LR.
TROTT F4717

123234 EVANS Mr M A. Daisy Cottage, Golding Lane, Mannings Heath, Horsham Sussex, RH13 6JX.
BARON Barron FURSE Furze HUNKIN F1881

123242 EVANS Mr Michael J. 32 Newton Road, Knowle, Solihull, West Midlands, B93 9HN. Tel:0564-774203
BAKER DAVEY ELSWORTHY EVANS MARTIN MILLS OPIE PERRY POOLE PRYOR F4123

123250 EVANS Mr Nicholas. 258 Kingston Road, Willerby, Hull, Humberside, HU10 6ND.
ATKINSON BOWSER Bowzer COULSON EVANS GAMESON Gamson HARRIS HAXBY HOLDSWORTH HOLROYD JENKINS JOHNSON KEARTON LLOYD MOSS POUND RATCLIFFE RATTLE Scar SCARR SEAMAR SKAR Skarr THOMAS WHITEHEAD WILSON F5381

123269 EVANS Mrs P M. 38 Pinecroft Rise, Sudbury, Suffolk, CO10 7PA.
RUFFLE F6564

123277 EVANS Mr Philip W. 7 Endwood Drive, Solihull, West Midlands, B91 1NX. Tel:021-705-3165
BURNETT EVANS KEY PROCTOR SAVAGAR WHYLEY WOODBINE F6154

123285 EVANS Mr Philip. 11 Tenterns Green, Ward Green, Barnsley, S Yorks, S70 5JY. Tel:0226-284033
BAILEY BEEVERS CATLIN CUSWORTH EVANS JACKSON ROCK SYKES WALKER WHITE WILDSIMTH F2268

123293 EVANS Mr Roger J. Chez Nous, South View Road, Long Lawford, Rugby, Warks, CV23 9BP. Tel:0788-571529
ASHTON Bristo Bristol BRISTOW Cosner Cousener Couzener Cusener Cusner Cussner CUZNER EVANS Hoter HUDSON Hutson LAUGHTON Mimack MIMMACK Mimmock Oter OTTER ROBINSON SOUTHWOOD STARK STONES Udel UDELL Yewdale Youdall Youdle F6511

123307 EVANS Mrs Sandra. (Steedman) Pendyce House, Station Road, Ivinghoe, Leighton Buzzard, Beds, LU7 9EB.
ADAMS BROOKS CHAMBERLAIN DRIFFIELD EVANS FOWLER FRISBY GEDGE GILHAM HOPKINS MIRTLE PETTIFER PICKET RIDLEY STEBBINGS STEEDMAN WATTS WOODHOUSE F4923

123315 EVANS Mr W. 59 Caesars Road, Newport, Isle Of Wight, PO30 5EB.
DAVIES EVANS LOCKYER PRINCE F5135

123323 EVENDEN Mrs Jean. 12 Curzon Avenue, Horsham, W Sussex, RH12 2LB.
Ainger Angel Angell ANGER EVENDEN Everenden Evernden TICKNER F1386

123331 EVERETT Mr David. 64 Trimpley Drive, Kidderminster, Worcs, DY11 5LB. Tel:0562-754220
EVERETT PEARCE F5851

123358 EVERETT Mrs J. (Habgood) 5 Woodhurst Avenue, Petts Wood, Orpington, Kent, BR5 1AR. Tel:0689-870344
BRADBURN GARRICK GRAY HABGOOD NEWSHAM PEARSON PLANT RATTRAY F3958

123366 EVINGTON Mr Jack A L. Weir Meadow, Oakford, Tiverton, Devon, EX16 9EW. Tel:03985-352
Euington Eveington Eventon Everington EVINGTON Evinton Evrington Eyngton F321

123374 EWEN Mr Graham. 84 Donbank Terrace, Aberdeen, AB2 2SD.
ARCHIBALD BAIRD CLARK COOPER DEMPSTER EWEN FOWLER REFORD RITCHIE TAYLOR WATT F4683

123382 EWENS Miss D. 59 John Dee Crescent, Orewa, NEW ZEALAND.
Ewen EWENS Unwin Unwins F7129

123390 EWING Mr Iain P. 33 Loftus Road, Shepherds Bush, London, W12 7EH. Tel:081-740-1271
ADAMS CAMPBELL DAVIS DOUGLAS DUN EWING FARLEY GWILLIM HALDER HOARE JAMES KING LAWRENCE LILLEY LLOYD MILLER NOSSITER PREECE PRITCHARD SMART WATTS WOOD WOSTEAR F5411

123404 EXTON Miss L S. 35a Mayflower Road, London, SW9 9JY.

ALLEN AYRE Burges BURGESSE Burgiss CAGE CODDINGTON CODLING Collington COLLINS Crosley Crosly CROSSLEY DEWEY DUNN DYBALL EXTON FEWKES FITCHET FOWELL Fowks Fukes Furkes GARNER Haden Haydon Hemingway HEMMINGWAY HEYDON HOGGINS Kedge LOVES MEADOWS Muggeson MUGGINSON Muggleston Mugliston NUBBS PLUM Plumb RAVENSCROFT RICHARDS ROE Rowe Rowel ROWELL Rowil SMITH SPOONER SYGR THORN Thorne Thornne Thurn TOON TURNER Waddingham WADDINGTON WATTS WHITBY WOOLLEY YOUNG F5893

123412 FAHERTY Mr Jan Edward. 14 Leonard Street, Stockton Heath, Warrington, Cheshire, WA4 2UP. Tel:0925-604253
ALLISON BOTT Faharty FAHERTY Fauarty Fauerty Feharty Feherty MAGRATH RUSTON TOWNSEND WILLIAMS F3768

123420 FAIERS Mr M. Knoll Cottages, Martley Road, Lower Broadheath, Worcester, WR2 6QG. Tel:0905-640875
BUNN DOWLING DUFFIELD FAIERS JARVIS MCCARTHY RECKNELL ROGERS TURNER YATES F4149

123439 FAIRBROTHER Mrs M. 22 Ermine Way, Stamford, Lincs, PE9 2XN.
CHINCHEN F1678

123447 FAIRCHILD Mr Mark. 50 Barley Farm Road, Exeter, EX4 1NN. Tel:0392-217988
ENDACOTT FAIRCHILD Fayerchild Fayerchilde Fayrechchilde Ferchild Ferchilde GLIDDON Glidon Glyddon SNELL Varchild Verchild Verchilde F4764

123455 FAIRFAX Mr J E. 9 The Ball, Bratton, Westbury, Wiltshire, BA13 4SB. Tel:0380-830837
FAIRFAX Feerfox Foirefax F2182

123463 FAIRLEY Mr G D. 28 St Johns Road, Altrincham, Cheshire, WA14 2NA. Tel:061-928-3571
BELL CLAYTON DALZIEL DONALDSON FAIRLEY HOPWOOD F135

123471 FAIRMAN Mrs Agnes. (Kinnish) 50 Green Lane, Bayston Hill, Shrewsbury, Shropshire, SY3 0NR. Tel:074372-2231
BEDDOES BOULTON EVANS GREENWOOD HASLEM KINNISH POSTLETHWAITE TOMLINSON F1274

123498 FAITHFULL Mr B C T. 35 Berice Drive, Lara, Victoria, 3212, AUSTRALIA.
FAITHFULL F6598

123501 FAITHFULL Dr Nigel T. Cwm Heulog, Clarach, Aberystwyth, Dyfed, SY23 3DP. Tel:0970-828734
Fairfoul Fairfoull Fairfull Faithful FAITHFULL Fayrfowel Faythefull Faythfule Faythfull Ffaithfull F1845

123528 FALL Mr D. 26 The Parklands, Erdington, Birmingham, B23 6LA.
FALL FROGGATT F6565

123536 FALLA Mrs Gillian. 101 Sweetbrier Lane, Heavitree, Exeter, Devon, EX1 3AP.
ANGEL BENN BERRY BEVERIDGE BRADLEY BRAITHWAITE CAMPBELL CAULFIELD CHEEKE CHURCHILD CROSSLEY DAVISON DAWSON DEAR DIXON DODDS DOWSON EKINS EMENS EMMERSON Fala FALLA Fallaw Fallow GIBBON GREENWELL Haddon HALL HATCHARD HAWDON HENDERSON HERON HLOMES Holden JOBSON LAWES LILLEY Lilly LOCK Locke MASON MCKIE MILLS MOAT Monday MONDEY PAPE ROBINSON Rowlate Rowlatt ROWLETT SANDERSON SAUNDERS SCHOFIELD SELBY SMITH TARN TEASDALE THOMPSON WALTON WATSON YOUNG F4753

123544 FALLOWS Mr G F. 17 Windermere, Lytton Grove, Putney, London, SW15 2ER.
FALAYS FALEGAS FALLOWES FALLOWS FALOYS FALWIZ Fellows Ffallowes HALLOWES F2086

123552 FARBUS Mrs Joan. (Prangnell) 35 Winston Road, Westville, Natal, 3630, SOUTH AFRICA.
BARNARD BATHE COLEMAN COLLINS COOLING EMES JEPSON LONG POTTERTON PRANGNELL READ SKINNER STRAW WARREN WOOSMAN WYKES F5180

123560 FARBUS Mr Norman. 35 Winston Road, Westville, Natal, 3630, SOUTH AFRICA.
DERRICK ELLEN FARBUS MART ROSE SHALLISH WELLS WILLIAMS F5181

123579 FARLEY Mr. Fearnlyes, Drews Close, Churchdown, Cloucester, GL3 2JZ. Tel:0452-713883
Fairly Farle Farleigh FARLEY Farlie Farly Ferly F1910

123587 FARMER Mrs Alice D S. 2 Molyneux Park Road, Tunbridge Wells, Kent, TN4 8DN.
ATHERALL CARD COOMBER CROUTCH FEAKINS GASELTINE PARKER ROOTES WEBB WICKENDEN F2522

123595 FARMER Mrs Pauline. 13 Balmoral Avenue, Beaumont Park, Huddersfield, W Yorks, HD4 5LR.
AUTEY BAILEY BATES BATTYE BEAUMONT BEEVER BLEWITT BOOTHROYD BOTTOMLEY BOWKER CASTLE CHARLESWORTH COOPER CROSLAND ELLIS FARMER FITTON FLETCHER GLEDHILL GREAVES HAIGH HARRIS Hawty HIRST HORSFALL KAYE LAWTON LEE LOCKWOOD Main Mane Mayne Mayor MEAR MILLS MORTON RAMSDEN REVEL ROBERTS SMITH STOTT SYKES THEWLIS THORNTON TRASLER WALKER WHITELEY WILKINSON WORTHINGTON F3175

123609 FARMER Mrs Val. 3 Tainton Street, Clontarf Beach, Queensland, 4019, AUSTRALIA.
BARTER BEST CHALLIS COOPER FARMER FRENCH HENDREN HURLEY MCCULLOGH MOORE MUDFORD RAYSON ROGERS RUSSELL WARD F5157

123617 FARNATH Mr Antony. 5 Laurence Grove, Tettenhall, Wolverhampton, West Midlands, WV6 9QN.
FARNAGH FARNARTH FARNATH FARNETH Farnorth FARNOTH F5276

123625 FARNDALE Mr Roy. 1 Lasham Court, Northampton, NN3 4BD. Tel:0604-414438
FARNDALE PODMORE ROWLEY TODD WINTRIP F1998

123633 FARQUHARSON Mrs Robert. (Wylie) Rr1, Tilbury, Ontario, N0P 2L0, CANADA. Tel:+1-519-682-1944
MACKLEM MARY PARRISH POOLE STRANG WILEY F5436

123641 FARR Mrs Marion. 60 Parsonage Road, Withington, Manchester, M20 9WQ. Tel:061-445-9281
BARTRAM BUTTON COLGRAVE CROFT KENEWELL MATTHEWS SKELTON SLACK TALBOT F322

123668 FARR Mrs Vera. (Chapman) 38 Lime Road, Hanham, Bristol, BS15 3AR. Tel:0272-675865
CHAPMAN COLES COLLINGS Collins EDWARDS Far FARR Farre Ffar Ffarre Humphreys Humphries HUMPHRIS Jefferey JEFFERY Jeffrey MONTAGU Montague PROUSE Sweating SWEETING F4840

123676 FARRALL-HUTCHINGS Mrs Rosemary. 21 Margaret Close, Whitley Wood, Reading, Berks, RG2 8PU. Tel:0734-876041
BLOWS FARRALL SELL WALLDUCK F5666

123684 FARRANT Mr E J. Saintsbury, Grove Mount, Ramsey, Isle Of Man.
FARRANT F7277

123692 FARRANT Mr Reginald. 5 Clift House Road, Ashton, Bristol, BS3 1RY. Tel:0272-634707
FARRANT Farrent GOOCH PHILLPOTTS WIDLAKE F2373

123706 FARRINGTON Mrs Linda. (Martin) 41 Grasmere Road, Chestfield, Whitstable, Kent, CT5 3NA.
BOULTER BRECKELL FARRINGTON GOLDSMITH LYON MARTIN MARTLAND MCCLINCHEY F2067

123714 FARROW Mr Richard. 6 Dolbeare Road, Ashburton, Devon, TQ13 7AS. Tel:0364-53530
BEAUMONT FARROW F4822

123722 FAULKNER Mrs Barbara. 13 Bathurst Parade, Bristol, BS1 6UB.
BETTS BOWMAN BRAY CLARKSON ELKINGTON FAULKNER GATTER GREEN HAWKINS HEADFORD HERRIOTT HOLE HOLT LOVELL MORLEY PASSMORE PRINCE RASHLEIGH ROWE SHIRE WOODEY YEWENS F3108

123730 FAULKNER Mrs Margaret. 24 Botany Road, Winton, Eccles, Manchester.
Falkner FAULKNER Highley HILEY Hollingrake HOLLINRAKE WORTHINGTON F2133

123749 FAULKNER Mrs Thelma J. (Grant) Harwood St, Maryborough, Queensland, 4650, AUSTRALIA.
BEATTIE FAULKNER GATHERCOAL Gathercole GRANT HORRIGAN JONES MOORE NEAL SHANAHAN TEMPLEMAN F5564

123757 FAUTLEY Mr Ray F. 7 Kingfisher Road, Downham Market, Norfolk, PE38 9RQ. Tel:0366-385168
Fately Faughteley Faulty Fauteley FAUTLEY Fautleys Fautly Fawtely F1414

123765 FAWCETT Mr Reg. 44 Chantry Lane, Great Grimsby, South Humberside, DN31 2LJ. Tel:0472-360278
ANDREW Andrews BLACKBURN CAPES COOK FAWCETT FITZGERALD GUY HERD HEWSON HILL HOLGATE KEYWORTH KIRTON LEWIS LILBURN MALKINSON MEARS

PRESTON QUICKFALL RAFFERTY ROGERS ROSE SHARP SUTTERBY WEST WRIGHT F2541

123773 FAYERS Mrs Evelyn. (Harris) 18 Colley Road, Great Baddow, Chelmsford, Essex, CM2 7JH. BULLOCK Bullocke FAYERS HARRIS HOWE HUNT KENT MANNING MANSFIELD TAMBLYN WEBSTER WILLIAMS F2874

123781 FEAKES Mr G W. Church View, Chapel Lane, Houghton, Huntingdon Cambs, PE17 2AM. Fake Fakes Feak Feake FEAKES Feek F6900

123803 FEAR Mr David. 121 Vandyke, Bracknell, Berks, RG12 4UT. FEAR JOHNS WARD F4218

123811 FEASEY Mrs Andrea. 4 Fen Cottages, Combs Lane, Stowmarket, Suffolk, IP14 2DA. Tel:0449-677454 BARBER BROWN BUCKLE CATTON CHAPLIN CRAPNELL GRIMWOOD HAGGER RICE RIDGEN SIMPSON THORPE WARD WRIGHT F155

123838 FEEST Dr A. 4 Westfield Close, Bath, Avon, BA2 2EA. FEEST F1731

123846 FELL Mr Frank. 2 Ashwood Avenue, Ramsbottom, Bury, Lancs, BL0 0BQ. Tel:0706-824689 Fel FELL Ffel F247

123854 FELLS Mr David. 57 Countrymans Way, Shepshed, Leics, LE12 9RA. CAUNT FELLS VERNON F2172

123862 FELTHAM Mr G A. 13 Kilmiston Avenue, Shepperton, Middx, TW17 9DL. BRYANT COLLETT COOMBES FELTHAM FIBCH MINTON ROACH F5836

123870 FELTHAM Ms Sharon. 972 Woodville Road, Villawood, NSW 2163, AUSTRALIA. Tel:+61-2-727-5976 ALDRIDGE BATH BRODERICK DILLON DOWDING Faltham Feltam FELTHAM Felton HART JARVIS Malender Malinder MALLINDER Mullender Mullinder PAGE POWER Read Reed REID ROSENTHAL Saxton Selar Seler SELLAR Seller Sextan Sextin SEXTON SWABEY TOLLEY TOWNSEND Veltam WALL WEBBY WESTWOOD WHITEWOOD YOUNG F4600

123889 FELTON Mr Roy. 40 Plymouth Road, Stirchley, Birmingham, B30 2PD. Tel:021-459-5549 FELTON PICKSTOCK F7401

123897 FENBY Mrs M. Peacehaven Cottage, Bolton, Nr Wilberfoss, York, YO4 5QS. Tel:07596-534 FENBY PORTUFIELD F4351

123900 FENCOTT Mrs Doreen. Pencoed Isof, Bynea, Llanelli, Dyfed, SA14 9TW. Tel:0554-773926 FENCOTT F4598

123919 FENDER Mrs R. 47 Cambridge Road, Bromborough, Wirral, Merseyside, L62 7HZ. Tel:051-334-6482 FENDER WOODFIN F4957

123927 FENN Richard. 31 Uffington Road, West Norwood, London, SE27 0RW. Fen FENN Fenne F7043

123935 FENNER Mr Christopher J F. 10 Singelton Way, Fulwood, Preston, Lancs, PR2 4PX. Tel:0772-712457 FENNER F4219

123943 FENNEY Mr Eric. 6 Clarendon Close, Winnersh, Wokingham, Berks, RG11 5JW. Tel:0734-794610 BULMER CLARKE DAVISON FAZAKERLEY FENNEY HARLEY JENNINGS STOCKDALE F5594

123951 FENNEY Mrs Margaret. (Davison) 6 Clarendon Close, Winnersh, Wokingham, Berks, RG11 5JW. Tel:0734-794610 ATKINSON BELL BROOK CHINN DAVISON ELLIS HANSON STOTT SYKES WHITELEY F5593

123978 FENTON Miss Jane. 1 Leaside Way, Bassett Green, Southampton, Hants, SO2 3DN. Tel:0703-557490 BARTLETT BLACKWELL DOBEDOE ECKERSLEY FENTON FITZPATRICK GALGANI GARGANI KENNETT LUCAS PECKHAM PEMBLE SHEPARD Shepherd SNELGROVE Snellgrove STANBRIDGE Stansbridge TAYLOR F5025

123986 FENTON Mr R O. 44 Reford Loan, Edinburgh, Scotland, EH13 0AX. Tel:031-441-2432 BRECHIN FENTON F517

123994 FERDINANDO Dr P. 22 Copperfield Drive, Thornhill, Cardiff, CF4 9DD. Ferdinand FERDINANDO Fernando F6692

124001 FERGUSON Mrs Danis J. (Peatfield) Wood View, 14 Whernside Grove, Carnforth, Lancs, LA5 9XH. ALEXANDER BEATTIE BELL BREWIS BRICE CADDY COLE CORBY ESDAILE FANSTONE FINDLAY GRILLS INGRAM JAMIESON MEAD PEATFIELD Petfield PHILLIPS Pitfield TAYLOR VINCENT F1605

124028 FERGUSON Mr Derrick G. Wood View, 14 Whernside Grove, Carnforth, Lancs, LA5 9XH. BAILEY BLAIR BURTON CAMPBELL CLARKE EMERY FERGUSON GARDINER GOLDFINCH HAYDON JEE SMITH WOODHALL F3950

124036 FERGUSON Mrs G Shirley. (Callaghan) 9 Lion Lane, Billericay, Essex, CM12 9DL. CALLAGHAN GEORGE JOHN Jones F4730

124044 FERGUSON Mrs Leslea. (Verrall) 5/30 Leiper Street, Stafford, Queensland, 4053, AUSTRALIA. Tel:+61-7-356-2197 BRODIE COCK COX CRAWFORD DERGES LINNETT PEARCE PONSFORD F5546

124052 FERGUSON Mr Michael. 6 Wrecclesham Hill, Farnham, Surrey, GU10 4JW. FERGUSON MAY F5018

124060 FERGUSON Mrs Phyllis. (Hibbert) Flat 4, 5 Marwick Terrace, St Leonards On Sea, East Sussex, TN38 0RE. HIBBARD HIBBERD HIBBERT F5070

124079 FERRAND Mr David F. 14 Cromwell Crescent, London, SW5 9QW. Tel:071-602-5299 BUSFEILD DAVIE FERRAND TOPHAM F1921

124087 FERRIER Mrs Heather. 4 Durham Crescent, Failsworth, Manchester, M35 0QL. FERRIER HOLLIN F5193

124095 FERRIMAN Mrs Elizabeth. (Wilson) 13 Braikenridge Close, Clevedon, Avon, BS21 5LA. Tel:0275-343228 CHILVERS POREL D'AGROND POWLEY SIBLEY SPENCER SPILLANE WHITMAN WILSON F6429

124109 FERRIS Mr C. South Holm, 17 Coombe Road, Dartmouth, Devon, TQ6 9PQ. Tel:0803-833740 FERRIS LUSCOMBE PILLAR TARRANT F5317

124117 FERRIS Mr R. 69 Redland Park, Bath, Avon, BA2 1SH. Tel:0225-333955 BARNETT BERRY CAIN FERRIS MIZEN MORRIS F4528

124125 FEW Mrs Janet. 12 Ranelagh Road, Lake, Sandown, Isle Of Wight, PO36 8NX. SEAR Sears Seear Seears Sier Siers F6908

124133 FFOULKES Mr Rodney. 44 Hamsey Road, Sharpthorne, East Grinstead, W Sussex, RH19 4PA. BRISCOE BURGESS FFOULKES FOULKES HATTON HUMPHREY WOODS F3011

124141 FICE Mr John. 8 Harptree Close, Nine Elms, Shaw, Swindon Wiltshires, SN5 9UU. Feese FICE Fis FISE Fits Fitz Fitze Fyz VICE Vise F683

124168 FIDIAM Mrs S P. (Nixon) Tees Bank House, 337 Coinscliffe Road, Darlington, Co Durham, DL3 8AN. Tel:0325-467550 BROWN BUNTON FEWSTER FIDIAM FOWLER MOWBRAY NIXON PAMLER PURVIS WATCHMAN WOOD F3679

124176 FIELD Mr Bob. 45 Moreland Road, Droitwich, Worcs, WR9 8RN. Tel:0905-773420 BATES BUCKINGHAM CASTLE CHURCHILL CLAYTON COLLETT FAULKNER FIELD HESTER HITCHCOCK HOUSE IVINGS JACKSON KEMP KIMBELL MATTHEWS NASH OAKLEY RICHMOND TAYLOR TURNER WATKIN F746

124184 FIELD Mr M. White Cottage, Waters Green, Brockenhurst, Hants, SO42 7RG. COOKE FIELD GOOD MARSON MUMBY MURCH SPRENT F1837

124192 FIELDEN Mr Keith. 81 De Bohun Court, De Bohun Avenue, Southgate, London, N14 4PZ. FIELDEN F7159

124206 FIELDER Miss Alexis Doreen. 1 Mayhill Close, Pinecrest, Thornhill, Cardiff, CF4 9DT. BLUNT BRINE BURGE COOPER DOBBINS EDITON FIELDER GETTY GUDERIAN JAMES MEREDITH MOULTON NEAL NEALE WATTS F242

124214 FIELDS Mrs P M. 10 Bonington Road, Mapperley, Nottingham, NG3 5JR. Tel:0602-621726 Field Fieldes FIELDS Padbury Podbury Portberrie PORTBURY Potberry Potbury SANDERS TAYLOR F6138

124222 FILBY Mr F N. 15 Cavendish Gardens, Ilford, Essex, IG1 3EA. FILBY GUNTHORPE F6566

124230 FINCHER Ms S. 5 Seymour Place, Canterbury,

Canterbury, CT1 3SF.
FINCHER F7161

124249 FINDON Mr Andrew. Suagros House, Old Fosseway, Tredinton, Shipston On Stour, CV36 4NN. Tel:0608-661083
Findal Findall Findalls Findan Findel Findell Finden Findern Finderne Findle FINDON Fyndorne F647

124257 FINERON Mr Paul. 2 Oaktree Lane, Haxby, York, YO3 8YL.
CORNBROUGH CRAWFORD CROFT DICKINSON FINERON MARSHALL ROMMANS SHERWOOD WOFFINDEN F6054

124265 FINN Mrs Felicity. 29 Warren Road, Banstead, Surrey, SM7 1LG. Tel:0737-373026
COOK FEARING HAYTON F1983

124273 FINN Mrs Linda. 20 Upper Park Road, St Leonards On Sea, E Sussex, TN37 6SL.
BONNER COBHAM FINN KINGDON RADFORD ROBERTS SOUNDY YOUNG F186

124281 FINNEMORE Mrs J. 211 Haunch Lane, Kings Heath, Birmingham, B13 0PJ.
Bennimore CONSTABLE Fenamor Fenemer Fenemore Fenimore Fenmer Fenmere Fennamore Fennemore Fenneymore Fennimore Fennymore Fiddimore Fillmore Filmer Filmore Finamer Finamoore Finamore Finemer Finemere Finemor Finemore Finimor Finmer Finmere Finmore Finnamoor Finnamoore Finnamore FINNEMORE Finneymoore Finneymore Finnymoor Finnymore Finymore Fynmer Fynnamore Fynnemore Fynneymoore Fynneymore Fynnimore Fynnymore GUPWELL HEMMING HUNT JACKSON LA TOUCHE Philimore Phillimore Philmore Phinamor Phinamore Phinnamore Phinnemore Phinnmore Phynemore Phynnamore Phynnemore Phynneymore Phynnimore Phynnymore PREES Vennimore WEBB WITHEY F6453

124303 FINNERTY Mrs J. 21 Long Lodge Drive, Walton On Thames, Surrey, KT12 3BY.
DAWSON F2505

124311 FINNESEY Mrs Sue. (Landers) 30 Park Avenue, Formby, Liverpool, L37 6EB. Tel:07048-76669
BASS BEADLE Biddell Biddle BOXALL Fennesey FINNESEY Finnessy Finnissy Goodgeon Goodgion GUDGEON HUTT LANDERS MARCHANT Marchent Merchant F2796

124338 FINNETT Miss J L. 12 Parkfield Crescent, South Ruislip, Middx, HA4 0RB.
GOTTERSON F6711

124346 FIORI Mrs Carole. (Softley) 3 Flash Lane, Enfield, Middx, EN2 9JH. Tel:081-363-7104
FRANCIS LAKEMAN MANCEAU PETERS POOLEY SCHUNTER SOFTLEY WILLEY F4996

124354 FIRTH Mr David. 20 First Avenue, Gillingham, Kent, ME7 2LG. Tel:0634-280393
BROOK CARROLL FIRTH LOWE NICHOLSON ROSENBERG F4325

124362 FIRTH Mr William. 49 Woodstock Avenue, London, NW11 9RG. Tel:081-455-7164
ANDREWS CROMPTON DAINES DAY FIRTH PERRY PRACEY STOCKS STOTT F3434

124370 FISHER Mr B. 21 Honeybrook, Waltham Abbey, Essex, EN9 3DD.
SLACK Slacke F7222

124389 FISHER Mrs Carol. (Horsfall) 51 Morley Street, New Plymouth, NEW ZEALAND. Tel:+64-6-758-7586
COOPER HORSFALL Horsfell Horsfield Mathers Mathew Mathews Mathus Matthew MATTHEWS REEVE SUTCLIFFE TOWNEND Vapent Vapont Vappers Vappon Veapond Veepon Veepond Veepont Veipon Vepans Vepend Veping Vepoint Vepond Veponn Vepound Vepoynte Veppine Verpende Verpent Verpond Veterepond Veterepont Vipam Vipan Vipant Vipart Vipe Vipeham Vipehan Vipen Vipend Vipent Viper Viphan Viphill Viphirs Viphors Viphours Vipin Vipind Viping Vipoint Vipon VIPOND Viponde Vipont Viport Vipos Vipound Vipounde Vipount Vipounte Vipout Vippars Vippen Vippin Vippon Vippur Vipun Vipus Vitropent Vitropond Vuipent Vupend Vypant Vypend Vyping Vypointe Vypond Vyponde Vypont Vyponte Vypounde F4400

124397 FISHER Mr F A. West View, Church Road, Bell House, Billericay, Essex, CM11 1RH. Tel:0268-711173
FISHER MELBOURNE RICHARDS SNELLGROVE WILKINS WOLSEY F3725

124400 FISHER Mrs Gillian. (Jackson) 4 Lindsey Drive, Healing, Grimsby, DN37 7NU. Tel:0472-887056
BATES FISHER JACKSON PAYNE SHERRY TOPP F6159

124419 FISHER Joan. 131 Swanwick Avenue, Toronto, Ontario, M4E 2A2, CANADA.
TAPE F7371

124427 FISHER Mrs Marilyn B. (Beynon) 10226 Hopeland Avenue, Downey, CA 90241-2159, USA. Tel:+1-310-927-9643
AULEY BEYNON CAW DEWAR DIXON ELLIS FISHER FOSTER GRIFFITH JONES JOYCE LEWIS LOWE LUMLEY NESBIT NICOL OWEN PARRY RAMSEY RICHARDS ROBERTSON SKIPPON TUCK F5616

124435 FISHER Mrs Mary L. (Coggeshall) Scrambles, Ware Road, Hailey, Herts, SG13 7PE.
COGGESHALL RICE SPURLING VIDLER WATERS F4088

124443 FISHER Mr Peter. 18 Cupola Lane, Grenoside, Sheffield, South Yorks, S30 3NQ. Tel:0742-452648
FISHER FULLELOVE Fulleylove Fullilove GELL HURRELL KETTLE RAGGETT F6205

124451 FISHWICK Mr William. 117 Cranborne Road, Wavertree, Liverpool, L15 2HY.
ALLEN FISHWICK PERRY RYCROFT F296

124478 FISK Mr Brian P E. 48 Benedict Close, Romsey, Hampshire, SO51 8PN.
FISK Fiske Fisks Fysck Fysk Fyske F3760

124486 FITCH Mrs V. 21 Sinah Lane, Hayling Island, Hants, PO11 0HH.
Farden FARTHING Farthinge Farthings F7047

124494 FITNESS Mr E W. 5 Woodlands Rise, Swanley, Kent, BR8 7JT.
FITNESS Fitnesse Fitnis Fittness Fytnes Fytnesse Fyttness F6816

124508 FITT Mrs Joan K. 14 Raymer Close, Stalbans, Herts, AL1 3QH.
BATEMAN FITT KIRWOOD LEDGER LITTON PATTE F1969

124516 FITTER Mrs Andrea. (Smith) 142 Halstock Crescent, Poole, Dorset, BH17 9BB.
DAVIES Lea LEE Legh Leigh Ley F618

124524 FITTER Mrs Margaret. 6 Avon Road, Keynsham, Avon, BS18 1LJ.
CHARLTON DAVIES FLEMING HEDGE HETT HUTCHINS KELSEY LAW LUCAS NICHOLSON PULLEY RAWBONE RAWLINS ROSS SNELSON SPENCELEY VICARS WOOTTON WYATT YORK F2627

124532 FITTER Williamina. Camilla Lace Cottage, Chapel Lane, Westhumble, Dorking Surrey, RH5 6AH.
CAMPBELL MILNE MURRAY THOMSON F2756

124540 FITZGERALD Mr Garrett. 28 The Grove, Upminster, Essex, RM14 2ET. Tel:04022-23405
CHRISTIE FITZGERALD GRAY GRIFFIN MAYALL WERNHAM F6178

124559 FITZGERALD Mrs Tona. 39 Oakgrove Road, Bishopstoke, Eastleigh, Hants, SO5 6LN.
BAKER COLLINS CORDERY COX GOODCHILD KEELEY VASS WILLIAMS F3459

124567 FITZPATRICK Kay. 5 Patton Street, Broken Hill, NSW 2880, AUSTRALIA. Tel:+61-8-088-2319
HANCOCK F5638

124575 FITZPATRICK Mr T. 23 Glen Crescent, Bacup, Lancs, OL13 0NP.
FITZPATRICK F6059

124583 FITZSIMONS Mrs Ann Marie. 277 Lower Hillmorton Road, Rugby, Warwickshire, CV21 4AB. Tel:0788-570679
BURDETT FARN FITZSIMONS MILLER NORMAN F957

124591 FLEET Mr B L. 44 Ferndale Avenue, Chertsey, Surrey, KT16 9RA.
OTHEN WATCHAM Watsham F6725

124605 FLEMING Mrs Jill. (Cottle) 8 Green Way, Colne Engaine, Colchester, CO6 2HB. Tel:0787-222080
ALP ANGIER BARR BEZANCE BEZANTS BLOWERS BURCH CLARKE COLE CORP COTTLE CURTIS DEWSON DODD DUNN EMERY FALLER FLEMING GENTLEMAN GOWEN GOWING GOYMER HALL HARRISON HAWKES HOLMES JONES KING LOCK LOVELOCK MARSHALL NOAD NUTTER PECK PETERS PHILLIPS PLUMB PLUMMER RAYNER REX REYNOLDS ROADS SILK SMITH STANNARD STEPHENS STEVENS TAYLOR WARD WEBB WENT WHITCHELO WHITE WITTS F3077

124613 FLEMING Mrs Tania. (Henson) 4 Lingards Drive,

Astley, Manchester, M29 7FD.
COCKSHOOT DULY FLEMING GLAZIER HENSON MARSHALL UNSWORTH YATES F1546

124621 FLETCHER Mr Barry. 21 Ilex Way, Middleton On Sea, Bognor Regis, W Sussex, PO22 6PQ. Tel:0243-584207
ACKRILL BEAVERS BILLING CABOURN COTTAM EMMERSON FARMER FLETCHER FOX FRESHNEY GELL HAITH HARVEY HASELTON HAZELTON HEAZELTON HESSLETON INCLES LAWRANCE RHODES RODGERS RUSELL RYLATT TAYLOR WARD WARNOCK WATTERS YARBOROUGH YOUNG F432

124648 FLETCHER Mr John S. Upper Moors Farm, Garway Hill, Hereford, HR2 8RT.
BARKER BROOKS FLETCHER HATELEY HATELY MALLETT PRITCHARD SPICER TEMPEST WILKINS WOODING F467

124656 FLETCHER Mr K B. 9 Myngs Terrace, Salthouse, Nolt, Norfolk.
BOWLEY FILBY FLETCHER FREEMAN ROBERTS ROE WEST WHITBY F398

124664 FLETCHER Mrs Mary. Lodge Farm, Shottle, Belper, Derbys, DE5 2DW. Tel:077389-243
FLETCHER MASON ROSE F121

124672 FLETCHER Mrs Rachel. 21 Ilex Way, Middleton On Sea, Bognor Regis, W Sussex, PO22 6PQ. Tel:0243-584207
BOFFIN COX EACOTT FRAMPTON HEATH HINKS HOPKINS LINDSEY NOAD TAYLOR F431

124680 FLINTHAM Miss B E. 15 Cranmer Grove, Mansfield, Notts, NG19 7JR.
FLINTHAM Flinton Flintum F6984

124699 FLOATE Mrs Sharon. (Sillers) 25 Sadleir Road, St Albans, Herts, AL1 2BL.
BAGGS BARTLETT CRANFORD CROOK HOOKER LOVE LOVELL MACFARLANE MCKINDLAY MULLENGER PETMAN PRECIOUS RANSLEY READ REED SELTH SILLARS SILLERS TWYMAN WOOLDRIDGE F76

124702 FLOATE Mr T C. 7 Harry Truslove Close, Radford, Coventry, CV6 3HE.
BUSH CROMPORN-BUSH F3290

124710 FLOOD Mr Eric. 66 Hickory Dell, Hempstead, Kent, ME7 3SL. Tel:0634 375972
BEST FLOOD FORD FORDRED PARKER F2824

124729 FLOOD Mr John P. Crestway, Redhill, Oxford Road, Denham Middx, UB9 4LD.
FLOOD F6892

124737 FLOODGATE Mr Geoff. 103 Stagsden, Orton Goldhay, Peterborough, Cambs, PE2 0RP.
FASNACHT FLACKETT FLADGATE FLAGGETT FLATGATE FLOODGATE F1264

124745 FLOODGATE Mrs Janet. 103 Stagsden, Orton Goldhay, Peterborough, Cambs, PE2 0RP.
BRONNE FREELAND ROGERS F1265

124753 FLOOK Miss C L. 3 Malling Road, Manchester, M23 8XE.
FLOOK Flooke Fluke Stewart-Cole STUART-COLE F3786

124761 FLOWER Dr John & Mrs Jean. 3 Rodway Hill, Mangotsfield, Bristol, BS17 3LQ. Tel:0272-563347
BANFIELD Barnfield Benfield CASTLE COULTRIP Coultrup FLOWER FRANCIS GARDINER GULLIFORD Hale HALES Hare HARES KING MARTIN Strode STROOD Stroud THROWER WITCOMBE F2206

124788 FLOWERS Mrs Dorothy. (Newton) Little Easthall Farmhouse, St Pauls Walden, Hitchin, Herts, SG4 8DH.
BACON BANCROFT BEARD BLOWER BRADBURY COMBS DIXON EELY FERNEHOUGH FISH FLOWERS HALLETT HANKEY HARRISON HILL HOLDGATE HOWARD LAWTON LINGLEY LOMAS MASON MIDDLETON NEWTON Ossie OUSEY Owsie Owzy Ozey REDFORD TIDMAN TURNER Ussey WALTON WATSON WHITEHEAD WILSON F2128

124796 FLOYD Mrs Su. (Atherton) Royal Oak House, 32 Nelson Street, Buckingham, MK18 1DA. Tel:0280-817173
ATHERTON BARNS BEEDLE BRISTOW BUCHER BUTLER CHEETHAM CLARKE COLES CONEY FLOYD FREE GADBURY GODFREY GOLBY GREEN GREY HAWSE HEATH HESTER HOBBS HOPKINS HULME IVES JAMESON JANES JONES JUDGE KING LITTLEPAGE LODER MARKHAM MILLER MORRIS NEWELL NEWETT NIBBS ORKNEY PAGE PARISH PARRISH PARSLOW PULLEY QUARTERMAIN READING ROADS SALMON SAUNDERS SEARE SHUCKBOROUGH SIME STANDISH STEEDEN STEVENS SUMMERS TEMPLE TOFIELD TUCKER TURNER TYLER WADE WATERFIELD WINDMILL WOODS F6314

124818 FLYNN Mrs Audrey. 7 Salisbury Gardens, Buckhurst Hill, Essex. Tel:081-504-8180
PADDON F6066

124826 FLYNN Mrs Brenda. 32 Auckland Oval, Darlington, Co Durham, DL3 0LJ.
Algarth Algate Algath BARRATT BRAMALL Bramma BREADON CANTY CHARLESWORTH Clark CLARKE DIXON DOUGHTY Duty FILDES GEBLER Halgarth Halgath HALLGARTH STARK TATTER F2690

124834 FLYNN Mrs R M G. 12 Loughborough Road, Hoton, Loughborough, Leics, LE12 5SF.
ANGRAVE Borowes Borrowe Borrowes Bossworth BOSWORTH Burrowe Burrowes BURROWS Clark CLARKE Hardie HARDY KIRK Kirke Macer MARCER Masser Mercer NEAL Neale NORTH Northe OLDERSHAW WOODROFFE Woodroofe Woodrooffe Woodruff WOOTON Wootton F6277

124842 FODEN Mr Edward John. 22 Johnstone Avenue, Werrington, Stoke On Trent, ST9 0DY. Tel:078130-3943
BARRATT BELLIS FODEN GILBERT PALMER ROBERTS SEEOCH SHUBOTHOM TURTON F600

124850 FOLEY Niall. 85 Upper Drumcondra Road, Dublin 9, IRELAND.
FARRELL F7278

124869 FOLLAND Mr P W J. 2 Brockenhurst Close, Canterbury, Kent, CT2 7RX.
FOLLAND F551

124877 FONE Mr J F. 17 The Walnuts, Branksome Road, Norwich, Norfolk, NR4 6SR.
EDMONDS FONE GOGGS WHITEFOORD Whiteford Whitfoord F1906

124885 FOOKS Mr John. 146 Glebelands, Pulborough, W Sussex, RH20 2JL. Tel:0798-873465
Fookes FOOKS Fowkes F1163

124893 FOOKS Mrs Meriel. 146 Glebelands, Pulborough, W Sussex, RH20 2JL. Tel:0798-873465
FOOT GREEN HUSKISSON KINDERSLEY WILLIAMS F1164

124907 FOORD Mrs Diane. 51 Farm Hill, Woodingdean, Brighton, E Sussex, BN2 6BG.
BALES BROWNINGS FREEMAN GADD HARROWELL HEANEY KEEN LIBBETTER MITCHELL NEWMAN PELLING SHOULDERS SMITH STRACHAN STUDLEY TIDEY WOODS F2664

124915 FOORD Mr K. 51 Farm Hill, Woodingdean, Brighton, E Sussex, BN2 6BG.
ASHWELL BROOKS COTTLE DODD ELLIOTT FOORD GALE HIVES HOWE KETLEY KETTON MITCHENOR NORTH PENFOLD PUDDIFOOT RAWSON RICH WRIGHT F2221

124923 FOOT Mrs Susan. 28 Augustine Road, St Pauls Cray, Orpington, Kent, BR5 3JZ.
LITTLEFORD F6937

124931 FORBES Alison. 19 Chamberlain Close, London, SE28 0EL. Tel:081-316-7184
CANTLON DUNNACHIE FORBES KERR MALCOLM MELDRUM THORNTON F2620

124958 FORD Mr A G. St Catherines Court, Salisbury Road, Redland, Bristol, BS6 7AT.
MACEY ROBINET Robinett Robinette Robnet Robnett Robnette F3583

124966 FORD Mr Conroy Herbert. 4 Clappers Orchard, Loxwood Road, Alfold, Cranleigh Surrey, GU6 8HQ. Tel:0403-752639
DARBY FORD HEBDITCH LEVY MARTIN NORGATE PAGE READ ROGERS TUTT F992

124974 FORD Mr David. 11 Lymington Avenue, Yateley, Camberley, Surrey, GU17 7EG.
A Baer A Bear A Beare A Beere A Bere A Beyre A'barre A'BEAR A'beare A'beere A'beyre Abair Abarre Abbeare Abbir Abear Abeard Abeare Abeer Abeere Abere Abeyre Abier Abitot Abore Abour Abuer Abure ALLE ATTE BERE BARNES BARTHOLOMEW BASSET Bassett Bear Beare BEAUCHAMP BEAUMONT Beire Bere BOSTOCK Bostok Bostoke BRAMPTON BRAVANT BREEDON Brewes Briouze BROWN Bruse BULMER BYE CAMBER Camville Canville Cheesat CLAPSHAW Clapshew Clapshin Clapsho CLAPSHOE Clapshoo Clapshow Clerk COLLINS Commens Commins Commons Cotgrave COTGREAVE Cotgreve Cottgrave CROFT Crofte Cummings CUMMINS Cummons D'ABITOT Dalbeare De Beare De Beauchamp De Beaumont De Bere De Bostock De Bostok De Boxtoc De Brampton DE BRAOSE De Breuse De Brewes DE

CAMVILLE De Esette De Esset DE ESSETE De Essette De Esshetes De Excetes De Ferrers De Ferrieres DE GAI De Gamaches De Gamage De Gamages De Gay DE GOURNAY De Hanslope De Harcourt De Harley DE HEVER De Kynardsley De Kynnardsley De Kynnardsleye De La Bear De La Beere DE LA BERE DE MANDEVILLE De Mineriis De Miners De Mortemer De Mynors De Neubourg De Neufmarche DE NEWBURGH De Newmarch De Pembridge De Pemprugge De Puleston De Pyuelisdon De Pyvelisdon De Pywelisdon De Remevill De Remeville De St Valery De St Valori De St Valory De Turberville De Varenne DE WARENNE De Warren DE WARWICK Delaber Delabere Dellabere Delliber DEVEREUX DUTTON Edgecomb EDGECOMBE EDWARDS Eirmonger Eirmunger Eliot Eliott Elliat Elliatt Elliot ELLIOTT Ellot ELLOWAY Ellyot Emens Emmans EMMENS Eyrmonger Eyrmunger FAITHFUL FARMER FENTON FERRERS FOSTER Gai Gamaches GAMAGE Gamages Gesset Gessett Gessut Giset Gissat Gissatt Gisset Gissett Gournay GRACE Gyssett HANSLOPE HARCOURT HARLEY HARTWELL HATTEN Hawkince Hawking Hawkings HAWKINS Hedgecomb Hedgecombe Helliot Helliott Hever HILL HOLDWAY Iermonger Iermunger Iernmonger Iernmunber Iesset IREMONGER Iremunger Ironmonger Ironmunger Jacett Jasett Jassat Jasset Jassett Jessat Jesseit Jesset Jessete Jesseth JESSETT Jessette Jessit Jessitt Jessott Jessut Jessutt Jeuset Jizat Jizet Juset Jusset Jyssett KEYTE Kinardsley Kinnersley KNIGHT KYNARDSLEY Kynnardsley Kynnardsleye Kynnersley KYVELYOC LARDUR LE CLERK LIDDIARD LOWMAN LOWTHER Malherbe Malherve MALT Mandeville MATHEW Mathews Matthews MAUDIT Mauditt Mauduit Mayduith Miners MORRIS Mortemer MORTIMER MYNORS Naish Naishe NASH Nashe Naysh Neace NEAL Nese Neufmarche Neufmenell NEW NEWLAND NEWMARCH Newmarsh NOAKE Noise Noke Nova Meinell Noyce NOYES Noys Noyse PARKER Peckman PEMBRIDGE Pembruge Pembrugge Penbrug Penbrugg Penebrugge Pickman PITMAN Pitmon Pittman Plokenet Pluckenet PLUCKNET Plukenet Plukent Plunkenet Plunknet Prescott PRESTHOPE PULESTON Pulleston Pyuelisdon Pyvelisdon Pywelisdon RANDOLPH Remevill REMEVILLE ROBERTS SIBLEY St Valeri St Valery ST VALORY Tailer Tailor TALBOT Taleboth Tayler TAYLOR Thoytes THOYTS Tiping TIPPING Tippinge TOWNSEND TREFOR Trevor Trublevill Trubleville Turbervile Turbervill TURBERVILLE Turbill Turville Tyler Typinge Typping Typpinge Warenne WARREN WEBB WIDMORE Wigmore WILCOCK WILLIAMS Wither WITHERS Wythers Yermonger Yermunger Yernmonger Yernmunger F748

124982 FORD Mr E J. Springfield, The Old Post Office, Rockhampton, Berkeley, Glous, GL13 9DT.
ABRAHAMS ALLEN ASTBURY BARTON BELLIS BOND BRODRIBB BURGES BURLEY COLLINS DORNEY FEAR FORD FOWLER FOXWELL FRYER GREENAWAY GREENWOOD HASELL HAYWARD HOPKINS INGRAM JACOBS JEFFERY JENKINS JONES KNOTT LIGHT LLOYD LONG MORGAN OWENS PARKINSON PENNY PROCTOR REEVES RIDDIFORD RIGG ROACH RUSSELL SCOTT STEPHENSON STUMP VIZARD VOWLES WATKINS WEAVER WETHERELL WILLCOX F1179

124990 FORD Mrs Hilary. (Mockridge) Hillcrest, Dumping Hill, Shebbear, Beaworthy, Devon, EX21 5SN. Tel:040928-259
BOARD Boon BOONE Bord BOWRING CARTER FLAY FORD GOODYEAR HEMBERY Hembry Hembury Keirle KERLE Kerrel Kierle Kirle Kyrle LANGFORD MOCKRIDGE Mogridge Muckridge SPARROW SURRIDGE WILCOX Willcox WILLIAMS F360

125008 FORD Miss Jenny. Flat 3, 90 Weymouth Road, Frome, Somerset, BA11 1HJ.
FORD SWIFT F237

125016 FORD Miss Jenny. 131 Whatcombe Road, Frome, Somerset, BA11 3AT. Tel:0373-472729
FORD SWIFT F6343

125024 FORD Mrs Marie. (Livermore) 4 Clappers Orchard, Loxwood Road, Alfold, Cranleigh Surrey, GU6 8HQ. Tel:0403-752639
DOORE HUGHES LANE LEE LIVERMORE MOORE MUNDAY NEW TRINDER F993

125032 FORD Mr Michael. 11 Lymington Avenue, Yateley, Camberley, Surrey, GU17 7EG.
Aleright Allright Allwright Alright ALWRIGHT ANDREWS ASTEN BARNARD BECK BLACKMAN Blackney BLAKENEY BUTLER Clace CLACEY Clacy CLARKE Clasey CORNMELL DEAN Deane DOLLERY Dougat Ducket DUCKETT Duget Dugget Duggett Ealslie Easlye Eeles Eesley Eesly Elesely Elesley Eleslye FORD GILES GLACEY GRIFFITHS HALL HERRIER Hildesley Hildisley Hildsley HILTON HUNT Iilsley Ildesley Ildslee Ildsley Illesley Illsley Illsly Ilseleye Ilselie Ilsey Ilslelye ILSLEY Ilsleye Ilslie Ilsly JOHNS KEEP LEGGE Mae Maie MANNERS MAY Maye MESSENGER MINCHIN MORTON NIGHTINGALE PARSONS Rummery RUMMEY Rummy Rumney SMITH STACE TAYLOR WILLIS Woodrofe Woodroff WOODROFFE Woodroofe Woodruff Woodrus YEATES F749

125040 FORD Mr R C C E. 98 Mays Lane, Chipping Barnet, Herts, EN5 2LL.
CASLAKE F6743

125059 FORD Mr Wilfred Penrose. Sarsden, Blackboys, Uckfield, East Sussex, TN22 5JU.
BONES BOWNESS FORD HARVEY SPENCE F5356

125067 FORDHAM Mr K J. 141 Forest Road, Loughborough, Leics, LE11 3HS.
Fordam Fordame FORDHAM Fordom F6907

125075 FOREMAN Mr Alan J. 46 The Old Yews, New Barn, Longfield, Kent, DA3 7JS.
FOREMAN Foremann Forman Formann Formen Fourman Fourmen Voorman F5968

125083 FOREMAN Mrs Jean. 89 Lister Road, Margate, Kent, CT9 4AF. Tel:0843-223827
CULLEN Cullin Cullindge Cullinge Cullyne FOREMAN STACEY F3103

125091 FOREMAN Mr M J. 12 Stoneleigh Close, Patcham, Brighton, E Sussex, BN1 8NQ.
CROFT FOREMAN F4948

125105 FOREMAN Mr Peter. Spurway, Cranston Road, East Grinstead, W Sussex, RH19 3HQ.
ALLMAN ARTIS AUGUST Baccus Backhouse Backhurst Backhust BACKUS Bakehouse Barckus Bauckas Baugust Bawgurst BEAKHOUSE Beakhurst Beaks Beakus BECK Beckus CHOWN CLIFTON DAVY DOWSETT FOREMAN FORMAN JAMES JEARY LASKEY MOSS NAUNTON ROWE SEWELL SOWELL WILDING F3773

125113 FOREMAN Revd Sheila. (O'Connor) 77 Felixtowe Road, Abbey Wood, London, SE2.
BATCHELOR BAX BIBLEY BROOKER BROOKS BUDGEN CONSTABLE CURTIS DENMAN EVANS FAIRBROTHER FOREMEN HORN HUGGETTT HUNT JONES KNOTTLEY MORRIS MOTT O'CONNOR PRITCHARD RINGWOOD SAVIN SAYER SPEED TILLMAN WALKER WEEKS WILLIAMS WOBBS F4705

125121 FORESTER M H. Idle Hill Cottage, Lyme Road, Axminster, Devon, EX13 5BL.
BROOKE CRUMP GIBBENS Harbert HERBERT MANNING MUSGROVE SPURLING TUTTLE WALDEN F1037

125148 FORRESTER Mrs Hilary. (Wallace) 120 Morningside Drive, Edinburgh, EH10 5NS.
BEBB DONKIN FOWLER GALBRAITH HANCOX HAWKES JERDAN WALLACE F6158

125156 FORRESTER Orville. Rr 1, Westport, Ontario, K0G 1X0, CANADA.
FORRESTER F7280

125164 FORRYAN Mr Mike. 21 Blakesley Road, The Meadows, Wigston, Leicester, LE8 1WD.
Fforian Forian Forrian FORRYAN Foryan F6311

125172 FORSYTH Mr A W & Mrs J R. (Springings) Little Throphinsty, Cartmel Fell, Grange Over Sands, Cumbria, LA11 6NU. Tel:05395-31727
BENN BIRKETT ELLERAY FLEMING FORSYTH QUAIL SPRIGINGS F2279

125180 FORSYTH Mrs Charlotte T W P. C/o Wickham Elms, Rectory Road, Great Waldingfield, Sudbury Suffolk, CO10 0TL. Tel:0787-74741
FORSYTH Forsythe PENMAN WISHART F1296

125199 FORSYTHE Mrs Judith. (Hodgson) 27 Cornsland, Brentwood, Essex, CM14 4HP. Tel:0277-222187
AYTON BAILEY BUNDOCK FARRER FURBISHER GODDARD HODGSON PIMM PYM WALKER F4527

125202 FORT Mr Andrew & Mrs Anita. (Cannon) 16 Crosby Close, Worthing, W Sussex, BN13 2RS. Tel:0903-60185

ALMOND BENJAMIN CANNON CHADBOURNE COLMAN COPSON CRABTREE DOBSON FENN FORT GILLETT GREEN HEPTONSTALL LAXTON LOVELL MARSHALL MILLS NORMINTON PAGE PALMER PRIOR PYLE SCOTT SUTTON THOMPSON UTTLEY VERNON F1157

125210 FOSTER Mr Anthony Erskine. 9 Brunswick Terrace, Hove, Sussex, BN3 1HL.
EVANS FIRMIN FOSTER RICHARDSON WOOD F1802

125229 FOSTER Mrs Dianne. Mansion View, Gwystre, Llandrindod Wells, Powys, LD1 6RN.
DEAN HARRIS HATT JANES LACEY MASON RIDGLEY WHARTON F136

125237 FOSTER Mr G A. 142 Cotswold Crescent, Walshaw Park, Bury, Lancs, BL8 1QP.
BRIGGS BURY DUXBURY ECCLES ENTWISLE FISH FOSTER GRIME HARWOOD HINDLE HOLDEN HUNT JEPSON KAY KIRKHAM LEACH LIGHTBOWN MANSDEN PICKUP SHONROCK SMALLEY SNAPE THOMPSON WALMSLEY WALSH WATSON F420

125245 FOSTER Mrs J A. 172 Grimsby Road, Humberston, Grimsby, South Humberside, DN36 4AG.
WATTAM F7152

125253 FOSTER Mr James H P. 68 Little Brook Road, Sale, Cheshire, M33 4WG. Tel:061-969-1548
ASCOUGH FORSTER FOSTER O HARA SUTTON F104

125261 FOSTER Mr John William. The Brent, Station Road, Thurgarton, Notts, NG14 7HD. Tel:0636-830557
FOSTER SAXBY F3515

125288 FOSTER Mrs Maureen. 44 Chatsworth Avenue, Great Barr, Birmingham, B43 6QN.
ALLSOP AVERILL BITHEL CLEWLOW CONOLLY COOPER GARNER HADDON HARVEY NORRIS RAND RUDD RUDGE SUMNER SWANWICK WALKER WILSON WOODWARD F1477

125296 FOSTER Mr R E. 488 St Marks Place, Upper Hale, Farnham, Surrey, GU9 0EU. Tel:0252-727294
DE PUTRON LIHOU MARQUAND ROBIN F4312

125318 FOSTER Dr Roy. 2a Belmont Park Road, Maidenhead, Berks, SL6 6HT. Tel:0628-76550
ASHLEY BULLOCK BURT BUSS DE SMITH EWENS FORWARD FOSTER HATKISS HEARN PAINE PARKES PARKS PURKISS STUDDS THORRINGTON VORST F1235

125326 FOSTER Mr Tony. Mansion View, Gwystre, Llandrindod Wells, Powys, LD1 6RN.
FOSTER FRY OSWALD SEWELL SKINNER SMART STREET F137

125334 FOSTON Mr Edward. 54 Sudbury Way, Beaconhill Green, Cramlington, Northumberland, NE23 8HH. Tel:0670-734567
FOSTON F5974

125342 FOTHERGILL Mrs J. 103 Upper Hird Street, Broomhill, Keighley, West Yorkshire, BD21 1NH.
FOTHERGILL GRAY HARDING HARES HARRIES ISAAC JOHNSON LANSDALE MRGATROYD ROTHERA RUSHWORTH SMITH TURNBULL WILD F6318

125350 FOULKES Miss Janice. 39 Windsor Road, Billinge, Wigan, Lancs, WN5 7LD.
BANKS BANNISTER EAVES FENTON FOWLER HANKINSON LAW TOWNSEND WADE WAITE F120

125369 FOX Mr Bryan Paul. Foxhaven, 27 Crossville Crescent, Foxhall Manor Park, Didcot, Oxon, OX11 7HE.
NEWMAN F5723

125377 FOX Mr D K. Tower House, 12 St Peters Hill, Stamford, Lincs, PE9 2PE. Tel:0780-63891
FLOWER F6092

125385 FOX Mrs D. 217 Broadway Lane, Throop, Bournemouth, Dorset, BH8 0AE.
DRAY FOAKES GAIR SOUTHGATE F1571

125393 FOX Mr David. 1 Canberra Road, Christchurch, Dorset, BH23 2HL. Tel:0202-482787
BIBB COLEY FOOT Foote FOX Foxe HEELEY HUNT Hunte KEMPSTER Kimpster MAYCOCK PARKES Parks F1715

125407 FOX Dr Dennis H. West Hythe, Upper Tockington Road, Tockington, Bristol, BS12 4LQ. Tel:0454-612754
FOX GITSOM GREEDY HERWIG ROY F4812

125415 FOX Mrs Elsie. 209 Northfield Road, Kings Norton, Birmingham, W Midlands, B30 1EA. Tel:021-458-3314
ANDERTON BURNS ELLWOOD FOX HATHAWAY HUNT JONES KENT LLOYD MOUNT ROWLEY TAYLOR WATKINS WILLIAMS F1541

125423 FOX Mrs Gillian. The Farm House, Clayton Lane, Bracklesham Bay, W Sussex, PO20 8JQ.
ASPLIN CHATER CHATTER DANGERFIELD ELLWELL ELWALL ELWELL OLDFIELD PARREY PARRY ROUND SUMMERS F4055

125431 FOX Mrs Joyce. (Russell) 14 St Bees Drive, Barrow In Furness, Cumbria, LA14 4PS. Tel:0229-826739
BOYCE BRAMWELL MCCLELLAND MCFADDEN MCMULLEN PATTON RUSSELL WALLACE F3523

125458 FOX Mrs Margaret. 19 Tremaine Close, Heamoor, Penzance, Cornwall, TR18 3QS.
BARKER JONAS MOON WARD F1070

125466 FOX Mr Peter N. Ten O'Clock Farm, Butterwick, Sedgefield, Cleveland, TS21 3ER.
BAISTER BLAKE BROOM BULLINGHAM BURLINGHAM FOX HASTE LINDRIDGE MILHAM NELSON PINKNEY WOOLF F495

125474 FRAMPTON Mr A R. 14 Snowdon Avenue, Bryn-Y-Baal, Clwyd, CH7 6SZ.
FRAMPTON F5650

125482 FRAMPTON Mrs C. 14 Snowdon Avenue, Bryn-Y-Baal, Clwyd, CH7 6SZ.
BANNING F5649

125490 FRAMPTON Mr T W. Middlecombe Brae, Middlecombe, Minehead, Somerset, TA24 8SN.
SCAPENS Scapings F6761

125504 FRANCE Mr Alan. 46 Kirkstall Close, Brinsworth, Rotherham, South Yorkshire, S60 5NP. Tel:0709-379240
FAIRCHILD FRANCE F4964

125512 FRANCIS Mrs Kathleen R. (Shaw) 2/109 Through Road, Burwood, Victoria, 3125, AUSTRALIA. Tel:+61-3-889-2818
BAXTER CANTRELL PLAISTED SHAW F4242

125520 FRANCIS Revd Kenneth. St Johns Vicarage, Princes Road, Felixstowe, Suffolk, IP11 7PL. Tel:0394-284226
ADKINS BRERETON DESORT FRANCIS HEATH MOTT NIELD SOMERWILL TOMAS WAKEHAM Weakham F5046

125539 FRANCIS Sheila. 14 Bryngwastad Road, Gorseinon, Swansea, West Glamorgan, SA14 SXG.
WHEELHOUSE F7027

125547 FRANKLAND Mr Stuart. 48 Rydal Drive, Worksop, Notts, S81 7PZ. Tel:0909-482056
FRANKLAND F3947

125555 FRANKLIN Mrs C A. Ballairdie Cottage, Abernyte, Perthshire, PH14 9RE.
HUMM MALONEY MELLISH TIGHE WELLER F3255

125563 FRANKLIN Revd Richard. St Andrews Vicarage, Oakfield Road, Wollescote, Stourbridge W Midlands, DY9 9DG. Tel:0384-422695
BURROWS COULING DREW FRANKLIN HUMPHRIES RIMELL Rymell Rymill Rymyll TOWNSEND F976

125571 FRASER Mrs Eleanor. (Radge) 82 Welholme Avenue, Grimsby, South Humberside, DN32 0BP.
LAING MILBURN RADGE RAGG WATT F6377

125598 FREARSON Marion. 38 Beech Crescent, Wheathampstead, Herts, AL4 8TD. Tel:058283-2773
FREARSON GREIG LEEFARR PIRIE SAMUEL SPARHAM F2355

125601 FREDEEN Mrs A Joan. (Brine) Box 1810, Lacombe, Alberta, T0C 1S0, CANADA. Tel:+1-403-782-3252
BRINE ENGLISH FORTUNE WARREN F4575

125628 FREELAND Ms Joan. 22 High Street, Clifton, Bristol, BS8 2YF. Tel:0272-732554
BELCHER Boas BOASE Boaz Bose Bowes DANN FAIREY FLEETWOOD Foddeslie FREELAND FROGLEY Froglie Frogly HECK HICHENS Hick Hicks Hitchens LAWRENCE LAY SALTER SELMES SUMNER Tayler Tresize TUSISE TYLER WAKEM WILLIS WILSON F2251

125636 FREEMAN Mrs Elizabeth. Bulwardine, Claverley, Wolverhampton, WV5 7AP.
BURTON GOODSON F6450

125644 FREEMAN Miss J R. 76 Highlever Road, London, W10 6PN.
BILLYARD STRAHORN F6567

125652 FREEMAN Mrs J. 20 Shenstone Avenue, Halesowen, West Midlands, B62 8QA.
FREEMAN LUDFORD-FREEMAN F3804

125660 FREEMAN Mr James D. 56 Culverden Down, Tunbridge Wells, Kent, TN4 9SG. Tel:0892-524665

ADKIN ALSTON COSTIDELL COTTEREL DIVES DOUBELL FREEMAN GLOVER HALE HOLMDEN JEWELL NEWBERY SEARLE SPIERS TULETT WHITLEY WHITMORE F1861

125679 FREEMAN Mr John. 25 Hillmead, Gossops Green, Crawley, Sussex, RH11 8RP. Tel:0293-524149
BISHOP BRADLEY BURGER CRINNION FREEMAN MAY ROBINSON STAGG F3059

125687 FREEMAN Mr John. 77 Fairview, Liversedge, W Yorks, WF15 6LL. Tel:0274-872227
ARCHER CLOUGH FREEMAN MACKENZIE F3126

125695 FREEMAN Mr John. 33 Ferrers Road, Doncaster, South Yorks, DN2 4BU.
ALDERMAN ATKINSON BALMER BLANSHARD CARTER CORBY CROOTE CURTIS DEAN FREEMAN GRAY HART JACKSON JEAKINS KIDDOR LOAKE NIXON NOBLE PAIN PEXTON PORTERIS RACHER RAWLINGS RICHARDSON RUSSELL SAUNDERS SPEIGHT TIPPING TRUELOVE VARVILL F3705

125709 FREEMAN Mr M K. 9 Ruth Gardens, Kettering, Northants, NN16 0PU.
BATES FREEMAN HOBBS STARMER WEST F2718

125717 FREEMAN Mrs P M. (Riley) 20 Oxford Street, Daventry, Northants, NN11 4AD.
BATES BEVAN COTTERALL DAVIES HOLMES LLEWELLYN MORGAN PIERCE RILEY SHANNON WALTERS WEEKS F130

125725 FREEMAN Mr Robert. 99 Wellfield Road, Hatfield, Herts, AL10 0BY. Tel:0707-266769
BATTS BENFIELD FREEMAN GOODISON STAYT WHISTLE F1633

125733 FREER Mr D E. 9 Percheron Way, Droitwich, Worcs, WR9 7RF. Tel:0905-775493
FREER GUTHRIE MERCHANT F4225

125741 FREESTONE Mr C J. 6 Cedar Road, Berkhamstead, Herts, HP4 2LA.
Freeston FREESTONE Freestonne Freston Freyston Frieston Friestone TATTERSON F5822

125768 FRENCH Mr Alan. 4 Quintin Close, Hailsham, East Sussex, BN27 3NQ.
FRENCH F3220

125776 FRENCH Mrs Christine. (Relf) Pound Cottage, The Pound, Ashburnham, Battle, E Sussex, TN33 9NR.
FRENCH RALF RALPH REALF RELF RELFE Relph ROLF ROLFE F1634

125784 FRENCH Mrs P. 10 Old Mill Road, Saffron Walden, Essex, CB11 3ER.
ADAMS ASHMAN BENSTEAD FRENCH HUNT NEWCOMBE SMITH F5838

125792 FRENCH Mr Peter E. The Moorings, Main Street, Chilthorne Domer, Yeovil Somerset, BA22 8RD.
ENGLAND FRENCH FRY GRIDLEY LAMB F3636

125806 FRESHWATER Mrs Barbara. (Brommer) 10042 Chapin Way, Sunland, CA 91040, USA.
ADDERLEY AIMIS BUSHELL LAMB LUCAS PEARSON RAYBOULD SHAW SIMMS WHITE F5640

125814 FRIDAY Mrs Nancy. (Roberts) 6 Davies Drive, Wem, Shrewsbury, Shropshire, SY4 5YW. Tel:0939-33965
FRIDAY ROBERTS F3397

125822 FRIGGLE Mr Rod. 3713 W 185th Street, Torrance, CA 90504, USA. Tel:+1-310-516-6104
Fragall FRAGEL Fragell Fragle Freagell Freagle Fregal Fregwill FRIGALL Friggell Friggle F5513

125830 FRISKNEY Dr C A. 11 North Over Road, Westbury On Trym, Bristol, BS9 3LN.
BUTTERY Freshney Freskney Frishney Friskeney FRISKNEY LOCKING F2530

125849 FRISON Theo. Koning Albert Street 34, B2800, Mechelen, BELGIUM.
FRISON F7282

125857 FRLAN Mrs Margaret D. 24 Rectory Gardens, Solihull, West Midlands, B91 3RL.
ALLEN BANKS HICKEN JACKSON MILTON POOLE STRATTON F7426

125865 FROST Mr Colin. 12 Highate Drive, West Knighton, Leicester, LE2 6HH.
BRIGHTMAN BROWN COX Davies DAVIS EDMONDS Edmunds FROST KIRK MRASURRS Pailing Palian PALIMG PALIN Paling RUTLAND SPRMCRR TOLLADAY TUTTY WALKER Walter Waltiar WARLTIER WARLTIRE Wartyre WILDE Wrightwril F4769

125873 FROST Mrs Maureen. 36 Redstone Road, Redhill, Surrey, RH1 6EA.
ASHFORD BALDWIN EADE FROST Kempsell KEMPSHALL MORLING WASSALL Wassell F2380

125881 FROST Mr R. 7 Honey Hill, Wimbotsham, Kings Lynn, Norfolk, PE34 3QD.
ABDALE Ebdale FROST JARVIS LEFEVRE MERRIKIN RUBYTHON SYDER TWITE WHITBY F3478

125903 FRY Mrs Joan. 9 Penmere Place, Falmouth, Cornwall, TR11 2QG.
BOSLEY CANNON GILL LOVELL WHITOAKS WHITTICKS WIDDOCKS WITTOCK F688

125911 FRY Mrs L. 4 Coronation Cottages, Routs Way, Rownhams, Southampton Hants, SO1 8JG. Tel:0703-737931
Blan BLANN Blans F2536

125938 FRY Mrs Maureen. (Randle) 7 Thornbury Close, Crowthorne, Berks, RG11 6PE. Tel:0344-774590
ALLDRITT CALDICOTT GIBBS HAYDEN LANGLEY MILLERCHIP MOORE RANDLE WALKER WYRESDALE F2735

125946 FRYATT Mrs Elizabeth. (Smurthwaite) 42 Manor Gardens, Buckden, Huntingdon, Cambs, PE18 9TN.
SMALFIT SMALLPIECE SMURFOOT SMURTHWAITE YATES F4830

125954 FRYER Mrs Betty. 9 Glenheadon Rise, Leatherhead, Surrey, KT22 8QT.
BEALEY BLUNT BROOKSBANK BRUETON COOCH COOMBE EYRES HARGROVE IRONSIDE NORMINGTON PHYSICK QUINTON ROBINSON SHORTLAND STYRING YATES F5029

125962 FRYER Mr Edward R. 31 Conway Road, Taplow, Maidenhead, Berks, SL6 0LB. Tel:0628-604522
FRYER GATES GEORGE HORTEN NEWELL OLFORD POOLE TIBBLES F515

125970 FRYER Mrs Joanne. 9 Fordingbridge Close, Oakwood Park, Allington, Maidstone, ME16 0DA.
CHRISTOPHER DEVERSON FRYER STAPLETON UPTON VINTEN F1345

125989 FRYER Mr John. 6 Meadowlands, Havant, Hants, PO9 2RP.
BAUGH F2365

125997 FUCHS Mr Peter. The Elwells, Dunton Bassett, Lutterworth, Leics, LE17 5JJ. Tel:0455-202370
BLACKALL CONNELL COOKE WATSON F1451

126004 FULLER Mrs B. 65 New Park Street, Devizes, Wiltshire, SN10 1DR.
BOBBY F6683

126012 FULLER Colin Michael. 14 Silver Birch Avenue, Culverstone, Meopham, Kent, DA13 0TP. Tel:0732-822835
CALLER CARLOW FULLER LILLEY Lilly PAIN PEEL F1440

126020 FULLER Mrs E M. 58 The Crescent, Theale, Reading, Berks, RG7 5AZ.
GALE GRAY HICKMAN NEALE STRATTON F2046

126039 FULTON Mr Kenneth T. 3 Meadway, Berkhamsted, Herts, HP4 2PL.
FULTON F7283

126047 FURNEAUX Mrs L M. 21 Orchid Court, The Avenue, Egham, Surrey, TW20 9HA. Tel:0784-430077
Hinard Hiner HYNARD Hyner F6051

126055 FURSE Mr David John. 50 Hallam Road, Mapperley, Nottingham, NG3 6HR.
BLANCHFORD FURSE HARVEY PIKE STOOKE F3873

126063 FURZE Miss Liz. Foinfield, Leeds Road, Otley, W Yorks, LS21 1DL. Tel:0943-462525
ELLIS Firrs Firs Furrs Furs FURSE Fursse FURZE HOAR HOARE F599

126071 FUSSELL Mrs R J. (Lock) Summerdown House, Bratton, Westbury, Wiltshire, BA13 4SW. Tel:0380-830486
COSSLETT LOCK F6035

126098 FUSSELL Mr S W. Summerdown House, Bratton, Westbury, Wiltshire, BA13 4SW. Tel:0380-830486
ALLEN BARRATT Barrett BOURN Bourne BUDDEN DANIEL FREEMAN FUSSELL HINE LEGG NOAD TURNER Whittleton WILSON WITTLETON F3062

126101 GABB Mr James G. 17 Meadow Croft, Upper Stratton, Swindon, Wilts, SN2 6JP. Tel:0793-825039
BURLEY CRADDOCK GABB LANGFORD MENCE WALDRON F17

126128 GABRIEL Mrs Ina. (Oclee) Little Orchard, 58 Cross Road, Tadworth, Surrey, KT20 5SU. Tel:0737-813571

MYHILL SPRATT F4385
126136 GAFFNEY Miss. 76 Horley Road, Redhill, Surrey.
BURDEN COMBES EDE MADDISON F2202
126144 GAFOUR Mrs M. Rosendale Cottage, Canworthy Water, Launceston, Cornwall, PL15 8UD.
BARBER BARRETT BENNETT CLARK Clarke CLEAVES Cleeves COOPER CUNNINGHAM DIXON ELLIS EVANS FRANCES GUNTER Haise Haman HAMMETT HARRYMAN HAYES HAYMAN Hays Hayse Herriman Heys HODGE Hoveden HOWES INGRAM KENDRICK KING LEDGER Mainard MAYNARD OVENDEN PARNELL RASPISON RIVERS RUSSELL Sacar SAKER SARGEANT Secker Seeker SELLIN Sergeant SMITH F140
126152 GAIN Dr Robin G. Minstead, Red Lion Lane, Sarratt, Herts, WD3 6BW. Tel:0923-268762
GAIN F616
126160 GAINFORD Mr J J. 79 Crowther Road, Wolverhampton, WV6 0HX. Tel:0902-751308
BUCKLEY DAWSON FINLAY FORRESTOR GAINFORD LITTLE SANDELANDS Sandilands WATTS F453
126179 GALE Mr Nigel. 51 Heron Way, Horsham, West Sussex, RH13 6DW. Tel:0403-64035
ALLEN BATEMAN BRANSTON BRITTAIN GALE JOHNSON RAWLINGS SPICER WOODROW F6467
126187 GALE Mr Robert E J. 17 Dalkeith Avenue, Kingswood, Bristol, BS15 1HH.
BAXTER BIDDLESCOMBE Bloor BLOWER COUSINS Cousons EVELEIGH GALE Gregory GREGREY MANSFIELD MORRIS NORTHOVER PARKER RAISON RALLS SELMAN WHITE WILLIAMS F2731
126195 GALL Mr Dickson. 10 Northfield Place, Aberdeen, Scotland, AB2 4SJ.
DICKSON GALL F3291
126209 GALL Mr Edward. 39 Edward Road, Oldbury, Warley, W Midlands, B68 0LZ.
BARNES BOTTFIELD BURFORD EVANS GALL HARTLE NORWOOD POTTS SPROT TAIT Tate F2196
126217 GALLAGHER Mr D. 32 Nursery Road, Rainham, Gillingham, Kent, ME8 0BE.
BARNARD BURNS DOUGLASS GALLAGHER LUCAS PEPPERELL SAUNDERS VIZE F4741
126225 GALLIGAN Mrs S R. 137 George Street, Kippa Ring, Queensland, 4021, AUSTRALIA.
ASTON HAMILTON HARRISON HREATHWOOD THOMPSON F5446
126233 GALLOWAY Mr Gerry. 39 Dulverton Road, Aigburth, Liverpool, L17 6AR.
CONNOLLY COOK FRAZER GALLOWAY F2951
126241 GALLOWAY Mr Ron. 15 Torver Close, Brunswick Green, Wideopen, Newcastle Upon Tyne, NE13 7HJ.
BAN DER BEN CHARLTON CRAIG CRAIGS FRENCH GALLOWAY HUNTRESS MORRIS PENMAN SPEEDY F1392
126268 GALVIN Mr D A. 30 Cliveden Road, Highams Park, London, E4 9RN.
BRADSHAW CRICK DAY DOFFIN FERRY GREENWAY HARVEY HEAP HENRIQUES IDE ISEMONGER JOHNSON LOWTHER MAPLEDORAM POND POOLMAN PUSSER RABBATTS STOCKS VALENTINE F6240
126276 GALVIN Mr Denis. 11 Waller Avenue, Blackpool, Lancs, FY2 9EL.
BALMFORD Balmforth Bamford BEDFORD BODMAN BOULTER BRIERLEY BUCKLEY COLEMAN COX Crathwell CRAUGHWELL CROSSLAND Crothwell Dagmell DAGWELL Ealey Ealy Eeley Eley Elie Elley Elly ELY GALE Galvan GALVIN Golvun GRADY Gready HILLIER KAY Kaye MANION Mannion MATTHEWS Rhoades RHODES Roads SEMLEY Slatery SLATTERY STAMP THOMPSON UNCLES WALTON Willshire WILSHER Wilshier WILTSHIRE WOOD F3239
126284 GAMBIER Mr R F. 25 Harrow-Piece, Maulden, Beds, MK45 2DG.
GAMBIER F6568
126292 GAMBLE Mrs Angela. (Fiske) 11 Minton Heights, Ashingdon, Nr Rochford, Essex, SS4 3EQ.
CHAPMAN COSH FISKE GAMBLE GREENHON HARE LEPLA ODELL F5855
126306 GAMBRILL Mr Kenneth Frederick. 30 Flowerdown Close, Totton, Hants, SO4 2UJ. Tel:0703-869905
BREWSTER FROST GAMBRILL F3289
126314 GANDER Mr Des. 67 Woolsery Avenue, Exeter, Devon, EX4 8BR.
GANDER F2175
126322 GANDER Mrs Frances. (Dunn) 1 Whitton Drive, Wealstone Lane, Upton, Chester, CH2 1HF.
BALMER BARRETT BENNION BOON BOULTON CRIMES CROCOMBE DUNN GANDER JONES LEWIS POTTER PRICE PRITCHARD RYDER F3623
126330 GANDY Mr Clifford N. Clare Park, Crondall, Farnham, Surrey, GU10 5DT. Tel:0252-850123
Gandee Gandey Gandie GANDY F1471
126349 GANN Mrs Josephine. Orchard Paddock, 90 Cupernham Lane, Romsey, Hants, SO51 7LF.
ARCHER FOYSTER GANN Ganne GLASCOTT HINDLEY OLIVER PARKER RICHARDSON Sencicle Seneschal Sensical Sensicall SENSICLE THOMAS WOODWARD F1834
126357 GARBUTT Mrs Mary E. (Baker) Rr4, Coldwater, Ontario, L0K 1E0, CANADA. Tel:+1-705-835-2821
BAKER BASKERVILLE BOYD Britain BRITTON BUNKUM CAMPBELL CASWELL GALL Gauld GILL HARVIE HEARD HOLLAND HOLLIS JOHNSON KEMP LANGMAN MCFARLANE MCLEOD RUTHERFORD SAUNDERCOCK TAYLOR THOMPSON TRIMBLE Wakelin WEAKLIM F4236
126365 GARD Mr Peter J. Upper Leys House, Leys Lane, Frome, Somerset, BA11 2JX. Tel:0373-63178
GARD F717
126373 GARDENER Mrs Hilary. 57 Yorktown Road, Sandhurst, Camberley, Surrey, GU17 8BS. Tel:0252-874405
MUCOCK MULCOCK F6428
126381 GARDENER Dr Patricia. 21a Highfield Road, Impington, Cambridge, CB4 4PF.
Brasier BRAZIER BROWN CAVE DICKERSON Dickinson GARDENER Gardiner Gardner Hubard HUBBARD Hubbart RINGWOOD ROBSON TREDGET Tredgett Treget Trudget F234
126403 GARDER Christine. 15 Littleton Place, Stoke, Plymouth, Devon, PL2 1DY. Tel:0752-551210
DEACON DINNER DYMOND NILES OLIVER POOLE RETALLICK TAPPER WEEKS F1990
126411 GARDINER Mrs Freda. (Shaw) The Coppice, Abbotts Lane, Widford, Ware, Herts, SG12 8RT. Tel:0279-842680
BUCKLEY CROMPTON GARDINER GARTSIDE HARGREAVES LEES SHAW STOTT TIMMINS WHITEHEAD F6011
126438 GARDINER Mr Norman. 23 Cranmore Close, Broadmead, Trowbridge, Wiltshire, BA14 9BU.
CULL DAVIS GARDINER GARDNER HAYNES MCKERCHER SKELDING SOPER SPARROW WOOLDRIDGE F2422
126446 GARDNER Mr I C. Strawberry Cottage, 3 Butter Street, Moonfleet, Weymouth, Dorset, DT3 4EE.
BONCEY BOYER BUTLER GARDNER MACKLIN MILO WHITELOCK F694
126454 GARDNER Mrs Nancy. 15 Farrer Parade, Port Macquarie, NSW 2444, AUSTRALIA. Tel:+61-6-583-1384
BUCKLAND CARPENTER DOWNES ELLIOTT GARDENER Gardiner HUTCHINSON JOASS JOHNSON LATIMORE MASON SMITH STONE TAYLOR TURBERVILLE UNICOMB WALKLEY WEAVER WELBY WORSLEY F4476
126462 GARDNER Mrs Susan. (Mutum) Balder View, Cotherstone, Barnard Castle, Co Durham, DL12 9NR.
ANNETT BIRKETT BURTON CLARK CLARKSON GARDNER HOPE MUTUM RIDDELL STORROW F4256
126470 GARDNER Mrs V P. (Currie) 2 Stratford Court, 68 The Parkway, Bassett, Southampton, SO2 3PN.
ALDERMAN BURNELL CURRIE CURRY FREEMAN NELSON PALMER POND TAMLIN TITCOMBE F6200
126489 GARNER Mr Barry Hugh. Rose Cottage, Babbs Lane, Doveridge, Derbys, DE6 5JT. Tel:0889-563923
BLOUNT COPESTAKE GARNER HORSLEY F365
126497 GARNER Mrs G. (Thain) Villa Landa, Bon Air Lane, St Saviour, Jersey, JE2 7LJ.
AINSCOW ANDERSON ARROWSMITH ASHALL ASHURST BAILEY BAIN BAXENDALE BIRD BORTHWICK BRADYLL BREMNER BRUCE BYRNE CALDERBANK CAMPBELL CARR Castel CASTLE CHEYNE CLARK Clarke CLERK Clerke CLOUGH CORMACK CORRIGAN CRUICKSHANK DANIEL DAVENPORT DAVIDSON Devenport Devonport DUGUID DUNCAN FAIRHURST FIELDING FISHWICK FOSTER FOWLER GAIR Gardner GARNER GEAR GEDDES GILMUIR GRAY GREEN GROAT HARRISON HARROW HATTLE HENDERSON HEYES HIGHAM HOPWOOD HORN KAY LAIRD LIPTROT LOCKHART Macdonald MACKAY MANSON MARSH MCDONALD MCINTYRE MCKAY MILLER

MILNE MITTON MUNRO Mytton NICOL OMAN PARKINSON PATTERSON PINCOCK Rainie Rainnie Rainy Ranny REILLY RENNIE Renny RIGBY ROSIE RYNE SHEARER SINCLAIR SMALLEY SMITH STANFORTH STEPHEN STUART SUTHERLAND TAYLOR THAIN Thaine THOMPSON TICKLE VALE WARBURTON WATERWORTH WELCH Welsh WESTHEAD WINSTANLEY F4176

126500 GARNER Mrs Gillian. Villa Landa, La Rue Du Froid Vent, St Saviour, Jersey, JE2 7LT. ASHALL BAIN BAXENDALE BIRD BORTHWICK BREMNER Castel CASTLE CHYNE CLARK Clarke Clerk Clerke CLOUGH Davenport DAVIDSON DEVENPORT DUGUID FIELDING FISHWICK Gair GARNER GEAR HENDERSON HEYES HIGHAM LIPTROT LOCKHART Macdonald MACKAY MANSON MARSH MATTLE MCDONALD Mckay PATTERSON PINCOCK Rainnie Rainny RENNIE Renny RIGBY ROSIE SMITH STEPHEN SUTHERLAND TAYLOR THAIN Thaine TICKLE VALE WELCH Welsh WINSTANLEY F53

126519 GARNETT Mrs S E. 1 Princes Street, Leamington Spa, Warks, CV32 4TY. Tel:0926-337983 ALLEN CADY COOK GARNETT HYATT JOHNSON KNEATH KNOTT LEES LILES F1556

126527 GARNHAM Ms Patricia F. 11 Bascraft Way, Godmanchester, Huntingdon, Cambs, PE18 8EG. Tel:0480-453502 ASHMORE GARNHAM PERRY SHAW WARNER F2066

126535 GARRATT-SMITH Mrs Melanie A. Trelawney, Fentonadle, St Breward, Bodmin, Cornwall, PL30 4PJ. Tel:0208-850362 BOXALL CHAPLIN DUNLOP HALLIDAY LANE MARSHALL OLSON SALLNOW SMITH STUBLEY F6324

126543 GARRETT Mrs Barbara A. 25 Robins Grove, Yateley, Camberley, Surrey, GU17 7PS. BARDWELL BELL BUNGAY FARRINGTON FORSDICK FRIEND GARRETT MONK PIPER SOUTHGATE F1401

126551 GARRETT Mr Eric V. Bradstones, Haw Lane, Olveston, Bristol, BS12 3EG. Tel:0454-613019 FISHER GARRETT ORGAN PHILLIMORE TAYLOR VOWLES F2851

126578 GARVIN Mr James. 19 Clonavon Terrace, Ballymena, County Antrim, N Ireland, BT43 5BE. Tel:0266-44660 Garvan Garven GARVIN Garvon F4888

126586 GASKELL Mrs Sally. 53 Nicholls Field, Harlow, Essex, CM18 6DZ. BASHAM BEAGLEY BOWLES COOPER CRAWFORD CROSBY CRUICKSHANK DALLEN DANDY DUGUID EVANS FARRAR FIRMAN GASKELL GLAZING GOODEN GRAY HARRIS HART HICKFORD HINDES HITCHMOUGH HORNE HOWE IRELAND JONHES KERR LAWFORD MAJOR MCDONALD MCGOURTY MERCER MILLER MITCHELL MONK MOOK MORTIMORE MOSS MUCH MURKIN OPPEN PATRICK PAWSEY PICKETT RANESLEY RIMMER ROWE ROWLING RUDKIN SAUNDERS SIMPSON STEVENS STONER THOMPSON TIMMINS VON OPPEN WAGSTAFFE WARNER WATSON WHEATLEY WHITEROD WHITFIELD WILKINSON WILSON F3082

126594 GASKIN Mr Paul. 8 Wadham Parade, Mount Waverley, VIC 3149, AUSTRALIA. Tel:+61-3-807-3044 GASKIN GILBERT LANE MADDOCKS MUDIE NEWLANDS THORNTON WOOD F5187

126608 GASKING Mr R A. St Ives, 1 West Road, Berkhamsted, Herts, HP4 3HT. GASKING F6717

126616 GASPARELLI Mrs Geraldine. (Travers) The Rose Cottage, 80 West Street, Carshalton, Surrey, SM5 2PR. Tel:081-647-2359 FURBER GALE GAMBEL Gamble Gambol HALLETT HODGES HOUCHELL Houchen Houtchell Howchell Howtchell HYDE LAST LLOYD NUTBEAM Ouchell Travas TRAVERS Traverse Traves Travis Traviss Trevass Trevis WATSON WHITEWAY F3595

126624 GASSON Mrs Vi. 29 Mayfair Avenue, Chadwell Heath, Romford, Essex, RM6 6UB. JAMES PREECE SCRIMSHAW F2467

126632 GATE Mr George. 3 Bolle Road, Alton, Hants, GU34 1PW. Tel:0420-83881 BATY CLOUGH GALL GATE MITCHELL SINCLAIR F1244

126640 GATER Mr Edward. 61 Barry Road, Bitterne, Southampton, Hants, SO2 5LT. Tel:0703-449435 BUNDY CHALCROFT COOPER DODD Eckton ECTON FUREY GATER LUFF MUSPRATT NIMMO PHILLIPS SNOOK TREMLIN F2417

126659 GATER Mr Michael. 268 Main Road, New Duston, Northampton, NN5 6PP. Tel:0604-752601 BARNSHAW BURTON FILKIN Gaiter GATER Gayter Gaytor HIGHAM JINKS RICKARDS RUSSELL TASSELL TILDESLEY USBORNE VAUGHAN F3163

126667 GATES Mrs Elinor M. (Anderson) 81 Burnham Lane, Slough, Berks, SL1 6JY. Acott ALLEN ANDERSON BARTON BROWN BUCKETT BUTCHER DADGE Dodge DOREY Eacott EYCOTT Gifkins GRANT GUY GWINNETT Jefkins JIFFKINS JIFKINS JOLIFFE RANDALL READ Rideout Ridet RIDETT Ridhett Ridout SCOTT SENNOCK SMITH SUMMERS TAYLOR TURNER Vey Vie VYE WELLARD Wellerd WHITE Willard WOODFORD WOODS F2244

126675 GATES Mr Stephen. 41 Gainsborough Crescent, Eastbourne, E Sussex, BN23 7NE. Tel:0323-766387 DRAPPER ELLIOTT GATES HOOKER LEOPPARD MARSHALL MAYELL SMALL WHITE F958

126683 GATFIELD Mr William James. 14 Lower Lambricks, Rayleigh, Essex, SS6 8DB. Tel:0268-775996 GATFIELD HOLMES MOUNTAIN ROGERS SACKER SAINT SHEPPARD TOWNSEND F2170

126691 GATHERCOLE Mr E E. 12 Cathsworth Road, Huntstanton, Norfolk, PE36 5DJ. Gathercoal GATHERCOLE Standley F6974

126705 GATTINESI Mr Peter. 73 Milton Mount Avenue, Pound Hill, Crawley, Sussex, RH10 3DP. ALLAN Arbridge ATHERTON BEADSON Beaton Beatson Beeson Beeston BEETSON Betson BUTT CASSIDY CLARK Clarke COOK COTTERELL DEARDEN DENNEY Denny DENSON DUNN FISHER GARNER GREEN HALL HAMER Harbadge Harbage Harbidge Harbige Harbridg HARBRIDGE Hewett Hewit HEWITT HILL HOBSON HOLLAND HOWARD Huet JACKSON JAMESON LARGE LAWTON LINDORES Longton LYNN MCDADE Mosedale MOSS Moudsdlae Moulesdale Moulsdale Moulsdel Moulsdell MOUSDALE NIGHTINGALE NUTALL OAKES PARR RATHBONE RIMMER SHANNON Sharrock SHORROCK SIMPSON STEVENSON TATNALL THIRSK UNDERWOOD VERNON VICKERS WALKER WALSH Walshe WHITWORTH WILLIAMS WOODVILLE WORRALL WREN WRIGHT F6323

126713 GAUNT Mr G A. 19 Valley View, Rudheath, Northwich, Cheshire, CW9 7HX. Tel:0606-45395 GRAY HATTON LONGBOTTOM F412

126721 GAUNT Mr L. 11 Station Road, Swinderby, Lincoln, LN6 9LY. BARNARD BIRKIN BRACKLEY DAY FAULCONBRIDGE GAUNT HANKIN INSKIP LOCKWOOD MANLEY MILLER NIXON ODELL RHODES SALVIN SEYMOUR SQUIRE STARR THOMPSON THORNHILL THURSTON TINKER TURNER WALKER F3316

126748 GAYE Mr I M. 44 Highfield Avenue, Waterlooville, Portsmouth, Hants, PO7 7PX. GAY GAYE MONCREIFF Moncreiffe Moncrieff Moncrieffe F3392

126756 GAZE Mr E W. 9a Hillberry Road, Forest View Park, Valley Road, Cinderford Glous, GL14 2JD. GAZE PAYNE F730

126764 GEAL Mrs L M. 3 Suffolk House, Queens Drive, Acton, London, W3 OHN. SWATTON F7002

126772 GEDYE Mr David James. 16 Colne Road, Bluntisham, Huntingdon, Cambs, PE17 3LU. ALLEN ARNOLD BARNETT BARROWCLIFF BONE BURKINSHAW CARPENTER CHETTLE COOMBE CRON Crone CUMING DOMAN Donan Dornan EDNEY FOX FROST GAUL Gedge GEDYE Giddy GILES GREASLEY HUMPLEBY JACKSON KITCHING LAMMIE MCTURK PAYNE PRIM SAWYER SPENCER STOREY SWINFIELD WATSON WAYTE WHITEHOUSE WILSON F3021

126780 GEDYE Mr Nicholas G E. Sydney House, Crossgate Peth, Durham, DH1 4PZ. Tel:091-386-9360 Geddy Gedie Gedy GEDYE Geedie Geedy Geedye Geydye Giddey GIDDY Giddye Gidi Gyddy Gyde Gydy F564

126799 GEERE Mr Jeremy. 46 Gibson Close, Abingdon, Oxon, OX14 1XT. ANGOLD AYRES BROWN BURNETT BURSEY BURWOOD CHAPMAN CHILVERS DREW FENNELL FULLER GARDNER GEER GEERE GUTTERIDGE HARDING HART HEWLETT HILLS MILES MUDGE PEMBRIDGE PLUMB RANSOME SANIGAR SHELDRAKE F2331

126802 GEESIN Mr Ron. Headrest, Scotsford Road, Broad Oak, Heathfield, E Sussex, TN21 8TU. BOLTON DOBSON DONALD DONALDSON GEESIN GEESING Geeson Gesynge Geysinge Gissing Gysynge KENNEDY LAWSON LEES MALCOLM PENNY SWAINSON TELFORD F2416
126810 GELDER Mr John. 25 Torre Close, West Bletchley, Milton Keynes, Bucks, MK3 6NG. GELDER Gilder Guelder F883
126829 GELL Miss Freda. 29 Pentland Gardens, Thorpe Park, Long Eaton, Nottingham, NG10 4FX. GELL F4042
126837 GELLING Mr Eric N. 1184 Clovelly Terrace, Victoria, British Columbia, V8P 1V6, CANADA. BRISCOE DRIVER EVANS FLETCHER GALE GELLING JENNINGS LAWSON MALCOLM PUTTERGILL RADFORD SHAW THEAKER WARTNABY F4380
126845 GENDLE Mr Eric. 13 Mayfield Road, Nunthorpe, Middlesborough, Cleveland, TS7 0ED. Tel:0642-324360 BULMER FOOTIT GENDLE KEEP MAUGHAM PRESTON WHITE F6284
126853 GENN Mr David. 10251 Algonquin Drive, Richmond, British Columbia, V7A 3A5, CANADA. Tel:+1-604-275-3535 GENN F4389
126861 GENT Mr R. 4 Winterton Gardens, Hackenthorpe, Sheffield, S12 4NA. GENT Ghent Jent Jhent F6753
126888 GERHARDT Mr E Alvin. 5 Bingham Court, Johnson City, TN 37604, USA. Tel:+1-615-929-3206 F4917
126896 GIBB Ms. 88a Grahams Road, Falkirk, Stirlingshire, Scotland, FK2 7DL. DUTHIE FORGIE GIBB MCCULLOCH TRAIL F343
126918 GIBBINS Mrs Shirley. (Aldridge) 98 Eden Park Avenue, Beckenham, Kent, BR3 3HW. ALDRIDGE BALLINGALL BANBROOK BULLOCKE CHITTAM FRANKLIN FRYER HARRINGTON LION LYON MORTON POMFRET POOLEY SPINKS WHEELER WILMOT F884
126926 GIBBONS Mrs C S. 82 Coningsby Gardens, Chingford, London, E4 9BD. Bracknal Bracknall BRACKNELL Collyer COLYER DAVIES DAVIS HALLS NIGHTINGALE F3599
126934 GIBBONS Mr Islwyn. 77 Gipsy Lane, Irchester, Wellingborough, Northants, NN9 7DJ. GIBBONS F3271
126942 GIBBONS Mr Trevor. 84 Main Street, Shadwell, Leeds, Yorks, LS17 8HN. Tel:0532-737171 BLUNDEL BRINDLE BROWN BUXTON EASTWOOD FRITH GIBBONS GREGORY LEE LIMB MANSFIELD PHILLIPSON SALISBURY SPRUSEN TAYLOR WESTON WHALLEY F5747
126950 GIBBS Mrs G. (Sidwell) 8 Freshwood Way, Wallington, Surrey, SM6 0RL. BONSER GIBBS SIDWELL TUTT VEALE WREN F5082
126969 GIBBS Mr George. 136 High Street, Wyke Regis, Weymouth, Dorset, DT4 9NT. Tel:0305-776719 GIBBS LEGG F4836
126977 GIBSON Mr Alan. 16 Chetwood Avenue, Great Crosby, Liverpool, L23 2UX. BOYD BULMER CHADWICK DOUGLAS GIBSON MAIN MAWDSLEY PENDLETON WHIRK F4334
126985 GIBSON Mrs Greta. (Kennedy) Wilderness, Damask Green Road, Weston, Hitchin, Herts, SG4 7DA. BARTON CONNELLY GIBSON KENNEDY PEARE PONSONBY REDWOOD SCAIFE SIMPSON WEDDALL Weddell F4544
126993 GIBSON Lady J. 3 Tipperlinn Road, Edinburgh, EH10 5ET. BURSBY CLARKE CLOUDSLEY GIBSON GREIG HINSHELWOOD STRAPP TULLY WATT WILLIAMSON F2692
127000 GIBSON Mr & Mrs W J B. (Bailey) 14 Dorset Road, Lytham St Annes, Lancs, FY8 2ED. BAILEY BAIN BALD BETHELL BISSELL BROTCHIE DAVIES DUNNETT EVANS GIBSON HAY HOLT HOPWOOD KINSEY LANGSTON MANLY MANSON MARKS MOSELEY NICHOLLS OAKLEY OLIVER PENLINGTON PERRIN PURCELL RUSCOE SIMPSON SINCLAIR STOBBIE STOBIE THOMPSON THOMSON THORLEY F5304
127019 GICHARD Mr H A. 81 Tavistock Road, Waipukurau, NEW ZEALAND. Tel:+64-6-858-9252 GICHARD F4474
127027 GIDDENS Mr R A. 3 Church Street, Baslow, Derbyshire, DE4 1RY. Tel:0246-583495 Gedding Geden Gedin Gedon Giddens GIDDINGS GIDDINS Gydding Gyddyng Gydin Gydon F6118
127035 GIDLOW Mr Charles And Mrs Doris. 3 Wykeham Court, Wykeham Road, Hastings, East Sussex, TN34 1UN. Tel:0424-439023 BAKER BATSON BOX GIDLOW HALL HARDY HEASMAN LASCELLES LOCKYER MESSENGER PITMAN THORRINGTON F3430
127043 GIGGINS Mr Brian. 1 Orchard Close, Towcester, Northants, NN12 7BP. GIGGINS Giggons Jeggeons Jeggins Jeggon Jegins Jegion Jegon Jiggins Jiggons Jyggyns RICHINGS TIMMS F271
127051 GILBERT Mr Anthony J. 9 Fir Tree Close, Coppenhall, Stafford, ST18 9BZ. Tel:0785-48264 DILKE GILBERT LAMPORT F1332
127078 GILBERT Mrs B. 12 Cavanna Close, Gosport, Hants, PO13 0PE. ARM CAMMEL DENBEIGH DENMAN GANN GILBERT HICKISSON HOTFIELD IMBER F1641
127086 GILBERT Mr Bernard H. 27 Cromwell Avenue, Aulesbury, Bucks, HP19 3PL. Tel:0296-81698 Abbingdon ABINGDON BITHELL GILBERT JILBERT KRINKS F3460
127094 GILBERT Mrs J M. 25 Salcombe Drive, Earley, Reading, Berks, RG6 2HU. Adman Admans ADNAM ADNAMS Adnum Adnums ATKINS GILBERT Hadnam Hadnams Hadnum Hadnums HATT HUBEN KENNERLEY MOORE NEVILL NEVILLE NEVILLES RIGBY WILLIAMS F653
127108 GILBERT Mrs Jackie. 67 Connaught Avenue, Chingford, London, E4 7AP. Tel:081-529-4440 ARGENT GOLDING MADDISON POPE STRAPP F2000
127116 GILBERT Mrs Margaret. (Owens) 16 Price Road, Kalorama, Victoria, 3766, AUSTRALIA. Tel:+61-3-728-4660 ABBOT BAKER BELLINGER BREWER BUNNEY BURNETT BURT BUTLER CHARLTON COLE COOK CORDRAN DAVIES DINGLE DOMING DOVEY FORSTER FOULSHAM FRIAR FULCHER GALE GILBERT GILES GOTER HAUGHTON HOLDWAY HUMPHREY HYDE JONES KEMISH KENT KIDGELL LAWRENCE MASON MEREFIELD MONDAY MONKTON NICHOLAS NORTH OSMAN OWENS PAICE PIERCE POOR PRATER ROBERTS SAUNDERS SHEPPARD SMALL SPICER STACY THOMPSON TILLS TOWLER TUFFIN UNDERWOOD WARNE WATERMAN WHITE WHITMARSH WILLIAMS YATES F5419
127124 GILBERT Mr R A & Mrs Sarah. Crags, 49 Ardholm Place, Lochadil, Inverness, IV2 4QG. Tel:0463-243896 CLEGHORN GILBERT GLEGHORN ROBERTS F1977
127132 GILCHRIST Mr David. 17 Contance Avenue, Trentham, Staffs, ST4 8TE. Tel:0782-643438 GILCHRIST SENIOR WELLS F3939
127140 GILCHRIST Mrs Marjorie W. (Calder) Claigan, Dunvegan, Isle Of Skye, Inverness, IV55 8WF. Tel:047022-215 BANNATYNE BELL BOYD BRAID CALDER CAMERON CAMPBELL Carsell CARZELL COLQUHOUN CRAIG DICK FERGUSON FORSYTH Forsythe FYFE GARTSHORE GIBSON GUNN JAMIESON KIRK KNOWLES LAING LANG LINN MACDIARMID MACDONALD MACKINNON MACNAUGHT MCFARLAN Mcfarlane MCKELVIE MCKENZIE MCLEAN MCNALL MCTAGGART MCTAVISH MITCHELL ORR Probait PROBERT PROCTOR RADFORD RANKIN Rankine REID SCOTT SHAW Sherifs Sherrifs SHIRREFFS SIMPSON SMITH SPEIRS STEWART STRATHERN THOMSON WALKER WARDEN WAYMAN WEIR WILSON WYLIE YOUNG F4158
127159 GILDER Miss Mary. 22 Woodhurst Road, Canvey Island, Essex, SS8 0HB. GILDER JELLEYMAN F1123
127167 GILDING Miss Gail. 2 Duck Lane, Haddenham, Ely, Cambs, CB6 3UE. Tel:0353-741354 BOOTLE GILDING F4294
127175 GILDING Mrs Joan. 4 Linford Estate, Clenchwarton, Kings Lynn, Norfolk, PE34 4BA. BACON Becan Becon Dey Die DYE Gelding Gilden GILDING Gildon Guilden Guilding Guildon Gylden Gylding Gyldynge LITTLEWOOD Lyttlewood Oxer OXLEY Oxxe Perrie PERRY Pery F3003
127183 GILES Mrs Heather. (Marten) 42 Kilndown Close, Allington, Maidstone, Kent, ME16 0PL. Tel:0622-676546 BAKER BUTCHER HARDEN Harding KEMP LUCAS MARTEN Martens Martin MCKINNON NASH NEWNHAM

SIMPSON TOOTH TURNER WATSON Wichington WICKINGTON Wiggington Wigginton Wigington Win Winn WOOD WYNN F2657

127191 GILES Mr L C. 23 Hollycombe Close, Liphook, Hants, GU30 7HR.
F3277

127205 GILI-ROSS Mrs Lynne. (Garnett) 9 Delany Drive, Freckleton, Preston, Lancs, PR4 1SJ. Tel:0772-634238
BEARD GARNETT HARRISON RUDINGS WHITCOMB F5940

127213 GILL Barbara. Rd1 Box 1645, Schuylkill Haven, PA 17972, USA.
Packson PAXSON Paxton F5342

127221 GILL Mr Derek C. Morning Calm, 74 Stafford Road, Petersfield, Hants, GU32 2JG. Tel:0730-62322
BIGNELL BLACKISTON CHILCOT GILL F1027

127248 GILL Mrs Kathleen. (Caldwell) 7 Hillcrest, Thornbury, Bristol, BS12 1AA. Tel:0454-412285
CALDWELL Calldwell Caudwell Cauldwell EDDY Edy GILL Malison Malisone Malisonn Mallesonne Mallingson MALLINSON Mallison Mallyson F4140

127256 GILL Mrs R P. 108 Foxley Lane, Purley, Surrey, CR8 3NB.
HARDWAY F7200

127264 GILL Mr Randal David. 5 Westburn Crescent, Bangor, Co Down, BT20 3RN, NORTHERN IRELAND. Tel:0247-465770
GILL HODKINSON KEARNEY F5765

127272 GILL Mrs S M. (Paveley) 9 Malory Close, Stone, Staffs, ST15 0JQ.
BASSIL BATTY BRACE BREARLEY EMBERTON GILL HASSAN MORRIS PAVELEY PAVELY WESTWOOD F1470

127280 GILLAM Mr M J. 17 Highdown Drive, Littlehampton, Sussex, BN17 6HJ.
GILLAM HAINES MACKALL Mackoll Macole Macoll F1818

127299 GILLARD Mrs D M. 4 Aintree Road, Furnace Greep, Crawley, W Sussex, RH10. Tel:0293-512459
BOLTON BONE CORNISH CRAIGIE HASLETT SHARPE SWAINSTON F446

127302 GILLARD Mr Peter J. 47 Stewart Street, Chelmsford, Essex, CM2 9BB. Tel:0245-257090
DOWSETT GILLARD JANES JOHNSTON MERRICKS MORTON PEPPIATT ROWLAND THOMPSON WOOD F2349

127310 GILLBERRY Col George. 20 Old Arncott Road, Ambrosden, Bicester, Oxon, OX6 0LT.
Gilberay GILLBERRY Gillbury F6939

127329 GILLESPIE Mr La Roux. 1300 E 109 St, Kansas City, MO 64131-3585, USA. Tel:+1-816-942-5497
IRETON F5530

127337 GILLETT Mrs A J. 62 Boyce Road, Stanford Le Hope, Essex, SS17 8RP.
HONEYWOOD Honywood Hunniwood F6763

127345 GILLETT Mr M J. 33 Marion Crescent, Maidstone, Kent, ME15 7DZ.
GILLETT HALES HILLS F5716

127353 GILLHAM Trixie. (Line) Meadowside, Penstraze, Chacewater, Truro, Cornwall, TR4 8PL. Tel:0872-560154
ALLEN AYRES BATES BECKETT BUCK COLEMAN DEAN Dickenson DICKINSON EMERSON Gailham Gilham GILLAM Gillham Gilliam GOSNEY Gozney JEANS KIRK KNOWLES LINE MARKLEY MORTIMER MOSS Muckley REEVE Reeves ROSE Sale SAYELL Sayle SIBLEY THOMPSON WARING Warren F3114

127361 GILLION Mr Richard B. 3 Windermere Close, Dunstable, Beds, LU6 3DD.
APPS BAXTER BRADDEN COUCH DAWSON ELLSOM EVANS FARRAR GILLION HAMBLY HARRIS ISAAC JOHNS LOBB MARSHALL MORGAN MULLER PHILLIPS PIPER REYNOLDS SENIOR SHAW SPINK THOMAS TOPPS WALKER YOUNG F1738

127388 GILLIVER Mr A. 36 West Common Gardens, Scunthorpe, South Humberside, DN17 1EH.
BLOOR DENTON DIBBLE GILLIVER SNOW THEAKER F6376

127396 GILMORE Miss K E. 36 Hills Road, Buckhurst Hill, Essex, IG9 5RS. Tel:081-505-3845
Gilmer GILMORE F5950

127418 GILMOUR Mrs Janet. (Neil) Stonebyres Farm, Eaglesham, Glasgow, G76 0PH. Tel:03553-3399
Fleeming FLEMING Gilmore GILMOUR Gilmur MALLCOH MCLAREN Mclauren Mcneil Mcneill NEIL Neill WATT F1214

127426 GILROY Mr David Lindsey. 10 Park Avenue, St Albans, Herts, AL1 4PB. Tel:0727-52959
ALLEN AUSTIN BEST BLAND BOYS BROWN BUTCHER CLARK CLIMPSON CORNISH CREED DARBY DAVIES DEIELIES DOVE DOWN DOWNE DURRANT ELLET ELYOTT FREE GILROY GOSNEL GOSNELL GROCER HARMER HOGG HOLDER HOLDSTOCK HOPPER HOW HOWE HUGHES JACOB JENNENS JENNINGS JENNINS JORDON KILBY LANES LIPSCOMBE LOWN MARDEN MARIOTT MAYNARD MEREDITH MILLES MILLWARD MISSING MULLENGER NASH NEEVE NEILSON NEVES PALMER POWELL PRATT PROBERT REDMAN REED ROSE SMITH SOUTHERNDEN SPILLET SPILLETT STEDMAN TEBBUT TILBIE TILBY Tilbye TILDEN TURNER VINCETT WALKER WELLS WHITE WILLIAMS F2877

127434 GILROY Mr H C. Avalon, Abbostford Road, Darnick, Melrose Roxburghshire, TD6 9AH.
Corrie Currer CURRIE Currier Curror Curry GILROY F2461

127442 GILSON Mrs B. Box 205, Didsbury, Alberta, TOM OWO, CANADA.
BALL COMAN Comin Comyn Cooman Cowman MARRIOTT RILEY TAGG F5177

127450 GIMBERT Mr Gordon W. Rural Route 1, Hillsburgh, Ontario, NOB 1Z0, CANADA.
GIMBERT F7285

127469 GINGELL Mr Nicholas. 54 Stoneleigh Road, Knowle, Bristol, BS4 2RJ.
CLEMENTS GAIN GINGELL HAMILTON F2716

127477 GINN Mr Cyril Herbert. 19a Theatre Street, Warwick, CV34 4DP. Tel:0926-498301
Bolton BOULTON Gen Gheen Gin GINN Ginne Gyn Gynne Simmonds SIMONDS Symmonds Symonds WEBB WRIGHT F5798

127485 GIRDLESTONE Mr K. 14 Eastern Crescent, Thorpe St Andrew, Norwich, Norfolk, NR7 OUE.
GIRDLESTONE F6569

127493 GIRDLESTONE Mr Mark. Cherry Tree Cottage, 192 Mile End Road, Colchester, CO4 5DY. Tel:0206-851777
GIRDLESTONE F310

127507 GIRVIN Mr Allister. 21a Croft Road, Ballygally, Larne, Co Antrim, BT40 2QP. Tel:0574-583582
ARMSTRONG Boner BONNER BROWN CRAIG Davidson DAVISON GIRVAN Girven Girvin GRAY Grey HARPER HUNTER KELL KENNEDY LENNON LOVE MCALISTER Mcallister MCILWAINE MCNALLY MCNEILL REID F4094

127515 GITTINGS Mr E K. 24 Wedgewood House, Churchill Gardens, London, SW1V 3BT.
Capis Cappes Cappis CAPPS Caps F6942

127523 GITTINS Mrs Sheila. (Raven) 85 Tower Hill, Great Barr, Birmingham, B42 1LQ.
ALVES DEARN GITTINS LALOR RAVEN RUSSON TOOLE F1171

127531 GITTUS Mrs P. 59 Elm Road, Evesham, Worcs, WR11 5DR.
GITTUS F1483

127558 GLADWISH Mr Victor E R. 2 The Orchard, Church Road, Broadbridge Heath, Horsham, RH12 3LF. Tel:0403-60261
Gladdish Gladish GLADWISH Gladwishe Gledewysh F435

127566 GLAISTER Mrs Ann. (Castree) 80 Sussex Avenue, Isleworth, Middx, TW7 6LB.
CASTREE F3608

127574 GLASCOE Mrs Gladys Zonena. 3 Pointer Close, Crossway, North Thamesmead, London, SE28 8PN. Tel:081-311-7628
ACKROYD GARNSWORTHY GARNWSORTHY RATHMELL F361

127582 GLASPER Mrs Susan. Carswell Farm, Ford Street, Wellington, Somerset, TA21 9NY. Tel:0823-622810
CHURCHYARD CROKER FRANCOMB JOLLEY PARRATT WOOLWARD F3228

127590 GLASSON Mrs Jean. 113 Martin St, Upper Hutt, 6401, NEW ZEALAND.
ARGALL CARPINTER CLARK COOK FLEMING FRASER GLASSON HOOPER HUBBARD LAWSON MCCARTHY MILNE MORRISON PEARCE RAE SMITH WARD WATSON WOODWARD F5494

127604 GLEDHILL Mr Fred G. 29 Homestead Road, Chelsfield, Orpington, Kent, BR6 6HN. Tel:0689-852887
BALLARD BATES BAXTER CRADDOCK DARNELL

GLEDHILL MURGATROYD ROWE WATSON WHITEHALL WILCOX F871

127612 GLEED-OWEN Mr Richard P. 19 Fairfield Drive, Mansfield, Notts, NG18 3EQ. Tel:0623-631086
AYRES BOULTER GLEED GREETHAM JONES MAYNARD POUND TEVLEN Tevlin WILLIAMS F1268

127620 GLENISTER Mr Andrew. 5 Graeme Court, Eastmead Avenue, Greenford, Middx, UB6 9RE. Tel:081-578-8351
Glanister Glenester GLENISTER GLENISTERS Glennerster Glinister F3933

127639 GLIBBERY Mr J J S. Lyndons, Goose Lane, Broadway, Ilminster Somerset, TA19 9RU.
Glibberry GLIBBERY Glibbury Glibree Glibrey F240

127647 GLINKA Mrs Ellen. (More) 7111 Delwood Road, Edmonton, Alberta, T5C 3A8, CANADA. Tel:+1-403-478-5737
DRYSDALE GAMBLE GILBEY IRVINE KAY MORE PERKINS RADFORD STEWART TEMPLETON THOMPSON F5471

127655 GLOVER Mr David C. 6 Baker Fold, Raglan Street, Halifax, W Yorks, HX1 5TX.
ADDISON ALDRED ALRED ATKINS ATKINSON BOLES BOWLES BULL COATES Cookes COOKS CROXTON DEBBRIDGE EVANS FLETCHER FRENCH GEORGE GLOVER GODDARD Greaves GREVES HARDING HASTINGS HAWORTH Hincks HINKS HOGG HOLGATE HOLMES JOHNS LANGFORD LARGE LAUGHTON LEESON LOCKEY LUDLOW MARTINDALE MITCHELL NEWCOMB Newcombe NUNALY Nunnaly PAGE PEACH PHELPS RAWCLIFFE RIDGLEY RINGROSE ROBERTS Shepheard SHEPPARD SMALL STANCOMB Stancombe SWEETING THORNTON TOPPER TOWNSEND VALE WARNER WAY WELLS WHITAKER Whittaker WIGMORE WILKINS WILLIAMS YEAMANS F6418

127663 GODBER Miss H. 1 Longfield House, Uxbridge Road, London, W5 2SR.
Godbear Godbeare Godbeer Godbeere GODBER F6920

127671 GODDARD Mrs J R. 11 Chandos Road, Newbury, Berks, RG14 7EP.
GODDARD SIDDONS F2071

127698 GODDARD Mrs J R. (Linden) 54 Shirley Drive, Hove, E Sussex, BN3 6UF.
GODDARD HARRIOTT MILLS PARVIN WILSON F1897

127701 GODDARD Mrs Jacqueline. 4 Shamrock Close, Tollesbury, Maldon, Essex, CM9 8SZ.
BRUCE GODDARD HAINSWORTH IVENS NUNN SCRUBY SIPTHORP STEVENS WINSPEAR F2554

127728 GODLEY Mrs Patricia Anne. (Revill) 91 Whitley View Road, Kimberworth, Rotherham, S Yorks, S61 2HJ.
GODLEY HARDCASTLE RAYNER REVILL SKELTON STOREY WALKER F6273

127736 GODMON Mrs D. The Two Brewers, Wargrave Road, Remenham, Henley On Thames, RG9 2LT.
MURFET F6722

127744 GODSMARK Mr Peter H. 459 Green Lane, Finham, Coventry, CV3 6EL.
EXLEY GODSMARK F1337

127752 GOLDER Mr R W. 28 Beaufort Avenue, New Cubbington, Leamington Spa, Warwickshire, CV32 7TA.
GOLDER F6841

127760 GOLDIE Mrs Gwen. The Cottage, 8 Woodborough Road, Putney, London, SW15 6PZ. Tel:081-788-4884
ASHDOWN BARTLETT ELLISON GOLDIE RICKETTS F2396

127779 GOLDING Mr A W. 122 Westpole Avenue, Barnet, Herts, EN4 0AR.
BARNES BENNETT BUNKER COLBY CRIPPS DAVY GARNHAM GARRARD GOLDEN GOLDING GRIFFITH JACKSON KEMP KNIGHT MILDENHALL MILES MOORE PHILLIPS PORTSMOUTH SCRINE STONER STUBBING TUCKER WHITEHEAD WIGGINS F705

127787 GOLDING Mrs P S. 48 St Michaels Avenue, Yeovil, Somerset, BA21 4LH.
BEADLE BIDDLECOMBE CRANE DANIELS EVANS EYERS GOLDING MELLOR MILLER NUTLEY OLD SUMMERFIELD WHITLOCK F3587

127795 GOLDING Mrs Stephanie. 122 College Road, Maidstone, Kent, ME15 6SU. Tel:0622-674410
COUTER GOLDING HILTON TRANAH WELLER WHITE F1934

127809 GOLDMAN Mrs Barbara. 952 Woodbourne Drive, Southampton, PA 18966, USA.
BALL SENTER F6130

127817 GOLDRING Mr Reginald. 81 Southampton Road, Cosham, Portsmouth, Hants, PO6 4SB.
CROAD GOLDRING TREAGUST F2274

127825 GOLDS Mrs Patricia. (Gregory) 49 Waldronhyrst, South Croydon, CR2 6NZ. Tel:081-688-7800
GOLD GOLDS GOLES GOULDS F5825

127833 GOLDSMITH Mr C F. Crosby Lodge, 17 Normandy Way, Fordingbridge, Hants, SP6 1NW.
ALLUM BARBER BENNETT BIDDLECOMBE BISHOP COOPER COXHEAD DENKLEY Doncklin Donkley Donklin DREW Dunckley Dunckling Dunkley Dunkling FARLEY FORD FOSTER GAUNTLETT GOLDSMITH HIBBERD HICKS HILL HOSKING JAGO MOUNTFORD MOYLE MUMFORD PILCHER POCOCK PROUD THOMAS WARNER WELCH WELLS WOOD Woods F5354

127841 GOLDSMITH Mrs Gladys A. (Coomber) 153 Junction Road, Burgess Hill, West Sussex, RH15 0JL. Tel:0444-232640
DUNCOMBE RADFORD F1759

127868 GOLDSMITH Mr Richard I. Hillview, 46 Mill Road, Hailsham, E Sussex, BN27 2HT. Tel:0323-843102
GOLDSMITH Gouldsmith HOBDEN THURGOOD F1962

127876 GOLDTHORPE Mr James W H. Autumn Hill, St Johns Road, Crowborough, Sussex, TN6 1RT. Tel:0892-661162
Gawthorpe Gawthrope Gawthropp Goldthorp GOLDTHORPE F5234

127884 GOLLAND Mr Jim. 49 Azalea Walk, Pinner, Middx, HA5 2EH.
BIRD DORE FISHER GLANLEY GOLLAND GURNEY LANGTHORN Langthorne LEHMANN MEDGETT Megett Midgett Midgitt STAFFORD WILSHIN F2471

127892 GOMERSALL Mr & Mrs M E. 65 East Park, Southgate, Crawley, W Sussex, RH10 6AR.
GOMERSALL F6791

127906 GOOCH Mrs R J. 44 First Avenue, Rossmoyne, WA 6155, AUSTRALIA.
BOAG Boak Boake Boeg Boog F6953

127914 GOODALL Sir David. Greystones, Ampleforth, York, YO6 4DU.
BYERS FRAYNE GOODALL HATCHELL LEVICK PEECOCK SIMS WHITTLE F3139

127922 GOODALL Mr P E. 3 Dixeys Cottages, Great North Road, London, N2 0NS.
GOODALL F6695

127930 GOODBODY Mr M I A. The Old Rectory, Wickham St Pauls, Halstead, Essex, CO9 2PJ.
BOURKE Goodbaudy GOODBODY F44

127949 GOODCHILD Mr Jeff. Basement Flat, 13 Albany Road, Montpelier, Avon, BS6 5LQ.
BIRTCHNELL BOYCE ELLISON FRASER GOODCHILD HAMPSON HODSON SHUTTLEWORTH WALKER F2050

127957 GOODCHILD Mrs R D. 7 Hazelhurst Crescent, Worthing, W Sussex, BN14 0HW.
CADDY DAY Fookes FOOKS FOSS GOLDSWORTHY GOODCHILD GRANT HIBBS LADNER MARKS Penney PENNY PHILLIPS RATCLIFF Ratcliffe ROBERTS SEABROOK STEER TREADAWAY Treadway Tredaway Tredway Wakeford WEAKFORD F6341

127965 GOODE Mr S. 27 Belchamps Way, Hawkwell, Hockley, Essex, SS5 4NU. Tel:0702-203069
DIXON Good GOODE Goodee RIDLEY STOKOE F3522

127973 GOODENOUGH Mr Anthony. 11 Wyndham Lane, Allington, Salisbury, Wiltshire, SP4 0BY. Tel:0980-610835
CALLOW CHILD Childs Chiles GOODENOUGH GREEN Manhire MENEAR Minear STOCKWELL Stockwill F3991

127981 GOODENOUGH Mrs Corrinne. (Diviani) 11 Wyndham Lane, Allington, Salisbury, Wiltshire, SP4 0BY.
BRADICK DIVIANI HITCHCOCK HUGGINS KEEN MASTERS NEAGUL NEAGUS RAYNER READ WALKER F3992

128007 GOODEY Mr Michael. Woodsdale, High Street, Horam, East Sussex, TN21 0EY.
GOODEY Goody HORSNELL TOOLE F5967

128015 GOODING Mrs Iris. C/o 13 Lord Crew Close, Newbold, Verdon.
GREASEY HENNESSEY F1531

128023 GOODING Mr Peter E. C/o 13 Lord Crew Close,

Newbold, Verdon, Leics.
GOODING F1532

128031 GOODLAD Revd Martin R. 61 Kingsmead Avenue, Worcester Park, Surrey, KT4 8UZ. Tel:081-337-1327
ALLEN BUXTON EXLEY GOODLAD HOOD RODGERS TAYLOR WELDON WHITELEY F5409

128058 GOODMAN Mr R S. Little Paddocks, Barton Orchard, Tipton St John, Sidmouth, Devon, EX10 0AN.
GOODMAN F6037

128066 GOODSIR Mr David. 31 Dahlia Way, Hebburn, Tyne & Wear, NE31 2QH.
GOODSIR GUTCHER F5835

128074 GOODWIN Mr B Arthur. 7 Copperfield Road, Cheadle Hulme, Cheadle, Stockport Cheshire, SK8 7PN.
GOODWIN HEMPSALL HOUGH MINIFIE NEWTON F2002

128082 GOODWIN Mrs Janice. 50 Empress Avenue, Woodford Green, Essex, IG8 9EA.
ANGEL Audridge Autheridg Autheridge AUTRIDGE Awdridg Awdridge Awtridg Awtridge BEAMOND BRIDGEMAN HARRIS LAUNDER LLOYD MULLIS Odrigd Odrigde Ottridg Ottridge PALMER STONE TAYLOR WARD F5975

128090 GOODWIN Mrs Juliet. (Belsey) 50 West Drayton Park Avenue, West Drayton, Middx, UB7 7QB. Tel:0895-442679
BATEMAN BELSEY BRAY CARR DAY DIGHT EWELL HUGGARD F4007

128104 GOODWORTH Mr William Arthur. 14 St Barnabas Road, Emmer Green, Reading, Berks, RG4 8RA. Tel:0734-471075
Goderthe Godworth Goodwerth Goodwerthe Goodwith GOODWORTH Goodworthy Gudworth F675

128112 GOOLD Mr Mark. 7 Oaks Avenue, London, SE19 1QY.
CHANDLER DIFFIELD GARDINER GOOLD POULTON STEVENS F5772

128120 GOOLD Mr Roy. Po Box 552, Clarkson, NY 14430-0552, USA.
Riseley RISLEY Rizley Wrisley F7356

128139 GORDON-JONES Mrs V. 40 Pargeter Street, Stourbridge, W Midlands, DY8 1AU.
BILLINGHAM Gauden Gorden Gordin GORDON F5809

128147 GORE Mr D. The Red House, Lower Basildon, Berks, RG8 9NG.
CALDWELL De Masny GORE Maine MANNY Mayenne MAYNE MAYNEY Meduana F51

128155 GORE Ms J M. 37 Lyncroft Gardens, Hounslow, Middx, TW3 2QT.
YARNEY F6136

128163 GORELY Mrs Margaret. Roselands Cottage, Doynton, Bristol, Avon, BS15 5SS.
ALLBERRY BAGLIN BROTHERIDGE BUCKNALL CLISSOLD CROWHURST GORELY HARRY KEWELL LEGGATT LYSTER RUSSELL STRUTTON TAYLOR TERRY F1013

128171 GORMAN Mrs C J. 6 Cotswold Close, Upton, Chester, Cheshire, CH2 1SW. Tel:0244-314896
BADGER BARNES BEBBINGTON BOOTH CRUMP LAURIE Lawrie SHERRY SULLIVAN F3570

128198 GORSUCH Mrs D. 19 Nelmes Road, Hornchurch, Essex, RM11 3HX.
GORSUCH Gossage F7106

128201 GORSUCH Mr T B. 19 Thorn Road, Swinton, Gt Manchester, M27 1QU. Tel:061-728-2079
De Gorsuch Garsh Garstwich Garstwick Gaurstage Georsich Gersey Gornish Gorsach Gorsedg Gorsedge Gorseeche Gorsehidge Gorsey Gorsh Gorshe Gorshich Gorshuch Gorsich Gorsiche Gorsidg Gorsiegh Gorsige Gorsitch Gorsitche Gorssage Gorssuck Gorstadge Gorstage Gorstige Gorston Gorstridge Gorstwick GORSUCH Gorsuche Gorsuchill Gorsuck Gorsutch Gorsuth Gorsyche Gortage Gortain Gortan Gortelow Gorten Gorter Gorth Gorthar Gorthy F3214

128228 GORSUCH Dr T. 17a Lime Tree Road, Norwich, Norfolk, NR2 2NQ.
GORSUCH F4976

128236 GOSDEN Mr Robin. 5 Goldings Way, Freshwater, Isle Of Wight, PO40 9NW.
Godsden GOSDEN Gosding Gosdon Goslin Gosline Gosling Gosolon Gosselin Gossline Gozling F575

128244 GOSIOR Mrs Janet. (Smart) 8215 185 Street, Edmonton, Alberta, T5T 1G9, CANADA. Tel:+1-403-481-4682
ANDERSON BARR DRUMMOND DUNCAN EASTON HAMILTON HARPER LONGMORE PURDON REID SMART TURNBULL WHITELAW WILSON F5437

128252 GOSNEY Mrs J O. Stafford House, 74 Alexandra Road, Farnborough, Hants, GU14 6DD. Tel:0252-542436
Golsney Golsny Gosnai Gosnay Gosne GOSNEY Gosny Gossney Goznay Gozney F2152

128260 GOSS Mr J. 3 Goodison Close, Fair Oak, Eastleigh, Hants, SO5 7LE.
COOMBS GOSS HAYWARD OLIVE PULLEN RICKMAN TOWLSON TRAVERS F4552

128279 GOSS Mrs M. (Brown) 3 Goodison Close, Fair Oak, Eastleigh, Hants, SO5 7LE.
BARR BROWN ETHEREDGE HANRAHAN HORNBY ROPER SALTER TOWERS WILKINSON YOUNG F5700

128287 GOSWELL Mrs M E. 87 Finchampstead Road, Wokingham, Berks, RG11 2PE. Tel:0734-791128
AYERS GOSWELL WATERMAN F2913

128295 GOTT Mr & Mrs J. 3 Packhorse Close, Marshalwick, St Albans, Herts, AL4 9TQ.
GOTT F6735

128309 GOTTS Mr I. 7a Sunderland Ave, St Albans, Herts, AL1 4HJ.
GOTTS F6995

128317 GOTTSCHALIC Mr Mart. 178 Rectory Road, Sutton Coldfield, West Midlands, B75 7RT.
ABEL DOLEMAN IRELAND MONK PYRKE RICHINS SANSUM STRETTON WHYBROW WORKMAN F6153

128325 GOUDGE Mr W A B. Trencreek, 21 Glenleigh Park, Sticker, St Austell Cornwall, PL26 7JB. Tel:0726-65794
BEST CARTER Chappel CHAPPELL Chapple CRAGGS ELLIS Goad Good Goodge Googe Goud GOUDGE Gouge SLEEMAN UDY YELLAND F2436

128333 GOULD Mr Allan. Place Farm, Glemsford, Sudbury, Suffolk, CO10 7QF.
BALDWIN BESTWICK BISHOP DAVIDSON GOULD HALLPIKE HARGER KELBRICK KIRKBY MAXWELL MELLOR SIMPSON TAYLOR WARDLE F1133

128341 GOULD Mr D E. 85 Thanington Road, Canterbury, Kent, CT1 3XD. Tel:0227-768796
GOULD F4695

128368 GOULD Mr Keith. 92 Twyn Carmel, Swansea Road, Merthyr Tydfil, Mid Glamorgan, CF48 1PF. Tel:0685-6502
ALLEN BAILEY BINNEY BOELS BOOKER BREWER BRINICOMBE BROKEHOUSE BROOK BUTCHER CARTWRIGHT CHALONS COLLINSON COTTAM COWLISHAW CURNOW DUNN EDDY EYRE FIELDING FREEMAN GILBERT GILLOTT GOULD HAIGH HALL HARDY HODGE HOWETT HUDSON JELBERT JENKIN KIRBY KNOTT LEAMAN LONGLEY MABBOTT MATHERS MIDDLEWICH MIDDLEWREK MOORHOUSE PALMER PEDRICK PERKINS PLACE RUSSELL SMITH STARKEY STEVENS WALKER WEDLOCK WILDGOOSE WINDLE F5894

128376 GOULD Mr Keith. 30 Dalkeith Road, Harpenden, Herts, AL5 5PW. Tel:0582-715303
ALDRIDGE ARMSTRONG ASHFORD BLAKEBURN BULMAN COLVIN COXON DAVY EARNSHAW EMERSON FISHER GARRET GOULD GREEN HALL HARDY HOWE HUDSON HUTCHINSON INGS IRWIN JOPLING LAUDER LEA LEAR LOCKYER PEEL SNAITH SPERRING STAR TOOMER TROTTER WEARMOUTH WILLIAMS WRIGHT F2012

128384 GOULD-BOURN Mr Phillip. 19 Mornington Road, Cheadle, Cheshire, SK8 1NJ. Tel:061-428-0199
BROCKLEHURST CATTERALL DURRANT GOULD-BOURN HILL KENYON PENKETHMAN RIVERS SMALL F1139

128392 GOULTY Dr George A. 2 Parkside Drive, Church Street, Old Catton, Norwich Norfolk, NR6 7DP. Tel:0603-405555
Galtie Galty Golty Goultie GOULTY F96

128406 GOUNDRY Mrs I. (Tait) Eastfield, Glebe Crescent, Washington Village, Tyne & Wear, NE38 7AW.
FENWICK KNOX SCOTT TAIT F3916

128414 GOUNDRY Mr M J. Eastfield, Glebe Crescent, Washington Village, Tyne & Wear, NE38 7AW. Tel:091-416-3373
BOOTH CHAPMAN CURRY GOUNDRY SIMPSON WHEATLEY F3915

128422 GOWENLOCK Prof B G. 49 Lygon Road, Edinburgh, Scotland, EH16 5QA.
Gouinlock Govanelokis Govanlock Govanlok

Govenlock Gowanloch Gowanlock GOWENLOCK F6570
128430 GOWLETT Mr D O. 26 Denton Close, Barnet, Herts, EN5 3AP.
Goulet Gowlet GOWLETT Gowlette Gullet TRICE Trise Tryce Tryse F6876
128449 GRACE Mr Mark A S. 39 Hasted Close, Saxon Court, Greenhithe, Kent, DA9 9HS. Tel:0322-380145
ADAMS ALLOTT BATEMAN Beadmead BENNINGTON BICKNELL Bidmade BIDMEAD Bidmeade Bidmeed BODEN BOWLES BRADLEY BROOKE CRESSELL CRISP DUDLEY Dugand DUGARD DURKIN FITZPATRICK FLATHER FRANCIS GARLAND GIFFORD GLEADHILL GLEADLE GLEDHILL GRACE GREEN Hauthorn HAWTHORN HOLBROOK LANE LITCHFIELD LOWNEY MACDONALD MANNING MINNIS MONKS O'CONNELL O'DONOVAN O'NEILL O'SULLIVAN OSBORNE PARR POPPLEWELL ROBERTS ROYDES SANDERS SEASTON SESTON SHILVOCK SMITH TOMKINS WILKES F1734
128457 GRACEY Mr W J. 4 Castlerobin Road, Belvoir Park, Belfast, N Ireland, BT8 4DW. Tel:0232-645598
BIGGAR EMERSON GRACEY F3912
128465 GRACEY-COX Mr Gerald. 64 Mill Street, Kidlington, Oxon, OX5 2EF. Tel:08675-5933
BUTTREY CORBETT COX EDMONDS GOUGE Haigwood HANNINGAN HEAVEN HOGWOOD HOLDSTOCK JORDAN PEARSON SAUNDERS F64
128473 GRADIDGE Mr & Mrs N W. 8 Forest Road, Chandlers Ford, Eastleigh, Hants, SO5 1LZ. Tel:0703-269513
BRAHAM Gradage Graddage GRADIDGE Gradige F1304
128481 GRADY Mrs Christine L. 147 Elmsfield Avenue, Norden, Rochdale, Lancs, DL11 5XA.
ANDERSON BRUCE BRYDON GUNN HENRY Mean Mein MIEN SEWELL SHARP Yool Yoole Yuil Yuile YUILL Yuille Yule Zuil Zuill Zuille F4222
128503 GRADY Mrs Sheila. 4 Manor Road, Scarborough, North Yorks, YO12 7RZ.
EDGERLEY HAWORTH SHARPLES WILKINSON F4317
128511 GRAHAM Mr C P. 27 Cedar Avenue, East Barnett, Herts, EN4 8DY.
BOUCH BUSHBY GRAHAM F3685
128538 GRAHAM Mrs Linda. Hallgarth, Great Hatfield Road, Withernwick, Hull, HU11 4TU.
BOSSA BRINT BROOKE ELWORTHY HARRISON PARRISH SHILLITO WHITTAKER WILSON WITHERWICK F5903
128546 GRAHAM Mr Robert. 11 Broadstairs Court, Grindon, Sunderland, Tyne & Wear, SR4 8NP. Tel:091-522-8955
GRAHAM F5044
128554 GRANNELL Miss Karen. 61 Hope Street, Millom, Cumbria, LA18 4JW. Tel:0229-775148
COWARD CUNNINGHAM GRANNELL INGLEBY MARSDEN MCCANN MCCARTIN F5068
128562 GRANNUM Guy. Tasma, Old Seaview Lane, Seaview, Isle Of Wight, PO34 5BJ.
Granam Granham GRANNUM Granom F6999
128570 GRANT Mr I C. 4 The Rise, Elmswood Gardens, Sherwood, Nottingham, NG5 4BA.
Fauvaque Fauvargue Fouargur FOVARGUE Fovarque F7158
128589 GRANT Mrs J. 110 Luxborough Towers, Luxborough Street, London, W1M 3LH.
CRANE HIDE HYDE MAYLIN MORGAN PLUMMER ROWLAY SAUNDERS TOTTMAN TRETT F2080
128597 GRANVILLE Mr Roy Henry. 54 Swiss Road, Ahston Vale, Bristol, Avon, BS3 2RT. Tel:0272-666194
Glanville Granfield GRANVILLE Grenvill GRENVILLE F1136
128600 GRAY Mr Alan. 48 Hatton Gardens, Mitcham, Surrey, CR4 4LG.
BRITTAIN FOXWELL GRAY WALES F672
128619 GRAY Mr Brian. 25 Linden Way, Droylsden, Manchester, M35 6QJ. Tel:061-370-3795
BARAN GRAY F1062
128627 GRAY Mrs E M. 17 Pyotts Hill, Old Basing, Basingstoke, Hants, RG24 0AR.
ADAMS BARDLEY BAYNES BURRELL DAVIS FITZGIBBON FITZGIBBON-HENCHY Gailward GALWARD GREEN HENCY HYTCH JARVIS MCKENZIE NICHOLS PRESTON RILEY ROWE SIMMONDS STIRK F2758
128635 GRAY Mrs Edith N. (Brown) 19 Gleniffer Crescent, Elderslie, Johnstone, Renfrewshire, PA5 9JH. Tel:0505-24281
NANGLE F1726
128643 GRAY Mr George R. Fulmar, East Road, Kirkwall, Orkney, KW15 1LX. Tel:0856-3147
BREMNER BROWN CARTER GILMOUR GRAY MANSON F3118
128651 GRAY Mrs Grace. 24 Durness Avenue, Bearsden, Glasgow, G61 2AL.
BORLAND GENTLEMAN F5299
128678 GRAY Mrs S A. 40 Little Minster Street, Winchester, Hampshire, SO23 9HB.
MITHAM F668
128686 GRAY Mrs S A. Jordan Cottage, Little Minster Street, Winchester, Hampshire, SO23 9HB.
MITHAM Mithem Mittham Mytham F6705
128694 GRAY Miss Sharon. 46 Willow Way, Hatfield, Herts, AL10 9QE. Tel:0707-270268
Earley EARLY FIORINI FUDGE GRAY Hackett Hinchley Hinchliff HULBERT Hurckett Hurcot Hurcott Hurcotte Hurcut Hurkett INCHLEY Inchliff MARSHALL MURKETT PLUMMER SIMS SMITH TURNER WILLIAMS WILTSHIRE F3463
128708 GREATHEAD Dr David. 29 Dale Lodge Road, Sunningdale, Ascot, Berks, SL5 0LY.
COLLETT FUGLER GREATHEAD HEWITT MERRIMAN SMITHSON WRIGHT F5979
128716 GREAVES Miss Valerie. Hermitage, Westbury, Shropshire, SY5 9QX.
CARTWRIGHT CLEGG DEWAR GREAVES PURSEY ROWLANDS STEVENTON STOKES F3246
128724 GREEN Mrs Brenda. (Huggett) 94 Dawson Avenue, Forrest Field, WA 6058, AUSTRALIA. Tel:+61-453-2053
ANDREW Bantack BANTICK BRYANT BUCKWELL Campion CHAMBERLIN CHAMPION CLACK CLARK CLARKE CLARY COOPER CROWHURST DRAKE Filpot GREEN Hollaway HOLLOWAY HUGGETT JACKSON JOHNSON Leaper Leder LEEPER LUCKET MANNING MILES NUNN NUTLEY PAGE PASK Paske PATTLE PENNES Phillpot Phillpott Philpot PHILPOTT RIVET ROWLAND RUSHBROOK SPARROW SPICER STEVENSON SULLIVAN TALBOT THOMAS Tombs Tomes TOOMBS TURNER VICARS WALES WATSON WICKENS WRIGHT F4392
128732 GREEN Mr Chris. 38 Birchfield Close, Coulsdon, Surrey, CR5 2SJ. Tel:081-668-3576
BASS BREWERTON DELLA ROCCA GREEN GRIMSEY HUMPHRIES OWEN STEVENS THOMAS TRASLER F4284
128740 GREEN Mr Eric Russell. 49 Dennis Road, Gravesend, Kent, DA11 7NN. Tel:0474-568854
AXTEN BISHOP BROAD BUYERS CHINNERY COOK GREEN HAMMON RUSSELL THOMAS F4538
128759 GREEN Mr Harry. 101 Mendip Vale, Coleford, Bath, BA3 5PP. Tel:0373-812531
AVEN CAZNELL CROW GLAYSHER GREEN HONE TEDMAN WATKINS F4858
128767 GREEN Miss J A. 23 Kenwyn Drive, Neasden, London, NW2 7NX.
COLEGATE Colgate Colget F6855
128775 GREEN Mr J F. 27 York Road, Holland On Sea, Essex, CO15 5NP. Tel:0255-812441
BORE BURROUGHS GEARY GREEN HOOKHAM PARSONS SMITHYMAN F542
128783 GREEN Mrs Joan. 44 Woodbridge Road, Leicester, LE4 7RG.
ELTINTON GREEN HUMBY PEGG SALMON TAYLOR TERREY F1491
128791 GREEN Mrs Kay. 13 Southlands Drive, Fixby, Huddersfield, W Yorks, HD2 2LT.
GORMAN F3089
128805 GREEN Ms Linda R. 186 Carlton Avenue East, Wembley, Middx, HA9 8PT.
BODDY Body DOCKERELL Dockerill Dockrell Dockrill GREEN HARDY RUMBOL STACEY SUMMERS F5785
128813 GREEN Ms Linda R. 337 Chapter Road, Dollis Hill, London, NW2 5ND.
BODDY GREEN HARDY RUMBOL STACEY SUMMERS F2680
128821 GREEN Mr Michael J. 45 Overbrook, Evesham, Worcs, WR11 6DD.
COAP GREEN MCVEIGH SHOOTER F2807
128848 GREEN Mr N W B. Grove Farm, Warham, Well Next The Sea, Norfolk, NR23 1NF.
FITZHERBERT GIBBS GREEN F5244
128856 GREEN Mrs P A. Balchins, White Lackington, Ilminster, Somerset, TA19 9EF.
BALCHIN CLEGG GILLARD GOLDSMITH JOHNSTON

LOESCHER RAPLEY ROBERTSON WELLS F6443

128864 GREEN Mrs P. 71 Hillfield Road, Little Sutton, S Wirral, L66 1JB. Tel:051-339-3315
HUBBERT MCLEAVY F2449

128872 GREEN Mr Ronald. 144 The Crescent, Horley, Surrey, RH6 7PA. Tel:0293-772840
Courtenage Courtnage Courtnedge Courtnege COURTNEIDGE Courtnidge GREEN HOGSDEN KNIGHT KNOPP F5663

128880 GREENE Mrs B M. 18 Welland Court, Cheltenham, Glos, GL52 3HS.
RICKERS F7181

128899 GREENER Mr Fred. 43 Northwood Road, Tullibody, Alloa, Clackmannanshire, FK10 2JT. Tel:0259-216427
CAIRNS GREENER F5215

128902 GREENGRASS Mr B H. 1 Cornwallis Close, Clover Hill, Norwich, Norfolk, NR5 9BJ.
GREENGRASS Greengrasse Grengres F6201

128910 GREENHALGH Miss Betty. 39 Plessey Terrace, Newcastle Upon Tyne, NE7 7DJ. Tel:091-281-1709
BARLOW BARROWCLOUGH BEARDMORE BINKLEY BOOTH BRADLEY BRATFORD BROWN BUXTON CARRAT CHAPMAN CLARKE COX DAVIS ELLIS FENNELL FISHER FRITCHLEY GARRET GREENHALGH GRIMES HARRISON HASLEGRAVE HESSELGRAVE HILL HIND HOLME KEYWORTH KITSON LATHBURY LOWE MALTBYE MARSON MARSTON MASSEY NEALE NUTHALL PEACE ROGERS SANDER SMITH SPENCER STARKEY TOPHAM TURNER VARLEY WALTERS WELBOURNE WESTON WHITE WILBRAHAM WILLIAMSON WOOD WOODCOCK WOODHOUSE YOOLE F1800

128929 GREENHALGH Mr C H. 35 Kathleen Road, Birmingham, B25 8AY.
BROOKES Cleulow Clewlow CLULOW EITE GREENHALGH F827

128937 GREENING Miss C M. 42 Valley Drive, Kendal, Cumbria, LA9 7AG. Tel:0539-729152
BOUGHTON Coiles Coils COX COYLE DODDS FARMER Greeneinge GREENING Greeninge Greenings Greenyng Greninge Grenynge Grinen Grining Grininges Grinnen Grinnin Grinning HATTON MADDISON Pool POOLE Yongue YOUNG Younge F5096

128945 GREENWELL Mrs Margaret Ann. (Sarsfield) 19 Long Acres, Gilesgate, Durham, DH1 1JF. Tel:091-386-6761
BAXTER MORRIS PEACOCK SARSFIELD TOWERS YOUNG F5595

128953 GREENWOOD Dr Arthur Alexander. R R 1 Box 40, Madrona Drive, Nanoose Bay, British Columbia, V0R 2R0, CANADA. Tel:+1-604-468-9770
GREENWOOD F6148

128961 GREENWOOD Mr Harold C. 108 The Ridgeway, Marshalswick, St Albans, Herts, AL4 9PR.
ADAMS ANSELL ATKINS ATKINSON BALL BENTALL BENWELL BLOYS BRIGHTWEN BROCKWAY CHAPLIN COLCOCK COOPER CORDER DAY DEANE DOW Dowe ELAM ELLWOOD FELLOWES Fellows GREENWOOD HAGEN Hagin HAYCOCK HORSNAILL HOW Huckelsby Hucklesbey HUCKLESBY KEMP KILBER LEVITT LIVERSEDGE Mark MARKE MARRIAGE MILLER PALMER PECKOVER PERRY PIPER POTTER QUICK REYNOLDS SEWELL SIBBEN SKEGG SPARROW TALBOT TAYSPILL TURNER WARNER WESTON WING WRIGHT YOUELL F2276

128988 GREER Mrs Aileen M. 314 Main Street, Kelty, Fife, KY4 0BB. Tel:0383-831589
BURTON GALLOWAY GREER KEANEY MAGUIRE MCGILLEN RAIT REID SNEDDON WALKER F2155

128996 GREGORY Mr Jim. The Green, Thorney, Peterborough, PE6 0QD. Tel:0733-270368
ABBOTT ALCOCK ALDERMAN ALLEN AMMONY AMORY ANNABLES ARMSTRONG ARNOLD ARSELING ASHLING ASHWORTH ATKINS AVELING BACON BAILEY BAINES BAKER BALDERSON BARBER BARNET BARRON BARTON BATES BATSON BEAGLES BEARD BEBEE BELLAMY BELLOM BERRIDGE BIRCH BLANCART BLANCHARD BONIFACE BOWLAND BOWLING BOYCE BRACE BRACER BRADSHAW BRASSAR BRETT BRIGGS BRITTAIN BROWN BROWNING BUCKWORTH BURGESS BUTT CAILLET CANHAM CARRINGTON CATLING CAUTLEY CAVE CHAPMAN CHARITY CLAPHAM COATES COBB COLBOURN COLES CONGREVE COOKE COWLEY CRANE CULY DARNELL DAY DEBENER DEBOO DECAY DELAHOY DELANOY DELEHAYE DELESPIER DENNISON DESBOROUGH DESCOUS DOBNEY DODMAN DOGGETT DOURNELLE DUBOIS EGAR EMONEY EMORY FALL FLETCHER FOREMAN FORSTER FOSTER FOWLER FREAR FULLARD GACHES GARNER GARRATT GEE GIBSON GILBY GIRDLESTONE GODDARD GODFREY GOODE GOODWIN GREEN GRICE GROUND HAIRSINE HALES HAMMERTON HANNOTE HARE HARKER HARRISON HART HEARNE HEMMANT HENSMAN HICKS HILL HILLIAM HOLDICH HOLIDAY HOLMES HOLT HOOLE HOPKINS HORNBY HORSEPOOL HUDDLESTONE HURN HURRY JACKSON JOHNSON JORDAN JOYCE KEMPTON KING KIRBY KISBY LANCASTER LAWSON LE PLA LEATON LECONTE LEFEVRE LEGRAINE LEHAIRE LENTON LEOPARD LEROY LETALL LOTTEE MALTSHIRE MARCHANT MARKILLY MARRIOTT MARSHALL MAXWELL MAYES MEASURES MILLFIELD MILLVILLE MORILLION MORRIS NASSAU ODEHAM OLDHAM PALMER PAREN PARNELL PASK PATEMAN PEACH PEARS PENRUDDOCK PERKINS PICKERING PINDER POPELY POPPLE PROVOST QUINCEY RANDALL REEDSHAW RHODES RIDLINGTON ROBINSON RUFF RUSSELL SANSBY SAUNDERS SAVAGE SAWFORD SCANDLING SCOTNEY SCOTT SCRIBO SEARLE SENECHAL SHARMAN SHARP SIGGEE SISSON SIX SLITE SLOTE SLY SMAILES SMITH SNUSHALL SOUTHAM SOUTHWELL SPEECHLEY STAPLETON STUBBS SUTTON TABOR TANSLEY TAYLOR TEGARDINE THACKER THOMPSON TURNELL ULYATT VENIN VENOY VINE WARNER WARREN WATSON WHITE WHITFIELD WHITTAM WILCOX WILKINSON WILSON WING WOODCOCK WOOLERTON WRIGHT YSERBY F5100

129003 GREGORY Mrs L. 67 Devonshire Gardens, Tilehurst, Reading, Berks, RG3 6FP.
BLOMFIELD BURWOOD BYNORTH CLARKSON GRAY MANTHORP PELLS ROCKCLIFFE WENT WORSWICK F4842

129011 GREGSON Mrs Florence Vera. 35 Western Road, Flixton, Manchester, Lancs, M31 3LB. Tel:061-748-0607
BOND CARUS FISHER LUDLOW MADDOCKS MOORE MORRIS PAINTER RICHARDS RICHARDSON SAWREY SHENTON SURGEY WATERHOUSE WHITE WILKES F1009

129038 GREGSON Mr T M. Mickle Vale, Warcop Appleby, Cumbria, CA16 6PF. Tel:09304-360
BARDGETT BLACKETT BRASS GREGSON OLDCORN RICHARDSON THORNBORROW WILKINSON F1246

129046 GREIFF Mrs Margaret. (Wootton) 99 Leicester Road, Thurcaston, Leics, LE7 7JH.
BAILEY BUTTERWORTH DUTTON GOODER GREIFF Grieff HIRST HURST WEBBER WOOD WOOTTON F775

129054 GRESTY Mr R J. Kenton, 24 Wood Lane, Fleet, Hampshire, GU13 9EA.
CRUTCHLEY EVAN Graistie Graisty Grasty Greesty Grestie GRESTY Greysty Griesty JONES KENWOOD Kingdom KINGDON Kyngdon MORRIS SYMMONS THOMAS WALSH F4643

129062 GREVE Mrs Lynda. (Turnbull) 500 Brunswick Street, Stratford, Ontario, N5A 3N6, CANADA.
JOLLY MCINTOSH MCNEIL TURNBULL WILLOUGHBY F5694

129070 GRIBBIN Mr David. Redthorn, Malacca Farm, West Clandon, Guildford, Surrey, GU4 7UG.
Gribban Gribben Gribbens GRIBBIN Gribbing Gribbings Gribbins Gribbon Gribbons Gribin Gribyn F2210

129089 GRIER Mr J C. 10a Cairneyhill Road, Crossford, Dunfermline, Scotland, KY12 8NZ.
Graeor Grayr Greair Greaor Greare Greares Grears Greary Greear Greeare Greeares Greears Greehar Greeor Greer Greere Greeres Greers Greery Greeve Greeves Greier Greir Greire Greires Greirs Greiw Greiwar Greor Grere Greres Griar Griars Griear Grieer GRIER Griere Grieres Grierr Griers Griev Grieve Grieves Grievs Grior Grire Grirre Griv Gryer Gryor F2537

129097 GRIFFIN Mrs Betty. 7 Grosvenor Court, Kenilworth Road, Leamington Spa, Warks, CV32 5TF. Tel:0926-423047
EVANS JENKINS JONES MICHAEL ROWLAND RUSSEL F1598

129100 GRIFFIN Mr Raymond. 202 Honey Pot Lane, Stanmore, Middlesex, HA7 1EE.
AYLETT CHANTS GRIFFIN LACKEY LIMBRICK LONG PUDDEPHATE THOMAS F6093

129119 GRIFFITHS Mr Alan. Fairwinds, Silver Street, Congresbury, Bristol, BS19 5EY. Tel:0934-838015
COCKER DALLING DAVIES DOBIE GRIFFITHS

MCGEORGE MCMURDO NUTTALL WHITTAKER WHITWORTH F1575

129127 GRIFFITHS Mrs Beryl. The Old Bakery, Briston, Melton Constable, Norfolk, NR24 2HL. Tel:0263-860417
BALZEBY KNIGHTS F6133

129135 GRIFFITHS Mrs Bidi. Bro Enlli, Ffordd Y Gaer, Aberaeron, Dyfed, SA46 0HZ. Tel:0545-570176
DAVIES GIBBON GRIFFITHS MAURICE MOSES NARBETT WILLIAMS F402

129143 GRIFFITHS Mr Bryngwyn. Maesllyn, 19 North Road, Builth Wells, Powys. Tel:0982-553384
BURCHELL DAVIES GRIFFITHS POWELL SKYRME F3795

129151 GRIFFITHS Mrs Cherry A. (Edwards) Fold Cottage, Ashton, Nr Leominster, Herefordshire, HR6 0DN.
BENNETT BROOKS EDWARDS HAINES HAYNES HUNT DAVIES JULYAN TAYLOR F5108

129178 GRIFFITHS Mr David. 17 Lincoln Street, Canton, Cardiff, CF5 1JX. Tel:0222-232186
BAMFORD CUTLER DE BREANSKI GARTON MOREL PYNE F1714

129186 GRIFFITHS Mr Derek. 86 Rushton Drive, Bramhall, Stockport, Cheshire, SK7 3LA. Tel:061-439-8730
FAUX GRIFFITHS MCCONNELL PARKER WEBSTER F4011

129194 GRIFFITHS Mrs J M. 6 Gardner Road, Titchfield, Fareham, Hants, PO14 4EF.
BUCKINGHAM Carsford Carysfort Caseford Casfeild Casfield Casford Cashford CASSFORD Cosfort CROFT Crofts GAMAGE GIBSON GOSDEN INGATE Kaysford Keysford TALLENT WINTER Woolner Woolno WOOLNOUGH WRIGHT F1225

129208 GRIFFITHS Mr Keith Raymond. 20 Pochard Drive, Poynton, Stockport, Cheshire, SK12 1JU. Tel:0625-859336
CHADWICK CHAMBERS GRIFFITHS HAMMERSLEY MOLINEUX STONEHEWER WRIGHT F4182

129216 GRIFFITHS Mrs L. 34 Stephen Drive, Sheffield, S10 5NX.
BUCK CHADWICK COLLINSON Lund LUNN Macmahon MARSH MCMAHON Meades Meads Medes MEEDS RATCLIFF Ratcliffe SHARP Sharpe SHELTON F4691

129224 GRIFFITHS Mrs M D. 36 Duchy Road, Harrogate, N Yorks, HG1 2ER.
PARLEY F6571

129232 GRIFFITHS Mr Martyn J. 15 Brookfield, Neath Abbey, Neath, West Glamorgan, SA10 7EG.
BEVAN COLLINS DAVIES EVANS GRIFFITHS HARE HODGSON JONES LEWIS LLEWELLYN MAINWARING REES STANFORD SUGDEN F3565

129240 GRIFFITHS Mr Peter N. 190 Tythebarn Lane, Shirley, Solihull, W Midlands, B90 1PF. Tel:021-744-1277
BROWN COLEMAN ESTLIN GOUGH GRIFFITHS HUMPAGE PARKER WALKER WIGGIN F2205

129259 GRIGG Mr Geoffrey J R. 10 Culver Close, Eggbuckland, Plymouth, Devon, PL6 5NL. Tel:0752-769580
GREIG Grig GRIGG GRIGGE GRIGGOR GRIGGS GRIGS F40

129267 GRIGG Mr George. Trengun, Warbstowe, Lanceston, Cornwall, PL15 8RW.
BARRIBALL COWLING CURTICE FERRETT GRIGG JASPER MILLS RUNDLE SQUIRE F134

129275 GRIMES Mrs Helen C. Per Ardva, 14 Cook Close, The Meadows, Dovercourt, Essex, CO12 3UE. Tel:0255-240095
ARNOLD AYLWARD BIRHIE CLARK CLARKE COOTE COWIE GRIMES HOLLAWAY HUNT KENDALL LAWRENCE LESLIE LODGE MASTIN MEARNS PALMER SAVILLE SMITH SOAFT STAMMERS TERRAS THOMSON TOPPEN TURNER WEBSTER WELLHAM WHITE WRIGHT YOUNG F712

129283 GRIMES Mrs Rita. (Cartwright) 13 Foxhall Road, Upminster, Essex, RM14 2DD.
ALLIT AMATT Aylett Baisy BAIZEY BATELEY Bayesy BECK BONE BOYTON BRETT BROWN BULL CARTWRIGHT CLARK Delay DENT DRANE DULLEA EWEN GRIMES Grimme GRYME Grymme Haylet Heard HERD KEMP LACEY LOKER MAYES MILLAR Miller MOORE MOSS OSBORN SPOONER WALPOLE Walpoole Warpole WAYLETT WHISSON WILLIAMSON Worpel F3379

129291 GRIMMETTE Mrs Winifred. (Bailey) 8 Hornbeam Close, Paddock Wood, Kent, TN12 6LL. Tel:0892-832196
BAILEY COOPER GRIMMETTE F4451

129305 GRIMMOND Mrs Gwendalyn. (Peters) 7/19 Cross St, Port Macquarie, NSW 2444, AUSTRALIA. Tel:+61-6-583-8924
BEVERIDGE BROWN BURNETT Crondace CROUDACE Cruddass Grammond Grimmand GRIMMOND Grummond PASCOE PEACOCK RAMSHAW TONKIN Tonking UREN WALLIS Wallish Walls F5428

129313 GRIMSHAW Mr James Arnold. 187 Claremont Road, Pendleton, Salford, Lancs, M6 8PA.
BARLOW BEECH GRIMSHAW HOUGH JACKSON KINGSWOOD KITTRIDGE RIGBY TAYLOR WEST WILLIAMS WINDLE WITHINGTON F2803

129321 GRIMSTEAD Mrs L S. 16 Beech Road, Basildon, Essex, SS14 1SQ.
GRIMSTEAD Grimsteed F6764

129348 GRINDER Mrs J B. (Goldsbury) 10 Kauri Crescent, Matamata, 2271, NEW ZEALAND. Tel:+64-7-888-7894
BONE ELLERY MITCHELL NEWMAN NODDER RICHARDS ROBERTS ROWE YEOMAN F5141

129356 GRINT Miss Marjorie. 31 Western Road, Havant, Hants, PO9 1NJ.
ADAMS ASTON BISHOP BRAY BROWNE BUTLER CHAPMAN DODSON Faviour Favour Feaveriere Feaveryear Feavier FEAVIOUR Feavour Feavyer Feavyour Fevier Fevyer GARDNER GILBERT GOODDEN GOWER GRINT HARRIS LANGHAM LOVERHAM MANNING MOORE PEARCE POOLE PORTER RICE SHOOSMITH SHORLAND SMITH UTTING WALKER WATLING F3037

129364 GRINTER Mrs Winnifred F. (Flanders) 204 St George Street, Brantford, Ontario, N3R 1W4, CANADA. Tel:+1-519-753-3222
BENTON FLACK FLANDERS GRAY GRINTER SAUNDERS SURRIDGE WINDLE F5484

129372 GRIST Mr Stephen. 16 Bath Road, Peasedown St John, Bath, Avon, BA2 8DH.
GRIST F1143

129380 GRISWOLD Mr James Wells. 65 High Street, -Exeter, New Hampshire 03833, USA. Tel:+1-603-772-3289
GRISWOLD F110

129399 GROM Ruth S. 9360 Babcock Blvd, Allison Park, PA 15101, USA.
BASTARD DALGLIESH LARHAM MONK STANFIELD F4161

129402 GRONOW Mr C. Endslieghley House, 4 Caroline Place, Claughton, Birkenhead Wirral, L43 1TR.
Gronnow Grono GRONOW Gruno F6918

129410 GROOCOCK Mr Norman H. The Bungalow, Baslow Road, Bakewell, Derbys, DE4 1AF. Tel:0629-812573
BINDLEY GREWCOCK GROCOCK GROOCOCK F6513

129429 GROOM Mr Paul C. Pine Tree Cottage, Sandhurst Road, Wokingham, Berks, RG11 3JQ. Tel:0734-784322
GROOM HAWKEN F2020

129437 GROSE Mr John. 31 Pennance Road, Falmouth, Cornwall, TR11 4ED. Tel:0326-315256
BENNETT EDDY GROSE HARVEY MATTHEWS POLGREAN TREWAVAS F1452

129445 GROSE Mr William James. 120 Foxcote, Wokingham, Berks, RG11 3PE. Tel:0734-734209
BAKER BRITTON BULLMORE COUSINS Groaes Groas Groass Groasse Groce Groos Groose Gros GROSE Gross Grosse Grouse Growse GUY HANSON MERCHANT SAWFORD SOBEY WELLS F2600

129453 GROUNDS Mr W T B. The Croft, Pant Lane, Austwick, Lancs, LA2 8BH. Tel:05242-51244
AITKEN ASPINALL BATTY Bibbey BIBBY ELCOCK GERMAIN German GROUNDS SCOTT SHEPHERD WAKE F2565

129461 GROUT Mr G E. 2 Windsor Court, Windsor Way, Polegate, E Sussex, BN26 6QG. Tel:0323-486092
ADAMS COX GODFREY GROUT HUGHES KENNEL LOWE PARISH SEABORN SEARS F5983

129488 GROVES Mr G D. 10 Salterns Point, Salterns Way, Lilliput, Poole Dorset, BH14 8LN.
GAGE GROVES WELLER F2207

129496 GROVES Mr Peter G. Netheredge, Sticklepath Hill, Barnstaple, Devon, EX31 2DW. Tel:0271-71841
AYSCOUGH BROWNE DICKINSON DODGESHUN FITCHETT GROVES HUTCHINSON INNOCENT MARTIN MAUDE MIDDLEBROOK NOLDA SHELMERDINE STOCKDILL TENNANT WALKER F2337

129518 GROVES-KIRKBY Mr C J. Caswell, Towcester, Northants, NN12 8EQ.
BLENNER HASSETT FITZGERALD GOODFELLOW GROVES HAYCROFT KIRKBY STANGER STRETTON F5631

129526 GRUNDY Mr Anthony Albert. 63 Oldershaw Road, East Leake, Loughborough, Leicestershire, LE12 6NF. Tel:0509-856397
GRUNDY F1771

129534 GRUNDY Mr John T. 11 Hebburn Drive, Bury, Lancs, BL8 1ED. Tel:061-764-8718
BARLOW DUMBILL GALE GIBSON GRUNDY HIRST F754

129542 GRUTCHFIELD Mr J. 1 Parsonage Road, Eastbourne, E Sussex, BN21 1JE.
Grudgefield Grudgfield GRUTCHEFIELD Grutchfield F6679

129550 GRYLLS Mr Richard G. 1 Longfield Road, Tring, Herts, HP23 4DQ. Tel:044282-5502
ARTHUR BRODHURST-HILL Greels Grells Grill Grilles GRILLS Grils Gryll Grylles GRYLLS Gryls Gryrlls HANCOCK NEWSON SHELDRAKE F4315

129569 GUBBINS Mr Robert. 133 Lovibonds Avenue, Orpington, Kent, BR6 8EN.
GUBBINS F7286

129577 GUBBINS Mrs Wendy. Stronwen, Whinwhistle Road, East Wellow, Romsey, Hants, SO51 6BH. Tel:0794-22602
Aplin APLON APPLETON APPLON BAIN BARNES BARTON BAY BENNETT BURRIDGE BUTCHER CALDER CHIVERTON CLARKE COOKE CREW DAY GALLOP GOODMAN GUBBINS HANSHAW HARBER HAYLES HAYWARD HENDEY HUCK HUNDERWOOD KINGSWELL Larcomb LARKAM Larkham LONG MCDONALD MCDONNELL MCGILLURAY MEW MOORE Patey PEATY RAYNER RICHARDS RIGGS ROSE ROWE SALTER SARRAL SMALL SNOW STALLARD THOMPSON UNDERWOOD WHEELER WOODFORD WOODMORE YOUNG F413

129585 GUESS Mr D. 31 Lammas Way, Letchworth, Herts, SG6 4LN.
GUESS F6913

129593 GUEST Mrs Margaret. (Sanderson) 35 Station Road, Hugglescote, Leics, LE6 2GA.
BAILEY COCKFIELD CODLING DOUGHTY DUELL GILL GUEST SANDERSON SHIMMIN STAFFORD WAKEFIELD WARD F358

129607 GUEST Mr Peter. 1 Mill Road, Angmering, W Sussex, BN16 4HP. Tel:0903-786878
BAKER BOXALL CREMER DOWNES EVANS GUEST JONES MEREDITH MICKMAN PETTITT RANSOM ROWLANDS SNELGAR TILSTON TUNGATE Tylston WELCH WHITE WRIGHT F351

129615 GUINN Mrs Meredith Jean. (Bowman) 5423 San Jose, Montclair, CA 91763-2038, USA. Tel:+1-714-986-3282
BUZZA EDWARDS NANKERUIS PEARCE ROGERS TREBILCOCK F5480

129623 GUISELEY Mr Eden. 17 Gresham Close, West Bridgford, Nottingham, NG2 7RQ.
ANDERSON BENTLEY CUSWORTH GUISELEY HOWELLS KENYON SHANN WALBANK WARREN F4300

129631 GULLIFORD Mr R J D. Lamb Cottage, Brutes Row, Blaenavon, Gwent, NP4 9BP.
GULLIFORD GULLIVER SKYRME WHITE F5124

129658 GULLIFORD Mrs Shelagh. (Effner) 18 Purslane, Abingdon, Oxon, OX14 3TR.
BOWDEN CARTER EFFNER FREEZER GOLLEDGE HARDING MUNTON SOUTHWICK TOKINS WELDISH F3757

129666 GUMM Mr Brian. 29 Gosmore Road, Hitchin, Herts, SG4 9AT. Tel:0462-433101
GUM Gumm SMURTHWAITE F3443

129674 GUNDERSON Bernice B. 3753 E 15th Street, Long Beach, CA 90804, USA.
DURKEE F7269

129682 GUNNELL Mr Peter Frederick. 31 Irving House, Park Row, Bristol, BS1 5LU.
BARTON GUNNELL F2052

129690 GUNSTONE Mr Len. 16 Mead House, Wedgewood Road, Twerton, Bath, BA2 1QN.
Gunsten Gunston GUNSTONE F7042

129704 GURNEY Revd Canon Richmond H. Dunelm, Gelt Road, Brampton, Cumbria, CA8 1QH. Tel:06977-2516
GURNEY F4530

129712 GURNEY Mrs S. (Seccombe) 18 Old Gardens Close, Tunbridge Wells, Kent, TN2 5ND. Tel:0892-522841
BETSWORTH BRADD DRAPER ENGLISH GOODE GURNEY HARDWICK LAMBERT LEWRY PEMBRIDGE QUINTON SECCOMBE SHARMAN SPASFORD WEBB WICKS WINDER F4103

129720 GURTEEN Mr A R. Sandcroft, 4 Rainton View, Fencehouses, Houghton-Le-Spring, Tyne & Wear, DH4 6NE. Tel:091-385-7202
GURTEEN F4388

129739 GUTHRIE Mr Melvyne Stewart. 21 Gilnahirk Park, Cherryvalley Knock, Belfast, N Ireland, BT5 7DX.
BUGLASS BURNETT GILLMAN GUTHRIE POTTS RUDDOCK SMITH F652

129747 GUTTERIDGE Mrs Anne C. (Buxton) 10 Soleoak Drive, Sevenoaks, Kent, TN13 1QD.
ABEL ADAMS ASKEW Benches BINKS BIRD Brierly BROWN Browne BUCKENHAM Buckingham BUCKTON Bucton BUXTON BYERLEY CARVAL Cerveil CHEETHAM CLAYTON COOK CREAK Creake CRISP CROOKS EAVES EDWARDS ENTWHISTLE Eves FELL FROST FULBECK GARROD GILLATT GREEN GUTTERIDGE HADFIELD HARRISON HARVEY HAYWOOD HILBERD HISTON HOVELL JACKSON JEFFREY JOHNSON JUPE KEEBLE KING LANDIMORE LANDYMORE MALLINSON MALTBY MAY NEWSTEAD ONIONS PAGE PALGER PERKIN RAGG RANDS RAYMOND RICHARDS RIDGEWAY RIDGWAY RIGBY SEWELL SHAW SHEPHERD Simonds SKONTS SYMONDS TEAGOE Tego THEEBLE TONGUE TUXFORD Tuxworth WALTON WARD WARDLEY WARREN WEDGER WELLS Wheatley Wheatly Whetley WHETLY WHITEHEAD WILBY WILCOCK WILLIAMS Willoughby WILSON Wortley WRAGG F4794

129755 GUTTERIDGE Mrs Joan. 9 Queens Cottages, Reading, Berks, RG1 4BE. Tel:0734-586801
BALLARD CREPIN HARRIS NEWINGTON Pae PAY Paye RACKSTRAW Rakestraw ROBERTS TURNER F2591

129763 GUTTERIDGE Mrs Maxine. (Howlett) 77 Malcolm Drive, Duston, Northampton, NN5 5NJ.
BANYARD BIRD BLAND BOOT BURROWS CHECKLEY GOLDBY GUTTERIDGE HEEPS HOWLETT ILIFFE MORSON OSBOURNE PICKFORD RIGBY SIBBARD THORNTON TURTON WILSON F5675

129771 GUY Mr O W. 10/276 Dorset Road, Croydon, Victoria, 3136, AUSTRALIA. Tel:+61-3-723-4688
BILLINGHAM COLVIN DAN DAY DURRANT GUY HART HENTY MORLEY WEBB F5427

129798 GUY Mrs Pat. Tirley House, 142 Cheltenham Road East, Churchdown, Glous, GL3 1AA.
BOND Farrett Feret Ferit FERRETT Firit GOLDING HUDSON LOBLEY ORMANDY ROBERTS STEPHENSON THACKRAY F1811

129801 GUYVER Mr Peter Donald. 3 Thurza Court, London Road, Isleworth, Middx, TW7 5DG.
CAVE Giver GUIVER GUYVER Gyva MEDCALF PALMER PARKER WICKINS WOODCOCK F33

129828 GWINNETT Mr Kenneth. Langton, Highfield Road, Hazel Grove, Stockport, Cheshire, SK7 6NS. Tel:061-483-7104
GWINNETT Gwinnutt Gwynedd Gwynett Gwynutt F4018

129836 GWYNNE Mr Thomas. 5 Newtonmere Drive, Wellington, Telford, Salop, TF1 3HG. Tel:0952-249109
GWYNN Gwynne LUNTS PRICE RUBOTHAM THOMAS WILSON F2288

129844 GYNES Revd David. 97 Kingsmead Avenue, Worcester Park, Surrey, KT4 8UT.
Ghieyes Ghines Ghisnes Ghiyes Ghuines Gines Guines GYNES Jeens Jines Joynes Jynes F3823

129852 GYNGELL Mr Roy. 22 Stanwell Gardens, Stanwell, Staines, Middx, TW19 7JY.
Gingell GYNGELL Gyngle F6218

129860 HABBERLEY Mr Edwin H. 21 Eaton Road, Duston, Northampton, NN5 6XR.
HABBERLEY Habberly Haberley Haberly F2912

129879 HACKER Mr Tom. 179a Churchill Avenue, Chatham, Kent, ME5 0DQ. Tel:0634-826198
CHARLES DRAKE HACKER HIGHAM F5107

129887 HACKSHALL Miss C J. 175 Hermon Hill, South Woodford, London, E18 1QQ.
HACKSHALL Hackshell Hacsell F7179

129895 HADDOCK Mrs J V. Scotsfield Cottage, The Avenue, Copdock, Ipswich, Suffolk, IP8 3JS.
BARKER BENNETT Clark CLARKE Clerk FAIRWEATHER Haddcock Haddick HADDOCK Hadduck Hadduk HAILS HARVEY Hay HAYE Hayes HAYWARD JAY Keridge KERRIDGE MILES MILLS Moise Moor MOORE MORSE

Moss MULLEY PARKER Pretty Prety PRITTY Ravel Revel Revell REVILL Ryell SMITH F6214

129909 HADDON Mr Gordon. 3 Redwood Grove, Bude, Cornwall, EX23 8EB. Tel:0288-353186
Adden Bebe Beby Beebey BEEBY Haddan HADDON Haden MAYCOCK Meacock Mecock Mecuk WRIGHT F1408

129917 HADDRELL Mr I N. 29 High Street, Staple Hill, Bristol, BS16 5HB.
HADDRELL Haddrill Hadrill F6622

129925 HADLER Mr Stuart. 9 Blake End, Kewstoke, Weston Super Mare, Avon, BS22 9LS.
GILL HADLER Hadlor HADLOW Hadlowe HOLNESS JACKSON F2011

129933 HADLEY Mr Andy. 60 Vicarage Road, Oakdale, Poole, Dorset, BH15 3BB. Tel:0202-666295
ARMOUR ARTHUR BAKER BALL BATH BECK BOND BROOKS BROWN BUST CHARLES COFFEL CRAIG CRAWFORD ELLIS FLUDDER FORD GALBREATH GILCHRIST GORDEN GORDON GRIFFIN GRISSELL HADLEY HAMILTON HARDING HARMSWORTH HOLLIS KENT LUNN MARKS MARSHALL MCBLANE MCCREATH MCILWRAITH MCLEAN MCPHEE MERRETT MILES NEIL NEWMAN PARRICK PENTLOE PODMORE REDING REID RIDGERS SCAIFE SEARLE SLOPER SMART SPENCER STARK STEVENSON TELFER WADHAM WEST WHINYARD WHITE WICKENS WOODWARD F1290

129941 HADWEN Mrs J. 91 Oak Avenue, Bare, Morecambe, Lancs, LA4 6HY.
Blackley Blakely Bleackley BLEAKLEY Bleekley Blekley F7190

129968 HAFFNER Mr Philip. 926 Mulholland Dr, Parksville, British Columbia, V9P 1Z4, CANADA.
HAFFNER Hafner Heffner Hefner F7287

129976 HAIGGER Mrs S. (Dix) 4 Plimsoll Avenue, Folkestone, Kent, CT19 6LJ.
BAKER BURT DIX HALL KIDHAM ROSSITER Sanders SAUNDERS TAPPENDEN Thompson THOMSON WILSON F628

129984 HAIGGER Mr Trevor. 4 Plimsoll Avenue, Folkestone, Kent, CT19 6LJ.
Aden CHAPMAN GATEHOUSE Haden HAGGER HARRIS Hayden HEYDON HOBDAY PENNY PHILPOTT Tong Tonge TONGUE WOOD F5677

129992 HAILE Mrs M. (West) 111 Leafields, Houghton Regis, Beds, LU5 5LU.
BILLINGHAM BRUDENWELL HAILE HOCKING LACE POSTLEWAITE SMILES WELCH WHITE WILLIAMS F6395

130001 HAILE Dr N S. Lot 1026, Pkns In Estate 54200 Ulu Kelans, Selangor, WEST MALAYSIA.
HAILE F6838

130028 HAILEY Mr John R. 1a Ashurst Walk, Croydon, Surrey, CR0 7JX.
HAILEY F6870

130036 HAILWOOD Mr Malcolm J F. 9 Penton Avenue, Staines, Middx, TW18 2NA.
Ailard Ailward Allward Allwood Alward Alwart Alwood Alyward Aylward BELLWOOD BROCKBANK BUTTERS CHARSLEY ELLWOOD FRANCIS HAILWOOD Halewood HALWOOD Haywood HIGGINBOTTOM IMISON LUMBY Penrhys PENRICE Penrise PLATT SWINBURN WILSON F5087

130044 HAINSBY Mr Kenneth. 20 Chaplains Close, Hales Barn, Haverhill, Suffolk, CB9 0DT.
BEDDING DEIGHTON HAINSBY HARRIS HILLS LEGOOD RAWLINS ROYAL F3775

130052 HAIRSINE Mr Robert. 10 Ormonde Road, Poole, Dorset, BH13 6DF.
BLANSHARD HAIRSINE HARESIGN HERRSEIN HERSENT HERSIN F4838

130060 HAISELL Mr James George. 2 Gifford Close, Caversham, Reading, Berks, RG4 0RF.
BAKER BARROW BRACKENBURY BROCK CHISHOLM DALE GARDNER HAISELL HALL Halsell Harsell Hassell Hazel HINDS LANES SIMPSON SMITH TAYLOR TERRY TOD WOOD F629

130079 HAISELL Mrs Marian. 2 Gifford Close, Caversham Park, Reading, Berks, RG4 0RF. Tel:0734-476625
ARIS AYRES BERRY BIRDSEYE CHAPMAN CREEK CRICK CURTIS DRAKE EAST FOWLER GOM GOMME GRIMSLEY GUMM HARBEY HOWES KING KINGE KINGS KINKAID LACEY MASTERS NORCOTE NORCOTT NORKETT NORTHCOTE PRITCHETT PULEE SHEERS SMYTHER SPENCER STAPOL TAPLIN TULEE WATTS F866

130087 HAKE Mrs Laraine. Chapel House, Leather Lane, Great Yeldham, Essex, CO9 4HX. Tel:0787-237686
ALABASTER HAKE LAWRENCE ORAM PARRISH F26

130095 HALBROOKS J C. 357 Snake Meadow Hill Road, Sterling, Connecticut, 06377, USA.
Alsebrook Bolbrook HALBROOK Halbrooks Haulbrook Haulbrooks Holbrock Holdbrook Holdbrooks Houlbrook Houlbrooks F6689

130109 HALES Mr Alfred E G. 34 Greenacres Avenue, Winnersh, Wokingham, Berks, RG11 5SX.
HALES F1029

130117 HALFYARD Mr Robert R. 9 Frontenac Drive, St Catherines, Ontario, L2M 2E1, CANADA.
HALFYARD Halfyards F7288

130125 HALL Mr David. Lodge Farm House, Westwood Heath Road, Coventry, West Midlands, CV4 8AA. Tel:0203-466786
AGAR ALLEN ATCHINSON BELL BELLCHAMBER BEVERIDGE BONE BOWMER CARWARDINE CLARK COCKBURN CRAWFORD CROSBY DAY DONALD DOUGHLY FORD GATE GEDDAS GIBBS GIRDWOOD GRANT HAFIELD HALL HANNAH HARRIS HEATH HOG HOPKINS HOWEY HUGHES HUMES HUNT IRVING LADYMAN LANCASTER LANE LITTLE LOCK MARK MARTIN MIDDLETON MORTIMER NEWTON NICHOLS OLIVER PARKER PERCIE PICK POWELL REDDY REID REYNOLDS RICHARDSON RICKETTS ROSBY SAUNDERS SHANKS SLYFIELD SMITH SNELLING STARLING TANNER TAYLOR THOMPSON TIMS URWIN WEETMAN WHITE WHITFIELD WILLIAMS WILTSHIRE WOOLFRY F3581

130133 HALL Mr Derrick A. 1 Upton Close, Park Street, St Albans, Herts, AL2 2NR. Tel:0727-873588
BROWN HALL STOWE WHITEHEAD F4513

130141 HALL Mrs Evelyn. (Barnes) 28 Santa Elena Avenue, Daly City, CA 94015, USA.
BARNES BOASE CRONIN DANIEL FURNISS MULCAHY MURRISH RAY RICHARDS RING TREMBATH WHITE F5111

130168 HALL Mr John. 9 Neville Grove, Warwick, CV34 5TU. Tel:0926-497452
BADNAGE BOLTON CLAYTON GODSOME GROVE HALL HUDSON HULSTON LANE PERRY POULSOM WOOLLEY F3023

130176 HALL Mrs Margery. (Lawn) 6 Budle Close, Blyth, Northumberland, NE24 5DS.
Clemo CLYMO GRENFELL Lathlane LATHLEAN Lethlean MILL ROWE Tresise Tresize TREZISE F4320

130184 HALL Mr Michael. Pleasant View Cottage, Erwood, Builth Wells, Powys, LD2 3EJ. Tel:0982-560676
BEWSEY COLLINS DANIELS DEW DURNFORD FRICKER GILBERT GREEN HALL HEDGECOCK HOARE JOHNSON LAKER LANGMEAD MITCHELL NEAL NEWMAN PEARSON PORTER ROSE TERRY VIRENDER WARD WHITE WILDING F6152

130192 HALL Mrs Patricia. 28 The Meadway, Cuffley, Herts, EN6 4ES.
BANNER BILLINGTON CAWLEY KERSEY LIDGETT Lidiart Ludgett Lydiart Lydiat Lydiate Lydiatt Lydyate PARTRIDGE THOMAS WICKLIN F2909

130206 HALL Mr Peter. 2 Uppermoor, Pudsey, W Yorks, LS28 7SG. Tel:0532-568098
BARRETT HALL LIGHTOWLERS MILLINGTON REED ROWBOTHAM F3838

130214 HALL Revd Philip. The Vicarage, Mayfield, Ashbourne, Derbyshire, DE6 2JR.
AMBROSE BRADLEY BUTTER CAITHNESS GILBERT HALL HARKNETT HARMAN MONCUR WALLIS F6444

130222 HALL Mrs Sandra E A. 27 Hastings Road, Kingsthorpe, Northampton, NN2 7RL.
CHANCE CLARKE DAVISON EADY GOODALL GRACE GREEN HALL HARRIS HAYFORD HUTTON LORD PAGE PATTERMASTER SIBLEY TIRRELL VELLEMOUTH WATTS WOODCOCK F2717

130230 HALL Mrs Veronica. (Steers) 24 Church Avenue, Farnborough, Hants, GU14 7AT. Tel:0252-545222
BROCKLEBANK DUNSTAN HALL HASWELL KELSEY LEDGER PETTIT STEER Steere Steeres Steers TAYLOR TYSON WATFORD WHITEHORN WIESEN WILSON F1770

130249 HALL Mr W M L. White Gables, Westcroft, Leominster, Herefordshire, HR6 8HF.

FOWLE HALL JONES MEADE REED F680
130257 HALLAM Mr & Mrs B. Unit 119 Lakewood, 43-71 Murtha Drive, Elanora, Queensland, 4221, AUSTRALIA. Tel:+61-7-598-1330
ARNOLD BROCK BUDGE CARTER COLES DICKER DIMENT FEARN FOX GATES HALLAM HODGE HOLMAN JENKINS KINSMAN LEIGH MACHEN MEWIS OVERALL PEARCY PERKINS RAINS REYNOLDS RICHARDS SPILLER SYMONS TAYLOR TRITHALL WELCOME WILLIAMS F5482
130265 HALLAS Mr Desmond. 12 Forest Close, Wendover, Alyesbury, Bucks, HP22 6BT.
Halas HALLAS Hallass F4666
130273 HALLETT Mrs Amy. Box 26, Ranfurly, Alberta, TOB 3TO, CANADA.
HALLETT F6162
130281 HALLETT Mrs E. 188 Elm Park Mansions, London, SW10 0AX.
BASSETT BELCHER DAVIS FORWARD HOLNESS JENNER MASTERS PRIDHAM SOAR WHEELER F5947
130303 HALLIDAY Major C John. C5 Baghdad Villa, Cowell Close, Sek Kong, HONG KONG.
Halladay HALLIDAY Holliday F7214
130311 HALLOWELL Mrs A. (Gumbley) 73 Whitelees Road, Littleborough, Lancs, OL15 8DR.
GUMBLEY Gumley Gumly F1647
130338 HALLS Mrs Patricia A M. 10 Fairbourne Drive, Mickleover, Derby, DE3 5SA.
WIGHTMAN F297
130346 HALLSWORTH Mr John Alaric. 82 High Street, Waddesdon, Aylesbury, Bucks, HP18 0JD.
BARRETT COCKAYNE HALLSWORTH HENSON HINKLEY PADGETT F4549
130354 HALPIN Mr Neil. Ael-Y-Bryn, Salem Cresent, Pwllheli, Gwynedd, LL53 5EA.
COULTHARD HALPIN HUTTON MAXWELL PERRY SMILES TUNSTALL WOOD YATES F6142
130362 HALSE Mr R C. Peaceavon, Wyre, Pershore, Worcs, WR10 2JB.
Halesse Hals HALSE F2226
130370 HALSON Mr David. 15 Den Avenue, Bognor Regis, W Sussex, PO21 1HE. Tel:0243-865113
COSTELLO COX Hallson Halsand HALSON Halsone STUBBS F1563
130389 HAMBLY Mr Allen D. 645 Newport Road, Cardiff, CF3 8DB. Tel:0222-778428
ALLEN BAKER BRADBEER DURRANT EDWORTHY GIBBS Hambley HAMBLY Hamley F2330
130397 HAMBLY Mrs G D. (Bates) Roseleigh, Trewetha, Port Issac, Cornwall, PL29 3RU.
BATES HAMBLY PLATT WEBSTER F6473
130400 HAMILTON Mr G M. 109 Beech Lane, Earley, Reading, Berks, RG6 2QD.
BARKER FLOCKHART HAMILTON MANNERING MICKLEBURGH MONTGOMERY ONGLEY WARNOCK F4778
130419 HAMILTON Mrs Joan S. 89 Oroua Street, Eastbourne, Wellington, 6304, NEW ZEALAND.
Allott BAILEY CLARK DILWORTH ELLERSHAW Elliot ELLOTT HAMILTON HARLIN HARTLEY HEAP HESLEDEN MAXWELL Mcgenet MCGEO Mcgeogh MCHANNETT Mcjannett Mcjenet Mcjennett NUTTALL PARKER PARSONS POLLARD PRESTON STOCKDALE TAYLOR TOMLINSON WHITAKER Whittaker WILLIAMSON WRIGHT YOUNG F4404
130427 HAMILTON Mr John Leslie. Meadowbrook Lodge, Barrows Lane, Sway, Lymington, Hants, SO41 6DD. Tel:0590-683540
COLLINS GALT Gault HAMILTON LANCE MORRISON STACEY F3740
130435 HAMILTON Mrs Leanne. 21 Akoonah Drive, Golden Square, VIC 3555, AUSTRALIA.
AVARBRIETER BATTY COLTMAN EZARD JONES RAWSON F5483
130443 HAMILTON Mr R S. 17 Wingate Road, Woodley, Reading, Berks, RG5 4JU.
BRIGHT FREEMAN GRUBB HINDS HOOLEY HUDSON KNIGHT WALDRAM F4082
130451 HAMILTON Mrs S P. Penglebe, Dunterton, Milton Abbot, Tavistock Devon, PL19 0QJ. Tel:0822-87462
DOLLERY JENKINS LONGMAN F2842
130478 HAMLEY Mr D W. 20 New Street, Cawston, Norwich, Norfolk, NR10 4AL.
COLEMAN HAMBLY HAMLEY PEDLER F35
130486 HAMMERSLEY Mr J & Mrs O N. 30 Kingsway, Fordsham, Warrington, Cheshire, WA6 6RU.
CLEWS DAVIES GRIPTON HALLIDAY HAMMERSLEY NOLAN RICE ROCHE STANLEY TAYLOR TIERNAN TRUBSHAW WARNER WILDE WRIGHT F1088
130494 HAMMERSLEY Mr R G. 2 Sarum Road, Tadley, Basingstoke, Hants, RG26 6ES.
Coales COLES Colles Hamersley HAMMERSLEY Hammersly Herle Hurl HURLE Hurll ROYAL Royale Royall F800
130508 HAMMOND Mr Brian Douglas. 7 Porthmeor Road, Holmbush, St Austell, Cornwall, PL25 3LT. Tel:0726-74763
AFFLECK ALLAN ANDERSON ATKINSON BAIRD BARRET BAYNES BEVERIDGE BISSETT BROWN BULPITT BUTTERS CHAPMAN CLEMENTSON COPE COULSON COXON CRAWFORD CUNNINGHAM DAVIDSON DEFTY DEIGHTON DINES DODGSON DOLTON DOUGLAS DRULY DUNCAN EASSON ERWIN FLEEMING FORGAN FOWLER FYALL GIVEN GOURLAY GRAY HAMMOND HEAD HETH HITCHIN HOLSWORTH HOOD HOOPER HUTCHEON HUTT HUTTON JERVIS KID KNIGHT LAMBERT LAWSON LEA LUMSDEN MATHEWSON MULLAM MULLEN MURRAY NESS NIX PACE PAGE PARISH POLLARD POTTS POWELL RAYNE REID RICHARD SMITH STAFFORD STOBBO SWIRREL TAIT TULLEY WHITEHOUSE WILLIAMSON WILSON WISEMAN WOODMAN F1530
130516 HAMMOND Mr David. 15 Jerome Road, Woodley, Reading, Berks, RG5 3NH. Tel:0734-695297
CHEWTER COX HAMMOND KERSLEY TRIBE F1141
130524 HAMMOND Mrs Eileen. 13 Belmont Close, Wickford, Essex, SS12 0HR.
BOARDMAN CARSBY COOPER FICKLIN FICKLING GOODWIN HAMMOND HEWITT NEVILL NIGHTINGALE PLUMMER SNOW F307
130532 HAMMOND Mr John. 25 Oakfield Drive, Leyland, Lancs, PR5 3XE.
HAMMOND F289
130540 HAMMOND Mr Joseph C. 1702 N Delaware, Roswell, New Mexico, 88201, USA.
HAMMOND F7289
130559 HAMPSON Mr Kenneth William. 26 Dolphine Close, Thamesmead North, London, SE28 8PY. Tel:081-311-2981
GILLINGHAM HAMPSON RUTT SEWELL SURREY WOODHAMS F3616
130567 HAMPSON Mrs Pauline. 10 Cherry Lane, Lawton Heath, Alsager, Staffs, ST7 3QZ.
AYRES BAGNALL BAMFORD BIRCH BLOOR BRELSFORD BUTLER BUXTON Edgeley Edgey EDGLEY Elgay GEORGE HAMPSON STANT STATHAM STRATTON F1646
130575 HANCOCK Mr G W. 18 Shetland Road, Leicester, LE4 6RR. Tel:0533-681674
ARCHER BOOT Boote ENGLAND GERRARD HANCOCK HEATON LAKIN Simms SIMS TOMPKINS F3533
130583 HANCOCK Mrs Margaret M. (Ingles) 36 Badsey Lane, Evesham, Worcestershire, WR11 6AZ. Tel:0386-41190
HANCOCK INGLES JARRETT LADBROOK Ladbrooke F6120
130591 HANCOCK Mr W H J. Mariquita Cottage, Ford Wivelscombe, Taunton, Somerset, TA4 2RJ.
BLAKE BREWER BUDD CONSTABLE HANCOCK HYNAFORD MICHELL PRING RICH TROTT WEBBAR F2401
130605 HANDCOCK Mrs Nora. (Gray) 14 Forstersteads, Allendale, Hexham, Northumberland, NE47 9AS.
BERWICK BEWICK Bewicke DICKSON Gan Gane Gawen Geon Geune Gilb Gonne Gown Goyne GRAY Guine Hancock HANDCOCK Jaine Jane JAYNE JOICE Joicey MORTIMER PRATT F5016
130613 HANDLEY Miss Alison E. 25 Oakdene Road, Marple, Stockport, Cheshire, SK6 6PJ. Tel:061-427-2418
HANDLEY Hanley HUDSON PRICE RENDERS WEBB F1196
130621 HANDLEY Mrs Evelyn. 45 Montalt Road, Woodford Green, Essex, IG8 9RS. Tel:081-504-4147
BEAR Beare BEBBINGTON Beer Bier BOSTOCK BOWSKILL CLARK DREW EARDLEY FISHLOCK GODFREY HANDLEY Hanley JESSOP JOHNSON KIRBY LANGFORD Lankford MCKNIGHT MOORBY SINKER SQUIRES Telfer TELFORD TILLY Vishlake WILLIS WOODROFF Woodroffe Yearsley Yurdley F2832
130648 HANDLEY Mrs Joan M. 82 Makins Road, Henley On Thames, Oxon, RG9 1PR. Tel:0491-575383
BARWIS FOOT FOOTE HANDLEY OSBORNE RYLAND STROUD WOOLLEY F6055
130656 HANDLEY Mrs R. 84 Gundagai Road, Junee, NSW 2663, AUSTRALIA.

CARR COMYNS DAWE HOCKIN LEWARNE MUNDAY SHUTTLEWORTH WAGHORN F5432

130664 HANDLEY Mrs Sybil. 25 Oakdene Road, Marple, Stockport, Cheshire, SK6 6PJ. Tel:061-427-2418
Aiken Aikin Aken Akins Auchain Baray Berie Berrie BERRY Berrye Bery Burie Burrey Eakings Eakins Eakons Ekens EKINS Ekynes Ekyns FORD Hackence Hackins Hakince Hakines Hakings Hakins HAMMOND HANSON Hawkins HIDE JUPP Oaking Oakins Okens Okins Okyn Okyns OSBORN Ouckins F1981

130672 HANDO Mr Ken. 3 The Paddocks, Herne Bay, Kent, CT6 6QX. Tel:0227-363334
ANDO ANDOE ANDOW HANDEL HANDELL HANDLE HANDO HANDOL HANDOLE HANDOLL F1396

130680 HANDS Mr S Arthur. 99 Lansdowne Avenue, Leigh On Sea, Essex, SS9 1LJ. Tel:0702-79972
Checket Checkets CHECKETTS Chicket GRIGSON HAMMOND Handes HANDS Hannes Hanns Hans PERKINS SINGLE Thownson Towenson TOWNSON WARREN F1949

130699 HANDSCOMB Mr Ralph. 15 Baden Terrace, Penyard, Merthyr Tydfil, Mid Glamorgan, CF47 0HR.
HANDSCOMB F5913

130702 HANKINSON Mr R D. 32 Queensway, Heald Green, Cheadle, Cheshire, SK8 3ED.
HANKINSON Hankison Henkinson F6927

130710 HANMER Mrs Judy. The Old Granary, Mill Road, Great Wilbraham, Cambridge, CB1 5JW.
FAIRCHILD Fairchilde Fairchilds Farchild Fearchilde Ferchell Ferchild Ferchilde GARNETT HANMER LYNN Verchell Verchild Verchilde F2035

130729 HANNA Mr & Mrs Chad. 161 St Peters Road, Early, Reading, Berks, RG6 1PG.
Chesham CHESSUM F7100

130737 HANNAFORD Miss L D. Flat 3 Summerfield Court, 141 Worcester Road, Malvern, Worcs, WR14 1ET.
HANNAFORD F6472

130745 HANNAH Chevalier David. 10 Cobden Terrace, Dalry, Edinburgh, EH11 2BJ. Tel:031-337-6241
ACHANY D'ANNETHE Hanna HANNAH Hannay F5927

130753 HANNAH Mr David. 3/74 Temple Park Crescent, Merchiston, Edinburgh, Scotland, EH11 1HZ. Tel:031-228-3434
HANNA HANNAH HANNAY HANNEY F1247

130761 HANNAM Rev D C. 2 Holway Cottage, The Mall, Swindon, Wiltshire, SN1 4JB.
Hanam Hanham HANNAM F6823

130788 HANNING Mr Roy N. Caretakers Flat, T A Centre, Sydenham Road, Croydon, Surrey, CR0 2EW.
ALCROFT Aldcroft Allcroft Haining Hainning Haning HANNING Hanyng Hayning PAYE F4163

130796 HANNINGTON Lt Col G. Chute House, Chute Forest, Andover, Hants, SP11 9DG.
HANNINGTON LE FEUVRE F3184

130818 HANNON Mrs Violet G G. (Dunn) 29 Huxley Street, Paddington, London, W10 4QQ.
CHADWICK DUNN GOTTLER HOY JOHNSON KOLTER LUTSKE NEWBURY POLUS SULLIVAN TEMPLE TISSER WATKINS F6529

130826 HANSELL Mrs Lorna. 19 Celandine Close, Whitebridge Park, Gosforth, Newcastle Upon Tyne, NE3 5JW.
HANSELL MCNIELL OLIVER F3454

130834 HANSFORD Mr Michael A. 23 Moray Avenue, Hayes, Middx, UB3 2AU.
HANCEFORD Hancford HANDSFORD HANSFARD HANSFORD F2029

130842 HANSON Mr Anders. 25 Lydgate Hall Crescent, Sheffield, S Yorks, S10 5NE.
JACKSON RADLEY WAKEFIELD WILLINGTON F5643

130850 HANSON Mr Keith. 50 Central Avenue, Birkdale, Southport, Lancs, PR8 3EQ. Tel:0704-74705
AXENALL BREWSTER DAVENPORT GRIMSDITCH Handsen Hansen HANSON Hantson Harrison MORTON SHAWCROSS F4985

130869 HANWELL Mr Adrian. 59 Western Road, Brentwood, Essex, CM14 4SU. Tel:0277-227708
BROCKBANK BROCKLEBANK CORDINER HANWELL HAWTHORN LEE LEMEN RILEY ROOM STEPHEN WALTON F1305

130877 HARBERTSON Mrs Jill. 182 Powder Mill Lane, Tunbridge Wells, Kent, TN4 9DT.
AMBLER Bagalew Bagalow Baggalew BAGGALEY Baggalow Baggley Bagley Ballson Balsom Balson BLACK BOLLSOM BRAMLEY BRAY BROOKES Brooks CESSFORD CHARLTON Colson Coson COULSON Coxon DALBY DARKER Daulby DAVIDSON DENNISON Dineson Dolby DOUGLASS Eccles Ekels FRENCH GOODALL Harberson HARBERTSON Harbison Harbutson Heckels HECKLES Herberson Herbertson Herbison Herbutson Hickles HICKLING HUGO JEW Mc Crackan MC CRACKEN MCCRACKAN MITCHELL OLIVER PICKFORD RICHARDSON Riddell RIDDLE ROBINSON ROBSON SIMPSON Sissford Spackman Spakeman SPEAKMAN STAPLETON STEPHENS Stevens TILLOTSON Utler UTLEY Uttler Uttley Westgarten WESTGARTH WHEATER WOOD F300

130885 HARBOTTLE Mr Garth & Mrs Marian. (Clough) 72 Green Lane, Stobhillgate, Morpeth, Northumberland, NE61 2HB. Tel:0670-514743
CHARLTON CLOUGH DOBSON FAIRBAIRN HARBOTTLE HENDERSON JEWELS WHITEHEAD F3967

130893 HARBRON Ms Patricia. The Mews, The Buttlands, Wells Next The Sea, Norfolk, NR23 1EU. Tel:0328-711364
HARBRON F6184

130907 HARDEN Mr Eric Arthur. 36 Biddenham Turn, Bedford, MK40 4AZ. Tel:0234-267141
HARDEN F568

130915 HARDIE Miss E S. 30 Orchard House, New Elvet, Durham, DH1 3DB.
AITKEN ARTHUR BLACK BROWN CRAM CRANNA CROOKS DICKSON DUNLOP GIBSON GRIEVE HAIG HARDIE HAY HUME HUSBAND JAFFREY JAMIESON LANSEMAN LINDSAY MIDDLEMISS PLAYFAIR SCOTT SKINNER STIRLING SWINTON THOMSON TOD WATSON WIGHT F461

130923 HARDING Mr A S & Mrs D. 9 Birch Close, Clifton, Brighouse, W Yorks, HD6 1XB. Tel:0484-718069
GLEDSTONE HARDING KIDD LEVIT TURNBULL F2526

130931 HARDING Mr David Richard. 7 Camden Park Road, Camden, London, NW1 9AU. Tel:071-485-9511
BOWDEN GIBBONS HARDING HEATON HILL HUGHES KELLEHER KELLY LANGSTONE MCNULTY O'DONNELL REARDON ROBINSON STAUNTON F1670

130958 HARDING Mrs Ellen E. (Strange) 77 Randalls Park Avenue, Leatherhead, Surrey, KT22 7NS.
BEASANT BROADWAY CECIL GEORGE HARTOP POWNEY ROE ROWE SPOONER STRANGE F2369

130966 HARDING Mr N. 102a Stourvale Road, Bournemouth, Dorset, BH6 5JB.
COURTNEY EATON GILL HANSFORD HARDEN HARDING JENKINS MILLER POND F2335

130974 HARDISTY Mr Owen. 51 Ravenbank Road, Luton, Beds, LU2 8EJ. Tel:0582-38268
AMBLER Hardesty Hardistie HARDISTY HILL PADGET Rathmall Rathmell RATHWELL SCHOFIELD Scholefield Scorefield SHEARD WALKER F6243

130982 HARDWIDGE Miss G M. 32 Arthur Road, Wokingham, Berks, RG11 2SY.
Hardwich HARDWIDGE Hardwitch F7074

130990 HARDY Mrs Betty. 53/299 Burns Bay Road, Lane Cove, NSW 2066, AUSTRALIA.
ACKROYD ARMSTRONG DIXON DUNN ELDIN EVANS FLOYD FORSTER GILBERT GRAHAM GREEN HARDY HOEY HURLE HUTCHINSON INGHAM JARVIS LASSAM MUFF PARDY RODDAM ROWLES THOMAS THORP THORPE F5425

131008 HARDY Mrs Louise. (Harrison) 103 Racecommon Road, Barnsley, South Yorks, S70 6JR.
HARDY HARMAN HINKS PANKHURST SCOTT F5292

131016 HARDY Mrs Lynn. 71 Park Avenue, Diffield, E Yorks, YO25 7EN. Tel:0377-42990
TUMBELTY F1961

131024 HARDY Mrs M E L. (Marriott) 61 St Thomas Road, Hardway, Gosport, Hants, PO12 4JU.
DOUGHTY ELWELL FRASER HOLLIER MARRIOTT SMITH SPEED WADE F4620

131032 HARDY Mr Ronald W. Brooklea, 21 Cheapside East, Rayleigh, Essex, SS6 9JU. Tel:0268-784431
BOTHEL BOTHELL HARDY HARVEY RACKHAM RULE TAYLOR F5417

131040 HARDYMAN Mr Brian. 26 St Annes Drive, Coalpit Heath, Bristol, BS17 2TH. Tel:0454-773807
BOULTON GROVES HARDYMAN POCKETT STROUD

WHITCHURCH F4559

131059 HARE Mr Godfrey. 12 Colburn Avenue, Caterham, Surrey, CR3 6HU. Tel:0883-342433
Abbett ABBOTT ADKIN AVERILL AVIS BAILEY BINES BONNICK BUCKENHAM CHRISTOPHER CLEMENTS COCK COX DOUBLE FLETCHER FORD FREEMAN GENTRY GOEBLE HALFAKER HARE HOGGART HORNE HORTSEED HUTSON JEMSON JORDAN JUNIPER KENT KNIGHT LAMB LAW LEECH LEVITT MALIN MARSHALL MAXWELL OLIVER PALMER PEAKE PORTER QUILTER RANSLEY REYNOLDS RICHARDSON RIVERS ROBINSON ROCHESTER ROLFE RYLEY SCRAFTON SCRIVENER SEABROOKE SEWELL STANES STARKEY STEREWOOD STEVENS STILL SUTTON WADE WALTER WARD WHITE WHOLEY WOODLEY WOOLMER F3212

131067 HARFIELD Mrs Tessa. 293 Cromwell Tower, Barbican, London, EC2Y 8DD.
DAVEY DITMAS DITMASS HARFIELD KERVILL KERVILLE PLAMPIN SWABY TRENDER WELLS F2082

131075 HARGREAVES Mr David Paul. 6 Avon Road, Scunthorpe, South Humberside, DN16 1EP.
ASHLEY Bramble BRAMBLES Bromble Brombles Hargrave Hargraves Hargreave HARGREAVES Hargrove Hargroves Legat Legatt Leggat Leggatt Leggit Leggitt Leggot Leggott Legot LEGOTT ROBSON Robsun SMITH TURNER F5737

131083 HARGREAVES Mrs Miriam Spokes. Rhadley, Post Office Lane, Hanwood, Shrewsbury, Shropshire, SY5 8LR. Tel:0743-860385
COOL HOLBROOK HOWELLS NEEDHAM Spok Spoke SPOKES Spookes Spooks WILLIAMS F684

131091 HARKER Mr Maurice G. 9 Curzon Place, Pinner, Middx, HA5 2TQ. Tel:081-866-0225
BURRELL FRANCIS FROST GARROD GREEN Harca Harcur HARKER Harkie Hearker Lollum Lulha LULHAM Lulhame Lulla Lullam Lullham Lullum MILES SCOTT SHELLEY F2866

131105 HARLEY Mr Mark. 6 Hexby Close, Walsgrave, Coventry, CV2 2BT.
HARLEY F4959

131113 HARLEY Mr Philip. 40 Overthorpe Close, Knaphill, Woking, Surrey, GU21 2LA.
HAMMETT HARLEY HAWKING RIGGS ROWSE WALLIS F494

131121 HARLING Mr John. 6 Fontwell Road, Little Lever, Bolton, Lancs, BL3 1TE.
FITZGIBBON HARLING LANCELEY PADGETT SPEAK TART TUCK WARBURTON F4112

131148 HARLOW Mrs Glennis. (Derbyshire) 178 Albert Road, Warragul, Victoria, 3820, AUSTRALIA. Tel:+61-56-236591
ANNABLE CORNISH DERBYSHIRE LOMAS OPIE TURNER WEEKS F4241

131156 HARLOW Mrs Roberta. 9 Trevose Gardens, Sherwood, Nottingham, NG5 3FU.
BALLARD BOULTON EDWARDS Emets Emetts EMMETS HARLOW Heiat Hiat Hiatt Hiet Hiett Highet Hyatt HYETT Hyot LEWIS NEWMAN SPARK WALTERS F1144

131164 HARMAN Mr David. 30 Audley Rise, Tonbridge, Kent, TN9 1XU. Tel:0732-770176
COWNE HARMAN Harmand Harmon HOLMAN HOMEWOOD Lucken LUKENS MARSHALL STAPLEHURST THOMAS TOOMER VINALL F1673

131172 HARMAN Mrs Margaret. (Tomlinson) Ashton, 27 Oaklands Park, Buckfastleigh, Devon, TQ11 0BW. Tel:0364-42461
COUCHMAN HARMAN HARTLEY JARRETT MIDMER RIDER SUNDERLAND TOMLINSON WARD WILD WILDE F5360

131180 HARNIMAN Mr James L. 5 Chouler Gardens, Stevenage, Herts, SG1 4TB.
HARNIMAN F6977

131199 HARPER Ms Audrey. 4 Thorndale Croft, Wetwang, Driffield, North Humberside, YO25 9XZ. Tel:0377-86319
BATEMAN BOAM BUTTON HARRISON HUNTRODS JOHNSON STONEHOUSE STRINGER F2822

131202 HARPER Mrs Margaret. 137 Hermitage Woods Crescent, St Johns, Woking, Surrey, GU21 1UH.
APPLETON ATKINSON COPITTS MUSGRAVE PATTERSON F2535

131210 HARPER Mr Peter. 24 Seaview Road, Mount Pleasant, Newhaven, Sussex, BN9 0NP. Tel:0273-514044
ALDCROFT BENTLEY BROMLEY CONNOR COOKE DOLLY DOYLE Grewby Groobey Grooby GRUBY HAINES HARPER HART JAMES LALLY LEAFE MCCARTHY MITCHELL PERRY PHILCOX POTTER RADLEY SAKER SHEPHERD SQUIER STOREY F2427

131229 HARPER Mrs R W. (Priddey) 24 Seaview Road, Mount Pleasant, Newhaven, E Sussex, BN9 0NP. Tel:0273-514044
AMPHLETT ARTHUR BLUCK BREE BURTON FFIDOE Fidoe GILDEA GORE KNOX LAMB LILWALL MATTEY MORGAN MOULE PEARSE PRIDDEY RAWLINGS RUSSELL RUTTLEDGE SMITH Stapilton Stapleton STAPYLTON TAYLOR VINCENT WATERS WATKINS WHITNEY WILLIAMS WIMBOW WINWOOD YEOMANS F2428

131237 HARRELL Mr R L. Yeld House, Yeld Bank, Shrewsbury Road, Church Stretton, Shropshire, SY6 6EZ. Tel:0694-722809
Haral Harald Harold Harolde Harould Harrall Harrel HARRELL Harrill Harrold F3387

131245 HARRIES Mr K. 58 Hall Green Lane, Hutton, Brentwood, Essex, CM13 2QU.
ADAMS ADDERSON Addison Addistone Aderson ADKIN ALEXANDER ALLMAN Allthorpe ALTHORPE ANGEL ARNOLD Asthy Attkin Attkins Aughton BALM Baum BEAUMONT Belcher BELLSHEAR BENNETT BLACKFORD BLYTH BRADSHAW BRATBY BRIGHTY Brity BROWN BROWNE BUSH Cason CASSON CHESTER CLARK CLAY CLEMENTS COOK CORBY CRAWLEY CUPIT DAKIN DAVENPORT DAVIS DAWSON Daykin DENT DUNTHORPE EATON ELLIS ESSEX EVERETT FARREN FOXLEY FRANCIS FREEMAN FROST GLADSTONE Goram GOREHAM Gorham Gorum GOSS GREENWOOD Gumbley GUMLEY GUNN GUYTON HAINES Hale HALES HARRIS HARRISON HARTOPP HASTE HAUGHTON HAYES HAZELL HEATH HODGKINSON HOPWOOD Horton HOWARD HUCKBODY HYAMS INGRAM JACKSON JONES KEMP KERCHIN Kerching KING KINGSBURY Kirchin Kirching KIRKMAN KNAPE KNIGHT Langton LANKTON LEAR LEE LESTER LILLEY LINCE LISSAMAN Lyssaman MANN MARKHAM MERRETT MOLD MORTIMER Mould MUSTON MYERSON NOBLE NORTH OAKLEY OATES Orton OVER PARSONS Payne PEIN Pine PLATTS POLLOCK POOLEY RANDLE RICHES RILEY ROBSON ROW RUDD RUSSELL SARSON Searson SERJEANT Sharp SHARPE SKEGGS SMALLBONES SMITH SPOWAGE STANWELL STEVENSON SWIFT TANNER TAYLOR TILER Tirrel TIRRELL Tirrol TOWN TOWNSEND TRIPTREE TUNWELL TURNER Tyler Tyrrell VIGERS Vigus WALTER WALTON WARD WASTELL WEEKES WHITE Wild Wilde WILKINS WILKS WILLIAMS WITARD Wvigus Wyld WYLDE F4674

131253 HARRIES-NICHOLAS Anna Avril. The Old Forge, Llanfairwaterdine, Knighton, Shropshire, LD7 1TU. Tel:05477-654
BEST BLACKMORE CODNER EVANS GERSHAM Gloyen GLOYN GUBBINGS HARRIES Hayman HAYMEN HELLIER Hellyer MADDICOTT MORGAN ROBBINS F3173

131261 HARRIMAN Mrs June R. Box 123, Griffith, New South Wales, AUSTRALIA.
ADAMS ASQUITH CAMPION GRIFFIN HARRIMAN KEENAN KEEP MAKINSON MORLEY RANBY SAVAGE TASKER WEAVER F5169

131288 HARRINGTON Mr Duncan. Ashton Lodge, Church Road, Lyminge, Folkestone Kent, CT18 8JA.
BRITTEN CLARKE HARINGTON HARRINGTON Herington Herrington NEWTON WILSON F2672

131296 HARRINGTON Mrs Elsie. St Martins, 106 New Road, Brading, Isle Of Wight, PO36 0AB.
DANIELS FARR HARRINGTON F2917

131318 HARRINGTON Mr Simon. 79 Austrey Road, Warton, Nr Tamworth, Staffs, B79 0HG.
BOYER CLOTHIER HARRINGTON HART HUNT TRULOCK F5712

131326 HARRIS Mr Bob. 12 Alandale Road, Sholing, Southampton, Hants, SO2 8DG.
DAVEY FLETCHER GREEN HARPER HARRIS HEAUME KIMBRELL LE HURAY LE LACHEUR LEGG LUQUAS LYLICK MITCHELL MOLES PRIAULX RANDELL Rose ROZE SEARBY Vian VYAN WEBB WOONE F3531

131334 HARRIS Mrs Brenda. (Twyford) 13 Chorley Wood Road, Leicester, LE5 6LE.
BATEMAN BRAIN BUTCHER HARRIS HOLLIDAY JEFFERIES MILSOM SMITH STANFORD TWYFORD F5031

131342 HARRIS Dr Colin D J. 42 Milton Crescent, Attenborough, Notts, NG9 6BE. Tel:0602-256062
CLEASBY GRAY GYDE HARRIS MALLAM PARSONS RIDEOUT F4893

131350 HARRIS Mr D Stephen. 2 Y Dolan, Morriston, Swansea, SA6 6BN. Tel:0792-700161

BEVINS COLLINS CROCOMBE GUBB HARRIS HAYES TONKIN F4703
131369 HARRIS Mrs F. (Lane) 3008 Se 154 Ave, Vancouver, WA 98684-5188, USA. Tel:+1-206-944-7502
EDWORTHY HARRIS HENLEY LANE PIERCEY POMROY SATTERLEY WHITEHEAD F5560
131377 HARRIS Mr H C. 33 Eden Road, Newton Aycliffe, Durham, DL5 5RL. Tel:0325-314328
BATES BIRD BRADLEY BURNHAM CHAPMAN CRANE DEXTER ELLIOT EVERET GILLAM GOODWIN HARRIS MILLS MOORE MOORFOOT PERKINS PINNOCK POOL REMMINGTON RICHARDS SHORTLAND STRONG THORNWELL F6347
131385 HARRIS Mr James. Jalna, Marl Edge, Prestbury, Macclesfield, Cheshire, SK10 4BT.
APPS BRINER BROOM BULL FARRANT HARRIS HEDDON HOOPER MAUNDER MUSCATT PYM SLADE TETT TROUT F5701
131393 HARRIS Mr John K. 5 Beaumont Road, Canford Cliffs, Poole, Dorset, BH13 7JJ. Tel:0202-700333
CLING EGGINS HARRIS MORGAN THOMAS F4431
131407 HARRIS Mr John R. 32 Leaside, Heacham, Kings Lynn, Norfolk, PE31. Tel:0485-71995
HARRIS HONEYWOOD F2949
131415 HARRIS Ms Judith. The Old Vicarage, Buckland Dinham, Frome, Somerset, BA11 2QR.
CLENDINNEN DAVIES EVANS FAIRBAIRN HARRIS HUDSON HUDSON-DAVIES LESLIE ROGERS WHALE F1146
131423 HARRIS Mrs Margaret. (Concha) 57 Cluny Gardens, Edinburgh, EH10 6BL. Tel:031-447-2264
AITKEN CAMPBELL Conachar Conch CONCHA Conchair CONCHAR Conchay Conchea Conchear Conched Concher Conchey Conchiar CONCHIE Conchier Conchor Conchy Concie Conckey Concky Conenochie Congie Coniqhar Conkey Conkie Conky Connachie Connalin Connochie Conqhar Conqhuar Conquer Conquher Conquie Conqut Couchie Counchie DICK GRASSICK Maccanch Maccanchie Macconchie Maconochie Mccanchie Mcconch Mcconchie Mcconchy Mcconcie Mccongie Mcconkie Mcconnachie Mcconnichie Mcconnochie Mcconochie Mcconochy Mcconockie MCTAVISH MOON ROBERTSON WILSON F5611
131431 HARRIS Mr Nick. Chestnut Cottage, 1 Rosemont Lane, Bath, Avon, BA2 4NE. Tel:0225-316765
BENNETT CHALLINGSWORTH DALLOW DAVIES DEVAN GARDNER GRAYSON GRIFFIN HARRIS HUMPHREYS ISSARD JONES LONG MANNERING MORELAND POILE POINTING REES THOMAS Tindal Tindale Tindall Tyndale TYNDALL WHITNEY WILLIS F1993
131458 HARRIS Mr Reginald C. 1021-9th Street South East, Calgary, Alberta, T2G 3B1, CANADA.
BARON BENNETTO HARRIS MATHEWS PREEN PROYBN VIVIAN F4393
131466 HARRIS Mr Ron. 51 Mount Park Road, Eastcote, Middx, HA5 2JS. Tel:0895-674921
F6203
131474 HARRIS Mrs Vahda. (Worsnop) 117 Stoops Lane, Bessacarr, Doncaster, S Yorks, DN4 7RS.
CLAUGHTON FROST KAY RICHELIEU WORSNOP F6017
131482 HARRIS Mr William. 57 Cluny Gardens, Edinburgh, EH10 6BL. Tel:031-447-2264
DOW HARRIS HARTLEY PATON F4365
131490 HARRIS Mrs Yvonne E. 60 Dover Road, Wyke Regis, Weymouth, Dorset, DT4 9DD.
ANDREWS ENGLISH GOAFE GOUGH SIMMONDS F878
131504 HARRISON Mrs Eileen. Chapel House Farm, Gill Lane, Longton, Lancs, PR4 4SR. Tel:0772-612183
BLUNDELL HARRISON HOLDEN HUNT MAYOR STANNANOUGHT SUTTON F1644
131512 HARRISON Mrs F E. (Morton) 5 Cumberland Avenue, Fixby, Huddersfield, West Yorks, HD2 2JJ. Tel:0484-534813
MORTON F5064
131520 HARRISON Mr G A. Woodlands, High Arcal Road, Himley, Dudley, West Midlands, DY3 4DB.
CLARICOATES Clattercoats F6685
131539 HARRISON Dr J. 6 Marston Avenue, Indooroopilly, Queensland, 4068, AUSTRALIA.
INVERARITY F7299
131547 HARRISON Mrs Janina. The Barn, Bishopton, Ripon, North Yorks, HG4 2QL.
ARTER Beldam BELDHAM BLACK BRACE Cheeseman CHEESMAN CHILD CHRISMAS CHRISTMAS DE LA RISEBREGGE DUFFELLS HAREWELL HARRISON Hubard HUBBARD HUTCHINS ILLMAN JONES KNIGHT LONGHURST Marchant MELLINGS MERCHANT MOLD Molde MORRIS PARKHURST PELLETT PREDDY PRIDDY RISBRIDGER ROBINSON RUSBRIDGER RYSBRUG Rysbrugg RYSEBRIGGER RYSHBRYGGE SAUNDERS SCONCE SCRAGG STEER Steere STEWART TIPTON WATFORD WHEELER WOLFE WOOLASTON F3878
131555 HARRISON Mr John Robin. 32 Ilkeston Road, Stapleford, Nottingham, NG9 8JL.
ALLEN BEVAN CHADBURN HARRISON HARTOP HARTOPP HOPCRAFT HOPCROFT SAXTON SKUCE SKUSE F209
131563 HARRISON Mrs Lesley. (George) 46 Oregon Drive, Upper Hutt, 6401, NEW ZEALAND. Tel:+64-4-526-8581
BROOKER BROWN Gellat Gellatt Gellot Gellott Gillat GILLATT Gillot Gillott Gyllot Gyllott Jellat Jellatt Jellet Jellett Jellot Jellott Jillat Jillatt MEGGITT POWELL Walmsley Wamsley Warmsley WORMSLEY F5493
131571 HARRISON Mrs Lynette. (Ison) 68 Bennett St, Dubbo, NSW 2830, AUSTRALIA.
FERGUSON HARRISON ISON KING PUGH RICKMAN TAYLOR TURNBULL WALTER Walters WILKINSON F5190
131598 HARRISON Mr Michael. 43 Symons Street, Etobicoke, Ontario, M8V 1T7, CANADA. Tel:+1-416-255-9718
HARRISON HEWGILL HUGEILL HUGILL MIDDLETON F5183
131601 HARRISON Mr Philip S. 14 Scarborough Road, Lytham St Annes, Lancs, FY8 3ES.
ALLEN CAUNCE HARRISON HART KAVANNAGH LAMB RATHBONE F5021
131628 HARRISON Mr W F. 90 Airedale Avenue, Cottingley, Bradford, W Yorks, BD16 1TL.
BEAUMONT Bownass BOWNESS DAVIDSON Davison Deninson Denison DENNISON FAWBERT HARRISON SEDGEWICK SHARP Sharpe Sidgwick F214
131636 HARROW Mr Brian. 71 Wantage Road, Didcot, Oxfordshire, OX11 0AE. Tel:0235-813649
HARROW F6189
131644 HARROWER Mr Noel. Culross, 11 The Crescent, Woodthorpe, Nottingham, NG5 4FX. Tel:0602-606012
HARROWER F52
131652 HART H D. 5248 N Le Claire, Chicago, IL 60630, USA.
DEWICK STAGG F7404
131660 HART Mrs N Margaret G. (Harvey) 15 Gilslake Avenue, Brentry, Bristol, BS10 6QN.
AUSTIN BAYFIELD BENDALL BOYES CURRY FISH GWILLIM HART HARVEY HESELTINE TUCKWELL TURNER VALLIS WESTON F3924
131679 HART Dr Simon. 1 Skibo Place, Kirkcaldy, Fife, KY2 5SJ. Tel:0592-204568
ALLEN HART PRADIER F4314
131687 HARTLEY Mrs Barbara. (Fern) 42 Duxbury Avenue, Little Lever, Bolton, BL3 1PX. Tel:0204-73459
FERN JACQUES WOOLFENDEN F4371
131695 HARTLEY Mr Derek C. 1 Carlan Stepps, Broadway, Ilminster, Somerset, TA19 9SD.
BARTLETT DEAN HARTLEY YOUNG F4952
131709 HARTLEY Mrs Sheila. (Watson) 76 Turf Lane, Royton, Lancs, OL2 6JB.
DEAN HALL MANSLEY MOSELEY MOTTRAM NICHOLSON SHEPLEY WARBURTON WATSON WORTHINGTON F1473
131717 HARTON Mr Terence A. 92 Claremont Grove, Pudsey, W Yorks, LS28 7DL.
BURN KELLY O'KELLY WARREN F5194
131725 HARTSOOK Mrs Liz. (Wooding) Box 313, Eston, Saskatchewan, S0L 1A0, CANADA. Tel:+1-306-962-3211
BALL BOURNE CHILTON EVANS FERREDAY GRINDLEY LEWIS MARTIN OWEN PITCHFORD RAMSELL WOODING F5165
131733 HARVEY Mrs Anne. (Williams) 19 Kendal Lane, Leeds, LS3 1AS.
Beddoe Beddoes BEDDOW Beddows HARRIS HUTT MACK Maurice MORRIS Morrish Morriss WILLIAMS WRIGHT F3963
131741 HARVEY Mrs Enid. (Hughes) Nessmynydd, Priest

Weston, Nr Chirbury, Montgomery, SY15 6DE.
EVANS GARBETT GENT GWILLIAM HUGHES PARKES ROBERTS F5224

131768 HARVEY Mrs H K. (Smith) Wesley Cottage, Silver Street, Bredgar, Sittingbourne, Kent, ME9 8ES. Tel:062784-427
BALDRY ELISHA ORTON PENFOLD SLAUGHTER SMITH F3980

131776 HARVEY Miss H. 30 Clare Street, New Town, Hobart, Tasmania, 7008, AUSTRALIA.
F5674

131784 HARVEY Mr Laurence C E. 29 Cecil Road, Enfield, Middx, EN2 6TJ. Tel:081-364-0441
GASCOINE OUTRAM Owtram F4432

131792 HARVEY Mr Neil. 1a Deards Wood, Knebworth, Herts, SG3 6PG. Tel:0438-813130
BROWN CATES COOK DEINSHBACK EASTON EMBREY FLEET HALE HARVEY MORRIS PHILLIPS ROBERTS TAYLOR WOODCOCK WOODS F4130

131806 HARVEY Mr P. The Square House, Lodsworth, Petworth, W Sussex, GU28 9DG. Tel:07985-543
BILTON CADLE CROUCH FRASER HARVEY MACDONALD PIBEL WAKELIN F5198

131814 HARVEY Mr Richard F. 50 Epping Road, Double Bay, NSW 2028, AUSTRALIA.
HARVEY PELLEW SEYMOUR F5531

131822 HARVEY Dr Timothy Corsellis. 275 Hagley Road, Edgbaston, Birmingham, B16 9NB.
BEATHAM CARSLAKE CORSELLIS DE CHAIR DEEKS DOUBLE ELLINGFORD FETHERSTON FIRMAN FREEBORN HARVEY LAWTON NAPPER RIVERS SQUIRE YULE F986

131830 HARWOOD Mrs Anne. (Bristow) 9 Church Road, Broadbridge Heath, West Sussex, RH12 3LD. Tel:0403-65968
BRISTOW GASTER HARWOOD HELLIWELL F5355

131849 HARWOOD Mrs Janet. (Jasper) Gull Rock, Treknow, Tintagel, Cornwall, PL34 0EP.
ANNALS BENGE CATT CLAPPERTON DURRANT HUDSON JASPER PALMER PRIER PUMPHREY F5951

131857 HASKELL Mr W A. Mohrengabe 11, 7501 Marxzell/pfaffenrot, W Germany.
BUTLER DENHAM Foule FOWLE FOYLE HASKELL Haskoll JENKINS MAYO PARSONS PHILLIPS F1779

131865 HASLAM Miss Fiona. Gruezi, The Plain, Brailsford, Derbys, DE6 3BZ.
GILBERT HAMPSON HANES HASLAM HOLTHAM METCALF SMALLEY UPTON WRIGHT YOUNG F197

131873 HASLER Mr Brian. 23 Southdown Road, Horndean, Hants, PO8 0ET. Tel:0705-595301
ATKINS BISHOP BRICE BURROWS BUTLER CHAPPLE CLARK CROWE CURTIS DAVEY DAVIS DOWNEHAM GARRAT GRIGGS HASLER HAYNE HILLMAN HOLLIDAY HOWELL JACKSON JENKINS KERR MARSHALL MASON MCDANNELL PATIENT RUDDELL SAVIL SEYMOUR SHARP SIMPSON TAKEL TURNER USHER WOOTEN WRIGHT F1505

131881 HASLETT Mr Martin K. 16 Beverley Road, Leamington Spa, Warwickshire, CV32 6PJ. Tel:0926-429254
ANDERSON Aslet Aslett BAXTER BIDEN BLACK BLACKADER Broadie BRODIE Brydie Brydy CHIVERTON CORPS DYER ELLIOTT Farrow HASLETT Haslut Haslutt Heslet HUSBAND JACOB JOHNSON KEADIE KINLOCH LEMMON LOVEDER MOORE PALMER PHAROAH POINDEN POOR PRYKE SIDEN SLATER SPARKS SPICE THOMAS WALLACE WEBSTER WESTLEY F507

131903 HASSALL Mr Clifford. 38 Brook House, Warrington Lane, Wigan, Lancs, WN7 3RP.
BINYON BRADSHAW BURKE FOLEY HASSALL MITCHELL F5651

131911 HASSALL Mr Mark. 21 Thornhill Square, London, N1 1BQ.
BEAVES CORY COULTHARD FOXLEY GELL HASSALL OWEN TOOGOOD F2111

131938 HASSARD-SHORT Miss Margaret. 56 De Beavoir Road, Reading, Berks, RG1 5NP.
CHEYNE COLSTON DALLY HASSARD-SHORT JOHN LONG MCKINTY MORGAN PEGLER WAYNESS F4427

131946 HASTINGS Mr Roy. 30 Oaklands Drive, Wokingham, Berks, RG11 2SB.
HASTINGS F348

131954 HASWELL Alan. 29 St Colians Place, Newton Stewart, Wigtownshire, Scotland, DG8 6LY.
HASWELL MACMURRAY MCMURRAY F1549

131962 HATCHELL Mrs Elizabeth. (Isaac) Heathcot, Pine View Close, Chilworth, Guildford, Surrey, GU4 8RS. Tel:0483-571430
ALLAMBRIDGE BAILEY BANSBACH Bansback Banspach Banspack BARJEW BERJEW BROOKE CLUCAS COLLINS CONRATH Conratt Courath Dodgson DODSON Dodsonne FENNER GERHARD Hatchel HATCHELL Hatchill HOOK ISAAC Isaacs Isack LUTZ OWEN PHILPOTT QUAYLE QUIGGAN QUIRK RILEY ROBINSON STUDDY F4124

131970 HATCHER Mrs Shirley. (Porter) 141 Priory Road, St Denys, Southampton, Hants, SO2 1JS. Tel:0703-584394
BUCKLAND BURNETT CAPEN JERRAM LANHAM LAWRENCE MILLER PITTMAN PORTER SALLIS STONE F1216

131989 HATFIELD Mr Frank E S. 212 High Street, Ongar, Essex, CM5 9JJ. Tel:0277-363428
ATTFIELD MERCER OLDHAM F5312

131997 HATHWAY Mrs T. Marine Bungalow, Sands Hill, Faringdon, Oxon, SN7 7PQ. Tel:0367-241886
CHAMPION COX Coxe FRY HATHWAY PECK F2786

132004 HATLEY Mrs Heather G. Kings Farm, Horningsea, Cambridge, CB5 9JG. Tel:0223-860588
BADCOCK BAREFOOT Bareford HATLEY THOMPSON F4721

132012 HATSWELL Mr & Mrs E D. Squires Cottage, Crawley Down, Crawley, W Sussex, RH10 4JQ.
Hatchwell HATSWELL Hatswill F6677

132020 HATT Mr Brian J. Greenacres, Swan Hill, Ellesmere, Shropshire, SY12 0LY.
Hat HATT Hatte F7020

132039 HAUGHEY Betty. 60 Leigh Road, Fareham, Hants, PO16 7SY.
BEAUMONT DAVIS GOREY HAUGHEY MILES NEWBERRY OSMOND POORE SABINE VANNER F2819

132047 HAUNTON Mr D J. 11 Melrose Road, Merton Park, London, SW19 3HF.
Hannton HAUNTON Hawnton F6701

132055 HAVELOCK Mrs Christine. (Allingham) 12 Ashdown, Maidenhead, Berks, SL6 8HU.
Alengame Alengham Alingame Alingham ALLINGHAM DOMINI Dominii Dominy DUNN FORD HILLS MARTIN Pen PENN Penne SMALLMAN THRASHER F3872

132063 HAVELOCK Mr Roger E. 33 Aspin Park Crescent, Knaresborough, N Yorks, HG5 8EZ.
HAVELOCK F146

132071 HAVER Mr Peter. 102 Dukes Mead, Fleet, Aldershot, Hants, GU13 8HF.
EMMERSON Haber Haffer HAVER Havre Havver Lauder LAWTHER Lowther F952

132098 HAVERS Mr Alan P. 98 Palmer Road, Angmering, Nr Littlehampton, W Sussex, BN16 4LW.
HAVERS PIGANY PITCHERS F5863

132101 HAVERS G E. 11 Cockney Hill, Tilehurst, Reading, RG3 4HF.
Avis HAVERS Havies Havors F7086

132128 HAW Mr Edward. 17 Fresia Way, Yaxley, Peterborough, Cambs, PE7 3WA. Tel:0733-244884
BRAMMEL CREW EATON HAW HOPKINS LAILEY MACKIFF TONG F5005

132136 HAWES Mrs Eugenie. (Kerger) 30 The Dale, Keston, Kent, BR2 6HW. Tel:0689-854664
BENSON BROCKLEHURST HAWES STUBBS WINCHCOMBE F4745

132144 HAWGOOD Mr David. 26 Cloister Road, Acton, London, W3 0DE. Tel:081-993-2897
Axcel Axcell Axel Axell EXCEL EXCELL Exel Exell HAWGOOD F2863

132152 HAWKE Mr A H. 30b St Pirans Road, Perranporth, Cornwall, TR6 0BJ.
HAWKE F1359

132160 HAWKES Mr Anthony Bryan. 10 Court Green Close, Cloughton, Scarborough, North Yorkshire, YO13 0AP. Tel:0723-870832
Hawker HAWKES HAWKINS Hawks LEY PETTY Shapcote SHAPCOTT Shepcote F1588

132179 HAWKES Dorothy. (Broady) 3 Darlington Street, Coppull, Chorley, Lancs, PR7 5AB.
BROADY FLETCHER FORD HALE HAWKES HUGHES KILLINGBECK LEE LUMB NORMANTON RIDGEWAY SPENCER TRAFFORD VINCENT F2961

132187 HAWKES Mrs Joan. (Pavey) 24 Wicklands Road, Hunsdon, Ware, Hertfordshire, SG12 8PD.
BEECHEY COOPER HUNTLEY PAVEY ROBERTS F3382

132195 HAWKINGS Mr David Thomas. 21 Frays Close, West Drayton, Middx, UB7 7PF.
CORNELIUS FOURACRE HARTNELL HAWKINGS HAWKINS

HOWELL JAMES OLIVER SNOOK TREASURE F631
132209 HAWKINS Mr A E. 6 The Grove, Waddesdon, Aylesbury, Bucks, HP18 0LF.
CUTTER HALSTEAD Hasted HAWKINS Haystead F6383
132217 HAWKINS Mr Dai. Y Garth, Nantmel, Ger Llandrindod, Powys, LD1 6EH. Tel:0597-823105
ADAMS ANNABALAH EDWARDS EVANS FLIGHT Hannibal Hannible HARTLEY HAWKINS HAYWARD Heartley HUGHES JONES Kilmaster KILMINSTER Kilmister Pierce PIKE PRICE ROBERTS SAMUAL SMITH STEPHENSON TAYLOR THOMAS WEBB Whitcomb WHITCOMBE WILLIAM WILLIAMS WORKMAN F5676
132225 HAWKINS Mr G D. 15 Kirkstone Crescent, Barrow In Furness, Cumbria, LA14 4ND. Tel:0229-823558
BROOKES BUTLER COVENTRY DEAN DYER HART HAWKINS HODKINSON JOINSON JOYNSON Kay Kaye KEAY MURRAY NASH PLANK REAY SIMS TIPPING WILKINSON F175
132233 HAWKINS Mrs Gylian. (Durrans) 21 Meadway, Harpenden, Herts, AL5 1JN. Tel:0582-763553
BATTY BAYFORD DURRANS HAWKINS HUTCHIN SKETCHLEY SYGROVE THURGOOD F4008
132241 HAWKYARD Mr Tom. 183 Ripon Road, St Nicholas, Stevenage, Herts, SG1 4RL. Tel:0438-740630
BRIGHT BUCKLEY CREASER DYSON HAWKYARD KINDER SETTLE WHITEHEAD WINDRAM F1923
132268 HAWORTH Mr Roy E. 23 Winston Avenue, Cleveleys, Blackpool, Lancs, FY5 2HU.
ASPINALL Aspinwall BARLOW BEDDOWS COATS Crowder CROWTHER HAMER HAWORTH HINDLE HOLDEN HOPE Houlden Howarth HOWE Howorth JACKSON KAY KEEN KEMPSON Kimpson Massay MASSEY Massy Massye MONTGOMERY Mountgomery NUTTALL OSBORNE Paine PAYNE Pollet Pollit POLLITT ROUSE Scoulcroft SCOWCROFT SMITH SPENCER WHEATCROFT WOOD F2313
132276 HAXELL Mr Michael. 11 Ryeland Avenue, Bridlington, North Humberside, YO16 5UN. Tel:0262-677067
Axall Axcell Axell BESSER COLE EADE Hacksall Hacksoll Hackwell Haxall HAXELL Haxill Haxoll Haxswel Haxwell RICHARDSON TALBOT F1631
132284 HAYCOCK Mr Sam. 15 Paxhill Lane, Twyning, Tewkesbury, Glous, GL20 6DU.
BAKER HAYCOCK F1017
132292 HAYES Mr J M E. 18 Heol Fair, Porthcawl, Mid Glamorgan, CF36 5LA. Tel:0656-784814
HAYES LODWICK F6001
132306 HAYGARTH Mr W L. Almeda, Abbey Park, Burghfield Common, Reading, Berks, RG7 3HQ.
BLORE CARPENTER DIXON GIDMAN HAYGARTH LLOYD LOGAN F4095
132314 HAYLAND Mrs Anne T. (Littlemore) 36 Bruce Avenue, Shepperton, Middx, TW17 9DW. Tel:0932-228651
HAYLAND LITTLEMORE MACKERETH STYLES F5394
132322 HAYNES Mrs Edna. (Cottenden) 12 Bolton House Road, Bickershaw, Wigan, Lancs, WN2 4AB. Tel:0942-866001
COTTENDEN Cottendesa Cottendon Cottenson Cottenton Cotterden Cotterdon Cottingden Cottonden Cottynden F3824
132330 HAYNES Mrs Jean. (Congrave) 40 Cowper Road, Harpenden, Herts, AL5 5NG.
Coggrave Colgrave Colgreve Congrave Congraves Congreave Congreaves Congreives CONGREVE Congreves Congrieve Conigrave Conygrave KEATS F167
132349 HAYNES Mrs Kathy. (Hutchinson) 5 Alfriston Road, Seaford, E Sussex, BN25 3QD. Tel:0323-890057
ADSETT BALCHIN BROWN CHAPMAN DREWETT GEERING GOLDSMITH GREENYER HAYNES HEAVER HENLEY HUTCHINSON HUTSON KNIGHT LOWER LUMMS MACE MILLER PETTITT RANGLER READ SMITH STEVENS TAYLOR WILLIAMS YORK F5350
132357 HAYNES Mrs Moyra. 1 Holywell Close, Abingdon, Oxford, OX14 2PU. Tel:0235-523326
ELLIOTT Hain Haines Hains HAYNES Heynes Heyns NICHOLLS Sherborn SHERBORNE Shirborne Shurbon Shurbone Shurbun SWINBURNE VARDY WILLIAMS F493
132365 HAYSOM Mr John. The Tynings, 2a Nore Road, Portishead, Bristol, BS20 9HN. Tel:0272-843649
Haisom Hasom Haysham HAYSOM Haysome Hayson F1868
132373 HAYTER Mr Graham. 8 The Land, Frampton Cotterell, Bristol, Avon, BS17 2LJ. Tel:0454-778923
DIKE HAYTER MIZEN REES RUDLEDGE F2850
132381 HAYWARD Mrs Patricia. 17 Sturton Way, Long Sutton, Spalding, Lincs, PE12 9BZ.
BOYD BOYLE BRAMMER BRUCE CAMPBELL CARMICHAEL CORDUKES COUTTS CRWAFORD CUMMINGS CURRIE CUTHBERTSON DAVIDSON DOCHERTY DOWLING GILKS GRAHAM HAYWARD IZAT JACK KIRKWOOD MARSHALL MAXFIELD MCLEOD MORTON NEVINS PEARSON RATCLIFFE ROBERTSON SMITHYMAN SPITTAL SPROULL STAWPERT STRATHERN STRUTHERS SUTHERLAND WESTWOOD WILLIAMSON WILSON F824
132403 HAYWARD Mrs Valerie. (Dallman) 10 Aldwyck Court, Leighton Buzzard Road, Hemel Hempstead, Herts, HP1 1SJ.
BONIFANT DALLMAN GRAVESTOCK HARROD Herrod HORTON NEARY REID THORPE TOFT F1600
132411 HAYWOOD Mr Charles. 22 Clifton Gardens, Golders Green, London, NW11 7FL. Tel:081-458-1897
Godwin GOODWIN Goodwyne F3769
132438 HAYWOOD Mrs P J. 48 St Wystans Road, Derby, DE3 3JY.
BUCKLEY CARR FLETCHER HAYWOOD HOBDAY HOLT PRICE PROBERT WEBBER F4692
132446 HAZELTON Miss May. 114 Erinvale Avenue, Belfast, N Ireland, BT10 0FP.
BEAVERS HASELTON HAZELTON HEASLETON HESSELTON RODGERS RUSSELL WARNOCK WATTERS YOUNG F430
132454 HAZON Mr Richard. 15 Mulberry Gardens, Gateshead, Tyne & Wear, NE10 0EJ.
BAILES COMERFORD GAVAN Haison HALL Hasson Haysand Hayzen Hazen Hazeon HAZON Hegesende Heisende WILSON F5270
132462 HEADLEY Mr George. 17 Runnymede, Kingswood, Bristol, BS15 4BG. Tel:0272-679931
GOUGH HEADLEY PAYLOR WEST WOODHEAD F2725
132470 HEADON Mr Mike. 2 Oxwich Road, Mochdre, Colwyn Bay, Clwyd, LL28 5AG.
CONROY COOPER GIBBS HADEN HEADON LAWRENCE PINCOMBE SAUNDERS TURNER WELSH F3439
132489 HEAL Mrs Jacqueline. 54 Hambrook Lane, Stoke Gifford, Bristol, BS12 6QD. Tel:0272-691910
ALLEN HEAL KENNEDY MATTHEWS NOTT OTTERY WALLBRIDGE WINTERSON F1679
132497 HEALES Mrs F S J. 37 Lenham Road, Sutton, Surrey, SM1 4BG.
CORNISH FARRIS HARRIS HEMMING PURVIS STAINES SWAIN WHITE F2371
132500 HEALEY Mrs Dyann L. Springs Farm, Lothersdale, Keighley, W Yorks, BD20 8HH.
ASHBY BASTOW BOOTHROYD BRADBURY BUTTERWORTH CHEETHAM CLEGG CROSSLEY DAVIES DIXON MCGILL OAKES SCHOLES SMETHURST WHIP WHITTAM F2560
132519 HEALY Mrs Doreen M. (Ayres) 39 Longdown, Fleet, Hants, GU13 9UY.
Dellar DELLER Staddan Stadden STADDON F3557
132527 HEARDER Mr I. Florence Hall, Shopford, Bewcastle, Cumberland, CA6 6PS.
HEARDER Herder Hurder F6998
132535 HEARLE Mr Barrie. 117 Kingrosia Park, Clydach, Swansea, W Glamorgan, SA6 5PJ.
HEARLE PETERS F2026
132543 HEARN Mrs D. (Brooker) 3 Blenheim Drive, Chilwell, Nottingham, NG9 5ES.
Booker BROOKER CAWLEY Coorley CORLEY Harn HEARN Hearne Hern OWENS PALFREY ROWE WATKINS F4168
132551 HEARN Mr Ron. 42 Whitehill Park, Whitehill, Bordon, Hants, GU35 9DS. Tel:0420-489992
ANNETTE HEARN Hearne Hern Herne HERON Hurn PAYNE PURNELL WALTER F994
132578 HEASMAN Mr William A. 8 Hammy Way, Shoreham By Sea, W Sussex, BN43 6GG.
Haysman Heaseman HEASMAN Heesman Heisman Heseman Hesman Hezman Hysman F1031
132586 HEATH Mrs C Patricia. (Moon) 6-4750 Uplands Drive, Nanaimo, British Columbia, V9T 5V1, CANADA. Tel:+1-604-758-5190
BATH BLOCKLEY CHECKER CHEQUER EGGLETON FREER GOODENOUGH HOWITT LAY Miffling MIFLIN Miphlin MOON NICHOLES SMITH STUMP F4399

132594 HEATH Mr Ciril. 29 Chalfont Way, Meadowfield, Durham, DH7 8UP. Tel:091-378-2094
HEATH F1018

132608 HEATH Prof Len. Forge Cottage, Yelverton, Devon, PL20 6BT.
CHAMP CHANDLER CRAFER DANCE HEATH HOBBS HULBERT HULCUP JEWELL PRATER Preater SPANSWICK STRUGNELL F645

132616 HEATH Mrs Vera. 15 Ashgrove Road, Ashford, Middx, TW15 1NS. Tel:07842-55006
FORBES GILES LAPPAGE WINGRAVE F2700

132624 HEATHER Mr C D. 40 Dene Road, Dartford, Kent, DA1 1LX.
HEATHER Heether Heither Hether F6829

132632 HEATHER Mr H O. 112 Wardown Crescent, Luton, Beds, LU2 7JT. Tel:0582-32279
BARLOW BURREN CROOK FARNORTH FARNOTH HEATHER MERCER PASS PEET TODHUNTER F5042

132640 HEATHER Mr Peter. 36 St Andrews Road, Coulsdon, Surrey, CR5 3HA.
AVARD BALDRY BATES BEEKEN BROOKS CEALY CHAPMAN CLAPSON CRASKE DRAKE FURNEAUX GIBBINS GILSON HALE HAMMOND HARDWICK HEATHER HILL JONES LIFFORD LOVELAND MILLER PUDDY SHARPEY SHURLOCK SMITH SOUTHGATE SUMNER SWIFT THYER WAKEFIELD WALTER WILKIE WYETH F6475

132659 HEATON Mrs Doreen. 4 South Crescent, Garlieston, Newton Stewart, Wigtowns, DG8 8BQ.
Berkenshaw Berkinshaw Berkumshaw Birkenshaw BIRKINSHAW Burkenshaw Burkinshaw Cochsha Cocksham Cockshatt COCKSHAW Cockshay Cockshutt FARROW GLASBY HALLEY HAYNE HEATON Hewison Hewitson HEWSON Hueson Hughson Huison Huson Northmoor Northmoore NORTHMORE PASH POTTER SHORE STANAWAY Stanway WHITEOAK F1167

132667 HEATON Mr Robert. 17 Bradford Road, Bingley, W Yorks, BD16 1DT.
HEATON F2810

132675 HEBBLETHWAITE Mr Paul. 55 Newfield Lane, Sheffield, S17 3DD. Tel:0742-363222
COLEY HEBBLETHWAITE PEACOCK F5810

132683 HEBBLETHWAITE Mrs Sheila M. (Pennington) Birch Heyes, 121 St James Avenue, Upton By Chester, Chester, CH2 1NN.
BAKER CAMDEN DUSART HAMMOND HEBBLETHWAITE PENNINGTON SAYLE F1482

132691 HEBDEN Mr J R. Aldergarth, Galphay, Ripon, N Yorks, HG4 3NJ.
Hebbton Hebdain Hebdan HEBDEN F6616

132705 HECKFORD Mrs Nancy M. 12 Well Lane, Welton, Daventry, Northants, NN11 5JU.
COWELL KENCH MAYOR F3431

132713 HECKMAN Mrs J. 3 Fencove Court, Old Saybrook, Connecticut, 06475, USA.
Sharp SHARPE F6879

132721 HEDGER Mr Garry. 79 North Roskear Road, Camborne, Cornwall, TR14 8PX. Tel:0209-710353
BARTLETT BEER BONE CHUGG CLARK Clarke DELVE DENNIS GILLOW GUBB HEDGER MUNDAY PARKHOUSE RIDD TUCKER VINCENT WYATT YEO F2637

132748 HEDGER Mr George. 67 South Avenue, Southend On Sea, Essex, SS2 5JA. Tel:0702-611104
COUZENS EWENS HEDGER LUDMAN MOREY F5239

132756 HEDGES Ms Fiona. 51 Hillview Road, Oxford, Oxon, OX2 0DA.
ABEL ANDERSON AYNSLEY BARTON BENNETT Bignall BIGNELL BIRD BLACK Boreman Borman Bourman BOWERMAN BUTLER CARNABY CORNWALL DE ACTON DE BIDDLESTON DE CLAXTON DE CREON DE EMELDON DE FELTON DE MOLTON DE SMYTHETON DELAVAL DIXON DOUGLAS EASTER Edgerton Edges Egenton EGERTON Egges Eginton FENWICK FRANKLIN GALLIMORE GARBETT Garbutt GERRARD GOODWIN GOWER GREY HACKLEY HALTON HEDGES Hegges HEMMINGS HILL Hodges HORSLEY House HOWSE Humphery HUMPHREY Humphries Humphry JACKSON JOYNER KING LOOKUP MARSDEN MASON MCKAY MERDLING METCALFE MITFORD MONTGOMERY MORRIT Morritt PADLEY PERCY PERKINS POPE POWIS PRENDERGAST REDDALL Rochester ROGERS Rotchester ROUND RUDCHESTER RUSH RUTHERFORD SANTOS SIMS SMITH SNOW STUART SWINBURNE TATE TAYLOR WIDDRINGTON Wodman WOODMAN F4972

132764 HEDLEY Mrs Jean. (Johnson) 12 Mitford Close, High Shincliffe, Durham, DH1 2QE.
BELL BOYES BRUNSWICK DIXON EARLE ENGLISH JAMES JOHNSON PATTINSON ROBINSON ROCHESTER SMITH THEW F4707

132772 HEDLEY Mr Tony. 4 St James Close, Hasland, Chesterfield, Derbyshire.
CRANE HALL HEDLEY F3990

132780 HEGAN Mr Russell. 7 Farm Close, Sedgley, Dudley, W Midlands, DY3 3NE. Tel:0902-882473
Eagan Eagin HAGAN Hagen Haggan Hagin Haygan Heagan Heagin Heagon HEGAN Heigan Higan Hogan O'hagan F560

132799 HEIGHES Mrs Susan. 27 Timber Bank, Frimley Green, Camberley, Surrey, GU16 6PL.
BEDWELL BROOKLAND COX GLEESON HEIGHES HUGGINS MCGARRY TARRY F4311

132802 HEIGHWAY Dr John D. 15 Bolton Avenue, North Hykeham, Lincoln, LN6 8JA. Tel:0522-681334
ADDISON BRADLEY CAMERON CHRISTIE DEAR Demont Diment DIMOND Dymond FERGUSON GRANGER GRIFFITHS Hayway HEELEY HEIGHWAY Heywaye Highway HORTON JOHNSON JONES LOWE MAULAM MOSELEY MULLERT ROWTON SANSON SHORT STAINER THOMAS Willemot Willemote WILLMOT Willmott Wilmot WORSLEY F6307

132810 HELLAWELL Mrs Lynne. (Waddington) 3 Green Crescent, Golcar, Huddersfield, W Yorks, HD7 4RF.
ALLISON ASPINALL Halliwell Hallowell HELLAWELL Helliwell Hellowell HINCHLIFFE HURST MARTIN MEAD WADDINGTON F4228

132829 HELLENS Mrs W J. 8 Westcroft Road, Forest Hall, Newcastle Upon Tyne, NE12 9JS. Tel:091-266-8185
BARTRAM BERTRAM BERTRIM CARR HELLENS HESLOP HUNTER MARLEY MOORHEAD SHEEL STEWART WELFORD F924

132837 HEMINGFORD Lord. The Old Rectory, Hemingford Abbots, Huntingdon, Cambs, PE18 9AN.
BAILEY BATTLE CLARK FRANCO GREVILE GROSSE HARBOTTLE HAYNES HERBERT ISLEY MCCLARE MOTT OKES RUDDOCK STICKALORUM THOMPSON F1951

132845 HEMINGTON Mr Roy E. 12 Jellicoe Close, Windsor Meadows, Slough, Berks, SL1 9HW.
Ainland AINLEY ALFORD Allford CHEESEMAN Cheesman Chezsman Emington Emmington FINCH Halford Hementon HEMINGTON Heminton Hemmington MOORLEN Morland Morlin Oseland OSLAND Oslin F2673

132853 HEMMING Miss S. 272 Cowick Road, Tooting, London, SW17 8LQ.
CANHAM COWLES CROOK DAVIES Davis Emans Emens Eming Emings Emmans Emmens Emming Emmings ENGLAND Hemans Hemens Heming Hemings HEMMING Hemmings HOARE LAND LEE Mathew Mathews Matthew MATTHEWS MURRAY Padget Padgett Paget PAGETT POTTER Sale Sales Sayle SAYLES YAUGHAN F5364

132861 HEMMINGHAM Mrs K E M. 31 Cressex Road, High Wycombe, Bucks, HP12 4PG.
DORLING F6748

132888 HEMMINGS Mr A. 11 Grummock Avenue, Ramsgate, Kent, CT11 0RR.
ASH EVANS HARDING MADGE F2929

132896 HENDERSON Mr Barry Wilbur. 21 King Edwards Road, Malvern Wells, Malvern, Worcs, WR14 4AJ. Tel:0684-565345
HENDERSON MCNAB F742

132918 HENDERSON Mrs Isabel. (Burns) 40 Fothringham Drive, Monifieth, Dundee, DD5 4SW. Tel:0382-534623
BURNS POWRIE F5032

132926 HENDERSON Mrs Pamela. (Linstead) 2 Higherwell Lane, Helston, Cornwall, TR13 8QT. Tel:0326-563390
LINSTEAD POOLE TAMS F3749

132934 HENDERSON Mr S. 28 Mikasa Street, Barrow In Furness, Cumbria, LA14 3EA.
HENDERSON MAUGHAN F4535

132942 HENDRA Mr Peter. 30 Fort Crescent, Margate, Kent, CT9 1HX.
ADAMS BONES BROWN COX DENN EMBLETON GILBERT GLANFALE HAMPTON HENDRA HODGE HOSKIN INGRAM JOBLING MICHELL NIXON PURVIS ROGERS SHAWTER F440

132950 HENLY Mr C R G. 9 Renfrew Drive, Wollaton, Nottingham, NG8 2FX. Tel:0602-283850

Bonehill BONELL Bonhill Bonill CHEESEMAN Cheesman Cheseman COLE Doleman DOLMAN Doman EDWARDS Finemore FINMORE Fynmore Godderidge Godderige Goderidge Goderige Godridge Godrige Goodridge Goodrige GOTHERIDGE Gotherige Gothridge Gothrige Gutteridge HARBER Hendley Hendly Henley HENLY JEPSON Nicholls NICHOLS Nickalls PARKIN Parkyn PETERS Scull SELF Selfe SIMPSON SKULL SLADE Standen STANDING TOGHILL TURNER F6469

132969 HENNEY Mr Graham. 7 High Trees, Shirley, Croydon, Surrey, CR0 7UR.
HENNEY F6795

132977 HENRY Mr Robert Mcdowall. Solway, 5 Maitland Terrace, Kildrochat, Stranraer, DG9 9EX.
Tel:0776-82278
BELL BRUTY CHAPMAN CLARK CORSON DALRYMPLE GEMMELL HENRY KENSETT MCCONCHIE MCKINNELL MCMIKEN RHODES SNATCHFOLD F1182

132985 HENSON Mr P B. 11 Potters Croft, Horsham, W Sussex, RH13 5LR. Tel:0403-61923
EASTER HENSON HUTCHINSON WIDDOWSON F1051

132993 HENWOOD Mr Glyn. 18 Gannet Close, Basingstoke, Hants, RG22 5QN.
BATTEN BICKFORD BLIGHT COATH CRUDGE DARLEY FEATELEY FRAMPTON GATRALL GODOLPHIN HARVEY HOOPER HOUGHTON HUNT JACKSON JONES KINGSWELL LOADEL MACEY PHILLIPS RANNALS SMITH STEPHENS SWEET THOMPSON THRIFT TWYCROSS UREN VAUGHAN WEBB WHITTINGTON WILLIAMS F2502

133000 HENWOOD Mrs Rose. 18 Gannet Close, Basingstoke, Hants, RG22 5QN.
ANDREWS ARMSTRONG BARRINGER CHANNON CHILLORY COOK HALL HARPER JEFFORD LOVEDAY MANNING MITCHELL PALMBY RUSTON RUTTER STOREY TAYLOR THORN UDALL WAKELY WARREN WATERMAN F1766

133019 HEPPELL Mr Cliff. 17 Ewbank Avenue, Fenham, Newcastle Upon Tyne, NE4 9NY.
Tel:091-273-6762
COCK HENDERSON Hephale Heple Heppel Heppele HEPPELL Hepple Langcake LONGCAKE MAXWELL MENSLEY MINSLEY Peal Peale PEDLAR PEEL Peil Peile Pele Piel Piele PONTON SAYERS Tweady Twedey Twedy TWEEDY F283

133027 HEPPELL Mr George A W. 10 Riseborough House, Rawcliffe Lane, Clifton, York, YO3 6NQ.
Tel:0904-624995
HEDINBURGH Heppel HEPPELL Hepple F6468

133035 HEPPLEWHITE Mrs Esme. (Newell) Trencrom, 102 Pinewood Avenue, Crowthorne, Berks, RG11 6RG.
HEPPLEWHITE F3567

133043 HERBERT Mr Eugene F. 29a Wharf Road, Birchgrove, NSW 2041, AUSTRALIA.
Tel:+61-2-810-8370
ARBER Arbor BLACKBURN DEVINE GEAKE GEE GUILFOYLE Harber KEENAN Kilfoyle MALONEY Moloney POWNEY F4464

133051 HERD Mrs Sheila. 2 Lady Row, The Street, Shotley, Ipswich Suffolk, IP9 1NA.
Birch BURCH Byrch F1279

133078 HERITAGE Mr John. 1 Butler Road, Crowthorne, Berks, RG11 6QZ. Tel:0344-774104
Eritage HERITAGE Herytayge Herytidge WILKINS F6482

133086 HERMON Mr G V. 46 Oakleigh Drive, Croxley Green, Rickmansworth, Herts, WD3 3DF.
ALLCOCK ELLCOCK FENNELL HERMON JAMES F4801

133094 HERON Mrs Ella Mansfield. 115 Newville Avnue, Anchorsholme, Cleveleys, Blackpool, FY5 3RG.
Tel:0253-860129
HERON KNOWLES MANSFIELD F3258

133108 HERON Mrs Margaret. (Leach) 42 Prickwillow Road, Ely, Cambs, CB7 4QT.
AHERNE HERON POWDRILL F6479

133116 HERRIDGE Mr Kevin A. Tree Topes, Upper Highland Road, Ryde, Isle Of Wight, PO33 1EA.
Hedage Herage Heredge HERRIDGE F6952

133124 HESELDEN Mr Alan J M. 81 Roxeth Hill, Harrow On The Hill, Middx, HA2 0JL.
Saissal Sasel Saycele Saycell Saycil Saysal SAYSELL Saysill Saysol Seysel Siscel Sysel F1978

133132 HETHERINGTON Elizabeth. 45 Laet Street, North Shields, Tyne & Wear, NE29 6NN.
ALLOTT BAKER DIXON HETHERINGTON HOTHAM HOWIE KNIGHT LOVE MANTHORPE WAYTE F612

133140 HEWER Mr D J. 7 Catchpole Lane, Great Totham, Maldon, Essex, CM9 8PY.
HEWER F6898

133159 HEWITT Mr J F. The Grange, 47 Bay View Road, Benllech, Gwynedd, Wales, LL74 8TT.
DAWSON GILL HEWITT HODGSON HOLMES NELSON PATRICKSON STEAD F3883

133167 HEWITT Mr John. 60 Cartland Road, Stirchley, Birmingham, West Midlands, B30 2SE.
Tel:021-443-2511
BULLAS CROWLEY HEWITT HINDS HIPKISS JONES MAKEPEACE MANDER RINGHAM SADLER F6117

133175 HEWITT Mr Thomas John. 16 Park Road, Southville, Bristol, BS3 1PU.
ADEY ADLAM BLAKE EGLINTON HARCOMBE HEWITT THOMPSON WILTSHIRE WINDOWS F3104

133183 HEWLETT Mrs Molly. 14 Kenilworth Drive, Willsbridge, Bristol, BS15 6UP.
Tel:0272-327620
ALDOM BROAD NOBLE POOL F3182

133191 HEXT Mr John M. Ivy Cottage, New Town Lane, West Pennard, Glastonbury Somerset, BA6 8NL.
Tel:0458-34170
Haxt Heaxt HEXT Hexte Hix Hixt F170

133205 HEXTER Mr Nick. 284 St Johns Road, Boxmoor, Hemel Hempstead, Herts, HP1 1QG.
Tel:0442-63456
HEXTER F2058

133213 HEYBYRNE Mr Ernest. 43 Bourne Close, Winterbourne, Bristol, BS17 1PJ.
HEYBYRNE F4045

133221 HEYS Mrs Susan. (Gates) 13 North Lane, Rustington, W Sussex, BN16 3PF.
BATCHELOR BOYTON BRYANT BRYER CUTLER DEAN ELLETT FRISBY GADD GATES GLADWIN GODFREY GOSNEY HEYS HOLLOWAY HOUSE INWOOD LUNN NEWMAN PEARSON POINTER REYNOLDS ROGERS ROSE RUSSELL SMITH SOTCHER STREET TROWBRIDGE WAREHAM WELLS WILBORN WOODRUFF F5210

133248 HIBBERT Mrs I. (Linnett) 195 King Street, Kettering, Northants, NN16 8QS.
ASHER DURLING KNOWLES LINNETT MOORE ORMISTON F6410

133256 HIBBITT Mrs Wendy. 2 Green Close, Writtle, Essex, CM1 3DX. Tel:0245-421265
HIBBITT THURGOOD F1024

133264 HICKEN Lesley. 19 Lilybank Close, Matlock, Derbyshire, DE4 3EH.
BAILEY GREAVES HAMLIN LOWE SHELDON SPALTON F59

133272 HICKLEY Revd P M. 372 Heath Road South, Northfield, Birmingham, B31 2BH.
Tel:021-476-1705
De Heckele Haccleia Heckley Heckly Hekle HICKLEY Hickly F533

133280 HICKLEY Mrs Teresa. (Brittain) 372 Heath Road South, Northfield, Birmingham, B31 2BH.
Tel:021-476-1705
BRITTAIN GUEST O'NEILL ONIONS PERCIVAL PLANT VENNERS F532

133299 HICKLING Mr Malcolm J Larkworthy. 38 Kingsley Road, Northampton, NN2 7BL.
Boyce BURNETT De Heckele De Hekelinge De Hekelingge De Hekelyng De Hekelyngg De Hichelle De Hickel DE HICKELING De Hickelinge De Hickelle De Hickelyng De Hickelynges De Hickland De Hickling De Hicklinge De Hicklingge De Hicling De Higeling De Hikeland De Hikeling De Hikelinga De Hikelinge De Hikelinges De Hikelingge De Hikelyng De Hikelynge De Hikligg De Hiklyng De Hitling De Hykeling De Hykelinge De Hykelingge De Hykelinggs De Hykelingh De Hykelyng De Hykelynge De Hykelyngge De Hykkelingh De Ikeling De Ikelinges De Ykeling Eccling Echel Echelinog Etcling Haccleia Heckeley Hecklay Heckley Heckly Heclay Heekley Heicklay Hekle Hiccle Hiccleton Hicel Hiceling Hichelyn Hichelyng Hickelle Hickelynge HICKFORD Hickingham HICKISSON Hicklain HICKLAND Hicklen HICKLENTON HICKLER HICKLES HICKLETON HICKLEY HICKLIN HICKLING HICKLING-BURNETT HICKLINGAM Hicklinge Hicklingem Hicklings Hicklingse Hicklington Hicklinse Hicklinton Hicklonton Hicklton Hickly Hicklye Hicklyn HICKMALT HICKMAN Hickmanes HICKMANS Hickmons

Hickson Hiclen Hiclin Hicling Hiclingham Hiclyng Hikal Hikalton Hikel Hikeley Hikeling Hikelton Hikelyng Hikelyngg Hikkling Hikley Hiklynge Hixling HUTCHINSON Hyckelyng Hycklinge Hycklyng Hykeling Hykelyn Hykelyng Hykling Hyklyng Hyklynge Icel Icelin Iceling Icelingham Icelingtun Icelintone Ichel Ichelin Icheltone ICKEL ICKELING Ickle Ickleton Ickling Icklingham Iclans Icles Icling Iclingas Ikel Ikeline Ikeling Ikelinge Ikelingham Ikling LANDER-BOYCE Larkeworthy LARKWORTHY Yclin Ycling Yclinham Yclinton Ykeling Ykling F160

133302 HICKS Mr Edward. 56 Gambier Parry Gardens, Gloucester, GL2 9RD. Tel:0452-418178
HICKS F1971

133310 HICKS Mr Peter George. 11 Georgia Road, Thornton Heath, Surrey, CR7 8DU.
HICKS F2463

133329 HICKS Mr Richard. 27 Middlethorpe Road, Cleethorpes, South Humberside, DN35 9QD. Tel:0472-603303
ANDERSON BROCKLEBANK CHALLENGER HICKS PERRIN F4330

133337 HICKS Mr Ronald L. Dunroamin, 3 Clare Terrace, Falmouth, Cornwall, TR11 3ES. Tel:0326-313061
Hick Hickes HICKS POULTON F4546

133345 HICKTON Miss D. 71 New Green Park, Wyken Croft, Coventry, CV2 1HS. Tel:0203-615299
HICKTON WEBSTER F7432

133353 HIERON Mr Harold. 1 Highwin, Highbury, Coleford, Bath Avon, BA3 5PA. Tel:0373-812656
HIERON Hiron Hirons Hyron Hyrons F1101

133361 HIGGINS Mrs Beryl. High Bank, Mill Hill Lane, Brockham, Betchworth Surrey, RH3 7LS. Tel:0737-843326
ANDERSON BODEN COOK EDWARDS EVERETT FLOYD HIGGINS NEWTON-COOK Overend OVERIN POPE ROWLINGSON SPIERS WESTON WOODHAMS F2988

133388 HIGGINS Mr George. 52 Devonshire Street, Keighley, W Yorks, BD21 2BL.
CARMICHAEL FISHER HIGGIN HIGGINS F3039

133396 HIGGINS Mrs J. Somerville House, Allendale Road, Hexham, Northumberland, NE46 2NB.
Belitha BELITHER Beuglas Bolitha Bolither BOOKLESS BOTTERILL Buckles Buglass Bugless Buickless Buigloss WILSON F1427

133418 HIGGINS Shirley. Woodcroft, Bucks Hill, Kings Langley, Herts, WD4 8DT.
AMER GREEN HEBORN HESTER F3028

133426 HIGGS Mr Carl J. 16 Partridge Grove, Spennells, Kidderminster, Worcs, DY10 4HH. Tel:0562-745170
BRADLEY CHETTER EDWARDS HALL HANCOX HAYWARD HIGGS JEAVONS NOAKE SHAKESPEAR SHORTER TAYLOR TUCKEY F4047

133434 HIGHAM Mrs Anne. 21 Lindsey Street, Epping, Essex, CM16 6RB. Tel:0378-74943
BOWDITCH BURDEN FISHER HIGHAM KEMP Liford Livard Liverd Livord LYFORD Lyvard Lyward MCGEE NETLEY F198

133442 HIGHLEY Ms Sue. 4 Church Road, Bexleyheath, Kent, DA7 4DA.
BLAKE DOBBS GITTINS GUYER HIGHLEY HULLINGHURST Perdu PURDUE F5133

133450 HIGMAN Mr Julian. 42 Aldworth Avenue, Charlton Heights, Wantage, Oxon, OX12 7EJ. Tel:02357-66931
ADAIR ADAMS ADYE AINSWORTH ALDHAM ALLARD ALLWOOD ANSON ARUNDELL AVERY BALME BARROW BARTY-KING BAYLEY BEAL BEECHEY BENSTEAD BERNARD BEST BETTY BILLANY BIRT BLAZE BRAY BROCKENSHIRE BRUNSKILL BULL BULLOCK BUTLER CARHART CARPENTER CARRIER CARTER CAUSTON CHATTERTON CHRISTIE CLOUGH COCK COLE COLEMAN COLLEY COLLINS CORNISH Crae CREE CROWE DAVIES DUNN Eliot ELLIOT Elliott Elliotte ELLIS ELTON ENGLAND FARINGTON FARO FARQUHARSON FAUSETT FENNER FLOWER Foord Foorde FORD Forde FRIEND FUKES GABBETT GAGE Garbed GARDINER Gardner GILBARD GILES GOODENOUGH GREENHALGH GRIER GRILLS GURDON HALEY Hallowes HALLOWS HANCOCK HARRIS HARRISON Hathersall HAVILLAND HAWKEY HAYMAN Hegman HELGREEN HELPS HENDERSON HENWOOD Hethersall HEWSON Hickman HICKS Higeman Higgman HIGMAN Higmann HINTON HOCKIN HODSON Hollows HOTHERSALL HOWARD HURRELL Huthersall Hygman Hykman JACKSON JOHNS JONES KENT KINGDON LAVIES LLOYD LOFTUS LUCAS LUMBY MACDOUGALL MACKENZIE Marilion Marillon MARSHALL MASSEY MAY Meurilyon Mewrillon MOCK MOORE Morillon Mourilon MOURILYAN Murillon NEWMAN NICHOL NOAKES NORMAN OLIVER OLIVER-BELLASSIS OSGOOD OWEN PAIGE PARKER PARTINGTON PAULET PEARCE PELHAM PENWARNE PHILIPS PICKHALL Pierce PIERCY PIGOTT POOLE PORTER PRETTYMAN RAIKES Read Reader Rede REED Reede REEDER Reider RICHARD RICHARDS RICKARD RIGBY ROBERTS ROBERTSON ROBINSON ROSE RUSSELL SAMBROOKE SANKEY SIMMONS SIMPSON SLADDEN SMITH SNOSWELL SPERNON SPIERS Squar SQUARE Squarr SQUIBBS Squire STAFFORD Stephenson STEVANS STEVENSON Stewkley STOKES STRANGEWAYS STUART Stutely STUTLEY SUTEHALL SWANSON SWORTON Tanar Taner TANNER TAUNTON TOM TONKIN Tonshet TOUCHET Touchette Toutchet TREMAYNE TRISTRAM TROTTER TRUEBODY Tuchett Tuchette Tushet Tutchet Varco VARCOE VAUGHAN VENABLES Verco Vercoe VERNON VERRIER Walch Walsh Walshe WALTON WEBBER Welch WELSH Welshe WENTWORTH WICKETT WILLIAMS WINGATE WITTS WOOD WOOLCOMBE-ADAMS WOOLMER YELLAN F740

133469 HIGNELL Mr Stephen. 117 Boroughbridge Road, York, N Yorks, YO2 6AA. Tel:0904-798695
HIGNELL F2823

133477 HIGNETT Mr Nicholas Julian. 1-3 Deanery Close, Pontesbury, Shropshire, SY5 0PS. Tel:0743-790228
HIGNETT F1159

133485 HILDER Mr Ian. 73 Valance Road, Lewes, E Sussex, BN7 1SJ.
HILDER SIZELAND F2168

133493 HILL Mr Anthony. Po Box 97, Bondi, NSW 2026, AUSTRALIA.
CHAPELL COLSTON DANN HAWKINS HILL JORY KILLICK MORRANT NEW OARE OLVER PROUT RAVENSCROFT READ SARJEANT STONE TREWIN WEEKS WHITE WINSOR F5559

133507 HILL Mrs Daphne. 12 Willow Drive, Bexhill On Sea, E Sussex, TN39 4PX.
ADAMS ANDREWS GREEN Kean Keen KEENE MARTIN Pain PAINE Payne SUMMERELL SUMMERHILL Summerille TAYLOR WATSON WELFORD F1930

133515 HILL Mrs G J. (Fantham) 16 Springfield Road, Wilbarston, Market Harborough, Leics, LE16 8QR.
BILSON Fantam FANTHAM Fanthom Fantom Fentham KIND TIDD TWEED F5216

133523 HILL Mr Godfrey. 35 Danycoed, Aberystwyth, Dyfed, SY23 2HD. Tel:0970-623028
CUDLIP HILL JONES MACEY Masey RATTENBURY Rundell RUNDLE SNELL TURNER WEATHERLEY F5130

133531 HILL Mr John Edward. 30 High Street, Linton, Swadlincote, Derbys, DE12 6QL. Tel:0283-760050
BATES CHAPMAN HILL KELLY LATEY NEWBOLD POTTER F5301

133558 HILL Mrs M. Po Box 176, Chelsea, Victoria, 3196, AUSTRALIA.
WHITELEY F3285

133566 HILL Mr Ralph W. 12 Willow Drive, Bexhill On Sea, Sussex, TN39 4PX.
ASTON BALLS BASFORD BATES CHILDERSTONE DAVIS EVANS FRYER HAMMOND HILL HUDSON JACKMAN KNIGHT Moyes MOYSE NICHOLLAS PLACE PLUMMER RACKHAM SMITH WELBROCK Welbrook WHINCUP Winckup Wincop WOOLLAMS F1975

133574 HILL Mr Raymond. 30 Regent Road, Horsforth, Leeds, W Yorks, LS18 4NP.
BROGDEN CRABTREE DENTON GREENACRE HILL LOFTHOUSE THOMPSON WHITEHEAD F3621

133582 HILL Mr Richard. 53 Hatfield Road, Ipswich, Suffolk, IP3 9AG. Tel:0473-726505
CLAYDON GALLAFANT HIGGLETON HILL KILLICK SMITHER F5052

133590 HILL Mrs Zena. (Reddick) 9544 Foxbury Way, Pico Rivera, CA 90660, USA. Tel:+1-310-949-8619
Beattie BEATTY Cleugh CLEUTH Clough DICKSON DUTTON HURLEY MAJOR MARSH Mccau Mccaw MCGAUGH

Nicholds Nicholls Nichols NICKOLDS Nickoless Nickols PRICE SPROTT WARD WHITEHOUSE WOODWARD F5426

133604 HILLIER Miss Melanie. Peckingell, Langley Burrell, Chippenham, Wiltshire, SN15 4LJ. BARNES BERRINGTON BUTLER CROFTS DUEL FLOWER FRANCIS FROST HILLIER JONES LYE MANN NEWMAN PARK REYNOLDS SELF WILLIS F3851

133612 HILLIKER Miss S P. Po Box 184, Sutherland, NSW 2232, AUSTRALIA. HILLIKER F6688

133620 HILLS Mr Brian. 32 Meadow Way, Farnborough Park, Orpington, Kent, BR6 8LW. Tel:0689-859747 De Helles Helles Hilles HILLS F1854

133639 HILTON Miss Dyan. 12 Northleigh, Bradford On Avon, Wiltshire, BA15 2RG. ABBOT Anam Anams Annanis ANNUM Annums Anum Anums BARTROP BESANT Besent BISHOP BOUCHER BOUGH CHINNOCK CHIVERTON COX DAVIS DELEMONT DIBBS DODGE Dowel DOWELL DOWNTON ELDRIDGE FARNHAM Folger FOOTMAN FORREST FOSTER Foulds FOULGER Foulkes Fulger GILLAM Gilliam GODWIN HAMMOND HEEKES HEWITT HEYLER HILTON LAWRENCE LEIGHT MASON MITCHELL MORGAN Navis Neavil Neavill Neaville Nevel Nevell Nevelle Neves Nevil Nevill NEVILLE Nevis Nowis PARSONS PHILLIPS POMEROY Pomery Pomroy PRICE PUDDEN PUDDING Pumeroy Pumrey ROUND SCALES SCARLETT SLADE STAGG STEPHENS STEVENS STROUD TRASK WALKER WILLIAMSON F3969

133647 HINCHLIFFE Mrs A. 12 The Meadows, Bournmoor, Houghton Le Spring, Co Durham, DH4 6HG. DAY GOODWIN HINCHLIFFE SINGLETON SMITH F3956

133655 HINE Mr D. Glenrue, 6 Butt Lane Close, Hinckley, Leicestershire, LE10 1LF. Hind Hinde HINE Hynd Hynde Hyne F2354

133663 HINE Mrs Eileen. 48 Stoneleigh Road, Solihull, W Midlands, B91 1DQ. GARNHAM MATHEWS F1989

133671 HINE Mrs Rita. Oakley Cottage, Westbury Lane, Purley On Thames, Reading, Berks, RG8 8DL. Tel:0734-843655 ASHWELL CHANDLER CHRISTMAS CUBIS DELLAR DIXON DOBSON EDWARDS FRY HARDING PONTING ROGERS ROSENDALE SHERGOLD SMART SMITH SPARROW STONE WALDRON WEEKS WHEATLEY F5660

133698 HINE Mr Tom. Oakley Cottage, Westbury Lane, Purley On Thames, Reading, Berks, RG8 8DL. Tel:0734-843655 HARDY HARRISON HARRISSON HINE MANN RICH SUTTON F1663

133701 HINES Dr Kenneth. 37 Woodside, Park Avenue, Walthamstow, London, E17 3NP. Tel:081-521-6567 ASTLEY CROMPTON CRUMPTON HINDES HINES TURNPENNY WEBSTER F5373

133728 HINSON Mrs Lucie. (Pinder) The Smithy, Grinton, Richmond, North Yorks, DL11 6HJ. Tel:0748-84454 COULTASS FANTHORPE HINSON PINDER PLAYFOOT POTTS F5341

133736 HINWOOD Miss C L. Appletree Cottage, Crossways Road, Grayshott, Hindhead Surrey, GU26 6HE. HINWOOD HIPPOTT LANGRIDGE PESTER RELF ROLFE SOLLY WITTS F2388

133744 HINXMAN Mr Richard. Fairthorn, Beckingham Street, Tolleshunt Major, Maldon, Essex, CM9 8LH. Anschamen Hanchman Hansemane Hanshmen Haunchman Haunsmen Henceman Hencheman Henchman Henchmen Hengestman Hengestmannus Hengstman Hengysman Henseman Hensheman Henshman Hensman Henxceman Henxeman Henxman Henxmen Henxstman Heynceman Heynsman Hinchman Hinckesman Hincksman Hincxman Hinesman Hingman Hingston Hinkman HINKSMAN Hinksmann Hinkson Hinshman Hinskman Hinsman Hinxeman Hinxksman HINXMAN Hinxon Hitchman Hnksman Hyckesman Hyncksman F6887

133752 HIRSCHBERG Mr Len. 40 Grenfell Road, Liverpool, L13 9BZ. Tel:051-226-8435 BAKER GREEN HERSEBERGER HIRCHBERG HIRSCHBERG HIRSHBERG F1327

133760 HIRST Mrs S J. (Wimpenny) 1 Miry Lane, Thongsbridge, Huddersfield, Yorks, HD7 2SA. AUBREY BAXTER BOOTHROYD BROOK BROWN CROSLAND EASTWOOD FIRTH GELDRT HAIGH HINCHLIFFE HORSFALL Penie Penny SCHOFIELD SYKES Whimpenie Wimpennie WIMPENNY Winpenny WOODCOCK WORDSWORTH F4906

133779 HISCOCK Mr David John. 57 The Street, Old Basing, Basingstoke, Hants, RG24 0BX. GENT Hedgcock Hedgecock HILLIEAR Hillier Hillyer HISCOCK Hiscocks Hiscox Hitchcock KEELER KIMBER F3041

133787 HISCOCK Mrs Isabel. (Allardice) 79 Elgin St, Gordon, NSW 2072, AUSTRALIA. Tel:+61-02-498-1628 ALLARDICE BABBINGTON BLAIKIE CASEY CURRIE DEMATT GOURLAY GRAINGER HISCOCK HOWDEN IMRIE MOFFATT PEARCE WATSON WOODBRIDGE F4460

133795 HISEY Mr Bill. 2237 Cambridge, TX 76054-2909, USA. Tel:+1-817-485-3148 BAIRD BLAIR BRYSON HEWETT HOWELL PROVEN WADEL WALLACE WILSON WRIGHT F6514

133809 HITCH Dr Dennis. 102 Rawcliffe Lane, Clifton Without, York, YO3 6QT. Tel:0904-651220 HITCH F81

133817 HITCHCOCK Mr Witgar. The Mill House, Bures, Suffolk, CO8 5BZ. Tel:0787-227367 Abrey ADAMS BATEY CHOATE Choit COOPER DUCE ENNALS FLINDERS FREEMAN GREENE GRIMWOOD HITCHCOCK Hitchicock HURSTHOUSE LARKING LEGG LEGGETT NEVILL NORTON OBREY OLDRING PEARSON Pearsons SPAWTON SQUIRRELL SUTERS SWEETLOVE THOMPSON WARD WATERMAN F199

133825 HITCHINS Mrs Janet. (Askam) 1 Fyfe Crescent, Baildon, W Yorks, BD17 6DR. Ascham ASKAM Askem Askham BAKER DAVY FIRTY HAWKINS HISCOCKS HITCHINS POTTS F3543

133833 HITCHON Mr J C. Tomann Cottage, 52 Lonmore, Gairloch, Ross-Shire, IV21 2DB. Tel:0445-2355 BARRETT CLARK DANIELS HAWORTH Hichen Hitchen Hitchin HITCHON F3888

133841 HOARE Mrs J. Garden Cottage, Emmetts, Ide Hill, Sevenoaks Kent, TN14 6BA. CONQUEST F7011

133868 HOATHER Mrs M S. 41 Parkside Drive, Watford, Herts, WD1 3AU. Tel:0923-222205 FOWLER HAWKEY SHEARS STEER F752

133876 HOBBIS Mr Arthur. Brookmede, Worcester Road, Shrawley, Worcs, WR6 6TD. BATE BOLLARD Emuss HEMUS HOBBIS Pensar PENSON Pensor PENZER PIPER F1720

133884 HOBBS Mr Graham. 1 Burcombe Villas, Chalford Hill, Stroud, Glos, GL6 8BN. Tel:0453-884778 CLARK HOBBS MACDONALD SEARING F4560

133892 HOBBS Mr H R. 59a Smeeth Road, St Johns Fen End, Wisbech, Cambs, PE14 8JF. ABBOTT DENTON HOBBS HODDELL HOLDEN NASH STANTON F5369

133906 HOBBS Mr James A. Rr 1 Backbone Road West, Box 253, Princeton, IL 61356, USA. Tel:+1-815-879-9531 BAXTER HOBBS SHEARD F4494

133914 HOBBS Mrs K Margaret. 3 Stepstone Lane, Knowle, Braunton, N Devon, EX33 2NB. COOK LYDDON MOORE F5196

133922 HOBBS Mr M R & Mrs W J. The Hollies, 124 Winchester Road, Shirley, Southampton, Hants, SO1 5RP. ADAMS AXFORD BALL BROOMFIELD CLARK CLARKE COOPER COTTON DAVIS ELLINGWORTH FRICKER GALE GETTINGS GIDDINGS GIDDINGS-PYLE GRAY GREEN Gyddings HOBBS HOBBS ALABY HORN HUMPHREY HURST HUTCHINGS JAMES KLIEN LAKE MEABY MOTT NASH OSMAN PARSONS PENNY PETTY PYLE-GIDDINGS RICHES SOAN TOOMER VIBERT WEAVER WEBB WELCH WOOLDRIDGE F4072

133930 HOBBS Mrs Margaret. Timbers Chase, Ruxbury Road, Chertsey, Surrey, KT16 6NJ. CASE CHURCH CLARK COOPEY CURTIS GOODWIN GUSTERSON HOBBS F737

133949 HOBBY Mr David. 22 Bradmore Way, Lower Earley, Reading, Berks, RG6 4DS. Tel:0734-862384 DAVIS GOODYEAR HOBBY F1106

133957 HOBHOUSE Mrs M A D. (Newton) Quantock Cottage Farm, Crowcombe, Nr Taunton, Somerset, TA4 4AP. Tel:09848-225

ALLEN AUGUST BOYD DEAKINS FARROW GIBBONS HALSTEAD HEATHER JENNET KELLEY LOVEDER MICKLAM MUSSON Muston NEWTON PARSONS REEVES WHITE F4503

133965 HOBLEY Mr Trevor Michael. 10 Hawarden Road, Clowyn Bay, Clwyd, LL29 8NA.
Hobblae Hobbley Hoblae Hoble HOBLEY Hobly Hublae Hubley Oble Obley F4833

133973 HOBSON Mr David G. 23 Gaunt Drive, Bramley, Rotherham, S66 0YJ.
HOBSON F7419

133981 HOBSON Mr F W. 34 Sycamore Road, Ecclesfield, Sheffield, S Yorks, S30 3YW.
HOBSON Hopson F6572

134007 HOBSON Dr J. Field Head, Netherton Fold, Netherton, Huddersfield, HD4 7HB.
BATEMAN BLASSON ELAND FROGGETT HOBSON IRTON KILLICK KIRKE SPENDLEY STANFEILD STANROYD WRENCH YOUNGS F4896

134015 HOBSON Michael E. 30 Catherine Road, Woodbridge, Suffolk, IP12 4JP. Tel:0394-382234
BREARLEY BROWN HAMMOND MOORE WILSON F2612

134023 HOBSON Mr Michael. 12 Church Balk, Thorne, Doncaster, S Yorks, DN8 5BU. Tel:0405-813943
BRAMHILL BRUNYEE HOBSON NICHOLLS NUTT F4319

134031 HOCKIN Mr J C. 33 Prospect Crescent, Swanage, Dorset, BH19 1BD.
BAINES BARTLETT CLOAK HOCKIN F3875

134058 HOCKING Mrs P A. 1 Park Avenue, Golden Square, VIC 3555, AUSTRALIA.
BILLINGS BOOKER FLEET GITTINS GREEN HOCKING HUMPHREY MAYNE MCMINN MORRISON PERRIN RODWELL ROWE SCARLETT TOWNSEND TREZONA VEITCH WILCOX F5553

134066 HOCKLESS Mrs J. 7 Mckenzie Court, Greensborough, Victoria, 3088, AUSTRALIA.
HOCKLESS Hockliss Ockless F7180

134074 HOCKNEY Mr R. 16 Jonas Drive, Wadhurst, E Sussex, TN5 6RJ. Tel:0892-882967
BENNETT COSSINS CRAWFORD CRAWLEY DELVES HOCKNEY ROBERTS F4021

134082 HODDER Miss J. 33 Napier Street, Kippa Ring, Brisbane, Queensland, 4021, AUSTRALIA.
GOODING MCKENZIE WANER F5142

134090 HODGE Mr B T. 5 Bell House Walk, Rockwell Park, Kingsweston, Bristol, BS11 0UE.
BRIGHT GREGORY HODGE JENNINGS LEONARD MCMULLEN Mcmullin Morris MORRISH TOOKEY Veal VEALE VENTON WEBBER F5646

134104 HODGE Mrs S J. 5 Bellhouse Walk, Rockwell Park, Kingsweston, Bristol, BS11 0UE.
BLACKWELL BOSTOCK BYTHEWAY CLUTTON Connah COOPER CUNNAH Dod DODD Peter PETERS STANTON Wild WILDE F4332

134112 HODGES Mr Albert E. 41 Brynawelon, Nant-Y-Glo, Brynmawr, Gwent, NP3 4BZ. Tel:0495-311951
HODGES Hoghes F6111

134120 HODGES Miss Alison Marina. 28 Hardwicke Road, Hastings, East Sussex, TN34 3PF.
EDWARDS Edwoods HODGES Hogges PRETLOVE Pretluv Prettlove Prettluv WELCH Welsh F308

134139 HODGES Mr John. 3 Arkwright Road, Milton Ernest, Bedford, MK44 1SE.
ABERCROMBIE Abercromby ADAMI BUCKBY Bugby Cladingbold CLARINGBOLD Claringbould CORRI ENGLAND Eyles GREENSLADE Hodge Hodgers HODGES HOLMES ILES Ingland Isles LEADLEY LEVERIDGE Merrall Merrell MERRILL Rannolds REYNOLDS Warrick WARWICK WHITEWOOD F3798

134147 HODGKINSON Mr A J. Kirkstead, 52 Kelso Close, Worth, Crawley Sussex, RH10 4XH.
ALLAKER Elleker Ellerker F6693

134155 HODGKINSON Mrs S J. 80 Dale End Road, Carlisle, Cumbria, CA1 3DE.
CLARK HODGKINSON LENNIE LITTLE ROBINSON F2792

134163 HODGKINSON Mr Wilfred John. 27 Thornton Road, Girton, Cambridge, CB3 0NP. Tel:0223-276869
Hodgekinson HODGKINSON Hodgkison Hodgkisson Hodgskinson F2

134171 HODGSON Mrs A J. 18 Hardwick Road, Sedgefield, Stockton On Tees, Cleveland, TS21 2AL. Tel:0740-20912
HODGSON MAKEPEACE MAUGHAM PIGNEY RICHARDSON RUTTER YOLE F3563

134198 HODGSON Mr Gordon. 11 Rocks Avenue, Cleckheaton, W Yorks, BD19 3YD.
Faucit FAWCETT Fawcitt GABBITAS Gabitas Gabittas HODGSON Hodgsone Hodson Hogson SAXTON Sexton F5786

134201 HODGSON Mr Kenneth. 8 Kassassin Street, Eastney, Southsea, Hants, PO4 9PS. Tel:0705-293511
CAMPBELL ENGLAND HODGSON HULL MACPHERSON PINFIELD PRIESTLEY SIMISTER WICKET WYNN F1953

134228 HODSDON Dr James D. 32 Kings Road, Cheltenham, Gloucs, GL52 6BG.
Hoddesden Hoddesdon Hodsden HODSDON F34

134236 HODSON Mr K G. Lightwood, Cirencester Road, Minchinhampton, Stroud Glous, GL6 9EL.
HODSON F2379

134244 HOFF Mr D E. 20 Alexandra Park, Scarborough, N Yorks, YO12 5EL. Tel:0723-377964
CLIMPSON HARRISON HOFF F6268

134252 HOGG Miss F. 7 Carrick Way, St Mawes, Truro, Cornwall, TR2 5BB.
GREENLAND HAWKER Hoff HOGG WHEELER F4048

134260 HOGG Mrs Margaret. 23 Pollard Street, South Shields, Tyne & Wear, NE33 2DP. Tel:091-456-9516
CRAIGS GODFREY GRAVETT HOGG MAPSTON RADFORD RAFFLE F469

134279 HOILE Mr B F. 41 Springhead Road, North Preston Estte, Faversham, Kent, ME13 7ET.
HOILE F6858

134287 HOLBROOK Mrs E M. 5 Higham Road, Woodford Green, Essex, IG8 9JN. Tel:081-504-3280
EATON Lacelet Laslet LASLETT Laslye Lasslet Lauslet Luslet F202

134295 HOLDCROFT Mr Gary. 1 Beacon Road, Romiley, Stockport, Cheshire, SK6 3HZ. Tel:061-430-7838
HOLCROFT HOLDCROFT F2677

134309 HOLDEN Miss A G. 95 Commonside, Ansdell, Lytham St Annes, Lancs, FY8 4DJ. Tel:0253-737800
BAINBRIDGE DUCKWORTH HAGUE HOLDEN MARTIN MOSELEY RANDLE WHITEHEAD WINTERBOTTOM F5610

134317 HOLDEN Mr John. 14 Goodwood Close, Burghfield Common, Reading, Berks, RG7 3EZ. Tel:0734-832727
BLOOR Bloore Blore Blowèr DANES FROST Golbey GOLBY Goldbey Goldby HADLAND Hebblethwait HEBBLETHWAITE Heblet Heblett HOLDEN SIMPSON SWARBROOK Swarbrooke Swarbrooks WYLIE F4671

134325 HOLDICH Mr R J. Wheelwrights Cottage, Great Hales Street, Market Drayton, Shropshire, TF9 1JW.
HOLDICH Holditch Houlditch F6863

134333 HOLDING Mr N H. 101 Manor Road, Cadington, Luton, Beds, LU1 4EF.
COTGROVE F6985

134341 HOLDIP Mr J A. 61 Blackthorn Ave, Toronto, Ontario, M6N 3H4, CANADA.
HOLDIP Holdup Holduppe Holdyp F7196

134368 HOLDSWORTH Miss E E. 55 Broadway Avenue, Harlow, Essex, CM17 0AG. Tel:0279-433370
ACOMB Anscomb Ascomb BAYLIS Brian BRYAN Bryon EVANS GREEN HOLDSWORTH Houldsworth JEFFERSON JENKINS PERRIS WILKES F3429

134376 HOLE Mrs Janet. 12 Roding Road, Loughton, Essex, IG10 3ED. Tel:081-508-0964
BAKER BELL COOK DAVIS FAIRFOOT MCGREGOR MEADE OTTAWAY POTTER RUSSELL THOMAS TITE F895

134384 HOLGATE Elizabeth. 29 Cupernham Lane, Romsey, Hants, SO51 7JJ.
EMMINS HOLGATE MURRAY TOWNLEY F92

134392 HOLLAND Mrs Nancy. 15 Cunningham Avenue, Wrexham, Clwyd, LL13 8SY.
Hellen HELLIN F7408

134406 HOLLAND Mr P A. 85 Farndale Drive, Guisborough, Cleveland, TS14 8JX.
ANGUISH Angus CLIFFE FARRALL HOLLAND WHITE F6476

134414 HOLLAND Miss R D. 24 Arbury Hall Road, Shirley, Solihull, W Midlands, B90 4PY.
ASKEY F6981

134422 HOLLAND Mrs Sheila. 62 Rodings Avenue, Stanford Le Hope, Essex, SS17 8DU.
BOWMAN CARNEY CHASEN EASHIOTT HAWKINS HOLLAND LUCASSI MALLETT MARSHALL NELSON PALMER

PHYTHIAN PYTHIAN RAWSTRONE F2568
134430 HOLLANDS Mr Thomas. 33 Evelegh Road, Farlington, Portsmouth, Hants, PO6 1DJ. Tel:0705-377378
BIGGS CATHERALL DICKSON HAMLIN HOLLANDS HOUGH MORGAN OVERINGTON WILLET F4037
134449 HOLLELY Mr Philip J. 9 Eden Grove, Swallownest, Sheffield, S31 0TP. Tel:0742-873981
HOLLELY F6291
134457 HOLLEY Mrs Roberta F. Northwinds, Les Landes Avenue, St Brelade, Jersey. Tel:0534-43769
BETSON DEITON FLEMING GRANTHAM GREENAWAY LAINCHBURY PEEL-SMITH TOLL F1355
134465 HOLLICK Mr D A. 10 Rushford Close, Shirley, Solihull, W Midlands, B90 4UF.
Holich HOLLICK Hollix Olick Ollick F6629
134473 HOLLIDAY Joan. 22 Kenilworth Road, Ashford, Middx, TW15 3EL.
BEECH BENNETT BRASH BURSTOW COSTIN CRONEY HARVEY HEWITSON HOLLIDAY JENNINGS PLUMB SPONG F1728
134481 HOLLIDAY Mrs M Elizabeth. (Merredew) The Anchorage, Blackstone, Ipplepen, Newton Abbot, Devon, TQ12 5QN. Tel:0803-812115
DOWSETT HINDLE HOLLIDAY MERREDEW NEWMAN REDINGTON SHEPLEY WEBB F3759
134503 HOLLINGSBEE Mrs Kathleen. (Reed) 5 St Andrews Way, Tilmanstone, Deal, Kent, CT14 0JH.
DARLEY Garat GARRATT Garrett Gear GEER Gere Ghere GODDARD GRAVES HACKFORD Hackforth HAYWARD Haywood HEWSON Heyward Heywood Hollandby Hollenby Hollendby Hollingberry HOLLINGSBEE KINGSFORD KINGSNORTH PAGE Read Rede REED Reid SMALLFIELD Smallvel STOREY Story SUMMERS TIDY WASHFORD F766
134511 HOLLINGSWORTH Mr Fred. Highfield House, 115 Wolverhampton Road, Pelsall, Walsall, WS3 4AD. Tel:0922-682688
ALCOCK ALLSOP ANDREWS ATKIN ATTENBOROUGH BARFOOT BLAZEDALE BRENTNALL BROOKS BYRON CHILD CLARK CLAY CLIFF COWLISHAW EAVES ELLEY ELLIS EVANS FRANKS GERMAN HALLAM HARVEY HAZELL HEARSON Hollingsworth HOLLINGWORTH HOLMES HOULT HUDDLESTON HUTCHINSON ILLSLEY KETTLE LAIN LAMB LAMIN LEVERNS MARROTT MELLORS PALING PAWLEY PAYN PENDLETON PIMBLETON PLUCKWELL PRATT Sale SEAL SIMPSON STANDLEY STEEVENS STRINGER THURLBY TRICKETT WAGG WARREN WHETTON WHITE WIDGOOSE WIGHTMAN WILLIAMS WILLIAMSON WOOD WOODWARD F937
134538 HOLLINS Mr Brian. 83 Merley Ways, Wimborne Minster, Dorset, BH21 1QW. Tel:0202-883048
HALLING Hallinge Hallinges Hauling Haulinge Hawlin Hawling Hawlings HOLLINS F460
134546 HOLLOWAY Mr John. 2 Blenheim Close, Raynes Park, London, SW20 9BD. Tel:081-543-9893
Bear Beare BEER Beere BLAIR Brabrook Brabrooke BRAYBROOK Braybrooke Britain Britan Briton Brittain Britten BRITTIN Britton BULL CHARLES COWLEY Craig CRAIK DENTON DUKE DUNMORE DYER FARMER FARROW Geffery Gefferys Geffry Geffryes Geofery Geoffry Goodwel GOODWELL Goodwill Goodwille GRAY Hail Haills Hails Hale Hales Halloway Hallowell HANLEY Hayle HAYLES Hincks Hinkes HINKS Hodgkin HODGKINS Hodgskin Hollaway HOLLOWAY Hollowell JACOB Jacobs Jeffary Jeffarys Jefferie Jefferies Jefferess JEFFERY Jefferye Jefferys Jeffre Jeffres Jeffress Jeffrey Jeffreys Jeffries Jeffris Jeffry Jeffrys Jefrys Jeoffries Jeoffrys KERR MANNING Matten MATTHEW MCKENZIE REID ROSS ROWLATT SARGEANT SCOTT SHORTLAND Tounsend Townesend Townsend Townshend TOWNSIN WAGSTAFF Wagstaffe Wood WOODS F5681
134554 HOLLOWELL Mr A J. 81 Cranbrook Road, Redland, Bristol, BS6 7BZ.
HOLLOWELL F4765
134562 HOLMAN Mr D C. 3 Harbour Court, North Parade, Portscatho, Truro Cornwall, TR2 5HH.
BRENDON HOLMAN PETER SHAW WALTON F3976
134570 HOLMES Mrs Brenda. (Appleton) 8 Manor Way, Shipton Road, York, YO3 6UH. Tel:0904-632707
APPLETON F4909
134589 HOLMES Mr C. 23 Usher Park Road, Haxby, York, N Yorks, YO3 3RX. Tel:0904-764422
AIRE ALLAN AMBLER AYRE BEAN BRIGGS BROWN CABLE CAMM CANBY CARTWRIGHT CHAM CHANN COOPER CORNER COWARD CUNDALL DAWSON DIXON DURHAM EELS ELLERY GUNESS GUNHOUSE HARRISON Haselgrove HASSELGRAVE Hazlegrave HODGSON HOGG HOLMES HORNBY HUDSON HUNT KETTLESTRING KETTLEWELL KIRBY KIRK LOLLEY LOWTHER MARSHALL MASON MOUNTAIN NICHOLSON OATES OUTHWAITE PALMER PEARSON REYNOLD RHEAM RICHARDSON SCADLOCK SCRUTON SHILBURN SMITH SNOWDEN SQUIRE STORK TAYLOR THREADGOLD WALKER WATSON WOOD WRIGHT F2419
134597 HOLMES Ms Mandy. 40 Newlyn Street, Rusholme, Manchester, M14 7PQ.
BRERETON HOLMES MEE RICHARDSON Skeeles SKEELS Worthan WORTHEN Worthin Worthing Worthon F3868
134600 HOLMES Margaret. Acaster, Willowfield Road, Halifax, W Yorks, HX2 7NF.
BEARD FARNELL JONES MERCER RIMMER RUSHWORTH WARRLOW F2902
134619 HOLMES Mrs Maureen. (Hill) 14 Church Lane, Garforth, Nr Leeds, Yorkshire, LS25 1HD.
ATKINS BENTON BUTTERY COWARD CRAVEN FOISTER GILL HILL HORSWOOD HUGHES KNOWLES MASSER MOORE MORGAN POTTS PRECIOUS SIMMONDS SKIDMORE TYASS YATES F5920
134627 HOLMES Mrs Susan. 191 Sutton Road, Walsall, West Midlands, WS5 3AW.
ADAMS ALLEN BENTLEY CAPEWELL Challanor CHALLENOR Challoner CONSTABLE COULSON COX DALE DALTON DAY DEAN DEEMING DUNHAM EASY Farthers FATHERS FRIEND GREEN HARTIN Harting HOLMES JORDAN Jorden LEACH LEWIS MEEKS PALMER REYNOLDS SOUTHAM SUTTON WARD F6458
134635 HOLMES Mrs Susan. 465 London Road, Boxmoor, Hemel Hempstead, Herts, HP3 9BE. Tel:0442-213934
Chriginton Credgington CRUDDINGTON Crudgeton CRUDGINGTON Crudington Cruginton F2845
134643 HOLROYD Mr J F. Deepfield, Luddington, Stratford Upon Avon, Warks, CV37 9SD.
GEORGE HAUXWELL Hawkswell HOLROYD THORNE F4154
134651 HOLT Mr A J. 43 Woodfield Grove, Hoole, Chester, CH2 3NY.
DODSWORTH FILLINGHAM HEWITSON HOLT HOWE SMALL STIRZAKER STRANGER TODD F4847
134678 HOLT Mr David M. 241 New Hey Road, Oakes, Huddersfield, W Yorks, HD3 4GH. Tel:0484-652744
AINLEY HOLT MILNES F2259
134686 HOLT Mr Douglas C. 6 Birch Drive, Silverdale, Carnforth, Lancs, LA5 0SE. Tel:0524-701742
CORBETT CRANFIELD DIGGLE DORAN EASTWOOD GAIR GARLICK GRIGOR HOLT MACPHERSON SHEPLEY F2154
134694 HOLT Mrs Joan. (Betts) 78 Gladstone Road, Sholing, Southampton, Hants, SO2 8GT. Tel:0703-448313
AISH Ash BETTS CHANNON DEWEY F203
134708 HOLT Mrs Julia C. 43a Beech Gardens, Lichfield, Staffs, WS14 9EB.
COSFORD CULLUM HOLLIDAY WYLDE F506
134716 HOLT Mrs S V. (Wilcoxon) 24 Greave, Romiley, Stockport, Cheshire, SK6 4PU.
WILCOXON F3200
134724 HOLTOM Mrs Carol. (Tipping) Rooksmoor, Church Bank, Binton, Stratford On Avon, Warks, CV37 9TQ.
DOLPHIN HICKMAN LEE SCONE TIPPING F3968
134732 HOLTZ Mrs Brenda. (Wilson) 1466 Plumber Avenue, Ottawa, Ontario, K1K 4A7, CANADA. Tel:+1-613-746-7340
BENNETT BINGHAM BRIDGEWATER CAMPBELL DRIFFIELD FITZPATRICK GORDON HILL JOHNSTON KELLY THOMAS WILSON F5545
134740 HOLYER Mr H J C. 10 Masonfield, Mannings Heath, Horsham, W Sussex, RH13 6JP.
CHAPRONIERE Hollier HOLYER Hoyler F6756
134759 HOMES Mr Alan. 3 Creswick Walk, Addington Road, Bow, London, E3 2AQ.
ALFLATT CRAMPTON FINLOW FULL HAYDEN HOMES LAYCOCK OFFIELD OFIELD REDMAYNE F965
134767 HOMEWOOD Mrs P. 14 Lincoln Close, Meads, Eastbourne, E Sussex, BN20 7TZ.

Tel:0323-645906
BOND CATLIN DALTON DIPLOCK FULLER HARDING HAWLEY NORRIS F2327

134775 HONE Mr Mark. 25 Daisyfield Court, Bury, Lancs, BL8 2BL.
HONE WATTIS F97

134783 HONES Simon. 20 Kingsdowne Road, Surbiton, Surrey, KT6 6JZ. Tel:081-399-4853
BOTTRELL COCKING CRAZE HONE NICHOLLS PENBERTHY ROWE STAMMERS SUMMERS WILCOX F3027

134791 HONEYBALL Mrs J. 13 Balham Grove, Balham, London, SW12 8AZ.
HONEYBALL F7128

134805 HONEYSETT Mrs Eileen. (Bush) 15 Grove Road, Northwood, Middx, HA6 2AP. Tel:0923-821613
Braban Brabham Brabon BRAYBAN Braybon BUSH HONEYSETT Honiset Honysett Hunniset KEILOR F6074

134813 HONY Mr B Vivian. The Old Forge, Polebrook, Oundle, Peterborough, PE8 5LP.
Tel:0832-272978
ALLEN BARON HARVEY HERRING Honey HONY THOMAS VIVIAN F2043

134821 HOOKWAY Miss A J. 2a Fairway Avenue, Borehamwood, Herts, WD6 1PR.
HOOKWAY F7293

134848 HOOLEY Mr David. 61 St Martins Road, Coventry, Warwickshire, CV3 6FD.
Tel:0203-411784
CROSSLAND CUBBIN DIBLEY FENNELL HOAD HOOLEY MARSDEN PLACKETT PLATT QUAYLE THORNLEY THORPE F3210

134856 HOOPER Mr David. 36 Flag Lane North, Upton Heath, Chester, CH2 1LE.
CLEMMOW Clemo Clemow EMBREY GILES HOOPER F617

134864 HOPE Mr Frank. 9 Braeside, Kirklevington, Yarm On Tees, Cleveland, TS15 9NB.
Tel:0642-782391
HOPE F65

134872 HOPKINS Mr V T. 120 Greenacres, Shoreham By Sea, W Sussex, BN43 5XL.
DA VALL Davell De Vall Divall HOPKINS Pain Paine PAYNE STEVENS F2558

134880 HOPKINS Mr W W. 4 Staleys Road, Borough Green, Sevenoaks, Kent, TN15 8RR.
Tel:0732-883629
BLAND BRISSLEY BUSHELL CHAPMAN COBB DOVE DOWN GLOYNE HARNETT HOPKINS MASKELL NEWMAN PILCHER RYDING SHEPHARD THOMAS URQUHART VINCER WATERS F1121

134899 HOPPER Mr D S. Roundwood, Littlemead Lane, Exmouth, Devon, EX8 3BU.
DANE ERRIDGE HOPPER LAMING LANGSTRETH MORTLEY PERRY RICE RIGDEN STACKHOUSE F944

134902 HOPPER Mr Philip. 16 Brockswood Lane, Welwyn Garden City, Herts, AL8 7BG.
BAMFORD FOWLER HOGG HOPPER MARRIOTT MARSH SIMPSON STOCKDALE WARRINGTON WASHINGTON F4849

134910 HOPPITT Mr C E. 4 Hilly Fields, Woodbridge, Suffolk, IP12 4DX.
BUTTRESS EVERS HOPPITT WRIGHT F2287

134929 HORA Miss Susan. 51 Eastern Avenue, Reading, Berks, RG1 5SQ. Tel:0734-261902
Da Hora De Hora Hansard HANSORD HENTSCH HORA HUGGINS MORTARA Vasey-Simons Vasie-Simons Vazey-Simons VAZIE-SIMONS F2575

134937 HORDERN Mr Richard. 1820 Grant Drive, Regina, Sask, S4S 4V4, CANADA.
HAWTHORN HORDERN PAUL F6149

134945 HORGAN Mr Kingsley B. 70 Eton Wick Road, Eton Wick, Windsor, Berks, SL4 6JL.
Tel:0753-866801
HORGAN F2862

134953 HORLINGTON Mr Edwin Arthur. 163 Walton Road, Walton On Naze, Essex, CO14 8NE.
Tel:0255-677178
DE HARTLYNGTON DE HERLINETUN HORLINGTON HURLINGTON F449

134961 HORN Mr Ross. 3/40 Victor Street, Holland Park, Brisbane, 4121, AUSTRALIA.
COLEMAN ELSLEY Macnee MAGNAY F7272

134988 HORNBUCKLE Mr I. 32 Buckingham Avenue, Hucknall, Notts.
CHAMBERLAIN HORNBUCKLE F1311

134996 HORNBY Mr Tony. 2 Bungalow, Glebe House, Shudy Camps, Cambridge, CB1 6RB.
Tel:0799-584359
CLONEY HORNBY MAGIN SHARP WESTON WHITTAM WIGNEY F2049

135003 HORNE Mrs Hope E. (Fletcher) R R #3, Bracebridge, Ontario, P1L 1X1, CANADA.
Tel:+1-705-645-4988
FLETCHER HOLTBY YOUNG F6287

135011 HORNER Mr C D. 46 Commercial Street, Scarborough, N Yorks, YO12 5EW.
Tel:0723-363525
CALVERT EDSON HADFIELD HESELWOOD HORNER KNAGGS LEGGOT SIMPSON WHILEY WILSON F6267

135038 HORNER Mrs Sylvia. 5 Weeton Avenue, Lytham St Annes, Lancs, FY8 3JE. Tel:0253-728413
HACKING HORNER MASKEW SCHOLES F3253

135046 HORROCKS Mr Derek. 32b College Road, Up Holland, Skelmersdale, Lancs, WN8 0PY.
COOPER CREWES CROSS HORROCKS MCNEAL MITTON PRIGG SANTUS SWEET TAYLOR WOOD F1288

135054 HORSFALL Miss Joanne. Plas Yn Cornel, Llansannan, Denbigh, Clwyd, LL16 5HS.
Tel:0745-77649
BECKWITH DOVERNER DUDLEY-WARD HORSFALL PLACE F3978

135062 HORSHAM Mrs Cynthia Ruth. 148 Hillson Drive, Fareham, Hants, PO15 6PA. Tel:0329-844523
BURRAGE DANCE DANCER FOUNTAIN HARRINGTON HERRINGTON HODGSON HODSON HOLDEN HORSHAM ILIFFE JONES RAGG SPOONER Thornell Thornelough THORNHILL Thornhull Thorningly Trace TRACEY Tracy WEBBERLEY WHITEHOUSE WIBBERLEY WRAGG F273

135070 HORSTMAN Mrs C. 38 Grandridge Close, Fulbourn, Cambridge, CB1 5HN. Tel:0223-880841
ALDERTON AVIS CARTER CHUTER CLOWTING ELLWICK FROST HAWES KITTS LAWS PALMER POLLARD SPRIGGS WALES F1294

135089 HORSTMAN Mr Eric P. 38 Grandridge Close, Fulbourn, Cambridge, CB1 5HN. Tel:0223-880841
ATKINSON CASSFORD DRAITEN DRAYDEN DRAYTON HESK HIGGS HORSTMAN Horstmann KING MANNING MOOR MOORE O'LLARD O'OLLARD OLLARD OSBORN OSBORNE RUSSELL TAYLOR TERRY TRUCKEL TRUCKELL TRUCKELLS TRUCKELS F1293

135097 HORSUP Mrs Sylvia. 341 Colchester Road, Ipswich, Suffolk, IP4 4SE. Tel:0473-712382
Hirsopp Horsop HORSUP Horsupp F111

135100 HORSWELL Mrs Evelyn. 44 Fairfield, Christchurch, Dorset, BH23 1QX.
HALLETT F7211

135119 HORTH Mr J R. The Old School House, Crookbank, Stonehaugh, Hexham Northumberland.
Hoath HORTH Horthe Hoth Hothe F6627

135127 HORTON Mrs Pat. (Goad) 9 Sutton Road, Bournemouth, Dorset, BH9 1RN. Tel:0202-520562
ADEY Beasant BEDFORD BESSANT COULTER DANKS DAVIES Eady GOAD GWINNUTT HORTON MILLARD MOLYNEUX RANN SCOTT Shepherd SHEPPARD SPITTLE STEELS Thompson THOMSON WARBURTON WHEELER WHITE Whiteing WHITING WILKES WILKINS F2146

135135 HORTON Mr Richard. 30 Newlands Drive, Halesowen, West Midlands, B62 9DY.
HORTON Hurton F7294

135143 HOSKINS Mr George D. 20 Sherwood Avenue, Ferndown, Wimborne, Dorset, BH22 8JT.
BARKER BROWN BROWNLOW CARR DODD GALES GEALE HADFIELD HOSKINS KIMBER KING LAKE MOORE SHARPE TOWERS WOODS F2363

135151 HOSKINS Mrs Judith. (Graham) 3 Mayfields, Keynsham, Bristol, Avon, BS18 1BW.
BOWES CHRISTIAN CORJEAGE GRAHAM HARKNESS HORNCASTLE JACKSON KENNEDY KENNISH KERMODE LOGAN LONGSTAFF Longstaffe LOONEY MILNER NICHOLSON QUALTROUGH QUAY;E ROBINSON THOMPSON WATSON WESTGARTH WHARTON WILSON F4891

135178 HOSKINS Mr R S. 40 North End, Meldreth, Royston, Herts, SG8 6NT. Tel:0763-262453
Hoiskins HOSKINS F604

135186 HOTTEN Miss Elizabeth. 37 Acacia Avenue, Hayes, Middx, UB3 2ND.
HOTTEN F6258

135194 HOUDE Mr John. Po Box 82, Glencoe, IL 60022, USA.
Clair Desrochers Desruisseaux Durocher HOUDE Houl Hould Houle Houlle Leclair Leclerc Oule

The best in French fashion direct to your door

FREE designer gift **FREE** returns **EASY** payment

Côté Femme sleeveless dress
£35

Références ecru shirt
£29

With La Redoute, you don't have to go to France to shop in Paris!

Request our Autumn-Winter 2001/2002 Collection for 730 pages of great value style for *la femme*, *l'homme* and *l'enfant* - delivered direct to you!

With top designers like **Lagerfeld** and **Ventilo**, exclusive labels including **Côté Femme**, plus stunning lingerie and essential sportswear, you'll find everything you need to stay ahead of the crowd. And our FREE returns service lets you try before you buy!

Request your new 730-page Collection today and claim a FREE designer gift (normally £24.99) when you order!

Côté Femme satin trousers
£29

Sous-entendus balconette bra
£23

Call FREE ***0500 777 888***
8am-11pm 7 days a week

www.redoute.co.uk
browse and buy on-line any time

Please send me the ***NEW*** La Redoute Collection. I will claim my ***FREE*** designer gift (normally £24.99) with my first order.

Please complete all your details clearly below :

RYC018

Mr/Mrs/Miss/Ms: Forename: ________

Surname: ________

Address: ________

Postcode: ________ Date of birth: / /

We search the files of credit reference agencies who record it. We use your information for our marketing. Applicants must be at least 18 years of age and resident in the UK, Channel Islands or BFPO Germany. We may refuse applications. To buy gift quote ref. 256.6290. Prop.: La Redoute (UK) Ltd. Registered Office: 245-249 Horbury Road, Wakefield, West Yorkshire, WF2 8RA. Registered in England No.192243.

LA REDOUTE

FREEPOST LS 6450
P.O. Box 777
Wakefield
WF2 8UZ

LA REDOUT

French fashion with la différer

French Autumn Style

strappy top by
Côté Femme
£14

F7295

135208 HOUGHTON Christine E. Rose Cottage, Heath Lane, Thatcham, Berks, RG13 4BS. Tel:0635-65419
Bethel BETHELL Bethelle BODGER BROWN Browne DIXON Dixson Ffrude FOWLER Frood Froode FROUD FROUDE Frude HANGER HENDEN HOUGHTON Lawrance LAWRENCE LE PINE Naramore NARRAMORE STEELS STONE Twelftree Twelftrees Twelftrick Twelftricks TWELVETREE Twelvetrees Twelvetrick Twelvetricks F2669

135216 HOUGHTON Mr G M. 12 East Crescent, Beeston, Nottingham, NG9 1QA.
HOUGHTON SIMKIN F5622

135224 HOUGHTON Mr Joe. 3 Hollywood Road, Bolton, Lancs, BL1 6HL. Tel:0204-47080
COOPER CORDOCK GREENWOOD Horton HOUGHTON Howton Hufton JANNEY Janny OGLE PRICE SARGARTSON Sargeantson Sargisson Seargantson Sergisson SMITH STOTHARD TREW True TURNER F3314

135232 HOUGHTON Mr John J. 25 The Greenway, Powick, Worcs, WR2 4RZ. Tel:0905-830643
BALDOCK FORSDICK HAYNES HOUGHTON PACKMAN POPE F4299

135240 HOULDER Mr Eric. 31 Fairview, Carleton, Pontefract, W Yorks, WF8 3NT.
DOBBY GREEN Holder HOULDER WOODGETT F949

135259 HOUNSELL Mrs Ann. 33 Quennevais Park, St Brelade, Jersey, JE3 8GB. Tel:0534-41795
AXFORD BROWN CLINGO D'ORR HOUNSELL PHILIPS ROBINS WHITE F1352

135267 HOUSHAM Mrs J. 57 Asquith Street, Gainsborough, Lincolnshire, DN21 2PQ.
HOUSHAM Howsam Howsham Howsom F7087

135275 HOVELL Mrs Michelle. 131 Queens Parade, Brighton, Brisbane, Queensland, 4017, AUSTRALIA. Tel:+61-7-269-9519
ANNISON DEACON FALKINDER FORSTER HOVELL JONES LODGE MADY PARKERSON F5441

135283 HOWARD Mrs C A. 100 Chapel Hill, Braintree, Essex, CM7 6QZ.
BAREHAM BARHAM BRIDGE BUTCHER HOWARD LEES TEECE WEBSTER WITT F6145

135291 HOWARD Mr George Eric. 4 St Anns Way, Shelton, Nr Newark, Nottingham, NG23 5JH. Tel:0949-51329
HOWARD F4015

135305 HOWARD Miss Michelle. 47 Norfolk Road, Wollaston, Stourbridge, West Midlands, DY8 4TA.
GREENWOOD HOWARD NEVIN Salsters SALTER Salters Saltters SHELDON F4517

135313 HOWARD Mr Stanley. 31 Becmead Avenue, Kenton, Harrow, Middx, HA3 8HD.
DAVIS HOWARD LEADNER MCLOUGHLIN MOCKETT RENDLE ROUX F6367

135321 HOWARD Mr Vic. Harggatan 8, 590 40 Kisa, Sweden. Tel:+46-0494-12806
CAVLEY HOWARD MANNING STALHAM F1684

135348 HOWARD-SMITH Mr Gordon. 303 Waterloo Street, Oldham, Lancs.
BEECH COOK CROW FOSTER FROST FULLERLOVE HARRISON HOWARD KIRKHAM MALLADEW MARCHBANKS PRIESTLEY SMITH SPENCER TAYLOR TOWNLEY TUFFS WILD WILSON F769

135356 HOWARTH Mrs Barbara J. (Fiddes) 2 Beaumont Road, Petts Wood, Orpington, Kent, BR5 1JN. Tel:0689-833136
Faddes Feddis Feedes Fettice Fettis Fettous FIDDES Fiddies Fiddis Fieldes Fittis F3610

135364 HOWARTH Mr Derek. 57 March Road, Wimblington, March, Cambs, PE15 0RW. Tel:0354-54323
ELKINGTON HASKAYNE HOWARTH LYON MARSDEN MAWDSLEY ROTHWELL SALISBURY TURNER YATES F2081

135372 HOWARTH Mr Robert. Conway, 23 Scape View, Golcar, Huddersfield, W Yorks, HD7 4DH. Tel:0484-655597
HOWARTH F6208

135380 HOWCROFT Mrs Rona. 58 Canton Court, Canton, Cardiff, CF1 9BG.
CAMERON CURTIS HOWCROFT SOLLISS SORRILL F1820

135399 HOWE Mrs B. 1 Hopes Hill Drive, Carlisle, Cumbria, CA1 3LB. Tel:0228-24882
DE QUERTON De Wharton Walton Warton Werfton WHARTON Whartonne Worton F1025

135402 HOWE Mrs Jean. 16 Roles Grove, Chadwell Heath, Romford, Essex, RM6 5LT.
BLEWITT BUCKTHORPE CURLE CURTIS FOWLER FRYER-KELSEY HONESS HOWE RABY-YOUNG YOUNG F3669

135410 HOWE Mrs Joan. 2 Cottesmore Drive, Heswall, Wirral, Merseyside, L60 1YG.
ARMSTRONG FISHER GREENWOOD HIND PAYNE WILSON F1256

135429 HOWELL Mr D G S. 28 Mincinglake Road, Stoke Hill, Exeter, Devon, EX4 7EA. Tel:0392-430152
ANSDELL AUST BAKER BAWDEN BISHOP BOOTH BOWDEN BRIGHT BRINING BRINNING BROWN BROWNING CALLEN CARSLAKE CAUNT Cerslake CHANNON CHARKER CLANFIELD Clap Clape CLAPP Clappe Cloup COOPER CROCKER CROOK DIMOND DYER ECCLES ELLACOMBE FAIRBRASS FLOUD FLOWERS FRYAR Fryer GLANFIELD GREEP GRIMES HARRISON HITCHCOCK HITT HORSLEY HOWELL HUDD HUGHES INNES JOY KARSLAKE KER Kerr Kerslake KIMBER KING LUXMOORE MAEER MAPLE NORRINGTON NOSWORTHY OTTON PARNACOTT PARSONS PASSMORE PERRIAM PICKFORD PINE PLUCK PRING QUICK RICHARDS SCAWIN Seamer SEARLE SETTERFIELD SEYMOUR SHEER SHILSTONE SHURVIN SLADE STANLAKE STIDWORTHY SUTHERLAND TEED THOMPSON TONGE VARLEY WARE WARREN WILMINGTON WINSLOW F1428

135437 HOWELL Mr Keith M. 8 Oakdale, Harrogate, N Yorks, HG1 2LL.
ABBS ANDREWS ASHLEY Ashly ASTON BASTARD BELL Bennet Bennett BEVEN BISGROVE BISS Bisse BLACKMORE Bonnet BROMFIELD Broomfield BULLER BUNNET Bunnett BUNTING CHAPPEL CHARD COMPTON COOK Cooke COOT COX CUMINGS DAVENPORT DAVIDSON DEAN Debell Dibbell DIBBLE Dibbley Dibel Dible Dibley EMERY Emmery Emory Emry EVANS FARENDEN Farnden Farrenden Foord FORD Forde FORDS FRANKLAND Franklin Frankling FRENCH Fullar FULLER GWIN HABERMEHL Haeffermehl Haffermehl HALL HALLET HAND Hande HARWOOD Herod Hews Heyward HILL HOWELL Howells HUGHES Hughs Huse Hutchenson HUTCHINSON INNINGS JOLLY JONES KENNY KETT KINDRICK Kitt KNOWLES LAIT Leait LEEK LEWIS LIGHT Lightning MAIN MARLIN MARTIN MERCER Michel MINNS Mitchel MITCHELL ONSLOW PALMER PARHAM PARRY PICKERING PIDGLEY Pool POOLE PORKER PORTER PRICE RAWLINS ROGERS ROOME RUFFE Rug RUGG SAGE SAUNDERS Scorse Scource SCOURSE SHEPHARD SHEPPARD SMITH Smyth STONE TAYLOR THOMPSON TOMLEY Tompson TUCK TUCKER WADE Watkin WATKINS WATTS WILLIAMS WOODROW F931

135445 HOWELLS Mrs A. Rozel, 5 Glebe Close, Dalston, Carlisle Cumbria, CA5 7JE.
Harsell Horsall HORSELL F6890

135453 HOWISON Mrs Sandie. Parkhill, Newburgh, Cupar, Fife, KY14 6HH. Tel:0337-40386
BRYCE BUNTEN BURNS CARRICK EDWARD EDWARDS HOOPER HOWISON LAWSON MACKENZIE MCDONALD MURDOCH NASH RUSSELL STIRLING TORRANCE WATSON F1299

135461 HOWLETT Mrs Betty J. (Reynolds) 63 Tamworth Road, Lichfield, Staffs, WS14 9HG.
AKERS ARMES Howlet HOWLETT Hullet Hullot KIRKBY REYNOLDS TAMS F5400

135488 HOWLETT Mrs Brenda. (Baker) Camberwell, Halfpenny Lane, Elm, Cambs, PE14 0AE. Tel:0945-581118
BAKER BAWN BEAGLES BURTENSHAW CATER CLOAKE COATES DAISLEY DARWOOD DAVIES DISTON EDWARDS HOBBS HOLT HOWLETT JUDAN LAMBERT LEWARNE LYNN MARKWICK PISSEY ROSE SETCHFIELD WELSFORD WHITE WILSON F6404

135496 HOYLE Ms Judith. 5 Crickmerry Bank, Market Drayton, Shropshire, TF9 2BQ. Tel:0630-638277
ASHBY BAKEWELL BENNETT CARTWRIGHT CORK Corke DODMAN EADE EDGERLEY FARDON GIRLING GOODWIN HALSEY HARKEY HARRUP HEMMINGS HOYLE JACKSON LOWE MASON MOORE OWEN RAWLINSON ROCKLEY SPEIGHT SWANWICK SWINDELLS TAYLOR THOMPSTONE WEALE WHITLOW WILLIAMS F2610

135518 HUBBARD Mrs Betty. 160 Wollaton Vale, Wollaton, Nottingham, NG8 2PL.
ARMISON BURGESS CASTLE GREEN HUBBARD F6264

135526 HUBBARD Mrs S. The Cottage, 84 Cademan Street, Whitwick, Coalville Leics, LE6 4AE.
PERRY F3279

135534 HUCKER Mr T W Gordon. Silver Birches, 4 Charlwood Drive, Oxshott, Surrey, KT22 OHD.
Tel:0372-842733
HUCKER F2301

135542 HUCKLEBRIDGE Mr Geoffrey. 35 Rosedale Gardens, Thatcham, Berks, RG13 4LE.
Tel:0635-865349
DOLLEN EAMES Hackelbridge Hockelburge HOSMER Hucclebridge Huckberry Huckelbridg Huckelbridge Huckelbrige Huckelbrigge Huckelburdge Huckelburge Huckellbridge Huckellburge Huckeridge Huckilbridge Huckleberry Hucklebourg Hucklebridg HUCKLEBRIDGE Huckleburdge Huckleburg Huckleburge Huckleburgh Huckleburie Hucklebury Hucklebur ye Huckridge Huckylbrygg Huclebridge Knucklebridge WEAVER WINTER F1412

135550 HUDDART Mr Dave. 13 Love Lane, Oldswinford, Stourbridge, W Midlands, DY8 2DA.
Tel:0384-397085
ABEL BELLAS CALVERT CANNON COWLING GREEN HINDSON HUDDART ORANGE SPEDDING F5748

135569 HUDDY Mr Grenfell. 63 Wood Vale, Muswell Hill, London, N10 3DL. Tel:081-883-4405
Hoddie Hoddy HODY HUDDY HUDY F3772

135577 HUDSON Mrs Ann. (Hammon) 14 Havengate, Horsham, West Sussex, RH12 4BH.
Tel:0403-64706
HAMMON HUDSON F6340

135585 HUGGETT Mrs Joan. 31 Duncan Way, Bushey, Watford, Herts, WD2 2BE.
HURN MITCHELL ROSS F1040

135593 HUGGINS Mr Alan. Ridgeway, 30 Ashbridge Rise, Chandlers Ford, Hampshire, SO5 1SA.
Tel:0703-263165
Huggens Huggin HUGGINS Huggons Hugins F2410

135607 HUGHES Mrs Anne E. (Steer) Spring House, Hadlow, Tonbridge, Kent, TN11 ODZ.
Tel:0732-850214
BOYCE FARMER HATHAWAY Hathway Havaway MANT SMITH STEER F2564

135615 HUGHES Mrs B I. 77 Threefields, Tanterton, Ingol, Preston Lancs, PR2 7BJ.
BRIDGE ENTWHISTLE LYLIES F3156

135623 HUGHES Mrs E M. Hafod Cerrig, Llangoed, Beaumaris, Gwynedd, LL58 8SA. Tel:0248-490407
Asnep ASNIP Asnipp BOWES BREARLEY COOKSON Greatbach GREATBATCH HENRY LAWSON LOVATT NORCOTT SHANDS SMEDLEY Wolgar WOLGER Woolgar Woolger F4735

135631 HUGHES Mr Eric G. Bryn Awel, 179 Eaton Road North, West Derby, Liverpool, L12 5HY.
Tel:051-226-1005
DOULL HUGHES JACKSON KELLY MCCOLL ROBINSON WILLIAMS F5303

135658 HUGHES Mr Geoffrey T. 217 Stoke Lane, Westbury On Trym, Bristol, Avon, BS9 3RX.
Tel:0272-683048
Azelwood Azlewood BENNETT BRENNAN CARROL CURTIS DEAN ENGLAND EVANS FOSTER FOWLER FRANCIS FRYERS Haselwood Haslewood Hazelwood HAZLEWOOD Hazzelwood Hazzlewood HONEL Honnour Honor HONOUR Honoure Honrel Hornal HORNEL Hornell Horner Hornur HUGHES JENKINS LEACK Leak Leake LLEWELLYN POWELL Reece REES Reese RENNEL Rennell Rice RINNEL Rinnell ROBERTS ROGERS SCOTT Stewart STOKES STUART WALKER F2183

135666 HUGHES Dr Goronwy Alun. Talwrn Glas, Afonwen, Mold, Clwyd, CH7 5UB.
BASSET Bassett BEER BOSHER DANIEL DAVIES EVANS HUGHES JAMES KEATING MORGANS NICHOLAS PARRY PHILLIPS PRICHARD PRITCHARD SIMON THOMAS F275

135674 HUGHES Mrs Judith. 222 William Street, Carleton Place, Ontario, K7C 1X3, CANADA.
Tel:+1-613-251-3154
CHALLENGER SHAW SITWELL WALKER F4568

135682 HUGHES Mrs Marion E. (Bush) 317 Luton Road, Harpenden, Herts, AL5 3LW.
BUSH F4868

135690 HUGHES Mrs Shelagh. (Turnbull) Fron Ednyfed, Ednyfed Hill, Amlwch Port, Anglesey, LL68 9HW. Tel:0407-831683
TURNBULL F3717

135704 HUGHES Mrs Yvonne. (Andrews) Applecroft, Meavy Bourne, Yelverton, Devon, PL20 6AR.
Tel:0822-854496
ANDREWS BICKERSTAFF DOLPHIN JORDAN KERKHOFF PILTER F5368

135712 HUISH Mr Frank. 20 Fairlawn, Albrighton, Wolverhampton, WV7 3QF. Tel:0902-373407
Hewish Hewishe Hiwis Huise HUISH Huishe Huyshe F1875

135720 HUITSON Mr Fredk. 1 Mccutcheon Street, Seaham, Co Durham, SR7 OJS. Tel:091-581-3366
Hewetson Hewitson Hewittson Hewson Hugheson Hughetson Hughson HUITSON F1254

135739 HULL Dr Peter. 49 North Grange Road, Bearsden, Glasgow, G61 3AG. Tel:041-942-1103
CORMACK CRAIG DENT FLETT HATCH HULL PIGG REID SHORTCLIFFE TENNANT WATERS WILLIAMSON F61

135747 HULL Mrs Rita. Rsd Maiden Gully Road, Maiden Gully, Victoria, 3551, AUSTRALIA.
CHAMBERLAIN GREAVES HOLT HULL MUNRO ROBERT RUSSELL SCOTT F5440

135755 HULLEY Mr Ray. Longview, Feldon Lane, Hemel Hempstead, Herts, HP3 OBB.
HALLEY Hanley HAWLEY HOOLEY Hooly Howley Hullay HULLEY HULLY ULLEY Ully Utley Whooley F4414

135763 HULME Mr Michael J. 19 Brook Road, Bomere Heath, Shrewsbury, Shropshire, SY4 3PU.
Tel:0939-290516
ARCHER BEECH COATES COLFOX CORNES COX DENNIS FOX FREEMAN FURBER GASCOIGNE GODING GRIFFITHS HULME JONES KENT MANNING MASTERS PRIESTLEY ROBINSON STEPHENS TOOGOOD WATSON WATTS WELLS WENLOCK WYCHERLEY F2291

135771 HULME Mr Wm. One Riddings Court, Morris Park, Hartford, Northwich Cheshire, CW8 1SB.
Tel:0606-871663
ALLCOCK ASH BYROM CLAYTON COUCH GASKELL GOODEVE HEATH HOUGHTON LOVELL MAGNES MAY MULLARD OSBALDESTON Osbaldiston Osbalston Osbason Osbenson Osberson Osbiston Osbornson Osbosen Osboston Osbostone PASSMORE PERKIN SHEPLEY SLATER SUSSEX SUTTON WALLWORTH F1847

135798 HUMBY Mr Michael. 2 Mulberry Close, Lancing, W Sussex, BN15 9AQ.
HUMBY F806

135801 HUME Mrs Margaret. Weetwood Cottage, Knowle Lane, Sheffield, Yorks, S11 9PL.
BLOW BROOMHEAD FOX HAKES HINCHCLIFFE MANUEL NETTLESHIP F5944

135828 HUMPHREY Mrs Eileen. 5 Rock Villas, Rock, Wadebridge, Cornwall, PL27 6LE.
COCK GILBERT HOW MIDDLETON SKINNER SPOONER YATES F2773

135836 HUMPHREYS Mrs A P. Flat 4 Rachaels Court, 36 Cemetery Road, Ipswich, Suffolk, IP4 2JA.
Scope SCOPES Skoopes Skopes F6807

135844 HUMPHRIES Mrs Grace. 34 Rosebery Avenue, Brighton, Sussex, BN2 6DE.
BEARD BONWICK COURTNELL HUMPHRIES JARMAIN MAJOR MARCHANT PRICE SARGENT SMITH F2356

135852 HUNKIN Mr Michael J. Flat 1, 73 Chaddesley Glen, Canford Cliffs, Poole, Dorset, BH13 7PB. Tel:0202-709302
HUNCKYNGE HUNKIN HUNKING HUNKINS F115

135860 HUNN Mrs G M. 48 Forge Road, Southborough, Tunbridge Wells, Kent, TN4 OEX.
ALLEN BRABON BULTITUDE HUNN MACHIN NEWMAN POWLEY TURNER UDALL WHITING F3867

135879 HUNNISETT Mrs Margaret. 69 Cornwall Road, Ruislip, Middx, HA4 6AJ.
AVIS BARWELL BLIGHT BRADER DRUETT GLADDEN HEARD HUNNISETT SUCKLING SUTTON WITT F1763

135887 HUNT Mr Allan. Clayton House, 49 Brighton Road, Crawley, W Sussex, RH10 6AX.
Tel:0293-546103
DYER EDMONDS MATON PITCHER POPEJOY SEAWARD TAYLOR F3415

135895 HUNT Mrs B M. 61 Beaufort Avenue, Fareham, Hants, PO16 7PE.
BALL CARTER JOHNSON LUCAS RANDALL ROBERTS SAMWAYS SMITH STONE F1607

135909 HUNT Mr Brian. 35 Beechwood Road, Redcliffe Bay, Portishead, Bristol, BS20 8ER.

Tel:0275-844831
ABBOT ALLAN BIBBY BICKERSTAFF CARR CHRISTIE DANDY GAYLER HERBERT HUMPHREY HUNT LINDAL MALCOLM MCGHIE MUNCASTER PATERSON PESCUD SHARP Sharpe SIMMONDS Simmons SPENCER STANNANOUGHT Symonds F1437

135917 HUNT Mr David H. The Elms, Wasperton, Warwick, CV35 8EB. Tel:0926-624514
FOSTER Heusser HUNT Hussard Huzerd HUZZARD Uzzett WATKINS F974

135925 HUNT Mr David M. 13 Shenfield Place, Brentwood, Essex, CM15 9AG. Tel:0277-224558
ADAMS ALLEN BANGS BROWN BUTT CAIRNS CHALMERS COLBOURN COOPER COTTRELL CROSS HARE HAXTON HEADLAND HOPKINS HUNT KIMBER KNIGHT LIVINGSTONE MCDONALD MEARNS MITCHELL MOORS MUNRO SIEVEWRIGHT SMITH Suvaret WARD WESTCOTT WITHERS F2636

135933 HUNT Mr Derek. 8 Stokes Avenue, Poole, Dorset, BH15 2EA.
ACKERMAN Edden Eddens Eddons Eden EDENS Edon Gum GUMM HERBERT HOWARD HUNT KENCH Kinch PARRY TELFORD F4885

135941 HUNT Mr Norman H J. 89c Hill House, Great Thurlow, Haverhill, Suffolk, CB9 7LA.
ALBON ARGENT ATHERTON AUTHERTON BAINES BANGS BENNET BOWN BUFFET BURTON BYFORD CAPP COOK CROW CUTHBERT DEAN DRAKE ELY EWIN GATHERCOLE Grainger GRANGER Gridiley GRIDLEY HAMMOND HAMSTEAD HAVERLAND Heinsby HENSBY HOLMS HUNT IVE Jarmain JARMAN Jarmin JOHNSON JONES KETCHINER LAPSLIE LOVEDAY Mackeinder MACKENDER MALT MARTIN MEDCALF Medcalfe Medtcalf Medtcalfe Metcalf Metcalfe MORGAN MORLEY MURRAY NEGONS NEWMAN NORMAN NOTLEY PAWSEY PLEDGER Reader REEDER REEVE RUTTERFORD SIME SMITH SPARROW STANLEY STIFF Sym TALBOTT TAYLOR TURNER VEAL Veil WALLACE WALLIS WEBB WHITE WHITEACRE WHITTAKER WIBROW WORDLY WORLLIDGE YULE F5995

135968 HUNT Mr Paul J. 29 Berkeley Close, Mountsorrel, Leics, LE12 7DN.
ALFORD BAINS BAUM BEAVER BELLAMY BENJAMIN BERRINGTON BONSER BOON Brearley BRIERLEY BROWN BRYANT BUHLER BURTON CARTWRIGHT CHRISTIAN COOPER CORNER CROWHURST CULLEY DENT EAGLESFIELD ECCLESTONE EVERY FARMER FAULKENER FERRIS GILL GLASSON GODDARD GRICE HARRIS HAWKINS HAWKSWORTH HAYNES HOBSON HODGKIN HUNT JARRETT KENWARD KILLEEN KILNER KNOTT LAW LIMBREY LOVE LOWER MAWBY MITCHELL NASH NICHOLSON NORMAN NORMANTON PARSONS PERRY PICK PRESTON PYCROFT Read REID RICH ROBERTS RUMMERY SEERS SHARRATT SKELLETT SNOW SPILLER TATTESHALL TAYLOR TIDMAS TOMKINS TURNER UNTHWAITE VESTRY WALKER WARREN WARTNABY WILLIAMS WILLIAMSON WILLSON WOOD YEARNSLEY YOUNG F4085

135976 HUNT Mr R L. 4 Grange Close, Ingrave, Brentwood, Essex, CM13 3QP.
HUNT INCE F4638

135984 HUNT Mr Ronald Albert. 12 Heath Road, Coldblow, Bexley, Kent, DA5 2DW. Tel:0322-527959
ALLUM Greenstead Greensted Grimstead Grinstead GRINSTED HAMPSON HARTRIDGE HUNT RICHES SKEGG STEPHENS SWINSCOW F2156

135992 HUNT Mr Stanley F. 19 Little Moss Lane, Pinner, Middx, HA5 3BA.
HUNT F3113

136018 HUNT Mr Wm A L. 23 Barn Park Road, Fremington, Barnstaple, Devon, EX31 3DN. Tel:0271-42530
BAYNES BENNETT DAVIDSON DE PRADINES GREEN HENDRY HUNT MILLER F5857

136026 HUNTER Mrs A L. (Miller) Holmlea, Craigend Farm, Stow, Galashiels, TD1 2RW.
FYFFE LAUGHLAN MCCALL MILLER F5013

136034 HUNTER Mrs Beverley A. 8 Spencer Street, Berala, NSW 2141, AUSTRALIA.
BROWN Coakaloff Coakleough Cockcroft Cockliffe Cocklough COCKROFT Coclof Colclough Coleclough Coltclough COSENS Cossens Coughlough Cousens Cousins Cowloff COXHEAD CROOK EYLES FOX HITCHEN HUNTER JACKSON LOWTHER Paine PAYNE Tailor TAYLOR Tonkiss TONKS WATKISS WOOLFORD F4453

136042 HUNTER Mr Cliff. Roselands, 4 Lingfield Avenue, Kingston Upon Thames, Surrey, KT1 2TN. Tel:081-549-7251
ATKINSON BAKER BARROW BROWN CAMPKIN CHURCHER CLEAVE COLLER CRICK CROSBY EVANS FREE GANGE GAY HINCKINGTON HOLDING HOW HOWE HUNTER LEWIS MARSHALL O'SULLIVAN OWEN PARTRIDGE SIBLEY SIMKINS SIMPKINS SLOUS SMITH STOCKWELL STOKES STRONG TAYLOR VINCE F1145

136050 HUNTER Mr E. 14 Glenhome Terrace, Dyce, Aberdeen, AB2 0EB. Tel:0224-723202
HUNTER LUDOVICK F586

136069 HUNTER Mr Gordon. 10 Young Avenue, Barassie Troon, Ayrshire, Scotland, KA10 6SJ. Tel:0292-313059
HUNTER F3481

136077 HUNTER Mr John Francis. 32 Kirkstone Avenue, Worsley, Manchester, M28 5JL. Tel:061-790-6651
CLOUGH DARBYSHIRE HUNTER LEVER MULVANEY ORMOND SCHOFIELD SCOBLE F3960

136085 HUNTER Mr M. 39 First Avenue, Wellingborough, Nothants, NN8 3PT.
CURRIE DOUGLAS GATT GRASSICK HUNTER STEVENSON F1544

136093 HUNTING Mr C. Pimlico Cottage, Little Beckford, Tewkesbury, Glos, GL20 7AL.
HUNTING UNTON F6179

136107 HUNTINGTON Mr Douglas. Bonaventure, New Domewood, Copthorne, West Sussex, RH10 3HE. Tel:0342-717362
BARKER BIRKS HUNTINGTON F3984

136115 HURD Mrs Valerie. (Darnley) 32 Glascote Close, Shirley, Solihull, West Midlands, B90 2TA.
DARNLEY REELEY F4947

136123 HURDEN Mr Oliver W J. Andromeda, 55 Coombe Farm Avenue, Fareham, Hants, PO16 0TS. Tel:0329-235745
HURDEN HURDING HURDON F519

136131 HURLEY Mrs B. 21 Elizabeth Drive, Jump Farm, Devizes, Wiltshire, SN10 3SB.
Peapell Peaple People PEPAL F6732

136158 HURLOCK Mr James B. Whitwell House, 33 Ruffa Lane, Pickering, N Yorks, YO18 7HN. Tel:0751-76425
CALPSON HURLOCK MCCLARTY MIDDLETON PETEGREE STROWGER Waight Waights Wait Waite Waites Waithe Waits Wate Wates Wayt Wayte Waytes WAYTH Waythe Wayths Weight Weighte Weights Whaite Whaites Whaits Whayte F3979

136166 HURMAN Mr R H. 10 Smeaton Street, Riverside, Cardiff, S Glamorgan, CF1 8EF.
CHARLEY GRAY Grey HARDING HARRIS HERBERT Herman Hermon Hirman HURMAN LANG RICH SLOMAN Slowman F4417

136174 HURST Mr Nicholas. 10 Aghnahoe Road, Cabragh, Dungannon, Co Tyrone N Ireland, BT70 1TN.
AGNEW ALLEN BELL CHAPMAN CLARKE Hearst Herse Herst Hirst HOPPER HURST JENKINSON MCKEOWN RAINEY F107

136182 HURST Mr Roy. 12 Mendip Close, Langley, Slough, Berks, SL3 8UB. Tel:0753-548611
HURST F3604

136190 HUTCHINGS Mr R L. 31 Norman Avenue, Abingdon, Oxon, OX14 2HQ.
SELLEN Sellon F7155

136204 HUTCHINSON Mrs G. 29 Southview Drive, South Woodford, London, E18 1NP.
Macraft Macro Macrow MAYCRAFT Maycroft F5796

136212 HUTCHINSON Mrs Jennifer. (Speechley) 48 Thomas More Hosue, Barbican, London, EC2Y 8BT.
BULLER CHILMAN COLLINGRIDGE COX CRINGLE EAST FOX GAY GIBBARD GREGORY Hillsden Hillsdon HILSDEN Hilsdon LAWRENCE Merie Merry MINNS Mirrie Mirry MOBBS MYRRY OVERTON PAYNE ROSE SMITH Speechley SPEECHLY STANGROOM STONESTREET THOMAS TINKLER TOWNSEND WATSON Whidley WHITBY F5327

136220 HUTCHINSON Mr Thomas. 82 Glenluce, Birtley, Chester Le Street, Co Durham, DH3 2HY. Tel:091-410-4383
BIRKETT Eveley EVELY FRIEND HALL HUTCHINSON KNIGHT LANGTHORNE Longthorne PEARCE PENGELLY

Sander SANDERS Saunders WAGGOTT WILLIAMS F2728
136239 HUTCHISON Mr Andrew. 4 Beechcrest View, Hook, Basingstoke, Hants, RG27 9RF.
BAKER BROAD COOK DINGLE GRAY HODGE HUTCHISON MCCUMISKEY MELIA MINARDS F1127
136247 HUTHNANCE Mr S L & Mrs E M. 15 Parkside Road, Reading, Berks, RG3 2DA. Tel:0734-507463
Bartell BARTLE Bartwell HUTHNANCE Huthnans Huthnes F876
136255 HUTTON Mrs Enid M. (Hochheimer) 3 Bryony Court, Heaton With Oxcliffe, Morecambe, Lancs, LA3 3QL. Tel:0524-424575
HOCHHEIMER HORNE WILKINSON F3313
136263 HUXFORD Mr R C. 5 Northcroft Court, South Warnborough, Basingstoke, Hants, RG25 1RW. Tel:0256-862800
Hexford Hucksford HUXFORD Scamel SCAMELL Scammell F882
136271 HYATT Mr Robert. 13 Albert Road, Hendon, London, NW4 2SH.
BENSTED Hiatt HYATT Hyett JACKMAN REEVES F4016
136298 HYDEN Mr Gene. 7911 Yancey Drive, Falls Church, Virginia, 22042, USA.
FEATHERSTONE HYDEN F6389
136301 HYDES Mr Nigel. 2 Stable Court, Marthesham Heath, Ipswich, Suffolk, IP5 7UQ.
CHAPMAN DRAKE GUEST HYDES MICKLETHWAITE MOYSER REECE TILLOTSON F6480
136328 HYLAND Mr G F. 35 Davenport Road, Stockport, Cheshire, SK2 6JU. Tel:061-483-6470
ANDERTON FRANCE GODLEY Hairbrun HALL Harberon Harbourn Harbourne HARBRON Harbrun Harburn HYLAND WEST F1102
136336 HYLAND Mrs K M. 35 Davenport Park Road, Stockport, Cheshire, SK2 6JU. Tel:061-483-6470
MORTIMER Mortimore PRATER Preater Preator WHALLEY F2719
136344 HYLANDS Mr David P. 38 Trevalyn Way, Rossett, Wrexham, Clwyd, LL12 0EJ. Tel:0244-571304
Heghland Heilland Hielan Hielaunde Highland Highlande Highlands Hiland Hilands Hyland HYLANDS F173
136352 HYNER Mr Leslie. 21 Sandy Lane, Cheam, Sutton, Surrey, SM2 7RD.
Haywood Heignwood Henywood Highner Hiner Hinor Hinord HYNARD HYNER Hynerd Hynor F381
136360 IBBETSON Mr B. 67 Moorhead Crescent, Shipley, W Yorks, BD18 4LQ.
CAMPBELL F3927
136379 IDE Mr Roger. 118 Maney Hill Road, Sutton Coldfield, W Midlands, B72 1JU. Tel:021-354-5874
BLAKE HANCOX IDE F2978
136387 IFOULD Mr Andrew M H. 8 Westward Close, Bosham, Chichester, Sussex, PO18 8QX. Tel:0243-573602
GROVER Hivel Iffold Ifold Ifolde IFOULD Ival Ivall Ivel Ivell Ivil Ivol Ivold Ivolde Ivoll Ivould Ivoulde F359
136395 ILES Mr D. 124 Clouds Hill Road, St George, Bristol, BS5 7LQ. Tel:0272-553534
BRAIN COGGINS ILES WARN F3640
136409 ILES Mr Donald Morton. 42 Willow Street, North Chingford, London, E4 7EG. Tel:081-529-1501
Ailes Eyles Hiles ILES Isles F2691
136417 ILES Mr Ronald Arthur. La Maison De Iles, 18 Woodland View, Lanivet, Bodmin, Cornwall, PL30 5HQ. Tel:0208-831688
Ailes Ayles Eales Eeles EYLES Hiles Hyles ILES Yeeles F4001
136425 ILOTT Mrs M W. Green Lane, Moorhouse, Newark, Notts, NG23 6LY.
HALLAM PINDER SAXELBY Saxilby F7030
136433 INCH Mr A R. 4 Garden Cottages, Bolnore Isaacs Lane, Haywards Heath, West Sussex, RH16 4BU.
INCH F6573
136441 INGALL Mr Martin. The Old Motor House, Bank Lane, Hildenborough, Tonbridge, Kent, TN11 8NR.
INGALL F7298
136468 INGLIS Pauline. 48 Carnegie House, Littlehampton Road, Worthing, W Sussex, BN13 1NW.
INGLIS TROWSDALE F2192
136476 INGOLD Mrs Carol. 18 Park Road, Raunds, Northants, NN9 6JL.
CLEAL COUN INGOLD MACE F427
136484 INMAN Mr Terence G. 8 Latymer Road, Lower Edmonton, London, N9. Tel:081-803-3967
BATES BOTT COOK HALLETT HASWELL INMAN MANSER NEWMAN O'HARA PARKS F607
136492 INNES Mr James. 88 Netherwood Tower, Muirhouse, Motherwell, Lanarkshire, ML1 2EQ. Tel:0698-53836
Ennis HEFFERNAN INNES Kellacher KELLAGHER Layden Lea LEE Leigh LEYDEN MADDEN MCGHEE Mcghie MCVAY Mcveigh Mcvey MULLEN Mullin O'keefe O'KEEFFE RENNIE Rinn Rynn SHANNON TAYLOR Tinne TUNNEY F1668
136506 INNES Mr Matthew. 27 Alexandra Terrace, Fraserburgh, Aberdeenshire, AB43 5PR.
INNES F3449
136514 INSULL Mrs M E. (Bevan) Gwernyrefail Fach, Cross Inn, Llandysul, Dyfed, SA44 6NH. Tel:0545-560236
BEVAN F6107
136522 IREDALE Mrs Sarah M. South Lodge Woodcroft, Chalton, Waterlooville, Hants, PO8 0BD. Tel:0705-594056
BOWLES BREACH COLTART HEIRONS IREDALE MOFFAT PEMBERTON PYBUS TAYLOR F2987
136530 IRELAND Mrs K F. Heythrop Cottage, Church Enstone, Chipping Norton, Oxon, OX7 4NN.
CARLSTROM COTON GORDON HEYWOOD HUNT IRELAND KIMBERLEY LAND Leamon LEMON LINCOLN LOWE RICE SUTTON F5136
136549 IRELAND Mr K J. 128 Penrice Road, Angaston, 5353, AUSTRALIA.
CAVNETT F6599
136557 IRELAND Mrs Shirley Maureen. (Cobie) 43 Princes Road, Langney, Eastbourne, E Sussex, BN23 6HS. Tel:0323-34217
CARTER COBIE COFFEEY IRELAND F3655
136565 IRVIN Mrs Dorothy. (Hind) 6 Wayside Close, Lymm, Cheshire, WA13 0NG. Tel:0925-754012
BEE BEER BEETHAM CHADWICK DERBYSHIRE DUCKWORTH FISHER GREGORY HEARFIELD HIND HOLDEN HOWARTH IRVIN KNOWLES MARTIN OAKLEY PIDDINGTON PYE STRUTT WARD F5746
136573 IRVINE Mr Joh H. 26 Murfield Street, Kirkcaldy, KY2 6SY. Tel:0592-260015
BAIRD HENDRY IRVINE F1573
136581 IRWIN Mrs Elva C. (Parsons) 2 Mahogany Drive, New Lambton, NSW 2305, AUSTRALIA.
BASS GEST Guest IRWIN PARSONS SOAR Soare Sore Sword F4488
136603 IRWIN Mr Harry E. 3707 Acosta Road, Fairfax, VA 22031-3801, USA.
Ervine ERWIN Irvin Irvine Irving Irwin F7274
136611 ISAAC Mr Geoffrey M. The Lodge, Dre Isaf, Ystrad Meurig, Dyfed, SY25 6AA. Tel:09745-303
ABBOTT Anstee ANSTEY AYRES BACON BENNETT CHANNEL CREW CROCKER CURRY FIGURES GRIFFITHS ILLSLEY ISAAC JOHNSON KERSLAKE LOVELOCK PAGE RICKARDS SCOTT SKULL SMITH VICKARY Vickery WEST F3124
136638 ISARD Mr J W. 11 Hazel Road, Reigate, Surrey, RH2 7LY. Tel:0737-244417
CARBERRY HEAD ISARD IZARD IZZARD LYNN STAUNTON THOROGOOD F2760
136646 ISHERWOOD Mr Philip. 74 Benhams Drive, Horley, Surrey, RH6 8QU.
ISHERWOOD MABEY TIDMAN WALTHAM F489
136654 ISLIP Mr R. 17 Newall Hall Park, Otley, W Yorks, LS21 2RD.
ISLIP F5970
136662 IVORY Mr D J. 51 Whitecross Avenue, Whitchurch, Bristol, Avon, BS14 9JF.
Ivereigh Ivery IVORY Ivry F2165
136670 IVORY Mrs P C. 108 Lime Walk, Chelmsford, Essex, CM2 9NJ.
Hendebourck Hendebourk Hendlebourck HEUDEBOURCK Heudebourk Heudebourq Hourdebourg Hudiberk F6646
136689 IZOD Mr A V. 11 Salterley Grange, Leckhampton Hill, Cheltenham, Glos, GL53 9QW.
IZOD F4874

136697 JABBETT Mr Derek. 95 Erdington Road, Aldridge, Walsall, WS9 0RN. Tel:0932-51555
JABBETT JOBBITT F2990

136700 JACKLIN Mr Arthur Stanley. 54 The Rise, Hillingdon, Uxbridge, Middx, UB10 0JN. Tel:0895-31660
HAM JACKLIN F534

136719 JACKMAN Mr Alan. 1 Bedford Gardens, Wokingham, Berks, RG11 2UX. Tel:0734-794906
ALDERTON ALLEN BENHAM CAMMIS GODDARD HARDY HINES HODGSON HUGHES JACKMAN JERROM KESSLEY KEW LISE LOADER MARLOW MARTIN MUDD NIND PAICE PINCHAM PINNELS POLDEN PURVER RICHES SANSOME SCAMMEL SMITH STEVENS WALDREN WEBB F390

136727 JACKSON Mr B D. 50 Selmeston Road, Eastbourne, E Sussex, BN21 2TB.
DEBENHAM JACKSON F3674

136735 JACKSON Mr B P. The Kedge, Oak Meadow, Birdham, Chichester, W Sussex, PO20 7BH. Tel:0243-512086
BENNELL BENNETT BROOKS CAUSER EDWARDS FRANCE HINKS JACKSON STACEY TIPTON WEATHERLAY WITHERS F4463

136743 JACKSON Mr Francis Arthur. 42 Birchfield Road, Coventry, Warks, CV6 2BD. Tel:0203-332809
BIRD BUGGINS BURGIN HORTON JACKSON LEWIN PENN SETCHEL SHUTTELWORTH WELBOURNE F793

136751 JACKSON Mr Jack A. 37 Medora Road, Romford, Essex, RM7 7EP.
Mannakay MANNAKEE Mannekee F7112

136778 JACKSON Mrs Joyce H. (Hancock) 5 The Tynings, Corsham, Wilts, SN13 9DE.
BRYANT DOWDING HANCOCK JACKSON NEWMAN SWANSBOROUGH TINSON F5740

136786 JACKSON Dr Lyn M. 10 Church Road, Whitchurch, Bristol, BS14 0PP.
CRUMLEY FOWLER JACKSON OAKES PICKUP RATCLIFFE SNAILHAM TAYLOR WALKER F2882

136794 JACKSON Mr Martin F. 7 Llys-Y-Berllan, Holywell, Clwyd, CH8 7QZ. Tel:0352-715983
BAILEY BULL HOLLOWAY JACKSON TIPPER F4452

136808 JACKSON Mrs Phyllis. (Plumb) Flat 1, Bourns Court, Ayshe Court Drive, Horsham, E Sussex, RH13 5RL. Tel:0403-63400
ASHMAN BATTY Battye BENSTEAD BURGOYNE BURROUGHS BUTT CHARLES COLLINS COMBER GARRETT GARWOOD GRANGE HALL HARVEY HIGHAM HOOKER HUNT JOINER MILNER MYERS PAYNE PLUM Plumb RIGHALL ROBERDS SEARLE SOUTH WATSON F1900

136816 JACKSON Mrs S E. 7a Oak Road, Sheffield, South Yorks, S12 3HT.
BODEN CHILDS DENNIS FOX HAGUES KNOWLES PEACE PEARSON PLANT WILBOURNE F5769

136824 JACKSON-MOONEY Mrs Marilyn. Ramsor Farm, Ramshorn, Oakmoor, North Staffs, ST10 3BT.
DEVLIN FRENCH GLEED HARRISON HOLMES JACKSON JONES OGDEN SLATER SOUTHERN WHITELEY F117

136832 JACOB Mr T W. 9 Wilmar Close, Uxbridge, Middx, UB8 1AS.
BRADLAUGHE JACOB Jacobs F5043

136840 JACOBS Mr David G. 14 Glasslaw Road, Bitterne, Southampton, Hants, SO2 5PE. Tel:0703-473292
ALEXANDER ALLEN AMBROSE ARLET Arlett ATKINS BAILEY BARBER Barnsberry BARNSBURY Barnsby BEAN BELCHAMBERS Bellchambers BENNET Bennett BISHOP BRADLEY Broadley BROOKES Brooks BROWNING BURGES BURNELL BUSH Caraher CARRAHER CARTER CLARK CLARKE COOK COUGHLAN Davies DAVIS DRIVER Faber Fabian Feban FEBEN Febin FENNING FORD GAGE GIBBS Goff GOFFE Gough GREEN GREENHAM Grinham HALLICK HANNEN HARRIS HAYTER HEARD HEATH Heth HIGGS HOLLAND HOLLES Hollon HOLLOWAY HOW HUNT Jacob JACOBS KNIGHT LEGGE LOCK LOCKE LYDDON MADDOX MARTIN MILLS MOORE MORGAN MORTIMER NEWMAN NEWTON Noyce NOYES Noys PENN Perkis PERRY POCOCK PONTON PORTER PRIOR Purchass PURKIS Randal RANDALL RANGER RICHARDS RICHARDSON RICKETTS ROACH ROGERS SLYFIELD SMITH SNELLING SPRIDDLE Steelman STEWART STILLMAN STRUGNEL VICKARY VOAK WATERMAN WATSON WHITE Willmot WILLMOTT Wilshear WILTSHIRE WOOLFRY YATES Yeats F5038

136859 JACOBS Mr Peter. 1 Eskdale Close, Horndean, Portsmouth, Hants, PO8 0DJ. Tel:0705-593413
ADAMS BEAUMONT BULL JACOBS LAMB PROCTOR SEXTON F451

136867 JACOBSEN Mrs E. 23 Grammar Street, Strathmore, Melbourne, 3041, AUSTRALIA.
BRAMBLE BRIDGES COATES COLENSO GRAVER JARVIS KITTO LARK LEIGH MOXLEY POWNCEBY SAMPSON F5536

136875 JACQUES Mrs Anne. 5 South Drive, Guiseley, Leeds, LS20 8JF.
BENTLEY BORRIDGE BRADLEY BUTLER COMMOFORD DUTTON EATCH ELLIOTT ENSTONE GAMBLE Gordon Instone JACQUES JOHNSON JORDAN MURRAY SMITH THOMPSON TURNER F3696

136883 JACQUES Miss J W. 5 The Enterdent, Godstone, Surrey, RH9 8EG.
Pointin POINTING Poynting F6843

136891 JALIL Mrs A Z. Ailsa Craig, Cooper Lane, Potto, Northallerton N Yorks, DL6 3HA.
BRICK BRIGGS COWAN COWARD DAVIES FRENCH FRICKLEY JEFFCOCK OWENS ROBSON SHANLEY THOMAS TRICKLEY TRICKLEY-COWARD F337

136905 JAMES Mrs A J. (Moss) 204 Wrexham Road, Whitchurch, Shropshire, SY13 1JE.
Andersen ANDERSON ELEMENT FERGUSON Hadwen HADWIN MERRICK MOSS TEWLEY Tooley TULEY Tuly WARD WILLS F5116

136913 JAMES Mrs Audrey. 3 Westview Close, Boroughbridge Road, York, YO2 6BE.
ADDISON CROWDER EXELBY PARKIN TIPLADY F5049

136921 JAMES Mrs C M. (Mainnie) 34 Sandtoft Road, Charlton, London, SE7 7LR. Tel:081-858-0926
FUNNELL JANES MENNIE F4009

136948 JAMES Miss Claire. 125 Parry Road, Wyken, Coventry, Warwickshire, CV2 3LW.
BOOTH BROOKS JANES SWALES WHALLEY F979

136956 JAMES Mrs E M. 20 Wray Park Road, Reigate, Surrey, RH2 0DD. Tel:0737-245486
BYARD F837

136964 JAMES Mrs Joan E. (Toogood) Alumuna, 24 Allsops Road, Launching Place, Victoria, 3139, AUSTRALIA. Tel:+61-5-964-7659
BLAIR BLAZELY DALE FLOYD HODGES JENKIN KIDDELL LUKE MADDEN MATHEWS MCGOLDRICK MUTBEAN PEARCE PEARD POULTON PURCHASE RICHARDS ROWE SMITH SQUIRE STATTON TOOGOOD UNDERLINE WALKER F5487

136972 JAMES Mr John. Trelowarth, 81 Salisbury Road, Ealing, London, W13 9TT.
BARTLE EADE HITCHINGS HOSKEN HOSKIN HOSKING JAMES JENKIN JOHNS KITTO LAMPRA MATTHEWS MITCHELL PASSMORE PERRY RICHARDS RODDA ROWE SILVESTER SMITH STEPHENS STEWART STRIKE SYMONS THOMAS TREGEMBO TRELOAR TRESIDDER WEARNE WILLIAMS F2068

136980 JAMES Mrs Lorna. 49 Ellengowan Crescent, Fairy Meadow, NSW 2519, AUSTRALIA.
BEAN CORNELL CREATON CROPPER DAVIS ELAND FARRANT JAMES KIRK LEVER MCDONAGH MCNAB MOODY MOULDS PAYNE RANKIN REEVES SALT TAYLOR WATERS WILSON F5516

136999 JAMES Mrs Mavis. (Lawry) 22 Adelaide St, Lawson, NSW 278', AUSTRALIA. Tel:+61-4-759-1996
BERRIMAN BUCKINGHAM CAWSTON DUNN ELLERY EVA FOYSTER GEORGE HOLLAH JAMES LAWREY LAWRY Lowry MARTIN MELVILLE OLIVER PASCOE ROWE RUSSEN SKEWES SOLOMON STONE STORER TONKIN TRIZISE WILTON F5764

137006 JAMES Mr W. Askew Green, Witherslack, Cumbria, LA11 6SA.
HIBERNIA IRELAND Irlond F7029

137014 JAMIESON Mrs Steph. 2 High Street, Yardley Gobion, Towcester, Nothants, NN12 7UB.
COPSON CUBBIN DAULMAN DUDLEY FERGUSON HOLLIS JAMIESON MALIN MIDDLETON ORR PARSONS F5125

137022 JANES Mr Bryan. 288 Southcote Lane, Southcote, Reading, Berks, RG3 3BL. Tel:0734-587466
JANES JOSEY F3490

137030 JANMAN Mr Ken. 66 Woodrow Drive, Wokingham, Berks, RG11 1RT.
GINMAN HARWOOD JANMAN F626

137049 JANSEN Mr Frank J. Greensleeves, 45 Knowle Park, Cobham, Surrey, KT11 3AA. Tel:0932-865865
CLEAVER Clever Cllever CRATHERN Darkin

DARKING JANSEN Janson F6039
137057 JAPING Mr H W D. 48 Pineheath Road, High Kelling, Holt, Norfolk, NR25 6RH.
BAKER COLLINS COUTTS GRANT HAY JAPING LAING NEAL SCORGIE STEPHEN SYKES THOMPSON VENNER F5273
137065 JARDINE Ms Shirley M. Po Box 92, White River Jct, VT 05001, USA.
JARDINE F7300
137073 JARMAIN Mrs D E. 7 Green Close, Rawcliffe Drive, Clifton Without, York, YO3 6PB.
Caesar CAESER Ceasar Ceaser DEADMAN Dedman HOVENDEN LEE Lock LOCKE READ Reed RYE STARLING F4905
137081 JARMAN Mr & Mrs D A E. 184 Thames Side, Laleham, Middx, TW18 2JH.
Playdell PLEYDELL F6806
137103 JARMAN Mr Lytton Proom. 27 Oakfield Road, Rugby, Warwickshire, CV22 6HU.
Tel:0788-562200
Prom PROOM Proome Prum Prume Prumme F3
137111 JARRETT Mr Keith. 20 Farmfield Road, Easington, Banbury, Oxon, OX16 9AP.
Tel:0295-266195
ADAMS Allblaster ARBLASTER BAILEY BATE BILKEY CATON CHAVASSIE CHESHIRE Chesshire Croyden CROYDON GRANGER GUTTERIDGE HALL Hallblaster HARTWELL HEATH HILL HINE Jarratt JARRETT KING MAIN Maine Mayne MICHELL Mitchell RATHBONE THOMPSON WILKES WILKINS YARRINGTON F1301
137138 JARRETT Mr Peter. Fieldfare, Lower Holway Close, Taunton, Somerset, TA1 2LN.
Ardy Eardy ERBACH Erback Garad Garard Garrad Garrard Garrat Garratt Garred Garretson Garrett Garretts Garrettson Garrison Garrit Garritt Garrod Garrould Gerad Geraddus Gerald Geralds Gerard Gerarde Gerardes Gerards Geratt Geraud Geret Gerold Gerrad Gerrard Gerratt Gerred Gerrett Gervaise Gervas Gervase Gervis Gorret Heardy Jarad Jarald Jarat Jared Jareld Jarelds Jaret Jarets Jarett Jaretts Jarrad Jarrard Jarrat JARRATT Jarred Jarret Jarrets JARRETT Jarretts Jarritt Jarrod Jarrold JARROT Jarrott Jarvie Jarvis Jeffette Jeofett Jeorrett Jereatt Jerrard Jerratt Jerreatt Jerred JERRETT Jerrold OULTON Yard Yarrat Yarratt Yarrott Yerratt F1741
137146 JARRITT Mrs B M. (Brockless) 5 Sutton Avenue, Rustington, W Sussex, BN16 2ES.
Tel:0903-774887
Brockhall Brockle Brockles BROCKLESS Brockleys Brocklis Brockliss Brocles Brocolo F5820
137154 JARVIS Mrs Georgina. (Troughton) 1 Suncourt, Rye Close, Worthing, West Sussex, BN11 5EG.
GUEST TROUGHTON F5696
137162 JARVIS Mr Matt. Wyndham House, 22 Desford Road, Kirby Muxloe, Leicester, LE9 9BB.
Tel:0533-394653
BARKER SHELTON TYRER F1640
137170 JARVIS-SMITH Mrs G. The Bungalow, Tyler Close, Canterbury, Kent, CT2 7BD.
Adkin ADKINS Atkin Darrant Durent Durrand Durrande DURRANT Durrent Garvasius Gervais Gervaise Gervase Gervasius Gervayse Gerveys Gervis Jarvas Jarves Jarvice Jarvies JARVIS Jerfeys Jervaulx Jervis Jervois Jervoise Pepeat Pepiat Pepiatt Pepitt Peppett PEPPIAT Peppiatt Peppit PEPPITT Peppytte Pepyat Screyvener Scribner Scribnor SCRIVENER SINFIELD Singfeild Singfield Sinkfeild Sinkfield SWINCKFIELD Synfield Yarvie Yeauman YEOMAN Yeouman Yeoumans Yomans Youman F2671
137189 JEACOCK Mr A. 19 Beechwood Gardens, Rainham, Essex, RM13 9HU. Tel:0708-523178
Jacock Jacocke Jacott Jacox Jaycock Jaycott Jaycox Jcock JEACOCK Jeacocke Jeacocks Jeacott Jeacox Jecock Jecox Jeycock Jeycocks F6960
137197 JEAL Mr Peter E. 69 West Avenue, Oldfield Park, Bath, Avon, BA2 3QD.
Geal Geale JEAL Jeale Jeall F7068
137200 JEE Mrs Sandra. Field House, Upper Chalkley, Horton, Chipping Sodbury Bristol, BS17 6QS.
Tel:0454-314390
DYER GEE GWATKIN GWATKINS JEE MILSOM F116
137219 JEEVES Mrs Valerie J. (Williams) 56 Red Scar Drive, Scarborough, North Yorks, YO12 5RQ.
Tel:0723-376817
ANDERSON WILLIAMS WILLIAMS F6301
137227 JEFFERS Mr D A. 64 South Court Avenue, Dorcehster, Dorset, DT1 2BZ.
GATRALL HOGG JEFFERS LONG PAMPHLETT PARTRIDGE PELLEY TAPP F6075
137235 JEFFERSON Mrs A R. (Hicklin) Stenson Fields Farmhouse, Stenson Road, Derby, DE3 7LP.
CAIN DEWSON DRAKEFIELD HICKLIN KINDER F4360
137243 JELLEY Mrs Sheila. 37 Copperkins Lane, Amersham, Bucks, HP6 5QF.
ADDINGTON ANSCOMB BRIDGEFORD HANSCOMB HOSIE JELLEY SWINYARD WATKISS F2608
137251 JELLOWS Val. 15 Tythe Close, N Springfield, Chelmsford, Essex, CM1 5SU.
Jealous Jellice Jellis JELLOWS F7139
137278 JEMMESON Mrs Christine. (Brown) 8 Dilston, Hyde Lane, Danbury, Chelmsford Essex, CM3 4RN.
BROWN CARTER CAYGILL Coachwith Coatesworth COATSWITH Coatsworth Coatsworthe Coteswith Cotesworth Cotsworth Cotsworthe Doan Doane DONE Donne Hadfeld HADFIELD Halliday Hasking Haskins Hatfield Holiday HOLLIDAY Holyday HOSKING Hoskings Hoskins Jameson Jammeson Jemeson Jemison Jemmerson JEMMESON Jemmieson Jemmison Jimmeson Jimmison KIRKBRIDE Kirkbright Knolson Knoulson Knowleson KNOWLSON Nollson Nolson Nolsonne Nowlson Pattinson PATTISON RACE Raice Rase RUTTER SAUNDERS SHIPLEY Smailes SMALES Solesby Solsby Solsbye Soulbie Soulesby SOULSBY Soulsbye Sowleby Sowlesby STALEY Stalley Stally Staly Stayly Stealy Steley Stelly THOMPSON F3518
137286 JENKIN Mr Richard G. An Gernyk, Chapel Road, Leedstown, Hayle, Cornwall. Tel:0736-850332
BIRD BOASE Bodener Bodinar Bodiner BODINNAR DREW Dunckley DUNKLEY Ebbs ENDERSBY FACER GRYLLS HARVEY HEBBES Hebbs Ibbs JENKIN MILLETT SEABROOK SHARMAN Shearman TONKIN Treouran TREVENEN TREWREN Truran F2508
137294 JENKINS Mr Graham James. 17 Manor Road, Stanford Le Hope, Essex, SS17 0NY.
Tel:0375-641367
BROOKS JAMES JAY JENKINS NASH F286
137308 JENKINS Miss Marian. (Allen) 63 Forest View Road, Tuffley, Glos, GL4 0BY. Tel:0452-528020
ALLEN AUBREY Ginner JENNER JONES LANSDELL LAVENDER LEWIS PRICE SHEPHARD F3466
137316 JENKINS Mrs Maureen. 38 San Reno Road, Aspley Guise, Milton Keynes, Bucks, MK17 8JY.
TREDGETT TRUDGETT F1537
137324 JENKINS Mrs Patricia Gwedoline. (Pearmain) Hamel, 63 Franklynn Road, Haywards Heath, West Sussex, RH16 4DT. Tel:0444-452673
JAMES PEARMAIN Pearman ROBERTS F6497
137332 JENKS Mr Mike R. 10 Horselydown Lane, Tower Bridge Square, London, SE1 2LN.
BLATHWAYT JENKES JENKS Jenkys WINTER WINTOUR WYNTER-BLATHWAYT F215
137340 JENKYN Mr A W. 8 Hurley Close, Boscombe Down, Amesbury, Wiltshire, SP4 7QZ. Tel:0980-623382
CARNE JENKYN TRESILLIAN F971
137359 JENKYN Mrs F M. 8 Hurley Close, Boscombe Down, Amesbury, Salisbury Wiltshire, SP4 7QZ. Tel:0980-623382
ELLSEY STREATER F972
137367 JENNER Mr D A. 98 Princes Avenue, Palmers Green, London, N13 6HD.
JENNER F872
137375 JENNER Mr Henry. 113 Denmark Road, Gloucester, GL1 3JW. Tel:0452-24180
HAWKINS JENNER PROUT VICK F3309
137383 JENNINGS Mrs Helen. 47 Cambridge Terrace, Malvern, South Australia 5061.
Tel:+61-271-7322
COLLINGWOOD FULTON HOWELL KEMP MARTIN MCSTAY PARKER REEVES WELCH F1666
137391 JENNINGS Miss J. 12 Leofric Court, Elvetham Road, Birmingham, B15 2LY.
JEFCOATE MCCOLL MCINNES TABOR F4922
137405 JENNINGS Mr John. 40 The Limes, Harston,

Cambridge, CB2 5QT. Tel:0223-871746
AMSEL Amzell ANCELL Ansell Anzell BARKER BARNARD BATESON BAXTER BENTON BRIGGS Burbidge BURBRIDGE BURKETT Burkitt CALDICOT CHALLIS COOPER COVELL Covil CUTMORE DUCKINS EDWARDS Empy GIDDINS GILLSON Girling GODFREY GREEN GREESON GURLING Haiden Haise Hansil Harden HARDING HARWOOD HAYDEN Haydon HAYES Hays Hayse HAYWOOD Heywood HILLS HOWARD IMPEY Impy JENNINGS JUDE KENT Kneeves Kneves LACK LAVENDER LEACH LOVE MATTHEWS MAYES Meriton MERRINGTON MORLEY MORLING Neaves NEEVES Neves NORMAN NORRIS OFFLEY PALMER Roiston ROYSTON Sarjeant Scair SCARR SERJEANT SINGLETON Siser SIZER Smethy SMITH SMITHY Smythees Smythies Soar Soare Soer SORE Stamford Standford STANFORD STANLEY SUTTON SWAN Syer Syser Tale TALL Talle TAYLOR Toll Tolle WEBSTER Websture WILSON WRIGHT YOUNG F4774

137413 JENNINGS Mr Paul. 28 Pendle Fields, Fence, Burnley, Lancs, BB12 9HN.
BARRATT BAYLIS BUCKLEY DAWSON IDIENS JENNINGS LABBETT LEEK MARSHALL MEERS MOUNDSDON PARKER POLLARD SKIDMORE SMITH SPEAKE STRONG TAYLOR WEBBER F5797

137421 JENNS Miss K. 58 Endhill Road, Kingstanding, Birmingham, B44 9RP. Tel:021-353-8001
BANNING CAPEWELL CATER JENNS KETTERIDGE LAYTON MEADOWS PAYNE PETERS PLATT PRITCHARD SHORE THOMPSON WHY F3024

137448 JENSEN Ms Elizabeth. 5 Mira Street, Gepps Cross, SA 5094, AUSTRALIA. Tel:+61-8-262-5827
BAKER BRAY CLIFTON CROWLEY GOSS GROSE HARRIS MORROW REMPHREY TREMBATH F5477

137456 JENSON Miss Valerie. 18 Pembroke Gardens, Rainham, Kent, ME8 8TD.
ASH BORSLEY BOWN BURGESS BURR CAMBERS COLLINS COOK COOPER DEVENPORT DEVEREUX GENSON GORE HOPPY JENSON JOHNSON LING LOYNS MANTON ODELL ONELY SHARMAN STEFFEN THOMPSON TRANTER VEASEY WARNER WILLETT WORSTER F2805

137464 JEPHCOTT Mr J A. 73 All Saints Avenue, Prettygate, Colchester, Essex, CO3 4PA. Tel:0206-561950
ANNIS BOWLEY Jefcoate Jefcut Jeffcoat Jeffcoatt Jeffcott Jephcoat Jephcote JEPHCOTT SALTS SEATON F20

137472 JEROME Dr Barry R. Rareridge, Rareridge Lane, Bishops Waltham, Southampton, Hants, SO3 1DX.
BISHOP BURFORD DURANT Durrant Frances FRANCIS HILL HOLT Jerom JEROME JOHNSON Jorham Jorum LANGLEY LEE LEGG LITTLE LUCAS Lukas MONK Parrot PARROTT RICHARDSON SHERMAN Skelton SKILTON SMITH TRUMPLET Trumplett WEBB WERNHAM WHITE WOODLEY WORSLEY WRIGHT F5040

137480 JERRARD Mr Rob. 19 Castle Close, Warwick, CV34 4DB.
BARTLETT DASHWOOD EASTMENT GERRARD JERRARD WHITE F177

137499 JERVIS Dr Graham. 42 Alexandra Road, Epsom, Surrey, KT17 4BY. Tel:03727-20909
BARKER CRUTCHLEY Husselbe HUSSELBEE Husselbury Husselby Husslebee Hustlebee JERVIS Rishin Rushen RUSHENT Rushin F6238

137502 JEWELL Mr & Mrs R. 82 Elmshott Lane, Cippenham, Slough, Berks, SL1 5QZ. Tel:0628-664791
BOWMAN Claiton Claton Clatton Clayton Cleaton Cleeton Cleiton Cleton Cleyton Cleytone ISAACS Jewel JEWELL Joule Juel Juele POWNEY F3380

137510 JEWITT Mr Cyril. 9 Hylton Road, Durham City, DH1 5LS. Tel:091-386-1502
Jeuit Jewet Jewett Jewit JEWITT Jueit Juet Juit F3829

137529 JOHNS Mrs Julie. Albert Cottage, Cox Park Farm, Cox Park, Nr Gunnislake Cornwall, PL18 9BB. Tel:0822-832898
Cloak Cloake CLOKE MEDLAND Merton Moorton Moreton Morten Morton Mourton Murten Murtin MURTON TRUSCOTT F2894

137537 JOHNS Miss P. 76 Northbourne Road, Eastbourne, E Sussex, BN22 8QP.
BAKER BENNYMEN COWLING FLOWERS FROST HUSBAND JOHNS LAMPEY PICTON THORN F825

137545 JOHNS Mrs Valerie. 32f West End House, West Street, Tavistock, Devon, PL19 8JY.
CRANCH DRAKE ISLIP KENDRICK PADDON SEARLE TRICKS F2415

137553 JOHNS Mr W N. Clonwithy Cottage, Lower Morton, Thornbury, Avon, BS12 1LF. Tel:0454-413500
EADE EDE GOFF HICKS JOHNS TREMAIN Tremaine Tremayne F1280

137561 JOHNSON Mrs Adele M. (Johnson) 218 Muir Crescent Nw, Medicine Hat, Alberta, T1A 6W5, CANADA. Tel:+1-403-526-6611
ADDIMAN ANDREW ANDREWARTHER BARKER BRAY DENNIS FALL HARRISON MORRIT PARKIN F5444

137588 JOHNSON Mrs Anthea. (Browne) Turbary, Goon Piper, Feock, Truro, Cornwall, TR3 6RA. Tel:0872-863941
ALFORD ASH BASTABLE BOWDEN BROWNE CHUDLEIGH DYKE ELLIS FOLLAND FOX GILLINGHAM HAYCRAFT HELMORE HODGES LINSCOTT MARTIN PENNY REED Shepard SHEPHERD SHEPPARD Shepphard Sheppherd STONE TOZER VICARY F4956

137596 JOHNSON Mr B T. Farthings, The Copse, Alderbury, Salisbury Wilts, SP5 3BL.
Rasey Razee RAZEY F7352

137618 JOHNSON Mr C P C. 24 Canterbury Drive, Washingborough, Lincoln, LN4 1SJ.
BAILEY BOYERS BURTON BYERS COOPER CROSS FISHWICK FRANCIS GLOVER HARRIS HARTLEY HAWARD JOHNSON MAHONEY NEAL PALMER PHILLIPS SIBBALD SOWERBY STEELS WARING F37

137626 JOHNSON Mrs Carol. (Hardy) 714 Richardson Road, Mt-Roskill, Auckland, NEW ZEALAND. Tel:+64-9-656793
BAKER BARRATT Barrett HARDY JOHNSON MANSFIELD MEASURES Measurier PICKERING SHERWIN Storah STORER F4171

137634 JOHNSON Catherine. 37 Bingham Road, Cotgrave, Notts, NG12 3JS. Tel:0602-894862
ASHTON BUTLER CLATER DOWNS FOSTER FOX HALL HUTCHINSON LISTER MARR MARSHALL NETTLESHIP RAYNE REDSHAW ROBINSON SHAW SPENCER STORRS WARD WATSON WILKINSON F370

137642 JOHNSON Mr Chris. Farthings, Honey Lane, Otham, Kent, ME15 8RJ. Tel:0622-861353
BEEVIS CREASY CUMING FENNIMORE HARPUM JOHNSON KITCHIN LEWIS MANSER Raisey Rasey Rasy RAZEY Razy WEBB F2596

137650 JOHNSON Ms D. Box 165, Central Butte, Saskatchewan, S0H 0T0, CANADA.
GRAHAM LEACH MITCHELL STEPHENSON THOMPSON TOLMIE VICARY F5462

137669 JOHNSON Mrs D. 91 Stretford House, Chapel Lane, Stretford, Manchester, M32 9AY.
CONDLIFFE F6872

137677 JOHNSON Dave. Jasmine Cottage, North Street, Barrow On Humber, South Humberside, DN19 7AP.
STUBBINGS F7368

137685 JOHNSON Mr David John. 19 Upper Park, Harlow, Essex, CM20 1TN.
ADAMS Amor AMOUR CARRIER CLIFT COUCHMAN DRAIN DRAPER FOTHERGILL Gardeiner Gardener Gardiner GARDNER GARROD Hibblet Hibblett HIBLET Hiblett HIGGIE HOWDON HUNTER-GARDNER JOHNSON MCINTOSH MUCKLESTONE PAGE SHUTTLEWORTH SHUTTLEWORTH-CLIFT SMITH SPERRIN STREATFIELD WATKINS WEBB F6115

137693 JOHNSON Mrs Diane J M. 26 The Ride, Kingswood, Bristol, BS15 4SY.
ANDROS BLINMAN BOWDEN BUSSELL CAREY CARTERET COOPER FREKE GARIS GOSSELIN GUILLAUME GUILLE HANCOCK HUSSEY ILES LEE REEVES ROUGIER VEEL F2245

137707 JOHNSON Mrs Eileen G. (Merring) 27 St Swithun'S Road, Kennington, Oxford, OX1 5PU. Tel:0865-739997
DEWEY LARKHAM MEERING MORICKTON TOMKIN F6223

137715 JOHNSON Mrs Elaine. 10 Elmfield Road, Davenport, Stockport, Cheshire, SK3 8SE.
BOOTH JOHNSON ROPER SINCLAIR F2572

137723 JOHNSON Ella. (Holseth) 7325 14th Avenue S, Richfield, MN 55423-3469, USA.
CLUTTON JENNINGS WILSON F5458

137731 JOHNSON Mrs Elspeth. 10 Church Street, Market Drayton, Shropshire, TF9 1AD.
BAILEY BROUGH BUTTER Butters D'IFFANGAR LEA LOMAS SHUFFLEBOTHAM SWAN Swann WOOLLISCROFT

F1813

137758 JOHNSON Mr Gordon. 123 Johnston Gardens, Peterculter, Aberdeen, AB1 0LD. Tel:0224-734017
BRISBANE COUBROUGH COULL GILLANDERS HOLT JOHNSON PERT F1780

137766 JOHNSON Miss H A. Lot 18 Dandenong-Hastings Road, Langwarrin 3910, AUSTRALIA.
FEAVER F7279

137774 JOHNSON Mrs Marian. Trent Lodge, Sutton Lane, Granby, Nottingham, NG13 9PY. Tel:0949-50845
AMOS BEER BENTLEY BLECHYNDEN BOWLES BULL CORCORAN EASTON FIFIELD FILES GILES HART MARSHALL MOORE MUMMERY TUTT WARD F2524

137782 JOHNSON Mrs Muriel. 66 Victoria Road, Flat 2, Exmouth, Devon, EX8 1DW. Tel:0395-275290
BARKER DEARDEN ELLIOTT Elyett FISHER HELLIWELL JAMES LAMB LAW LAWTON LOWERY Lowrey MARSDEN MCFARLANE Noakes NOKES OSBORN Osborne POWLESLAND REYNOLDS SAGE STANBURY THATCHER WHITTAKER YOUNG F2648

137790 JOHNSON Mr Peter. 29 Dane Close, Alsager, Stoke On Trent, Staffs, ST7 2HZ. Tel:0270-877126
BLAKE CAPPER FRIAR GOODIER HENSHALL HOLLINSHEAD HULSE JOHNSON PLANT STRETCH F2145

137804 JOHNSON Mr Philip Galbraith. 71 Market Street, Edenfield, Ramsbottom, Lancs, BL0 0JQ. Tel:0706-824794
CHARNLEY HALLAM JOHNSON F166

137812 JOHNSON Mr R A. (Lamley) 116 Grevill Road, Warwick, CV34 5PL. Tel:0926-401909
DUCK JOHNSON Lambley LAMBLY LAMLEY Walin Wallen WALLIN F5302

137820 JOHNSON Mr Robert L. Setter, Mid Yell, Shetland, ZE2 9BJ. Tel:0957-2153
ABERNETHY AITCHISON ANDERSON ARNOTT ARTHUR ARTHURSON BAIN BARTLESON BIGLAND BLANCE BROWN CHARLESON CHEYNE CHRISTIE CLARK CLUNESS COPLAND COUTTS DANIELSON DAVIDSON DEMPSTER DEYELL DONALDSON FARQUHAR FINDLAYSON FORBES FORDYCE FRASER GALT GARDNER GARSTER GARTHSON GAUNSON GEORGESON GILBERTSON GRAY GREEN GUNN GUTHRIE HALCROW HANSON HARRISON HART HAWICK HAY HENDERSON HENRY HERCULESON HOSEASON HUGHSON HUNTER INKSTER IRVINE ISBISTER JAMESON JAMIESON JEROMSON JOHNSON LAURENCESON LEASK MALCOLMSON MANN MANSON MATHEWSON MOAR MOODY MOUAT Mowat NEVEN Nicholson NICOLSON NINIAN NISBET ODIE OLLASON OMAND PARK PETERSON PETRIE PHILLIP POLE PORTEOUS Portice RAMSAY RATTER REID RENDALL ROBERTSON Rusland RUSSLAND SANDISON SCOLLAY SHARP SINCLAIR SMITH SMOLLETT SPENCE STOVE SUTHERLAND TAIT THOMASON Thompson TULLOCH URQUARTH WILLIAMSON WINCHESTER WISHART YOUNG F1208

137839 JOHNSON Mr Roy. Rr 1, Ridgeville, Ontario, L0S 1M0, CANADA.
JOHNSON F7302

137847 JOHNSON Miss S L. Turbary, Goon Piper, Feock, Truro, Cornwall, TR3 6RA.
BROWN FLEMING GRANTHAM JOHNSON SHORE TOWN WATERMAN F6355

137855 JOHNSTON Miss Anne. 16 Ardvarna Park, Belfast, Northern Ireland, BT4 2GH. Tel:0232-760636
BARRON FALCONER JOHNSTON MCMILLAN NICOL ROBERTSON SUTHERLAND URQUHART WATT F3971

137863 JOHNSTON Ms Audrey D. 3 Thomas Street, Clontare Beach, Queensland, 4019, AUSTRALIA. Tel:+61-7-283-4494
ALEXANDER DUNNINGHAM JOHNSTON MCPHERSON STOKES STUBBIN WARD F5145

137871 JOHNSTON Mr Colin. 32/10 Mount Street, Hunters Hill, NSW 2110, AUSTRALIA.
Casling CASTLING F7041

137898 JOHNSTON Mr Kenneth E. 1 Langley Road, Isleworth, Middx, TW7 5AH.
BRACHER COX FRANCIS FURNELL JOHNSTON SMITH SNOOK YEATES F2685

137901 JOHNSTON Mrs Lynn. 94 Torkington Road, Hazel Grove, Stockport, Cheshire, SK7 6NR.
ANGEL BALL BENNETT CHAMBERS COAD DINGLE LEAMAN SOUTHWORTH TAYLOR F6360

137928 JOHNSTON Mr Robert A. 480 Lee Avenue, Woodstock, Ontario, N4S 6Y3, CANADA.
Jhonson Johnson JOHNSTON F7076

137936 JOHNSTONE Mrs Agnes. 48 East Street, Horncastle, Lincs, LN9 6AA.
ADAMS BETHUNE BURNS CUTHILL GELLATLEY GOUCK GREY HAY HOUSTON HUNTER JAMIESON JOHNSTON KINGO KINGOW MARSHALL MITCHELL MORRIS MOUAT Mowat MURRAY PITBLADDO REEDIE ROBERTSON SANDILANDS SHANKS SHEPHERD SKINNER SMART SUTHERLAND WINWICK F3116

137944 JOHNSTONE Mr Graham. 2 Arundel Close, Bower Grange, Bedlington, Northumberland, NE22 5YJ. Tel:0670-824007
BRAMLEY BRIGGS Dracot Dracote Dracott Draycot Draycote DRAYCOTT Galsthorp Galsthorpe Gellesthorp Gellesthorpe Gelsthorp GELSTHORPE Gillsthorp Gillsthorpe Gilsthorp Gilsthorpe HALL Jacques Jakes JAQUES Johnston JOHNSTONE JUDD MACDONALD Mcdonald POLLARD F5362

137952 JOHNSTONE Mrs Sheila M. (Godden) Knightsfield, Ifield Green, Crawley, W Sussex, RH11 0ND. Tel:0293-522992
AMBROSE GIBBONS GODDEN JOHNSTONE MIDDLETON YEO F5081

137960 JONAS Mrs W. (Tiquet) 89 Bower Hill, Epping, Essex, CM16 7AW.
DANELLE JONAS Lasad Le Sade Malnoury MANOURY MARCHAND PIGGINS SADE SOULARD Soullard Tickat Ticket Tickett Ticquet TIQUET VIAR Viard YON F6177

137979 JONES Mrs (Betty) Audrey. (Plant) 37 Long Meadows, Ponteland, Newcastle Upon Tyne, NE20 9DX.
EARNSHAW GRAVELEY KNAPTON PLANT ROBINSON ROBSHAW TURNER WESTERMAN F5620

137987 JONES Mr Alan. 9 Bryntirion Terrace, Llanfair Road, Abergele, Clwyd, LL22 7BG. Tel:0745-825411
ANKERS BOODLE Buddle COBBE GOORE GOUGH MATHER Mathers MORGAN NICKSON Nixon PARSONAGE PEEL PHILLIPS PICKSTOCK PIGG RALPHS SALADINE Travis TREVIS WOOD F2994

137995 JONES Aneurin M. Heulwen, Heol Aberystwyth, Cardigan, Dyfed, SA43 1LU. Tel:0239
HOWELL LEWIS-HOWELL OWEN-LEWIS F1710

138002 JONES Mrs Ann. (Peachment) 1 Green Close, Epping Green, Epping, Essex, CM16 6PS. Tel:0378-76929
PEACHMENT F897

138010 JONES Mr Antony. 1 Oaklands, Oakhill Road, Horsham, West Sussex, RH13 5LG.
BRYER BURGESS GIRLING HELLIER LARKE PILCOCKS POONEY RADFORD READ WARD F4953

138029 JONES Mr Arthur. 13 George Street, Leyland, Preston, Lancs, PR5 2NY. Tel:0772-422710
Block Blog BLOGG Bloog CHASTNEY DRINKWATER GREAVES HARDY HARMER JONES NICHOLS PIERREPONT THURSBY WITHNELL F3030

138037 JONES Mr Arthur. 44 Aubreys, Letchworth, Herts, SG6 3TU.
Anders ANDERSON Anderwes Andrew Andrewe Andrewes ANDREWS Andro Androess Androwes Andrus Cavill Claidon Claiton Claydon CLAYTON Cut Cutt Cutte CUTTS Hanchant Hanchatt Hanchent HANCHET Hanchett Hanchiott Hantchett Haseler Haslar Hasle HASLER Hastler Hatchet HATCHETT Henshot HIDE Hyde OVERTON SALMON Saman Sammond Sammons Samon Saval Saveall Savell Savil Savile SAVILLE Savle Seavell F2519

138045 JONES Mrs Barbara Mary. (Sinden) Nyasa, 3 Cradoc Close, Brecon, Powys, LD3 9UA. Tel:0874-625939
CHAMBERLAIN COLLEY COMER HODGE JONES NEEDHAM NESBIT RENTON SINDEN YEOMAN F3516

138053 JONES Mr C A & Mrs M T. (Kinmonth) 40 Keble Road, Maidenhead, Berks, SL6 6BA. Tel:0628-782856
ALLEN JONES KINMOUTH WYNNE F4679

138061 JONES Mr Charles R. 4 Scott Drive, Lexden, Colchester, Essex, CO3 4JA.
CLEMENTS HISLOP HUTCHINGS JONES LUKE SAINSBURY SHARPE WESTON F1436

138088 JONES Mr Christopher David. Three Darnford Lane, Boley Park, Lichfield, Staffs, WS14 9RW.
CHUMBLEY FRENCH GRINDLEY HITCHENER ITCHENER

Jarvis JERVIS PRITCHARD RODENHURST F5780

138096 JONES Mr Christopher. 7 Guildings Way, Kings Stanley, Stonehouse, Glos, GL10 3LF. Tel:0453-826705
FAGAIN HONEY MANSELL ROACH SHAPCOTT TURNER F4273

138118 JONES Mr David E. Beachan, Farr, Inverness, IV1 2XF.
BARRATT BILLINGTON DESOER DOVEY GRIFFIN HARDING JONES RICHARDS ROOTSEY SIMCOCK TOMLINSON WRIGHT F1688

138126 JONES Mr Dyfrig. Kingsmead, 18 Cae Rex, Llanblethian, Cowbridge, S Glamorgan, CF7 7JS.
ADAMS GAINSFORD Goodwin GOODWYN JENKINS JONES POWELL TURNERS WATERS WILLIAMS F5946

138134 JONES Mrs Evelyn. 8 Eastbourne Avenue, Bath, Avon, BA1 6EW. Tel:0225-316807
BALSDON CHAMPION KEBBY WALL F2140

138142 JONES Mrs G. (Elflett) 47 Laurel Walk, Horsham, West Sussex, RH13 5NR.
Alefleet Alflatt BROWNSELL DELLAR Elfleet ELFLETT Elflitt GARNER PARNELL WILDERSPIN F4252

138150 JONES Mrs Geraldine A. 5 Slessor Close, Monxton Road, Andover, Hants, SP11 8HH.
BISHOP COLE CRILLY DOLAN EDWARDS FISHER GETHIN HAWORTH Howarth HOWELL KENNISON REDFERN SHERBORNE Sherburn SHORT STINCHCOMBE THOMAS TROTMAN WHEELER WILLIAMS Willsher Wilsheir WILTSHIRE F2129

138169 JONES Mr Graham D. 33 Strafford Avenue, Clayhall, Ilford, Essex, IG5 0TJ. Tel:081-550-9273
Bennet BENNETT BURROUGH CARY CLARK Clarke D'isigny D'isney Desney DISNEY GLOVER GLUE HARDY HICKS Hix JONES NIPPER TOMKINSON TOPLIS F4659

138177 JONES Mrs J M. 1 Stencills Road, Walsall, WS4 2HJ.
HARDWICK Hardwicke Hardwyck F6740

138185 JONES Mr J W. 107 Porters Avenue, Dagenham, Essex, RM9 5YU.
BOOT CAMBRIDGE CANTRELL DONAWAY DONOVAN EYRE GREEN JONES LEIVERS NEEDHAM OLIVER PAVITT RUFFIAT RUSEL RUSELL RUSSELL RUSSIAL SHAW SKINGLEY WALKER F930

138193 JONES Mrs J. (Barlow) 23 Berry Way, Newton Longville, Milton Keynes, MK17 0AS.
BALDWYN BARLOW BURLOW KEY MORGAN RUSH STEGER TILDESLEY TIPPING WINTER F4828

138207 JONES Mrs Jane Mary. (Jones) Llwyn Ysgaw, Llaniestyn, Pwllheli, Gwynedd, LL53 8SL. Tel:0758-83527
EDWARDS GRIFFITH JONES ROBERTS THOMOS WILLIAMS F4589

138215 JONES Jeremy. Benwick, 35 Harewood Gardens, Longthorpe, Peterborough Cambs, PE3 6NF. Tel:0733-331897
COPEMAN JONES LAWRENCE NIGHTINGALE PEEL STAPLETON F1495

138223 JONES Mrs Joan. 39 Lytton Avenue, Penn, Wolverhampton, W Midlands, WV4 4HL. Tel:0902-332950
EDWARDS Hobson HOPSON PIKE ROBINSON TURNER Way WHALE F1567

138231 JONES June H. 153 Ashfield Road, Bispham, Blackpool, Lancs, FY2 0BU. Tel:0253-58708
BROWN FORREST GRAHAM HILTON LOWNDES MAKIN MERCER PRISTNUM THORNTON F3257

138258 JONES Mrs K M. 19 The Close, Cleadon, Sunderland, Tyne And Wear, SR6 7RG.
BARNETT GARGETT LUMLEY SAYER SCOTT SHELDON F3471

138266 JONES Mrs Kathryn. (Stoker) 17 Forth Court, South Shields, Tyne & Wear, NE34 0NP. Tel:091-456-5681
FAREN TOFT WHATCROFT F5685

138274 JONES Mr Keith. Apple-Garth, Belton Road, Whitchurch, Shropshire, SY13 1JB. Tel:0948-2737
JONES Parrie PARRY Pary Perry F5905

138282 JONES Mr Kenneth. 21 Alyn Drive, Rossett, Wrexham, Clwyd, LL12 0HQ.
CLUBBE HALL MORT F1816

138290 JONES Mrs L. (Hooper) 27 Rugby Close, Broadstairs, Kent, CT10 2XA.
FAITHFUL HANDSCOMB HOOPER KING LANCEFIELD ROOTS RUSSELL VICKERS F5816

138304 JONES Mr Leslie. 21 Carol Close, Upper Stoke Holycross, Norwich, Norfolk, NR14 8NN.
DAVIES HARGREAVES HEAPS HILL JONES OPENSHAW OVEREND OWENS F563

138312 JONES Mrs Lynda. (Elson) 63 Deepdene Vale, Dorking, Surrey, RH4 1NJ.
BALCOMB BAX CHAMBERS CROUCHER DENGATE Ealson Ellson ELSON FULLER GURR HEATH KNIGHT LONGHURST MARSHALL MUNN NORWOOD RUMMERY SAYERS SISLEY SMITH WEEDON F2112

138320 JONES Mr Malcolm. 24 William Street, Trethomas, Newport, Gwent, NP1 8DQ. Tel:0222-885266
Brees BREESE DAVIES EVANS INWOOD JENKINS JONES MORGAN REILLY RICHARDS ROWLANDS Silcock Silcocks SILCOX WATKIN WATKINS F1579

138339 JONES Miss Mary A. 17 Dunster Gardens, Cheltenham, Glous, GL51 0QT.
BEVAN CURTIS DUTFIELD EVANS FULWELL GILES GREEN HINTON HOPPER HUGHES JONES LOVERIDGE MASON MORRIS PURSER ROSE SMITH SUMMERS TANDY WEBB WILLIAMS F1946

138347 JONES Mrs Mary F. 4 Scott Drive, Lexden, Colchester, Essex, CO3 4JA.
AIREY COLLINS GALL HEASMAN LUFKIN MITCHELL STEPHENSON TANSLEY TWEED WAKELING F741

138355 JONES Mrs Mary. (Naylor) Llainwen, Llanfair Yn Neubwll, Holyhead, Anglesey Gwynedd, LL65 3HL.
ALLEN Allin BUTT HOBSON JONES NAYLOR NOBLE ROWLANDS SCOTT SHAW SHORT Talbert TALBOT THOMPSON F3338

138363 JONES Mrs Maud. 4 Holly Close, Clayton Le Woods, Chorley, Lancs, PR6 7JN. Tel:0772-321214
BROTHERTON DODD FITZELL Fizzel Fizzell FLETCHER Gervis HODGKINSON Hodkinson Hodskinson JARVIS Jervis NOTT Phizell PRESCOT Prescott TOMLINSON WILKINSON F2932

138371 JONES Maureen. 26 Greenside Crescent, Waterloo, Huddersfield, W Yorks, HD5 8QJ.
BROWN CUSICK DIAMOND JACKSON JONES MCARTHY O'BRIEN WHISTON F3086

138398 JONES Michael. 17 Forth Court, South Shields, Tyne & Wear, NE34 0NP. Tel:091-456-5681
AMBREY BRAIN CHALCROFT EMANUEL HALL HEAM HEAMES HOTHAM HOUGH JONES LAWFORD MORGAN POWELL SHEPPARD TALBOT THOMAS F1282

138401 JONES Mrs Olwyn C. (Parry) Bryn Clyd, Maes Llan, Eglwysbach, Gwynedd, LL28 5UB.
ANSON ATKINSON BAXTER BRIDGE CORNTHWAITE COTTON DAVIES DAWSON EVANS FARRINGTON Ffoulkes Ffoulks FOULKES Foulks GRIFFITH HALL HOLME HOW JOHNSTON Johnstone JOHSTONE JONES LINDSAY Lindsey Linzer LLOYD MESSENGER MORRIS NICHOLSON OLIPHANT OWEN OWN PARRY PRITCHARD RICHARDSON ROBERTS ROWLAND Sanders Saunder SAUNDERS Scorr Scorre Scorrs Scur Scure SCURR Scurre Scurres Skur Skurr SMITH STEPHENSON SYMOND THOMAS Tideman Tidiman TIDYMAN Tydeman Tydiman Tydman Wait WAITE WALKER Wate WILLIAMS WYNNE F888

138428 JONES Mr Owen. Anneddwen, Llanfihangel-Y-Creuddyn, Aberystwyth, Dyfed, SY23 4LB. Tel:09743-387
JONES LEWIS F5219

138436 JONES Mrs P. 43 Derby Road, Watford, Herts, WD1 2LZ.
BRICKEL COOKE HUMM JONES MIDWOOD RICH F2037

138444 JONES Mr Peter M. 9 Proctor Close, Grace Park, Brislington, Bristol, BS4 5HT. Tel:0272-710871
BRADSHAW DUFF KING LAWRANCE LEE LIGGINS NOTT SMITH STADON WEST F3053

138452 JONES Mr Peter Meurig. Tir Y Dail, Cae Groes, Y Bala, Gwynedd, LL23 7AQ. Tel:0678-520944
GRIFFITHS MICHAEL MORGAN PEREGRINE Pergrin F4209

138460 JONES Mrs R A. Po Box 674, Charters Towers, Queensland, 4820, AUSTRALIA.
Jeaves Jeeve JEEVES Jeve Jeves F7108

138479 JONES Mr Robert. 40 Lockingwell Road, Keynsham, Bristol, BS18 2HN.

ATHERTON BAKER BLACK HARRIS ISMADE Ismead JONES LARKIN MORTIMORE READ ROWLEY SPROD Sprood STEVENS STOCK THATCHER THOMAS Vearine VEARING WATTS WILKINS WILLIAMS WOOKEY YARD YOUNG F1836

138487 JONES Roger. Rosebank, Harmer Hill, Shrewsbury, SY4 3EE.
BAKER DENNIS GANE JONES MAIDEN MAYALL MEREDITH MIDDLETON MIDELTON PAISH SMITH SPOFFORTH TRUMP TUCKER WHITEHEAD WISH WRAY WRIGHT F423

138495 JONES Mrs Sheila. 114 Church View Gardens, Kinver, Stourbridge, W Midlands, DY7 6EF.
BETTS LANSDELL Love Loves LOVETT MECROW MORETON MOSSON O'CALLAGHAN F2986

138509 JONES Mrs Susan Jane. (Rushby) 4 Hunters Crescent, Totton, Southampton, Hants, SO4 2FA. Tel:0703-871028
ATTENBOROUGH CLEWES COOK HOPKINS JACKSON LOWBRIDGE REDFERN ROWLEY RUCHBY WEEDON F5074

138517 JONES Mrs Trina. (Greaves) 6 Rossio Grove, Wendouree, Victoria, 3355, AUSTRALIA.
BARNES BARRACLOUGH BLACKWELL CALLAGHAN CASTLE CROSS CROTON CURELL DARRAGH DAVIS EDMONDS FRANCIS GOULD GREAVES GREENWOOD HAYWOOD HUTCHINS JOHNSON JONES KEILLOR LAWSON LOWSON LUFF NEED PUDDLE READIE SHINE STANLEY STEPHENSON THOMAS VORCE WHITTON WILSHER WITHNELL F5468

138525 JONES Mr W A M. 30 Silver Birch Close, Woodham, Surrey, KT15 3QW. Tel:0932-343108
EVANS JONES MORGAN WATKINS F5091

138533 JONES Mr William L. 56 Regent Crescent, Skipton, N Yorks, BD23 1BE. Tel:0756-794774
BARFOOT BATTY CONYERS DAVIES DONKERSLEY ELEY Ely HILL JONES JOWETT MILLS OLIVER PITCHERS Redding RIDDING Simms SIMS SMITH TOULMIN WARNES F2886

138541 JONES-HARDWICK Mrs Joyce. (Hardwick) 1 Stencills Road, Walsall, W Midlands, WS4 2HJ. Tel:0922-26320
DYKE GOULD HARDWICK HAWKINS KENDRICK F4010

138568 JORDAN Mrs Bernice. (Alexander) 19 Holly Road, Poynton, Cheshire, SK12 1PA.
ALEXANDER JUDD Sheen SHIN F4143

138576 JORDAN Mrs G. (Lazenby) 70 White Hill Road, Brinsworth, Rotherham, S60 5JQ. Tel:0709-368214
JORDAN LAZENBY F6126

138584 JORDAN Mrs J E. 3 Glenwell Gardens, Newtonabbey, Co Antrim, N Ireland, BT36 7SZ. Tel:0232-849646
ADAMSON ARMSTRONG ATKINS BAUMFORTH BEATTIE BENNETT BEXTON CHAPLIN CLAREBROUGH COPLEY DAVIES DIVERS Diverse FIELDING Firth Firthe FYRTH GARNER GILL Haire HALAY Haley HALL HARE HIRST HORNCASTLE HUDSON Hurst JENNINGS JOHNSTON JORDAN KEN KITCHEN Kitching MARSHALL MOSS NICKSON Nycson OXLEY PICKLES POLLARD RAMSDEN RILEY SHELTON SPEIGHT Speyght TAYLOR THOMPSON Thomson TODD Tomson TWELLS Twelves WEST WRIGHT F3601

138592 JORDAN Mrs Louise. 232 Raedwald Drive, Bury St Edmunds, Suffolk, IP32 7DN. Tel:0284-704934
Dabby Darbey Darbie DARBY Derbey Derbie Derby Jordain JORDAN Jorden Jordon Jordun Jurdain Jurden Jurdon Jurdun Maisters MASTERS Mesters Musters F5658

138606 JORDAN Mrs Patricia. Kittoch Mill, Carmunnock, Glasgow, G76 9BJ.
JORDAN SCOULAR Scouller TOMLIN WALLBRIDGE F2776

138614 JORDAN Mrs Sarah. (Euren) Po Box 35, Albany, Auckland, 10, NEW ZEALAND.
ACKERMAN Akerman BALDWIN BARR BEARD BISHOP BRENNAN BRODIE CAFFERY Caffrey CAPON Cardell CORMACK COUPAR CURDELL Dane DAWN Dawne Euren FRANCIS GALE Gear GEIR GEORGE GORDGE Gorg Gorge GREEN HALLIDAY HASKING HOPKINS Hoskin Hosking JACK JACOB JOHN JONES JORDAN KING Loveys LOVIS LYALL MACKAY Magowan MALCOLM MARLEY Martin MATHESON Mcewan MCGOWAN MCKEOWN MCKILL MCLELLAN MILLER Morley MORTIN MOWAT MUNRO MURRAY Neene Neenes Nennis NINNIS PATERSON PROUDLOVE RAE ROSS ROWE SANDISON SIMPSON SUTHERLAND SWAINE THOMSON TREGONNING TROUNSON UREN VINCENT WEBB WILSON Youren F5439

138622 JOSEPH Dr A P. 25 Westbourne Road, Edgbaston, Birmingham, B15 3TX. Tel:021-454-0408
ABRAHAM BLOCH GLEIBERMAN HARRISON JACOB JACOBS JOSEPH JUNG LAZARUS LEVI LEVY MINDELSOHN PEDOTT PENNEY PENNY ROGERS WEINSTEIN F513

138630 JOSEPH Mr Charles Anthony Norman. 21 Church Street, Ashley, Newmarket, Suffolk, CB8 9DU. Tel:0638-730146
COOPER JOSEPH NORMAN PLAINE PLANE WILKIN WOODGATE F2323

138649 JOSLIN Mr C W. 61 Wentworth Avenue, Cambridge, Ontario, N1S 1G8, CANADA. Tel:+1-519-623-4865
BERRY JOSLIN MOSELEY MOUL MUGFORD ROGERS F5550

138657 JOSLIN Mr Peter W. Sunsets, 9 Heysham Avenue, Heysham, Lancs, LA3 2DH. Tel:0524-51588
BOND EYRE HOLMES JOSLIN OMEROD PARROTT SHERWIN THOROGOOD TOCKLEY WEATHERILL F3973

138665 JOSLING Mr Peter. 61 Golden Dell, Welwyn Garden City, Herts, AL2 4EE. Tel:0707-327917
JOSLING F2518

138673 JOWITT Mrs Diana. (Ratcliff) Heatherlea, 37 Briton Hill Road, Sanderstead, South Croydon, Surrey, CR2 0JJ. Tel:081-651-5643
AGER BOXALL BUTLAND CHALLESS CHANNALL COWLING DE LACY EVANS DEXTER EVANS INGHAM JONES JOWITT LEA MAY MILNER MORPHEW POTTER RATCLIFF TUPPEN WHITEHEAD WRIGHT F5088

138681 JOYNES Mr P E. 13 Jersey Close, Church Hill, Redditch, Worcs. Tel:0527-60056
Gines JOINES JOYNES WATTON F6122

138703 JOYNES Miss P. 1 Watson Terrace, Morpeth, Northumberland, NE61 1UE.
BIRCH GORSE GOSS HEPWORTH JOYNES LINFORD PEACOCK REECE ROWLEY SIMPSON F1116

138711 JUBB Mr Michael. Elliscroft, Elrig, Newton Stewart, Wigtownshire, DG8 9RD. Tel:098-87-437
JUBB F1468

138738 JUDD Mrs B L. 70 Priory Crescent, Upper Norwood, London, SE19 3EE. Tel:081-771-2654
Garrad GARRARD Garrett Garrod Garrott Gerrard JOHNSON PILLING WILKINSON F4246

138746 JUDD Mr Ivan L. 57 Digswell Rise, Welwyn Garden City, Herts, AL8 7PT.
JUDD LYE OSMAN PAIN PERREN SHEPPEARD F3776

138754 JUDGES Mrs R E. 238 Barton Road, Luton, Beds, LU3 7NH.
JUDGES F6963

138762 JUFFS Mr Paul. 1 Poplar Road, Breaston, Derbys, DE7 3BH.
JUFFS F4862

138770 JUNIPER Mr M G. 83 Thronhill, North Weald, Essex, CM16 6DP.
FENN FENNE Janniper Jeneper Jenever Jenifer Jeniffer Jenivere Jennever Jenniper Jennipher Jinnifer Jumper Junevar Junifer JUNIPER Junipher Juniver Junyver F481

138789 JUPP Mr David. 12 Mountwood, Hurst Park, East Molesey, Surrey, KT8 9RP. Tel:081-979-8653
JUP JUPE JUPP JUPPE F1207

138797 JUPP Mr Peter. 28 Shenley Road, Dartford, Kent, DA1 1YE. Tel:0322-276327
JUPP F3741

138800 JURD Mrs G L. 219 Westmount Road, Eltham, London, SE9 1XZ.
HUEGDON Hugdon F7191

138819 KANE Mr David J. 4 Ozanan Close, Fordley, Northumberland, Tyne & Wear, NE23 7BW.
BIRD DINNING DODDS ELSON KANE MILLS MOSS MURPHY WAKE WATSON F3962

138827 KANE Mrs Susan. 5/66 Clarence Road, Wood Green, London, N22 4PL.
BARNES DEWAR DODD GIBSON PEET PHILBIN PLATT THORPE F2781

138835 KAPPHAN Mrs J C. 1 Walter Street, Glen Waverley, Victoria, 3150, AUSTRALIA.
Palaie Palay PALEY Payley F6861

138843 KASSELL Mr T. 26 Richmond Road, Brompton On Swale, North Yorks, DL10 7HE.
KASSELL F6965

138851 KAY Miss E Margaret. 40 Linton Avenue, Leeds, W Yorks, LS17 8PX. Tel:0532-686026
ABBOTT ALMOND ANDREW APPLETON ARNFIELD Babbington BABINGTON BARKER BARLOW Bebbington Bebington BIBBY Boden BOTTOMLEY BOWDEN CLAYTON COOK Crichlow CRITCHLEY Cruchlow Doan Done DUNN ELLISON GREENHALGH GREGSON GRESTY GRIMSHAW HACKNEY Heginbotham HIGGINBOTHAM Higginbottom HOLT KAY KIRKPATRICK MARSH MILNER MOTTRAM PASS RIDGWAY ROTHWELL ROUTLEDGE SHALLCROSS THOMPSON THORNELY Thorniley Thornley TOPPIN WILD WRIGHT YOUNG F2266

138878 KEALEY Mrs Anne. 46 Towers Lane, Cockermouth, Cumbria, CA13 9EE.
BALLANTINE BENN BROWN BUSHBY DALE DIXON ELLIOT GLOVER GREEN HODGSON HOWLETT JERVIS MOORE NIXON OLIVER PEARSON PICKERING RICHARDSON ROUND RUDD SANDERSON SAUNDERS SHACKLEY SHARPE SURTEES WALLACE WHALE WISEMAN F6402

138886 KEANE Mrs S A. 9 Savick Road, Fulwood, Preston, Lancs.
BRINDLE BROMLEY COOPER COWARD DEAN DICKINSON DUGDALE FARRINGTON FORREST RABY REID RICHARDSON RIGBY SHARPLES SOUTHWORTH SOWERBUTTS TEARLE TOWERS WELCH F3649

138894 KEARLEY Mrs Susan. (Kerr) 27 Mellow Ground, Haydonleigh, Swindon, Wiltshire, SN2 3QJ. Tel:0793-728337
ALLEN DUNN FULBROOK Fullbrook HOOK HUDSON KEARLEY KERR O'DONNELL PRATT QUIRIE F2782

138908 KEARSEY Dr H A. 2 Beeching Close, Upton, Didcot, Oxon, OX11 9JR.
HINWOOD KEARSEY Kersey F6785

138916 KEARSEY Mr Jack. 47 Lilliesfield Avenue, Barnwood, Gloucester, GL3 3AQ. Tel:0452-618444
KEARSEY Kersey F4523

138924 KEDGE Mr Thomas. 2 York Road, Brentford, Middx, TW8 0QP. Tel:081-568-9752
Cadge Cage Kadge KEDGE Keg Ketch SMITH F531

138932 KEECH Mr John. 2 Webster Place, Mill Road, Stock, Essex, CM4 9LF. Tel:0277-840259
KEECH NEALE WHITTY WILLIS F2040

138940 KEEFE Mrs Myrtle. (Harrington) 867 Wildwood Trail, Santa Rosa, CA 95409, USA. Tel:+1-707-539-0840
FIELDING GRAY HOYLE WOOD F5691

138959 KEENE Dr David E. 20 Clare Lawn Avenue, East Sheen, London, SW14 8BG. Tel:081-876-5122
Austen AUSTIN Botoler Botollien BUTLER GOODVIGHT Kean Keane Keen KEENE Keens Kene Kens F193

138967 KEEP Mr David. 81 Hurst Road, Sidcup, Kent, DA15 9AQ. Tel:081-302-3052
BELL GELDART KEEP SEDWELL SOUTHERBY F4555

138975 KEEP Dr P J. 7 Bluebell Crescent, Eaton, Norwich, Norfolk, NR4 7LE. Tel:0603-58668
Ceep Cepe Keap Keape Kebbe Kebe KEEP Keepe Keeppe Kep Kepe Kibbe Kibe Kipe Kippe Kyppe F654

138983 KEER Mrs Brenda M. (Green) 39 Dover Road, Wanstead Park, London, E12 5DZ. Tel:081-989-7336
GREEN HUNTER F5383

138991 KEETCH Mr David. 54 The Leas, Darlington, Co Durham, DL1 3DA. Tel:0325-483906
CRABB CROZIER KEETCH KING MADLE F5072

139009 KEETCH Mrs Pam. (Damsell) White Walls, 42 Rectory Lane, Little Bowden, Market Harborough, Leics, LE16 8AS.
DAMSELL F5802

139017 KEETLEY Mr Leonard. 67 Albert Park Road, Malvern, Worcs, WR14 1RR. Tel:0684-569810
KEETLEY F833

139025 KEETON Mrs Shirley. (Mann) 43 Beeversleigh, Clifton Lane, Rotherham, South Yorks, S65 2AD. Tel:0709-370801
CARBUTT Denton KEETON Mann MANNS RHODES DENTON F5055

139033 KEEVILL Mrs N. 69 Downs View, Chalford Hill, Stroud, Glos, GL6 8NB.
BASEBE BEAUCHAMP CODY DOLMAN Keevil KEEVILL Keeville Kevil Kevill MILLARD F4052

139041 KELLETT Mrs Anne. Eton College, 88 Gresham Road, Staines, Middx, TW18 2AE.
CLARKE F3169

139068 KELLEY Mr Tom. 29 Hoppingwood Avenue, New Malden, Surrey, KT3 4JX. Tel:081-942-7884
Arman Armar Armer Armour COOKE DANIEL FLOOD FRANCES Hamer Harman Harmar Harmen HARMER Harmon Harmour KELLEY MUNFORD TOWNSHEND WILLIAMSON WILLIM F2303

139076 KELMAN Miss A D. 14a Roger Street, Muswellbrook, NSW 2333, AUSTRALIA.
Kalman Kellman KELMAN Kelmon F6817

139084 KELSEY Mrs Linda. (Cunningham) Khobar, Ridgway, Pyrford, Woking, Surrey, GU22 8PW. Tel:0932-347605
ANDERSON BATTLE BELL BIRD BROWN COLLINS CUNNINGHAM DOUCH DOUSE ELLIOT GREGOOSE HONIE LINDSELL LOUGH MULLARD NICHOLL NICHOLSON NIXON OSBORNE PENFOLD POWELL RIDLEY SEARLE SMITH SPENS STOCK TINLINE TOFT WEBB WILLIAMS WOODHAM F4644

139092 KELVIN Dr Patricia. Orchard House, 66 Ladder Hill, Wheatley, Oxon, OX9 1HY.
CURRIE EMETT GAWLER GOLDEN GREENFIELD HACKWOOD HOBBS MOORS PHILLIPS WILSON F143

139106 KEMP Miss D V M. 43 Kent Gardens, London, W13 8BU.
ALDERTON BARTLETT BURGESS ELPHICK HAMERTON HANCOCK HARDWICK HARTNUP HOWARD Keggan KEGGIN KEMP Kiggin SHAW SMITH WILLETT F6090

139114 KEMP Mrs Irene. 18 Eileen Avenue, Southport, Queensland, 4215, AUSTRALIA.
ARMSTRONG BAKER BROADHURST BROWNING BUCHANAN BUCHMAN BURLEY CHRISTIE COLLETT COLLINS CRAPP CROSS CULSHAW EDWARD FOGG HAY HOARE HUGHES JACKET KAY KEMP KIDNEY LAWN LENAN Linnane LITTLEJOHN MCMULLIN MEALING MOORCROFT MOSLEY MYFORD NEIGHBOUR REDMOND ROBINSON SAMMON STEPHENS STEPHENSON Stevenson SWALES WARRINGTON WOOD F5420

139122 KEMP Mr Michael. 38 Bancroft Street, Bulwell, Nottingham, NG6 9HF.
FRANCIS GARNER HOPKINSON KEMP NEWELL PAYNE RIMMINGTON SHUTTLEWORTH SIMS TEASDALE F1382

139130 KEMP Mr W J. 1 Lister Road, Stafford, ST16 3NB. Tel:0785-53930
BARTLET Camp Campe Cimp GREGORY KEMP Kempe Kimp Kimpe MOSELEY F4943

139149 KENDAL-WARD Mr Clifford. 3 Marchfield Terrace, Edinburgh, EH4 7AE. Tel:031-336-3081
BRADLEY BROADHURST BROADLEY FAWCETT FORSTER GARTON GLEDHILL GRAY HAMILTON HAMMETT HAWKER HOGGART HOLLAND HOUGHTON HUBANK HURLEY JACKSON KERSHAW KNOWLES MEASE MORTIN MORTON NEWTON RAWCLIFFE SEARLE SHAW SMETHAM SQUIRE STANDEVEN STEPHENSON THOMPSON TURNER WALKER WARD WATSON WHARTON WOOTON WRANGHAM F6169

139157 KENDALL Mr P G. 5 The Drive, Hailsham, Esat Sussex, BN27 3HN. Tel:0323-840024
BRUDENELL COTTRELL KEEN KENDALL KIMBER F2808

139165 KENDON Mrs E C P. (Horne) 14 Culme Close, Oundle, Peterborough, Cambs, PE8 4QQ. Tel:0832-272369
COLE FAGG HOBDAY WILLIAMS F3766

139173 KENDRICK Mrs Maureen. (Wall) 6 Dark Orchard, Tenbury Wells, Worcs, WR15 8DH. Tel:0584-811054
ASHLEY DIGGORY Dukes GONDERTON JUKES Juks KENDRICK OWEN PEDLEY WALL F5298

139181 KENNEDY Miss Cecilia. 7 Bonney Way, Swanley, Kent, BR8 7BL.
BETHELL CHESHIRE CRUMP HOPKINS KENNEDY KENNETT KIRWAN LAMBERT MCDONNOUGH MCDONOUGH MORGAN RYAN SEDDON F708

139203 KENNEDY Mrs Margaret M. (Power) Po Box 718, Shepparton, Victoria, 3630, AUSTRALIA.
ALLEN BRENNAN BROUGHALL Brughall CALVERT Charteris CHARTERS CLARKE Clemason Clementson Clemison CLEMSON Coad COADE Code CROWE DAVIS DUNNING Elise Ellice Elliess ELLIS FAIL Faulkingham Flinn FLYNN FOLKINGHAM FRAHER Frahir Frehr Fryor GILHAM GOSLING HALL HALLIDAY HAMM HOADLEY HUNTER KAY KENNEDY LAIDLAW-MCLAUGHLAN LANGLEY LEACH LORNE LOVE MCGIBBON Mclaghlin Mclaren Mclaughlan MCLAUGHLIN Mclauglan Mclauglin Mclauran Mclauren MCLAURIN MILLS PARKINSON PATON

PETERSON Phraher POLLOCK Pooer POWER QUAIN Quan Quinn Raher SHORT SULLIVAN TAIT Thomasson Thomisson THOMPSON THOMSON TILBROOK Tomasson Tomisson Tomson VAUGHAN WALSHAW Welshaw WILDE WOODCOCK YULE F4127

139211 KENNER Ms Joan. C/o Kelvedon, 25 Marius Road, Balham, London, SW17 7QU.
BUSH Keenor Kena Kennar KENNER Kennor Kenor Kiner Kinnear Kinner Kinnuer Kinver Kyner Kynner PYE F977

139238 KENNETT Jo. The White House, Headcorn Road, Sutton Valence, Kent, ME17 3EH.
RICHARDS F7354

139246 KENNEY Lillian. 12150 Peack Road, Plymouth, IN 46563, USA.
BORROR F7240

139254 KENT Mr Alan J. 6 Clarendon Road, Bournemouth, Dorset, BH4 8AJ. Tel:0202-763712
COX ELVY JACKSON KENT TUDGEY F2761

139262 KENT Mrs Barbara. 17 Red Hill, Stourbridge, W Midlands, DY8 1NA.
Waggestaff Waggstaf Waggstafe Waggstaff Waggstaffe Wagstaf Wagstafe WAGSTAFF Wagstaffe F2299

139270 KENT Major James. Old Naggs Head, Wereham, Kings Lynn, Norfolk, PE33 9AP. Tel:0366-500764
EMBLETON HOBSON KENT MANN SMALLBONES SMITH THOMPSON WARNES WILKINGSON F548

139289 KENYON Mrs Marjorie V. (Nicholson) Beach Croft, Drigg Road, Seascale, Cumbria, CA20 1NX. Tel:09467-28146
NICHOLSON F3728

139297 KEOUGH Mr E. Po Box 3934, 1000 Oaks, CA 91359, USA.
APPLEBY HAW Howe Kehoe Keogh KEOUGH Laight LATES LEWIS Maddison MADISON NELSON PATTISON F5698

139300 KEPPIE Mr J C. 5 Abercorn Avenue, Edinburgh, EH8 7HP. Tel:031-661-3791
CAPIE CAPPIE Cappy Kapie Keppey KEPPIE Keppy F1966

139319 KERLOGUE Mrs J G. Dittisham House, Lyons Gate, Dorchester, Dorset, DT2 7AZ.
KERSLAKE F7004

139327 KERNER Mr S R J. 65 Liverpool Grove, London, SE17 2HP. Tel:071-708-1770
BEEDELL HELLINGS KERNER LEWORTHY RAWLE SPAULL WIGNALL F3833

139335 KERR Mrs Amanda. (Flashman) Sea Splash, 2 Marine Drive, Goring By Sea, West Worthing, West Sussex, BN12 4QN.
BEDDINGFIELD BLADEN DAY FLASHMAN HOLDER WEEKS F4926

139343 KERR Mrs Christine Doris. (Arnold) 4 Glencregagh Park, Belfast, Co Antrim, N Ireland, BT6 ONT.
ARNOLD CAVE CHANNING HISTED ISTED F731

139351 KERRIDGE Mr Andrew. 93 Neville Road, Limbury, Luton, Beds, LU3 2JG. Tel:0582-576731
BIELBY BURRELL CLEMENTS FIRTH FLINTOFT HARTSHORN Hartshorne INMAN KERRIDGE METCALF MOOK PICKERING ROSE WILEY YAXLEY F3942

139378 KERRIGAN S A. 167 Everard Drive, Colston, Glasgow, G21 1XW.
COWAN DICK FORREST GLENFIELD KERRIGAN LAW MARR PETTIGREW REWCASTLE THOM F2941

139386 KERRY Mrs S J. 8 Windermere Way, Farnham, Surrey, GU9 ODE.
ANSELL Ansiel Ansill BARNES BATHURST BRADEY BURROUGHS Burrows BUTLER CLARK Clarke Fake Feak FEAKES Feaks FULLER GATES GOODWIN HALFHEAD Harpam HARPHAM Harpum HILL Holt HOPKINSON HOULT Keeley KEELY Kerrey Kerrie KERRY KIRKHAM LOVEDAY LUCAS Lucasse MALKIN MARSH Maulkin Oddie ODDY OWEN PENSTON Penstone POTTS Ranbie RANBY Randbie RELF Relph SEARS Siers STACEY SUNNUCKS TANNER TURLEY TURVEY TUSTIN WIDDOWSON WILLIAMSON Willson WILSON WOOD F2611

139394 KERSHAW Mr Colin. 33 Chaucer Street, Royton, Oldham, Lancs, OL2 6RG.
KERSHAW F3763

139408 KERSHAW Mrs P J. (Goode) 18 Frog Hall Drive, Wokingham, Berks, RG11 2LF.
CHATER GOODE MUNDAY PITHAM F1341

139416 KERSHAW Mrs Pamela. (Alleyn) 22 Burdon Lane, Cheam, Surrey, SM2 7PT. Tel:081-643-1666
ALLEN ALLEYN KERSHAW F4277

139424 KERSHAW Mr Walter Donald. 9 Chester Court, Winchester Road, Southampton, Hants, SO1 2TP. Tel:0703-778840
EASTWOOD HEGINBOTTOM F1739

139432 KERSLAKE Mr Signey Ian. 14 Coniston Crescent, Loughborough, Leics, LE11 3RH. Tel:0509-261741
BARROW DROWN FERRIS FURSE GRATTON KERSLAKE F4807

139440 KERSLEY Mr & Mrs D M R. Candleford, 12 Hazelbank Close, Sheet, Petersfield, Hants, GU31 4BY. Tel:0730-264083
Kearsley Kearsly Kerseley KERSLEY Kersly Kiersley F7077

139459 KESTERTON Mr Malcolm. 97 Rustlings Road, Sheffield, S11 7AB. Tel:0742-666864
ALBIN BARTLETT BERESFORD Casterson Casterton Cesterson Cesterton Cestreton Chesterson Chesterton DAVIS GETHING HAINES HOLLAND Kesterson KESTERTON KILOW PAYTON ROSON RUTTER STEEDMAN SWAIN TREVOR VILLAGE WAKSTEAD WATTS YATES F2515

139467 KETTER Mr Paul. 1311 Candlelight Ave, Duncanville, TX 75137, USA.
KETTER F7303

139475 KETTERINGHAM Mrs S G. Croft House, Great Tosson, Thropton, Morpeth Northumberland, NE65 7NW.
CHADWICK DALTON GATENBY KETTERINGHAM SHARPLES SHONE SYMS TYM F270

139483 KEVAN Mrs N. (Edwards) 1 Fischer St, Port Macquarie, NSW 2444, AUSTRALIA. Tel:+61-06-583-7603
ADIAR ALLERTON ARMITAGE BIRCHALL BOLLAND DOWLAN Dowland DOWLING EDWARDS FIDLER GILLOTT GUY HERON JOHNSON Keavan KENNEDY KEVAN Kevand Keven MASON Mcgoffock Mcgoffog Mcguffie MCGUFFOG MCLAUGHLAN MUSKER NEILSON PORTER ROB THOM TOATTERSALL WALLACE WILCOCK WOODS F4383

139491 KEVERN Mrs Veronica Tabert. Chyvounder, Richards Lane, Illogan, Redruth Cornwall, TR16 4DQ. Tel:0209-215564
BERRYMAN CARVASSO Corvouso Curnoe CURNOW Kevan Keveren KEVERN KEVERNE KEVERYN LAMPREY Landery LANDRY Laundery Laundry QUICK ROSEWALL SPARGO STEPHENS STEVANS TABERT TREMBATH F3209

139505 KEW Mrs P. (Filewood) 3 Esplanade Court, Brighton Road, Worthing, Sussex, BN11 2BL. Tel:0903-208566
FILEWOOD Fillwood Fylewood F6392

139513 KIDDLE Mrs B. (Cross) 2 Carmel Villas, Wincanton, Somerset, BA9 9EF.
Crose CROSS Crosse Keddle Kettle KIDDLE Kiddle-White Kidel Kidell Kihol Kittle F5203

139521 KIDDLE Mr William. 3 Chelmer Garth, Paston, Peterborough, Cambs, PE4 7XX. Tel:0733-572789
DOBSON KIDALL KIDDALL KIDDLE F156

139548 KIDMAN Mr Thomas H F. 36 London Road, Cirencester, Glos, GL7 1AG.
KIDMAN F346

139556 KIDNER Mr Peter. Highfield, Gas Lane, Hinton St George, Somerset, TA17 8RX.
Chebbott Chetemore CHIBBETT Chibott Clibbott Cubett Cubitt Elworlthie Elworthe ELWORTHY GEBBETT Gibett Jebett Ketenor Ketner KIDNER Kitner Kitnor Kittnor Kybbet Kybet Kydenor Kyne Kytemore Kytner Kyttner F5095

139564 KIDWELL Mr A P. 21 Oakhill Road, Ashtead, Surrey, KT21 2JG.
BIRT BROWNING Kadwell Kedwell KIDWELL NORMAN POOK F2376

139572 KIELLOR-EDWARDS Mrs A. Ringstrasse 40, W-6501 Dexheim, GERMANY.
Kiellar Kieller KIELLOR F7096

139580 KILBORN Mr H M H. 18 Horncastle Road, Lee, London, SE12 9LA.
KILBORN F2033

139599 KILBOURNE Mr L B. 2 Pawley Gardens, Eyres Monsell Estate, Leicester, LE2 9AE. Tel:0533-774349
HARDISTY KILBOURNE F3562

139602 KILBURN Mrs Audrey. (Knowles) Rosewell

Cottage, Ladywood, Droitwich, Worcestershire, WR9 0AJ. Tel:0905-52443
BAKER HALFARD Halfred HALFYARD Halfyeard HARVEY Hellard Hembrough HEMBROW Hoar HOARE Hore Knol Knoll KNOWLES Noll Nowel Nowell SPERRING TAPP TILLY Whore F1616

139610 KILDUFF Mrs Christi. 3416 Echo Springs Road, Lafayette, CA 94549, USA.
KILDUFF Killduff F7098

139629 KILDUFF Christi. 3470 Vista Oaks Dr #205, Martinez, CA 94553, USA.
KILDUFF F7304

139637 KILLER Mr David. Crud Yr Awel, Llanrhystud, Dyfed, SY23 5AA.
KILLER Killhard Killhare Kyllar F189

139645 KILLOCK Mrs Diane H. 44 Florence Avenue, Wilsden, Bradford, W Yorks, BD15 0HE.
DUNHAM Dunholm JANNEY Jenney STANLEY F2258

139653 KILLON Miss M R. Elstree Manor, Edgwarebury Lane, Elstree, Herts, WD6 3RF.
Comford Conford Cornfoot CORNFORD Cornfort Killan KILLON F6762

139661 KILVINGTON Mrs J. (Walker) 8 Newlay Wood Crescent, Horsforth, Leeds, West Yorks, LS18 4LW.
BOLDY BROWN FITZ KILVINGTON STOKES WALKER WEST WRIGHT F5921

139688 KIMBER Ms J. 21 The Towers, Victoria Road, Netley Abbey, Southampton Hants, SO3 5DR.
AKEHURST CHITTUCK CLEVELAND DIMOND DOWN DOWSING DREWS HOILES KIMBER KING LAVINGTON LEEKS LINCH REEVES SIMPSON SINFIELD TOVELL VARNDELL WYATT F3879

139696 KIMMINS Mr John. 72 Skippers Meadow, Ushaw Moor, Co Durham, DH7 7QJ.
CHAMPION KIMMINGS KIMMINS KIMMONS MCCLURE PENNICK PENNOCK F2464

139718 KIMPTON Mr W J. Mess 1.04, Rfa Argus, Bfpo 433.
BURGESS KIMPTON NANCARROW THOMAS F3310

139726 KINDT Mrs H. 5 Toll Close, Mareeba, Queensland, 4880, AUSTRALIA.
ALDERDICE Alderdyce Allderdice F6821

139734 KINDT Helen. 9 Toll Close, Mareeba 4880, AUSTRALIA.
ALDERDICE F7224

139742 KING Mr A E T. 5 Ogwell Mill Road, Bradley Barton, Newton Abbot, Devon, TQ12 1PG.
KING F7049

139750 KING Carole. 39 Lopez House, Willington Road, London, SW9 9NF.
Wathew Wathews Wathey Watthew WATTHEWS F7385

139769 KING Mr David R. Chantry, Cowley, Exeter, Devon, EX5 5EJ. Tel:0392-78628
ADAMS BRITAIN COLBRIDGE COLLINS CRASKE EDWARDS KING KITCHEN MESSENGER PARRY SELLICK SMITH STENLAKE WOOD WOODCOCK F1672

139777 KING Mrs Elizabeth. (Morgan) 25 Harries Street, Tenby, Dyfed, SA70 7NA. Tel:0834-4338
BEAGLEY BRIGHTWELL CARMAN EMMETT GOMM HACKER KING LEVETT MORGAN MUSSELWHITE NORWOOD SANDALL SCOTT F3223

139785 KING Mr G M. 27 Avondale Road, Hove, E Sussex, BN3 6ER.
BROMLEY EUSTACE Fardel FARDELL Fardle GREENE KING SALTMARSH Saltmarshe Saltmash WATTS YOUNG F5915

139793 KING Mr Geoffrey. 6 Ryles Close, Macclesfield, Cheshire, SK11 8DA. Tel:0625-611288
DAVIES KING WILLIAMS F4787

139807 KING Mrs Gillian. Penlee, Delamer Road, Bowdon, Altrincham Cheshire, WA14 2NT. Tel:061-928-0096
BIRD BOULTER CONYERS COSWAY FORSYTH JAMES KING LAURANCE MICHAEL NASH PODMORE STUBBS WINNALL F2358

139815 KING Mrs M E E. (Cleverdon) 25 Clifton Crescent, Falmouth, Cornwall, TR11 3QQ.
BATTEN CLEVERDON GILBERT GLOYN HARVEY HOLE KING OLIVER PRISK STONEMAN F4298

139823 KING Mrs M. (Travess) Middle Mellings, Tilkey Road, Coggeshall, CO6 1QN.
BAKER LADWELL TRAVERS TRAVES TRAVESS F5683

139831 KING Miss Mary. 21 Homecross House, Fishers Lane, Chiswick, London, W4 1YA.
BARRETT BRAY CHISNALL DANIELS DRIVER GREEN WALDEN Walding Waldren Wallden WATTS WINTERTON F2149

139858 KING Ms Pamela. 69 Hillcrest, Monkseaton, Whitley Bay, Tyne & Wear, NE25 9AF.
CALVELEY CALVERLEY FENTON GOLIGHTLEY RITSON STOBBART WHITE F2130

139866 KING Mr Patrick. Bachau, Newchapel, Boncath, Dyfed, SA37 0ET.
CHAPMAN CORNELL DEARMAN FROST HARRIES HAUGHTON HOPKINS HUMPHREYS IRVINE IVES KING LYLES MORRIS MOTTON PITTS RUSSELL SESSIONS SHIPLEY SQUAREY F6103

139874 KING Mrs S C. (Lamb) 85 Homestead Road, Hatfield, Herts, AL10 0QR. Tel:0707-260399
CLARKE COWAN DAMMANN HAILES HALES LAMB PITTILLA WARDROPER WHITE F831

139882 KINGAN Mrs D F. Loch Hill, Po Box 21, Akaroa, NEW ZEALAND.
KINGAN F6675

139890 KINGDON Mr John. 1 Pound Close, Rod Lane, Ilton, Ilminster Somerset, TA19 9ET.
BOND DIDHAM Kingdom Kingdome Kingdomme KINGDON Kingdone Kingdonne Kyngedon Kyngedone Liteljohns Littlejohn LITTLEJOHNS Littlejon Littlejons Lytteljohns Lytteljons PUNCHARD STACEY WALKER F830

139904 KINGDON Mrs Judith. (Smith) 1 Pound Close, Rod Lane, Ilton, Ilminster Somerset, TA19 9ET.
RAM Rame Ramm Ramme SMITH F5671

139912 KINGETT Mr Edward. 86 Devonshire Avenue, Woking, Surrey, GU21 5QB. Tel:0932-347505
Kingeet Kinget KINGETT Kingette Kinggett Kingzett Kynget STEVENS F4978

139920 KINGSMAN C. 156 Silverleigh Road, Thornton Heath, Surrey, CR7 6DS.
BAILEY HACKWELL POLLARD YOUNG F1222

139939 KINGSMILL Mr A J. Coremansstraat 24, Bus 6, 2600 Antwerp, BELGIUM.
KINGSMILL F7183

139947 KINGSTON Mr M J. 13 Maple Drive, Kings Worthy, Winchester, Hants, SO23 7NG.
DIGWEED F6745

139955 KINGSWELL Mr John. Clodiagh House, 34 Knighton Park, Barton On Sea, New Milton, Hampshire, BH25 7PG. Tel:0425-610287
BUSHNELL JENNINGS KINGSWELL PERRY PITT WHEELER F2954

139963 KINGWELL Mr Peter F. 8 Moyeady Avenue, Rugby, Warwicks, CV22 5HE.
INGS Kingswell Kingswill KINGWELL Kingwill Kingwyll Kyngwill Kyngwyll Langabear Langabeare Langabere LANGSBEAR Langsbeare Langsbere STICKLAND F3547

139971 KINNISON BOURKE Mrs Judith. Rose Cottage, Chapel Row, Herstmonceux, Hailsham E Sussex, BN27 1RB.
ALCHORN AUSTIN BALCOMBE BARNEY BIRKMYRE BOURKE BUCKLAND BURTON CLARK COLLINS COPPARD CROFT DOHORTY EADES EARLE FLETCHER FORD GARLICK GIBBONS HADOCK HARRIS HORSECRAFT HOVER HUGGETT HUMPHRIES KINNISON KNOWLTON LANGAN LAVELLE LILY LONGHURST MARTIN MATES MAUGHAN MEWETT MILLINGTON MILLWARD MULLARD PAINTER PANKHURST PARSONS PHILLIPS PRICE RADBURN RUTHERFORD SANKEY SAVAGE SEYMOUR SHEPHERDLEY Shipherdley SIMMONS SLADE SMITH SOMMERVILLE SOUTHERTON TICEHURST TUFTON TUPPEN TUTT WALLS WARD WATKINS WILDASH WINTERS WOOD F3133

139998 KINROSS Mrs Elaine. (Russell-Lilley) 25 Mayfield Drive, Bare, Morecambe, Lancs, LA4 6ES.
RUSSELL-LILLEY F7394

140007 KINVIG Mrs Ellen B. Jones Flat Road, R R 3, Summerland, British Columbia, V0H 1Z0, CANADA.
KINVIG F7305

140015 KIPLING Mr Paul Gerard. 42 Abbotsham Road, Bideford, Devon, EX39 3AP. Tel:0237-475438
KIPLING PEARSON F3166

140023 KIPPS Mr Brian. 2 Blundell Crescent, Southport, Merseyside, PR8 4RF. Tel:0704-66003
BLANCHARD CHANDLER HAYES KIPPS PARKER F4003

140031 KIPPS Mrs Carol. (Smitten) 2 Blundell Crescent, Southport, Merseyside, PR8 4RF. Tel:0704-66003
ELLINGHAM LEESON REYNOLDS SMITTEN WARNER F4004

140058 KIRBY Mrs Eileen. (Vickers) 64 Brampton Lane, Armthorpe, Doncaster, S Yorks, DN3 3HX. Tel:0302-831272
ALLCORN CHRISMAS Christmas DEAN GOODSELL HOWELL JESSUP PHILCOX STICKLAND Strickland THORPE TODMAN VICKERS F3706

140066 KIRBY Mrs S. 54 Weymouth Street, Hemel Hempstead, Herts, HP3 9SJ.
BIRD CRUSE ECCLES HOUGHTON KEEN RICHARDSON VERRINDER F4034

140074 KIRCHER Mr Robert H. Pfingstweid Strasse 8-B, W-6382 Friedrichsdorf 1, GERMANY.
KIRCHER F7306

140082 KIRKHAM Mrs Betty. Box 50, Lucindale, SA 5272, AUSTRALIA.
BOSSISTOW DURE ELLIS EVANS HILLIARD KIRKHAM LAMBORNE LEE LUKE MITCHELL NUTTALL RAE TAYLOR F4403

140090 KIRKMAN Mr Ken. 35 Albury Drive, Pinner, Middx, HA5 3RL. Tel:081-866-9191
ABBOTT DAVENPORT GRAFTON HARPER KIRKMAN LAIRD MURPHY NEWBERRY POPLE RICHBELL ROY SHAW TAYLOR WIGHTMAN F1979

140104 KIRSOPP Mr & Mrs E. 14 The Drive, Shotley Bridge, Consett, Co Durham, DH8 0DL. Tel:0207-504488
BISHOP KERSHOPE KIRSOPP F1180

140112 KITCHING Mr Donald. Brookside, Newbiggin, Heads Nook, Carlisle, Cumbria, CA9 9DH. Tel:0768-86609
KITCHING MAUGHAN WOOD F4871

140120 KITCHING Mr Ron. 2 Allnut Avenue, Basingstoke, Hants, RG21 2BW. Tel:0256-22011
DUBERY GERHARD KITCHING WILLIS F1919

140139 KITE Mrs G E. 7 Gravel Road, Bromley, Kent, BR2 8PE.
DAVEY Davy GOODE Landray LANDREY Landry Landy Laundrey Lawndrey Lawndrie ROWE VAGUE F1775

140147 KITT Mr David. 46 Hyholmes, Bretton, Peterborough, Cambs, PE3 8LJ. Tel:0733-266077
Carol Carrol CARROLL DOWNEY GAREY Keet Kit KITT Kitts Kyte MORGAN POLLOCK STITT F1008

140155 KITT Miss P. 8 Nutfield Grove, Filton, Bristol, BS12 7LJ.
COLE GALLIFORD HARRIS HODGES KITT MEAKER F3477

140163 KITTRIDGE Mrs Maud. (Ough) 119 Clevelode, Malvern, Worcs, WR13 6PD.
HENDY KITTRIDGE OUGH RUTTER TRESSIDER HALL F5969

140171 KLINKERT Mr Graham. 22 Richmond Close, Ware, Herts, SG12 0EN.
BLAXHILL CORDERY DYER FURRELL GILES HINDE F2065

140198 KNAPP Mrs Shirley. 20 Sycamore Avenue, Hatfield, Herts, AL10 8LZ. Tel:0707-264099
COCHRANE DIGSWELL HALSEY KNAPP NASH F2674

140201 KNELL Mrs Eileen. (Bregazzi) 72 Plantation Road, Poole, Dorset, BH17 7LP.
Baggazzi Begazzi Biggazzi Bragarri Bragazzie Braggazzi Bregazzi BREGAZZIE Breggazi Brigazzi KNELL OVER F4653

140228 KNIGHT Mr Howard Marriage. 327 Nore Road, Portishead, Bristol, BS20 8EN. Tel:0275-845113
Marag Marage Maragh Marayge Maregge Mariadge Mariag Mariage Mariche Maridge Marige Marigg Marrage Marraige Marredge Marrege Marriadg Marriag MARRIAGE Marriages Marrich Marriche Marridg Marridge Marrige Marriges Marryadge Marryage Maryadge Maryge F4191

140236 KNIGHT Mrs J. 21 Croft Road, Mortimer Common, Reading, Berks, RG7 3TS.
CLARK HILLINGWORTH MANN PLACE SEDGWICK SMITH STONAH STONEY YATES F2260

140244 KNIGHT Joan M. 12 Sandy Ridge, Chislehurst, Kent, BR7 5DR.
ABLETT FRANKLIN F1877

140252 KNIGHT Mr K W G. 78 Ramshill Road, Paignton, Devon, TQ3 3PL. Tel:0803-852268
Gourney GURNEY Gurnie Gurny Gurnye F3550

140260 KNIGHT Miss Margaret A. Baringama, Po Box 141, Leeton, Nsw, 2705, AUSTRALIA. Tel:+61-6-953-2347
BOYLE BURGES DAVIS DOHERTY FAHEY GILLESPIE HOLMES KNIGHT LLOYD ROURKE SMITH WITHERS F5161

140279 KNIGHT Mrs Mary. (Clark) Kingswood, 238 Barton Hill Road, Barton, Torquay, Devon, TQ2 8LA. Tel:0803-311876
Avason AVESTON Avoison BARRETT BASKERVILLE DAVIES Ffray Frie FRY Frye GRIFFITHS HART HIGHLAND KNIGHT STRANG Veal VEALE WILLIAMS F5635

140287 KNIGHT Mr R G H. Po Box 55, Mooloolaba, Queensland, 4557, AUSTRALIA.
GLASSON GOODERHAM HOPPER KNIGHT MATTHEWS PEIRPOINT PERRY PITTAM SKEATES STANSBIE TREZISE F5557

140295 KNIGHT Mrs Rosa L. 6 St Margarets Crescent, Roath, Cardiff, CF2 5AU. Tel:0222-486144
BANTON Bouant BURROWS BUSBY CAPLE COX DAVID FOURACRE FOWLER HORTON HUTCHINS ISBELL JENKINS KNIGHT LEWIS Loines Loins Lowins Loyn LOYNS POWELL ROBERTS RUSSELL STEBBING Stebling WEBB WHITE WILLIAMS F4434

140309 KNIGHT Mr T D. 1 Blacksmiths Lane, South Littleton, Evesham, Worcs, WR11 5TW.
AINGE BIRD Byrd DAVIS DRAKE FLETCHER Geaden Geadon GEDEN Gedon Geeden Geedon Geyden Geydon GISBORNE HALL HEWINS Huins INGRAM JEFFRIES KNIGHT MORRIS TAYLOR YATES F686

140317 KNIGHTS Mrs Christine. Packridge Farm, Packridge Lane, Romsey, Hants, SO51 9LL.
ANTHONY APPLEBY BEWEN BRADSHAW BRANCH BROWN CLARK EDWARDS Enew ENNEW Gardener Gardiner GARDNER GLAZIER GRAY HALL HEARD JONES KNIGHTS LESLIE MORRIS PHILLIPS POTTER PRIOR ROSE SELBY SIMONS THOMAS Vos VOSS Vox WADLEY Willemore Willmer WILMER Wilmore YOUNG F2447

140325 KNIGHTS Mr Philip. 6 Ruskin Close, Pound Hill, Crawley, Sussex, RH10 3TP. Tel:0293-885586
BARNETT BENDER BURROWS KNIGHTS SPARLING F2032

140333 KNOTT Mrs Patricia A. 4 Craigendoran Avenue, Helensburgh, Strathclyde, G84 7AZ.
CLARK DONOVAN MAGUIRE O SULLIVAN PRIVETT STONEHAM F425

140341 KNOW Mr M P. 35 Chadacre Road, Southend, Essex, SS1 3QX.
JARVIS KNOW NORGROVE PANNELL F1865

140368 KNOWLES Mr Frank. 1 Mayfield Close, Bishops Cleeve, Cheltenham, Glos, GL52 4NA.
de Cnol de Knol de Knoll de Knolle Knol Knole Knoles Knoll Knolle Knolles KNOWLES F315

140376 KNOWLES Mr J. 43 Coldyhill Lane, Newby, Scarborough, N Yorks, YO12 6SF. Tel:0723-365607
KNOWLES Nowls F5206

140384 KNOWLES Mrs Joan. 252 Hylton Road, Worcester, WR2 5LA.
CARDO SWAIN F3218

140392 KNOWLING Elizabeth. 21 Wallaford Road, Buckfastleigh, Devon, TQ11 0AR.
FRENCH GIDLEY HEATH HEXT HOARE KNOWLING LEWIS MUDGE WHITEWAY F894

140406 KRONER Mrs Jean Kay. 22 Simmer Piece, Fenstanton, Huntingdon, Cambs, PE18 9LT. Tel:0480-66022
BARRINGER BATTERSBY F3486

140414 KUCK Miss Marjorie A C. Anderida, Dene Lane West, Lower Bourne, Farnham Surrey, GU10 3PS.
AMIES CARDEN FLOOK KUCK PEARCE SALMON TRAIL F342

140422 KYFFIN Mrs Ruth Louise. 6 Churchill Place, Blakenhale Road, Garretts Green, Birmingham, B33 0XB.
BEACON CUFFIN KIFFIN KYFFIN KYFFYN LABERT LAMBERT F357

140430 KYNE Mr C R. 20 Elizabeth Drive, Theydon Bois, Essex, CM16 7HJ.
KYNE F2722

140449 L'HUILLIER Mrs Linda. 3243 Anston Road, Green Bay, WI 54313, USA.
BOND COWLING CURTIS HARVEY HOOPER HOSKING JAMES NICHOLLS POLLARD RODDA F5547

140457 LABRAM Mrs Jacqueline. 11 Sadlers Lane, Dibden Purlieu, Hants, SO4 5LZ.
LABRAM Labrum F7218

140465 LACEY Mr & Mrs J E. 3 Park View House, Brock Street, Bath, Avon.
GUPPY LACEY WATTS WHITE F1058

140473 LACEY Mrs Nancy. (Henry) 103 Lonsdale Drive, Rainham, Gillingham, Kent, ME8 9JB.
BATES BRENTON DICKSON FORD GULLY HATFIELD HENRY JONES LACEY LLOYD RICHARDSON ROGERS SELWAY VAUGHAN F4585

140481 LACY Mr A J. 1 The Mount, Snydale Road, Normanton, West Yorks, WF6 1NU.
LACY F5879

140503 LADD Mr Roger. 27 Chaucer Court, New Dover Road, Canterbury, Kent, CT1 3AU.
LADD F5804

140511 LAFLIN Mr John & Mrs Shirley. (Swaffield) The White Cottage, Great Wymondley, Hitchin, Herts, SG4 7ET. Tel:0438-357143
Lafflin LAFLIN Lafling Laughlin Laughling SWAFFIELD Swafield Swathfield Swayfield F3180

140538 LAFLIN-BARKER Mrs S. 757 Pershore Road, Birmingham, B29 7NY.
LAFLIN PREEN Preene Prene F7103

140546 LAING Mr Hugh. Springbank, Salts Lane, Loose, Maidstone, ME15 0BD.
ASHDOWN DONNISON LAING WOODGER F3034

140554 LAING Mr Iain. 11 Falkland Street, Glasgow, G12 9PY. Tel:041-339-5724
ALLOWAY BENSON BLAIR CRESSWELL FEATHERSTONE FOX GLEW HANLEY HOLMES KENDAL LAING LAWSON MERRICK NEILSON POWELL RYMER SHEARSMITH WATKINSON WHARTON WHITECROSS F5241

140562 LAIRD Miss Annie E C. Hillhead, St Ola, Kirkwall, Orkney Island, KW15 1SX.
LAIRD F2632

140570 LAKE Mr Edward. Cherry Tree Cottage, 8 Sandringham Road, Lytham St Annes, Lancs, FY8 1EZ. Tel:0253-712260
BLUNT LAKE LEWIS WEBB F1100

140589 LAKE Mr G T. 1140 Kildonan Place Sw, Calgary, Alberta, T2V 4B1, CANADA.
LAKE LATCHAM OLDFIELD OVERFIELD ROWE F6295

140597 LAKER Mrs Patsy. 13 College Road, Southwater, Horsham, W Sussex, RH13 7EE. Tel:0403-730143
LAKER F178

140600 LAMACQ Mr R R. 30 Cheriton Avenue, Clayhall, Ilford, Essex, IG5 0QN.
LAMACQ Lamaroq Larmacq F6833

140619 LAMBERT Mr David. 15 Morelands Road, Purbrook, Portsmouth, Hants, PO7 5PT.
FRADD HARDY LAMBERT WESTON F1125

140627 LAMBERT Mr & Mrs M J. 47 Chesterfield Road, Cambridge, CB4 1LN. Tel:0223-425269
ALDRIDGE ALEXANDER ARMES ATMORE BRIDGES BROWN Browne BUBBINGS BURRELL COGMAN CRASKE DAINES DUNN DUNNETT DUNTHORNE EDWARDS ELY FOUNTAIN FURNESS GOWEN GRAY GREEN GRIMSON HOLMES ISBILL JEARY JENNINGS LAKE LAMBERT MANN MATHEWS Matthews NELSON NORTON RICHES SHARPE SMITH TANN UTTING VINCENT VINES WHITE WINTER F4725

140635 LAMBERT Mr Rowland & Mrs Evelyne. 84 Blendworth Lane, Harefield Estate, Southampton, Hants, SO2 5HG.
HOPE JONES Lambard Lambart LAMBERT Lampard Lamperd MARSHALL WEBSTER Winter WINTERS F6303

140643 LAMBOURNE Mr D C. 2/25 Chestnut Street, Carnegie, Victoria, 3163, AUSTRALIA.
LAMBOURNE SANDELLS F5456

140651 LAMPEN Mr B R. 47 Stokenchurch Plc, Bradwell Common, Milton Keynes, Bucks, MK13 8AU. Tel:0908-675611
Lampayne LAMPEN Lampin Lampine Lamppyn Lampyn F3617

140678 LANCASTER Mrs Elizabeth S. Little Drawdykes, 4 Whiteclosegate, Carlisle, Cumbria, CA3 0JD.
BELLAS BELLASIS BROWNRIGG CALLANDER CAMPBELL CARRUTHERS CHALMERS CRERAR CROSBY FORBES HINDSON HOLLIDAY KINNIBURGH LANCASTER MCDOWALL MCRAE MOSES STEWART F1095

140686 LAND Mr Bryan. 10 Taverham Road, Drayton, Norwich, Norfolk, NR8 6RX. Tel:0603-867272
ARCHER LAND F2418

140694 LANDEG Mr A B. Am Huellepfuhl 36a, 1000 Berlin 20, GERMANY.
LANDEG F3646

140708 LANDER Mrs Jane. 43 Hazelhurst Road, Kings Heath, Birmingham, B14 7PH. Tel:021-444-3193
Baggetripe Baketerpe Baudrip Broadbribb Broadrib Broderib Broderibb Broderibbe Broderip Broderipp Broderybb Brodrib BRODRIBB Brodrip Brodripp Brodrybbe CARR LANDER F2100

140716 LANE Mrs D I. 17 Riddell Gardens, Baldock, Herts, SG7 6JZ. Tel:0462-491451
BEECH CATTERHOLD DENMAN GOULDER KNIVETON LANE TAYLOR F4194

140724 LANE Mr Don. 46 Blackburn Road, Padiham, Burnley, Lancs, BB12 8JZ.
ALTREE BARLOW CHADWICK COOPER HILL HUGHES HUMPHREY HUMPHRY JONES LANE LLOYD MANN MCCRACKEN MCCRACKIN SABIN WOODDEN WOODDIN F5378

140732 LANE Miss J C. Carveiche, Luxulyan, Bodmin, Cornwall, PL30 5EE.
Carvath Carveighe Carverth Carverthe CARVETH Carvolth Cerveth F6574

140740 LANE Mrs Lynn B. Hatherley Brake, 104 Old Road, East Cowes, Isle Of Wight, PO32 6AX.
BAYNHAM HAMLETT KARN LANE PRICE WATKINS WILLIAMS WILSON F715

140759 LANE Mrs Lynn. (Jones) Newsparrowend, Brinkers Lane, Wadhurst, E Sussex, TN5 6LS.
BARNETT FORTUNE HAWKINS JONES POULTER POULTON POWELL PRICE PRICE-JONES RUMSEY SCHULZE Schutze WILLIAMS F2164

140767 LANE Mrs Margaret. (Kelly) 32 Cheviot Way, Upper Hopton, Mirfield, W Yorks, WF14 8HW.
BAILEY CADDICK CORBETT CORCORAN DAVIES DOWNES DOWNS DULANTY DUNN DUNNILL Ellwell ELWELL GLANAN GRAINGER GRIFFITHS HALES HODGSON HUGHES HUNT IRVINE IRVING JENNINGS JONES KELLY LANE MCHALE MICHAEL MICKMAN NICKLIN POTTER PRIAL PRYAL PRYALL SCANLON SHARP SIVETER Siviter SOUTHALL WALL WELLS WILLS WILSON F1429

140775 LANGDON Mr S John. Oaklands, East Village, Crediton, Devon, EX17 4BY. Tel:0363-866463
LANGDON WERRY F5390

140783 LANGFORD Mr Peter. 7 William Burt Close, Weston Turville, Aylesbury, Bucks, HP22 5QX.
GEORGE HEPTINSTALL LAMBORN LANGFORD LESTER PURSER ROBERTS THOMERSON WRIGHT F4848

140791 LANGHAM Mrs Marjorie. Dietersheim, Church End, Fringford, Bicester Oxon, OX6 9DP.
COLLINRIDGE MARTIN MEAGER SHEPHERD F1618

140805 LANGHORN Mr Stuart. 7 Furze Street, Carlisle, Cumbria, CA1 2DL. Tel:0228-46019
BISHOP DAVIDSON LANGHORN MILBURN ROBINSON F1266

140813 LANGMAN Mrs R. (Haile) Little Timbers, 28 Longmeadows, Darras Hall, Ponteland, Newcastle Upon Tyne, NE20 9DY.
BEATTIE CATTON ELLIS FLINT Hail HAILE Hale KERSHAW ROBERTSHAW RUCK SKILLERN F1513

140821 LANGMAN Mr S J. 28 Longmeadows, Darras Hall, Ponteland, Newcastle Upon Tyne, NE20 9DY. Tel:0661-23436
ANSDELL GENTLE LANGMAN SOUTHAM F1514

140848 LANGMEAD Mr Sydney R. Shore Footings, Old Road, Galmpton, Brixham, Devon, TQ5 0NE. Tel:0803-844022
ALLEN DUKE GORDEN LANGMAID Langmate LANGMEAD Langmede LASKEY Longmaid Longmaide Longmate Longmead Longmeade Longmede PROWSE TILL YEATES F239

140856 LANGRIDGE Mr Frederick. Ivy Lodge, High Street, Worle, Weston Super Mare, BS22 0EQ. Tel:0934-629472
LANGRIDGE POOR STICKLEY F4879

140864 LANGRIDGE Mr L W. 2 Rowantree Raod, Enfield, Middx, EN2 8QA. Tel:081-363-0795
BLANCHFLOWER BUCHAN BURNETT CATTO CLARK Clarke Colven COLVIN DOWNES ELEMENT Fidgeon FITZJOHN Fugion HEATH HENDERSON HOBBS KING Landbridge Landridge Langbridge Langredge LANGRIDGE Langrish Lawrance LAWRENCE MOONLIGHT NUNN PRUDENCE RITCHIE SCOTT SIMPSON SPENCER TRAIL Traill WALCH Welch WELSH WILLIAMS F2014

140872 LANGRIDGE Mr N R. 26 Grainge Way, Hawghley,

Suffolk, IP14 3PP.
BOLTON Bone BOON Boone Boulton Bowen
LANGRIDGE Modell MUDDLE Mudle F5782

140880 LANGSTON Mrs M. (Creighton) 16 Abbots Close, Rainham, Essex, RM13 9LA. Tel:04027-58672
COLE COLEMAN CREIGHTON DALE DYMOND FELLOWS LANGFORD PILBEAM ROMAINE F5209

140899 LANKSHEAR Mr A F. 30 Earlswood, Skelmersdale, Lancs, WN8 6AT.
LANKSHEAR F6612

140902 LANNON Mr Allan C. 6 Burnett Place, Thurso, Caithness, Scotland, KW14 8RF. Tel:0847-62636
BOOTH DUNSTAN DUSTAN FRASER HEGG LINEKAR MELVELLE MELVEN MELVILLE MELVIN ROSS SCOTT F1349

140910 LANSBERRY Mrs K C. 45 Park Terrace East, Horsham, W Sussex, RH13 5DJ.
PATTENDEN F6862

140929 LANSDELL Mrs Judith. West Ho, Westfield Lane, Etchinghill, Kent, CT18 8BZ. Tel:0303-862498
Landsdale Landsdell Landsell Lansdale Lansdall LANSDELL F408

140937 LANYON Mr Claud. Yew Tree House, Vicarage Street, Painswick, Glos, GL6 6XS.
LANYON F4333

140945 LAPPIN Alice. 155 Stamfordham Road, North Fenham, Newcastle Upon Tyne, NE5 3JN.
LAPPIN TORLEY F161

140953 LARARD Mrs F A. 12 Pinewood Road, St Ives, Ringwood, Hants, BH24 2PA.
ALLEN ATKINSON Larad LARARD Larrad Larrard Larred Larrod NELL POOLE QUINTON RUMENS VEALE WRIGHTON F1955

140961 LARDEN Mr R. 10 Conway Crescent, Short Heath, Willenhall, W Midlands, WV12 5TP.
LARDEN F6575

140988 LARKUM Mr M. 27 Park Road, Cheam, Surrey, SM3 8PY. Tel:081-642-2150
DENNY LARKUM F1838

140996 LASHBROOK Mr George. 32 Winchester Street, Taunton, Somerset, TA1 1QG. Tel:0823-337233
Lashbrok LASHBROOK Lashbrooke Lashbrooks F1238

141003 LASKEY Mr A. 19a Lilac Close, Newark, Notts, NG24 4LD.
GRESHAM HAMLYN LASKEY MANN SKEPPER F3347

141011 LATCHAM Mr Paul. The Old Rectory, Eardisley, Herefordshire, HR3 6NS.
Lachem LATCHAM Latchem F7130

141038 LATCHFORD Mr Derek. 48 Lode Road, Bottisham, Cambs, CB5 9DJ. Tel:0223-811454
LATCHFORD F2947

141046 LAUDER Mrs J S. (Whitworth) 20 Sutherland Close, Barnet, Herts, EN5 2JL.
ANDERSON ATTWELL BURDON EADIE FULLER HANNAH HATLEY KNOTT LATHER LAUDER LEGGATT MATHEWS MCELROY MCEWN MCILROY PENKETH POWELL RIDDLE SHORTER STONE WALKER WALLACE WARE WHITWORTH WILSON F3225

141054 LAVENDER Mr A T C. 91 Brenton Road, Penn, Wolverhampton, WV4 5NS.
ADDIS Dike DYKE Lander Launder LAVENDER F5705

141062 LAVER Mrs Ann. High Elms, Ripley Lane, West Horsley, Surrey, KT24 6JJ. Tel:04865-3304
BANKS BIRCH COX CURTIS DEAN EMMOTT GOODIER Goodyer GOWENLOCK HADLEY Haldern HAMMOND HARROP HARTLEY Hawthorn HESFORD Horden HORDERN JACKSON LAVER Lavor LOVATT MILNER MUNCASTER PRICKETT Prockter Procter PROCTOR RINGER Sagar SAGER SALMON SHIPP Swaine Swayne SWEAINE SWINDELLS Swindles Swyndells THOMPSTONE TRAVIS TRUBODY Truebody F1496

141070 LAW Jane. (Armour) Walker House, Marrick, Richmond, N Yorks, DL11 7LQ. Tel:0748-84342
ARMOUR ELLISON F1639

141089 LAW Mrs Yvonne. 86 Goddard Way, Saffron Walden, Essex, CB10 2ED.
CODLING COLES CREMER CUGAN HIGGINS JACOB LANGLEY LAW TREMAIN WARRY F1192

141097 LAWCOCK Mr Richard. 5 Chervil Close, Folksworth, Peterborough, Cambs, PE7 3SZ.
ANDERTON ARRANDELL ASHTON BARACLOUGH BEAL BLITHMAN BROWN BUCK BUTLER CHAPMAN CLIFFORD CROMPTON DOBSON DOWNS EMMERSON EYRE FOSTER FOX GOLDSBOROUGH GRAYSON HALL HARE HEPWORTH HEWITT HILTON HINDE HORNSEY HOUGHT HOWCROFT HUDSON JACOB JAQUES JOHNSON LAW LAWCOCK LAYCOCK LOWCOCK LUNDE MOOR MURPHY NETTLESHIP NEWMARCH PAGDIN PATTISON PICKERING RAYLEY SARGE SHAW SHEPHERD SIDEBOTTOM SMITH STANNIFORTH SUTTON THISLETON THOMPSON TOMSONE WADSWORTH WARD WARRINGTON WATSON WILLIAMSON F131

141100 LAWER Mrs E. Chy An Glas, Lanner Green, Lanner, Redruth Cornwall, TR16 6DJ. Tel:0209-211766
GREET HEBBARD LAWER MARTAIN MARTIN Martyn WATTERS F2813

141119 LAWES Mrs W M. 3 Brockenhurst Road, Manor Park, Aldershot, Hants, GU11 3HH.
HOLLANDS LAWES LAWS SILLENCE TURNER F2687

141127 LAWFORD Mr Clive. Storgata 23, N-4340 Bryne, Norway.
BICKERS Brimacombe Brimicombe Brimmicombe Brinecombe BRINICOMBE Brinnacombe Caxton Clackson Claxon Claxson CLAXTON DYE HANNAFORD LAWFORD Nuthal NUTHALL SCREACH Screech VATCHER F293

141135 LAWLESS Mr Howard. The Sycamores, Legh Road, Knutsford, Cheshire, WA16 8LS.
BREYMAYER BURGESS CHALONER HARNWELL LAWLESS MOULT NUTTALL RILEY F5077

141143 LAWLESS Mrs Margaret. 11 Roman Hackle Avenue, Wymans Brook, Cheltenham, Glos, GL50 4RF. Tel:0242-574952
CROWLEY DOVE EASTERBROOK EDEN Hares Haress Haris Harise Hariss Harries HARRIS Harrise Harrisse Hawis LAWLESS F4654

141151 LAWRANCE Mrs Brenda. 25 Bramber Road, Seaford, Sussex, BN25 1AG. Tel:0323-490779
AYLING BROWN BUTCHER BYE CROSS CROUCH FINCH FLESHER FLETCHER FOWLE GARRETT HALL HAYWARD HINTON HORNBY HORNSBY JENNINGS JUTSON LAWSON LETHIEULLIER MARSH MILLIQUET MOODY NICHOLLS NICHOLS PALMER PELLETT POCOCK RAYDEN RUTTER SADLER SAIL SCHOEN SMITH WELCH WORKMAN F2812

141178 LAWRENCE Dr Danny. 40 Holkham Avenue, Chilwell, Beeston, Nottingham, NG9 5EQ. Tel:0602-259755
Crab CRABB Crabbe Grill GRYLL Grylls HALEY HAND Hands Laurance Laurence Lawrance LAWRENCE Lorrens MOON Moone SOUTHERN WALLIS F2399

141186 LAWRENCE Freda. Brades, Lower Penkridge Road, Acton Trussell, Stafford, ST17 ORJ. Tel:0785-713377
BELLINGHAM HAMMOND HIBBS HOWARD Ibbs JACKSON LAWRENCE RIDER Shettle Shuttel Shuttell SHUTTLE TALBOT F1014

141194 LAWRENCE Mrs Georgina. 85 Hamilton Road, Gillingham, Kent, ME7 1QL.
CHALTON CLEMENTS FAWCETT FOSSETT GREENAWAY KIBBLE ROSE SCAMMELL F2864

141208 LAWRENCE Mr Leonard George. Rosehill Farm, Mylor Bridge, Falmouth, Cornwall, TR11 5LZ. Tel:0326-74356
CHARLESVORTH HUMPHRIES LAWRENCE UNWIN F886

141216 LAWRENCE Mrs Madeline. 2 Slepe Farm Cotts, Organford, Lytchett Minster, Poole Dorset, BH16 6HS. Tel:0202-625513
BRIMMELL BUCKLE CLARKE DRINKWATER FENN GILBERT LITTLE MOSELEY PEARCE PURROCK ROAN ROGERS SYMES SYMONDS TERRETT WALL WATTS WYMAN F1504

141224 LAWRENCE Mrs Polly. (Rubery) 2 Chamberhouse Mill, Thatcham, Newbury, Berks, RG13 4NU. Tel:0635-866814
ALSOP BARTLETT BATEMAN BAYLIS BRITTON BROWN CROOME DERRICK EDWARDS FLOOK FRANCIS GOUGH HANDY HARRIS HAWKINS HENDING HENDY HIGHAM KING LOVE MACGUIRK MARTIN MCGUIRK NEWBURY OSBORNE PALMER PERRY POWELL Rewbury Robery Rowberry Rowbery Rowbory Rowbree Rowbrey Rowbury Rubbery Rubbra Ruberry RUBERY Rubra Rubrey SHEPHERD STABBINS Tawcock TILLY TOCOCK Toecock Toocock Towcock TURNER Twocock VOWLES WAYMOUTH WEYMOUTH WILLY YOUNG F1

141232 LAWRENSON Mr Brian. 51 Bay Road, Wormit, Fife, DD6 8LW.
COCKERILL Laurenson LAWRENSON THOMPSON F3129

141240 LAWS Mr John P. Midina, 12 Syston Grove, Lincoln, Lincs, LN5 8TJ. Tel:0522-523436

De Lawze De Lors Larse LAW Lawes LAWS Lawse Mclaws F2117

141259 LAWSON Mr Clifford John. 22 Porthill Drive, Shrewsbury, Shropshire, SY3 8RS. Tel:0743-354085
GOODEVE F2770

141267 LAWSON Mrs Madeline. (Palmer) 72 Collinswood Drive, St Leonards On Sea, E Sussex, TN38 0NX. Tel:0424-422405
Brookman BROWN BRUCKMANN Brueckman Dussec DUSSEE HALL HODGES HOSKIN Hoskins JOHNSTONE LAWSON PALMER POWIS SCRIVENER Scrivenor Shephard SHEPPARD SHERIDAN SWIFT WARREN F6312

141275 LAWSON Mr Paul. 65 Sussex Road, Lowestoft, Suffolk, NR32 4HG. Tel:0502-517478
CADE DUNKLEY LAWSON MALTBY ROBINSON SNEEZUM F4942

141283 LAWSON Mr R K. 78 New Brighton Road, Emsworth, Hampshire, PO10 7QS.
BANKS CHRISTIAN CURPHEY FORSYTH HARDMAN HEATH JAMES LAWSON LLOYD LOVELY MCGILL ROSSER SKERRATT SORTON TOFT F1884

141291 LAWTON Mrs Brenda. 11 Maylands Grove, Barrow In Furness, Cumbria, LA13 0AN. Tel:0229-831314
CAIRN CAIRNE CALLISTER CARTER CASSON CLUCAS COSTAIN CUBBON DOBSON EASTHAM EDMONDSON GAITSKELL GARDNER GAWN GAWNE GELL GIBSON GOAD GOODALL GREENWOOD HUDDLESTON HUNTER JACKSON JAMES KELLY KENDALL KINRY KIRKBY LOWEY MADDRELL MANSELL MCYLVORREY MOORE NORRIS PERKS PICKERILL PILLING POOLE POSTLETHWAITE RADCLIFFE RICHARDSON SILVERWOOD TAUBMAN TAYLOR TOWNSON WAINEMAN WARD WATTERSON WILSON WRIGHT F1430

141305 LAWTON Mr Guy. 17 Condover Park, Condover, Shrewsbury, Shropshire, SY5 7DU. Tel:0743-738153
BRETTEL FENTON LAWTON LEECH LUKE OLIVER ROCHFORT SMALLWOOD WORKMAN F6465

141313 LAX Mr Alistair. 5 Bradwell Road, Tilehurst, Reading, Berks, RG3 6SD. Tel:0734-414267
COUTTS HARVEY LAX OUGHTRED ROBINSON SMITH F820

141321 LAY Mrs Sylvia. (Hudson) Portway Cottage, Childrey, Wantage, Oxon, OX12 9UQ. Tel:023559-612
BRIDGES FROGLEY Froglie Froode FROUD Froude Frowde Frude Hogson HUDSON Hutson JAMES LAY Lea Lee Leigh Locket LUCKET Luckett F5263

141348 LE BRETON Mrs M. 43 Ullswater Crescent, Radipole, Weymouth, Dorset, DT3 5HF.
BRAY CATTLE LE BRETON F3681

141356 LE CLERCQ Mr Paul M. 4 Nicolle Close, Clarendon Road, St Helier, Jersey, JE2 3YS.
AMY CONNOR DU HEAUME HAMON HOLMES LE CLERCQ PINKET VASSE F3500

141364 LE MESSURIER Mr Colin. 38 Gaviots Way, Gerrards Cross, Bucks, SL9 7DX. Tel:0753-883063
LE MESSURIER Le Mesurier Lemessurier Lemesurier Messurier Mesurier F3683

141372 LE TOCQ Mr & Mrs L C. 12 St Peters Grove, York, YO3 6AQ. Tel:0904-654049
BATTAM BRAGG COLTMAN CROSSMAN DADD DAW FOREMAN HAYMAN POPE PORTER F1407

141380 LE-CLUSE Jane. 31 Rosehill, Billingshurst, W Sussex, RH14 9QN.
DE LE CLUSE HENBEST Henvest Hinbest Hinves Hinvest KEMPSHALL Le Cluse MOULAND F2384

141399 LE-FEVRE Barbara. 53 Helmores, Laindon West, Basildon, Essex, SS15 6SA. Tel:0268-415919
HOWARD JONES LE-FEVRE LEFEVER SMITH F2900

141402 LEACH Mr Dennis. Meadow Cottage, Treburley, Launceston, Cornwall, PL15 9PU.
BIRCH BUNN DAVIES DAWSON DOWDEN ENGLISH FENN HEARN LEACH MCGREGOR NEWTON PAYNE PEARCE PUDDEPHATT REEVE SHRIMPLIN SMITH WOODRUFF F4927

141410 LEACH Mr John. 209 Lower Mortlake Road, Richmond, Surrey, TW9 2LP. Tel:081-940-0803
BARLOW HARE LEACH LEEDS NEWTON QUINCEY F1237

141429 LEAHY Mr David. 33 Varty Avenue, Raheen, Limerick, IRELAND.
NAMMOCK F7325

141437 LEAK Dr Anthony. 16 Gladstone Road, Ipswich, Suffolk, IP3 8AT.
LEAK F3671

141445 LEAKE Mrs Jane. 8 Hunslet Road, Burntwood, Walsall, Staffs, WS7 9LA. Tel:0543-683520
BUSTIN DARNELL HAND HARTBURN HINE JEFFERY LEAKE TIVEY WATTHEY F2584

141453 LEASK Madam A. 1 Vincent Road, Sheringham, Norfolk, NR26 8BP.
LEASK F3710

141461 LEATHARD Mr David. 43 Topside, Grenoside, Sheffield, S30 3RD.
BLAKELOCK CHRISTELOW CHRISTOPHER DAVIES DOMINEY HAWKER HUTCHINSON JOPLING PARKINSON SLADE F5609

141488 LEATHER Dr Simon R. The Lighthouse, 80 High Street, Peebles, Tweedale, EH45 8SW. Tel:0721-22377
LEATHER F3709

141496 LEATHER Miss Sue. 60 West Road, Buxton, Derbyshire, SK17 6HG.
HOLLAND MALKIN NAYLOR PAMPLIN RYLANCE SALE SHARROCK STIRZAKER WANT F2957

141518 LEBUTT Ms M. 6204 Taywood Road, Apt G, Englewood, OH 45322, USA.
Laybutt Lebatt LEBUTT Leybutt F6978

141526 LEDGER Mrs Lorna. Yeomans, Holland Road, Oxted, Surrey, RH8 9AU. Tel:0883-713231
FOWLE HAWES HOCKEY LEDGER PRITCHARD STEVENS VOUSDEN WELLING WILLIAMS F417

141534 LEDWELL Mrs Maureen. 7 Dukes Avenue, Theydon Bois, Essex, CM16 7HG.
BROWN DISLEY LEDWELL MALKIN F899

141542 LEE Mrs Beryl. (Davies) 41 Wentworth Drive, Bromborough, Wirral, L63 0HZ. Tel:051-334-0031
BIRDSALL BUERDSALL BUERDSELL DAVIES MILLER SALADIN SALADINE F3054

141550 LEE Mrs Elsie Harrison. Trunkwell Lodge, Beech Hill, Reading, Berkshire, RG7 2AT. Tel:0734-884593
CRIPPS HARRISON-CRIPPS HEYWORTH POTTER PRING F2101

141569 LEE Mr Eric A. Camelot Caravan Park, Longtown, Carlisle, Cumbria, CA6 5SZ.
ASTLE BATCHER BOWERS CASTLEDINE CLIPSON Clipston Clipstone DICKEN DIMBLEBY FRANKLIN LEE LONGDEN MEADOWS PEARSON Phipps PHIPS RUFF SEDGELEY Sedgely SHAW SPRIGGS TROWELL WYATT F2605

141577 LEE Mr G N. 8 Eton Street, Barry, South Glamorgan, CF6 8PH.
BEST HOPKIN JAMES LEE Leigh MORDECAI PARR PHILPIN POTTER SANDERS Saunders WILLIAMS F4639

141585 LEE Mrs Jeanne M. (Bradfield) 16 Broadley Avenue, Birchington On Sea, Kent, CT7 9UA.
BRADFIELD LEE MARSH MOCKRIDGE MOGGERIDGE MOGRIDGE SEXTON WEST F457

141593 LEE Miss Margaret Ream. 15 Bedford Court, Oakwood Lane, Leeds, LS8 2PL. Tel:0532-400936
LEE Realme REAM Reame Rheam Rheame SCHOLEY SMITH TURPIN WOOLHOUSE F5922

141607 LEE Mrs Margaret. 60 Chantryfield Road, Angmering Village, W Sussex, BN16 4LY. Tel:0903-783643
MUDLE SLIM SLINN SPARGO F1833

141615 LEE Mrs Monica. (Fyles) Camelot Caravan Park, Longtown, Carlisle, Cumbria, CA6 5SZ. Tel:0228-791248
Addinson ADINSON ALKER ALLEN Allinson ALLISON ALMOND ARNOLD ATKINSON BACKHOUSE BATES BEAMONT Beaumont BIBBY BIRD BIRKHEAD BLACKLEDGE BLAND BOOTH BRACEBRIDGE BRADGATE BRIAN BROUGHTON BURROW CARTER CLARKE CLARKSON COOPER CORWEN COWARD CROFT CROSFIELD DANN Danson DAWSON DEAKEN Dicconson DICKINSON DONISTHORPE Durandesthorpe FAIRCLOUGH FALLOWS FELL Fildes Files FISHER Fyldes FYLES GIBSON GREAVES GREEN GREGSON GROVES Helm HELME HEXTALL HILL HOBKYN HUGGAN ILIFFE IRONMONGER JACKSON JESON JOHNSON KILNER KIRBY LASENBY Lazenby LECYTHWATE LION LIQUORISH LUCAS LUCK MEADOW MERRALL Merrell Merrill MOORE OSWIN PARKINSON PEDDER PEGG PICKARD PINLEY PRATT PRIOR PYWELL RAINFORD Rainforth RAYSON RENCHER Rensher ROBINSON ROLSON RONSON

ROTHWELL ROWE SANDER SAUNDERSON SCLATER SEEDE SHAWE SISSON SMITH SPEIGHT SUTTON SWAN Usteison VSTEISON WALLIN WARD WATSON WEAVER WHEATLEY WOODLAND F2604

141623 LEECH Augustus. 429 Walton Road, East Molesey, Surrey, KT8 0EJ.
CHALKLEY COLEMAN GRICE JEFFERY LEECH PLAYLE F2559

141631 LEECH Mrs M R. 7 Prentices Lane, Woodbridge, Suffolk, IP12 4LF.
TROTT F7372

141658 LEES Mr David. 183 Northridge Way, Hemel Hempstead, Herts, HP1 2AS.
COOPER EASTWICK Lea Leace Leas Lease Lee LEES Leese PLOUGHWRIGHT PROWSE F74

141666 LEES Mrs Lynn. 84 Highcliffe Close, Wickford, Essex, SS11 8JY.
BRACEY SABAN F2197

141674 LEES Mr Ralph Alan. 23 Sapcote Road, Burbage, Leicester, LE10 2AS. Tel:0455-230339
BLACK LEES F5410

141682 LEESON Mr F L. 108 Sea Lane, Ferring, W Sussex, BN12 5HB.
AVERY BARTLETT BOWMAN BREAKSPEAR IVENS KEARSE Leason LEESON Lesson POLLARD F46

141690 LEGEZA Mrs Louise. (Passmore) 1448 Lake Road, Conneaut, OH 44030, USA. Tel:+1-216-593-2515
GILL HARPER JEFFERY LIFECHILD PACOCK PASSMORE PASTMOOR PEARCE PEATCH SALTER SNELL WILLIAMS F5648

141704 LEGG Mrs Brenda C. (Ockenden) Abbotts Lea, 1 Crabtree Lane, Lancing, W Sussex, BN15 9PF.
BAKER BALLARD CLAXTON DAY GLANVILLE HOAD KRAKER LEGG NASH OCKENDEN PAMPHILON RAWLINGS ROSE ROSS STONE STOREY TIDY WEBB WHITE F2833

141712 LEGG Mrs V E M. 5 Reculver Walk, Senacre, Maidstone, Kent, ME15 8QE.
FABIAN Fabyan Pheban Pheben F6739

141720 LEGGE Mr Brian. 64 Vulcan Way, Islington, London, N7 8XR.
DUNSBY FRENCH HOPCROFT LEGG LEGGE LLOYDE LOCK LOCKE SEYMORE STONE TAYLOR WELLER F6014

141739 LEGGETT Mrs Joan. (Sutherland) Crossmount House, Kinloch Rannoch, Perthshire, PH16 5QF.
BANKS BRASH CUMMING Denham DENHOLM FARR Farre FERGUSON Ghorst Gorse GORST Gourlay GURLEY HART KIRBY LINDSAY MACLEOD MARSHALL MCKERETH MCNEE ROBERTSON SCOTT THOMSON VANDERSTEGEN WOLFE F4115

141747 LEGGETT Mr L. 102 Sylvan Avenue, Timperley, Altincham, Cheshire, WA15 6AB.
GILL HOWARTH Ledgate LEGAT LEGATE Leget Leggate LEGGATT LEGGETT LEGGOTT LIDGATE LIDGETT LIGGETT F93

141755 LEGUTKI Mr G. 1936 East Fifth Street, Ontario, CA 91764, USA.
Sciner Skiner SKINNER Skynner F6781

141763 LEIGH-DUGMORE Mr C H. 26 Sandhurst Road, Four Oaks, Sutton Coldfield, W Midlands, B74 4UE.
Dougsmore DUGMORE F6922

141771 LEIR NICHOLSON Mr R P. Milton Abbey School, Blandford Forum, Dorset, DT11 0BZ. Tel:0258-880484
AINSLIE JAMES JEKYLL LEIR WADHAM-WILLIAMS F3435

141798 LEITCH Mrs Sheila. (Deans) Wye View, Glasbury On Wye, Powys, HR3 5NU. Tel:0497-847354
ARMSTRONG BARTLETT BELL BRUCE CHRISTIE CRAWFORD DAVIE DEANS DOUGLAS ELIOTT GOWANS Griffith GRIFFITHS HISLOP Hyslop JAFFRAY Jeffray Jeffrey KENNEDY Leach LECKIE Leech LEITCH LIDDELL Liddle MCINTYRE MELLIS Millar MILLER Millstone MILSON NEILSON Nelson ODLIN PRICE PRYCE REECE ROBERTS ROBERTSON RUTHERFORD VAUGHAN WHITTINGTON WILLS YOUNG F1195

141801 LEITH Mr Ronald. 152 King Street, Aberdeen, AB2 3BD.
Leath LEITH Lythe SCORGIE F6686

141828 LEM Mr R J. Springfield House, Sway Road, Brockenhurst, Hants, SO42 7SG.
LEM LEMM Lemme Lems Lemson F1885

141836 LEMMENS Mr Gerard W C. Golding House, High Street, Cranbrook, Kent, TN17 3EJ. Tel:0580-712660
LEMMENS MACGILLIVRAY MACLEOD F5106

141844 LENG Mr A J. 1 Moushill Cottage, Moushill Lane, Milford, Godalming Surrey, GU8 5BH.
Aislabie AISLABY LENG F6751

141852 LENHAM Mr Terence. 83 Greenfield Road, Middleton On The Wolds, North Humberside, YO25 9VL.
LENHAM F7044

141860 LEONARD Mr A. Po Box 134, East Sandwich, MA 02537, USA.
NYE F7331

141879 LEONARD Mr Eleanor. (Mcgough) 3957 Acoma Drive, Ormond Beach, FL 32174, USA. Tel:+1-904-676-9444
BASSETT Bourke BURKE JAMES LEONARD LOMAS MAKIN Mcgaugh MCGEOUGH Mcgough ROUNDTREE Rountree F5645

141887 LEONARD Mr R B. 26 Filwood Drive, Kingswood, Bristol, BS15 4HS.
LEONARD F2185

141895 LEOPOLD Mrs Heather. (Porteous) 29 Milton Road, Hanwell, London, W7 1LQ. Tel:081-567-8291
LETHBRIDGE LISTER NORTHMORE PORTEOUS ROGERS F2088

141909 LEPOMME Mrs Glenys. (O'Keefe) 10 Hinton Street, Redcliffe, QLD 4020, AUSTRALIA.
FISHER FLANDERS GLIDDON MORPHETT POWELL SHOOBRIDGE WINSER WYKE F5575

141917 LERWILL Dr C J. Holly Cottage, Boarded Barn Road, Wakes Colne, Colchester, CO6 2AU.
Lerwell LERWILL Lurwell F7154

141925 LETCHFORD Mrs Anne. Amberley, Vicarage Close, Cookham, Berks, SL6 9SE. Tel:06285-27007
BRUNSDEN BUTLER DORMOR HARMSWORTH LETCHFORD LUMBER PARR REEVES WHEELER F951

141933 LETCHFORD Mrs Barbara. 7 Fairlie Avenue, Macleod, Victoria, 3085, AUSTRAILIA.
ALLEN GUTTIS HURFORD LESBY LETCHFORD NORMAN PETERS PILE UNDERWOOD WOOLNER F3544

141941 LETHBRIDGE Mrs Joyce. 55 Oriel Road, Portsmouth, Hants, PO2 9EG.
BATEMAN BLEACH CARTER CLARKE HOGSFLESH HUSKISSON READ REED SHEEHAN TULL F1020

141968 LEVER Mr C. 68 Tower Street, Heywood, Lancs, OL10 3AD.
ACKERNLEY BEASLEY HIRST LEVER MIDGLEY WALKER F4352

141976 LEVER Mr R J A. 51 Links Road, Ashtead, Surrey, KT21 2HL.
Leaver LEVER F2480

141984 LEVITT Mr J R. 56 Mill Hill Avenue, Pontefract, West Yorks, WF8 4JJ. Tel:0977-797070
ANSON Beachell BEACHILL Bearchill CROMACK Crummack FLETCHER FOSTER Heppenstall Heppinstall Heptinstall HEPTONSTALL HILL Leavitt Leavitte Levet Levett Levit LEVITT MARLAND PICKARD WALKER WATSON WEBSTER F5351

141992 LEWARNE Mr Peter. 21 Teviot Road, Keynsham, Bristol, Avon, BS18 1QS. Tel:0272-862783
LEWARNE F2034

142018 LEWCUN Mr Marek. 63 The Oval, Bath, Avon, BA2 2HD.
ADAMS ALBERT ALLEN AMER ANDREWS ASHFORD ATKINS BABB BACON BATH BATT BAYLEY BEVIS BICKHAM BUCKLAND BUCKLER BURROW BUTT CARPENTER CARRIER CASELEY CHAMPION CHAPPERLIN CLARKE CLIFFORD COLLINS COMMONS CROOK DARBY DAVIS DAWS DOWLING DREW DUCY EARLE ELLIOT FILDER FOX FREEMANTLE GANE GARDNER GAUNTLETT GAY GEORGE GIBBS GRAVES GREEN GREENLAND HAINE HARDING HARDS HARRIS HIGGENS HILL HOCKADAY HOWELL HOWLETT HUISH HUNT HUTCHINGS JERRETT JONES KING LAFFER LANGDON LEGG LEWIS LOVELL LUMBARD MARCHANT MARSHMAN MASON MAYNARD MERRIFIELD MILLARD MILLS MITCHELL MORGAN NEALE NEEDES NOAD NOTLEY NOYES ODBER PAGE PALMER PARIS PARSONS PAUL PINE PITCHER POBJAY POUND PRATT PRYOR PUTLY RAND RANDALL RICHARDSON ROBINSON ROWE SANDELL SANGER SANTS SAWYER SEAMAN SHUTTLER SIMS SKEAINES SLEDGE SMITH SMITHFIELD SNAILUM SPENDER STRUDWICK SYMES TANNER TOTTLE TOVEY TYLEE UNDERHILL VALE VERRIER WARD WARMOUTH WATTS WEBB WELLS WEST WESTCOTT WHEELER WHITAKER WHITTLE WHITTOCK WIDDOWS WILLIAMS WINCHESTER WITT

WOODFORD F2284

142026 LEWIS Mr Adrian. 31 Lammack Road, Blackburn, Lancs, BB1 8JW. Tel:0254-583706
COTTLE GAY HAYES LEWIS MILLS SIMMONS SYMONDS F1791

142034 LEWIS Mrs Ann. (Harries) Aran, 1 Wellington Gardens, Aberaeron, Dyfed, SA46 0BQ.
ARTHUR BEVAN BROWN DAVIES EDWARDS HARRIES JABES JONES LEWIS F1445

142042 LEWIS Mrs Dorothy M. 102 Roseberry Avenue, Gloucester, GL1 5EJ.
Banckes Bancks Bankes BANKS Bushal Bushall Bushel BUSHELL Conet Connet CONNETT GRIFFITHS Griffits Griffitts HEATH KINGHCOTT KINGTON LEWIS OWEN PARR PAUL RICE Sargeant Sargeaunt SARGENT Sarjeant Sarjeaunt Sarjent Sealwood SELLWOOD Selwood SPAIN WISE Wyse F3333

142050 LEWIS Mr E J. 95 Ruskin Avenue, Long Eaton, Notts, NG10 3HX. Tel:0602-734472
Clark CLARKE DIMENT DOWNTON Hewish HUISH JEFFORD LEWIS Liddel LIDDLE SARLING SCRIVEN VARLEY WILLEY WILLIAMS F6552

142069 LEWIS Mrs Heather. (Webster) Oakwood, The Grange, Everton, Lymington, Hants, SO41 0ZR. Tel:0590-643335
ASQUITH CAMPBELL GAWEN HIRST UPSTONE WEBSTER F6249

142077 LEWIS Mrs J. (Earl) 84 Melrose Avenue, The Ridge, Yate, Bristol, BS17 5AW.
EARL HARRIS LEWIS MOORE PUGH SHORTMAN SMITH TOWNSEND F2208

142085 LEWIS Mrs Janet A. (Hickling) 20 Heights Road, Upton, Poole, Dorset, BH16 5QL.
ADKIN Atkin BOOT CRAFTS Crofts DAKIN FOOTITT HARRISON HICKLING HUDSON LAUNDER Launders POXSON SPENCER WATERS WINFIELD F503

142093 LEWIS Mrs L M. 2 Kingsbury Court, Llwydcoed, Aberdare, Mid Glamorgan, CF44 0YN.
DAVIES GRIFFITHS HOWELLS HUMPHREYS LEWIS VAUGHAN WILLIAMS F3512

142107 LEWIS Mr L. 23 Lucastes Avenue, Haywards Heath, W Sussex, RH16 1JU. Tel:0444-450177
BARTON FALLOWS HUMBER KEOGH LEWIS MAY PALMER RASHBROOK SALMON TWAITS F3611

142115 LEWIS Ms Mandy. 12 Heol Y Llan, Burry Port, Dyfed, SA16 0AP. Tel:05546-5461
JAMES NEWMAN PETERSEN F1129

142123 LEWIS Mrs Margaret. 121 Moss Avenue, Mt Helen, Victoria, 3350, AUSTRALIA.
BENNETT Bennetts EDGERTON EGERTON Ferrian FURRIAN GROOM HAMMOND Handscombe HANSCOMBE HONOUR KNUCKEY Lacie LACY LAKE LANGFORD LISTER Longford Lyster MADDOCKS Maddox Mailes MALES Nuckey PARSONS PORTER RAVENSCROFT RIDER Ryder STRATTON Tannat TANNATT WILLIAMS WRIGHT F5151

142131 LEWIS Mr Roger. 35 James Road, Dorchester, Dorset, DT1 2HB. Tel:0305-262659
COX FANCETT GOULD LEWIS MILDENHALL SAMPSON SAUNDERS SCOTT SELLWOOD F2985

142158 LEWIS Mr T R. 59 Private Road, Mapperley, Nottingham, NG3 5FQ. Tel:0602-607042
ALSOP BAKER BENGE BERRY BIGLEN BULL BYARD BYATT BYETT CLIFFORD CLOTHIER COLE CRIPS CURTIS DAVIES GOULD GREEN GREENE HAYES HEAZEL HILL HOPKINS HUNTLEY HUSSEY LAMBOURN LEWIS MANSELL MARKLOVE MEE NEALE PAGINTON PALMER PENNY PONTING PORTER READ ROBERTS ROWLAND SHEAN SHEPARD SHERMAN SMITH SPICER TIMOTHY TONKIN TRAYHERN VOKINS WAITES WATTS WILLIAMS WRIGHT F1011

142166 LEWIS Vera. 46 Oliver Court, Union Street, Bedford, MK40 2UU. Tel:0234-342892
ABRAHAM ARMES BUTLER COLLIER FOLLETT FRANCIS GAME GAUCHERON HILL HOLMES HUMBERSTONE JONES KEMP LANGRISH LATTIMER LEWIS LICKFOLD LITTLEJOHN MORGAN SAVAGE SHEPHARD SMITH STONE TANSLEY WARNER F760

142174 LEWIS Mrs Wendy. (Freeland) 95 Ruskin Avenue, Long Eaton, Nottingham, NG10 3HX. Tel:0602-734472
BENSKIN Benskyn BICKERTON Bigerton Biggerton BRILL Davey DAVIE Davy Fearn FEARNS Fern Ferns Freedland Freedlander FREELAND Friedland Friedlander GLOVER Hicks HIGGS HOMER MALLINSON MASON Perceval PERCIVAL Percivall Ricket Rickets RICKETTS Rochester ROSENSTRAUGH STRINGER Wollarton Wollerton WOOLERTON Woollaton Woolloton F504

142182 LEWIS-JONES Mr Raymond. Lodge Farm, Tilford Road, Farnham, Surrey, GU9 8HU. Tel:0252-716403
CLAYTON HALSTEAD HALSTED F1942

142190 LEWSEY Mr Andrew Walter. 120 Beechwood Drive, Bonhill, Alexandria, Dumbartonshire, G83 9LY. Tel:0389-55322
LEWSEY F1321

142204 LEYLAND Mrs Sheila. (Boardman) 34 Weymouth Drive, Hindley Green, Wigan, Lancs, WN2 4QX. Tel:0942-58323
BEATSON BOARDMAN CROSTON HART HOLDEN SCHOFIELD SWINDELL WESTWELL F5788

142212 LEYSHON Mr Thomas Taliesin. 2 Box Close, Fleetsbridge, Poole, Dorset, BH17 7AR. Tel:0202-671548
CHURCHHOUSE DAVIES EDWARDS EVANS GWYLIM LEYSHON LEYSHONE NICHOLAS PHILLIPS VAUGHAN F3390

142220 LICKFOLD Dr Gordon. 33 Parsonage Road, Henfield, W Sussex, BN5 9JG. Tel:0273-492398
Leckfold Leckford Licfold Lickefolde Lickfauld LICKFOLD Lickford Lyckfold Lykfauld F45

142239 LICKISS Dr Paul D. 38 Meadow Drive, Knutsford, Cheshire, WA16 0DT.
Lickas Lickass Lickes Lickess Lickis LICKISS Liclkas Likis Likiss F6973

142247 LICKLEY Mr James. June Cottage, Shere Road, West Horsley, Leatherhead Surrey, KT24 6EQ. Tel:04865-4056
LICKLEY Likely Likly MAIR F2475

142255 LIDSTONE Mr Hugh. 11 Furzehatt Avenue, Plymstock, Plymouth, Devon, PL9 8LJ. Tel:0752-403537
Leadston LEADSTONE Ledestone LEDSTON Ledstone Lesson LIDSTONE Lisson Liston Lydeston LYDSTON Lydstone Lysson F4054

142263 LIGGAT Mr Thomas Stewart. 28 Bryn Road, Coychurch, Bridgend, Mid Glamorgan, CF35 5EY.
CAMPBELL CYSTER DONALD GILLANDERS LIGGAT Liggatt MACDONALD MACKENZIE STEWART TEBBUTT WHITE F1494

142271 LIGGETT Eric & Sheila. High Dam Barn, Arkholme, Carnforth, LA6 1BE. Tel:05242-21895
LIGGETT F285

142298 LIGGETT Mrs S. 232-12875 Railway Avenue, Richmond, British Columbia, V7E 6K3, CANADA.
BUCHAN COUTTS CROSS FROST LIGGET PHILPOTS PIKE Pyke ROBINSON SMITH STEAD Steed STINSON TOON TRISTRAM WALLACE WARWICK WATERFIELD WEBSTER WHEATLEY F4175

142301 LIGHT Dr John. 29 Longfield Road, Tring, Herts, HP23 4DG.
BARBER BELL BULLOCK BUTTMAN DAVIS DUNKLEY FAWCUS GRAFTON GRAY GRIME HANKIN HARRIS HAWKINS HIDE HORNER HORWOOD ISHERWOOD JEFFERY JOHNSON KNOX LIGHT PARSONS PEARN PEARS SHEPHERD SHORT STOCK TAYLOR WAITE WHITE WILLANS WOLSTENHOLME F724

142328 LIGHTFOOT Mr Daryl H. Po Box 574, Toronto, NSW 2283, AUSTRALIA.
COCKBURN CREED FIELDER GILBERT GILL GLOVER HUNTER MACDONALD SADDS SCHAW F5470

142336 LIGHTON Mr Kenneth. 40 Haepham Road, Gainsborough, Lincs, DN21 1SW. Tel:0247-610350
Laighton Laton Layton Leaton Leighton Lighten LIGHTON Lyghton Lyton Lyttone F3834

142344 LILE Mr Brian. 41 Cwm Aur, Llanilar, Aberystwyth, Dyfed, SY23 4NT.
LILE F1402

142352 LILLEY Mr C C. 23 Gildingwells Road, Woodsetts, Worksop, Notts, S81 8QB. Tel:0909-566837
GRAVES LILLEY LILLY LILY PERCY SANDERS Saunders WALKER WARR WOODS F6080

142360 LILLEY Mrs M A. Hazelcot, Hibbert Road, Braywick, Maidenhead Berks, SL6 1UT. Tel:0628-24969
ASHBY Askell Aswell BECKENSALE BEDDINGTON BOULTON BREEZE BROWN CHAMBERLAIN COBB COLEMAN COXHEAD CRIPPS CROFTS ELAND Essell FAVELL

GADD GOSLING Haskell Hassel Haswell Hawsell Haysel HERBERT Hessell HITCHCOCK Hoswell HOWES HUNTER Husle Hussell HUZZELL IND Israel Issel JENNINGS KEMPTON KING LILLEY MAYELL MEGGISON Osell Oswald Ozell PAGGINTON PEARCE PRECIOUS RUSSELL SEXTON STAINES STEPTOE STREET TAPLIN TULL Ursell Urswell Ushil Ussell Ussol Ussould Uswell Uzald Uzle Uzzeel Uzzele UZZELL WELLS WIGG WILDER WILSON F1090

142379 LILLIMAN Mr L J. 194 Roding Road, Loughton, Essex, IG10 3BS. Tel:081-508-9265
LEWIS Liliman Lilleyman Lillieman LILLIMAN Lillyman Lilyman Lyliman Lylleyman Lylliman Lyllyman WATSON F1830

142387 LILLINGTON Mr B D. 19 Woodlands Avenue, Wanstead, London, E11 3RA.
LILLINGTON Lyllington F7141

142395 LILLY Mrs Janet. 61 Stanway Road, Shirley, Solihull, W Midlands, B90 3JF.
Alden ALLDEN Aulden BLOOMER Brownell BROWNHILL DOWLER DRAWBRIDGE GEE Hallden Holden Holttum HOLTUM Houlton HUGHES JACKSON Jee Liley Lilley Lillie LILLY Lily LLOYD Lyllye OSEMAN REYNOLDS STRETTON THOMAS F1839

142409 LINCOLN Miss M B. 16 Walmead Croft, Harborne, Birmingham, B17 8TH.
ADKINS BIDDLE BUYCE CONSTABLE CURTIS GREEN HARRIS HEWITT HILL HUMPHREY LEEK LINCOLN MARCH MOGG MOULD MULLINGTON NURFUR OLIVER RUSSELL TURNER WILLETT WITHERS WRIGHT F4914

142417 LINCOLN Mr Maurice A. 8 Reay Gardens, Westerhope, Newcastle Upon Tyne, NE5 2NB. Tel:091-286-9506
ARMSTRONG BENSLEY DAVIDSON DYKES HENDERSON HUDSON LINCOLN MAKENS TEASDALE F3341

142425 LINDEGAARD Mrs D P. (Pillinger) 49 Clayfield Road, Brislington, Bristol, BS4 4NH. Tel:0272-776176
BURCHILL HONOUR LEAR PILLINGER SUMMERILL F3613

142433 LINDER Mr K J. Brackenwood, Hollybush Ride, Wokingham, Berks, RG11 3QP.
Lindar Lindars LINDER Lindor F6603

142441 LINDFIELD Mr Alan. Southview, Maplehurst, Horsham, W Sussex, RH13 6QY. Tel:0403-864389
Lendfild LINDFIELD Linfeeld Linfeild Linfeile Linfield Linfields Linnild Linveild Linvile Linvill Linville Lyndfeild Lynfeild Lynfelde F1046

142468 LINDO Mr & Mrs Albert W. 4 Cedar Way, Slough, Berks, SL3 7TT.
LINDO Lindoe Lindow Lyndo F6651

142476 LINDOP Mr Granville V F. 36 Woodland Hill, Whitkirk, Leeds, W Yorks, LS15 7DG.
LINDOP MCCLOUD Mcleod MCMANUS F4121

142484 LINDSAY Mrs Barbara. (Harriss) 29 Campfield Road, Broughty Ferry, Dundee, DD5 2NG.
HARRISS MACEY NEWMAN RATTERY Rattray F5045

142492 LINDSAY Mrs H. 25 Black Bull Lane, Fulwood, Preston, Lancs, PR2 3PT.
ASHTON CAMPS EGLIN FOTHERGILL RIDEHALGH F2779

142506 LINDSAY Mrs L M. (Hubert) 10 Exeter Road, Chichester, W Sussex, PO19 4EF.
CHAPPLE LANDER LINDSAY LINDSEY Linsey PORTER WARD F2059

142514 LINDSAY Mrs Shirley M. (Woolmer) 8 Old Oak Road, Kingston, Ontario, K7M 7K3, CANADA. Tel:+1-613-549-8331
ALLCHURCH CASTELL LEIGH LINDSAY NEAL WOOLMER F4108

142522 LINES Mr Jack M. 940 So 16th Avenue, Yakima, Washington, 98902, USA. Tel:+1-509-248-7214
APLIN BASSETT BEDIENT BLIZZARD BUDD CLARK COLLINS CULVER DALLIBER DENNE ELGAR ELWELL FOCHE GARWOOD HALSNODE HANCOCK JOHNSON JORDAN KEMBLE KNIGHT LADD LAUGHEAD LOWE O'HARA PAGE PORTER RAINES ROWE SYMONS WALLING WEST WRYGHT F5538

142530 LINES Mrs Olive E. (Sims) 12 Whitebarn Crescent, Hordle, Lymington, Hants, SO41 0FY. Tel:0425-620623
ADEY BLUNT JARVIS LINES PEACHY SIMS THOMPSON WHEELER F1945

142549 LINES Mr Wayne. 50 Red Barn Lane, Fareham, Hants, PO15 6EB. Tel:0329-221150
A'COURT Acourt ADAMS BAYLEY COLLIER DREA EACOTT Folland Follard FOLLON GRAY HAYTER JAMES Line LINES LUSH Lynes SHIPSEY WHITE F2952

142557 LINFORD Mrs O M. (Bearup) 79 Cassio Road, Watford, Herts, WD1 7BN. Tel:0923-229925
Bearhop BEARHOPE Bearop BEARUP Beerup F1778

142565 LINGLEY Mr A J. 21 Beck Lane, Horsham St Faiths, Norwich, Norfolk, NR10 3LD.
ALDHAM Everard Everett EVERITT Germany Hewet Hewett HEWITT Huet Jarmy Jermany JERMY Linele Lingey LINGLEY Lingly Lingy Linley Molett Mollet MOLLETT Oldham Overard Overitt POINTER Townsend TOWNSHEND WATTS WOODCOCK Woodkok F2622

142573 LINKLATER Mr John. 4c Donald Place, Aberdeen, AB2 4UF.
LINKLATER F3493

142581 LINTER Mr G J. 19 Anson Road, Goring By Sea, Worthing, Sussex, BN12 6JB.
LINTER PRATT F2374

142603 LINTON Elaine. 37 Fisher Avenue, Kilsyth, Glasgow, Stirlingshire, G65 0LT.
LINTON STEWART F1426

142611 LISLE Ms Rebecca A. Highlands, Poplar Hill, Shillingstone, Blandford Dorset.
BOYERS ERSKINE LISLE MARSDIN MEARBECK MOORHOUSE PORTEOUS REYNOLDS WORSNOP F1103

142638 LISNEY Mrs M I. 119 Draycott Avenue, Kenton, Harrow, Middx, HA3 0DA. Tel:081-907-5097
BARKER CHAMBERLIN CROUCH DOIDGE FREWIN GERRETT HARRIS KNIGHT LISNEY LISNEY PREECE ROWTON YALDEN F2122

142646 LITTLE Canon John. St Andrews Vicarage, Towne Gate, Heddon On The Wall, Newcastle Upon Tyne, NE15 0DT.
ABBOTT BELLAS BLAND DENT HOLME LITTLE RICHARDSON SANDES WHALLEY F6474

142654 LITTLE Mrs Emily Louise. 75 Billington Road, New Cross, London, SE14 5QH.
HOBBS VALENTINE F3267

142662 LITTLE Mr John. 3 The Knoll, Oxton, Birkenhead, L43 5UZ. Tel:051-652-6364
ARMSTRONG BROWN LITTLE VOUNG F1675

142670 LITTLE Mr Stephen. 25 Audley Park Road, Bath, Avon, BA1 2XJ. Tel:0225-310180
BELL COOMBS CRAWFORD CUNINGHAME DIROM FOTHERINGHAM GREENLAW HAIG HAYES KOWIESON LITTLE MARCH MARTIN MUIR NICOL PASLEY PETER PRINGLE PRUDDEN READ SKENE SOMERVILLE SPEARING SPINK TINSLEY F1657

142689 LITTLECHILD Mr S C. White House, The Green, Tanworth In Arden, Solihull W Midlands, B94 5AL.
LITTLECHILD F141

142697 LITTLEWOOD Mrs J H. 40 Grasscroft Road, Marsh, Huddersfield, West Yorkshire, HD1 4LP.
BROWN BROWNE HOWARTH LAMBERT LITTLEWOOD F3084

142700 LITTLEWOOD Mr W H. 29 Woodfield Road, Thornton Cleveleys, Lancs, FY5 4EQ. Tel:0253-826024
ALLEN STOTT F4376

142719 LIVERMORE Mr Alan. 75 Richmond Park Road, Kingston On Thames, Surrey, KT2 6AF.
LEE LIVERMORE NEW F6100

142727 LIVINGSTONE Mr Charles MacBeath Noble. 45 Silton Grove, Stockton On Tees, Cleveland, TS18 5AT. Tel:0642-583347
LIVINGSTON Livingstone MUNDIE NOBLE F3204

142735 LIVINGSTONE Mrs D J. 37 Antlers Hill, Chingford, London, E4 7RX. Tel:081-529-0540
BRADY BRIND DIXON HUNT KINSEY LIVINGSTONE LOCK MACKIE MORRIS WHEELER F1742

142743 LLANWARNE Mrs Margaret K. 8 The Glade, Woodside Road, Sevenoaks, Kent, TN13 3HD. Tel:0732-460709
GREENING JONES Lanwarn Lanwarne Lanwerne Lanworn Llanwarn LLANWARNE SCHOLES F3240

142751 LLEWELLYN Mrs Jean. (Macdonald) 34 Windlehurst Road, High Lane, Stockport, Cheshire, SK6 8AB.
Broman BROMHAM BROOKS Brooman Bruman Brumman COLE DEMPSTER DENNISON FIELD HOWELLS Llewellyn Llewelyn LLEWHELLIN MCKENZIE Mckinzie Norbery Norburie NORBURY TOLMIE WEIR F5413

142778 LLOYD Mr A Wyn. Ysgubor Isa, Llanfair D C,

Ruthin, Clwyd, LL15 2UN. Tel:08242-2747
HUGHES JONES LLOYD MORRIS OLDFIELD WYNNE F3511

142786 LLOYD Mrs Anne. 4 Mornington Terrace, Newham On Severn, Glous, GL14 1BG.
BRADBURY LLOYD SUTHERLAND F447

142794 LLOYD Miss Annie. 4635 Stoner Avenue #4, Culver City, CA 90230-5773, USA. Tel:+1-310-398-3924
BEVAN DAVIES HERBERT LLOYD MARGAM MORGAN MORGANS F5572

142808 LLOYD B. Route 41, Silver Lake, New Hampshire 03875, USA.
EVANS F981

142816 LLOYD Miss E N V. Maesbrook Nursing Home, Church Road, Moele Brace, Shrewsbury, SY3 9HQ.
LLOYD F3273

142824 LLOYD Mr J. 48 Bury Road, Harlow, Essex, CM17 0EE. Tel:0279-430052
LLOYD F3468

142832 LLOYD Mr John William. 68 St Marys Walk, Middlesbrough, Cleveland, TS5 7SD. Tel:0642-816927
LLOYD F179

142840 LLOYD Mrs Joyce. 68 St Marys Walk, Middlesbrough, Cleveland, TS5 7SD. Tel:0642-816927
DICK DOW DOWE ELDER HOWLETT LINCOLN LLOYD F180

142859 LLOYD Mr Julian Edward. 1 Royston Road, Manchester, M16 0EU.
BAKER BARNARD BENCE BENNION CURTIS DAVIS FERLY FISHER GARRATT GILL GOULDING GUEST HEAP HIGGINS HILL HINTON HYDE ILLINGSWORTH JONES LAVINGTON LEVOT LLOYD MANNING NEWMAN ORMEROD PACKER PENY PILKINGTON PLATT POPE PRIDE ROLLINSON SLATER SUTTCLIFFE TANNER WAKERLEY WAKLEY WALKERLEY WALKEY WALKLEY WEAKLEY WEBB WEBSTER WETMOTH WOOD F1233

142867 LLOYD Mrs June. 27 Sunnydown Road, Olivers Battery, Winchester, Hants.
Stranach STRANACK Strannach Strannack Strannock F2616

142875 LLOYD Mrs Leanne. 19 Dean St, Cal Gully, VIC 3556, AUSTRALIA.
ALLEN ALLIS BEER BLATCHFORD BLEWETT BOWATER BRABBINS BUTLER COOPER COWLEY DRUERY DYALL GLOVER GOWAN GROSE HUEY IVES KELLETT LLOYD MCKEMMISH NANCARROW PASCOE PEARCE PROSSOR RIDGE ROBINS ROBINSON SISSONS TUCK TUNSTALL WATERS WEBSTER WEST WILLIAMS F5518

142883 LLOYD Mrs Mary. (Walker) 14 Royston Road, Davyhulme, Manchester, M31 1QG.
ARMSTRONG BULMAN CORNER GRAHAM JOHNSTONE RUDDICK STARLING STORROW WALKER WAUGH F3648

142891 LLOYD Mr Peter. 82 Great Albert Road South, Great Malvern, Worcs, WR14 3DX.
BEVERLEY CREED EVANS Floyd GOOSEMAN LLOYD Lloyde Loyd Loyde NEWMAN Reece REES Rheese Rhys SANDERSON SAUNDERSON THOMPSON F1810

142905 LLOYD Mr Philip E. 268 Upper Chorlton Road, Manchester, M16 0BN.
ASTINGTON BENNETT DICKINSON DRINKWATER GOLDSWORTHY GOSLING HUSSEY JOHNSON LLOYD NEAVE NETTELL Nettle RALPH RATHBOURNE Shoal Shoale Shole SHOLL Showle SIMPSON THOMAS WOOLCOCK F355

142913 LOACH Mrs B M. 18 Berwood Farm Road, Sutton Coldfield, W Midlands, B72 1AJ.
AINSBURY BALE KIRBY LOACH SHELLEY Slason SLAWSON Slawston Sloson Slowson F396

142921 LOADER Mr T A. 3 Bourne Cottages, Bourne Hill, Wherstead, Ipswich Suffolk, IP2 8NH. Tel:0473-601319
COTTERILL DUNCAN EDWARDS HILLMEN LEESE LOADER PEGLER F4141

142948 LOBB Mr Rodney Bown. Meadow Farmhouse, Bathingbourne Lane, Sandown, Isle Of Wight, PO36 0LU. Tel:0983-867499
LOBB F3302

142956 LOBBETT Mr Keith A. 130 Hair Street, Wainuiomata, Wellington, NEW ZEALAND.
Labbett LOBBETT Lobet Lobett F7010

142964 LOBLEY Mr Phillip N. 25 Langthorne Crescent, Grays, Essex, RM17 5XA.
LOBLEY F6714

142972 LOCHRIE Mrs Rebecca. (Pudney) 41 Hillview Avenue, Kilsyth, Glasgow, Stirlingshire, G65 0DJ.
Lochery LOCHRIE LOUGHARY Loughery PATRICK ROSS SINCLAIR F1425

142980 LOCKE Mr C C. 3 Blackbrook Drive, Lodge Moor, Sheffield, Yorks, S10 4LS.
COLE FEARNLEY LOCK RYCROFT WATERWORTH F988

142999 LOCKE Mrs Enid. (Woodhams) High Chantry, 36 Blacksmiths Hill, Benington, Herts, SG2 7LQ. Tel:043885-211
BODY BOX BRIDER BUTSON DAVIES KESTLE LOVERING MILLS OLDHAM RICHARDS STEVENS WILLIAMS WILLMOTT WOODHAMS F3686

143006 LOCKE Mr R David. 4 Rathmore Road, Cambridge, CB1 4AD. Tel:0223-411180
CONWAY ELMORE HOUSLEY LOCKE MASON PRIESTLEY Priestnall WALKER F1789

143014 LODDER Mr G J. 3 The Green, Walditch, Bridport, Dorset, DT6 4LB. Tel:0308-56250
ARMITT BIGNELL BROWN BURGESS CLEAN FLOYD HARPER Hurden HURDING LODDER MARTIN MULLETT ROSS SARD THURSFIELD TRENT WALLER WEBSTER F1700

143022 LODGE Mr Alan. 450 Hatfield Road, St Albans, Herts, AL4 0XS. Tel:0727-869785
DEARNLEY DONKERSLEY HINCHLIFFE LODGE LOFT MARSHALL MOSS PITT SHARP TOLSON F3507

143030 LODGE Mr Brian. 4 Avon Drive, Bedford, Beds, MK41 7AB. Tel:0234-267531
BROADWAY FARMER Frapell Frappell Frapple FRAPWELL LIDDIARD Lidiard LODGE Lydiard MARKHAM Rappel SMILEY Smilie Smilley Smillie Smyley Smylie Smyly Wrapple F2077

143049 LODGE Mrs E J. 14 Elliot Place, Trowbridge, Wiltshire, BA14 9TQ. Tel:0225-767775
DRYDEN GROOM HUMBLE NEALE NORMAN PLEDGER PRIN QUINTON F3371

143057 LODGE Ursula J. 182 Coates Way, Garston, Watford, WD2 6PE.
O'BASE F7332

143065 LOGAN Mrs A M. 60 Mickleton Road, Earlsdon, Coventry, CV5 6PQ. Tel:0203-676736
CALVERT CHRISTIAN JACKSON MORELAND SHUFFLEBOTHAM F2423

143073 LOGAN Mr & Mrs Peter. Rury, 9 Blaen Y Myarth, Llangynidr, Powys, NP8 1NQ. Tel:0874-730900
FALCONER LOGAN PORTER THOMSONE WILSON F3589

143081 LOGUE Mrs V E. 307-8880 No 1 Road, Richmond, British Columbia, V7C 4C3, CANADA.
MILEMAN F6856

143103 LOMAS Mrs Helen. 26 Berrow Court, Gardens Walk, Upton Upon Severn, Worcester, WR8 0JP.
CLAYTON HAWKINS F1719

143111 LOMAS Mr Peter D R. 28 Park Avenue, Ashbourne, Derbyshire, DE6 1GA.
Lemas Lemess Lomacks Lomalghs Lomalls Lomals LOMAS Lomase Lomass Lomasse Lomath Lomax Lomaxe Lomes Lomhas Lomis Lommas Lomos Lomous Lomus Loomas Loumas Lowmas Lumas Lumhales Lumhalghs F2590

143138 LOMBARD-BEAHEN Mrs Janet. (Beahen) 4016 Idaho Avenue North, Minneapolis, Minnesota, 55427-1447, USA.
BACHILER BOOKE JENKINS Lambard Lambert LEWIS LOMBARD Lombart Lombert Lumbard Lumbart Lumber Lumbert Lumbort Puddington Purington Purrington PURRINTON WING F4498

143146 LONG Mrs Joan. 14 Seely Avenue, Calverton, Nottingham, NG14 6NF.
CAULDWELL DAVIS Fullwood FULWOOD LESTER LONG MOSS SCOTT SWIFT F4915

143154 LONG Mr John M B. Pax House, 14 Ellis Road, Bedford, MK41 9DW. Tel:0234-353860
BANWELL How HOWE LONG F3332

143162 LONG Dr L H. Compass Cottage, Stoke Hill, Exeter, Devon, EX4 7JH.
DRAKE JUSTICE MELWAYE Millway F3954

143170 LONG Mrs Mary. Woodbine Cottage, 8 Shrubbery Road, Gravesend, Kent, DA12 1JW.
Coashman Coteford COUCHMAN Coushman Cowchman Cudaford Cuddeford CUDDIFORD Cushman Cuteford Cutresfourd CUTTIFORD HUBBARD Olsborn Orsborn OSBORN Osborne Osbourn Osbourne Osburn Ozborne RASBERRY Rasbury RESBURY STARTUP Tap

TAPP Tappe Taype TYLER Tylor F4496
143189 LONG Mr Roland. 5 Paddock Close, Wyke, Bradfrod, BD12 9LB.
BROWN LITTLE NATTRASS PURTON SISSONS TUCKER F3042
143197 LONG Mr Sidney Howard. 90 Southfield Road, Oxford, OX4 1PA.
Baser Bazer BEAZER Beeser Beser Besor Besser Bezer DEAN GOODEARL LEWIS LONG SILCOCKS STEVENS F5265
143200 LONGLEY Mr Peter. 115 Cooden Sea Road, Bexhill On Sea, E Sussex, TN39 4TA. Tel:04243-2270
JACKSON LONGLEY MCDONALD NYE REEVE F634
143219 LONGMAN Mr D A. Woodstock, Violet Way, Loudwater, Rickmansworth Herts, WD3 4JP. Tel:0923-773858
ADAMS FORFITT Langaman LANGMAN Longeman LONGMAN MOFFAT MYHILL PICKERDITE ROBERTS WILLIAMS F2651
143227 LONGMIRE Mrs J A. Finchams Farm, The Ling, North Lopham, Diss Norfolk, IP22 2NJ.
LONGMIRE SOMERSCALES F6577
143235 LONGMORE Dr H J A. Lynnhurst, Lochmaben, Lockerbie, Dumfriesshire, DG11 1NH. Tel:0387-810252
Langmoor Langmore Langmuir Langmuire Longmoor LONGMORE Longmuir Longmuire F3827
143243 LOOSEN Mrs Mary. (Whitaker) 46 Groveland Road, Newbury, Berks, RG13 1SS.
ALLEN BRADLEY BROUGHTON CHAMBERS FALKINGHAM STEVENSON TRUEMAN WHITAKER F2581
143251 LOPTSON Mr Peter. Dept Of Philosophy, University Of Saskatchewan, Saskatoon, Saskatwhewan, S7N 0W0, CANADA.
BAIRD BRYANT CAMERON MCCULLOCH MCCULLY METCALF MUNRO ROSS STANLAKE THOMPSON F868
143278 LORANGER Mrs Joyce C. (Freeman) 1534 Voorhees Avenue, Manhattan Beach, CA 90266, USA.
AUSTIN BAUGH BENNION FERNEYHOUGH FOXEN FREEMAN GLOVER GODFREE LANGTON LOWE MARRIOTT PIDDOCK TITLEY WATSON F4475
143286 LORD Prof John V. 4 Orchard Lane, Ditchling, Hassocks, W Sussex, BN6 8TH. Tel:07918-4718
BISHOP BLAKEY BOWKER CLYST CORNER DAVIS DERRY DIXON EDWARDS GRAY HAMPSON HAYWARD HEATON HOOPER HOUGHTON KIRKHAM LONEY LORD MARGERISON MASON MATHEWS OKELL PRICE REEVES SCOTT SHEPHERD SMITH STEANE TREVELYAN WATSON F2136
143294 LORD Mr K J. 71 Dawpool Drive, Bromborough, Wirral, Merseyside, L62 6DF. Tel:051-334-5036
BROXHAM ENSOR GEORGE LORD MACE NICHOLS PARSONS ROBERTS SIMS WESTACOTT WHITE F3545
143308 LORD Mr M J. 30 Dalby Avenue, Bushby, Leicester, LE7 9RD.
BACON BAKER LORD MEEK MOSS NELSON OLLEY TAYLOR F4921
143316 LORD Mr Roland Alan. 22 Elizabeth Crescent, East Grinstead, West Sussex, RH19 3JA. Tel:0342-325149
CLARKE DYKE PREDDY F6543
143324 LORIMER Mrs Daphne. (Freeth) Scorradale House, Orphir, Orkney, KW17 2RF.
FREETH HAPGOOD HOME MACDONALD POCOCK F739
143332 LORRAIN Mrs P. 19 The Croft, Bishopstone, Salisbury, Wiltshire, SP5 4DF.
BEST DE VEAR GILES GOATLY JOPLEN KEENE MINIFIE PENFOUND SNOOK WYER F2096
143340 LOUGHRAN Mrs P M. 10 Spencer Avenue, Earlsdon, Coventry, Warks, CV5 6NP. Tel:0203-713625
BALE BECKETT BRICK CALLAGHAN EASINGWOOD FINCH GREEN HARRIGAN HAYES HORRIGAN LOUGHRAN LYNCH MAISLAND WALMSLEY WALSH F4276
143359 LOUKES Mrs Elizabeth. (Rogers) 87 Hayes Street, Bunbury, WA 6230, AUSTRALIA.
BLOWS COAD FRANCE INKSTER JONES LOUKES MATTHEW ROGERS SUMMERLAND WISHART F5568
143367 LOVATT Mr S E. 23 The Newlands, Wallington, Surrey, SM6 9JX.
Lovat LOVATT Lovet Lovett WEARY Werrey Werrie Werry Wheary Wheery Wherry F6388
143375 LOVE Mr B. 5 Thonock Road, Westgate, Morecambe, Lancs, LA4 4RG. Tel:0524-415297
LOVE F4269
143383 LOVE Mr W H. 33 Slievecoole Park, Belfast, Northern Ireland, BT14 8JN.
LOVE F4156
143391 LOVEDAY Mrs C. 9 Stirling Court, Holmes Chapel, Crewe, Cheshire, CW4 7JG.
Gausby Gisbey Gisby Gosbee Gosbey Gosbie GOSBY Gousby F6848
143405 LOVEGROVE Mr Roger. 11 Marlborough Road, Bowes Park, London, N22 4NB. Tel:081-888-5609
LOVEGROVE F3063
143413 LOVELL Mr Mark. 61 Charnwood Avenue, Westone, Northampton, NN3 3EE.
Louvell Lovel LOVELL F2748
143421 LOVELL Mr Percy. West Lea, Wylam Wood Road, Wylam, Northumberland, NE41 8HZ. Tel:0661-852161
Bain Ban Bane Baun BAWN FUDGE HOPES LEONARD LOVELL SOMIRELL Summerhill Summerlille F4030
143448 LOVELLE Mrs Gillian. (Boyers) Highfield, Grove Lane, Waltham, Grimsby, South Humberside, DN37 0HD.
BOYERS BRIGGS DENYER HOWARD IVES LOVE PATTERSON ROSE ROSS SANDERSON SHEPHERD F5050
143456 LOVETT Mr Cliff. 24 Lenham Close, Winnersh, Berks, RG11 1HR. Tel:0734-792926
EDWARDS JACKSON LOVETT WOODHOUSE F389
143464 LOW Mrs Audrey. (Bradshaw) 62 Ridgeway Avenue, East Barnet, Herts, EN4 8TN. Tel:081-440-5956
BRADSHAW COLLYER KNIGHT LOW PALMER F3802
143472 LOW Miss Helen Keay. 136 Crieff Road, Perth, PH1 2NY. Tel:0738-35731
DUFF GLASS LOW F5777
143480 LOWE Mrs Doris. 106 Eton Road, Ilford, Essex, IG1 2UG.
BORTON CALLINGHAM CARTER CHANCE CHITTENDEN COSTER DAGWELL Frewen FRUEN GOODALL HUNT MATTHEWS MURRELL PASKENS Paskins PHILLIPS READ STRUGNELL WEBSTER WYETH F2063
143499 LOWE Mr J J W. 4 St Marks Close, Evesham, Worcs, WR11 6EU. Tel:0386-48910
ASH BAKER BAWDEN BURCHELL GEE LOWE MESSAM WILLEY YOCKNEY YOUNGASH F263
143502 LOWE Miss K M. 18 Moat Bank, Bretby Lane, Burton On Trent, Staffs, DE15 0QJ.
CACKETT CARLTON CHETTER COLLINS DAY DODD HAIGH HARRIS JOHNSON LEONARD LOWE MANSELL MERRYFIELD MITCHELL MORGAN NICKLESS OSBORNE OXSPRING PEPLOW PETTIT PODMORE POTTER REYNOLDS SURREY THORINGTON THORNTON WARD WATTS F1558
143510 LOWE Mrs P G. Gatsby, 311 Dyke Road, Hove, Sussex, BN3 6PE.
BURGIS HEGBIN F6731
143529 LOWE Mrs V. (Hodges) 81 Cradlebridge Drive, Ashford, Kent, TN24 0RL.
BRAYBROOK Braybrooke EDWARDS HODGES LEGGETT LOWE PIGGE ROSE RUTTER WILTSHIRE WOOTTON F648
143537 LOWE-PONSFORD Mrs Barbara. 61 Caves Lane, Bedford, MK40 3DW. Tel:0234-212123
BRUNDRITT GILLETT JUDKINS Leading Leadon LEEDEN MATTS PONSFORD PROWSE SMITH WALDRON F2686
143545 LOWES Mr Peter. 43 Millfield Avenue, Northallerton, N Yorks, DL6 1AT. Tel:0609-774589
LOWES F385
143553 LOWIS Mr David. 6 Doomgate, Appleby In Westmorland, Cumbria, CA16 6RB.
BEATHAM BELLAS BENSON BRUNSKILL COCKFIELD COWPERTHWAITE ELLWOOD HUNTER LANCASTER LOWIS MARTIN MOSS MURRAY NICHOLSON NIXON RICHARDSON SEDGWICK WATSON F579
143561 LOWTH Mr G M. 20 Cedarland Crescent, Nuthall, Nottingham, NG16 1AH. Tel:0602-277525
Louth Louthe LOWTH Lowthe F6121
143588 LUCAS Mrs Avril. (Otty) 27 Alms Hill Road, Sheffield, S11 9RR.
DRAKE FELL OTTY SWINN THEAKSTONE F5882
143596 LUCAS Mrs Maureen. 18 Lewry Close, Hedge End, Southampton, Hants, SO3 4EW.
CARVOSSO COURT DAVEY GENDALL HARRY LEGGO MATTHEWS MOLES REDWOOD RICHARDS TIDBOULD F1094
143618 LUCAS Mr Michael J. 8 Bleakley Avenue, Notton, Wakefield, W Yorks, WF4 2NT.
GOMERSALL HINES LAWTON LUCAS MARGERSON

Periman Perriman PERRYMAN SKELTON Swailes Swails SWALES WILLIAMS F2709
143626 LUCAS Mr Robin. Vassars, Common Road, East Tuddenham, East Dereham Norfolk, NR20 3AH. Tel:0603-880356
VASSAR F145
143634 LUCAS Mrs Sharron. (Delamere) 8 Bleakley Avenue, Notton, Wakefield, W Yorks, WF4 2NT.
BROSTER De La Mare Dela Mare Delamare DELAMERE Delimare Dellamare FELLOWS FREEMAN JENKS KING LAWTON MINCHER STANLEY F2703
143642 LUCAS-HOGBIN Mrs Vivienne. 39 Natal Road, Brighton, Sussex, BN2 4BN. Tel:0273-691327
ALDRIDGE LUCAS PENN F614
143650 LUCE Mrs J. 43 Winchester Way, Willingdon, E Sussex, BN22 0JS.
CORKE HALL HINSON JENKINS LUCE F2875
143669 LUCY Mrs Nina. (Clements) 183 Well Lane, Willerby, Hull, HU10 6HT. Tel:0482-655347
LUCY F3712
143677 LUDLAM Miss H. 38 Sun Road, Swanscombe, Kent, DA10 0BH.
COALES DAYKIN DUNSTER JENNER LUDLAM PAYNE F2827
143685 LUDLOW Mr Douglas. The Orchard, Pembury Road, Tunbridge Wells, Kent, TN2 4ND. Tel:0892-824430
BEWSEY BINGLEY CURRIE HARDIE LOWLOW LUDLOW PEPLER RENTMORE F4424
143693 LUKE Dennis E. 38 Primrose Ridge, Godalming, Surrey, GU7 2NX.
ALLUM BALL BARNET Barnett Benats Bennatts BENNET Bennett BOLTON BRIGGS BRISTOW Britnall BRITNELL BROWN Brutenell Brutennell BUNCE BUTLER CARPENTER COLLINS DARVEL DELL DICKER EATON EMMANS Frood FROUD GOODCHILD GREENING HALL HARDING HATCH HEARN Hearne Hern Herne HOARE HOLLOWAY Holoway Holway HOPKINS HUGHES HUNT HUSSEY JONES JORDAN KEEN KENSEY Kinsey LACK Lacke LUKE MARTIN MAY MEAD MONK Nicholls NICHOLS OAKES Oaks Pearce PEERCYE PEWSEY Pisey POTTINGER PRICE Pusey RANCE Raunce Rodgers ROGERS RUSSEL SANDERS Saunders SEARS Seears Seers SMEE SMITH Snowden SOWDEN STEVENS TAYLOR THOMPSON TOOVEY Toovye Tovy TURNER WALKER WARD Warde WARNER WATSON WELCH WESTFIELD WHITE WILKINS WILLIAMS WRAYLER F2675
143707 LUKE Mrs E M. Langdon, 165 Newbridge Hill, Bath, Avon, BA1 3PX. Tel:0225-422255
COBBETT COX CRISP HORNSBY HYDE LUKE PUCKETT ROBINSON VYE WICKHAM F6319
143715 LUKSYS Miss Anne. 38 Springfield Road, Millfield, Peterborough, Cambs, PE1 2JG.
HARRIS MARCHANT Merchant WATKINS WOODWARD F4776
143723 LUMLEY Mrs M L. 22 Trem Y Nant, Wrexham, Clwyd, LL13 7QL.
Loemle LUMLEY Lymley F6882
143731 LUMMIS Mr Eric. 44 Brackendale Road, Camberley, Surrey, GU15 2JR. Tel:0276-22413
AGAR CREASEY Lammesse Londnys Lonney Lonys Louenes Louenesse Louneis Lovenes Loveness Lownes LUMMIS Lumnes Lumnis Lumys Lundnes Lunnis F6247
143758 LUMSDEN Mr John. Earlsdene, 19 Meadow Road, Pickering, North Yorks, YO18 8NW. Tel:0751-75023
ANTHONY BRATT CLAYTON FAIRBAIRN HANDY LUMSDEN MEARS RUTHERFORD SMART SMITH TURNER WALTON F4167
143766 LUND Mrs Dawna. 1732 Parkview Cir, Redlands, CA 92374, USA.
BARKLE BARTLE CARNSEW EUSTICE HARVEY HOCKIN PHILLIPS PIERCE POOLEY F5476
143774 LUNTLEY Mrs A P. 23 Castle Mound, Barby, Rugby, Warwick, CV23 8TN.
BATES BAXTER BRADWELL HARRISON Holderfield Holifield Hollifield Hollyfield HOLYFIELD JAMES JENNINGS Lantley Lantly LAWSON LISTER LUNTLEY Luntly TREDWELL F1660
143782 LUSH Dr G J. Flat 6, Waverley Court, 41 Steeles Road, London, NW3 4SB. Tel:071-586-0181
LUSH F2660
143790 LUSH Dr Gordon. 6 Waverley Court, 41 Steeles Road, London, NW3 4SB.
LUSH Lushe F7121
143804 LUTLEY Mr A J. 22 Basing Way, Thomas Ditton, Surrey, DT3 0NX.
LUTLEY F6948
143812 LYALL Mrs Margaret. Woodward Street, Repton, NSW 2454, AUSTRALIA.
Barbar Barbarr Barber Barbor BARBOUR Chenower Chenoweth Chenowethe Chenowight Chenowith Chenoworth Chenowth Chenowyth Chenswath Chensweth Chenwith Cheynoweth Chnweth Chynouth CHYNOWETH Chynowith CRANSTON Genower KENNEDY MCGOWAN Mcgurran MORRIS Oxenham Oxinham Oxman OXNAM Oxsonham Polick Pollak Pollick Pollicke Pollique Polloc POLLOCK Pollok POPPINS Shortal SHORTALL Shortel Shortell Shorthill Shortill F4405
143820 LYALL Mr R T. Woodward Street, Repton, NSW 2454, AUSTRALIA.
FRASER GIBSON LINDSAY Lyal LYALL Lyel Lyell F4406
143839 LYDDIETH Mr John. C/o Burra Folly, Limpley Stoke, Bath, Avon, BA3 6HA.
BARRATT Barrett Boun BOWN BOWN BRAY Brown CAVE CHAPMAN LASBURY LAWRENCE Lideath Lyddiatt LYDDIETH LYDDIETH Lydeat Lydiat Lydiate Lydiath Lydiatt Lydieth MAY WHITE F3720
143847 LYE Mr Bryan. Quernhow, Gt North Road, Sinderby, Thirsk, N Yorks, YO7 4LG. Tel:0845-567221
LYE F5866
143855 LYELL Mrs Jean. (Stevenson) 80a Southview Terrace, St Judes, Plymouth, Devon, PL4 9DH. Tel:0752-225160
BOYD IRISH LUXTON Lyall LYELL Lyle STEVENSON TANCOCK WEBBERLEY F2733
143863 LYES Mr W J. 2 Riverwood Road, Frenchay, Avon, BS16 1NX. Tel:0272-569213
Lies Lise Lize LYES Lys Lyse F4737
143871 LYNALL D G. 3 Denecote Lodge, 6 Westminster Road, Poole, Dorset, BH13 6JL.
Linall Lineall Linehill Linell LYNALL Lynehill Lynell Lynold F6578
143898 LYNCH Mrs Georgina. (Harvey) Southside, 63 Parklands Road, Chichester, W Sussex, PO19 3DX. Tel:0243-788732
DAWE HARVEY HILDER JEZZARD MELLERS METTERS NAGBY PORTER SELLENS TOOGOOD F259
143901 LYNCH Mr J P. 63 Parklands Road, Chichester, W Sussex, PO19 3DX.
KING LYNCH MACKIE MILLER NEILL PLAYER WADMORE WHELAN WILLIAMS F260
143928 LYNDS Mrs Doris. (Adams) 28 Longfield Avenue, Newbarn, Longfield, Kent, DA3 7LE. Tel:0474-703659
ADAMS ALAND Lind Linde Linds Lines Lynd Lynde LYNDS Lynes Lynn Lyns F2013
143936 LYNE Mr Arthur. 52 Falmouth Road, Truro, Cornwall, TR1 2HR.
JEFFERY JOHNS LYNE SLEEMAN F4279
143944 LYON Mrs A. 4 Fairclough Road, Rainhill, Prescot, Merseyside, L35 9JG.
ARNELL ATKINSON BEAL BLAKEY BLENKARN CHAPMAN DENT FLETCHER LYON LYTH MARWOOD MATTHEWS NAWTON PROCTER RICHARDSON RIVERS THOMPSON WILD WILLIS YATES YEATES F571
143952 LYON Mr John R. Poachers, 6 Harvest Court, Welwyn, Hertfordshire, AL6 0NG. Tel:043871-7633
BRUMBY LYON F4515
143960 LYONS Mrs Vi. 14 Lynwood Grove, Sale, Cheshire, M33 2AN.
HARDBOTTLE POLLOCK POWELL STEPHENS F874
143979 LYUS Mr B W. Shepstone, Holmesdale Road, South Nutfield, Surrey, RH1 4JE.
Lias Lyas LYUS F6940
143987 MAC DOWELL Mr Thomas. Flat 1, Albany House, The Embankment, Bedford, MK40 3PA.
BLAIN MAC DOWELL F5720
143995 MACDONALD Mrs Frances. 2077 Prospect Street, Apt 703, Burlington, Ontario, L7R 1Z4, CANADA.
AYLWIN Aylwyn F7228
144002 MACDONALD Linda Harney. 6696 Hollow Dale Drive, Apt 8, Salt Lake City, UT 84121, USA.

HARNEY F7290
144010 MACDONALD Mrs Noreen. (Howat) 664 Buckingham, Lincoln Park, Michigan, 48146, USA.
CUMMING DICK DICKSON HARROLD HOWAT LENNOX MACDONALD MURCHISON RATTRAY F4440
144029 MACDONALD Mr Robert. 61 Armstrong Street, Sunshine, Victoria, 3020, AUSTRALIA.
Tel:+61-3-311-2948
CARTLEDGE DUNNINGTON FOUNTAIN GLEDHILL GREENALD MACDONALD PARKER PARKINSON SMITH WILLIAMS WYKE F5584
144037 MACFADYEN Mrs Elizabeth. (Bone) 2 Martlet Drive, Spateston, Johnstone, Renfrewshire, PA5 0SJ.
ADAM ARTHUR BANKS BONES BRYDON CARR CASWELL COWING FAULDS FRASER HILLHOUSE HYNES JACKSON LAPSLEY LENNOX MACFADYEN MCDONALD POTTS ROSE SCOTT SHOTTON SLIMAN SMITH TURNER WATSON WOOD F3814
144045 MACFARLANE Mr Robert. 11 Fairfield Crescent, Oakwood, Hexham, Northumberland, NE46 4LH.
BYWORTH FEATHERSTONEHAUGH JORDAN MATSON MCARTHY NEWTON TAYLOR F3675
144053 MACFARLANE-DUNN Mrs A. 1 Abbey Road, West Moors, Wimborne, Dorset, BH22 0AU.
BENDALL CROCKETT DANIELS DUNN FLETCHER JONES MACFARLANE PARRY STOCKER TRENCHARD F2479
144061 MACFAWN Jeff. Po Box 289, Armdale, Nova Scotia, B3L 4K1, CANADA.
MCFAWN F7324
144088 MACHIN Mrs Betty. (Paton) 84 Eleanor Crescent, Westlands, Newcastle, Staffs, ST5 3RF.
AUSTIN CAPPER COMER COOMER CRAIG CROMPTON DAVIES DINGLEY DOORBAR DUNLOP KERR MACHIN MCCULLOUGH MCHOUL PARKES PATON REID F1055
144096 MACHIN Mrs Muriel. 23 Nicholas Road, Beeston, Nottingham, NG9 3LP. Tel:0602-228837
ATTENBOROUGH COOKSEY DAVIS FOSTER ROWBOTHAM F2362
144118 MACKAY Mr Christine. Po Box 114, Coolum Beach, 4573, AUSTRALIA.
A'teuill Atral Atril Atrill Atterill ATTRILL F7227
144126 MACKAY Mr Donald. 25 Largie Road, Glasgow, Scotland, G43 2RD.
Ailmer Aimer Alemar Alemer Aylmar AYLMER Elmar Elmer HUBBLE MACKAY MOYCE F1898
144134 MACKAY Mrs Fay. Caddon Mill, Clovenfords, Selkirkshire, TD1 3LZ.
LOTHIAN MACKAY THOMSON WALKER F2945
144142 MACKENZIE Mr Donald G. 12 Garven Road, Stevenston, Ayrshire, KA20 3NX.
MACKENZIE ROSS F1490
144150 MACKENZIE Mrs G D. (Hoye) 78 Steade Road, Sheffield, Yorks, S7 1DU. Tel:0742-557520
Cabble CABLE CAMPBELL Christal Christall CLUNES Cornewall Cornewell Cornwall CORNWELL Cristal CRISTALL DINGWALL EVANS FENCOTT HOY Hoye INNES MACKENZIE Mckenzie MORGAN OWEN RAMSAY Sim SIME SMITH THACKWAY F1234
144169 MACKENZIE Mrs Joyce. (Egan) 30 Withenfield Road, Northen Moor, Wythenshawe, Manchester, M23 9BS.
BENBOW BRISCOE CARTER COURT DAVIES EGAN HOLMES JENKINS JENNINGS MARSH MORRAM MORRAN Morvam PEUDU TATTERSALL TAYLOR THORPE WEBB F5943
144177 MACKIE Miss Linda. 110 Alexandra Street, Bardon, QLD 4065, AUSTRALIA.
ANDERSON BAKES BARTLETT BREWER CUMMIN Cumming DORMAN KEAY LEE MACKIE MOORE NESBITT PAULL RANDALL THOMSON TONKIN WHATMOUGH WHYTE F5521
144185 MACKLEY Mr Peter. 5 Leslie Gardens, Rayleigh, Essex, SS6 8SZ. Tel:0268-773577
MACKLEY F3951
144193 MACKLIN Mrs Maureen. 117 Eastfield Road, Belgrave Drive, Hull, HU4 6DU.
Tel:0482-571083
SHREEVE Shreeves Shreve Shreves Shrieve Shrieves F1173
144207 MACKMAN Mr Bev. 35 Sitwell Gr, Acomb, North Yorks, YO2 5JG. Tel:0904-781752
MACKMAN MACKMIN MAKEMAN MAKMAN F2576
144215 MACKNIGHT Mr John Eric. 3 Alicewell Villas, Cox Green, Sunderland, Tyne & Wear, SR4 9JU.
Tel:091-534-3268
DAVISON INGRAM MACKNIGHT SPALDING STAVOLD WILLIAMS F3503
144223 MACLACHLAN Mrs Rowena. (Fletcher) 157 Redford Cr, Stratford, Ontario, N5A 1P3, CANADA.
BURNEY DELMAGE DOLMAN FLETCHER LYNES MARKES MCLACHLAN PHILLIPS TIGHE WESLEY F5442
144231 MACLEOD Mrs Irene. 10 Warwick Road, Bishop Auckland, Durham, DL14 6LT.
ARMSTRONG CRON DEANS FISHER GRIERSON HOWIE MARSHALL MCMEEKAN MCMURDO NICOLSON PEACOCK STEVENSON TANNOCK UNDERWOOD F1516
144258 MACMILLAN Mrs Betty. 414 Eleventh St West, Cornwall, Ontario, K6J 3B8, CANADA.
Galland Gallon Gaulon Gaylinge Gealing Gilland GOILLON Golding Golland Gollin Gowland Gowling Gulling Gullon Valpi VALPY F7453
144266 MACQUISTEN Mr F A. 15 The Oaks, Common Mead Lane, Gillingham, Dorset, SP8 4SW.
Coistain Eysteinn GLENDENNING Huisdean Huisdeinn M'cristain M'cristan M'cuistan M'cuisten M'cuistin M'cuiston M'huchison M'huison M'hustan M'qhuiston M'queaston M'queestan M'queeston M'queiftoun M'queisoun M'queistene M'queistine M'quesistein M'questan M'questen M'questin M'questine M'question M'queston M'quiestan M'quistan M'quistein M'quisten M'quistin M'quistine M'quistion M'quiston M'uistine M'utchon Maccoistain Maccuiston Machuison Mackuisten Macqueechan Macqueifstoun Macquesten Macquestian Macquestion Macquiftion Macquistan Macquistani Macquistation MACQUISTEN Macquister Macquistin Macquistini Macquistion Macquiston Macuistian Macuiston Macwhistan Macwhiston Macwisdon Maquiston Mccrustian Mccuestian Mccuestion Mccuistain Mccuisten Mccuister Mccuistians Mccuistin Mccuistion Mccuiston Mccusten Mccustin Mccuston Mchoustone Mchuistonn Mchutcheon Mckqueistein Mckquestein Mcquest Mcqueston Mcquiften Mcquifton Mcquinston Mcquistan Mcquisten Mcquistian Mcquistin Mcquistion MCQUISTON Mcquseten Mcqustin Mcqustion Mcquston Mcuisten Mcuisthon Mcuistian Mcuistine Mcuistion Mcuiston Mcwhiston Meccustin Mkhuthin Mkhutkhon Mkquefton Mkquiton Monfcuiftion F521
144274 MACRAE Mrs F. Holme Mains Farm, Dores Road, Inversness, IV1 2DH.
MACRAE MCRAE F1959
144282 MACRAE Miss Jane A. 20 Princess Crescent, London, N4 2HJ.
BARHAM CHAPMAN COX DANIELS Elfick ELPHICK GOLDSMITH GRINSTED HARMAN Harriatt HARRIOTT Hayyot Herriott HOOK LASHMAR MASON MEDHURST MORSE RICKS SILSBY STEDFORD F3164
144290 MACRAE Mr John. Whitelands, London Road, Rivenhall End, Witham, Essex, CM8 3HA.
ANGUS BEETHAM BEMROSE CAMPBELL COUSANS HINCHLIFFE ILINGWALL LEITCH LEVERS MACAULAY MACDONALD MACDOUGALL MACINTOSH MACIVER MACRAE MCRAE MURRAY NAYLOR NORWOOD PATERSON ROBINSON SLIGHT SOWERBY WARNOCK YOUNG F5308
144304 MADDOCKS Lady Patricia. 11 Lee Road, Aldeburgh, Suffolk, IP15 5HG. Tel:0728-453443
BUXTON DUCK HOLMES WILLIAMS F522
144312 MADGE Mr Paul. 25 Hayes End, South Petherton, Somerset, TA13 5AG.
MADGE F6447
144320 MAFANT-MASSON Mme Isabelle. Coursiere De Lilas, 6bis Avenue De Mondon, 43000 Polignac, FRANCE.
MALFANT F7310
144339 MAGLOCHLAINN Mr P A. 46 Malone Avenue, Belfast, NORTHERN IRELAND.
MAGLOCHLAINN Mclaughlin F6645
144347 MAGUIRE Mrs M L. (Fairbairn) 14 Atherton Heights, Bridgewater Road, Wembley, Middx, HA0 1YD.
BLOOMFIELD CULLEN FAIRBAIRN MANHIRE F2041
144355 MAGUIRE Mrs M. 45 Manor Park, Maids Moreton, Bucks, MK18 1QX.
ANDREWS AUSTEN BACK BOURNE CROMP DRYLAND EARL FISHER GILES GOODWIN GOULD GOWER HALL HARDRES

HIGGINS JOHNCOCK MAGUIRE MATSON MOLL NEWMAN NOKES NORRINGTON NORTON ROSS SAWKINS WHITEWOOD WILMSHURST F1972

144363 MAHAN Mrs Jeanne. (Naugle) 19 Eastgate Drive, Daly City, CA 94015, USA.
BLACKSHAW DE DUNLOP DICKINSON FAWKES FURNESS HOOD LEONARD NEWLIN WALKER WILSON F7398

144371 MAHONEY Mr Shaun. 19 Benslow Rise, Hitchin, Hertfordshire, SG4 9QX. Tel:0462-451636
BRIGHT CASELDEN CHANDLER MAHONEY QUANCE RICH SHEARS TOWNSEND WAYE F4507

144398 MAIN Mrs Margaret. (Hamlin) 26 Bushmead Road, Whitchurch, Aylesbury, Bucks, HP22 4LG.
HAMLIN MAIN MITCHELL PARTRIDGE PEVALIN READ WARREN F4327

144401 MAINWARING Mr Clive. 90 Monkmoor Road, Shrewsbury, Shropshire, SY2 5AY. Tel:0743-56324
BIRBECK EBREY Mainewaring MAINWARING Mannering Manwaring Maynwaring F354

144428 MAIRIS Mr Henry. 17 Dean House, 24 Church Avenue, Ruislip, Middx, HA4 7HT.
MAIRIS Mareis Mares Mareys Maries Maris Marrays Marreys Marys F2930

144436 MAJOR Mrs J D. Po Box 5413, Wellesley Street, Auckland, NEW ZEALAND.
FANCOURT ISHAM F7275

144444 MALBY Mr T A. Richmond House, Plud Street, Wedmore, Somerset, BS28 4BE.
MALBY F6845

144452 MALCOLM Mrs Doris. (Wright) Bay Nook, 45 Sands Lane, Bridlington, YO15 2JG. Tel:0262-672767
AUSTWICK CHURCH EDDISON WRIGHT F6165

144460 MALES Mr R J. 2 Grasmere, Macclesfield, Cheshire, SK11 8PL.
ANCHRET BELL CAWOOD DEARMAN EASTHO[E JONES LEWIS Madle Mailes Male MALES Masle Mayles NORTH PRESLAND ROSERS STRATTON SYMPSON WIGGINS F4839

144479 MALIN Mr John. 197 Sturminster Road, Stockwood, Bristol, BS14 8EL. Tel:0272-834276
BEER MALIN NEWTON F3012

144487 MALIPHANT Dr Gordon. 18 Owen Street, Wellington, Somerset, TA21 8JY.
Malefant MALIPHANT Malliphant Maıophant F2218

144495 MALLEN Mr Russell. 66 Newmans Lane, Loughton, Essex, IG10 1TH. Tel:081-502-0941
BENSON COOMBE HANDSON MALLEN ORGAN WARNE F2151

144509 MALLERY Mr Alan A. 6 Stanbury Avenue, Watford, Herts, WD1 3HW.
MALLERY Mallory Malory F1466

144517 MALLETT Miss J M. 29 Abbey Road, West Moors, Wimborne, Dorset, BH22 0AX.
HOPPER Mallet MALLETT F6715

144525 MALLPRESS Mr Richard J. 38 Restharrow Road, Weavering, Maidstone, Kent, ME14 5UH. Tel:0622-735400
BRAY CLIMPSON Climson Clympson Clymson JEAL LAMDEN Lamdin Mallpress MALPRESS Maltpress NEVILL WARWICK F3578

144533 MALTBY Mr Eric N. 114 Fallowcourt Avenue, London, N12 0BG.
BOAG BOAGEY MALTBY MARTIN Maultby SAMPLE THOMPSON WILLEY F1331

144541 MANCE Mr G O. 30 St Lawrence Gardens, Eastwood, Leigh On Sea, Essex, SS9 5YD. Tel:0702-529598
DAVIS MANTZ MILES WALTON F6272

144568 MANCELL Mr Leslie. Edgmond Acres, R R 1, Merlin, Ontario, N0P 1W0, CANADA.
ARMSTRONG Boyce BOYS BROWN DOVE FRANKLIN HANCOCK IMESON Maben MABIN Mabine Mabon Mancel Mancell Mansel MANSELL Maunsel Maunsell PAINE POPPLEWELL Rumlea RUMLEY SMITH THOMPSON VESTER WILKINSON F4459

144576 MANCHESTER Mr Jack. 79 Calm Lands Road, Meltham, Huddersfield, West Yorks, HD7 3HQ. Tel:0484-850199
MANCHESTER F6290

144584 MANDER Revd D S. 12 Menheniot Crescent, Langore, Launceston, Cornwall, PL15 8PD. Tel:0566-772853
MANDER F6333

144592 MANDEVILLE Mr R W. 72 Cedar Road, Sturry, Canterbury, Kent, CT2 0JL.
MANDEVILLE Manvell Manville F6850

144606 MANDRY Mr L P. 12 Fernside Road, Balham, London, SW12 8LL.
ADAMS BARTLEY BEATON BOOLE BURT CARNES COVERLEY EGLIN ELKINS EVERRETT GREENLEES GRIMMER HANN HOFORD JACKSON JOHNSON LAUGHTON LEE MANDRY MITCHELL MUNN PARK PEARCE PRICKETT ROBERTS ROE SMITH SWAEN SWAN THOMPSON TOMPSON TRUBEY TUFIREY VEVIAN WARE WHITING WILKINSON WRIGHT YATMEN F1455

144614 MANFORD Mrs Penelope Jane. (Griffiths) 34 Powderham Road, Hartley Vale, Plymouth, Devon, PL3 5SG. Tel:0752-773140
BUTTLE EDWARDS GREENING GRIFFITHS HALL JAMES MALLETT SADLER TAYLOR F3682

144622 MANGHAM Mr Colin. 10 Tor Avenue, Greenmount, Bury, Lancs, BL8 4HG. Tel:0204-886771
BOOTH BROADHEAD BROADLEY DOUGLASS DUCK HAWORTH MANGALLS MANGHAM OXLEY SMITH SPEIGHT TAYLOR TRUELOVE TURNER WRIGHT F5122

144630 MANGHAM Mrs Dorothy Anne. (Sanford) 10 Tor Avenue, Greenmount, Bury, Lancs, BL8 4HG. Tel:0204-886771
BESSTON GRUMMETT HOWARD JOHNSON SAMFER Sandford SANFORD F6089

144649 MANLEY Mr Frank Roy. 23 Surridge, High Legh, Knutsford, Cheshire, WA16 6PU. Tel:0925-754533
COUPLAND MANLEY F7436

144657 MANLEY Mr J D. 38 West Road, Stansted, Essex, CM24 8NQ.
ABRAHAM ALWAY ASH BAILEY BAKER BARNES BEAGLEY BEALE BLAKE BLANCHET BLAND BROOKE BROWN CARPENTER CARTER CHASE CLIST COOKE COOPER CROSS CUMBERS DEATH DENNIS DICKS ELWAY EMES FOXWELL FREE FREEMAN FRY FURLOW GORING GRANT GRUBY HALE HARRIS HARRISON HILEY HILLMAN HORSLEN HYDE KEEP KNIGHT LAMBERT LARKE LEGH LOVELL MANLEY MILLER MONTAGUE NORGATE NORTON OCKLEY PALMER PARR PERRIN PERRY PRIOR PRITCHARD RANSTED RICHARDS ROFFEY RUMBLE RUSSEL SHAUGHNESSY SIMONS SINNOTT SMITH SPRAGUE STEVENS STEWARD STREATER SULLIVAN SUMMERS THORN TOWERS TREMAN TURNER TWOSE WARD WATKINS WAY WHITE WILLEY WINTERBOURN WRENCH F679

144665 MANLEY Mrs M. 23 Hyburn Close, Bricket Wood, St Albans, Herts, AL2 3QX. Tel:0923-671147
INSTRELL F2173

144673 MANLEY Miss Patricia. 6 Heol Crwys, Penyraber, Fishguard, Dyfed, SA65 9EJ.
HENNESSY IVEY MANLEY MANNIX PYRKE F990

144681 MANN Mr A G. 11 Colne Close, Worthing, Sussex, BN13 3LP.
BATES BEAMS GOWER HULL MANN MEADOWS STAGGS WEBB WILLIAMS F959

144703 MANN Mr D E. 9 Launceston Road, Wigston Magna, Leicester, LE8 2GZ.
ARNOLD BELL BLAND BODENHAM BROUGHTON Clark CLARKE HANSON Man MANN SHERRIF Sherriff SNAITH WHETSTONE WIGGINS F2821

144711 MANN Mrs P D. 4 Waddington Avenue, Old Coulsdon, Surrey, CR5 1QE.
BARNES BLENCH BURTON CANFIELD CHIVERS DEWAR EDWARDS ELLIS HAYTHORPE HERMERY HUTCHINSON LEEDS MANN ROSE STOAKLEY WEST WHITHAM WHITTOME WITTAM F1853

144738 MANN Revd Ralph. Broadwell Rectory, Moreton In Marsh, Glous, GL56 0TU. Tel:0451-31866
GRAINGER IMMS KINLAY MANN F615

144746 MANNERS Mr Peter. 2 Swinfen Broun Road, Lichfield, Staffs, WS13 7AP. Tel:0543-262622
BEADLE EVERETT FOSTER HUXLEY JACKMAN LONGLEY MANNERS F4898

144754 MANNERS Mr Tony. Birdland, Copt Hall Road, Ightham, Sevenoaks Kent, TN15 9DT.
BOWEN BUTLER GRAHAM HAWES MANNERS PRIEST RAWLINGS SMITH STONEHAM WALDEN F1852

144762 MANNING Mr Ernest James. 4 Sherrards Way, Barnet, Herts, EN5 2BJ. Tel:081-449-3814
CHAPMAN CLIFFORD HUNT MANNING PECK SLADE WITHAM F3153

144770 MANNING Mrs G M. 1 Cottage, Little Chilton Farm, Ferryhill, Co Durham, DL17 0PG.
Eales Eals EELES Eells Eels F7094

144789 MANNING Mrs N. 2 Sheppards Close, Haywads Lane, Child Okeford, Nr Blandford Forum, DT11 8DS.
TIMBERLAKE Timberlick Timlic F6824

144797 MANNING Mr Peter. 18 Stratford Avenue, Rainham, Gillingham, Kent, ME8 0EP.
CLARK CUSHWAY DEDE GIBBS HARE HAWKINS HUNTRODS LEMERES LOVE;; MANNING MANNION MEGNIN PEACOCK PUGH PYNN RICHARDS SHARP SIMONS SMITH TUESHAW WINES F4859

144800 MANNING Mr Peter. Third Acre, Leeds Road, Lightcliffe, Halifax, W Yorks, HX3 8NH. Tel:0422-204150
ANCHOR ARMITAGE BEAUMONT BROOK HAYDEN JARVIS KERNEY LOCKWOOD MANNING MILLS Milnes MOWBRAY PARKER PEARSON SANDERSON SEYMOUR SWIFT TATE THEWLIS YATES F5071

144819 MANSBRIDGE Mrs G. 42 Ulverscroft Road, Cheylesmore, Coventry, W Midlands, CV3 5EZ.
Mainsbridge MANSBRIDGE F6917

144827 MANSON Mrs Denise. 2 Cadwell Road, Lydiate, Merseyside, L31 4JU.
BRAMHALL HARGREAVES HARTLEY OVERSBY F1691

144835 MANTELL Mr H J. 169 Isabella Drive, Farnborough, Kent, BR6 7UF.
Mantel MANTELL Mantle F6752

144843 MANTERFIELD Elizabeth. Riseholme, 28a Hillcrest Gardens, Hinchley Wood, Esher Surrey, KT10 0BS. Tel:081-398-7629
EVENDEN Mandefield Manderfield Manderville Mandeville MANTERFIELD SHIRLEY Soughthe Southe SOUTHEE Southey Southie Southy F3102

144851 MANTHEY Mrs Dorothy. (Sear) 1279 North 85th Street, Wauwatosa, Wisconsin, 53226, USA. Tel:+1-414-453-8781
BAVE EMERY HARRISON HEATHFIELD MARTIN PAGE PHILLIPS REEVES SEAR THORNE F5491

144878 MANTHORPE Mrs Heather. 45 Wallasey Crescent, Ickenham, Uxbridge, Middx, UB10 8SA.
BARNS BROOK BULMER CHAPMAN FREELOVE GREET HOW Howe JOHNSON KIFF LAMBURN LAWRENCE O'BRIAN RAGAN STORER TESTAR TYLER VINCENT WEBBER F2217

144886 MANUEL Janet D. 230 Rolling Road, Gaithersburg, MD 20877, USA.
SHAW F7362

144894 MARBECK Miss J. 8 Maungarei Road, Remuera, Auckland 5, NEW ZEALAND.
MARBECK F7095

144908 MARDLIN Mr Stuart Barry. Malting Yard, 24 Silver Street, Great Barford, Bedford, MK44 3HU. Tel:0234-870988
AYRE BUNDY COLLINS DRAPER ISHERWOOD LEAF LESTER MARDLIN Marlin Maudley Mawdling POULTON SAYWELL Sewell VEY WILSON WOODCRAFT F3735

144916 MARFELL Mr Terry. 39 Comp 23, Fanny Bay, British Columbia, V0R 1W0, CANADA.
Marfel MARFELL Marfill F7206

144924 MARFLEET Mr J K. 4 Robottom Close, Huncote, Leicester, LE9 6BB.
MARFLEET F6579

144932 MARGERISON Mr John M. 474 Liverpool Road, Rufford, Ormskirk, Lancs, L40 1SQ. Tel:0704-821562
CAMPBELL COOK Cooke COOPER Gerrison Mar-Gerrison Margerinson MARGERISON Margesson Marginson Margison Marjoryson MCKUNE MELLING F2876

144940 MARGRETT Mr B. 51 Oakleaf Drive, Polgate, E Sussex, BN26 6PS. Tel:0323-484568
Magget Maggot Maggott Magit Magitt Magot Margaret Margarete Margarets Margarett Margarette Margarettes Margaretts Margarott Margarts Margate Margates Margats Margattes Margatts Margeret Margerets Margeretts Margerit Margerts Marget Margets Margett Margetto Margetts Margitt Margitts Margrat Margrata Margrate Margratt Margratte Margrave Margreate Margreath Margret Margrete Margrets MARGRETT Margrette Margretts Margrit Margrits Margritt Marguerit F3618

144959 MARKER Lt Col S N & Mrs I J. Green Ridges, 25 Gladsdale Drive, Pinner, Middx, HA5 2PP.
ATTWELL BALL HENNING MARKER F6580

144967 MARKOW Mrs H. (Bryce) 62 Heatherfield, Bolton, Lancs, BL1 7QF.
BRYCE HANKINSON RIGBY SANKEY WORTHINGTON F3908

144975 MARKWELL Mr F C. 48 Howard Road, Kings Heath, Birmingham, B14 7PQ.
MARKWELL F6581

144983 MARKWICK Mr David. 577 Bexhill Road, St Leonards On Sea, E Sussex, TN38 8AX.
AVLING BEAN MARKWICK SPRAY F4060

144991 MARKWICK Mr M G. 101 Hownslow Road, Twickenham, Middx, TW2 7HA.
Gradage GRADDAGE F6734

145009 MARLBOROUGH Mrs D P E. 31 Glenwood Road, West Moors, Ferndown, Dorset, BH22 0EN. Tel:0202-872957
BAILEY BIRD BRISTOW CLEMENTS CROWLEY Fellender FELLINDER HILL JAMES JONES MARLBOROUGH Valendar VALENDER Velender Vellender WALL WILSON F2678

145017 MARLEY Mrs Gloria M C. 15 Ashwood Drive, Broadstone, Dorset, BH18 8LN.
BAILEY Bayley CAMPBELL DAVIS ELLIOTT FARMER Gawman Goeman Goman Goreman GORMAN Gormon GOWMAN Holland HULLAND LEE Marely Marleigh MARLEY Marly Merely Murlye SCADDING SPRAGUE TAYLOR WEBSTER Windgate WINGATE Wingeatt Wingett F2973

145025 MARLEY Mr R. 52 Woodbine Road, Blackwood, Gwent, NP2 1QF. Tel:0495-9792
MARLEY MOREY F1988

145033 MARQUIS Mrs Pauline. (Toms) Chalon, Le Douit Lane, Landes Du Marche, Vale, Guernsey.
DENE DOCKING TOMS F3842

145041 MARR Ms M. (Parker) 5 Boyne View, Trimdon Village, Co Durham, TS29 6JZ. Tel:0429-882122
BUDDLES FINAN FORBES GLENWRIGHT MARSHALL PARKER PRICE ROBERTSON F3862

145068 MARRIAGE Mrs June. 22 Cintra Road, Norwich, Norfolk, NR1 4AE.
ARNOLD ELSTON FERGUSON FLEXMAN HAMMOND MARRIAGE SNELLING TOULSON WATTS WITCHER F3019

145076 MARRISON Mr Pete. 49 Mollanbowie Road, Balloch, Alexandria, Strathclyde, G83 8EL. Tel:0389-58277
MARRISON F416

145084 MARRS Mrs Frances. (Harrison) The Old Smithy, Crosby Garrett, Kirkby Stephen, Cumbria, CA17 4PR.
BEWLEY COOPER FAULDER HARRISON MARRS MOSSOP PARKER PERCIVAL STRICKLAND WIGHAM F5093

145092 MARRS Mrs Stella. 6 Cartha Road, Dumfries, Dumfriesshire, Scotland, DG1 4JB.
Corrie CURRIE Euart EWART LAUDER LOCKHART Maher MARRS Mayer MOFFAT Myers Neilson NELSON PATERSON Patterson RICHARDSON F2567

145106 MARSDEN Mrs Betty. 39 Scholes Moor Road, Holmfirth, Huddersfield, W Yorks, HD7 1SN.
BLOOMFIELD CORNISH RHODES WILLIS F2679

145114 MARSDEN Mr John Brian. # 806-556 Laurier Avenue West, Ottawa, Ontario, K1R 7X2, CANADA. Tel:+1-613-233-9657
MARSDEN Marsdens Marsdin Marsdon Marskin Marston Mersden F4486

145122 MARSDEN Mr John. 3 Hesketh Road, Sale, Cheshire, M33 5AA. Tel:061-973-2099
GREEN MAGINNES MARSDEN SPENCER F934

145130 MARSDEN Mr N L. 39 Smethurst Lane, Pemberton, Wigan, Lancs, WN5 8BG. Tel:0942-217764
BILLINGTON BIRCHALL Marchden Marchdene Marclsden Marsdean Marsdeane MARSDEN Marsdene Marshdean Marshden Marzden Mercden Merclden Merclesden Merlsden Mersceden Mersden F1681

145149 MARSH Mr Alan & Mrs J. Broadacres, Oakley Straight, Wimborne, Dorset, BH21 1SB.
BAILEY CHILDS GOULD JENKINS LANGRIDGE MARSH MORGAN PRIVETT SEEVIOUR STEEL F1850

145157 MARSH Mrs Joan. (Blake) 7 Eversley Close, Rhyl, Clwyd, LL18 4US.
Astin Austen AUSTIN BECKETT Hiorne HIORNS Iorne Iorns Irons MARKS SHAW F3594

145165 MARSH Mr Ronald. 6 Hawks Place, Bognor Regis, West Sussex, PO22 9LZ. Tel:0243-825970
DANIELS IDE MARSH F4304

145173 MARSH Mr Terence G. 57 Adeyfield Road, Hemel Hempstead, Herts, HP2 5DP. Tel:0442-256689
GARRAD Garrard MARSH MERSH Mesh REEVES

SPENCER F4033

145181 MARSHALL D. 30 Westfield Close, Dorridge, Solihull, B93 8DY.
FRANKS MARSHALL MENZIES WRIGHT F1597

145203 MARSHALL Mr David. 14 Scott Avenue, Simonstone, Burnley, Lancs, BB12 7YH. Tel:0282-74279
ABRAHAM BAKE CHAPMAN MARSHALL PEACOCK RAMSBOTTOM RILEY STOCKDALE WILKINSON F3680

145211 MARSHALL Mr Geoff. Measum House, Arkendale, Knaresborough, North Yorks, HG5 0RF.
BALEY FEASBY GRANGE HUTCHINSON IDDESON INGLEBY JOHNSON LISTER MARSHALL MASON RUDD WALBANK YATES Yeates F4262

145238 MARSHALL Miss Iris Ethel Eliza. The Willows, Witton Bridge, North Walsham, Norfolk, NR28 9AH. Tel:0692-650861
COLE GRIMES Grymes KEEN Keene LARTER Lawter Marschel Marshal MARSHALL Martial ROTHWELL SELF Selfe Selth TOOLEY WHITWORTH Wodehouse WOODHOUSE F5283

145246 MARSHALL Mr John W. 1 Wood Burcote, Towcester, Northants, NN12 7JR.
MARSHALL WOODIWISS F5128

145254 MARSHALL Mrs Marion. (Birtles) 9 Broadfield Close, Denton, Manchester, M34 1BN.
BIRTLES DUNN Dunne HARDIE JOHNSON MARSDEN MAYO Mayoh SIMNETT WHITMORE F5984

145262 MARSHALL Mr Philip. 46 Meadow Bank Avenue, Sheffield, S Yorks, S7 1PB. Tel:0742-554683
HALEY WILDE F3730

145270 MARSHFIELD Mrs Barbara M. (White) Woodbury, Newtown, West Tisbury, Salisbury, Wilts, SP3 6NY. Tel:0747-870484
ANNING BRIGHTMAR HUTCHINGS INGRAM MARSHFIELD MASHFIELD PASSMORE WILLINGHAM F723

145289 MARSHFIELD Mr Gordon. 8 Tichborne Road, Harefield Estate, Southampton, Hants, SO2 5HZ. Tel:0703-463118
BARTON BULL COOKE DEVENISH DOWNER HAMMOND HEAL HOLLIER JACKMAN JAMES JOHNSTON LACEY LINNINGTON MARSHFIELD MILLAGAN NEWIN PERKINS PRESSEY PRIDDLE ROFFE SCOVELL SERAGE SNOW STEPHENS URRY WHITTINGTON F582

145297 MARSHMAN Mr Eric R. 13 Government Road, Nords Wharf, NSW 2301, AUSTRALIA.
ASHTON BICKLE CARTER COLLIER COUZNER DIKE HAWKEY HEWETT MARSHMAN MILLS MITCHELL PASCO PASCOE SANDERS STRAIGHT STREIGHT STRIGHT WILLIAMS WOODWARD F4489

145300 MARSON Mrs Hilda. (Wheeler) 20 The Bury, Pavenham, Bedford, MK43 7PX.
BODDINGTON Crede CREED HOOPER Lad LADD Lads MARSON Mason Massom Musson Muston WHEELER Wheler Whiler Whylr Willson WILSON F956

145319 MARSON Mrs Jacqueline. (Meredith) 14 Laburnam Close, Kidsgrove, Stoke On Trent, Staffs, ST7 1BB. Tel:0782-786353
ALDRIDGE Alldridge BOAST Bost JORDAN LANCASTER Marsdon MARSON Marston MEREDITH NIGHTINGALE Oldridge OLIVER Olliver Olyiker PARR POSTON RENWICK SPARRY STOKES Totley Totlie Totly Tottey Tottie TOTTY WHEATLEY WICKHAM WILLIAMS F792

145327 MARSTON Mr Geoffrey. Saltaire, 62 Henderson Drive, Kintore, Inverurie, Aberdeen, AB51 0FB. Tel:0467-32808
ABBOT Abbott Abott Abut BOOTH Brunskell Brunskil BRUNSKILL HORNER HUDSON KITCHEN Leedam LEEDHAM Marsten Marstin MARSTON Masten Maston Mooras Moorehouse Moorehowse MOORHOUSE SIMPSON WALKER F4582

145335 MARTIN Mrs A M. (Ainslie) Glen Dhu, Kinchurdy Road, Boat Of Garten, Inverness-Shire, PH24 3BP.
Ainsley AINSLIE Ainsly Angely Annesly BLAYLOCK CARR CHAPELHOW Chaplow Dracas DRACASS Dracus Drakas Drakehouse Drakes HIND JONES MARTIN MCCAREY REVITT SIMPSON STEPHENSON F3981

145343 MARTIN Mr Adrian. 27 Newlands, Whitfield, Dover, Kent, CT16 3NB.
BUDD COULTER DENNIS Farnan Farnin FARNON FORD FURNELL GODDEN Goddon KEILTY Kielty MAY Monday MOON MUNDAY NEWLAND PRECTER Vollar VOLLER WESTON F3136

145351 MARTIN Mr Anthony E C. Elton, Foxley Lane, Binfield, Bracknell, Berks, RG12 5DB. Tel:0344-51073
CROWCOMBE DIXON MARTIN F3794

145378 MARTIN Mr Anthony John. 5 Otlinge Close, Orpington, Kent, BR5 3SH.
BERRIMAN CASSELL CLINCH DIPLOCK EDWARDS EMMERSON FOWLER FULLER LEEVES LEWRY MARTIN PAIN PAINE SIMMONDS SQUIBB WELLS F814

145386 MARTIN Mrs B J. 28 Chichester Park, Woolacombe, Devon, EX34 7BZ.
ANDREW Andrews CLOSE DALGLEISH GARMSTON Handley HANLEY KIMLIN LOWRY MABBETT MARTIN MORGAN PALLETT PEARCE PRGANELL SCUDAMORE SKIDMORE TROWER F5742

145394 MARTIN Mrs C X. Keston Lea, Main Road, Filby, Great Yarmouth, NR29 3HN.
ANSTIS BAKER BATCHELOR BUSBY COUCH GOLDS HENSTUS JACKSON JOHNSON KERSLEY KITCHELL LANGLEY LIGHT MARTIN MITCHELL MORLEY NAILARD PENGILLY PROUDLEY RANDALL REBOUSE SATCHER SAYERS TAYLOR TUPPER WATTS WOODLING F2138

145408 MARTIN Mr Charles. 4 Delphi Court, Hope Road, Shanklin, Isle Of Wight, PO37 6EL.
BLANE CULLY DRAKES MARTIN MITCHELL OAKLEY OSGODBY PEARCE SANDELL SHANNON F2516

145416 MARTIN Mr David. 14 Sevenoaks Avenue, Croydon 3136, AUSTRALIA.
MARTIN F7311

145424 MARTIN Mr E W. 23 Rogerson Close, Hundon, Sudbury, Suffolk, CO10 8SB.
BALDOCK CAPPS CROTOSHINSKY DELLER EDBROOK HIBBERT HURRELL MARTIN NANKEWELL RAMSDEN F913

145432 MARTIN Mrs Elsie H. 207 Hendricks Road, Perkiomenville, PA 18074, USA.
BEST COLLINS CRUDGINGTON DUFFIELD DUFFILL EDMONDS FEARNALL HALLOWAY HAYES HOLLOWAY MOLE SPILLSBURY SPILSBURY THATCHER F323

145440 MARTIN Mr J. 27 Firs Crescent, Harrogate, North Yorks, HG2 9HF. Tel:0423-872997
HALDANE MACKNIGHT MARTIN WRIGHT F3752

145459 MARTIN Mr Jeffrey. Morellos, Providence Hill, Bursledon, Southampton, Hants, SO3 8AU.
Aishley ANDREWS Androwes Androws ASHLEY Ashly Assheley BAKER Beaman Beaumont Behmen BEMAN Campantin Champante Chanel CHANNEL Cheynel Cheynell CHIAMPANTE CULL Dibben DIBDEN Emerie EMERY Emrey Emry Feilder FIELDER GOOD HEWLET Hewlett HICKS Holas HOLLIS Hulet Hulett JORDAN Jordon Kerby Kerkeby Kirby Kirkbey KIRKBY Lainson LAINSTON Lenson Leynstone Liant LOADER Loder LYANT Lyon Lyons Lyont MARKS Marsters Marten MARTIN Master MASTERS Moreten Moreton Morten Morton NICHOLAS Oseman OSMAN Peckam PECKHAM Sawuer SAWYER Snelgar SNELGROVE Snellgrove Soughyer THOMAS Walten WALTON Warn WARNE Wiat Wyat WYATT F90

145467 MARTIN Mrs Kathleen. Keepers Cottage, Shougle, Birnie, Elgin Morayshire, IV30 3RP. Tel:034-386285
BREMNER FARQUHARSON HAY HUNTER MARTIN RIDDELL SHEPHERD STEPHEN THOMSON F3234

145475 MARTIN Mrs L. 36 Wynford Road, Frome, Somerset, BA11 2DP.
Grimston GRIMSTONE F6987

145483 MARTIN Mr M D. 33 King Edwards Road, Malvern Wells, Worcs, WR14 4AJ. Tel:0684-574647
MARTYN F1117

145491 MARTIN Mrs M J. 30 Lancaster Road, Kettering, Northants, NN16 8PB.
MARLOW WALLIS F915

145505 MARTIN Mrs Margaret J. 80 The Avenue, Alverstoke, Gosport, Hants, PO12 2JU.
CROWTHER DAINTON PREW ROUSE SUMMERS WHEATCROFT F3558

145513 MARTIN Mrs Marion. (Bushell) 16 Back Road, Calne, Wiltshire, SN11 0BA.
BUSHELL BUTLER CRANE DAVIS HESTER HOOPER KIMBER LONG PIDDINGTON F6097

145521 MARTIN Mrs Nancy. (Edwards) Victoria, 100 Langney Road, Eastbourne, E Sussex, BN22 8AQ.
DALMON EDWARDS HUGGETT F1551

145548 MARTIN Mr Peter. 2 Lime Tree Way, Apley Park, Wellington, Telford, TF1 3PJ. Tel:0952-253103
BANCROFT BUDDING CORNELIUS MARTIN MORTIMER F6155

145556 MARTIN Mr Philip. 8 Derwent Close, Tangmere, Chichester, West Sussex, PO20 6FQ. Tel:0243-531929
Alis Alison Allis ALLISON Alliss ANDERSON BEAMAN Beamand Beament Beaumont Beeman BURTON CANE CLARK COLEMAN GOING HILLS Mardin Marrten Martaine Marteham MARTEN MARTIN Martine MARTYN Myttyne Senet Sennett Sennitt Sinnatt Sinnett SINNOT Sinnott Sionoid Synot Synott F5324

145564 MARTIN Mr Rex. High Beeches, Wych Cross, East Sussex, RH18 5JP.
Chapel Chaple Chappel CHAPPLE DAVE Davey Davie Davy DAY FOX GODSMITH Leningham Lenington Lenningham Lennington Linington LINNINGTON MARTIN Travena Travenor TREVENA Trevenor Trevin Trivin F6032

145572 MARTIN Mr Russell. 4 North Street, Nazeing, Essex, EN9 2NL. Tel:099289-2169
BELCHER BOWATER HARRINGTON MARTIN MERCOTE MURCOTT NETTLEINGHAM NETTLINGHAM F2763

145580 MARTIN Mr Simon. 70 Greenslate Road, Billinge, Wigan, Lancs, WN5 7BQ.
BARRY BILLING BROWN BURGESS CALDWELL CHANDLER CLARKE Cobstake COPESTAKE Copstake Coupestack Coupstak Coupstake Cowpstake DE MORTAGNE De Mountanys Plaine De Muntein Demunteny DUNN EDWARDS EMBRIDGE GADSBY HALLIWELL HARRIS JONES MARTIN MAXFIELD Monntegne Montaigne Mountagne Mountaigne Mountaine Mountane Mountany Mountayne Mountenay Mounteney Mounteneye Mountenney Mounteny Mountnay MOUNTNEY Mowntayne PARRY REDGATE RUNGE SHAILES SIMPSON SMITH TAYLOR TOLMAN WHITHILL WILLIAMS F5878

145599 MARTINSON Mrs Genevieve. (Canfield) 1144 North Gordon, Wichita, KS 67203, USA. Tel:+1-316-942-7120
Camfield Campfield CANFIELD F7251

145602 MARTY Mrs Erin. Korakonui, Rd 3, Te Awamutu, 2400, NEW ZEALAND.
AINSWORTH ARNOLD BLACKBURN BROWN COOMBS CROSSMAN DONALDSON HOWARTH JENNER KIMBER MELLING MILLER MORTIMER NETTIN ROSE SKUTT TATTERSALL TAYLOR WELCH F5515

145610 MARTYN Mr George. Rr1, Caledon Village, Ontario, LON 1CO, CANADA. Tel:+1-519-927-5155
MARTYN F5569

145629 MARVILL Mrs Kathleen. 87 Derby Road, Chellaston, Derby, DE7 1SB. Tel:0332-700987
COOPER GIBSON MARVILL SANSOM F4790

145637 MARYON Mr A J. 37 Pickards Way, Wisbech, Cambs, PE13 1SD.
BRECHIN DUNCAN GOLLAN KINGSTON MARYON ROSE F4040

145645 MASH Revd W E J. 16 The Leases, Beverley, East Yorkshire, HU17 8LG. Tel:0482-881324
BRAMLEY MASH SPENCE F5952

145653 MASLEN Mrs Diana. 69 Ashlands Road, Cheltenham, Glous, GL51 ODF. Tel:0242-243986
MASLEN F1241

145661 MASLENKI Mrs Dorothy M. R R 3 Spiers Road, Kelowna, British Columbia, V1Y 7R2, CANADA.
BARRETT BEVIN COLCHIN COOMBER FRANKS GWILLIM HOPGOOD PALMER PLAYER POWELL SMITH TAYLOR WAREHAM WAY F5697

145688 MASLIN Mrs Wendy. 8 Rufford Close, Fleet, Hampshire, GU13 9TJ. Tel:0252-620887
ACRILL BAKER BARRETT BEALE BOOTH BOULDRAM BROOK BROWN CHATTEN CLARK CLEGG COATES COOKE CORDEN CRANSON CURWOOD DEAN DEAR DEE DICKSON DISHMAN DUNFORD EXON HACKETT HAGGAS HALL HARBOR HARRISON HEMINGWAY HEWSON MARSH MARTIN MASLIN MCCANN MEDCALF MONTAGUE MOODY OLDROYD PALMER RUSHTON SENIOR SHARMAN SIMPSON SMITH SPITTLEHOUSE STANLEY STELL SUGDEN SWALES THARALD TURNER WATKINSON WHITE WILKINSON WOOD WRIGHT F1653

145696 MASON Mr A Kenneth. 58 Lancaster Road, Garstang, Preston, Lancs, PR3 1JA.
BROOKS MASON SHELMERDINE F5217

145718 MASON Mrs Beryl E. (Barford) 19 Elgar Avenue, Surbiton, Surrey, KT5 9JH.
BARFORD FITCH GOODCHILD GORDON HEDGES INNS LEAVER MCCARTNEY F5988

145726 MASON Mrs D. 57 Green Street, Brockworth, Gloucester, GL3 4LX. Tel:0452-862949
CODDELL FENNER FURBY GREEN HODGES MASON MIDDLETON PATES TURNER F1371

145734 MASON Miss F M. The Nook, Stainton Court, Penrith, Cumbria, CA11 0EN.
BROUGH JACKSON MASON NEWBY RITSON F3573

145742 MASON Mr John. Lanson, Barrow Lane, Pilton, Shepton Mallet, BA4 4BH. Tel:074989-414
Birnes Birns Burnes BURNS Byrnes Byrns COLGAN DORAN DUCKHAM GAGNAL Granvill Granville Grenvill GRENVILLE HACKETT HOOKWAY HORTON HUMPAGE KNOWLES LANNING LOWE MARTIN PARKER PICKERING ROBINSON SMITH TIMMINS TONKES URCH WILLIAMS F1098

145750 MASON Mr R J. 46 Norman Avenue, Abingdon, Oxon, OX14 2HL.
AYRES BIGGS BOTHAMLEY BRIGHOUSE CHAPLIN DAVYS HENDRY JUMP KING LINE LYON MASON MAWBY MAWDSLEY PHEASANT RAINFORD RIMMER RUMBLE SHELDRICK TINGLE VINTERS F2883

145769 MASON Mrs Shelagh Avril. (Maddison) 46 Field Avenue, Canterbury, Kent, CT1 1TR.
COOK HOLMES KEMP MADDISON MASON SAVAGE TERRY F3386

145777 MASON Valerie. 4 Walker Crescent, Raymond Terrace, Nsw 2324, Australia. Tel:+61-049-872150
WATERS F1152

145785 MASSEY Mrs Barbara. 48 Daw End Lane, Rushall, Walsall, W Midlands, WS4 1JR.
MASSEY SALIS F6394

145793 MASSEY Mr G. Bank Cottage, Somersham, Huntingdon, PE17 3DJ.
MASSEY F7312

145807 MASSEY Mr Geoffrey. 12 The Bank, Somersham, Huntingdon, Cambs, PE17 3DJ. Tel:0487-840853
AYLETT Candalant Candalent Candalett CANDELENT Candelow Candlent HODSON JOHNSON MASSEY Massy Massye TONKS F1938

145815 MASSINGHAM Mr Mortimer. Clare House, Clare Road, Cromber, Norfolk, NR27 ODD.
MASSINGHAM F7313

145823 MASTERS Mrs Beryl. (Sharpe) 181 Ingrave Road, Brentwood, Essex, CM13 2AB. Tel:0277-215254
ASPLAN Asplin BUSH COLEMAN Cracklin Crackling Cracknel CRACKNELL Dillnot Dillnott DILNOT Dilnott DINES Everet EVERETT Everit Everitt GRAY HIPSEY Hipsy Ipsey Ipsy KEEBLE KEMP KING KITSON KNOTT MANNING MASTERS NEWBERY OWEN PRIOR REVELL ROE SHARPE Spear SPEER Spier SUTTON F1174

145831 MASTERS Mr O G F. The Haven, Hope Cove, Kingsbridge, South Devon, TQ7 3HQ.
MASTERS F5380

145858 MATHER Mr Donald. 136 Porthpean Road, St Austell, Cornwall, PL25 4PN. Tel:0726-74645
FARNSWORTH FORSTER HODGE JONES MATHER MOON ORGAN Pasco PASCOE Paskow SAUNDERS SMITH STAHL STUBBS TURNER Vage Vagg VAGUE Veague F4615

145866 MATHER Mr Geoff. 18 Ravenswood Avenue, Crowthorne, Berks, RG11 6AY. Tel:0344-775651
BAKER BANCROFT HANNAM MATHER RADFORD SAINT SAMWAYS SCOTT SIMS TRASK WALLACE WATSON WIBBERLEY F2553

145874 MATHER Mrs Mary L. (Shearmur) 13 Horsell Park Close, Woking, Surrey, GU21 4LZ. Tel:0483-771986
SHEARMUR F516

145882 MATHERS Mrs Barbara. (James) Rr2 Site 15 Comp 4, Lumby, B C, V0E 2G0, CANADA. Tel:+1-604-547-9690
BLANEY BONFIELD CLAYTON MATHER Mathers RAWLING SMITH STROUD F5527

145890 MATON Mr C R. 7 Montague Road, Berkhamstead, Herts, HP4 3DS.
Maten MATON Matten Mattin Matton Matyn Matyne F6800

145904 MATTERN Mrs D M. (James) 43 Wooteys Way, Alton, Hampshire, GU34 2JB.
BENNETT BIRD ROSS F7399

145912 MATTHEWS Mrs Audrey. (Learoyd) 6 Alstead Road, Histon, Cambridge, CB4 4EX.
ARUNDEL DEAN GOODAIR HEMINGWAY INGHAM LEAROYD MATTHEWS PARKER ROBERTS STRINGER VARLEY F4795

145920 MATTHEWS Mrs B. 58 Denzil Avenue, Netley

Abbey, Southampton, Hants, SO3 5BA.
CRISP HATCH HAYNES HOLLINGDALE MATTHEWS OAKLEY RICHENS SKINNER F2970

145939 MATTHEWS Dr C J. 58 Durfold Road, Petersfield, Hants, GU13 4HA. Tel:0230-64456
BELL BOND CHAMBERS CONZON EVANS GLANVILLE HUGH LLOYD MATTHEWS PAGE PULEN SELFE TARGETT TROUNCE F1277

145947 MATTHEWS Mr D A T. Springfield, Upper Lyde, Hereford, HR4 8AF.
MATTHEWS F3268

145955 MATTHEWS Mrs Elizabeth. (Hutton) 3 Carroll Place, Llandudno, Gwynedd, LL30 2AL.
EDWARDS ELVEY HARRISON HUTTON LUNT ROBINSON F6483

145963 MATTHEWS Mr Gerald. The Larches, Black Torrington, Beaworthy, Devon, EX21 5PU.
ADDAMS Davey Davie DAVY FRYER GWYNNE MATTHEWS ROBERTS WHEREAT F5259

145971 MATTHEWS Mrs Jeanne H. Little Orchard, Sampford Peverall, Tiverton, Devon, EX16 7EG. Tel:0884-820579
BALDOCK BARNES BOWEN CAMPBELL ELLIOTT HEAD JOWETT LANGFORD MUMMERY PILLING PINHORN ROBINSON TAGGART TORDOFF VANDERPLANK WORSNOP F3790

145998 MATTHEWS Mr Jonathan. White Willows, 16 Copperfields, Beaconsfield, Bucks, HP9 2NS. Tel:0494-670671
BUTT COLEMAN HOOKE JEFFCOTT LUMB MATTHEWS MUMFORD SPRAGGS STRUTT TRASK F2697

146005 MATTHEWS Mr Lionel F. Flat 1, 13 The Hornet, Chichester, West Sussex, PO19 4JL. Tel:0243-536638
MATTHEWS F5728

146013 MATTHEWS Mr M. 33 Emerald Street, The Groves, York, YO3 7LQ.
ALMONDROYD BENTLEY BOWEN BUTCHER MATTHEWS MULLIDGE ORMONDROYD PARKER PUNNETT SANDWELL F3856

146021 MATTHEWS Mr W E. 58 Harwood Road, Heaton Mersey, Stockport, Cheshire, SK4 3AZ. Tel:061-432-0741
BARON BICKERSTAFFE BRIGHTMAN COPE DAVIES DONAVAN DOYLE LAMB MATTHEWS PARKINSON TELSTON F2386

146048 MATTINGLEY Miss Anne. 101 Minterne Waye, Hayes, Middx, UB4 0PF. Tel:081-561-6778
MATTENLEY MATTENLY MATTINGLEY F2079

146056 MATTINGLY Mr Geoffrey. 29 St Francis Avenue, Bitterne, Southampton, Hampshire, SO2 5QL. Tel:0703-462814
Ailes Ails Ayels AYLES BAILEY DOWN Eales MATTINGLY Mattlingley F6236

146064 MAULE Dr Andrew. 8 Westland Close, Amesbury, Wiltshire, SP4 7QS. Tel:0980-624309
BRIDCUT CHIDGLEY HARDING HOLYOAK MAUL MAULE F6186

146072 MAUN Mr Charles. 42 Station Road, Pinhoe, Exeter, Devon, EX1 3SD.
ELBOURNE MARQUISS MAUN MOORE MORRISON PRINCE RICKETT F4808

146080 MAUNDER Mrs F B D. Ten Tors, Totnes Road, Ipplepen, Newtown Abbot Devon, TQ12 5TD.
DOVE EPPS F3293

146099 MAVINS Mrs Yvonne. Box 6 Grp 70, R R 1 Anola, Manitoba, R0E 0A0, CANADA. Tel:+1-204-866-2922
CHANDLER COYNE Dibble Dibblee DIBLEY Dibly Le Scelleur LE SEELLEUR Le Selleur Le Sulleur Mabane Mabin Mabyn Mauin Mauings Mauven Mauvin Mauving Mavein Maveing Maven Mavene MAVIN Mavine Maving Mavinge Mavings MAVINS Mavius Mawevyn Mawven Mawvin Maying Mayvan Mayvens Meavin Meavine Meven Mevens Mevins MORAN RENOUF Skeg Skegg Skegge SKEGGS Skegs Skig Skigg Skiggs Skigs F4402

146102 MAW Mrs Jean. 111 Wolfreton Lane, Willerby, Hull, HU10 6PS.
BARNET BARNETT BOULTON FOSTER JONES MARLOR MAW PAULSON Pearson SEDDON WEBSTER F2654

146110 MAWBY Mrs Elizabeth M. 140 Oswestry Road, Ellesmere, Shropshire, SY12 0BY.
AITCHISON BARR BAYTHROP BROWNLIE CALTENACH COLIN CROMPTON DE BOARD ELLIMAN FAIRHURST GARLAND GIBBONS GIBSON GRANT HOOLE INGLIS JONES LEWIS LORD MARKS MAWBY MCARTHUR MCDONALD MCGEACHAN MOSS MURRAY NORRIS PORTOR ROUND THORNICROFT WEBB WOODWARD F4419

146129 MAXWELL Mrs Margaret T. (Anderson) Akaroa, 7 Meadowside, Gatehouse Of Fleet, Castle Douglas, Kirkcudbrightshire, DG7 2LG. Tel:0557-814551
ANDERSON Carsom CORBOM Corsam Corsamme Corson INGLES INGLIS Micol MURRAY NICHOL Nichole Tod TODD F5322

146137 MAY Mr A & Mrs V. Auchlee Cottage, Longside, Peterhead, Aberdeenshire, AB42 7UF. Tel:077982-301
BARCLAY BEATON DUNCAN GLENNIE MATHEW MAY MILNE MORRICE PENNY WILLOX F4610

146145 MAY Mrs Gill. 20 Moreland Drive, Gerrards Cross, Bucks, SL9 8BB. Tel:0753-885602
DALE ELSOM GIBSON HARDING KIRK MAY WELLS F428

146153 MAY Mrs Gwen M. 33 Harebeating Crescent, Hailsham, W Sussex, BN27 1JH.
Phicocks Philcocks PHILCOX Phillcox F6865

146161 MAY Mr Robert. 6 Carlson Court, North Haven, Adelaide, South Australia 5018. Tel:+61-08-248-5225
HAGAN HALL HOLLIDGE LEE MAY MILLER SIZER WOOD F1659

146188 MAY Mr Sidney T. 77 Chaucer Drive, Lincoln, LN2 4LT. Tel:0522-543358
CAPPER GOMPERTZ MAY NORTON SHEPHARD F6457

146196 MAYBANK Mr R. 52 Arden Crescent, Dagenham, Essex, RM9 6TP.
MAYBANK Maybanke Maybanks F6925

146218 MAYCROFT Mrs Sheila. 1 Spring Valley, Upper Milton, West Super Mare, Avon, BS22 9AS. Tel:0934-416221
CHURCHYARD Hacraste Haycraft Haycroft Macraft Macraste Macroft Makecraft Marcroft Maycraft Maycraught MAYCROFT Mecraft Mecroft MEDCROFT Moorcroft F2039

146226 MAYER Mr & Mrs W E. 145 Town Lane, Whittle Le Woods, Chorley, Lancs, PR6 8AG. Tel:0257-262068
AMALRIC BAUGH BRADSHAW COLLEY FURNEVALL HARVEY HAYES HILTON HOLDEN HORROCKS LEECH MALLOWS MARE Mayer MAYERS MEARE MERE NUTTALL SAUNDERS SMITH TOOTILL WARD WEATHERHEAD WILLMOT F2840

146234 MAYERS Mr & Mrs R S. 51 Sylvan Road, Exeter, Devon, EX4 6EY.
INNES Kikke KIKKIE Mares MAYERS MECKLENBURGH MORTIMORE ROGERS TITSHALL Trathan TRATTAN F1210

146242 MAYHEW Mr Clive. 28 Windmill Road, West Croydon, Surrey, CR0 2XN.
MAYHEW F1665

146250 MAYHEW Mr N M. 3 Oakdene, Kirton, Ipswich, Suffolk, IP10 0NS. Tel:03948-402
MAYHEW SEARLE F3467

146269 MAYHEW Mr Reginald William. 19 Hammers Gate, Chiswell Green, St Albans, Herts, AL2 3DZ.
AINSBY COBB DOWSING KALEY KENTLETON MAYHEW MCKAIN MIDDLETON RAMPLING RICE F2898

146277 MAYNARD Mrs Bernice. 15 Orchard Way, Cranfield, Beds, MK43 0HU. Tel:0234-750660
DANDO KIDDLE VERINDER F940

146285 MAYNARD Mrs Lois. 9 Gaylyn Way, Fareham, Hants, PO14 3AR.
ALDIS BAILEY BALES BLAND COOPER JEREM KING LAWRENCE LOWDEN MARSHALL MILLAR PETTY POPE ROBERTS SIMLETT SUTTON SWINNARD WATERMAN WRIGHT F2368

146293 MAYNARD Mr M J. 26 Whitby Road, Woolwich, London, SE18 5SE. Tel:081-855-6600
BROWN HILLMAN MAYNARD PLUCKNETT PROUT WHALESBY F2403

146307 MAYNE Mr John. Twigg House, Cansiron Lane, Ashurst Wood, East Grinstead, Sussex, RH19 3SF.
DEE MAYNE F3659

146315 MAYNE Mrs L A. 3 Setley Way, Martins Heron, Bracknell, Berks, RG12 6QF.
BEEBY BLOMILEY BUTLER BUTTERFIELD CHEW CRANN CREIGHTON CRETON GOULDBOURNE GRESTY HARDY KEW LARGE LEVIT MARSDEN MAYNE PCIKERING RICHARDSON SMITH WHITE WILSON F1263

146323 MAYOH Mr Peter. 73 Ashkanasy Crescent, Evatt,

2617, AUSTRALIA.
MAYOH F7314

146331 MCALPINE Mrs Wendy. Po Box 202, Yarram, 3971, AUSTRALIA.
AISBETT ANDERSON ARMITAGE CROSS FROST NASH PEARCE ROBINSON TUNN WALKER F4216

146358 MCAULEY Mr Douglas. 53a Storie Street, Paisley, PA1 2HT. Tel:041-887-6791
BELL BOYLE BROGAN BROWN BURNS Byrns COOPER COUTTS DAGNEN DEGNEN Docherty DOUGHERTY HUGHES KING MCAULEY MCCREADIE MCFARLANE MCGUINESS MCNEIL MCNICOL MCPHEE MELVILLE MILLER Selbie SELBY SWAN TELFORD WILLIAMSON WINTOM F6188

146366 MCAUSLIN Mrs Jean. (Macdonald) 4 Gallow Hill, Peebles, Tweeddale, EH45 9BG.
ALLAN BLACK HILL INSCH MACDONALD MCINTOSH MILLS ROBSON ROSS F1889

146374 MCBREARTY Mrs Irene. 20 Farm Street, Mount Maunganui, 3002, NEW ZEALAND.
ANSTEY CORNISH GILLARD HOSKING LANGDON NEWSON SMITH STEVENSON WILLS F5504

146382 MCCALL Mr Ivan. Apt 28 Tyrone House, Adelaide Street, Belfast, Co Antrim, BT2 8HR. Tel:0232-320826
MCCALL Mccaul Mccaull Mccoll F1560

146390 MCCANN Mrs M. 17 Renshaw Street, Eccles, Manchester, M30 0PQ. Tel:061-789-5541
ARNOLD BUGG DAVENPORT FAWCETT GOLDSTRONG KILLIGREW MCCANN PIERCE SPRINGETT YOUNG F4254

146404 MCCARTHY Mrs Margaret Elizabeth. (Trewren) 69 Whitehill Road, Cambridge, CB5 8LU.
OWEN Owens Trewran TREWREN Truran Truron F4628

146412 MCCLUNG Mr H R. 1431 Parkside Drive, Columbus, IN 47203, USA.
MCCLUNG F7323

146420 MCCLURE Mr Robert David. 84 Kings Road, Belfast, BT5 6JN, NORTHERN IRELAND. Tel:0232-796031
ALDWORTH Alldworth Allworth Alworth Lewers Loures Lures Mabry Mabury Maclure Mayberry MAYBURY Mcclewr Mcclour Mccloure Mcclower Mccluer Mccluir Mccluire MCCLURE Mciloure Mcilure Mclewer Mclure F6401

146439 MCCOLGAN Brian. 51 Wingfield Road, Norwich, Norfolk, NR3 3HF. Tel:0603-666660
Greaney Greeny Greney Grening Grenney Grennie Grenny Griney Grinime Grining GRINNEY Grinning MCCOLGAN F6373

146447 MCCONNELL Mrs B F E. 55 Front Street, Tynemouth, Tyne & Wear, NE30 4BX. Tel:091-257-0597
BRACK CARR MARTIN MOFFITT ROBSON F5269

146455 MCCORMACK Ms B. 30 Dordells, Lee Chapel North, Basildon, Essex, SS15 5DB.
DOHERTY JONES MORRIS F4738

146463 MCCOURT Mrs Maureen. 117 Falstones, Basildon, Essex, SS15.
OAKFORD OCKFORD OKEFORD F2974

146471 MCCRAIGHT Mrs P A. 4 High View, Portishead, Bristol, BS20 8RF.
DAVIES F3275

146498 MCCREA Mr Nigel. 2 Kiln Bolton, Kiln Ride, Upper Basildon, Berks, RG8 8TB.
MCCREA F4536

146501 MCCREDIE Mr Gordon. Gemini Cottage, Hurlford, Scotland, KA1 5NP.
MCCREDIE F5080

146528 MCCULLOCH Mr Don. 35 Princeton Street, Kenmore, Brisbane, Australia 4069.
BAIRD DAWSON DOWNIE Gagie GEGGIE MCCULLOCH SALMON F996

146536 MCCULLOCH Mrs Janet. Pen-Y-Bryn, 13 Cae Rex, Llanblethian, Cowbridge, S Glamorgan, CF7 7JS. Tel:0446-773296
ARCHIBALD BAIRD BROWN CHALMERS CLERK COCHRANE COWAN CRANSTON CUNNINGHAM DUFF EDMUND FIFE FISHER FORBES FYFE GARDINER HALL HODGART HOLMES HOUSTON JACK JOHNSTON JOHNSTONE LAMMIE LENNOX LINDSAY LOGAN MAILLEN MCALLISTER MCCLELLAND MCDONALD MCDOWALL MCKISSOCK MELVIN MILLAR MINNIS MORRISON NISBET ORR OSWALD RAE ROUGHEAD SHAW SHEDDEN SLOAN SLOANE TAIT THOMSON TORRANCE WALKER WHITEFORD F1003

146544 MCCULLOCH Mrs M A I. 19 Vienna Way, Strathpine, Queensland, 4500, AUSTRALIA.
Arlosh LOSH TEGNER F6832

146552 MCCULLOCH Mrs M. Barrymore, Marbury Road, Comberbach, Northwich Cheshire, CW9 6AU.
Huntinford HUNTINGFORD F6787

146560 MCCULLOCH Mr Robert. Pen Y Bryn, 13 Cae Rex, Llanblethian, Cowbridge, S Glamorgan, CF7 7JS. Tel:0446-773296
ALLARDYCE ANDERSON BALLANTYNE BELL BROWN BULLOCH CAMPBELL CARUTH COOLEY COOPER CORBETT DINGWALL DIVER DOCHERTY DUNCAN GARDNER GIRDWOOD GLASS HALDANE HALL HARLEY HILL JAMIESON KEDDIE KIETH KIRK LYNN MARK MARSHALL MATTEWSON MCCORD MCCULLOCH MCPHERSON MONTGOMERY MOORE MORISON MOWBRAY NICHOLL NICOL PENNYCUICK PETERKIN REEKIE RUSSELL SELKIRK SIMMERTON SPENCE STEWART SUTHERLAND TAYLOR TRAINOR WATSON WILSON F1004

146579 MCDONALD Mr K R. 2 Greenfields, Stansted, Essex, CM24 8AH.
TESKEY F7126

146587 MCDONALD Mr Keith. 1 Chestnut Avenue, Caversham Park Village, Reading, Berks, RG4 0NS. Tel:0734-476072
ALLBERRY BOWDEN BRADRIDGE BULL CAMERON CAULDOCK CORDERY DRAPER FOALE FORREST FRICKER GADDES GARDINER JAMES KEYES LIVINGSTONE MCDONALD PERKINS PLANE PODGER PRESLEY RYDER SHEPHERDLY SHIPPERLEY SHIRAFS STACEY F4588

146595 MCDONALD Mr Ronald. 22 Dunecht Road, Westhill, Skene, Aberdeenshire, AB32 6RH.
MCDONALD MCINTOSH SMITH F4860

146609 MCDONALD Mrs S C. 22 Compton Road, Winchmore Hill, London, N21 3NX.
CROWE GATLEY GLAVE GORDON KING ORTON TURNER WALKER WITTLETON F610

146617 MCDONAUGH Miss Pat. 12 Mountford Close, Wellesbourne, Warwick, CV35 9QQ.
BASKOTT HUGHES LOMAS MCDONAUGH WILLIAMS F1391

146625 MCDONNELL Mrs Rita. (Chapman) 18 Highgate Avenue, Lepton, Huddersfield, W Yorks, HD8 0EE. Tel:0484-607501
BOOTH Boothe CHAPMAN Fellowes FELLOWS Goodinson GOODISON HORTON MCDONNELL SHAW STORER F3081

146633 MCDONNELL Mrs V. (Liddall) 71 Timberbank, Vigo Village, Meopham, Kent, DA13 0SN. Tel:0732-823156
BAKER BRAY BUSHELL Cheeseman CHEESMAN CHIVERS CLIFTON COCKBURN ELLIS Grobety GROBITY HUNT HURST LIDDALL MCDONNELL PICKETT SHEFFORD F1826

146641 MCDOUGALL Miss E. 5 Spangate, Blackheath Park, London, SE3 9RS.
BASSANO CUTLACK SAVIGNAC F6614

146668 MCDOUGALL Mrs Frances Edith. 32 David St, Albany, WA 6330, AUSTRALIA. Tel:+61-9-841-2823
BALDWIN CAREY EASTLAND THOMAS VENNING WOODROW F4645

146676 MCDOUGALL Mr Maurice. 16 St Georges Road, Cullercoats, Northumberland, NE30 3LA. Tel:091-252-5681
BROWNE HESELTINE LOCK MCDOUGALL PULMAN SHARP WALLER WILSON F6187

146684 MCEVOY Mr Michael. 145 Bury Street, Ruislip, Middx, HA4 7TQ. Tel:0895-675763
LATHLIEFF MCEVOY SHAW STANLEY VIDLES F1536

146692 MCEWAN Miss V G. 14 Rickleton Avenue, Chester Le Street, Co Durham, DH3 4AE.
Macewan MCEWAN Mcewen Mckeown F7145

146706 MCEWEN Mrs Marion. (Stonehouse) Box 49, Beaumont, Alberta, T0C 0H0, CANADA. Tel:+1-403-929-8912
CALLUM CRAVEN ELLIOTT GAULT MARSHALL MCEWEN NOBLE STONEHOUSE F4429

146714 MCEWEN-KING Mrs Margaret. Beck House, Hornby Road, Caton, Lancs, LA2 9QR. Tel:041-204-3692
BOUSTEAD BURTON GRAY GREASON HIRD PENMAN WALTON F839

146722 MCEWEN-KING Mr Robin. Beck House, Hornby Road, Caton, Lancs, LA2 9QR. Tel:041-204-3962
GALTRESS JOHNSON KING SMITH TAYLOR F838

146730 MCFARLAND Paul. 127 Goldhawk Road, London, W12 8EN. Tel:081-743-3819
COWEN DREW GILL GWYN HOODLESS JACQUES

MCFARLAND OSLER PADDY PICKTON QUINTON RUDGE SCOTT STUART TIBBS F2265

146749 MCGEORGE Mr Hugh David. 19 Vanbrugh Fields, Blackheath, London, SE3 7TZ.
Macjore MCGEORGE MCJORE Mcjorys F3638

146757 MCGHEE Mrs Nan. 82 Durward Avenue, Glasgow, G41 3UE.
BROWN CAMPBELL DUCKWORTH DUNLOP GILMOUR GIRVAN KNIGHT KNOWLES Macauley MALCOLM MARTIN MCAULEY MCGEE Mcghee Mcgie MERCER REYBURN ROBERTSON ROSS SMELLIE Smillie SMITH Smylie STEWART SWANSTON WATSON WOODS F1585

146765 MCGLADDERY Mr John. 15 Taylor Court, Warwick, CV34 4QT. Tel:0926-497048
MCGLADDERY MCGLATHERY F1291

146773 MCGLINCY Mrs Maria. (Ashley) 29 Hallams Yard, Skipton, N Yorks, BD23 1JN.
ASHLEY ASHWORTH BENNETT DOHERTY DRURY GLOVER HAGAN MCGLINCEY MCGLINCY F1722

146781 MCGOWAN Mr Alan B. 22 Orchard Way, Aldershot, Hants, GU12 4HW.
VINDEN F6608

146803 MCGOWAN Mr Alan. 105 High Street, Aldershot, Hants, GU11 1BY.
AYRES BALL BOWERS CHARLESWORTH COULL CRAIG DAVIS DUFFIN DUNN ELSLEY FAIRBAIRN GOWER GUNNER HAWKINS LEECH MACE MANSELL MARTIN MAY MCBETH MCGOWAN MOTH MYLES PANNELL PATON PETRIE PRATT SANSON SAUNDERS SHEPHERD SNELLER THOMSON TRENCH VINDEN WOOLTORTON F3151

146811 MCGREGOR Mr C S. 8 The Grove, Guisborough, Cleveland, TS14 8BG.
BARTLE BOYD BROWN CLAYTON Cleaton DONALD DUNBAR DURCAN Durkin ELLIS FOLEY FORSYTH HALL HARLAND Hogarth HUGGART JOHNSON MCGREGOR MCNAIR OXLEY PEARSON REID SILVERLOCK SIMS SYKES Tarbart Tarbat TARBERT Tarbet TAYLOR WADSWORTH WALLACE White WHYTE F6421

146838 MCGREGOR Mrs Margaret. 3 Henbury Road, Westbury On Trym, Bristol, Avon, BS9 3HQ.
WHITTINGTON F72

146846 MCGREGOR Dr Richard. 43 Alder Crescent, Luton, Beds, LU3 1TG. Tel:0582-571326
Aichinhead Aikenhead Aikenheid AITKENHEAD Akenhead Akinhead Akinheid Calhom Callam CALLUM Calum CARD CART Collum Curt FRENCH Gregor Grigor Kart Lovekyn Luckin LUCKING Luckyn Lukin M'gregor M'grigor Macgregor Macgrigor Mackgregor Mackgrigor Mcgreagor Mcgreger MCGREGOR Mcgreogar Mcgrigor Mckgregor Mckgrigor Recassel REUCASSEL Rowcassel Rucassel F3729

146854 MCINTOSH Mrs L J. Cartref Melys, Drury Lane, Drury Buckley, Clwyd, CH7 3DY.
Tel:0244-549154
BACKHOUSE BARLOW BAYBUTT BLAMIRE BOOTH BOWNESS BUTTERWORTH DIXON HOLME HOLMES ION KEPPIE LAYCOCK LICKBARROW LONGSTAFFE MASKRAY MOORBY POTTER POWLEY SHARP SHAWE THORNBORROW WADESON F429

146862 MCINTOSH Mr Thomas Slimmond. 16 Cheviot Way, Duns, Berwickshire, TD11 3HB. Tel:0361-83351
DICKSON Macdonald Mackintosh MCDONALD MCINTOSH SLIMMOND F3120

146870 MCINTYRE-CLARK Mrs Doris. (Mcintyre) 33 Walesby Lane, New Ollerton, Notts, NG22 9RB.
Tel:0623-861233
BURRELL CLARK GIRDLESTONE HUNTER JARVIS MCINTYRE WALKER WONNACOTT F6275

146889 MCKAY Mr Donald. 25 Largie Road, Glasgow, G43 2RD.
MACKAY F3937

146897 MCKELLAR Mrs M. 9 Homebush Court, Heathmont, Victoria, 3135, AUSTRALIA.
BAIRSTOWN DORRELL DRAKE HUDSON JOHNSON MOORE OUTRAM ROEBUCK SHAW STANDRING F5532

146900 MCKENNA Mr Derek. 1 Loggie, Loch Broom, Ullapool, Ross Shire, IV23 2SG.
Tel:085485-231
BERRY FRENCH GARD KIRKPATRICK LEAR MCKENNA MITCHELL STANTON WARREN F5214

146919 MCKENNA Mrs Julie. (Pennington) 1 Loggie, Loch Broom, Ullapool, Ross-Shire, IV23 2SG.
Tel:0854-85231
CAMM CARTER KING LOVE MAWSON PENNINGTON RICHARDSON SALT THISTLETHWAITE Thistlewhate WILLIAMSON F5904

146927 MCKENZIE Mr James. 56 Gladstone Avenue, South Perth, WA 6151, AUSTRALIA. Tel:+61-9-367-6286
BAGGETT Baggot Baggott Bagot BOWEN BOYLE BUZZA COLLIER CUFF Deveraux Devereau DEVEREUX HALLIDAY HAYMES KENTISH M'caughan M'kenzie M'lean Macaughan Mackenzie Maclean MCCAUGHAN Mckeighan MCKENZIE MCLEAN NOMES O'boyle POLARD ROBERTSON WARD F5422

146935 MCKEOWN Miss A. 14 Taplow Street, Anfield, Liverpool, L6 0AB.
BANKS HOBBS HOULT JUDGE LAPPIN LAPPING MALLINSON MCCANN MCKEOWN MCNURTY MINSHULL O GORMAN QUINN WRIGHT F5297

146943 MCKEOWN Mrs Barbara. (Hooper) 25 Braemar Road, Worcester Park, Surrey, KT4 8SN.
AMY CARR HOOPER JOLLY SALMON SEAR STOKES F3025

146951 MCKERRELL OF HILLHOUSE Madam May. Magdalene House, Lochmaben, Lockerbie, DG11 1PD.
Tel:0387-810439
Carleton Carol Charleton Hillhouse Kerrill Mackerel Mccarol MCKERRELL Mckerrill F6024

146978 MCKEVITT Mr Laurence. 5 Cross Lane, Lichfield, Staffs, WS14 9SY. Tel:0543-415397
ATKINSON BRADBURN BRADLEY BURROWS GRAHAM GREEN HOARE LAWTON MCKEVITT MERRIMAN PLATT RAWSON ROACH STARR STOCKHAM WILKS WOODWALL Woodwell F1231

146986 MCKIE Mrs Ann. (Bagwell) 102 Silverdale Road, Earley, Reading, Berks, RG6 2LU.
Tel:0734-268752
BAGWELL BOUND DUNMILL EDMED HARRIS HARWOOD MARKHAM PEARD ROSE RULE SHEAN SWANNELL F3930

146994 MCLACHLAN Mrs Mary. (Wall) 26 Queens Court, East Clyde Street, Helensburgh, G84 7AH.
GRAHAM WALL F4989

147001 MCLAIN Mrs Charlene. 1875 Church Street Se, Salem, Oregon 97302, USA. Tel:+1-503-399-1546
BENTLEY GRINSTED HAYNES LANHAM RANDALL SPEARING WORSFOLD F331

147028 MCLARDY Mr James Donald. 22 Altcar Road, Formby, Liverpool, L37 8DT. Tel:07048-74527
MCLARDY F3482

147036 MCLAREN Mrs Mary. Bankhead Of Kinloch, Meigle, Blairgowrie, Perthshire, PH12 8QY.
GREWAR MCARA MCLAREN MILNE NEISH F955

147044 MCLEAN Mrs Adele. (Warren) 41 Cameron St, Portland, Victoria, 3305, AUSTRALIA.
Tel:+61-55-231068
JOSE MATHEWS ROWE WARREN F4386

147052 MCLEAN Mr B. 8 Marwood Court, Whitley Bay, NE25 9XR.
OVINGTON F7338

147060 MCLEAN Mrs Denise Anne. (Wade) 1 Bridge Of Westfield, Thurso, Caithness, KW14 7QN.
BURNS HOLDSWORTH MCLEAN MURRAY O'HARA SKINNER WADE WINN F6003

147079 MCLEISH Mrs V. (Garland) 1 St Johns Road, Stansted, Essex, CM24 8JP.
BASTABLE Clibborn CLYBORN DUNNE GARLAND Maher MEAGHER WINN F3911

147087 MCLEOD Mrs Heather. Shougle Farm Cottage, Birnie, Elgin, Moray, IV30 3RP.
ADAM BIRD BRUTON COUTTS FRASER JEFFCUTT MCDONALD MCLEOD SCREEN SMITH F3206

147095 MCMEEKIN Mr John. 18 Grieve Croft, Bothwell, Glasgow, G71 8LU. Tel:0698-853895
BLACK DENHOLM FERGUSON GROSSET HAY HOGG MCMEEKIN MILNE F5255

147109 MCMILLAN Mr John Leslie. Fir Tree Cottage, Pedham Road, Hemblington, Norwich, NR13 4QD.
Tel:060549-344
BRENNAND CORLETT CULLIMORE MCMILLAN F1964

147117 MCMINN Mr Ian. 10 Baroncroft Road, Liverpool, L25 6EH. Tel:051-428-1572
Mackman Mackmen Mackmin Mackminn Macmain Macmaine Macmane Macmean Macmin Makmin Makmun Mcmain Mcmean Mcmeans Mcmeen Mcmein Mcmen Mcmenn Mcmim Mcmin Mcmina Mcmine Mcmines MCMINN Mcminne Mcminnies Mcminnis Mcmuin Mcmunn Mcmuns Mcmyn Mcmyne Mcmynn Muckmen F3171

147125 MCMURDY Mrs Elizabeth. 13 Willow Street, Kippa Ring, Queensland, 4021, AUSTRALIA.
Tel:+61-7-284-9420

ALEXANDER BENNETT Carlton Carton Cauton CAWTON Coulton FRIEND FRY GILLANDER Gillinder Labourn Laburn Laybourn LAYBOURNE Layburn LEWIS Leybourne Leyburn Leyburne RUSSELL F5431

147133 MCNALLY Mrs B C. 4 Wrights Road, South Norwood, London, SE25 6RY.
JUKES F1997

147141 MCNAMARA Miss B R. Po Box 6764, Knoxville, Tennessee, 37914-2847, USA.
Wheeldon WHEELTON Whelton F6810

147168 MCNAMARA Mrs G. 8811 State Line Road, Olive Branch, MS 38654-8395, USA.
EDGAR F7271

147176 MCNAUGHTON Mrs Moera. (Hutchinson) 11 Heath St, Mount Maunganui, 3002, NEW ZEALAND.
HUTCHINSON MCNAUGHTON NEWBY NICHOLLS SMITH STEADMAN F5174

147184 MCNEIL Mrs June. (Percival) 241 Acton Lane, Chiswick, London, W4 5DD. Tel:081-994-8328
BARTLEY BELL BUCKLEY FREEMANTLE HILLIARD HUTCHINSON IVES O'BRIEN PERCIVAL RIPPINGHAM F1849

147192 MCNULTY Mr Peter. 439 Maplin Park, Slough, Berks, SL3 8YG.
WICKHAM F4063

147206 MCQUIRE Mrs S E. Deer Dell, Botany Hill, Sands, Farnham Surrey, GU10 1LZ.
Grafam Graffham GRAFHAM F6789

147214 MEAD Mr Alan. 29 Kingston Road, Ewell, Surrey, KT17 2EG. Tel:081-939-6474
HAYWARD MEAD MICKLEBURGH WADDINGTON WILCOCK F5089

147222 MEADOWS Miss Elaine. 149 Muirhead Avenue, Liverpool, L13 0AX.
BAMBER BLUNDELL BOWRIN DALTON DAVENPORT JONES MEADOWS NEWTON SEDDON SUMNER WATKINSON F3826

147230 MEADOWS Mrs Evelyn. (Ringwood) 20 Durrants Drive, Croxley Green, Rickmansworth, Herts, WD3 3NP. Tel:0923-35737
ALLWRIGHT BARTRUM BLIGHT BRISTOW CARTER RINGWOOD ROUT SAUNDERS SORRELL SULLIVAN F1857

147249 MEADOWS Mr Roger. Waterlea, Charlton, Kilmersdon, Bath, Somerset, BA3 5TN. Tel:0761-37855
CARTER HUTTON JACKSON LEVER MEADOWS SCARISBRICK VON HUTON F205

147257 MEADS Mr Steve. 49 Hythe Field Avenue, Egham, Surrey, TW20 8DD. Tel:0784-458811
BLACKBURN BULLEN EILES HORTON KNOWLES MEADS WOOLLEY F2981

147265 MEASURES Mr J H P. 50 Upton Park, Chester, CH2 1DG. Tel:0244-380986
BLACKBOURN BLACKBURN BLENKEY BROWN CON CONN DAVIDSON DAVY EASON EVISON GALBRAITH GAMBLE HAMILTON HARRIS HERMITAGE HODGSON HOOLEY INGRAM JOHNSON JONES LARGUE LONGBOTTOM MASON MEASURES MORRISON NEESHAM NEESOME NEWTON PEARSON PHILIPSON PITTS PORTER POSINET POSINETT POSNET POSNETT REDFOORD REIDFOORD ROBINSON SHARP SHARPE SMITH SNAITH STAMP STOREY SURFLEET THOMPSON TOLLANDS WASHINGTON WHITE WIGELSWORTH WOLFE F1572

147273 MEASURES Mr Peter. C/o 9 Hemington, Peterborough, Cambs, PE8 5QJ.
HUMPHREY MEASURES F329

147281 MEECHAM Mrs Vera. (Schofield) 12 Coronation Road, Brierfield, Nelson, Lancs, BB9 5BS.
ASHWORTH BROOKS CLARKE CLEGG GRIMSHAW HELLEWELL MAWDSLEY MEECHAM PHEASEY PICKUP SCAIFE SCHOFIELD TAYLOR TRICKET WOODALL F646

147303 MEES Mr Reginald W. 22 Harold Thorpe Gardens, Swindon, Wiltshire, SN2 3EA.
BRALIND COOMBES GAISFORD MEES F5914

147311 MEGGINSON Mr Derek. 84 Hovingham Drive, Scarborough, Yorkshire, YO12 5DT.
ALLAN ANDERSON BAMFORTH BARBER BAXTER BEAUMONT BERKIN BLAIR BOOTH BOYCE BROWN BURTON CHESTER COLE CONSTABLE COTTON CRADDOCK FLETCHER GELLEY HALL HARWOOD JACKSON JEFFERSON KEATLEY LEE LLOYD MALEY MARFLITT MARSHALL MEGGINSON OWEN PARKIN PENNOCK SALT SEDMAN SMITHSON TEMPLE THEAKER TOPCLIFF TRUEFITT WATSON WEATHERILL WILLIS F5017

147338 MEGSON Mr John R. 11/6 South Oswald Road, Edinburgh, Scotland, EH9 2HQ.
Tel:031-667-0479
ALLAN BROADBENT BROADLEY ELLIS HARRISON HEBBLETHWAITE HOYLE JOHNSON Magson MARSLAND Megginson Meggison MEGSON POLLARD SCHOLEFIELD SCOTT STOTT TANKARD TURNER WATSON WOOD WOODHEAD F410

147346 MEIER Mrs Elizabeth. (Potts) 3680 Potosi Avenue, Studio City, CA 91604, USA.
Tel:+1-818-769-2865
BAIN BELL BLAIR BOWDEN FEATHERSTONE GOATER GOURLEY HODGSON MACK OXLEY PORTEOUS POTTS STODDART TAYLOR TEMPERLEY F5577

147354 MELMOTH Mr George. 14a Chardmore Road, Stoke Newington, Hackney, London, N16 6JD.
Tel:081-806-9369
HELMOTH MEALEMOUTH MEALMOUTH Meldmouthis MELEMOUTH MELLMOUTHE Melmath MELMETH Melmore MELMOTH Melmoth-Brooks Melmott MELMOUTH Melmouthes Melwoth Milmoth Milmouthes Molmoth WELMOTH F2232

147362 MELROSE Mr Paul. 3 Middleton Close, Wigston, Leicester, LE8 1WF. Tel:0533-811012
ANNIS DAKIN HINGLEY INGLEY PARKES PARKIN SHELLEY SHEPHARD TRIVETT WILLOOUGHBY F6213

147370 MELSOM Mr A J. 2 Chiltern View, Saunderton, High Wycombe, Bucks.
MELSOM Melsome Melson F7450

147389 MEMBREY Mrs Pauline. 66 Powisland Drive, Derriford, Plymouth, Cornwall, PL6 6AD.
CARNELL COLE COLLINGS HENLY MEMBREY PIZZEY POMROY ROBERTS TOLMAN TREMBLETT F828

147397 MEMORY Mr Jim. 5 Chilworth Gate, Silverfield, Broxbourne, Herts, EN10 6NN. Tel:0992-448130
Breton BRITTEN Eales EYLES Mambery Membery Membrey Membry Memmery Memorry MEMORY Mowbery Mowbray PANTLING SPENCER F6515

147400 MENASCHE Mrs Cynthia Mary. (Porter) 18 The Common, Ashstead, Surrey, KT21 2ED.
Tel:0372-273781
ABBEY GODDARD HYATT PORTER SANDERSON SHAW F5316

147419 MENHENOTT Mr David C S. Arluck, Carn View, Gwennap, Redruth, Cornwall, TR16 6BE.
Tel:0209-821180
JAMES MATTHEWS MENHENETT MENHENICK MENHENIOT MENHENOTT ROBERTS F1365

147427 MENNIE Mr Peter. 8 Elm Hill, Warminster, Wiltshire, BA12 0AU. Tel:0985-212275
MENNIE F1026

147435 MENNIM Mr A M. Croft Cottage, Sutton Onthe Forest, York, YO6 1DP.
Mannon Mennar MENNIM Menon F6931

147443 MEREDITH Dr K E G. Hillside View, The Hollies, Nailsworth, Glous, GL6 0AW.
MEREDITH F6772

147451 MERINGO Mr B V J. 6 Rue Windsor, 92200 Neuilly-Sur-Seine, FRANCE.
Marenchi Marenco MARENGO F6719

147478 MERRETT Mr Roy. 34 Pilgrims Way, Cuxton, Rochester, Kent, ME2 1LG.
ANCOCK CRAMPTON HILL HOARE JENNER JONES MERRETT NEWMAN PURFIELD F1727

147486 MERRETT Mrs Shirley M. (Curtis) 23 Bush Spring, Baldock, Herts, SG7 6QT.
Tel:0462-893738
ATKINSON BELL BISHOP BLETSOE BOTTRILL BRIDGFORD CHARLES COLLEIS COX CURTIS EVERSHED FITZHUGH GAISFORD GOODYEAR GRIFFIN HIGGINSON HOLLOWAY JOLLIFFE LABRUM MERRETT MONK PARKHOUSE PEIRCE PIERCE PLUCKNETT SHRIVES TOMBS WELLS WESTCOMBE F3304

147494 MERRICK Mrs Joanna. 23 Raven Lane, Billericay, Essex, CM12 0JB. Tel:0277-659124
DE CROSS GONZALES FOSTER HARTLEY MARTIN RUBERY SAVORY SHERINGHAM STAPLETON F807

147508 MERRICK Mr Keith. Harbourne, Conifer Walk, Kings Acre, Hereford, HR4 0SW.
Tel:0432-342500
GALLIERS GARLICK LERICHE MADDOX MERRICK MORETON PHILLIPS PRILE ROGERS STACEY F1936

147516 MERRICK Mrs Laurel. Hotel Mackay, 179 Victoria Street, Mackay, Nth Queensland, 4740, AUSTRALIA.
PARKES POPE F7001

147524 MERRIGAN M. 14 Rochestown Park, Dun Laoghaire, Co Dublin, IRELAND.

MERRIGAN F7316
147532 MERRILL Dr John. Brickyard Farmhouse, Owston, Oakham, Leics, LE15 8DH.
BARTON BURROWS FORSTER GALLOWEY GREEN HENSHAW HOLLINS HOLMES HUDSON LOCKETT Merel Merell Meriell Merill Merrel Merrell Merril MERRILL Meryl NANSON PICKERING SCOTT SHORE STEELE TINSLEY TIPPING WALFORD F2345
147540 MERRIMAN Mr Richard. 42 Castle Gardens, Kimbolton, Huntingdon, Cambs, PE18 0JE.
Meriman Merrieman MERRIMAN Merryman Mirryman F7317
147559 MERRITT Mr David C. 12 Edgar Court, Edgar Close, Swanley, Kent, BR8 7JJ. Tel:0322-665974
De Meriet Marrett Meriet Merit Merot Merrat Merrett Merriott MERRITT Meryt F2715
147567 MERRITT Mr Michael. 87 Worcester Road, Chichester, W Sussex, PO19 4EB.
COPPARD COX HODGSON HODSDEN HYDE LAMBERT LAMBOURN MERRITT MOSS MUNDAY NEWTON PAGE PERRIN SALTER TRIBE WHITE F2478
147575 MERRYWEATHER Mr Alan. Frithwood Cottage, Bussage, Stroud, Glos, GL6 8AE. Tel:0453-882428
AMIEL BEECH BERLE BROADWAY CHANDLER CHRISTIRE CLARKE COLLINS COX CULLIMORE DEANE DIVE DRAPER EARDLEY EASTAWAY EVANS FIELD FROST HAMILTON HARVEY HURCOMBE IVE JARVIS JONES KENT LAMBERT LEAVERSUCH LUKERS LUTMAN MABBUTT MERRYWEATHER MOORE MORGAN MORTIMER OLVERSON OLVESON OXLEY PRUER READING RICHARDS ROBERTS ROBERTSON RUSSELL SANDERSON SHEPPARD SKELLING SKILLING STEPHENS STRACHEY STREET TRINDLER TYSSEN UPHILL WALHOUSE WALL WELCH WELSH WILLIAMS WINSOR F4791
147583 MESLEY Dr Robert J. 21 Charts Close, Cranleigh, Surrey, GU6 8BH. Tel:0483-276528
BARTLETT BESS Best DALLEY Dally Daubner DOBNER Dolley Dolly GREGORY Haward HAYWARD HOPKINS Howard Measley Medgley MESLEY Messley MIDGLEY MITCHELL Redknap REDKNAPP Rednap ROGERS ROSE SOPER Woodhouse WOODISS F6021
147591 MESSENGER Mr J F. 37 Overhill Way, Park Langley, Beckenham, Kent, BR3 2SN.
Massinger MESSENGER Messinger F18
147605 METCALFE Mr C S. 28 South Road, Hayling Island, Hants, PO11 9AE.
Medcalf Medcalfe Metcalf METCALFE F2466
147613 METCALFE Mr Edward. 18 Larch Rise, Barrow In Furness, Cumbria, LA13 0JZ. Tel:0229-829606
ARMITAGE ATKINSON BALL BANTAN BARRETT BATESON BATTEY BATTY BAYLIFFE BELL BOUSKILL BOWATER BRADLEY BUCKLE BURROWS BUTLER CHARNLEY CLARK COOKNELL COOKSEY COOPER COWDEN COWLEY CRAIN Craine CRESSWELL CUM Cumbe CUMBERLAND DIXON DOWNING DRAKE EDMONDSON ELLERSHAW EMMOTT EVANS FAULKNER FERGUSON FORRESTER FURNACE GARDENER GARRETT GELDART GOSSE GREENFIELD GREENHILL GREGSON GUY HARRISON HARTLE Hartley HASBURY HEWITT HOLME Holmes HOMER Howel Howele Howell Howelle HOWL Howlle INGHAM INGLEBY INGLEY INGSLEY. JAUNDRELL JEAVONS JESSON KELLY KILLEY KINGS LAMBERT LEACH LIVERMORE LOUGHRIDGE LOWE MARSH MARSHALL MASHITER MAUDSLEY METCALFE MILLER MITTEN MOORBY MOORE MOSELEY NAIL NEAL Neale NOCK OLGAN PALMER PARDOE PARKER PATTISON PEARSON PERRY PHILLIPSON POLLOCK PRIEST QUAYLE RIPLEY RISHFORTH RONKSLEY RUMNEY SADLER SERGENTSON SHAW SIDAWAY SIMPSON SKEELS SKIRROW SMITH STEVENS STURMAN SWIFT TALBOT TATE Thompson THOMSON THRUSSELL TIERNEY TOMLINSON Tompson Tomson TOWNSON WAINWRIGHT WALKER WALLING WALTERS WARING WATERSON WEST WHITE WHITEHEAD WHITEHOUSE WHITFIELD WICKS WILCOCK WILLIAMS WILLIS WILLMAN WINTER WOODHOUSE YOUNG F4710
147621 METCALFE Mr Peter. 20 Brushwood Avenue, Flint, Clwyd, CH6 5TY. Tel:0352-732950
ASHTON BARCLAY Barcley Barkley BELLIS BENJAMIN Buckley BULKELEY Bulkley DAVIES EDWARDS EVANS FOULKES HODGKINSON HUGHES JOHNSON JONES LEE Leigh Madchoff Makoff Mariot MARRIOTT Marrit Matcalf Medcalf Meriot Merrit METCALFE Metcalph Metcelf NORMAN PARRY REDFERN ROBERTS SMEDLEY TAYLOR WHITNEY WILLIAMS WYNNE F1270
147648 METHERELL Mrs B D. 2808 Grants Lake Blvd, 703 Sugar Land, Texas, 77479, USA.
Metherall METHERELL Mythrell F6648
147656 METHERINGHAM Mrs D W. 25 Tintagel, Great Lumley, Chester Le Street, Co Durham, DH3 4NF.
Meatheringham METHERINGHAM F6980
147664 METSON Mr W. 62 Stephen Road, Barnehurst, Kent, DA7 6EE.
Metsom METSON Midsom Mitsom F7217
147672 MEW Mrs Joyce. 8 Brooks Street, Broken Hill, NSW 2880, AUSTRALIA.
ANTHONY BOLLEN BROADBENT BRUFF Brugh CARTHEW FRANCIS GARVIE GROSE INMAN MCLENNON MCNAB NORTHEY OATES PROUT ROGERS SCHOOLAR SPRAGG SWEET THORN TRENWITH F4407
147680 MEWES Mr Peter S. 14 Pymers Mead, Dulwich, London, SE21 8NQ. Tel:081-670-1828
MEWES F401
147699 MEWTON Ms Angela J. 23 Glenville Avenue, Enfield, Middx, EN2 0ER.
MEWTON Mouton Muton F3884
147702 MICALLEF Mrs Elizabeth. (Irving) 13 Woodfield, Bamber Bridge, Preston, Lancs, PR5 8EB. Tel:0772-628298
ELLSNORTH Irvine IRVING Irwin LITHERLAND MICALLEF NICKSON QUINN F3470
147710 MICKLEBURGH Mr John. 32 Orchard Close, New Denham, Uxbridge, Middx, UB9 4BB.
BRANSBY BREED CHAMPION DARTON EAGLE FOX JACKSON Meckleburgh Mecklenburgh Mickelburgh Mickleboro Mickleborough MICKLEBURGH Muckleburgh MUNDHAM ROBINSON F6239
147729 MIDDLETON Mr D G. 31 Perton Road, Wightwick, Wolverhampton, WV6 8DE. Tel:0902-762020
CALVERT Ciplin Collar COLLARD Gardiner GARDNER Garner Garvis Gervis JAMES Jarvis JERVIS Kiplin KIPLING Kiplinge Kypling Kyplinge Medilton Medulton MIDDLETON Midleton Myddleton Pontin PONTING Ponton ROBSON F1705
147737 MIDDLETON Mr David. 3 Derwent Road, North Shields, Tyne & Wear, NE30 3AH. Tel:091-258-1377
MIDDLETON Wooard WOOLARD Woollard F5965
147745 MIDDLETON Mr Eric. 26 Thornton Avenue, Redhill, Nottingham, NG5 8PA.
BROWN BUNTING COLLARD DAVISON DRYSDALE GIBSON GREENWOOD JACKSON MARTIN MIDDLETON NEWTON NORTH RICHARDSON TAYLOR TUCKER UNWIN WOOD F6196
147753 MIDDLETON Mrs Janet. (Hargreaves) 10 Thornfield Avenue, Longridge, Preston, PR3 3HL.
HARGREAVES F1409
147761 MIDDLETON Mrs Karen M. (Smith) Boat Harbour Road, Rd1, Whitianga, 2856, NEW ZEALAND. Tel:+64-8-436-3838
CROOK EASTWOOD MIDDLETON SMITH WEEDEN F5489
147788 MIDDLETON Mrs Sheila. (Pearson) 24 Willana Avenue, Hamlyn Heights, Geelong, Victoria, 3215, AUSTRALIA.
BLACK COWGILL GRISENTHWAITE HOBSON HUDSON MIDDLETON PEARSON SLATER SLINGSBY WHITING F5567
147796 MIDDLEYARD Mr G T. Fairport, 1 Miterdale, Woodthorpe, York, YO2 2SX.
MIDDLEYARD F6842
147818 MIDGLEY Mr R Neil. 16 Longlands Bank, Thongsbridge, Holmfirth, W Yorks, HD7 2FR. Tel:0484-684261
BERRY BRADLEY BRETT CHADDERTON CUNDALL GRUNDY Haliday Halladay HALLIDAY HARDING HARDY HARRISON HASTIE ISHERWOOD LINNEY Midgeley MIDGLEY MORRIS PARR PERRY SHARPER SMITH SWALES THOMPSON WALTON WHITTAKER F3090
147826 MIDGLEY Mrs V. 8 Longmead Drive, Sidcup, Kent, DA14 4NV.
BATE DOWNTON FOUNTAIN LUCAS PIKE TRUDE WARHAM WATTS WHITE WOODFIELD F3157
147834 MIDWINTER Mrs M. Wansdyke House, Claverton Down Road, Bath, BA2 7AS.
Faux FAWLK MIDWINTER Mywynter F7017
147842 MIDWINTER Mr S J. 21 Avon Road, Scunthorpe, DN16 1EP.
MIDWINTER F4499

147850 MILBOURN Mrs J. (Edwards) 8 Playfield Road, Edgware, Middx, HA8 0DF.
BRASSINGTON COLLINS EDWARDS HURST MILBOURN MORGAN SHARP STANDING WAGSTAFF F5859

147869 MILDENHALL Mrs Sheila. 5 Milton Court, Ickenham, Uxbridge, UB10 8NB.
ALYWARD BASSE CRAME DAYCOCK GARDINER Gardner HURKETT JACOBS LUCAS MARTIN MILDENHALL PILKINGTON RICHARDSON ROBINSON VINCENT F2242

147877 MILEHAM Mrs Sheila. 31 Faire Road, Glenfield, Leicester, LE3 8EE. Tel:0533-874394
ALLSOPP BIRCH BREWIN COOK FAITHFULL GEARY GOAD HOOK LEE MILEHAM RUSSELL SMITH WILCOX F1680

147885 MILES Mrs Gloria. (Evans) 13 Chelmer Court, London Road, Basingstoke, Hants, RG21 2DT. Tel:0256-27046
BASFORD BLUNDELL BURTENSHAW CARRINGTON COCHRANE COCKBURN COMBER CROFTS EADE EBBINS Ede EGGLISHAW EGLISHER ENGLAND Evans EVINS FRUTS GARTON GREEN GRIFFIN HAYNES HEAVER Hollies HOLLIS HUGHES JACKSON JONES LANE LEWIS MACFARLANE MARTIN MILES NEALE OXLEY Paine PARKINSON PARRY PATCHOM PAYNE ROBERTS SELLIS SMART STEER STEVENS TAYLOR WILLIAMS F3433

147893 MILES Mrs S. 11 Lanacre Avenue, Grahame Park, London, NW9 5FN.
CHALLIS DURRANT WILLIAMS F1941

147907 MILES Mrs Stella Mary. (Mealing) 83 Harford Drive, Watford, Herts, WD1 3DQ. Tel:0923-224570
LAMB LATCHAM MADDAFORD MEALING MILES PEACHEY POPE SELMES WORBOYS F4413

147915 MILFORD Mr H E. 85 Marlborough House, Granby Way, Devonport, Plymouth, PL1 4HG. Tel:0752-500820
COURTER de Luly GLANVILLE Glean Glenn GLINN Glyn Glynn HICKS LOBB Luliere Lulliere Lully LULY MILFORD Neut Newt Newte NUTE PENGELLY SNELL F1160

147923 MILFORD Mrs Valerie. 47 South Street, Havant, Hants, PO9 1BY. Tel:0705-472755
LANE NEWBY POWELL Renakers Runacles RUNACRES TURNER F1381

147931 MILHENCH Mr Roy. 6 Tame Street, Uppermill, Saddleworth, Oldham Lancs, OL3 6BA. Tel:0457-873675
M'gilhauche M'gilhauk Macgilhauch Macgillhench Macilhench Magilhauche Makclouch Makgilhauch Makgillhauch Makkilauche Makkillauche Makylhauche Mcgilhauch Mciihaush Mckilhauche MILHENCH Millhench F3901

147958 MILLARD Mr Andrew. Flat 1, 16 Rowlinson Road, Oxford, OX2 6UE.
Boddimead Boddimeade Boddimede Boddymead Boddymeade Boddymede Bodimaid Bodimead BODIMEADE Bodimeaid Bodimede Bodiment Bodyman Bodymand Bodymead Bodymeade Bodymede BROOK BROOKSBY BUTTON Camack CAMMACK CARTER CHAPMAN CLARK CLARKE Costa COSTER CRABB Cummock EDWARDS FOMM HATCH HEARD JOWETT LINCOLN LITTLECHILD MILLARD MILLS ONWIN PRICE REDINGTON ROBERTSON Sabell SABLE Spriddell SPRIDDLE STOKES Unwin WADSWORTH WEATHERLEY F2818

147966 MILLARD Mr Peter. 4 Jubilee Cottages, Brownshill, Stoud, Glous, GL6 8AR. Tel:0453-882670
BRIGGS FRANCIS MILLARD Millward SKARDON WATERS F2856

147974 MILLEDGE Mr Derek. 128 Bullbrook Drive, Bracknell, Berks, RG12 2QS.
APTED BRAY GARDNER HUTCHINGS Hutchins La Marechal LE MARECHAL Le Mareschal Le Marishall Le Marshall Mellidge Melwyche Milage MILLEDGE Millidge Molledge STANTON VYE F1944

147982 MILLER Mrs Barbara. 41 Alexandra Street, Marton, 5151, NEW ZEALAND.
BELL BURTON CRADDICK HARDEN MARSHALL RENOLDS TAYLOR F4318

147990 MILLER Mrs Brenda. 21640 Chalon, St Clair Shores, Michigan, 48080, USA. Tel:+1-313-777-1779
JOHNSTON-CAMPBELL MOFFAT-BELL F7414

148008 MILLER Enid. 437 Laceby Road, Grimsby, DN34 5NA.
BARRON CLARVIS MILLER F7429

148016 MILLER Mrs Florence. (Ford) Riverhurst, Central Butte, Sask, S0H 3P0, CANADA. Tel:+1-306-353-2043
CAMERON FORD LANGSTAFF MILLER NORMAN PARKS SNELL F5463

148024 MILLER Mr Ian L. 23 Dewar Place Lane, Edinburgh, EH3 8EF.
MILLER WARNES F3934

148032 MILLER Mr John. 54 Cornwall Road, Ruislip, Middx, HA4 6AN. Tel:0845-672443
MILLER NEWMAN F1860

148040 MILLER Mrs Joy. 40 Lariggan Crescent, Penzance, Cornwall, TR18 4NH. Tel:0736-64211
BOUNSALL Bounsell EVELEIGH Everleigh FULFORD Grainger GRANGER MARTIN Martyn MATTHEWS PERKIN Perkins SLEEP Sleepe F795

148059 MILLER Ms K. 210c Walmersley Road, Bury, Lancs, BL9 6LL.
APPERLEY BRIAN BROWN BURNELL BURNHOLE Burnoll CARPENTER COOPER DAVEY Davy FELL HELIE Horam HURAM LEWIS MILLER ORAM PRATT SMITH TURBERVILLE Whoram F2802

148067 MILLER Mrs Margery G. (Mombrun) 7 Winston Road, Exmouth, Devon, EX8 4LR.
BAKER De Monbrun FARROW JENNES Mambrun MASON Membrun MILLER Mimbrun Mombrom Mombrum MOMBRUN Monbrun Mornborn Mumbrun PARKER VALLE WALSH F2645

148075 MILLER Mrs Pamela. (Brightling) 28 Knight Street, Walsingham, Norfolk, NR22 6DA. Tel:0328-820824
BRIGHTLING RANDALL F1656

148083 MILLER Mr Roderick D. 14 Heywood Close, Hartland, Devon, EX39 6HS. Tel:0237-441689
IMBER KITCHER MILLER SEAGER Segar Seger F3141

148091 MILLETT Mrs Ruth. The Old House, 63 Goose Street, Beckington, Bath, BA3 6SS.
ANDREWS BORWICK FOULGER HALLIWELL HEARNSHAW MILLETT PAGE PHIPPEN ROBINSON F236

148105 MILLICHAMP Mr M E. Orchard End, 80 Wallingford Road, Goring, Oxford, RG8 0HN.
MILLICHAMP Millichap Millichop F6660

148113 MILLINGTON Mr Douglas. 3 Ashfield Drive, Gleadless, Sheffield, South Yorks, S12 2QW. Tel:0742-391990
ADAMS Addams Adhams APPLEBY BALL BARGH BELL BINGHAM Bromehead Bromhead BROOKS BROOMHEAD BURTON CHAPMAN CHARLES CREW Crewe DAVIS DUNBAR FIRTH HOLMES KING Kitchen KITCHIN Kitching LEE MERRITT MILINGTON Milinton Millington Millinton Myllington OSBORN PALFREY PALING Palling PARKE PARKER Payling PEARCE SLATER SOUTHALL WILLIAMS WRIGHT F5329

148121 MILLINGTON Miss L. 31 March St, Kotara, Newcastle, NSW 2289, AUSTRALIA. Tel:+61-4-957-5857
BARTHOLOMEW BAWN Bohan BOHEN BOHUN BRADLEY BRANSBY BROUGH CHRISTIE Civill CROSS DRAPER FELSTEAD FRANCIS GINN GRATTON GRAY Grey HARDY HUNT HUTCHINS JACKSON MATCHAM Milligeton MILLINGTON Mulyncon MURPHY PITT ROSE SAVILLE Seville SMEDLEY SYKES TURNBULL TURNER WEYMSS WHITTLE WHYSALL F4698

148148 MILLINGTON Mr William. 28 Cronton Avenue, Whiston, Prescot, Merseyside, L35 3SH. Tel:051-426-3477
MILLINGTON F305

148156 MILLO Mr Royston. Bourne Court, Ragged Appleshaw, Andover, Hants, SP11 9HX. Tel:0264-772801
ABLETHORPE AYRES BAXTER BRAWN BUTLER CLARKE COOK COOKE COX DANIEL FEAR FLETCHER FOWLER GARLEY GIDDINGS GIDGEON HALL HARVEY JOHNSON KNIGHT LANTAFF LEVER LOVELL MALLARD OLD PARKER PARROTT RADFORD REED ROWNING STANTON THORNICROFT TUCK VERNON WATTS WAYMAN WELCH WILLIAMSON WILLS F2453

148164 MILLS Mr James. 1 Pental Road, North Caulfield, Victoria, 3161, AUSTRALIA.
MILLS PERRY F4243

148172 MILNER Miss Brenda. 35 Willow Park Road, Wilberfoss, York, YO4 5PS.
ASHCROFT BUSSEY CARR CLEVELAND LISTER LOWE

MIDGELEY MILNER RAPER F6106
148180 MILNER Mr Robert. 411 Cheadle Road, Cheddleton, Leek, Staffs, ST13 7BH. Tel:0782-550112
BENTLEY COXON HOBSON HULME LEESE MILLER Millner Milnar MILNER Milnor Mylner OULSNAM ROE STICKLAND F112
148199 MILSOM Mr Peter. 12 Welholme Road, Grimsby, S Humberside, DN32 0DU. Tel:0472-349794
AMOS COLBERT HORSEWOOD MILSOM NICHOLSON REVILL SELLERS SLEIGHTHOLM WALSH F6326
148202 MILSOM Mr Peter. 2/31 Albany Road, Bexhill On Sea, East Sussex, TN40 1BY. Tel:0424-219113
Badam Baddam BADHAM LUCK LYNN Melksham Melsom Melsum Milksham.MILSOM Milsum F5226
148210 MILTON Mrs Gail. Box 472, Eston, Saskatchewan, S0L 1A0, CANADA.
CRUIKSHANK CUMMING DONALD DOUGLAS EDWARD FLANNIGAN HARRIS HOPPER LESLIE MCADAM MCCULLOUGH MEADOWS MILTON ROE SIMPSON SIVEWRIGHT SMITH STRACHAN F5573
148229 MIMMS Mr Peter. 20 Lonsdale Road, Bournemouth, Dorset, BH3 7LX. Tel:0202-557069
Mimes Mimmes MIMMS Mims F54
148237 MINERS Mrs Rhoda. Bostennor, Wheal An Wens, Marazion, Cornwall, TR17 0DF.
BOYES BROOKER ELDERTON HALSEY HARDING HEAD POWELL SHEPHERD SYLVESTER TREAGUS F2262
148245 MINNEY Barrie. 2 Stanley Cottages, Sheffield Park, Nr Uckfield, East Sussex, TN22 3QG.
Minell Miney Minin Minnal Minnell MINNEY Minnie Minny Miny F7034
148253 MINSHULL Mr Tony Freer. Priory Park Hotel, 4 Avenue Road, Great Malvern, Worcs, WR14 3AG. Tel:0684-565194
Minshall MINSHULL Mynshule F821
148261 MINSON Mr Roland & Mrs Carol. (Dexter) 1844 Nancy Circle, Thousand Oaks, CA 91362, USA. Tel:+1-805-494-3674
BAKER BELL CRIPPS DAWSON DEXTER Eckersall ECKERSLEY FRIEND HAGUE Haig HALLETT LEE LOVE MCPHAIL MINSON SADLER WALTON WHITFIELD WOODCOX F5510
148288 MINTER Mrs M. (Attenborough) 237 Mccaffrey Drive, Rankin Park, NSW 2287, AUSTRALIA.
ABELL Adenburgh ALDRED ALLAN Attenboro ATTENBOROUGH Attenborrow Attenburgh BACON BAMFORD BARNES Barrotcluff BARROWCLIFFE BLAKE Bourke BURKE COLLINS COOKE CORBRIDGE Coshar Coshier COSIER Cozier Crozier DEVLIN EDMISTON Edmonston GALLOWAY GIBSON GOULD GREAVES Guild HAMMERTON HATHERLY Hibbard HIBBERD Hibbert Hibbird HOLLAMS HOY HUDSON HUTTON IRELAND KIRKE Leabeater Leabter LEADBEATER Leadbetter LEAKE LEWIS LISTER Macknamay MAGEE MALROY Mcname MCNAMEE Melroy MELVILLE Milroy MINTER MORPHEW MORSE MOULTRY Noakes NOKES PINCHES PRATT SCOTT SIDNEY SMEDLEY SMITH STEWART STROUD Stuart Thompson THOMSON TICKNER TILBERRY WAKEFIELD Wakeford WALKER WEIGHTON Wighton WILKINSON WILLMOTT YATES YOUNG F5551
148296 MINTER Mr R E. 7 Warwick Hall Gardens, Bromsgrove, Worcs, B60 2AU.
GROVE Le Meneter MANN MINTA MINTER Mintor Myntor Myntur PENTON F3631
148318 MINTERN Mr Frederick. 37 Royds Crescent, Rhodesia, Worksop, Notts, S80 3HF. Tel:0909-481884
MINTERN Minterne Minton F5931
148326 MIRRINGTON Mr R D. 184 Maldon Road, Colchester, Essex, CO3 3AY.
MERRINGTON F6582
148334 MIST Mrs Coral. 2 Horewood Road, Easthampstead, Bracknell, Berks, RG12 4LY.
BOWMAN BUNN BYRNE DUFFIELD DYKE ERSWELL FARLEY MIST WHITE F1926
148342 MITCHELL Durno. 17 St Marys Close, Southam, Warwickshire, CV33 0EW. Tel:0926-817667
BAYLEY BOWDEN BRICE CORDINER DURNO HANDLEY KILBY MACKIE MITCHELL MOTTRAM MURRAY STEPHEN WEBSTER F1052
148350 MITCHELL Mr Harold. 31a Fairfax Road, Bingley, N Yorks, BD16 4DR. Tel:0274-563153
CURRELL GOMERSALL HOYLE LISTER MITCHELL SCURRAH F2630
148369 MITCHELL Ms Iris. 9800 Horton Road Sw, Apt 506, Calgary, Alberta, T2V 5B5, CANADA.
HERSANT Hersent F6983
148377 MITCHELL Mr John D. 28 St Johns Rise, Woking, Surrey, GU21 1PW. Tel:0483-762674
APPLEDORE COUCH CREWS DICKERSON GARRARD GIRLING IAGO JAGO KING MILLS MITCHELL WOOLMER F109
148385 MITCHELL Mr John Trevor Drew. 91 Bath Street, Abingdon, Oxon, OX14 1EG. Tel:0235-521036
ASHE DREW MITCHELL SYMES F2494
148393 MITCHELL Mrs K A. 10 Ducks Meadow, Marlborough, Wiltshire, SN8 4DE.
CROSSKILL F6808
148407 MITCHELL Mr K D B. 10 Ducks Meadow, Marlborough, Wiltshire, SN8 4DE.
Foulton FULTON F1985
148415 MITCHELL Mr Leslie. Trehelig, New Road, Zeals, Warminster, Wilts, BA12 6NG.
HAYWARD LEWIS MITCHELL STEDMAN F5271
148423 MITCHELL Mrs Lorna. (Conway) 12 Park View, Balmullo, St Andrews, Fife, KY16 0DN. Tel:0334-870254
AULD CARR CONWAY FERGUSON GRANT HALL MCDONALD MCGREGOR MORRISON SHAW WATSON F3167
148431 MITCHELL Mrs Mary. (Ledger) 34 Craigs Park, Edinburgh, EH12 8UL.
CHUME LEDGER LOVELL MITCHELL POFFLEY F4364
148458 MITCHELL Mr Raymond. 6 Anscomb Gardens, Newcastle Upon Tyne, NE7 7BB.
BRADLEY GRAY MITCHELL PEABODY RICHARDSON SLATER F2283
148466 MITCHELL Mrs V E. 36 Broadlands Ave, Hockley, Essex, SS5 5EW.
BUCHANAN MCGLASHAN F7188
148474 MITCHINSON Mrs Petra E. 91 Heathfield Drive, Mitcham, Surrey, CR4 3RD.
Batey Batty BATY Beattie Beaty BELL FRENCH GRAHAM HOY JOHNSTON Ketchen KETCHIN Kitchen Kitchin Mackie MATTHEWSON Mattinson Mattison Mccie Mckay Mckey MCKIE Michelson Michinson Mitcheison Mitchelson Mitchenson Mitcheson MITCHINSON Mitchison MUSGRAVE Roantree Rontrey Rountree Rowentree ROWNTREE TURNBULL Woodal WOODALL Wooddle Woodell Woodhall Woodle F524
148482 MOAR Mr John W H. Muce Cottage, Marwick, Birsay, Orkney, KW17 2NB. Tel:085672-268
ANDERSON BAIKIE BALLANTYNE Ballenden Bellenden BELLIE BRECK CAPTAIN FLETT Folsetter FOLSTER Gadie Gady GAUDIE HUNTER Hunto Huntow JOHNSTON MEADOWS Midhouse MOAR Moir More Mouat Mouatt MOWAT Oliver OLLAY Philip PHILIPS Sclaitter Sclater Sklaitter SLATER Stainsgair STANGER Stenger Stensgarth STICKLER TAYLOR WOOD F1671
148490 MOBBERLEY Linda. 20 Orme Road, Hirael, Bangor, Gwynedd, LL57 1AY.
MCDONALD MOBBERLEY PARRY WILLIAMS F1363
148504 MOBBS Mrs Annita. (Williams) 2/3 Bell Cottages, Derby Road, Doveridge, Derbyshire, DE6 5JU. Tel:0889-566165
CHAMBERS HOUGHTON RUSHTON WEBB WHEELER WILLIAMS F4788
148512 MOBBS Mr Christopher. 94 Southlands Avenue, Orpington, Kent, BR6 9ND. Tel:0689-853228
MOBBS NICHOLAS F4561
148520 MOCK Mr Jack H. 13 Kingsfield, Bradford On Avon, Wiltshire, BA15 1AN. Tel:02216-5626
Chapel CHAPELL Chappel Chappell FAGG Fagge MOCK Mocke Mok F458
148539 MOFFATT Mr Charles. 12 Thompson Ave, North Sydney, Nova Scotia, B2A 1X8, CANADA.
Moffat MOFFATT Moffet Moffit F7138
148547 MOFFATT Mrs Linda. 2 Burley Road, Winchester, Hampshire, SO22 6LJ.
Scudamore Skidgemore Skidgmore SKIDMORE Skidsmore Skitmore Skudemore F2550
148555 MOFFATT Mrs Linda. 28 Abbotts Ann Road, Winchester, Hants, SO22 6NB.
Scudamore Skidgmore SKIDMORE Skitmore F7365
148563 MOFFATT Mr Trevor. 24 Karen Way, Great Sutton, South Wirral, Cheshire, L66 4LL. Tel:051-339-6297
BENTLY GURNEY JENKINS MCMAHON MOFFATT SHARP F4283
148571 MOGER Mrs Doreen. 14 Sylvan Avenue, Bitterne,

Southampton, Hants, SO2 5JU.
GALE MOGER F2706

148598 MOGFORD Mr Anthony. 42 Old Coach Road, Playing Place, Truro, Cornwall, TR3 6ET. Tel:0872-865087
APLIN HANCOCK MOGFORD SMITH TITTERTON F4806

148601 MOGGS Mr Bernard. 2 Greenfinch Close, Tilehurst, Berks, RG3 5SY. Tel:0734-421552
MOGGS TERRY WINGROVE F863

148628 MOHAMED Mrs J. 285 Sheffield Road, Glossop, Derbyshire, SK13 8QY.
BROAD F6459

148636 MOHUN Mr Charles Reynell. 1 The Cottage, Albaston, Gunnislake, Cornwall, PL18 9AL. Tel:0822-833718
Mohon MOHUN F2167

148644 MOIR Colonel Claud. 17 Sunbury Place, Dean Village, Edinburgh, EH4 3BY. Tel:031-225-6175
BELL CLELAND MILLIGAN MOIR MORE MUIRHEAD MURRAY WATSON F5343

148652 MOLE Mrs S M. (Hinton) 2 Second Avenue, Charmandean, Worthing, W Sussex, BN14 9NX.
BOYER CHRISTOPHER DICKSON HINTON JOHNS MARTIN MOLE RANDLE TOOMER WILSON F856

148660 MOLL Miss Irene. 30 Harecroft Gardens, Kings Lynn, Norfolk, PE30 2BY.
BARBER LIVOCK MOLL WARD F1695

148679 MOLLAND Mrs Sheila. 132 Salterton Road, Exmouth, Devon, EX8 2PD. Tel:0395-263265
ASHFORD LOVERING WADHAM YOUNG F5414

148687 MOLLER Mrs Patricia. (Knight) 7 Sutton Court, Eastcote Avenue, West Molesey, Surrey, KT8 2HB.
KNIGHT-PITT Polglaise POLGLASE Polglass Polglaze F5398

148695 MOLLOY Denise. Po Box 556, Ballarat 3353, AUSTRALIA.
HODGE F7291

148709 MOLONEY Mr Kevin. Avoca, Bridge Road, Chertsey, Surrey, KT16 8JN.
HARRINGTON HOOKEY F6044

148717 MOLYNEUX David. 42 Keswick Road, Great Bookham, Leatherhead, Surrey, KT23 4BH.
Moleyns Molinaux Molineus Molineux Molinex Molino Mollenas Mollineaux Molyneaux MOLYNEUX Molynox Moulineaux Mulinex Mullenax Mullenneix Mulliner Mullinox F6909

148725 MONAGHAN Mrs Valerie. (Ketteridge) 65 Parc-Y-Felin, Creigiau, Cardiff, CF4 8PA. Tel:0222-890842
BOGGIS Bogis BRADFORD Burges BURGESS Chefens CHEFFINS Chefins Chevins Chivins COLLEDGE Coolidge Coolledge Coollidge FOX Hocket HOCKETT Ketridge KETTERIDGE Kettridge Kitteredge RINGSTEAD Ringsted Vigors Vigours VIGUS Vikers F4648

148733 MONCK Peter. The Flat, 6 Temple Street, Sidmouth, Devon, EX10 9AY. Tel:0395-515622
ARCHER BATCHELOR Le Moigne MOIGNE MONCK MONK Monke Monks Moyne Munck Munk SPELLER F2915

148741 MONEY Mr K A & Mr R. Dubai College, Po Box 837, Dubai, UNITED ARAB EMIRATES.
MONEY Monie Monies Monney F6637

148768 MONK Mr Douglas. 5 Dalewood Close, Emerson Park, Hornchurch, Essex, RM11 3PJ.
BROOKS CAPPER CROOK DEACKES DICKS EMERTON FAWCETT Forster FOSTER FREEMAN GARE GARROW GARROW-MONK HANDCOCK HARRIS HERBERT JOHNSTON LOWNDES MCDONALD MCSHANE MELBOURNE MILNE Monck MONK NICHOLS PHILLIPS SAFFERY SMEED SOWDEN SPARKS TATUM THACKER F2135

148776 MONK Mrs M. 52 Wivenhoe House, Fairways, Ferndown, Wimborne Dorset, BH22 8BB.
MONK ROWE F2338

148784 MONNERY Mrs Mary. (Barr) 5 The Boulevard, West Worthing, Sussex, BN13 1JZ. Tel:0903-501081
ARNATI BANGS BUNT GOATCHER MONNERY MUNNERY PORDAGE ROLLS F6168

148792 MONTGOMERY Mr Roy. 102 Sunnymead Drive, Waterlooville, Hants, PO7 6BX. Tel:0705-254007
ALDRIDGE APPLETON BILLET BRIGHT Brite COLLINS FERRIS FISHER FOSTER HOLLAND LEGROVE MONTGOMERY PEARCE RICKETTS STEFENS SWAIN Swayne Talmadge TALMAGE WEDGE F2483

148806 MOODY Mrs C M. 24 Nightingale Drive, Towcester, Northants, NN12 7RA.
BRECKON COVERDALE KESSELL Kissell PICKARD RICHARDSON SIMPSON TONKIN WARDALE Wardell Wardill Wardle F2628

148814 MOONEY Mr & Mrs L W. (Webber) 25 Elmar Road, Liverpool, L17 0DA.
COCKRAM FISHER HAGGETT JAMES MAYHEW MOONEY RAY WEBBER F5680

148822 MOORCOCK Mr P S. 175 Hawes Lane, West Wickham, Kent, BR4 9AG.
MOORCOCK Morecock F826

148830 MOORE Mr Christopher Halliday. 6 Lonsdale Terrace, Edinburgh, EH3 9HN.
DUNCAN HALLIDAY JOHNSTONE MARTIN MCINTYRE MILLAR MOORE POLLOCK RILEY RUTHVEN F372

148849 MOORE Mr Donald. 28 Cleveland Road, South Woodford, London, E18 2AL. Tel:081-530-4934
CORKIN MOORE MORE PEACH POPE F6065

148857 MOORE Mr Fred. 9 Rakeway, Saughall, Chester, CH1 6AZ.
Brat BRATT Brett Moor MOORE Moores Moors More Mores F1329

148865 MOORE Mr G W R. 24 Campion Close, Hillingdon, Uxbridge, Middx, UB8 3PY. Tel:0895-442804
BURRAGE Burridge CARLILE CARLISLE CARLYLE FAIRFAX-CARLISLE MOORE PIERREPOINT THACKERAH F5014

148873 MOORE Mr Gary. 102 Tintagel Close, Andover, Hampshire, SP10 4DB. Tel:0264-351130
FORD HONEY MOORE STEVENS TIZZARD F3137

148881 MOORE Mr George R. 7 Ferndene Road, Herne Hill, London, SE24 0AQ.
MOORE TURNER F3188

148903 MOORE Mr Hugh. 7 Cuffelle Close, Chineham, Basingstoke, Hants, RG24 0RH. Tel:0256-25741
BOLT LIDSTER MOORE F4074

148911 MOORE Mrs Irene. 25 Westbrook Drive, Macclesfield, Cheshire, SK10 3AQ.
BOOTH BOYNE RADFORD SHAWCROSS TIMMONS TULLY F927

148938 MOORE Mr J C. 120 Parrys Lane, Stoke Bishop, Bristol, BS9 1BJ.
Barratt BARRETT Barrot BLOWER BODNUM BRADFORD BURFORD BUSLEY Butcher BUTCHERS CANNOCK CLARKE Croom CROOME DAVIS DERRETT DUNSTONE Friar FRYOR HILL HOPKINS Mallet MALLETT MASTON Moor MOORE More PEARCE PINNELL POLE Pool Poole POPE Randall RANDELE Rendele ROBERTS Sansom Sansome SANSUM THOMAS TUCKER VICARY Vickery WATKINS WILKINS F3988

148946 MOORE Mr J E. 68 Layard Square, London, SE16 2JF.
Leffen LEFFIN Liffen Liffin F6777

148954 MOORE Ms Joyce B. (Collins) Silver Birches, Lowford, Bursledon, Southampton Hants, SO3 8EP.
APPLEBY COLLINS CORRY CRUTCHLOW GOLDING JOHNSON MORTON MOSS PLUCK RANDALL F2240

148962 MOORE Mrs Linda. (Chivers) 102 Tintagel Close, Andover, Hants, SP10 4DB. Tel:0264-351130
BROUGHTON CHIVERS GREEN PRITCHARD RANDALL STAIRE WEST F3138

148970 MOORE Mrs M R. 1 Cambridge Close, Lawn, Swindon, Wiltshire, SN3 1JQ.
Belainy BELANEY Belanie F6875

148989 MOORE Mrs Norma. 24 Puller Road, High Barnet, Herts, EN5 4HF. Tel:081-364-9766
Appeling APPLIN CLAYTON CORDWELL EDIS GINSBERG Ginsburg PAMPHILION POPKIN SINETT F3221

148997 MOORE Mrs Pam. 37 Minismere Road, Keynsham, Bristol, BS18 1PY. Tel:0272-862966
BEECHENO HICKS IGGULDEN LEWIS REAVELL STINCHCOMBE F287

149004 MOORE Mrs Patricia. (Taylor) 128 Foliejohn Way, Maidenhead, Berks, SL6 3XZ.
ANDERSON BELL BOOKER CHICK CONCHIE COULTER EASLICK GIGG HAWKEN HICKS KNOX LOCK MAHONEY MALLETT MASSEY MCLAUGHLIN MIDDLETON MILES MOORE MORRISON RICHARDS SHERWIN TAYLOR TILL VASSIE WALKER WOODS F367

149012 MOORE Mr Peter H. 37 Swanley Lane, Swanley, Kent, BR8 7JE. Tel:0322-664169
BARKER DANIEL GURNEY HAINSBOROUGH Moor MOORE

More Weeler Whealer Wheelar WHEELER Wheeller Wheiler Wheler Wheller F4114

149020 MOORE Mr R. 1 Cambridge Close, Lawn, Swindon, Wiltshire, SN3 1JQ.
SILVERTHORNE F6961

149039 MOORE Mr Robert. 103 Cedar Road, Northampton, NN1 4RW. Tel:0604-718860
AUSTIN BLAKEMORE CRUTCHLEY FELTON FOSTER GOODEY LUMMAS MALIN MOOR MOORE OGDEN PAINE PHILLIPS UNDERWOOD WOOLEY F6380

149047 MOORE Miss Rosemary C. 4252 Fair Avenue, Apt 3, North Hollywood, CA 91602, USA.
BINNS BLAKE CHALLENGER CLARE HIBBS HOBSON LAMB NEWCOMBE NUTT ROUGHTON SMITH THORN Thorne TIPPER TOMLINSON YOUNG F4128

149055 MOORE Mrs Rosemary Joan. 4 Hillside, Brandon, Suffolk, IP27 0NL. Tel:0842-811212
BAGGARIDGE BOXALL Cain CANE DOWDEN DRAPER ELLIOTT-WELLS PALMER ROWNEY WELLS F2228

149063 MOORE Vivienne Seonaid. Rivendell, 33 Doocot Road, St Andrews, Fife, KY16 8QP.
AINSLIE ALLAN ANDERSON Blackie Blaickie BLAIKIE Burnet BURNETT CAVERS COCKBURN CURRIE DARLING DICKSON DODDS Dods Eddislaw Eddisly EDGELAW Edglaw Edslaw Ennislie Enslie FAIR FORREST FORTUNE Fraiter FRATER Gardener GARDINER Gardner GRAY GREENFIELD Greive GRIEVE HALL HENDERSON HOGG HOOD HUGHES IRVINE Ischer Johnson JOHNSTON Johnstone KERR LAUDER LAWSON Liddel LIDDLE MERCER PATERSON PENNY PRINGLE ROBSON SCOTT SIMPSON Simson Sommers SOMNER Steel Steil STEILL Sumner Sympson Symson TAIT TOOK Tuck TURNBULL USHER VEITCH WHITE WILSON YULE F1289

149071 MOORE Mrs W J. 138 The Avenue, Highams Park, London, E4 9RD.
BAKER CLARK Clarke LANE LEAVENS F7424

149098 MOORHEN Mrs Wendy. (Lorenz) 2 Field Hurst, Langley Broom, Langley, Berks, SL3 8PQ.
BEARDMORE Bolton BOULTON BROWN GILCHRIST GRAVES HAMES HARTHORN HOPE Ingal Ingale INGALL Lee LEIGH LOCKETT LORENZE MOORHEN NOBLE RILEY ROBERTSON Robinson Robson ROCLIFF Ryley SHAW Shawe Waley Walley WARING WHALEY Whalley Whawley Willson WILSON WOOD F4883

149101 MOORHOUSE A R. 179 Makepeace Raod, Northolt, Middx, UB5 5UJ.
FARMERY F7276

149128 MOORHOUSE Mrs M. 3 The Meridians, Stour Road, Christchurch, Dorset, BH23 1RA. Tel:0202-471284
BARBER BISHOP HAVIS MUNDAY MUNDY F1457

149136 MOORHOUSE Miss Margaret. 5 Summerhill Avenue, Steeton, Keighley, W Yorks, BD20 6RU. Tel:0535-653945
GOUGH MOORHOUSE MYERS WALKER F2359

149144 MOORMAN Mr Robert. 66 St Thomas'S Road, Hardway, Gosport, Hants, PO12 4JX.
BOVEY KNOWLES Mooreman MOORMAN MOREMAN Morman NORWAY STRIPE Varrant Varrent VERRANT Verrent WELLINGTON Yoltan Yolten Yolton Youltan Youlten Youltin YOULTON F859

149152 MOOT-CRAVEN Ms P M. 2 Coach House, Town Hall Lane, Swanage, Dorset, BH19 1EX.
ARCHER ARMSTRONG BACON BAKER BROOK Brooke Brookes Brooks CAMPBELL CASTLETON COOPER CRAVEN EADON EATON ELLIOTT FIELD FOX FULL GUTHERSON Gutterson HALL Heaton Hewison HEWSON JEPSON LATHAM Lathem Laytham LEE MERCER Moffat Moffatt Moffet Moffett Moffit MOFFITT OXSPRING REANEY SWAN TASKER TITTERTON TOPHAM WORMALD F5933

149160 MORAN Mrs Susan. (Clark) Milestone, Amercombe, Pensford, Avon, BS18 4JQ.
BYNER CLARK LEE MAYCOCK MILLER MINGAY PARSONS PYCROFT F4852

149179 MORCOM Mr D M T. Zeals, Selworthy, Minehead, Somerset, TA24 8TR. Tel:0643-862205
MORCOM Morcombe Morcome F791

149187 MORETON Mrs M E. 6 Rosevale Place, Richmond, Nelson, NEW ZEALAND.
AIMERS ALLAN ARTHUR BARNET BAULDIE BERTRAM BLACK BROWN BROWSTER BRUCE CLARK CORMIE CRICHTON DEUCHARS DICK DUNCAN EMERY FEATHERS FORBES FORD GALLICHAN GLASS GRANDIN GUTHRIE HEAND HENDRY HUBERT IRELAND JOHNSTON JONES Kelley KELLIE LEONARD LESLIE MITCHELL MORETON MOYES NAIRNE NICOL NICOLLE PHIN RATTRAY RENOUF ROUTLEDGE SCOTT SMITH SPENCE STEPHEN STORRIE SUTHERLAND SWANKIE TAYLOR THOMSON WARDEN WATT WHITTON WILSON WRAY F4177

149195 MORETTI Mr A. 49 Brook Street, Wymeswold, Loughborough, Leics, LE12 6TT. Tel:0509-880871
HASTINGS HOLNESS JAQUES MARRIOT PALMER PAYNE TALBOT F4798

149209 MOREY Mrs Isabel. 123 Ashcroft Road, Ipswich, Suffolk, IP1 6AE. Tel:0473-464017
MARLEY MOREY TYERS F6241

149217 MORFORD Miss Audrey P. 43 Martin Road, Copnor, Portsmouth, Hants, PO3 6JZ. Tel:0705-660669
MORFORD POLHILL STANDFORD F2858

149225 MORGAN Mrs Barbara. 18 Glanmore Crescent, Newport, Gwent, NP9 8AX. Tel:0633-275227
BLOODWORTH Stackwell STOCKWELL Stokewell Treeman Trewman Trueman TRUMAN Trwman F5024

149233 MORGAN Mrs Dorothy. 24 Scotland Drive, Dunfermline, Fife, KY12 7SY.
CASTLE CHALMERS HUTCHEON HUTCHESON LOW MACDONALD MACINNES MIDDLETON WALKER WATSON F1313

149241 MORGAN Mr Edward. The Glen, Stonehouse Lane, Bulkley, Malpas Cheshire, SY14 8BQ. Tel:0829-720306
ELLERY GODDARD HUGHES JONES MORGAN PRITCHARD ROBERTS F960

149268 MORGAN Mrs J S. 53 Middleton, South Bretton, Peterborough, Cambs, PE3 6XH.
LYON RUDKIN STANTON F3677

149276 MORGAN Mrs June. Pokey Cottage, 74 Ringmore Road, Shaldon, Teignmouth, Devon, TQ14 0AB. Tel:0626-873423
LANG F295

149284 MORGAN Miss N J. 8 Wexham Close, Luton, Beds, LU3 3TU.
ALLEN BODD CLIST COURT HAYWARD HURLEY MORGAN SMITH STRANGE F2968

149292 MORGAN Mr Norman Canning. 15 West Park Avenue, Newby, Scarborough, Yorkshire, YO12 6HH. Tel:0723-363162
ALLEN CANNING CHISHOLM COCKBAIN HAMBROGE HAMILTON HOMRETH KERR MCKAY MORGAN MORRISON Mylevoirrey PRICE ROBERTS SHIMMIN F3588

149306 MORGAN Mr Paul L. 4 Elmgate Gardens, Edgware, Middx, HA8 9RT. Tel:081-959-2836
BLORE CHAPMAN COLES HARRIS MORGAN OAKDEN PARKER PARR PAUL PITZ F1389

149314 MORGAN Mrs Rosemary Olivia. (Harvey) 31 St Davids Close, West Wickham, Kent, BR4 0QY.
HARVEY JAMES Lewes LEWIS WETTER F1197

149322 MORGAN Mr Roy. 12 Beacon Square, Emsworth, Hants, PO10 7HU.
ELLISON HILTON MORGAN NEILD REYNOLDS ROSS F3065

149330 MORGAN Mrs Sheila. 12 Beacon Square, Emsworth, Hants, PO10 7HU.
CLARKE FODEN HOPE LIGHTFOOT RHEAD ROWE WAINWRIGHT F3064

149349 MORGAN Mr Thomas E. 1716 Jamestown Place, Pittsburgh, PA 15235, USA. Tel:+1-412-371-6979
APPLEGATE BATTERSON GEORGE MCCULLOUGH MORGAN ROSS RUTHERFORD STEWART F6140

149357 MORING Mrs P D. (Hockey) 5 Vales Close, Sutton Coldfield, W Midlands, B76 8LJ. Tel:021-351-2291
CHANNELL FEHNERS GOODING HEWSON HICKS HOCKEY MAYO REES F4910

149365 MORLEY Mrs A J. 30 Briar Place, Eastbourne, E Sussex, BN23 8DB.
BAKER BARR GREEN RANSOM REARDON TUNNELL WELLS F477

149373 MORLEY Mrs A. (Hulme) Madrigal, Furnace Lane, Broad Oak, Brede, E Sussex, TN31 6ES.
BLABY CAYFORD COX HALFPENNY HARVEY HULME MACKERETH MORLEY OLLIS PARKS RICH F5919

149381 MORLEY Mr Gwilym Ryan. Welton, Queen Street, Spooner Row, Wymondham, Norfolk, NR18 9JN. Tel:0953-607627
MORLEY MORLYE F2527

149403 MORLEY Mrs Janet. (Henderson) 1 Hillbrow

Close, Wood Street Village, Guildford, Surrey, GU3 3DF. Tel:0483-235240
ANDERSON ARMSTRONG AVISON BARNETT BEATTIE BENNETT BENSTED BININGTON BINNINGTON BLUNT BROOK CARLTON CARR DANDRIDGE DAWSON DURRAN ELLIOTT FLETCHER FLIGHT GREEN HEDGES HENDERSON HINCHLIFFE HODGSON IRONSIDE IRONSIDES KING LUCOP MILBOURNE MORLEY MORRELL MUMFORTH PAYNE RHODES ROGERSON SHAW STOCKTON STORER WALKER WARD WILSON F2341

149411 MORLEY Mrs June. 8 Fairfield Road, Havant, Hants, PO9 1BA.
Linington LINNINGTON F7065

149438 MORLEY Mrs N W. Chart House, Bowesden Lane, Shorne, Kent, DA12 3LA.
ELLIOTT MAWBEY MIDDLEDITCH PATTENDEN F387

149446 MORNINGSTAR Mrs Beryl L. 30 Shrewsbury Street, Stratford, Ontario, N5A 2V5, CANADA.
ASQUE BECKHAM CHILD GIBBONS HEWITT HILLIER RADFORD SHINKFIELD F5621

149454 MORRELL Mr Andrew. 39 Hele Road, Torquay, Devon, TQ2 7PP. Tel:0803-311168
HALE HAMMOND LEITHAL MCMULLIN MORRELL SWEET WEBB F4593

149462 MORRELL Ms Vivienne. 37 Edinburgh Terrace, Wellington 2, NEW ZEALAND.
ALLSWORTH BURGE COULSON JONES MORRELL MORRIS RALPH READ SHECKELL TANKARD F5189

149470 MORREN Mr D G. 20 Hill Street, Kingston, Ontario, K7L 3M3, CANADA.
Morran MORREN Morrin O'morren F7208

149489 MORRIS Mrs Barbara. 74 Portsmouth Road, Camberley, Surrey, GU15 1JN.
AGNEW BASNETT DEANE DINNAGE GUY HARVEY HENWOOD HUGHES HURD JACKSON Kilberry Kilbery KILBURY Killberry LITTLEMORE MAYER MORRIS OWEN PATCHING RICE STAGG TOTTY WAREHAM Watley Whatley WILBRAHAM WILLSTEAD WOTTLEY F1122

149497 MORRIS Miss C A. 36 Church Street, Ground Floor Flat, Helston, Cornwall, TR13 8TQ.
Brealey Brearey BREARLEY CINDEREY DOUGHTY Doutty Hicken HICKIN Hicklin JONES Maurice Morrice MORRIS Morrish Morriss Tregoning TREGONNING Tregony Tyack Tyacke Tyacks TYERS F3715

149500 MORRIS Mr H D. 36 Mount Crescent, Pinewood Estate, Morriston, Swansea, SA6 6AP.
SYKES F4880

149519 MORRIS Mr H K. 6 Guardians Road, Patrington, Hull, N Humberside, HU12 0NX.
ABRAHALL BAKER BARGE BUTTERS ELLIS WALKER WOODS F6173

149527 MORRIS Mrs J F. 36 Southbank Road, Kenilworth, Warks, CV8 1LA.
GIBBS F6338

149535 MORRIS Mrs June. (Billingham) 25 The Glade, Furnace Green, Crawley, W Sussex, RH10 6JS.
BILLINGHAM CLEAVE STANESBY STANSBY STOPPANI F284

149543 MORRIS Mrs Kay. 62 Imperial Close, North Harrow, Middx, HA2 7LW.
FELLOWES HICKSON PENRY WHITTINGTON F2015

149551 MORRIS Mr Raymond. Bryn Goch, Christchurch, Aberbeeg, Gwent, NP3 2DB.
MILLS MORRIS OLDING F3479

149578 MORRIS Mrs Rita. 18 Briarswood, Springfield, Chelmsford, Essex, CM1 5UH.
BARNES BINGHAM CLARK CROUCH DOWNTON HARGRAVE HEWITT LEWIS LONDON MEAD MUGGLETON PAINE PAWLEY STACEY F4635

149586 MORRIS Mrs Valerie J A. (Price) Odessa, Bulls Lane, Wishaw, Sutton Coldfield, B76 9QN. Tel:021-351-5460
PRICE WHATTON F3514

149594 MORRIS Mr Walter A. 45 Syon Park Gardens, Osterley, Isleworth, Middx, TW7 5NE. Tel:081-560-2084
MORRIS F1522

149608 MORRISH Ms Adrienne. 5349 North Cliff Drive, Rocklin, CA 95677, USA. Tel:+1-916-624-8778
BADCOCK BILLINGS BUDD BURT Goyan Goyen GOYNE LANG LANKSBURY LEACH Leech Leich Michel Mitchel MITCHELL Morish Morrice MORRISH PROUT Stacey Stacie STACY Thom Thoms Tom TOMS TRATHEN Trattan Tratten F4481

149616 MORRISON Mrs Ann. Dornock House, Annan, Dumfriesshire, DG12 6SU. Tel:0461-40217
BRYSON CAW LOWTHER MORRISON SPALDING STIRLING F1410

149624 MORRISON Mrs Barbara E. (Drinkwater) Kipton Ash, Weasenham St Peter, Kings Lynn, Norfolk, PE32 2SZ.
BRACEWELL BULCOCKE DRINKWATER FOWLES HARTLEY HEMSLEY RILEY SMITHIES SUTCLIFFE F5771

149632 MORRISON Mrs Corona. (Sheppard) 4 Malba Place, Esperance, WA 6450, AUSTRALIA.
BENTLEY BLAND BUCHANAN CARTER CASSADY CRAWFORD EASTON FINLAY FOUNTAIN GARRETT GODKIN GOODBRAND HALE HATRICK LARY LOCKE LYND MCCOLLUM MENZIES MILLER MORRISON MUNE NICOLL RAE RENTON SHEPPARD STEEL THORNE WEBB WILSON F4447

149640 MORRISON Mr Edward. 35 Fern Towers, Harestone Hill, Caterham, Surrey, CR3 6SL.
Campion CHAMPION KENT MORRISON SLEEPER Snocks Snook SNOOKS Snouke Snoukes Snouks Stammer STAMMERS Stammus WAKE WASSELL F1092

149659 MORRISON Mr Geoffrey. 12 St Michaels Road, Broxbourne, Herts, EN10 7JL.
BELCHER GRINELL HINTON LOVEGROVE MILLER MORRISON PATRICK RIVERS SHEPHERD SMITHSON SPICKETT WILSON F5738

149667 MORRISON Mrs Pat. Rose Cottage, 1 Throop Road, Templecombe, Somerset, BA8 0HR.
BROAD KEMPTON F1421

149675 MORT Mrs K A. (Barker) 62 Stoney Lane, Weeke, Winchester, Hants, SO22 6DP. Tel:0962-882914
ALLEN BARKER Ficher Fischer FISHER Hobbes HOBBS Hobes Hobs Hoobes MARTIN MORT F1534

149683 MORTER Mr Ian. 60 Buxton Road, Chaddesden, Derby, DE2 4JL. Tel:0332-672985
ADAMS DAY DOMINY JONES MORTER NEWCOMBE F1948

149691 MORTIBOY Mr P N. 72 Uplands, Stevenage, Herts, SG2 7DW.
CHAMBERS CHAMNESS Champness Coombes COOMBS JELFES KIRBY Mortbois Morteboyce MORTIBOY Mortiboyes MORTIBOYS SEVIER WHATELEY F1749

149705 MORTIMER Mrs G. (Reeve) Fir Tree Farm, Metfield, Harleston, Norfolk, IP20 0LP.
BULLINGHAM CLARK Clarke Haward HOWARD LEONARD LOVICK MORTIMER REEVE ROBINETT WADE F5755

149713 MORTIMER Mrs Isobel. (Pullen) 54 Roseberry Avenue, Linsdale, Leighton Buzzard, Beds, LU7 7RQ.
AMOS DIX EVANS FREESTONE MORTIMER PULLEN RICHARDSON SINFIELD SOMES F3708

149721 MORTIMER Mrs Rochelle S. Clare House, Clare Road, Cromer, Norfolk, NR27 0DD. Tel:0263-511559
DYSON MASSINGHAM MORTIMER F1645

149748 MORTLOCK Mr H C. 40 Parkwood Road, Hastings, E Sussex, TN34 2RW. Tel:0424-753511
MORTLOCK F2016

149756 MORTON Mrs Catherine. 7 Westville Avenue, Ilkley, Yorks, LS29 9AH. Tel:0943-600815
CARIOLI DAGLEISH DALGLEISH MORTON F3131

149764 MORTON Mr Martin. 30 Hillway, London, N6 6HJ. Tel:081-340-5972
LEA MACFARLANE MORTON STROUD TURLEY F250

149772 MORTON Mr Richard. 40 The Rising, Billericay, Essex, CM11 2HN. Tel:0277-655593
BENT FLETCHER HAMER MORTON NEWBOLD Rodger RODGERS Rogers SHARPLES SHEPHARD TYSON WILCOCK Wilcox F6527

149780 MOSS Mr Alan. 11 New Street, Kirkeaton, Huddersfield, W Yorks, HD5 0DG.
FAIRHURST MARROW MOSS F3094

149799 MOSS Mrs Bridget H. (Knowles) 10 Strettitt Gardens, East Peckham, Tonbridge, Kent, TN12 5ES.
Knoles Knollys KNOWLES QUINEY Quinney Quiny RILEY THOMPSON F4596

149802 MOSS Mrs Dawn. 12 Gordon Avenue, Donnington, Chichester, W Sussex, PO19 2QY. Tel:0243-774824
Cuell Cuill Cule Keuell Kevel Kevell Kewel KEWELL Kewylle Kul F991

149810 MOSS Mr Geoffrey. 31 Orchard Road, Beacon Park, Plymouth, Devon, PL2 2QY.
BLAMEY CORNELIUS MOSS F5892

149829 MOSS Mrs Gill. 16 High Street, Stilton, Peterborough, Cambs, PE7 3RA. Tel:0733-244373

CASSELS LOBJOIT F4106
149837 MOSSOP Mrs S. 9 Rakeway, Saughall, Chester, CH1 6AZ.
Chrimes Chrymes CRIMES Crims Crymins Gregorey Gregorie GREGORY F1330
149845 MOTLEY Mrs Joyce. (Clough) 20 Boston Road, Spilsby, Lincolnshire, PE23 5HD. Tel:0790-52612
BLOIS CABORN CLOUGH COCKSEDGE COOKE COTTAM GRAVES HALLGATH METCALFE MOTLEY F603
149853 MOTT Mrs Elizabeth. 14 South View, Broadmayne, Dorchester, Dorset, DT2 8ET.
CHELL HAYLOCK F2853
149861 MOTT Mr John W. 71 Molesey Close, Hersham, Walton On Thames, Surrey, KT12 4PZ.
GILBERT HORWOOD MOTT F2254
149888 MOTTERSHEAD Mrs Barbara. 44 The Green, Southwick, Sussex, BN42 4FR.
BOOK BOONE BRAY BURNETT CAINS CALLUM CLARKE COLES COOMBE CROSSMAN CRUDGE DEACON FISHER FULIAMES GARLAND GIMLETT HADDY HALL HAWKEN HOSKING HUMPHRIES HURFORD JONES KIMBER LAWRENCE LINES PERRY PETERFIELD PETT PHELPS POMEROY READE REEP ROGERS Ruegg RUGG SMITH SOADY SPEAR STEPHENS SWEET TOWNSEND WATERS WILLIAMS WILTON F2644
149896 MOULD Mr Clifford. 4 Manor Court, 25 Avenue Elmers, Surbiton, Surrey, KT6 4SH. Tel:081-390-0099
GARNER Mole MOULD F5715
149918 MOULD Mrs L A. (Madden) 104 Greenway Lane, Warsash, Southampton, Hants, SO3 9HS.
ASHLEY BARTON CHARLES FARMER JONES MADDEN MOULD SAMWELLS SWINDEN TURNER F3865
149926 MOULDER Mr M D. 49 Earlstock Close, Crownhill, Plymouth, Devon, PL6 5QN.
MOULDER F6667
149934 MOULE Mr Jocelyn. 10c Charlotte Street, Cabot, Bristol, BS1 5PX. Tel:0272-272570
COSSHAM KINDERSLEY Mold Molde MOLE Moul MOULD Moulde MOULE PARSABLE F3237
149942 MOULES Mrs Ann M. (Rhodes) 14 Fenwicks Lane, Fulford, York, YO1 4PL. Tel:0904-658239
MOULES RIPPON UTTON WILLIS F5120
149950 MOULIN Mrs Faith. 33 Court Avenue, Yatton, Bristol, BS19 4EP.
DAWSON MOSS REEKS SYMONS WHITCHER F4539
149969 MOULTON Mrs D E. (Freeman) 37 Severns Field, Epping, Essex, CM16 5AP. Tel:0378-75469
FREEMAN HASKELL QUINNELL WATTS F903
149977 MOUNSEY Ms S C. 57 Romsey Road, Winchester, Hants, SO22 5DE.
BOWATER BRADBURY CARTWRIGHT CRADDOCK CRUTCHLEY DAVIES EARDLEY ELEMENT HAYNES HICKMANS HILTON KINSEY LEA LENCH LIVERSAGE MOORE MORREY MOUNSEY PARKER PEPLOW PRICE PRITCHETT QUINTON REEVES THURSFIELD WARD WESTWOOD WILSON F2982
149985 MOUNTAIN Mrs Alida M. 3 White Horse Close, Longford, Coventry, Warks, CV6 6NE.
GRANT ISBISTER MOUNTAIN F6477
149993 MOUNTFORD Mr Basil W. 3 Bowen Close, Bramhall, Stockport, Cheshire, SK7 1NJ.
BASS CAPNER CLARKE COLDICOTT COLEBROOKE COOKE ELLIS GREGORY HATCHER HUMBER KIMBER KNIGHT LANCASHIRE Lankester Montford MOON MOUNTFORD Mountfort PRYCE Rhoden RICHARDS Riches Ridges RODEN WALTON WHEELER F1703
150002 MOUNTFORD Mrs P M. 3 Bowen Close, Bramhall, Stockport, Cheshire, SK7 1NJ.
BEATON DAMBY DOOLITTLE FORDRED GILL HARVEY HOILE HOLLAND MEESON MILNE SHUTTLEWORTH Sim SIME Simes Simm Sym Symm THOMASON TOLLEY WEBSTER WHITE WOOLLARD WRIGHT WYATT F1704
150010 MOURANT Mrs Anne. (Turner) Little Mead, Claremont Road, St Saviour, Jersey, JE2 7RT. Tel:0534-34948
DUFFETT TURNER F4932
150029 MOWAT Mr J A S. 17 Culland View, Crich, Matlock, Derbyshire, DE4 5DA.
FINDLAY FLEEMING GEMMEL GUNN KERR MOWAT STEVENSON WILSON F6397
150037 MOWATT Mr A. Rr #1, Fergus, Ontario, N1M 2W3, CANADA.
MOWAT F7319
150045 MOWBRAY Mr David. 17 The Close, Coaley, Dursley, Glous, GL11 5EP. Tel:0453-890553
MOUBRAY MOWBERRY MOWBRAY F119
150053 MOWER Mrs Judith. 114 St Margarets Road, Lowestoft, Suffolk, NR32 4HN.
BAILEY BIRD GRAMMER JENKERSON MANE MONK SAMPSON WILLMOTT F2137
150061 MOWFORTH Dr Clive. 13 Jubilee Road, Kingshill, Dursley, Glos, GL11 4ES. Tel:0453-548920
BURROWS HEYWOOD HOPKINSON MOWFORTH SAWYER SNEESTON SUTCLIFFE F4258
150088 MOXEY Mr John. Summer Winds, Paradise, Boscastle, Cornwall, PL35 0AW. Tel:0840-250327
Mockcy Mockey Mocksay Moxay Moxcay Moxcey Moxe MOXEY Moxhae Moxhay Moxhaye Moxhey Moxie Moxley Moxsay Moxsaye Moxsey Moxseye Moxsie Moxsy Moxsye Moxxey Moxy Moxye Moxzay Moxzie Moxzye Mucksay Muoxhey F3548
150096 MOXON Mr D. 15 Dorothy Hodgkin Court, Beccles, Suffolk, NR34 9XN. Tel:0502-712832
BROWN CLARKSON HOWSON HUDSON LEVITT MOXON PLOWS TURTON F5852
150118 MOYLE Mrs Sheila A. (Ryder) Menerdue Farm, Carnmenellis, Redruth, Cornwall, TR16 6PE. Tel:0209-860512
BEAN BILBROUGH DAVEY HIRST KING MASTERSON MYERS RYDER TAYLOR F4825
150126 MOYLE Mr Terry. Trenoweth, Dartford Road, South Darenth, Dartford Kent, DA4 9HY. Tel:0322-862368
CURNOW EADE EXELBY HARRIS JAMES MARTIN MOYLE NICHOLLS RETALLACK TRIPCONY F2344
150134 MUELLER Mr Frank P. 2317 Riverbluff Parkway #249, Sarasota, FL 34231, USA.
Burdet BURDICK Burdit F7245
150142 MUGFORD Mrs S K. (Blamey) Treveor Farm, St Michael Penkivel, Truro, Cornwall, TR2 4AF.
BLAMEY MUGFORD ROBERTS SYMONS TRUDGEON Trudgian F4543
150150 MUGGLETON Mr R A L. 116 Mere Road, Wigston, Leicester, LE8 1RL.
ADAMS BAKER BATCHELOR BATE BOWLER BRETON BURDETT CASSELDINE CHENEY CHESTER CLARKE COLEMAN DURHAM EVERARD FALKNER GILBY GLADWIN GOULD HUNT LOLE MANSELL MELLARD MUGGLETON NOBLE PARKER RANDALL RASTALL RAWBONE ROBINSON RONALDS SHARMAN SHERRARD SWANSON WHITING WILLCOX YORK F4682
150169 MUKERJI Mrs Jenny. 1 Elsdon Road, Goldsworth Park, Woking, Surrey, GU21 3NX.
ADAMS ALEXANDER AYTO BAKER BLANCHARD COLES GOODCHILD IVEY NIXON F805
150177 MULES-BERRY Mr A W. White House Bungalow, Saltburn Lane, Saltburn By Sea, Cleveland, TS12 1HA.
Meulles Mewles Moels Molis Mule MULES Mulys F7036
150185 MULLETT Mrs Anita. (D'Arcy) 16 Trent Crescent, Melksham, Wiltshire, SN12 8BG. Tel:0225-703667
D'ARCY MULLETT PORTER SCOTT WOODWARD F3432
150193 MULLETT Miss M E. 273 Eltham High Street, London, SE9 1TY. Tel:081-850-5697
MULLETT F4967
150207 MULLEY Mrs P R. 5 Viceroy Close, Colchester, Essex, CO2 8BQ.
BANHAM MULLEY Mully F6814
150215 MULLICE Mr J. 17 Camp Road, Gosport, Hants, PO13 0XU.
BELL BEMEY FORD GREEN HARRIS Mules Mulles MULLICE Mullies Mullis Mulliss Mullize Mullys Mulys PICKENGILL TAYLOR F4516
150223 MULLINS Mrs Pamela. 62 Frosthole Crescent, Fareham, Hants, PO15 6BD.
ADAMS DYER FARWELL FLEMING GURD HIBBERD MASTERMAN MULLINS SKEY TRUE F4280
150231 MULLISS Mr John. 6 Little Woodlands, Windsor, Berks, SL4 3RF.
Hullice Hullious Hullis Hulliss MULLIS PELLS F4767
150258 MULVEY Mr D. 22 Cranberry Road, Partington, Manchester, M31 4FQ.
MULVEY F7422
150266 MUNDAY Mr A. The Laurels, 92 Countess Road, Amesbury, Salisbury, Wiltshire, SP4 7AT.

Tel:0980-623914
LEAT TOON Toone Toones Toons Towan Towen TOWN Towne Townes Towns TUNE Tunes F5911

150274 MUNDAY Mr P J. 82 Paygrove Lane, Longlevens, Gloucester, GL2 0BG.
TOPE F2061

150282 MUNIS Mrs D. 3 Bessie Street, East Bentleigh, VIC 3165, AUSTRALIA.
CITTIL CLARKE DAVIES DOHERTY MARSH MIRK PINE RIDDIFORD SPENCER F5507

150290 MURFITT Mrs Patricia A. (Hudson) Pytts House, Church Lane, Fulbrook, Burford, Oxon, OX18 4BA. Tel:0993-823193
HUDSON MURFITT MURFOOT MURPHEY F6094

150304 MURGATROYD Mrs Marjorie. 5 Park Crescent, Gildersome, Morley, W Yorks, LS27 7EA. Tel:0532-535790
BEDFORD BROOK BROUGH LACE LEE QUAYLE F2491

150312 MURIE Mr David J B. 2 Liff Park, Liff, Dundee, DD2 5PH.
BISSETT BOYD LEITH MCKAY MCMILLAN MCPHAIL MURIE ROLLO ROY F3078

150320 MURLEY Mr Fred. Apple Cottage, 3 School Road, Hythe, Southampton, Hants, SO4 6BJ. Tel:0703-840454
BOWER BOWERS BUCKINGHAM CROSS DOWN GRENFELL MURLEY NORTHCOTT ROBINS TREZONA F936

150339 MURPHY Mr D W. Elgstien 34, 4600 Kristiansand S, NORWAY.
Thaik THAKE Theak F6630

150347 MURPHY Mrs Evelyn M. 10 Fairways, Dilton Marsh, Westbury, Wiltshire, BA13 3RU.
AGER BROOKES CRAWFORD EARP Erp LEADBETTER LIVERSEDGE MADDOCKS Maddox MURPHY TILT TRAVERS WILLINGTON F2339

150355 MURPHY Mrs H M. 36 Cardinal Avenue, St Budeaux, Plymouth, Devon, PL5 1UW.
GOLDSWORTHY MADDY MUNN F2031

150363 MURRAY Mrs E C. 15 Galashiels Road, Stow, Galashiels, Selkirkshire, TD1 2RQ.
CHRISHOLM PRINGLE WADDELL WATSON F5012

150371 MURRAY Mr John R. 30 Havis Road, Stanford Le Hope, Essex, SS17 8ET. Tel:0375-670887
ARMSTRONG BROWN DAVIDSON DOBIE DOUGLAS DUNCAN EDGAR FORRESTER GASS GRIEVE HALLIDAY JACKSON JOHNSON KYLE LILLICO LITTLE MURRAY PATTISON PENMAN RUTHERFORD SCOTT STOREY WAUGH WILSON F5408

150398 MURRAY Mrs Marjorie. (Sore) 48 Keldholme, Wildridings, Bracknell, Berkshire, RG12 7RP.
FULLER Soar Soare Soer SORE SUTTON SWAISLAND Swaseland TOWNSEND TURNAGE WALTER Walters WEAR Weare F4540

150401 MURRAY Mr Walter Weir. 209 Palomino Drive, Oakdale, PA 15071-9315, USA.
BARRAS GRAY MURRAY TURNER F6551

150428 MURRAY Mr William T. 29 Stobshaw Terrace, Tweedbank, Galashiels, Selkirkshire, TD1 3RN. Tel:0896-55329
TANNAHILL F2312

150436 MURRELLS Mr Donovan John. 428 Bedonwell Road, Abbey Wood, London, SE2 0SE. Tel:081-310-6773
Merrell Merrells MURRELL MURRELLS Murrill Murrills F27

150444 MURTELL Mr A T. Flat B, 58 Kensington Gardens, Ilford, Essex, IG1 3EL. Tel:081-554-6388
HONEYWELL Martell Mertell Mirtell MURTELL Myrtle F1848

150452 MUSK Mr D J. 8 Bristol Road, Bury St Edmunds, Suffolk, IP33 2DL.
MUSK Muske Must Muste F6780

150460 MUSPRATT Mr David. Spring House, Mill Hill, Alresford, Hants, SO24 9DD.
Masprat Maspratt Misprat Mispratt Mosbrate Mospert Mosprat Mospratt Mossprat Mousprat Mursprat Musbert Muserate Mushprat Mushrat Mushratt Muspard Muspart Muspered Musperet Muspert Muspirt Musprate MUSPRATT Muspret Musprett Muspritt Musprot Musprote Musprotte Musprout Muspurt Muspurte Mussprat Musspratt Mustprat Mustpratt Mustrap Mustrop Mustrope Mustsprat Mustsprit F3959

150479 MUSTOE Mrs P K. 52 Garth Drive, Chester, CH2 2AG. Tel:0244-380250
ARNOLD ASHTON DOBSON GATHERCOLE GOUGH HANDERIN JELLEY JONES MADDERN Musto MUSTOE SLAUGHTER WALKER F4719

150487 MUSTON Mrs Theresa M. 2 Alma Green, Stoke Row, Henley On Thames, Oxon, RG9 5RB.
ACLAND CONEYBEARE MILTON RIORDAN WATKINS F574

150495 MUTLOW Mrs J S. 8 Isaacs Road, Barton, Torquay, Devon, TQ2 8NB.
CLEMSON HARDY MUTLOW SYMONS VENN F4766

150509 MUZEEN Mr Robert. 54 Goodliffe Gardens, Tilehurst, Reading, Berks, RG3 6FZ. Tel:0734-426774
MOZEEN MUZEEN F2387

150517 MYALL Mr P. 54 Yew Tree Close, Yeovil, Somerset, BA20 2PD.
MIGHILL MIHILL MYALL STARLEY F1443

150525 MYLAM Mr Cyril A. 87 Wansunt Road, Bexley, Kent, DA5 2DJ. Tel:0322-523350
GARLING Milam MILEHAM Millham MYLAM F1068

150533 MYNOTT Martin. 20 Pasquier Road, London, E17 6HB.
MYNOTT F7388

150541 NADIN Revd Dennis Lloyd. 79 Bishopsfield, Harlow, Essex, CM18 6UN. Tel:0279-430176
HAMER HARRISON JONES LLOYD NADEN NADIN NADON NAIDEN NAYDEN NEDEN Neyden YARWOOD F341

150568 NAIRN Mr George. 77 Primrose Crescent, Dalkeith, Midlothian, EH22 2JR. Tel:031-663-3821
Alders Aldhous Aldhouse Aldhowse Aldis Aldous ALDUS Alduse Alldiss Audas Awdas Awdis Awdus Mcnairn Mcnairna Mcnairne Naern Naerne NAIRN Nairne Nairon Narn Narne Narryn Neaum Neorne Oldis Orders Skelden Skelding SKELDON TATE F3678

150576 NAISH Mrs Sandra. 77 Athelstan Road, Bitterne, Southampton, Hants, SO2 4DE.
BAKER BARRATT BURTON CALLEN FURNELL Stingermore Stingjemor Stinjamore STINJEMOR VINEY F4289

150584 NALDER Mr Adrian. 14 Willow Way, Ferndown, Wimborne, Dorset, BH22 9SR. Tel:0202-891191
MERCER NALDER F456

150592 NANCARROW Mr Arthur. Higher Castle Farm, Trematon, Saltash, Cornwall, PL12 4QW. Tel:0752-843783
NANCARROW F2599

150606 NANKIVELL Mr Edmund. 9 Robina Lodge, Station Road, Preston Park, Brighton, BN1 6SF. Tel:0273-504979
Nankeval NANKIVELL Nanscuval Nanskievel Nanskivell F475

150614 NAPTHINE Mrs Betty. (Vernon) Milestone, Hoads Hill, Wickham, Hampshire, PO17 5BX. Tel:0329-833234
ALEXANDER ALLMAN BASNETT BOARDMAN BODEN BOULTER BRISCALL BRUCE CARTWRIGHT COOPER CROXFORD CUMMINS DARLINGTON DUNN DUTTON EADE FURMSTON HASSALL HICKMAN Naphthen Napkin Napten Napthen NAPTHINE Napthing PICKERING PRESTON RAVENSCROFT VERNON WADE WILLIS F3568

150622 NARRACOTT Mr John K. 89 The Greenway, Ickenham, Middx, UB10 8LX. Tel:0895-633646
LASKEY F2255

150630 NASH Mrs E R. (Collins) 203 Little Bushey Lane, Bushey, Herts, WD2 3RZ. Tel:081-950-2006
COLLINS COTTON HYSLOP KEYS KITCHENER NASH WARNER F4676

150649 NASH Mrs Janet. (Runagall) 13 Upper Shott, Cheshunt, Herts, EN7 6DR.
RUNACLE RUNAGALL F1276

150657 NASH Mrs Prue. 17 Haglane Copse, Lymington, Hants, SO4 8DT. Tel:0590-673427
BULLEY DRYDEN ENDACOTT HANCOCK HOCKING HOSKEN NORTHCOTT YABSLEY F2488

150665 NASON Mr H E. Fredericton R R No 10, Beaverdam, New Brunswick, E3B 6H6, CANADA.
NASON Nasson Nassone Nassonne F7193

150673 NAULTY Denis. 339 Kingsway, Dundee, DD3 8LQ. Tel:0382-84730
DONACHIE MCGUCKIN MCVEIGH NAULTY F2408

150681 NAYLOR Mrs Pat. (Hughes) 13 Hazelhurst Road, Burnham, Bucks, SL1 8EE. Tel:0628-660375
BROWNLEE BRYANT GILMURRAY GLOVER GUNN HOBBS HOLMES HUGHES NAYLOR TOPLEY F4343

150703 NEALE Miss Janice. 5 Melbourne Road,

Wallington, Surrey, SM6 8SF. Tel:081-647-9369 JARVIS Josclen Joslen Joslin JOSLING Joslyn Neal NEALE ROBINSON F5994

150711 NEALE Mr Kenneth John. 10 Oak Street, Gelli Pentre, Rhondda, Mid Glamorgan, CF41 7NP. Tel:0443-430997
BELL HODGE NEALE F4329

150738 NEATH Mr Richard. 2 Harpley Road, Defford, Worcester, WR8 9BL. Tel:0386-750380
BLUNN COVERLEY KNOTT MCKELL NEATH TIPTUN F4410

150746 NEECH Mrs S E. 114 The Street, Rockland St Mary, Norwich, NR14 7HQ.
Neach Nech Neche NEECH Neeche Nich Niche Nyche F7014

150754 NEEDHAM J R. Deputy Directors Bungalow, Alsager College Of Higher Education, Alsager, Stoke On Trent, ST7 2HL. Tel:0270-873847
Nedham NEEDHAM F3377

150762 NEEDLE Mrs Thelma. 52 Richmond Road, Abergavenny, Gwent, NP7 5RE. Tel:0873-852650
AVERY BATCHELOR BLANCHARD BROWN DOWDING DRISCOLL GOUGH HARDING HYDE JUKES KINNERSLEY LANGFORD MITCHELL NEEDLE PLASTER POOLE SMITH STEAD THOMAS TROTMAN WITHERS F266

150770 NEELAND Mr John Robert. 2 Nw 41st Terrace, Kansas City, MO 64116-1759, USA.
Kneeland Kneland Nealand NEELAND Neelands Neland Newland Neyland F7326

150789 NEESHAM Mr G F. 6 Arbutus Close, Dorchester, Dorset, DT1 1PZ.
Meesham Neasham NEESHAM Nesham F2791

150797 NEGUS Mrs Christina. (Batty) 27 Chadwick Avenue, Rednal, Birmingham, B45 8ED. Tel:021-453-4458
Allist Alliste Allys Alys Batte Battey Battie BATTY Battye Bower Bowyer BOYER ELLIS Ellys FORREST Forret GRAY GRIFFIN KING Kinge Kynge NEGUS OLDERSHAW Pidgin Piggen Piggin Pigging Piggings PIGGINS ROSS TINDALE Tindall Tindell Tindle Tyndale Valance Valence Vallance VALLENCE Vallens WALKER Woddle Woodal WOODALL Wooddall Woodle F3446

150800 NEIGHBOUR Mr Michael K. 27 Knutsford Avenue, Watford, Herts, WD2 4EQ. Tel:0923-244907
HOCKING MILBURN NEIGHBOUR SCANTLEBURY SEABROOK SHILCOCK SIMMONS SYDNEY F673

150819 NEIL Mr William. 11 Chequers Road, Chorlton, Manchester, M21 1DX.
FERAN FERN NEIL RAMSEY F6084

150827 NEILL Mrs Norma C. Colywell, Commonside, Westwoodside, Doncaster, DN9 2AR. Tel:0427-752692
CALLUM CRUISE Ealam ELAM Ellam Ellom Ellum HESLIN KENDALL LLOYD F388

150835 NEILLEY Doreen. Glenelg, Moura, Queensland, AUSTRALIA.
BELL FORWOOD FREEMAN HARVEY HEAVENOR HIGGINS MCKENZIE MCPHEARSON MOLLOY NEILLEY NOBLE SMYTH F5423

150843 NELLIST Mrs Joyce. Marsham Lane House, Marsham Lane, Gerrards Cross, Bucks, SL9 8HD.
BRECKON CONYARD Coolin Coulin Couling COWLING DURRANT EGGLESTON Fennick FENWICK Gillens GILLIATT GILLINGS GRASBY HARLAND HOLDERNESS HUMPHREY Jellings LEADLEY LOWTHER MATTHEWS MAWER MELBOURNE MILEHAM NELLIST NOBBS PRUDOM SHREEVE SISSONS WARNES F2815

150851 NELSON Dr Geoffrey. 32 Clun Road, Northfield, Birmingham, B31 1NU. Tel:021-475-5329
BENTON FARROW NELSON PITCHER RAINEY Ranye F6316

150878 NELSON Mrs J. 127 Mandeville Road, Aylesbury, Bucks.
BEECHENO Bircheno F6790

150886 NELSON Mrs Joan. 2 The Whistlers, St Ives, Huntingdon, Cambs, PE17 6EE.
Ayre Ayres BROWNING CLEMENTS Comberlege Comberlidge Comblidge Cumberlege Cumberlidge CUMBLIDGE Cumlege Eayre EKINS EYRE Hair Hare KING NELSON PAGE F3799

150894 NELSON Mrs Joy. (Robson) 52 Eleventh Street, Parkhurst, Johannesburg, 2193, SOUTH AFRICA. Tel:+27-11-788-7470
ARNALL BOYS COWLING EWELL FEATONBY MOORE MUDDLE PAUL ROBSON F4491

150908 NELSON Ms Judith. 1603 Mill Creek Road, Manahawkin, New Jersey, 08050, USA.
Polan POLAND Polland Powland F7127

150916 NESBIT Mr John. 6 Grasmere Avenue, Sutton Coldfield, West Midlands, B74 3DG.
CONYERS DORRINGTON NESBIT F3691

150924 NESBITT Mr Bob. Carie Old Manse, Lawers, Aberfeldy, Perthshire, PH15 2PB. Tel:05672-773
ASKEW BARTLEY DOVE-SMITH NESBITT RIDLEY-SMITH SCOTT SMITH THOMPSON WILSON F5792

150932 NESFIELD Mrs Susan. (Thompson) 64 Shelton Avenue, East Ayton, Scarborough, N Yorks, YO13 9HB.
Fatherston Fatherstone Fatterstone Featherston FEATHERSTONE Fetherston Fetherstone Hornee Hornesey Hornsay Hornsaye Hornsea HORNSEY Hornsie Hornsy Knisfield Nasfield Nashfylde Nastfeild Nastfield Nesfeald Nesfeeld Nesfeld Nesfelde Nesfelld NESFIELD Nessfield Nestfield Nisfield Tetherston THOMPSON Thomson Tomeson Tompson Tomson F6382

150940 NETCOTT Mrs D P. Addington House, The Village, Burrington, Bristol Avon, BS18 7AD.
BARR COLES HARMER Natcott NETCOTT Notcott Notcutt Tather Teather Tethe TETHER Tetther Tither F2429

150959 NETHERCOTT Mr Arnold W. 1310 Brydges St, London, Ontario, N5W 2C4, CANADA.
Neathercot Neathercotte Neithercot Neithercote Neithercott Neithercut Neithercutt Nethercoat Nethercoate Nethercoats Nethercot Nethercote NETHERCOTT Nethercut Nethercutt F6628

150967 NEUHOFER Mr Keith. Small Oaks, Doles Lane, Wokingham, Berks, RG11 4EB. Tel:0734-790296
BEECHEY DE L'AUNE DE NOYERS MAROLLEAU NEUHOFER PAROISSIEN F1405

150975 NEVILLE Mrs Deidre F. (Luke) 30 Musgrave Avenue, East Grinstead, W Sussex, RH19 4BS. Tel:0342-325257
Attwell Atwell BAILEY BATSON BROWN De Gryndenham GREENHAM Greneham Grenham Grinham Gryndeham Gryndenham HOCKEY LUKE Nevil Nevile NEVILLE POPE SOUTHWOOD F2214

150983 NEVILLE Mr Edward D. 1 Shaves Lane, New Milton, Hants, BH25 5DJ.
APPS BRAXTON DERING FOREMAN GREEN HUNT JACKMAN KNIGHT MOORE NANCARROW NEVILL NEVILLE RUSSELL WELLS WEST WORLIDGE F2694

150991 NEVILLE-JONES Mrs S F. Audlem House, 68 Blake Hill Crescent, Lilliput, Poole, Dorset, BH14 8QS. Tel:0202-700355
IRVINE IRVING F4739

151009 NEVILLE-TOWLE Cdr Felix. Badnam Cottage, High Street, Bursledon, Southampton, Hants, SO3 8DJ. Tel:0703-403271
NEVILLE TOWLE F6304

151017 NEVITT Mr T J. 123 Friary Road, Peckham, London, SE15 1PY. Tel:071-639-6827
CORNFORD DYER ELAN GARNER HORLOCK NEVITT THURLEY F5793

151025 NEW Mr R L. 139 Cubbington Road, Leamington Spa, Warks, CV32 7AP. Tel:0926-425915
CHURCH EDEN HARRIS NEW F230

151033 NEWARK Mrs Mary E. Trequite, 40 St Marwenne Close, Marhamchurch, Bude Cornwall, EX23 0HX. Tel:0288-361508
JUTSUM NEWARK PARKER STEVENS F1083

151041 NEWBERY Mrs L M. (Griffiths) 13 Norwood House, Pennsylvania Road, Exeter, EX4 6TR.
BOWEN Cowan COWEN CUNLIFFE DAWSON DERRY HOWELL WEBSTER WILSON WRAY F3785

151068 NEWCOMB Mr James E. 37 Crosby Road, Birkdale, Southport, Merseyside, PR8 4TE. Tel:0704-68475
CARLING JOHNSON JONES NEWCOMB POPPLEWELL TEWKESBURY WALLBANK F6276

151076 NEWELL Mr Michael John. 19 Glamis Road, Newquay, Cornwall, TR7 2RY.
LANYON NEWELL F4629

151084 NEWENS Mr A S. The Leys, 18 Park Hill, Harlow, Essex, CM17 0AE. Tel:0279-420108
BRUNT CALCOT Calcott Callcot Callcott CAULCOT Caulcott CLARK CLOSE FRITH FURSEDON Fursedonn

Furssedon Furssedonn HARDING HONEY MOORE Newans Newen NEWENS Newin Newins PENNANT POWELL ROGERS SHEEN SHERRATT SWAIN YOUNGER F3181

151092 NEWHAM Mr Kenneth. 23 The Drive, Morden, Surrey, SM4 6DH.
BASS Baycroft BEACROFT BEAZLEY Becroft Beecroft BENTON BUTTENSHAW Buttinshaw Buttonshaw DENGATE Deverson DEVESON Devison GRANLEESE Granlese Granleze Granlise HICKS LARKIN MCCANN Neuham Newam NEWHAM Newum O'BRIEN PEISLEY POPE SWAN Whiddington WHITCOMBE WHITTINGTON Witcom Witcombe F3859

151106 NEWLANDS Mrs Noreen. (East) 97 Stamford Park Road, Mt Roskill, Auckland, 1004, NEW ZEALAND. Tel:+64-9-659-648
BARCLAY BRECHIN BROOMFIELD CHILCOTT CHRISTER EAST FOGGIN KIRKLAND OATES POWELL F4484

151114 NEWMAN Mr A E. 155 Laverock Avenue, Richmond Hill, Ontario, L4C 4K1, CANADA.
NEWMAN F7328

151122 NEWMAN Mrs Elsie G. (Cook) 11 Horndean Close, Roehampton, London, SW15 4BE. Tel:081-788-4221
COOK F3579

151130 NEWMAN Mr James Bernard Havard. 4 Pullar Court, Bridge Of Allan, Stirling, Scotland, FK9 4SS. Tel:0786-833760
ARNOTT HAVARD KEITH NEWMAN F1632

151149 NEWMAN Mrs M. 10 Hasluck Gardens, Barnet, Herts, EN5 1HT.
CANSICK Chusick Kansick F6803

151157 NEWMAN Mr Paul L. 3 Red House Lane, Leiston, Suffolk, IP16 4JZ.
GWINNELL HAY LAWRENCE NEWMAN NEWMAN F3806

151165 NEWMAN Mr Sheridan L. 275 Woodgrange Drive, Southend On Sea, Essex, SS1 2SQ. Tel:0702-466146
BRIDGE COTTON EVERITT FREEMAN GOLDSTONE MAYNARD NEWMAN PAYNE WALLAKER Wisbey WISBY F4207

151173 NEWNES Mrs Frances. 46 Waveney Road, Hunstanton, Norfolk, PE36 5DQ.
FLINT NEWNES NORTH PHILLIPS POXTON TWYMAN F1118

151181 NEWTON Mr Charles A. 6 Yeatmans Close, Enmore Green, Shaftesbury, Dorset, SP7 8LU.
BISHOP BROADFOOT DUNDON GROOM HACKET HOPKINS MESSENGER NEWTON PADDISON PRIOR RAY Sharp SHARPE STUBBS F1419

151203 NEWTON Mr Derek. 62 Egerton Road North, Chorlton Cum Hardy, Manchester, M21 1SQ. Tel:061-881-6648
CORNEY HALL NEWTON F4056

151211 NEWTON Mrs L E. (Marwood) Meadow View, Chestnut Avenue, Bucknall, Lincoln, LN3 5DU.
ASH BEE CLAY Coals COLES COWHAM CUMBERWORTH HOUSEHAM Housham Howsam Mariot Marod Marriott Marrod Marrot Marrott MARWOOD MASSEY TIDSWELL MURDEN Murdin NEWTON SANDERSON Storey STORY THISTLETON F6231

151238 NEWTON Mr Laurence. 14 Roffrey Avenue, Hampden Park, Eastbourne, E Sussex, BN22 0AE.
ANDREWS ELLIS HOARE Hooar Hore MILLER NEWTON REAL ROBERTSON Royal Ryal SPILLER F463

151246 NEWTON Mrs Rosemary D. 6 Yeatmans Close, Enmore Green, Shaftesbury, Dorset, SP7 8LU.
DEADMAN HOOK KENWOOD MARTIN METLAND MUGGERIDGE STAPLEY TOMPSETT TWORT WOODGATE F1420

151254 NEWTON Mrs Susan. (White) 10 Hornyold Road, Malvern, Worcs, WR14 1QQ. Tel:0684-563671
BROTHWELL DANIEL DAWSON GARNER GILFOYLE HAUGHTON HOUGH HULME Kilfoyle LEYLAND LYTHGOE Morison MORRISON OTTIWELL PETTIT SUTCLIFFE WHITE WILSON F4416

151262 NEX Mr L W M. 30 Meadowside, Sandford, Crediton, Devon, EX17 4NN.
NEX F5222

151270 NEYLAN Mrs Edith. (Scotney) 96 Mein Street, Scarborough, Queensland, 4020, AUSTRALIA. Tel:+61-7-203-6016
ATKINS BARRY BROWN BUTCHER DARKER ELLIS FINNEGAN GOULDING GUDGE HARRISON HAYES HYLAND KENNEDY KILMINSTER MACHINDER MCFARLANE MONAGHAN NEYLAN POPPLE RAWSON RYAN SCOTNEY SEXTON SHAW SMITH SPEARING SPEECHLEY STIRLING YEATMAN YORE F5485

151289 NICE Mr A. Waterpark, Holsworthy, Devon, EX22 6LZ.
NICE F7329

151297 NICHOLAS Mr P J. 25 Sarnfan, Baglan, Port Talbot, West Glamorgan, SA12 8DY. Tel:0639-881490
BARRELL BOON CURRIE CURRY DAVIS ENOCH FOLLEY FOLLY FOUND FRANCIS GRIFFITHS JENKIN Jenkins JONES KEY LEWIS MURRAY NICHOLAS PHILLIPS SUFF WATKINS WILLIAM Williams F1992

151300 NICHOLAS Mr Peter. Hilltop Cottage, Hillview Road, Loxton, Axbridge, Somerset, BS26 2XJ.
BARRIBALL CRISP GOODWIN HARTWELL JEFFCOTT JOHNSON LANGTON NICHOLAS F6462

151319 NICHOLLS Mr David. 59 Furze Road, Worthing, Sussex, BN13 3BH.
BLADES GIDDINGS HILL KIDD LONGTHORN NICHOLLS OAKES TERRY WATSON WHITTME F404

151327 NICHOLLS Mrs E M. 27 Eynsford Road, Greenhithe, Kent, DA9 9HB. Tel:0322-383244
BARBER FRANKLIN KEMP KEMSLEY KING MEAL Meale Meel Meele NICHOLLS NICHOLS SMITH SPRAY Treadle TREADWELL Treddell Treddle Tredwell Treedle Truddle F1406

151335 NICHOLLS Mr Stephen. 47 Langland Drive, White Cross, Hereford, HR4 0QG.
COMLEY LEWIS NICHOLLS SAYELL F1109

151343 NICHOLSON Miss Annette. 72 Kiln Lane, Milnrow, Rochdale, Lancs, OL16 3JN.
MACK Mackay MARSHALL MCDONAL Mcdonald MCKAY MELLOR NICHOLSON Nickleson PHILLIPS WADDINGTON F4013

151351 NICHOLSON Mr John. 25 Brunwin Road, Rayne, Braintree, Essex, CM7 5BU. Tel:0376-49742
ADAM ADDAMS ATKINSON BAKER BARKER BARRETT BARSON BLANCHARD BROWN CARNEEY CARTER CHALKER CHURCHILL CLARK Clarke CLARKSON CLIFF COCKSHUT COLLETT CUTTING DARBY DAVIES DAVIS DAY DEVERAL DEWES DICKINSON EDERINGTON EGLESTONE ERSKINE EYRES FLEETHAM GIBBS GILBERT GILL GROVES HAWXWELL HOSKINS INGLIS JARRETT JENKINS KERSHAW KING KNOWLES LAMB LAMBERT MARCH MEE NEWMAN NICHOLSON OCHTERLONY PEEL PIKE POOL POOLE POUNCE PRESSLEY PRESTON ROBINSON ROSE RYDER SCOT SERGEANT SHARP Sharpe SMITH SPENCER STEVENSON STRACHAN SUTTON VAUGHAN VINCENT WAITE WATKINSON WATSON WILKS WRIGHT F5750

151378 NICHOLSON Mr Ken. 13 Kingswood Crescent, Shrewbury, Shropshire, SY3 8UU. Tel:0743-354553
GAY GRAHAM HALL HAMPTON LAMBERT LAWSON MELLING NASH NICHOLSON POWELL SCURR Siddal SIDDALL SPEAK STACEY STEVENS THRALL WILLIAMS F4024

151386 NICHOLSON Mrs R. 46 Buffalow Bch Road, Whittianga, NEW ZEALAND.
MELLSOP Melsop Melsopp F7089

151394 NICKSON E J. 60 Aspin Oval, Knaresborough, North Yorkshire, HG5 8EL. Tel:0423-869850
LEEKEY Leeky NICKSON F371

151408 NICKSON Mrs Jeanne. (Twitchin) 60 Aspin Oval, Knaresborough, North Yorkshire, HG5 8EL. Tel:0423-869850
BALLINGER COLLINS Tutching Twitchen TWITCHIN F885

151416 NICOL Mrs Ruth. Captain Jan, Granville Road, St Margarets Bay, Dover Kent, CT15 6DT.
BARLOW CASTLE CORSTORPHINE EYRE HEAVER HILL MOFFAT NICOL F2785

151424 NIELD Mrs B. (Du Feu) 41 Midhurst Gardens, Hillingdon, Middx, UB10 9DN.
Bontemps BONTEMS BRADBERRY CALVERT CLARKSON EDWARDS FRAZIER HOWES ISLES JOHNSON KAYE LAMPARD NIELD PARDEY PIM Pimm Pym Pymm SMITH STEVENS THACKRAY WINN F4148

151432 NIELD Mrs Lilian. (Wallwork) 24 Grindsbrook Road, Radcliffe, Manchester, M26 0JS. Tel:061-764-3928
CADMAN Cartman LEES NIELD PLATT TAYLOR WALLWORK WOLFENDEN F5760

151440 NIEURZYLA Mr John. 34 Queens Road, Whitley Bay, Tyne & Wear, NE26 3BH. Tel:091-251-1536
DODDS GALLON LILLIE NIEURZYLA NIEUZYLA F162

151459 NIGHTINGALE Ms Christine E. 208 Earlham Road, Norwich, Norfolk, NR2 3RW.
BECKLEY HARVEY LAVENDER NIGHTINGALE URSELL F4937

151467 NIGHTINGALE Mr John. 60 Cromwell Road, Beckenham, Kent, BR3 4LN.
BATES BATH Jutten JUTTON MALLETT NIGHTINGALE RAYNER WESTON WROOT F2517

151475 NILSSON Mrs Margaret. (Tallis) 24 Icknield Close, Bidford On Avon, Alcester, Warwicks, B50 4BZ. Tel:0789-772943
ALDINGTON BALLARD DAVIES Davis FOGWELL GOODRIDGE HAWKINS KENT LANGDON LANGDON-DAVIES TALLIS Talliss TREZISE WEYMOUTH F661

151483 NIONS Mrs Margaret Ellen. (Cottam) 6 Pershing Place, Tanilba Bay, Port Stephens, NSW 2301, AUSTRALIA. Tel:+61-49-824335
CARTER COTTAM GRAFTER HOOLE HORN-MORGAN MERYICK MONKHOUSE NAPTHALY TILL WINNELL F7451

151491 NISBET Miss A. Altona, Mid Yell, Shetland.
Nesbit Nesbitt NISBET Nisbett F6792

151505 NIXON Miss Dorothy. 35 Rockland Road, Waterloo, Liverpool, L22 9QH.
BENNETT DIXON NIXON TEBAY F4090

151513 NIXON Mr Michael. Grenwood, Blind Lane, Tanworth In Arden, Solihull Warks, B94 5HT.
Adkins ATKINS Bloar Bloer Blore BLOWER BOYARD Byard Chetten Chetwin Chetwind Chetwym Chetwyn CHETWYND COLLINS COOPER Dickson DIXON Dixson DRAYTON FORTESCUE Fortesque JONES Nickson Nigson Nixen NIXON Nixson Nixsone Noxon RAWLETT Rollett SMITH TILL F1435

151521 NIXON Dr R C C. 129 Ridgeway Road, Sheffield, S12 2SQ. Tel:0742-398510
BECKTON Bentcliff BILLCLIFF Biltcliff Bintcliff DOBSON GRAYSON Hinchcliff Hinchcliffe HINCHLIFFE JACKLIN Jackling Jaglen Jaglin Jaklin LIGGETT MUSCROFT Nickson NIXON RIPLEY Rippley F6204

151548 NIZETTE Mrs Billie D. 727 Enterprise House, Kings Head Hill, Chingford, London, E4 7NF. Tel:081-524-4297
BEAMISH BEGGS BREE DENMAN GAMBLING GOSTELOW KEMP MADDICK MCILWAIN MCMURTREY MORRIS NEALE OSBORN ROUNCE SPRINGALL STOKES F1535

151556 NOBLE Mr Frank. 63 Musters Road, Ruddington, Nottingham, NG11 6JB. Tel:0602-211456
CHANTER DAWSON NOBLE WARWICKS F4656

151564 NOBLE Mrs H. Appletrees, Blakes Road, Wargrave, Reading Berks, RG10 8LA.
NOBLE F2684

151572 NOBLE Mrs Jean C. (Barnes) 12 Sherwood Crescent, Woodhatch, Reigate, Surrey, RH2 7QL. Tel:0737-248732
BARNES CHARMAN Corbeet Corber CORBET Corbett Corbit Corbitt Corbut COVENTRY NOBLE ROE WEALE F3004

151580 NOBLE Mrs June A. (Spencer) 142 Cuffley Hill, Goffs Oak, Waltham Cross, Herts, EN7 5EY. Tel:0707-873800
ARMAN ARMON BESWICK CORREN FRENCH GLAZEBROOK MARTIN NOBLE POLLEY SPENCER STAPLETON TUCKER F232

151599 NOBLE Kevin. 24 Northumberland Road, Coundon, Coventry, CV1 3AQ.
ATHERDEN BRANT BURTON BUTLER CHANDLER CROSS DRURY EVANS FINCH FOWLER HAGUE HALLOT HAMMOND HARVEY HOME HUNT JELLEY KEETLEY KIRK LEAKEY Lickey LLOYD MARSH MARSHALL METFORD MOWBRAY NOBLE PECK ROWLAND RUSSELL SMITH TINDAL TONG TURVEY WARD WARREN WARRY WITHAM WOOD F2525

151602 NOBLE Mr Len. Delamere, 157 Whitehill Road, Ellistown, Leics, LE6 1ER. Tel:0530-61186
ANDREWS AXFORD BACON BERRY BURGESS COUCHER DAVIE DAY DIKE DOBSON FISHER GARRARD HAZEL HAZLEHAND HISCOCK HUMBY KIMMER MARSHALL MESSENGER NOBLE NOYCE POOL Poole POWELL ROBERTS ROBINS RUDDLE RUSS Russe SMITH STACEY STEVENS TARRANT THORNTON WAFORD WESTALL WISE WOOD WOOTTON F5749

151610 NOCK Mr Terry. 64 Napier Road, Gillingham, Kent, ME7 4HD. Tel:0634-55576
. COOPER DARBY GURNEY HALL NOCK NORTHERN PEARCE F1087

151629 NODEN Mrs D A. 1 Welton Park, Welton, Nr Daventry, NN11 5JW.
BAINES Bane BAYNES HAWORTH SKELTON SMALLPAGE F426

151637 NOKES Mrs Christine. 5 Norfolk Grove, Great Wyrley, Walsall, WS6 6JS.
EVANS HODGES JARVIS NOKES PREECE TRISTRAM WILLIAMS F1338

151645 NOKES Dr David C B. 54 Hayfield Hill, Cannock Wood, Nr Rugeley, Staffs, WS15 4RS. Tel:05436-73303
CRAWFORD GASKIN Gaskine Gaskines Gaskins GODWIN Noak Noake Noakes Noaux Nock Nocke Nok Noke NOKES Noks Nookes F108

151653 NORMAN Mr Adrian R D. The North Wing, Crowcombe Court, Crowcombe, Taunton, Somerset, TA4 4AD. Tel:09848-613
ALLEINE BAGEHOT BLAKE BOWDING BOXER DE MERLE FORSTER LUER MERDON NORMAN PRANKERD SHERMAN TRAVIS TUNNICLIFFE VERMUYDEN YEO F2583

151661 NORMAN Mrs B. 4 Rochester Gardens, Market Harborough, Leics, LE16 9LR.
Poudrel Powderell POWDRILL F6620

151688 NORMAN Mr John C. 31 Derry Hill Road, Redhill, Nottingham, NG5 8HQ.
BILLINGS BOLLAND BOLLONS BREEZE BULLAMORE FALKENER FAULKNER GRIMMER HUNT JERVIS KING LACK LAW LEMONS LITTLEWOOD MAXON MAXSON NORMAN PARISH REED RINGHAM ROSAMOND SHARPE THIRST THURST TYLER UTTERIDGE YALLOP YALLUP F4102

151696 NORMAN Mrs Kathryn F. 6 Peter Street, South Croydon, Victoria, 3136, AUSTRALIA.
DEAR KETTLE KLOODHOUSE NORMAN VARNEY F5429

151718 NORMAN Mr Leslie V T. Greensleeves, Thaxted, Essex, CM6 2PY.
COWCHER MARSDEN NORMAN TUFF WRIGHT F1895

151726 NORRINGTON John & Jeannette. 1a Woodcote Park Road, Epsom, Surrey, KT18 7EY. Tel:0372-725134
Norington NORRINGTON F2762

151734 NORRIS Mr & Mrs. 190 Beckenham Road, Beckenham, Kent, BR3 4RJ.
CHIPPENDALE Chippindale F7148

151742 NORRIS Mr Chris. 27 Sheraton Drive, Tilehurst, Reading, Berks, RG3 5UZ. Tel:0734-415805
COLLIER EDWARDS ELSTOB FARROW FRANKLAND HOLBURN MIKOSZ MILFORD NORRIS STRICKLAND WASS WILKS WREN F4726

151750 NORRIS Mrs Valerie. 10 Queens Avenue, Byfleet, Weybridge, Surrey, KT14 7AD. Tel:0932-353444
ATKINS BATTEN BIRCH BROXTON CULVERHOUSE ELVISH FIELD HOWARTH HULSON HULSTON JOHNSON LEWORTHY OSBORN SHARPLES VOICE F3196

151769 NORTH Mr Derek. Andranus, Dexter Lane, Hurley, Atherstone Warks, CV9 2JG. Tel:0827-873460
BACON BEARDMORE BIRKETT BLUMFIELD BOTT BULL CAPP CHRISTIAN COCK CORBETT DEXTER DICKINSON DOOLEY FERBON GRANEY GRAVES HEBB JACKSON KNIGHT LANE LEE LITTLEDYKE MEE MOORE NORTH SHAW SHENTON SHIMIELDS SINGLETON SLANEY SMEETON SMITH STARNELL THOMPSON TOPLISS TRYNER WHITEHOUSE WILD WOOLHOUSE WRIGGLESWORTH F2889

151777 NORTH Mr George & Mrs June. 277 South Farm Road, Worthing, W Sussex, BN14 7TL.
BARRETT BENNETT FORBES GILL KEEN LANE LIFFORD MCINTOSH NORTH PITTOCK F2755

151785 NORTH Mr John. 6 Newbrough Crescent, Newcastle Upon Tyne, NE2 2DQ. Tel:091-281-0769
ABDY BURTON CREE GOSE HARRISON LINNELL MORTON NORTH ROBINSON SENIOR SIDDALL SMITH TROTT TURTON F1561

151793 NORTH Mrs Patricia. 66 Heathend Road, Alsager, Stoke On Trent, ST7 2SH.
BRIODY DOWNEY GOBLE NORTH F1438

151807 NORTHEY Mr Robert. 5 Wallace Avenue, Lisburn, Co Antrim, BT24 4AA.
NORTHEY F6512

151815 NORTHROP Mr Fred. Bon Accord House, 20 St Margarets Square, Cambridge, CB1 4AP. Tel:0223-411188
BODGER CHARTER COLLIN Collings Collins Collis COOK Cooke COOPER HARVEY HITCH HULL KEFFORD

Natrup Nauthorp Nauthrop Nawthorp Northorp NORTHROP Northrope Northroppe Nortop Nortrap Notrup PEARCE Peirce Petit Petite PETTIT Pettite Pierce PRIME REYNOLDS Willmot Willmott Wilmot WILMOTT WRIGHT F41

151823 NORTON Mrs C. Walnut Cottage, Potton Road, Hilton, Cambs, PE18 9NG.
Gelliart Gilliart GILLIATT F7059

151831 NORTON Mrs J C. (Sponder) 90 Buckland Way, Worcester Park, Surrey, KT4 8NS.
Tel:081-337-8840
Ponder Spander Spaunder Spawder Spawnder SPONDER F4275

151858 NOTLEY Lt Col G M N. 22 Gosford Road, Kirkcaldy, Fife, KY2 6TZ. Tel:0592-260093
CONWAY DIMENT Dowdall DOWDELL Dowdwll GALE LEGG MACIVER MACKENZIE NOTLEY OZARD PARK READ SKINNER STOCKLEY STREET TARREL F4350

151866 NUNN Mr Donald. Meadow Cottage, Bangors Road South, Iver, Bucks, SLO 0AP. Tel:0753-652654
BEARD BOYDEN LOND LOVE NUNN ROSE SAVIDGE SIMPSON SUTTON WARREN F6416

151874 NUNN Mr John. 17 Sunningdale Avenue, Ipswich, Suffolk, IP4 5SH. Tel:0473-725738
Bilbeart Gelbert Gilbard Gilbart Gilberd GILBERT Gilburd Gilburt Gillbard HASTE Nonne Nun NUNN Nunns Nunny F82

151882 NUNNE Mrs Alice. 4 Woodstock Road, Poole, Dorset, BH14 8DS. Tel:0202-744164
EVANS FOOT HANKERD HORN JOHNSON MORGAN NASH F1053

151890 NUTSFORD Miss S G. 22 Rowlands Lane, Thornton-Cleveleys, Lancashire, FY5 2QU.
Knuttesforde NUTSFORD F6655

151904 NUTT Mr W. 43 High Street, Peterborough, Cambs, PE7 3RA.
NUTT F7187

151912 NUTTER Mr E J. 27 Feniscliffe Drive, Blackburn, Lancs, BB2 2UF. Tel:0254-209543
ASPIN ATKINSON BARNES BLACKBURN BRIGGS BRITCLIFFE CORNER DUERDEN DUGDALE ETHERINGTON FISHWICK HORNBY IRELAND JACKSON LAKELAND LANG MITCHELL NUTTER PARKER SHAW SHUTTLEWORTH SLINGER STRICKLAND TATLOW UNSWORTH WARING WELLS WHALLEY WRIGLEY F2984

151920 NUTTING Mrs Mary. 89 Forbes Avenue, Potters Bar, Herts, EN6 5NQ. Tel:0707-57479
BLENHEIM FINCH NUTTING WARD F3172

151939 NYE Mr Donald Charles. 77 Southfield Road, Worthing, W Sussex, BN14 9EQ. Tel:0903-30114
NYE F1413

151947 O'BRIEN Mrs Catherine. (Musgrave) 11 Keyes Avenue, Cardiff, CF2 5QQ. Tel:0222-766784
BUCK MAHONEY MUSGRAVE O'BRIEN ROBERTS F4771

151955 O'CONNELL Mrs Jill. (Casbon) Cheney Hill Farm, Edgmond, Newport, Shropshire, TF10 8EH.
Tel:0952-810157
BARRETT BURROWS CASBON SAUNDERS F3361

151963 O'CONNELL Mr Stephen John. 1 Royston Road, Manchester, M16 0EU.
BREHONY O'CONNELL F1232

151971 O'DONOGHUE Rod. The Coach House, Little Gaddesden, Berkhamsted, Herts, HP4 1PH.
Donaghue Donahue DONOGHUE Donohoe Donohue O'donaghue O'donahue O'DONOGHUE O'donohoe O'donohue F7334

151998 O'LOUGHLIN Mrs Dianna. 19 Thirlmere Road, Hatherley, Cheltenham, Glos, GL51 5NQ.
Tel:0242-236497
CHATER CHEATER DAVIS GIBBS GURD JARVIS JONES MARTIN POOK RENDALL SANDERS SHORT SIMMONS SOPER TOOTH TYNDALL WHITE F1842

152005 O'MAHONEY Mr John Paul. 23 Thorncliffe, Two Mile Ash, Milton Keynes, Bucks, MK8 8DT.
Tel:0908-567718
Mahoney MAHONY O'mahoney O'mahony Pierce PIERSE F3852

152013 O'NEIL Mr John William. 32 Springwood Drive, Blaise Dell, Henbury, Bristol, BS10 7PU.
Tel:0272-508248
BENNY WILLIAMS BRADSHAW NORRIS O'NEILL ROACH SLAUGHTER VICCARS F4178

152021 O'NEILL Mrs Christine. (Dawson) 36 Glossop Road, Sanderstead, South Croydon, Surrey, CR2 0PU.
BROWN CHAPMAN CROFT FIELDING HANWAY JONES LANGTON MCARTHY MURRAY O SULLIVAN O'NEILL OWENS PADDISON POWER ROBERTS ROLLINSON SARGEANT SMITH WALLER WILSON F5092

152048 O'RAW Mr Joseph. 10 Aldersyde Avenue, Craigneuk, Wishaw, Lanarkshire, ML2 7RE.
Tel:0698-350945
ALLAN BRUCE CASSIDY CRAWFORD DOBBIE Gilmer GILMORE Gilmour LARID MADDEN MCCAUGHAN MCCLUSKEY Mccluskie Mcclusky MCDONALD Mcdonnell MCFARLANE Mcluskie Mclusky MUIR O'RAW O'rawe O'row Raw Rawe RUSSELL SHAW SKIMMING SMITH STRATHEARN TORSNEY F1965

152056 O'SHEA Mr Brian. 131 Norwood Road, London, SE24 9AF. Tel:081-674-6093
ASH ETHERINGTON JAMES LEAK LEAVER LOUTH LOWTH F5389

152064 O'SHEA Ms Margaret. (Butler) Little Llwygy, Lower Cwmyoy, Abergavenny, Gwent, NP7 7NY.
Tel:0873-890536
AZEVEDO BONNER BUTLER HOOPER O'BRIEN ROCHE TIBBLES F3353

152072 O'SHEA Mr Peter. 480 Vardon Road, Stevenage, Herts, SG1 5BJ. Tel:0438-359732
SADLEIR SADLER F6245

152080 O'SULLIVAN Mrs Leanne. (Mole) 67 Mclennan Street, Woody Point, Queensland, 4019, AUSTRALIA. Tel:+61-7-284-9537
ALDER ALLUM BUNBURY CANNAN CHAMP GLOVER GODDARD HEWITT HOBBS Hutchings HUTCHINS MADDOCK MOLE MOVE STEPHENS STOCK TIBBLE VIVIEN WARD WASHBAND F5144

152099 O'SULLIVAN Miss M. 16 The Priory, Epsom Road, Croydon, Surrey, CR0 4NT.
BALL GIBSON Hellier Hellyer HILLIER Hillyer JONES O'SULLIVAN SHAW WHITE F1317

152102 OAKELEY Mrs Doreen. 26 Woodstock Close, Hedge End, Southampton, Hants, SO3 4NG.
EDE FLOWER GODWIN GOULD MARSHALSEA PADWICK SHILLING WARNER WELLS WILKINSON F881

152110 OAKLEY Mr Denis. Swaledale, Thompsons Lane, Denmead, Portsmouth, Hants, PO7 6NB.
Tel:0705-251046
ALLEN ARBER BRADWELL BREWSTER BRIDGE BROWN FFLETHE GAME GIBSON GOODY GOWERS HARBOROUGH HARWOOD HILL HOLT HUTCHINSON LORD MALYN MERRILLS Oackley Oackly Oakely OAKLEY Oaklie Oakly Occle Ochely Ockeley Ockle Ockley Ockly Ocle Oclee Ocley Ocleye Ocly Okelee Okeley Okelie Okely Okle Okly PATTISON RAINER REVE RICHMOND Rithoak Rithock SANDERSON STRUTT THISTLEWOOD WOOLLARD Wreakoke Writhoak F3643

152129 OAKLEY Mrs Pamela Jill. (Heath) Bucklands, Coppice Row, Theydon Bois, Essex, CM16 7ER.
Tel:0992-813442
AUSTIN CLARK DEAN EMERTON HEATH HUNTER JONES LAMBERT PARKER POTTER SATTERTHWAITE THOMPSON F2816

152137 OASTLER Mr P C. 12 Cranemoor Avenue, Highcliffe, Christchurch, Dorset, BH23 5AN.
OASTLER F6778

152145 OATES Dr D K. 4 North Avenue, Exeter, Devon, EX1 2DU.
OATES Oats Otes F3359

152153 OCKEY Mr Edward. Longvida, 15 Upper Pines, Woodmansterne, Banstead Surrey, SM7 3PU.
Oakey OCKEY F7411

152161 OFFLEY Mr Harold G. 21 Forest Road, Cherry Hinton, Cambridge, CB1 4JA.
Offelow OFFILER OFFLEY Offly Ofley Ofly F2767

152188 OLDCORN Mr A C. 68 Queen Elizabeth Road, Humberston, Grimsby, DN36 4DE.
HUGHES OLDCORN F6379

152196 OLDFIELD Mrs Judith. Trinett Howe, Brisco Road, Egremont, Cumbria, CA22 2EJ.
Tel:0946-821077
ALLISON ASHLEY ATKINSON BAINES BAKER BARNES BENN BENTHAM BIBBY BOND BOUCH BROCKLEBANK BROWN CHAMBERS COOKE COOPER CORNTHWAITE COTTOM COWEN CRAGG CRAYSTON DICKINSON DODD DONALDSON FAWCETT FERGUSON FRANCIS GERMAN GILPIN HALSAL HARRINGTON HARRISON HUDDLESTON JACKSON KESKET KITCHIN. KNIGHT LYON MANSERGH MASON MILBURN OLDFIELD PAGE PARK PARTRIDGE PEILE PONSONBY PRATTSON RICHARDSON RODGER SEDGEWICK SHARP SHERWEN SIMPSON SPEIGHT STABLE THOMPSON TICKLE TYSON VICKARS WINTHROP

YARE YEADON F3860
152218 OLDHAM Mr Orlando Winter. 58 Glenville Way, Denton, Manchester, M34 1BS.
FINDLATER GEE MILLWARD OLDHAM SEDDON WINTER F5104
152226 OLDING Mrs C A. 66 English Road, Shirley, Southampton, Hants, SO1 3QF.
ALCE Als BRAKE BROWN Browne CHERRETT CROCKETT FALL FREELOVE GAMLIN KNELLER KNIGHT MAIN Mains MIDDLETON MUMFORD NEWTON OLDEN OLDING Reakes REEKS ROCKETT TRUELOVE WHITE WILKINSON WILLIS WOODHEAD F2204
152234 OLDROYD Mrs Jean. (Finch) 20 Regent Street, Horbury, Wakefield, WF4 6EP. Tel:0924-279157
ATKINSON Bacchus BACKHOUSE Backhus Backus FINCH Finche Fink Fynche Greenhoff Greenhough Greenhow Greenhowe GREENOUGH Hessitt Hewet Hewit HEWITT Huit KING Kinge Kyng Kynge Limbard LIMBOARD Limbord Lun Lund LUNN MOAT Moate Mote Myer MYERS PEPPER RENTON Rentone RINGROSE ROBSON TOWNEND Townsend Townshend WARD Warde F3602
152242 OLIVER Mr C W. Culverkeys, Beddlestead, Chelsham, Warlingham, Surrey, CR3 9QN. Tel:0959-77332
BEARE BOASE HOLLEBON OLIVER ORAM STEPHENS F602
152250 OLIVER Miss Elaine. 11 Curlew Bay Road, Otahuhu, Auckland 6, NEW ZEALAND.
CLEAL MEDHURST OLIVER PENFOLD RITCHIE TAYLOR F4480
152269 OLIVER Mrs Helen. (Herbert) 143 Norfolk Avenue, Sanderstead, South Croydon, Surrey, CR2 8BY.
ARNDELL CONQUEST FLOWERDAY HERBERT HUMBLE MEADS OLIVER PURYER SEAR F4086
152277 OLIVER Miss Rosemary. 11 Gravel Road, Bromley, Kent, BR2 8PE.
CHATTERTON COTTINGHAM CREIGHTON WATERLAND F3098
152285 OLIVEY Mr Brian C. 18 Winnington, Fareham, Hampshire, PO15 6HP. Tel:0329-236568
BISH Bisshe BOLT BONNEAU Bysh Byshe DELETO DONALDSON FAUTLEY Fortley FURBY GUTCH HEADDON LELLIOTT MINERS Minors O'livey Olivah OLIVE Olivee OLIVEY Olivie Olivy Olyvye PROUD Sambidge SAMBRIDGE STRIBLING Tissard TIZARD Tizzard Tyzard URRY WINCHCOMB Winchcombe WOODFORD F28
152293 OLLEVEANT Mrs Ivy Alexandra. 56 Malpas Road, Runcorn, Cheshire, WA7 4AN.
MCGOWAN OLLEVEANT F1887
152307 OLMSTEAD Mr J W. 18 Wedgewood Drive, Winnipeg, M B, R3T 2J8, CANADA.
OLMSTEAD F7337
152315 OLSEN Mr R G. 44 Wakefield Drive, Moreton, Wirral, Merseyside, L46 3RW. Tel:051-677-6358
GREEN LOCKYER MARSHALL STEADMAN F5818
152323 OLVER Mr Brian Wenmoth. 20 Mill Street, Warwick, CV34 4HB. Tel:0926-491905
OLVER WENMOTH Wenmouth F2381
152331 OMAN Mr John. Beechwood, Nigg Station, Tain, Ross-Shire, IV19 1QL. Tel:0862-86216
FRASER GEDDIE OMAN ROSS F1566
152358 ONION Catherine. 224 Penn Road, Wolverhampton, West Midlands, WV4 4AA.
Oniens ONION Onions Onyon F7136
152366 OPENSHAW Mr Roy. 345 Peppard Road, Emmer Green, Reading, Berks, RG4 8XG. Tel:0734-470007
ALLEN OPENSHAW WEAVER F4713
152374 ORBELL Mr E. 33 Vandyke Road, Oadby, Leicester, LE2 5UB.
Orbal Orbel ORBELL Orble F6666
152382 ORDERS Mr D C. Casa Da Boneca, Marthinha, 2765 Estoril, PORTUGAL.
Auders Audis Audus ORDERS F6625
152390 OREGAN Mrs Irene Grace. (Patterson) 4 Station Approach, Birchington On Sea, Kent, CT7 9RD.
BEECROFT BROWN CHESTER COWIE DIXON GROVE Groves O'REGAN PATTERSON PORTER TWIGG YALLOP F5117
152404 ORME Dr John E. 10 Causeway Gardens, Dore, Sheffield, S17 3EY. Tel:0742-360085
ALDRED AYLING BENNETT BERRY BRINKWELL CHARLTON DUNN EMERY GREENHALGH HARRISON HIGGENBOTHAM HILL IVIL Ivill LOMAX MARLAND MILLIGAN MORRIS ORME Ormerod ORMROD OVER PEARSON PERCIVAL PIPER PRICE ROBINSON SANDIFORD SAUL SMALL UPPERTON WALLWORK WOLSTENCROFT WOOD F2021
152412 ORMEROD Mr Ian. Gambleside, 33 Stapenhall Road, Monkspath, Solihull W Midlands, B90 4XX. Tel:021-745-4209
Homerode Omerod Omerode Omroyde ORMEROD ORMEROD Ormeroyd Ormrod Ormroyd RUSHTON WADDINGTON F3624
152420 ORMSTON-STRAW Mrs Joan. 13 Goldrings Road, Loughton, Essex, IG10 2QR.
BILL GILBEY HAGAR INMAN ORMSTON STRAW F1922
152439 ORR Mrs E. Achnabreck, 9 Rushfield, Helens Bay, Co Down, BT19 1JZ, NORTHERN IRELAND.
FENWICK F7402
152447 ORRELL Dr Richard. 3 Woodthorne Croft, Shadwell, Leeds, LS17 8XQ. Tel:0532-697126
HOWELL ORRELL F5733
152455 ORRIDGE Mr David. 113 Taverners Road, Rainham, Gillingham, Kent, ME8 9AG.
CARTWRIGHT HASLER ORRIDGE SPLAINE F2740
152463 ORTON Mrs C. 34 Outwoods Drive, Loughborough, Leics, LE11 3LT. Tel:0509-266720
BRYAN Bryans Buckstone BUXTON CARTLEDGE Cartlidge CLARKESTONE Clarkson CLARSON COOK CRAMP FOULDS GEE HALLAM MANSELL MEE ORTON WAIN F3539
152471 ORTON Mr David. 56 Hazel Road, Purley On Thames, Reading, Berks, RG8 8HR. Tel:0734-428809
BREWARD JACKSON Meares Mears Meers MERES Oerton ORTON Overton Owerton WRIGHT F3556
152498 ORTON-MAGGS Mr John D. 31 Trinity Road, St Johns, Narborough, Leicester, LE9 5BU. Tel:0533-867604
Magges MAGGS Mags Meg Meggs Mogg F4260
152501 ORYS Mrs S A. 20 Denton Rise, Denton, Newhaven, East Sussex, BN9 0QN. Tel:0273-516288
AVERY BROOKS COOK DAWSON DEWEL DEWELL FLETCHER FOOT FRITH HANDEL JEWKES Jukes KITE LAKER LAMBERT LANGRIDGE MACE MAITLAND MOECKX MOORE OAKLEY ORYS SHAKESPEARE SMART SOMMERAYNS Sommerijns THACKER THORNTON TYNAN WHEELER F3756
152528 OSBORN Mr Bob. Bramlea, 4 Fosseway Court, Ilchester, Somerset, BA22 8JT.
ANDREWS Asborn BELLAMY COLE COOL CROUCH DAVIES DUNKOIN ELLIS FRY GAY GLANCEY HAMPTON Hosbon JACKSON LINCOLN Osban Osband Osbon Osbond OSBORN Osborne Osbourn Osbourne Osburn Osburne Ozborn Ozbourn Ozbourne Ozburn Ozburne REID ROBSON SHARPLIN SHOEBRIDGE STOTEN STROUD SYMES WARD WARREN Wasborn Washbourne F1735
152536 OSBORNE Mr Bruce. Tower House, Tower Road, Tadworth, Surrey, KT20 5QY.
CANTELLS DICKINSON DONOVAN OSBORN OSBORNE SOUTER-OSBORN STEER VERRAL WASHBOURNES F3704
152544 OSBORNE Mrs Jean M. Little Whiligh Farm Cottage, Ticehurst, Sussex, TN5 7JX.
BASHFORD BEST BRIGDEN CARPENTER COLE HALLETT HARLETT F537
152552 OSBORNE Mrs Margaret. (Clayden) 10 The Close, Rayners Lane, Pinner, Middx, HA5 5DU.
AINGE ALGAR BOND CLACK CLAYDEN FRAYNE HURREN JEFFERY SHELDRAKE F5842
152560 OSBORNE Mr Richard. 36 Troutbeck Crescent, Bramcote, Beeston, Nottingham, NG9 3BP.
BAGSHAW BUCKNALL CHADWICK DALBY MAGSON MELLOR F3351
152579 OSTAFEW Mrs Daphne. (Rose) 20 Walrond Road, Swanage, Dorset, BH19 1PB. Tel:0829-424613
BROWN BUSHROD FRANCIS HATTON HEARN LEAR MARKS OWEN ROCKETT WEST F5849
152587 OSWALD Mr John. 88 Hereford Road, Monmouth, Gwent, NP5 3HH.
BRAGG CLOAKE COOK CROSS DEAL EMENY OSWALD PASS SHARP THORNS WORTLEY F6109
152595 OSWALD-JONES Mr M. Lamkyns, Horsmonden, Tonbridge, Kent, TN12 8BJ. Tel:0892-722607
LAMPKYN F6583
152609 OTTER Mrs Glynis M. Laburnum Cottage, Lowdham Road, Gunthorpe, Notts, NG14 7ES.

DAVISON DAWSON GILES MASON F3554
152617 OUTHET Miss Edna. 150 Falsgrove Road, Scarborough, Yorks, YO12 5BE.
OUTHART OUTHET OUTRED F3538
152625 OVERINGTON Mr N G. 15 Grove Avenue, Honeybourne, Evesham, Worcs, WR11 5PW.
Ouerington OVERINGTON F7006
152633 OWEN Mrs Angela. (Wright) Bryn Awelon, Station Road, Trawsfynydd, Gwynedd, LL41 4TE. Tel:0766-87447
BLANKS BUTLER ELSON MONTGOMERY OWEN SHARPE TREFOR WRIGHT F5232
152641 OWEN Mr & Mrs G. 26 Dorchester Road, Upton, Poole, Dorset, BH16 5NR.
BEARD BRAGG CORBETT DANGERFIELD ELDRIDGE HANCOCK HAYWOOD HOGBEN Hogbin HUGHES IGGULDEN LEES PEARSON PETTIT PRITCHARD SETTERFIELD TRIVELLI WILKINS F2563
152668 OWEN Mr John D B. 36 Oxford Drive, Kippax, Leeds, W Yorks, LS25 7JG. Tel:0532-861182
BENJAMIN BRIGHTON DAVIDSON Hawyn HOPKINSON LAMPLOUGH OWEN RHODES RIMMINGTON SPIVEY WHITE Woewen Woewin Wowen Wowin F1994
152676 OWEN Mr Ken. 7 Chestnut Way, Formby, Merseyside, L37 2DP. Tel:07048-75090
MARSHALL F1976
152684 OWEN Mrs Pat. Shenley Grounds Farm, Whaddon Road, Calverton, Milton Keynes, MK19 6EN. Tel:0908-501746
ASHBY GARDNER HILLYARD LEA LUCAS MASON OWEN SCRIPPS F2346
152692 OWEN Mr Robert. 2 Dalar Wen, Denbigh, Clwyd, LL16 3HT. Tel:0745-813173
BROWN FENNA MEESON MORRIS ROBERTS F4872
152706 OWEN Mr W H P. 20 Trembel Road, Mullion, Helston, Cornwall, TR12 7DY.
OWEN F1568
152714 OWENS Mr Edward R. Pinecroft, Station Road, Sibsey, Boston Lincs, PE22 0SA. Tel:0205-750284
EDGE GARDNER HOLLAND JONES LEWIS OWENS PETERS POTTER POUNTNEY SPRANG WILLIAMS F2831
152722 OWENS Mrs Ruth. (Sanderson) Pinecroft, Station Road, Sibsey, Boston Lincs, PE22 0SA. Tel:0205-750284
BURDEN CHALLAND COLES DEAR ELKINS GRANT HIGGINS HINDS KIMBER MACKLIN MULLIN SANDERSON SHERLOCK F2830
152730 OWST Mrs Margaret. (Whitton) Willow House, 34 Braids Walk, Kirkella, East Yorkshire, HU10 7PD. Tel:0642-653056
ANDERSON BURTON HART MADDISON OWST WHITTON F4245
152749 OXENBOULD Mr William Michael. 19 Summerhill Crescent, Liverton, Newton Abbot, Devon, TQ12 6HG.
MUDGE OXENBOULD F2797
152757 PACK Mr R O. 4 Edgehill Road, Midanbury, Southampton, SO2 2AJ.
PACK Packe Pake Park Pax Peck F6298
152765 PACKARD Brigadier. 143 Thomas More House, Barbican, London, EC2Y 8BU. Tel:071-628-6904
BROOKS HARRISON LUKE NUTTER Paccard Paccarde PACKARD Pakkarde SEPPINGS WOOLLEY F2158
152773 PACKER Mr G M. 2 Cranbourne Road, Old Swinford, Stoubridge, West Midlands, DY8 1QZ.
CROWTHER EATWELL HALL KING LONG MARCHANT PACKER F5684
152781 PACKER Mrs W E. 2 Cranbourne Road, Old Swinford, Stourbridge, W Midlands, DY8 1QZ.
FLAVELL HARWOOD KING MINTERN Minterne SLINGSBY TIMMINS VEASEY F4229
152803 PACKHAM Mr John. 16 Westbury Road, New Malden, Surrey, KT3 5BE. Tel:081-942-1660
BARTLET BAYLISS BOND BUTLER CHURCH COOPER Fleming FLEMMING FRY HEMS MORRIS PACKHAM PAGE Peckham POOLEY Pooly Powley Powly ROWING Seagall Seagle Seagul SEAGULL Segull SEYMOUR SHRIMPTON TUNKS WENN WILLAN WRIGHT F544
152811 PADBURY Mr A J. 376 Northborough Road, Norbury, London, SW16 4TS.
PADBURY F6993
152838 PADDISON Mr Peter. 69 Wyatts Drive, Thorpe Bay, Southend-On-Sea, SS1 3DG.
BAULDOCK BOOTH DORCAS GALE GOUGER HARRIS JACKSON JENNINGTON KIRK LANCASTER MARRIS NEWTON NICHOLSON OLIVER PADDISON SARGENT SHAW STAMP SWABY TATTERSHALL WALKER WOOD WRIGHT F3342
152846 PADDLE Mrs Alison M. 9 Cliff Terrace, Kendal, Cumbria, LA9 4JR.
Paddel PADDLE Padle Padwell F7071
152854 PADMOS Ruth. 1365 Sun Crest Road, Kingsville, Ontario, N9Y 2T7, CANADA.
WOONTON F7378
152862 PAGAN Mr A C. 10 Highmill, Ware, Herts, SG12 0RX.
LANDRETH PAGAN F6584
152870 PAGE Miss A K. 85 Roundshill, Kenilworth, Warwickshire, CV8 1DW.
EMMERSON GIBBONS LEONARD PAGE RICHARDSON ROWE UNWIN F1348
152889 PAGE Mr Brian. 12 Beechwood Avenue, St Albans, Herts, AL1 4YA. Tel:0727-860809
BURTON CASTLE CATLING COCK COLES COUCHMAN DAWSON GARRAT HARVEY HILL MEDLOCK MITCHELL MULLET MUNDAY PAGE PERRIDGE PIPER RICHARDS SMITH WILLIAMS F2017
152897 PAGE Mrs June. 19 Carlyle Road, Staines, Middx, TW18 2PU.
STEVENSON F3264
152900 PAGE Mr L H. 69 Highcliff Drive, Leigh On Sea, Essex, SS9 1DQ. Tel:0702-471878
BURCHELL Embry EMBURY FULLMAN HOWARD KIFF Kiffet LEE MUNDEN PAGE SHEPHERD THOMAS F2307
152919 PAGE Mr M G. 29 Devon Road, Swindon, Wiltshire, SN2 1PQ. Tel:0793-532483
COMLEY GROCOAN LITTLE PAGE F2256
152927 PAGE Mr Robert A. 178 Hopgarden Road, Tonbridge, Kent, TN10 4QZ.
BUCHAN CALDER MCWILLIAM PAGE STORRAR THAIN F2975
152935 PAGET Mr John. Elm Farm, Burnett, Keynsham, Bristol, BS18 2TF. Tel:0272-864276
CHARLES HILL HUNT PAGET WARREN F192
152943 PAICE Mr Leon. 9 Wilbye Grove, Inns Court, Knowle, Bristol, BS4 1XN.
Archard Archart BAKER BIDDER BROOMFIELD Bydder Fordar Fordard Fordat Forden FORDER Forderd Fordet Hached Hatchard Hatchat Hatcherd Hatchet HATCHETT HAWKSHAW HUGHES HUNT Hunte Hunter Huses LITTLE London LONNON Mallenson MALLESON Mallinson Mallison Merrick Merryck Meryck MEYRICK Myrech Myrick Oakshott Ockshaw ORCHARD Orchart Orcheard Orchet Orchett Pace PAICE Paise Payce Pays Payse PEATER Peise Peiter Peter Petre Petter Petterd PHILLIPS Renault Rennaulds RENNOLDS Renold Reynolds SMITH THOMAS WALL Walle Waller Weddon Whall Whalle WHEADON Wheaton WHITE Whitton Widdon F650
152951 PAIN Mr Reginald. Spindrift, Kingsmark Lane, Chepstow, Gwent, NP6 5LZ. Tel:0291-622137
PAIN Paine Pane Payne F6108
152978 PAINTER Mr Howard F J. Normandie, Penoweth, Mylor Bridge, Falmouth Cornwall, TR11 5NQ. Tel:0326-74016
BAKER COOK Cooke CUTBUSH ELVIS Gardiner GARDNER HEWER MYTTON OAKES PAINTER SELMAN STACEY STEWARD WILTSHIRE WOODSBY F2826
152986 PALGRAVE Mr & Mrs D A. Crossfield House, Dale Road, Stanton, Bury St Edmunds Suffolk, IP31 2DY.
PALGRAVE SPILLING F6585
152994 PALK Mr George. Marley Grange, South Brent, Devon, TQ10 9JT. Tel:0364-73634
Cocker COKER PALK VOOGHT F950
153001 PALLANT Mr E W. 31 Hieght Drive, Linthwaite, Huddersfield, W Yorks, HD7 5SU.
BROWN CARR CLEMENTS GRANGE HABLY HAZELTON PALLANT PITT RIDLEY ROBINSON SOCKET Sockett STEEL STOCKTON TELFORD F2919
153028 PALMER Mrs B. 17 Ardney Rise, Catton, Norwich, Norfolk, NR3 3QH.
ANDREWS PALMER F3635
153036 PALMER Mr Barry John. 9 Beechfield, Hoddesdon, Herts, EN11 9QH. Tel:0992-464026
Fiveash GLAZIER-BUSS SNOOR VIVASH Viveash Vivish Vivosh F5973
153044 PALMER Mr D H. Whitegates Farm, Rushton, Kettering, Northamptonshire, NN14 1QS. Tel:0536-710291

PALMER F3076
153052 PALMER Mrs D. 40 Park Court, Grosvenor Park Road, Walthamstow, London, E17 9PE.
CUSS GLASS HIMPFEN PETTS SIBLEY F2108
153060 PALMER Mrs E B. 15 Lowther Street, Maldon, Victoria, 3463, AUSTRALIA.
MATTHEWS MCFARLANE F4971
153079 PALMER Mrs E M. 244 Gladstone Street, Peterborough, PE1 2BS.
ALLSOP CARTER CROFTS Grave GRAVES Greaves GREEN MOULDS STEWARD Stewart Stuart WILKINSON F4746
153087 PALMER Mr Jack. 5 Avondale Crescent, Cwmbran, Gwent, NP44 1UA.
FARR JACKSON MACDONALD PALMER RUSHWORTH F6040
153095 PALMER Mr John E G. Taw Cottage, Wonersh, Nr Guildford, Surrey, GU5 0PR. Tel:0483-34667
Coneybear Coneybeare Coneybeer CONIBEAR Conibeare Conibeer Connibear Connibeare Connibeer Conybear Conybeare Conybeer COSTER Cuneybear Cuneybeare Cuneybeer Cunibear Cunibeare Cunibeer Cunnibear Cunnibeare Cunnibeer Cunybear Cunybeare Cunybeer FORSTER GAMMON PALMER WEEKS F4939
153109 PALMER Mrs Marjorie. (Littlewood) 21 Brassington Road, Heaton Mersey, Stockport, Cheshire, SK4 3PN.
BALLS DENT HENDERSON LITTLEWOOD MEADOWCROFT OAKES PALMER PEAKE ROBERTS ROBINSON F5895
153117 PALMER Revd Norman E. 4 St Augustines Close, Bexhill On Sea, East Sussex, TN39 3AZ. Tel:0424-218573
BROOKS DAVIS LEECH PALMER F953
153125 PALMER Mrs V S. Redgables, Brookwood Hosp Est, Knaphill, Woking Surrey, GU21 2RQ.
Deaven Deavon Deven DEVON F7207
153133 PANKHURST Mr Terry. 18 Garrard Way, Wheathampstead, Herts, AL4 8PE. Tel:058283-2817
BATCHELOR CARPENTER ENGLAND HAWES MUDD Panckhurst Pancoast Pancurst Pancus Pankherst PANKHURST Penkhurst REMINGTON VANNER F558
153141 PANRUCKER Mr Alfred. 39 Outing Close, Southend On Sea, Essex, SS1 2UX.
PANRUCKER F2252
153168 PARDY Mrs June. 9 Parkfield Crescent, Park Lane, Kimpton, Herts, SG4 8EQ. Tel:0438-832754
COLE RULE F1422
153176 PARISH Mr Ivor. 8 Farm Close, Kidlington, Oxon, OX5 2BE.
ALINGTON CRIPPS Crips CUMMING DUNN EARLE Godsal Godsale GODSALL Godsell HALL HARDIMAN HENDERSON HESLOP HOGARTH HONEY LOCKIE LUPTON MARWOOD NELLES NORRIS NUTT PARISH PARNABY Parrish PEMBERTON PHELPS SHAYLE STOBBS TAYLOR TINDELL Tindle WEAVER F2521
153184 PARK Mr Keith. 19 Penybryn, Mountain Ash, Mid Glamorgan, CF45 3TJ. Tel:0443-478754
BOULTON DIXON LEWIS MESSENGER PARK PECK PREDDY SOURBUTTS STANTON WEBB F1000
153192 PARK Mrs M Y. Keilthustag, Andreas, Isle Of Man.
BROOK BROOKE Brookes Brooks ESCRICK ESCRICKE Eskrett ESKRICK Eskricke Eskrit Eskritt Estrick F6125
153206 PARK Mrs Marjorie Edith. 211a Crescent Road, East Barnet, Herts, EN4 8SB. Tel:081-440-1688
BRYANT CROUCHMAN HITCH SEARS F3174
153214 PARK Mrs Sheila. (O'Donnell) 6 Alvara Road, Alverstoke, Gosport, Hants, PO12 2HY. Tel:0705-583554
BALCOMBE BECKETT BRYANT BURKE DAY DONOVAN GEES MULLINS O DONNELL F4829
153222 PARK Mrs Tracey June. (Skuse) 19 Penybryn, Mountain Ash, Mid Glamorgan, CF45 3TJ. Tel:0443-478754
DILLMAN SKULL SKUSE SQUIRES TYLER WALDRON WEBB F1001
153230 PARKER Mr Alan. 22 Edenham Road, Hanthorpe, Bourne, Lincs, PE10 0RB.
BOWN DERBYSHIRE EADY GUILFORD LAKE NEAL PARKER SHILLAKER SWANN WALLIS F3695
153249 PARKER Mrs B M. 8 Crawford Close, Lillington, Leamington Spa, Warwickshire, CV32 7HA.
BATEMAN EDKINS FRANKLIN GODFREY HAYNES Hearn Hearne Heiron Herne Heron HICKMAN Hierne Hieron Highorne Hiorne Hiorns Hiren Hirens Hirin HIRON Hirone Hirons HOBBIS Hurn Hurne Hyearnes Hyerne Hyorn Hyron Hyrone Hyrons Hyryn Iron Irons Lancashire LANKESTER MATTHEWS MELEN MOORE QUINEY SILLS TARPLEE TOWNSEND TUNBRIDGE WINTER F3315
153257 PARKER Mr David. 96 Waverley Avenue, Twickenham, Middlesex, TW2 6DN.
BECKLEY BELLAMY BOND COPE GLASS LANK NEWNHAM PRETLOVE STONESBRIDGE WALTON F3572
153265 PARKER Mrs G L. (Cleak) 31 Highfield, Letchworth, Herts, SG6 3PY. Tel:0462-685603
Clake CLEAK Cleake Click Clique HANKINS PARKER F1226
153273 PARKER Mr Gordon. 25 Meeting Lane, Penketh, Warrington, Cheshire, WA5 2QU. Tel:092572-8712
ALEXANDER CARR COCKERAM Cockerham DIXON HARRISON HUDDLESTON KERR MOORHOUSE Morehouse PARKER SINGLETON SUTTON TIMMIS WALKINSHAW WARRILOW F1843
153281 PARKER Mr Ivor M. 60 Chantry Road, Gosport, Hants, PO12 4NF. Tel:0705-580930
BAKER BARNETT BARTRAM BOND CHICK CORK COX Curl Curle DADD FRIEND Hereford HEX HURFORD JONES Kearle KEIRL Keirle LOCKIER MANTELL MILLS Pafford PALMER PARKER Pavard Paverd PAVORD PINNEY SPURLE STOCKMAN TIVER Wattes WATTS WINSOR WOODFORD F719
153303 PARKER Mrs Joan. 4 Dale Avenue, Mapperley, Nottingham, NG3 6BU.
Bilbie BILBY COACHIFOR COOK Cooke DAUBNEY IDENDEN LEWIS PARKS PHIPPS SWOFFER WILLIAMS F2838
153311 PARKER Mr M A. 5 Dawn Close, Heavitree, Exeter, Devon, EX1 3DU. Tel:0392-75589
CHANEY HOOPER NOWELL PACKER PARKER TOLLEY F4747
153338 PARKES Mr Ron. 21 The Warren, Billericay, Essex, CM12 0LW.
PARKES Parks F2586
153346 PARKINS Mrs Judith. (Rowbottom) 68 Garth Crescent, Coventry, CV3 2PQ. Tel:0203-459471
BAKER Biram BRISTOW BYRAM Byron FIELD FORREST LANE MALE MOORE PARRY Reubotham Rewbotham ROWBOTTOM RYDER SIMPSON WHITEHOUSE WOOLDRIDGE Woolridge F6471
153354 PARKINSON Mr Barry John. Po Box 200, Croydon, Victoria, 3136, AUSTRALIA. Tel:+61-3-726-9695
ASH BARNETT BARRIBALL BLACKADDER BRIANT BROWN BURNS CURNOW EDIE FRANCIS HAMILTON HICKEY JASPER JOB LEAN LUSKEY MARTIN MORCOMB MORRISON MULLONEY NICHOLLS OLD PARKINSON PHILLIPS PRIOR REED REID REYNOLDS STEELE TOSPELL TREGONNING TRELLEGAN TREMAINE TREWEEK VINCENT WHITBURNE WILLIAMS F5537
153362 PARKINSON Mr Colin & Mrs Susan. 25 Stirling Crescent, Testwood, Totton, Southampton Hants, SO4 3BN. Tel:0703-869162
BOOR FISHER GLOVER HORSFIELD JAY JENNER LOFTHOUSE MARSH PARKINSON PURVIS F1059
153370 PARKS Theodore E. Po Box 590, Milwaukee, WI 53201, USA.
PARK Parke Parkes Parks F7341
153389 PARNELL Mrs Ann. (Jolin) 344 Archer Road, Stevenage, Herts, SG1 5QH. Tel:0438-725809
JOLIN F3863
153397 PARNELL Mr R V & Mrs S J. (Barrick) 103 Applegarth Avenue, Guildford, Surrey, GU2 6LT. Tel:0483-571028
ADAMS AXFORD BAKER BAKHEN BARRICK BARTER BARTLETT BENNETT BINGHAM BROOK BUCKLEY BUNGEY BUTCHER CASTILLION CHALK CLARKE COFFIN COGGRELLE Curl CURLE Davies DAVIS DEARLOVE DIBDEN DOWDEN DRODGE DUKES DUNKINSON DURRANT FOSTER FOXLEE Foxley FROST GARSON GARSTON GATES GILLINGHAM GOLDWIRE GOLDWYRE GOLSTON GOODCHILD GUY Guye HARTNETT HASKELL HAWKINS HAWTHORN HEWITT HILES HOBBS HOOKEY HOPKINS HOUSE HOWSE HUQUENAN JOLIN KEEP Kerle Kerley KITCHER LAMBIE LEAT MANVELL Manville MARTIN MCINTYRE MILLER MUNDEN Naish NASH NINEHAM Ninham Ninnim OXFORD PARISH PARNELL PARSONS PEASCOD PENNY PERNELL PICOT PINEL POWELL PRENTICE PURNELL READ Reade SAMBER SHOTTER

SMIRK Smirke SMITH SPELT ST PIER ST PIERRE TESTER THORN THORNE TOURNEFORTE TROWBRIDGE Ullyat Ullyett ULYAT Ulyate Ulyatt Ulyet VEAL Veale WADE WARN WARNE WARWICK WEEKES WEST WITT WITTS WORT Yeats F2293

153400 PARR Mrs P Hoare. Beech View, 34a Rhind Street, Bodmin, Cornwall, PL31 2EL.
BAUDRIER BLOWEY FREEMAN HOAR Hoare JERMY LUND MORSE SCOTT F2647

153419 PARRETT Mrs Heather. (Dodd) Wendover, School Lane, Stedham, Midhurst, Sussex, GU29 0NT.
FROST GOSNEY F2348

153427 PARRINGTON Mrs S E. (Edwards) 2 The Homestead, Gallows Green, Alton, Stoke On Trent, ST10 4BN. Tel:0538-702240
BAILEY BENBOW Bendbow BROOKES CLULOW COOMBES EDWARDS FLETCHER Parinton Parnton PARRINGTON SALT WHISTON F5387

153435 PARRY Mr Maurice Glyn. The Banquet House, Princess Road, Rhuddlan, Rhyl, Clwyd. Tel:0745-590580
PARRY F4564

153443 PARSELL Mr Jim. Jan, Imble Close, Pembroke Dock, Dyfed, SA72 6PJ. Tel:0646-683349
PARSELL F1333

153451 PARSLOE Mr J. 1 Woodcote Green House, Woodcote Green, Epsom, Surrey, KT18 7DF.
ALEXANDER BURLAND GAMLEN HANDY PARSLOE F6228

153478 PARSONAGE Mrs Jean. 26 Gillity Avenue, Walsall, West Midlands, WS5 3PJ.
BEDNALL F4266

153486 PARSONS Dr A M. 14 Woodlands, St Neots, Cambs, PE19 1UE.
CRAWFORD EDWARDS HOLMES MESNARD PARSONS SEAGER WHITE F1905

153494 PARSONS Mr Alan. 160 Coleshill Heath Road, Chelmsley Wood, Solihull, West Midlands, B37 7SN.
BOX CHECKLEY DYKE PARSONS F5721

153508 PARSONS Miss Beryl. Chandos, Stoke Close, Stoke D'Abernon, Cobham Surrey, KT11 3AE. Tel:0932-862060
BIRD COLESELL Coleshil COLLINS Colsel Coucell Coulsell HINES HOGSFLESH KNOTT NICHOLLS Not Nott PARSONS Ribbens RIBBINS WARNER F1107

153516 PARSONS Elizabeth Jane. (Hasell) Icelton Farm, Wick St Lawrence, Weston Super Mare, Avon, BS22 0YJ. Tel:0934-515704
BAKER BALL BOWLE BRIANT BRIMBLE Brookes BROOKS BROWN Browne Chapell Chappel CHAPPELL Clark CLARKE COCK COLE COOK COURT CULLIFORD Davies DAVIS EDWARDS FELTHAM FROST GAGE GILL GOULD HARRIS HARSE Hasel HASELL Hassell Hazel Hewelet Hewitt HEWLETT HICKS HILLMAN Hix HUISH LEAKEY LIGHT LOUCH MAPSTONE MARTIN MAY PARSONS PLUMBLEY POPLE Powel POWELL SHOPSTONE STABBINS TOOGOOD VOWLES WALKER WALLIS WARD WELSH WINSTONE Yates YEATES F3069

153524 PARSONS Mr Iain Hughes. Far Hills, Capon Tree Road, Brampton, Cumbria, CA8 1QL. Tel:06977-2127 or 3003
BENNETT HUGHES PARSONS TRIPPICK TRIPPIOCK F1662

153532 PARSONS Mrs Jill. 9 Moera Place, Whangaparaoa, NEW ZEALAND.
PLUMRIDGE F7346

153540 PARSONS Mr Malcolm C. 420 Middle Road, E Greenwich, RI 02818, USA.
BEST BLACKALER HENWOOD JACKSON KNEEBONE LUXTON PARSONS PUTT RENFREY F4448

153559 PARSONS Mr R C. 1 Rosslyn Court, Rosslyn Avenue, East Barnet, Herts, EN4 8DJ.
PARSONS F3154

153567 PARSONS Mr T B. 54 Attimore Road, Welwyn Garden City, Herts, AL8 6LP. Tel:0707-338089
Ffranceys Francies FRANCIS Francys Frannceys Frauncys GREENE Taltersale Tatarsole Tatashal Tatersall Tatershal Tatersole Tateshale Tateshalle TATTERSHALL Tattsal Tattsil Titsel Titterel Tittersal Tittersale Tittersall Tittersell Totterel F3193

153575 PARTINGTON Mr Harry. 19 Greville Court, Greville Park Road, Ashtead, Surrey, KT21 2QN. Tel:0372-273097
PARTINGTON F6199

153583 PARTRIDGE Canon Tim. Bugbrooke Rectory, Northampton, NN7 3PB. Tel:0604-830373
ASHBY BILLINGHAM CURTIS DODD EALES HEFFORD HOWARD KIRTON LOVELL MOORE PARTRIDGE PATRICK PHIPPS PICKERING SAXBY TIBBS TURLAND F790

153591 PARTRIDGE Mrs Joy. (Russell) 73 Park Road, Rydalmere, NSW 2116, AUSTRALIA. Tel:+61-2-638-1881
Allen ALYN BAKER BINE BRUCE BUCHANAN COLLEY DICKER Docker ENGLISH Eva EVANS EVEA FRY GARLAND HACKETT HICKS HUMPHRIES JAMES JONES LAMB LIDDICOAT LUKE MASON MAYNARD MILGATE OATES PARTRIDGE PLAYFORD PLUMBER PRICE PUGH RICKARD ROBERTS RUSSELL SELMES STIRLING TAYLOR THOMAS TICEHURST TILLMAN TONKYN TREWELLA URQUHART USTICK WEBB WEBDAY Wibday F4384

153605 PASCOE Mr Allen. 2318 Maue Road, Miamisburgh, Ohio, 45342, USA. Tel:+1-513-866-2379
ANDERSON BAIN Baine BECKERLEG FORBES FULLERTON GLENNIE HANCOCK HEAD JAMES LIBBY MATTHEWS MCMASTER MEARNS PASCOE PETRIE RUTTER SMITH TONKIN TRAIL TRELOAR TRENWITH TRY WALKER WILLIAMS F4485

153613 PASS Mrs E Ann. (Abbott) Kohima, Hague Street, Glossop, Derbyshire, SK13 8NS.
ABBOTT BARNES COATES GODDARD GREATOREY GULLY HATTON PASS SMITH WOODHOUSE F4908

153621 PATCHETT Mr John H. 13 Russell Avenue, Queensbury, Bradford, W Yorks, BD13 2AL. Tel:0274-880268
ACKROYD AKROYD BOTTOMLEY BRAMLEY BRIGGS BURWIN COCKROFT EMSLEY FOSTER GREENWOOD HALSTEAD HEAP HOLROYD KERSHAW NICHOLSON NUNNS PATCHETT RUSHWORTH SCOTT SIDNEY SIMPSON SUMMERSCALES TAYLOR WARBURTON WHITWORTH F8

153648 PATCHING Mr Colin. 19 Rogate Close, Worthing, W Sussex, BN13 2DU. Tel:0903-60226
Patchen Patchin PATCHING F3606

153656 PATE Mr George. 61 Pine Grove, Monton, Eccles, Manchester, M30 9JW.
BARR BAXTER BROWN CHALMERS CURRIE MITCHELL MUNRO PATE STEWART VEITCH F3442

153664 PATERSON Mr Allan. 39 Boston Avenue, Hornby, Christchurch 4, New Zealand. Tel:+64-03-496-819
BOULT GEE HILL PATERSON F693

153672 PATES Miss Helen J E. 20 Myles Court, Goffs Lane, Goffs Oak, Waltham Cross Herts, EN7 5PP. Tel:0707-876143
ALMOND BRADBURY BROWN BULLARD DRAPER MOSELEY PEARTS F567

153680 PATON Mrs I. (Wilson) 26 Cairn Terrace, Galston, Ayrshire, KA4 8QF. Tel:0563-821211
PATON WILSON F4179

153699 PATON Mr K. 36 Wychwood Avenue, Lymm, Cheshire, WA13 0NE.
CHRISTIE HADDEN MCCURRACH Mcgrouther MCGRUTHER MCKENZIE PATON F3885

153702 PATT Mrs Susan. (Rendall) 21 Meadowside, Ashford, Barnstaple, Devon.
BENTERMAN HUMPHRIES PATT F5274

153710 PATTEN Mrs. The Coach House, Millbank, Lymm, Cheshire, WA13 9DG.
CORRIGAN ESLIN HEWITT F7407

153729 PATTEN Mr E D A. 302 The Cedars, Abbey Foregate, Shrewsbury, SY2 6BY. Tel:0743-243549
COULSELL GRISDALE LOWTHER MALONEY MCNALLY PATTEN REARDON SIMSON STURROCK F2321

153737 PATTERSON Mrs Joan. (Wilby) Glencoyne, York Road, Barlby, Selby, North Yorks, YO8 7JP.
GILL HOLMES KAYE LAMB PATTERSON PICKET ROSE WILBY F6015

153745 PATTERSON Mrs V. 5 Ryemead Lane, Wyke Regis, Weymouth, Dorset, DT4 9NS.
BEHENNA BURLEY COLLETT CURNOW MORCOM NORTHEY PATTERSON F4815

153753 PATTISON Mr Chris. 57 Clarence Road, Moseley, Birmingham, West Midlands, B13 9UH. Tel:021-449-6302
DINSDALE HOLTON LLOYD MOUL MUNDAY PALMER PATTISON PICKERING SPENCE TAYLOR F2257

153761 PATTISON Mr I T. 2 Ogilvy Square, Worcester, WR3 7LU.
MAP Mapp Mapps Maps F6988

153788 PATTISON Mr John M. 53 Upavon Way, Carterton,

Oxon, OX18 3AS.
Edbroke Edbrook EDBROOKE Pattenson Patteson Pattesone Pattinson PATTISON Tam TAME Taym F2124

153796 PATTISON Mrs Joyce. 190 Grange Road, Hyde, Cheshire, SK14 5NU.
BEELEY MOORS PATTISON PRIESTLEY SMITH WOOD F2739

153818 PAULING Mrs Norina. 11 Horton Road, Middleton Cheney, Banbury, Oxon, OX17 2LE.
BISHOP DUMBLETON HOWLETT MILLWARD Millwood Milward Milwood Paulienge Paulin PAULING Paulling Pawlin Pawling PRICKETT Pualing Sharrog SHEARWOOD Sherwood F6095

153826 PAULING Mr Robert. Po Box 292, Neutral Bay, New South Wales, 2089, AUSTRALIA.
ACKLING BRANSCOMBE GLENISTER GREGG GUMLEY HEFFERNAN HUMPHREYS LANG PAULING F5581

153834 PAVEY Mrs Valerie. 9 Magpie Road, Eastbourne, E Sussex, BN23 7RG.
FUNNELL KEMP PAVEY SUTER SWAIN F1191

153842 PAVITT Mr D H. Bulls Bridge House, Cowfold, W Sussex, RH13 8DT.
COOMBS DOWD DUNNING HERITAGE HUMBERSTONE Kirkley KIRTLEY MCDOUGAL Mcdowall MCDOWELL Mcdugal O'dowd PAVITT Pearman PERMAIN Perman WATSON F1995

153850 PAWLEY-WHITE Mr George. Chy'N Elyn, Tregenna Lane, Camborne, Cornwall, TR14 7QU. Tel:0209-712974
Pauley PAWLEY WHITE F1806

153869 PAYLER Mr Roy. Highfield, 8 Church Lane, Kislingbury, Northampton, NN7 4AD. Tel:0604-830615
PALEY PAYLER TUNGATE F5094

153877 PAYNE Mr A D. 164 Boldmere Road, Birmingham.
BREMNER DRIVER INGLEFIELD LIGHT NICHOLS PARRY PAYNE SKILLINGTON TRATMAN WARDON F2539

153885 PAYNE Mrs Angela M. (Wright) 14 Gorselands Close, Ash Vale, Aldershot, Hants, GU12 5EF. Tel:0252-26156
ALLEN BLIN COX HARRIS HICKS PETTIT SPARKES STOYLE WILTON WRIGHT F2696

153893 PAYNE Mr Brian. 7 Fairbairn Road, Cambridge, CB4 1UG. Tel:0223-423896
COUSINS PAYNE WESTON F3528

153907 PAYNE Mr Charles. Beara House, Beara Cross, Bratton Fleming, Barnstaple, Devon, EX31 4TG. Tel:0598-710607
BADLAND FITZJOHN HUNT PAYNE F5717

153915 PAYNE Mrs E S. Beara House, Beara Cross, Bratton Fleming, Barnstaple, Devon, EX31 4JG. Tel:0598-710607
KINSEY POSTINGS PUGH WHITMORE F4718

153923 PAYNE Miss K. 67 Chestnut Drive, Pinner, Middlesex, HA5 1LX.
HILL EARLE JILL PAYNE SHARLAND TROTT F4986

153931 PAYNE Mr R A. 81 Mayes Lane, Ramsey, Essex, CO12 5EL.
ANSCOMBE CLARK FOWLER HAMPTON HARTFIELD LILLEY LISTER LODGE PAYNE F3074

153958 PAYNTER Helen. 54 York Street, Morningside Qld, Australia 4170. Tel:+61-07-399-8746
BERESFORD HOPGOOD PAYNTER WILKINSON F2964

153966 PAYNTER Mr Terence M. 5 Welby Crescent, Winnersh, Wokingham, Berkshire, RG11 5SW. Tel:0734-791193
PAYNTER F4843

153974 PEACOCK Mrs Christine. (Dawe) 96 Elm Grove, Hayling Island, Hampshire, PO11 9EH. Tel:0705-465713
BEDFORD BLAND BUNCE DAWE EVANS JOHNSON LANE LENTON MCLEAN F5132

153982 PEACOCK Mrs Janice. (Harman) 51 Old North Road, Royston, Herts, SG8 5EP.
BISHOP CAVEEN EARL FITZGERALD GELLING HARMAN HOLMAN JEWSON JOY MILLETT MURRAY NEEDLER OTT PEACOCK SIMPSON TWORT F2413

153990 PEAK Mrs Ruth. (Mayson) 22 Ashworth Park, Knutsford, Cheshire, WA16 9DE. Tel:0565-651086
BATCHELOR BURNETT DAVISON EVANS GOODWIN MATON MAYSON MEEK NAYLOR SMITH WILSON F3205

154008 PEAKE Mr A R. 142 White Edge Moor, Liden, Swindon, Wiltshire, SN3 6LY.
BREWER CARPENTER CORNOCK DEATH KIDGER Laimbear LAIMBEER Limebear Limebeer PEAKE STARLING TUCKER TYLER F4505

154016 PEAKE Mr Andrew. 14 Tudor Street, Dulwich, SA 5065, AUSTRALIA. Tel:+61-8-332-8884
BOTTING ELLIOTT GRAHAM HUNT MCCOLLAH PEAK PEAKE TOWNSEND WILSON F4462

154024 PEAKER Mr R. 16 Wyreside Drive, Hambleton, Blackpool, Lancs, FY6 9DP.
BOLTON BOWN CLAY Cocayn Cockayne Cockeyn Cockin COCKING COOPER DAVIES HARDWICK HAYES HAYWARD HUGHES HURST MILLINGTON MITCHEL MOORE NELSON Peacar PEAKER Peeker Pekar Peker PENDLEBURY PORTER POSTLES RHODEN RIMER ROBINSON ROWLEY SALTER SIMPKIN SMITH STUBBS TEBB THOMPSON TURTON VAUGHAN WESTWOOD WILKINSON WORTHINGTON F2933

154032 PEARCE Mrs C M. (Delanay-Lewis) 20 Meadow Way, Westergate, Chichester, PO20 6QT. Tel:0243-542900
DAVIES DELAHAY EDWARDS GRIFFITH GRIFFITHS LEWIS LLEWELLYN F2589

154040 PEARCE Mr David John. 4 Brookfield Close, South Street, Braunton, Devon, EX33 2AN.
BUSTIN GEEN HICKS HINTON MANLEY MARLES PEARCE PHILLIPS Sanders SAUNDERS TUCKER TURNER WILLIAMS F5929

154059 PEARCE Mr Frank T. 16 Scratton Fields, Sole Street, Gravesend, Kent, DA12 3AS. Tel:0474-814530
Belchamber Belchambers BELLCHAMBERS CARLICK CUNNINGHAM FISHER FLIGHT FOOT HERMAN Hermann Hurman LANGMAID Lile LILL Lille LINES LUNN SHALDERS Shaulders TOOGOOD WATTS F1756

154067 PEARCE Major J A. 20 Meadow Way, Westergate, Chichester, Sussex, PO20 6QT. Tel:0243-542900
BOUCHET CRESPEL DE BEAUREGARD DE BEAUREGARDE EAGLES HARDESTY HIGHAM LINDGREN LINFITT MAW PEARCE RIEDER WARLTERS WILSON F1746

154075 PEARCE Mr John. 4 Jackson Croft, Morland, Penrith, Cumbria, CA10 3AU.
HEAGUE MORRISS PEARCE STANIER WALTER F1745

154083 PEARCE Mrs K J. Trefa, Fore Street, Marazion, Cornwall, TR17 0AD.
Thorp THORPE F6923

154091 PEARCE Miss K M. 3 Cecil Avenue, Enfield, Middx, EN1 1PT.
BRANCH HEATH HONER KITE PEARCE ROLES WITNEY WORTHINGTON F1590

154105 PEARCE Mrs Lily. (Turley) 36 Scrimshaw House, Oxford Street, Walsall, West Midlands, WS2 9JD. Tel:0922-641589
ALLEN LOOTES Loots MYERS TURLEY F4337

154113 PEARCE Mrs Marjorie. 12 Cotswold Way, Tilehurst, Reading, Berks, RG3 6SH.
ADDISON BOYDE DILLEY GILGRAVES JOY F3057

154121 PEARCE Mrs Olive. 4 Tudor Court, Park Road, High Barnet, Herts, EN5 5SH.
CLEAVE MINCHINTON PEARCE F3251

154148 PEARSE Mr Michael. 56 Valletort Road, Stoke, Plymouth, Devon, PL1 5PN. Tel:0752-562224
D'albamarle D'amirel D'amll D'aumarle Damarel Damarell Dambrell DAMEREL Damerell Dameril Damerill Damiral Dammarel Dammarell Damrel Damrell F6302

154156 PEARSON Mrs A L. 3312 East Costilla Ave, Littleton, CO 80122, USA.
Morell Morrel MORRELL Morrill F6664

154164 PEARSON Miss Ann. 4 Clifford Dibben Mews, Avenue Road, Southampton, Hants, SO2 1AL.
BREEZE CHESNEY COLMAN GARGRAVE LANGLEY PEARSON SIMES STUBBINGTON TALBOT WEIGHELL F6194

154172 PEARSON Mr Euan. 4 Beeches Road, Farnham Common, Bucks, SL2 3PR. Tel:0753-644734
ATKINSON BROOK DRAKE HODGSON KNAPTON OLDRIDGE PEARSON POGMORE SELLERS THURNTON F5294

154180 PEARSON Mr Geoffrey. 22 Lea Road, Ampthill, Beds, MK45 2PT. Tel:0525-404153
PEARSON POWELL F4631

154199 PEARSON Mr James. 60 Mansel Road East, Millbrook, Southampton, Hants, SO1 9DW. Tel:0703-777384
NORTHOVER PEARSON F1035

154202 PEARSON Mr P E. 13 Summit Drive, Freckleton, Preston, Lancs, PR4 1PP. Tel:0772-635569
BAKER BIRD PEARSON F5708

154210 PEARSON Mr Paul Robert. 4 Lionheart Road, Bearwood, Bournemouth, Dorset, BH11 9UB.
ARNOLD BAINES BAKER BOLLAND BOWLAND BROWN CALLAWAY CANNING CANNINGS CLARKE COBB COLE DALE DEAN FORDER FUDGE GREEN JEFFERY KING LEGG LOVELESS NEALE PADLEY PEARSON PENNY PERCY PIERCY STICKLAND TRIM WALKER WILKINSON WILSON YEATS F5358

154229 PEAT Dr John. 3 Dean Way, Storrington, Pulborough, W Sussex, RH20 4QN. Tel:0903-744970
EASTWOOD PEAT QUENETT STAINER F312

154237 PEATLING Mr Robert. 36 Park Lane, Wimborne Minster, Dorset, BH21 1LD.
PEATLING F3016

154245 PEAVER Mr R H. Edinburgh House, Cromer Road, Holt, Norfolk, NR25 6DZ.
DEVENPORT GREENHALGH PHILLIPS REVELL F721

154253 PEBERDY Mr R B. 38 Randolph Street, Oxford, OX4 1XZ.
Paybody Peabody PEBERDY Pebody Pepperday F262

154261 PECK Mr George. 6 Gresham Close, Newquay, Cornwall, TR7 2LF.
BOOSEY GODBOLD HURST MASON PECK REDGEWELL RODDA F2498

154288 PEDERSEN Mrs Muriel. (Orvis) 202 Carshalton Road, Sutton, Surrey, SM1 4SA. Tel:081-643-1493
ARCHER BACK BANTCOCK COPE DAVIES HURREN MEADOWS MULLEY ORVIS RATTLE F5079

154296 PEEL Mrs J E. (Wormald) Brook Cottage, Weeke Hill, Dartmouth, Devon, TQ6 9DB.
ADDINGTON HORSFORD HOSFORD OLNEY PARKS PEEL ROCKWELL WORMALD F1809

154318 PEELING Mrs J. 5 Solent View Close, Seaview, Isle Of Wight, PO34 5HZ.
HOPKINS LISTER PEELING SHINGLETON TINSLEY WAGG WRIGHT F415

154326 PEERS Miss E. 23 Westbrook Way, Wombourne, Wolverhampton, Staffs, WV5 0EA.
Tillstone TILSTON F6888

154334 PEGG Mr Raymond. 14 Hillcrest Drive, Beverley, E Yorks, HU17 7JL.
BROMLEY MCINNES PEGG F5233

154342 PEGLER Mrs Bernice. (Floyd) 76 Leap Valley Crescent, Downend, Bristol, Avon, BS16 6TN. Tel:0272-564964
ALFORD BAILEY Baily BALE Barnes BARNS BARRETT BARTLETT BLAGDON Bower BOWERY BRAIN Braine Brayne BREADY Breddy BRITTON BROWN BUSKIN Bustin CHEW COALMAN Coleman COULES Cowles COX DAVIS DAWES Daws DYER Finegan Finigan FINNIGAN FLOYD FOWLER GARROT GINGELL Gingle GOMER GRAVELL HARFORD HARRIS HARRISON HASKINS HOLLOWAY HOOD JAY KING LEAR LONG Lovel LOVELL MILLER MONK Monke Moreton MORTON MUGGLEWORTH Mugleworth Neads NEEDS NEWMAN NOBLE O'CONNELL PALMER Peglar PEGLER PILLINGER Pincot PINCOTT POLLINGER Pool POOLE PURDY RENDLE Renuall ROACH Roache ROGERS Scrace SCRASE SEWARD Shiell SHILL Shirt SHORT SHURT SNOW TAYLOR TREGILGUS TRIM WATTS WELCH Welsh WHITE Willmot WILLMOTT Wilmot Wilmott WILSON WREYFORD F4078

154350 PELLETIER Andre. 8788 Boul St Michel, Montreal, H1Z 3C2, CANADA.
PELLETIER F7342

154369 PEMBER Denis. 23 Du Maurier Road, North Lake 6163, AUSTRALIA.
PEMBER F7343

154377 PENDRED Mrs Mary. 72 Thistle Drive, Stanground, Peterborough, Cambs, PE2 8HY.
BALLARD BROUGHTON BULLARD EDEN HUDSON JARMAN LOVEDAY LOVELL PENDRED PHILLIPS ROBINSON STEWARD STEWART STORER WARD F7440

154385 PENFOLD Mr Leonard William. 12 Grove Court, Waltham Abbey, Essex, EN9 1BE. Tel:0992-715268
MANHOOD PENFOLD REED F896

154393 PENGELLY Mr Anthony Clive. 6 Smallcombe Road, Paignton, Devon, TQ3 3SL. Tel:0803-526918
PENGELLY F947

154407 PENGELLY Mr Joe. 36 Thorn Park, Mannamead, Plymouth, Devon, PL3 4TE. Tel:0752-661100
LYNE PENGELLY F2382

154415 PENGELLY Mr Richard A. Byways, Wern Goch Road, Cardiff, S Glam, CF2 6SD. Tel:0222-764418
BLACKMORE BRIGHT BURNARD CHUBB CROSS HUDSON LUXTON PENGELLY SLEEP WARREN F4510

154423 PENHALE Mr G W. 1 Albany Place, West Ferry, Dundee, DD5 1NR.
PENHALE PENHALL F1306

154431 PENIKET Mr & Mrs P F. (Ashmore) 44 Eggington Road, Wollaston, Stoubridge, West Midlands, DY8 4QJ. Tel:0384-397204
Parnacoat Parnacote PARNACOTT Parnecoat Parnecote Parnecott Parnecut Parnecutt Parnicoat Parnicote Parnicott Parnicutt Parnycoat Parnycote Parnycott Parnycutt Peenicott Penacot Penecad Peneceard Penecett Penecod Penecot Penecud Penekat Peneket Penekett Peneycud Peneycudd Peneycutt PENICAD Penicade Penicard Penicat Penicate Peniceard Peniced Penicet Penicoat Penicoate PENICOD Penicode Penicoot Penicord Penicorde Penicot Penicote Penicott PENICUD Penicudd Penicut Penicutt Peniend Penikat Penikate Peniked PENIKET PENIKETT Penikid Pennacott Pennaket Pennecett Penneket PENNEKETT Penneycidd Penneycod Penneycud Pennicad Pennicade PENNICARD Pennicarde Pennicate PENNICEARD Pennicoad Pennicoate Pennicod PENNICODD Pennicode Pennicood Pennicoot PENNICORD Pennicorde Pennicot Pennicote PENNICOTT Pennicotte PENNICUD Pennicudd Pennicutt Penniend Pennikat Pennikate Penniket PENNIKETT Pennikide PENNYCAD Pennycade Pennycard Pennycate Pennyceard Pennycid Pennycoad Pennycod Pennycodd Pennycode Pennycoed Pennycord Pennycorde Pennycot Pennycote PENNYCOTT PENNYCUD PENNYEND Pennykate Pennyrott Penocod Penycad Penycard Penycat PENYCATE PENYEAD F2496

154458 PENN Mrs Monica J. Champneys, 28 Petvin Close, Street, Somerset, BA16 0SX.
BENNETT CHESHIRE COLESBY DEVIS FLYNN GLOYNS GOODSON HIGGINS HIGGINSON HOTCHKISS HUGHES LEWIS MCMAIN PENN SANDERS SMALL STOCKER TAYLOR VINCENT WALTON WARD WARDEN WATHEW F2905

154466 PENNEY Mr Colin. Coppers, Oak Lane, Minster, Sheppey Kent, ME12 3QW. Tel:0795-872788
BAILEY BARLING BRISLEY PENNEY Pennie Penny TWIGG WHALEBONE WILDISH F1925

154474 PENNINGTON Mr Leslie. 6 Cross Lane, Grappenhall, Nr Warrington, Cheshire, WA4 2LW. Tel:0925-601597
BIGGINS EDWARDS FERGUSON MILLER PENNINGTON STIRZAKER TAYLOR WESTERN WILLIAMSON F527

154482 PENPRASE Mr Robert. 353 Liverpool St, West Hobart, TAS 7000, AUSTRALIA. Tel:+61-02-341927
COWIE LITTLE PENPRASE WAINE F5525

154490 PENTELOW Miss Joyce. 14 Bentham Road, Brockwell, Chesterfield, Derby, S40 4EZ. Tel:0246-230650
ASHCROFT BESTER HAWKES JAMES KNIGHTS LENTON Pentelo Penteloe PENTELOW Pentler Pentlo Pentloe Pentlow WELLS F3719

154504 PEPPERDINE Mr John. 17 Proctor Road, Sprowston, Norwich, Norfolk, NR6 1LA.
PEPPERDINE QUIPP QUIPPE F48

154512 PERCY Mr K. 63 The Ridgway, Sutton, Surrey, SM2 5JX. Tel:081-642-9151
LAIDLAW MCCREATH ROULSTON SHEWARD WHITEHOUSE F2143

154520 PERCY Miss Mabel. 19 Sycamore Avenue, Guide Post, Choppington, Northumberland, NE62 5NU.
BELL DAVISON GRAY LAWS NORRIS PATTERSON Pearcy PERCY REAY THOMPSON YELLOWLEY F6129

154539 PERKINS Miss Dorothy. 58 Lugard Road, Aigburth, Liverpool, Merseyside, L17 0BB. Tel:051-727-4419
BARKLEY HUTTON LEYLAND MARSHALL MOORE Parkin Pearkins PERKIN PERKINS Prevost Provest Provis PROVOST REID WILLIAMS F496

154547 PERKINS Mr Francis. Sunnyholme, Whitsands Road, Swaffham, Norfolk, PE37 7BJ.
PERKINS F810

154555 PERKINS Mr Jim. 23 Poundley Close, Castle Bromwich, Birmingham, B36 9SZ.

ANDREW CLARK CLARKE Parkins Parkyns PERKINS Perkyns Pirkins Pirkyns Purkins Purkyns Pyrkins Pyrkyns SABIN SANDERS SHAKESPEARE SPARGO TEW WATERS F1689

154563 PERKINS John & Eileen. (Hankey) 1 Glebeside, Witton Gilbert, Durham, DH7 6SD. Tel:091-371-0671
ADAMSON ANGUS ARROWSMITH ASHLEY BAINBRIGG BAKER BARREN BAZELY BEAVIS BELL BICKERSTAFF BILKE BISHOP BLACKET BRAMLEY BRIGGS BROADBENT BROWN BUCK CHAPMAN CHENEY CHURCHILL CLARK COLE COLLEY COUSSENS CURRY DAGLISH DAVISON DAWSON DONKIN DOWSON DRYDEN ELLIOTT ELLIS GAUDEN GAUNT GOLIGHTLY GOOKE GOWLAND GRAHAM GREAVES GREENWAY GRIEVE HALL HALLET HANKEY HAYNE HAYWELL HEAVISIDE HELLIER HERRON HIRST HOLMES HOPKINSON HOPPER HOWSON HUDSON JACKSON JOHNSON KEATT KIRKLY LEIGHTON LITTLE LOBLEY LOWES LUMMON MEECH NATTERAS PARKER PASSMORE PATTISON PERKINS PLOWMAN PYMER RAIN RAWES RAYNE ROBINSON ROPER RUTTER SCHORAH SIMES SLACK SMORTHWAITE SOULSBY STEPHENSON STEVENSON SWITHINBANK TALBOT TEASDALE THOMPSON THORNER TIBBS TIMPERLEY TOMKINS VALENCE WAITON WALKER WALLBRIDGE WATERHOUSE WATSON WEARS WHEATLEY WILKS WILLIAMS WILLIS WILSON WINSKILL F2689

154571 PERKINS Mr John Philip. 24 Withens Avenue, Sheffield, S6 1WE.
DUCK PERKINS PIGG SPANTON F3750

154598 PERKINS Mrs Margaret. 8 Steadman Avenue, Manor Farm Estate, Cosby, Leics, LE9 5UZ.
Cloughs Clous CLOWES Clows ELLIS GRANT HALBARD Halbert HASTINGS Holbard JORDAN Langdail LANGDALE Langdayle Langdell Langdill PERKINS RICHARDSON Toesland TOSELAND Tosland WAGSTAFFE F2765

154601 PERKINS Mr R V. 45 St Mary Street, Farcet, Peterborough, Cambs, PE7 3AR. Tel:0733-242214
ASKIN BLAKELEY BROADHEAD BURTON BUTTLE COPLEY FARRAR FISHER HAINSWORTH HALDSWORTHE HAUMSHAW HEAP Holdsworth ISSOTT JOHNSON LAMBERT MITCHEL PERKINS RICHARDSON ROBINSON SLATER SUNDERLAND SWALLOW TALBOT F4800

154628 PERKINS Mr Stephen. Ludshott Manor, Bramshott, Hants, GU30 7RD.
JORY Mitre MITTER PERKINS Pilston PULESTON Pulieston Puliston F592

154636 PERKS Mr Ken. 38 Glynde Way, Thorpe Bay, Essex, SS2 4TS. Tel:0702-586517
Pearkes Pearks Perkes PERKS Pierkes Pierks Pirkes Pirks Purkes Purks F1880

154644 PERKS Mrs O W R. 11 Hawthorne Walk, Beck Row, Bury St Edmunds, Suffolk, IP28 8UD. Tel:0638-711072
WINDRIDGE F6134

154652 PERKS Mr R F. 147 Barns Road, Cowley, Oxford, OX4 3RB. Tel:0865-773291
PERKS F3815

154660 PERRAUDIN Mrs R. 7 Higham Road, Woodford Green, Essex, IG8 9JN. Tel:081-504-2275
BRAY F201

154679 PERRETT Mrs P S. 36 Elm Court Gardens, Crowborough, E Sussex, TN6 1BP.
Parrett Parrott PERRETT F6733

154687 PERRIN Mrs Marjorie H. (Port) 4 Beaumont Street, Herne Bay, Kent, CT6 8LX.
ABBOTT GURNEY HEATHCOTE KNOWLES LANCASTER PERRIN PORT SCRIVENS SPICER F5790

154695 PERRINS Mr Nigel R. 18 Hill End Grove, Bradford, W Yorks, BD7 4RP. Tel:0274-571060
CAWTHORNE DANIEL HORSFALL PERRINS F218

154709 PERRIS Mr C R. 73 Hamilton Avenue, Pyrford, Woking, Surrey, GU22 8RU.
Coney CONWAY COWARD CURRY DOWN HUTTON LAGER LANSDOWN LOCK Locke MOSS Perres PERRIS PORTCH PURCHASE SCOTT SEALY Silley SPRAGG SWASH Waistell WASTELL F2588

154717 PERRON Guy. Cp 6700, Sillery, Quebec, G1T 2W2, CANADA.
PERRON F7344

154725 PERROW Mr J R. 2 Field House, Bassingby, Bridlington, N Humberside, YO16 4UH.
Parrow Perow Perowe PERROW F7051

154733 PERRY Mr Alan. 29 High Street, Stoke Sub Hamdon, Somerset, TA14 6PR. Tel:0935-822703
BAKER BLACKER COX GRANT HISCOCKS LILLINGTON MOGGRIDGE PERRY PICKARD SHEPPARD F2421

154741 PERRY Mrs Barbara. (Ward) Virginia Cottage, Gainsborough Road, Girton, Newark, Notts, NG23 7HX.
CLARKE WARD F1521

154768 PERRY Mr D T A. 35 Williams Orchard, Highnam, Glos, GL2 8EL. Tel:0452-417929
Comeada Comeaddowe Comeado Comeadow Comeadowe Comeda Comedo Commeda Commedo Commody Coromeadow Coweddow Cowmadow Cowmaydo Cowmaydy Cowmeaddowe COWMEADOW Cowmeadowe Cowmeadoy Cowmeda Cowmeddow Cowmeddowe Cowmedo Cowmedow CROWMEADOW PERRY F4428

154776 PERRY Ms K. 14 Underwood Close, Dawlish, Devon, EX7 9RY.
PERRY SLANN F2493

154784 PERRY Mr Laurence. 20 Ewell Close, Chorley, Lancs, PR6 8TT.
BLAMIRES BREAREY FISHER PERRY F3994

154792 PERRY Mr Leonard H. 22 Perch Drive, Mile End, Coleford, Glous, GL16 7DG. Tel:0594-34168
DUGGINS Englethorpe Glaconbury Glassenbury GLASTONBURY GREEN Ingamthorp Ingarthorp INGLETHORPE Inglethrapp Inglethropp LAUGHER Lawer Lawgher MILLS PACE PACEY PERRY POWELL PROSSER SHORE SPIERS WINDOW WREN WRENN F277

154806 PERRY Mrs M J. (Sylvester) 105 Clinton Crescent, Hainault, Essex, IG6 3AW.
BURKITT HANDSLEY HARLING JENKINSON KENDRICK MITCHELL MOSSOP NELSON OLLIVE PERRY PHILLIPS ROWELL ROWLE SYLVESTER WHEELER WHITE WOODWARD F4420

154814 PERRY Mrs Marion E. (Halls) 9 Bodleian Close, Daventry, Northants, NN11 4RY. Tel:0327-78401
HALLS PERRY F3874

154822 PERT Mr & Mrs G H. 189 Dominion Road, Worthing, Sussex, BN14 8LH. Tel:0903-35836
PERT F649

154830 PESKETT Mrs Shirley. (Cook) 11 Gun Road Gardens, Knebworth, Herts, SG3 6ED. Tel:0438-813979
BALDRY COOK HARBER LEE MARCH MILLS MITCHELL NUNN PARSONS PENFOLD PESKETT TICKNER TREAGUST VINCE F368

154849 PETCOFF Mrs Muriel. (Cameron) Box 36, Riverhurst, Sask, SOH 3P0, CANADA.
ALEXANDER ALLAN CAMERON GLEN HARVIE JACK F5464

154857 PETERS Dr C D. 34 Combe Road, Combe Down, Bath, Avon, BA2 5HY. Tel:0225-833605
HEYSETT Heyssett PETERS ROUSE Rousi Rowse F6354

154865 PETERS Mr D. Purbeck Cottage, Chalk Lane, East Horsley, Leatherhead Surrey, KT24 6TH.
Peter PETERS F3294

154873 PETERS Mr Michael H. 10 Gore Court Road, Sittingbourne, Kent, ME10 1QN.
ADY ADYE BARLING BARTON BASSAGE BRIGHAM BROOKE BROWN BROWNE BURCHETT CHALFONT COOT DE BOUVERIE De Bouveries DE BRYN DE LA PIERRE DE ROS ELVEY EVE FFARNFOULD FITZGERALD FORSYTHE FORTRYE FRYAR GERRARD GRAHAM GREEN Grosshurst GROVEHURST GULBY GUMBERT HARMS HARRIS HECKLES HENMAN HEXTALL HOYLE HUDSON HUNTER JACKSON JAMESON KISBEY MAPLE MARKWELL MATSON MIDDLESTON MILWAY MUNNE NICHOLSON NORRES PACKHAM PAGE PEARSON PEDDER PETERS PEYFORER PLAYNE RATCLIFFE RICKARD ROWLAND SMITH Steel STEIL STOKES SYMINGES THIEFFRIES TURNBULL WALLER WALTER WATSON WAUGH WETENHALL WHITMAN WILLIAMS WOOD WOOLARD F2899

154881 PETLEY-JONES David. Tremywawr, Llanfair Caereinion, Powys, SY12 0BZ. Tel:0938-810841
ABERNETHY ALFFEWE ALPHEIGH AMIS APLETREFEUD ARMYAS ASHBURNHAM ASHDOWNE ASTLEY BADLESMERE BAILLIE BALE BAMBURGH BARLINGHAM BARNWELL BARRE BATTISFORD BEAUMONT BELKNAPPE BERKELEY BETTELEY BIGHAM BINGLEY BIRCH BIRCHENSTY BIRD BIRSTY Blackley BLAKELY BLYKE BODULGATE BONVILE BOURCHIER Bourgchier BOYD BRANDON BROCKET BROWN BUCKLAND Burcher BURLEY BURWASH BYNG CAM CAME CAMPBELL CANTELUPE CARLTON CAWSTON CHAWORTH CHEYNEY CLOPTON COBHAM COMBRIDGE COOKE CORBET Corbett CORBY COTTY CREYE CROMER CROWMER CUMYN D'UZES DANIEL

DARKYNHOLL DE BAR DE BOHUN DE BRAOSE DE CLAVERING DE HADINDEN DE HEVRE DE LA QUEULLE DE LEYBURNE DE LOUVAINE DE MANDEVILLE DE MONTFORT DE QUINCY DE RIDELSFORD DE SANDFORD DE SAY DE SEGRAVE DE STUTEVILLE De Toeni De Toni DE TONY DE TRIE DE VALLERIES DE WAER DE WAUTHAM DE WESTON DELAWARE DEVEREUX DODDINGTON DROWET DRUMMOND DUNCAN DUNN EARDNEY EATON ERINGTON EVEREST EVERINGHAM EWINGS EYNES FARMER Fevyear FEVYER FIENNES Fines FISHER FISK FLEMING FOLIOT FRANKLIN FREMLYN FRENCH FRITH GABRIEL GATTACRE GEORGE GIBSON GOATER GOUSAL GOUSHILL GRAHAM GRIFFITHS GUILDFORD HAINES HALDEN HALDENE HALL HALYBURTON HAMMOND HARCOURT HARROWER HASSALL HASTINGS Haute HAWTE HEAD HINTON HOLCROFT HOTOFT HUSSEY INCE JACOB JERMY JOHNSTON JONES KEITH KER KIRKBY KYNASTON LA ZOUCH LAMBE LATHOM LAUDER LAWNDY LE BRUNE LEIGH LEYCESTER LINGEN LIVINGSTONE LLOYD LOCKYER LUCK LYNKHULL LYONS MACKENZIE MASSY MAUREWARD MAXWELL MILLER MILLS MINCHIN MOODIE MOORE MORRISON MORTIMER MOTON MULOCK MURRAY MYERS NEVILLE NISBET NISBETT NISELL NORTHWOOD NOTTON O'HARA OLIPHANT PAGENHAM PAISEY PATRICK PATTERSON PAUL PAULIN PEARSON PEMBERTON PENBURY Petle PETLEY Pettely PEVEREL PEVERELL PIERREPOINT Pitle Pittley PLUMLEY POLHILL PONTON PORTER POWELL POYNTZ PRAYERS PRETTY PULESTON REED RIVERS ROE SALE SALES SALTON SANDBACH SANKEY SCOULLER SETON SEYLIARD SLIGHTER SMOULT SOUTHILL STANFORD STANGRAVE STIRLING STREATFEILD SUDEN SUMMERS SYDNEY TAILBOYS TANSER Tansur TAYLOR TERRY THEOBALD THICKNESSE THOMAS THOMPSON THORP TIMBERDEN TIPTOFT TODD TYMBERDEN VAVASOUR VILLIERS VIPONT WAKE WALLEYS WALLIS WASSELL WATERS WEMYSS WHASSALL WHITMORE WHITNEY WHITTON WILLOUGHBY WINGFIELD WISEMAN WOODCOCKE WOODGATE WOODVILLE WOTTON WYKINGE WYVERTON F1219

154903 PETTET Mrs Rita. (Thorner) 30 Ashbarn Crescent, Winchester, Hants, SO22 4LW.
CLARK CLAYTON COPP ELLENDEN FINNIS HOLE JORDAN KINGSFORD LEONARDS PACKER PETTET PETTIT RAMSAY ROWSELL THORNER TINCKNELL WICKARDS WICKERS F1115

154911 PETTIFER Miss Joyce M E. 123 Gretton Road, Winchcombe, Cheltenham, Glous, GL54 5EL.
BONNER PETTIFER TANFIELD F333

154938 PETTIGREW Mrs Pat. 2 Third Avenue, Lancing, W Sussex, BN15 9PU.
CAIGER JEFFERY F2720

154946 PETTINGER Miss Joyce. 15 Syringa Street, Marsh, Huddersfield, W Yorks, HD1 4PD.
BEASTON BEST BIELBY BOLT BORODALE BORROWDALE BRADLEY BURTON BUTLER CLEMENT Clemmet COWPER CROSLAND Crossland FLETCHER FORD FRANK GILES GOUNDRILL HARDING HESSEY HUNTER Jiles JOHNSON MASON MATTHEWS Mayson PARKIN PETTINGER RABY ROBINSON SHARP SHEPHERD SMITH SPENCER SUTCLIFFE THORP THWAITES TOMLINSON TROTTER TUNE WOMERSLEY F3049

154954 PETTIT Mrs Marina Helen. 42 Dunham Close, Bedford, MK42 0LU. Tel:0234-341920
HUNT PORTER SHEDDEN Sheddon TAYLOR F3097

154962 PETTMAN Miss Sheila. 57 London Road, Hertford Heath, Hertford, Herts, SG13 7RJ. Tel:0992-586098
BROADBRIDGE DUKER GOLDFINCH HAINES MANKTELOW PETMAN PETTMAN RICE SHUTTLEWORTH F5315

154970 PETYT Mr Anthony. 10 Station Street, Sandal, Wakefield, W Yorks, WF1 5AF. Tel:0924-255047
CURTIS FORMAN FOSTER HISCOCK HODGSON LAUND LEECH PALMER PEGG Petit Pettie PETTY Pettyt PETYT ROBINSON SMART TIPLADY WILLAM YOUNG F1996

154989 PEWSEY Mr Philip. 80 Hamstel Road, Southend On Sea, Essex, SS2 4PF. Tel:0702-467377
PEWSEY F2916

154997 PEYMAN Miss S E. 15 The Grovelands, Lancing, West Sussex, BN15 8HY.
PEYMAN Pyeman F7178

155004 PHANCO Mr Graeme M. 1 Carleith Terrace, Duntocher, Clydebank, Scotland, G81 6HZ.
ERSKINE Fancho Fanco Fanker Fanko Funcko HORN Howieson HOWISON KIRKWOOD MCFARLANE MORRIS Pfankuch PHANCO STABLES TAYLOR F1509

155012 PHELPS Mr R. Lyndley Croft, Bridge Road, Cranleigh, Surrey, GU6 7HH.
Felps PHELPS Philps F6665

155020 PHENNA Mr Edward. Trigfa Glyd, 19 Tyn Y Coed Road, Great Orme, Llandudno Gwynedd, LL30 2QA. Tel:0492-878984
FENNA FENNAH PHENNA PHENNAH F10

155039 PHILLIP Mr Richard D. 25 Denton Drive, Wallasey, Wirral, L45 7QS.
AYRTON CARTER DARLINGTON DIXON DOOLEY EVERARD HOLDSWORTH HOLGATE MILNES PHILLIP WHITELEY F3060

155047 PHILLIPS Mrs C. 3 Moseley Road, Cheadle Hulme, Cheshire, SK8 5HO.
BUNCE BURGESS GRAHAM HARRIS HARRISON MASSEY MCCLELLAND PHILLIPS REYNOLDS SMITH F6370

155055 PHILLIPS Dr Christopher. 34 Chestnut Court, 65 Mulgrave Road, Sutton, Surrey, SM2 6LR.
BARRATT BRAWN CHESTER COLLINS DODD HARVEY HILL HIPWOOD MORRIS PEARSON PHILLIPS POWELL ROGERS SMITH SOLLOM WALKER WEBB WHITBY F4837

155063 PHILLIPS Mrs D. 2204 West Houston Ave, Spokane, WA 99208-4440, USA.
POTTER Potterf Pottier F7060

155071 PHILLIPS Mrs Helen. (Sparry) 28 Tawbury Close, Oakenshaw South, Redditch, Worcs, B98 7YZ. Tel:0527-546871
PHILLIPS SPARRY F5776

155098 PHILLIPS Mr Ian R. 5 Windsor Court, York Close, Horsham, W Sussex, RH13 5PH.
Brannen BRENNAN BRIGGS PEARSON Philip Philips Phillip PHILLIPS RAE RAWNSLEY Rea STEVENSON THOMSON F1628

155101 PHILLIPS Mr Ivor David. Waverley, Elmley Castle, Pershore, Worcs, WR10 3HS. Tel:0386-710337
CADWALLADER EVANS HAYWARD MINCHIN OLDHAM PHILLIPS SIMONS SYMONDS THOMAS WALKLEY WEBSTER WOODWARD F761

155128 PHILLIPS Mrs Margaret. (Horswill) 12 High Street, Broseley, Shropshire, TF12 5HE. Tel:0952-883154
HORSEWELL HORSEWILL HORSWELL HORSWILL F1617

155136 PHILLIPS Mr Michael S. 33 Olney Road, Emberton, Olney, Bucks, MK46 5BX.
CHALMERS LEDGERWOOD MANETTE MANUELL MINETTE PHILLIPS SHERIDAN F6387

155144 PHILLIPS Mr Paul. 71 Osborne Road, East Cowes, Isle Of Wight, PO32 6RZ. Tel:0983-290293
HARVEY HILL NEEDHAM SLADE THWAITES TILSED WEBB YOUNG F5336

155152 PHILLIPS Mr Richard. 5 Cedar Avenue, Beeston, Nottingham, NG9 2HA.
BOULTON BUSSEY DANCE DENHAM FITZGERALD HODGET JOHNSON LOWE MASON MATTHEWS PHILLIPS SAMPSON WELLS WHEELER WHITTAKER F4391

155160 PHILLIPS Mr Stephen. 18 South Road, Ash Vale, Aldershot, Hants, GU12 5AJ. Tel:0252-331982
CULE F4854

155179 PHILLISKIRK Mr Thomas. 141 Whitefield Crescent, Penshaw, Houghton Le Spring, Tyne & Wear, DH4 7QX. Tel:091-584-4945
Feliskirke Felixkirke Felyxkyrk Filiskirk Filiskyrke Filliskirke Fylleskyrke Le Felicekyrk Pheliskyrk Philickerke PHILLISKIRK Philliskirke Phyllykyrk F5885

155187 PHILPOT Mr I E. 11 Cefn On Meadows, Lisvine, Cardiff, CF4 5FL.
Friant Friate Friatt Frient Friett Friitt Friott FRYATT Goimar Goimer Goimor Goimour Goimur Goymar GOYMER Goymor Goymour Goymur F6812

155195 PHILPOT Mrs Pamela. (Baxter) 31 Chichester Drive, West Saltdean, Sussex, BN2 8SH.
BARNARDIER BAXTER HITCHINS PHILPOT REAY WRIGHT F5977

155209 PHILPOTT Mr B G. Brimar, Church Lane, Manby, Louth, Lincs, LN11 8HL. Tel:0507-327431
Felipot Felpot Felypot Ffillopott Ffillpot Ffilpot Ffilpott Filepot Fillepotte Fillpot Fillpott Fillpotte Filpott Fylopot Fylpot Fylpott Phelipot Phelipote Phelipott Phelpot Phelpotte Phelpottes Philepot Philipot

Philipott Philippot Philippotte Phillipott Phillpot Phillpotts Philpootte PHILPOT Philpote PHILPOTT Philpotte Philpotts Philputt Philypot Philypott Phylpot Phylpott Phylpotte Phylypot Phylypotte F204

155217 PHILPOTT Mr John Austin. 78 Ashleigh Road, Exmouth, Devon, EX8 2JZ. Tel:0395-276443
CARR DAVY Filpot Filpott GAYDON GULLICK HOLNESS HORNE LAMPERT MONCKTON RUSSELL OSMOND Philcock Philcott Philipot Phillpot Phillpott Philpot PHILPOTT Phylpote Phylpott F4264

155225 PHILPOTT Mr R M. 35 Berkeley Road, Kenilworth, Warks, CV8 1AQ. Tel:0926-54980
BERG BIRCHER Burcher Cook COOKE FITZGERALD FLACK GRIFFITHS HARRIS Harriss Keneally Kenealy Kenelly KENELY Kennely Line Lines LYNE Lynes NELMES O'SHEA Phillpott Phillpotts Philpot PHILPOTT REA ROBERTS SHEA SHORT STEPHENS F1441

155233 PHILSON Mrs M. 3/5 Chartwell Avenue, Glenfield, Auckland, NEW ZEALAND.
DEWDER Duder Filson PHILSON F6690

155241 PHIPPARD Mr Michael. 36 Wellesley Drive, Crowthorne, Berks, RG11 6AL.
PHIPPARD F6500

155268 PHIPPS Mr G H. 99 Acomb Crescent, Newcastle Upon Tyne, NE3 2BD. Tel:091-285-5491
PHIPPS F105

155276 PHIPPS Mrs O. 21 Hillside Crescent, Northwood, Middx, HA6 1RP. Tel:0923-823359
ALDOUS Baldery Baldrey Baldry BALORT BLOCK BOTWRIGHT BRANDSON Branson BROWN Buckenham BUCKINGHAM BURLINGHAM BUTTON Cachpole CAPON CATCHPOLE Coats COLLINS COOK COOPER DEWELL ENGLISH FEAST Fish Fisk FISKE FLETCHER FLORRY Flory Flurry FULCHER Fulger Fulshire GARDINER Gardner GOATH GOATS GREENWOOD HEWITT Huet Huit JAMES KING LEMAN Lemman Lemon LEWIS LIMER Limmer MANNING May Mayes MAYS MILLES Mills ORIVER PACKARD PAIN PARSONS Payne PEDDER PLUMBLEY Plumbly Reddit Reddy REDHEAD Right Ring RINGE Rite Sier Sirret SKIPPER SMITH Spaul SPAWL Sporle STANWARD STURGEON SYRE SYRETT THWAITE Thwaites TILL Toakely TOAKLEY Toaklove Tockeley TURNER VESSEY Waites Wallace WALLIS WEBB WOOD Woodward WOOLNER WOOLNOUGH WOOLWARD WRIGHT F6028

155284 PICK Mrs D. Kingsmead, Medbury Road, R D Hawarden, NEW ZEALAND.
Batey BATY Batye Bayty DYALL F7107

155292 PICKERING Mrs Isabel. (Baldwin) Lescrow Farm, Passage Lane, Fowey, Cornwall, PL23 1JS. Tel:0726-832437
BALDWIN PICKERING F3135

155306 PICKERING Mrs P R. (Heath) 443 Doncaster Road, Ardsley, Barnsley, South Yorks, S71 5ER.
FITZPATRICK HEATH SWINSON WESTON F5284

155314 PICKETT Mr Henry F W. 16 High Street, Aylesford, Kent, ME20 7BG. Tel:0622-719823
PICKETT F6160

155322 PICKNELL Miss P M. 31 Friston Avenue, Eastbourne, E Sussex, BN22 0EL.
CARPENTER KINGSFORD MACKETT MEEK PICKNELL PICKNOLL VENN WEATHERSBEE F5015

155330 PICKSTONE Mr Alan & Mrs Elsie. (Fish) 31 Lyndhurst Avenue, Hazel Grove, Stockport, Cheshire, SK7 5PN.
Bickston Peckton Pexton Pickstan Pickston PICKSTONE Pickstones Picton Pigston Pixston Pixstone Pixton Pixtone Theckston F4969

155349 PICKUP Mrs Annie Atkinson. (Holt) 227 Bradford Road, Wrenthorpe, Wakefield, W Yorks, WF1 2AT.
ATKINSON SMALLMAN F6431

155357 PICKUP Mr Trevor. 51 Kingsley Road, Shirley, Southampton, Hants, SO1 3QP. Tel:0703-786961
BENNETT BURDFIELD FREEMAN GATES MCCARTY PANNEL PARSONS PICKUP PORTER QUIN SEAGRAVE SUTTON TINGLEY VINCENT WHITE F6234

155365 PIDWELL Mr Christopher. 16 St Michaels Road, Decoy, Newton Abbot, Devon, TQ12 1DJ. Tel:0626-68002
PIDWELL F4873

155373 PIENKOS Mrs Ann. Langdale, Proffits Lane, Helsby, Warrington Cheshire, WA6 9JX.
ATKINSON BARBER FLICK FOUNTAIN GADSBY HANNAM HANSON HOBBS KNIGHTS LUCAS PHILLIPS ROWNTREE SHEPHERD SPIVEY STEVENSON SWALES SWALLOW TAPSELL WOOTON F2937

155381 PIERSON Mr Mark. 30 Jeffreys Road, Cressing, Braintree, Essex, CM7 8JQ. Tel:0376-20994
BLAKE CHISHOLM DE CARLE HARVEY PIERSON THOMPSON THOMSON VEYSEY WELLS F4255

155403 PIFF Mr Reginald E G. 3 Woodend, Pirbright Road, Farnborough, Hants, GU14 7BA. Tel:0252-542593
PIFF F3308

155411 PIKE Mr Christopher. Stone Cottage, Norwich Road, Roughton, Norwich, Norfolk, NR11 8NA.
GARDENER PIKE ROTHERA THAXTER UNDERWOOD F6353

155438 PIKE Mrs R J. 24 Heath Crescent, Griffith, NSW 2680, AUSTRALIA.
JAMES LANCASTER PALLISTER PIKE SHINGLES SKINNER TOY F5433

155446 PIKE Mr Robin. 195 Long Lane, Tilehurst, Reading, Berks, RG3 6YW.
PIKE F783

155454 PIKETT Mrs Jean Ann. (Royle) 84 Ridge Langley, Sanderstead, South Croydon, Surrey, CR2 0AR.
Colet COLLETT CRIDDLE Cridle HEADLAND LEE Pickett Piket PIKETT Pykett Rayle Royal Royall ROYLE Ryle F6350

155462 PILBEAM Mrs Norma. (Cooper) 45 Heather Court, Stockbridge Road, Chichester, W Sussex, PO19 2HJ.
COOPER PILBEAM Pilbeame Pilbean Pilbin Pillbeam Pilvin Procktor Procter PROCTOR F4950

155470 PILCHER Mrs E J. 61 Drayton Bridge Road, Hanwell, London, W7 1ET.
BUCK DELLER DYMENT GRANGER KNOPP MOULE SADLER SAPSED UHRMACHER WASS F2326

155489 PILGRIM Mr Peter J. 2 Pickering Close, Timperley, Altrincham, Cheshire, WA15 6PT. Tel:061-980-7581
BINNS EYRE FULTHORP Fulthorpe MASSEY PILGRIM WEBSTER F4625

155497 PILKINGTON Mr David G. 48 Gough Way, Cambridge, CB3 9LW. Tel:0223-354019
ANDERSON CALVER DOXEY DUNNING KIPPING MILLAR PILKINGTON SLACK TWEEDALE F3609

155500 PILL Mr David. 9 Springwood Hall Gardens, Huddersfield, W Yorks, HD1 4HA. Tel:0484-429191
BANN BEAMONT BENNETT BENT BOOTH BRIDEOAKE BROTHERTON CALDWELL CORNS ECKERSLEY EVANS Forster FOSTER GREEN HALTON HENSHAW HILTON HOUGHTON HUGHES HUGHSON LANGHAM NAYLOR PARSLOW PILL PINCHES PUGH SMITH STREET THOMAS TUNSTALL WAKEFIELD WARD WATSON WEEDALL WELSBY WIBLING WIGGINS WILLIAMSON WILMOT WORSLEY WRIGHT F2230

155519 PILLING Mrs K V. 2 Willow Way, Darras Hall, Ponteland, NE20 9RJ. Tel:0661-71526
HAWKES LAMPWRIGHT PIEARSON PILLING VARLEY YOUNGMAN F3000

155527 PIM Mr F Bewley. 134 Glebe Avenue, Ickenham, Uxbridge, Middx, UB10 8PG. Tel:0895-636745
PIM Pimm Pym F3747

155535 PIMLETT Mr Kenneth. Derwenfa, Gellifor, Ruthin, Clwyd, LL15 1RY.
PIMLETT F3762

155543 PINCHING Mr A A. 11 Braemar Avenue, Wood Green, London, N22 4BY. Tel:081-888-8910
CHANCELLOR LEEDHAM PINCHING RICKERBY UNDERWOOD F5258

155551 PINDER Mr William E. 27 St Leonards Grove, Bradford, W Yorks, BD8 9PN.
GREEN HOOPER PINDER WHITE F4026

155578 PINGRAM Mr Frederick. Crooked Oak, 10 Woodland Way, New Milton, Hants, BH25 5RT. Tel:0425-638271
Ingam Ingraham Ingrarum Pangeram Pangerham Peagram Peagrem Peagrim Peagrum Peagrym Pegram Pegrem Pegrim Pegrum Pegrym Pelgram Pelgrem Pelgrin Pelgrum Pelgrym Pemgram Pemgrem Pemgrin Pemgrum Pemgrym Pengeram Pengerham Pengram Pengrem Pengrim Pengrum Pengrym Pigram Pigrem Pigrim Pigrum Pigrym Pilgram Pilgrem Pilgrin Pilgrum Pilgrym

Pimgram Pimgrem Pimgrin Pimgrum Pimgrym Pinckam Pinckham Pinckomb Pinckombe Pincomb Pincombe Pingeram Pingerham PINGHAM Pingram Pingrem Pingrim Pingrum Pingrym Pinkam Pinkham Pinkomb Pinkombe Pringham Pygrem Pygrim Pygrum Pygrym Pylgram Pylgrem Pylgrin Pylgrum Pylgrym Pymgram Pymgrem Pymgrin Pymgrum Pymgrym Pyngeram Pyngerham Pyngram Pyngrem Pyngrim Pyngrum Pyram F5365

155586 PINHORN Mr M. Norman'S Place, Newbridge, Yarmouth, Isle Of Wight, PO41 0TY.
Penhorn Penhorne PINHORN Pinhorne Pynhorn F7050

155594 PINION Mrs Barbara. (Allen) 61 Damolly Road, Newry, Co Down, N Ireland, BT34 1QR. Tel:0693-62716
ALLEN BURDEN FISHER MATHEWS Matthews MILLER PALMER Penion PINION Pinnion Pinnions F697

155608 PINKNEY Mrs P. (Peggy) 2 Old Common, Furneux Pelham, Buntingford, Herts, SG9 0LQ. Tel:0279-777503
ADAMS ALLSOP CAULTON COLE CRESSWELL Halloway HARRISON HEPPLE HOLLOWAY Holoway JOHNSON MOSSOM NEWTON NICHOLSON PARKIN PINKNEY Rayner RAYNOR SHIELLAW SHILLAW Sladdin SLADEN Sladin WAKE WILLIAMS F587

155616 PINKNEY Mr Simon. 30 Burnt Oak, Cookham Rise, Maidenhead, Berks, SL6 9RN.
CASTLE COX De Picquigny De Pinkeni DIXON Peneni Pinchene Pinchengi Pincheni Pinckney Pinkeigni Pinkeney Pinkeni Pinkeny PINKNEY POLLARD Pynhenye Pynkenheye Pynkney RUSSELL WILKERSON F3211

155624 PINNELL Miss Patricia. 102 Westward Road, Cainscross, Stroud, Glous, GL5 4JA. Tel:0453-763254
PINNELL F2432

155632 PINWILL Mr Norman C. Bryn Y Wawr, Synod Inn, Llandysul, Dyfed, SA44 6JB. Tel:0545-580135
BEAN DE CARTERET DESPERQUES-COUTANCHE FOOT Foote Foott Footte GOODALL KITSON L ANGLOIS MOURANT Penwell Penwill Pinhoul Pinoil Pinwell PINWILL POPPLEWELL STANLEY THOMAS WARD WILKES WORSNIP F572

155640 PIPE Mr E John. 17 Hornchurch Hill, Whyteleafe, Surrey, CR3 0DA.
SOUTHEY F6280

155659 PIPER Mrs D J. 33 Dellfield Road, Hatfield, Herts, AL10 8EW.
PIPER Pipers Pipper Pyer F6935

155667 PIPER Mr George A. 37 Penfold Road, Folkestone, Kent, CT19 6DQ.
BENNICKE BRICKENDEN BRIENT CHURCH HORTON HUNT JAFFREY LANYON MAY PIPER F6038

155675 PIPER Mrs Margaret. 56 Western Street, Swindon, Wiltshire, SN1 3JR. Tel:0793-525886
GRADY HOUSSART MOWLING F1529

155683 PIPER Mr William. Sutton House, Sutton Valance, Maidstone, Kent, ME17 3HH.
BARNES Detmar DETTMER Dittmar Dittmer DROUGHT FREEMAN HAMLEY HANGER JACKSON KELLAWAY Kelleway Kelloway Kelway KEMPSON KIRBY LEAR MAITLAND MILLS PAINTER F4418

155691 PIPER-SMITH Mrs Martyna. (Walle) 10 Rodney Close, Langney Point, Eastbourne, E Sussex, BN23 6AR.
ALLBRIGHT BARTLETT BOLTON BROMFIELD CALCRAFT CHALK COLE COWLEY EARLY FAULKNER FRAMPTON KNIGHT MITCHAM NAGLE PIPER PLUMRIDGE REAKES RILEY ROWE SLADE SMITH STAIRS WALLE WHITE WINTER F5097

155705 PIRRIE Mr David. 26 The Green, Bathgate, West Lothian, Scotland, EH48 4DB.
GOODFELLOW HERRIES HOPE JAPP NICHOLSON Nicolson PIRIE Pirrie RENWICK SUTTIE WATT Whigam WHIGHAM F2364

155713 PITCAIRN Mrs Margaret Gaywood. (Thompson) 10 Farmerie Road, Hundon, Sudbury, Suffolk, CO10 8HA. Tel:0440-86467
BELLARS BROWNLIE FORREST GAYWOOD GRAYSON HUTLEY MEIKLE PEEL PITCAIRN SIGSWORTH THOMPSON WAIND WILSON F6045

155721 PITMAN Mrs F. Le Petit Coin Du Pre, Victoria Road, St Saviour, Jersey, JE2 7QG. Tel:0534-33795
SIMS F5051

155748 PITT Mr John. Moorview, 4 Bole Hill, Sheffield, S8 8QE. Tel:0742-508401
ENSOR PITT F1882

155756 PITTAM Mrs Brenda. (Berkshire) Aurora, Moorend, Yardley Gobion, Towcester, Northants, NN12 7UF. Tel:0908-542474
Barkshire BERKSHIRE Birkshire Burkshire GLENN Offa OFFER PARKER PITTAM F6062

155764 PITTMAN Mrs Susan. 27 Old Chapel Road, Crockenhill, Swanley, Kent, BR8 8LL.
BICKNELL DUNN EAST FOSTER HAWKINS LONG MEDHURST MILLS ONN SCARBOROUGH F2736

155772 PITTOCK Mr I M. Beach Lodge, Tower Hill, Tankerton, Whitstable, Kent, CT5 2BW.
PITTOCK Pttock-Buss F7151

155780 PITTS Mr J. 21 Elm Grove, Toddington, Dunstable, Beds, LU5 6BJ. Tel:05255-4615
COOKE HAYWARD HOLWAY NATION Nations Pits Pittes Pittis PITTS Pyttes REED RUSSELL F2414

155799 PIZER Mr R. 6 Drews Court, Churchdown, Gloucestershire, GL3 2LD.
Payser Pazzer PIZER Poiser POIZER Poyser Poysor Poyzer Pysor PYZER Spizer Spoiser Spoizer Spyzer F3894

155802 PLACE Mr John. 11 Bramble Close, Pontefract, W Yorks, WF8 4RT. Tel:0977-791353
FOWLER OVERD PLACE F5861

155810 PLANT Mr John. 50 Dorset Gardens, Rochford, Essex, SS4 3AH. Tel:0702-548319
BELLERBY BOISTON BOUSFIELD CASTLEHOWE DUNN LATHOM MILES PLANT SCOTT F4126

155829 PLANT Mrs S. 1 Thornbury, Church Road, Hendon, London, NW4 4QW.
GILLINGHAM F7122

155837 PLANT Mr W K. 22 Chapel Court, Chelford, Macclesfield, Cheshire, CW3 8LF.
PLANT F6661

155845 PLANTEROSE Mr Donald. 19 Rectory Close, Guildford, Surrey, GU4 7AR. Tel:0483-64430
CARTWRIGHT COLWELL DALE DRIVER GREGORY NEWTON PLANTEROSE F6327

155853 PLATT Mrs Margaret. (Bell) Westbury, 27a Waveney Close, Wells-Next-The-Sea, Norfolk, NR23 1HU.
BACON BELL BROUGHTON DUNN SAWYER Wollard Woolard WOOLLARD Woolward F3326

155861 PLATTS Miss M. 47 Coldwell Lane, Sheffield, S10 5TJ.
Alcard Allcar ALLCARD Allcart F7150

155888 PLEDGER Mr P. 2 Warner Road, Selsey, W Sussex, PO20 9AL.
PLEDGER F3822

155896 PLEYDELL Mr John A. 5 Ladies Mile, Knutsford, Cheshire, WA16 0ND. Tel:0565-632493
ALLARD AWRE Baile Bailey Bayle BAYLEY BENNETT BLEEKE BUTLER CHAPMAN CLEMENTS HYETT JONES KEENE KING LATHAM LEIGH MAYNARD MAYO MEDLICOTT MORRIS PEARSE Pladal Pladall Pladel Pladell Pladle Pladwel Pladwell Plaidal Plaidall Plaidel Plaidell Plaidwel Plaidwell Platel Platwall Playdal Playdall Playdel Playdell Playdwel Playdwell Pleadal Pleadall Pleadel Pleadell Pleadles Pleadwel Pleadwell Pledal Pledall Pleddle Pledel Pledell Pledle Pledwel Pledwell Pleidal Pleidall Pleidel Pleidell Pleidwel Pleidwell PLEYDELL PLEYDELL-WILTON Ploydel Ploydell Plydel RIDER WILTON WINTLE F510

155918 PLUDOWSKA Miss Halina. 3 Amberley Court, 32 Stanley Road, Wimbledon, London, SW19 8RF.
CALLOW MINTER MOORE VILLIERS VINCENT F4974

155926 PLUMB Mr George R. Flat 5, 15 Portman Square, London, W1H 9HD. Tel:071-935-0478
PLUMB PLUMBE F692

155934 PLUMB Miss M. 44 Belvoir Road, Cambridge, CB4 1JJ.
AVES BUCKLEY PARR PLUMB F3551

155942 PLUMMER Mrs Winifred. (Farr) 2 Fernside Cottages, Yarbridge Cross, Brading, Sandown Isle Of Wight, PO36 0BP.
HARRIS WILLIS F2511

155950 POCHIN Miss Mary. 23 Beaudesert, Boney Hay, Chase Terrace, Walsall, WS7 8JD.
Brewin Briten BRITTAIN Brittan Britten Brittin Britton BRUIN BULLAMORE Bullimore CARTWRIGHT DAVIS FISHER GROCOCK Groocock

PARKER POCHIN SPEECHLEY F4897
155969 POCOCK Mrs Sally J. (Finlinson) 2 Fairmantle Street, Truro, Cornwall, TR1 2EG.
AKED BALDWIN EDWARDS FINLINSON FOWLER Fozard FOZZARD HOGG JOHNSON PHILP SAYER SHERRY SIMPSON STOCKLEY STROUD SUTCLIFFE TERRY WALKER WHEELEY WILKINSON F811
155977 POINTER Mr Russell W H. Carreg Dan, Whitsands Road, Swaffham, Norfolk, PE37 7BJ. Tel:0760-23858
DEW POINFON POINTER POINTUR PUINTUR F1119
155985 POINTON Mrs B A. 96 Emma Road, London, E13 0DR.
POINTON Poynton F7005
155993 POINTON Miss D. 79 Rufford Drive, Whitefield, Greater Manchester, M25 6PN.
BOWLER LOMAS ROWLANDS SKIPBOARD WILKES WILKS WILLIAMS F5309
156000 POLKEY Mr Andrew. 12 Royal Avenue, Long Eaton, Notts, NG10 1NU. Tel:0602-733830
BIRKIN PALKE POLKEY F159
156019 POLKINGHORNE Mr Clive. 43 Langley Cr, Griffith, 2680, AUSTRALIA. Tel:+61-6-962-1650
BREADNER BUIK COAD GIBSON JONES KING PEARCE POLKINGHORNE THOMPSON TONKIN F5556
156027 POLKINGHORNE Mrs Wendy. (Bested) 43 Langley Cr, Griffith, 2680, AUSTRALIA. Tel:+61-6-962-1650
BASSINGTHWAIGHTE BASTARD BROADHEAD CHALKER DENCH ISAACS KEMBER SPENCER STEWART UNDERHILL UNDERSHILL WORSTER WRIGHT F5555
156035 POLLARD Mrs Christine. 127 High Street, Melbourn, Nr Royston, Herts, SG8 6AP. Tel:0763-261548
BAKER DOUGHTY JACKSON NICHOLLS POLLARD WASHBOURN F169
156043 POLLARD Mrs Jacqueline. 9 Beechwood Close, Brighton, E Sussex, BN1 8EP.
CONNATTY F2510
156051 POLLARD Mr Kevin. 71 Murray St, Anglesea, VIC 3230, AUSTRALIA.
DOWNEY Downie EDWARDS HAWKEN Hawkin Hawkins Hocken Hockin JONES KEAST LATHLEAN LEATHAN Lethan PARKER POLLARD RAWLINGS ROBINS SAMPSON VAGUE WAINWRIGHT WALKER F5528
156078 POLLARD Mr Robert. 28 Layland Road, North Skelton, Cleveland, TS12 2AQ.
BENNINGTON COLEMAN DOBSON DORKS HOLDEN LAING LINDO MOTHERLOVE NORTON POLLARD SEXTON SMITHSON TUBB WRIGHT F6396
156086 POLLETT Mrs Pamela. (Whalley) 18 Cadbury Farm Road, Yatton, Avon, BS19 4HW.
BROCK DUDLEY GREEN HOLLINGS POLLETT PRIOR RANNS WHALLEY F3689
156094 POLLIKETT Mr Edward C. 42 Beresford Road, Chandlers Ford, Eastleigh, Hants, SO5 2LY. Tel:0703-263277
Poleykett Pollecutt Polleycutt POLLICOTT Pollicutt POLLIKETT F144
156108 POLLITT Mr N. 9 Garnet Court, Marlow, Bucks, SL7 2AN.
Palet Palett Pallet Pallett Paulet Paulett Paulit Paullet Paulot Pawlet Pawlete Pawlett Polet Polett Poliet Polit Pollert POLLET Pollett Polliet Polliot Pollit Pollitt Pollitte Pollot Poolit Poulett Poulette Powlet Powlett Powlit F3936
156116 POLLOCK Mrs Frances. (Newton) Box 429, Central Butte, Sask, S0H 0T0, CANADA. Tel:+1-306-796-2088
GRIEVE MACALLUM POLLOCK F5460
156124 POMEROY Mr A M J. 182 Kings Hall Road, Beckenham, Kent, BR3 1LT.
POMEROY Pomery Pomroy Pomry F6727
156132 POND Mr Edward. The Coach House, 99 Blackheath Park, London, SE3 0EU. Tel:081-852-9842
BRITTAN BROWN ELLIS POND SEABROOK SKINNER F3480
156140 PONIEWIERSKI Mrs B. 39 Winston Road, Sheldon, Australia, OLD 4157. Tel:+61-617-206-3214
APPS BALL BROOKER CALLOW CALLOWAY CHANTLER FIELD GILPIN JORDAN MARKWICK MARQUICK MITCHELL NOCK OVERTON PACKHAM PARKES RICHARDSON SLATER TILL TILLEY TUTT VENESS WHICK WICK WINTER F732
156159 PONTER Mr Christopher. West Lodge, Maidenhead Road, Cookham, Berks, SL6 9DA. Tel:0628-522693
PONTER F4992
156167 PONTING Mrs Alice. 9 Crossways, Swanvale, Falmouth, Cornwall.
Pantin Pontin PONTING Pontyn F7111
156175 POOK Mr Simon J. 203 Coombfield Drive, Darenth, Kent, DA2 7LF.
BARTHOLOMEW BATCHELOR BISHOP BROOKER BUNTING CLAPSON CUNDY DENNY DEWGATE DUNK DUNNETT FRANKLIN GILDERSLEEVE GLADWELL GREENLAND HARVEY HOOD LANDEN LUSTED MORRIS PATEY POOK SLATTERY SPRAY THOMPSON F4684
156183 POOL Mrs Beth. 2/15 Woodall Place, Glenfield, Auckland 10, NEW ZEALAND.
CAINS Goodair Goodaire GOODARE Goodayre Goodear Goodeare Gooder Goodere Goodheir Goodier Goodyear Goodyeare GORRIE Gudeare HAIGH NICHOLLS Nichols NICKLES ROWLEY RUSH SIDDALL STUBBS WALL WATSON WHITTLE F4411
156191 POOLE Mrs Brenda. 14 Roche Avenue, Rochford, Essex, SS4 1NG. Tel:0702-546056
BLIZZARD CLINTON DUNN GIVENS GOODWIN NOBLE PERKINS PLAYER POOLE RUSSELL SARGENT SHAXTED UMPELBY UMPLEBY VIZER WHEAL F3145
156205 POOLE Miss Catherine. 19 Pear Tree Close, Bransgore, Christchurch, Dorset, BH23 8NH.
Noades NODES F7056
156213 POOLE Mrs E. (Downes) 16 James Street, Llanbradach, Caerphilly, Mid Glamorgan, CF8 3LJ. Tel:0222-864823
SEABORNE Seabourne Seaburne Sebron Sebronde Seybon Shebrond F3870
156221 POOLE Mr John S N. 9 Cwrt-Y-Camden, Brecon, Powys, LD3 7RR. Tel:0874-622832
BURNEY CLOSSON COOMBS DARWENT DAVIS FELTHAM LANE LESLIE MACBURNIE MANDELLI POOLE RIXON SHORLAND SIRMAN WARREN F658
156248 POOLE Mr Keith E. Smestow Gate Farm, Swindon, Nr Dudley, W Midlands, DY3 4PJ.
BENNETT FACER HARIS HARRISON INGRAM JONES LANE MIDLAM POOLE ROLLASON F2907
156256 POOLE Mr R. 41 Barngate Street, Leek, Staffs, ST13 8AP. Tel:0538-387109
DALE FISHER MYCOCK PEACH POOLE SHELDON F113
156264 POOLEY Mr John. Newlands, 47 Alderton Hill, Loughton, Essex, IG10 3JD.
FOOT FORSTER LAMPITT LUXMORE PEELESS POOLEY RICHARDSON ROBINSON YEO F5238
156272 POOLEY Lieutenant Kevin. Sneinton House, 2 Boston Road, Nottingham, Notts, NG1 1ED. Tel:0602-504364
Besgrove Besgrow BISGROVE Bosgrove Hisgrave HISGROVE Hissgrove Hosegrave Isgro ISGROVE Isgroves F2979
156280 POPLETT Dr I J F. 7 Victoria Avenue, South Croydon, Surrey, CR2 0QP.
AGNEW ASHDOWN Ashdowne Boplet CUTHBERT DALBY Garlet Garlett Garlot Jarlet JARLETT Jarlot LADD Ladde LUSH PALMER Poplet POPLETT Popplett Puplet Puplett Pupplett STOTT Toplett F4036
156299 POPPLESTONE Ms J. 496 Portswood Road, Portswood, Hants, SO2 3SP.
POPPLESTONE F7347
156302 POPPLETON Mr D A. 11 Rookery Drive, Nantwich, Cheshire, CW5 7DD. Tel:0270-625535
BRAMLEY CLEOBURY KAY LAPPALE MAXWELL POPPLETON VAUGHAN WALKER F6449
156310 PORRETT Miss S J. 4 Emmanuel House, Rochester Row, London, SW1P 1BS.
BIDDLECOMBE BREWSTER BROCK DIXON DYBALL FORSTER Hibgame Hibgin Hipgam Hipgham HIPKIN Hipkins Hypgame Hypgham LEATHERDALE MONEY PATTEN PILCH PORRETT RAYMENT Selcock Selcocks SILCOCK Silcox Sillcock Sillcocks WENN WHITMORE F1433
156329 PORTCH Mr Alan. 32 Cheapside East, Rayleigh, Essex, SS6 9JU.
CORDELL HAWKES PORTCH SAPSFORD SEAMONS SIDNEY STEVENS TWINEHAM F2315
156337 PORTER Ms Angela. (Benson) 51 Lavender Rise, West Drayton, Middx, UB7 9AP.
BENSON DENMAN EVANS HILL KIRBY LEE MORGAN WALTERS F3549

156345 PORTER Mr David Roy. 4 Devonshire Crescent, Leeds, W Yorkshire, LS8 1EP. Tel:0532-664164
PORTER F3953

156353 PORTER Mrs Dorothy. 24 Haddenham Road, Wilburton, Ely, Cambs, CB6 3RG.
Tel:0353-740476
CROXON Croxton GROOM LEACH PLEDGER PORTER ROBERTS SULMAN Sunman WARREN F1721

156361 PORTER Mr R C. 106 Dowson Road, Hyde, Cheshire, SK14 5BN. Tel:061-368-5799
PORTER F380

156388 PORTER Mr Stanley William. 108 Heatherstone Avenue, Dibden-Purlieu, Southampton, SO4 5LA.
Tel:0703-845298
ARTHUR PORTER STAPLES F4946

156396 PORTER Prof Vincent. 19 Wentworth Mansions, Keats Grove, London, NW3 2RL.
Tel:071-794-7366
CAVE DILLINGHAM MORTON PORTER WOOD F3733

156418 PORTUS Mrs Doreen. (Todd) 26 Fir Tree Close, Hilton In Cleveland, Yarm, Cleveland, TS15 9JZ.
KIRKBY MASSAM PORTUS SUNLEY TODD WORSLEY F3455

156426 POST Mr Herbert. 3044 Sunrise Drive, Crown Point, IN 46307, USA.
BIRCH BRASSINGTON EVANS HOLT ROBINSON F5155

156434 POSTLETHWAITE Mr Sidney. 9 Manor Road, Swanage, Dorset, BH19 2BH.
FRANCIS POSTLETHWAITE SPRULES F2270

156442 POTTER Mrs Marigold. (Roberts) 84 Swanfield Street, London, E2 7DS.
BARGENT BEAGLEHOLE BENNETT DAVID FIRMAN FORSTER HENRY HICKS HOBBS JONES NASH POWELL ROBERTS ROWE TIPPETT F3857

156450 POTTER Dr Robert. 98 Addison Road, Hove, E Sussex, BN3 1TR. Tel:0273-203545
BOWDEN BROOK LAST MOUNTJOY POTTER RUNDELL F3881

156469 POTTS Mr Michael. Brooke House, The Parade, Parkgate, S Wirral, Cheshire, L64 6RN.
Tel:051-336-1494
POTTS F738

156477 POULTON Mr G F. Northend House, Woodford, Berkley, Glous, GL13 9JN.
POULTON F6678

156485 POULTON Mrs Rosalie. 4 The Greenway, Pattingham, Wolverhampton, Staffs, WV6 7DA.
BELLIS JONES MAKEN MAKIN MATTHEWS WRIGHT F2737

156493 POVEY Mr R. Po Box 6061, Westgate, 1734, SOUTH AFRICA.
Corbet CORBETT DENNIS FELL HOLWELL MCCALLUM NIVEN PATERSON PHILLIPS POVEY REID ROSS F4965

156507 POWELL Mrs A G. 13 Elgin Road, Pwll, Llanelli, Dyfed, SA15 4AD.
SPRANGE F6968

156515 POWELL Mr Alan A. 1 St Davids Close, Forest Park, Penpedairheol, Hengoed Mid Glamorgan, CF8 8BL. Tel:0443-832614
AMESBURY ARKILL BERRY CRUMP DENLEY DOVEY GODWIN HAYES KEYSELL LANDEG LAYTON PAGET POWELL PROSSER ROSS WHITNEY F364

156523 POWELL Mrs Anne. (Fradd) 23 Fairview Road, Lancing, West Sussex, BN15 0PA.
BENHAM FRADD POWELL TOUGH F5917

156531 POWELL Mrs Brenda. Fircroft, Feniton, Honiton, Devon, EX14 0DE.
BRIDGEMAN CASIER EVANS GLOYN HORSEY JOSLIN POWELL SHORT VICARY F5741

156558 POWELL Mr Colin F. 11 Gomshall Avenue, Wallington, Surrey, SM6 8NY. Tel:081-688-3488
BENNETT BULLOCK CHEAL HUNT JONES KNIGHT MARCH MOBSBY POWELL VAUGHAN F1683

156566 POWELL Mrs Dorothy. 2 Glen Usk View, Caerleon, Gwent, NP6 1FY.
ARSSOLOM CARTHEW KING POWELL SWEET F5800

156574 POWELL Mrs E. 48 Heathend Road, Alsager, Cheshire, ST7 2SH.
ADAMS BILLINGTON GROCOTT LAWTON POWELL RODDY STONIER TAYLOR F4066

156582 POWER Miss Margaret. 32 Rosebank Road, Hanwell, London, W7 2EN.
Bansgrove Bramsgrove BRANSGROVE BUNNET Bunnett CLAMP DAWES Daws Far FARR FOX HICKERSON Hickinson LATTEN Macdewell MACDUELL Mcdowel Mcduell MEANEY NIXON POLLARD POWER QUIDDINGTON Quittenden WILMOT Wilmott F2746

156590 POWLING Mr Robert D. 35 Limes Avenue, Chigwell, Essex, IG7 5NX.
POWLING F5753

156604 POWNEY Mr Barry. 10 Basil Close, The Richmonds, Abbeybale, Gloucester, GL4 9TJ.
Tel:0452-502141
ALLEN CHARLES COOLEY FARQUHAR Fleet Fleete Foot FOOTE HENDERSON MCEACHEN Poney Pouny Poutney POWELL POWNEY Powny RAE SHARP Shewry SHUREY Shurrey Shury SLATER SPLINGARD TREVISS WALL WATSON F19

156612 POXON Mr Gareth. Karibuni, Park Lane, Gayton, Northants, NN7 3HB.
Paxen Paxon Paxson Paxton Pockson Pockton Pocson Pocton Pogson Poxan Poxen POXON Poxson Poxton F3282

156620 PRACY Mr David & Mrs Sara. 16 Shooters Drive, Nazeing, Waltham Abbey, Essex, EN9 2QD.
Tel:0992-893264
Pracey PRACY F1609

156639 PRAGER Mrs A C. 157 Hornchurch Road, Hornchurch, Essex, RM12 4SZ.
DYER FARR FRANCIS GUBB LUSBY MORGAN PLATT PRAGER VENABLES F2552

156647 PRAGNELL Mr Reginald Thomas. 44 Leighfield, Mortimer Common, Reading, Berks, RG7 3TT.
Tel:0734-333030
ALLEN ANDERSON AUFRERE BRETT BULL CAIN CANNELL CARPENTER CARTER CONWAY CORBET CORLETT FINCH GARDNER HERBERT IDEN JOLLIFFE KILLIP MACKETT NEVILL NEWEN NEWMAN O'HAGEN PELHAM PRAGNELL SANDYS URRY WESTMORLAND WHARTON WHEELER WILKINSON WILLIAMS WILLOUGHBY F4708

156655 PRALAT Mr Peter. 94 The Wye, Daventry, Northants, NN11 4PX.
INNOCENT F6002

156663 PRANGNELL Mr R D. 32 Middle Furlong, Bushey, Watford, Herts, WD2 3SZ.
Pragnell Prangell Prangle Prangnall PRANGNELL Staresmore Starmore Starsmeare Starsmor STARSMORE F4722

156671 PRANKERD Mrs Ethelyn Haskoll. (Reed) 65 Coronation Road, Blackwood, Gwent, NP2 1ED.
Tel:0495-225037
BEER CHAPMAN GILL HASKELL HASKOLL LAMEY LAMLEY MOORLE PHILP PRANKERD REED F2962

156698 PREBBLE Mrs D. (Stevens) 4 Eastglade, Northwood, Middx, HA6 3LD.
ARCHER BLACKMORE BULLED COLE DARVELL ELSE FRESHWATER FRY GREEN KEELER MUNDEN NOTT PARHAM PARTRIDGE RATCLIFFE SEDGWICK STEVENS TWOHEY WINSLOW F3784

156701 PREBBLE Mr G. 4 Eastglade, Northwood, Middx, HA6 3LD. Tel:0923-821992
ARCHER BEETS BLACKMORE DARVELL-STEVENS FRY MUNDEN PARTRIDGE RATCLIFFE STEVENS-DARVELL WINSLOW F6052

156728 PREEN Mr F E. 1 Westlake Avenue, Sandown, Isle Of Wight, PO36 9NJ.
I'anson JANSON PREEN SPLEEN SPREEN TEARNAN F1135

156736 PRENDERGAST Mr Michael J. 79 Payne Close, Great Sankey, Warrington, Cheshire, WA5 1DU.
Tel:0925-413460
PRENDERGAST SAUNDERS F5690

156744 PRESBURY Mrs Hilary. 64 Dupont Gardens, Glenfield, Leicester, LE3 8LD.
Tel:0533-873028
DAVIES DAVIS FEARN HALES HEALD LEWIS Presburrie PRESBURY Presby Prestbury Prisbrey Prisbry THOMAS TOMLINSON WILLIAMS F29

156752 PRESLAND Mr & Mrs A. 35 Lodge Road, Rushden, Northants, NN10 9HA.
PRESLAND Pressland Prestland F7171

156760 PRESLAND Mr Ian. 7 Rothbury Close, Sholing, Southampton, Hants, SO2 8JX. Tel:0703-445035
GATESMAN Henbest Henrest Henvest Hinrest HINVEST MARWOOD Moxan Moxham MOXON Preistland PRESLAND Pressland Prisland F5060

156779 PRESLAND Mrs J Mary. 19 Millbrook Lane, Eccleston, St Helens, WA10 6QX.
Tel:0744-23141
BEEDLE Beneworth BENNIWITH Benworth Biddle

CHASTER Chester CUTHBERT FEUALL Feuell Fewel Fewell Fuel Fuell Gowan GOWARD Gowen Lambard LAMBERT PRESLAND Pressland ROUS Rouse SPINKS TROBRIDGE Troubridge Trowbridge WEBBER WILSON F5602

156787 PRESTON Mrs B. 55 Albemarle Gardens, New Maldon, Surrey, KT3 5BB.
O'dowd O'DOWDE YEATS F2280

156795 PRESTON Mr Barry. 7 Beccles Close, Hamworthy, Poole, Dorset, BH15 4BS. Tel:0202-676766
ADAMS Aish ASH Ashe AXTENCE Aysh Ayshe BATT BUDDEN BULLEN BUTT Chiddel Chiddle Chidtell CHISTELL CULL CUTLER Dogerel Doggrel DOGGRELL Dogrel Dogrell DURDALE Durdel Durdell Exten Extence Extens FARLEY Fearley Fifed FIFET Fiffed Fiffet Fiffird Fiffoot Fifird Fifoot FISHER Gard Gird Gourd GRAY GURD GUY HAILEE Hailey Haily Haley HARDING HICKS Luxal LUXALL Luxel Luxell MACHAM MASTERS Matcham OLIVER PRESTON SANKEY Slie Sly SLYE SMART STONE Tayler TAYLOR WAREHAM Warham WATTS Werham WHITE Whitelock WHITLOCK Wilcocks Wilcox WILKINS WILLCOCKS WILLCOX Willkins F842

156809 PRESTON Mrs G M. Wendens, Thrimley Lane, Farnham, Bishops Stortford Herts, CM23 1HX.
CALLADINE Callerdine CANADINE CANARDINE Canderdine CANDERDYNE CANNADINE CANNADYNE CARADIN Carden Cardin Carding CARDON Carodine CARRADINE Carradyne Carrodine CARROWDYNE Carwarden Carwardin CARWARDINE CARWARDYNE CAWARDIN DE KAREWARDYN KAWRDIN Keanodine KENDERDINE KENWARDEN F2835

156817 PRESTON Mr Graham C. Charnwood, 15 Chescombe Road, Yatton, Bristol.
COLTON COULTON HEATH HIGGINS RICHARDS WEAD F3005

156825 PRESTON Mrs M. (Barlow) Pinecottage, Crossroads, St Day, Redruth, Cornwall, TR16 5PN. Tel:0209-820691
BARLOW F4757

156833 PRESTON Patricia. 87 Taunton Road, Ashton Under Lyne, Lancs, OL7 9EB. Tel:061-330-1270
ASHTON AUSTIN BAGNALL CRANMER CUFF DAWSON ELKIN FEARON GARNISS JENNINGS KELSEY LEES LEESE F171

156841 PRESTON Mr Roy. 12 Eastgate, Whitworth, Rochdale, Lancs, OL12 8UB.
PRESTON F3612

156868 PRICE Mrs Aleda. 66 Medway Road, Oldham, Lancs, OL8 4NP.
CLARK CLARKE HAYCOCK HOLT POWELL SORBY TETLOW WARREN F557

156876 PRICE Mr Dick. 12 Briar Close, Waterford Park, Radstock, Bath Avon, BS3 3EL. Tel:0761-435475
AHSMAN CURTIS PRICE STEEDS TREASURE WEBB F2281

156884 PRICE Mrs Elaine. (Woodling) 38 Kitchener Road, Highfield, Southampton, Hants, SO2 3SG. Tel:0703-554847
BROWN EDMONDS PENNY RAY SHUTLER TAYLOR WOODLING F864

156892 PRICE Miss J D. 8 Dalston Drive, Didsbury Park, Manchester, M20 0LG.
ARMIGER BYNG GRAHAM HENDRICK HENZELL HENZEY HOPSON HUDSON LACK NICKLIN PRICE RICHES ROEBUCK SKILBECK TYZACK F2375

156906 PRICE Mrs Jill. (Brider) 35 Lynn Road, Terrington St Clement, Kings Lynn, Norfolk, PE34 4JU. Tel:0553-828605
Breda Brida BRIDER Bryder Clabbone Clabborn Clabborne Clabbourn Clabbourne Clabbun Clabburn Claiborn Claiborne Claybon CLAYBORNE Cleborne Cleyburn Cleyburne Cliberon Cliborne Clibrone Cliburne Cliggon F3418

156914 PRICE Mrs M. Cwmearl, Sarn, Newtown, Powys, SY16 4HW.
ADKINS BARNETT BAYLISS BRAY COX DAVIES EVANS GORE HUGHES JENKINS JONES JUDSON LLOYD MINTON POWELL PRICE PRYCE RICHARDS RIDDING ROBERTS Tibott TONKS TYBBOT VAUGHAN WEBSTER WILLIAMS F4349

156922 PRICE Mrs Margaret. Sinnaid, Chetnole, Sherborne, Dorset, DT9 6NY.
BLOOM CARNELLEY CLARKE COCKERILL COX DOWNING JOY LATHAM PAYNE SERGEANT SNOW F3525

156930 PRICE Mr Martin. Thorwood Cottage, Knoll Road, Godalming, Surrey, GU7 2EL.
Ayles Barrat Barret BARRETT Barrott BENNETT Birch BURCH EYLES FLOWER FRANCIS GODWIN GURNEY HARRIS HARWOOD HOLMES Homes Ives LEWIS Mudg MUDGE NAPPER PRICE RICHARDS Sheepheard Sheepherd Shepard Shepheard SHEPHERD Shepperd STOCKHAM STRONG Stronge THOMAS Thompson THOMSON Tomson WAKEFIELD WATERS Weakfield WILCOX WILLIAMS Woakfield F6358

156949 PRICE Mr Norman. 7 Park Lane, Trecynon, Aberdare, Mid Glamorgan, CF44 8HN. Tel:0685-873493
PRICE F1285

156957 PRICE Mr Peter C. 35 Wadham Road, Woodthorpe, Nottingham, NG5 4JB. Tel:0602-263678
CARVER HEATH MASON PAGE Persuire PRICE PURSER Pursuir SEARCY Sercy TAINTON Taynton THORNTON F4973

156965 PRICE Mr Ronald A. Aeron Retreat, Ciliau Aeron, Lampeter, Dyfed, SA48 8DE.
BOYCE Boys ORAM PRICE SARGISSON SAUNDERS TRAYLEN WITTED F3227

156973 PRICE Mr Victor James. 269 Robin Hood Lane, Birmingham, W Midlands, B28 0DJ.
BANNOCKS CRUTCHLEY PRICE F1693

156981 PRICE Mr W L. 10 Windsor Avenue, Irlam, Manchester, M30 6HP. Tel:061-775-6531
ALVIS FISHER FRANKLIN MORGAN PIERCE PRICE ROBERTS TAYLOR F3458

157007 PRICE Mr Wilfred. 78 Lower Hester Street, Northampton, NN2 6BL.
PRICE F2397

157015 PRIDDLE Mr R. The Maltings, 29/31 Chapel Street, Alconbury, Huntingdon Cambs, PE17 5DY. Tel:0480-891066
PRIDDLE F84

157023 PRIDMORE Mr W A. 3 Orchard Croft, Millhouse Woods Lane, Cottingham, N Humberside, HU16 4HG. Tel:0482-848318
BALE EMERY ENGLISH GIDDINGS PEAR PRIDMORE REYNOLDS ROBINSON SOFTLEY F4022

157031 PRIESTLEY Mr Francis Joseph. 41 King George V Cottages, Minley Road, Cove, Farnborough Hants, GU14 9UB. Tel:0252-542542
CLANCEY CORRON LOAN MCGUFFIE PRIESTLEY QUIG F4820

157058 PRIME Mr C. 475 Rickstones Road, Rivenhall, Essex, CM8 3HH.
CLARKE CLAYTON JESSOP MURRAY PRIME SMOOTHY F5986

157066 PRIMMER Mrs J. 28 Glenmore Avenue, Mossley Hill, Liverpool, L18 4QF.
FLETCHER KENT LOUGH MCKENNA MCWHOR PRIMMER VOCE F5280

157074 PRINCE Mrs B J. 35 Sopers Lane, Poole, Dorset, BH17 7EW.
ABRAHAM BROWN BUMBY Burmby CLAY DACRE Dacres Daiker Daikers Daker Dakers Dayker Daykers FRENCH GEORGE PRINCE ROLPH STRUDWICK F2095

157082 PRINCE Miss Eileen. 121 Heather Drive, Monroeville, PA 15146, USA. Tel:+1-412-372-0298
PRINCE STINTON F4443

157090 PRINGLE Mr K. 14 Mentone Avenue, Aspley Guise, Milton Keynes, MK17 8EQ. Tel:0908-582220
Merdex Merdox Merdu Merdy Merdyson Mordall Morday Morddew Morddle Mordeu Mordew Mordex Mordey Mordle Mordne Mordow Mordu MORDUE Mordy PRINGLE Pringles Pringleton F729

157104 PRINT Mr M A. 32 St Peters Close, Evesham, Worcs, WR11 6EW.
PRINT F7412

157112 PRIOR Mrs Pamela. (Mckenna) 22 Water Mill Way, Hanworth, Middx, TW13 4NG. Tel:081-894-6327
CALLAN MCKENNA MORGAN MURPHY THORNTON F5275

157120 PRIOR Mr Richard Ian. 21 Lambert Gardens, Shurdington, Cheltenham, Glous, GL51 5SW. Tel:0242-862404
DE GRESLEY DE LONGFORD DE STAFFORD DE TOENI HYDE Langeford Langeforde Langfit LANGFORD Langforde Longeford Longeforde Longfford Longfforde LONGFORD Longforde MORGAN PRIOR Todnie Tony F2057

157139 PRITCHARD Mr & Mrs A C. Carangill, 61 Brownsmuir Park, Lauder, Berwickshire, TD2 6QD. Tel:05782-529
BACKHOUSE Bone Bowen BOWN HALL NEEDHAM PRITCHARD RAMSAY SCOTT SUMNER WHILLANCE Whillans Willans F3469

157147 PRITCHARD Mrs Edna E. (Evans) 4 Cil Coed, Bangor, Gwynedd, LL57 4TT. Tel:0248-351999
COOPER CREESY DUFFIN EVANS FOULKES HOWE HUGHES JONES LAWRENSON LEWIS LEYLAND PAICE PRITCHARD ROBERTS SEWELL SEYMOUR SMITH WILLIAMS F3831

157155 PRITCHARD Mrs Hilda Caroline. (Flavell) 2 Blackthorn Place, Cedar Way, Bellfields, Guildford Surrey, GU1 1NF. Tel:0483-571249
Favel Flavel FLAVELL PAULEY Pawley F3537

157163 PRITCHETT Mrs R E. Sunset House, Arlington, Bibury, Cirencester Glos, GL7 5ND.
Joblin Joplin JOPLING Joplyn F6607

157171 PROBERT Mr Eric D. 62 Sidmouth Road, Chelmsford, Essex, CM1 5LS. Tel:0245-259914
Amies AMIS Amise Amiss Amisse Amys Amyss BAKER BOUGH BRIMMEL Brimmell BUCK COCK ELLIS GREGORY HALLIER Hallin Halling Hallings HALLINS HARRISON HARTLEY HILL HOBBS HOLDER Hollin Holling Hollings Hollins Loveredg Loveredge LOVERIDGE Loveridges Loverodg Loverodge Lovradge Lovridge Lovridges MADDOCKS Maddox Merick Merike MERRICK Merricke Meyrick Meyricke MITCHELL PHILLIPS PITT Pitts PLEVY POYNER PRITCHARD Probard Probards Probart Probarts Probat Probate Probates Probats Probatt Probatts PROBERT Proberts Probet Probets Probett Probetts Probit Probits Probitt Probitts Rame Rames REAMES Reem Reeme Reemes Reems Reme Remes Rhame Rhames Rheem Rheeme Rheemes Rheems Shewel SHEWELL SHORTMAN SMITH THORP THORPE F1583

157198 PROCTER Mr Thomas. 21 South Road, Weston Super Mare, Avon, BS23 2HA. Tel:0934-417457
CRANSTON MAUDSLEY PROCTER TIPTAFT F1736

157201 PROCTOR Miss Patricia E. 5 Redruth House, Grange Road, Sutton, Surrey, SM2 6RT.
BARTLETT JOHNSONS PROCTOR WILLMOTT F4899

157228 PROFFIT Mr A E. 32 York Avenue, West Kirby, Wirral, L48 3JF.
PROFFIT Profit Prophet F7413

157236 PROSSER Mr Brynley George. 8 New Park Road, Crosskeys, Gwent, NP1 7AE. Tel:0495-271066
PROSSER F1411

157244 PROUDFOOT Mrs. (Bennett) 7 Kidston Court, Market Street, St Andrews, Fife, KY16 9NS. Tel:0334-73684
BABINGTON BENNETT GREGOIRE PROUDFOOT WILLIAMS F1240

157252 PROUDFOOT Mr Joseph E. 19 Bewdsey Close, Stevenage, Herts, SG1 2LA.
PROUDFOOT STANILAND F4547

157260 PROUT Miss Iris. 1 Forth House, Kent Street, Northam, Southampton Hants, SO1 1SF.
APPLETON BARTHOLMEW MINDENHALL PROUT Sprout TAPHOUSE TRODD F5730

157279 PROWSE Mrs M. 1 The Orchard, South St, Uley, Gloucestershire, GL11 5ST.
Prouse Prouze Provs PROWSE F7090

157287 PROWSE Mr Michael. Clonearl, 13 Guildford Road, Fleet, Hants, GU13 9EN.
MILES MITCHELL PROUSE PROWSE F659

157295 PROWSE-GIRDLESTONE Jane. Cherry Tree Cottage, 192 Mile End Road, Colchester, Essex, CO4 5DY. Tel:0206-851777
De Rie Pratellis Preaux Preux Probus Prouse Prouz Prouze PROWSE F309

157309 PRUDAMES Mrs A. 2 Cannonbury Cottages, Churchbury Lane, Enfield, Middx, EN1 3LR.
PRUDAMES Prudham Prudome F6720

157317 PRUEN Ms T C. Flat 3, 5 Suffolk Square, Cheltenham, Glos, GL50 2DR. Tel:0242-521421
Prewen Prewin Prewine Prewne Proeuen Prouen Prouin Prowen Prowne Prowyne Pruan PRUEN Pruene Pruenèn Pruine Prun Prune Prunne Prunnen Pruyn Pruyne Pruynen Pruynes Pryne F3672

157325 PRYOR Mr Ben P. 228 Airport Road, Griffin, GA 30223-4769, USA. Tel:+1-404-227-6678
PRYOR F5563

157333 PRYOR Estella. (Yule) 1512 N E Hogan Drive, Gresham, OR 97030, USA.
Eule Ewel Eweles Ewell Ewels Hoole Juel Jule Uhl Uhles Uiles Uoel Yeaull Yeel Yeell Yehl Yeil Yeill Yell Yeoale Yeouls Yeowell Yeuell Yeuille Yeul Yeules Yeull Yeulle Yewell Yewl Yoall Yoele Yoell Yol Yole Yoll Yooil Yool Yooll Yoolo Yooly Youan Youel Youell Youels Youhill Youil Youile Youill Youille Youl Youle Youles Youlie Youll Youlla Youlle Youlley Youllie Youlo Youlow Youly Yowel Yowil Yowle Yual Yuall Yuel Yuell Yuelle Yuelo Yuial Yuie Yuiell Yuil Yuile Yuille Yuillie Yuills Yuir Yul YULE Yull Yulle Yullie Yullow Yuls Yuyll Ywill Zoule F7379

157341 PRYOR Mr James. 1/11 Church Street, Berwick, VIC 3806, AUSTRALIA. Tel:+61-3-707-4333
CHAMPION GUSWELL PRYOR TURPIN F5492

157368 PUDNER Mr Brian. Midtown Farm, Torpenhow, Wigton, Cumbria, CA5 1JF. Tel:09657-385
HILLARY LAZONBY Pudener Pudnar PUDNER Pudnor Putnar Putner Putnor Puttener F4138

157376 PUGH Dr David. Brookville, Trerhyngyll, Cowbridge, South Glamorgan, CF7 7TN. Tel:0446-772023
CATHRALL PUGH F5898

157384 PUGH Revd Leslie. 11 Corston Grove, Blackrod, Bolton, Manchester, BL6 5TB. Tel:0204-696717
BLAND MARTIN PUGH SAXTOM F4831

157392 PUGH Mr R. The Storey Arms, Libanus, Brecon, Powys, LD3 8NL. Tel:0874-623598
FELLOWS HAWKINS JONES PUGH F4046

157406 PULLAN Mr Roy. 12 Acacia Avenue, Wilmslow, Cheshire, SK9 6AX. Tel:0625-525865
BOOTH DORMAN HARDMAN MARBECK MITCHELL PULLAN Pullein Pulleyn Whitamore Whitimore Whittamore WHITTEMORE Whittimore F852

157414 PULLAR Mr Adrian. 21 De Tany Court, St Albans, Herts, AL1 1TW.
SHIRT F176

157422 PULLAR Mrs B. 30 Awamoa Road, Oamaru, North Otago, NEW ZEALAND.
Hoar HOARE Hore F6811

157430 PULLAR Mr David. 1 Kemble Close, Willenhall, West Midlands, WV12 4DQ. Tel:0902-602070
KIDSON MOCKFORD POOLER PULAR Pullar PULLER SUMMERHILL THOMAS F55

157449 PULLEN Mrs Doris E. (Lord) 155 Venner Road, Sydenham, London, SE26 5HX.
BAILEY Bancks Bankes BANKS Combs Coombes COOMBS EVANS GARRAD Garratt Garred GARRETT Garrod HOLLEY Holly Jewel JEWELL LORD PULLEN WEBB F655

157457 PULLEN Mrs Patricia Eleanor. (Cowper) Little Hanger, 26 Kings Hill Beech, Alton, Hants, GU34 4AL. Tel:0420-63264
COWPER F4864

157465 PULLIN Mr F E. 55 Purfleet Road, Aveley, South Ockendon, Essex, RM15 4DR. Tel:0708-865103
LEAH PULLIN WEAVERS F3723

157473 PULVERTAFT Mr David. Tucketts, Trusham, Newton Abbot, Devon, TQ13 0NR.
Polvertoft Polvertofte PULVERTAFT PULVERTOFT Pulvertofte F67

157481 PUNTER John. Old Orchard, 14 Croye Close, Andover, Hants, SP10 3AF. Tel:0264-323347
Davaries DE VRIES PUNTER F2834

157503 PURCELL Miss Margaret. 128 Redbank Road, Bispham, Blackpool, Lancs, FY2 9DZ. Tel:0253-53909
Graless Gralis Graliss Grayless GRAYLIS Grealis Greles Grelis Greslas HEAP Made Maid Mayde Mead MEADE Meaith Meath Meatt Meed Mesid Nicholls NICHOLS PURCELL RYAN SHARPLES Sharpless Sharplesse STEEL Steele F6310

157511 PURCHASE Mrs Nancy. (Schneider) 1108 Yorkshire Road, Starkville, Mississippi, 39759-4014, USA.
BONE BRINE COOPER HARWIN PAGE PHIPPARD Purchas PURCHASE SPURGEON TALBOT Talbott F7395

157538 PURDON Mrs J. 41 Middlebrook Drive, Ringwood North, Victoria, 3134, AUSTRALIA. Tel:+61-3-876-4319

BAYNES BLOW CASTLE ELDRIDGE GLEW GOODWIN GOUGH HOGG JOHNSON LECOTT NAILOR NOYSE OLLEY PARTRIDGE POSTGATE PUDNEY PURDON ROTHWELL SALLETT SIBLEY SIMONS SURMAN TURVEY WARE WHITNEY F5524

157546 PURDUE Mrs Liz. 11 Test Road, Whitchurch, Hants, RG28 7LP. Tel:0256-892947
PURDUE F1578

157554 PURDY Miss Norma M. 25 Langmere Road, Watton, Thetford, Norfolk, IP25 6LG.
BETTS BRUCE COOK HARRISON LINCOLN MANN MORRIS NORMAN PURDY REEVE F5860

157562 PURSEY Mr E. 12 Meadfoot Road, Streatham Vale, London, SW16 5BL.
PURSEY F1654

157570 PURSEY Mrs Jacqui. 4 Mill Green, Basildon, Essex, SS13 3PA. Tel:0268-550242
LAMING METTERS PURSEY STRICK STRIKE F2872

157589 PURSLOW Mr Duncan. 19 St Michaels Road, Claverdon, Warwickshire, CV35 8NT.
LERRY PURSLOW Trahearn Trahern TRAHERNE Trehearn Trehearne Trehern Treherne F2799

157597 PURVES Mrs W. 1a Willington Street, Maidstone, Kent, ME15 8JW. Tel:0622-38837
BAKER BALDWIN LUCAS NEWTON PURVES TAYLOR UPTON WRIGHT F7437

157600 PURVEUR Mrs S D. 7 Vicarage Close, Aylesford, Kent, ME20 7BB.
Perver Perveur Purceur Purver PURVEUR Purveure Purvey Purveyor Purvier Purviour Purvor Purvur F5900

157619 PUSEY Mr W E N. 57 Reynards Close, Winnersh, Wokingham, Berks, RG11 5NU. Tel:0734-783900
BUCKLAND CALTHORPE HUGHES Pewsey POOK PUSEY ROUT TRODD TUGGEY WEBBER WISHART F2113

157627 PUTNAM Mr B L. 11th Chem Co, Box 232, Opo, NY 09160, USA.
Putman PUTNAM F7166

157635 PUTTENHAM Mr J H. 48 San Fernando Drive, Hamilton, Ontario, L9C 2C2, CANADA.
Putnam PUTTENHAM Puttnam F7114

157643 PYATT Mr L A. 173 Heath Row, Bishops Stortford, Herts, CM23 5DW.
DOWSING HAMILTON JONES OTTEY PYATT SHAWCROFT F464

157651 PYE Mrs Anne. 36 Alwyne Drive, Shipton Road, York, YO3 6RS. Tel:0904-635659
BENN Clark CLARKE DODGSON FOY GILL HALLIDAY HARDISTY Holliday Holyday IRVING LITTLE MANN STAMP F6488

157678 PYE Mr W K. 86 Cherry Tree Walk, Stretford, Manchester, M32 9AS.
BAKER CASHMORE FAIRHURST GASKILL HORSEFIELD JACKSON MOORHOUSE NAYLOR OLIVERSON PYE SWIFT TAYLOR F2460

157686 PYLE Mr P B. 13 Arismore Court, Marine Parade West, Lee On Solent, Hants, PO13 9ED. Tel:0705-552255
PYLE F4533

157694 PYRAH Dr Roger D. Raikes Head, 90 Raikes Road, Skipton, North Yorkshire, BD23 1LU. Tel:0756-792642
BATLEY DALE MURRAY PYRAH TOWNEND F3690

157708 QUARMBY Mrs Jean. (Robertson) 12 Asher Reeds, Langton Green, Tunbridge Wells, Kent, TN3 0AL. Tel:0892-862731
Ap Ithel Armer ARMOUR Bethel BETHELL Bethll Bithel BURTON Bythall Bythel Bythell CHIRSTIE Christie Chrystie DAINTY Highley HILEY Iley JENNISON LOVE MORLEDGE PARTON ROBERTSON RUSHTON VICKERY F1479

157716 QUARMBY Mr Raymond. 12 Asher Reeds, Langton Green, Tunbridge Wells, Kent, TN3 0AL. Tel:0892-862731
BARBER BOTTOMLEY CHAMBLEY Goodaire Goodayre GOODEARE GOODYER GUDGER HAIGH HIRST MOORHOUSE Morehouse QUARMBY SHAW SWALLOW WALKER F1478

157724 QUARTERMAN Mr A A. 5 Cottesmore, Bracknell, Berks, RG12 4YL. Tel:0344-51479
BLOSS Catterment COOKE CREED FARMER GOOD HARRIS HICKES KINGSBURY PHILLIPS QUARTERMAIN Quartermaine QUARTERMAN Quartermane Quatremaine REASON REECH ROBERTS SIDYE SMITH WARNER YOUNG LEVEN F2764

157732 QUAST Mrs Ruth. (Momsen) 1646 Rome Avenue, St Paul, MN 55116, USA. Tel:+1-612-698-3160
BAIGENT GATES GRAY GROVER HARROW LANGRISH LILLYWHITE ROBERTS SALMON STEBBING F5580

157740 QUESTED Mrs Marjorie. (Locker) 30 Court Hill, Sanderstead, Surrey, CR2 9NA. Tel:081-657-8652
BIRKS FAULKNER GAGE HEYES LOCKER MAWSON NORTH QUESTED REDMAN ROBINSON TARBUCK F549

157759 QUINCEY Dr P G. Gander Bank, Buggen Lane, Neston, Merseyside, L64 6QB.
QUINCE QUINCEY Quincie Quincy Quinse Quinsey Quinsy F335

157767 QUINLAN Mr Kevin. 19 Woodward Avenue, Strathfield, NSW 2135, AUSTRALIA. Tel:+61-2-642-2923
BONNER BRANSTON MASON F5561

157775 QUINLIVAN Mrs Joyce. (Clemson) 4 Thomson Street, Griffith, NSW 2680, AUSTRALIA. Tel:+61-6-962-1850
BURRELL CALLICOTE CHROM CHROMN CLEMSON FROGGATT GALE JARDINE LUFF SHARP WHITE F5613

157783 QUINLIVAN Mr Walter John. 4 Thomson Street, Griffith, NSW 2680, AUSTRALIA.
MULHARE STAUNTON F5612

157791 QUINTIN-ARCHARD Mr Dennis Howell. Barn Cottage, Great Wolford, Shipston On Stour, Warwickshire, CV36 5NQ.
ARCHARD DAVIES FRANCIS HOWARD ORCHARD SKINNER SMITH THWAITES VIDLER F5328

157805 QUINTON Mrs Pauline Helen. 10 Addison Pavement, Pitsea, Basildon, Essex, SS13 3JB. Tel:0268-555384
BARBER CONSTANTINE DAVIS QUINTON TINNAMS WALKER F2870

157813 QUIRKE Mrs Wendy. (Spear) 13 Innismore Grove, Ballincollig, Co Cork, Ireland.
BUCKTON SPEAR Speare Speer SPENCER F4331

157821 QUIRKE Mr William. 13 Innismore Grove, Ballincollig, Co Cork, IRELAND.
Cuirc O'cuirc O'quirk Quirk QUIRKE F5647

157848 QUY Mrs Betty Winifred. (Harvey) 18 Hadden Way, Greenford, Middx, UB6 0DH.
CONTENCIN ENEVER Enever-Harvey HARVEY HARVEY-ENEVER Quie Quoy Quoye QUY Quye F2115

157856 RABBETTS Mr Philip L. 6 Kirkly Close, South Croydon, CR2 0ET.
BARTON BEECHING MCKIE RABBETS RABBETTS SWIFT F6375

157864 RACKHAM Mrs Carol A. 10 The Chase, Billericay, Essex, CM11 2DL. Tel:0277-654957
ASHCROFT AVERY BAKER BANNAN BENSTEAD DOLMAN EVERSON HARRIS HODSON HOLLIDAY IVES JACKSON JONES MACKENZIE MAYES RACKHAM ROXBY SHELDRAKE F375

157872 RADFORD Mrs Jean. 3 Bathurst Road, Winnersh, Wokingham, Berkshire, RG11 5JB. Tel:0734-784212
BLAKE BLYTH BOLTON HOUSE KEMP MARKWELL RADFORD SMITH STANLEY F6102

157880 RADNEDGE Mr David. 6 Recreation Road, Earlham, Norwich, Norfolk, NR2 3PA. Tel:0603-505544
EARL FEAR MCGILL RADNAGE RADNEDGE Radnege RADNIDGE Ranedge RUDD F2848

157899 RADOMSKA Mrs Pauline. 3 Sandy Lane, Hucknall, Notts, NG15 7GR.
COLEMAN CORBY GHENT GIBSON SOUTHWELL F5262

157902 RAFFERTY Mrs Gabrielle L. (Lingard) Penaluna Cottage, 36 New Road, Barripper, Camborne, Cornwall, TR14 0QS.
BUTLER Dickson DIXON DREW DUCKWORTH EYLEY GARNER HASLAM LINGARD Malia Malley Mealey Melia MORTON O'MALLEY F7393

157910 RAFFILL Mr D. 126 Heol Y Bardd, Bridgend, Mid Glamorgan, CF31 4TD.
PARSONS Rafeil Raffaell Raffel RAFFELL Raffil RAFFILL Raffille RAFFILLS Raffle Rafflle Rafield Rafil Rafill Rapgael Raphall Raphel Raphele Raphell Raphiel Raphil Rasil Rassel F4755

157929 RAIL Dr John. York Lodge, 9 West Ridings, East Preston, Littlehampton, West Sussex, BN16 2TD. Tel:0903-772048
ENGLISH RAIL REAL ROUTLEDGE F5604

157937 RAILTON Mr Keith. 61 Styvechale Avenue, Earlsdon, Coventry, W Midlands, CV5 6DW. Tel:0203-676742

DENT KEITH RAILTON TURBERFIELD F2277
157945 RAIMBAULT Yves. 9 Rue Mayet, 75006 Paris, FRANCE.
RAIMBAULT F7349
157953 RAINBIRD Mr Gerald. 7 Collingwood Road, Horsham, West Sussex, RH12 2QN. Tel:0403-53660
LEE PAYNE RAINBIRD Rainburd SHARP WESTWOOD WITNEY F5803
157961 RAINBIRD Mrs Rosemary. Orchard Cottage, 2 Beach Road, West Mersea, Colchester, Essex, CO5 8AA.
RAINBIRD Raynbeard Raynbird F6877
157988 RAINE Mrs Lesley. (Macknight) 32 Tintagel, Great Lumley, Chester Le Street, Co Durham, DH3 4NF.
ERRINGTON KIRTLEY MACKNIGHT SPOOR TELFORD F3484
157996 RALLS Mr Stanley. 46 Bridge Street, Whaddon, Royston, Herts, SG8 5SQ. Tel:0223-207242
CATHCART COLLINGS LEADBETTER PICKARD RALLS ROBERTS TRAIL WILSON F3899
158003 RAMSDEN Mr Joseph W. 6 Park View, Whitburn, West Lothian, EH47 0AD. Tel:0501-40669
CUTLER EDGELAR Edglar RAFTER RAFTON RAMSDEN THEAKER F5195
158011 RAMSEY Mrs Eileen. (Wright) 19 Highlands Drive, Burton On Trent, Staffs, DE15 0TY. Tel:0283-65709
BECK BRIGGS FEATHERSTONE FEATHERSTONE-BECK Gilstrap Gilthorp Gilthrop GILTRAP LYONS SHERWIN WRIGHT F1347
158038 RANCE Mr Frederic A. 26 Wolverton, Skelmersdale, Lancs, WN8 8NA. Tel:0695-21648
BURROWS HOPLEY RANCE TRUBSHAW F529
158046 RANDALL Mrs S M. 1 Crabtree Villas, Crabtree, Laira, Plymouth Devon, PL3 6EN.
CREMAR DUSTIN EDE KENDALL PRIDEAUX SKELTON WOTTON F2938
158054 RANDELL Prof B. 26 Osbaldeston Gardens, Newcastle Upon Tyne, NE3 4JE.
COLMAN GREEN RANDELL STEWARD F5250
158062 RANDS Mr R M. 14 Mount Way, Chepstow, Gwent, NP6 5NF.
LUCKETT PEARSON RANDS F6041
158070 RANSOM Mr David M. 14 Kings Way, Burgess Hill, W Sussex, RH15 0TQ.
BIFFEN Bignal Bignall BIGNEL Bignell BUCKMAN GUMBRELL KENNARD NEAL PEDLEY RANSOM SAYERS F2243
158089 RANSOM Mr Stuart. 27 Barn Way, Wembley Park, Middx, HA9 9NS.
BAKER Cockerill COCKRILL HUDDY MCCOLLOCH POLKINGHORN Polkinghorne PRESTON RANSOM STEWARD WALTER F4356
158097 RASON Mrs D. 1 South Drive, Orpington, Kent, BR6 9NG.
FISHENDEN Fishington Fissenden F6910
158100 RATCLIFFE-ALLEN Mrs J. Oak Hill Cottage, Lords Wood, Highbridge, Colden Common Hants, SO5 7HR.
Aves AVIS BOVINDON DEVONSHIRE F6864
158119 RATEAU Mr Michel. 25 La Barriere, 24150 Mauzac, FRANCE. Tel:+33-5322-5608
RATEAU F7350
158127 RATHBONE Mr Derek. 4 Lea Croft, Clifford, Wetherby, W Yorks, LS23 6EY. Tel:0937-844022
FOSTER RATHBONE WRAGG F2927
158135 RATHBUN Mr Frank H. 11308 Popeshead Road, Fairfax, VA 22030, USA.
Rathbone RATHBUN Rathburn F7351
158143 RATTRAY-ALLAN Mr Andrew J. Wickham Elms, Rectory Road, Great Waldingfield, Sudbury Suffolk, CO10 0TL. Tel:0787-74741
BAXTER CROSS CUDDIE DUFF HAMILTON Hamiltone Hamiltown HART LYALL Lyell MALLOCH MUIR PENMAN RATTRAY THOMSON WALKER F1295
158151 RATTRAY-ALLAN Mrs Dorothy. (Patfield) Wickham Elms, Rectory Road, Great Waldingfield, Sudbury Suffolk, CO10 0TL. Tel:0787-74741
PATFIELD F1297
158178 RAVEN Mrs Margaret. 76 Chesterfield Road, Leyton, London, E10 6EN.
BUNDOCK LENCH PETTICAN RAVEN F1340
158186 RAVENSDALE Mrs J H. 4 Griffith Gardens, Ashby De La Zouch, Leics, LE6 5PE. Tel:0530-415028
DINAN RAVENSDALE ROSHIER F1255
158194 RAWBONE Mr Peter. 1 Hollyberry Grove, Holmer Green, High Wycombe, Bucks, HP15 6XB.
RAWBONE F4129
158208 RAWCLIFFE Mr Charles P. 35 Comely Bank Road, Edinburgh, EH4 1DS. Tel:031-332-5296
AYRE BELL DOWSON HAGGER HAZEL RAWCLIFFE ROBINSON WATSON WILSON F3668
158216 RAWCLIFFE Mrs Hilda. 93 Warrenside Close, Blackburn, Lancs, BB1 9PE.
COOPER FLETCHER FOWLER HALL HOLMES LEIGH-TRAVIS PARSONAGE RAWCLIFFE ROBINSON WILLIAMSON F2998
158224 RAWDON Mr Stan. Keble Cottage, 98a Hursley Village, Winchester, Hampshire, SO21 2JY. Tel:0962-75258
Rawden Rawdin Rawding RAWDON F2118
158232 RAWES Mrs B G. 18 Oldfield Crescent, Cheltenham, Glos, GL51 7BA.
ARROWSMITH BUNDAY FORD HARLOW HEWITT JOHNCOCK MARTIN PEAKE REEVES SETTERFIELD F2078
158240 RAWES Mr Julian. 11 Trowscoed Avenue, Cheltenham, Glous, GL53 7BP. Tel:0242-245259
BAGNALL LANCASTER MULEY RAWES Raws Rawse WILSON F3061
158259 RAWLEY Ms E M. 6 Carol Close, Brighton, Sussex, BN1 8QG. Tel:0273-502650
CHARLES HUNT OWEN Raily Raley Rawleigh RAWLEY Rawly Rowley F6399
158267 RAWLING Mrs G. 48 Westburn Avenue, Keighley, Yorks, BD22 6AW. Tel:0535-605421
BARTLETT BLAKE CROCKER HOPPER LAMPLUGH MATTHEWS PENROSE RAWLING SHEDD STEPHENS F1517
158275 RAWLINGS Mr Stephen. 33 Grove Road, Basingstoke, Hants, RG21 3BE. Tel:0256-472619
BARNEY BLACK BLACKMAN BLACKWELL BOWERS CARTER CHITTLE HARDY PAGE RAWLINGS THOMAS TURTON F1712
158283 RAWSON Mr David. 5 Savery Street, Southcoates Lane, Hull, E Yorks, HU9 3BG.
CUPPLEDYKE RAWSON TWYNAM F1467
158291 RAY Mr J D. 32 South Road, Hayling Island, Hants, PO11 9AE. Tel:0705-468245
NAPIER RAY F2490
158305 RAYBOULD Mrs J Laura. (Oliver) Barnet Cottage, Vention Lane, Lower Lydbrook, Glos, GL17 9RL.
BARTRAM BORMAY COPPENDALE DONNISON HUTCHINSON LANCASTER MITCHEL OLIVER ROE SPURR WATSON WHITWELL WILLIAMSON F5819
158313 RAYBURN Mr Alan. 5 Solva Drive, Nepean, Ontario, K2H 5R4, CANADA. Tel:+1-613-828-8510
CALHOUN CARSON CLUGSTON COBEAN COOK JOHNSTON LOGAN OLIVER PURDON REBURN F5159
158321 RAYMENT Mr David C. 20 Leasway, Wickford, Essex, SS12 0HF.
EASTLAKE Estlake Raiment Raymant RAYMENT Raymint Raymont Reyment F7008
158348 RAYMOND Mrs Gwyneth. Low Green Farm, Lindale, Grange Over Sands, Cumbria, LA11 6ND. Tel:05395-34780
LLOYD-JONES MARTIN MASON PYNEN RAYMOND REDMOND TAYLOR F2295
158356 RAYNOR Mr J Barrie. 23 Carisbrook Avenue, Leicester, LE2 3PA. Tel:0533-703756
HAWLEY RAYNOR SAVILLE F4238
158364 REA Mr George. 4 Orchard Dene, Rainhill, Merseyside, L35 0LT. Tel:051-430-6062
CANDIE CANDO CANDOW CANDY KANDOW KENNEDY RAE RAY REA WRAY F5856
158372 READ Mr Colin. 16 Spring Close, Burwell, Cambridge, CB5 0HF. Tel:0638-741749
BLYTHE CRONE READ F3904
158380 READ Mr John F W. 16 Thorncroft, Saffron Walden, Essex, CB10 2AZ. Tel:0799-523142
BLOOMFIELD COLEMAN IMPEY LIZARS PHILLIPS READ SAFFELL SHIMELL THOMPSON WOODHOUSE F5961
158399 READ Mrs Lorna. (Edwards) 19 Tukes Avenue, Bridgemary, Gosport, Hants, PO13 0SA.
BATEY BROWNING DARGUE DARGUES DART DOWNTON GODDARD GOODYER GREGORY HALL HART JOHNS MILES MURRELL PILESLY PLUMMER PURVES READ RICHARDS RINTOUL SIMMONDS SOANE STEPHENS TRASH TYRRELL UPHAM WILLIS F4614
158402 READ Mr Norman. 21 Gainsborough Road, Bournemouth, Dorset, BH7 7BD. Tel:0202-349822

CALL HAWES MATTHEWS MILFORD MITCHELL SANDERS SMITH WRIGHT F4387

158410 READ Mr Philip. 5 Camellia Close, Three Legged Cross, Wimborne, Dorset, BH21 6UD. AMEY READ VINE F2045

158429 READMAN Mr Anthony. 18 Somerfiled Lane, Stainsacre, Whitby, N Yorks, YO22 4NU. Tel:0947-604710 READMAN F1696

158437 REAR Mrs Marjorie. (Alais) 4 Manor House Road, Newcastle Upon Tyne, NE2 2LU. Tel:091-281-1231 ALAIS Alay Aley Alliace Allies BARFORD BARKER CREASEY FORD GARRATT HENN LEAVER REAR Reare Reares Reeher Reer Reir SCOTT F190

158445 REAR Mr R M. 106 Malleson Road, Gotherington, Cheltenham, Glos, GL52 4EY. Tel:0242-674470 Agate ALLISON ANDREWS ARMS ATKINSON BIGWOOD BOOTHROYD BRIGGS BURDEN Burdon BURGESS Buthroyd DOUGLAS DYER DYSON GRAHAM Grayham GRIFFITHS Griffs Griffus HALLAS HENDERSON Higate HIGHGATE HOBBS Hyat Hygate JONES MARSHALL Mathews Mathus MATTHEWS MAY Miels MILES MORGAN Morgans OWEN OWENS PECK PETCH PIERCE RANGER REAY RUDD SHADWELL SIMPSON SLINGSBY Standford STANDFORTH Stanforth Staters Stathers STATTERS THOMPSON TUCK VINE WATSON WEST WILES WILSHIRE WILSON Wyles F3375

158453 REDGATE Mrs Brenda. (Street) 31 Nene Close, Stretton, Burton On Trent, Staffs, DE13 0YA. Tel:0283-44886 STREET F7446

158461 REDMAN Mrs M. (Smith) 297 Benfleet Road, Benfleet, Essex, SS7 1PR. COPITHORNE NEVILL REDMAN WAKE F4144

158488 REE Mr Jack. 69 Brent Way, Finchley, London, N3 1AR. Tel:081-346-3297 REE THUSTIN F777

158496 REE Mrs P. (Jones) 45 Field View, York, YO3 6ES. HARISON JAMES JONES LAVERICK MARSHALL OSMOND SNOWBALL YOUNG F5078

158518 REED Mrs Alison. (Homer) 37 Highdale Close, Summerfield Estate, Llantrisant, Mid Glamorgan, CF7 8QE. HARRISON HOMER LADD REED F892

158526 REED Miss Anne B M. 36 Somers Road, Southsea, Hants, PO5 4PU. BOWERS MAYBANK MCKAY SMITH WILKINSON F4157

158534 REED Mr Christopher. 27 Tivoli Crescent, Brighton, Sussex, BN1 5NB. NEGROPONTE F7327

158542 REED Mr Eric. 27 Ash Close, Thornhill, Southampton, Hants, SO2 5SD. BARNES EVANS GOLD HEATH JENVEY JONES REED WISEMAN WRANN F982

158550 REED Mr Frank. 68 Dorchester Road, Ipswich, Suffolk, IP3 8RH. Steff Steffe Steph Stephe Stief Stife STIFF Stiffe F95

158569 REED Mr G E. 15 Reservoir Road, Rednal, Birmingham, W Midlands, B45 8PJ. BEEDOM BOWNS BUCKOKE CASWELL CHALTON CROSS DENT EDRIDGE FRIER FRYER GAY GODFREY GROVE HOARE JACKSON JARRETT JEFFERY KNIGHT MASON PARGETER PRESTIDGE REED ROBINS SHEPHER SHOTTON TENANT TOWNSEND TURNER F989

158577 REED Dr J L. Willow Tree House, Westleigh Drive, Bromley, Kent, BR1 2PN. ABBOTT ALLIN GUSTARD REED THOMPSON F4667

158585 REED Mr Martin. North Lodge, West Broyle, Chichester, W Sussex, PO18 9AJ. Tel:0243-779906 COFFIN FISH HOWE LOVE REED STANYON STIDWORTHY F2667

158593 REED Mr Pater. 57 Mayfield Avenue, Orpington, Kent, BR6 0AJ. Tel:0689-837274 COMBER COOMBER MOISEY Moissy MOYSEY Moysie Moysse Moysy Moyzey Opey OPIE Oppie Oppy REED Rooby Rouby Rubby Rubey Rubie RUBY Suttaby Sutterbee Sutterbie SUTTERBY Wesbrook Westbroke WESTBROOK WESTBROOKE F555

158607 REED Mr William A. 22 Gainsborough Road, New Malden, Surrey, KT3 5NU. Tel:081-337-7735 ASHPOOL REED SIMPKINS WALSH F4290

158615 REEDER Mr Brian. 20 Bernard Crescent, Ipswich, Suffolk, IP3 9LJ. Tel:0473-710177 REEDER F3737

158623 REES Mr Howard D. 47 St Marys Close, Attenborough, Beeston, Nottingham, NG9 6AT. DAVEY GODDARD HUMBER F5847

158631 REES Mrs Idwen. (Thomas) Tan Dinas, Rhos Lan, Criccieth, Gwynedd, LL52 0NL. ELLIS OWEN OWENS ROBERTS THOMAS F3436

158658 REES Mr Malcolm. 48 Broomhill Road, Dartford, Kent, DA1 3HT. Tel:0322-225567 ABRAHAM ATKINS Baetson Baettson BATSON Battson BEDDOW BROWNE CHARLESWORTH CLARKE DANIEL DAVID DAVIES DYER ELY EVANS GROUT HARRY HODDS HOLLOWAY HOUSDEN HOWELL HUGHES JARY Jeary JENKINS JOHN JONES LEWIS LLEWELLYN MADDOCKS MADDOX MARSH MARTIN MORGAN MORT Morter NATHANIEL NEWBY OVERILL PHILLIPS PRICE REES ROBERT ROSSER ROYAL SHEPARD STARLING THOMAS WILKIN WILLIAM WILLIAMS WINTER F4630

158666 REEVE Mr Allan I. 16a Blackfriars Lane, Chirnside Park, Victoria, 3166, AUSTRALIA. Tel:+61-3-735-3279 ARBUTHNOT BOON FORREST HAMILTON HART REEVE RICHARDSON SUMMERS WEBB WINTER F5154

158674 REEVES Mrs Betty. (Foote) 28 Cedar Gardens, Upminster, Essex, RM14 3DL. FOOT Foote F1733

158682 REEVES Mr Francis G. 162 Kent House Road, Beckenham, Kent, BR3 1JY. Tel:081-778-4145 REEVES F5735

158690 REEVES Mrs Helen. Agra, 89 Acreman Street, Sherbourne, Dorset, DT9 3PH. Tel:0963-816346 COWELL MORRISON REEVES ROBSON SHAW WATSON WILLS F970

158704 REEVES Mrs Merlynne. 6 Rolvenden Road, Wainscott, Strood, Rochester Kent, ME2 4NY. Tel:0634-710404 BEARSBY BOWEN DAVIES HATTON NEEDS PERRITT POUND QUELCH REEVES SCOONS F4068

158712 REGAN Mrs K M. 236 Birchover Way, Allestree, Derby, DE3 2RR. AUCKLAND BAULDING BULHAND BULLEN CONSTABLE GOLDTHORP THOMPSON WILSON F2793

158720 REID Mrs Anna. 32 Anderida Road, Lower Willingdon, Eastbourne, E Sussex, BN22 0PU. Tel:0323-505434 HARDMAN F1484

158739 REID Mr Clive & Mrs Anne. 54 Rhyd-Y-Defaid Drive, Sketty, Swansea, SA2 8AL. Tel:0792-771333 BURTON CRUSCOMBE DAWSON DEERE GWILLIM GWYON HERBERT HOWELL JAMES JENKIN LACY LLOYD MINNET MORRIS PORTREY PRICE REID SAMUEL STOBO SYMONDS THOMAS WILLIAMS F3629

158747 REID Mrs J E M. (O'Mara) 503 Sidcup Road, Mottingham, London, SE9 4ET. Tel:081-857-0184 Arm Arme Armes ARMS BODLEY CHICK Falbrick Falbrook Fallbrick FOOT Fulbrick Fulbrook FULLBRICK HARRIS MARA Meara O'MARA O'meara O'THAM Philbrick Philbrook SEYMOUR Wannister Winister Winnester WINNISTER F347

158755 REID Mrs M R. 171 Symes Road, Hamworthy, Poole, Dorset, BH15 4PY. Tel:0202-678218 BRASSEY HUNT MOYES REID THOMPSON F622

158763 REINKE Mrs Ailsa. (Compton) 1 Chapman Street, Proserpine, Queensland, 4800, AUSTRALIA. Tel:+61-7-945-2168 COMPTON DAWE GRAY HANNINGTON HOW ILLIDGE MILLER PRITCHARD Sobey SOBIE Soby WINSER F5167

158771 RELF Sqn Ldr Brian. 11 Hanbury Drive, Biggin Hill, Kent, TN16 3EN. REALF RELF RELPH RICOLFIS RICWULF RIULF F2885

158798 RELF Mr Chris & Mrs Helen. 4 Blacklands Road, Upper Buckleybury, Reading, Berks, RG7 6QP. BRIDGLAND BROWNJOHN DEACON HODDINOTT PHIPPEN PRATTEN RELF SPERRING WATSON WOODLEY F802

158801 RELF Miss G E M. 43 Winterbourne Lodge, Warren Drive, Lewes, E Sussex, BN7 1HD. Tel:0273-474079 Ralf Realff RELF Relfe Relph Rolph F233

158828 RENAULT Mr Kenneth C. La Source, Rue Du Tapon, St Saviour, Jersey, JE2 7UL. Tel:0534-54801 MACKENZIE F6345

158836 RENDELL Mrs M. 17 Western Avenue, Thorpe,

Egham, Surrey, TW20 8QB.
COLLINS FROUDE HOARE PARFETT ROBINI WOODHOUSE F879

158844 RENOWDEN Mr P A. 41 Lakeside Drive, Norton Canes, Cannock, Staffs, WS11 3RH.
RENOWDEN F2906

158852 RESTORICK Mrs R A. 71 Medeswell, Orton Malborne, Peterborough, Cambs, PE2 0PB.
Restarick RESTORICK Restrick F6866

158860 REVANS Mr William Godfrey. 23 Johnson Close, Leigh, Lancs, WN7 4QJ. Tel:0942-678534
REVANS F1375

158879 REVIE Mr George Martin. 20 Blackthorn Drive, Gosport, Hants, PO12 4AZ. Tel:0705-588731
BERSEY REVIE SCOLIN WOODLEY F2668

158887 REYNER Mr Robert. 29 Scorton Avenue, Perivale, Greenford, Middx, UB6 8LA.
REYNER SIZELAND F5367

158895 REYNOLDS Mr Brian. Po Box 11, Telopea, New South Wales, 2117, AUSTRALIA.
BROMAGE DUNNING FERGUSON KIFFT Kift REYNOLDS SMALLBONES F5579

158909 REYNOLDS Dr C F. Div Of It Csiro, Po Box 1599, Macquarie Centre, N Ryde, NSW 2113, AUSTRALIA.
PHIPSON F6647

158917 REYNOLDS Mrs E M. (Hart) 4 Maple Avenue, Poynton, Stockport, Cheshire, SK12 1PR. Tel:0625-872471
ALLEN BENTLEY HART HAWLEY HULSE JORDAN MITCHELL REYNOLDS VOKES WHITWORTH F3527

158925 REYNOLDS Mrs Edna. (Jones) 54 Parkhill Road, Bexley, Kent, DA5 1HY.
COURT GODWIN HAYBALL KENWARD MAYERS NORRINGTON REYNOLDS TREVIGAN WEDLAKE WOOLCOTT F4049

158933 REYNOLDS Mr Ian. 17 Macdonald Street, Chifley, ACT 2606, AUSTRALIA. Tel:+61-6-282-1705
Reinolds Rennels Rennoles Rennols Renoldeg REYNOLDS F6509

158941 REYNOLDS Mrs Irene. (Heath) 9 Polperro Way, Hucknall, Nottingham, NG15 6JS. Tel:0602-635588
BROWN Crokestone Croxton CRUXTON HEATH JOHNSON LAWTON WALKER F505

158968 REYNOLDS Mr John Francis. 7 Devonshire Drive, Draycott Park, Rugeley, Staffs, WS15 1LA.
BICKLEY COLE COOPER MARSHALL MORGAN MUDWAY REYNOLDS STACKHOUSE WHITEHOUSE F5889

158976 REYNOLDS Mrs Patricia. 20 Lilac Place, Yiewsley, West Drayton, Middx, UB7 8LR. Tel:0895-444442
ALDWIN ANDERSON BALMFORTH BEASLEY BECKETT BROTHERTON BUTLER DEAMER DRAPER FAULKNER HULLAW HUSBAND JENKINS KNAGGS LAMB LYNAS MACEY MUNNS PARLOUR REYNOLDS ROFFEY TAYLOR WILKINSON F2997

158984 REYNOLDS Mr Peter. 66 Aylesbury Close, Norwich, Norfolk, NR3 3LB.
CHURCHILL CROSS FERGUSON KNELL LAPRAIK LEES MARTIN REYNOLDS VENUS F3744

158992 RHODES Mrs B. 30 Kingsley Road, Allestree, Derby, DE3 2JH.
GRAHAM HUGHES JONES MURRAY REES WILLIAMS F3453

159018 RHODES Mrs Janet. 34 Redwood Avenue, Wollaton, Nottingham, NG8 2SG. Tel:0602-284232
ATKINSON BRANDON BRUMPTON GOODCHILD OLDHAM RHODES TYLER F3117

159026 RHODES M. 134 Sunnybank Crescent, Brinsworth, Rotherham, S Yorks, S60 5JJ.
Baddgeer BADGER BADGERS Badier Badjer Bagger CHAPMAN GOODBUN HILL LAND NASH Ramskar RAMSKER ROBERTS SANDERSON SHORT SMITH STONES TURTON WATKINSON F744

159034 RHYS Mrs Stella. (Ruthven) 6 Windermere Road, Barnehurst, Bexleyheath, Kent, DA7 6PW.
ABBOTT ALLEN CANDISH FISSENDEN LANGLEY Melbourne MILBORNE Milbourn Milbourne PARROCK RICHMOND Ruthen Rutheson Ruthsen Ruthson Ruthvan RUTHVEN Ruthvin Ruttum TAMPLIN WEBSTER WITT F1447

159042 RICHARDS Mrs Auriel. (Wren) 39 Westhawe, Bretton, Peterborough, PE3 8BA. Tel:0733-268409
BELTON BINGHAM BLACKBURN COATES Eelborn FAULKS Frisby FRIZBY GREEN Hais Hayes HAYS HEATH Heays Heoth JOHNSON MICHELSON MIDDLETON MILLER MORTON MUSSON NICKS NIX PEARSON Peirson Pierson REVELL SEARSON SMITH TOON Welband Welborn Welbourn WHEELBAND WILBORN WILBURN WREN F3072

159050 RICHARDS Mrs C A. The Lawns, Woods Lane, Cliddesden, Basingstoke Hants, RG25 2JG.
VERLANDER F6610

159069 RICHARDS Mr David J. 8 Dorchester Close, Stoke Mandeville, Bucks, HP22 5YR. Tel:0296-613929
CHAPMAN HAZARD HOODINOTT PAYNE RICHARDS F4550

159077 RICHARDS Mr Donald. 39 West Hawe, Bretton, Peterborough, PE3 8BA. Tel:0733-268409
ABBOTT BEEKEN CONNERTON CUBBY ELDERKIN FARNSWORTH GILL GRAY HAMMOND HILLS HOOPER HOSMER HUNT LINDSEY NORRIS RICHARDS SMITH TURNER WITNEY WRIGHT F6525

159085 RICHARDS Mrs E. Llanwnwr, Goodwick, Dyfed, SA64 0JL.
EDMONDS Edmons Edmunds STOBIE Stobo F7142

159093 RICHARDS Mr Geoffrey. Ashton Lodge, Ashton Road, Hilperton, Trowbridge Wilts, BA14 7QY. Tel:0225-751420
BASTABLE BETTY COWEY CRAFFORD EVETTS MURRELL RICHARDS F1788

159107 RICHARDS Mr Jack R. 2 The Green, Codicote, Hitchin, Herts, SG4 8UR. Tel:0438-820006
BAYLISS DAVIS EARESS HIAM HIGHAM HILL JONES MONNOX NIGHTON OFFELOW OFFILER Offler OFFLEY Offlow PEARS POOLE RICHARDS RUSSELL SMALL TAFT TAYLOR WATTON F3035

159115 RICHARDS Mrs Jacqueline. 6 Cowleaze Close, Shrivenham, Swindon, Wilts, SN6 8EH. Tel:0793-782984
ABEL AKEHURST AKNOS AKVOS AYERS BARKER BRIGGS COOMBE COWARD FRANCIS FRASER HARPER LE ROY MARCHE RICHARD RICHARDS SIMS SMALLMAN TIPTON TOMLINS TUCKER WILLY F5757

159123 RICHARDS Miss Kathleen. 14 Adelaide Court, Copers Cope Road, Beckenham, Kent, BR3 1TT. Tel:081-650-7652
IVERSON RAVEN RICHARDS SOUTHGATE F4826

159131 RICHARDS Miss Laura. Hastingleigh, Highcotts Lane, West Clandon, Guildford Surrey, GU4 7XA.
BAINES BUTTERWORTH FRIDDLE GARDNER GRACE HARRISON Landram Landrem Landrim LANDRUM LEWIS NIGHTINGALE OWEN PORTER RICHARD RICHARDS SIMMONDS TEDDER F2219

159158 RICHARDS Mr Patrick. 4 Pine Tree Drive, North Upton Lane, Barnwood, Gloucester, GL3 3AJ.
ANGEL BUTTON COTHER CRANE EATON FERRIS Galder GAULDER Gauler GREGORY Haines HAYNES HEATH JONES LOVEDAY PICKETT RICHARDS Welborn Welborne Welburn Wilbourn WILBOURNE F4813

159166 RICHARDS Mr Robert Paul. 135 Stockport Road West, Bredbury, Stockport, Cheshire, SK6 2AN. Tel:061-430-3298
CALDERBANK GEE JOULE MILLS PICKERING VIVYAN WRAY F4014

159174 RICHARDS Mr W H F. 88 Wilbury Road, Letchworth, Herts, SG6 4JJ. Tel:0462-673182
BAILEY Bauch Bauche Baucke Baugh Baughe BELTON Betridge Betteredge BETTERIDGE Bettridge Bitteredge BOUCH Bouche Boucke BOUFFEY Bough Boughe Bowch Bowche Bowgh BRIDGFORD CAMPBELL CARTWRIGHT COLLIS DAVIES ESCOTT EVANS GARLAND GOODRED GREENSLADE HARRAD HARWOOD HIBBERT HILL HOPKINSON HUDSON HUGHES JOHNS JONES LEWIS LODGE LUDGATE MADDOX MORGAN NADEN NADIN NIXON NOVELLO PEARCE PERKINS RICHARDS ROBINSON ROTHERY STANDLEY Stanley Stanly TUNNICLIFF TURRALL WEIR F2075

159182 RICHARDSON Mr F. 7 Rudland Way, High Etherley, Bishop Aukland, Co Durham, DL14 0HH. Tel:0388-832417
BAINBRIDGE MONAGHAN MORAN RICHARDSON F3603

159190 RICHARDSON Mrs J A Carew. (Buckett) 127 Marvels Lane, Grove Park, London, SE12 9PP.
CAREW Carewe Caro Caroe Carrew Carro Carrow Caru Carue F3751

159204 RICHARDSON Mr John Peter. 12 Havant Road,

Emsworth, Hants, PO10 7JE. Tel:0243-374113 BAILEY CUDBIRD GLASSPOOLE MACHIN MILBANK RICHARDSON SWANN VASSAR F4619

159212 RICHARDSON Mr Mick. 8 Wythwood, Haywards Heath, W Sussex, RH16 4RD. Tel:0444-452524 BAILEY BIRKETT CARTER COULTHARD FLEMING HILL KEY LEWIS MILLER MOULDEN PYECROFT RAVEN RICHARDSON SCOTT THOMAS WARREN WILKINSON F4208

159220 RICHARDSON Miss Sarah. 21 Avon Road, Scunthorpe, S Humberside, DN16 1EP. ARROWSMITH BALL BEDFORD COATES FENTON JENSEN MADES MOORE MORRIS MORRITT RICHARDSON F2766

159239 RICHARDSON Mrs V A. (Moore) 50 Wentworth Crescent, Ash Vale, Aldershot, Hants, GU12 5LF. Tel:0252-311834 BRETT DOW GROVES HADMAN HAWES HOOK RUSSELL SIVIER STEWARD STOW UPCHER Upsher VACHER VAUGHAN F4562

159247 RICHARDSON Miss Valerie. 40 Madingley, Birch Hill, Bracknell, Berkshire, RG12 4TF. AWSON BANT BIRKS Boden BOWDEN GREENHALL HUMPHREYS Humphries MASON RICHARDSON WHARTON WOODS F4881

159255 RICHES Mrs Lesley A. 185 Colchester Road, West Bergholt, Colchester, Essex, CO6 3JY. CALLEN FLEXEN FUNDELL PHEBY RICHES SCOWEN F6352

159263 RICHINGS Mr Matthew Henry. 10 Bower Road, Ashton, Bristol, BS3 2LN. Tel:0272-669462 RICHINGS F4935

159271 RICHMOND A F. 19 The Orchards, Epping, Essex, CM16 7BB. BEDDING BROAD BUDD DANIEL RICHMOND START THURLOW F910

159298 RICKARD Mr Kenneth Edward. 10 Brackendale, Potters Bar, Herts, EN6 2LU. Tel:0707-50939 RICKARD F3231

159301 RICKARD Mr Mostyn. 7 Tilney Way, Lower Earley, Reading, Berks, RG6 4AD. BLATCHFORD EVANS FRANKLIN RICKARD F1439

159328 RICKARD Mr Robert. 3154 Paradise Way, Zephyrhills, Florida, 33541, USA. Tel:+1-813-782-7073 Recard Reccard Recceard Receard Recerd Rechard Recheard Recherd Reckard Reckeard Record Ricard Riccard Riccord RICKARD Rickarde Rickeard Rickerd Ricord F5520

159336 RICKARDS Mrs B A. (Linfoot) 21 Grange Close, Shaw Mills, Harrogate, N Yorks, HG3 3HX. Tel:0423-771475 COATES CONNOR CULLEN GILMORE HEPPTONSTALL LINFOOT SHIRE F3513

159344 RICKCORD Mr Michael. 3 Church Street, Little Shelford, Cambridge, CB2 5HG. Riccord Riccords RICKCORD Rickcords Rickoard Rickord Rickords Ricord Ricords F3987

159352 RICKMAN Mr David. 41 Marlbrook Lane, Bromsgrove, Worcs, B60 1HP. Tel:021-445-2372 RICKMAN F2868

159360 RIDD Mrs Anne. Higher Tippacott Farm, Brendon, Lynton, Devon, EX35 6PU. Tel:05987-343 RIDD WADDINGTON F6047

159379 RIDDEL Mrs Jessie S. (Gibson) Flat 3/2, 12 Henrietta Street, Glasgow, G14 0BG. Besset Bessot Biset Bisit Bisot Bissat BISSET Bissit Bissot Bizat Bizet Bizett Bizit Bizot Bizzet Bysset CALDER Caulder Fraiser Fraser FRAZER Frissel Frissell Frizzel Frizzell GIBSON HAY HENDERSON Mansey Meness Mengeis Menges Mengies Mengus Mengzies Meniss Mensies Menyeis Menzeis Menzie MENZIES Minges Moinzies Mowncey Ridal Riddal Riddall RIDDEL Riddell RIDDELS Riddle Ridley Ridlon ROBERTSON Ruddal Ruddel Ruddell Rydall Ryedale Sauland Sunderland Surrland Sutheland SUTHERLAND SUTHERLANDS Suthland Suylerland Suyrland F3521

159387 RIDDICK Miss Averil. 4 Roseberry Mount, Dursley, Glous, GL11 4PR. Tel:0453-543600 Grove GROVES RIDDICK Ruddick Ruddoch Ruddock F281

159395 RIDGEON Mr David C E. Rectory Farm, Madingley Road, Coton, Cambridge, CB3 7PG. Tel:0223-354812 JOHNSON MILLER RIDGEON SCALES F4834

159409 RIDGERS Mr C. 57 Highclere Gardens, Roborough, Plymouth, Devon, PL6 7EB. BUDD RIDES RIDGERS RIGERS F520

159417 RIDOUT Mr William. Hollyburn, New Road, Northchurch, Berkhamstead Herts, HP4 1LN. Tel:0442-875862 MUNDAY Redout Rideout RIDOUT Ridoutt Ridoux F1417

159425 RIEDSTRA Lutzen H. 24 St Andrew Street, Stratford, Ontario, N5A 1A3, CANADA. Reidstra RIEDSTRA Rietstra F7355

159433 RIGARLSFORD Mr F J. 339 Rainham Road, Rainham, Essex, RM13 7TB. Tel:04027-51752 RIGARLSFORD F5993

159441 RIGBY Mr Alan F. Hillhead, Ashill, Cullompton, Devon, EX15 3NQ. Tel:0884-840294 Bennats Bennatts BENNETS Bennetts BLOM DAWE GEE HARE MARTHOLM RIGBY TAYLOR THOMAS VEALE WEDLOCK WHOMES WOOD F2056

159468 RIGBY Mrs Ann P. Meadlands, 3 Pickwick, Corsham, Wiltshire, SN13 0JD. Tel:0249-713228 BOWNASS BROOKES CATTON CULLEN DAY FLYNN GARDENER GRICE HARRISON HIBBARD JONES KIRKHAM LILLEY MILLS PADMORE PODMORE RIGBY SLAYMAKER SMITH F1044

159476 RIGGALL D E. 27 Queenswood Road, Sutton Coldfield, West Midlands, B75 6UB. Giggall Rigal RIGGALL Righall Ryeauld F7037

159484 RILEY Mrs June. 3 Bilberry Close, Locks Heath, Southampton, Hants, SO3 6XX. Ing Inggs INGS Inngs KENCHINGTON Kenchinton Kinchington F942

159492 RILEY Mrs M A. (Hall) Zenith, 28 Eastbourne Street, Glodwick, Oldham, Lancs, OL8 2BZ. BARNES BEARDSALL BOLTON BOND CARDING COLLIER COWAP CROMPTON DALTON DAWS FIELDING FOGG HADFIELD HALL HANCOCK HARDY HOLT HUXLEY MARLOR MILHENCH MILLS MOSS NAYLOR NORMAN OAKES OGDEN PERDIKOU RAMSDEN ROTHWELL RUSHTON SHAW SMETHURST STOTT TAYLOR TURNER Twaemlow TWAMLOW WALTON WHITTAKER WILD WOOD F1039

159506 RILEY Mr Stanley. 83 Carrwood, Hale Barns, Altrincham, Cheshire, WA15 0ET. LEADBETTER PENDER PINCHON PYE RILEY ROSKELL STANLEY F1846

159514 RING Mr A D. 8 Newton Road, Dovercourt, Essex, CO12 4JD. AMNER COLLINS HART JAMES PAPE READING RING SIMONS WILDMAN F4069

159522 RINGHAM Mrs Norma. 23 Margaret Close, Whitley Wood Lane, Reading, Berks, RG2 8PU. Tel:0734-868809 COOPER COX CROOK HULME MURDIN READE READER RINGHAM THURBON F2621

159530 RIPPIN Ms Lynda. 29 Bargate, Lincoln, LN5 8DD. Bickerdyke Bigadag Bigadyke BIGGADIKE Biggerdag Biggerdike CAVE Dickerday Dickerdyke Digadag Diggerdyke Doodles DUDDLES Dudles Hotchkis HOTCHKISS Kave Ripen Ripin Riping Ripon Rippen RIPPIN Ripping Rippon F4775

159549 RISDALE Mr K H. 110 High Street, Riseley, Bedford, MK44 1DF. Tel:0234-708281 Rezle Risdal RISDALE Wrassell Wresle Wressell Wrossell F4714

159557 RITCHIE Mrs Jean. 14 Glenview Road, Via Mooloolah, Queensland, 4553, AUSTRALIA. CHILD SARGENT TANNER F5571

159565 RITCHIE Mrs Sally. 39 Grosvenor Road, Caversham, Reading, Berks, RG4 0EN. DAY GOWER HENRY MAGGS MOSES NICHOLS POWEL POWELL SANDLES SCORER WATKINSON F6296

159573 RIVAS Dr Peter. 57 Hemmingford Road, Islington, London, N1 1BY. Barrett Barrit BARRITT BREARLEY EYLES FUDGE Isles PERRY PRIESTLEY SANDS Sandys Sans Shippen SHIPTON STANSFIELD Wales WALLOP Walls Wals Weals WHALES Whalls Whals F5352

159581 RIVERS Mrs J E. (Shurlock) 20 Herons Close, North Oulton Broad, Lowestoft, Suffolk, NR32 3LB. Tel:0502-563052 BALCHIN Balchine Balchylde Baldchild Ballchin Ballchine BULLEN CHANDLER Chittie CHITTY COOPER DENDY EARTHY EDWARDS ELIOT Ffulk

Ffulke Folkes FREEMAN Fulk FULKE GARRAT Garratt GODDARD Graffham GRAFHAM Hillier HILLYER LARRANCE Laurence Ledgard LEDGER LEE Lidger Lock LOCKE Lydger MATCHWICKE MIALL MILLS MORRIS NEIGHBOUR NOY PAGE PECK PETCH PRATT PRENTICE PULLEN RIVERS Sharlock Sharlocke Sherlock Shirlock SHURLOCK STEDMAN STENNING STEVENS STONE TICKNER WEST WILSON WORSFOLD Worsfolde F411

159603 RIVETT Mr Eric. 30 Bernhard Gardens, Polegate, E Sussex, BN26 5JN. Tel:03212-3982
RIVETT F1931

159611 RIX Mrs M A. Clapstile Farm, Apheton, Sudbury, Suffolk, CO10 8BN.
GOLDING F6970

159638 RIX Mr R W. 7 Mead Court, Common Mead Lane, Gillingham, Dorset, SP8 4ND.
RIX F6635

159646 RIXON Mrs Olive. (Chappell) 7 Holtsmere Close, Garston, Watford, Herts, WD2 6NG.
CHAPELL CHAPPELL CHAPPELLE CHAPPLE EVANS MOON MOONE F1007

159654 ROACH Mr Christopher. 36 Brookside, Hertford, Herts, SG13 7LL. Tel:0992-587796
HEWINGS JAMES ROACH F1016

159662 ROBB Mr Eric G. 4 Alanwood Park, Bangor, Co Down, N Ireland, BT20 5PT. Tel:0247-466755
GAWLEY F191

159670 ROBB Miss H L. 244 Queens Esplanade, Thorneside, Queensland, 4158, AUSTRALIA.
Stere Sterrey STERRY Stirry F6851

159689 ROBERTS JOHNSON Miss E. Dunholme, Deaf Hill, Trimdon Station, Co Durham. Tel:0429-880321
EDWARDS ROBERTS F5774

159697 ROBERTS Mr & Mrs. Tegfan, 8 Sutherland Crescent, Blythe Bridge, Stoke On Trent, Staffs, ST11 9JU.
Standaven Standavens Standeen Standeeven Standeon Standevan Standevans STANDEVEN Standevens Standever Standevins Standhaven Standhavens Standheaven Standheavens Standheven Standivan Standiver Standoven Standven Standwen Standwin Stannonen F6975

159700 ROBERTS Mr Andy. 9 Connaught Road, New Malden, Surrey, KT3 3PZ. Tel:081-942-7591
BROWN BURBIDGE CORBETT DAVIES De Fowell Ffowell FLOYD PRICE Foghill Fouhel Fouhell Fowel FOWELL Fowhell Fowhill GABB HARROLD MORGAN PEARDON POWELL PRICE ROBERTS Sketch Skich SKITCH TROWBRIDGE Voghill Vowel WORKMAN ZACHARY F5936

159719 ROBERTS Mrs Ann M. (Sims) 69 Heol-Y-Hendre, Rhuddlan, Clwyd, LL18 5PG. Tel:0745-591335
EVANS JONES LEWIS F3900

159727 ROBERTS Ms C. 12 Victoria Drive, Eastbourne, E Sussex, BN20 8JS.
RABBITT F6385

159735 ROBERTS Mrs Constance. (Boothby) 36 Heol Isaf, Rhiwbina, Cardiff, South Glamorgan, CF4 6RJ.
BOOTHBY EDWARDS GRIFFITHS MORGAN PHILLIPS ROBERTS F2370

159743 ROBERTS Mr David G E. Gorwel, Llanarth, Dyfed, SA47 0NN. Tel:0545-580204
BEYNON DAVIES EDWARDS GETHING GRIFFITHS JONES MORGAN OWEN ROBERT ROBERTS WILLIAMS F1565

159751 ROBERTS Mr Donald John. Pinewoods, Ashley Priors Lane, Torquay, Devon, TQ1 4ES. Tel:0803-324480
COULMAN DUSTAN FRIEND HEATH JOHNS KNAPMAN LONG LOT LYELL LYLE PALMER PERING REDSTONE ROBERTS F3702

159778 ROBERTS Mrs Dorcas. Rhoslan, Greefield Road, Ruthin, Clwyd, LL15 1EP. Tel:08242-4684
EVANS ROBERTS THOMAS F2465

159786 ROBERTS Mr Edward. 7 Westbrook Square, West Gorton, Manchester, M12 5PF.
HUGHES OWEN ROBERTS SEBER WILLIAMS F6079

159794 ROBERTS Mr G. Berwyn, 5 Rhiw Bank Avenue, Colwyn Bay, Clwyd, LL29 7PH.
MOSES ROBERTS ROWLAND Rowlands SOLOMON F4542

159808 ROBERTS Mrs Joyce. 28 Admirals Road, Park Gate, Southampton, Hants, SO3 6QF.
FRY Preace Preas Preast PREECE Prees Preest Priest Reece Rees Robarts Robbarts Robberts ROBERTS Sanders SAUNDERS Stairs STARES Stears Steres STURGESS F1449

159816 ROBERTS Mr Kenneth. 24 Alton Close, Ashton In Makerfield, Wigan, WN4 9TX. Tel:0942-716209
ROBERTS F6071

159824 ROBERTS Mr Martin. Stowlands, 2 Golden Avenue Close, Angmering On Sea, Sussex, BN16 1QS.
ELLIOTT FIRKS MANCHEE ROBERTS TRESCOWDRICK VIDLER F5758

159832 ROBERTS Ms Tanya. 11717 Kingtree Street, Wheaton, Maryland, 20902, USA. Tel:+1-301-942-7591
HEATON HURLBUT F5526

159840 ROBERTS Mr Tim. 67 Falmouth Road, Chelmsford, Essex, CM1 5JA.
BOLGER BULGER GRIFFIN HUDSON HUNKING KIPPS MARSHALL MARTIN NOCKELS O'DONOGHUE PRIDIE REED ROBERTS ROBINSON SHERMAN SKERMAN SOLLY WALSH F1343

159859 ROBERTS Mrs Tracey. 14 Tregarrick Close, Helston, Cornwall.
BLEE F873

159867 ROBERTSON Mr Alexander John. 8 Narbeth Crescent, Llan-Yr-Afon, Cwmbran, Gwent, NP44 8RJ. Tel:0633-872196
HAWKINS ROBERTSON F6016

159875 ROBERTSON Mr Charles. Po Box 40, Bilbul, Griffith, NSW 2680, AUSTRALIA. Tel:+61-6-963-5356
GANNON JARRETT MADDEN MCKINNON ROBERTSON RUTTER STOREY F5474

159883 ROBERTSON Mr Hamish. 44 Lancaster Gate, London, W2 3NA. Tel:071-723-0721
BUDDS BURGESS CHALMERS COLEMAN CRICKETT CUTHBERT FORMAN HARFLETE HORNE HOUGHAM INGRAM IRVINE KNOTT MCLEISH MEAL MELVILLE NOAKES OGILVY PAIN POTTER PROUDE PRYOR RATTRAY ROBERTSON SARGENT SHEPHERD SMITH SOLLY WICKES YOUNG F690

159891 ROBERTSON Miss Irene N. 10 Forfar Road, Kirriemuir, Angus, DD8 5BY.
FINDLAY FLEMING LEIGHTON MORRIS RENNIE ROBERTSON SINCLAIR F2726

159905 ROBERTSON Mr Keith. 3/32 Chandos Road, Redland, Bristol, BS6 6PF. Tel:0272-733460
BEERS BETTS BLACK BLOXHAM BROMMAGE BROOKS BROWN BUDDLE CAIRNS CHISHOLM CORBY COULTHARD CROOKS CROSS CUNCLINGTON DALTON DRURY FAWCETT GAVIN GREEN GRUMMEL HALL HAMILTON HAY HAYES HILTON HONE HUNTER JOBSON MANCILL MARK MELDRUM MOLE NICHOLLS NICHOLS NORMAN PARSONS PINDER RICHARDS ROBERTSON THOMPSON UPTON VACHER VICKERS WAILS WATKINS WRIGHT F2001

159913 ROBERTSON Mrs Linda. (Barnett) 33 Gorse Avenue, South Sheilds, Tyne & Wear, NE34 7PP. Tel:091-456-7007
BARNETT BRAWLEY DURSTON EVERY JAMES JONES LUKE MEAKER MEDLIN MITCHELL NICHOLLS PURSEY RICHARDS THOMAS F1015

159921 ROBERTSON Mrs Margaret. (Mathieson) 27 Arthur Place, Cowdenbeath, Fife, KY4 8NR.
MATHIESON F929

159948 ROBERTSON Mrs Margaret. 12 Commercial Street, Lerwick, Shetland Isles, Scotland, ZE1 0AN.
LAWSON Lowson ROBERTSON F2721

159956 ROBERTSON Mr Simon. 70 Punch Croft, New Ash Green, Kent, DA3 8HR. Tel:0474-872144
ALFOUNDER BAKER BARTLETT BEAVIS BIDDLE BLOMFIELD BOREHAM BOWERS BURROWS CAMERON CAMP CLARKE CLEARS CRADOCK DALE DOUGLAS GATES GORDON GREIG GYE HAILS HALES HALL LEECH LOWS MARSH MILLAR MILLER MOOR MORLEY MUNDEN OTLEY PAGE PATRICK PAYNE RAINBIRD RAYNER REEVE ROBERTSON RUDDOCK RUST SAMS SHICKLE SPURGEN STYLEMAN SYER SYMONDS TOLTON WAITMAN WILSON WOODS WORLLEDGE WYATT F4132

159964 ROBINSON Mr Andrew. 52 Victoria Avenue, Saffron Walden, Essex, CB11 3AE. Tel:0799-21895
ADAMS AFFLECK BARLOW BOWIE BRIMSON BURGESS CARFRAE CLOUNIE Cloutie CORBETT CUMMINS CUTMER DUNN FARLEY FLEMING FLETCHER GELSTON Gilston GRIFFIN HAMILTON HAZELL HILTON HINDLEY HULME HURST IRELAND LINDLEY Livans Livens LIVINGS MAYLOR MCMURRAY ORR Phathain Phathian PHETHEAN Phethian Phthyan PHYTHIAN PLATT Plum PLUMB RENNIE Rickson RIXON Rixson

ROBERTSON ROBINSON RUSHTON SHARPE Strachan STRAIN THOMAS TOTTENHAM Tottingham Tottnam VICKERS WARDLE F3475

159972 ROBINSON Mr Barry L. 32 Croham Mount, South Croydon, Surrey, CR2 0BR. Tel:081-657-7399 ADAMS DIGHT DITE DREW DYTE EDEN KETTLETY KITTLETY MOWER ROBINSON SKERTEN SKERTON SKIRTEN SKIRTON STIDARD STIDDARD WHALE F1472

159980 ROBINSON Mr Brian. 111 Fulthorpe Avenue, Mowden Estate, Darlington, Co Durham, DL3 9XJ. Tel:0325-461422 ADDISON CRAGGS HALL HINDHAUGH JEWSON LOCKEY REED ROBINSON F3505

159999 ROBINSON Mr David. 7 Consfield Avenue, New Malden, Surrey, KT3 6HB. CATCUM CROWLEY HOWE LATHAM OLLIFFE SPIELMAN WHITE F2309

160008 ROBINSON Mr Dennis. 83 Elm Tree Road, Lower Bredbury, Stockport, SK6 2EG. Tel:061-430-6447 BESWICK BURTON CARSEY Cassey CRAWSHAW DEAN DOANE Done EPTON FURNESS Hamblett HAMLET HARRISON LISTER NORTH ROBINSON SILLITTO WOOD F5114

160016 ROBINSON Mr G Howard. 68 Jackroyd Lane, Newsome, Huddersfield, HD4 6RD. Tel:0484-421321 Sedgewick SEDGWICK Sidgewick Sidgwick Sigiswick F4821

160024 ROBINSON Miss Gillian. 5 Adelaide Court, Copers Cope Road, Beckenham, Kent, BR3 1TT. Tel:081-658-7438 ANDREWS ARMITAGE BARKER BEE CRAVEN DEY ELLORS GOODMAN GREENWOOD HICKSON HIRST HOLDSWORTH LATHAM MELLOWS MOLYNEUX MOREL Rickard RICKARDS Rickeard ROBINSON TAYLOR THOMPSON F3693

160032 ROBINSON Mrs Gloria. 35 Hatherton Avenue, Cullercoats, North Shields, Tyne & Wear, NE30 3LG. JOHNSON LIMERICK LYALL MAVIN F5710

160040 ROBINSON Ivy. 48 Wheelers, Epping, Essex, CM16 5AL. Tel:0378-73691 NORKETT F911

160059 ROBINSON Mr John. 34 Greatfield Road, Kidderminster, Worcs, DY11 6PH. BENNETT ILES ROBINSON F5848

160067 ROBINSON Miss Marion. 133 Rodmell Avenue, Saltdean, Brighton, East Sussex, BN2 8PH. Burbidge BURBRIDGE DODD FATHERS JOHNSTON MERCER F6322

160075 ROBINSON Mrs Maureen. (Richardson) 71 Broadway, York, YO1 4JP. DOBBING FALLA FORTH Furth MOODY MORALEE Moraley Morally Moraly PASSMOOR SWINNEY TROBE TROLLOPE TURNBULL F5871

160083 ROBINSON Mrs S M. Flat H, Eleanor House, George Place, Plymouth Devon, PL1 3NZ. GODDANEW JOYNES MASFORD OUTRAM OWTRAM PONTEFRACT REDMORE REYNOLDS F1166

160091 ROBINSON Mrs Sheila. 2 Tynedale Road, South Shields, Tyne & Wear, NE34 6EX. WEIR F7406

160105 ROBINSON Ms V J. 4 Burmarsh, Sutton St Nicholas, Hereford, HR1 3BW. Gruit Gruitt GRUT Grute Grutt F7205

160113 ROBINSON Mr Walter. 47 Anthony Crescent, Alvaston, Derby, DE2 0GH. FAULKNER ROBINSON F6157

160121 ROBSON Mr Andy. 38 Edinburgh Road, Jarrow, Tyne And Wear, NE32 4BD. BLACK HAVARD HENDERSON JOHNSON NIXON PRINGLE SAMS WALTON F5751

160148 ROBSON Mrs Carol. 20 Thirlmere Crescent, Normanby, Cleveland, TS6 0EV. BAINBRIDGE BINNS COOKE CRUDDAS FELTON PEPPER ROBSON WATT F3450

160156 ROBSON Mrs Geraldine. 71 Cranbrook Road, Parkstone, Poole, Dorset, BH12 3BW. Tel:0202-743902 BENNALLACK BROOKES HINDMARSH KNIGHT MALONEY NASH ROBSON UPHILL F2132

160164 ROBSON Mrs Hilda M. Pinewood, 1 Coed Y Bryn, Flint Mountain, Clwyd, CH6 5QP. BAILDON BALCKER Bayldon BOOTH BRIGHT CARTER CATCHPOLE CAUNT CHEATLE De Luttele De Lutteley De Lutteleye DEWHURST GRABHAM HICKMAN Letteleye LILLYCRAP Lutely Lutlay LUTLEY Lutleye Lutlie Lutly Luttelay Luttele Luttelegh Lutteley Lutteleye Luttey Luttley Luttly Lyteleye Lytley Lytteleghe MARRIOTT MASSEY SMEDLEY THOMPSON TOON VIOLETT VOILETT WYATT F1328

160172 ROBSON Mr J K. 30 Church Street, Norton, Malton, N Yorks, YO17 9HS. BAKER LAMB Read REED Rheed ROBSON SADLER SEDMAN UMPLEBY F1748

160180 ROBSON Mrs J M. (Davy) 442 Reading Road, Winnersh, Wokingham, Berks, RG11 5EP. Tel:0734-785295 DAVY DEPLEDGE LANGFORD MURPHY WHITAKER F4571

160199 ROBSON Mrs M G. 12 Spring Terrace, North Shields, Tyne And Wear, NE29 0HQ. BAKER GLENWRIGHT Haslipp HESLOP LINDGREEN Lindgren MOUNSEY PARR ROBSON SYMES URWIN YEOMAN F3627

160202 ROCHESTER Mr G N. 18 Burns Green, Bennington, Herts, SG2 7DA. ROCHESTER F4720

160210 ROCHESTER Miss Lynn. 14 Long Grove, Baughurst, Basingstoke, Hants, RG26 5NY. GLENDINNING NEWTON ROCHESTER STOKOE F3398

160229 RODDHAM Mrs Doris. (Elmes) 67a Hill Corner Road, Chippenham, Wiltshire, SN15 1DR. ELEMES ELMES HOOD HUDD F5323

160237 RODEN Mr Peter F C. 6 Yew Tree Avenue, Bradford, W Yorks, BD8 0AD. Tel:0274-542193 Beaseley Beasle Beasley Beasly Beazeley Beazley Beeasly Beeseley Beesely Beeslay Beesle Beeslee BEESLEY Beesly Beezeley Beezely Beezley Beezly Beisley Beisly Beseley Besley Besly Bessley Beuisley Beysley Bezeley Biesley Biesly Biezley Bisley Bisly Byesley CARLISLE CREWE DUGDALE FOX GUY HENSMAN Raudinge Rawdon Raydon Reuden Rhoaden Rhodan Rhoddan Rhodden RHODEN Rhodin Rhoding Rhodon Roadding Roaden Roading Roadinge Roadon ROBINSON Rodan Rodden Roddin Rodding Roddon RODEN Rodend Rodene Rodhenn Rodin Rodine Roding Rodinge Rodinn Rodon Rodone Rodyn Roeden Roedon Rohden Roiden Rooden Roodin Rooding Roodinge Roodon Roodyng Roudan Rouden Rowadon Rowdan Rowden Rowdin Rowding Rowdinge Rowdon Royden Spoad Spoade SPOARD Spoarde SPODE Spood Spoode Spoward VOUGHTON WEETMAN Weightman Wetman Wheatman Whiteman Wightman Woden F210

160245 RODGERS Miss Linda. 12 Beacon Avenue, Loughborough, Leicester, LE11 3HP. BESWICK KNIFTON RODGERS ROGERS F4607

160253 RODGERS Mr Walter Shaw. 80 Marsh Lane, Shepley, Huddersfield, W Yorks, HD8 8AS. Tel:0484-602945 BOOTH DEARNLEY DENBY DYSON ENGLAND HEPPENSTALL JUBB KENWORTHY LOCKWOOD RODGERS Rogers SHAW WATSON F2787

160261 ROFFEY Dr Clifford. 72 Moggs Mead, Petersfield, Hants, GU31 4NX. Tel:0730-67780 CALLAWAY FRENCH ROFFEY TREACHER F3650

160288 ROGERS Mrs Barbara. 85 Old Winton Road, Andover, Hants, SP10 2DB. Tel:0264-361341 Clayden Claydon CLEDEN Cledon MATHEWS ROGERS STANMORE F1729

160296 ROGERS Mrs Beryl. Town House, Thoroughfare, Halesworth, Suffolk, IP19 8AR. ALLEN DOW DUNHAM EDWARDS LINES Lynes Pettingale Pettingall Pettingel PETTINGILL Portingall WEBB F1548

160318 ROGERS Mr Hugh. 95 High Street, Bottisham, Cambridge, CB5 9BA. ARTER DODD ROGERS F3898

160326 ROGERS Mrs Janet. 90 Fore Street, Topsham, Exeter, Devon, EX3 0HQ. Tel:0392-877312 CULLISS SEELHOFF F2477

160334 ROGERS Mrs Janette. 27 Statham Street, Derby, DE3 1HR. HOLLISTER Holsor Olester Olser F7063

160342 ROGERS Mr P S. 31 Wheatlands Road East, Harrogate, N Yorks, HG2 8QS. Tel:0423-504734 DURMAN GALT HIGGS LANG LAVER MILLAR SWORD UDALE VIVERS F4116

160350 ROGERS Mr Ronald. 92 Colin Gardens, Hendon,

London, NW9 6ER.
BILTON COLLARD FLOYDE FOLLETT FROST HARRIS JAMES NICHOLAS ROGERS F678

160369 ROGERS Mr Tim. 27 Stoneacre Avenue, Sheffield, S12 4NT. Tel:0742-484424
HARVEY ROGERS SERGEANT F6008

160377 ROGERS Mrs Wendy. The Mint House, 94 High Street, Hurstpierpoint, West Sussex, BN6 9PX.
GIBSON HERDSFIELD LICRECE Liquorish RINGROSE SAMPLE F6548

160385 ROGERSON Mrs Dorothy Vera. (Cottier) 7 Derbe Road, St Annes On Sea, Lytham St Annes, Lancs, FY8 1NJ. Tel:0253-723431
BERRY CALLISTER CASTILL CLEWER CORKISH CORLETT COTTIER DAVIES DUTTON FAYLE GANNON HOGG JOHNSON KENYON KILLIP LEWNEY MARTIN MCAVOY MUDIE MYLREA PATTISON ROGERSON SHEPPARD STEPHEN F4661

160393 ROGERSON Mr L G. Nantcol, Llandre, Aberystwyth, Dyfed, SY24 5AA. Tel:0970-828000
BARLOW ROGERSON SKERRATT F6029

160407 ROLLINSON Mr Peter. Grandon, Wayside Road, Basingstoke, Hants, RG23 8BH.
BRYANT CROSS F4306

160415 ROLLS Mr P. 194 Kings Road, Harrogate, N Yorks, HG1 5JG.
HARDISTY Roles ROLLS Rowls F2366

160423 ROOK Mrs Beryl. (Maddever) Brook House, Ravenstone, Olney, Bucks, MK46 5AR. Tel:0908-55380
Dabie Daby DAVEY Davie Davy Madaver Maddaver Maddeford MADDEVER Maddifor Maddiford Maddiver Madefield Madefor Madeford Madever Madifor Madiford Madiver F997

160431 ROOTES Mrs Maureen Elizabeth. (Alexander) The Denes, Caxton Road, Bourn, Cambs, CB3 7SX. Tel:0954-718044
ALEXANDER GUTHRIE JOHNSTONE Mackay MACKIE WHYTE F4672

160458 ROPER Mr Robert S. 136 Buersil Avenue, Rochdale, Lancs, OL16 4TX.
ADAMS ALLEN BARNES BEARD BIDDER BIRKENSHAW BLACKWELL BRADBURY BRIGGS BRUCE BUNTING BURROWS CARR CRABTREE CUBITT DAGLISH DODDS FOSTER FOX FURNESS GOOCH GRISSELL HAWTHORN LEE LOCKE LONGRIDGE LORD PETO RANDLES RASTRICK RAYNER ROPER ROSE SMITH SPENCER STANTON STENSON STEPHENSON WARRINGTON WEALLENS WEATHERBURN WILD WILSON F1606

160466 ROSAMOND Mr Frederick George. 21 Huntingdon Road, Brampton, Huntingdon, Cambs, PE18 8PB. Tel:0480-453972
Rasiman Rosaman ROSAMOND Rosamund Rosemunde Rosiman Rosoman Rosomand F3010

160474 ROSCOE Mr John. Longvue, 166 Stockingstone Road, Luton, Beds, LU2 7NJ. Tel:0582-24876
ABBOTT ALLISON BENSON BLACK BOOTHMAN BURNS DODD EDWARDS EVANS GASKELL Hawat Hewet Hewett Hewiss Hewit HEWITT HINDLE Howat Howatt Howitt Huet Huett Huitt Huot JACKSON JONES LANE MOORE NUTTER OWENS PARKINSON PARTRIDGE PHILLIPS Roscho Roschow Rosco ROSCOE Roscow Roscowe Roskow Rosow Rosscho SMITH STALKER WALSH WATSON WILLNER Willnor Wilnal Wilnall Wilner Wilnor Woosencroft Wosencroft WOSONCROFT F2820

160482 ROSE Miss Doris. 20 Arderne Road, Timperley, Altrincham, Cheshire, WA15 6HJ.
ASHBROOK BURFORD LEWIS ROSE VARNEY F2470

160490 ROSE Mr G F. Po Box Hm 530, Hamilton Cx, BERMUDA.
ROSE F6859

160504 ROSE Mrs Janet R. (Bond) 18 Highview Gardens, Chiltern Park, St Albans, Herts, AL4 9JX.
ALLEN BOND HIRD HOLLAND WAKE F4634

160512 ROSE Mrs Marjorie W. 205a Peter Street, Macclesfield, Cheshire, SK11 8ES.
Bewshea Bewshear BEWSHER F6652

160520 ROSE Mrs Mary. Edelweiss, 29 Elizabeth Avenue, Hove, E Sussex, BN3 6WA. Tel:0273-502615
Randall RANDELL Randle Randles Randole Randoll Ranulf F2924

160539 ROSENTHAL Mrs Molly. Tandderwen, Prion, Denbigh, Clwyd, LL16 4RS.
BARTLETT BURTON RAVENHILL F1086

160547 ROSEVEAR Mr Alan. 7 Trinder Road, Wantage, Oxon, OX12 8EE. Tel:02357-3722
GOTHERIDGE ROSEVEAR STREET WYATT F728

160555 ROSIER Mrs Margaret E. (Bryant) 71 Greenfield Crescent, Cowplain, Waterlooville, Hants, PO8 9EL.
BRYANT VERYARD WEEKS F1147

160563 ROSS Miss H A. 15 Lawhead Road Est, St Andrews, Fife, KY16 9ND. Tel:0334-73188
BROWN CHALMERS DREWETT HYDE MACPHERSON RAIT ROSS THORP TREASURER WHITEHEAD F2566

160571 ROSS Mr Howard. 118 Willoughby House, Barbican, London, EC2Y 8BL.
BARRASS BOOKER CHEAL GARGETT KELL LYNES MCKAY MORGAN ROSS TAYLOR F6113

160598 ROSS Mrs Judy. 10 Penlee Road, Stoke, Plymouth, PL3 4AU.
FAIRFAX RICH ROBSON STRAIGHT UPHILL F6244

160601 ROSSER Mrs Valerie. 4 Le Jardin De L'Est, St Mary, Jersey, JE3 3DG. Tel:0534-83615
ALAVOINE ALMOND BARRETT BELGROVE BUCKERIDGE Buckridge Child CHILDS DURRANT EARLES FLUCK Gardener GARDINER HARRIS HIGH ILSLEY KRELLE LLEWELLYN Llewelyn ROSSER SADLER SLATTER SPARROW SPINK STOCK TEMPLER Waeich WAEICK WALLAGE WASHFORD Wolfe WOOLFE Worledge F1351

160628 ROSSINGTON Mr Douglas T. 24 Kilner Close, Unsworth, Bury, Lancs, BL9 8AD.
ROSSINGTON TURTON F2329

160636 ROSSINGTON Mr Richard. 26 Station Road, Higham On The Hill, Nuneaton, Warks, CV13 6AG.
ARROWSMITH ATKIN BARNSLEY BOYER BRADLEY BROADBENT BROWN CATLOW CLAPHAM COOKE COOLING COTTINGHAM DENNIS FERGUSON FOSTER FOWLER HARTLEY HAUGHTON HEWITT HOLT HOWARD HOWITT KEY KIRKPATRICK LILLEY MACMYN Mcmyn PEEL PEEL-STEPHENS Peele RADFORD RICHARDSON ROGERS ROSSINGTON RUSHWORTH SHAW SMITH STEPHENS TIGHE WILSON WOODALL F4358

160644 ROSSITER Mr C A. 523 Locking Road, Weston Super Mare, Avon, BS22 8QU.
BAWDEN HILL ROSSITER WATTS F966

160652 ROSSITER Mr Rex. 28 Mulberry Gardens, Sherborne, Dorset, DT9 4BZ. Tel:0935-814339
ADAM BESTER CONWAY CROSS DAW DEMELLWEEK EATON JOHNS PARROTT ROSSITER F4109

160660 ROUGHTON-SKELTON Mr H. 32 Southview Road, Marlow, Bucks, SL7 3JP. Tel:0628-485523
DE STIRRUP GANE NIND PICTON ROUGHTON SHARPE SKELTON F1097

160679 ROUNCE Mr Bill. 40 Salcombe Avenue, Jarrow, South Tyneside, Tyne & Wear, NE32 3SY. Tel:091-489-8474
BELL CAWTHORN CAWTHORNE ROUNCE F2036

160687 ROUND Mrs Mary. 20 Coldiers Green, Meltham, Huddersfield, W Yorks, HD7 3JH.
ROUND RUSSON F3093

160695 ROUNDING Mrs B L. 58 West Hill, East Grinstead, West Sussex, RH19 4EP.
PRESTON F7415

160709 ROUTLEDGE Mrs M J. 27 Atherley Road, Shanklin, Isle Of Wight, PO37 7AU.
BABINGTON BRAZIER CRANE FLICKER HARDING HEWETT HINTON PETTS ROUTLEDGE TREADWELL F1878

160717 ROUTLEDGE Mr Robert Clive. Linden Lea, 1 Linden Road, Broom, Ferryhill Co Durham, DL17 8BD.
ELLERBY RODNEY ROUTLEDGE TALBOT F98

160725 ROWBOTHAM Mrs Sue. Boscombe, 222 Gloucester Road, Cheltenham, Glous, GL51 8NR. Tel:0242-580035
BAINBRIDGE BRAILEY BRAYLEY COHN IONS LILLEY QUICK STUBBS TAYLOR WOOD F379

160733 ROWE Mr John W. 109 Winton Drive, Croxley Green, Rickmansworth, Herts, WD3 3QS. Tel:0923-34920
BELL BRADSHAW DYBALL FAWCETT Rew Rosevear ROSEVEARE Rosevere Row ROWE Willoghby WILLOUGHBY Wollacot WOLLACOTT Woolacott Woollacot Woollacott F1325

160741 ROWE Mrs Kathleen Joyce. (Minihan) 67 Brentwood Raod, Romford, Essex, RM1 2EU.
BLAKE EDWARDS GARSIDE GRAHAM MINIHAN MINIHIN MORRIS SCOTT F6470

160768 ROWE Mr S. 5 Sandpiper Close, Burton Latimer,

Kettering, Northants, NN15 5TF.
APPLIN BOILING HEWSON MUNDAY ROWE TALBOT F4373

160776 ROWE Mrs Shirley. (Clark) 26 Aberdeen Gardens, Leigh On Sea, Essex, SS9 3RH. Tel:0702-558232
ASHDOWN CASTELL CLARK HALL HARRIS Postan Posten Postern Posterne POSTON Roe Row ROWE WELLOCK WOOLNOUGH F4613

160784 ROWELL Miss Diana. 48 Swallow Lane, Golcar, Huddersfield, West Yorks, HD7 4NB.
BASSETT FAULKNER MALPASS ROWELL SPEED F5022

160792 ROWETT-JOHNS Mr Jeremy. Crown House, Clifton On Teme, Worcestershire, WR6 6EN. Tel:08865-304
JOHNS ROWETT F819

160806 ROWLAND Mrs Jean E. (Frearson) 4 Baker Street, Irthlingborough, Northants, NN9 5PR.
ALDERMAN ALDRIDGE FREARSON Freason Freerson Freeson Freeston KING PUTTOCK ROWLAND SHORT STEWART Stuart F5006

160814 ROWLAND Mr Robert C. Traine Farm, Wembury, Plymouth, Devon, PL9 0EW.
ACKLAND ANTHONY ATWILL COCK CROSS HORN LUSCOMBE MARSHALL MOSES ORGAN ROWLAND TREGELLAS WORTHYLAKE F2502

160822 ROWLANDS Mr David. Bwthyn Hir, Llanerfyl, Welshpool, Powys, SY21 0HA. Tel:093888-372
CREIGHTON-BROWNE HUTCHINGS LLOYD PENTLOW PIKE ROWLANDS SHEPPARD F920

160830 ROWLANDS Mrs L. 6 Linbery Close, Oakerthorpe, Derbys, DE5 7NF.
Pining Pinni PINNING Pynning F6883

160849 ROWLANDS Miss Linda. 14 Oakbrook Court, Graham Road, Sheffield, S10 3HR.
ARNOLD Beetleson Beetleston BEETLESTONE Betleston Bittleson Bittlestone Born Bourn BOURNE BROOMHEAD BUTLER CHATWELL Chatwin Chatwynd Chetwall Chetwyn Chetwynd EDWARDS FISH GLOVER HARDY Hargrave Hargraves Hargreave HARGREAVES Hibard Hibbard Hibbart HIBBERD Hibbert Hiberd HUNT Hybard Hyberd Ibbert Ibbot KELLINGLEY Kellinley Killingley Killinley METCALF Morrice MORRIS Morryce Pinin Pining Pininge Pinins Pinni Pinnin PINNING Pinninge Pinnings Pins Pynin Pynnin Pynninge ROWLAND STAMFORD Stamforth STEAD Steade Sted Stede Steed Steede Vesey VESSEY Vessie Vessy WALL Yap YAPP Yappe Yarnold F5246

160857 ROWLANDS Mrs S A. 18 Marine Terrace, Aberystwyth, Dyfed, SY23 2AZ.
ALBAN CANTON EINON F6621

160865 ROWLANDS Mrs Shirley June. (Jeram) 9 Hollybank Lane, Emsworth, Hants, PO10 7UD.
JERAM MORCOM SANDELL F1753

160873 ROWLEY Ms Janet Maureen. (Price) 21a Grosvenor Road, Birmingham, B20 3NW. Tel:021-356-0115
Acheson ADDENBROOKE ADENBROOKE Aldrich ALDRIDGE Allbut ALLPORT Alport Anbrook ATKINSON Auport Aupott Awport BAKER BARMS BATHER Bathoe Beebee BELL BIBBINS BIRD BRADFORD BRAGG BRETTELL BROWN Burd BURNETT BUTLER CARTWRIGHT Caulfield Cawfield Cirsop CLARKE CLEMPSON CLIFF COLLINS Coney COOK COOPER CORFIELD COUNDLEY COVILL COWEN COWINS COWNEY Cownley Crisopp EADES Eeds ELLERBY ELLIOT Favell FAVILL Felloe FELLOW FISHER Flavell FLETCHER FORSTER FOSTER GILBERTS GILL GOLD GREEN GREGORY HALE HAMMOND HARDWICK HART HAWARD HAWKES Hawkesford HAWKSFORD Heeds HERDMAN HICKMANS HIGGINBOTTOM HILL Hirdman HODGES Hodgetts HOLLAND HOLLIGRENE Hordwyck HUMPHREY JOHNSON JONES Kershope KIRSOPP KNOWLES LEA Lee LITTLE LOW MARSH MASON MILLER MINNINGS NASH Neale NEIL Neill NOTAS OAKLEY Oldridge OLIVER Parkeshouse Parshouse Parsus PARTRIDGE Pauton PAWTON PERRY PERSEHOUSE PIPE Porton PRETTY PRICE Pursehouse Rawlinson REA REACHER REED RIDLEY ROBINSON ROLLASON Rollison ROSTELL ROWLEY RUSSON RUTHERFORD SCOTT Scudamore SEAGER SEWELL SHAKESPEARE SHELTON Sherwood SHEWARD Shewell Shuard SKIDMORE SMITH SPARRY SPRATT STEPHENS STOKES TONKE TURNER VERNON WAINWRIGHT WARD Weastherell WETHERAL Wetherill Whetherill WHITEHOUSE WILKINSON Willets WILLIS WILLMORE Wilmer WILSON WRIGHT WYLEY Yates F5086

160881 ROWLING Mr Harold. Home Brow House, Westmeston, Sussex, BN6 8XG.
ROWLING F597

160903 ROWLSON Mrs J S. 14 Essenden Court, Stony Stratford, Milton Keynes, Bucks, MK11 1NW. Tel:0908-562853
ABBOTT BARNARD BENTLEY BIRD CATTLEY JONES MAYHEW WARD F6356

160911 ROWSON Mrs Belinda. (Read) 140 Burwood Road, Matamata, NEW ZEALAND. Tel:+64-7-888-5343
ANDERSON DARBY DRING HUTCHINSON INGLE MARSH READ ROBINSON ROWSON F5188

160938 ROY Dr R J. 9 Church Street, Mears Ashby, Northants, NN6 0DN.
BARTWELL BEVINGTON HARRAP HOWLETT HUDSON JONES MALLALIEU ROY SLATER STEEPLE F6274

160946 ROYALL Revd Arthur. Carmelite House, 10 Pit Lane, Swaffham, Norfolk, PE37 7DA.
BARKSHIRE Berkshire CHANEY Cheney Cheyney ELVIN Goodberry Goodboddie GOODBODY Roial Royal ROYALL Royals Royle RYAL Ryals Ryell F1829

160954 ROYDEN Mr Mike. 36 Barndale Road, Mossley Hill, Liverpool, L18 1EN. Tel:051-734-5723
CARLILE CLARKE DILWORTH ELLIS HUGHES HUMPHRIES KINSELLA KNOX Roden Rowden ROYDEN Roydon Ryden WEBB WESLEY WIGGINS F1635

160962 ROYLE Mrs P M. (Deane) 6 Aviary Road, Worsley, Manchester, M28 4WF. Tel:061-790-2811
BARLOW Barlowe Dane Dean DEANE Deans Dene Rayle Royal Royale ROYLE Ryle STANSFIELD F2131

160970 RUDD Mr John. 1 Grove Road, Leytonstone, London, E11 2AN.
HAMMOND RUDD F5667

160989 RUDDICK Mrs Moira. 14 Moor Place, Gosforth, Newcastle Upon Tyne, NE3 4AL. Tel:091-285-7279
BELL HARRISON PARK F3242

160997 RUDDLE Mrs Valerie. (Hill) 26 The Middlings, Sevenoaks, Kent, TN13 2NN. Tel:0732-450355
GILL GREGORY HILL RUDDLE F4694

161004 RUDGE Mrs A J. Po Box 48-155, Blockhouse Bay, Auckland 7, New Zealand.
F3055

161012 RUDMAN Mr Mike. 71 Ellerdine Road, Hownslow, Middx, TW3 2PN.
BARNUM RUDMAN F75

161020 RUGMAN Mr Michael A. Micros, Inner Down, Old Down Tockington, Bristol Avon, BS12 4PR.
EDWARDS JACKSON LATHAM RUGMAN F2248

161039 RUGMAN Mr P. 157 Sandbach Road, Alsager, Stoke On Trent, Cheshire, ST7 2AX.
Ruggman RUGMAN Rugmand Rvgman F6889

161047 RUGMAN Mrs Sue. 107 Clowne Road, Stanfree, Chesterfield, Derby, S44 6AR. Tel:0246-824537
FERNANDES FURNANDIZ HALL HERRINGTON F1489

161055 RUMBOLD Mr Mike. 3 West Street, Weedon Bec, Northampton, NN7 4QU.
RUMBOLD F2306

161063 RUMSEY Mrs M E. 29 Queens Road, Alton, Hants, GU34 1JG.
RUMSEY WINDEBANK Windybank F6788

161071 RUNCHMAN Mrs Theresa. (Flack) 83 Clyde Way, Rise Park, Romford, Essex, RM1 4XT. Tel:0708-768462
AMEY CHURCHILL MCCOMBIE RUNCHMAN STERN F206

161098 RUNDEL Mr R. 140 Robin Way, Chipping Sodbury, Avon, BS17 6JT. Tel:0454-321626
LEWORTHY RUNDEL F1376

161101 RUSDEN Miss Beatrice Amelia. 44 Nursery Road, Bishops Stortford, Herts, CM23 3HL.
RUSDEN F2482

161128 RUSHTON Mrs J. 162 Marlow Bottom Road, Marlow, Bucks, SL7 3PP.
Roccker ROCKER Rockerby F6992

161136 RUSLING Miss Freda M. 73 Cairns Road, Crosspool, Sheffield, S Yorks, S10 5NA.
BARR BARRETT BEDDOW BRIERLEY BURNETT COLBRIDGE CURR HALIFAX HOLROYD JARVIS JONES LUCAS OAKES RENSHAW RHODES RIPPER RUSLING SCOTT SUGDEN WILSON WOODCOCK F4075

161144 RUSSAM Mr Eric. 202 Luddington, Stratford On Avon, Warwickshire, CV37 9SJ. Tel:0789-750850
RUSSAM F1099

161152 RUSSELL Mrs Doris. (Mcalpin) 8600 Hickory Hill Lane, Huntsville, AL 35802-3552, USA.
Macalpin Macalpine Mcalpin Mcalpine MCAPLIN Mccalpin Mccolpin Mccoppin Mccorpin F7321

161160 RUSSELL Mr G. 34 Abbey Road, Bush Hill Park, Enfield, Middx, EN1 2QN.
Popeley POPELY Popley F6938

161179 RUSSELL Mrs Joan Audrey. (Cross) 7 Netherlands Road, Morecambe, Lancs, LA4 5SJ. Tel:0524-421876
BROADLEY CROSS RAMSBOTTOM SHARPLES WALMSLEY F5295

161187 RUSSELL Mrs June. 43 St Marks Road, Orle, Weston Super Mare, Avon, BS22 0PL. Tel:0934-510660
RUSSELL WEBB F1686

161195 RUSSELL Ms L. 37 Pomfret Avenue, Luton, Beds, LU2 0JJ.
FAGAN RUSSELL WILLIS F4984

161209 RUSSELL Mr Michael. 171 Hinchcliffe, Orton Goldhay, Peterborough, Cambs, PE2 0ST.
BASTARD KEY WEBSTER WILKS F703

161217 RUSSELL Mr P A. 16 Witney Road, Ducklington, Witney, Oxon, OX8 7TX. Tel:0993-704282
Russel RUSSELL F6182

161225 RUSSELL Mr T W. 97 Heathway, Northumberland Heath, Erith, Kent, DA8 3LZ. Tel:0322-347177
BARRATT DAW DUNN FLUTE FREEMAN GOLDSACK HEBBES MAKEHAM RUSSELL VALE F5346

161233 RUSSELL Mrs W. 33 Bell Barn Shopping Centre, Cregoe Street, Lee Bank, Birmingham, B15 2DZ.
Funell Funnel FUNNELL Funnelle F7192

161241 RUSSON Mr Donald Frank. 6 South View Road, Christchurch, Dorset, BH23 1JH. Tel:0202-484148
RUSSON F2347

161268 RUST Mrs Jessie Ann. (Cowie) Bauchlaw Farm, Banff, Banffshire, Grampian, AB45 3TJ. Tel:0261-812182
Cow Cowe COWIE FARQUHAR HORN Horne Roust RUST F3718

161276 RUTLAND Mr & Mrs E R. Gilbtona, Grange Road, Cookham Rise, Berks, SL6 9TH.
BLICK BUCKLE COX DONGWORTH GODFREY PIPER RUTLAND SCARR SHACKLEFORD Trindal TRINDER WILLIS F2727

161284 RUTTER Mrs Chris. (Bailey) Millburn House, Kirkcudbright, Galloway, DG6 4ED. Tel:0557-30926
BAILEY Bayley BIBBINS BLOOD Blud Bludd DABBS EBORALL HALL HUNT LEWIS LINTON MACE NORRIS PRITCHARD PUGH PURSALL RUTTER SMART SMITH WINSPER F4107

161292 RYALL Mr David H. Colleytown Cottage, Chittlehampton, Umberleigh, North Devon, EX37 9QT. Tel:0769-540576
BAVERSTOCK BEBBINGTON CHETTER COLEMAN DICKSON DIXON ELLERY ELLIOTT FROST GAMBLE GIFFORD GILLARD HIGNETT HOSKINS HOULSTON LAWTON LUCKES NELSON PERRIAM RICHES ROBERTS RYALL STONE TINSLEY TUFFEY WESTCOTT F4057

161306 RYAN Mrs Jill. (Humphreys) 3101 37th Avenue, Vernon, British Columbia, V1T 2Y3, CANADA. Tel:+1-604-545-1066
GREENWOOD Humpherys HUMPHREYS Humphries LIVINGSTONE TIDMARSH WARE Weare F5514

161314 RYCROFT Mr Christopher. Scarr House, Stainland, Halifax, West Yorks, HX4 9PN.
FIRBY LUMBY RYCROFT SEWELL THOMPSON WEATHERHEAD WEBSTER F5112

161322 RYE Mr J. 18 Wantworth Close, Hadleigh, Ipswich, Suffolk, IP2 5SA.
BOURTON BUTSON DINE DINES GAIGE HUBBARD NEWPORT RYE WEAVER F6210

161330 RYE Mr Tony. 24 Netherfields Crescent, Dronfield, Sheffield, S18 6UX. Tel:0246-419903
BISHOP BROWN CAMPBELL DUFFIELD ELLIS GARBUTT GRAHAM HANSON HICKLETON LAMBERT MOORE POTTS RICHARDSON RYE TALLAND UPTON WAINWRIGHT WARHURST F5932

161349 SABELL Mr Nigel. 40 Patch Lane, Bramhall, Stockport, Cheshire, SK7 1HX.
BAWDEN BAYLISS BRITTAIN DONE MEEK MYCOCK SABELL F2025

161357 SACKETT Miss M. 53 Surley Row, Caversham, Reading, Berks, RG4 8LX.
ANDREWS Barratt BARRETT BEDINGFIELD BREENS BROCKMAN BROOKER BROWN CLIFFORD DARBY DAWSON Derby Falconer FAULKNER Fawkener FEWEL Fewell FOX Fuel Gooding GOODWIN HAYWARD KIRKHAM MARSHALL MARTINELLI MILLER MILLS NAIL Neal Newby NEWMAN NUBY PATERSON Patterson Pattison PERRIN Peterson Pole POWEL Powell RAY ROBERTS Sacket SACKETT Sackette Saket SAMUEL SAMUELS SLADE SMITH WARD WELLS Wills Wray F1503

161365 SACKVILLE Dr Andrew. 7 Rutland Crescent, Ormskirk, Lancs, L39 1LP. Tel:0698-575808
COULTHART DEAN MANDEVILLE SACKFIELD SACKVILLE SIGSWORTH F4051

161373 SADGROVE Dr P C. 12 Orange Hill, Lutterworth, Leicestershire, LE17 4BT.
Sadgrave Sadgrouge SADGROVE Sadgrowe Salgrove Satgrove Sedgrave Sedgreves Sedgrove Sedgrow Sidgrave Sudgrave Sudgrove F6786

161381 SADLER Mr. 18 Edward Place, Dunblane, Perthshire, FR15 9HN.
SADLER F1221

161403 SAGAR Mr John H. 8 Morrell Avenue, Horsham, W Sussex, RH12 4DD.
SAGAR Sager Saghar Sagher Seagar Seager Segar Seiger F241

161411 SAINES Mrs Pat. 2 Kingway Avenue, Selsdon, South Croydon, Surrey, CR2 8NE.
ALDERSON BAKER GANNON HORSLEY LANCASHIRE OSBORNE SAINES SMITH STOCKBRIDGE F801

161438 SAINSBURY Mr John. The Beeches, 73 Ninian Road, Roath Park, Cardiff, CF2 5EN.
Sainsberry SAINSBURY SAINTSBURY SAINTSBURYE SAYNSBURY SEINESBERIA SEYNISBURY Seynsbury Sinisbury F3354

161446 SAINT Mrs K. Florando, Manilla, NSW 2346, AUSTRALIA.
ADCOCK BATTEN BOWDEN BRAY BREWERTON CHINNER CLARIDGE COOK COX DARLINGTON DENNIS DUDDEN FLACK GALE GEORGE GLASSON HAMBLEN HENSHALL HOCKIN HOWES HUNT LOCK MASLEN MIELL NELSON PETERS RICHARDSON SAINT SIMS SINNOTT SOLOMON TILL WADWORTH WARD WILLIAMS WRENTMORE F5539

161454 SALE Mr L J H. 109 Kilmorie Road, London, SE23 2SP.
CHAMP F7387

161462 SALISBURY Ms P. 2 Peddles Lane, Charlton Mackrell, Somerton, Somerset, TA11 6AQ.
BURDEKIN Burdikin Burdykin F7199

161470 SALLIS Ms Jean. 18a Brandreth Avenue, St Anns, Nottingham, NG3 3BX.
BLOUNT Bramby BRAMLEY COLLIS COLLIS ELLIOT ELLIOTT GOLDING SALLIS SPENCER F4025

161489 SALMON Miss M A. The Herts Cheshire Home, St Johns Road, Hitchin, Herts, SG4 9DD. Tel:0462-432618
FITZJOHN GOODMAN HICKS JACKSON JENNINGS MYRING SALMON F2238

161497 SALMON Ms M M. 3 Campbell Road, East Ham, London, E6 1NP.
SALMON Salomon F6996

161500 SALMON Peter F. Hill Top House, 37 St Johns Avenue, Kidderminster, Worc, DY11 6AU.
CLAYALL CLEAL COOPER DAVIS DODGE DUVALL GROVES HAMBLIN Hamblyn LITTLEJOHN MUNFORD PITT SALMON STAPLE Stapol F1589

161519 SALMON Mr R. 9 Grebe Avenue, Scotton, Richmond, North Yorks, DL9 3NU.
Alick Alix ALLICK Allix Chanterelle Chantrall Chantrel CHANTRELL HANBY Mennell MEYNELL MORROW NICHOLSON NIXON PAY SALMON WARDELL F5990

161527 SALMON Miss Stella M. 20 Pelham Square, Brighton, E Sussex, BN1 4ET. Tel:0273-688559
BROAD Garrad Garrard GARROD HARDING HOLLOWAY Lothian LOWTHIAN SALAMON SALOMON Salomons Solomon Solomons TROTT F349

161535 SAMMES Mr Edward. 118 Hag Hill Rise, Taplow, Maidenhead, Berks, SL6 0LT.
Sam Same Sames SAMMES Samms Sams F1002

161543 SAMMY Mrs Valerie. (Bray) 61 Allerton Road, London, N16 5UF.
BRAY FOWELL GOODALL GRIMWOOD HITCHCOCK

MCDONALD OGG WILLS F1538
161551 SAMPLES Mrs Barbara A. (Whitehead) 10 Axholme Road, Thingwall, Wirral, Merseyside, L61 1BJ. Tel:051-648-3757
COMBS MANTELL SAMPLES WESTON WHITEHEAD F6170
161578 SAMPSON Mr Ken. 7 Morley Court, Morley Road, Lewisham, London, SE13 6DG.
SAMPSON F2451
161586 SAMUEL Mrs Ruth. (Hargrave) Le Cateau, 12 Park Road, Sudbury, Suffolk, CO10 6QB. Tel:0787-74820
Bilbrough BILLBROUGH Billbruff CHURCHER DENT DUFF FURNAS Furnass Furness GUY HARGRAVE Hargraves HOSSELL MAYER Sellwood Sillwood STAFFORD Tillwood WEALAND Wealands WELLS Whitemore WHITMORE WRIGGLESWORTH ZILLWOOD F3385
161594 SAMWELL Mrs Connie. (Shippen) 56 Main Street, Scholes, Leeds, LS15 4DH.
CUTLER Scheppyn SHIPPEN Shippin Shippon F5832
161608 SANCHEZ Mrs R. (Eade) 45 Riverside Gardens, Romsey, Hants, SO51 8HN.
AYLING COOPER EADE MARTIN WAKELING F3401
161616 SANDERS Mrs B. Ambarvalia, High Street, Conington, Cambridge, CB3 8LT.
Camphilon Campilyon Campilyone Camplechon Camplechone Camplegean Camplegin Camplegon Campleiane Campleijohn Camplejean CAMPLEJOHN Camplejoyne Camplesham Campleshon Campleshone Campleson Camplethon Campleton Campleyon Campligon Camplijohn Camplisham Camplishon Capleion Champloshon Compleshon F7198
161624 SANDERS Mrs Brigit. Town Yeat, High Nibthwaite, Ulverston, Cumbria, LA12 8DI.
COLLINGWOOD COOKE Dadd Dades Darde DARDS Deards MCGOWAN F6390
161632 SANDERS Captain Charles B. 69 Westbury Leigh, Westbury, Wilts, BA13 3SF. Tel:0373-823724
SANDERS F5266
161640 SANDERS Mrs Elizabeth J. (Haddington) 28 Waterloo Crescent, Wokingham, Berkshire, RG11 2JJ. Tel:0734-790963
DARNBROUGH EAMES HADDINGTON HILL KITSON PADDON SANDERS STONEHOUSE WALMSLEY WEEKS F4783
161659 SANDERS Mrs Jean. 59 Heather Road, Bloxwich, Walsall, West Midlands, WS3 2QA. Tel:0922-404127
FARNELL HARTSHORN Hartshorne KANE KEANE KEENS MARSHALL MILLWARD MINTON TAYLOR F5067
161667 SANDERS Mrs Lillian G. (Simmons) 212-2969 Kingsway Drive, Kitchener, Ontario, N2C 2H7, CANADA. Tel:+1-519-893-2784
BASSETT BROWNING DIXON FERGUSON GIBSON HANLEY HIBBS JACKSON JENKINS KING MANTLE MEATCHAM Metcham Mitcham PEARSON SCRACE SEDGER Simmonds SIMMONS Simons Symons WEST F5589
161675 SANDERS Mrs Marian. (Meyer) Route 2, Box 25, Alden, Iowa, 50006, USA. Tel:+1-515-648-3846
CUNNINGHAM DOIDGE HUNTER JOLLY F4441
161683 SANDERS Mrs N. (Uzzell) 3 Beechfield, South Otterington, Northallerton, North Yorks, DL7 9JJ. Tel:0609-771210
UZZELL F6150
161691 SANDERS Mr Wilfrid F. 212-2969 Kingsway Drive, Kitchener, Ontario, N2C 2H7, CANADA. Tel:+1-519-893-2784
BARRADELL Barrowdale Boradale BUTLER Cockram COCKRAN EYRE HOLMES SANDERS Saunders SAYER SMITH STEVENSON F4701
161705 SANDERSON Mr David. St Andrews Vicarage, 225 Prince Of Wales Road, Sheffield, Yorkshire, S2 1FB. Tel:0742-399346
BROWNSELL COCKERAM DUFFIELD GODFREY GRAY HAGTHORPE HEMSWORTH HINDS LARKMAN MORRISON MOY PIGGOT ROBINSON SANDERSON TASH TINKER F644
161713 SANDERSON Mrs Hilda. (Butterworth) 41 Little London, Silverstone, Nr Towcester, Northants, NN12 8UP.
BUTTERWORTH F6542
161721 SANDERSON Mr John T. 26 Briarside, Shotley Bridge, Consett, Co Durham, DH8 0AF. Tel:0207-592230
ATKINSON BARRON BELL BRIGNAL CAIRNS FENDER HARLEY HOGGET OXLEY PAUL RUDD SAMPLE SANDERSON Sandison TINDLE WILLIS WILSON F2028
161748 SANDERSON Mr Peter. 21 The Sycamores, Baldock, Herts, SG7 5BJ. Tel:0462-3700
SANDERSON F6042
161756 SANDFORD Revd E Noel T. 3 Madeira Road, Clevedon, Avon, BS21 7TJ. Tel:0275-874035
SANDFORD SEYMOUR F5955
161764 SANDS Mr R. Greensleves Cottage, 47 Oast Road, Hurst Green, Oxted Surrey, RH8 9DU. Tel:0883-713976
SANDS F2193
161772 SANGER Mrs Vicki. (Taylor) 46 Probert Avenue, Griffith, NSW 2680, AUSTRALIA.
BLYTON BOBBIN BORMAN BURDES CARNELL HAGHAN HIGHLAND HIRISON HYLAND PALMER SANGER TAYLOR TRICKEY TURLEY WARNER WATSON WYATT F5540
161780 SANGER-DAVIES Mr Peter. Further West, Udimore Road, Broad Oak, Rye, E Sussex, TN31 6DG. Tel:0424-882115
BOARD HARDING HIGGON PANKHURST SANGER F5371
161799 SANHAM Mr Chris. 44 Mansfield Road, Hampstead, London, NW3 2HT.
SANHAM SANHAM Sanhum Sannam Sannum Sanom Seniohm Sinom F3783
161802 SANKEY Mr Tim. 16 Church Road, Owlsmoor, Camberley, Surrey, GU15 4TJ. Tel:0344-771965
SANKEY F556
161810 SANTAANA Ms Pat A. 29 Gilda Court, Watford Way, Mill Hill, London, NW7 2QN.
DOLTON FRUSHER MARSHALL PRICE ROSE ROSS WILKINS WILLIAMS WORRALLO F4002
161829 SAPSFORD Mrs Joan E. 70 The Mead, Carpenders Park, Watford, Herts, WD1 5BU.
GULLY HILL MOORE F4704
161837 SARAH Mr Ted T. 239 Bermont Avenue, Munroe Falls, OH 44262-1105, USA. Tel:+1-216-688-2013
EDWARDS GREET Greete HARRIS HODGE MATTHEWS ROBERTS ROWE RUNDLE Sara SARAH WILLIAMS F4473
161845 SARE Mr G T. 12 Burghley Road, Stone Manor Park, Lincoln, LN6 7YE. Tel:0522-500443
SARE SAYER F1822
161853 SARNEY Mrs Tracy. 56 Sandison Road, Hallett Cove, South Australia 5158.
Boar Boor BOORN Boorne Bore Born Bourn Bourne Etheredge ETHERIDGE Ethrige Etrich Etridge Marcklew Marclu Markclew Markelew MARKLEW Marklewe Marklow Marklue F313
161861 SAUL Mrs C. Broadgate, Bodmin Street, Holsworthy, Devon, EX22 6BH. Tel:0409-254111
ASHER BARBER BATH BULLEN CARTMEL Cartmell ELLINOR EVANS HARDING HOBBS JENKINSON KNIGHT MANNERS MANNING Nail NEAL Neale PEARSON REDMAN REEVES ROSE SAUL SAUNDERS SHEARMAN SMITH TAYLOR F5928
161888 SAUNDERCOCK Mrs Jan. 6 Ordnance Avenue, Lithgow, New South Wales, 2790, AUSTRALIA.
BARRETT BATHGATE BELLAMY BETTS BUCKLEY CAMERON CARPENTER CURRY DOEL FORRESTER FOSTER FROST GALLOWAY GIBSON JENKINS KENTWELL LEAHY LYELL Lyle MILLER MORAN NEVILLE NOBLE POLL REES SAUNDERCOCK SEARLE SINGLETON STEWART TAYLOR TRAYHURN WALSH WATTS F5170
161896 SAUNDERS Mr Alan. 35 Arun Road, West End, Southampton, SO3 3PR.
GOSLING KITCHING OXFORD POLLY SAUNDERS SEDGWICK SHAMBROOK WILLS F3666
161918 SAUNDERS Mr Albert J. Kenilworth, 1 Heatherley Road, Camberley, Surrey, GU15 3LW. Tel:0276-62538
SAUNDERS F6255
161926 SAUNDERS Mr F G. 51 Pinnocks Lane, Baldock, Herts, SG7 6DD.
SANDERS F4227
161934 SAUNDERS Mr Jack. Watersmeet, 55 Devon Road, Cheam, Surrey, SM2 7PE.
BRINGINSHAW F6724
161942 SAUNDERS Miss P A T. 24 Westgate, Chichester, W Sussex, PO19 3EU.
CHANEY Garrett Jaraitt JARRETT PAGET PATMORE F6434
161950 SAUNDERS Mr P J. Higher Colmer, Modbury, Ivybridge, Devon, PL21 0SG. Tel:0548-82210
ANGEL DALLY FLEW FLORANCE HERRIARD HODGE HOLLAND LINTON MINTERN SANDUM SAUNDERS TOBY WIGGOT F2385

161969 SAUNDERS Mrs Ronna. Veniscombe, 6 Argyll Street, Ryde, Isle Of Wight, PO33 3BZ. Tel:0983-64406
BONHAM CARPENTER NORRIS Sargeant SARGENT Sarjent Sergeant VIGIS F1038

161977 SAUNDERS Mrs Ruth. (Passey) 53 Fifth Road, Newbury, Berks, RG14 6DP. Tel:0635-49099
PASSEY F3929

161985 SAVAGE Mrs Betty. Culver Keys, Broadmore Green, Rushwick, Worcester, WR2 5TE.
Garside Garsyde GARTSIDE F788

161993 SAVAGE Mrs C. (Avann) 11 Orchard Road, Hook Norton, Oxon, OX15 5LX. Tel:0608-737261
Avan AVANN Avenn F5938

162000 SAVAGE Mr Ken. 53 Linden Drive, Sheerness, Kent, ME12 1LG.
ALLEN BETSON BETTS BRENCHLEY CHAMBERS HALLS JARVIS MARSHALL PARHAM PARSONS PEARCE REED SAVAGE SAYWELL WILLIAMSON YATES F1177

162019 SAVAGE Mrs Sheila. 10 Wellington Square, Cheltenham, Glos, GL50 4JU.
GOODING SAVAGE F3961

162027 SAVILE-ATKINSON Mr John. Northdene, 7 Fleet Avenue, Dartford, Kent, DA2 6NL.
ACKROYD ATKINSON BEAUMONT FLEWIN FRANCIS GREEN JAGGER LAWSON LITTLEWOOD SAVILE F363

162035 SAVIN Mrs Margaret. (Carter) 36 Ramley Road, Lymington, Hants, SO41 8GT. Tel:0590-677259
ASTON ATTWOOD BARRINGTON BECK BERRY BUTCHER CARTER EVANS GAMES HAMILTON HOSKEN JAMES MARCHMENT MORGAN ROBERTS RUDMAN SAVIN SCRASE SUMMERS THOMAS THORNE WRIGHT F4845

162043 SAVOR Mrs J. 1099-88th Ave W Apt 233, Duluth, MN 55808, USA.
Andrew Andrewe ANDREWS BILLING Billings Bylling COCK Cocks Cox Gaulson GOLDSTON Goldstone Golson Goulson Gunthorp Gunthorpe Gunthrip Gunthrup GUNTRIP MASON Morse MOSS Pincomb Pincombe PINKHAM REDWOOD Trewalla TREWOLLA Trewoola F4395

162051 SAVORY Mr Chris. 28 Albert Road, Polegate, E Sussex, BN26 6BS.
Saueri Sauery Savare Savari Savarie Savary Saverey Saveri Saverie Savery Saverye Savoery Savori Savorie SAVORY Savourey Savouri Savourie Savoury Severy F1891

162078 SAWBRIDGE Miss Maureen. 55 Heaton Avenue, Bolton, Lancs, BL1 5PG.
DIX MCCURDY SAWBRIDGE F3800

162086 SAWYER Mr Derek. 155 Westfields, St Albans, Herts, AL3 4JU.
CAMPION FOX GRESWELL HATFIELD LAWRENCE MORRIS READ SAWYER SHACKLETON SHAW F4210

162094 SAWYER Mr Edward Anthony. 50 Gerard Road, Alcester, Warwickshire, B49 6QQ. Tel:0789-763577
PHILLIPS SAWYER F311

162108 SAWYERS Mr & Mrs R. 6 Titchfield Close, Oaklands, Burgess Hill, W Sussex, RH15 0RX.
BAINES BARKER BARRETT BECKINSALE BENNETT BLAXILL BOTTING CANNON CHIPPERFIELD CLAYDEN FOREST GATTY JENKIN LAW MORTLOCK PARR RANKIN RULE SAWYERS STAPLE TOWNSEND F5807

162116 SAYCE Miss M A. The Old Orchard, 39 Highfields, Shrewsbury, Shropshire, SY2 5PQ.
SAYCE F3276

162124 SCADDEN Mr R W. 8 Copse Drive, Wokingham, Berks, RG11 1LX. Tel:0734-785267
HARRIS SCADDEN SCADDING SCADENG TAYLOR F5706

162132 SCADDEN Mrs Shirley. (Burne) 15 Madden Place, Masterton, NEW ZEALAND. Tel:+64-6-378-6423
BURNE SCADDEN F5164

162140 SCADDING Mrs Linda. 52 Woodmere, Barton Hills, Luton, Beds. Tel:0582-583626
DESCON JONES SCADDING SPELLER THURGOOD WARWICK WIBERD F422

162159 SCALES Mr Robert E. Box 2525, Williams Lake, British Columbia, V2G 4P2, CANADA.
INGHAM PERKINS SCALES F6840

162167 SCANDLING Mr Brian. 10 Harrington Court, Meltham, Huddersfield, West Yorks, HD7 3ED. Tel:0484-852564
SCANDLING F6209

162175 SCARBOROUGH Mrs Enid. Box 196, Redcliffe, Queensland, 4020, AUSTRALIA. Tel:+61-7-203-7889
BELL CURRAN MULLEN ROSSITER SCARBOROUGH TREVANNION F5488

162183 SCARLE Mr David. Chimneys, 94 Church Lane, Cossall, Nottingham, NG16 2RW. Tel:0602-307471
BURROWS COOPER DEANEY HOBSON HOLLAND SCARLE WARD F6025

162191 SCARLETT Mrs Kath. (Taylor) 30 Oaklands Park, Bishops Storford, Herts, CM23 2BY.
EDIS HOGGARTH JONES ROSSELL SCARLETT SHILTON TAYLOR WILKINSON F1334

162205 SCHAUMLOFFEL J. 10a Euston Avenue, Adelaide, S Australia 5063.
BROADBRIDGE CASLEY CLAPCOTT CRICK HAWKE STANDLEY STANLEY STENTIFORD TROWBRIDGE F1604

162213 SCHEIG Mrs Mary. (Beardsley) 16301 Fairway Woods Dr, Unit 801, Ft Myers, FL 33908, USA. Tel:+1-813-433-4456
BEARDSLEY F5466

162221 SCHMIDL Muriel Jean. 6 Tilesford Park, Throckmorton, Pershore, Hereford And Worcester, WR10 2LA. Tel:0386-552065
Brearley BRIERLEY HORROCKS LORD NUTTALL ROBERTS ROSCOW WHITTAKER F2216

162248 SCHMUKI Mrs Bette. (Atkinson) W271 S3581 Oak Knoll Drive, Waukesha, WI 53188, USA. Tel:+1-414-547-9160
ATKINSON BELL BURNAND MALIM OUTHWAITE POWELL F4442

162256 SCHOFIELD Miss Alison C. 8 Walnut Avenue, Chichester, W Sussex, PO19 3EE.
ASHWORTH ASPDEN AUDSLEY BARLOW BRIGGS BRINDLE BURY BUTTERWORTH CARUS COCKER DUXBURY ECCLES ENTWISLE FISH GREGSON GRIME HARWOOD HINDLE HOLDEN HUNT JEPSON KAY KERSHAW KIRKHAM KNOWLES LEACH LEIGH LIGHTBROUWN MARSDEN NIGHTINGALE NORBURY PICKUP SCHOFIELD SHAW SHORROCK SUMNER TAYLOR THOMASSON THOMPSON TOMLISON WALKER WALMSLEY WALSH WATSON WHOWELL WORSLEY F1370

162264 SCHOFIELD Mrs Eileen Beatrice. (Stansfield) 82 North Street, Whitwick, Leics, LE6 4EA. Tel:0530-831499
STANSFIELD TITTERINGTON F2503

162272 SCHOLES Mr Stafford. 38 College View, Esh Winning, Durham, DH7 9AB. Tel:091-373-4958
BECK GLADDLE HERRING JOHNSON QUINN SCHOLES WILLS F1404

162280 SCHONNBERG Mrs Jean. 19d Cavendish Road, Southsea, Hants, PO5 2DG.
Beddoes BEDDOW BENNET BIGGS BLOCKLEY BROOKS BURGESS Canduck CONDUCT Conduit Cundwick FLETCHER GILBERT GORDON HARRISON LITTLEJOHN LITTLETON MASON STREET F1638

162299 SCHULTZ Mr John. 1085 Bowen Drive West, North Tonawanda, NY 14120-2828, USA.
Neames Nimes Nimms NIMS F7330

162302 SCHUMER Miss B P. 1 Manor Gate, 12 St Johns Avenue, London, SW15 2AU.
CALCUTT GASH LAZENBY F1251

162310 SCOLTOCK Mr John K. 43 Peacroft Lane, Hilton, Derby, DE6 5GH. Tel:0283-733441
Scaltock Scawtock SCOLTOCK F2492

162329 SCOTT Mr B E. 3 Penn Hill Park, Yeovil, Somerset, BA20 1SE.
BREWSTER DEATH DIVER DRIVER FROST JARY SCOTT STEARN STERN WOBY F4811

162337 SCOTT Mr C R. Po Box 2547, Kensington, Maryland, 20895, USA.
POYTHRESS SCOTT F6825

162345 SCOTT Mrs Carolyn. (Guiver) 24 Walnut Crescent, Noble Park, VIC 3174, AUSTRALIA. Tel:+61-79-82970
ADLAM EDMEADES FRANKLAND GOWLETT GUIVER HILLIER LITTLETON POLE RUDD SARGENT WARRENER F4215

162353 SCOTT Craig R. Po Box 4016, Merrifield, VA 22116-4016, USA.
SCOTT F7358

162361 SCOTT Miss E. 12 Benson Street, Cambridge, CB4 3QJ.
FERGUSON GITTINS GRAYLAND HIRON HOLLOWAY PERRY SCOTT SMALLWOOD STANLEY STRONG WINGFIELD F5722

162388 SCOTT Mrs G Jane. (Hales) Beacon Ridge, Portscatho, Truro, Cornwall, TR2 5EN.

Tel:0872-58468
CAVIL CLEMO DAVIES GEORGE HERBERT KESSELL SCOTT SCUTT F2261

162396 SCOTT Mr & Mrs G. 53 Whitegates, Longhorley, Morpeth, Northumberland, NE65 8UJ.
ALDAM ALLCOCK AMORRY ANDREW BADGER BARKER BARKS BIRD BRADLEY CLOVER DADDY EAST ELLIS ELLISON FAULKNER FLETCHER FREEMAN GLEW GRAYSTON HARTLEY HEYS HOGER LONSDALE MARIS MARSH NETTLESHIP NEWTON PARRY PERRY PLENDER POTTER PRESTON RICE ROBERTS SAGGERS SCOTT SHAW SHIPHAM SMITH SOWERBY SWANNOCK TAYLOR THURSTON TRIPP VICKARS WALKER WARE WELLOCK WILLIAMS WINDLE WRATHALL F5870

162418 SCOTT Mrs Gillian. 18 Chandag Road, Keynsham, Bristol, Avon, BS18 1NR.
STUCKEY TIMBRELL-ROBINSON F207

162426 SCOTT Mrs Gloria. (Johnston) 20 Forest Road, Brantford, Ontario, N3S 6W1, CANADA.
MULHOLLAND F5511

162434 SCOTT Mr James H J. 8 The Avenue, Yeovil, Somerset, BA21 4BJ. Tel:0935-73665
ADYE EDWARDS GUMTER LATIE LITTEM SCOTT F4818

162442 SCOTT Mrs M P. (Mccarthy) 40 Eden Road, Joydens Wood, Bexley, Kent, DA5 2EG.
BRUNT BULLIONS HOLMES KERR MCCARTHY SCOTT SINCLAIR WIGGS F939

162450 SCOTT Mr Peter & Mrs Erica. 20 Lateward Road, Brentford, Middx, TW8 0PL. Tel:081-560-6044
BOVINGTON EVANS JONES LEWIS LLOYD Milichamp Milichip Millichamp MILLICHIP MORGAN PALMER RICHARDSON Rook ROOKE RUTTER SCOTT SPARKES THOMAS WAITE F2529

162469 SCOTT Mr Peter R. Rebels Roost, Pettaugh Road, Stonham Aspel, Stowmarket, Suffolk, IP14 6AU. Tel:0449-711414
BAKER BANKS BARNES BARTON CLAYTON COUSINS DAVILL DIXON DURRANT ELLIOTT GIBSON HARCOCK HATELY HOWARD HUDSON KIRLEW LARTER LUCAS MASTERSON MOULTON NOBLE OCTON PHILPOT SCOTT SHEPHARD TALLANT TOWNSEND WEAVIS WILLIAMS WYTHE F3501

162477 SCOTT Mr R K. 43 Darenth Road, Dartford, Kent, DA1 1LS.
SCOTT F4556

162485 SCOTT Mr Roy. 3 Ivory Road, Norwich, Norfolk, NR4 7DT.
BAKER SCOTT SPARKS TURNER F3771

162493 SCOTT Mr Thomas. 42 Goodhew Close, Yapton, Arundel, W Sussex, BN18 0JA.
GRAY RENDALL SCOTT SEATTER THOMPSON F1550

162507 SCOTT-SAUNDERS Mr Timothy. 157 Parkwood Road, Bournemouth, Dorset, BH5 2BW. Tel:0202-431680
ANDERSON ANDREW AUCHINLECK AUCHTERLONY BAILLIE BARNET BLACK CHAMNEY Cognard CONYERS CRICHTON DAVIDSON FEAD FLEMING GALBRAITH GOODE GRAHAM HALIFAX HAMPDEN HAYES Hays Hewet HEWETT Hewitt HOGAN IRVING KENDALL KIRKPATRICK LEE LOGIE MARCH MARTYN MOLLISON NORTHEY PAGE RODGERS SAUNDERS SCOTT Sharrier Sharyer SHAYER WALLER WEBSTER WEST WHITBURN WILLIAMSON F4521

162515 SCRIVENER Miss Maureen. 24 Sheldrake Drive, Ipswich, Suffolk, IP2 9NY.
LEVETT-SCRIVENER SCRIVENNER TRIGG-SCRIVENER WILLIS F5026

162523 SEABROOK Mr David. 7 Beech Close, Newport, Shropshire, TF10 7ED.
AMBLER ARCHER ELLIOTT HOLLOWAY MADDAMS MASSEY SEABROOK WADE WARRINGTON F2914

162531 SEAGER Dr D A. 36 Squires Road, Shepperton, Middx, TW17 0LG.
WADHAM F6702

162558 SEAMARK Mr Robert Walter. 22 Curzon Street, Long Eaton, Notts, NG10 4FT. Tel:0602-729828
SEAMARK F255

162566 SEARANCKE Mrs Peggy. (Aplin) 27 Miro Street, Masterton, NEW ZEALAND.
APLIN SEARANCKE F5424

162574 SEARLE Mr C G. 28 Mallroy Crescent, Fareham, Hampshire, PO16 7QA.
Searl SEARLE Serle F6747

162582 SEARLE Mr Roy. 7 North Common Road, Uxbridge, Middx, UB8 1PD. Tel:0895-32388
GOHNS HANDY HUMBY IRELAND PEARN PICKFORD SEARLE VEAL F1120

162590 SEARLE Lt Col S J. 6 Heather Grange, Hartley Wintney, Hampshire, RG27 8SE. Tel:025126-3647
COX LE TISSIER RILEY SEARL SEARLE Serl Serle SERLO F2598

162604 SECCOMBE Mr Derek. 29 Victoria Terrace, Bedlington, Northumberland, NE22 5QB. Tel:0670-827212
Seacombe SECCAS Seccomb SECCOMBE Secombe F2753

162612 SECCULL Mr J R. Grove Bungalow, Great Milton, Oxford, OX9 7NS. Tel:0844-278100
SEACOLE SECCULL SECOLL F816

162620 SECHIARI Mr Jeff. Manor Side East, Mill Lane, Byfleet, Weybridge Surrey, KT14 7RS. Tel:0932-341084
ALSOP ANGEL ARGENTI BRAY BRIDGE BROADWOOD BROWN BYERS CALVOCURESSI CARR COCKBURN COWARD CROW DAVIES DINNEN DONKIN EVOMY FRANKLIN FURBER GAWLER GIBSON GOODACRE HAFNER HEWLETT HOFF HUGAL HUNTER JOHNSON KENNEDY KING MALONEY MAVROCORDATOU OATS PEARSON RALLI RICHARDSON RIDLEY ROCHESTER RODOCANACHI RUSSELL SCOTT SECHIARIA SENIOR SEWARD SHELDRAKE SHIELD SPARKE SPENCER WAITE WATSON WHEELER WILSON WITHERS WONTNER F3083

162639 SECKFOLD Mr Roy J. Po Box 346, Gosford 2256, AUSTRALIA.
SECKOLD F7359

162647 SEDGE Mrs Daphne. (Pells) 29 Millbank, Leighton Buzzard, Beds, LU7 7AS. Tel:0525-373193
BETTS GAME HOMEWOOD PELLS PINDER SERSHALL F4626

162655 SEKULLA Mr Michael. 231 Milton Road, Cambridge, CB4 1XQ. Tel:0223-423431
Belfrage Beridge Berige BERRIDGE COCKERTON Cockeson Cokerton Coketon Cokton Empey Empy IMPEY Impy Onion Onyen Poulter Powlter POWTER Simkin SIMPKIN Union UNWIN Unwyn F637

162663 SELBY Mr Philip G F. 18 Green Walk, Market Deeping, Lincs, PE6 8BQ. Tel:0778-342547
ALLEN BLACKMAN CLARKE DAWSON DUNMORE HUDSON KIRK MOUNT SELBY F3050

162671 SELDON Mr A E J. Green Tiles, 7 Belmont Close, Uxbridge, Middx, UB8 1RF.
BARNES COLLINS ELLINGHAM NANNON ODELL SELDON TAYLOR WHITTAL F6235

162698 SELDON Mr Peter. 81 Shilton Road, Carterton, Oxford, OX18 1EN.
SELDON F3343

162701 SELF Mr Robert John. 29 New Lane, Havant, Hants, PO9 2JJ.
DYER EGGAR PAGE SELF F4796

162728 SELKIRK Mr James. 84 Piccadilly Close, Greenlands Road, Chelmsley Wood, Birmingham, B37 7LQ.
MADDOR MCGREGOR MCINNES MCLAREN RUTHERFORD SELKIRK F2083

162736 SELLEY Mrs Maureen. (Pryor) Windyridge, Plymouth Road, Horrabridge, Yelverton, Devon, PL20 7RL.
AVARD BAILEY BATCHELOR HOOPER KEMP NEALE Prier Prior Prower Pryer PRYOR SELLEY Selly Sulley Sully Zelley Zelly F3995

162744 SELLORS Mrs Ruby. 12 Palmerston Street, Westwood, Jacksdale, Notts, NG16 5JA.
CASTLEDINE EAGLE HALLAM LIMB POLLITT SELLORS WOODWARD F5899

162752 SELLS Mr William F. 62 Aylesham Way, Yateley, Camberley, Surrey, GU17 7NT. Tel:0252-876680
CHARGE HARBIRD HOLLIMAN HOSIER JENNINGS MILLINGTON PERRY SELLS F3590

162760 SELLWOOD Mr Richard. 4 Westmead Drive, Newbury, Berks, RG14 7DJ. Tel:0635-43527
COOMBES DYER SELLWOOD F2267

162779 SELMER Susan. 6062 Lake Nadine Place, Agoura Hills, CA 91301-1421, USA.
RUSH F7357

162787 SENIOR Mrs H. 11 Rahopara St, Castor Bay, Auckland 9, NEW ZEALAND.
SENIOR F7360

162795 SEPHTON Mr Robert S. 2 Owestry Road, Oxford, OX1 4TL. Tel:0865-245167
KENNERLEY SEPHTON F3110

162809 SERGEANT Mrs Verney. 70 Ravenswood Drive, Solihull, W Midlands, B91 3LP.

Tel:021-705-5306
DONNELLY ECKERSLEY LEAMAN LYTH MARCHANT MOORE SERGEANT SMITH VERNEY F2963

162817 SERMON Mr John S. Hill Rise House, Hethe, Bicester, Oxon, OX6 9HD. Tel:0869-278105
BROMLEY SERMON Sirman Sirmon SURMAN F803

162825 SEVERN Mrs S M. 23 Holland Way, Hayes, Bromley, Kent, BR2 7DW.
ALLEN BARNFIELD BARWICK BENNETT Bermingham BIRMINGHAM BOWDEN BRAITHWATE Burbage BURBIDGE Burbridge DELVE ELLERY ELLISON FRY GALE Gardener Gardiner GARDNER GRIFFITH HARDY Hursell Hussel HUSSELL Hustle MORTON PARKER ROBERTS Seven Sevens SEVERN Severns Sivorn STICKLAND STONEHOUSE Travers Traverse Travis Trevers Treverse Treves TREVIS Trives WALTON WESLEY WHITTLE WILDGOOSE Willgoose WILLIAMS F5997

162833 SEWARD Mr Robert G. Wheal Lucky, Rundlestone, Yelverton, Devon, PL20 6SS. Tel:082289-444
BROWN COLEMAN CROSS EAMES EDLIN HARDING KEYS KIRKHAM MYERS SEWARD F2273

162841 SEWELL Mr E R A. Bay House, Aldbourne, Marlborough, Wilts, SN8 2DW.
REYNOLDS THOMPSON F5109

162868 SEYMOUR Mr Alan J. 166 Tottington Road, Bury, Lancashire, BL8 1RU.
OLIVER Seamer Seamor Seamour Seymer SEYMOUR F1364

162876 SEYMOUR Dr John. 36 Christchurch Road, Sidcup, Kent, DA15 7HQ. Tel:081-300-3182
BEATER COX DAVIE FORES Pool POOLE Seamar Seamer Seamour Semer Seymer SEYMOUR SPERLING Spurling STEPHENS Stevens F4131

162884 SEYMOUR Mrs Wendy. 18 Martha Street, Donvale, Victoria, 3111, AUSTRALIA.
CANHAM CHAMBERLAIN GARWOOD HANKIN HANSFORD SEYMOUR STONE WITCHELL F5475

162892 SHACKELL Mrs F M. Dairy Cottage, Leigh Farm, Winsham, Chard, Somerset, TA20 4HT.
DENNETT SHACKELL SHECKELL F1805

162906 SHADDICK Mr Donald. 49 Callington Road, Brislington, Bristol, BS4 5BZ.
SHADDICK Shaddock F2489

162914 SHAFTO Miss Val. 70a Whittingham Road, Mapperley, Notts, NG3 6BH.
FAYERS HOLMES MAXFIELD Metcalf METCALFE Schaften Schaftin Schafting Schafto Schafton Shaften Shaftin Shafting SHAFTO Shaftoe Shafton STAPLETON TURNER WAKE WARD F3052

162922 SHAILES Mr David. 28 Erlesmere Gardens, Ealing, London, W13 9TY. Tel:081-840-6896
SHAILES F5399

162930 SHAKESHAFT Mr Ronald. 2 Abbotsfield Gardens, Barrow In Furness, Cumbria, LA13 9JX. Tel:0229-825113
HELM Helme SHAKESHAFT F598

162949 SHAKESPEARE Mr Clive Gordon. 49 Wainsford Road, Everton, Hants, SO41 0JR.
LANCASTER MCWILLIAM SHAKESPEARE STANLEY F400

162957 SHAKESPEARE Mr Roy William. 303 Eachelhurst Road, Walmley, Sutton Coldfield, Warks, B76 8DS.
Schackespaer Schackespaere Schackespaerr Schackespear Schackespeare Schackespearr Schackespeer Schackespeere Schackespeir Schackespeire Schackespeirr Schackespeirre Schackesper Schackesperr Schackesperre Schackespier Schackespiere Schackespierr Schackespir Schackespirr Schackespyrr Schaexspaer Schaexspaere Schaexspaerr Schaexspear Schaexspeare Schaexspearr Schaexspeer Schaexspeere Schaexspeir Schaexspeire Schaexspeirr Schaexspeirre Schaexsper Schaexspere Schaexsperr Schaexspier Schaexspiere Schaexspierr Schaexspierre Schaexspir Schaexspirr Schaexspyr Schaexspyrr Schaickspaer Schaickspaere Schaickspaerr Schaickspear Schaickspeare Schaickspearr Schaickspeer Schaickspeere Schaickspeire Schaickspeirr Schaickspeirre Schaicksper Schaickspere Schaicksperr Schaicksperre Schaickspier Schaickspiere Schaickspierr Schaickspierre Schaickspir Schaickspirr Schaickspyr Schaickspyrr Schaiksspaer Schaiksspaere Schaiksspaerr Schaiksspear Schaiksspeare Schaiksspearr Schaiksspeer Schaiksspeere Schaiksspeir Schaiksspeire Schaiksspeirr Schaiksspeirre Schaikssper Schaiksspere Schaikssperr Schaikssperre Schaiksspier Schaiksspiere Schaiksspierr Schaiksspierre Schaiksspir Schaiksspirr Schaiksspyr Schaquespaer Schaquespaere Schaquespaerr Schaquespear Schaquespeare Schaquespearr Schaquespeer Schaquespeere Schaquespeir Schaquespeirr Schaquespeirre Schaquesper Schaquespere Schaquesperr Schaquesperre Schaquespier Schaquespiere Schaquespierr Schaquespierre Schaquespir Schaquespirr Schaquespyr Schaquespyrr Schayxpyr Schayxspaer Schayxspaere Schayxspaerr Schayxspear Schayxspeare Schayxspearr Schayxspeer Schayxspeere Schayxspeir Schayxspeire Schayxspeirr Schayxspeirre Schayxsper Schayxspere Schayxsperr Schayxsperre Schayxspier Schayxspiere Schayxspierr Schayxspierre Schayxspir Schayxspirr Schayxspyrr Scheackespaer Scheackespaere Scheackespaerr Scheackespear Scheackespeare Scheackespearr Scheackespeer Scheackespeere Scheackespeir Scheackespeire Scheackespeirr Scheackespeirre Scheackesper Scheackespere Scheackesperr Scheackesperre Scheackespier Scheackespiere Scheackespierr Scheackespierre Scheackespir Scheackespirr Scheackespyr Scheackespyrr Scheikspaer Scheikspaere Scheikspaerr Scheikspear Scheikspeare Scheikspearr Scheikspeer Scheikspeir Scheikspeire Scheikspeirr Scheikspeirre Scheiksper Scheikspere Scheiksperr Scheiksperre Scheikspier Scheikspiere Scheikspierr Scheikspierre Scheikspir Scheikspirr Scheikspyr Scheikspyrr Scheixspeirr Scheykespaer Scheykespaere Scheykespaerr Scheykespear Scheykespeare Scheykespearr Scheykespeer Scheykespeere Scheykespeir Scheykespeire Scheykespeirr Scheykespeirre Scheykesper Scheykespere Scheykesperr Scheykesperre Scheykespier Scheykespiere Scheykespierr Scheykespierre Scheykespir Scheykespirr Scheykespyrr Scheyquespaer Scheyquespaere Scheyquespaerr Scheyquespear Scheyquespeare Scheyquespearr Scheyquespeer Scheyquespeere Scheyquespeir Scheyquespeire Scheyquespeirr Scheyquespeirre Scheyquesper Scheyquespere Scheyquesperr Scheyquesperre Scheyquespier Scheyquespiere Scheyquespierr Scheyquespierre Scheyquespir Scheyquespirr Scheyquespyrr SHAKESPEARE Shakesperr Shaykspaer Shaykspaere Shaykspaerr Shaykspear Shaykspearr Shaykspeer Shaykspeere Shaykspeir Shaykspeire Shaykspeirr Shaykspeirre Shayksper Shaykspere Shaykspere Shaykspere Shayksperre Shaykspier Shaykspiere Shaykspierr Shaykspierre Shaykspir Shaykspirr Shaykspyr Shaykspyrr Shayxpaer Shayxpaere Shayxpaerr Shayxpear Shayxpeare Shayxpearr Shayxpeer Shayxpeere Shayxpeire Shayxpeirr Shayxpeirre Shayxper Shayxpere Shayxperr Shayxperre Shayxpiere Shayxpierr Shayxpierre Shayxpir Shayxpirr Shayxpyr Shayxpyrr Sheackespaer Sheackespaere Sheackespaerr Sheackespeare Sheackespearr Sheackespeer Sheackespeere Sheackespeir Sheackespeire Sheackespeirr Sheackespeirre Sheackesper Sheackespere Sheackesperr Sheackesperre Sheackespier Sheackespiere Sheackespiero Sheackespierr Sheackespierre Sheackespir Sheackespirr Sheackespyr Sheackespyrr Sheacksspeare Sheacksspearr Sheacksspeere Sheacksspeire Sheacsspier Sheaksspaer Sheaksspaere Sheaksspaerr Sheaksspear Sheaksspeer Sheaksspeir Sheaksspeirre Sheakssper Sheaksspere Sheakssperr Sheakssperre Sheaksspiere Sheaksspierr Sheaksspierre Sheaksspir Sheaksspirr Sheaksspyr Sheaksspyrr Sheaquespaer Sheaquespaere Sheaquespaerr Sheaquespear Sheaquespeare Sheaquespearr Sheaquespeer Sheaquespeere Sheaquespeir Sheaquespeire Sheaquespeirr Sheaquesper Sheaquespere

Sheaquesperr Sheaquesperre Sheaquespier
Sheaquespiere Sheaquespierr Sheaquespierre
Sheaquespir Sheaquespirr Sheaquespyr
Sheckespaer Sheckespaere Sheckespaerr
Sheckespear Sheckespeare Sheckespearr
Sheckespeer Sheckespeir Sheckespeire
Sheckespeirr Sheckespeirre Sheckesper
Sheckespere Sheckesperr Sheckesperre
Sheckespier Sheckespierr Sheckespierre
Sheckespir Sheckespirr Sheckespyrr Sheixspaer
Sheixspaere Sheixspaerr Sheixspear
Sheixspeare Sheixspearr Sheixspeer
Sheixspeere Sheixspeir Sheixspeire
Sheixspeirre Sheixsper Sheixspere Sheixsperr
Sheixsperre Sheixspier Sheixspiere
Sheixspierr Sheixspierre Sheixspir Sheixspyr
Sheixspyrr Shekespaer Shekespaere Shekespaerr
Shekespear Shekespeare Shekespearr Shekespeer
Shekespeere Shekespeir Shekespeire
Shekespeirr Shekespeirre Shekesper Shekespere
Shekesperr Shekesperre Shekespier Shekespiere
Shekespierr Shekespierre Shekespir Shekespirr
Shexpaerr Shexspaer Shexspaere Shexspear
Shexspeare Shexspearr Shexspeer Shexspeere
Shexspeir Shexspeire Shexspeirr Shexspeirre
Shexsper Shexspere Shexsperr Shexsperre
Shexspier Shexspiere Shexspierr Shexspierre
Shexspir Shexspirr Shexspyr Shexspyrr
Sheykspaer Sheykspaere Sheykspaerr
Sheykspeare Sheykspearr Sheykspeer
Sheykspeere Sheykspeir Sheykspeire
Sheykspeirr Sheykspeirre Sheyksper Sheykspere
Sheyksperr Sheyksperre Sheykspier Sheykspiere
Sheykspierr Sheykspierre Sheykspir Sheykspirr
Sheykspyr Sheykspyrr F6413

162965 SHAMBROOK Mr B J. 2 Hillsborough Park, Camberley, Surrey, GU15 1HG.
SHAMBROOK Shambrooke F6766

162973 SHAMBROOK Mr Roy. 29 Fairlawn Grove, Chiswick, London, W4 5EJ. Tel:081-995-7354
Clemmow Clemo Climo CLYMO HOLMAN KITTO KITTOW NORRIS OPIE Oppie Opy RULE SHAMBROOK Sharnbrook F1781

162981 SHANKLAND Mrs A & Mr I T. 63 Church Lane, Colden Common, Winchester, Hants, SO21 1TR.
Shankiland SHANKLAND Skanlin F7072

163007 SHANKS Mrs J R. Pencarrow Road Rd3, Hamilton, NEW ZEALAND.
MCBRATNEY F7322

163015 SHANKS Mrs Joyce. (Fotherby) 24 Glenbank Close, North Hykeham, Lincoln, LN6 8TW.
BLUNDEN ECOPPE FOTHERBY GREENBERRY KNOWLES MUSSON POWDRILL SHANKS STENT F6286

163023 SHAPCOTT Miss J A. 75 Windsor Drive, Dartford, Kent, DA1 3HW.
Shapcot Shapcote SHAPCOTT F6951

163031 SHAPLAND Mr P & Mrs J. 8 Hawksley Rise, Oughtibridge, Sheffield, S30 3JB. Tel:0742-863251
BARLOW BATTY CARTER CHAPPLE CHILCOTT CLINTON DOUGHTY ELWORTHY Grasby GREASBY MACHIN RAY Raye SHAPLAND Shappland SHORE TRICK WADSWORTH WILSHAW Wray F4928

163058 SHAPLEY Mr John F. Willow Tree Cottage, Salford, Chipping Norton, Oxon, OX7 5YN. Tel:0608-642478
Shapleigh SHAPLEY Shaplie Shaplye F3707

163066 SHARLAND Mr M I. 7 Dene Bridge, Howdden Le Wear, Crook, Co Durham, DL15 8JP.
SHARLAND F6962

163074 SHARON Margaret M. 8824 Finch Court, Burnaby, British Columbia, V5A 4K5, CANADA.
SHARON F7361

163082 SHARPE Mr Joseph. 79 Kentstone Close, Kingsthorpe, Northampton, NN2 8UJ.
ARNOLD ASH Ashe BALCOMB Balcombe Balcoumb Balcourt Balkam Balkham Ballcomb Ballcombe Baucomb Baucombe Baukham Baulcomb Bawcom Bawcomb Bawcombe Broadrick BRODERICK Brodrick COOPER ELLIS GADD GENESIS HARLING Kenley KINLEY LAYZELL Pain PAINE Payne Phipps PHIPS SCREEN Sharp SHARPE STACE WALKER WOODALL F4188

163090 SHARPLES Ms Barbara. Brooklands, 54 Park Lane, Great Harwood, Blackburn, Lancs, BB6 7RF.
DANIEL FEATHERSTONE GOODILL RODDY F3837

163104 SHARPLES Ms Rosemary. 201 Slade Lane, Levenshulme, Manchester, M19 2AE.
RENNIE SHARPLES F2993

163112 SHARPLESS Mrs Wendy. (Barron) 27 Bury Road, Epping, Essex, CM16 5ET.
BARNES BARRON BROADBRIDGE HUNKIN MILLS F1162

163120 SHARRED Mr S T C. 30 Upton Road, South Yardley, Birmingham, W Midlands, B33 8SY. Tel:021-784-0024
Sharrard Sharred Sherard SHERRARD F1595

163139 SHAW Mr Bertram. 26 Carr Manor Road, Leeds, LS17 5AZ.
FOTHERINGHAM Fotheringhame Foulis FOWLIS LINKLATER MATCHES MURRAY SHAW F2943

163147 SHAW Mrs Evelyn. (Oates) Barnawartha, Victoria, 3688, AUSTRALIA. Tel:+61-6-026-7357
OATS F5592

163155 SHAW Mrs G. (Fennell) 168 Bardon Road, Coalville, Leics, LE6 3BJ. Tel:0530-839784
BAKER BREWIN CUFFLIN DEAKIN FENNELL GREASLEY HODGES JEFFCOAT LOVETT PRATT SHAW SPEED STEELS TALBOT UPTON WILLN WORTLEY F5396

163163 SHAW Mrs Janet. (Tomsett) 6 Granada Place, Glendowie, Auckland 5, NEW ZEALAND.
ALLAWAY COX INGRAM PHILPOT REEVE THOMPSON TOMSETT WIGHT WOODGATE WOOLFORD F5566

163171 SHAW Mrs Marjorie. 7 Tamworth Road, Ashby De La Zouch, Leics, LE6 5PW.
HARTILL HUTCHCRAFT LINDLEY MAJOR SCOTT SPENCER SYLVESTER F5339

163198 SHAW Mrs Patricia. 6 Carnarvon Road, Preston, Lancs, PR1 8PU.
BINGLE F7425

163201 SHAW Mr Paul. 17-2465 Oriole Drive, Nanaimo, British Columbia, V9T 3P2, CANADA. Tel:+1-604-756-2626
BURGESS CHRISTIE DEASE HAKEN HUMPHREY MERRICK O'BRIEN RICE ROBERTS SHAW WOOD F4470

163228 SHAW Mrs Sandra M. 13 Woodhill Crescent, Rampside, Barrow In Furness, Cumbria, LA13 0QE. Tel:0229-825908
BOOTH HORN SMITH WILLIAMS F99

163236 SHAW Miss Susan L. 4440-H Shadow Hills Circle, Santa Barbara, California, 93105, USA. Tel:+1-805-683-9018
FOX MAXALL SCHOLEFIELD SHAW WRIGLEY F4307

163244 SHAW Mrs Wendy. (Johnson) 11 Copper Close, Carine, WA 6020, AUSTRALIA. Tel:+61-9-448-2882
Carlin CAROLAN Caroline CLIBBORN DAVIES Davis HOOD HORN Johnson JOHNSTON Johnstone KNIGHT Mceachern MCKECHNIE SCOTT SHAW SMITH WHITE Whyte WINTLE WOOD F4492

163252 SHAWCROSS Ms K. 155c Junction Road, London, N19 5PZ.
BLAND Gandal Gandall Gandell Gandle GENDALL Gendell Gendle Gengell Robben Robbens Robbin Robbins Roben Robens Robin ROBINS Shalcross Shalcrosse Shallcross Shallcrosse SHAWCROSS Shawcrosse Snowden SNOWDON WISEMAN Yandal Yandall Yandell Yandle YENDALL Yendell Yendle F3746

163260 SHAWL Mr Harold. 2 Elm Close, Newark, Notts, NG24 1SG.
ARDEN BLAZER DARLOW KING LEMMON PRIDMORE SHAUL WALES WILES WYE F2127

163279 SHAYLER Mrs Cynthia. (Perry) 127 Cot Lane, Kingswindford, West Midlands, DY6 9SD. Tel:0384-294419
CASTLE PERRY SHAYLER SPITTLE WESTON F7438

163287 SHEAR Mr Peter. 63 Braemar Road, Lillington, Leamington Spa, Warwickshire, CV32 7EZ.
ALCOCK CLUTTERBUCK EDGINGTON HARRIS SHEAR Sheare Sheares Shears Sheer Sheere Sheeres Sheers Sheir Sheire Sheires Sheirs Shere Sheres Shier Shiere Shiers Shire Shires F3327

163295 SHEARAN Mr P D. 44 Glen View, Gravesend, Kent, DA12 1LP.
Coles COULES Cowles Cowls FAYLE Gillson Gilson MITCHELL Pott POTTS THORPE F3778

163309 SHEARDOWN Mr Frank. The White House, Oare, Faversham, Kent, ME13 7UA. Tel:0795-533123
GLEW GREENFIELD HORSWOOD IREMONGER Ironmonger SHEARDOWN Sheerdown Sheredonne Sheredown Sheredowne F1586

163317 SHEARN Mrs Susan. (Akerman) 96 Exeter Street, Salisbury, Wiltshire, SP1 2SF. Tel:0722-336854
AKERMAN ALEXANDER BOARD COX DALE DICK GREGG MCKENZIE SAVIDGE SCHONSTADT SMITH STEEVENS VERITY F1755

163325 SHEEHAN Mrs B C. 2808 N Florida No 88, Lakeland, FL 33805, USA.
CHOICE Choyce F6605

163333 SHEEHAN Betty. Pob 92582, Lakeland, FL 33804-2582, USA.
CHOICE Choiyce F7253

163341 SHEEHAN Mrs Elaine. 44 Florida Avenue, New Lambton, NSW 2305, AUSTRALIA. Tel:+61-049-573276
BAINES BOWERMAN BUTTON CLAYDEN LEE PARKINSON PRYDE PUDDING RUMBALL THOMPSON F78

163368 SHEFFIELD Mr Neil. 67 Greenland Crescent, Chilwell, Nottingham, NG9 5LD.
CHADBOURNE COTON HOLLAND JARMAN OLIVER SHEFFIELD SIDWELLS STANLEY F3793

163376 SHEFFIELD Mrs Yvonne D. (Huddlestone) 8 Shires Close, The Murreys, Ashtead, Surrey, KT21 2ND. Tel:0372-278799
HUDDLESTON HUDDLESTONE HUDLESTON F124

163384 SHELDON Mr J F. Ashbourne, Surrey Gardens, Effingham, Surrey, KT24 5HH.
SHELDON F6932

163392 SHELDRAKE David. 8 Fairview Avenue, Stanford Le Hope, Essex, SS17 ODW.
BERRY DOWLER DYER GRIFFIN HEWITT HOVER HOWARD PARKER SHELDRAKE WHITE WILLIS F2271

163406 SHELLARD Mrs Pamela. (Tolcher) 9 Stirtingale Avenue, Bath, Avon, BA2 2NQ.
BENCE COLE DENCH FOURACRE JAQUES MUTTER RUSSELL SHELLARD TOLCHER WINSOR F4348

163414 SHELTON Marjorie. 4 Fountain Court, Ufford, Stamford, Lincs, PE9 3BJ. Tel:0780-740729
SHELTON F2094

163422 SHEPHERD Mrs Lorelle. (Sumner) Sandycroft, 8 Jesmond Park West, Newcastle Upon Tyne, NE7 7BU. Tel:091-281-3757
SUMNER F3620

163430 SHEPPARD Mr A H. 711 Whitton Avenue West, Northolt, Middlesex, UB5 4LE. Tel:081-864-9065
OSGOODBY F3497

163449 SHEPPARD Ms G. 23 Bryanston Road, Bitterne, Southampton, Hants, SO3 7AP.
LUFFMAN SHEPHERD SHEPPARD WILGRESS WILLGRESS WILLIAMS WILTSHIRE WINKLE F5736

163457 SHEPPARD Mr M. 12 James Road, Branksome, Poole, Dorset, BH12 1EA.
LONGMORE F7308

163465 SHEPPARD Mrs P J. South View Farm, Holme, Newark, Notts, NG23 7RZ. Tel:0636-703886
ATKINSON BILTON BOURNE CORBETT FRANKS HANCER HUTCHINSON PASCHOUD RECKERBY SHEPPARD STENNETT WILLIAMSON F4296

163473 SHEPPARD Mr Peter J. 4 Belvedere Close, Fleet, Aldershot, Hants, GU13 8JP.
CLENCH JERRETT MADGE OTTER SHAVE SHEPPARD F943

163481 SHEPPARD Mr Richard. 41 Belvoir Street, Mapperley, Nottingham, NG3 5GN. Tel:0602-606128
DAGWORTHY F2532

163503 SHEPPEY Mr G Clive. 106 Kingswood Avenue, Bromley, Kent, BR2 ONP.
FOGG GARDNER SHEPPEY WILDBLOOD F3043

163511 SHERBORN Mr D R. 161 Marine Parade, Brighton, Sussex, BN2 1EJ.
ALLMAN BANCE DISMORE DODSON SAVAGE SHERBORN F860

163538 SHERBORNE Mr John. 22 Miro Street, Masterton, 5900, NEW ZEALAND.
Sherborn SHERBORNE Sherbourne F7003

163546 SHERGOLD Mrs Doreen. 30 Naseby Close, Binley, Coventry, CV3 2HS.
JONES Shargold Sheargold Shergall SHERGOLD Shergoll Shirgold WOOD F306

163554 SHERIDAN Mr James F. 12 Cornelscourt Hill Road, Foxrock, Dublin, Ireland, D18.
DONNELLY PETTIGREW RYAN SHERIDAN F3115

163562 SHERLOCK Mrs Caroline. 24 Champion Grove, Camberwell, London, SE5 8BW.
BARBER BRAY BROOKES CHAMBERLAIN DAVIDSON DURNFORD DYMOCK FARR FILLINGHAM FORSTER FOWNES Gattey GATTY HISCUTT JOHNSON LIDDELL LYNDALL MARTYN OLIVER RIDPATH SCHWEITZER SENNERTH Urswick Urswyk URWICK WARTON WHITBY F1089

163570 SHERLOCK Mr G S. 81 High Street, Offord D'Arcy, Huntingdon, Cambs, PE18 9RH. Tel:0480-811889
CHADDERTON Chaderton Scurlock Sharlock Shearlock Sherloc SHERLOCK Shirlock Shurlock F4239

163589 SHERMAN Mrs Frances. (Stamper) 19 Market Place, Dalton In Furness, Cumbria, LA15 8AX. Tel:0229-64891
Coopland Copeland COUPLAND Cowpland MCCUNE Mcewan Mcewen Mckune Pool POOLE Pull STAMPER F1655

163597 SHERRARD Mr John S. 34 Juniper Way, Tilehurst, Reading, Berks, RG3 6NB.
Sharred Sherard Sherrad SHERRARD Sherratt Sherreard Sherred Sherret Sherrott F4537

163600 SHERRY Mr Norman F. 68 Campbell Crescent, East Grinstead, Sussex, RH19 1JS. Tel:0342-327541
ABBS COOPER FERNEE Ferney Ferny FLIGHT Furney Furny SHARY SHERRY TAYLOR TUCKER WISEMAN F554

163619 SHERWELL Mr G L. 59 Liverpool Drive, Keysborough, Victoria, 3173, AUSTRALIA.
SHERWELL F6967

163627 SHERWEN Mr Nigel. 27 Glen Park Road, Wallasey, Wirral, L45 5JL.
SHERWEN Sherwin F7391

163635 SHERWIN Mr Ronald. Flintstones, Stisted, Braintree, Essex, CM7 8BX.
ANDREWS BARKER BARRETT FOXLOWE PERRY SHERWIN WAGSTAFF WIGGINS F2098

163643 SHEW Mr B. 18a Queens Avenue, Whetstone, London, N20 0JE.
FLUDGER HOVEY SHEW SNOSWELL F1170

163651 SHILLABEER Mr C. 16 Fernside Road, Talbot Park, Bournemouth, BH9 2LA.
SHILLABEER Shillibeer F6708

163678 SHILLING Ms A E. 14 Ashfield Lane, Ashford, Barnstaple, North Devon, EX31 4BY.
SHILLING Shillinge Shillings F6759

163686 SHILTON Mrs Ethel. 66 Mercian Way, Slough, Berks, SL1 5LY. Tel:0628-603387
ADSHEAD CHERRY Crier CRUMPTON CRYER CURRALL Emet Emit Emmet EMMETT Emmit Enit GOLDER Goldier Goulder Haliwell Halliwell Heliwell HELLIWELL HOLLAND HOYLE SHILTON SMITH WELLS WOODFIELD WRIGHT F815

163694 SHIMMIN Mr T J. 38 College Road, Clontarf, Queensland, 4019, AUSTRALIA.
ELLISON GIFFORD HUNTER LANGRIDGE LONGMUIR PAYNE QUIRK RICH SHIMMIN F5147

163708 SHIPP Mr H F. 13 Cadogan Park, Woodstock, Oxford, OX7 1UW.
Popkess POPKISS F6653

163716 SHIPP Mr Ken. 30 Goose Green Road, Snettisham, Norfolk, PE31 7PW.
BAILEY Bayley CHRISTIE PLEDGER SHIP Shipp F3440

163724 SHIPP Mrs Pam. The Haven, Boundary Raod, Rowledge, Farnham Surrey, GU10 4EP. Tel:025125-2390
HIRST HURST SHIP SHIPP F1835

163732 SHIPP Mrs Yvonne. The Elms, Capps Lane, All Saints, South Elmham, Halesworth Suffolk, IP19 0PD.
COCKADAY DENNINGTON DOWNING FRANCIS HADDOCK LAMBERT LINGHAM MARSHAM PINK SHIPP F5934

163740 SHIPTON Mr David. 97 Laindon Road, Billericay, Essex, CM12 9LG.
BIRKETT BRAY BROOK COLE CUMMIN DORRELL FULLAGAR HARGREAVES HART HIGGINS HUGHES HUNT KEAR KINGSTON SHIPTON SINCLAIR TILBURY TUCKWELL WAIT WHITEHEAD WINDSOR F4677

163759 SHIRE Mr A W & Mrs D M M. Springfield, Long Road West, Dedham, Colchester, Essex, CO7 6ES. Tel:0206-322650
PEARCE SHIRE F4573

163767 SHIRLEY Mrs Betty. 10256 Glencoe Drive, Cupertino, CA 95014, USA.
Sherley SHIRLEY Shirly Shurley F6847

163775 SHIRLEY Mr E W. 8 Delmar Gardens, Brockhill, Wickford, Essex, SS11 7NA.
ATKINS Autey AUTY Awty AYLMER BAILEY Barratt Barrett BERRETT BILLINGHAM BOOTHBY BROOKS BROWN BRUMMET BURTON CARROLL CHILDS Chiles CLARE COBBEAL CONLEY COURCHE Courchja COX DAVIES Detanon DETNON DIPPLE DREA Drisdale DRISDALL DUNSDON EASTON ENGLISH Eyston Foch Foche Fooch FOSH Fouache Fouch Fouche Foucher FRANNIE GARROTT GILL Glascock Glascoe Glascow GLASGOW GREEN GUY HASTINGS Hawkins HAYDON HIGGINSON HORRIX HOWKINS HUGGETT HYDE IRONS JOHNSON JOLLIFFE JONES KEHOE KLELTY Lauday LAWDAY LEDEUX Loveday MACDONALD MAETRIC MALANDIE Malindine MARSH MARSHALL MCKEOWN Merner MERNOR MORRISON MORTON NEAL Neale Oute PATTERSON PETERS PHILLIPS PHILLO POWLEY RAYNOR READING Rose ROZEE Ruse SHIRLEY SIMPSON SOMERS STEVENS SWITZER TAPLEY THOMPSON TIMMS Toy TOYE WAITE WILSON F4019

163783 SHOESMITH Mrs Lilian. (Holmes) Green Gables, 221 Midgeland Road, Marton Moss, Blackpool, Lancs, FY4 5HL. Tel:0253-62406
ASHCROFT BALL BILLINGTON BUXTON CROSS DEWHURST FAIRCLOUGH FISHER FLEETWOOD HALL HIGHAM HOLMES KIRK LUCAS MELLING Millner MILNER MOORE NIVEN PARKINSON RICHMOND SINGLETON SPARLING TAYLOR TUNSTALL WALKER YEATES F4079

163791 SHONE Mr John C & Mrs Judy. (Shield) 15 Knoll Street, Island Bay, Wellington, 6002, NEW ZEALAND. Tel:+64-4-383-8882
BRAILEY CLIFF HANNIGAN JENKIN LEECH LEONARD PHELAN SHIELD SHONE SMITH STANTON F4472

163805 SHORE Mr B W. The Breck, 25 Westerham Road, Oxted, Surrey, RH8 0EP.
D' Escures DE SCURES Schoor Schoore Schor Shoar SHOARD Shoare Shoord Shor Shord Shorde SHORE F6031

163813 SHORE Mrs Eveline W. (Coomer) 2 Poplar Grove, Albert Street, Newcastle Under Lyme, Staffs, ST5 1JW. Tel:0782-616380
Bealin Bellin Boylin Boyling BURROUGHS BYOLIN Byollin Byolling COOMER DOUASTON HANCOCK JONES MALPASS SHORE F3855

163821 SHORLAND Mr Frederick. 6 Montroy Close, Henleaze, Bristol, BS9 4RS. Tel:0272-629182
AVERY DUNN HAMBLETON ILES SHORLAND SHORT F4518

163848 SHORTALL Dr Myles. Laurel Lodge, Downshire Road, Newry, Co Down, Northern Ireland, BT34 1EE. Tel:0693-67534
BOURKE Breslain Breslawn BRUSLAUN CAHILL FOGARTY HARFORD LIDWELL Lidwill MORROGH O'cahill O'FOGARTY RUSSELL SHORTALL Shortell Shortle F4135

163856 SHORTMAN Mr & Mrs D A. Carmina, 12 Stangeways, Watford, Herts, WD1 3SP.
Bainton BAYNTON Bayton PETLEY SHORTMAN STREETING F2817

163864 SHOUKSMITH Mrs K E. Red Roof, Lords Moor Lane, Strensall, N Yorks, YO3 5XF. Tel:0904-490303
CRABB MACNAUGHT Shanksmith Shonksmith Shooksmith Shoucksmith SHOUKSMITH Shucksmith TORBIT F6490

163872 SHRAPNELL Mr D A. 13a Charlton Road, Weston Super Mare, Avon, BS23 4HB.
SHRAPNELL F6587

163880 SHRIMPTON Ms V. 143a Grosvenor Road, Langley Vale, Epsom Downs, Surrey, KT18 6JF.
Shimpton SHRIMPTON Srimpton F7061

163899 SHUKER Mr N H. Wherley Rough House, Prees, Whitchurch, Shropshire, SY13 2BH.
Shewker Shooker Shucker Shugar SHUKER Shulker Sucker Sugar Suger Suker F3850

163902 SIDDALL Mr Gordon. 17 Bowden Wood Crescent, Darnall, Sheffield.
COOPER DAWSON GARNETT HEWITT HINCHLIFFE MITCHELL SACKFIELD SIDAL SIDDAL SIDDALL SIDLE SMITH TAYLOR WAGSTAFFE F735

163910 SIDEBOTHAM Mrs Joyce. (Harrison) Rostherne, Greenfield Road, Holmfirth, Huddersfield, HD7 1LA.
COLVARD HASLAM LEWERS LEWIS SIDEBOTHAM TISSINGTON F656

163929 SIEBER Mrs B. (Roper) 8 Tapestries Hall, Straight Road, Old Windsor, SL4 2RN.
LEVERETT ROPER SHELDRAKE F3419

163937 SIEGEL Ernestine. Po Box 13302, Tampa, FL 33681-3302, USA.
REEDER F7353

163945 SILCOCK Mrs E. New Lodge Farm, Over Wallop, Stockbridge, Hants, SO20 8HU. Tel:0264-781433
ARMSTRONG BODLE COURTHOPE GIBBONS LAMBE LATCHFORD LUSHINGTON LUSIGNAN MARCHANT Marchante Merchant Merchante SILCOCK WALTER F2431

163953 SILCOCK Mrs Pauline. (Lord) 84 Pyms Road, Wem, Shropshire, SY4 5UU. Tel:0939-234635
BARKER DYER FOX Haward Hawk HAWKE HAYWARD HEATH Heyward Howard KEYS Laud Loid LORD Loyd LUDKIN POTTLE TUCKER WRIGHT F6202

163961 SILK Mr A. 20 Sandhill, Shrivenham, Swindon, Wiltshire, SN6 8BQ.
SILK Silke Silks F6936

163988 SIMMONDS Mrs E. 1 Epping Green, Hemel Hempstead, Herts, HP2 7JP. Tel:0442-216722
CANNON FRIENDSHIP GOMER MCCLELLAND PINN SEAGE F4734

163996 SIMMONDS Miss M G. 4 Pathfinder Way, Ramsey, Huntingdon, Cambs, PE17 1LX.
SIMMONDS F4876

164003 SIMMONS Mrs Eileen Winifred. 3 Weeke Manor Close, Winchester, Hants, SO22 5JE.
COSSINS HADLAND HUMPHRIES POOLE TUCKER TURPIN VOCKINS WOOD F1049

164011 SIMMONS Mrs Valerie. 53 Patricks Copse Road, Liss, Hants, GU33 7DW.
BACK BURROUGHS CANHAM CLIFTON COLES DUNCAN ELDRIDGE FRIER HARROLD HART HOWELLS LEY MANSFIELD MAY MCGILLOWAY OLD PRESDEE PRESTON PYM RATCLIFFE REYNOLDS SANDALL SHILLING SIMMONS SMITH SQUIBS STICKLAND TURNER F5375

164038 SIMMS Mrs Dorothy A. 9 Broad Mark House, Ash Lane, Rustington, W Sussex, BN16 3BT. Tel:0903-772439
ALCHORNE BODLE BODYLL BRIDLE BRISTOW BRYDELL BULL CHEALE DE LA CHAMBRE HAMPSON HOLNEY HOWARD MORLEY REYNOLDS WALKER WEDGE F1807

164046 SIMONS Mr John Wenden. 6 Parkwood Grove, Sunbury On Thames, Middx, TW16 6QJ. Tel:0932-787685
SIMONS F472

164054 SIMONS Miss Mary. 30 Farrowdene Road, Reading, Berks, RG2 8SD. Tel:0734-860408
BOYER COPLEY SIMONS WATTS F541

164062 SIMPSON Mrs Catherine. (Mcgrath) 1 Marsh Terrace, Darwen, Lancs, BB3 0HF. Tel:0254-703924
ABBA CAINE GARSDEN GREEN HALL HEWITT MACK MCCGRATH SHORROCK SIMPSON F1828

164070 SIMPSON Mrs Dorothy. (Gregory) 20 Wearside Drive, Durham, DH1 1LE.
GREGORY JAMES JONES LOCKYER MILES PRICE F4425

164089 SIMPSON Mrs E. 2 Stella Grove, Tollerton, Notts, NG12 4EY. Tel:06077-2287
FOINQUINOS F5331

164097 SIMPSON Mrs Eileen. (Jack) 12 Newlyn Avenue, Litherland, Liverpool, L21 9LD.
CROFT FORSHAW HENNIGAN JACK LITTLE LUCAS SHIELS SIMPSON TURNER F4268

164100 SIMPSON Mr Graham. Bon Accord, Eaton Bishop, Hereford, HR2 9QW. Tel:0981-250540
Curam Curem Curm CURME Curmi Curn Curom Currum F24

164119 SIMPSON Mrs J M. 17 Gwynns Walk, Hertford, Herts, SG13 8AD.
ANDREWS F3955

164127 SIMPSON Mr John W. 22a Rances Lane, Wokingham, Berkshire, RG11 2LH. Tel:0734-781358
BARRY CALLAWAY HAYWARD MCEWEN PASSMORE PAULL SIMPSON SNELL F3046

164135 SIMPSON Miss Joyce Mary. 38 Elm Grove, Hayling Island, Hants, PO11 9EF. Tel:0705-463457
BARNES JEFFS NEWPORT SIMPSON WARD F6104

164143 SIMPSON Mrs Julia D A. (Waud) 17 Standhill Avenue, Carlton, Notts, NG4 1LG. Tel:0602-874382
EADES Eads Eedes Heeds KNIGHT ORFORD RAINBOW

Wand WARD WAUD Waude Waudebie Waudie Waund Woad F3540

164151 SIMPSON Mr K A. 15 Greenacre Close, North Tawton, Devon, EX20 2TR.
HEWITON LINDSAY NICHOLSON NORTH PRESTON SCURR SHIELDS SIMPSON WILSON F4731

164178 SIMPSON Mr M A. 12 Hailsham Close, East Preston, West Sussex, BN16 1DW. Tel:0903-770040
ANSCOMBE CALLAWAY COOTE DAMP FOXCROFT JOYES LEWIS OLDFIELD SHELLEY SIMPSON F4189

164186 SIMPSON Mr O John. 63 Ravensbourne Gardens, Clayhall, Ilford, Essex, IG5 0XH. Tel:081-550-0491
DAVIS SIMPSON YOUNG F4497

164194 SIMPSON Mr P P. 49 Anzac Street, Takapuna, Auckland 9, NEW ZEALAND.
HECKS Hex Silkston SILKSTONE F7170

164208 SIMPSON Mrs Thelma. 45 Leyster Street, Morecambe, Lancs, LA4 5NF. Tel:0524-420908
ALLAN BENSON GAUNT HALL HAWLEY HOLME MONKS SIMPSON WALTON WOODHOUSE F3219

164216 SIMPSON Mrs Vera C. (Rance) 3 Stoney Butts, Lea, Preston, Lancs, PR2 1RT. Tel:0772-720416
CURWEN RANCE ROSS F3464

164224 SIMPSON Mr William. 20 Wearside Drive, Durham, DH1 1LE.
CHATWIN PARKER SIMPSON SINCLAIR TATE F5703

164232 SIMS Mrs Beryl. The Old Mill, Bramford, Ipswich, Suffolk, IP8 4AU.
ASHWELL Ashwill BARBER BECKETT Bethel BETHELL CHITTLEBOROUGH Chittleburrow Corbet CORBETT DAWKINS DICKINSON GRAY JANAWAY LUMKIN Lumpkin Markam MARKHAM NOY Noye SALMON SAUNDERS SIMS UNGLESS WARD WILLIAMS F123

164240 SIMS Mr David. 19 Barford Road, Kenilworth, Warwickshire, CV8 2AY.
BAILEY HENNING SIMS F473

164259 SIMS Mrs E J. 13 Valerie Street, Ashmore, Queensland, 4214, AUSTRALIA.
AYSCOUGH CASWELL GREENHALGH HALL HEMPSTEAD OWENS PEARSON PICKERING SIMS WRIGHT F5478

164267 SIMS Mrs Eileen. 63 Sevenoaks Road, Orpington, Kent, BR6 9JN.
ATKINSON BAYTON BELLAMY BRAN FRANKUM HAYLES KING KNIBBS MILES MILSOM PITMAN SIMS SNOOK WOODS F1142

164275 SIMS Mrs Joan. 8 The Orchards, Epping, Essex, CM16 7BB.
GALLOWAY LAX PORTER SIMS TINWELL WILKIE F908

164283 SIMS Mr M A. Warelyn, 15a Howard Road, Great Bookham, Surrey, KT23 4PW.
JEWEL Juell Seem Sems SIMS Symes Symmes Symms F4342

164291 SIMS Mrs Marion. (Purchall) Owl Cottage, Broom Way, Oatlands Park, Weybridge Surrey, KT13 9TG. Tel:0932-842327
Parchall Parshall Pershall Porchel Purchal PURCHALL Purchel PURCHELL Purchil Purchill Purshale Purshall SIMS TIPLADY F4067

164305 SINDEN Mrs J. (Maskell) 84 Longridge Avenue, Saltdean, Brighton, E Sussex, BN2 8RB.
MASKELL F3896

164313 SINDEN Mrs Julie. 14 Chestnut Drive, Kingswood, Maidstone, Kent, ME17 3PD.
BATCHELOR OTTAWAY WICKENDEN F995

164321 SINFIELD Mrs Dorothy M. 2324 Kawartha Hts Blvd, Peterborough, Ontario, K9K 1S5, CANADA.
BAKER BASTICK BRISTOW BROOKS FISHER FREMONT GREEN KNIGHTLEY Knightly LATHAM MASON MUNDAY Randall RANDELL Randle REDMAN Saber SAUBERE Sober Sobere SOONS STARKEY Starkie Starky Weston WHISTON WINCHESTER Wiston F3160

164348 SINGLEHURST Mr Dennis. 292 Fort Austin Avenue, Crownhill, Plymouth, Devon, PL6 5SR. Tel:0752-701029
CUDLIP SINGLEHURST F3684

164356 SINNICK Mrs N M. 27 Mistover Road, Wareham, Dorset, BH20 4BY.
JAMES ORCHARD SINNICK F3592

164364 SISSONS Mrs Joy. (Banks) 9 Anvil Close, Stannington, Sheffield, S6 5JN.
BANKS COBB HOLAH KILBY PLANT RAWLINSON RUSLING SISSONS TEASDALE WALL F5754

164372 SIZER Mr P D. Sunset, Court Road, Newton Ferrers, Plymouth, Devon, PL8 1DD.
Sizar SIZER Sizor Syzar Syzer F7143

164380 SKEGGS Mrs Anita. 2 St James Close, East Cowes, Isle Of Wight, PO32 6PP. Tel:0983-292518
Dearl DEARLE Derl Derle SKEGGS F224

164399 SKELLY Mr D W. Clovelly, Bolthouse Close, Launceston Road, Tavistock Devon, PL19 8LN. Tel:0822-614153
ALFORD COLE FUGE HUTCHING JEFFERY OKE ROBERTS SCOFFERN SKELLY F1189

164402 SKELLY Mrs Moira. (Blackman) 25 Leazes Park, Hexham, Northumberland, NE46 3AX.
AITKEN BLACKMAN BOSANKO GEDDES LYST PARKER SKELLY SKERRY TODD F4237

164410 SKELTON Mr Colin D'Arcy. Lostock, 24 Margaret Road, Blundellsands, Liverpool, L23 6TR. Tel:051-924-2855
D'ARCY MANSON SKELTON F5200

164429 SKERN Miss Brenda. 239 Boothferry Road, Hessle, N Humberside, HU13 9AP. Tel:0482-649283
GROVES PROCTOR SKERN F3764

164437 SKERRY Mr M W. 24 Wheatley Drive, North Wootton, Kings Lynn, Norfolk, PE30 3QQ.
CHILVERS GOGLE MATSELL SKERRY TWITE WING F4995

164445 SKEWS June. 17 Restrop Road, Purton, Swindon, Wiltshire.
SKUSE F2459

164453 SKINNER Mr J. 7 Mersey Road, Worthing, W Sussex, BN13 3NF. Tel:0903-67971
HUBBARD MEETEN Meetens Meeting Meetten Mitton Mutton SKINNER F2406

164461 SKINNER Mr Neville J. 60 Gunton Drive, Lowestoft, Suffolk, NR32 4QB. Tel:0502-573913
CATCHPOLE DUNNETT SKINNER SPALL F6270

164488 SKINNER Mr Stephen. 16 Ennismore Avenue, Chiswick, London, W4 1SF.
NEWALL SKINNER WHITEHEAD F1743

164496 SKITTRALL Mrs P. 17 Windmill Avenue, Dereham, Norfolk, NR20 3BE.
Skitterall SKITTRALL Skittrell F7185

164518 SKLINAR Mrs C. 1 New Lane, East Ardsley, Wakefield, WF3 2DP.
DAY DUNCAN HEBDEN MILLS OFFICER RIACH SIDDLE WHEELDON WILKINSON F2633

164526 SKOYLES Mr E R. 7 Little How Croft, Abbots Lanley, Watford, Herts, WD5 0BR.
Scoles Skayles Skoils SKOYLES F6944

164534 SKUES Mr Keith. Lambs Meadow, Castle Hill, Holmesfield, Sheffield, South Yorkshire, S18 5WQ. Tel:0742-891300
SKEWES SKEWIS SKEWS SKUCE SKUES SKUSE F1713

164542 SKUES Mrs Valerie. 16 Lower Drive, Seaford, E Sussex, BN25 3AS. Tel:0323-894436
CAFFYN COOKE FRENCH Scues Scuse Skewes Skewis Skews Skewys Skuce SKUES Skuse Skuys F1674

164550 SKULL Mrs M F. 53 Manor Road, Brackley, Northants, NN13 6ED.
BEVAN BEVIN LEWIS SWEETMAN WARNER F706

164569 SKYRM Mr Ian. Lodge Farm, Broadheath, Tenbury Wells, Worcs, WR15 8QS. Tel:08867-234
DICKSON SKERM Skirm SKYRM SKYRME F2626

164577 SLADE Mrs Lou. (Morrell) 2200 Garland St, Lakewood, CO 80215, USA. Tel:+1-303-237-0279
BEST CHARTER JEREMY NAUGHTY ORKEY RHIND SLADE WAIT F5654

164585 SLADE Mrs M. Brookfield, The Wash, Hargrave, Bury St Edmunds, IP29 5HH.
Hadenham Hadham HADINGHAM F6969

164593 SLADE Mr R. 33 Boundary Close, Kingsdown, Swindon, Wiltshire, SN2 6TG. Tel:0793-823479
DEW GARDOM KELLAWAY KILLICK LEY SLADE VINES F4305

164607 SLADER Mrs Ann. (Rogers) 15 Foster Drive, Hitchin, Herts, SG4 9EH.
ALLEN DIMMACK PARSONS ROGERS SLADER TOFT F6305

164615 SLANN Mr Francis. 44 Ash Grove, Chinley, Stockport, SK12 6BQ.
BARLOW BENNETT CORNER EYERS FRANCIS HALE HATHAWAY KEEN LAURENCE LYONS MALLALIEU MANIFOLD OFFER SHAWCROSS SLANN F1393

164623 SLATER Mrs A K. Perins View, Bridge Road, Alresford, Hants, SO24 9ET.
AYRES BOYLES BROWN CHRISTIAN COE DOTCHEN

Dotchin FATKIN FINNEY HARDWICK HARRIS Harriss JONES LADDS LEONARD MARTIN NEWTON REDMOND ROBBINS SKELTON SLATER SMITH WRIGHT F5987

164631 SLATER Mr B R & Mrs R J. 50 Melbourne Road, Bramhall, Stockport, Cheshire, SK7 1LS. BARRETT BARTON BEEKIN BONNER BOWN BRIDGES BURGESS BUTLER CLIFFORD CORBETT CROWE DAWSON DEPEAR DYER FAWKES HALL HART HOLDEN HUBBARD LAND LEADBEATER LEES MAPP MARSH MEADOWS MOORE MOUNTCASTLE NICHOLLS OLIVER PARKER PHILLIPS POLLARD ROOME SALMON Saman SCLATER SEATON SLATER SPILBURY STANLEY VICARIS WARD WATSON WEEKS WINSTANLEY YARRANTON F5061

164658 SLATER Dr Lucy J. 30 Oxford Road, Cambridge, CB4 3PW. Tel:0223-353987 DALTON SLATER F226

164666 SLATFORD Mr J M. St George'S Famrhouse, High Street, Ripley, Woking Surrey, GU23 6AE. SLATFORD F6852

164674 SLEE Mr David. 147 Queens Road, Teddington, Middx, TW11 0LZ. ABRAHAM COMBEN FLANN HOWARD PARKIN SLEE TITTERTON F419

164682 SLEMMINGS Mr Barry. 34 Pretoria Road, Romford, Essex, RM7 7AS. Clemmings LACK PEER Slayman Slemands Slemans SLEMMINGS SLEMONDS Sleymans F6442

164690 SLEMMONDS Mr Sam. 47 Sulivan Road, Fulham, London, SW6 3DT. Tel:071-736-8979 SALAMAN Slammon Slamon SLAYMAN SLEAMAN SLEMAN SLEMANS Slemen Slemens Slemmen Slemmens Slemming SLEMMINGS SLEMMON SLEMMONDS SLEMMONS SLEMON SLEMONS Sleuthman SLIMAN SLIMANS Slimin Sliming Slimings Slimmand SLIMMANDS SLIMMING SLIMMINGS Slimond Slymand Slymin Slymins F5231

164704 SLOAN Mrs Patricia. (Neville) 26 Aylsham Close, Tilehurst, Reading, Berks, RG3 4XG. CANNON COLEMAN DUCKETT GILES HAWKINS JEFFS JEROME LOCK Nevel Nevil Nevill NEVILLE SHERWOOD SNAREY SOMERVILLE Sommerville Thorp THORPE TULL WARRICK Warwick F1501

164712 SLOBOM Mrs J M. Little Tudors, 44 Marshalls Drive, St Albans, Herts, AL1 4RQ. Schlobohm Schlobohn Sloban Slobin SLOBOM Sloburn Slowbohm Slowburn F7167

164720 SLOW Mrs Joan. (Witts) 404 Mutton Lane, Potters Bar, Herts, EN6 3AT. Tel:0707-54917 BERRY PLUMB SLOW WITTS F3186

164739 SLUCUTT Mr Mike & Mrs Mary. 5 Deverose Court, Hanham, Bristol, BS15 3SW. Bluecock Gassard Gasserd Gazard GAZZARD Gissard Gizard Gizzard Gossard Gozard Gozzard Guyzard Hucutt Milden MILDON Mylden Myldon Slewcock Slewcott Slocock Slocutt Sloocock Slowcock Slowcoke Slucett SLUCOCK Slucott SLUCUTT Sluggate Sluggut TASKER F2724

164747 SMALLEY Mrs Dawn. 19 Silver Birches, Barkham, Wokingham, Berks, RG11 4YZ. GODDARD PAGE F674

164755 SMALLEY Mrs Gwyneth. (Hughes) 414 Burnley Road, Cliviger, Burnley, Lancs. COOMBE HOCKADAN HUGHES OWEN Owens F6534

164763 SMALLSHAW Mr R. 5 Heathacre, Bath Road, Colnbrook, Bucks, SL3 0HX. SMALLSHAW Smalschaghe Smalschawhe Smalsha Smalshagh Smalshaw Smalshawe Smalshew Smalshey Smalshowe Smawshaw F6775

164771 SMALLWOOD Mr David. 67 Station Road, Fernhill Heath, Worcester, WR3 7UP. SHERRIES SHERRIS SMALLWOOD F6321

164798 SMEDLEY Lady Beryl. (Harley Brown) 11a Beehive Lane, Ferring, W Sussex, BN12 5NN. BROWN CROSS DALY GUBB HARLEY MORRIS RENDLE SATCHELL SMEDLEY F6441

164801 SMEETON Mr E Brian. 15 St Johns Way, Piddington, Northampton, NN7 2DL. Tel:0604-870591 BERRINGTON CHURCH GREENHAM LAMBOURN LAMBOURNE ROBERTS SMEETON F2195

164828 SMERDON Mrs B. 18 Clarendon Gardens, Wembley, Middx, HA9 7QW. BOYDEN-ROBERTS PEARE SMERDON F3742

164836 SMERDON Mr D W. 17 Walnut Lane, Milton, New York, 12547, USA. Smardon Smerden SMERDON F7186

164844 SMITH Mr Alec. 83 Blount Avenue, East Grinstead, West Sussex, RH19 1JN. Tel:0342-323937 COOK FISHER JESSON SCOTT SMITH VANN WATSON F3687

164852 SMITH Mr Andrew J. 44 Bolton Crescent, Basingstoke, Hants, RG22 6BD. Tel:0256-843690 COX PURSE SMITH WATTS F1156

164860 SMITH Mr Andrew. 20 Thornton Drive, Hoghton, Preston, Lancs, PR5 0LX. Tel:0254-854223 ALDEN BARKER BIRD BLOWERS BRETT BURROWS CATCHPOLE CHAPMAN COOK COOPER FRIEND LANKESTER Levet LEVETT Levitt MEADOWS OSBORNE PEASEY SHEPPARD SMITH WALTON WARD WOOD F5105

164879 SMITH Mr Anthony. 132 Brancaster Lane, Purley, Surrey, CR8 1HH. Tel:081-668-7794 ALFREY BALDING BENNETT BIRD BLANCHARD Blanched Blanshard BUDD BURTENSHAW CHAPMAN COLLIER COOPER DENDY FANNIPAT FORREST GORING Gorring GORRINGE GRAY Grey HAMMOND HARES HARMAN HEDGER HINKS HOLTORF JONES KENT LANCASTER LENTZ LIKEMAN LOVELL MERRETT MOGGE MORLEY PARKES ROBERTS SAVOURS SCHULTZ SCOVELL SMITH THARP WELLINGS WHEBLE WOODWARDS F2253

164887 SMITH Mr Antony. 12 Western Road, Henley On Thames, Oxon, RG9 1JL. Tel:0491-574668 BOWLEY BURGESS BUTLIN CHAPPELL COGGINS COLES DIXON FLETCHER GROVER HATHAWAY HAYLER LANGTON MCCLURE PANKHURST SLOTMAN STOCKLEY SWAIN TREACHER VAUX F1043

164895 SMITH Mr Aubrey. 27 New Coventry Road, Sheldon, Birmingham, B26 3BA. Tel:021-743-9527 BERRIDGE DUFFIN HARRIS HURST KENT LESSON ROBERTS SMITH Trueman TRUMAN F5844

164909 SMITH Mr B. 17 Cavendish Close, Lowestoft, Suffolk, NR32 3DU. BIRDE CHILD CHILDS DUDLEY EVANS FOY HINTON HUGHES MORETON MORTON OLNEY OSBORNE PALMER REYNOLDS SHIPMAN SHIPTON THICKBROOM TYLER WILLIS WOOD F6064

164917 SMITH Mrs Barbara. (Brown) 45 The Bryn, Trethomas, Newport, Gwent, NP1 8GP. BRADDON BROWN GREEN HOCKEN PHIPPS PUCKEY SMITH STACEY STEPHENS THOMAS F4608

164925 SMITH Mrs Beryl. 78 Roberta Drive, Christchurch, New Zealand 2. Tel:+64-03-332-1584 FILL VANT F1165

164933 SMITH Mrs C M P. (Papworth) 81 Westfield Avenue, Rushden, Northants, NN10 9RD. MILLARD PAPWORTH F1947

164941 SMITH Clive. Buildings Farm, Thorney Road, Newborough, Peterborough Cambs, PE6 7PT. Tel:0733-810212 COLLIER COLYER SMITH SMYTH F870

164968 SMITH Mr D & Mrs S. 242 Hawthorn Road, Bognor Regis, W Sussex, PO21 2UP. Tel:0243-828988 HASKELL HAYDEN Haydon Horn HORNE HUNT PRATT SMITH TREMAIN Tremaine Tremayne TRIBE Warbey Warboys Warby WORBEY WORBOYS Worby F1065

164976 SMITH Mr D J. 124 Stepehnson Way, Bourne, Lincs, PE10 9DD. ATKIN BANKS BARDSLEY BARLOW Beebe Beebey BEEBY BIRKIN BIRKS BROOKS Brownlee Brownley BROWNLOW BULL CHADWICK CHESTER CLAYTON Cockayn COCKAYNE CROMPTON DUROSE FRANKFIELD GALLEY GERVES GILDING GODBER GOODMAN GREGORY HALFORD Jarvis JERVIS KERSHAW KIRKBY MAYO MORAN MOSS Neal NEALE NEEDHAM ROSTRON SMITH TAGG TAYLOR THORNTON Tole Towl TOWLE Tull WHEATLEY WILLIAMS WINFIELD WRIGHT F3892

164984 SMITH Mrs D M. (Jones) 11 Hatfield Road, Southport, Merseyside, PR8 2PE. ARCHER GAUNT HIME JONES MACKINDER MATHEWS MILLER SKINNER STEWART WILKINSON F6309

164992 SMITH Mr David. 35 Oak Close, Copthorne, Crawley, West Sussex, RH10 3QT. ALGAR CLARINGBOULD DANDO DILKS DIVIANI DREW FARRENT KITE MEPSTED PAIN PIERCE READE REEVES SOWTEN STOAKES TORRANCE TOTTLE WELFORD WILLIAMS F5727

165018 SMITH Mrs Dianne. (Spence) 67 St Catherines Drive, Leconfield, N Humberside, HU17 7NU. Abbot ABBOTT ANDREW Andrews CAMP Champ CHARLTON FRYER Harneiss Harnes HARNESS

Harniss HARPER Holm Holme HOLMES Hume JACKSON SPENCE Teal TEALL WEST F5743

165026 SMITH Miss E A. 17 Green Close, Eastburn, Nr Keighley, West Yorks, BD20 8UX. Tel:0535-652991
BALDWIN EDMONDSON HODGSON MITCHELL NORRIS RAMSDEN REDMAN SHACKLETON SHAW SMITH WHEATLEY F4913

165034 SMITH Mr E. 6 Girton Close, Peterlee, Co Durham, SR8 2NF.
BROXHOLME CHARLTON EASEY EASY FLEURY FOWLER GLANVILLE HEASEY Heasie HEASY NEEL PEERS POWER SMITH VICKERS F2150

165042 SMITH Mr Earle K. 2 Hazel Drive, Horringer, Bury St Edmunds, Suffolk, IP29 5ST.
GOUGH LEMUNYAN PHIPPEN PINCKNEY TOBY F1801

165050 SMITH Mr Edward. 64 Blackshaw Lane, Royton, Oldham, Lancashire, OL2 6NR. Tel:0706-845219
SMITH WOOD F4865

165069 SMITH Mrs Elizabeth. 70 New Green Park, Wyken Croft, Coventry, CV2 1HS. Tel:0203-618419
BARNACLE TAYLOR F6409

165077 SMITH Mrs Elizabeth. (Singer) 6 Gordon Road, Kemnay, Inverurie, Aberdeen, AB5 9NB. Tel:0467-43378
SINGER F3633

165085 SMITH Mrs Elizabeth. 1 Sussex Close, Hoddesdon, Herts, EN11 8JS.
FAIRCHILD FITCH GILES MARTIN F855

165093 SMITH Mr F J & Mrs P E. 153 Upton Road, Moreton, Wirral, Merseyside, L46 0SQ.
FOXALL HUGHES KELLY LAWRENCE MITTON MORGAN NEWALL ROBERTS ROUND SMITH STEENTON THOMAS THOMASON WALL F4506

165107 SMITH Mrs Frances M. 14 Pitt Road, Maidstone, Kent, ME16 8PA.
COPE GURNEY JARVIS LIVERMORE PLATT RUTHERFORD SPILLETT WAKEFIELD WRIGHT F1071

165115 SMITH Mr Frank D. 10 Whitburn Close, Ladybridge, Bolton, Lancs, BL3 4UY. Tel:0204-655672
F439

165123 SMITH Mrs Freda. (Power) 234 Hoylake Crescent, Ickenham, Uxbridge, Middx, UB10 8JW.
BRUSH CHAPELL HARKNESS HAYMAN LEGASSICK Legassicke MARCHANT POWER F2177

165131 SMITH Mr G A. 14 Butler Road, Crowthorne, Berks, RG11 6QY. Tel:0344-773842
SMALLS Thecher TILNEY Tracher Traker Tratcher TREACHER Treker Tricker Troacher Trocker Trouchor F2603

165158 SMITH Mrs G M. 17 Tatton Lodge, Moorside, Knutsford, Cheshire, WA16 6JD. Tel:0565-650715
DAMP DAMPIER DEGGE GALE HEWITT JEANS LOVE ORCHARD PYE STIRRUP SWIFT F2469

165166 SMITH Mrs Gillian. 6 Seymour Close, Cox Green, Maidenhead, Berks, SL6 3EZ. Tel:0628-37942
SPARNON SPERNON F492

165174 SMITH Ms H. 6 The Limes, Spencer Gate, St Albans, Herts, AL1 4AJ. Tel:0727-42131
BOESE F339

165182 SMITH Mr I E. 11 Swanage Grove, Hart Station, Hartlepool, Co Durham, TS24 9RR.
ANMEAR BENNISON BORLEY COWHILL Cowull DAVISON DRYDEN FAVELL GILL JACQUES SMITH TURNER WILSON F3647

165190 SMITH Mr Irvine. 1 Anslow Lane, Rolleston On Dove, Staffs, DE13 9DS.
Bateson Battenson BATTINSON Battison Battisson Bettinson Bettison CONSTANTINE HODGSON Pattenson Pattinson Pattison TERRY F4960

165204 SMITH Mr J M. 1 Orchard Close, Preteigne, Powys, LD8 2HF. Tel:0544-267126
BARRAS PICKLES PIERREPONT ROOLEY SMITH TOWNROW F5834

165212 SMITH Mr J M. 10 Holmlea Road, Goring, Reading, RG8 9EX. Tel:0491-873218
BUTTERY CUSWORTH GODLEY LOWE PICKERING PLATT SEWELL SHIMELD SMITH STOKER F4558

165220 SMITH Mr J. 39 Newberry Road, Weymouth, Dorset, DT4 8LP. Tel:0305-783827
BANKS BULL HART MILLS SMITH SONE WALLER F4861

165239 SMITH Mr James E. Box 232, Thamesville, Ontario, NOP 2KO, CANADA.
GASTON HERBISON MCCURLIE MCKENZIE STEWART TURNER WILD WILSON F5498

165247 SMITH Mrs Jean. (Willis) 3 Greenfields Road, Wombourne, Staffs, WV5 0HP. Tel:0902-895938
Arkenstall Arkingstall Arkingston ARKINSTALL Arkinston Arkinstone Coger COGGER Couger Cougger Harkinstall Harkinstone MADELEY Madely ROGERS WILLIS F1176

165255 SMITH Mrs Jennifer. Avalon, Swan Lane, Edenbridge, Kent, TN8 6BA.
BAILEY BURRIDGE Haw HOARE Hore JENKINS JENNINGS ROOM SMITH Warr Weare Whore Woar Woare WOOR Woore F1669

165263 SMITH Mr Jim. 21 The Grove, Caterham, Surrey, CR3 5QD.
BAKER BARNES BERRY BROWNE COLE COLLINS COOKE DUNCAN GILBERT HAMMOND HEMSLEY HOLMWOOD HYDE JOHNSON LUCK MARTIN MICHEL PARKER ROGERS SMITH WICKENDEN F984

165271 SMITH Mrs Joan. 40 St Thomas Road, Chiswick, London, W4 3LD. Tel:081-994-7239
ATKINS BURLETON DANZEY HOPKINS JENKINS PALMER RIDGEWELL ROBERTS SMITH TOMLINS WARREN F1794

165298 SMITH Mrs K M. (Gilder) 47 Elmstone Drive, Tilehurst, Reading, Berks, RG3 5NS.
Aylett BREESE BYATT Eylett GILDER HUNT ILETT Ilette Ilott OSBORN Osborne PRIOR WILSON F4609

165301 SMITH Mrs M. 4 Winchester Drive, Brandon, Durham, DH7 8UG. Tel:091-378-9364
CLEASBY EDGAR ELLIOT HEATHERINGTON LAWS SMITH F196

165328 SMITH Mrs M. 25 Glastonbury Close, Stafford, ST17 0PB.
TURP Turps F6793

165336 SMITH Mr Malcolm D. 15 Ainslie Wood Gardens, Chingford, London, E4 9BL. Tel:081-524-2491
COLE FOSTER LINDSAY MCADAM MELLOR OAKFORD SMITH F1892

165344 SMITH Mr Malcolm. 6 The Sycamores, Vesey Close, Sutton Coldfield, W Midlands, B74 4QL.
BARTLETT BLYDE BLYTH BLYTHE BONEHAM COLLIER DRAPER INGRAM JONES LABRUM MARLOW SMITH WEST WORRALL F376

165352 SMITH Miss Margaret K M. 83 Harrow Way, Carpenders Park, Watford, Herts, WD1 5EH.
BROOK Brooke Brookes Brooks CROWHURST HAMPTON PARKER SMITH F3656

165360 SMITH Mrs Mary Helen Fenton. 2 Burford Close, Burford Green, Market Harborough, Leicestershire, LE16 9LF.
FENNER Fenteman Fenterman FENTIMAN Fentoman FENTON Fentyman SMITH VENTERMAN Ventyman F590

165379 SMITH Mr Merle. 1730 Cleveland Avenue, San Jose, CA 95126, USA. Tel:+1-408-292-5047
JOANES JOHNSON MCGREW WISEMAN F6289

165387 SMITH Mrs Monica. 76 New Road, Hadleigh, Benfleet, Essex, SS7 2RL.
COOLING GOODSON GRIFFIN MITCHELMORE SCALLEY SPELLER WAITE F3224

165395 SMITH Mrs Olive M. (Davis) 14 Fasach, Glendale, Isle Of Skye, IV55 8WP. Tel:047-081-278
ASTON COLEMAN DAVIS HERBERT KEENE PEDLEY THURSFIELD TOMLINSON WALLEY F2546

165409 SMITH Mr P. 6 Nuthatch, Longfield, Dartford, Kent, DA3 7NS.
SALLABANK Sallabanks F6964

165417 SMITH Mrs Pauline. (Oxley) 1730 Cleveland Avenue, San Jose, CA 95126, USA. Tel:+1-408-292-5047
ALLEN BOOTH EGGERS FULLER HEDGES NOLBLE OSGOOD OXLEY WARRINER WRIGHT F6288

165425 SMITH Mr R B M. 3 Holland Avenue, West Wimbledon, London, SW20 0RN. Tel:081-946-4938
Re'foy Re-Foy REFOY F2393

165433 SMITH Mr Ray. 65 Ashgrove Road, Horfield, Bristol, Avon, BS7 9LF.
BUFFERY BUFFREY BUFFRY BURRIS SILVERTHORN SILVERTHORNE SMITH F726

165441 SMITH Mr Robert. 4 Redman Grove, Sneyd Green, Stoke On Trent, ST6 2LS.
ALLEN BAVENHILL Benian Benion BENNION Benyen BENYON BOOTE BROUGHTON CADDY Dael Dail

DAINTRY DALE Deal DIMMOCK EMERY EWARDS GROCOTT GROOM HALLAM HARDING KEELING MADDOX MARE MARKLEW MAYER Mayor Mear Meyer NELSON PHILLIPS POOLE RAWSON SHENTON SMITH TAYLOR THOMA TOMPSON WALTERS WEBBER WHITAKER Whittaker WINKLE F1461

165468 SMITH Mr Roy. 132a Marlow Bottom, Marlow, Bucks, SL7 3PH. Tel:0628-476666
ALVIS ATKINSON BICKERDIKE BYERS HARRY JAMES MARSHALL PRICE SMITH THOMAS F1533

165476 SMITH Mr Royston Derek. 39 Trevale Road, Rochester Upon Medway, Kent, ME1 3NZ. Tel:0634-404988
Allingham BARBER BARDEN BELL BROAD BUBBERS DULY HALLINGHAM MACKAY MARSHALL PEAL SEAGER SHARP SMITH WARD F2836

165484 SMITH Mrs Sandra. 45 Meek Street, Dubbo, NSW 2830, AUSTRALIA. Tel:+61-6-882-8372
Badtemp BATEUP Batup Beatup Beleus Bellaies BELLAS Bellasse Bellis Belows BROWN BURTON CROSS DAVISON FISHBURN HALL Hardin Harten HARTIN Harton HARVEY Haughton HOLMES Horton HUCKEL Hutton Johnson Johnston Johnstone LATTER LINDLEY LOVE Madeleigh MADELEY Madely Madlee Madley Maidley Martin Richards RICHES RILEY Ritchies ROBINSON SALE TAYLOR Troath TROTH Trough WALKER WARING WILLIAMS WILSON F4693

165492 SMITH Mrs Sarah. Penhill Farm, Pendomer, Yeovil, Somerset, BA22 9PA.
ASHLING COWARD MAGGS MILLIS UNICUME WERE F4740

165506 SMITH Sheila. 3 The Cottages, Wymondham Road, Bunwell, Norwich, NR16 1NB.
Calcleugh CALDCLEUGH Caldeleugh Caldelough Cartclough Coldcleugh F1577

165514 SMITH Mr Sidney John. 37 Alspath Road, Meriden, Coventry, CV7 7LU.
CANNING COX CURTIS HAWKES HIORNS HUMFORD PARSONS F2044

165522 SMITH Mrs Stella. 72 Blackborough Road, Reigate, Surrey, RH2 7DF.
CHAPMAN CUBBON DRURY F2420

165530 SMITH Mr T M. 24a Ashford Road, Top Of Cul-De-Sac On Right, Swindon, Wilts, SN1 3NR.
ALWAY BAKER BERRY BIRD BRISTOW CHAMBERS CLOUGH COLE COOPE COTES CURNOCKE FRY GOLDING HARDMAN HARVEY HOOPER HOWLETT JAMES LEES LOMAX LONG LOYD MASKIL MAY MORSE NEAL NUTTALL PALMER POVEY PYKE SMITH TAVENDER WIGGINS WORKMAN F5306

165549 SMITHERAM Mrs J. 11 Barkworth Way, West Chiltington, Pulborough, West Sussex, RH20 2PQ.
BROCKENSHIRE BULLOCK CHAPMAN CROWL Crowle Gommo Goodge GOUDGE GUMMOW KENT PASCOE RANDALL RETALLICK RICHARDS ROBINS Rundle SMITHERAM SNELL THOMAS TONKIN TREGONING TRETHEWEY TRUSCOTT VIVIAN F4250

165557 SMURTHWAITE Mr Richard. 16 Grove Road, Worthing, Sussex, BN14 9DG. Tel:0903-212518
BALLARD LENG SMURFITT SMURTHWAITE F484

165565 SNAPE Mr Albert. Willow House, 122 Main Street, Thringstone, Coalville Leics, LE6 4NB.
KINGHT SNAPE SPRATTON-KNIGHT THOMPSON F340

165573 SNEE Mr Patrick. 73 Prestwick Road, Ayr, Scotland, KA8 8LQ. Tel:0292-284079
CARTY CLARK GRATTAN SNEE F5101

165581 SNELL Mr Rodger. 36 Manby Street, Lincoln, Lincs, LN5 8NW. Tel:0522-514035
BALMONT HAMPSON HERRICK RAY SHAW SNELL WARD WINTER F1183

165603 SNELLING Mrs Amanda J. (Richmond) 2 Roseleigh Cottages, Holland Lane, Oxted, Surrey, RH8 9AR.
ADAMSON APPLEBY ASHDOWN ASHTON ASQUITH BINKS BROOKE BULMER CHAPMAN CRAIG CUNLIFFE DOWSON GANDER HART HICKMAN HILLS LODGE RABBATTS REID RICHMOND SMALL SMITH SNELLING STRATTON SUTHERLAND SWINBURNE TAYLOR TEMPLE WILLOUGHBY F5942

165611 SNELSON Mr Adrian J. 40 Tennyson Avenue, Turramurra, NSW 2074, AUSTRALIA.
SNELSON F6914

165638 SNOW Dr Donald R. Department Of Mathematics, Brigham Young University, Provo, Utah 84602 Usa. Tel:+1-801-378-2366
Snaw SNOW Snowe F1664

165646 SNOW Mrs P M. Mayfield, Hinckley Road, Desford, Leics, LE9 9JE.
BAILISS DAVIS HORNBUCKLE JORDEN MANSELL PHIPPS PRYCE SAXON SNOW WOOD F6371

165654 SNOW Mrs Pauline. (Titt) Trem Y Foel, Aberhosan, Machynlleth, Powys, SY20 8RA.
BULLIN BUTLER CABLE CHAMBERLAIN DONOHUE GONEY HALL HODGE PALMER SMITH SNOW TAYLOR THOMPSON TITT WEEKS WHITTAKER WILSON F4668

165662 SNOWDEN Mr Frederick N. 72 Patching Hall Lane, Chelmsford, Essex, CM1 4DB. Tel:0245-353450
BICKLEY BRINSFORTH CARTER DALTON HOBSON KAY SNOWDEN WARDLE F4816

165670 SNYDER Mrs D. 610 S Tanglewood Drive, Springfield, OH 45504, USA.
SUGG F7032

165689 SOBEY Mr Peter. 511 Bath Road, Saltford, Bristol, BS18 3HQ.
BROWN EVANS HARE HERLEY HILL SCHALLER Sobee SOBEY Sobie Soby Sobye F4029

165697 SOLE Mr F T W. 17 Hyholmes, Bretton, Peterborough, Cambs, PE3 8LG. Tel:0733-261234
BEESLEY BODEN BOSWORTH ELLIOTT FULLER GABRIEL HOWARD JUDD MULLENOX NICHOLSON OVERALL PATE SOLE THOMPSON TRAFFORD F4339

165700 SOLES J E W. 301 Lutterworth Road, Nuneaton, Warks, CV11 6PW.
LEEDHAM SOLES Soules F7418

165719 SOLMAN Mr David. 68 Greenway Close, Friern Barnet, London, N11 3NT.
LODDIGES F5868

165727 SOLOMONS Mr Norman H. 15 Manor Avenue, Kidderminster, Worcs, DY11 6EA. Tel:0562-751896
COONEY DAVIS DONAVAN ISAACS JACOBS MEISLER RABIN SOLOMON Solomons F2320

165735 SOLOMONS Mrs Veronica A. 15 Manor Avenue, Kidderminster, Worcs, DY11 6EA. Tel:0562-751896
BARTLETT Boddy BODY COLE COLLEY DAVEY GRIFFIN HOBBS MOSS OLIVER PEAGAM POLLARD RENDLE TUCKER WILLIAMS F2285

165743 SOPER Mr P. Parsons Close, Oakham Road, Tilton On The Hill, Leicester, LE7 9DJ. Tel:053-754-267
GOSNALD GOSNOLD JOHNSON Soaper Soapper SOPER Sopper F2788

165751 SORRELL Mr Geoffrey A. 26 Coppice Close, Chase Terrace, Walsall, Staffs, WS7 8BJ. Tel:0543-684340
ASHTON HARVEY SORRELL STATHAM F4941

165778 SORTWELL Mr Andrew. 10 Constable Walk, Woodford, Kettering, Northants, NN14 4EZ.
SALTWELL SORTWELL F770

165786 SOULSBY Mr Bill. 44 Ripon Gardens, Jesmond, Newcastle Upon Tyne, NE2 1HN.
DUFFAUT MESSENGER SOULSBY THOMPSON F3422

165794 SOUTAR Mrs J. 247 Uxbridge Road, Hampton Hill, Middx, TW12 1AS.
STEER Thomas Tomas Tomes TOMS F6019

165808 SOUTHAM Mrs Noelle. 8 Bindon Close, Parkstone, Poole, Dorset, BH12 4DS. Tel:0202-730007
LE QUEUX MILLS PADBURY Sotham Sothams Sotheran Sothern Sotherne Sothoran Souden SOUTHAM Southan Southarn Southart Southen Southham Southin Southon Southorn Southorne Southoun Southran Southren Southron Southurn Southwell Souton Soutten Sowtan Sowtharn Sowthern Sowton Sowtun Sutham Suthern Sutherns Suthers Suthon Suthorn Sutton F1488

165816 SOUTHERN Mrs C I. 86 Mill Lane, Churchtown, Southport, Merseyside, PR9 7PE.
Yeaman Yeamon YEOMAN F6706

165824 SOUTHERN Mrs Rosemary. (Hale) 54 Hillcrest Drive, Southdown, Bath, Avon, BA2 1HE. Tel:0225-315720
ALLEN ANDREW AUSTIN BARLOW BEDDOWES BEER BIRCHALL BLAKEMAN BRUCE CAMERON COX DAVEY DICKETTS Follan Folland Follen Follin FOLLON FORBES FORD FRASER GAISFORD GRAY GREENWAY GUILDFORD HALE HAYWOOD Horrall Horrell

Horrill HORROLL JOHNSON JORDAN MACDONALD MARTIN MATTHEWS MOLYNEUX NEWMAN OSBORNE PHIPPEN PRICE SAINSBURY SOUTHERN Sprig Sprigg SPRIGGS Sprigs STEPHENS WALTON Wavin Weavin WEAVING F3128

165832 SOUTHEY Mr E A. Brambles, 3 Latimer Road, New Barnet, Herts, EN5 5NU. Tel:081-440-3741
Southay Southee SOUTHEY Southy Sowthe Sowthy F3122

165840 SOUTHEY Mrs Valerie. 6 Cambridge Road, Salisbury, Wiltshire, SP1 3BW.
EVANS HARLE SOLOMAN STUCKEY F1416

165859 SOUTHIN Mrs Pamela J. (Allan) Loganberry Cottage, 33 Conger Lane, Toddington, Beds, LU5 6BT. Tel:05255-3788
ALLAN AYLESWORTH BRENT GAMPBELL Hawkins HILL HOPKINS O'NEIL OSBORNE PIGGINS ROUTLEY Routly F3698

165867 SOUTHIN Mr Steven B. Loganberry Cottage, 33 Conger Lane, Toddington, Bedfordshire, LU5 6BT. Tel:05255-3788
BANNOCK ELLIS Ginman GREGORY JANMAN Southey SOUTHIN Sowethee VAUGHAN F3697

165875 SOUTHWELL Mrs Eileen M. 50 Deutscher Street, Avondale Heights, Victoria, 3034, AUSTRALIA.
SOUTHWELL F6906

165883 SOUTHWORTH Mr Edwin. 3 Larch Grove, Bamber Bridge, Preston, Lancs, PR5 6GX.
BROMLEY SOUTHWORTH TURNER WELCH F539

165891 SOUTHWORTH Mrs Pam. (Herring) The Bungalow, Cannister Lane, Gipsey Bridge, Boston, Lincs, PE22 7HD.
BENNETT HERRING SPRIDGEN TOYNE WHITE WOODCOCK F6036

165905 SOUTTER Mr Elwyn. 60 Artlone Road, Randalstown, Co Antrim, BT41 3HX, NORTHERN IRELAND.
Soutar Souter Souttar SOUTTER Sowter Suter F6540

165913 SOWTER Mr R A. 2 Hill House Road, Downend, Bristol, BS16 5RR.
SOWTER F6588

165921 SPACKMAN Mr Gordon W. 18 Whilestone Way, Swindon, Wiltshire, SN3 4HS.
SPACKMAN Spakman Speckman WEBB F6022

165948 SPACKMAN Mrs Linda. 27 Keats Road, Banbury, Oxon, OX16 9QY.
BISHOP CHESTER HUMPHREY PETCH PITTAM Polentine Polintine Polinton Pollendine Pollentine Pollindyne Pollington POLLINTINE Polyngton F2811

165956 SPARROW Mr Robert Arthur. 48 Lloyd Road, Worcester Park, Surrey, KT4 8SA. Tel:081-337-4204
HARCUS ROBBINS SPARROW F4292

165964 SPATHAKY Mr Mike. 9 Fairstone Hill, Oadby, Leicester, LE2 5RL. Tel:0533-713494
BOLSOVER CREE MONTAGUE F4958

165972 SPAUGHTON Mr Bernard. 8 Aragon Avenue, Ewell, Surrey, KT17 2QG.
BACHELOR BORNE BROCK BROWNSTON BURGESS COLVERD DELVE DORAN DOWNEY DREW HEANES HOLMES LEE MACKEY MOORE MORTIMER PARTRIDGE PHILIP PHILLIPS ROLLESTONE SAPSFORD SHUTE SPAUGHTON STRIDE TREMLETT WAY WHITELEY WILCOCKS F12

165980 SPAUGHTON Mrs C. 30 George Street, Fenny Stratford, Bletchley, Milton Keynes, MK2 2NR.
BARTON CARD Carde CORNFORD FOSTER HONEYGETT HOOK Hooke LEWIS PETTER POCOCK PONTING Venes VENESS VENICE Venus F208

165999 SPAWTON Mrs Eirlys. Honeysuckle Cottage, Cotham, Newark, Notts, NG23 5JT.
ADLAM AILWORTH ARCHER ASHER ATKINSON AUSTEN BADCOCK BAILEY BAKER BALDWIN BARNARD BARNES BATE BAXTER BELLAMY BENTLEY BETTESS BLABER BRAND BROOK BROOKING Brooks BROOM BURLEY BURRUP BURTON CALCROFT CASTELL CHAPMAN CHARLES CHILD Childe CLARK CLEMENTS COLE Coles CROOM Croome CROSSMAN CUFFE DEAR DICKSON DIXON DOVE DREW EDGE ELLIOTT EMERY FERRIS FIRMIN FOOTITT FORDS FOWLER FOX FRANCOMB GLANCEY GROVE GUYON HALL HAMMOND HANCER HANDLEY HANSON HEDGECOCK HICKS HILL HITCHCOCK HOLE HOPKINS HORRELL HOUGH HUNT HURN INGRAM INNALL JEFFREY Jeffreys JENKINS JOHNS JOHNSON KELLAND KILLEN KILLINGBECK LEE LEWTY LICKFOLD LUDCOCK LUMBER LUTY MACKERNES Maquernes MEREDITH MILLS MITCHELL MOORE NICHOLSON ORTON OSBORNE OUGHTON PEATE PETRE PIERCY POLLEY PONTING PRESTON PRICE PRIDE PURNELL QUEENSBOROG RATH RAWLINS SADLER SAYER Sayers SELF SHORT SINGLETON SLADE SMEDLEY Spaldon Spalton Sparkes SPARKS SPAWTON Spolton STARKEY STUBBS TEBBUT THEEDAM THEOBALD THOMAS THOMPSON TILL Tilley TILLY TOVEY TRENEMAN VOWLES WAIT Waite WATKINS WETHERLY WHITCHURCH Willis WILLS WITHERLEY WRATH F3080

166006 SPEAKE Mr John. 211 Milton Road, Cambridge, CB4 1XG. Tel:0223-423974
Spake Spate Speak SPEAKE Speakes Speaks Specke Speecke Speke Spoake F4261

166014 SPEAR Arzella Brashear. Box 603, Bedford, TX 76095, USA.
BRASHEAR F7243

166022 SPEAR Mr Peter J W. 58 Gally Hill Road, Church Cookham, Aldershot, Hants, GU13 0RU.
BAKER DAUNT DAVID DAVIS ETHERIDGE FULJAMBE JEPSON KNIGHT MIGNON ODDY OGDEN SPEAR TICKNER TUFFNELL WRIGHT F3177

166030 SPEET Mr John B. 16 Blantyre Street, Winton, Eccles, Gt Manchester, M30 8HY. Tel:061-789-8398
DOBSON HURST LIVESEY LONGSWORTH SPEATE SPEET SPEIGHT F2114

166049 SPEIRS Mrs Charlotte B H. (Sellar) 15 Cairnview Crescent, Aberdeen, AB2 5DR.
FERGUSON FORBES Fories Forist Forister FORREST FRASER HAMILTON MACDONALD Macintosh Mackintosh MANSON Mcdonald MCINTOSH Mintie MINTY Mouat MOWAT Mowatt RIACH Rosey ROSIE Rosy Rozie SELLAR SUTHERLAND F4606

166057 SPENCE Mrs W. 17 Prince Charles Crescent, Scremeston, Berwick Upon Tweed, TD15 2RH.
Hawkard Hawkhead HAWKYARD F6617

166065 SPENCER Mrs Barbara Ann. (Bowdler) 26 Westbury Road, Heath Farm, Shrewsbury, Shropshire, SY1 3HW.
BOWDLER F1067

166073 SPENCER Mrs Barbara E. (Roberts) Oak Cottage, 43 Dargate Road, Yorkletts, Whitstable, Kent, CT5 3AD. Tel:0227-273074
BARROW BRADLEY DAVIS FRENCH GRANVILLE LYNCH O'RIELLY OREILLY ROBERTS SPENCER WALKER F851

166081 SPENCER Mr Christopher John. 17 Black Bull Lane, Fulwood, Preston, Lancs, PR2 3PT. Tel:0772-717275
ADAMS BOYLE FIELDING GRIME HALLIWELL HATKILL JACKMAN KELBRICK MAGSON MCGREAVY MOORBY MOORES MOTTRAM MURPHY NEWSHAM SPENCER SQUIRE TAYLOR TOOBY WALKER WILSON F4529

166103 SPENCER Mr Garry Brian. Merrihaven, Rebels Lane, Great Wakering, Essex, SS3 0QE. Tel:0702-586595
BEETHAM BEETON BUNTING GODING HOLT JACQUES PRESTON SPENCER WILKES F2869

166111 SPENCER Mrs Jennifer. Clovelly House, 113 London Road, Bozeat, Northants, NN9 7JR.
BERRIL DRAGE HAYNES LINE MALIN PARTRIDGE PETTIT ROBERTS SPENCER WARREN F1819

166138 SPENCER Mrs M M. (Holland) 2 Juniper Court, Neal Close, Northwood, Middx, HA6 1TJ.
BOARDMAN Crosland CROSSLAND DALGLESH HOLLAND F848

166146 SPENCER Mr Raymond. 72 Oakleigh Park Drive, Leigh On Sea, Essex, SS9 1RS.
BUSHELL MARRIOTT MARSHALL PARKER SPENCER TUCKWOOD F4359

166154 SPENCER Mr Tony. 10 Dumas Close, Yateley, Camberley, Surrey, GU17 7XZ. Tel:0252-870695
BANNISTER BIRD BRYANT COOPER DIVAL HOLLAND LEVINS LUFFMAN MATTHEWS MAYTUM MULLINDER STAMP TOLHURST TULLY WAKEFORD F2544

166162 SPENDLOVE Mr D H. 35 Sutton Park Avenue, Colchester, Essex, CO3 4SX.
SPENDLOVE F6687

166170 SPICER Mrs Mary. (Truin) 108 Osborne Road, New Milton, Hants, BH25 6AA. Tel:0425-612227
HENDY KINCHIN PLAYFOOT READER SPICER Splayfoot TRUIN VERNEY WRIGHT F5412

166189 SPICER Mrs V. (Craig) 2 Ash Grove, Harefield, Middx, UB9 6EU. Tel:0895-822446

ANDERSON ASHTON BAILEY BURROWS COX CRAIG DRINKWATER GOODYEAR HANSTEAD HERBERT HINTON HUTCHINGS JOHNSON KELLY MONTAGU MONTAGUE PLUMBRIDGE SMITH SPICER TRUMPER WILKINSON WILLMOTT WOODBRIDGE F6230

166197 SPIERS Miss Doris. 40 Plymouth Road, Stirchley, Birmingham, B30 2PD. Tel:021-459-5549
CARTER CRESSE CLARA DANIELS DAVIS DUTTON FITTON GALE GREENING HAMPTON HARPER HAWKER HEWINGS INGRAM IRONS KITCHINGS NEWMAN ROBERTS SHERWOOD SPIERS Spire SPIRES WEBB YEATES F5314

166200 SPIERS Mr James William. 42 Pendragon Road, Perry Barr, Birmingham, B42 1RN.
HOBBS SPIERS F6430

166219 SPIERS Miss S M. 27 Woodend Drive, Aberdeen, AB2 6YJ.
RIVER Rivers Ryver Ryvers Speir Speirs Spier SPIERS Spire Spires Spyer Spyers Spyre Spyres F6989

166227 SPILLER Mrs M J. 29 Gainsborough Court, Station Avenue, Walton On Thames, Surrey, KT12 1NH.
Poke Poock POOK Pooke F6930

166235 SPINK Mr Reginald. 6 Deane Way, Eastcote, Ruislip, Middx, HA4 8SU. Tel:081-866-6899
ACKRELL APPLEYARD BRADLEY NEWBOLD SPINK STURDY WRIGHT F6257

166243 SPINKS Mr William Hugh. 48 Durrington Lane, Worthing, West Sussex, BN13 2QU. Tel:0903-61546
BELL BRIDGER BUDD HARBER HEDGER HOLLAND KITCHEN-HEDGER KNELL LUCKHURST MARTIN PHARON REEVE SMALE Spinckes Spincks SPINK Spinkes SPINKS VALLER WATERS F1580

166251 SPITTAL Mr Charles Jeffrey. The Shieling, 162 Church Road, Frampton Cotterell, Bristol, BS17 2ND.
Spitell SPITTAL Spittall Spittle Spittles Spitull Spytell Spyttle Spytull Spytyll F2594

166278 SPONG Mr & Mrs G S. Tilehurst, 98 Fairfield Drive, Dorking, Surrey, RH4 1JJ.
KNOWLES Nolls Nowles Spon SPONG Sponge Spoung Spounge F7104

166286 SPOONER Mrs Alison M. (Kirkwood) Pine View, Tow Path, Shepperton, Middx, TW17 9LL.
KIRKWOOD F2444

166294 SPOORS Mr Gerald. 10 Bewley Grove, Oakerside Park, Peterlee, Co Durham, SR8 1PP. Tel:091-586-3905
ELLIOT HUNTER MAUGHAM SPOORS WILSON F6440

166308 SPRATLEY Mr Rodney. Flat 1, 7 Westwood Road, Southampton, Hants, SO2 1DL.
SPRATLEY F5759

166316 SPRATT Mr Clive. 426 Baddow Road, Great Baddow, Chelmsford, Essex, CM2 9RB.
ANSON BAKER BARKER BOULTON BROOK CANDY COPSEY CRUSE FUNNELL GOODING HAYWOOD NORMAN POUNCEY SMITH SOMERWELL SOUTHCOMBE SPRATT STEVENS F2879

166324 SPRIET Maurice. 4 Rue Honore De Balzac, 59960 Neuville En Ferrain, FRANCE.
SPRIET F7367

166332 SPRINGATE Mr B A. 24 Salisbury Road, Hove, East Sussex, BN3 3AE.
SPRINGATE Springett F7175

166340 SPRINGFORD Mr G T C. 30 Parklawn Avenue, Epsom, Surrey, KT18 7SL.
Springbat Springbatt Springbett SPRINGFORD F7184

166359 SPRY Mr J W. 5 St Teilos Way, Watford Farm Estate, Caerphilly, Mid Galmorgan, CF8 1FA.
BASKERFIELD HENTON JORDAN POWELL REYNOLDS ROBLIN SEECOMBE SIMPSON Spray Sprey SPRY THOMAS WAKELY WOODLEY F5972

166367 SPURR Mr B P. 70 Hunters Way, Durban North, Natel, SOUTH AFRICA.
Spor Spur SPURR Spurre F7024

166375 SQUIRE Mr David M. 2 St Stephens Avenue, Ealing, London, W13 8ES.
Blatnauer Blatner CRUWYS EASTMOND HUXTABLE PARKHURST Platmaner Platnancer PLATNAUER Platner POWNEY SILVERSTON SMITH Sockburn SQUIRE Stockborn Stockborne Stockbourn Stockbourne STOCKBURN F478

166383 SQUIRES Mrs Mona. (Wright) 6705 Lotus St, Reno, Nevada, 89506, USA. Tel:+1-702-972-7945
BARKER BARTON HOMER HOOPER LETTON LYTTON PAVEY SCRANAGE SQUIRES WRIGHT F4136

166391 STABLER Mr I C. 22 Fernwood Close, Brompton, Northallerton, North Yorkshire, DL6 2UX.
FAMILTON PUNSHON Stabeler Stabelor STABLER Stabley Stablor Stabulor Steabler Wainman WAYMAN F5311

166405 STACEY Mr Geoffrey. 46 Ashdene Road, Withington, Manchester, M20 9RZ. Tel:061-445-1091
HESLING F1960

166413 STACEY Mr Kenneth. Wildwood, 122 Queens Road, Walton On Thames, Surrey, KT12 5LL. Tel:0932-220265
STACEY Staci Stacy Stasey Stasy F2004

166421 STACEY Miss Marjorie. 34 Ambleside Close, Thingwall, Wirral, L61 3XQ. Tel:051-648-4554
BELLAMY Broham BROUGHAM Browgham Browham Browholme FOSBERY PALLETT F57

166448 STACEY Mr R & Mrs G. 20 The Croft, Cocking, Midhurst, Sussex, GU29 0HQ.
ABURROW LANE ROWE SIMPSON STACEY SWALLOW TERRY F254

166456 STACK Mr Clive. 85 Chester Road South, Kidderminster, Worcs, DY10 1XF.
COYNE OLNER STACK F2658

166464 STACK Mrs Marilyn. 26 Garfield Street, Kettering, Nothants, NN15 6BU. Tel:0536-516369
BAYLEY BOND BONELL BOTT BROMLEY BUTTERWORTH CRADDOCK GOODIER GOUGH HALL HARLEY HARVEY HITCHENER HODDY HUNT HUTCHINGS KENINGALE MORGAN OAKLEY RENDER RUSH TUNNICLIFFE WALDRON WILSON WOODWARD F2528

166472 STAFFORD Mr James. 4 Bradley Hall Cottage, Bradley Hall Farm, Grappenhall, Warrington, WA4 4SL. Tel:0925-754383
STAFFORD Stafforde Staford Staforde Stefford Stifford Stofford Stratford F3652

166480 STAINER Mr Lloyd. Crookham, Field Dalling Road, Bale, Fakenham, Norfolk, NR21 0QS. Tel:0832-878017
Briand BRIARD Briart DE LA HAYE Delahay Delahaye Diamond Dimand Dimmond DIMOND JARVIS LE RICHE Leriche QUERIPEL STAINER Stanier Stayner Steiner Stenner WOODMAN F3577

166499 STAMPS Ms Helen. (Paty) 1280 Lake Stone Lea Drive, Oxford, Georgia, 30267, USA. Tel:+1-404-786-3176
BEHENNA BREAY HARBOURNE HEAD PATY F4449

166502 STANBRIDGE Mrs Daphne. (Longland) Alandale, 6 Buckland Road, Lower Kingswood, Tadworth, Surrey, KT20 7DP.
HAM LONGLAND F5235

166510 STANDISH-HAYES Mr D G. Little Short Close, Shaw Green Lane, Prestbury, Cheltenham, Glos, GL52 3BP. Tel:0242-574100
BURLTON CARR COCHRAM Cockram GOFF Gough HAYES MORTIMER SWEET F2925

166529 STANDRING Mr B. 121, Wentworth Road, Harborne, Birmingham, B17 9SU.
Standering Standrin STANDRING F7115

166537 STANIER Dr Alan M. 24 Chaplain Drive, Colchester, Essex, CO4 3EA.
ADAMS BERRIMAN BONAS CLIFT KIMBER LEHAIR READ SKIPPER STANIER WHITEHOUSE F70

166545 STANILAND Mrs M G. (Chaffe) 30 St Peters St, Stamford, Lincs, PE9 2PF.
BOWERMAN CHAFFE RICE F6156

166553 STANLEY Mrs Adeline. (Netcott) 24 Greenford Close, Orrell, Wigan, Lancs, WN5 8RH. Tel:0695-632844
MILES Natcott NETCOTT NORRIS PAYNE PRINCE STANLEY F5877

166561 STANLEY Mr David H. The Priests House, Eastwell, Melton Mowbray, Leics, LE14 4EL. Tel:0949-60463
ASHER DERRICK FIELDING FOLLOWS HULL SAVAGE SHEPPARD STANLEY THORNHILL WOOD WRIGHT F5211

166588 STANLEY Mr Douglas George. 58 Quorn Gardens, Leigh On Sea, Essex, SS9 2TB. Tel:0702-557181
RUSSELL STANLEY F4618

166596 STANLEY Mr I H. Spring Cottage, 47 Corser Street, Old Swinford, Stourbridge W

Midlands, DY8 2DE.
DAVIDSON POWERS STANLEY WIELD WILLMOTT F757

166618 STANTON Mrs Corrine R. 9 Dace, Dosthill, Tamworth, Staffs, B77 1NT.
Yearl YEARLE Yerl Yerle F6820

166626 STANTON Mrs D. 94 Everton Road, Hordle, Lymington, Hants, SO41 0FD. Tel:0425-619427
STANTON F5778

166634 STAPLES Mr Peter. 3 The Mews, Hamilton Road, Reading, Berks, RG1 5RA. Tel:0734-662701
BOWTLE COLLINS COOK PATRICK STAPLES WELLS F4804

166642 STAPLEY Mrs M. (Kemp) Chalkwood, Southfleet Avenue, Longfield, Kent, DA3 7JG. Tel:0474-703512
ADAMS AUSTIN BALDY Bax BELL BELSON BENTLEY BISHOPPS BLACKLOCKS BLASKET BOX BROWNE BROWNING CHANDLER CHURCH CLEMENS Clements CROFTS CULLEN DANIELS Dobble Dobell Double DUBLE DUKE EARL ELGAR ESSEX FAGG FREEMAN FRIEND FULLER GANN GARDINER GIBBS GILES GREENLAND HEARN HOBBS HOLMAN HOLMES HOOKER HOPPER HOWLAND Humphreys HUMPHRIES JORDAN JOY KEMP KNIGHT LEWIS NIXON NORRINGTON PACKING PAY PETTIT PHILLIPS PILCHER PRICE REEVES REYNOLDS SAINT SAUNDERS SAVAGE SHARPE SMIDDITT Smithet STAPLEY SWINERD Swinnard Swinyard Swynnyard TERRY TRITTON TURNER WALLACE WARDEN WARE Warlow WATSON Whollo WHORLOW WIGMORE WILKINS WOODHAMS WORGER F2520

166650 STAPLEY Mrs Shirley. 5 Quarry Park Road, Peverell, Plymouth, Devon, PL3 4LW. Tel:0752-224569
CANN GILLEY GLANVILLE HANNAFORD JEWELL ODNEE PENGILLEY POPHAM STAPLEY WILLIAMS F2224

166669 STARKEY Mr A. 28 Bishops Way, Meltham, Huddersfield, HD7 3BW.
STARKEY Starkie Starky F6934

166677 STARKS Mr & Mrs R W. 8 Juniper Road, Bitterne, Southampton, Hampshire, SO2 4EH.
ARFMAN CASH CRICK GLADDIS GRIST LLOYD ROBERTS STARKS THOMAS F2956

166685 STARR Mrs Sylvia. 3 Gaywood House, North Street, Bedminster, Bristol, BS3 3BA.
ASHFORD BARRETT Brown BROWNE CHANT Chaunt GOLD INGLIS Neades NEADS Needs Plumbly PLUMLEY Plumly PORCH Portch RACEY REED STARR VIRGIN WHITE F2394

166693 STARTUP Miss Stancy J. Po Box 275, Masterton, NEW ZEALAND.
STARTUP F6905

166707 STEANE Miss Sheila. 50 Lawford Lane, Bilton, Rugby, Warks, CV22 7JS.
BALDWIN CHURCH Eales HALES Hayles Hosborn LESTER LOWE NEAL OSBORN Osborne Stean STEANE WALTON WELLS F3474

166715 STEBBENS Mr Carl. 10 Shetland Close, Edgbaston, Birmingham, B16 0RF. Tel:021-455-8783
Stebben STEBBENS Stebbin Stebbing Stebbings Stebbins WARRAD WARWOOD WHARRAD Wharrod WHORWOOD WORRAD WORROD F1302

166723 STEDMAN Mr J R. Barn Cottage, 5 Middle Street, Brockham Green, Betchworth Surrey, RH3 7JT.
AITKEN ALEXANDER ANDERSON BAXTER BEDFORD BENNETT Boneface Boneyface BONIFACE Bonniface Bridon BRYDON CAVERS CHAPMAN Christoffer Christopher Christophers COCK COLEMAN CREWS Cruse Cruwys DABBS DEVERELL FENWICK FIDDES FIELD FREELAND GOLDSMITH GOODMAN HEWARD HOLLOBON JEFFREY KEMPSEY Kemsey KIRK LINE LISTER Lyne MATTHEWS MCBRIDE MCDOUGAL MCLURE MITCHELL PASCOVY PAWSON POLSON Poulson RENWICK SHEPERD SHERWOOD SIMMONDS STACE STEDMAN TAPLEY THORPE TICKNER WARD WICKERS WOODS F1899

166731 STEED Mr David. Spratling Court Farm, Manston, Ramsgate, Kent, CT12 5AN.
STEED F562

166758 STEEL Mr Don. Brooking, Jarvis Lane, East Brent, Highbridge Somerset, TA9 4HS.
BEER BISKET BROOKING CURRIE FERGIE GARDNER GOODMAN HARVEY HARVIE HONEYCOMBE JENNER KITCHENER MITCHELL NORRIS PEPPERELL PROWSE SOLE STEEL WALDOCK F657

166766 STEEL Mrs Phyllis. 38 Station Road, Steeton, Keighley, W Yorks, BD20 6RY.
BROWN HOTCHKISS TUDOR F264

166774 STEELE Mrs C A. 47 Barlows Road, Tadley, Basingstoke, Hants, BD8 0AD.
DIBDEN Dibdon Diffden Dirdin F6949

166782 STEELE Ms Joan. (Beckingham) 65 Ford Road, Lesmurdie, WA 6076, AUSTRALIA.
BECKINGHAM FALCONER FORBES KIMMER MILNE SMITH STEELE THOMSON WHITEBREAD F5517

166790 STEENMEIJER Mr Johan A A. 38 Rock Grove, Brighton, East Sussex, BN2 1ND. Tel:0273-696206
MCCOLL MCEVOY PALMER F6344

166804 STEER Mr Christian. Woodland View, The Ridge, Cold Ash, Newbury, Berks, RG16 9JB.
ADAMS ALDERMAN ANNETS AYERS BEDWELL BEECHEY BINKS BROWN BRUAN CARPENTER CARTER CARVEY Carvy Cavey Cavy CHAMBERLAIN COLLINGWOOD COOLEY COOPER COWLEY CREW CUMMINS EARWOOD EMMONS EPPS FAR FOREMAN FOX FREESTONE GIDDENS Giddings GIDDINS GILES GOODCHILD GRACE GRALE GRINGLE HANKS HENSELL HOPKINS HUDSON KITE KNOWLER LAPPER LOVEGROVE LOVELOCK MASE MILES MOULDER NICHOLS PENCOTT PORTER POUND PRESTON PUSHLEY RANSLEY SMITH SNATT SPANTON Spenton STEEL Steele STEER SWAN TAYLOR TEAL TERRY VICKERY WALCRAFT WHALE WHITE WOODEN F699

166812 STEER Mrs Sylvia. (Cleary) 344 Lower Luton Road, Wheathampstead, St Albans, Herts, AL4 8JQ.
ASHLEY BEAL BELL BLETCHER CARBERRY CHELL CLEARY COATES COLLS CONNOLY CORRIGAN CROW FENWICK FINCHETT HAMER HARDCASTLE HENRY HOLMES HOUGHTON HUNTER MOORES SHAW TRIBECK F4017

166820 STEGGLES Mr Keith. 22 Godwin Walk, Ryehill Estate, Northampton, NN5 7RW.
BLACKWELL DUFFETT Holmewood Holmwood HOMEWOOD Homwood JARVIS Steggalls Steggells STEGGLES Stigals Stygals Stygles Wardell WARDIELL Wardle WELLMAN Welman F5041

166839 STEIB Mr William H. 4116 Water Oak Place, Virginia Beech, VA 23452, USA.
ALLEN AMBLER BINNS BOLTON GANT LEACH PICKLES RIDDIOUGH TORDOFF F6546

166847 STEINBACK Mrs Beverley A. 149 Anzac Avenue, Redcliffe, Queensland, 4020, AUSTRALIA. Tel:+61-7-283-3056
ANDERSON BLAKE BLAND BRADSHAW Cornwall CORNWELL FROOD Frood Froud Froude Fround HORLER HOWARD-OSBORNE HUNTLEY LUMBER MCDONALD Osborn OSBORNE Osbourn Osbourne PARKIN POLLARD Ridsdall Ridsdell RIDSDILL Risdall Risdell RUTLEY WILSON WINTER F4495

166855 STENHOUSE Mrs Anne. 47 Peartree Close, Anstey, Leicester, LE7 7TD. Tel:0533-363977
ADAMS CRINKLEY GOLDING HARDING MILLS STAFFORD TARRY TIPLER WHITEHEAD F2047

166863 STENNER Mrs Virginia. (Laurie) Clashaidy, 20 Heatherdown Road, West Moors, Ferndown, Dorset, BH22 0BY. Tel:0202-891275
ANTELL BARR BOYES BRADLEY BRUNT BUCK BURGES BURGESS CARWELL COOMBES CURTIS DAMPNEY DRY FOXALL FULLER FURNELL GAINES GILMORE GODWIN HARVIE HOUSE JOY JUKES LARNEY LAURIE LOCKE MCCANN MCPHAIL MITCHELL MOODY PACKMAN PATTEN PIERCE POLLENDINE SADLER SHANNON STENNER TRIM WEAVER WEEKS WOODGER F5830

166871 STEPHEN Mrs Alison J. Newhaven, 16 Jill Court, Ringwood, Victoria, 3134, AUSTRALIA.
Hickin HOCKING F6945

166898 STEPHENS Mr B. 1 Wade Close, Eastbourne, E Sussex, BN23 6AW. Tel:0323-639321
BLAKE BOFF Boof BRETT BULT CHINNOCK HANKEY HOSIER JONES Llewelin Llewellin LLEWELLYN Llewelyn PHILLIPS PITTARD ROBINSON STEPHENS Tocker Toker TUCKER WATTS F6393

166901 STEPHENS Mr Paul N M. 22 Voss Park Drive, Llantwit Major, South Glamorgan, CF6 9YE.
BARNES BLEWITT GRIFFITHS JONES MORGAN PEARSON ROGERS STEPHENS F4777

166928 STEPHENSON Mr Martin. 3 Eden Close, Witham, Essex, CM8 1LA. Tel:0376-513202
ALDEN BINNING DAWSON FLUX HARRISON MASLIN STEPHENSON SULLIVAN F6005

166936 STEPHENSON Mr Robert G. 1142 Pine Bluff Avenue, Point Pleasant, NJ 08742, USA. Tel:+1-908-899-4422
DIXON DUNBABIN STEPHENSON F4398

166944 STEPTOE Mr Michael John. 46 Seaforth Grove, Southend On Sea, Essex, SS2 4EW. Tel:0702-611677
STEPTOE F3105

166952 STERRY Mrs Cecily. (Boswell) Watergate House, Upper Basildon, Reading, Berks, RG8 8NT. Tel:0791-671293
BEARDSLEY Bertwisle Bertwistle Betwisell BIRTWISLE Birtwistle BOSWELL Botweazle DYSON GREGSON HAIGH HARRISON HEMINGWAY HIRST HOLLINGWORTH PORTER Rishforth Rishworth Rushfirth RUSHFORTH Rushworth SLACK STERRY TAYLOR F1599

166960 STEVENS Mrs Ann M. (Wilson) 29 Grey Street, Griffith, NSW 2680, AUSTRALIA.
ATLEE BARKER BEAUMONT BRUNT CANNON CHADWICK CHURCH CLARKE DUNMO Dunmow EDWARDS HADAWAY HART HUTCHINSON KNIGHTS LAMPARD LANGTON Lilley LILLY MCGEOCH MOORHOUSE NEVILL RAY Sargeant SARGENT Seargent Sergeant STEVENS STREET TRUMAN WARE WESTON WILSON F5168

166979 STEVENS Mr Bernard. 12 Chaseden Road, Hemel Hempstead, Herts, HP1 3NL.
CRITTAL HOLBROOK MURPHY RICHARDS ROSSITER STEEVENS STEPHENS STEVENS F2649

166987 STEVENS Mrs F J. 15 Radnor Rise, Somerville, Victoria, 3912, AUSTRALIA.
BROOKS CHALMERS GOSLING MACKENZIE PHILPOT Philpott SECKER F4195

166995 STEVENS Mr Henry L. 139 Marine Parade, Brighton, Sussex, BN2 1DF. Tel:0273-607535
HARDING JOUXSON LOVELL STEVENS F2084

167002 STEVENS Mr Hugh. Cambrian House, Upper St Johns Road, Burgess Hill, West Sussex, RH15 8HB.
Adames ADAMS Addes ADDS Ade Ades Adze ANDREWS Astwick AUSTWICK BAKER BELL Bennet BENNETT Bish Bishe Bisshe Blanchet BLANCHETT Boud Boude BOWD Bowde BRAGG BYSH Byshe Bysshe Colles COLLIS Colliss Dorrel Dorrell Dorril DORRILL DUKE EDWARDS Faudington FAWDINGTON FELLOWS FRANKLIN Frankling FRYER GILDON GILL GOODMAN HARMER HARVEY HAYWARD HILDER HODSON HOWARD Jefferies JEFFERY Jeffrey Jeffries JOHNSON KERCHEVALL KING KIRTLAND KNIGHT LADE LEACH LEDGER Lilley LILLY LOVEGROVE MAYER Meakin Meaking Meakings MEAKINS Mekins MOON Moone Murfee MURPHY NEWINGTON OXLEY Paddington PAILLING Paleing Palin Pardington Partington Patdenden PATTENDEN Pattender Pattentine Pattenton Pattington Peddenden Peddington Petterden PINER PRICE Ren Renne SEYFANG STEVENS Swayesland Swayseland SWAYSLAND SWEBY SWIFFEN TAYLOR THOMAS TODD TOMKIES TOPPING Traughton TROUGHTON Trouton Trowton TUTT Tutte Tutty Tuttye Walborn Walborne Walbourn Walbourne WALBRAN WALBURN Walburne WALKER Welburn WELLS WILMHURST Wilmshurst Wimpset Wimpshurst Wimset Wimsherst Wimshurst Woollman WOOLMAN Worcester WORSTER WREN Wrenne WRENSTED WRIGHT ZUPPINGER F5227

167010 STEVENS Mrs J. Oystese, Bell Green, Cratfield, Halesworth, Suffolk, IP19 0DH.
BUTCHER CHAMBERS CONNOLD FISK KERSEY STEVENS STOLLERY WHATLING F4270

167029 STEVENS Ms M L. 11 Kingshill Close, Malvern, Worcs, WR14 2BP.
BARNES Bavins Beavans Beavins BEVAN Bevance Bevans Bevens Bevin Bevince BEVINS BIFFIN BROOKES BUSHELL Chettle Chitell CHITTLE COLLINS DAY GREENAWAY HALSE KIMBER Linam LINEHAM Lynam Lyneham Pound POUNDS RUDDLE Rudell SANDFORD SMART SMITH SOUTHEY STEPHENS Stevens TRICKS Trix WESTON WHEELER F1344

167037 STEVENS Mrs Margaret. Po Box 66, 8 Keswick Street, East Bentleigh, Victoria, 3165, AUSTRALIA.
BECK BROWN BRYANT BUDGE CHOLMELEY CIVELL Civil CLISSOLD COLLINGS De Ceville DONALDSON EASTON FARNHAM GARNIER Guernier HALCOTT HAMPSHIRE HOBDAY HORSEMAN HORWOOD HUGHES HUTCHISON JACOBS JONES KING LITTLE LOURIE MACDONALD MCLEOD NELSON ORBY PAINE PARRY Payne PILKINGTON RICH SHEAHAN SNELLING SQUIER STEVENS TUFF VIZARD WRIGHT Yealding YIELDING F5509

167045 STEVENS Mrs Megan. (Lloyd) 38 Salisbury Gardens, Downend, Bristol, BS16 5RE.
COULSTING DURSLEY EDDOLLS FIDO HOLLIS LLOYD F4164

167053 STEVENS Mr Noel. 3 Severn Close, Maisemore, Gloucester, GL2 8ET. Tel:0452-526111
ACKLAND HALE HURCOMBE KIRK PAYNE ROWLEY SQUIRE STEPHENS VINALL WARDEN F4869

167061 STEVENS Mrs Olive G. (Fairall) 16 Grange Court Drive, Bexhill On Sea, E Sussex, TN39 4AX.
DANN FAIRALL STEVENS F1084

167088 STEVENS Mr Peter. 40 Avenue Gardens, Teddington, Middx, TW11 0BH.
AVENT BENN BENSON CARDIGAN COCKERTON CORBER CORFIELD DIXON DYER HENDERSON IRONMONGER LANGTON LAW LITTLEDALE LOVELL MALLOTT MATYEAR MAY OXENHAM PATRICKSON PLAISTER ROBERTSON SIMONDS SMITH STEVENS WALKER WEBB F535

167096 STEVENS Mr Roy. 5 Farleigh Crescent, Swindon, Wiltshire, SN3 1JY. Tel:0793-521548
ALLEN BURDEN KILBECK Pafford PALSER Parser Pasard Paser Pasher Passard Passer Passerd Passwer Payser Payzer Pazer Pazzard PAZZERD Posheart Purser RADFORD SALTER SANDFORD Sheild SHIELD Shill Steevens Stephans Stephens STEVENS Stevins WEBB WILLIAMS F1458

167118 STEVENS Miss Ruth. 2 Mill Yard, Countess Wear, Exeter, Devon, EX2 6LL.
Emberry EMBERY Emburie Embury HOOKWAY LANG MANNING Steevins Stephens STEVENS F4617

167126 STEVENS Mrs Susan. 40 Avenue Gardens, Teddington, Middx, TW11 0BH.
ASHFORD BODY BONES CAMPLING GALPIN HEMMING TULK TURTLE TUTTERIDGE VIDGEN F536

167134 STEVENSON Ms Janet H. 23 Byron Gardens, Sutton, Surrey, SM1 3QG.
NESBITT STEVENSON F1879

167142 STEVENSON Mrs M R. 41 Wepre Lane, Connahs Quay, Deeside, Clwyd, CH5 4JR.
SNELHAM F7366

167150 STEVENSON Mrs Sheila J. (Thornley) 2 Weldon Way, Gosforth, Newcastle Upon Tyne, NE3 3HX.
BLACKAH Blacker Blakey GASKIN PINHORN THORNLEY F1082

167169 STEWART Miss Agnes B. 9 Bruce Square, Kilconqulias, Leven, Fife, KY9 1LA.
BALDIE NESS SIMPSON SMALL STEWART F2798

167177 STEWART Mrs Catherine S. (Barclay) 51 Gainsborough Rise, Bedford, Beds, MK41 7NS. Tel:0234-347554
ALSTON BARCLAY BOWIE DOW RICHARDSON ROBERTSON ROXBURGH STIRLING STOBIE F4006

167185 STEWART Ms F. 90 Middleton Road, London, E8 4LN.
BLOMFIELD Bloomfield F7109

167193 STEWART Mrs I. 8 Mylis Close, Sydenham, London, SE26 6JL.
Odam Odham ODHAMS Oldhams F7146

167207 STEWART Mr Iain. 51 Gainsborough Rise, Bedford, Beds, MK41 7NS. Tel:0234-347554
BLACK CLARK MCINTOSH PRINGLE REID SCOTT STEWART WRIGHT F4005

167215 STEWART Dr R H M. Donkleywood House, Donkleywood, Hexham, Northumberland, NE48 1AQ. Tel:0434-240303
Machomas Macthomas Mcthomas Steart Stert Steuard Steuarde Steuart Steuarte Stevarde Stevarte Steward STEWART Stirt Stiuard Stiubhard Stiubhart Stiward Stuard Stuarde Stuart Stuerd Sturt Stuward Stwyarde Styward Stywarde Thamson Thamsone Thompson THOMSON Thomsone F585

167223 STEWART Mrs Ruth. Bundilla, Ballengarra, NSW 2441, AUSTRALIA. Tel:+61-6-585-8232
DONNITHORNE HERD ISAACS JOHNSTON MANDERSON MCINNES NORRIS OATAWAY RINTOUL STONE TAYLOR TOMS TREWEEK WESTLAKE F5618

167231 STEWART Mrs Sylvia. (Payne) 14 Hyacinth Close, Creekmoor, Poole, Dorset, BH17 7YX.
BAIGENT Baijeant Baijent EDGINGTON Edginton

JACKSON Pain Paine PAYNE Wakeley Wakelin Wakely WAKERLEY Wakerly WHITE F4522

167258 STEWARTSON Ms A F. 67 Southway, London, NW11 6SB.
BELL CHALMERS FORRESTER HENDRY LITTLEJOHN NOTLEY ROBERTS STEWARDSON STEWARTSON F5989

167266 STIBBLES Revd George. St John Stone Priory, Sandbrook Way, Woodvale, Southport, PR8 3RN. Tel:0704-77722
Stabil Stablis Stabyl Steeble Stibbillis STIBBLES Stibils Stibles STIBLIS Stibls Stibulis Stibull STUBBLES Stubil Stubyl F2042

167274 STICHBURY Mr Michael. 3 Chapel Close, Capel St Mary, Suffolk, IP9 2ES.
Stichberry STICHBURY Stickbury Stitchberry Stitchbury Strichbury F7125

167282 STICKLAND Michael. 3 Beaufort Gardens, The Ridge West, St Leonards On Sea, East Sussex, TN37 7PQ.
Steckland Stecklen Stecklian Steclin Stecquelin Stekland Steklen Stequelain Stequelin Stichling Stickeland Stickeling Stickelonde Sticklaine Sticklan STICKLAND Sticklane Sticklang Sticklen Sticklend Stickler Sticklin Stickling Sticklinge Sticklings Sticklonde Sticland Stictland Stikland Stuckland Styckland Stycklinge Stycland Stykklande F1539

167290 STICKLAND Mrs S. 146 Alumhurst Road, Bournemouth, Dorset, BH4 8HW.
COOPER FEAR HIGBID KIDD MASTER ROBIE VILLER F5858

167304 STICKLAND Mrs Sarah. Fernhurst, Garden Lane, Witley, Surrey, GU8 5QB.
HEATH SHOEBRIDGE F3201

167312 STILES Mrs Betty. (Stockdale) 60 London Road, Coalville, Leicester, LE6 2JA. Tel:0530-839947
BOWMAN STOCKDALE F1652

167320 STILL Mrs Sandra J. 24 Connaught Avenue, Grays, Essex, RM16 2XX.
YENDALL F1716

167339 STILLMAN Mr H. 48 Delane Drive, Winnersh, Wokingham, Berks, RG11 5AT.
LEE STILLMAN STYLEMAN F4809

167347 STOCK Mrs S. 8 Albert Road, Breaston, Derby, DE7 3DL.
DAFT F392

167355 STOCK Mrs V M. (Sheldon) 25 Ravenscroft, Covingham, Swindon, Wilts, SN3 5AE.
ALGER ALMOND BALCKETT BETTERIDGE Blacket Blackett BLACKETT SHELDON BURROW CHAPMAN CHESSON CLARK GURNEY LORD MITCHELL NEWMAN PANNELL PEARSON RICKARD SHELDON Shelton SHILDON Shilton Squance SQUINCE Squints STOCK F3362

167363 STOCKER Mr T. 10 Greenway Lane, Charlton Kings, Cheltenham, Glos, GL52 6LB. Tel:0242-525893
HUGHEA STOCKER F5287

167371 STOCKTON-LINK Mrs S. Severn, 101 Woodthorpe, Woodthorpe Drive, Blewdley, Worcs, DY12 2RL.
Stocken STOCKTON Stocton F6837

167398 STODDART Mrs Jean. 28 Lowes Barn Bank, Merry Oaks, Durham City, DH1 3QL. Tel:091-386-5679
FITZSIMMONS HOWIE JAMIESON LIGHTBODY MCDOWAL MCINTYRE NAIRN STODDART WAINMAN WILSON F1398

167401 STOKER Mr Michael. 39 Woodbourne, Weybourne, Farnham, Surrey, GU9 9EE. Tel:0252-28252
BARRETT CHERRY DAVIES KNIGHT LONGWORTHY MORRISON POLLARD Stokald Stokel Stokeld Stokell STOKER Stokoe SUMMERS WATSON F5033

167428 STOKES Mrs Christine. (Finlayson) 3 Holyrood Walk, Corby, Northants, NN18 9JD.
MURRAY F7381

167436 STOKES Mr F H. 29 Moreton Close, Crookham, Fleet, Hants, GU13 0LQ.
CHUBB HENNING SCOBLE STOKES F2361

167444 STOKES Ms Hilda. (Richardson) 31 Brunswick Road, Fair Oak, Eastleigh, Hants, SO5 7FF.
BIRCH CHILDS CHOULES Chouls Chowles GRANT Hilard Hilierd Hilliar HILLIARD Hillier Hillierd MALPAS MERRYWEATHER MIDDLETON-SALT RICHANS RICHARDSON RICHENS Richenson Richerson Richinson SALT SIMMONDS Simonds SPENCER Symonds Symons F716

167452 STOKES Mr Raymond E. 87 Sallows Shaw, Sole Street, Cobham, Kent, DA13 9BP.
ALMON Almond BATTEN Batting BETTERIDGE BRISTOW Bristowe EAST HALEY HANNENT Hannet Horseman HORSMAN HUSSEY KING NEAL Neale STOKES STONE TURNER WELCH WELLON WEST F3144

167460 STOKES Mr W P. 41 Ludlow Road, Feltham, Middx, TW13 7JE.
BARNES BARNS GRIFFITHS LODGE STOKES F1511

167479 STONE Mr C F. 37 Windsor Way, Polegate, E Sussex, BN26 6QF.
BROADIST CREASER PARSONS STONE WATTS WHITWELL F2457

167487 STONE Mrs Christine. 10 Society Road, Shepton Mallet, Somerset, BA4 5GF.
DAWSON DENHOLM FOWLER HALLETT HOWARD KENDALL LANE LAWRENCE PAULL POOR F718

167495 STONE Mr Donald. 31 Exeter Road, Dawlish, Devon, EX7 0AB. Tel:0626-863663
STONE F5767

167509 STONE Mrs Judith. (Dell) 31 Exeter Road, Dawlish, Devon, EX7 0AB. Tel:0626-863663
DELL F5768

167517 STONE Mrs Lilian. (Maynard) 9 Jubilee Crescent, Edmonton, London, N9 7NU. Tel:081-805-2725
BUFTON CAMM CARTWRIGHT CLARK DITZEL DIXON MAYNARD MEMORY SMITH F890

167525 STONE Mrs M A. 37 Windsor Way, Polegate, E Sussex, BN26 6QF.
BOXSHALL HOLMES NEAL SARGENT SPURGEON F2456

167533 STONE Mrs Margaret. 12 Westminster Court, Cambridge Park, Wanstead, London, E11 2PU.
ALLARD APPLETON BARRETT BATTERSBY BAZELEE BLOOM BRISON BRYSON BURROUGHS DEEBLE DUCK EDGER FAWKES GLANFIELD GRAY HURSE JOSEPH JUDD LATE MEGGS MORGAN NIXON PERCIVAL POLE ROBINS ROWBOTTAM SCARNELL SCARNING SHAVE SMITH SNELLING STREETON TOLSON UNDERWOOD WARD WEDMORE WILLIAMS F2841

167541 STONE Mrs R P. 11 Chaffers Mead, Ashtead, Surrey. Tel:0372-273134
ANDREWS BULLEY CLARK COLLINS GLOUGH KINGHORN OXLADE PETTIT WILDING WOOLFREY F5865

167568 STONE Mr Trevor. 4 Oak Avenue, Killinghall, Harrogate, North Yorks, HG3 2RT.
BALES CROSS DOMONEY HARRISON HENCHEB HOPKINS HUDSON LACEY LEFTLY PYBUS ROBSON SHIPPEY STONE WEST WITHERS F6262

167576 STONER Mr Peter. 25 Bristol Gate, Brighton, E Sussex, BN2 5BD.
MAPLESDEN NYE STONER WALKER F3803

167584 STONES Mr H. 8 Pixie Lane, Braunton, Devon, EX33 1AZ.
BAINBRIDGE BOWSER DALEY DAVISON DIXON GREGORY HUGHF STOCKBURN STODDART VART WHITFIELD F809

167592 STONES Mr Robert. Clifton Cottage, High Street, Malpas, Cheshire, SY14 8NN. Tel:0948-860760
ABBEY ABSALON ALCOCK ALDRED ARNOUX ASQUITH ASTBURY BADDELEY BALL BALMER BARR BARRY BENNETT BENTLEY BLAKE BOARDMAN BRETTEL BRIAND CADDICK CADDOCK Caddocke CALCOTT CALDWELL CATHERALL CHAFFERS CHAMBERLAIN CHILD CLEGGS CLEWES CLIVE CLOKIE CLOWES COGHILL COLLINSON COMPTON CRANE DANIEL DAVENPORT DIBB DRESSLER DRINKWATER DUNBAVAN DUNBIBBIN DUNDERDALE DUVIVIER ELERS FALXMAN FARQUAR FISHLEY FRYE GILBODY GILDEA GRASTON GRATTON GREATBACH HANCOCK HARLING HERTZ HEWSON HEYES HOLLINS HOLT HOSTAGE HUGHSON HURDUS HURTEN HUSON JOYCE LAWRENSON LOWDIN LOWE LUCOCK LUND MACDOWELL MANIFOLD MANZINI MANZONI MARSH MARSH-CALDWELL MARSHALL NEALE OULSNAM PALMER PENNINGTON PODMORE POVEY PRICE PRICE-WOOD PROTAT RANDALL RAVILIOUS REID RIDGWAY ROUBILIAC SADLER SHARRATT SKARRAT SMITH-BARRY SOLON SOQUI SORTON SPRIMONT STAMFORD STUBBS TASKER TITTENSOR TOFT TOWNE TRAFFORD TUSHINGHAM VOYEZ WHIELDON WILEMAN WOLFE WOOD F3235

167606 STORER Mr Norman. Rievaulx Cottage, Lake Lane, Barnham, Bognor Regis, West Sussex, PO22 0AJ. Tel:0243-551662
BEDFORD HELM JAMES JESSOP KNOWLES PARRY STORER TIDSWELL F6406

167614 STOREY Mr Harold J. 2 Orchard Close, Cheadle Hulme, Cheshire, SK8 7ET.
FLAVELL FOWNES GRIFFITHS F4541

167622 STOREY Mrs M C. 77 Arundel Drive, Carleton, Poulton Le Fylde, Lancs, FY6 7TE.
Lewtas LEWTUS Lutas LUTUS MYLES RAWLINSON ROSE Rowlinson F1974

167630 STORM Mr Alan. Plow House, Little Casterton, Stamford, Lincs, PE9 4BE.
STORM F2300

167649 STORMONT Miss Anne. 18 Osprey Close, Lower Wick, Worcester, WR2 4BX.
BROWN CHAPMAN DARTON DIMOND ELLIS GETHIN GREEN GREENING HAGGER HARDING HOLLINGSWORTH JONES MANN MOULD ROGERS SKIGGS SPILLER STORMONT SUMMERHAYES WORRALL F1620

167657 STORRAR Mr Jim. 20 Avenue Road, Brentford, Middx, TW8 9NS. Tel:081-560-8820
STORRAR F1497

167665 STOTE Mr Brian. 22 Chetwode Close, Allesley Park, Coventry, W Midlands, CV5 9NA.
BROOMFIELD Crosland Crosley Crossland CROSSLEY Petifer Petipher Pettifer Pettipher PITTIPHER Stoat Stoate Stoatt STOTE F2754

167673 STOTT Mr Iain J C. 7 Delamere Close, Peterborough, Cambs, PE1 4RX. Tel:0733-348213
COOPER ENTWISTLE GORD HAYCOCK MURRAY OSBORNE ROBERTS STOTT F3161

167681 STOTT Mr W T. Tree Cottage, Lammas Gardens, East Bridgford, Nottingham, NG13 8LQ.
STOTT F6589

167703 STOUT Mr Tom. 3 Thorkel Road, Thurso, Caithness, Scotland, KW14 7LW. Tel:0847-65973
CALDER SEATTER STEVENSON STOUT F1459

167711 STOW Mrs Sandy. 18 Alice Street, Clontarf, Queensland, 4019, AUSTRALIA.
CALLANAN CLIFTON COLE DOUGLASS FRANKLIN GREEN GROVER HATTER LEE MUSGRAVE NORRIS PALMER ROBINSON STEPHENSON STOW TILLCOCK WHIPP F5447

167738 STOWELL Mr John. Belmont, The Street, Godmersham, Canterbury, Kent, CT4 7DU.
De Stavele De Stawele De Stawell De Stawelle De Stawille De Stawylle De Stoill De Stouill De Stoule De Stoville De Stowill De Stowille Howell Mcstoile Mcstole Showell Shoyell Stafeld Staile Stauwill Stavold Stavwill Stawel STAWELL Stawle Stawyll Stayell Stayle Steole Steul Stewell Stewill Steywel Stoal Stoale Stoall Stoel Stoell Stoelle Stoewell Stoffell Stohel Stohell Stohill Stohl Stoiel Stoiell Stoil Stoile Stoiles Stoils Stol Stole Stoles Stoll Stolle Stolles Stols Stool Stoole Stooles Stools Stoolus Stouall Stouel Stouell Stouil Stoul Stouwell Stoval Stovald Stovall Stovel Stoveld Stovell Stovill Stovold Stovoll Stowal Stowall Stowals Stoweel Stoweils Stowel Stoweld Stowele Stoweley STOWELL Stowells Stowels Stowhil Stowhill Stowil Stowilles Stowl Stowldwell Stowle Stowles Stowold Stowole Stowoll Stowvel Stowwell Stowyll Stoyel Stoyell Stoyels Stoyl Stoyle Stoyles Stoyll Stoylls Stoyls Stoyoll Stuell Stul Stule Stules Stull Stweall Stwell Styell F4584

167746 STOYLE Mr Ian. Fairfield, Thorverton, Devon, EX5 5NG.
ELLACOMBE ELLICOMBE STOYLE F1760

167754 STRACHAN Mr G. 5 Wentworth Close, Daventry, Northants, NN11 4NY.
STRACHAN Strahan Strauchan Strawn F6088

167762 STRADLING Mr Frank. 10 Yeolls Crescent, Lovedean, Portsmouth, Hants, PO8 9SH.
BICKERDIKE BOLTON BUTTERS BUTTIS HARLAND HOOPER HOPKINSON MATTINGLY STRADLING STRETCH STRITCH WEBBER F1621

167770 STRALEY Mr Richard. 7 Tanners Close, Mill Lane, Brockworth, Glous, GL3 4QN. Tel:0452-864506
BRUSH Brushe Brusshe Fanston FANSTONE Fanstonne GOUCH PUYRAVEL STODGELL STRALEY Stroehle Stroele Strohl STROHLE Strole Vanston Vanstone F3191

167789 STRATFORD Dr Mike. 10 Ashford Road, Fulshaw Park, Wilmslow, Cheshire, SK9 1QE. Tel:0625-583239
BECK BRADLEY CLOTWORTHY DROUGHT LONGFORD Macharg Maharg MEHARG NEWING ROBERTSON SINGLETON Stafford STRATFORD Wale WHALE Wheale F126

167797 STRATFULL Mr J. 10 Black Path, Polegate, E Sussex, BN26 5AP.
DYER STRATFIELD Stratford Stratfull F1970

167800 STRATHEARN Mrs Lucy E. (Cock) 4 Meredith Street, Redcliffe, Queensland, 4020, AUSTRALIA. Tel:+61-7-284-6564
CHALK COCK HOLDAWAY HORTON MORE PRIDHAM SANDERS SCUFFLE TANCOCK TUBB TURNER WYETH F5576

167819 STRATTON Mrs M D. 37 Olympic Way, Bishopstoke, Eastleigh, Hants, SO5 6PS. Tel:0703-694413
ADAMS BENNETT HAWKINS MODDY MOODY NEWMAN STRATTON F1161

167827 STRETTON Mrs Elizabeth. 7 Rockingham Road, Bispham, Blackpool, Lancs, FY2 0LP.
BRADBURY GOODCHILD HINES HULL MATTHEWS MCCANN ROBERTS STRETTON WINTERBOURNE F3250

167835 STRICKLAND Mrs Helen. (Ruddick) Station House, Armathwaite, Carlisle, Cumbria, CA4 9PW. Tel:0699-2340
GRANT MCBURNIE MCROBERTS MUSE RUDDICK STRICKLAND F3923

167843 STRINGER-CALVERT Mr David W J. 8 Lynchet Close, Market Lavington, Devizes, Wiltshire, SN10 4BY.
ADDISON BATEY BELL BRAMWELL BRUCE CALVERT Cantill CANTRILL CLARKSON CLAYTON CRADDOCK DAVISON HARTLEY HODGSON HORN MCLACHAN MCNALLY PARK PARKINSON PEACOCK PERUIM RAW ROBINSON RYDER SARGISON SMITHSON STRINGER THOMAS TOMLIN WALKER WARRINER WORTHINGTON YARE F753

167851 STROBRIDGE Ms Jill. 59 Melville Street, Edinburgh, EH3 7HL.
CRAVEN JANNAWAY RIX ROBINSON STROBRIDGE Strobryg Strobrygge Strowbridge Strubridge YOUNG F2940

167878 STRONACH Mr David. 8 Grenadier Drive, Thornlie, WA 6108, AUSTRALIA. Tel:+61-9-459-0192
ATTWOODS BOWDEN BROWN BURGAR CHAPMAN CHOULS COLLINS COTES DICKMAN EGGLETON FOULIS GOODALL GOODMAN HAYES HIGH HILLIER HOPE JACOBS KIMBER LEE LONG MCLEOD MEAD NEATE RUDDLE SMITH SPAINSWICK STRONACH SUGG YOUNG F5522

167886 STRONACH Mrs Edna. 128 New Street, St Helens, Lancs, WA9 3XF.
DAVISON DUCKWORTH GORE LEICESTER MCDONALD RIGBY SPARKS STRONACH F2227

167894 STRONG Mr Peter J. South Gate, Chapel Street, Tiverton, Devon, EX16 6DF. Tel:0884-253700
BRIDGEMAN STRONG F3349

167908 STROPHAIR Mr Robert. 11 Baswich Crest, Stafford, ST17 0HL. Tel:0785-49164
SCORER Strafair Straffair Strafhair Straughair STRAUGHAIRE Straugheir Straughier Strawhair Strofair Strofare Stroffair Stroghare STROPHAIR Stropheir STROUGHAIR Stroughare Strowhair F5652

167916 STUBBINGS Mr Edward H J. 75 Swifts Green Road, Luton, Beds, LU2 8BW.
BURROWS CLARKSON FEARMAN HOLT Stebbing Stebbings Stubben STUBBINGS Stubbins WARD F5047

167924 STUBBS Mrs Jane. 16 Le Brun Road, Eastbourne, E Sussex, BN21 2HZ. Tel:0323-36953
ALBORN ANCKLEY ANDERSON ASHTON BAILY BALL BLENCARN BROTHERS BROUGH BULL BULLOCK BURROWS CARROW CARTER CHAMBERS CHAPLIN CHAPMAN CHERRY CLARK CLARKSON COLLINS COOK COOPER COX Daill DALE DAVIS DAWLEY DEW DUNHAM EASTON EATON EDWARDS EVANS FALDO FALLOWFIELD FLINT FOX FRASCH GILLIANS GODFREY GOODALL GREEN GREIG GREY GYLMAN HALL HALLAM HANCHETT HANSCOMBE HARRIS HARRISON HARVEY HOMBSTRON HUGHES HUGHNOWNE HUMBERSTONE ILIFFE IRELAND JENNINGS JOHNSON JONES KEEN KERWIN KERWINY KIRBY Kirwin LAWRENCE MANUEL MARRIOT MARSHALL MARTIN MCCARTHY MEAGRE MILLS MOSSEY MOULES NEWMAN NOOT NORWELL PAPPER PAPWORTH PECK PICKERING POO PROUDE RAVENS RICHARDS ROWLEY SIMPKINS SKEGG SMITH SMOOTHMAN SOLE SPOONLEY STUBBS STURMAN SWAIN TANSLEY TAYLOR THOMPSON

TODD TOPPING TOWNSEND TUVEY WALBY WALKER WARD WATSON WILBRAHAM WILKINS WILKINSON WINTER WOODCOCK WRIGHT F623

167932 STUBBS Mrs S G. 68 Timms Avenue, Kilsyth, Victoria, 3137, AUSTRALIA. Tel:+61-3-725-2245
AITKEN BRANDON BROADBENT CHARIE Collings COLLINS GOODALL HAMILTON HOGG JEFFREY KIRK MACHIN MCNAE NELSON PEEBLES PRICE PRITCHARD RAGGETT RAWLE READ SPENCE STUBBS VERNON WILDBLOOD F5558

167940 STURGES Mrs Maria. (Hollingsworth) Osmington House, Christchurch Road, Tring, Herts, HP23 4EF. Tel:0442-822814
GOODING HOLLINGSWORTH How HOWE MAYHEW NEAL Neale Pecket PECKITT Piat Prickett Pyatt PYETT Ramsay RAMSEY STURGES YORK Yorke F2865

167959 STURROCK-MCMOORE Mr Ron. 16 Byrd Street, Laindon, Essex, SS15 5QP.
ANDREWS BROWN CAMPKIN CHINERY DUGGIN ENGLISH FINCH GODWINE GRIGG KEMP LUCK MCDANIEL MOORE NORRIS PULLINGER REEVES RICHARDS SEWELL STURROCK F581

167967 STURT Mr David. 147a Isledon Road, Finsbury Park, London, N7 7JP. Tel:071-609-9761
GLADDERS GREENWELL MARSHALL STURT F5799

167975 STUTTLE Mr M J. 2 Grey'S Cottages, St James'S Place, Babbacombe Downs Road, Torquay Devon, TQ1 3LR.
Stettle Stuttell STUTTLE F7102

167983 STYLE Mrs Patricia. 12 Ridge Avenue, Marple, Stockport, Cheshire, SK6 7HJ.
Tel:061-427-4680
ARROWSMITH BARNETT COCKRILL CRAWFORD DARROCH FOSTER GOODMAN STYLE WILLIAMS F5811

167991 STYLES Mr Haydn G. Fulford House, Fulford Road, West Ewell, Surrey, KT19 9QZ.
Tel:081-393-0110
HEATH NINNIS PAYNE PRICE RICHARDS ROOTS STILES STYLES WEBB F6251

168009 STYLES Mr Victor J. 40 Campion Close, Warsash, Southampton, Hants, SO3 9DE.
Tel:0489-578232
MILLARDS PIMM PIMM (NORRIS) STYLES TIDMARSH F583

168017 SUDDARDS Mr A D. 1 St Andrews Road, Blundellsands, Liverpool, L23 7UP.
Tel:051-924-7272
BOTTOMLEY DENISON Dennison Engel Ingall Ingel Ingell INGLE Ingles Southard Southers Sudard Suddard SUDDARDS Suddart Sudderd Sudderds Sudders Suddert Sudderth Suddorth Sudert Sudord Suthard Suthast SUTHERS Sutherst Suthert Suthworth Suttherd WILKINSON Ynkel F4192

168025 SULLIVAN Mrs D. 62 Harwood Road, Heaton Mersey, Stockport, Cheshire, SK4 3AZ.
DRISCOLL DUNMALL HERRIVEN PERRY RODWELL SULLIVAN SWATMAN THOMPSON F6381

168033 SULLIVAN Mrs Phyllis. (Pring) Glenmuir, Corsock, Castle Douglas, Kirkcudbrightshire, DG7 3DH. Tel:06444-661
BARKER CHAPMAN CLARK DUDLEY Faranden Farendon Farindon Farnden Farrenden Farringdon FARRINGTON GIBBINS GODLEY HALL Lale Leal LEALL LEE Lisle MARSH PENFOLD Precias Precions PRECIOUS Precise Prescious Preshas Presheas Preshess Preshouse Preshus Presise Presses Pressius Presson Pressus Pretcious Preticouss Pretious Pretiouss Pretius Pretyus PRING PULLING Sampear Sampeere Samper Sampher Samphey Samphier SAMPHIRE Samphur Sampier Sampieri Sampiers Sampire SANSBURY SHIELD SPARKS SWEET F3615

168041 SUMMERER Mrs Marion. 411 Rockland Road, Campbell River, B C, V9W 1N7, CANADA.
Tel:+1-604-923-4912
BAILY BURMAN COOPER GARDNER KIRSTING MACKERELL SAVILLE SPICE WALLER F5591

168068 SUMMERFIELD Mr Mark A. 33 Barnborough Street, Burley, Leeds, LS4 2QY.
DUNSTAN EDWARDS FLAXMAN LOCKE MORTER RICHARDS RISBRIDGER STEVENS SUMMERFIELD TAYLOR TRIGGS F3365

168076 SUMMERFIELD Mrs Rita. 8 High Street, Portbury, Bristol, Avon, BS20 9TW.
Tel:0275-373464
CARR COLEMAN LADD MAY PALMER PERRY SELWAY SPILLER TURNER UNDERWOOD WASHER F919

168084 SUMMERFIELD Mr Ted. 59 Roman Way, Stoke Bishop, Bristol, BS9 1SP.
BROAD FRY HOOPER PEACOCK SUMMERFIELD SWEET TOGHILL F1768

168092 SUMMERS Mrs D E. 3 The Uplands, Thorpences, Leiston, Suffolk, IP16 4NQ.
BIRCH DEAN OSGOOD Scruce SCRUSE F2688

168106 SUMMERS Mr Eric William. 25 Riverside, Egham, Surrey, TW20 0AD.
Biurst BYHURST ROBINSON SUMMERS F3051

168114 SURMAN Mrs Maureen. 23 Upper Close, Woodgate Valley, Bartley Green, Birmingham, B32 3SN.
Cyrmon Serman Sermon Sirman Sirmon SURMAN F3727

168122 SURRIDGE C. Box 255, Stirling, Ontario, K0K 3E0, CANADA.
STUTT F7369

168130 SUSANS Mr H R. 52 Clarence Road, Ponders End, Enfield, Middx, EN3 4BW. Tel:081-804-6110
SUSAN SUSANS SUZAN SUZANS F2019

168149 SUSOEFF Mrs Marilyn. (Toyne) 1063 Elizabeth Drive, Bridgeville, Pennsylvania, 15017, USA.
Tel:+1-412-941-5241
COUSENS COX CUTLER FLETCHER GARDNER HANCOCK JENKINS KINGTON MATTOCKS MAWKINSON MELLS PEARSON SMITH TINSON TOYNE F4664

168157 SUSSEX Mr Roger. 22 Woodlands Bank, Dalgety Bay, Fife, KY11 5SX. Tel:0383-823053
SUSSEX F1982

168165 SUTCLIFFE Mrs Annie. 20 Brindale Road, Brinnington, Stockport, Ches, SK5 8BZ.
DORMAN FRENCH JEFFERSON SAUNDERS SPICER F6334

168173 SUTCLIFFE Mrs E M. (Rundle) 19 Ware Road, Tonwell, Ware, Herts, SG12 0HN.
ADAMS BEDELLA BREWER DOWRICK KEMP LUKE NANKIVELL RUNDLE SUTCLIFFE TONKIN F1916

168181 SUTCLIFFE Mr Glenn. South Lodge, Holdenhurst, Bournemouth, Dorset, BH8 0EF.
ATTHILL CUMBERLAND HAMILTON HEWETSON Hewson HORRY KIDD LAMPORT MATHEW Matthew MAXWELL MOIR PATTON PIKET TABINER WOODWARD F2191

168203 SUTHERLAND Mr George H. 8 Glenlockhart Valley, Edinburgh, EH14 1DE.
Bain BAINE Bayne BLAIR BUCHAN DOW DRUMMOND DUFF FALCONER GORRIE GRAY GREENLAW GUNN HAY HENDERSON HORNE KEDDIE Keddy KENNEDY Kid KIDD Kiddie Kiddy MARSHAL MCINNES MCLEOD MILLER MURRAY ROSS SCOTT SINCLAIR STALKER SUTHERLAND TAYLOR THOMSON F1257

168211 SUTTLE Mrs Susan. (Bird) 8 The Banks, Wellingborough, Northants, NN9 5YX.
BARNES BIRD CARTER CLIFTON DAY DEAMER DEVERELL GOBEY Newberry NEWBURY RODELL TUFFNELL F1685

168238 SUTTON Mr Anthony. Clevedon House, 6 All Saints Lane, Clevedon, Bristol, BS21 6AA.
SUTTON F6320

168246 SUTTON Mrs Connie. (Craig) 80 Derby Road, Heaton Moor, Stockport, Cheshire, SK4 4NF.
BLACK CRAIG FARGLE MALCOLM MORTON NEIL SAWERS STEEL WALKER WOODBURN F6220

168254 SUTTON Mrs G H. (Gaught) 36 High Street, Linton, Swadlincote, Derbyshire, DE12 6QL.
Tel:0283-761344
GAUGHT Gault Gaut GAWGHT GAWT Goult Gout F5794

168262 SUTTON Mr Geoffrey. 80 Derby Road, Heaton Moor, Stockport, Cheshire, SK4 4NF.
LEES SUTTON TORKINGTON WYATT F6219

168270 SUTTON Miss J L. 26 Wellington Road, Old Colwyn, Colwyn Bay, Clwyd, LL29 9NE.
Quarrey Quarrie QUARRY F6713

168289 SUTTON Mrs N A. (Cox) 36 Trelawn Place, Howick, Auckland, 1705, NEW ZEALAND.
CONLEY CONNELY COX HAWKINS HENDERSON OGDEN PILKINGTON SUTTON WALLETT F5565

168297 SVOBODA Mrs J. (Trummel) 3491 Tracy Drive, Santa Clara, CA 95051, USA.
BEILBY FISHER GROVES HODGSON PARKINSON STEAD F5438

168300 SWADLING Mr Ralph H. 10 Mackley Way, Harbury, Leamington Spa, Warwickshire, CV33 9NP.
SWADLING F465

168319 SWAIN Mr Claude. 29 Springhead, Tunbridge

Wells, Kent, TN2 3NY. Tel:0892-534659
SWAIN Swaine Swane Swanne Swayne F36

168327 SWAN Mr F John. 38 St Andrews View, Derby, DE2 4LH. Tel:0332-367843
BARKER DELANEY FOSSEY GEARY HART LINE SWAN WILSON WISE F1954

168335 SWANBOROUGH Mrs Sue. 18 Wentworth, Yate, Bristol, BS17 4DJ.
BLITHE F691

168343 SWANN Mr B P. 24 Dalston Close, Heatherside, Camberley, Surrey, GU15 1BT. Tel:0276-28598
COKER CUBITT GROVER HARBORD PICTON SWAN SWANN F5037

168351 SWART Mr Edward R. 276 Beechlawn Drive, Waterloo, Ontario, N2L 5W7, CANADA. Tel:+1-519-746-4119
ARUNDELL BRIDLE BURNELL GLIDE HOWSON OWEN POWELL RILEY SOUTHGATE VINCE F5149

168378 SWAYNE Mr Geoffrey. 6 New Cottages, Hawkeshead Lane, North Mymms, Hatfield Herts, AL9 7TF.
Swain Swaine SWAYNE F4198

168386 SWAYNE Mrs Mary. (Cranstoun) 51 Brisbane Street, Largs, Ayrshire, KA30 8QP. Tel:0475-686589
ADAMS BAYLIS CARRUTHERS CRANSTOUN LEGGE LOVIE MARSHALL SWAYNE THOMSON WEBSTER F4894

168394 SWEETING D C. 15 Jupiter Road, Ipswich, Suffolk, IP4 4NT.
SWEETING F7384

168408 SWIFT Mr Kenneth. 27 Fairfields, St Ives, Huntingdon, Cambs, PE17 4QG. Tel:0480-69560
HALLILEY INMAN KEMP SWIFT WHITELEY F6282

168416 SWIGGS Mr John Noel. Pinehaven, Driving Lane, Par, Cornwall, PL24 2RH.
BOVEY JOHNS NICHOLLS SWIGGS THOMAS F606

168424 SWINBANK Mr J A. Orchard House, Brierley, Barnsley, S72 9JQ.
ELLERSHAW FAWCETT FLYN FLYNN HESELTINE PRATT REES SMITH SWINBANK TAYLOR THWAITE WEAVER WHITEHEAD WILSON F5281

168432 SWINBURN Mrs Linda. 10 Southgate Road, Sunnybank, Bury, Lancs, BL9 8DZ. Tel:061-766-2674
FAULDER SWINBURN F2328

168440 SWINFIELD Dr G. 53 Roman Road, Faversham, Kent, ME13 8PZ.
SWINFIELD Swingfield Swynfield F6611

168459 SWINNERTON Col I S. Yew Tree Cottage, Blackford, Stoke Street, Milborough Nr Ludlow, SY8 2ET.
Swenarton Swenerton Swinarton Swinerton SWINNERTON Swinnington Swynerton Swynnerton F6590

168467 SWINSCOE Mr David. 103 Crossways, Peterchurch, Hereford, HR2 0TQ. Tel:0981-550595
BASSETT BLORE GALLIMORE HODGKINSON OKEOVER PHILLIPS RIVETT SHORE F4139

168475 SWINTON Mr A J. 47 Ellerslie Road, Loganlea, Queensland, 4131, AUSTRALIA.
SWINTON F6834

168483 SWORDS Miss M. 9 Janred Court, Sea Road, Barton On Sea, New Milton Hants, BH24 7PF.
Sword SWORDS F6741

168491 SYGROVE Mr D C. 8 Brincliffe Close, Walton, Chesterfield, Derbyshire, S40 3DU. Tel:0246-235347
SEGRAVE SIGRAVE SIGROVE SYGROVE F999

168505 SYKES Mrs G. 29 Stowe Crescent, Ruislip, Middx, HA4 7SR.
CHAPPUIS SHOPPEE F4919

168513 SYKES Mr J A. 71 Bank End Land, Almondbury, Huddersfield, W Yorks, HD5 8EW.
BATTY BEDFORD Bedforth BEST DAWSON DUNFORD DYSON FARRAND KAYE ROEBUCK SCARGILL Sikes SMITH SYKES TAYLOR WALKER F2296

168521 SYKES Mrs Joyce. 17 Wellfield Road, Marsh, Huddersfield, Yorkshire, HD3 4AX.
BARDEN BROOK GROOM JACKSON LORD LOWES OLLEY RICHES SKIPPON VERTIGAN F2595

168548 SYKES Ms Vivienne. 10 Colvestone Crescent, Hackney, London, E8 2LH. Tel:071-254-1299
BREWER HERBERT ROLLS SETHLE SETTLE SUTTLE F3329

168556 SYLVESTER Dr D G H. Almondsbury Field, Tockington Lane, Almondsbury, Avon, BS12 4EB.
Silvester Silwester SYLVESTER F4853

168564 SYLVESTER Mrs Nicolette. 143 Elmer Road, Middleton On Sea, Bognor Regis, W Sussex, PO22 6HZ. Tel:0243-582045
BOWERS HINKS PRITCHARD SILVESTER SYLVESTER TRACE F350

168572 SYMONDS Mrs D G. 27 Haig Road, Aldershot, Hants, GU12 4PS.
BLORE DAVIES EWINS HAYWARD JEPSON NEWSOME PEEL RADFORD RANDALL SPRINKS SUMMERFIELD WAKLEY WEAKLEY F1380

168580 SYMONDS Dr John L. 14 Taloombi Street, Cronulla, NSW 2230, AUSTRALIA.
BAULCH BOULTON CAWSE CLOGG CROCKER GILLARD GUMMOW HITCHINS LITTLE LLOYD OSBORNE SYMONS TRAHER VERRAN WHITE F4172

168599 SYMONS Mr K. Kendall, 8 Uplands, Tavistock, Devon, PL19 8ET.
GLADSTONE SOLOMON SYMONS VERCOE WHITING F441

168602 TABEART Mr Colin. 238 Hunts Pond Road, Titchfield Common, Fareham, Hants, PO14 4PG.
ABBET ANDERSON Ascue ASKEW AYERS Ayres Ayscough BALLS BARRET BARRON BODINGTON BOWYER BRADSHAW BRIGHTLY Brightwell BUTCHER CHILVERS COPEMAN Crawlie Croley CROWLY DICKENS FISHER FOWLER GILBERT GILL Grudgefeild Grudgefeld GRUDGEFIELD HALL HALLS HATCH Heires HENMAN LAMBERT LANGFORD LAW LAWRENCE MASH MATTHEWS NICHOLAS NIGHTINGALE NIX PANNIFER PECK Pennifer PETTIT Pleasance PLEASANT Poll POWELL POWLES PRETTY RICHES RIDGE RISELEY Risely Risly ROOF Ryseley Rysley SABERTON SAUNDERS SAVAGE Savidge SAVIGE SEE SHARP SHELTON SPURDEN SPURGEON Spurgon Tabat TABBAT Tabbatt Tabbit Tabet Talbot Tawbutt TAYLOR Tbet THWAITES Tibbot TINDSLEY Tindsly Towler Twaites Twaits Tynsly WALKER WOODWARD F4647

168610 TAFT Mrs Pat. 27 Holmwood Avenue, Kidderminster, Worcestershire, DY11 6DB. Tel:0562-753446
BAKER GARDNER GREGG LETTICE PENSON POTTER F87

168629 TAGGART Miss Julie. 5 Botheby Wood, Skipton, N Yorks, BD23 1NE.
APPLETON HALL LINTON Medcalf Metcalf METCALFE PICKERING TAGGART TWEDALE Tweddale Tweddle Tweedale Twydale F3732

168637 TAIT Mrs B. (Walker) 26 Sunnybanks, Hatt, Saltash, Cornwall, PL12 6SA.
ASHTON AXFORD BALHATCHET BARRIE BAXTER BRIERE CHANNON CHITTY EARL MILLER PINK ROUX SHORT Spearing SPIRING Spuring Spyring Spyryng TAIT TAYLOR THOMPSON WALKER F4316

168645 TALBOT Mr Thomas. 3 Drum Wynd, Ellon, Aberdeenshire, AB41 9GN. Tel:0358-22308
FRANKS HEATH PLIMMER Plummer Plymer SWIFT TALBOT Talbott Talbut WHITMORE F5242

168653 TALBOT-ASHBY Mr Peter. 32 Palleg Road, Lower Cwmtwrch, Swansea Valley, SA9 2QE.
APPELBEE APPLEBEE APPLEBIE APPLEBY ASHBY CANNING DANIELS GARRARD GLADWELL LLOYD MARKHAM MAY MILLER PASK PRICE RICHARDSON TALBOT WARD WELHAM F633

168661 TALLANTIRE Dr Philip. Thanet Well, Hutton Roof, Penrith, Cumbria, CA11 0XX.
Talantire Talantyre Talentire Talentyre Talintire Talintyre TALLANTIRE Tallantyre Tallentire Tallentyre Tallintire Tallintyre F1253

168688 TALLISS Mr Anthony Charles. 4 Leyfields Crescent, Warwick, CV34 6BA. Tel:0926-493967
Tailles Taillis Tallis TALLISS Tayles Taylis Tolas WILKES F2849

168696 TAMBLIN Mrs L. 14 Copper Leaf Close, Moulton, Northampton, NN3 1HS.
ANDREWS BAKER BARTLETT BATTS Beakerfield BEVAN BRADLEY BRITTON BROWN CARDEW Chapman CLARK Clarke COLBAK COUCH CROSS ELSON Elsone FEAR FLETCHER HARRISON HASELY Haywood HENDON Heywood HIGHWOOD HILL HUNT JEPMAN KANE KEEN PEARCE Pearse PROBERT RICHARDS ROGERS Scull SKULL SMITH SNELL SUMNER TOY TRINDER VIZARD WAKEFIELD WIDGER F2960

168718 TAMBLIN Mr Stuart. 14 Copper Leaf Close, Moulton, Northampton, NN3 1HS.
ANEAR BADCOCK BEDLAKE BLACK Blacke BODDY Body

BONFIELD BRAMBLE BROAD BUCKLER BURNETT COLLING Collings DAYTON Deacon Deighton DINGLEY Dingly DUMBLE Eakings Eakins Easom Ekings EKINS FISHER FOX GOODMAN HAMBLY Hamly HANCOCK Handcock HARDING HART HOBY HOLKYN HOLMAN ISOM JANE JAY JOHN Johns KNIGHT LANGLEY Langly LANGMAN Larrat Larratt LARRETT LEWIN Lewing LOASBY Loseby LOWE Lowesby LOWETH Mais Marsden Marson MARSTON MAYES Mays MEADOWS MITCHELL MOOR NEAL NEEDHAM NICHOLAS Nicholls Oliver OLVER PEARN Pearne Pern Robbins ROBERTS ROBINS Robinson ROOTHAM ROPER Rotham Roton ROWE Saerson Sanders SARSON SAUNDERS Searson SHAWLER Simmons SKILLINGTON SLOGGETT SMITH SNELL STAYNES STOOKES Symonds SYMONS Tamblenson Tambleson TAMBLIN Tambling Tamblingson TAMBLINSON Tamlin Thomlin TILLEY Tilly Tomlin Tomlyn TREGENNA Trelisick TRELISSICK Trelizick Trelysick Trethack TRETHAKE WARD Warrenton Warrington WATERS WATTS WHITE WHITTLE WILLIAMS Worlich Worlington Worrington WORTHINGTON Wrootham Wrotham F2959

168726 TAMES Mr K S. Malton Lodge, 21 Howard Road, Reigate, Surrey, RH2 7JE. Tel:0737-243833
BRAY Coningston CONISTON Conningston Cuniston Cunningston Cunniston FARRO Farrow PAGE STAMP TABOR TAMES Tamms Tams WHITE WHITEHEAD F1557

168734 TAMM Mrs E A. (Spear) 166 Swanshurst Lane, Moseley, Birmingham, B13 0AW. Tel:021-777-7004
Baymont BEAUMONT Bemond Bemont CALKIN CAULKIN CAWKEN Cawkins DEACON HOCKING Hoskin HOSKINS Hoskyns PAGET Piff PITT Pitts Slater SLATTER Slaughter Spare SPEAR Speare Spears SUTTON WAITHMAN F1475

168742 TANN-WATSON Mrs Lynne. 2 Abthorpe Avenue, Kingsthorpe, Northampton, NN2 8NS. Tel:0604-842413
BAYLISS BRAND Caudle Caudwell CAULDWELL CHARLESWORTH COLTON GROVE KNIGHT LANE LOUTHAN LUCAS MARSHALL Stableford STAPLEFORD TANN TAYLOR TRICKETT F6391

168750 TANNER Mr J C. Half Way Tree, Wellingtonia Avenue, Crowthorne, Berks, RG11 6AF. Tel:0344-772401
BEVAN CURNOW DAVIES GABRIEL LAWRY LLEWELYN LUKE MAYBERRY MORGAN MORLEY NOALL PEARSON PRYOR REEDMAN REES RICHARDS STEVENS TANNER WALKER WILSHERE F570

168769 TANNER Mr James. Willowfield, Fords Heath, Shrewsbury, SY5 8QG.
TANNER F320

168777 TANNER Mr & Mrs S J. The Roost, 3 Rose Hill, Lovedean, Portsmouth Hants, PO8 9QU.
AYLING CHRISTY COLLIS COTTON COUCH CROSBIE CROUCH DOWLING DRURY FARMER FILLARY FOOT GREEN HALL HARE HUMPHREYS JUDD LEACH LEADBITTER MILES NOAKES PAGE PERRATON Philery PRESTON ROBINSON RYDER SAVAGE SEFFORD SHIRLEY STEWARD Stewart Stuart TANNER THOMAS VINCE VOYCE WAITE WALKER WELLS WHITEWAY WINSLAIDE YEATS F778

168785 TANNER Mrs Sarah. (Hinton) 2 Hospital Road, Sevenoaks, Kent, TN13 3PH. Tel:0732-740136
ASHTON CARTWRIGHT EVANS Henton HINTON LUXFORD NEVE STORR TANNER F4534

168807 TANSLEY Mr B. 77 Bishops Road, Kings Lynn, Norfolk, PE30 4NU. Tel:0553-762045
TANSLEY F3029

168815 TANSLEY Mr William. Thorncliffe, Gortonronach, Lochgair, Longilphead, Argyll, PA31 8SB. Tel:0546-86371
BARLOW CHADWICK CLARKSON COPLEY FIDLIN HEATON HESTERMANN HOLLINPRIEST HOLMES LEIGO F6339

168823 TAPSON Mrs Ursula. 7 St Anthonys Drive, Wick, Bristol, BS15 5PW. Tel:027582-2016
TAPSON F1057

168831 TARLING Mr John. 81 Forest Avenue, Fishponds, Bristol, BS16 4DA. Tel:0272-658873
KNIGHT Tarlin TARLING Teirling Thurling Torlon F4422

168858 TATCHELL Mr James A. Via Principe Evgenio 60, 00185 Rome, ITALY.
Tachell Tatchel TATCHELL F7057

168866 TATLER Mr C C. 8 Camden Way, Dorchester, Dorset, DT1 2RA.
Hilborn HILBORNE Hilbourn Hilbourne Hilburn Hillbourn Hillbourne Tather TATLER Tatley Tatlow Tatter Tattle Tattler F6796

168874 TATLER Mr C R. 12 Hallcroft, Ratho, Edinburgh, Scotland.
TATLER F6591

168882 TAYLOR Mr A J C. 60 Ashley Road, Farnborough, Hampshire, GU14 7HB.
BICKELL CARRUTHERS CUDLIPP Edgcom Edgcomb EDGCOMBE Edgcum Edgcumb Edgcumbe Edgecomb Edgecombe Edgecome Edgecumb Edgecumbe Egcom Egcumbe Eggecom Eggecombe Eggecumbe GRAY Hedgecombe Hitchcombe PADBURY TAYLOR THORPE F138

168890 TAYLOR Mrs B. (Weller) 27 The Uplands, Gerrards Cross, Bucks, SL9 7JQ. Tel:0753-885059
BRION HIATT WELLER F5801

168904 TAYLOR Mrs D M. 3 New Cottages, Homestall Road, Ashurstwood, Sussex, RH19 3PG. Tel:0342-823319
TEMPLETON F5763

168912 TAYLOR Mr David. 11 Athol Road, Bramall, Stockport, Cheshire, SK7 1BR. Tel:061-439-8656
ATHERTON BRAMSKILL BROOMFIELD DARE DAWSON GASKELL GEORGE HAINES HOLDEN HOLHURST LEIGH MASSEY PALMER RACKLEY SCHOFIELD SHELDON F6369

168920 TAYLOR Mrs Diedre M. 93 Balmoral Road, Morecambe, Lancs, LA3 1SS. Tel:0524-412284
BOOTH COURTNEY CROFT DEAN DRURY GIDDENS HARE HOLLIDAY HUMPHREY LEAH LYTHGOE MARKEY PAGE RIORDEN SECKER SHARPLES TAYLOR TIPPING TRUELOVE F2263

168939 TAYLOR Mrs Ethel M. (Waddelow) 12 Little Aston Hall, Aldridge Road, Little Aston, Sutton Coldfield, B74 3BH. Tel:021-353-9670
FITZJOHN MORDEN TRUSS WADDELOW Waddilow Waddilowe Wadelow Wadiloe WADLOW Wadlowe F15

168947 TAYLOR Mrs Eva. 54 Smethurst Lane, Bolton, Lancs, BL3 3QE. Tel:0204-64045
BLYDE CARDY COOKSON COPPLESTONE DICKINSON GOTOBED GREGORY HAINES Haynes HULSE JONES KAY LEESON NORRIS PANKHURST PLIMLEY Purdie PURDY TAYLOR WILLIAMS YEOMANS F3168

168955 TAYLOR Mr F. 265 Telegraph Road, Heswall, Wirral, Merseyside, L60 6RN. Tel:051-342-5922
BURGESS HOOLEY MALTBY TAYLOR F3026

168963 TAYLOR Mrs Frances. (Byford) 16 Mount Avenue, Rayleigh, Essex, SS6 7HS. Tel:0268-771196
BAYFORD Biford BYFORD BYFORT F1862

168971 TAYLOR Miss Frederica. 5 Trinity Place, Bull Street, Stratford On Avon, Warwickshire, CV37 6DU. Tel:0789-204647
LAGLAND LANCASTER WILLIAMS F3245

168998 TAYLOR Mr Ian. 25 Westingway, Bognor Regis, W Sussex, PO21 2XX.
BUCKHAM BULLEN MOYES TAYLOR F6403

169005 TAYLOR Mr Jack. 5 French Gardens, Cobham, Surrey, KT11 2AJ. Tel:0932-64985
PAMMENT PAYNE TAYLOR F2229

169013 TAYLOR Mrs Janice. 5 Thornton Close, Little Lever, Bolton, BL3 1NZ.
BARKER BRADLEY DAVIES GRUNDY MCKAY NOTHER PARKER TAYLOR WEBB WILKINSON F4354

169021 TAYLOR Mrs Joan. Box 408, Northampton, WA 6535, AUSTRALIA.
AUSTIN BOASE HIGH JONES KING MORRIS ROBERTS RYDER TAYLOR F5150

169048 TAYLOR Mrs Kathleen. (Caisley) 25 Rosedale Crescent, Pine Hills, Guisborough, Cleveland, TS14 8HZ. Tel:0287-638552
CAISLEY F4263

169056 TAYLOR Mr Lionel. Tresilian, 8 Laburnum Grove, Burscough, Lancashire, L40 0ST.
COCKCROFT DRAPER HAIGH HAWORTH JESSOP LOCKLEY RIGBY SLATER STEVENS TAYLOR WADE F3555

169064 TAYLOR Mrs M. 164 Cardigan Road, Bridlington, E Yorks, YO15 3NB.
AYRES GEARY WAINES WALLIS WEBB F3125

169072 TAYLOR Mrs O. White Cottage, 3 Townside, Haddenham, Bucks, HP17 8BG.
ALLMARK Hallmark F6769

169080 TAYLOR Mrs P J. 4 Chestnut Close, Hampton, Evesham, Worcs, WR11 6PA.

DITCHAM SMOWTON F3281
169099 TAYLOR Miss Patricia A. 89 Newsborough Road, Shirley, Solihull, W Midlands, B90 2HB. Tel:021-745-2867
CAWLEY GAYDEN Gaydon Geaden Geden TAYLOR TREHERNE F2859
169102 TAYLOR Mrs Penelope Ann. 16 Roper Close, Rainham, Gillingham, Kent, ME8 9QX. Tel:0634-373761
CLOUD HARRISON NEIGHBOUR ROBINSON SEARLES TAYLOR F2888
169110 TAYLOR Mr R & Mrs M. 64 Wansbeck Avenue, Cullercoats, North Shields, Tyne & Wear, NE30 3DJ.
DAVISON JOHNSTON SABISTON TAYLOR F1243
169129 TAYLOR Mr Richard. 81 Mountbatten Avenue, Sandal, Wakefield, W Yorks, WF2 6HE. Tel:0924-256644
Aldrid Aldridge CLAYDON COBB DAVISON DINES FAILES FORTH GREEN JOHNSON JOLLY KIDD MAUD MECK MITCHELL MONUMENT Oldrid Oldridge Oldroid OLDROYD Oldroyde POLLYN POSTLE SHIRLEY SKINNER STANFORD SUGARS Tailor Taler Talor Tayler TAYLOR TUCK WHITE F1967
169137 TAYLOR Mr S C. 29 Upland Drive, Colchester, Essex, CO4 4PZ.
Ball Balle BALLS Mintar MINTER Mintor Myntar Mynter Peach Peache PEACHEY Peachie Peachy Peachye Pech Peche Pechie SADLER F303
169145 TAYLOR Mrs Sylvia. (Rees) 12 Blaen-Y-Coed, Radyr, Cardiff. Tel:0222-843189
BETTS GAMMON HALL MAY REES F7454
169153 TAYLOR Mrs Val. Glen Cottage, Bridge, Nr Redruth, Cornwall, TR16 4QG.
NELSON SALTER F4531
169161 TAYLOR Mr W J. 30 Peregrine Drive, Darwen, Lancs, BB3 0JL. Tel:0254-774589
COURT Currey CURRIE Curry FAIRCLOUGH Feakes Ffoks FOAKES Fokes Foks Folkes HALEWOOD LEDINGHAM LLOYD MCPHIE PINHAY TAYLOR TOWNLEY WALLACE F751
169188 TAYLOR Mr Warwick G. 17 Vallis Way, Hook, Chessington, Surrey, KT9 1PX. Tel:081-397-2920
BUTEUX GUYVER KNIPE TAYLOR WILKS F5953
169196 TAYLOR Mr William Boneham. 4 The Courtyard, Bishopthorpe, York, YO2 1RD. Tel:0904-707063
BONEHAM Boomham F43
169218 TAYLOR-DICKSON Mr James. 57 Clonmel Road, London, SW6 5BL.
BLYTH CLARK DICKSON DOUGAL FRANKHAM HENDERSON LANDELLS SHELL TAYLOR WILSON F2022
169226 TAYTON Mr K J J. Stoneycroft House, Shirenewton, Chepstow, Gwent, NP6 6RQ.
BAXTER BRITON HAMER SMITH TAYTON F3352
169234 TAZEWELL Mr Frank Toms. 47 Mays Lane, Stubbington, Hants, PO14 2EN.
BARFOOT BRASSINGTON GANNAUAY PIKE PUGSLEY RUSSELL SMITH TASWELL TOMS WADE F1592
169242 TAZEWELL Mrs Mollie. 47 Mays Lane, Stubbington, Hants, PO14 2EN.
BRISON COWLES GROVES KING MARTIN PHAROAH POOR PRATT READ SIBLEY F1593
169250 TEAGUE Mrs Dorothea. 18 Manor Way, Petts Wood, Kent, BR5 1NW.
ALLINSON AULT BARKER BLUNDELL COLE ELMS HOMEWOOD POBGEE SILK TEAGUE TULLOCH WEEKLY F1199
169269 TEARLE Miss Barbara M. 9 Burrows Close, Headington, Oxford, OX3 8AN.
TEARLE F6594
169277 TEASDALE Mrs Margaret. (Acornley) 3 Cumberland Grove, Norton, Stockton On Tees, Cleveland, TS20 1NT.
Acarnley Ackernley ACORNLEY F3441
169285 TEBAY Mr Philip John Holt. 13 Belmont Road, West Kirby, Wirral, L48 5EY.
HOLT TEBAY F1908
169293 TEBBIT Mr Arthur L. Birds Hill, Chalk Lane, East Horsley, Surrey, KT24 6TJ. Tel:04865-2850
Tebaud Tebbet TEBBIT Tebbot Tebbut Tebet Tebit Tebot Theobald Thibaud Thibault Tibaud Tibbet Tibbets Tibbit F6266
169307 TEBBLE Mr N. 4 Brights Crescent, Edinburgh, Scotland, EH9 2DB.
Tebbel TEBBLE F6728
169315 TEBBS Mrs Pauline. 10 Ainthorpe Close, Burdon Park, Tunstall Village, Sunderland, SR3 2DA. Tel:091-523-6843
BRINDLEY COLLEY GRAHAM MASON MAULE MEEK ROWLEY SCOTT SHROUDER SMITH STANSFIELD F1388
169323 TEDD Mr Michael R. The Old Manse, 107 Forest Gate, Anstey, Leicester, LE7 7FJ. Tel:0533-366394
ASTON BALDWIN Baldwyn Birtchnell BROXHOLME BURCHNALL CARTER COLDICOTT CULL FOSTER GILES Goyles HITCH Holihead Hollehead Holleyhead Hollyhead HOLYHEAD KINNERSLEY LAUGHTON Lawton LITTLE LOWE MASON MEEK ONIONS PERE POVEY Radcliff Radcliffe Ratcliff RATCLIFFE ROBERTS ROBINSON Tead Ted TEDD Tedde Tedds Tede Teds Tidd Tudd WILKES F3877
169331 TEECE Mr Brian V. 4 Eastville Avenue, Rhyl, Clwyd, LL18 3TH. Tel:0745-351284
TEECE Tees Teese F2412
169358 TEESE Mrs M. F1/6 Bronte Court, Williamstown, Victoria 3016, Australia.
CHALLIS GORE GREGSON HURLE MAYOH NELSON WINDROSS F1698
169366 TEGGIN Mr Robert. 33 Ellys Road, Radford, Coventry, Warks, CV1 4EW. Tel:0203-256422
TEGGIN TEGIN F5718
169374 TEMPLE Mrs Daisy. 14 Castle Rise, Belmsthorpe, Stamford, Lincs, PE9 4JL.
BERRIDGE CHAPPEL CODRINGTON DALE DORMAN HARRIS HURLEY KELLAND KELLOND SHARPE SNOWBALL TEMPLE WEARE WHEARE F1486
169382 TEMPLE Mr M. Ploggs Hall East Barn, Whetsted, Five Oak Green, Tonbridge, Kent, TN12 6SE. Tel:0892-834563
LONG POOLE PRUST TEMPLE F4423
169390 TEMPLETON Mr John. The Pikers Pad, Hillside Walk, Storrington, West Sussex, RH20 3HL. Tel:0903-745521
INGLIS KENT MOLISON STRACHAN TEMPLETON YOUNG F5340
169404 TENNET Mr H W. 19 Glendining Avenue, Dunedin, 9001, NEW ZEALAND.
BECK GLEN GRAY MURRAY PATRICK PETCH ROBINSON SIMON TENNET F4439
169412 TEPPER Mr Philip. 30 Edenfield Road, Prestwich, Manchester, M25 8EE. Tel:061-740-4860
BENNETT BENNION GREEN MANSON MILLER MORRIS MOSES ROBERTSHAW SMITH WARD WILLIAMS F5817
169420 TERRELL Mr William. 13 Buckstone Shaw, Edinburgh, Lothian, EH10 6XP. Tel:031-445-1080
LOTHIAN RYDER TERRELL F2784
169439 TERRY Mr Steve. Rountre, Fernleigh Road, Grange Over Sands, Cumbria, LA11 7HT.
AUSTIN BARRET CARLTON CATLOW Chatlow COOPER CRONKSHAW ENTWISTLE FRANCE GILKES GRACE HANSON HINDLE HORTON HOYLE KESBEY LINGARD NAYLOR NUTTALL PILKINGTON Pilkinton RILEY SHIRLEY SIDES TERRY Walkman Warkman Warpman WEST WILCOCK WORKMAN F345
169447 TERRY Mrs V. 12 Mount Avenue, Harold Park, Romford, Essex, RM3 0DE.
Goard GOURD F7082
169455 TEULON Mr Alan E. 54 Clarence Avenue, Northampton, NN2 6NZ. Tel:0609-711755
TEULON F6486
169463 TEVENDALE Mr Brian K. 15 Field Drive, Clive, Shrewsbury, Shropshire, SY4 3LB. Tel:0939-28524
Tavendale Tavidale Taviotdale TEVENDALE Tevidale Tevindale Teviotdale TIVENDALE Tividale Tivindale Tiviotdale F3974
169471 TEW Mr Alan J. 43 Chanctonbury Way, Woodside Park, London, N12 7AA. Tel:081-445-5692
Bounce BUNCE Bunch Chew DOVE DUMBELTON Penil Pennil Pennill Penny Pinel Pinell PINNEL Pinnell Pynnell TEW Toe Too Tue F3032
169498 THACKER Mrs Margaret E. The Lilacs, High Road, Whaplode, Spalding Lincs, PE12 6TG. Tel:0406-370037
BAILEY KING KNOWLES PARSONS F2211
169501 THAIN Mrs Jean. (Turnbull) 101 Lethame Road, Strathaven, Strathclyde, ML10 6EF. Tel:0357-22501

CARRUTHERS CRAIG FORD GEMMELL KERR LAIDLAW MCCRIRICK MCKERROW MERRY Mirrey SATTERTHWAITE TITMUS TURNBULL F4020

169528 THAIN Mrs Jean. 31 Riverdale Gardens, Twickenham, Middx, TW1 2BX.
BARLEY BRADLEY BRIGHT BRUFORD DOBLE FENTON HARTLEY HORSMAN KEMP MARGETTS MESTON SAVAGE STANILAND THAIN TUNKS F2018

169536 THATCHER Miss U R. 15 Stoney Lane, Hailsham, East Sussex, BN27 2AP.
BLAINEY CULVERHOUSE ENSBY LEMON NORTHCOTE RINGE THATCHER WILKES F4038

169544 THEAKER Mrs D A. 89 Burringham Road, Scunthorpe, S Humberside, DN17 2DF. Tel:0724-846993
BRASIER LYNAUGH THEAKER WINKWORTH F641

169552 THEXTON Mr Neil. 31 Caton Green Road, Brookhouse, Lancaster, Lancs, LA2 9JJ.
ATKINSON BAISBROWN BARNES Besbrowne Bisborwn Bysbrown DICKINSON FARRER GOOSE GORST MITCHELL Orman Ormand ORMOND Ormonde Seddan Sedden SEDDON STAINTON Stenton STEWARDSON STIRZAKER STRETCH Sturzaker Thaxton Theaxton Theckston THEXTON THIRNBECK TOWNLEY WARRINER WINSTER F1469

169560 THIRSK Mr James Wood. 1 Hadlow Castle, Hadlow, Tonbridge, Kent, TN11 0EG. Tel:0732-850708
CHAPMAN COWPER ELLA GOODHAND HALL HUTTON SIMPSON THIRSK WILKIE WOOD F2846

169579 THISTLEWOOD Revd Michael J. 9 Lightburn Road, Ulverston, Cumbria, LA12 0AU. Tel:0229-54687
THISTLEWOOD F1168

169587 THODAY Mr Alan F. 5 The Hollins, Holloway, Matlock, Derbyshire, DE4 5BA. Tel:0629-534344
THODAY THODY F127

169595 THOMAS Mrs Angela. 81 Crabtree Lane, Lancing, W Sussex, BN15 9NH.
ARMSTRONG Blacklock Blaiklock BLAYLOCK Blellock BREWER DIMBLEBY ENGLAND Ingland ROBEY Roby Rolf ROLFE Rolph THOMAS Troubridge TROWBRIDGE WILSON F163

169609 THOMAS Mrs Anne Usher. 30 Brigbourne Drive, Seaton, Workington, Cumbria, CA14 1JG. Tel:0900-63090
ROBERTS SIMPKINS SMART USHER WILLIAMS F4934

169617 THOMAS Mrs Brenda. (Briddick) 6 Mount Gardens, Bare, Morecambe, Lancs, LA4 6AS. Tel:0524-423729
Bradach Braddick Braddock Braddocke Bradick Braidack Bredack Breddack BRIDACK Briddack Briddeck BRIDDICK Briddock Brideck Bridick Bridock Broddock F6216

169625 THOMAS Mrs Bronwen. (Glenister) 36 Faraday Road, Croydon South, Victoria, 3136, AUSTRALIA.
BEATTY BESLEY BRADSHAW BRUNT BULLER CATTERSON CHAPMAN CRESSWELL DAVIES DICKINSON DUMONT GLENIE GLENISTER HOLDEN HOOD JONES MORGAN MOYLE NEIL OPIE OUSLEY POLLOCK PRINCE PUTNAM RICHARDS SCOTT THOMAS THORNE WALDIE WELLS WILSON F4461

169633 THOMAS Janet E. Po Box 245, Novinger, MO 63559, USA. Tel:+1-816-488-6616
Genning Gennings Gennins Gilling Ginning Ginnings Ginnins Jellings Jenings Jenkins Jenning JENNINGS Jennins Jilling Jining Jinnings Jinnins STEWART F7301

169641 THOMAS Miss June. 19 Melton Walk, Hemilngton, Middlesborough, Cleveland, TS8 9NB. Tel:0642-595562
BIGGINS BLAKE BONE BUCHANAN FIELD HARDY JUDE PEARMAN THOMAS F3355

169668 THOMAS Mr Kenneth Gordon. 10 Brompton Road, York, YO3 6NJ. Tel:0904-638239
HAYNES THOMAS WILLIAMS F3411

169676 THOMAS Mrs Lola D. (Bramich) 18 Mortensen Road, Nerang, Queensland, 4211, AUSTRALIA.
AUSTIN BARCLAY BONNEY Bonny BOTT Bramich BROMWICH FUDGE HOLLINS KELCEY F5500

169684 THOMAS Mr Michael John. 17 Richmond Place, Ilkley, West Yorks, LS29 8TJ.
Dereham DERHAM Dyrram Dyrrham F7131

169692 THOMAS Mr N L. Holly Lodge, Norwich Road, Salhouse, Norfolk, NR13 6QQ.
BARRETT BARTLETT HORNBY Hornsby O'neil O'NEILL O'niel TARRANT TAYLOR THOMAS Willet Willett Willoit Willot WILLOTT F980

169706 THOMAS Mr Peter. Roding View, London Road, Abridge, Romford Essex, RM4 1X8. Tel:037881-3256
THOMAS WYATT F909

169714 THOMAS Mr Ronald P H L. Farthings, Hillcrest Drive, Tunbridge Wells, Kent, TN2 3AG. Tel:0892-535844
THOMAS F4715

169722 THOMAS Mrs Rosemary. 118 Milton Road, Weston Super Mare, Avon, BS23 2UW. Tel:0934-622095
COOKE CREBER CROSSLEY FLEET HICKS SKERRETT THOMAS WELLINGTON F4729

169730 THOMAS Mrs Sheila F. (Cooper) 8 Glebelands, Claygate, Esher, Surrey, KT10 0LF.
ABBOTT ADAMS ALLEN ARMITAGE BAILEY BALDERSON Baley BEAL BODMEAD BOLDERSTONE BROWN CANN CHANDLER CLARKE CONGRAVE CONGREVE CONGRIEVE COOPER CRABB Delahoy DELANOY EMMERSON FERRABY FREEMAN GEARL GEARLE GILLOTT Girle GOODCHILD Gotsheim GOTYHEIN GREGORY HANDSEL Hansell HAYDEN INGRAM JOHNS JOHNSON JONES KNIGHT LAWSON LAWSON-FREEMAN LINCOLN Martin MARTYN MECK MONIMENT MONUMENT MOORE NASH OSMAN OTHEN PAINE Payne POINTER Poynder QUINCE Quincey RICKETTS ROGERS ROWELL Ruffell RUFFIED SHARP SMITH SONGHURST SPENCER STAMPERS THOMAS TRING VINCE WHITBY WIGG WINCHWORTH WINKWORTH WORBEY WORRALL F2966

169749 THOMPSON Mr Allan. 83 Victoria Road, Sherwood, Nottingham, NG5 2NL. Tel:0602-603928
ARCHER EASTON MARSHALL MASSEY OSCROFT SOULBY STORER TEBBUTT THOMPSON WATSON F3127

169757 THOMPSON Mrs Ann. 2 Baron Street, Fenton, Stoke On Trent, Staffs, ST4 3PH. Tel:0782-332510
BURROUGHS LEE Simms SIMS STIMPSON Stimson WILLIAMSON F758

169765 THOMPSON Mrs Brenda S. 73 Threlfall Road, Blackpool, Lancs, FY1 6NW.
Anthorn Hathorn Hathorne Hauthni Hawthen Hawthorn HAWTHORNE Hawthornthwaite Hawtyn Haythorne Horethorn Horthorn Horton Hothorne Houghton Orton F6986

169773 THOMPSON Mr Charles. Coombers Farm, Partridge Lane, Newdigate, Surrey, RH5 5EE. Tel:0306-77248
EDWARDS HART HILL HOWELL JORDAN MORRIS SAGE SOUTHGATE THOMPSON F5066

169781 THOMPSON Mr Christopher. 6 Briar Lane, Carshalton, Surrey, SM5 4PX. Tel:081-647-4916
ALLINGHAM ATKINSON BACKHOUSE BEE BELL BILLOP BILLOPP BOORER BOWMER BROADHEAD CARR CLARK COATES COLDWELL COWELL DAVIS DEARMAN DONALDSON ELRINGTON FARMAR FERRIS GAMBLE GILES GODSALVE GREEN HALL HARRIS HASWELL HAZELWOOD HEDLEY HUITSON HUME HUNTER KITSON KNOTT MASON MILLS MITCHELL MOORE MUNDAY NEWTON PAXTON PEACOCK PEASE PRANKEARD RHODES RICHARDSON ROBSON SEVERS SMITH SPRY STRATTON STRINGER THOMPSON WARD WELFOOT WHITE WILLIS F3812

169803 THOMPSON Mrs E R. 18 Pentland Road, Bushey, Watford, Herts, WD2 3QN.
ALLWOOD BRASIER GRAGG HUNTINGTON JONES OSWIN THOMPSON VANN WILLIS F2186

169811 THOMPSON Mrs Elizabeth. 42 Slade Valley Avenue, Rothwell, Kettering, Northants, NN14 2HR. Tel:0536-712347
BRERETON F172

169838 THOMPSON Mr Ian. 6 Ferndale Avenue, Frankby, Wirral, Merseyside, L48 1NW.
FLANAGAN GOODMAN HALL MARSH THOMPSON WEATHERCUP F5823

169846 THOMPSON Dr Jean. (Mcintosh) 62 Ringway, Garforth, Leeds, West Yorks, LS25 1BZ.
ATKINSON BUCKLE VARLEY F5376

169854 THOMPSON Mr Keith. 8 Byron Close, Bletchley, Milton Keynes, MK3 5BD.
BONEHILL Bonel Bonell Bonhil Bonhill Bonnel Bonnell BYWORTH CHARNLEY EDMONDSON FRENCH HICKMANS MOWBRAY REAY THOMPSON F4824

169862 THOMPSON Mr Leslie H. Gable Cottage, Rookery Road, Staines, Middx, TW18 1BT.

Tel:0784-454902
CHILTON CHINNEREY FLETCHER GIBSON LOCKETT MAINWARING Mannering Manwaring MARSHALL Mison Misson MYSON Mysson PARDOE Pardow Pinckney PINKNEY PRINCE Pyncknaye Pyncknye REVELL SALT SANDERS Sparehawke SPARHAWKE Sparrowhawk STANFIELD Stansfield TEAGUE THOMPSON Thomson Tigue Tompson Tomson F1893

169870 THOMPSON Mrs Margaret. (Sleath) 3 Higher Chelburn, Summit, Littleborough, Lancs, OL15 9QX.
SLEATH F5252

169889 THOMPSON Mr & Mrs P H. (Smith) 46 Grange Avenue, Old Normanton, Derby, DE3 8DG. Tel:0332-768149
Antcliff Antcliffe ANTLIFF Antliffe BARKER BURNELL LINGS MARRIOTT PACEY PEMBERTON RADFORD REDGATE SHORT SMITH TANSLEY THOMPSON TYERS F2009

169897 THOMPSON Mrs Sylvia. 45 Pollock Walk, Dunfermline, Scotland, KY12 9DA.
BURNS COX FLOCKHART HANKEY JASPER KIRKWOOD LLOYD MADDOCKS Milliner Millner MILNER ROBERTS THOMPSON F857

169900 THOMSON Mrs Coral. (Shaw) 34 Kingwell Lane, Worsbrough, Barnsley, S Yorks, S70 4HA. Tel:0226-203553
BEARDSHALL LONG SHAW THOMSON F1790

169919 THOMSON Miss Margaret L. 16 Reed Close, Eltham Road, London, SE12 8UD.
BOONE DUNLOP INGLIS JAMES MCPHEE STIRRAT THOMSON F5220

169927 THOMSON Mr Peter D. 26 Lee Lane, Royston, Barnsley, South Yorkshire, S71 4RT. Tel:0226-722449
FOWLER HARTLEY RAMAGE THOMSON F4323

169935 THOMSON Mrs S M. (Schlamp) 3 Caesars Way, Shepperton, Middx, TW17 8HT.
BETTRIDGE BIRD CLEAVER CLITHEROE FRANKLIN GARDINER JOWETT KARBY MARSHALL NOKES OWEN Sharpenton Sharpentyne Sharperton Sharpertone Sharpertonn Sharpertonne SHARPINGTON Sharpinton Sheppington SNELSON SPRINGETT TALLENTINE F6006

169943 THOMSON Mrs S M. 14 Doubledays, Cricklade, Swindon, Wiltshire, SN6 6AU.
BARBER BETTRIDGE BIRD CLITHEROE HARROLD JOWITT MARSHALL NOKES OWEN SHARPINGTON SPRINGETT F1894

169951 THORBURN Revd Peter. 12 Drake Road, Wells, Somerset, BA5 3JX. Tel:0749-672919
THORBURN F3998

169978 THORNE Mrs Rita. The Stable, Sandyway Farm, Off Walsall Road, Lichfield, Staffs, WS13 8JJ. Tel:0543-264560
BUNTING GRAHAM JAMES KIDD MORTON OXLEY RUSSELL SMITH THORNE F2950

169986 THORNETT Mrs Marian R L. (Blunn) Cae Derwen, Church Lane, Nantmel, Llandrindod Wells, Powys, LD1 6EH. Tel:0597-823013
Blon Blune BLUNN Blunne Deaken DEAKIN DUTTON Hackerson HACKESON Hacksun HAYNES HOLCRAFT Holcroft LEWIS Mealey MELLEY Melly Meloy OCRAFT PARSONAGE Personage SMITH THORNETT F6007

169994 THORNHILL Mr C E. Warren Cottage, Warren Road, Southrepps, Norwich Norfolk, NR11 8UN.
BECK BELTON THORNHILL F168

170003 THORNTHWAITE Mr Leslie. Wear Bridge House, Bouth, Ulverston, Cumbria, LA12 8JB. Tel:0229-861486
THORNTHWAITE F759

170011 THORNTON Glenda. 4020 Duplin Drive, Greensboro, NC 27407, USA.
PHILLIBROWN F7345

170038 THORNTON Sheila. (Graham) Littlemoor Farm, Littlemoor, Queensbury, Bradford Yorkshire, BD13 1DB. Tel:0274-882479
AMBLER CHAFFER FIRTH GRAHAM HASTE HELSOP JAGGER PRATTEN SPARKES THORNTON F593

170046 THORNTON Mr W Roy. 2 Eleanor Place, Gt Barton, Bury St Edmunds, Suffolk, IP31 2QT. Tel:028487-578
GENT MILLHOUSE THORNTON F5069

170054 THOROWGOOD Miss L. Lesser High Birks, Clapham, Via Lancaster, Lancs, LA2 8HD.
BERTRAM BOYCE BRINDLEY GURR HARDS HICKS LOFT TAYLER THOROWGOOD WHITEHEAD F5711

170062 THORPE Mr Leslie. 62 Holtby Street, Manchester, M9 1AR.
ELY MCCALLAM Mccullam Mcellam Mcellum MERRIN Thorp THORPE Thorrp F3213

170070 THOULD Mr Robert H. 27 Hawthorn Road, Evesham, Worcs, WR11 6HP.
Theuld Thold Thole THOULD Thowell Thowld F319

170089 THUBRON Mr R Stanley. Whitburn House, 47 Front Street, Whitburn, Sunderland, SR6 7JG. Tel:091-529-2059
Thubboron Thubbron THUBRON F3761

170097 THURSFIELD Mr Mark. 2/32 Moat Lane, Yardley, Birmingham, B26 1TJ. Tel:021-783-1908
BADSEY BRIDGEN MINSHULL THURSFIELD WINDRIDGE F1005

170100 THURSTON Mrs Margaret. 14 Bournelea Avenue, Burnage, Manchester, M19 1AF. Tel:061-432-3466
CAINK DUCKETT GREEN F701

170119 TICEHURST Mr Alan M. 49 Gore Park Road, Eastbourne, E Sussex, BN21 1TG. Tel:0323-36474
ARNDALE GILLINGHAM KEBBY MARLOW NORKETT STRATTON TICEHURST TYHURST F3075

170127 TICEHURST Revd John. The Manse, Exeter Road, Braunton, Devon, EX33 2BN. Tel:0271-812574
GALBRAITH TICEHURST F630

170135 TICKNER Mr Arthur G. 4 Pound Place Close, Shalford, Guildford, Surrey, GU4 8HL. Tel:0483-69596
GRAHAM JONES LANE LANGFORD MCGIL NEWTON OWEN POTTER Ticknar TICKNER Ticknor Ticner Tikner TUCKER Tyckner Tycner Tykener Tykenore Tykner F132

170143 TICKNER Mr V J. 24 Crown Gardens, Brighton, Sussex, BN1 3LD. Tel:0273-727671
ALDRED ALEXANDER BETSWORTH Bettsworth BINSTED Bird Birt Blakesley BLAXLEY BONE BROOKS BURT Carwood CAWOOD CHUTER Clout Cloute CLOUTT CLOUTTE Clowte COCKE Cocks COLLYER COOK COPUS Cox DE FRESNE De Ticheners De Tichenoure De Tykenore DUNMORE EMM Emms FELPES FRANKS GAMMIDGE GRAVATT GROVER GUNNER HALL HAMMOND HAMOND HARRAS HARRIS HARVIE HEATH HENCHMAN HOLDFORTH HOUNSOME KEMP LANE LEGGE LOVE NOVELL Nowell OAKESHOTT Okeshot Oxeate PARKER PEARCE PIPER PLEDGER POOLE REED RUSSELL SCOONES Scoons Searl SEARLE Serle SHARMAN SHEAT SMITH SMITHERS STENT STEVENS Striddick Stridduck STRUDWICK STURT TAYLOR Techener Techiner Techinor Technear Teckner Tecner Teknor TERRY Tetchener Tetchner Tichenar Tichener Tichenner Tichiner Tichinor Tichinour Tichmour Tichnar Tichner Tichnore Tickerner Tickernor Tickiner Tickinor Ticknar TICKNER Tickno Ticknor Ticknore Ticknour Ticne Ticner Ticnor Tikner TILLEY Tilly Tinchiner Titcharton Titchener Titchenor Titchiner Titchner Titchoner Tochener Tockne Tockner Touchener Trikner Tuchener Tuchenor Tuchiner Tuchinor Tuckne Tuckner Tupne TURNER Tutchener Tutchiner Twichener Twychener Twychenor Tycenare Tychenar Tychener Tychenor Tychenour Tychiner Tychinor Tychyner Tyckener Tyckner Tycknor Tycknore Tycknour Tycne Tycner Tyeknor Tygnor Tykenar Tykener Tykenor Tykenore Tykenour Tyknar Tyknare Tykner Tyknere Tyknor Tyknore Tyknour Tylkenor Tynchiner Tynchyner Tynckor Tytchenor WELLS WILLIAMSON York YORKE F822

170151 TIDSALL Mr Peter E. The Spinney, Penny Long Lane, Derby, DE3 1AW.
DANGERFIELD Tideswell TIDSALL Tidsell Tidza Tisdall WINROW F7177

170178 TIGHE Mr M F. Strath Colin, Pettridge Lane, Mere, Wiltshire, BA12 6DG.
ABBOTT ALLAN ALLEN BAILY BAKER BLICK BOOKLAND BRATFIELD BUTCHER CARTER CLARK COGGER COLLINGE Colven Colville Colvin COLWELL CURD DOBSON EDMONSON EDMUNDSON ELLIS ELPHICK FEW FREEMAN Fryman HARPER HAZELL HUMPHREY LETT LOVELOCK LOWE MCCONCHY MINCHIN MORGER PICKETT RANDALL RICHARDSON SAVERY SHERMAN SIMS SLOPER STEPHENS SWADLING Swatling TAWS Tawse TIGHE

TURK WHITE WINSTONE Woodhouse WOODHURST Woodus F1209

170186 TIGWELL Mr M J. 21 Bovington Heights, Marlow, Bucks, SL7 2JR. Tel:0628-473588
HEMMINGS PENNEY Tigal Tigalle TIGGALL TIGWELL Tygal Tyghall F835

170194 TILBURY Mr Charles. C/o 0212, A-1010 Wien, Schubertring 5, AUSTRIA. Tel:+43-1-711943817
BURFORD CANTRILL CLAY Claye COX CUBLEY DRAPER FLETCHER HAYBITELL HICKMAN HOLLELY HOLLOWAY LEIGHTON MATLEY NICKIN ORGAN SALE TILBURY WALTERS WILLEY WYERS F2201

170208 TILL Mr Arthur Thomas. 55 Brunswick Avenue, New Southgate, London, N11 1HR.
TILL F2996

170216 TILLER Mr C F R. Swanthorpe House, Farnham, Surrey, GU10 5HH.
ANDERSON BELL BENHAM BERTIE BLANDFORD BRACHER BREWER BUDDEN BURT BUTT COMPTON CROOKE DORE Elfe EVERLEY EYRES Farnehill Farnell Farnhill Farnol Feltam FELTHAM Fernell FORD FRANCIS FRICKER FRY FURNELL GERRARD GRAY Halleck HARRIS Hascol Hascoll HASKELL HAYLOCK HEYTER HILLIER HUNT INGRAM JEFFERY JENKINS KING LAMPARD LANE Larcomb Larcombe LARKAM Larkham LOCK LONG LUCAS LUSH LUTER Maihoo MANSTONE MAYHEW Mayo MORTIMER MOXHAM Nickland NICKLEM Nicklen OSBORNE PARHAM PENNY Pike Pothecary Potticarie POTTICARY PRIEST PYKE RAWKINS RICHMOND ROGERS SAMWYAS SANGER SCAMMELL SINGLETON STANGMORE STICKLAND SWEETAPPLE SYME Thrumboy Thrymbie Tillar TILLER Tillier Tilyer Topp TOPPE Trembe Trimbie TRIMBY Trymbie Tylyer WARDNER Warner WEBB Whicker WHITCHER Whitear Whitier WILKINS WOODFORD Yealf YELF Yelfe Yellowes YOUNG F4955

170224 TILLEY Mr John. 35 Point Hill, London, SE10 8QW.
MISTOVSKY TILLEY F5395

170232 TILMOUTH Mr James E. 23 Romford Road, Warsash, Southampton, Hants, SO3 9GZ. Tel:0489-57665
MANNERS Tillemuth TILLMUTH TILMOUSE TILMOUTH Tyllemuth TYLLEMUTHE F2897

170240 TILY Mrs Janet. (Brodribb) 22 Prestbury, Yate, Bristol, BS17 4LB. Tel:0454-314279
Baggetripe Baketerpe Baudrip Broaderib Broaderibb Broadrib Broadribb Broadrip Broadripp Broderibb Broderip Broderipp Brodrib BRODRIBB Brodrip Brodripp Broerib Tiley TILY F3918

170259 TIMBERS Miss S M. 21 Ash Close, Watlington, Oxon, OX9 5LW.
Timber TIMBERS F6744

170267 TIMINEY Mrs K M. 227 Warning Tongue Lane, Cantley, Doncaster, S Yorks, DN4 6TT. Tel:0302-530037
ANDREWS APPLEYARD BELSTEN Belstone Bilstone BOLTON Bulstone CLAY COATH Doveton DRAKE Duffton Duftan DUFTON FARRER GRIMSHAW KEIGHLEY LANGLEY MANN OSBORNE PEARSON ROSS STEPHENSON TOOGOOD WADE WESTMORLAND F1603

170275 TIMPERLEY Mr Dave. 111 Chester Road, Hazel Grove, Stockport, Cheshire, SK7 6HG. Tel:061-487-2868
TIMPERLEY F3807

170283 TIMS Mr John. 84 Amberley Road, Hilsea, Portsmouth, Hants, PO2 0TQ. Tel:0705-691950
CRIPPS Timbs Times Timms TIMS F3639

170291 TINLEY Miss R. 16 Lincoln Road, North Hykeham, Lincoln, LN6 8HE.
ALMOND CROPLEY GLASIER Glaysier Glayzier Glazier PARNELL PEPPER PINNER TAYTON Threadgold Tindley Tingley TINLEY TREADGOLD Tredgold Tredgould F6292

170305 TINNEY Mr T M. Po Box 1980, Salt Lake City, UT 84110, USA.
Teney Tenney Tennie TINNEY F6640

170313 TIPPER Mr Michael. 234 Monkmoor Road, Telford Estate, Shrewsbury, Shropshire, SY2 5SP. Tel:0743-51437
COVENTRY EVA EVERISS GINDLER GIRDLER GOODCHILD GREEN HARRIS HARTSHORN HYDE MILLS POTTER RICHARDS SCONSE SCOTT SCOUSE SKIDMORE SPRAGG TAGG TIPPER TROUNCE WALDRON WILLIAMS WILSON WOODHOUSE F2450

170321 TISDALL Miss Margaret E. 10 Aldhelm Court, Southville Road, Bradford On Avon, Wilts, BA15 1HW. Tel:0225-868231
AYRES COOMBES EARL TISDALL TURNER F5906

170348 TITCOMBE Mrs J. (Sunderland) 18 Radway Road, Shirley, Southampton, SO1 2PW.
Ackroyd AINLEY AKEROYD Aneley ARMITAGE ASHFORTH BARBER BATES BATSON Beamand BEAUMONT BERRY BINGLEY BLAKE BOLER BRADFURTH BRADLEY BRAMMER BRAY BROOKE BROWN BURDEN BUTHROYD BUTLER CARPENTER CHARLESWORTH CLAYTON COLE COLLIER COOPER CRABTREE CROWTHER CUTHBERT DAWSON DICKINSON Durrance DURRANS DYSON EASTWOOD ELLIS EVANS FAHERTY FARRAND FELL Fells Footitt FOOTTIT FRANCIS FRANKLIN Futtit GARSIDE GREEN GREENAWAY GREENWOOD GRIFFIN GRIMES HAGGOT HAIGH HANBY Handley HARDY HARRISON HARTLEY HAUKES HEY HILL HIND HINDER Hinds HIRST HODSON HOLLICK HORSFALL HOSKINS HOWARTH HURST INGHAM JONES KAY KAYE KENNEDY KITCHEN KNOTT LAW LEE Libsy LIVESEY Livsay LOCKWOOD Lucy MALLINSON Mallison MARSDEN MARSHALL MAUGHAM MELLOR MILLER MITCHELL MOORHOUSE Morehouse NEW NOAD NOBLE NORTH PAINTER PALMER PEARSON PIRIE PRANGLEY PRESELEY PRIDDY REDFORD Rigley SADLER SCHOFIELD Scolefield Sedgwick SHARP SHEARD SHEDWICK SHERWIN SMITH SOUTH SPIVIE SPIVY Stanage STANIDGE STANLEY STEP SUNDERLAND TANNER THEWLIS THOMAS Thoulouse TIDCOMB TITCOMBE Twedge TWIGGE TYAS VIZARD WALKER WARREN WATTS WESTON WHEELER WHITEHEAD WILKINS WOOD WRIGHT WRIGLEY F2007

170356 TITCUMB Mr Duncan N. Birch House, Chapel Lane, Curridge, Newbury, Berks, RG16 9DX. Tel:0635-201238
FRENCH HAZELL ILSLEY STRATTON TITCUMB F4467

170364 TITE Mrs D. 9 York House, Carlisle Lane, London, SE1 7LE.
BISSMIRE NAGLE TITE F7033

170372 TITFORD Mr John. Yew Tree Farm, Hallfieldgate, Higham, Derby, DE5 6AA. Tel:0773-520389
TITFORD F1803

170380 TITHER Mrs Mary. 22 Oakleigh Drive, Croxley Green, Rickmansworth, Herts, WD3 3EF.
BORRINGTON TITHER F2662

170399 TITHERADGE Mrs Ann. 129 Kipling Avenue, Woodingdean, Brighton, E Sussex, BN2 6UF. Tel:0273-305798
Tetheridge Tidridge TITHERADGE Titheridge Tytheridge F6330

170402 TITTENSOR Mrs E M. 7 Westridge Drive, Beaumout Park, Huddersfield, Yorks, HD4 7AX. Tel:0484-652129
BANNER FOX LYON TETSER TIDSER TITSALL TITTENSOR WEBB F2908

170410 TITTERTON Mr & Mrs J E. 7 Cecil Aldin Drive, Tilehurst, Reading, Berks, RG3 6YP.
Teturton Tidderton TITTERTON Tydrington F7101

170429 TITTERTON Mrs M J. (Woffindin) 145 Rotherham Road, Maltby, Rotherham, S66 8LP.
WOFFINDIN F3576

170437 TOBIN Dr John A. The Old House, Stanford In The Vale, Faringdon, Oxfordshire, SN7 8HY.
COOPER GROSSMITH KEET PARKER ROGERSON SWANSON TOBIN F973

170445 TODD Mr C. 13 Ryal Walk, Kenton Bar Estate, Newcastle Upon Tyne, NE3 3YE.
TOD TODD TOOD F6366

170453 TODD Mr Charles. 7 Mill Hill Drive, Winshill, Burton On Trent, Staffs, DE15 0BD. Tel:0283-63181
ANALL ANDERSON BIRRELL DUNCAN GALLOWAY HONEYMAN LILLIE ROBERTSON SCOTT SHANKS SIMPSON TOD TODD F1462

170461 TODD Mr J Ian. Cherub Cottage, Lelant, St Ives, Cornwall, TR26 3EL.
BLAIR CLAYTON FERGUSON FOULIS HOSKIN MARSH REA SOUTHALL TODD F2750

170488 TODD Mr Philip. Dressors, The Street, Eversley, Basingstoke, RG27 0PJ.
COOPER DODDS GRAY GRIEVE HALL KENNETT MANLY MOXEY TODD VIGERS YELLOLY F4211

170496 TOLL Mr Ken C. 20 North Road, Three Bridges, Crawley, W Sussex, RH10 1JX.

Toel TOLE TOLL Tolle VANT F118
170518 TOLLER Miss Gail. 112 Bush Avenue, Little Stoke, Bristol, BS12 6NF. Tel:0272-696834
ANDICOT BAKER BALL CARPENTER CHICK Dowlen Dowlin DOWLING ELEY Elley Ely Endicote HELLIER Helyar Hillier Hollier HUGHES KEMPSTER MILLARD PAUL Paull PRIDDLE PRIOR Pryor RICHARDS RICHINGS SCOTT TAYLOR Toler TOLLER WEBBER F1006
170526 TOLLIDAY Miss Hazel. 105 Lichfield Road, Copnor, Portsmouth, Hants, PO3 6DF.
BOYS BUDD BURGESS CRIPPS FORD HENBEST KERSWELL LOVELL PARFITT PAUL ROWSE SAUNDERS TOLADY TOLLADAY TOLLIDAY TOOLADAY F2438
170534 TOMBLESON Dr Philip. 30 Lewes Road, Ditchling, Sussex, BN6 8TU.
TOMBLESON F2991
170542 TOMBS Mrs Elizabeth. (Muckett) 58 Radway Road, Upper Shirley, Southampton, Hants, SO1 2PJ. Tel:0703-772227
ARSCOTT BARBER BARTHOLOMEW BINSTEAD BIRCH BRADLEY BUDDLE FAIRMAN FILLINGHAM GOOD HAWKINS HOLFORD HUGHES JOHNSON KNOWLER LOCK MILLS MINTER MUCKETT PECK READ REVELL SEYMOUR SHEEN SPEERSHOT TOMBS F4983
170550 TOMLINSON Mrs Charmaine Jane. Pathways, 109 Ridge View Road, Whetstone, London, N20 0HG.
TOMLINSON F3185
170569 TOMLINSON Mrs Christine. (Linney) 8 Colmore Avenue, Spital, Bebington, Wirral, L63 9NL.
BAILEY BARRET HIGHAM HOLT LINNEY POWNALL RICHARDSON RILEY SHIELDS SYKES WALPOLE WEBB F1465
170577 TOMLINSON Mr Colin. 4 Kennerleigh Garth, Leeds, LS15 8NJ. Tel:0532-602106
TOMLINSON F3977
170585 TOMLINSON Mrs Kim. 37 North Rocks Road, Broadsands, Paignton, Devon, TQ4 6LF.
Ewen EWIN FARRANT Hasking Haskings HASKINS JACKMAN Pinck Pincke PINK Pinke Thomlinson Tomasson Tominson TOMLINSON Wethers WITHERS F5208
170593 TOMPKINS Mrs Blanche. (Lane) 360 West 20th Street, San Bernardino, CA 92405, USA. Tel:+1-714-883-7468
BEDFORD BLOW CADD CONNER TOMPKINS F5597
170607 TOMS Mr Alan. 197 Park Road, Formby, Liverpool, L37 6EW. Tel:07048-72244
BENHAM BROWN COOPER HANCOCK HUGHES MABER MARSHALL RATTIE ROBINSON TOMS F865
170615 TONKIN Mr & Mrs John. Moorview, Lockengate, Bugle, St Austell Cornwall, PL26 8RU. Tel:0208-831285
Collect Collet COLLETT FOLLEY HODGE KNIGHT NICHOLLS Rouncefield ROUNSEFELL Rounsevell Rounsfull Rounsifield TONKIN F2178
170623 TONKIN Mr K & Mrs E. 10 Clauds Close, Hazlemere, Bucks, HP15 7AE.
ALLEN BEGBIE BOWN CHAPMAN COLLARD COLLINS COUCH COX DENNIS FIELD FINCH HAMILTON HERBERT ILES MARCH MORTON MUNDAY PICKETT PUSHMAN TONKIN WAYE WILLIAMS WISE YELLAND F3099
170631 TOOK Mr Reginald. 56 Pinhill Road, Banbury, Oxfordshire, OX16 7NQ. Tel:0295-254909
CLIFTON PERKIN TOOK VOISEY VOYSEY WESTLAKE WORDEN F1079
170658 TOOKE Mr & Mrs. 1 Woodside Close, Caterham, Surrey, CR3 6AU.
EDKINS TOOK Tooke F6699
170666 TOOMBS P E. 5 Fairway Close, Oldland Common, Bristol, Avon, BS15 6SA.
GILLAM HOUGHTON PEACHEY REEVE REYNOLDS F148
170674 TOOMBS Mr S R. 5 Fairway Close, Oldland Common, Bristol, Avon, BS15 6SA.
COLE CONQUEST CRISP Crispe DEAN JAKES LAURANCE LAURENCE Lawrance Lawrence RIPLEY SELL Tombs TOOMBS F147
170682 TOOP Mr Leslie John. 63 Trinity Lane, Waltham Cross, Hertfordshire, EN8 7EL. Tel:0992-27137
TOOP F1261
170690 TOOP Mr P A. 70 Malyons Road, Lewisham, London, SE13 7XG.
TOOP F6673
170704 TOOTLE Mr Roy Joseph. 16 Manchester Road, Knutsford, Cheshire, WA16 0NT. Tel:0565-652104
KENNEDY MCGREAVY Mcgreevy MORRIS MORROW RIGBY Tootal Tootel TOOTELL Toothill Tootill Tootle WILCOX F246
170712 TOTTEM Mr Kenneth. 124 Carlton Avenue, Sudbury Court, Wembley, Middx, HA0 3QX. Tel:081-904-7807
TOTTEM F781
170720 TOTTERDELL Mrs M E. 46 Hillside, Horsham, Sussex, RH12 1NG.
Totterdale TOTTERDELL F6844
170739 TOULMIN Dr George. 30 Coltham Road, Cheltenham, Glous, GL52 6RN. Tel:0242-517109
Eddlestone EDELSTON Edleston Edlestone Littlejohn LITTLEJOHNS NASH Talmin Tolmin Tolmine Tolming Toulman TOULMIN Toulmine Toulming Towline Towlinge Towlmin Towlmine Towlming Towlminge F362
170747 TOUT Mrs M D. 9 Dene Close, East Dean, Eastbourne, Sussex, BN20 0JJ.
Barclay BARKBY BARKLEY CHANDLER Chantler FAULKS FITCHET Fitchett GODDARD Haward HAYWARD Haywood Heyward Heywood MANTON TOUT F2233
170755 TOVEY Mrs Susan M. (Delicate) 22 Chestnut Walk, Elson, Gosport, Hants, PO12 4BH. Tel:0705-502475
Daddecot Deddicott Dedicoat Dedicott Delicata DELICATE Delicati Delicoat Delicut Deligate Dellicate Dellicott Derricott Derriscott Didicoat Dilleket Dillicate Dillicoat Doddicott Gelicot Gelicut Jelicot Jellicott Jellicult TOVEY Tovi Tovie Tovy F4519
170763 TOWEY Mr P. 11 Church Lane, Teddington, Middx, TW11 8PA.
FREATHY F6592
170771 TOWLER Mr Derek R. Livety Cottage, High Street, Stebbing, St Dunmow, Essex, CM6 3SQ.
BARNES LILLY TOWLER F4817
170798 TOWN Miss Audrey. 33 New Lane, Skelmanthorpe, Huddersfield, W Yorks, HD8 9EY.
ASKHAM BATTY BINNS CHARLESWORTH COWPER DAKIN DEVONPORT GOLDTHORPE GREEN HEMINGWAY MAURICE MIDGLEY MINSELL MINSHELL MORRIS ODDY POLLARD PRIEST RICHARDS ROTHWELL Rowarth ROWORTH SKELTON SMITH SMITHSON TOMLINSON TOWN WEBSTER WILKINSON F1500
170801 TOWNEND Mr Roy B. 102 Coniston Avenue, Dalton, Huddersfield, Yorks, HD5 9PZ. Tel:0484-512237
BECK COLE DOWSON DUKE MARTIN MINOGUE MORTON NAVIN PICKLES REED SWAINE SYKES TIERNAN TOWNEND F1081
170828 TOWNER Mr R N. 23 Chaucer Drive, Liverpool, L12 0LH.
TOWNER F6143
170836 TOWNROW Mr Ronald James. 53 Meyrick Avenue, Luton, Beds, LU1 5JN. Tel:0582-33336
FELMINGHAM TOWNROW F5999
170844 TOWNSEND Mr Charles. 5721 Antietam Drive, Sarasota, FL 34231-4903, USA. Tel:+1-813-924-9170
TOWNSEND F5686
170852 TOWNSEND Mr John. 95 Arbor Lane, Winnersh, Wokingham, Berks, RG11 5JE. Tel:0734-785463
BAKER BOWDEN BUDD DOWINING GILL HARBERT HARNETT KEELING MOLYNEUX PARSONS TOWERSON TOWNSEND WILKINSON F2176
170860 TOWNSEND Mrs Margaret. (Portsmouth) Brynawelon, Trelydan, Welshpool, Powys, SY21 9HL. Tel:0938-552479
HOPELY PORTSMOUTH SMAIL TOWNSEND TULIP WILTCHER F922
170879 TOWNSEND Mrs Margaret. (Toghill) 24 Tilting Road, Thornbury, Bristol, BS12 1ES.
ASH BRITTEN BROAD BURTON FREEGARD PADFIELD TOGHILL F4142
170887 TOWNSEND Mr William. 19 Whalebone Avenue, Chadwell Heath, Romford, Essex, RM6 6DA.
BEARMAN TOWNSEND F4366
170895 TOZER Revd R E. 4 Church Road, Snape, Suffolk.
Toozer Tosere TOZER F6972
170909 TRACY Mrs Helen. Beehive Park, Rydal, Nsw, 2790, AUSTRALIA. Tel:+61-6-355-6265
BRENNAN BROWN BURKE CAIN CAMPBELL Deignen DIGNIN EGAN FERGUSON FIDDES FLANAGAN HOGG

JENNINGS Keane LEACH MILNE PELLY ROCK Rocks SAUNDERS THOM F5162

170917 TRAINI Diane M. 715 Shady Drive, Trafford, PA 15085, USA.
Wolseley Woosley WOOZLEY F7417

170925 TRAVELL Mr R J. 3 Regent Square, Bow, London, E3 3HQ.
Tuffen TUFFIN F7053

170933 TRAVERS Mrs J A. (Dicks) Lansdowne Villa, Heyford Road, Steeple Aston, Bicester, Oxon, OX6 3SH.
BREWER DICKS GROVES TRAVERS F3928

170941 TREADGOLD Mr L G. 6657 Camelia Drive, San Jose, CA 95120, USA.
Threadgold TREADGOLD Tredgold F7221

170968 TREADWELL Mrs Shirley. (Harvey) Creston, 124 White Dirt Lane, Catherington, Waterlooville, Hants, PO8 0TW. Tel:0705-591423
BARTHOLOMEW BUNDAY Bundy EDWARDS FOSTER HARVEY KENT PAYNE PEARSON RUSSELL SEARLE STICKLAND Strickland TREADWELL WILSON F1175

170976 TREGARTHEN Mrs Muriel. (Sanders) Kaycroft, 10 Park View, Truro, Cornwall, TR1 2BN. Tel:0872-73861
KENDALL MEWTON ROWE SANDERS SMITH STANHOPE TREGARTHEN WHITE F4100

170984 TREGENZA Mr Paul. 70 Gloucester Road, Norbiton, Kingston On Thames, Surrey, KT1 3RA. Tel:081-549-6091
Traganza Tragenza Treganza Tregensa Tregensagh Tregensith Tregenso Tregensoe Tregensow Tregensyth TREGENZA Tregenzo Treginsa Treginza F4271

170992 TREGONNING Mrs Margaret. 140 Pacific Parade, Army Bay, Whangaparaoa, 1463, NEW ZEALAND.
BACON BELL HAGART JACKSON KAYE LASKEY SIMPSON STUBBS WEATHERALL F5578

171018 TRELEVEN Mr J. C/o Intern Tennis Fed, Palliser Road, Barons Court, W Kensington, W14 9EN.
TRELEVEN Treliving F6668

171026 TREPESS Mr Pickard. C/o The Institute Of Drilling & Prod, Leoben Minin Univ, Leomben, Austria A8700. Tel:+43-3842-46416
TREPAS TREPASSE TREPES TREPESS TREPPASS TREPPESS TREPUS F926

171034 TRESCOTT Mrs S M. (Ewart) 19 Delves Wood Road, Beaumont Park, Huddersfield, W Yorks, HD4 7AS. Tel:0484-656234
ANDERSON BURTON CHAPMAN DIMITRESCO EWART FISHER KAYE QUARMBY SHAW F4504

171042 TRESEDER Mr Errol. 131 St Thereses Court, Raglan Road, Devonport, Plymouth, PL7 4NQ.
HAMBLY Tredeser Tresedder TRESEDER Tresidder Tresider Tresodern Tresseder Trezedar Trezeder Trezodar F5941

171050 TRETHEWEY Mrs Madeline. Treslo, Carolyn Road, St Austell, Cornwall, PL25 4LJ. Tel:0726-63838
De Lobbe Lob LOBB Lobbe Lobe Trethevy Tretheway TRETHEWEY Trethewy Trethue F1418

171069 TREVANION Mr Denis. 58 Chatsworth Way, Carlyon Bay, St Austell, Cornwall, PL25 3SN.
TREVANION F1873

171077 TREVATHAN Mr Ken. Oban Street, Lawrence, Otago, NEW ZEALAND. Tel:+64-3-485-9893
BALL BENNET BUNT HERD HEWETT HICKS PARSONS PASSONS SAUNDRY TREVATHAN F4471

171085 TREVYLLIAN Mrs Sheilagh. 3 Augustus House, Tundridge Lane, Bristol, Avon, BS5 8SE.
SHORLAND SOWDEN Trevilian Trevillian TREVYLLIAN F765

171093 TREWARTHA Mr Michael. Lower Ground Floor Flat, 1 West Hill Road, Brighton, E Sussex, BN1 3RT. Tel:0273-727615
ODGERS SHEPSTONE TREWARTHA F511

171107 TRIBE S E. 2233-6th Street, E Courteney, British Columbia, V9N 7T8, CANADA.
Tribb TRIBE Trybe F7079

171115 TRIBE Mr T. 16 Pitts Orchard, Sturminster Newton, Dorset, DT10 1ER. Tel:0258-72440
TRIBE F2116

171123 TRITT Mr D. 4072 Goose Lane Sw, Granville, OH 43023, USA.
Dritt Trait Trate TRITT Tritten F7370

171131 TROTT Mr John. Sleepers Hold, Mill Lane, Witnesham, Suffolk, IP6 9HR.
BEACH HANNON O HANNON TROTT F5034

171158 TROTT Mr Robert M. 24 The Greenwood, Guildford, Surrey, GU1 2ND. Tel:0483-570082
BISHOP BOND BOUGHTWOOD BROOM BYSHOP COOK DIMOND DOBLE DOE ELSON Elsone Elston Elstone FARMER FINCH GOWERS HALES HEARD KIRBY LOWE MILL MORGAN NORMAN NUNN OTHAM PRIDDICE PRING RUSSELL SALTER SELLER SKINGLEY SORRELL SPRAGUE TROTT F1403

171166 TROTTER Mrs Christine. The Oaks, 15 Faris Barn Drive, Woodham, Weybridge, KT15 3DZ. Tel:0932-346303
BARRETT Birdsal BIRDSALL Birdsell Birdsill DUCKETT GOODWILL Limbard Limbert LIMBORD LUN MITCHELL NEWLOVE PROCTER ROBSON THOMPSON TROTTER VAUSE F2543

171174 TROUPE Miss M E. 13 Welldale Crescent, Stockton On Tees, Cleveland, TS19 7HU.
BLACK CLAYTON CLEMENT JONES MASON ROBERTSON RYDER TROUP TURNPENNY F4991

171182 TROWBRIDGE Mr C W. Darcy'S Field, Ford Lane, Frilford, Oxon, OX13 5NS. Tel:0865-391411
BONICK BURTON CHOWN CREED CULLIMORE DURMAN FAULKNER FFORD FOYLE GRINTER HAMLYN HARDIMAN HAYSOM HEWITT HOPKINS JONES LANGDON LOGSDON PERCY SCAMEL SHERGOLD SHERRELL STEVENS Trobarge Troberege Trobridge Troubridge TROWBRIDGE Trowerbridge Trubreg Trubridge VEAL VINCENT F3890

171190 TRUEMAN Mrs June. 89 Valley View Road, Rochester, Kent, ME1 3NX.
BIBLE LETHERLONG MYTTON SEAMAN Search SHARP Sharpe SURCH F3031

171204 TRUNKS Mr E R. 5 Whitmore Road, Winchcombe, Cheltenham, Glous, GL54 5HR.
TRUNKS F3292

171212 TRUSSLER Mr Geoffrey. 22 Linden Avenue, Old Basing, Hants, RG24 0HG. Tel:0256-473829
TEMPLER TRUSSLER F2141

171220 TUBB Mr A P. 43 Graham Avenue, Mile Oak, Portslade, E Sussex, BN41 2WN.
F3190

171239 TUCK Mr Frederick. Tanglewood, Fugelmere Road, Fleet, Hants, GU13 9BB.
AUSTIN TUCK F4501

171247 TUCKER Mrs O J. (Penny) 12 Carlisle Road, Romford, Essex, RM1 2QP.
ARMITAGE ASTRIDGE BILES EMM HOLLOWAY LEAVER Lever LONG Penney PENNY F3394

171255 TUDOR Mr David Linthwaite. 2 Harbour Wall, Stoke Bishop, Bristol, Avon, BS9 1EA. Tel:0272-682470
GERARD GERRARD JARRARD JERRARD KENT THORNE TODER TUDOR F1844

171263 TUDWAY Mr S W. 7 Heath Lawns, Fareham, Hampshire, PO15 5QB.
De Medewe De Wythnesham Meadowe MEADOWS Medew Medewe Medowe Onwhynne Pierrepont Tadway Tedway Tidway Todway Tudwaie TUDWAY Tudwaye Tudwey UNWIN Unwine F7153

171271 TUFF Mrs H. Little Laurels, Bourton On The Hill, Moreton In Marsh, Glos, GL56 9AH.
Treglawn Tregloan Treglohan Treglone Treglowan TREGLOWN F5279

171298 TUFF Mrs Kathleen. (Barratt) 8 Clifton Place, York, YO3 6BJ. Tel:0904-656734
ARCHER BARRATT BARRETT DAVIES MULDOWNEY TUFF WILLIAMS F6009

171301 TUFFS Jenny. 14 Robin Hood Close, St Johns, Woking, Surrey, GU21 1SS.
BALL EADE TUFFS F487

171328 TULEY Mr G. 5 Murray Place, Stonehaven, Kincardineshire, AB3 2GG.
TULEY Tuly F6672

171336 TULL Mrs Christopher Stuart. The Rectory, Bishopsnympton, South Molton, North Devon, EX36 4NY.
TULL F5228

171344 TUNNA Miss G. Old Gwilliam, Lyth Mill, Shropshire, SY3 0AU.
TUNNA Tunnah F7066

171352 TUNNICLIFF Mr R J. 24 Beechwood Avenue, St Albans, Herts, AL1 4YA.
FUTCHER HOLAH TUNNICLIFF F6649

171360 TUNSTILL Mr John. Old Telephone Exchange,

Eckington, Pershore, Worcs, WR10 3AP. Tel:0386-750133
HEADWORTH Opperman OPPERMANN Tonstal Tunstale TUNSTALL TUNSTILL VON BARGEN F3722

171379 TUPHOLME Mrs Susan. 11 Shoreham Drive, Moorgate, Rotherham, S Yorks, S60 3DT.
ADDLESEE ADDLESHAW BOURN BOX DESFORGES FENSOM FLACK SNAPE TUNE TUPHOLME WOFFENDEN F399

171387 TUPPEN A E. 64 Chesil Street, Winchester, Hants, SO23 8HX.
GREGORY Tifton Tupen Tupenn TUPPEN TUPPEN-LASHMAR Tuppenn Tuppin Tuppyn TUPPYN-SCRASE Tuppyne Tuppyng Tupton F1061

171395 TUPPER Mrs Val. (Jillott) 2 Birchfield Avenue, Tettenhall, Wolverhampton, W Midlands, WV6 8TG. Tel:0902-753931
COATSWORTH Gillette Gilliot Gillot Gillott GROUT JILLOTT TUPPER WOODHOUSE F2699

171409 TURLEY Mr Albert W. 32 Cogate Road, Paddock Wood, Tonbridge, Kent, TN12 6UE. Tel:0892-833616
PENVELL Penvil Penvill Penville STANDEN WOOLLETT F2757

171417 TURNAGE Mr Robert William. 40 Chelsworth Drive, Plumstead, London, SE18 2RA.
BARRETT BORTON CRAWLEY HUGO LAYZELL MACROFT SPARROW SPELLER TURNAGE WHITTINGHAM F5127

171425 TURNBULL Mr John. 5 St Georges Court, Wardley Park, Gateshead, Tyne And Wear, NE10 8ED. Tel:091-469-5240
BROWN CARR CLASPER CROSBY FLETCHER GRAHAM MILNE NETTLESHIP PEARSON TURNBULL F3667

171433 TURNBULL Mr S J. Po Box 375, St Marys 2760, AUSTRALIA.
MORIER TURNBULL F7318

171441 TURNER Mr Alan. Banc Y Felin, Aberbechan, Newtown, Powys, SY16 3AW. Tel:0686-630606
ABLITT ADER Adgor ADGORE ALDER ALEXANDER ALFORD ANDREWS ASPINALL ATHER AUSTIN BAKER BARNETT BARRETT BARTLETT BASSETT BATES BEAUMAN BEECHING Benet BENNET Bennett Bennit BEST BILLING BLACK BODDY BOOKMASTER BOWES BRANCHETT BRENCHLEY BRIDGES BROWN BROWNING BUCKINGHAM BUNCE BUNGAY BURROUGHS BURROW BURTON BUSHELL BUTLER BUTTINGTON CACKET CAISTER CARRYER CHAMBERLAIN CHAMBERS CHAMPION CHAPMAN CHURCH CLINCH COCK COLDRAKE Coldrick COLLINS COOK COPPIN COPPING Coppings Coppins COSSENS Couldrake CROWHURST CUTTS DALE DALTON DANE DAY DEAN DEARMAN DENNE DOWNS DREWETT DUNK Durk EAGLES EARL EASTES ELLIS EVANS EXTON FAGG FARLOW FARROW FILMER FINN FLOOD FOORD FOSTER FRENCH FRYAR FRYDAY GILBERT GOSLING GOUGE GRAHAM GREENSTED GRIMSHIRE GROVE HADWIN HALES Halford HALL HANCOCK HARRATAGE HARVEY HAZELL HENWOOD HIGGS HILL HIND HODGSON HOLMES HORNBY HUDSON JACKSON Jefferies JEFFRIES JONES JORDAN KEEN KENNARD KEYS KISBY KITCAT KNIGHT LANGLEY LAW LAWRENCE LEE LEWIS LOVELL MERSH MESSENGER MILES MILLER MOON MORRIS MOSS ODELL PAGE PARKER PAYNE PERRY PHILLIPS PILCHER PINK POTTER POWELL RAN RANDALL READ REDMANS RICHARDS RICKETS RIDER ROBSON ROWLAND SEAD SEAGERS Segers SELUY SETH SHARP SHARPE SINDEN SKILLER SMITH Snoad SNODE SOPER SPENCER STANDLEY STEVENS STONAGE STONE STORY STRIDE SULLY SYFLEET TAYLOR TOWNSEND TURNER UPWOOD USHER VINCE VINCENT WAITE WALKER WARD WATTS WEDD WELLS WEST WHITE WILDING WILLIAMS Willshire Wilshier Wilshire WILTSHIRE WINDEBANK WISHAM Wissam WOLLACOTT Wyssam Wyssom YEAT F1390

171468 TURNER Mrs Anne. (Whittington) 45 Brookside Glen, Brookside, Chesterfield, S40 3PG.
BROWN FANTOM HALLAM HODGKINS TRIGG WEBSTER WHITTINGTON WINSOR F4884

171476 TURNER Mr C R. 1 Newham Road, Stamford, Lincs, PE9 1BZ. Tel:0780-53932
BARLOW BLANCHFIELD CARTWRIGHT EASTGATE JUDD MARLOW MORRIS THORROLD TURNER WARD F3552

171484 TURNER Dr Charles. 5 Mill Road, Great Gransden, Sandy, Beds, SG19 3AG. Tel:07677-525
ALDRIDGE FLINDERS FULLER HUDSON MARSDEN OKINS TURNER F4212

171492 TURNER Mrs D E. 37 Sutton Park, Blunsdon, Swindon, Wiltshire, SN2 4BB.
ALEXANDER GLOVER HAMMOND MILESON NORTON SCOTT SHARP SHIPGOOD TURNER F3476

171506 TURNER Mrs Dorothy. (Sidery) 4 Old Manor Close, Bexhill On Sea, E Sussex, TN40 1SL. Tel:0424-212392
SIDERY F1229

171514 TURNER Mrs E. (Leech) 140 Railway Road, Stretford, Manchester, M32 0QD.
FORSTER GARNER LEECH SHAW WOODHOUSE F5288

171522 TURNER Miss H E. 25 Briar Place, Larkspur Estate, Langney, Eastbourne E Sussex, BN23 8DB.
Bevele Bevelle Bevile BEVILL Beville CLARK Comber Comer Constabile CONSTABLE COOMBER Cunstable DOYLE DRURY ELPHICK FISHER FORD GILES GILL HOWELL MARTIN Read REED Reid Ried SCRIVENS SHORTER Stephens STEVENS Varnham Varnon Verham Vernham VERNON WARREN YOUNG F3944

171530 TURNER Mrs Helen E. 15 Garden Wood, Inchmarlo, Kincardineshire, Scotland, AB31 4AW. Tel:03302-3667
BREMNER Brimner Brymer MCKEAN Pait PATE Peat Pett ROBERTS SCOTT WHYTE F2935

171549 TURNER Mr Hilton. 210 South Park Street, New Wilmington, PA 16142, USA. Tel:+1-412-946-2784
ANDERSON BALL BEAR Beer Bonite BONITHAN Bonity BORROUGHS BOTTERS BROAD Burroughs Burrows CALLARD COKE COLLINS CONGDON DEACON DINGLEY FOX HARDY HILTON JOLLIFFE LANDER LAYCOCK LEIGH LUSCOMBE LYTE Maab Mabb MABE MADDOCK Maib Mayab MAYALL MOORE NEWBURGH O'TOOL O'toole Pain PARKHOUSE Pine PUNE Pyne Ralph Rolf ROLPH SHELLABEAR SLATER SQUANCE SQUIRE STANNING Stonige TOMS Tool Toole TRELEVAN TURNER WAREHAM WAVELL WHITE WILCOCK WOODFORD WOODS YOUNG F5570

171557 TURNER Mrs Janet. (Bazley) 54 Weymouth Road, Frome, Somerset, BA11 1HJ. Tel:0373-462636
BAZLEY COLLINS MUNDAY MUNDY PAVER RUSSELL F267

171565 TURNER Dr John M. 15 Lingdales, Formby, Liverpool, L37 7HA. Tel:07048-71549
BINNINGTON BLENKIN Blenking CARR HAGAR HARPER MARTIN PARKER SMITH SONLEY Sonly Sunlay Sunley TURNER F1718

171573 TURNER Mrs K M. (Smith) 606 Spring Bank West, Hull, Humberside, HU3 6LJ.
BINKS DAVIS Davison DEIGHTON Hewartson HEWITSON HIRD LODGE ROBSON SMITH STOTT WALKER F5377

171581 TURNER Mrs M. (Welch) 6 Andrew Road, Howick, Auckland, NEW ZEALAND.
HALL JACKMAN KING LEANING PUDDY SCANNELL TURNER WELCH F5503

171603 TURNER Mrs R A. 27 Burley Close, London, SW16 4QQ.
Lewar LEWER Lewir Luer F7173

171611 TURNER Captain Richard. 11 Hill Street, Caernarfon, Gwynedd, LL55 1PL. Tel:0286-4611
CRUMACK DAVIES TURNER F4430

171638 TURNER Mr Robin A C. 107 Millfields, Writtle, Chelmsford, Essex, CM1 3LJ. Tel:0245-421229
CHOWNE COTTINGHAM CROOKSHANK D'AGUILAR GAULER HILL-COTTINGHAM RACHANCE TURNER WALLER WILLCOX WILTON F2097

171646 TURNER Miss Rosemary. 5 Mallards Road, Woodford Green, Essex, IG8 7DF. Tel:081-559-2644
ALLEN BALL BRANT BROWN GREENING Grinen HAYDEN LOCK OWEN PARKER PARSLOW PETTIT REDRUP REGAN SAMSON SHARP SHEEN STOKES TURNER WILLIAMS F5359

171654 TURNER Mr & Mrs S R. 21 Hertford Road, Stevenage, Herts, SG2 8RZ.
ADAM Adkins ARMSTRONG ATKINS BAKER Balch BALDOCK Ballantine BALLANTYNE BARR Baulch BILLINGS BLISS BOLCH Bolche BROWN Bur BURR BUSWELL Buzell CAIRNS CASSELS Cassils CLAY DIBBLE Dible DICKINSON DRYNAN DUNLOP DUNMORE Dybble FERGUSSON FINDLAY FINLAY FLEMING FRENCH Gardener GARDINER Gardner GEMMELL GRANT HAMILTON Hebron HEPBURN HICKMAN HOLMAN HOLTOM Holton Jack JACKS Kairns Kay KETCHER

KEY LAMBERT Lamburd Lamburn LANGHAM LAWRIE LENOX LINDSAY Lochawe Lochoar LOCHORE Marr MARSHALL MARTIN MCAPLIE MCCOLM MCLUCKIE MEAKINS Meekins Mekins MILLAR MILLER MOFFAT Moir Moore MORE Muir PARISH PARKER Parrish ROGERS ROSS RUSSELL SABIN Sabine Sabyn SANDY Scot SCOTT Seagar SEAGER Seger SHARP SHEDDEN Sheeden Shifeley Shifferley SHIFLEY SMITH SNEDDON SOLLAWAY Spendalow SPENDELOW Spendillo Sprot SPROTT STEEL Steele STEVENSON STORIE Story TAYLOR TEMPLEMAN THORN Thorne TORRIE Tory TREEN TURNER WALLACE WATSON Willis WILLS WILSON YOUNG Zeager Zeger F2934

171662 TURNER Mrs Sandra. Po Box 712, Charters Towers, Queensland, 4820, AUSTRALIA. Tel:+61-7-770-4431
BALLANTINE BEDFORD BROWN BUCKLEY BUTTERWORTH CARROLL CONNOR DALGLEISH DYNES FARMER FRIER GREIG HARDIE HILL HOWE JACKSON KING LEISHMAN LING MOORE MORTIMER PAYNE PEARSON PENTLAND PHILLIPS PRICE SMALL TAYLOR THOMSON TURNER WELDONE WILSON WOLFE F5472

171670 TURNER Mr Thomas. 26 Barry Avenue, Grimsby, South Humberside, DN34 5LS. Tel:0472-78652
BLISS COOPER DANNAN TURNER WILKINSON WILSON F243

171689 TURNER Mr W A. 25 Briar Place, Larkspur Estate, Langney, Eastbourne E Sussex, BN23 8DB.
CALADINE DOBSON DRAYCOTT FLINT HIGGINBOTTOM HILL KING MAY TURNER F3945

171697 TURNROSS Mr Arthur. 1 Old Albert Terrace, Runcorn, Cheshire, WA7 1DB. Tel:0928-568281
TURNROSS F225

171700 TURRALL Mrs D. (Bruce) 4 Oatlands Drive, Paignton, Devon, TQ4 5JL. Tel:0803-526064
BRUCE F5887

171719 TURVILL Mrs Mary. Fletching House, 18 Archery Fields, Odiham, Basingstoke Hants, RG25 1AE.
ELLISTON ENGLISH HARLING HARVEY PACKER STAFFORD TURVILL F157

171727 TURVILL Mr Reginald W. 33 Audley Crescent, Hereford, HR1 1BW. Tel:0432-265646
Dalve Delues Delvas Delve DELVES JORDAN Tarvall Terevall Tervil Torvill Turuell Turuill Turval Turveile Turvell TURVILL Turville Turvyle UPTON F1248

171735 TURVILLE Mr Cyril Leonard. 10 Gynsill Lane, Anstey, Leicester, LE7 7AG. Tel:0533-876996
TURVILLE F4981

171743 TUTCHER Mrs Jane. (Raistrick) 67 Dunton Road, Broughton Astley, Leics, LE9 6NA. Tel:0455-282342
CAPPS COTTEY COX CRABB MARTIN MEAR RAISTRICK THOMPSON TUTCHER WILKINS F5030

171751 TWEDDLE Mr Michael John. 72 Oakleigh Park Drive, Leigh On Sea, Essex, SS9 1RS.
BELL BUCKLEY GAFFNEY KELLY KILDEA LEE PHELAN ROBINSON STEWART STOBBS TILLEY TWEDDLE WAUGH F4187

171778 TWELLS Mr Donald F. Windrode, Rectory Lane, Heswall, Wirral, L60 4RY. Tel:051-342-4753
Twell TWELLS Twelves F5709

171786 TWELVES Mr J A. 119 Oakdale Drive, Heald Green, Cheadle, Cheshire, SK8 3SN.
TWELVES F6642

171794 TWENTYMAN Mrs Mary. (Clayton) 13 St Abbs Fold, Odsal, Bradford, West Yorks, BD6 1EL.
BARKER BOND BRISTOW CLAYTON CORDINGLEY DALES EVENING FILLINGHAM GLAISTER HUDDART JACKSON JOHNSON LOWE MAWSON MOSS NEWBORN PITTS RANSOM ROOK ROWNSON SIMPSON TWENTYMAN WILLS F5134

171808 TWIDDY Mr David Rodney. 31 North Villiers Street, Leamington Spa, Warwickshire, CV32 5XY. Tel:0926-315860
Tweedy Twiddy F6425

171816 TWIST Mrs Eleanor. (Eales) 6 Coles Avenue, Alford, Lincs, LN13 0AH.
Branston BRAUNSTON BUBB CAPEL CAPELL CHAMBERLAIN Chamberlayne Chamberlin Clark CLARKE EALES Eals Eels Eyles FIELD HARPER Harpur HOWLETT JACKSON Jakes Jaques JEAQUES Moreton MORTON Murdin MURDING PINNER SMITH STOCKHALL THORNE TWIST WEBSTER WENTWORTH Wintworth WRIGHTON F768

171824 TWIST Mr Geoff. 17 Hill Rise, Kilgetty, Dyfed.
BIRCH BURNS DIXON FAIRCLOUGH GERRARD HARDMAN HOLDEN HOLDING HOVEY LARGE LEA LITHGOE MATHER MORRIS PICKERING RHODEN ROUGHLEY SMITH TOPPING Twis Twiss TWIST VALENTINE WALTON WEBB WOODS F785

171832 TWORT Mr Thomas James. 35 Sompting Avenue, Broadwater, Worthing, W Sussex, BN14 8HS.
FOX ONGLEY Tourt Turte TWORT WILKINSON F2904

171840 TYLER Mrs Beryl Thorold. Cedarwood, Gormston, Eaton Constantine, Shrewsbury Shropshire, SY5 6RL.
HOWARD SARGENT TYLER WATSON F808

171859 TYNAN Mrs K J. (Juby) 5 Gloucester Avenue, Welling, Kent, DA16 2LL.
BUSSELL EDGINTON GALBALLY GALE JUBY LOCK PETFORD STAITE STEPHENS YAXLEY F3673

171867 TYRRELL Mr B. 6 The Hiron, Coventry, W Midlands, CV3 6HT.
Tirrell Turrell Tyrell TYRRELL F6797

171875 TYRRELL Mrs Cecilia. 63 Millcroft, Carlisle, Cumbria, CA3 0HT. Tel:0228-21515
BAIN ELLIS JOHN MURRAY ROSS SHENNAN STEVENSON WARNES F5662

171883 TYRRELL Mr P. 30 Hitchman Drive, Chipping Norton, Oxfordshire, OX7 5BG. Tel:0608-641216
BOSWORTH FAIRMAN WITHERS F2695

171891 TYRRILL Mr John. 41 Wooburn Manor Park, Wooburn Green, High Wycombe, Bucks, HP10 0ES. Tel:0628-523509
BICKLE BOWSHER EDWARDS HOLLAND HONOUR HOWITT HUGGILL LUNN MARSHALL SWALLOW Tarle Tarrall Tarrel Tarrell Tarrill Taurel Tearle Terall Terel Terell Terill Terle Terold Terrald Terrall Terrel Terrell Terril Terrill Terroll Terryl Teryl Tirall Tirel Tirell Tirolde Tirral Tirrall Tirrel Tirrell Tirril Tirrill Tirrold Tirrolde Tirroll Torell Torill Torrell Tourell Tourle Tourlle Turel Turell Turil Turill Turl Turle Turral Turrall Turrel Turrell Turril Turrill Turrle Turrold Turroll Tyrald Tyrall Tyrel Tyrell Tyrie Tyril Tyrill Tyrol Tyrold Tyroll Tyrral Tyrrall Tyrrel TYRRELL Tyrril Tyrrill Tyrrol Tyrrold Tyrrolde Tyrroll WEST WILLRING F4509

171905 TYSOME Mrs Pat. 8 Frogmore Gardens, North Cheam, Surrey, SM3 9RZ.
BOWEN HYATT HYETT KEELEY SOLOMON TUBBS F1757

171913 TYSON Mr Colin. 40 Trent View, Ermine West, Lincoln, LN1 3PF. Tel:0522-524661
BARKER BOND CLINNGH COOKE COUCH HARVEY HOLLINGSWORTH HORNER LONGNEY MORRIS PARTLETT PRESSWOOD REYNOLDS RICHARDS SHARMAN SIMPSON TYSON WHEATLEY F6139

171921 TYSON Mrs Doreen M. (Coates) 181 Littlecoates Road, Grimsby, S Humberside, DN34 5TF.
COATES DREWERY Drewry Drury FRANKISH LARGE MARTIN RHODES SMITH Tison TYSON F5058

171948 TYSON Ms Mary. 73 Forge Mill Road, Redditch, Worcs, B98 8HQ.
BRIGGS KENDALL POPPITT ROBINSON SHEPHERD TYSON F1559

171956 ULLATHORNE Mr G. 29 Parkhouse Road, Lower Pilsley, Chesterfield.
ULLATHORNE Ullithorne F6958

171964 ULPH Mr Colin. 281 Upper Shoreham Road, Shoreham By Sea, W Sussex, BN43 6BB.
ALF ALFF ALP ALPE ALPHE ALPS AULPH HULF OLFE ULF ULFE ULPH F714

171972 UNDERHAY Mrs Mary. (Binks) 110 Church Road, Teddington, Middx, TW11 8PY. Tel:081-977-7655
BINKS GULL HICKS UNDERHAY F5956

171980 UNDERWOOD Mrs F I. (Watkins) 52 Kings Lane, South Heath, Gt Missenden, Bucks, HP16 0QY.
COX CRIDLAND DRAYDON DYKE EDEN HAWKINS HITCHINS HOLMES KYNNERSLEY UNDERWOOD WATKINS F2922

171999 UNDERWOOD Mr Ken. 27 Church Street, Werrington, Peterborough, Cambs, PE4 6QB. Tel:0733-578898
BARTON CHALKLEY CHILDERLEY DOLLIMORE FOSTER GODFREY MILES UNDERWOOD F1224

172006 UNSWORTH Mrs Catherine. (Lewis) Spurs Lodge, Sagars Road, Styal, Cheshire, SK9 4HE.
AHSTON BAILEY BARRATT Barrett BENNETT BRUNT CROOKS DAVIS FROWEN GRINDALL HUNTER JOHNSON

Layland LEWIS LEYLAND LLEWELLYN MARSH MICHEAL MORGAN MURPHY NORRIS PAINTER PLATT POCKET SARSFIELD SHAW SIMMONDS SMITH SOUTHWARD THOMAS THORNHILL TOWNSEND UNSWORTH WOOD F3808

172014 UNSWORTH Mr John. 68 Norton Lees Road, Sheffield, S8 9BZ.
Crammond CRAMOND UNSWORTH F2965

172022 UNWIN Mrs Jeanette A. (Racine) 191 Rolleston Road, Burton On Trent, Staffs, DE13 0LD.
ARCHER CONDON EVATT GREEN HEWITT OLDHAM PORTER SEDDING STOREY WELLS F6242

172030 UPHAM Mr R. Kwai Lo, Winterhay Green, Ilminster, Somerset, TA19 9PL. Tel:0460-57283
ACKLAND ANDREWS BAKER CROSS PUDDICOMBE SPURWAY UPHAM WESTAWAY WILLIAMS F4936

172049 UPTON Miss Sheila May. Foston Cottage, 6 Main Street, Stonesby, Melton Mowbray, Leics, LE14 4QX. Tel:066478-394
BRADBURY CRISP FOSTER HELLABY JONES MEE Meigh MILLINGTON OLDHAM REDSHAW RILEY UPTON F3414

172057 URE Mrs Karen. 80 Campbell Street, Toowoomba, Queensland, 4350, AUSTRALIA.
BRIDGER CAMPBELL CLARKE COULTER DEANS DUFFY DUNNE HALL HORNE HULHERAN JOHNSTON JONES KELLY MCGIBBON MILES MILLS NISBET O'CONNEL OSMOND PHILLIPS ROONEY SCOTT SHEEHY SPARLING STROUD TOMS WALSH F5421

172065 UREN Mr Harold. 10 Bidston Avenue, Wallasey, Wirral, L45 3LJ. Tel:051-638-7830
UREN F4285

172073 USHER Mrs Barbara. 46 Warren Road, Wilmington, Dartford, Kent, DA1 1PL.
BROAD CHAPMAN CHURCH DAVIS EVERSFIELD MILLEN SHEPHERD SMITH SUMMERTON TICKNER USHER WILLIAMS F2855

172081 USSHER Ms Jemma. 12 Pebble Beach Drive, Runaway Islands, Queensland, 4216, AUSTRALIA.
RAINES Rainsraynes Rayns F7147

172103 UTTERIDGE Mr Tom & Mrs Brenda. (Cooper) Russets, 14 Wysall Lane, Keyworth, Nottingham, NG12 5AG. Tel:06077-2580
COOPER HUMAN NORTHROP Uteridge Utridge Utterage UTTERIDGE Uttrage Uttrege Uttridge F56

172111 UTTRIDGE Mrs Mary. (Mcneilly) 11 Fiddington Clay, Market Lavington, Devizes, Wiltshire, SN10 4BT.
BAILEY CLARKE CRAIG FULLERTON MCNEILLY MORRELL NEATE SLADE SPENCE WRIGHT F3345

172138 VALENTINE Miss Mary P. 74 Balshaw Lane, Euxton, Chorley, Lancs, PR7 6HU.
CONNOLLY ROGERS VALENTINE F3416

172146 VALENTINE Mr Peter. 350 London Road, South Stifford, Grays, Essex, RM16 1AB.
Flower FLOWERS PHILBRICK VALENTINE WADE F272

172154 VALLIS Mr Carrol. (Godfrey) Oak Cottage, Littlefield Green, White Waltham, Maidenhead, Berks, SL6 3JL.
LACEY MOSS VALLIS WAIT WARRINGTON WOODMANSEE F5864

172162 VAN DER WERFF Mrs M B (Betty). 175 Commerce St, Whakatane, Bay Of Plenty, 3400, NEW ZEALAND.
BLACK BUTLER CLARK CURTIS HENDERSON MCARTNEY NUTTALL SMITH STONE F5548

172170 VAN EEDEN Mrs Sandra M. (Hidson) 5 Wheatlands Crescent, Hayling Island, Hants, PO11 9SH.
CROSSMAN HERBERT HIDSON LAKE LEE PREBBLE Whorm Whormes WORMS F5385

172189 VANDER AVORT Luc. Gotje 9, Sint Anna, B8000, Brugge 1, BELGIUM. Tel:+32-15-335874
Van Der Avert Van Der Avoird Van Der Avoirt Van Der Avoort Van Der Avort Vander Avort VANDERAVORT F7434

172197 VANSTONE Mr David. 4 Mill Street, Torrington, N Devon, EX38 8AL.
Fanstone VANSTONE VODEN F4097

172200 VARCOE Mr Christopher. Grace's Cottage, Trevereux Hill, Limpsfield Chart, Oxted Surrey, RH8 0LT.
VARCOE F500

172219 VARILONE Mrs B. 91 Newtown Road, Woolston, Southampton, Hants, SO2 9HX.
BOSWELL FOSTER PRIMMER Rendel Rendell RENDLE RUSTON SCOREY SMITH VALENTINE WINDEBANK Windibank Windybank F1032

172227 VARLEY Mrs Mary. Ascot House, Cherry Tree Avenue, Newton Upon Ouse, York, YO6 3EN.
AUDAER MOISER F4322

172235 VARTY Mrs B L. (Crouch) Allendale House, Fishergreen, Ripon, Yorkshire, HG4 1NL.
Chapel Chapell Chappel CHAPPELL CROUCH FAIRBURN MACMILLAN VARTY F5949

172243 VARTY Mrs Joyce. (Groening) 2 Mooney St, Telegraph Point, NSW 2441, AUSTRALIA.
BERRY FRASER GOUGH KNOWLES LINNANE MORRIS PENN ROYLE STIDOLPH F5583

172251 VAUGHAN Mrs Barbara. 67 Keynesham Road, Bitterne, Southampton, Hants, SO2 5EX.
Berbridge Bergidge Birbage Birbidge Birbridge BISHOP BREEDON Burbage BURBIDGE Burbridge CLARKE CROWDER GREEN HATCHER HENWOOD PLATTS SHAW STRATHAM F1400

172278 VAUGHAN Mr Christopher. 51 Greenacre Close, Swanley, Kent, BR8 8HT. Tel:0322-613431
VAUGHAN F3022

172286 VAUGHAN Mr F J. 11 Hillside Gardens, Kenton, Harrow, Middlesex, HA3 9UW.
HATTERSLEY ROSE STOBBS VAUGHAN F3388

172294 VAUGHAN Mr John. 1 Roxton Drive, The Reddings, Cheltenham, Glous, GL51 6SQ.
BETTY BOOBYER DORROFIELD GEARY KNOWLTON ORIEL Oriell Orriel Orriell RHODES SAUNDERS THOMAS VAUGHAN F39

172308 VAUGHAN Mr T G. 11 Mangotsfield Road, Mangotsfield, Bristol, BS17 3JG. Tel:0272-564588
VAUGHAN F4863

172316 VAUTIER Mrs Jean I. (Barker) Dunblane, Rue Des Buttes, St Mary, Jersey, JE3 3DE.
BAILEY BARKER BURGESS DOREE FINNIS HABBERLEY HUMM LAPLEY LARDEN LEE Leplay Lepley LIPLEY MCCARTHY SMITH F1354

172324 VEACOCK Mr I S. 190 Gurney Close, Barking, Essex, IG11 8JZ. Tel:081-591-0316
BATTCOCK BIGGS DALTON LINSLEY OLDROYD ROFEY RYDER TRIMMER F6072

172332 VEAL Miss M B. 30 Milton Carr, Ridings Park, York, YO3 6PU.
Beal BENTHAM BOOTH Colley COLLY DUNN Dunne Gravel GRAVIL Gravill Graville JAMES VEAL Veale Veall Vele F6386

172340 VEALE Mr Charles Winston. 78 Crowshott Avenue, Stanmore, Middx, HA7 2PE. Tel:081-907-4483
Veal VEALE F1762

172359 VEALL Dr R M. 1 Plants Close, East Wellow, Romsey, Hants, SO51 6AW. Tel:0794-22192
LE PAGE LUCAS Luquas Vale VEAL Veale VEALL Veel Veile Vele F829

172367 VEARNCOMBE Mr Kenneth. 5 St Michaels Park, Aughton Green, Ormskirk, Lancs, L39 6TF. Tel:0695-422315
Fearncombe Ferncombe VEARNCOMBE Verncombe F5624

172375 VEECOCK Mrs I R. 71 Queen Annes Grove, Ealing, London, W5 3XP.
Veaco Veacock VEECOCK F6994

172383 VENABLES Mr Michael Knowles. Arrow Lawn, Kington, Herefordshire, HR5 3AL. Tel:0544-230431
VENABLES F88

172391 VENING Mrs J. 178 Abbots Road, Abbots Langley, Herts, WD5 0BL.
VENING Venning F7055

172405 VENN Mr Denis Harold. 17 Walliscote Rd, Henleaze, Bristol, Avon, BS9 4RZ. Tel:0272-629833
BLEASE HAYES MEARS POULTON TREACHER VAUGHAN VENN F3651

172413 VENN Mr Ian A. 22 Becketts Close, Feltham, Middx, TW14 0BG. Tel:081-751-1872
BAGWELL BARNES BRISTOR COOTE GILHAM LOFTS STALLAN TILL VENN YATES F2318

172421 VERNALL Mrs Sue. 90 Campbell Street, Karori, Wellington, 6005, NEW ZEALAND.
DEW HAYMAN MASON MILLARD MILTON PARKE PARKER SHUTER Varnol Vernal VERNALL Vernalls Vernals Vernel Vernell Vernoll Vernols WATERMAN F5534

172448 VERNON Mrs Esther. (Brough) 31 Intake Avenue, Mansfield, Notts, NG18 5EJ.
BEAVEN BROUGH KNIFTON LAURENCE LYMN MISSON

ROBINSON SPAVOLD STANLEY VERNON F5985
172456 VERRALL Mr Michael S. 80 Falkland Road, Dorking, Surrey. Tel:0306-740713
Fairall FAIRHALL VERRALL Verrell Verrells Verrill Verrills F235
172464 VERRINDER Mr Stanley. 19 Hazeldene, Seaford, E Sussex, BN25 4NQ.
Verinder Verrender VERRINDER F7216
172472 VESEY Mrs J. 63 Hurstcourt Road, Sutton, Surrey, SM1 3JD.
ABON ALBERRY DAVIS GARNER HANDLEY HUME IMAGE Tiffen TIFFIN Vaisey VASEY Vesey WICKENDEN F4716
172480 VIALLS Mrs Christine M. Yew Tree Lodge, 25 Gladstone Street, Kibworth, Leics, LE8 0HL.
Vial Viall VIALLS Vials F6593
172499 VICARY Mr Ian Scott. 17 Lansdown Drive, Abergavenny, Gwent, NP7 6AW. Tel:0873-854929
VICARY F5962
172502 VICARY Mr Michael Jago. 17 Springfield Avenue, Telscombe Cliffs, Peacehaven, E Sussex, BN10 7AR. Tel:0273-584371
BOWKER COUTTIE JAGO PARFETT ROBINS VICARY F512
172510 VICK Mr Gordon. South Riding, The Plains, Wetheral, Carlisle, Cumbria, CA4 8LA.
ASKAM ASKHAM AXE DUCKENFIELD Duckinfield GAUNT LEE MITCHELL PLANT SUTCLIFFE VICK WHITEHEAD F6461
172529 VILLATA Mrs Lynnette. (Fisher) Po Box 37, Beelbangera, NSW 2680, AUSTRALIA. Tel:+61-6-963-5359
ALLEN BEACON BRYDON CANNON COLE FISHER HAMILL LAPPAN LEE LINDSAY LOYNDS PARTRIDGE POOLE RHODES SAWYER SCOWN SHEEHAN SHORT TAMSETT TYE F5457
172537 VILLIERS Mr Peter Denis. 17 Furrowfelde, Kingswood, Basildon, Essex, SS16 5HB.
DE VILLERS VILLERS F2705
172545 VINALL Mrs Joan. Kynance Cottage, 11 St Johns Road, Mortimer, Reading Berks, RG7 3TR. Tel:0734-332841
BOSWELL FLAY KING TONG VINALL WILLIAMS WOOLFORD F2656
172553 VINCE Mrs A. (Laver) 18 Walmers Avenue, Higham, Rochester, Kent, ME3 7EJ.
BOLTWOOD CLARK CLARKE DREWRY DRURY HOW HOWE LAVER RAYNER SURRIDGE UNDERWOOD WRIGHT F5218
172561 VINCENT Mr E F J. 22 Gloucester Road, Staple Hill, Bristol, Avon, BS16 4SH. Tel:0272-567660
GLOVER HARRIS NANCE PRICHARD RICHARDS THOMAS VENNER VINCENT WATERS YEO F3813
172588 VINE Mrs Ann. 22 Bishops Court Gardens, Chelmsford, Essex, CM2 6AZ. Tel:0245-267854
CALLAHAN COUSINS HAMMOND HUTCHINS JONES LACEY PARSONS RIMELL VINE F2087
172596 VINGOE Miss S L. 14 Franklin House, Tyrrel Way, West Hendon, London, NW9 7QA. Tel:081-202-8668
BADCOCK BLEWETT BREACH HARVEY HOCKING JAMES MANN NORTH PAYNE POPE TREGURTHA VINGOE WILLS F1324
172618 VIVIAN Revd A. Parsonage Farm, Parsonage Road, Newton Ferrers, Plymouth, PL8 1AT.
HARNDEN VIVIAN WHITLAMB F3699
172626 VIVIAN Mr Barry E. The Red House, Hagley Road, Fleet, Hants, GU13 8LH. Tel:0252-615795
VIVIAN Vivyan Vyvyan F2336
172634 VOCE Mr Alan. The Forge, 5 Church Path, Halberton, Tiverton, Devon, EX16 7AT.
BENNETT BROMFIELD COPP GUY HOARE HUNT JEFFERIES KNIGHT MATTHEWS MILDON REDWOOD SATHERLEY STILES THORNE VOCE WORTHYLAKE F1377
172642 VOCE Mrs Eileen. 5 Church Path, Halberton, Devon, EX16 7AT.
BLYTHE BOWEN COLLINS FIRBER FURBER HARGEST LAND MORRIS WHITE WOOD F1378
172650 VOGAN Mr Mark. 95 Magazine Farm Way, Colchester, Essex, CO3 4ER. Tel:0206-768693
Fychan GAMBLE MADILL MOFFAT Moffet Murdoch MURDOCK Vaghan Vahan Vaughan VOGAN VOGHAN Vogin Vougan Voughan Voughen Voughn Voughon F3779
172669 VOICE Mr A J. 11 Thatchers Close, Horsham, W Sussex, RH12 4TL.
VOICE F6768
172677 VOLLANDS Mr Ian. 215 Overpool Road, Great Sutton, South Wirral, L66 2JF. Tel:051-355-8025
VOLLANDS F268
172685 VOLLANDS Mrs S E. (Cullimore) 215 Overpool Road, Great Sutton, South Wirral, L66 2JF.
CULLIMORE VOLLANDS F269
172693 VOOGT Mrs Helen. (Warne) Harkaway Farm, R M B 3070, Euroa, Victoria, 3666, AUSTRALIA. Tel:+61-5-795-2042
CARRON FUNSTON SEARLE WARNE WILLIAMS F5693
172707 VOTIER Mrs A. 49 Darfield Road, Crofton Park, Brockley, London, SE4 1ET.
Vautier Voiter Votia VOTIER Votyer F7120
172715 VOWLES Mr Douglas F. 15 Lilliput Court, Chipping Sodbury, Bristol, BS17 6EB. Tel:0454-327990
VOWLES F4092
172723 VOWLES Mrs Thelma Ruth. (Wentworth) R D 3 Matamata, 2271, NEW ZEALAND.
BAX CRYER EVANS KEEDWELL MULLOY NINCHWORTH PIERS ROBERTS TEBBUTT WENTWORTH F4669
172731 VYSE Mr Clifford. 9 Herne Close, Toddington, Beds, LU5 6AF.
CHAPMAN Vice Vise VYSE Vyze F4857
172758 WADDINGTON Mr D. 9a Bold Street, Accrington, Lancs, BB5 6RH.
WADDINGTON F7373
172766 WADDINGTON Roger. 4 Commercial Street, Norton, Malton, North Yorkshire, YO17 9ES. F5826
172774 WADDINGTON Dr W B. 12 Swan Street, Seagrave, Loughborough, Leics, LE12 7NL. Tel:050981-2348
WADDINGTON F3121
172782 WADE Mr R K. 48 Cannonbury Park North, London, N1 2JT.
ADCOCK ADDISON ATKINSON BELL CONSIT CONSITT FRYER PAWSON PYBUS SALT STARKEY VASEY WADE WARNER WHITELOCK WICKHAM WINTOUR F476
172790 WADKINS Mr Dennis Peter. 50 Canonbury Road, Enfield, Middx, EN1 3LW. Tel:081-366-6361
WADKINS F2896
172804 WADMAN Mr E W. 38 Audley Avenue, Torquay, Devon, TQ2 7PD.
WADMAN F6681
172812 WAGER Mrs Barbara. 38 Loosen Drive, Woodlands Park, Maidenhead, Berks, SL6 3UT.
BARNARD BRIGHTMAN BUTTANSHAW BUTTENSHAW BUTTONSHAW COTHER DUNT EVENDEN GODENCH GODINCH GORRIDGE GOWER GRIMES HILL LEE LYFORD MEADEN NORRIS SMITH WAGER WARDAL WARDEL WARDLE WOODLEY F332
172820 WAGHORN Mrs Fay. 74 Dean Parade, Lemon Tree Passage, NSW 2301, AUSTRALIA. Tel:+61-4-982-3146
APPLE CHAMBERLAIN CLEMENTSON HUGHES INGERSOLE MAPPLES MORTON ROWE STANFORD WADSWORTH WIGMAN F5175
172839 WAGHORN Mr R J. 64d Enderley Avenue, Hamilton, NEW ZEALAND.
Waggon WAGHORN Waghorne Wagon F7105
172847 WAIN Mr Alan. 40 Dunster Road, West Bridgford, Nottingham, NG2 6JE.
BROWN Browne CAVE Creepel Creeple Crepell Creple Creppill Crepple Cripil Criple Crippel Cripple Cripwel Cripwele CRIPWELL DUNMORE Dunsmore ETHERINGTON Hetherington Marsden MARSON Marston MORRIS WAIN Waine Wainer Wane Wayne Wayner Wean Weane Wein Wene F4165
172855 WAINE Mrs Elizabeth. 35 Ambleside Terrace, Dundee, DD3 0DB.
AITCHISON AUCHTERLONIE BALDWIN GLOVER HEAP HINDLE LAWRIE PARIS WAINE F1896
172863 WAITE Mrs L M. (Dykes) 21 Lawn Avenue, Burley In Wharfdale, Ilkley, W Yorks, LS29 7ET. Tel:0943-862510
BARKER BEECROFT BROTHERTON DAVEY DYKES FARRAR HARDY SWALE WALKER WILSON WOOD F3628
172871 WAKEFORD Dr David. Carpalla Villa, Foxhole, St Austell, Cornwall, PL26 7TY. Tel:0726-822675
ANDERSON ATKINS BALCHIN BEEDIE BERRY BLAND BROOMFIELD BUGG CAPELIN Caplin COLEMAN COOK CURTIS DEATH DEER DICKIE DOWDEN EAMES Eemes

ELKINS FINDLAY FORESTER FREEMAN FREWER FROST GAY HARDING HART HODGES HULL HUNT JAMES KING LAMB LARBY MANNING MARKEL MATHEWS Matthews MEARNS METCALF MICKLEFIELD MILNE MOIR MONK MOWER NOBLE Norie NORRIE Parry PERRY POBJOY PRESS SALTER SIMMONDS SIMPSON SLIGHT SMITH STEPHEN Steven THORNTON TINSON WAKEFORD WARNER WATTS WEST WESTLAKE WILKINS WRIGHT F916

172898 WAKEHAM Mr & Mrs R L. (Ashton) 27 Croham Manor Road, South Croydon, Surrey, CR2 7BJ. ASHTON BALLARD BEER BRANT BREEDEN BROWN COLEMAN DAMMERELL EDMUND ESDAILE GALE HAMNET HAMNETT HANNINGTON HARLOW HERBERT HILL HODGES HOOPER HOPKINS KING LAKE LINNELL MARTIN NEWTON PAINE PEMBER PERRY ROW SANDFORD SMITH SPRATT STRANGE THORNETT TREE TREMLETT WAKEHAM WILLIAMS WOOD F1423

172901 WAKELAM Nick & Jacqui. 5 Moresby Close, Westlea, Swindon, Wiltshire, SN5 7BX. ANDREW Andrews ARCHER BAKER BARDILL BARTLET BURTON CARTER CASTLE CHARLTON CHEETHAM COCKERELL DUESE GARTON GODWIN GRIMSHAW HEAR HILL HOLLIDAY HOWARTH HUBBARD KERSHAW LINDSEY MOORE MURFIN MURTON PALIN REVILL SANSOM SELF SHORT SIMISTER SIMS SORE STARBUCK WAKELAM Wakelem WALLACE Whakelam WHALE WOODALL F2174

172928 WAKELAM Mr William Gerard. Hill Crest, Ewyas Harold Common, Abbey Dore, Herefordshire, HR2 0JF. Tel:0901-240663 BARTON BRUERTON O'CONNELL TOMBLISON WAKELAM F2099

172936 WAKELING Mr A L W. 9 Queen Street, Brightlingsea, Essex, CO7 0PH. Wakelen Wakelin WAKELING F7195

172944 WAKEMAN Mrs Elizabeth. 48 Cambridge Road, Lee On The Solent, Hants, PO13 9DH. DOWNES DUNN MILNE WAKEMAN F2707

172952 WALE Mrs Diana. 6 Landguard Manor Road, Shanklin, Isle Of Wight, PO37 7HZ. BACHELOR BATCHELOR CARTER FARRANT MILLS RICHARDSON SHOOSMITH TIZZARD WALE WARDER WAVELL F1785

172960 WALES Mrs P. 5 Foxglove Close, Simons Park, Wokingham, Berks, RG11 2NF. ALLEN BOND GODDARD WALES F779

172979 WALFORD Mr G C. 2 Chestnut Drive, Shenstone, Lichfield, Staffs, WS14 0JH. Tel:0543-480412 WALFORD F3396

172987 WALKER Mrs Alice. (Hackley) 305 S 10th Ave, Yakima, WA 98902, USA. Tel:+1-509-453-2762 CHICKIE CLAYDEN GRANGER HACKIEY LAMBERT F5605

172995 WALKER Mrs Audrey. 30 St Michaels Road, Farnborough, Hants, GU14 8NE. Tel:0252-545864 BUDDEN Butten Button Cheeseman CHEESMAN Chiesman HINDES HUNNEYBALL PROWSE WALKER F1786

173002 WALKER Beverly. 220 W Olympic Pl #209, Seattle, WA 98119, USA. Tonkein Tonken TONKIN Tonkyn F7021

173010 WALKER Mr C P. 11 Oakfield Crescent, Aspull, Wigan, Lancs, WN2 1XJ. FLASBY KNOWLES MORT Tildesley Tinsley TYLDESLEY WALKER WILD YEATES F2602

173029 WALKER Mr Christopher. 15 Bankfield Avenue, Wistaston, Crewe, Cheshire, CW2 6RJ. CAVE COLLIER CULLEDGE HUDSON HULSE LOVAT STOCKDALE WALKER F4224

173037 WALKER Mr David. 1 Grange Avenue, Falkirk, Stirlingshire, FK2 9ER. Tel:0324-2216 DAVIS DONNELLY GOODFELLOW GOURLEY IRVINE KENNEDY MCCLEAN MILLIGAN WALKER F5223

173045 WALKER Mrs Doreen. (Irwin) Lindrene, 7 Burnleys Buildings, Flockton, Wakefield, W Yorks, WF4 4DL. Tel:0924-848746 BELCHER BROWN BUCHANAN CAMPBELL DINSMORE GREENOP IRWIN JACKSON KIPLIN WILSON F3880

173053 WALKER Mrs Eunice. Greystone Farm, Over Silton, Thirsk, N Yorks, YO7 2LH. Camby Canbe CANBY HODGSOM HOWE KELLET Kellett LASKEY Lasky PATTERSON Pattison VERRAN Verron F3925

173061 WALKER Mr Graham. 100 Sutherland Road, Croydon, Surrey, CR0 3QJ. BROWNE BUCK GAMBLING HUGGETT WALKER F2607

173088 WALKER Dr J M. 8 Walton Street, Oxford, OX1 2HG. Tel:0865-514515 ASBURY EYKYN GASK JOHNSON WALKER F2241

173096 WALKER Mrs Jill. (Galloway) 10 Dorly Close, Shepperton, Middx, TW17 8RT. ALLEN MAY BEAK CHILTON CRAMP CRAMPE CROMPE DARE DEAR FEREBEE GALLOWAY GLOVER HILL HUBBARD JONES KNIGHT LIPSCOMBE MILLHOUSE NEWTON PACKHAM PANKHURST PAYNE PEGLER PIRIE POLDING POULDEN POWLING SHELTON SHOEBRIDGE TROWNSON TRULL WALKER WILLIAMS F6101

173118 WALKER Mr John C. 19 Neath Road, Tonna, Neath, West Glamorgan, SA11 3DQ. Tel:0639-642775 ANDERSON BATTEN BECK BLIGHT BROWN CLEMENT DAVIES ELLIOT FOREHEAD FOWARD GOODRIDGE HIBBET Hibbett HIGGINS HITCHINGS HUDSON LEACH MARTIN Martyn MAY MAYNARD Maynards MORGAN Mynard Mynards OWEN Owens PASCO Pascoe Pashco PEAK Peake PEARCE ROWLAND Rowlands RYAN STONE THOMAS TOMS WALKER WALTON F3861

173126 WALKER Mrs Lori. 138 Kennington Bay, Winnipeg, Manitoba, R2N 2L5, CANADA. CROASDALE F6886

173134 WALKER Mrs M. 34 Paddock Way, Oxted, Surrey, RH8 0LG. CRAIG CUMMING REID SUTHERLAND F5251

173142 WALKER Mrs Margaret. White Haven, 36 Tudor Avenue, Dymchurch, Kent, TN29 0LT. Tel:0303-872805 BACK CONNINGTON CURD HAMMOND MERRYWEATHER PRITCHARD SILVERWOOD VINTEN WOOD F2634

173150 WALKER Mrs Molly. (Goodsell-Weller) 13660 Greenview Drive, Sun City West, AZ 85375, USA. Tel:+1-602-584-5418 BARNES GOODSELL RUMENS Rumings Rummens Rummings Rummins WELLER F3461

173169 WALKER Mr R S. 11 Mount Pleasant Close, Buckingham, MK18 1DN. BALL BRACEY CHERRY GIBBS GILLIAT STEVENSON STINSON WALKER WORLOCK F6349

173177 WALKER Dr Raymond F. 13660 Greenview Drive, Sun City West, AZ 85375, USA. Tel:+1-602-584-5418 ADEY BALL BORROWS BROMLEY BUSH HIGGITT MANTON RALPH WALKER YATES Yeates F3462

173185 WALKER Mrs Rita. (Spivey) 9 Dyson Hill, Honley, Huddersfield, W Yorks, HD7 2JJ. Tel:0484-663065 ALLEN MUSPRATT PLEWS RIPLEY SCHOFIELD SPIVEY F4065

173193 WALKLATE Mr Neil. 4 Smiths Row, St Nicholas, Cardiff, South Glamorgan, CF5 6SG. Tel:0446-760031 Waklet Walkelate Walklat WALKLATE Walklet Walklett Walklot Wauklet F13

173207 WALL Mr C. 18 Anthony Crescent, Alvaston, Derby, DE2 0GA. BOLLEN DUCE WALL WHEELER F4678

173215 WALL Mr John. Hurdcot, Berkeley Heath, Berkeley, Glos, GL13 9ES. Tel:0453-810361 BRISLAND GRANT-TAYLOR KILFOY WALL F5205

173223 WALL Mr Philip. 9 Woburn Close, Trowbridge, Wiltshire, BA14 9TJ. AGUS Blomfield BLOOMFIELD Farmer Farmor FERMOR HENSTRIDGE HILL KRALL RANDALL Randell RICHARDS ROWDEN Rowdon SARGENT Sarjeant Sarjent Self SELFE Sergeant Sergent Serjeant Shergall SHERGOLD Shergoll SWEET WALL WELLS WESTON F1772

173231 WALL Mrs S A. 53 Beechfield Road, Bromley, Kent, BR1 3BT. FINCH HARRIS MCKINNEY NORRY OLIVER WALL F4867

173258 WALLACE Mr Neil. 2 Meadow Gardens, Beccles, Suffolk, NR34 9PA. RITCHIE SHAW WINNING F5770

173266 WALLACE Mrs Rosemary E. (Richards) Wilroa, 26 Elliott Street, Caboolture, Queensland, 4510, AUSTRALIA. Tel:+61-7-495-6292 CHAMPION RICHARDS SHUTE TIMMINS WALLACE F5435

173274 WALLACE Mr Ted. 21 Southglen Road, Brantford, Ontario, N3R 6Z8, CANADA. BOORMAN BOREHAM BROWN CLARKE COLEY DOUBLE GARROD HORTON LEANEY LUNDY MARSHALL PAYNE WALLACE WHITTLE F4174

173282 WALLBRIDGE Mrs Lillian M. 4 Rothwell Close, Paulsgrove, Portsmouth, Hants, PO6 4DR.

Tel:0705-381435
DE-REDING OAKES WALLBRIDGE WARD WEBB F969

173290 WALLER Mr J D. Les Abris, La Brecque Phillippe, Alderney, Channel Islands. Tel:0481-822328
COTTON CROWTHER DENNETT ELLIS HALSTEAD HELLIWELL JACKMAN JOHNSON MIDGLEY NORTON PATCHETT PICKLES RAY RIGBY UNSWORTH WALLER F4265

173304 WALLER Mrs Nora Jean. 90 Arthur Road, Rainham, Kent, ME8 9HU.
ARNOLD CHINNAH FELTHAM GODDEN LITTLEFIELD MARSH OBALSTON RICHE Richie SPONG Sponge F2609

173312 WALLEY Dr Stephen. 11 Acrefield Drive, Cambridge, CB4 1JW.
BAYLEY BENNION BERKS BLANTHEM BULEY BURROWS DERBYSHIRE DRYLAND DUDDLESTON GRINDLEY GUERIN HOOSON MASSIE MEREDITH NEWTON PEAK PICKEN PODMORE ROBINSON WALLEY F1048

173320 WALLIS Mr Bruce Wakeman. 11 Maltings Road, Gretton, Corby, Northants, NN17 3BZ. Tel:0536-770342
WAKEMAN F2159

173339 WALLIS Mr N J & Mrs L E. 55 York Street, Charters Towers, Queensland, 4820, AUSTRALIA. Tel:+61-77-872124
CLUNE DINGLE FOY HAYNES MALONEY MCELROY O'LOUGHLIN PARKER WALLIS WESTON F4169

173347 WALMSLEY Mr Basil. 30 Knockdene Park South, Belfast, BT5 7AB, NORTHERN IRELAND. Tel:0232-654648
FAIRBAIRN WALMSLEY F4278

173355 WALPOLE Diana. 24 Friday Street, Minchinhampton, Stroud, Glous, GL6 9JL.
ALDRIDGE BISHOP CLACK HILL KEELING KIDMAN LATCH LATHAM MCLELLAND TRUMPER F1137

173363 WALROND Mr Lionel F J. Eton Villa, 5 Slad Road, Stroud, Glous, GL5 1QJ.
CHARD Valeran Waldron Waldrond Waleran Walerand Waleraund Wallrond Walran Walrand Walrauen Walraund Walron WALROND F1601

173371 WALTERS Mrs Edna. (Sheppard) 39 Stallcourt Avenue, Roath, Cardiff, CF2 5AL.
ALMER ELLIS JONES SHEPHERD SHEPPARD STUBBS VICKERS WALTER WRAGG F4851

173398 WALTERS Mr J S. 30 Stowe Street, Middlesborough, Yorkshire, TS1 4ND.
WEDLAKE WIDLAKE WINNER F6398

173401 WALTON Mr Alan. 50 Beech Grove, Mitcham, Surrey, CR4 1LH.
WALTON WORMALL F5901

173428 WALTON Mr Geoffrey. 17 Shaftesbury Road, Epping, Essex, CM16 5BH.
AVERY BARTLETT BURGESS CLEMENTSON COOK HARROP HOTSON JACKSON LOW MARTIN MECKLENBURGH MORGANS OVERS STAR WADDINGTON WADE WALTON F3357

173436 WALTON Mr Michael. 7 Tavistock Road, Cambridge, CB4 3NB.
BECKETT Blenco Blencoe Blencow BLENCOWE BLENCOWES Blenko Blinco Blincoe Blincow Blinko Blyncho Brookes BROOKS COTTON GAUNT PASHLEY SHENTON Shinton WALTON Woodmancey Woodmansee WOODMANSEY F1515

173444 WANKLING Mr Gerard. 10 Woodville Estate, St Helier, Jersey.
BAYLIS Bayliss GIDLEY MARDLIN Thurnall Thurnel THYRNALL Wancklen WANKLIN WANKLING Wanklyn F5644

173452 WANN Mrs J. 30 Laburnam Grove, Richmond, N Yorks, DL10 5AR.
ALLEN ASHTON Autey Autie AWTEY BERRY Bisbie BISBY Biszby Bizbie Bizby BROOKES CARR CROSS CROSSLEY EARLY GARRETT GREAVES Grieves JUSTICE KIMBERLEY LEECH REVILL THOMPSON WALKER WATERFIELD WEST WESTWOOD Yardley YEARDLEY F4347

173460 WANSTALL Miss Alison. 4 Cambrian Close, Bursledon, Southampton, Hants, SO3 8GW. Tel:042121-2489
FOLWELL GOLDFINCH JOINER LIDDIARD MILES MILLARD MUTTON SUTTON TILLEY WANSTALL WILKINS F2342

173479 WANT Mrs Julia. 78 The Warren, Old Catton, Norwich, Norfolk, NR6 7NN. Tel:0603-405309
DAWS FRENCH GOULDER JEFFERSON JEFFS REEVES WANT WEST F5614

173487 WARBOYS Mr Ralph C T. 71 Longstanton Road, Oakington, Cambridge, CB4 5AB. Tel:0223-232487
Warbois Warboise WARBOYS F4554

173495 WARD Mr A E. 162 Swithland Lane, Rothley, Leicester, LE7 7SF.
WARD F6211

173509 WARD Mrs Anne. 67 Rosebank Crec, Pennsylvania, Exeter, Devon, EX4 6EJ. Tel:0392-55242
HUNT LEADER METSON NEWTON SPILLER STARTUP F4587

173517 WARD Mr David R K. 17 Merley Drive, Highcliffe, Christchurch, Dorset, BH23 5BN. Tel:0425-275808
Bangam BINGHAM Binghame Byngham HINSLEY INSLEY Insly Tilley TILLY WARD F3048

173525 WARD Mr Dennis. Weald Cottage, Main Street, Beckley, Sussex, TN31 6TL.
MECHAM F7382

173533 WARD Mr G S. 38 Chennells Way, Horsham, W Sussex, RH12 5TW.
BISTOW CLARK DRAPER EASTON FLANDERS HARRIS HENSON HOWARD JARVIS LINNELL LUTHER PACKWOOD PAINE PALMER SHIRLEY SMITH THOMPSON TOMLIN VORLEY WARD F1787

173541 WARD Mr J D. 27 Emberson Way, North Weald, Epping, Essex, CM16 6DL. Tel:037882-2702
WARD F905

173568 WARD Mrs J. 3 Rutland Avenue, Thornton-Cleveleys, Lancs, FY5 2DU.
CARTMEL GORSE WHALLEY F3254

173576 WARD Ms Jennifer. 15 Corona Road, Cambridge, CB4 3EB.
HADFIELD HARDINGTON KEATING LOMAS SUCKSMITH WALTERS WARD WOODHEAD F4415

173584 WARD Mrs Joan. 41 Mildenhall, 25-27 Westcliff Road, Bournemouth, Dorset, BH4 8AY.
FANCY FRANCIS F1493

173592 WARD Mr Leonard B. Surfirs, Crackington Haven, Bude, Cornwall, EX23 0JP. Tel:0840-3359
BRAY MARSHALL SANDERCOCK WARD F667

173606 WARD Mrs M C. 2 Russell Street, Eastwood, NSW 2122, AUSTRALIA.
Allcroft HOLCROFT Holdcroft Howlcrofte MCGREGOR Oldcroft F7292

173614 WARD Dr Mark. 7 Cornfield Road, Lee On The Solent, Gosport, Hants, PO13 8HZ.
BAILEY BAWDEN Bowden Duffen DUFFIN Glaspole GLASPOOL Graddon GRAHAM GRATTON HANCOCK HAWKIN Hawkins Hockin Hockins KERSHAW LAKE LUXTON MATTHEWS PAINTER SOUTHERD SOUTHWELL STONEMAN WARD WATERAGE Wateridge Wedlake WIDLAKE F2377

173622 WARD Mrs Merle. 1159 Sunnybrae Road, Kelowna, B C, V1Z 2N9, CANADA.
BRADSHAW BUCHANON HARVEY KEMP KIRKIN MORRELL ROBERTS SHERWIN THOMPSON WALKER WILEY Wily Wylay Wylie F5596

173630 WARD Mr Michael. 19 Orchard Close, Blundeston, Lowestoft, Suffolk, NR32 5AF.
BOGGIS ELEY FINCH HOPPINS MUNSEY REVILL SPINDLER TURNER WARD WOLFE F2194

173649 WARD Peter & Chris. (Yates) 14 Stowe Crescent, Ruislip, Middx, HA4 7SS.
Brian BRYAN BUCKLEY BULLOCK FALLOWS HALL HITCHEN Hitchin Hitchon Hollier HULSE INSKIP IRVING Lacey LACY LUXTON OBERY Obrey Olier OLLIER PLATT Poiser POYSER RICE Scarratt SCHOFIELD Skarratt SKERRATT Skerrett Skerritt STARKEY STATHAM WARD Woberry Wooberry YATES F1796

173657 WARD Mr R B. 20 Manor Way, Chesham, Bucks, HP5 3BH. Tel:0494-771593
Drewett DREWITT Druet DUNBAR HAMMETT HARRIS OKINES Okins PHILIPS PILL Wade WARD Warde WHETTER F1584

173665 WARD Mr Roland. 77 Eary Veg, Tromode Park, Douglas, Isle Of Man. Tel:0624-621596
ARNOT Arnott ASHLEY BOWDEN FRANCIS GREENWOOD HALE HARKER MOORE STORR WARD F5766

173673 WARD Mrs Yvonne J. (Fryer) Y Wern, Old Mill Road, Dwygyfylchi, Penmaenmawr, Gwynedd, LL34

6TG. Tel:0492-623396
BRADLEY DUTCH Friar Frier Fryar FRYER HARTLEY LUCAS Mair Mare MAYER Mayers Mear Meyer Meyers Pitanay PITAWAY Pittaway Pounal Pounall Pownal POWNALL ROGERS F4780

173681 WARDELL Mr Fred G. 101 Christie St, Toronto, Ontario, M6G 3B1, CANADA. Tel:+1-416-531-6922
BESTWICK BUCKINGHAM CHANCE CLEWS EDGE ELFORD HILL STINSLEY THOMPSON TINSLEY WAIN WARDLE WESTWOOD F4487

173703 WARDLE-ROBINSON Mrs C. (Prior) 74 Southport Road, Ormskirk, Lancs, L39 1LX.
FFITZER FITZER GUY OLIVE PRIOR F6081

173711 WAREING Mrs Ada M. (Leyland) 13 Bagganley Lane, Chorley, Lancs, PR6 0EW.
BELLAS CRAIG HAYSTON LEYLAND SCOTSON SEDGWICK STEPHENSON WARMBY WILSON F6164

173738 WARKCUP Mrs Janet. (Mcarthur) 3 Bertana Drive, Mudgeeraba, Queensland, 4213, AUSTRALIA. Tel:+61-7-530-5523
BLANDY FERRIS MATTHEWS METCALFE MOCK WALKCUP WARCUP F5625

173746 WARLAND Mr Peter Andrew Auchmuty. 45 North Court, Hassocks, W Sussex, BN6 8JS. Tel:0273-844685
AUCHMUTY CHATTING FEARDON FULLER MAY PRICE STONE Warlan WARLAND Warlon Warlond F5199

173754 WARN Mr P. 36 Mitchell Road, Orpington, Kent, BR6 9TP.
Waren WARN Warne Wearn Wearne F7156

173762 WARNE Mrs Doris. 89 Gloucester Road, Newbury, Berks, RG14 5JN. Tel:0635-34147
Brae BRAY Brey Glasspole GLASSPOOL Glasspoole HORSEMAN LEE MARSH RUSTELL SMITH THURSTAIN Thurston WARNE WINKWORTH F983

173770 WARNE Mrs Vivien A. (Gill) 2 Braddons Hill, Woodford, Plympton, Plymouth Devon, PL7 4RT.
BARFOOT BLATCHFORD CHAPMAN CLARKE Farrow Gerram GILL HOLDER JERAM Jerom Jerram MCLEAN MOODY PARSONS PHAROAH PROUSE Prowse Train TREIN Trien Warkman WARNE WATERMAN WILCOCKS WORKMAN F4058

173789 WARR Mr Edward. 1 Finlay Close, Faversham, Kent, ME13 7SH.
WARR F394

173797 WARR Mrs Patricia. 13 Brown Street, Toowoomba, Queensland, 4350, AUSTRALIA.
BANKS DAVIS FROGATT FROGGATT FULLELOVE HULME LOUGHLIN MAKER O LOUGHAN F5469

173800 WARREN Mr Frank. 10 Bonython Road, Newquay, Cornwall, TR7 3AN.
CULLEN RICHARDS TRETHEWEY WARREN F2723

173819 WARREN Mrs Helen. 49 Prideaux Road, Eastbourne, Sussex, BN21 2NE.
GREAVES PAULSON PEASANT QUIBELL WABY WARREN WEDGE WRAGG YORK F436

173827 WARREN Mr Ian. 6 Wedgberrow Close, Droitwich, Worcs, WR9 8RS.
BRIDGE DROVER GREEN GRETTON Hayward HAYWOOD Heywood HOLLAND HUGHES JOHNS KIRKHAM Orgil ORGILL PARTRIDGE PAYNE STALEY TONKS WARREN WRIGHT F5827

173835 WARREN Mr John. 7 Winnham Drive, Fareham, Hants, PO16 8QE. Tel:0329-283037
DUNSTAN JOHNSON KEMP MESSENGER PETERS QUINNELL RUFF STILES Styles WARREN F709

173843 WARREN Mrs Julie K. (Woodcock) 292 Southborough Lane, Bromley, Kent, BR2 8AA.
DIMENT ELLIS HOARE PEARMAN TRUDGETT F4761

173851 WARREN Mrs May. (Morris) Mayden, Chestnut Way, Longwick, Aylesbury, Bucks, HP17 9SD. Tel:08444-3595
BERRISFORD BROWN BURGESS CATCHPOLE COLEY COLWELL HANSOM HATCH HAWES HAWKES HEMERS MINSHIN MORRIS NICHOLSON PEXTON PILGRIM POOLE TESCH WALTERS WARREN WATHAM ZEDDI ZEDY F4706

173878 WARREN Dr Michael D. 2 Bridge Down, Bridge, Canterbury, Kent, CT4 5AZ. Tel:0227-830233
CLARKE COMPTON GEARING REEKS TAYLOR WARREN F3830

173886 WARRENDER Mrs J E. (Hancock) 6 Rimu Street, Matamata, North Island, NEW ZEALAND.
BRENTON BREWER CARNE ELLERY HANCOCK MITCHELL MOORMAN PORTLOCK WARRENDER F5140

173894 WARRY Mr M J. 3 Lukin Street, Mt Morgan, Queensland, 4714, AUSTRALIA.
Warie WARRY Wary Wharry Worie F6738

173908 WARRY Mr R. 4 Ravenscroft Road, London, W6 0UG.
WARRY F5957

173916 WARSOP Mrs Sarah. Oaklands, Old Church Road, East Hanningfield, Chelmsford, Essex, CM3 8BG. Tel:0245-400372
BRIGNOLL CORNER ELGIE LANGBORNE MEAD PRESTON WINN F5875

173924 WARTH Mr K E. Wass Hael, 57 Stephenson Road, Hanwell, London, W7 1NN.
WARTH F6656

173932 WARWICK Mr Herbert D. 43 Oak Tree Drive, Guildford, Surrey, GU1 1JL. Tel:0483-66559
ADDLEY ARNOTT AXFORD BATCOCK BLEE BOWYER BUNDLE CARPENTER Chety Chetye CHILMAN CHITTY COOK CUTT DAY DELL EDWARDS FARRALL FARRELL FIELD FIELDER FLAHERTY GALLAZI HARGREAVES HASEMAN HOOKER HOWELL KEENE LIPSCOMB MEARS MELLISH MORRIS MURRAY NEEDHAM OTWAY PAYNE PENFOLD PENNY POTTER READ RICE RUSSELL SHARP SHAW SILCOX SNELGROVE SPIKESMAN STEDMAN STEVENS STEVENSON STONE STREET STRINGFELLOW TAYLOR TOONE WARWICK F978

173940 WARWICK Captain Ronald W. Castle Cottage, Nunney, Somerset, BA11 4NH.
ATKINSON GENT HOLT MACNAUGHTON WARWICK F1642

173959 WASS Mr Robin. 20 Links Avenue, Whitley Bay, Tyne & Wear, NE26 1TG. Tel:091-252-5310
Vaus Vause Was WASE WASS WASSE Waus F5415

173967 WATERALL Mrs W E. 86 High Street, Loscoe, Derbys, DE7 7LF.
ALLSOP Allsopp Alsop Alsope F6736

173975 WATERFIELD Mrs P. 51 Sheridan Crescent, Baughurst, Basingstoke, Hants, RG26 5HQ.
OATES WATERFIELD F3067

173983 WATERS Mr Jeremy D. 30 Parsons Green, London, SW6 4UH.
BEVINGTON BOLAM FARDON LAMB LESANT LOVELL MORRIS SANTO WALTERS WATERS F509

173991 WATERS Mrs Lorraine. (Walkey) 1 Goverseth Hill, Foxhole, St Austell, Cornwall, PL26 7UZ. Tel:0726-882825
ECCLES-JONES HODGE ROWE SKEWS TRUDGEON WALKEY F2623

174009 WATERS Mr Roland. 74 Shirley Drive, Hove, East Sussex, BN3 6UL.
ALLCORN COMBS CRUTTENDEN FOSTER GASTON HERMITAGE JASPER LAMBERT MOCKFORD WATERS F5924

174017 WATKINS Mrs C E. 28 Windsor Crescent, Frome, Somerset, BA11 2EA.
ADDIS DARLING FINCH MANNION VOWLES WATKINS F6151

174025 WATKINS Mr David. 31 Fairwater Drive, Woodley, Reading, Berks, RG5 3JG. Tel:0734-661401
CROXTON HARWOOD JERVIS PEMBERTON PERROTT SOUCH SURRIDGE TRAVERS WIGGINS WRIGHT F2070

174033 WATKINS Mr John. 4 Elizabeth Grove, Oakham, Dudley, West Midlands, DY2 7TG. Tel:0384-235392
ANDREWS BREWER GLAZE HONEY JEFFRIES LANCASTER PARSHOE WATKINS F6175

174041 WATKINS Mrs Linda. 121 Rempstone Road, Merley, Wimborne, Dorset, BH21 1TR.
BALE FACEY HENDEBOURCK INSTONE LOWE RILEY SQUIRES TAYLOR WATKINS F4835

174068 WATKINS Mrs Rosemary. (Osborne) 8401 Kalview Drive, Vernon, B C, V1B 1W8, CANADA. Tel:+1-604-549-3004
BEALE COCKRAM DAVIS GATES ROBBENS SWAN WOOLLEY F5182

174076 WATKINS Mrs Shirley. 2 Ilmington Close, Glenfield, Leics, LE3 8BF. Tel:0533-874988
CAPELL DRIVER DURAN DURRAN KNAPP PEBERDY SATCHELL SEENEY SMITH SNAREY F589

174084 WATNEY Dr D. Larchwood, 15 Lower Saxonbury, Crowborough, East Sussex, TN6 1EB.
ACRES WATNEY F5366

174092 WATSHAM Mrs A. Redhouse Farm, Bildeston, Suffolk, IP7 7EG.
Pudeney PUDNEY Putney F7040

174106 WATSON Mrs Brenda. 6 East View Fields, Plumpton Green, Lewes, E Sussex, BN7 3EE. Tel:0273-890757

Gartley GARTLY HAWLEY WARREN F4920
174114 WATSON Mrs Doris. (Hunt) 9 Jennings Road, Lower Parkstone, Poole, Dorset, BH14 8RY. BARKER BAXTER CLARKE GATES HUNT LOCH NUNN F4866
174122 WATSON Mr H F. Highfield House, Kitty Briggs Lane, Grantham, Lincs, NG31 7JR. WATSON F5912
174130 WATSON Miss I M. 60 Gordon Street, Dargaville, Northland, 0300, NEW ZEALAND. ADCOCK ALSOP AMPLEFORD ARSCOTT ATTON BEEBYE BELTON BOND COX CRAINE DERHAM DICKINSON FRISBY HALL HILL JACKSON KING KNIGHT LEE LIFLY PONSFORD POWLESLAND ROOTS SEWARD SMEETON SMITH STIRGIS WALDREN WALKER WATSON WEBSTER WELLS F4595
174149 WATSON Mr J R S. 4 Welton Close, Stocksfield, Northumberland, NE43 7EP. Tel:0661-842828 HEDLEY JOBLING STEWART WATSON F219
174157 WATSON Mrs Jill Scott. 65 Chalfont Road, Oxford, OX2 6TJ. COPE DUNCKLEY GIBSON GURD MCDADE PARKE PICKERING RUDDELL SCOTT WATKINS WILSON F5009
174165 WATSON Mr Joseph. East View, Main Road, Claybrooke Magna, Leics, LE17 5AH. WATSON F6046
174173 WATSON Mr Kenneth. 47 Stockbridge Road, Elloughton, Brough, N Humberside, HU15 1HW. Tel:0482-668437 BULMAN FLEMING LEFFLER LITTLEWOOD LIVERSEDGE PARKINSON POSTLE RAINFORTH WATSON WHITING F5845
174181 WATSON Mrs Margaret A. 56 Elstow Road, Kempston, Bedfordshire, MK42 8HJ. BIRD JENKS F265
174203 WATSON Mr Paul. Jubilee House, Coles Lane, South Petherton, Somerset, TA13 5AF. Basil Basill BASSIL Bassill BULMER CALOW FITCH HOLLOWELL READ Reade SABAN Seaban SEAGO Seagoe TOMPKINS WATSON F6489
174211 WATSON Mr Rex. 29 Woodland Road, Sawston, Cambridge, CB2 4DT. ASKFORD BARLOW BRUMPTON BURROWS BUTTERWORTH COTTAM CROSSLEY Daubener Daubeney Daubner DAUBNEY DAWSON Emmet Emmett Emmot EMMOTT GEORGE GIBSON GREEN HARRISON HARTLEY HAYES Haywood Heyes HEYWOOD Holden HOLDING Holme Holmes HULME KEAP KIPPAX Lovelee Loveley LOVELY Lovlee MACKINDER Makinder Needlay Needler NEEDLEY PARKINSON PEARSON SCHOFIELD Scholefield Scholfield SHEARMAN SMITH SPENCER THORNTON Tindal Tindale TINDALL WATSON Whitaker WHITTAKER WIGGINS Wolstancroft WOLSTENCROFT Woolstancroft Woolstencroft Worstencroft YATES F3765
174238 WATSON Mr Stephen. 42 St Edwards Road, Gosport, Hants, PO12 1PP. EDMEADES ODD PEEN TWOCOCK WATSON WATTS WOTTON F2653
174246 WATT Mrs Arlene C. (Adam) 7 Glebe Park, Banchory, Kincardineshire, AB31 3YT. Tel:03302-4172 ADAM CLARK LEDINGHAM PIRIE STOTT WATT YOUNGSON F3561
174254 WATT Mr John Lochrie. 1325 Chuckanut Drive, Bellingham, Washington, Usa 98226. Tel:+1-206-734-2174 LOCHRIE PAXTON WATT F3222
174262 WATTERSON Mrs. 17 Darley Dale Avenue, Great Barr, Birmingham, B44 9UW. CASHMORE DAVIES EVANS FORDE HIGGESON HILL HODGSON HOOTON LAWRENCE LEWIS MEADE PIE REECE REYNOLDS SAVAGE SMITH STRINGER STYLES WILLIAMS WOODWARD WORKMAN F1751
174270 WATTON Ms Dawn. 150 South Kinson Drive, Bournemouth, Dorset, BH11 8AD. ANSTY BOTHAMLEY BRADSTOCK BREAKER BROWNING COLLINS COOMBS DEAN DUGDALE KELLEWAY RANDALL REEKES VALLANCE WATTON WILLIS F5839
174289 WATTON Ms Dawn. 276 Ferme Park Road, Crouch End, London, N8 9BL. Anstey Anstie ANSTY ATKIN BOTHAMLEY Bottomley Bracher Bradstock BRADSTOCKE BRAKER Breaker Bredestock Broadstock BROOMHEAD Brownienge BROWNING BURSEY Cam Came CAMM COLLINS Colons COOMBS COOPER Corben CORBIN Corbyn DAVENPORT DAVIES Davis DEAN Devonport DUGDALE Dugdell HUGHES Hutchens Hutchings HUTCHINS JANES Kellaway KELLEWAY Kelloway Michell MITCHELL MURPHY Oakeley OAKLEY Okeley Okely Osborn OSBORNE Osburn PERKINS PRITCHARD RANDALL ROBERTS SANDERS SAUNDERS SCOTT Sharly Sherley SHIRLEY THOMAS THOMPSON TITHER TROTTLE Tyther VALLANCE Vallence Vallens WATTON WILLIAMS WILLIS WOODS F1520
174297 WATTON Mrs Margaret. White Cottage, Codmore Hill, Pulborough, W Sussex, RH20 1BQ. Tel:07982-5296 BALL Biday Bitheway Byday BYTHEWAY CARR CLEWER Cluer COURT HORTON QUINEY QUINTON Rud RUDD Rudde WATTON Whatton F2547
174300 WATTS Mr Colin. 4 Silvertrees, Emsworth, Hants, PO10 7ST. BIGGS CHIVERS COBURN COLEMAN DREDGE FORD GEORGE GRANT JANES LONG MITCHELL PALMER TAYLOR WATTS F3907
174319 WATTS Mr G E. 7 The Priory, Abbotskerswell, Newton Abbot, Devon, TQ12 5PP. Aple APLEY Aply Aplye Aplyn Appeley Apple Appley Applye BARON BAWDEN BILKEY Bilky Boaden Bowden BROAD BROWN Carlion Carlyan CARLYON CHEGWIDEN CLOTWORTHY COCK Collam Collom Collomb Collombe Colomb Cullombe CULLUM Cullumbe CURRIE DADDOW DALGLEISH DELLAMAYNE DENHOLM DEVENSHER GOSLEY GRIFFIN HARRIS HILLIER HOBLIN Hoblyn HOCKEN HOYTE IRVINE JENKIN JOHN KING Lanion LANYON LEIGH MASON MCEWAN MCRAE MICHELL NIGHTINGALE NORTHERN Novderen ODGERS PIRIE Raschelegh Raschelye Rasely RASHLEIGH Rasle Rasselegh Rasshelegh Rayshelegh REID RIDDOCH RITCHIE Sharplin SHARPLING SIMPSON SLADE SMITH TOM TONKIN TREGILGAS Trelvalscois TREVALSCUS Trevascus TRUGIAN VIVIAN WADHAMS Water Waters Wates Wats Watters Wattes Wattie Wattis WATTS Wattus WILLIAMS Worters Worts F1874
174327 WATTS Mr J. 3 Poplar Avenue, Stoke Bishop, Bristol, BS9 2BE. Buteland BUTLAND Buttland F6784
174335 WATTS Mrs Jean. (Holmes) 9 Dryden Road, Scunthorpe, South Humberside, DN17 1PW. Tel:0724-861333 DERBYSHIRE ENGLAND HEWITT HOLMES SAYERS SOUTH SWALLOW WATTS F5603
174343 WATTS Mrs Nina. (Silk) 4 Silvertrees, Emsworth, Hants, PO10 7ST. ALLEN BELLAMORE CHURCHER DAVIES DEADMAN EWEN GREEST MAY MEGGS NEWMAN PAINTER PARKER PHILLIPS POOLE POOR SILK SPENCER STAGG TAYLOR TOPP WHITCOMB F3906
174351 WATTS Mrs Pearl. (Towse) 21 Apthorpe Way, North Arbury, Cambridge, CB4 2NJ. TOWSE WATTS F3676
174378 WATTS Peter & Isobel. 44 Clough Avenue, Sale, Cheshire, M33 4HU. ABBOTT BEBBINGTON BOWDLER GODFREY PERRY ROGERS STEBBINGS TEW WATTS WHITE F2189
174386 WATTS Mr Robert H. 34 Cherry Orchard, Wootton Under Edge, Gloucestershire, GL12 7HT. Tel:0453-842979 Alden Cawdery Corderie CORDERY ELDEN Eldin Eldon HART HERBERT KENCH WARNER Warrell Wat WATT WATTS WILLMOTT Wilmot Wilmott Worel Worell Worrel WORRELL Worrill F150
174394 WATTS Mr William. 42 Wentworth Crescent, Ash Vale, Adlershot, Hants, GU12 5LE. Tel:0252-25698 NICHOLLS SIMMONS WATTS F3882
174408 WAUGH Mrs Lois. 58 Pownall Crescent, Margate, Queensland, 4019, AUSTRALIA. COLVARD COLVERD DYSON HORAN KERSHAW ROWE TAYLOR WILKS F5445
174416 WAY Mr David. 37 Sandersfield Road, Banstead, Surrey, SM7 2DH. COX FOLLETT WAY F468
174424 WEARE Bob. 1 Greenfield Drive, Gt Tey, Nr Colchester, Essex, CO6 1AA. Ware Wear WEARE Were Wheare F7045
174432 WEARMOUTH Mrs P. 25 Spring Garden Lane, Ormesby, Middlesborough, TS7 9JB. BEHAGG BUTLER CARTER ENGLISH FEWSTER GOODWIN HALL OSWALD PARKE WEARMOUTH F6478

174440 WEATHERALL Mr & Mrs K. 7 Lisburn Street, Milton, South Otago, NEW ZEALAND.
WEATHERALL Witherall F7097

174459 WEATHERHEAD Mrs Elizabeth. (Seth) 85 Balmoral Avenue, Galashiels, Selkirkshire, TD1 1JJ. Tel:0896-4728
Seath SETH F3383

174467 WEAVER Christine. 14 Du Maurier Close, Redfields Road, Church Crookham, Fleet Hants, GU13 0YA.
WINDON F1907

174475 WEAVER Mrs Iris M. (Jones) 71 Downside Close, Blandford, Dorset, DT11 7SD. Tel:0258-451239
BIRD HEMMING HOUGHTON JAMES JONES WALDRON WEAVER F5881

174483 WEAVERS Mr Frank. 8 Beechnut Lane, Solihull, W Midlands, B91 2NN. Tel:021-704-1543
BILLING WEAVERS F1362

174491 WEBB Mr A. 9 Drysdale Close, Weston Super Mare, Avon, BS22 8HH.
WEBB F6746

174505 WEBB Mrs Barbara. 15 Whittal Street, Kings Sutton, Banbury, Oxon, OX17 3RD.
CANNELL DOWDESWELL MENHAM PIDOUX ROBSON THORNLEY F3147

174513 WEBB Mr Gerald. 100 Queens Crescent, Chippenham, Wiltshire, SN14 0NP. Tel:0249-652427
ADAMS BAYLIS BULLOCK COCKINS COLE COLLINS DICKS ENDALL FOX GEORGE HAYNES HEWLETT HITCHCOCK HOWSE Hulet JELKS JONES LINDSAY MORRIS ROWLAND SATES Seyts SIMPSON SMART SMITH TAYLER TIMMES VENNIMORE WEBB F1526

174521 WEBB Mr John A. 10 Fairway, Littlehampton, W Sussex, BN17 6PY.
ANDREWS COX KING LANDER Launder Lavender SIMPSON SMITH WEBB WOODS F1956

174548 WEBB Mrs Pat. Garden Flat, 12 Eastern Villas Road, Southsea, Hants, PO4 0SU. Tel:0705-752816
HOGBEN MARCHANT ROSE TAYLOR F1935

174556 WEBB Mr Peter David. 15 St Lawrence Lane, Ashburton, Devon, TQ13 7DD. Tel:0364-52855
ATKINS BELLAMY CROCKER FINCHER HOWARD PERRY SCUFFHAM WEBB WHITE F2055

174564 WEBB Mrs Phyl. 22 Abbey Road, Eastbourne, Sussex, BN20 8TE.
APPS ARKELL BADCOCK BAKER BARNES BEALE BENNETT BISHOP BLACKMAN BOONE BRAZIER BRIANT BUMSTEAD BURTON BUSS CAREY CHEESEMAN CHEESMAN CLEWLOW COLTON DUTTON EARLE EASTWOOD EDWARDS FARNS FORD FOSTER FRANKLIN FREEMAN FRYER GALLOP GILPIN GOODALE GOTT GROVES HANSON HARMAN HARRIS HILLER HOAD HOWELL HUNTER HUTCHINSON JAMES KENDALL KEYS LARGE LEVETT MANN MARSHALL MATTHEWS MONK MORRIS PAGE PARKS PENNELS PETTITT PHILLIPS PHIPPS PUNTER RANGLEY ROBERTS SEDGWICK SELLINGS SHOESMITH SIMMONS STROUD SYMONDS TALBART TASKER TURNER WEBB WINBORN WOOD WORSEY WRIGHT YOUNG F228

174572 WEBB Mr Ronald. 22 Abbotsferry Road, Galashiels, Selkirkshire, TD1 3RX. Tel:0896-4779
CLARK HERBERT KINGSTONE MORGAN OWEN RAVEN THOMAS VOSS WEBB WRIGHT F4944

174580 WEBB Miss Sheila. 27 Epsom Lane South, Tadworth, Surrey, KT20 5TA.
BOES Dracopp DRACUP Hillindrake HOLLINRAKE WEBB F6180

174599 WEBB Mr Stanley. 11 Harefield Road, Rickmansworth, Herts, WD3 1LY. Tel:0923-772996
ALDRIDGE BANNISTER Bennet BENNETT BEST BISHOP BISSE Brickel BRICKELL Brickle Caish CASE CASH Cass Casse CHALK Chalke COLLIER Coombes COOMBS CROSS EXTON FARROW FOY GAISFORD GALE GOOCH HARTE HAYNES Hellyer Hillier HILYEAR HODDER HOPKINS Howel HOWELL HUSSEY IMBER JOLLIFFE LOCKE LUSH MUSSLEWHITE NOBLE ROBERTS ROOK Rooke Scoates SEYMOUR Skotes SKOTS SOUTHGATE STICKLER STRIDE TRAVERS TUTTEN VILLIS WEBB WELDON WOODS F1870

174602 WEBBER Mrs B A L. Hilltop, Chester Street, St Asaph, Clwyd, LL17 0RE. Tel:0745-583980
ASKEN CUTHBERTSON GILLAIT GRATTON HARRISON HORTON JACKMAN JENNINGS PYDD RICKETT ROCK SCROWTHER SHORT STERLAND TULIP F4702

174610 WEBBER Mrs Edith. 404 West Pawnee, Apt 221, Wichita, KS 67213, USA.
GALE F4397

174629 WEBBER Mr Thomas M. 63 Hanover Close, Yew Tree Gardens, Nailsea, Avon, BS19 2XR. Tel:0275-853306
CARNELL SELWAY WEBBER F3571

174637 WEBLEY Mrs M A. 30 Sedbury Road, Sompting, Sussex, BN15 0LL.
BAGOT BRINSLEY BURTON Dabhoirean Daveren Daverin Daverrennes DAVOREN Davren De Vesci Derbridge Doorbridge Dubhdabhoireann Durbidg Durbidge DURBRIDGE Edsar Edsau Edsaw Edsawe Edscer EDSER Edsir Edsor Edzcer JEFFREYS Knowden KNOWLDEN Knowleden LETT LLOYD MAY Nolden Noulden O'davoren O'duvdavoren PEARCE RANDALL RUTLAND SARSFIELD STONE SWAIN THYNNE TICKNER VESEY Vessey WEAVER Webbel Webbeley Webberley Webbly WEBLEY Webly Weebyly Weobley Whibley Wibelai Wibley WINTER F32

174645 WEBSTER Mr D M. Meadowbank, Wrexham Road, Llanfair D C, Clwyd, LL15 2RU.
ATTY WEBSTER F3542

174653 WEBSTER Mr K M. 73 Downie Park, Dundee, DD3 8JW.
ALEXANDER DORWARD DUNDAS ESPLIN HIGH PEEBLES ROBERTSON ROSS WEBSTER F3403

174661 WEBSTER Ms Lisa. 95 Lincoln Road, Bush Hill Park, Enfield, Middlesex, EN1 1JU. Tel:081-363-9300
BANNING BELL BOLTON DALTON GILLAM Gomm GOOM HEFFER Hefford LEVINS PERRYMAN PITHER Pithers F6535

174688 WECKERT Mrs Annette. (Mackrill) Po Box 262, Scone, NSW 2337, AUSTRALIA. Tel:+61-6-545-2871
MACEY Mackerell Mackerill Mackrell MACKRILL PILL POLDEN Polten Poulden SKINNER WARD WHITE WILLS F5502

174696 WEDD LEIGH Ms Imogen. (Wedd) Oak Villa, 90 Hadlow Road, Tonbridge, Kent, TN9 1PA.
BUDGETT COTTER DUNKIN FROST INKERSOLE PATTISON WEDD F3983

174718 WEDD Mr Edward. 20 Lone Tree Avenue, Impington, Cambridge, CB4 4PG. Tel:0223-232193
WEDD F2969

174726 WEDDELL Mr Thos Lumsden. 9 Downing Drive, Kirkhill, Morpeth, Northumberland, NE61 2YB. Tel:0670-515828
LUMSDEN F1047

174734 WEEKES Mr Michael A. 12 Frederick Road, Fishbourne, Chichester, West Sussex, PO19 3JQ.
HOLLANDS WEEKES Weeks WHALE F6435

174742 WEEKLEY Mr Derek. 10 Churchill Avenue, Clevedon, Bristol, BS21 6QW.
Weakly WEEKLEY Wickland Wicklin F1913

174750 WEIBEL Mrs P. 43 Emily Street, Murrumbeena, VIC 3163, AUSTRALIA.
ADAMS ARMSTRONG BEER CHURCHILL GILLON HUGHES MEWKILL OFFORD PALMER PILGRIM SEERS TITLEY TOWNSEND TOWSEY WELCH F5506

174769 WEIGHT Mr G A J. 69 St Peters Street, Gharb, Gozo, MALTA.
Waight Wayt WEIGHT Weights F6783

174777 WEIR Mr David A. 2 Stoney Lane, Brinsley, Notts, NG16 5AL. Tel:0773-712499
BLACKWOOD DAVIES HODGE Hutchenson HUTCHESON Hutchison JOHN LORIMER Lorrimer Lottimer MADDOX MORRISON PRESTON TODD WEIR Wier F1315

174785 WEIR Mr J M. Hermiston, 2 Harborough Close, West Chiltington, West Sussex, RH20 2PS.
PEARSON WEIR F4890

174793 WEIR Mrs May. (Weston) 7 Kipling Avenue, Balby, Doncaster, S Yorks, DN4 9EE. Tel:0302-857113
BARBER COOK FRETWELL HENDERSON PRITCHETT SEVERN WEIR WESTON F5695

174807 WEIR Mrs Norma S. (Neal) 5 Carlisle Grange, 22a Grange Road, Eastbourne, East Sussex, BN21 4HJ.
BAKER BATCHELOR BEXHILL BUTLER COMBER CORNFORD CORNWELL DENNETT DRYNAN FLINT GATES GOFFE HOLE LOGAN MACDONALD MCCOLM NEAL NORMAN

OSBOURNE PIKE PILFORD REYNOLD SMITH TURNER WARD Weekerson WEIR WICKENS Wickerson Wickeson WILKINSON WINTER F5679

174815 WEIR Mrs Rosemary W. 2 Stoney Lane, Brinsley, Notts, NG16 5AL. Tel:0773-712499
Ayers AYRES BAKER COOPER CROCKER Eyre Eyres Hollioake HOLLYOAK HUNT LEWIS MERRALL Merrill Nailer Nailor Nayler NAYLOR PALNT ROBINSON ROSE SHAW Sheappheard Shepherd SHEPPARD VEAL VEALE WALTERS WIGLEY Woans WONES YEOMANS F1316

174823 WELBY Mr Daniel. Botschaft Road, Postfach 1500, 5300 Bonn 1, GERMANY.
Wealby Weelebee Welbe Welbeaby Welbee Welbey Welbie WELBY Welbye Wellbe Wellbee Wellbey Wellbie Wellby Wellbye Wellebye Welliaby Welsby Whelby Wheleby Wilby Willby Willebey F6928

174831 WELCH Miss M. 11 Wind Street, Aberdare, Mid Glamorgan, CF44 7LL. Tel:0685-878257
BAINTON BAYNTON BETTS ENGLAND HARDING WELCH F5930

174858 WELCH Ms M. 13801 89th Avenue, Surrey, B C, V3V 6K7, CANADA.
BELLERBY BOYES Boys Broun Broune BROWN Browne CLARK Clarke CLOSE Corzer COWTON Crocer Croser Crosier Crossier Crosyer CROZIER DARLEY DUNN Ellard FOX Foxes GAMBLE Garbart Garbertt Garbut GARBUTT HARPER HELLARD HOGGARD JOHNSON Jonson PRINCE RICHARDSON SEDGEFIELD Sedgfeild Sedyfeild SMITH Tramer Trammer TRANMER WARD Witte WITTY F5185

174866 WELCH Mr N. Coldsides, Burtree Gate, Cockerton, Darlington, DL2 2XX.
CHOYCE FLEMING GARRAWAY GRIBBIN PICKERING F4744

174874 WELCH Mr Vivian S. Box 847, Grenfell, Sask, S0G 2B0, CANADA. Tel:+1-306-697-3589
TURNER WELCH F6508

174882 WELCHMAN Mr B D. The Cottage, Manor Terrace, Paignton, Devon, TQ3 3RQ.
WELCHMAN Welshman F6990

174890 WELDON Mr Albert. 53 Buxton Avenue, Heanor, Derbyshire, DE7 7UN.
Welden WELDON Weldone Wellden Welldon WELTDEN F2512

174904 WELLS Mrs A M. 18 Limecroft Close, West Ewell, Surrey, KT19 9RE.
CARSLAKE F7140

174912 WELLS Mr Colin Durant. Cae Coch, Brynsiencyn, Llanfairpwll Gwyn, Gwynedd, LL61 6SZ. Tel:0248-430308
ASHTON BRADSHAW BRIDGE CHESHIRE CULVERWELL DURANT German HAMPSHIRE Jarman JERMAN Jermyn LLEWELLYN SALTER TREMBLETT Tremlett F4743

174920 WELLS Mrs Dorothy. (Reditt) 3 Orchard Drive, Meopham, Kent, DA13 0LN.
BUTTERS Hayhoe Hayhow Heigho HEYHOE KEMP POWELL Redditt Redhead Redit REDITT RICE WATKINS F4592

174939 WELLS Mr Eric. 55 Holt Park Road, Adel, Leeds, LS16 7QS. Tel:0532-610683
ADAMSON BRIGGS COLE LUPTON MOSS PERKIN WARDMAN WARREN WELLS YOUNG F3836

174947 WELLS Miss J W. 2 Gatesbield, New Road, Windermere, Cumbria, LA23 2LA.
ASKEW BEEBY HUTCHINSON SHARP Sharpe TURNER WALLIS WELLS WOOLLEY F3844

174955 WELLS Mrs June. (Mowatt) 9 Lower Lees Road, Slough, Berkshire, SL2 2AB.
BALSDON BURSTOW DREW DREWMILK HOWARD JENKINS LINDSAY MOWAT MOWATT NELSON PACKHAM SEAWARD STURROCK STUTELEY WARD WHEELER F4637

174963 WELLS Mrs M. (Gullick) 106 Alexandra Road, Hemel Hempstead, Herts, HP2 4AG.
ATTWELL BARNES BAWTREE Bawtrey Bawtry BEACHAM Beachim BEARNE BEAUCHAMP Beecham Beechim BROWN BUTTON CHURCHILL Clements CLEMETS Colet Colett Collet COLLETT COLLINS CORBETT DEAR Deer DICKENSON Dickinson Dickison DIXON DODDS DRURY Dury EASTON EMERY GAYFORD GRAY GREEN GULLICK GULLOCK Harrhy HARRY HAYES HILL HILLIARD Hilliyard HILLYARD HOBBS HODGES HOGG JAMES JOHNSON JONES KNAPP LABRUM LAND LANG LANGFORD MANLEY MOIST Mulin Mulins MULLIN Mullins OGILVY PADFIELD PARTRIDGE RENDLES RIGGS ROGERS ROSS SMITH STEED Steeds STENSON STOKE STOKES STONEHOUSE STRANGEWAYS TALLING THOMAS WAUGH WELLS WIDCOMBE WISE Witcom WOOD F1205

174971 WELLS Mr O R. Kaisen Strasse 61, D-7890, Waldshut, WEST GERMANY.
De Welles WELLS Wels F6804

174998 WELSBY Mrs Sandra Jean. (Kay) 22 Parkstone Avenue, Carleton, Poulton Le Fylde, Lancs, FY6 7PF. Tel:0253-885050
HARLOW HARRISON HIGSON HILTON KAY MILLS PARKER PRESCOD ROSTRON SEEDALL SIMEY STOVEY SULLIVAN WELSBY WOODS YATES F5655

175005 WELSFORD Mrs L J. 3 Gleneagles Drive, Henbury, Bristol, BS10 7PS.
BRETT BROOKS DIBBLE DUCKHAM KITSON LAND OUTRAM PELLOW TREVAIL TREVEAL TREVEALE WELSFORD F2593

175013 WELSH Mr T M. 54 Westbourne Road, Olton, Solihull, W Midlands, B92 8AU.
LITTLEHALES F6757

175021 WENDEN Mr K C. 23 Oxford Road, St Leonards, E Sussex, TN38 9SR.
WENDEN Wending Wendon Windin F6836

175048 WENT Mr Derrick. Woodside Cottage, Camp Road, Ross On Wye, Herefordshire, HR9 5NJ. Tel:0989-65262
WENT F841

175056 WERRY Ms Evelyn. (Moore) 25-310 Westminster Avenue, London, Ontario, N6C 5H4, CANADA. Tel:+1-519-432-6432
COYSTEN COYSTON MOORE WERRY WITHEY F5467

175064 WESSELS Mrs Ann. 14 Dymoke Road, Hornchurch, Essex, RM11 1AA. Tel:0708-751403
BAILEY BERRY CURTIS FIELDER GALE MILLS PEACOCK F1481

175072 WEST Mr Alan. 19 Clevedon Gardens, Cranford, Middx, TW5 9TT.
ABBOTT ARMSTRONG ATKIN ATKINSON BABER BANCROFT BARNET BEE BELLAMY BENSON BOWLES BRACKENBURY BRADBURY BURRELL COOK COULSON CREASEY CURTIS EDWARDS ELLIS EVANS FOSTER GUNNING HARRISON HARSE HAW HODGES HODGSON HUGHES JACKSON JESSOP JOHNSON MACHIN MORSE PEGLY PRICE PROUDFOOT RADFORD RENNISON ROBINSON ROSSINGTON SCHOLEY SCOLEY SEABRIGHT SEVIAR SINDERSON STANHOPE STARMORE STROPES TAYLOR TETHER THOMPSON VALLEY WEST WILLEY WILLIAMS WILLOWS YEARDLEY F1220

175080 WEST Mr & Mrs Alfred. Northangle, Ms-5, Dubbo, NSW 2830, AUSTRALIA. Tel:+61-68-829142
ANCELL BENCE BOAK BROWN BULEY BURTON BUTLER COMER COX DREW Drewe FURNELL GOBLE GRINSDALE HAMMOND Hansel HOPPER HOPSON HOYLAND JACKWAY KARNEE LIPTROP LONDON MARCH MARSH MILES MORGAN MUNDAY PINK RIGERS Valler VOLLER WALLACE WALLIS WARREN WEBBER WEST WHEELER WHITE WITTS F4363

175099 WEST Mr Arthur. 47 Sheraton Road, Newton Aycliffe, Co Durham, DL5 5PQ. Tel:0325-312664
ADAMSON CLARK CLARKE DAUBER GOLDSBOROUGH MASON WEST F6417

175102 WEST Mr Barry. 3 The Limes, Hitchin, Herts, SG5 2AY. Tel:0462-451981
CARR COOKE HARRIS WEST F4557

175110 WEST Mr D W. Ivy Mount, Welland Road, Hanley Swan, Worcester, WR8 0DE.
KENT LEE LOVELAND WEST F2971

175129 WEST Revd Derek. 16 Buckland Avenue, Slough, Berks, SL3 7PH.
Douce Douse Dowce Dowes Dows DOWSE F1474

175137 WEST Mrs Helen. (Dodds) 2808 15th Street, Vernon, B C, V1T 3V8, CANADA. Tel:+1-604-542-7735
CANT DODDS PAXTON REDPATH SCOTT F5606

175145 WEST Mr Leonard E. 30 Linnell Road, Rugby, Warwickshire, CV21 4AN. Tel:0788-567081
BLEEK BUBB SKEET WEST F414

175153 WEST Mrs Margery. (Wood) 248 Wakefield Road, Lightcliffe, Halifax, West Yorks, HX3 8TZ. Tel:0422-201230
BAKER COPPING DOWNBOROUGH DRAKE SPENCER THORNTON WALLACE WITTON WOOD F5843

175161 WEST Mrs Marion B. (Griffin) Ivy Mount, Welland Road, Hanley Swan, Worcester, WR8 0DE.

ANDERSON BIRD GREENWELL GRIFFIN HARRISON NEWTON PERRINS F5633
175188 WEST Mrs Maureen. 5 Barlborough Avenue, Whitehouse Farm, Stockton On Tees, Cleveland, TS19 0QL.
COGDON KELL THIRWALL TOLSON F2531
175196 WEST Mr Richard. 2 Ellacombe Road, Longwell Green, Bristol, BS15 6AZ.
AYLING Baigbie Baikbie Beagbie Beagby Begbee Begbey BEGBIE Begbio Begby Bigbie Bigby CORYNDON DOUGHTY FISHER HATHERLY MASLIN Sargeant Sargent SARJEANT TAYLOR TILDESLEY Tildsley Tildsly Tinsley WEST WINCHESTER F1752
175218 WEST Mrs Rosalie. 11 Dozmere, Feock, Truro, Cornwall, TR3 6RJ.
AINGER CREAMER DOY ENGLISH FENBY FENN HARDY HARLAND HARPER HOWMAN JACKSON JACOB JORDAN LANGLEY LEVITT NELSON NORTON OMBLER PAWLEY PERRIT SIMPSON STEVENSON WHITING F4749
175226 WEST Mrs S M. 9 Avocet Lane, Martlesham Heath, Ipswich, IP5 7SF.
Gomeldon Gumbelton GUMBLETON F6802
175234 WESTALL Mr A F. 8 Stoneham Close, Petersfield, Hants, GU32 3BX.
BROOKER CURTIS GRAHAM LAMBOURN WESTALL F2861
175242 WESTAWAY Mr Robert. 129 Nowell Road, Barnes, London, SW13 9BX.
COLES Westawaie WESTAWAY Westawaye Westerway Westeway Westoway Westway F2873
175250 WESTERMAN Miss Margaret. 18 Reynolds Gardens, Moulton, Spalding, Lincs, PE12 6PT. Tel:0406-370794
WESTERMAN F5291
175269 WESTMACOTT Mr John. 1 Salisbury Close, Wokingham, Berks, RG11 4AJ.
BERNERS BIGLAND BYGLANDE CARYL KENNETT LAROCHE ROWE VARDY WESTMACOTT F663
175277 WESTMACOTT Mr John. 18 Wakefield Close, Ronkswood, Worcester, WR5 1QR. Tel:0905-352869
Wasmecoat Wesmacott Wesmicot Westemecott Westmacet Westmackit Westmacoat WESTMACOT WESTMACOTE WESTMACOTT Westmacotte Westmacutt Westmaggott Westmaket WESTMANCOAT Westmancote WESTMANCOTT Westmancourt Westmarrott Westmarutt Westmecet Westmecott Westmicott Westmoncoat Westmoncote Westmuchett Westmuckett WESTNACOTT F1314
175285 WESTMORE Mr Terence. 87 Old Road, East Cowes, Isle Of Wight, PO32 6AU.
Bert Birt Birte Birtt Bortt Bourt Burrtt BURT Burte Burtt Bust Butt Byrt Byrtt Wesmoor Wesmoore Wesmor Wesmore Wessmor Westemore Westmare Westmeer Westmer Westmond Westmoor Westmoore Westmor WESTMORE F962
175293 WESTOBY Mrs Sue. (Roffey) 11 Edendale, Oulton Broad, Lowestoft, Suffolk, NR32 3JZ.
KENT MARTIN PERKINS REDSTONE SMALE Westabee Westabie Westaby Westabye Westauby Westbe Westbie Westby Westebee Westebey Westebie Westeby Westebye Westerbey Westerbie Westerby Westerbye Westibie Westiby Westibye Westobe Westobie WESTOBY Westobye Westorby Westorebie Westybye Whesterby F4997
175307 WESTON Mrs Denise. (Barty) 73 Downside Close, Blandford Forum, Dorset, DT11 7SD. Tel:0258-456686
BARTY BEARDMORE BENNETT FERRIMAN JOHNSON KIDWELL MILLINGTON NUTT PAVOR PIERCE PLANT ROMNEY SALT SANDERS SHARLAND TOINTON TOWERS-PIERCE WESTON WILDER F6030
175315 WESTON Mrs Joyce. (Benham) 10 Bruxby Street, Fosseway, Syston, Leicester, LE7 8NB. Tel:0533-696460
Banham Beenham BENHAM TILLEY Tillie Tilly Tylley Wesson Westetun Westington WESTON Westone Westun F3713
175323 WESTON Mr R V. 145a High Street, Uckfield, E Sussex, TN22 1HP. Tel:0825-762676
BEESON DOWNES Downs DUMBRELL HALL RUSSELL STEPNEY TITMUS WESTON WISTON F1545
175331 WESTON Mrs Sheila R. (Trenbath) 6 Benedict Close, Halterworth, Romsey, Hants, SO51 8PN. Tel:0794-515382
BLANDIMORE DAMER Dammer FARGUS GILLETT RAHR TRENBATH F2072
175358 WESTON Mrs Thelma. (Hill) 42 Miner St, Charters Towers, Queensland, 4820, AUSTRALIA. Tel:+61-7-787-2756
FINNEY LARKIN MARKS MURPHY St Clair ST CLARE ST CLERE WILSON F5533
175366 WESTON-WEBB Mr A P. 77 Village Gardens, Baglan Moors, Port Talbot, West Glamorgan, SA12 7LP. Tel:0639-822777
BOWSHER Ffoulkes FOULKES WEBB WESTON F2235
175374 WESTREN Mrs V. (Anderson) 17 Russell Road, Felixstowe, Suffolk, IP11 8BG. Tel:0394-284027
ANDERSON BARRY BERRY PECK WESTREN F4979
175382 WESTWELL Mrs J E. (Dykes) Summerlands, 2 St Michaels Lane, Bolton Le Sands, Carnforth, Lancashire, LA5 8LG. Tel:0524-823897
APPLEYARD ARMITAGE CLAPHAM DODGSON DUGDALE FEARNSIDE FIELDHOUSE FIRTH GRANT HAINSWORTH HARTLEY HOWARTH LAMBERT LANGSTROTH LEE LOFTHOUSE NEWSOME OUTWAITE POLLARD PRESTON ROBERTS ROBINSON THORPE WESTWELL WHITEHEAD WOOD WRIGHT F3485
175390 WETTERN Mr John. 15 The Green, Fetcham, Surrey, KT22 9XE. Tel:0372-459277
CADIC DEAN F3404
175404 WETTON Mrs C. (Wilson) 7 Mersey Road, Bulkington, Nuneaton, Warks, CV12 9QB.
NEWMAN WETTON WILSON WOLFE F3452
175412 WEYERS Mrs Elizabeth. (Blackhall) 27 Old Road, Old Harlow, Essex, CM17 0HD. Tel:0279-436637
Blackall BLACKHALL GREEN GROSVENOR Grovenor Grovesnor LOWE Offspring OFSPRING SCOTT SHAW F4233
175420 WEYMAN Mr W E. 28 Rotherfield Road, Henley On Thames, Oxon, RG9 1NN.
HANSCOMBE JUSTICE NAILER NAYLER NAYLOR PAULIN TAYLER WEYMAN F676
175439 WHALEY Mr David. The Old Rectory, Oxhill, Warwick, CV35 0QR.
Ap Eignion BENYON CHARNOCK CLIFFORD CLINCH CRIDLAND DALRYMPLE DIXON HARINGTON Harrington LARNER MONCKTON Piggot PIGOT ROBINSON SHRUBB Shurb THARP Tharpe Thorp Thorpe WHALEY Whalley YATE F1883
175447 WHALLEY Mrs Sylvia. 189 Oldham Road, Ashton Under Lyne, Lancs, OL7 9AS. Tel:061-339-4635
BOYD CAVE CRUTCHLEY DAVIES DEAN HILTON HOWARD HOWARTH MILLS WRIGLEY F1630
175455 WHARTON Mr D F. Barbican House, St Stephens Way, Coolinge Lane, Folkestone Kent, CT20 3RD.
GOSLETT Gostlett F6707
175463 WHATMORE Mr Derek E. 9 Elizabeth Avenue, Hove, East Sussex, BN3 6WA. Tel:0273-505564
BALL BROOKER Faithful FAITHFULL FRY GILBERT HOLLAND HURREN Hurrian JEWELL Newberry NEWBERY Newbury PAIN Paine Payn Payne Searl SEARLE Serle SOAMES Somes STEPHENS Watmer Watmoor Watmor WATMORE Wattmore Whatmoore WHATMORE F2434
175471 WHATMORE Mr Geoffrey. Morewood House, Defford Road, Pershore, Worcs, WR10 1JE.
WATMER WATMORE WATMOUGH WATTMORE WHATMORE F2837
175498 WHATMORE Mrs Sheila. 9 Elizabeth Avenue, Hove, E Sussex, BN3 6WA. Tel:0273-505564
BATES BLOMBERG Burnes Burness BURNS COOKE CRAPP DOWDING GALE GRIMES HANCOCK HARRIS LAY LITTLE WASHINGTON Whittenberie Whittenberrye Whittenborough Whittenburrough WHITTENBURY Witenbury Wittenburg F2435
175501 WHATMOUGH Mrs M M. Lindens, 3 Gilbraltar Hill, Lincoln, LN1 3BW.
FLEAR F6971
175528 WHEATER Mr J G. 2 Chadwick Hall Road, Rochdale, OL11 4DJ.
WHEATER F7124
175536 WHEATLEY Mr Steve. 18 Orchard Way, Hurstpierpoint, W Sussex, BN6 9UB. Tel:0273-835500
BALCHIN TRUCKLE WHEATLEY F2641
175544 WHEATLEY Ms Susan. (Wheatley) 32a Grove Road, New Barnet, Herts, EN4 9DE.
WHEATLEY F3238

175552 WHEELDON Mrs Glenna. 102 Bilsand Road, Glenrothes, Fife, KY6 2ED. Tel:0592-754757
BOA BRUNTON COUTTS CRUIKSHANK DODDS KIRK MILLAR OLIVER POWRIE SMITH THOMSON F2857

175560 WHEELDON Mr Howard. 17 Russell Avenue, Sprowston, Norfolk, NR7 8XE. Tel:0603-408468
FAWCETT WHEELDON F4940

175579 WHEELER Mr John Arthur. 132 Quarella Road, Bridgend, Mid Glamorgan, CF31 1JT. Tel:0656-663709
CARTER HEATH SULLIVAN WHEELER F3700

175587 WHELAN Mr Bernard. 16 Moat Farm Lane, Bishampton, Pershore, Worcs, WR10 2NJ. Tel:0386-82375
Atkins BROOK CLIFF Cliffe CROWTHER DAVID ESARTT GOFF Gough HATKINS HIATT HODGSON Hyatt Hyett ISAAC Isaak LEWIS LOCOCK Lowcock MIDDLETON MILLINER MOUNCEY Mouncy OWEN Pole Pool POOLE Powell ROBINSON Sanders Sarle SAUNDERS SCARLETT Scorlett SEARLE SHELTON Whalen Wheelan WHELAN WILSON WOOD YEWDALL F1131

175595 WHELAN Mrs Patricia Rose. (O'Donnell) 10 Poplar Avenue, Crosby, Liverpool, L23 2SU. Tel:051-924-5265
CAVANAGH CLARKE CUTLER Gilgan Gilgin GILLIGAN Kavanagh KINSELLA LYNN MCCONNELL MCMANUS O'DONNELL F5632

175609 WHERRY Mr Tony. 2 Redfern Avenue, Redhill, Worcester, WR5 1PZ. Tel:0905-358532
TOZER WHERRY F66

175617 WHETHERLY Mrs S. 13 Haviland Grove, Upper Weston, Bath, Avon, BA1 4JP.
Spranklin SPRANKLING F7013

175625 WHIELDON Miss Margaret. 217 Breedon Street, Long Eaton, Nottingham, NG10 4EU.
Bouldy Boultbee Boultbey Boultbie BOULTBY Boultley START Starte Stert Stirret Sturt Whinyates Windgeat Windyates WINGATE Wingett Wynniatt F611

175633 WHIFFEN Mrs Jeannine. (Allkins) 74 Dereham Avenue, Ipswich, Suffolk, IP3 0QF.
Alken Alkens ALKIN Alkins Alkyn Alkyne Alkynes Alkyns Allckin Allcoin Allekin Allken Allkin ALLKINS Allkyn Allkyne Allkynes Aulkin Aulkyns Awlkyns BOLTON Boulton GARRETT HUDSON HUSKINS TASKER WARRINGTON F4525

175641 WHIFFEN Mr John C. 19 Sylvan Way, Coney Hall, West Wickham, Kent, BR4 9HA.
ALLEN BYRNE DOYLE HOMEWOOD HONEYBALL JACKSON KATES NEVILLE OAKEY PAMMENT PURKIS RIXSON ROBINSON ROWLING STENNETT TUNNARD WALL WALLAGE WORLEDGE F5702

175668 WHIFFING Mrs Sally. (Brealey) 21 Trewithan Parc, Lostwithiel, Cornwall, PL22 0BD.
BREALEY Brealy Brearley Brearly Brereley Brerely Brerley Brierley Bryerly EDWARDS HICKMAN MUSSELLWHITE Tretheway TRETHEWEY Trethewy Whiffen WHIFFIN Whiffing Wiffen Wiffin F2325

175676 WHINHAM Mr David A. 7 The Beeches, Goddard Avenue, Hull, North Humberside, HU5 2BG. Tel:0482-470207
Whinam WHINHAM Whinholm Whinnem Whinnim Whinnom F3520

175684 WHISKIN Mr David. 16 Westland Drive, Brookmans Park, Hatfield, Herts, AL9 7UQ. Tel:0707-54911
EAMER FUTCHER GARNON GIDLEY JENNINGS KING LEVERSUCH LITTLE MALONEY MANFIELD MCGHIE SIMKINS STURGEON WEBBER Whisken WHISKIN Whisking Whiskins Whiskyn WISKEN Wiskens WISKIN Wisking Wiskins Wyskin F2234

175692 WHISLER Wilton M. 121 South 168, Seattle, WA 98148-1611, USA.
CRAWFORD F7260

175706 WHITAKER Mrs M. 20 Darvall St, Rosanna 3084, AUSTRALIA.
WITHELL F7376

175714 WHITBY Mrs Alison. (Walker) 2 Market Hill Cottages, Clopton, Woodbridge, Suffolk, IP13 6SB. Tel:0473-735686
WALKER WHITBY F3841

175722 WHITBY Mrs J E. (Hickey) 3 Brambles Close, Syon Lane, Isleworth, Middx, TW7 5BX.
BANHAM BLAND GUMM HEYWOOD HICKEY JEX REEVE SNOWLING WHITBY F3993

175730 WHITCHER Mrs Muriel. 5 Hyland House, Furlong Road, Bourne End, Bucks, SL8 5AE.
MURSELL F1366

175749 WHITCROFT Mrs Evelyn V. (Russell) 36 Beechmount Park, Newry, Co Down, N Ireland, BT34 1LA. Tel:0693-64026
MCMORDIE RUSSELL F3335

175757 WHITE Mrs Clare. The Fighting Close Cottage, Southam Street, Kineton, Warwickshire, CV35 0LN. Tel:0926-640221
BRINDLEY CLARK Clarke COOK Cooke ELLIS HACKETT HASLAM HAYES JANION MAYOH MCALISTER Mcallister OTTEWELL Ottiwell Ottowell Otwel PARR Railton RAYTON RICHARDSON SHAW TAYLOR WEBSTER Wrayton Wreaton F2573

175765 WHITE Mr Colin. 3 Hogarth Close, College Town, Camberley, Surrey, GU13 4FG. Tel:0276-600939
WHYARD WIARD WYARD F2580

175773 WHITE Miss D M. Rupert Lodge, Lyndhurst Road, Landford, Salisbury, Wiltshire, SP5 2AF.
Deacon Decon Dekon Diccon Dickens Dicker Dicking DICKON DICKSON Diggen Dikkon Dikon Dixon Dyckon Dykon Dyxon Gnawdaby Gnordaby HALL HODGSON LUXFORD Mill Milles MILLS Mylles Nawdaby NORDABY PEDERICK Petherick Rocliffe Routcliff Routleff Routleft Routley Routliff Rowcliff Rowcliffe ROWTCLIFF Rowtcliffe Rowtly SMITH THOMPSON Thomson Tompson Tomson WILLIAMS F624

175781 WHITE Mr David G. Well Cottage, 109 Westbrook, Bromham, Chippenham, Wiltshire, SN15 2EE. Tel:0380-850624
ABRAMS BACON BOND ENGLISH GEORGE HOPKINS LEE MITCHELL NEATE OATLEY PAYNE SHERGOLD SLADE SUDERY WHITE WOOTTON F6171

175803 WHITE Mrs E J. 22 Mynchen Road, Knotty Green, Beaconsfield, Bucks, HP9 2BA. Tel:0494-673980
CARR CURRY FLINN HALL-ROBINSON HELLARD HUSSEY PATTISON PEARCE ROBSON SHEWARD WELCH WEST WHITE F1682

175811 WHITE Miss Elfrida. Nyanza, Kiln Lane, Stokenham, Kingsbridge Devon, TQ7 2SF. Tel:0548-580456
COLE Cool Coole Cooll Cul Cull WHITE F2092

175838 WHITE Mr Homer L. 581 Garden Lane, Pasadena, CA 91105, USA.
ALLEN ANGOVE BUTLER EDWARDS GOYDEN NANCARROW NOBLE REPPIN ROUSE SAMPSON WHITE F4232

175846 WHITE Mr John. 41 Alton Road, Fleet, Hants, GU13 9HW. Tel:0252-615573
BAVERSTOCK CHUBB CRABB DAY DOBLE EYLES HOPKINS KINGSBURY SAUNDERS SIGGERY VASS WADDING WESTON WHITE WILLIAMS WITCH F877

175854 WHITE Miss K Nancy. 41 Springfield Road, Linsdale, Leighton Buzzard, Beds, LU7 7QS. Tel:0525-384365
BULL Egelton Eggelton Eggleton ROBERTS Sedgbear SEDGBEER Sedgberry Sedgbury Sedgebear Sedgeberry Sedgebury Vicars Vicas Viccars Vickars VICKERS Vickhouse Vickous Vicr Vicres Vicrs Vicus Vigers Vuckis WEBBER WHITE F4781

175862 WHITE Mrs L M. (Allen) 88 Rowlings Road, Winchester, Hants, SO22 6HL.
ALLEN COLLAR Coller DAVIDGE JACKSON JAMES MARSH MERRY TITCOMBE TRODD WHITE F1066

175870 WHITE Mr Leonard Charles. 6 Clovelly Way, Orpington, Kent, BR6 0WD. Tel:0689-828849
BAKER CANNINGS CLINKERBERRY GODWIN GOOSE LYDIARD OSBORN SMITH STRETCH WRIGHT F4105

175889 WHITE Mrs Margaret. Lon Bhan, 2 Ardhallow Bungalows, Bullwood, Dunoon Argyll, PA23 7QL. Tel:0369-4811
BLAIR CAMERON CAMPBELL CLARK CRAWFORD LEITCH MCBETH MCLEAN MCLEOD ROBERTSON SHEARER SMEATON TURNER WHITE F2778

175897 WHITE Mr Martin. 70 Ashleigh Road, Exmouth, Devon, EX8 2JZ. Tel:0395-266600
ANDERTON WHITE F677

175900 WHITE Mrs Norma. (Greenwood) Po Box 2170, Big Bear City, CA 92314-2170, USA. Tel:+1-714-585-8962
COCKCROFT GREENWOOD TEMPEST F4190

175919 WHITE Olive. 10 Stewards Green Road, Epping,

Essex, CM16 7BX. Tel:0378-74717
CHOAT WARD F906

175927 WHITE Mr P W C. Cobwebs, Hale Green, Chiddingly, E Sussex, BN8 6HQ. Tel:0825-872525
CAREY Cary Kari F1804

175935 WHITE Mr Peter. 1 Moorland Road, Fulford, York, YO1 4HF. Tel:0904-658461
Aber Abri Alberie Alberry Albery Auberie Aubery AUBRAY Aubraye Aubrey Aubreye Aubrie Awberie Awbery Awberye Awbrey Awbreye Horberry Horbery Horbury Opberry Opbury Orbery F6018

175943 WHITE Mr Richard. 17 Bridge Gardens, East Molesey, Surrey, KT8 9HU. Tel:081-979-5354
Beasley Beasly BEAZLEY Beazly Beezly GILHAM Gillam GOUJON Kettel KETTLE NARES WALLER WHITE F3591

175951 WHITE Mr Robert. Townbury House, 11 Blackfriars Street, Salford, M3 5AB. Tel:061-834-4919
ALLCOCK BACKSHALL BIRKITT BOSTOCK BUTLER CHATFIELD CHELTON COLBY COWARD MILLETT NORMAN RIMMINGTON SEAL STREET TRANTER WASHER WHITE WILLIAMSON F3495

175978 WHITE Mr Roy. Picton Lodge, High Street, Bury, Huntingdon Cambs, PE17 1NQ. Tel:0487-314558
CARTER COOPER FINCH KETLEY QUILTER WHITE F1937

175986 WHITE Mrs S. Dower House Cottage, Flishinghurst, Cranbrook, Kent, TN17 2QA.
Bearda Beardah Beardall Beardar Beardaw Bearden BEARDER Beardin Beardo Beardoe Beardon Beardow Berdall Berdoe Berdow EGGBEER Eibbot Eibert FEATHER GREENWOOD Hebbat Hebberd Hebert Hepert Herbert Hibbart HIBBERT Hibort Hobort Hubberd Hubbert Hubert Hybbart INMAN THURLBY WHITTLES F3593

175994 WHITE Mrs Sheila. (Brown) 1 Tuffley Road, Westbury On Trym, Bristol, Avon, BS10 5EQ.
ALAND BOWLES BRAMBLE BROWN FARMER GARDINER Gardner Gauler GOLDING HOLLAND MITCHELL Olden OLDING PANTING Sellings Selvin Selwin Selwyer SELWYN Selwynne Sulivan F6420

176001 WHITEAWAY Mrs P R. Church House, 16 Church Street, Dawlish, Devon, EX7 9QR.
NANFAN Whiteaway WHITEWAY F7160

176028 WHITEHEAD Mrs Martha. 32 Quail Hollow Drive, San Jose, CA 95128, USA. Tel:+1-408-559-3797
ALDRICH F5543

176036 WHITEHEAD Dr Maurice. 92 Millhouse Woods Lane, Cottingham, North Humberside, HU16 4HB. Tel:0482-840285
ARBOUIN CROOKE HIBBERT MOLLESON VALENS F2629

176044 WHITEHEAD Mr Robert. 4 Laurel Close, Cheriton, Folkestone, Kent, CT20 3PP.
BARTLETT JUDD MOORE OSBORN OSBORNE SURRIDGE TOMBS VINEY WATKINS F1064

176052 WHITEHOUSE Mrs Janette. (Hubball) 42 Upper Meadow Road, Quinton, Birmingham, B32 1NX. Tel:021-422-8307
AKER BEWICK CALLEAR GREEN HABBERLEY HOLLAND HUBBALL JENNINGS KING MASKELL MATTHEWS MILLGROVE OSBORN POWELL ROBERTS WATERHOUSE WHITEHOUSE F6495

176060 WHITEHOUSE Mr Robert. 2 Rivermead Avenue, Darlington, Durham, DL1 3SG.
BUSBY CHRISTIENSEN DAFFON GREEN REEVES WATSON WHITEHOUSE WILSON F776

176079 WHITEMAN Mr Neil. 1 Beacon Hill House, Court Road, Newton Ferrers, Plymouth Devon, PL8 1DB.
AITKEN BRIERLEY DIGBY FREEMAN JACKSON KINGSTONE LARWARDINE MALE WHITEMAN F4990

176087 WHITESIDE Dr Don. 4 Newgale Street, Nepean, Ontario, K2H 5R2, CANADA.
Quitesyd Qwythedws WHITESIDE Whitesides Whitsid Whitside Whitsyd Whittsyde Whyteside Whytsd Whytsyd F7374

176095 WHITESTONE Mr Peter. Applehurst, Lowbands, Redmarley, Glos, GL19 3NF. Tel:0452-840587
WHITESTONE F3249

176109 WHITFORD Mr A H G. 73 Kneller Gardens, Isleworth, Middx, TW7 7NR.
KIRKHAM MARTIN WHITFORD F2292

176117 WHITHAM Mr F. 67 Rossendale Road, Burnley, Lancs, BB11 5DQ.
HESKETH KNIGHT Qwittwham RUFFLEY TRESEDER Whitam WHITHAM Whitquam Whittam Whittham Whitwam Whitwham Witham Wittam Wittom F2474

176125 WHITING Mr Anthony E G. Butt Lodge, Butt Lane, Goulceby, Louth, Lincs, LN11 9UP. Tel:0507-343778
ALLISON ASHLEY BLADES BRACKENBURY BROUGHTON BUTTERS CLARKE COOK COTCHIEFER CRAWFORD DAVIS DAWSON EAST EHRHARDT FLINTOFF GUY HARDY HATCLIFFE HEATON HEREWARD HOLLIER JESNEY JONES KIRKBY LEONARD LINGARD LLOYD MARTIN PLUMPTON SOUTHWELL STEPHENSON THOMSON TOMLINSON TRAFFORD TRUE TUXWORTH WAITE WALKER WEST WHITEING WHITING WHITINGE WHITTING WHYTINGE WHYTTYNG WRIGHT F2038

176133 WHITING Mrs Susan. (Screeton) 254 Ryebank Road, Chorlton Cum Hardy, Manchester, Lancs, M21 1LU.
Acheson Aitcheson Aitchison ATTCHISON BRAY BROOMHEAD CREETON Francland Frankeland FRANKLAND NUTTALL PRIOR Screaton Screeton Screton Scruton Skreetan Skreeton THOMAS WILLIAMS F5668

176141 WHITLEY Mr Thomas. 64 Odd Road, Tower Hamlets, Dover, Kent, CT17 0DW. Tel:0304-215317
DENHAM DOBSON FOREHAM RUDD SEABORN SHARWOOD WHITLEY F5254

176168 WHITLOCK Mr Peter M. 3804 Kilarney St, Port Coquitlam, British Columbia, V3B 3G6, CANADA.
Whitelock Whitelocke WHITLOCK Wittlock F6615

176176 WHITMARSH W E. 43a Kiln Ride, Wokingham, Berks, RG11 3PJ. Tel:0734-733018
BUCKETT EAST HOOPER JOHNSON JONES LEAVER MUTTER STREET WHITMARSH WISE F2747

176184 WHITMORE Mr H C G. 4 Heather Close, Horsham, W Sussex, RH12 4XD. Tel:0403-65178
BUCKLER GATHERCOLE HEMMINGS LEADER WHITMORE F5063

176192 WHITNEY Mr Colin. 22 Leatham Close, Birchwood, Warrington, Cheshire, WA3 6PX. Tel:0925-811911
WHITNEY Whittney Whittneye Witeneie Witney F304

176206 WHITNEY Mr J G. 129 Bagley Close, Kennington, Oxford, OX1 5LU. Tel:0865-736545
AIME Germain GERMAINE WHITNEY Whitteney Whyteneye Witenie Wittney Wyteney Wytteneye F639

176214 WHITNEY Mr M M. Les Portes, Mainsat 23700, FRANCE.
Eatall EATWELL Etwall Yetwale F6737

176222 WHITNEY Mrs Shaena. 129 Bagley Close, Kennington, Oxford, OX1 5LU.
CHENNELL LITTLETON WATCHCORN WHITNEY F640

176230 WHITTA Mr Rex A. 14 Candler Street, Scarborough, N Yorks, YO12 7DF. Tel:0723-375740
JUDD MALT Rolt ROUGHT Roult Rowlt WHITTA Whittaw Whitto Whitton F4259

176249 WHITTAKER Mr E J W. 60 Exeter Road, Kidlington, Oxford, OX5 2DZ. Tel:08675-3592
BERRIDGE BESWICK HARDY HASLAM NICHOLSON PAGE RYE WHITTAKER F5902

176257 WHITTAKER Mrs Jill. (Ferry) 20 Maybridge Drive, Solihull, West Midlands, B91 3NE.
BRAMPTON BRINKLOW BROOKER BULLINGER BURROWS CARPENTER CHALKLEY CLEMMEY CORNISH CROXFORD DAVIS DYE EMMONS FERRY FROMANT GREASLEY HAINES HURDLESTONE KNIGHT LANE LEVETT LOVELL MAYHEW MERCER OWEN PACK PARTRIDGE PERREN POCOCK ROYS SAVAGE SHEPHARD STUDDS SWEBY TEMPLE TOMS URRY WALKER WARWICKSHIRE WESLEY F2390

176265 WHITTALL Mr J R. 8 Orme Road, Worthing, W Sussex, BN11 4EX.
WHITTALL F6828

176273 WHITTARD Mr M A. 63 Ridge Park Avenue, Mutley, Plymouth, Devon.
WHITTARD F6815

176281 WHITTINGHAM Dr J S. Turner House, 153 Cromwell Road, London, SW5 0TQ. Tel:071-373-5560
BETTS BULLEN COTTERELL CRANE DANBY DRAKE

DUPUIS FIELD GOOSE HALSE HARPUR I'ANSON JORDAN KINGSLEY MALLORD MARSHALL MELLER MUNRO POUND SHAW TURNER F4281

176303 WHITTINGTON Mr J C. 56 Buchanan Road, Walsall, West Midlands, WS4 2EN. CADDEL Caddell Caddle Caudle SANDARS WHITTINGTON F1555

176311 WHITTLE Miss Helen M. Elmfield, Toddington Lane, Littlehampton, W Sussex, BN17 6JX. AVIS BARKER BLACKWELL BRADFORD EDWARDS EVANS GARDNER WARREN WHITTLE F1782

176338 WHITTLE Mr Laurance. 73 Grammar School Road, Hull, East Yorks, HU5 4NY. Tel:0482-48195 DRESSER Hairsign HAIRSINE Haresine Harsen Harsin Harsine Hersan MUMBY Pammenter Parmenter PARMENTIER Parminter VINEY WHITTLE F5253

176346 WHITTON Mr Geoffrey. Berry Brow, The Knoll, Cranham, Glos, GL4 8HR. Tel:0452-812417 WHITTON F4846

176354 WHITWELL Revd Martin Corbet. 11 Hollies Drive, Baystone Hill, Shrewsbury, Shropshire. Tel:0743-874241 CORBET WHITWELL F3241

176362 WHITWORTH Mr B A. La Jaoniere, Val Au Bourg, St Martins, Guernsey. Tel:0481-36723 Braithwait BRAITHWAITE Chevalier CHEVALLIER COYNE FISON Fyson LUCK STOREY TROWER WHITWORTH WOOLNOUGH F1463

176370 WHORLEY Edward. 190 Stockbridge Road, Winchester, Hampshire, SO22 6RW. Tel:0962-853685 CHAMBERS FARLEY KING MANICOM PACKHAM PARSONS TOWNSHEND Verley Verli Verly Virly Warle Warley Wawley Wharley Whawley Whearly Wherley Wherly Whirley Whorely Whorlay Whorle WHORLEY Whorlie Whorlly Whorly Wirley Worlye F1596

176389 WHYMAN Mr Mark. 7 Rockwood Close, Guisborough, Cleveland, TS14 7BG. BOSS BURNET CLEASBY Peniman Penneyman PENNIMAN PENNYMAN PENNYMON PENYMAN PERRYMAN Ponnyman F1271

176397 WHYTE Mr J S. Wild Hatch, Coleshill Lane, Winchmore Hill, Amersham, Bucks, HP7 0NT. Tel:0494-722663 Hepbern HEPBURN MARSHAL Mershal Quhyt WATSON White Whyt WHYTE F6328

176400 WICKENS Mrs Betty. (Beasley) Two Ways, 72 Vincent Crescent, Brampton, Chesterfield, Derbyshire, S40 3NP. Tel:0246-566270 BONSALL FLEAR OLDFIELD SMITH WHEATCROFT WILKINSON F5237

176419 WICKS Mr R Paul. 126 Kings Avenue, Watford, Herts, WD1 7SA. Tel:0923-56853 BEGBIE Bigbie Glenister GLENNERSTER HELMORE MCGREGOR Mcgrigor TRICKER WHEATCROFT WICKS F1687

176427 WICKSTEAD Mrs E Y. 18 The Glade, Furnace Green, Crawley, W Sussex, RH10 6JT. WICKSTEAD Wicksteed Wixsted F6819

176435 WIGGIN Mrs Sue. (Wrigglesworth) 75 Pittneys, Paston, Peterborough, Cambs, PE4 7BB. ANGELL HART MURRAY-ROUCHARD NEWLAND PASTERFUL ROBBINS ROCHARD WIGGIN WRIGGLESWORTH F4083

176443 WIGGINTON Mr R. 39 Church Hill Close, Solihull, W Midlands, B91 3JB. Wiggington WIGGINTON F6933

176451 WIGGLESWORTH Mr George. Hatters Mill, Lea Wood, Lea Bridge, Matlock, Derbyshire, DE4 5AA. ARMYTAGE BAINES BARNES BLACKBOURNE Bramfete Bramfit BRAMFITT Bramfoot Brumfet Brumfit Brumfitt Brumphit CLARK CURTIS DARGUE DENTON FOSSCROFT GOLDIE GOODCHILD HANTY Hazmalalch Hazmalhalch Hazmonalsh Heshmonhalsh Hesmalhalch Hesmalhalsh Hesmanlanch Hesmaulansh Hesmelhals Hesmelhelch Hesmolash Hesmonhalsh Hessenhanch HEZMALHALCH Hezmolalch Hezmonalsh Hezmonhalch HOLMES INMAN JAGGER JOWETT MALLON NEWTON OGLONBY OSWELL POUNDER RATCLIFFE RAYNER ROTHWELL STOTT TURNOCK WALSH WIGGLESWORTH WILKINSON WILLAN WILLIAMSON F6313

176478 WIGGS Mr M E. Bradenham, Moorlane, Rickmansworth, Herts, WD3 1LH. ROBERTSON WIGGS F1872

176486 WIGHT Mr K. 87 Alfred Road, Kingston, Surrey, KT1 2TZ. Tel:081-546-5811 DITSON TARBIT WIGHT F5935

176494 WIGHTON Mrs Winsley. Station House, Clarke St, Penola, 5277, AUSTRALIA. Tel:+61-8-737-2882 BOON COLENSO Colensoe COMFORT DAWES ENNIS Innes PITMAN RICHARDSON SUMMERFIELD WINSTANLEY F5585

176508 WIGZELL Mr Ray. 25 Offens Drive, Staplehurst, Kent, TN12 0LS. ATWOOD CALCUTT DEAN HAINES HINES MASON Wigsell WIGZELL F3036

176516 WILBY Mrs J. 52 Temple Avenue, Temple Newsam, Leeds, West Yorks, LS15 0JT. ALDRED CROOKES CRYER DAMMS DRAPER EATON ELLIOT GREAVES HOLLAND HUTCHINSON MOUNTAIN SNOWBALL STEPHENSON STOKES TAYLOR WALKER WATSON WILBY F5261

176524 WILCOCK Mr Gerald. 73 Ormond Avenue, Hampton, Middx, TW12 2RT. GLOVER GRACE HOLDING JONES LEA MUNRO PICKERING SPRAGUE WILCOCK F2751

176532 WILCOCK Mrs June. (Gibbons) 14 The Green, St Leonards On Sea, East Sussex, TN38 0SU. Tel:0424-432498 GIBBONS PENLEY RADFORD RIDDY WALTERS F4924

176540 WILD Mr Alan Eric Albert. 85 Maxwell Gardens, Orpington, Kent, BR6 9QT. Tel:0689-829150 CAMERON CLELLAND CLEMSON COUTT KILLENBACK MCPHIE SCAID SCOTT WALLACE WILD F3869

176559 WILD Mr David E G. 96 Victoria Avenue, Porthcawl, Mid Glamorgan, CF36 3HA. Tel:0656-784163 DAVID EDWARDS JERIES LEWIS RICHARD THOMAS WILD F5896

176567 WILDBORE Mrs Daphne. Shoreham Cottage, 1 Beech Manor, Manor Park, Pontesbury, Shropshire, SY5 0PW. HICKS Roussel ROUSSELL VERINDER Verrinder Whitbourn Whitbourne Whitburn WILDBORE F3216

176575 WILDE Mrs Ann. Po Box 185, Shasta, CA 96087-0185, USA. Tel:+1-916-241-1110 ANDREWARTHA Burberry BURBERY Eudey EUDY GOLDSWORTHY HOSKIN Hosking Hoskins JONES PASCOE SMART STEPHENS Stevens WILD Wilde F4444

176583 WILDE Mrs Josephine. (Jacks) 11 Seafaring Drive, Corona Del Mar, CA 92526-1433, USA. Tel:+1-714-759-0306 LEGGOTT MANN MARQUAND OSBOURNE PARROTT RIGBY SELLER WILDE F5642

176591 WILDIG Mr Reginald. 14 Shefford Road, Seabridge, Newcastle Under Lyme, Staffs, ST5 3LE. Tel:0782-618625 EDWARDS KEY MALPASS PRICE ROBINS WEATHERHOGG Weeldig Welldig Whildig Widdig Wilddigg Wildeck Wildeg Wildegg Wildegge Wildic Wildick Wildicke Wildidd WILDIG Wildigage Wildige Wildiges Wildigg Wildigge Wildiggs Wildigh Wildigs Wildike Wildin Wilding Wildinge Wildis Wilduck Willdeck Willdeg Willdege Willdegg Willdegge Willdic Willdick Willdicke Willdidge Willdig Willdige Willdigg Willdigge Willdike Willdin Willding Willdinge Willdizz Willdog Willduck Willgig Wooldig Wyldig Wyldigg F211

176605 WILDY Mr Edward A. 167 Carlisle Road, Browns Bay, Auckland 10, NEW ZEALAND. VAILE WILDY F6896

176613 WILES Mr E. 448 Haslucks Green Road, Shirley, Solihull, W Midlands, B90 1DE. FISHER GROUNDS PLAYER SMYTH Smythe WILES F4912

176621 WILES Dr Robert. 31 Coxford Drove, Maybush, Southampton, Hants, SO1 6FE. AICKEN ALLEN AMAS BETTS BOLE BOOTH BOYD BROWN BUDDEN CALLUM CANE CARRINGTON COLEMAN COOPER COWSLADE CROSBY CUTTING DICKLEY EDGAR FEATHERBY FERGUSON FLEMING FLETCHER FRIBENS FRISTAN GLASGOW GOODMAN GOULDEN GRAINGER HAMILTON HANCOX HASSALL HAWKINS HONEYSETT HORN HUBBARD HUME JONES KENNEDY KENNETT LE SAGE LYON MARSDEN MARTIN MASKELYNE MILEHAM MILLER MITCHELL MORGAN MUSGRAVE MUSTOE NIXON PALFREY PHILCOX POTTINGER PRICE PRIGG RUFFLES

RUSHFORTH SCRAFIELD SERGEANT SMITH STAINES STEVENSON STOCKWELL THORNTON TOOMER TRIGG TURNER WHITMORE WICKS WILES F2828

176648 WILKES Mr Colin. 17 Cavendish Drive, Waterlooville, Porstmouth, Hampshire, PO7 7PJ.
BAKER FAITHFULL FISHER GREEN KIMBER MASON MINTRAM'NEWMAN WILKES WILKINS YOULDON F2942

176656 WILKIN Mr Neil R. 48 Railway Street, Barnetby Le Wold, Sth Humberside, DN38 6DQ. Tel:0652-688741
DEVANNEY FAULDING HARDEY HIRST ROBERTS SKINNER TROUGHT WEBSTER WHITELEY WHITEWOOD WILKIN F5966

176664 WILKINS Miss Doris. 87 Broadfield Road, Knowle Park, Bristol, BS4 2UW.
CARTER PAINTER WILKINS F4949

176672 WILKINS Mr P. 21 Pine Trees, Weston Favell, Northamptonshire, NN3 3ET.
AYLEN BATES BENSLEY CRUTTENDEN D'OYLY DAY DUKE EVERNDEN FREESTONE FRENCH GILLETT HERRIET HESELTON HISCOCK HOLMSTEAD JEX NOAKES PHILLIPS PILGRIM REDGWELL RICHARDSON ROUTLEDGE STEPHENS THORNTON WARMOLL WEBB WILKINS F1112

176680 WILKINS Mr Robert. 368 Pine Avenue, St Labert, Quebec, J4P 2N8, CANADA.
WILKINS F7375

176699 WILKINSON Mr Alan J. Corner Cottage, Mill Lane, Osgodby, Market Rasen, Lincs, LN8 3TB.
WILKINSON F6048

176702 WILKINSON Mr J. 29 Kenmore Drive, Bradford, West Yorks, BD6 3JL. Tel:0274-572401
ACKROYD BENTLEY BLAND BRIGGS CRAVEN EMSLEY FEARNLEY HAINSWORTH HERITAGE HEWITT HORSFALL HOWLETT HUTCHINSON LAMB NAWTHORP NEVISON NORTH PATCHETT Pickles Picles Pigheles PIGHILLS PRIESTLEY PUGH ROBERTSHAW SHARP SPENCER STOTT TAYLOR WHITLEY WILKINSON WOODFORD F6400

176710 WILKINSON Mrs Mary. 13 Beech Leaze, Alveston, Bristol, BS12 2NF. Tel:0454-411181
BOOTH FARREN HERBERT JEACOCK MUGG SPRIGGS TOOTH WILKINSON WILLIS F2104

176729 WILKINSON Mrs O R. (Jones) 56a Pastures Hill, Littleover, Derby, DE3 7BA.
JONES WILKINSON F4789

176737 WILKINSON Mrs P. 11 Woodside, Ponteland, Newcastle Upon Tyne, NE20 9JA.
BESWICK HADFIELD HODGSON LINGLEY MASSEY NEWSHAM SEYMOUR F5745

176745 WILKINSON Mrs Sally. (Bushell) Combestone, Ware Lane, Lyme Regis, Dorset, DT7 3EJ.
Hamon Hoeman Holeman Hollman Holman HOMAN Homanes JUPP WELLER WOOD F6027

176753 WILKINSON Mrs Valerie. 14 Beehive Road, Goffs Oak, Herts, EN7 5NL. Tel:0707-873746
CYPHER HARNIESS METHVEN ODELL PITTMAN STAKER STATHERS TUGGEY WILKINSON F5886

176761 WILKINSON Mrs Winifred. 277 Rosalind Street, Ashington, Northumberland, NE63 9AZ. Tel:0670-816114
Arcle ARKLE GREENS Hardie HARDY LAWSON LITTLE LOCKEY Lockie Mahan Mahon MAHONE Medne MEDNIS MILLER Mohane PATRICK SKELLY STEAD THOMPSON TROTTER WARD WATSON F1091

176788 WILKINSON Wynyard R T. 99d Talbot Road, London, W11 2AT. Tel:071-229-0539
GORDON LOVELL MAIR PITTAR ROGER TWENTYMAN F832

176796 WILKS Mrs S M. 9 Talbot Road, Carshalton, Surrey, SM5 3BP. Tel:081-647-1356
DOLBEAR Dolbeare PALMER SLADE WILKS F4902

176818 WILLERTON Mr J. 6 Girton House, Manor Fields, Putney, London, SW15 3LN.
De Welleton De Wilghton De Willeghton De Wilughton De Wylgton Walerton Wallerton Welerton Wellerton Whelerton Whilerton Whillerton Wilerton Willarton Willatan Willaton WILLERTON Willertone Willinton Willirton Williton Willoughton Wilughton Wolerton Woliton Wollarton Wollaton Wollerton Woolarton Woolerton Woollaton Woollerton Woolorton Wooloton Wylarton Wyllerton F6670

176826 WILLIAMS Mrs A J. 11 Highfield Crescent, Aberbargoed, Bargoed, Mid Glamorgan, CF8 9DW.
BARRELL F1456

176834 WILLIAMS Mr Adrian. 28 Trinity Street, St Ebbes, Oxford, OX1 1TY. Tel:0865-247202
FLEMING WILLIAMS F5036

176842 WILLIAMS Mr Alan. Cloverley Hall, Calverhall, Whitchurch, Shropshire, SY13 4PH.
ARMSTRONG BOSTOCK CHADWICK CURROUGHS DAVIES ENTWISTLE OPENSHAW PUGH WILLIAMS F3835

176850 WILLIAMS Ms B A. 823 3rd Street Nw, Calgary, Alberta, T2N 1P1, CANADA.
Astrage Astride ASTRIDGE F7084

176869 WILLIAMS Mrs Beryl. (Holley) 4 Samuel White Road, Hanham, Bristol, Avon, BS15 3LZ.
CONDUIT DUNN HARMAN HOLLEY NELSON WILLIAMS F3653

176877 WILLIAMS Mrs C Eira. 32 Harrington Drive, Cheltenham, Glos, GL51 6ER. Tel:0242-233253
BREES BREEZE BRYAN DAVIES EDWARDS EVANS FRANCIS GWILLIM JONES LEWIS LLOYD MASON MEREDITH MORGAN MORRIS OWENS POWELL PRICE SIMMONDS TAILOR THOMAS WIILIAMS WILLIAMS F4728

176885 WILLIAMS Mrs Celia. (Collingwood) 36 Napier Road, Hamworthy, Poole, Dorset, BH15 4NA.
AKED Bates Beardsal Beardsall Beardsel Beardsell Beats BELL Bets BETTS Birdsal BIRDSALL Birdsel Birdsell Boardsall Boardsell BONE Burdsal Burdsall Burdsel Burdsell CHAPMAN Colingwood Colinwood COLLINGWOOD Collinwood Cornal Cornall Cornel CORNELL CRISP DEAN Drewes Drews Drewse DRUCE Druse ENGLAND FINNEY Geckes Gecks Gex Grimesdale Grimsdal Grimsdall Grimsdel GRIMSDELL GUNTON HARRINGTON HAWKS HILL Jacks Jakes Jeackes Jeakes Jeaks Jeckes Jecks JEX Jexe JUST Lacey Lackey Lackie Lacy LAKEY Lakie Laky Leakey Leakie Leaky Manday Mandey Mandie Mandy Marten Martin Marton MAWER Menday Mendey Mendie Mendy Minday Mindey Mindie Mindy Monday Mondey Mondie Mondy Moore Moretin Moreton MORLEY Mortin MORTON Mower MUNDAY Mundey Mundie Mundy PACE Pase Pass Paye Polton Poolton POULTON Pulton Pye Sanders SAUNDERS Sharp SHARPE SIDNEY Sidny SMITH STADHAM Statames Statems Statham STATHAMS Statmas Statms Stattam Stattum Sydney Sydny Thwait Thwaites Thwaits TIMMINS Twait Twaite TWAITES Twaits Twite Weles Welles WELLS Wels WILLIAMS F2443

176893 WILLIAMS Mr Charles John. 4 Cotshore Drive, Radbrook Green, Shrewsbury, Shropshire, SY3 6DL. Tel:0743-53148
BAKER BREES BURRELL CANTER JACK MORRIS RUTLEDGE THOMAS Thomasina Thomson VOOGHT WATERS WILLIAMS F274

176907 WILLIAMS Mrs D Kay. 3 The Spinney, Madeley Heath, Crewe, Cheshire, CW3 9TB. Tel:0782-751018
HEATH HOOK JOHNSON OLDHAM PHELPS PICKERING PROUDLOVE SPIERS WOODALL F2509

176915 WILLIAMS Mr David. Redcroft, Pannierman Lane, Nunthorpe, Middlesborough, TS7 0NX. Tel:0642-722452
ADAMS HORTON JAMES MACFARLANE MAUD WILLIAMS F5027

176923 WILLIAMS Mr Derek F. 32 Harrington Drive, Cheltenham, Glos, GL51 6ER.
ASHMAN BADMAN BAKER BARWELL Bedman BOWEN CARTER CHAPMAN CLEMENT DAVIES ELFORD Engeram EVANS FILER GREEN GREENE GRIFFITH HANCOCK HAYNES HENRY HORLER Ingraham INGRAM JENKIN KINGMAN LANSDOWN LEIGH MAGGS MATTHEW Moorhouse MOREHOUSE NASH OAKELEY OAKLEY Ockley Okeley POW POWELL PRITCHARD REES RICHARD ROBERT Roberts SCOURFIELD Scurfield Seaverne SEVERNE SLADE STOKES TALBOT WILLIAM WILLIAMS WOGAN F5714

176931 WILLIAMS Mrs Doris. 57 Kyle Crescent, Whitchurch, Cardiff, CF4 1ST.
BEAVAN BOX DAVIS HUGHES JONES LOGAN PAYNE PORTER RICHARDS RUTTER TAYLOR WILLIAMS F2775

176958 WILLIAMS Ms Eileen. 9 Scotforth Road, Lancaster, Lancs, LA1 4TS. Tel:0524-35660
BOWEN CARNE COOK CURLING DAVIES DAVIS DENHAM DODDRELL EATON EDWARDS EVANS FENNELL FIELD FINZEL Fyelde GEORGE GRIFFITH Griffiths HALE

HALL HARAL Harall Harel Harell Harold Harral Harrall Harrel Harrell HARRISON Haword HAYTER HOWARD INGRAM JENKIN Jenkins JONES LEWES LISTER LLOYD LOUGHER MILLARD MORGAN MORRIS OLDHAM PARFITT PARRY PENDRY PHILLIP PHILLIPPS Phillips PICTON Playfair PLAYFERE POWELL PRICHARD RAMSDEN ROBINSON ROGERS Sampson SAMSON SPEIGHT Tayler TAYLOR TURBERVILL WALKER WARD WARLOW WHETTING WHITAKER WILD WILLIAMS F2794

176966 WILLIAMS Mrs Eunice. 24 George Street, Langley Mill, Nottingham, NG16 4DJ. Tel:0773-712372
BURTON MARTIN RANDALL SIMONS THURMAN WILKINSON WILLIAMS F1651

176974 WILLIAMS Mrs Frances. (Griffiths) 8 Court Close, Little Dewchurch, Herefordshire, HR2 6PT. Tel:0432-840355
Bold Bosstake BOSTOCK Bostocke BOULD COLCLOUGH Cowclough GRIFFITHS HEWITT INGRAM JAMES LLOYD Pool POOLE PRICE ROBINSON THOMAS F5688

176982 WILLIAMS Mr G E. Manor Wood, Coltishall, Norwich, Norfolk, NR12 7DU.
Angel ANGELL AXWORTHY AYRES Bare Bear Beare BEAZLEY BELL BERE BISHOP BOURNE BROUGHTON BROWN CHAPMAN Dellow DILLON DOWNING Duller DULLOW Elbet ELLET Elliott GAY GIBBS GILES GRAY HAWKE HENDERSON HILL HOCKING HORN Illet KENT LAMONT LEWIS MACKENZIE MICHELL SEARLE THORPE WHALE WILLIAMS F1078

176990 WILLIAMS Mrs Gaynor. 17 Woodview Road, Risca, Newport, Gwent, NP1 6QJ.
BRUSH EVANS HARTNOLL WILLIAMS F1267

177008 WILLIAMS Miss H. 96 Howard Avenue, Hamilton, Ontario, CANADA L9A 2W5. Tel:+1-416-575-1472
DAVIES JENKINS JONES PARRY PRICE PROFSER PROSSER THOMAS WILLIAMS F3183

177016 WILLIAMS Mrs Heather. (Bamfield) Lenton House, Mold Road, Ruthin, Clwyd, LL15 1SL. Tel:08242-4998
BAMFIELD EDMUNDS PERRIN REVILL SHEPHERD WILLIAMS F4732

177024 WILLIAMS Mrs I L. 11 Grange Avenue, Ryde, Isle Of Wight, PO33 3LS.
CLARK Comyns COULTER CROW CUMMINS Doleman Dolman DOUGH Doulman DOWLMAN Dowman ELLIS EVANS FARRANCE FIELDSEND FIELDSON Fieldston Fieldstone GIBSON GILLIES GLOVER GRANT GREAVES GREEN HASE Hayes JONES LANGHELT LAURIE LEWIS MCARTHUR MCKENZIE MCLEAN MCLEOD MORRIS OASTLER Ostler PALMER PEARCE PHILIPS ROBINSON Serich SERREDGE SMITH STOKES THOMSOM WARR WEBB WILLIAMS WRIGHT F165

177032 WILLIAMS Mrs J D. 14 Lawn Terrace, Treforest, Pontypridd, Mid Glamorgan, CF37 1DA.
BENJAMIN COLE JACKMAN RUSHTON SINGER STEPHENS TAPPER WHITMARSH WHITMORE F3107

177040 WILLIAMS Mrs Jean. (Smith) 18 Valley View, Clutton, Bristol, BS18 4SN. Tel:0761-52772
ORGAN SMITH YOUNG F2989

177059 WILLIAMS Mrs Jean. (Maule) 27 Mossford Court, Barkingside, Ilford, Essex, IG6 2BS.
Archbald ARCHBOLD Archbould Archibald Archibalde Archibauld Archibaulde Archibold Archibould Archiboulde Mae Mall Maoul Maul MAULE Maw F4421

177067 WILLIAMS Mrs Joan N. (Roberts) 63 Meliden Road, Prestatyn, Clwyd, LL19 8RH.
FENNELL SHILL F6329

177075 WILLIAMS Mrs Joan. 15 Drygrounds Lane, Felpham, Bognor Regis, Sussex, PO22 8PS.
BRIMBLE CARTER FLOWER FRY RADFORD RATTLE READING Redding SAVAGE WALLACE Wallis F2625

177083 WILLIAMS Mr John D. 7 Oakfield Terrace, Ammanford, Dyfed, SA18 2NG.
Berant Besant BESSANT Bezzant F6880

177091 WILLIAMS Mrs Judith. Rosenleek, 2 Badgers Walk, Angmering, Littlehampton, West Sussex, BN16 4DT. Tel:0903-775382
COLLINGWOOD DAWE FOGG GILES KING PARSONS PITTS SLEE STACEY WEBB F5407

177105 WILLIAMS Mr Keith. 82 Moggs Mead, Petersfield, Hants, GU31 4PH. Tel:0730-63400
BARNSHAW GWILLIM PARRY F4117

177113 WILLIAMS Mrs Laura. (Jelf) 23 Bryn Offa, Wrexham, Clwyd, LL13 7UL. Tel:0978-352533
BLUNT BRACE ELEMENT GARDINER JELF F4751

177121 WILLIAMS Mr M L P. 75 Baldwin Avenue, Eastbourne, East Sussex, BN21 1UL. Tel:0323-33622
GARLICK PRANCE SEABROOK F6445

177148 WILLIAMS Mrs M L. 164 Westward Road, Chingford, London, E4 8QJ.
Beacher Becher BEECHER Bychar F6950

177156 WILLIAMS Revd Michael E. 8 Westbrook Lane, Horsforth, Leeds, LS18 5RG.
GRESSIER HALLAM F1010

177164 WILLIAMS Prof Michael. 152 Hangingwater Road, Nethergreen, Sheffield, S11 7ET.
BEAKE EMERY GRAVENOR GRAY GULLIDGE JARRETT LEAVES MORGAN POLL YERBURY F1022

177172 WILLIAMS Nona. Po Box 225, Ben Lomond, CA 95005, USA.
SIMPSON F7364

177180 WILLIAMS Mr Owen. 7 Svenskaby, Orton Wistow, Peterborough, Cambs, PE2 6YZ. Tel:0733-39195[illegible]
ATKINS BAILEY BALDRY BAREFOOT Barfoot Barfor[illegible] Bauldry Bayley BIGGERSTAFF BILL BOTT BUTLER CANTERELL Cantrell CASHMORE CASSERLEY CHANDLER CHENNELLS CHILD CLARK Clarke COLEMA[illegible] Copperthwaite COPPERWHEAT Copperwhite Copperwick COSTIN CUTLER DAWSON DUFFIN FALLA FELTON FENN FIELD FLETCHER FOWLER GATES GINGER GLENISTER GODWIN Goodwin GRANGER GRANTHAM GRAY GRIFFIN HALL HALSEY HARRIS HAWKINS HEATH HILL Hobbes HOBBS HOLLAND HONNOR Honor HONOUR HORTON Joiner JOYNER JUDGE KEMP KEMPSTER KENNISON KING KINGHAM KNOWLING LEE MALLAT Mallet MCCUBBIN MEACHER MEAD MINORS MISKIN MORTON MOSS MYAS Myass Myers NEIGHBOUR PAINE PARISH POOL Powell PRICE PROVICE Provis PUDDEPHATT Puddifoot Rhodes RICHARDS RICHARDSON RICKARD RING ROADS RYLEY Schieldt SCHILDT SEDWELL SIDDOWNE SIMMONS SMITH STALEY STANBRIDGE STRANKS SURREY SUTTON TAYLOR THORN TOMLIN TOMLYN TURNER TURPIN VARNEY WARE WESTWOOD WHITE WILKES WILLIAMS WINDMILL F545

177199 WILLIAMS Mr Paul. Grange Cottage, Grange Farm, Redbourne, Gainsborough, Lincs, DN21 4JE.
DOUGLAS DRURY GLODE HERING HOWDEN LUSBY OLDERSHAW SCRIMSHAW SHEE TAYLOR TUCKER WILLIAMS F5976

177202 WILLIAMS Mrs Pearl. (Bradley) 24 Oaks Close, East Cowes, Isle Of Wight, PO32 6EH.
BRADLEY Bramble Bromley BRUMBLEY Brumley ROBBINS Robins F6127

177210 WILLIAMS Mr Peter. 155 Blackcarr Road, Baguley, Manchester, M23 9PB. Tel:061-998-1291
DALE DAVIES JONES POTTS WILLIAMS WOODWARD F3405

177229 WILLIAMS Mr R Desmond. Bonnett Cottage, Marsden, Cirencester, Glos, GL7 7ET.
ARCOLL BRIGHT CREEMER FORSTER JOYCE WILLIAMS F5138

177237 WILLIAMS Mrs R P. (Norton) High Cottage, 10 Lower Road, Harmer Hill, Shrewsbury, SY4 3QZ. Tel:0939-290693
BERRY HITCHMAN LAKER MOORE NORTON PAGET PRIC[illegible] ROUSE SEABRIGHT WILLIAMS F6195

177245 WILLIAMS Mrs Rae. Merryoak, The Drive, Godalming, Surrey, GU17 1PH.
CHRISTOE Ezzy Hissy HIZZY Issy F2551

177253 WILLIAMS Mr Robert G J. 97 Airport Road, Hengrove, Bristol, BS14 9TD. Tel:0272-777724
BROWN HOPGGOD HOPGOOD MASTERS TOVEY WILLIAMS F1190

177261 WILLIAMS Mrs Susan. (Springate) 99 Mayfair Avenue, Worcester Park, Surrey, KT4 7SJ. Tel:081-330-0394
Springall Springat SPRINGATE Springet Springett F5980

177288 WILLIAMS Mrs Val. Greyholme, Frieth, Nr Henley On Thames, Oxon, RG9 6PJ.
BERRY CRISFORD EASTWOOD HEDGES KINSEY KYNSEY MCINTOSH MYHILL SALTER STEWART F2571

177296 WILLIAMS Mrs Vina. (Wales) 76 Dinorben Close, Fleet, Hants, GU13 9SJ. Tel:0252-621500
ATKINSON BULLOCK DISNEY GILL LINTON PEACH

TEWSON Tulson Tuson Wailes WALES Whailes WILKINSON F3801

177318 WILLIAMS-ELLIS Mrs E A. 18 Wilton Street, London, SW1X 7AX.
ALTESTON DENNETT HAMOR HARGREAVES HATTON HODSON HOGTON HOUGHTON KEARSLEY KNOWLES LIVEYEY LYVESEY PENDLEBURY RIGBY ROBINSON SANDERSON WITHINGTON WOODS F6091

177326 WILLIAMSON Mr Dennis J. 51 Hillsway Crescent, Mansfield, Notts, NG18 5DR. Tel:0623-634663
GREGORY LYGO SPINKS WILLIAMSON F5831

177334 WILLIAMSON Mr James Alan. 32 Sizergh Road, Bare, Morecambe, Lancs, LA4 6TL.
CLEWS NEWTON WILLIAMSON F4394

177342 WILLIAMSON Mrs M. Staneycarth, Burravoe, Yell, Shetland, ZE2 9AY.
PAPLAY F7340

177350 WILLIAMSON Mr Michael. 2 Sale Hill, Broomhill, Sheffield, S10 5BX.
ANDERSON BONE CLARKE HAWKER MINCHIN PEEL PRITCHARD STANSFIELD WILLIAMSON F2513

177369 WILLIAMSON Mr Trevor. 8 Wayland Drive, Adel, Leeds, LS16 8LX. Tel:0532-672499
CARTWRIGHT ETHERIDGE EYRE FOWLER JAMES LAKE LINTON MAJOR WAREHAM WILLIAMSON F3457

177377 WILLING Ms June. 15 Strathcona Gardens, Glasgow, G13 1DN.
FENN GODDART HARDCASTLE LLEWELYN PLEASANCE TIDD WELLARD WILLING F2275

177385 WILLINGTON Mr C J. 75 Sherwood Road, Tunbridge Wells, Kent, TN2 3LD.
WILLINGTON F7018

177393 WILLIS Mr Alan. 12 Upleatham Street, Saltburn By Sea, Cleveland, TS12 1LQ. Tel:0287-623983
ASKHAM AUSTIN BACON BAINBRIDGE BARKER BEAN BEDFORD BENSON BENTLEY BOBBINS BOLTON BRITTON BROOMHEAD BROWN BULLIVANT BURK BURKE CALVERT CLARKE CLARKSON COLLINS COPPARD COPPINDALE COX DOWSON FALLADOWN FEATHERSTONE FOSTER FULBROOK FULLER GARDINER GIBSON GROOM HARDISTY HARDY HARMAN HARRISON HICK HODGSON HORSEFIELD HUNT HUNTER JACKSON KIRK LEABERRY LEDGER LEWIS LISTER LUND MARJESON MCMAHON MEAKIN MILBURN MOORE NEWTON NICHOLSON PAGDIN PALMER PENROSE PLUMB POND PRIOR PRYOR RHODES ROBSON SCHOLEY SHAFTEN SHAFTOE SHEPPARD SHERRATT SKELTON SKINNER SMITH STAINTON STENSON STEVENS SWALLOW THACKRAY THORP THORPE TIPLADY TURPIN WATERHOUSE WELLS WHITFIELD WILLIS WILSON WOOD WOOLDER WRIGHT WROE F5098

177407 WILLIS Mrs Ann. 31 Hawkins Way, Wokingham, Berks, RG11 1UW.
BURROWS HEAD Walden Waldin WALDRON WILLIS F1242

177415 WILLIS Mrs B J. (Kington) 24 Clevedon Road, Nailsea, Bristol, BS19 1EH.
KINGTON F4768

177423 WILLIS Mrs Vee. (Goring) 19 Curzon Avenue, Horsham, W Sussex, RH12 2LA.
Goaring Goreing GORING Goringe Gorring Gorringe F2769

177431 WILLMOT Revd Philip. 34 Hatherley Road, Winchester, Hants, SO22 6RT.
WILLMOT F2953

177458 WILLMOTT Mr Henry. 59 Bushfields, Loughton, Essex, IG10 3JR. Tel:081-502-1240
PIDGEON Willmot WILLMOTT Wilmot Wilmott F5873

177466 WILLOWS Mrs Denise. (Roth) 7 Rosewarne Court, Hyde Street, Winchester, Hants, SO23 7HL.
BOWDEN BROADHURST FARRELL KEY MCGILL WARDLE WILLOWS F1442

177474 WILLS Mr Dick. Narracombe Farm, Ilsington, Newton Abbot, Devon, TQ13 9RD.
Tel:0364-661243
BRAIM CORBYN CROCKWELL FURSLAND GOTBED LEARE NOSWORTHY RENDELL WILLS F3843

177482 WILLS Mr E M. 24 Ashcroft, Chard, Somerset, TA20 2JH. Tel:0460-64258
Benet Bennat Bennatt Bennet BENNETT Bennetts BROWN LAMBSHEAD SALTER STOYLE WILLS F1250

177490 WILLS Mrs Elizabeth S. (Clark) 19 Flawforth Avenue, Ruddington, Notts, NG11 6LH.
Tel:0602-215535
BAILEY BARBER CLARK COOPER ELPHICK GARROD GINGELL PENNEY PHILLIPS REED SHRIMPLING SINDEN STREETER F6123

177504 WILLS Mr R G & Mrs G. 11 Martin Close, Southfields, Lee On Solent, Hants, PO13 8LG.
Tel:0705-550310
ABET ARNOLD BAKER BOBBET Bobit Boorman BOREMAN Bowman Cockrell COCKRILL COGGER COOK CORT Court Crab CRABB Crabbe ELLIS FLANDERS Flinders Florry FLORY Flurry GOOK HARLEY HOLLAND JAMES JOHNSON KNIGHT LAKE LEE MARTIN NUGENT Randle RAYNER RENDLE Roleston Rolestone ROLSTONE Rowlestone Rowlston Rowlstone SHARMAN Sherman SHREWSBURY Shrowsbury SMITH Tavener TAVERNER THOMPSON TINGAY WEEKS WILKINSON WILLS YOUNGS F4520

177512 WILLSON Mr Peter. 17 Toucan Way, Basildon, Essex, SS16 5ER.
WILLSON F1611

177520 WILLSON-LLOYD Mrs V J. 5 Rowan Avenue, Ravenshead, Nottingham, NG15 9GA.
AUNGER BRAY SKEWES F5272

177539 WILSDON Mrs Glynis. (Dray) 21 Churchdown Road, Malvern, Worcs, WR14 3JX.
BENNETT BULLOCK BUTTON DRAY KING PULCHRO PYER SILVER Willsdon WILSDON F799

177547 WILSON Mr A C. 32 Colne Avenue, Millbrook, Southampton, Hants, SO1 9NU. Tel:0703-786099
BRIDGEMAN CROSSLEY LAVERSUCH Recks Reeks RICKS WILSON F689

177555 WILSON Mrs D. 1 Elsicker Lane, Warmfield, Wakefield, W Yorks, WF1 5TW.
ALLEN CHAMP CHARLES CRIMBLE HOLGATE HOWELL JENKS JEPSON Jinks KING NARROWAY O'GANAGH RAMSHAW SMITH VIVIAN WALKER WILSON WOODCOCK F2062

177563 WILSON Mr David V. 114a Sidney Road, Walton On Thames, Surrey, KT12 3SA. Tel:0932-222035
FORREST F3654

177571 WILSON Mr David. Rana, 230 London Road, Wokingham, Berks, RG11 1SW. Tel:0734-784855
BUSWELL EDLIN HIGGS JOHNSON MATTHEWS MILLS PARCELL PATES PERRY ROUTLEDGE SAICH SAUNDERS SECKINGTON SHIRT TAMKIN WILSON F1650

177598 WILSON Dr E J. 8 Orchard Way, Hurst Green, Oxted, Surrey, RH8 9DJ.
Barrel Beriall Berrill BORRELL Borrill Burhill Burrall Burrell Burrill Buryll F7113

177601 WILSON Mr Ernest. 26 Bodle Crescent, Bexhill On Sea, E Sussex, TN39 4BG. Tel:0424 221580
Balcombe BALKHAM BISSENDEN BOURNE Dunc DUNK Dunke ELDRIDGE SMITH TERRY WILSON F68

177628 WILSON Miss Eunice. 143 Harbord Street, Fulham, London, SW6 6PN.
Thirkell THIRKILL THRELKELD WILSON F9

177636 WILSON Dr George S. 1 Gorse Road, Blackburn, Lancs, BB2 6LY. Tel:0254-5664
ALKER Awain BENN BIBBY CULSHAW FLETCHER Hade HEAD Houlker JACKSON Kilshaw Oldham Owain Owdem OWEN Whilson Willson WILSON F3597

177644 WILSON Mrs Hilary. (Vipan) 39 Tritton Gardens, Dymchurch, Romney Marsh, Kent, TN29 0NA.
DUGDALE MAYLIN VIPAN F5370

177652 WILSON Mr James. 6 The Sycamores, Vesey Close, Sutton Coldfield, W Midlands, B74 4QL.
BALMER BATSON ELLERY HIGGINS LANE LEE MCNALLY PALMER TONKS TURNER WILSON F377

177660 WILSON Mr John. 71 Ancaster Avenue, Scartho, Grimsby, South Humberside, DN33 3LH.
Tel:0472-70038
WILSON F38

177679 WILSON Mrs June. Tundergarth Mains, Lockerbie, Dumfireshire, Scotland, DG11 2PU.
ARMSTRONG COATES FORSTERS NOBLES WILSON F3266

177687 WILSON Mrs K. (Eade) North Villa, Huttoft Road, Sutton On Sea, Lincs, LN12 2RU.
BEAL Beel Beeles BLOW CATER CHAPMAN EADE Eades Ede Head JANNEY KEAL LANGTON Longley Longton SCOTT SIMONS SMITH VEAR Vearah Verah Vere VICKERS WILLINGHAM WILSON F5123

177695 WILSON M E. 33 Archery Rise, Durham, DH1 4LA.
ALLEN Ashwode ASHWOOD BAILEY BARRETT BATE BOYD BURDETT CADMAN CARR CHAMBERS CLARK Clarke CLEAVER COLES COLLINS COOK CRAIG CRISP DAVIES Davis DICKENS EVANS FREEMAN GOUGH HABBERLEY HENDERSON HERBY HITCHMAN Hodgekins HODGEKISS Hodgskiss HOWKINS HUMBLE LOWREY Madin MAIDEN MARRIOTT MASON Mayden Meaden

METCALFE MOTT NEGUS Nicholls NICHOLS OLIVER PARKER RAPPITT RATCLIFFE REDHEAD RODHAM SMITH STANTON Staunton SUMMERS TESTER THIRLWELL TOMKINS Tompkins TRENHOLME TURNER WARNES WATCHMAN WHITEHOUSE WILSON WRIGHT F720

177709 WILSON Mrs M M. (Green) Gien Mie, Walpole Road, Ramsey, Isle Of Man. Tel:0624-816330
BUCKLEY DUNCAN GASSON GREEN HOLLAND F5332

177717 WILSON Mr Malcolm. 4 St Mawgan Close, Bodmin, Cornwall, PL31 2BW.
ADAMS Cuming CUMMING Cummings GILDEN Gilding Hurle HURRELL LEE PEARCE WILSON F4111

177725 WILSON Mrs Marjorie. R R 4, Stratford, Ontario, N5A 6S5, CANADA.
BAKER BANCROFT CARTLEDGE COATES Coats COOK Cotes CROWTHER CURL Curle GILLMAN HACKER HAMLYN HICKS Kearl Keirl LAW LUMLEY MILES Pengelly PENGILLY PETCH PIPE SCARR SLEIGHTHOLME Slightholm Slitom TALBOT VANN VANNER WALDEN WILLERTON WILLOWS WILSON F4408

177733 WILSON Mrs P A. Hillside, Station Road, Gedney Hill, Spalding, Lincolnshire, PE12 0NP.
HURST JAKEMAN LLOYD MAY PEERS WALKER WARWICK WILSON F5918

177741 WILSON Mrs P. 16 Hawkswood, Covingham Park, Swindon, Wiltshire, SN3 5AH.
REYNISH F6755

177768 WILSON Mr R G. Hockham Lodge, Shropham, Attleborough, Norfolk, NR17 1ED.
Tel:0953-498240
BAGNALL HARRISON LEATHERS MARRIOTT NICOLL O'DONNELL PAUL WILSON F5131

177776 WILSON Mr Robert W. 22 Demage Lane, Upton By Chester, Chester, CH2 1EL. Tel:0244-381110
ALDERSON BANKS BLACKALL HOWE HUMPHREYS JAMES PYLES WEBB WILSON F4576

177784 WILSON Mr Ronald H. 34 Cumber Drive, Brixham, Devon.
COOL Coole F2577

177792 WILSON Mrs Ruth. 10 Pelham Road, Wallasey, Merseyside, L44 3AD.
BRYANT BURDEKIN Burkikin Dickenson DICKINSON FRANKLIN FRASER Frasor Frazer Freser FURBER GRESHAM JOHNSTON Johnstone MCDONALD PALMER SOWERBY F682

177806 WILSON Sarah. 127 Goldhawk Road, London, W12 8EN.
BULL GURNEY HAYES MAIR SHARP STEELE WILSON F2200

177814 WILSON Mr Terry. Po Box 664, Sarnia, Ontario, N7T 7J7, CANADA. Tel:+1-519-542-0190
BALLANTINE CRAVEN FEWSTER FRASER HILL LOCKWOOD MCPHERSON PULLAR WELCH WILSON F5139

177822 WILSON-CROOME Mrs O. White Hart, Alswear, Devon, EX36 4LG.
GRAHAM LITTLE POTT STAVERT SUMMERFIELD TIMBERLAKE F3845

177830 WILSON-PAISLEY Mr Duncan. Glen Annan House, Beechgrove, Moffat, Dumfries, DG10 9RS.
PAISLEY F7339

177849 WILTON Mr Robert. Rond Anneth, Hannafore Road, Looe, Cornwall, PL13 2DD.
WILTON F2729

177857 WILTSHIRE Mrs E I. 26 Simmil Road, Claygate, Esher, Surrey, KT10 0RT.
BURKIN DUNMAN F6595

177865 WINBANKS Mrs Anne. (Davies) 31 Lockwood Road, Baronia, 3155, AUSTRALIA. Tel:+61-3-762-1698
BOYD DAVIES GALE GRANT GREENLAND MCDONALD PROCTOR F7400

177873 WINBANKS Mrs Jessie L. (Overton) 31 Lockwoods Road, Boronia, VIC 3155, AUSTRALIA.
Tel:+61-3-762-16981
AXFORD BALL CLEGG Hurben Hurlen HURLEY MADDICKS OVERTON PARR RUMBELOW SHARPE TURNER F5554

177881 WINCH Mr Jack. 23 Arkleston Road, Paisley, Scotland, PA1 3TE. Tel:041-889-0458
BLACKHURST BRIANT GRIFFIN HULSON MESSER RAMSAY REDPATH UNDERDOWN WINCH YELLAND F530

177903 WINCHESTER Mr C C. Beech Cottage, Old Odiham Road, Alton, Hants, GU34 4BW.
CHAPPEL Chapple HOVEY MCINTOSH MESSENGER NOBLE SOUTHWARD Suddart WINCHESTER WOLVERSON F1808

177911 WINCHESTER Dawn. 49 Aukland Close, Enfield, Middx, EN1 4PR. Tel:081-805-3572
WINCHESTER F3006

177938 WINCHESTER Mrs Winifred. 109 Silvester Road, Cowplain, Waterlooville, Hants, PO8 8TR.
ALLEN BAYLY BUGLER CARBIS CARTER DAVEY FARLEY FOLEY GARTZ GIBBS HANSFORD HELMORE LOVERIDGE MAISH MEECH MILLS PALMER POOLE ROWE STAPLE TRAVERS WILLSON WINCHESTER F2946

177946 WINDER Mrs Mary Elizabeth. 246 Singlewell Road, Gravesend, Kent, DA11 7RE.
Tel:0474-365299
WINDER F3876

177954 WINDER Mr R G. Overdale End, Ashtead, Surrey, KT21 1PZ. Tel:0372-277277
De Wynder WINDER Wynder F94

177962 WINDRIDGE Mrs Nora. The Stone House, Church Street, Yetminster, Dorset, DT9 6LG.
BENTLEY F987

177970 WINGATE Mr Guy. 37 Seamead, Stubbington, Fareham, Hampshire, PO14 2NG.
BELL BROOKS CRAIG GORDON GOVAN HANDY HAW KYTHELL REAVELY Revely RIPPETH ROSS SCOTT SNAITH SOUTHERN Sutheran TAYLOR WINGAT WINGATE F3509

177989 WINGHAM Mrs Gaynor. (Holloway) 17 Greenholm Road, Eltham, London, SE9 1UQ.
ALLWRIGHT BEATON BRADMAN BUNCE BUSHNELL GREEN HEATH Hickson HISCOCK Hixon HIXSON HOLLOWAY JONES KIFT LEWENDEN MARSHALL MESSENGER MUNDAY Mundy NICHOLAS PENFORD Rothero ROTHEROE Rotherough WESCOMBE WINGHAM F5010

177997 WINGROVE Mr Richard John. 1 Oakhurst, Lichfield, Staffs, WS14 9AJ. Tel:0543-264452
BARNSLEY BLOCKLEY WICKS Wingrave WINGROVE F2618

178004 WINSOR Mr Stephen. 17 Llwyn Estyn, Deganwy, Conway, Gwynedd, LL31 9RA. Tel:0492-582000
CARTER Cossens Cossons COUSENS Couzens CREW DAVIES GAY HILL JONES JOSEPH MASON MILSOM MORGAN PRINCE ROWBOTHAM SHUTE Shutt SMITH SNAPE SQUIRES SUTTON THOMPSON WARING WHITE WILSON Windsor WINSOR F4378

178012 WINTER Mr Gerald. Briggs Road, Rmb 6675, Warragul, Victoria, 3820, AUSTRALIA.
KENNER MATTHEWS WINTER WOOD F4457

178020 WINTER Mr Peter. The Post House, Enochdhu, Blairgowrie, Perthshire, PH10 7PB.
Tel:0250-881202
BAILEY COLLARD DAVIS GODFREY HILL INMAN MULLINS NEWTON WINTER YANDLE F5888

178039 WINYARD Mr John K. 1 Churchdown Close, Boldon Colliery, Tyne & Wear, NE35 9HA.
WINYARD F7039

178047 WISDOM Mr Peter. 1 Farleigh Close, Charlton Kings, Cheltenham, Glos, GL52 6XX.
Tel:0242-238415
BRILL BROWN ELLERTON HIGGIN HILL HOUSEMAN MUNDAY RODWELL WISDOM F2710

178055 WISEDALE Mr Norman. 45 Woodlands Drive, Thelwall, Warrington, Cheshire, WA4 2JL.
GROUNDS HOWARD WARHAM WISEDALE F4762

178063 WISHART Mr J G. Milton House, Milton Of Balgonie, Glenrothes, Fife, KY7 6PX.
Wisehart Wishard WISHART Wisheart F2441

178071 WISSON Mrs Doreen. 68 Cambria Road, Camberwell, London, SE5 9AS.
FISHBURN WISSON F608

178098 WITHERIDGE Mr J M. 6 Nore Close, Darland, Gillingham, Kent, ME7 3DG.
Watheridge Weatheredge Weathereg Weatheridge Weatherige Wetheredg Wetheredge Wetheridge Wetherudge Wetheryde Wetheryg Whetherige Witherage Witheredg Witheredge Witheridg WITHERIDGE Wyderidge Wyetherayge Wytheridge Wytherug Wytherydg F7197

178101 WITHERS Mr M. 27 Old Movilla Road, Newtownards, Down, BT23 3HH. Tel:0247-810787
BREWER BROWN Browne BURROUGHS FERGUSON JOHNSTON MCKINLEY MCVEIGH SEYMOUR Weathers Wether Wethers WITHERS Wythers F696

178128 WITHERSPOON Mr Claude F. 402 Camp Drive, Grand Prairie, TX 75051-4908, USA.
WITHERSPOON F7377

178136 WITHINGTON Mrs Andrea. (Hanby) 20 Beech Drive, Ellington, Morpeth, Northumberland,

NE61 5EU.
CORBETT DAMANT FREEMAN GOLDSPINK HAMERSLY HANBY MARTIN MCGRAN MELLOR NAYLOR POTTS TEE TWIGGER WARD WITHINGTON F5353

178144 WITHY Mrs Barbara. (O'Connell) Osiers, 152 Langley Road, Langley, Slough Berks, SL3 7TG.
GIBSON O'CONNELL WITHY F3410

178152 WITT Mrs. Carmargue, The Hawthorns, Main Road, Marchwood Hants, SO4 4UZ.
BARON FAGAN Fagen Fagin FELLOWS GAMBLE HULL Joice Joy JOYCE Joys PEARSE PENDER Philips PHILLIPS Philps TIDMAN Warrity Wharty WHERTY WITT F2190

178160 WOGAN Mr Jack. Gwgan, 5 Rhiw Grange, Colwyn Bay, Clwyd, LL29 7TT. Tel:0492-530042
GWEAWN GWGAN Hoogan Ogan WOGAN F4799

178179 WOLEDGE Mr H S. 23 The Woodlands, Beverley, North Humberside, HU17 8BT.
VICKERAGE Vickress Vickris F6624

178187 WOLFE Mr William. 1800 Dover Drive, Newport Beach, CA 92660-4419, USA.
Tel:+1-714-646-6410
HUMPHREY NEWBERRY F5505

178195 WOLFORTH Mrs Anne R. (James) 8 Blenheim Court, West Meads, Aldwick, W Sussex, PO21 5QB.
FRY GURNEY JAMES JONES JOWERS LAKE LANGRIDGE NEWBERRY Newbury RENWICK Wolford Wolfork Wolfort WOLFORTH Woolford Woolforth Worfolk Worfolke F1747

178209 WOLSTENHULME Mr Leslie. 156 New Road Side, Horsforth, Leeds, West Yorks, LS18 4DP.
Tel:0532-589929
COWARD CULM DIXON DUNKERLEY VICKERS WOLSTENHOLME F6077

178217 WOMBWELL Mr Stanley Arthur. 7 Tarragon Close, Lower Earley, Reading, Berks, RG6 2GW.
Tel:0734-869307
Womball Wombel Wombell Wombewell Wombill Womble Wombwel WOMBWELL Womel Womell Womewell Woombell Woombill Woombwell F704

178225 WOOD Mr A P. 193 Darlington Lane, Stockton On Tees, Cleveland, TS19 ONF. Tel:0642-678719
CASSON LORAINE Lorraine MCCURLEY REDICAN SCRUTTON TOWELL WOOD F4690

178233 WOOD Mrs Anita. 4 Hookwater Close, Chandlers Ford, Hampshire, SO5 1PS.
ASHALL ATHERTON BARTON BEWICK BIRCHALL BROADFOOT BUCKLEY BUTTERWORTH CHILDS Crankshaw Cranshaw Cronkshaw CRONSHAW DENNET DICKINSON FISHER Garrat Garratt Garret GARRETT GREENALL GRIFFITHS HART HOLDER KNIGHT MARSH OLLERTON Radcliff Radcliffe Ratcliff RATCLIFFE RICHARDSON ROBERTS SMITH Spibey SPIBY Spivey Spivy VALENTINE VALLAR Valler Vollar Voller WARD WOOD F1149

178241 WOOD Mrs Anne. (Hargreaves) 28 Hillcrest Avenue, Scarborough, Yorkshire, YO12 6RQ.
Tel:0723-363982
BARNES BARNS HALLAM HARGREAVES RICHARDS F352

178268 WOOD Mr Ashleigh J. 94 Brown Avenue, Church Lawton, Stoke On Trent, Staffs, ST7 3EP.
AINSWORTH GRESTY HAMMOND MOSS STOCKTON WHITEHURST WOOD F114

178276 WOOD Mr Bernard & Mrs Joyce. Kemplay House, 7 Kemplay Foot, Eamont Bridge, Penrith Cumbria, CA10 2BD. Tel:0768-63941
FARR FENTON FROST NEILSEN PRICE WOOD F1394

178284 WOOD Mr C. Copper Cottage, Mill Corner, Northiam, Rye Sussex, TN31 6HT.
Tel:0797-252503
BAKER COOPER HOOPER HOWARD OMER WOOD F3644

178292 WOOD Mr Colin. 14 Thatch Leach, Chadderton, Oldham, OL9 9QX.
BUCKLEY WOOD F4545

178306 WOOD Mr Des. 28 Hillcrest Avenue, Scarborough, Yorkshire, YO12 6RQ.
Tel:0723-363982
WOOD F353

178314 WOOD Mr Donald. 4253 N Granadilla Drive, Moorpark, CA 93021-2137, USA.
WOOD Woods F5586

178322 WOOD Mrs E L. (Thompson) 14 Whitecroft, Nailsworth, Glous, GL6 ONS.
BAYLISS BERRY BISHOP CANNING COOK DANIEL DYER ETHERIDGE FOUNTAIN FRENCH GOLD GREEN HAMMOND HICKMAN HIGGS HUTTON JORDAN LAKE MACNALLY MARTIN PAGE PETTMAN PRICE SEWARD TAYLOR THOMPSON TRESIZE WILKINS WOOD YOUNG F4570

178330 WOOD Revd Eric. The Master House, Hugh Sexeys Hospital, Bruton, Somerset, BA10 0AS.
Tel:0749-813369
ADLARD BATEMAN CRABTREE GOOCH GOWAR HONE JUPE LEIGHTON MEADEN NICHOLSON PROCTER ROE SEXEY WOOD F1858

178349 WOOD Mrs Gwendoline. (Curtler) Curtwood House, Stonebow, Thronton Le Beans, Northallerton, N Yorks, OL6 3SR.
CURTLER OLDHAM RIDLEY ROBLET F3972

178357 WOOD Mr J Norman. 14 Vale Drive, Wallasey, Merseyside, L45 1LY. Tel:051-639-7943
BEARD HENDERSON KEIL KEILL MCDOUGAL MCKEE POSTLETHWAITE SPENCE STEWART WOOD F152

178365 WOOD Mr John. 21 Regina Crescent, Walsgrave, Coventry, CV2 2EP. Tel:0203-621699
BARLOW BILLINGSLEY HEWLETT REBBECK SNOOK THATCHER WHITFIELD WHITING WOOD F6317

178373 WOOD Mrs Kathleen. (Twaddle) 26 Glenmavis Crescent, Carluke, Lanarkshire, ML8 4JL.
Tel:0555-770992
BLAKE Toudell Tuedell Twaddel TWADDLE Twedale Tweddell Tweddle Twodell F3619

178381 WOOD Mr Norman Arthur. 53 Park Avenue, Longlevens, Gloucester, GL2 0EA.
Tel:0452-411688
BARNFIELD CHORLTON DOD Dodd FARMER Gelliman HARGREAVES HARRIS HERBERT JELLIMAN Jellyman Juliman KIBBLEWHITE KITE Kyte OWEN PARTINGTON Plaistead PLAISTED Plastead Playstead Playsted TAYLER Taylor TRIGG VALE WHITEHEAD Willesden Willsden Willsdon Wilsden WILSDON WOOD YOUNG F2010

178403 WOOD Mrs P. Kviabol, Sheep Pen Lane, Seaford, E Sussex, BN25 4QR. Tel:0323-894920
BAKER BIRTLES BLAKE BLUNT BRANDRYTH BROOKER CAVENDISH COLEMAN COLESHILL COX CURTIS DEMAN EDMONDSON ELLIS FENWICK GOUSHILL HADDON HALL HARDWICK HARTLEY HIERON HILLS HUGHES IRVING JEWELL LATHAM LOWE LOWER LUXFORD MAYNARD METCLAFE PENFOLD PHILLIPS RADFORD RICHARDSON ROE SAUNDERS SHEPHERD SILLIFANT STEVENS TUCKER VERNON WATERWORTH WILBRO WILSON WILTON WOOD F2650

178411 WOOD Mrs Pat. (Shacklock) The Masters House, Sexeys Hospital, Bruton, Somerset, BA10 0AS.
Tel:0749-813369
ABBOTT BARKER BILTON CLARK CLARKE CUMBERLAND GILLIOTT Haither HAND HATHER Hother MESSETTER NETTLESHIP READ Schacklock SHACKLOCK Shacklocke Shadlock Shalselock Shatlock Shocklach Shokelach Sholiche SMOKE STAPLETON TOMPKIN WASS WIGHTMAN WILSON WINGFIELD WOOD F1859

178438 WOOD Mr Sidney. Valhallagatan 21, 26162 Glumslov, SWEDEN.
Sanda Sandah Sando SANDOE Sandow Sandowe F6947

178446 WOOD Mr Steven. 4 Montague Terrace, Lincoln, Lincs, LN2 5BE. Tel:0522-511617
BALDERSON BLANCHARD COULSON FRANKLIN MCCOIG STOREY WOOD F6222

178454 WOOD Mr T J M. Penrhyn, 4 Georgian Houses, Ludborough Road, North Thoresby, Grimsby Lincs, DN36 5RF. Tel:0472-840566
BOURNE CHARLESWORTH GOLDFINCH GOLDFINCH HEAD MARSH PHAYER RICHARDSON Shewbridge Shobridge SHOEBRIDGE SHOEBRIDGE Shoobridge Shoubridge Shrowbridge Shubridge WOOD F3598

178462 WOOD Mr Tom. A Georgian Houses, North Thoresby, Grimsby, Lincs, DN36 5RF.
SHOEBRIDGE F7363

178470 WOOD Mr William. Westholme, North Side, Shadforth, Durham, DH6 1LJ. Tel:091-372-0371
ARCHBOLD BONES CATCHESIDE CHALDER HADDOCK HUNTER MAINS REAY WILSON WOOD F4779

178489 WOOD Mrs Win. 5953 Broken Arrow Street, Simi Valley, CA 93063-5715, USA.
Tel:+1-805-584-1088
ASHCROFT CRITCHLEY MARSHALL ROSCOE SHERWOOD F5641

178497 WOODCOCK Mr Anthony L S. 34 Dean Court,

Portsmouth Road, Horndean, Portsmouth Hants, PO8 9NN. Tel:0705-595900
WOODCOCK F595

178500 WOODCOCK Mrs M. 17 Coopers Holt Close, Skellingthorpe, Lincoln, LN6 5SY. Tel:0522-695711
ALDRED COVE CRESSWELL DAWBER HENSHAW KEMP LANE OATES PEET F3529

178519 WOODEN Terence. 6 Heath Rise, Westcott, Dorking, Surrey, RH4 3NN.
WOODEN F7028

178527 WOODFIELD Mr R H. Braymor House, Queens Avenue, Canterbury, Kent, CT2 8AY.
HESSNAN LARTER NUELLE WOODIFIELD F4998

178535 WOODGER Mr J P. St Dunstans Vicarage, Bedminster Down, Bristol, BS13 7AA.
Wodier WOODGER Woodyear F6601

178543 WOODHEAD Mrs Margaret A. 12 Church Street, Edwinstowe, Notts, NG21 9QA. Tel:0623-824455
BARRASS BULLEN COMERY Comrie Cowan FAIRLESS Frailes HASTINGS HAUGH MCCOWAN WATKIN WOODHEAD F1697

178551 WOODHOUSE Mrs Janet. (Moore) 44 Cartier Close, Old Hall, Warrington, Cheshire, WA5 5TD.
BIDDLESTONE HOPKIN MOORE SLACK STREETS TIDY F3444

178578 WOODHOUSE Mr R M. 44 Cartier Close, Old Hall, Warrington, Cheshire, WA5 5TD.
HALL PRITCHARD WENT WILLIAMS WOODHOUSE F3445

178586 WOODIWISS Mr Alfred. 33 Grosvenor Road, London, W4 4EQ. Tel:081-994-3421
WOODDISS WOODIS WOODISE Woodiwis Woodiwise WOODIWISS WOODIWISSE WOODWIS WOODWISE WOODWISS F6087

178594 WOODIWISS Mr F. 4 Barratt Close, Attenborough, Beeston, Nottingham, NG9 6AE.
Woodiwis WOODIWISS F6813

178608 WOODS Mr Edward. The School House, 75 Rayleigh Road, Eastwood, Leigh On Sea, Essex, SS9 5UU.
BLACKMAN BRASIER BROWN BYSOUTH DILLON FENN GILBEY HARRINGTON HAWE HOLDOWAY JEMSOB KYBERD MASON PARKER F5653

178616 WOODS Mrs Hilary R. (Jackson) 3 Blackpool Road, Carleton, Poulton Le Fylde, Lancs, FY6 7QB. Tel:0253-883148
BLOOD CRAFTS FITCH HALL HARRIMAN JACKSON LOYLEY NEWBY NORMAN TIERNEY TIVEY WHILEY WOODS F5600

178624 WOODS Mr J F. 23 Knights Avenue, Clapham, Bedford, MK41 6DF. Tel:0234-352368
BULLENT HOLNES MILLER MORLEY PRESTON RICHARDSON SADLER STANDING WELLER WOODS F4696

178632 WOODS Mr Kenneth. 1 Braodacres Garth, Carlton, Goole, East Yorks, DN14 9QD.
GOFF SANDLAND SCHOFIELD WOODS F6146

178640 WOODS Mr L A. 136 The Causeway, Petersfield, Hants, GU13 4LL.
ACASTER Ackaster AKESTER Akister De Acastre Pettie PETTY Sanderson SAUNDERSON Wood Woodde Woode WOODS F4563

178659 WOODS Mrs O A. Wythop, 41 Accommodation Road, Horncastle, Lincs, LN9 5AP.
CAMERON Ellias Elliot ELLIS HARRIS Jenkins Jenkinson JINKENS Jinkins LEAR Leer Lyer Parfrey PARR PUREFOY Purfrey THYNNE F2789

178667 WOODS Mrs S M. (Eggleton) 7 East Hill, Charminster, Dorchester, Dorset, DT2 9QL. Tel:0305-265614
EGGLETON HASKETT RIDDLE WHURR F5245

178675 WOODWARD Mr Philip. 34 Deakin Leas, Tonbridge, Kent, TN9 2JX. Tel:0732-359312
ACASTER BRABFORD GLOVER HODGKINSON RAWDING F5656

178683 WOODWARD Miss Tessa Elizabeth. 32 Cypress Court, Waterloo Street, Cheltenham, Glos, GL51 9BY.
BLACKWELL CLARK FORD FOWLER KILMISTER MALINS MELSOME POPE RIDDIFORD SELMAN Selmon WOODWARD WORKMAN F660

178691 WOOF Mr Clifford. 6 Elm Close, Shipham, Winscombe, Avon, BS25 1UG. Tel:0934-842064
DODD HINDMARSH TURNBULL Woff Woffe Wolf Wolfe WOOF Wooff F4134

178705 WOOLDRIDGE Mrs Marilyn C. (Edwards) 26 Chestnut Avenue, Wokingham, Berkshire, RG11 2UU.
BARTLETT BUCKINGHAM BURBIDGE BURBRIDGE BURLE CARTER CARVER CHAMPION COBLEY COFFIN DODD EDWARDS GARRETT GREGORY HALL HEEREBERT HEYDEN HOPES KNIGHT LEADER MOORE PAGE PAYNE PHIPPS SOLICE TAYLOR TUCKER WELLAVIZE WELLAWYSE WEST WESTBURY WHEELER WILLAVISE WOOLDRIDGE F2225

178713 WOOLFENDEN Mr Jack. 52 Oxenholme Road, Kendal, Cumbria, LA9 7HH. Tel:0539-722964
Wolfenden Wolfendon Wolfinden WOOLFENDEN Woolfendon Woolfinden Woolindon F5011

178721 WOOLGAR Mrs M J. 6 Marlborough Court, West Meads, Bognor Regis, West Sussex, PO21 5QH.
Wolgar Wolger WOOLGAR Woolger Woollgar Worger F7176

178748 WOOLLAN Mr M J. The Pines, Manor Road, Trimley St Mary, Ipswich, Suffolk, IP10 0TU.
Wolen Wolens Wollam Wollams Wollan Wolland Wollands Wollans Wollen Wollend Wollens Wollin Wollins Wolloms Wollon Wollons Woolam Woolams Woolan Woolans Woolen Woolham Woollams WOOLLAN Woolland Woollands Woollans Woollen Woollend Woollends Woollens Woollham Woollhams Woolliams Woollin Woollins Woollon Woollons F7162

178756 WOOLLER Mr James. 37 Manor Way, Polegate, East Sussex, BN26 5AS.
Woller Wooler WOOLLER F4302

178764 WOOLLEY Mr M. 4 Penrith Avenue, Macclesfield, Cheshire, SK11 8PP.
Woley Wolley Wooley WOOLLEY F6997

178772 WOOLLEY Mrs Sheila E. 56 Branksome Drive, Filton, Bristol, BS12 7EF. Tel:0272-696006
CORBER CURBER F2939

178780 WOOLLINGS Miss B. 2 Chelmer Road, Witham, Essex, CM8 2EU.
Wollings Woolings WOOLLINGS F6897

178799 WOOLNER Mr George J. 34 Dolphin Square, Plymstock, Plymouth, Devon, PL9 8RW. Tel:0752-406187
BARRON BARRON NEE WELLER BROMLEY CONEYBEARE Coneybeer CRUMWELL GORDON GROVE KINGWELL NEILL OLIVER STAMP UPHAM WELLER WOOLNER F3424

178802 WOOLRICH Mr Alfred Edgar. 9 Woodsend Close, Burton Joyce, Nottingham, NG14 5DY. Tel:0602-312449
Wolridge Wolrych Wooldridge WOOLRICH Woolriche Woolridge Woolrych F6232

178810 WOOLVEN Mr Dave. 2 Aspen Way, Malpas Park, Newport, Gwent, NP9 6LB. Tel:0633-858359
WOOLVEN F1113

178829 WOOLVETT Mr Brian L. 2 Halsey Road, Elizabeth East, SA 5112, AUSTRALIA.
Wolvert WOOLVETT Woolvitt F6957

178837 WOOLVIN Mr Richard. 2/17 Percy Road, London, W12 9PX.
WOOLVIN F437

178845 WOOLWARD Mrs Mary. (Eplett) 20 South Vale, Upper Norwood, London, SE19 3BA. Tel:081-653-0949
BAWDEN BROWN COX DAVIES ELLERY Eplet EPLETT EPOLITE Epplet Epplett Eptlett HARRIS HARVEY HAYWARD HEPPETT HEPPOLETTE HICKS JAMES JENKIN Jenking Jenkyn JOSEPH Kendal KENDALL Kendell Kendle LONGDEN MARTIN Martyn MORGAN NICHOLLS OLIVER PENNY POLKINGHORNE Poolton POULTON Pulton REID RICHARDS SCREEN SMITH TREGLOAN Treglorn Treglorne Treglowan Treglowhan Treglown TREGONING Werkman Willabay Willbey Willbie Willbo WILLOUGHBY Willowby WORKMAN F2126

178853 WOON Mr D T G. The Rowans, Main Road, Little Oakley, Harwich, Essex, CO12 5EB. Tel:0255-880257
BELLINGHAM BENNETT GALE GEORGE PARDON TOZER VENNING WHITE WOON YOUNG F2294

178861 WOOTTON Mr David G. Stanmore Place, Church Road, Chrishall, Royston, Herts, SG8 8QT. Tel:0763-838400
BENTLEY EVEREST HOLMES SELLMAN WHALE WOOTTON F4201

178888 WOOTTON Mr Walter Stanley. 42 Windmill Court, Fairstead, Kings Lynn, Norfolk, PE30 4XP. Tel:0553-760189
PHILLIPS WOOTTON F745

178896 WORKMAN Mrs Anne E. (Scott) 7 Cuikenburn, Penicuik, Midlothian, EH26 0JG.
BRODIE GOODWIN GRIMMOND Grimond POTTS RITCHIE Rouckston Rouckstone Roukston Roukstone Rukston RUXTON SCOTT SMITH TAYLOR F3849

178918 WORNHAM Mr M David. 20 The Parklands, Droitwich, Wrocs, WR9 7DG.
WARNHAM WERNHAM Wirdnam WIRNHAM WIRONAM WORNHAM WYRDENHAM WYRNHAM F813

178926 WORRALL Mr David Frank. 213 Brunswick Park Road, New South Gate, London, N11 1EL.
Bail BALE Beale BROOKES BROOKS CHATER COUPLAND Cpoeland FLAVELL HASSELL Hazzael HULBARD HULBERT NEEDHAM PAYBODY PEABODY PEBODY POTTERTON POTTINGTON POTTOTON RHODES Rodes SPERRY Tebbet TEBBETT Tebbutt WHORRALL WORALL WORRALL F5333

178934 WORRALL Mr J R. Hillcrest, Old St Johns Road, St Helier, Jersey, JE2 3LG.
HOLBERY NOLLOTH ROBERTS STAMMERS WHINCOP WORRALL F6336

178942 WORRALL Mr Raymond. 39 Prospect Hill, Whitby, North Riding, YO21 1QE. Tel:0947-604230
BIELBY MOLYNEUX SNOWDEN WORRALL F666

178950 WORSDELL Brigadier Geoffrey W. 27 Bereweeke Road, Felpham, Bognor Regis, W Sussex, PO22 7EG.
Wasdal Wasdall Wesdal Wesdall Westal Westall Wisdal Wisdall Wordsell Worsdale Worsdall Worsdel WORSDELL Worsdoll Worstall Worstoll Wosdale Wosdell Wostil Wostill Wostoll F60

178969 WORSTER Mr Norman George. 41 Alde Lane, Aldeburgh, Suffolk, IP15 5DZ. Tel:0728-453075
DYSON ELENGAM MORTLOCK Tredacke Tredanic Treddinnick Tredenack Tredeneck Tredenicke Tredick Tredinick TREDINNICK Tredyck Tredynnacke Wooster Worcester Worcestre Worsetar Worseter WORSTER Worsyter Wosetar Woseter Woster Wyssetour F609

178977 WORTH Mr A F N. 25 Highcroft Drive, Four Oaks, Sutton Coldfield, W Midlands, B74 4SX.
Werth Wirth WORTH F6782

178985 WORTH Mrs M V. (Moore) 8 Rock Avenue, Barnstaple, Devon, EX32 9AP.
Holiock Holiocke HOLYOAKE Holyoke JENNENS MOORE PAYN F4603

178993 WORTHINGTON Mrs Barbara. 31 Fairview Crescent, Almondbury, Huddersfield, W Yorks, HD5 8ER.
ACKROYD DODGSON ELLEBY JEPSON JOHNSON SHAW SWALLOW TAYLOR WALKER WORTHINGTON F2282

179000 WOTHERSPOON Mr David. 9 Callander Drive, Larbert, Stirlingshire, FK5 3ET. Tel:0324-553584
Aiken AITKEN BAIRD BUCHANAN CARLAW CHALMERS COOK FISHER Gardener GARDINER Gardner GLEN Gooch GOUCH HAMILTON HENDERSON HUNTER Matheson MATHIESON PATERSON RICHARDSON ROBERTSON SHAW SHIELDS SINCLAIR TURNBULL WAUGH Weatherspoon Wedderspon Wetherspoon Witherspoon Witherspoons WOTHERSPOON F3426

179019 WOTTON Mr G H. Hamull, High Street, Bursledon, Southampton, SO3 8DJ. Tel:0703-402963
SWAFFIN TERRY WOTTON F3536

179027 WOZENCROFT Mrs Karen. (Barbero) 57 Glebe Street, Bedwas, Newport, Gwent, NP1 8AD.
BARBERO BEYNON COLLINS MOSES PRICE RUMSEY F4493

179035 WRAGG Mr Leonard. Appt 1705, 1285 Cahill Drive E, Ottawa, Ontario, K1V 9AY, CANADA.
ABBS BRACEY WRAGG F3488

179043 WRAY Mr Harold. Raw Bank Farm, Beestonley Lane, Stainland, Halifax, HX4 9PS. Tel:0422-371831
ACRES BARR BEDFORD LANE-FOX MACKIE PRENTICE TUER WALTON WRAY F1033

179051 WRAY Mrs Joan. Raw Bank Farm, Beestonley Lane, Stainland, Halifax, HX4 9PS. Tel:0422-371831
ANGEL Angell CARTER HOLMES HOPE HUMES LAMBTON Loaten LOATON Loten Loton PUNTER Streadar Streader STREDDER Streder F1034

179078 WRIGHT Mrs Annie. (Baron) 2 The Newlands, Outgang Road, Pickering, North Yorks, YO18 7EP.
BARNES BARON BOOTH BREAKS BUCKLEY CHARNLEY CHERRY CLEGG CRAVEN DILWORTH GREEN HAWORTH HAYHURST HEAPS HIGSON HOLT KEALING KERSHAW LAW LORD OLIVE RIGG ROCHELLE RUSHTON TOWNSEND WALKER WHITTAKER WOLFENDEN WOODS WRIGHT F3787

179086 WRIGHT Mrs B. 7 Northbrook Road, Shirley, Solihull, West Midlands, B90 3NT. Tel:021-744-6919
ALLINSON BEARD BROWN BUCKLEY CANESFORD DAVIES HANSON KEIGHLEY MORTIMER NAGGINSON PARKINSON PEARSON SHUTT F5073

179094 WRIGHT Mr B. 66 Illshaw Close, Winyates Green, Redditch, Worcs, B98 0QZ.
MOGG Mugg F7135

179108 WRIGHT Mrs Brenda. 19 Queensway, Little Stoke, Bristol, BS12 6LQ.
LACEY F2048

179116 WRIGHT Mr D I W. Flat 2, 107 Belvedere Road, London, SE19 2HY.
ANSLOW BAGLEY BLACK BROUGHALL BROWNING BUCKLEY BURTON Calcot Calcott CALCUTT Callcott Callcut Callcutt Caulcott Cawcott Cawket Cawkett Clewes Clews CLOWES COOPER COTTON DAITON Davies DAVIS Dayton GIBB HALL HALLKINS Holkins JEFFRIES JOHNSON KELLY LEITCH Mickelwright MICKLEWRIGHT PLANT REID REYNOLDS Sara Sary SCADDAN Scadden Scaddon SEARY Seery Sery SHEDDEN Smallshare SMALLSHAW Smallsher SMALLSHIRE Smalshaw Smalshire SMITH WEBB WILSON WRIGHT F4186

179124 WRIGHT Mr D. 71 Island Wall, Whitstable, Kent, CT5 1EL.
ELVE Elvey Elvy F6600

179132 WRIGHT Mr David N. 2 Holmes Close, Wokingham, Berks, RG11 2SG. Tel:0734-784814
BATESON WRIGHT F231

179140 WRIGHT Mr David. 12 Shelley Grove, Loughton, Essex, IG10 1BY. Tel:081-508-2403
CRANE FAULKNER FOWLER GRIFFIN GUNN HAMILTON HENRIQUES HOWE SHARP WARREN WILSON WRIGHT F1300

179159 WRIGHT Mrs Evelyn. 70 Church Road, Woburn Sands, Milton Keynes, Bucks, MK17 8TA.
GALBRAITH HARE HARMER PAQUELIN ROBERTS THRALE WILSON F7423

179167 WRIGHT Mrs Gill. 75 Merrieleas Drive, Chandlers Ford, Eastleigh, Hants, SO5 2FQ.
ANDREWS HENNING LEVEY LEWER MUNDY PEWSEY F796

179175 WRIGHT Mr Graham. 20 Greenwood Road, High Green, Sheffield, S Yorks, S30 4GW.
EDGELEY Edgely Edgley Edgly F4096

179183 WRIGHT Mrs Iris. (Hamilton) 12 Shelley Grove, Loughton, Essex, IG10 1BY. Tel:081-508-2403
BRADSHAW COOPER CRANE HAMILTON MOORE ROGERS SPRINGAY WILSON F5704

179191 WRIGHT Mrs J M H. (Ellicott) Flat 8, Heathmount Hall, Crossbeck Road, Ilkley, West Yorks, LS29 9JN.
BROWN BURN BURNS COPPIN ELLICOTT ERRINGTON HAMBLEY Hambly Hamley Hamly TAYLOR WEAR F5084

179205 WRIGHT Mrs J M. 257 Chesterfield Road, Temple Normanton, Chesterfield, Derbyshire, S42 5DE.
ASHMORE BROCKELSBY Brocklesby BULBECK BUSH FOX MARRIOTT MAYHEW WRIGHT F5726

179213 WRIGHT Mr J R. 2 Low Road, Debenham, Suffolk, IP14 6QU.
BROWN DAW HAYMAN KELLAWAY KNOTT LEGASSICK PENNY PROWSE WILLOTT WRIGHT F2893

179221 WRIGHT Mr James Henry. D'argon, Wexham Street, Stoke Poges, Bucks, SL3 6NX.
DUNKERLEY MAY TULETT WRIGHT F1374

179248 WRIGHT Mrs Jean. (Ellicott) Flat 8, Heathmount Hall, Crossbeck Road, Ilkley, W Yorks, LS29 9JN.
BROWN ELLICOTT ERRINGTON HAMBLEY LAXTON WEAR F4023

179256 WRIGHT Mrs Joan A. 26 Leggfield Terrace, Hemel Hempstead, Herts, HP1 2LL. Tel:0442-65224
BROOKS LAKE LOWNDES MARLBOROUGH Marlbrough MORAN ROFFE Rolfe WELLING WRIGHT F3622

179264 WRIGHT Lisa Rose. Toblerone Cottage, 84 Victoria Road, New Barnet, Herts, EN4 9PE.
WRIGHT F1367

179272 WRIGHT Mr M C. 284 Ringwood Road, Totton, Southampton, Hants, SO4 3EN. Tel:0703-666788

BLAKE SILLENCE WRIGHT F847
179280 WRIGHT Mr M L. Tamarisk, Warren Road, Kingsbridge, Devon, TQ7 1LB. Tel:0548-852069
ROBEY WAINWRIGHT WRIGHT F5841
179299 WRIGHT Ms Melanie. 4 Marquis Way, Bearwood, Bournemouth, Dorset, BH11 9TN.
ARMER CALLEN CONLEY CONNETT FOLLOWS LUCAS MULLEY PENNACK TAUERNER WRIGHT F935
179302 WRIGHT Mr Philip Thomas. 15 New House Park, St Albans, Herts, AL1 1UA. Tel:0727-833693
COTTERELL COTTRELL IRONS WRIGHT F2562
179310 WRIGHT Mr Stephen. 9 Boynton Drive, Mapperley, Nottingham, NG3 3EP. Tel:0602-583063
DILLWORTH MCROBERT WRIGHT F5243
179329 WRIGHT Dr Steve. 277 Mauldeth Road, Burnage, Manchester, M19 1FF. Tel:061-248-7433
GIBSON SALKELD SULLIVAN WATSON WRIGHT F928
179337 WRIGHT Mr Stuart. 498a Grey St, Brantford, Ontario, N3S 7L4, CANADA. Tel:+1-519-758-5338
BENCE BOLTON BRAMBLE DYER HAMMOND HARRIS HAYWARD HULL JEFFERIES LABBITT MATHEWS NEATE SENDALL SHEPHERD SIMONDS SIMPKINS THORN WILCOX WOODHAM YOUNG F4328
179345 WRIGHT-NOOTH Mr Peter. 7 Norman Drive, Hatfield, Doncaster, S Yorks, DN7 6AQ. Tel:0302-840162
DUPERRON FELL IRVING NOOTH ROY SEARLE VERIT WHITEHEAD WRIGHT F4053
179353 WRIGHTSON Mrs Mavis. (Coombs) 58 Eastwick Road, Walton On Thames, Surrey, KT12 5AR. Tel:0932-226930
Coombes COOMBS Coomes F5103
179361 WRIXON Dr Anthony. 1 Woodgate Close, Grove, Wantage, Oxon, OX12 0NF. Tel:02357-65005
BLANCHARD BUNDY FIELDS GOLDING Goulding HALLETT HERRINGTON KENT SHEPPARD SMALL TRUMAN WELLSTEAD WRIXON F2921
179388 WYATT Mr Kevin. 26 Cavendish Close, Goring By Sea, Worthing, W Sussex, BN12 6DP. Tel:0903-505629
CUCKNEY F483
179396 WYATT Mr Peter A H. 35 Livonia Road, Sidmouth, Devon, EX10 9JB.
ASHFORD BATCHELDER DAVIS DAW FOSTER GWYN HORLER PROBERT WEST WYATT F3534
179418 WYATT Lt Col R J. 33 Sturges Road, Wokingham, Berks, RG11 2HG.
Wiat Wiot Wyat WYATT F782
179426 WYBORN Mr Robert H. 1515 Kerfoot Road, White Rock, British Columbia, V4B 3L9, CANADA.
Wiborn WYBORN Wyborne Wyburn F6904
179434 WYLLIE Mr Arthur. 40 Maberley Street, Aberdeen, AB1 1NB. Tel:0224-637910
M'KENZIE Mackenzie SINCLAIR WATT Wylie WYLLIE F4579
179442 WYLLIE Mr H R. Oaks Knowle, Blakes Lane, Tadley, Hants, RG26 6PU.
AUSTEN Austin Austyn Borden BURDEN MCINTOSH MCNEIL Semens SEMMONS Simmonds Simmons Symonds Vylie Weyle Wily Wylie WYLLIE Wylly Wylye F3758
179450 WYLY Mr Peter. 8 Burnham Close, Culcheth, Cheshire, WA3 4LJ. Tel:0925-763485
BROUGHAM BROWHAM F2398
179469 WYNNE-DAVIES Mrs L. 47 Wyndcliffe Road, Charlton, London, SE7 7LP.
Edrup REDRUP Rethrop Rudroppe F6709
179477 YABSLEY Mr D John. 9 South Croft, Henleaze, Bristol, BS9 4PS.
CLARK DOWN HAYDON HURLEY JENKINS OSBORNE PARSLOW PERKINS SURRIDGE YABSLEY F3781
179485 YALE Mr John. 15 Rectory Avenue, Corfe Mullen, Wimborne, Dorset, BH21 3EZ. Tel:0202-690628
YALE Yales F153
179493 YARDE Mrs Doris M F. 40 Gurnsey Close, Lampton, Middx, TW5 0PH.
FLEETWOOD FULLER F1523
179507 YARDLEY Mr Michael J. Howletts Hall, Chignall St James, Chelmsford, Essex, CM1 4TP.
NICHOLLS YARDLEY F2732
179515 YATE Mr Jeremy C A. 2 Church Lane, Bishops Castle, Shropshire, SY9 5AF. Tel:0588-638705
ASHWOOD AUDLEY BOYCOTT CAIRNS COURT DANE DAVIES GIBBS GUEST HART HUNTER MCCOY MILMINE MOYLE NAIRNE NORTHEY PITTS PRYCE RANDALL REYNOLDS ROKER STEEN WRIGHT WYER YATE F6547
179523 YATES Dr David. 20 Martingales Close, Ham, Richmond, Surrey, TW10 7JJ.
BENNETT BLACKHURST FAIRCLOUGH Gelicho Gelico Gellico GRIFFITHS Jelico JELLICOE PEERS SEFTON Sephton WILDING YATES F1524
179531 YATES Mr Eric. Court Baron, Higher Cheriton, Payhembury, Honiton Devon, EX14 0JL.
ABBERLEY ALLEN BEER BEVINS BILLEAU BRIGHAM BRUNT CLULOE COULTER CREEN DALE FARLEY FARMER FISHER FLETCHER GRIMES KENT MEWBURN PASCO PATTON PYE RANDLES TRELEAVEN TROSSE VARNHAM YATES F1372
179558 YATES Mrs Eva. (Goudie) 11 Gressy Loan, Lerwick, Shetland, ZE1 0BD. Tel:0595-4947
YATES F3564
179566 YATES Mrs Hazel. 17 Greenhill Gardens, Alveston, Bristol, BS12 2PD. Tel:0454-412555
ADAMSON BOWMAN FENWICK YATES F1140
179574 YATES Mrs Patricia. 20 Martingales Close, Ham, Richmond, Surrey, TW10 7JJ.
AITKEN ARMSTRONG BROWN CREE FORESTER GIBSON GRANT HALLUM HUNTER MCLAREN SMITH WILSON F1525
179582 YEARBY Mr John. 64 Victoria Avenue, Shanklin, Isle Of Wight, PO37 6LY. Tel:0983-863173
YEARBY Yerby F4526
179590 YEATS-EDWARDS Mrs T K. (Kiddle) 23 Pine Road, Four Marks, Alton, Hants, GU34 5EZ. Tel:0420-64382
Keddall Keddle Kidal Kiddall Kiddell Kiddill KIDDLE Kidel Kidil Kydal Kydel Kydil Shufflebotham Shufflebothom Shufflebottam SHUFFLEBOTTOM F3600
179604 YELLAND Mr John. 12 Avon Crescent, Durban North, 4051, SOUTH AFRICA.
BARRETT DOIG FOY HUNTER NEWLAND QUIRK ROSS WEBBER YELLAND F5153
179612 YEO Mr L J. 39 Carne Street, Pentre, Rhondda, Mid Glamorgan, CF41 7LQ. Tel:0443-436605
BANBERY DAVIES EVERY HARRIES HUGHES JONES MORRIS PALMER PEARCE PROTHEROE SMITH WOOLFE YEO F4091
179620 YODER Mr H Walter. 1422 Wealthy S E, Grand Rapids, MI 49506, USA.
HOWE F7297
179639 YORKE Mr Colin. 11 Tower Road, Portishead, Bristol, BS20 8RE. Tel:0275-849447
YORKE F4844
179647 YOUNG Mrs Cerisa. (Pierpoint) 109 Glannant Way, Cimla, Neath, W Glamorgan, SA11 3YW.
Auckley BOSWORTH BOWEN BRUSH Conley CONNELLY CONNER Connerlly Connerly COOK DRANE HAINES HARDIE Haynes HUGHES MEALING NIVEN OAKLEY Ockly Pearpoint Peirpoint Pheopoint PIERPOINT TONKS YOUNG F5290
179655 YOUNG Mr David. 11 Ffordd Mon, Rhosddu, Wrexham, Clwyd, LL11 2LL.
CRAMMOND CRAMOND GAMESON WILLIAMSON YOUNG F3957
179663 YOUNG Mrs O. 3 Oak Dene, Ealing, London, W13 8AW.
BOWES BROWN CHRISTOFFER CRUSE DEDE HALL LEMERES MITCHELL NICHOLSON PHILIPSON PROUDFOOT TAPLEY TOUCHARD WALKER WARD F2231
179671 YOUNG Mr Robert S F. 5 Richford Road, Stratford, London, E15 3PG. Tel:081-519-5502
CHARLTON COX EDWARDS REYNOLDS SHOTTON WATSON WHEELER YOUNG F1502
179698 YOUNG Mr Roger. Chalcroft, Cliff Way, Compton Down, Winchester Hants, SO21 2AP.
Yong Yonge YOUNG Younge F1920
179701 YOUNG Mrs S C. 25 Tuson Drive, Widnes, Cheshire, WA8 9EZ. Tel:051-423-2059
BURTON CARSON CASH TASKER TRICKETT F2768
179728 ZANKER Miss Patricia. 7 Wickstead Close, Kettering, Northants, NN15 6HJ. Tel:0536-523521
ZANKER F1543

MORE ADDRESSES:
Addresses of Record Offices and other archive sources, as well as organisations associated with Family History can be found in Section G.

SECTION E - SPECIAL STUDIES

This section contains:
Place Studies
Special Studies
Index to Maiden Names in Section D.
Index to One Name Studies in Section C.

As with the rest of this Directory the information has been provided by the people concerned. We have not extracted information from other directories, advertisements or county society magazines.

The reference number relates to the name and address of the contributor to be found in Section D. The F number is the file number in our system, which is also at the end of their address in Section D.

PLACE STUDIES

ANSTEY LEI (1700+) 169323 F3877
ASHLEYHAY DERBYSHIRE 113395 F6237
ASTON ABBOTS BUCKS 177180 F545
AUCHTERMUCHTY EAST FIFE 173746 F5199
AYLTON COURT HEREFORD & WORCS 133639 F3969
BLACKHALL CO DURHAM 135720 F1254
BRAMSHOTT HAMPSHIRE 127191 F3277
BRINKWORTH WILTSHIRE 132950 F6469
BURNHAM ESSEX 120553 F3809
CASTLE BENOWN IRELAND 150835 F5423
CAULDON STAFFORDSHIRE 105791 F6260
CHIPPING CAMPDEN GLOUCESTERSHIRE 153249 F3315
CHITTLEHAMPTON DEVON 161292 F4057
CREEKSEA ESSEX 120553 F3809
CUBBINGTON WARWICKSHIRE 153249 F3315
DARLINGTON CO DURHAM 124826 F2690
DARTMOOR DEVON 105333 F2545
DRY DRAYTON CAMBRIDGESHIRE 162655 F637
DUCKLINGTON OXFORDSHIRE (HISTORY & ARCHAEOLOGY) 147958 F2818
EASINGTON CO DURHAM 135720 F1254
EAST KENT - SURNAMES INDEX (CENSUS AND PARISH REGISTERS) 151416 F2785
EAST ORCHARD DORSET 141585 F457
EDWINSTOWE NOTTS 178543 F1697
EGTON NORTH YORKSHIRE 113778 F6325
FECKENHAM RURAL HISTORY OF 127477 F5798
FERRYDEN ANGUS 137758 F1780
FOWLMERE CAMBRIDGESHIRE 133809 F81
GREAT YARMOUTH COBHOLM ISLAND 113395 F6237
GREATER MANCHESTER ABSTRACTS 1004-1837 142859 F1233
GROWTH AND DEVELOPMENT OF HAMMERSMITH-BROMLEY-BOW-POPLAR-HACKNEY AND THE CITY OF LONDON 162051 F1891
GROWTH AND DEVELOPMENT OF WANDSWORTH-SOUTHWARK AND BEDDINGTON ALL OF SURREY 162051 F1891
HAILSHAM LOCAL HISTORY 127868 F1962
INDEX TO COURT CASES IN OLD COUNTIES OF LANCASHIRE CHESHIRE AND GLOUCESTERSHIRE 1100-1750 142859 F1233
KENT (INDEX OF PROBATE AN UNPULISHED MATERIAL) 131288 F2672
KIMBOLTON CAMBRIDGESHIRE 111414 F4925
KINGHAM GLOUCESTERSHIRE 144738 F615
KIRTLING RURAL HISTORY OF 127477 F5798
KIRTON IN LINDSEY 177199 F5976
LANCASHIRE HISTORY PARTICULARLY BURY AREA 162868 F1364
LEAVENING EAST RIDING 172766 F5826
LICKFOLD SUSSEX 142220 F45
LIPHOOK HAMPSHIRE 127191 F3277
LITTLE COMBERTON NEAR PERSHORE 109398 F7433
LITTLE THURROCK ESSEX 105848 F5923
LLANFYRNACH PEMBROKESHIRE 129135 F402
LODSWORTH SUSSEX 142220 F45
LURGASHALL SUSSEX 142220 F45
MERIDEN WARWICKSHIRE 100420 F1298
MICHAELSTOW CORNWALL 128082 F5975
MIDDLESEX ALL NAMES AT THE FOLLOWING PLACES RUISLIP-EASTCOTE-NORTHWOOD-ICKENHAM-HAREFIELD-PINNER 131466 F6203
MONTROSE ANGUS 137758 F1780
MOUNTAIN ASH MID GLAMORGAN 131938 F4427
NEWHALL DERBYSHIRE 112003 F1591
NORTH LAMBETH SURREY 122211 F2655
OLD SEAHAM MAPS 1853-1939 135720 F1254
OLD SUNDERLAND 135720 F1254
OSGATHORPE LEICESTERSHIRE 112003 F1591
PENDENNIS CASTLE FALMOUTH CORNWALL & ITS SOLDIERS 104671 F3215
PLEASHEY CASTLE ESSEX 148121 F4698
POLRUAN-BY-FOWEY CORNWALL 155292 F3135
RUTLAND LEICESTERSHIRE 112003 F1591
SALWARPE WORCESTERSHIRE 124176 F746
SHOTTLE DERBYSHIRE 113395 F6237
SITTINGBOURNE MILTON KENT 109398 F7433
SOUTH HETTON CO DURHAM 135720 F1254
SOUTH OCKENDON ESSEX 105848 F5923
ST JENNYS CORNWALL 173592 F667
ST KEVERNE CORNWALL 150126 F2344
SWADLINCOTE DERBYSHIRE 112003 F1591
THORNEY CAMBRIDGESHIRE 128996 F5100
TINGEWICK BUCKS 124796 F6314
UPHAM HAMPSHIRE 109355 F3839
WANTAGE OXFORDSHIRE 160547 F728
WELLS-NEXT-THE-SEA ST NICHOLAS PARISH RECORDS 1659-1899 155853 F3326
WELTON LE MARSH LINCOLNSHIRE 125865 F4769
WEST ORCHARD DORSET 141585 F457
WIMBLEDON VILLAGE & COMMON SURREY 141585 F457
WISBECH ST MARY 1805-1880 153893 F3528
WITLEY COURT WORCS 133639 F3969
YARDLEY GOBION NORTHANTS 137014 F5125

SPECIAL STUDIES

11TH MANCHESTER REGIMENT 1917-1919 109479 F566
138 SQUADRON SPECIAL OPERATIONS EXECUTIVE 1939-1945 177199 F5976
16TH MANCHESTER REGIMENT 1915-1917 109479 F566
1851 CENSUS FOR CHANNEL ISLES-INDEX & TRANSCRIPTS 131326 F3531
1939-1945 WARTIME MEMORIES 157449 F655
19TH CENTURY EAST END LONDON & RIVER THAMES 120057 F4081
355 PANZERDIVISION TOTENKOPF 1939-1945 177199 F5976
49TH-66TH REGIMENT OF FOOT - 2ND BATTALION 113395 F6237
72ND HIGHLANDERS IN IRELAND INDIA & ENGLAND 1866-1876 179000 F3426
7TH REGIMENT OF ROYAL FUSILIERS 1845-1856 127868 F1962

ABNEY PARK CEMETERY (STOKE NEWINGTON) 165719 F5868
ACASTER MERCHANTS OF YORK 1200-1400 178640 F4563
ANGLO-INDIAN GENEALOGY 113158 F5867
ANGLO-JEWISH GENEALOGY 138622 F513
ANY INFORMATION ON NAME AUCHMUTY 173746 F5199
ANY WARLAND EMMIGRATIONS 173746 F5199
AQUILA (CHRISTAIN NAME) 154504 F48
ARMY RECORDS (3RD DRAGOONS, 6TH INNISKILLING DRAGOONS, ROYAL DUBLIN FUSILIERS) 1750-1920 110159 F2825
AUSTIN AND VARIATIONS (AS A CHRISTIAN NAME) 102628 F681
AYLESBURY UNION WORKSHOUSE AND CUDDINGTON WORKHOUSE 1869-1883 153818 F6095
BAPTISMS MARRIAGES & BURIALS FOR ASPLEY GUISE 1500-1812 130222 F2717
BAPTISMS MARRIAGES & BURIALS FOR EVERSHOLT BEDS 1557-1900 130222 F2717
BAPTISMS MARRIAGES & BURIALS FOR LITTLE HARROWDEN NORTHANTS 1813-1900 130222 F2717
BAPTISMS MARRIAGES & BURIALS FOR RIDGMONT 1500-1812 130222 F2717
BAPTISMS MARRIAGES & BURIALS OF HUSBORNE CRAWLEY 1557-1980 130222 F2717
BEAMERS TWISTERS & DRAWERS AMALGAMATION (UNION) 174211 F3765
BEAN NAME CONNECTED WITH CINQUE PORTS 104841 F2139
BLACKSMITHS 113395 F6237
BLACKSMITHS OF NORWICH NORFOLK 100641 F2142
BOOK & MAP COLLECTION OF CORNWALL 142905 F355
BOOK & MAP COLLECTION OF MANCHESTER 142905 F355
BOOKS BOUND BY SAMUEL OR HENRY HOGG 134252 F4048
BOW STREET RUNNERS 1800-1839 159034 F1447
BOX CHURCH WILTSHIRE 148121 F4698
BRILL & LUGGERSALL TRAMWAY 1860-1935 117897 F455
BRITISH CLIMATE 112003 F1591
BRITISH SHIPS THAT WENT DOWN AND CREW WITH OR NEAR HMS HOOD (2ND WORLD WAR) 143715 F4776
BUILDING INDEX OF SOLDIERS OF THE BRITISH ARMY 1914-1918 106186 F5937
BURNLEY MINERS STRIKE 1972 152412 F3624
C OF E CLERGY IN ENGLAND 1600-1700 154539 F496
CABINET MAKERS IN 18C FALMOUTH CORNWALL 104671 F3215
CARADON - SHADOWS OF THE PAST (BOOK) 162973 F1781
CARTE DE VISITE (VICTORIAN PHOTOGRAPHS) PARTICULARLY SOUTHERN ENGLAND 150266 F5911
CARVERS AND CARVING TRADE 1800-1960 118907 F2433
CENSUS'S 1841-1881 FOR HUSBORNE CRAWLEY 130222 F2717
CHAPELS 151513 F1435
CHARTISM IN WORCS & BLACK COUNTRY (STAFFS) 118907 F2433
CHARTISTS 170704 F246
CHRISTIAN NAME OF MELIAN 114669 F5384
CHRUCH RECORD GROUP 170968 F1175
CHURCH BELL RINGING 170968 F1175
CHURCHYARDS 151513 F1435
CINEMAS FOR SILENT FILMS IN SCOTLAND PRE 1925 135658 F2183
CIRCUS & MUSIC HALLS 1890-1920 135658 F2183
CIRCUS PROPRIETORS AND ARTISTS MAINLY VICTORIAN 171565 F1718
CLANDESTINE MARRIAGE 105848 F5923
CLERGY AFFECTED BY PARLIAMENTARIANS 1642-1660 110787 F5670
CLERGY AFFECTED BY THE STUART RESTORATION 1660-1662 110787 F5670
COACH HOUSES IN CHELTENHAM & BIRMINGHAM 163287 F3327
COAL MINING LIFE DURHAM OF 19TH CENTURY 169617 F6216
COINS TOKENS & MEDALLIONS OF CORNWALL 146307 F3659
COLDSTREAM GUARDS 1900-1912 173517 F3048
COLLECTION OF DRAWINGS & PHOTOGRAPHS OF BUILDINGS IN GREATER MANCHESTER BEFORE 1750 142859 F1233
COLLECTION OF ESTATE & ORDINANCE SURVEY MAPS OF GREATER MANCHESTER 1004-1837 142859 F1233
COLLECTION OF POST CARDS OF WATER COLOUR PAINTINGS BY ALFRED ROBERT QUINTON 124974 F748
COLLECTION OF RYDER WILLS OF COVERDALE YORKS 1590 TO 1830 118486 F4324
COLLECTION OF SCOUTING MEMORABILIA 164720 F3186
COMBMAKERS INDEX 108375 F547
COPPER TRADE BETWEEN CHILE & SWANSEA 19C 135658 F2183
CORDWAINERS IN 19C FALMOUTH CORNWALL 104671 F3215
CORN MILLERS IN LANCS 1775-1915 135658 F2183
CORNISHMEN SERVING IN WW1 173835 F709
CUSTOMS OFFICERS IN LONDON & DISTRICTS 154539 F496
DATABASE OF SIX MILLION NAMES (BIRTHS MARRIAGES DEATHS WILLS SCHOOL ENTRIES CIVIC OFFICERS ETC) 124656 F398
DISCOVER BACKGROUND OF JOHN BEALEY IN CAMBORNE 102911 F4235
DISCOVERY OF NW PASSAGE OF SIR JOHN FRANKLIN EXPEDITION 1845 TO 1888 109061 F2074
DOMESTIC HANDLOOM WEAVING IN BLACKBURN AREA 17C TO 19C 144932 F2876
DUKE OF BEDFORD'S ESTATE AT WOBURN BEDFORDSHIRE 153818 F6095
DURHAM MINERS FEDERATION 1871-1900 118907 F2433
EARLY RAILWAY ENGINEERS AND CONTRACTORS 160458 F1606
EAST SUSSEX CENSUS 1851 AND 1841 103934 F3320
EDWIN WARD PEARLY KING 1910-1977 102717 F1984
EMIGRATION AND SETTLEMENT C17TH+ IN AUSTRALIA CANADA NEW ZEALAND SOUTH AFRICA AND USA 135852 F115
ENGLISH COUNTRY DANCING INCLUDING MORRIS AND SWORD 162868 F1364
ENGLISH FOLK CUSTOMS 162868 F1364
EPIDEMICS 112003 F1591
FAMILY SAMPLERS BY ELIZABETH COLEMAN 1765 141623 F2559
FAMILY SAMPLERS BY SARAH CHALKLEY 1720-1740 141623 F2559
FAMILY WILLS FROM 1826 163414 F2094
FARMING AND NEEDLE MAKING COTTAGE INDUSTRIES 127477 F5798

FARMING FAMILIES OF EAST LEAKE 1798-1900 AND BEFORE 124834 F6277
FARMING FAMILIES OF NEATH & DULAIS VALLEYS 129232 F3565
FARRIER'S 113395 F6237
FARRIERY AND VETERNINARY HISTORY 143006 F1789
FISH FACTORS MANAGERS AND PORTERS IN MIDDLESEX AND SURREY POST 1550 162051 F1891
FOLK SONGS IN ENGLAND 162868 F1364
FOLKLORE & LEGENDS OF BERKSHIRE 124974 F748
FOLKLORE & LEGENDS OF HAMPSHIRE 124974 F748
FOREIGN & MILITARY (SEE FORM) 133639 F3969
FREEMEN OF LONDON 154539 F496
FREEMEN OF STAFFORD 139130 F4943
FULLER'S IN THE FORCES 1750-1920 173746 F5199
GOLD SILVER AND ALLIED TRADES WHO WENT TO INDIA 1760-1860 176788 F832
GOODISON BRASS MUSICAL INSTRUCMENTS 1830-1890 125725 F1633
GRAVESTONES & MEMORIALS FOR PONTEFRACT 1801 ONWARDS 135240 F949
HADRIANS WALL & ROMAN HISTORY 174815 F1316
HANDLOOM WEAVERS OF RENFREWSHIRE 128651 F5299
HERALDRY 100897 F3319
HISTORIC MUSICAL INSTRUMENTS 162868 F1364
HISTORY OF BODMIN GRAMMAR SCHOOL CORNWALL 1874-1973 111279 F5056
HISTORY OF CHINA CLAY AND CHINA STONE IN SOUTH EAST BRITAIN 170615 F2178
HISTORY OF EDUCATION 131938 F4427
HISTORY OF EXTRACTION INDUSTRIES IN AND AROUND HENSBARROW (ST AUSTELL) GRANITE 170615 F2178
HISTORY OF NURSING 131938 F4427
HISTORY OF OWNERSHIP FO WHITWELL HALL NEAR REEPHAM NORFOLK 126063 F599
HISTORY OF THE TODD FAMILY IN NORTH EAST GLASGOW 1530 TO PRESENT 146129 F5322
HMS CUBBITT WWII 1943-1946 156175 F4684
HOBBS' MAKING HORSE COLLARS COUNTRYWIDE FROM 1680 TO 1930 133884 F4560
HUGUENOT GLASSMAKERS FROM TORRAINE FRANCE 156892 F2375
HUMAN GENETICS 151513 F1435
HUME LANCASTER 1814-1850 BOTH PAINTERS 103942 F3524
HYWEL AP SYR MATHEW CHIEF BARD GENEALOGIST AND SOLDIER 132217 F5676
GREATER BIRMINGHAM BURIAL INDEX 157430 F55
ILLUSTRATED ARTICLE OF THE MITCHELLS OF MITCHELLSFORT 148415 F5271
INDEX OF DURHAM COUNTY (86 PARISHES) MARRIAGES TO 1837 160679 F2036
INDEX OF PARISH REGISTER INDEXES FOR LANCASHIRE CHESHIRE DERBYSHIRE AND DURHAM 142859 F1233
INDEX OF REGISTERS FOR ST MARY THEUIRGIN WALTON ON THE HILL 1586-1837 102512 F3325
INDEXES OF IRISH RECORDS (150000 INDIVIDUALS) 144797 F4859
INDEXING COLINGHAM PARISH RECORDS 1694-1759 149063 F1289
INDO-CHINA STEAM NAVIGATION CO LTD 161942 F6434
INDUSTRIAL ASPECTS 122211 F2655
INHABITANTS OF COWGILL/COGHILL ROW CLAYTON YORKS 1825-1906 160024 F3693
IRISH PALATINE FAMILIES 101192 F1799
IRISH WHO SERVED IN FRENCH MILITARY/NAVY 1700-1800 150835 F5423
JACQUES (JAMES) PARMENTIER HISTORICAL PAINTER 176338 F5253
JAMES HOLLAND 1799-1865 WATER COLOUR ARTIST 160504 F4634
JEWELLER AND SILVERSMITH RICHARD ATTENBOROUGH 156493 F4965
JOHN BADGER & SONS (WM BADGER & SONS) PORTABLE STEAM ENGINES 1854 159026 F744
JOHN EDMUNDS & CO SILK MANUFACTURERS 1840-1859 111155 F3810
JOHN EVANS AUTHOR POET POLEMICIST AND METHODIST PREACHER 132217 F5676
JOHN STEWART & CO 1870-1928 (SHIPPING COMPANY) 179671 F1502
JOHN WARLTIRE (1739-1810) CHEMIST AND LECTURER AUTHOR 125865 F4769
KILT MAKER AND TAILOR WILLIAM ROSS 156493 F4965
LAMBETH (PARISH) APPRENTICES 1856-1911 152099 F1317
LAMBETH SETTLEMENTS EXAMINATIONS TO 1829 152099 F1317
LANDED GENTRY OF CO DURHAM/BUCKS/SURREY 154539 F496
LAWRENCE TRAVELLING THEATRE 151157 F3806
LEE GYPSIES OF SOUTH EAST ENGLAND 102717 F1984
LEEDS POTTERY CREAMWARE 1780-1865 102407 F356
LEEDS-LIVERPOOL CANAL COMPANY & EMPLOYEES 102407 F356
LIFE OF REV JOHN HENRY SHOLL 1842-1905 (WESLEYAN METHODIST) 142905 F355
LIFE OF REVD ROBERT CAMPBELL DROUGHT 155683 F4418
LIGHTERMEN & WATERMEN ON THE RIVER THAMES 100897 F3319
LINCOLNSHIRE REGIMENT 1914-1918 173517 F3048
LINCOLNSHIRE WATCH CLOCK AND BAROMETER MAKERS 1700-1900 174122 F5912
LISNEY (FORENAME) 142638 F2122
LIST OF CORNWALL & DEVON FAMILIES WHO MOVED TO BURNLEY LANCS 1872-1873 152412 F3624
LOCAL HISTORY OF CHIPSTABLE SOMERSET 139130 F4943
LOCAL HISTORY OF STAFFORD(SHIRE) 139130 F4943
LOCAL HISTORY OF SYDENHAM/PENGE/FOREST HILL/DULWICH/BECKENHAM 157449 F655
LOCAL/SOCIAL/POLITICAL/INDUSTRIAL HISTORY 137294 F286
MALDEN AREA DEMOGRAPHY AND FAMILY RECONSTRUCTION GROUP PROJECT 105619 F462
MANOR OF MERE WILTSHIRE 148121 F4698
MARIE LLOYD 1870-1922 178454 F3598
MATHEMATICAL & SURGICAL INSTRUMENT MAKERS 160504 F4634
MEDIAEVAL HISTORY OF WEST SOMERSET 10TH TO 15TH CENTURIES 139556 F5095
MEMBERS OF THE FAMILY IN ROYAL NAVY 1883-1948 104094 F2499
MERCHANTS OF LONDON & CO DURHAM 1600-1900 154539 F496

METHODIST CHURCH PLANS & CLASS TICKETS 130389 F2330
MILITARY HISTORY/SOLDIERS LIVES HANTS 179418 F782
MILLS OF YORKSHIRE & LANCS 1700-1900 154539 F496
MORMONS IN 19C LANCS 174211 F3765
NAIL MAKING 107131 F327
NAVAL HISTORY 131938 F4427
NAVAL MEMBERS OF THE HILL'S FAMILY 1760-1830 133620 F1854
NAVAL RECORDS MOSTLY HELD AT KEW/PRO 158593 F555
NURSE EDITH CAVELL (1865-1915) 176591 F211
NURSING HISTORY 160504 F4634
OCCUPATIONS (SEE FORM) 133639 F3969
OLD COINS (BRITISH & FORIEGN) 174815 F1316
OLD HAND & DIAMOND INN COEDWAY SHREWSBURY 139203 F4127
ORIGINAL PEARLY KINGS & QUEENS GUILD 1952 102717 F1984
OYSTER FISHERY INDUSTRY 125075 F5968
PEOPLE WHO WORKED AT CASTLE ASHBY AND COMPTON WYNYATES BETWEEN 1894 AND 1914 143715 F4776
PILGRIM/PURITON EMIGRATION TO NEW ENGLAND 1600-1640 154296 F1809
PIPE MAKERS 142018 F2284
PLACE NAMES AND WELSH LANGUAGE IN RADNORSHIRE AREA 132217 F5676
PLACE NAMES OR LOCATIONS WHICH INCLUDE 'MARSDEN' 145114 F4486
PLACENAMES INCORPORATING COLEY 114758 F3150
PLAIN AND DECORATIVE PLASTERWORK 162868 F1364
POOR LAW MIGRATION 105848 F5923
PORTSMOUTH LOCAL HISTORY 170968 F1175
PUBLICANS AND INNKEEPERS OF SLEAFORD LINCS 102296 F344
QUAKERS AND HORTICULTURAL BUSINESS - STOKE NEWINGTON 18TH AND 19TH CENTURIES 165719 F5868
RAF INDEX & RESEARCH 177628 F9
RAILWAY & PUBLIC WORKS CONTRACTORS 165115 F439
RAILWAYS AND TRAMWAYS 168017 F4192
RARE CHRISTIAN NAMES 131288 F2672
RECONSTRUCTIONS OF FAMILY TREES (FROM TRANSCRIPTS) FOR FOXTON CAMBRIDGE 137405 F4774
REGENCY COACH BUILDERS 160504 F4634
RESEARCHING FAMILIES INVOLVED IN COPPER INDUSTRY AROUND 1750 148415 F5271
RESEARCHING THE ANCESTRY OF ACTOR PETER DUEL 132179 F2961
REVD RICHARD HUME LANCASTER 1772-1853 103942 F3524
ROCKING HORSE MANUFACTURERS 100897 F3319
ROMANO-BRITISH MOSAICS 124974 F748
ROYAL ANCESTRY OF SIR RICHARD DE LA BERE OF KENNERSLEY 124974 F748
ROYAL NAVAL AIR SERIVCE SUBMARINES 1914-1920 162329 F4811
ROYAL NAVAL RECORDS 138983 F5383
SAILING SHIP THE BRILLIANT LEFT TOBERMORY MULL SCOTLAND 1837-1838 FOR AUSTRALIA 139203 F4127
SCOTTISH MIGRATION FROM TINGWALL SHETLAND ISLES TO AUSTRALIA AND NEW ZEALAND 139203 F4127
SETTLEMENT RECORDS OF WORCESTERSHIRE 123331 F5851
SHIPBUILDING BY HILL'S OF SANDWICH KENT 1750-1814 133620 F1854
SHROPSHIRE BURIAL INDEX 138487 F423
SITUATION IN SHEFFIELD IN 1800'S 128031 F5409
SLAIDBURN MANOR COURT ROLLS (YORKSHIRE) 166081 F4529
SOUTH AFRICA RESEARCH 130230 F1770
SOUTH SHIELDS FOOTBALL CLUB 110671 F5286
SOUTH SHIELDS SHIP YARDS 1790-1890 110671 F5286
ST JOHN AMBULANCE 164720 F3186
ST VINCENT & TRINIDAD WEST INDIES 141739 F4115
STEAN(E) ENTRIES FROM RUGBY ADVERTISER 1850-1980 166707 F3474
STEAN(E) FROM HARBRO' MAGNA PR'S AND BTS FROM 1500 166707 F3474
STUDY OF BIBLE CHRISTIAN MISSIONARY WORK ENGLAND TO CANADA AND WISCONSIN USA 1840 TO 1882 121932 F5179
SUBMARINE THETIS 1939-1940 177199 F5976
SUBSIDY ROLLS AND LAND TAXES RELATING TO HUNTS 166413 F2004
SUSIE COOPER POTTERY 141739 F4115
TANNERS (LEATHERMAKERS) INDEX (ENGLAND 1500+) 169323 F3877
THAMES FISHERMEN AND WATERMEN 1550-1850 162051 F1891
THAMES LIGHTERMEN 105848 F5923
THE GREAT POACHING AFFRAY AT BERKELEY (COTGROVE WOOD) 18/19 JANUARY 1816 124982 F1179
THE POTTERS OF STOCK AND BUTTSBURY ESSEX 1480-1745 105619 F462
TOBACCO PIPE MAKERS 142018 F2284
TOTENKOPFVERBANDE 1925-1945 177199 F5976
TRANSCRIBING MANORIAL COURT ROLLS FROM LATIN 166081 F4529
TRINITY HOUSE PILOTS FROM GRAVESEND UP TO LONDON BRIDGE 120057 F4081
TURNPIKE TOLL COLLECTORS 158747 F347
VILLAGE HISTORY OF WANTAGE/ABINGDON AREA 141321 F5263
VOLUNTEER YEOMANRY CAVALRY TROOPS IN BRK'S 1794-1828 161799 F3783
VULCAN MOTOR CAR COMPANY 1901-1930'S 134864 F65
WALKER/UNWIN NAMES USED TOGETHER OR AT DIFFERENT TIMES 105449 F2495
WARLAND PRISON RECORDS OR DEPORTATIONS 173746 F5199
WARLAND'S IN THE FORCES 1600-1950 173746 F5199
WILLANS JAMES 300 YEARS ON 157139 F3469
WINDMILLS OF SUSSEX AND SURREY 103853 F6043
WOLVERTON RAILWAY WORKS 1880-1920 153818 F6095
WOMBWELLS CIRCUS AND BOSTOCK WOMBWELL CIRCUS 178217 F704
WOODMEN/HURDLEMAKERS OF KIRTLING 127477 F5798
WOODWORKING PLANES 173657 F1584
WORKS OF ANDREW CURRIE SCULPTOR 1812-1891 127434 F2461
YORKSHIRE CLAY TABACCO PIPE MAKERS 109630 F5739

Let us know of your Special Studies, and any Special Interests you have. We would particularly like to hear of unusual sources that may be of use to the Family Historian. So why not write today.

INDEX TO MAIDEN NAMES
Found in Section D

ELSOM	115878
ELSON	138312
EMM	112747
EPLETT	178845
EUREN	138614
EVANS	111007
EVANS	147885
EVANS	157147
EVERITT	115193
EWART	171034
FAIRALL	167061
FAIRBAIRN	144347
FANTHAM	133515
FARMER	112143
FARR	155942
FENNELL	163155
FERN	131687
FERRIDGE	112569
FERRY	176257
FIDDES	135356
FIELD	119237
FILEWOOD	139505
FINCH	152234
FINLAYSON	167428
FINLINSON	155969
FISH	155330
FISHER	117560
FISHER	172529
FISKE	126292
FITTON	110523
FITZJAMES	110183
FLACK	161071
FLANDERS	129364
FLASHMAN	139335
FLAVELL	157155
FLEMING	111376
FLETCHER	135003
FLETCHER	144223
FLOYD	154342
FOOTE	158674
FORD	148016
FORTIER	117455
FOSTER	104949
FOSTER	112941
FOTHERBY	163015
FRADD	156523
FRAYNE	119377
FREARSON	160806
FREELAND	142174
FREEMAN	143278
FREEMAN	149969
FREETH	143324
FROGGATT	117900
FRYER	173673
FURZE	120030
FYLES	141615
GALLOWAY	173096
GARDENER	109975
GARLAND	147079
GARNETT	127205
GARRAN	114669
GATES	133221
GAUGHT	168254
GELEIT	108391
GEORGE	131563
GERMAN	117609
GIBBONS	176532
GIBSON	121150
GIBSON	159379
GILDER	165298
GILL	173770
GLEDHILL	110345
GLENISTER	169625
GLOVER	105155
GLOVER	109363
GLOVER	113999
GOAD	135127
GODDEN	137952
GODFREY	108189
GODFREY	172154
GODSON	120162
GOLDRING	106666
GOLDSBURY	129348
GOLLINGS	118621
GOODE	139408
GOODSELL-WELLER	173150
GORING	177423
GOUDIE	179558
GRAHAM	135151
GRAHAM	170038
GRANT	123749
GRAY	130605
GREAVES	138517
GREEN	138983
GREEN	177709
GREENWOOD	175900
GREGORY	112852
GREGORY	127825
GREGORY	164070
GRELLIS	120057
GRIFFIN	118494
GRIFFIN	175161
GRIFFITHS	144614
GRIFFITHS	151041
GRIFFITHS	176974
GROENING	172243
GUIVER	162345
GULLICK	174963
GUMBLEY	130311
GUY	119040
HABGOOD	123358
HACKLEY	172987
HADDINGTON	161640
HAIGH	115258
HAILE	140813
HALE	165824
HALES	162388
HALL	109819
HALL	116246
HALL	159492
HALLS	154814
HAMILTON	117889
HAMILTON	179183
HAMLIN	144398
HAMMETT	104477
HAMMON	135577
HANBY	178136
HANCOCK	119296
HANCOCK	119636
HANCOCK	136778
HANCOCK	173886
HANKEY	154563
HANSON	104396
HARDING	116076
HARDWICK	138541
HARDY	137626
HARGRAVE	161586
HARGREAVES	147753
HARGREAVES	178241
HARLEY BROWN	164798
HARMAN	153982
HARRIES	142034
HARRIGAN	120332
HARRINGTON	138940
HARRIS	111031
HARRIS	117730
HARRIS	123773
HARRISON	131008
HARRISON	145084
HARRISON	163910
HARRISS	142484
HART	111198
HART	158917
HARVEY	108030
HARVEY	131660
HARVEY	143898
HARVEY	149314
HARVEY	157848
HARVEY	170968
HARWOOD	119512
HASELL	153516
HAWKINS	104922
HEATH	152129
HEATH	155306
HEATH	158941
HENDERSON	149403
HENLEY	104884
HENRY	140473
HENSON	124613
HERBERT	110019
HERBERT	152269
HERRATY	122114
HERRING	165891
HIBBERT	124060
HIBBS	118559
HICKEY	175722
HICKLIN	137235
HICKLING	142085
HICKS	101168
HIDSON	172170
HILL	134619
HILL	160997
HILL	175358
HINCHLIFFE	109509
HIND	136565
HINTON	148652
HINTON	168785
HOCHHEIMER	136255
HOCKEY	149357
HOCKLEY	114618
HODGE	117072
HODGES	143529
HODGSON	125199
HOLLAND	166138
HOLLEY	176869
HOLLINGSWORTH	167940
HOLLOWAY	120472
HOLLOWAY	177989
HOLMES	163783
HOLMES	174335
HOLSETH	137723
HOLT	120952
HOLT	155349
HOMER	158518
HOODLESS	107441
HOOKER	103705
HOOPER	138290
HOOPER	146943
HORNE	108952
HORNE	139165
HORSFALL	124389
HORSWILL	155128
HOWARD	117854
HOWAT	144010
HOWLETT	129763
HOYE	144150
HUBBALL	176052
HUBERT	142506
HUCKSTEPP	108502
HUDDLESTONE	163376
HUDSON	141321
HUDSON	150290
HUGGETT	128724
HUGHES	131741
HUGHES	150681
HUGHES	164755
HULL	109983
HULME	149373
HUMMERSTONE	115096
HUMPHREYS	161306
HUNT	174114
HUNTER	122394
HUTCHINSON	132349
HUTCHINSON	147176
HUTTON	145955
HYDE	122378
INGLES	130583
IRVING	147702
IRWIN	173045
ISAAC	131962
ISON	131571
IVERSON	103233
JACK	164097
JACKS	176583
JACKSON	101893
JACKSON	124400
JACKSON	178616
JAMES	102830
JAMES	145882
JAMES	145904
JAMES	178195
JARVIS	117676
JARVIS	120588
JASPER	131849
JELF	177113
JENKINS	110027
JERAM	160865
JILLOTT	171395
JOHNSON	104671
JOHNSON	132764
JOHNSON	137561
JOHNSON	163244
JOHNSTON	162426
JOLIN	153389
JONES	110906
JONES	138207
JONES	140759
JONES	158496
JONES	158925
JONES	164984
JONES	174475
JONES	176729
JOSLIN	107794
JUBY	171859
KAY	110663
KAY	174998
KEECH	119911
KEEN	113638
KELLY	118362
KELLY	140767
KELSALL	121665
KEMP	166642
KENNEDY	126985
KERGER	132136
KERR	138894
KETTERIDGE	148725
KIDDLE	179590
KILLICK	106534
KINGTON	177415
KINMONTH	138053
KINNISH	123471
KIRKLAND	111694
KIRKWOOD	166286
KNIGHT	109223
KNIGHT	148687
KNOTT	107190
KNOWLES	139602
KNOWLES	149799
LAMB	139874
LAMLEY	137812
LANDERS	124311
LANE	117641
LANE	131369
LANE	170593
LAURIE	166863
LAVER	172553
LAWN	130176
LAWRY	136999
LAZENBY	138576
LEACH	133108
LEAROYD	145912
LEDGER	148431
LEECH	171514
LEGG	112712
LEVETT	117862
LEWIS	172006
LEYLAND	173711
LIDDALL	146633
LINDEN	127698
LINE	127353
LINES	112925
LINFOOT	159336
LINGARD	103004
LINGARD	157902
LINNETT	133248
LINNEY	170569
LINSLEY	122440
LINSTEAD	132926
LIPPETT	123072
LITTLEMORE	132314
LITTLEWOOD	153109
LIVERMORE	125024
LLOYD	167045
LOCK	126071
LOCKER	157740
LONGLAND	113433
LONGLAND	166502
LOONEY	116572
LORD	157449
LORD	163953
LORENZ	149098
LOVETT	108103
LOWRIE	122882
LUKE	117927
LUKE	150975
MACDONALD	142751
MACDONALD	146366
MACKNIGHT	157988
MACKRILL	174688
MADDEN	149918
MADDEVER	160423
MADDISON	145769

Surname	Number
MAINNIE	136921
MALSON	119695
MANGAN	112844
MANN	119059
MANN	139025
MARKS	119180
MARRIOTT	131024
MARSDEN	112364
MARSDEN	119997
MARSHALL	100757
MARSHALL	120650
MARSHALL	121355
MARTEN	127183
MARTIN	101060
MARTIN	104744
MARTIN	123706
MARWOOD	151211
MASKELL	164305
MATHIESON	159921
MAULE	177059
MAXFIELD	102350
MAY	105775
MAY	119954
MAYNARD	167517
MAYSON	153990
MCALPIN	161152
MCARTHUR	173738
MCCARTHY	162442
MCEVOY	115533
MCGOUGH	141879
MCGRATH	164062
MCINTOSH	169846
MCINTYRE	146870
MCKENNA	157112
MCNEILLY	172111
MEALING	147907
MEREDITH	145319
MERREDEW	134481
MERRICK	109177
MERRING	137707
METCALFE	100196
MEYER	161675
MIDGLEY	114464
MILES	106755
MILLER	136026
MILLS	102326
MINIHAN	160741
MOCKRIDGE	113069
MOCKRIDGE	124990
MOIR	106968
MOLE	152080
MOMBRUN	148067
MOMSEN	157732
MOON	132586
MOORE	121290
MOORE	159239
MOORE	175056
MOORE	178551
MOORE	178985
MORE	127647
MORGAN	116408
MORGAN	139777
MORRELL	164577
MORRIS	173851
MORTON	131512
MOSS	136905
MOULDEY	108960
MOWATT	174955
MUCKETT	170542
MULLISS	116173
MURGESS	111406
MUSGRAVE	151947
MUTUM	126462
NASH	106380
NAUGLE	144363
NAYLOR	138355
NEAL	174807
NEALE	102253
NEIL	127418
NETCOTT	166553
NEVILLE	164704
NEWDICK	100013
NEWELL	133035
NEWING	102210
NEWMAN	109215
NEWNS	121835
NEWTON	124788
NEWTON	133957
NEWTON	156116
NICHOLS	107158
NICHOLS	118303
NICHOLSON	139289
NIXON	124168
NORTON	102229
NORTON	177237
O'CONNELL	178144
O'CONNOR	125113
O'DONNELL	153214
O'DONNELL	175595
O'KEEFE	141909
O'MARA	158747
OATES	163147
OCKENDEN	141704
OCLEE	126128
OLIVER	158305
ONIONE	123013
ORVIS	154288
OSBORNE	174068
OTTY	143588
OUGH	140163
OVERTON	177873
OWEN	112321
OWENS	114456
OWENS	127116
OXLEY	165417
OXSPRING	122246
PALMER	141267
PAPWORTH	164933
PARKER	145041
PARKES	123137
PARKINSON	109630
PARNELL	120618
PARRY	138401
PARSONS	136581
PASSEY	161977
PASSMORE	141690
PATFIELD	158151
PATON	144088
PATTERSON	152390
PATY	166499
PAVELEY	127272
PAVEY	132187
PAYNE	167231
PEACHMENT	138002
PEARCE	107662
PEARMAIN	137324
PEARS	111457
PEARSON	110507
PEARSON	147788
PEATFIELD	124001
PEGGY	155608
PELLS	162647
PEMBERTON	119075
PENDLEBURY	119822
PENNINGTON	132683
PENNINGTON	146919
PENNY	171247
PERCIVAL	147184
PERKINS	104515
PERRIN	111104
PERRY	163279
PETERS	129305
PEYTON	106003
PIERPOINT	179647
PIKE	113891
PILLER	116998
PILLINGER	142425
PINDER	133728
PLANT	137979
PLUMB	136808
POPE	120723
PORRITT	103187
PORT	154687
PORTEOUS	141895
PORTER	131970
PORTER	147400
PORTSMOUTH	170860
POTTS	147346
POWELL	101524
POWER	139203
POWER	165123
PRANGNELL	123552
PRETLOVE	108847
PRICE	149586
PRICE	160873
PRIDDEY	131229
PRING	168033
PRIOR	173703
PRYOR	162736
PUDNEY	142972
PULLEN	149713
PURCHALL	164291
PURKIS	100749
RACINE	172022
RADGE	125571
RAISTRICK	171743
RANCE	164216
RANDLE	125938
RATCLIFF	138673
RAVEN	102520
RAVEN	127523
RAVENSDALE	105791
RAWNSLEY	112267
READ	160911
REDDICK	133590
REDITT	174920
REED	134503
REED	156671
REES	123161
REES	169145
REEVE	149705
RELF	125776
RENDALL	153702
RENWICK	115061
REVELL	118370
REVILL	127728
REYNOLDS	111414
REYNOLDS	135461
RHODES	149942
RICE	101672
RICHARDS	173266
RICHARDSON	115223
RICHARDSON	160075
RICHARDSON	167444
RICHES	102288
RICHMOND	165603
RIDGE	107670
RIGDEN	107948
RIGGS	116815
RILEY	125717
RIMMER	114995
RINGER	105066
RINGWOOD	147230
ROBERTON	104035
ROBERTS	125814
ROBERTS	156442
ROBERTS	166073
ROBERTS	177067
ROBERTSON	157708
ROBSON	150894
ROFFEY	175293
ROGERS	143359
ROGERS	164607
ROLLAND	115266
ROPER	163929
ROSE	152579
ROTH	177466
ROTHERHAM	120383
ROW	116882
ROWBOTTOM	153346
ROWE	116092
ROYLE	115932
ROYLE	155454
RUBERY	141224
RUDDICK	167835
RUMENS	113824
RUNAGALL	150649
RUNDLE	168173
RUSHBY	138509
RUSSELL	125431
RUSSELL	153591
RUSSELL	175749
RUSSELL-LILLEY	139998
RUTHVEN	159034
RYDER	150118
SADLER	118699
SAMPSON	101826
SANDERS	170976
SANDERSON	129593
SANDERSON	152722
SANFORD	144630
SARSFIELD	128945
SAWYER	111546
SCHLAMP	169935
SCHNEIDER	157511
SCHOFIELD	147281
SCOTNEY	151270
SCOTT	178896
SCREETON	176133
SEAR	144851
SECCOMBE	129712
SEDGMAN	114480
SELLAR	166049
SENIOR	116327
SETH	174459
SHACKLOCK	178411
SHARPE	145823
SHAW	100579
SHAW	125512
SHAW	126411
SHAW	169900
SHEARMUR	145874
SHELDON	167355
SHEPPARD	149632
SHEPPARD	173371
SHIELD	163791
SHIPPEN	161594
SHURLOCK	159581
SIDERY	171506
SIDWELL	126950
SILK	174343
SILLERS	124699
SILVESTER	116653
SIMMONS	161667
SIMPSON	108154
SIMS	142530
SIMS	159719
SINDEN	138045
SINGER	165077
SKUSE	153222
SLEATH	169870
SMART	118877
SMART	128244
SMELT	106550
SMITH	103608
SMITH	110132
SMITH	117366
SMITH	124516
SMITH	131768
SMITH	139904
SMITH	147761
SMITH	158461
SMITH	169889
SMITH	171573
SMITH	177040
SMITTEN	140031
SMOKER	106151
SMURTHWAITE	125946
SOFTLEY	124346
SONE	116955
SORE	150398
SPARRY	155071
SPEAR	157813
SPEAR	168734
SPEECHLEY	136212
SPEECHLY	107344
SPENCE	165018
SPENCER	151580
SPIVEY	173185
SPONDER	151831
SPRENGER	121681
SPRINGATE	177261
SPRINGINGS	125172
STAFFORD	109576
STAMPER	163589
STANSFIELD	162264
STEEDMAN	123307
STEER	135607
STEERS	130230
STEVENS	156698
STEVENSON	122416
STEVENSON	143855
STOCKDALE	167312
STOKER	138266
STOKES	114782
STONEHOUSE	146706
STONES	117145
STRAITH	121126
STRANGE	130958
STRANGEWAYS	109797
STREATFIELD	116297
STREET	158453

SUMNER	163422
SUNDERLAND	170348
SUTHERLAND	141739
SWAFFIELD	104310
SWAFFIELD	140511
SWALES	103845
SYLVESTER	154806
SYMONDS	114642
TAIT	128406
TALLIS	151475
TAYLOR	149004
TAYLOR	161772
TAYLOR	162191
THAIN	126497
THOMAS	123110
THOMAS	158631
THOMPSON	115592
THOMPSON	150932
THOMPSON	155713
THOMPSON	178322
THORNER	154903
THORNLEY	167150
THORP	121584
TIPPING	134724
TIQUET	137960
TITT	165654
TODD	156418
TOGHILL	170879
TOLCHER	163406
TOMLINSON	131172
TOMS	145033
TOMSETT	163163
TOOGOOD	136964
TOWSE	174351
TOYNE	168149
TRAVERS	126616
TRAVESS	139823
TREBILCOCK	121398
TRENBATH	175331
TREWREN	146404
TROUGHTON	137154
TRUIN	166170
TRUMMEL	168297
TURLEY	154105
TURNBULL	129062
TURNBULL	135690
TURNBULL	169501
TURNER	150010
TWADDLE	178373
TWITCHIN	151408
TWYFORD	131334
TWYMAN	115517
UGLOW	118648
URCH	113670
UZZELL	161683
VERNON	150614
VERRALL	124044
VICKERS	140058
VINES	111554
VINEY	119776
VIPAN	177644
WADDELOW	168939
WADDINGTON	132810
WADE	110477
WADE	147060
WADHAM	116580
WALDEGRAVE	108553
WALES	177296
WALKER	100056
WALKER	115525
WALKER	119555
WALKER	122769
WALKER	139661
WALKER	142883
WALKER	168637
WALKER	175714
WALKEY	173991
WALL	139173
WALL	146994
WALLACE	125148
WALLE	155691
WALLWORK	151432
WARD	101923
WARD	103314
WARD	154741
WARNE	172693
WARNER	101656
WARREN	147044
WARRINGTON	115355
WATKINS	105457
WATKINS	171980
WATSON	100528
WATSON	131709
WAUD	164143
WEBB	102989
WEBB	105996
WEBBER	148814
WEBSTER	142069
WEDD	174696
WEEDON	108200
WEISS	116734
WELCH	171581
WELLER	168890
WENTWORTH	172723
WEST	129992
WESTON	174793
WEYMOUTH	104930
WHALLEY	156086
WHEATLEY	175544
WHEELER	145300
WHITAKER	110914
WHITAKER	143243
WHITE	115436
WHITE	116238
WHITE	145270
WHITE	151254
WHITEHEAD	107654
WHITEHEAD	161551
WHITTINGTON	171468
WHITTON	152730
WHITWORTH	141046
WILBY	153737
WILCOX	103659
WILCOXON	134716
WILLCOX-JONES	112976
WILLIAMS	110701
WILLIAMS	118230
WILLIAMS	131733
WILLIAMS	137219
WILLIAMS	148504
WILLIS	165247
WILSON	111708
WILSON	121339
WILSON	124095
WILSON	134732
WILSON	153680
WILSON	166960
WILSON	175404
WILTSHIRE	111155
WIMPENNY	133760
WITTS	164720
WOFFINDIN	170429
WOOD	121541
WOOD	175153
WOODCOCK	173843
WOODGER	122068
WOODHAMS	142999
WOODING	131725
WOODLING	156884
WOOLMER	142514
WOOTTON	129046
WORMALD	154296
WORSNOP	131474
WRATH	105643
WREN	113123
WREN	159042
WRIGGLESWORTH	176435
WRIGHT	144452
WRIGHT	152633
WRIGHT	153885
WRIGHT	158011
WRIGHT	166383
WYLIE	123633
YATES	173649
YOUNG	116637
YULE	157333

INDEX TO
ONE NAME STUDIES

Found in Section C.

A'BEAR	124974
ACRES	100544
ADDIS	100323
ADLAM	100366
ADRIAN	100374
AGAR	100404
AGUTTER	100420
AIRNS	109924
AISH	101974
AISLABY	141844
ALABASTER	130087
ALAIS	158437
ALBAN	160857
ALDERDICE	139726
ALDERDICE	139734
ALDERSLEY	108332
ALDERSON	100625
ALDERSON	100633
ALEFOUNDER	100706
ALLABY	100781
ALLAKER	134147
ALLBERRY	100870
ALLCARD	155861
ALLISTONE	101117
ALLMARK	169072
ALLSOP	173967
ALVEY	101206
AMANET	101222
AMBRIDGE	106925
AMPHLETT	112151
AMSDEN	101338
AMY	101346
ANGEL	101516
ANNETT	121371
ANNING	145270
ANSCOMB	137243
ANSTIS	101591
APPLEBY	168653
APTHORP	101664
ARCH	101680
ARGENT	118796
ARKLE	101710
ARKWRIGHT	101729
ARMIN	101753
ARNISON	101850
ASH	101974
ASHBRIDGE	101982
ASHBY	110698
ASHE	102032
ASHFIELD	102040
ASHMOLE	111147
ASHWORTH	102121
ASKEY	134414
ASLETT	102156
ASPELING	102180
ASTRIDGE	176850
ATTREE	102423
ATTRILL	144118
ATTWELL	144959
ATTWOOLL	102458
ATYED	102474
AUSTERBERRY	102547
AVANN	161993
AVENS	102652
AVIS	158100
AYLWIN	143995
AYTON	102725
BABB	114677
BABER	102776
BABER	118249
BADBY	102792
BADGERS	159026
BADHAM	102822
BAIGENT	102857
BAKES	103276
BALCHIN	128856
BALDWINSON	113115
BALL	144959
BALLARD	103500
BALM	103519
BANGAY	103594
BANGS	103608
BANHAM	150207
BANKS	157449
BANWELL	103675
BARCHARD	100781
BARDSLEY	103780
BARLEY	103861
BARNELL	119814
BARNHURST	104019
BARRATT	143839
BARRETT	104116
BARROW	104175
BASKER	104345
BASLINGTON	104388
BASSANO	146641
BASTARD	161209
BATH	104558
BATTEN	104582
BATTINSON	165190
BATY	155284
BAUGH	125989
BAUGHEN	104639
BAZZONE	104787
BEAMISH	104833
BEARSBY	158704
BEART	100889
BEATSON	104906
BECKERLEG	105082
BECKHAM	105112
BEDENHAM	105147
BEDSER	105244
BEDWARD	104493
BEECHENO	150878
BEECHER	177148
BELAM	105333
BELANEY	148970
BELBIN	105341
BELCHER	105368
BELL	105430
BELTZUNG	105570
BENBOW	105589
BENDING	105597
BENIANS	105619
BENNEWITH	105783
BENTING	107077
BEQUETTE	105104
BERESFORD	105880
BERJEW	122041
BESSANT	177083
BETHEL	106100
BETSER	106119
BETTINSON	106135
BETTS	106151
BEVERLEY	104647
BEVIS	106224
BEWICK	130605
BEWSHER	160512
BIBLE	122025
BIDDULPH	106348
BIDWELL	106364
BILLINGS	106453
BILLYARD	125644
BIRCHENOUGH	106615
BIRDSALL	171166
BIRKBECK	106674
BIRTWHISTLE	106739
BISSMIRE	170364
BIX	118222
BLACK	102180
BLAKE	107107
BLANN	125911
BLEAKLEY	129941
BLEEK	107263
BLENCOWE	120936
BLENCOWES	173436
BLIGH	107336
BLISS	107387
BLOCK	107409
BLOMFIELD	167185
BOAG	127906
BOBBY	126004
BODFISH	107603
BODIMEADE	147958
BODMAN	107611
BOFF	107646
BOGG	115568
BOLSOVER	165964
BONEHAM	169196
BONIFACE	107808
BONSER	122173
BONTOUX	107867
BOOTH	107921
BORRELL	177598
BORROR	139246
BOTTERILL	108073
BOTTLE	108081
BOURREE	108170
BOUSFIELD	108235
BOUTAL	108243
BOVINDON	158100
BOWDLER	108294

BOWN	143839	CARPENTER	108219	CRAFER	116629	DUDGEON	108820
BOWYER	108499	CARSLAKE	174904	CRAM	116718	DUFALL	120960
BOYD	108545	CARVETH	140732	CRAMOND	179655	DUFF	113077
BOYES	108626	CASBOLT	112488	CRANFIELD	116742	DUFTON	170267
BOYLETT	108650	CASLAKE	125040	CRASKE	139769	DUGMORE	141763
BRACKPOOL	108707	CASTLING	137871	CRAWFORD	175692	DUJARDIN	121029
BRADLAUGHE	136832	CAVE	112682	CREE	165964	DUMPER	121088
BRAMMAGE	109231	CAVE	112690	CREPIN	129755	DUNBAR	112984
BRASHEAR	166014	CAVEEN	153982	CRESPEL	154067	DUNCALF	114561
BRASS	109037	CAVNETT	136549	CREWS	116890	DUNMAN	177857
BRATLEY	109916	CAWTE	112720	CRIPPEN	116971	DUNMORE	121266
BRECKON	101443	CAWTHORNE	160679	CROASDALE	173126	DUNMOW	100250
BREWARD	109185	CESAR	112755	CROCOMBE	117056	DUNNICLIFFE	121347
BREWIN	109231	CESSFORD	130877	CROSSER	116068	DUNSTALL	121371
BREYMAYER	141135	CHADDERDON	112763	CROSSKILL	148393	DURBRIDGE	174637
BRICKETT	113468	CHADWICK	112798	CROWFORD	116785	DURHAM	121479
BRIMSON	109371	CHADWICK	112801	CROWMEADOW	154768	DURKEE	129674
BRINGINSHAW	161934	CHAFFIN	120642	CRUDDINGTON	134635	DUXBURY	121517
BRINGLOW	117757	CHAMP	161454	CRUDGE	149888	DYALL	155284
BRISON	109401	CHANDLER	112917	CRUTTENDEN	117420	EACHUS	121649
BROADY	132179	CHAPRONIERE	134740	CRUXTON	117439	EAGLES	121738
BROATCH	109541	CHARLETON	113190	CUFFE	117498	EARLAND	121789
BROMELL	109592	CHATFIELD	113255	CUFLEY	117501	EARWICKER	121797
BROOKBANK	109665	CHEGWYN	112399	CULLING	117587	EASEY	165034
BROOKING	109711	CHEKE	113271	CULVERHOUSE	151750	EAST	121800
BROUGHAM	166421	CHESSUM	130729	CURME	164100	EASTERLING	121843
BROWHAM	179450	CHILTON	113379	CUTLACK	146641	EASTLAKE	158321
BROXTON	151750	CHIPPENDALE	151734	CUTTEN	117919	EATWELL	176214
BRUNDISH	110302	CHISLETT	113409	CUZNER	123293	EBBOTT	121932
BRUTON	110337	CHOICE	163325	DACRE	157074	ECCLESHALL	105260
BRYANT	100382	CHOICE	163333	DADLEY	115487	EDGAR	147168
BRYANT	160555	CHOWINGS	113468	DAGWORTHY	163481	EDGCOMBE	168882
BUCHANAN	148466	CHRISTMAS	113506	DALLISON	118087	EDKINS	170658
BUDWORTH	110620	CHURCH	113522	DALRYMPLE	118109	EDMANS	121975
BUIST	110655	CHURCHWARD	113549	DALTON	118125	EDMONDS	159085
BUNDOCK	114073	CLAPP	135429	DAMEREL	154148	EDNAY	122009
BUNGAY	110744	CLARICOATES	131520	DANGERFIELD	170151	EELES	144770
BUNNETT	110760	CLASPER	113980	DANKS	118257	EGAN	122289
BUNNEY	110779	CLAUGHTON	113921	DARTNELL	113468	EGERTON	122300
BUNNING	110787	CLAXTON	113948	DARVALL	118338	EINON	160857
BUNTING	110809	CLAYBURN	113980	DASHWOOD	113468	ELAM	150827
BUNYAN	110825	CLEGG	108294	DAVISON	118907	ELEY	122408
BURDEKIN	161462	CLEMETT	114103	DAVOREN	174637	ELLA	122432
BURDGE	110876	CLIFFORD	114138	DAYMAN	119083	ELLINGWORTH	112003
BURDICK	150134	CLIVES	114197	DE VILLE	119172	ELSEGOOD	122750
BURGIS	143510	CLOTHIER	114200	DEARLE	164380	ELSLEY	134961
BURGOYNE	110973	CLUB	101109	DEBNEY	119288	ELVE	179124
BURGUM	110981	COARE	114251	DELICATE	170755	ELVISH	151750
BURKIN	177857	COATH	114278	DELLER	119350	EMERY	122831
BURNETT	111015	COBBETT	114308	DENDLE	119393	ENGERT	122866
BURNISTON	111058	COBBING	114324	DENLEY	103993	ENIFFER	122874
BURREE	111120	COBELDICK	114332	DENNING	119415	ENSTONE	122890
BURVILLE	111244	COCKBURN	114375	DENNIS	119466	EPLETT	178845
BUSHBY	111309	COCKINGS	114391	DENNISTON	119482	ERWIN	136603
BUTLAND	174327	CODD	114421	DENNY	119490	ESSERY	122971
BUTLER	111392	CODGBROOK	100927	DERHAM	169684	ESSLEMONT	122998
BUTLIN	100323	COGHILL	114510	DERUSETT	119547	ETHERIDGE	111414
BUTTERWORTH	100005	COKER	105333	DEVALL	119598	EUSTACE	123056
BUTTERWORTH	111481	COLAM	114537	DEVITT	119601	EVINGTON	123366
BUTTRESS	111473	COLEGATE	128767	DEVON	153125	EWENS	123382
BYARD	136956	COLEMAN	134961	DEVONISH	119644	EXCEL	132144
BYETT	142158	COLFER	114766	DEVONSHIRE	158100	FABIAN	141712
CAINAN	118222	COLLIER	114839	DEWDER	155233	FAHERTY	123412
CAINS	111627	COLWELL	115053	DIBDEN	166774	FAIRCHILD	123447
CAKE	111635	CONDLIFFE	137669	DIBLEY	101559	FAIRFAX	123455
CAKEBREAD	111643	CONGREVE	132330	DIGGORY	119830	FAITHFULL	123498
CALBERSON	111651	CONQUEST	133841	DIGWEED	139947	FALL	123528
CALDCLEUGH	165506	COOKSEY	115363	DILNOT	123137	FALLA	123536
CALL	111716	COOKSON	115398	DINWOODIE	119946	FALLOWS	123544
CALLINGHAM	112828	COOL	109789	DISS	119989	FANCOURT	144436
CAMMISH	111872	COOPS	115657	DITZEL	167517	FARMERY	149101
CAMPER	111902	COOTER	115665	DOBSON	120111	FARNOL	101052
CAMPION	111910	COPPARD	115754	DOBSON	120138	FARRANT	123684
CAMPLEJOHN	161616	COPSEY	115800	DOCKREE	112542	FARRANT	123692
CANFANY	110086	CORBET	151572	DOHERTY	120421	FARRELL	124850
CANFIELD	145599	CORBIN	115827	DOLLING	101559	FARTHING	124486
CANNADINE	156809	CORBY	115851	DONOGHUE	151971	FAUTLEY	123757
CANNELL	109924	CORFIELD	115916	DOO	120324	FAWLK	147834
CANSELL	107328	CORNFORD	139653	DOREY	100234	FEAKES	123781
CANSICK	151149	CORNISH	115991	DORLING	132861	FEAVER	137766
CANTON	160857	CORSON	115029	DORRELL	120391	FELL	123846
CANTRILL	112003	COTGROVE	134333	DOUBT	120413	FELTHAM	123870
CAPON	112011	COTTEE	111317	DOUGHTY	120448	FENBY	123897
CAPPS	127515	COTTON	116130	DOUST	120480	FENN	123927
CARCAS	112054	COUTTS	116262	DOWSE	175129	FENNER	123935
CARDOZA	112070	COX	116491	DRAPER	120693	FERDINANDO	123994
CAREW	159190	COZENS	116564	DRYHURST	120847	FERRETT	129798
CARMICHAEL	108383	CRABBE	116599	DUCKETT	120898	FIANDER	120766

Surname	Number
FICE	124141
FICKLIN	130524
FIDDES	135356
FIELDEN	124192
FIELDSEND	177024
FILBY	124222
FINCHER	124230
FINDON	124249
FINLINSON	155969
FISHENDEN	158097
FISK	124478
FITNESS	124494
FITZJOHN	168939
FLEAR	175501
FLINT	123196
FLINTHAM	124680
FLOOD	124729
FOINQUINOS	164089
FORDHAM	125067
FOREMAN	125075
FORRESTER	125156
FORRYAN	125164
FOSBROKE	109428
FOVARGUE	128570
FRAMPTON	125474
FREATHY	170763
FREE	103209
FRESHNEY	108634
FRISON	125849
FROGGATT	123528
FROST	125873
FRYATT	155187
FUDGE	120766
FULTON	126039
FULTON	148407
FUNNELL	161233
FUTCHER	171352
GABB	126101
GAMBIER	126284
GANDER	126314
GANN	126349
GARNSWORTHY	127574
GARVIN	126578
GASKING	126608
GATFIELD	126683
GATHERCOLE	126691
GEER	102504
GEESIN	126802
GELDER	126810
GELL	126829
GENT	126861
GILL	111430
GILLARD	127302
GILLBERRY	127310
GILLIATT	151823
GILLINGHAM	155829
GILSTON	113115
GIMBERT	127450
GIRDLESTONE	127485
GIRVAN	127507
GLANDER	112801
GLASCOCK	117102
GLASSON	115959
GLENISTER	169625
GLENISTERS	127620
GLIBBERY	127639
GODBER	127663
GODDARD	127671
GODDING	120006
GODSON	120162
GOGGIN	109614
GOLDER	127752
GOLDFINCH	178454
GOLDING	159611
GOMERSALL	127892
GOODALL	127922
GOODBODY	127930
GOODLIFFE	112003
GOODWORTH	128104
GORICK	110086
GORRIE	102695
GORSUCH	128198
GOSBY	143391
GOSDEN	128236
GOSLETT	175455
GOSNALD	165743
GOTT	128295
GOTTERSON	124338
GOTTS	128309
GOULTY	128392
GOURD	169447
GOWENLOCK	128422
GOWLETT	128430
GOYMER	155187
GRADDAGE	144991
GRAFHAM	147206
GRANNUM	128562
GREENWOOD	128953
GRIBBIN	129070
GRIER	129089
GRIGG	129259
GRIMSTEAD	129321
GRIMSTONE	145475
GRONOW	129402
GROSE	129445
GROTTICK	112801
GRUT	160105
GRUTCHEFIELD	129542
GRYLLS	129550
GUBBINS	129569
GUESS	129585
GUISELEY	129623
GULLICK	174963
GUMBLETON	175226
GUNSTONE	129690
GUNTHORPE	124222
GUYVER	129801
GYNES	129844
HACKSHALL	129887
HACKWOOD	139092
HADDRELL	129917
HADINGHAM	164585
HAFFNER	129968
HAILE	130001
HAILEY	130028
HALBROOK	130095
HALFYARD	130117
HALLAM	136425
HALLAS	130265
HALLETT	135100
HALLIDAY	130303
HALSE	130362
HALSTEAD	142182
HAMBROOK	100498
HAMMOND	130540
HANKINSON	130702
HANNAM	130761
HANSFORD	130834
HANSON	100382
HARBERTSON	130877
HARBRIDGE	126705
HARDISTY	160415
HARDWAY	127256
HARDWICK	138177
HARDWICK	138541
HARDWIDGE	130982
HARDY	176761
HARDYMAN	131040
HARINGTON	131288
HARMAN	131164
HARNEY	144002
HARNIMAN	131180
HARROWER	131644
HASSARD-SHORT	131938
HATCHELL	131962
HATSWELL	132012
HATT	132020
HAUNTON	132047
HAVELOCK	132063
HAVERS	132101
HAWKES	132160
HAWKYARD	166057
HAWTHORNE	169765
HAZELTON	110876
HEARDER	132527
HEATHER	132624
HEBDEN	132691
HECKS	164194
HEELIS	106631
HEGBIN	143510
HEMINGTON	132845
HEMS	104434
HENNEY	132969
HENNING	144959
HENRIQUES	112070
HERITAGE	133078
HERNIMAN	107034
HERRIDGE	133116
HERSANT	148369
HEUDEBOURCK	136670
HEWER	133140
HEXT	133191
HEXTER	133205
HIBERNIA	137006
HICKLIN	133299
HICKS	107409
HILBORNE	168866
HILDER	133485
HILLIKER	133612
HINWOOD	138908
HINXMAN	133744
HISCOCK	104000
HITCHON	133833
HOARE	157422
HOBLEY	133965
HOBSON	133981
HOCKING	166871
HOCKLESS	134066
HODGE	148695
HODGKINSON	134163
HODSDON	134228
HOGWOOD	128465
HOILE	134279
HOLAH	171352
HOLCROFT	173606
HOLDICH	134325
HOLDIP	134341
HOLLICK	134465
HOLLISTER	160334
HOLYER	134740
HONEYBALL	134791
HONEYCOMBE	166758
HONEYWOOD	127337
HONOUR	135658
HOOKWAY	134821
HOPPER	144517
HORSELL	135445
HORSUP	135097
HORSWILL	155128
HORTH	135119
HORTON	135135
HOSIE	137243
HOSKINS	135178
HOUCHELL	126616
HOUDE	135194
HOUSHAM	135267
HOVENDEN	117552
HOWE	179620
HUDDLESTONE	163376
HUDSWELL	106739
HUEGDON	138800
HUGGINS	135593
HUISH	135712
HULL	135739
HULLEY	135755
HULSTON	151750
HUNKIN	135852
HUNTINGFORD	146552
HURDEN	136123
HURST	136174
HUSTHWAITE	103721
HYLANDS	136344
HYNER	136352
INCH	136433
INGALL	136441
INGHAM	162159
INVERARITY	131539
IRELAND	137006
IRONSIDE	149403
ISARD	136638
ISGROVE	156272
ISHAM	144436
ISHERWOOD	136646
IVORY	136662
JACOB	136832
JARDINE	137065
JEACOCK	137189
JEAL	137197
JEE	137200
JEEVES	138460
JELLOWS	137251
JENNINGS	169633
JEPHCOTT	137464
JESSETT	124974
JOHNSON	137839
JOHNSTON	137928
JOPLING	157163
JOSLING	138665
JUDGES	138754
JUNIPER	138770
JUPP	113468
KASSELL	138843
KEARSEY	138908
KELMAN	139076
KEMP	139130
KEMPSHALL	125873
KENINGALE	166464
KERKHOFF	135704
KERNER	139327
KERSLAKE	139319
KERSLEY	139440
KESTERTON	139459
KETTER	139467
KIDDLE	179590
KIDNER	139556
KIDWELL	139564
KIELLOR	139572
KILDUFF	139610
KILDUFF	139629
KILLON	139653
KING	139742
KINGAN	139882
KINGSMILL	139939
KINVIG	140007
KIRCHER	140074
KITCAT	171441
KITCHENER	166758
KNIPE	112895
KYFFIN	140422
KYNE	121029
LABRAM	140457
LAFLIN	140538
LAILEY	102024
LAKER	140597
LAMACQ	140600
LAMPKYN	152595
LANDEG	140694
LANDON	110493
LANDRETH	152862
LANDRUM	159131
LANGHELT	177024
LANGMEAD	140848
LANKSHEAR	140899
LAPEYRE	108170
LARDEN	140961
LASHBROOK	140996
LATCHAM	141011
LAWLESS	141135
LAWS	141240
LAWSON	102687
LE MESSURIER	141364
LE SEELLEUR	146099
LEA	109932
LEACH	141410
LEATHER	141488
LEBUTT	141518
LEES	141658
LEESON	141682
LEFFIN	148946
LEGGETT	141747
LEITH	141801
LEM	141828
LENG	141844
LENHAM	141852
LERWILL	141917
LEWER	171603
LEWIS	102180
LEWORTHY	151750
LICKFOLD	142220
LICKISS	142239
LICKLEY	142247
LIDSTONE	142255
LIGGETT	142271
LILLINGTON	142387
LINDER	142433
LINDFIELD	142441
LINDO	142468
LINFITT	154067
LINNINGTON	149411
LINTER	142581
LISNEY	142638
LITTLECHILD	142689

LITTLEFORD	124923
LITTLEHALES	175013
LLANWARNE	142743
LOBBETT	142956
LOBDELL	112763
LOBLEY	142964
LONGMAN	143219
LONGMIRE	143227
LONGMORE	163457
LORD	157449
LOSH	146544
LOVEGROVE	143405
LUCOP	149403
LUMLEY	143723
LUSH	143790
LUTKIN	117978
LUTKIN	117986
LUTLEY	143804
LUTYENS	100889
LYDDIETH	143839
LYFORD	133434
LYNALL	143871
LYUS	143979
MACKMAN	144207
MADDEVER	160423
MAGGS	152498
MAGLOCHLAINN	144339
MAGNAY	134961
MAHONY	152005
MAIRIS	144428
MALBY	144444
MALFANT	144320
MALIPHANT	144487
MALLERY	144509
MALLETT	144517
MANDEVILLE	144592
MANHOOD	154385
MANNAKEE	136751
MANSBRIDGE	144819
MANTELL	144835
MAP	153761
MARA	158747
MARBECK	144894
MARENGO	147451
MARFELL	144916
MARFLEET	144924
MARGRETT	144940
MARKER	144959
MARKWELL	144975
MARNELL	107956
MARRIAGE	140228
MARSDEN	145122
MARSHFIELD	145270
MARSTON	145327
MARTIN	145416
MASSEY	145793
MASSINGHAM	145815
MASTERSON	120316
MATON	145890
MAUNDRELL	110469
MAVINS	146099
MAYBANK	146196
MAYCROFT	146218
MAYHEW	146242
MAYNE	128147
MAYOH	146323
MCAPLIN	161152
MCBRATNEY	163007
MCCLUNG	146412
MCCLURE	146420
MCCREA	111716
MCCURLEY	118974
MCEWAN	146692
MCFAWN	144061
MCGLASHAN	148466
MCGREGOR	173606
MCMINN	147117
MEADOWS	171263
MECHAM	173525
MEGSON	147338
MEIKLEHAM	119679
MELLSOP	151386
MELMOUTH	147354
MELSOM	147370
MENNIM	147435
MEREDITH	147443
MERRIGAN	147524
MERRIMAN	147540
MERRINGTON	148326
MERRITT	147559
MERRY	106275
MESSENGER	147591
METCLAFE	105813
METHERELL	147648
METHERINGHAM	147656
METSON	147664
MEWHA	109150
MICKLEBURGH	147710
MIDDLEYARD	147796
MIDWINTER	147834
MILDRED	118192
MILEMAN	143081
MILLHOUSE	173096
MILLICHAMP	148105
MILLIER	106631
MILNER	148180
MIMMS	148229
MINNEY	148245
MITHAM	128686
MOCK	148520
MOFFATT	148539
MOGG	179094
MOLYNEUX	148717
MONEY	148741
MORDEN	168939
MORIER	171433
MORRELL	154156
MORREN	149470
MORTIBOY	149691
MOTH	120766
MOULDER	149926
MOUNTCASTLE	164631
MOWAT	150037
MOWBRAY	150045
MOWELS	107034
MOXEY	150088
MULCOCK	126373
MULES	150177
MULLETT	150193
MULLEY	150207
MURFET	127736
MURRELLS	150436
MURTELL	150444
MUSK	150452
MYNOTT	150533
NADIN	150541
NAGLE	170364
NAMMOCK	141429
NANFAN	176001
NASON	150665
NEALE	118125
NEECH	150746
NEELAND	150770
NEESHAM	150789
NEGROPONTE	158534
NEIGHBOUR	150800
NETHERCOTT	150959
NETHERSELL	110973
NEWMAN	151114
NEWMAN	151157
NEX	151262
NICE	151289
NIEURZYLA	151440
NIMS	162299
NISBET	151491
NODES	156205
NOKES	151645
NORRINGTON	151726
NORTHMORE	132659
NUNES	112070
NUTSFORD	151890
NUTT	151904
NYE	141860
O'BASE	143057
O'CARRAGHER	112046
O'DONOGHUE	151971
OASTLER	152137
ODHAMS	167193
OETLING	111082
OFFLEY	159107
OLIVER	115088
OLIVEY	152285
OLMSTEAD	152307
ONION	152358
ORBELL	152374
ORDERS	152382
ORIEL	172294
ORMEROD	152412
ORRIDGE	152455
OSWALD	152587
OTHEN	124591
OUSEY	124788
OUTHET	152617
OVERINGTON	152625
OVINGTON	147052
OXENBOULD	152749
PACKARD	152765
PADBURY	152811
PADDLE	152846
PAGAN	152862
PAISLEY	177830
PALEY	138835
PALGRAVE	152986
PANKHURST	153133
PAPLAY	177342
PARK	153370
PARKES	147516
PARLEY	129224
PARSONAGE	108561
PARSONS	100382
PATCHETT	153621
PATTENDEN	140910
PATTISON	153788
PAVELEY	127272
PEAK	154016
PEATLING	154237
PELLETIER	154350
PEMBER	154369
PENDRILL	103101
PENHALE	154423
PENIKET	154431
PENNYMAN	176389
PEPAL	136131
PEPPERDINE	154504
PERKINS	154555
PERKINS	162159
PERRETT	154679
PERRON	154717
PERROW	154725
PEYMAN	154997
PHELPS	155012
PHENNA	155020
PHILCOX	146153
PHILLIBROWN	170011
PHILPOTT	155209
PHILPOTT	155217
PHILSON	155233
PHIPSON	158909
PICKERDEN	101974
PIGG	135739
PILBEAM	155462
PILLINGER	142425
PILTER	135704
PIM	155527
PIMBLE	115320
PINDER	136425
PINHORN	155586
PINNING	160830
PINWILL	155632
PIPER	155659
PITE	112623
PITTOCK	155772
PITTS	155780
PLANT	155837
PLEDGER	155888
PLEYDELL	137081
PLUCKNETT	147486
PLUMRIDGE	153532
POINTING	136883
POINTON	155985
POLAND	150908
POLKEY	156000
POLLET	156108
POLLIKETT	156094
POLLINTINE	165948
POMEROY	156124
PONTING	156167
POOK	166227
POPE	147516
POPELY	161160
POPKISS	163708
POPPLESTONE	156299
POPPLEWELL	155632
POTTER	155063
POULDEN	173096
POULTON	156477
POWDITCH	100773
POWDRILL	151661
POWLING	156590
POWNEY	156604
POXON	156612
POYTHRESS	162337
PRACY	156620
PRANCE	177121
PREEN	140538
PRESBURY	156744
PRESLAND	156752
PRESSICK	101443
PRESTON	156841
PRIDDLE	157015
PRIEST	103179
PROOM	137103
PROTHERO	118222
PROUDFOOT	157252
PROWSE	157279
PRUDAMES	157309
PUCKMORE	106631
PUDNEY	174092
PULESTON	154628
PULKER	101699
PULLEN	157449
PULVERTAFT	157473
PURSEY	157562
PUTNAM	157627
PUTTENHAM	157635
PYMAN	113832
QUADLING	121991
QUARRY	168270
QUARTERMAN	157724
QUINCEY	157759
QUIPPE	154504
QUY	157848
RADNEDGE	157880
RAIMBAULT	157945
RAINBIRD	157961
RAINES	172081
RANDELL	160520
RATEAU	158119
RATHBUN	158135
RATHMELL	127574
RAVENSDALE	105791
RAWDON	158224
RAWES	158240
RAYMENT	158321
RAYTON	175757
RAZEY	137596
RAZEY	137642
REAR	158437
REDRUP	179469
REEDER	163937
REFOY	165425
RELF	158771
RENOWDEN	158844
RESTORICK	158852
REYNISH	177741
RHOADES	110876
RHODES	109924
RICHARDS	108294
RICHARDS	139238
RICKERS	128880
RICKET	121630
RIDDELS	159379
RIDOUT	159417
RIEDSTRA	159425
RIGGALL	159476
RIMER	105678
RISLEY	128120
RIVER	166219
RIX	159638
ROBY	113867
ROCKER	161128
RODEN	160237
ROLLS	160415
RONALDS	120065
ROSE	160490
ROSSINGTON	160636
ROUFFIGNAC	108081
ROUNCE	160679
ROWLING	160881
ROWORTH	170798
ROYALL	160946
ROYDEN	160954

Surname	Number
RUDMAN	161012
RUFFLE	123269
RUGG	149888
RUGMAN	161039
RUMSEY	161063
RUNACRES	112801
RUSH	162779
RUSSON	161241
RYCROFT	161314
SACKFIELD	161365
SADGROVE	161373
SAGAR	161403
SALLABANK	165409
SALMON	161497
SAMPEY	119245
SANDOE	178438
SANHAM	161799
SANKEY	161802
SANT	109940
SAVIGNAC	146641
SAXELBY	136425
SCALES	162159
SCAPENS	125490
SCOLTOCK	162310
SCOPES	135836
SCORGIE	141801
SCOTT	162337
SCOTT	162353
SCRIVEN	104558
SEACOLE	162612
SEAR	124125
SEARLE	162574
SECKOLD	162639
SELLEN	136190
SENIOR	162787
SERMON	162817
SESSIONS	139866
SEXTON	123870
SHAKESPEARE	162957
SHAMBROOK	162965
SHANKLAND	162981
SHAPCOTT	163023
SHARLAND	163066
SHARON	163074
SHARPE	132713
SHARPINGTON	169935
SHAW	144886
SHEARMUR	145874
SHELDON	163384
SHEPPEY	163503
SHERBORNE	163538
SHERRARD	163120
SHERRIS	164771
SHERWELL	163619
SHERWEN	163627
SHILLABEER	163651
SHILLING	163678
SHIRLEY	163767
SHIRT	157414
SHOEBRIDGE	178454
SHOEBRIDGE	178462
SHOLL	142905
SHRAPNELL	163872
SHRIMPTON	163880
SHROFF	116343
SHUKER	163899
SHUTTLE	141186
SIDWELL	126950
SILK	163961
SILKSTONE	164194
SILLERS	124699
SILVERTHORNE	149020
SIMPSON	177172
SINGS	118311
SIZELAND	133485
SIZER	164372
SKELLY	176761
SKIDMORE	148547
SKIDMORE	148555
SKINNER	141755
SKITTRALL	164496
SKOYLES	164526
SKYRM	164569
SLACK	124370
SLATFORD	164666
SLOBOM	164712
SMALLSHAW	164763
SMELT	106550
SMERDON	164836
SNELGROVE	117536
SNELHAM	167142
SNELSON	165611
SNOW	165638
SOBEY	165689
SOLE	165697
SOMERSCALES	143227
SONLEY	171565
SOPER	165743
SOUTHWELL	165875
SOWTER	165913
SPAUGHTON	165972
SPEAKE	166006
SPEDDING	114596
SPENDLOVE	166162
SPIERS	166219
SPILLING	152986
SPODE	160237
SPONG	166278
SPOTTISWOODE	120359
SPRACKLING	104000
SPRANGE	156507
SPRANKLING	175617
SPRIET	166324
SPRINGATE	166332
SPRINGFORD	166340
SPURLE	114987
SPURR	166367
STALEY	100854
STANDEVEN	159697
STANDRING	166529
STANESBY	149535
STARKEY	166669
STARTUP	166693
STERRY	159670
STEWART	169633
STICHBURY	167274
STICKLAND	167282
STOBIE	159085
STOCKTON	167371
STOTT	167681
STOWELL	167738
STRAHORN	125644
STRATH	121126
STRETCH	137790
STUBBINGS	137677
STUTT	168122
STUTTLE	167975
SUGG	165670
SUSAN	168130
SUTHERLANDS	159379
SWAFFIELD	140511
SWAIN	168319
SWATTON	126764
SWEETAPPLE	110744
SWEETING	168394
SWINFIELD	168440
SWINNERTON	168459
SWINTON	168475
SWORDS	168483
TAMPIN	104973
TAPE	124419
TATCHELL	168858
TATLER	168866
TATLER	168874
TEARLE	169269
TEBBLE	169307
TEDD	169323
TEECE	169331
TEGNER	146544
TEMPLETON	169390
TENNANT	135739
TESKEY	146579
TETLOW	120537
THAIN	126500
THAKE	150339
THETFORD	107980
THEXTON	169552
THIRKELL	177628
THISTLEWOOD	169579
THODAY	169587
THOMERSON	140783
THOMPSTONE	141062
THORPE	154083
THUNDER	105228
THURKETTLE	119229
TICKNER	170135
TIDSALL	170151
TILMOUTH	170232
TILSTON	154326
TIMBERLAKE	144789
TIMBERS	170259
TIMOTHY	142158
TIMPERLEY	170275
TINNEY	170305
TITE	170364
TITHERADGE	170399
TITTENSOR	170402
TITTERTON	170410
TOCOCK	141224
TOIN	102296
TOLL	170496
TONKENS	113115
TONKIN	173002
TOOK	170658
TOOP	170690
TOTTERDELL	170720
TOWNER	170828
TOWNSEND	123870
TOZER	170895
TRAPNELL	102555
TREADGOLD	170941
TREGENZA	170984
TRELEVEN	171018
TRIBE	171107
TRIBE	171115
TRICE	128430
TRIP	119547
TRITT	171123
TROTT	123218
TROTT	123226
TROTT	141631
TROTT	171158
TRUSS	168939
TUDWAY	171263
TUFFIN	170925
TULEY	171328
TUNE	150266
TUNNA	171344
TUNNICLIFF	171352
TUNSTILL	171360
TURNBULL	171433
TURNPENNY	133701
TURP	165328
TWELVES	171786
TYE	117811
TYRRELL	171867
TYRRELL	171891
TYZACK	156892
UDEN	118370
ULLATHORNE	171956
ULPH	171964
UNWIN	171263
UPWOOD	171441
UREN	104108
URWICK	163562
VAILE	176605
VANDERAVORT	172189
VEECOCK	172375
VENABLES	172383
VENING	172391
VENN	172413
VERLANDER	159050
VERNALL	172421
VERRALL	172456
VERRINDER	172464
VERYARD	160555
VIALLS	172480
VICKERAGE	178179
VINDEN	146781
VIRR	112119
VIVIAN	172626
VOICE	172669
VOTIER	172707
WADDELOW	168939
WADDINGTON	152412
WADDINGTON	172758
WADHAM	162531
WADMAN	172804
WAGHORN	172839
WAGSTAFF	139262
WAKELAM	172901
WAKELING	172936
WALKLATE	173193
WALROND	173363
WANSBROUGH	103748
WARDER	106224
WARLTERS	154067
WARN	173754
WARRY	173894
WARTH	173924
WARWICK	173940
WASSALL	125873
WATCHAM	124591
WATERLAND	152277
WATTAM	125245
WATTHEWS	139750
WEARE	174424
WEATHERALL	174440
WEAVERS	174483
WEBB	174491
WEBLEY	174637
WEDLAKE	173398
WEEKS	160555
WEIGHT	174769
WELBY	174823
WELCHMAN	174882
WELDON	174890
WELLS	174971
WENDEN	175021
WESTAWAY	175242
WESTERDALE	100927
WESTOBY	175293
WESTON	175323
WHALEY	175439
WHATMORE	175471
WHEALE	118656
WHEATER	175528
WHEELHOUSE	125539
WHEELTON	147141
WHELAN	143901
WHINHAM	175676
WHITEHOUSE	154512
WHITESIDE	176087
WHITESTONE	176095
WHITEWAY	176001
WHITLOCK	176168
WHITNEY	176222
WHITTALL	176265
WHITTARD	176273
WICKSTEAD	176427
WIGGINTON	176443
WIGZELL	176508
WILDIG	176591
WILDY	176605
WILKES	176648
WILKINS	176680
WILLERTON	176818
WILLINGTON	177385
WILTON	177849
WINDEBANK	161063
WINDER	177954
WINGROVE	177997
WINROW	170151
WINYARD	178039
WISDOM	178047
WITHELL	175706
WITHERIDGE	178098
WITHERSPOON	178128
WOODEN	178519
WOODGER	178535
WOODIWISS	178594
WOOLGAR	178721
WOOLLAN	178748
WOOLLEY	178764
WOOLLINGS	178780
WOOLVETT	178829
WOONTON	152854
WORMS	172170
WORRALL	178942
WORSDELL	178950
WORTH	178977
WORTHEN	134597
WRIGGLESWORTH	176435
WYARD	175765
WYBORN	179426
WYLLIE	179442
YALE	179485
YEARLE	166618
YEEND	122173
YEOMAN	165816
YULE	157333
ZANKER	179728

SECTION F

ARTICLES AND PROJECTS

CONTENTS

INTRODUCTION

This section contains, articles, details on projects, and information on how to both submit information for the next directory, and the British Genealogical Database. It is broke, for our convenience into two parts. The items in section F2, needed a full page format, which uses up a lot more room, while those in section F1 could be in the two column magazine format, that gets so much more information into the available space. All the articles etc are by the two authors except the two guest articles, who have special knowledge of their subject.

You will find there is also an article at the beginning of section B, which covers how name variants came about and our peculiar spelling.

There are less articles in this years directory than last years, yet you will see because they are generally larger they take up more pages. Only the Getting Started article is an updated version of last years, all the others are totally new and different. Although last year we did announce the setting up of the Family History Club of Great Britain, a year further and you can see some ideas coming into practise, and yet more coming up.

Perhaps, readers who have seen the 91 directory would like an update, on some of the items mentioned. Last year we reported problems with some members of the Federation of Family History Societies, I am glad to report that I have met a number of their officers over the last year, including their Chairman, Richard Ratcliffe, and their project co-ordinator John Perkins, and vice-president Elizabeth Simpson, all of whom I have visited at their homes. I also attended several conferences, hosted or run by or with the Federations member societies, and got on with everyone there. The original communication problems have therefore been overcome, and I hope that in the future, we shall be able to work together on some of the larger projects. Neither the Family History Club of Great Britain or Time Travellers (a new group run by the club, to assist those doing one name, place studies, and family reconstructions) are members of the Federation. You will see that the Federations President Col Iain Swinnerton has listed his one name study in this directory, as have many other established figures within the Family History Society world.

Some readers felt my comments last year about the Guild of One Name Studies, was too strong, and that I was over influenced by letters I had received from some of their members. They felt it was not the Guilds fault if some of their members did not abide by the spirit and rules. I felt it was right that I balance my previous comments, with this view so that you have a balanced picture.

The article about which I received the most mail was the one on re-regression, using Hypnosis to release inherited memories of events your ancestors experienced. Letters and phone calls were generally in favour from psychologists and psychiatrists, and surprisingly well over half of GP's liked the article. I had expected about 50% for GP's. Many people who worked in hospitals or the health field told me about hypnosis being used more and more in hospitals now. A number of interesting experiences were reported. This, of course, was the article that was chosen to be misquoted any time by anybody who wished to criticise what we are doing.

I have spoken to so many of our readers over the last year at different points, so perhaps I can update you on our news over the last year. Tracey had our second son Aaron, on Monday 16th December 1991, and being Tracey, she was working when she went into labour, and back at her desk in well under a week. Our first son Adam, who will be 3 on the 11th September, was diagnosed a Special Needs child, with learning difficulties, this means he has developed slower than expected, so effectively we have two babies, although Adam is now walking, and starting to feed himself. Having had every test possible without finding anything wrong with him, we ended up with the Genetic service, and had a genetic nurse come and record our family tree for us. An interesting experience, and a change to see someone else at work interviewing us. They so far have not found anything, although I am looking forward to seeing the specialist again, and this led me to look at how the project to record Family History Data could be of use to the medical profession. Adam is a happy, contented child, who enjoys everything, including the special school he attends daily, and really looks forward to his taxi picking him up in the morning. Adam is special, and if some Doctor came along with a magic cure, although of course we would have to take it, it would be a pity to change such a special child, with all his smiles and excitement, when you return to the room after only being out of sight for a few minutes.

More of you now have computers, and some are writing your own programs, not so difficult is it, and it really does make life easier. Perhaps I can offer a challenge, can any of you, devise a routine that will match name variants. I know there are some, but I have yet to see one that gets a good match on those we want, yet eliminates those we do not. Try with some of the variants in section B, and if you think you have a good match, let me know, and I will give you a disk containing a selection of names to match. This you will appreciate is of great use for the BGD, and for other applications, like matching health records to patients. While on the subject of patients how about devising a system for outpatient departments, that schedules appointments based on Doctors habits, like starting an hour late, having long appointments to start, getting very short just before lunch. Starting late after lunch, and going through the afternoon getting shorter again towards the end. Some of us who have had to spend up to 4 hours at a time waiting in corridors with small children would really appreciate an appointment system that worked.

Getting back to Family History, you will probably of heard by now of the Family Tree Researcher series we are starting. These are two series of low cost booklets. The RED guides, looks at records by location such as the Public Record Office (PRO), or County Record Offices. While the YELLOW guides looks at a subject, such as Military Records or Census Returns. The question is, do you have an area you are experienced in that you could write one of these guides on. 32 to 64 A5 pages, is not a lot, and I am sure you will agree that you could do a lot better than me. Remember it is the quality of information that interests readers, the computer does the typesetting and correct spelling, and we can put up with the criticism we get about our use of the English language can't we ? Although the guides are intended to be low cost, there are small royalties available to authors, so at least you can make your hobby pay for itself, but remember only fiction authors get rich.

Can you organise, if so how about organising a small group to collect and enter information for the British Genealogical Database, or other projects we are working on. Perhaps a family reconstruction of a place might excite you, if so you will find "A Project of Your Own" exciting.

Finally, if you have a project, any project, we will encourage, and help you all we can. So please let us know what you are doing, or if you wish, telephone us and if I have made a comment or suggest something you do not agree with, then please tell us, there is always room for another opinion.

GETTING STARTED

by Keith Park

In this article we look at where to start if you want to trace your family tree, how to go about it, and where you can find out facts about you and your ancestors. We also look at a few ideas to make life easier.

The starting point is what you know, you progress from here to find out what your parents and relations know, and then we look at records in various places. We also need to know how to check out our family tree, and make sure it really is ours, and not just a collection of people who 'sort of fit'.

You are keen to get started so lets. Get a piece of paper and put your name in the centre on the left hand side about halfway down. Next add your father and mothers name, so as to start a chart, shown like the one in fig. 1. Next add your grandparents, you will probably be able to do this much yourself.

People generally go through the same pattern. They are born, often christened, go to school, get a job, get married, have children, retire, die and get buried. Some may also join a military service and later leave, receive particular honours, divorce and re-marry, be widowed

FIGURE 1: Below is a five line pedigree chart, which you can see gives you 30 ancestors by only going back on the parent lines, many if not all of these would have had other children giving other branches of your extended family.

GGGFATHER
GGFATHER
GGGMOTHER
GRANDFATHER
GGGFATHER
GGMOTHER
GGGMOTHER
YOUR FATHER
GGGFATHER
GGFATHER
GGGMOTHER
GRANDMOTHER
GGGFATHER
GGMOTHER
GGGMOTHER
YOU
GGGFATHER
GGFATHER
GGGMOTHER
GRANDFATHER
GGGFATHER
GGMOTHER
GGGMOTHER
YOUR MOTHER
GGGFATHER
GGFATHER
GGGMOTHER
GRANDMOTHER
GGGFATHER
GGMOTHER
GGGMOTHER

and re-marry etc. So there are many public events, but in order to get a family tree, we need only to know when the person was born or christened, died or was buried and it is helpful to know when they were married. It is also helpful to know where any of these events happened, and the cause of death.

So next let's get a piece of paper and list for each of the people on the chart the information we know.

Next check anything in your possession such as an old family bible, or old documents, copies of birth, marriage, or death certificates, look at the back of old photographs for any dates, names of people, other notes etc.

Now its time to go visiting. Make a list of all the people you feel would be useful to talk to. Start with your own parents if you can, and then select the older person first, (just in case they are no longer with us in a few months time). Most people follow a set interview procedure, with fixed questions. If you choose this approach start with the date of birth and marriage, where these occurred, and then do the same for their parents, but you may also need death and place of death, and so on. A checklist of questions can be found on page 10.

I personally have found this restricting, and it is better to get them going, and not interrupt too much, but just to write everything down, as fast as I can. When I cannot keep up I leave a gap. When they come to a natural end I then go back to ask them about the areas I could not write down fast enough. Next going from the beginning I look for the information I need, and ask questions about missing dates, this often sets off a whole lot more memories, and on you go. Often for several hours. If you get information that does not match other information you know or is suspicious on logical grounds, marriage date too close to birth date etc, then ask questions around that point, which may prompt more memories, don't challenge what they are saying. If you were to challenge, then you will find some people will adjust their story to line up with anything you want, while others will stick rigidly to their story, but will not tell you anymore. While with them also ask if they know anyone else who is researching their family tree, and if that person is any relation to them, or if they know of any other person you can see who could help with your research. From this you will be able to deduce if they are likely to be researching the same ancestors. Also ask about any old bibles, and newspaper cuttings, death certificates or other documents in their possession. Finally if you are still in a position to absorb more information ask to see any old photographs they have and ask questions about the individuals in the photographs.

You will see when you get to this point you have much more information than you need to just create a family tree, you could write a whole family history. You know about the families, you have gossip, rumours, facts, snippets from the past, and you will find you need some time to organise, or re-write this information before your ready for the next visit. You may find on occasions it is worth going back and asking people more questions, often they will have thought of a lot more after your first visit, and you may have information to prompt them with now.

After talking to several people you will come across inconsistencies, but then all we have so far is leads that need confirming.

So where do we go next ?

Luckily since 1837 all births have been recorded in London, and the indexes to these records are held at St Catherines House, the address is in section G (Useful Addresses). There is a large book covering every 3 month period. They are organised alphabetically by surname, and give surname, first name, date of birth, the registration district and number. Scotland has a different system introduced in 1855. With this information you can order a copy of a birth certificate. Now St Catherines House is a very crowded place, and not convenient for everyone, so copies of their indexes have been made available on microfilm and can be viewed at a number of major libraries and in the Family History Centres run by the Church of Jesus Christ and Latter Day Saints (LDS), better known as the Mormons. Addresses in section G (Useful Addresses). The Mormons have reasons connected with their religious beliefs for tracing their ancestors, and are always helpful to anyone doing the same. If you normally avoid religious groups, and places, then I would like to point out I have found the Mormons to be always friendly and helpful, and they never once brought up the subject of religion.

The Mormons (LDS), have also microfilmed many parish registers, and other documents, and can get items they don't have at their centre in a few days notice for only a minimal charge. They can also get census returns on microfilm, (we will discuss this later). They also have a major index of events their members have recorded. This is called the International Genealogical Index (IGI), and is organised by surname within county, with similar sounding surnames listed together. Copies of this index can also be seen in some libraries and in other places.

Once you get back to 1891, you have another source of information, this is the census returns. Census's have been taken every 10 years since 1841, with the exception of one during the 2nd world war. The 1841 census is a little short of detail, but the 1851, 1861, 1871, 1881 and 1891 also 1891) census contains details on everyone who lived in every house in Britain. You not only find out the household, but other adults and children, their relationships, jobs they had, ages, and places of birth. Following these back you see the family grow and can estimate the marriage year from the age of the oldest child. You can see this information on microfilm at any LDS centre, at county record offices in the county, and some libraries. My choice has been the County Record Office, as often I want to look at several possible towns or villages across several censuses, and therefore the number of films I look at in day can be quite large. You can find someone not listed where you expected, and where you least expected to find them. The family is there but no one by the name you are looking for. If the person you are looking for is also under 13, try to find the grandparents, and the other children of the grandparents, and usually you will find them, as the census records who was sleeping in a specific house on a particular night. If they are over 13, they could be working, often in another house in the same area. Luckily in many counties enthusiasts have created indexes to some of the censuses and these are often, although not always, available at the county record office. County record offices cover a very wide range of information, much of which is helpful to you, but you will usually need a readers ticket to gain access. In most cases readers tickets are free, but usually you will have to have some form of identification such as a driving licence. You should of course check up on this by telephone, as well as checking opening hours, and whether you have to book to reserve a microfilm reader. There is a complete list of both County Record Offices and LDS Family History Centres in section G (Useful Addresses).

The next source of information, also usually available in county record offices is the parish church records, and sometimes non-conformist church records. Sometimes you will find they have copies of Bishops Transcripts, so lets look at each of these.

The parish church r gisters contains amongst other things, christenings, weddings and burials. Periodically a copy had to be made of these registers and sent in to head office (The Diocese). These are known as Bishops Transcripts. If the record you are looking for is not in the parish registers, it will not be in the Bishops Transcripts, but if you cannot read the writing in the parish registers or they have been lost, destroyed or are still in the church then the Bishops Transcripts can be most useful. If the records are still at the church, you can see them but you will need to make an appointment with the vicar, curate or whoever is in charge of the church.

There are many other sources.

It is good practise, not only to find out where people were buried but when they died. This will help you to eliminate some obvious errors, but will also add depth to your research. If possible also find out what it was they died of.

Initially, you will find you make very rapid progress, then you reach a point, where it will take longer to find out the next part. This is a good point to consider lodging what you have with the British Genealogical Database (BGD), you will find a separate article on this, but it is a good idea to get into the habit of recording your information full and submitting it from the beginning. As you get information back you will start to see how really useful this will be.

A pack of 20 different forms you will find useful is being published by the Family History Club of Great Britain in October 1992. You can photocopy these for your own use, but not for re-sale. Packs of each form will also be available. Packs of 20 different forms costs £3.75 including explanation notes on how to use them and postage.

There is a lot of very useful advise in the Scottish Ancestors article, which is relevant to English, Welsh and Irish researchers as well as Scottish.

Finally, consider joining the Family History Club of Great Britain, the magazine will keep you informed, and introduce you to new sources, and you will have access to the databases, and be informed of the various books in the low cost Family Researcher series as they come out.

Enjoy yourself, and remember at all times, it is a hobby, absorbing, exciting, but understand others who do not see the same priorities or interest in your research as you do.

A MAJOR PROJECT OF YOUR OWN

Do you feel you would like to take on a major research project. Something you can do on your own or with friends, and will be of great interest to others. If so then I have the project for you.

Take a place, any place, but ideally one both near to you, having some significance to you, and being a practical size, by this I mean a village or small town not a city.

Now the project is to re-construct all the families that have ever lived there. As simple as that. Your source material is the same as you would usually use for family history, initially of course census returns and parish registers. This is a sizable task, and not something you can finish in a couple of weekends.

You will of course need access to a computer, or recruit someone to help you who has one, although you can start with a paper system, and transfer it later, you will find progress much faster using a computer.

Having decided you have the time, and interest to take this on, then write to the Family History Club of Great Britain, and ask them to record your study. There is no cost for this, but if you join the club, or pay £10 per annum to belong to the Special Project Study Group (Time Travellers), you will receive a disk of computer programs designed to make the project easier, a computer file identifying everyone in this directory studying your place of interest, and a pack of other information. As and when sufficient news is available you will also get a newsletter, and you will have immediate access to data within the British Genealogical Database (BGD), relating to the place you are studying. Information will also be included on various special processing the club can do with your data for you.

The advantage of registering your study, includes being advised if someone else is doing a similar study, and others becoming aware that you have the study in hand, and as registering costs you nothing it would be a wise first step. You will also get a specification sheet showing how census, and parish register data can be put into the British Genealogical Database, and notes suggesting how you get started.

The next step is to identify your source material and where you can get access to it. Find out which libraries have copies of census microfilm, if your relevant county record office is not nearby, Mormon centres likewise have access to these films. If you want to work at home, see if there is a copy available for loan in your area, rent a copy, or buy a copy from the PRO (see Section G Useful Addresses). A visit to a county record office or library will still probably be necessary to identify which films you need. If working from home you will also need to borrow, hire or buy a microfilm viewer. Secondhand ones are available cheaply (from around £30).

The census' are the obvious starting point as families on these are at least partly constructed, and by going across the years you identify older and younger children, in most cases.

If working on paper, rather than with a computer, the best way to start is by creating a card for each family, for each census, showing the census year and surname on the top. Record the address, and all the information shown for each individual, at this point exactly as it is recorded. Don't try to edit or correct data when you are capturing it. The term daughter in law used in the 1851 census means step daughter not wife of son. You would of course discover this, but if you recorded it differently it could be difficult to work out. Always also record any reference, or page numbers that will allow you to get back to the source data.

Once you have gained some experience yourself, you will be able to encourage others to do similar studies nearby, and working with them, account for people who slipped over from one place to somewhere nearby.

Once you have constructed families, and worked back to the earliest records you will have a unique record, of great use to genealogists and family historians interested in your chosen place, but also useful for all other types of studies, such as average age of marrying, and child bearing, number of children, illegitimacy, and other facts through the years.

You can get some idea of the size of the task you are setting yourself from the population, generally populations were smaller the further back you go. For a typical population of 1,000 people you can expect to find about 30 christenings per year, and as before the industrial revolution most parishes number only a few hundred, you will see you can make rapid progress through the centuries. One study I have looked at had 500 inhabitants in 1676 growing to 1,172 in 1801. This period involved 2,783 baptisms, 815 marriages and 2711 burials, quite a large number but minute compared with the contents of this book. You should however not under estimate the time it will take to track down every record, including wills, of all these people. One estimate I have seen suggests 1500 hours would be necessary. To totally reconstruct a parish of 1,000 people over 300 years. 1,500 hours is about 9 months, with 8 hours a day 5 days a week. During a study of people doing similar studies, many said they would not do anything of this size again, but several in fact did go on to do similar studies. These cases are not genealogists or family historians, but people interested in social history, collecting data for statistical analysis. As far as I know in all these cases, everything was done by hand. With a computer time would be saved, and faster progress made. Of course, using commonly available records; census', parish registers and the like, you could reconstruct the majority of the people in a parish, with a computer, in a smaller amount of time than suggested above. Therefore, you should not be put off from starting by the size of this estimate, and once you have the project in hand it is likely you will find others who wish to help.

Of course eventually you will want the fruits of your labour to be made public, and of use to other people through the centuries to come. I would suggest that all the reconstructed families are added to the British Genealogical Database (BGD), but you may also like to make the source data available on a computer disk to schools, colleges, and universities for them to use in studies or teaching exercises, or to publish the information in a booklet or on microfiche for depositing in county record offices or libraries. Some of you however, will find the information prompts you into writing your own book on your chosen place. Working with others through the Family History Club of Great Britain you will be able to compare your researches with results others have. How did the age of marriage or family size depend on occupation, and did it differ from other areas ? How did infant deaths, and deaths of mothers in childbirth differ from other areas for the same period, and why should this be ?

I think you can see, it would be only too easy to forget about publishing, and family history and go off into a world of your own, researching all types of theories. However as no meaningful results can be obtained until the source data is complete, hopefully you will put off the urge until the family reconstruction phase is complete, and you have entered all you research in the BGD, that is if you have not done so on the way.

Remember with studies, like learning to walk, it is necessary to get one foot moving in front of the other and once started to keep going. Putting it off to next month or next year means you will probably never get started. If you don't have time yourself, think who can you encourage to take on your chosen area. Why not make a list and get a group interest in areas around you.

THE FAMILY HISTORY CLUB OF GREAT BRITAIN

Last year a new National Club was set up, for everyone researching family history with ancestors associated with Great Britain and Ireland. The club is a non-profit corporation with no shareholders or dividends, run entirely for the benefit of members. Since last October it has grown steadily and is currently larger than some county family history societies, but still has some way to go to catch up the largest. Continued growth is expected. The club over the last year has been able to help many people, and has a number of projects up and running with more now coming on stream. The British Genealogical Database, covered in detail in another article is one of these. In this article I want to look at some of the databases up and running now, some being built, the club magazine and the future.

At the point of writing this, the club was still run by its founders, but within the next 6 months a committee will be elected to run it. During this initial period, a series of referendums have been issued which has allowed the members to define the way the members wished the club to go. This approach means the club is still devolving, driven by what the members see as needed, and greater use to them. An example of this is training material or courses. The members have identified a need, some have suggested content, other structure, and the ways to meet these requirements are being looked at in detail. Within a few months, a course or courses will be announced, to exactly fit what the members wanted.

This directory, was an identified need, suggested by the smaller Family History Computer Club, and many of the suggestions from this small club, lead to the establishment of the Family History Club of Great Britain, and to the British Genealogical Database (BGD), also detailed in this directory.

Members are kept informed of progress, and new services by the bi-monthly journal "Family Twigletts', which is free to members, or can be subscribed to separately. Besides giving news of projects it also contains a range of articles, such as looking at an unusual source, name studies, and other articles ranging from memories of earlier times to how to get your own book into print.

At the centre of the clubs activities are computer databases, which although the most advanced anywhere, there is no need for members to have any knowledge of computers to use them, and get the benefits. Many people just pose a problem and get a solution. The databases cover, sources, interests, special studies, places to stay economically, collectors, an article database and much more. Perhaps we should just look at some in a little more detail.

The B&B database contains places throughout the UK, where you could stay while doing research or visiting other areas. There are about 800 economic B&B's, guesthouses or small hotels, many with proprietors who have an interest in Family History or Local History.

Name and Address Database. A rapidly growing database, which contains the names and addresses, often telephone numbers and other information on nearly 40,000 people known to be researching their family history. The entries are indexed forward as and when people move, which means it can give you up to date addresses for people you have lost touch with, or address where you only know a name.

The sources database started its life as Tracey's card system, she used to tell people where they could find various types of records. When it grew too big, it was converted to a computer system, which has rapidly grown, yet will grow even more rapidly over the next 6 months. The useful addresses section of this directory you will see carries reference numbers, this is part of the source databases list of places sources are held. Club members are involved in expanding this database now, and eventually it will also be used with the British Genealogical Database (BGD), to suggest automatically where people should look to further various branches of their research. For example if the BGD entry said a person was a surgeon, and the dates matched, the sources database could tell them where to look to find the relevant directory of surgeons. If a person disappeared from local records, maybe a muster roll exists, and can identify if they went off to war.

The British Genealogical Database (BGD), is of course the most ambitious database project, and hopes to record connected up family trees, together with a lot of information on each person. Advanced computer programs will use a form of pattern matching, to suggest likely links to other known family trees, and of course through the sources database suggest how you verify this. You will see from the article on the BGD, that in fact it is much more than this, it will be of enormous use for medical research, allowing doctors to examine hereditary problems, and skills without a life times experience of Family History, and a spare 10 years to build sufficient data. The BGD is available to everyone. You do not have to be a club member to enter or obtain information. Neither is there any cost, so like this directory, it will grow rapidly. The club is about to launch a program to encourage people to undertake family reconstructions of complete villages, which besides being an interesting collection of projects in their own right, will also add data to the BGD. It is hoped other clubs and societies will also help with this project, especially as all the advantages will be freely available to their members.

The club also encourages the recording of history, both from a traditional viewpoint, but also encourages less conventional ways which makes history fun for everyone.

The Club is also actively involved with the Family Tree Researcher series of Booklets, this covers two groups of low cost guides. The RED guides looks at locations. RED guides will cover the Public Record Office, County Record Offices, and Scottish Records initially, with other titles being announced later. The YELLOW guides, will look at subjects, and cover subjects such as Parish Registers, Military Records, Census Returns, Genetics, Education, Health, with the first being Photography, Copying and Dating Old Photographs. Several authors are involved at present, but if you would like to write one of the guides then please contact the club.

The long term objectives include bringing family history to everyone. We will encourage everyone, of any age, background, race, colour, sex, religion or education standard. A project was attempted over the last year, which had to be suspended when time ran out, but hopefully can be re-activated in the future. This project was to produce a 32 page booklet explaining how to go about researching your family history, and to have this delivered by the Royal Mail to every home in England, Scotland, Wales and Northern Ireland. With 23.5 million copies it would have been the largest circulation publication ever to have been produced in Britain, requiring 6 print works to print it. The project was so large that it took so long to get prices, and get all the various parts, printers, distributors etc, that in the end there was not enough time to sell the required amount of advertising to make it pay for itself. The work that has been already done will make it easier when we are ready.

The most ambitious of the long term objectives revolves around a National Family History Centre. This is not a single library, or building, but a complex containing, hotels, food halls, displays, collections, libraries, research areas, lecture halls, audio visual facilities, video studios, book shops and much more. The equivalent of the National Exhibition Centre, or National Agricultural Showground, but with all the facilities for the Family Historian and their family, right down to a creche and supervised amusement areas for the children.

The benefits of membership can therefore be summarised as sharing knowledge and experience through the magazine, and knowledge through the databases. Using computer technology that would be beyond the capabilities of any small group of people or individuals. You will see that by working together we can make this both a useful and exciting club to belong to.

SO WHAT DOES IT COST;

Membership Type	Annual Membership	Joining Fee
Full Member	£15.00	£7.50
Young (15-18)	£12.00	£3.00
Junior (11-16)	£8.50	£1.50
OVERSEAS MEMBERSHIP:		
Credit Cards at UK rates or:		
AUSTRALIA	$41.04	$17.10
USA	$31.32	$13.05
CANADA	$36.90	$15.38
NEW ZEALAND	$58.32	$24.30

Life Membership is also available at £150.00 plus joining fee of £7.50

The joining fee is a once only charge. Membership runs for a full 12 months. There is no additional joining fee when transferring from Junior or Young to Full membership.

All use of the systems are included, there are no additional charges every time you want to use the clubs facilities.

TRACING SCOTTISH ANCESTORS

by David W. Webster

PART ONE. PREPARATION

Introduction

The comment was made in a book published recently by the Scottish Record Office that family tree research in Scotland in the period before 1855 should be approached with "optimism tinged with realism".

The reason for this is that, while there is a wealth of material to consult, there are very often gaps in the material, particularly the Old Parish Registers (OPR's). In other words, you should be prepared for the situation where you come up against a dead-end in the OPR's. Sometimes it is possible to use other sources to work round this block, sometimes not, so that it has to be accepted that that line has been taken back as far as is possible.

If you are about to undertake your first venture into genealogy then you're in for an absolutely fascinating, at times extremely frustrating, but above all satisfying experience. You may think that all you're going to do is to trace the family tree, but along the way you will become enmeshed in the necessity to learn all about the country and a range of aspects of Scottish society, since they impinge on your research. You'll also end up with an excellent knowledge of Scottish geography.

There is tremendous satisfaction involved in successfully tracing a family tree. In one way this comes from the detective work involved; piecing together the various bits of information and clues from a range of sources, and proving a certain link. At the same time you will also become involved in finding out what society was like at that period, and how it could have influenced your ancestors actions or general lifestyle, or possibilities for a career, etc., etc.

Another way of describing the situation is to say that it's like a large jigsaw puzzle, except that the picture you're putting together is not known in advance, there are no straight edges, and there can often be an ambiguous fit between two pieces which is not shown to be false until further neighbouring pieces turn out not to fit, so that you have to go back one or more generations and start again.

General Background

Firstly, you are fortunate. Not just because you have Scottish ancestors, but because, with the exception of the systems in Australia and New Zealand, the Scottish statutory registration system is the best in the English speaking world.

The Scottish system of compulsory registration started in 1855. Tracing a tree back to that point is normally straightforward as long as the surnames involved are not too common or the families involved didn't move around the country a lot. The work involved is mainly concerned with the birth and marriage registers. The complete statutory indices for Scotland are held at New Register House (NRH) in Edinburgh.

It is possible, however, to use the statutory registers to go back much further. This involves the use of the death registers. Let us say that we can find the death certificate of someone aged 80 who died in 1860. This will provide a place and year of birth of 1779 or 1780. In addition the death certificate will show the names of the parents of the deceased. Assuming that their child was born when they were 30 would give dates of birth back to the late 1740's. Remember, though, that it was the exception rather than the rule that people survived to the age of 80 in the eighteenth century.

In a similar manner, a marriage certificate in the late 1850's or 1860's will provide valuable information regarding events before 1855.

The only drawback with using the death registers is that it can take quite a long time to trace a certificate if the year of death is not known, or if it is not possible to tie down the death to a period of a few years through the comments on marriage certificates regarding whether or not the parents are alive. Without such information, it may be necessary to check a large number of possibilities, especially in the first few years of statutory registration after 1855, because the indices do not give the age at death. In later years this information in the indices allows the immediate elimination of many entries.

In addition to the birth, marriage, and death records held at New Register House, there is also a group of records termed the Minor Records, which consists of births, marriages, deaths in various circumstance outside Scotland, e.g. reported by British consuls. The Minor Records also include service records from 1881 with deaths for the two world wars and the Boer War (1899-1902). It should be noted, however, that these war records are incomplete, especially for WWII, in the sense that not all deaths of Scottish persons were reported to the General Register Office. Note, however, that most Scottish military records are held by the Public Record Office in England.

There are, of course, other sources which are the main ones to use for a search prior to 1855. These are the Old Parish Registers (OPR) and the associated christening and marriage indices, the censuses from 1841 to 1891, the International Genealogical Index (IGI), and a range of sources held at the Scottish Record Office (SRO) concerning wills and other inheritance information, ownership of land and property, other legal transactions, litigants and criminals, taxpayers, government officials, various professions such as lawyers, doctors, the clergy, etc., trade and business, electors and elected, the sick and insane, the poor, and migrants.

In addition to the SRO records there are valuable sources at most local and district libraries and archives.

PREPARATION

There are three areas which you should take some time to prepare before even starting to think about visiting New Register House in Edinburgh. Time spent on preparation can, however, prove to be invaluable in the long run and well worth the effort and frustration of not starting straight away on the actual tree research.

Relatives

The first is to gather as much information as possible from relatives regarding the family tree. Such information should relate not just to the bare facts of who married whom etc., but you should also take care to record all the anecdotal information which is available.

Anecdotal information on its own may not be of great value to the tree, but it can sometimes be a piece of the jigsaw puzzle, which together with other information, confirms a certain generation link, i.e. without this anecdotal information, the link in question might well have just remained a probability. In addition, such information fills out the bare branches of the tree.

If you need to approach elderly relatives who haven't heard from you for some time, proceed with care. If you rush things they may become suspicious of your motives, so that you don't get the valuable information which they have. So take time and care to approach them, and to fully explain the reason for the contact. Properly done, you'll most probably find that they are only too happy to talk to you about the "old days". If it's at all possible visit and discuss the family tree rather than doing it by letter.

In summary, the categories of information which you are seeking are names and places, documents and photographs, and reminiscences.

When visiting try to use a tape recorder rather than taking notes, - the conversation will flow much better. Prepare for this meeting by having a list of questions ready. Don't immediately challenge apparent anomalies. They may not be anomalies, and, even if they are, better to let the conversation flow and steer it back later to the area of doubt.

Be prepared for confusion between generations, individuals, etc. Ask questions regarding when events happened in relation to known events, as well as finding out dates where available. Cross reference where possible by asking about the age of relatives etc. compared to the relation to whom you are talking. Ask not just about persons' occupations but also about whether they worked for themselves or for someone else.

If it's necessary to approach distant relatives by post, then send them the tree which you have so far and ask them to add anything they can; send copies (not originals) of any documents or photographs which you have; and, finally, send them a prepared list of questions with plenty room on the paper for their answers. A reply paid envelope may help the situation.

It may well turn out to be the case that someone else in the family has previously researched the tree. If so, a lot of work may already have been done for you. On the other hand, take care and time to check that the work previously done is accurate. It often happens that someone puts together all the certificates they can lay their hands on, and makes a tree, but fills gaps where they occur by making assumptions. You have been warned!

Background Reading

The next area of preparation is to read books giving full details of how to trace a Scottish family tree. In my opinion, the best such book is "Tracing Your Scotish Ancestry" by Kathleen B. Cory. The best guide to the sources at New Register House and The Scottish Record Office and how to use them is the book published in 1990 by Cecil Sinclair of the Scottish Record Office, - "Tracing Your Scottish Ancestors".

If you know that the family came from certain areas of Scotland, then spend a little time now to learn about the geography of the places involved if they are unfamiliar to you. Again it's a case of a little time spent now potentially saving a lot of possibly wasted time later on.

Similarly, if you are a bit vague on the history of Scotland, spend a little time on reading it up, not just in terms of the standard history book information, but also from the social point of view, e.g. when did the railways come to Scotland and lead to a much greater mobility? Before the railways came, how easy was it to travel in Scotland?, - etc., etc.

Recording of Information

The last type of preparation is to decide how you're going to handle all the information which you'll be collecting. After a couple of years it could easily be the case that you have information on several hundred people. Keeping track of that amount of information needs some careful thought.

Do you prefer to use a card index system, or are you familiar with computers, in which case you should obtain and evaluate available software packages. If you have an IBM compatible then the best shareware genealogy package I've come across is Brothers' Keeper.

Whatever type of system you decide to use, you need to realise that you have to have some systematic method of recording the mass of information which you'll be generating.

PART TWO - RECORDS AVAILABLE

Introduction

Part one of this article dealt with the necessary preparation. In this second part we look at the subject of searching the Scottish statutory records. Note that part 2 deals only with the structure and organisation of the records. Part 3 will deal with the recommended methods for searching these records.

The General Register Office For Scotland

At the eastern end of Princes Street, opposite what used to be the North British Hotel, now the Balmoral Hotel, are the two buildings in Scotland of most importance to the genealogist.

Directly fronting onto Princes Street, with "the man on the horse" statue right outside is General Register House, home of the Scottish Record Office. Next to it, but set back about 50 yards, is New Register House, home of the Registrar General for Scotland.

Here in New Register House are kept the records of every birth, death and marriage in Scotland since the 1st January 1855. Also kept here are the pre-1855 Old Parish Registers (OPR's) for the 901 parishes, along with the records of the censuses in 1841, 1851, 1861, 1871, 1881, and 1891.

Unlike England, the Scottish system allows the actual register entries, or microfiche copies of these to be consulted for the approriate fee. There is no restriction on the number of entries which are consulted during a day's search.

Getting Started

It is possible to book a place in advance, but only a limited number of places are made available for advance booking (approximately a quarter of the total), so that the date you are given may be some weeks away.

The rest of the available places in the search rooms are made available for searchers who turn up on the day. Be warned,- at peak times of the year, late spring and summer, it may be necessary to be in the queue outside New Register House at 8 am or shortly after to be sure of obtaining a place. The opening hours are currently 9 am to 4.30 pm Monday to Thursday, and 4 pm on a Friday. New Register House is closed in the evenings, weekends, and public holidays.

At present there are three different search rooms. The largest is "the Dome" which has 25 places, all equipped with a microfilm/fiche reader. The Dome search room is intended for those who want to search in the statutory indexes, OPR's, and censuses. In addition this room has, at present, 8 computer terminals for accessing those indexes on computer. Finally, there are several separate microfiche readers.

The two other search rooms are Room 28 with 13 places which is for those whose interest is limited to the OPR's and censuses, and the library where there are normally 12 places available for researchers whose interest is limited to the statutory records.

Work will start in the near future to extend the Dome search room. This will probably result in the closing of one or both of the other search rooms.

Tickets can be purchased for a 1 day, 1 week, 1 month, or 3 month period. The cost varies according to the records to be searched. If you are only interested in the statutory indexes this currently costs £9 for a single day. Access to just the OPR's and censuses currently costs £8 for a single day. A ticket for such restricted searches is available only for a single day. Combining all three, a so-called inclusive search, costs £15 for a single day, £50 for a week, and £300 for a quarter (the information on the cost of a monthly inclusive ticket is not available at present). Prices are current as at January 1992.

After paying the relevant amount, you'll be directed to the correct search room. Here the staff will welcome you, and, if you are new to searching, will give you instruction in the systems. Don't be afraid to ask questions, at this time, or later.

Note that you are only allowed to use pencil in the search rooms. It is best to come prepared even though pencils can be bought.

<u>The Statutory Indexes</u>

Compared to England and Wales where statutory recording began in 1837, Scotland was relatively slow in introducing statutory recording, not starting until 1855, some 18 years later. This delay is more than made up for, however, by the thoroughness with which the system was set up.

At the beginning, in 1855, ambitions were very high, and the amount of information recorded in certificates was much more than today. It can be a tremendous bonus to find that someone in the tree was born, married, or died in 1855, since, for example, there will also be information on their birth certificate concerning the number of siblings, how many alive and how many deceased, the ages and places of birth of the parents, as well as the normal information.

It was soon realised that too much information was being required. This led to a decrease in the information registered. For a few years this led to the omission of too much information. In other words, the pendulum swung too far the other way. From about 1860 onwards, depending on the type of certificate, various information was restored so that the certificates are largely as we know them today.

Most of the indexes are now held on computer. You no longer have to look through the large index books (called the "paper indexes"), except (at present) for births 1855 to 1859 , marriages 1855 to 1865, and deaths 1855 to 1861. By the time you visit New Register House this will have changed, since it is the intention to computerise all the indexes.

If you do have to use the paper indexes, take care to remember that there are addenda at the back of both the male and female indexes, which should be checked if you can't find a relevant entry in the main index. There is normally an annotation in the main index to point out that there is an entry in the addenda. For the computerised indexes these addenda have, of course, been included.

Especially if you are unfamiliar with computer terminals, take all the time necessary to learn how to operate and how to use the computerised indexes. It's much faster and more convenient than using the paper indexes as long as you learn how to do things properly. Again, the search room staff will only be too happy to assist you.

Note that there are separate indexes for males and females.

Remember that the indexes refer to the year of registration, not the year of the event, so that a birth, death, or marriage which occured in late December may not be registered until the following year and be indexed accordingly.

<u>Birth Indexes and Certificates</u>

The information in the computer index is the full name, parish of birth, the registration district reference number, and number of the entry. The paper index does not give the registration district number, just the name. You need to to look up this number on the large alphabetical lists of parishes. From 1929 onwards for all parishes, but also for some parishes in 1928, the index also shows the maiden name of the mother. Note that there are separate indexes for female and male births. In addition, note that "Mc" and "Mac" are treated separately.

All birth certificates have now been microfilmed so that you will not see the actual registers.

For the years 1855 to 1915 the fiches are available on a "self-service" basis, i.e. you go to the drawer yourself and extract the fiche you require. This self-service concept will be extended to other periods and certificates in the future. Only three can be consulted at the same time, and must be returned before a further three fiches are obtained.

For other years an order slip must be filled in, and an attendant will bring the fiche. Again, only 3 can be ordered at the same time.

Entries in the statutory registers of births from 1861 give,-

1. entry number of the record,
2. name,
3. date, time and place of birth,
4. sex,
5. father's name and rank or profession/occupation,
6. mother's name and maiden name,
7. date and place of marriage,
   (unfortunately not for 1856 to 1860)
8. signature and qualification of the informant, and
   address if different from the place of birth given in 3.

Always remember to look at the first, narrow column which gives the number of the record. It is here that there will be an indication that there is an amendment or addition to the entry. Once the entry has been recorded, it cannot be altered, only augmented.

This may involve something as minor as an insignificant spelling error, or something of major interest such as an additional name, or paternity action. Information on simple corrections is normally at the back of the register, but other information is held separately in the Register of Corrections.

In 1855 only there was extra information, consisting of the ages and places of birth of the parents (the latter might only give the county), plus the number of previous children (but not names) and how many were still alive.

Between 1856 and 1860, the information on the date and place of the parents' marriage was dropped, being restored in 1861.

There were changes in the type of certificate in 1966 and 1972, but these related only to the format of the form, the information recorded remaining the same.

In the column giving the informant, you will sometimes see the annotation "present". This means that the informant was present at the registration, nothing more.

If you wish it, an extract, i.e. a copy, of a birth certificate can be ordered. The current cost of this when applying in person is £7.50, or £9.50 by post.

There has been discussion for some time regarding the possibility of making available a service to supply simple photocopies of the certificates, i.e. the entries in the registers. Most family tree researchers do not not require the fully legal format of the formal extract, - a simple photocopy would suffice. As yet, however, such a service is not available.

Many people make a hand written copy of the certificate. If you chose to do this, then develop the discipline of copying out every last word on the certificate. Don't fall into the trap of using shortcuts or abbreviations. You may be sure at the time that you'll recall what your hieroglyphics mean at a later stage. More likely, you won't, so that you might have a long journey back just to double check one or two facts. It's a matter of personal preference whether you make up standard "forms" for making hand written copies, but these do have the advantage of giving you a routine to follow.

The birth certificate is the only certificate on which there is no doubt about the age involved, - zero. In other words, don't place absolute reliance on ages and dates given on certificates. Mostly they are correct or, at least, nearly correct, but I can guarantee that you'll come across a father who doesn't give the correct date for his marriage.

Remember that in the case of an illegitimate birth, there may not be any information concerning the father. In a similar vein, if the mother's surname is not specifically noted as her maiden name, then it is possible that the parents were not married at the time of the birth.

One great advantage of the Scottish system compared to that in England and Wales is the information on the place and date of the marriage, apart from the unfortunate gap bewteen 1856 and 1860.

Marriage Indexes and Certificates

The marriage indexes give the full name as reported on the certificate of those getting married. This should be emphasized, since not everyone gave the fully correct information. In other words, although someone was born "John Smith Brown", they may be described on the marriage certificate as plain "John Brown". Similarly, someone born as "John Brown" may have adopted an additional name to that shown on his birth certificate later in life.

In the paper indexes, at present for 1855 to 1865, the information is the registration district and the number of the entry in the register. As for births, the additional, time-saving information in the computer indexes is the registration district number.

Between 1855 and 1863 the name in the female index is the maiden name with the married name alongside in brackets. If a widow married there will be two entries, one under her maiden name, the other under her former married name. From 1864 onwards, however, the married surname is not shown, until 1929.

From 1929 onwards (and for a few parishes in 1928) there is also given the surname of the spouse, so that you don't have so many possible records to cross check, if any. This is because there are separate indexes for females and males so that an entry of possible interest in the one index can be cross-checked in the other.

Currently, the registers from 1918 to date have been microfilmed and are are supplied as fiches. Before that date, the actual register, or a copy, is made available. At present there is no self service facility.

Entries in the statutory registers of marriages from 1856 onwards give, -

1. entry number of the record,
2. details of the date, place, and form of the marriage, i.e. whether according to the banns and forms of a church,
3. the names, ranks, professions, occupations, ages, usual residences, and marital status (i.e. batchelor, spinster, widow, etc.) of groom and bride as well as the relationship to each other (occupation not always for the bride),
4. the maiden name of the bride and previous married name if previously married,
5. the names, ranks, and professions of the fathers of the bride and groom, as well as whether they are deceased at the date of the marriage,
6. similar information regarding the mothers of the groom and bride except that there is not always information regarding the profession,
7. For regular marriages, the name of the officiating minister or registrar (from 1940), together with the names of the witnesses,
8. For irregular marriages, the date of conviction (up to 1939), decree of declaration or Sheriff's warrant,
9. place and date of registration.

Again, check that very first column. You may never come across an example, but it's here that an annotation will lead you to a clerical error, or, much more interesting, a divorce or bigamous marriage.

In 1855, the extra information was both the present and usual residence if different, and details of any former marriages along with the number of children, living and deceased.

The format of the marriage certificate changed in 1922, 1966, and 1972, but with two exceptions, the information recorded did not change. The first relates to the relationship, if any, of the bride and groom. The recording of this ceased in 1921. Prior to that, you may find that the negative information regarding there being no such relationship is recorded as "none". This, however, is not consistent,

The second is that from 1972 onwards the date of birth rather than ages of bride and groom are given, together with the places of their births.

In addition, from 1922 onwards, the words "or divorced" are added to the marital status.

The information on whether parents are alive at the date of a marriage can be very useful in terms of reducing the period which it is necessary to search for a death certificate in the case where the year of death is not known. For the same reason, it can be well worthwhile tracking down the marriage certificates of brothers and sisters of your direct ancestor.

Extracts are available at the same cost as for a birth certificate, given above.

The information on a marriage has to be treated with considerably more care than that on a birth certificate!

Ages can be found to be several years in error, especially if there is a large difference in the age of those concerned. This may not always have been a deliberate "massaging" of an age,- it could be the case that someone genuinely believed that they were a certain age.

In the case of both parents being deceased, the information on their full names should be treated with care.

There is an understandable tendency to promote professions or occupations "one rung up the ladder", so don't always believe what is recorded.

Remember too, that, in the situation where someone signs using their mark, this will probably indicate that they are illiterate and are therefore not able to check the accuracy of the information which has been written down.

Again, it cannot be emphasized too much how important it is to record all the information. At first sight, the witness's names aren't too important, but what if they are relatives of the bride and groom, - this was quite often the case, - and they don't turn up in other records?

Death Indexes and Certificates

At present the indexes are computerised from 1862 onwards. The information given is the name of the deceased plus the registration district, registration district number, and record number. In the case of the paper indexes, the registration district number is not given.

For females, the treatment of the maiden name varies. For 1855 the death is indexed under her married name with her maiden name alongside. For 1856 to 1858 the maiden surname is not shown. Between 1859 and 1865 there are entries under both the maiden and married name (if married) with maiden name alongside. In theory, there will be entries under all the married names, if married more than once, but this relies on the person reporting the death knowing all the details.

For the period 1866 to 1973 a married woman is indexed under both her maiden and married names. Note, however, that a widow might revert to her maiden name, so that there could be no entry under her maiden name.

From 1974 onwards, the situation is the same as for 1866 to 1973 except that the maiden surname of the deceased's mother is also shown for males and females.

In the 1866 index the entries relating to a few parishes show the reported age at death, and, by 1868, this practice was universal. Note, however, that, in earlier years, including 1866 and 1867, there are often erroneous entries showing the age at death as 0. In other words, the age at death figure is only reliable for 1866 and 1867 if it is greater than 0. The reason for this is a quirk of the computer programme which should be corrected at some time in the future.

At present, the death certificates for 1855 to 1883, and for 1940 to date have been microfilmed and are therefore made available as fiches. For other years, the original registers, or copies, with appropriately black covers, are made available.

As yet no self service system is in operation so that order slips must be filled in for each record you want to consult, with a maximum of 3 allowed at the one time.

Entries in the statutory registers of deaths from 1861 to date give, -

1. entry number of the record,
2. name, rank and profession or occupation,
3. marital status with name(s) of spouses if married,
4. when and where the death occurred,
5. sex,
6. age,
7. father's name, rank and profession or occupation, and whether deceased,
8. mother's name, rank and sometimes occupation, plus maiden name and whether deceased,
9. cause of death, and duration of illness if applicable, with physician's name,
10. signature and qualification (relationship to deceased if any) of informant, and residence if different from that given earlier for the deceased.

Again check that first column. It will be here that there will be an annotation if, for example, the death resulted from an accident leading to a fatal accident enquiry, and, possibly, newspaper reports.

In 1855 the extra information consisted of the place of birth of the deceased, how long he or she had been resident in the district, details of marriage(s) including information on all issue both living and deceased, and, finally, the burial place together with the undertaker by whom this latter information has been certified.

From 1856 to 1860 the only extra information was the burial place and the name of the undertaker or other person certifying this information. During this period the marital status of the deceased is shown, but not the names of any spouse(s), this latter being restored in 1861 onwards.

From 1861 onwards the burial place information was no longer given.

There were changes in the format of the certificate in 1966 and 1972, but, with one minor exception, this only involved the format change. The exception relates to

1966 onwards, when a specific question is asked regarding the occupation in the case of a female death.

Even if the death occurred in a hospital, the usual residence of the deceased is given.

The death certificate contains a wealth of information, but take care. If the informant is the spouse of the deceased the accuracy of the information is more than likely good, but if the informant is anyone else, even a son or daughter, there is a good chance that some of the information is not quite accurate, or even completely wrong, especially if the deceased's partner predeceased them and there are no uncles or aunts to ask, so that the son or daughter has no-one who can be asked for information. In this situation, be especially suspicious of information such as a maiden name until otherwise confirmed.

If you are fortunate to have an ancestor who died in 1855, and all the information is given as well as informant being the spouse the liklihood is that all the information is accurate, then you will see that this can be a tremendous bonus.

Don't forget that the name of the informant can provide valuable information not only in terms of the name of a son, daughter, or other relation, but also that, if the informant lives at an address other than that of the deceased, then you have a valuable lead for a check in the relevant census. Remember that the surname of a married daughter will most likely be different from that of the deceased.

Compared to the English death certificate and its relative paucity of information, it can be seen that Scottish death certificates provide a rich haul of information making it well worthwhile spending quite some time to locate them even when there is considerable uncertainty as to the year of death, or whether it took place in 1855 or later.

Other Records

In addition to the three main sets of records there are also registers of still-births from 1939. These registers, however, are not open for public search and extracts are only issued in exceptional situations, such as those involving legal purposes.

The adopted children register started in 1930. Confidential information about the natural parents will not be revealed except in clearly defined circumstances, e.g. to an adopted person who has reached the age of 17 years and to whom the information relates.

The separate divorce register started in May 1984. Prior to this date the recording of a divorce was by an annotation in the first column of the marriage certificate.

Minor Records

In addition to the statutory records for births deaths and marriages as described above, there is a further type of statutory record indexed under the heading "Minor Records".

These records relate to births, deaths and marriages outside Scotland and relating to Scots. They comprise, -

Marine register of births and deaths, from 1855;
Air register of births and deaths, from 1948;
Service records, from 1881;
War registers, from 1899;
Consular returns of births, deaths and marriages, from 1914;
High Commissioners' returns of births and deaths, from 1964;
Registers of births, deaths and marriages in foreign countries, for 1860 to 1965;
Foreign marriages, from 1947.

These records cannot be relied on 100% since they are patchy and incomplete.

Note that the service records relate to births deaths and marriages involving someone who declared that they were of Scottish origin. Service records relating to details of a person's service are held at Kew.

There are three War Registers. The first is for deaths of Scottish soldiers in the Boer War (1899-1902). The second relates to deaths of Scottish persons serving as warrant officers, NCO's, and men in the army and petty officers and men in the navy during the first world war. The third and last relates to deaths of Scottish members of the armed forces during the second world war. In all three cases, the returns are incomplete.

All these categories of minor records are indexed on one combined series of microfiches, with separate indexes for males and females. If you think that you need to consult such a record, order the fiche for the relevant period. If there is an approriate entry, the search room staff will assist you to order the separate register involved. Note that the amount of information supplied varies greatly.

PART THREE - SEARCHING SCOTTISH STATUTORY RECORDS, CENSUSES, AND OLD PARISH REGISTERS

Part one of this article dealt with the necessary preparation, while part two was about the structure of the Scottish statutory records.

In this third part we will consider methods and search strategies to use when searching the statutory records as well as the censuses and the Old Parish Registers (OPR's).

WHERE TO START ?

The best place to start is with your own birth certificate and work back from there. At this stage it is best to work backwards all the time. Once you become more expert in the subject, you may be able to do some tracing forward of lines of interest.

Even if someone else in the family has already carried out some family tree work it is a good idea to use the checking of this as a way of learning how to trace the tree.

First Generation

On your birth certificate is shown the place and date of your parents' marriage. First check if the place of marriage shown is a parish in its own right, or if it is part of a parish of a different name. To assist you with the latter situation, the search rooms in New Register House have copies of various gazeteers.

Next take the less common of the surname of your father's surname and your mother's maiden name and look up the marriage index for the year of marriage shown on the birth certificate. Note down the details, i.e. registration district, district number if shown, and entry number for all possible marriages which fit the facts you have.

If there are no appropriate entries, then try one, then two years either side of the year you started with. If this still doesn't give any possibilities, check the starting information and whether you are using the indexes correctly.

Once you have some entries which could include the correct one, look up the index for your other parent for the same year, and cross check entries against those already found. Normally, this process will give you just one entry to check, but, very very occasionally, there may be more than one entry which has to be checked. If this happens, then you will need to know the names of at least some of your grandparents in order to identify the correct marriage.

Order the relevant record and note down all the details shown on the marriage certificate.

Using the ages shown, work out the most likely two years of birth for your parents. Two years are involved, since the marriage certificate doesn't indicate if the birthdays have past at the date of the marriage, or are still to come. In other words, if someone still has to have their birthday, their age will increase by one, so that the year of birth will be one year earlier.

Remember that there is no way of knowing if the ages shown on the marriage certificate are accurate.

Starting with the two most likely years, check the birth indexes. If the surname involved is not too common and/or there is a middle name, then it should not take too long to locate the correct entry. If a commoner surname is involved together with a common first name, and there is no middle name, it is helpful, if at all possible, to know where the birth took place, so that the search can be limited to that parish, otherwise there could be a large number of possible entries to check.

If the entries are not found in the two most likely years, then check several years either side. If there is still no success, first recheck the marriage certificate in case you have incorrectly noted down some fact. It's surprising just how often this can happen, especially if you are searching several lines in parallel.

If you still have no success, then start considering spelling variations of the surname involved, as well as checking on possible variants of the first name. It could be the case, for example, that a certain given name is shown on the birth certificate, but a pet name has been adopted later in life, or another name altogether, and it is this latter name which is shown on the marriage certificate.

As far as spelling variations of surnames are concerned, use as many sources as possible to produce possible variants. Don't be surprised if variants look completely different, - it's the pronunciation which is important.

If there is still no success in finding a relevant entry, then you have to consider the probability that the birth did not take place in Scotland.

When checking possible entries, the clue that it is the correct one is given by the names of the parents being the same as those on the marriage certificate. Only if you are unlucky enough to meet the situation involving very common names for the child and parents involved, including the mother's maiden name, could there be the possibility of ambiguity which would need further investigation to prove one way or the other.

Subsequent Generations

Now you have the birth certificates, you also have the information on the places and dates for your grandparents' marriages. In other words, you have completed one cycle, and must now go through exactly the same procedure as described above, but for the two separate grandparental lines.

Once you have the marriage certificates for your grandparents, followed by their birth certificates, you then have the places and dates for the marriages of your 4 sets of great-grandparents.

This procedure continues until you come up against the 1855 barrier.

BEFORE 1855

There are two general search strategies which can be followed to take the tree back before 1855.

The first is to use only the information you have collected so far and search further in the censuses and Old Parish Registers (OPR's).

The second search strategy might at first appear to take longer but can often be more efficient in overall terms. This is to generate as much information as possible from the 1861, 1871, 1881, and 1891 censuses on places of birth, siblings and other relations, etc., together with searching for death certificates. If you are fortunate to find a death certificate for someone who died in the late 1850's at a great age, say 80, you have already taken the tree back to the 1770's without becoming involved in the possible complications of the OPR's.

Death Certificates

The best way to search for a death certificate when the year is not known is to establish the range of years to search by using information from sources such as marriage certificates. These record the fact if a parent is deceased. Finding the marriage certificates for siblings of your direct ancestor can be a worthwhile investment. The best way of generating sibling information is by searching the censuses.

First search for the death certificate of the wife involved, since, statistically, it is more likely that she outlived her husband. This will then provide you with two more bits of information, - the note on the death certificate as to whether she was a widow already at the time of her death plus, possibly, another address to check in the censuses. In addition, since there should be entries for the wife's death both under her married and maiden names, together with the fact that, for some periods the maiden name is shown in brackets alongside the married name, the death of a married female is easier to find.

Censuses

Censuses of the population started in Scotland in 1801, and continued thereafter every 10 years, but for 1801, 1811, 1821, and 1831, with a very few exceptions, only the statistical summary reports survive, i.e. the detailed personal information was destroyed.

Starting in 1841, the full details survive in the form of the enumerators' books. The returns for individual households are available to the public for the censuses between 1841 and 1891 inclusive. In Scotland it used to be the case that census records were closed for a period of 90 years, so that the 2001 census would have become available now but for the fact that we have had to fall in line with the English practice of a closed period of 100 years.

All of the 1841 to 1891 censuses are available on microfilm at New Register House. These census returns were recorded by district or parish, each district or parish having a registration number. These were then further sub-divided into enumeration areas or books, each book having it's own number. The start of each enumeration book deatils the area covered, this description improving with later censuses.

Census returns are not indexed by the name of the persons involved, but are listed in the order of the households and then streets or dwellings surveyed by the particular enumerator. In towns and cities it is quite common for a street to be split among many different enumeration books.

A limited number of censuses for a few areas have been indexed by surname by local family history societies. It's worth checking the position.

It is a great assistance to have an address before searching a census. Without this information, particularly in the case of a large parish or a search involving a town of any size, a search may take days rather than hours. Only in the case of a small, rural parish will a search without an address take a reasonable time.

One helpful index is available, this being the indexing of the street names for all cities and most towns of any size. In other words, starting with the address, you can, in this case, limit the number of enumeration books which have to be consulted.

It's always worth looking at the whole of an enumeration book, and, possibly those for ajoining areas, since it's often the case that relatives of those you are searching for lived nearby. Maps can be a useful help.

Don't be surprised if you can't find an address at all. Especially if there is a large number of years between that for which you have the address and the census year, it could be the case that the address did not exist at the time of the census.

With the exception of 1841 the information given in a census is the names of the occupants of the household, relation to the head of the household, marital status, age, rank profession or occupation, and parish of birth.

Before giving details of the various censuses one important point must be made. This is that the hundreds of enumerators employed for the purpose of the censuses were given a set of rules and regulations to follow. In most cases these were strictly followed, and most departures from the required practices were picked up and corrected by the supervisors. Some departures from the rules, however, still occasionally slipped through. This is not always a drawback for the genealogist, - it can be the reverse. Some 1841 enumerators recorded exact ages.

In the 1841 census there is no information on marital status or relationship to the head of the household. In addition, above the age of 15, ages were rounded down to the nearest 5 years, i.e. 24 would be recorded as 20. Most importantly from a genealogical point of view the place of birth is not given, only the answer to whether born in the county or not.

Additional information in other censuses is whether blind deaf or dumb in the 1851 census; number of children in each family between the ages of 5 and 15 attending school and number of rooms with one or more windows in the 1861 census; whether deaf and dumb, blind, imbecile or idiot, or lunatic, number of children between the ages of 6 and 18 attending school or being educated at home, and the number of rooms with one or more windows in the 1871 census; whether deaf, blind, imbecile or idiot, or lunatic, and number of rooms with one or more windows in the 1881 census; whether employed or employer, whether speaking Gaelic, whether deaf and dumb, blind, lunatic, imbecile or idiot, and the number of rooms with one or more windows in the 1891 census.

As well as the "land" censuses there is some information on shipping. This varies from census to census.

Remember that the enumerator could only record what he was told. When replying to the question regarding their parish of birth, someone might remember the parish where they grew up and not be aware that they were born in a different parish. In addition there are numerous examples of an enumerator recording what he thought he heard rather than the real information, this most often applying to the name of a parish unknown to the enumerator but similar to one he did know. In addition, those who were illiterate could not check what the enumerator had written down.

Once you have exploited the potential of death certificates and the censuses, the next step is to move on to the Old Parish Registers (OPR's).

<u>The Old Parish Registers</u>

Prior to the introduction of statutory recording in 1855, records were kept locally in the parishes by the minister or session clerk of the parish or church concerned. In 1855 the OPR's were "called in" to Edinburgh, and those which arrived and have survived are now kept in New Register House, microfilms being available to searchers.

The OPR's are patchy, there being relatively few parishes for which the records are complete for the time period over which they exist. Most of the records relate to baptisms and marriages or calling of banns (proclamations), with very few records of deaths or hiring out of mortcloths.

There was no standard form of recording information, so that this varies from parish to parish, and even within a parish with passage of time and the involvement of different ministers and clerks. The degree of conscientiousness also understandablely varies, with some OPR's, regardless of the actual information, immaculately kept, while others are a frustrating mess with obvious mistakes and omissions.

For baptisms, or occasionally births, the least information found is the fact that a child had been baptised or born i.e. no name or sex, the date, and name of the father. This quite frequent lack of information on the mother can most often mean a dead end as far as her line is concerned.

At the other extreme, there will also be information on the name of the mother in the standard Scottish form of her maiden name, - Scottish women have never lost their name on marriage,- the date of the birth as well as that of the baptism, and the place of residence and occupation of the father. Occasionally there will be names of witnesses at the baptism, sometimes stating the relationship. For upper class births there can, in addition, often be a great deal extra information concerning the parents of the father and mother.

Even if you come up against a parish which only provides the minimum information there is a small chance that the baptism will also be registered in the parish from which the mother originally came if diffferent from the present residence, and the OPR for that parish may provide more information. A similar comment applies to marriages if the bride and groom came from different parishes. If anything, the "two OPR" recording of marriages is more frequent than that of births.

The minimum information found in OPR records of marriages or proclamations is the names of those proclaimed and their parish of residence. In fact, there are a number of OPR's where the parish of residence is only shown if different from that in which recorded, i.e. one has to assume that the lack of such information is an indication that one or both the parties live in the parish of recording.

At best the good OPR's will provide full information on the origin of both parties, i.e. giving a certain place in the same or another, named parish, together with the occupation of the male, and, occasionally, the name of the father of the female, and, very occasionally, the mother.

Similar comments as for births apply to upper class marriages.

Where death or mortcloth hire records exist they are often completely unhelpful, not even giving age. Occasionally OPR's will give information on age and origin and/or residence.

There are 901 OPR's, the earliest surviving being that for Errol in Perthshire in 1553, but starting dates in the early 1700's are the most common. It must be realised that the OPR's are in essence the registers of the established Church of Scotland with very few entries relating to non-members. Records for other denominations, where they exist, are most likely to be found in the Scottish Record Office.

Whereas, for the statutory records, it can be stated that a birth or other event did not take place in Scotland if it is not in the post-1855 records (assuming that there is certainty concerning details such as spelling), no such statement can be made for the OPR's.

Reasons for a record not being made of a birth or marriage can range from laxity on behalf of the minister or session clerk concerned to a positive decision on the part of the family or minister not to record the events, for reason, for example, of legislation to which they took exception or found, quite simply, to lead to unnecessary expense, e.g. the Stamp Act of 1783 which imposed a tax of 3d for every entry of a birth/baptism, marriage/proclamation or death.

Especially for OPR's which are extant for the 16th and 17th centuries, and sometimes the early 18th century, it will be necessary to develop a knowledge of the handwriting styles of those times in order to be able to decipher them. In addition, be prepared for wide variations in spelling not just of place names but also of given and surnames.

Some OPR's are jumbled up as regards the chronological order of recording events, and require great care. In a similar vein it is not uncommon to find an elder child or children being registered on the baptism of the youngest, newly arrived member of a family. In particular, many people preferred to have their records made by the kirk so that there were numerous multiple baptisms in 1854 immediately prior to the start of statutory recording.

The information in the OPR's is indexed in two closely related forms. The first involves the fact that OPR source information is included in the International Genealogical Index (IGI) prepared by the Mormon Church. The latest available at the time of writing is the 1988 IGI. This list records first by county, and then by surname, i.e. there are separate sets of microfiches for each county. The previous IGI is the 1984 edition, which, while it contains fewer records, has the advantage for a search where the county is not known, of being in the form of one index by surname for the whole of Scotland.

Both these editions of IGI give only the basic information of the names, date, and parish. It it most often the case that further details can be found by consulting the actual entry in the OPR.

The standard of extraction of the OPR records in the IGI indexes leaves something to be desired. Simply because a birth or marriage does not show up in IGI84 or IGI88 do not believe that there is not an OPR record. Similarly there is some hearsay information included which can not be substantiated from other sources.

The IGI should only be used as a guide, and some time should be spent to develop an understanding of how the index is structured and organised, in particular the treatment of Mc and Mac, including the IGI peculiarity that McMillan without a space is indexed separately from Mc Millan with a space; the treatment of similarly spelt surnames, and the way in which given names are indexed exactly as they are shown in the OPR, even if it is obvious that there is a mistake and the intent is absolutely clear.

A better index is now available. Also produced by the Mormom Church it relates only to information from the OPR's, but considerable time and care has been taken in the production of the two indexes, one for baptisms/births, the other for marriages/proclamations. The organisation of both indexes is the same as that for IGI88, i.e. indexed first by county and then surname. Note that the method of treating similar surnames is different from that used in the IGI indexes.

Pre-1855 uncertainty
As can be readily appreciated from the above, it is most often the case that, unless there is corroborative information, links established using only the OPR's as a source can only ever be speculative, however powerful is the circumstantial evidence such a naming patterns, since there is no guarantee that there are unrecorded births or marriages which would fit the facts equally well.

Having said that, research using the OPR's can involve fascinating detective work, and it can give great satisfaction to find and then prove a link via the OPR's using other tools such as wills, property transfers etc.

From census or death certificate information one can first check the relevant OPR. Beyond that generation one is most often involved in deduction, i.e. given that the earliest OPR baptism of a child for a certain couple is, say, 1780, then one should start looking for the marriage first around 1760. But, as stated above, the fact that there is only one record which apparantly fits this requirement, e.g. only one possible entry for the whole of the period 1730 to 1765, this is not proof that there was not another marriage which also fits the facts but which was not recorded, or was recorded in an OPR no longer extant. Once a marriage has been found, then this gives a latest date for the two births, and so on and so on.

Particular care should be taken to avoid the assumption that people did not move much between parishes or counties. This was most often the case, but a surprising degree of mobility did exist. Similary, make sure that you check the geography well enough, so that you can decide if it is necessary to check the index for one or more neighbouring counties. Be aware if you are involved with a parish right on the border of a county that the county to which it belonged may change with time.

SUMMARY

Searching in the OPR's can be supremely satisfying, - stretching your detective ability and deductive powers to the limit to find what initially looks an unlikely but possible link when is later corroborated. On the other hand it can also be unbelievably frustrating. After a long painstaking search which requires all your knowledge of the subject you find a very uncommon surname which leads you back one or more generations further, so that the situation looks very promising and then, a gap in the OPR of interest. A complete, utter and absolute blank wall, with little or no chance of other sources helping you. Be prepared for both sets of feelings inside the same day!

To describe how to handle the myriad possible situations you will encounter in the OPR's, as well as the censuses, and many other sources, particularly in the Scottish Record Office is beyond the scope of an article such as this. A book could be written about it.

And there we are in luck. Within the last year or so two books have been published which are, in my humble opinion, unlikely to be bettered. The first is "Tracing Your Scottish Ancestry" by Kathleen B. Cory, published by Polygon, Edinburgh, in 1990, ISBN 0 7486 6054 2. This combines a detailed description of the sources with a wealth of practical and detailed advice on how to carry out your search which no other book has, including a story of an actual search, - 23 pages long. The second book relates mainly to Scottish Record Office sources and is "Tracing Your Scottish Ancestors - Scottish Record Office", author Cecil Sinclair, published by HMSO, Edinburgh, in 1990, ISBN 0 11 494118 1, price £5.95, 160 pages. This book covers, in a comprehensive, lucid and logical manner all possible Scottish Record Office sources likely to be of use to the genealogist, and what's better, how to access them quickly and efficiently.

Good reading and good hunting!

JEWISH ANCESTRY

by Dr A P Joseph

The first problem in this context is defining what or who is a Jew. Whatever definition is chosen, it is nearly always possible to find examples of people who do not fall within it and yet consider themselves Jewish. The Jewish journalist, Barbara Amiel, has stated recently "We have all debated this exquisite question ... but by now the answer ... seems to be ... in general, we are a tribe, a group of people that have inter-married for a few thousand years, been formed by pressures outside and within and probably all share one or two relatives about ten generations back. Like any tribe, I suspect, after long enough, nature and nurture combine and acquired characteristics seem to take on an inherited value".

Given this somewhat loose concept of the people about whom this genealogical article is written, it is perhaps relevant to summarise briefly the history of the Jews in England. The first known Community arrived with William the Conqueror from Normandy and for the next two centuries or so the Mediaeval Jewish Community flourished, although from time-to-time subjected to appalling atrocities such as the Massacre of York in 1190. The main function of Mediaeval Jewry was to provide the financial infrastructure for the economies that supported a Christendom which officially disapproved of money lending and the charging of interest. In 1290 Edward I issued his Edict of Expulsion and the Anglo-Jewish Mediaeval Community thereby ceased. For approximately the next three centuries there was virtually no Jewish presence in England, although the occasional Portuguese Jewish adventurer, such as Sir Edward Brampton (a companion of Perkin Warbeck at the time of the Wars of the Roses) is to be found in the pages of English History. In Elizabethan times small groups of Portuguese Jews began to settle in London and were known as "Conversos". Openly they professed Christianity but secretly maintained their loyalty to Judaism and a well-known example amongst their ranks is Ruy Lopez, both a famous physician and chess player, who ministered to Elizabeth I. (A less pleasant word for the "Conversos" is "Marranos" which means "Swine"). In 1656 the Portuguese Dutch Jew, Menasseh ben Israel, successfully petitioned Cromwell to allow the Jews to return to England and the small Crypto Community was then able to flourish openly. An interesting quirk of English history is that the Edict of 1290 has never been formally repealed but since it only referred to the Jews living in the Realm at the time, it can have no modern force.

The first significant Jewish Community in the Resettlement Era was Sephardi and this is essentially a group of Jews deriving from Italy, Spain or Portugal. Before the end of the 17th century the other major section of Jewry (the Ashkenazim) were also returning and by

1700 both Communities were flourishing side by side. Although Jewish immigration to England continued steadily throughout the 18th century, serious problems concerning employment and destitution arose in London and these were solved by many hawkers and peddlers colonising port towns all along the South Coast, which Communities form the backbone of the early history of Provincial Anglo-Jewry. For full details of their stories refer to Cecil Roth's "The Rise of Provincial Jewry 1740-1840".

The modern Anglo-Jewish Community influxed to England in the last quarter of the 19th century, fleeing appalling persecution from Russia and Eastern Poland. In many cases these immigrants were using Britain as a staging post on their way to America. Nearer to our own time many refugees, similarly fleeing the persecution of Nazi Germany, entered these Islands in the 1930's.

How best should a person living in England today, either fully Jewish or with some strands of Jewish ancestry, set about researching their Jewish pedigree? In the first instance the usual secular approaches of listing all family reminiscences, interviewing as many elderly relatives as possible, obtaining birth, marriage and death certificates from St Catherines House, checking probates and Census Returns etc. are entirely appropriate. A word of caution at this point concerns skill in interpreting phonetic representations of names and remembering that, at least in the early years of the civil registration system, immigrants, who were not familiar with our customs, were more likely to escape the net. Civil registration was compulsory from July 1st 1837 but penalties for non registrants were not imposed until 1874.

The most significant Collections of specific Jewish records are probably those held by the Synagogues themselves and will vary in their quality, both of antiquity and accessibility, according to how well they have been preserved. The oldest Sephardi and Ashkenazi London Congregations have some records going back to the early 18th or even late 17th centuries and include various primary sources, such as some circumcision registers (males only!), marriage lists and cemetery interments. Probably the most important addresses are the Archivist at the Bevis Marks Congregation, 2 Ashworth Road, London W9, and the Archivist at the Office of the Chief Rabbi, Adler House, Tavistock Square, London WC1. The records of Anglo-Jewish Archives (which has recently been disbanded) have been dispersed and those of genealogical significance are now in the Society of Genealogists' Headquarters. They include the Colyer-Fergusson Collection of Pedigrees, the Hyamson Papers and the D'Arcy Hart Papers. Jewish newspapers can be an important source and in this context the Jewish Chronicle, published continuously weekly since November 1841, is the senior representative of the genre. The Jewish Historical Society of England, founded in 1893, has published over thirty volumes of Transactions and some ten volumes of Miscellanies, including many communal histories and specific genealogical articles. They have also published an index to Anglo-Jewish Probates up to 1848 and an extract of many Jewish obituaries that appeared in the Gentleman's Magazine between 1760 and 1850.

Denization and naturalisation papers are most important sources and are available in the Public Record Office, although the papers themselves are subject to the usual hundred year closure rule that applies to the Censuses.

So far I have considered the researching of Jewish genealogy from the somewhat narrow standpoint of the Anglo-Jewish Community. However, considering the wider canvas, societies for promoting the study of this topic have now been formed in Holland, France and Switzerland; the Australian Jewish Historical Society offers assistance with the records throughout Australasia and in the U.S.A. there are some thirty or more State Jewish Genealogical Societies devoted to the pursuit. Each Society tends to produce its own journal or newsletter for contact but probably the best overview is to be found in "Avotaynu" published from Teaneck, New Jersey. It goes almost without saying that the records at the Mormon Family History Library in Salt Lake City include much of Jewish importance. Finally, the records in the Modern State of Israel, particularly the Central Archive for the History of the Jewish People in Jerusalem, may also prove invaluable. In this context, it is worth mentioning that the first International Jewish Genealogical Seminar was held in Jerusalem in 1984 and was followed by the Second of the series in London in July 1987. The Third (and to date the latest so far) was held in Salt Lake City in July 1991. The attendance of participants at each seminar has increased each time and this enthusiasm seems set to continue expanding for the foreseeable future.

Tracey's Comments: I have been through our source database and other books I have, and have extracted the following which may help you in your search for Jewish Ancestors.

AVOTAYNU, 1485 Teaneck Road, Teacneck, New Jersey 07666, USA.
The Secretary, Jewish Historical Society of England, 33 Seymour Place, London, W1H 5AP.

The Court of the Chief Rabbi, Adler House, Tavistock Square, London WC1H 9HP. They have proceedings books 1876-1938 and 1940 to date, Case Files of adoptions, conversions, divorces, Jewish and Marital Status around 1945 to today, and Certificates of Evidence containing details of applicants dates and place of birth and/or marriage abroad from 1922-1966. There is no public access to these records but you can write and a search will be carried out for you for a fee.

The offices of the United Synagogue, Woburn House, Tavistock Square, London WC1H 0EZ. They have printed annual lists of members arranged alphabetically by congregation 1885-1939. Registers of births, marriages and burials of defunct congregations ranging from 1770 to 1965 depending on which Synagogue. Registers of Closed Burial Grounds 1796-1872.

The LDS Library in Exhibition Road, South Kensington, London has a microfilm of all the Jewish holdings at Salt Lake City in the USA. These records can be ordered for a fee.

COULD YOU WRITE AN ARTICLE ?

Could you write a specialist article for the next directory, an article for Family Twigletts, or one of the guides in the Researcher Series ? If so we would like to hear from you. So why not drop us a note today with your ideas. If you don't feel you could write an article, but feel there is a need for one on a particular subject, then we would welcome your suggestions.

Tracey

LOOKING AT HISTORY FROM DIFFERENT VIEWPOINTS

Last year we had an article looking at this time from a 1,000 years in the future. Now we are going to bring back Oliver Cromwell to have another go at ruling the country today. This is designed to be fun, and cause discussion, so don't take it seriously. What would you do if you were Lord General - Protector of the Realm for a week ?

DIARY OF LORD GENERAL PROTECTOR OF THE REALM

by Oliver Cromwell

Monday May 3rd 1993
A shock to the system, re-incarnated in 1993 to have another go at the job I started in 1649. Started by visiting Parliament. It hadn't changed much, many members still only part time, or receiving retainers from other interested parties. I presumed it was all the alcohol being consumed in the bars that made them all so badly behaved. Action - closed the bars, but with no improvement, so suspended Parliament.

Spent the rest of the day finding out what was going on, getting my hair cut, and getting a modern uniform.

Tuesday May 4th 1993
Things are now so expensive, took a taxi ride, in a black cab, that moved in spurts but didn't seem to make much more progress than I could walking. Offered the good man a penny when I got out and learnt some new words.

It would appear that many innocent people have been released from Prison over the last two years, but thousands of innocents are still locked up. Also many people locked up waiting for trial (they call it remand). Many police forces, applying laws differently, some give warnings, some prosecute. Drug cases appear most unequal. Government agencies give out drugs in some areas, and police take no action against offenders, nearby another force prosecutes, and people end up in prison. Action - decided to release all prisoners. Those that have homes to go to can go home today. Others to be released as soon as possible.

Had a driving lesson at 5pm, seems such a slow way to travel, but I haven't seen any horses, perhaps they have been poisoned by the fumes and become extinct. Figured out most of the controls. Stalled at one junction right across the road, I didn't know what to do, helpful suggestions from other drivers who make their cars make noises, found I had a button in the centre of my wheel which did the same, had fun making my car make noises and waving back at people waving to me. I think they would have gone on all day, but time was short so I had to move on.

Wednesday May 5th 1993
River Thames has improved. Got the hang of new money, if the Government doesn't have enough, just print some more. Difficult to see therefore why they need to raise tax.

Got hit over the head by a highwayman, they call them muggers now, had to go to hospital. Wasted a lot of time in casualty waiting for the end of the tea break. National Health Service is a good idea, asked lots of questions. Also found out the highwayman who hit me and three parts out of four property crimes and crimes against people are caused by people raising money to buy drugs on the black market. I'll sort that out tomorrow.

Action - made a few adjustments to the National Health Service, like making surgeons only work privately or for the NHS, so they don't need to create waiting lists, so as to divide the work between their two sources of income. Found wards closed but spare nurses sitting in groups. It appears all work had to be done in the morning before rounds, and therefore a lot of staff needed in morning and spare later on. Action - moved rounds to evening, now they can work throughout the day, share out labour and operate all wards.

Had another driving lesson at 5pm, but got the police to close the A406 so I could practise without being disturbed. Although I only closed one road, it was really unpopular. Don't think I will do that again.

Thursday May 6th 1993
Started by getting rid of most crime, the black market in drugs, and other problems. Made all drugs available through pharmacists to anyone who had seen a Doctor and received counselling, and still in need. With no one to buy, the black market will disappear, without the black market no new people will be enticed in, so effort can be placed on helping those receiving supplies to release themselves. We will also know how many and who they are.

Met a group of my descendants, was interested to hear what they thought happened in my time. Some of it was right. Surprised to learn that there is restrictions on information, secrets acts, data protection acts. Seems to be far too much law no one knows what the law is ... really confusing for everyone.

Took my driving lesson this evening, near the Thames, saw a road going down into the river, so thought it was a ford, got rather wet, and lost the car, it turned out the road was for launching boats, although there was nothing to say it wasn't a road.

Friday May 7th 1993
Decided to have a day of action. Started by having breakfast with some of the political leaders. Told them all laws would be repealed, that they could not define and explain in a reasonable sized book that people could understand. This went down much better than I expected. Agreed in the end they could have two books, one effecting ordinary people and one on business topics. One of them suggested a ring binder approach where pages could be replaced as laws needed modifying.

While on subject of law, decided to give all the Judges a taste of their own medicine, so sent them all to fill some of the empty places now in prisons. That may quicken reform. Perhaps I will send the magistrates, another self appointed group, next week.

Had a driving lesson at lunch time in one of the Royal Parks. Lots of bodies laying about everywhere. Had to be careful as some of them were still alive. I even saw some get up and walk away. I was going to arrange burial for the others, but when I went back later they had all gone.

Some politicians and church people want action on prostitution. I thought they wanted it stopped, I said impossible, but no they want it legalised. Licenced brothels seem a good idea, better for everyone so agreed, but said they had to keep records of those using, for health monitoring, some worried faces about this, politicians want to be exempted on security grounds.

Found out Scotland is often used to try out new ideas, new taxes, and laws before extending to the rest of Britain. Discovered the fact Britain is one of only a few countries to drive on left of road. Decided to try out driving on right in Scotland. Will start with buses and lorries on Monday, and if they work, cars can change over the following Thursday.

After lunch declared freedom of speech, and most importantly of information. All Government documents to go into public access, with no destruction. Documents relating to inquests and similar are no longer to be destroyed. I found out about microfilm and other technologies, there really is no excuses to destroy anything now.

Saturday May 8th 1993
Funny, no one turned up for work today, thought it was something I had done, but appears they take an extra day off every week now. Had the people I wanted to see brought in. The police got a little carried away, smashed down doors, and roughed them up a little, so it took a little while before we could get going. One thing did come out of this, the need for an Independant Police Complaints Unit, with its own independent investigators to sort out what is going on. The need for a citizens charter also came up, setting out the rights of the individual, no imprisonment without a trial, no lengthy remands, no police interrogators without a lawyer present. Needs a bit more work. Changed the role of the police from finding evidence to get a case to fact finding only, leaving the prosecution counsel to decide if to proceed or not. Equal access to facts to be given to defence. Still not happy, current system doesn't work at all, seems just a lottery.

Had a flight in a helicopter, seems a good idea, seemed a bit more difficult to drive, probably a good job or the sky would be as busy as the roads. I don't think I will get the man to teach me to fly the thing he seemed very nervous, especially when I pointed out how handy it was to have the runaway helicopter catchers, wires on large steel towers spread across the country. I went down to Longleat for lunch, but flying back I spotted a large number of lions in the grounds. Could this be why so many people have moved to the city, or could they be everywhere. Perhaps that is what happened to all those missing bodies in the park. I shall have to be careful.

Investigated business failures after lunch. Removed corporation tax and regional grants as they cancelled each other out. Without corporation tax to avoid, Companies will be able to plan to have something in the kitty for a rainy day, so business failures will be down. With less failures there will be more businesses, therefore a need to go where people are - therefore no need for regional grants, which in most cases only seem to go to big companies who don't need them. Sorted the other major reason for businesses failing, by telling the banks they were to have loan contracts, with their business customers, no more variable overdrafts, withdrawn at a whim. Any breach of a fair contract will leave them liable to pay compensation.

Had tea with the Royal Family in Windsor Castle. Very friendly, and far more knowledgeable than I expected. They know about the lions, and said there were tigers and wolves at Longleat as well. I heard some rumours about some newspapers, some of the information was said to be from insiders. I am not sure it is right, that those who so many listen to, should repeat unfounded rumours.

Spent the evening with some disabled people, was taught a simple sign language called Makaton, which meant I could talk to people unable to talk or hear me, great fun. I am sure if more people took the time to talk or should I say wave to these people they would understand their needs better, and find they could play a useful part.

Sunday May 9th 1993
Got up and made my way to church, but the first church I went to wasn't open this week, found another but it only had a small number of old people in it. The city appears empty, must be a big church somewhere I haven't found.

Learnt to drive over the last week so took the opportunity after lunch to go for a drive. Found a big wide road which I followed, but ended up where I started. Roads used to go from one place to another, so don't see why this road went from nowhere back to nowhere, without going through a single place. It was labelled M25, avoided other roads labelled M in case they didn't go anywhere either.

Get someone to explain to me tomorrow why towards evening there was so many people in such a hurry to go around the circle, surely they have found out it gets them back to where they started !!!

Stayed up all night looking for the church where all the people had gone. But decided first thing Monday morning it must be a long way away, as all the people where arriving back by train at stations all around the city.

Heard of a club called the Family History Club of Great Britain, who is said to make history fun, and exciting. Can't imagine history being fun, all dull dates and things isn't it !!

MONEY

The following shows some of the different types of currency we have had over time.

4 farthings	1 penny
12 pennies (d)	1 shilling (s)
20 shillings	1 pound (£)
21 shillings	1 guinea
5 shillings	1 crown
24 pence	1 florin (2s)
4 pence	1 groat
1 pound	1 sovereign
1 unit	1 pound
1 lurel	1 pound
1 broad	1 pound
10 shillings	1 angel
15 shillings	1 ryal or noble
15 shillings	1 spur ryal
30 shillings	1 rose ryal
12 pence	1 testoon

A more complete list can be found in the 91 directory on page 521.

THE BRITISH GENEALOGICAL DATABASE (BGD)

by Keith Park

The power and storage capabilities of computers have been expanding and at the same time dropping in price, and soon we will be at the point where all known Family Trees can be recorded, connected up and accessible. Although technology with the capacity necessary is not widely available yet, we expect it to be before all the information can be obtained and put together.

This database will share several functions, the first and more obvious is in helping to find branches and extensions to your Family Tree, or possibilities that may link up. It will of course allow you to record the work you have done so that it is not lost, and can be handed on to future generations.

The database will also be a major aid to researchers interested in genetics, inherited abilities, susceptibility to medical problems as inherited problems. At a time when more knowledge of genetics is being discovered it is clear that if this branch of medical science is to be allowed to develop to give us all the potential benefits, it will be necessary for Doctors to put together Family Trees without a lifetimes experience of Family History.

The legal profession will also be able to use the database to help solve some of the more difficult inheritance problems, and could one day bring you a windfall from a relative you didn't realise you had.

After eighteen months looking at the design problems of the system, it has been decided to keep the way information is input as simple as possible, and allow several input formats, the first two of these are now being announced, but before we look at this, let us look at how you can actually submit your information.

By one means or another we need to get information onto computer disks. If this was all done by us, then progress would be slow, to say the least, and the old maxim 'that many hands make light work' needs to be employed. Ideally therefore, if you do not have a personal computer, you should find someone who has or someone who has access to one. As a last resort we can get someone to key it in for you from paper input. If you or they have a program to record Family History, it is likely that it will be able to output information in what is known as GEDCOM format. This is perfectly acceptable as it stands, although we would prefer to have other known information added if possible, this can be done by getting a program (FREE) from us which will read a GEDCOM File, display the information for you to check, and allow you to add more information such as cause of death, and where they died, this "killing off" is particularly useful to those interested in using the database to help with medical research. This additional information is stored with your original information in such a way as not to disturb the basic GEDCOM structure, which allows you to load a copy of your information into any computer running a program that can read a GEDCOM File.

If you have access to, or have a computer but do not have a Family History Program that produces GEDCOM output, then you can enter the information very simply through a question and answer style program available as part of the free set of programs available from us.

The second format will allow input of descendent charts, which can be typed in any normal word processing program. If you wish to use this option, then please read the specification later in this article.

To get a set of programs, that will work on an IBM PC compatible computer, send us a disk that has been formatted on your computer, together with an envelope for us to return it to you, and a note saying which computer you have, and as much information as you know. For example; do you have a colour screen, hard disk, printer etc. Once you have your disk back, you will be able to use the programs straight away. You can also copy the programs and give copies to anyone else.

Once you have the information entered, you can copy it onto a disk (we include instructions for this), and send it to us. We will run a program to check your disk is readable, and back the information up to a second disk, which is stored at another place as a safeguard against fire. As soon as the main programs are ready, we will add the disks to the system, and will hold your disk. After a few months, we will extract for you the information you put in plus information that appears to link to it or information which may need further research to link to your information, and return your disk containing this information. You will of course be able to send in modified information at any time, and once up and running we should be able to get information in and out again within a few weeks. There is no cost to you, for the programs or to use the system.

Another system is currently being built, called the British Source Database (BSD), this will contain references to all types of records, where located, periods covered etc. Eventually, the two systems will work together so you will get not only projections back, forwards, sideways etc from the British Genealogical Database, but lists of where to look to resolve problems, overcome holdups and generally progress.

Information which was collected in order to create the name variant section of the Family History Knowledge Directory, will shortly be converted to form the British Variant Database (BVD), and will work with the other databases to help identify potential links.

A further Database the British Intelligent Database (BID), is also being constructed which is a combined database of all directories, advertisements and similar. This will also eventually link up, and allow you to know who else has been doing similar research even if they have not entered their research into the BGD. Members of the Family History Club of Great Britain have already volunteered to build the BSD, and BID, but we can always do with more volunteers. You do not have to be a member of the club to help, although I think you will soon realise these databases form only a fraction of the projects currently in hand, and with all the other advantages many of you will decide to join.

I am sure some people will not think this project is possible, but didn't they say there was no need for The Family History Knowledge Directory, and that the project wouldn't work. Two years later, it has become well established, and is both the worlds largest Genealogical Directory and technologically most advanced. In a few years we will all wonder how we managed before the databases were available.

In a year or two, we will see computers with optical disks in Record Offices, they are already in some libraries now, and I am told common in American libraries. We hope to be able to supply the BGD on optical disk, together with the source database (BSD). Does this sound like something from the next century, well the Mormon Church are issuing well known databases like their International Genealogical Index (IGI) on optical disk today, and the GEDCOM format we mentioned earlier is in use by them to build 'Ancestral File', a similar project to the British Genealogical Database (BGD). So hopefully, you will see this project although vast and will take years to fully develop can be operational and of great use this year.

One final point, who is making money out of this? No one, the programs are free, as is submitting and extracting data. Computer Club Ltd is registered under the Data Protection Act, as holding and maintaining these resources.

STRAIGHT TEXT LAYOUT FOR SUBMITTING INFORMATION TO BGD

You can enter this information in any word processor, text editor etc. If you do not have access to a computer you can use this layout to type or write out sheets, which we can get volunteers to enter for you.

If you are able, output the information to disk, as a print file (ASCII). If you are not able to do this, or don't understand, then press enter at the end of each line, and write on the disk label the name of the word processor you used. We will be able to convert your file to ASCII. If you are unsure about anything relating to this, then put some information on a disk and send it in, saying it is a test. We will then look at it and tell you of any problems. You can use the QUES: tag to ask us questions, or confirm you have defined the information correctly (tags are explained below).

This method uses two principles, Descendent Charts and position identification, let me explain this.
A Descendent Chart looks like :-

```
GRANDFATHER
GRANDMOTHER
     FATHER
     MOTHER
          YOU
          YOUR WIFE/HUSBAND
               YOUR FIRST CHILD
               YOUR SECOND CHILD
          YOUR BROTHER/SISTER
          THEIR SPOUSE
               THEIR CHILDREN
     YOUR FATHERS BROTHER/SISTER
etc
```

You will see that each generation is inset in such a way that all brother/sisters are on the same vertical line.This is easier to achieve if you step each generation in by 2 characters, but larger steps are shown here to make the effect more obvious. All surnames are shown in capitals (KEITH). Female first names are in lower case with a capital at the front (Tracey). The descendent is listed first followed by the spouse in all cases. Maiden names are shown after married in brackets (SKUSE). You add a / before and after the Surname (/PARK/). Following the name, other information can be included, as this can continue onto other lines as needed. A continuation line is shown by one or more hyphens (-) at the beginning of the line. The different types of information is shown by a tag followed by a colon ":" for example MARR: for marriage, BIRT: for birth, a list of initial codes is shown at the end of this article. If you wish you can indent lines with one or more hyphens (-), to show linked items, as in:-

```
Tracey/PARK/(SKUSE)
-BIRT:18 APR 1964
--PLAC:CIRENCESTER, GLS
-CHR:1964
--PLAC:ASHTON KEYNES, WIL
--NOTE:Godparents, Phyllis Matthews, Hilda Skuse, Harold Long
-MARR:08 AUG 1986
--PLAC:CHIPPENHAM, WIL
and so on
```

You can also indicate the same in a straight string as in;

```
Tracey /PARK/(SKUSE) BIRT:18 APR 1964 PLAC:CIRENCESTER, GLS :CHR:1964
-PLAC:ASHTON KEYNES, WIL NOTE:Godparents, Phyllis Matthews, Hilda Skuse,
-Harold Long :MARR:08 AUG 1986 PLAC:CHIPPENHAM, WIL
```

You will see in this case there is a colon before the tag, when the item changes. Alternatively you can put related items in square brackets [] as in;

```
Tracey /PARK/(SKUSE) [BIRT:18 APR 1964 PLAC:CIRENCESTER, GLS] [CHR:1964
```

-PLAC:ASHTON KEYNES, WIL NOTE:Godparents, Phyllis Matthews, Hilda Skuse,
-Harold Long] [MARR:08 AUG 1986 PLAC:CHIPPENHAM, WIL]

In both of the last two examples you can see a hyphen (-) used at the beginning of continuation lines.
It looks complex at first, but if you try it you will find it works quite well.

We mentioned originally, the use of both descendent charts and positioning, so let me now explain positioning.

Let us first look at a tree.

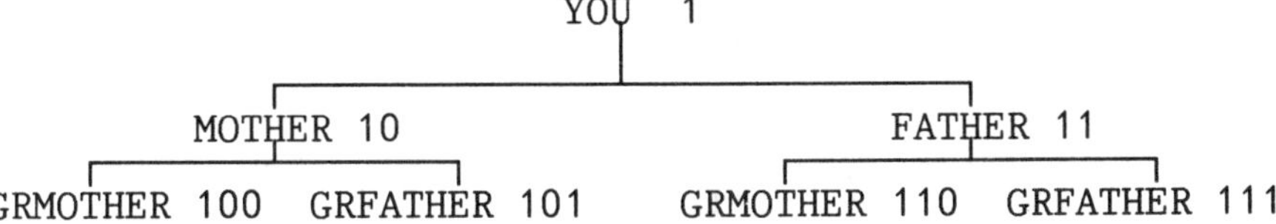

You will see against each individual, I have written a number where zero (0) represents a female, and one (1) a male, and uniquely details the position in your tree. The number of digits also shows the generation. This is shown in the Descendent Chart with a tag of TREE:

The descendent chart can if you wish be broken into many parts, even down to individuals if you wished, provided that at least one person in each section of the descendant chart has a TREE: or LINK:ID tag. To indicate a break from one section of the chart to another either leave two blank lines, or draw a line with the hyphen or minus symbol or underline.

You will see that as you start with descendent charts for different ancestors you could repeat large common sections. This is not necessary, and as soon as a person who is in another descendent chart is mentioned, the section below does not need to be repeated. It is a good idea to put the sequence number with the TREE: or LINK:ID tag on these so the computer definitely recognises them as the same person.

When information is missing you can put a ? For example, Mary/?/ for a Mary where you do not know the Surname of a person or 187? when you know its 1870-1879, but do not know when. Dates should all be written in the format Day Month Year, and can be:-

18 Jun 1990	ABT 1806
Jun 1990	1806/1808
1990	BEF 1949

The prefixes ABT for about, BEF for before, and AFT for after can be used. Once this project is up and running a fuller specification with more options will be available, price £2.95. This will contain extended examples. Information will be available (FREE), on disk, if you send a formatted computer disk and a return envelope.

TAGS FOR USE WITH TEXT SUBMITTED FOR BGD

We have tried to make these tags where possible, similar to those used with GEDCOM. The idea is to allow you to record every piece of known information on each individual.

Start the sheet by defining you are using this specification and follow this with the name, address, and other information on the submitter.

For example:-
SPEC:1
SUBM:KEITH PHILIP /PARK/
SUBF:1000

ADDR:19 PENYBRYN TERRACE, MOUNTAIN ASH, MID GLAMORGAN CF45 3TJ
PHON:0443-478754
TREE:1
WIFE:TRACEY JUNE /PARK/ (SKUSE) LINK: SKUSE.BGD 1

We could put much more down at this time if we wished or we can give more details in the main chart. The risk of entering too much at this time is of confusing which information relates to which person.

The LINK: tag shows that Tracey's Ancestry is defined in another file called SKUSE.BGD, and she would have a TREE: tag of 1 in this file. If LINK: is used all files must be submitted together.

LINK: can be used anywhere.

You may wish to identify two people in your chart as being the same person. This can be done where they are a descendant with the TREE: tag, if not then use LINK:ID1 for the first LINK:ID2 for the second and so on. Both linked people will, of course, show the same number. The DATE: tag can be omitted if the date immediately follows another tag, for example:-

BIRT: DATE:01 OCT 1949 PLAC:Malmesbury CTY:WIL

Is the same as:- BIRT:01 OCT 1949 PLAC:Malmesbury CTY:WIL

The county can be written in full or abbreviated to a three letter code which can be the codes used in Family History Knowledge UK directories, the Chapman County Codes or the British Standard County Codes.

The PLAC: CTY: tags can be omitted if you use the format TAG DATE PLACE COUNTY

For example:- BIRT: 01 Oct 1949 Malmesbury WIL

DEAD or ALIVE. You should know if the people are dead or alive, and you will see there are several tags you can use. Ideally, where people are dead you will be able to show the information with DEAT:, DEAC:, PLAC:, DATE: etc. Sometimes you will know they are dead but have no other information, such as burial, will, or probate in this case the DEAD: tag is useful. The LIVI: or LIVC: tags allow you to define that a person is still alive. The LIVC: tag should in theory not be necessary, if you do use it, please do so sparingly. It defines a person to be alive and that all information relating to them is to be kept confidential. This means that you never end up with a whole in the middle of your tree, due to a wish not to offend someone sensitive about information.

CONFIDENTIAL. You will see in the last paragraph we discussed LIVC:, for very rare cases. More often you will find only certain information is confidential. You can mark any individual piece of information confidential, by adding a ! after the tag. For example;
Jane /WILKS/
-BIRT:
--DATE:!16 JAN 1945
--PLAC:Newmarket SFK
defines just the date of birth as confidential.

Although we feel that the list that follows should cover just about all eventualities, and you will see you have both the NOTE: and COMM: tags to add notes, we have also allowed you to define your own tags and these can be referred to as TAG1: to TAG9: and TAGA: to TAGZ, If you use these then put a statement following SPEC:1 similar to:

SPEC:1

TAG1:=MASONIC ACTIVITIES
TAG2:=EMIGRATED

You can also define your own personal tags, to contain information not to be added to the database.Tags have to be 3 or 4 characters followed by a colon. You define these as items to be ignored by making it equal to 4 capital X's (XXXX), so if you defined your own code for a possibility as GUES: then you would add

SPEC:1
GUES:=XXXX

Any sub item of this will also automatically be omitted.

Hopefully, you will soon get use to this and find it a useful form of shorthand for doing all your research notes. The normal format for Tags are TAG:DATE or DATE RANGE,PLACE,COUNTY. HUSB: and WIFE: also allow for a name before the date.

The first list of TAGS are:

TAG:	DESCRIPTION
ADDR:	ADDRESS (Information will not be used for mailing lists)
ABIL:	Abilities (Music, painting etc)
ADOF:	Shows the family a child has been adopted by (use FAMF: and FAMM: to identify adopted parents. Link can be used.)
ADOP:	ADOPTION. Shows a child is adopted. (use FAMF: and FAMM: to identify birth parents. Link: will also be handy)
AGE:	Age in years unless otherwise indicated
ALIA:	ALIAS (another name, or pet/nickname)
ANUL:	ANNULMENT
APER:	APPEARANCE. (eye colour, hair colour, height etc)
BAPM:	BAPTISM (ADULT)
BARM:	BAR MITZVAH
BASM:	BAS MITZVAH
BIRT:	BIRTH
BLES:	BLESSING
BLOO:	BLOOD type (o,a,b,ab, + or -)
BRUP:	Brought up by
BURI:	BURIAL
CEME:	CEMETERY
CENS:	CENSUS. Format CENS:year,information. Try to include ADDR: and OCCU: tags.
CHAR:	Reserved for later expansion. (Character set in use)
CHIL:	CHILD Used where you know there was a child but do not know the name. Can also be used with other formats not defined here.
CHR:	CHRISTENING
COMM:	COMMENT same as NOTE:
CONF:	CONFIRMATION
CONT:	CONTINUATION Same as hyphen (-)
CREM:	CREMATION
CTR:	COUNTRY (not required for UK)
CTY:	COUNTY
DATE:	DATE
DEAC:	CAUSE OF DEATH. Please give whatever your source states, if you interpret this as something else by todays labels, then you can add this as a NOTE: Please try to use a SOUR: tag to identify where you came across this information.
DEAD:	DEAD. Shows that the person is dead, when no information is known about the death.When possible use DEAT: and DEAC:
DEAT:	DEATH

DIR:	DIRECTORY ENTRY
DIV:	DIVORCE
EDUC:	EDUCATION
ELEC:	ELECTION REGISTER
ENDF:	End family. Allows you to define the end of a family. You will not normally use this. This would be useful if entering family group record sheets, which I have not explained in this article.
ENDE:	End entry, same as : before the next tag, or a].
ENDP:	End person, and continue with previous person at same level.
ENGA:	ENGAGEMENT
FAMC:	Reserved for computer system. (Family child)
FAMF:	Reserved for computer system. (Family father)
FAMM:	Reserved for computer system. (Family mother)
FAMS:	Reserved for computer system. (Family record pointer)
FILE:	File name (optional). You may find it useful.
GENE:	GENETIC INVESTIGATION
GEND:	Doctor involved in investigation, name or file number
GENS:	Genetic material/ sample held by.
HON:	HONOURS RECIEVED
HUSB:	HUSBAND
LAW:	MENTION IN COURT (automatically treated as confidential to any person tagged LIVI: alive)
LEVL:	Level, not defined in this initial specification
LINK:ID	LINK ID shows two people to be the same
LINK:	LINK to another file
LIVC:	LIVING CONFIDENTIAL. Defines a person as alive at the point of submission, and that the person wishes information on them to be kept confidential at this time. Please use sparingly, very few people will need this. The system will not be used for direct mail or other similar purposes.
LIVI:	LIVING. Confirms that at the point of submission the person was not dead. The computer tags the individual LIVI: submission date.
MARB:	MARRIAGE BANNS
MARC:	MARRIAGE CONTRACT
MARL:	MARRIAGE LICENCE
MARR:	MARRIAGE. It is only necessary to show this in one person in each pair. Where there are numerous Marriages either show it in the other person, or put just before the HUSB: or WIFE: tag
MARS:	MARRIAGE SETTLEMENT
MEDI:	MEDICAL PROBLEMS This information will only be released to the individual, to anyone doing medical research or to the person who submitted the information, when the person is alive.
MILL:	MILITARY SERVICE
NAME:	NAME. Provided to ease updating of manual sheets.
NAMR:	RELIGIOUS NAME. (not religion, see RELI:)
NAMS:	NAMESAKE - PERSON NAMED AFTER (LINK ID can be used)
NATU:	NATURALISATION
NEWS:	NEWSPAPER
NOT ID:	Defines two people not to be the same person. Only to be used where confusion if known to occur, for example two people born in the same place in the same year. It makes sense only to use this if you define the other person and their family.
NOTE:	same as COMM:
OCCU:	OCCUPATION
OLD:	Reserved for later system expansion. (Oldest sibling)
OTHE:	OTHER FAMILY (spouse and children of other relationship or marriage). Relates to the person immediately before at the same level.)

PARE:	Reserved for latter expansion. (Parent)
PHON:	TELEPHONE NUMBER (UK std format or international format)
PLAC:	PLACE. (Can have county code as last 3 characters)
PROB:	PROBATE
QUAL:	QUALIFICATIONS
QUAY:	Reserved for later expansion. (Quality of information)
QUES:	Question to computer operator, or explanation where you are unsure of the way to show information.
REFN:	Reserved for computer system use. (Reference number)
REGF:	Reserved for later expansion. (re-regressed from)
REGR:	Reserved for later expansion. (re-regressed to)
RELI:	RELIGION
RETI:	RETIREMENT
SEPT:	SEPERATED, but not divorced.
SEX:	M or F (useful when used with the CHIL: tag)
SIBL:	Reserved for later system expansion. (Sibling)
SOUR:	SOURCE OF INFORMATION
SPEC:	format SPEC:1 (THIS SET)
STIL:	STILLBORN Often their will be no name
SUBF:	SUBMITTERS FILE/MEMBERSHIP NUMBER. If you don't know your file number or do not have one then make sure you include your name and address. File numbers are shown in section D of Family History Knowledge UK Directories as the last item and starts with an F.
SUBM:	SUBMISSION BY (Name)
TAG:	Reserved for computer system use.(Used with user tags)
TAGn:	USER DEFINED TAGS. Where n can be 1-9 and A-Z
TITL:	TITLE
TREE:	POSITION INDICATOR
UPDR:	UPDATE REQUEST. Any developments to file number. Service not provided on start up, but tags can be put in ready now. The format is UPDR: file/membership number.
VAR:	Variant name spelling. Format VAR:name1,name2,...namen
WIFE:	WIFE similar to HUSB: defines spouse
WILL:	WILL
WITN:	WITNESS
YOUN:	Reserved for later system expansion. (Youngest sibling)
	for use with dates
ABT:	ABOUT
AFT:	AFTER. The date or year or after
BEF:	BEFORE. The date or year or before.

There is no limit to line length, characters in a name, number of lines per file, or the amount of information you submit. Spaces with the exception of leading spaces to show generations, are not critical. Please do not use any of the tags defined as reserved.

Example file.

The idea of course is to put in as much information as possible, and any real file would therefore take up many pages. There is no limit to what you can enter and it is a case of the more the better. All the information in this example is fictitious.

```
SPEC:1
FILE:JACOB22.BGD
TAGS:=SEPARATED
TAG1:=EMIGRATED
PRIV:=XXXX
SUBM:Jane /SMITH/(JACOBSON)
```

```
ADDR:125 Church Rd, Frompton-Under-Hill, WIL
PHON:0891 123456
TREE:1
HUSB:JOHN /SMITH/ LINK:SMITH.BGD 1 LINK:DAVIES.BGD 1

STEPHEN JOHN /JACOBSON/ LINK: ID1
-[BIRT: 17 NOV 1898 PLAC: SOUTHAMPTON HAM
-SOUR: BIRTH CERTIFICATE]
-TREE:11
-DEAT:1991 AGE:92 BURI:PORTSMOUTH HAM SOUR:GRAVESTONE
-WIFE:GERALDINE /JACOBSON/ (ELVIN) NORWICH NFK DATE:12 JAN 1900
--TREE:10
--DEAT:ABT 1950 DEAC:CANCER BURI:PORTSMOUTH HAM
    Jane /SMITH/(JACOBSON) 01 APR 1920 PORTSMOUTH HAMPSHIRE TREE:1
    -CHR:12 MAY 1920 Frogbottom Church HAM
    -RELI:C of E
    -CONF:1932 Frogbottom Church HAM
    -EDUC:C OF E School, Frogbottom, Portsmouth, HAM
    -MILL:1939-1945 Ambulance Corps.
    -APER:EYES=HAZEL, HAIR=BLOND, HEIGHT=5FT 2IN
    -APER:!WEIGHT=12ST 6OZ
    -MARR:02 JUN 1949 Portsmouth Cathedral HAM
    -MEDI:1970 Breast Cancer
    -MEDI:1990 Cancer detected in bones
    -BLOO:A+
    -OCCU:Bookkeeper RETI:1980
    -HUSB:JOHN /SMITH/ 01 MAY 1918 FROMPTON-UNDER-HILL WIL
    --CHR:15 MAY 1918 Methodist Chapel Frompton-Under-Hill WIL
    --RELI:Methodist
    --MILL:1939-1945 RAF Airframe Mechanic
    --BLOO:O+
    --APER:EYES=BLUE, HAIR=BROWN, HEIGHT=6FT 2IN
    --ABIL:MUSIC
    --DEAT:08 JUN 1952 Swindon WIL DEAC:heart attack
    --BURI:16 JUN 1952 Minety WIL
        Mary/SMITH/ 16 AUG 1949 DEAT:12 JAN 1951 Swindon WIL
        -DEAC: PNEUMONIA BURI:Swindon WIL
        Irica/SMITH/ 23 SEP 1950
        -QUAL:FCA (Accountant)
        -ADDR: 12 The Common, Fincheley Green BKM
        DAVID /SMITH/ 23 SEP 1950 NOTE:Twin
        -BLOO:A+
        -ABIL:MUSIC
        -MARR:15 JUN 1970 Leigh church WIL
        -WIFE:Janet/SMITH/(GREY)1954 Swansea GLA
        --BLOO:O+
        --DIV:MAY 1974
            JAMES /GREY/ 02 MAY 1970 ALIA: JAMES /SMITH/
            -BLOO:A+
            ANTHONY /SMITH/ 12 MAY 1971
            -BLOO:O+
            Hellen /SMITH/ 18 SEP 1974
            -BLOO:!AB+
            - PRIV: (PRIVATE NOTE) FATHER PROBABLY DR WILLIAMS
        -WIFE:Marion/SMITH/ (DAVIES) 1960 CARDIFF GLA
        --MARR: 12 OCT 1976 ST MARYS, CARDIFF GLA
        --LINK: DAVIES.BGD 1
            Ammy/SMITH/ 06 NOV 1989 CTR:CANADA
```

-MEDI: SPECIAL NEEDS - SEVERE LEARNING DIFFICULTIES
-NAMS:Ammy/WESTWOOD/ LINK:DAVIES.BGD 100
STIL: 15 FEB 1953 SEX:M
PHILIP/SMITH/ 28 DEC 1954
TAG1:1974 CTR:W AUSTRALIA
WIFE:Claire /SMITH/ (LEECH) ABT 1958 PERTH CTR:AUSTRALIA
-MARR: BEF 1990
JAMMIE/SMITH/ 17 FEB 1990 PERTH CTR:AUSTRALIA

JOHN /WYATT/
-TITL:LORD WILTSHIRE 02 MAY 1842
-MILL:Army- Field Marshall
-TREE:1101
-ADDR: DEVIZES CASTLE, DEVIZES WIL
-DEAT: 1899 DEAC:FALL WHILE HUNTING
-WIFF:Mary/WYATT/(RIX) ABT 1850
--TREE:1100
--DEAT: 17 NOV 1898 PLAC: SOUTHAMPTON HAM
--DEAC: GROWTH IN NECK
ELLEN /JACOBSON/(WYATT) 1872
-VAR:WIAT
-TREE 110
-DEAC:CHILDBIRTH
-HUSB:ANTHONY /JACOBSON/ 1870
--TREE:111
EDGER PAUL /JACOBSON/ 1896 DEAT:1908 DEVIZES CASTLE
-DEAC:Drowned in castle mote
STEPHEN JOHN /JACOBSON/ LINK: ID1
Anthia /JACOBSON/17 NOV 1898 NOTE:TWIN
-DEAT 19 NOV 1898

I have tried to show most types of tags being used, over two segments. In order to save room I have omitted much of the detail that would be repetitive in an example of this type. You will see, that you can read a brief history of this family from the little I have shown properly completed. You will see that you would know about where they lived, the pattern of childbearing, education, health and religion and of course much more. Try to use both the PLAC: tag to show their various addresses, showing date ranges if necessary, and the SOUR: source tag to show where you obtained the information from, if the same information is confirmed in more than one source then show all of them as separate following SOUR: Statements.

SOME USEFUL TIPS:-
1. Draw some lines at half inch intervals vertically on a piece of paper, this will help you to line up generations.
2. Break the job into manageable sized pieces. One way to do this is to sketch a family tree, and start a new chart for each set of great-grandparents (4 charts), and then go back in two or three generation steps, doing the same. Another way would be to look at the family tree and have a segment for each family. Remember to include a TREE: tag in each segment.
3. Once in a computer system, it is easy to correct information, add additional information when found, and keep your charts up to date. If you are building it on paper, for someone else to enter, then please make sure all the information can be clearly read.
4. Remember you can use the TREE: tag or the Link: IDn (where n is a number) to connect up segments of your chart. It is usually easier for someone who does not know the family to enter a number of smaller and therefore simpler segments, than it is to enter a very complex chart. Using segments you will also not loose too much of the chart space by stepping in for each generation.
5. Try to always kill off (in the records of course) your ancestors and their families, this helps

you to eliminate obvious errors, and makes the submitted material of much wider interest, and useful for medical research. Please show the source of your knowledge of the cause of death.

6. As soon as you have some done, please send it in, you can add more as often as you like. Don't wait until you finish your research, because there is always more to find out, you will never complete all possible research. If you send a second disk while we still hold a previous one we will return the oldest disk, if you say that the second disk includes the information in the earlier disk.

7. You can put a letter to us on the disk if you like, but if you do please use the file name READ.ME likewise when you get a disk back you should look for a file called READ.ME. Always put your name and address, on a piece of paper, just in case the disk cannot be read for some reason, or has been damaged in the post.

GENETICS - AN INTRODUCTION

You are absolutely unique, there is and will never be anyone exactly the same as you. Below the obvious differences of size, shape, weight, and colour, there are so many other differences which governs how we see the world, through sound, sight, taste, feel and smell. Some of these differences are accounted for by our culture, upbringing, the food we eat and our experiences. There are however many similarities, some insignificant, others more important, some obvious, some not, that is part of our biological inheritance.

Each of us started, with an event, the coming together of two simple cells. One provided by each parent. From the mother comes what is often called an egg, about the size of a pin head, from the father a sperm many times smaller. When these two meet a genetically unique life story begins. In normal cells each brings half the genetic material required. A process of mitosis then happens, this is the constant process of cell division that creates a body. The definition or program for which is encapsulated into every cell.

In the nucleus of each cell we find chromosomes, tiny thread like chains. Normally an equal number from each parent, 22 matching pairs plus two chromosomes, which can be a matching pair in a girl (XX) and a different pair (XY) in a boy. As all females have two identical X chromosomes, you can see it is the father that provides either an X or Y and decides the sex of each child.

Along the chromosomes, can be found genes, and patched into the 46 chromosomes, it is estimated there are at least 100,000 genes. Some of which have been identified, yet the exact function of most have not. The genes can have 2 or more Alleles, or conditions, some of which are dominant to others. However, even such a vast number can't account for every difference, and research into immunities gained would suggest it is how and where the genes touch each other which can store so much information.

The pattern of inherited characteristics, will differ depending on the number of Alleles, the chromosome it is on, and the population it is in. Perhaps we could explain this with two examples:

Example One: - Colour Blindness (CB)

Found in 8% of men and 0.4% of women. (However, 15% of women are carriers and can pass it on to their children).

GRANDFATHER	X Y	1 Normal (Y) + 1 Defective (X) gene	= CB
MOTHER	X X	2 Normal (X) genes	= OK
DAUGHTER	X X	1 Normal (X) + 1 Defective (X)	= OK
HUSBAND		1 Normal (X) + 1 Normal (Y)	= OK
DAUGHTERS SON		1 Defective (X) + 1 Normal (Y)	= CB

As a normal gene masks the effect of a defective gene and is said to be dominant. You can see from the Grandfather the colour blindness has jumped and next appears in the grandson. Of course he has an equal chance of inheriting the good X from his mother, and therefore has only a 50% chance of being effected. Likewise a daughter has a 50% chance of being a carrier. This is of course not the whole story, as some women are colour blind, but this is thought to be the effect of a different gene.

Example Two: - BLOOD TYPE
There are three Alleles relating to blood type, known as type A, type B, and (neither) type O. As each person has two genes you can have:-

OO OA OB AA BB AB Genes
O A B A B AB Blood Types

As A or B is dominant to O you can see that a person with blood type A could be OA or AA. A simple diagram can be used to determine which possible blood groups the children will have, and even predict the occurrence.

FATHER OA MOTHER OO
CHILDREN can be OO OA OB AB any blood type

FATHER AA MOTHER OB
CHILDREN can only be AO Blood type A

FATHER AO MOTHER OO
CHILDREN can be AO or OO Blood type A or O

You can see therefore where the father was a blood type O and mother was blood type A in our BGD example, we assumed the daughters blood group of AB might wish to be flagged as confidential, as in this case it was impossible for the stated father in fact to be the father.

If you give people an incompatible blood type in a transfusion, the blood defences attack the invading blood, forming clots which can be fatal, which accounts for the high mortality rate when blood transfusions first took place before they understood about blood types.

Family Trees are often drawn by people researching potential genetic inheritances, these trees look similar to any other except in the symbols they use.

Two basic symbols are used □ for male and ○ for female
The shape is filled in to show an effected person and a dot is put in the centre to show a carrier.

■ effected male

⊙ female carrier

A line is put through ⍁ to show the person is now dead, so our colour blindness family tree might look like this;

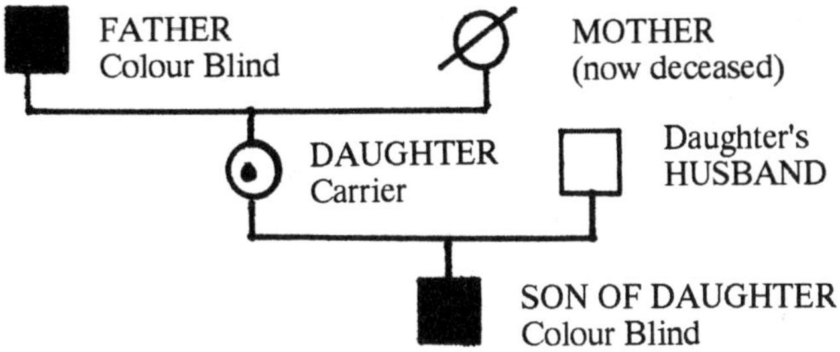

FATHER
Colour Blind

MOTHER
(now deceased)

DAUGHTER
Carrier

Daughter's
HUSBAND

SON OF DAUGHTER
Colour Blind

Now you could carry out the same exercise with various complaints or illnesses, and identify not only who is effected, but who are likely to be carriers, and therefore who may develop a problem. The sister of the boy above, has a 50% chance of being a carrier. It follows therefore that her male children have a 25% chance of being colour blind, and therefore it would make sense to have their colour vision checked.

I have used colour blindness in my example as it is non-fatal and therefore perhaps we feel less emotional about it than conditions which result in early death, but the same could apply. One of the best known examples of this is in the progeny of Queen Victoria, who had haemophilia (inability of the blood to clot), this condition has luckily not been passed down to our current Royal Family, but has effected many of the branches, and been responsible for wiping out many of the Royal Families members throughout Europe.

This brings us onto another point, inbreeding. You will see that the likelihood of two effected genes getting passed on is greatest where inbreeding occurs, and this could be marriages within a small religious community such as the Amish in America, or in small tightly nit communities such as Scottish Islands or small welsh mining communities. Geographic or communication barriers tend to increase the probability, while emigration, large distance movements tend to reduce the chance except when the people who moved live within a self contained community.

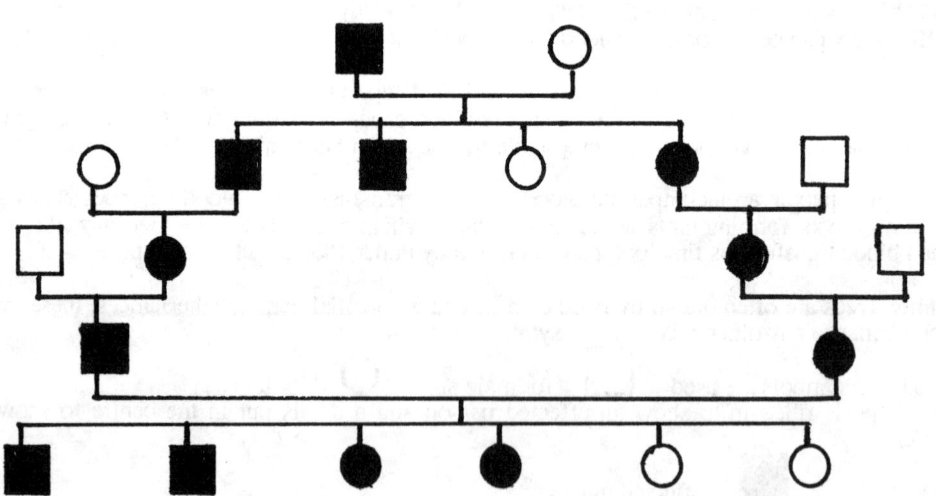

This illustration shows the position when the condition is dominant, here the chance of the lower line being effected the possibilities in this case are high when both parents are effected.

1 Parent effected on 1 gives YN NN
2 Parents effected gives YN NN YY NY 75%

When the condition is not dominant a YN is a carrier. Therefore with one effected parent you don't get an effected person unless it is on the sex (XY) chromosomes. But with two effected people you have 100% chance (all children will be effected), and with two carriers a 25% chance of being effected.

There are a very wide range of disorders that have already been identified as being genetically inherited, and this area, and the ability to selectively screen potential or likely people to have a problem offers the best opportunities of improvements in health care. It also posses an ethical problem, if you can predict certain people will have a higher chance of getting certain cancers, would that not effect their life insurance premiums, after all insurance companies are expert gamblers, and work out probabilities all the time.

Before we leave this, perhaps it would be useful to point out that none of us are pure, we all have some effected genes. Sometimes we would call them different Alleles. Put this book down and fold your arms, did you tuck in your right or left hand. Even this is an inherited trait, as is the ability to roll your tongue, taste certain chemicals, and so much more.

On the positive side, you can inherit abilities or skills, interests, and probably memories. We discussed inherited memory and hypnosis in last years directory.

If you want to look at your genetic family tree, may I suggest you look at cause of death and age at death for each of your ancestors. If they all lived to a hundred, then you haven't learnt much except that the odds are that you will also, but if they all died at an early age of similar problems, and you are approaching that age, then perhaps a check up would be in order, just to put your mind at rest, and just perhaps you might catch a potentially dangerous condition before it gets a hold.

Medicine has progressed a bit over the years, and problems have different names, at different periods, so if you feel there is a possibility why not get your research together and ask your GP, to give it a quick look over, my feeling from previous discussions of hypnosis and the like, you will find half the doctors consider this to be rubbish, while the other half may feel you have discovered a major breakthrough and get all their patients tracing their family histories. Perhaps you would let me know what you find, and remember to send in all your data to the British Genealogical Database.

GENETICS is an enormous subject, we have only lightly touched here, a more detailed overview will be available as a Family Tree Researcher YELLOW guide. If you want a copy, let us know and we will tell you when it is available.

WEIGHTS and MEASURES

The following is a list of weights and measures of the past and the current, showing their equivalents.

Linear Measure	*Metric Equivalent*
1 inch	25.3999 millimetres
1 foot (12 inches)	0.30480 metre
1 yard (3 feet)	0.914399 metre
1 pole (5.5 yards)	5.02919 metres
1 chain (22 yards)	20.11678 metres
1 furlong (220 yards)	201.16778 metres
1 mile (1,760 yards)	1.60934 kilometres
1 league (3 miles)	4.82802 kilometres
100 links (1 chain)	20.11678 metres
10 chains (1 furlong)	201.16778 metres
8 furlong (1 mile)	1.60934 kilometres

Square Measure	
1 square inch	6.45159 sq. centimetres
1 square foot (144 sq in)	9.29028 sq. decimetres
1 square yard (9 sq ft)	0.836126 sq. metre
1 perch (30.25 sq yards)	25.29280 sq. metres
1 rood (40 perches)	10.11712 ares
1 acre (4,840 sq yards)	0.40468 hectare
1 square mile (640 acres)	258.99824 hectares

(30.25 sq. yards = 1 rod, pole or perch)

Measure of Capacity	
1 gill (.25 pint)	1.42058 decilitres
1 pint (4 gills)	0.56823 litre
1 quart (2 pints)	1.13646 litres
1 gallon (4 quarts)	4.5459631 litres
1 peck (2 gallons)	9.0917 litres
1 bushel (8 gallons)	3.6366 dekalitres
1 quarter (8 bushels)	2.90935 hectolitres

(16 fluid ounces = 1 pint)
(1 barrel = varies from 31 to 42 gallons)

Metric Length	
10 millimetres (mm)	1 centimetre (cm)
10 centimetres	1 decimetre (dm)
10 decimetres	1 METRE (m)
10 metres	1 dekametre (dam)
10 dekametres	1 hectometre (hm)
10 hectometres	1 kilometre (km)

Metric Capacity	
10 millilitres (mil)	1 centilitre (cl)
10 centilires	1 decilitre (dl)
10 decilitres	1 litre (lit)
10 litres	1 dekalitre (dal)
10 dekalitres	1 hectolitre (hl)

Continued on Page 1076

FAMILY HISTORY KNOWLEDGE UK 1994

	1991	1992/3	1994
NUMBER OF PAGES	528	1,088	?
PEOPLE SUBMITTING	3,200+	7,300+	?
SURNAMES - TOTAL	17,596	35,179	?
SURNAMES - Sect C Only	11,984	19,579	?
ENTRIES - Section C	51,511	106,040	?
1ST VARIANT ADDITIONAL	138,000	751,593	?
SECT C + 1ST LINK	189,511	851,633	?
EQUIVALENT TO OVER	200,000	1,000,000+	?

(How these figures are calculated can be found in Section A - Introduction).

You will see from the above table the growth rate of this directory. Last year we thought it was a fantastic achievement with the equivalent of over 200,000 entries, twice the worlds largest. This year now the equivalent to over a million entries, and still daily coming across people who have not heard of this directory, so what will next year bring ?

You will have noticed we titled this edition 92/93, this does not mean we are missing a year, but are changing the time it is published. The target this year of April was impossible to meet, and while our original November close was designed for publication at the beginning of the year, it is clear that many people do the majority of their research over the Autumn and Winter, and therefore an early year close, and publishing for next autumn seems sensible. You will also have noticed that most year books come out in advance of the year on their cover. So our 94 edition will come out during the summer of 93.

Given the growth of this directory, it is not sensible to plan to get next years into a single book. We are therefore at this time going to say it will be two volumes, although it might have to be three. As costs increase as the number of pages grow, there is a limit to how far we can go with this directory, and as there is a strong possibility that the 94 edition will be the last, we are making a special edition, and adding two other optional volumes. The first of these is an additional section by name within place, so you can find out who is researching ancestors from the same place. This will allow you to share work with them, and approach them if you wish to see if they have come across any branches of your research, remembering that most people have only listed their main interest. This section is available for this years directory on microfiche costing £5.00.

The other optional section is a special compilation of Family History Sources, the ultimate reference book on where to look to solve those difficult problems. You will see as any or all of these could overflow into more volumes it is starting to look like an encyclopaedia set.

These are of course optional volumes, and as such you can choose what you wish to have, if any. There is no commitment.

FAMILY HISTORY KNOWLEDGE UK 1994 (2 volumes) will cost £19.95 (pre-published price) and we expect £25 when published.
The Optional section by PLACE will cost £8.95 pre-published, and we estimate £12.00 when published.
The Optional section on SOURCES will also cost £8.95 pre-published, and we estimate £12.00 when published.

This edition was sold to people who ordered before it was published at a special price of £14.95, and it turned out to be twice the size, and took a lot more time to build and cost a lot more to print. They still got it at the £14.95 option price. Likewise if you order in advance at the option price the price is guaranteed. All you pay for on dispatch is the cost of the post and packing.

If you are in this edition, then you will receive a computer printout of your entries, for you to check and correct. If you have an IBM compatible computer then also read the section below on computer input options.

A lot of time was taken up in the production of this years directory by trying to work out what had happened in peoples research. If you just send us a list, we don't know if this is instead of, as well as, or some of the entries modified. Therefore please mark additions or modifications for us, and if the modification is not obvious then put what it was, and what it should be now. You can of course send in modifications at any time, and we do prefer to have information as early as possible, and then keep it up to date.

Everyone in the 91 edition was sent computer update forms, all but a few returned them.

This year, you will receive a sheet showing your entries after you have submitted it and it has been entered. This will allow you to make corrections before the next edition goes to the printers, and as you will get a new printout of all entries every time an amendment is made, it means you can use these sheets for your amendments. There are times of the year when we can't keep up, so please don't chase us up for these sheets, if you have sent it in just prior to a bank holiday, or after the closing date. While this edition is as accurate as we could get it, the next, possibly being the last, has to be error free.

You will find that on this years form there are additional questions to previous years, this is not only for the directory, but to help us decide where we go from here.

You will see the form also allows you to join the Family History Club of Great Britain, Time Travellers, a special interest group for people doing place, one name studies and family reconstructions, and of course magazine subscription.

If you are not in this issue, then please either complete the form, or give the same information on a sheet of paper. There is no cost or commitment involved with being included in this directory, and no limit of lines. If you have any difficulties with the form, just tell us what you want to achieve, and we will do our best to comply. We use a form only to make it easy for you to provide information and speed up data entry.

Please don't wait until the closing date to submit entries, as firstly you may forget, and secondly it helps us to spread the load. If your information changes during the year you can send in additional information or modifications. There is no cost to you.

Other information required:

1) Please list all variants you know of to each name on another piece of paper.
2) Please list any studies, collections or special interest you have. Collections are not in this directory, but held as another database. For example, it could be a study of a place, name or item.
3) Please list all address you have had lived at over the last five years. This allows us to flag old addresses on our database, saving unnecessary postage, and also to help people who have lost track of your current address.

Closing date for entries: 15th January 1993. We will, however, include all information received after that date up to the point we need to typeset the pages for the printer, subject to space being available. Information received subsequently, will be included in the next issue. Please do not leave it until the closing date, but send in your entries early, you will then be sent a proof of your entries, that you can correct if necessary.

Publication Date: After the increase in volume this year, and the difficulty in getting everything in, we are allowing longer. Publication is provisionally set for some time during the summer of 93, so expect to see it in August or September.

Data Protection Act: The registered data user is Computer Club Ltd. Our computer databases are not hired out as mailing lists, and the directory contains a method which allows us to see if others are using it as a mailing list. Last year the GRD, and Northumbria Heritage used the 91 directory as a mailing list. There is an option on the form which allows you to specify if you wish to be sent information we felt may interest you. This year we sent out for example details on the Genealogical Bibliographies produced by Stuart Raymond (see advertising section). All our information is now kept on a computer system, manual records are not practical, so we are no longer offering to hold records on cards.

Additional Explanation of Columns: The idea of having both Known and Research columns, is to help you to understand the entry and cut down unnecessary correspondence. The KNOWN columns indicate the dates from and to that you know information for, while the RESEARCH columns show the period you either are researching or would like to know information for. It is up to you how you use this, you can just enter "ALL" across all columns if that is your requirement, or you can be specific or you can for example say you know information for 1860-1940, but are researching this and earlier say from 1500-1940.

If you have any problems with the form, ideas for improvements etc you can call Tracey on the club lines: 0443-475900 or 0443-478754 9am to 9pm Monday to Saturday plus most Sundays. If you do not get an answer please try again later, there are odd occasions when we have to leave the office unwomand, such as getting the groceries. If you call from overseas, please look at the time difference, we will answer your call, but are not at our best at 4.30am. Our home and office are on the same telephone lines.

OTHER INFORMATION REQUIRED:

Names and Addresses: If you know of people interested in Family History, then we would like to know their names and addresses. Addresses more than three years old, are often so far out of date as to not be worth using. Please therefore check your source if it a magazine, newspaper, directory or similar, to see when it was published.

Many county societies have printed interests in their magazines, so far we have seen very few of these. Please first let us know which copies you have, and we will let you know which we would like to borrow. We will return them, and repay you the postage you spend on sending them to us. We have purchased every directory we can identify, but again like the magazines we would like to hear of which ones you have come across. We do not use information directly from other directories or magazines but mail these people details of this directory and a form to allow them to put an entry in the next issue. Some societies object to this, but we feel it is up to the individual to decide to enter information or not. We never disclose where we obtained names and addresses from. If any individual requests that their name be removed from our mailing lists, we flag them deleted at once.

Besides the use as a mailing list, the database also allows us to put back in touch, researchers when they have lost contact with each other.

Studies, Collections and Special Interests: Do you know of someone interested in a particular subject, building a collection, or researching a subject. If so we would like to know. Please don't assume someone else will tell us. There is no limit to the areas we want to index. Collectors will not appear in the directory but will be listed on one of our databases. Some studies and special interests will be listed, but a much wider collection will be added to our databases. You will see that these areas overlap, while a person might collect old cameras, or photograph grave stones, some items cannot be collected because they are too big, expensive or impractical. An example of this second group might be railway carriages, or historic maps.

Our Errors: If you notice any errors we have made, then please let us know. Spelling and typesetting errors, are of little interest unless they make the information contained inaccurate. There will be errors in this book, not because we were careless, but because the only way not to make a mistake is not to do anything.

FREE SUBMISSION OF INTERESTS FOR FAMILY HISTORY KNOWLEDGE UK 1994

SURNAME: ____ F:______

FIRST NAMES: ____

MAIDEN NAME (if required): ____________________________________

ADDRESS: ____

____

______________________________ POSTCODE: ____________________

TELEPHONE: (_______)______________________ Include in Directory ? Y/N

FAX NO: (________)______________________ Include in Directory ? Y/N

DO YOU HAVE AN IBM COMPATIBLE COMPUTER ? Y/N

DO YOU HAVE ANOTHER COMPUTER ? Make:__________________________

IF YOU HAVE A COMPUTER, COULD YOU USE/READ
A GEDCOM FILE ? Y/N

WILL YOU BY MID 93 HAVE SUBMITTED YOUR KNOWN INFORMATION
TO THE BRITISH GENEALOGICAL DATABASE ? Y/N

DO YOU WISH TO RECEIVE OFFERS THAT WE THINK MAY INTEREST
YOU ? (Our mailing list is not sold or rented out) Y/N

DO YOU WISH TO ORDER (Please circle the price):-

94 EDITION (2 volumes) PRE-PUBLISHED PRICE (Paperback)	£19.95
SUPPLEMENTS TO 94 EDITION -	
VOL 3 STUDIES BY PLACE - PRE-PUBLISHED	£8.95
VOL 4 SOURCES - PRE-PUBLISHED	£8.95
92/93 EDITION - PAPERBACK	£18.95
91 EDITION - PAPERBACK	£18.95
(Please add £10 to each you wish to have in Hardback)	
HANDOUT ON BRITISH GENEALOGICAL DATABASE (when released)	£2.95
FAMILY TWIGLETTS SUBSCRIPTION (Free to FHCGB Members) 6 copies	£8.40
TIME TRAVELLERS (Free to FHCGB Members) per annum	£10.00
PACK OF 20 FORMS YOU CAN COPY	£3.75
OPTIONAL - Enrol me as a member of the Family History Club of Great Britain (£15.00 per annum plus £7.50 joining fee)	£22.50
OPTIONAL - I enclose a donation of	£_____

Make Cheques/Postal Orders Payable to: FAMILY HISTORY CLUB
Please charge my Credit Card:

NO:____ EXPIRES:__________

Send to: FAMILY HISTORY CLUB, 19 Penybryn, Mountain Ash, Mid Glamorgan CF45 3TJ
Or Credit Card Orders accepted on 0443-475900 (Telephone or Fax).

See Page 1057 for instructions on completing this form

SURVEY OF FAMILY HISTORY KNOWLEDGE - UK

Please complete in Block Capitals, as clearly as you can. Place can be the name of a town, village or an area (ie north, south, central etc). Known are the dates you know information for, while Research are the dates you wish to find out information or are currently researching.

SURNAME	COUNTY	PLACE	Known FROM	Known TO	Research FROM	Research TO
Skuse	Wiltshire	Leigh	1850	1960	1700	1850

You may continue on another sheet if necessary.

INSTRUCTIONS FOR COMPLETING 1994 ENTRY FORM

There is no cost to you to be included in this directory. You may if you wish order a copy, but you are under no obligation to do so.

1. Complete the block at the end of this section, continuing on another sheet if necessary. Pay particular attention to letters that can be misread. Where several name variations are being researched, include only the main one and include a separate sheet listing all the other name variations. Include British and Irish names only.

2. Complete the address sheet which you will notice has several questions, which you can answer by crossing out the option that does not apply.

3. Special Interests or other studies. Please give us details. See Information Required defined elsewhere in this section.

5. Make a note of the following address and send this form to Family History Club, 19 Penybryn, Mountain Ash, Mid Glamorgan, CF45 3TJ, as soon as you can, but not later than the 15th January 1993.

6. Should your knowledge or interest subsequently change prior to April 1993, then write stating that you have already completed a form and giving the amended information. Do not hold onto the form as you may forget to post it later.

7. If you know of anyone else who should be included then tell them. Information can be supplied on plain paper if they do not have a form available, or if you do not wish to damage the book.

INSTRUCTIONS FOR COMPLETING 1994 ENTRY FORM

IF YOU HAVE AN IBM COMPATIBLE COMPUTER

If you have an IBM compatible computer you can maintain your own interest list, and submit it on computer disk instead of paper.

We are creating a set of computer programs, which will allow you to do this, and to output information for inclusion in other directories as well. If you wish to use this option send a floppy disk formatted on your computer to us, and we will return it with the programs, and if you had information in this directory, the data we have (so you don't have to re-key it). There is no cost for this. If you send in your disk before the computer programs are available we will hold your disk until they are. The computer disk will also contain a definition of the information required, so those of you who like to fiddle with the beastie, can write your own programs if you wish. Please put in a note with the disk, stating the type of computer you have, if you have a hard disk, colour screen etc. Please also state if you use Microsoft Windows. .

You may also be interested to know that the Family History Club of Great Britain operates a (FREE) shareware program for members. Time Travellers, their special interest group for people doing one name studies, place studies, and family reconstructions, also has free software available - see Useful Addresses and Articles sections.

If you have written any programs, that you are happy to share with others, then please send us a copy, (but don't forget to give us some instructions). You will, I am sure, find the article on the British Genealogical Database exciting. Volunteers are always appreciated, so if you could spare some time to enter information for some of the databases being built, please let us know.

SECTION G

USEFUL ADDRESSES

Introduction
In this section we are trying to provide as many addresses and other information as we can, which will help you in your research. This section is broken into the following sub-sections:-

- National Organisations
- Addresses of Computer Software Suppliers
- Miscellaneous.
- ARCHIVES
  - National
    - Channel Islands
    - England and Wales
    - Isle of Man
    - Ireland
    - Scotland
  - County, Local and Special
    - England and Wales
    - Isle of Man
    - Ireland
    - Scotland
  - Mormon Family History Centres

Within each of the above sections the archives are arranged within counties under their county code. A full list of codes is available on the last printed page.

All except the Mormon Centres have been checked by telephone during June 1992. If you find any information has changed, then please let us know.

This list is, we believe, the most complete list of places records are held available. If you find or know of any place that holds records that could be of use to Family Historians, then please let us know.

Key:
O: Opening Hours
L: Location
C: Charges (relates to any charges the offices make for the use of their facilities ie entrance fee or in the case of postal research, some record offices make a charge for this service etc)
P: Parking
R: Research undertaken for you
X: Photocopies or copies of microfilm
B: Booking in advance required (usually because a restricted number of researchers can be accommodated at any one time)
T: Readers Ticket
D: Facilities for disabled researchers
PC: Portable computers allowed in search area
S: Bookshop/Book sales,
CARN: (County Archive Research Network), these Readers Tickets are usually issued free, but you will need one piece of identification, showing your address and in some cases a photograph, check with the office for what is required. A number of Record Offices belong to this scheme and your ticket can be used in any participating office throughout England and Wales.
NOTE: Gives details of information we have come across which we felt was necessary to bring to your attention.
[EDURC01] A unique reference is shown in square brackets which identifies each archive and is part of the Sources Database. If you need to ask or tell us anything in relation to an archive you may find it convenient to use this.
PENCILS all record offices require you to use pencil only, PEN is not allowed. Most of the offices listed close for a lunch break, so check with them individually if this is the case. Most of the offices below also stipulate a last request for documents which can be anything up to an hour before they close.

NATIONAL ORGANISATIONS:
Family History Club of Great Britain, 19 Penybryn, Mountain Ash, Mid Glamorgan, CF45 3TJ. Telephone: 0443-475900 or 478754. 9am to 9pm Monday to Saturday. The Family History Club is a new National Club whose objectives include the establishment of numerous computer databases to help you with your research, and a wide range of help and projects. A separate article on the club will be found in Section F1.

Time Travellers, c/o Family History Club of Great Britain, 19 Penybryn, Mountain Ash, Mid Glamorgan CF45 3TJ. A group set up by the Family History Club of Great Britain to register and encourage people to undertake place studies and family reconstructions. (See article in Section F1). Membership; Free to club members or £10 per annum. Registering of a study is free. Advice and computer software is available.

Society of Genealogists, 14 Charterhouse Buildings, Goswell Road, London, EC1M 7BA. Telephone: 071-251-8799. O:10am to 6pm Tuesday to Saturday, late nights Wednesday and Thursday to 8pm, closed Mondays. Located: in a cul-de-sac at the junction of Goswell Road and Clerkenwell Road about 500 yards north of the Barbican Underground Station. The society has a unique library containing a vast amount of information of interest to the Family Historian. It has a wide range of card indexes, microfiche, and various other indexes. The library is open to non-members for a fee, telephone for current charges. Other services include a quarterly magazine "The Genealogists Magazine" available free to members, and members have use of their library and members room at no extra charge, they may borrow printed books with certain exceptions. Their membership fee is related to the area of the country where you live (or overseas), so therefore you should telephone them to find out how much it will cost you to join. The majority of their members live within the London area.

The Scottish Genealogy Society, Library and Family History Centre, 15 Victoria Terrace, Edinburgh, EH1 2JL. Tel: 031-220-3677. The library is open to members and contains printed books, manuscripts, foreign periodicals, monumental inscriptions from various counties and districts, a copy of the Mormons IGI and microfiche indices to old Parochial Registers of Scotland on a county basis as far as this project has progressed. They also produce a quarterly journal "The Scottish Genealogist", free to members. Single copies available for £3.25 each. O: Tuesday 10.30am to 5.30pm, Wednesday 2.30pm to 8.30pm and Saturday 10am to 5pm.

The Institute of Heraldic and Genealogical Studies, Northgate, Canterbury, Kent CT1 1BA. Tel:0227-768664. A Charitable educational trust, studying the history and structure of the family, engaged mainly in teaching and research. It has a heraldic and genealogical library containing, manuscripts, indexes, research guides and unique collections of research for London, Sussex, Kent and Hampshire. They also have around 20,000 genealogical cases indexed by surname. Access to the library is by appointment only on Monday, Wednesday and Friday 10am to 4.30pm.

Association of Professional Genealogists in Ireland (A.P.G.I), The Genealogical Office, 2 Kildare Street, Dublin 2, Ireland. The main regulating body for commercial genealogical research in records for the whole of Ireland.

Association of Ulster Genealogists and Record Agents (A.U.G.R.A), 54 Rosscoole Park, Belfast, BT14 8JX, Northern Ireland. A similar organisation to A.P.G.I, but concentrating mainly on the province of Ulster.

Ulster Genealogical & Historical Guild, 68 Balmoral Avenue, Belfast, BT9 6NY, Northern Ireland. Tel:0232-681365.

Association of Genealogists and Record Agents (A.G.R.A), 15 Dover Close, Hill Head, Fareham, Hampshire PO14 3SU.

Association of Scottish Genealogists and Record Agents (A.S.G.R.A), 3 Warrington Crescent, Edinburgh EH3 5LA.

Federation of Family History Societies, The Administrator, C/o The Benson Rooms, Birmingham and Midland Institute, Margaret Street, Birmingham B3 3BS. Can tell you if there is a local family history society, who is a member of the Federation, near you.

Guild of One Name Studies, Box G, 14 Charterhouse Buildings, Goswell Road, London EC1M 7BA. An organisation set up by the Federation of Family History Societies to register the first person to claim all research of a particular name. NOTE: The FHK 1992/3 (this directory) contains more one name studies than any other source. All but a few of the Guilds Members, you will find listed within these pages. You will also find a very large number of studies that are not registered with the Guild. If you are undertaking a study then please let us know.

County Societies. Each county has at least one Family History Society. These societies hold local meetings and produce magazines mostly quarterly. Some societies produce members interest directories, but in some cases these are constructed from historic information within their card systems. Some societies maintain indexes to their area, and some of these will be found in County Record Offices. Most societies welcome volunteers to join them in their indexing operations. If you wish to meet with others in your area interested in family history, then you may like to join your local society. Most will welcome you to a few meetings so you can decide if you fit in before expecting any commitment from you. Most members do not attend meetings and their only benefit is the magazine. It is often suggested that you should join numerous societies in each of the areas your ancestors come from, and this practise is widely followed, but you will have to decide if the additional magazines on their own justifies the expense. You can find out information about the local societies by contacting the Federation of Family History Societies, the county record office for the area or major library. Not all local Family History Societies are members of the Federation. NOTE: Many societies have a principle, of not replying to you if you do not include a stamped addressed envelope, leaving many people to believe that the societies are not active.

Association of Family History Societies of Wales 18 Marine Terrace, Aberystwyth, Dyfed SY23 2AZ.

Scottish Association of Family History Societies 4 Loftus Road, Downfield, Dundee, DD2 9TE.

MISCELLANEOUS:

FAMILY TWIGLETTS. A bi-monthly magazine, free to members of the Family History Club of Great Britain, and £8.40 per annum to others. Single copy £2.00. Edited by the Authors of this Directory, it contains articles by Family Historians, reminiscences of life in earlier times by other members, series on special topics like Scottish records, getting your book into print and unusual sources. Available from the Family History Club of Great Britain, 19 Penybryn, Mountain Ash, Mid Glamorgan CF45 3TJ. Credit Card orders accepted on 0443-475900.

BRITISH GENEALOGICAL DATABASE (BGD), c/o Family History Club of Great Britain, 19 Penybryn, Mountain Ash, Mid Glamorgan CF45 3TJ. A database of information relating to British Ancestors. This is new, but within a year or so should be one of your most useful resources. A fuller description of this can be found in the Articles and Projects section (Section F). There is no cost to you in using this service, which also provides (Free) some computer programs that can help you.

COMPUTERS IN GENEALOGY. A quarterly publication of the Society of Genealogists to help genealogists in the use of computers, to share experience, to minimise effort in organising information and designing programs, and to report progress in such applications. It is intended to cater for the amateur genealogist considering the purchase or use of a computer to the professionals needing to process records of genealogical interest. For more details contact Mr Eric D Probert, Editor, Computers in Genealogy, Society of Genealogists, 14 Charterhouse Buildings, Goswell Road, London EC1M 7BA.

FAMILY TREE MAGAZINE, 15/16 Highlode Industrial Estate, Stocking Fen Road, Ramsey, Huntingdon, Cambs PE17 1RB. Tel:0487-814050. A monthly magazine for Family Historians and Genealogists. They also have a new quarterly magazine, started this year (92) called Family Tree Computer Magazine for those of you interested in computers as well.

LOCAL HISTORY Magazine, 3 Devonshire Promenade, Lenton, Nottingham, NG7 2DS. Tel:0602-700369. A magazine covering local history topics, also of interest to Family Historians.

HISTORY GUILD, PO Box 199, Swindon, Wiltshire SN3 4BR. A book club based around History. A monthly magazine will keep you informed of the latest/best books on history subjects, from biography to local history, from monarchy to revolution. Like most book clubs the books are usually discounted slightly but around half of the discount is then lost by their practise of charging packaging on each book.

COLLIE BOOKS LTD, 22a Langroyd Road, London SW17 7PL. Tel:081-767-7421. This company produces two mail order catalogues containing books at well below list prices. These books, mainly publishers overstocks, represent very good value for money. Most appear to be between a quarter and half the normal list price. The Collie Books main catalogue covers both aspects of history, and a number of general interest titles, while their second catalogue called 'Postcript' contains around 500 books mainly connected with history.

The NATIONAL TRUST, 36 Queen Anne's Gate, London, SW1H 9AS.

NATIONAL TRUST FOR SCOTLAND, 5 Charlotte Square, Edinbrugh EH2 4DU.

COMPUSERVE. This is a on-line service you can connect your computer to using a modem. You are charged for time connected, for communication lines and you still have to pay your own telephone bill. Within compuserve there are hundreds of information services and club groups (Forum). One of the club groups is Genealogy Forum. You will find compuserve contains mainly American information. UK contact address: 15/16 Lower Park Row, PO Box 676, Bristol BS99 1YN. Tel:0272-255111.

BULLETIN BOARD: There are a number of people who use their computer to provide an information/communication service to others. Like the compuserve service you need both a computer and modem. You can connect to one of these services by dialling 0483-579631 (8N1). This bulletin board is run by Mike Fisher and he will probably be able to put you in touch with others. Like most bulletin boards it operates on a single line, so you may have to try several times before you can connect.

COMPUTER SOFTWARE SUPPLIERS AND SHAREWARE
NOTE: The Family History Club of Great Britain offer a FREE shareware system to members.

PAF (Personal Ancestral File), Church of Jesus Christ and Later Day Saints, 339 Garrets Garden Lane, Sheldon, West Midlands B33 0UA

PEDIGREE Software, 123 Links Drive, Solihull, West Midlands B91 2DJ

SHAREWARE Marketing, 3a Queen Street, Seaton, Devon EX12 2NY

ADVANTAGE (shareware), 56 Bath Road, Cheltenham, Glous GL53 7HJ

KINGSWAY Computer Services (shareware), 72 Glencoe Road, Sheffield S2 2SR

VASSTEC Ltd (shareware), 1485 Dumbarton Road, Glasgow G14 9XL

PDSL (shareware), Winscombe House, Beacon Road, Crowborough, Sussex TN6 1UL

RED DRAGON (shareware), 3 Oaklea Court, Rhyl, Clwyd LL18 4NP

GEMINI Shareware Ltd, Weston Business Park, The Airport, Locking Moor Road, Weston Super Mare, Avon BS24 8RA

OTHER SOURCES:

Please see the advertising section in this book.
Both your local library and record office will know other addresses covering local history societies, and much more.

NATIONAL ARCHIVES

CHANNEL ISLANDS
Greffe, Royal Court House, Guernsey, Tel:0481-725277 O:9am to 1pm 2pm to 4pm Monday to Friday B: NOTE:Registrar General of Births Deaths and Marriages [CGSYN01]

Ecclesiastical Court, 12 New Street, St Peter Port, Guernsey[CGSYN02]

Judicial Greffe, State Building, 10 Hill Street, Royal Square, St Helier, Jersey, Tel:0534-502300 O:9am to 1pm 2pm to 5.30pm Monday to Thursday 2pm to 5pm Friday R:£6 per hour NOTE:Legal Records open to Lawyers only [CJSYN01]

States Offices, Royal Square, St Helier, Jersey C:£8 per hour for search and then £5 per certificate NOTE:No public access to civil registration records, so you must write to the Superintendent Registrar. NOTE:However, a microfiche copy of indexes from 1842-1900 is now lodged at two places, but only gives name and book number. So search is still required if more than one name exists on the same date. [CJSYN02]

ENGLAND AND WALES ARCHIVES
National Library of Wales, Aberystwyth, Dyfed, SY23 3BU, Tel:0970-623816 O:9.30am to 6pm Monday to Friday, 9.30am to 5pm Saturday. L:Between Bronglais Hospital and the University Campus. C: R: X: B:for viewers T: D: [EDFDN01]

Royal Air Force Personnel, Management Centre, Easton Avenue, Glos GL4 7PN[EGLSN01]

ST CATHERINES HOUSE, 10 Kingsway, London WC2B 6JP, Tel:071-242-0262 O:8.30am to 4.30pm Monday to Friday. NOTE:Civil registration records of births, marriages and deaths in England and Wales since 1837. Also has some Regimental Registers and others. NOTE:(POSTAL ENQUIRIES) General Register Office, Smedley Hydro, Southport, Merseyside PR8 2HH. [ELNDN01]

OFFICE OF POPULATION CENSUSES AND SURVEYS, St Catherines House, 10 Kingsway, London WC2B 6JP, Tel:081-876-3444 ext. 2602 O:9.30am to 4.50pm Monday to Friday R:£11.75 per search [ELNDN02]

PRINCIPAL REGISTRY OF THE FAMILY DIVISION, Somerset House, Strand, London WC2R 1LP, Tel:071-936-6960 O:10am to 4.15pm Monday to Friday C:£2 made payable to H M P G (Her Majesty's Paymaster General) NOTE:Holds post 1857 probate

(Wills) records of England and Wales. NOTE:(Postal Searches) Probate Sub Registry, Duncombe Place, York. YO1 2EA, including name of Deceased, Date of Death and last known Address [ELNDN03]

PUBLIC RECORD OFFICE, Chancery Lane, London, WC2A 1LR, Tel:081-876-3444 O:9.30am to 5pm Monday to Friday. T:proof of identity required on visit NOTE:You need the readers ticket to get to the documents [ELNDN04]

BRITISH LIBRARY, Department of Manuscripts, Great Russell Street, London WC1B 3DG, Tel:071-323-7513/4 (direct) or 071-636-1544 (switchboard) O:10am to 4.30pm Monday to Saturday O:9am to 5pm Monday Friday Saturday, 9am to 9pm Tuesday to Thursday (Main Reading Room). X: T: D: NOTE:Enquiries should be made in advance to the Manuscript Librarian, Manuscript Collection NOTE:apply in advance for readers ticket [ELNDN05]

BRITISH Library Newspaper Library, Colindale Avenue, London NW9 5HE, Tel:071-636-1544 (switchboard) or 071-323-7353/5/6 and 081-200-5515 (Direct Lines) O:10am to 4.45pm Monday to Saturday P: X: T: D: [ELNDN06]

MANORIAL SOCIETY OF GREAT BRITAIN, 65 Belmonth Hill, London SE13 5AX, Tel:081-852-0200 NOTE:Has an index of manors, and their lords and stewards. NOTE:Enquire in writing before visiting, they will then let you know if they have anything there. Supply name and address of person you're looking for, with estimated time period [ELNDN07]

GUILDHALL LIBRARY, Aldermanbury, London EC2P 2EJ, Tel:071-260-1863 O:9.30am to 5pm Monday to Friday and Saturday. Although closed between 1pm and 2pm on Saturday and are not able to produce documents between 12 and 2pm. NOTE:Holds many London original parish registers, Livery Companies, long runs of peerages, directories etc. [ELNDN08]

COLLEGE OF ARMS, Queen Victoria Street, London, EC4V 4BT. NOTE:You can call at the College Mondays to Fridays and get advice from one of the officers. However there is no public access to the records, but they will do searches for you for a fee. [ELNDN09]

IMPERIAL WAR MUSEUM, Department of Documents, Lambeth Road, London SE1 6HZ, Tel:071-416-5000 O:10am to 6pm Monday to Sunday [ELNDN11]

NATIONAL ARMY MUSEUM, Department of Records, Royal Hospital Road, Chelsea, London SW3 4HT, Tel:071-730-0717 O:10am to 5.30pm Monday to Sunday T: [ELNDN12]

ROYAL AIR FORCE MUSEUM, Department of Aviation Records (Archives), Aerodrome Road,Hendon, London NW9 5LL, Tel:081-205-2266 O:10am to 5pm Monday to Friday B: [ELNDN13]

RECORD OFFICE OF THE HOUSE OF LORDS, London SW1A 0PW, Tel:071-219-3074 O:9.30am to 5pm Monday to Friday B: [ELNDN14]

ROYAL COMMISSION ON HISTORICAL MANUSCRIPTS, Quality House, Quality Court, Chancery Lane, London WC2A 1HP, Tel:071-242-1198 O:9.30am to 5pm Monday to Friday R:no charge for small enquiries NOTE:Has detailed information on parish registers and all other archives that have been inspected. [ELNDN15]

Minstry of Defence Army Records, Bourne Avenue, Hayes, Middx UB3 1RF[EMDXN01]

BODLEIAN Library, Department of Western Manuscripts, Bodleian Library, Oxford OX1 3BG, Tel:0865-277000 O:9am to 10pm (term), 9am to 7pm (vacation) Monday to Friday, 9am to 1pm Saturday C: T: [EOXFN01]

PUBLIC RECORD OFFICE, Ruskin Avenue, Kew, Richmond, Surrey TW9 4DU, Tel:081-876-3444 O:9.30am to 5pm Monday to Friday, Closed first two weeks in October for stocktaking T:proof of identity required [ESRYN01]

Modern Records Office, University of Warwick Library, Coventry CV4 7AL, Tel:0203-523523 O:9am to 1pm and 1.30pm to 5pm Monday to Thursday, 9am to 1pm and 1.30pm to 4pm Friday P: X: B: D: S: [EWARN01]

IRELAND

GENERAL REGISTER OFFICE, Oxford House, 49-55 Chichester Street, Belfast, BT1 4HL, Northern Ireland, Tel:0232-235211 O:9.30am to 4pm Monday to Friday [IANTN01]

PUBLIC RECORD OFFICE of Northern Ireland, 66 Balmoral Avenue, Belfast, BT9 6NY, Tel:0232-661621 O:9.15am to 4.45pm Monday to Friday NOTE:Holds official records of the 19th century, private papers from 17th century, and pre-1900 church and school registers. [IANTN02]

GENEALOGICAL OFFICE, 2 Kildare Street, Dublin 2, Ireland, Tel:010-353-1-765521 O: [IDUBN01]

LAND REGISTRY OFFICE, Ely Place, Dublin 2, Ireland, Tel:010-353-1-725194 O:10.30am to 4.30pm Monday to Friday [IDUBN02]

NATIONAL ARCHIVES, Four Courts, Dublin 7, Ireland, Tel:010-353-1-733833 (direct line) O:10am to 5pm Monday to Friday X: D:By prior arrangement NOTE:Have collections of many government and private papers including transportation papers, census returns etc. NOTE:Hopefully from September 92 will be located at Bishops Street, Dublin 2. Telephone 010-353-1781666 [IDUBN03]

NATIONAL LIBRARY OF IRELAND, Kildare Street, Dublin 2, Ireland, Tel:010-353-1-618811 O:10am -9pm Monday, 2pm-9pm Tuesday and Wednesday, 10am to 5pm Thursday, 10am to 1pm Saturday T:Identification required only issue tickets during particular times. Phone for details. [IDUBN04]

THE REGISTER GENERAL, 8-11 Lombart Street (off Pear Street), Dublin 2, Ireland, Tel:010-353-1-711000 O:9.30am to 12.30pm 2.15pm to 4.30pm Monday to Friday NOTE:They hold the registers of all births, deaths and marriages since 1864, (non-catholic from 1845). [IDUBN05]

REGISTRY OF DEEDS, Chancery Street, Dublin 1, Ireland, Kings Inns, Henrietta Street, Dublin 1, Ireland, 010-353-1-732233 O:10.30am to 4.30pm Monday to Friday [IDUBN06]

STATE PAPER OFFICE, Birmingham Tower, The Castle, Dublin 2, Ireland, Tel:010-353-1-792777 NOTE:Houses records before partition which belonged to the Chief Secretary's Office, ie. records of convictions and sentences. [IDUBN07]

ISLE OF MAN
GENERAL REGISTRY, Finch Road, Douglas, Isle of Man, Tel:0624-675506 O:9am to 1pm 2.15pm to 4.30pm Monday to Friday [MIOMN01]

SCOTLAND
SCOTTISH RECORD OFFICE, HM General Register House, Princes Street, Edinburgh, EH1 3YY, Tel:031-334-0380 O:8.45am to 4.30pm Monday to Thursday, 8.45am to 4pm Friday. T: [SMLNN01]

GENERAL REGISTER OFFICE FOR SCOTLAND, New Register House, Edinburgh EH1 3YT, Tel:031-334-0380 O:8.45am to 4.30pm Monday to Thursday 8.45am to 4pm Friday C:phone for complete list [SMLNN02]

NATIONAL LIBRARY OF SCOTLAND, Manuscripts, George IV Bridge, Edinburgh EH1 1EW, Tel:031-226-4531 O:9.30am to 8.30pm Monday to Friday 9.30am to 1pm Saturday T: [SMLNN03]

COURT OF THE LORD LYON, New Register House, Edingburgh EH1 3YT, Tel:031-556-7255 O:10am to 4pm Monday to Friday [SMLNN04]

WEST REGISTER HOUSE, Charlotte Square, Edingburgh EH2 4DF, Tel:031-556-6585 O:9am to 4.45pm Monday to Friday Closed third week of November [SMLNN05]

COUNTY, LOCAL AND SPECIAL

ENGLAND AND WALES

AGY
LLANGEFNI Record Office, Shirehall, Llangefni, Gwynedd LL77 7TW, Tel:0248-750262 O:9am to 5pm Monday to Friday. CARN: [EAGYC01]

AVN
BATH City Record Office, Guildhall, Bath, Avon BA1 5AW, Tel:0225-461111 O:9am to 5pm Monday to Friday NOTE: Telephone in advance, sometimes closed at short notice. NOTE:Parish Register Records (Bath City only) up to 1840, Census returns in Library [EAVNC01]

BRISTOL Record Office, B Bond Warehouse, Smeaton Road, Bristol BS1 6XN, Tel:0272-225692 O:9.30am to 4.45pm Monday to Thursday Closed Friday and Saturday P:Nearby R:£12 per hour X:on request. B: [EAVNC02]

BRISTOL University Library, Tyndall Avenue, Bristol, BS8 1TJ, Tel:0272-303030 O:9.15am to 4.45pm Monday to Friday B: [EAVNU01]

BDF
BEDFORDSHIRE County Record Office, County Hall, Cauldwell Street, Bedford, MK42 9AP, Tel:0234-363222 O:9am to 5pm Monday to Friday. Open 10am first Thursday in month R:by post £15 per hour [EBDFC01]

BKM
BUCKINGHAMSHIRE Record Office, County Hall, Alyesbury, Bucks HP20 1UA, Tel:0296-395000. Fax:0296-383166 O:9am to 5.15pm Tuesday to Thursday 9am to 4.45pm Friday Closed Monday B:to 7.45pm first Thursday of each month CARN: [EBKMC01]

BUCKINGHAMSHIRE Archaeological Society, County Museum, Church Street, Aylesbury, HP20 2QPO:10am to 4pm Wednesday B: [EBKML01]

BRK
BERKSHIRE Record Office, Shire Hall, Shinfield Park, Reading, RG2 9XD, Tel:0734-233182 O:9am to 5pm Tuesday and Wednesday, 9am to 9pm Thursday, 9am to 4.30pm Friday. Not open Monday. L:30 minutes by bus from Reading Railway station. C: P: R: X: B: CARN: NOTE: Census' are not held here, but at Reading Reference Library. [EBRKC01]

Institute of Agricultural History and Museum of English Rural Life, University of Reading, PO Box 229, Whiteknights, Reading, RG6 2AG, Tel:0734-875123 O:10am to 4.30pm Tuesday to Saturday (library) L:Part of University at Whiteknights B: NOTE:Reader Ticket required for long visits once only visit no ticket [EBRKS01]

READING University Library, PO Box 223, Whiteknights, Reading, RG6 2AE, Tel:0734-875123 O:10am to 4.30pm Tuesday to Saturday L:Part of University B: NOTE:Reader Ticket required for long visits, once only visits no ticket [EBRKU01]

CAE
CAERNARFON Record Office, Victoria Dock, Caernarfon, Gwynedd, Tel:0286-679095 Fax:0286-679637 O:9.30am to 5pm Monday to Friday, late night to 7pm Wednesdays. CARN: [ECAEC01]

GWYNEDD County Offices, Shirehall Street, Caernarfon, Gwynedd LL55 1SH, Tel:0286-679089 Fax:0286-679637 NOTE:For site addresses see Caernarfon, Dolgellau and Llangefni. [ECAEC02]

CAM
CAMBRIDGE County Record Office, Shire Hall, Cambridge, CB3 0AP, Tel:0223-317281 O:9am to 5.15pm Monday to Thursday, 9am to 4.15pm Friday, Tuesday evenings by appointment only 5.15pm to 9pm. L:In Castle Street, half a mile north of city centre. P:Nearby X: CARN: D: PC: [ECAMC01]

CAMBRIDGESHIRE Record Office, Grammar School Walk, Huntingdon, PE18 6LF, Tel:0480-425842 O:9.00am to 12.45pm 1.45pm to 5.15pm, Monday to Thursday, 9.00am to 12.45 pm 1.45 pm to 4.15 pm Friday, P:nearby X: B:second Saturday in the month 9.00 am to 12 noon. CARN: [ECAMC02]

Centre of South Asian Studies, Laundress Lane, Cambridge CB2 1SD, Tel:0223-338094 O:9.30am to 5.00pm Monday to Friday B: NOTE:Proof of identity required [ECAMS01]

Scott Polar Research Institute, Lensfield Road, Cambridge CB2 1ER, Tel:0223-336555 O:10am to 12.30pm 2.30pm to 5pm Monday to Friday B: [ECAMS02]

CAMBRIDGE University Library and Archives, Department of Manuscripts, West Road, Cambridge CB3 9DR, Tel:0223-337733 O:9.00am to 6.45pm Monday to Friday, 9.00am to 12.30pm Saturday, closed one week in September B: T: [ECAMU02]

CHURCHILL Archives Centre, Churchill College, Cambridge, CB3 0DS, Tel:0223-336087 or 336178 O:9.00am to 12.30pm 1.30pm to 5.00pm Monday to Friday B: [ECAMU03]

Trinity College Library, Trinity College, Cambridge CB1 1TQ, Tel:0223-338488 O:9am to 5pm Monday to Friday B: [ECAMU04]

CGN
Cardiganshire Area Record Office, County Office, Marine Terrace, Aberystwyth SY23 2DE, Tel:0970-617581 O:9am to 1pm 2pm to 4.45pm Tuesday and Thursday B:microfiche only [ECGNC01]

CHS
CHESHIRE Record Office, Duke Street, Chester, CH1 1RL, Tel:0244-602559 O:9.15am to 4.45pm Monday to Friday also last Saturday of month and late first Wednesday of month P:Not at record office, but nearby. R:by post X: B:Microfiche viewer or table or both D: NOTE: Also includes the Chester Diocesan Record Office. [ECHSC01]

CHESTER City Record Office, Town Hall, Chester CH1 2HJ, Tel:0244-324324 O:9.30am to 7.30pm Monday, 9.30am to 5.30pm Tuesday to Thursday, 9.30am to 5pm Friday. L:in Princess Street. B:required after 5.30pm on Monday [ECHSC02]

STOCKPORT Archive Service, Central Library, Wellington Road South, Stockport SK1 3RS, Tel:061-474-4530 O:9am to 8pm Monday to Friday 9am to 12noon Saturday B: [ECHSL01]

TAMESIDE Local Studies, Stalybridge Library, Trinity Street, Stalybridge SK15 2BN, Tel:061-338-2708 or 061-338-3831 O:9am to 7pm Monday to Wednesday and Friday, closed on Thursday, 9am to 4pm Saturday [ECHSL02]

CLV
CLEVELAND County Archives, Exchange House, 6 Marton Road, Middlesbrough, Cleveland TS1 1DB, Tel:0642-248321 O:9am to 5pm Monday Wednesday Thursday 9am to 9pm Tuesday 9am to 4.30pm Friday R:Specific enquiries, no charge B: T: [ECLVC01]

CMA
CUMBRIA Record Office, 140 Duke Street, Barrow In Furness, Cumbria LA14 1XW, Tel:0229-831269 O:9am to 5pm Monday to Friday. P:limited street parking nearby R:limited X: CARN: [ECMAC01]

CUMBRIA Record Office, The Castle, Carlisle, Cumbria CA3 8UR, Tel:0228-23456 O:9am to 5pm Monday to Friday. L:within the Castle grounds. C: P:at the Castle and nearby. R: X: CARN: [ECMAC02]

CUMBRIA Record Office, County Offices, Kendal, Cumbria LA9 4RQ, Tel:0539-721000 O:9am to 5pm Monday to Friday. C: P:limited R: X: CARN: [ECMAC03]

CMN
CARMARTHENSHIRE Record Office, County Hall, Carmarthen, Dyfed SA31 1JP, Tel:0267-233333 O:9am to 7pm Monday 9am to 4.30pm Tuesday to Thursday and Saturday 9am to 4.15pm Friday R:charges just for photocopies [ECMNC01]

CON
CORNWALL Record Office, County Hall, Truro, TR1 3AY, Tel:0872-73698 O:9.30am to 5pm Tuesday to Thursday, 9.30am to 4.30pm Friday, 9am to 12noon Saturdays. C: R: X: B: CARN: S: [ECONC01]

Royal Institute of CORNWALL, County Museum, River Street, Truro, TR1 2SJ, Tel:0872-72205 O:10am to 1pm 2pm to 5pm Monday to Saturday B: [ECONL01]

CWD
CLWYD Record Office, The Old Rectory, Hawarden, Deeside, Clwyd CH5 3NR, Tel:0244-532364 O:9am to 4.45pm Monday to Thursday, 9am to 4.15pm Friday. R:up to half an hour free of charge T: [ECWDC01]

CLWYD Record Office, 46 Clwyd Street, Ruthin, Clwyd LL15 1HP, Tel:08242-3077 O:9am to 4.45pm Monday to Thursday, 9am to 4.15pm Friday. R:Limited to half an hour free of charge T: CARN: [ECWDC02]

DBY
DERBYSHIRE Record Office, (POSTAL) County Offices, Matlock, Derbyshire, DE4 3AG. (SITE) Ernest Bailey Building, New Street, Matlock, Tel:0629-580000 O:9.30am to 4.45pm Monday to Friday. P:Limited R:£5.50 for half an hour B: [EDBYC01]

DEV
DEVON Record Office, Castle Street, Exeter, Devon, EX4 3PU, Tel:0392-384253 O:9.30am to 5pm Monday to Thursday, 9.30am to 4.30pm Friday, also open some Saturdays. P: R:telephone for charges. X: T:£2 per day, £13 per annum, £6.50 for OAP's. Indentification needed NOTE:Also the Dean and Chapter Archives [EDEVC01]

West DEVON Record Office, 3 Clare Place, Coxside, Plymouth, PL4 0JW, Tel:0752-385940 O:9.30am to 5pm Monday to Thursday, 9.30am to 4pm Friday, also open some Wednesday evenings. P: R:telephone for charges. X: T:£2 per day, £13 per annum, £6.50 for OAP's. Identification needed [EDEVC02]

North DEVON Record Office, Tuly Street, Barnstaple, Devon, EX32 7EJ, Tel:0271-47068 O:9.30am to 5pm Monday, Tuesday, Friday, 9.30am to 4pm Wednesday, 9.30am to 7pm Thursday also open some Saturdays to 4pm R:telephone for charges. X: B:for fiche T:£2 per day, £13 for six months, £6.50 for OAP's. Identification needed D: PC: [EDEVC03]

EXETER University Library, Stocker Road, Exeter EX4 4PT, Tel:0392-263870 O:9am to 5pm Monday to Saturday B: T: [EDEVU01]

DFD
University College of North Wales Library, Department of Manuscripts, Bangor LL57 2DG, Tel:0248-351151 O:9am to 1pm 2pm to 5pm Monday to Friday (9pm on Wednesday in term) [EDFDU01]

DOR
DORSET Record Office, Bridport Road, Dorchester, Dorset DT1 1RP, Tel:0305-250550 O:9am to 5pm Monday to Friday, 9.30am to 12.30pm Saturday. R: B: T: [EDORC01]

DUR
DURHAM Record Office, County Hall, Durham DH1 5UL, Tel:091-386-4411 O:8.45am to 4.45pm Monday to Friday B:readers [EDURC01]

TYNE & WEAR Archives, Blandford House, Blandford Square, Newcastle Upon Tyne NE1 4JA, Tel:091-232-6789 O:8.45am to 5.15pm Monday to Friday with late night opening on Tuesdays to 8.30pm. L:Nearest station is Central. P:nearby R:limited X: B:for microfilm [EDURC02]

GATESHEAD Central Library, Local Studies Collection, Price Consort Road, Gateshead NE8 4LN, Tel:091-447-3478 O:9.30am to 7.30pm Monday and Thursday 9.30am to 5pm Tuesday Wednesday Friday [EDURL01]

NEWCASTLE UPON TYNE City Libraries, Central Library, Princess Square, Newcastle upon Tyne NE99 1DX, Tel:091-261-0691 O:9.30am to 8pm Monday to Thursday 9.30am to 5pm Friday 9am to 5pm Saturday X: D: [EDURL02]

South TYNESIDE Central Library, Prince George Square, South Sheilds, Tyne and Wear NE33 2PE, Tel:091-427-1818 O:9.30am to 7pm Monday to Thursday 9.30am to 5pm Friday 9.30am to 1pm Saturday P: X: D: S: [EDURL03]

Oriental Section, Elvet Hill, Durham DH1 3TH, Tel:0385-64971 O:8.45am to 5pm Monday to Saturday (term), 9am to 1pm 2pm to 5pm (vacation) B: [EDURS01]

DURHAM University Library, Department of Special Collections, Palace Green, Durham DH1 3RN, Tel:0385-64466 O:9am to 5pm Monday to Friday (9am to 12.30pm Saturdays during term) B: T: [EDURU01]

DURHAM Dean and Chapter Library, The College, Durham DH1 3EH, Tel:091-386-2489 O:10am to 1pm 2.15pm to 5pm Monday to Friday Closed in August B: [EDURU02]

Archives and Special Collections, University Library, 5 The College, Durham DH1 3EQ, and The Prior's Kitchen, The College, Durham DH1 3EQ, Tel:091-374-3610/1, Tel:091-374-3615/6 O:10am to 1pm 2pm to 5pm Monday to Friday (Tuesday to 8pm during term) Closed three weeks during summer P: NOTE:Currently split across two buildings, merging into one building (University Library) at end of 92. [EDURU03]

ESS
ESSEX Record Office, PO Box 11, County Hall, Chelmsford CM1 1LX, Tel:0245-430067. Fax:0245-352710 O:9.15am to 5.15pm Tuesday to Thursday, 9.15am to 4.15 Friday and 10am to 8.45pm Mondays. R: X: B:microfilm readers CARN: D:prior notice PC:prior notice S: [EESSC01]

ESSEX Record Office, Stanwell House, Stanwell Street, Colchester, Essex CO2 7DL, Tel:0206-572099 O:10am to 5.15pm Monday 9.15am to 5.15am Tuesday to Thursday 9.15am to 5pm Friday P:nearby R: X: B: [EESSC02]

ESSEX Record Office, Central Library, Victoria Avenue, Southend-on-Sea, SS2 6EX, Tel:0702-612621 O:9.15am to 5pm Monday to Thursday 9.15am to 4.15pm Friday B: [EESSC03]

REDBRIDGE Central Library, Local History Room, Clements Road, Ilford EG1 1EA, Tel:081-478-7145 O:9.30am to 8pm Monday to Friday 9.30am to 4pm Saturday B: [EESSL01]

BARKING AND DAGENHAM Local History Studies, Valence Library, Valence House, Becontree Avenue, Dagenham, Essex RM8 3HT, Tel:081-592-4500 O:9.30am to 7pm Monday Tuesday Thursday and Friday 9.30am to 1pm Wednesday and Saturday P: B:One week in advance [EESSL02]

HAVERING Reference and Information Library, St Edwards Way, Romford, Essex RM1 3AR, Tel:0708-46040 O:9.30am to 8pm Monday to Friday 9.30am to 5pm Saturday D:On request [EESSL03]

GLA
GLAMORGAN Archive Service, County Hall, Cathays Park, Cardiff CF1 3NE, Tel:0222-820282 O:9am to 4.45pm Tuesday to Thursday, 9am to 4.30pm Fridays, not open Mondays. R:£12 per hour B: [EGLAC01]

West GLAMORGAN Record Office, County Hall, Oystermouth Road, Swansea SA1 3SN, Tel:0792-471589 O:9am to 4.45pm Monday to Wednesday. B:5.30pm to 7.30pm Monday [EGLAC02]

University of SWANSEA Library, Singleton, Swansea SA2 8PP, Tel:0792-205678 O:9am to 5pm Monday to Saturday, Closed Saturday in vacation B:up to 10pm evenings [EGLAU01]

GLS
GLOUCESTERSHIRE Record Office, Clarence Row, Alvin Street, Gloucester GL1 3DW, Tel:0452-425295 O:9am to 5pm Monday to Friday, with late night opening to 8pm on Thursdays. C:£2 per day £1.50 over 60's. P: R:£12 per hour X: T:£20 for six months (£10 for OAP's). D: [EGLSC01]

GNT
GWENT County Record Office, County Hall, Cwmbran, Gwent NP44 2XH, Tel:0633-832214. Fax:0633-838225 O:9.30am to 5pm Tuesday to Thursday, 9.30am to 4pm Fridays. R:£11.75 per hour [EGNTC01]

HAM
HAMPSHIRE Record Office, 20 Southgate Street, Winchester, Hants SO23 9EF, Tel:0962-846154 O:9am to 4.45pm Monday to Thursday, 9am to 4.15pm Friday and 9am to 12noon Saturday. P:limited R:limited X: CARN: D: [EHAMC01]

PORTSMOUTH City Record Office, 3 Museum Road, Portsmouth, Hants PO1 2LE, Tel:0705-829765 O:9.30am to 5pm Monday to Thursday, 9.30am to 4pm Fridays. P: CARN: [EHAMC02]

SOUTHAMPTON City Records Office, Civic Centre, Southampton, SO9 4XR, Tel:0703-223855 O:9am to 5pm Monday to Friday. [EHAMC03]

Army Museums Ogilby Trust, Connaught Barracks, Duke of Connaught's Road, Aldershot GU11 2LR, Tel:0252-24431 O:9.30am to 5pm Monday to Friday [EHAMS01]

Royal Naval Museum, HMS Naval Base, Portsmouth, Hants PO1 3LR, Tel:0705-733060 O:10.30am to 5pm Monday to Friday C:£1 and 75p for OAP/Children P: NOTE:You can get details of their holdings by sending a 24p A5 envelope. NOTE:Holds ships logs from 1757 and have 42,000 photographs. Copies of photographs available £2.23-£3.76 plus postage. [EHAMS02]

SOUTHAMPTON University Library, Highfield, Southampton SO9 5NH, Tel:0703-559122 O:9am to 1pm 2pm to 5pm Monday to Friday B: [EHAMU01]

HEF
HEREFORD Record Office, The Old Barracks, Harold Street, Hereford HR1 2QX, Tel:0432-265441 O:10am to 4.45pm Monday, 9.15am to 4.45pm Tuesday to Thursday, 9.15am to 4pm Friday. L:near TA Centre R:£8.40 per hour X: B:microfilm readers CARN: [EHEFC01]

HRT
HERTFORDSHIRE Record Office, County Hall, Hertford SG13 8DE, Tel:0992-555105 O:9.15am to 5.15pm Monday to Thursday 9.15am to 4.30pm Friday [EHRTC01]

HUM
HUMBERSIDE Archive Office, County Hall, Beverley, North Humberside HU17 9BA, Tel:0482-867131 Fax:0482-885035 O:9.15am to 4.45pm Monday to Thursday, Late night Tuesday to 8pm, and 9.15am to 4pm Friday. L:Off Champney Road. P:nearby X: B: [EHUMC01]

SOUTH HUMBERSIDE Area Record Office, Town Hall Square, Grimsby DN31 1HX, Tel:0472-353481 O:9.30am to 12noon 1pm to 5pm Monday to Thursday 9.30am to 12noon 1pm to 4.15pm Friday B: [EHUMC02]

KINGSTON UPON HULL City Record Office, 79 Lowergate, Hull HU1 2AA, Tel:0482-595102 or 595110 Fax:0482-595062 O:8.45am to 4.45pm Monday to Thursday 8.45am to 4.15pm Friday (by appiontment) X: B:Late nights alternate Wednesdays S: [EHUMC03]

HULL University, Brynmor Jones Library, Cottingham Road, Hull HU6 7RX, Tel:0482-462665 O:9am to 1pm 2pm to 5pm Monday to Friday B: [EHUMU01]

HUN
HUNTINGDON County Record Office, Grammar School Walk, Huntingdon, PE18 6LF, Tel:0480-425842 O:9am to 5.15pm Monday to Thursday, 9am to 4.15pm Friday. CARN: [EHUNC01]

IOW
ISLE OF WIGHT County Record Office, 26 Hillside, Newport, Isle of Wight PO30 2EB, Tel:0983-823820 O:9am to 5.30pm Monday to Thursday, 9am to 5pm Friday. X: CARN: [EIOWC01]

KEN
KENT Centre for Kentish Studies, County Hall, Maidstone, Kent ME14 1XQ, Tel:0622-671411 ext 4360 O:9am to 5pm Tuesday to Friday. L:adjacent to HM Prison, opposite Maidstone East BR Station. C: R: X: B: CARN: D: S: NOTE:Non UK residents are charged £11.50 entry fee for part/whole day. [EKENC01]

WEST KENT Area Archives Office, Central Library, The Drive, Sevenoaks, Kent, Tel:0732-452384 O:9.30am to 5.30pm Monday to Wednesday and Friday 9.30am to 8pm Thursday 9am to 5pm Saturday B:microfiche [EKENC02]

KENT Archives Office, SOUTH EAST KENT Area, Central Library, Grace Hill, Folkestone, CT20 1HD, Tel:0303-57583 O:9am to 6pm Monday and Thursday, 9am to 7pm Tuesday and Friday, 9am to 1pm Wednesday, 9am to 5pm Saturday B: [EKENC03]

KENT Archives Office, NORTH EAST KENT Area, Ramsgate Library, Guildford Lawn, Ramsgate CT11 9A1, Tel:0843-593532 O:9.30am to 5.30pm Monday To Wednesday and Friday 9.30am to 5pm Thursday B: [EKENC04]

HYTHE Town Archives, Town Council Offices, Oaklands, Stade Street, Hythe, Kent CT21 6BG, Tel:0303-66152 O:9.30am to 1pm 2pm to 4.45pm Wednesday P: B: D:By Prior Arrangement [EKENC05]

KENT Archives, The Precincts, Canterbury, Kent CT1 2EH, Tel:0227-463510 O:9.30am to 4.30pm Monday to Thursday. L:within Canterbury Cathedral by the Chapter House. C: R: X: B: CARN: D: NOTE:Non UK residents are charged £11.50 entry fee for part/whole day. [EKENC06]

ROCHESTER upon Medway City Archives, Civic Centre, Strood, Rochester, Kent ME2 4AW, Tel:0634-732714 O:9am to 12.45pm 2pm to 4.45pm Monday to Thursday L:Situated behind civic centre in Strood, enter through door beneath Tower Clock. R:on some enquiries X: B: CARN: D: S: [EKENC07]

BEXLEY Libraries and Museums Department, Local Studies Section, Hall Place, Bourne Road, Bexley DA5 1PQ, Tel:0322-526574 O:9am to 5pm Monday to Saturday [EKENL01]

MEDWAY Heritage Centre, Dock Road, Chatham, Kent, Tel:0634-407116 O:10am to 40pm Wednesday to Saturday, 2pm to 5pm Sunday (summer months) or by appointment. [EKENL02]

BROMLEY Public Libraries Archives Section, Central Library, High Street, Bromley KENT BR1 1EX, Tel:081-460-9955 O:9.30am to 6pm Monday Wednesday Friday, 9.30am to 8pm Tuesday and Thursday, 9.30am to 5pm Saturday R: B:24 hours notice [EKENL04]

LAN
LANCASHIRE Record Office, Bow Lane, Preston, Lancs PR1 8ND, Tel:0772-54868 O:10am to 8.30pm Tuesday, 10am to 5pm Wednesday to Friday. R: CARN:idenification needed [ELANC01]

Greater MANCHESTER County Record Office, 56 Marshall Street, New Cross, Manchester M4 5FU, Tel:061-832-5284 O:9am to 5pm Monday to Friday and some Saturdays. P: X: B:microfilm readers. CARN: D: [ELANC03]

WARRINGTON Library, Museum Street, Warrington WA1 1JB, Tel:0925-571232 O:9.30am to 7pm Monday, Tuesday Friday, 9.30am to 5pm Wednesday 9.30am to 1pm Thursday and 9am to 1pm Saturday [ELANL01]

ROCHDALE Libraries, Local Studies Department, Area Central Library, Esplanade, Rochdale OL16 1AQ, Tel:0706-47474 O:9.30am to 7.30pm Monday and Thursday, 9.30am to 5.30pm Tuesday and Friday, 9.30am to 5pm Wednesday, 9.30 to 4pm Saturday B:microfiche reader only [ELANL02]

ST HELENS Local History and Archives Library, Central Library, Gamble Institute, Victoria Square, St Helens WA10 1DY, Tel:0744-24061 O:9.30am to 8pm Monday and Wednesday 9.30am to 5pm rest of week X: B:viewers D: [ELANL03]

MANCHESTER Central Library Archives Department, St Peter's Square, Manchester M2 5PD, Tel:061-236-9422 O:9am to 12noon 1am to 9pm Monday, 9am to 12noon 1pm to 5pm Tuesday to Friday B: [ELANL04]

National Museums and Galleries on MERSEYSIDE, Archives Department, 64-66 Islington, Liverpool L3 8LG, Tel:051-207-3697/8 O:9am to 5pm Monday Tuesday Thursday and Friday, 10am to 5pm Wednesday B: [ELANL05]

LIVERPOOL Record Office and Local History Department, City Libraries, William Brown Street, Liverpool L3 8EW, Tel:051-207-2147 O:9am to 7.30pm Monday to Thursday, 9am to 5pm Friday and Saturday R: T: [ELANL06]

Local Studies Centre, BOLTON Reference Library, Central Library, Le Mans Crescent, Bolton BL1 1SE, Tel:0204-22311 O:9.30am to 7.30pm Monday Tuesday Thursday Friday, 9.30am to 1pm Wednesday 9.30am to 5pm Saturday X: D: [ELANL07]

WIRRAL Archives Service, BIRKENHEAD Reference Library, Borough Road, Birkenhead L41 2XB, Tel:051-652-6106/7/8 O:10am to 8pm Monday Tuesday Thursday and Friday, 10am to 1pm, 2pm to 5pm Saturday [ELANL08]

OLDHAM Library Service, Local Studies Library, 84 Union Street, Oldham OL1 1DN, Tel:061-678-4654 O:10am to 7pm Monday Wednesday Thursday, 10am to 1pm Tuesday, 10am to 5pm Friday, 10am to 4pm Saturday [ELANL09]

BURY Metropolitan Borough Council, Textile Hall, Manchester Road, Bury BL9 0DR, Tel:061-797-6697 or 061-705-5871 (out of hours) O:10am to 1pm 2pm to 5pm Tuesday P: X: B:By appointment for other days (same hours as Tuesday) [ELANL10]

TRAFFORD Library Service, Sale Library, Tatton Road, Sale M33 1YH, Tel:061-973-3142 O:9am to 7.30pm Monday Tuesday Thursday, 9am to 5pm Tuesday and Friday, 9am to 4pm Saturday [ELANL11]

WIGAN Record Office, Town Hall, Leigh WN7 2DY, Tel:0942-672421 O:10am to 4pm Monday to Friday B: [ELANL13]

SALFORD Arhives Centre, 658/662 Liverpool Road, Irlam, Manchester M30 5AD, Tel:061-775-5643 O:9am to 4.30pm Monday to Friday B: [ELANL14]

Maritime Museum, Merseyside, L3 4AA, Tel:051-208-0001 O:10.30am to 4.30pm Tuesday to Thursday P: X: D: NOTE:Shipping archives, emigration documents and both originals and copies of diaries. [ELANS01]

John Rylands University Library of MANCHESTER, Deansgate, Manchester M3 3EH, Tel:061-834-5343 O:10am to 5.30pm Monday to Friday 10am to 1pm Saturday B: T: [ELANU01]

LIVERPOOL University, Sydney Jones Library, PO Box 123, Liverpool L69 3DA, Tel:051-709-6022 O:9am to 12pm 1pm to 5pm Monday to Friday B: [ELANU02]

LIVERPOOL University Archives Unit, PO Box 147, Liverpool L69 3BX, Tel:051-794-2000 O:9.30am to 5pm Monday to Friday B: [ELANU03]

LEI

LEICESTERSHIRE Record Office, 57 New Walk, Leicester LE1 7JB, Tel:0533-473236. Fax:0533-548950 O:9.15am to 5pm Monday Tuesday Thursday, 9.15am to 7.30pm Wednesday, 9.15am to 4.45pm Friday, 9.15am to 12.15pm Saturday P:Wigston address, parking nearby R: X: CARN: D:limited access, give notice of your visit. S: NOTE:Move expected July 92 to Long Street, Wigston. During move will be closed for 12 weeks. [ELEIC01]

LIN

LINCOLNSHIRE Archives Office, St Rumbold Street, Lincoln LN2 5AB, Tel:0522-525158 (search room appointments), 0522-526204 (enquiries and other services) O:2pm to 7.45pm Monday 9am to 5pm Tuesday to Friday 9am to 4pm Saturday C: P: R: X: B:advised T:LAO requires 2 passport photos, and proof of identity. [ELINC01]

LND

Greater LONDON Record Office, 40 Northampton Road, London EC1R 0HB, Tel:071-606-3030 O:9.30am to 7pm Tuesday 9.45am to 4.45pm Wednesday to Friday, Closed Monday L:Underground to Farringdon, Angel or Kings Cross. P: D: NOTE:Also known as Corporation of LONDON Records Office. Holds the Middlesex Archives also. [ELNDC01]

WESTMINSTER Diocesan Archives, Archbishop's House, Ambrosden Avenue, London SW1P 1QJ, Tel:071-938-3580 O:10am to 1pm 2pm to 5pm Monday to Friday B: [ELNDC02]

BARNET Local History Library, Ravensfield House, The Burroughs, Hendon, London NW4 4BE, Tel:081-202-5625 O:9.30am to 5pm Monday to Friday except Wednesday open until 7.30pm, 10am to 5pm Saturday B: [ELNDL01]

Local History Library, BATTERSEA Library, 265 Lavender Hill, London SW11 1JB, Tel:081-871-7467 O:9am to 9pm Monday to Friday 9am to 5pm Saturday X: B:Saturdays D:Reference Library only [ELNDL02]

BRENT Leisure Services, Grange Museum of Local History, Neasden Lane, London NW10 1QB, Tel:081-908-7432 O:12am to 5pm Monday, Tuesday, Thursday and Friday 12am to 8pm, Wednesday 10am to 5pm

Saturday B: [ELNDL03]

CAMDEN Public Libraries, Local History Library, Swiss Cottage Library, 88 Avenue Road, London NW3 3HA, Tel:071-413-6523 O:10am to 7pm Monday and Thursday, 10am to 6pm Tuesday and Friday, 10am to 5pm Saturday [ELNDL05]

CHELSEA Public Library, Local Studies Department, Old Town Hall, King's Road, London, SW3 5EZ, Tel:071-352-6056/2004 O:10am to 8pm Monday Tuesday and Thursday, 10am to 1pm Wednesday, 10am to 5pm Friday and Saturday X: B:For viewers D: [ELNDL06]

CHISWICK District Library, Duke's Avenue, Chiswick, London W4 2AB, Tel:081-994-5295/1008 O:9am to 8pm Monday to Wednesday, 9.30am to 5pm Friday, 9am to 5pm Saturday, Closed Thursday P: D: [ELNDL07]

Local History Library EALING Central Library, 103 Ealing Broadway Centre, Ealing, London W5 5JY, Tel:081-567-3656 O:9am to 7.45pm Tuesday Thursday Friday, 9am to 5pm Wednesday and Saturday, closed Monday P: B: D:possiblity of some arrangements. [ELNDL08]

FINSBURY Local History Collection, Finsbury Library, 245 St John Street, London EC1V 4NB, Tel:071-609-3051 O:9am to 8pm Monday Tuesday Thursday, 9am to 1pm Wednesday and Friday, 9am to 5pm Saturday B:Saturday after 10am 24 hours notice for rest of week D:By arrangement [ELNDL09]

GREENWICH Local History Library, Woodlands, 90 Mycenae Road, Blackheath, London SE3 7SE, Tel:081-858-4631 O:9am to 5.30pm Monday Tuesday, 9am to 8pm Thursday, 9am to 5pm Saturday B: [ELNDL10]

HACKNEY Archives Department, Rose Lipman Library, De Beauvoir Road, London N1 5SQ, Tel:071-241-2886 O:9.30am to 5pm Monday Tuesday Thursday, B: [ELNDL11]

HAMMERSMITH AND FULHAM Archives, Shepherd's Bush Library, 7 Uxbridge Road, London W12 8LJ, Tel:081-741-5159 O:9.30am to 8pm Monday, 9.30am to 1pm Tuesday Thursday, 9.30am to 1pm one Saturday per month R:limited B: [ELNDL12]

HARINGEY Libraries, Museum and Arts Department, Bruce Castle Museum, Lordship Lane, London N17 8NU, Tel:081-808-8772 O:1pm to 5pm Monday to Saturday B: [ELNDL13]

Local History Library, HOLBORN Library, 32-38 Theobalds Road, London WC1X 8PA, Tel:071-413-6345 O:10am to 7pm Monday and Thursday, 10am to 6pm Tuesday and Friday, 10am to 5pm Saturday. Closed Wednesday B: D: [ELNDL14]

HOUNSLOW Library Centre, 24 Treaty Centre, High Street, Hounslow London TW3 1ES, Tel:081-570-0622 O:9.30am to 5.30pm Monday Wednesday Friday Saturday, 9.30am to 8pm Tuesday and Thursday P: X: D: [ELNDL15]

ISLINGTON Archives, Islington Central Library, 2 Fieldway Crescent, London N5 1PF, Tel:071-609-3051 O:9am to 8pm Monday to Thursday, 9am to 5pm (for library) Friday and Saturday X: B:Appointment hours 10am to noon, 2pm to 4pm, 5pm to 7pm depending on staff availability D: [ELNDL16]

KENSINGTON AND CHELSEA Libraries and Arts Service, Central Library, Phillimore Walk, London W8 7RX, Tel:071-937-2542 O:10am to 8pm Monday Tuesday Thursday and Friday, 10am to 1pm Wednesday, 10am to 5pm Saturday B: [ELNDL17]

LAMBETH Archives Department, Minet Library, 52 Knatchbull Road, London SE5 9QY, Tel:071-733-3279 O:10.30am to 7.30pm Monday, 9.30am to 1pm Tuesday Thursday Saturday B: [ELNDL18]

LEWISHAM Local History Centre, The Manor House, Old Road, London SE13 5SY, Tel:081-852-5050 O:9.30am to 5pm Monday Thursday Friday, 9.30am to 8pm Tuesday B: [ELNDL19]

Local History, Marleybone Library, Marleybone Road, London NW1 5PS, Tel:071-798-1030 O:9.30am to 7pm Monday and Thursday, 9.30am to 5pm Tuesday Wednesday Friday Saturday B: [ELNDL20]

WIMBLEDON Central Reference Library, Wimbledon Hill Road, London SW19 7NB, Tel:081-946-1136 O:9.30am to 7pm Monday Tuesday Thursday Friday, 9.30am to 5pm Wednesday and Saturday [ELNDL21]

MITCHAM Public Library, London Road, Mitcham, Surrey CR4 2YR, Tel:081-648-4070 O:9.30am to 7pm Monday Tuesday Thursday Friday, 9.30am to 1pm Wednesday, 9.30am to 5pm Saturday P: X: D: [ELNDL22]

Local Studies Library, Morden Road, London, SW19 3DA, Tel:081-542-2842/1701 O:9.30am to 7pm Monday Tuesday Thursday and Friday ,9.30am to 1pm Wednesday, 9.30am to 5pm Saturday P: X: B: D: [ELNDL23]

Archives and Local History Unit, Southgate Town Hall, Green Lanes London N13 4XD, Tel:081-982-7453 O:9am to 5pm Monday to Saturday P: R:limited B:for viewers D: [ELNDL24]

SOUTHWARK Local Studies Library, 211 Borough High Street, London SE1 1JA, Tel:071-403-3507 O:9.30am to 8pm Monday and Thursday, 9.30am to 5pm Tuesday and Friday, 9.30am to 1pm Saturday B: [ELNDL25]

STRATFORD Reference Library, Water Lane, London E15 4NJ, Tel:081-534-4545 (office hours) or 081-534-1305 (evenings or Saturday) O:9.30am to 7pm Monday Tuesday Thursday Friday, 9.30am to 5pm Wednesday and Saturday X: B: D:by prior arrangement [ELNDL26]

TOWER HAMLETS Libraries, Local History Library, 277 Bancroft Road, London E1 4DQ, Tel:081-980-4366 O:9am to 8pm Monday and Thursday, 9am to 6pm Tuesday and Friday, 9am to 5pm Wednesday and Saturday B: [ELNDL27]

WALTHAM Forest Archives, Vestry House Museum, Vestry Road, Walthamstow, London E17 9NH, Tel:081-509-1917 or 081-527-5544 O:10am to 5.30pm Monday to Friday B:need to make appointment with Manager of Museum for access to archives. [ELNDL28]

WESTMINSTER ABBEY Muniment Room and Library, London SW1P 3PA, Tel:071-222-5152 O:10am to 1pm 2pm to 4.45pm Monday to Friday B: [ELNDL29]

WESTMINSTER CITY Libraries, Archives Section, Victoria Library, 160 Buckingham Palace Road, London SW1W 9UD, Tel:071-798-2180 O:9.30am to 7pm Monday to Friday, 9.30am to 1pm 2pm to 5pm Saturday [ELNDL30]

VICTORIA AND ALBERT MUSEUM, National Art Library, Cromwell Road, London SW7 2RL, Tel:071-589-6371 O:10am to 5pm Tuesday to Saturday T: [ELNDS01]

BRITISH LIBRARY INDIA OFFICES LIBRARY AND RECORDS, 197 Blackfriars Road, London SE1 8NG, Tel:071-928-9531 O:9.30am to 5.45pm Monday to Friday, 9.30 to 12.45 pm Saturday T: [ELNDS02]

SCHOOL OF ORIENTAL AND AFRICAN STUDIES LIBRARY, Malet Street, London WC1E 7HP, Tel:071-263-6013 O:9am to 8pm Monday to Thursday, 9am to 6.30pm Friday (term), 9am to 5pm Monday to Friday (vacation), 9.30am to 12.30pm Saturday [ELNDS03]

BRITISH MUSEUM, Cromwell Road, London SW7 5BD, Tel:071-589-6323 O:10am to 5.50pm Monday to Sunday B: T: [ELNDS04]

BRITISH ARCHITECTURAL LIBRARY, Royal Institute of British Architects, Manuscripts and Archives, Collection, 66 Portland Place, London W1N 4AD, Tel:071-580-5533 O:10.30am to 5pm Monday, 10am to 8pm Tuesday, 10am to 5pm Wednesday to Friday, 10am to 1.30pm Saturday B: [ELNDS05]

ROYAL ASTRONOMICAL SOCIETY LIBRARY, Burlington House, Piccadilly, London W1V 0NL, Tel:071-734-4582/3307 O:9.30am to 5pm Monday to Friday B: [ELNDS06]

INSTITUTE OF CIVIL ENGINEERS, 1-7 Great George Street, London SW1P 3AA, Tel:071-222-7722 O:9.15am to 5.30pm Monday to Friday B:in advance [ELNDS07]

NATIONAL MARITIME MUSEUM, Manuscripts, Greenwich, London SE10 9NF, Tel:081-858-4422 O:10am to 5pm Monday to Friday R:limited [ELNDS08]

INSTITUTE OF ELECTRICAL ENGINEERS, Archives Department, Savoy Place, London WC2R OBL, Tel:071-240-1871 O:10am to 5pm Monday to Friday B:desirable NOTE:Holds archives of its members and some other institutions connected with electricity. List of members from 1871-1992. Also documents relating to the history of electricity. Journals and some companies/EEC records. [ELNDS09]

LAMBETH PALACE LIBRARY, London SE1 7JU, Tel:071-928-6222 O:10am to 5pm Monday to Friday NOTE:Holds marriage allocations for licences granted by the Archbishop of Canterbury. NOTE:You may need a letter of introduction to gain access, telephone first for requirements. [ELNDS10]

LINNEAN SOCIETY OF LONDON, Burlington House, Piccadilly, London W1V 0LQ, Tel:071-434-4479 O:9.30am to 5.30pm Monday to Friday B: [ELNDS11]

SCIENCE MUSEUM LIBRARY, South Kensington, London SW7 5NH, Tel:071-589-3456 O:10am to 6pm Monday to Saturday, 11am to 6pm Sunday B: T: [ELNDS12]

TATE GALLERY ARCHIVES, Millbank, London SW1P 4RG, Tel:071-821-1313 O:10am to 1pm 2pm to 5.50pm Monday to Saturday, 2pm to 5.50pm Sunday B: [ELNDS13]

ROYAL COLLEGE OF PHYSICIANS OF LONDON, 11 St Andrews Place, London NW1 4LE, Tel:071-935-1174 O:9am to 5pm Monday to Friday [ELNDS14]

SOCIETY OF FREINDS' LIBRARY, Friends House, Euston Road, London NW1 2BJ, Tel:071-387-3601 O:10am to 5pm Tuesday to Friday B:only 2 fiche viewers NOTE:closing end of August 92 to end of December for building work. [ELNDS15]

BRITISH LIBRARY OF POLITICAL AND ECONOMIC SCIENCE, 10 Portugal Street, London WC2A 2HD, Tel:071-405-7686 O:9.30am to 7pm Monday to Friday, 9.30am to 9.20pm Tuesday late opening T: [ELNDS16]

ROYAL COLLEGE OF SURGEONS OF ENGLAND, 35-43 Lincoln's Inn Fields, London WC2A 3PN, Tel:071-405-3474 O:10am to 6pm Monday to Friday, Closed in August B: [ELNDS17]

INSTITUTE OF COMMONWEALTH STUDIES, 27-28 Russell Square, London WC1B 5DS, Tel:071-580-5876 O:10am to 7pm Monday to Wednesday, 10am to 6pm Thursday and Friday (term) 10am to 5.30pm (vacation) B: [ELNDS18]

ROYAL COMMONWEALTH SOCIETY LIBRARY, 18 Northumberland Avenue, London WC2N 5BJ, Tel:071-930-6733 O:10am to 5.30pm Monday to Friday B:appointment only T: [ELNDS19]

ARCHIVE OF ART AND DESIGN, 23 Blythe Road, London W14 0QF, Tel:071-603-1514 O:10am to 1pm 2pm to 4.30pm Tuesday to Thursday B: T: [ELNDS20]

ROYAL INSTITUTION OF GREAT BRITAIN, 21 Albemarle Street, London W1X 4BS, Tel:071-409-2992 O:Michael Faraday Museum 1pm to 4pm Monday to Friday B: NOTE:Concerned with Science particularly Physics. [ELNDS21]

CHURCH HOUSE RECORD CENTRE, Church House, Dean's Yard, London SW1P 3NZ, Tel:071-222-9011 NOTE:See Church Commissioners - Archives [ELNDS22]

SOCIETY OF ANTIQUARIES OF LONDON, Burlington House, Piccadilly, London W1V 0HS, Tel:071-734-0193/437-9954 O:10am to 5pm Monday to Friday. Closed from July until 7th September 92. B: [ELNDS23]

WELLCOME INSTITUTE FOR THE HISTORY OF MEDICINE LIBRARY, 200 Euston Road, London NW1 2BP, Tel:071-383-4414 O:9.45am to 5.15pm Monday Wednesday Friday, 9.45am to 7.15pm Tuesday and Thursday T: [ELNDS24]

DR WILLIAMS'S LIBRARY, 14 Gordon Square, London WC1H 0AG, Tel:071-387-3727 O:10am to 5pm Monday Wednesday Friday, 10am to 6.30pm Tuesday and Thursday, Closed first two weeks of August [ELNDS25]

BUSINESS ARCHIVES COUNCIL, 185 Tower Bridge Road, London SE1 2UF, Tel:071-407-6110 [ELNDS26]

ROYAL SOCIETY, 6 Carlton House Terrace, London SW1Y 5AG, Tel:071-839-5561 O:10am to 5pm Monday to Friday B: [ELNDS27]

COURT OF THE CHIEF RABBI, Alder House, Tavistock Square, London WC1H 9HP, Tel:071-387-5772 Fax:071-383-4920 R:write for details of charges NOTE:No public access for purely genealogical purposes. They have researchers who will carry out searches for you, for a fee. NOTE:The major classes of pre-1837 registers have been microfilmed by the Church of the Latter Day Saints and are available in their libraries. [ELNDS28]

THE UNITED SYNAGOGUE, Woburn House, Tavistock Square, London WC1H 0EZ, Tel:071-387-4300 Fax:071-383-4934 R: [ELNDS29]

Church Commissioners Archives, 15 Galley Wall Road, South Bermondsey, London SE16 3PB, Tel:071-222-7010 O:9.30am to 5pm Monday to Friday B: NOTE:Holds records of General Synod and Church Commissioners. NOTE:Write before visiting giving an outline of your research. You will be notified of any records relavent to your research. [ELNDS30]

UNIVERSITY OF LONDON LIBRARY, Senate House, Malet Street, London WC1 7HU, Tel:071-636-4514 O:9.30am to 5.30pm Monday to Saturday B: T: [ELNDU01]

IMPERIAL COLLEGE ARCHIVES, Room 455, Sherfield Building, Imperial College, London SW7 2AZ, Tel:071-589-5111 B: NOTE:Holds papers of scientific interest and administration to college(s) [ELNDU02]

KINGS COLLEGE LONDON, Liddell Hart Centre for MILITARY ARCHIVES, Strand, London WC2R 2LS, Tel:071-836-5454 O:9.30am to 5.30pm Monday to Friday (term), 9.30am to 4.30am (vacation), Closed two weeks in August B: [ELNDU03]

UNIVERSITY COLLEGE LONDON, Manuscripts Room, The Library, Gower Street, London WC1E 6BT, Tel:071-387-7050 O:10am to 5pm Monday Wednesday and Thursday, 10am to 8pm Tuesday, 10am to 5pm Friday B: T: [ELNDU04]

CITY OF LONDON POLYTECHNIC, Fawcett Library, Old Castle Street, London E1 7NT, Tel:071-283-1030 (Polytechnic), Tel:071-320-1000 (Library) O:11am to 5pm Monday 9am to 5pm Tuesday to Saturday [ELNDU05]

MDX

LOCAL HISTORY LIBRARY, Civic Centre Library, PO Box 4, Civic Centre, Harrow Middlesex HA1 2UU, Tel:081-863-5611 O:9am to 8pm Monday Tuesday Thursday, 9am to 6pm Friday, 9am to 5pm Saturday, Closed Wednesday B:proof of identity required [EMDXL01]

LOCAL STUDIES COLLECTION, Hillingdon Borough Libraries, Central Library, High Street, Uxbridge, Middlesex UB8 1HD, Tel:0895-50600 O:9.30am to 8pm Monday to Friday, 9.30am to 5pm Saturday B: D: [EMDXL02]

TWICKENHAM LOCAL STUDIES LIBRARY, Garfield Road, Twickenham, Middlesex TW1 3JS, Tel:081-891-7271 O:10am to 6pm Monday Friday, 10am to 8pm Tuesday, 10am to 5pm Wednesday and Saturday, Closed Thursday X: B: D:by prior arrangement NOTE:local studies Afternoons only [EMDXL03]

MER

DOLGELLAU Record Office, Cae Penarlag, Dolgellau, Gwynedd LL40 2YB, Tel:0341-422341 O:9am to 4.45pm Monday to Friday. CARN: [EMERC01]

NBL

NORTHUMBERLAND Record Office, Melton Park, North Gosforth, Newcastle Upon Tyne NE3 5QX, Tel:091-236-2680 B:Microfilm readers [ENBLC01]

BERWICK Branch Record Office, Berwick Borough Council Offices, Wallace Green, Berwick Upon Tweed, Northumberland TD15, Tel:091-236-2680 or 0289-330044 on Wednesdays O:10am to 1pm 2pm to 5pm Wednesday X: [ENBLC02]

MORPETH Records Centre, The Kylins, Loansdean, Morpeth NE61 2EQ, Tel:0670-514343 [ENBLC03]

NEWCASTLE UPON TYNE University Library, Newcastle upon Tyne NE2 4HQ, Tel:091-232-8511 O:9.15am to 5pm Monday to Friday B: [ENBLU01]

NFK

NORFOLK Record Office, Central Library, Norwich, Norfolk NR2 1NJ, Tel:0603-761349 O:9.15am to 5pm Monday to Friday 9.15am to 12noon Saturday L:Microfilm searchroom located at Shirehall, Market Avenue, Norwich X: B: CARN: D: [ENFKC01]

NTH

NORTHAMPTONSHIRE Record Office, Woottan Hall Park, Northampton NN4 9BQ, Tel:0604-762129 O:9am to 4.45pm Monday to Wednesday, 9am to 7.45pm Thursday and 9am to 4.15pm Friday. Open some Saturdays. NOTE:Some time restrictions on obtaining documents, phone in advance to book [ENTHC01]

NTT

NOTTINGHAMSHIRE Archives Office, County House, High Pavement, Nottingham NG1 1HR, Tel:0602-504524 O:9am to 4.45pm Monday to Friday, late night Tuesdays to 7.15pm, 9am to 12.15pm Saturdays. L:opposite Shire Hall. X: CARN: [ENTTC01]

BRITISH GEOLOGICAL SURVEY LIBRARY, Kegworth, Nottingham NG12 5GG, Tel:0602-376111 O:9am to 4.30pm Monday to Friday B: [ENTTS01]

NOTTINGHAM University Library, Manuscripts Department, University Park, Nottingham NG7 2RD, Tel:0602-506101 O:9am to 5pm Monday to Friday B: [ENTTU01]

OXF
OXFORDSHIRE Archives, County Hall, New Road, Oxford OX1 1ND, Tel:0865-810187 P:nearby B: CARN: [EOXFC01]

The Centre for Oxfordshire Studies, Top Floor, Oxford Central Library, Westgate, Oxford OX1 1DJ, Tel:0865-815749 O:9.15am to 7pm (Closed 5pm Wednesday and Saturday) B:fiche/film viewers recommended NOTE:Holds GRO indexes 1837-1983 [EOXFL01]

NUFFIELD College Library, Oxford OX1 1NF, Tel:0865-278550 O:9.30am to 1pm 2pm to 6pm Monday to Friday. B: [EOXFU01]

RHODES House Library, South Parks Road, Oxford, OX1 3RG, Tel:0865-270909 O:9am to 5pm Monday to Friday, 9am to 1pm Saturday C: B: T: [EOXFU02]

St Antony's College, MIDDLE EAST Centre, Oxford OX2 6JS, Tel:0865-59651 O:9.30am to 5.15pm Monday to Friday, closed two weeks at Easter and Christmas and for August B: [EOXFU03]

PUSEY House Library, Pusey House, 61 St Giles, Oxford, OX1 3LZ, Tel:0865-278415 O:9.15am to 4.45pm Monday to Friday closed 1pm to 2pm each day B. T: [EOXFU04]

PEM
PEMBROKESHIRE Record Office, The Castle, Haverfordwest, Dyfed SA61 2EF, Tel:0437-763707 O:9am to 4.45pm Monday to Thursday, Friday closing at 4.15pm also some Saturdays. [EPEMC01]

POW
POWYS Archives, County Library Headquarters, Cefnllys Road, Llandrindod Wells, Powys LD1 5LD, Tel:0597-2212 O:9am to 5pm Monday to Thursday, 9am to 4pm Friday. [EPOWC01]

SAL
SHROPSHIRE Record Office, Shirehall, Abbey Foregate, Shrewsbury, Shropshire SY2 6ND, Tel:0743-252851 O:9.30am to 5pm Monday to Thursday, closed Wednesdays, 9.30am to 4pm Fridays. B: T: [ESALC01]

SHROPSHIRE Libraries, Local Studies Department, Castle Gates, Shrewsbury SY1 2AS, Tel:0743-361058 O:9.30am to 12.30pm 1.30pm to 5.30pm Monday and Wednesday 9.30am to 12.30pm 1.30pm to 7.30pm Tuesday and Friday, 9.30am to 12.30pm 1.30pm to 4pm Saturday. Closed Thursday [ESALL01]

SFK
SUFFOLK Record Office, Raingate Street, Bury St Edmunds, Suffolk IP33 1RX, Tel:0284-722522 O:9am to 5pm Monday to Thursday, 9am to 4pm Friday, 9am to 5pm Saturdays. L:opposite New Shire Hall and the Police Station. C: P:limited R: CARN: NOTE:Documents required on Saturday must be ordered by 1pm on Friday [ESFKC01]

SUFFOLK Record Office, Gatacre Road, Ipswich, Suffolk IP1 2LQ, Tel:0473-264541 (direct line) 0473-230000 (switchborad) O:9am to 5pm Monday to Thursday, 9am to 4pm Friday, 9am to 5pm Saturdays. L:.75 mile from city centre C: P: R: X: and printout copies from microfilm B: CARN: D: NOTE:documents required on Saturday must be ordered by 1pm on Friday NOTE:They have a coffee machine and small seating area for drinks, also a small garden. [ESFKC02]

SUFFOLK Record Office, Central Library, Clapham Road, Lowestoft NR32 1DR, Tel:0502-566325 O:9.15am to 5pm Monday to Thursday and Saturday, 9.15am to 6pm Friday L:off main shopping centre, first floor of library. C: R: CARN: [ESFKC03]

SOM
SOMERSET Record Office, Obridge Road, Taunton, Somerset TA2 7PU, Tel:0823-337600 O:10.30am to 4.50pm Monday, 9am to 4.50pm Tuesday to Thursday, 9am to 4.20pm Friday and 9.15am to 12.15pm Saturday. P:for 14. R: X: B: [ESOMC01]

SRY
SURREY Record Office, County Hall, Penrhyn Road, Kingston Upon Thames, Surrey KT1 2DN, Tel:081-541-9065 O:9.30am to 4.45pm Monday to Friday, closed Thursdays. B: [ESRYC01]

SURREY Record Office, Guildford Muniment Room, Castle Arch, Guildford GU1 3SX, Tel:0483-573942 O:9.30am to 4.45pm Tuesday to Thursday B:9.30am to 12.30pm 1st and 3rd Saturday of month [ESRYC02]

CROYDON Local Studies Library, Katherine Street, Croydon, Surrey CR0 6ND, Tel:081-679-5414 O:10am to 7pm Monday 10am to 6pm Tuesday to Friday (exept Wednesday when closed), 9am to 5pm Saturday D: [ESRYL01]

KINGSTON Museum and Heritage Centre, Wheatfield Way, Kingston-upon-Thames, Surrey KT1 2PS, Tel:081-546-5386 O:10am to 5pm Monday to Friday P: X: B:two or three days in advance [ESRYL03]

RICHMOND Local Studies Library, Old Town Hall, Whittaker Avenue, Richmond Surrey TW9 1TP, Tel:081-940-5529 O:10am to 5pm Tuesday, 1pm to 8pm Wednesday, 10am to 6pm Thursday and Friday, 10am to 5pm Saturday (closed Monday) Closed for Lunch 12.30pm to 1.30pm X: B: D:By prior arrangement [ESRYL04]

SUTTON Central Library, St Nicholas Way, Sutton, Surrey SM1 1EA, Tel:081-770-4782 O:9.30am to 8pm Tuesday to Friday, 9.30am to 5pm Saturday, Closed Monday P: X: B: D: [ESRYL05]

ROYAL BOTANIC GARDENS LIBRARY, Kew, Richmond TW9 3AE, Tel:081-940-1171 O:9am to 5pm Monday to Friday B: T: [ESRYS02]

SSX
East SUSSEX Record Office, The Maltings, Castle Precincts, Lewes, BN7 1YT, Tel:0273-482356 O:8.45am to 4.45pm Monday to Thursday, 8.45am to 4.15pm Friday. R: X: CARN: S: [ESSXC01]

West SUSSEX Record Office, (POSTAL) County Hall, Chichester, West Sussex PO19 1RN (SITE) Sherburne House, Orchard Street, Chichester PO19 1RN, Tel:0243-533911 O:9.15am to 4.45pm Monday to Friday. L:opposite County Hall. P: X: CARN: D: S: [ESSXC02]

Sussex Combined Services Museum, Redoubt Fortress, Royal Parade, Eastbourne, Sussex [ESSXL01]

ROYAL GREENWICH OBSERVATORY, Herstmonceux Castle, Hailsham BN27 1RP, Tel:0323-833171 O:9am to 5.30pm Monday to Friday B: B:Saturdays and Evenings by Appointment [ESSXS01]

STS
STAFFORDSHIRE Record Office, County Buildings, Eastgate Street, Stafford ST16 2LZ, Tel:0785-223121 O:9am to 5pm Monday to Thursday, 9am to 4.30pm Fridays and 9.30am to 1pm Saturdays. P:nearby X: B: T: D: S: [ESTSC01]

LICHFIELD Joint Record Office, Lichfield Library, The Friary, Lichfield WS13 6QG, Tel:0543-256787 O:10am to 5.15pm Monday to Friday, Wednesdays close at 4.30pm. R: B: [ESTSC02]

William Salt Library, Eastgate Street, Stafford ST16 2LZ, Tel:0785-52276 O:9am to 5pm Tuesday to Thursday 9am to 4.30pm Friday [ESTSL01]

KEELE University Library, Keele ST5 5BG, Tel:0782-621111 O:9.30am to 5pm Monday to Friday 9.30am to 12noon Saturday. Closed ten days at Easter, August Bank Holiday and Christmas B: [ESTSU01]

WAR
WARWICKSHIRE Record Office, Priory Park, Cape Road, Warwick CV34 4JS, Tel:0926-412735 O:9am to 5.30pm Monday to Thursday, 9am to 5pm Fridays and 9am to 12.30pm Saturdays. R:limited £15 per hour T: [EWARC01]

BIRMINGHAM Archives Dept, Central Library, Chamberlain Square, Birmingham, B3 3HQ, Tel:021-235-4219/4217. Fax:021-233-4458 O:9am to 5pm Monday to Saturday (except Wednesday). X: CARN: D: PC: NOTE:Holds historical records that relate to the City of Birmingham and the Anglican Diocese of Birmingham. Also has some records relating to STS, WAR, and WOR which were acquired before the county record offices were set up. [EWARC02]

COVENTRY City Record Office, Mandela House, Bayley Lane, Coventry CV1 5RG, Tel:0203-25555 O:8.45am to 4.45pm Monday to Thursday, 8.45am to 4.15pm Friday B: [EWARC03]

DUDLEY Archives and Local History Department, Dudley Library, St James' Road, Dudley DY9 9EL, Tel:0384-55433 O:9am to 1pm 2pm 5pm Monday Wednesday and Friday, 2pm to 7pm Tuesday and Thursday first and third Saturday in month 9.30am to 12.30pm B: [EWARL01]

WALSALL Archives Service, Local History Centre, Essex Street, Walsall WS2 7AS, Tel:0922-721305 O:9.30am to 5.30pm Tuesday and Thursday, 9.30am to 5pm Friday, 9.30am to 7pm Wednesday, 9.30am to 1pm Saturday. Closed Monday [EWARL02]

WOLVERHAMPTON Borough Archives, Central Library, Snow Hill, Wolverhampton WV1 3AX, Tel:0902-312025 O:10am to 1pm and 2pm 5pm Monday to Saturday [EWARL03]

BILSTON Branch Library, Mount Pleasant, Bilston WV14 7LU, Tel:0902-353830 B: [EWARL04]

SANDWELL Local Studies Service, Smethwick Library, High Street, Smethwick, Warley B66 1AB, Tel:021-558-2561 O:9.30am to 7pm Monday and Friday, 9.30am to 6pm Tuesday Wednesday Thursday, 9am to 1pm Saturday B: [EWARL05]

Local Studies Collection, Central Library, Homer Road, Solihull, West Midlands B91 3RG, Tel:021-704-6977 O:9.30am to 5.30pm Monday to Wednesday, 9.30am to 8pm Thursday and Friday, 9.30am to 5pm Saturday P: D: [EWARL06]

Shakespeare Birthplace Trust Records Office, Henley Street, Stratford-upon-Avon CV37 6QW, Tel:0789-204016 O:9am to 5.30pm Monday to Saturday, 10am to 5.30pm Sunday [EWARS01]

BIRMINGHAM University Library, Special Collections Department, Main Library, PO BOX 363, Brimingham B15 2TT, Tel:021-472-1301 O:9am to 5pm Monday to Friday, Closed second week of July B: [EWARU01]

WIL
WILTSHIRE Record Office, County Hall, Trowbridge, Wiltshire BA14 8JG, Tel:0225-753641 O:9am to 5pm Monday to Friday. CARN: P: L:Across the road from main Council Offices (County Hall) [EWILC01]

WOR
WORCESTER Record Office, County Hall, Spetchley Road, Worcester WR5 2NP, Tel:0905-763763 O:10am to 4.45pm Monday, 9.15am to 4.45pm Tuesday to Thursday and 9.15am to 4pm Fridays. L:off jct 7 of M5 P: X: B:microfilm readers CARN: [EWORC01]

WORCESTER, Fish Street, Worcester WR1 2HN, Tel:0905-765922 O:10am to 4.45pm Mondays, 9.15am to 4.45pm Tuesday to Thursday, 9.15am to 4pm Friday L:off High Street X: B: T: CARN: [EWORC02]

YKS
West YORKSHIRE Archives, Registry of Deeds, Newstead Road, Wakefield, W Yorks WF1 2DE, Tel:0924-290900 O:9am to 8pm Monday, 9am to 5pm Tuesday to Friday. R:exact dates on information required [EYKSC01]

North YORKSHIRE Record Office, County Hall, Northallerton, N Yorks DL7 8AD, Tel:0609-777585 O:9am to 4.45pm Monday, Tuesday and Thursday, 9am to 8.45pm Wednesday, 9am to 4.15pm Friday. L:Malpas Road, Northallterton. P: B:appointment only. D: [EYKSC02]

SHEFFIELD Record Office, (POSTAL) Central Library, Surrey Street, Sheffield S1 1XZ. (SITE) 52 Shorham Street, Sheffield, Tel:0742-734756 O:9.30am to 5.30pm Monday to Thursday, 9am to 4.30pm Saturday. B: T: [EYKSC03]

YORK City Archives, Art Gallery Buildings, Exhibition Square, York YO1 2EW, Tel:0904-651533 O:9.30am to 12.30pm and 2pm to 5.30pm Tuesday to Thursday. L:to the right of the Art Gallery. B:necessary [EYKSC04]

DONCASTER Archives Department, King Edward Road, Balby, Doncaster DN4 0NA, Tel:0302-859811 O:9am to 12.30pm and 2pm to 5pm Monday to Friday R:details necessary [EYKSL01]

Local History Section, Library, Crown Street, Darlington, DL1 1ND, Tel:0325-469858 O:9am to 1pm and 2pm to 7pm Monday to Friday, 9am to 1pm 2pm to 5pm Saturday [EYKSL02]

West YORKSHIRE Archives, 15 Canal Road, Bradford BD1 4AT, Tel:0274-731931 O:9.30am to 5pm Monday to Thursday, alternate Thursdays until 8pm R: B: [EYKSL03]

BARNSLEY Archive Service, Central Library, Shambles Street, Barnsley S70 2JF, Tel:0226-283241 O:9.30am to 1pm and 2pm to 6pm Monday to Wednesday, 9.30am to 1pm and 2pm to 5pm Friday, 9.30am to 1pm Saturday B: [EYKSL04]

West YORKSHIRE Archives, Central Library, Northgate House, Northgate, Halifax HX1 1UN, Tel:0422-357471 (direct line after 5pm) 0422-357257 (main switchborad) O:10am to 8pm Monday to Friday, except Wednesday 10am to 12noon, 10am to 5pm Saturday B:10am to 12noon Wednesday [EYKSL05]

YORK MINSTER Library, Dean's Park, York YO1 2JD, Tel:0904-625308 O:9am to 5pm Monday to Friday B: [EYKSL06]

West YORKSHIRE Archives, Central Library, Princess Alexandra Walk, Huddersfield HD1 2SU, Tel:0484-513808 O:9am to 8pm Monday to Friday, 9am to 4pm Saturday R: B: [EYKSL07]

ROTHERHAM Metropolitan Borough, Brian O'Malley Central Library, Walker Place, Rotherham S65 1JH, Tel:0709-382121 O:9.30am to 7pm Monday Tuesday Thursday Friday, 9.30am to 5pm Wednesday, 9am to 5pm Saturday [EYKSL08]

West YORKSHIRE Archives, Chapeltown Road, Sheepcar, Leeds LS7 3AP, Tel:0532-628339 O:9.30am to 5pm Monday to Friday B: [EYKSL09]

BROTHERTON COLLECTION, University of Leeds, Woodhouse Lane, Leeds LS2 9JT, Tel:0532-431751 O:8.45am to 5pm Monday to Friday B: B:Saturday [EYKSS01]

YORKSHIRE Archaeological Society, Claremont, 23 Claredon Road, Leeds LS2 9NZ, Tel:0532-456362 O:9.30am to 5pm Monday Thursday and Friday, (closed Monday if open on previous Saturday), 2pm to 8.30pm Tuesday and Wednesday, 9.30am to 5pm first and third Saturday of the month [EYKSS02]

YORK University, Borthwick Institute of Historical Research, St Anthony's Hall, Peasholme Green, York YO1 2PW, Tel:0904-642315 O:9.30am to 12.50pm and 2pm to 4.50pm Monday to Friday. Closed two weeks in August Bank Holiday B: [EYKSU01]

SHEFFIELD University Library, Western Bank, Sheffield S10 2TN, Tel:0742-768555 O:9am to 9.30pm Monday to Thursday, 9am to 5pm Friday, 9am to 1pm Saturday (term), 9am to 12.30pm (vacation) B: T: [EYKSU03]

IRELAND
ANT
LINENHALL LIBRARY, 17 Donegall Square North, Belfast, Northern Ireland[IANTL01]

DUB
Dublin Corporation Archives, City Hall, Dame Street, Dublin 2, Tel:010-353-1-6796111 O:by appointment only X: B: D: [IDUBL01]

REPRESENTATIVE CHURCH BODY LIBRARY, Braemor Park, Churchtown, Dublin 14, Ireland, Tel:010-353-1-979979 O:9.30am to 5pm Monday to Friday [IDUBS01]

ISLE OF MAN
IOM
MANX Museum Library, Kingswood Grove, Douglas, Isle of Man, Tel:0624-675522 O:10am to 5pm Monday to Friday R:limited [MIOML01]

SCOTLAND
ABD
GRAMPIAN Regional Archives, Old Aberdeen House, Dunbar Street, Aberdeen AB2 1UE, Tel:0224-481775 O:10am to 5pm Monday to Friday R:limited B: [SABDL01]

ABERDEEN City Archives, Town Hall, Aberdeen AB9 1AQ, Tel:0224-276276 O:9.30am to 12.30pm 2pm to 4.30pm Monday to Friday B:appointment necessary if achivist isn't there no access to records. [SABDL02]

GRAMPIAN Health Board Archives, 1-7 Albyn Place, Aberdeen AB9 8QP, Tel:0224-589901 O:9am to 5pm B: [SABDS01]

ABERDEEN University Library, Department of Manuscripts and Archives, Kings College, Aberdeen AB9 2UB, Tel:0224-480241 O:9.15am to 4.30pm Monday to Friday B: [SABDU01]

AGL
ARGYLL AND BUTE District Archives, Argyll and Bute District Council, Kilmory, Lochgilphead PA31 8RT, Tel:0546-602127 O:9.15am to 1pm 2pm to 5.15pm Monday to Thursday, 9am to 1pm 2pm to 4pm Friday [SAGLL01]

AYR
AYRSHIRE SUBREGIONAL Archives, County Buildings, Wellington Square, Ayr, Tel:0292-266922 x 2138 O:10am to 4pm Wednesday NOTE:To make an appointment other days telephone 041-227-2405 [SAYRL01]

CUMNOCK AND DOON VALLEY District Reference Library, Library Headquarters, Council Offices, Lugar, Ayrshire KA18 3JQ, Tel:0290-22111 O:9am to 4.30pm Monday to Friday P: X: [SAYRL02]

DFS
DUMFRIES AND GALLOWAY Regional Library Service, Ewart Public Library, Catherine Street, Dumfries DG1 1JB, Tel:0387-53820 O:10am to 7.30pm Monday to Wednesday and Friday 10am to 5pm Thursday Saturday R:limited B: [SDFSL01]

DUMFRIES Archive Centre, 33 Burns Street, Dumfries DG1 2PS, Tel:0387-69254 O:11am to 5pm Tuesday

Wednesday Friday 6pm to 9pm Thursday evening B:microfiche [SDFSL02]

STRANREAR Branch Library, Co Wigtown, London Road, Stranrear D69 8ES, Tel:0766-2153 [SDFSL03]

FIF
DUNFERMLINE Central Library, Abbot Street, Dunfermline, Fife KY12 7NW, Tel:0383-723661 O:10am to 7pm Monday Tuesday Thursday Friday 10am to 1pm Wednesday 10am to 5pm Saturday X: B: [SFIFL01]

KIRCALDY Central Library, War Memorial Grounds, Kircaldy, Fife KY1 1YG, Tel:0592-260707 O:3pm to 6.45pm Monday to Thursday 10am to 4.30pm Saturday X: B: [SFIFL02]

The Hay Fleming Reference Library, St Andrews Branch Library, Church Square, St Andrews, Fife, Tel:0334-73381 Enquiries 0334-53722 O:10am to 7pm Monday to Wednesday and Friday 10am to 5pm Thursday Saturday X: [SFIFL03]

ST ANDREWS University Library and University Archives, North Street, St Andrews KY16 9TR, Tel:0334-76161 O:9am to 5pm Monday to Friday [SFIFU01]

INV
MORAY District Record Office, Tolbooth, High Street, Forres IV36 0AB, Tel:0309-673617 O:8.40am to 5pm Monday to Friday B: [SINVL01]

HIGHLAND Regional Archives, Genealogical Research, Inverness Library, Farraline Park, Inverness, Tel:0463-236463 O:9am to 5.30pm Monday to Friday 9am to 6.30pm Tuesday Thursday 9am to 5pm Wednesday Saturday L: opposite the bus station C: R: X: [SINVL02]

MLN
CITY OF EDINGBURGH District Council Archives, Department of Administration, City Chambers, High Street, Edinburgh EH1 1YJ, Tel:031-225-2424 O:9.30am to 4.30pm Monday to Thursday B: [SMLNL01]

ROYAL BOTANIC GARDEN, The Library, Inverleith Row, Edingburgh EH3 5LR, Tel:031-552-7171 O:8.30am to 1pm 2pm to 5pm Monday to Thursday 8.30am to 1pm 2pm to 4.30pm Friday B: [SMLNS01]

SCOTTISH CATHOLIC ARCHIVES, Columba House, 16 Drummond Place, Edinburgh EH3 6PL, Tel:031-556-3661 O:9.30am to 5.30pm Monday to Friday B: [SMLNS02]

LOTHIAN Health Board, Medical Archives Centre, Edinburgh University Library, Edingburgh EH8 9LJ, Tel:031-650-1000 O:9am to 5pm Monday to Friday [SMLNS03]

National Monument Records of SCOTLAND, Royal Commission of Ancient & Historical Monuments of Scotland, John Sinclair House, 16 Bernard Terrace, Edinburgh EH8 9NX, Tel:031-662-1456 O:9.30am to 4.30pm Monday to Friday [SMLNS04]

ROYAL COLLEGE OF PHYSICIANS OF EDINBURGH, 9 Queen Street, Edingburgh EH2 1JQ, Tel:031-225-7324 B: NOTE:Must be a member of the Fellowship [SMLNS05]

Royal College of Surgeons of Edingburgh, Nicholson Street, Edinburgh EH8 9DW, Tel:031-556-6206 O:9am to 5pm Monday to Friday [SMLNS06]

Scottish United Services Museum, The Castle, Edinburgh EH1 2NG, Tel:031-225-7534 O:10am to 5pm Monday to Saturday, 2pm to 5pm Sunday [SMLNS07]

Edinburgh University Library, Special Collections Department, George Square, Edinburgh EH8 9LJ, Tel:031-667-1011 O:9am to 5pm Monday to Friday Closed second week of August B: T: [SMLNU01]

New College Library, Mound Place, Edinburgh EH1 2LU, Tel:031-225-8400 O:9am to 5pm Monday to Friday B: T: [SMLNU02]

Heriot-Watt University Archives, Riccarton, Currie, Edinburgh EH14 4AS, Tel:031-449-5111 O:9.15am to 5pm Monday to Friday [SMLNU03]

OKI
Orkney Archives, The Orkney Library, Laing Street, Kirkwall KW15 1NW, Tel:0856-3166 O:9am to 1pm 2pm to 5pm Monday to Friday B: [SOKIL01]

PER
Perth and Kinross District Archives, Sandeman Library, 16 Kinnoull Street, Perth PH1 5ET, Tel:0738-23329 O:9.30am to 5pm Monday to Wednesday, 9.30am to 8pm Thursday Friday, 9.30am to 1pm Saturday R:by post £10 per hour B:necessary [SPERL01]

Perth Museum and Art Gallery, George Street, Perth PH1 5LB, Tel:0738-32488 O:10am to 5pm Monday to Saturday B: [SPERS01]

Dundee University Library, Archives and Manuscripts Department, Dundee DD1 4HN, Tel:0382-23181 [SPERU01]

RFW
Renfrew District Council Central Library, High Street, Paisley PA1 2BB, Tel:041-887-3672 or 889-2360 O:9am to 8pm Monday to Friday 9am to 5pm Saturday X: B:for Viewers [SRFWL01]

SEL
Border Regions Archealogical and Local History Centre, St Mary's Mill, Selkirk TD7 3EU, Tel:0750-20842 O:9am to 5pm Monday to Thursday, 2pm to 4pm Friday P: R:Limited X: B: D:under review [SSELL01]

SHI
Shetland Archives, 44 King Harald Street, Lerwick ZE1 0EQ, Tel:0595-3535 O:9am to 1pm 2pm to 5pm Monday to Thursday, 9am to 1pm 2pm to 4pm Friday [SSHIL01]

STD
MITCHELL LIBRARY, Glasgow District Libraries, North Street, Glasgow G3 7DN, Tel:041-221-7030 O:9.30am to 9pm Monday to Friday, 9.30am to 5pm Saturday. R:Limited [SSTDL01]

Strathclyde Regional Archives, Mitchell Library, North Street, Glasgow G3 7DN, Tel:041-227-2405 O:9.30am to

4.30pm Monday to Thursday 9.30am to 4pm Friday B: [SSTDL02]

Royal College of Physicians and Surgeons of Glasgow, 234-242 St Vincent Street, Glasgow G2 5RJ, Tel:041-221-6072 O:9.15am to 5pm Monday to Friday B: [SSTDS01]

Business Archives Council of Scotland, Glasgow University Archives, The University, Glasgow G12 8QQ, Tel:041-339-8855 O:9am to 5pm Monday to Friday, closed Wednesday NOTE:Would be helpful to know when you are intending to go, then they can get information out in advance. [SSTDS02]

Greater Glasgow Health Board Archives, University of Glasgow, Glasgow G12 8QQ, Tel:041-330-5516 O:9am to 5pm Monday to Friday [SSTDS03]

Glasgow University Library, Special Collections Department, Hillhead Street, Glasgow G12 8QE, Tel:041-339-8855 O:9.15am to 9pm (term) 9.15am to 4.45pm (vacation) Monday to Friday, 9.15am to 12.15pm (term only) Saturday T: [SSTDU01]

Glasgow University Archives, The University, Glasgow G12 8QQ, Tel:041-339-8855 O:9am to 5pm Monday to Friday B:Evenings in term by appointment T: [SSTDU02]

Strathclyde University Archives, University of Strathclyde, Glasgow G1 1XQ, Tel:041-552-4400 O:9am to 5pm Monday to Friday B: [SSTDU03]

Scottish Record Society, Department of Scottish History, University of Glasgow G12 8QQ, Tel:041-339-8855 (switchboard) [SSTDU04]

Strathclyde Univesity Archives, Livingstone Tower, 26 Richmond Street, Glasgow G1 1HX, Tel:041-552-4400 (switchboard) [SSTDU05]

STI
Central Regional Council Archives Department, Unit 6, Burghmuir Industrial Estate, Stirling FK7 7PY, Tel:0786-50745 O:9am to 5pm Monday to Friday P: X: D: [SSTIL01]

TAY
City of Dundee District Council Archive and Record Centre, 21 City Square, Dundee DD1 3BY (POSTAL), Tel:0382-23141 O:9am to 1pm 2pm to 5pm Monday to Friday X: B: D:prior arrangement NOTE:(callers use 1 Shore Terrace) [STAYL01]

Dundee University Library, Archives and Manuscript Department, Dundee DD1 4HN, Tel:0382-23181 O:9.30am to 4.45pm Monday Wednesday Friday, 9.30am to 1.30pm Thursday R: B: [STAYU01]

MORMAN (LDS) FAMILY HISTORY CENTRES

The Church of Jesus Christ and Later Day Saints (LDS), known as Mormons after the prophet Mormon, have religious reasons for tracing family trees. They put enormous resources into this exercise, and make a lot if not all of their records available to people like you and me, interested in family history. They have, besides their own records, microfilm copies of St Catherines House Indexes and copies of census. You will find they do not preach to you or mention religion so if you normally avoid religious groups you do not need to feel uncomfortable when visiting these centres. The telephone numbers in most cases are of the home of one of their members and you need to phone to find out when the centre is open and to book a seat. There is no charge, but a donation tin is usually on display. An article on why they are so interested in tracing their family trees can be found in our 91 directory. We have not telephoned all of these numbers over the last few weeks, and if you find any are wrong numbers then please let us know.

CHANNEL ISLANDS
JSY
ST HELIER Family History Centre, Ru De La Vallee, St Mary, Jersey, Tel:0534-82171 [CJSYM01]

ENGLAND AND WALES
AVN
BRISTOL Family History Centre, 721 Wells Road, Whitchurch, Bristol, Tel:0272-838326 [EAVNM01]

YATE Family History Centre, The Meeting House, Wellington Road, Yate, Avon, Tel:0454-323004 [EAVNM02]

BDF
ST ALBANS Family History Centre, Cutenhoe Road & London Road, Luton, Beds, Tel:0582-22242/482234 [EBDFM01]

BRK
READING Family History Centre, 280 The Meadway, Tilehurst, Reading, Berks, Tel:0734-427524/410211 [EBRKM01]

CAM
CAMBRIDGE Family History Centre, 670 Cherry Hinton Road, Cambridge CB1 4DR, Tel:0223-247010 [ECAMM01]

PETERBOROUGH Family History Centre, Cottesmore Close, off Atherstone Avenue, Netherton Estate, Peterborough, Cambs, Tel:0733-263374 [ECAMM02]

CHS
CHESTER Family History Centre, 50 Clifton Drive, Blacone, Chester, Cheshire, Tel:0244-390796 [ECHSM01]

CLV
BILLINGHAM Family History Centre, The Linkway, Billingham, Cleveland TS23 3HJ, Tel:0642-563162 [ECLVM01]

CMA
CARLISLE Family History Centre, Langrigg Road, Morton Park, Carlisle, Cumbria CA2 5HT, Tel:0228-26767 [ECMAM01]

CON
HELSTON Family History Centre, Clodgey Lane, Helston, Cornwall[ECONM01]

CWD
RHYL Family History Centre, Rhuddlan Road, Rhyl, Clwyd[ECWDM01]

DEV
PLYMOUTH Family History Centre, Hartley Chapel, Mannamead Road, Plymouth, Devon, Tel:0752-688998/668666 [EDEVM01]

DOR
POOLE Family History Centre, 8 Mount Road, Parkstone, Poole, Dorset, Tel:0202-730646 [EDORM01]

DUR
SUNDERLAND Family History Centre, Linden Road, off Queen Alexander Road, Sunderland, Tyne & Wear, Tel:091-528-5787 [EDURM01]

ESS
ROMFORD Family History Centre, 64 Butts Green Road, Hornchurch, Essex RM11 2JJ, Tel:0402-458412 [EESSM01]

GLA
CARDIFF Family History Centre, Heol y Deri, Rhiwbina, Cardiff, South Glamorgan CF4, Tel:0222-620205 [EGLAM01]

MERTHYR TYDFIL Family History Centre, Nanty Gwenith Street, George Town, Merthyr Tydfil, Mid Glamorgan, Tel:0685-722455 [EGLAM02]

SWANSEA Family History Centre, Cockett Road, Swansea, West Glamorgan[EGLAM03]

GLS
CHELTENHAM Family History Centre, Thirlestaine Road, Cheltenham, Glous, Tel:0242-523433 [EGLSM01]

FOREST OF DEAN Family History Centre, Wynols Hill, Queensway, Colesford, Glos[EGLSM02]

HAM
PORTSMOUTH Family History Centre, Kingston Crescent, Portsmouth, Hants, Tel:0705-696243 [EHAMM01]

HUM
HULL Family History Centre, 725 Holderness Road, Hull, Yorks, Tel:0482-794250 [EHUMM01]

IOW
NEWPORT Isle of Wight Family History Centre, Chestnut Close, Shide Road, Newport, Isle of Wight, Tel:0983-529643 [EIOWM01]

KEN
MAIDSTONE Family History Centre, 76b London Road, Maidstone, Kent ME16 0DR, Tel:0622-757811 [EKENM01]

LAN
ASHTON Family History Centre, Tweedale Street, Rochdale, Lancs OL11 3TZ, Tel:0706-526292 [ELANM01]

LIVERPOOL Family History Centre, 4 Mill Bank, Liverpool L13 0BW, Tel:051-228-0433 [ELANM02]

CHORLEY Family History Centre, 33-41 Walter Street, Chorley, Lancs, Tel:02572-69332 [ELANM03]

MANCHESTER Family History Centre, Altrincham Road, Wythenshawe, Manchester M22 4BJ, Tel:061-902-9279 [ELANM04]

RAWTENSTALL Family History Centre, Haslington Road, Rawtenstall, Rossendale, Lancs, Tel:0706-213460 [ELANM05]

LEI
LEICESTER Family History Centre, Thorpe Hill, Alan Moss Road, Loughborough, Leicester, Tel:0509-214991 NOTE:Presently closed due to fire damage. Contact Mr S Presbury 0533-873028 for more information. [ELEIM01]

LND
WANDSWORTH Family History Centre, 149 Nightingale Lane, Balham, London SW12, Tel:081-673-6741 [ELNDM01]

HYDE PARK Family History Centre, 64/68 Exhibition Road, South Kensington, London SW7 2PA, Tel:071-589-8561 [ELNDM02]

MDX
STAINES Family History Centre, 41 Kingston Road, Staines, Middlesex, Tel:0784-50709/453823 [EMDXM01]

NFK
NORWICH Family History Centre, 19 Greenways, Eaton, Norwich, Norfolk, Tel:0603-52440 [ENFKM01]

KINGS LYNN Family History Centre, Reffley Lane, Kings Lynn, Norfolk, PE30 3EQ, Tel:0553-67000 [ENFKM02]

NTH
NORTHAMPTON Family History Centre, 137 Harlestone Road, Northampton, NN5 6AA, Tel:0604-587630 [ENTHM01]

NTT
MANSFIELD Family History Centre, Southridge Drive, Mansfield, Nottinghamshire NG18 4FT, Tel:0623-26729 [ENTTM01]

NOTTINGHAM Family History Centre, Hempshill Lane, Bulwell, Nottingham NG6 8PA, Tel:0602-274194 [ENTTM02]

SFK
IPSWICH Family History Centre, 42 Sidegate Lane West, Ipswich, Suffolk IP1 3DB, Tel:0473-723182 [ESFKM01]

SSX
CRAWLEY Family History Centre, Old Horsham Road, Crawley, Sussex RH11 8PD, Tel:0293-516151 [ESSXM01]

WORTHING Family History Centre, Goring Street, Worthing, W Sussex[ESSXM02]

STS
LICHFIELD Family History Centre, Purcell Avenue, Lichfield, Staffordshire, Tel:0543-262621/414843 [ESTSM01]

NEWCASTLE UNDER LYME Family History Centre, The Brampton, PO Box 285, Newcastle Under Lyme, Staffordshire ST5 0TV, Tel:0782-620653 [ESTSM02]

WAR
COVENTRY Family History Centre, Riverside Close, Whitley, Coventry, Tel:0203-301420 [EWARM01]

SUTTON COLDFIELD Family History Centre, 185 Penns Lane, Sutton Coldfield, Birmingham, West Midlands, Tel:021-384-2028 [EWARM02]

WOR
REDDITCH Family History Centre, 321 Evesham Road, Crabbs Cross, Redditch, Worcs B97 5JA, Tel:0527-550657 [EWORM01]

YKS
SHEFFIELD Family History Centre, Wheel Lane, Grenoside, Sheffield, South Yorkshire S30 3RL, Tel:0742-453231 [EYKSM01]

HUDDERSFIELD Family History Centre, 2 Halifax Street, Birchencliffe, Huddersfield, West Yorkshire HD3 8BY, Tel:0484-420352 [EYKSM02]

YORK Family History Centre, West Bank, Acomb, York, Tel:0904-785128 [EYKSM03]

LEEDS Family History Centre, Vesper Road, Leeds, West Yorkshire LS5 3QT, Tel:0532-585297 [EYKSM04]

IRELAND
DOW
BELFAST Family History Centre, 401 Holywood Road, Belfast, Co Down, Northern Ireland BT4 2GU, Tel:0232-768250 [IDOWM01]

DUB
DUBLIN Family History Centre, Ireland Dublin Mission, The Willows, Finglas, Dublin 11, Tel:010-353-1-4625609 [IDUBM01]

LDY
LONDONDERRY Family History Centre, Racecourse Road, Blemont Estate, Londonderry, Northern Ireland[ILDYM01]

ISLE OF MAN
IOM
DOUGLAS Family History Centre, Woodside, Woodbourne Road, Douglas, Isle of Man, Tel:0624-675834 [MIOMM01]

SCOTLAND
ABD
ABERDEEN Family History Centre, North Anderson Drive, Aberdeen, Grampian, Scotland, Tel:0224-692206 [SABDM01]

AYR
KILMARNOCK Family History Centre, Whatriggs Road, Kilmarnock, Ayrshire KA1 3QY[SAYRM01]

FIF
KIRKCALDY Family History Centre, Winifred Crescent, Forth Park, Kirkcaldy, Fife, Tel:0592-640041 [SFIFM01]

MLN
EDINBURGH Family History Centre, 30a Colinton Road, Edinburgh E10, Tel:031-337-3049 [SMLNM01]

STD
GLASGOW Family History Centre, 35 Julian Avenue, Glasgow, Strathclyde G12, Tel:041-357-1024 [SSTDM01]

PAISLEY Family History Centre, Campbell Street, Johnstone, Strathclyde PA5 8LD, Tel:0505-20886 [SSTDM02]

TAY
DUNDEE Family History Centre, Bingham Terrace, Dundee, Tayside, Tel:0382-451247 [STAYM01]

Continued from page 1051.

International Paper Sizes

A0 (46.75 x 33.125 in)	1189mm x 841mm
A1 (33.125 x 23.375 in)	841mm x 594mm
A2 (23.375 x 16.5 in)	594mm x 420mm
A3 (16.5 x 11.75 in)	420mm x 297mm
A4 (11.75 x 8.25 in)	297mm x 210mm
A5 (8.25 x 5.875 in)	210mm x 148mm
A6 (5.875 x 4.125 in)	148mm x 105mm
A7 (4.125 x 2.875 in)	105mm x 74mm

Envelope Sizes

DL (4.75 X 8.625 in)	110mm x 220mm
C5 (6.375 x 9 in)	162mm x 229mm
C4 (9 x 12.75 in)	229mm x 324mm

Postage Guide
The actual number of sheets of paper you can get within a particular postage weight will vary according to the thickness of the paper. The same, of course will apply to both the envelope and any stamped addressed envelope enclosed. The following is intended as a guide only and assumes A4 80gms (standard) paper and an average weight C5 envelope.

60gms (currently 24p first, 18p second)
Envelope and 10 sheets
Envelope, 9 sheets and SAE
Envelope, 9 sheets, SAE and Postcard

100gms (currently 36p first, 28p second)
Envelope and 18 sheets
Envelope, 17 sheets and SAE
Envelope, 16 sheets, SAE and Postcard

150gms (currently 44p first, 34p second)
Envelope and 28 sheets
Envelope, 26 sheets and SAE
Envelope, 26 sheets, SAE and Postcard

200gms (currently 54p first, 41p second)
Envelope and 37 sheets
Envelope, 36 sheets and SAE
Envelope, 35 sheets, SAE and Postcard

Overseas postage rates are based on 10gm steps.
C5 Envelope is 6 gms (approx)
1 sheets of paper is 4.5gms (approx)

There is a more complete list in the 91 directory on page 520.

CHARLES FARROW RESEARCH

Genealogical, Heraldic, Historical, Legal & Manorial Research

in

NORFOLK, SUFFOLK & CAMBRIDGESHIRE

• • • • • • • • • • • • • • • • •

* Family Histories Compiled *
* Parish Registers Transcribed *
* Photographic Service *

• • • • • • • • • • • • • • • • •

Charles W Farrow FInstLEx

32 Varvel Avenue, Sprowston, Norwich, NR7 8PH, England

SECTION H

ADVERTISING

CHURCH POSTCARDS

ILLUSTRATE YOUR FAMILY HISTORY

Bring your Family History to life with old postcards of the churches where your ancestors were baptised, married or buried. Send SAE (3IRCs) for details

PICTURE PAST

47 Manor House Park, Codsall, Staffordshire, WV8 1ES, England

VIDEO-GENEALOGY

THE BEST WAY TO TELL YOUR FAMILY STORY.

IF YOUR ANCESTORS CAME FROM BRITAIN,
THIS IS YOUR IDEAL RECORD.
YOUR OWN FAMILY DOCUMENTARY.

From information supplied by you, we visit places where your ancestors lived and produce a video to suit your requirements. Each documentary lovingly created by professionals with over 20 years' British Television and film experience.
Each programme supplied on the video format of your choice and converted to the television standard of any country.

Commissions for 1992/93 being undertaken now.

Details in our FREE Colour brochure:
**DE BRÉANSKI FILM AND VIDEO,
17 LINCOLN STREET,
CANTON, CARDIFF CF5 1JX
WALES. GREAT BRITIAN**

FAMILY TREE RESEARCHER SERIES

RED GUIDES:
Looking at a location.
For Example: Public Record Office (PRO)

YELLOW GUIDES:
Looking at a subject.
For Example: Census'

These A5 guides of between 32 and 64 pages (possibly larger) are at economic prices.

Write or Call for current list and Publication Dates of others.

FAMILY HISTORY CLUB OF GREAT BRITAIN

19 Penybryn, Mountain Ash,
Mid Glamogran CF45 3TJ
Tel: 0443-475900 or 0443-478754

SECTION I - REFERENCE

In order to use every last small space available this section is spread throughout the book - see contents page (page 1) for locations.

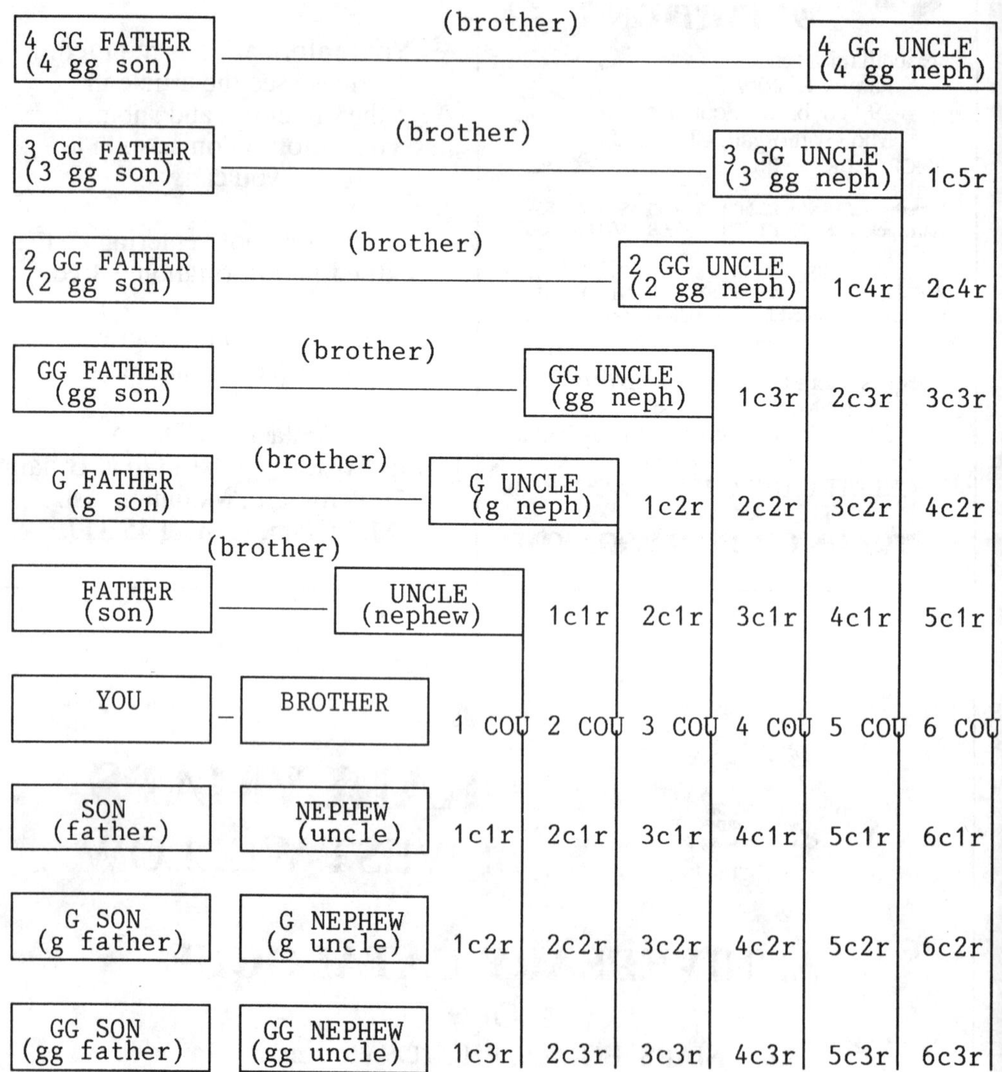

RELATIONSHIP CHART

CODES: G = Great or Grand, C = Cousin and R = Removed.

Expalnation:

Above is a chart showing various family members and thier relationships across the generations. This chart may help you to see how some of your ancestors that you come across are related to you. To determine the relationship of the brothers/sisters of your direct ancestors, follow the horizontal line from the direct ancestor. To determine your relationship to the children of the brothers/sisters of your direct ancestors, follow the vertical lines down.

For example:-

The brother of your 4 ggfather is your 4 gguncle. Your relationship is shown in ( ), 4 ggneph. The son of your 3 gguncle is your 1c4r and the grandson of your gguncle is you 2c1r.

MAP OF ENGLAND, WALES, SCOTLAND and NORTHERN IRELAND

Showing counties prior to 1974.

COUNTY CHART

( ) = Pre 1974, [ ] = Part of a previous county, * = New county. Full description at end.

County	Code	Was/Now	Surrounding Counties
ENGLAND	ENG		
*AVON	AVN	([GLS,SOM,WIL])	GLS,SOM,WIL
BEDFORDSHIRE	BDF		BKM,CAM,HRT,HUN,NTH
BERKSHIRE	BRK		BKM,GLN,HAM,MDX,OXF,SRY,WIL
BUCKINGHAMSHIRE	BKM		BED,BRK,GLN,HRT,MDX,NTH,OXF
CAMBRIDGESHIRE	CAM	([HUN],CAM)	BED,ESS,HRT,LIN,NFK,NTH,SFK
CHESHIRE	CHS		CWD,DBY,DEN,FLN,LAN,SAL,STS,
*CLEVELAND	CLV	([DUR,YKS])	DUR,NYK
CORNWALL	CON		DEV
CUMBERLAND	CUL	CMA	DFS,DUR,LAN,NBL,ROX,WES
*CUMBRIA	CMA	(CUL,[LAN],WES)	BRD,DUR,LAN,DGY,NBL,NYK
DERBYSHIRE	DBY		CHS,LAN,LEI,NTT,STS,SYK,YKS,WYK
DEVONSHIRE	DEV		CON,DOR,SOM
DORSET	DOR		DEV,HAM,SOM,WIL
DURHAM	DUR	[CLV],DUR	CUL,CLV,CMA,NBL,NYK,YKS,WES
EAST RIDING	ERY	HUM	NRY,WRY
*EAST SUSSEX	SXE	(SSX)	KEN,WSX
EAST YORKSHIRE	EYK	HUM	
ESSEX	ESS		CAM,GLN,HRT,MDX,SFK
GLOUCESTERSHIRE	GLS	[AVN],GLS	AVN,GNT,HEF,MON,OXF,SOM,WAR,WIL,WOR
*GREATER LONDON	GLN	([KEN],LND,MDX,[SRY])	BKM,BRK,ESS,HRT,KEN,SRY
HAMPSHIRE	HAM		BRK,DOR,SRY,SSX,SXW,WIL
HEREFORDSHIRE	HEF	H&W	BRE,GLS,MON,RAD,SAL,WOR
*HEREFORD & WORCESTER	H&W		GLS,GNT,POW,SAL,STS,WAR,WMD
HERTFORDSHIRE	HRT		BED,BKM,CAM,ESS,GLN,MDX
*HUMBERSIDE	HUM	(EYK,[LIN])	LIN,NTT,NYK,SYK,WYK
HUNTINGDONSHIRE	HUN	[CAM]	BED,CAM,NTH
ISLE OF WIGHT	IOW	HAM	
KENT	KEN		GLN,SRY,SSX,SXE
LANCASHIRE	LAN	([CMA],LAN)	CHS,CMA,CUL,DBY,MSY,NYK,WES,WYK,YKS
LEICESTERSHIRE	LEI	(LEI,RUT)	DBY,LIN,NTH,NTT,RUT,STS,WAR
LINCOLNSHIRE	LIN	([HUM],LIN)	CAM,HUM,LEI,NFK,NTH,NTT,RUT,YKS
LONDON	LND	City	ESS,GLN,KEN,MDX,SRY
*MERSEYSIDE	MSY	([CHS,LAN])	CHS,LAN
MIDDLESEX	MDX	GLN	BRK,BKM,ESS,HRT,LND,SRY
NORFOLK	NFK		CAM,LIN,SFK
NORTH RIDING	NRY	NYK	DUR,ERY,WES,WRY
*NORTH YORKSHIRE	NYK	(YKS)	CLV,CMA,DUR,HUM,LAN,SYK,WYK
NORTHAMPTON	NTH		BED,BKM,CAM,HUN,LEI,LIN,OXF,RUT,WAR
NORTHUMBERLAND	NBL		BEW,BRD,CMA,CUL,DUR,ROX
NOTTINGHAMSHIRE	NTT		DBY,HUM,LEI,LIN,SYK,YKS
OXFORDSHIRE	OXF	[BRK],OXF	BRK,BKM,GLS,NTH,WAR,WIL
RUTLAND	RUT	LEI	LEI,LIN,NTH
SHROPSHIRE	SAL		CHS,CWD,DEN,HEF,MGY,POW,RAD,STS,WOR
SOMERSET	SOM	[AVN],SOM	AVN,DEV,DOR,GLS,WIL
*SOUTH YORKSHIRE	SYK	(YKS)	DBY,HUM,NTT,NYK,WYK
STAFFORDSHIRE	STS		CHS,DBY,LEI,SAL,WAR,WMD,WOR
SUFFOLK	SFK		CAM,ESS,NFK
SURREY	SRY	[GLN],SRY	BRK,GLN,HAM,GLN,KEN,LND,MDX,SSX,SXE,SXW
SUSSEX	SSX	ESX,WSX	HAM,KEN,SRY
*TYNE & WEAR	T&W	([DUR,NBL])	DUR,NBL
WARWICKSHIRE	WAR		GLS,LEI,OXF,NTH.STS,WOR,WMD
*WEST MIDLANDS	WMD	([STS,WAR])	STS,WAR,WOR
WEST RIDING	WRY	[NYK],SYK,WYK	DBY,ERY,NRY,LAN,NTT
*WEST SUSSEX	SXW	(SSX)	HAM,SRY,SXE
*WEST YORKSHIRE	WYK	(YKS)	DBY,LAN,NYK,SYK
WESTMORLAND	WES	CMA	CUL,LAN,YKS
WILTSHIRE	WIL		AVN,BRK,DOR,GLS,HAM,OXF,SOM
WORCESTERSHIRE	WOR	H&W	GLS,HEF,SAL.STS,WAR
YORKSHIRE	YKS	[HUM],NYK,SYK,WYK	CUL,DBY,DUR,LAN,LIN,NTT,WES
WALES	WLS		
ANGLESEY	AGY	GYN	
BRECONSHIRE	BRE	POW	CGN,CMN,GLA,HEF,MON,RAD
CAERNARVONSHIRE	CAE	GYN	DEN,MER
CARDIGANSHIRE	CGN	DFD	BRE,CMN,MGY,PEM,RAD
CARMARTHENSHIRE	CMN	DFD	BRE,CGN,GLA,PEM
*CLWYD	CWD	(DEN,FLN,[MER])	CHS,GYN,POW,SAL
DENBIGHSHIRE	DEN	CWD	CAE,CHS,FLN,MER,MGY,SAL
*DYFED	DFD	(CGN,CMN,PEM)	GYN,POW,WGM
FLINT	FLN	CWD	CHS,DEN
GLAMORGANSHIRE	GLA	SGM,WGM,MGM	BRE,CMN,MON
*GWENT	GNT	(MON,[BRE])	GLS,HEF,MGM,POW,SGM,WOR
*GWYNEDD	GYN	(AGY,CAE,[DEN],[MER])	CWD,DFD,POW
MERIONETHSHIRE	MER	[CWD],GYN	CAE,DEN,MGY
*MID GLAMORGAN	MGM	([BRE,GLA])	GNT,POW,SGM,WGM
MONMOUTHSHIRE	MON	GNT	BRE,GLA,GLS,HEF
MONTGOMERYSHIRE	MGY	POW	CGN,DEN,MER,RAD,SAL
PEMBROKESHIRE	PEM	DFD	CGN,CMN
*POWYS	POW	([BRE],MGY,RAD)	CWD,DFD,GNT,GYN,HEF,MGM,SAL,WGM,WOR
RADNORSHIRE	RAD	POW	BRE,CGN,HEF,MGY,SAL,

*SOUTH GLAMORGAN	SGM	([GLA])	GNT,MGM
*WEST GLAMORGAN	WGM	([GLA])	DFD,MGM,POW
SCOTLAND	SCT		
ABERDEENSHIRE	ABD	GMP	ANS,BAN,INV,KCD,PER
ANGUS	ANS	TAY	ABD,KCD,PER
ARGYLLSHIRE	ARL	STD	BUT,DNB,INV,PER
AYRSHIRE	AYR	STD	DFS,KKD,LKS,RFW,WIG
BANFFSHIRE	BAN	GMP	ABD,INV,MOR
BERWICKSHIRE	BEW	BRD	ELN,MLN,NBL,ROX
*BORDERS	BRD	(BEW,PEE,ROX,SEL)	CMA,DGY,LTN,NBL,STD
BUTE	BUT	STD	
CAITHNESS	CAI	HLD	SUT
*CENTRAL	CEN	(CLK,[PER],STI)	FIF,LTN,STD,TAY
CLACKMANNANSHIRE	CLK	CEN	ARL,KRS,STI
DUMFRIESSHIRE	DFS	DGY	AYR,CUL,KKD,LKS,PEE,ROX,SEL
*DUMFRIES & GALLOWAY	DGY	(DFS,KKD,WIG)	BRD,CMA,STD
DUNBARTONSHIRE	DNB	STD	ARL,LKS,PER,RFW,STI
EAST LOTHIAN	ELN	LTN	BEW,MLN
*FIFESHIRE	FIF	FIF	CEN,CLK,KRS,PER,TAY
*GRAMPIAN	GMP	(ABD,BAN,KCD,MOR)	HLD,TAY
*HIGHLANDS	HLD	([ARL],CAI,INV,NAI, SUT,ROC)	GMP,STD,TAY
INVERNESS-SHIRE	INV	HLD	ABD,ARL,BAN,MOR,NAI,PER,ROC
KINCARDINESHIRE	KCD	GMP	ABD,ANS
KINROSS-SHIRE	KRS	TAY	CLK,FIF,PER
KIRCUDBRIGHTSHIRE	KKD	DGY	AYR,DFS,WIG
LANARKSHIRE	LKS	STD	AYR,DFS,DNB,MLN,PEE,RFW,WLN,
*LOTHIAN	LTN	(ELN,MLN,WLN)	BRD,CEN,STD
MIDLOTHIAN	MLN	LTN	BEW,ELN,LKS,PEE,SEL,WLN
MORAY	MOR	GMP	BAN,INV,NAI
NAIRNSHIRE	NAI	HLD	INV,MOR
ORKNEY ISLES	OKI		
PEEBLESHIRE	PEE	BRD	DFS,LKS,MLN,SEL
PERTHSHIRE	PER	TAY	ABD,ANS,ARL,CLK,DNB,FIF,KRS,INV,STI
RENFREWSHIRE	RFW	STD	AYR,DNB,LKS
ROSS & CROMARTY	ROC	HLD	INV,SUT
ROXBURGHSHIRE	ROX	BRD	BEW,CUL,DFS,MLN,NBL,SEL
SELKIRKSHIRE	SEL	BRD	DFS,MLN,PEE,ROX
SHETLAND ISLES	SHI		
STIRLINGSHIRE	STI	CEN	CLK,DNB,PER,WLN
*STRATHCLYDE	STD	([ARL],AYR,BUT,DNB, LKS,RFW)	BRD,CEN,DGY,HLD,LTN,TAY
SUTHERLAND	SUT	HLD	CAI,ROC
*TAYSIDE	TAY	([PER],ANS,KIN)	CEN,FIF,GMP,HLD,STD
WEST LOTHIAN	WLN	(LTN)	LKS,MLN,STI
WESTERN ISLES	WIS		
WIGTOWNSHIRE	WIG	DGY	AYR,KKD

IRELAND (Eire)	IRL	
CARLOW	CAR	KID,KIK,LEX,WEX,WIC
CAVAN	CAV	FER,LET,LOG,MEA,MOG,WEM,
CLARE	CLA	GAL,LIM
CORK	COR	KER,LIM,TIP,WAT
DONEGAL	DON	FER,LET,LDY,TYR
DUBLIN	DUB	KID,MEA,WIC
GALWAY	GAL	CLA,MAY,OFF,ROS,TIP,
KERRY	KER	COR,LIM
KILDARE	KID	CAR,DUB,LEX,MEA,OFF,WIC
KILKENNY	KIK	CAR,LEX,TIP,WAT,WEX
LEITRIM	LET	CAV,FER,LOG,ROS,SLI
LEIX	LEX	CAR,KIK,KLD,OFF,TIP
LIMERICK	LIM	COR,KER,TIP,WAT
LONGFORD	LOG	CAV,LET,ROS,WEM
LOUTH	LOU	ARM,MEA,MOG
MAYO	MAY	GAL,ROS,SLI
MEATH	MEA	CAV,DUB,KLD,LOU,MOG
MONOGHAN	MOG	ARM,CAV,LOU,MEA
OFFALY	OFF	GAL,KLD,LEX,MEA,ROS
ROSCOMMON	ROS	GAL,LET,LOG,MAY,OFF
SLIGO	SLI	LET,MAY,ROS
TIPPERARY	TIP	COR,GAL,KIK,LEX,LIM
WATERFORD	WAT	COR,KIK,TIP
WESTMEATH	WEM	CAV,LOG,MEA,OFF,ROS
WEXFORD	WEX	CAR,KIK,WIC
WICKLOW	WIC	CAR,DUB,KLD,WEX

NORTHERN IRELAND		NIR
ANTRIM	ANT	DOW,LDY,TYR
ARMAGH	ARM	DOW,LOU,MOG
DOWN	DOW	ANT,ARM,MOG
FERMANAGH	FER	DON,LET,MOG,TYR
LONDONDERRY	LDY	ANT,DON,TYR
TYRONE	TYR	ANT,DON,DOW,FER LDY,MOG

OTHERS	
CHANNEL ISLES	CHI
ALDERNEY	ALD
GUERNSEY	GSY
JERSEY	JSY
SARK	SRK
ISLE OF MAN	IOM

The above is a list of county codes for England, Wales, Scotland, Northern Ireland, Ireland and a few others. The list is split into the relevant countries and then organised alphabetically by county. The first column is the full county name, the * signifies that it is a new county. The second column is the 3 digit county code. The third column shows what the county (3 digit code) was prior to 1974 or is now. The ( ) contains the codes prior to 1974, and [ ] contains that part of a county which has been used/distributed to create the new one. If there are no brackets then it is the current county code. The fourth column gives you the counties that border the county both prior to 1974 and now. This column is intended to give you an idea of where the county is in relation to others in the country, but also if you have ancestors living on or close to border lines it will also help you to see which other counties may need checking out. This list does not include area codes ie South Wales (SWL).

COUNTY CODES

Code	County
???	Not Specified
ABD	ABERDEENSHIRE
AGY	ANGLESEY
ALD	ALDERNEY
ALL	ALL
ANS	ANGUS
ANT	ANTRIM
ARL	ARGYLLSHIRE
ARM	ARMAGH
AVN	AVON
AYR	AYRSHIRE
BAN	BANFFSHIRE
BDF	BEDFORDSHIRE
BDS	BORDERS
BEW	BERWICKSHIRE
BKM	BUCKINGHAMSHIRE
BRE	BRECONSHIRE
BRK	BERKSHIRE
BUT	BUTE
CAE	CAERNARVONSHIRE
CAI	CAITHNESS
CAM	CAMBRIDGESHIRE
CAR	CARLOW
CAV	CAVAN
CGN	CARDIGANSHIRE
CHI	CHANNEL ISLANDS
CHS	CHESHIRE
CLA	CLARE
CLK	CLACKMANNANSHIRE
CLV	CLEVELAND
CMA	CUMBRIA
CMN	CARMARTHENSHIRE
CON	CORNWALL
COR	CORK
CUL	CUMBERLAND
CWD	CLWYD
DBY	DERBYSHIRE
DEN	DENBIGHSHIRE
DEV	DEVONSHIRE
DFD	DYFED
DFS	DUMFRIESSHIRE
DNB	DUNBARTONSHIRE
DON	DONEGAL
DOR	DORSET
DOW	DOWN
DUB	DUBLIN
DUR	DURHAM
EAG	EAST ANGLIA
ELN	EAST LOTHIAN
ENG	ENGLAND
ERY	EAST RIDING
ESS	ESSEX
EYK	EAST YORKSHIRE
FER	FERMANAGH
FIF	FIFESHIRE
FLN	FLINT
GAL	GALWAY
GLA	GLAMORGANSHIRE
GLS	GLOUCESTERSHIRE
GMP	GRAMPIAN
GNT	GWENT
GSY	GUERNSEY
GYN	GWYNEDD
HAM	HAMPSHIRE
HAR	ISLE OF HARRIS
HEF	HEREFORDSHIRE
HIL	HIGHLANDS
HMC	HOME COUNTIES
HRT	HERTFORDSHIRE
HUM	HUMBERSIDE
HUN	HUNTINGDONSHIRE
INV	INVERNESS-SHIRE
IOM	ISLE OF MAN
IOW	ISLE OF WIGHT
IRL	IRELAND
JSY	JERSEY
KCD	KINCARDINESHIRE
KEN	KENT
KER	KERRY
KID	KILDARE
KIK	KILKENNY
KKD	KIRCUDBRIGHTSHIRE
KRS	KINROSS-SHIRE
LAN	LANCASHIRE
LDY	LONDONDERRY
LEI	LEICESTERSHIRE
LET	LEITRIM
LEX	LEIX
LIM	LIMERICK
LIN	LINCOLNSHIRE
LKS	LANARKSHIRE
LND	LONDON
LOG	LONGFORD
LOU	LOUTH
LTN	LOTHIAN
MAY	MAYO
MCA	MERICA
MDX	MIDDLESEX
MEA	MEATH
MER	MERIONETHSHIRE
MGM	MID GLAMORGAN
MGY	MONTGOMERYSHIRE
MID	MIDLANDS
MIL	MILITARY
MLN	MIDLOTHIAN
MOG	MONOGHAN
MON	MONMOUTHSHIRE
MOR	MORAY
MSY	MERSEYSIDE
NAI	NAIRNSHIRE
NBL	NORTHUMBERLAND
NFK	NORFOLK
NIR	NORTHERN IRELAND
NRY	NORTH RIDING
NTH	NORTHAMPTON
NTT	NOTTINGHAMSHIRE
NWL	NORTH WALES
NYK	NORTH YORKSHIRE
OFF	OFFALY
OKI	ORKNEY ISLES
OXF	OXFORDSHIRE
PEE	PEEBLESHIRE
PEM	PEMBROKESHIRE
PER	PERTHSHIRE
POW	POWYS
RAD	RADNORSHIRE
RFW	RENFREWSHIRE
ROC	ROSS & CROMARTY
ROS	ROSCOMMON
ROX	ROXBURGHSHIRE
RUT	RUTLAND
SAL	SHROPSHIRE
SCT	SCOTLAND
SEL	SELKIRKSHIRE
SFK	SUFFOLK
SHI	SHETLAND ISLES
SLI	SLIGO
SOM	SOMERSET
SRK	SARK
SRY	SURREY
SSX	SUSSEX
STD	STRATHCLYDE
STI	STIRLINGSHIRE
STS	STAFFORDSHIRE
SUT	SUTHERLAND
SWL	SOUTH WALES
SXE	EAST SUSSEX
SXW	WEST SUSSEX
SYK	SOUTH YORKSHIRE
T&W	TYNE & WEAR
TAY	TAYSIDE
TIP	TIPPERARY
TYR	TYRONE
WAR	WARWICKSHIRE
WAT	WATERFORD
WCY	WEST COUNTRY
WEM	WESTMEATH
WES	WESTMORLAND
WEX	WEXFORD
WIC	WICKLOW
WIG	WIGTOWNSHIRE
WIL	WILTSHIRE
WIS	WESTERN ISLES
WLN	WEST LOTHIAN
WLS	WALES
WMD	WEST MIDLANDS
WOR	WORCESTERSHIRE
WRY	WEST RIDING
WSX	WESSEX
WYK	WEST YORKSHIRE
YKS	YORKSHIRE